Pronunciation table 發音表

CONSONANTS 子音／輔音

K.K.	IPA	範例
p	p	**p**ack
b	b	**b**ack
t	t	**t**ie
d	d	**d**ie
k	k	**c**lass
g	g	**g**lass
tʃ	tʃ	**ch**urch
dʒ	dʒ	**j**udge
f	f	**f**ew
v	v	**v**iew
θ	θ	**th**row
ð	ð	**th**ough
s	s	**s**oon
z	z	**z**oo
ʃ	ʃ	**sh**oe
ʒ	ʒ	mea**s**ure
m	m	su**m**
n	n	su**n**
ŋ	ŋ	su**ng**
h	h	**h**ot
l	l	**l**ot
r	r	**r**od
j	j	**y**et
w	w	**w**et

VOWELS 母語／元音

K.K.	IPA	範例
ɛ	e	b**e**d
æ	æ	b**a**d
i	iː	sh**ee**p
ɪ	i	pr**e**tty
ɪ	ɪ	sh**i**p
ɑ	ɑː	c**al**m
ɑ	ɒ	p**o**t
ɔ	ɔː	c**au**ght, h**o**rse
ʊ	ʊ	p**u**t
u	uː	b**oo**t
ʌ	ʌ	c**u**t
ɚ	ɜː	b**ir**d
ə	ə	bett**er**
e	eɪ	m**a**ke
o	əʊ	b**oa**t
aɪ	aɪ	b**i**te
aʊ	aʊ	n**ow**
ɔɪ	ɔɪ	b**oy**
ɪr	ɪə	h**ere**
ɛr	eə	h**air**
ʊr	ʊə	p**oor**
eɚ	eɪə	pl**ayer**
oɚ	əʊə	l**ower**
ɔɪɚ	ɔɪə	empl**oyer**
aɪr	aɪə	t**ire**
aʊr	aʊə	fl**ower**

特別符號

; 此符號之前為K.K.音標, 後為IPA音標。IPA
音標所表示的是英國標準音 (R.P.)。
/ˈ/ 表示主重音。
/ˌ/ 表示次重音。
/◂/ 表示重音轉移。
/ʳ/ 在詞尾表示美式英語中 /r/ 通常發音, 在英式
英語中如果後接的詞以元／母音開始也要
發音。
/ɪ̈/ 表示有些人以 /ɪ/ 發音, 有些人以 /ə/ 發音。
/i/ 表示英式英語一般發 /iː/ 音, 但美式英語則
發 /i/ 音。
/ə/ 表示 /ə/ 可發音可不發音。
/o/ 表示美式英語以 /ɔ/ 或 /əʊ/ 發音。
/ɑ, ɔ, ɜ/ 這三個音標專用於美式英語, 音值等於
/ɑː, ɔː, ɜː/。

W.T.GRAHAM

朗文

進階

英漢雙解

詞典

第二版
Second Edition

Longman
Active
Study
English-Chinese
Dictionary

出版人：吳天祝
Publisher: T C Goh

主審：陳善偉
Chief reviser: Chan Sin Wai

審訂：謝福榮
Reviser: Floyd Xie

翻譯：謝福榮　李仕健　錢華
Translators: Floyd Xie　Li Shijian　Howard Qian

責任編輯：陳麗敏
Executive editor: Lilian Chan

編輯：李建元
Editor: Dominic Lee

平面設計：梁若基
Graphic designer: Timothy Leung

校對：朱建中　季忠　張瑾之
Proofreaders: Jackson Zhu　Jidd Ji　Kitty Zhang

排版：麥兆華　王瑩　姚俐
Pagemaking: Mak Siu Wa　Annie Wang　Judy Yao

朗文

進階 英漢雙解 詞典

第二版
Second Edition

Longman
Active
Study
English-Chinese
Dictionary

Bilingual Edition 雙語版

Chief Reviser: Dr. Chan Sin Wai

主審：陳善偉博士

Longman 朗文

This edition is published under the imprint of Longman,
which is an imprint of Pearson Education Group.

Published by
Pearson Education North Asia Limited
18/F., Cornwall House
Taikoo Place
979 King's Road
Quarry Bay
Hong Kong
Tel: 3181 0000
Fax: 2565 7440
e-mail:info@ilongman.com
Website:http://www.ilongman.com

培生教育出版北亞洲有限公司
香港鰂魚涌英皇道 979 號
太古坊康和大廈十八樓
電話：3181 0000
圖文傳真：2565 7440
電子郵遞：info@ilongman.com
網址：http://www.ilongman.com

First published 2001
Third impression 2002
二〇〇一年初版
二〇〇二年第三版
ISBN 962 00 1476 6

Produced by Pearson Education North Asia Ltd., Hong Kong
SWTC/03

The
publisher's
policy is to use
**paper manufactured
from sustainable forests**

Contents

目錄

Study notes 學習提示:

New words 新詞 **1337**

Appendices 附錄:

To our readers

致讀者

常言道：「萬丈高樓從地起」，我們學習英語，也必須先打好根基，循序漸進，才可把英語運用自如。

《朗文進階英漢雙解詞典》是為中等程度的英語學習者而編纂的，目的是幫助他們進一步鞏固已有的英語基礎，使他們對英語的各個方面有更深入的認識，從而提高他們理解及運用英語的能力。

本詞典收詞量豐富，詞目和片語超過45,000條，例句達55,000句，堪稱同類型詞典之冠。其中包括九十年代常用詞彙，例如camcorder（手提攝錄機）、colour prejudice（種族偏見）等，另特別收錄2,000多個二十一世紀最新詞彙，如cyberspace（網際空間）、website（網站）等，以配合時代需要。除此之外，本詞典還具以下幾項特色：

1. 以專頁詳細列出一些常用詞的各種時態、各項釋義、相關詞組／片語等，並附以大量例句，深入淺出，使讀者容易理解，便於學習。

2. 「用法說明」提示詞的特別用法，指出詞與詞之間的區別，教你如何選用適當的詞。

3. 「有用句型」指示常用的句型，並以紅色框線及網底突出，使人一目了然。

4. 九個「學習提示」針對常犯的文法錯誤，重點講解錯誤原因。

5. 「拼寫提示」提供拼寫的基本知識。

6. 十六頁彩色全頁插圖，透過多項實用主題，介紹常見事物的中英文名稱，並配以相關的練習，加強讀者的應用能力。

7. 六個精心編撰的附錄，包括地名、不規則動詞表、標點符號等，提供實用的英語知識。

8. 隨書附送學習光碟，以練習形式教你使用詞典的正確方法，使讀者可從遊戲中學習。

本詞典從九五年展開翻譯工作到付印成書，共經歷了六個寒暑。這本詞典能夠順利完成，全有賴我們一群盡責用心的編、譯、校，以及排版人員，在此謹向他們致以衷心謝意。

在編譯本詞典的過程中，我們得到香港中文大學翻譯系系主任陳善偉博士在百忙之中抽空為我們審校譯文，在此謹致謝意。為了詞典能趕及本年初出版，陳博士除犧牲了一個悠閒暑假外，還要連續多晚挑燈工作，令本部門同人深為感動，就此向陳博士再三致謝。

本詞典編譯工作繁浩，雖然我們已力求審慎，但仍難免會有疏漏，懇請各專家、學者及讀者不吝指正為幸。

培生教育出版北亞洲有限公司
辭典部
二零零一年二月

Preface by Dr Chan Sin-wai

陳善偉博士序

　　《朗文進階英漢雙解詞典》是一本編得好、譯得好的詞典，是一部非常適合中等程度和具有一般英語水平人士使用的語文參考書。

　　在編的方面，這本詞典有幾點是優勝於其他同類詞典的。首先是收詞方面，共計有四萬五千條，較其他同類進階詞典內容多出三分之一。所選的詞匯大部份都是中學各學科及社會上流行的用語，包括科技新詞，並且標示其最常用的程度，以符合學習上的需要。其次是釋義方面，運用二千個常用字來解釋詞義，明白易懂，不會有釋義中有太多難字而不明其義的情況出現。其三是例句方面，由於選自大量英語語庫資料，不但文字深入淺出，而且內容與我們生活息息相關，都是我們常用的表達方式，都是我們認識的事物，所以很容易理解，也很容易接受，真正達到使用詞典學習常用英語的效果。其四是學習提示方面，特別將意義相近的詞在文法上加以說明和區分，以免錯誤使用。另外亦有「有用句型」，可供反覆練習，舉一反三。

　　在譯的方面，《朗文進階英漢雙解詞典》漢語翻譯忠實準確，有助學習者提高雙語能力。詞典名之為雙解詞典，中文解釋當然非常重要。詞典在詞匯方面譯名準確，翻譯人名地名等專有名詞方面亦是採用最流行最常用的譯名，妥妥當當地處理了中港台三地同名異譯的問題。其次，例句的翻譯完全達到信順的境界，不但句子的意思交待得準確，而且表達得非常流暢地道。要達到這個水平，翻譯方面必須留意很多問題，例如語域的不同，單複數的分別及搭配的變化等。《朗文進階英漢雙解詞典》在這些地方都刻意求工，確保譯文的質素。從雙解詞典的詞與例句中不但可以認識到英語的使用和字句的意義，而且可以掌握到漢語的表達和翻譯的技巧。

　　《朗文進階英漢雙解詞典》有這樣高的水準是長期努力和精心編纂的結果，是值得欣賞的集體成就。

陳善偉

二零零零年十一月

陳善偉，現任香港中文大學翻譯系系主任及翻譯系教授。英國倫敦大學博士。八零至八五年在中文大學中國文化研究所翻譯研究中心從事漢英翻譯及編輯工作。八五年至今在翻譯系任教。出版著作作共計四十冊，其中字典方面有《漢英翻譯大辭典》（光碟版），翻譯研究方面有《漢英英漢翻譯學百科全書》，文學翻譯方面漢譯英作品有《高陽小說英譯》，英譯漢作品有《我的兒子馬友友》。

Preface by Prof Huang Shuanfan

黃宣範教授序

為什麼又要編一部新的詞典？

這通常至少有兩個因素。其一是語言本身或對語言的了解已經有了明顯的變化；其二是詞典編纂的科技有了重大的突破。這兩個因素之間其實有互為因果的關係，而朗文出版公司過去多年來推出的一系列英語詞典應該都跟這兩個因素有關。

七十年代後期大量機讀 (machine-readable) 英語語料庫的建立開啟了英語詞典編纂的新頁。以出版英語史上第一部英語詞典而聞名於世的朗文出版公司在這方面一向居於領航者的地位。過去二十多年朗文以其獨特的眼光自行（或合資）建立了三種相當寶貴的語料庫，包括 Longman Lancaster English Language Corpus，Longman English Learners' Corpus 及 British National Corpus，並且利用這些語料庫而連續推出幾部相當成功的英語詞典，其中對台灣的讀者而言可能以 Longman Dictionary of Contemporary English（《朗文當代高級詞典》，中譯本名為《朗文當代英漢雙解詞典》）最足稱道。

這一本《朗文進階英漢雙解詞典》同樣反映了朗文英語詞典系列已確立多年且為內行人所稱許的一些特色。這至少包括下列幾項：

1. 標出每個詞出現的頻率（稱為詞頻）。龐大的語料庫使朗文英語詞典的編輯群對英語的詞頻深具信心。例如 anxious 或 angry 是屬於最常用的 2001-3000 字之一；apparent 或 approve 是屬於最常用的 1001-2000 字之一；而 argument，apart 或 appeal（名詞）是最常用的 1000 字之一。有了詞頻的知識，讀者對英語的理解就更有把握。假定有兩個同義詞，它們的詞頻很不一樣，那麼它們的意義就可能也很不一樣了。

2. 用法 (usage) 及語法句型 (useful pattern) 的處理更見成熟。朗文獨創的 Learner's Corpus 使本詞典的編者可以更有效地掌握每個關鍵詞的用法和語法。例如 commit 的受詞常指 crime 一類的字眼；decide 之後可接各種不同的補語：decide to, decide that, decide whether, decide on。Different 這個形容詞之後可以接不同的介詞：different from, different to; different than。其他還有數以千計的用法說明或語法句型難以一一詳述。

3. 所有單字的定義都控制在最常用的 2000 詞之內。這項創新首見於上面提到的《朗文當代高級詞典》之第一版，目前已成為其他詞典仿效的對象。

詞典的編纂已經成為與語料庫有高度依存關係的工作。朗文英語詞典系列以其開風氣之先的姿態為詞典界帶來種種新的可能。這是新一代讀者們最值得慶幸的事。

黃宣範

二零零一年一月

黃宣範，國立台灣大學語言學研究所教授兼語文中心主任。

Preface by Prof Zhang Boran

張柏然教授序

《朗文進階英漢雙解詞典》在堅持優良傳統的基礎上，吸收了現代語言學與詞典學的研究成果，並借助最新的資訊科技，使詞典編纂與出版領域有着廣闊的發展前景。這本詞典在編寫釋義、排列義項、描述語法性質、選擇例句、描述語用特點方面，全面、客觀地反映了當代英語的特點，務求更能配合讀者的需要。

1. 重視資料庫的建設及其在詞典編纂中的應用

《朗文進階》的一大特色，是盡量增加收詞量，覆蓋更多領域的詞彙。在收錄的 45,000 餘條詞目之中，包括了 20 世紀 90 年代由於社會發展、科技進步而產生的詞彙，另更特別增收 2,000 個 21 世紀最新詞彙以配合時代的需要。它除了客觀描述英語在新時代的使用情況，也沒有忽視英語的歷時性，恰如其分地反映了英語的演變。而隨着語言教學越來越重視學習者交際能力的培養，《朗文進階》除收錄書面語外，還利用資料庫中大量常用的口語材料，讓學習者可從而提高語言交際能力。資料庫因而得以全面運用於詞典編纂的各個方面，使詞典內容更見充實。

2. 堅持傳統與創新並舉，改進詞典的結構形式

釋義方面，《朗文進階》使用了 2,000 個的釋義詞彙 (Longman Defining Vocabulary)，即用最常用的單詞和通俗的文體，簡明扼要地對詞項進行釋義。這樣的釋義深入淺出，易懂易記，便於學習。同時，詞典還為讀者提供了一些詞項的使用語境，憑釋義準確判斷詞項的語法特徵，包括詞性語法搭配情況及詞彙搭配情況，從而保證了詞項的正確使用。

一個詞有這麼多意義，在詞目中該怎麼安排呢？有的詞典着眼於歷史，從最早的意義講起；有的詞典著眼於當代，從最常用的意義講起。《朗文進階》根據資料庫提供的詞頻信息，將詞按使用頻率排列，從最常用的意義講起，這樣讀者就不必費時去瀏覽一些較罕用的意義。詞典使用者可根據所提供的信息，比較和選擇能準確表達意思的詞語。詞典還分別以一至三個 * 號來表示最常用的 1000 至 3000 個單詞。這些信息無疑是讀者準確使用字詞的有力保障。

一般語文詞典採用的代碼系統均十分複雜難記。為方便讀者，《朗文進階》僅採用了四個最常用的字母 C/U,T/I 分別表示可數 / 不可數名詞、及物 / 不及物動詞，其餘的語法特徵均用完整的單詞在方括號中標註出來，如 [never before a noun], [always before a noun], [T: F+ that], [C+sing/pl verb], [T, usually passive] 等，閱讀起來極為方便。

一部詞典非但要釋義準確，還要有豐富的例子。例子有兩個作用：一是印證詞義，二是深化釋義，說明所釋詞目在日常會話和寫作中的實際用法。《朗文進階》在舉例方面，利用了龐大的資料庫，例證可信手拈來，所提供的例證貼切適用。此外，這部詞典漢譯詳實，對於初學者尤為稱便，在查詢之餘尚可兼學翻譯，一舉兩得。

3. 加強用法說明，重視充實語用信息，全面、客觀地反映當代英語的特點

把英語作為外語來學習的人有一個大難題，就是不清楚詞怎麼用才合乎規矩。這裏面有詞的概念意義問題，有詞的內涵意義問題，也有詞義容易混淆的問題，還有語法形式問題。特別是語用學的興起，使得詞典編纂者的目光不再局限於語言的正確性，同時還注重語言的得體性。關於這些，《朗文進階》在詞條後附加「用法說明」、「學習提示」、「拼寫提示」、用紅色框線及網底標示句型等途徑，都給了讀者一些語用的提示。此外，詞典還有全頁彩圖共16個主題，並配以相關的練習，這對廣大讀者尤其是學生起着溫故知新的作用。

在英語學習詞典家族中，朗文詞典一向是頗受莘莘學子歡迎的。這次，《朗文進階》更隨書附送學習光碟，教讀者使用詞典的正確方法，方便這高科技世代的讀者更有效快捷地取得所需的資訊。

這部《朗文進階英漢雙解詞典》還有其他特色，茲不一一列舉。我相信廣大讀者必將視之為一位百問不厭且有趣的良伴益友。

張柏然

二零零零年十二月

張柏然，現任南京大學雙語詞典研究中心教授兼博士生導師，為中國翻譯工作者協會副會長。

Guide to the dictionary

詞典用法説明

SPELLING 拼寫

Different spelling
不同的拼寫法

‡**judg·ment** /ˈdʒʌdʒmənt; ˈdʒʌdʒmənt/ *n* (also 又作 **judgement**) **1** [C] an official decision given by a judge or a court of law: 〔法官或法院的〕判決; 裁決: *The judgment was given yesterday.* 法院的判決於昨天宣佈。

不同的拼寫法在括號內列出。

British and American spelling
英式和美式拼寫法

‡**col·our**¹ /ˈkʌlə; ˈkʌlər/ *n* (**color** *AmE* 【美式】) **1** [U] the quality which allows you to see the difference between, for example, a red flower and a blue flower when they are both the same size and shape 彩色; 色彩: *an insect that can change colour* 會變色的昆蟲 | *colour television* 彩色電視

美式拼寫法在括號內列出。

Irregular plurals
名詞複數不規則變化

***mouse** /maʊs; maʊs/ *n* **1** [plural is 複數為 **mice** /maɪs; maɪs/] a small furry animal with a long tail that lives in houses and in fields 老鼠; 耗子: *a field mouse* 田鼠 | *I think we've got mice in the kitchen.* 我想我們廚房裡有老鼠。 **2** [plural is 複數為 **mouses**] a small box connected to a computer by a wire which you move around on a surface in order to work the computer 〔電腦〕鼠標

如果某個名詞複數變化是不規則的, 用這樣的方式列出。

po·ta·to /pəˈteto; pəˈteɪtəʊ/ *n* **potatoes** [C; U] a round white vegetable with a thin brown or yellow skin, that is cooked and served in many different ways: 馬鈴薯; 土豆: *I've peeled the potatoes.* 我已給馬鈴薯削了皮。

Irregular verbs
動詞時態不規則變化

*****hope**¹ /hop; həʊp/ *v* **hoped, hoping** **1** [I; + (that)] to want something to happen and have some confidence that it probably will happen 希望; 期望: *I hope he comes tomorrow.* 我希望他明天來。 | *She hopes to go to college next year.* 她盼望明年上大學。

這個動詞的拼法是否會隨着時態變化而有所改變? 我們這樣列出其變化。

SOUND/PRONUNCIATION 讀音

Sound
讀音

★**ap·ple** /ˈæpl̩; ˈæpəl/ *n* **1** a hard round fruit with white juicy flesh and red, green, or yellow skin 蘋果

每個單詞的讀音都會這樣標出。

Stress
重音

‡**a·bil·i·ty** /əˈbɪlətɪ; əˈbɪləti/ *n* **abilities** [C; U] skill and power to do something 能力: *She has the ability to think and write clearly.* 她具有清楚地思考和寫作的能力。

應讀作 ab<u>i</u>lity 還是 <u>a</u>bility?

For more information on pronunciation turn to Sound/Pronunciation.
有關讀音的詳細説明，見 "讀音" 部分。

MEANING 釋義

Definitions
釋義

★**egg**¹ /ɛg; eg/ *n* **1** [C;U] a rounded object with a hard shell, which can contain a baby bird, insect, or snake; eggs are often eaten as food 〔雞、鳥、蛇等的〕蛋；〔昆蟲等的〕卵: *Each female lays five or six eggs.* 每隻雌鳥下五、六個蛋。

單詞的釋義簡明易懂。讀者可能不認識的單詞，概用大寫字母排印，如此處所示。這些單詞均可在本詞典中查到。

cock·le /ˈkɒkl̩; ˈkɒkəl/ *n* a small SHELLFISH 鳥蛤

More than one meaning
一詞多義

a·cute /əˈkjut; əˈkjuːt/ *adj* **1** very great or severe (used of bad situations) 劇烈的，嚴重的〔指壞的狀況〕: *She was in acute pain.* 她痛得很厲害 | *an acute lack of food* 嚴重缺少食物 **2** showing an ability to understand things clearly and deeply 尖鋭的；深刻的: *an acute analysis of the political situation* 對政治形勢的深刻分析 **3** able to notice small differences 敏鋭的: *Dogs have an acute sense of smell.* 狗有敏鋭的嗅覺。 **4** *tech* less than 90 degrees (used of an angle) 【術語】成鋭角的〔指角度〕

許多單詞是一詞多義的，最常用的字義會排在首位，但別忘記查看其他義項。

Examples
例句

‡**la·ter** /ˈletɚ; ˈleɪtəʳ/ *adv* **1** after some time 較晚地；後來: *I can't do it now, but I'll do it later.* 我現在不能做，但我稍後會做。 | *At first they said 32 people had died, but later they said it was 15.* 起初他們説有三十二人喪命，但後來又説是十五人。 | *She had a cup of coffee and read for a while. Later that afternoon she took a walk down to the beach.* 她喝了杯咖啡，看了會兒書。下午晚些時候又散步去了海濱。

單詞的用法以許多有用的例句説明。

GRAMMAR 文法

Parts of speech
詞類

> ‡**age¹** /edʒ; eɪdʒ/ *n* **1** [C;U] the number of years that a person has lived 年齡: *He is 10 years of age.* 他十歲。| *At your age you should know better.* 在你這個年齡應該更懂事了。| *She died at the age of 79.* 她七十九歲謝世。| *What ages are your children?* 你的孩子們都幾歲了?
> **age²** *v* **aged, aging** *or* **ageing** [I;T] to become older and weaker or make someone seem older and weaker (使)〔某人〕變老: *After his wife's death he aged quickly.* 自妻子死後,他老得很快。| *The illness has aged him.* 他因病衰老。

這些字母標出單詞的詞類。

Word families
派生詞

> **ea·ger** /ˈigɚ; ˈiːgəʳ/ *adj* having a strong desire to do something or a strong interest in something 渴望的; 熱衷的: *I was very eager to meet him.* 我渴望和他見面。| *He's eager for success.* 他渴望成功。| *crowds of eager tourists* 一羣羣熱切的遊客 — **eagerly** *adv* — **eagerness** *n* [U]

不同詞類的派生詞通常會如此標示。

Countable and uncountable nouns
可數與不可數名詞

> **lace¹** /les; leɪs/ *n* **1** [U] a very fine cloth with a lot of holes in it, which is used to decorate clothes and other things 網眼織物; 花邊; 飾帶: *lace curtains* 網眼紗簾 **2** [C] a string or cord which goes through two holes on the edges of clothes or shoes in order to fasten them together 鞋帶; 繫帶

這兩個字母表示這個名詞是否可以用複數形式。
[C] 表示可以,
[U] 表示不可以。

Transitive and intransitive verbs
及物與不及物動詞

> ‡**ar·rive** /əˈraɪv; əˈraɪv/ *v.* **arrived, arriving** [I] **1** to reach a place 到達; 抵達: *What time does the plane arrive in New York?* 飛機甚麼時候到達紐約? | *The train arrived late at the station.* 火車到達車站時已晚點了。**2** to happen 來臨: *At last our holidays arrived.* 我們的假期終於來臨了。

> *∗**ar·rest¹** /əˈrɛst; əˈrest/ *v* [T] **1** to catch someone and declare that they are believed to be guilty of a crime 逮捕, 拘留〔某人〕: *He was arrested **for** stealing a car.* 他因偷汽車而被捕。

這些字母表示這個動詞是否後接直接受詞[賓語]。
[I] 表示這個動詞不能跟受詞[賓語], [T] 則表示可以。

Verbs followed by prepositions 動詞後接介詞	⚑⚑**ab·scond** /æbˋskɑnd; əbˈskɒnd/ *v* [I] *fml* to run away suddenly and secretly, usually because you have done something wrong【正式】〔通常因做了壞事而〕潛逃: *He absconded* **with** *all the money.* 他攜了所有款項潛逃。| *They absconded* **from** *the police station.* 他們從警察局潛逃了。	這個單詞後常跟的介詞用粗體標出。
Verbs followed by other grammatical patterns 動詞後接其他語法結構	⚑**care·ful** /ˋkɛrfəl; ˈkeəfəl/ *adj* **1** taking care 小心的: *We were careful not to mention it to his wife.* 我們很小心，避免向他妻子提及此事。| *You should be more careful* **with** *your money.* 你花錢的時候應更加謹慎一些。| *a careful driver* 小心翼翼的駕駛員 | *Be careful crossing the road.* 過馬路要當心。 □USEFUL PATTERNS 有用句型 to be careful (not) to do something; to be careful with something; to be careful doing something...; to be careful where/who/what/how...	有用句型指出通常與這個動詞連用的語法結構。
Phrasal verbs 片語[短語]動詞	**arrive at** sthg *phr v* [T] to reach a situation or decision: 達成，得出〔結論、決定等〕: *After many hours' talk, the committee arrived at a decision.* 經過許多小時的討論，委員會終於達成了一項決定。	這表明使用片語[短語]動詞 arrive at 時，受詞[賓語]總是放在介詞 at 後面。
	thrash sthg ⌐ **out** *phr v* [T] to reach agreement about a problem or produce a decision by talking about it in detail 徹底討論〔以達成協議或做出決定〕: *After a long argument we thrashed out a plan.* 經過長時間的爭辯後，我們終於訂出了一個計劃。	箭頭⌐表示既可以說 thrash the plan out，也可以說 thrash out the plan。
Choosing the right word 選擇正確的用詞	⚑**kid**[1] /kɪd; kɪd/ *n.* **1** [T] *infml* a child or young person【非正式】小孩；年輕人: *My kids are two and six.* 我的兩個孩子，一個兩歲，一個六歲。| *college kids* 大學生 | *It's immoral putting kids in uniform and sending them to fight a war.* 讓孩子們穿上軍裝去作戰是不道德的。	正式與非正式: 在學生的作文中用這個字是否正確?

Usage Notes
用法說明

‡**much²** *det, pron, n* **more, most 1** used in questions asking about the amount of something that there is 多少〔用於問句詢問數量〕: *How much cheese have we got left?* 我們還剩下多少乾酪? | *How much does it cost?* 這東西多少錢?**2** *fml* a large amount【正式】許多; 大量: *I have much pleasure in welcoming you today.* 今天我能來歡迎你, 十分榮幸。 | *Much of what he says it ture.* 他說的很多都是實話。

■USAGE 用法: Much is not usually used in simple statements. Instead use **a great deal of** or **a lot of** ☆ 在簡單的陳述句裡 much 不常用, 而用 **a geat deal of** 或 **a lot of**: *She's got* **a lot of** *money.* 她有很多錢。 | *We've already collected* **a great deal of** *information.* 我們已經搜集了很多信息。 | **a lot of** *trouble* 很多麻煩 | **a great deal of** *discomfort* 很不舒服

對單詞作出補充說明, 並解釋相近詞語的意義和用法。

Opposites
反義詞

‡**hap·py** /ˈhæpɪ; ˈhæpi/ *adj* **happier, happiest 1** feeling, expressing, or giving pleasure and satisfaction 高興的; 愉快的; 幸福的; 滿意的: *a happy child* 快樂的孩子 | *You look very happy* 你看上去很高興。 | *a happy marriage* 美滿的婚姻 | *I'm not very happy about their decision.* 我對他們的決定不太滿意。 —opposite 反義 **unhappy**

列出反義詞。

Related words
有關詞匯

a·the·ist /ˈeɪθɪɪst; ˈeɪθi-ɪst/ *n* a person who does not believe in the existence of God 無神論者 – compare 比較 AGNOSTIC –**atheistic** /ˌeɪθɪˈɪstɪk; ˌeɪθiˈɪstɪk/ *adj*

列出有關的詞或可能混淆的詞。

Idioms
慣用語

* **hab·it** /ˈhæbɪt; ˈhæbɪt/ *n* **1** [C;U] something you do regularly, often without thinking 習慣: *She has the annoying habit of biting her fingernails.* 她有咬指甲的惡習。 | *He smokes only out of habit.* 他吸煙只是一種習慣。 | *I can't get him to break the habit.* 我無法令他改掉這一習慣。**2** [C] a special set of clothes worn by members of some religious groups 法衣 **3 be in the habit of doing something** to do something regularly 定期做某事: *We're in the habit of meeting for lunch on Fridays.* 我們總是在星期五見面並共進午餐。

慣用語和固定片語[短語]在此列出。相近或可替換的片語[短語]在相關詞組中列出。

A, a

A, a /eɪ; eɪ/ **A's, a's** *or* **As, as** the 1st letter of the English alphabet 英語的第一個字母

A a note in Western music 〔西洋音樂中的〕A 音; A 調

★★ **a** /ə; ə; *strong* 強讀 eɪ; eɪ/ *indefinite article, det* (also **an** before a vowel sound 在元音前用 **an**) **1** one 一個: *There was a man standing by the door.* 在門邊站着一名男子。| *She's an artist.* 她是位藝術家。**2** used before some words of quantity 〔用於某些數量詞前〕: *a few weeks* 幾個星期 | *a lot of people* 許多人 | *a little water* 一點水 **3** every 每; 任何的: *A bicycle has two wheels.* 腳踏車有兩個輪子。**4** every or each 每一: *six times a day* 每天六次 | *£3 a packet* 每包三英鎊 | *We're paid ten pounds an hour.* 人家付我們每小時十英鎊。**5** used before someone's name when you do not know the person 有位, 有個〔用於不認識的人的名字前〕: *There's a Mr Robinson on the telephone for you.* 有位羅賓遜先生來電話找你。—see 見 AN (USAGE 用法) **6** when you have several points you want to make, you can order them and show where each one starts by using "a", "b", "c", etc.; teachers and speakers on technical subjects do this, and some people use them in conversation 第一〔要表述數個論點時, 可使用 a, b, c 等順序進行羅列; 教師和演講者常這樣做, 有些人在交談中也使用這幾個字母〕: *There are two reasons why the plant has failed to flower: a, it hasn't had enough light and, b, the temperature hasn't been sufficiently high.* 這株植物不能開花有兩個原因; 第一, 光照不足, 第二, 溫度不夠。| *"Do you think he'll get the job?" "Well, I don't really because, a, he hasn't got the qualifications and, b, he hasn't got much experience."* "你認為他能得到這份工作嗎?" "哦, 我認為他不能, 原因是, 首先是他資歷不夠, 其次是他經驗不多。"

ab·a·cus /ˈæbəkəs; ˈæbəkəs/ *n* **abacuses** a frame holding wires on which small balls can be moved, used for counting 算盤

★ **a·ban·don** /əˈbændən; əˈbændən/ *v* [T] **1** to leave someone or something for a long time or for ever 放棄, 離棄, 遺棄〔某人, 某物〕: *The sailors abandoned the sinking ship.* 船員們放棄了下沉的船。| *He abandoned his wife.* 他遺棄妻子。| *an abandoned building* 棄置的建築物 **2** to stop an activity without finishing it or getting the result you want 〔未完成或未獲得預定結果而〕放棄; 中止: *The search was abandoned when night came.* 由於天色已晚, 大家放棄了搜尋。**3** **abandon**

yourself to to allow yourself to be completely controlled by a feeling 放縱自己; 盡情: *He abandoned himself to despair.* 他陷入絕望中。**–abandonment** *n* [U]

a·base /əˈbes; əˈbeɪs/ *v* **abased, abasing** *fml* 〔正式〕 **abase yourself** to behave in a way that makes you lose pride or respect for yourself 自貶

a·bashed /əˈbæʃt; əˈbæʃt/ *adj* uncomfortable or ashamed in the presence of others 羞愧的; 侷促不安的: *He looked suitably abashed as his mistakes were pointed out.* 錯誤給人指出來時, 他的臉上立即露出羞慚的神色。

a·bate /əˈbet; əˈbeɪt/ *v* **abated, abating** [I] *fml* to become less strong 〔正式〕減弱; 降低: *The ship waited in the harbour until the storm abated.* 在暴風雨減弱之前, 船一直在港內等着。

ab·at·toir /ˈæbətwɑr; ˈæbətwɑːʳ/ *n BrE* a building in which animals are killed for meat〔英式〕屠宰場

ab·bess /ˈæbɪs; ˈæbɪs/ *n* a woman who is the head of a religious establishment for women called a CONVENT 女修道院院長

ab·bey /ˈæbɪ; ˈæbi/ *n* a building in which nuns (NUN) or monks (MONK) live or lived 修道院

ab·bot /ˈæbət; ˈæbət/ *n* a man who is the head of a religious establishment for men called a MONASTERY 男修道院院長

ab·bre·vi·ate /əˈbriːvɪ,et; əˈbriːvieɪt/ *v* **abbreviated, abbreviating** [T] to make something shorter, usually a word, a talk or a piece of writing 縮短〔單詞、談話或文章〕; 縮寫

ab·bre·vi·a·tion /ə,briːvɪˈeʃən; ə,briːviˈeɪʃən/ *n* a short form of a word, usually used in writing; for example, 'adj.' is an abbreviation for 'adjective' 縮略語, 縮寫〔例如 adj. 是 adjective 的縮寫〕

ab·di·cate /ˈæbdə,ket; ˈæbdɪkeɪt/ *v* **abdicated, abdicating 1** [I] to officially give up the position of king or queen 正式放棄王位; 讓位; 遜位: *The King abdicated in favour of his son.* 國王讓位給兒子。**2** **abdicate responsibility** to refuse to be responsible for something any longer 放棄責任 **–abdication** /,æbdəˈkeʃən; ,æbdɪˈkeɪʃən/ *n* [C;U]

ab·do·men /ˈæbdəmən; ˈæbdəmən/ *n tech* a part of your body below your chest, that includes your stomach and bowels〔術語〕腹部 **–abdominal** /æbˈdɑmənḷ; æbˈdɒmɪnḷ/ *adj* : *abdominal pains* 腹痛

ab·duct /æb'dʌkt; æb'dʌkt/ v [T] to take someone away unlawfully, often by force 誘拐, 綁架〔某人〕: The police think the missing woman may have been abducted. 警方認為那失蹤的女人可能已被綁架。 –abduction /-'dʌkʃən; -'dʌkʃən/ n [C;U]

a·bet /ə'bɛt; ə'bɛt/ v -tt- [T] aid and abet to help someone to do something wrong or dishonest 幫助他人幹壞事或欺詐

a·bey·ance /ə'beɪəns; ə'beɪəns/ n fml《正式》in abeyance not in use at the moment 中止; 暫擱; 緩辦: These rules are temporarily in abeyance. 這些規則暫停執行。| an old custom that has fallen into abeyance 已不再奉行的舊習俗

ab·hor /əb'hɔr; əb'hɔːr/ v -rr- [T; not in progressive forms 不用於進行式] to hate something very much 憎恨, 痛恨, 厭惡〔某事物〕: Most people abhor cruelty to children. 大多數人痛恨虐待兒童的行為。

ab·hor·rent /əb'hɔrənt; əb'hɒrənt/ adj hateful or unacceptable 可恨的; 可惡的: The idea of killing animals for food is abhorrent to many people. 許多人覺得為了吃肉而殺死動物是可惡的行為。| I find his behaviour abhorrent. 我發覺他的行為很可惡。 –abhorrence n [U]

a·bide¹ /ə'baɪd; ə'baɪd/ v abided, abiding [T] can't abide to dislike something very much 非常討厭〔某事物〕: I can't abide noisy children. 我非常討厭吵鬧的孩子。| He never could abide queuing. 他非常討厭排隊。 –see 見 BEAR² (USAGE 用法)

abide by sth phr v [T] to follow or obey rules, agreements, and decisions 遵守〔規則、協議和決定〕: If you join the club you must abide by its rules. 你如果參加俱樂部, 就必須遵守它的規章。

a·bide² v **abode** /ə'bod; ə'bəud/, **abided**, **abiding** to stay or live somewhere (a word which is no longer used in modern English) 逗留, 居留〔此詞在現代英語中不再使用〕

a·bid·ing /ə'baɪdɪŋ; ə'baɪdɪŋ/ adj lasting for a long time 持續的; 持久的: The experience left me with an abiding hatred of dogs. 那次經歷使我從此對狗憎恨不已。

a·bil·i·ty /ə'bɪlətɪ; ə'bɪlɨti/ n abilities [C; U] skill and power to do something 能力: She has the ability to think and write clearly. 她有清楚思考和寫作的能力。| a person of great musical ability 音樂才華很高的人 | a job more suited to his abilities 更能發揮他才能的工作

ab·ject /æb'dʒɛkt; 'æbdʒekt/ adj 1 abject poverty extreme poverty, deserving great pity 赤貧; 一貧如洗 2 an abject apology an apology showing lack of pride or self-respect 卑聲下氣的道歉

a·blaze /ə'blez; ə'bleɪz/ adj [never before a noun 不能用於名詞前] 1 on fire 着火的: The wooden house was quickly ablaze. 那木屋很

快便燒了起來。 2 very bright 明亮的; 發光的: The village was ablaze with light. 整個村莊燈火通明。

a·ble /'ebl; 'eɪbəl/ adj 1 able to do something having enough power, skill, knowledge, time, or money to do something 能夠〔有力量、技能、知識、時間或金錢〕幹某事: Will you be able to come? 你能來嗎? | We might be able to afford a new car next year. 我們明年也許能買得起新車。| I was only able to do three questions in the exam. 在考試中我只做出三道題。| I wasn't able to contact him. 我不能聯絡上他。| At last I was able to get the door open. 我終於把門弄開了。 2 clever or skilled at doing something 聰明能幹的; 熟練的: a very able student 十分能幹的學生

a·bly /'ebli; 'eɪbli/ adv with skill 巧妙地: She organized the meeting very ably. 她把會議組織得很巧妙。

ab·nor·mal /æb'nɔrml; æb'nɔːməl/ adj different from what is usual or expected and so worrying in some way 反常的; 不正常的: She was afraid the child was abnormal. 她怕這孩子有些不正常。| abnormal levels of radiation 異常的輻射能級 –abnormally adv: He was behaving abnormally. 他舉止反常。| It was abnormally hot. 天氣熱得反常。 –abnormality /ˌæbnɔr'mælətɪ; ˌæbnɔː'mælɨti/ n abnormalities [C; U]

a·board /ə'bɔrd; ə'bɔːd/ adv, prep [never before a noun 不能用於名詞前] on or into a ship, aircraft, train or bus 在船〔飛機、火車、公共汽車〕上; 上船〔飛機、火車、公共汽車〕: The boat is ready to leave. All aboard! 船要開了, 請各位上船! | The plane crashed, killing everyone aboard. 飛機墜毀了, 機上人員全部遇難。

a·bode /ə'bod; ə'bəud/ n fml your home, or the place where you live《正式》住所; 住處: She has the right of abode in the U.K. 她有英國的居住權。| a person of no fixed abode 居無定所的人

a·bol·ish /ə'bɑlɪʃ; ə'bɒlɪʃ/ v [T] to bring something to an end by law〔依法〕廢除; 廢止: Slavery was abolished in England in the 19th century. 英國在十九世紀廢除了奴隸制。 –abolition /ˌæbə'lɪʃən; ˌæbə'lɪʃən/ n [U]: the abolition of the death penalty 廢除死刑

a·bom·i·na·ble /ə'bɑmənəbl; ə'bɒmɨnəbəl/ adj extremely bad, unpleasant, or shocking 極壞的; 討厭的; 令人震驚的: The judge said it was the most abominable crime he had ever heard of. 法官說這是他聽說過的最可惡的罪行。 –abominably adv

ab·o·rig·i·nal /ˌæbə'rɪdʒənl; ˌæbə'rɪdʒɨnəl/ adj belonging to or concerning the people who have lived in a place from the earliest times 土著的

ab·o·rig·i·ne /ˌæbə'rɪdʒəni; ˌæbə'rɪdʒɨni/ n (also 又作 **Aborigine**) a member of one of the tribes living in Australia when European people arrived 〔澳大利亞〕土著居民

a·bort /ə'bɔːt; ə'bɔːt/ v **1** [I; T] to end a PREGNANCY, usually intentionally, when the baby is still too small to live 使墮胎; 使〔胎兒〕流產; 小產: *The doctor had to abort the baby.* 醫生不得不把胎兒打掉。 | *Many women abort spontaneously in the early weeks of pregnancy.* 很多婦女在懷孕的最初幾週小產。 **2** [T] to end a plan or process before it has been finished 使〔計劃, 過程〕夭折, 中止: *The space flight had to be aborted because of difficulties with the computer.* 那次太空飛行因電腦故障而不得不中止。

a·bor·tion /ə'bɔːʃən; ə'bɔːʃən/ n [C; U] the intentional ending of a PREGNANCY when the baby is still too small to live 墮胎; 人工流產: *She was advised to have an abortion.* 她被勸墮胎。 | *a debate on the question of abortion* 關於墮胎問題的爭論

a·bor·tive /ə'bɔːtɪv; ə'bɔːtɪv/ adj unsuccessful (used of actions or plans) 不成功的〔指行動、計劃〕: *an abortive attempt by the army to take power* 軍方企圖奪權但行動失敗

a·bound /ə'baʊnd; ə'baʊnd/ v [I] fml 〔正式〕 **1** to exist in large numbers 大量存在: *Rumours abound on the subject of his marriage.* 關於他婚姻的流言多極了。 **2** to contain large numbers of 盛產: *The rivers abound with fish.* 這些河裡有很多魚。

★★**a·bout**¹ /ə'baʊt; ə'baʊt/ prep **1** on a particular subject 關於; 對於: *We talked about the weather.* 我們談論天氣。 | *a book about birds* 一本關於鳥類的書 | *I haven't had time to think about your idea yet.* 我還沒時間考慮你的意見。 **2** in a place 在〔某處〕裡: *He's somewhere about the house.* 他就在這房子裡的甚麼地方。 | *There were books lying about the room.* 房間裡到處散放着書。 **3** about someone in someone's appearance, or their way of behaving 〔從外表、行為中顯出〕某人有…的氣質〔特點〕: *There was something mysterious about him.* 他顯得有點神祕。 **4** what about, how about: a a phrase used when you are introducing a new idea into a conversation …怎麼樣〔怎麼辦〕〔用於會話中引入新看法〕: *Yes, but what about animals? They have rights as well, don't they?* 是啊, 可是動物怎麼辦? 牠們也有權利, 對不對? **b** a phrase used when you are suggesting that someone could do something, or inviting them to do it …怎麼樣〔用於建議某人做某事, 或者邀請別人做〕: *How about a drink?* 喝一杯好不好? | *How about coming round for a meal later?* 過一會兒來吃飯怎麼樣?

★★**about**² adv **1** in a place, often not doing very much 〔悠閒地〕在某處; 呆着: *People were lying about in the sun.* 人們在躺着曬太陽。 | *We spent the morning just sitting about.* 我們就這麼坐着打發了一個早上。 **2** in a place and able to be used or obtained 在附近; 在用得着或取得到的地方: *Is there a pair of scissors about?* 近旁有剪刀嗎? | *Is your mother about?* 你媽媽在附近嗎? | *I'm afraid there's no-one about to deal with your query at the moment.* 恐怕現在周圍沒人能解答你的疑問。 **3** near to a particular amount 大約: *There were about 50 people there.* 那兒大約有五十個人。 | *He arrived about ten minutes later.* 他大約是十分鐘後到的。 **4 be about to do something** to be just going to do something 正要做某事: *We were about to leave when the phone rang.* 我們正要離開, 電話鈴響了。 | *They're about to move house.* 他們快要搬家了。

★★**a·bove** /ə'bʌv; ə'bʌv/ adv, prep **1** adv, prep higher than something or over it 高於, 在…之上: *The sky above us was clear and blue.* 我們頭上的天空晴朗蔚藍。 | *flying just above the surface of the water* 貼在水面上飛 | *We could hear shouting coming from the flat above.* 我們能聽到樓上傳來的叫喊聲。 | *Birds were circling round in the sky up above.* 鳥兒在天上盤旋。 –see picture on page 764 見 764 頁彩圖 **2** adv, prep more than a particular number or amount 超過〔一定的數量〕: *Don't let your overdraft rise above £1000.* 別讓你的透支超過一千英鎊。 | *The temperature had risen to above freezing.* 溫度已經升到冰點以上。 | *children aged seven and above* 七歲及七歲以上的孩子 **3** adv, prep higher in rank or power than someone else 〔級別或權力〕高於: *He's just above me in the hierarchy.* 他只是級別比我高。 | *Anybody of the rank of captain and above will be invited.* 上尉及上尉以上軍官都會受到邀請。 **4** adv on an earlier page or higher up on the same page 上述: *The figures given above show that pollution is still increasing in an alarming way.* 上述數字表明污染仍在驚人地增加。 **5 above something, above doing something** too good, too honest, or too proud to do something 〔因優良、誠實、自負而〕不至於做某事: *I'm sure he's above stealing.* 我肯定他不會偷東西的。 **6 above all** most important of all; you use this when you are coming to your most important point 最重要的〔用於談到最重要的觀點時〕: *For this job, you need to be reliable and you need to be good with people but, above all, you need a sense of humour.* 這份工作要求你為人可靠, 善於和人相處, 但最重要的是你要有幽默感。

a·bove-board /ə'bʌv,bɔːd; ə,bʌv'bɔːd◂/ adj [never before a noun 不能用於名詞前] open and honest 光明正大的; 誠實的: *His part in the affair was quite aboveboard.* 在這件事上, 他的行為相當光明磊落。

a·bra·sive /ə'breɪsɪv; ə'breɪsɪv/ adj **1** rough (used to describe a substance which will make a surface smooth and clean) 粗糙的〔用於形容能使平面光滑乾淨的物體〕 **2** rather

---

A

rude and offensive 很粗魯的; 粗暴的: *Her manner is particularly abrasive.* 她的態度特別粗暴。

a·breast /ə'brest; ə'brest/ *adv* [never before a noun不能用於名詞前] **1** side by side and facing the same direction 並排; 並肩: *lines of soldiers marching five abreast* 五人並行的士兵列隊 **2** keep/be abreast of to know the most recent facts about something 知道〔某事的〕最近動態: *She read the papers to keep abreast of the latest developments.* 她經常看報瞭解形勢。

a·bridge /ə'brɪdʒ; ə'brɪdʒ/ *v* abridged, abridging [T] to make a speech or a piece of writing shorter by taking parts out 刪節, 節略〔語言或文章〕: *This book is an abridged version of Dickens' original novel.* 這本書是狄更斯小説原作的節寫本。–**abridgment** *n*

*a·broad** /ə'brɔd; ə'brɔːd/ *adv* [never before a noun 不能用於名詞前] to or in another country 到國外; 在國外: *He lived abroad for many years.* 他在國外住了很多年。| *Are you going abroad this summer?* 今年夏天你去國外嗎?

a·brupt /ə'brʌpt; ə'brʌpt/ *adj* **1** sudden and unexpected 突然的; 出其不意的: *The train came to an abrupt halt.* 火車突然剎車。**2** rough and rather rude in the way you speak or behave〔説話、行為〕粗魯的, 無禮的: *She had a rather abrupt manner.* 她的態度相當粗魯。–**abruptly** *adv* –**abruptness** *n* [U]

ab·scess /'æb,sɛs; 'æbses/ *n* a swelling on or in your body containing a thick yellow-ish liquid called PUS 膿腫

ab·scond /æb'skɑnd; əb'skɒnd/ *v* [I] *fml* to run away suddenly and secretly, usually because you have done something wrong〔正式〕〔通常因做了壞事而〕潛逃: *He absconded with all the money.* 他攜了所有款項潛逃。| *They absconded from the police station.* 他們從警察局潛逃了。

*ab·sence** /'æbsn̩s; 'æbsəns/ *n* **1** [C;U] the state or time of not being in a place, or of being away 不在; 缺席: *Please look after the house during my absence.* 我不在時, 請幫我照看房子。| *Absence makes the heart grow fonder.* 眼不見, 心更念〔人不在, 情更深〕。**2** [U] non-existence or lack 不存在; 缺乏: *The biggest problem facing the police is the absence of reliable information.* 警方面臨的最大問題是缺乏可靠的情報。

ab·sent¹ /'æbsn̩t; 'æbsənt/ *adj* **1** not present 缺席的; 不在的: *Four students are absent from class today.* 今天有四名學生缺課。**2** [only before a noun 只用於名詞前] showing lack of attention to what is happening 漫不經心的; 心不在焉的: *an absent look on his face* 他臉上一種心不在焉的神情

ab·sent² /æb'sent; əb'sent/ *v fml* 〔正式〕**absent yourself** to stay away 不到場; 缺席: *He absented himself from the meeting.* 他沒有出席會議。

ab·sen·tee /,æbsn̩'ti; ,æbsən'tiː◂/ *n* a person who stays away 缺席者: *There are fewer absentees in the summer because the children are healthier.* 夏天孩子們身體較為健康, 所以缺席者也較少。| *an absentee landlord* 遙領地主〔房主〕

ab·sen·tee·is·m /,æbsn̩'tiːzəm; ,æbsən'tiːɪzəm/ *n* [U] the act of staying away from school or from your place of work with no good reason 曠工; 曠課: *The level of absenteeism in this factory is much too high.* 這家工廠的曠工率過高。

ab·sent·ly /'æbsn̩tli; 'æbsəntli/ *adv* in a manner showing lack of attention 漫不經心地; 心不在焉地

absent-mind·ed /,···◂/ *adj* forgetful or too concerned with your thoughts to notice what is happening or what you are doing 心不在焉的 –**absent-mindedly** *adv* –**absent-mindedness** *n* [U]

*ab·so·lute** /'æbsə,lut; 'æbsəluːt/ *adj* **1** complete and total 完全的; 純粹的; 絕對的: *a man of absolute honesty* 絕對誠實的人 | *That's absolute nonsense!* 那純粹是胡説八道! **2** having limitless power 有無限權力的; 專制的: *the power of an absolute monarch* 專制君主的權力 **3** not depending on or measured by comparison with other things 絕對的; 不依靠他物或與他物比較而言的: *In absolute terms, wages have risen, but not in comparison with the cost of living.* 從絕對意義上説, 工資有所增長, 但與生活費用相比就並非如此了。–compare 比較 RELATIVE

*ab·so·lute·ly** /'æbsə,lutli; 'æbsəluːtli/ *adv* **1** completely 完全地; 絕對地: *It's difficult to cross the desert by car, but not absolutely impossible.* 乘汽車穿越沙漠很困難, 但不是完全不可能的。| *I'm absolutely exhausted.* 我筋疲力盡。**2** a word used to show that you completely agree with someone 當然; 對極了〔用於完全同意別人〕: *"Do you think so?" "Absolutely!"* "你認為是這樣嗎?" "肯定是!"

ab·so·lu·tion /,æbsə'luʃən; ,æbsə'luːʃən/ *n* [U] forgiveness given by the Christian church for an offence against a religious law〔基督教的〕赦罪

ab·solve /æb'sɑlv; əb'zɒlv/ *v* absolved, absolving [T] to free someone from a responsibility or duty, or from having to be punished for a wrong 免除〔責任〕; 赦免〔罪責〕: *The report absolved her from all blame.* 這份報告免除了她所有的責任。

*ab·sorb** /əb'sɔrb; əb'sɔːb/ *v* [T] **1** to take in heat, light, or a liquid 吸收〔熱、光、液體〕: *The drug is absorbed through the skin.* 該藥通過皮膚吸收。**2** to understand or take in information 理解, 獲取〔信息〕: *We are constantly absorbing new ideas.* 我們經常吸收新思想。**3** to accept or deal with something easily, without any serious effects 吸收, 消化〔某物〕: *The company has been able to absorb these extra costs.* 公司已經能夠負擔這些

額外成本。**4** to take all someone's interest or attention 全貫貫注；專心致志: *The new baby absorbs all her energy.* 新生嬰孩使她耗盡精力。**5** to gain control over a smaller group or company 併吞: *The company has absorbed all its rivals.* 這家公司兼併了所有對手。–**absorption** /-ɔrpʃən; -ɔːpʃən/ *n* [U]

ab·sorbed /əbˈsɔrbd; əbˈsɔːbd/ *adj* giving all your attention to something 全神貫注的: *He was soon absorbed in his book.* 他很快就專心看書了。| *She is absorbed by her own problems.* 她全神貫注於自己的問題。

ab·sor·bent /əbˈsɔrbənt; əbˈsɔːbənt/ *adj* able to take in liquids 能吸收液體的

ab·sorb·ing /əbˈsɔrbɪŋ; əbˈsɔːbɪŋ/ *adj* very interesting 極有趣的；引人入勝的: *I find my new course absorbing.* 我覺得新課程非常有趣。

ab·stain /əbˈsten; əbˈsteɪn/ *v* [I] **1** to intentionally not do something you enjoy doing 戒除: *Jack was advised to abstain from alcohol for a few days.* 傑克被勸告要戒幾天的酒。**2** to not vote, rather than voting for or against something 〔投票〕棄權: *I couldn't decide who to vote for, so in the end I abstained.* 我無法決定該選誰,因此最後棄權。

ab·sten·tion /æbˈstɛnʃən; əbˈstenʃən/ *n* [C; U] an act of not voting rather than voting for or against something 〔投票〕棄權: *50 votes for, 35 against, and 7 abstentions* 50 票贊成,35 票反對,7 票棄權

ab·sti·nence /ˈæbstənəns; ˈæbstɪnəns/ *n* [U] the act of keeping away from things you enjoy 禁戒〔喜愛的事物〕

ab·stract¹ /æbˈstrækt; ˈæbstrækt/ *adj* **1** general, and not related to a particular situation 抽象的;非具體的;理論上的: *an abstract argument about justice* 關於正義的抽象辯論 | *abstract thought* 抽象思維 **2** not trying to represent objects as they would be seen by a camera (used of works of art) 抽象派的〔指藝術〕: *an abstract painting* 抽象派畫作

abstract² /ˈæbstrækt; ˈæbstrækt/ *n* **1** a shortened form of a speech or piece of writing 〔演講、文章等的〕摘要 **2** something that does not try to represent an object as it would be seen by a camera (used of works of art) 抽象派作品〔指藝術〕: *a large abstract by Picasso* 畢加索的大幅抽象畫作

ab·stract³ /æbˈstrækt; əbˈstrækt/ *v* [T] to separate out important pieces of information from a speech or piece of writing 摘錄,節錄〔演講、文章等的要點〕

ab·stract·ed /æbˈstræktɪd; əbˈstræktɪd/ *adj* lost in thought, and so not noticing what is happening 心不在焉的;出神的 –**abstractedly** *adv*

ab·strac·tion /æbˈstrækʃən; əbˈstrækʃən/ *n* **1** [U] a state in which you are thinking deeply and do not notice what is happening around you 出神;心不在焉 **2** [C] an idea which is general and not related to the material world 抽象概念: *A good judge must consider all the facts of a case as well as the abstraction "justice".* 好的法官不但要考慮抽象的"正義"概念,而且要考慮案件的全部事實。

ab·struse /æbˈstrus; əbˈstruːs/ *adj fml* difficult to understand 〔正式〕深奧的;難懂的: *a rather abstruse argument* 相當深奧的論點

ab·surd /əbˈsɝd; əbˈsɜːd/ *adj* foolish or senseless 愚蠢的;不合理的;荒謬的: *It's absurd not to wear a coat in such cold weather.* 這麼冷的天氣不穿一件外套,真是荒唐。–**absurdly** *adv* –**absurdity** /əbˈsɝdəti; əbˈsɜːdəti/ *n* **absurdities** [C;U]

a·bun·dance /əˈbʌndəns; əˈbʌndəns/ *n* **1** an **abundance of** a very great quantity of 大量;豐富: *The country has an abundance of skilled workers, but not enough jobs.* 這個國家有大量技術熟練的工人,卻沒有足夠的就業機會。**2** in **abundance** in large numbers or great quantity 大量: *There was food and drink in abundance.* 有很多飲品和食物。

a·bun·dant /əˈbʌndənt; əˈbʌndənt/ *adj* existing in great quantity 大量的;豐富的: *abundant supplies of oil and gas* 石油和天然氣供應充裕 –**abundantly** *adv*

a·buse¹ /əˈbjuz; əˈbjuːz/ *v* **abused, abusing** [T] **1** to say very rude or cruel things to someone 辱罵 **2** to treat someone cruelly or violently 虐待: *She had been beaten and sexually abused.* 她被毆打和性虐待。**3** to use something badly or wrongly 濫用;妄用: *He had abused his power.* 他濫用職權。

*a·buse² /əˈbjus; əˈbjuːs/ *n* **1** [U] rude or cruel words 辱罵;刻薄的話: *He greeted me with a stream of abuse.* 他見到我就連聲辱罵。**2** [U] cruel or violent treatment of someone 虐待: *physical abuse of children* 對兒童施以體罰 **3** [C;U] wrong or bad use of something 妄用;濫用: *the problem of drug abuse* 濫用藥物問題 | *This is an abuse of your position.* 這是濫用你的職權。

a·bu·sive /əˈbjusɪv; əˈbjuːsɪv/ *adj* using unkind, rude, or cruel language 辱罵性的: *an abusive letter* 罵人的信 –**abusively** *adv*

a·bys·mal /əˈbɪzml; əˈbɪzməl/ *adj* very bad 極糟的: *The food was abysmal.* 食物糟透了。

a·byss /əˈbɪs; əˈbɪs/ *n* **1** a deep hole which appears to have no bottom 深淵 **2** a strong feeling that there is no hope 絕望感: *an abyss of despair* 絕望的深淵

A/C an abbreviation for 〔縮〕 = ACCOUNT¹ (5)

a·ca·cia /əˈkeʃə; əˈkeɪʃə/ *n* **acacias** or **acacia** a tree found mainly in hot countries 金合歡

*ac·a·dem·ic¹ /ˌækəˈdɛmɪk; ˌækəˈdemɪk/ *adj* **1** concerning the teaching or studying of subjects taught to provide skills for the mind, especially in a college or university 〔尤指大專院校〕教學上的: *academic subjects* 學科 | *academic qualifications* 學術資格 **2**

not practical or useful 脫離實際的: *What car to buy is a purely academic question for me, because I can't afford one at all!* 對我而言，買甚麼車這個問題純屬空談，因為我根本沒錢買車!

a·cad·e·mic² *n* a college or university teacher 大學教師

a·cad·e·my /ə'kædəmɪ; ə'kædəmi/ *n* **acad·emies 1** a society of people interested in encouraging art, science, or literature〔藝術、科學、文學等的〕學術機構; 學院; 學會 **2** a school for training in a special art or skill 專科院校: *a military academy* 軍事學院 | *an academy of music* 音樂學院

ac·cede /æk'sid; ək'siːd/ *v* **acceded, acceding** *fml*【正式】**accede to something: a** to agree to do or accept something 同意某事; 接受某事: *He finally acceded to our request.* 他最終同意了我們的請求。**b** to take a high post or position after someone has left it 繼任; 就職

ac·cel·e·rate /æk'sɛlə,ret; ək'seləreɪt/ *v* **accelerated, accelerating 1** [I] to move faster 加速: *The car accelerated.* 汽車加快了速度。| *Jack accelerated to overtake the bus.* 傑克加速以超過那輛公共汽車。**2** [T] to make something happen more quickly 使加快; 促進: *a plan to accelerate the growth of tourism* 一項促進旅遊業發展的計劃 **–acceleration** /æk,sɛlə'reʃən; ək,selə'reɪʃən/ *n* [U]

ac·cel·e·ra·tor /æk'sɛlə,retə; ək'seləreɪtəʳ/ *n* the piece of apparatus in a motor vehicle which is used to increase speed〔汽車的〕加速器, 加速裝置 –see picture on page 209 見 209 頁彩圖

ac·cent¹ /'æksɛnt; 'æksənt/ *n* **1** a particular way of speaking, usually connected with a country, area, or class〔常指某一國家、地區、或階層的〕口音, 腔調: *He speaks with a strong Welsh accent.* 他說話帶有很濃的威爾士口音。**2 the accent** particular importance given to something 重點: *The accent of the report is on safety.* 報告的重點在安全方面。**3** importance given to a word or part of a word by saying it with more force〔加在詞或音節上的〕重音: *The accent in the word "important" is on the second syllable.* "important"一詞的重音是在第二個音節。**4** the mark used above a part of a word in writing or printing to show what kind of sound is needed when it is spoken〔加在書寫或印刷的字母上方的〕重音符號: *Some people write "café" with an acute accent on the "e".* 有些人寫"café"時, 在"e"上面加個重音記號。

ac·cent² /æk'sɛnt; ək'sent/ *v* [T] to pronounce a word or a part of a word with more force 重讀〔一個詞或其中一部分〕

ac·cen·tu·ate /æk'sɛntʃu,et; ək'sentʃueɪt/ **accentuated, accentuating** [T] to make something more important or noticeable

強調; 着重指出: *The dark frame accentuates the brightness of the picture.* 深色畫框更加襯托出這幅畫的明亮色彩。**–accentuation** /æk,sɛntʃu'eʃən; ək,sentʃu'eɪʃən/ *n* [U]

ac·cept /ək'sɛpt; ək'sept/ *v* **1** [I;T] to agree to receive something 同意接受〔某事物〕: *I'm delighted to accept this gift.* 我樂於接受這份禮物。| *The Unions accepted the company's offer.* 工會接受了公司的提議。**2** [I;T] to agree to do or use something 同意做〔某事〕; 同意使用〔某物〕: *He asked her to marry him, and she accepted.* 他向她求婚, 她答應了。| *I never believed that the government would accept free and fair elections.* 我從不相信政府會同意進行自由公正的選舉。| *They refuse to accept new technology.* 他們拒絕使用新技術。**3** [T; +that] to agree that something is true 相信; 承認〔為事實〕: *I accept that it's dangerous, but I want to try.* 我承認這很危險, 但是我想試一試。| *He refused to accept the fact that he was getting old.* 他不肯承認自己老了這一事實。

> **□ USEFUL PATTERNS 有用句型**
> to accept that…; to accept the fact that…

4 [T] to let someone join a course or organization 接受〔某人〕加入: *The college only accepts local students.* 這所學院只招收本地學生。**5** [T] to suffer something unpleasant or difficult without trying to prevent it or change it 忍受: *He accepted the situation for years.* 這種情況他忍受了好些年。**6 accept responsibility** to agree that you are responsible for something 承擔責任

ac·cep·ta·ble /ək'sɛptəbl; ək'septəbəl/ *adj* satisfactory 令人滿意的; 可以接受的: *Your work is not acceptable.* 你的工作做得不夠好。| *This solution was acceptable to everyone involved.* 這個解決方法大家都能接受。–opposite 反義 **unacceptable –acceptably** *adv* **–acceptability** /ək,sɛptə'bɪlətɪ; ək,septə'bɪlɪ̩ti/ *n* [U]

ac·cept·ance /ək'sɛptəns; ək'septəns/ *n* [U] **1** agreement to receive something or someone 接受; 收受: *The Unions recommended acceptance of the offer.* 工會建議接受那個提議。| *Two weeks after applying for the job I received a letter of acceptance.* 申請這份工作的兩週以後, 我收到了一封信, 接受我去工作。**2** agreement that something is true 承認: *their acceptance of the theory* 他們對這一理論的承認 **3** the act of suffering something unpleasant or difficult, without trying to prevent it or change it 忍受; 承受: *his acceptance of defeat* 他承受失敗 **4 gain acceptance, win acceptance** to become popular or liked 受歡迎; 受人喜愛: *The idea is gaining acceptance.* 這個主意受人喜愛。

ac·cess /'æksɛs; 'ækses/ *n* **1** [C] a way to reach or enter a building 接

近或進入之路: *The only access to that building is along a muddy track.* 去那幢樓的唯一途徑是一條泥濘小路。 **2** [U] the ability or right to obtain or use something〔使用、獲取的〕能力, 權利: *Students need easy access to books.* 要使學生很方便就能借到圖書。| *Do you have access to that information?* 你有辦法得到那條信息嗎? **3** [U] the right to see someone〔看望的〕權利: *The court gave him access to his child at weekends.* 法庭給他週末探望孩子的權利。

ac·ces·si·ble /æk'sɛsəbl; ək'sesɪ̩bəl/ *adj* **1** possible to reach 可到達的: *The island is accessible only by boat.* 只有坐船才能到達那個島。 **2** easy to understand and enjoy (used of a book or work of art) 容易理解、欣賞的〔指書、藝術品〕: –opposite 反義 **inaccessible** –**accessibility** /æk,sɛsə'bɪlətɪ; ək,sesɪ̩-'bɪlɪ̩ti/ *n* [U]

ac·ces·sion /æk'sɛʃən; ək'seʃən/ *n* [U] *fml* the act of taking up a high position〔正式〕就任: *her accession to the throne* 她即位女王

ac·ces·so·ry /æk'sɛsərɪ; ək'sesəri/ *n* **accessories 1** something which is not a necessary part of something larger but which makes it more useful, effective or beautiful 附件: *Accessories for this car include a roof rack and a radio.* 這輛汽車的附件包括車頂架和收音機。 **2 accessories** things such as hats, shoes, and gloves, which you wear or carry and which often match your clothes 配襯衣服的物品〔如鞋、帽、手套〕: *a black dress with matching accessories* 配套的黑色女禮服 **3** *law* a person who helps another in doing something criminal〔律〕同謀; 從犯

★**ac·ci·dent** /'æksədənt; 'æksɪ̩dənt/ *n* **1** something unpleasant, undesirable, or damaging that happens without intention or by chance 意外事件; 事故: *There's been a serious accident on the motorway.* 高速公路上發生了一起嚴重事故。| *He was killed in a climbing accident.* 他在登山事故中遇難。| *She had an accident with the tin opener and cut her hand.* 她用開罐器時闖了禍, 割破了手。| *Don't be angry with me — it was an accident.* 別生我的氣——這是個意外。 **2 by accident** by chance 偶然: *He opened her letter by accident.* 他無意中拆了她的信。| *We met by accident.* 我們偶然相遇。

ac·ci·den·tal /,æksə'dɛntl; ,æksɪ̩'dentl◂/ *adj* happening by chance, not by plan or intention 意外的; 偶然的 –**accidentally** *adv*

accident-prone /'··· ·/ *adj* more likely to have accidents than most people 易遭遇意外的

ac·claim¹ /ə'klem; ə'kleɪm/ *v* [T] to praise publicly 稱讚: *The new drug has been acclaimed as the most important discovery for years.* 這種新藥被公認是近年來最重大的發現。

acclaim² *n* [U] strong expressions of approval and praise 歡呼; 喝采; 稱讚: *The*

book received considerable acclaim. 這本書備受讚揚。

ac·cla·ma·tion /,æklə'meʃən; ,æklə'meɪʃən/ *n* [C;U] loud sounds of approval and praise 歡呼; 喝采

ac·cli·ma·tize /ə'klaɪmə,taɪz; ə'klaɪmətaɪz/ *v* **acclimatized, acclimatizing 1** [I;T] to become accustomed to the general weather conditions in a new part of the world (使)適應氣候; (使)服水土: *It took several days to get acclimatized to the atmosphere in Mexico City.* 花了幾天時間才適應墨西哥城的氣候。 **2 acclimatize yourself to something** to become accustomed to something 習慣於某事: *He can't acclimatize himself to working at night.* 他不習慣晚上工作。 –**acclimatization** /ə,klaɪmətə'zeʃən; ə,klaɪmətaɪ'zeɪʃən/ *n* [U]

ac·co·lade /,ækə'led; 'ækəleɪd/ *n* strong praise and approval 讚揚; 讚頌: *His new book received the highest accolade from the critics.* 他的新書受到書評人的高度讚揚。

ac·com·mo·date /ə'kamə,det; ə'kɒmədeɪt/ *v* **accommodated, accommodating** [T] **1** to provide someone with a place in which to live or stay 為〔某人〕提供住宿 **2** to have enough space for something or someone 容納: *enough shelves to accommodate all our books* 有足夠的書架來放我們所有的書 **3** *fml* to change things to help someone or to do what someone wants〔正式〕使適應; 遷就: *We will make every effort to accommodate the needs of our clients.* 我們將盡一切努力來滿足顧客的需求。

ac·com·mo·dat·ing /ə'kamə,detɪŋ; ə'kɒmədeɪtɪŋ/ *adj* willing to help, by changing things if necessary 樂於助人的; 隨和的

★**ac·com·mo·da·tion** /ə,kamə'deʃən; ə,kɒmə'deɪʃən/ *n* [U] somewhere to live, for example a room, flat, house or hotel room 住所; 住處: *The high cost of accommodation makes life difficult for students in London.* 由於住宿費用昂貴, 住在倫敦的學生感到生活困難。

■ USAGE 用法: In British English the word **accommodation** is uncountable and is not, therefore, used in the plural ☆在英式英語中, **accommodation** 為不可數名詞, 所以不用複數形式: *The university offers excellent* **accommodation** *for summer visitors.* 這所大學為夏季來訪者提供了最好的住宿。| *The school provides* **accommodation** *for all its students.* 學校為所有學生提供住宿。(Note that it may be used in the plural in American English. 注意在美式英語中可用複數形式。)

---

ac·com·pa·ni·ment /ə'kʌmpənɪmənt; ə-'kʌmpənimənt/ *n* **1** something which is used or provided with something else 伴隨

物 **2** music played to support singing or another instrument 伴奏

ac·com·pa·nist /ə'kʌmpənɪst; ə'kʌmpən̩ɪst/ *n* a person who plays a musical accompaniment 伴奏者

★**ac·com·pa·ny** /ə'kʌmpənɪ; ə'kʌmpəni/ *v* **accompanied, accompanying** [T] **1** *fml* to go with someone, especially on a journey 〖正式〗伴隨, 陪同〔某人〕: *The Governor was accompanied to the palace by a military escort.* 州長由衛隊陪同進入宮殿。 **2** to appear with someone or something 伴同〔某人〕; 配有〔某物〕: *A series of colour photographs accompanies the text.* 課文配有一系列彩色照片。 **3** to make supporting music for someone 為…〔某人〕伴奏: *The singer was accompanied by a famous pianist.* 一位著名鋼琴家為這歌手伴奏。

ac·com·plice /ə'kʌmplɪs; ə'kʌmpl̩ɪs/ *n* a person who helps someone to carry out a crime 同謀犯; 幫兇, 從犯

ac·com·plish /ə'kʌmplɪʃ; ə'kʌmplɪʃ/ *v* [T] to succeed in doing something 做成功, 完成〔某事〕: *We tried to arrange a meeting but accomplished nothing.* 我們試圖安排一次會議, 但一無所成。

ac·com·plished /ə'kʌmplɪʃt; ə'kʌmplɪʃt/ *adj* good at something 擅長於…的; 有造詣的: *an accomplished singer* 有造詣的演唱家

ac·com·plish·ment /ə'kʌmplɪʃmənt; ə'kʌmplɪʃmənt/ *n* **1** [U] the act of finishing work completely and successfully 完成; 成就: *When he had finished, he felt a real sense of accomplishment.* 完工以後, 他覺得有種真正的成就感。 **2** [C] a skill 才藝: *Being able to play the piano well is just one of his accomplishments.* 鋼琴彈得好僅僅是他的其中一種才藝。

ac·cord¹ /ə'kɔrd; ə'kɔːd/ *v* [I] *fml* to agree 〖正式〗一致: *The evidence of the second witness does not accord* **with** *that of the first.* 第二個證人的證據和第一個的不一致。

accord² *n* **1** [C;U] agreement 一致; 協議: *The two governments are completely in accord on the question of preserving peace.* 兩國政府在維護和平的問題上是完全一致的。 | *accords between neighbouring states* 兩個鄰國之間的協議 **2 of your own accord** without being asked 主動地; 自願地 **3 with one accord** with everybody agreeing 一致(同意)地

ac·cord·ance /ə'kɔrdns; ə'kɔːdəns/ *n* **in accordance with** in agreement with or in obedience to 按照: *Seat belts must be worn, in accordance with the law.* 按照法律規定必須繫上安全帶。

ac·cord·ing·ly /ə'kɔrdɪŋlɪ; ə'kɔːdɪŋli/ *adv* **1** *fml* for the reason just given 〖正式〗從而; 因此: *We see that you have an income of less than £2000 a year. Accordingly, we have decided to grant you free tuition.* 我們發現你的年收入低於二千英鎊。因此, 我們決定免去你的學費。–see Study Note on page 1325 見

1325 頁學習提示 **2** in a suitable way 相應地: *Some events are very formal. Others are very informal. You have to dress accordingly.* 有的社交場合很正式, 有的則很隨便, 你得根據不同情況穿着服裝。 | *If you change your address, please notify the office accordingly.* 如果你的地址有變, 請據此通知辦公室。

★**according to** /·'····/ *prep* **1** as said by someone or shown by something 根據; 依照: *According to our records, you still have six of our desks.* 根據我們的記錄, 你還有六張我們的書桌。 | *According to George, she's a really good teacher.* 據喬治說, 她真是個好老師。 **2** in a way that agrees with something 視…而定: *We will be paid according to the amount of work we do.* 我們的報酬視工作量而定。

■ USAGE 用法: **1** Do not use **according to** when giving your own opinion. Instead use phrases such as, **in my opinion**.... ☆發表自己的意見時不用 **according to**, 而要用 **in my opinion** 等。 **2** Do not use **according to** with words like **opinion** or **view**. ☆**according to** 不和 **opinion** 或 **view** 搭配。Compare 比較: **According to** *the government*.... 按照政府的説法...。 | *In the government's* **view/opinion**.... 政府的看法〔意見〕是...。

ac·cor·di·on /ə'kɔrdɪən; ə'kɔːdiən/ *n* a musical instrument like a box; you play it by pressing both sides in and out to force air through it while working the keys with your fingers 手風琴

ac·cost /ə'kɔst; ə'kɒst/ *v* [T] to go up to and speak to someone, especially a stranger, often in a threatening manner or with the offer of sex 走上前去跟〔陌生人〕説話〔常以威脅口氣, 或提供性服務〕

★**ac·count**¹ /ə'kaunt; ə'kaunt/ *n* **1** [C] a written or spoken report 報道; 敍述: *Give us an account of what happened.* 把發生的事情告訴我們。 | *There was an account of the train crash in the paper.* 報紙上有一篇關於火車事故的報道。 **2** [C] a sum of money kept in a bank which may be added to and taken from 〔銀行的〕賬戶: *I've got an account with First City Bank.* 我在第一城市銀行有個賬戶。 | *My salary is paid directly into my bank account.* 我的工資直接存入銀行賬戶。 **3 accounts** [pl] a record or statement of money received and paid out by a bank, business, person or group 〔銀行的〕賬目: *The accounts show that business is beginning to improve.* 賬面顯示, 營業開始好轉。 | *She does the accounts for a London firm.* 她為倫敦的一家商行管賬。 **4** [C;U] an arrangement which allows you to take goods away and then pay for them later 賒賬: *I'll pay for the shirt now,* *but could you put the shoes on my account, please.* 這件襯衫的錢我現在付，但請把這雙鞋的記在我的賬上。| *Could I take them on account?* 我能賒賬購買嗎？ **5** [C] a statement of money owed 欠賬: *Please pay your account immediately.* 請立刻結清你的欠賬。 **6 by all accounts** according to what everyone says 人人都說; 據說 **7 of great account** of great importance 很重要的 **8 of no account** of no importance 不重要的 **9 on account of** because of 因為; 由於 **10 on no account, not on any account** not for any reason 決不; 切莫: *He must not go there on any account.* 他決不可以去那裡。| *On no account must he go there.* 他絕對不可以去那裡。 **11 on someone's account** out of consideration for someone's wishes 為某人的緣故: *Don't stay up late on my account.* 不要為了我而熬夜。 **12 put/turn something to good account** to really make the best use of something, often unexpectedly 充分利用某事物 **13 take something into account, take account of something** to give proper consideration to something when making a judgment or decision 考慮到某事; 體諒某事: *You must take her illness into account.* 你必須考慮到她的病情。

account[2] *v* **account for something** to give an explanation or reason for something 解釋某事; 說明理由: *He can't account for his mistake.* 他無法解釋他的錯誤。| *How do you account for the fact that you've arrived late every day this week?* 你怎麼解釋本週每天都遲到？

ac·coun·ta·ble /ə'kauntəbl; ə'kauntəbəl/ *adj* [never before a noun 不能用於名詞前] responsible and prepared to give an explanation for your actions 對…負有責任的, 有解釋義務的: *I am not accountable to you for my decisions.* 我沒有義務向你說明我的決定。 –**accountability** /ə,kauntə'bılətı; ə-,kauntə'bıl̩ʒti/ *n* [U]: *demands for an increase in police accountability* 對加強警方責任的要求

ac·coun·tan·cy /ə'kauntənsı; ə'kauntənsi/ *n* (**accounting** *AmE*【美式】) [U] the work or job of an accountant 會計工作

ac·coun·tant /ə'kauntənt; ə'kauntənt/ *n* a person whose job is to keep and examine the money accounts of businesses or people 會計(員、師)

ac·cu·mu·late /ə'kjumjə,let; ə'kju:mjṵleɪt/ *v* **accumulated, accumulating** [I;T] to make or become greater in quantity or size 積累; 積聚: *We've accumulated a large number of books over the years.* 幾年來我們積累了大量書籍。 –**accumulation** /ə,kjumjə'leʃən; ə-,kju:mjṵ'leɪʃn/ *n* [C;U]: *an accumulation of work while I was ill* 我生病時積壓下來的工作

ac·cu·ra·cy /'ækjərəsı; 'ækjṵrəsi/ *n* [U] exactness or correctness 精確; 準確 –op-

posite 反義 **inaccuracy**

*·**ac·cu·rate** /'ækjərıt; 'ækjṵrət/ *adj* exactly correct 準確的; 精確的: *Give me an accurate report of what happened.* 就發生的情況給我寫一份確切的報告。| *Is the station clock accurate?* 火車站的鐘準不準？ –opposite 反義 **inaccurate** –**accurately** *adv*

ac·cu·sa·tion /,ækjə'zeʃən; ,ækjṵ'zeɪʃn/ *n* [C;U] a statement saying that someone has done something wrong or criminal 控告, 譴責〔某人〕: *We were shocked by the accusation that he'd stolen the money.* 他被控告偷錢, 我們都很震驚。| *She's made some pretty serious accusations against the director.* 她對導演提出了非常嚴重的控告。| *accusations of fraud* 告發詐騙行為

*·**ac·cuse** /ə'kjuz; ə'kju:z/ *v* **accused, accusing** [T] to say that someone has done something wrong or has broken the law 控告, 譴責〔某人〕: *He was accused of murder.* 他被控謀殺。| *Are you accusing me of cheating?* 你是在指責我作弊嗎？| *Her teacher accused her of stealing the books.* 她的老師指責她偷書。| *an accusing look* 譴責的神情 –**accuser** *n*

□ USEFUL PATTERNS 有用句型
to accuse someone of something; to accuse someone of doing something

ac·cused /ə'kjuzd; ə'kju:zd/ *n fml*【正式】**the accused** a person charged with a crime 被告: *The accused pleaded not guilty.* 被告申辯無罪。

ac·cus·tom /ə'kʌstəm; ə'kʌstəm/ *v* [T] to make someone used to something 使習慣於〔某事〕: *He had to accustom himself to the cold weather of his new country.* 他不得不使自己習慣那個新國家的寒冷天氣。

ac·cus·tomed /ə'kʌstəmd; ə'kʌstəmd/ *adj* **1 get accustomed to something** *fml* to become used to something【正式】習慣於某事: *It took ages to get accustomed to living abroad.* 要花上好幾年時間才習慣在國外居住。[RELATED PHRASE 相關詞組 **be accustomed to something**] **2** [only before a noun 只用於名詞前] usual 通常的: *sitting in her accustomed place at the table* 坐在桌子旁邊她慣常坐的位置上

ace /es; eɪs/ *n* **1** a playing card that has a single mark on it and usually has the highest or the lowest value〔紙牌的〕幺點, "A"牌 **2** *infml* a person of the highest class or skill in something【非正式】王牌; 第一流好手: *an ace skier* 滑雪好手

ache[1] /ek; eɪk/ *v* **ached, aching** [I] **1** to have or suffer a continuous, but not violent, pain〔持續地、隱隱地〕疼痛: *I'm aching all over.* 我渾身疼痛。| *My head aches.* 我頭痛。 **2 be aching to do something** *infml* to have a strong wish to do something【非正式】渴望做某事: *She was aching to go to the party,*

A

but her parents wouldn't let her. 她渴望去參加聚會，但她父母不讓她去。
ache² *n* a continuous, dull pain〔持續而隱約的〕疼痛: *He's always complaining about his aches and pains.* 他老是抱怨東痛西痛。| *a headache* 頭痛

■ USAGE 用法: **1 Backache, headache, stomachache, toothache** are the most common nouns formed from **ache.** ☆ **backache, headache, stomachache, toothache** 是以 **ache** 結尾構成的最常用的名詞。**2 Headache** is always countable ☆ **headache** 總是可數: *I've got a* **headache.** 我頭痛。The other nouns are usually uncountable ☆其他名詞常不可數: *I've got* **toothache** 我牙痛，but some people treat them as countable, especially when they are talking about a sharp, sudden pain ☆但有人把這些當作可數名詞，尤指突然、劇烈的疼痛時: *The meal gave me* **stomachache/a stomachache.** 這頓飯引起了我的胃痛。

a·chieve /əˈtʃiːv; əˈtʃiːv/ *v* **achieved, achieving** [T] **1** to succeed in doing something 完成，實現〔某事物〕: *He will never achieve anything if he doesn't work harder.* 要是他不更努力一點，他將永遠一事無成。| *We were all exhausted, but felt we had achieved quite a lot.* 我們都累極了，但是感到已取得相當大的成就。**2** to get something as the result of action or effort 獲得，取得〔某事物〕: *As a result of advertising, we've achieved a big increase in sales this year.* 由於做了廣告，我們今年的銷售額獲得了大幅增長。–**achievable** *adj*

a·chieve·ment /əˈtʃiːvmənt; əˈtʃiːvmənt/ *n* **1** [U] the successful finishing or gaining of something 完成；達成: *Passing the exam gave her a real sense of achievement.* 考試及格使她有一種真正的成功感。**2** [C] something successfully finished or gained, especially through skill and hard work 成就；成績；成功: *a remarkable achievement* 令人注目的成就 | *He has broken two world records in one day, which is quite an achievement.* 他在一天之內打破了兩項世界紀錄，那真是了不起的成績。

ac·id¹ /ˈæsɪd; ˈæsⵧd/ *n* **1** [C;U] a chemical substance which may destroy things it touches 酸〔一種對所接觸的物體有腐蝕性的化學物質〕: *The acid burnt a hole in the carpet.* 酸把地毯燒了個洞。| *nitric acid* 硝酸 **2** [U] *slang* the drug LSD〔俚〕迷幻藥 **3 acid test** a test or trial which will prove whether something is as valuable as it is supposed to be 嚴峻的考驗，決定性的試驗〔以證明某物是否如所說的那麼有價值〕: *It looks good, but will it work? That's the acid test!* 這看上去不錯，但是會不會有效? 這得驗證一下!

acid² *adj* **1** having an unpleasantly sour taste 有酸味的 **2** unkind or hurtful 尖酸的; 尖刻的: *an acid remark* 尖刻的話
acid rain /ˌ···ˈ·/ *n* rain which damages trees and plants because it contains acid put out into the air by industry〔由工業所釋放出來的酸所造成的和對樹及其他植物有害的〕酸雨–see picture on page 470 見 470 頁彩圖
a·cid·i·ty /əˈsɪdətɪ; əˈsɪdⵧti/ *n* [U] the quality of being acid 酸性; 酸味
ac·knowl·edge /əkˈnɒlɪdʒ; əkˈnɒlɪdʒ/ *v* **acknowledged, acknowledging 1** [T; +that] to accept something and be prepared to admit it 認可，承認〔某事物〕: *When the results were announced, the Prime Minister acknowledged defeat.* (投票)結果公佈後，首相承認失敗。| *He finally acknowledged that they had been defeated.* 他終於承認他們已被擊敗。| *She acknowledged having made a mistake.* 她承認犯了個錯誤。

□ USEFUL PATTERNS 有用句型
to acknowledge something; to acknowledge that…, to acknowledge doing something

2 [T] to accept something as being legal or real, or as having value 承認〔某事是合法的、真實的或具有價值〕: *The terrorists refused to acknowledge the court.* 恐怖分子拒絕承認法庭 (有權審訊他們)。| *She is acknowledged as an expert on the subject.* 她被公認是這個學科的專家。| *She is acknowledged to be their best tennis player.* 她被公認為她們當中最佳的網球選手。

□ USEFUL PATTERNS 有用句型
to acknowledge something; to acknowledge someone or something as; to acknowledge someone or something to be

3 [T] to state that you have received something 告知收到〔某物〕: *We must acknowledge his letter.* 我們必須通知他已收到了他的來信。**4** [T] to show that you recognize someone, for example by smiling or waving〔以微笑或招手等〕表示認識〔某人〕; 打招呼: *He walked right past me without even acknowledging me.* 他從我身邊走過，連個招呼也沒打。
ac·knowl·edg·ment /əkˈnɒlɪdʒmənt; əkˈnɒlɪdʒmənt/ *n* (also 又作 **acknowledge-ment**) **1** [U] the act of accepting or admitting something 承認; 認可: *the Prime Minister's acknowledgment of defeat* 首相承認失敗 **2** [C] something given, done, or said as a way of thanking or of showing that something has been received 謝禮; 謝意; 表示收到〔某物〕的回音; 回執: *I wrote to them three weeks ago, and I haven't had an acknowledgement yet.* 我三星期前給他們寫了封信，至今未有回音。**3 in acknowledgement of**

in recognition of 致謝; 答謝: *He was given a gold watch in acknowledgement of his services.* 大家給他一隻金錶, 以答謝他的服務。

ac·ne /ˈækni; ˈækni/ *n* [U] a condition, common among young people, in which spots appear on the face and neck 痤瘡; 粉刺

a·corn /ˈekɔːn; ˈeɪkɔːrn/ *n* the fruit of the OAK tree 橡樹果實; 橡栗

a·cous·tic /əˈkuːstɪk; əˈkuːstɪk/ *adj* **1** of sound or the sense of hearing 聲音的; 聽覺的 **2** making its natural sound, not helped by electrical apparatus 不藉助電動裝置而發出自然聲音的; 原聲的: *an acoustic guitar* 原聲吉他

a·cous·tics /əˈkuːstɪks; əˈkuːstɪks/ *n* **1** [U] the scientific study of sound 聲學 **2** [pl] the qualities of a place, especially a hall, which make it good or bad for hearing music and speeches〔尤指大廳內的〕音響效果: *The acoustics of this concert hall are excellent.* 這音樂廳的音響效果極佳。

ac·quaint·ance /əˈkweɪntəns; əˈkweɪntəns/ *n* **1** [C] a person who you know, especially through work or business, but who is not a close friend 相識的人; 泛泛之交 **2** [sing;U] knowledge obtained through personal experience rather than careful study 認識; 了解; 體驗: *I have some acquaintance* **with** *the language.* 我對這種語言有些了解。 **3** **make someone's acquaintance** *fml* to meet someone for the first time〔正式〕結識某人

ac·quaint·ed /əˈkweɪntɪd; əˈkweɪntɪd/ *adj fml*〔正式〕**1** **be acquainted with something** to be familiar with something 熟悉某事; 了解某事: *I am already acquainted with the facts.* 我已了解這些事實。 **2** **be acquainted with someone** to be slightly known to someone socially 認識某人: *We are already acquainted.* 我們已經相識。 **3** **get/become acquainted with someone** to get to know someone 結識某人

ac·qui·esce /ˌækwiˈes; ˌækwiˈes/ *v* **acquiesced, acquiescing** [I] *fml* to agree, often unwillingly but without arguing〔正式〕默許; 默認: *He acquiesced* **in** *the plans his parents had made for him.* 他勉強同意了父母為他擬定的計劃。 **–acquiescence** *n* [U] **–acquiescent** *adj*

★**ac·quire** /əˈkwaɪə; əˈkwaɪər/ *v* **acquired, acquiring** [T] **1** *fml* to get something, especially by your own work, skill, or action〔正式〕〔尤指靠自己的工作、技能或行動而〕獲得, 得到〔某物〕: *I managed to acquire two tickets for the concert.* 我設法弄到了兩張音樂會的票子。 | *The company has recently acquired a new office building in central London.* 這家公司最近在倫敦市中心弄到了一幢新的辦公大樓。 | *Typing is a skill well worth acquiring.* 打字是一項值得掌握的技能。 **2** **acquired taste** something that you may learn to like after a while 逐漸養成的嗜好: *Some alcoholic drinks are an acquired*

taste. 有些酒是慢慢喝上癮的。

★**ac·qui·si·tion** /ˌækwəˈzɪʃən; ˌækwəˈzɪʃən/ *n* **1** [U] the act of acquiring something 獲得; 取得 **2** [C] something that you have acquired 獲得物: *This car is my latest acquisition.* 這輛汽車是我最近得到的。 | *Intel is the latest acquisition of this American computer company.* 英特爾公司最近兼併的這家美國計算機公司。

ac·quis·i·tive /əˈkwɪzətɪv; əˈkwɪzətɪv/ *adj* keen on getting and possessing things (a word used to express disapproval) 貪得無厭的〔用於表示不贊許〕: *He's very acquisitive and has filled his house with things.* 他貪慾很重, 家裡堆滿了東西。 **–acquisitiveness** *n* [U]

ac·quit /əˈkwɪt; əˈkwɪt/ *v* [T] **1** to give a decision in a court of law that someone is not guilty of a crime 宣判〔某人〕無罪: *They acquitted him* **of** *murder.* 他們宣判他被控的殺人罪不成立。 | *He was acquitted.* 他被判無罪。 **–opposite** 反義 **convict** **2** **acquit yourself well/badly** *fml* to perform well or badly〔正式〕表現好〔不好〕: *She acquitted herself rather well in the exam.* 她在考試中表現良好。

ac·quit·tal /əˈkwɪtl; əˈkwɪtl/ *n* [C;U] the act of declaring someone to be not guilty, or the condition of being found not guilty in a court of law (被)宣判無罪 **–opposite** 反義 **conviction**

a·cre /ˈekə; ˈeɪkər/ *n* a unit for measuring land, equal to 4,840 square yards or about 4,047 square metres 英畝〔相等於4840平方碼或約4047平方米〕: *The total area of a football field is about two acres.* 一個足球場的總面積大約是兩英畝。

a·cre·age /ˈekərɪdʒ; ˈeɪkərɪdʒ/ *n* [U] the area of a piece of land measured in acres〔以英畝計算的〕土地面積

ac·rid /ˈækrɪd; ˈækrɪd/ *adj* stinging your eyes and nose 辛辣的; 刺激性的: *the acrid smell of burning wood* 燃燒木頭所發出的刺鼻氣味

ac·ri·mo·ny /ˈækrəmoni; ˈækrəməni/ *n* [U] bitter feeling between people, often strongly expressed 苛刻; 刻薄; 刻毒 **–acrimonious** /ˌækrəˈmoniəs; ˌækrəˈmoʊniəs/ *adj* **–acrimoniously** *adv*

ac·ro·bat /ˈækrəbæt; ˈækrəbæt/ *n* a person skilled in performing difficult physical actions, such as walking on their hands or on the high wire, especially at a CIRCUS (2)〔尤指馬戲團的〕雜技演員 **–acrobatic** /ˌækrəˈbætɪk; ˌækrəˈbætɪk/ *adj*

ac·ro·bat·ics /ˌækrəˈbætɪks; ˌækrəˈbætɪks/ *n* [pl;U] the art or tricks of an acrobat 雜技

★**a·cross** /əˈkrɔs; əˈkrɔs/ *adv, prep* **1** *adv, prep* from one side of something to the other side 橫過; 穿過; 從一邊到另一邊: *We walked across the bridge.* 我們從橋上走過。 | *She stood up and marched*

A

across the room. 她站起來, 大步走到房間的另一端。 | *He drew a straight line across the page.* 他在該頁上劃了一條橫線。 | *We got to the river, and then realized that we had no way of getting across.* 我們走到河邊, 結果發現無法過河。 | *The stream measures six metres across.* 這條小溪有六米寬。 **2** *prep* on the other side of a road or river 在〔路或河流〕的另一邊: *They live just across the road from us.* 他們就住在我們對面, 在馬路的另一邊。–see picture on page 764 見 764 頁彩圖

⭐**act¹** /ækt; ækt/ *v* **1** [I] to do something 採取行動: *The council must act before more people are killed on that road.* 市政委員會必須採取行動, 以防更多的人在那條道路上死於車禍。 | *He had to act swiftly.* 他必須迅速行動。 **2** [I] to behave 舉止; 表現: *The report said that the doctor had acted correctly.* 報告說醫生的診治正確無誤。 | *She's acting very strangely these days.* 她這幾天舉止非常奇怪。 **3** [I;T] to represent a character, especially in a play or film 〔尤指在戲劇或電影中〕扮演〔角色〕, 表演: *Jerome Flynn is acting in Shakespeare's "As You Like It".* 傑羅姆·弗林正在莎士比亞的"皆大歡喜"中扮演一個角色。 | *He's acting the part of Orlando.* 他扮演奧蘭多一角。 | *I can't take her seriously because she always seems to be acting.* 我不會對她認真, 因為她似乎總是在演戲。 **4** [I] to produce an effect 有功效; 起作用: *Does the drug take long to act?* 這藥是否需很長時間才發揮作用? | *It acts on the nervous system.* 它對神經系統起作用。 **5 act as: a** to do a job which is not your usual one, sometimes for only a short time 〔臨時〕擔任; 充當: *She's acting as caretaker while the real one is on holiday.* 原來的那位看管人去度假了, 她是臨時代一下的。 | *His wife's fed up with acting as an unpaid secretary.* 他的太太膩透了當沒報酬的祕書。 **b** to operate as 起...作用; 充作: *The electric wire acts as a fence to keep the animals in.* 這電線起柵欄的作用, 把動物關在裡面。 **6 act for** to represent another person in legal or business affairs 代理; 代表: *the solicitor acting for the buyer* 代表買方的律師 **7 act on** to take action according to advice, suggestions, or information 按照〔勸告、建議或信息〕行動: *They acted on our advice.* 他們按照我們的勸告行事。

act sthg ↔ **out** *phr v* [T] to express thoughts and feelings in actions and behaviour rather than in words 把〔想法等〕付諸行動; 實行

act up *phr v* [I] *infml* to behave or perform badly 〔非正式〕表現差; 出毛病: *His car is acting up again.* 他的汽車又在出毛病了。

⭐**act²** *n* **1** *fml* something that someone has done 〔正式〕行為; 舉動: *a foolish act* 愚蠢的行為 | *an act of cruelty* 殘忍的行為 **2** (also 又作 **Act**) a law 法案: *Parliament has passed an act banning the drug.* 國會通過了一項禁止毒品的法案。 | *the Gun Control Act* 槍枝管制法案 **3** (also 又作 **Act**) one of the main divisions of a play 〔戲劇的〕一幕: *Hamlet kills the king in Act 5, Scene 2.* 哈姆雷特在第五幕第二場中殺死了國王。 | *at the end of the first act* 第一幕的末尾 **4** one of a number of short events in a television show or a theatre or CIRCUS (2) performance 〔電視節目、戲劇或馬戲中的〕一段表演, 節目: *The next act will be a snake charmer.* 下一個節目是耍蛇人的表演。 **5** *infml* an example of insincere behaviour used to influence people's feelings 〔非正式〕裝模作樣: *He doesn't really mean it. It's just an act.* 他不是真的有那個意思, 只不過作作樣子而已。 **6 get in on the act** *infml* to get a share of an activity, and especially any advantages that may come as a result 〔非正式〕〔尤指有利可圖時〕插手, 參與行動

act·ing¹ /ˈæktɪŋ; ˈæktɪŋ/ *n* [U] the art of representing a character, especially in a play or film 演技

acting² *adj* [only before a noun 只用於名詞前] appointed to carry out the duties of an office or position for a short time 代理的: *Our director is in hospital, but the acting director can see you.* 我們的主管住院了, 但代理主管可以見你。

⭐**ac·tion** /ˈækʃən; ˈækʃən/ *n* **1** [U] doing things for a purpose 行動; 動作: *We're tired of talking about the problem — now is the time for action!* 我們已經厭倦老是談論這個問題——現在是該行動了! | *What's your plan of action?* 你們的行動計劃是甚麼? | *The police had to take firm action to deal with the protestors.* 警方只得採取堅決的行動來對付抗議者。 **2** [C] something that you do 行為; 舉動: *His prompt action saved her life.* 他迅速的行動救了她的命。 | *a very kind action* 充滿善意的舉動 | *The baby watched all its mother's actions.* 嬰孩注視著母親的一舉一動。 **3** [C] effect 作用: *Photographs are produced by the action of light on film.* 照片是光線對軟片發生作用而形成的。 **4** [U] fighting or a fight between armies and navies 〔陸軍和海軍的〕戰鬥; 軍事行動: *the results of military action* 戰果 | *Her husband was killed in action.* 她丈夫在戰事中陣亡。 **5** [C] a charge or matter for consideration by a court of law 訴訟: *If he doesn't pay us soon we'll have to bring an action against him.* 如果他不馬上付錢給我們, 我們只好對他起訴。 | *a libel action* 誹謗罪訴訟 **6 the action** the main events in a play or book 〔劇本等的〕情節, 故事: *The action takes place in a mountain village.* 故事發生在一個山村裡。 **7** [C] the way in which something moves or works 動作姿態; 活動(方式): *The horse had a fine jumping action.* 那匹馬做了個漂亮的跳躍動作。 | *studying the action of the heart* 研究心臟的活動 **8 action-packed** full of exciting action 充滿激烈動作的 **9 action replay**

---

the showing again, usually more slowly, of a piece of a film in which you see a particularly interesting part of a sports event 〔體育比賽中特別精彩部分的錄像鏡頭的〕即時重播 **10 in action** doing a typical activity 在活動中: *He's a very good tennis player: you ought to see him in action.* 他是位網球高手: 你應該去看看他打球。**11 out of action** unable to move or operate 停止活動; 發生故障: *Can I borrow your car? Mine's out of action.* 我可以借用你的車嗎? 我的車壞了。**12 put into action** to begin to use a plan or idea 開始實行〔計劃或想法〕: *The government is now putting the new policy into action.* 政府正開始實施這項新政策。

ac·tiv·ate /'æktə,vet; 'æktɪ,veɪt/ *v* **activated, activating** [T] to make something start working 使〔某物〕活動; 開動: *This button activates the heating system.* 撳動這按鈕, 暖氣系統就開始運作。 **–activation** /,æktə-'veʃən; ,æktɪ'veɪʃən/ *n* [U]

⋆**ac·tive¹** /'æktɪv; 'æktɪv/ *adj* **1** doing things or always ready or able to do things 有活動力的; 活躍的; 積極的: *Although he is over 70 he is still active.* 雖然他年逾七十, 仍仍然很活躍。| *an active member of the club, who goes to every meeting* 俱樂部中一位每次會議必出席的積極分子 | *an active volcano* 活火山 | *an active chemical* 活性化學物質 **–op**posite 反義 **inactive 2** *tech* relating to or containing a verb which has the person or thing doing the action as the subject; in the sentence "The boy kicked the ball", "kicked" is an active verb 〔術語〕〔動詞〕主動語態的〔如在 "The boy kicked the ball" 中, "kicked" 是主動語態動詞〕 **–opposite** 反義 **passive¹** (2) **–actively** *adv*

active² *n* [sing] *tech* 〔術語〕 **the active** the active part or form of a verb 主動語態

ac·tiv·ist /'æktɪvɪst; 'æktɪˌvɪst/ *n* a person taking an active part in a political movement 〔政治運動中的〕積極分子

⋆**ac·tiv·i·ty** /æk'tɪvətɪ; æk'tɪvɪti/ *n* **activities 1** [U] movement or action 活動(性); 活潑; 能動(性): *a day full of activity* 熱鬧的一天 | *There's been a lot of activity in the town centre today.* 今天市中心一直是熙熙攘攘的。| *political activity* 政治活動 | *economic activity* 經濟活動 **–op**posite 反義 **inactivity 2** [C] something done for pleasure, interest or education 〔基於娛樂、興趣或教育的〕活動: *Among her activities are swimming and photography.* 游泳和攝影是她的兩項活動。| *classroom activities* 課堂活動 **3** [pl] things done by a group, often one opposed to the government, to advance their aims 〔常指反政府集團為實施其目標的〕行動: *the activities of the New National Party* 新民族黨的活動 | *terrorist activities* 恐怖活動

⋆**ac·tor** /'æktə; 'æktə/ *n* a person who acts in a play or film or on television 演員

ac·tress /'æktrɪs; 'æktrɪs/ *n* a woman who acts in a play or film or on television 女演員

⋆**ac·tu·al** /'æktʃuəl; 'æktʃuəl/ *adj* [only before a noun 只用於名詞前] **1** existing as a real fact, and not existing just as an idea 真實的; 實際的: *The actual cost of the repairs was a lot less than we had expected.* 實際的修理費用比我們預期的要低很多。**2** really; you use this expression when you are saying something which is not what people might expect from the last thing you said 事實上, 實際上〔用於表示所説的內容可能與人們預期的不一樣〕: *I did my best to encourage her, but in actual fact, I don't think she's got much chance.* 我盡可能鼓勵她, 但實際上我認為她機會不大。

⋆**ac·tu·al·ly** /'æktʃuəlɪ; 'æktʃuəli/ *adv* **1** a word used to show that you are giving the real information about something 實際地; 真實地: *We didn't actually go up the Eiffel Tower, though we saw it.* 雖然我們看到了埃菲爾塔, 我們實際上並沒有上去。| *The people who actually have power are the owners of big industries.* 真正掌權的人是大企業家。**2** a word used to correct the wrong idea in a polite way 實際上 〔用於有禮貌地糾正錯誤説法〕: *It isn't expensive. Actually, it's very cheap.* 這東西不貴。實際上, 還挺便宜。| "*He's in his office.*" "*Actually, he's at lunch.*" "他在辦公室裡。" "其實, 他在吃午飯。" **3** you use "actually" when you are politely correcting someone, or giving an opinion which is different from theirs, or telling them something unexpected 〔用於有禮貌地糾正某人説話, 表示與他人不同的看法或講述出人意料的事〕: "*You can really taste the butter in this cake.*" "*Well, actually, I used margarine.*" "你真能在蛋糕中嚐出黃油味道。" "哦, 不過, 我用的是人造黃油。" | "*You've finished that letter, haven't you?*" "*Well, no, I haven't, actually.*" "你已寫好了那封信, 是不是?" "哦, 不, 我實際上還沒寫好。"

■ USAGE 用法: Do not use **actually** when you mean "at the present time". Instead use phrases such as, **at present, currently, at the moment, nowadays** ☆表示"現在"不能用 **actually**, 但可用如下短語, **at present, currently, at the moment, nowadays**: *Where are you working at the moment?* 你現在在哪兒工作? | *She is currently directing her third film.* 她正在導演她的第三部影片。

ac·u·men /ə'kjumɪn; 'ækjuˌmən/ *n* [U] *fml* ability to think and judge quickly and well 〔正式〕敏鋭; 精明: *Her business acumen has made her very successful.* 她靈活的經商頭腦使她的生意十分興隆。

ac·u·punc·ture /'ækjuˌpʌŋktʃə; 'ækjuˌpʌŋk-**

A

tʃ゚ʳ/ n [U] the method of stopping pain and curing diseases by pricking certain parts of the body with needles, used especially in China 針刺(療法); 針灸

a·cute /ə'kjut; ə'kjuːt/ adj **1** very great or severe (used of bad situations) 劇烈的, 嚴重的(指壞的狀況): She was in acute pain. 她痛得很厲害。| an acute lack of food 嚴重缺少食物 **2** showing an ability to understand things clearly and deeply 尖銳的; 深刻的: an acute analysis of the political situation 對政治形勢的深刻分析 **3** able to notice small differences 敏銳的: Dogs have an acute sense of smell. 狗有敏銳的嗅覺。**4** tech less than 90 degrees (used of an angle) 【術語】成銳角的(指角度) –compare 比較 OBTUSE –**acutely** adv: acutely embarrassing 十分侷促不安 –**acuteness** n [U]

AD /,e'di; ,eɪ'diː/ since the birth of CHRIST; an abbreviation for the Latin phrase **anno domini**; you use AD when you are giving dates 〔縮〕公元: a battle in 1649 AD 發生於公元 1649 年的一次戰役

★**ad** /æd; æd/ n infml an advertisement 〔非正式〕廣告

ad·age /'ædɪdʒ; 'ædɪdʒ/ n an old wise phrase 格言, 諺語

ad·a·mant /'ædə,mænt; 'ædəmənt/ adj fml determined not to change your mind 〔正式〕強硬的; 不動搖的; 堅決的: He's absolutely adamant. 他非常強硬。| She's adamant that she won't go. 她堅決不去。–**adamantly** adv

Ad·am's ap·ple /ˌædəmz 'æpl; ˌædəmz 'æpəl/ n the part at the front of the throat that is seen to move when a person, especially a man, talks or swallows 喉結, 喉核

★**a·dapt** /ə'dæpt; ə'dæpt/ v **1** [T] to make something suitable for a new need or purpose 使適合, 使適應〔某事物〕: He adapted an old car engine to use in his boat. 他改裝了一台舊車引擎來驅動他的小艇。| The author is adapting his novel for television. 作者正把自己的小説改編成電視劇。| The car has been specially adapted for use by the handicapped. 這輛車經過特別改裝供殘疾人士使用。| We must adapt our methods to the new circumstances. 我們必須使我們的方法適應新情況。| Some birds are well adapted to life on water. 有些鳥完全適應水上生活。**2** [I] to change your behaviour or ideas to fit a new situation 適應新環境: The children have adapted well to life in the country. 孩子們很容易便適應了鄉間的生活。

a·dap·ta·ble /ə'dæptəbl; ə'dæptəbəl/ adj able to change your behaviour or ideas so as to manage well in a new situation (a word used to express approval) 能適應的; 適應性強的〔含褒義〕–opposite 反義 **unadaptable** –**adaptability** /ə,dæptə'bɪlətɪ; ə,dæptə'bɪlẹti/ n [U]

ad·ap·ta·tion /,ædəp'teʃən; ,ædæp'teɪʃən/ n

[C;U] something adapted or the process of adapting 適應; 改編; 改編物: a new adaptation of the book for television 由本書新改編的電視節目 | Darwin explained the adaptation of living things to their environment. 達爾文解釋了生物對環境的適應現象。

a·dap·tor /ə'dæptɚ; ə'dæptəʳ/ n (also 又作 **adapter**) a PLUG that makes it possible to use more than one piece of electrical machinery from a single SOCKET 轉接器; 多頭插座

★★**add** /æd; æd/ v **1** [T] to put something together with something else 增加, 添加〔某物〕: Mix the flour and salt. Add the water. 把麵粉和鹽和在一起。再加水。| Add a few more names to the list. 名單上再加幾個名字。| The tower was added in 1232. 這塔是 1232 年增建的。**2** [T] to put numbers or amounts together and calculate the total 加; 相加〔數、量等以求總和〕: If you add 5 and 3 you get 8. 5 加 3 等於 8。| Add 5 to 3. 把 3 加上 5。| Add the travel costs and the hotel bill together. 把旅費和旅館賬單加在一起。**3** [T; + that] to say something else when speaking 補充説〔某事〕: "Susan's left home," she said. "I don't understand why," she added. "蘇珊離家出走了," 她説。"我不知道為甚麼," 她補充説。| Have you anything to add, John? 你還有甚麼要補充的嗎, 約翰? | I should like to add that we are pleased with the result. 我想補充的是, 我們對結果很滿意。**4** add insult to injury to make a bad situation even worse 既傷害又侮辱; 雪上加霜; 更糟的是: He helped himself to my dinner and then, to add insult to injury, asked me to wash up. 他擅自把我的飯吃了, 還得寸進尺要我替他洗碗。

add sth ↔ **on** phr v [T] to join on 添造〔某物〕; 加造: We're going to add another room on to our house. 我們打算給房子加造一個房間。

add to sth phr v [T] to increase something 增加〔某物〕: The rise in electricity costs has added to our difficulties. 電費上漲增加了我們的困難。

add up phr v **1** [I;T **add** sth ↔ **up**] to put numbers or amounts together and calculate the total 〔把數字〕相加〔以求得總數〕: Add the costs up. 把成本加起來。| He's not fit to work in a bank. He can barely add up. 他不適合在銀行工作。他幾乎連加法也不懂。**2** [I] infml to make sense 〔非正式〕講得通; 有道理; 合乎情理: His story just didn't add up. 他講的故事根本不合情理。

add up to sth phr v [T] **1** infml to result in 〔非正式〕結果是; 導致: What it adds up to is that she won't let me go. 事情的結果是她不讓我走。**2** to result in a particular total 總計達: This adds up to 1,000 miles. 這加起來總計達一千英里。

ad·ded /'ædɪd; 'ædɪ̩d/ adj [only before a noun 只用於名詞前] further 附加的; 增加的;

更多的: *It's cheap, and it has the added advantage of being much faster.* 它不只便宜，還具有快得多這個額外優點。

added to *prep* in addition to something 除…以外；附加上: *It's cheap, added to which it's much faster.* 它便宜，除此以外，它還快得多。

ad·den·dum /ə'dɛndəm; ə'dɛndəm/ *n* **ad·denda** /ə'dɛndə; ə'dɛndə/ *tech* something that is added at the end of a speech or piece of writing〔術語〕〔講演或文章的〕補充；補遺；補編

ad·der /'ædə; 'ædəʳ/ *n* a small poisonous snake found in northern Europe and northern Asia 蝰蛇〔一種產於北歐和北亞地區的小毒蛇〕

ad·dict /'ædɪkt; 'ædɪkt/ *n* a person who is unable to free himself from a harmful habit, especially of taking drugs 耽溺於不良嗜好的人〔尤指吸毒者〕: *a drug addict* 吸毒者

ad·dict·ed /ə'dɪktɪd; ə'dɪkt‚ɪd/ *adj* unable to stop taking or using something 沉溺於…的；無法擺脫某種嗜好的: *addicted to heroin* 吸海洛因成癮的 | *My children are hopelessly addicted to television.* 我的幾個孩子都成了電視迷，簡直是不可救藥了。

ad·dic·tion /ə'dɪkʃən; ə'dɪkʃən/ *n* [C;U] a strong need which makes you dependent on something bad, for example drugs 沉溺；(吸毒)成癮: *the growing problem of heroin addiction among young people* 年輕人吸食海洛因成癮這一日趨嚴重的問題

ad·dic·tive /ə'dɪktɪv; ə'dɪktɪv/ *adj* making you addicted to something 使人上癮的: *This drug is highly addictive.* 這種毒品很容易使人上癮。

★★ad·di·tion /ə'dɪʃən; ə'dɪʃən/ *n* **1** [U] the addition together of several numbers〔幾個數字的〕相加；加法 **2** [C] something added 增加物: *A newly born child is often called an addition to the family.* 新生嬰兒常常被說成是家庭中新添的成員。 **3 in addition** besides; you use this expression when you add another thing to what you have already mentioned 除…之外〔用於對已提到的事物進行補充〕: *Candidates should fill in and return the form. In addition, they should enclose a recent, passport-size photograph.* 應徵者應填好表格並寄回，除此以外，還應附上一張新拍的護照上用的那種尺寸的照片。 | *In addition to giving a general introduction to computers, the course also provides practical experience.* 課程除了介紹一般電腦知識外，還提供實際操作的機會。

★ad·di·tion·al /ə'dɪʃənl; ə'dɪʃənəl/ *adj* added to something already there 附加的；添加的: *An additional charge is made for heavy bags.* 重的行李要額外收費。**–additionally** *adv*

ad·di·tive /'ædətɪv; 'ædɪ‚tɪv/ *n* a substance added in small quantities to something

else so as to improve the quality, or add colour or taste 添加物；添加劑

★ad·dress¹ /ə'drɛs; ə'drɛs/ *v* [T] **1** to write a name and address on an envelope or parcel〔在信封或包裹上〕寫姓名和地址 **2** *fml* to direct what you say to a person or group〔正式〕對…作演說；向…講話: *The queen addressed the crowd.* 女王向羣眾發表講話。| *Address your remarks to the chairperson, please.* 請把話講給主席聽。**3 to address yourself to something** *fml* to consider something carefully so that you can decide what should be done about it〔正式〕致力於某事；着手某事: *We must address ourselves to the problem of drugs among young people.* 我們必須着手解決青年人吸毒的問題。

★ad·dress² /ə'drɛs; ə'drɛs/ *n* **1** details of where someone works or lives, including the number of the building, name of the street and town 住址；地址: *I can't read the address on this letter.* 我看不清這封信上的地址。**2** a formal speech 演講

ad·ept /ə'dɛpt; ə'dɛpt/ *adj* highly skilled 擅長的；精通的；拿手的: *Be careful when you play cards with him — he's very adept at cheating.* 和他玩牌時你要小心──他極善於欺詐。**–adeptly** *adv*

★ad·e·quate /'ædɪkwɪt; 'ædɪkw‚t/ *adj* enough for the purpose, and no more 足夠的；充分的: *The city's water supply is no longer adequate for its growing population.* 這城市的用水已經不再足夠供應日益增長的人口了。| *A teacher's salary is barely adequate to support a family.* 教師的薪水剛夠勉強維持一家生計。**–opposite** 反義 **inadequate –adequately** *adv* **–adequacy** *n* [U]

ad·here /əd'hɪr; əd'hɪəʳ/ *v* **adhered, adhering** [I] **1** to stick firmly 黏着；附着: *Glue makes one surface adhere to another.* 膠水使一個表面黏附着另一個表面。**2 adhere to something** to firmly support an idea or belief 堅持某個觀點或信念: *She adhered to the view that a broad education was important.* 她堅持認為全面的教育是重要的。

ad·her·ence /əd'hɪrəns; əd'hɪərəns/ *n* [U] firm support for certain beliefs or ideas 堅持；信奉: *his strict adherence to his religious beliefs* 他絕對信奉自己的宗教信仰

ad·her·ent /əd'hɪrənt; əd'hɪrənt/ *n* a person who supports a particular idea, opinion, or political party〔某種思想、主張或政黨的〕追隨者，擁護者

ad·he·sion /əd'hiʒən; əd'hi:ʒən/ *n* [U] the state or action of one thing sticking to another 黏着；附着；黏合

ad·he·sive /əd'hisɪv; əd'hi:sɪv/ *n* a substance, such as GLUE, that can make things stick together 黏性物質〔如膠水〕；黏合劑 **–adhesive** *adj*

ad hoc /'æd 'hɑk; ‚æd 'hɒk/ *adj* made or arranged for a particular purpose 特別〔專門〕安排的: *an ad hoc committee set up to*

A

deal with the water shortage 解決缺水問題的特別委員會

a·dieu /ə'dju; ə'dju:/ *n* **adieus** *or* **adieux** /ə'djuz; ə'dju:z/ *lit* goodbye 〔文〕再見

ad·ja·cent /ə'dʒesnt; ə'dʒeɪsənt/ *adj fml* very close or next to 〔正式〕鄰近的; 毗連的: *The two families live in adjacent streets.* 這兩戶人家住在相鄰的兩條街上。| *His office is adjacent to mine.* 他的辦公室與我的辦公室相鄰。

ad·jec·tive /'ædʒɪktɪv; 'ædʒ ktɪv/ *n* a word which describes a noun 形容詞: *The word "black" in the phrase "a black car" is an adjective.* 在短語 "a black car" 中, black 這詞是個形容詞。 –**adjectival** /,ædʒɪk'taɪvl; ,æ-dʒ k'taɪvəl/ *adj*: *an adjectival phrase* 形容詞短語 –see Study Note on page 1330 見 1330 頁學習提示

ad·join /ə'dʒɔɪn; ə'dʒɔɪn/ *v* [I;T] *fml* to be next to something 〔正式〕貼近; 鄰近; 毗連: *Our house adjoins theirs.* 我們的房子和他們的相鄰。| *The two buildings adjoin.* 這兩幢大樓相毗連。| *the adjoining room* 隔壁的房間

ad·journ /ə'dʒɜn; ə'dʒɜ:n/ *v* [I;T] to stop a meeting or a trial for a short time or until a slightly later date 使〔會議、審訊〕暫停; 休會; 延期: *This trial has been adjourned until next week.* 這次審訊已推遲到下週舉行。| *The committee adjourned for an hour.* 委員會休會一個小時。 –**adjournment** *n* [C;U]: *The court met again after an adjournment of two weeks.* 法庭在休庭兩週之後重新開庭。

ad·ju·di·cate /ə'dʒudɪ,ket; ə'dʒu:dɪkeɪt/ *v* **adjudicated, adjudicating** [I;T] *fml* to judge or make an official decision 〔正式〕裁判; 裁決: *She's been asked to adjudicate a singing competition.* 她獲邀請擔任歌唱大賽的評判。| *The union needs someone to adjudicate on the dispute.* 工會需要有人來裁決這場爭執。 –**adjudicator** *n*

ad·junct /'ædʒʌŋkt; 'ædʒʌŋkt/ *n* something that is added or joined to something else but is not a necessary part of it 附屬物; 伴隨物

***ad·just** /ə'dʒʌst; ə'dʒʌst/ *v* **1** [T] to correct or slightly change the position of something 調節; 調整: *He adjusted his tie.* 他整理一下領帶。 **2** [I] to change to suit a particular situation or new conditions 適應: *He adjusted quickly to the heat of India.* 他很快就適應了印度的炎熱氣候。 –**adjustable** *adj*: *an adjustable chair* 可調節的椅子 –**adjustment** *n* [C;U]: *I've had to make a lot of adjustments.* 我必須做許多調整。

ad lib[1] /'æd'lɪb; ,æd'lɪb / *adj* spoken or performed without preparation 即興; 無準備的: *ad lib remarks* 即興的話 –**ad lib** *adv*: *She spoke ad lib.* 她作了即興演説。

ad lib[2] /· '·/ *v* **-bb-** [I;T] *infml* to say something or play music without preparation or planning 〔非正式〕即興表演; 即興演奏: *The*

actress forgot her lines but ad libbed very amusingly. 女演員忘了台詞, 但她的即興表演讓人開懷大樂。

ad·min·is·ter /əd'mɪnəstə; əd'mɪn stə / *v* [T] **1** to direct or control the affairs of a country, company or organization 管理, 治理〔國家、公司或組織〕: *Mr Jones administers the company's accounts.* 瓊斯先生管理公司的賬目。 **2** *fml* to give a drug to someone 〔正式〕給〔某人〕餵藥: *She administered the medicine to the sick woman.* 她給生病的女子餵藥。 **3** to make sure a law or test is used properly 執行; 實施: *The courts administer the law.* 法庭執行法律。

***ad·min·is·tra·tion** /əd,mɪnə'streʃən; əd-,mɪn 'streɪʃən/ *n* **1** [U] the control or direction of affairs, for example in a country or business 管理; 行政: *You will need some experience in administration.* 你需要一些管理方面的經驗。 **2** **the Administration** the national government of the U.S.A. (美國)政府; 內閣: *the Clinton Administration* 克林頓政府

***ad·min·is·tra·tive** /əd'mɪnə,stretɪv; əd'mɪn-stratɪv/ *adj* to do with the control or direction of affairs in a country or business 管理的; 行政的: *His responsibilities are mainly administrative.* 他的責任主要是行政方面的。 –**administratively** *adv*

ad·min·is·tra·tor /əd'mɪnə,stretə; əd'mɪn-streɪtə / *n* a person who controls or directs the affairs of a country or business 〔國家或公司的〕管理者; 行政官員

ad·mi·ra·ble /'ædmərəbl; 'ædmərəbəl/ *adj* considered worthy of praise and respect 令人欽佩的; 極佳的: *an admirable attempt* 令人欽佩的嘗試

ad·mi·ral /'ædmərəl; 'ædmərəl/ *n* [C] an officer who holds a very high rank in a navy 海軍上將; 海軍將官

Ad·mi·ral·ty /'ædmərəltɪ; 'ædmərəlti/ *n BrE* 〔英式〕 **the Admiralty** the government department which controls the navy 海軍部

ad·mi·ra·tion /,ædmə'reʃən; ,ædm 'reɪʃən/ *n* [U] a feeling of pleasure and respect 讚美; 欽佩: *I was filled with admiration for his courage.* 我對他的勇氣充滿了欽佩之情。

ad·mire /əd'maɪr; əd'maɪə / *v* **admired, admiring** [T] **1** to approve of and respect someone or something 欽佩, 讚賞〔某人、某事物〕: *We all admired her for the way she saved the children from the fire.* 我們都欽佩她從火中救出孩子的壯舉。 **2** to look at someone or something with pleasure 欣賞〔某人、某事物〕: *Stop looking in the mirror admiring yourself!* 別對着鏡子自我欣賞了! | *They admired the garden.* 他們欣賞着園中的景色。 –see 見 WONDER (USAGE 用法) –**admirer** *n*: *He is one of her many admirers.* 他是她眾多的愛慕者之一。

ad·mis·si·ble /əd'mɪsəbl; əd'mɪs bəl/ *adj* acceptable or allowed 可接受的, 可容許的:

admissible behaviour 可容許的行為 | facts admissible in court 法庭上可接受的事實 – opposite 反義 **inadmissible**

*★**ad·mis·sion** /əd'mɪʃən; əd'mɪʃən/ n **1** [U] permission given to enter a building or a country, or join a school or club 入場〔入境; 入學; 入會〕許可: They campaigned for the admission of women **to** the club. 他們發起運動, 使婦女也可加入該俱樂部。 | the admission of refugees into France 容許難民進入法國 **2** [U] the cost of entering 會費; 入場費; 門票: Admission £1 門票一英鎊 **3** [C] a statement saying that something bad or unpleasant is true 承認; 供認: His admission of guilt surprised everyone. 他承認有罪, 使大家吃驚。

★★**ad·mit** /əd'mɪt; əd'mɪt/ v **-tt- 1** [I;T; + (that)] to agree, often unwillingly, that something bad or unpleasant is true 〔通常不情願地〕承認, 供認: Few politicians admit their mistakes. 政客很少會承認自己的錯誤。 | She'll never admit that she is wrong. 她決不會承認自己做錯了。 | The prisoner admitted to the murder. 那囚犯承認了謀殺罪。 | John admitted breaking the window. 約翰承認打碎了玻璃窗。 | "You're right," she admitted. "你做得對," 她承認說。

□ USEFUL PATTERNS 有用句型
to admit that…; to admit (to) something; to admit (to) doing something

2 [T] to allow someone or something to enter a place 允許〔某人或某物〕進入: There were no windows to admit air. 沒有窗戶可讓空氣流入。 **3** [T] to allow someone to join a club or organization 允許〔某人〕加入〔某俱樂部或組織〕 **4 be admitted to** to be taken in to hospital until you are better 被送進〔醫院〕: He was admitted **to** hospital suffering from burns. 他因燒傷而被送進醫院。

ad·mit·tance /əd'mɪtns; əd'mɪtns/ n [U] **1** the right to enter a place 進入權 **2 gain admittance** to be allowed to enter a place 獲准進入: Journalists were unable to gain admittance. 記者們未獲准進入內。 –see 見 ADMISSION (USAGE 用法)

ad·mit·ted·ly /əd'mɪtɪdlɪ; əd'mɪtɪdlɪ/ adv you use "admittedly" when you allow that there are facts which do not support your idea 無可否認地; 確實地: I don't know why you're so against him. Admittedly, he's rather odd, but he's a very kind person. 我不明白你為甚麼如此反對他。無可否認, 他相當古怪, 但他是個很善良的人。 | I think this is the best bed we're going to find. It's not very cheap, admittedly, but I think we won't regret spending the money on it. 我認為這是我們能找到的最好的牀。無可否認, 這牀不很便宜, 但是我認為我們花錢買它也不會後悔。

ad·mon·ish /əd'mɒnɪʃ; əd'mɒnɪʃ/ v [T] fml to warn someone gently that they have

done something wrong 〔正式〕〔溫和地〕訓誡, 警告〔某人〕: The witness was admonished by the judge for failing to answer the question. 證人因未能回答問題而受到法官的警告。 –**admonition** /ˌædmə'nɪʃən; ˌædmə'nɪʃən/ n [C;U]

a·do /ə'du; ə'duː/ n **without more ado/ without further ado** with no further delay 不再拖延; 乾脆

ad·o·les·cent /ˌædl'ɛsnt; ˌædə'lesənt◂/ n a boy or girl in the period between being a child and being a grown person 青少年; 青春期之男孩〔女孩〕 –see 見 CHILD (USAGE 用法) –**adolescent** adj

*★**a·dopt** /ə'dɒpt; ə'dɒpt/ v [T] **1** to take someone else's child into your family and make it legally your child 收養, 領養〔別人的孩子〕: He was adopted as a baby. 他在嬰兒時期被人收養。 –compare 比較 FOSTER **2** to begin to have or use an idea, plan, or way of doing something 採用; 採取: We adopted the new method of production. 我們採用了新的生產方法。 | The government is adopting a tougher approach to crime. 政府正採取更嚴厲的對策解決犯罪問題。 **3** to formally approve and accept something 採納〔某事物〕: The committee adopted her suggestions. 委員會採納了她的建議。

a·dop·tion /ə'dɒpʃən; ə'dɒpʃən/ n [C;U] the act of adopting a child 〔孩子的〕收養, 領養: If you cannot have children of your own, why not consider adoption? 如果你不能生孩子, 為甚麼不考慮領養〔一個〕呢?

a·dop·tive /ə'dɒptɪv; ə'dɒptɪv/ adj [only before a noun 只用於名詞前] fml having adopted a child (used of parents) 〔正式〕收養〔了孩子〕的: her adoptive parents 她的養父母

a·dor·a·ble /ə'dɔrəbl; ə'dɔːrəbəl/ adj attractive, charming, and worthy of love 迷人的; 漂亮的; 可愛的: What an adorable child! 多可愛的孩子!

ad·o·ra·tion /ˌædə'reɪʃən; ˌædə'reɪʃən/ n [U] deep love and respect 愛慕; 敬重

a·dore /ə'dɔr; ə'dɔːʳ/ v **adored, adoring** [T; not in progressive forms 不用於進行式] **1** to love someone deeply and respect them very much 敬愛, 敬重〔某人〕: an adoring look 敬慕的目光 | He adores his elder brother. 他敬重哥哥。 **2** infml to like something very much 〔非正式〕非常喜歡〔某事物〕: She adores the cinema./ She adores going to the cinema. 她很喜歡去看電影。

a·dorn /ə'dɔrn; ə'dɔːrn/ v [T] to decorate something and make it attractive 裝飾〔某物〕: a Christmas tree adorned **with** lights 以燈光裝飾的聖誕樹 –see 見 DECORATE (USAGE 用法)

a·dorn·ment /ə'dɔrnmənt; ə'dɔːrnmənt/ n **1** [U] the act of adorning something 裝飾 **2** [C] something that improves the beauty of something else 裝飾品

a·dren·a·lin /ə'drɛnḷɪn; ə'drɛnəl-ɨn/ *n* [U] a chemical substance made by your body when you are feeling anger, fear, or anxiety, which gives you more strength to take action 腎上腺素〔因生氣、恐懼或焦慮而在體內產生的一種激素〕

a·drift /ə'drɪft; ə'drɪft/ *adv* **1** not tied to anything, and moved about by the sea or wind (used of boats)〔指船〕〔隨風浪〕漂流地，漂泊地 **2 have gone adrift** to no longer be working as intended 脫節；出問題: *Our plans seem to have gone adrift.* 我們的計劃似乎出問題了。

a·droit /ə'drɔɪt; ə'drɔɪt/ *adj* quick and skilful in thought or action 機敏的；靈巧的: *a journalist adroit at asking questions* 善於提問題的記者 **–adroitly** *adv* **–adroitness** *n* [U]

ad·u·la·tion /,ædʒə'leʃən; ,ædʒʊ'leɪʃən/ *n* [U] praise that is more than is necessary or deserved 諂媚；阿諛；恭維

★**ad·ult** /ə'dʌlt; 'ædʌlt/ *n* a fully grown person or animal 成年人〔動物〕 **–adult** *adj*: *an adult lion* 成年的獅子

a·dul·ter·ate /ə'dʌltə,ret; ə'dʌltəreɪt/ *v* **adulterated, adulterating** [T] to make a substance weaker or of poorer quality by adding something else to it 攙雜；攙假: *wine adulterated with water* 攙了水的酒 **–adulteration** /ə,dʌltə'reʃən; ə,dʌltə'reɪʃən/ *n* [U]

a·dul·ter·er /ə'dʌltərɚ; ə'dʌltərər/ *n* a married man who has sexual relations with someone who is not his wife 姦夫

a·dul·ter·ess /ə'dʌltərɪs; ə'dʌltərɨs/ *n* a married woman who has sexual relations with someone who is not her husband 姦婦，淫婦

a·dul·ter·y /ə'dʌltərɪ; ə'dʌltəri/ *n* [U] sexual relations between a married person and someone to whom they are not married 通姦 **–adulterous** *adj*

★**ad·vance[1]** /ə'dʌvæns; əd'vɑːns/ *v* **advanced, advancing 1** [I] to improve in understanding or development 取得進展；改進: *Scientists have advanced greatly in their knowledge of physics.* 科學家對物理學的了解已取得巨大進展。**2** [T] to help or support a cause 促進；推進: *This policy will do nothing to advance world peace.* 這項政策絕不會促進世界和平。**3** [I] to move forward in position, usually in order to attack someone 前進；推進〔通常為了攻擊某人〕: *Napoleon's army advanced on Moscow.* 拿破崙的軍隊向莫斯科推進。**–compare** 比較 **RETREAT 4** [T] to bring something forward to an earlier date or time 把〔某事〕提前: *The date of the meeting was advanced.* 會議的日期提前了。**5** [T] to provide money earlier than the usual or proper time 預付〔錢〕: *The company will advance you £200 until your salary is paid.* 在給你發工資前，公司將預付給你二百英鎊。**6** [T] to introduce or suggest something 提出〔建議、看法〕: *The report advances the idea that safety standards should be improved.* 這份報告提出安全標準應該改進。

★**advance[2]** *n* **1** [C] forward movement 前進: *the advance of the enemy* 敵軍的前進 **2** [C; U] improvement or progress 進展；進步: *There have been great advances in medicine in the last 50 years.* 醫學在過去五十年有很大的進展。**3** [C] money that is paid or lent before the proper time 預支；貸款: *Some authors are given an advance on their books.* 有些作者可得到預支的稿費。**4 in advance** before a date or time 預先: *We always pay the rent in advance.* 我們總是預付房租。**5 make advances to someone** to try to become someone's friend or start a sexual relationship with them 接近某人；向某人求愛

advance[3] *adj* happening before something else 預先的；事前的: *We were given no advance warning of his arrival.* 我們沒有預先接到他將到達的通知。

★**ad·vanced** /əd'vænst; əd'vɑːnst/ *adj* **1** having a very developed industry (工業)先進的，領先的: *the advanced industrial nations of the world* 世界上先進的工業國家 **2** at a high level of knowledge or skill 高級的；高深的；先進的: *advanced studies* 高深的研究 | *an advanced child* 智力超前發育的孩子

ad·vance·ment /əd'vænsmənt; əd'vɑːnsmənt/ *n* [U] improvement or development 進步；發展；促進: *the advancement of science* 科學的進步 **2** being moved to a more important position or job 擢升；升級: *He's very concerned about his own advancement at work.* 他十分關注自己在工作中的提升。

★★**ad·van·tage** /əd'væntɪdʒ; əd'vɑːntɪdʒ/ *n* **1** [C] something that may help you to be successful or to get something that you want 有利條件；優勢: *Her experience gave her a big advantage over the other applicants.* 她的經驗使她與其他求職者相比具有很大的優勢。**2** [C;U] a favourable condition resulting from something 好處；利益；優點: *Is there any advantage in getting there early?* 早到達那兒有甚麼好處呢？| *This method has the advantage of saving fuel.* 這種方法有節約燃料的優點。| *the advantages of living in the country* 住在鄉間的好處 **3 to your advantage** useful or favourable for you 對你有利: *It's to your advantage to contact him.* 和他接觸對你有利。**4 take advantage of** to make use of someone or something, sometimes unfairly 利用〔某人或某物〕: *I'll take advantage of your offer.* 我將從你的提議中受益。| *I'm afraid he's just taking advantage of your generosity.* 我想他不過是在利用你的慷慨。**–opposite** 反義 **disadvantage**

ad·van·ta·geous /,ædvən'tedʒəs; ,ædvən'teɪdʒəs/ *adj* helpful to a particular aim 有利的；有益的 **–opposite** 反義 **disadvan-**

tageous –**advantageously** *adv*

ad·vent /ˈædvɛnt; ˈædvent/ *n fml* 〖正式〗**the advent of** the start of an important event, period, or invention〔重要事件、時期或發明的〕到來，來臨: *People are much better informed since the advent of television.* 自從有了電視，人們的見聞遠比以前廣了。

ad·ven·ture /ədˈvɛntʃɚ; ədˈventʃərˈ/ *n* [C;U] a journey, activity, or experience that is strange, exciting, and often dangerous 奇遇；冒險的經歷: *her exciting adventures in the Himalayas* 她在喜瑪拉雅山驚心動魄的歷險 | *a life of adventure* 冒險生涯

ad·ven·tur·er /ədˈvɛntʃərɚ; ədˈventʃərərˈ/ *n* a person who has or looks for adventures 冒險家

ad·ven·tur·ous /ədˈvɛntʃərəs; ədˈventʃərəs/ *adj* **1** eager to take risks and try new things 愛冒險的 **2** exciting and full of danger 驚險的；充滿危險的: *an adventurous life* 驚險的生活 –opposite 反義 **unadventurous** –**adventurously** *adv*

ad·verb /ˈædvɝb; ˈædvɜːb/ *n* a word which describes or adds to the meaning of a verb, an adjective, another adverb, or a sentence, and which answers such questions as when? or where?〔用於描述動詞、形容詞、其他副詞或句子，或者增加其意義，並能夠回答"如何?"、"何時?"、"何地?"等問句〕副詞: *In the sentences "He ran slowly" and "It was very beautiful", "slowly" and "very" are adverbs.* 在句子 "He ran slowly" 和 "It was very beautiful" 中，"slowly" 和 "very" 就是副詞。–see Study Note on page 1330 見第 1330 頁學習提示 –**adverbial** /ædˈvɝbɪəl; ədˈvɜːbɪəl/ *n, adj*

ad·ver·sa·ry /ˈædvɚˌsɛrɪ; ˈædvəsəri/ *n fml* 〖正式〗**adversaries** an enemy or someone you are competing against 對手；敵手

ad·verse /ədˈvɝs; ˈædvɜːs/ *adj fml* unfavourable to you 〖正式〗不利的；逆的；反對的: *The proposal has attracted a lot of adverse comment.* 這提案已引起許多反對的意見。| *adverse weather conditions* 惡劣的天氣情況 –**adversely** *adv*

ad·ver·si·ty /ədˈvɝsətɪ; ədˈvɜːsɨti/ *n* **adversities** [C;U] difficulties or problems 逆境；厄運；困難: *A good friend will not desert you in time of adversity.* 好朋友不會在人患難時棄你而去。| *He met with many adversities.* 他遭遇過許多不幸。

ad·ver·tise /ˈædvɚˌtaɪz; ˈædvətaɪz/ *v* **advertised, advertising** **1** [I;T] to tell the public about something, such as an event, service, or article for sale, for example in a newspaper or on television 為⋯做廣告；登廣告: *I advertised my house in the "Daily News".* 我在《每日新聞》上為房子登了廣告。| *a poster advertising shampoo* 洗髮劑的廣告招貼 **2** [I] to ask for someone or something by placing a notice somewhere like a newspaper or shop window〔在報紙或商店櫥窗

等〕做廣告以徵求〔某人或某物〕: *We should advertise for someone to look after the garden.* 我們應登廣告招聘人來照料花園。 –**advertiser** *n*

ad·ver·tise·ment /ˌædvɚˈtaɪzmənt; ədˈvɜː-tɪ̩smənt/ *n* (also 又作 **ad, advert** *infml* 〖非正式〗) something used for advertising things, such as a notice on a wall or in a newspaper, or a short film shown on television 廣告

ad·ver·tis·ing /ˈædvɚˌtaɪzɪŋ; ˈædvətaɪzɪŋ/ *n* [U] the business of encouraging people to buy goods through advertisements 廣告業

★**ad·vice** /ədˈvaɪs; ədˈvaɪs/ *n* [U] an opinion given by one person to another on how that other should behave or act 勸告；忠告: *I asked the doctor for her advice.* 我徵求這位女醫生的意見。| *On her advice I am staying in bed.* 遵照她的囑咐，我正臥牀休息。| *Let me give you a piece of advice.* 讓我給你一個忠告。

> ■ USAGE 用法: The word **advice** is uncountable and is not, therefore, used in the plural ☆ **advice** 這詞是不可數名詞，因此不能有複數形式: *She gave me a lot of good advice.* 她給我許多忠告。| *Ask your teacher for advice.* 向你的老師徵詢意見。| *a piece of excellent advice* 一個絕好的忠告

ad·vi·sab·le /ədˈvaɪzəbl; ədˈvaɪzəbəl/ *adj* [never before a noun 不能用於名詞前] sensible or wise 合情理的；明智的: *It is advisable always to wear a safety belt when you're driving.* 駕駛汽車時最好總是繫上安全帶。–opposite 反義 **inadvisable** –**advisability** /ədˌvaɪzəˈbɪlətɪ; əd̩vaɪzəˈbɪl̩ti/ *n* [U]

★**ad·vise** /ədˈvaɪz; ədˈvaɪz/ *v* **advised, advising** **1** [T] to tell someone what you think they should do 勸告，忠告〔某人〕，向〔某人〕提建議: *The doctor advised me to take more exercise.* 醫生建議我多做運動。| *I advised him that he should join a union.* 我勸他加入工會。| *Can you advise me where to stay?* 你能建議我該住在哪兒嗎?

> □ USEFUL PATTERNS 有用句型
> to advise someone; to advise someone to do something; to advise someone that they should do something; to advise someone how, where, when... etc.

2 advise against something, advise someone against something to warn someone not to do something 勸阻某事；勸阻某人做某事: *Lawyers advised against signing the contract.* 律師勸阻説不能簽這份合約。| *He advised me against giving up my job.* 他勸我不要放棄我的工作。**3** [I;T] to act as a professional adviser to someone 擔任〔某人的〕

顧問: *the experts who advise the President* 擔任總統顧問的專家 | *She advises* **on** *legal matters.* 她擔任法律事務顧問。 **4** [T] *fml* to inform someone about something 〖正式〗通知; 告知: *We wish to advise you that you now owe the bank £500.* 你現欠銀行五百英鎊, 特此通知。

★**ad·vis·er** /ədˈvaɪzə⁻; ədˈvaɪzɚ/ *n* (also 又作 **advisor** *AmE* 〖美式〗) a person whose job is to give advice, especially to a government or business 〔尤指政府或企業的〕顧問: *the President's special adviser* **on** *foreign affairs* 總統的外交事務特別顧問

ad·vi·so·ry /ədˈvaɪzəri; ədˈvaɪzəri/ *adj* having the power or duty to advise people 顧問的, 提供諮詢的

ad·vo·cate¹ /ˈædvəˌket; ˈædvəket/ *v* **advocated, advocating** [T] to suggest or support an idea, plan, or action, often in public 主張; 鼓吹; 提倡; 擁護: *The opposition party advocates an immediate reduction in transport costs.* 反對黨主張立即減運輸費用。

ad·vo·cate² /ˈædvəkɪt; ˈædvəkət/ *n* **1** *law* a lawyer who speaks in favour of someone or against them in court 〖律〗律師 **2** a person who publicly supports an idea or way of life 〔某種思想或生活方式的〕倡導者, 支持者: *He is a strong advocate* **of** *prison reforms.* 他竭力主張監獄改革。

aer·i·al¹ /ˈɛriəl; ˈɛəriəl/ *n* a wire put up on top of a building or a car to receive radio or television broadcasts 天線 –see pictures on pages 209 and 729 見 209 頁和 729 頁彩圖

aerial² *adj* [only before a noun 只用於名詞前] from the air or happening in the air 從空中的; 空中發生的: *aerial photographs* 從高空拍攝的照片 | *an aerial battle* 空戰

aer·o·bics /ɛˈrobɪks; eəˈrəʊbɪks/ *n* [U] a form of very active physical exercise which is usually done in a class to music, and is intended to strengthen your heart and lungs 〔加強心肺功能的〕增氧健身操; 氣健術: *She does aerobics twice a week.* 她每週做兩次增氧健身操。 | *an aerobics class* 增氧健身班

aer·o·drome /ˈɛrəˌdrom; ˈeərədrəʊm/ *n* (**airfield** *AmE* 〖美式〗) a small airport 〔小型的〕飛機場

aer·o·dy·nam·ics /ˌɛrodaɪˈnæmɪks; ˌeərəʊdaɪˈnæmɪks/ *n* [U] the scientific study of objects moving through the air 空氣動力學 –**aerodynamic** *adj*: *aerodynamic laws* 空氣動力學定律

aer·o·plane /ˈɛrəˌplen; ˈeərəpleɪn/ *n* (**airplane** *AmE* 〖美式〗) a flying vehicle that has wings, and is driven by at least one engine 飛機 –see picture on page 991 見 991 頁彩圖

aer·o·sol /ˈɛrəˌsɑl; ˈeərəsɒl/ *n* a small container from which liquid can be forced out in the form of a fine mist 噴霧器

aes·thet·ic /ɛsˈθɛtɪk; iːsˈθetɪk/ *adj* (also 又作 **esthetic** *AmE* 〖美式〗) related to a sense of beauty, especially in art 美學的; 審美的; 美的: *The building is functional but has little aesthetic interest.* 這幢建築物很實用, 但缺少美感。 –**aesthetically** /-klɪ; -kli/ *adv*

aes·thet·ics /ɛsˈθɛtɪks; iːsˈθetɪks/ *n* (also 又作 **esthetics** *AmE* 〖美式〗) [U] the study or science of beauty, especially in art 美學

a·far /əˈfɑr; əˈfɑːr/ *adv* *lit* 〖文〗 **from afar** from a great distance 從遠處

af·fa·ble /ˈæfəbl; ˈæfəbəl/ *adj* friendly and easy to talk to 和藹可親的; 易於交談的 –**affably** *adv* –**affability** /ˌæfəˈbɪlətɪ; ˌæfəˈbɪləti/ *n* [U]

★**af·fair** /əˈfɛr; əˈfeər/ *n* **1** [C] an event or set of connected events 事情; 〔互有聯繫的一組〕事件: *The meeting was a noisy affair.* 這次會開得吵吵鬧鬧。 | *the Watergate affair* 水門事件 **2** **affairs** [pl] matters needing attention or connected with a particular subject 事務; 事態; 業務: *The minister deals with important affairs of state.* 這位部長處理重要的國務。 | *foreign affairs* 外交事務 **3** [C] a sexual relationship between two people not married to each other, especially when one of them is married to someone else 私通; 〔尤指非配偶間的〕性關係

★**af·fect** /əˈfɛkt; əˈfekt/ *v* [T] **1** to influence or to cause a result or change in something 影響: *The nurses' strike affects all hospitals.* 護士罷工影響所有的醫院。 | *How was the village affected by the storm?* 那村子受暴風雨的影響有多大? **2** to cause feelings of sorrow, anger, or love 使產生悲痛 〔憤怒、愛〕的感情: *She was deeply affected by the news of his death.* 他去世的消息使她深感悲痛。

■ USAGE 用法: Compare 比較 **affect** and 和 **effect**. **Affect** is usually a verb ☆**affect** 通常是動詞: *The new law will affect all of us.* 新的法律對我們大家都有影響。 **Effect** is usually a noun ☆ **effect** 通常是名詞: *The new law will have an effect on all of us.* 新的法律對我們大家都有影響。 The verb **effect** is very formal and means "to cause or produce" ☆**effect** 作為動詞是很正式的用詞, 意思是"造成或產生": *to effect a change in government policy* 使政府的政策產生變化

---

af·fec·ta·tion /ˌæfɪkˈteʃən; ˌæfekˈteɪʃən/ *n* [C;U] behaviour which is not natural and which aims to make people admire you 不自然的行為; 矯揉造作: *All that talk about art is just an affectation. She doesn't really know the first thing about it.* 那一番關於藝術的談話不過是裝模作樣。 她實際上對藝術一竅不通。

---

af·fect·ed /əˈfɛktɪd; əˈfektʃd/ *adj* not real, natural, or sincere 不真實的; 不自然的; 做作的: *She has a really affected voice on the phone.* 她在電話裡的聲音聽起來很不自然。– opposite 反義 **unaffected**

af·fec·tion /əˈfɛkʃən; əˈfekʃən/ *n* [U] a feeling of love or fondness 愛慕; 慈愛; 鍾愛

af·fec·tion·ate /əˈfɛkʃənɪt; əˈfekʃənɪt/ *adj* showing love or fondness towards people 慈愛的; 鍾愛的; 愛慕的 –**affectionately** *adv*

af·fil·i·ate¹ /əˈfɪlɪˌet; əˈfɪlɪeɪt/ *v* **affiliated, affiliating** [I] (of an organization) to join or have a close connection with a larger organization〔某組織〕加入, 併入〔更大的組織〕: *We hope that other groups will affiliate* **with** *the Party.* 我們希望其他小派別加入本黨。–**affiliated** *adj*: *a group of affiliated companies* 幾家分公司 | *a medical centre affiliated* **to** *the University* 附屬於大學的醫療中心 –**affiliation** /əˌfɪlɪˈeʃən; əˌfɪlɪˈeɪʃən/ *n*: *He never tried to hide his political affiliations.* 他從不設法掩蓋自己的黨派關係。

af·fil·i·ate² /əˈfɪlɪət; əˈfɪlɪət/ *n* an organization which is joined to a larger organization 分支機構; 分會; 分公司: *The firm is an affiliate of a major company.* 這是一家大公司的分公司。

af·fin·i·ty /əˈfɪnətɪ; əˈfɪn̩tɪ/ *n* **affinities** [C; U] **1** close similarity or connection 類同; 相似; 緊密關係 **2** strong attraction or feeling of shared interests 吸引力; 親和力: *He feels a strong sense of affinity* **with** *this village.* 他深深地愛上了這村莊。 | *She has a natural affinity* **with** *other women.* 她對其他婦女有一種自然的親切感。

af·firm /əˈfɝm; əˈfɜːm/ *v* [T; +that] *fml* to declare, often for the second or third time, that something is true〔正式〕斷言, 重申〔某事物〕: *The minister affirmed that the government's intention to reduce taxes.* 這位部長重申政府準備減稅的打算。–**affirmation** /ˌæfɚˈmeʃən; ˌæfəˈmeɪʃən/ *n* [C;U]

af·fir·ma·tive /əˈfɝmətɪv; əˈfɜːmətɪv/ *adj* *fml*〔正式〕**1** showing agreement or giving the answer 'yes' 肯定的; 贊成的: *an affirmative answer* 肯定的回答 **2 answer in the affirmative** to answer 'yes' 作肯定的回答 –opposite 反義 **negative** –**affirmatively** *adv*

af·fix /əˈfɪks; əˈfɪks/ *v* [T] *fml* to fix, fasten, or stick〔正式〕使固定; 繫住; 黏上: *A stamp should be affixed to the envelope.* 郵票應該貼在信封上。

af·flict /əˈflɪkt; əˈflɪkt/ *v* [T] to cause severe suffering or pain 使受痛苦; 使苦惱; 折磨: *He was afflicted* **with** *blindness.* 他受失明之苦。 | *afflicted* **by** *terrible wounds* 受重傷的折磨

af·flic·tion /əˈflɪkʃən; əˈflɪkʃən/ *n* [C;U] *fml* something causing suffering or pain〔正式〕痛苦; 苦惱; 折磨

af·flu·ent /ˈæflʊənt; ˈæflʊənt/ *adj* having plenty of money or other possessions 富有的; 富裕的 –**affluence** *n* [U]

*af·ford /əˈford; əˈfɔːd/ *v* [T] **1** to have enough money to do or buy something without difficulty 負擔得起; 買得起: *Can you afford £35,000 for a house?* 你能花三萬五千英鎊買幢房子嗎? | *Since she lost her job, she can no longer afford to go on holiday.* 她失業以後, 再也花不起錢去度假了。

□ USEFUL PATTERNS 有用句型
to afford something; to afford to do something

2 to be able to do something or let something happen without risk or damage to yourself 經得起; 受得住: *You can't afford to lose their support.* 失去他們的支持你會不行的。 | *She can afford to be rude to her neighbours now she's moving.* 既然她要搬家, 她就不怕對鄰居無禮了。 | *We can't afford any more trouble.* 我們再也經不起麻煩了。**3** *fml* to provide with〔正式〕提供: *The tree afforded us shelter from the rain.* 這棵樹為我們提供了避雨的地方。

af·front /əˈfrʌnt; əˈfrʌnt/ *n* an act or remark that is rude to someone or hurts their feelings 侮辱; 冒犯

a·field /əˈfild; əˈfiːld/ *adv* **far afield** far away 遠離; 在遠處: *Don't go too far afield or we might lose you.* 不要走得太遠, 否則我們會找不到你的。 | *We get a lot of tourists from Europe, and some from even further afield.* 我們的遊客很多來自歐洲, 有些來自更遠的地方。

a·flame /əˈflem; əˈfleɪm/ *adj* [never before a noun 不能用於名詞前] on fire 着火的; 燃燒的

a·float /əˈflot; əˈfleʊt/ *adj* [never before a noun 不能用於名詞前] **1** floating on water 在水中漂浮的 **2 stay afloat, keep afloat** to stay or keep out of debt 不欠債的

a·foot /əˈfʊt; əˈfʊt/ *adj* [never before a noun 不能用於名詞前] being prepared or already happening 正準備中; 在進行中: *There is a plan afoot to pull down the old building.* 目前正計劃拆除這幢舊建築物。

*a·fraid /əˈfred; əˈfreɪd/ *adj* [never before a noun 不能用於名詞前] **1** worried or frightened about something that might happen 擔心的; 憂慮〔可能發生的事情〕的: *She looked lonely and afraid.* 她看上去孤孤單單, 憂心忡忡。 | *He was afraid* **of** *being bitten.* 他怕被咬。 | *I was afraid of upsetting her.* 我怕令她不安。 | *My aunt was afraid that she might catch a cold.* 我姨母擔心她自己可能染上感冒。 | *He was afraid the plane would crash.* 他擔心飛機會墜毀。

□ USEFUL PATTERNS 有用句型
be afraid of something; be afraid of doing something; be afraid that…

2 afraid of someone/something frightened

because someone or something is unpleasant or will hurt you 害怕某人[某事]: *The child is afraid of the dark.* 這孩子怕黑。| *He's afraid of Bill.* 他怕比爾。**3 afraid to do something** nervous or unwilling to do something because you are worried about what might happen 不敢做某事: *She was afraid to go out alone at night.* 她不敢晚上單獨外出。**4 I'm afraid** a phrase used to show that you are sorry about something or to disagree politely with someone 恐怕〔用於感到遺憾或有禮貌地表示不同意時〕: *I can't come to the party, I'm afraid.* 我恐怕不能來參加聚會。| *"Is Richard there?" "I'm afraid not."* "理查德在嗎?""恐怕不在。"| *I'm afraid that these facts are incorrect.* 恐怕這些事實不正確。**5 afraid for** worried or concerned about someone or something 為〔某人、某事〕擔心: *During the flood she was afraid for her father and his house.* 洪水期間她為父親和他的房子擔心。

a·fresh /əˈfreʃ; əˈfreʃ/ *adv fml* again from the beginning 〔正式〕重新: *We decided to close down the business and start afresh.* 我們決定先關閉商行, 再重新開張。

Af·ri·can[1] /ˈæfrɪkən; ˈæfrɪkən/ *adj* connected with Africa or coming from Africa 非洲的

African[2] *n* a person from Africa 非洲人

af·ter[1] /ˈæftə; ˈɑːftər/ *prep* **1** in the time following something 〔時間上〕在…以後: *We'll leave after breakfast.* 我們吃完早餐以後動身。| *I'll phone you some time after six o'clock.* 我六點多給你打電話。**2 day after day, week after week, etc.** every day, every week, etc. 每天; 每週等: *I hated having to sit in a classroom day after day.* 我討厭日復一日地坐在教室裡。**3** following someone or something 在…之後; 跟在…後面: *"P" comes after "O" in the alphabet.* 在字母表裡, "P" 在 "O" 後面。| *I ran after her.* 我追她。**4** because of something that has happened 由於; 因為: *After the way he treated me I never want to see him again.* 因為他這樣對待我, 我再也不想見他了。**5** looking for someone or trying to catch them 尋找; 搜尋: *The police are after me.* 警方正在追緝我。**6** trying to get something 想得到: *I think he's only after your money!* 我認為他只是想要你的錢! **7 be named/called after someone** to be given the same name as someone 以某人之名命名: *He was named Jack, after his father.* 他以父親的名字取名為傑克。**8 after all : a** in spite of things which had been done or thought earlier 畢竟: *There are two r's in "earring". You see, I was right after all.* earring 中有兩個 r。你瞧, 畢竟是我對。| *I was feeling a bit tired, but then David said he was going, so I decided to go after all.* 我覺得有點累, 可戴維說他要去, 所以到頭來我也決定去。**b** don't forget; a phrase used when you are giving force to your opinion with good reasons 別忘了〔用於強調自己的觀點〕: *You can't expect him to understand. After all, he's only six years old.* 你不能指望他理解。別忘了, 他才六歲。

■ **USAGE** 用法: Do not use the phrase **after all** to refer to the time when something happens. **After all** has two main uses. ☆指某事發生的時間, 不用 **after all. After all** 有兩個主要用法。**1** To show that something is true in spite of what has been done or said before ☆畢竟; 終究: *She said she wasn't going to come, but she turned up after all.* 她說不會來, 但終究還是露面了。| *I didn't believe you, but you were right after all!* 我本來不相信你, 但歸根結底是你對了! | *I've changed my mind, I think I'll have a coffee after all.* 我改變主意了, 想想還是要一杯咖啡。In this use **after all** usually comes at the end of a sentence. ☆在這種用法中, **after all** 常出現在句尾。**2** To introduce an idea that explains or supports what you are saying ☆別忘了〔用於提出一個觀點以解釋或支持所說情況〕: *It's not his fault. He's only obeying orders after all.* 這不是他的過錯, 別忘了他只是執行命令。| *Don't be too hard on her. After all she's only a child.* 別對她管得太嚴, 別忘了她還是個孩子。| *Of course he can afford it. After all he is a millionaire!* 他當然付得起, 別忘了他是個百萬富翁!

---

9 after that : a you use "after that" when you move on to the next stage in a story that you are telling 接着〔用於進入話題的下一部分〕: *They mixed the clay and sand, and then added some water. After that, they rolled the mixture into a ball.* 他們混合了沙和土, 然後加點水。接着, 他們把它搓成一團。**b** you use "after that" when you give the next in a group of instructions 接着〔用於在一系列說明中, 帶出下一步的做法〕: *Mix the clay and sand. Then add the water. After that, roll the mixture into a ball.* 把沙和土混在一起, 然後加水, 接着把它搓成一團。**c** you use "after that" when you go on to the next stage of a process that you are describing 然後〔用於在描寫的過程中, 提及下一步〕: *The letters are taken to the sorting office and sorted. After that, they are sent out to the main postal towns, where they are sorted again.* 信件被送到分揀處分類, 然後送往主要的郵政城鎮, 在那裡再次分揀。

af·ter[2] *adv, conj* later than someone or something else 在…之後: *I went to live in France, and soon after I met my wife.* 我去法國定居, 不久以後便遇到了我的妻子。| *John came last Tuesday, and I arrived the day after.* 約翰是上星期二來的, 我比他晚一天到。| *Soon after he'd left I realized that* *he'd left his coat.* 他離開沒多久, 我就發現他把外套忘了。

af·ter·ef·fect /ˈæftərəˌfɛkt; ˈɑːftərɪˌfekt/ *n* an unpleasant effect or result 〔不良的〕後效; 副作用: *the after-effects of the new drug* 新藥的副作用

af·ter·life /ˈæftəˌlaɪf; ˈɑːftəlaɪf/ *n* [sing] the life that is thought by some people to follow death 來世

af·ter·math /ˈæftəˌmæθ; ˈɑːftəmæθ/ *n* [sing] the period following an unpleasant event such as an accident, storm, or war 〔不幸事件如事故、暴風雨、戰爭等的〕後果; 餘波: *There was confusion in the aftermath of the accident.* 事故過後一片混亂。

☆**af·ter·noon** /ˌæftəˈnun; ˌɑːftəˈnuːn/ *n* the period which begins at about midday and ends at about six o'clock 下午: *on Tuesday afternoons* 星期二下午 | *I like to sleep in the afternoon.* 我喜歡午睡。 | *an afternoon walk* 午後散步 | *in the late afternoon* 傍晚

☆**af·ter·wards** /ˈæftəwədz; ˈɑːftəwədz/ *adv* (also 又作 **afterward**) later, after something else has happened 以後; 後來: *She had her supper and then went to bed soon afterwards.* 她吃過晚飯很快就上牀了。

☆**a·gain** /əˈɡɛn; əˈɡeɪn/ *adv* **1** once more 再一次; 又: *Could you explain it again, please?* 請再解釋一遍, 好嗎? | *I'd love to go to Africa again.* 我很想再去一次非洲。 | *We had to listen to his jokes yet again!* 我們還得再聽一次他的玩笑! **2** you use "again" when you are going to make another point of the same kind as your last one 再者; 此外: *Let's now compare this screen with the last one we looked at. Again, we see that colour is very important.* 讓我們把這個屏幕和剛才看的比較一下。此外, 我們發現色彩是十分重要的。 **3** back to the same place or same condition as before 如前; 恢復原狀: *She was ill for a long time, but she's well again now.* 她病了很長時間, 不過現在又好了。 | *I can't wait to be home again.* 我迫不及待要回家。 **4 again and again** repeatedly many times 再三地: *The government keeps coming out with the same excuses again and again.* 政府屢次提出相同的藉口。 **5 then again, there again** on the other hand 另一方面: *He might get the job, but then again he might not have the right qualifications.* 他可能得到這份工作, 但另一方面, 他可能沒有合適的資格。

☆**a·gainst** /əˈɡɛnst; əˈɡenst/ *prep* **1** in opposition to someone or something 反對; 與…相反: *We discussed the arguments for and against capital punishment.* 我們就贊成或反對死刑的論點進行了討論。 | *The government have threatened to use force against the rebels.* 政府揚言要使用武力來對付反叛者。 | *We're playing against a team from the North next week.* 下星期我們要和北方隊比賽。 | *It is important that we*

win the battle against inflation. 贏得反通貨膨脹的鬥爭是很重要的。 **2** touching something or pressing on it 靠; 碰: *He leaned his bike against the wall.* 他把腳踏車靠在牆上。 | *The rain was beating against the window.* 雨打在窗戶上。–see picture on page 764 見764頁彩圖 **3** as a defence or protection from something 防備; 預防: *We're insured against burglary.* 我們保了盜竊險。 **4 against the law** not allowed by the law 違法的: *It's against the law to sell alcohol to children under 18.* 賣酒給十八歲以下的孩子是違法的。 **5** in the opposite direction to the wind or to the movement of water 逆, 對着〔風或水流〕: *trying to sail against the wind* 盡量逆風航行 | *We had to row against the current.* 我們不得不逆水划行。

☆**age**[1] /eɪdʒ; eɪdʒ/ *n* **1** [C;U] the number of years that a person has lived 年齡: *He is 10 years of age.* 他十歲。 | *At your age you should know better.* 在你這個年齡應該更懂事了。 | *She died at the age of 79.* 她七十九歲謝世。 | *What ages are your children?* 你的孩子們都幾歲了? **2** [U] one of the periods of life 一生的某一時期: *You don't get your pension until you reach retirement age.* 你到了退休年齡才能領取養老金。 | *Who will look after you in old age?* 你老了誰來照顧你? **3** [U] the state of being old 高齡; 老年: *His back was bent with age.* 他老得背都駝了。 **4** [C] a particular period of history 歷史時期: *the history of painting through the ages* 幾世紀以來的繪畫史 | *the age of television* 電視時代 **5 an age, ages** a long time 長時間: *I haven't seen her for ages.* 我很久沒見她了。 **6 come of age** to become an adult in law and be allowed to vote and get married 成年; 達到〔准予投票、結婚等〕法定年齡 [RELATED PHRASE 相關詞組 **be of age**] **7 over age** too old to do a particular thing because the rules do not allow it 超過規定年齡 **8 under age** not legally old enough to do something 不到規定年齡

age[2] *v* **aged, aging** or **ageing** [I;T] to become older and weaker or make someone seem older and weaker (使)〔某人〕變老: *After his wife's death he aged quickly.* 自妻子死後, 他老得很快。 | *The illness has aged him.* 他因病衰老。

☆**aged**[1] /eɪdʒd; eɪdʒd/ *adj* [never before a noun 不能用於名詞前] a word used to say how old someone is …歲的: *a man aged 40* 四十歲的男人

ag·ed[2] /ˈeɪdʒɪd; ˈeɪdʒɪd/ *adj* **1** very old 年老的: *an aged man* 老翁 **2 the aged** very old people 老人: *care of the sick and the aged* 照顧病人和老人

age·less /ˈeɪdʒlɪs; ˈeɪdʒləs/ *adj* never showing signs of growing old 不見老的

☆**a·gen·cy** /ˈeɪdʒənsɪ; ˈeɪdʒənsi/ *n* **agencies** a business that arranges services for people 代理處; 經銷處: *I got this*

A

job through an employment agency. 我通過職業介紹所找到了這份工作。

a·gen·da /ə'dʒɛndə; ə'dʒɛndə/ n 1 a list of the subjects to be talked about at a meeting 〔會議的〕議程 2 **on the agenda** being considered and talked about 正在討論: *Protecting the environment is very much on the agenda.* 保護環境是個熱門話題。

★**a·gent** /'edʒənt; 'eɪdʒənt/ n 1 someone who represents the business affairs of another person or of a firm 代理商; 經銷商: *Our agent in Rome deals with all our Italian business.* 我們在羅馬的代理商負責我們在意大利的所有業務。2 someone who works for a government and tries to find out the secrets of other governments 特務: *a secret agent* 間諜 3 something that causes a particular result 作用物: *Soap is a cleansing agent.* 肥皂是一種洗滌劑。

ag·gra·vate /'ægrə,vet; 'ægrəveɪt/ v **aggravated, aggravating** [T] 1 to make a problem worse or more serious 使〔問題〕更壞; 加劇: *The lack of rain aggravated the already serious lack of food.* 雨水少使原來就嚴重的糧食短缺問題更加嚴重。2 to annoy someone 惹惱〔某人〕: *His little habits really aggravate me!* 他的小習慣真叫我生氣! | *an aggravating way of interrupting people* 惹人生厭的插話方式 –**aggravation** /,ægrə'veʃən; ,ægrə'veɪʃən/ n [U]

ag·gre·gate /'ægrɪgɪt; 'ægrɪgət/ n [C;U] a total 總計

ag·gres·sion /ə'grɛʃən; ə'greʃən/ n [U] angry or violent behaviour in which you attack someone 侵犯; 侵略: *an act of aggression* 侵略行為 | *feelings of aggression* 侵略感

ag·gres·sive /ə'grɛsɪv; ə'gresɪv/ adj 1 always ready to argue with people or attack them 好爭吵的; 好攻擊的: *He has a very aggressive manner.* 他有一種十分好鬥的態度。2 forceful, and determined to succeed 強有力的; 決心成功的: *If you want to succeed in business you must be aggressive.* 如果你想在事業上成功, 就必須有闖勁。| *an aggressive marketing campaign* 一次積極進取的銷售活動 –**aggressively** adv

ag·gres·sor /ə'grɛsə; ə'gresər/ n fml a person or country that begins a fight or war without a good reason 〔正式〕侵略者; 侵略國

ag·grieved /ə'grivd; ə'griːvd/ adj fml feeling angry and upset because you have been treated unfairly 〔正式〕受委屈的; 憤憤不平的

a·ghast /ə'gæst; ə'gɑːst/ adj [never before a noun 不能用於名詞前] suddenly filled with surprise, fear, and shock 吃驚的; 嚇呆的

ag·ile /'ædʒəl; 'ædʒaɪl/ adj 1 able to move quickly and easily 敏捷的 2 able to think quickly (used of someone's mind) 靈活的 〔指大腦〕–**agility** /ə'dʒɪləti; ə'dʒɪləti/ n [U]

ag·i·tate /'ædʒə,tet; 'ædʒəteɪt/ v **agitated, agitating** 1 [T] to make someone feel worried 使〔某人〕不安; 使焦慮 2 [I] to argue strongly in public for or against political or social changes 鼓動; 煽動: *people agitating for political reforms* 鼓動政治改革的人

ag·i·ta·tion /,ædʒə'teʃən; ,ædʒə'teɪʃən/ n [U] 1 a strong feeling of worry 焦慮不安 2 public argument or actions for or against political or social changes 鼓動; 煽動; 騷動

ag·i·ta·tor /'ædʒə,tetə; 'ædʒəteɪtər/ n a person who tries to encourage political or social changes by public argument or actions 鼓動者; 煽動者

a·glow /ə'glo; ə'gləʊ/ adj [never before a noun 不能用於名詞前] lit bright with colour and warmth 〔文〕放光彩的; 發熱的

ag·nos·tic /æg'nɒstɪk; æg'nɒstɪk/ n someone who believes that it is not possible to know whether there is a God or whether there is life after death 〔對於上帝或來世〕不可知論者 –compare 比較 ATHEIST –**agnostic** adj –**agnosticism** /-tə,sɪzəm; -tɪsɪzəm/ n [U]

★★**a·go** /ə'go; ə'gəʊ/ adv in the past 以前: *He left ten minutes ago.* 他是十分鐘前離開的。| *How long ago did she die?* 她是多久以前死的? | *That all happened a long time ago.* 這些都是很久以前的事了。

■ USAGE 用法: 1 We nearly always use **ago** with the past tense of verbs, but not with perfect forms (formed from have). ☆我們幾乎總是把 **ago** 和動詞的過去式連用, 但不和 **have** 構成的完成式連用。Compare 比較 *I came here a year ago* 我一年前來到這兒 and 和 *I have been here for a year/since 1990.* 我來這兒一年了 [我自 1990 年以來一直在這兒]。2 When we want to show the difference between a time in the past and a time even further back we use **before (that)** or **previously** instead of **ago** ☆要表示過去某一時間和較遠的過去某一時間的差別時, 用 **before (that)** 或 **previously** 代替 **ago**: *My grandfather died five years **ago***; *my grandmother had already died three years **before (that)**/three years **previously**.* 我祖父五年前去世了; 我祖母比他早三年就去世了。

---

a·gog /ə'gɒg; ə'gɒg/ adj [never before a noun 不能用於名詞前] infml excited about something, and keen to know what will happen next 〔非正式〕激動的; 渴望的; 急切的

ag·o·nize /'ægə,naɪz; 'ægənaɪz/ v **agonized, agonizing** (also 又作 **agonise** BrE 〔英式〕) [I] infml to spend a lot of time worrying about something or trying to make a decision 〔非正式〕焦慮: *Nina has been* *agonizing* **over** *whether to take the job abroad.* 尼娜為是否要接受這份海外工作而焦慮不安。

ag·o·nized /'ægə,naɪzd; 'ægənaɪzd/ *adj* (also 又作 **agonised** *BrE*【英式】) showing great pain or suffering 痛苦的: *an agonized cry* 痛哭

ag·o·niz·ing /'ægə,naɪzɪŋ; 'ægənaɪzɪŋ/ *adj* (also 又作 **agonising** *BrE*【英式】) causing great pain or worry 使人痛苦的; 令人焦慮的: *an agonizing decision* 令人痛苦的決定

ag·o·ny /'ægənɪ; 'ægəni/ *n* **agonies** [C;U] very great pain or suffering in your mind or body〔身心的〕極度痛苦: *He lay in agony until the doctor arrived.* 他十分痛苦地躺在那裡, 直到醫生來。| *She was suffering agonies of doubt.* 她疑慮不安, 十分痛苦。

a·grar·i·an /ə'grɛrɪən; ə'grɛəriən/ *adj* concerning farmland or its ownership 土地的; 土地所有權的

★a·gree /ə'gri; ə'griː/ *v* **agreed, agreeing** **1** [I; +(that)] to have the same opinion about something 同意, 贊成〔某事〕: *She agreed* **with** *me.* 她同意你的意見。| *We agreed that the government should do more to protect the environment.* 我們贊成政府為保護環境多做點事。| *We agreed* **on** *a price for the car.* 我們商定了汽車的價格。| *I agree* **with** *you* **about** *this.* 在這方面我同意你的意見。**2** **agree to something, agree to do something** to say that you will do something else has suggested 接受某事; 答應做某事: *The government will never agree to the plan.* 政府決不會接受該計劃。| *She agreed to look after the cat for the weekend.* 她答應週末照看貓咪。**3** **be agreed** to have reached the same decision about something 達成一致決定: *We were all agreed that the government has not done enough to tackle this problem.* 我們一致認為政府在解決這個問題上做得不夠。**4** **agree with something** to believe that something is right 相信某事正確: *I don't agree with hitting children.* 我認為打孩子不對。**5** **not agree with someone** *infml* to make someone ill【非正式】使某人不舒服: *Strawberries don't agree with me.* 我吃草莓不舒服。**6** [I] to be in accordance with something or be the same as something 一致: *The two statements agree in everything except the smallest details.* 除了一些細枝末節, 兩份聲明在其他方面完全一致。

a·gree·a·ble /ə'griəbl̩; ə'griːəbəl/ *adj* **1** pleasant, enjoyable, or acceptable 令人愉快的; 愜意的: *The weather was very agreeable.* 氣候十分宜人。–opposite 反義 **disagreeable** **2** **agreeable to something** willing to do or accept something 樂於做某事; 欣然接受某事

a·gree·a·bly /ə'griəblɪ; ə'griːəbli/ *adv* pleasantly 令人愉快地: *I was agreeably surprised.* 我感到又驚又喜。

★a·gree·ment /ə'grimənt; ə'griːmənt/ *n* **1** [U] the state of having reached the same opinion or feeling about something 相合; 一致: *They finally reached agreement after long discussions.* 經過長時間的討論, 他們最終取得了一致意見。–opposite 反義 **disagreement** **2** [U] the act of showing that you accept something 認可; 同意: *The committee needs your agreement.* 委員會需要你的認可。**3** **in agreement** having the same opinion about something as someone else 同意; 一致: *We are all in agreement about the need to tackle inflation.* 我們一致認為該對付通貨膨脹了。**4** [C] an arrangement or promise made between people or countries 協議; 協定; 合約: *an arms-control agreement* 軍備控制協定 | *You have broken our agreement.* 你破壞了我們之間的協議。

★ag·ri·cul·ture /'ægrɪ,kʌltʃə; 'ægrɪ,kʌltʃər/ *n* [U] the practice of farming, especially of growing crops 農業; 農耕 –**agricultural** /,ægrɪ'kʌltʃərəl; ,ægrɪ'kʌltʃərəl◂/ *adj*

a·ground /ə'graʊnd; ə'graʊnd/ *adv* **run aground, go aground** (of a ship) to touch the bottom of a sea or lake and be unable to move〔船〕擱淺

ah /ɑ; ɑː/ *interj* a word used to express surprise, pity, pain, or pleasure! 啊! 喲!〔表示驚奇、憐憫、痛苦或喜悅〕: *Ah! I hurt my foot on that stone.* 喲! 我踩在那塊石頭上, 弄傷了腳。| *Ah, there you are!* 啊, 原來你在這兒!

a·ha /ɑ'hɑ; ɑː'hɑː/ *interj* a word used to express surprise, satisfaction, or understanding 啊哈!〔表示驚奇、得意或理解〕: *Aha, so it's you hiding there!* 啊哈, 原來是你躲在那裡!

★a·head /ə'hɛd; ə'hed/ *adv, adj* **1** *adv* in front of you 在前面: *There were quite a few cars on the road ahead.* 前面的路上有好幾輛汽車。| *He ran ahead to see what was happening.* 他奔到前面去看出了甚麼事。| *There was a roadblock straight ahead* **of** *us.* 我們正前方有路障。**2** *adv* into the future 將來; 未來: *We must look ahead and try to plan for the future.* 我們必須未雨綢繆, 作好打算。| *It's important to plan ahead.* 未雨綢繆是很重要的。**3** *adv, adj* more advanced than someone else or winning in a competition against them 勝過: *Our team was ahead at half time.* 上半場結束時我隊領先。| *We're ahead* **of** *all the other companies in this field.* 在這個範疇上, 我們公司勝過其他任何一家公司。| *I think we might finish the project ahead of schedule.* 我想我們可能提前完成計劃。

a·hoy /ə'hɔɪ; ə'hɔɪ/ *interj* a greeting shouted on a boat 啊嗨!〔船隻與船之間的招呼〕

aid¹ /ed; eɪd/ *v* [T] to help or give support to someone 援助, 幫助〔某人〕–see 見 HELP¹ (USAGE用法)

★aid² *n* **1** [U] help that is given to someone 幫助: *I managed to go up the mountain with*

A

the aid of a guide. 在嚮導的幫助下, 我爬到了山頂。**2** [U] money, food, and services given to people who need them〔食物、金錢、服務等的〕援助: *They are sending aid to the victims of the disaster immediately.* 他們馬上為災民送去了援助。| *overseas aid* 海外援助 **3** [C] a thing that helps you do something 有助之物: *A dictionary is an important aid in learning a new language.* 在學習一種新語言時, 詞典是重要的工具。**4 in aid of** in support of 以支援或幫助: *What is the money in aid of?* 這筆錢準備用來做甚麼? **5 go to someone's aid** to help someone 幫助某人: *He went to the aid of the injured man.* 他去幫助那個受傷的男人。

aide /ed; eɪd/ *n* a person employed to help a government minister〔政府部門的〕助手; 助理

AIDS /edz; eɪdz/ a very serious disease, which destroys the body's defences against infection; an abbreviation for **Acquired Immune Deficiency Syndrome**〖縮〗艾滋病, 愛滋病〔獲得性免疫缺綜合症〕

ail /el; eɪl/ *v* [I;T] *old fash* to become ill and grow weak〖老式〗生病; 有病

ail·ing /ˈelɪŋ; ˈeɪlɪŋ/ *adj* ill or weak, and not getting better or stronger 生病的; 有病的: *his ailing mother* 他有病的母親 | *the country's ailing economy* 國家的病態經濟

ail·ment /ˈelmənt; ˈeɪlmənt/ *n* an illness that is not serious 小病痛; 不適

★aim¹ /em; eɪm/ *v* **1** [I;T] to point or direct a weapon towards an object you want to hit 瞄準: *He aimed the gun carefully.* 他小心地用槍瞄準。| *He aimed it at the bottles.* 他瞄準了瓶子。**2 aim to do something, aim at doing something** to direct your efforts and plans towards making something happen 旨在做某事; 致力於做某事: *The company aims to increase sales overseas.* 公司致力於增加海外銷售額。| *I'm aiming at getting a good job in advertising.* 我立志要在廣告界謀一份好工作。**3** [T] to direct something at someone in order to influence them 針對〔某人〕: *an advertising campaign aimed at young people* 一項以年輕人為對象的廣告宣傳運動

★aim² *n* **1** [U] the act of pointing a weapon 瞄準; 對準: *Her aim was very good.* 她瞄得很準。**2 take aim** to point a weapon at something 瞄準: *He took aim, then fired.* 他瞄準了, 然後開槍。**3** [C] the thing that you are trying to do or get 目標; 目的: *The project was set up with the aim of helping young unemployed people.* 制訂這個計劃的目的是為了幫助年輕的失業人士。

aim·less /ˈemlɪs; ˈeɪmləs/ *adj* without any clear purpose 無目的的; 無目標的: *His life was aimless.* 他的生活沒有目標。–**aimlessly** *adv*

ain't /ent; eɪnt/ *v* short for "am not", "is not", "are not", "has not", and "have not";

many people do not consider this to be correct English ☆ "am not", "is not", "are not", "has not", "have not" 的縮約式; 很多人認為這是英語中的不規範用法: *We ain't coming.* 我們不來了。| *They ain't got it.* 他們沒有弄到它。

★air¹ /ɛr; eəʳ/ *n* **1** [U] the mixture of gases which surrounds the Earth and which we breathe 空氣; 大氣: *She opened the window to get some fresh air.* 她打開窗讓新鮮空氣進來。**2 the air** the space around you above the ground 天空; 空中: *She threw the ball into the air.* 她把球拋向空中。**3** [sing] a general appearance or feeling 神態; 氣氛: *There was an air of excitement in the stadium.* 運動場上瀰漫着一種激動的氣氛。| *He had an air of sadness about him.* 他有一種悲傷的神情。| *The city had a depressing air.* 這個城市氣氛蕭條。**4 by air** by plane 坐飛機: *We decided to go by air.* 我們決定坐飛機去。**5 air travel** travel by plane 坐飛機去旅行 **6 disappear into thin air** to disappear completely 無影無蹤 **7 give yourself airs, put on airs** to behave as if you are more important than you really are 擺架子; 裝腔作勢 **8 on the air** broadcasting on the radio or television 正在廣播或播映 [RELATED PHRASE 相關詞組 **off the air**]

air² *v* **1** [I;T] to dry in a place that is warm and has plenty of dry air 晾乾; 曬乾: *You should always air clothes thoroughly.* 你總應該把衣服徹底曬乾。| *Hang those shirts up to air.* 把那些襯衫掛起來晾乾。**2** [T] to make a room fresh by letting in air 使通風: *I'll open the windows to air the room.* 我開窗給房間通通風。**3** [T] to make your ideas known to other people 發表〔意見〕: *The discussion will give everyone a chance to air their views.* 這次討論將使每個人都有機會來發表自己的意見。–**airing** *n* [always 常作 **an airing**]: *Let's give the room a good airing.* 讓我們給房間透透氣。

air·borne /ˈɛrbɔrn; ˈeəbɔːn/ *adj* **1** carried about by the air (used of seeds) 由空氣傳播的〔指種子〕**2** flying in the air (used of aircraft) 在空中飛行的〔指飛機〕

air·bus /ˈɛrˌbʌs; ˈeəbʌs/ *n* a plane for carrying large numbers of passengers on short flights 空中客車;〔作短程飛行的〕大型客機

air-con·di·tion·ing /ˈ· ·ˌ··/ *n* [U] the system that uses machines to keep air in a building cool 空調〔系統〕–**air-conditioned** *adj*

★air·craft /ˈɛrˌkræft; ˈeəkrɑːft/ *n* [plural is 複數為 **aircraft**] a plane of any type, with or without an engine 飛機; 航空器

aircraft car·ri·er /ˈ··· ˌ···/ *n* a warship that carries aircraft and has a large flat surface where they can take off and land 航空母艦

air·field /ˈɛr fild; ˈeəfiːld/ *n* an open area,

smaller than an airport, where aircraft may land and take off 飛機場

air force /ˈɛrˌfors; ˈeəfɔːs/ *n* the part of the military organization of a country that is concerned with fighting in the air 空軍

air·host·ess /ˈɛrˌhostɪs; ˈeəˌhəʊstɪs/ *n* a woman who looks after passengers in a plane 空中小姐

airing cup·board /ˈ···ˌ··/ *n* a warm dry cupboard used for airing clothes 烘衣櫃

air·less /ˈɛrlɪs; ˈeələs/ *adj* without fresh air 不通風的: *The room was hot and airless* 這房間熱不透風。

air·lift /ˈɛrˌlɪft; ˈeəˌlɪft/ *n* the carrying of a lot of people or supplies by aircraft, often to or from a place that is difficult to get to 空運 *—***airlift** *v* [T]

*★***air·line** /ˈɛrˌlaɪn; ˈeəlaɪn/ *n* a business that runs a regular service for carrying passengers and goods by air 航空公司

air·lin·er /ˈɛrˌlaɪnɚ; ˈeəˌlaɪnəʳ/ *n* a large plane used for carrying passengers 大型客機; 班機

air·lock /ˈɛrˌlɑk; ˈeəlɒk/ *n* **1** the air blocking the flow of a liquid in a tube or pipe 氣塞 **2** an enclosed space through which air cannot accidentally pass, for example in a spacecraft〔太空船等的〕氣密艙

air·mail /ˈɛrˌmel; ˈeəmeɪl/ *n* [U] the system of sending letters and parcels by air 航空郵政

air·man /ˈɛrmən; ˈeəmən/ *n* **airmen** /-mən; -mən/ a person of low rank in a country's air force 空軍士兵

air·miss /ˈɛrˌmɪs; ˈeəˌmɪs/ *n* **airmisses** a situation in which two planes very nearly hit each other in the air 險些發生的撞機事故

air·plane /ˈɛrˌplen; ˈeəpleɪn/ *n* the usual American word for《美式》= AEROPLANE

*★***air·port** /ˈɛrˌport; ˈeəpɔːt/ *n* a place you arrive at or leave from when travelling by plane 飛機場 *–see picture on page 991* 見 991 頁彩圖

air raid /ˈ· ·/ *n* an attack by military aircraft 空襲

air·ship /ˈɛrˌʃɪp; ˈeəʃɪp/ *n* an old type of aircraft containing gas to make it lighter than air and with an engine to make it move〔舊時的〕飛艇

air·sick /ˈɛrˌsɪk; ˈeəˌsɪk/ *adj* sick because of the movement of an aircraft 暈機的

air·space /ˈɛrˌspes; ˈeəspeɪs/ *n* [U] the sky above a country, regarded as the property of that country 領空

air·strip /ˈɛrˌstrɪp; ˈeəˌstrɪp/ *n* a small stretch of land used by aircraft to take off and land 臨時飛機跑道; 簡易機場

air ter·mi·nal /ˈ··ˌ··/ *n* a building at an airport where passengers wait before getting on their plane 航空終點站;〔旅客候機的〕機場大廈

air·tight /ˈɛrˈtaɪt; ˈeətaɪt/ *adj* not allowing air to pass in or out 不透氣的; 密封的: *airtight containers* 密封容器

air·waves /ˈɛrˌwevz; ˈeəweɪvz/ *n* **on the airwaves** on radio or television 廣播; 播映

air·wor·thy /ˈɛrˌwɚði; ˈeəˌwɜːðɪ/ *adj* safe to fly (used of aircraft) 適航的〔指飛機〕 *–***airworthiness** *n* [U]

air·y /ˈɛrɪ; ˈeərɪ/ *adj* **airier, airiest 1** having plenty of fresh air inside (used of buildings) 通風的〔指建築物〕: *The room was large and airy.* 這房間又大又通風。**2** not based on facts or not very practical 不實際的: *his airy plans* 他的不切實際的計劃 | *airy schemes to become a millionaire* 要當百萬富翁的空想計劃 **3** joking and not seeming to care about things that should be taken seriously 漫不經心的; 輕率的: *She dismissed my objection with an airy wave of her hand.* 她漫不經心地揮揮手, 不理我的反對。 *–***airily** /ˈɛrəlɪ; ˈeərɪlɪ/ *adv*

aisle /aɪl; aɪl/ *n* a passage between rows of seats in a church, theatre, or cinema, or between rows of shelves in a large shop〔教堂、劇院等座位或大商店貨架間的〕走道, 過道

a·jar /əˈdʒɑr; əˈdʒɑː/ *adj* [never before a noun 不能用於名詞前] not quite closed (used of a door) 微開的〔指門〕; 半開的

a·kin /əˈkɪn; əˈkɪn/ *adj fml*《正式》**akin to something** similar to something 與某物相似

à la carte /ˌɑləˈkɑrt; ˌæ lə ˈkɑːt/ *adj, adv French* choosing food from a list where each dish has its own separate price《法》照菜單點菜(的): *We ate à la carte.* 我們按菜單點菜。 | *an à la carte menu* 點菜單

a·lac·ri·ty /əˈlækrətɪ; əˈlækrɪtɪ/ *n* [U] *fml* great willingness《正式》欣然; 樂意

a·larm[1] /əˈlɑrm; əˈlɑːm/ *n* **1** [U] sudden fear and anxiety when there is the possibility of danger 驚恐; 驚慌: *There is no need for any alarm — you are quite safe.* 不必驚慌 — 你挺安全。**2** [C] something such as a bell, noise, or light which is used to give a warning 警報物〔如鈴、響聲、光等〕 **3 raise the alarm, sound the alarm** to warn people of danger, especially by shouting 發出警報〔尤指喊叫〕

alarm[2] *v* [T] to make someone feel afraid and anxious 使〔某人〕驚慌不安: *Parents are very alarmed at the amount of violence on television.* 父母們對電視裡過多的暴力鏡頭感到不安。

alarm clock /ˈ·· ·/ *n* a clock that can be set to make a noise at a certain time to wake you up 鬧鐘

a·larm·ing /əˈlɑrmɪŋ; əˈlɑːmɪŋ/ *adj* very worrying 擔心的: *There has been an alarming increase in violent crime.* 暴力犯罪在驚人地增長。

a·larm·ist /əˈlɑrmɪst; əˈlɑːmɪst/ *n* a person who warns other people of danger unnecessarily 大驚小怪的人 **-alarmist** *adj*

a·las /ə'læs; ə'læs/ *interj lit* a word used to express sadness 〖文〗哎呀! 唉!〔表示悲傷〕

al·be·it /ɔːl'biːɪt; ɔːl'biːɪt/ *conj fml* although 〖正式〗儘管; 雖然: *It was a very important, albeit small, mistake.* 這個錯誤雖小但很嚴重。

al·bi·no /æl'baɪnəʊ; æl'biːnəʊ/ *n* a person or animal born with very white skin and hair, and pink eyes 患白化病的人或動物〔皮膚毛髮呈白色, 眼呈粉紅色〕

*★**al·bum** /'ælbəm; 'ælbəm/ *n* **1** a book used for collecting things such as photographs or stamps 黏貼簿〔如照相簿, 集郵冊等〕 **2** a record which plays for about 20 minutes on each side 唱片

al·bu·men /æl'bjuːmən; 'ælbjʊmʃn/ *n* [U] the white or colourless part of an egg 蛋白; 蛋清

al·che·my /'ælkəmɪ; 'ælkəmi/ *n* [U] the science of trying to find a way to turn metals into gold 煉金術 **–alchemist** /-ɪst; -ʃst/

*★**al·co·hol** /'ælkə,hɒl; 'ælkəhɒl/ *n* [U] **1** the colourless liquid present in drinks such as wine and beer; alcohol can make people drunk 酒精 **2** drinks containing this liquid 含酒精的飲料: *I never drink alcohol.* 我從不喝酒。

al·co·hol·ic[1] /,ælkə'hɒlɪk; ,ælkə'hɒlɪk◂/ *adj* containing alcohol or related to alcohol 含酒精的; 酒精的 **–opposite** 反義 **non-alcoholic**

alcoholic[2] *n* a person who cannot stop the habit of drinking too much alcohol 酗酒者; 酒鬼

al·co·hol·is·m /'ælkəhɒl,ɪzəm; 'ælkəhɒl-ɪzəm/ *n* [U] the disease caused by the continued drinking of a lot of alcohol 酒精中毒

al·cove /'ælkəv; 'ælkəʊv/ *n* a partly enclosed space in the wall of a room where you can put furniture or shelves 〔大房間內一小部分凹入牆裡可放牀、椅的〕凹室

al·der·man /'ɔːldəmən; 'ɔːldəmən/ *n* **aldermen** /-mən; -mən/ a local government officer 地方官員

ale /eɪl; eɪl/ *n* [U] a type of beer, especially one that is pale in colour 淡色啤酒

a·lert[1] /ə'lɜːt; ə'lɜːt/ *adj* **1** quick to notice what is happening 警覺的; 機靈的 **2 alert to something** knowing about a danger or problem 對某事警覺的: *We were alert to the dangers of the plan.* 我們對該計劃的危險有所警覺。 **–alertness** *n* [U]

alert[2] *n* **1** a situation in which people are ready and watching for danger 警戒狀態 **2 on the alert** ready and watching for danger 防備着; 警戒着

alert[3] *v* [T] to warn someone of a danger or problem 警告〔某人〕: *We must alert young people to the dangers of smoking.* 我們必須警告年輕人吸煙的危害。

A lev·el /'eɪ,levl; 'eɪ,levəl/ *n* the higher of the two standards of examination formerly taken at most British schools; an abbreviation for **Advanced Level** 〖縮〗〔英國普通教育文憑的〕高級考試

al·gae /'ældʒiː; 'ældʒiː/ *n* [pl] very small, simple plants that live in or near water 藻; 藻類

al·ge·bra /'ældʒəbrə; 'ældʒʃbrə/ *n* [U] a branch of MATHEMATICS in which signs and letters are used to represent numbers 代數學; 代數 **–algebraic** /,ældʒə'breɪɪk; ,æld-ʒʃ'breɪ-ɪk/ *adj*

al·go·rith·m /'ælgə,rɪðəm; 'ælgərɪðəm/ *n* a list of instructions to a computer which are carried out in a fixed order 〔電腦的〕計算程序; 算法

a·li·as[1] /'eɪlɪəs; 'eɪliəs/ *n* a false name, especially one used by a criminal 〔尤指罪犯用的〕化名

alias[2] *prep* a word used when you are giving someone's alias 又名; 化名: *The police are looking for Stephen Smith, alias Edward Ball.* 警方正在尋找斯蒂芬·史密斯, 又名愛德華·保爾。

al·i·bi /'ælə,baɪ; 'ælʃbaɪ/ *n* proof that a person was in another place at the time of a crime and so could not have done it 不在犯罪現場的證據: *He didn't have an alibi for the night of the murder.* 對那晚的謀殺案, 他沒有不在犯罪現場的證據。

a·li·en[1] /'eɪlɪən; 'eɪliən/ *adj* **1** belonging to another country or race 外國的; 異族的 **2** different and strange 相異的; 不同的; 陌生的: *an alien environment* 陌生的環境 | *Their ideas are quite alien to our way of thinking.* 他們的想法跟我們的截然不同。

alien[2] *n* **1** a foreigner who is not a citizen of the country where he or she is living 外僑 **2** a creature from another world 外星人

a·li·en·ate /'eɪljə,neɪt; 'eɪliəneɪt/ *v* **alienated, alienating** [T] to make someone stop feeling friendly or sympathetic 使〔某人〕疏遠: *The government has alienated a lot of people with this new policy.* 這條新政策使許多人疏遠了政府。

a·li·en·a·tion /,eɪljə'neɪʃən; ,eɪliə'neɪʃən/ *n* [U] a feeling of not belonging to or not being part of your surroundings 疏離感: *The increasingly dull nature of many industrial jobs has led to the alienation of many workers.* 許多工業界的工作越來越枯燥乏味, 使很多工人產生了一種疏離感。

a·light[1] /ə'laɪt; ə'laɪt/ *v* [I] *fml* 〖正式〗 **1** to get off a vehicle at the end of a journey 〔旅途終了時〕從…下來; 下車 **–see** 見 TRANSPORT (USAGE 用法) **2** (of a bird) to come down from the air onto a surface 〔鳥〕飛落

a·light[2] *adj* [never before a noun 不能用於名詞前] burning 燃燒着: *The fire was still alight.* 火仍燒着。

a·lign /ə'laɪn; ə'laɪn/ *v* [T] **1** to arrange

something into a straight line, or into the same line as something else 排成直線; 排列: *The pictures were all aligned perfectly.* 畫整整齊齊地排成一行。**2 align yourself with someone, be aligned with someone** to come into agreement with someone else because you have the same aims 與某人一致; 與某人結盟: *They aligned themselves with the workers in the struggle for freedom.* 在爭取自由的鬥爭中, 他們與工人結盟。

a·lign·ment /ə'laɪnmənt; ə'laɪnmənt/ *n* **1** [U] a position in which something is in a straight line 直線排列; 隊列 **2** [U] the act of forming into a group with other people who have the same aims 結盟 **3** [C] a group of people who have the same aims 聯盟: *new political alignments forming before the election* 競選前結成的新政治聯盟

a·like[1] /ə'laɪk; ə'laɪk/ *adj* [never before a noun 不能用於名詞前] similar 相像的: *The two brothers are very much alike.* 兩兄弟長得非常相像。

alike[2] *adv* **1** in a similar way 同樣地: *She treats all her children alike.* 她對所有的孩子一視同仁。**2** equally 同等地: *a training course for employed and unemployed alike* 就業者和失業者同樣可以參加的培訓班

al·i·men·ta·ry /ˌælə'mɛntəri; ˌælɪ'mɛntəri/ *adj tech* concerning food and the way it is treated in your body 〔術語〕食物的; 消化的

al·i·mo·ny /'æləˌmoni; 'ælɪməni/ *n* [U] money that someone has to pay regularly to their former partner after they have been divorced (DIVORCE) 〔離婚後一方付給對方的〕贍養費

★**a·live** /ə'laɪv; ə'laɪv/ *adj* [never before a noun 不能用於名詞前] **1** living and not dead 活着的: *Is he still alive?* 他還活着嗎? | *We want to keep the debate alive.* 我們想繼續辯論。**2** active and full of life 活躍的: *She's so alive!* 她真是活躍! **3** alive to something having full knowledge of something 完全知曉某事: *He was alive to the dangers of the work.* 他很清楚這工作的危險性。**4** alive with covered with or full of living things 充滿(活物)的: *The place was alive with people.* 這地方滿是人。**5** come alive to become interesting and full of life 變得有趣; 活躍起來

al·ka·li /'ælkəˌlaɪ; 'ælkəlaɪ/ *n* **alkalis** or **alkalies** [C;U] *tech* a substance that forms chemical salts when combined with acids 〔術語〕鹼 —**alkaline** /-ˌlaɪn; -laɪn/ *adj*

★★**all**[1] /ɔl; ɔːl/ *det, predeterminer, pron* **1** the whole of something 全部: *He ate all his food.* 他吃完了他的全部食物。| *He ate it all.* 他把它全吃掉了。| *We walked all the way into town.* 我們一路走到市中心去。| *We worked hard all last year.* 我們去年全年都在努力工作。**2** every one of 每一個的; 大家的: *I've invited all the people in the office.* 我邀請了辦公室裡所有的人。| *All children like toys.* 每個孩子都喜歡玩具。| *Are you all*

hungry? 你們大家都餓了嗎? | *There are twenty questions on the paper. Please answer them all.* 試卷上有二十個問題, 請全部回答。| *We invited thirty people, but not all of them came.* 我們邀請了三十個人, 但他們不是全都來。**3 all in** with everything included 包括一切; 總的: *an all-in price of £50* 總價五十英鎊 **4 all out** using all your strength or making as much effort as you can 竭盡全力地: *an all-out attack on the enemy* 對敵人全力進攻 **5 not at all** not in any way 根本不: *I'm afraid I don't agree with you at all.* 恐怕我根本不同意你的意見。| *He's not at all shy.* 他一點也不害羞。

★★**all**[2] *adv* **1** completely 全部: *She sat all alone.* 她獨自一人坐着。| *I got all dirty.* 我弄得一身髒。**2** for each side 各方: *The final result of the match was three all.* 比賽的最後結果是(雙方)各得三分。**3 all but** almost 幾乎: *We've all but finished here.* 做到這我們幾乎要完成了。| *It's all but impossible.* 這幾乎是不可能的。**4 all over** everywhere in a place 到處: *We've been looking all over for you.* 我們一直在到處找你。| *They've travelled all over Europe.* 他們遊遍了歐洲。**5 all the same** even so 即使如此: *Sometimes young children can be so difficult, but they're lovely all the same.* 有時小孩子會叫人頭痛, 但不管怎麼樣他們還是挺可愛的。

Al·lah /'ælə; 'ælə/ *n* the Muslim name for God 真主, 安拉〔伊斯蘭教對所信奉的神的稱呼〕

al·lay /ə'le; ə'leɪ/ *v* [T] *fml* to make a feeling like fear, anger, or doubt less strong 〔正式〕減輕〔恐懼、憤怒、疑惑等〕

all clear /ˌ· '·/ *n* a signal telling you that a danger has passed 解除危險的信號

al·le·ga·tion /ˌælə'geʃən; ˌælɪ'geɪʃən/ *n fml* a statement suggesting that someone has done something bad or criminal, but which is not supported by proof 〔正式〕〔說某人做壞事或犯罪, 但無證據的〕指控, 陳述: *These allegations of cruelty must be investigated.* 對這些暴行的指控必須受到調查。

al·lege /ə'lɛdʒ; ə'lɛdʒ/ *v* **alleged, alleging** [T;+that] *fml* to state that something is true before giving proof 〔正式〕〔無證據地〕宣稱: *The police allege that the man was murdered.* 警方聲稱這男子是被人謀殺的。

al·leged /ə'lɛdʒd; ə'lɛdʒd/ *adj* suggested, but not proved to be true 〔未經證實而〕聲稱的: *The alleged crimes took place last month.* 據稱這樁罪行是上個月發生的。—**allegedly** /ə'lɛdʒɪdli; ə'lɛdʒɪdli/ *adv: He had allegedly committed several other crimes.* 據稱他還犯下了其他幾樁罪行。

al·le·giance /ə'lidʒəns; ə'liːdʒəns/ *n* [C;U] loyalty and support given to a leader, a country, or an idea 〔對領袖、國家、思想等的〕忠誠: *We had to swear allegiance to our country.* 我們得宣誓效忠祖國。

A

al·le·go·ry /ˈæləˌgorɪ; ˈælɪˌgɔri/ n [C;U] a story, poem, or painting in which the characters and actions represent good and bad qualities 諷喻; 寓言 —**allegorical** /ˌælə-ˈgɔrɪkl; ˌælɪˈgɒrɪkəl/ adj

al·le·lu·ia /ˌæləˈlujə; ˌælɪˈluːjə/ n, interj – see 見 HALLELUJA

al·ler·gic /əˈlɜːdʒɪk; əˈlɜːdʒɪk/ adj having an allergy or caused by an allergy 過敏的; 過敏引起的: He is allergic to cats. 他對貓過敏。 | an allergic rash 過敏性皮疹

al·ler·gy /ˈælədʒɪ; ˈælədʒi/ n **allergies** a condition in which your body is very sensitive to something that you eat or breathe so that it makes you feel ill or suffer in some way 過敏反應; 過敏症

al·le·vi·ate /əˈliviˌet; əˈliːvieit/ v **alleviated, alleviating** [T] to make suffering or an unpleasant situation less severe 減輕; 緩和 – **alleviation** /əˌliviˈeʃən; əˌliːviˈeiʃən/ n [U]

al·ley /ˈælɪ; ˈæli/ n a narrow street between buildings in a town 胡同; 小巷; 弄堂

★**al·li·ance** /əˈlaɪəns; əˈlaiəns/ n 1 [C;U] a close agreement between countries or groups for a shared purpose 〔國家、團體間的〕聯盟: We are hoping for an alliance between government and industry. 我們希望政府和工業界能結成聯盟。2 [C + sing/pl verb] a group of people or countries formed to look after the interests of its members 集團; 同盟: the Western alliance 西方集團

al·lied /əˈlaɪd; ˈælaid/ adj 1 joined by a political agreement 結盟的; 聯合的: the allied nations 諸盟國 2 related or connected in some way 有關聯的

al·li·ga·tor /ˈæləˌgetər; ˈælɪˌgeitəʳ/ n a large animal with a long body and a hard skin that lives on land and in rivers in parts of America and China 短吻鱷〔產於美洲和中國江河地帶的一種體大皮硬的動物〕

al·lit·er·a·tion /əˌlɪtəˈreʃən; əˌlɪtəˈreiʃən/ n [U] the appearance of the same sound at the beginning of two or more words that are close to each other (as in "Round the rocks runs the river") 頭韻(法)〔相近幾個詞的起頭音相同, 如 Round the rocks runs the river〕

al·lo·cate /ˈæləˌket; ˈæləkeit/ v **allocated, allocating** [T] to keep or give something for a particular purpose 分配; 配給〔某事物〕: That space has already been allocated for building a new hospital. 那塊空地已撥出來興建新醫院了。 | the amount of money allocated to the National Health Service 撥給國民保健用的款額

al·lo·ca·tion /ˌæləˈkeʃən; ˌæləˈkeiʃən/ n 1 [U] the allocating of things for a particular purpose 分配; 配給 2 [C] a share of something, such as money, that is allocated to a particular person or for a particular purpose〔款項等的〕份額

al·lot /əˈlɑt; əˈlɒt/ v **-tt-** [T] to give some-

thing to someone as their share 撥給, 分配〔某事物〕: Two rooms had been allotted to me. 兩個房間已分配了給我。

al·lot·ment /əˈlɑtmənt; əˈlɒtmənt/ n 1 a share of something such as money that is given to someone〔款項等的〕份額 2 a small piece of land rented out by a town council in Britain for growing vegetables〔英國市政府出租給個人種蔬菜的〕小塊土地

★★**al·low** /əˈlau; əˈlau/ v 1 [T] to give permission for someone to do something or have something 允許, 准許〔某人做某事〕: We don't allow smoking in our offices. 我們辦公室不許抽煙。 | They allow us four weeks holiday a year. 他們一年准我們放假四週。 | As a child, I was never allowed to stay up late. 小時候, 大人從不許我熬夜。

□ USEFUL PATTERNS 有用句型
to allow something; to allow someone something; to allow someone to do something

2 [T] to let someone go somewhere 允許〔某人去某處〕: Dogs are not allowed in the children's play area. 狗不准進入孩子的遊戲場地。 | I'm afraid you're not allowed in. 恐怕你不准進去。3 [T] to make it possible for something to happen 容許〔某事發生〕: We must not allow inflation to rise any further. 我們決不容許通貨膨脹進一步發展。

□ USEFUL PATTERN 有用句型
to allow something to happen

4 [T] to keep or give an amount of time or money for a particular purpose 給予〔金錢或時間〕: Allow ten days for delivery. 給十天時間交貨。 | I've allowed myself three weeks to get the job finished. 我給自己三週時間完成這項工作。

□ USEFUL PATTERNS 有用句型
to allow an amount; to allow yourself an amount

5 **allow for something** to take something into consideration so that you can deal with it if it happens 考慮到某事; 估計到某事 6 [+ that] fml to admit that something is true〔正式〕承認: I allow that there may have been some mistake. 我承認可能出了某種錯誤。

al·low·a·ble /əˈlauəbl; əˈlauəbəl/ adj acceptable and so permitted 允許的; 准許的

al·low·ance /əˈlauəns; əˈlauəns/ n 1 an amount of money that is given to someone regularly 定期補助; 津貼: an allowance of £5,000 a year 每年五千英鎊的津貼 | a travelling allowance 出差補貼 2 **make allowances for something** to take facts into consideration when making a decision or judgment 考慮到某事; 為某事留出餘地

al·loy /ˈælɔɪ; ˈælɔɪ/ *n* a metal made by mixing together two or more different metals 合金

★**all right¹** /ˌ·ˈ·/ *adj* [never before a noun 不能用於名詞前] **1** safe, unharmed, or healthy 安全的; 無害的; 健康的: *Is the driver all right after the accident?* 事故發生後, 駕駛員安然無恙嗎? **2** satisfactory and acceptable 還行的; 可接受的: *Is the food all right?* 食物還可以嗎?

all right² *adv* **1** in an acceptable or satisfactory way 可接受; 還行: *Is John getting on all right at University?* 約翰在大學裡過得還行吧? **2** a word used when you are agreeing to do something 行(用於同意做某事): *"Will you help me?" "All right."* "你能幫我嗎?" "行。"—see 見 ALRIGHT (USAGE)

all-round /ˈ· ·/ *adj* [only before a noun 只用於名詞前] having ability in many things 全能的; 多面手的 **–all-rounder** /ˌ·ˈ··/ *n*

al·lude /əˈlud; əˈluːd/ *v* **alluded, alluding** *fml* 〔正式〕**allude to something** to speak about something in an indirect way 間接提到某事; 暗指某事

al·lure /əˈlʊr; əˈljʊəˈ/ *n* [sing] attraction or charm 吸引力; 魅力

al·lur·ing /əˈljurɪŋ; əˈljʊərɪŋ/ *adj* very attractive 迷人的; 誘惑人的

al·lu·sion /əˈluʒən; əˈluːʒn/ *n* [C;U] *fml* an act of speaking about something in an indirect way 〔正式〕暗指; 間接提及: *He made several allusions to my failure.* 他幾次間接提到了我的失敗。

al·lu·vi·al /əˈluviəl; əˈluːviəl/ *adj* made of soil put down by rivers, lakes, or floods 〔江、湖、洪水等〕沖積而成的; 淤積的

★**al·ly¹** /əˈlaɪ; əˈlaɪ/ *v* **allied, allying** [T] **ally yourself with someone** to join with someone and support them politically 與某人結盟: *They allied themselves with America during the war.* 戰爭期間他們與美國結盟。

al·ly² /ˈælaɪ; ˈælaɪ/ *n* **allies** a person or country that helps or supports another one, especially in war 〔尤指戰爭中的〕盟國; 盟友

al·ma·nac /ˈɔlmə‚næk; ˈɔːlmənæk/ *n* a book giving a list of the days of a year, and also information about the movement of the sun, the moon, and the sea 曆書; 年曆; 天文曆

al·might·y /ɔlˈmaɪti; ɔːlˈmaɪti/ *adj* **1** **Almighty** having the power to do anything (used of God) 全能的, 萬能的(指上帝): *God Almighty* 萬能的上帝 **2** *infml* very big or loud 〔非正式〕巨大的; 極響的: *There was an almighty crash.* 一起慘重的撞車事故發生了。

al·mond /ˈæmənd; ˈɑːmənd/ *n* a kind of nut 杏仁; 扁桃仁

★★**al·most** /ˈɔl‚most; ˈɔːlməʊst/ *adv* very nearly but not quite 幾乎; 差不

多: *I lived in India for almost two years.* 我在印度住了差不多兩年。 | *She's been very ill, but she's almost better now.* 她一度病得很重, 但現在差不多痊癒了。 | *I almost forgot that it was his birthday today.* 我差點忘了今天是他的生日。 | *Almost everybody who was invited came.* 被邀請的人幾乎都來了。

alms /amz; ɑːmz/ *n* [pl] money, food, or clothes given to poor people (a word which is no longer used in modern English) 〔錢、食品、衣服等〕施捨物〔現代英語中不再使用〕

a·loft /əˈlɔft; əˈlɒft/ *adv* [never before a noun 不能用於名詞前] high up in the air 高高地; 在高處

★★**a·lone** /əˈlon; əˈləʊn/ *adv, adj* **1** without other people 獨自的〔地〕; 孤獨的〔地〕: *He lives alone.* 他獨自一人生活。 | *I was alone in the room.* 我一個人呆在房間裡。 | *She had never been on holiday alone.* 她從沒一個人度過假。 | *She alone knew his real identity.* 只有她知道他的真實身分。 **2** [only after a noun 只用於名詞後] only 僅僅; 只有

■ **USAGE** 用法: **Alone** is neither good nor bad ☆**alone** 一詞無褒貶意義: *She lives on tea and cake when she's alone.* 她獨自一人時只喝點茶和吃點蛋糕過日子。**Solitary** and **lone**, when used of things, mean that there is only one ☆ **solitary** 和 **lone** 用來修飾事物時, 表示只有一個: *a solitary/lone tree in the garden* 花園裡唯一的一棵樹, but used of people they may show sadness, like **lonely** or (especially in American English) **lonesome** ☆但用來修飾人時, 可以表示愁悶, 如 **lonely** 或 **lonesome** 〔美式英語常用〕: *Come over and see me; I'm feeling a bit lonely/lonesome.* 過來看看我吧, 我感到有點寂寞。

★★**a·long¹** /əˈlɔŋ; əˈlɒŋ/ *prep* moving or positioned on a road, river, etc. 沿着, 順着〔路、河等〕: *She walked along the road.* 她沿着馬路走。 | *I love driving along narrow country lanes.* 我喜愛沿着狹窄的鄉間小路開車。 | *There were trees all along the river bank.* 沿着河岸樹木成行。 | *Their house is just a bit further along this road.* 順着這條路再過去一點就是他們的房子。—see picture on page 764 見 764 頁彩圖

★★**a·long²** *adv* **1** forward 向前: *She was cycling along, singing to herself.* 她騎着腳踏車, 一路上唱着歌。 | *I walked along behind him.* 我跟在他後面往前走。 **2** to a place 到〔某處〕: *You go straight to the restaurant. I'll come along later.* 你直接去飯店, 我隨後就到。 | *The others will be along soon.* 其他人馬上就到。 **3** with you 一起; 一道: *Is it all right if I bring the children along?* 我帶孩子們一起來行嗎? **4** **all along** during the whole of a period of time 一直; 始終:

A

I'd known all along that the idea wouldn't work. 我早知道這主意行不通。**5 along with** with 和... 一起: *Along with many other people, I'm very worried about the situation.* 和許多人一樣, 我也很擔心局面。

*a·long·side /ə,lɒŋˈsaɪd; ə,lɒŋˈsaɪd/ *prep, adv*
1 next to and in line with the edge of something 在...旁邊; 與...並排: *We brought our boat alongside theirs.* 我們把船靠在他們的(船)旁邊。**2** together with something or someone else 與...在一起: *Scientists are working alongside the police to discover the cause of the explosion.* 科學家協同警方查找爆炸的起因。

a·loof /əˈluf; əˈluːf/ *adj* apart and distant from other people, or not joining in and doing things with other people 疏遠的; 避開的: *He kept himself aloof from the others.* 他跟其他人保持距離。–**aloofness** *n* [U]

a·loud /əˈlaʊd; əˈlaʊd/ *adv* (also 又作 **out loud**) **1** in a voice that people can hear 出聲地: *The teacher asked her to read the poem aloud.* 老師叫她朗誦那首詩。**2** in a loud voice 大聲地; 高聲地: *The pain caused him to cry aloud.* 他痛得大喊大叫。

al·pha /ˈælfə; ˈælfə/ *n* the first letter (α) in the Greek alphabet 希臘語字母表中第一個字母 (α)

al·pha·bet /ˈælfə,bɛt; ˈælfəbet/ *n* the set of letters used in writing any language, arranged in order〔按順序排列的〕一套字母; 字母表

al·pha·bet·i·cal /,ælfəˈbɛtɪkl̩; ,ælfəˈbetɪkl◂/ *adj* arranged in the order of the alphabet 字母表的; 按字母順序的: *The names are listed in alphabetical order.* 姓名按字母順序排列。–**alphabetically** /-klɪ; -kli/ *adv*

al·pine /ˈælpaɪn; ˈælpaɪn/ *adj* concerning or existing in high mountains 高山上的

*al·read·y /ɔlˈrɛdɪ; ɔːlˈredi/ *adv* **1** before a particular time, or before expected 已經: *He had already left by the time I got there.* 我到那裡時他已經走了。| *The meeting doesn't start for another half hour, but quite a few people are already here.* 會議再過半小時才開始, 但好些人已經到了。**2** before 以前: *"Would you like to have lunch with us?" "No, thank you, I've already eaten."* "你想和我們一起吃午飯嗎?" "不, 謝謝, 我已吃過了。" –see 見 JUST² (USAGE用法)

> ■ USAGE 用法: **1** Compare 比較 **already** and **yet**. We use **already** mainly in positive sentences ☆**already** 主要用於肯定句中: *I've **already** asked her.* 我已問過她。We use **yet** mainly in questions and negatives ☆**yet** 主要用於疑問句和否定句中: *Have you asked her **yet**?* 你問過她嗎? | *I haven't asked her **yet**.* 我還沒問過她。**2** Compare 比較

already and 和 **all ready**. *We're **all ready*** means that all of us are ready. ☆*We're **all ready*** 一句的意思是指我們大家都準備好了。

al·right /ɔlˈraɪt; ɔːlˈraɪt/ *adv* = all right

> ■ USAGE 用法: In the past, people considered **all right** the only correct form, but **alright** is very common now. 過去人們認為 **all right** 是唯一正確的形式, 但 **alright** 現在已很常見。

al·so /ˈɔlso; ˈɔːlsəʊ/ *adv* as well 亦, 也, 同樣, 並且: *She speaks German and French, and also Spanish.* 她會說德語和法語, 也會說西班牙語。| *I've seen his latest film, and I've also seen a few of his earlier ones.* 我看過他最近的電影, 也看過一些較早期的電影。| *It was not only cold and windy, but also raining!* 天氣不僅寒冷多風, 而且下雨。| *"The Moon, the Moon" is available on CD. It's also available as a cassette.* "月亮, 月亮" 可以在鐳射唱片上找到, 也可以在錄音帶上找到。–see Study Note on page 1325 見 1325 頁學習提示

al·tar /ˈɔltɚ; ˈɔːltəʳ/ *n* a table used in a religious ceremony 祭壇; 聖餐室

al·ter /ˈɔltɚ; ˈɔːltəʳ/ *v* [I; T] to change in some way (使) 改動, 變更: *It's still the same book. Only the cover has been altered.* 這仍是同一本書, 只是封面改了。| *The government's policy on this hasn't altered.* 政府在這方面的政策並沒有改變。

al·ter·a·tion /,ɔltəˈreʃən; ,ɔːltəˈreɪʃən/ *n* **1** [C] a change in something 變化, 變動: *The Bill went through Parliament with only a few minor alterations.* 該法案只作了一些改動便在議會通過了。**2** [U] the act of changing something 改動, 更動

al·ter·ca·tion /,ɔltəˈkeʃən; ,ɔːltəˈkeɪʃən/ *n fml* a noisy quarrel《正式》爭辯, 爭吵, 吵嘴

al·ter·nate¹ /ˈɔltɚnɪt; ɔːlˈtɜːnɪt/ *adj* [only before a noun 只用於名詞前] **1** happening in a regular way, first one thing and then the other thing 交替的; 輪流的: *a week of alternate rain and sunshine* 時晴時雨的一週 **2** alternate days, alternate weeks, etc. every second day, week, etc. 每隔一天; 每隔一週等等: *He works on alternate days.* 他每隔一天上班。

al·ter·nate² /ˈɔltɚ,net; ˈɔːltəneɪt/ *v* **alternated, alternating 1** [I] to follow regularly, with first one thing happening and then the other 交替; 輪流: *Her moods alternated between cheerfulness and despair.* 她的心情忽喜忽悲。| *Periods of heavy rain alternated with periods of drought.* 有時是大雨滂沱, 有時是乾旱一片, 交替更迭。**2** [T] to do first one thing and then the other 輪流: *We alternated periods of work and rest.* 我們工

A

作與休息輪流進行。 **–alternation** /ˌɔːltɚˈneɪʃən; ˌɔːltəˈneɪʃən/ *n* [C;U]

al·ter·na·tive¹ /ɔlˈtɝnətɪv; ɔːlˈtɜːnətɪv/ *adj* [only before a noun 只用於名詞前] **1** able or suitable to be used or done instead of something else 可選擇的: *When traffic is bad use the alternative route.* 交通堵塞時可走另一條路。 **2** different from what is usual or accepted 不同一般的; 非傳統性的: *alternative technologies* 非傳統性技術 | *alternative medicine* 非傳統性藥物

alternative² *n* something that can be used or done instead of something else 可選擇的東西; 替代物: *We had to fight: there was no alternative.* 我們必須鬥爭: 別無選擇。 | *Many farmers are now growing maize as an alternative* **to** *wheat.* 很多農民現在種植玉米來替代小麥。

al·ter·na·tive·ly /ɔlˈtɝnətɪvli; ɔːlˈtɜːnətɪvli/ *adv* a word used when you are suggesting an alternative to the first suggestion 或者, 要不〔用於作為一種選擇〕: *I could pick you up on my way into town or, alternatively, we could meet in town.* 我可以讓你搭順風車去市中心, 或者我們也可以在那裡才碰頭。

al·though /ɔlˈðo; ɔːlˈðəʊ/ *conj* **1** in spite of something 雖然; 儘管: *I recognized her at once, although I hadn't seen her for ten years.* 儘管我們有十年沒見面, 但我一眼就認出她來了。 | *Although it was raining we decided to go for a walk.* 雖然在下雨, 我們仍決定出去走走。 **2** but 然而; 但是: *I think she's going to apply for the job, although I'm not sure.* 我想她要申請這份工作, 但我也不能肯定。

al·ti·tude /ˈæltəˌtjud; ˈæltɪˌtjuːd/ *n* [C;U] the distance that something is above sea level 高度; 海拔: *They were flying at a low altitude.* 他們在做低空飛行。

al·to /ˈælto; ˈæltəʊ/ *n* a singing voice that is quite high for a man and quite low for a woman 男聲最高音; 女聲最低音

al·to·geth·er /ˌɔltəˈgɛðɚ; ˌɔːltəˈgeðəʳ/ *adv* **1** completely 全然; 完全: *It's not altogether a bad idea.* 這主意並非一無是處。 | *We've now stopped making this product altogether.* 我們現在已完全停產這種產品。 | *This is an altogether different problem.* 這是一個完全不同的問題。 | *What he's saying is not altogether true.* 他說的並不都是真的。 **2** considering all things 總而言之; 總的說來: *It will look very ugly and cost a lot of money. Altogether, I'm not too keen on the idea.* 那樣會既難看又花錢。總之, 我不太喜歡這主意。

al·tru·is·m /ˈæltruˌɪzəm; ˈæltruː-ɪzəm/ *n* [U] concern for the happiness of other people rather than your own 利他; 無私 **–altruistic** /ˌæltruˈɪstɪk; ˌæltruˈɪstɪk/ *adj* : *His motives were entirely altruistic.* 他的動機是完全無私的。

al·u·min·i·um /ˌæljəˈmɪnɪəm; ˌæljuˈmɪnɪəm/ *n* (**aluminum** /əˈlumɪnəm; əˈluːmɪnəm/

AmE 〖美式〗) [U] a silver-coloured metal that is light and easily shaped 鋁

al·ways /ˈɔlwez; ˈɔːlwɪz, -wəz/ *adv* **1** all the time or every time 總是; 一直: *We've always lived here.* 我們一直住在這兒。 | *The sun always rises in the east.* 太陽總在東方升起。 | *She's always late!* 她老是遲到! | *He's always criticizing me!* 他總是批評我! **2** for ever 永遠; 始終: *I shall always love you.* 我將永遠愛你。 **3 can always, could always** a phrase used when you are suggesting what someone could do 總可以〔用於建議某人可以做某事〕: *If she's not in the office, you could always try phoning her at home.* 如果她不在辦公室, 你還可以打電話去她家試試看。

am /əm; əm; *strong* 強讀 æm; æm/ the first person singular present tense of BE 動詞 BE 的第一人稱單數現在式: *I am living in London now.* 我現在住在倫敦。 **–see** 見 'S (USAGE用法)

AM /ˈe ˈɛm; ˌeɪ ˈem/ a system of broadcasting by radio in which the strength of the sound waves varies; an abbreviation for **amplitude modulation** 〖縮〗調幅

a.m. /ˈe ˈɛm; ˌeɪ ˈem/ letters which follow numbers to show that a time is before midday 午前, 上午: *the 8 a.m. train from London* 上午八時從倫敦開出的火車 | *We arrived at 11 a.m.* 我們上午十一點到達。 **–compare** 比較 **P.M.**

a·mal·gam·ate /əˈmælgəˌmet; əˈmælgəm-eɪt/ *v* **amalgamated, amalgamating** [I] (of businesses or organizations) to join together to form a larger business or organization 〔企業或組織〕合併, 聯合: *The two companies amalgamated two years ago.* 這兩家公司在兩年前合併了。 **–amalga·mation** /əˌmælgəˈmeʃən; əˌmælgəˈmeɪʃən/ *n* [C;U]

a·mass /əˈmæs; əˈmæs/ *v* [T] to collect things such as money or facts in very large amounts 收集; 積累

am·a·teur¹ /ˈæməˌtʃur; ˈæmətəʳ/ *n* **1** a person who does something for enjoyment and not as their job 業餘愛好者: *Only amateurs may compete in the Olympic Games.* 只有業餘運動員才能參加奧運會比賽。 **2** a person without much experience or skill in a particular activity 外行: *Those builders were really only amateurs.* 那些建築工人真的只是些外行。

amateur² *adj* **1** done for enjoyment and not as a job 業餘的: *amateur football* 業餘足球運動 | *an amateur detective* 業餘偵探 **2** not very skilfully done 技術不熟練的; 外行的: *The performance was rather amateur.* 表現只屬業餘水平。 **–amateurism** *n* [U]

am·a·teur·ish /ˌæməˈtɜrɪʃ; ˈæmətərɪʃ/ *adj* not very skilfully done 不熟練的; 外行的

a·maze /əˈmez; əˈmeɪz/ *v* **amazed, amazing** [T] to make you feel very surprised 使驚愕 〖驚奇〗: *It amazed me to hear that you were* leaving. 聽說你要走，我很驚訝。 **–amazed** adj: Everyone looked amazed when he walked in. 他走進來時每個人都顯出驚奇的神色。**–amazement** n [U]

a·maz·ing /ə'mezɪŋ; ə'meɪzɪŋ/ adj very surprising and causing pleasure or admiration 令人驚異的；了不起的: What an amazing film! 多了不起的一部電影！ | It's so fast — it's amazing! 多快呀——真叫人驚訝！

am·bas·sa·dor /æm'bæsədə; æm'bæsədər/ n an important official representing his or her country in the capital city of another country 大使，使節: the British Ambassador to Spain 英國駐西班牙大使

am·ber /'æmbə; 'æmbər/ adj, n [U] **1** a hard yellowish-brown clear substance used for making jewellery 琥珀: clear amber beads 純淨無瑕的琥珀珠子 **2** a yellowish-brown colour 琥珀色

am·bi·dex·trous /,æmbə'dekstrəs; ,æmbɪ'dekstrəs/ adj able to use either hand with equal skill 左右手都能靈巧使用的

am·bi·ence /'æmbɪəns; 'æmbɪəns/ n (also 又作 **ambiance** AmE 《美式》) [U] the character or feeling of a place 環境；氣氛: The restaurant has a pleasant ambience. 這小餐館環境幽雅宜人。

am·big·u·ous /æm'bɪgjuəs; æm'bɪgjuəs/ adj not clear, and able to be understood in more than one way 意義不明確的；模稜兩可的: an ambiguous reply 模稜兩可的答覆 – **ambiguity** /,æmbɪ'gjuətɪ; ,æmbǐ'gju:əti/ n **ambiguities** [C;U]: There were several ambiguities in her statement. 她的陳述中有幾處模稜兩可的地方。

am·bi·tion /æm'bɪʃən; æm'bɪʃən/ n **1** [U] strong desire to obtain success, power, or riches 志向；抱負；雄心；野心: a politician full of ambition 野心勃勃的政客 **2** [C] something that you very much want to do or obtain 追求的目標: His main ambition is to be famous. 他追求的主要目標是成名。

am·bi·tious /æm'bɪʃəs; æm'bɪʃəs/ adj **1** having a strong desire to be successful, powerful, or rich 有抱負的；有雄心的: an ambitious young man 有雄心的年輕人 **2** daring and difficult to do successfully 費勁的: This is the most ambitious project I've ever taken on. 這是我承擔過的最費勁的工程。

am·biv·a·lent /æm'bɪvələnt; æm'bɪvələnt/ adj not clear in your mind about whether you like or dislike something 有矛盾心理的: I have a very ambivalent attitude towards giving to charity. 對於是否要捐助慈善事業，我態度矛盾。 **–ambivalence** n [U]

am·ble /'æmbl; 'æmbəl/ v **ambled, ambling** [I] to walk slowly because you are not in a hurry 緩步；漫步: He was ambling along by the riverside. 他沿着河邊漫步。

am·bu·lance /'æmbjələns; 'æmbjǐləns/ n a motor vehicle for carrying sick or wounded people to hospital 救護車

am·bush /'æmbʊʃ; 'æmbʊʃ/ v [T] to attack someone after hiding and waiting for them 伏擊 **–ambush** n

a·me·li·o·rate /ə'miljə,ret; ə'mi:liəreɪt/ v **ameliorated, ameliorating** [T] fml to make a situation better or less difficult 《正式》改進，改善 **–amelioration** /ə,miljə'reʃən; ə-,mi:liə'reɪʃən/ n [U]

a·men /'eɪmɛn; ɑ:'mɛn/ interj a word said by Christians at the end of a prayer 阿門〔祈禱的結束語〕: for ever and ever, Amen 直到永遠，阿門

a·me·na·ble /ə'minəbl; ə'mi:nəbəl/ adj willing to be guided or influenced by something 順從的；服理的: I've always found him very amenable. 我一直覺得他能服從教導。 | She is amenable to reason. 她是講道理的。

a·mend /ə'mɛnd; ə'mend/ v [T] to make changes to something that has been written or said 修改〔某物〕: The law has been amended recently. 這項法律最近作了修正。

a·mend·ment /ə'mɛndmənt; ə'mendmənt/ n [C;U] a change made to something that has been written 修正；修正案: The government is proposing several amendments to the Bill. 政府對該議案提出了幾項修正。

a·mends /ə'mɛndz; ə'mendz/ n **make amends** to do something for someone to show that you are sorry about something harmful or unkind that you did to them 賠罪；補償: How can I ever make amends for such unkindness? 我怎樣來補償過去這些不善之處呢？

a·me·ni·ty /ə'mɛnətɪ; ə'mi:nǐti/ n **amenities** a public place where people can go for pleasure or entertainment 文娛康樂場所: Local amenities include parks and swimming pools. 本地的文娛康樂場所包括公園和游泳池。

A·mer·i·can /ə'mɛrɪkən; ə'merǐkən/ adj belonging to or connected with the United States of America 美國的: the American dollar 美元

American foot·ball /·,····'··/ n (**football** AmE《美式》) [U] an American ball game similar to football 美式足球；美式橄欖球 – see picture on page 957 見 957 頁彩圖

A·mer·i·can·ism /ə'mɛrəkən,ɪzm; ə'merǐ-kənɪzəm/ n a word or phrase of English that is used in the United States 美式用語

am·e·thyst /'æməθɪst; 'æmǐθǐst/ n [C;U] a purple stone used in jewellery 紫(水)晶

a·mi·a·ble /'emɪəbl; 'eɪmɪəbəl/ adj fml pleasant and friendly 《正式》和藹的；友善的: She proved to be a most amiable companion. 她的表現說明她是個最可親的同伴。 – **amiability** /,emɪə'bɪlətɪ; ,eɪmɪə'bɪl̩əti/ n [U]

am·i·ca·ble /'æmɪkəbl; 'æmǐkəbəl/ adj pleasant and without argument 友善的；平心靜氣的: We reached an amicable agreement. 我們達成一項友好協議。 **–amicably** adv

a·mid /ə'mɪd; ə'mɪd/ *prep* (also 又作 **amidst** /ə'mɪdst; ə'mɪdst/) *fml* 〖正式〗 in the middle of a lot of things 〖正式〗在…當中: *Amid all the noise and excitement, suddenly I heard a voice that I knew.* 在一片喧鬧和興奮之中, 我忽然聽到了一把熟悉的聲音。

a·miss /ə'mɪs; ə'mɪs/ *adj fml* 〖正式〗**1 something is amiss** = something is wrong 出毛病: *I knew that there was something amiss.* 我知道有點兒不對勁。 **2 take something amiss** to be angry about something or feel hurt because you have understood it wrongly 〔因誤會而〕對某事惱火〔見怪〕

am·mo·ni·a /ə'mʊnjə; ə'mʊniə/ *n* [U] a strong gas or liquid with a sharp unpleasant smell, used in cleaning substances 氨; 阿摩尼亞

am·mu·ni·tion /ˌæmjə'nɪʃən; ˌæmjɨ'nɪʃən/ *n* [U] **1** bullets and explosives fired from a weapon 彈藥 **2** information that can be used against someone 攻擊某人的材料: *The tax increases will be used as ammunition by the opposition.* 增稅會被反對派用作攻擊的砲彈。

am·ne·si·a /æm'niːʒiə; æm'niːʒiə/ *n* [U] *med* loss of memory 〖醫〗記憶缺失

am·nes·ty /'æm,nɛstɪ; 'æmnɪsti/ *n* **amnesties** an official declaration of forgiveness given by a state to political criminals 〔對政治犯的〕大赦, 赦免: *The President granted an amnesty on Independence Day.* 總統在獨立紀念日簽署了大赦令。

a·mok /ə'mʌk; ə'mʌk/ *adv* **run amok** to run around in a wild and uncontrolled way often destroying things or killing people 四出瘋狂砍殺

a·mong /ə'mʌŋ; ə'mʌŋ/ *prep* (also 又作 **amongst** /ə'mʌŋst; ə'mʌŋst/) **1** in the middle of a lot of people or things 在…中間: *He stood among the bricks and rubble that had been his home.* 他站在碎磚瓦礫中間, 這裡曾是他的家園。| *My purse is somewhere among all this mess.* 我的錢包就在這堆亂糟糟的東西當中。| *She loves being among a lot of people.* 她喜歡呆在一大羣人中間。 **2** in a particular group of people or concerning a particular group of people 在〔某一特定人羣〕中; 有關〔某特定人羣〕: *Unemployment is especially high among young men under 25.* 二十五歲以下的年輕人中失業率特別高。| *There is a lot of anger among women about this new law.* 婦女當中有許多人對這條新法律感到氣憤。| *There has been much discussion about this among politicians.* 政客對此議論紛紛。| *Just talk among yourselves for a few minutes.* 你們自己談上幾分鐘吧。 **3** between three or more people 在〔三人或三人以上〕之中: *The money was divided equally among them.* 錢由他們平分了。–see 見 BETWEEN (USAGE 用法) **4 among other things** a phrase used when you are giving just one thing as an

example 除了別的以外〔用於只舉一件事為例〕: *He was, among other things, a poet and a painter.* 除了別的以外, 他還是個詩人和畫家。

a·mor·al /eɪ'mɒrəl; eɪ'mɔrəl/ *adj* not caring whether something is right or wrong 無是非觀念的; 非道德性的

am·o·rous /'æmərəs; 'æmərəs/ *adj* concerning sexual love or wanting sexual love 性愛的; 多情的: *He was giving me amorous looks.* 他含情脈脈地看着我。

a·mor·phous /ə'mɔːfəs; ə'mɔːfəs/ *adj* having no fixed form or shape 無固定形式或形狀的: *an amorphous blob of jelly* 一滴無固定形狀的果子凍

a·mount[1] /ə'maʊnt; ə'maʊnt/ *n* a quantity of something 數量: *Large amounts of money were spent on the bridge.* 這座橋耗費了大量金錢。

amount[2] *v* **amount to something a** to mean something without stating it directly 相當於〔等於〕某物: *His words amounted to a refusal.* 他的話等於拒絕。 **b** to make a total of a particular amount 總計; 合計: *His debts amount to over £1,000.* 他欠債總數達一千多英鎊。

amp /æmp; æmp/ *n* **1** (also 又作 **ampere** /'æmpeə; 'æmpeə'/ *fml* 〖正式〗) a measure of a quantity of electricity 安培: *a 10 amp fuse* 十安培的保險絲 **2** see 見 AMPLIFIER

am·phet·a·mine /æm'fɛtə,miːn; æm'fɛtəmiːn/ *n* a drug which makes people feel very excited 安非他明〔一種興奮藥劑〕: *Amphetamine abuse can lead to physical exhaustion.* 濫用安非他明能導致體力衰竭。

am·phib·i·an /æm'fɪbɪən; æm'fɪbɪən/ *n* an animal that is able to live both on land and in water 兩棲動物 **–amphibious** /æm'fɪbɪəs; æm'fɪbɪəs/ *adj*

am·phi·thea·tre /'æmfə,θɪətə; 'æmfɨθɪətə'/ *n* (**amphitheater** *AmE* 〖美式〗) a large open area with rows of seats around it, used for performing plays 圓形劇場; 露天競技場

am·ple /'æmpl; 'æmpəl/ *adj* **1** enough of something and some more 充足的; 充裕的: *Don't hurry. We have ample time.* 別着急。我們有充裕的時間。 **2** large 大的; 寬敞的: *a garden of ample proportions* 寬敞的花園

am·pli·fi·er /'æmplə,faɪə; 'æmplə'faɪə'/ *n* (also 又作 **amp** *infml* 〖非正式〗) an instrument used in radios and record players (RECORD PLAYER) that makes sounds or signals louder 放大器; 擴音器; 揚聲器 **–see** picture on page 730 見 730 頁彩圖

am·pli·fy /'æmplə,faɪ; 'æmplɨfaɪ/ *v* **amplified, amplifying** [T] **1** to increase sound from electrical instruments 放大, 增強〔聲音〕 **2** to explain something in greater detail 詳述〔某事物〕: *This statement needs to be amplified.* 這項聲明需要進一步闡述。 **–amplification** /ˌæmpləfə'keɪʃən; ˌæmplɨfɨ'keɪʃən/ *n* [U]

A

am·pu·tate /ˈæmpjəˌtet; ˈæmpjʊ̩teɪt/ v **amputated, amputating** [I;T] to cut off a part of someone's body for medical reasons 截肢: *She had to have a leg amputated.* 她只得把一條腿截去。–**amputation** /ˌæmpjəˈteʃən; ˌæmpjʊ̩ˈteɪʃən/ n [C;U]

a·muse /əˈmjuz; əˈmjuːz/ v **amused, amusing** [T] **1** to make someone laugh or smile 把〔某人〕逗樂; 使〔某人〕笑: *We were very amused by her comments.* 我們被她的評論逗得哈哈大笑。**2** to keep someone happy and prevent them from losing interest 給〔某人〕提供娛樂[消遣]: *It's a toy which will amuse children for hours.* 這是一種能使孩子們玩幾小時都玩得津津有味的玩具。| *The children amused themselves by playing games.* 孩子們玩遊戲取樂。

a·muse·ment /əˈmjuzmənt; əˈmjuːzmənt/ n **1** [U] the feeling that you have when you are amused by something 樂趣; 興味: *I listened in amusement.* 我津津有味地聽着。**2** [C] something which gives people pleasure or entertainment 娛樂活動: *Big cities have theatres, football matches, and many other amusements.* 大城市裡有戲劇、足球賽以及許多其他的娛樂活動。

a·mus·ing /əˈmjuzɪŋ; əˈmjuːzɪŋ/ adj making you laugh or smile 有趣的; 逗笑的: *an amusing story* 引人發笑的故事

★★an /ən; ən; *strong* 強讀 æn; æn/ indefinite article, det see 見 A

> ■ USAGE 用法: The choice of **a** or **an** before a set of letters like *UN* or *FM* depends on how we say the first letter, not on whether the letter itself is a vowel or a consonant. Put **a** if we say the letter with a consonant sound ☆在諸如 *UN* 或 *FM* 的一組字母前該選用 **a** 還是 **an,** 取決於其第一個字母如何發音, 而並非取決於這字母本身是元音字母還是輔音字母。如果該字母發音以輔音起首, 就用 **a**: *a UN official* 一位聯合國官員。Put **an** if we say the letter with a vowel sound ☆如果該字母發音以元音起首, 就用 **an**: *an FM radio* 一台調頻收音機

a·nach·ro·nis·m /əˈnækrəˌnɪzəm; əˈnækrənɪzəm/ n a thing which is no longer suitable because it belongs to the past 時代錯誤; 不合時代的事物 –**anachronistic** /əˌnækrəˈnɪstɪk; əˌnækrəˈnɪstɪk◂/ adj

a·nae·mi·a /əˈnimiə; əˈniːmiə/ n (also 又作 **anemia** AmE 〖美式〗) [U] the unhealthy condition of not having enough red cells in your blood 貧血症 –**anaemic** /əˈnimɪk; əˈniːmɪk/ adj

an·aes·the·si·a /ˌænəsˈθiʒə; ˌænʊ̩sˈθiːziə/ n (also 又作 **anesthesia** AmE 〖美式〗) [U] the use of pain-killing drugs in medicine〔藥物的〕麻醉(術)

an·aes·thet·ic /ˌænəsˈθɛtɪk; ˌænʊ̩sˈθetɪk/ n (also 又作 **anesthetic** AmE 〖美式〗) [C;U] a drug which stops feelings of pain; an anaesthetic is given either in a limited area (**local anaesthetic**) or in the whole body (**general anaesthetic**), when a patient becomes unconscious during a medical operation〔使局部或全身失去知覺的〕麻醉劑

a·naes·the·tist /əˈnɛsθətɪst; əˈniːsθ⒦tɪst/ n (also 又作 **anesthetist** AmE 〖美式〗) a person who gives an anaesthetic to a patient before a medical operation 麻醉師

a·naes·the·tize /əˈnɛsθəˌtaɪz; əˈniːsθ⒦taɪz/ v **anaesthetized, anaesthetizing** (also 又作 **anaesthetise** BrE 〖英式〗, **anesthetize** AmE 〖美式〗) [T] to make someone unable to feel pain by giving them an anaesthetic 使〔某人〕麻醉; 施麻醉劑於〔某人〕

an·a·gram /ˈænəgræm; ˈænəgræm/ n a word or phrase made by changing the order of the letters in another word or phrase, for example 'silent' is an anagram of 'listen' 變位詞[改變單詞或片語中字母位置而構成另一單詞或片語, 例如 silent 是 listen 改變字母次序後形成的另一單詞]

a·nal /ˈenl; ˈeɪnl/ adj involving or connected with a person's ANUS 肛門的

an·al·ge·sic /ˌænælˈdʒizɪk; ˌænəlˈdʒiːzɪk/ n tech a drug which stops you from feeling pain〔術語〕止痛藥 –**analgesic** adj

a·nal·o·gous /əˈnæləgəs; əˈnæləgəs/ adj fml 〖正式〗analogous to something similar to something else in certain ways 類似[相似]於某事物

a·nal·o·gy /əˈnælədʒi; əˈnælədʒi/ n **analogies 1** [C] a degree of similarity 類似, 相似: *He drew an analogy* **between** *the way water moves and the way light travels.* 他把水的流動和光的傳播作類比。**2** [U] **by analogy** by comparing something with another similar thing 通過類比

★an·a·lyse /ˈænlˌaɪz; ˈænəlaɪz/ v **analysed, analysing** (also 又作 **analyze** AmE 〖美式〗) [T] to examine something carefully in order to find out about it 分析〔某事物〕: *The chemicals were analysed in our laboratories.* 這些化學物質在我們的實驗室裡作了分析。| *This problem needs to be analysed in detail.* 這個問題需作詳細分析。

★★a·nal·y·sis /əˈnæləsɪs; əˈnæl⒦s⒦s/ n **analyses** /-siz; -siːz/ [C;U] a careful examination of something which helps you to understand and explain it 分析: *His analysis of the accident showed what had happened.* 他對事故的分析說明了事故發生的經過。

an·a·lyst /ˈænlɪst; ˈænəl⒦st/ n **1** a person who makes an analysis of a subject and gives opinions about it 分析者; 分析家: *political analysts* 政治分析家 **2** see 見 PSYCHOANALYST

an·a·lyt·ic /ˌænlˈɪtɪk; ˌænəlˈlɪtɪk◂/ adj (also

A

又作 **analytical** /-kl; kəl/) using reason or able to use reason 分析的; 善於分析的

an·ar·chis·m /ˈænəˌkɪzəm; ˈænəkɪzəm/ n [U] the political belief that society should have no government or laws, but people in society should work together and help each other 無政府主義 **–anarchist** n

an·ar·chy /ˈænəkɪ; ˈænəki/ n [U] a state of complete disorder and confusion, when no-one is in control and no-one follows any rules or laws 混亂狀態; 無政府狀態 **–anarchic** /ænˈɑːkɪk; æˈnɑːkɪk/ adj

a·nath·e·ma /əˈnæθəmə; əˈnæθ ɔ̩ mə/ n fml [sing; U] something that you hate very much 《正式》令人厭惡的東西: Those opinions are an anathema to me. 那些意見真令我厭惡。

a·nat·o·my /əˈnætəmɪ; əˈnætəmi/ n **anato-mies 1** [U] the scientific study of the bodies of living things and the way their parts fit together 解剖學 **2** [C] the way that the parts of a living thing or a body fit together (生物體) 結構: the anatomy of a rabbit 兔子的身體結構 **–anatomical** /ˌænəˈtɒmɪkl; ænəˈtɒmɪkəl/ adj

an·ces·tor /ˈænsestə; ˈænsəstəʳ/ n a person from whom someone is descended 祖先; 祖宗: My ancestors came from Spain in the eighteenth century. 我的祖先是十八世紀的西班牙人。 **–ancestral** /ænˈsestrəl; ænˈsestrəl/ adj [only before a noun 只用於名詞前]

an·ces·try /ˈænsestrɪ; ˈænsəstri/ n **ances-tries** [C;U] the people from whom some-one is descended 祖先; 世系: British citizens of Indian ancestry 印度裔英國公民

an·chor¹ /ˈæŋkə; ˈæŋkəʳ/ n a heavy hooked metal object that is dropped into the water to stop a boat moving away 錨

anchor² v **1** [I] to stop sailing and lower the anchor 拋錨泊(船): We anchored just off Cape Town. 我們剛離開開普敦就拋錨停駛了。 **2** [T] to fix something firmly into a place or a position 使〔某物〕固定

an·chor·age /ˈæŋkərɪdʒ; ˈæŋkərɪdʒ/ n a place where ships may stop and lower their anchor 拋錨處; 錨地

an·cho·vy /ˈæntʃəvɪ; ˈæntʃəvi/ n anchovies a small fish with a strong, salty taste 鯷魚

an·cient /ˈenʃənt; ˈeɪnʃənt/ adj **1** belonging to times long ago 古代的; 遠古的: ancient Rome 古羅馬 | ancient ruins 古代廢墟 **2** very old 很舊的; 老式的: That car's ancient! 那車老掉牙了!

an·cil·la·ry /ænˈsɪlərɪ; ænˈsɪləri/ adj fml or tech providing help or support for the people who work in an organization 《正式或術語》輔助的; 支援性的

and /ənd; ənd, ən, strong 強讀 ænd; ænd/ conj **1** used to join two words or expressions 和; 與; 又; 及; 同: I need a knife and fork. 我需要一副刀叉。 | my mother and father 我的父母 | He was cold and hungry.

他又冷又餓。 | She started shouting and screaming. 她開始又喊又叫。 | Three hun-dred and fifty people were there. 有三百五十人在那兒。 **2** used to show that two things happen at the same time or almost at the same time 〔用於表示兩件事同時發生或者幾乎同時發生〕: I looked at the book and realized that it was not the one I wanted. 我看了那本書一眼, 知道不是我想要的那本。 | I woke up and got out of bed. 我醒來後就起牀。

an·ec·dote /ˈænɪkˌdot; ˈænɪkdəʊt/ n a short amusing story about something that has happened 軼事; 趣聞 **–anecdotal** /ˌænɪkˈdotl; ænɪkˈdəʊtl◂/ adj

a·ne·mi·a /əˈniːmɪə; əˈniːmiə/ n see 見 ANAEMIA

a·nem·o·ne /əˈnɛmə̩ni; əˈneməni/ n **1** a garden plant with red, white, or blue flowers 銀蓮花 **2** a small sea animal with a jelly-like body 海葵

an·es·the·si·a /ˌænəsˈθiʒə; ˌæn ɔ̩ sˈθiːziə/ n see 見 ANAESTHESIA

anesthetic n see 見 ANAESTHETIC

anesthetist n see 見 ANAESTHETIST

anesthetize v see 見 ANAESTHETIZE

a·new /əˈnju; əˈnjuː/ adv lit in a new or dif-ferent way 《文》重新; 再度: beginning life anew after retirement 退休後重新開始生活

an·gel /ˈendʒəl; ˈeɪndʒəl/ n **1** a messenger from God, usually represented as a person with wings and dressed in white 天使 **2** a person who is very kind and cares for others 〔天使般〕善良體貼的人 **–angelic** /ænˈdʒelɪk; ænˈdʒelɪk/ adj

an·ger¹ /ˈæŋgə; ˈæŋgəʳ/ n [U] a strong feel-ing of displeasure that you feel when someone has behaved in a cruel or unkind way towards you 憤怒; 氣憤: She returned, full of anger at the way she had been treated. 她回來了, 因別人對待她的態度而感到滿腔氣憤。 | I can feel nothing but anger at your behaviour. 我對你的行為感到的只是憤怒。

anger² v [T] to make someone feel angry 使〔某人〕發怒[生氣]: His attitude had angered me. 他的態度激怒了我。

an·gle¹ /ˈæŋgl; ˈæŋgəl/ n **1** the space be-tween two lines that meet or cross each other, measured in degrees 角: The roads join at an angle of 90 degrees. 這兩條路相交成九十度的角。 **2** at an angle sloping, and not upright or straight 傾斜的; 不直的: The plant was growing at an angle. 那株植物長歪了 **3** a point of view 角度; 觀點: We need to tackle this problem from a different angle. 我們需要從另一個角度來解決這個問題。

angle² v angled, angling [T] **1** to represent something from a particular point of view 從某一角度來表述〔某事〕: She angles her reports to suit the reader. 她從某種特定角度來寫報道, 以迎合讀者。 **2** be angling for something to be trying to make someone offer something to you without asking for it directly 拐彎抹角地向〔某人〕索取某物

an·gler /ˈæŋglə; ˈæŋglər/ n someone who fishes with a hook and line 釣魚者

An·gli·can /ˈæŋglɪkən; ˈæŋglɪkən/ n a member of a branch of the Christian religion 英國聖公會教徒 **–Anglican** adj

an·gli·cize /ˈæŋglə͵saɪz; ˈæŋglɪˌsaɪz/ v **anglicized, anglicizing** (also 又作 **anglicise** BrE 【英式】) [T] to make something sound or appear English 使英語化; 使英國化

an·gling /ˈæŋglɪŋ; ˈæŋglɪŋ/ n [U] the activity of fishing with a hook and line 釣魚: angling equipment 釣魚用的裝備 **–angling** v [I; only in progressive forms 只用於進行式] : I really enjoy angling. 我真的喜歡釣魚。

An·glo-Sax·on /ˌæŋgloˈsæksn; ˌæŋgləʊˈsæksən/ n a member of the people who lived in England from about 600 to 1066 AD 盎格魯撒克遜人 **–Anglo-Saxon** adj

*★***an·gry** /ˈæŋgrɪ; ˈæŋgri/ adj **angrier, angriest** very annoyed 發怒的; 生氣的: He gets angry at the slightest thing. 他為一件最小的事也會發怒。| It really makes me feel angry. 那件事真使我生氣。| I'm very angry **with** him. 我很生他的氣。**–angrily** adv

> ■ USAGE 用法: Do not use **angry** to describe a person's character. Instead, use words like **quick-tempered** (fairly weak) or **bad-tempered** (stronger). ☆ 描述人的性格時不用 **angry**, 而應使用 **quick-tempered**(意思較弱)或 **bad-tempered**(意思較強)。

an·guish /ˈæŋgwɪʃ; ˈæŋgwɪʃ/ n [U] very great grief or pain 〔精神上的〕極度痛苦: She suffered great anguish. 她遭受極大的痛苦。 **–anguished** adj: anguished cries 痛苦的呼喊

an·gu·lar /ˈæŋgjələ; ˈæŋgjʊlə/ adj **1** having sharp corners 有尖角的 **2** very thin (used of people) 很瘦的〔指人〕: her thin angular face 她瘦削的臉

*★***an·i·mal**[1] /ˈænəml; ˈænɪˌməl/ n a living creature; "animal" is sometimes used for all living creatures, sometimes for all creatures except humans, and sometimes just for mammals (MAMMAL) 動物〔有時指所有動物, 有時指除人以外的所有動物, 有時僅指哺乳動物〕: The forest is full of wild animals. 森林裡到處是野獸。| Of all the animals, we are the cleverest. 在所有的動物中, 我們人類是最聰明的。

animal[2] adj **1** connected with animals or made from animals 動物的; 動物製成的: animal fats 動物脂肪 **2** concerning only your body, not your mind or spirit 肉體的: We are told to suppress our animal instincts. 我們被要求壓抑我們肉體的本能。

an·i·mate[1] /ˈænəmɪt; ˈænɪˌmət/ adj having life 有生命的 **–opposite** 反義 **inanimate**

an·i·mate[2] /ˈænə͵met; ˈænɪˌmeɪt/ v **animated, animating** [T] **animate someone's face** to make someone look excited and full of life 使某人臉上有生氣: Laughter animated his face for a moment. 笑使他臉上一時增添了生氣。

an·i·ma·ted /ˈænə͵metɪd; ˈænɪˌmeɪtɪd/ adj full of life and excitement 栩栩如生的; 生氣勃勃的; 活躍的: an animated debate 一場熱烈的辯論

an·i·ma·tion /ˌænəˈmeʃən; ˌænɪˈmeɪʃən/ n [U] **1** excitement and interest 生氣; 興奮; 活躍: They were full of animation as they talked of their holiday. 他們興奮地談論着假期的事。 **2** the making of films in which people and things that are drawn seem to move and talk 動畫片的製作

an·i·mos·i·ty /ˌænəˈmɑsətɪ; ˌænɪˈmɒsɪti/ n **animosities** [C;U] a feeling of hatred and anger 仇恨; 憎惡; 敵意: There was a lot of animosity between the two countries. 兩國之間敵意很深。

an·i·seed /ˈænɪ͵sid; ˈænɪˌsiːd/ n [U] the strong-tasting seeds of a plant; aniseed is used in sweets, medicines, and alcoholic drinks 大茴香子〔用於糖果、藥品和酒類〕

an·kle /ˈæŋkl; ˈæŋkəl/ n the part of your body where your foot joins your leg 腳踝

an·nals /ˈænlz; ˈænəlz/ n [pl] fml a record of the past events of a nation or society, written year by year 〔正式〕編年史; 年鑑; 年報: She has an important place in the annals of British politics. 她在英國政治史上佔有重要的地位。

an·nex /əˈnɛks; əˈneks/ v [T] to take control of land or property without permission 兼併; 併吞; 霸佔: The country was annexed at the beginning of the war. 那個國家在戰爭初期被併吞了。 **–annexation** /ˌænɛkˈseʃən; ˌænekˈseɪʃən/ n [C;U]: the annexation of Austria 奧地利的吞併

an·nexe /ˌɑˈnɛks; ˈæneks/ n (**annex** AmE 【美式】) a building joined to or positioned near the main building 附屬建築物: a hospital annexe 醫院的附屬建築物

an·ni·hi·late /əˈnaɪə͵let; əˈnaɪəleɪt/ v **annihilated, annihilating** [T] to destroy something or defeat someone completely 殲滅; 消滅; 毀滅: The city had been virtually annihilated. 那城市實際上被全毀了。 **–annihilation** /ə͵naɪəˈleʃən; ə͵naɪəˈleɪʃən/ n [U]

an·ni·ver·sa·ry /ˌænəˈvɜsərɪ; ˌænɪˈvɜːsəri/ n **anniversaries** a date which is remembered because it is an exact number of years after an event 週年紀念日: Today is the tenth anniversary of the country's independence. 今天是本國獨立十週年紀念日。| our wedding anniversary 我們的結婚紀念日

An·no Dom·i·ni /ˌænoˈdɑmə͵naɪ; ˌænəʊˈdɒmɪˌnaɪ/ fml 【正式】see 見 AD

an·no·tate /ˈæno͵tet; ˈænəteɪt/ v **annotated, annotating** [T] fml to add notes to a book in order to explain certain parts of it 〔正

式〕〔給書作〕註釋, 註解: *an annotated text* 有註釋的文本 –**annotation** /ˌænəˈteɪʃən; ˌænə-ˈteɪʃən/ *n* [C;U]

an·nounce /əˈnaʊns; əˈnaʊns/ *v* **announced, announcing 1** [T; +that] to state something publicly 宣佈, 宣告〔某事物〕: *He suddenly announced that he was leaving.* 他突然宣佈他要離開。 | *The winner of the competition will be announced later today.* 比賽的獲勝者將於今天稍後時候宣佈。 | *The election results were announced to the waiting crowd.* 選舉結果向等待的人羣宣佈了。 | *"John's dead," she announced.* 她向大家宣佈, "約翰死了。"

□ USEFUL PATTERNS 有用句型
to announce something; to announce something to someone; to announce that…

2 [T] to introduce people when they arrive at a formal occasion 宣佈〔某人〕到達: *The guest of honour was announced.* 有人宣佈貴賓已到達。

an·nounce·ment /əˈnaʊnsmənt; əˈnaʊnsmənt/ *n* **1** [C] a public statement 通告; 佈告: *I've got an important announcement to make.* 我有件重要事情要宣佈。 **2** [U] the act of saying something publicly 宣佈; 宣告; 公佈: *the announcement of the trade figures* 貿易數字的公佈

an·nounc·er /əˈnaʊnsər; əˈnaʊnsər/ *n* a person who gives information to people, especially on radio or television 〔尤指電台、電視台的〕播音員, 節目主持人

an·noy /əˈnɔɪ; əˈnɔɪ/ *v* [T] to make someone feel rather angry 打擾〔某人〕; 使〔某人〕煩惱: *He was beginning to annoy me.* 他開始使我心煩。

an·noy·ance /əˈnɔɪəns; əˈnɔɪəns/ *n* **1** [U] the feeling of being annoyed 煩惱; 氣惱: *He showed signs of annoyance.* 他露出氣惱的神情。 **2** [C] something which annoys you 令人煩惱的事物: *The noisy traffic is a continual annoyance.* 交通噪音時時刻刻令人煩惱。

an·noy·ing /əˈnɔɪɪŋ; əˈnɔɪ-ɪŋ/ *adj* making you feel angry 討厭的; 惱人的: *an annoying delay* 惱人的延誤

an·nu·al¹ /ˈænjuəl; ˈænjuəl/ *adj* **1** happening or done every year or once a year 每年的; 一年一次的: *an annual holiday* 年假 | *the annual meeting* 年會 **2** calculated over a period of one year 以年計算的: *What's his annual income?* 他的年薪是多少? –**annually** *adv*

annual² *n* **1** a plant that lives for only one year or one season 一年生〔一季生〕植物 **2** a book or magazine for children which appears once each year 〔供兒童閱讀的〕年鑑, 年刊

an·nu·i·ty /əˈnuətɪ; əˈnjuːʃᵻti/ *n* **annuities** a fixed sum of money paid each year to a person for a stated number of years or until they die 年金; (每年的) 養老金

an·nul /əˈnʌl; əˈnʌl/ *v* **-ll-** [T] *tech* to declare officially that a marriage, agreement, or law no longer exists 〔術語〕解除〔婚約〕; 廢止〔契約、法律等〕–**annulment** *n* [C;U]

an·ode /ˈænəʊd; ˈænəʊd/ *n tech* the part of an electrical instrument such as a BATTERY which collects electrons (ELECTRON); the anode is often a rod or wire shown as (+) 〔術語〕陽極, 正極

a·noint /əˈnɔɪnt; əˈnɔɪnt/ *v* [T] to put oil or water onto a person's head as part of a religious ceremony 〔在宗教儀式上〕塗油[水]於〔人頭〕

a·nom·a·ly /əˈnɒməlɪ; əˈnɒməli/ *n* **anomalies** *fml* a person, thing, or fact that is different from what is usual and which may be impossible to explain 〔正式〕畸形人或物 –**anomalous** /əˈnɒmələs; əˈnɒmələs/ *adj*: *anomalous results* 異常的結果

a·non¹ /əˈnɒn; əˈnɒn/ *adv lit or infml* soon 〔文或非正式〕不久; 立刻: *See you anon.* 待會兒見

anon² a word written at the end of a piece of writing to show that it is not known who wrote it; an abbreviation for ANONYMOUS 〔縮〕無名氏; 作者不詳

an·o·nym·i·ty /ˌænəˈnɪmətɪ; ˌænəˈnɪmᵻti/ *n* [U] **1** the condition of not having your name known 匿名; 無名; 姓氏不明: *The author prefers anonymity.* 那作者寧願匿名發表其作品。 **2** the condition of not having any interesting and different qualities 無特色; 無個性特徵: *the anonymity of hotel rooms* 旅館房間的毫無特色的佈局

a·non·y·mous /əˈnɒnəməs; əˈnɒnᵻməs/ *adj* done, made, or given by someone whose name is not known 匿名的; 無名的; 不具名的: *an anonymous letter* 匿名信 | *an anonymous gift* 不知是誰送的禮物 –**anonymously** *adv*

an·o·rak /ˈænəˌræk; ˈænəræk/ *n BrE* a short coat with a cover for your head 〔英式〕帶風帽的外套 –see picture on page 210 見 210 頁彩圖

an·o·rex·ic /ˌænəˈreksɪk; ˌænəˈreksɪk/ *adj* suffering from a disease which makes you very afraid of becoming fat, and so afraid to eat 患厭食症的

an·oth·er /əˈnʌðər; əˈnʌðər/ *det, pron* **1** one more of the same kind 再一; 又一: *Would you like another biscuit?* 你要不要再來一塊餅乾? | *I had one drink, then decided that I needed another.* 我喝了一杯, 然後決定再要一杯。 **2** a different one 別的; 另一個的: *This car's falling to bits. We must get another one.* 這輛車已破爛不堪。我們必須另買一輛。 | *We were glad the war was happening in another country.* 這場戰爭在別的國家發生, 我們感到慶幸。 | *The women were in one room, the men in another.* 婦女們住在一個房間, 男人們住在另一間。

A

★an·swer¹ /ˈænsə; ˈɑːnsəʳ/ *n* **1** [C;U] a reply to what someone says, asks, or does 回答; 答覆; 應答: *He rang the doorbell but there was no answer.* 他按了門鈴, 但是無人回答。| *She can't give us an answer yet.* 她尚無法答覆我們。| *I think I know the answer to your problem.* 我想我知道你問題的答案。| *Her only answer to their threat was to laugh.* 她對他們的威脅只是報以一笑。 **2 in answer to something** as a reply to what someone says, asks, or does 作為對某事物的回答: *In answer to your previous question: I don't think so.* 我對你前一個問題的回答是: 我不以為然。 **3** [C] a result which you get when calculating with numbers 答案; 解答: *The answer is 255.* 答案是 255。 **4** [C] an action which gets rid of a problem 解決辦法: *There is no easy answer to the problem of unemployment.* 對失業問題沒有容易的解決辦法。

★answer² *v* **1** [I;T; +that] to reply to something that someone has said or asked 回答; 答覆: *You didn't answer his question.* 你沒有回答他的問題。| *Why didn't you answer?* 你為甚麼不回答? | *Answer your mother, John!* 回答你母親的話, 約翰! | *I answered with a smile.* 我以微笑作答。| *He asked her why, but she answered that she didn't know.* 他問她為甚麼, 但她回答說她不知道。| *"I don't know," she answered.* "我不知道," 她回答說。

□ USEFUL PATTERNS 有用句型
to answer; to answer someone; to answer a question; to answer that...; "..." she answered

2 answer the telephone to pick up the telephone when it rings 接電話 **3 answer the door** to open the door when someone knocks on it 〔有人敲門後〕開門 **4 answer a description, answer to a description** to fit a description 與描述相符: *The police have seen a man answering to his description.* 警方已發現一名其相貌特徵相符的男子

■ USAGE 用法: Compare 比較 **answer, reply, respond.** ☆ **1 Answer** and **reply** are both common verbs for answering questions, but **reply** is a little more formal. **Respond** is very formal. ☆ **answer** 和 **reply** 都是表示回答問題的常用動詞, 但是 **reply** 略更正式。**respond** 是很正式的用詞。 **2** With an object we must use *to* after **reply** and **respond**, but not after **answer**. ☆ 帶賓語, 在 **reply** 和 **respond** 後必須用 *to*, 但 **answer** 後不用 *to*。Compare 比較 *They did not* **answer** *my question* 他們沒有回答我的問題 和 *They did not* **reply to/respond to** *my enquiry.* 他們沒有回答[答覆]我的詢問。

answer back *phr v* [I;T **answer back**] *infml* to reply rudely 〔非正式〕回嘴; 頂嘴: *Don't answer me back!* 別跟我頂嘴!

answer for *phr v* **1** [T **answer for** sbdy/sthg] to state that someone has certain qualities 對...負責; 為...負責: *I can answer for his honesty.* 我可以對他的誠實負責。 **2** [T **answer for** sthg] to be punished for an action 承受...的後果; 受報應: *One day you will have to answer for this.* 你總有一天要為此受報應。 **3 have a lot to answer for** to have done a lot of things that have had bad results 〔對已產生的不良後果〕負很大的責任: *Town-planners have a lot to answer for.* 城市規劃者負有很大的責任。

an·swer·a·ble /ˈænsərəbḷ; ˈɑːnsərəbəl/ *adj* **answerable to someone, answerable for something** having to explain your actions to someone 向某人負責; 對某事物承擔責任: *He is answerable to the Managing Director.* 他向總經理負責。| *We should be answerable for all our actions.* 我們應該對自己的一切行動負責。

ant /ænt; ænt/ *n* a small insect which lives on the ground in large groups 螞蟻

an·tag·o·nis·m /ænˈtægəˌnɪzəm; ænˈtægənɪzəm/ *n* [U] active opposition or hatred between people or groups 對抗; 對立; 敵對: *The two men felt a strong antagonism towards each other.* 這兩人互相持有很強的敵對態度。

an·tag·o·nist /ænˈtægənɪst; ænˈtægənʌst/ *n* an opponent in a fight or competition 對手; 敵手

an·tag·o·nis·tic /ænˌtægəˈnɪstɪk; ænˌtægəˈnɪstɪk/ *adj* showing opposition or hatred towards someone 對抗的; 敵對的; 對立的

an·tag·o·nize /ænˈtægəˌnaɪz; ænˈtægənaɪz/ *v* **antagonized, antagonizing** (also 又作 **antagonise** *BrE* 〔英式〕) [T] to make someone feel angry with you 引起〔某人〕的敵對[對抗]: *I wouldn't antagonize him, if I were you.* 如果我是你的話, 我不會與他為敵。

Ant·arc·tic /ænˈtɑrktɪk; ænˈtɑːktɪk/ *n* **the Antarctic** the very cold most southern part of the world 南極(地區)

an·te·ced·ent /ˌæntəˈsidṇt; ˌæntɪˈsiːdənt/ *n* *fml* a person, thing, or event that comes before something related to it 〔正式〕先例; 先行者

an·te·date /ˈæntɪˌdet; ˈæntɪdeɪt/ *v* **antedated, antedating** [T] *fml* to come before something else in time 〔正式〕先於; 早於

an·te·lope /ˈæntḷˌop; ˈæntɪləʊp/ *n* a graceful animal like a deer, able to run very fast 羚羊

an·te·na·tal /ˌæntɪˈnetḷ; ˌæntɪˈneɪtḷ◂/ *adj* [only before a noun 只用於名詞前] *tech* of the period of time before a woman gives birth 〔術語〕產前的: *an antenatal clinic* 產前檢查診所

an·ten·na /ænˈtɛnə; ænˈtenə/ *n* **1** [plural is

antennae /-ni; -niː/] one of two long thin sensitive organs on the heads of some insects 觸角; 觸鬚 **2** [plural is **antennas**] *AmE* the AERIAL of a radio or television 〖美式〗〔收音機或電視機的〕天線

an·ter·i·or /æn'tɪrɪə; æn'tɪərɪəʳ/ *adj* **1** *fml* earlier in time 〖正式〗先前的; 先於的 **2** *tech* nearer the front 〖術語〗靠前部的

an·them /'ænθəm; 'ænθəm/ *n* a religious song of praise written for a special occasion 讚美詩; 聖歌; 頌歌

an·thol·o·gy /æn'θɑlədʒɪ; æn'θɒlədʒɪ/ *n* **anthologies** a collection of works by different writers in one book 〔詩、文等的〕選集: *an anthology of poetry* 一部詩選

an·thro·poid /'ænθrə,pɔɪd; 'ænθrəpɔɪd/ *adj* like a human 像人類的; 似人的: *anthropoid apes* 類人猿

an·thro·pol·o·gy /,ænθrə'pɑlədʒɪ; ,ænθrə-'pɒlədʒɪ/ *n* [U] the scientific study of the human race, including its different beliefs, customs, and social habits 人類學 –**anthropologist** *n* –**anthropological** /,ænθrəpə'lɑ-dʒɪkl; ,ænθrəpə'lɒdʒɪkəl/ *adj*

an·ti·bi·ot·ic /,æntɪbaɪ'ɑtɪk; ,æntɪbaɪ'ɒtɪk/ *n* a drug such as PENICILLIN, which is used to destroy harmful bacteria and to cure infections in a person's body 抗菌素; 抗生素

an·ti·bod·y /'æntɪ,bɑdɪ; 'æntɪ,bɒdɪ/ *n* **anti-bodies** a substance produced in the blood which fights infection 抗體

an·tic·i·pate /æn'tɪsə,peɪt; æn'tɪs½peɪt/ *v* **anticipated, anticipating 1** [T; +that] to expect something 期望, 預期〔某事〕: *He's anticipating trouble when the factory opens again.* 他預料工廠重新開工時會有麻煩。| *We anticipate that there will be a lot of opposition to the plan.* 我們預料該項計劃會遭到許多人的反對。| *I anticipated meeting a few problems.* 我預料會遇到幾個問題。

□ USEFUL PATTERNS 有用句型
to anticipate something; to anticipate doing something; to anticipate that…

2 [T;+that] to see what is likely to happen and taken action in order to be ready 預料到〔會發生甚麼事並採取措施〕: *I tried to anticipate the kind of questions they might ask me at the interview.* 我設法事先預測一下他們在採訪時會問我甚麼問題。| *We had anticipated that the enemy would try to cross the river and had destroyed the bridge.* 我們料到敵人可能設法渡河, 所以把橋毀了。

□ USEFUL PATTERNS 有用句型
to anticipate something; to anticipate that…

–**anticipation** /æn,tɪsə'peʃən; æn,tɪs½'peɪ-ʃən/ *n* [U] –**anticipatory** /æn'tɪsəpə,torɪ; æn-,tɪs½'peɪtərɪ/ *adj*

an·ti·cli·max /,æntɪ'klaɪmæks; ,æntɪ'klaɪ-mæks/ *n* something unexciting, ordinary, or disappointing, which comes after something exciting 高潮突降〔指精彩的高潮之後出現平淡或令人失望的結局〕; 令人掃興的結尾: *Coming home again was a bit of an anti-climax.* 重返老家有點讓人掃興。

an·ti·clock·wise /,æntɪ'klɑkwaɪz; ,æntɪ-'klɒkwaɪz/ *adj, adv* (**counterclockwise** *AmE* 〖美式〗) in the opposite direction to the movement of the hands of a clock 逆時針方向的〔地〕: *Turn it anticlockwise.* 請逆時針方向轉動。

an·tics /'æntɪks; 'æntɪks/ *n* [pl] odd behaviour, usually intended to amuse people 〔旨在逗笑的〕滑稽動作; 古怪行為

an·ti·cy·clone /,æntɪ'saɪklon; ,æntɪ'saɪ-kləʊn/ *n tech* an area of high air pressure, causing either hot or cold settled weather conditions 〖術語〗高氣壓; 反氣旋

an·ti·dote /'æntɪ,dot; 'æntɪdəʊt/ *n* **1** a substance that stops or controls a poison working inside a person's body 解毒劑: *The poison has no known antidote.* 這種毒藥沒有解藥能解。**2** something which helps you to change a difficult situation 〔能改變困境的〕方法: *We need an antidote to our present political troubles.* 我們需要一種能解決目前政治難題的方法。

an·ti·freeze /,æntɪ'friz; 'æntɪfriːz/ *n* [U] a chemical substance put in water to stop it from freezing; antifreeze is used especially in car engines 〔尤指用於汽車發動機的〕防凍劑; 抗凝劑

an·tip·a·thy /æn'tɪpəθɪ; æn'tɪpəθɪ/ *n* [U] a strong feeling of dislike or hatred 憎惡; 憎恨; 反感: *the President's well-known antipathy to trade unions* 總統對工會反感眾所周知 –**antipathetic** /æn,tɪpə'θetɪk; ,æntɪpə'θe-tɪk/ *adj*

an·ti·quat·ed /'æntə,kwetɪd; 'ænt½kweɪt½d/ *adj* belonging to the past and not suited to modern needs or conditions 過時的; 陳舊的; 落伍的: *antiquated laws* 過時的法律 | *an antiquated machine* 陳舊的機器 –see 見 OLD (USAGE 用法)

an·tique /æn'tik; æn'tiːk/ *n* an old object, such as a piece of jewellery or furniture, which is rare and valuable 古物; 古玩; 古董

an·tiq·ui·ty /æn'tɪkwətɪ; æn'tɪkw½tɪ/ *n* **antiquities 1** [C] a building, ruin, or work of art from the ancient world, especially from ancient Rome or Greece 〔尤指古羅馬或古希臘遺留下來的〕古跡, 古物 **2** [U] ancient times 古代; 古老: *the temples of antiquity* 古廟 **3** [U] great age 古老; 高齡: *a building of great antiquity* 一座很古老的建築物

an·ti-Sem·i·tis·m /,æntɪ'semə,tɪzəm; ,æntɪ'sem½tɪzəm/ *n* [U] hatred of the Jewish people 反猶太主義 –**anti-Semitic** /-sə'mɪ-tɪk; -s½'mɪtɪk/ *adj*

an·ti·sep·tic /,æntə'septɪk; ,ænt½'septɪk◂/ *n*

A

[C;U] a chemical substance able to prevent infection in a wound by killing harmful bacteria 消毒劑; 防腐劑

an·ti·so·cial /ˌæntɪˈsoʃəl; ˌæntɪˈsəʊʃəl/ *adj* **1** causing annoyance by showing no concern for other people 有害公眾利益的; 妨害他人的: *It's antisocial to play your radio so loud at this time of the night.* 在夜間這個時候你把收音機開得這麼響, 是妨害他人的行為。 **2** not liking to mix with other people 不愛與人交往的; 不合羣的: *Jane's very friendly, but her husband's rather antisocial.* 簡很友善, 但是她的丈夫有點孤僻。

an·tith·e·sis /ænˈtɪθəsɪs; ænˈtɪθ⅟ₔsɪs/ *n* **antitheses** /-ˌsiz; -siːz/ the exact opposite of something 相對; 對立: *The antithesis of death is life.* 與死亡相對的是生存。

ant·ler /ˈæntlə; ˈæntlər/ *n* one of the long horns with branches on the head of a male deer 鹿角

an·to·nym /ˈæntəˌnɪm; ˈæntənɪm/ *n tech* a word opposite in meaning to another word; for example, "hot" is the antonym of "cold" 〖術語〗反義詞〔例如"hot"是"cold"的反義詞〕

a·nus /ˈeɪnəs; ˈeɪnəs/ *n tech* the opening through which solid food waste leaves your bowels 〖術語〗肛門

an·vil /ˈænvɪl; ˈænv⅟l/ *n* an iron block on which hot metals are hammered and shaped 鐵砧

★**anx·i·e·ty** /æŋˈzaɪətɪ; æŋˈzaɪəti/ *n* **anxieties** [C;U] **1** a feeling of fear and worry about something uncertain 憂慮; 焦慮; 擔心: *I sensed her anxiety.* 我感覺到她的焦慮。 | *Sometimes it helps to talk about your fears and anxieties.* 有時候, 説出你所害怕和擔心的事是有好處的。 **2** great eagerness to do something and worry that you might not be able to do it 渴望; 熱切; 急切

★**anx·ious** /ˈæŋkʃəs; ˈæŋkʃəs/ *adj* **1** nervous or troubled 憂慮的; 焦慮的; 擔心的: *I was rather anxious about the children when they didn't come home from school.* 孩子們還未從學校回來, 我有點替他們擔心。 | *an anxious wait for our examination results* 焦慮地等待考試結果 **2** very eager to do something 渴望的; 急切的: *She was anxious not to offend her guests.* 她不想使客人感到不高興。 | *We were anxious that everyone should know the truth.* 我們急於讓大家都知道事實真相。 | *He was anxious for news.* 他急於知道消息。

□ USEFUL PATTERNS 有用句型
be anxious to do something; be anxious that someone should do something; be anxious for something

–see 見 NERVOUS (USAGE 用法) – **anxiously** *adv*

★**an·y**[1] /ˈɛnɪ; ˈeni/ *det, pron* **1** no matter which one or no matter what kind

任何一個; 無論哪個: *They're all free — take any you like.* 它們都是免費的——你隨便拿吧。 | *Any child would know that.* 任何一個孩子都知道這一點。 | *Any help would be welcome.* 樂意接受任何幫助。 **2** [used only in negatives and questions 只用於否定句和疑問句] some 一些; 一點: *Have you got any money?* 你有沒有錢? | *He hasn't got any imagination.* 他連一點想像力也沒有。 | *Are there any letters for me? I never seem to get any.* 有我的信嗎? 我似乎從來沒收到過甚麼信。–see 見 SOME (USAGE 用法)

any[2] *adv* [used only in negatives and questions 只用於否定句和疑問句] at all 絲毫; 一點點: *I can't stay any longer.* 我一刻也不能留下去了。 | *Do you feel any better?* 你感覺好一點了嗎?

★**an·y·bod·y** /ˈɛnɪˌbɑdɪ; ˈeniˌbɒdi/ *pron* (also 又作 **anyone**) **1** any person or people, no matter who 無論誰; 任何人: *Anybody can cook if they try.* 任何人只要肯嘗試都會烹飪。 | *He thinks he's cleverer than anyone else.* 他自認為比誰都聰明。 **2** [used only in negatives and questions 只用於否定句和疑問句] any person 任何人: *Is there anybody there?* 有人在那兒嗎? | *There wasn't anyone in the building.* 大樓裡沒任何人。 | *If anybody asks for you, I'll tell them you've gone out.* 如果有人要見你, 我會對他們説你出去了。–see 見 EVERYBODY (USAGE 用法)

an·y·how /ˈɛnɪˌhaʊ; ˈenihaʊ/ *adv* **1** carelessly, not in a regular or ordered way 隨隨便便地; 雜亂無章地: *His clothes had been thrown down just anyhow.* 他的衣服到處亂扔。 **2** see 見 ANYWAY

an·y·one /ˈɛnɪˌwʌn; ˈeniwʌn/ *pron* see 見 ANYBODY

■ USAGE 用法: Compare 比較 **anyone** and 和 **any one**. Anyone refers to a person ☆**Anyone** 指人: *I don't want* **anyone** *to know my secret.* 我不想有人知道我的祕密。 **Any one** can refer to a person or thing and it is often followed by of ☆**Any one** 可用於指人或事物, 而且後面常常跟 of: *There are three possible answers and I can accept* **any one** *of them.* 解決辦法可能有三個, 我可以接受任何一個。

★**an·y·thing** /ˈɛnɪˌθɪŋ; ˈeniθɪŋ/ *pron* **1** [used only in negatives and questions 只用於否定句和疑問句] any thing 任何事物: *There wasn't anything in the cupboard.* 櫥櫃裡甚麼東西也沒有。 | *You can't believe anything she says.* 她説甚麼你都不能信。 | *Would you like anything to eat?* 你想吃點甚麼嗎? **2** any thing or things, no matter what 無論何事: *Surely anything's better than a war!* 無論發生甚麼事, 肯定比戰爭好! | *He'll do anything for a quiet life.* 他要千方百計過安定的生活。 **3** **anything but** not

A

at all 根本不; 決不: *She's anything but poor!* 她根本不窮! **4 not anything like** not at all 全然不; 決不: *It isn't anything like as cold as it was yesterday.* 今天全然不像昨天那麼冷。**5 as easy as anything, as fast as anything, etc.** very easy, fast, etc. 非常容易; 非常快, 等等: *The exam was as easy as anything.* 考試非常容易。**6 or anything** a phrase used to say that there are other possibilities 或甚麼事物〔表示存在其他可能性〕: *Would you like a biscuit or anything?* 你想不想吃塊餅乾或其他甚麼東西?

★an·y·way /ˈɛnɪˌwe; 'eniwei/ *adv* (also 又作 **anyhow**) **1** used when you are saying something which supports something else that you have just said 無論如何〔用於表示所說的內容證實已提到的另一件事〕: *I don't think he's the right person for the job, and he hasn't got any qualifications anyway.* 我認為他不是做這份工作的適當人選, 無論如何, 他缺乏資歷。**2** used when you are saying that something is true in spite of something else 不管怎樣; 儘管…還是: *It wasn't quite the right colour, but I bought it anyway.* 儘管顏色不那麼適合, 但我還是買下了。**3** used when you are continuing with a story or changing the subject〔用於繼續講述某事或改變話題〕: *Anyway, I must go now, so I'll talk to you later.* 反正我現在必須走了, 那麼我以後跟你談吧。

★an·y·where /ˈɛnɪˌhwɛr; 'eniweər/ *adv* **1** in or to any place, no matter where 無論哪裡; 隨便哪裡: *Sit anywhere you like.* 你喜歡坐在哪裡就坐在哪裡。| *I'd be willing to go and work anywhere in the world.* 我願意去世界上任何地方工作。**2** [used only in negatives and questions 只用於否定句和疑問句] in or to any place 在任何地方; 去任何地方: *Did you go anywhere yesterday?* 你昨天去了甚麼地方嗎? | *We didn't go anywhere on holiday this year.* 今年假期我們甚麼地方也沒去。

★a·part /əˈpɑrt; ə'pɑːt/ *adv* **1** separated by a distance 相隔; 相距: *She was standing a little apart from the others.* 她站着的地方與別人相隔一段距離。| *The two buildings are three miles apart.* 這兩幢建築相距三英里。| *He and his wife are living apart.* 他和妻子分居住。**2** into parts 拆開; 分開: *He took the clock apart to repair it.* 他把鐘拆開來修理。| *I'm afraid the chair has fallen apart.* 恐怕那把椅子已經散了。**3 apart from: a** except for 除…以外; 撇開…來說: *a good piece of work, apart from a few slight faults* 除了一些小缺點外, 不失為一件好作品 **b** in addition to 除…還; 而且: *The Government has plenty of problems to deal with, apart from inflation.* 除了通貨膨脹, 政府還有許多問題要解決。**4 tell apart** to be able to see the difference between things 區別; 區分: *I can't tell the two boys apart.* 我無法區分這兩個孩子。

a·part·heid /əˈpɑrthet; ə'pɑːtheɪt/ *n* [U] the political separation by law of people of different races, especially the separation of black and white people in South Africa〔尤指南非的〕種族隔離

★a·part·ment /əˈpɑrtmənt; ə'pɑːtmənt/ *n* **1** the usual American word for 〖美式〗= FLAT⁴ –see 見 HOUSE¹ (USAGE 用法) **2** a large or splendid room 大的〔豪華的〕房間: *the Royal Apartments* 帝王套間

apartment house /·'····/ *AmE* a large building containing many apartments 〖美式〗公寓大樓

ap·a·thet·ic /ˌæpəˈθɛtɪk; ˌæpə'θetɪk◁/ *adj* not interested in anything 無興趣的; 漠然的: *This year's students are a rather apathetic bunch.* 今年的這批學生是相當冷漠的一羣人。**–apathetically** /-klɪ; -kli/ *adv*

ap·a·thy /ˈæpəθɪ; 'æpəθi/ *n* [U] lack of interest, or lack of desire to do something 無感情; 無興趣; 冷淡; 漠然: *There is a sense of public apathy about the government's latest policies.* 對於政府最近宣佈的政策, 公眾態度冷漠。

ape¹ /ep; eɪp/ *n* an animal like a monkey, but larger and without a tail; a GORILLA is a kind of ape 猿〔如大猩猩〕

ape² *v* **aped, aping** [T] to try to copy a person's behaviour, manners, or speech 模仿〔人的行為, 舉止或說話〕

a·per·i·tif /əperiˈtif; ə,perɪ'tiːf/ *n* an alcoholic drink that people have before a meal 〔餐前飲用的〕開胃酒

ap·er·ture /ˈæpətʃər; 'æpətʃər/ *n* a hole, crack, or other narrow opening 孔; 隙; 窄的缺口

a·pex /ˈepɛks; 'eɪpeks/ *n* the top or highest point of something 頂; 頂點: *the apex of a triangle* 三角形的頂點 | *the apex of his career* 他事業的頂峯

a·phid /ˈefɪd; 'eɪfjd, 'æfjd/ *n* a small insect that lives by sucking the juices of plants 蚜蟲

aph·o·rism /ˈæfəˌrɪzəm; 'æfərɪzəm/ *n* a short and clever saying that expresses something that people believe to be true 格言; 警句

aph·ro·dis·i·ac /ˌæfrəˈdɪziˌæk; ˌæfrə'dɪziæk/ *n* a medicine or drug that causes sexual excitement 催慾藥; 春藥

a·piece /əˈpis; ə'piːs/ *adv* old fash each 〖老式〗每一; 每個: *The apples cost sixpence apiece.* 蘋果每個六便士。

a·pol·o·get·ic /əˌpɑləˈdʒɛtɪk; ə,pɒlə'dʒetɪk◁/ *adj* saying that you are sorry for doing something wrong or causing trouble 有歉意的; 抱歉的: *He was very apologetic.* 他十分抱歉。| *He wrote me an apologetic letter.* 他給我寫了一封道歉信。**–apologetically** /-klɪ; -kli/ *adv*: *He smiled apologetically.* 他歉然一笑。

a·pol·o·gize /əˈpɑləˌdʒaɪz; ə'pɒlədʒaɪz/ *v* **apologized, apologizing** (also 又作 **apolo-**

A

gise *BrE* 〖英式〗) [I] to say that you are sorry for doing something wrong or causing trouble 道歉: *I'll apologize* **to** *her tomorrow.* 我明天向她道歉。| *He apologized* **for** *being late.* 他因遲到而道歉。| *She didn't even apologize!* 她連一點歉意都沒有!

a·pol·o·gy /ə'pɒlədʒɪ; ə'pɒlədʒi/ *n* **apologies 1** [C;U] a statement saying that you are sorry for doing something wrong or causing trouble 道歉; 謝罪; 認錯: *That is completely untrue — I demand an immediate apology.* 這全是假的──我要求立即道歉。| *Please accept our apologies for any inconvenience we have caused.* 若有不便, 敬請原諒。| *She can't come; she sends her apologies.* 她不能來, 所以派人來表示歉意。| *I wrote a letter of apology.* 我寫了封道歉信。**2 an apology for something** *infml* a very bad example of something 〖非正式〗勉強代替某物的東西; 不像樣的代用品

ap·o·plex·y /'æpə‚plɛksɪ; 'æpəpleksi/ *n* [U] *old fash* a serious illness in which you suddenly lose the ability to move or feel anything 〖老式〗中風; 卒中 **–apoplectic** /‚æpə-'plɛktɪk; ‚æpə'plektɪk•/ *adj*

a·pos·tle /ə'pɒsl; ə'pɒsl/ *n* **1** one of the 12 men chosen by Jesus Christ to teach his message 使徒〔尤指耶穌基督派出傳佈福音的十二門徒之一〕**2** a person who believes strongly in certain ideas and tries to spread them 〔某種思想的〕狂熱信仰者, 鼓吹者

a·pos·tro·phe /ə'pɒstrəfɪ; ə'pɒstrəfi/ *n* the sign (') used in writing 〔書寫中的〕撇號(') **a** to show that one or more letters or figures have been left out (as in *don't* for *do not* and *'47* for *1947*) 〔表示字母或數字的省略, 如 *don't* 代替 *do not*, *'47* 代替 *1947*〕**b** before or after *s* to show possession or relation 〔放在 s 之前或之後, 表示所有格〕(as in 如 *John's coat, James' coat, St James's Park, lady's coat, ladies' coats, children's coats*) **c** before *s* to show the plural of letters and figures 〔放在 s 前表示字母和數字的複數〕(as in 如 *There are 2 f's in "off"* and 和 *Your 8's look like S's.*)

ap·pal /ə'pɔl; ə'pɔːl/ *v* **appalled, appalling (appall** *AmE* 〖美式〗) [T] to shock someone so deeply that they are very upset 使〔某人〕驚駭: *We were appalled to hear that she had been murdered.* 聽到她被謀害的消息, 我們都驚駭萬分。| *People were appalled* **by** *reports of the famine.* 人們因關於饑荒的報導而感到驚駭。| *I was appalled* **at** *how old she looked.* 我見她容貌蒼老, 驚駭不已。

ap·pal·ling /ə'pɔlɪŋ; ə'pɔːlɪŋ/ *adj* **1** shocking and terrible 駭人聽聞的; 令人震驚的 **2** *infml* very bad 〖非正式〗極糟的; 很嚴重的: *an appalling waste* 嚴重的浪費 | *an absolutely appalling play* 糟糕透頂的劇本 **–appallingly** *adv*

ap·pa·ra·tus /‚æpə'reɪtəs; ‚æpə'reɪtəs/ *n* [C;

U] a set of instruments, machines, tools, or materials needed for a particular purpose 器械; 裝置; 儀器; 設備: *a piece of apparatus in a gym* 健身房的一件器械 | *The television men set up their apparatus ready to film.* 電視攝像人員架起器械, 準備拍攝。

ap·par·el /ə'pærəl; ə'pærəl/ *n* [U] clothes worn on an important occasion (a word no longer used in modern English) 〔重要場合穿的〕衣服, 服飾〔現代英語中已不使用〕

★**ap·par·ent** /ə'pærənt; ə'pærənt/ *adj* **1** clearly seen or understood 明顯的; 顯而易見的: *Her anxiety was apparent to everyone.* 大家都看得出她焦慮不安。| *The reasons for his anger soon became apparent.* 他生氣的理由大家很快就明白了。**2** seeming to be real or to exist 表面的; 貌似真的: *I was shocked by his apparent lack of concern for other people.* 他似乎對他人漠不關心的樣子使我感到很吃驚。

ap·par·ent·ly /ə'pɛrəntlɪ; ə'pærəntli/ *adv* **1** a word used when you do not know something for certain, but have heard that it is true 顯然; 顯而易見〔用於表示對某事並不肯定, 但聽說是事實〕: *I wasn't there, but apparently she tried to drown him.* 我當時不在場, 但是很顯然她想淹死他。| *"Did she succeed?" "Apparently not."* "她成功了嗎?" "似乎沒有。" **2** seeming to be but not necessarily so 似乎; 看來: *She looked up and smiled, apparently pleased to see him.* 她抬起頭笑一笑, 似乎很高興見到他。

ap·pa·ri·tion /‚æpə'rɪʃən; ‚æpə'rɪʃən/ *n* a dead person that you think you see appearing as a spirit 幽靈; 鬼怪

★**ap·peal¹** /ə'pil; ə'piːl/ *n* **1** [C;U] a strong request for something 呼籲; 要求: *His appeal for help went unanswered.* 他要求幫助, 但無人應答。| *Local people are launching an appeal for money to build a new hall.* 當地民眾為籌集建造一座新大會堂的經費作出呼籲。**2** [U] the power to make you feel attracted or interested 感染力; 吸引力: *Films of that sort have lost their appeal.* 那類電影已經失去了吸引力。**3** [C;U] a request to a higher court to change the decision of a lower court 上訴: *You have the right of appeal.* 你有上訴權。| *His appeal was turned down by the High Court.* 他的上訴被高等法院駁回。

★**appeal²** *v* [I] **1** to make a strong request for something 呼籲; 要求; 懇請: *The government is appealing* **to** *everyone to save water.* 政府正呼籲大家節約用水。| *The charity appealed* **for** *more money.* 慈善團體呼籲募集更多的錢。**2 appeal to someone** to please, attract, or interest someone 對某人有吸引力; 使某人感興趣: *Does the idea of working abroad appeal to you?* 你對出國工作感興趣嗎? | *His books don't appeal to me at all.* 他寫的書我一點也不感興趣。**3** to request a higher law court to change the decision of a lower court〔向上級法院〕上訴

ap·peal·ing /ə'piːlɪŋ; ə'piːlɪŋ/ *adj* **1** showing that you want something 懇求的; 哀訴的: *He gave me an appealing look.* 他對我露出懇求的神情。**2** attractive or interesting 吸引人的; 有趣的: *The idea of a free holiday is rather appealing.* 免費度假的主意頗有吸引力。–opposite 反義 **unappealing** (for sense 2) –**appealingly** *adv*

⋆⋆**ap·pear** /ə'pɪr; ə'pɪəʳ/ *v* **1** [I] to come into view 顯露; 出現; 呈現: *A ship appeared on the horizon.* 一艘輪船出現在地平線上。**2** [I] to begin to be seen or used 開始出現[使用]: *Several new products have recently appeared on the market.* 幾種新產品最近開始在市場上出售。| *Credit cards first appeared about 20 years ago.* 信用咭大約在二十年前開始使用。**3** [I; +complement] to seem 好像; 看來: *She appeared upset at the news.* 她好像對這個消息感到不安。| *He appears to be very happy.* 他看來十分快樂。| *People appear to like this new product.* 看來人們喜愛這種新產品。

> □ USEFUL PATTERNS 有用句型
> to appear to be something; to appear to do something; to appear + adj

4 it appears that... a phrase used when you are saying that something seems to be true, although you find it surprising 好像; 看來: *It appears that he no longer works for the company.* 他好像不再為那公司工作了。| *It appears that I was wrong.* 看來是我錯了。**5** [I] to be printed and put on sale 出版: *His first novel appeared last month.* 他的第一部小說上個月出版了。**6** [I] to be present in a court when you have been accused of a crime 出庭受審: *He appeared in court, charged with attempted murder.* 他因被控企圖謀殺而出庭受審。**7** [I] to perform publicly in a play, show, or film〔在戲劇、表演或電影中〕公開演出: *He's currently appearing in "Hamlet" at the National Theatre.* 他現正在國家劇院演出《哈姆雷特》。

⋆**ap·pear·ance** /ə'pɪrəns; ə'pɪərəns/ *n* **1** [sing] coming into view or arrival 出現; 到達: *The thieves ran off at the appearance of the police.* 那幾個賊看到警察來了就逃走了。| *His sudden appearance shocked everyone.* 他突然出現使人人驚愕。**2** the time when something is first present or first used 首次出現[使用]: *Television viewing has increased since the appearance of satellite TV.* 自衛星電視面世以來，看電視的人越來越多了。**3** the way you look to other people 外表; 外貌; 外觀: *Her pale appearance worried her mother.* 她蒼白的面容使母親擔心。| *He gave the appearance of being bored.* 他露出厭倦的神情。**4** a public performance in a play, show, or film〔在戲劇、表演或電影中的〕公開演出: *His first public*

appearance was at the age of 5. 他首次演出時年僅五歲。**5** the official presence of a person in court when they have been accused of a crime 出庭受審 **6 keep up appearances** to continue to behave in your usual way because you are too proud to admit to other people that you have suffered a loss of money or social position 裝門面; 保持體面 **7 put in an appearance** to go to an event for a short time〔在公開場合短暫的〕露面: *I suppose I'd better put in an appearance at the party.* 我想我還是在聚會上露一下面為好。**8 to all appearances** a phrase used when you are saying that something seems to be true 就外表來看: *To all appearances he seems happy.* 從外表看來他似乎心情愉快。

ap·pease /ə'piz; ə'piːz/ *v* **appeased, appeasing** [T] to make someone calm or less angry by giving them what they want 使〔某人〕平息, 撫慰, 滿足 –**appeasement** *n*

ap·pend /ə'pɛnd; ə'pend/ *v* [T] *fml* to write something at the end of a longer piece of writing《正式》附加; 增補: *I append a list of those shops which sell our products.* 我附上一張銷售我們產品的商店名單。

ap·pend·age /ə'pɛndɪdʒ; ə'pendɪdʒ/ *n* something that is joined to something larger or more important 附加物; 附屬物

ap·pen·di·ci·tis /ə,pɛndə'saɪtɪs; ə,pendɪ'saɪtɪs/ *n* [U] a painful condition caused when your appendix becomes infected 闌尾炎

ap·pen·dix /ə'pɛndɪks; ə'pendɪks/ *n* **appendixes** *or* **appendices** /-də,siz; -dɪ½siːz/ **1** a small tube in your body which is closed at one end and joined to your bowel at the other end 闌尾 **2** additional information which is placed at the end of a book〔書後的〕附錄

ap·per·tain /,æpɚ'ten; ,æpə'teɪn/ *v fml*《正式》**appertain to something** to belong or be related to something 屬於某事物; 與某事物相關的: *the responsibilities appertaining to the leadership* 領導的職責

ap·pe·tite /'æpə,taɪt; 'æpɪ½taɪt/ *n* [C;U] a strong physical desire for something, especially food 食慾; 胃口: *Don't eat any sweets before dinner or you'll spoil your appetite.* 飯前不要吃糖果，否則會壞了你的胃口。| *I completely lost my appetite while I was ill.* 我生病時一點食慾也沒有。–see 見 DESIRE² (USAGE 用法)

ap·pe·tiz·er /'æpə,taɪzɚ; 'æpɪ½taɪzəʳ/ *n* something small which you eat or drink before a meal〔正餐前用的〕開胃小吃或飲料

ap·pe·tiz·ing /'æpə,taɪzɪŋ; 'æpɪ½taɪzɪŋ/ *adj* looking and smelling good and therefore making you feel hungry (used of food) 刺激食慾的, 開胃的〔指食物〕–opposite 反義 **unappetizing**

ap·plaud /ə'plɔd; ə'plɔːd/ *v* [I;T] **1** to show

A

that you liked a play, actor, or performance by hitting your hands together 鼓掌 〔表示讚賞〕 **2** to express strong approval of someone or something 讚許; 贊成: *We must applaud the council's decision not to close the hospital.* 我們必須對市政委員會不關閉那家醫院的決定表示讚許。

ap·plause /ə'plɔz; ə'plɔːz/ *n* [U] loud praise for a performance or performer, in which people hit their hands together repeatedly 熱烈鼓掌; 喝采

*ap·ple** /'æpl; 'æpəl/ *n* **1** a hard round fruit with white juicy flesh and red, green, or yellow skin 蘋果 –see picture on page 504 見 504 頁彩圖 **2 be the apple of your eye** *infml* to be the person or thing that you love the most 〔非正式〕最珍愛的人[物]: *He was the apple of his father's eye.* 他是父親的掌上明珠。

ap·pli·ance /ə'plaɪəns; ə'plaɪəns/ *n* a machine that does a particular job in your home 〔家用的〕器具; 器械: *electrical appliances such as dishwashers and washing machines* 諸如洗碗機和洗衣機之類的家用電器 –see 見 MACHINE¹ (USAGE 用法)

ap·plic·a·ble /'æplɪkəbl; ə'plɪkəbəl, 'æplɪkəbəl/ *adj* suitable for or relating directly to a particular person or situation 適用的; 合適的: *This rule is not applicable to foreigners.* 這條規則不適用於外國人。

ap·pli·cant /'æplɪkənt; 'æplɪkənt/ *n* a person who makes a formal, written request, for example for a job or university place 〔職位或大學入學等的〕申請人

*ap·pli·ca·tion** /,æplɪ'keɪʃən; ,æplɪ'keɪʃən/ *n* **1** [C] a formal written request for something 申請 (書): *I wrote five applications for jobs but got nothing.* 我寫了五封求職信, 但一無所獲。| *Do I have to fill in an application form?* 我必須填寫一份申請表格嗎? **2 on application** by making a formal written request 申請; 請求: *Details will be sent on application.* 詳情函索。 **3** [C;U] the putting of something to practical use 應用; 施用: *Let's see if the results of the survey have a practical application.* 讓我們看看調查結果是否能被實際應用。 **4** [C;U] the process of putting something onto a surface 敷用; 塗抹: *a second application of paint* 再上一遍油漆 **5** [U] careful and continuous attention or effort 用功; 專心: *He worked with great application to learn a new language.* 他專心致志地學習一種新的語言。

ap·plied /ə'plaɪd; ə'plaɪd/ *adj* able to be used in a practical way 應用的; 實用的: *applied mathematics* 應用數學 –opposite 反義 **pure**

*ap·ply** /ə'plaɪ; ə'plaɪ/ *v* **applied, applying 1** [I] to request something, especially in writing 〔尤指書面〕申請: *I'll apply for the job today.* 我今天就申請這份工作。

2 [T] to use something such as a method or a law 應用, 運用〔方法、法律等〕: *Apply as much force as is necessary.* 需要多少力量就用多少力量。| *to apply a new method* 運用一種新方法 **3** [T] to put something onto a surface 敷用; 塗抹: *Apply some medicine to his wound.* 在他的傷口上塗一些藥。 **4** [I] to have an effect on something or to be directly related to it 適用於〔某物〕; 與〔某物〕直接有關: *This rule does not apply.* 這條規則不適用。| *This question applies only to married men.* 這個問題只適用於已婚男子。 **5 apply yourself, apply your mind** to work hard with careful attention 專心; 致力於: *He applied himself to his work.* 他專心做自己的工作。

*ap·point** /ə'pɔɪnt; ə'pɔɪnt/ *v* [T] **1** to choose someone formally for a position or job 任命; 委任: *We must appoint a new teacher soon.* 我們必須迅速委派一名新教師。| *They appointed him to be chairman.* 他們任命他為主席。 **2** *fml* to arrange or decide a time or day on which to do something 〔正式〕約定; 指定: *Let's appoint a day for our next meeting.* 讓我們約定下一次會面的日期。 –**appointed** *adj*: *She wasn't there at the appointed time.* 她沒有在約定的時間到那裡。

*ap·point·ment** /ə'pɔɪntmənt; ə'pɔɪntmənt/ *n* **1** [C] an arrangement to meet someone at a particular time and place, especially a formal or official meeting 約見; 約會: *I have an appointment with the doctor.* 我已與醫生約好看病。| *Make an appointment to see your dentist as soon as possible.* 盡快與你的牙醫約好診治一下。| *I'm afraid I won't be able to keep my appointment.* 很抱歉, 我無法履約。 **2 by appointment** to meet at a particular time 根據事先約定: *The doctor will only see you by appointment.* 要事先約定, 醫生才會替你診治。 **3** [U] the choosing of someone for a position or job 任命; 委任; 派遣: *He is responsible for the appointment of all new staff.* 他負責選派所有的新員工。 **4** [C] a job 〔委任的〕職位: *I've applied for a teaching appointment in London.* 我申請了在倫敦的一個教職。

ap·por·tion /ə'pɔrʃən; ə'pɔːʃən/ *v* [T] *fml* to divide something and share it out 〔正式〕分配; 分攤: *It was difficult to apportion the blame for the accident.* 要分清這次事故的責任是很難的。| *He apportioned his possessions among his children.* 他把財產分給孩子。

ap·praise /ə'prez; ə'preɪz/ *v* **appraised, appraising** [T] *fml* to judge the value, quality, or condition of something 〔正式〕估價; 評價; 鑑定: *The students' work is carefully appraised.* 學生的作業得到仔細評定。 –**appraisal** *n*

ap·pre·cia·ble /ə'prɪʃɪəbl; ə'priːʃəbəl/ *adj* enough to be felt, noticed, or considered important 可感覺到的; 可注意到的; 被認為重

要的: *an appreciable difference* 明顯的差異 –**appreciably** adv

*ap·pre·ci·ate /əˈpriʃɪˌet; əˈpriːʃieɪt/ v **appreciated, appreciating** 1 [T] to understand and enjoy the good qualities or value of something 欣賞, 鑑賞, 賞識〔某事物〕: *They don't appreciate good wine.* 他們不會品嚐美酒。| *I appreciate your help.* 我感激你的幫助。 2 **I would appreciate it if...** a rather formal phrase used to ask someone to do something 如果...我將十分感激〔這是個相當正式的短語, 用於請求別人幫助〕: *We would appreciate it if you would provide further information.* 如果你能提供進一步的資料, 我們將非常感激。 3 [T;+that] to understand something 領會, 體會, 充分認識〔某事物〕: *I do appreciate the fact that the project will be very expensive.* 我完全理解, 這項工程花費十分巨大。| *We appreciate that the task will not be easy.* 我們明白到這個任務並不容易。 4 [I] to increase in value over time 增值: *Houses in this area have all appreciated in value since the new road was built.* 自從新道路建成以後, 這個地區的房子都增值了。 –**ap·pre·ci·a·tion** /əˌpriʃɪˈeʃən; əˌpriːʃiˈeɪʃən/ n [C;U]

ap·pre·cia·tive /əˈpriʃɪˌetɪv; əˈpriːʃətɪv/ adj feeling or showing understanding, admiration, or gratefulness 有欣賞力的; 有眼力的; 感激的 –**appreciatively** adv

ap·pre·hend /ˌæprɪˈhɛnd; ˌæprɪˈhend/ v [T] fml to take a person who breaks the law into police control〔正式〕逮捕; 拘押

ap·pre·hen·sion /ˌæprɪˈhɛnʃən; ˌæprɪˈhenʃən/ n 1 [U] anxiety or fear about the future 憂慮; 恐懼; 擔心: *She waited for news with great apprehension.* 她憂心忡忡地等待消息。 2 [C;U] fml the act of seizing a person who breaks the law〔正式〕逮捕; 拘押

ap·pre·hen·sive /ˌæprɪˈhɛnsɪv; ˌæprɪˈhensɪv/ adj worried or anxious about what might happen 憂慮的; 擔心的 –**apprehensively** adv

ap·pren·tice /əˈprɛntɪs; əˈprentɪs/ n a person who has agreed to work for a skilled employer for a fixed period and usually for low wages, in order to learn a skill 學徒; 徒弟

ap·pren·tice·ship /əˈprɛntɪsˌʃɪp; əˈprentɪsʃɪp/ n [C;U] the time you spend as an apprentice 學徒期; 學徒年限: *I've got to serve a three year apprenticeship.* 我必須做三年學徒。

*ap·proach¹ /əˈprotʃ; əˈprəʊtʃ/ v 1 [I;T] to move nearer to something or someone approaching 靠近; 接近: *We approached the house.* 我們走近那幢房子。| *I moved out of the way as the procession approached.* 當隊伍走近時, 我讓開了道。| *Inflation is approaching 10%.* 通貨膨脹率正接近百分之十。 2 [I;T] to come nearer in time〔時間上〕臨近: *The day was fast approaching when we would have to leave.* 我們要離開的日子快到了。 3 [T] to

speak to someone about something for the first time, especially to ask for something or offer something〔尤指有求於人時〕與〔某人〕接洽, 打交道: *Did he approach you about lending him some money?* 他有沒有向你提及借錢給他的事? 4 [T] to begin to consider something 開始考慮〔某事〕: *He approached the difficulty with great thought.* 他開始用心考慮如何去解決那個困難。

approach² n 1 [U] the act of moving nearer to something or someone 靠近: *At our approach, the animals fled.* 當我們走近時, 野獸紛紛逃走。 2 [U] the fact of coming nearer in time〔時間的〕臨近: *At the approach of winter the weather grew colder.* 冬天將臨, 天氣轉冷。 3 [C] a road or path leading to a place 通道;〔通向某處的〕道路: *All approaches to the town were blocked by snow.* 所有進城的道路都被雪封住了。 4 [C] a way of doing something or considering something 方法; 方式: *a new approach to teaching English* 英語教學的新方法 5 [C] an act of speaking to someone for the first time, usually because you want something from them〔初次〕與〔某人〕打交道; 接觸: *They have made several approaches to that company with a view to doing business.* 他們為了做生意已跟那家公司接觸了好幾次。

ap·proa·cha·ble /əˈprotʃəbl; əˈprəʊtʃəbəl/ adj 1 friendly and easy to talk to 易親近的; 平易近人的; 隨和的 –opposite 反義 **unapproachable** 2 able to be reached in a particular way 可達到的: *That village is only approachable on foot.* 去那個村子只能步行。

ap·pro·ba·tion /ˌæprəˈbeʃən; ˌæprəˈbeɪʃən/ n [U] fml praise or approval〔正式〕讚許; 認可; 批准

*ap·pro·pri·ate¹ /əˈproprɪt; əˈprəʊprɪ-ɪt/ adj correct or suitable 適當的; 合適的; 恰當的: *His clothes were not appropriate for the occasion.* 他的服裝並不適合那個場合。| *The ambassador will be provided with facilities appropriate to his status.* 大使將獲提供與他的身分相符的設施。| *You should complain to the appropriate authorities.* 你應該向有關當局投訴。 –opposite 反義 **inappropriate** [U] –**appropriately** adv –**appropriateness** n [U]

ap·pro·pri·ate² /əˈproprɪˌet; əˈprəʊprieɪt/ v **appropriated, appropriating** [T] fml to steal or take something for your own use〔正式〕盜用, 挪用〔某物〕: *He was accused of appropriating government money.* 他被控挪用公款。

*ap·prov·al /əˈpruvl; əˈpruːvəl/ n [U] 1 favourable opinion or judgment 贊成; 讚許: *I hope this plan meets with your approval.* 我希望該項計劃能得到你的贊成。 2 official permission 批准; 通過: *We have to wait for the council's approval before we can start to build.* 我們必須等待市政委員會的批准後才能

開始興建。**3 have/get something on approval** to buy something and take it home with an agreement that you can take it back to the shop if you decide that you do not want it 買下後可退換的商品

☆☆**ap·prove** /ə'pruv; ə'pru:v/ *v* **approved, approving 1 approve of** to believe that something or someone is good or acceptable 贊成; 稱許: *I don't approve of smoking.* 我不贊成抽煙。| *My parents don't approve of my friends.* 我的父母不喜歡我的朋友。| *I approve of your decision.* 我贊成你的決定。**2** [T] to agree to something officially 批准; 通過; 認可: *The Council hasn't approved the plans yet.* 市政委員會尚未批准那些計劃。

☆**ap·prox·i·mate**[1] /ə'prɑksəmɪt; ə'prɒksɪ̣mɪ̣t/ *adj* nearly correct but not exact 近似的; 大約的: *Can you give me an approximate price for the job?* 你能否告訴我幹這工作大約要多少工錢? **–approximately** *adv*: *We've got approximately £300.* 我們大約收到三百英鎊。

ap·prox·i·mate[2] /ə'prɑksə,met; ə'prɒksɪ̣meɪt/ *v* **approximated, approximating: approximate something, approximate to something** to be very similar to something 近似於某事物

ap·prox·i·ma·tion /ə,prɑksə'meʃən; ə,prɒksɪ̣'meɪʃən/ *n* **1** a number or calculation that is not exact but is good enough 近似數, 近似值; 概算 **2** something which is not correct in every detail, but which is near enough 近似的東西

a·pri·cot /'eprɪ,kɑt; 'eɪprɪ̣kɒt/ *n* a small soft yellow fruit with a furry outside and a single large stone inside 杏

A·pril /'eprəl; 'eɪprɪ̣l/ *n* (also 又作 **Apr** *abbreviation* 〖縮〗) the 4th month of the year 四月

April fool /,··'·/ *n* a person who has been deceived by a trick played on the morning of April 1st, which is called **April Fools' Day** 在愚人節(4月1日)早上受愚弄者

a·pron /'eprən; 'eɪprən/ *n* a piece of cloth or plastic that you put over the front of your clothes to keep them clean, for example while you are cooking 圍裙; 圍腰布

apt /æpt; æpt/ *adj* **1 apt to do something** likely to do something or having a tendency to do it 易於做某事物; 有做某事物的傾向: *This kind of shoe is apt to slip on wet ground.* 這種鞋在濕地上容易打滑。| *She is apt to forget.* 她生性健忘。**2** exactly suitable 恰當的; 貼切的: *an apt remark* 恰當的話 **–aptly** *adv*: *He was aptly punished for his behaviour.* 他因自己的行為受到恰如其分的懲罰。

ap·ti·tude /'æptə,tjud; 'æptɪ̣tju:d/ *n* a natural ability to learn something quickly and to do it well 〔學習方面的〕資質, 才能, 天資: *She has a real aptitude* **for** *maths.* 她在學習數學方面有真正的天分。

a·quar·i·um /ə'kwɛrɪəm; ə'kweəriəm/ *n* **aquariums** *or* **aquaria** /-rɪə; -riə/ a glass container for fish and other water animals, or a building with many of these 玻璃養魚缸; 水族箱; 水族館

A·quar·i·us /ə'kwɛrɪəs; ə'kweəriəs/ *n* one of the signs of the ZODIAC 寶瓶宮〔黃道十二宮之一〕

a·quat·ic /ə'kwætɪk; ə'kwætɪk/ *adj* living or happening in or on water 水生的; 水棲的; 水中的: *aquatic plants* 水生植物 | *Aquatic sports include swimming and rowing.* 水上運動包括游泳和划船。

aq·ue·duct /'ækwɪ,dʌkt; 'ækwɪ̣dʌkt/ *n* a bridge built to carry water across a valley 高架渠; 導水管; 渡槽

aq·ui·line /'ækwə,laɪn; 'ækwɪ̣laɪn/ *adj fml* long and curving (used of someone's nose) 〖正式〗狀如鷹嘴的〔指人的鼻子〕

Ar·a·bic nu·me·ral /,ærəbɪk'njumərəl; ,ærəbɪk 'nju:mərəl/ *n* one of the signs used for numbers in the English and many other alphabets such as 1, 2, 3, 4 阿拉伯數字〔如1, 2, 3, 4等〕

ar·a·ble /'ærəbl; 'ærəbəl/ *adj* used for growing crops or suitable for growing crops 〔土地〕適於耕作的, 可耕的: *arable land* 可耕的土地

ar·bi·tra·ry /'ɑrbə,trɛrɪ; 'ɑ:bɪ̣trəri/ *adj* not decided by rules or reason but by chance or a person's personal opinion 任意的; 武斷的: *an arbitrary selection of books* 任意選定的書 | *arbitrary decisions which make no sense* 毫無意義的武斷決定 **–arbitrarily** /'ɑrbə,trɛrəlɪ; 'ɑ:bɪ̣trərɪ̣li/ *adv*

ar·bi·trate /'ɑrbə,tret; 'ɑ:bɪ̣treɪt/ *v* **arbitrated, arbitrating** [I;T] to act as a judge in an argument especially at the request of both sides 仲裁; 公斷

ar·bi·tra·tion /,ɑrbə'treʃən; ,ɑ:bɪ̣'treɪʃən/ *n* **go to arbitration** to ask a third person to settle an argument between two people 提請仲裁: *The men agreed to go to arbitration to settle their pay claim.* 那些人同意通過仲裁來解決他們的工資要求。

arc /ɑrk; ɑ:k/ *n* part of a circle or any curved line 弧; 弧線

ar·cade /ɑr'ked; ɑ:'keɪd/ *n* a covered passage, especially with an arched roof, with shops on one or both sides 〔一邊或兩邊設有商店的〕拱廊式街道: *a shopping arcade* 拱廊購物商場

arch[1] /ɑrtʃ; ɑ:tʃ/ *n* **1** the top curved part over a doorway, window, or bridge 〔門廊、窗、橋等的〕拱頂 **2** the raised part of the bottom of your foot 足底弓

arch[2] *v* [I;T] to form something into the shape of an arch 拱起; 使〔某物〕成弓形: *The cat arched her back in anger.* 那隻貓氣得拱起了背。

ar·chae·ol·o·gy /,ɑrkɪ'ɑlədʒɪ; ,ɑ:ki'ɒlədʒi/ *n* (also 又作 **archeology**) [U] the study of ancient times by examining the buried remains of buildings and tools 考古學 **–ar-**

chaeologist *n* –**archaeological** /ˌɑːkɪəˈlɒdʒɪkl; ˌɑːkiəˈlɒdʒɪkəl/ *adj* –**archaeologically** /-klɪ; -kli/ *adv*

ar·cha·ic /ɑːˈkeɪk; ɑːˈkeɪ-ɪk/ *adj* belonging to the past and no longer used 古時的; 已不通用的: *archaic language* 古語

arch·bish·op /ˌɑːtʃˈbɪʃəp; ˌɑːtʃˈbɪʃəp◂/ *n* a priest of very high rank in some branches of the Christian church, responsible for the churches in a large area 〔基督教會的〕大主教

ar·cher /ˈɑːtʃə; ˈɑːtʃəʳ/ *n* a person who shoots with a BOW³(1) and ARROW, usually for sport 弓箭手; 射箭運動員

ar·cher·y /ˈɑːtʃəri; ˈɑːtʃəri/ *n* [U] the sport of shooting with a BOW³(1) and ARROW 射箭(術); 射箭運動

ar·chi·pel·a·go /ˌɑːkəˈpeləˌgo; ˌɑːkɪˈpeləgəʊ/ *n* **archipelagoes** *or* **archipelagos** a group of small islands 羣島

★**ar·chi·tect** /ˈɑːkəˌtekt; ˈɑːkɪˌtekt/ *n* a person who plans new buildings and who is responsible for making sure that they are built properly 建築師; 設計師

★**ar·chi·tec·ture** /ˈɑːkəˌtektʃə; ˈɑːkɪˌtektʃəʳ/ *n* [U] **1** the art and science of building, including its planning, making, and decoration 建築學 **2** the style or manner of building 建築風格; 建築式樣: *the architecture of ancient Greece* 古希臘的建築風格 | *Gothic architecture* 哥特式建築式樣 –**architectural** /ˌɑːkəˈtektʃərəl; ˌɑːkɪˈtektʃərəl/ *adj* –**architecturally** *adv*

ar·chives /ˈɑːkaɪvz; ˈɑːkaɪvz/ *n* [pl] **1** a collection of old papers, reports, letters, and photographs of a particular group or country, kept for historical interest 檔案; 案卷 **2** a place for storing such historical material 檔案室; 檔案館

Arc·tic /ˈɑːktɪk; ˈɑːktɪk/ *n* **the Arctic** the very cold, most northern part of the world 北極; 北極區 –**arctic** *adj*: *arctic weather conditions* 北極的氣候情況

ar·dent /ˈɑːdnt; ˈɑːdənt/ *adj* having strong feelings of admiration or love for something or someone 熱情的; 熱烈的; 熾烈的; 強烈的: *an ardent supporter of government policies* 政府政策的熱烈支持者 | *her ardent admirers* 她的熱情崇拜者 –**ardently** *adv*

ar·dour /ˈɑːdə; ˈɑːdəʳ/ *n* (**ardor** *AmE* 〖美式〗) [U] *fml* a strong feeling of excitement, admiration, or love 〖正式〗熱情; 熱心: *patriotic ardour* 愛國熱情

ar·du·ous /ˈɑːdjʊəs; ˈɑːdjuəs/ *adj* needing hard and continuous effort 艱巨的; 艱苦的: *an arduous climb* 艱辛的攀登 | *arduous work* 艱苦的工作 –**arduously** *adv*

are /ə; əʳ *strong* 強讀 ɑː; ɑːʳ/ the present tense plural of BE ☆ BE 的現在式複數

★★**ar·e·a** /ˈɛrɪə; ˈeəriə/ *n* **1** the size of a flat surface measured by multiplying the length by the width 面積: *What's the* area of the front garden? 前花園的面積是多少? **2** a particular place or division of a town, a country, or the world 地區; 區域: *I was born in a very poor area of London.* 我出生於倫敦一個十分貧窮的地區。 | *The Sahara desert is one of the driest areas in the world.* 撒哈拉沙漠是世界上最乾旱的地區之一。 **3** a particular space or surface 〔專用的〕空地, 地面: *a room with a dining area at one end* 一頭用作飯廳的房間 | *a parking area* 停車場 **4** a subject or activity 學科; 領域; 範圍: *developments in the area of language teaching* 語言教學領域的發展 | *What area do you work in?* 你的研究領域是甚麼?

a·re·na /əˈrinə; əˈriːnə/ *n* an enclosed area used for sports or public entertainments 運動場; 公共娛樂場所

aren't /ɑːnt; ɑːnt/ **1** short for 縮略式 = "are not": *They aren't here.* 他們不在這兒。 | *Aren't you coming?* 你不來嗎? **2** used in questions as a short form of "am not" 〔在問句中用作 am not 的縮約式〕: *I'm your friend, aren't I?* 我是你的朋友, 不是嗎?

ar·gu·a·ble /ˈɑːgjuəbl; ˈɑːgjuəbəl/ *adj* **1** able to be questioned or doubted 可爭論的; 有爭議的: *The government claim that their policies will help the unemployed, but that's arguable.* 政府聲稱他們的政策將幫助失業者, 但是這種說法是有爭議的。 **2** **it is arguable that...** a phrase used when you are giving your opinion about something 有論據的; 可論證的〔用於表示對某事的看法〕: *It is arguable that the government has no right to interfere in this matter.* 說政府無權干涉此事是有論據的。 –**arguably** *adv*

★★**ar·gue** /ˈɑːgju; ˈɑːgjuː/ *v* **argued, arguing** **1** [I] to fight or disagree with someone using words 爭辯; 爭論; 爭吵: *Do what you are told and don't argue with me.* 叫你怎麼做就怎麼做, 別和我爭論。 | *They're always arguing about money.* 他們總是為錢爭吵。 **2** [I;T,+that] to provide reasons for or against something, especially in a clear order 辯論: *He argues well.* 他好辯善辯。 | *It could be argued that sending men to the moon is a waste of money.* 可以認為把人送上月球是浪費金錢的。 | *She argued her case very well.* 她為自己辯護得十分成功。 | *Ministers argued* **for** *and* **against** *the proposals.* 部長們為同意或反對這些提案進行了辯論。

★★**ar·gu·ment** /ˈɑːgjəmənt; ˈɑːgjə̩mənt/ *n* **1** [C] an unfriendly disagreement, often with people shouting at each other 爭論; 爭吵: *They're always having arguments* **about** *money.* 他們總是為錢爭吵不休。 **2** [C] a reason given to support or disprove something 〔贊成或反對某事的〕理由, 論據, 論點: *We listened to all the arguments* **for** *and* **against** *the plan.* 我們聽了所有贊成和反對該項計劃的論點。 **3** [U] the use of reason to decide something 辯論; 説理: *We should try to settle this affair by argument, not by fighting.* 我們應該試圖用説理而不是打架的方式來解決這件事。

ar·gu·men·ta·tive /ˌɑrgjəˈmɛntətɪv, ˌɑːgjə-ˈmentətɪv/ *adj* often disagreeing or arguing with people 好爭論的; 愛爭辯的

a·ri·a /ˈɑrɪə; ˈɑːrɪə/ *n* a song that is sung by only one person in an OPERA〔歌劇中的〕咏歎調; 獨唱的唱段

ar·id /ˈærɪd; ˈærˌd/ *adj* **1** having very little rain and so very dry 乾旱的; 乾燥的: *arid soil* 乾燥的土壤 | *an arid region* 乾旱的地區 **2** without interest or imagination 枯燥的; 無生氣的: *arid theories* 枯燥乏味的理論 | *an arid existence* 枯燥的生活

Ar·ies /ˈɛriz; ˈeəriːz/ *n* one of the signs of the ZODIAC 白羊宮〔黃道十二宮之一〕

★**a·rise** /əˈraɪz; əˈraɪz/ *v* **arose** /əˈroz; əˈrəʊz/, **arisen** /əˈrɪzn; əˈrɪzən/, **arising** [I] **1** to happen or appear 發生; 出現: *New difficulties are constantly arising as we do the work.* 我們從事這項工作時, 新的困難不斷出現。**2** *lit* to get up〔文〕起牀

ar·is·toc·ra·cy /ˌærəˈstɑkrəsɪ; ˌærˌˈstɒkrəsi/ *n* **aristocracies** the people of the highest social class, people from noble families and with titles of rank 貴族; 權貴

ar·is·to·crat /əˈrɪstəˌkræt; ˈærˌstəkræt/ *n* a member of the highest social class 貴族(成員) –**aristocratic** /əˌrɪstəˈkrætɪk; ˌærˌstə-ˈkrætɪk/ *adj*

a·rith·me·tic[1] /əˈrɪθmə,tɪk; əˈrɪθmətɪk/ *n* [U] the science of calculation by numbers 算術 –compare 比較 MATHEMATICS

ar·ith·met·ic[2] /ˌærɪθˈmɛtɪk; ˌærɪθˈmetɪk/ *adj* (also 又作 **arithmetical** /-ɪkl; -ɪkəl/) connected with the science of calculation by numbers 算術的 –**arithmetically** /-klɪ; -kli/ *adv*

★**arm[1]** /ɑrm; ɑːm/ *n* **1** [C] one of your two upper limbs 手臂; 上肢: *She carried the box under her arm.* 她攜下挾着盒子。| *He was shot in his left arm.* 他左手臂中彈。**2** [C] something that is shaped like an arm or moves like an arm 臂狀物: *the arm of a chair* 椅子的扶手 | *the arm of a record player* 唱機的唱頭臂 | *a narrow arm of the sea* 一段狹長的海灣 **3 arms** [pl] weapons used in war 武器 **4 arm in arm** with arms joined together 臂挽着臂: *They walked arm in arm.* 他們臂挽着臂地走路。**5 be up in arms** to be very angry and ready to argue or fight about something 奮起戰鬥; 竭力反對: *The women are up in arms over their low rate of pay.* 婦女們正竭力反對給予她們的低報酬。**6 welcome someone with open arms** to show that you are pleased to see someone by holding your arms out towards them to take hold of them 張開雙臂〔熱烈地〕歡迎某人 **7 welcome something with open arms** to be very pleased that something has happened 熱烈地歡迎某事

arm[2] *v* [T] to supply someone with weapons 向〔某人〕提供武器; 武裝: *The country armed itself in preparation for war.* 該國正武裝起來準備打仗。

ar·ma·da /ɑrˈmɑdə; ɑːˈmɑːdə/ *n lit* a collection of armed ships〔文〕艦隊

ar·ma·ments /ˈɑrməmənts; ˈɑːməmənts/ *n* [pl] weapons and other fighting apparatus used in a war 武器及裝備; 軍備

arm·band /ˈɑrm,bænd; ˈɑːmbænd/ *n* a band of material that you wear round your arm to show that you have an official position; people sometimes wear black armbands to show that someone has just died 臂章;〔服喪時戴的〕黑臂紗

arm·chair /ˈɑrm,tʃɛr; ˈɑːmtʃeər/ *n* a chair with supports for your arms 扶手椅 –see picture on page 730 見 730 頁彩圖

★**armed** /ɑrmd; ɑːmd/ *adj* **1** carrying a weapon or weapons 帶有武器的: *Both men were armed.* 那兩名男子均帶有武器。**2 armed robbery** a crime in which a person steals something and in which they are carrying a weapon, usually a gun 持槍搶劫 **3 armed with something** having or knowing something useful 裝備, 配備某物: *I went to the meeting armed with various facts and figures.* 我準備好各種事實及數據去出席那次會議。**4 armed to the teeth** carrying a lot of weapons 武裝到牙齒的〔全副武裝的〕

armed forc·es /ˌ··· ˈ··/ *n* [pl] the military forces of a country, usually the army, navy, and air force 武裝力量; 武裝部隊〔通常指國家的陸、海、空三軍〕

arm·ful /ˈɑrm,fʊl; ˈɑːmfʊl/ *n* all that a person can hold in one or both arms〔單臂或雙臂的〕一抱之量: *She was carrying an armful of books.* 她抱着一大疊書。

ar·mi·stice /ˈɑrməstɪs; ˈɑːmˌstˌs/ *n* an agreement made during a war to stop fighting, usually for a limited period of time 停戰; 休戰(協定)

ar·mour /ˈɑrmər; ˈɑːmər/ *n* (**armor** *AmE*〔美式〕) [U] **1** strong metal or leather protection that men and horses used to wear in battle 盔甲; 甲冑 **2** strong metal protection on fighting vehicles, ships, and aircraft〔戰車、軍艦和飛機的〕裝甲

ar·moured /ˈɑrmərd; ˈɑːməd/ *adj* (**armored** *AmE*〔美式〕) protected by a hard metal covering 裝甲的: *an armoured car* 裝甲汽車

ar·mour·y /ˈɑrmərɪ; ˈɑːməri/ *n* **armouries** (**armory** *AmE*〔美式〕) a place where weapons are stored 軍械庫

arm·pit /ˈɑrm,pɪt; ˈɑːm,pɪt/ *n* the hollow place under your arm at your shoulder 腋窩

★**ar·my** /ˈɑrmɪ; ˈɑːmi/ *n* **armies** [+sing/pl verb] **1** the military forces of a country trained to fight on land 陸軍 **2** a large group of people, especially one that is organized for a purpose 大羣人〔尤指為某一目的而組織起來的〕: *An army of workers are building the Channel Tunnel.* 一大批工人正在建造英吉利海峽隧道。

a·ro·ma /ə'rome; ə'rəumə/ *n* a strong pleasant smell from food and drink〔食物或飲料的〕芳香; 香味: *the aroma of fresh coffee* 新煮咖啡的芳香 —**aromatic** /,ærə'mætɪk; ,ærə'mætɪk◂/ *adj*: *Aromatic herbs are often used in cooking.* 芳香的植物常用於烹調。

a·rose /ə'roz; ə'rəuz/ *v* the past tense of ARISE ☆ ARISE 的過去式

★★**a·round** /ə'raund; ə'raund/ *adv, prep* **1** *adv, prep* moving or positioned in a circle 圍繞; 環繞; 圍着: *She spun the wheel around.* 她轉動輪子。 | *He put a belt around his waist.* 他在腰上繫了一根腰帶。 | *We sat around the table.* 我們圍桌而坐。 | *People were standing around the fire.* 人們站在火的四周。 | *The children gathered around to listen to the story.* 孩子們圍成一圈聽故事。 | *a large tree measuring three metres around the trunk* 一棵樹幹周長三米的樹 **2** *adv* so as to face the other way 轉過來; 向相反方向: *Turn the clock around so that I can see it.* 請把鐘轉過來讓我看一下。 | *He swung around to look at me.* 他轉過身來看我。 **3** *adv, prep* visiting all the parts of a place, or a lot of different places 到處; 各處: *They've been travelling around together.* 他們一起去各地旅行。 | *We're driving around France this summer.* 我們今年夏天將開着車在法國各地跑。 | *A guide showed us around the castle.* 一位導遊領我們參觀城堡。 **4** *prep* near a place 在⋯附近: *A lot of the people who live around here work in London.* 許多住在這裡附近的人在倫敦工作。 **5** *adv* to someone's house 去〔某人〕的家: *He invited us around to his house for a meal.* 他請我們去他家吃飯。 **6** around a corner turning a corner or past a corner 拐彎: *He disappeared around the corner.* 他一拐彎就不見了。 | *The post office is just around that corner.* 郵局就在那拐角處。 **7** this way around, the other way around, the right way around, etc. a phrase used to say which way something is facing or in which order things are placed 朝這邊; 朝那邊; 朝方向對的這一邊, 等等: *You've got that hat on the wrong way around.* 你那頂帽子戴反了。 | *Those two numbers should be the other way around.* 那兩個數字的位置應顛倒過來。 **8** *adv* in a place and able to be used or obtained 在附近: *Is there any paper around?* 這裡有沒有紙? | *I'm afraid there's no one around to deal with your query at the moment.* 我想現在這裡沒人能回答你的詢問。 **9** *prep* about 大約: *There were around 50 people at the meeting.* 大約有五十人出席了會議。

a·rouse /ə'rauz; ə'rauz/ *v* **aroused, arousing** [T] **1** to wake someone up 喚醒〔某人〕: *Aroused from a deep sleep, he was rather*

short tempered. 他從熟睡中被叫醒, 顯得相當惱火。 **2** to make someone have a particular feeling 喚起; 激起; 引起: *Her behaviour aroused the suspicions of the police.* 她的行為引起了警方的懷疑。 **3** to make someone sexually excited 激起〔某人〕的性慾

ar·raign /ə'ren; ə'reɪn/ *v* [T] *tech* to call or bring someone before a court of law to face a charge〔術語〕提堂審訊; 傳訊

★**ar·range** /ə'rendʒ; ə'reɪndʒ/ *v* **arranged, arranging 1** [T;+that] to make plans for something to happen and to agree with other people that it will happen 安排, 準備〔某事物〕: *I've arranged the meeting for 2 pm.* 我已把會議安排在下午二時。 | *He didn't arrange to come with me.* 他沒有約好和我一起來。 | *Can you arrange for a taxi to collect us?* 你能安排一輛計程車來接我們嗎? | *I arranged that we should meet at the station.* 我已安排好我們在車站見面。

□ USEFUL PATTERNS 有用句型
to arrange something; to arrange to do something; to arrange for someone to do something; to arrange that...

---

2 [T] to put things in a certain order or position so that they are neat or attractive 整理, 排列, 佈置〔某物〕: *The food was arranged beautifully on the plates.* 食品在盤子裡放得整整齊齊十分好看。 **3** [T] to set out a piece of music in a certain way, for example for different instruments 改編〔樂曲〕 **4** an arranged marriage a marriage in which parents choose a partner for their children〔由父母作主的〕包辦婚姻

★**ar·range·ment** /ə'rendʒmənt; ə'reɪndʒmənt/ *n* **1** arrangements [pl] plans and preparations for something to happen 安排; 籌備; 準備: *He's making arrangements for the wedding.* 他正在籌備婚禮。 | *travel arrangements* 旅行準備[安排] **2** [C] an agreement with someone to do something 商定: *I have an arrangement with my boss to do some of my work at home.* 我與老闆説好, 有些工作我帶回家做。 **3** by arrangement arranged in advance 根據事先安排 **4** [C] a group of things that have been put in an attractive or neat order 整理[排列]好的東西: *a beautiful flower arrangement* 美麗的插花樣式 **5** [U] putting into position or order 排列; 整理: *The arrangement of furniture in the office is being changed.* 辦公室的家具正被重新安放。 **6** [C] the setting of a piece of music〔樂曲的〕改編

ar·ray¹ /ə're; ə'reɪ/ *v* [T] *fml*〔正式〕**1** to place soldiers in order ready for battle 把〔士兵〕排成作戰陣勢; 部署: *The soldiers were arrayed on the opposite hill.* 士兵們在對面的小山上擺好陣勢。 **2** to dress someone in fine clothes 盛裝; 打扮: *Arrayed in all her finery, she felt ready to meet the world.* 她花枝招展地打扮起來, 覺得能出去見人了。

A

array² *n* **1** an attractive show or collection 陳列; 展示: *There was an impressive array of film stars at the premiere.* 在首映式上, 電影明星紛紛露面, 蔚為壯觀。**2** *lit* clothes for a special occasion 〖文〗〔特殊場合穿的〕衣服; 盛裝

ar·rears /əˈrɪrz; əˈrɪəz/ *n* [pl] **1** money that is owed and should have been paid 〔過期未付的〕欠款: *There were huge arrears to be paid.* 有大筆款項尚待支付。**2 be in arrears** to be behind in a payment and so owe someone money 拖欠的: *Sally was two months in arrears with her rent.* 薩麗拖欠了兩個月的房租。

★**ar·rest¹** /əˈrɛst; əˈrest/ *v* [T] **1** to catch someone and declare that they are believed to be guilty of a crime 逮捕, 拘留〔某人〕: *He was arrested for stealing a car.* 他因偷汽車而被捕。**2** *fml* to stop the growth or development of something 〖正式〗阻止, 抑制〔某事物〕: *Doctors successfully arrested the growth of the disease.* 醫生們成功地阻止了病情的惡化。**3 arrest someone's attention** to make someone notice something 吸引某人的注意力

arrest² *n* **1** [C;U] the act of arresting someone 逮捕; 拘留: *The police made several arrests at the football match.* 警方在足球賽時逮捕了幾個人。**2 under arrest** not allowed to go free because you have been arrested 被捕; 被拘留

★**ar·riv·al** /əˈraɪvl; əˈraɪvəl/ *n* **1** [U] the act of arriving 到達; 抵達: *The arrival of Flight 208 from Singapore has been delayed.* 新加坡來的 208 號航班誤點了。| *On my arrival home I was greeted by my parents.* 我回到家時, 雙親迎接了我。**2** [C] a person that has arrived 到達的人: *The new arrivals waited in the reception area.* 新來的人在接待處等候。

★**ar·rive** /əˈraɪv; əˈraɪv/ *v* **arrived, arriving** [I] **1** to reach a place 到達; 抵達: *What time does the plane arrive in New York?* 飛機甚麼時候到達紐約? | *The train arrived late at the station.* 火車到達車站時已晚點了。**2** to happen 來臨: *At last our holidays arrived.* 我們的假期終於來臨了。

  arrive at sthg *phr v* [T] to reach a situation or decision 達成, 得出〔結論、決定等〕: *After many hours' talk, the committee arrived at a decision.* 經過許多小時的討論, 委員會終於達成了一項決定。

ar·ro·gant /ˈærəgənt; ˈærəgənt/ *adj* proud and self-important in an unpleasant way 傲慢的; 驕傲自大的: *Elizabeth thought he was an arrogant, selfish man.* 伊莉莎白認為他是個又傲慢又自私的男人。| *arrogant behaviour* 傲慢的舉止 **–arrogantly** *adv* **–arrogance** *n* [U]: *His arrogance made him unpopular.* 他的傲慢使他不得人心。

ar·row /ˈæro; ˈærəʊ/ *n* **1** a thin straight stick with a point at one end and feathers at the other, which is used as a weapon or in

sport 箭 **2** a sign like an arrow (→) used to show the direction or position of something 箭頭; 箭號: *Follow the arrows for the footpath.* 請沿着箭頭所指的小路走。

ar·se·nal /ˈɑrsṇl; ˈɑːsənəl/ *n* a store of weapons and explosives 軍火庫; 兵工廠: *The police found an arsenal of guns and explosives in the terrorists' house.* 警方在恐怖分子的家中發現一大批武器和炸藥。

ar·se·nic /ˈɑrsnɪk; ˈɑːsənɪk/ *n* [U] a very strong poison 砒; 砒霜

ar·son /ˈɑrsṇ; ˈɑːsn/ *n* [U] the crime of setting fire to property in order to cause damage 縱火〔放火〕罪 **–arsonist** *n*

★★**art** /ɑrt; ɑːt/ *n* **1** [U] the skill of drawing or painting 藝術; 美術: *Tania is going to study art in Italy.* 塔尼婭打算去意大利學美術。**2** [U] objects such as paintings that are considered to be beautiful 藝術品; 美術品: *an art collection* 藝術品收集 **3** [U] the production of things like painting, music, or literature 藝術創作: *She devoted her life to her art.* 她把一生奉獻給藝術創作。**4** [sing] something which needs a lot of skill 技藝; 技術; 技巧: *the art of making friends* 交友技巧 **5 the arts** [pl] the production or performing of things like music, plays, or films 藝術創作〔表演〕: *The government provides a lot of financial support for the arts.* 政府對藝術創作提供了大量的資助。**6 arts** [pl] subjects, especially those taught at university, that are not considered a part of science 人文學科; 文科: *There is heavy competition for places on courses leading to arts degrees.* 文科學位課程的入學名額競爭很激烈。

ar·te·fact /ˈɑrtɪˌfækt; ˈɑːtɪˌfækt/ *n* see 見 ARTIFACT

ar·te·ry /ˈɑrtəri; ˈɑːtəri/ *n* **arteries 1** a blood vessel that carries blood from your heart to the rest of your body 動脈 **2** *tech* a main road, railway, or river 〖術語〗〔公路、鐵路、河流等的〕線 **–arterial** /ɑrˈtɪriəl; ɑːˈtɪəriəl/ *adj* [only before a noun 只用於名詞前]: *arterial roads leading into the capital* 通往首都的公路幹線

art·ful /ˈɑrtfəl; ˈɑːtfəl/ *adj* clever and skilful, often in a way that is not completely honest 精明的; 狡猾的; 欺詐的: *an artful attempt to gain our sympathy* 博取我們同情的狡猾企圖

ar·thri·tis /ɑrˈθraɪtɪs; ɑːˈθraɪtɪ̩s/ *n* [U] a disease causing pain and swelling in the joints of your body 關節炎 **–arthritic** /ɑrˈθrɪtɪk; ɑːˈθrɪtɪk/ *adj, n*

ar·ti·choke /ˈɑrtɪˌtʃok; ˈɑːtɪ̩ˌtʃəʊk/ *n* **1** (also 又作 **globe artichoke**) a plant with a leafy kind of flower that can be eaten as a vegetable 洋薊, 朝鮮薊〔其葉片狀花可作蔬菜食用〕 **2** (also 又作 **Jerusalem artichoke**) a plant with a potato-like root that can be eaten as a vegetable 菊芋〔其塊根似馬鈴薯, 可食用〕

ar·ti·cle /ˈɑrtɪkḷ; ˈɑːtɪkəl/ *n* **1** a particular thing or object, especially one of a group 物品; 物件: *Burglars stole several articles of value from the house.* 竊賊從那幢房子裡偷盜了幾件昂貴的物品。**2** a piece of writing in a newspaper or magazine 文章; 論文: *An article **on** unemployment* 一篇有關失業的文章 | *I've read an article **about** her.* 我已讀到一篇有關她的文章。**3** *tech* the words "a" or "an" (**indefinite article**) and "the" (**definite article**) 【語法】冠詞〔不定冠詞為"a"和"an", 定冠詞為"the"〕

ar·tic·u·late¹ /ɑrˈtɪkjəlɪt; ɑːˈtɪkjʊlɪt/ *adj* expressing or able to express thoughts and feelings clearly 表達清楚的; 表達力強的: *She is a very bright and articulate child.* 她是個既聰明又説話伶俐的孩子。–**articulately** *adv*

ar·tic·u·late² /ɑrˈtɪkjəˌlet; ɑːˈtɪkjʊleɪt/ *v* **articulated, articulating** [I;T] to speak clearly and effectively 清楚有力地講: *He articulated each word carefully.* 他把每個詞都講得清清楚楚。–**articulation** /ɑrˌtɪkjəˈleʃən; ɑːˌtɪkjʊˈleɪʃən/ *n* [U]

ar·tic·u·la·ted /ɑrˈtɪkjəˌletɪd; ɑːˈtɪkjʊleɪtɪd/ *adj* consisting of two parts that are joined together by a metal bar (used of vehicles) 鉸接的〔指車輛〕: *a huge articulated lorry* 大型鉸接式貨車

ar·ti·fact /ˈɑrtɪˌfækt; ˈɑːtɪˌfækt/ *n* (also 又作 **artefact**) a tool or other small object made by a person 人工製品

ar·ti·fice /ˈɑrtəfɪs; ˈɑːtɪfɪs/ *n fml* 【正式】**1** [C] a clever trick 巧計 **2** [U] the use of clever tricks and deceit 詭計; 欺騙

ar·ti·fi·cial /ˌɑrtəˈfɪʃəl; ˌɑːtɪˈfɪʃəl◂/ *adj* **1** not natural but made by people 人造的; 人為的: *artificial flowers* 人造花 | *This drink contains no artificial colours.* 這飲料不含任何人造色素。**2** not real or sincere 矯揉做作的; 虛假的: *She welcomed me with a rather artificial smile.* 她以虛偽的微笑歡迎我。–**artificially** *adv*

artificial res·pi·ra·tion /ˌ·····ˈ··ˈ··/ *n* [U] the forcing of air into the lungs of a person who has stopped breathing by pressing their chest and blowing air into their mouth 人工呼吸

ar·til·le·ry /ɑrˈtɪləri; ɑːˈtɪləri/ *n* [U] **1** large guns often on wheels or fixed in one place 大砲; 火砲 **2** the part of the army that uses large guns 砲兵(部隊)

ar·ti·san /ˈɑrtəzṇ; ˌɑːtɪˈzæn/ *n* a person who does skilled work with their hands 手藝人; 工匠

art·ist /ˈɑrtɪst; ˈɑːtɪst/ *n* **1** a person who paints, draws, or produces pieces of art 藝術家; 美術家 **2** see 見 ARTISTE

ar·tiste /ɑrˈtist; ɑːˈtiːst/ *n* (also 又作 **artist**) a professional singer, actor, or dancer 藝人〔指職業歌手、演員或舞蹈家〕

ar·tis·tic /ɑrˈtɪstɪk; ɑːˈtɪstɪk/ *adj* **1** concerning or typical of art or artists 藝術的; 藝術

家的; 美術的; 美術家的: *artistic freedom* 藝術自由 **2** having or showing imagination and skill in art 有藝術想像力的; 有藝術技巧的; 藝術性強的: *All the children in the family are artistic.* 家中所有小孩都有藝術才華。–**artistically** /-kli; -kli/ *adv*

art·ist·ry /ˈɑrtɪstri; ˈɑːtɪstri/ *n* [U] the skill of someone like an artist, musician, or actor 藝術才華; 藝術性: *His artistry is admired all over the world.* 他的藝術才華舉世讚譽。

art·less /ˈɑrtlɪs; ˈɑːtləs/ *adj* simple and natural, without any deceit 天真自然的; 純樸的: *an artless village child* 純樸的農村孩子 | *an apparently artless question* 一個聽來很單純的問題 –**artlessly** *adv*

art·y /ˈɑrti; ˈɑːti/ *adj* **artier, artiest** trying to appear artistic or stylish (a word used to show disapproval) 冒充愛藝術的; 附庸風雅的〔含貶義〕–**artiness** *n* [U]

as¹ /əz; əz; *strong* 強讀 æz; æz/ *adv, prep* **1** used when you are comparing things, or saying that they are like each other in some way 同樣地; 像…一樣: *He's not as old as me.* 他年紀沒我大。 | *She's the same age as me, but not as clever.* 她年紀和我一樣, 卻不如我聰明。 | *We must get to the hospital as quickly as possible.* 我們必須盡快去醫院。**2** being or considered to be a particular thing 作為; 如同: *He was trying to make his living as a painter.* 他試圖以作畫為生。 | *He's working as a window cleaner at the moment.* 他現在是窗戶清潔工。 | *I had been to Ireland many times as a child.* 我年幼時曾去過愛爾蘭多次。 | *As a writer, I need to spend a lot of time observing people.* 身為作家, 我需要花許多時間觀察人。 | *She regarded me as an enemy.* 她把我當作敵人。 | *They treated the whole thing as a joke.* 他們把整件事情當作一個笑話。–see 見 LIKE³ (USAGE 用法)

as² /əz/ *conj* **1** used when you are comparing things, or saying that they are like each other in some way 像…一樣: *He's not quite as brilliant as his brother is.* 他不像他弟弟那樣聰明。 | *She can run just as fast as I can.* 她能跑得和我一樣快。 | *She failed the exam, just as I had done the year before.* 她考試沒及格, 與我前一年的情況一樣。

■ USAGE 用法: In negative comparisons, we can use **not as** or **not so** ☆在作否定比較時, 我們可以用 **not as** 或 **not so**: *He's not as old/not so old as you.* 他年紀沒我大。

2 while something is happening 當…的時候: *As I was getting onto the bus, I realized that I had left my purse at home.* 我上了公共汽車, 才發覺把錢包留在家裡了。 | *He called to me as I walked past.* 我走過時他叫了我一聲。 | *I talked to each of the guests as they arrived.* 客人到達時, 我跟每一位都談了幾句。

3 because 因為; 由於: *As it was now November, it was getting quite cold.* 現在已經是十一月了，天氣變得相當冷。| *I didn't bother to stop and chat to Sarah, as I had spoken to her earlier that day.* 我沒有停下來與莎拉聊天，因為那天早些時候我已經和她説過話了。| *As you're so clever, perhaps you can sort out this problem for us!* 你這麼聰明，也許能為我們解決這個問題！**4** though 雖然; 儘管: *Tired as I was, I was determined to get the job finished.* 我儘管累，還是決定把工作做完。**5 as it is** in fact 事實上; 實際上: *I hoped things might get better, but as it is they seem to be getting worse!* 我原希望情況會好轉，但實際上似乎越來越糟！**6 as it were** a phrase used when you are saying that something is true in a certain way 可以説是; 似乎就是: *He is my best friend, my brother, as it were.* 他是我最好的朋友，可以説如同我的兄弟。**7 as well** also 也: *Dick came up to London with us. Judy came as well.* 狄克和我們一起來倫敦，朱迪也來了。

as for /ˈ··/ *prep* used when you are starting to talk about a new subject 至於: *We've got a spare bed for you, but as for the children, I'm afraid they'll have to sleep on the floor.* 我們有一張空牀讓你用，至於孩子，恐怕他們只能睡地板了。| *Alison hasn't been much help. As for George, he's quite useless.* 艾莉森幫不了大忙，至於喬治，他更是一點用處也沒有。

as if /ˈ··/ (also 又作 **as though**) *conj* in a way that suggests that something is true 好像; 彷彿: *She looked as if she'd been crying.* 她看上去好像在哭。| *He stared at me blankly, as if he didn't believe me.* 他茫然地盯着我，似乎不相信我説的話。| *He shook his head as if to say no.* 他搖搖頭，好像是要説"不"。

as of /ˈ··/ *prep* (also 又作 **as from**) from a particular time 從…時起: *As of today you are in charge.* 從今天起，由你負責。

as regards /ˌ·ˈ·/ *prep* concerning or regarding a particular thing 關於; 至於: *As regards your recent enquiry, I am sorry to inform you that we have no job vacancies at the moment.* 關於你最近的垂詢，我遺憾地通知您我們現在沒有空缺職位。

as to /ˈ··/ *prep* concerning or regarding a particular thing 至於; 關於: *He's very uncertain as to whether it's the right job for him.* 這件工作是否合適他，他毫無把握。| *We had been given no guidance as to what was expected of us.* 至於要我們做甚麼，沒人給我們作任何指導。

a.s.a.p. /ˌe ɛs e ˈpi; ˌeɪ es eɪ ˈpiː/ a written abbreviation for〖縮〗= **as soon as possible** 盡早

as·bes·tos /æsˈbɛstəs; æsˈbestəs/ *n* [U] a solid substance which does not burn and which is used as protection against fire or heat 石棉

as·cend /əˈsɛnd; əˈsend/ *v* [I;T] *fml* to move upwards or move to the top of something〖正式〗攀登; 登高; 上升: *The plane ascended rapidly after take-off.* 飛機起飛後迅速上升。–opposite 反義 **descend**

as·cen·dan·cy /əˈsɛndənsɪ; əˈsendənsi/ *n* (also 又作 **ascendency**) [U] *fml* power or influence over someone〖正式〗優勢; 權勢; 支配地位

as·cent /əˈsɛnt; əˈsent/ *n* **1** [C] moving or climbing upwards 攀登; 登高; 升高: *The team hope to make a successful ascent of the mountain.* 該隊伍希望能成功登上這座山。**2** [U] the process by which someone develops and becomes more advanced〔地位、職務等的〕上升; 提升: *a rapid ascent to a position of power* 迅速攀上有權勢的地位 **3** [C] a path or road which slopes upwards 斜坡; 上坡路

as·cer·tain /ˌæsəˈten; ˌæsəˈteɪn/ *v* [T;+that] *fml* to discover or get to know something〖正式〗查明; 弄清; 確定: *The police are trying to ascertain the facts.* 警方正試圖查明事實真相。

as·cet·ic /əˈsɛtɪk; əˈsetɪk/ *n* a person whose simple, often religious way of life allows no physical pleasures 苦行者; 禁慾主義者 – **ascetic** *adj fml*〖正式〗

as·cribe /əˈskraɪb; əˈskraɪb/ *v* **ascribed, ascribing** [T] **ascribe something to** to believe that something is the result of a particular thing or the work of a particular person 把某物歸於: *He ascribes his success to skill and hard work.* 他把自己的成功歸因於技術和勤奮。

ash /æʃ; æʃ/ *n* [U] (also 又作 **ashes** [pl]) **1** the soft grey powder that remains after something has been burnt 灰; 灰燼: *cigarette ash* 煙灰 | *The house burnt to ashes.* 房子燒成灰燼。**2 ashes** [pl] the remains of a dead person after burning 骨灰: *Her ashes were scattered over the sea.* 她的骨灰撒在大海裡了。**3** [C;U] a type of forest tree, or its wood 梣; 白蠟樹

a·shamed /əˈʃemd; əˈʃeɪmd/ *adj* [never before a noun 不能用於名詞前] feeling shame, guilt, or sorrow about something 羞恥的; 害臊的; 慚愧的: *He felt ashamed of his old clothes.* 他衣着陳舊，感到羞慚。| *I was ashamed to admit what I had done.* 我羞於承認自己所做的事。| *You should be ashamed of yourself.* 你應該自我慚愧。–**ashamedly** /əˈʃemɪdlɪ; əˈʃeɪmˌɪdli/ *adv*

□ USEFUL PATTERNS 有用句型
to be ashamed of someone/something;
to be ashamed to do something

ash·en /ˈæʃən; ˈæʃən/ *adj* very pale because of shock or fear (used of a person's face)〔指由於震驚或害怕而臉色〕灰白的; 蒼白的

a·shore /əˈʃɔr; əˈʃɔːr/ *adv* on or onto the

shore or land from the sea 在[向]岸上; 在[向]陸上: *We came ashore at Dover.* 我們在多佛爾上了岸.

ash·tray /'æʃ,tre; 'æʃtreɪ/ *n* a small dish for cigarette ash 煙灰缸

Ash Wednes·day /,·'··/ *n* the first day of LENT 聖灰星期三〔四旬節的第一天〕

A·sian /'eʃən; 'eɪʃən/ *n* (also 又作 **A·si·at·ic** /,eʒɪ'ætɪk; ,eɪʃɪ'ætɪk/) a person from Asia 亞洲人 **–Asian** *adj*

★**a·side**[1] /ə'saɪd; ə'saɪd/ *adv* to the side or out of the way 在[向]旁邊; 在[向]一邊: *She stepped aside to let them pass.* 她站到一邊, 讓他們通過. | *He put his work aside for a time.* 他暫時擱下自己的工作.

aside[2] *n* a remark in a low voice not intended to be heard by everyone present 〔非説給別人聽的〕低聲説的話

★★**ask** /æsk; ɑːsk/ *v* **1** [I;T] to make a request for someone to tell you something 問; 詢問: *Can I ask a question?* 我可以提個問題嗎? | *She asked me several difficult questions.* 她問了我幾個難題. | *I think I'd better ask him who he is.* 我想我最好問一下他是誰. | *We need to ask where to go next.* 我們需要問一問接下來去哪兒. | *He asked me if I would like a drink.* 他問我要不要來一杯飲料. | *"How old are you?" she asked.* "你年紀多大了?" 她問道.

□ USEFUL PATTERNS 有用句型
to ask a question; to ask someone a question; to ask (someone) who, where, why, how, etc.; "…?" he asked

2 ask someone to do something to say to someone that you would like them to do something for you 請求[要求]某人做某事: *She asked me to lend her some money.* 她要求我借些錢給她. | *I needed someone to sort out my money for me, so I asked Jim.* 我要有個人替我理財, 因此找了傑姆. **3** ask for something, ask someone for something to say to someone that you would like them to give you something 向某人要某物: *I sat down at a table and asked for a cup of tea.* 我在桌旁坐下, 要了一杯茶. | *She's never asked me for money.* 她從不向我要錢. **4** ask for someone to say that you would like to talk to someone on the telephone 要求與某人通電話: *I phoned the office and asked for Jane.* 我打電話到辦公室, 要跟簡講話. **5** ask someone somewhere to invite someone somewhere 邀請某人去某處: *I asked her in for a drink.* 我請她進來喝一杯. | *He hadn't been asked to the party.* 他沒被邀請赴聚會. **6** ask after someone to ask whether someone is well 問候某人: *I met Mark in town, and he asked after you.* 我在城裡遇到馬克, 他向你問候. **7** be asking for trouble to be behaving in a way which will cause trouble for you 自找麻煩

■ USAGE 用法: Compare 比較 **ask, inquire, question.** Ask is the usual verb for questions ☆**ask** 是表示"問"問題的常用動詞: *"When were you born?" he asked.* "你是甚麼時候出生的?" 他問道. | *He asked me the time.* 他問我幾點鐘了. **Enquire** (or **inquire**) is more formal ☆**enquire** 〔或**inquire**〕較正式: *"What is your date of birth?" he enquired* "你是甚麼時候出生的?"他問道. But we cannot use **enquire** before a pronoun object (*me, you, him, her, us, them*). ☆但是 **enquire** 不能用於代詞賓語〔代名詞受詞〕(me, you, him, her, us, them)前面. The verb **question** means "to ask a person a lot of questions" ☆動詞 **question** 表示"盤問"〔即問某人許多問題〕: *The police questioned the suspect for several hours.* 警方對那嫌疑犯盤問了好幾個小時.

a·skew /ə'skju; ə'skjuː/ *adv* [never before a noun 不能用於名詞前] not straight or level 歪地; 斜地: *He wore his hat askew.* 他歪戴着帽子.

a·sleep /ə'slip; ə'sliːp/ *adj* [never before a noun 不能用於名詞前] **1** sleeping 睡着的; 熟睡的: *Be quiet! The baby is asleep.* 請安靜! 嬰兒在睡覺. **2** fast asleep, sound asleep sleeping very deeply 睡得很熟; 沉睡 **3** unable to feel anything (used of an arm or a leg that has been in one position for too long) 〔手或腳因長久固定於某一位置而〕麻木的; 無感覺的 **4** fall asleep to go into a state of sleep 入睡

as·par·a·gus /ə'spærəgəs; ə'spærəgəs/ *n* [U] a plant whose young green stems are eaten as a vegetable 蘆筍; 石刁柏

★**as·pect** /'æspɛkt; 'æspɛkt/ *n* **1** a particular side or characteristic of a situation 方面: *The training course covers every aspect of the job.* 培訓課程包括這項工作的各個方面. **2** the direction in which a window, room, or front of a building faces 〔窗、房間、建築物的〕朝向: *The house has a southerly aspect.* 這幢房子朝南. **3** *lit* appearance 〖文〗外貌; 臉容: *Her face wore a melancholy aspect.* 她臉帶憂鬱的神色.

as·per·sion /ə'spɝʒən; ə'spɜːʃən/ *n fml* 〖正式〗 **cast aspersions on** to suggest that someone is not very good at something (a phrase which is often used in a humorous way) 誹謗; 中傷〖常帶幽默〗: *She cast aspersions on my driving.* 她諷刺我的駕駛技術.

as·phalt /'æsfɔlt; 'æsfælt/ *n* [U] a hard black substance that is used to make the surface of roads 〔用於鋪路面的〕瀝青

as·phyx·i·ate /æs'fɪksɪ,et; æs'fɪksɪeɪt/ *v* **asphyxiated, asphyxiating** [T] *fml* 〖正式〗 to kill someone by making them unable to breathe 〖正式〗使〔某人〕窒息而死: *She was*

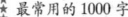

A

asphyxiated by the smoke. 她被煙窒息而死。–**asphyxiation** /æsˌfɪksiˈeʃən; æsˌfɪksiˈeɪʃən/ *n* [U]

as·pi·rant /əˈspaɪrənt; əˈspaɪərənt/ *n fml* a person who hopes for and tries to get something important《正式》追求者; 希冀者

as·pi·ra·tion /ˌæspəˈreʃən; ˌæspɜˈreɪʃən/ *n* a strong desire to have or do something, especially something important 渴望; 熱望; 志氣; 抱負: *He has aspirations to become a great writer.* 他有志成為一名大作家。

as·pire /əˈspaɪr; əˈspaɪər/ *v* **aspired, aspiring, aspire to something, aspire to do something** to have a strong desire to do something and aim to do it 渴望做某事: *She aspires to be prime minister.* 她渴望成為首相。–**aspiring** *adj: an aspiring young actress* 雄心勃勃的年輕女演員

as·pirin /ˈæspərɪn; ˈæsprɪn/ *n* [C;U] a common medicine that reduces pain and fever 阿司匹林〔退熱鎮痛藥〕: *She took two aspirins.* 她服了兩片阿司匹林。| *a bottle of aspirin* 一瓶阿司匹林藥片

ass /æs; æs/ *n* an animal like a horse but smaller and with longer ears 驢

as·sail /əˈsel; əˈseɪl/ *v* [T] *fml*《正式》**1** to attack someone violently 攻擊〔某人〕: *The police were assailed with rocks.* 警察受到石塊攻擊。**2 be assailed by** to be worried or troubled by problems 困擾: *Tom was assailed by doubts.* 湯姆滿腹狐疑。

as·sai·lant /əˈselənt; əˈseɪlənt/ *n fml* an attacker《正式》攻擊者

as·sas·sin /əˈsæsɪn; əˈsæsɪn/ *n* a person who murders someone for political reasons 暗殺者, 刺客

as·sas·sin·ate /əˈsæsɪnˌet; əˈsæsɪneɪt/ *v* **assassinated, assassinating** [T] to murder an important person for political reasons 暗殺, 行刺〔政要人物〕–see 見 KILL¹ (USAGE 用法) –**assassination** /əˌsæsɪnˈeʃən; əˌsæsɪˈneɪʃən/ *n* [C;U]

⋆**as·sault**¹ /əˈsɔlt; əˈsɔːlt/ *n* [C;U] a violent attack, often on a person〔常指對人的〕襲擊; 攻擊: *a vicious assault on an old lady* 對一位老婦的狠毒襲擊 | *The captain led an assault against the castle.* 隊長率隊攻擊城堡。| *He was sent to prison for assault.* 他因襲擊他人而入獄。

assault² *v* [T] to attack someone violently 猛襲〔某人〕

as·sem·ble /əˈsɛmbl̩; əˈsembəl/ *v* **1** [I;T] to gather or collect together 集合; 聚集: *The schoolchildren assembled in the hall to listen to the headmaster.* 學生集合在禮堂聽校長講話。| *The books are assembled on the shelves in alphabetical order.* 書按書名字母順序放在書架上。**2** [T] to put the different parts of something together 裝配〔某物〕; 安裝〔某物〕: *It was easy to assemble the bookcase myself.* 我自己裝配書櫃很容易。

⋆**as·sem·bly** /əˈsɛmblɪ; əˈsembli/ *n* **assemblies** [C;U] the meeting of a group of people for a particular purpose 集會; 集合: *School assembly will begin at nine o'clock.* 學校九點鐘舉行大會。

assembly line /əˈ···ˌ·/ *n* a production process in a factory where each worker does one particular job and then the work is passed on a moving band to the next worker〔工廠中的〕裝配線, 流水作業線

as·sent /əˈsɛnt; əˈsent/ *v* [I] *fml* to agree to something《正式》同意; 贊成: *The committee would not assent to the proposal.* 委員會不會同意那個提議。–opposite 反義 **dissent** –**assent** *n: The director has given her assent.* 那位董事已表示贊成。

as·sert /əˈsɝt; əˈsɜːt/ *v* **1** [T;+that] to state an opinion forcefully 宣稱; 斷言: *The lawyer asserted his belief in his client's innocence.* 律師堅稱當事人是清白的。**2** [T] to behave in a determined way in order to make other people recognize something 維護; 堅持; 表明: *She asserted her independence by going out alone.* 她獨自外出以表示自己的獨立性。**3 assert yourself** to behave in a strong and determined way so that people take notice of you 表現自己〔以吸引他人注意〕; 出風頭

as·ser·tion /əˈsɝʃən; əˈsɜːʃən/ *n* [C;U] a forceful statement or claim 主張; 斷言; 申述: *He repeated his assertions that he was not guilty.* 他反覆申述自己無罪。

as·ser·tive /əˈsɝtɪv; əˈsɜːtɪv/ *adj* behaving in a confident, determined way so that people take notice of you 斷言的; 肯定的; 自信的; 武斷的: *You must be more assertive if you want people to listen to you.* 如果你要人們聽從你, 你必須表現得更自信。–**assertively** *adv* –**assertiveness** *n* [U]

⋆**as·sess** /əˈsɛs; əˈses/ *v* [T] **1** to think carefully about a situation or problem, and make a judgment about it 評價, 判斷〔某事物〕: *We must assess the political situation carefully.* 我們必須謹慎判斷政治形勢。**2** to judge the quality, amount, or value of something 評估, 確定〔某事物的質量、數量或價值〕: *Teachers have to assess their students' work regularly.* 教師必須定期評估學生的學業。| *It's difficult to assess exactly how much damage was caused.* 很難精確估計造成了多大的損失。–**assessment** *n* [C;U]

⋆**as·set** /ˈæsɛt; ˈæset/ *n* **1** [C] something that is useful and helpful 寶貴〔有益〕的東西; 優點; 長處: *A sense of humour is a great asset.* 具有幽默感是一大長處。**2 assets** [pl] *fml* the property of a person or a company which can be sold to pay off debts《正式》資產; 財產

as·sid·u·ous /əˈsɪdʒʊəs; əˈsɪdjuəs/ *adj* working hard or paying great attention to detail 刻苦的; 勤奮的; 努力的 –**assiduously** *adv*

as·sign /əˈsaɪn; əˈsaɪn/ *v* [T] **1** to give something to someone to use 分配〔某物供某人使用〕; 分派: *They have assigned me a small* *room.* 他們給我分配了一個小房間。

2 to give someone a job to do 分配〔工作給某人〕: *Guards were assigned to watch the hotel day and night.* 警衛被分配去日夜守護那家旅館。 **3** to send someone to a place, usually to do a job 派〔某人去某處工作〕: *He was assigned to Tokyo.* 他被派往東京工作。

as·sign·ment /ə'saɪnmənt; ə'saɪnmənt/ *n* **1** [C] a job which you are given to do 任務; 工作; 作業: *The newspaper is sending her on a special assignment to India.* 報社派她去印度執行一項特別任務。 **2** [U] the act of giving someone a job to do 委派; 指派; 分配

as·sim·i·late /ə'sɪmɪˌet; ə'sɪmḻleɪt/ *v* assimilated, assimilating **1** [I;T] to make an accepted part of or become an accepted part of a group or country (使)同化: *America has assimilated many people from Europe.* 美國同化了許多來自歐洲的人。 | *They assimilated easily into their new jobs.* 他們很容易地適應了新工作。 **2** [T] to understand something properly 理解; 消化: *You have to assimilate the facts, not just remember them.* 你必須理解這些事實, 而不是僅僅記住它們。 –assimilation /ə,sɪmɪ'eʃən; ə,sɪmḻ'leɪʃən/ *n* [U]

★**as·sist** /ə'sɪst; ə'sɪst/ *v* [I;T] *fml* to help or support someone 〔正式〕幫助; 協助: *Two nurses assisted the doctor in performing the operation.* 兩位護士協助醫生施行手術。–see 見 HELP[1] (USAGE 用法)

★**as·sist·ance** /ə'sɪstəns; ə'sɪstəns/ *n* **1** [U] help and support 幫助; 援助: *Our organization needs more financial assistance.* 我們的組織需要更多的財政援助。 **2** come to someone's assistance to help someone 幫助某人

as·sist·ant /ə'sɪstənt; ə'sɪstənt/ *n* a person who helps someone in a job, and is under that person's direction 助手; 助理: *This is my assistant, Sally.* 這是我的助手, 名叫薩麗。 | *He is an assistant cook.* 他是個助理廚師。

★**as·so·ci·ate**[1] /ə'soʃɪˌet; ə'səʊʃɪeɪt/ *v* associated, associating **1** [I;T] to join or be connected with someone or something (使)聯合; (使)結交; (使)參與: *He associates with some very strange people.* 他跟一些奇怪怪的人來往。 | *I am not associated with any political group.* 我不參與任何政治組織。 **2** [T] to connect ideas in your mind 聯想: *I don't associate the two ideas.* 我不把這兩種想法聯繫在一起。 | *She associates summer with holidays.* 她一到夏天就聯想到假期。

as·so·ci·ate[2] /ə'soʃɪt; ə'səʊʃɪḻt/ *n* a person connected with another person, especially in work 同事; 夥伴; 合夥人: *He's not a friend, just a business associate.* 他不是朋友, 只是生意上的夥伴。

★**as·so·ci·a·tion** /ə,sosɪ'eʃən; ə,səʊsɪ'eɪʃən/ *n* **1** [C] an organization of people joined together for a particular purpose 協會; 社團: *an association to help blind people* 一個幫助盲人的團體 | *the Association of Scientific Workers* 科學工作者協會 **2** in association with together with someone or something else 與...聯合〔合夥〕: *The council is working in association with the Department of Education.* 該委員會正與教育部聯合工作。 **3** [U] the act of connecting things in the mind 聯想

as·sort·ment /ə'sɔrtmənt; ə'sɔːtmənt/ *n* a group of mixed things or of various kinds of the same thing 各式各樣東西的混合; 什錦: *An assortment of strange objects lay on her desk.* 她桌子上鋪滿了各種奇怪的物品。 | *an assortment of biscuits* 各式餅乾 –assorted *adj*: *a bag of assorted sweets* 一袋什錦糖果

★**as·sume** /ə'sjum; ə'sjuːm/ *v* assumed, assuming **1** [T;+that] to believe that something is true without any real proof 假定, 假設〔某事物〕: *If he's not here in five minutes, we'll assume he isn't coming.* 如果他過五分鐘不來, 我們就認為他不會來了。 | *Assuming it rains tomorrow, what shall we do?* 明天下雨的話, 我們該怎麼辦? | *I assumed that she was American but she was actually Canadian.* 我原以為她是美國人, 但她實際上是加拿大人。 **2** [T] to begin to use or have something, sometimes without the right to do so 行使〔權力〕; 〔有時指無權〕僭奪: *He will assume responsibility for the new staff.* 他將負責管理新員工。 | *The army has assumed control of the government.* 軍方奪取了政府的控制權。 **3** to pretend to have a quality or way of behaving 假裝; 裝出: *He assumes a well-informed manner, but in fact he knows very little.* 他裝出一副消息靈通的樣子, 但實際上他所知甚少。 –assumption /ə'sʌmpʃən; ə'sʌmpʃən/ *n* [C;U]: *Our assumption that we would win was mistaken.* 我們以為自己會贏, 但這種想法錯了。

as·sur·ance /ə'ʃʊrəns; ə'ʃʊərəns/ *n* **1** [C] a firm statement or promise 斷言; 保證: *He gave repeated assurances that he would finish the work.* 他反覆保證會做完那件工作。 | *an assurance of your loyalty* 你表示忠誠的保證 **2** [U] (also 又作 self-assurance) strong belief in your own ability and powers 自信; 信心; 把握: *The new teacher lacks assurance in the classroom.* 那位新教師上課缺乏自信。 **3** [U] *BrE* insurance against events that are certain rather than possible 〔英式〕保險: *life assurance* 人壽保險

★**as·sure** /ə'ʃʊr; ə'ʃʊər/ *v* assured, assuring [T] **1** to tell someone that something is certainly true, in order to make them feel more confident 使〔某人〕確信〔放心〕; 向〔某人〕保證: *I assure you that this medicine cannot harm you.* 我向你保證該藥對你沒有損害。| *I can assure you of his good intentions.* 我可以向你保證, 他的用意是好的。

> ☐ USEFUL PATTERNS 有用句型
> to assure someone of something; to assure someone that...

2 to make someone feel certain of having something 保證〔某人〕得到〔某物〕: *Our clients are assured of a trouble-free holiday.* 我們保證顧客一定能有一個無憂無慮的假期。| *We can assure you a carefree retirement.* 我們可以保證你退休後生活無憂無慮

> ☐ USEFUL PATTERNS 有用句型
> to assure someone of something; to assure someone something

as·sured /ə'ʃʊrd; ə'ʃʊəd/ *adj* **1** (also 又作 **self-assured**) confident in your own abilities 自信的; 有把握的: *He has an assured and relaxed manner.* 他的態度自信而從容。 **2** having or showing certainty 確定的; 有保證的; 必然的: *Her success as a singer looks assured.* 她作為歌手看來是有成功的把握的。–**assuredly** /ə'ʃʊrɪdlɪ; ə'ʃʊərɪdlɪ/ *adv*

as·te·risk /'æstə‚rɪsk; 'æstərɪsk/ *n* **1** a mark like a star (*), used to make you look at a note at the bottom of a page 星號(*)〔用以指示讀者看書頁下部的注釋〕 **2** a mark like a star (*), often used in grammar to show that something is incorrect 星號(*)〔常用於語法書中表示某句或某詞是不正確的〕

as·te·roid /'æstə‚rɔɪd; 'æstərɔɪd/ *n* one of many small planets (PLANET) between MARS and JUPITER〔火星和木星之間的〕小行星

asth·ma /'æsmə; 'æsmə/ *n* [U] a disease which makes breathing very difficult at times 哮喘(病) –**asthmatic** /æz'mætɪk; æs‚'mætɪk/ *adj, n*: *He is asthmatic.* 他是個哮喘病人。

as·ton·ish /ə'stɒnɪʃ; ə'stɒnɪʃ/ *v* [T] to fill someone with great surprise 使〔某人〕驚駭; 使驚駭: *Kate's memory for names and faces astonishes me.* 凱特對姓名和人臉的記憶力令我大為驚異。–**astonished** *adj*: *I was astonished to find out how rich they are.* 我發現他們這麼有錢, 大為吃驚。–**astonishing** *adj*: *Her performance in the play was astonishing.* 她在戲裡的演出讓人吃驚。

as·ton·ish·ment /ə'stɒnɪʃmənt; ə'stɒnɪʃmənt/ *n* [U] great surprise 驚訝; 驚駭

as·tound /ə'staʊnd; ə'staʊnd/ *v* [T] to fill someone with shock and surprise 使〔某人〕震驚: *He was astounded when he heard that he had won.* 他聽說自己贏了大為驚訝。–**astounding** *adj*

a·stray /ə'stre; ə'streɪ/ *adv* **1 go astray** to go off the right path and get lost 迷路; 離開正道; 誤入歧途 **2 lead someone astray** to introduce someone to bad habits 把某人引入歧途: *The attractions of the big city soon led the young man astray.* 大城市的誘惑很快把那年輕人引入歧途。

a·stride /ə'straɪd; ə'straɪd/ *adv, prep* with a leg on each side of something 兩腿分開; 跨着: *He was sitting astride his horse.* 他兩腿叉開騎在馬上。

as·trin·gent /ə'strɪndʒənt; ə'strɪndʒənt/ *adj* **1** able to tighten up someone's skin or stop bleeding 收斂的; 止血的 **2** severe and bitter 嚴厲的; 尖刻的: *an astringent remark* 尖刻的話

as·trol·o·gy /ə'strɒlədʒɪ; ə'strɒlədʒɪ/ *n* [U] the art of understanding the supposed influence of the stars and planets (PLANET) on events and on people's character 占星術 –**astrological** /‚æstrə'lɒdʒɪkl; ‚æstrə'lɒdʒɪkəl/ *adj* –**astrologically** /-klɪ; -klɪ/ *adv* –**astrologer** /ə'strɒlədʒə; ə'strɒlədʒə/ *n* adv

as·tro·naut /'æstrə‚nɔt; 'æstrənɔːt/ *n* a person who travels in a spacecraft 宇航員; 太空人

as·tro·nom·i·cal /‚æstrə'nɒmɪkl; ‚æstrə'nɒmɪkəl/ *adj* **1** concerning the study of the stars 天文學的 **2** *infml* extremely large 〔非正式〕極大的; 天文數字的: *Astronomical sums of money will be needed for this plan.* 實施這項計劃將需要巨額資金。–**astronomically** /-klɪ; -klɪ/ *adv*

as·tron·o·my /ə'strɒnəmɪ; ə'strɒnəmɪ/ *n* [U] the scientific study of the sun, moon, and stars 天文學 –**astronomer** *n*

as·tute /ə'stjut; ə'stjuːt/ *adj* clever and quickly able to see something that is to your advantage 精明的; 敏銳的; 狡黠的 –**astutely** *adv* –**astuteness** *n* [U]

a·sy·lum /ə'saɪləm; ə'saɪləm/ *n* **1** [U] protection and shelter, especially when it is given by a government to people who have left their country for political reasons 〔尤指政治性的〕避難, 庇護: *The refugees were granted political asylum.* 那些難民得到政治庇護。 **2** [C] *old fash* a hospital which treats illnesses of the mind 〔老式〕精神病院; 瘋人院

★**at** /ət; ət; *strong* 強讀 æt; æt/ *prep* **1** in a particular place 在〔某處〕: *He was standing at the door.* 他正站在門口。| *I'll be at home this afternoon.* 我今天下午在家。| *I bumped into Mary at the post office.* 我在郵局碰見了瑪麗。| *The children are all at school.* 孩子們都在學校。| *We spent five hours waiting at the airport.* 我們在機場等了五個小時。| *They live at number 24 Bridge Street.* 他們住在布里奇街第24號。–see picture on page 764 見 764 頁彩圖 **2** when it is a particular time 在...時: *I'll see you at two o'clock.* 我兩點鐘見你。| *We got home at* *midnight.* 我們半夜時分到了家。| *I got up at dawn.* 我天亮就起牀了。| *He died at Christmas.* 他在聖誕期間去世。**3** towards someone or something 對着; 朝...的方向: *He picked up a stone and threw it at me.* 他撿起一塊石頭, 向我扔來。| *There's no need to shout at me!* 用不着對我大喊大叫! | *He shot at the bird, but missed.* 他對着小鳥開槍, 卻打偏了。| *She looked at me and smiled.* 她看着我微笑。**4** because of something 因為; 由於: *I was very surprised at the outcome of the discussions.* 我對討論的結果感到非常驚奇。| *We all laughed at his jokes.* 聽了他的笑話, 我們都哈哈大笑。**5 good at something, bad at something, etc.** able to do something well, badly, etc. 擅長某事, 不擅長某事等等: *She's not very good at tennis.* 她對打網球並不在行。| *I'm very bad at cooking.* 我做飯燒菜很不在行。**6** used to show the cost, speed, age, or rate of something 〔表示價格、速度、年齡、比率等〕: *The book is being sold at £3.95.* 該書以 3.95 英鎊的價格出售。| *We were driving along at sixty miles per hour.* 我們以每小時六十英里的速度駕車前行。| *He left school at sixteen.* 他十六歲時離校。| *Unemployment is increasing at an alarming rate.* 失業人數正以驚人的速度增加。

ate /et; et/ the past tense of EAT ☆ EAT 的過去式

> ■ USAGE 用法: Most British people say /et/, though some of them say /eɪt/. Most Americans say /eɪt/, and many Americans consider that /et/ is incorrect. ☆大多數英國人讀 /et/, 但是有些英國人讀 /eɪt/。大多數美國人讀 /eɪt/, 而且許多美國人認為 /et/ 這個讀法是不正確的。

a·the·is·m /ˈeθɪˌɪzəm; ˈeɪθɪ-ɪzəm/ *n* [U] disbelief in the existence of God 無神論

a·the·ist /ˈeθɪɪst; ˈeɪθɪ-ˌɪst/ *n* a person who does not believe in the existence of God 無神論者 –compare 比較 AGNOSTIC –**atheistic** /ˌeθɪˈɪstɪk; ˌeɪθɪˈɪstɪk/ *adj*

ath·lete /ˈæθlit; ˈæθliːt/ *n* a person who is very good at sports, and is physically strong and active 運動員; 運動健將

ath·let·ic /æθˈlɛtɪk; æθˈletɪk/ *adj* **1** connected with athletes or athletics 運動的; 運動員的 **2** physically strong and active, and good at sports 〔人〕身強力壯的; 擅長體育運動的

ath·let·ics /æθˈlɛtɪks; æθˈletɪks/ *n* [U] sports demanding strength and speed, such as running and jumping 體育運動; 田徑運動 –see picture on page 957 見 957 頁彩圖

at·las /ˈætləs; ˈætləs/ *n* a book of maps 地圖冊; 地圖集

at·mo·sphere /ˈætməsˌfɪr; ˈætməsfɪəʳ/ *n* **1** the mixture of gases that surrounds the Earth, or any other PLANET 大氣; 大氣層 **2** the air, especially in a room 〔尤指室內的〕空氣: *a smoky atmosphere* 煙霧騰騰 **3** the general character or feeling of a place 氣氛; 氛圍; 環境: *Since the bomb exploded in the hotel, the atmosphere has been tense.* 自從那枚炸彈在旅館中爆炸以來, 氣氛一直緊張。

at·mo·spher·ic /ˌætməsˈfɛrɪk; ˌætməsˈferɪk/ *adj* **1** [always before a noun 只能用於名詞前] of or concerning the Earth's atmosphere 大氣(層)的: *atmospheric pressure* 大氣壓 **2** beautiful and full of mystery 有感染力的; 富於製造氣氛的: *atmospheric music* 製造氣氛的音樂

at·oll /ˈætɑl; ˈætɒl/ *n* a ring-shaped island made of CORAL 環礁珊瑚島; 環礁

at·om /ˈætəm; ˈætəm/ *n* the smallest piece of a substance that can exist alone or can combine with other substances to form a chemical chain 原子

atom bomb /ˈ··· /ˈ (also 又作 **atomic bomb** /·ˌ·· ·/) *n old fash* a bomb that uses the explosive power made by splitting atoms 〔老式〕原子彈

a·tom·ic /əˈtɑmɪk; əˈtɒmɪk/ *adj* **1** of or concerning an atom or atoms 原子的 **2** working on or moving by the power made by splitting atoms 原子能的; 原子動力的 –**atomically** /-klɪ; -klɪ/ *adv*

atomic en·er·gy /·ˌ·· ··· / *n* [U] the power made by splitting atoms; it is used to make electricity, and in NUCLEAR weapons 原子能; 核能

a·tone /əˈton; əˈtəʊn/ *v* **atoned, atoning, atone for something** to make repayment for something bad that you have done 贖罪; 補過: *He tried to atone for his sins by a life of prayer.* 他想以終生虔誠禱告來贖罪。– **atonement** *n* [U]

a·tro·cious /əˈtroʃəs; əˈtrəʊʃəs/ *adj* **1** extremely cruel and shocking 兇惡的; 殘暴的; 惡毒的: *atrocious crimes* 殘暴的罪行 **2** *infml* very bad 〔非正式〕糟透的; 惡劣的: *an atrocious meal* 一頓粗劣不堪的飯 –**atrociously** *adv*

a·troc·i·ty /əˈtrɑsətɪ; əˈtrɒsɪtɪ/ *n* atrocities an act of great evil or cruelty 極大的罪惡; 暴行: *Many atrocities were committed during the war.* 戰爭期間發生了許多暴行。

★**at·tach** /əˈtætʃ; əˈtætʃ/ *v* [T] **1** to fix, fasten, or join one thing to another 縛; 繫; 連接; 固定: *Please attach a photograph to the application form.* 請在申請表格上貼一張照片。| *There's a health club attached to the hotel.* 酒店附設健身俱樂部。**2 be attached to** to be connected to a group or organization, especially for a short time 〔尤指短期地〕加入; 參加: *I was attached to the art department for three months during my training.* 我受訓期間在藝術系待了三個月。**3 be attached to someone** to be fond of someone 喜愛某人, 依戀某人: *I am very attached to her.* 我很喜歡她。**4 attach importance to something** to

A

think that something is important 認為某事重要；重視某事

at·tach·ment /əˈtætʃmənt; əˈtætʃmənt/ n **1** [C] something that can be fixed to something else 附屬品；附件: *This machine has a special attachment for cutting metal.* 這部機器有一個用於切割金屬的附屬裝置。**2** [C;U] fondness or friendship 喜愛；依戀；友情

at·tack[1] /əˈtæk; əˈtæk/ v **1** [I;T] to use violence against someone or against a place especially with weapons〔尤指用武器〕攻擊，進攻〔某人〕: *The enemy attacked at night.* 敵軍在夜間發起攻擊。| *She was attacked on her way home.* 她在回家路上遭人襲擊。**2** [T] to speak or write strongly against someone〔口頭或文字〕攻擊，抨擊，非難〔某人〕: *The minister has been strongly attacked by the newspapers for his comments.* 部長因其發表的言論而受到各家報紙的強烈抨擊。**3** [T] to harm or damage something, especially by a continuing action〔尤指不斷地〕侵襲，侵害〔某物〕: *This disease attacks most crops.* 這種病害侵襲了大部分莊稼。**4** [T] to begin to deal with something with determination〔幹勁十足地〕着手處理〔某事〕: *We should attack the problem at once.* 我們應立即着手解決這個問題。– **attacker** n

at·tack[2] n **1** [C;U] an act of violence intended to harm 攻擊；進攻: *There has been an attack on the president's life.* 有人行刺總統。| *vicious attacks* 惡毒的攻擊 | *nuclear attack* 核攻擊 **2** [C] a piece of writing that is strongly against someone or something〔文字〕攻擊；抨擊；非難: *The article contained an attack on government policy.* 文章包含着對政府政策的攻擊。**3** [C] a sudden and severe period of illness〔疾病的〕突然發作: *an attack of malaria* 瘧疾的發作 **4 come/be under attack** to suffer violence or strong disapproval 受到攻擊〔抨擊〕: *The city is under attack.* 該城正遭攻擊。| *The headmaster came under attack for his views.* 校長因其所持觀點而受到攻擊。

at·tain /əˈten; əˈteɪn/ v [T] to succeed in gaining something, especially after effort〔尤指經過努力而〕達到，獲得: *He attained the position of company director.* 他終於當上了公司董事。–**attainable** adj –**attainment** n

at·tempt[1] /əˈtɛmpt; əˈtɛmpt/ v [T] to make an effort to do something which may be difficult 嘗試；試圖；企圖: *The second question was so difficult I didn't even attempt it.* 第二道題太難了，我連試都沒試。| *I attempted to speak but was told to be quiet.* 我想開口說幾句，但是有人叫我別作聲。

> □ USEFUL PATTERNS 有用句型
> to attempt something; to attempt to do something

at·tempt[2] n **1** an effort made to do something 嘗試；企圖；努力: *I passed my driving test at the second attempt.* 我考到第二次才通過駕駛執照考試。| *It was his attempt at humour but nobody laughed.* 他想幽默一下，但是沒人被他逗笑。| *He made several attempts to escape.* 他好幾次試圖逃跑。

> □ USEFUL PATTERNS 有用句型
> an attempt at something; an attempt to do something

2 an attempt on someone's life an effort made to kill someone 企圖謀殺某人: *The President has survived two attempts on his life.* 有人兩次行刺總統，但總統仍安全無恙。

at·tend /əˈtɛnd; əˈtɛnd/ v **1** [I;T] to be present at an event 出席；參加: *I shall be attending the meeting.* 我將出席會議。| *How many children attend the school?* 多少孩子在這所學校上學？| *Unfortunately, I was unable to attend.* 遺憾的是，我未能出席。**2** [I] *fml* to give your attention to something〔正式〕注意；傾聽: *Are you attending to what I am saying?* 你在聽我說的話嗎？**3** [T] *fml* to go with someone in order to look after them〔正式〕陪伴，伴隨〔某人〕: *The Queen was attended by her bodyguard.* 女王由其衛士伴隨。

> ■ USAGE 用法: People who **attend** a play or concert are the **audience**; people who **attend** a religious service are the **congregation**; people who **attend** a game, such as football, are **spectators**. ☆看戲或聽音樂會的人叫 **audience**（觀眾；聽眾）；做禮拜的人叫 **congregation**（會眾）；去看比賽（例如足球賽）的人叫 **spectators**（觀眾）。But an **attendant** is someone whose job is to look after a public place ☆但是，**attendant** 是指受雇看管公共場所的服務人員: *a swimming-pool attendant* 游泳池工作人員

attend to sbdy/sthg *phr v* [T] to deal with something or look after someone 處理〔某事〕；照顧〔某人〕: *I have an urgent matter to attend to.* 我有一件急事要辦。| *She's attending to the baby.* 她在照顧嬰兒。

at·tend·ance /əˈtɛndəns; əˈtɛndəns/ n **1** [C;U] the act of being present, especially regularly〔尤指經常的〕出席，到場: *Attendance at school is required by law.* 法律規定兒童必須上學。| *Church attendances have fallen in recent years.* 去教堂做禮拜的人數近年來下降了。**2** [sing] the number of people present at an event 出席〔到場〕人數: *The public meeting attracted a large attendance.* 公開集會吸引了許多人出席。**3 in attendance on** *fml* going or being with someone in order to help them〔正式〕照顧；護理: *A doc-*

tor is in attendance on the Queen. 一位醫生正在照顧女王。

at·tend·ant /ə'tɛndənt; ə'tɛndənt/ *n* a person who looks after a place or person 服務員; 侍者: *a museum attendant* 博物館接待員 –see 見 ATTEND (USAGE 用法)

★**at·ten·tion** /ə'tɛnʃən; ə'tɛnʃən/ *n* [U] **1** the act of fixing your mind on something, especially by watching or listening carefully 注意; 留心; 專心: *I felt I had her full attention.* 我感到她非常留意我。 | *He likes to be the centre of attention.* 他喜歡成為大家注意的人物。 | *Your request will receive your full attention.* 我們會充分考慮你的請求。 **2 pay attention** to listen carefully and give your full thought to something 注意; 留心; 專心: *The teacher told the students to pay attention.* 教師要學生專心聽講。 | *I didn't pay attention to what she said.* 我沒留心她說了甚麼。 **3 attract/catch someone's attention** to make someone notice something 引起某人注意: *I tried to attract the waiter's attention.* 我想引起侍者的注意。 **4** particular care or notice 關心; 關注; 照應: *Old cars often need a lot of attention to keep them working.* 舊汽車需要常常維修保養才能正常運行。 **5 at/to attention** standing straight and still like a soldier 立正; 立正姿勢

at·ten·tive /ə'tɛntɪv; ə'tɛntɪv/ *adj* **1** taking careful notice of things 注意的; 專心的: *The class was very attentive and quiet.* 這班學生非常專心和安靜。 **2** kind and helpful 關心的; 體貼的: *He was very attentive to his grandmother and did everything for her.* 他十分關心祖母, 甚麼事情都替她做。 –opposite 反義 **inattentive** –**attentively** *adv* –**attentiveness** *n* [U]

at·tic /'ætɪk; 'ætɪk/ *n* the room at the top of a house just below the roof 屋頂閣樓; 頂樓

at·tire /ə'taɪr; ə'taɪr/ *n* [U] *fml* clothes 〖正式〗服裝; 穿着

★**at·ti·tude** /'ætə,tjud; 'ætɪtjuːd/ *n* **1** a way of feeling, thinking, or behaving 態度; 看法: *I found her attitude very unfriendly.* 我覺得她的態度非常不友好。 | *She has a very odd attitude to money.* 她對金錢的看法很古怪。 | *His attitude* **towards** *me was always rather cold.* 他對我的態度總是相當冷淡。 | *Attitudes have changed since I was young.* 我成年後對許多事情的看法都有了改變。 **2** *fml* the position in which someone is standing or sitting 〖正式〗姿勢

★**at·tor·ney** /ə'tɜnɪ; ə'tɜːnɪ/ *n* the usual American word for 〖美式〗= LAWYER

★**at·tract** /ə'trækt; ə'trækt/ *v* [T] **1** to make someone like or admire someone or something 吸引〔某人〕: *She was attracted by his smile.* 她被他的笑容吸引住了。 | *I've always been attracted to tall women.* 我總是對於高個子的女人有好感。 **2 attract attention** to be noticed and receive attention 引起注意; 受

到注意: *Her novel has attracted a lot of attention.* 她的小說受到了廣泛的注意。 **3** to cause interest, or make something come near 招引〔某物〕: *Flowers attract bees.* 花招引蜜蜂。 | *I am not attracted to city life.* 城市生活對我沒有吸引力。

★**at·trac·tion** /ə'trækʃən; ə'trækʃən/ *n* **1** [U] the ability to attract people 吸引力: *The idea of travelling to the moon holds little attraction for me.* 去月球旅行的想法對我沒有多少吸引力。 | *physical attraction* 引力 **2** [C] something which people admire and are interested in 吸引人的事物: *The main attraction of this town is its excellent theatre.* 這座城市最吸引人的地方是其出色的戲院。 | *tourist attractions* 旅遊勝地

★**at·trac·tive** /ə'træktɪv; ə'træktɪv/ *adj* **1** causing interest or pleasure 有吸引力的: *The idea is very attractive.* 這主意很吸引人。 **2** pretty or HANDSOME (used of a person) 漂亮的, 英俊的〔指人〕: *an attractive man* 一個英俊的男人 **3** pleasant to look at 漂亮的: *The garden looks very attractive.* 這個花園看上去很漂亮。 –see picture 見 BEAUTIFUL (USAGE 用法) –**attractively** *adv* –**attractiveness** *n* [U]

at·tri·bute[1] /'ætrə,bjut; 'ætrɪbjuːt/ *n* a quality forming part of the nature of a person or thing 性質, 屬性: *Kindness is one of his many attributes.* 仁慈是他的許多好品性之一。

at·trib·ute[2] /ə'trɪbjut; ə'trɪbjuːt/ *v* **attributed, attributing, attribute something to** to believe something to be the result or work of 把某事歸因於; 認為是某事的結果: *Jim attributes his success to hard work.* 吉姆認為自己的成功是努力工作的結果。 | *This song is usually attributed to J. S. Bach.* 這首歌通常被認為是巴哈所作的。

at·tuned /ə'tjund; ə'tjuːnd/ *adj* **be attuned to something** to be used to or ready for something 習慣於某事物, 適應某事物: *I'm not really attuned to his way of thinking yet.* 我還不太適應他的思維方式。

au·ber·gine /'obɛr,ʒin; 'əʊbəʒiːn/ *n* [C;U] *BrE* a large fruit with a purple skin that is eaten as a vegetable 〖英式〗茄子

au·burn /'ɔbən; 'ɔːbən/ *adj* reddish-brown (used especially of hair) 赤褐色的〔尤指頭髮〕 –see picture on page 469 見 469 頁彩圖

auc·tion[1] /'ɔkʃən; 'ɔːkʃən/ *n* **1** a public meeting to sell goods to the person who offers the most money 拍賣: *a furniture auction* 家具拍賣 **2 by auction, at auction** at an auction 被拍賣: *The paintings will be sold by auction.* 這些畫將被拍賣。

auction[2] *v* [T] to sell something at an auction 拍賣

auc·tio·neer /,ɔkʃən'ɪr; ,ɔːkʃə'nɪər/ *n* a person who is in charge of an auction 拍賣人

au·da·cious /ɔ'deʃəs; ɔː'deɪʃəs/ *adj* *fml* willing to be daring and take risks 〖正式〗大膽的; 冒險的 –**audaciously** *adv*

A

au·dac·i·ty /ɔːˈdæsətɪ; ɔːˈdæsɜ̩tɪ/ *n* [U] behaviour which is daring and often disrespectful 大膽或魯莽的行為

au·di·ble /ˈɔdəbl; ˈɔːdɜ̩bəl/ *adj* loud enough to be heard 聽得見的 –opposite 反義 **inaudible**: *His reply was barely audible.* 他的回答幾乎聽不見。 –**audibly** *adv* –**audibility** /ˌɔdəˈbɪlətɪ; ˌɔːdɜ̩ˈbɪlɜ̩tɪ/ *n*

✱ **au·di·ence** /ˈɔdɪəns; ˈɔːdɪəns/ *n* [+sing/pl verb] **1** the people listening to or watching a performance, speech, or television show 聽眾; 觀眾: *The audience was very excited.* 觀眾非常激動。 | *a radio audience of 10 million* 一個有一千萬聽眾收聽的廣播節目 | *a member of the audience* 觀眾[聽眾]的一員 | *Cinema audiences have declined.* 電影觀眾愈來愈少。 **2** a formal meeting between somebody powerful and somebody less important 正式拜見; 謁見: *He had an audience with the Pope.* 他謁見了教皇。

au·di·o /ˈɔdɪˌo; ˈɔːdɪəʊ/ *adj* [always before a noun 只能用在名詞前] *tech* connected with or used in the broadcasting or receiving of sound radio signals 〔術語〕音頻的; 聲頻的

audio·vis·u·al /ˌ···ˈ····◂/ *adj* using pictures and sound in educational materials 視聽教學的: *The school's audio-visual equipment includes videos and cassettes.* 學校的視聽教學器材包括錄像機和磁帶。

au·dit /ˈɔdɪt; ˈɔːdɜ̩t/ *v* [T] to make an official examination of the accounts of a business 審計, 查核〔賬目〕–**auditor** *n*

au·di·tion¹ /ɔˈdɪʃn; ɔːˈdɪʃən/ *n* a performance given by a singer, actor, or dancer as a test of their ability for a particular job 〔歌手、演員、舞蹈演員等的〕試唱, 試演

audition² *v* [I;T] to give or make someone give an audition (使)試演; 試唱

au·di·to·ri·um /ˌɔdəˈtɔrɪəm; ˌɔːdɜ̩ˈtɔːrɪəm/ *n* the space in a theatre where people sit when listening to or watching a performance 聽眾席; 觀眾席

aug·ment /ɔɡˈmɛnt; ɔːɡˈment/ *v* [I;T] *fml* to make something become bigger by adding to it 〔正式〕(使)增大, (使)擴大: *He augments his income by working in the evenings.* 他在夜間工作以增加收入。

au·gur /ˈɔɡə; ˈɔːɡər/ *v* **augur well/ill** *lit* to be a sign of good or bad things in the future 〔文〕預示吉[兇], 是好[壞]的兆頭: *This rain augurs well for the farmers.* 這場雨對農民是個吉兆。

au·gust /ɔˈɡʌst; ɔːˈɡʌst/ *adj* *lit* noble and grand 〔文〕高貴而威嚴的

Au·gust /ˈɔɡəst; ˈɔːɡəst/ (also 又作 **Aug**) *n* the 8th month of the year 八月

aunt /ænt; ɑːnt/ (also 又作 **aunt·ie**, **aunt·y** /ˈæntɪ; ˈɑːntɪ/ *infml* 〔非正式〕) *n* the sister of your father or mother, or the wife of your uncle 姑母; 姨母; 伯母; 嬸母; 舅母: *Take me swimming, Auntie Jane!* 簡姨, 帶我去游泳吧! | *My aunt lives in the country.* 我的姑母住在鄉下。–see picture on page 503 見503頁彩圖

au pair /o ˈpɛr; ˌəʊ ˈpeər/ *n* (also 又作 **au pair girl** /· ·· ·/) a young foreign woman who lives with a family in order to learn their language, in return for doing light work in the house 做換工的姑娘〔為學習當地語言而寄住在別人家裡並幫助做些輕微家務的年輕外國女子〕

au·ra /ˈɔrə; ˈɔːrə/ *n* an effect or feeling that seems to surround and come from a person or place 〔人或地方的〕氣息, 氣氛: *There was an aura of decay in the village.* 這個村莊裡有一種衰敗的氣氛。

au·ral /ˈɔrəl; ˈɔːrəl/ *adj tech* of or related to the sense of hearing 〔術語〕聽覺的: *aural skills* 聽力技能

aus·pic·es /ˈɔspɪsɪz; ˈɔːspɜ̩sɜ̩z/ *n* [pl] **under the auspices of** *fml* with the support and approval of 〔正式〕在…的贊助下: *This conference has been arranged under the auspices of the United Nations.* 這會議是由聯合國贊助舉辦的。

aus·pi·cious /ɔˈspɪʃəs; ɔːˈspɪʃəs/ *adj fml* promising or showing signs of future success 〔正式〕吉祥的; 預示成功的: *We are gathered here on this auspicious occasion...* 在這良辰吉日, 我們聚集在這裡... –**auspiciously** *adv*

aus·tere /ɔˈstɪr; ɔːˈstɪər/ *adj* **1** without comfort or enjoyment 簡樸的; 艱苦的: *Life in the monastery was austere.* 廟宇裡的生活很艱苦。 **2** very serious 嚴肅的: *an austere manner* 嚴肅的態度 **3** plain and without decoration 樸素的 –**austerely** *adv* –**austerity** /ɔˈstɛrətɪ; ɔːˈsterɜ̩tɪ/ *n* [U]

au·then·tic /ɔˈθɛntɪk; ɔːˈθentɪk/ *adj* known to have been made, painted, or written by a particular person or at a particular time and known not to be a copy 真的; 原作的: *This is an authentic Roman coin.* 這是一枚真正的羅馬硬幣。 –**authenticity** /ˌɔθənˈtɪsətɪ; ˌɔːθenˈtɪsɜ̩tɪ/ *n* [U]

au·then·tic·ate /ɔˈθɛntɪˌket; ɔːˈθentɪkeɪt/ **authenticated, authenticating** [T] to prove that something is authentic and not a copy 鑑定〔某物〕為真的 –**authentication** /ɔˌθɛntɪˈkeʃən; ɔːˌθentɪˈkeɪʃən/ *n* [U]

✱ **au·thor** /ˈɔθə; ˈɔːθər/ *n* **1** the writer of a book, article, play, poem, or any piece of writing 作者 **2** the person who produces an idea or plan 創始者; 倡議者

au·thor·i·tar·i·an /ɔˌθɛrəˈtɛrɪən; ɔːˌθɒrɜ̩ˈteərɪən/ *adj* demanding that rules and laws must always be obeyed, and that personal freedom is not important 權力主義的; 專制的: *an authoritarian style of government* 專斷的施政作風 –**authoritarian** *n*: *He's a strict authoritarian.* 他是個絕對的權力主義者。 – **authoritarianism** *n* [U]

au·thor·i·ta·tive /əˈθɔrəˌtetɪv; ɔːˈθɒrɜ̩tətɪv/ *adj* **1** having or showing power and the ability to command or control others 有權威的; 命令式的: *an authoritative voice* 命令式的口氣 **2** that can be completely trusted 可靠的; 可信賴的 –**authoritatively** *adv*

au·thor·i·ty /əˈθɒrətɪ; ɔːˈθɒrɪ̩ti/ *n* **authorities 1** [U] the power or right to control and command people 權力; 權威: *She enjoys exercising her authority* **over** *her staff.* 她喜歡對職員指手畫腳, 施展權勢。 | *Young people have no respect for authority these days.* 年輕人現在不把權威當回事情。 **2 in authority** having power over other people 掌權: *She has no respect for people in authority.* 她不尊敬掌權的人。 **3** [U] the right to do a particular thing 〔做某事的〕權力: *I do not have the authority to sign any contracts.* 我沒有簽合同的權力。 **4** [C] a person or group with the power or right to control and command people 有支配權的人或集團; 當局; 官方: *The government is the highest authority in the country.* 政府是國家的最高權力機關。 | *the local education authority* 地方教育機構 **5 the authorities** the government or a government department 政府或政府部門: *The authorities have refused to allow him to enter the country.* 當局拒絕他入境。 **6** [U] the ability to influence people 影響力: *Although she has no official position in the party, she has a lot of authority.* 她在黨內雖不擔任正式職務, 但是很有影響力。 **7** [C] a person who knows a lot about a subject and is respected 權威人士: *She is an authority* **on** *Roman history.* 她是羅馬史的權威。

au·thor·ize /ˈɔːθəˌraɪz; ˈɔːθəraɪz/ *v* **authorized, authorizing** (also 又作 **authorise** *BrE* 〔英式〕) [T] to give permission 批准; 允許: *Who is authorized to sign these invoices?* 誰有權簽署這些發票呢? | *I cannot authorize payment of this bill until it has been checked.* 在經過核對以後, 我才能批准支付這張賬單。

□ USEFUL PATTERNS 有用句型
to authorize something; to authorize someone to do something

–**authorization, authorisation** /ˌɔːθərəˈzeɪʃən; ˌɔːθəraɪˈzeɪʃən/ *n* [C;U]

au·to·bi·og·ra·phy /ˌɔːtəbaɪˈɒɡrəfɪ; ˌɔːtəbaɪˈɒɡrəfi/ *n* **autobiographies** a book written by someone about their own life 自傳 – compare 比較 BIOGRAPHY –**autobiographical** /ˌɔːtə‚baɪəˈɡræfɪkl; ˌɔːtəbaɪəˈɡræfɪkəl/ *adj* –**autobiographically** /-klɪ; -kli/ *adv*

au·toc·ra·cy /ɔːˈtɒkrəsɪ; ɔːˈtɒkrəsi/ *n* **autocracies** [C;U] rule by one person with unlimited power 獨裁政治; 專制制度

au·to·crat /ˈɔːtəˌkræt; ˈɔːtəkræt/ *n* **1** a ruler with unlimited power 獨裁者 **2** a person who gives orders without considering the wishes of other people 獨斷專行的人 –

autocratic /ˌɔːtəˈkrætɪk; ˌɔːtəˈkrætɪk•/ *adj* –**autocratically** /-klɪ; -kli/ *adv*

au·to·graph¹ /ˈɔːtəˌɡræf; ˈɔːtəɡrɑːf/ *n* a famous person's name, written in their own handwriting 〔名人的〕親筆簽名: *We asked the singer for her autograph.* 我們請那位歌手給我們簽名留念。

autograph² *v* [T] to sign something with your own name 親筆簽名於〔某物〕: *I've got an autographed copy of her book.* 我有一本她親筆簽名的書。

au·to·mate /ˈɔːtəˌmeɪt; ˈɔːtəmeɪt/ *v* **automated, automating** [T] to make something work by machinery and without the work of people 使自動化: *The factory is now fully automated.* 這家工廠現已全實現了自動化。

au·to·mat·ic /ˌɔːtəˈmætɪk; ˌɔːtəˈmætɪk•/ *adj* **1** able to work or move by itself without needing the operation of a person (of a machine) 自動的〔指機器〕: *The heating system here has an automatic temperature control.* 這裡的暖氣系統有自動化的溫度調節控制。 | *This washing machine is fully automatic.* 這台洗衣機是全自動的。 **2** done without thinking, especially as a habit 不經思考的; 習慣性的: *The movements needed to ride a bicycle soon become automatic.* 騎腳踏車所需要的動作很快就變成了習慣性的動作。 **3** certain to happen, without the need for further action 〔無需採取進一步行動而〕必然發生的: *You will get an automatic pay increase every year.* 你的薪金每年會自然增長。 –**automatically** /-klɪ; -kli/ *adv*

au·to·ma·tion /ˌɔːtəˈmeɪʃən; ˌɔːtəˈmeɪʃən/ *n* [U] the use of machines that need little or no human control 自動化

au·to·mo·bile /ˈɔːtəməˌbil; ˈɔːtəməbiːl/ *n fml, AmE* a car 〔正式, 美式〕汽車: *the automobile industry* 汽車工業

au·ton·o·mous /ɔːˈtɒnəməs; ɔːˈtɒnəməs/ *adj* having autonomy 自治的: *Catalonia is an autonomous region of Spain.* 加泰羅尼亞是西班牙的一個自治區。 –**autonomously** *adv*

au·ton·o·my /ɔːˈtɒnəmɪ; ɔːˈtɒnəmi/ *n* [U] the right of self-government or management of your own affairs, usually of a state or group within a country 自治; 自主

au·top·sy /ˈɔːtɒpsɪ; ˈɔːtɒpsi/ *n* **autopsies** an examination of a dead body to discover the cause of death 驗屍

*★***au·tumn** /ˈɔːtəm; ˈɔːtəm/ *n* (also 又作 **Autumn**) [C;U] the season between summer and winter 秋天; 秋季: *I left England last autumn.* 我於去年秋天離開了英國。 –**autumnal** /ɔːˈtʌmnl; ɔːˈtʌmnəl/ *adj*

aux·il·i·a·ry /ɔːɡˈzɪljərɪ; ɔːɡˈzɪljəri/ *adj* giving help or additional support 輔助的: *auxiliary workers* 輔助工人 –**auxiliary** *n* **auxiliaries**

auxiliary verb /ˌ···ˈ·/ *n tech* a verb that is used with another verb to show differences such as person and tense; in English the auxiliary verbs are **be, do,** and

have〖術語〗助動詞〔與另外一個動詞連用, 以表示人稱與時態的區別; 英語中的助動詞是 **be**, **do** 和 **have**〕(e.g. in 如在 *"I am running", "I didn't climb", "they have heard"* 當中)

a·vail¹ /ə'veɪl; ə'veɪl/ *n lit*〖文〗**to no avail** without success 無用; 徒勞: *We tried and tried, but it was all to no avail.* 我們試了又試, 可全都是徒勞無功。

avail² *v* **avail yourself of** *fml* to make use of a chance to do something〖正式〗利用〔某物〕: *You should avail yourself of every opportunity to improve your English.* 你應該利用每一個機會來提高你的英語水平。

★a·vai·la·ble /ə'veɪəbḷ; ə'veɪləbəl/ *adj* **1** able to be obtained or used 可得到的; 可使用的: *I'm sorry, Madam, those shoes are only available in small sizes.* 很抱歉, 太太, 那種鞋只有小號的。| *When will the paperback edition be available?* 那本書的平裝版何時才能買得到? **2** free to see or talk to someone 有空會面、交談的: *The doctor is not available just now.* 醫生現在沒有空。| *I will be available on Monday.* 我星期一有空。–opposite 反義 **unavailable** – **availability** /ə,velə'bɪlətɪ; ə,veɪlə'bɪlḁti/ *n* [U]

av·a·lanche /'æv̩,lɑ:ntʃ; 'ævəlɑ:ntʃ/ *n* **1** a large mass of rocks or snow and ice crashing down the side of a mountain 雪崩 **2** a lot of things happening or coming at the same time 同時發生的許多事情: *An avalanche of letters landed on the doormat.* 來信如雪片般落到門墊上。

a·vant-garde /ə,vɑnt'gɑrd; ,ævɒ:ŋ 'gɑ:d/ *adj* based on the newest and most modern ideas in music, theatre, and literature 前衛派的, 先鋒的〔指在音樂、戲劇、文學方面〕: *an avant-garde painter* 前衛派畫家

av·a·rice /'ævərɪs; 'ævərḁs/ *n* [U] *fml* extreme desire for wealth〖正式〗貪婪; 貪慾 – **avaricious** /,ævə'rɪʃəs; ,ævə'rɪʃəs/ *adj*

Ave *n* a written abbreviation for〖縮〗= AVENUE

a·venge /ə'vendʒ; ə'vendʒ/ *v* **avenged, avenging** [T] *fml* to do harm to someone in return for something bad that they have done〖正式〗為某人報復, 復仇: *He avenged his brother's death by burning the house.* 他燒了那所房子, 為哥哥的死報了仇。–**avenger** *n*

av·e·nue /'ævə,nju; 'æv̩,nju:/ *n* **1** a wide road in a town, often between two rows of trees〔城市的〕大街, 林蔭道: *My address is 11 Carlton Avenue, Bristol.* 我的住址是布里斯托市卡爾通大街十一號。**2** a way of getting something done 方法; 途徑: *They explored every avenue but could not find a solution.* 他們每一種方法都試過了, 但是沒有找到解決辦法。

★av·e·rage¹ /'ævərɪdʒ; 'ævərɪdʒ/ *n* **1** [C] the amount found by adding together several quantities and then dividing by the number of quantities 平均數: *The average of 3, 8, and 10 is 7.* (數字) 3, 8, 10 的平均數是 7。| *The price of cars has increased by an average of 6%.* 汽車的價格平均上漲了6%。**2** [U] a level or standard regarded as usual or ordinary 一般水平; 平均標準 **3 above average** better than average 高於一般水平: *Tanya is good at maths* 坦尼亞的數學很好—遠遠高於一般水平。[RELATED PHRASE 相關詞組 **below average**] **4 on average** usually 通常: *On average babies start walking at a year old.* 嬰兒一般都是在一歲時開始走路的。

average² *adj* [only before a noun 只用於名詞前] **1** calculated by making an average of a number of quantities 平均的: *What is the average rainfall for July?* 七月份的平均降雨量是多少? **2** regarded as usual or ordinary 普通的; 通常的: *The average British family has two children.* 普通的英國家庭有兩個小孩。| *I am of average weight.* 我的體重屬於中等。**3** neither good or bad in quality 不好不壞的; 一般的: *The film was just average — nothing special.* 這部影片只屬一般 — 沒有甚麼特別之處。

average³ *v* **averaged, averaging** [T] to do or have something usually, as an average 平均為: *Our company averages 20 enquiries a day.* 我們公司平均每天接到二十次詢價。

average out *phr v* [I] *infml* to come to an average quantity or standard over a period of time〖非正式〗〔在一段時間內〕達到一般水平: *My hours of work average out at about 35 a week.* 我的工作時間為每週三十五小時。

a·verse /ə'vɜs; ə'vɜ:s/ *adj* **averse to** opposed to 反對的: *I don't drink usually, but I am not averse to the occasional glass of champagne.* 我通常不喝酒, 但也不反對偶爾來一杯香檳。

a·ver·sion /ə'vɜʒən; ə'vɜ:ʃən/ *n* [sing] a strong dislike for something 厭惡; 反感: *She has an aversion to cats.* 她討厭貓。

a·vert /ə'vɜt; ə'vɜ:t/ *v* [T] **1** to prevent something unpleasant from happening 防止, 避免〔令人不愉快的事情〕: *An accident was only averted by her quick thinking.* 她思維敏捷, 才避免了一起事故。**2** *fml* to turn away〖正式〗轉移; 移開: *He quickly averted his gaze.* 他很快把目光移開。

a·vi·a·ry /'eɪvɪ,ɛrɪ; 'eɪvɪərɪ/ *n* **aviaries** a large cage or enclosure for keeping birds in 大鳥籠; 鳥舍

a·vi·a·tion /,eɪvɪ'eʃən; ,eɪvɪ'eɪʃən/ *n* [U] **1** the development and production of aircraft 飛機製造業 **2** the business of operating aircraft 航空; 飛行術

a·vi·a·tor /'eɪvɪ,etə; 'eɪvɪeɪtə/ *n old fash* the pilot of an aircraft〖老式〗飛行員

av·id /'ævɪd; 'æv̩d/ *adj* doing something a lot because you enjoy it〔出於喜歡而〕大量做某事的; 渴望的: *Liz is an avid reader.* 利茲是個廢寢忘食的讀者。–**avidly** *adv*

av·o·ca·do /,ɑvə'kɑdo; ,ævə'kɑ:dəʊ◂/ (also

又作 **avocado pear** /ˌ····'·/) *n* a green tropical fruit with a large stone and smooth oily flesh 鱷梨, 牛油果

★★a·void /ə'vɔɪd; ə'vɔɪd/ *v* [T] **1** to make an effort not to do something or to stop something from happening 避免〔做某事〕; 防止〔發生某事〕: *A healthy diet will help you avoid heart disease.* 健康的飲食會助防止心臟病。| *She avoided answering most of my questions.* 她對我問的很多問題都避而不答。| *He left the room to avoid having to speak to her.* 他離開了房間, 免得跟她說話。

□ USEFUL PATTERNS 有用句型
to avoid something; to avoid doing something

2 to keep away from a person, place, or thing 避開: *Turn right here to avoid the city centre.* 在這兒朝右轉以繞過市中心。| *The doctor's told me to avoid alcohol.* 醫生叫我不要喝酒。**–avoidable** *adj* **–avoidance** *n* [U]: *tax avoidance* 逃稅

a·vow /ə'vaʊ; ə'vaʊ/ *v* [T;+that] *fml* to state or admit something openly 〔正式〕聲明; 公開承認 **–avowal** *n* [C;U]

a·vowed /ə'vaʊd; ə'vaʊd/ *adj* [only before a noun 只用於名詞前] openly declared or admitted 公開宣稱的; 公開承認的: *an avowed Communist* 公開承認的共產主義者

a·wait /ə'wet; ə'weɪt/ *v* [T] *fml* 〔正式〕**1** to wait for something 等候, 等待〔某人〕: *I am awaiting their reply.* 我在等他們的回音。**2** to be ready for someone 〔為某人〕作好準備: *A warm welcome awaits you.* 你將受到熱烈的歡迎。

a·wake¹ /ə'wek; ə'weɪk/ *adj* [never before a noun 不能用於名詞前] **1** not asleep 醒着的: *She lay awake for hours, thinking.* 她躺在牀上思考問題, 好幾個小時還沒有睡。**2 awake to something** *fml* conscious of something 〔正式〕意識到某事物: *He is awake to the difficulties he faces.* 他意識到自己所面臨的困難。**3 wide awake** not at all sleepy 毫無睡意; 異常清醒

awake² /ə'wek; ə'weɪk/ *v* **awoke** /ə'wok; ə-'wəʊk/ *or* **awaked, awaked** *or* **awoken** /ə'wokən; ə'wəʊkən/, **awaking** (also 又作 **awaken**) *fml* 〔正式〕**1** [I;T] to stop sleeping 醒過來: *I awoke to the sound of birds singing.* 我聽到鳥鳴聲醒了過來。| *The noise awoke me.* 喧鬧聲把我吵醒了。**2 awake to something** to become conscious of something 意識到某事物: *Suddenly they awoke to the danger.* 他們突然意識到了危險。

a·wak·en·ing /ə'wekənɪŋ; ə'weɪkənɪŋ/ *n* **1** the beginning of a feeling or activity 覺醒: *There was an awakening of concern for the environment.* 大家開始關注環境問題。**2 a rude awakening** a shock felt when you find out or suddenly understand something unpleasant 猛然醒悟, 突然明白〔不愉快的事態〕

★★a·ward¹ /ə'wɔrd; ə'wɔːd/ *v* [T] to officially give a prize or money to someone for a special reason 〔由於原因而〕授予〔某人〕獎品〔獎金〕: *He was awarded the Nobel Prize for Literature.* 他獲頒諾貝爾文學獎。| *The judge awarded a large sum of money to the families of the dead.* 法官判給死者家屬一大筆錢。

□ USEFUL PATTERNS 有用句型
to award something to someone; to award someone something

award² *n* a prize or money, given by an organization for a special reason 〔由於原因而由某一機構所授予的〕獎品, 獎金: *the award for Best Actress* 最佳女演員獎 | *The University sometimes gives awards to students with financial difficulties.* 有時候大學會給有經濟困難的學生頒發獎學金。

★★a·ware /ə'wɛr; ə'weə/ *adj* having knowledge or understanding 知道的; 意識到的: *Women are often more aware of their feelings than men.* 女人通常比男人更為清楚自己的感覺。| *Are you aware that there is a problem?* 你意識到有個問題嗎? | *I'm quite aware of how you must feel.* 我十分清楚你肯定會有甚麼感覺。| *She is very politically aware.* 她的政治意識很強。– opposite 反義 **unaware –awareness** *n* [U]

□ USEFUL PATTERNS 有用句型
be aware of something; be aware that...

a·wash /ə'wɑʃ; ə'wɒʃ/ *adj* [never before a noun 不能用於名詞前] **1** covered with water 被水覆蓋的: *The river flooded, and soon the streets were awash.* 河水泛濫, 街道很快便被淹沒了。**2 awash with something** *infml* having too much of something 〔非正式〕某物充沛的; 某物充斥的: *The office is awash with computers but there's no money for new staff.* 辦公室裡有大量電腦, 卻沒有錢招聘新雇員。

★★a·way¹ /ə'we; ə'weɪ/ *adv* **1** moving from a place 從〔某地〕移開; 離開: *He got into the car and drove away.* 他鑽進汽車便駕車離開了。| *She walked away from the house.* 她離開了那所房子。| *Go away!* 走開! –see picture on page 764 見764頁彩圖。**2** distant from a place 距離〔某地〕: *Is your house far away?* 你的家遠嗎? | *They live three miles away.* 他們住在三英里以外的地方。**3** not at home or at your usual place of work 不在家; 不在工作單位: *She's away on holiday at the moment.* 目前她正出門度假去了。| *He had to go away on business.* 他得因公外出。**4** in a safe place 在安全地方: *I'll put the plates away.* 我去把盤子收起來。**5** so as to be gone …掉; 消失: *The water had all boiled away.* 水燒乾了。**6** all the time or continuously 不斷地; 一直地: *They worked away all day.* 他們整天不停地工作。

away² *adj* [only before a noun 只用於名詞前] played at the sports field of your opponent〔體育比賽〕客場的; 在對方場地進行的: *We've got an away match next week.* 下週我們要去客場比賽。

awe /ɔ; ɔ:/ *n* [U] **1** a feeling of respect mixed with fear or admiration 敬畏: *I watched the powerful ocean with awe.* 我驚嘆地看着擁有千鈞之力的海洋。 **2 in awe of** someone having feelings of respect and fear for someone 對某人感到敬畏: *He is in awe of his father.* 他敬畏父親。

awe·in·spir·ing /'···, ·· / *adj* causing feelings of awe 令人敬畏的

awe·some /'ɔsəm; 'ɔ:səm/ *adj* causing feelings of awe 令人敬畏的: *an awesome account of the terrors of war* 描寫戰爭恐怖的令人畏懼的報道 | *an awesome responsibility* 令人感到敬畏的責任

awe·struck /'ɔ,strʌk; 'ɔ:strʌk/ *adj fml* filled with awe〔正式〕敬畏的; 畏懼的: *We sat in awestruck silence after hearing the truth at last.* 我們終於聽到了事實真相, 嚇得一聲不響地坐在那裏。

aw·ful /'ɔful; 'ɔ:fəl/ *adj* **1** very unpleasant and shocking 糟糕的; 可怕的: *The pain was awful.* 疼痛得厲害極了。 | *That's awful news.* 那消息真可怕。 **2** *infml* not very well〔非正式〕不好的; 難受的: *I feel awful.* 我感覺很難受。 **3** *infml* not very pleasant〔非正式〕令人不快的: *What an awful day!* 多麼糟糕的一天! | *The food tasted awful.* 食物的味道很糟糕。 **4 an awful lot** *infml* very many or very much〔非正式〕許多; 大量: *I've got an awful lot of things to do.* 我有一大堆事要做。 | *Big dogs need an awful lot of food.* 大狗吃得特別多。 | *Babies cry an awful lot!* 嬰兒哭起來真沒完沒了。

aw·ful·ly /'ɔfuli; 'ɔ:fəli/ *adv infml* very〔非正式〕很; 非常: *It's awfully cold in here.* 這裏冷得厲害。 | *That's an awfully good idea.* 那個主意好極了。

a·while /ə'hwaɪl; ə'waɪl/ *adv fml* for a short time〔正式〕一會兒; 片刻

awk·ward /'ɔkwəd; 'ɔ:kwəd/ *adj* **1** lacking skill in moving your body easily or confi-

dently 笨拙的; 不靈活的: *He is rather awkward with his hands.* 他的手腳不靈巧。 **2** difficult to use or do 難用的; 不便的: *an awkward size* 不合適的尺碼 | *This machine is awkward to clean.* 這部機器很難清潔。 **3** causing difficulty or uncomfortable feelings 引起不便的; 令人不舒服的: *Our visitors came at an awkward time.* 我們的客人來得很不是時候。 | *She asked me some very awkward questions.* 她問了我幾個令人尷尬的問題。 | *an awkward silence* 尷尬的沉默 **4** unwilling to help 不肯幫忙的: *Stop being so awkward!* 不要總給人出難題! **–awkwardly** *adv* **–awkwardness** *n* [U]

aw·ning /'ɔnɪŋ; 'ɔ:nɪŋ/ *n* a covering made of strong cloth, used as protection from sun or rain 遮篷; 涼篷

a·woke /ə'wok; ə'wəʊk/ the past tense of AWAKE ☆ AWAKE 的過去式

a·wok·en /ə'wokən; ə'wəʊkən/ the past participle of AWAKE ☆ AWAKE 的過去分詞

axe¹ /æks; æks/ *n* **axes** /'æksɪz; 'æksɪz/ (also 又作 **ax** *AmE*【美式】) a tool with a heavy metal blade on the end of a long handle, used to cut wood 斧; 斧頭 –see picture on page 958 見 958 頁彩圖

axe² *v* **axed, axing** (also 又作 **ax** *AmE*【美式】) [T] to reduce costs, plans, or services or to stop them completely 削減〔開支〕; 取消〔計劃〕; 停止〔服務〕: *The new school project was axed by the government.* 興建新學校的計劃被政府取消了。

ax·i·om /'æksɪəm; 'æksɪəm/ *n* a statement that is accepted as true by most people 公理 **–axiomatic** /,æksɪə'mætɪk; ,æksɪə'mætɪk/ *adj*

ax·is /'æksɪs; 'æksɪs/ *n* **axes** /'æksiːz; 'æksiːz/ **1** the imaginary line around which something moves 軸; 軸線: *The Earth turns on its axis.* 地球繞着地軸線旋轉。 **2** a line at the side (X-axis) or bottom (Y-axis) of a GRAPH, along which things are measured 圖表的軸線

ax·le /'æksl; 'æksəl/ *n* a bar with a wheel on each end 輪軸

aye /aɪ; aɪ/ *adv dialect* yes〔方言〕是; 對: *Aye, aye, sir.* 是, 長官。

az·ure /'æʒə; 'æʒər/ *adj* bright blue 蔚藍的: *the azure sky* 蔚藍色的天空

B, b

B, b /biː; biː/ **B's, b's** *or* **Bs, bs 1** the 2nd letter of the English alphabet 英語的第二個字母 **2** when you have several points you want to make, you can order them and show where each one starts by using "a", "b", "c", etc; teachers and speakers on technical subjects do this, and some people use them in conversation 第二〔當要表述幾個要點時，可使用 "a"，"b"，"c" 等順序進行羅列；教師和專業學科的演講者使用這種方法，還有一些人在會話中也這樣用〕: *There are two reasons why the plant has failed to flower: a, it hasn't had enough light and, b, the temperature hasn't been sufficiently high.* 這株植物不開花有兩個原因：第一，光照不足；第二，溫度不夠高。| *"Do you think he'll get the job?" "Well, I don't really because, a, he hasn't got the qualifications and, b, he hasn't got much experience."* "你想他能得到這份工作嗎？" "嗯，我認為他不能，因為第一，他資歷不夠；第二，他經驗不多。"

b. a written abbreviation for 〔縮〕= BORN 出生: *b. 1885* 生於1885年

BA /ˌbiː ˈeɪ; ˌbiː ˈeɪ/ **1** an abbreviation for BACHELOR OF ARTS; a first university degree not in a scientific subject 〔縮〕文學士學位: *He has a BA.* 他有文學士學位。 **2** a person who has a BA 文學士: *John Stephens, BA* 文學士約翰·斯蒂芬斯

baa /bɑː; bɑː/ *n* the sound that a sheep or lamb makes 〔羊或小羊叫聲〕咩

bab·ble /ˈbæbl; ˈbæbəl/ *v* **babbled, babbling** [I] **1** to talk quickly and foolishly, or in a way that is hard to understand 胡言亂語；含糊不清地說: *What are you babbling on about?* 你在胡言亂語些甚麼？ **2** to make continuous sounds like a stream 作潺潺聲: *a babbling stream* 潺潺的小溪 | *The baby babbled away for hours.* 這嬰孩一連幾個小時咿咿呀呀。 – **babble** *n*

babe /beɪb; beɪb/ *n* **1** *old fash* a baby 〔老式〕嬰兒 **2** *AmE slang* a woman, usually a young one 〔美俚〕年輕婦女；小妞

ba·boon /bæˈbuːn; bəˈbuːn/ *n* a large monkey 狒狒

★★**ba·by** /ˈbeɪbɪ; ˈbeɪbi/ *n* **babies 1** a very young child, usually one who has not yet learnt to speak 嬰孩〔常指尚未學說話的〕嬰兒: *It's a baby girl.* 這是個女嬰。| *a tiny baby* 小嬰兒 –see 見 CHILD (USAGE 用法) **2** a very young animal or bird 幼畜；雛鳥: *a baby monkey* 幼猴 **3** something younger or smaller than others like it 比較年幼的人；比較小的東西: *She's the baby of*

the class. 她是班級中年齡最小的。 **4** *infml* something that is the special responsibility of a particular person 〔非正式〕歸某人管的事物: *You'd better ask Peter about that — it's his baby.* 這事你最好問彼得——這是他管的。 **5** *AmE slang* a word used to address someone you love 〔美俚〕寶貝兒〔用於稱自己所愛的人〕

baby car·riage /ˈ···, ···/ *n* the usual American word for 〔美式〕= PRAM

ba·by·hood /ˈbeɪbɪˌhʊd; ˈbeɪbihʊd/ *n* [U] the period of time when you are a baby 嬰兒期

ba·by·ish /ˈbeɪbɪɪʃ; ˈbeɪbi-ɪʃ/ *derog* 〔貶〕 **1** like a baby 像嬰兒的；孩子氣的: *They told him it was babyish to cry.* 他們對他說，哭哭啼啼太孩子氣了。 **2** suitable for a baby 適於嬰兒的: *That toy's too babyish for a six-year-old.* 這玩具對六歲的孩子來說太容易了。

baby-mind·er /ˈ···ˌ···/ *n* *BrE* a person who looks after your baby 〔英式〕受雇照料嬰兒的人；褓姆

baby-sit /ˈ··· ·/ *v* **baby-sat, baby-sat, baby-sitting** [I] to look after children while their parents are out 受雇代外出的父母照看小孩: *I'm baby-sitting for Mrs Davis tonight.* 今晚我臨時要為戴維斯太太照顧孩子。 – **baby-sitter** *n*: *We couldn't go out because we couldn't get a baby-sitter.* 因為沒找到臨時照顧孩子的人，我們無法外出。

bach·e·lor /ˈbætʃələ; ˈbætʃələr/ *n* an unmarried man 未婚男子；單身漢

Bachelor of Arts /ˌ··· ·ˈ·/ *n* –see 見 BA

Bachelor of Sci·ence /ˌ··· ·ˈ··/ *n* –see 見 BSC

★★**back¹** /bæk; bæk/ *n* **1** the part of your body that is behind you, opposite your chest, and goes from your neck to your bottom 背部；背脊: *He was lying on the floor on his back.* 他仰臥在地板上。| *She was carrying a baby on her back.* 她揹着嬰孩。–see 見 PAIN (USAGE 用法) **2 the back** the part of something that is opposite the front 後面；後部；背面: *Please write your address on the back of the cheque.* 請把你的地址寫在支票背面。| *The index is at the back of the book.* 索引在書後面。| *We couldn't hear very well because we were right at the back of the hall.* 我們坐在大廳後面，所以聽不清楚。 **3** the part of a chair that you lean on when you are sitting 椅背 **4 be glad to see the back of** to be glad when you do not have to see someone or something any more 因不用再看見〔某人或某事〕而高興 **5**

★★ 最常用的 1000 字　　★ 最常用的 1001-2000 字　　★ 最常用的 2001-3000 字

behind someone's back in a way that is unknown to the person concerned 背着某人: *The decision was taken behind my back.* 這項決議是背着我作出的。| *They've been talking about me behind my back.* 他們老在背後談論我。**6 put someone's back up** to annoy someone 使某人生氣 **7 the back of beyond** a place that is far away from other places 與外界隔絕的地方 **8 turn your back on someone** to refuse to help or see someone 拒絕幫助[見]某人

back² *adv* **1** in the direction that is behind you 在後面: *She stepped back to look at the painting.* 她退回去看那幅畫。| *He turned round and looked back towards the town.* 他轉過身往後面的市中心看看。**2** where someone or something was before 回原處: *I put the book back on the shelf.* 我把書放回書架上。| *We'll be back home tomorrow.* 我們明天回家。**3** away from a person or thing 離開[某人或某物]: *Stand back from the fire.* 站得離爐火遠一點。**4** in someone's possession again 再回到[某人]手裡: *She gave the book back to me.* 她把書還給我。| *I don't know if I'll ever get my money back.* 我不知道是否還能拿回我的錢。**5** in reply 回覆: *I'll phone you back later.* 稍後我會給你回電話的。| *I wrote to her but she never wrote back.* 我給她寫信,但她從不回信。**6** towards or in an earlier time [追溯至以前]早在...: *This law was brought in back in 1968.* 這條法律早在1968年就制訂了。

*★**back³** *adj* [only before a noun 只用於名詞前] **1** at the back 後面的: *I always use the back door.* 我總是使用後門。| *the back wheels of the car* 汽車的後輪 **2** owed from an earlier time 拖欠的: *The company owes me £500 in back pay.* 公司欠我五百英鎊薪水。**3 back road, back street** a small road in a town or city [鎮裡或城市裡的]小馬路

*★**back⁴** *v* **1** [I] to move backwards 後退: *He backed out of the room.* 他向後退出了房間。| *The car backed out of the garage.* 車倒開駛出了車庫。**2** [T] to make a vehicle move backwards 倒[車]: *She backed the car down the drive.* 她順着車道倒車。**3** [T] to support someone, often by giving them money 資助[某人]: *We persuaded a couple of firms to back the project.* 我們勸說幾家公司贊助該項目。**4** [T] to put money on a person or animal in a race 下賭注於[賽馬或比賽]: *I backed three horses and they all lost!* 我在三匹馬上下了注,可是牠們都輸了!

back away *phr v* [I] to move away from someone or something because you are frightened [因害怕而]離開[某人或某物]

back down *phr v* [I] to admit that you were wrong about something 承認錯誤

back onto sthg *phr v* [T] (of a building) to have something at the back [建築物]背對着: *The house backs onto open fields.* 這幢房子背對着開闊的田野。

back out *phr v* [I] to decide that you will not do something that you had agreed to do 決定不履行[允諾的事]: *They backed out of the deal at the last minute.* 他們在最後關頭變了卦,決定不做這項交易。

back sbdy/sthg ↔ **up** *phr v* [T] to support someone or something, especially by showing that they are telling the truth 支持[某人或某事][尤指反映真情]: *The evidence seems to back up what you are saying.* 證據似乎都支持你所說的話。

back·bit·ing /ˈbæk,baɪtɪŋ; ˈbækbaɪtɪŋ/ *n* [U] unkind talk about someone who is not present 背後說人的壞話

back·bone /ˈbækˈbɒn; ˈbækbəʊn/ *n* **1** [C] the row of bones in the centre of your back 脊骨 **2** [sing] the part of a group that provides the main support [團體的]骨幹; 中堅; 主要成分: *Small farmers form the backbone of our nation!* 小農是我們國家的主要支柱。**3** [U] strength of character 毅力; 骨氣: *"No backbone," said the old man. "That's the trouble with young people today!"* "沒有骨氣,"這老人說。"這是當今青年人的毛病。"

back·break·ing /ˈbæk,breɪkɪŋ; ˈbækbreɪkɪŋ/ *adj* very hard and needing a lot of effort 勞累的; 累人的: *backbreaking work* 勞累的工作

back·date /ˈbækˈdeɪt; ,bækˈdeɪt/ *v* **backdated, backdating** [T] to make something come into operation from an earlier date 使[某事物]從過去某日開始有效: *The increase in pay agreed in June will be backdated to January.* 六月時同意增加的工資將從一月算起。

back·drop /ˈbæk,drɒp; ˈbækdrɒp/ (also 又作 **backcloth** /-,klɒθ; -,klɒθ/) *n* a situation in which something happens 背景: *The events of the 1930s provided the backdrop for the film.* 這部電影以三十年代的那些事件為背景。

back·er /ˈbækə; ˈbækəʳ/ *n* someone who supports a plan or a person with money [對計劃或他人的]贊助人; 資助者

back·fire /ˈbæk,faɪr; ,bækˈfaɪəʳ/ *v* **backfired, backfiring** [I] **1** to make a loud noise as a result of an explosion in the engine which comes too soon (used of a motor vehicle) 引擎回火, 逆火[指汽車] **2** to have an effect opposite to the effect intended 產生事與願違的後果: *His plan to get rich backfired and he lost all his money.* 他的致富計劃事與願違, 結果把錢都虧掉了。

back·gam·mon /ˈbæk,gæmən; ˈbækgæmən/ *n* [U] a game for two players, using round wooden pieces and DICE on a special board 西洋十五子棋[一種使用圓木棋子和骰子的雙人棋戲]

*★**back·ground** /ˈbæk,graʊnd; ˈbækgraʊnd/ *n* **1** [C] the scenery or ground behind the main objects or people in view, a picture or a photograph 背景; 後景: *This is a photo*

of my house; in the background you can see the mountains. 這是一張我家房子的照片; 在背景處你可以看到山脈。 **2** [C;U] the conditions that exist when something happens and that help to explain it 〔發生事情時的〕情況: *The election took place against a background of widespread unemployment.* 選舉在一片失業聲中舉行。 | *I'll need a bit more background information before I can help you.* 我需要再了解一點背景情況, 然後才能幫助你。 **3** [C] a person's family, experience, and education 個人的背景資料〔包括家庭、經歷和教育狀況〕: *She's from a rather disturbed background.* 她出身於一個很不安定的家庭。 **4 in the background** not noticed very much 不顯眼的: *She's got a lot of power, but she likes to remain in the background.* 她很有權勢, 但喜歡居於幕後。

back·hand /ˈbækˈhænd; ˈbækhænd/ *n* a stroke in tennis made with the back of the hand turned in the direction of movement 〔網球的〕反手擊球: *He's got an excellent backhand.* 他的反手功夫很出色。 –compare 比較 FOREHAND

back·hand·ed /ˈbækˈhændɪd; ˌbækˈhæn-dɪ̣d◂/ *adj* **backhanded compliment** a remark about someone that sounds pleasant but is usually not intended kindly 〔隱含諷刺的〕恭維話

back·hand·er /ˈbækˈhændə; ˈbækhændəʳ/ *n infml* money given to someone in order to influence their actions or decisions 〔非正式〕賄賂

back·ing /ˈbækɪŋ; ˈbækɪŋ/ *n* **1** [U] help or support, especially by giving money 幫助; 支持; 資助: *The plan has plenty of backing, and will probably succeed.* 該計劃得到許多支持, 相信會成功。 **2** [C;U] any kind of material that is put on the back of an object to protect it 襯背; 背托: *a cardboard backing* 硬紙襯背 **3** [C] the music or singing that helps and supports the main singer or musician 伴奏; 伴唱

back·lash /ˈbæklæʃ; ˈbæklæʃ/ *n* **1** a strong but usually delayed feeling by many people against a growing belief or practice, especially towards a political or social development 〔對某項政治或社會事態發展的〕強烈反應, 強烈反對; 抵撞; 後衝: *a sudden violent backward movement* [U]

back·log /ˈbækˌlɒg; ˈbæklɔg/ *n* a lot of things needing to be done that were not done at the proper time 積壓待辦的事務: *After his holiday, he had a large backlog of work to deal with.* 假期過後, 他有一大堆積壓的工作要處理。

back·pack /ˈbækˌpæk; ˈbækpæk/ *n AmE* a special type of bag that you carry on your back 〔美式〕背包 –**backpacker** *n* –**backpacking** *n* [U]

back·ped·al /ˈbækˌpɛdl; ˌbækˈpedl/ *v* **-ll- (-l- AmE 〔美式〕) 1** to PEDAL backwards,

on a bicycle 〔在自行車上〕倒蹬 **2** *infml* to do or say something differently from the way you were going to do or say it 〔非正式〕出爾反爾; 變卦

back seat /ˌ·ˈ·◂/ *n* **1** a seat at the back of a car 〔汽車的〕後座 **2 take a back seat** to take a less important position 接受次要的位置: *She won't take a back seat to anyone.* 她不會接受低於任何人的職位。

back·side /ˈbækˈsaɪd; ˈbæksaɪd/ *n infml* the part of your body on which you sit 〔非正式〕臀部; 屁股

back·stage /ˈbækˈsteɪdʒ; ˌbækˈsteɪdʒ/ *adv* **1** behind the stage in a theatre 在後台 **2** secretly 祕密地

back street /ˈ·◂/ *n* a street away from the main streets of a town or city 〔遠離大街的〕後街小巷

back·stroke /ˈbækˌstrok; ˈbækstrəʊk/ *n* [sing, U] a swimming stroke done on your back 仰泳

back·track /ˈbækˌtræk; ˈbæktræk/ *v* [I] **1** to go back over the same path 原路返回 **2** to change a promise or intention and say or do something different 出爾反爾; 變卦

back·up /ˈbækˌʌp; ˈbækʌp/ *n* **1** [U] help which you have in addition to, or instead of, other support 後備; 替代物 **2 backup copy** a copy of information stored on a computer which you keep separate in case the main copy is lost 後備副本: *Make a backup copy, just in case you lose the file.* 複製一份後備副本, 以防文件丟失。

back·ward /ˈbækwəd; ˈbækwəd/ *adj* **1** in the direction that is behind you 向後的: *He gave a backward glance to see if he was being followed.* 他向後瞥了一眼, 看看是否有人在跟蹤。 **2** slow to learn things 遲鈍的: *a backward child* 遲鈍的孩子 **3** not having modern factories or a modern way of life 落後的: *a backward country* 落後的國家

back·wards /ˈbækwədz; ˈbækwədz/ *adv* (also 又作 **backward** *AmE* 〔美式〕) **1** in the direction that is behind you 向後地: *She stepped backwards to let him past.* 她後退幾步, 讓他通過。 **2** towards the past 倒退; 回顧: *We must look forwards, not backwards.* 我們必須往前看, 而不是往後看。 | *He described the new law as a step backwards.* 他把新法規說成是一種倒退。 **3** in the opposite way to the way that is usual 相反地: *Can you say the alphabet backwards?* 你能倒背英文字母表嗎? **4 backwards and forwards** first in one direction and then in the opposite direction 來回地; 往返地 **5 know something backwards** to know something perfectly 瞭如指掌

back·wa·ter /ˈbækˌwɒtə; ˈbækwɔːtəʳ/ *n* **1** a part of a river where the water does not move 死水 **2** a place not influenced by outside events or new ideas 閉塞地區; 窮鄉僻壤: *There's nothing for young people in this* *village; it's a real backwater.* 對年輕人來説, 這村裡一無所有, 真是一處窮鄉僻壤。

back·woods /'bæk'wʊdz; 'bækwʊdz/ *n* **the backwoods** uncleared land far away from towns 遠離城鎮的叢林地帶

back·yard /'bæk'jɑrd; ˌbæk'jɑːd◂/ *n* **1** *BrE* a yard behind a house, covered with a hard surface 《英式》〔鋪了硬地面的〕後院 **2** *AmE* an area of ground behind a house, usually covered with grass 《美式》〔常為草地的〕後院

ba·con /'bekən; 'beɪkən/ *n* [U] salted or smoked meat from the back or sides of a pig 醃豬肉, 熏豬肉(豬的背肋部分) –see picture on page 504 見 504 頁彩圖 –see also MEAT (USAGE 用法)

bac·te·ri·a /bæk'tɪrɪə; bæk'tɪərɪə/ *n* [pl] very small living things, some of which cause disease; they exist in water, soil, air, plants, and the bodies of people and animals 細菌

★**bad** /bæd; bæd/ *adj* **worse** /wɜrs; wɜːs/, **worst** /wɜrst; wɜːst/ **1** not good or unpleasant 不好的; 令人不快的: *a bad smell* 難聞的氣味 | *The boys were punished for their bad behaviour.* 男孩們因為行為不檢而受到了懲罰。 | *I have some bad news for you, I'm afraid.* 對不起, 我有些壞消息要告訴你。 **2** not very skillful or of a low standard 不熟練的; 拙劣的: *She is a bad teacher.* 她是個蹩腳的老師。 | *I'm bad at maths.* 我的數學很差。 **3** unwell or hurt 不舒服的; 疼痛的: *She's got a bad leg.* 她的腿很痛。 **4** damaging or harmful 損害的; 有害的: *Smoking is bad for your health.* 吸煙對健康有害。 | *Pollution is having a bad effect on plants and animals.* 污染對動植物產生壞影響。 **5** serious or severe 嚴重的: *a bad cold* 重感冒 | *The winter's been bad this year.* 今年冬天極為寒冷。 **6** not fit to eat 不能吃的: *This fish has gone bad.* 這條魚不能吃了〔壞了〕。 **7 bad language** offensive language 粗言穢語 **8 bad debt** a debt that is unlikely to be paid 不大可能收回的賬; 壞賬 **9 feel bad** to feel ashamed or sorry 感到羞愧或抱歉: *I do feel bad about missing your birthday.* 錯過了你的生日我實在是抱歉。 **10 have a bad name** to have lost people's respect 聲譽不好: *That car has a bad name among motorists.* 那車在駕車人士之間已失去信譽。 **11 in a bad way** very ill or in serious trouble 病得很重; 情況嚴重 **12 it's too bad, that's too bad** *infml* I'm sorry 《非正式》感到遺憾: *It's too bad you couldn't come last night.* 很遺憾你昨晚沒能來。 **13 not bad** *infml* quite good 《非正式》不錯: *"How are you?" "Not bad, thanks."* "你好嗎?" "不錯, 謝謝。" | *This cake isn't at all bad.* 這蛋糕不錯。 –**badness** *n* [U]

bade /bæd; bæd, beɪd/ the past tense and past participle of BID ☆ BID 的過去式和過去分詞

badge /bædʒ; bædʒ/ *n* anything, especially a piece of metal or plastic, worn to show a person's job, rank, or membership of a group 徽章, 證章〔金屬或塑料製成, 表示職業、等級或會員身分等〕

bad·ger¹ /'bædʒə; 'bædʒəʳ/ *n* an animal which has black and white fur, lives in holes in the ground, and is active at night 獾〔一種毛色黑白, 居於地穴中並在夜間活動的動物〕

badger² *v* [T] to persuade someone by asking them again and again 吵着要; 煩擾: *The children badgered me to take them to the cinema.* 孩子們吵着要我帶他們去看電影。

★**bad·ly** /'bædli; 'bædlɪ/ *adv* **1** in a bad way 不好; 差: *badly made clothes* 縫製得不好的衣服 | *The book was badly written.* 這本書寫得很差。 | *I played very badly today.* 我今天打[玩、彈]得不好。 –opposite 反義 **well 2** very much 非常: *They want money badly.* 他們很需要錢。 | *He is badly in need of help.* 他非常需要幫助。 | *The whole area has been badly affected by snow storms.* 整個地區受到了暴風雪的嚴重影響。

badly-off /ˌ··'·/ *adj* **worse-off**, **worst-off** [never before a noun 不能用於名詞前] poor 窮困的

bad·min·ton /'bædmɪntən; 'bædmɪntən/ *n* [U] a game like tennis played by two or four people who hit a small feathered object called a SHUTTLECOCK over a high net 羽毛球(運動)

bad-tem·pered /ˌ·'···◂/ *adj* feeling angry and dissatisfied 生氣的; 覺得不滿的: *Why are you so bad-tempered this afternoon?* 你今天下午為甚麼這麼生氣?

baf·fle /'bæfl; 'bæfəl/ *v* **baffled, baffling** [T] to confuse someone greatly 使〔某人〕困惑; 難倒〔某人〕: *I was completely baffled by his remark.* 我被他的話完全弄糊塗了。 –see 見 ANGRY (USAGE 用法) –**bafflement** *n* [U] –**baffling** *adj*: *a baffling question* 令人為難的問題

★**bag¹** /bæg; bæg/ *n* **1** a container made of material such as paper, plastic, or leather, used to carry things in 包, 袋子〔常以紙、塑料、皮革製成〕: *a shopping bag* 購物袋 | *a polythene bag* 塑膠袋 –see picture on page 244 見 244 頁彩圖 **2** a woman's handbag 女式手提包: *Where's my bag?* 我的提包在哪裡? **3** the things in a bag 一袋之物: *Tom ate a whole bag of cherries.* 湯姆吃了一整袋櫻桃。 **4 bags of** lots of 許多: *bags of ideas* 好多主意 **5 have bags under your eyes** to look very tired 看上去很疲倦 **6 in the bag** *infml* certain to be won 《非正式》穩操勝券的; 十拿九穩的: *The contract is in the bag.* 這份合約是十拿九穩的。

bag² *v* **-gg-** [T] **1** to put things into bags 把…裝進袋中 **2** to get the right to do or have something which a lot of other people would like 獲得做〔某事〕的權利; 佔有〔某物〕: *She's bagged us a couple of seats in the front row.* 她在前排給我們佔了幾個座位。

bag·gage /ˈbæɡɪdʒ; ˈbæɡɪdʒ/ *n* [U] all the cases and bags you take when you travel 行李

bag·gy /ˈbæɡɪ; ˈbæɡi/ *adj* **baggier, baggiest** *infml* hanging loosely (used of clothes)〔非正式〕寬鬆而下垂的〔指衣服〕: *His trousers were baggy at the knees.* 他的褲子在膝蓋處很寬鬆。

bag·pipes /ˈbæɡ,paɪps; ˈbæɡpaɪps/ *n* [pl] a musical instrument in which air stored in a bag is forced out through pipes to produce the sound 風笛: *to play the bagpipes* 吹風笛

bail¹ /bel; beɪl/ *n* [U] money left with a court of law so that a prisoner can be set free until they are tried 保釋金: *The prisoner was released on bail.* 這個犯人交了保釋金後獲釋放。| *The judge granted bail.* 法官給予保釋。**2 stand/go bail for someone** to pay money so that someone may be set free in this way 為某人交保釋金 **3** [C] either of two small pieces of wood laid on top of the stumps (STUMP¹) in cricket〔板球〕三柱門上的橫木

bail² *v*

　　bail out *phr v* **1** [T **bail** sbdy ↔ **out**] to obtain someone's freedom by paying money called bail to show that you are sure that they will appear in court later〔交保釋金способ某人〕保釋出來〔保證將來到庭應訊〕: *Clark was charged with robbing the bank. His family paid £5000 to bail him out.* 克拉克被控搶劫銀行。他的家人付了五千英鎊將他保釋出來。**2** [T **bail** sbdy ↔ **out**] to help someone out of a difficult situation which they have got into, usually through their own fault 幫助〔某人〕脫離困境 **3** [I;T **bail** sthg ↔ **out**] to remove water from a boat to prevent it sinking〔從船上〕舀出水〔以免下沉〕: *Quick — start bailing out!* 快 — 開始舀水! **4** [T **bail** sbdy/sthg ↔ **out**] to help a person or a business out of difficulties by providing money〔用錢〕幫助〔某人或某企業〕擺脫困境 **5** [I] to escape from an aircraft by PARACHUTE 跳傘: *The pilot bailed out of the burning plane.* 飛行員跳傘逃離著了火的飛機。

bai·liff /ˈbelɪf; ˈbeɪlɪf/ *n* **1** *law* an official, especially one who takes possession of goods or property when money is owed〔律〕財產查封官; 執達吏 **2** a person who looks after land for the owner 地主的管家

bait¹ /bet; beɪt/ *n* **1** [U] food used to attract and catch fish, animals, or birds 誘餌: *The fisherman put the bait on the hook.* 漁夫把誘餌裝在鈎子上。**2** [C;U] something you use to attract someone when you want them to do something 誘惑物

bait² *v* [T] **1** to put bait on a hook to catch fish or in a trap to catch animals 裝上餌(以捕魚或獸) **2** to make someone angry intentionally 激怒, 挑惹〔某人〕

baize /bez; beɪz/ *n* [U] thick green cloth

used to cover tables on which certain games are played 綠色的厚桌面呢〔鋪在某些遊戲桌上作襯墊〕

bake /bek; beɪk/ *v* **baked, baking** [I;T] **1** to cook in an OVEN 烘; 烤; 焙: *to bake bread* 烘麵包 | *The bread is baking.* 麵包正在烘製中。**2** to make something hard by heating it 焙乾; 烤硬: *In former times, bricks were baked in the sun.* 從前, 磚是放在太陽下曬硬的。–see 見 COOK¹ (USAGE 用法)

baked beans /, ·'· / *n* [pl] small white beans cooked with tomatoes (TOMATO); people usually buy them in tins 烘豆〔小白豆子加番茄製成, 常以罐裝出售〕

bak·er /ˈbekə; ˈbeɪkər/ *n* **1** a person who bakes bread and cakes, especially professionally 麵包師 **2 baker's** a shop which sells bread and cakes 麵包[糕餅]店: *The baker's has got Christmas cakes already.* 麵包店已經有聖誕節的蛋糕了。| *I'm just going to the baker's.* 我正要去麵包店。

bak·er·y /ˈbekərɪ; ˈbeɪkəri/ *n* **bakeries** a place where bread and cakes are baked or sold 麵包烘房; 麵包店

bal·ance¹ /ˈbæləns; ˈbæləns/ *v* **balanced, balancing 1** [I;T] to get into a steady position and not allow to fall to one side or the other, especially when this is difficult (使)保持平衡: *She balanced the cup on top of a huge pile of books.* 她把杯子放在一大堆書上使其保持平衡。| *When you learn to ride a bicycle, you have to learn to balance.* 你學騎腳踏車時得學會保持平衡。**2** [T] to give equal importance to two or more things 使〔兩件或更多的事物〕同等重要; 使均衡; 兼顧: *They have to balance the demand for a better service* **with** *the need to keep costs down.* 他們既需要有更好的服務, 亦需要控制成本。**3** [I;T] to prevent something from becoming too unequal 使相稱; 和...相等: *His imagination is balanced by great practicality.* 他既有想像力, 又很務實。**4** [T] to consider one thing in relation to another 權衡; 斟酌: *You have to balance the advantages of living in the country* **against** *the disadvantages.* 你應該把在鄉村生活的利弊權衡一下。**5 balance the books** to show that the money that has been paid out is equal to the money that has been paid in 結算賬目 **6 balance the budget** to make sure that your income will be as much as you intend to spend 使收支平衡

★**balance²** *n* **1** [sing;U] a condition of being steady and not falling over 平衡: *He's got something wrong with his ears, and his balance isn't very good.* 他的耳朵有點毛病, (身體)平衡性也不大好。**2 keep your balance** to stay in a steady position without falling to one side or the other, even when it is difficult 保持平衡 [RELATED PHRASE **lose your balance:** *As she reached out from the ladder, she lost her balance and fell.* 她從梯

子上下來時, 身體失去平衡, 摔了下來。] **3 off balance** in an unsteady physical position 〔身體〕不穩: *The blow knocked him off balance and he fell.* 那一擊打得他搖搖晃晃, 摔倒在地。**4** [C;U] a steady state in which everything has equal power or is in the right relationship to everything else 均衡: *The balance of nature is being upset by intensive agriculture.* 自然界的平衡正被精耕細作的農業所打亂。**5 strike a balance** to find a middle way between two things 力求折衷; 達到平衡: *If you want your children to grow up well, you have to strike a balance between firmness and affection.* 如果你想讓孩子們健康成長, 就要做到嚴格和慈愛兼顧。**6** [C] an amount that remains 結餘; 餘額: *My bank balance is only £72.* 我的銀行存款只有七十二英鎊。| *The accountant said that the balance at the end of the last financial year was £97,000.* 會計師說上一個財政年度末的結餘為 97,000 英鎊。**7** [U] fairness in reporting different views on a subject 〔報導的〕不偏不倚: *the need for balance in the reporting of political affairs* 報導政治事件時需要不偏不倚 **8** [U] a state of mind in which you are calm and reasonable 鎮定; 沉着: *It's no use getting worked up at every small crisis. You need to keep a sense of balance.* 一遇到小小的急難就激動是沒甚麼用的。你需要保持鎮定。**9 on balance** taking everything into consideration 總的説來; 全面考慮之後: *I think on balance I preferred the old system.* 總的説來, 我覺得自己更喜歡舊體制。**10 in the balance** in a state of uncertainty where the result could be good or bad 〔後果好壞〕未定, 懸而未決: *The future of the nation is in the balance.* 國家的前途安危未卜。

bal·anced /ˈbælənst; ˈbælənst/ *adj* **1** fair 公平的; 公正的: *a balanced judgment* 公正的判決 | *a balanced account* 合理的描述 **2** good because everything is in the correct relationship to everything else 均衡的: *a balanced diet* 均衡的飲食 | *a balanced budget* 收支平衡的預算 **3** having a firm sensible mind 心態穩定的: *She's very well balanced.* 她情緒十分穩定。–opposite 反義 **unbalanced** (for sense 3)

balance of pay·ments /ˌ···ˈ··/ *n* [sing] (also 又作 **balance of trade**) the amount of money coming into a country in comparison with the amount going out 〔一國的〕國際收支差額

balance of pow·er /ˌ···ˈ··/ *n* [sing] **1** a position in which power, especially political or military power, is evenly balanced on all sides 〔政治、軍事的〕力量均勢: *The growth of the new political party upset the balance of power.* 新政黨的壯大打破了力量均勢。**2 hold the balance of power** to be able to make one side more powerful than the other by giving it your support 能夠左右局勢; 舉足輕重

bal·co·ny /ˈbælkənɪ; ˈbælkəni/ *n* **balconies 1** a place for people to stand or sit on, built out from the upper part of a building 陽台: *You can see the sea from our balcony.* 你從我們的陽台上就能看到海。–see picture on page 729 見 729 頁彩圖 **2** the seats upstairs in a theatre 〔戲院的〕樓座

bald /bɔld; bɔːld/ *adj* **1** with little or no hair on the head 〔頭〕禿頂的 –see picture on page 469 見 469 頁彩圖 **2** stated directly with no attempt to soften the unpleasant truth 直截了當的; 不加修飾的: *a bald statement of the facts* 對事實直截了當的陳述 – **baldness** *n* [U]

bald·ing /ˈbɔldɪŋ; ˈbɔːldiŋ/ *adj* becoming bald 變禿的: *a balding man* 頭髮漸禿的男人

bald·ly /ˈbɔldlɪ; ˈbɔːldli/ *adv* spoken plainly, and sometimes even cruelly 不加掩飾地; 直截了當地: *The doctor told her baldly she was going to die.* 醫生直截了當地告訴她, 她快要死了。

bale¹ /beɪl; beɪl/ *n* a large mass of soft material, tightly tied so that it can be moved 大包; 大捆: *a bale of cotton* 一捆棉花 | *a bale of straw* 一捆稻草

bale² *v* **baled, baling**

bale out *phr v* **1** [I] to escape from an aircraft by PARACHUTE 〔從飛機上〕跳傘: *The pilot baled out of the burning plane.* 飛行員從着火的飛機上往外跳傘。**2** [I;T **bale** sthg ↔ **out**] to remove water from a boat to prevent it sinking 將水戽〔抽〕出船外(以免沉沒): *Quick! Start baling out!* 快! 開始戽水〔抽水〕!

bale·ful /ˈbeɪlfəl; ˈbeɪlful/ *adj* full of hate and desire to do harm 懷恨的; 惡意的: *a baleful look* 惡毒的眼神 –**balefully** *adv*

balk /bɔk; bɔːk/ *v* see BAULK

★**ball** /bɔl; bɔːl/ *n* **1** a round object used in a game or sport 球: *to throw a ball* 扔球 | *The ball bounced into the road.* 球彈到了馬路上。**2** anything of a similar shape 球狀物: *a ball of string* 線團 | *a snow-ball* 雪球 **3** **ball** a rounded part of the body 〔人體的〕球狀部分: *the ball of the foot* 腳趾球 | *an eye-ball* 眼球 **4 on the ball** *infml* showing up-to-date knowledge and an ability to think and act quickly 〔非正式〕內行; 機靈; 敏捷: *That new secretary is really on the ball.* 那個新祕書的確很在行。**5 play ball** *infml* to CO-OPERATE 〔非正式〕合作 **6 keep the ball rolling** to continue something 繼續做某事 **7 start the ball rolling** to begin something 開始做某事 **8** a large formal occasion for social dancing 大型舞會 **9 have a ball** *infml* to have a very good time 〔非正式〕玩得很痛快

bal·lad /ˈbæləd; ˈbæləd/ *n* a simple song or poem which tells a story 歌謠; 敘事詩

bal·last /ˈbæləst; ˈbæləst/ *n* [U] **1** heavy material which is carried in a ship to keep it steady 壓載物; 壓艙物 **2** broken stone used as a bed for railway lines or as the bottom part of a road〔鐵路、道路所用的〕道碴, 道牀

ball bear·ing /ˌ·ˈ··/ *n* **ball bearings** metal balls moving in a ring round a bar in a machine so that the bar may turn more easily〔滾珠軸承的〕滾珠

ball·cock /ˈbɔl,kɒk; ˈbɔːlkɒk/ *n* an apparatus for opening and closing a hole through which water passes, worked by a hollow floating ball which rises and falls with the level of the water 浮球旋塞; 浮球閥

bal·le·ri·na /,bæləˈrinə; ,bæləˈriːnə/ *n* a female ballet dancer 芭蕾舞女演員

bal·let /ˈbælɪ; ˈbæleɪ/ *n* **1** [C] a kind of dance in which a story is told without speech or singing 芭蕾舞 **2** [U] the art of doing such dances 芭蕾舞藝術: *She has studied ballet for six years.* 她學芭蕾舞已有六年了。**3** [C + sing/pl verb] a group of ballet dancers who work together 芭蕾舞劇團: *The Bolshoi Ballet is coming to London.* 大劇院芭蕾舞團將來倫敦。

bal·lis·tics /bæˈlɪstɪks; bəˈlɪstɪks/ *n* [U] the scientific study of the movement of objects that are thrown or forced through the air, such as bullets fired from a gun 彈道學; 發射學

bal·loon¹ /bəˈlun; bəˈluːn/ *n* **1** a small bag made of rubber or a similar material that can be blown up, used as a toy or to decorate your house when you have a party 玩具氣球; 裝飾性氣球 **2** a bag of strong light material filled with gas or heated air so that it can float in the air; some balloons carry people in a basket under them〔有吊籃可載人的〕熱氣球

balloon² *v* [I] to get bigger and rounder 膨脹(呈氣球狀): *Her skirt ballooned out in the wind.* 她的裙子被風吹得鼓了起來。

bal·loon·ing /bəˈlunɪŋ; bəˈluːnɪŋ/ *n* [U] the sport of flying in a balloon 乘氣球運動 – **ballooning** *v* [only in progressive forms 只用於進行式]

bal·lot¹ /ˈbælət; ˈbælət/ *n* **1** the action or system of secret voting 無記名投票: *The ballot is an important part of the democratic process.* 無記名投票是民主進程的一個重要的部分。| *Let's have a ballot on it.* 讓我們就此事進行無記名投票。**2** **at the ballot box** by secret voting 通過無記名投票: *The issue will be decided at the ballot box.* 這問題將通過無記名投票來決定。

ballot² *v* [T] to find out what people think by a secret vote 以無記名投票了解民意: *The General Workers' Union balloted its members on the issue of safety.* 總工會通過無記名投票了解會員對安全問題的意見。| *Balloting took place last Thursday.* 上星期四進行了無記名投票。

ball·point /ˈbɔl,pɔɪnt; ˈbɔːlpɔɪnt/ *n* a pen which has a ball at the end that rolls ink

onto the paper 圓珠筆, 原子筆

ball·room /ˈbɔl,rum; ˈbɔːlrum, -ruːm/ *n* **1** a large room for formal social dancing 舞廳

balm /bɑm; bɑːm/ *n* **1** [C;U] oily liquid with a strong but pleasant smell, used as medicine or to lessen pain〔鎮痛等用的〕香油, 藥膏 **2** [U] something which comforts you after your feelings have been hurt 安慰(物)

balm·y /ˈbɑmɪ; ˈbɑːmi/ *adj* soft and warm (used of air) 溫和的, 和煦的〔指氣候〕

bal·us·trade /,bæləˈstred; ,bæləˈstreɪd/ *n* a row of upright pieces of stone or wood with a bar along the top, guarding the outer edge of any place from which people might fall 欄杆; 扶欄

bam·boo /bæmˈbu; ,bæmˈbuːˀ/ *n* [U] a tall plant of the grass family, or its hard, hollow, jointed stems, often used for making furniture 竹; 竹子

bam·boo·zle /bæmˈbuzl; bæmˈbuːzəl/ *v* **bamboozled, bamboozling** *infml*〔非正式〕 **bamboozle someone into doing something** to trick someone into doing something 騙某人做某事

***ban¹** /bæn; bæn/ *v* **-nn-** [T] to forbid, especially by law〔尤指法律上〕禁止: *He was banned from driving for three months.* 他被禁止駕駛三個月。| *All strikes have been banned.* 一切罷工活動都已受到禁止。

> □ USEFUL PATTERNS 有用句型
> to ban something; to ban someone from doing something

ban² *n* an order banning something 禁令: *a ban on smoking* 禁煙令 | *The union has imposed a ban on overtime.* 工會已實施禁止加班的條例。

ba·nal /bəˈnæl; bəˈnɑːl, bəˈnæl/ *adj* very ordinary, and not so interesting 平庸的; 乏味的: *a banal remark* 陳詞濫調 –**banality** /bəˈnælətɪ; bəˈnæl ̩ti/ *n* [C;U]

ba·na·na /bəˈnænə; bəˈnɑːnə/ *n* **1** a long tropical fruit, with a yellow skin and a soft inside 香蕉 –see picture on page 504 見 504 頁彩圖 **2** **bananas** mad or stupid 發瘋的; 愚蠢的: *Just stop that noise! You're driving me bananas.* 別吵了! 你要把我逼瘋了。

***band¹** /bænd; bænd/ *n* **1** a thin flat narrow piece of material, often circular; a band can be used for fastening things together or it can be part of a piece of clothing or machinery〔捆紮用的〕帶子; 箍帶;〔衣服或機器上〕帶狀部分: *a rubber band* 橡皮筋 **2** [+ sing/pl verb] a group of people formed for a common purpose and often with a leader 一隊; 一夥; 一幫; 一組: *a band of armed men* 一幫持械的男人 **3** [+sing/pl verb] a group of musicians 樂隊: *a jazz band* 爵士樂隊 | *The band is touring the country next month.* 樂隊下個月在鄉村巡迴

演出。 **4** a line of a colour or pattern different from that of the area on either side of it 〔與底子的色彩或圖案不同的〕條紋; 條飾: *There was an orange band on the snake's back.* 蛇背上有一條橙色的紋。 **5** one of the parts of the whole range of something 段; 條; 帶: *people in the $60,000-$80,000 income band* 收入幅度在六萬元至八萬元的人

band² v

band together *phr v* [I] to get together in a group, usually with some special purpose 〔為某種特殊目的〕聯合, 團結

ban·dage¹ /ˈbændɪdʒ; ˈbændɪdʒ/ **(gauze** *AmE* 〖美式〗**)** *n* a long narrow piece of material, for binding round a wound or round a part of the body that has been hurt 繃帶

bandage² v **bandaged, bandaging** [T] to tie a bandage round a part of someone's body 〔用繃帶〕包紮: *The doctor bandaged his broken ankle.* 醫生把他受傷的腳踝包紮起來。

B & B /ˌbiː ən ˈbi; ˌbiː ən ˈbiː/ an abbreviation for bed and breakfast, a service offered by a guesthouse or other place where you can stay the night; you get a bed for the night and breakfast, but no other meals 〖縮〗〔旅館等供應的〕住宿及早餐

ban·dit /ˈbændɪt; ˈbændɪt/ *n* an armed robber, usually working in a group, who attacks travellers in wild places 〔持械的〕強盜, 土匪〔常結成一幫, 在荒僻處襲擊路人〕

band·stand /ˈbændˌstænd; ˈbændstænd/ *n* a raised place, open at the sides but with a roof, where a band plays 〔有頂棚的〕室外音樂演奏台

ban·dy¹ /ˈbændi; ˈbændi/ *adj* **1** curved outwards at the knees (used to describe legs) 膝部向外彎曲的〔指腿〕 **2 bandy-legged** /ˌ·····◂/ having bandy legs 兩腿膝部向外彎曲的

bandy² v **bandied, bandied, bandying**

bandy sthg ↔ **about/around** *phr v* [T] to say things to other people carelessly, without thinking about them properly 輕言; 傳播: *Several different figures have been bandied about, but these are the correct ones.* 有幾種不同的數字在流傳, 但這些才是正確的。

bane /beɪn; beɪn/ *n* **the bane of your life** the greatest cause of continual trouble to you 一生的禍根

bang¹ /bæŋ; bæŋ/ *n* **1** a sudden loud noise 砰地一聲: *The door shut with a bang.* 門砰地一聲關上了。 **2** a sharp blow 猛擊; 重打: *a bang on the head* 頭上重重的一擊 **3 go off with a bang** (of a social occasion) to be very successful 〔社交活動〕極為成功的

bang² v **1** [T] to hit something sharply 重擊〔某物〕: *He fell and banged his knee.* 他跌倒了, 撞傷了膝蓋。 **2** [T] to move something violently and with a loud noise 猛撞〔某物〕: *She banged the chair against the wall.* 她把椅子猛地往牆上撞過去。 **3** [I] to move

violently and with a loud noise 砰砰地移動: *Somewhere a door was banging in the wind.* 有一扇門在風中砰砰作響。 | *There's someone banging about upstairs.* 有人在樓上砰砰地走來走去。

bang³ *interj* a word used to represent a loud noise 〔用於代表一種很大的聲音〕: *Bang! Another firework flew into the air.* 砰! 又一枚炮仗飛向空中。

bang⁴ *adv infml* 〖非正式〗 **1** directly or exactly 恰好; 正好: *The sales figures are bang on target.* 銷售額正好達到指標。 | *The lights went out bang in the middle of Act 2.* 燈光正好在第二幕進行到一半時熄滅了。 **2 bang on** exactly correct 完全正確 **3 Bang goes...** a phrase you use when something you would like or the chance of it suddenly disappears 〔用於想得到的東西或某種可能〕突然消失: *Bang goes our free time this weekend.* 這個週末我們的休息時間成了泡影。

bang·er /ˈbæŋə; ˈbæŋər/ *n infml* 〖非正式〗 **1** a SAUSAGE 香腸 **2** a noisy FIREWORK 爆竹

ban·gle /ˈbæŋgl; ˈbæŋgəl/ *n* a band worn round the arm or ankle as a decoration 手鐲; 腳鐲

bangs /bæŋz; bæŋz/ *n* [P] the usual American word for a 〖美式〗= FRINGE¹(1)

ban·ish /ˈbænɪʃ; ˈbænɪʃ/ *v* [T] to send someone away, usually from their own country, as a punishment 把〔某人〕驅逐出境: *banished by the government* 被政府驅逐出境 **–banishment** *n* [U]

ban·is·ter /ˈbænɪstə; ˈbænɪstər/ *n* a row of upright pieces of wood or metal with a bar along the top guarding the outer edge of stairs 〔樓梯外側的〕扶手, 欄桿

ban·jo /ˈbændʒəʊ; ˈbændʒoʊ/ *n* a stringed musical instrument with a long neck, and a body like a drum, used to play popular music 班卓琴〔一種長頸鼓狀弦樂器〕

★★bank¹ /bæŋk; bæŋk/ *n* **1** an organization which performs services connected with money, and which usually has local offices in which money is kept for customers and paid out on demand 銀行: *I drew some money out of the bank.* 我從銀行提了些錢。 **2** a place where something is stored, especially products of human origin for medical use 庫; 貯藏所〔尤指貯藏以人體取出的有機物作醫療用的場所〕: *Hospital blood banks have saved many lives.* 醫院血庫拯救了很多人的生命。 **3** land along the side of a river or lake 河岸 **4** a long pile of earth which is heaped up in a field or garden 〔在田野裡或花園裡的〕長條形的土堆 **5** a mass of a substance such as snow or mud 〔雪、土等〕堆, 團: *The banks of dark cloud promised rain.* 黑雲堆集預示有雨。 **6** a SANDBANK 沙洲; 沙灘

bank² v [I;T] to put or keep money in a bank 把〔錢〕存入銀行: *Who do you bank with?* 你在哪家銀行存款? | *Did you bank that* *cheque?* 你有沒有把那張支票存進銀行？

bank on sbdy/sthg *phr v* [T] to depend on 依靠; 指望: *I'm banking on you to help me with the arrangements.* 我要靠你來幫我安排呢。| *"I do hope the weather will be good on Saturday." "Don't bank on it."* "我真希望星期六是個好天氣。""別指望了。"

bank up *phr v* [I;T **bank** sthg ↔ **up**] to form into a mass or heap 堆起; 堆積: *The wind had banked the snow up against the wall.* 風把雪吹到牆邊積成一堆。

bank ac·count /'· ·,·/ *n* an arrangement for someone to keep money in a bank and take it out when they want to 銀行帳戶: *How much money have you got in your bank account?* 你的銀行賬戶裡有多少錢？

bank·er /'bæŋkə; 'bæŋkəʳ/ *n* a person who owns a bank or who shares in the control of a bank 銀行業者; 銀行家: *International bankers are gathering in Rome.* 國際銀行業者聚集在羅馬。

bank hol·i·day /,·'···/ *n* in the United Kingdom, an official public holiday, not a Saturday or Sunday, when the banks are closed 〔英國除星期六、星期日以外的〕銀行假日, 公眾假日

bank·ing /'bæŋkɪŋ; 'bæŋkɪŋ/ *n* [U] the business of a bank or a banker 銀行業: *a career in banking* 銀行業生涯 | *the international banking system* 國際銀行業體制

bank note /'· ·/ *n* a piece of paper money printed for the national bank of a country for public use 鈔票; 紙幣

bank·rupt¹ /'bæŋkrʌpt; 'bæŋkrʌpt/ *adj* **1** unable to pay your debts 無力還債的; 破產的 **2** **go bankrupt** to become unable to pay your debts 破產

bank·rupt² *v* [T] to make someone bankrupt or very poor 使〔某人〕破產, 使〔某人〕窮困

bank·rupt·cy /'bæŋkrʌptsɪ; 'bæŋkrʌptsi/ *n* **bankruptcies** [C;U] the state of being bankrupt 破產狀態: *The company is threatened with bankruptcy.* 公司面臨破產的威脅。| *Bankruptcies increased during the last quarter of 1990.* 1990年最後一季度破產事件大為增加。

bank state·ment /'· ,··/ *n* a list of payments into and out of your bank account; the bank sends you statements regularly 〔由銀行定期寄給賬戶的〕銀行結單

ban·ner /'bænə; 'bænəʳ/ *n* **1** a long piece of cloth on which a sign or message is painted, usually carried by people 橫幅標語: *The marchers' banners said "We want work."* 遊行者的橫幅上寫着"我們要工作"。 **2** *lit* a flag 〔文〕旗幟

banns /bænz; bænz/ *n* [pl] a public declaration in church of an intended marriage 〔在教堂宣佈的〕結婚預告

ban·quet /'bæŋkwɪt; 'bæŋkwɪt/ *n* a formal dinner for many people in honour of a special person or occasion, especially one at which speeches are made 〔尤指有致辭的〕宴會

ban·ter /'bæntə; 'bæntəʳ/ *v* [I] to speak playfully or jokingly 開玩笑; 戲謔 **–banter** *n* [U]: *The actress exchanged banter with reporters.* 女演員與記者們互相開玩笑。

bap·tis·m /'bæptɪzəm; 'bæptɪzəm/ *n* [C;U] a Christian religious ceremony in which someone becomes a member of the Church 〔基督教的入教〕洗禮 **–baptismal** /bæp'tɪzml; bæp'tɪzməl/ *adj*

Bap·tist /'bæptɪst; 'bæptɪst/ *n* a member of a branch of the Christian church which believes that baptism should be only for people old enough to understand its meaning 浸信會教友〔認為洗禮應對已長大成人並能了解洗禮意義者施行〕

bap·tize /bæp'taɪz; bæp'taɪz/ *v* **baptized, baptizing** (also 又作 **baptise** *BrE* 〔英式〕) [T] to perform the ceremony of baptism 行洗禮儀式

★★bar¹ /bɑr; bɑːʳ/ *n* **1** something solid that is long and straight 棒; 條: *an iron bar* 一根鐵棒 | *a bar of chocolate* 一塊條形巧克力 **2** a long piece of wood or metal across a door, gate, or window that keeps it shut or prevents movement through it 〔木、金屬等〕栓, 柵, 欄: *There were metal bars across the windows of the prison.* 監獄的窗戶有金屬柵欄。 **3** one of the rooms in a building called a PUB where people can buy and drink alcohol 〔酒店裡的〕酒吧間 **4** a room in a hotel, theatre, or other public building where people can buy and drink alcohol 〔旅館、戲院或其他公共場所裡的〕酒吧間 **5** the high table where drinks are served in a bar 〔酒吧〕櫃台 **6** a place where food and drink are sold 小吃店; 賣小吃的櫃台: *a coffee bar* 咖啡店〔櫃台〕 **7** in America, a place where people buy and drink alcohol 〔美國的〕酒吧間 **8** a group of notes in music 〔樂譜的〕小節: *She sang the first three bars of the song.* 她唱了這首歌的前三小節。 **9** a bank of sand or stones under the water 沙洲 **10 behind bars** in prison 坐牢, 在獄中 **11 prisoner at the bar** the person being tried in a court of law 在法庭上受審的人

bar² *v* **-rr-** [T] **1** to close something firmly with a bar 閂上〔某物〕: *to bar the door* 閂上門 **2** to keep in or out by barring something 把〔某物〕關在裡面〔外面〕: *They barred themselves in.* 他們把自己關在裡面。 **3** to block something 阻擋〔某物〕: *to bar the way to the city* 阻擋通往市裡的路 **4** to forbid something, or forbid someone from doing something 禁止(做)〔某事〕: *Smoking has been barred in the office.* 辦公室裡禁止抽煙。| *The protesters were barred from entering the building.* 抗議者被禁止進入大樓。

bar³ *prep* except 除…以外: *The whole group was at the party, bar John.* 除了約翰以外, 全

組的人都參加了聚會。

bar·bar·i·an /bɑrˈbɛrɪən; bɑːˈbeəriən/ *n* an uncivilized person, especially one who is rude and wild in behaviour 野蠻人: *The barbarians conquered Rome.* 野蠻人征服了羅馬。 –**barbaric** /bɑrˈbærɪk; bɑːˈbærɪk/ *adj*: *barbaric people* 野蠻人 | *a barbaric punishment* 野蠻的懲罰 –**barbarism** /ˈbɑrbə.rɪ.zəm; ˈbɑːbərɪzəm/ *n* –**barbarous** /ˈbɑrbərəs; ˈbɑːbərəs/ *adj*

bar·bar·i·ty /bɑrˈbærətɪ; bɑːˈbærˌti/ *n* **barbarities** [C;U] cruelty of the worst kind 殘暴; 暴行: *The barbarities of the last war must not be repeated.* 上次戰爭的暴行絕不可重演。

bar·be·cue¹ /ˈbɑrbɪ.kju; ˈbɑːbɪkjuː/ *n* **1** a metal frame on which you cook meat and other food over an open fire outdoors〔室外用的〕金屬烤架 **2** an outdoor party with food cooked on a barbecue〔烤肉〕野餐

barbecue² *v* **barbecued, barbecuing** [T] to cook meat and other food on a barbecue 在燒烤架上烤〔肉〕

barbed /bɑrbd; bɑːbd/ *adj* **1** with one or more sharp points 有倒鈎的; 有刺的 **2** intended to hurt someone and make them feel upset 尖刻的: *a barbed remark* 諷刺的話

barbed wire /ˌ· ˈ·/ *n* [U] wire with short sharp points in it 有刺鐵絲網: *a barbed-wire fence to keep the animals in* 用來把動物圍住的有刺鐵絲籬笆

bar·ber /ˈbɑrbɚ; ˈbɑːbəʳ/ *n* **1** a person, usually a man, who cuts men's hair〔常指以男性為服務對象的男性〕理髮師 **2** **barber's** the place where a barber works 理髮店: *He's gone to the barber's.* 他去理髮店理髮了。| *You can get them in the barber's.* 你可以在理髮店找到他們。

bar·bi·tu·rate /ˌbɑrbɪˈtjʊret; bɑːˈbɪtʃʊrˌt/ *n* [C] *tech* a drug that makes people calm and sends them to sleep〔術語〕巴比土酸鹽〔一種鎮靜劑、安眠藥〕

bard /bɑrd; bɑːd/ *n lit* a poet〔文〕詩人

bare¹ /bɛr; beəʳ/ *adj* **1** not covered by anything 赤裸的: *bare feet* 赤腳 | *bare floorboards*（沒有鋪地毯的）光地板 **2** empty 空的: *The cupboard was completely bare.* 碗櫃全空了。**3 with your bare hands** using only your hands, but no tools or weapons 徒手地: *He killed her with his bare hands.* 他赤手空拳殺死了她。**4** [only before a noun 只用於名詞前] the most basic, with nothing added 最基本的; 加以發揮的: *the bare facts of a case* 最基本的事實真相 –**bareness** *n* [U]

bare² *v* **bared, baring** [T] to uncover something so that it can be seen 使〔某物〕裸露: *The animal bared its teeth in anger.* 那野獸憤然露出牙齒。

bare·back /ˈbɛr.bæk; ˈbeəbæk/ *adj*, *adv* riding without a SADDLE 不用馬鞍的[地]: *a bareback rider* 不用馬鞍的騎手

bare·faced /ˈbɛr.fest; ˌbeəˈfeɪstˑ/ *adj*

shameless 厚顏無恥的: *a barefaced lie* 無恥的謊言

bare·foot /ˈbɛr.fʊt; ˈbeəfʊt/ *adj*, *adv* not wearing any shoes 赤腳的[地]

bare·head·ed /ˈbɛrˈhedɪd; ˌbeəˈhedˌd◂/ *adj*, *adv* not wearing a hat 光着頭(的); 不戴帽(的)

bare·ly /ˈbɛrlɪ; ˈbeəli/ *adv* only just 僅僅: *We have barely enough money to last the weekend.* 我們的錢只能勉強維持到這個週末。| *I can barely understand what he's talking about.* 我只能勉強明白他在説些甚麼。–see HARDLY (USAGE 用法)

bar·gain¹ /ˈbɑrgɪn; ˈbɑːgˌn/ *n* **1** an agreement, especially one to do something in return for something else 交易; 協議: *He made a bargain with his wife: "You do the shopping and I'll do the cooking."* 他跟太太達成協議: "你買東西我做飯。" **2** something that is both cheap and good value 便宜貨: *These shoes were a real bargain.* 這些鞋子買得確實合算。| *bargain prices* 廉價 **3 drive a hard bargain** to get an agreement very much in your own favour 達成對自己極有利的協議 **4 into the bargain** a phrase used when you are stating forcefully that something is true in addition to everything else you have said 此外〔用於強調所説的屬實〕: *She had to look after a house, her sick mother—and four children into the bargain.* 她必須照管一所房子, 照料生病的母親, 此外還有四個孩子。

bargain² *v* [I] **1** to talk about the conditions of a sale, agreement, or contract 談價; 談條件: *We bargained with her about the price.* 我們跟她討價還價。| *They were bargaining over a horse.* 他們為買馬討價還價。**2 he hadn't bargained for/on...** he had not expected that something would happen and did not include it in his plans 沒考慮到; 始料不及: *I hadn't bargained for such heavy rain, and I got very wet.* 我沒料到會下這麼大的雨, 所以渾身都濕透了。

barge¹ /bɑrdʒ; bɑːdʒ/ *n* a boat with a flat bottom used mainly for carrying heavy goods on a CANAL or river 平底載貨船; 駁船

barge² *v* **barged, barging** [I] (also 又作 **barge your way**) to move rudely and ungracefully, often hitting against things 魯莽地衝撞: *He barged onto the bus before everyone else.* 他衝衝撞撞地搶在別人前面擠上了公共汽車。| *She barged her way into the room.* 她闖進了房間裡。

barge in *phr v* [I] to rush in rudely or interrupt 闖入: *The door burst open and the children barged in.* 門突然打開, 孩子們闖了進來。

bar·i·tone /ˈbærə.ton; ˈbærˌtəʊn/ *n* a singing voice lower than a TENOR and higher than a BASS 男中音

bark¹ /bɑrk; bɑːk/ *v* **1** [I] to make the loud,

B

sharp sound of a dog or fox〔狗或狐狸等〕吠，叫: *The dog always barks at the postman.* 這隻狗老朝着郵遞員叫。**2** [T] to shout something in a sharp voice 大聲喊叫；吼: *The officer barked an order at us.* 那軍官向我們大聲下達命令。**3 bark up the wrong tree** *infml* to try to do something based on a mistaken idea〔非正式〕認錯目標；打錯主意

bark² *n* **1** [C] the loud, sharp sound made by a dog or fox〔狗或狐狸的〕吠聲 **2 his bark is worse than his bite** *infml*〔非正式〕= he seems more unpleasant or difficult than he really is 他看上去兇，其實不然 **3** [U] the strong outer covering of a tree 樹皮

bar·ley /'bɑːlɪ; 'bɑːli/ *n* [U] a grain plant like grass grown for food and also used in the making of beer 大麥

bar·man /'bɑːmən; 'bɑːmən/ *n* **barmen** /-mən; -mən/ a man who serves drinks in a BAR¹; a woman who does this is called a **barmaid** /'bɑːmed; 'bɑːmeɪd/ 酒吧間男招待〔酒吧間女招待叫做 barmaid〕

bar·my /'bɑːmɪ; 'bɑːmi/ *adj infml* foolish or a little mad〔非正式〕呆笨的；瘋瘋癲癲的: *You must be barmy to play football in this weather.* 這種天氣還踢足球，你一定是瘋了。

barn /bɑːn; bɑːn/ *n* a large farm building where crops are stored or animals are kept 穀倉；牲口棚

barn·yard /'bɑːnjɑːd; 'bɑːnjɑːd/ *n* a yard on a farm with barns and other buildings round it 穀倉場院

ba·rom·e·ter /bə'rɒmətə; bə'rɒmtər/ *n* an instrument which measures the air pressure; you use it to judge probable changes in the weather 氣壓計；晴雨表

bar·on /'bærən; 'bærən/ *n* **1** a British nobleman of the lowest rank 男爵〔英國貴族中爵位最低者〕**2** a very powerful businessman〔工商業〕大王；巨頭: *an oil baron* 石油大王 | *a press baron* 報業大王 **–baronial** /bə'rəʊnɪəl; bə'rəʊniəl/ *adj*

bar·on·ess /'bærənɪs; 'bærənɪs/ *n* **1** a woman who is the wife of a baron 男爵夫人 **2** a British noblewoman of the lowest rank〔英國的〕女男爵

bar·on·et /'bærənɪt; 'bærənɪt, -net/ *n* a British nobleman with the rank of KNIGHT¹ (2) whose title passes on to his son when he dies 準男爵，從男爵〔英國的一種世襲爵位〕

bar·rack /'bærək; 'bærək/ *v* [I;T] *infml* to interrupt someone giving a speech by shouting at them〔非正式〕〔給演講的人〕喝倒采；起哄: *They barracked the speaker throughout the meeting.* 他們在會上對發言者喝倒采。

bar·racks /'bærəks; 'bærəks/ *n* [plural is 複數為 **barracks**] a building or group of buildings that soldiers live in 兵營；營房: *The barracks is in Kingsdown Road.* 營房在金斯當路上。

bar·rage¹ /'bærɪdʒ; 'bærɑːʒ/ *n* **1** a pile of earth or stones built across a river, usually to control the level of the water 攔河壩；堰

barrage² /bə'rɑːʒ; 'bærɑːʒ/ *n* **1** the continuous firing of a number of heavy guns 掩護火力網 **2** a large number of questions or complaints which are made very quickly one after the other 連珠砲似的問題[埋怨]: *a barrage of criticism* 一連串的批評

bar·rel /'bærəl; 'bærəl/ *n* **1** a round metal, plastic, or wooden container with a flat top and bottom 圓桶；琵琶桶: *a beer barrel* 啤酒桶 –see picture on page 244 見 244 頁彩圖 **2** the long part of a gun that looks like a tube 槍[砲]管: *a rifle barrel* 來福槍管；步槍管

bar·ren /'bærən; 'bærən/ *adj* **1** unable to produce a good crop (used of land) 貧瘠的〔指土地〕**2** not able to produce young (used of female animals) 不孕的；不生育的〔指雌性動物〕**3** useless or producing no result 無用的；無結果的: *a barren argument* 毫無結果的爭論 –compare 比較 FERTILE, FRUITFUL **–barrenness** *n* [U]

bar·ri·cade¹ /ˌbærə'ked; 'bærɪˌkeɪd, ˌbærɪ'keɪd/ *n* a quickly-built wall of vehicles or heavy objects put across a road or passage to block the advance of the enemy〔用車輛、重物等迅速疊起阻止敵軍前進的〕路障，街壘

barricade² *v* **barricaded, barricading** [T] **1** to put a barricade across something 設路障於: *Demonstrators had barricaded the street.* 示威者在街上設起了路障。**2 barricade yourself in** to shut yourself in a room or building and put something heavy against the door in order to protect yourself against your enemy 把門堵起來，躲在房中〔避開敵人〕: *The terrorists barricaded themselves in the embassy.* 恐怖分子把門堵起來，躲在使館裡面。

★bar·ri·er /'bærɪə; 'bærɪər/ *n* **1** something used to keep people or things apart and prevent or control their movement 障礙；屏障: *The police put up barriers to control the crowd.* 警察設置了屏障來控制人羣。| *The cream acts as a barrier against infection.* 這種藥膏可作為一種屏障，防止感染。**2** something which prevents people from talking to each other, agreeing with each other, or succeeding in their aims 隔閡，障礙: *the language barrier* 語言障礙 | *Lack of confidence is the biggest barrier to investment in this industry.* 缺乏信心是投資這一工業的最大障礙。

bar·ring /'bɑːrɪŋ; 'bɑːrɪŋ/ *prep* **1** except for 除...之外: *The whole group was at the party, barring John.* 除了約翰以外，全組的人都參加了聚會。**2** if the thing mentioned does not happen 除非: *Barring any unexpected problems, we'll finish the job tonight.* 除非有任何意外問題，否則我們將於今晚完成這項

B

工作。

bar·ris·ter /ˈbærɪstə; ˈbærḷstɚ/ *n* a lawyer in England who has the right to speak and argue in the higher courts of law〔在英格蘭,有權在高等法院出庭辯論的〕(訟務)律師

bar·row /ˈbærəʊ; ˈbærəʊ/ *n* **1** a small cart with a roof made of material from which fruit and vegetables are sold in the street〔在街上用以賣水果、蔬菜的〕手推車 **2** a WHEELBARROW 獨輪小車

bar·ter /ˈbɑːtə; ˈbɑːtɚ/ *v* [I;T] to exchange goods for other goods 作以物易物交易: *They bartered farm products for machinery.* 他們用農產品交換機器。| *bartering for food* 用貨換食品 **–barter** *n* [U]

★**base**¹ /beɪs; beɪs/ *n* **1** the lowest part of something, especially the part on which it stands 底部; 基礎: *a lamp with a heavy base* 底座很重的燈 | *leaves at the base of the stem* 莖上的葉子 **2** a centre from which something is controlled and plans are made 總部; 基地: *Our company's base is in London, but we have branches all round the world.* 我們公司的總部在倫敦,但分公司遍及世界各地。| *a military base* 軍事基地 **3** the original part from which something develops or from which other things are made 基礎部分; 根基: *A knowledge of human biology is a useful base for training as a nurse.* 對培訓護士來說,人體生物學知識是有用的基礎。 **4** the part of something where it is joined to something else 基部; 連接處: *the base of the leaf* 葉子的根部 **5** a chemical substance which combines with an acid to form a salt 鹼 **6** any of the four points which a baseball player must touch in order to make a run〔棒球的〕壘

★**base**² *v* **based, basing, be based** to have a centre for your work or an activity 駐紮; 設立以...為中心: *They're based in Birmingham, but they travel all over the West Midlands.* 他們的總部在伯明翰,可是他們遍遊西米德蘭茲。| *a London-based firm* 總部設在倫敦的公司

base sthg on sthg *phr v* [T] **1** to make or develop something using something else as a starting point 基於〔某事物〕; 以〔某事物〕為根據: *You should always base your opinions on facts.* 你的意見應該以事實為依據。| *The film is based on the book by D.H. Lawrence.* 這部電影是根據 D.H. 勞倫斯的書改編的。

★**base·ball** /ˈbeɪsbɔːl; ˈbeɪsbɔːl/ *n* [U] a game played with a BAT and a ball called a baseball between two teams of nine players each, on a large field with four bases; baseball is popular in America 棒球〔在美國很流行〕: *a baseball player* 棒球手 | *a baseball team* 棒球隊

base·ment /ˈbeɪsmənt; ˈbeɪsmənt/ *n* a room or rooms in a house which are below street level 地下室 –see picture on page 729 見 729 頁彩圖

bash¹ /bæʃ; bæʃ/ *v* [T] *infml* to hit something or someone hard, so as to break it or hurt them〔非正式〕猛擊〔某人、某物〕: *He bashed her over the head with a brick.* 他拿磚對着她的腦袋猛擊。| *I've just bashed my head on the door.* 我的頭剛撞在門上。

bash² *n infml* 〔非正式〕 **1** a hard blow 猛擊; 痛擊: *He gave me a bash on the nose.* 他在我鼻樑上猛的一拳。 **2 have a bash** to try to do something even though you might not succeed 試試看: *I'll have a bash at rowing the boat, although I've never done it before.* 雖然我從未划過船,但我要試試看。

bash·ful /ˈbæʃfəl; ˈbæʃfəl/ *adj* lacking confidence, especially when talking to people you do not know 局促不安的; 羞怯的〔尤指和不認識的人談話時〕: *a bashful smile* 羞怯的笑容 | *bashful teenagers* 害羞的少年人 **– bashfully** *adv* **–bashfulness** *n* [U]

★**ba·sic** /ˈbeɪsɪk; ˈbeɪsɪk/ *adj* **1** more necessary and important than anything else 根本的; 基本的: *the basic rules of good driving* 良好駕駛技術的基本規則 **2** simple and having only the things which are really necessary 簡單的; 起碼的: *The accommodation is very basic.* 住所(的陳設)十分簡單。

basic *n* **1 BASIC** (also 又作 **Basic**) a very commonly used computer language BASIC 程式語言〔一種極常用的電腦語言〕 **2 basics** [pl] the simplest and most important things 基本要素: *When you get down to basics, love counts for more than possessions.* 當你認真地想想基本道理時,(會發現)愛情比財富重要得多。| *She did a short course to learn the basics of carpentry.* 她上短期班學習木工的基本原理。

ba·sic·ally /ˈbeɪsɪklɪ; ˈbeɪsɪklɪ/ *adv* a word used when you are giving a fact or statement which you think is the most important one 基本上; 根本上: *Basically, he's a nice person, but he doesn't always show it.* 他基本上是個好人,並且不經常表現出來。| *He's basically nice.* 他基本上是好的。| *Basically, we need more money.* 我們實際上需要多點錢。

ba·sin /ˈbeɪsn̩; ˈbeɪsn̩/ *n* **1** a round container for holding liquids or mixing foods 盆; 碗 **2** a WASHBASIN 洗臉盆 **3** an area of land from which water runs down into a river 盆地; 流域: *the Amazon Basin* 亞馬遜河流域

★**ba·sis** /ˈbeɪsɪs; ˈbeɪsḷs/ *n* **bases** /ˈbeɪsiːz; ˈbeɪsiːz/ **1** the most important principle or fact from which something is made or developed 基礎; 根據: *What is the basis for your opinion?* 你的看法有甚麼根據? | *The lectures formed the basis of a new book.* 新書以這些演講的內容為基礎。 **2** an agreed arrangement〔獲同意的〕安排: *She works for us on a part-time basis.* 她以兼職形式為我們工作。

bask /bɑːsk; bæsk/ *v* **1** [I] to lie or sit in

pleasant warmth, usually from the sun 曬太陽; 取暖: *I was lying on the sand, basking in the sunshine.* 我躺在沙灘上曬太陽。**2 bask in someone's approval** to enjoy the fact that someone likes you or approves of you 受某人的喜愛或讚許

bas·ket /'bɑːskɪt; 'bɑːskɪt/ *n* **1** a container made from narrow pieces of wood or plastic woven together 籃; 筐; 簍: *a shopping basket* 購物筐 | *a wastepaper basket* 廢紙簍 –see picture on page 244 見 244 頁彩圖 **2** a basket and the things it contains 一籃; 一筐: *a basket of apples* 一籃蘋果 **3** an open net fixed to a metal ring high up off the ground, through which players try to throw the ball in the game of basketball 〔籃球的〕籃

bas·ket·ball /'bɑːskɪt,bɔl; 'bɑːskɪtbɔːl/ *n* **1** [U] an indoor game between two teams of five players each, in which each team tries to throw a large ball through the other team's basket 籃球(運動) –see picture on page 957 見 957 頁彩圖 **2** [C] the ball used in this game 籃球

bass¹ /bes; beɪs/ *adj* deep or low in sound (used of a male singing voice or a musical instrument) 低音的〔指男歌手的聲音或樂器〕: *He has a fine bass voice.* 他的聲音低沉優美。 | *a bass drum* 低音鼓

bass² /bes; beɪs/ *n* **1** the lowest male singing voice 男低音(歌手) **2** the lowest range of sounds in written music 〔樂譜的〕低音部 **3** see 見 DOUBLE BASS

bas·soon /bæ'sun; bə'suːn/ *n* a wooden musical instrument which makes a deep sound and is played by blowing 巴松管〔一種木製低音管樂器〕

bas·tard /'bæstəd; 'bæstəd/ *n* **1** a child of unmarried parents 私生子 **2** *slang* a person who has behaved very badly to another person 〔俚〕討厭鬼; 壞蛋: *You bastard! How could you do this to me!* 你這臭小子! 怎麼可以這樣對我! **3** *slang* a person you feel fond of or sorry for 〔俚〕傢伙〔對其喜愛或感到惋惜〕: *You lucky bastard!* 你這走運的傢伙!

baste /best; beɪst/ *v* **basted, basting** [T] **1** to join pieces of cloth together in long loose stitches 〔用長針腳〕粗縫; 疏縫 **2** to pour melted fat over meat that is cooking 〔往烤肉上〕塗油脂

bas·ti·on /'bæstʃən; 'bæstiən/ *n* something that strongly defends a particular principle or activity 堡壘: *His club doesn't allow women members. It's one of the last bastions of male chauvinism.* 他的俱樂部不接受女會員, 這是大男子主義的最後堡壘之一了。

bat¹ /bæt; bæt/ *n* **1** a specially shaped wooden stick used for hitting the ball in various games 球棒; 球拍 –see 見 BASEBALL, CRICKET², TABLE TENNIS **2** a flying animal that looks like a mouse and is active at night 蝙蝠 **3 off your own bat** *infml*

without being told or forced to 〔非正式〕主動地; 自覺地: *Have you done all this work off your own bat?* 這些工作都是靠你自己完成的嗎?

bat² *v* **-tt- 1** [T] to hit a ball with a bat 用球棒擊〔球〕; 用球拍打〔球〕 **2** [I] to have a turn to hit the ball in a game of cricket or BASEBALL 〔板球、棒球〕輪到擊球: *Who's batting now?* 現在輪到誰擊球? **3 not bat an eyelid** *infml* to show no feeling or surprise 〔非正式〕不露聲色; 處之泰然: *She heard the news without batting an eyelid.* 她聽了這個消息後, 一點也不動聲色。

batch /bætʃ; bætʃ/ *n* a number of things or people to be dealt with at one time 〔人或物的〕一批: *a batch of bread* 一爐麵包 | *the next batch of students* 下一批學生 | *The prisoners were released in batches of 20.* 犯人每二十個一批, 逐批釋放。

bat·ed /'betɪd; 'beɪtɪd/ *adj* **with bated breath** with a great desire to know 極想知道: *He waited for the news with bated breath.* 他屏息靜氣地等候消息。

★**bath¹** /bæθ; bɑːθ/ *n* **baths** /bæðz; bɑːðz/ **1** (**bathtub** *AmE* 〔美式〕) a container in which you sit to wash your whole body 浴缸; 澡盆 **2 baths** a public swimming pool 公共游泳池 **3 have a bath, take a bath** to sit in a bath and wash your body 洗澡

bath² *v* **1** [T] to give a bath to someone 給〔某人〕洗澡: *He's bathing the baby.* 他在給嬰兒洗澡。 **2** [I] to sit in a bath and wash your body 洗澡: *She baths every morning.* 她每天早晨都洗澡。

■ USAGE 用法: **1** When talking about what you do to get clean say **have a bath/take a bath** ☆談論洗澡時用 **have a bath/take a bath:** *I have a bath every morning.* 我每天早晨都洗澡。 **2** When talking about swimming in the sea or a river use the verb **bathe** or the expression **go for a bathe** ☆談論在海裡或河裡游泳時用動詞 **bathe** 或詞語 **go for a bathe:** *Further along the beach we saw some people bathing.* 沿着海灘再往前走, 我們看見有些人在游泳。 | *Let's go for a bathe.* 我們去游泳吧。 (Do NOT use **have/take a bath** with this meaning. 此義不能用 **have/take a bath**) **3** When talking about lying in the sun use the verb **sunbathe** ☆談論曬太陽時用動詞 **sunbathe:** *They spent the afternoon sunbathing.* 他們一整個下午在曬太陽。 | *A week of swimming and sunbathing will do you the world of good.* 游泳和曬日光浴一個星期會對你大有好處。(Do NOT use **have/take a bath** with this meaning. 此義不能用 **have/take a bath**)

bathe¹ /beð; beɪð/ **bathed, bathing** *v* **1** [I] to

swim for pleasure 游泳: *I like to bathe in the sea.* 我喜歡在大海裡游泳. **2** [T] to cover or wash something gently with water or other liquid〔用水或其他液體〕浸, 洗: *Bathe your ankle twice a day.* 每天浸洗腳踝兩次. **3** [I] *AmE* to sit in a bath and wash your body《美式》洗澡 **4 be bathed in light** to be covered in light 沐浴在日光中: *The fields were bathed in sunlight.* 田野沐浴在陽光中. – see 見 BATH² (USAGE 用法) –**bathing** *n* [U]: *Bathing is dangerous near the rocks.* 在礁石附近游泳很危險. | *a bathing suit* 游泳衣

bathe² *n* **have a bathe, go for a bathe** to swim for pleasure 游泳

bath·er /'beðə⟨; 'beɪðə⟨/ *n* a swimmer 游泳者

bath·robe /'bæθ,rob; 'bɑ:θrəʊb/ *n* **1** a loose piece of clothing that you wear before and after you have a bath or swim 浴衣 **2** the usual American word for《美式》= DRESSING GOWN

*★**bath·room** /'bæθ,rum; 'bɑ:θrʊm/ *n* **1** a room containing a BATH and usually a TOILET〔一般有馬桶的〕浴室; 盥洗室 **2** the usual American word for the 《美式》= TOILET: *Can I use your bathroom, please?* 請問我能用你的廁所嗎?

bath·tub /'bæθ,tʌb; 'bɑ:θtʌb/ *n* –see 見 BATH¹

bat·man /'bætmən; 'bætmən/ *n* **batmen** /-mən; -mən/ an officer's personal servant in the armed forces 勤務兵

bat·on /bə'tɑn; 'bætɒn/ *n* **1** a short thin stick used by a CONDUCTOR to show the beat of the music〔樂隊指揮用的〕指揮棒 **2** a short thick stick used as a weapon by a policeman 警棍

bats·man /'bætsmən; 'bætsmən/ *n* **batsmen** /-mən; -mən/ the player in cricket who tries to hit the ball with a BAT¹ (1)〔板球的〕擊球手

bat·tal·ion /bə'tæljən; bə'tæljən/ *n* a group of 500-1000 soldiers made up of four or more companies (COMPANY(5)) 營〔由四個或四個以上的連組成, 士兵五百至一千名〕: *The second battalion is going abroad.* 第二營正開赴國外.

bat·ter¹ /'bætə⟨; 'bætə⟨/ *v* **1** [T] to hit a person repeatedly 連續擊打〔某人〕; 毆打: *She had been battered by her drunken husband.* 她被喝醉酒的丈夫毆打. | *battered to death* 毆打至死 **2** [I;T] to hit or beat against something repeatedly 連續猛擊〔某物〕: *Someone was battering on the door.* 有人在用力敲門. | *The ship was battered against the rocks.* 那艘船重重地撞在礁石上. | *a battered old car* 一輛殘破的舊汽車 | *They battered the door down.* 他們撞開了門.

batter² *n* [U] **1** a mixture of flour, eggs, and milk, beaten together and used in cooking〔麵粉、雞蛋和牛奶等調成的〕麵糊 **2** a person who bats (BAT² (2)) 擊球員

bat·tered /'bætəd; 'bætəd/ *adj* **1** knocked and worn 破舊的; 用壞的: *a battered copy of "Treasure Island"* 一本破舊的《金銀島》| *a battered teddy bear* 一隻玩舊了的玩具熊 | *a battered old car* 一輛殘破的舊汽車 **2** repeatedly beaten 不斷受毆打的: *a refuge for battered wives* 受毆打的妻子的避難處

bat·ter·ing /'bætərɪŋ; 'bætəri/ *n* repeated beating which results in damage〔導致損害的〕持續的擊打: *The house took a real battering in the 1987 gales.* 這幢房子在 1987 年的強風中受到重創.

bat·ter·ing ram /'··· ·/ *n* a large heavy log used in the past during war for breaking through the doors and walls of castles and towns〔古時的〕破城槌〔攻城時用以撞門牆, 一端裝有鐵板的巨木〕

bat·ter·y /'bætərɪ; 'bætəri/ *n* **batteries 1** a small apparatus which provides electrical power, which you put inside something such as a radio 電池 **2** a number of big guns fixed in a warship or fort 排砲 **3** a line of small boxes in which hens are kept and specially treated so that they will lay eggs frequently〔使母雞頻繁下蛋的〕孵蛋箱組; 層架式雞籠: *battery hens* 在層架式雞籠中飼養的母雞 | *She won't buy battery eggs. She'll only have free-range ones.* 她不會買層架式雞籠裡的雞下的蛋, 她只會買自由放養的雞下的蛋. **4** a set of things of the same kind that happen together or are kept together〔相似的〕一組, 一套: *They gave her a whole battery of tests to try to find out what she's allergic to.* 他們給她做了一連串的試驗, 看她對甚麼東西過敏.

*★**bat·tle¹** /'bætl; 'bætl/ *n* **1** a fight between enemies or opposing groups 戰鬥; 戰役: *the Battle of Waterloo* 滑鐵盧戰役 | *It was one of the worst battles of the First World War.* 這是第一次世界大戰中最慘烈的戰役之一. **2** a struggle to obtain something or prevent something〔為求得到某物、防止某事而進行的〕鬥爭: *a battle **for** power in the government* 政府內部的一場權力鬥爭 | *the battle **against** inflation* 制止通貨膨脹的鬥爭 | *the battle against cancer* 抗癌鬥爭 –compare 比較 WAR

*★**battle²** *v* **battled, battling** [I] to struggle in order to do or obtain something〔為做某事或得到某物而〕鬥爭: *Firemen are still battling to get the fire under control.* 消防隊員仍在奮力控制火勢.

bat·tle·field /'bætl,fild; 'bætlfi:ld/ *n* a place at which a battle is fought 戰場

bat·tle·ground /'bætl,graund; 'bætlgraund/ *n* **1** a place at which a battle is fought 戰場 **2** a subject about which people disagree strongly 激烈爭論的課題

bat·tle·ments /'bætlmənts; 'bætlmənts/ *n* [pl] a low wall round the roof of a castle or fort, with spaces to shoot through〔城堡或堡壘上的〕城垛, 雉堞

bat·tle·ship /'bætl,ʃɪp; 'bætlʃɪp/ *n* the largest kind of warship, with the biggest guns and heaviest armour 戰艦; 主力艦

bau·ble /ˈbɔbḷ; ˈbɔːbəl/ *n* a cheap, bright decoration or piece of jewellery 廉價飾物; 廉價珠寶

baulk /bɔk; bɔːk/ *v* (also 又作 **balk**) baulk at something to be unwilling to face or agree to something difficult or unpleasant 猶豫不決; 畏縮不前: *Sally baulked at the idea of doing the exam again.* 薩莉拿不定主意, 不知要不要再考一次。

bawd·y /ˈbɔdɪ; ˈbɔːdi/ *adj* mentioning sex in a rude and amusing way 猥褻的: *bawdy jokes* 猥褻的笑話

bawl /bɔl; bɔːl/ *v* [I;T] to shout or cry in a loud hard voice 高聲叫喊; 哭喊: *The baby bawled all night.* 嬰兒哭喊了一夜。| *He bawled an order at me.* 他向我大聲發令。

bay /be; beɪ/ *n* **1** a part of the sea or of a large lake enclosed in a curve of the land 海灣; 灣: *the Bay of Biscay* 比斯開灣 | *We went swimming in the bay.* 我們去了海灣游泳。**2** any one of the parts into which a building or space is divided 〔建築物的〕隔間: *This parking bay is reserved for staff only.* 這個停車間是留給員工的。**3** hold someone or something at bay, keep someone or something at bay to keep someone or something a safe distance away 不讓某人或某事物接近: *He kept me at bay with a knife.* 他用刀阻止我接近。**4** a horse whose colour is reddish-brown 栗色馬

bay·o·net /ˈbeənɪt; ˈbeɪənət/ *n* a long knife fixed to the end of a soldier's gun 〔裝於步槍上的〕刺刀

bay win·dow /ˌ·ˈ··/ *n* a window that sticks out from a building and is built up from the ground 凸窗

ba·zaar /bəˈzɑr; bəˈzɑːr/ *n* **1** a marketplace or a group of shops, especially in the Middle East 〔尤指中東的〕集市; 商業區 **2** a sale to collect money in order to help a person or organization 義賣會: *a church bazaar* 教會義賣會

BBC /ˌbi biˈsi; ˌbiː biːˈsiː/ *n* [U] the British radio and television broadcasting company that is paid for by public money; an abbreviation for **British Broadcasting Corporation** 〔縮〕英國廣播公司: *She's a producer at the BBC.* 她是英國廣播公司的製作人。| *It's on BBC tonight.* 它在今晚的英國廣播公司節目中播出。

BC /ˌbiˈsi; ˌbiːˈsiː/ *adv* before the birth of CHRIST; you use BC when giving dates 公元前: *Rome was founded in 753 BC.* 羅馬建立於公元前753年。

★★**be** –see page 82 見 82 頁

★★**beach¹** /bitʃ; biːtʃ/ *n* a shore of a sea or lake covered by sand or small stones 海灘; 湖濱 –see 見 SHORE¹ (USAGE 用法)

beach² *v* [T] to push or drive a boat or large animal onto the shore 推、送〔船或大型動物〕至岸上

bea·con /ˈbikən; ˈbiːkən/ *n* **1** a fire on a hill, tower, or pole, used as a signal 烽火〔用作信號〕**2** a light or radio signal to sailors or pilots as a guide or warning 信號燈; 無線電信號〔用於引導或警告船員或飛行員〕**3** an encouraging example that shows how something worthwhile can be done 指引物

bead /bid; biːd/ *n* **1** a small ball of glass or other material with a hole through it, often threaded on a string and worn as jewellery 〔有孔的〕小珠: *She was wearing a string of green beads.* 她戴着一串綠色的珠子。**2** a small drop of liquid 珠狀物; 滴: *beads of sweat* 汗滴

bead·y /ˈbidɪ; ˈbiːdi/ *adj* beady eyes small, round, and shining eyes 圓而晶亮的小眼睛

beak /bik; biːk/ *n* the hard horny mouth of a bird 鳥嘴, 喙

bea·ker /ˈbikɚ; ˈbiːkər/ *n* **1** BrE a drinking cup with no handle 〔英式〕〔無柄的〕酒杯 – see picture on page 244 見 244 頁彩圖 **2** a small glass cup shaped for pouring, as used in a chemical LABORATORY 燒杯

beam¹ /bim; biːm/ *n* **1** a long heavy bar of wood, especially one of the main ones used to support the roof of a building 〔建築物的〕樑 **2** a line of light shining out from some bright object 光線; 光束: *a moonbeam* 一道月光 | *a laser beam* 激光〔雷射光〕束 **3** radio waves sent out along a narrow path in one direction only, often to guide aircraft 〔導航用的〕射束, 波束 **4** a bright look or smile 愉悅的神情; 微笑: *"How nice to see you!" she said, with a beam of welcome.* "見到你多好呀!" 她笑臉相迎地道。**5** off beam *infml* not exactly correct 〔非正式〕不完全正確

beam² *v* **1** [I] (used of the sun and other shining objects) to send out light 〔太陽或其他發光體〕發光: *The sun beamed down.* 陽光照耀。**2** [I;T] to smile brightly and happily 喜笑顏開; 面露喜色: *He beamed a cheerful welcome.* 他笑着表示熱誠歡迎。**3** [T] to send a radio signal out in a certain direction 定向發出〔無線電信號〕: *The signal is beamed to a satellite.* 這個信號被發至衛星。

bean /bin; biːn/ *n* **1** a seed of a plant, grown for food; beans are usually sold dried or tinned 豆, 豆類〔常曬乾後或罐裝出售〕: *baked beans* 烘豆 **2** a seed container of the bean plant with the seeds inside it, eaten as a fresh vegetable 豆莢; 莢果: *green beans* 嫩菜豆; 青菜豆 –see picture on page 504 見 504 頁彩圖 **3** a seed of certain other plants, from which food or drink can be made 豆形果實: *coffee beans* 咖啡豆 | *cocoa beans* 可可豆 **4** full of beans *infml* full of life and eagerness 〔非正式〕精力充沛; 精神旺盛

bear¹ /bɛr; beər/ *n* a large, heavy animal with thick, rough fur 熊

★★**bear²** *v* **bore** /bɔr; bɔːr/, **borne** /bɔrn; bɔːrn/ [T] **1** to carry something from one

B

★be /bɪ; bi; *strong* 強讀 bi; bi:/ *v*

present tense 現在式	past tense 過去式	past participle 過去分詞
I **am**, I'**m**	I **was**	**been**
You **are**, you'**re**	You **were**	present participle 現在分詞
He / she / it **is**, he'**s**/ she'**s** /	He / she / it **was**	**being**
it'**s**		
We **are**, we'**re**	We **were**	negative short forms 否定縮略式
You **are**, you'**re**	You **were**	**aren't isn't wasn't,**
They **are**, they'**re**	They **were**	**weren't**

For the pronunciation of these forms look them up in the dictionary at their own place. 上述各種形式的發音，可參閱本詞典各自的詞條。

1 [auxiliary verb] used to form the continuous tenses of verbs 用於構成動詞的進行語態: *Where are you going?* 你現在去哪裡? | *She was reading a book.* 她正在看書。| *We're leaving tomorrow.* 我們將於明天離開。| *I'm working at the moment.* 我現在正在工作。

2 [auxiliary verb] used to form the passive of verbs 用於構成動詞的被動語態: *He was attacked by three men.* 他被三個人襲擊。| *The building was decorated last year.* 這幢房子去年已粉刷過了。| *Has the telephone been repaired yet?* 電話修理好了沒有?

3 [auxiliary verb] used to show what will happen or what must happen 用於表示將會發生或一定發生: *He's to meet the president next week.* 他將於下星期會見總統。| *You're to get this finished by tomorrow morning.* 你必須在明天早上之前完成它。

4 [auxiliary verb] used to show what might happen 用於表示可能會發生: *If you were to invest your money wisely, you could make quite a nice profit.* 如果你明智地投資你的錢，你可以獲得相當不錯的利潤。

5 [+ complement] used to give the name, date or position of something, or to describe it in some way 用於表示某物的名稱、時間或位置，或對其作某種描述: *This is Mr Stevenson* 這是史蒂芬遜先生。| *"What's that? It's a hammer."* "那是甚麼?""那是錘子。" | *Today is Monday.* 今天是星期一。| *She's a doctor.* 她是醫生。| *The book is on the table.* 書在桌子上。| *The concert was last night.* 音樂會在昨晚舉行。| *January is the first month of the year.* 一月是一年的第一個月。| *This house is very old.* 這屋子很古老。| *He's a very clever man.* 他是個很聰明的人。

6 **there is, there are, etc.** a phrase used to say that something or someone exists, or to say where they are 表示某物或某人的存在，或表示其位置所在: *Suddenly there was a loud scream.* 突然傳來大聲的尖叫。| *There were three people in the room.* 房間裡有三個人。| *There is a possibility that he will arrive late.* 他有可能會遲到。

place to another 運走，攜帶〔某物〕: *The seeds are borne long distances by the wind.* 種子被風吹得很遠。| *They arrived bearing gifts for us.* 他們攜禮物來看我們。**2** to support the weight of something 負荷; 負重: *I don't think that branch will bear your weight.* 我想那樹枝承受不住你的體重。**3** to have or show a mark or sign 有; 顯示; 表明: *The letter bore his signature.* 這封信有他的簽名。| *All the furniture bears the family's coat of arms.* 所有的家具上都有這個家族的盾形章徽。**4** to suffer and accept something unpleasant without complaining 容忍; 忍受: *He bore the pain bravely.* 他勇敢地忍着痛。| *This last disappointment was almost more than I could bear.* 最近這次的

失望幾乎讓我無法忍受。

■ USAGE 用法: Compare 比較 **abide, bear, endure, stand, tolerate 1** We use *can't* with **abide, bear, endure** and **stand** to show great dislike. *Can't* **stand** is very common ☆ *Can't* **stand, abide, bear, endure, stand** 連用表示極不喜歡，can't **stand** 很常用: *I can't* **stand** *him/his attitude!* 我沒法忍受他/他的態度! We use **abide** mainly with people ☆ **abide** 主要用於指人: *I can't* **abide** *that man!* 我受不了那個男人! We use **bear** and **endure** for really serious things ☆ **bear** 和 **endure** 用於非常嚴重

的情況: *He couldn't* **bear/endure** *listening to reports of the disaster.* 聽到關於災難的報導, 他受不了。 **2** We use **bear, endure** and **stand** with things that are painful or uncomfortable. **Endure** suggests pain that lasts for a long time ☆ **bear, endure, stand** 用於指痛苦或令人不舒服的事物。**endure** 指持續很久的痛(苦): *Try to* **bear/stand** *the pain as long as you can.* 試盡量力去忍住痛。| *She* **endured** *great pain for many years.* 多年來她忍受了很大的痛苦。 **3** We use **tolerate** with people or behaviour, but not with pain ☆ **tolerate** 指忍受人或行為, 但不指痛苦: *I won't* **tolerate** *your rudeness!* 我絕不容忍你的粗魯無禮!

5 can't bear to dislike someone or something very much 極不喜歡〔某物或某人〕: *I can't bear travelling.* 我很討厭旅行。| *I can't bear that man!* 我厭惡那個男人! **6** *lit* to give birth to a child 〔文〕生〔孩子〕: *She had borne three children.* 她生了三個孩子。| *He wanted her to bear him a son.* 他要她給他生個兒子。 **7** to produce fruit or flowers 結果, 開花: *It's an old tree and hasn't borne any fruit for years.* 這是棵老樹, 好幾年沒結果子了。 **8 bear the brunt of something** to suffer the worst effects of something 承受最壞結果; 首當其衝: *As always, it's the poor who will bear the brunt of the economic recession.* 和往常一樣, 窮人在經濟衰退中首當其衝。| *These two cities bore the brunt of the fighting.* 在這場戰爭中, 這兩個城市首當其衝。 **9 bear a grudge** to continue to feel angry with someone for a long time after they have done something to hurt you 懷恨: *I was furious at the time, but I don't bear him any grudge.* 當時我火冒三丈, 但現在我對他毫不懷恨。 **10 bear left, bear right** to turn left or right 往左轉; 往右轉: *Bear left at the next roundabout.* 在下個環形路口向左轉。 **11 bear something in mind** to consider something when you are making a decision or a judgement 〔作決定或判斷時〕考慮某事: *Please bear in mind that there are a lot of other people interested in buying the property.* 請記住有很多人對購置房地產很感興趣。 **12 it doesn't bear thinking about** = it is too terrible to think about 不堪設想 **13 bear no relation/resemblance to something** to be very different from something 和某事物大不相同: *His story bears no relation to the truth.* 他的陳述和事實出入很大。 **14 bear witness to something** to show that something is true or exists 表明某事物真實或存在: *His latest film bears witness to his great acting ability.* 他最近一部影片證明了他的演技精湛。

bear down on sbdy/sthg *phr v* [T] to move nearer to someone or something quickly and in a threatening way 逼近〔某人或某物〕: *We tried to row away as the ship bore down on us.* 那艘輪船逼近我們時, 我們力圖划開。

bear sthg ↔ **out** *phr v* [T] to show that something is true 證實〔某事〕: *His story was borne out by several witnesses.* 他的陳述為幾個證人所證實。

bear up *phr v* [I] to show courage and remain cheerful when you have a lot of difficulties 支持住; 堅忍不拔

bear with sbdy *phr v* [T] to be patient with someone 容忍, 忍耐〔某人〕: *If you'll just bear with me for a few minutes, I will explain everything.* 如果你能耐心地等幾分鐘, 我會解釋一切的。

bear·a·ble /ˈbɛrəbl̩; ˈbɛərəbəl/ *adj* able to be suffered or accepted 可忍受的; 可接受的: *The pain was just bearable.* 這種痛勉強忍受得住。| *His salary increase made life more bearable.* 他的工資增加了, 使生活好過了些。 -opposite **unbearable**

beard /bɪrd; bɪəd/ *n* hair on a man's chin and cheeks 鬍鬚: *Not all men have beards.* 不是所有的男人都有鬍鬚。| *John no longer wears a beard.* 約翰不再蓄鬚了。 -see picture on page 469 見 469 頁彩圖 -compare 比較 MOUSTACHE **bearded** *adj*: *a tall, beared man* 留鬍子的高個子男人 | *a grey-bearded old man* 一個鬍子灰白的老人

bear·er /ˈbɛrɚ; ˈbɛərəʳ/ *n* **1** *fml* a person who brings or possesses something such as an official letter 〔正式〕〔如公文等〕攜帶者, 持有者: *Please help the bearer of this document.* 請協助持本文件者。 **2** a person who helps to carry something 幫助提〔抬〕〔物〕者: *The bearers carried the coffin to the grave.* 扶靈者把棺木抬到墓地。| *the flag-bearer* 擎旗者

bear·ing /ˈbɛrɪŋ; ˈbɛərɪŋ/ *n* **1** [sing] someone's way of holding or moving their body, especially when this shows their behaviour or character 舉止; 姿態: *her proud, upright bearing* 她那高傲、軒昂的舉止 **2** [C] *tech* the part of a machine which holds another part so that it can turn or move more easily 〔術語〕軸承 **3** [C] *tech* a direction or angle as shown by a compass 〔術語〕〔羅盤顯示的〕方位, 方向: *We need to take a bearing.* 我們需要取一個方向。 **4 have a bearing on something** to have a connection with or an influence on something 和某事物有關係, 對某事物有影響: *What you said has no bearings on the matter.* 你說的和這事沒關係。 **5 lose your bearings** to become confused 搞糊塗: *In all this mass of details I'm afraid I've rather lost my bearings.* 面對這一堆瑣碎事, 恐怕我已被弄糊塗了。 [RELATED PHRASE 相關詞組 **get your bearings**]

beast /bist; biːst/ *n* **1** *lit* an animal 〔文〕動物, 野獸 **2** a person or sometimes a thing that you think is very unpleasant 惹人討厭的人或事物: *a beast of a job* 惹人討厭的工作 |

Her husband was a real beast. 她的丈夫真是個畜生。| *You beast!* 你這個畜生! **–beastly** *adj*: *beastly weather* 討厭的天氣 **–beastliness** *n* [U]

★**beat¹** /biːt/ *v* **beat, beaten** /'biːtn̩; 'biːtn̩/ **1** [T] to defeat someone or do better than they 打敗〔某人〕; 勝過〔某人〕: *She beat Holly Wilson in the finals.* 她在決賽中擊敗了霍莉・威爾森。| *She's hoping to beat the world 1000 metre record.* 她希望打破一千米世界紀錄。**–see** 見 **WIN¹** (USAGE 用法) **2** [T] to hit someone repeatedly, usually with a hard object〔常以硬物接連地〕打〔某人〕: *The students were beaten by the police.* 學生被警察打。**3** [I;T] to hit something hard and continuously〔連續地〕重敲,重打〔某物〕: *The rain was beating against the windows.* 雨打在窗戶上。| *The police beat the door down.* 警察強行把門砸開。| *They beat the drums.* 他們擊鼓。**4** [I;T] to move regularly 有規律地動; 跳動: *You can hear its heart beating.* 你能聽到牠的心臟在跳動。| *The bird beat its wings rapidly.* 鳥急速地拍打着翅膀。**5** [T] to mix something well with regular movement of a fork or spoon〔用叉子或匙〕打, 攪拌: *Beat two eggs and add them to the mixture.* 先打好兩個雞蛋, 然後加入混合物中。**6 beat about the bush** to delay talking about or answering questions about the most important part of a subject 轉彎抹角; 旁敲側擊; 拖延談及正題 **7 Beat it!** *slang* Go away! 〔俚〕走開! **8 beat someone at their own game** to use successfully against someone a method which they use themselves 以其人之道還治其人之身 **9 beat someone to it** to do something before someone else 先於某人做某事 **10 beat time** to make regular movements or noises with your hands and feet at the same speed as a piece of music 打拍子 **11 it beats me** *infml* I can't understand it〔非正式〕我不明白

beat down *phr v* **1** [I] (of the sun) to be very hot and bright〔太陽〕曝曬 **2** [I] (of the rain) to come down very hard〔雨〕下得很大 **3** [T **beat** sbdy ↔ **down**] to persuade someone to reduce a price 勸〔某人〕減價, 殺價: *He wanted £50 for the dress, but I beat him down to £40.* 這件衣服他要價五十英鎊, 但我把價錢壓到四十英鎊。

beat sbdy/sthg **off** *phr v* [T] to prevent an attacker from succeeding 擊退; 逐走: *He managed to beat the dogs off.* 他把狗趕走了。

beat sthg ↔ **out** *phr v* [T] **1** to make sounds by beating 敲出〔聲音〕: *The drummers beat out their music.* 鼓手們敲出樂曲。**2** to put out a fire by beating 撲滅〔火〕

beat sbdy **to** sthg *phr v* [T] to defeat someone by being the first to do something 搶先一步; 捷足先登: *They had hoped to win a big contract in Japan, but they were beaten to it by a German company.* 他們原

希望能在日本獲得一份巨額合同, 但被一家德國公司捷足先登。

beat sbdy ↔ **up** *phr v* [T] *infml* to hurt someone badly by hitting〔非正式〕揍; 痛打: *The boys robbed the old man and then beat him up.* 男孩們搶了那老人的東西, 還把他揍了一頓。

beat² *n* **1** [C] a single movement or blow, especially as part of a group〔連續敲打中的〕一擊; 敲擊: *one beat of the drum every 60 seconds* 每隔六十秒敲一下鼓 **2** [sing] a regular sound produced by or as if by repeated beating 有規律的敲擊聲: *the beat of the drum* 敲鼓的聲音 **3** [sing] a regular timing in music or poetry 節拍; 拍子: *Every member of the band must follow the beat.* 樂隊的每個成員都必須跟着拍子演奏。| *music with a strong beat* 節奏強烈的音樂 **4** [C] the usual area for which someone, especially a policeman, is responsible in their job〔尤指警察的〕巡邏路線

beat³ *adj* [never before a noun 不能用於名詞前] **1** *infml* very tired〔非正式〕非常疲勞的: *I'm dead beat after all that work!* 我做完所有的工作後累得要命! **2** defeated 被打敗的: *I had to admit that I was beat.* 我得承認我被打敗了。

beat·en¹ /'biːtn̩; 'biːtn̩/ the past participle of BEAT ☆ BEAT 的過去分詞

beat·en² *adj* **1** shaped by beating, e.g. with a hammer or by people's feet 被錘薄的; 被踏平的: *a plate made of beaten gold* 用金箔製成的盤子 | *We followed a well-beaten path through the forest.* 我們沿着一條踏得很平的小路穿過森林。**2 off the beaten track** not often visited 人跡罕至的: *Every year they go camping somewhere off the beaten track.* 他們每年都到人家不大去的地方野營。

beat·er /'biːtə; 'biːtər/ *n* **1** a tool used in the kitchen to mix eggs and other things 拍打器; 攪拌器: *an egg beater* 打蛋器 **2** a tool used for beating floor coverings 拍打〔地毯等的〕工具: *a carpet beater* 地毯撣子

beat·ing /'biːtɪŋ; 'biːtɪŋ/ *n* **1** an act in which one person hits another hard many times, usually with something such as a stick; a beating is sometimes given as a punishment〔常以棍棒〕責打〔有時作為懲罰〕: *The child had been given a severe beating.* 這孩子挨了一頓痛打。**2** a bad defeat, especially in a game or competition〔尤指遊戲、比賽的〕慘敗: *Our team took quite a beating. The score was five-nil.* 我隊遭到慘敗, 比分是 5 比 0。**3 take some beating** be so good that it will be difficult for anything else to be better 好得難以超越: *Your chocolate puddings take some beating.* 你的巧克力布丁比誰的都好。

beat-up /ˌ·'·◂/ *infml adj* in very bad condition because used so much or treated so badly〔非正式〕破舊的; 破爛的: *a beat-up old car* 一輛破破爛爛的老爺車

beau·ti·cian /bjuːˈtɪʃən; bjuːˈtɪʃən/ *n* a person who gives beauty treatments to your face or nails 美容師

beau·ti·ful /ˈbjuːtəfəl; ˈbjuːtɪฺfəl/ *adj* giving great pleasure to your mind or senses 美麗的: *a beautiful girl* 美麗的女孩 | *a beautiful sunset* 美麗的日落 —**beautifully** *adv*

> ■ USAGE 用法: **1 Beautiful** is quite a strong word to describe a person's appearance. **Pretty, handsome, good-looking** or **attractive** may be more suitable words. ☆ 形容人的外貌, **beautiful** 是一個意義很強的詞。**Pretty, handsome, good-looking** 或 **attractive** 可能更適宜一些。**2** We use **beautiful** and **pretty** to describe women, children and things, but usually not men ☆ **beautiful** 和 **pretty** 用於形容女人、小孩和東西，但通常不用於男人: *a beautiful girl* 美麗的女孩 | *a beautiful house* 漂亮的房子 | *a pretty child* 漂亮的孩子 | *a pretty picture* 好看的畫。We use **good-looking** to describe men and women, but not things. We use **handsome** to describe men, or women who are **good-looking** in a strong, healthy way. We use **attractive** to describe men, women and things ☆ **good-looking** 用於形容男人和女人，但不用於描寫東西。**handsome** 用於形容男人或健美的女人。**attractive** 用於形容男人、女人和東西: *an attractive young man* 有魅力的青年 | *an attractive pattern* 引人注目的圖案

beau·ti·fy /ˈbjuːtəˌfaɪ; ˈbjuːtɪฺfaɪ/ *v* **beautified, beautifying** [T] to make something beautiful 使美麗; 美化

beau·ty /ˈbjuːtɪ; ˈbjuːti/ *n* **beauties 1** [U] the quality of being attractive to look at or hear, or pleasing to the mind 美; 美麗: *a poem of great beauty* 極美的詩 | *the beauty of the scenery* 景色之美 **2** [C] someone beautiful, usually a woman, or something beautiful 美人; 美的東西: *She is a great beauty.* 她是個大美人。 | *the beauties of nature* 大自然的美景 **3** [C] *infml* someone or something very good or very bad 《非正式》很好[很糟]的人[東西]: *That apple is a real beauty.* 那蘋果真是個佳品。 | *That black eye is a real beauty!* 那隻黑眼睛真是好看! **4** the beauty of the advantage of the 優點: *The beauty of my idea is that it would cost so little!* 我的主意奧妙之處在於它花費極少!

beauty spot /ˈ··· / *n* a place known for the beauty of its scenery 風景點; 名勝

bea·ver /ˈbiːvə; ˈbiːvəʳ/ *n* a water and land animal of the rat family with a broad flat tail which builds walls across streams 河狸; 海狸

be·calmed /bɪˈkɑːmd; bɪˈkɑːmd/ *adj* unable to move forward because of lack of wind (used of a sailing ship) 〔因無風而〕不能航行的〔指帆船〕

be·cause /bɪˈkɒz; bɪˈkɔz/ *conj* a word you use when you are giving a reason for something 因為: *"Why can't I go?" "Because you're too young!"* "我為甚麼不能去?" "因為你年紀太小了!" | *We couldn't go out because it was too cold.* 因為天氣太冷, 我們不能外出。

because of *prep* for the reason given 由於: *The event was called off because of the rain.* 由於下雨, 運動會的比賽項目被取消了。

beck /bek; bek/ *n* **be at someone's beck and call** to always have to be ready to do everything someone asks 聽命於某人

beck·on /ˈbekən; ˈbekən/ *v* [I;T] to show someone with a movement of the finger or hand that you want them to move nearer 〔用手勢〕示意, 召喚〔某人〕: *She's beckoning to you.* 她在示意要你過去。 | *She beckoned me to follow her.* 她示意要我跟她走。

be·come /bɪˈkʌm; bɪˈkʌm/ *v* **became** /bɪˈkem; bɪˈkeɪm/, **become, becoming 1** [+ complement] to begin to be something 變為; 成為: *He became king in 1938.* 他於1938年成為國王。 | *The weather became warmer.* 天氣變暖和了。**2** [T] *fml* to be right or suitable for 《正式》相稱; 合適: *That sort of behaviour does not become a person in your position.* 這種行為不應出自一個像你這樣身分的人。

become of sbdy/sthg *phr v* [T] to happen to somebody or something, often in a bad way 發生某種情況; 遭遇: *Whatever became of that nice girl you used to share a flat with?* 過去和你合住一個單位的那個可愛的女孩子後來怎麼了?

> ■ USAGE 用法: **Become** is not always the best word when you describe a change in a person or thing. To describe a change in colour you can use **turn**, or **go** if it is a temporary change ☆ 當描寫人或事物的變化時, **become** 並非總是最適當的詞。描寫顏色的變化可以用 **turn**, 如果是暫時的變化, 還可用 **go**: *The leaves are turning brown.* 葉子變成褐色。 | *His face turns/goes red when he is angry.* 他生氣時臉會變紅。We can use **go** or **become** in these expressions ☆ 在以下這些表達中, 可以使用 **go** 或 **become**: *to go/become deaf* 變聾 | *to go/become blind* 變瞎 | *People go mad; meat goes bad.* 人發瘋; 肉變壞。

be·com·ing /bɪˈkʌmɪŋ; bɪˈkʌmɪŋ/ *adj old fash* 《老式》(a word which is sometimes used in a humorous way 有時表示幽默) **1** looking very good on the wearer 〔穿在身上〕合適的: *Blue always looks very becoming on her.* 她穿藍色的服裝總是很合適的。**2**

B

proper or suitable 適當的; 宜適的: *His laughter was not very becoming on such a solemn occasion.* 他在這麼莊嚴的場合發笑有點不太得體. –opposite 反義 **unbecoming**

bed¹ /bɛd; bɛd/ *n* **1** [C;U] an article of furniture to sleep on 牀: *a room with two beds* 有兩張牀的房間 | *a comfortable bed for the night* 晚上睡覺用的舒服的牀 | *It's time for bed.* 是睡覺的時候了. | *She's gone to bed.* 她去睡了. | *She's in bed.* 她在睡覺. | *He helped me into bed.* 他幫我上牀. **2 make a bed** to make bed ready to sleep in 鋪牀: *When I've done the washing up, I'll make the beds.* 等我洗完碗, 我來鋪牀. **3** [C] a surface that forms the base or bottom of something 基座; 底部: *The hut rests on a bed of cement.* 茅舍建在水泥地基上. | *I served the chicken on a bed of lettuce.* 我端上一盤以萵苣作菜底的雞. | *the bed of the river* 河牀 | *the seabed* 海底 **4** [C] a piece of ground in which plants grow in a garden 苗圃; 花壇: *a flowerbed* 花壇 **5** [C] a band of rock of a certain kind lying above or below others 礦牀; 地層: *The building stands on a bed of rock.* 這幢樓建在岩牀上. **6 bed and breakfast** a service offered by a guesthouse or other place where you can stay the night; you get a bed for the night and breakfast, but no other meals 〔旅館等提供的〕宿夜牀位和早餐 **7 a bed of roses** *infml* a happy comfortable state 〔非正式〕稱心如意的境遇; 安樂窩 **8 he got out of bed on the wrong side** *infml* = he's in a bad temper 〔非正式〕發脾氣, 心緒不好 **9 go to bed with someone** to have sexual relations with someone 與某人性交: *He tried to get her to go to bed with him.* 他想讓她和他睡覺.

bed² *v* **-dd-** [T] to fix on a base or beneath the surface 安裝; 固定; 嵌入; 埋置: *The machine is bedded in cement.* 這台機器是安置在水泥地上的.

bed down *phr v* [I + adv/prep] to make yourself comfortable for the night when you have not got a proper bed 〔沒牀時〕使自己安睡

bed·clothes /'bɛd,kloz; 'bɛdkloʊðz/ *n* [pl] the sheets and covers that you put on a bed 牀上用品〔如被單、牀罩等〕

bed·ding /'bɛdɪŋ; 'bɛdɪŋ/ *n* [U] **1** sheets and other things which you use to make your bed 〔被單、牀罩等〕牀上用品 **2** something soft on which a person or animal can sleep 〔人用的〕寢具; 〔動物歇息的〕墊草

be·deck /bɪ'dɛk; bɪ'dɛk/ *v* [T] *fml* to decorate something 〔正式〕裝飾〔某物〕: *The cars were all bedecked with flowers for the ceremony.* 為了這次慶典, 汽車都裝飾上了花.

be·dev·il /bɪ'dɛvl; bɪ'dɛvəl/ *v* **-ll-** *BrE* 〔英式〕 **-l-** *AmE* 〔美式〕 [T] to cause problems to someone continually 使〔某人〕大為困擾

bed·lam /'bɛdləm; 'bɛdləm/ *n* [U] *infml* a

wild noisy place or activity 〔非正式〕喧鬧的地方[活動]

bed·pan /'bɛd,pæn; 'bɛdpæn/ *n* a low wide vessel used by a sick person for emptying their bowels without getting out of bed 〔病人在牀上用的〕便盆

be·drag·gled /bɪ'dræɡld; bɪ'dræɡəld/ *adj* with the clothes and hair in disorder 衣冠不整的; 頭髮濕濡的: *a bedraggled appearance* 不修邊幅的樣子

bed·rid·den /'bɛd,rɪdn; 'bɛd,rɪdn/ *adj* unable to get out of bed because of illness or old age 〔因疾病或年邁〕臥牀不起的

✲bed·room /'bɛd,rum; 'bɛdrʊm/ *n* a room for sleeping in 臥室

bed·side /'bɛd,saɪd; 'bɛdsaɪd/ *n* the side of a bed 牀邊: *He was called to the bedside of his sick father.* 他被叫到父親的病牀邊. | *a bedside lamp* 牀頭燈

bed·sit·ter /ˌ·'··/ (also 又作 **bed·sit** /'··/) *infml* 〔非正式〕 *n* a room used for both living and sleeping in 臥室兼起居室的兩用房間 –see 見 HOUSE¹ (USAGE 用法)

bed·spread /'bɛd,sprɛd; 'bɛdsprɛd/ *n* a decorative cloth cover for a bed 牀罩

bee /bi; biː/ *n* **1** a black and yellow insect that makes HONEY and buzzes (BUZZ) 蜜蜂 **2 a bee in your bonnet** *infml* a fixed idea 〔非正式〕固執的想法: *He has a bee in his bonnet about health foods.* 他對於保健食品有一套固執的想法.

beech /bitʃ; biːtʃ/ *n* **1** [C] a tree with a smooth grey trunk, spreading branches, and green leaves 山毛櫸 **2** [U] the wood of this tree 山毛櫸木

beef¹ /bif; biːf/ *n* [U] the meat of farm cattle 牛肉 –see 見 MEAT (USAGE 用法)

beef² *v* **beef about something** *infml* to complain continually about something 〔非正式〕發牢騷; 抱怨: *Stop beefing about your pay and do some work!* 別再抱怨工錢(太少)了, 做點兒事吧!

beef·y /'bifi; 'biːfi/ *adj* **beefier, beefiest** *infml* big, strong, and perhaps fat (used of a person) 〔非正式〕粗壯的〔指人〕

bee·hive /'bi,haɪv; 'biːhaɪv/ *n* see 見 HIVE (1)

bee·line /'bi,laɪn; 'biːlaɪn/ *n* **make a beeline for something** *infml* to go quickly and directly towards something 〔非正式〕直奔; 逕往: *The children made a beeline for the swings.* 孩子們朝着鞦韆直奔.

been /bɪn; bɪn/ *v* **1** the past participle of BE ☆ BE 的過去分詞: *They've been photographed.* 他們被拍下照片了. **2** gone and come back from 去過; 到過: *Have you ever been to India?* 你去過印度嗎? **3** arrived and left 來過: *I see the postman hasn't been yet.* 我看郵差還沒有來過. –see 見 GO¹ (USAGE 用法)

✲beer /bɪr; bɪəʳ/ *n* [U] a bitter alcoholic drink made from MALT and hops (HOP³)

啤酒: *Do you like beer?* 你喜歡啤酒嗎? **2** [C] a drink of beer 一份啤酒: *We had several beers.* 我們喝了好幾杯啤酒。**3** [U] any of several kinds of drink, usually non-alcoholic, made from roots or plants〔由植物或植物根釀造的通常不含酒精的〕飲料: *ginger beer* 薑味汽水 –**beery** *adj:* *unpleasant beery breath* 難聞的啤酒氣息

bees·wax /'biz,wæks; 'biːzwæks/ *n* [U] wax made by bees, used for making furniture polish and candles 蜂蠟〔可製家具亮漆或蠟燭〕

beet /bit; biːt/ *n* **1** [C;U] (also 又作 **sugar beet**) a plant with a thick root underground, used as a vegetable or made into sugar 甜菜 **2** the usual American word for〔美式〕= BEETROOT

bee·tle /'bitl; 'biːtl/ *n* an insect with hard wing coverings 甲蟲

beet·root /'bit,rut; 'biːtruːt/ (**beet** *AmE*〔美式〕) *n* **beetroot** or **beetroots** [C;U] a plant with a large round red root, which is cooked and eaten as a vegetable 甜菜根: *beetroot salad* 甜菜根沙拉 –see picture on page 504 見 504 頁彩圖

be·fall /bɪ'fɔl; bɪ'fɔːl/ *v* **befell** /bɪ'fɛl; bɪ'fel/, **befallen** /bɪ'fɔlən; bɪ'fɔːlən/ [I;T] *fml* (usually used about something bad) to happen to someone as if by fate〔正式〕〔常指壞事〕降臨, 發生: *Some misfortune must have befallen them.* 某種災禍必定是降臨到他們的頭上了。

be·fore¹ /bɪ'for; bɪ'fɔːr/ *adv* at an earlier time or on an earlier occasion 從前; 以前: *Haven't I seen you somewhere before?* 我以前在哪兒見過你嗎? | *He had never been to London before.* 他以前從沒到過倫敦。

before² *prep* **1** earlier than 在...以前: *We must leave before lunch time.* 我們必須在午飯以前離開。 | *They got there before us.* 他們比我們先到達那裡。**2** ahead of someone or something 在〔某人或某物〕之前: *Her name comes before mine on the list.* 她的名字在名單上排在我的前面。**3** in front of someone or something 在〔某物或某人〕前面: *She had to give evidence before a magistrate.* 她在地方法庭法官面前得拿出證據來。**4** in a more important position 比...更重要: *Your family should come before everything else.* 你的家庭應該比其他一切都重要。**5** **before that** you use "before that" when you are showing what order events happen in 在此之前〔用於表示事情按何種順序發生〕: *In five minutes' time we'll have the news, but before that let's go over to the London Weather Centre for the weather forecast.* 五分鐘以後我們就能聽到新聞了, 可是在此之前我們先撥到倫敦氣象中心聽聽天氣預報吧。

before³ *conj* earlier than the time when something happens 在...前: *I'd like to talk to you before you go.* 你走之前我想和你談

談。 | *We must consider all the facts before we make a decision.* 我們做決定以前必須考慮到所有的事實。

be·fore·hand /bɪ'for,hænd; bɪ'fɔːhænd/ *adv* before something else happens 預先; 事先: *If you knew what was going to happen, why didn't you warn us beforehand?* 要是你知道會發生甚麼事, 為甚麼不事先提醒我們?

be·friend /bɪ'frɛnd; bɪ'frend/ *v* [T] *fml* to act as a friend to someone who needs your help〔正式〕〔對需要幫助者〕待之如友; 照顧: *He befriended me when I was young.* 我年輕時他如同朋友一般地照顧我。

beg /bɛg; beg/ *v* **-gg-** **1** [I;T] to ask people in the street to give you money or food〔在街上〕乞討〔食物或錢等〕: *He lives by begging.* 他靠乞討為生。 | *She sat at the station begging for money.* 她坐在火車站討錢。**2** [I;T] to ask for something with great eagerness or anxiety 懇求; 請求: *to beg for forgiveness* 懇求原諒 | *Could I beg a favour of you?* 能求你幫個忙嗎? | *He begged me to stay.* 他懇求我留下。

□ USEFUL PATTERNS 有用句型
to beg for something; to beg someone to do something

3 [I] (of a dog) to sit up with its front legs held against its chest〔狗〕前腿收於胸前站立 **4** **going begging** *infml* able to be taken or used〔非正式〕可拿走的; 可用的 **5** **I beg your pardon** you use this expression when you are saying that you are sorry, or when you did not hear what someone said and you want them to say it again 請再說一遍〔用於道歉時或沒聽清別人的話〕 **6** **beg the question: a** to take as true something that is not yet proved〔對未經證實的事情〕信以為真 **b** to avoid answering a question 避免回答問題

beg·gar¹ /'bɛgɚ; 'begɚ/ *n* **1** a person who lives by begging 乞丐 **2** *infml* a person, especially a man〔非正式〕傢伙〔尤指男人〕: *So you're off to Hong Kong tomorrow, you lucky beggar!* 那麼明天你就要動身去香港了, 你這幸運的傢伙! **3** **beggars can't be choosers** *infml* poor people have to take anything they can get and must not hope to get exactly what they want〔非正式〕要飯的哪能挑肥揀瘦; 飢不擇食

beggar² *v* [T] *fml* to make someone very poor〔正式〕使〔某人〕貧窮

be·gin /bɪ'gɪn; bɪ'gin/ *v* **began** /bɪ'gæn; bɪ'gæn/, **begun** /bɪ'gʌn; bɪ'gʌn/, **beginning** **1** [I] to start 開始: *Tell me when to begin.* 告訴我甚麼時候開始。 | *Work on the new railway will begin in 1995.* 修築新鐵路的工作將於 1995 年開始。 | *The story began with a plane crash.* 這個故事以一宗飛機墜毀事件為開端。 | *I began by explaining the situation.* 我以解釋情況作為開端。**2** [T] to start something 開始〔某事〕: *They're beginning a new serial on BBC 2 next week.* 他們下週在英國廣播公司二台啟播一個新的連續劇。| *It's beginning to rain.* 天開始下雨。| *She began learning English last year.* 她去年開始學英語。

□ USEFUL PATTERNS 有用句型
to begin something; to begin to do something; to begin doing something

3 [I] to come into existence 始於: *The war began in 1979.* 戰爭始於 1979 年。**4 to begin with: a** firstly; when you are speaking or writing and you have several points you want to make, you can order them and introduce them with expressions such as "to begin with," and "secondly," 首先〔當說話或寫作時有幾個觀點要表述，可以按順序依次用"to begin with" 和 "secondly" 來表示〕: *It can't be done. To begin with, there's no time to plan it, and secondly, we haven't got enough men.* 首先，沒時間訂定計劃；第二，人手不夠。**b** at first 起初; 開始: *To begin with, the weather was dreadful, but it improved later in the week.* 這週初天氣很糟，但後來好轉了。–see 見 START¹ (USAGE 用法)

be·gin·ner /bɪ'gɪnə; bɪ'gɪnər/ *n* a person who is just beginning to do or learn something 初學者; 新手

★**be·gin·ning** /bɪ'gɪnɪŋ; bɪ'gɪnɪŋ/ *n* [C;U] the starting point or origin 開端; 起源; 開頭: *She knows that book from beginning to end.* 她對那本書瞭如指掌。| *at the beginning of the month* 在月初

■ USAGE 用法: **1** Note the use of the preposition at in the phrase **at the beginning** ☆注意詞組 **at the beginning** 中介詞 at 的用法: *As I mentioned* **at the beginning** *of my letter...* 如我在信的開頭所說... | *He arrived* **at the beginning** *of the lunch hour.* 午飯開始時他就到了。| *at the* **beginning** *of the century* 在本世紀初 **2** When you want to contrast an early time with a later time use **at first** ☆以較早的時間和較晚的時間作對照時，可用 **at first**: **At first** *we thought it was a joke but then we realized it was true.* 開頭我們以為這是個笑話，但隨後我們發覺這是真的。| *Nobody liked her* **at first** *but she soon became quite popular.* 起初沒人喜歡她，但不久她就變得很受歡迎了。

be·grudge /bɪ'grʌdʒ; bɪ'grʌdʒ/ *v* begrudged, begrudging [T] **1** to feel angry about doing something that you do not want to do 〔因不想做而〕抱怨, 生氣: *I begrudge spending so much money on train fares.* 我不願在火車票上要花這麼多錢。**2 begrudge someone**

something to feel angry that someone should have something 妒忌某人有某事物: *We shouldn't begrudge him his success.* 我們不該妒忌他的成功。

be·guile /bɪ'gaɪl; bɪ'gaɪl/ *v* **beguild, beguiling** [T] *fml* 〔正式〕 **1** to charm someone 迷住〔某人〕: *Her eyes and voice beguiled me.* 她的眼睛和聲音迷住了我。**2 beguile someone into doing something** to deceive or cheat someone into doing something 騙某人做某事: *He beguiled me into lending him my bicycle.* 他騙我把腳踏車借給他。–**beguiling** *adj*

be·half /bɪ'hæf; bɪ'haːf/ *n* **on behalf of** (also 又作 **in behalf of** *AmE* 〔美式〕) for someone or in someone's interests 代表〔某人〕; 為了〔某人〕的利益: *The President can't be here today, so I'm going to speak on his behalf.* 會長今天不能來，所以我來代表他講話。| *On behalf of everyone here, I'd like to thank you both very much for coming.* 我代表在座的諸位，感謝你們兩位的光臨。

★**be·have** /bɪ'heɪv; bɪ'heɪv/ *v* **behaved, behaving 1** [I + adv/prep] to act in a particular way 舉止; 表現: *She behaved with great courage.* 她表現出很大的勇氣。| *He's been behaving very oddly lately.* 最近他一直舉止古怪。| *My car has been behaving well since it was repaired.* 我的汽車自修理後一直運行正常。**2** [I] to act in a socially acceptable or polite way 舉止端正; 行為規矩: *He'll have to learn how to behave.* 他得學會舉止得體。**3 behave yourself** to act in a socially acceptable or polite way 舉止得體; 守規矩: *Just stop being naughty and behave yourself!* 別再淘氣了，規矩些! **4 behaved** behaving in the stated way 守規矩的: *a very badly behaved child* 很不守規矩的孩子

★**be·hav·iour** /bɪ'heɪvjə; bɪ'heɪvjər/ *n* (**behavior** *AmE* 〔美式〕) [U] **1** a way of behaving 舉止; 行為: *It was very odd behaviour for a policeman.* 對一個警察而言，這種舉止非常奇怪。**2 be on your best behaviour** to be very polite 舉止有禮

be·head /bɪ'hɛd; bɪ'hed/ *v* [T] to cut someone's head off 砍〔某人〕的頭; 斬首

★**be·hind**¹ /bɪ'haɪnd; bɪ'haɪnd/ *adv, prep* **1** *adv, prep* at the back of something 在〔某物〕後面: *A stream runs behind the house.* 一條小河從屋後流過。| *She ran out from behind a tree.* 她從樹後跑出來。| *a house with a large garden behind* 後面有個大花園的房子 –see picture on page 764 見 764 頁彩圖 **2** *adv* late or slow 遲; 慢: *We're a month behind with the rent.* 我們已經拖欠了一個月的租金。**3** *adv, prep* less successful than someone else 落後於: *We finished three points behind the leaders.* 我們最終以三分落後於領先者。**4** *adv* where something or someone was before 在原來的地方: *The others went for a walk but I stayed behind.* 其他人去散步，我卻留下沒走。| *I had left my* *handbag behind.* 我離開時忘了帶手提包。 **5** *prep* causing something 作為引起〔某事〕的原因: *I think that John is behind all this.* 我想這些事的起因都在約翰身上。 **6** *prep* supporting someone 支持〔某人〕: *The country is firmly behind the prime minister.* 舉國上下都堅定地支持首相。

behind[2] *n old fash* the part of your body that you sit on〔老式〕屁股; 臀部

be·hind·hand /bɪˈhaɪndˌhænd; bɪˈhaɪndhænd/ *adj, adv fml* late〔正式〕遲(的); 慢(的): *We're a month behindhand with the rent.* 我們已經拖欠了一個月的租金。

be·hold /bɪˈhold; bɪˈhəʊld/ *v* **beheld** /bɪˈheld; bɪˈheld/, **beheld** [T] *lit* to see someone or something〔文〕見到; 看

beige /beʒ; beɪʒ/ *n,adj* [U] a pale dull yellowish brown 米黃色(的) –see picture on page 243 見 243 頁彩圖

★**be·ing** /ˈbiɪŋ; ˈbiːɪŋ/ *n* **1 come into being** to begin to exist 開始存在: *When did the club first come into being?* 俱樂部是甚麼時候成立的? **2** [C] a creature 生物: *a human being* 一個人 | *a being from outer space* 外星人

be·la·bour /bɪˈlebɚ; bɪˈleɪbəʳ/ *v* (**belabor** *AmE*〔美式〕) [T] to talk about something for too long 囉嗦: *He kept belabouring the point until we were all absolutely fed up with it.* 他不斷重複同一論調, 我們都煩透了。

be·lat·ed /bɪˈletɪd; bɪˈleɪtɪd/ *adj* delayed or arriving too late 延誤的; 來得太遲的: *a belated apology* 為時已晚的抱歉 –**belatedly** *adv*

belch /beltʃ; beltʃ/ *v* **1** [I] to pass gas noisily from your stomach out through your throat 打嗝 **2** [T] to throw something out with force or in large quantities 大量吐出; 噴出: *chimneys belching smoke* 冒出濃煙的煙囪

bel·fry /ˈbelfri; ˈbelfri/ *n* **belfries** a tower for a bell, for example on a church〔教堂等的〕鐘塔, 鐘樓

be·lie /bɪˈlaɪ; bɪˈlaɪ/ *v* **belied, belied, belying** *fml* [T] to give a false idea of something〔正式〕掩飾; 給人錯覺: *Her smile belied her feelings of displeasure.* 她的笑容掩飾了她不快的感覺。

★**be·lief** /bɪˈlif; bɪˈliːf/ *n* **1** [sing;U] the feeling that something is true or that something really exists 相信; 信仰: *belief in God* 相信 (有)上帝 | *my belief that he is right* 我相信他是對的 **2** [sing;U] trust or a feeling that someone or something is good or can be depended on 信任; 信心: *her misplaced belief in her husband* 她對丈夫錯誤的信任 | *The failure of the operation has shaken my belief in doctors.* 手術的失敗動搖了我對醫生的信心。 **3** [C] an idea which is considered true, often one which is part of a system of ideas 信念; 信條; 信仰: *my religious beliefs* 我的宗教信仰 | *strongly-held beliefs* 堅定的信念 **4 beyond belief: a** too strange to be believed 難以置信的: *His story is beyond belief.* 他的故事難以置信。 **b** very great 很大的

be·lie·va·ble /bɪˈlivəbl; bɪˈliːvəbəl/ *adj* that seems real and can be believed 可信任的 – opposite 反義 **unbelievable** –**believably** *adv*

★**be·lieve** /bɪˈliv; bɪˈliːv/ *v* **believed, believing** [*not in progressive forms* 不用於進行式] **1** [T + (that)] to think that something is true 相信: *I don't believe these figures.* 我不相信這些數字。 | *You can't believe anything she says.* 無論她説甚麼, 都不能相信。 | *It's hard to believe that she's only 25.* 真難相信她才二十五歲。 **2** [T + (that)] to have an opinion 以為; 認為; 想: *I believe that she will win the next election.* 我認為她在下屆選舉中會贏。 | *70% of the people asked believe the government's policies are right.* 接受諮詢問的人有百分之七十認為政府的政策是正確的。 | *The jury believed her to be innocent.* 陪審團認為她無罪。 **3** [T] to think that someone is telling the truth 相信〔某人説真話〕: *I believe her.* 我相信她。 | *The police don't believe him.* 警方不相信他。 **4 believe it or not** you use this expression when you are surprised or you think that the person you are talking to will be surprised 信不信由你〔用於表示驚訝〕: *I asked for an extra week's holiday and, believe it or not, she agreed!* 我要求多請一星期的假, 信不信由你, 她同意了! **5 believe me** you use this expression to add force to what you are saying 相信我〔用於加強語氣〕: *I don't like it any more than you do, believe me.* 説真的, 我和你一樣不喜歡這個。 **6 would you believe it** you use this expression when you are surprised or shocked 你能相信嗎〔用於表示驚奇或震驚〕: *"He was back again only two days later." "Well! Would you believe it!"* "才過了兩天他又回來了。""啊! 你能相信嗎!" **7 make believe** to pretend 假裝: *He's making believe he's really ill. He just wants your sympathy.* 他假裝真的在生病, 只想博得你的同情。

believe in *phr v* **1** [T **believe in** sthg] to think that something exists 相信〔某物存在〕: *Do you believe in fairies?* 你相信有神仙嗎? **2** [**believe in** sbdy] to have faith or trust in someone 信任〔某人〕; 信仰: *Christians believe in Jesus.* 基督徒信仰耶穌。 **3** [**believe in** sthg] to have confidence in the value of something 認為〔某物〕有價值: *Jim believes in going for a run every morning.* 吉姆認為每天早上跑步是有益的。

be·liev·er /bɪˈlivɚ; bɪˈliːvəʳ/ *n* **1** someone who believes in God 信仰上帝者 **2** someone who believes in something 相信〔某事〕的人: *He's a great believer in the benefits of exercise.* 他深信鍛鍊有益。

be·lit·tle /bɪˈlɪtl; bɪˈlɪtl/ *v* **belittled, belittling** [T] *fml* to make something seem small or unimportant and not very good〔正式〕輕視; 貶低: *Don't belittle yourself.* 別小看你自

己。| *You mustn't belittle your efforts.* 你不要小看自己所做的努力。

*bell /bɛl; bɛl/ *n* a round hollow metal object, which makes a ringing sound when struck or when a movable hanging part hits the inside 鐘; 鈴: *a bicycle bell* 腳踏車鈴 | *a doorbell* 門鈴

bel·lig·er·ent /bəˈlɪdʒərənt; bɪˈlɪdʒərənt/ *adj* angry and ready to fight 怒氣沖沖的; 好鬥的: *I felt tired and belligerent.* 我覺得又疲倦又想和人打一架。

bel·low /ˈbɛloʊ; ˈbɛləʊ/ *v* **1** [I] to make the loud deep hollow sound typical of a BULL¹ (1) 吼; 大聲叫 **2** [I;T] to shout something in a loud, deep voice 咆哮; 怒吼: *"Go away!"* *he bellowed.* "滾吧!"他怒吼道。 **–bellow** *n*

bel·ly /ˈbɛlɪ; ˈbɛlɪ/ *n* **bellies 1** *infml* the part of the human body, between the chest and the legs, which contains the stomach and bowels〔非正式〕肚子; 腹部 **2** a surface or object curved or round like this part of your body 腹狀物; 腹狀部: *the belly of the plane* 飛機的機腹

bel·ly·ache /ˈbɛlɪˌek; ˈbɛlɪeɪk/ *v* **bellyached, bellyaching** [I] *infml* to complain repeatedly, especially about something unimportant〔非正式〕〔尤指小事〕抱怨, 發牢騷: *Stop bellyaching about the colour and get on with the job!* 別再抱怨顏色了, 繼續幹活吧!

belly but·ton /ˈ··ˌ··/ *n infml* your NAVEL〔非正式〕肚臍

bel·ly·ful /ˈbɛlɪˌfʊl; ˈbɛlɪfʊl/ *n infml*〔非正式〕**a bellyful of something** too much of something 某物過量: *I've had a bellyful of your complaints.* 我已經聽夠了你的怨言。

*be·long /bɪˈlɔŋ; bɪˈlɒŋ/ *v* [I] to be in the right place 處於〔適當位置〕, 該在: *That chair belongs in the other room.* 那把椅子應該放在另一個房間裡。| *I don't really feel I belong here.* 我真的覺得自己並不適合呆在這裡。

  belong to *phr v* **1** [T **belong to** sbdy] to be owned by someone 屬於〔某人〕: *That dictionary belongs to me.* 那本詞典是我的。**2** [T **belong to** sthg] to be a member of a group or to be connected with a group 是…的成員; 與…有關: *Which party do you belong to?* 你是哪一黨派的?

be·long·ings /bɪˈlɔŋɪŋz; bɪˈlɒŋɪŋz/ *n* [pl] the things which belong to you 所有物; 財產: *She lost all her belongings in the fire.* 她在那場火災中失去了所有的財產。

be·lov·ed /bɪˈlʌvɪd; bɪˈlʌvɪd/ *n* [sing] *fml* a person you love very much〔正式〕被熱愛的人 **–beloved** *adj*

*be·low /bəˈlo; bɪˈləʊ/ *adv,prep* **1** *adv,prep* lower than something 在〔某物〕下面; 在〔某物〕以下: *He lives in the flat below me.* 他住在我下面那一層的單位。| *We could hear shouting coming from the room below.* 我們能聽到下面房間裡傳來的叫喊聲。| *miners who work below ground* 在地底下工作的礦工 **–see picture on page 764** 見 764 頁彩圖 **2**

adv, prep lower in rank〔等級〕低於: *I have four people working below me.* 我有四個下屬。| *the rank of captain and below* 上尉及上尉以下的軍銜 **3** *adv* further on in a piece of writing 在下文中: *More details are given below.* 下文中載有更多細節。| *See page 82 below.* 見下面第八十二頁。**4** *prep* less than a particular amount〔數量〕少於, 在…以下: *children below the age of seven* 七歲以下的孩子 | *We must get inflation down to below 10%.* 我們必須把通貨膨脹控制在百分之十以

*belt¹ /bɛlt; bɛlt/ *n* **1** a band of cloth or leather that you wear around your waist〔布或皮的〕腰帶: *a dress with a matching belt* 配腰帶的衣服 **–see picture on page 210** 見 210 頁彩圖 **2** a moving band of rubber used for driving a machine or for carrying things along 傳動帶; 輸送帶: *Put your suitcases on the moving belt.* 把你的手提箱放在傳送帶上。**3** an area where a particular thing is common or where a particular type of person lives 地帶; 地區: *the corn belt of the USA* 美國的玉米種植地帶 | *the commuter belt* 月票居民帶〔指使用公共交通工具上下班者在郊區的居住地帶〕

belt² *v* **1** [T] to fasten something with a belt 用帶子束緊 **2** [T] *infml* to hit someone or something〔非正式〕打, 擊〔某人或某物〕: *Shut up or I'll belt you!* 閉嘴, 否則我揍你! **3** [I+ adv/prep] *infml* to move or travel very fast〔非正式〕快速行進: *We absolutely belted down the motorway.* 我們沿着高速公路飛馳。**4 belt up** *infml*〔非正式〕= shut up 閉嘴: *Belt up, will you!* 你閉嘴, 好不好!

  belt sthg ↔ **out** *phr v* [T] to shout or sing something loudly 大聲喊[唱]: *The Sergeant Major belted out the orders.* 軍士長大聲喊出命令。

be·moan /bɪˈmon; bɪˈməʊn/ *v* [T] *fml* to express deep sorrow about something〔正式〕為〔某事〕悲嘆: *He bemoaned his fate.* 他悲嘆自己的命運。

be·mused /bɪˈmjuzd; bɪˈmjuːzd/ *adj* confused, as if you do not know what is happening 困惑的; 茫然的; 發呆的: *She looked totally bemused.* 她看上去一臉困惑。

*bench /bɛntʃ; bentʃ/ *n* **1** a long seat made of wood or stone for two or more people 長櫈: *a park bench* 公園的長櫈 **2** a long strong work table 工作枱 **3 the bench** the seat where a judge sits in court, or the judge 法官席; 法官: *What is the opinion of the bench?* 法官有甚麼意見?

*bend¹ /bɛnd; bend/ *v* **bent** /bɛnt; bent/, **bending 1** [I] (also 又作 **bend down, bend over**) to move the top part of your body down towards the ground 彎腰; 傾身: *He bent down to pick up a book.* 他彎下身子拾起一本書。**–see picture on page 992** 見 992 頁彩圖 **2** [I] to move into a curved position 彎曲: *I can't get this wire to bend.* 我無法把

into a curved position 使〔某物〕彎曲, 弄彎: *You've bent your fork.* 你把叉子弄彎了。 | *Bend your knees a bit more.* 膝蓋再彎一點。 **4 be bent on something** to be determined to do something 一心一意做某事; 決心做某事: *She is bent on getting into publishing.* 她決心要進出版界。 **5 bend over backwards** to make every effort to help someone 竭力幫助〔某人〕 **6 bend the rules** to allow yourself or someone else to do something which is really against the rules 放寬規定

bend² *n* **1** a curved part of a road or river 〔路、河的〕彎曲處: *Slow down, this is quite a sharp bend.* 減速, 這是一個急轉彎。 **2 round the bend** *infml* mad 〔非正式〕瘋的: *He really drives me round the bend!* 他真要把我逼瘋了!

*★***be·neath** /bɪ'niːθ; bɪ'niːθ/ *adv,prep* **1** *fml* under or below 〔正式〕在…下; 低於: *She could feel the warm sand beneath her feet.* 她可以感覺到腳底下溫熱的沙子。 | *We looked down from the hills at the valley beneath.* 我們從山上俯瞰下面的山谷。 **2 beneath someone** not worthy of someone 不值得某人〔做〕: *He considered that manual work was beneath him.* 他認為那體力勞動的工作不值得他去做。

ben·e·fac·tor /'bɛnə,fæktə; 'bɛnˌfæktəʳ/ *n* a person who helps other people by giving money; a woman who does this is called a **benefactress** /-trɪs; -trˌs/ 捐助者〔女捐助者叫做 benefactress〕

be·nef·i·cent /bɪ'nɛfəsn̩t; bɪ'nɛfˌsənt/ *adj fml* kind and generous 〔正式〕仁慈的; 慷慨的

ben·e·fi·cial /ˌbɛnə'fɪʃəl; ˌbɛnˌ'fɪʃəl/ *adj* having a good effect 有用的; 有益的: *These measures should prove beneficial* **to** *the economy.* 這些措施應該對經濟有益。

ben·e·fi·cia·ry /ˌbɛnə'fɪʃərɪ; ˌbɛnˌ'fɪʃəri/ *n* **beneficiaries 1** a person who receives something and is helped by it 受惠者; 受益人 **2** a person who is left money or property by someone who has died 〔遺囑的〕受益人

*★***ben·e·fit¹** /'bɛnəfɪt; 'bɛnˌfɪt/ *n* **1** [C] something which helps you 益處; 好處: *Modern technology has brought many benefits.* 現代技術帶來了很多益處。 **2 have the benefit of something** to have something which is useful or helpful to you 得益於某物: *She had the benefit of a good education.* 她因受過良好的教育而獲益。 **3 of benefit to someone, to someone's benefit** useful or helpful to someone 對某人有用[有益]: *The money was of great benefit to me.* 這筆錢對我非常有用。 **4 for someone's benefit** in order to help someone 為了幫助某人: *I did it for your benefit.* 我為幫你而做了這件事。 **5** [U] money which is given by the government to people who

need it 〔政府發放的〕救濟金: *You should be able to claim unemployment benefit.* 你應該可以申請失業救濟金。 **6 give someone the benefit of the doubt** to accept that someone is telling the truth, even though you do not necessarily believe them 〔不大相信但仍〕承認某人說實話

*★***benefit²** *v* **1** [T] to be useful or helpful to someone 對〔某人〕有益: *These changes in the law will benefit many people.* 這些法律上的變更會使很多人受益。 **2 benefit from something, benefit by something** to gain as a result of something 因某事物而獲益; 得益於某事物: *Who would be most likely to benefit from the old man's death?* 那老人死後, 誰最可能獲益?

be·nev·o·lent /bɪ'nɛvələnt; bɪ'nɛvələnt/ *adj* kind and helpful 慈善的; 仁慈的 **–benevolence** *n* [U] **–benevolently** *adv*

be·nign /bɪ'naɪn; bɪ'naɪn/ *adj* **1** kind and gentle 慈祥的; 和善的 **2** favourable (used of the weather) 宜人的〔指天氣〕 **3** not dangerous (used of a disease or TUMOUR) 無危險的, 良性的〔指疾病或腫瘤〕 **–benignly** *adv*

bent¹ /bɛnt; bɛnt/ the past tense and past participle of BEND ☆ BEND 的過去式和過去分詞

bent² *adj BrE infml* 〔英式, 非正式〕 **1** dishonest (used of people in official positions) 不誠實的〔指官員〕 **2** HOMOSEXUAL 同性戀的

bent³ *n* a natural ability and interest 天賦; 天生愛好: *She's got an artistic bent.* 她有藝術天賦。

be·queath /bɪ'kwɪð; bɪ'kwiːð/ *v* [T] *fml* to leave money, property, or ideas to other people after you die 〔正式〕將〔財物等〕遺贈〔遺留〕〔給別人〕: *My aunt bequeathed me her gold watch.* 我的姨母把她的金錶遺留給我。 **–bequest** /bɪ'kwɛst; bɪ'kwɛst/ *n*: *He left a bequest of £5,000 to his children.* 他給孩子們留下五千英鎊的遺產。

be·reaved /bə'riːvd; bˌ'riːvd/ *adj fml* having suffered the death of a close friend or relative 〔正式〕受喪失親友之痛的: *The Prime Minister has sent letters of condolence to the bereaved families.* 首相給失去親人的家庭寄去了安慰信。 **–bereavement** *n* [U]

be·reft /bə'rɛft; bˌ'rɛft/ *adj* bereft of something completely without something 失去某物: *She was bereft of all hope.* 她毫無希望了。

be·ret /bə're; 'bɛreɪ/ *n* a flat, round cap with a tight headband, usually made of wool 貝雷帽〔通常為毛織的扁圓便帽〕

ber·ry /'bɛrɪ; 'bɛri/ *n* **berries** a small soft fruit with seeds; berries grow on bushes or trees 漿果〔長在灌木上或樹上〕

ber·serk /'bɜːsɜːk; bˌ'sɜːk/ *adj* **go berserk** to lose control, especially to become very angry and violent 勃然大怒

berth¹ /bɜːθ; bɜːθ/ *n* **1** a place where a ship

B

can be tied up in a harbour〔船舶的〕停泊地 **2** a bed in a ship, train, or aircraft〔船、火車或飛機上的〕臥舖 **3 give someone/something a wide berth** *infml* to avoid someone or something dangerous or unpleasant 【非正式】避開〔危險或令人不快的〕人或物

berth² *v* [I;T] to come or be brought into a port to be tied up (使)停泊: *The ship berthed next to the quay.* 船停泊在碼頭邊。

be·seech /bɪˈsiːtʃ; bɪˈsiːtʃ/ *v* **besought** /bɪˈsɔːt; bɪˈsɔːt/ *or* **beseeched, besought** *or* **beseeched** *lit* to ask someone to do something in an urgent and anxious way【文】祈求; 懇求; 哀求: *I beseech you to pardon him.* 我懇求你原諒他。–**beseechingly** *adv*

★**be·set** /bɪˈset; bɪˈset/ *v* **beset, beset, besetting** [T] to cause severe problems or difficulties to someone or something 困擾〔某人或某物〕: *the difficulties which beset the project* 這計劃的重重困難 | *He was beset by doubts.* 他疑慮重重。

★**be·side** /bɪˈsaɪd; bɪˈsaɪd/ *prep* **1** next to someone or something 在〔某人或某物〕旁邊: *He came and stood beside me.* 他過來站在我旁邊。–see picture on page 764 見 764 頁彩圖 **2** compared to something or someone 與〔某物或某人〕相比: *This year's profits don't look very good beside last year's.* 與去年的相比, 今年的利潤看來不太好。**3 beside yourself** unable to control yourself because you feel so strongly, usually anger or grief〔常因發怒或悲傷〕不能自制; 發狂: *He was beside himself with rage.* 他氣得發狂。

be·sides¹ /bɪˈsaɪdz; bɪˈsaɪdz/ *adv* in addition; you use this word when you make another point or give another reason that you have just thought of 此外; 而且〔用於表示剛想到的另一個觀點或理由〕: *I don't think I'm going to Scotland for Christmas. It's such a long way. Besides, I haven't got much money left.* 我想我在聖誕節不會去蘇格蘭, 路太遠了, 而且, 我的錢也所剩無幾了。–see Study Note on page 1325 見 1325 頁學習提示

besides² *prep* in addition to something 除〔某物〕以外: *There were three other people at the meeting besides Mr Day.* 除了戴伊先生以外, 還有另外三人出席了會議。

■ USAGE 用法: **Besides** means "as well as" but **except** means "leaving out; but not". So *All of us passed besides John* means that John passed too, but *All of us passed except John* means that John did not pass. ☆ **besides** 的意思是 "除…外還有", **except** 的意思是 "不包括在內; 但沒有"。所以 *All of us passed besides John* 的意思是 "約翰也及格了", 但 *All of us passed except John* 表示 "約翰不及格"。

---

be·siege /bɪˈsiːdʒ; bɪˈsiːdʒ/ *v* **besieged, be-**

sieging [T] **1** to surround a place with armed forces 圍攻; 包圍: *The castle was besieged in the last century.* 上個世紀這城堡受到了圍攻。**2 besieged with, besieged by** to have a lot of demands made on you all at once 一下子被〔很多要求〕包圍: *The police have been besieged by people wanting information about the accident.* 警察一下子被探聽事故消息的人們圍住了。

be·sot·ted /bɪˈsɒtɪd; bɪˈsɒtˌɪd/ *adj* so fond of someone or something that you are unable to think or behave sensibly 陶醉的; 痴迷的: *He's completely besotted with her.* 他完全被她迷住了。

★**best¹** /best; best/ *adj* [superlative of GOOD, GOOD 的最高級] **1** the most good 最好的: *She is the best tennis player in the world.* 她是世界上最好的網球員。| *She's my best friend.* 她是我最好的朋友。| *I want to do what is best for the children.* 我要做對孩子最有益的事。**2 the best part of something** most of something 某物的大部分: *We spent the best part of a year in London.* 我們去年大部分時間在倫敦度過。

★**best²** *adv* [superlative of WELL, WELL 的最高級] **1** most well 最好地: *Which picture do you like best?* 你最喜歡哪幅畫? | *I asked how I could best help them.* 我問怎樣才能best 幫助他們。| *Tuesday would suit me best.* 星期二對我最合適。**2 as best you can** as well as you can 盡最大努力: *Just answer the questions as best you can.* 你盡量回答這些問題吧。**3 had best** a phrase you use when you are telling someone that they should do something 應該; 最好〔用於告訴某人該做某事〕: *You had best tell her straight away.* 你最好立即告訴她。

best³ *n* [sing] **1 the best** the thing or person that is most good or most successful 最好的人; 最佳之物: *Only the best is good enough for him.* 只有最好的東西才能夠符合他的要求。| *We all want the best for our children.* 我們都希望給自己的孩子最好的東西。**2 your best** your greatest effort 最大的努力: *I did my best to finish it on time.* 我盡了最大努力按時完成。| *We'll try our best to get there by lunch time.* 我們盡力在午飯以前去到那裡。**3 at your best** full of life and looking attractive 生氣勃勃; 富有吸引力: *I'm not at my best at six o'clock in the morning!* 早晨六時我並不處於最佳狀態! **4 all the best** an expression you use to give someone your good wishes when you are leaving them or they are leaving you 祝一切順利〔用於告別時的祝願〕**5 at best** if the best thing happens 充其量; 至多: *At best we'll only make a small profit this year.* 我們今年至多只能獲一點小利。**6 make the best of something** to accept something that is not very good, and use it or enjoy it in the best way that you can 充分利用; 盡力而為: *I couldn't afford to give up my job, so I just had to make the best of it.*

我無法放棄工作,所以我只得盡力而為。

bes·ti·al /'bestɪəl; 'bestɪəl/ adj fml cruel and behaving like an animal (used of a person's behaviour) 〖正式〗殘酷的; 野獸般的〔指人的行為〕: bestial cruelty 獸性般的殘酷 – **bestiality** /,bestɪ'ælətɪ; ,bestɪ'ælↄti/ n [U]

best man /,·'·/ n the friend and attendant of a man who is getting married 男儐相

be·stow /bɪ'sto; bɪ'stↄu/ v fml 〖正式〗bestow something on/upon someone to give something to someone 將某物贈予某人: Many gifts were bestowed on them. 有很多禮物贈給他們。 – **bestowal** fml 〖正式〗n [sing]

best·sel·ler /,·'·/ n a book that sells in very large numbers 暢銷書

bet¹ /bɛt; bet/ n 1 an agreement to risk money on the result of a future event 打賭: I won my bet. 我打賭贏了。 | I've got a bet with my father that the Conservatives won't win the next election. 我和父親打賭,保守黨不會在下屆選舉中得勝。 | I think I'll put a bet on that horse. 我想把賭注下在那匹馬身上。 2 your best bet = the best thing that you can do 能做的最好的事: Your best bet is to say nothing about it. 你最好是對此事絕口不提。

bet² v bet, bet, betting 1 [T] to risk money on the result of a future event 打賭: I bet you £5 that they'll win the next election. 我和你賭五英鎊, 他們會在下屆選舉中得勝。 | I never bet money on horse races. 我從不在賽馬裡賭錢。 2 I bet infml 〖非正式〗= I'm sure 我肯定: I bet it will rain tomorrow! 我肯定明天會下雨!

be·tray /bɪ'tre; bɪ'treɪ/ v [T] 1 to be disloyal or unfaithful to someone 出賣, 背叛〔某人〕: I never believed that he would betray us. 我從不相信他會背叛我們。 2 fml to tell people secret information 〖正式〗泄露〔祕密〕: He betrayed the plan to a rival company. 他把計劃泄露給一家對頭公司。 3 to show your real feelings or intentions 顯示, 暴露〔真實感情或意圖〕: Her face betrayed her nervousness. 她臉上的表情顯示了她的緊張不安。

be·tray·al /bɪ'treəl; bɪ'treɪəl/ n [C;U] the act of betraying someone or something 出賣; 背叛: a betrayal of my principles 對我的原則的背棄行為

be·troth·al /bɪ'troθəl; bɪ'trↄuðəl/ n old fash a promise to marry someone 〖老式〗許配; 訂婚

be·trothed /bɪ'troθt; bɪ'trↄuðd/ adj old fash having promised to marry someone 〖老式〗已訂婚的

★bet·ter¹ /'bɛtɚ; 'betər/ adj 1 [comparative of GOOD, GOOD 的比較級] more good 較好的, 更好的: She's much better at maths than I am. 她的數學比我好得多。 | This film is better than his last one. 這部影片比他上次那部好。 2 improved in health 〔健康〕有所好轉的: I'm feeling a little better today. 今天我感覺好些了。 | When

you're better you must come and visit us. 你(身體)好些以後一定要來探望我們。 3 your better half your husband or wife; an expression that is usually used humorously 丈夫或妻子〔常含幽默〕 4 the better part of something more than half of something 大半: We haven't seen her for the better part of a year. 我們有大半年沒有見到她了。

★better² adv [comparative of WELL, WELL 的比較級] 1 in a better way 更好地: She swims much better than she used to. 她游泳游得比過去好多了。 2 to a greater degree 更: He knows the town better than I do. 這城鎮他比我了解得更清楚。 | I like this picture better than the other one. 和另一幅相比, 我更喜歡這張畫。 3 had better a phrase you use when you are telling someone that they should do something 最好還是; 應該: You'd better go home now. 你最好是現在回家。 | I'd better not tell him what happened. 我最好還是不告訴他出了甚麼事。

> ■ USAGE 用法: 1 Had better/'d better are used in conversation when giving firm advice about what a person should do, especially to avoid a problem ☆ Had better/'d better 用於會話中, 對應該做的事, 尤指該避免的問題, 提出堅定的勸告: You'd better go now or you'll be late. 你最好現在去, 否則你會遲到的。 | We'd better take out medical insurance for our holiday. 我們最好為假期投一個醫療保險。 | I think I'd better phone to say I'll be late. 我想我最好還是打電話說一聲我會晚些到。 2 Note that you'd better is a very direct way of giving advice which can also be used to give an order ☆ 注意 you'd better 是一種直截了當提意見的方法, 也能用作發命令: Look, you'd better ring me tonight. 聽着, 你最好今晚打電話給我。 | Hadn't you better apologize? 你不應該道歉嗎? | You'd better not show your face here again. 你最好別再來這兒露面了。 For this reason, do NOT use you'd better if you want to make a polite suggestion. Instead use phrases such as, Why don't you...? Why not...? It might be a good idea to... ☆ 所以, 如果想有禮貌地提建議, 不要用 you'd better, 可以用 Why don't you...? Why not...? It might be a good idea to... 代替。 3 Note that had better/'d better are followed by the infinitive WITHOUT 'to'. ☆注意 had better/'d better 後用不帶 "to" 的不定式。

better³ n 1 change for the better to change and become better 好轉: Let's hope that things will soon change for the better. 讓我們來希望事情會好轉吧。 2 get the better of someone to defeat someone or make them

seem foolish 打敗某人; 戰勝某人; 佔某人的
上風。 *She always manages to get the better of
me.* 她老是設法佔我的上風。

better[4] *v* [T] to improve on something 改進
〔某事〕: *We made record profits last year,
and we're hoping to better them this year.* 去
年我們的利潤創了紀錄, 我們希望今年更好。

★★**be·tween** /bə'twin; bɪ'twiːn/ *adv, prep*
1 *adv, prep* (also 又作 **in between**) in the space in the middle of two
things or people 〔空間〕在〔兩者〕之間: *a village somewhere between London and
Oxford* 位於倫敦和牛津之間某處的小村子 |
I was sitting between my parents. 我坐在父母
中間。–see picture on page 764 見 764 頁彩
圖 **2** *adv, prep* (also 又作 **in between**) in the
time after one thing has finished and before another thing has begun 〔時間〕在…之
間: *I'll phone you between five and six this
evening.* 今晚五點到六點之間我打電話給你。|
*I ate breakfast and lunch, but nothing in be-
tween.* 我吃了早飯和午飯, 但兩餐之間沒吃
東西。**3** *prep* above one amount and below
another 〔數量〕在…中間: *children aged between eight and ten years* 年齡在八歲到十歲
之間的孩子 **4** *prep* done or shared by two
people 由兩人一起做或分享: *The bonds between them are very strong.* 他們兩人之間的
關係很緊密。| *The money was divided be-
tween the two sons.* 這筆錢由兩個兒子分了。
5 between you and me a phrase you use
when you are telling someone something
that is secret 只在你我之間〔用於告訴某人祕
密時〕: *Between you and me, I think she's
pregnant.* 這是我們私下裡說的話, 我想她有孕
了。**6 few and far between** rare or in-
frequent 少有的; 稀疏的: *Good managers
are few and far between.* 好經理已經不多見
了。

> ■ USAGE 用法: Compare 比較 **be-
> tween** and 和 **among.** Use **between**
> when you are talking about only two
> people or things ☆說到只有兩個人、兩
> 件事物時用 **between**: *I divided the
> chocolates **between** the two children.* 我
> 把巧克力分給了兩個孩子。Use **among**
> when you are talking about more than
> two people or things ☆說到多於兩個人
> 或兩件事物時用 **among**: *I divided the
> chocolates **among** all the children.* 我把
> 巧克力分給了孩子們。

bev·er·age /'bevrɪdʒ; 'bevərɪdʒ/ *n fml* a
drink, for example tea, coffee or wine 〔正
式〕飲料〔如茶、咖啡、酒〕

be·ware /bɪ'wɛr; bɪ'weər/ *v* [I only in infinitive and imperative form 只用於不定式和命
令式] a word used to warn someone to be
careful about something 注意; 當心〔用於警
告某人小心某物〕: *Beware **of** signing any
agreement without studying it carefully.* 在沒

有仔細研究以前, 簽協議要當心。| *He warned
us to beware.* 他提醒我們要當心。

be·wil·der /bɪ'wɪldə; bɪ'wɪldəʳ/ *v* [T] to
make you feel confused 使迷惑; 弄糊塗: *His
attitude bewildered me.* 他的態度把我弄糊塗
了。–**bewildered** *adj*: *She looked completely
bewildered.* 她看上去完全糊塗了。–**bewilder-
ment** *n* [U]

be·witch /bɪ'wɪtʃ; bɪ'wɪtʃ/ *v* [T] **1** to produce
a magic, often harmful, effect on someone
施魔術於〔某人〕; 蠱惑〔某人〕 **2** to attract
someone's complete attention, as if by
magic 令人着迷的; 令人消魂的: *She had a
bewitching smile.* 她有令人着迷的笑容。

★★**be·yond** /bɪ'jɑnd; bɪ'jɒnd/ *adv, prep*
1 *adv, prep* on or to the
further side of something 在〔到〕較遠的一
邊: *He wouldn't travel with us beyond the
border.* 他不會和我們越過邊境去旅遊的。|
*He said he would come with us as far as the
river but not beyond.* 他說他會跟着我們走到
河邊, 但不過河。**2** *prep* more than or
further than 比…更多; 比…更遠: *The level
of inflation has now risen beyond 10%.* 通貨
膨脹率現在已超過百分之十。**3** *prep* except
除…以外: *I know nothing beyond what I've
already told you.* 除了已經告訴你的以外, 我
一無所知。**4 beyond you** too difficult for
you to understand 難以理解

bi·as[1] /'baɪəs; 'baɪəs/ *n* [C;U] **1** a tendency
to be either for or against something or
someone 偏見; 傾向性: *His plays show a
definite left wing bias.* 他的劇本表現出明確的
左翼傾向性。| *She was accused of political
bias.* 她因有政治偏見而被指控。**2** a tendency
to be good at particular things 偏愛: *Her
scientific bias showed itself in early childhood.* 她對科學的偏愛早在兒童時代就表現出
來了。

bias[2] *v* **-s-** *or* **-ss-** [T] to influence someone
so that they have either a favourable or
unfavourable opinion about something
although they do not necessarily know all
the facts about it 使〔某人〕有偏見; 使有傾向
性: *His background biases him **against**
foreigners.* 他的背景使他對外國人抱有偏見。|
*I admit I'm rather biased **in favour of** our
candidate.* 我承認我相當偏向於支持我們的候
選人。| *He described the report as biased
and inaccurate.* 他認為這篇報導既有偏見又
不準確。

bib /bɪb; bɪb/ *n* a cloth tied under a child's
chin to protect its clothes when it is eating
〔繫於小孩下巴底下的〕圍脖, 圍嘴

bi·ble /'baɪbl; 'baɪbl/ *n* the holy book of
the Christians 聖經 –**biblical** /'bɪblɪkl; 'bɪb-
lɪkəl/ *adj*

bib·li·og·ra·phy /,bɪblɪ'ɑgrəfɪ; ,bɪblɪ'ɒgrəfɪ/
n **bibliographies** a list at the end of a book
which names all the books and articles
which the writer used to help them write
their book 〔書後的〕參考書目

---

bi·car·bon·ate /baɪˈkɑːbənɪt; baɪˈkɑːbə-nə̩t/ n (also 又作 **bicarbonate of soda** /·ˌ··· ·ˈ··/, **bicarb** /ˈbaɪkɑːb; ˈbaɪkɑːb/ infml 〔非正式〕) [U] a white chemical powder used in baking or as a medicine for your stomach〔用於烘製食物及作胃藥的〕碳酸氫鈉

bi·cen·te·na·ry /ˌbaɪˈsɛntə,nerɪ; ˌbaɪsɛnˈtiː-nərɪ/ n **bicentenaries** the day or year exactly 200 years after a particular event 二百週年: The company's bicentenary was in 1974. 1974 年是這家公司成立二百週年。

bi·cen·ten·ni·al /ˌbaɪsɛnˈtenɪəl; ˌbaɪsenˈte-nɪəl/ n the usual American word for 〔美式〕 = BICENTENARY

bi·ceps /ˈbaɪsɛps; ˈbaɪseps/ n [plural is 複數為 **biceps**] the large muscle on the front of your upper arm〔上臂前側的〕二頭肌

bick·er /ˈbɪkə; ˈbɪkɚ/ v [I] to argue with someone about something unimportant〔為小事〕爭吵, 吵嘴: Stop bickering will you! 你別鬧了, 好不好! | They're always bickering about money. 他們經常為錢吵嘴。

***bi·cy·cle** /ˈbaɪsɪkl; ˈbaɪsɪkəl/ n (also 又作 **bike**) **1** a vehicle with two wheels which you move by pushing its pedals (PEDAL) round and round with your feet 腳踏車; 自行車: She's learning to ride a bicycle. 她在學騎腳踏車。 **2** by **bicycle** travelling on a bicycle 騎腳踏車: Let's go by bicycle. 我們騎腳踏車去吧。–see 見 TRANSPORT (USAGE 用法)

***bid¹** /bɪd; bɪd/ n **1** an offer to pay a certain price for something that is being sold 出價: I made a final bid of £20. 我最後出價二十英鎊。 **2** an offer to do some work at a certain price 投標; 招標: Bids for building the bridge were invited from British and American firms. 英國及美國的公司獲邀參加建造那座橋樑的投標。 **3** a chance to make a declaration in certain card games of the number of games that you think you will win〔玩紙牌時的〕叫牌 **4** an attempt to do or get something 努力; 企圖: The criminal made a bid for freedom by trying to run away. 罪犯企圖逃跑以獲得自由。 | a bid to overthrow the government 顛覆政府的企圖

bid² v **bid, bid, bidding** [I;T] **1** to offer to pay a certain price for something that is being sold 出價: I can afford to bid £50, but no more. 出價五十英鎊我負擔得起, 但再多就不行了。 | Who will bid £10 for this beautiful plate? 誰願出價十英鎊買這個漂亮的盤子? **2** to make a bid in a game of cards 叫牌 – **bidder** n: The buildings will be sold to the highest bidder. 這些大樓將賣給出價最高的人。

bid³ v **bade** /bæd, bed; bæd, beɪd/ or **bid, bidden** /ˈbɪdn; ˈbɪdn/ or **bid, bidding** lit 〔文〕 **1** bid someone good morning to say good morning 向某人說早安: He bid me good morning as he passed. 他走過時向我說了一聲早安。 **2** [T] to order or tell someone to do something 命令, 吩咐〔某人做某事〕: She would never do as she was bidden. 她從不按別人的吩咐去做。 | She bade him come. 她吩咐他來。

bid·ding /ˈbɪdɪŋ; ˈbɪdɪŋ/ n **do something at someone's bidding, do someone's bidding** to do something that someone has asked you to do 按某人的吩咐做某事

bide /baɪd; baɪd/ v **bided, biding, bide your time** to wait, usually for a long time, until the right moment 等待良機

bi·det /ˈbiːdeɪ; biːˈdeɪ/ n a kind of small low bath which you can sit on to wash your bottom〔洗下身的〕坐浴盆

bi·en·ni·al¹ /baɪˈɛnɪəl; baɪˈenɪəl/ adj happening once every two years 每兩年一度的: The city's biennial jazz festival begins next week. 這個城市兩年一度的爵士音樂節下週開始。

biennial² n a plant which lives for two years and produces seed in the second year 兩年生植物

bier /bɪr; bɪəʳ/ n lit a movable frame like a table, used for supporting a dead body at a funeral 〔文〕棺材架; 停屍架

bi·fo·cals /baɪˈfoklz; baɪˈfəʊkəlz/ n [pl] glasses which have an upper part made for looking at distant objects, and a lower part made for reading〔遠近兩用的〕雙光眼鏡 – see 見 PAIR¹ (USAGE 用法)

****big** /bɪg; bɪg/ adj **bigger, biggest 1** of more than average size, amount, or importance 大的; 重大的: There's a big parcel for you. 有個大包裹給你。 | the biggest ship that's ever been built 所造過的最大的船 | There's been a big rise in house prices this year. 今年房價漲幅很大。 | The big question is what to do next. 重要的問題是下一步該做甚麼。 **2** used when asking the size, amount, or importance of something 多大; 多重要〔用於詢問尺寸、數量、重要性〕: How big is their house? 他們的房子有多大? | We need to find out just how big the problem is. 我們需要查清楚問題到底有多大。 **3** too big for your boots infml believing yourself to be more important than you really are〔非正式〕自以為是; 自命不凡

big·a·my /ˈbɪgəmɪ; ˈbɪgəmɪ/ n [U] the crime of being married to two people at the same time 重婚罪: He was charged with bigamy. 他被指控犯了重婚罪。–**bigamist** n – **bigamous** adj

Big Broth·er /ˌ· ·ˈ··/ n a government or political leader who has too much power over society and limits your freedom 老大哥〔專制政府或政治組織的領導者〕

big·ot /ˈbɪgət; ˈbɪgət/ n someone who thinks, unreasonably, that their own opinions are correct, especially about matters of religion, race, or politics, and doesn't pay attention to the opinions of other people〔尤指宗教、種族、政治方面〕盲信者,

頑固者 –**bigoted** adj: He was arrogant and bigoted. 他既傲慢又頑固。

big·ot·ry /'bɪgətrɪ; 'bɪgətri/ n [U] the holding of strong, unreasonable opinions, and unwillingness to pay attention to the opinions of other people 頑固; 偏狹

big·wig /'bɪg,wɪg; 'bɪgwɪg/ n infml a person with a high position in an organization 〖非正式〗〔組織中的〕要人, 大頭頭

bike /baɪk; baɪk/ n (also 又作 **bicycle**) a vehicle with two wheels that you ride by pushing its pedals (PEDAL) round and round with your feet 腳踏車, 自行車

bi·ki·ni /bɪ'kinɪ; bɪ'kiːni/ n a garment in two pieces which women wear for swimming 比基尼式泳裝, 三點式泳裝

bi·lat·er·al /baɪ'lætərəl; baɪ'lætərəl/ adj including or concerning two people or two countries 雙方的; 雙邊的: a bilateral agreement 雙邊協定 –**bilaterally** adv

bil·ber·ry /'bɪl,bɛrɪ; 'bɪlbəri/ n bilberries a low bushy plant which grows in Northern Europe and produces small dark blue fruit 北歐越橘樹〔一種低矮的灌木, 結深藍色的小果子〕

bile /baɪl; baɪl/ n [U] a bitter liquid produced in your LIVER[1] which helps your body to DIGEST food 膽汁

bilge /bɪldʒ; bɪldʒ/ n [U] infml foolish talk 〖非正式〗傻話; 瞎說: Don't give me that bilge! 別跟我瞎說!

bi·lin·gual /baɪ'lɪŋgwəl; baɪ'lɪŋgwəl/ adj 1 spoken or written in two languages 兩種語言的: a bilingual dictionary 雙語詞典 2 able to speak two languages equally well 能說兩種語言的: a bilingual secretary 會講兩種語言的祕書

bil·ious /'bɪljəs; 'bɪliəs/ adj feeling sick and having a headache 患病的; 頭痛的: Fatty food makes some people bilious. 多脂肪的食物使某些人患病頭痛。–**biliousness** n [U]

★★ **bill**[1] /bɪl; bɪl/ n 1 a list of things bought or services supplied and their price 賬單: She paid the bill and left the restaurant. 她付了賬便離開飯店。| the gas bill 煤氣賬單 2 a plan for a law, written down for the government to consider 議案; 法案: M.P.s rejected the bill by 240 votes to 138. 下議院議員以240票對138票駁回了這項議案。3 AmE a piece of paper money 〖美式〗鈔票; 紙幣: a five-dollar bill 一張五元的鈔票 4 the beak of a bird 鳥嘴; 喙

bill[2] v [T] 1 to send a bill to someone 送賬單給〔某人〕: They've forgotten to bill me for the wine. 他們忘了給我開酒單。2 to advertise someone who is going to appear in a show 用海報宣傳: She was billed to appear in a new play in London. 海報上宣傳了她參演在倫敦上演的一齣新戲。

bill·board /'bɪl,bord; 'bɪlbɔːd/ n a large board in a public place, on which notices are put 招貼板; 廣告牌

bil·let /'bɪlɪt; 'bɪlɪt/ v [T] to provide lodging for soldiers in a private house, especially for a short time 〔尤指短期〕給〔士兵〕提供住宿處: The soldiers were billeted in private houses. 士兵被安頓在民宅裡。

bil·li·ards /'bɪljədz; 'bɪljədz/ n [U] a game played by two people on a cloth-covered table called a **billiard table**; the players use long sticks to knock balls into pockets at the sides of the table 桌球, 枱球戲

bil·lion /'bɪljən; 'bɪljən/ det, n, pron billion or billions 1 the number 1,000,000,000 十億 2 BrE old fash the number 1,000,000,000,000 〖英式, 老式〗萬億 –**billionth** det, n, pron, adv

bil·low[1] /'bɪlo; 'bɪləʊ/ n a rolling mass of smoke or mist 滾滾而來的煙或霧: Billows of smoke rose from the chimney. 滾滾濃煙從煙囱裡冒出來。

billow[2] v [I] 1 (of smoke) to rise and roll in a large mass 〔煙〕滾滾而出: Smoke billowed out of the burning building. 濃煙從那幢着火的建築物裡滾滾冒出。2 to fill with air and move about in the wind 〔在風中〕揚起: Her skirt billowed in the wind. 她的裙子在風中揚起。–**billowing** adj: billowing sails 揚起的帆

bil·ly goat /'··· /' n a male goat 公山羊

bi·month·ly /baɪ'mʌnθlɪ; baɪ'mʌnθli/ adv, adj 1 appearing or happening every two months 兩月一次地[的]: a bimonthly magazine 雙月刊 2 happening twice a month 一月兩次地[的]: a bimonthly meeting 一月兩次的會議

bin /bɪn; bɪn/ n a large container, usually with a lid, used for storing things in or putting waste in 〔帶蓋的〕大貯藏箱, 廢物箱

bi·na·ry /'baɪnərɪ; 'baɪnəri/ adj tech 〖術語〗1 consisting of two things or two parts 由兩部分組成的 2 **binary system** a number system using the two numbers, 0 and 1, as a base, used especially with computers 二進制計數法〔尤用於電腦〕

bind[1] /baɪnd; baɪnd/ v [T] **bound** /baʊnd; baʊnd/, **bound** 1 to tie something firmly 縛 [捆、紮]緊: His hands and feet had been bound. 他的手腳被捆在一起。2 to strengthen or decorate something with a binding 裝訂; 鑲邊: The book hasn't been bound yet. 這本書還沒有裝訂。| You'll have to bind the edges of the rug. 你要給小地毯鑲上邊。3 to make substances stick together in a mass 使黏結: Add a beaten egg to bind the mixture. 加一隻打好的雞蛋, 讓混合物黏起來。4 to unite people 聯合: They are bound together by their religious beliefs. 他們因宗教信仰而聯合起來。5 to force someone to do something 迫使〔某人做某事〕: The agreement bound him to secrecy. 協議使他要保守祕密。

bind sbdy **over** phr v [T] BrE law (of a court of law) to order someone to cause no more trouble for a certain period of time〖英式, 律〗命令〔某人〕具結[保證]不再滋事

bind² n infml **a bind** something that is difficult or annoying〖非正式〗困難、困擾的事物: *It's a real bind not having a telephone.* 沒有電話真使人煩惱。

bind·er /'baɪndə; 'baɪndər/ n **1** a machine or person that binds things, especially books 裝訂機; 裝訂工: *Your book is still at the binder's.* 你的書仍放在裝訂工那兒。 **2** a hard cover with metal rings inside for holding sheets of paper together 活頁夾

bind·ing¹ /'baɪndɪŋ; 'baɪndɪŋ/ n **1** [C] a book cover 書的封面: *a book with a beautiful leather binding* 一本有漂亮的皮封面的書 **2** [U] a band of material that is sewn or stuck along the edge of something in order to make it stronger or more attractive 滾條; 鑲邊

binding² adj having the legal power to force someone to obey a promise or an agreement 有約束力的; 必須遵守的: *a binding agreement* 有約束力的協議

binge /bɪndʒ; bɪndʒ/ n a period of drinking a lot of alcohol 酗酒; 狂飲

bin·go /'bɪŋgo; 'bɪŋgəʊ/ n [U] a game of chance played for prizes, in which players mark numbers on cards as the numbers are called out to them 賓戈遊戲〔一種彩票式遊戲〕

bi·noc·u·lars /baɪ'nɑkjələrz; bɪ'nɒkjʊləz/ [pl] a pair of glasses used for making distant objects look nearer 雙筒望遠鏡: *Shall we take the binoculars? There might be some interesting birds to look at.* 我們要帶雙筒望遠鏡嗎? 也許有些有趣的鳥可以看看。 – see 見 PAIR¹ (USAGE 用法)

bi·o·chem·is·try /,baɪo'kɛmɪstrɪ; ,baɪəʊ'kemɪstri/ n [U] the scientific study of the chemical processes that take place in living things 生物化學

bi·o·de·gra·da·ble /,baɪo,dɪ'greɪdəbl; ,baɪəʊdɪ'greɪdəbl/ adj able to decay naturally by the action of bacteria 能被細菌分解的: *biodegradable substances such as paper and wood* 諸如紙、木等能被細菌分解的物質

bi·og·ra·pher /baɪ'ɑgrəfə; baɪ'ɒgrəfər/ n a writer who writes biographies 傳記作家

bi·og·ra·phy /baɪ'ɑgrəfɪ; baɪ'ɒgrəfi/ n **biographies** [C;U] an account of a person's life written by someone else 傳記: *Boswell wrote a famous biography of Dr. Johnson.* 鮑斯威爾寫了一本著名的約翰遜博士傳記。| *a writer specialising in biography* 專業傳記作家 –**biographical** /,baɪə'græfɪkl; ,baɪə'græfɪkəl/ adj

bi·o·lo·gic·al /,baɪə'lɑdʒɪkl; ,baɪə'lɒdʒɪkəl/ adj **1** relating to biology, or to the way in which living things live and behave 生物學的; 和生物有關的 **2** using living things such as bacteria as weapons 用生物〔作為武器〕的: *biological warfare* 生物戰; 細菌戰 | *biolo-*

gical weapons 生物武器 **3** using natural chemicals called ENZYMES in order to clean things 用酶(清潔)的: *biological washing powder* 含酶洗衣粉

bi·ol·o·gy /baɪ'ɑlədʒɪ; baɪ'ɒlədʒi/ n [U] the scientific study of living things 生物學: *human biology* 人類生物學 | *She has a degree in biology.* 她有生物學的學位。| *a biology lesson* 一堂生物學課 –**biologist** n

bi·on·ic /baɪ'ɑnɪk; baɪ'ɒnɪk/ adj infml having greater powers than those of ordinary human beings, for example greater strength or speed〖非正式〗超越人力的〔如速度、力量〕

bi·par·tite /baɪ'pɑrtaɪt; baɪ'pɑ:taɪt/ adj agreed or shared by two groups 雙方的: *a bipartite agreement* 雙邊協議

bi·ped /'baɪped; 'baɪped/ n tech an animal with two feet〖術語〗兩足動物

bi·plane /'baɪ,plen; 'baɪpleɪn/ n an aircraft with two sets of wings, one above the other 雙翼飛機

birch /bɜrtʃ; bɜ:tʃ/ n **1** a tree with smooth wood and thin branches 樺樹〔木光滑, 枝細長〕 **2 the birch** a wooden rod used in the past for punishing people 樺樹條〔過去作體罰用〕

☆**bird** /bɜrd; bɜ:d/ n **1** a creature with wings and feathers which can fly 鳥 **2** BrE infml a young woman (a word which is considered offensive to women)〖英式, 非正式〗少婦, 小妞〔這個詞被認為是對婦女無禮〕 **3 early bird** infml a person who gets up early or arrives early〖非正式〗早起或早到的人 **4 kill two birds with one stone** infml to get two good results from one action〖非正式〗一箭雙鵰; 一舉兩得

bird of prey /,· · '·/ n a bird that kills other birds and small animals for food 食肉鳥; 猛禽

bird's-eye view /,· '·/ n a general view seen from high up 鳥瞰: *a bird's-eye view of Paris* 巴黎城鳥瞰圖

bi·ro /'baɪro; 'baɪərəʊ/ n [C;U] tdmk a pen with a small metal ball at the end〖商標〗〔拜樂牌〕圓珠筆: *a black biro* 一支黑圓珠筆 | *a short note written in biro* 用圓珠筆寫的短箋

☆**birth¹** /bɜrθ; bɜ:θ/ n **1** [C;U] the act, time, or process of being born 出生; 誕生: *the birth of her first baby* 她的第一個嬰兒的出生 | *Last year there were more births than deaths.* 去年的出生人數多於死亡人數。| *She weighed eight pounds at birth.* 她出生時重八磅。**2 give birth** to have a baby 生產; 分娩: *She gave birth to a fine healthy baby.* 她生了一個漂亮健康的嬰兒。**3** [U] your family origin 出身; 家世: *He was of noble birth.* 他出身高貴。**4 by birth** because of where you were born 由於出生在某處: *She was French by birth.* 她是法國血統的。**5 the birth of something** the beginning or origin of something 開始; 起源: *the birth of television*

電視的起源 | *the birth of a nation* 一個國家的創建

birth con·trol /ˈ· ·ˌ·/ n [U] the act of limiting the number of children born, for example by CONTRACEPTION 節育〔如通過避孕〕: *More and more third world countries are encouraging birth control.* 越來越多的第三世界國家正在鼓勵節育。

***birth·day** /ˈbɜːθˌde; ˈbɜːθdeɪ/ n the day in each year which is the date on which someone was born 生日: *Happy birthday!* 生日快樂! | *a birthday party* 生日聚會

birth·mark /ˈbɜːθˌmɑːk; ˈbɜːθmɑːk/ n an unusual coloured mark which someone has on their body when they are born 胎記; 胎痣

birth·place /ˈbɜːθˌples; ˈbɜːθpleɪs/ n the place where you were born 出生地

birth·rate /ˈbɜːθˌret; ˈbɜːθreɪt/ n the number of births for every 100 or every 1000 people in a particular area during a given time 出生率: *a birthrate of three per 100* 百分之三的出生率

bis·cuit /ˈbɪskɪt; ˈbɪskət/ n BrE 〔英式〕 1 a small flat cake, usually sweetened 餅乾 2 **take the biscuit** infml to be the best, worst, most surprising or most annoying thing you have ever seen or heard of 〔非正式〕所見到或聽到的最好〔最壞、最驚人、最惱火〕的事: *He's done some stupid things before, but this really takes the biscuit!* 他以前也做過些傻事, 但要數這次最糟糕!

bi·sect /baɪˈsekt; baɪˈsekt/ v [T] tech to divide something into two equal parts 〔術語〕把〔某物〕二等分 **–bisection** /baɪˈsekʃən; baɪˈsekʃən/ n [U]

bi·sex·u·al /baɪˈsekʃuəl; baɪˈsekʃuəl/ adj 1 sexually attracted to both men and women 對男女兩性都有性慾的 2 possessing both male and female sexual parts 雌雄同體的: *a bisexual plant* 雌雄同株的植物 **–bisexuality** /baɪˌsekʃuˈæləti; baɪˌsekʃuˈælˌti/ n [U]

***bish·op** /ˈbɪʃəp; ˈbɪʃəp/ n 1 a Christian priest in charge of the churches and priests in a large area 〔基督教的〕主教 2 one of the pieces in a game of CHESS 〔國際象棋中的〕象

bish·op·ric /ˈbɪʃəprɪk; ˈbɪʃəprɪk/ n the area for which a bishop is responsible 主教管轄區

bi·son /ˈbaɪsn; ˈbaɪsən/ n a large wild animal like a cow 野牛

bis·tro /ˈbɪstrəʊ; ˈbiːstrəʊ/ n a place where you can eat and drink, especially in France; bistros are usually small and quite cheap 〔尤指法國的〕小酒吧, 小餐館〔通常很廉價〕

***bit**¹ /bɪt; bɪt/ n 1 a small piece or quantity of something 一點; 一些: *Would you like another bit of cake?* 你想再吃點蛋糕嗎? | *I've been doing a bit of Christmas shopping.* 我在買一點聖誕節用的東西。 | *We*

need a bit of good luck. 我們需要一點好運。 2 a metal bar that is put in a horse's mouth and used for controlling its movements 馬嚼子; 馬銜 3 a part of a tool for cutting or making holes 刀頭; 鑽頭 4 **a bit** slightly 稍微; 有點: *This coffee's a bit cold.* 這咖啡有點冷。 | *I'm a bit tired.* 我有點累。 5 **a bit of** a phrase you use when you are saying what something is, but want to make it seem less strong 有點〔用於減輕語氣〕: *We've got a bit of a problem with the computer.* 我們的電腦有點問題。 | *This rain's a bit of a nuisance.* 這雨有點討厭。 6 **for a bit** for a short time 一會兒: *I'm just going out for a bit.* 我只出去一會兒。 7 **not a bit** not at all 一點也不: *He wasn't a bit embarrassed.* 他一點也不尷尬。 8 **bits and pieces** small things of various kinds 各種各樣的零碎東西: *I went home to pick up a few bits and pieces that I needed for the weekend.* 我回家取了一些週末需用的零星雜物。 9 **bit by bit, a bit at a time** gradually 逐漸地: *We're getting the house sorted out bit by bit.* 我們正在一點一點地整理房子。 10 **every bit as** just as 同樣: *She's every bit as clever as her brother.* 她像她哥哥一樣聰明。 11 **to bits** into small pieces 成為碎片: *Her dress was all torn to bits.* 她的衣服都被撕成了碎片。 | *The bridge was blown to bits by the explosion.* 那座橋被炸得粉碎。

■ USAGE 用法: Use **a bit** before adjectives ☆ **a bit** 用於形容詞前: *I'm a (little) bit tired* 我有點累; and **a bit of** before nouns ☆ **a bit of** 用於名詞前: *a bit of money* 一點錢 | *a bit of a problem* 一點問題

---

bit² the past tense of BITE ☆ BITE 的過去式

bitch¹ /bɪtʃ; bɪtʃ/ n 1 a female dog 母狗 2 a woman who is unkind and bad-tempered 惡婆娘; 潑婦: *You bitch!* 你這惡婆娘!

bitch² v [I] infml to complain about other people in a nasty way 〔非正式〕抱怨; 埋怨: *She's always bitching about the children, but they're not really naughty.* 她老是抱怨那些孩子, 可是他們並非真的淘氣。

bitch·y /ˈbɪtʃi; ˈbɪtʃi/ adj bitchier, bitchiest saying unkind things about other people (used of women) 說別人壞話的〔指女人〕: *She made a few bitchy remarks about her flatmate.* 她說了些有關和她同住的人的壞話。 **–bitchily** adv **–bitchiness** n [U]

bite¹ /baɪt; baɪt/ v [T] bit /bɪt; bɪt/, bitten /ˈbɪtn; ˈbɪtn/, biting 1 [I;T] to cut, crush, or seize something with your teeth 咬: *He bit into the apple.* 他咬了一口蘋果。 | *I was afraid the dog might bite me.* 我怕那狗會咬我。 2 [T] (of some insects) to prick your skin painfully 〔某些昆蟲〕咬, 叮: *I've been bitten by a mosquito.* 我被蚊子叮了。 3 [I] (of fish) to take food on a fisherman's hook and so get caught 〔魚〕咬餌: *The fish aren't biting today.* 魚今天不上鈎。 **4** [I] (of a piece of machinery) to touch a surface firmly or move against a surface without slipping 〔機械〕抓緊, 貼緊: *The ice on the road was so hard that the car wheels would not bite.* 路上的冰極硬, 因此車輪打滑。 **5** [I] to begin to have an unpleasant effect 開始產生不良後果: *The economic sanctions are really beginning to bite.* 經濟制裁真的開始產生不良後果。 **6 bite someone's head off** *infml* to speak to someone rudely and angrily 〔非正式〕蠻橫粗暴地對某人説話 **7 bite the dust** *infml* to be killed or defeated 〔非正式〕被殺死; 被擊敗

bite sthg. ↔ **back** *phr v* [T] *infml* to prevent yourself from saying something 〔非正式〕把〔話〕嚥下去

bite² *n* **1 take a bite, have a bite** to bite something that you are going to eat 咬下一口: *She took a large bite of the cake.* 她咬了一大口蛋糕。 **2 have a bite to eat** *infml* to eat a small meal 〔非正式〕吃少量的飯 **3** a wound caused by biting 咬傷: *His arm was covered in insect bites.* 他的手臂被蟲子咬得傷痕累累。 **4** the act of a fish taking food on a fisherman's hook and so getting caught 〔魚的〕吞餌

■ **USAGE** 用法: We can use the word **bite** (verb and noun) when talking about many kinds of insect ☆談及多種昆蟲時都可用 **bite** 〔動詞和名詞〕: *They had been **bitten** all over by mosquitoes/fleas/red ants.* 他們渾身都被蚊子 [跳蚤、螞蟻] 咬了。 | *They were covered in mosquito **bites**.* 他們被蚊子咬得渾身是傷。For some insects, however, we use the word **sting**: *He had been **stung** by an angry wasp/bee/scorpion.* 他被一隻兇猛的黃蜂 [蜜蜂、蠍子] 螫了。 | *His eye was swollen from a particularly bad bee **sting**.* 他的眼睛被一隻特別厲害的蜜蜂螫得腫了起來。

---

bit·ing /'baɪtɪŋ/ *adj* **1** very cold 極冷的: *a biting wind* 刺骨的寒風 **2** cruel 尖刻的: *He made some biting remarks.* 他説了些刻薄的話。

bit·ten /'bɪtn̩/ the past participle of BITE ☆ BITE 的過去分詞

★**bit·ter¹** /'bɪtɚ; 'bɪtəʳ/ *adj* **1** having a sharp, unpleasant taste 有苦味的; 苦的: *The coffee tasted bitter.* 這咖啡嚐起來有苦味。 **2** angry and unhappy 生氣的; 不快的: *He feels very bitter about the way he was treated.* 別人那樣待他, 他很不快。 **3** making you feel very angry and unhappy 令人傷心的: *The result was a bitter disappointment to me.* 這結果使我傷心失望。 **4** filled with hate or caused by hate 懷恨的; 抱怨的: *They are bitter enemies.*

他們是死敵。 | *The bitter fighting continued for several years.* 這場充滿仇恨的戰爭持續了幾年。 **5** very cold (used of the wind or weather) 寒冷的〔指風或天氣〕: *a bitter winter wind* 冬天刺骨的寒風 **6 do something to the bitter end** to continue to do something to the end, even though it is unpleasant or difficult 拼到底 –**bitterly** *adv* –**bitterness** *n* [U]

bitter² *n* [U] *BrE* a type of beer 〔英式〕苦啤酒: *A pint of bitter, please.* 請來一品脱苦啤酒。

bit·ty /'bɪtɪ; 'bɪti/ *adj* consisting of a lot of small parts or pieces which do not seem to go together very well 零碎的; 拼湊的: *a rather bitty collection of short stories* 七拼八湊的短篇小説集

bi·tu·men /bɪ'tjumən; 'bɪtʃʊmˌn/ *n* [U] a black sticky substance used in road-making 瀝青

biv·ou·ac¹ /'bɪvu,æk; 'bɪvʊ-æk/ *n* a soldiers' camp in which the soldiers sleep in the open without tents 〔軍隊的〕野營地, 露營地

bivouac² *v* **bivouacked, bivouacking** [I] to spend the night in the open without tents 野營露宿

bi·zarre /bɪ'zar; bɪ'zɑːʳ/ *adj* very strange or unusual 奇異的; 不尋常的: *He had a bizarre appearance and manner.* 他外貌古怪, 行為異常。–**bizarrely** *adv*

blab /blæb; blæb/ *v* -bb- [I] *infml* to tell people something that should be a secret 〔非正式〕泄露祕密

★**black¹** /blæk; blæk/ *adj* **1** of the colour of night 黑色的: *She wore a black dress.* 她穿了一件黑色的衣服。 | *black clouds* 烏雲 –see picture on page 243 見 243 頁彩圖 **2** without cream or milk (used of tea and coffee) 不加奶油或牛奶的〔指茶或咖啡〕: *Two black coffees, please.* 請來兩杯黑咖啡。 **3** belonging to a race of people with dark skins 黑種人的: *the problems of black people living in Britain* 居住在英國的黑人的問題 **4** very bad (used of situations) 極糟的〔指情況〕: *Things were beginning to look very black for us.* 對我們來説, 事情開始顯得很糟糕。 **5 black and blue** covered in dark marks as the result of being hit 〔被打得〕青腫的: *He was black and blue all over.* 他渾身青一塊紫一塊的。 **6 black and white** containing only the colours black, white, and grey 黑白的; 灰白的: *a black and white photograph* 黑白照片 **7 in black and white** in writing 書面的: *I want this agreement in black and white.* 我要求以書面形式把這項協議寫出來。 **8 black eye** an area of dark skin around someone's eye caused by being hit 〔被打成〕青黑色的眼眶 **9 black hole** an area in outer space into which everything near it, including light itself, is pulled 〔外太空的〕黑洞〔能吸入鄰近一切物質, 包括光〕 **10 a black look** an angry look 怒氣沖沖的一眼:

She gave me a black look. 她對我怒目而視。 **11 black magic** magic that is used for evil purposes 巫術；魔法 **12 black market** the system by which goods are bought and sold unlawfully at a time when such trade is controlled 黑市（交易）: *They bought butter on the black market during the war.* 戰時他們在黑市上買黃油。 **-blackness** *n* [U]

black² *n* **1** [U] the colour of night 黑色: *old ladies dressed in black* 穿黑衣的老婦 **2** [C] a person of a race which has dark skin (a word which is considered offensive by some people) 黑人〔有些人認為這是無禮的用詞〕 **3 in the black** having money in a bank account 〔銀行存款〕有盈餘: *Our account is in the black this month.* 我們的賬戶這個月有盈餘。

black³ *v* [T] **1** to make something black by covering it with a black substance 把〔某物〕弄黑: *They blacked their faces.* 他們把臉塗黑。 **2** to refuse to work with particular goods or people 抵制；拒絕合作: *The trade union blacked a firm that refused to pay proper wages.* 工會對一家不肯付合理工資的公司進行了抵制。 **3 black someone's eye** to hit someone on or near their eye, causing the skin round their eye to become dark 把某人的眼睛打得青腫

black out *phr v* [I] **1** to faint 昏厥: *I must have blacked out, because I don't remember anything about the accident.* 我當時一定是昏過去了，因為我不記得關於那次事故的任何情況。

black·ber·ry /ˈblækˌberi; ˈblækbəri/ *n* **blackberries** a dark sweet fruit which grows wild or is grown in gardens 黑莓〔野生或園栽的果實〕 -see picture on page 504 見 504 頁彩圖

black·bird /ˈblækˌbɜːd; ˈblækbɜːd/ *n* a common European bird of which the male is black with a yellow beak 黑鸝；黑唱鶇

black·board /ˈblækˌbɔːd; ˈblækbɔːd/ *n* a dark smooth board used in schools for writing or drawing on with chalk 黑板

black·cur·rant /ˌblækˈkɜːrənt; ˌblækˈkʌrənt◂/ *n* a garden fruit with small round black berries 黑醋栗，黑加侖子

black disc /ˌ· ˈ·/ *n* a record 唱片: *The album is available on compact disc and black disc.* 這套唱片集以鐳射唱片和普通唱片兩種形式出售。

black·en /ˈblækən; ˈblækən/ *v* [T] **1** to make something black 使〔某物〕變黑: *The walls had been blackened by smoke.* 牆被煙熏黑了。 **2** to make something appear bad 詆毀，敗壞〔某事物〕: *They tried to blacken the party's reputation.* 他們企圖敗壞該黨的名譽。

black·head /ˈblækˌhed; ˈblækhed/ *n* a small, black spot on someone's skin 黑頭粉刺

black·jack /ˈblækˌdʒæk; ˈblækdʒæk/ *n* **1** [U] a card game usually played for money 〔常

用來賭錢的〕二十一點牌戲 **2** [C] *AmE* a short stick used as a weapon 〔美式〕〔作武器用的〕短棒

black·leg /ˈblækˌleg; ˈblækleg/ *n BrE* a person who continues to work when other people have stopped working to demand more money or better conditions (a word used to express disapproval) 〔英式〕罷工期間繼續上工的人；工賊〔含貶義〕

black·list /ˈblækˌlɪst; ˈblækˌlɪst/ *n* a list of people who are not approved of for some reason or who are to be punished 黑名單: *He had been placed on a blacklist.* 他被列入了黑名單。 **-blacklist** *v* [T]: *They had been blacklisted for non-payment of debts.* 他們因無力償還債務而被列入黑名單。

black·mail¹ /ˈblækˌmel; ˈblækmeɪl/ *n* [U] the crime of obtaining money from someone by threatening to make known something unpleasant 敲詐；訛詐；勒索

blackmail² *v* [T] to obtain money from someone by blackmail 敲詐；勒索: *Don't think you can blackmail me.* 別以為你可以敲詐我。 **-blackmailer** *n*

black·out /ˈblækˌaut; ˈblækaut/ *n* **1** a period when a place is made completely dark, either during wartime or when the electric power supply fails 〔戰時的〕燈火管制；〔因停電引起的〕燈火熄滅 **2** a loss of consciousness for a short time 暫時性昏迷: *He had had a blackout after the accident and could not remember what happened.* 事故發生後他暈過去一陣子，不記得出了甚麼事。

black·smith /ˈblækˌsmɪθ; ˈblækˌsmɪθ/ *n* a person who makes and repairs things made of iron, such as horseshoes 鐵匠；鍛工〔尤指馬蹄鐵匠〕

blad·der /ˈblædə; ˈblædər/ *n* **1** a bag of skin inside your body, in which waste liquid called URINE collects before it is passed out 膀胱 **2** a bag of skin, leather, or rubber which can be filled with air or liquid 囊狀物；球膽

blade /bleid; bleɪd/ *n* **1** the flat cutting part of a knife, sword, or other cutting tool 刀鋒；刀刃 **2** the flat wide part of an OAR or a PROPELLER 槳葉；螺旋槳葉 **3** a long flat leaf of grass 草葉

*blame¹ /blem; bleɪm/ *v* **blamed, blaming** [T] **1** to believe or state that someone is responsible for something bad 責怪；歸咎於: *He always tries to blame other people when things go wrong.* 出了問題他總試圖怪罪他人。 | *Opposition parties have blamed the government for the rise in inflation.* 反對黨把通貨膨脹的增長歸咎於政府。 | *The failure of the talks was blamed on the British government's unwillingness to compromise.* 會談的失敗歸咎於英國政府不願妥協。 **2 be to blame for something** to be responsible for something bad 應對某事承擔責任: *They were not to blame for the accident.* 他們不應

對那次事故承擔責任。**3 don't blame, can't blame** a phrase used when you are saying that you understand why someone has done something and you do not think that they were wrong to do it 不責怪，無可厚非〔用於表示理解某人為何做某事，認為某人這樣做沒有不妥〕: *You can't really blame him for putting his own interests first.* 你確實不能怪他把自己的利益放在首位。| *'I've finally given up my job.' 'I don't blame you!'* "我終於辭了職。""我不怪你!"

□ USEFUL PATTERNS 有用句型
to blame someone; to blame someone for something; to blame something on someone

blame² *n* [U] **1** responsibility for something bad 對錯事應負的責任: *No one is entirely free from blame in this affair.* 這件事每個人都或多或少有過失。**2 lay/put the blame on someone** to state that someone is responsible for something bad 認為某人〔對錯事〕有責任 **3 take/bear the blame for something** to accept that you are responsible for something bad 承擔某事的責任: *We were ready to take the blame for what had happened.* 我們準備對已發生的事情承擔責任。

■ USAGE 用法: **1** The following sentences have a similar meaning, but note how the nouns **blame** and **fault** are used in different ways ☆下列句子意思相近，但注意名詞 **blame** 和 **fault** 的不同用法: *They were **not to blame** for the accident.* 他們不應對那次事故負責任。| *The accident was **not their fault.*** 那次事故不是他們的錯。**2** In conversation **fault** is more commonly used than **blame** to say that someone is (or is not) responsible for something bad which has happened ☆在會話中說某人對已發生的壞事應負責任〔或不應負責任〕時，**fault** 比 **blame** 更常用: *It's all **your fault!** I should never have listened to you.* 都是你的錯! 我早就該不再聽你的。| *Don't blame me! It's not **my fault** you were late.* 別怪我! 你遲到不是我的錯。

blame·less /ˈbleɪmlɪs; ˈbleɪmləs/ *adj* free from blame or guilt 無可責難的; 無罪的: *She had led a blameless life.* 她的一生沒有過失。 **–blamelessly** *adv*

blame·wor·thy /ˈbleɪmˌwɜːði; ˈbleɪmˌwɜːðɪ/ *adj fml* deserving blame 〔正式〕應受責備的

blanch /blɑːntʃ; blæntʃ/ *v* **1** [T] to put fruit or vegetables into boiling water for a very short time 用沸水速煮〔水果或蔬菜〕: *Blanch the almonds to remove the skin.* 用沸水燙一下杏仁，把皮去掉。**2** [I] to become pale with fear or cold 〔因恐懼或寒冷而〕變蒼白: *She blanched when she saw me.* 她看到我就臉都

白了。

blanc·mange /bləˈmɒnʒ; bləˈmɒnʒ/ *n* [C;U] a sweet dish made with flour, sugar, and milk, and eaten cold 牛奶凍〔一種由麵粉、糖、牛奶等做的冷凍甜食〕

bland /blænd; blænd/ *adj* **1** without much taste 味淡的: *I find her food very bland.* 我覺得她吃的東西很淡。**2** showing no strong feelings or opinions so as to avoid offending people 〔為不冒犯他人而〕不激動的，情緒平穩的，溫和的: *He criticized television's bland coverage of the election.* 他批評電視新聞對選舉溫和的報道。 **–blandly** *adv* **–blandness** *n* [U]

blank¹ /blæŋk; blæŋk/ *adj* **1** having nothing on, for example no writing or no sound 空白的; 無字跡的: *a blank page* 空白的一頁 | *a blank cassette* 一盒空白磁帶 | *Please write your name in the blank space at the top of the page.* 請把你的名字寫在這頁最上面的空白處。**2** without expression, interest, or understanding 沒有表情的; 沒有興趣的; 不理解的: *I tried to explain, but he just gave me a blank look.* 我試圖解釋，但他只是莫名其妙地看了我一眼。| *She looked completely blank.* 她看上去一片茫然。**3 blank cheque** a signed cheque on which the amount of money has not yet been written 〔簽了名而未填上金額的〕空白支票 **4 blank verse** poetry that does not RHYME 無韻詩 **–blankly** *adv* **–blankness** *n* [U]

blank² *n* **1** an empty space on a piece of paper 〔紙上的〕空白處: *In this exercise you have to fill in each blank with one word.* 這個練習題你要在每個空白處填上一個單詞。**2 my mind was a complete blank** = I couldn't remember or think of anything 我的腦子裡一片空白 **3** (also 又作 **blank cartridge**) a CARTRIDGE that contains an explosive but no bullet 〔有火藥而無彈頭的〕空彈

blan·ket /ˈblæŋkɪt; ˈblæŋkɪt/ *n* **1** [C] a thick woollen covering used especially on beds to protect you from the cold 毛氈; 毯子: *We might need an extra blanket tonight.* 今晚我們可能需要多一張毯子。**2** [C] a thick covering of something over an area 厚的覆蓋物: *The valley was covered with a blanket of snow.* 山谷覆蓋着一層雪。**3** [only before a noun 只用於名詞前] including all people or all cases 共通的; 總括的: *We are introducing a blanket ban on smoking in the building.* 我們正實施在大樓內全面禁煙。

blare /blɛr; bleər/ *v* **blared, blaring** [I] to make a loud, unpleasant noise 發出難聽刺耳的鳴響: *blaring car horns* 刺耳的汽車喇叭聲 **–blare** *n* [U]: *the blare of a brass band* 銅管樂隊刺耳的吹奏聲

blare out *phr v* [I;T **blare** sthg ↔ **out**] to make a loud, unpleasant noise or loud, unpleasant music 發出刺耳的聲音或音樂: *The radio blared out the news.* 收音機大聲地播出

新聞。| *Loud music was blaring out.* 響亮的音樂聲刺耳地傳出來。

bla·sé /ˈblɑːze; ˈblɑːzeɪ/ *adj* not feeling excited about something because you have experienced it many times before 〔因經歷過多次而〕無動於衷的: *You're being very blasé about it: aren't you glad you won the prize?* 你對此無動於衷: 你得了獎難道不高興嗎?

blas·pheme /blæsˈfiːm; blæsˈfiːm/ *v* **blasphemed, blaspheming** [I] to speak without respect about God or holy things 褻瀆〔上帝或聖物〕: *He can hardly speak without blaspheming against God.* 他不褻瀆上帝就說不了話。 –**blasphemous** /ˈblæsfɪməs; ˈblæsfɪmɐs/ *adj*: *blasphemous talk* 褻瀆神明的說話

blas·phe·my /ˈblæsfɪmɪ; ˈblæsfɪmi/ *n* **blasphemies** [C;U] disrespectful language about God or holy things 褻瀆神明的言詞: *Their conversation was full of blasphemies.* 他們的交談中滿是褻瀆神明的話語。

blast¹ /blæst; blɑːst/ *n* **1** a sudden strong movement of wind or air 一陣疾風; 一股氣流: *the icy blasts of the north wind* 一陣凜冽的北風 | *a blast of hot air from the oven* 從爐子裡傳出的一股熱氣 **2** an explosion 爆炸: *The windows were shattered by the blast.* 窗子被炸得粉碎。 **3** a very loud and usually unpleasant sound of a brass wind instrument 〔銅管樂器的〕噪聲: *He blew several loud blasts on his horn.* 他吹了幾聲響亮的喇叭。 **4 at full blast** playing as loud as possible 極響地: *She had the radio on at full blast.* 她把收音機開到最響。

blast² *v* [T] to make a hole in something by using an explosion 炸開〔某物〕: *They've blasted a tunnel through the mountain.* 他們在山上炸開了一條隧道。

blast off *phr v* [I] (of a space vehicle) to rise up into the air 〔太空船〕發射, 升空

blast³ *interj* a word used to express anger 該死〔表示憤怒〕: *Oh blast! I forgot to phone John.* 該死! 我忘了給約翰打電話。

blast·ed /ˈblæstɪd; ˈblɑːstɪd/ *adj* [only before a noun 只用於名詞前] a word used to express anger and give force to what you are saying 該死的〔表示憤怒, 加強語氣〕: *Make that blasted dog keep quiet!* 別讓那條該死的狗亂叫啦!

blast fur·nace /ˈ· ˌ··/ *n* a steel container where iron is separated from iron ORE by the action of heat 鼓風爐; 高爐

blast-off /ˈ· ·/ *n* the moment when a space vehicle leaves the ground and moves up into the air 〔太空船的〕發射, 升空時刻

bla·tant /ˈbleɪtnt; ˈbleɪtənt/ *adj* very noticeable and without shame (a word used to express disapproval) 無恥的, 露骨的〔含貶義〕: *his blatant disregard for the law* 他對法律的公然漠視 | *a blatant lie* 彌天大謊 – **blatantly** *adv*

blaze¹ /bleɪz; bleɪz/ *v* **blazed, blazing** [I] **1** to burn with a bright flame 熊熊燃燒: *A fire was blazing in the corner of the room.* 爐火在房間角落裡熊熊燃燒着。 **2** (of light) to be very bright 〔光〕照亮: *Lights blazed in every room.* 每個房間都燈火通明。 **3 his eyes blazed with anger** = he looked very angry 他的眼中閃着怒火 **4 blaze a trail** to do something new and exciting which other people can copy or follow 作開路先鋒; 做先導

blaze² *n* **1** a large fire 火焰; 烈火: *Firemen soon brought the blaze under control.* 消防隊員很快控制了大火。 **2 a blaze of light, a blaze of colour** a bright show of light or colour 燈火通明; 五彩繽紛 **3 a blaze of publicity** a sudden large amount of attention given to someone or something 突然受到公眾注意

blaz·er /ˈbleɪzə; ˈbleɪzər/ *n* a short coat often with the special sign of a school or club on it 〔印有學校、俱樂部等徽號的〕輕便上衣

blaz·ing /ˈbleɪzɪŋ; ˈbleɪzɪŋ/ *adj* **1** very hot (used of the sun or the weather) 熾熱的, 炎熱的〔指太陽或天氣〕: *the blazing heat of the sun* 太陽的炎熱 | *It was a blazing hot day.* 那天很炎熱。 **2 blazing row** a very angry and loud argument 大吵大鬧

bleach¹ /bliːtʃ; bliːtʃ/ *v* [T] to make something white or lighter in colour 使〔某物〕變白; 漂白: *His hair had been bleached by the sun.* 他的頭髮被太陽曬得顏色變淡了。

bleach² *n* [U] a strong substance used to clean things or to make things lighter in colour 漂白劑

bleak /bliːk; bliːk/ *adj* **1** cold, unattractive, and without trees or flowers 蕭瑟的; 荒涼的: *The landscape was bleak and uninviting.* 這景色荒涼, 毫不誘人。 **2** cold, dull, and grey (used of the weather) 陰冷的〔指天氣〕: *a bleak winter's day* 陰沉的冬日 **3** without hope 沒有希望的: *Our future looks very bleak.* 我們的前景很黯淡。

blear·y /ˈblɪərɪ; ˈblɪəri/ *adj* unable to see well because of tiredness or crying (used of someone's eyes) 睡眼惺忪的; 視線模糊的: *He sat rubbing his bleary eyes.* 他坐着揉他模糊的眼睛。 –**blearily** *adv*: *She looked at me blearily.* 她迷迷糊糊地看着我。

bleat /bliːt; bliːt/ *v* [I] **1** to make the sound that a sheep or goat makes 作羊咩聲 **2** to speak or say something in a weak, complaining voice 低聲訴苦: *"I don't want to go,"* *he bleated.* "我不要去," 他嘀嘀咕咕地說。 –**bleat** *n*

bled /blɛd; blɛd/ the past tense and past participle of BLEED ☆ BLEED 的過去式和過去分詞

bleed /bliːd; bliːd/ *v* **bled** /blɛd; blɛd/, **bled** [I] to lose blood from your body 流血: *Your nose is bleeding.* 你的鼻子在流血。

bleep¹ /bliːp; bliːp/ *n* a short, high, repeated

B

sound sent out by an electrical apparatus 〔電子儀器發出的〕嗶嗶聲

bleep² /v 1 [I] (of a machine) to make a short, high sound 〔機器〕嗶嗶聲 2 [T] to call someone using a bleeper 〔用傳呼機〕召喚〔某人〕: *Bleep Doctor Rice – it's an emergency!* 用傳呼聲召萊斯醫生 — 有緊急情況!

bleep·er /'blipɚ; 'bli:pəʳ/ *n* a small machine which you carry in your pocket, and which bleeps when you are needed somewhere 傳呼機

blem·ish¹ /'blɛmɪʃ; 'blemɪʃ/ *v* [T] to spoil the beauty or perfection of something 損害〔某物的〕完美; 玷污: *His reputation had been severely blemished by the scandal.* 他的名譽因這次醜聞而受到了嚴重的玷污。

blemish² *n* a mark that spoils the appearance of something 瑕疵

blend¹ /blɛnd; blend/ *v* 1 [T] to mix things together thoroughly 混合: *Blend the cocoa* **with** *the milk and water.* 把可可、牛奶和水混合在一起。| *Blend the sugar, flour, and eggs* **together.** 把糖、麵粉、雞蛋和在一起。2 [I] to go well together 調和; 相配: *Their voices blend well* **with** *each other.* 他們的嗓音互相配合得很好。

blend in *phr v* [I] to be similar to surrounding things, and so be not easily seen or noticed 融為一體: *These houses seem to blend in well* **with** *their surroundings.* 這些房子和周圍的環境似乎融為一體。| *Chameleons can change their colour to blend into their surroundings.* 變色蜥蜴能改變自身的顏色, 和周圍環境融成一體。

blend² *n* something produced by blending or mixing several things together 混合物: *my favourite blend of coffee* 我最喜歡的混成咖啡 | *His manner was a blend of friendliness and respect.* 他的態度友好而恭敬。

blend·er /'blɛndɚ; 'blendəʳ/ *n* a small electric machine used for making solid foods into a smooth liquid 食物攪拌器

bless /blɛs; bles/ *v* blessed *or* blest /blɛst; blest/, **blessed** *or* **blest** [T] 1 to ask for God's favour and protection for something 祈求上帝保佑; 求神祝福: *The priest blessed the ship before it left port.* 牧師在船離港前為船祝福。2 to make something holy 使〔某物〕神聖: *The bread and wine had been blessed by the priest.* 麵包和酒經牧師祝福成為聖物了。3 **be blessed with something** to be lucky enough to have something such as a skill or good quality 有幸得到某物〔如技術或優質〕: *We were both blessed with good health.* 我們倆有幸身體健康。4 **Bless you!** a phrase that you say to someone who has just sneezed (SNEEZE) 長命百歲〔在別人打噴嚏時說〕

bless·ed /'blɛsɪd; 'blesɪd/ *adj* 1 *fml* holy and favoured by God 〔正式〕神聖的; 受上帝祝福的: *Blessed are the peacemakers.* 使人和睦的人有福了。2 very nice, and giving a rest

from something unpleasant 非常怡人的; 使人舒服的: *a few moments of blessed silence* 令人愉悅的片刻寧靜

bless·ing /'blɛsɪŋ; 'blesɪŋ/ *n* 1 an act of asking for or receiving God's help and protection 〔向上帝的〕祈福; 〔上帝的〕保佑: *The blessing of the Lord be upon you all.* 願主保佑你們大家。2 **your blessing** your approval or encouragement 你的同意; 你的鼓勵: *The government has given its blessing to the new plan.* 政府已批准了該項新計劃。| *The agreement was made with the President's blessing.* 總統同意簽署這項協議。3 **a blessing in disguise** something which seems unpleasant at first but is really the best thing that could have happened 〔開始不好但實際上是〕禍中得福: *Failing my exams turned out to be a blessing in disguise.* 考試不及格到頭來卻因禍得福。

blew /blu; blu:/ the past tense of BLOW ☆ BLOW 的過去式

blight¹ /blaɪt; blaɪt/ *n* [sing] something which damages or spoils things 導致破壞的因素

blight² *v fml* [T] to spoil something 〔正式〕破壞; 毀損: *Her life was blighted by ill health.* 她的一生被疾病所摧毀。

***blind¹** /blaɪnd; blaɪnd/ *adj* 1 unable to see 瞎的: *She had been blind from birth.* 她天生瞎眼。2 not reasonable or not controlled 不講道理的; 控制不住的: *He was in a blind panic.* 他陷於盲目的驚慌狀態。| *Love is blind.* 愛情是盲目的。3 **blind to something** not conscious of something 沒有意識到某事物: *Is the government blind to the needs of the elderly?* 政府難道看不到老年人的需要嗎? 4 **blind corner** a corner that is difficult to see round when you are driving 駕駛時很難看到的拐角 5 **blind drunk** extremely drunk 酩酊大醉 6 **blind spot** a part of the road behind you that you cannot see when you are driving 〔駕駛者後面兩側一帶〕不易看見的地方 7 **as blind as a bat** completely blind 完全看不見東西的 8 **not take a blind bit of notice** to take no notice at all 毫不注意: *I've told her a hundred times, but she never takes a blind bit of notice.* 我跟她說過幾百次了, 可是她毫不理會。9 **turn a blind eye to something** to pretend not to notice something 假裝看不見某事物: *You girls shouldn't be in here, but I'll turn a blind eye to it, just this once.* 你們女孩子不該進這兒來, 但我就睜一隻眼閉一隻眼, 下不為例。–**blindly** *adv* –**blindness** *n* [U]

blind² *v* [T] 1 to make someone unable to see something 使〔某人〕看不見〔某物〕: *He was blinded by the smoke.* 他被煙燻得看不見了。2 to stop someone from being conscious of something 蒙蔽〔某人〕: *The government's optimistic words must not blind us* **to** *the dangers of rising inflation.* 政府樂觀的言詞不該使我們忘記通貨膨脹上升的

危險。

blind³ *n* a piece of cloth or other material which can be pulled down to cover a window 窗簾; 遮簾

blind al·ley /ˌ· ˈ··/ *n* a road with no way out at the other end 死胡同, 死巷

blind date /ˌ· ˈ·/ *n infml* an occasion arranged for someone to meet a person of the opposite sex whom they have never met before, with the intention of forming a relationship with them 〔非正式〕〔男女雙方經人介紹〕初次會面: *We met on a blind date.* 我們經人介紹見了面。

blind·fold¹ /ˈblaɪndˌfold; ˈblaɪndfəʊld/ *v* [T] to cover someone's eyes with a piece of material to prevent them from seeing 〔用一塊布〕蒙住〔某人〕的眼睛

blindfold² *n* a piece of material that covers someone's eyes to prevent them from seeing 蒙眼布: *He tore off his blindfold.* 他扯下了蒙眼布。

blink¹ /blɪŋk; blɪŋk/ *v* **1** [I;T] to open and shut your eyes quickly, several times 眨眼睛: *She blinked as she came into the light.* 她走到有亮光的地方時直眨眼睛。| *Blink your eyes to get the grit out.* 你眨眨眼睛, 把沙粒弄出去吧。 **2** [I] (of a light) to flash rapidly on and off 〔燈光〕閃爍不定

blink² *n* **1** an act of blinking 眨眼; 閃爍 **2 on the blink** *infml* not working properly (used of a machine) 〔非正式〕失靈; 出毛病〔指機器〕

blink·er /ˈblɪŋkɚ; ˈblɪŋkəʳ/ *n* the usual American word for the INDICATOR on a car 〔美式〕〔汽車的〕閃光信號燈

blink·ered /ˈblɪŋkɚd; ˈblɪŋkəd/ *adj* **1** wearing blinkers 戴眼罩的 **2** unable to understand or accept anything except ideas that are familiar to you already 〔除了自己熟悉的觀點以外〕無法理解的, 無法接受的: *The Prime Minister is completely blinkered in her opinions.* 首相固執己見, 對她的意見置之不理。

blink·ers /ˈblɪŋkɚz; ˈblɪŋkəz/ *n* [pl] a pair of leather pieces that are fixed beside a horse's eyes so that it can only see straight ahead 馬眼罩

blip /blɪp; blɪp/ *n* a short, regular sound or image produced by an electrical machine 〔電子機器發出的〕短而規則的聲音或圖像

bliss /blɪs; blɪs/ *n* [U] complete happiness 極樂; 至福

bliss·ful /ˈblɪsfəl; ˈblɪsfəl/ *adj* making you feel extremely happy 極樂的: *We spent a blissful two weeks on our own.* 我們自己度過了極為愉快的兩星期。–**blissfully** *adv*

blis·ter¹ /ˈblɪstɚ; ˈblɪstəʳ/ *n* **1** a painful watery swelling under your skin 〔皮膚上的〕水泡, 水腫: *New shoes always give me blisters.* 新鞋子老把我的腳磨起了泡。**2** a small swelling on the surface of paint or rubber 氣泡

blister² *v* [I;T] to form blisters 起水泡: *My hands blister very easily.* 我的手很容易起水泡。| *The heat blistered the paint on the door.* 高溫使門上的油漆起了泡。

blis·ter·ing /ˈblɪstərɪŋ; ˈblɪstərɪŋ/ *adj* **1** very hot (used of the sun or the weather) 炎熱的; 酷熱的〔指太陽或天氣〕 **2** expressing great anger 憤怒的: *a blistering attack on the government* 對政府的猛烈攻擊

blithe /blaɪð; blaɪð/ *adj* done without careful thought 漫不經心的: *a blithe remark* 漫不經心的話 –**blithely** *adv*

blitz /blɪts; blɪts/ *n* **1 the Blitz** the attacking of British cities from the air during the second world war 二次世界大戰時對英國的空襲 **2** a period during which you make a great effort and do a job quickly 閃電式行動

bliz·zard /ˈblɪzɚd; ˈblɪzəd/ *n* a severe storm with strong winds and snow 暴風雪 –see 見 WEATHER (USAGE 用法)

bloat·ed /ˈbloʊtɪd; ˈbləʊtɪd/ *adj* **1** unpleasantly swollen 腫脹的: *the bloated body of a drowned animal* 淹死的動物那腫脹的屍體 **2** *infml* very full of food 〔非正式〕飽脹的

blob /blɑb; blɒb/ *n* a drop of a thick liquid 一滴: *There was a blob of paint on the floor.* 地板上有一滴油漆。

bloc /blɑk; blɒk/ *n* [+sing/pl verb] a group of people or nations that take action together 集團; 陣營: *The Eastern bloc is gathering next week in Berlin.* 東歐集團下週在柏林集會。

block¹ /blɑk; blɒk/ *n* **1** a solid piece of something such as wood or stone 〔木、石等的〕一大塊: *The floor was made of wooden blocks.* 地板是用木塊拼成的。| *a block of ice* 一塊冰 **2** a large building divided into separate parts 〔大建築物的〕棟, 座, 幢: *a block of flats* 一幢住宅樓宇 | *an office block* 一幢辦公大樓 **3** a large building or a group of buildings built between two streets in a town or city 街區; 街段: *She lives two blocks from here.* 她住的地方距離這兒兩個街區遠。| *I'm going for a walk round the block.* 我在街區周圍散散步。**4** a quantity of things considered as a single unit 一組; 一批: *He had bought a block of shares in the business.* 他買了這家企業的一批股票。**5 a mental block** an inability to understand 無法理解: *I'm afraid I've got a real mental block about computers.* 恐怕我對電腦真的一竅不通。**6 the block** a large piece of wood on which people's heads were cut off in the past 〔昔時的〕斷頭台

block² *v* [T] **1** to prevent things from moving through or along something 阻塞: *Something's blocking the pipe.* 有東西塞住了管道。| *My nose is blocked and I can't breathe properly.* 我鼻子堵塞, 呼吸不暢順。| *Quite a lot of roads are blocked.* 許多道路也堵塞。**2** to prevent something from happening 阻止: *The government have blocked our plans.* 政府阻撓了我們的計劃。

block sthg ↔ **out** *phr v* [T] **1** to try very hard not to think about something 竭力不想〔某事〕 **2** to stop light or a signal from reaching somewhere 堵住〔燈光〕; 阻擋〔信號〕

block sthg ↔ **up** *phr v* [T] to prevent things from moving through or along something 阻塞: *The sink's got blocked up again.* 水槽又阻塞了。

block·ade /bləˈked; blɒˈkeɪd/ *v* **blockaded, blockading** [T] to prevent goods from reaching a place by the use of military power 封鎖: *Ships have blockaded all the major ports.* 輪船已封鎖了所有主要港口。 – **blockade** *n*

block·age /ˈblɑkɪdʒ; ˈblɒkɪdʒ/ *n* something that prevents movement through a pipe or tube 阻礙物

block let·ters /ˌ· ˈ··/ *n BrE* (also 又作 **block capitals** /ˌ· ˈ···/) [pl] letters that are written in their CAPITAL form〔英式〕印刷體大寫字母: *He wrote her name in block letters, MARY.* 他用印刷體大寫字母寫她的名字: MARY。

bloke /blok; bləʊk/ *n BrE infml* a man〔英式, 非正式〕人; 傢伙

blond /bland; blɒnd/ *adj* **1** light yellow in colour (used of hair) 淡黃色的〔指頭髮〕 – see picture on page 469 見 469 頁彩圖 **2** having light-coloured hair and skin (used of a man) 毛髮及皮膚淺色的〔指男人〕

blonde[1] /bland; blɒnd/ *adj* having light-coloured hair and skin (used of a woman) 金髮白膚的, 毛髮及皮膚淺色的〔指女人〕–see picture on page 469 見 469 頁彩圖

blonde[2] *n* a woman with light-coloured hair and skin 金髮白膚的女子

blood /blʌd; blʌd/ *n* [U] **1** the red liquid which flows through your body 血; 血液: *She had lost a lot of blood, and was very weak.* 她失了很多血, 非常虛弱。 **2** a person's family background 血統; 家世: *a woman of noble blood* 有貴族血統的女子 **be in your blood** to be a skill or quality that you have naturally, and that other members of your family also have〔技能、品質等〕與生俱來的, 遺傳下來的: *Her family have been farmers for hundreds of years, so farming is in her blood.* 她家裡人幾百年來都是農民, 所以她天生就是種田的料子。 **4 make your blood boil** to make you extremely angry 使人極為憤怒: *His attitude to women really makes my blood boil sometimes!* 他對婦女的態度有時真叫我怒火中燒! **5 make your blood run cold** to make you very afraid 使人非常害怕; 使人不寒而慄

blood·bath /ˈblʌd,bæθ; ˈblʌdbɑːθ/ *n* the violent killing of many people 血洗; 大屠殺

blood·cur·dling /ˈblʌd,kɜːdlɪŋ; ˈblʌd,kɜːd-lɪŋ/ *adj* very frightening (used of someone

that you hear) 令人毛骨悚然的〔指聽到的事〕: *bloodcurdling cries of pain* 令人毛骨悚然的叫痛聲

blood·hound /ˈblʌd,haund; ˈblʌdhaʊnd/ *n* a large hunting dog with a very good sense of smell〔嗅覺靈敏的〕大獵犬

blood·less /ˈblʌdlɪs; ˈblʌdləs/ *adj* **1** very pale (used of someone's skin) 沒有血色的; 蒼白的〔指膚色〕: *her bloodless cheeks* 她蒼白的雙頰 **2** without killing or violence 沒有殺戮或暴力的: *a bloodless coup* 不流血的政變

blood poi·son·ing /ˈ· ,···/ *n* [U] a serious illness caused by an infection in your blood 敗血症; 血中毒

blood pres·sure /ˈ· ,··/ *n* [U] the force with which blood travels through your body 血壓: *He's got high blood pressure.* 他患有高血壓症。

blood·shed /ˈblʌd,ʃed; ˈblʌdʃed/ *n* [U] fighting in which people are violently killed or hurt〔戰鬥中的〕殺戮, 流血: *The authorities are trying to prevent further bloodshed.* 當局正力圖阻止進一步的流血傷亡。

blood·shot /ˈblʌd,ʃat; ˈblʌdʃɒt/ *adj* red (used of someone's eyes) 充血的〔指眼睛〕

blood sport /ˈ· ·/ *n* a sport in which a bird or animal is killed 狩獵運動; 獵殺活動: *I am against all blood sports.* 我反對一切獵殺活動。

blood·stain /ˈblʌd,sten; ˈblʌdsteɪn/ *n* a mark where blood has fallen on something 血跡 –**bloodstained** *adj*: *bloodstained clothing* 血跡斑斑的衣服

blood·stream /ˈblʌd,strim; ˈblʌdstriːm/ *n* the blood as it flows around your body 血流;〔循環於體內的〕血液: *The poison has entered her bloodstream.* 毒藥已進入了她的血液中。

blood·thirst·y /ˈblʌd,θɜːstɪ; ˈblʌd,θɜːsti/ *adj* having too much interest in violence 嗜殺的; 耽於暴力的

blood ves·sel /ˈ· ,··/ *n* one of the tubes in your body through which your blood flows 血管

blood·y[1] /ˈblʌdɪ; ˈblʌdi/ *adj* **bloodier, bloodiest 1** covered with blood 有血的; 流血的: *a bloody nose* 流血的鼻子 **2** with a lot of wounding and killing 血腥的; 殺戮的: *a bloody battle* 血腥的戰鬥 **3** [only before a noun 只用於名詞前] *BrE infml* used for giving force to what you are saying (a word which some people consider not to be polite)〔英式, 非正式〕非常的〔用於加強語氣, 有些人認為不禮貌〕: *Don't be a bloody fool!* 別當大傻瓜!

bloody[2] *adv BrE infml* a word used for giving force to what you are saying (a word which some people consider not to be polite)〔英式, 非正式〕非常; 太〔用於加強語氣, 有些人認為不禮貌〕: *It's bloody cold in here!* 這裡面冷得要命!

bloody-mind·ed /ˌ·ˈ···◂/ *adj BrE infml*

intentionally being unhelpful and making difficulties for other people 〔英式, 非正式〕故意刁難的 –**bloody-mindedness** n [U]

bloom¹ /blum; blu:m/ n **1** a flower 花: *What beautiful blooms!* 多美的花啊! **2 in bloom** fully open (used of a flower) 盛開〔指花〕

bloom² v [I] **1** (of a tree) to produce flowers 開花: *The roses are blooming.* 玫瑰花正在盛開。 **2** to look very healthy and well 看上去很健康: *Jane is positively blooming with health these days.* 簡這些日子以來確實身體健康起來。

blos·som¹ /ˈblɒsəm; ˈblɒsəm/ n **1** [C;U] the flowers of a fruit tree 〔果樹的〕花: *apple blossom* 蘋果樹的花 **2 in blossom** with its flowers fully open (used of a tree) 開滿花的〔指樹〕

blossom² v [I] **1** (of a tree) to produce flowers 〔樹〕開花 **2** to develop in a pleasing way 發展; 成長: *a blossoming friendship* 發展中的友誼 | *Sally is blossoming into a beautiful girl.* 莎莉長成一個美麗的女孩。

blot¹ /blɒt; blɒt/ n **1** a drop of a liquid which has fallen onto something and made a mark 污漬: *a blot of ink* 一滴墨水漬 **2** something that spoils something 污點 **3 blot on the landscape** something that spoils the appearance of a place 破壞景色的東西: *That new building is a real blot on the landscape.* 這棟新樓真煞風景。

blot² v **-tt-** [T] **1** to dry a surface with a soft cloth or paper 〔用軟布或紙〕弄乾 **2 blot your copybook** infml to do something to spoil your good record 〔非正式〕玷污自己的好名聲

blot sthg ↔ out phr v [T] **1** to make something difficult or impossible to see 使〔某物〕難以看到; 遮住〔某物〕: *The mist blotted out the sun.* 霧靄遮住了太陽。 **2** to destroy a memory or a thought, so that you no longer think about it 抹掉〔記憶或念頭〕: *She had tried to blot out the memory of that terrible day.* 她試圖在記憶裡抹掉那可怕的一天。

blotch /blɒtʃ; blɒtʃ/ n a coloured mark on something, especially a large and irregular mark 大斑點 –**blotchy** adj

blot·ter /ˈblɒtə; ˈblɒtər/ n a large piece of blotting paper on which paper with writing on can be pressed to dry the ink 〔大張的〕吸墨紙

blotting pa·per /ˈ·· ˌ·· / n [U] thick soft paper used to dry writing in wet ink 吸墨紙

blouse /blaʊs; blaʊz/ n a shirt worn by a woman or girl 女襯衫

*****blow¹** /bloʊ; bloʊ/ v **blew** /blu; blu:/, **blown** /bloʊn; bloʊn/ **1** [I] to send air out through your mouth 〔從嘴裡〕吹出: *She put her lips to the whistle and blew.* 她用嘴唇吹哨子。 **2** [I] (of the wind) to move and cause a current of air 〔風〕吹: *The wind had been blowing all night.* 風颳了整整一夜。 **3** [T+adv/prep] (of the wind or an explosion)

to move something or make it fall 〔風〕吹動〔某物〕; 〔爆炸〕炸落〔某物〕: *The wind was so strong that it blew several trees down.* 風很猛, 颳倒了幾棵樹。 | *His hat was blown off.* 他的帽子吹走了。 | *Both his legs were blown off in the blast.* 他的兩條腿都在爆炸中炸斷了。 **4** [I+adv/prep] to move or fall because of the wind or a current of air 〔因風或氣流而〕移動, 掉落: *I was afraid the roof might blow off.* 我生怕屋頂會被颳走。 | *leaves blowing about in the wind* 在風中飛揚的葉子 **5** [T] to make something such as a horn or whistle make a sound by blowing into it or forcing air through it 吹響〔喇叭、哨子〕: *The referee blew his whistle.* 裁判吹響了哨子。 **6** [I] (of something such as a horn or a whistle) to make a sound 〔喇叭、哨子〕吹響, 鳴響: *Car horns were blowing behind me.* 汽車喇叭在我身後響起。 | *They were still losing 4-3 when the whistle blew.* 哨子吹響時, 他們仍以 4 比 3 落後。 **7 blow a fuse** to cause an electrical FUSE to stop working suddenly 燒斷保險絲 **8 a fuse has blown** = an electrical FUSE has stopped working suddenly 保險絲燒斷了 **9** [T] infml to spend a lot of money, often foolishly 〔非正式〕揮霍: *We blew all our savings on a holiday.* 我們在一個假日裡揮霍掉了所有的存款。 **10** [T] infml to lose a good chance to do something 〔非正式〕失去〔做某事的〕好機會: *I had the chance to go to the United States this summer, but I've blown it!* 今年夏天我本來有機會去美國, 但我失掉了! **11 blow hot and cold** to keep changing your mind about something or someone, sometimes seeming very keen and sometimes seeming not at all keen 反覆無常; 打不定主意 **12 blow your nose** to force air out through your nose in order to clear it, for example when you have a cold 擤鼻子 **13 blow your own trumpet** to speak too proudly about good or clever things that you have done 自吹自擂; 自誇 **14 blow your top** infml to become very angry 〔非正式〕大發雷霆: *When he saw the figures he blew his top.* 他看到這些數字便大發雷霆。

blow sthg ↔ out phr v [T] to blow air onto a flame or candle so that it stops burning 吹滅〔火焰或蠟燭〕

blow over phr v [I] (of a storm or an argument) to stop 〔暴風雨、爭論〕停止: *We didn't dare go out until the storm had blown over.* 直到暴風雨停了我們才敢出去。 | *They had an enormous row, but it'll probably blow over within a day or two.* 他們大吵了一場, 但過一兩天大概就不會吵了。

blow up phr v **1** [T **blow** sthg ↔ **up**] to destroy something by means of an explosion 炸毀: *The bridge was blown up by terrorists.* 橋被恐怖分子炸毀了。 **2** [I] to explode 爆炸: *The plane blew up as it was taking off.* 飛機起飛時爆炸了。 **3** [T **blow**

B

sthg ↔ **up**] to fill something such as a tyre with air 給〔輪胎等〕充氣: *Make sure you blow up the tyres before setting off.* 出發之前你一定要給輪胎打足氣。| *blowing up balloons* 給氣球充氣 **4** [T **blow** sthg ↔ **up**] to make a photograph larger 放大〔照片〕: *I want to have the picture blown up so that I can put it on the wall.* 我要把這張照片放大，這樣可以掛在牆上。**5** [I] (of a storm) to begin 〔暴風雨〕開始: *I think there's a storm blowing up.* 我想暴風雨要來臨了。

*★**blow²** n **1** an act of hitting someone hard with your hand or with a weapon〔用手或武器〕重擊: *He had received a severe blow to the head.* 他的頭部受到重重的一擊。**2** a shock or disappointment 打擊; 失望: *The news was a terrible blow to us all.* 這消息對我們大家是一個可怕的打擊。**3** **a blow for something** something which helps a system or an idea 支持某事物〔如體制或想法〕: *striking a blow for freedom of speech* 為支持言論自由而奮鬥 **4** an act of blowing 吹; 擤: *Give your nose a good blow.* 用力擤一下你的鼻子。| *Give a big blow.* 用力吹一下。**5** **blow-by-blow account** an account of something which gives details of everything that happened 詳盡的報道 **6** **come to blows** to start fighting 動手打起來: *I'm sure they're going to come to blows one of these days.* 我肯定他們這幾天會互相毆打起來。

blow³ *interj old fash* a word used to show anger〔老式〕該死!〔用於表示憤怒〕

blow-dry /'· ·/ v [T] to dry hair with an electric dryer held in your hand〔用手握式電吹風〕吹乾〔頭髮〕–**blow-dry** n: *They charge £10 for a cut and blow-dry.* 剪髮加吹風他們收費十英鎊。

blow·lamp /'blo,læmp; 'bləʊlæmp/ n a lamp which gives a small, very hot flame, used for example for burning off paint 噴燈

blown /blon; bləʊn/ the past participle of BLOW ☆ BLOW 的過去分詞

blow·out /'blo,aʊt; 'bləʊaʊt/ n **1** the bursting of a tyre 輪胎爆破: *He had a blowout on the motorway.* 他的輪胎在快車道上爆了。**2** *infml* a very big meal〔非正式〕盛宴

blow·pipe /'blo,paɪp; 'bləʊpaɪp/ n a tube used for blowing small stones or poisoned arrows used as a weapon 吹矢槍〔能吹出小石頭或毒箭的管子, 用作武器〕

blub·ber /'blʌbɚ; 'blʌbə'/ n [U] the fat of sea animals, especially whales (WHALE), from which oil is obtained 海獸脂肪〔尤指鯨脂〕

blud·geon /'blʌdʒən; 'blʌdʒən/ n [T] **1** to hit someone repeatedly with something heavy 用重物連續毆打〔某人〕**2** **bludgeon someone into something** to force someone to do something, often by threatening them〔常以威脅方式〕迫使某人做某事

*★**blue¹** /blu; bluː/ adj **bluer, bluest 1** of the

colour of the clear sky or of the deep sea on a fine day 藍色的: *She was wearing a dark blue dress.* 她穿着一件深藍色的衣服。| *He painted the door blue.* 他把門漆成藍色。| *My hands were blue with cold.* 我的手都凍得發紫了。–see picture on page 243 見 243 頁彩圖 **2** *infml old fash* sad and without hope〔非正式, 老式〕沮喪的; 憂鬱的 **3** *infml* concerned with sex〔非正式〕下流的; 色情的: *blue films* 黃色電影 **4** **blue blood** the quality of being born into a noble family 貴族出身: *He's convinced he's got blue blood in his veins.* 他相信自己血管中流着貴族的血。**5** **do something till you are blue in the face** to do something for ever; without ever being successful 一直幹; 永不成功: *You can telephone her till you're blue in the face but she'll never come.* 不管你怎麼打電話給她, 她也不會來。

blue² n **1** [U] the colour that is blue 藍色: *a woman dressed in blue* 穿藍色衣服的女子 | *A light blue would be nice for the door.* 門用淡藍色應該不錯。**2** **out of the blue** very suddenly and unexpectedly 非常突然地; 意外地: *John arrived, completely out of the blue.* 約翰突然來了。**3** **the blues** a type of slow, sad music from the Southern US〔美國南部一種感傷、緩慢的〕布魯斯音樂: *a well-known blues singer* 一位知名的布魯斯音樂歌手

blue·bell /'blu,bɛl; 'bluːbel/ n a blue bell-shaped flower 藍色風鈴花

blue·ber·ry /'blu,bɛrɪ; 'bluːbəri/ n **blueberries** a small bush which grows in North America and produces small dark blue fruit〔北美洲的〕烏飯樹〔產深藍色小果子〕

blue·bot·tle /'blu,bɑtl; 'bluː,bɒtl/ n a large blue fly 反吐麗蠅; 青蠅

blue-col·lar /,· '···•/ adj [only before a noun 只用於名詞前] relating to workers who do hard or dirty work with their hands 藍領階級的; 體力勞動者的: *a blue-collar union* 藍領工人工會

blue·print /'blu,prɪnt; 'bluː,prɪnt/ n **1** a plan for making a machine or building a house 藍圖〔製造機器或建築房屋的設計圖〕**2** a description of a plan or an idea, saying how it will work 藍圖; 行動計劃: *The report is a blueprint for the reform of the whole tax system.* 這份報告是整個税制改革的藍圖[計劃]。

bluff¹ /blʌf; blʌf/ v [I] to try and make someone think that you are in a stronger position than you really are, often by pretending to be very confident 虛張聲勢: *I knew that he was only bluffing.* 我知道他只是虛張聲勢。

bluff² n [sing;U] the action of bluffing 虛張聲勢: *He threatened to dismiss me from my job, but it's all bluff.* 他威脅說要解雇我, 但那只是虛張聲勢罷了。| *We all thought his threats were just a bluff.* 我們都認為他的恐嚇只是虛張聲勢而已。

bluff³ *adj* rough, cheerful, and direct, perhaps without considering the feelings of other people 直爽的; 爽快的; 粗率的

blun·der¹ /ˈblʌndə; ˈblʌndəʳ/ n a stupid unnecessary mistake 不智之舉; 愚蠢的錯誤

blunder² v 1 [I] to make a stupid unnecessary mistake 犯〔愚蠢而不必要的〕錯誤 2 [I+adv/prep] to move awkwardly or unsteadily, because you cannot see〔因看不見而〕跟蹌蹌地走: He blundered through the dark forest. 他在黑暗的森林裡跌跌撞撞地前進。

blun·der·buss /ˈblʌndəˌbʌs; ˈblʌndəbʌs/ n an old kind of gun which has a barrel with a wide mouth〔老式的〕大口徑槍

blunt¹ /blʌnt; blʌnt/ adj 1 not sharp 鈍的, 不鋒利的: This knife's blunt. 這把刀很鈍。 2 telling the truth directly, without trying to be polite or kind 直率的; 直言不諱的: To be quite blunt, I think you've made an awful mess of things. 坦率地說, 我認為你把事情搞得一塌糊塗。–**bluntness** n [U]

blunt² v [T] 1 to make something blunt 使〔某物〕弄鈍 2 to make a feeling weaker 把〔感覺〕減弱: The bad weather has rather blunted their enthusiasm for going camping. 惡劣的天氣使他們去野營的熱情大大減退。

blunt·ly /ˈblʌntli; ˈblʌntli/ adv said in a rough, direct way without trying to be polite or kind 直率地: To put it bluntly, there's no way you're going to pass this exam. 直率地說, 你將沒法通過考試。

blur¹ /blɜ; blɜːʳ/ n [sing] something that you cannot see clearly, or that you cannot remember clearly 模糊不清的東西: The houses appeared as a blur in the mist. 房子在霧中隱隱約約看不清楚。 | My memory of the accident is only a blur. 我對那場事故的記憶已模糊。

blur² v -rr- [T] 1 to make something difficult to see clearly or difficult to see through 使〔某物〕模糊不清: Tears blurred my eyes. 淚水模糊了我的眼睛。 | a very blurred photograph 一張很模糊的照片 2 to make something less clear 使〔某物〕不清晰: The article tries to blur the distinction between race and religion. 那篇文章試圖混淆種族和宗教的區別。

blurt /blɜːt; blɜːt/ v

blurt sth ↔ **out** phr v [T] to say something which you should not say, suddenly and without thinking〔對不應該說的事〕脫口而出: Peter blurted out the news before we could stop him. 我們來不及阻止, 彼得就脫口說出了這個消息。

blush /blʌʃ; blʌʃ/ v [I] to become red in the face, from shame or because people are looking at you〔因害羞或被人注視而〕臉紅: Stop it! You're making me blush! 別這樣! 你弄得我都臉紅了! | He blushed with shame. 他羞紅了臉。–**blush** n: His remarks brought a blush to my cheeks. 他的話讓我紅了臉。

blus·ter /ˈblʌstə; ˈblʌstəʳ/ v [I] to speak

loudly, roughly, and angrily 氣勢洶洶地說; 咆哮 –**bluster** n [U]

blus·ter·y /ˈblʌstri; ˈblʌstəri/ adj rough and windy (used of the weather) 惡劣的〔指天氣〕; 風大的

BO /ˌbi ˈo; ˌbiː ˈəʊ/ n [U] an unpleasant smell coming from a person's body; an abbreviation for **body odour**〖縮〗體臭; 狐臭

bo·a /ˈboə; ˈbəʊə/ n (also 又作 **boa constrictor**) a large South American snake that kills animals by crushing them 蟒蛇

boar /bor; bɔːʳ/ n 1 a male pig that is kept for breeding 公豬; 種豬〔未閹的〕 2 a wild pig 野豬

⋆**board¹** /bord; bɔːd/ n 1 [C] a long thin flat piece of cut wood 木板 2 [C] a flat piece of wood or plastic used for a particular purpose 板; 牌: She pinned the list up on the notice board. 她把名單釘在佈告牌上。 | a chess board 棋盤 3 [C] a group of people who have responsibility for a particular organization or activity 委員會; 理事會; 董事會: the school's board of governors 學校董事會 | the English Tourist Board 英國旅遊局 | a board of examiners 考試委員會 4 [C+sing/pl verb] (also 又作 **board of directors**) a committee of the directors of a company which is responsible for the management of the company〔公司的〕董事會: He's joined the board of Intel. 他加入了英特爾公司的董事會。 | The Board is meeting the union today. 董事會今天和工會會談。 5 [U] the cost of meals 伙食費: I pay £50 a week for board and lodging. 我每星期付五十英鎊的膳宿費。 6 **above board** completely honest and known about by everyone 誠實的; 光明正大的 7 **across the board** for all groups or all the members of a group 全體地; 包括所有人的: a wage increase of 10% across the board 全體加薪百分之十 8 **go by the board** (of a plan) to be no longer possible or practical〔計劃〕落空: We had intended to get a new car, but that's gone by the board now that I've lost my job. 我們本打算買輛新車, 但現在我丟了工作, 這計劃也就落空了。 9 **on board** in or on a ship or public vehicle 在船上; 在公共交通工具上: Get on board! 上船! | I went on board, but felt sick almost immediately. 我上了船, 但幾乎立刻感到想吐。 10 **take something on board** to understand or accept something fully 完全理解[接受]某事物: I don't think he's really taken her objections on board. 我想他並沒有完全接受她的反對意見。

board² v 1 [T] to get onto a ship or into a public vehicle 上〔船或公共交通工具〕: Passengers should board the train now. 乘客現在應該登上列車。 2 [I] (of a plane) to be ready for passengers to get in〔飛機〕讓乘客登機: Flight 387 for New York is now boarding at Gate 15. 飛往紐約的 387 號班機在 15

號閘門等候乘客登機。**3 board with someone** to live in someone's house and receive meals there in return for payment 在某人家寄宿

board·er /'bordə; 'bɔːdər/ n **1** a pupil who lives at his or her school 寄宿生; 住校生 **2** a person who pays to live in another person's house and receive meals there 寄膳宿者: *Mrs Brown takes in boarders, I think.* 我認為布朗太太是招收寄宿的人。

boarding card /'·· ·/ n (also 又作 **boarding pass**) an official card which allows you to get on a plane or ship 登機證; 登船卡

boarding house /'·· ·/ n a private lodging house, not a hotel, that supplies meals 供膳宿的私人住房

boarding school /'·· ·/ n [C;U] a school at which the pupils live 寄宿學校: *My son goes to boarding school.* 我的兒子在寄宿學校上學。

board·room /'bord,rum; 'bɔːdruːm/ n a room in which the directors of a company hold meetings〔公司董事會的〕會議室

board·walk /'bord,wɔk; 'bɔːdwɔːk/ n AmE a footpath made of wooden boards, usually by the sea《美式》〔常在海濱〕用木板鋪成的人行道

boast¹ /bost; bəust/ v **1** [I; +that] to talk too proudly about something that you have got or something that you have done 自我吹噓; 自誇: *She's boasting* **about** *the fact that she's just passed her driving test.* 她在誇耀自己剛通過了駕駛考試。| *He boasted* **of** *his many achievements.* 他誇耀自己有許多成就。| *Don't believe him; he's just boasting.* 別信他; 他只是在自吹自擂。| *They boasted that they'd won every match they'd played this season.* 他們誇口説他們贏得了本賽季的每一場比賽。**2** [T] to have something that is unusual and desirable 擁有〔不尋常或稱心的東西〕: *It's a tiny village but it boasts three shops.* 這是個小村莊, 但居然有三家商店。

boast² n an act of talking too proudly about something that you have got or something that you have done 自誇; 吹噓

boast·ful /'bostfəl; 'bəustfəl/ adj expressing too much pride in yourself or in things that you have done 自誇的; 吹噓的 – **boastfully** adv – **boastfulness** n [U]

boat /bot; bəut/ n **1** a vehicle for travelling across water, usually a small one 小船, 小艇: *a fishing boat* 漁船 | *a sailing boat* 帆船 | *They crossed the river in a boat.* 他們坐小船過河。**2 by boat** in a boat or ship 坐木船或輪船: *We're going by boat.* 我們坐船去。

■ USAGE 用法: A **boat** is usually smaller than a **ship**, or travels shorter distances ☆ **boat** 常比 **ship** 小, 或者航程較短: *a fishing* **boat** 漁船 | *a* **boat** *across the English Channel.* 穿過英吉利

海峽的船。But in ordinary speech we sometimes use **boat** even for a large passenger ship, travelling a long distance ☆但在一般會話中有時也用 **boat** 指航程長的大型客船: *There were over 2000 passengers on the* **boat**/**ship** *going to America.* 這艘開往美國的客輪上有二千多名乘客。

boat·swain /'bosn; 'bəusən/ n see 見 BOSUN

boat train /'· ·/ n a train that takes people to or from a ship〔與船聯運的〕火車

bob¹ /bab; bɒb/ v **-bb- 1** [I] to move quickly and repeatedly up and down on water〔在水面上下〕快速疾動: *The small boat was bobbing up and down on the rough sea.* 小船在洶湧的海面上下顛簸。**2 bob a curtsy** to bend your knees and bend your body forwards as a sign of respect 行屈膝禮或鞠躬禮〔表示尊敬〕

bob² n **1** a woman's hairstyle in which the hair is cut short to the same length all round〔女子的〕短髮式 **2** [plural is **bob**] infml a former British coin, worth 5p〔非正式〕先令〔舊時英國錢幣; 值五便士〕

bob·bin /'babın; 'bɒbˌn/ n a small roller on which thread is wound, for example in a sewing machine 繞線筒

bob·ble /'babl; 'bɒbəl/ n a small woolly ball for decorating clothes, especially woolly hats〔裝飾衣服用, 尤用於毛線帽的〕小羊毛球

bob·by /'babı; 'bɒbi/ n **bobbies** BrE infml a policeman《英, 非正式》警察

bob·sleigh /'bab,sle; 'bɒbsleı/ n a small vehicle that runs on metal blades and is used for sliding down snowy slopes 雪橇

bode¹ /bod; bəud/ v **boded, boding** lit **bode ill** to be a sign of bad things in the future〔文〕主兇; 是不好的兆頭: *Their current unpopularity bodes ill for the Nationalists' chances in the next election.* 他們現在不得人心, 這預示着民族黨在下屆選舉中將有機會落敗。[RELATED PHRASE 相關詞組: **bode well**]

bode² the past tense of BIDE ☆ BIDE 的過去式

bod·ice /'badıs; 'bɒdˌs/ n the part of a woman's dress above the waist 婦女連衣裙的上身

bod·i·ly¹ /'badlı; 'bɒdˌli/ adj [only before a noun 只用於名詞前] relating to your body 人體的; 身體的: *He likes his bodily comforts.* 他喜歡肉體上的享受。

bodily² adv taking hold of someone's whole body〔身體〕整個兒地: *She refused to move, so her mother picked her up bodily and carried her to bed.* 她不肯動, 所以她媽媽把她整個兒地抱起來送到牀上。

bod·y /'badı; 'bɒdi/ n **bodies 1** [C] the physical parts of a person as opposed to their mind or soul; sometimes "body" means all the physical parts of a person, and sometimes just the main, central part, without the arms and legs 身體; 軀體; 軀幹: *Her body was covered from head to toe in painful red spots.* 她身上從頭到腳布滿了令她很痛的紅點。| *They buried the body in an unmarked grave.* 他們把屍體埋在一個沒有標記的墓穴裡。| *He had a wound on his leg and two more on his body.* 他腿上有一處傷，身上還有兩處傷。**2** [C] the main part of something 主體部分: *We sat in the body of the hall.* 我們坐在會場的大廳中。**3** [C] a large amount of something 大量: *a substantial body of opinion that rejects this theory* 拒絕接受這個理論的意見很多 | *We have collected a large body of data.* 我們收集了大量數據。**4** [C; sing/pl verb] a group of people who do something together in a planned way 群體; 團體: *The House of Commons is an elected body.* 下議院是經選舉組成的機構。| *The governing body of the college meet every Thursday.* 學院的行政管理部門每週四開會。**5** [U] good strong taste that wine has 〔酒的〕醇厚, 濃郁: *I like a wine with plenty of body.* 我喜歡味道醇厚的酒。**6** [U] strength and firmness that your hair has 〔頭髮的〕硬挺: *Use a conditioner to give your hair more body.* 用護髮劑可使頭髮更硬挺。**7** [C] *tech* a physical object 〔術語〕物體 **8** -bodied having a certain kind of body 具有…軀體[形體]的: *a wide-bodied plane* 機身寬闊的飛機 | *a full-bodied wine* 醇烈的酒 **9 keep body and soul together** to have enough money and food to live on 勉強維持生活; 餬口 **10 over my dead body** a phrase used to show your determination that something will not happen 除非我死〔用於表示肯定某事不會發生〕: *You'll come into this house over my dead body!* 除非我死, 不然你休想進這幢房子!

body build·ing /'·· ‚··/ *n* [U] doing regular special exercises to make your muscles bigger and stronger 健美運動

bod·y·guard /'bɑdɪ‚gɑrd; 'bɒdigɑːd/ *n* a man or group of men whose duty is to guard an important person 保鏢; 保衛人員

bod·y·work /'bɑdɪwɜ‑k; 'bɒdiwɜːk/ *n* [U] the main outside parts of a motor vehicle, as opposed to the engine and wheels 〔汽車的〕車身

bog /bɑg; bɒg/ *n* [C;U] a large area of soft wet ground into which your feet sink when you try to walk on it 沼澤區; 泥塘 **-boggy** *adj*

bo·gey /'bogɪ; 'bəugi/ *n* (also 又作 **bogy, bo·gie**) **1** (also 又作 **bogey man**) an imaginary evil spirit, often used to frighten children 〔常用來嚇唬兒童的〕鬼怪 **2** a cause of fear, especially an imaginary one 〔尤指想像出來的〕恐懼的根源 **3** a piece of dry MUCUS in your nose 乾了的鼻屎

bog·ged down /‚bɑgəd'daun; ‚bɒgəd'daun/ *adj* unable to move forward or advance 無法移動[進展]的: *The car got bogged down in the mud.* 汽車陷入泥濘之中。| *The talks with the staff are bogged down on the question of working hours.* 和員工的會談在有關工作時間問題上陷入了僵局。

bog·gle /'bɑgl; 'bɒgəl/ *v* **the mind boggles** = something is very surprising or difficult to understand 令人驚訝; 難以理解: *The mind boggles at the idea of underwater football.* 一想到水底足球賽這意念, 就覺得難以想像。

bo·gus /'bogəs; 'bəugəs/ *adj* false, but pretending to be real 假冒的; 偽造的

bo·he·mi·an /bo'himɪən; bəu'hiːmiən/ *n old fash* a person, especially an artist, who lives in a very informal way and does not follow the usual rules of social life 〔老式〕〔尤指藝術家〕放蕩不羈的人 **-bohemian** *adj*

boil¹ /bɔɪl; bɔɪl/ *v* **1** [T] to cause a liquid to reach the temperature at which liquid changes into a gas 煮沸: *Make sure you boil the water for at least five minutes.* 一定要把水煮沸至少五分鐘。| *Shall I boil the kettle?* 要我把水壺裡的水煮沸嗎? **2** [I] (of a liquid) to reach this temperature 〔液體〕沸騰: *Is the milk boiling yet?* 牛奶煮沸了嗎? **3** [T] to cook food in water at 100°C 〔用開水〕煮〔食物〕: *Boil the potatoes for 20 minutes.* 把馬鈴薯煮二十分鐘。| *a boiled egg* 煮好的蛋 **4 boil dry** to boil until there is no liquid left 煮乾: *Don't let the pan boil dry.* 不要把鍋燒乾了。-see 見 COOK¹ (USAGE 用法) **5 make someone's blood boil** to make someone very angry 使某人怒火中燒: *It made my blood boil to see someone treat a child like that.* 看見有人那樣對待孩子, 我怒火中燒。

boil away *phr v* [I] **1** to be reduced to nothing by boiling 煮乾, 燒乾: *The water had all boiled away and the pan was burned.* 水全部燒乾, 平底鍋也燒焦了。**2** to boil continuously 不斷沸騰: *The kettle was boiling away merrily on the stove.* 水壺裡的水在爐灶上吱吱沸滾。

boil down to sthg *phr v* [T] a phrase used when you are stating what something really is or really means 歸結為〔某事物〕; 總而言之: *It's a very complex situation, but basically it boils down to a power struggle between the trade union and the directors.* 形勢很複雜, 但歸根到底是工會和董事之間的權力鬥爭。

boil over *phr v* [I] to boil and flow over the sides of a container 沸溢: *Turn off the gas. The milk is boiling over.* 關上煤氣; 牛奶開得溢出來了。

boil² *n* **1** [sing] an act or state of boiling 煮沸; 沸騰: *Give the clothes a good boil to get them white.* 把這些衣服好好煮一煮, 讓它們白一些。**2 bring something to the boil** to heat liquid until it boils 將某物煮開 **3 on the boil** boiling 沸騰的: *Heat the mixture until it is* *just on the boil.* 把這混合物加熱到正好沸騰。 [RELATED PHRASE 相關詞組: **off the boil**] **4** [C] a painful infected swelling under your skin 癤子

boil·er /'bɔɪlə; 'bɔɪləʳ/ *n* a large container in which water is boiled to provide heat, for example in a house 鍋爐

boiler suit /'·· ,·/ *n* a piece of clothing like a pair of trousers and a shirt made in one piece; boiler suits are worn for doing dirty work 連衫褲工作服

boil·ing /'bɔɪlɪŋ; 'bɔɪlɪŋ/ *adj* **1** very hot 極熱 的: *I'm boiling.* 我熱極了。| *It's boiling in the sun.* 太陽底下熱極了。 **2** boiling hot extremely hot 熱到極點的 **3** **boiling with rage/anger** extremely angry 氣憤至極的: *I was absolutely boiling with rage when I came out of the interview.* 面試出來時, 我簡直氣到了極點。

boiling point /'·· ·/ *n* **1** [C;U] the temperature at which a liquid boils 沸點: *Water has a boiling point of 100°C.* 水的沸點是攝氏一百度。| *Heat the milk until it reaches boiling point.* 把牛奶煮至沸點。 **2** [U] the point at which high excitement or anger breaks into action 極度興奮; 盛怒

bois·ter·ous /'bɔɪstərəs; 'bɔɪstərəs/ *adj* noisy, cheerful, and rough 喧鬧的; 活躍的; 粗魯的: *a group of boisterous children* 一羣喧鬧的孩子 **–boisterously** *adv*

bold /bəʊld; bəʊld/ *adj* **1** brave, confident, and willing to take risks 勇敢的; 自信的; 願冒險的: *The council has announced its bold, new plans for the city centre.* 市議會宣佈了大膽改造市中心的新計劃。 **2** clear and strong (used of the appearance of something) 清晰的; 顯著的〔指某物的外表〕: *the bold shape of the cliffs* 懸崖清晰的輪廓 | *bold colours* 顯眼的顏色 **–boldly** *adv* **–boldness** *n* [U]

bol·lard /'bɒlɑːd; 'bɒləd/ *n* a short thick post used to mark the edge of a road〔標誌馬路邊緣的〕安全柱, 矮椿

bol·shie /'bɒlʃi; 'bɒlʃi/ *adj BrE infml* (also 又作 **bolshy**) bad-tempered, and unwilling to do what people tell you to do〔英, 非正式〕壞脾氣的; 不合作的

bol·ster¹ /'bəʊlstə; 'bəʊlstəʳ/ *v* [T] (also 又作 **bolster** sthg ↔ **up**) to give necessary support and encouragement to something 支持, 鼓勵〔某事物〕: *Let's hope this achievement will bolster her confidence.* 我們希望這項成績能鼓起她的信心。| *The government is introducing measures to bolster up the economy.* 政府正推行促進經濟發展的措施。

bol·ster² *n* a long round PILLOW 長而圓的枕頭; 墊枕

bolt¹ /bəʊlt; bəʊlt/ *n* **1** a metal bar that slides across to fasten a door or window〔門、窗上的〕插銷, 閂 **2** a screw with no point, which fastens into a piece of metal called a NUT to hold things together 螺栓 **3** **bolt of lightning** a flash of lightning 閃電 **4** **make a bolt**

for it to run away suddenly 突然逃跑 **5** **bolt from the blue** a piece of news that is unexpected and very surprising 晴天霹靂

bolt² *v* **1** [I] to run away suddenly, often because you are afraid〔因害怕而〕突然逃跑: *He bolted for the door.* 他向閘口逃去。| *The horse bolted and threw me in the mud.* 馬突然狂奔, 把我摔到泥裡。 **2** [T] (also 又作 **bolt** sthg ↔ **down**) to eat something very quickly 匆匆吞下〔某物〕: *Don't bolt your food!* 別狼吞虎嚥! | *I bolted down a couple of sandwiches.* 我匆匆吞下幾塊三明治。 **3** [T] to fasten something with a bolt 用插銷閂住; 用螺栓拴住: *I bolted the two parts together.* 我把這兩部分用螺絲栓起來。| *She bolted the door.* 她把門閂起來。

bolt³ *adv* **bolt upright** standing or sitting very straight and stiffly 挺直地〔坐或站〕: *He heard the strange noise again, and sat bolt upright in bed.* 他又聽到了那奇怪的響聲, 於是挺直身子坐在牀上。

★bomb¹ /bɒm; bɑm/ *n* **1** a container filled with explosive 炸彈: *A bomb had been planted in the hotel.* 旅館給人放了一枚炸彈。 **2** **the bomb** NUCLEAR bombs in general 原子彈: *How many countries have got the bomb now?* 現在有多少國家擁有原子彈? **3** **go like a bomb** *BrE infml* to go very well〔英, 非正式〕非常有效地(進行): *The party went like a bomb.* 聚會辦得很成功。

bomb² *v* **1** [I;T] to attack a place with bombs, especially by dropping them from aircraft 投炸彈襲擊〔某處〕: *London was very badly bombed during the war.* 戰時倫敦飽受轟炸。| *a bombing raid* 空襲 **2** [I+adv/prep] *infml* to travel very quickly〔非正式〕疾行; 飛馳: *bombing along the motorway* 沿着高速公路飛馳

bom·bard /bɒm'bɑːd; bɑm'bɑːd/ *v* [T] **1** to attack a place heavily with gunfire 砲擊, 砲轟〔某地〕: *The warships bombarded the port.* 戰艦砲轟港口。 **2** to aim or direct a lot of something at someone〔向某人〕提出很多〔事情〕: *The speaker was bombarded with questions.* 演講者受到了連珠砲般的質問。 **–bombardment** *n* [C;U]

bomb·er /'bɒmə; 'bɑməʳ/ *n* **1** an aircraft that carries and drops bombs 轟炸機 **2** a person who puts bombs into buildings and other places 投彈手

bomb·shell /'bɒmʃel; 'bɑmʃel/ *n infml* a piece of unpleasant news that comes unexpectedly and is a great surprise〔非正式〕令人震驚的消息: *The news of the defeat came as an absolute bombshell to us.* 戰敗的消息令我們大為吃驚。

bo·na fi·de /'bəʊnə 'faɪdɪ; ˌbəʊnə 'faɪdi◂/ *adj* real, not just pretending 真正的: *The hotel car park is only for bona fide guests.* 旅館停車場是本旅館的客人專用的。

bo·nan·za /bə'nænzə; bə'nænzə/ *n* something that makes you very rich suddenly and unexpectedly 飛來財源; 致富之源

bond¹ /bɑnd; bɔnd/ n **1** [C] something that joins people together, such as a shared feeling 維繫, 紐帶〔如相通的感情〕: *the bond* **between** *mother and child* 母親和孩子間的感情關係 | *two countries united in the bonds of friendship* 兩國由友誼的紐帶連結起來的國家 **2** [C] an official paper in which a government or an industrial firm promises to pay back with interest money that has been lent 公債; 債券: *National Savings bonds* 國家儲蓄債券 **3** [sing] a state of being stuck together 結合; 黏合: *This new glue makes a firmer bond.* 這種新膠水的黏合力較強。 **4 bonds** [pl] *lit* ropes used for tying up a prisoner 〔文〕鐐銬

bond² v [T] **1** to stick things firmly together 黏合: *Bond the rubber to the wood.* 把橡膠和木頭黏合起來。 **2** to make people feel close and united 使〔人〕聯合起來

bond·age /'bɑndɪdʒ; 'bɔndɪdʒ/ n [U] *lit* the condition of being a slave or a prisoner 〔文〕奴役; 束縛

bone¹ /bon; bəʊn/ n **1** [C;U] the hard parts of your body, which are covered by flesh and skin 骨; 骨骼: *He broke a bone in his leg.* 他腿部骨折。 | *a dog gnawing a bone* 啃著一根骨頭的狗 | *fragments of bone* 骨頭碎片 **2 bone of contention** something that causes argument 爭論的原因; 爭執之所在: *That island has been a bone of contention between our two countries for years.* 那個島多年來一直是我們兩國之間爭執的焦點。 **3 have a bone to pick with someone** to have something to complain about to someone 向某人埋怨某事; 對某人不滿: *I've got a bone to pick with you.* 我對你有意見。 **4 make no bones about doing something** to feel no doubt or shame about doing something 對做某事毫不猶豫〔毫無顧忌〕: *She made no bones about telling me what she thought of me.* 她毫無顧忌地告訴我她對我的看法。

bone² v **boned, boning** [T] to take the bones out of a piece of meat or fish 剔去〔魚或肉〕的骨頭: *Could you bone the meat for me, please?* 請你替我把這塊肉的骨頭去掉好嗎? –**boned** *adj*

bone-dry /ˌ·ˈ·◂/ *adj* completely dry 完全乾的; 乾透的

bone-i·dle /ˌ·ˈ··◂/ *adj* extremely lazy 懶到極點的

bone·less /'bonlɪs; 'bəʊnləs/ *adj* without bones 無骨的

bon·fire /'bɑn,faɪr; 'bɒnfaɪəʳ/ n a large fire built outside, either for pleasure or to burn unwanted things 篝火, 營火, 火堆

bon·go /'bɑngo; 'bɒngəʊ/ n **bongos** or **bongoes** (also 又作 **bongo drum** /'·· ·/) a small drum that you play with your hands 小手鼓

bon·ho·mie /ˌbɑnə'mi; 'bɒnəmi/ n *lit* [U] cheerful and easy friendliness 〔文〕愉快; 親切, 友好

bon·kers /'bɑŋkɚz; 'bɒŋkəz/ *adj* [never before a noun 不能用於名詞前] *BrE infml* mad 〔英式, 非正式〕發瘋的: *You're completely bonkers.* 你完全瘋了。

bon·net /'bɑnɪt; 'bɒnॢt/ n **1** a soft hat that is tied under the chin, usually worn by babies 〔繫於頦下, 常為嬰兒戴的〕軟帽: *a pink, knitted bonnet* 編織的粉紅色軟帽 **2** *BrE* a metal lid over the engine of a car 〔英式〕汽車引擎蓋: *Can you open up the bonnet?* 你能把引擎蓋打開嗎? –see picture on page 209 見 209 頁彩圖

bon·ny /'bɑni; 'bɒni/ *adj* **bonnier, bonniest** pretty and healthy 美麗而健康的: *a bonny baby* 健康可愛的嬰兒

bo·nus /'bonəs; 'bəʊnəs/ n **1** an additional payment made to people who work for a business 額外津貼; 獎金: *The workers got a Christmas bonus.* 工人們得到了一份聖誕節獎金。 **2** a pleasant thing that is in addition to what you expect 額外令人高興的事: *It's a real bonus that my mother lives so near our new house.* 我母親住得離我們的新居這麼近, 真是額外的好。

bon·y /'boni; 'bəʊni/ *adj* **bonier, boniest 1** very thin (used of a person or a part of their body) 很瘦的〔指人或身體的一部分〕: *long, bony fingers* 細長的手指 **2** full of bones (used of fish or meat) 多骨的〔指魚或肉〕

boo¹ /bu; buː/ *interj, n* **boos** a shout of disapproval or strong disagreement 噓聲〔表示不滿或不贊成〕

boo² v **booed, booing** [I;T] to show that you do not like someone, or that you disagree with them, by shouting "Boo!" 噓〔某人〕〔表示不贊成或不喜歡〕; 向〔某人〕喝倒彩: *The crowd booed the speaker.* 人羣向發言者喝倒彩。 | *He was booed off the stage.* 他被噓聲哄下了台。

boob¹ /bub; buːb/ v [I] *infml* to make a foolish mistake 〔非正式〕犯荒唐的錯誤

boob² /bub; buːb/ n **1** a foolish mistake 荒唐的錯誤 **2 boobs** *infml* a woman's breasts 〔非正式〕〔女人的〕胸脯

boo·by prize /'bubi ˌpraɪz; 'buːbi praɪz/ n a prize given as a joke for the worst performance in a competition 末名獎〔用於開玩笑〕

booby trap /'·· ·/ n a hidden bomb 餌雷: *Watch out! There may be a booby trap.* 小心! 可能有餌雷。 –**booby trap** v [T] **-pp-**: *They were afraid that the room might be booby trapped.* 他們害怕房間裡可能埋設了餌雷。

★★book¹ /buk; bʊk/ n **1** a collection of sheets of paper fastened together in a strong paper cover; you use books for reading or for writing in 書; 書籍: *a book about gardening* 關於園藝的書 | *Open your book on page six.* 把書翻到第六頁。 **2 books** [pl] written records of money or names kept by an organization〔記錄賬目、人名等的〕簿冊: *How many names have you on your books?* 你的通訊錄中共有多少個人名? **3** any collection of things fastened together between cardboard or plastic covers 本; 冊; 簿: *a book of stamps* 集郵簿 | *a book of matches* 一包紙板火柴 **4 by the book** according to the rules 依照規則 **5 in someone's bad books** *infml* not liked very much by someone because you have done something which annoyed them〔非正式〕〔因曾惹惱某人而〕很不受某人喜歡 [RELATED PHRASE 相關詞組 **in someone's good books**]

book² *v* **1** [I;T] to arrange in advance to have something 預訂; 預約: *I've booked a table for two.* 我預訂了一張兩個座位的餐桌。| *Be sure to book in advance to make sure of getting a seat.* 一定要事先預訂以確保有座位。**2 be fully booked, be booked up** to have no places free because they have all been booked in advance 預約滿了的: *I'm sorry, we're completely booked up this week.* 對不起,本週的座位已預訂滿了。**3** [T] *infml* enter someone's name officially in police records, with the charge made against them〔非正式〕〔警方〕將〔某人〕記錄在案: *He was booked on a charge of speeding.* 他因超速開車被警方記名。

book in *phr v* **1** [I;T **book** sbdy ↔ **in**] to have a place kept for someone at a hotel 為〔某人〕預訂旅館房間: *I've booked you in at the Grand Hotel.* 我在格蘭飯館為你預訂了一個房間。| *We've all booked in at the same hotel.* 我們大家在同一家旅館預訂了房間。| *I booked into a small hotel in the town centre.* 我在鎮中心預訂好一家小旅館(的房間)。**2** [I] to report your arrival at a hotel desk, airport, etc.〔在旅館、機場等處〕辦理登記手續: *We booked in at 3 o'clock.* 我們在三點鐘辦理了登記手續。

book·a·ble /'bʊkəbl; 'bʊkəbəl/ *adj* able to be booked in advance 可預約的; 可預訂的: *All seats in the theatre are bookable.* 戲院的所有座位都可預訂。

book·case /'bʊk,kes; 'bʊk-keɪs/ *n* a piece of furniture with shelves for putting books on 書架; 書櫥 –see picture on page 730 見 730 頁彩圖

book·ends /'bʊk,ɛndz; 'bʊkendz/ *n* supports to hold up a row of books 書靠; 書擋

book·ing /'bʊkɪŋ; 'bʊkɪŋ/ *n BrE* an arrangement that you make in advance to have something such as a theatre seat or a hotel room kept for you〔英式〕預訂: *All bookings must be made at least three weeks in advance.* 所有預訂都必須提前至少三個星期辦理。

book·keep·ing /'bʊk,kipɪŋ; 'bʊk,ki:pɪŋ/ *n* [U] the activity of keeping the accounts of a business or organization 簿記; 登記賬目 – **bookkeeper** *n*

book·let /'bʊklɪt; 'bʊklɪ̩t/ *n* a small book giving information 小冊子

book·mak·er /'bʊk,mekə; 'bʊk,meɪkəʳ/ *n* (also 又作 **bookie** /'bʊkɪ; 'bʊki/ *infml*〔非正式〕) a person who takes money that people risk on the result of competitions or races, and who pays the winners 賭注登記人

book·mark /'bʊk,mɑrk; 'bʊkmɑ:k/ *n* something put between the pages of a book so that you can find a particular page easily 書籤

book·stall /'bʊk,stɔl; 'bʊkstɔ:l/ *n* a table or small shop open at the front, where books and magazines are sold 書攤; 書亭

book to·ken /'· ·,··/ *n* a card that can be exchanged for books 書券: *He gave me a £5 book token for my birthday.* 他送我一張價值五英鎊的書券作為生日禮物。

book·worm /'bʊk,wɝm; 'bʊkwɜ:m/ *n* a person who is very fond of reading 書呆子; 極愛讀書的人

boom¹ /bum; bu:m/ *v* [I] **1** to make a loud deep hollow sound 發低沉聲, 隆隆作響: *The guns boomed.* 大砲隆隆作響。**2** to grow rapidly in value〔價值〕迅速增長: *Business is booming.* 生意日趨興隆。

boom out *phr v* [I;T **boom** sthg ↔ **out**] to say something in a loud, deep voice 發出低沉聲: *His answer boomed out.* 他以低沉的聲音回答。| *He boomed out his answer.* 他以低沉的聲音説出答案。

boom² *n* a rapid growth or increase in something 迅速增長: *There has been a boom in exports this year.* 今年的出口激增。| *a population boom* 人口激增

boo·mer·ang /'bumə,ræŋ; 'bu:məræŋ/ *n* a curved stick which comes back to you when you throw it into the air, used for hunting by Australian ABORIGINES 回飛鏢〔澳大利亞土著打獵用的曲形木棒, 擲出後飛回原處〕

boon /bun; bu:n/ *n* a thing which is a great help or comfort to people 裨益; 便利: *A car is a real boon when you live in the country.* 在郊外居住, 有輛汽車確實方便。

boor /bʊr; bʊəʳ/ *n* an extremely rude person 極粗魯的人 **–boorish** *adj*

boost¹ /bust; bu:st/ *v* [T] **1** to increase something 增加, 提高〔某物〕: *to boost prices* 提高價格 | *plans to boost production by 30% next year* 明年增產30%的計劃 **2** to improve 增進; 改善: *Let's try to boost his self-confidence.* 讓我們來增強他的自信心吧。

boost² *n* **1** an increase in amount〔數量的〕增加, 提高: *a boost in share prices* 股價的提高 **2** an action that brings help or encouragement 幫助; 鼓勵: *Pay increases would give a great boost to teachers' low morale.* 加薪也許能鼓起教師低沉的士氣。

boost·er /'bustə; 'bu:stəʳ/ *n* **1** a machine which provides additional power or force

起推動作用的機器: *a booster rocket* 助推火箭 **2** a substance that increases the effectiveness of a drug or medicine〔增強藥效的〕輔助藥劑: *Children have the measles injection at 18 months and need a booster at 5 years.* 孩子十八個月時接受預防麻疹的注射，五歲時需要再注射以增強藥力。

***boot¹** /but; buːt/ *n* **1** a shoe that covers your whole foot and ankle 長統靴: *army boots* 陸軍靴 | *wellington boots* 惠靈頓長靴 –see picture on page 210 見 210 頁彩圖 **2** an enclosed space at the back of a car for bags and boxes〔汽車後部的〕行李箱 –see picture on 209 見 209 頁彩圖 **3 get the boot, be given the boot** *infml* to be dismissed from your job〔非正式〕被解雇: *If he keeps behaving so badly, he'll soon get the boot.* 如果他繼續表現得這麼差勁，很快會被解雇的。**4 the boot is on the other foot** *infml* the situation has now changed completely and someone else has power or control〔非正式〕情況完全改變而被其他人掌權; 局勢逆轉 **5 lick someone's boots** *infml* to try to gain someone's favour by being too polite and too obedient〔非正式〕奉承某人; 拍某人馬屁 **6 put the boot in** *BrE infml* to kick someone hard, usually when they are already on the ground〔英, 非正式〕〔常在某人倒地後〕猛踢 **7 to boot** *fml* a phrase used when you are adding something to what you have just said〔正式〕而且; 並且〔用於補充說明〕: *He is dishonest, and a coward to boot.* 他不誠實, 而且懦弱。**8 too big for your boots** *infml* having too high an opinion of yourself〔非正式〕自以為是

boot² *v infml* [T] to kick〔非正式〕踢: *He booted the ball up the field.* 他把球踢到前場。

  boot sbdy ↔ **out** *phr v* [T] *infml* to send someone away rudely and forcefully or dismiss them from a job〔非正式〕攆走, 解雇〔某人〕: *They booted him out for being drunk at work.* 他們把他解雇了, 因為他在工作時間喝酒酒。

boot·ee /buˈtiː; ˈbuːtiː/ *n* a baby's soft woollen boot〔幼兒的〕毛絨鞋

booth /buð; buːð/ **booths** /buðz; buːðz/ *n* **1** a small building put up for a short time where goods are sold or games are played 售貨棚; 攤位 **2** an enclosed place big enough for one person at a time〔可容一人的〕小間; 亭子: *a telephone booth* 電話亭 | *a voting booth*〔選舉的〕投票間

boot·leg /ˈbutleg; ˈbuːtleg/ *v* **-gg-** [I;T] to make, carry, or sell alcoholic drink unlawfully 非法私釀[運賣]酒: *bootlegging smuggled whisky* 非法走私的威士忌酒

boot·y /ˈbuti; ˈbuːti/ *n* [U] valuable goods taken from a place by a victorious army 戰利品

booze¹ /buz; buːz/ *v* **boozed, boozing** [I] *infml* to drink a lot of alcohol〔非正式〕暴飲; 痛飲: *He spends every night boozing with his friends.* 他每晚都和朋友狂飲一番。

booze² *n* [U] *infml* alcoholic drink〔非正式〕酒; 含酒精飲料

booz·er /ˈbuzə; ˈbuːzər/ *n infml*〔非正式〕**1** a person who drinks a lot of alcohol 豪飲者, 酒徒, 酒鬼 **2** *BrE* a PUB〔英式〕酒館

booze-up /ˈ··/ *n BrE infml* a party at which a lot of alcohol is drunk〔英式, 非正式〕狂飲作樂的聚會

***bor·der¹** /ˈbɔːdə; ˈbɔːdər/ *n* **1** the dividing line between two countries 國界; 邊境: *soldiers guarding the border* 守衛邊境的士兵 | *He lives near the Malawi border.* 他住在馬拉維邊境附近。**2** a band of something round the edge of an object for decoration 邊, 飾邊: *a green mat with a white border* 帶白邊的綠色地毯 **3** a thin piece of land with flowers in it, usually round the edge of an area of grass〔常沿草地周圍的〕狹長花壇

bor·der² *v* [T] **1** to be along the edge of something 以〔某物〕為邊界: *fields bordered by woods* 以樹林為界的田野 **2** to have a common border with 交界, 與…接壤: *the area where Finland borders Russia* 芬蘭和俄國交界處

  border on sthg *phr v* [T] to be almost like something 近似〔某物〕: *His remarks bordered on rudeness.* 他的話近乎粗魯。

bor·der·line¹ /ˈbɔːdəˌlaɪn; ˈbɔːdəlaɪn/ *n* the point at which two states or conditions are very close together and very similar to each other 邊界線; 國界線; 分界線: *the borderline between madness and genius* 介乎於瘋狂和天才之間的狀態

borderline² *adj* [only before a noun 只用於名詞前] not belonging clearly to one type or group 不明確屬於某一類的; 含混的: *I'm not sure whether he'll pass the exam — he's very much a borderline case.* 我不能肯定他考試是否會及格──他的情況很難說。

bore¹ /bɔ; bɔːr/ *v* **bored, boring 1** [I;T] to make a deep round hole in something 鑽孔; 挖洞: *This drill can bore through solid rock.* 這台鑽機能鑽透堅固的岩石。| *They bored a well for the villagers.* 他們為村民鑽了一口井。**2** [T] to make someone feel uninterested 使〔人〕厭煩: *Politics bore me nowadays.* 政治如今使我厭煩。**3 her eyes bored into me** = she looked hard at me 她緊盯着我

bore² *n* **1** a person who talks in an uninteresting way〔以無聊的談話〕惹人厭煩的人: *He's such a bore!* 他真討人厭! **2 a bore** *BrE infml* something which is uninteresting and annoying〔英式, 非正式〕令人討厭的事物: *It's a bore having to go to school when the weather's so lovely.* 在這麼好的天氣要去上學, 真討厭。**3** a measurement of the width of a gun barrel or pipe〔槍管或管子的〕口徑, 內徑

bore³ *v* the past tense of BEAR² ☆ BEAR² 的過去式

---

bored /bɔːd; bɔːd/ adj **1** tired and uninterested 厭倦的: *The students all looked bored.* 學生們看上去都不耐煩了。| *She was bored with her job.* 她厭倦了自己的工作。**2 bored to tears** extremely bored 極厭倦的

bore·dom /'bɔːdəm; 'bɔːdəm/ n [U] the feeling of being bored 厭倦: *She didn't try to hide her boredom.* 她不想掩飾自己的厭倦。

bor·ing /'bɔːrɪŋ; 'bɔːrɪŋ/ adj dull and not interesting 乏味的; 厭煩的; 無聊的: *a boring film* 乏味的電影

***born** /bɔːn; bɔːn/ adj **1** [never before a noun 不能用於名詞前] brought into existence at the beginning of your life 出生的; 誕生的: *He was born in 1964.* 他生於 1964 年。**2** [only before a noun 只用於名詞前] able to do something easily and well 天生的: *a born teacher* 天生的教師 **3 born and bred** having grown up from birth in a place 土生土長的: *She was born and bred in Yorkshire.* 她是個土生土長的約克郡人。**4 -born** born in the place mentioned 〔某地〕出生的: *an American-born writer* 美國出生的作家

borne /bɔːn; bɔːn/ **1** the past participle of BEAR² ☆ BEAR² 的過去分詞 **2 -borne** carried as stated 由⋯攜帶〔傳播〕的: *Some plants have windborne seeds.* 有些植物靠風傳播種子。

bo·rough /'bʌrə; 'bʌrə/ n a town, or an area of a large town, with powers of government 享有自治權的市鎮〔區域〕: *the London Borough of Islington* 倫敦伊斯林登自治區

***bor·row** /'bɒrə; 'bɒrəʊ/ v [T] **1** to take something for a certain time, intending to return it 借〔某物〕: *Can I borrow your dictionary for a moment?* 我能借你的詞典用一下嗎? | *I borrowed £5 from my mother.* 我向媽媽借了五英鎊。**2** to take or copy words or ideas 借用〔詞語或觀念〕: *English has borrowed words from many languages.* 英語借用了多種不同語言的詞語。

bos·om /'bʊzəm; 'bʊzəm/ n **1** a woman's breasts 婦女的胸部: *She held the child to her bosom.* 她把孩子抱在懷裡。**2 a bosom friend** a very close friend 知心朋友; 密友

boss¹ /bɒs; bɒs/ n infml an employer 〔非正式〕雇主; 老闆: *I'm my own boss.* 我自己是老闆。| *Where's the boss?* 老闆在哪裡?

***boss²** v [also 又作 **boss** sbdy **about/around**] to tell someone what to do 差遣〔某人〕: *She's always bossing me about.* 她老把我呼來喝去。

boss·y /'bɒsi; 'bɒsi/ adj **bossier, bossiest** enjoying giving orders too much 愛發號施令的; 專橫的: *a bossy school captain* 專橫的校長 **–bossiness** n [U]

bo·sun /'bəʊsn; 'bəʊsən/ n (also 又作 **boatswain**) a chief seaman on a ship 水手長

bot·a·ny /'bɒtəni; 'bɒtəni/ n [U] the scientific study of plants 植物學 **–botanical** /bə-'tænɪkl; bə'tænɪkəl/ adj [only before a noun 只用於名詞前]: *botanical gardens* 植物公園

botch /bɒtʃ; bɒtʃ/ v [T] infml (also 又作 **botch** sthg ↔ **up**) to do a job badly or in an awkward way 〔非正式〕〔笨手笨腳地〕弄糟: *You've really botched that up!* 你把那活兒真弄得一團糟! **–botch** n (also 又作 **botch up**): *I've made a terrible botch of mending the car.* 我把這輛汽車越修越壞。

***both** /bəʊθ; bəʊθ/ predeterminer, det, pron **1** the one as well as the other 兩者; 雙方; 倆: *Both the contestants were given a prize.* 兩個參賽者都得了獎。| *Both of my children are at school now.* 我的兩個孩子目前都在上學。| *Both suggestions are good.* 兩個建議都很好。| *We both enjoy dancing.* 我們倆都喜歡跳舞。| *They were both embarrassed by his praise.* 他們倆都被他稱讚得尷尬了。| *He's had two wives, and divorced them both.* 他有過兩位太太, 又和她們都離了婚。**2 both...and...** not only...but also... 不但⋯而且⋯; 既⋯又⋯: *We visited both New York and Washington.* 我們不但訪問了紐約, 還訪問了華盛頓。| *I felt both excited and apprehensive.* 我既激動又擔心。

***both·er** /'bɒðə; 'bɒðəʳ/ v **1** [T] to annoy or worry someone 打擾, 煩擾〔某人〕: *Does the heat bother you?* 這麼熱你煩不煩? | *I'm busy: don't bother me now.* 我很忙; 現在別打擾我。| *I could tell that something was bothering him.* 我可以說他有些事很傷腦筋。| *It doesn't bother me what you do.* 你所作的沒有打擾我。**2 not bother** not to make the effort to do something 不用操心〔做某事〕: *Don't bother to return it.* 不用還了。| *He never even bothered to say goodbye.* 他連再見都懶得說。| *Don't bother about the washing up.* 碗碟不用洗了。

□ USEFUL PATTERNS 有用句型
not bother to do something; not bother doing something; not bother about something

---

3 I can't be bothered = I am not going to do something because I do not want to make the effort 我不想出力〔懶得〕〔做某事〕: *I can never be bothered to make my bed in the morning.* 早上我總是懶得鋪好牀鋪。

bother² n **1** [U] trouble or inconvenience 麻煩; 不便: *We had a lot of bother finding our way here.* 我們費了很大的勁才找到這裡。| *It was no bother.* 這沒甚麼麻煩。**2 a bother** something or someone that is annoying or difficult 令人煩惱或麻煩的事或人: *I'm sorry to be such a bother.* 對不起, 我這麼麻煩人。

bother³ interj a word used to show annoyance 討厭〔表示煩惱〕: *Bother! I've lost my keys.* 討厭! 我丟了鑰匙。

***bot·tle¹** /'bɒtl; 'bɒtl/ n **1** a glass or plastic container for liquids 〔玻璃或塑料的〕瓶 – see picture on page 244 見 244 頁彩圖 **2** the quantity held by a bottle 一瓶之量: *Add*

---

half a bottle of wine. 加半瓶酒。

bottle² *v* **bottled, bottling** [T] to put something into bottles 將〔某物〕裝入瓶中: *After making the mint jelly, she bottled it in small jars.* 她做完薄荷凍，把它裝進小瓶子裡。

bottle sthg ↔ **up** *phr v* [T] to keep your troubles or worries to yourself, without telling other people about them 壓抑，隱藏〔自己的煩惱〕: *She had bottled up her fears for too long.* 她已把恐懼壓抑得太久了。

bottle bank /'·· ·/ *n* a place where members of the public can leave bottles so that the glass can be used again 玻璃瓶回收處

bot·tle·neck /'bɑtl,nɛk; 'bɒtlnek/ *n* **1** a place where a road becomes narrow and where the traffic must slow down 瓶頸路段; 狹窄路段 **2** something that makes activity slower 阻礙進展的事物: *a serious bottleneck in production* 嚴重妨礙生產流程的環節

*★**bot·tom** /'bɑtəm; 'bɒtəm/ *n* **1** [C] the lowest part of something 底; 底部: *at the bottom of the stairs* 在樓底 | *some tea left at the bottom of your cup* 剩在你杯底的一些茶 **2 the bottom** the ground under the sea, a lake, or a river 海〔湖、河〕底: *They sent the enemy ship to the bottom of the sea.* 他們把敵船擊沉到海底。 **3 the bottom** the least important or powerful part of something 最不重要〔最沒有力量〕的部分: *I'm no good at maths — I'm always at the bottom of the class.* 我數學不好——我的成績在班裡總是排最末。 | *He started life at the bottom but quickly worked his way up.* 他從基層幹起，很快便升了上去。 **4 the bottom** the far end 盡頭; 末端: *I'll walk with you to the bottom of the road.* 我陪你走到這條路盡頭。 | *at the bottom of the garden* 花園盡頭 **5** [C] the part of your body on which you sit 臀部: *He fell on his bottom.* 他跌坐在地上。 **6 at the bottom of something** the cause of something 某事的原因: *Who is at the bottom of all this trouble?* 是誰惹了所有這些麻煩? **7 get to the bottom of something** to find the cause of something 發現某事的原因 **8** [only before another noun 只用於另一名詞前] lowest or last 最低的; 最後的: *the bottom rung of the ladder* 梯子的最低一級 –compare 比較 TOP¹

bot·tom·less /'bɑtəmlɪs; 'bɒtəmlịs/ *adj* **1** very deep 很深的: *a bottomless pit* 很深的坑 **2** having no limit 無限的: *The supply of money seemed bottomless.* 錢似乎取之不盡。

bough /bau; bau/ *n lit* a main branch of a tree 〖文〗大樹枝; 粗樹枝

bought /bɔt; bɔ:t/ past tense and participle of BUY¹ ☆ BUY¹的過去式和過去分詞

boul·der /'boldɚ; 'bəuldə/ *n* a large stone or rock 巨石

boule·vard /'bulə,vard; 'bu:lva:d/ *n* a wide street with trees on each side 林蔭大道

bounce¹ /bauns; bauns/ *v* **bounced, bouncing 1** [I] to spring back or up again after hitting a surface 反跳; 彈起: *The ball bounced several times.* 球反彈了幾次。 **2** [T] to throw something, for example a ball, against a surface so that it bounces 使〔球〕彈起: *bouncing a ball against a wall* 把球擲向牆壁使其彈回 **3** [I + adv/prep] to walk quickly because you are happy 〔因高興而〕飛快地走: *She bounced into the room.* 她蹦蹦跳跳地走進房間裡。 **4** [I] (of a cheque) to be returned by a bank as worthless 〔支票〕遭銀行退票

bounce² *n* [C;U] the act or action of bouncing 跳動; 彈回: *The ball gave a high bounce.* 球高高地彈起來。 | *The ball has plenty of bounce.* 這球彈力很好。

bounc·ing /'baunsɪŋ; 'baunsɪŋ/ *adj* a **bouncing baby** a healthy, active baby 健康活潑的嬰兒

bounc·y /'baunsɪ; 'baunsi/ *adj* **1** full of life and eager for action 富有生氣的; 躍躍欲試的: *She was bouncy and cheerful.* 她精力充沛，興高采烈。 **2** able to bounce well 彈性好的: *a bouncy ball* 彈性強的球

*★**bound¹** /baund; baund/ *adj* **1 bound to** a phrase you use to say that you think someone will certainly do something, or something will certainly happen 一定會〔用於表示相信某人一定會做某事或某事一定會發生〕: *She's bound to pass her driving test.* 她一定會通過駕駛考試的。 | *That tree's bound to fall over next time there's a strong wind.* 下一次再有強風，那棵樹一定會颳倒。 | *In a group as big as this, you're bound to get occasional disagreements.* 你在這麼大的一個集團裡，一定會不時遇到不同的意見。 | *I knew that he was bound to have told her about our plans.* 我知道他肯定已把我們的計劃告訴她了。 **2** [never before a noun 不能用於名詞前] having a legal or moral duty to do something 有法律或道德上的義務的: *The government is bound by its agreement with the unions.* 政府有義務和工會訂定協議。 | *I felt bound to tell you.* 我覺得有義務告訴你。 **3** (of a book) fastened within covers 〔書〕裝訂好的; 有封面的: *a small book bound in leather* 皮裝封面的小書 **4 bound up in something** very busy with something or very interested in something 忙於某事; 對某事極有興趣: *She's very bound up in her work at the moment.* 她現在忙於工作。 **5 bound up with something** closely connected with something 與某事物有密切關係: *His future is closely bound up with that of the company.* 他的前途和公司的前途息息相關。 **6** intending to go in a particular direction or to a particular place 準備到…去的: *She got on a boat bound for Ireland* 她上了一艘開往愛爾蘭的船。

bound² *v* **1** [I+adv/prep] to move with large jumps 跳; 躍: *The animals bounded away.* 動物都跳開了。 **2** [T] to mark the boundaries or edges of a place 以…為界; 毗鄰:

The village was bounded by trees. 這個村子以樹木為界。

bound³ *n* **1** a large jump 一跳; 一躍: *With one bound he was over the wall.* 他縱身一躍, 跳過了牆。**2 bounds** [pl] the limits beyond which it is impossible or undesirable to go 邊界; 界限; 限制: *His suggestions go beyond the bounds of reason and possibility.* 他的建議超出常理, 沒有可能實行。| *His greed for power knows no bounds.* 他的權力欲沒有止境。**3 out of bounds** (of a place) forbidden 〔地方〕不准進入: *The pub was definitely out of bounds to us.* 那家酒館肯定不准我們進去。

bound⁴ the past tense and past participle of BIND ☆ BIND 的過去式和過去分詞

bound·a·ry /'baʊndərɪ; 'baʊndəri/ n boundaries **1** the dividing line between surfaces, spaces, or countries 界線; 邊界: *A river forms the boundary between the two countries.* 河流成了兩國的邊界。**2** the outer limit of something 界限; 範圍: *the boundaries of human knowledge* 人類知識的範圍

bound·less /'baʊndlɪs; 'baʊndləs/ adj without limits 無限的: *He has boundless energy and enthusiasm.* 他有無窮的精力和熱情。

boun·te·ous /'baʊntɪəs; 'baʊntiəs/ adj lit giving or given freely 《文》慷慨; 豐富的: *bounteous gifts* 豐富的禮物

boun·ti·ful /'baʊntəfəl; 'baʊntɪfəl/ adj lit in large quantities 《文》大量的; 充足的: *a bountiful supply* 充足的供應

boun·ty /'baʊntɪ; 'baʊnti/ n lit [U] generosity 《文》慷慨; 大方: *a rich lady famous for her bounty to the poor* 一位以對窮人慷慨大方著稱的有錢女士

bou·quet /bo'ke; bəʊ'keɪ/ n **1** a bunch of flowers given to someone or carried at a formal occasion 〔贈給某人或在正式場合手捧的〕花束: *The bride carried a wonderful bouquet of roses.* 新娘捧着一束美麗的玫瑰。**2** the smell of a wine 〔酒的〕芬芳, 香味: *a rich bouquet* 濃郁的酒香

bour·bon /'burbən; 'bʊəbən/ n [C;U] a type of American WHISKY 〔美國產的〕波旁威士忌酒

bour·geois /,bur'ʒwɑ; 'bʊəʒwɑ:/ adj old fash of or typical of the MIDDLE CLASS 〔老式〕中產階級的

bour·geoi·sie /,burʒwɑ'zi; ,bʊəʒwɑ:'zi:/ n **the bourgeoisie** the MIDDLE CLASS 中產階級

bout /baʊt; baʊt/ n a short period of great activity or illness 一陣, 一場〔激烈活動或疾病〕: *a bout of fever* 一陣發燒

bou·tique /bu'tik; bu:'ti:k/ n a small fashionable shop 賣時裝的小商店; 精品店

bo·vine /'bovaɪn; 'bəʊvaɪn/ adj tech relating to a cow or ox 《術語》牛的: *bovine tuberculosis* 牛結核病

bow¹ /baʊ; baʊ/ v **1** [I;T] to bend your head or the top part of your body forward, often as a sign of respect 低頭; 鞠躬〔以示敬意〕:

Everyone bowed as the Queen walked into the room. 女王走進房間時每個人都鞠躬行禮。| *He bowed his head in shame.* 他羞愧得低下了頭。**2 bow to** to accept or obey something 接受, 服從〔某事物〕: *I bow to your greater experience.* 我佩服你經驗比我豐富。

bow out phr v [I] to stop doing something or leave in order to let someone else take your place 退出〔讓別人接替〕: *He bowed out of the competition to let the younger members take part.* 他退出這次比賽, 讓年輕人參加。

bow² /baʊ; baʊ/ n **1** a bending forward of the upper part of the body, or the head, to show respect 鞠躬; 點頭致意: *He moved aside for her with a polite bow.* 他禮貌地鞠躬, 退避一旁讓她過去。**2 take a bow** to come on stage to receive praise at the end of a performance 鞠躬謝幕 **3** the front part of a ship 船頭; 艦首 –compare 比較 STERN

bow³ /bo; bəʊ/ n **1** a piece of wood held in a curve by a tight string and used for shooting arrows 弓 **2** a long thin piece of wood with a tight string fastened along it, used for playing musical instruments that have strings 〔弦樂器的〕弓 **3** a knot with two circles and two loose ends used for tying up shoes and for decorations 蝴蝶結: *She tied the ribbon in a loose bow.* 她把飾帶打了一個鬆的蝴蝶結。

bowed /baʊd; baʊd/ adj curved or bent 彎曲的: *bowed legs* 弓形腿; 羅圈腿

bow·els /'baʊəlz; 'baʊəlz/ n [pl] **1** tubes from your stomach which carry the waste matter out of your body 腸 **2** the deep inner part of something 內部; 深處: *deep in the bowels of the earth* 在地下深處

bow·er /'baʊə; 'baʊə/ n lit a pleasant, shaded shelter under the trees 《文》樹蔭處

bowl¹ /bol; baʊl/ n **1** [C] a deep uncovered container 碗; 缽; 盆: *a washing-up bowl* 洗碗盆 | *a flower bowl* 花盆 | *a sugar bowl* 糖缽 –see picture on page 244 見 244 頁彩圖 **2** [C] the contents of a bowl 一碗〔一缽, 一盆〕之物: *a bowl of sugar* 一缽糖 **3 bowls** [U] a game in which people roll big wooden balls as near as possible to a smaller ball 滾木球戲

bowl² v [I;T] to throw or roll a ball to a player in a game such as cricket, so that they can hit it 〔在遊戲中, 如板球〕投〔球〕給擊球員

bowl sbdy ↔ **over** phr v [T] **1** to knock someone or something down put-over翻〔某物〕: *Someone ran round the corner and nearly bowled me over.* 一個人從轉角處跑來, 幾乎把我撞倒。**2** to give a pleasant surprise to someone 使〔某人〕驚喜: *Your news has completely bowled me over.* 你的消息真讓我喜出望外。

bow-legged /'bo,lɛgɪd; 'bəʊ,leg'd⁴/ adj having legs which curve outwards at the knee 弓形腿的; 羅圈腿的

bowl·er /'bolə; 'bəʊlə'/ n 1 a person who bowls in a game of cricket 〔板球的〕投球手 2 (also 又作 **bowler hat** /ˌ·· '·/ BrE 〔英式〕) a man's round black hard hat, worn especially by British businessmen 〔英用黑色圓頂的〕常禮帽〔尤為英國商人所戴〕

bowl·ing /'bolɪŋ; 'bəʊlɪŋ/ n a game in which balls are rolled in order to knock down a group of sticks or other objects 滾木球戲 – **bowling** v [U]: tenpin bowling 十柱保齡球戲

bow tie /ˌboʊ'taɪ; ˌbəʊ'taɪ/ n a tie fastened at the front with a knot in the shape of a BOW³ (3) 蝶形領結

*★**box¹** /baks; bɒks/ n 1 a container with stiff sides and often with a lid, usually made of cardboard or wood 箱; 盒: a box **of** matches 一盒火柴 | a shoebox 鞋盒 –see picture on page 244 見 244 頁彩圖 2 the contents of a box 一盒[一箱]的容量: He's eaten a whole box **of** chocolates. 他吃了一整盒巧克力。 3 a small room or enclosed space 小間; 包廂: a box at the theatre 戲院包廂 | the witness box in a law-court 法庭的證人席 | the signal box on a railway line 鐵路的信號亭 | a telephone box 電話亭 4 **the box** BrE infml television 〔英式, 非正式〕電視: They show old films on the box every night. 他們每晚在電視裡放映舊影片。

box² v 1 [T] to put things in a box or boxes 把〔東西〕裝箱〔裝盒〕: The oranges were quickly boxed and sent off. 橘子很快裝箱送了出去。 2 [I;T] to fight someone with your hands 〔用手〕打〔某人〕 –see 見 BOXING (USAGE 用法) 3 **box someone's ears** infml to hit someone on their ears, especially as a punishment 〔非正式〕打某人耳光〔尤指作為懲罰〕

box sbdy/sthg ↔ **in** phr v [T] to enclose in a small space 把…困在狹小的地方: She feels completely boxed in living in that tiny flat. 她住在那套狹小房間裡感到非常局促壓抑。

box·car /'baks,kar; 'bɒkskɑː'/ n AmE a roofed railway carriage that carries goods 〔美式〕〔鐵路上用的〕有蓋貨車車廂

box·er /'baksə; 'bɒksə'/ n a person who boxes, especially professionally 〔尤指職業〕拳擊手: a heavyweight boxer 重量級拳擊手

box·ing /'baksɪŋ; 'bɒksɪŋ/ n [U] the sport of fighting with tightly closed hands 拳擊運動 –see picture on page 957 見 957 頁彩圖

Boxing Day /ˈ·· ·/ n [C;U] a public holiday in England and Wales, on the first day after Christmas that is not a Sunday 節禮日〔英格蘭和威爾士的法定假日, 在聖誕節次日, 遇星期日則順延〕

box num·ber /ˈ· ˌ··/ n a number used as a mailing address, especially in replying to newspaper advertisements 〔報紙廣告中為讀者覆信用的〕信箱號碼

box of·fice /ˈ· ˌ··/ n a place in a theatre, cinema, or concert hall, where tickets are sold 〔戲院、電影院或音樂廳的〕售票處, 票房: I'll wait for you at the box office. 我在售票處等你。

*★**boy¹** /bɔɪ; bɔɪ/ n 1 a young male person 男孩: Our new baby is a boy. 我們新生的嬰兒是個男孩。 | The school is for both girls and boys. 這所學校是男女同校的。 2 a son, especially a young one 兒子〔尤指年幼者〕: My little boy's hurt himself. 我的小兒子把他自己弄傷了。 3 **the boys** infml a man's male friends 〔非正式〕〔男子的〕男性朋友: He's having a night out with the boys. 他和一羣男性朋友晚上出去玩了。

boy² interj AmE infml an expression used to show a strong feeling, like excitement 〔美式, 非正式〕好傢伙; 嘿!〔表示興奮等或強烈感情〕: Boy, what a game! 嘿!真是一場精彩的比賽!

boy·cott /'bɔɪ,kat; 'bɔɪkɒt/ v [T] to refuse to do business with someone or take part in something as a way of showing your disapproval (聯合)抵制; 拒絕參加: They're boycotting the shop because the people who work there aren't allowed to join a union. 他們抵制那家商店, 因為店員沒有獲准加入工會。 | to boycott a meeting 拒絕參加會議 –**boycott** n

boy·friend /'bɔɪ,frend; 'bɔɪfrend/ n a male friend of a girl or woman who she likes very much, and with whom she may sometimes have a sexual relationship 男朋友: This is my boyfriend, Jim. 這是我的男朋友吉姆。

boy·hood /'bɔɪhʊd; 'bɔɪhʊd/ n [C;U] the state or time of being a boy (男子的)童年(時期): a happy boyhood (男孩)幸福的童年

boy·ish /'bɔɪɪʃ; 'bɔɪ-ɪʃ/ adj like a boy 男孩似的, 男孩子氣的: his boyish laughter 他那天真爛漫的笑聲 | her boyish figure 她那男孩般的身材 –**boyishly** adv –**boyishness** n [U]

boy scout /ˌ· '·/ n a SCOUT² (2) 童子軍隊員

BR /ˌbi 'ar; ˌbiː 'ɑː'◂/ an abbreviation for British Rail (the British railway system) 〔縮〕英國鐵路公司〔英國鐵路系統〕

bra /bra; brɑː/ n (also 又作 **brassiere** fml 〔正式〕) a piece of clothing worn by woman under their clothes to support their breasts 乳罩 –see picture on page 210 見 210 頁彩圖

brace¹ /bres; breɪs/ n 1 something used for supporting or strengthening something 支撐物 2 a wire worn inside the mouth, usually by children, to straighten their teeth 〔常為兒童使用的金屬絲〕牙齒矯正器 3 [plural is 複數為 **brace**] a pair of birds or animals 一對, 一雙〔鳥獸〕: three brace of pheasants 三對野雞 4 **braces** [pl] BrE bands, often made of elastic, worn over the shoulders to hold up trousers 〔英式〕(褲子的)吊帶〔常用鬆緊帶做〕 –see picture on page 210 見 210 頁彩圖 –see 見 PAIR (USAGE 用法)

brace² v **braced, bracing** [T] 1 to make

something stronger 加固〔某物〕: *We had to brace the walls when we put the new roof on.* 我們蓋新屋頂時要給牆壁加上支架。**2 brace yourself** to prepare yourself, usually for something unpleasant or difficult 準備迎接(困難); 振作精神: *Brace yourself for a shock!* 準備面對打擊吧!

brace·let /'breslɪt; 'breisl̩t/ *n* a band, usually of metal, that you wear round your wrist or arm for decoration 手鐲; 臂鐲 –see picture on page 210 見 210 頁彩圖

brac·ing /'bresɪŋ; 'breisiŋ/ *adj* fresh and health-giving (used especially of air) 新鮮的, 令人振奮的〔尤指空氣〕: *the bracing sea air* 清新的海風

brack·en /'brækən; 'brækən/ *n* [U] a plant which grows in forests and becomes a rich red-brown in autumn 蕨; 羊齒植物

brack·et¹ /'brækɪt; 'brækl̩t/ *n* **1** a piece of metal or wood fixed to a wall to support something 〔金屬或木製的〕托架, 托座: *The shelf rested on two strong brackets.* 架子擱在兩根牢靠的撐架上。**2** (also 又作 **square bracket**) either of the pair of signs [ ] used around a word or sentence in a piece of writing to enclose information 方括號[]中的一個 **3** (also 又作 **round bracket**) either of the pair of signs ( ) around a word or sentence in a piece of writing 圓括號( )中的一個 **4** a group of people who share a similar income or age 〔收入、年齡等的〕同等級的一類人: *This product is aimed at people in the 16-25 age bracket.* 這種產品是以十六至二十五歲之間的人為目標。

brack·et² *v* [T] **1** to enclose something in brackets 把〔某物〕置於括號內 **2** to consider certain people or things as similar 把〔某種人或物〕歸入同一類: *Don't bracket me and my friends together with those idiots!* 別把我和我的朋友與那些白痴相提並論!

brack·ish /'brækɪʃ; 'brækiʃ/ *adj* not pure (used of water) 不純淨的〔指水〕 –**brackishness** *n* [U]

brag /bræg; bræg/ *v* **-gg-** [I;T] to talk too proudly about yourself, or your possessions 自誇; 吹噓〔財產〕: *Don't brag!* 別吹牛! | *He bragged of having won first prize.* 他自誇說曾獲得一等獎。| *He bragged about his family background.* 他吹噓自己的家庭背景。

braid¹ /bred; breid/ *v* [T] the usual American word for 〔美式〕= PLAIT²

braid² *n* **1** [U] threads of silk or other material twisted to form a narrow decorative border 〔絲線等編成的〕總帶; 鑲邊: *gold braid* 金色總帶 **2** [C] the usual American word for a 〔美式〕= PLAIT¹

braille /brel; breil/ *n* [U] a way of printing with raised round marks which blind people can read by touching 〔盲人用的〕點字, 盲文

＊brain¹ /bren; brein/ *n* **1** the organ of your body in the upper part of your head, which controls thought, feeling, and physical activity 腦: *The brain is extremely delicate.* 腦是非常精細的。| *He suffered brain damage in the accident.* 他的大腦在事故中受到損害。**2** the ability to think clearly and intelligently 腦力; 智能: *a good business brain* 精明的商業頭腦 | *He's nice, but he hasn't got much of a brain.* 他人很好, 但腦子不太靈。| *You were born with a brain — use it!* 你有天資——好好利用吧! **3** *infml* a person with a very good mind 〔非正式〕智力高的人: *Some of the best brains in the country are here tonight.* 全國一些最優秀的人才今晚雲集在這裡。**4 be the brains of something** *infml* to be the person who organizes something, such as a business 〔非正式〕成為某事的組織者〔如企業〕: *Speak to Sheila — she's the real brains behind the outfit.* 說到希拉——她是公司名副其實的幕後策劃者。**5 have something on the brain** to think about something continually, often when you do not want to 〔常指不由自主地〕總是想著某事物: *I've got that stupid tune on the brain.* 那無聊的調子一直在我腦海裡縈繞。| *You're terrible — you've got sex on the brain!* 你真可怕——腦子裡裝的全是男女之事!

brain² *v* [T] *infml* to hit someone on the head very hard 〔非正式〕猛擊〔某人〕的腦部

brain·child /'bren,tʃaɪld; 'breintʃaild/ *n* [sing] *infml* someone's idea or invention, especially if it is successful 〔非正式〕構想; 發明: *This scheme was the brainchild of the town's mayor.* 這方案是鎮長的主意。

brain drain /'· ·/ *n* a movement of large numbers of skilled people from their own country to other countries where they can earn more money 人才外流

brain·less /'brenlɪs; 'breinləs/ *adj* silly and stupid 蠢的; 笨的 –**brainlessly** *adv*

brain·storm /'bren,stɔrm; 'breinstɔːm/ *n* *infml* 〔非正式〕**1** *BrE* a sudden inability to think clearly 〔英式〕腦猝病: *I don't know why I forgot those papers: I must have had a brainstorm.* 我不知道為甚麼忘了那些論文: 我一定是精神錯亂了。**2** the usual American word for 〔美式〕= a BRAINWAVE

brain·storm·ing /'bren,stɔrmɪŋ; 'breinstɔːmiŋ/ *n* [U] a method of finding answers to problems in which all the members of a group think very quickly of as many ideas as they can 獻計獻策; 羣策羣力

brain·wash /'bren,wɑʃ; 'breinwɒʃ/ *v* [T] to make someone change their beliefs by very strong persuasion 對〔某人〕洗腦; 把思想強加於〔某人〕: *Don't let all those advertisements brainwash you into buying that soap.* 別受那些廣告的影響而去買那種肥皂。| *The new regime attempted to brainwash the masses.* 新政府試圖對羣眾進行洗腦。–**brainwashing** *n* [U]

brain·wave /'bren,wev; 'breinweiv/ *n BrE*

B

infml a sudden clever idea 〖英式, 非正式〗靈機; 靈感: *I've just had a brainwave!* 我突然想到了一個妙計!

brain·y /'breɪni; 'breɪni/ *adj* **brainier, brainiest** *infml* clever 〖非正式〗聰明的

braise /brez; breɪz/ *v* **braised, braising** [T] to cook meat or vegetables slowly in liquid in a covered dish 〔用文火〕燉〔肉或蔬菜〕 – see 見 COOK¹ (USAGE 用法)

brake¹ /brek; breɪk/ *n* **1** the part of a vehicle which makes it go slower or stop 車閘, 制動器, 剎車: *Always check the brakes before going on a journey.* 出門以前總要先檢查一下剎車。–see picture on page 209 見 209 頁彩圖 **2 put the brakes on something** to slow down or stop something 使某事減速或停頓: *The government has put the brakes on spending by increasing interest rates.* 政府用提高利率來抑制消費。

brake² *v* **braked, braking** [I] to make something slow or stop by or as if by using a brake 〔用剎車〕使〔某物〕減速或停下: *She braked suddenly to avoid hitting the car in front.* 為了不撞上前面的汽車, 她突然剎車。

bram·ble /'bræmbl; 'bræmbəl/ *n* a common wild bush of the rose family, especially the wild BLACKBERRY 懸鈎子屬植物〔尤指野生黑莓〕

bran /bræn; bræn/ *n* [U] the crushed skin of wheat and other grain, separated from the flour 麥麩; 糠

★**branch¹** /brɑːntʃ; brɑːntʃ/ *n* **1** the part of a tree which grows from the trunk 樹枝: *an overhanging branch* 懸垂的樹枝 **2** a part of something larger which can be separated from it and is usually less important 分支: *a branch railway* 鐵路支線 **3** a division of an organization, group, or subject 分支機構; 部門: *Which branch of medicine are you studying?* 你學的是醫學的哪一個分支? | *Our firm has branches in most major cities.* 我們公司在大多數主要城市有分公司。

branch² *v* [I] to become divided into or form branches 把…分開; 使…分岔: *Turn off where the road branches to the right.* 在那條岔道往右轉。

branch off *phr v* [I] to leave a main road or a planned course of action 〔路〕分岔; 離開既定路線

branch out *phr v* [I] to add to the range of your activities 擴大活動範圍: *The bookshop has decided to branch out into selling tapes and records.* 書店已決定擴大經營範圍, 加售磁帶及唱片。

brand¹ /brænd; brænd/ *n* **1** a class of goods which are the product of a particular firm or producer 商標; 牌子: *What is your favourite brand of soap?* 你最喜歡甚麼牌子的肥皂? **2** a mark made by burning, usually to show ownership 〔標示所有權的〕烙印, 印記: *These cattle have a particularly distinctive brand.* 這些牛都有特別與眾不同的烙印標記。 **3** a

particular quality or way of acting 特性; 獨特的行為方式: *his unique brand of journalism* 他那獨一無二的新聞報道風格 | *a peculiar brand of humour* 獨特的幽默感

brand² *v* [T] **1** to mark something by burning it, usually to show who owns it 〔常為標示所有權〕打上烙印: *Our cattle are branded with the letter B.* 我們的牛都打上了字母 B 的烙印。 **2 brand someone as something** to say that someone has a bad character of a particular kind 加某種〔不好的〕名譽於某人: *The newspapers have branded all football supporters as troublemakers.* 報紙把所有的足球支持者都說成是惹事生非的人。

bran·dish /'brændɪʃ; 'brændɪʃ/ *v* [T] to wave something about in a violent or excited way 〔猛烈地或興奮地〕揮舞: *He stormed into the house brandishing an axe.* 他揮舞着斧頭, 氣沖沖地衝進房子。

brand name /'· ·/ *n* the name given to a product by its maker 商標名稱

brand-new /,· '··◄/ *adj* new and completely unused 嶄新的; 全新的

bran·dy /'brændɪ; 'brændi/ *n* **brandies** [C; U] a strong alcoholic drink made from wine 白蘭地酒

brash /bræʃ; bræʃ/ *adj* too confident often because of lack of experience 〔常因缺乏經驗而〕輕率的, 莽撞的 – **brashly** *adv* – **brashness** *n* [U]

brass /brɑːs; brɑːs/ *n* [U] **1** a very hard bright yellow metal, a mixture of COPPER and ZINC 黃銅: *a brass curtain ring* 銅窗簾環 **2** [+ sing/pl verb] the set of musical instruments made of brass and played by blowing them 銅管樂器: *a brass band* 銅管樂隊 **3 get down to brass tacks** *infml* to come to the really important facts or business 〖非正式〗言歸正傳; 談實際問題

bras·si·ere /brə'zɪr; 'bræziəʳ/ *n* see 見 BRA

brass·y /'bræsɪ; 'brɑːsi/ *adj* **brassier, brassiest 1** like brass in colour 黃銅色的 **2** loud and unpleasant in sound 〔聲音〕響亮刺耳的 **3** *infml* shameless and too self-confident in manner or appearance (used of women to express disapproval) 〖非正式〗厚顏無恥的〔指婦女〕

brat /bræt; bræt/ *n* a badly-behaved child 頑童

bra·va·do /brə'vɑːdo; brə'vɑːdəʊ/ *n* [U] the showing of courage or confidence to make other people think you are brave 虛張聲勢; 逞強的行為

brave¹ /brev; breɪv/ *adj* courageous and ready to suffer danger or pain 勇敢的; 無畏的: *brave soldiers* 勇敢的士兵 | *a brave attempt at a smile* 強作笑容 – **bravely** *adv*: *"I'll try," she said bravely.* "我會試一試", 她勇敢地說。– **bravery** /'brevərɪ; 'breɪvəri/ *n* [U]: *an act of outstanding bravery* 大無畏的舉動

brave² *n* a young North American Indian man 北美印第安青年人

brave³ v **braved, braving** [T] to face danger or difficulties without showing fear 勇敢面對〔危險或困難〕: *She braved her parents' displeasure by marrying him.* 她不顧父母的不快而和他結婚。

bra·vo /'bravo; 'brɑːvəʊ/ interj, n a word used to show your approval when someone, especially a performer, has done well 好!〔用於向演員喝采〕

brawl /brɔl; brɔːl/ n a noisy quarrel or fight, often in a public place〔常指在公共場所〕吵架; 打架 –**brawl** v [I]

brawn /brɔn; brɔːn/ n [U] muscle 肌肉 – **brawny** adj: *his brawny arms* 他那肌肉發達的手臂

bray /bre; breɪ/ v [I] **1** to make the sound that a donkey makes 發出驢叫聲 **2** to make a loud, unpleasant noise 發出刺耳的響聲: *He brayed with laughter.* 他呵呵地大笑起來。 –**bray** n

bra·zen¹ /'brezn; 'breɪzən/ adj without shame 不知羞恥的: *a brazen lie* 恬不知恥的謊言 –**brazenly** adv

brazen² v **brazen it out** to face trouble or blame with confidence and without shame even when you have done something wrong〔即使做錯了事也〕厚着臉皮幹下去

bra·zi·er /'breʒɚ; 'breɪzɪəʳ/ n a metal container for burning coal 火盆; 火鉢

*★**breach** /britʃ; briːtʃ/ n **1** [C;U] an act of breaking or not fulfilling a law, a promise, or a custom〔對法令、承諾、習俗的〕破壞, 違反, 不履行: *Your action is a breach of our agreement.* 你的行為違反了我們的協定。 **2** [C] an opening, especially one made in a wall by attackers 缺口;〔尤指牆上被攻破的〕破洞 **3** a breach of confidence the action of telling people things that you should not tell anyone 泄密 **4** a breach of the peace fighting in a public place 破壞治安〔鬥毆〕 **5** in breach of not fulfilling 違反: *You are clearly in breach of your contract.* 你顯然違反了你的合約。 –**breach** v [T]

*★**bread** /bred; bred/ n [U] **1** a common food made of baked flour 麵包: *a loaf of bread* 一條麵包 | *a slice of bread* 一片麵包 | *bread and cheese* 塗乳酪的麵包 | *brown bread* 黑麵包 –see picture on page 504 見504頁彩圖 **2** food considered as a means of staying alive 食物; 糧食: *our daily bread* 食糧 **3** slang money〔俚〕錢 **4** bread and butter: **a** bread spread with butter 塗黃油的麵包 **b** infml a way of earning money〔非正式〕生計; 謀生之道: *He doesn't just write for fun: it's his bread and butter.* 他寫作不是為了樂趣: 這是他的謀生之道。 **5** know which side your bread is buttered infml to know what will be of most gain to yourself〔非正式〕知道自己的利益所在

bread·crumb /'bred,krʌm; 'bredkrʌm/ n a very small bit of bread 麵包屑

bread·line /'bred,laɪn; 'bredlaɪn/ n on the

breadline extremely poor 十分貧困

breadth /bredθ; bredθ/ n [C;U] **1** the distance from one side of something to the other 寬度; 闊度: *He travelled the length and breadth of the country.* 他走遍全國, 到處遊歷。–compare 比較 LENGTH(1) **2** a wide range 廣度: *His book showed the great breadth of his learning.* 他的書顯示了他學識淵博。

bread·win·ner /'bred,wɪnɚ; 'bred,wɪnəʳ/ n the person who works to earn most of the family's money 掙錢養家的人: *My mother is the breadwinner in our family.* 我母親是掙錢維持一家生活的人。

*★**break**¹ /brek; breɪk/ v **broke** /brok; brəʊk/, **broken** /'brokən; 'brəʊkən/ **1** [I] to separate into pieces suddenly or violently 破裂; 破碎: *I dropped the glass and it broke.* 我把玻璃杯掉在地上打碎了。 | *Suddenly the rope broke.* 繩子突然斷了。 | *A piece of the branch had broken off.* 一根樹枝斷下來了。 | *The box fell and broke open.* 盒子掉下來裂開了。 **2** [T] to cause something to separate into pieces by hitting it or dropping it 打破, 擊破; 折斷: *Be careful you don't break that dish.* 小心別打碎了那個碟子。 | *He fell and broke a bone in his leg.* 他跌倒, 腿骨折了。

■ USAGE 用法: Compare 比較 **break, tear, cut, smash, crack, burst.** You cannot **break** soft things like cloth or paper, but you can **tear** them, which means "pull apart so as to leave rough edges", or **cut** them, which means "divide by using a sharp edge" ☆布或紙等柔軟的東西不能打破或折斷, 所以不能用 **break**; 只能撕〔扯〕破, 用 **tear**; 或以利刃剪斷或割斷, 用 **cut**: *He tore the letter into pieces.* 他把信撕成碎片。 | *I cut the cake with a knife.* 我用刀把蛋糕切開。 Things made of glass or china may **break** (or **be/get broken**) or **smash**, which means "break suddenly into small pieces" ☆玻璃或瓷器製品可以破碎 (**break**), 或被打碎 (**be/get broken**), 或粉碎 (**smash**): *The dish smashed on the floor.* 碟子掉在地板上摔得粉碎。 **Crack** means "break without the parts becoming separated" ☆ **crack** 表示裂開, 但沒成為碎片: *You've cracked the window, but luckily you haven't broken it.* 你把玻璃窗弄裂了, 幸而沒有弄碎。 **Burst** means "break suddenly by pressure from inside" ☆ **burst** 表示由於內部壓力而爆開: *She blew up the paper bag until it burst.* 她向紙袋裡吹氣, 直到紙袋爆開為止。

3 [I] (of a machine) to stop working〔機器〕中斷運行: *We used to have an electric lawn mower, but it broke.* 我們以前有一台電動割

草機, 但它壞了。**4** [T] to cause a machine to stop working 弄壞〔機器〕: *Don't keep switching the kettle on and off like that — you'll break it.* 不要老那樣反覆開關那水壺, 你會把它弄壞的。**5** [T] to fail to keep a law or a promise 不遵守, 違背〔法律或諾言〕: *I'm afraid you're breaking the law.* 我恐怕你違反了法律。| *She had no intention of breaking her promise.* 她無意背約。**6** [T] to destroy someone's ability and determination to continue doing something 摧毀〔繼續做某事的能力和決心〕: *They'll never break her spirit.* 他們永遠不能摧毀她的意志。| *They beat him up and tortured him, and in the end they broke him.* 他們毆打他, 折磨他, 最後弄垮了他。**7** [I] to have a rest from doing something 中止〔休息一下〕: *Let's break for lunch.* 我們停一下吃午飯吧。**8** [T] to cause something to end 使〔某事〕結束: *We need to have talks to try to break the deadlock.* 我們需要進行談判以打破僵局。| *She drinks a lot, but she's trying to break the habit.* 她喝很多酒, 但正盡力戒掉這習慣。| *A loud crash broke the silence.* 一聲爆響打破了寂靜。**9** [I] (of a boy's voice) to become deeper 〔男孩的嗓音〕變得低沉: *He was still young, and his voice had not yet broken.* 他年齡尚小, 嗓音還沒有變。**10 break a journey** to have a rest in the middle of a journey 旅行途中休息 **11 break someone's fall** to stop someone from falling too far or hurting themselves too much 承托住某人〔使某人摔得不遠或不重〕: *Fortunately some of the lower branches broke his fall.* 幸好一些低處的樹枝承托着他, 他摔得並不厲害。**12 break a record** to beat a record by doing something better or faster than anyone else 打破紀錄: *He won the 100 metres and broke the world record.* 他贏得了百米賽跑的金牌並打破了世界紀錄。**13 break a code** to manage to understand a secret way of talking or writing 破譯密碼 **14 break someone's serve** to win a game when someone else is serving in a game of tennis 〔網球〕接(發)球得分: *She has to break her opponent's serve now if she wants to win this match.* 如果她想要贏得這場比賽, 現在就得破對手的發球局。**15 break news to someone** to tell someone something 告訴某人消息: *My father came and broke the bad news to me.* 我爸爸來告訴了我這個壞消息。**16 news breaks** = news becomes known 消息傳開: *I remember I was sitting in the garden when news of war broke.* 我記得戰爭爆發的消息傳來時, 我正坐在花園裡。**17 day breaks** = it begins to get light 天破曉: *Day was just breaking as I got up.* 我起牀時天剛破曉。**18 a storm breaks** = a storm begins 暴風雨來臨 **19 a wave breaks** = a wave comes onto the shore 波浪拍岸: *We sat on the beach watching the waves breaking on the shore.* 我們坐在海灘上看波濤拍岸。**20 break the back of something** to finish the main part or the worst part of a job 完成工作最主要或最艱巨的部分: *I think we've broken the back of the painting now.* 我想我們已完成了油漆工作的最艱巨的部分。**21 break cover** to run out from a hiding place 從隱蔽處跑出來 **22 break even** to end up having gained as much money as you have spent 不盈不虧; 收支平衡: *We reckon the company should break even by next year.* 我們估計公司到明年應該會收支平衡。**23 break free, break loose** to become free from someone or something 〔從某人或某物處〕分離出來: *He managed to break free and escape.* 他設法逃跑了。**24 break new ground** to do something new 開始新的事情; 開闢新天地: *This research is really breaking new ground.* 這項研究確實開闢了一片新天地。**25 break the ice** to make people feel more comfortable with each other at a social event 〔在社交活動中〕使氣氛活躍; 打破沉默: *We need to have a few drinks to help break the ice.* 我們需要喝上幾杯來活躍一下氣氛。

break away *phr v* [I] to move away from someone, or escape from them 離開, 逃離〔某人〕: *Two policemen were holding him, but he managed to break away.* 兩個警察抓着他, 但他設法逃脫了。

break down *phr v* **1** [T **break** sthg ↔ **down**] to make something such as a door fall to the ground by hitting or kicking it 〔把門等〕擊倒, 踢倒在地: *When the police arrived they had to break down the door.* 警察到達時要把門砸開。**2** [I] (of a machine) to stop working 〔機器〕不能運轉: *The car broke down on the motorway.* 汽車在高速公路上抛錨了。**3** [I] to fail 失敗: *The peace talks have broken down.* 和平談判破裂了。| *Finally his resistance broke down.* 他的抵抗最終失敗了。**4** [I] to lose control and start laughing or crying 失去控制〔開始笑或哭起來〕: *He broke down and wept when his mother died.* 他的母親去世了, 他失聲痛哭起來。**5** [T **break** sthg ↔ **down**] to separate something into different parts or change it into a different form 把...分解: *Fats cannot easily be broken down by the body.* 脂肪不易被人體分解。

break in *phr v* **1** [I] to enter a building by force, for example in order to steal something 闖入〔如為偷東西〕: *Somebody had broken in and taken everything of value.* 有人闖進來過, 拿走了所有值錢的東西。–see 見 THIEF (USAGE 用法) **2** [I] to interrupt when someone is speaking 插話: *Sorry to break in on you like this.* 對不起, 這麼打斷了你的話。| *"Don't tell them that," she broke in angrily.* "別把那告訴他們," 她生氣地插嘴說。**3** [T **break** sbdy ↔ **in**] to make someone familiar with a new job or a new situation 使〔某人〕熟悉〔新工作或新情況〕: *There's a lot to learn, but we'll try to break you in gently.* 有很多東西要學, 但我們會盡量

使你慢慢熟悉起來。**4** [T **break** sthg ↔ **in**] to wear something new so that it becomes more comfortable 穿〔新衣物等〕使逐漸合身〔合腳〕: *These shoes are quite new, so I'm still breaking them in.* 這雙鞋子很新, 所以我仍然要把它穿至合腳。

break into sthg *phr v* [T] **1** to enter a building by force 闖入: *Thieves had broken into the house through an upstairs window.* 竊賊從樓上的窗子闖進房子裡。**2** to begin to do something suddenly 突然開始做〔某事〕: *She broke into song.* 她突然唱起歌來。| *We all broke into laughter.* 我們都突然笑起來。| *He broke into a run.* 他突然跑起來。**3** to use a part of something that you had been keeping 使用〔保存的〕一部分: *We had to break into our savings to pay for the repairs.* 我們得動用積蓄來付修理費。

break sbdy **of** sthg *phr v* [T] to cure someone of a bad habit 使〔某人〕戒除〔壞習慣〕: *He still smokes 40 cigarettes a day, but we're trying to break him of the habit.* 他仍然一天抽四十支煙, 但我們在設法使他戒掉這個壞習慣。

break off *phr v* **1** [T **break** sthg ↔ **off**] to remove a part of something by breaking it 折斷〔某物〕: *We broke off a few branches.* 我們折斷了幾根樹枝。**2** [I] to become separated from the main part of something by being broken 斷開: *I dropped the teapot and the handle broke off.* 我把茶壺掉在地上, 壺柄斷了。**3** [T **break** sthg ↔ **off**] to end a relationship or an agreement 中斷〔關係或協議〕: *The government has said that it will not break off diplomatic relations.* 政府說不會中斷外交關係。| *They've broken off their engagement.* 他們解除了婚約。**4** [I] to stop saying or doing something suddenly 突然住口; 突然停止: *She started talking, then broke off when the telephone rang.* 她開始講話, 但電話鈴一響就突然住了口。

break out *phr v* [I] **1** (of something bad) to start suddenly 〔壞事〕突然發生; 爆發: *We're all hoping that war won't break out.* 我們都希望戰爭不會爆發。| *A fire broke out at the factory.* 工廠發生了火災。**2 break out in spots** to become covered in spots suddenly 突然出現斑點: *Her face had broken out in spots.* 她臉上出現了許多斑點。| *He broke out in a rash.* 他長滿了疹子。**3** to escape from a prison 越獄逃跑: *Three prisoners broke out of a top security prison last night.* 三個犯人昨晚從看守最嚴密的監獄裡越獄逃走了。

break through *phr v* **1** [T **break through** sthg] to force your way through something 突破; 突圍: *Some members of the crowd managed to break through the police barrier.* 人羣中有些人設法衝破了警方的屏障。**2** [I] to suddenly become seen 突然出現: *The day started off cloudy, but later the sun broke through.* 天一開始陰陰的, 但後來太陽鑽了出來。

break up *phr v* **1** [I;T **break** sthg ↔ **up**] to break or separate into smaller pieces 打碎; 碎開: *The car was broken up for scrap.* 汽車被撞得粉碎, 成了廢物。| *Police were called in to break up the crowd.* 警察被召來驅散人羣。| *The ice started to break up when the warm weather came.* 天氣轉暖, 冰層開始破裂。**2** [I;T **break** sthg ↔ **up**] to end 結束: *The meeting broke up after only half an hour.* 會議只開了半小時就結束了。| *Demonstrators managed to get in and break up the council meeting.* 示威者進去中止了議會會議。**3** [I] to end a marriage or other relationship 〔夫妻〕離異; 〔關係〕破裂: *Their marriage broke up after two years.* 他們的婚姻兩年後破裂了。| *The relationship wasn't working, so we decided to break up.* 這種關係無法繼續下去, 所以我們決定分手。**4** [I] to stop going to school or college because the holidays are starting 終始放假: *When do we break up?* 我們甚麼時候放假? | *We broke up last Friday.* 我們上週五放假。

break with sbdy/sthg *phr v* [T] to end a friendship, relationship, or connection with someone 結束, 斷絕〔友誼、關係或聯繫〕: *He broke with the Labour Party and stood for parliament as an independent.* 他脫離了工黨, 以無黨派人士的身分競選議員。| *breaking with the old traditions* 與舊傳統決裂

★break² *n* **1** a hole or opening in something where it has broken or split 破裂處; 裂縫: *There was a break in the cable.* 電纜上有條裂縫。**2** a short pause when you rest from an activity 休息; 間歇: *I think it's time for a coffee break.* 我想是時候喝杯咖啡休息一下了。| *We worked for four hours without a break.* 我們連續不斷地工作了四小時沒休息。**3** an act of ending a friendship, relationship, or connection with someone or something 〔友誼、關係、關係的〕斷絕: *After her break with the Conservative Party, she joined the Social Democrats.* 她和保守黨脫離關係後, 加入了社會民主黨。| *a break with the past* 摒棄過去 **4 break of day** the time of day when it first starts to get light 破曉時分 **5** a lucky chance to do something 機遇; 好運: *This job could give me the break I've been waiting for.* 這份工作也許可以為我提供一個我一直在等待的機遇。

break·age /'breɪkɪdʒ; 'breɪkɪdʒ/ *n* **1** [C] the action of breaking something 損害; 破損: *All breakages must be paid for.* 所有的破損都必須得到賠償。**2** [U] *fml* the act of breaking something 〔正式〕損害; 破壞: *The vase is insured against accidental breakage.* 這花瓶保了意外損害險。

break·a·way /'breɪkəˌweɪ; 'breɪkəˌweɪ/ *adj* [only before a noun 只用於名詞前] separate from a larger group 脫離〔組織〕的: *a break-*

B

away faction within the political party 從那個政黨中脫離出去的派別

break·down /'brɛk,daʊn; 'breɪkdaʊn/ *n* **1** a failure in the operation of a machine or system〔機器或體系的〕故障，損壞: *The trip took longer than we expected because our car had a breakdown.* 我們的汽車出了故障，所以比原來預計的多走了一些時間。| *a breakdown of law and order* 法規和秩序的破壞 **2** a failure in agreement or understanding〔協議、默契的〕破裂; 失敗: *a breakdown in the talks* 會談破裂 **3** (also 又作 **nervous breakdown**) a medical condition of being unable to manage because of anxiety or worry〔因焦慮、擔心而〕衰弱 **4** a detailed description of something so that you can understand it better 詳細解釋: *I'd like a breakdown of these figures, please.* 請給我這些數字分成細目。

break·er /'breɪkə; 'breɪkər/ *n* a large wave that rolls onto the shore〔沖擊岸邊的〕大浪

★**break·fast** /'brɛkfəst; 'brɛkfəst/ *n* [C;U] the first meal of the day 早餐: *He has breakfast at seven o'clock.* 他七點鐘吃早餐。| *She ate a hearty breakfast.* 她吃了一頓豐盛的早餐。| *She likes eggs for breakfast.* 她早餐喜歡吃雞蛋。 –**breakfast** *v* [I]: *We breakfasted on orange juice and eggs.* 我們早餐喝橙汁和吃雞蛋。

break-in /'· ·/ *n* the illegal entering of a building using force 非法闖入: *£7000 was stolen in the break-in.* 在非法闖入(事件)中，七千英鎊被偷走了。

break·neck /'brɛk,nɛk; 'breɪknek/ *adj* **at breakneck speed** extremely fast and usually dangerously 高速而危險的

break·through /'brɛk,θru; 'breɪkθruː/ *n* an important discovery or advance, often made suddenly and after earlier failures〔常指經過失敗後作出的〕重大發現，突破: *Scientists have made a major breakthrough in their treatment of the disease.* 科學家在治療那種疾病方面取得了重要的突破。| *a scientific breakthrough* 科學上的突破

break·up /'brɛk,ʌp; 'breɪkʌp/ *n* **1** the coming to an end of a relationship or an organization〔關係或組織的〕終止，破裂: *the breakup of a marriage* 婚姻的破裂 | *the breakup of the alliance* 聯盟的瓦解 **2** a division into smaller parts 分裂; 分解: *the breakup of the large farms* 大農場的分解

break·wa·ter /'brɛk,wɔtə; 'breɪk,wɔːtər/ *n* a thick wall built out into the sea to lessen the force of the waves near a harbour 防波堤

breast /brɛst; brest/ *n* **1 breasts** the two parts of a woman's body that produce milk〔婦女的〕乳房 **2** the upper front part of the body between the neck and the stomach 胸部，胸脯: *a bird with an orange breast* 橘黃色胸脯的鳥 **3** the part of your body where your feelings are supposed to come from

心情; 內心: *He felt a surge of pride in his breast.* 他心中覺得有一份自豪感。 **4 make a clean breast of something** to admit the truth about something bad you have done 坦白說出事實〔指壞事〕

breast·stroke /'brɛst-,strok; 'brest-strəʊk/ *n* [U] a way of swimming on your front, pulling your arms back from your head and kicking your legs outwards 蛙泳

★**breath** /brɛθ; breθ/ *n* **1** [U] air taken into and breathed out of your lungs 呼吸，氣息: *He gabbled out his story, scarcely pausing for breath.* 他急促又含糊地說了他的故事，幾乎連氣都沒喘一口。 **2** [C] a single act of breathing air in and out〔一次〕呼吸，一口氣: *Take a deep breath and start again from the beginning.* 深深地吸一口氣，再從頭開始。 **3** a **breath of fresh air** a little clean, pure air〔文〕清淨的空氣: *Let's step outside a moment for a breath of fresh air.* 我們出去走一會兒，吸一口新鮮空氣吧。 **4 out of breath** having difficulty in breathing easily, for example after running〔如跑完以後〕氣喘吁吁; 上氣不接下氣 **5 get your breath back** to be able to breathe easily again 喘過氣來; 恢復正常呼吸: *Hang on a minute — let me get my breath back!* 稍等一下 — 讓我緩過氣來! **6 hold your breath** to stop breathing deliberately 屏息: *She can hold her breath for over a minute.* 她能屏住氣超過一分鐘。 **7 take someone's breath away** to surprise or shock someone very much 使某人十分驚訝〔震驚〕: *The way he spoke to his boss fairly took my breath away.* 他跟老闆說話的方式讓我驚訝極了。 **8 under your breath** in a low voice or whisper 低聲; 耳語

breath·a·lyze /'brɛθə,laɪz; 'breθəl-aɪz/ *v* **breathalyzed, breathalyzing** (also 又作 **breathalyse**) [T] (of the police) to measure the amount of alcohol that the driver of a car has drunk with a special apparatus called a **breathalyzer**〔警方對駕駛者〕作呼氣測醉檢驗

★**breathe** /brið; briːð/ *v* **breathed, breathing** **1** [I;T] to take air into your lungs and let it out again 呼吸: *Get off! I can't breathe.* 下來! 我沒法呼吸了。| *He was breathing very heavily.* 他氣喘吁吁。| *Don't breathe those fumes!* 別吸入那些難聞的氣味! **2 breathe something over someone** to send something out of your mouth towards someone 向某人噴(氣): *Don't stand so close; you're breathing garlic all over me.* 別站得這麼近，你嘴裡的大蒜味道都呼到我這裡來了。 **3** [T] to say something softly 輕聲說: *"Shh," he breathed.* "噓," 他輕聲說。 **4 not breathe a word of something** to say nothing about something 不將某事告訴〔某人〕: *Don't breathe a word of this to anyone!* 不要將這件事告訴任何人! **5 breathe again, breathe more easily, breathe a sigh of relief** to feel calm again after feeling anxious〔不安之後〕

鬆一口氣 **6 breathe new life into something** to make something become more exciting or full of life 使某事物變得更富有活力，給某事物注入新生命 **7 breathe down someone's neck** to watch someone extremely closely 密切監視某人 **–breathing** *n* [U]: *machines monitoring her breathing* 監測她呼吸的儀器

breathe in *phr v* [I;T **breathe** sth ↔ **in**] to take air into your lungs 吸氣: *Breathe in slowly.* 慢慢吸氣。| *They breathed in the scent of the roses.* 他們吸進了玫瑰的香味。

breathe out *phr v* [I;T **breathe** sth ↔ **out**] to let air or gas out of your lungs 呼氣: *"Hold your breath," said the doctor. "Now breathe out."* "屏住氣," 醫生説, "現在呼氣。"

breath·er /'briðə; 'briːðəʳ/ *n infml* a short pause for a rest 〔非正式〕短暫的休息

breathing space /'·· ·/ *n* [sing; U] a short period when you are free from work or worry 休息的機會; 喘息的時間

breath·less /'breθlɪs; 'breθləs/ *adj* **1** breathing heavily or with difficulty 氣喘吁吁的; 呼吸困難的 **2** causing you to stop breathing because of being excited or afraid 〔因激動或害怕而〕令人屏息的: *a breathless pause* 令人屏息的停頓 **–breathlessly** *adv*

breath·tak·ing /'breθˌteɪkɪŋ; 'breθˌteɪkɪŋ/ *adj* very exciting or shocking 激動人心的; 令人震驚的 **–breathtakingly** *adv*: *breathtakingly beautiful* 美得令人驚嘆

bred /bred; bred/ the past tense and past participle of BREED ☆ BREED 的過去式和過去分詞

breech·es /'brɪtʃəz; 'brɪtʃɪz/ *n* (**britches** *AmE* 〔美式〕) [pl] trousers which go to your knees 長及膝部的褲子; 馬褲

breed¹ /briːd; briːd/ *v* **bred** /bred; bred/, **bred, breeding 1** [I] (of animals) to produce young 〔動物〕生育; 繁殖: *They won't breed if you keep them in a cage.* 如果你把牠們養在籠裡, 牠們便不會繁殖。 **2** [T] to keep animals or plants for the purpose of producing young animals or developing new plants 〔為育種而〕飼養, 培育: *He's bred a new variety of rose.* 他栽培了新品種的玫瑰。| *The winning horse was bred in Ireland.* 那匹獲勝的馬是在愛爾蘭飼養的。 **3** [T] to cause a condition or feeling to develop 滋生; 產生; 引起: *Flies and dirt breed disease.* 蒼蠅和污物會引起疾病。| *Don't hit them back; violence breeds violence.* 別對他們作出反擊; 暴力只會招致暴力。

breed² *n* [+sing/pl verb] **1** a particular class of animal or plant 〔牲畜或植物的〕品種 **2** a particular kind of person or object 〔人或物體的〕種類: *the first of a new breed* **of** *lasers* 第一本新類型激光

breed·er /'briːdə; 'briːdəʳ/ *n* a person who breeds animals or plants 飼養員; 栽培者

breed·ing /'briːdɪŋ; 'briːdɪŋ/ *n* [U] **1** the producing of young of animals or plants 〔動物

的〕繁殖; 〔植物的〕生殖 **2** the business of keeping animals or plants in order to obtain new and better kinds, or young for sale 〔動物的〕飼養; 〔植物的〕培植: *good breeding stock* 良種種畜 **3** training in good manners, often thought to be related to high social position 教養: *a person of excellent breeding* 教養優秀的人

breeding ground /'·· ·/ *n* **1** a place where animals go to produce their young 〔動物的〕繁殖地 **2** a place where something can develop easily 〔某物的〕滋生地, 溫牀: *These village wells are the breeding ground* **of** *disease.* 村裡的這些井是疾病之源。

breeze¹ /briːz; briːz/ *n* a light gentle wind 微風; 和風: *A cool breeze was blowing.* 涼爽的微風在吹拂着。 **–see** 見 WIND¹ (USAGE 用法)

breeze² *v* **breezed, breezing** [I +adv/prep] to go quickly and in a carelessly confident way 飄然出現, 漫不經心地行動: *He just breezed in and sat down, without even apologizing!* 他飄飄然地走進來坐下, 連道歉都不說一聲!

breez·y /'briːzɪ; 'briːzi/ *adj* **1** having fairly strong but gentle winds blowing 有微風的: *a fine breezy morning* 微風吹拂的美好的早晨 **2** cheerful and carelessly confident 歡快的; 怡然的: *a breezy manner* 輕鬆愉快的態度

breth·ren /'breðrən; 'breðrən/ *n* [pl] a word used when you are talking to people in church, or talking about the members of a religious group 教友們; 諸兄弟〔用於在教堂稱呼教友, 或提到宗教團體的成員時〕

brev·i·ty /'brevətɪ; 'brevⱪti/ *n* [U] **1** shortness in time 短暫: *the brevity of the meeting* 簡短的會議 **2** the quality of expressing things in very few words 簡潔: *the wonderful brevity of her writing style* 她格外簡潔的寫作風格

brew /bruː; bruː/ *v* **1** [I;T] to make beer 釀造 (啤酒) **2** [T] to mix something with hot water to prepare a drink 沖 (飲料) **3** [I] to become ready for drinking after being mixed with hot water and left for a few minutes (used of tea) 沖好〔指茶〕: *We let the tea brew for five minutes.* 我們讓茶沖泡五分鐘。 **4 be brewing** (of something bad) to be starting to develop 〔壞事〕在醞釀中: *Trouble's brewing.* 麻煩快來了。| *A storm was brewing.* 暴風雨即將來臨。 **–brew** *n*: *a strong brew of beer* 醇烈的啤酒

brew·er /'bruːə; 'bruːəʳ/ *n* a person or company that produces beer 啤酒釀造者; 啤酒公司

brew·er·y /'bruːərɪ; 'bruːəri/ **breweries** *n* a place where beer is made 啤酒廠

bri·ar /'braɪə; 'braɪəʳ/ *n* [C;U] see 見 BRIER

bribe¹ /braɪb; braɪb/ *v* **bribed, bribing** [T] to persuade or influence someone in a position of power by giving them gifts or favours 向〔有權者〕行賄; 收買: *He bribed the*

B

police officer. 他賄賂警官。| *I bribed her into giving me the documents.* 我賄賂她，讓她給我提供文件。

bribe² *n* something offered or given when bribing someone 行賄物: *The official was accused of taking bribes from local businessmen.* 那位官員被指控接受了當地商人的賄賂。

brib·er·y /'braɪbəri/ *n* [U] the giving or taking of bribes 行賄; 受賄: *He was charged with bribery.* 他被控受賄〔行賄〕。

bric-a-brac /'brɪkə,bræk; 'brɪkə,bræk/ *n* [U] small objects of various kinds, for decoration in a house 小擺設; 小飾物

*★**brick¹** /'brɪk; brɪk/ *n* **1** [C;U] a hard piece of baked clay used for building 磚; 磚塊: *They used yellow bricks to build the house.* 他們用黃磚造了這座房子。| *The house is made of brick.* 這房子是用磚造的。**2** [C] something in the shape of a brick 磚狀物: *a brick **of** ice cream* 一塊冰(淇淋)磚

brick² *v*

brick sth ↔ **up** *phr v* [T] to fill something completely with bricks 用磚堵住〔某物〕: *They've bricked up the windows in the old house.* 他們用磚把這幢舊房子裡的窗堵住了。

brick·lay·er /'brɪk,leə; 'brɪk,leɪər/ *n* a workman who builds walls with bricks 砌磚工人; 泥水匠 **–bricklaying** *n* [U]

bride /braɪd; braɪd/ *n* a girl or woman who is about to be married, or is just married 新娘: *The bride wore a beautiful white dress.* 新娘穿了一件美麗的白色連衣裙。

bride·groom /'braɪd,grum; 'braɪdgru:m/ *n* (also 又作 **groom**) a man who is about to be married, or just married 新郎

brides·maid /'braɪdz,med; 'braɪdzmeɪd/ *n* an unmarried girl or woman, usually one of several, who helps the bride on the day of the marriage ceremony 女儐相; 伴娘 –compare 比較 BEST MAN

*★**bridge¹** /brɪdʒ; brɪdʒ/ *n* **1** [C] something built to take a road or railway over a river, road, or railway 橋; 橋梁: *We crossed the river there because it was the only bridge for miles.* 因為那是方圓幾里內唯一的一座橋，所以我們在那兒渡河。| *a railway bridge* 鐵路橋 | *a bridge **over** the Thames* 泰晤士河上的一座橋 **2** the bridge the part of a ship on which the captain and other officers stand when they are controlling it 〔船上的〕駕駛台; 艦橋 **3** [U] a card game for four players 橋牌 **4 the bridge of the nose** the bony upper part of your nose, between your eyes 鼻梁

bridge² *v* **bridged, bridging** [T] **1** to build a bridge across something 在〔某物〕上架橋: *to bridge a river* 在河上架橋 **2 bridge the gap** to reduce the difference between two things 減少分歧: *an attempt to bridge the gap between different cultures* 試圖減少不同文化之間的分歧

bri·dle¹ /'braɪdl; 'braɪdl/ *n* leather bands put on a horse's head to control its movements 馬籠頭; 馬勒

bridle² *v* **bridled, bridling 1** [T] to put a bridle on a horse 給〔馬〕套上籠頭 **2** [I] to show anger or displeasure, especially by making a proud upward movement of your head and body 昂首挺胸〔表示憤怒或不悅〕: *He bridled **at** my request.* 他頭一揚，對我提出的要求嗤之以鼻。

*★**brief¹** /brif; bri:f/ *adj* **1** not lasting for very long 短暫的: *I'll just have a brief look at the newspaper.* 我正要瀏覽一下報紙。**2** using only a few words and not describing or talking about things in detail 簡短的; 簡潔的: *a brief letter* 一封簡短的信 | *I'll try to be brief.* 我將盡量簡短一些。**3 in brief** using only a few words and giving only general points rather than details 簡單地說; 簡而言之: *Here is the news in brief.* 這是新聞摘要。| *In brief, he says "no".* 他簡短地說了一個 "不" 字。**–briefly** *adv*: *She spoke briefly.* 她簡短地發了言。

brief² *n* **1** a set of instructions about someone's duties or jobs 〔職責或工作的〕訓令; 指示: *His brief was to improve the company's sales figures.* 他的指示是要增加公司的銷售額。**2 briefs** [pl] men's UNDERPANTS or women's KNICKERS 男子三角褲; 女子內褲

brief³ [T] to give instructions or necessary information to someone 給〔某人〕指示; 為〔某人〕提供資訊: *The officer briefed his men **on** what tactics to use.* 指揮官指示士兵採取何種策略。**–briefing** *n* [C;U]: *Before the meeting, let me give you a briefing.* 開會以前，我先給你簡單說一下情況。

brief·case /'brif,kes; 'bri:fkeɪs/ *n* a flat case for carrying papers or books 〔扁平的〕公文包; 公事包

bri·er /'braɪə; 'braɪər/ *n* (also 又作 **briar**) [C;U] a wild bush covered with prickles, especially the wild rose bush 荊棘〔尤指野薔薇〕

bri·gade /brɪ'ged; brɪ'geɪd/ *n* [+sing/pl verb] **1** a part of an army, of about 5000 soldiers 旅〔約五千名士兵〕**2 the Fire Brigade** the organization responsible for putting out fires 消防隊

brig·a·dier /,brɪgə'dɪr; ,brɪgə'dɪər/ *n* an army officer of high rank 〔陸軍的〕准將, 旅長

*★**bright** /braɪt; braɪt/ *adj* **1** full of light or shining strongly 明亮的; 閃光的: *What a bright sunny day!* 好一個艷陽天! | *a bright light* 明亮的燈光 **2** cheerful 歡快的: *You look very bright and cheerful this morning.* 今天早晨你看上去容光煥發，興高采烈的。| *bright eyes* 流露喜悅的眼神 **3** strong, clear, and easily seen (used to describe a colour) 鮮艷的〔形容色彩〕; 清晰的: *bright blue* 寶藍色 **4** quick at learning things 聰明的: *a very bright child* 很聰明的孩子 **5 a bright idea** a clever idea 好主意 **6** showing hope or signs

of success 有希望的; 前途光明的: *You have a bright future ahead of you.* 你的前途光明遠大。–**brightly** *adv* –**brightness** *n* [U]

bright·en /ˈbraɪtn; ˈbraɪtn/ *v* [I;T] to make or become brighter (使)發亮; (使)快活; (使)有希望 (also 又作 **brighten up; brighten sthg ↔ up**): *The weather is brightening.* 天逐漸放晴。| *She brightened up when she heard the good news.* 她一聽到那個好消息就高興起來。| *A few flowers should brighten up the room.* 放點鮮花能使房間變得明朗。

*★**bril·liant** /ˈbrɪljənt; ˈbrɪljənt/ *adj* **1** very bright or splendid in appearance 光輝的; 燦爛的: *a brilliant blue sky* 碧藍的天空 | *brilliant light* 燦爛的燈光 **2** very clever 很聰明的: *a brilliant student* 非常聰明的學生 | *a brilliant idea* 絕妙的主意 –**brilliance** *n* [U] –**brilliantly** *adv*

brim¹ /brɪm; brɪm/ *n* **1** the top edge of a container 〔容器的〕邊, 緣: *The glass was full to the brim.* 玻璃杯裡的液體滿得快要溢出來了。**2** the bottom part of a hat which turns outwards to give shade, or protection against rain 帽檐 **3** -**brimmed** having a brim (used of hats) 有...邊的〔指帽子〕: *a wide-brimmed hat* 闊邊帽

brim² *v* -**mm**- [I] to be very full 注滿; 充盈: *a brimming cup of coffee* 滿滿的一杯咖啡 | *His eyes brimmed with tears.* 他熱淚盈眶。

brim over *phr v* **1** [I] to be very full of a liquid, so that the liquid comes out 充溢; 充滿 **2** be **brimming over with** to be full of a pleasant feeling, and show it in the way that you behave 洋溢着〔歡樂的情感〕: *He was brimming over with joy.* 他滿懷喜悅。

brim·ful /ˈbrɪmˈful; ˈbrɪmˌful/ *adj* [never before a noun 不能用於名詞前] full to the top or overflowing 滿到邊的; 充盈

brine /braɪn; braɪn/ *n* [U] water containing salt, used for preserving food 〔醃食物用的〕鹽水

*★★**bring** /brɪŋ; brɪŋ/ *v* **brought** /brɔt; brɔːt/, **brought 1** [T] to carry something to or towards a place 帶來, 拿來〔某物〕: *Bring your books with you when you come.* 你來時把書帶來。| *I've brought a present for you.* 我給你帶來了一份禮物。| *She brought me some flowers.* 她帶給我一些鮮花。| *Can I bring a friend to the party?* 我能帶朋友來參加聚會嗎?

> □ USEFUL PATTERNS 有用句型
> to bring something; to bring something for someone; to bring someone something

2 [T+adv/prep] to move something somewhere 把〔某物〕移至〔某處〕: *He brought his hand down onto the table.* 他把手放下來擱到桌上。**3** [T] to cause something to happen or start 導致; 使發生; 使開始: *Money doesn't necessarily bring happiness.* 金錢並不一定帶

來幸福。| *The scene brought tears to my eyes.* 那場面使我流淚。**4** [T+adv/prep] to cause or persuade someone to come to a place 使〔某人〕來到; 說服〔某人〕來到: *The noise brought several people out of their houses to see what was going on.* 吵鬧聲使得好幾個人跑出門來看出了甚麼事。| *The fair brings a lot of tourists to the town.* 展銷會把很多遊客吸引到鎮上。**5** [T+adv/prep] to cause someone or something to be in a particular state 使〔某人、某事物〕處於某種狀態: *That brings the total to £200.* 那將使總數達到二百英鎊。| *Let's hope that we can soon bring this war to an end.* 希望我們不久能結束這場戰爭吧。| *The club brought me into contact with a lot of people.* 俱樂部使我和很多人建立了聯繫。| *This dispute must be brought to an end.* 這場爭執必須結束。**6** can't **bring yourself to do something** to be unable to do something because it is so unpleasant 不忍心做某事: *I couldn't bring myself to kill the poor creature.* 我不忍殺害那可憐的動物。**7** **bring a charge against someone** to say officially to someone that it is believed that they have done something illegal 對某人提起訴訟: *He was arrested, and a charge of murder was brought against him.* 他被逮捕並指控犯了謀殺罪。**8** **bring a child into the world** to give birth to a child 生孩子

bring sthg ↔ **about** *phr v* [T] to cause something to happen 使〔某事〕發生; 引起: *This crisis has been brought about by the stupidity of our politicians.* 這場危機是由我們政客的愚蠢行為而引起的。

bring sthg/sbdy ↔ **along** *phr v* [T] to bring someone or something with you to a place 帶上〔某人或某物〕: *Please come to the party, and bring a few friends along if you like.* 請來參加聚會, 如果願意的話還可帶幾位朋友來。

bring back *phr v* **1** [T **bring** sbdy/sthg ↔ **back**] to bring someone or something with you when you return to a place 帶回〔某人或某物〕: *If you're going to the shop, could you bring back a few things for me?* 如果你要去買東西, 能給我帶點兒東西回來嗎? | *We'll take you to the concert, and we can also bring you back.* 我們帶你去(聽)音樂會, 還可以送你回來。**2** [T **bring** sthg ↔ **back**] to cause something to return 使〔某物〕返回; 使恢復: *Those songs certainly bring back a lot of memories.* 那些歌確然喚起對往事的許多回憶。| *a campaign to bring back the death penalty* 要求恢復死刑的運動

bring down *phr v* **1** [T **bring** sthg ↔ **down**] to cause something to come down to a lower place or a lower level 使〔某事物〕降低〔落下〕: *Gunmen shot at the plane and brought it down.* 槍手朝飛機開槍並將它擊落。| *The government is determined to bring down inflation.* 政府決心降低通貨膨脹。

2 [T **bring** sbdy/sthg ↔ **down**] to cause a person or a government to lose their position of power 使〔某人〕失勢; 使〔政府〕倒台: *This latest crisis could well bring down the government.* 最近這次危機足以令政府倒台。

bring sthg ↔ **forward** *phr v* [T] **1** to introduce or suggest a new idea 提出〔新主意〕; 提議: *Several new proposals have been brought forward.* 已提出了幾項新建議。**2** to decide that something will take place at an earlier time than had been planned 提前: *The meeting has been brought forward to Tuesday.* 會議已提前至星期二舉行。

bring in *phr v* **1** [T **bring** sthg ↔ **in**] to introduce something 引進; 提出: *The government is bringing in new laws to protect children.* 政府正提出制定保護兒童的新法律。**2** [T **bring** sbdy ↔ **in**] to ask someone to take part in something, especially in order to help with a problem 請〔某人〕參與〔尤指為幫助解決問題〕: *We need to bring in a few experienced people to get the job finished on time.* 我們需要請幾個有經驗的人來幫忙, 以便按時完成工作。**3** [T **bring** sthg ↔ **in**] to earn a particular amount of money 獲利; 賺錢: *She's bringing in £200 a week.* 她每星期賺二百英鎊。| *This new tax will bring in a lot of extra money for the government.* 這項新稅收將為政府帶來一大筆額外收益。**4 bring in a verdict** to give a particular VERDICT in a court of law 作出裁決; 宣佈判決: *The jury brought in a verdict of guilty.* 陪審團宣判〔被告〕有罪。

bring sthg ↔ **off** *phr v* [T] to succeed in doing something difficult 圓滿完成〔困難的事〕: *It will be a great achievement if they manage to bring it off.* 如果他們獲得成功, 這將是一項了不起的成就。

bring on *phr v* **1** [T **bring** sbdy/sthg ↔ **on**] to cause someone or something to grow, develop, or improve 使〔某人或某物〕發展, 進步, 改進: *The shock nearly brought on a heart attack.* 這打擊幾乎引起了心臟病發作。| *He was given special coaching to bring him on.* 他受到了特殊訓練以便提高水平。**2 bring something on yourself** to cause something unpleasant to happen to you 給自己招來〔不愉快的〕事情

bring out *phr v* **1** [T **bring** sthg ↔ **out**] to produce a new product 生產〔新產品〕: *The company has just brought out a new range of cosmetics.* 公司剛生產出新系列的化妝品。**2 bring out the best in someone** to make someone behave very well 使某人表現出色: *The crisis brought out the best in everyone.* 大家在這場危機中表現得很好。[RELATED PHRASE 相關詞組: **bring out the worst in someone**] **3** [T **bring** sbdy **out**] to encourage someone to talk to other people and feel at ease with other people 鼓勵〔某人〕隨便交談

bring sbdy ↔ **round** *phr v* [T] **1** to cause

someone to regain consciousness 使〔某人〕甦醒: *We tried everything we could think of to bring her round.* 我們想盡了法子讓她甦醒。**2** to persuade someone to change their opinion so that it is the same as your opinion 説服〔某人〕; 使〔某人〕改變主意

bring sbdy ↔ **to** *phr v* [T] to cause someone to regain consciousness 使〔某人〕甦醒

bring up *phr v* **1** [T **bring** sbdy ↔ **up**] to educate and care for a child 養育, 培養〔孩子〕: *I think that both parents should be involved in bringing up the children.* 我認為父親和母親都應為養育孩子出一分力。| *She was a polite and well brought up child.* 她是個懂禮貌、有教養的孩子。–see 見 RAISE[1] (USAGE 用法) **2** [T **bring** sthg ↔ **up**] to introduce a subject during a conversation 〔在會話中〕提出〔話題〕: *I didn't dare bring up the question of money.* 我不敢提出金錢的問題。| *All these problems were brought up at the last meeting.* 所有這些問題都在上次會議上被提出來。**3** [T **bring** sthg ↔ **up**] to be sick 噁心; 嘔吐: *He ate his dinner and then promptly brought it all up again.* 他吃完晚飯又馬上都吐了出來。

brink /brɪŋk; brɪŋk/ *n* **be on the brink of something** to be about to do or experience something wonderful or terrible 瀕臨某事物〔美妙或糟糕的事〕的邊緣: *Scientists say they are on the brink of a major discovery.* 科學家説他們將有重大發現。[RELATED PHRASE 相關詞組: **come/bring someone to the brink of something**]

brisk /brɪsk; brɪsk/ *adj* quick and active 輕快的; 活潑的: *a brisk walk* 輕快的步伐 –**briskly** *adv* –**briskness** *n* [U]

bris·tle[1] /ˈbrɪsl; ˈbrɪsəl/ *n* [C;U] short stiff coarse hair 短而粗硬的毛: *His chin was covered with bristles.* 他的下巴長滿了鬍子楂。

bristle[2] *v* **bristled, bristling** [I] (of hair or fur) to stand up stiffly 〔毛髮〕豎立: *The cat's fur bristled.* 貓豎起了身上的毛。

bristle with sthg *phr v* [T] to be full of something 充滿〔某物〕: *The market place bristled with activity.* 集市的買賣十分熱鬧。

Brit /brɪt; brɪt/ *n infml* a British person 〔非正式〕英國人

britch·es /ˈbrɪtʃɪz; ˈbrɪtʃəz/ *n* [pl] –see 見 BREECHES

Brit·ish /ˈbrɪtɪʃ; ˈbrɪtɪʃ/ *adj* from or connected with Britain 不列顛的; 英國的

brit·tle /ˈbrɪtl; ˈbrɪtl/ *adj* hard but easily broken or damaged 硬而易碎的; 脆的: *brittle glass* 易碎的玻璃

broach /brəʊtʃ; broʊtʃ/ *v* **broach a subject** to introduce as a subject of conversation 提出話題: *At last he broached the subject of the new contract.* 最後他提出了新合同的問題。

★broad /brɔːd; brɔːd/ *adj* **1** wide 寬的; 闊的: *He was tall, with broad shoulders.* 他個子高, 肩膀寬。| *the broad horizon* 開闊的眼界 **2** used in giving measurements 〔指寬度〕...寬:

four metres broad 四米寬 **3** not limited, but including a lot of different things or people 廣泛的: *The course appeals to a broad range of people.* 這門課程吸引了很多人來參加。**4** general, and not including a lot of details 概括的; 粗略的: *Give me a broad idea of your plans.* 給我概括地介紹一下你的計劃。**5 in broad daylight** during the day, where it is light 在白天; 在光天化日之下: *The raid took place in broad daylight.* 搶劫發生在光天化日之下。**6** showing clearly where the speaker comes from 地方口音重的: *She spoke broad Scots.* 她說話帶有很重的蘇格蘭口音。

broad bean /ˌ·ˈ·/ *n* a large flat bean 蠶豆

broad·cast¹ /ˈbrɔdˌkæst; ˈbrɔːdkɑːst/ *n* something sent out by radio or television 無線電廣播; 電視播放: *The broadcast suffered from technical problems.* 廣播節目出了技術故障。– **broadcast** *adj: broadcast news* 廣播新聞

broadcast² *v* **broadcast, broadcast 1** [I;T] to send out something on radio or television 〔無線電〕廣播; 〔電視〕播放: *The BBC broadcasts to all parts of the world.* 英國廣播公司向世界各地廣播。| *The BBC will broadcast the news at 10 o'clock.* 英國廣播公司將於十點鐘播送這條新聞。**2** [T] to make something widely known 傳播; 散佈: *He broadcast the news of his pay rise.* 他把自己加薪的消息四處傳播。–**broadcaster** *n* –**broadcasting** *n* [U]

broad·en /ˈbrɔdn; ˈbrɔːdn/ *v* **1** [I;T] (also 又作 **broaden out; broaden** sthg ↔ **out**) to make or become wider (使)變寬; 變闊: *The river broadens out here.* 這條河在此處開始變得寬闊。| *plans to broaden the road* 拓寬馬路的方案 **2** [T] to make something less limited 擴大〔某事物〕: *We need to broaden our campaign.* 我們需要擴大宣傳活動的範圍。**3 broaden someone's mind** to make someone more willing to accept different ideas or customs 使某人心胸開闊: *Travel broadens the mind.* 旅遊使人心胸開闊。

broad·ly /ˈbrɔdli; ˈbrɔːdli/ *adv* in general 大體說來: *Broadly, I agree with you.* 大體說來，我同意你的看法。

broad·mind·ed /ˈbrɔdˌmaɪndɪd; ˌbrɔːdˈmaɪndɪd◂/ *adj* willing to respect the opinions or actions of others even if they are very different from your own 心胸開闊的; 寬宏大量的; 能容納不同意見的 –opposite 反義 **narrow-minded** –**broadmindedness** *n* [U]

broad·side /ˈbrɔdˌsaɪd; ˈbrɔːdsaɪd/ *n* a strong spoken or written attack 〔口頭或書面的〕猛烈攻擊: *She delivered a broadside against government policies.* 她對政府的政策進行了猛烈的抨擊。

bro·cade /broˈked; brəˈkeɪd/ *n* [U] decorative cloth usually of silk, often with a raised pattern of gold or silver threads 〔織有金銀絲浮花的〕錦緞; 織錦

broc·co·li /ˈbrɑkəli; ˈbrɒkəli/ *n* [U] a vegetable whose young green flower heads are eaten 花椰菜; 花莖甘藍

bro·chure /broˈʃʊr; ˈbrəʊʃəʳ/ *n* a small book giving instructions or the details of a service 〔詳細介紹服務項目的〕小冊子: *a holiday brochure* 度假須知小冊子

brogue /brog; brəʊg/ *n* **1** a way of speaking 土腔; 方言口音 **2 brogues** [pl] strong shoes with a pattern made in the leather 皮革上有裝飾性花紋的厚皮鞋 –see 見 PAIR (USAGE 用法)

broil /brɔɪl; brɔɪl/ *v* [I;T] the usual American word for 〖美式〗= GRILL

broke¹ /brok; brəʊk/ past tense of BREAK¹ ☆ BREAK¹ 的過去式

broke² *adj* [never before a noun 不能用於名詞前] *infml* 〖非正式〗**1** completely without money 身無分文的: *I'm always broke by the end of the week.* 到了週末我總是身無分文。**2 go broke** to lose so much money that you have to close your business 破產

bro·ken¹ /ˈbrokən; ˈbrəʊkən/ past participle of BREAK¹ ☆ BREAK¹ 的過去分詞

★**broken²** *adj* **1** damaged, spoilt, or made useless by breaking 破碎的; 損壞的: *Be careful of the broken glass.* 小心碎玻璃。| *a broken leg* 骨折了的腿 | *a broken clock* 壞了的鐘 **2** interrupted 中斷的; 不連貫的: *a broken journey* 斷斷續續的旅程 | *broken sleep* 斷斷續續的睡眠 **3** without hope 沒有希望的: *a broken spirit* 消沉的意志 | *a broken man* 絕望的人 **4** destroyed by the separation of a husband and wife 〔夫妻〕離異的, 破裂的: *a broken marriage* 破裂的婚姻 | *a broken home* 破裂的家庭 **5** not kept 不被遵守的: *a broken law* 未被遵守的法律 | *broken promise* 失信的諾言 **6** imperfectly spoken or written 〔講或寫得〕不好的, 拙劣的: *broken English* 蹩腳的英語

broken-down /ˌ··ˈ·◂/ *adj* needing repair (used to describe cars and machines) 需要修理的〔形容汽車和機器〕

broken-heart·ed /ˌ·· ˈ·◂/ *adj* filled with grief 心碎的; 極度悲傷的: *He was broken-hearted when his son died.* 他兒子死時, 他悲痛欲絕。

bro·ker /ˈbrokɚ; ˈbrəʊkəʳ/ *n* a person who does business for someone else, for example in buying and selling shares or foreign money 〔股票、外幣等的〕經紀人, 掮客; 〔買賣的〕代理人, 中間人

brol·ly /ˈbrɑli; ˈbrɒli/ *n* **brollies** BrE infml an UMBRELLA 〖英式, 非正式〗傘

bron·chi·tis /brɑnˈkaɪtɪs; brɒŋˈkaɪtɪs/ *n* [U] an illness of the two tubes connecting the WINDPIPE with the lungs; it causes severe coughing 支氣管炎

bronze¹ /brɑnz; brɒnz/ *adj* **1** made of bronze 青銅製的 **2 bronze medal** a piece of bronze that you win when you come third in a race or competition 銅牌; 銅質獎章 **3** the colour of bronze 古銅色的; 青銅色的

bronze² n **1** [U] a metal made mainly of copper and tin 銅錫合金; 青銅 **2** [C] a bronze medal 銅牌 **3** [U] a dark yellowish-brown colour 古銅色; 黃褐色

bronzed /brɑnzd; brɒnzd/ adj made attractively brown by the sun 曬成古銅色的: handsome young men bronzed by the sun 皮膚被太陽曬成古銅色的英俊年青人

brooch /broʧ; brəʊʧ/ n a decoration worn on women's clothes, fastened on with a pin 〔婦女的〕胸針, 飾針 –see picture on page 210 見 210 頁彩圖

brood¹ /brud; bruːd/ n a family of young birds 一窩雛鳥

brood² v **1** [I] to sit on eggs as a hen does 孵蛋 **2** to think about something angrily or sadly for a long time 〔不快或難過地〕想; 沉思: Don't just sit there brooding — do something! 別老是坐在那裡想 — 做點兒事情!

broody /'brudɪ; 'bruːdɪ/ adj **1** wanting to sit on eggs (used of hens) 想孵卵的; 要抱窩的〔指母雞〕**2** wanting to have a baby (used of women) 想要生孩子的〔指婦女〕

brook /bruk; brʊk/ n a stream 溪; 小河

broom /brum; bruːm/ n a large brush which has a long handle and is used for sweeping 〔長柄的〕掃帚

broom·stick /'brum,stɪk; 'bruːm,stɪk/ n the long thin handle of a broom 掃帚柄

broth /brɔθ; brɒθ/ n [U] thin soup made by cooking meat and vegetables in water and then removing them 〔肉、蔬菜的〕原汁清湯: chicken broth 雞湯

broth·el /'brɔθəl; 'brɒθəl/ n a house where men can pay women to have sex 妓院

★**broth·er** /'brʌðɚ; 'brʌðəʳ/ n **1** a male relative with the same parents 兄弟: John and Peter are brothers. 約翰和彼得是兄弟。| John is Peter's brother. 約翰是彼得的哥哥〔弟弟〕。–see picture on page 503 見 503 頁彩圖 **2** a male member of a religious group, especially a MONK 〔教會中的〕男教友〔尤指修士〕: a Christian brother 基督教修士 | Evening prayers will be read by Brother John. 晚禱文由約翰修士來唸。

broth·er·hood /'brʌðɚ,hud; 'brʌðəhʊd/ n **1** [U] the feeling of being united with other people as if you were brothers 手足之情; 兄弟般的關係: the brotherhood of man 男人的手足之情 **2** [C] a society of men living a religious life 兄弟會; 修士會

brother-in-law /'··· ·'·/ n brothers-in-law **1** the brother of your husband or wife 內兄, 內弟; 大伯, 小叔 **2** the husband of your sister 姐夫, 妹夫 –see picture on page 503 見 503 頁彩圖

broth·er·ly /'brʌðɚlɪ; 'brʌðəlɪ/ adj kind and typical of a brother 兄弟的; 兄弟般的: brotherly advice 兄弟般的勸告

brought /brɔt; brɔːt/ the past tense and past participle of BRING ☆ BRING 的過去式和過

去分詞

brow /brau; braʊ/ n fml 〖正式〗**1** an EYEBROW 眉; 眉毛 **2** your FOREHEAD 額 **3** the brow of a hill the upper part of a hill 山脊

brow·beat /'brau,bit; 'braʊbiːt/ v browbeat, browbeaten /'bitn; biːtn/, browbeating [T] to force someone to obey by using fierce looks or words 〔用神情或言詞〕威逼〔某人〕: Don't let them browbeat you into doing all the dirty work. 別讓他們逼你幹這一切非法勾當。

★**brown¹** /braun; braʊn/ adj of the colour of earth, wood, or coffee 棕色的; 褐色的: brown shoes 褐色的鞋子 | He's very brown after his holiday. 他度假回來後, 皮膚曬成了褐色。| brown rice 糙米 | brown paper (棕色) 包裝紙 –brown n [C;U]: We chose brown. 我們選了棕色。| a dark brown 深褐色 –see picture on page 243 見 243 頁彩圖

brown² v [I;T] to make or become brown (使)變成褐色: First, brown the meat in hot fat. 首先, 把肉放在燒開的油裡炸成褐色。

browse /brauz; braʊz/ v browsed, browsing [I] **1** to feed on the leaves and young parts of bushes and trees 〔牲畜〕吃〔草、樹葉等〕**2** to look at things, especially books, without any particular purpose, for enjoyment 隨意翻閱; 瀏覽: I enjoy browsing through old magazines. 我喜歡隨意翻閱舊雜誌。–browse n: While you were out I had a good browse through your books. 你出去時, 我把你的書全都瀏覽了一遍。

bruise¹ /bruz; bruːz/ n a discoloured place where the skin of a person or fruit has been damaged by a blow or fall 〔人體或水果等碰傷後產生的〕青瘀, 傷痕

bruise² v bruised, bruising [T] to cause one or more bruises on something 使〔皮肉〕青腫; 碰傷〔皮膚等〕: She fell and bruised her knee. 她摔了一跤, 膝蓋被擦傷。| a bruised finger 青腫的手指

brunch /brʌnʧ; brʌnʧ/ n [C;U] infml a meal combining breakfast and the meal eaten in the middle of the day called lunch and eaten in the middle of the morning 〖非正式〗〔將早、午餐合而為一的〕早午餐

bru·nette /bru'nɛt; bruː'net/ n (also 又作 brunet AmE〖美式〗) a woman of a fair-skinned race with dark hair 〔毛髮黑色的〕白種女子 –see picture on page 469 見 469 頁彩圖

brunt /brʌnt; brʌnt/ n bear the brunt to suffer the heaviest part of something unpleasant 首當其衝: I had to bear the brunt of his anger. 他發脾氣時, 我是首當其衝。

brush¹ /brʌʃ; brʌʃ/ n **1** [C] a thing consisting of hairs on a handle that you use for things like putting paint on something, cleaning dirt off, or making your hair tidy 刷子; 毛刷; 掃帚; 畫筆: a dustpan and brush 畚箕和掃帚 | a clothes brush 衣刷 | a toothbrush 牙刷 | a paintbrush 畫筆; 油漆用的刷子 **2**

[C] an act of brushing (一)刷; (一)拂; (一)揮: *I'll just give my hair a quick brush.* 我要把頭髮很快地梳一下。 **3** [U] (also 又作 **brush-wood**) small branches of trees or bushes 〔樹或灌木的〕小枝條 **4** [U] small rough trees and bushes, or land covered by these 灌木(區); 雜樹地帶 **5 have a brush with someone** *infml* to have a short and unpleasant meeting or argument with someone 〔非正式〕和某人發生小衝突: *I've just had a brush with the law.* 我剛和警察發生過小衝突。

brush² *v* [T] **1** to clean something or make something tidy with a brush 〔用刷子〕刷〔某物〕: *Have you brushed your teeth?* 你刷了牙沒有? | *I brushed my hair.* 我刷了頭髮。 **2** to pass lightly over something 揮, 拂〔某物〕: *The wind gently brushed his cheek.* 風輕拂着他的臉頰。 **3 brush past someone, brush by someone** to move past someone, perhaps carelessly or angrily, so that you touch them 〔因不小心或生氣而〕擦過某人; 掠過某人

brush sbdy/sthg ↔ **aside** *phr v* [T] to refuse to consider something seriously 漠視, 不顧〔某事物〕: *He brushed the difficulties aside.* 他不顧困難。

brush sbdy/sthg ↔ **away** *phr v* [T] **1** to refuse to consider something seriously 漠視, 不顧〔某事物〕: *She brushed his arguments away.* 她不理會他的論點。 **2** to remove something with a brushing movement 刷去; 揮掉: *She brushed away a tear.* 她拂去一滴淚珠。 | *He brushed away a fly.* 他揮掉一隻蒼蠅。

brush sthg ↔ **up** *phr v* [T] to study a subject again in order to relearn what you have forgotten 重溫; 複習: *I must brush up my French before I go to Pairs.* 去巴黎之前, 我必須溫習一下法語。

brush-off /'· ·/ *n* give someone the brush-off to refuse to be friendly or to listen to someone 〔非正式〕拒絕某人; 讓某人碰釘子: *I wanted to ask her out to dinner but she gave me the brush-off.* 我想請她出去吃飯, 但她讓我碰了個釘子。

brusque /brʌsk; brʌskʲ/ *adj* quick and rather impolite 粗魯的; 唐突的: *He had a rather brusque manner.* 他態度相當粗魯。 – **brusquely** *adv* – **brusqueness** *n* [U]

brus·sels sprout /ˌbrʌslz 'spraut; ˌbrʌsəlz 'spraut/ *n* (also 又作 **sprout**) a green vegetable that is a small tight ball of leaves 球芽甘藍

bru·tal /'brutl; 'bruːtl/ *adj* **1** rough, cruel, and insensitive 粗暴的; 殘忍的; 無理性的: *a brutal attack* 蠻橫的攻擊 **2 the brutal truth** a fact that is true but unpleasant 嚴峻的事實 – **brutally** *adv* – **brutality** /bruˈtælətɪ; bruːˈtælˌti/ *n* [C;U]: *the brutality of war* 戰爭的殘忍

bru·tal·ize /'brutlˌaɪz; 'bruːtələaɪz/ *v* **brutalized, brutalizing** (also 又作 **brutalise** *BrE* 〔英式〕) [T] **1** to make someone brutal 使

〔某人〕殘忍〔變得無情〕 **2** to treat someone in a brutal manner 虐待〔某人〕 – **brutalization** /ˌbrutləˈzeʃən; ˌbruːtəl-aɪˈzeɪʃən/ *n* [U]

brute /brut; bruːt/ *n* **1** a rough, cruel, and insensitive person 粗暴〔殘忍〕的人; 無理性的人: *Her husband is a real brute.* 她丈夫真是個野蠻的人。 **2** an animal, especially a large one (a word used to express disapproval) 野獸〔含貶義〕 **3 brute force, brute strength** force used without any intelligence 蠻力; 蠻勁: *In the end I had to use brute force to open the box.* 到最後我只好用蠻力打開箱子。

brut·ish /'brutɪʃ; 'bruːtɪʃ/ *adj* very cruel 野蠻的; 殘忍的: *Their life is nasty, brutish, and short.* 他們活得庸俗、野蠻而且簡慢無禮。

BSc /ˌbi es 'si; ˌbiː es 'siː/ (also 又作 **BS** *AmE* 〔美式〕) **1** an abbreviation for BACHELOR OF SCIENCE, a first university degree in a science subject 〔縮〕〔大學理科初級學位〕理學士: *He has a BSc in Chemistry.* 他擁有化學理學士學位。 **2** someone who has a BSc 理學士: *Mary Jones, BSc* 瑪麗·瓊斯理學士

bub·ble¹ /'bʌbl; 'bʌbəl/ *n* a hollow ball of liquid containing air or gas 泡; 水泡; 氣泡: *The water's boiling; look at the bubbles.* 水開了; 看那些氣泡。 | *soap bubbles* 肥皂泡 | *to burst a bubble* 戳破一個氣泡

bubble² *v* **bubbled, bubbling** [I] **1** to form bubbles or rise as bubbles 冒泡; 沸騰: *The gas bubbled to the surface of the water.* 氣體成泡升到水面上。 **2** to make the sound of bubbles rising in liquid 發出噗噗聲: *We could hear the pot bubbling away quietly on the fire.* 我們能聽見爐火上的水壺在輕輕地發出噗噗聲。 **3 bubble over with joy** to show great happiness 喜形於色

bubble gum /'·· ·/ *n* [U] CHEWING GUM that can be blown into bubbles 泡泡糖

bub·bly¹ /'bʌblɪ; 'bʌblɪ/ *adj* **1** full of bubbles 充滿泡沫的 **2** full of life 生氣勃勃的: *a bubbly personality* 活潑的個性

bubbly² *n* [U] *old fash infml* 〔老式, 非正式〕= CHAMPAGNE

buck¹ /bʌk; bʌk/ *n* **1** a male deer or rabbit 雄鹿; 雄兔 **2** *AmE infml* an American dollar 〔美式, 非正式〕一美元

buck² *v* **1** [I] (especially of a horse) to jump up and kick with the back legs 〔尤指馬〕跳起並用後足踢 **2** [T] to throw a rider off by doing this 〔馬〕躍起, 把〔騎手〕摔下: *The horse bucked its first rider off.* 馬躍起, 把第一位騎手摔了下去。

buck up *phr v* **1** [I] to hurry up or make more effort 趕快; 更努力 **2** [I;T **buck** sbdy ↔ **up**] to make or become more cheerful 使打起精神; 變得歡欣鼓舞

buck·et¹ /'bʌkɪt; 'bʌkˌt/ *n* **1** a round plastic, metal, or wooden container with a handle, for carrying liquids 水桶; 提桶 –see picture on page 244 見 244 頁彩圖 **2** (also 又作 **bucketful**) the contents of a bucket 一桶的

量: *Give each tree a bucket of water.* 給每棵樹澆一桶水。**3 the rain came down in buckets** = it rained very hard 大雨傾盆而下
bucket² *v*

bucket down *phr v* [I] *BrE infml* to rain very hard 〔英式，非正式〕大雨傾盆而下

buck·le¹ /ˈbʌkl; ˈbʌkəl/ *n* a metal fastener for joining the ends of a belt or for decoration 〔帶子的〕搭扣; 扣形裝飾物: *The buckle's come off my sandal.* 我涼鞋上的搭扣脫落了。–see picture on page 210 見 210 頁彩圖

buckle² *v* **buckled, buckling 1** [I;T] to fasten with a buckle 〔用搭扣〕把…扣住[扣緊]: *He buckled his belt tightly.* 他把腰帶扣得緊緊的。| *The straps buckled up easily.* 這帶子很容易扣住。| *The two ends buckle together at the back.* 兩端在背後扣住。| *He buckled on his sword.* 他把劍扣掛在身上。**2** [I;T] to make or become bent through heat, shock, or pressure 〔通過加熱、撞擊、加壓〕使彎曲; 變彎曲: *The wheel of my bicycle was buckled in the accident.* 我的腳踏車輪子在事故中撞得變了形。| *The wheel buckled.* 輪子扭曲了。

buckle down *phr v* [I] *infml* to begin to work seriously 〔非正式〕開始認真做: *She buckled down to work.* 她開始認真工作。

bud¹ /bʌd; bʌd/ *n* **1** a young flower or leaf before it opens 蓓蕾; 葉芽 **2** come into bud to form buds 發芽: *My roses are just coming into bud.* 我的玫瑰花正在萌芽。**3** *AmE* 〔美式〕= BUDDY (2)

bud² *v* **-dd-** [I] to produce buds 發芽; 萌芽

Bud·dhis·m /ˈbʊdɪzəm; ˈbʊdɪzəm/ *n* [U] a religion of east and central Asia growing out of the teaching of Buddha and teaching that pureness of spirit is the answer to suffering 佛教 –**Buddhist** *n, adj*

bud·ding /ˈbʌdɪŋ; ˈbʌdɪŋ/ *adj* [only before a noun 只用於名詞前] beginning to develop 開始發育[發展]的: *a budding poet* 嶄露頭角的詩人

bud·dy /ˈbʌdɪ; ˈbʌdi/ *n* **buddies** *infml* 〔非正式〕**1** a good friend (usually used of a male friend of a man) 好朋友〔常指男子的男性朋友〕: *They're real buddies.* 他們是真正的好朋友。**2** *AmE* a way of talking to someone, especially a man, who you are angry with 〔美式〕傢伙, 老兄; 喂〔稱呼語, 尤指惹人生氣的男子〕: *Get out of my way, buddy!* 喂, 別擋道呀!

budge /bʌdʒ; bʌdʒ/ *v* **budged, budging** [I;T] **1** to move a little (使)微微移動: *I can't budge this rock.* 我挪不動這石頭。| *This rock won't budge at all.* 這石頭一動也不動。**2** to change a publicly stated position 改變〔立場〕: *The union refused to budge on its demand for an 8% rise.* 對於加薪百分之八的要求, 工會拒絕讓步。

bud·ger·i·gar /ˈbʌdʒərɪˌɡɑr; ˈbʌdʒərɪɡɑːʳ/ *n* (also 又作 **budgie** *infml* 〔非正式〕) a small

brightly coloured bird, often kept in a cage in British houses 〔英國家庭常養於籠中的〕虎皮鸚鵡

★bud·get¹ /ˈbʌdʒɪt; ˈbʌdʒɪt/ *n* **1** a plan of how to arrange private or public spending 預算: *the family budget* 家庭預算 | *In his annual budget the Chancellor announced a rise in income tax.* 財政大臣在年度預算中宣佈增加所得稅。**2** the quantity of money stated in these plans 預算額: *a budget of £10,000,000* 一千萬英鎊的預算額 | *running the Council on a very tight budget* 以極緊絀的預算主持議會

budget² *v* [I] to plan private or public spending within the limits of a certain amount of money 制定預算; 按預算來安排開支: *We're having to budget very carefully at the moment.* 現在我們要精心安排開支。| *She budgeted for a new car.* 她為買輛新車而計劃節省開支。–**budgetary** *adj*

budget³ *adj* cheap and good value 經濟的; 價廉物美的: *a budget buy* 買來價廉物美的東西 | *budget holidays* 花費經濟的假期

bud·gie /ˈbʌdʒɪ; ˈbʌdʒɪ/ *n infml* 〔非正式〕–see 見 BUDGERIGAR

buff¹ /bʌf; bʌf/ *adj* pale brown 淺黃色的: *a buff envelope* 淺黃色的信封

buff² *v* [T] (also 又作 **buff** sth ↔ **up**) to polish metal with something soft, so that it shines 〔用軟物〕擦亮〔金屬〕

buff³ *n infml* a person who is very interested in and knows a lot about the stated subject 〔非正式〕迷; 愛好者; 行家: *a film buff* 電影迷 | *He's a bit of a wine buff.* 他對酒有點著迷。

buf·fa·lo /ˈbʌfləˌo; ˈbʌfələʊ/ *n* **buffaloes** or **buffalos** any of several kinds of cattle with long flattish curved horns, found mainly in Asia, Africa, and North America (北美)野牛; (亞洲)水牛

buff·er /ˈbʌfə; ˈbʌfəʳ/ *n* **1** one of a pair of plates on springs fixed to a railway carriage or engine, or to the end of the railway track, which reduce the shock if the train hits anything 〔鐵路車輛的〕緩衝器 **2** protection 〔起緩衝作用的〕保護物: *The Prime Minister's popularity in the country acted as a buffer against criticism from his colleagues.* 首相在國內深得民心, 這使同僚對他的批評沒有產生很大影響。

buf·fet¹ /ˈbʌfɪt; ˈbʌfɪt/ *v* [T] to push or throw something repeatedly with great force 連續重擊〔某物〕: *We were buffeted by the wind and rain.* 我們不斷遇到風雨的襲擊。

buf·fet² /ˈbuˈfe; ˈbʊfeɪ/ *n* **1** a meal, often laid out on a long table, and usually consisting of cold food, which people serve for themselves and eat standing up or sitting down near by 自助餐 **2** an informal restaurant which serves meals to travellers 〔為旅遊者服務的〕簡易餐館

buffet car /ˈbʊfe ˌkɑr; ˈbʊfeɪ ˌkɑː/ *n* a part

of a train where you can buy food and drink〔火車的〕餐車

buf·foon /bʌˈfuːn; bəˈfuːn/ n a rough and noisy fool 醜角; 粗俗而愚蠢的人 **–buffoonery** n [U]

bug /bʌg; bʌg/ n **1** an insect, especially one which does damage or which people do not like〔尤指有危害性或令人討厭的〕蟲子: *The bed was full of bugs.* 牀上到處是臭蟲。**2** a small living thing causing disease 病菌; 病毒: *There are some nasty bugs going around at the moment.* 現在一些討厭的病毒正在流行。| *He picked up a bug on his travels.* 他在旅途中感染了病菌。**3** something wrong with a piece of ELECTRONIC apparatus, especially a computer〔電子儀器, 尤指電腦的〕毛病: *We'll have to iron out the bugs in that new program.* 我們要排除那個新程序中的故障。**4** an apparatus for listening secretly to other people's conversations 竊聽器: *The police tested the room for bugs.* 警察檢查房間, 看有沒有竊聽器。**5** infml a very strong but often not lasting interest in something〔非正式〕一時的狂熱: *She's been bitten by the travel bug.* 她迷上了旅遊。

bug² v **-gg-** [T] **1** to fit a place with a secret listening apparatus 在〔某處〕裝竊聽器: *The embassy was bugged.* 大使館裡裝了竊聽器。**2** infml to annoy someone〔非正式〕煩擾, 惹惱〔某人〕: *What's bugging you?* 甚麼叫你煩惱了?

bug·gy /ˈbʌgi; ˈbʌgi/ n **buggies** a seat on wheels used for pushing a young child; buggies fold and are light so that you can carry them〔摺疊式〕輕便嬰兒車

bu·gle /ˈbjuːgl; ˈbjuːgəl/ n a brass musical instrument, played by blowing, used especially for army calls 號角; 軍號 **–bugler** n

★**build¹** /bɪld; bɪld/ v **build** /bɪlt; bɪlt/, built, building **1** [I;T] to make things like houses, factories, or ships 蓋; 建築; 建造: *They're building a new bridge.* 他們正在建造新橋。| *The house was built of honey-coloured stone.* 這棟房子是用蜜色的石頭蓋的。**2** [T] to develop something gradually 發展; 建設: *It's our party's aim to build a better society.* 我們黨的目標是建設一個更美好的社會。| *to build confidence between the two countries* 發展兩國間的信任關係 **3** build on something to use one success to gain another one 在成功的基礎上進一步發展: *He hopes to build on the increase in productivity by opening new factories.* 他希望通過開辦新工廠來進一步提高生產力。

build sthg ↔ **in** phr v [T] to form something as a fixed part of something else and not add it on afterwards 把〔某物〕嵌〔插、建、袋〕入

build on phr v **1** [T **build** sthg ↔ **on**] to add another part to a building 添建: *The garage was built on to the west end of the house in the 1930s.* 這個車庫是三十年代時在

房子西面加建的。**2** [T **build on** sthg] to use something as a base for further development 以〔某事物〕作為發展基礎: *Her new job will allow her to build on her previous experience in marketing.* 她可以憑藉過去的推銷工作經驗來開展她的新工作。

build up [I;T **build** sthg ↔ **up**] to make or become greater in quantity 使增加; 使增進: *After four o'clock the traffic begins to build up.* 四點鐘以後交通開始擁擠起來。| *She built the business up from nothing.* 她白手起家, 生意日漸興隆。| *You need to build up your strength.* 你需要養精蓄銳。

build² n [C;U] the shape and size of the human body 體形; 體格: *a tall man with a powerful build* 體格強壯的高個子男人 | *We are of the same build.* 我們的體形相同。

build·er /ˈbɪldə; ˈbɪldər/ n a person whose job is building, especially someone who owns a building company 建造者〔尤指建築商〕: *a local firm of builders* 由建築商組成的本地公司

★**build·ing** /ˈbɪldɪŋ; ˈbɪldɪŋ/ n **1** [C] something with a roof and walls, such as a house, a factory, or an office block 建築物; 房屋: *The World Trade Center is one of the world's tallest buildings.* 世界貿易中心是世界上最高的建築物之一。| *historic buildings* 古建築 **2** [U] the process or business of making buildings 建築; 建築業

building so·ci·e·ty /ˈ··· ·ˌ···/ n **building societies** an organization in Britain into which people pay money in order to save it and gain interest, and which lends money to people who want to buy houses〔英國〕購屋互助協會〔接受會員存款並貸款給擬購房的會員〕

build·up /ˈbɪldʌp; ˈbɪldʌp/ n a gradual increase 逐漸增加: *a military buildup* 軍事擴充 | *the buildup of traffic on the road* 公路交通流量的增長

built /bɪlt; bɪlt/ **1** the past tense and past participle of BUILD ☆ BUILD 的過去式和過去分詞 **2** **-built** formed in the stated way 有...體形的: *a heavily-built man* 體態笨重的男子

built-in /ˌ· ˈ··◂/ adj planned as part of something and fixed into it 成為〔某物〕組成部分的; 固定的: *a built-in washing-machine* 有固定裝置的洗衣機

built-up /ˌ· ˈ··◂/ adj covered with buildings 佈滿建築物的: *a built-up area* 建築物林立的地區

bulb /bʌlb; bʌlb/ n **1** the round root of certain plants; bulbs grow leaves and flowers once a year, often in the spring〔某些植物的〕球莖, 鱗莖 **2** any object of this shape, especially the glass part of an electric lamp 球狀物〔尤指電燈泡〕: *a light bulb* 電燈泡

bul·bous /ˈbʌlbəs; ˈbʌlbəs/ adj fat and round with a narrow top 又肥又圓的: *a bulbous nose* 滾圓的鼻子

Bulgarian¹ /bʌlˈgɛrɪən; bʌlˈgeərɪən/ *adj* from or connected with Bulgaria 保加利亞的

Bulgarian² *n* **1** [C] a person from Bulgaria 保加利亞人 **2** [U] the language of Bulgaria 保加利亞語

bulge¹ /bʌldʒ; bʌldʒ/ *n* a swelling of a surface caused by pressure 膨脹; 鼓起部: *a bulge in the wall* 牆上鼓起的一塊

bulge² *v* **bulged, bulging** [I] to swell out 鼓起; 膨脹; 凸出: *a bulging stomach* 脹鼓鼓的肚子 | *His pockets were bulging* **with** *money.* 她的口袋裡鼓鼓囊囊地裝滿了鈔票。

bulk /bʌlk; bʌlk/ *n* **1** [U] great size or quantity, often combined with inconvenient shape 大塊, 大量, 大團〔常指令人感到不便〕 **2** **the bulk of** the greater part of 大部分; 主要部分: *The bulk of the work has already been done.* 大部分的工作已經完成了。 **3 in bulk** in large quantities and not packed in separate containers 大批的; 大量的; 散裝的: *We buy the goods in bulk.* 我們成批地採購這種貨。

bulk·y /ˈbʌlki; ˈbʌlki/ *adj* **bulkier, bulkiest** large and of an inconvenient shape 龐大的; 巨大的: *a bulky parcel* 笨重的包裹

bull /bʊl; bʊl/ *n* **1** the male of the cow, kept on farms to be the father of young cattle 〔未閹的〕公牛 **2 a bull in a china shop** *infml* a rough careless person in a place where skill and care are needed 〔非正式〕魯莽的人; 亂闖禍的人 **3 take the bull by the horns** *infml* to face difficulties in spite of fear 〔非正式〕不畏艱險, 挺身面對困難

bull·dog /ˈbʊldɒg; ˈbʊldɒg/ *n* a fierce dog of English origin, with a short neck and short thick legs 鬥牛狗

bull·doze /ˈbʊldəʊz; ˈbʊldəʊz/ *v* **bulldozed, bulldozing** [T] **1** to force objects and earth out of the way with a bulldozer 〔用推土機〕推[削]平 **2 bulldoze someone into doing something** to force someone into doing something 強迫某人做某事

bull·doz·er /ˈbʊldəʊzə; ˈbʊldəʊzər/ *n* a heavy machine used to make the surface of the ground level 推土機

bul·let /ˈbʊlɪt; ˈbʊlɪt/ *n* a small piece of metal with a rounded or pointed end, fired from a gun 槍彈; 子彈

bul·le·tin /ˈbʊlətɪn; ˈbʊlətɪn/ *n* **1** a short official notice or news report intended to be made public without delay 公告; 公報; 佈告: *Here is the latest bulletin about the President's health.* 這是關於總統健康情況的最新公告。 **2** a short printed newspaper produced by an organization or group 〔某一組織或團體的〕小報, 會刊

bulletin board /ˈ··· ·/ *n* the usual American word for 〔美式〕= NOTICEBOARD

bull·fight /ˈbʊlfaɪt; ˈbʊlfaɪt/ *n* a form of entertainment in Spain, Portugal, and Latin America in which a man fights, and usually kills, a BULL 〔西班牙、葡萄牙、拉丁美洲作為娛樂的〕鬥牛 **–bullfighter** *n* **–bullfighting** *n* [U]

bul·lion /ˈbʊljən; ˈbʊljən/ *n* [U] large pieces of gold or silver 金[銀]條; 金[銀]塊: *gold bullion* 金條

bul·lock /ˈbʊlək; ˈbʊlək/ *n* a young BULL which has had its sex organs removed so that it cannot breed 閹牛; 小公牛

bull·ring /ˈbʊlrɪŋ; ˈbʊlrɪŋ/ *n* a circular place surrounded by rows of seats where bullfights take place 鬥牛場

bull's-eye /ˈ· ·/ *n* the middle of a round board with circles on it which people try to hit when shooting 靶心; 鵠的: *Congratulations! It's a bull's-eye!* 恭喜! 擊中靶心了!

bul·ly /ˈbʊli; ˈbʊli/ *v* **bullied, bullying** [I;T] to use your strength to hurt or frighten people who are not as strong as you are 欺侮[人]; 橫行霸道: *He had been bullied at school.* 他在學校裡受人欺侮。 | *The older boys bullied us* **into** *stealing for them.* 年長的男孩逼我們替他們偷東西。 **–bully** *n* **bullies**

bul·rush /ˈbʊlrʌʃ; ˈbʊlrʌʃ/ *n* a tall grasslike plant that grows beside rivers 水燭; 香蒲

bul·wark /ˈbʊlwək; ˈbʊlwək/ *n* a strong wall built for defence or protection 堡壘; 壁壘

bum¹ /bʌm; bʌm/ *v* **1** *BrE infml* the part of your body on which you sit 〔英式, 非正式〕屁股 **2** *AmE infml* someone who has no home and lives by begging 〔美式, 非正式〕流浪乞丐 **3** *infml* someone who is considered worthless, lazy, or unable to do their job 〔非正式〕懶漢; 沒用的人; 做事差勁的人

bum² *v* **-mm-** [T] *infml* to ask for something without waiting for someone to offer it to you 〔非正式〕討[東西]; 乞求[某物]: *Can I bum a cigarette off you?* 我可以向你要支煙嗎?

bum about/around *phr v* [I] to travel around to different places for pleasure, usually with very little money 〔常以很少的錢〕到處遊蕩

bum·ble /ˈbʌmbl; ˈbʌmbəl/ *v* **bumbled, bumbling** [I] *infml* to speak without making much sense, or so that the words are hard to hear clearly 〔非正式〕語無倫次; 結結巴巴: *What are you bumbling on about now?* 你喃喃地在說些甚麼?

bum·ble·bee /ˈbʌmblbi; ˈbʌmbəlbiː/ *n* a large hairy bee which makes a loud noise when flying 熊蜂; 大黃蜂

bum·bling /ˈbʌmblɪŋ; ˈbʌmblɪŋ/ *adj* moving or behaving in a confused or disorganized way 笨手笨腳的; 手忙腳亂的: *You bumbling idiot!* 你這個笨手笨腳的傻瓜!

bump¹ /bʌmp; bʌmp/ *v* **1** [I;T] to hit or knock something by accident 〔意外地〕撞; 撞上[某物]: *Mummy, I've bumped my head.* 媽媽, 我碰了一下頭。 | *I bumped my knee against the wall.* 我的膝蓋撞在牆上。 | *Those cars are going to bump into each other.* 那些

汽車將要相撞了。**2** [I+adv/prep] to move along in an uneven way because the ground is not smooth 〔在高低不平的路面上〕顛簸而行: *We bumped along the track to the farm.* 我們沿着小路朝着農場顛簸前進。

bump into sbdy *phr v* [T] *infml* to meet someone by chance 〔非正式〕偶遇〔某人〕; 邂逅〔某人〕: *Guess who I bumped into this morning?* 猜猜今天早晨我碰見了誰?

bump sbdy ↔ **off** *phr v* [T] *infml* to murder someone 〔非正式〕謀殺〔某人〕

bump sthg ↔ **up** *phr v* [T] *infml* to increase something 〔非正式〕增加〔某物〕: *You need a good result to bump up your average.* 你需要取得好成績, 才能提高平均分。

bump² *n* **1** the sound of something hitting something else 碰撞聲: *We heard a bump in the next room.* 我們聽到隔壁房間傳來砰的一聲。**2** a car accident which is not very serious 〔不太嚴重的〕撞車事故: *I've just had a bump in the car.* 我的汽車剛才撞了一下。**3** a raised round swelling on your body, often caused by someone hitting you 〔常因碰撞而引起的〕腫塊: *He had a nasty bump on his head.* 他頭上腫起了一大塊。**4** an uneven part of a flat surface 〔平面上的〕隆起處: *bumps in the road* 路上的隆起處

bum·per¹ /ˈbʌmpə; ˈbʌmpɚ/ *n* **1** a bar fixed on the front and back of a car to protect it if it knocks against something 〔汽車車身前後的〕保險槓 –see picture on page 209 見 209 頁彩圖 **2 bumper-to-bumper** very close together and not moving very fast (used of traffic) 緊接着的, 開不快的〔指交通〕

bumper² *adj* [only before a noun 只用於名詞前] larger or greater than usual 特大的; 豐盛的: *a bumper crop of potatoes* 馬鈴薯大豐收

bump·y /ˈbʌmpɪ; ˈbʌmpi/ *adj* **bumpier, bumpiest** not smooth 高低不平的: *a bumpy road* 崎嶇的道路 | *a bumpy ride* 顛簸的旅程

bun /bʌn; bʌn/ *n* **1** a small round sweet cake 小圓麵包; 小圓糕點 **2** hair fastened into a tight round shape at the back of your head 〔盤在腦後的〕圓髮髻: *She wears her hair in a bun.* 她把頭髮盤成一個髻。

bunch¹ /bʌntʃ; bʌntʃ/ *n* **1** a number of things of the same kind fastened, held, or growing together at one point 束; 串; 紮; 捆: *I gave her a bunch of flowers.* 我送給她一束花。| *a bunch of bananas* 一串香蕉 | *a bunch of keys* 一串鑰匙 **2** *infml* a group of people who are similar in some way 〔非正式〕羣; 夥: *They're all nice in my department, but John is the best of the bunch.* 我部門裡的人都很好, 而約翰是同夥中最好的。| *My students are quite a nice bunch.* 我的學生是一羣好孩子。

bunch² *v* [T] to form into close groups 使成一束〔一羣〕: *The leaders are bunched together a long way ahead of the other runners.* 領先者聚在前面跑, 遠遠超過其他選手。

bun·dle¹ /ˈbʌndl̩; ˈbʌndl̩/ *n* **1** a number of things tied together or wrapped up so that you can carry them easily 〔一〕捆; 〔一〕束 〔一〕紮 **2 a bundle of nerves** extremely nervous 極度緊張的: *I'm a bundle of nerves.* 我緊張極了。

bundle² *v* **bundled, bundling** [I+adv/prep; T+adv/prep] to move or hurry in a rather quick and rough manner 匆忙地走或移動: *The police bundled him into a car and drove away.* 警察匆匆把他推上汽車, 揚長而去。| *We all bundled into the bus.* 我們都擠上了公共汽車。| *They bundled the children off to school.* 他們匆匆把孩子趕去上學。

bundle sthg ↔ **up** *phr v* [T] to collect things together quickly and untidily 把〔東西〕亂堆在一起: *She bundled up her knitting and went to answer the phone.* 她匆匆把編織物亂塞, 然後去接電話。

bung¹ /bʌŋ; bʌŋ/ *n* a round piece of rubber, wood or other material used to close the hole in a container 塞子

bung² *v* [T + adv/prep] *BrE infml* to put, push, or throw something somewhere quickly and carelessly 〔英式, 非正式〕投, 扔, 擲〔某物〕: *Bung the butter in the fridge, will you?* 把黃油扔到冰箱裡去, 好嗎?

bung sthg ↔ **up** *phr v* [T] *infml* to block something 〔非正式〕堵住, 塞住〔某物〕: *My nose is bunged up.* 我的鼻子塞住了。

bun·ga·low /ˈbʌŋgəˌlo; ˈbʌŋgələʊ/ *n* a house which is built on one level 平房 –see 見 HOUSE (USAGE用法) –see picture on page 729 見 729 頁彩圖

bun·gle /ˈbʌŋgl̩; ˈbʌŋgəl/ *v* **bungled, bungling** [I;T] to do something badly 把〔某事〕搞糟: *He'll bungle the job.* 他會把工作搞糟的。–**bungler** *n*

bun·ion /ˈbʌnjən; ˈbʌnjən/ *n* a painful swelling on your big toe 拇趾囊(炎)腫

bunk /bʌŋk; bʌŋk/ *n* **1** [C] a narrow bed fixed to a wall on a ship or train 〔車、船上靠壁而設的〕鋪位, 臥鋪 **2** [C] (also 又作 **bunk bed**) one of two beds placed one above the other, often for children 〔常為小孩用的〕雙層牀的上鋪或下鋪 **3** [U] *infml* nonsense 〔非正式〕廢話; 胡說: *That's a load of bunk.* 那是廢話連篇。**4 do a bunk** *BrE infml* to leave without telling anyone 〔英式, 非正式〕逃之夭夭; 擅自離開

bun·ker /ˈbʌŋkə; ˈbʌŋkɚ/ *n* **1** a place to store coal, usually on a ship or outside a house 〔船上或室外的〕煤艙, 堆煤處 **2** a shelter, usually built underground, for protection against military attack 掩體; 地堡 **3** a large hole on a GOLF COURSE 〔高爾夫球場的〕沙坑

buoy¹ /bɔɪ; bɔɪ/ *n* a floating object fastened to the bottom of the sea which shows ships where there are rocks or where it is safe to go 浮標; 航標

buoy² *v* [T] **1** to keep something at a high

B

level 使〔某物〕浮起 **2** to keep someone cheerful 使〔某人〕振奮: *Her spirits were buoyed up by hopes of success.* 成功的希望振奮了她的精神。

buoy·an·cy /ˈbɔɪənsɪ; ˈbɔɪənsi/ *n* [U] **1** the tendency of an object to float or the power of a liquid to make something float 浮性; 浮力: *the buoyancy of light wood* 輕質木材的浮性 **2** the ability of prices or business to return to a high level after a problem 〔價格或生意的〕回升能力: *the buoyancy of the American market* 美國市場的復甦 **3** the ability to remain cheerful or to recover quickly from disappointment 保持愉快心情; 恢復樂觀 –**buoyant** *adj*: *The financial markets are still buoyant.* 金融市場仍然行情看漲。

bur·ble /ˈbɜːbl; ˈbɜːbəl/ *v* **burbled, burbling** [I] **1** to make a sound like a stream flowing over stones 發出汨汨聲 **2** to talk quickly but in a way that makes little sense 嘮叨; 絮絮不休: *He burbled on for hours.* 他絮絮叨叨地說了幾個小時。

bur·den[1] /ˈbɜːdn̩; ˈbɜːdn̩/ *n fml* 〔正式〕 **1** something heavy that you have to carry 擔子; 負荷 **2** something which continually worries you or is difficult to bear 〔困擾人的〕重擔, 負擔: *the burden of responsibility* 責任的重擔

****burden**[2] *v* [T] *fml* 〔正式〕 **1** to give someone a lot of heavy things to carry 加負荷於〔某人〕; 使負重: *Burdened with so much equipment, I climbed with difficulty.* 我揹著這麼多設備, 登山很吃力。 **2 burden someone with something** to cause someone a lot of worry or trouble 用某事煩擾某人: *I won't burden you with my problems.* 我不想拿我的問題來煩你。

bu·reau /ˈbjʊro; ˈbjʊərəʊ/ *n* **bureaux** /ˈbjʊroz; ˈbjʊərəʊz/ **1** *BrE* a large desk or writing-table with a wooden cover which slides over the top to close it 〔英式〕大書桌, 寫字枱 **2** the usual American word for 〔美式〕= CHEST OF DRAWERS **3** a division of a government department 〔政府機構的〕局, 部, 處 **4** an office where a particular kind of work is done 〔做某種工作的〕辦公室: *an information bureau* 詢問處

bu·reauc·ra·cy /bjʊˈrɒkrəsɪ; bjʊəˈrɒkrəsi/ *n* **bureaucracies 1** [C;U] a system of government by many officials who are appointed rather than elected; **bureaucracy** sometimes means these officials 官僚制度; 官僚 **2** [U] a system of doing things officially which is annoying, unnecessarily difficult to understand, and usually ineffective 官僚主義; 官僚作風

bu·reau·crat /ˈbjʊrə,kræt; ˈbjʊərəkræt/ *n* an official who works in a government department and who follows all the rules carefully, perhaps too carefully 〔墨守成規的〕官僚, 官僚主義者

bu·reau·crat·ic /ˌbjʊroˈkrætɪk; ˌbjʊərəˈkrætɪk/ *adj* taking a long time to do things because there are lots of official rules 拖拖拉拉的; 官僚作風的: *bureaucratic procedures* 煩瑣拖拉的程序

bur·ger /ˈbɜːgɚ; ˈbɜːgəʳ/ *n* small pieces of meat made into a round flat shape and fried before eating 〔圓形的〕(煎)肉餅

bur·glar /ˈbɜːglɚ; ˈbɜːgləʳ/ *n* someone who gets into a house or shop illegally in order to steal things 〔潛入住宅或商店的〕竊賊 – see 見 THIEF (USAGE 用法)

burglar a·larm /ˈ·· ·,·/ *n* an apparatus that makes a loud warning noise when a thief breaks into a building 防盜警報器

bur·glar·y /ˈbɜːglərɪ; ˈbɜːgləri/ *n* **burglaries** [C;U] the crime of entering a building by force with the intention of stealing things 入屋盜竊罪

bur·gle /ˈbɜːgl̩; ˈbɜːgəl/ *v* **burgled, burgling** (also 又作 **burglarize** /ˈbɜːglə,raɪz; ˈbɜːgləraɪz/ *AmE* 〔美式〕) [I;T] to break into a building and steal from it 入屋盜竊: *I was burgled while I was out last night.* 我昨晚外出時家中被盜。

bur·i·al /ˈbɛrɪəl; ˈbɛriəl/ *n* [C;U] the act or ceremony of putting a dead body into a grave 埋葬; 葬禮

bur·ly /ˈbɜːlɪ; ˈbɜːli/ *adj* big and strong (used of a person) 粗壯的, 結實的〔指人〕 –**burliness** *n* [U]

burn[1] /bɜːn; bɜːn/ *v* **burnt** /bɜːnt; bɜːnt/ *or* **burned** /bɜːnd; bɜːnd/, **burnt** *or* **burned 1** [I] to be or catch on fire 着火; 燃燒: *the whole city was burning.* 整座城市好像都在燃燒。 | *The wood was damp, so didn't burn easily.* 木頭濕了, 所以不容易着火。 **2** [T] to damage, hurt, or destroy something by means of heat or fire 燒壞; 燒傷; 燒毀: *You should burn all those old papers.* 你應該把那些舊文件全都燒掉。 | *I burnt my hand on the iron.* 我的手給熨斗燙傷了。 | *Careful you don't burn the meat.* 小心別把肉燒焦了。 | *If you go out in this hot sun you'll get burned.* 太陽這麼熱, 你要是出去, 會給曬黑的。 **3** [I] (of food) to be spoilt by being cooked too much or too quickly 〔食物〕燒焦, 燒糊: *Oh no, the potatoes have burnt.* 啊, 不好了, 馬鈴薯燒糊了。 **4** [T] to use something for power, heating, or lighting 燒, 點〔燈、燭等〕; 加熱: *This boiler will burn oil or coal.* 這個鍋爐使用油或煤。 **5** [I] to be or feel very hot 發燙; 感到灼熱: *My face was burning.* 我臉上火辣辣的。 **6 burning with** full of a strong feeling 充滿〔強烈感情〕的: *She was burning with desire.* 她慾火中燒。 **be burning to do something** to be very eager to do something 渴望做某事: *I was burning to tell everyone the news.* 我急於要把這消息告訴每一個人。 **8 burn your boats/bridges** to do something which means that you will not be able to change your mind and do something different later 自絕後路; 破釜沉舟: *We must be careful not to burn our boats.* 我們必須當心，不要自絕後路。

burn away *phr v* [I] to disappear by being burnt 燒掉: *The wood had burnt away to nothing.* 木頭已燒成了灰燼。

burn down *phr v* **1** [I] (of a building) to be destroyed by being burnt〔建築物〕被燒毀: *The cinema burnt down last year.* 電影院去年被燒毀了。**2** [T **burn** sthg ↔ **down**] to destroy a building by burning it 燒毀〔建築物〕: *The school was burnt down by vandals.* 學校被人縱火燒毀了。

burn sthg ↔ **off** *phr v* [T] to remove something by burning 燒掉〔某物〕: *He was badly injured in the accident, and all his hair was burnt off.* 他在事故中嚴重受傷，頭髮也全部燒掉了。

burn out *phr v* **1** [I] to stop working because of damage caused by heat 燒壞: *The engine had burned out.* 引擎給燒壞了。**2 the fire burned out, the fire burned itself out** the fire stopped burning because there was nothing left to burn 火燒完自滅 **3 burn yourself out** to become ill or very tired by working too hard〔因拼命工作而〕得病或累垮

burn up *phr v* **1** [I] to be destroyed by being burned 燒毀: *The rocket burnt up when it re-entered the earth's atmosphere.* 火箭重入地球大氣層時焚毀。**2** [I] (of a fire or a flame) to burn more brightly or more strongly〔火、火焰〕燒得更亮［更旺］ **3** [T **burn** sthg ↔ **up**] to use a lot of fuel 耗費〔燃料〕: *This engine really burns up petrol!* 這引擎真費汽油。

■ USAGE 用法: In British English **burned** is used as the past tense or past participle of **burn** only if the verb is intransitive ☆在英式英語中，只有當 **burn** 是不及物動詞時，才用 **burned** 作為該動詞的過去式或過去分詞: *The fire* **burned** *brightly.* 火燒得很旺。But if the verb is transitive **burnt** is more usual 但如果是及物動詞，**burnt** 則更常用: *She* **burnt** *his letters.* 她燒了他的信。

---

burn[2] *n* a place on your skin where you have been burned 燒傷[灼傷]處: *Many of the victims suffered severe burns.* 許多罹難者嚴重燒傷。

burn·ing /'bɜːnɪŋ; 'bɜːnɪŋ/ *adj* **1** being on fire 燃燒的: *a burning house* 着火的房子 **2** very hot 火熱的: *a burning fever* 高燒 **3** [only before a noun 只用於名詞前] very important or urgent 極重要的；緊急的: *The environment is one of the burning issues of our time.* 我們的當務之急是環境問題。**4** [only before a noun 只用於名詞前] powerful or very strong (used of feelings) 強烈的[情感情]；有力的: *a burning desire* 迫切的慾望 | *a*

burning ambition 勃勃野心

bur·nished /'bɜːnɪʃt; 'bɜːnɪʃt/ *adj* polished with something hard and smooth (used of metal) 擦亮的〔指金屬〕

burnt /bɜːnt; bɜːnt/ the past tense and past participle of BURN[1] ☆ BURN[1] 的過去式和過去分詞

burnt-out /ˌ· '··◂/ *adj* **1** completely destroyed by fire 全部燒毀的 **2** very tired and possibly ill from too much hard work 精疲力盡的

burp /bɜːp; bɜːp/ *v infml*〔非正式〕**1** [T] to help a baby to get rid of stomach gas, usually by rubbing or gently striking its back〔用摩背或輕輕拍背的方法〕使〔嬰兒〕嗝 **2** [I] to make a noise as stomach gas suddenly rises to your mouth 打嗝 **–burp** *n*

bur·row[1] /'bɜːrəʊ; 'bʌrəʊ/ *n* a hole in the ground made by an animal such as a rabbit, in which it lives or hides〔兔子等動物所掘的〕地洞

burrow[2] *v* **1** [I+adv/prep] to move in a particular direction by digging 打地洞; 掘穴: *They burrowed under the fence.* 他們在籬笆下掘洞。**2** [I;T] to press close to someone or under something as if looking for warmth, safety, or love 偎依; (使)貼近: *He burrowed under the bedclothes.* 他鑽進被窩裡。

bur·sar /'bɜːsə; 'bɜːsəʳ/ *n* someone in a college or school who is responsible for the accounts〔學校裡〕管財務的人

bur·sa·ry /'bɜːsəri; 'bɜːsəri/ *n* a sum of money given to a student to help pay for a course of study 獎學金; 助學金

burst[1] /bɜːst; bɜːst/ *v* **burst, burst, bursting 1** [I;T] to break open or apart suddenly because of too much pressure inside, causing the contents to come out (使)爆炸; (使)炸裂; (使)脹破: *Don't drive over those nails — you'll burst a tyre.* 別輾過那些釘子——車輪會爆的。| *Help! I've got a burst water pipe!* 幫幫我! 水管裂了! | *That balloon will burst if you leave it in the sun.* 如果你把那氣球丟在太陽下面，它會爆破的。**2 be bursting with** to be very full of something 充滿〔某物〕的: *The town is bursting with tourists.* 市鎮上擠滿了遊客。–see 見 BREAK (USAGE 用法) **3 burst open** to open violently and suddenly 猛然打開: *The door burst open and the police stormed in.* 門猛然打開，警察闖了進來。**4** [I+adv/prep] to move suddenly and quickly in a way that is noticed 衝; 闖: *He burst angrily into the room.* 他怒氣衝衝地闖進房間。**5 bursting to do something** extremely keen to do something 急不可待地做某事: *She's bursting to tell you her news.* 她急於要告訴你她的消息。**6** [I] to make a sudden loud noise 突發巨響: *A cheer burst from the crowd.* 人羣中爆發出一片歡呼聲。**7 burst into flames** suddenly to begin to burn 突然起火

---

burst in on sbdy *phr v* [T] to interrupt someone suddenly and noisily 插嘴;〔吵吵嚷嚷地〕打斷〔某人〕: *They burst in on me while I was working.* 我正在工作的時候，他們突然闖了進來。

burst into sthg *phr v* [T] to start doing something, for example, crying, laughing, or singing 突然〔哭、笑、唱〕起來: *She burst into tears.* 她突然哭起來。 | *We burst into fits of laughter.* 我們突然大笑起來。

burst out *phr v* **1 burst out laughing/crying** to begin laughing or crying suddenly 突然笑〔哭〕起來 **2** [I] to say something suddenly and with strong feeling〔激動地〕突然説: *"I don't believe it!" he burst out.* "我不相信！"他突然喊道。

burst² *n* **1** the result of something which has burst 缺口; 裂口: *a burst in the water pipes* 水管上的裂口 **2** a sudden short period of great activity, loud noise, or strong feeling 爆發; 一陣: *a burst of laughter* 一陣大笑 | *a burst of machine-gun fire* 一陣機槍掃射

***bur·y** /ˈbɛrɪ; ˈberi/ *v* **buried, buried, burying** [T] **1** to put a dead body into a grave 埋葬: *She was buried next to her late husband.* 她被葬在亡夫旁邊。 **2** to cover something up either intentionally or accidentally〔故意或偶然〕掩埋，埋藏: *The dog has buried a bone in the garden.* 狗把一塊骨頭埋在花園裡。 | *His glasses were buried under a pile of newspapers.* 他的眼鏡掩埋在一堆報紙下面。 **3 bury yourself in something** to work very hard at something on your own 埋頭做某事: *After his wife's death, he buried himself in his business.* 妻子死後，他埋頭做生意。 **4 bury the hatchet** *infml* to become friends again after a quarrel《非正式》言歸於好

***bus¹** /bʌs; bʌs/ *n* **1** a large motor vehicle which takes people from one place to another 公共汽車: *I hope she catches the bus.* 我希望她能趕上公共汽車。 | *You're going to miss the bus.* 你會趕不上公共汽車。 –see picture on page 991 見 991 頁彩圖 **2 by bus** travelling in a bus 乘公共汽車: *Let's go by bus.* 我們坐公共汽車去吧。 –see 見 TRANSPORT (USAGE 用法)

bus² *v* **-ss-** [T] to move people by bus 用公共汽車運送: *The village children are bussed to the school in the nearest town.* 村裡的孩子們是用公共汽車送到最近的城裡上學的。

bus con·duc·tor /ˈ· ·ˌ··/ *n* someone on a bus who is in charge of selling tickets 公共汽車售票員

bush /bʊʃ; bʊʃ/ *n* **1** a low woody plant, smaller than a tree and with many stems 灌木; 矮樹: *a rose bush* 玫瑰花叢 –see picture on page 729 見 729 頁彩圖 **2 the bush** uncleared wild country in Australia or Africa〔澳大利亞或非洲的〕未開墾的叢林地帶

bush·y /ˈbʊʃɪ; ˈbʊʃi/ *adj* **bushier, bushiest** growing thickly (usually used of hair) 濃密的〔常指毛髮〕: *a bushy beard* 濃密的大鬍子 |

a bushy tail 毛茸茸的尾巴 –**bushiness** *n* [U]

bus·i·ly /ˈbɪzɪlɪ; ˈbɪzɪli/ *adv* in an active way 忙碌地: *She bustled around busily.* 她走動地忙來忙去。

***busi·ness** /ˈbɪznɪs; ˈbɪznəs/ *n* **1** [U] the work you do as a job to earn money 職業; 工作: *I'm in the insurance business.* 我在保險行業。 | *He's here on business, not for pleasure.* 他來這裡出差，不是來玩的。 **2** [U] the production, buying, and selling of goods and services 生意; 交易: *She wants to go into business when she leaves college.* 她大學畢業後想經商。 | *He set up in business as a property developer.* 他以做房地產開發商而開始立足於商界的。 **3 do business with someone** to buy something from someone, or sell something to them 和某人做生意: *It's a pleasure to do business with you.* 和你做生意很愉快。 **4** [U] the amount or value of trade being done 營業額; 貿易額: *"How's business?"* "營業額如何？" | *Business is booming.* 營業額激增。 **5** [C] an organization which provides a service or buys and sells something 商行; 商店: *He runs a small travel business in town.* 他在城裡開了一家小型旅遊服務商店。 | *It's a very profitable business.* 這是一家賺錢的商店。 **6** [U] your responsibility or concern 職責; 責任: *What I do with the money is none of your business.* 我怎樣處理這筆錢與你無關。 **7** [sing; U] a situation, event, or matter for talking about together 討論的情況或事情: *Let's get down to the main business of the meeting.* 我們來討論一下會議的主要議題吧。 | *It's a strange business.* 這是件奇怪的事情。 | *Investing in shares is a risky business.* 投資股票是件冒險的事情。 **8 have no business to do something, have no business doing something** to have no right to do something 無權做某事 **9 get down to business** to start dealing with the most important subject 開始處理最重要的事 **10 out of business** no longer able to operate as a business 不再經營: *These big increases in rent could put a lot of small shops out of business.* 房租的大幅度增加會使許多小商店停業。

busi·ness·like /ˈbɪznɪsˌlaɪk; ˈbɪznəs-laɪk/ *adj* acting quickly, calmly, and with common sense 效率高的; 做事冷靜而注重實際的: *Kate conducted the meeting in a businesslike way.* 凱特有條不紊地主持會議。

busi·ness·man /ˈbɪznɪsˌmæn; ˈbɪznəsˌmən/ *n* **businessmen** /-mən; -mən/ **1** a man who works in business, for example as the owner, director, or manager of a company 商人; 實業家 **2** a man who knows how to make money from good deals 生財有道的人: *You won't be able to knock the price down. He's a very good businessman.* 你無法把價錢壓下來的。他是個很會做生意的人。

busi·ness·wom·an /ˈbɪznɪsˌwʊmən; ˈbɪz-nəsˌwʊmən/ *n* **businesswomen** /-ˈwɪmɪn;

-'wɪmɪn/ **1** a woman who works in business, for example as the owner, director, or manager of a company 女商人; 女實業家 **2** a woman who knows how to make money from good deals 生財有道的女子

bus·ker /'bʌskə; 'bʌskəʳ/ *n* a person who plays music in the street for money 街頭藝人

bus stop /· ·/ *n* a fixed place where buses stop for passengers 公共汽車站: *I saw him waiting at the bus stop.* 我看見他在公共汽車站等車。

bust¹ /bʌst; bʌst/ *v* **busted, busted** *or* **bust** [T] *infml* 〖非正式〗 **1** to break something 打破, 打碎〔某物〕: *I bust my watch this morning.* 今天早上我把手錶摔壞了。**2** (of the police) to take someone to a police station because they have done something wrong 〔警察〕拘捕〔某人〕: *He was busted for possessing marijuana.* 他因藏有大麻而被逮捕。**3** (of the police) to enter a place without warning to look for something illegal 〔警察〕突擊搜查〔違禁物品〕

bust up *phr v infml* 〖非正式〗 **1** [I] to quarrel and end a relationship 爭吵並結束關係: *I've bust up with my boyfriend.* 我和男朋友吵架後分手了。**2** [T **bust** sthg ↔ **up**] to spoil something and make it come to an end 破壞, 毀壞〔某事物〕: *"Why are the police here?" "Apparently Greenpeace are planning to bust up the meeting."* "警察為甚麼在這兒?" "看樣子綠色和平組織打算破壞這次會議。"

bust² *n* **1** a piece of SCULPTURE showing someone's head, shoulders, and chest 半身雕塑像〔包括頭、肩、胸部〕**2** a woman's breasts 〔女人的〕胸部 **3** a measurement round a woman's breasts and back 胸圍: *She's got a 34-inch bust.* 她的胸圍是三十四英寸。

bust³ *adj infml* 〖非正式〗 **1** broken 破裂的; 損壞的: *My watch is bust.* 我的手錶壞了。**2** **go bust** (of a business) to fail because it cannot pay the money that it owes, so that it has to close 〔企業〕破產的: *I'm not surprised he went bust, considering the risks he took.* 以他所冒的險來看, 我對他破產並不驚訝。

bus·tle¹ /'bʌs; 'bʌsəl/ *v* **bustled, bustling** [I] to move in a hurried and determined way because you are very busy 忙忙碌碌; 熙熙攘攘: *She bustled about the house.* 她在房子裡忙個沒完。–**bustling** *adj*: *a bustling market town* 繁忙熱鬧的市鎮

bustle² *n* [U] excitement, noise, and great activity 忙亂; 喧鬧: *the bustle of a big city* 大城市的喧鬧

bust-up /· ·/ *n infml* 〖非正式〗 **1** a fight 毆鬥: *There was quite a bust-up last night outside the cinema.* 昨天晚上電影院外面發生了一場激烈的毆鬥。**2** the end of a relationship following a serious quarrel 〔激烈爭吵後的〕關係破裂: *the bust-up of their*

marriage 他們婚姻的破裂

bus·y¹ /'bɪzɪ; 'bɪzɪ/ *adj* **busier, busiest 1** having a lot of work or other things to do so that you are not free for anything else 忙碌的; 沒空的: *She's busy now. Can you come back later?* 她現在正忙着。你能稍後再來嗎? | *I was too busy working to notice the time.* 我忙於工作, 沒注意到時間。| *a busy man* 大忙人 **2** full of work or activity 繁忙的; 熱鬧的: *a busy day* 忙碌的一天 | *one of the busiest airports in the world* 世界上最繁忙的機場之一 **3** in use (used of telephones) 佔線的〔指電話〕: *I'm sorry, sir, the line is busy.* 對不起, 先生, 電話忙着。–**busily** *adv*

busy² *v* **busied, busied, busying: busy yourself with something** to give yourself something to do 使自己忙於某事: *He busied himself with answering letters.* 他忙於寫回信。

bus·y·bod·y /'bɪzɪ,bɒdɪ; 'bɪzɪ,bɑdɪ/ *n* someone who takes too much interest in other people's affairs and may try to give advice which is not wanted. 愛管閒事的人

but¹ /bət; bət; *stong* 強讀 bʌt; bʌt/ *conj* **1** a word you use when you are saying something which is opposite to or different from something else that you have just said 然而, 但是〔用於表示和剛才所說的相反或不同〕: *I'd like to go, but I can't.* 我想去, 但是無法去。| *It costs a lot of money, but it's well worth it.* 這要花許多錢, 但很值得。| *We were going to come and see you, but it rained so we stayed at home.* 我們本打算來看你, 可是下雨了, 所以我們留在家裡。| *The house was small but pleasant.* 房子雖小, 但很舒適。| *He won not one but two prizes!* 他得的不是一項獎, 而是兩項獎! **2** a word you use when you are surprised by what someone else has just said, and are also pleased, shocked, angry, etc〔表示驚奇、愉快、震驚、憤怒等〕: *"They've decided to close the school down." "But that's ridiculous!"* "他們已決定關閉學校。" "那可真荒唐!" | *"Mary's leaving tomorrow." "But she only arrived yesterday!"* "瑪麗明天走。" "但她昨天才到呀!" | *"He's finally managed to get a job." "But that's wonderful news!"* "他終於得到了一份工作。" "這可真是大好消息!" **3** a word you use when you are introducing a new subject 〔用於引入新話題〕: *Later in the programme we'll be discussing the progress of the war. But first here are the news headlines.* 在後面的節目中我們將討論戰爭的進程。現在請先聽新聞提要。| *I'm sure there's a lot more that could be said on this subject, but let's move on to our next question.* 關於這個題目肯定還有很多可以談論, 但我們講下一個問題吧。**4** used after expressions such as "I'm sorry" and "excuse me" 〔用於"對不起"、"請原諒"等套語後〕: *I'm sorry, but could you repeat that, please?* 對不起, 能不能請你再說一遍? | *Excuse me, but haven't I met you somewhere before?* 對不

起, 我以前在哪兒碰到過你們嗎? **5 but then** an expression you use when you are adding something that shows that a fact is not surprising 但另一方面〔用於補充說明某事並不令人驚訝〕: *It's not a very sophisticated computer, but then it only cost a few hundred pounds.* 這不是甚麼很精密的電腦, 不過只值幾百英鎊。

***but²** *prep* **1** except 除了…以外: *There's no one here but me.* 除了我以外, 這裡沒別人。| *All but one of the ships were destroyed.* 除了一艘船以外, 其他所有的船都毀了。**2 but for** except for the efforts of a particular person or the effects of a particular thing 要不是; 如果沒有: *But for her, I would have drowned.* 要是沒有她, 我便淹死了。| *But for his help, I would probably still be stranded there now.* 要不是他幫忙, 我可能現在還困在那裡。**3 the next but one** the one after the next one 再下一個 **4 the last but one** the one before the last one 倒數第二個

butch /butʃ; butʃ/ *adj BrE infml* dressing and behaving too much like a big strong man (used of women) 〔英式, 非正式〕男性化的〔指女人〕

butch·er¹ /ˈbutʃə; ˈbutʃɚ/ *n* **1** someone who works in or owns a shop which sells meat 屠夫; 肉商 **2 butcher's** a shop which sells meat 肉店; 肉鋪: *I'm just going to the butcher's to get something for dinner.* 我正要去肉店買點肉做晚餐。

butcher² *v* [T] **1** to kill animals for their meat 屠宰〔牲口〕 **2** to kill people in a cruel way 屠殺〔人〕–see KILL (USAGE 用法)

but·ler /ˈbʌtlə; ˈbʌtlɚ/ *n* the chief male servant of a house 男管家

butt¹ /bʌt; bʌt/ *v* [I;T] to hit or push against something with the head or horns 〔用頭或角〕頂撞, 衝撞

butt in *phr v* [I] *infml* to interrupt a conversation when you have not been asked for your opinion 〔非正式〕插嘴: *I wish you wouldn't keep butting in* **on** *us.* 我希望你別在我們談話時不斷地插嘴。

butt² *n* **1** the thick end of a tool or weapon 柄; 〔工具或武器等〕粗的一端: *a rifle butt* 步槍柄 **2** the small piece of a cigarette which is left when you have finished smoking 煙蒂 **3** someone that people make fun of 取笑的對象; 笑柄: *Poor John was the butt of all their jokes.* 可憐的約翰總是成為他們說笑的對象。**4** *infml* the part of your body that you sit on 〔非正式〕屁股: *Get off your butt and do some work.* 別老坐著, 做點事吧。

but·ter¹ /ˈbʌtə; ˈbʌtɚ/ *n* [U] a fairly solid yellow fat made from cream and spread on bread or used in cooking 黃油; 奶油 –see picture on page 504 見 504 頁彩圖 **2 butter wouldn't melt in his mouth** *infml* – he looks as if he would never do anything wrong but this is not really so 〔非正式〕表面上老實(其實不然) **–buttery** *adj*

butter² *v* [T] to spread something with butter 塗黃油於〔某物〕: *Shall I butter your bread for you?* 我給你的麵包抹上黃油, 好嗎?

butter sbdy ↔ **up** *phr v* [T] *infml* to praise or please someone because you want them to do something for you 〔非正式〕奉承〔某人〕; 巴結〔某人〕

but·ter·cup /ˈbʌtə‚kʌp; ˈbʌtɚkʌp/ *n* a small plant with yellow flowers which grows in fields 毛茛〔一種開黃花的植物〕

but·ter·fly /ˈbʌtə‚flaɪ; ˈbʌtɚflaɪ/ *n* **butterflies** **1** [C] a delicate insect which has large beautifully-coloured wings 蝴蝶 **2 have butterflies in your stomach** *infml* to feel very nervous before doing something 〔非正式〕〔做某事之前〕感到十分緊張 **3** [U] (also 又作 **butterfly stroke**) a way of swimming on your front in which you move both your arms together over your head 蝶泳

but·ter·scotch /ˈbʌtə‚skɒtʃ; ˈbʌtɚskɒtʃ/ *n* [U] a sweet food made from sugar and butter boiled together 黃油硬糖, 奶油糖果

but·tock /ˈbʌtək; ˈbʌtək/ *n* **buttocks** the two fleshy parts of your body on which you sit 臀部

but·ton¹ /ˈbʌtn; ˈbʌtn/ *n* **1** a small hard object, usually fixed to one part of a piece of clothing and passed through a hole in another part to join them together 鈕扣: *Do your buttons up, Mary.* 扣上鈕扣, 瑪麗。–see picture on page 210 見 210 頁彩圖 **2** a small object or piece of apparatus that is pressed to start a machine 按鈕: *Which button do I press first?* 我先撳哪個按鈕?

button² *v* [T] to close or fasten something with buttons 用鈕扣扣住〔某物〕: *Button your coat! It's cold outside.* 扣好外套吧! 外面很冷。

button sthg ↔ **up** *phr v* [T] **1** to close or fasten something with buttons 用鈕扣扣住〔某物〕 **2** *infml* to complete something successfully 〔非正式〕順利完成〔某事物〕: *The new contract is all buttoned up now.* 新合同現在已擬訂好了。

but·ton·hole¹ /ˈbʌtn‚həul; ˈbʌtnhoul/ *n* **1** a hole for a button to be put through to fasten a shirt or coat 鈕孔; 扣眼 **2** *BrE* a flower to wear in a buttonhole or pinned to your coat or dress 〔英式〕胸花〔佩帶在鈕孔上或別在衣服上的花朵〕

buttonhole² *v* **buttonholed, buttonholing** [T] *infml* to stop someone and force them to listen to you 〔非正式〕強迫〔某人〕聽: *She buttonholed me in the corridor and asked me for another pay rise.* 她在走廊裡強拉住我, 要求再加工資。

but·tress¹ /ˈbʌtrɪs; ˈbʌtrɪs/ *n* a support for a wall 扶壁

buttress² *v* **1** to support something with a buttress 以扶壁支撐〔某物〕 **2** *fml* to support or strengthen something 〔正式〕支持或支撐〔某事物〕: *Buttressed by its past profits, the* *company managed to survive for another five years.* 公司憑着以往利潤的支撐, 設法又度過了五年。

bux·om /'bʌksəm; 'bʌksəm/ *adj* attractively healthy-looking, usually with large breasts (an old-fashioned word which is now usually used humorously) 豐滿的; 健美的〔老式説法, 現在常表示幽默〕

★★★ **buy¹** /baɪ; baɪ/ *v* **bought** /bɔt; bɔːt/, **bought, buying 1** [I;T] to obtain something by paying money 購買〔某物〕: *We bought the flat for £50,000.* 我們花了五萬英鎊買下這套房間。| *Let me buy you a drink.* 讓我請你喝杯酒吧。| *They bought the car secondhand from their neighbours.* 他們從鄰居那裡買下了這輛二手汽車。| *When prices are low, I buy.* 我趁價錢便宜時買東西。

□ USEFUL PATTERNS 有用句型
to buy something for someone; to buy someone something; to buy something + adjective

2 [T] *infml* to be willing to believe something 〔非正式〕相信, 接受〔某事物〕: *The police will never buy a story like that.* 警察永遠不會相信那樣的故事。**3 buy time** *infml* to delay an action or decision that seems to be coming too soon 〔非正式〕拖延時間: *He tried to buy time by doing a lot of talking.* 他不斷談話, 企圖拖延時間。

buy sbdy ↔ **off** *phr v* [T] to pay someone money so that they do not carry out a threat or cause trouble 收買〔某人〕〔以擺脱威脅或麻煩〕

buy sbdy ↔ **out** *phr v* **1** [T] to gain control of a business by buying all the shares which you do not already own 買下...的全部股份 **2 buy yourself out** to pay money so that you can leave the army before you should 出錢使自己免服役: *He bought himself out of the army.* 他花錢使自己從軍中退役。

buy sthg ↔ **up** *phr v* [T] to buy all of something that it is possible to buy 全部買下; 買光: *All the suitable building land has been bought up by property developers.* 所有適合建築的土地都被房地産開發商買下了。

buy² *n infml* something bought, especially something of value at a low price 〔非正式〕買的東西〔尤指便宜貨〕: *It's a good buy at that price!* 用這個價買下確實便宜!

★ **buy·er** /'baɪə; 'baɪər/ *n* **1** someone who chooses and buys things to be sold in a large shop 〔大商店的〕採購員 **2** someone who is buying 購買者; 買主: *We've got a buyer for our flat!* 我們這套房間有了買主。

buzz /bʌz; bʌz/ *v* **1** [I] to make the continuous sound that bees make 發出嗡嗡聲 **2** [I] to be full of people talking excitedly 充滿〔興奮的談話〕聲音: *The room buzzed with excitement.* 房裡充滿了一片興奮的説話聲。**3**

[I;T] to call someone by using a buzzer 用蜂鳴器傳呼: *She buzzed* **for** *her secretary.* 她按蜂鳴器叫自己的祕書。**4 buzz off** *BrE infml* go away 〔英式, 非正式〕走開: *Buzz off and stop bothering me.* 走開, 別打擾我。

buzz² *n* **1** the sound of bees 〔蜜蜂的〕嗡嗡聲 **2** a feeling of excitement 興奮感 **3 give someone a buzz** *infml* to telephone someone 〔非正式〕給某人打電話: *I'll give you a buzz tomorrow.* 明天我給你打電話。

buz·zard /'bʌzəd; 'bʌzəd/ *n* a large brown bird that kills and eats other creatures 鵟, 鵟鷹〔一種食肉巨鷹〕

buz·zer /'bʌzə; 'bʌzər/ *n* a piece of electrical machinery that makes a buzzing sound 蜂鳴器

★★ **by¹** /baɪ; baɪ/ *prep* **1** near 在...旁邊; 靠近: *He was standing by the window.* 他站在窗邊。–see picture on page 764 見 764 頁彩圖 **2** past 經過: *She rushed by me.* 她奔過我身邊。**3** through using or doing something 靠; 由; 通過: *The burglars got in by an open window.* 竊賊從一扇開着的窗子進來。| *He makes his living by writing.* 他靠寫作為生。**4** used to show who did something or what caused something 被; 由〔表示行為者是誰或起作用的事物是甚麼〕: *The house was built by my father.* 這房子是我父親造的。| *a play by Shakespeare* 莎士比亞寫的戲劇 | *The school was damaged by fire.* 學校在火災中受損。**5** no later than a particular time 不遲於; 到〔某時〕之前: *I've got to get this finished by Friday.* 我要在星期五之前把它做好。**6** in accordance with something 根據; 按照: *By law employers have to make sure that their machinery is safe.* 根據法律, 雇主應確保機械安全。| *He never plays by the rules.* 他從不按規則行事。**7** used in measurements and numbers 〔用於量度或數目中〕: *a room 15 feet by 20 feet* 一間十五英尺寬二十英尺長的房間 | *Divide the total by three.* 總數除以三。| *What's seven multiplied by eight?* 七乘以八是多少?

★★ **by²** *adv* **1** past 經過: *She moved aside to let me get by.* 她移到一邊讓我通過。**2 by and by** *infml* a little bit later 〔非正式〕不久以後; 過一會兒 **3 by and large** in general 大體上; 總的説來: *By and large I agree with you.* 總的説來, 我同意你的意見。

bye /baɪ; baɪ/ *interj infml* (also 又作 **bye-bye**) a word used when you leave someone or someone leaves you 〔非正式〕再見

by-e·lec·tion /'· ·,··/ *n* a special election held when a Member of Parliament suddenly dies or leaves his or her position 〔國會議員的〕補缺選舉

by·gone /'baɪɡɒn; 'baɪɡɒn/ *adj* [only before a noun 只用於名詞前] of a time long ago 過去的; 以往的: *relics of a bygone age* 舊時的遺跡

by·gones /'baɪɡɒnz; 'baɪɡɒnz/ *n* **let bygones be bygones** *infml* to forgive and forget the bad things in the past 【非正式】過去的就讓它過去吧

by·pass¹ /'baɪ͵pæs; 'baɪpɑːs/ *n* **1** a road around a busy town 〔繞過鬧市的〕旁道: *the Oxford bypass* 牛津旁路 **2** a way of directing blood through new tubes to avoid the part of someone's heart which is not working properly 分流術〔使血液流經新的管道而不經過心臟功能欠佳的部分〕

bypass² *v* [T] to avoid something 繞過; 避開: *Can we bypass Derby?* 我們能避開德比嗎? | *I bypassed the usual complaints procedure by writing directly to the owner of the company.* 我繞過通常的投訴程序, 直接寫信給公司老闆。

by-prod·uct /'· ͵··/ *n* **1** something additional which is produced when making or doing something else 副產品: *Silver is often obtained as a by-product during the separation of lead from rock.* 從礦石中提取鉛時, 往往可獲得銀這種副產品。 **2** an ad-ditional result, sometimes unexpected or unintended 意外收穫; 附帶的結果

by·stand·er /'baɪ͵stændɚ; 'baɪ͵stændəʳ/ *n* someone standing near, but not taking part in what is happening 旁觀者: *The police asked bystanders about the accident.* 警察向旁觀者了解事故經過。 | *I was just an innocent bystander.* 我只是一個無辜的旁觀者。

byte /baɪt; baɪt/ *n tech* a unit of computer information 【術語】〔電腦的〕二進位位組; 位元組

by·way /'baɪ͵we; 'baɪweɪ/ *n* a small road or path which is not much used or known 小路; 偏僻小徑

by·word /'baɪ͵wɝd; 'baɪwɜːd/ *n* a person, place, or thing that is taken as repre-senting some quality 〔人、地、物的〕別名; 代名詞: *The general's name had become a by-word **for** cruelty in war.* 那位將軍的名字在戰爭中成為殘暴的代名詞。

C, c

C, c /siː; siː/ *C's, c's or Cs, cs* **1** the 3rd letter
of the English alphabet 英語的第三個字母 **2**
when you have several points you want to
make, you can order them and show
where each one starts by using "a",
"b", "c", etc.; teachers and speakers on
technical subjects do this 第三〔要表述幾個
論點時, 可使用 a, b, c 等順序進行羅列; 教師
和講者常用此方法〕: *There are three factors
which have contributed to the plant's failure
to flower: a, the day length has been too
long; b, the temperature has not been
sufficiently high; and, c, the growing medium has been too acid.* 導致這植物未能開花
的因素有三個: 第一, 白日過長; 第二, 溫度不夠
高; 第三, 生長環境酸性過強。

c 1 a written abbreviation for 〔縮〕= CENT **2**
a written abbreviation for 〔縮〕= CIRCA 大
約: *c 1834* 約 1834 年

C an abbreviation for 〔縮〕= CENTIGRADE
or CELSIUS 攝氏: *100°C* 攝氏 100 度

cab /kæb; kæb/ *n* **1** a taxi 出租汽車, 計程車,
的士: *Shall we walk or take a cab?* 我們步行
(去)還是坐計程車(去)? **2** by cab travelling in
a cab 坐計程車: *Let's go by cab.* 我們坐計程
車去吧。 **3** the part of a bus or railway engine in which the driver sits or stands 〔公
共汽車或火車的〕司機室 **4** a horse-drawn
carriage for hire in former times 〔舊時的〕
出租馬車

cab·a·ret /ˌkæbəˈreɪ; ˈkæbəreɪ/ *n* [C;U]
entertainment, usually singing and dancing, in a restaurant or club at night 〔餐館或
俱樂部中的〕歌舞表演

cab·bage /ˈkæbɪdʒ; ˈkæbɪdʒ/ *n* [C;U] a
large round vegetable with thick green
leaves 椰菜; 包心菜 –see picture on page
504 見 504 頁彩圖

cab·in /ˈkæbɪn; ˈkæbɪn/ *n* **1** a small room
on a ship usually used for sleeping 〔船上
的〕客艙 **2** a small roughly built wooden
house 小木屋: *a log cabin* 小木屋 **3** the
enclosed space at the front of an aircraft
in which the pilot sits 〔飛機的〕駕駛艙

cab·i·net /ˈkæbənɪt; ˈkæbḷnɪt/ *n* **1** a piece
of furniture, with shelves or drawers, used
for storing or showing things 樹; 櫃: *She
keeps her most expensive china in a glass
cabinet.* 她把她最值錢的瓷器放在一個玻璃櫃
裡。 | *a medicine cabinet* 藥品櫃 **2** [+ sing/pl
verb] the most important ministers of the
government, who meet as a group to make
decisions or to advise the head of the
government 〔政府〕內閣: *The cabinet meets
next week to discuss education.* 內閣於下週
開會討論教育問題。

ca·ble[1] /ˈkeɪbl; ˈkeɪbəl/ *n* **1** [C;U] thick, heavy
rope usually made of wire, used on board
ships and to support bridges 〔船上、吊橋等
處用的〕粗索, 繩纜 **2** [C;U] a set of wires
which carry electricity, television signals,
or telephone messages 電纜: *a cable
connecting the printer to the computer* 聯接
打印機和電腦的電纜 | *an underwater tele-
phone cable* 海底電話電纜 **3** [C] *fml* a TELE-
GRAM 〔正式〕電報 **4** [U] CABLE TELEVI-
SION 有線電視

cable[2] *v* **cabled, cabling** [I;T] to send something by TELEGRAM 發電報; 用電報把…發
往…: *He cabled the news to London.* 他用電
報把消息發往倫敦。 | *I cabled him some
money.* 我電匯了一些錢給他。

cable car /ˈ·· ·/ *n* a vehicle which is
supported in the air by a cable, used for
carrying people to the tops of mountains
纜車

cable tel·e·vi·sion /ˌ·· ···ˈ··/ *n* [U] a system
of broadcasting television by cable, usually
paid for by the user 有線電視

cack·le /ˈkækl; ˈkækəl/ *v* **cackled, cackling**
[I] **1** to make the noise made by a hen 〔母雞〕
咯咯叫 **2** to laugh loudly and unpleasantly
with a sound like this 咯咯地笑: *The old man
cackled with amusement.* 那位老人高興得咯咯
大笑。

cac·tus /ˈkæktəs; ˈkæktəs/ *n* **cactuses** *or* **cacti**
/taɪ; taɪ/ a desert plant protected by sharp
prickles, with thick fleshy stems and leaves
仙人掌

ca·dav·er /kəˈdævə; kəˈdeɪvəʳ/ *n fml* a dead
human body 〔正式〕〔人的〕屍體

ca·dence /ˈkedns; ˈkeɪdəns/ *n* **1** a regular beat
of sound 節奏; 韻律 **2** the rise and fall of the
human voice 〔人聲音的〕抑揚頓挫

ca·det /kəˈdɛt; kəˈdɛt/ *n* a person studying to
become an officer in one of the armed

forces or the police 軍官學校[警官學校]的 學員

cadge /kædʒ; kædʒ/ v **cadged, cadging** [I;T] *infml* to get or try to get something by asking, often seeming to be taking advantage of someone 〖非正式〗乞討; 索取: *He cadged 50p for cigarettes from me yesterday.* 他昨天向我討了五十便士買香煙。

cae·sar·e·an /sɪ'zɛərɪən; sᵻ'zɪərɪən/ n (also 又作 **cesarean**) an operation in which a woman's body is cut open to allow the baby to be taken out, when an ordinary birth may be difficult or dangerous 剖腹產 (手術)

ca·fe /kə'fe; 'kæfeɪ/ n (also 又作 **café**) a small restaurant where drinks and light meals are served 咖啡館; 小餐館

caf·e·te·ri·a /ˌkæfə'tɪrɪə; ˌkæfᵻ'tɪərɪə/ n a restaurant, often in a factory or college, where people collect their own food and drink and carry it to a table〔常設在工廠或大學裡的〕自助餐廳[食堂]

caf·feine /'kæfiːn; 'kæfiːn/ n [U] a chemical substance found in coffee and tea which makes people feel more active 咖啡因, 咖啡鹼

cage /kedʒ; keɪdʒ/ n an enclosure made of a framework of wires or bars, used especially for keeping animals or birds in 鳥籠; 獸籠 –**caged** adj: *a caged bird* 關在籠中的鳥

cag·ey /'kedʒɪ; 'keɪdʒi/ adj infml secretive or unwilling to give information 〖非正式〗保密的: *She's very cagey about her past life.* 她對自己過去的生活守口如瓶。 –**cagily** adv

ca·jole /kə'dʒol; kə'dʒəʊl/ v **cajoled, cajoling** [T] to persuade someone to do something by using false praise or deceit 哄騙: *I was cajoled into taking the job.* 我被哄騙接受了那份工作。

*****cake** /kek; keɪk/ n **1** [C; U] a sweet food made by baking flour, eggs, fat, and sugar 糕餅, 蛋糕: *a birthday cake* 生日蛋糕 | *Would you like a piece of cake?* 你要不要來一塊蛋糕? **2** [C] a flat shaped piece of something 餅狀物; 塊狀物: *a fish cake* 魚餅 | *a cake of soap* 一塊肥皂 **3 be a piece of cake** infml to be very easy 〖非正式〗非常簡單; 易如反掌: *That exam was a piece of cake!* 那次考試容易極了! **4 have your cake and eat it** infml to have both the choices that are offered 〖非正式〗兩全其美; 兩者兼得: *You spend all your money on beer and then complain about being poor. You can't have your cake and eat it.* 你把所有的錢都花在啤酒上, 卻又抱怨自己窮。兩者是不可兼得的。 **5 go/sell like hot cakes** to be sold very quickly 銷售得很快: *Those pictures are going like hot cakes.* 那些畫銷路非常好。

caked /kekt; keɪkt/ adj thickly covered or formed into a hard mass 被厚厚覆蓋起來的; 結成塊的: *My boots were caked with mud.*

ca·lam·i·ty /kə'læmətɪ; kə'læmᵻti/ n **calamities** [C; U] a sudden terrible event that causes great loss and suffering 災難; 重大的不幸: *It would be an absolute calamity for these villages if the river flooded again.* 如果河水再次泛濫, 那對這些村莊無疑是一場天大的災難。

cal·ci·um /'kælsɪəm; 'kælsiəm/ n [U] a silver-white metallic ELEMENT found in bones, teeth, and chalk 鈣

*****cal·cu·late** /'kælkjəˌlet; 'kælkjᵿleɪt/ v **calculated, calculating** [I; T; +(that)] to find out or make a firm guess about something, often by using numbers 計算; 算出; 估算: *Have you calculated the total yet?* 你把總數算出來了嗎? | *The experts have calculated that the market for these computers will expand by 200% next year.* 專家們預計明年這種電腦的市場將擴大百分之二百。 | *We'll have to calculate how much we can spend on advertising.* 我們必須計算一下我們能在廣告上花費多少錢。

□ USEFUL PATTERNS 有用句型
to calculate something; to calculate (that)…; to calculate when, how much….

---

cal·cu·lat·ed /'kælkjəˌletɪd; 'kælkjᵿleɪtᵻd/ adj **1** intentionally planned to gain a particular result 故意的; 蓄意的: *a calculated threat* 蓄意的威脅 **2 a calculated risk** something you decide to do although you know that it may have bad results 預計有風險的事; 成敗參半的事: *I took a calculated risk when I bought those shares.* 我買那些股票時已把風險計算在內。

cal·cu·lat·ing /'kælkjəˌletɪŋ; 'kælkjᵿleɪtɪŋ/ adj making careful plans to get what you want, without considering the effects on other people (a word used to express disapproval) 有心計的, 用盡心機的〖含貶義〗: *a cold, calculating killer* 一個冷酷而工於心計的殺手

cal·cu·la·tion /ˌkælkjə'leʃən; ˌkælkjᵿ'leɪʃən/ n [C; U] the result of using numbers to work out an amount 計算(的結果): *The calculations are based on the latest statistics.* 計算結果是以最新數據為基礎的。

cal·cu·la·tor /'kælkjəˌletɚ; 'kælkjᵿleɪtəʳ/ n a small machine which can perform calculations 計算器[機]: *a pocket calculator* 袖珍計算器 –see picture on page 763 見 763 頁彩圖

cal·cu·lus /'kælkjələs; 'kælkjᵿləs/ n [U] a way of making calculations in MATHEMATICS about quantities which are continually changing, such as the speed of a falling stone or the slope of a curved line 〔數學〕微積分

cal·dron /'koldrən; 'kɔːldrən/ n see 見

CAULDRON

cal·en·dar /ˈkælənddɚ; ˈkælˌ ndəʳ/ *n* **1** a list showing the days and months of the year 日曆; 月曆: *a desk calendar* 案頭日曆 | *According to the calendar, Christmas falls on a Monday this year.* 從日曆上看，今年的聖誕節是星期一。 –see picture on page 763 見 763 頁彩圖 **2** a system for fixing the beginning, length and divisions of a year and putting the days, weeks and months in a particular order 曆法: *the Muslim calendar* 穆斯林曆法 **3** *a calendar month* one of the 12 divisions of the year 曆月〔一年十二個月份中的一個〕: *From January 1st to February 1st is one calendar month.* 從1月1日到2月1日是一個曆月。

calf /kæf; kɑːf/ *n* **calves** /kævz; kɑːvz/ **1** the young of the cow or of other large animals such as the elephant 小牛;〔象等大動物的〕仔，幼獸 –see 見 MEAT (USAGE 用法) **2** the fleshy back part of your leg between your knee and your ankle〔人的〕小腿肚

cal·i·bre /ˈkælɪbɚ; ˈkælˌbəʳ/ *n* (also 又作 **caliber** *AmE*〖美式〗) **1** [sing; U] the quality of something or someone〔人或物的〕質量: *This work is of a very high calibre.* 這項工作做得很出色。 **2** [C] the size of a bullet or the inside size of a gun 子彈的直徑; 槍的口徑

cal·i·co /ˈkælɪkəʊ; ˈkælɪkəʊ/ *n* [U] a heavy cotton cloth （厚）棉布

call¹ /kɔl; kɔːl/ *v* **1** [I; T] to say something in a loud voice because you want someone to hear you 大聲叫喊; 高聲說出: *She called to her friends.* 她大聲向她的朋友們呼喚。 | *I heard someone call my name.* 我聽見有人呼喚我的名字。 | *"Hello," she called.* "你好，" 她大聲說。 | *He called for help.* 他大聲呼救。 **2** *be called* to have a particular name 叫作: *She was engaged to a man called Fred Emmerson.* 她與一個叫弗雷德·艾默遜的男人訂了婚。 | *What's your dog called?* 你的狗叫甚麼名字？ | *Her latest novel is called "The Lonely City".* 她最近寫的一部小說叫《孤獨的城市》。 **3** [T] to give something or someone a name 把〔某人或某物〕喚作; 給…取名為: *What are you going to call the baby?* 你們準備給嬰兒取個甚麼名字？ | *If I had a son, I'd call him Joshua.* 如果我有個兒子，我就給他取名為喬舒亞。 | *Her full name is Patricia, but her friends all call her Pat.* 她的全名為帕翠西婭，但她的朋友都叫她帕特。 **4** [T] to say that someone or something has a particular quality or is a particular thing 把…說成; 稱…是…: *Are you calling me a liar?* 你說我是在撒謊嗎？ | *She called me stupid and incompetent.* 她認為我又笨又無能。 **5** [T] to ask someone to come to where you are, either by shouting to them, or by telephoning them or sending them a message〔喊叫、打電話或送口信〕叫某人來: *My mother was calling me.* 媽媽在叫我去。 | *He called me over to his desk.* 他叫我到他的書桌那兒去。 | *The minister has* called union leaders to a meeting. 部長召集工會領導人開會。 | *I'd better call a doctor.* 我最好是去請醫生來。 **6** [I; T] to telephone someone （給人）打電話: *I picked up the phone and called my office.* 我拿起了電話打給我的辦公室。 | *I just called to ask how you were.* 我打電話只是想問問你好嗎。 **7** [T] to arrange for something to take place 安排舉行〔某事物〕: *The president called an election.* 總統宣佈舉行選舉。 | *The prime minister has called an emergency meeting of the Cabinet to discuss the crisis.* 首相已召集內閣開緊急會議，討論這次危機。 **8** [I] to make a short visit to someone 〔短時間〕拜訪某人: *I'll call to collect the money tomorrow.* 我明天來收錢。 | *I called at my aunt's on my way home.* 我在回家的路上，去了姨母家一趟。 **9** [I] (of an animal) to make its usual cry 〔動物〕叫喚，鳴，啼: *I could hear doves calling in the woods.* 我能聽見鴿子在樹林裡鳴叫。 **10** *call a halt to something* to make something stop 使某事物停止 **11** *call something to mind* to remember something 記起某事: *He did tell me his name, but I can't call it to mind now.* 他的確告訴了我他的名字，但我現在想不起來了。

call back *phr v* **1** [T *call* sbdy ↔ **back**] to call someone so that they return towards you 叫住; 叫回來: *I was about to leave when my secretary called me back.* 我正準備離開時，我的祕書叫住了我。 **2** [I] to make another visit to someone 再次造訪: *I asked the salesman if he could call back later.* 我叫推銷員稍後再來。 **3** [I; T *call* sbdy ↔ **back**] to telephone someone who you tried to telephone earlier, or who tried to telephone you earlier 再〔給某人〕打電話; 回電話（給某人）: *It's engaged, so I'll call back later.* 電話佔線，我遲些時候再打吧。 | *Mrs Evans is busy at the moment — shall I get her to call you back?* 伊萬斯太太現在正忙著——我待會兒叫她打電話給您好嗎？ –see 見 TELEPHONE¹ (USAGE 用法)

call for *phr v* **1** [T *call for* sthg] to demand something 要求〔某事物〕: *Opposition leaders have called for a public enquiry.* 反對派領導人要求進行公開調查。 **2** [T *call for* sbdy] to collect someone 接〔某人〕: *I'll call for you at eight o'clock.* 我八點鐘來接你。

call in *phr v* **1** [T *call* sbdy ↔ **in**] to ask someone to come in 請〔某人〕: *I think we'd better call in a doctor.* 我想我們最好還是去請醫生來吧。 **2** [I] to make a short visit to someone 〔短時間〕拜訪: *I'll call in to see you this afternoon.* 今天下午我來看你。 | *Call in on us if you're in town.* 如果你在城裡的話，來看看我們吧。

call sthg ↔ **off** *phr v* [T] **1** to say that something will not take place 取消〔某事〕: *The match was called off because of the bad weather.* 由於天氣不好，比賽取消了。 **2** to order a dog or other animal to keep away from someone 叫〔狗或其他動物〕走開: *Call your dog off!* 叫你的狗走開!

call on sbdy *phr v* [T] **1** to visit someone 拜訪〔某人〕: *I called on my uncle while I was in London.* 我在倫敦時探訪了我的叔叔。 **2** (also 又作 **call upon** sbdy) to ask someone to do something 要求〔某人做某事〕: *Opposition groups have called on the government to change the tax laws.* 反對派團體要求政府修改稅法。

call sbdy ↔ **out** *phr v* [T] **1** to order someone to come and help 使…出動; 召集〔某人來幫忙〕: *The army was called out to help the police clear the streets.* 軍隊出動協助警察把街道清場。 **2** to order someone to stop work 給…下令罷工: *The union immediately called the men out on strike.* 工會立刻下令工人罷工。

call sbdy ↔ **up** *phr v* [T] **1** to order someone to join the armed forces 徵召…入伍: *All men aged between 18 and 30 were called up.* 凡介乎十八至三十歲的男子均被徵召入伍。 **2** to telephone someone 〔給某人〕打電話: *I'll call you up this evening.* 我今晚會打電話給你。

★★call² *n* **1** a demand for something to be done 要求: *There have been many calls for a ceasefire in the war.* 要求停火的呼聲不斷。 **2** a conversation on the telephone, or an attempted conversation 〔一次〕電話; 通話: *I had a call from the managing director this morning.* 總經理今晨給我打了個電話。 | *There's a call for you.* 有一個電話找你。 –see 見 TELEPHONE¹ (USAGE 用法) **3** a cry made by a bird or an animal 〔鳥或動物的〕叫聲: *We heard the familiar call of the cuckoo.* 我們聽見布穀鳥熟悉的叫聲。 **4** **make a call, pay a call** to visit someone 拜訪: *I'm hoping to pay a call on my parents while I'm in London.* 我希望在倫敦期間去看看我的父母。 **5** **no call for** no need for; a phrase you use when you disapprove of something that someone has done 不需要〔表示不贊成某人做某事〕: *There was no call for you to say those unpleasant things to her.* 你不應該對她說那些令人不高興的事。 **6** **on call** ready to work if you are needed 隨時待命; 隨叫隨到: *Which doctor is on call tonight?* 今晚哪位醫生值班?

call box /'··/ *n* a small hut or enclosure containing a public telephone 公共電話亭

call·er /'kɔlə; 'kɔːlə^r/ *n* **1** a person making a telephone call, especially when spoken to by the OPERATOR 打電話的人〔尤指接線員用語〕: *I'm sorry, caller, the number is engaged.* 對不起, 先生〔女士〕, 電話佔線。 **2** a person who makes a short visit 來訪者; 拜訪者: *John's a regular caller here.* 約翰是這兒的常客。

call girl /'··/ *n* a PROSTITUTE who makes her arrangements by telephone 應召女郎〔用電話召喚的妓女〕

call·ing /'kɔlɪŋ; 'kɔːlɪŋ/ *n* **1** a strong desire to do a particular job, especially one which helps other people 〔對做某種工作, 尤其協助他人工作的〕強烈慾望; 使命感; 感召 **2** *fml* a profession 〔正式〕職業; 行業

cal·li·pers /'kælɪpəz; 'kælɪ͵pəz/ *n* (also 又作 **calipers** *AmE* 〔美式〕) [pl] metal supports fixed to the legs to help a person with weak legs to walk 〔裝在腿上幫助腿力弱者行走的〕雙腳規形架

cal·lous /'kæləs; 'kæləs/ *adj* cruel and having no sympathy for the sufferings of other people 冷酷無情的; 無同情心的 – **callously** *adv* –**callousness** *n* [U]

cal·low /'kælo; 'kæləʊ/ *adj* young and without experience (a word used to express disapproval) 初出茅廬的, 無經驗的〔含貶義〕: *a callow youth* 初出茅廬的年輕人

cal·lus /'kæləs; 'kæləs/ *n* an area of thick hard skin 硬皮; 老繭: *He had calluses on his hands.* 他的手上有老繭。

calm¹ /kɑm; kɑːm/ *adj* **1** quiet and not worried or excited 鎮靜的; 沉着的; 心平氣和的: *The police chief advised his men to stay calm and not to lose their tempers.* 警官勸他手下的人保持鎮靜, 不要發脾氣。 **2** not windy 無風的: *It became calm after the storm.* 暴風雨過後, 天氣又平靜下來了。 **3** smooth and still 平靜的: *The sea was calm.* 海上風平浪靜。 –**calmly** *adv*

calm² *n* [sing; U] **1** a time of peace and quiet without excitement or worry 平靜; 安靜; 心平氣和 **2** an absence of wind or rough weather 〔天氣〕無風; 平靜

calm³ *v* [T] to make someone less excited, worried, or angry 使〔某人〕鎮定〔平靜〕: *She tried to calm the baby by giving it some milk.* 她給嬰兒餵些牛奶, 使他安靜下來。

calm down *phr v* [I; T **calm** sbdy ↔ **down**] to become or make someone less angry, excited, or worried 使〔某人〕安靜下來: *For goodness sake, calm down!* 看在上帝的份上, 安靜點吧! | *It was difficult to calm my brother down.* 要使我弟弟安靜下來是很困難的事。

cal·o·rie /'kæləri; 'kæləri/ *n* **1** a measure used for the amount of heat or ENERGY (3) that a food will produce 卡路里〔食物所產生的熱量或能量單位〕: *One thin piece of bread has 90 calories.* 一薄片麵包有九十卡路里的熱量。 | *I can only eat 1500 calories a day on this diet.* 按此節食法, 我每天只能攝取一千五百卡路里的熱量。 **2** a measure of heat 〔熱量單位〕卡〔路里〕

calves /kɑvz; kɑːvz/ the plural of CALF ☆ CALF 的複數

cam·ber /'kæmbə; 'kæmbə^r/ *n* [C; U] a slight downward curve on both sides of a road which causes water to run off 〔路面以利於排水的〕微拱曲面, 中凸形

cam·cord·er /'kæm͵kɔrdə; 'kæm͵kɔːdə^r/ *n* a machine which you carry around and use to take films on a VIDEO CASSETTE 手提攝錄機

came /kem; keɪm/ the past tense of COME ☆ COME 的過去式

cam·el /'kæml; 'kæməl/ n a large long-necked animal with one or two large humps (HUMP) on its back, used for riding or carrying goods in desert countries 駱駝

cam·e·o /'kæmɪˌo; 'kæmi-əʊ/ n **1** a short piece of writing describing a character or situation, or a small part in a film or play acted by a well-known actor〔由名演員飾演的〕電影〔戲劇〕片段, 小品 **2** a piece of jewellery consisting of a raised shape on a background of a different colour stone 多彩浮雕寶石

*★**cam·e·ra** /'kæmərə; 'kæmərə/ n **1** an apparatus for taking photographs or making films 照相機; 攝影機 **2 in camera** fml in secret〔正式〕祕密地: The court met in camera. 法庭不公開審訊。

cam·e·ra·man /'kæmərəˌmæn; 'kæmərə-mæn/ n **cameramen** /-mɛn; -men/ a person who operates a camera for films or television〔電影或電視的〕攝影師

cam·ou·flage /'kæməˌflɑʒ; 'kæməflɑːʒ/ v **camouflaged, camouflaging** [T] to hide something, especially a military object, by covering it with branches, paint, or nets so that it looks like part of the surroundings〔尤指軍事上的〕偽裝, 掩飾 –**camouflage** n [C; U]

*★**camp¹** /kæmp; kæmp/ n **1** [C; U] a place where people live in tents or huts usually for a short time 營地: a military camp 軍營 | It was getting dark, so we pitched camp beside the stream. 天漸漸黑了, 於是我們在小河邊紮營。 | Let's go back to camp. 我們回營地去吧。 **2** [C] a group of people who share the same ideas, especially in politics 陣營〔尤指政治觀點相同的一羣人〕: This is the policy favoured by the antinuclear camp. 這項政策得到反核陣營的支持。

camp² v [I] **1** to stay in a place for a short time and sleep in a tent 宿營: We camped down by the river. 我們在河邊宿營。 **2 go camping** to go on a holiday in which you sleep in a tent 露營(度假): We're going camping in France next year. 明年我們將去法國露營度假。

　　camp out phr v [I] to sleep outdoors in a tent 露營 –**camping** n [U]: Camping doesn't appeal to me at all. 露營對我一點吸引力都沒有。 | Where can I buy camping equipment? 我在哪裡可以買到露營設備呢?

*★**cam·paign¹** /kæm'pen; kæm'peɪn/ n a set of organized military, political, or business actions intended to obtain a particular result 戰役; 運動: a successful election campaign 成功的競選活動 | an advertising campaign 廣告宣傳活動 | a campaign against smoking 反吸煙運動

campaign² v [I] to lead or take part in a campaign 領導〔參加〕運動: Sally is campaigning for women's right to equal pay. 莎莉正發起為婦女爭取同工同酬權利的運動。 –**campaigner** n

camp bed /ˌ·'·/ n a light narrow bed that folds flat and can be easily carried 行軍牀; 折疊牀

camp·er /'kæmpə; 'kæmpər/ n **1** a person who camps 宿營者 **2** a motor vehicle big enough to live in while you are on holiday 露營車

camp·site /'kæmpˌsaɪt; 'kæmpsaɪt/ n a place like a field where you can have a holiday in a tent 營地

cam·pus /'kæmpəs; 'kæmpəs/ n [C; U] the grounds of a university, college, or school 校園: Do you live on campus? 你住校嗎?

*★**can¹** /kən; kən; strong 強讀 kæn; kæn/ v past tense 過去式 **could** /kʊd; kʊd/ negative short forms 否定縮略式 **can't, cannot, couldn't** [modal verb 情態動詞] **1** to be able to do something or know how to do something 會: Can you swim? 你會游泳嗎? | I can't hear very well. 我聽不太清楚。 | Can you see those people over there? 你能看見在那邊的那些人嗎? | She can speak French fluently. 她能說一口流利的法語。 | I can't remember where I put it. 我記不得把它放在哪裡了。 | We couldn't afford a holiday last year. 去年我們沒有錢去度假。 | I can't stop and chat — I'm in a hurry. 我不能停下來聊天——我正忙着呢。 **2** to be allowed to do something 允許〔做某事〕: You can't play football here. 你不能在這兒踢足球。 | You can wait in here if you like. 你如果願意, 可以在這裡等。 | He said that I could borrow his car. 他說我可以借他的車的。 **3** [only in negatives 只用於否定句] used when you are saying that something is impossible 不可能: It can't be true! 這不可能是真的! | "There's Steven over there." "But it can't be — he's in Australia." "史蒂文在那裡。" "這不可能, 他現在在澳大利亞。" | Things can't go on as they are. The situation must get better soon. 事情不可能像現在這樣發展下去。情形肯定會很快好轉起來的。 **4 can you** a polite way of asking someone to do something 您能…〔表示有禮貌地請別人做某事〕: Can you help me carry this box, please? 請您幫我搬這個箱子好嗎? | Can you tell me the way to the railway station? 您能告訴我去火車站怎麼走嗎? **5 can I, can we, etc.** a polite way of asking someone if they will let you do something 我能…; 我們能…〔表示有禮貌地詢問別人是否同意你做某事〕: Can I borrow your pen, please? 我能借你的鋼筆用一用嗎? **6 can't you** a way of telling someone angrily to do something 你就不能…〔表示憤怒地要求別人去做某事〕: Can't you keep quiet for a minute? 你不可以安靜一會兒麼? –see Study Note on page 1318 見 1318 頁學習提示

can² /kæn; kæn/ v -nn- [T] to preserve food

C

by putting it in a closed metal container in which there is no air 把〔食品〕裝入密封罐頭: *The fish is brought ashore and canned immediately.* 魚被捕上來後便立即裝罐。| *canned sardines* 罐裝沙丁魚

can³ /kæn; kæn/ *n* **1** a small closed metal container in which food or drink is preserved 罐頭〔食品〕: *He opened a can of beans.* 他開了一罐豆子。| *a can of beer* 一罐啤酒 | *The park was littered with empty beer cans.* 公園內到處扔有空啤酒罐。–see picture on page 244 見 244 頁彩圖 **2** a container with a lid used for holding liquids such as oil or petrol 〔裝液體的〕罐, 壺

ca·nal /kəˈnæl; kəˈnæl/ *n* a long, narrow bit of water made for boats to travel along or to bring or remove water from an area 運河: *the Panama Canal* 巴拿馬運河

ca·nar·y /kəˈnɛrɪ; kəˈnɛəri/ *n* **canaries** a small yellow bird usually kept as a pet for its singing 金絲雀

can·cel /ˈkænsl; ˈkænsəl/ *v* **-ll- (-l-** *AmE* 〖美式〗) [T] **1** to state or decide that something will not happen 取消: *My mother's not well so I've cancelled my trip to New York.* 媽媽身體不好, 所以我取消了紐約之行。| *We regret to announce that the 11.05 train to Bristol has been cancelled.* 我們遺憾地宣佈, 11 時 05 分去布里斯托爾的火車取消了。**2** to inform someone that you no longer want something 放棄; 取消: *I've cancelled my subscription to that magazine.* 我已取消訂閱那份雜誌。**3** cancel a cheque to draw a line through a cheque so that it can no longer be used 註銷支票

  cancel sthg ↔ out *phr v* [T] to be exactly equal but opposite to something else and therefore to produce no effect 抵銷: *Our profits overseas are cancelled out by our losses at home.* 我們在海外的盈利抵銷了我們在國內的虧損。

can·cel·la·tion /ˌkænsəˈleʃən; ˌkænsəˈleɪʃən/ *n* [C; U] a decision not to do something or to stop something being done for you or sent to you 取消; 註銷: *The flight is fully booked, but if there are any cancellations we'll let you know.* 航班的機票已被預訂一空, 不過如果有人取消預訂的話, 我們會通知你的。| *The cancellation of the order led to the closure of the factory.* 訂單被取消導致這家工廠倒閉。

can·cer /ˈkænsə; ˈkænsər/ *n* **1** [C; U] a serious disease in which the body's cells increase too fast, producing a growth which may cause death 癌; 癌症: *lung cancer* 肺癌 | *He's got cancer of the throat.* 他患了咽喉癌。**2** **Cancer** one of the signs of the ZODIAC 巨蟹宮, 巨蟹座

can·cer·ous /ˈkænsərəs; ˈkænsərəs/ *adj* having the disease of cancer 患癌症的, 癌性的

can·did /ˈkændɪd; ˈkændɪd/ *adj* directly

truthful, even when telling the truth is uncomfortable or unwelcome 坦白的; 坦率的: *Go on, give me your candid opinion.* 說下去吧, 把你的意見坦白的告訴我。–**candidly** *adv*: *She talked quite candidly about her unhappy marriage.* 她對自己不愉快的婚姻直言不諱。

can·di·da·cy /ˈkændɪdəsɪ; ˈkændɪdəsi/ *n* (also 又作 **canditature** *BrE* 〖英式〗) [C; U] the fact of being a candidate, usually for a political office 候選人資格或身分: *He announced his candidacy for the next presidential election.* 他宣佈參加下屆總統競選。

can·di·date /ˈkændədet; ˈkændɪdət/ *n* **1** a person who wants to be chosen for a job, or for a position given as the result of an election 候選人: *Her supporters have nominated her as a candidate for the post of union representative.* 她的支持者提名她為工會代表的候選人。| *a presidential candidate* 總統候選人 **2** a person taking an examination 投考者, 應考人

can·dle /ˈkændl; ˈkændl/ *n* **1** a round stick of WAX containing a length of string, which gives light when it burns 蠟燭 **2** **can't hold a candle to** *infml* to be not nearly as good as something 〖非正式〗比不上 –**candlelight** *n* [U]

can·dle·stick /ˈkændlˌstɪk; ˈkændlˌstɪk/ *n* a holder for one or more candles 燭台

can·dour /ˈkændə; ˈkændər/ *n* (**candor** *AmE* 〖美式〗) [U] the quality of being sincerely honest and truthful 坦率; 坦白

can·dy /ˈkændɪ; ˈkændi/ *n* **candies** *AmE* [C; U] a shaped piece of boiled sugar or chocolate 〖美式〗糖果

cane¹ /ken; keɪn/ *n* **1** [C; U] the hard smooth often hollow stem of certain plants such as BAMBOO 〔籐、竹等的〕莖: *cane furniture* 籐製家具 | *We need some canes to support the raspberry bushes in the garden.* 我們需要些竹竿來支撐花園中的山莓樹。**2** [C] a stick used to help you while walking or used to hit someone as a punishment 拐杖; 〔懲戒用〕籐條: *My brother was given the cane for fighting at school.* 我的弟弟因在學校打架而受了藤條鞭打。

cane² *v* **caned, caning** [T] to punish someone by hitting them with a cane 以籐條懲罰

ca·nine /ˈkenaɪn; ˈkeɪnaɪn/ *adj* tech of or like a dog 〔術語〕(似)犬的

can·is·ter /ˈkænɪstə; ˈkænɪstər/ *n* a metal container used for holding a dry substance or a gas 〔裝乾貨或氣體的〕金屬罐

can·ker /ˈkæŋkə; ˈkæŋkər/ *n* [C; U] an area of soreness caused by a disease which attacks the flesh, especially the mouth and ears, of animals and people and the wood of trees 潰瘍; 瘡; (果樹的) 枝枯病

can·na·bis /ˈkænəbɪs; ˈkænəbɪs/ *n* [U] a drug made from the dried leaves of the HEMP plant, often smoked to give a feeling of pleasure, but whose use is illegal in many countries 大麻; 大麻製品

canned /kænd; kænd/ *adj* preserved in a tin (used of food) 罐裝的〔指食物〕

can·ni·bal /'kænəbḷ; 'kænˌbəl/ *n* an animal or person that eats the flesh of its own kind 殘食同類的動物或人 −**cannibalism** *n* [U]

can·ni·bal·ize /'kænəbḷˌaɪz; 'kænˌbəlaɪz/ *v* **cannibalized, cannibalizing** (also 又作 **cannibalise** *BrE* 〔英式〕) [T] to take a machine to pieces in order to use the parts in other machines 拆取機器部件〔以用於其他機器上〕

can·non¹ /'kænən; 'kænən/ *n* **cannons** *or* **cannon** a big gun, fixed to the ground or on wheels 〔固定於地面或裝有輪子的〕大砲; 加農砲: *a 15th century cannon* 十五世紀的大砲

cannon² *v* **cannon into** to run into someone or something violently 猛撞: *He came running round the corner and cannoned into me.* 他從拐彎處奔過來, 撞了我一個滿懷。

cannon ball /'···/ *n* a heavy iron ball fired from a cannon (加農)砲彈

can·not /'kænɒt; 'kænət/ *fml* can not 〔正式〕不能; 不可以: *Mr Smith is sorry that he cannot accept your kind invitation to dinner.* 史密斯先生無法接受你的宴請, 深表歉意。 −compare 比較 CAN'T

can·ny /'kænɪ; 'kæni/ *adj* clever and not easily deceived especially in money matters〔尤指在金錢方面〕精明的, 不易上當的

ca·noe¹ /kə'nu; kə'nuː/ *n* a long light narrow boat, pointed at both ends, and moved by a PADDLE held in the hands 獨木舟

canoe² *v* **canoed, canoeing** [I] **1** to travel in a canoe 乘獨木舟 **2 go canoeing** to go out in a canoe on the sea or a river for sport or pleasure 划獨木舟〔作為運動或消遣〕 −**canoeing** *n* [U]: *Canoeing is hard work on the arms.* 划獨木舟很費臂力。 −**canoeist** *n*

can·on /'kænən; 'kænən/ *n* **1** an established law of the Christian Church (基督教)教規 **2** *fml* a generally accepted standard of behaviour or thought〔正式〕準則; 標準 **3** a Christian priest with special duties in a CATHEDRAL 大教堂教士 −**canonical** /kə'nɑnɪkḷ; kə'nɒnɪkəl/ *adj*

can·on·ize /'kænənaɪz; 'kænənaɪz/ *v* **canonized, canonizing** (also 又作 **canonise** *BrE* 〔英式〕) [T] to declare a dead person to be a SAINT 把(死者)封為聖徒: *Joan of Arc was canonized in 1920.* 貞德在1920年被封為聖女。

can o·pen·er /'··· ···/ *n* see 見 TIN OPENER

can·o·py /'kænəpɪ; 'kænəpi/ *n* **canopies** a cover fixed over a seat or bed, used either for decoration or for shelter〔牀或座位上的〕罩蓋, 篷〔作為裝飾等〕

canst /kənst; kənst/ *strong* 強讀 kænst, kænst/ **thou canst** *biblical* (when talking to one person) you can 〔聖經〕〔講話時〕你能

cant /kænt; kænt/ *n* [U] insincere talk about religion or morals〔宗教或道德方面〕偽善的話

can't /kænt; kɑːnt/ short for 〔縮約式〕= can not: *I can't come with you: I'm busy.* 我不能和你一起來, 我沒空。 | *You can swim, can't you?* 你會游泳, 不是嗎? −compare 比較 CANNOT

can·tan·ker·ous /kæn'tæŋkərəs; kæn'tæŋkərəs/ *adj* bad-tempered 脾氣壞的 −**cantankerously** *adv*

can·teen /kæn'tin; kæn'tiːn/ *n* **1** a place in a factory, school, or office where people go to eat and drink〔工廠、學校、辦事處等的〕食堂, 餐廳: *I always have lunch in the canteen.* 我總是在餐廳裡吃午飯。 **2** a small container in which water or other drink is carried〔裝水或飲料的〕壺 **3** *BrE* a box which contains a set of knives, forks, and spoons〔英式〕〔裝有一套刀、叉、湯匙的〕餐具盒

can·ter /'kæntə; 'kæntər/ *n* the movement of a horse which is faster than a TROT but slower than a GALLOP〔馬的〕中速跑: *We set off at a canter.* 我們策馬以中速跑着上了路。 −**canter** *v* [I]

can·vas /'kænvəs; 'kænvəs/ *n* **1** [U] strong rough cloth used to make tents, sails, or bags 帆布 **2** [C; U] strong rough cloth used by artists for oil paintings〔帆布料的〕畫布: *She showed me her canvases.* 她給我看她作的畫。 **3 under canvas** in a tent 在帳篷裡: *It's fun sleeping under canvas.* 睡在帳篷裡很有樂趣。

can·vass /'kænvəs; 'kænvəs/ *v* [I; T] **1** to try and persuade people in a certain area that they should support or vote for a particular political party〔為政黨拉選票而〕游説: *I'm canvassing for votes tonight.* 我今晚準備為拉選票而游説。 **2** to try and find out what people think about a particular subject 徵求意見; 進行民意調查: *Let's canvass opinion before beginning the campaign.* 在舉行活動前, 我們去做一下民意調查吧。

can·yon /'kænjən; 'kænjən/ *n* a deep and narrow valley often with a river flowing through it 峽谷: *the Grand Canyon* 大峽谷

cap¹ /kæp; kæp/ *n* **1** a soft flat hat with a curved part sticking out at the front worn by men or boys, or as part of a uniform〔有帽舌的〕軟帽, 便帽: *a schoolboy's cap* 學生帽 **2** the top or end of an object which is used to protect it 蓋; 罩: *Put the cap back on the bottle.* 把瓶蓋蓋上。 **3** a small round object fitted inside a woman to allow her to have sex without having children〔婦女避孕用的〕子宮帽 **4 go cap in hand** to go without pride to someone in order to ask for something〔為獲取某物而〕謙卑地去找〔某人〕: *He went cap in hand to the director to ask for more money.* 他恭恭敬敬地去向董事多要些錢。

cap² *v* **-pp-** [T] **1** to cover something 覆蓋:

Clouds capped the hills. 烏雲覆蓋着山頂。**2** to improve on what someone has said or done 勝過; 超過: *He capped my story by telling a better one.* 他講了一個故事, 比我講的更有趣。**3 to cap it all** in addition to everything else 此外; 更加: *His wife left him, his car was stolen, then to cap it all he lost his job!* 他妻子抛棄了他, 汽車也被偷走了, 更倒霉的是他連工作也丢了!

ca·pa·bil·i·ty /ˌkepəˈbɪlətɪ; ˌkeɪpəˈbɪlˌti/ *n* **capabilities** [C; U] the quality of being able to do something 能力; 才能: *Could you explain the machine's technical capabilities to me?* 你可以給我講解一下這機器的性能嗎? | *Do you think the super powers will use their nuclear capability?* 你認為超級大國會利用他們的核力量嗎?

★**ca·pa·ble** /ˈkepəbļ; ˈkeɪpəbəl/ *adj* **1** skilful and effective 有才能的; 有成效的: *a very capable doctor* 很高明的醫生 | *Don't worry, she's very capable.* 不要擔心, 她很能幹。**2 capable of something, capable of doing something** having the power, skill, or other qualities needed to do something 有能力做某事的: *Don't annoy her: she's capable of making life very difficult for people she dislikes.* 不要惹惱她: 她能讓那些她不喜歡的人沒好日子過。 | *Would you say he is capable of murder?* 你是說他會殺人嗎? **3 capable of** *fml* able to be 《正式》能夠: *a remark capable of being misunderstood* 一句易被誤解的話 –opposite 反義 **incapable** –**capably** *adv*

★**ca·pac·i·ty** /kəˈpæsətɪ; kəˈpæsˌti/ *n* **capacities 1** [sing; U] the amount that something can hold, produce, or carry 容量; 容積: *The seating capacity of this theatre is 500.* 該劇場可容納五百人。 | *The machine is working at full capacity.* 機器正在開足馬力投產。 | *This factory has a productive capacity of 200 cars a week.* 這家工廠的生產能力為每週二百輛汽車。 | *The seating area was filled to capacity, so we had to stand.* 座位已滿了, 所以我們只好站着。**2** [C; U] an ability to do something 能力: *He has a great capacity for enjoying himself.* 他很會自得其樂。 | *Her capacity to remember facts is remarkable.* 她的記憶力很驚人。**3** [C] a position of responsibility 地位; 身分: *I'm speaking in my capacity as minister of trade.* 我以貿易部長的身分說話。 | *They took him on in an advisory capacity.* 他們請他擔任顧問。

cape /kep; keɪp/ *n* **1** a loose covering for the top part of your body without separate arm-coverings 披肩; 斗篷: *A bicycle cape will protect you in wet weather.* 腳踏車雨披可以使你在雨天騎車不被淋濕。**2** a piece of land going out into the sea 海角; 岬: *the Cape of Good Hope* 好望角

ca·per /ˈkepə; ˈkeɪpər/ *v* [I] *old fash* to jump about or dance in a happy way 《老式》雀躍; 〔歡快地〕跳躍: *We watched the lambs capering in the fields.* 我們看着小羔羊在田野裡歡快地蹦蹦跳跳。

ca·pil·la·ry /ˈkæpļˌɛrɪ; kəˈpɪləri/ *n* **capillaries** a very fine hairlike tube which carries blood around your body 毛細血管

★**cap·i·tal**¹ /ˈkæpətļ; ˈkæpˌtl/ *n* **1** [C] the most important city in a country or area 首都; 省會: *Paris is the capital of France.* 巴黎是法國的首都。 | *the financial capital of Europe* 歐洲金融中心 **2** [U] a sum of money, especially one used to produce more money or to start a business 資金: *The bank put up the capital for his new enterprise.* 銀行將資金投入他的新企業。 | *a successful firm that offers investors a high return on capital* 一家經營得法、給予投資者高額資金回報的商行 **3** [C] (also 又作 **capital letter**) a letter which is written or printed in its large form, used especially at the beginning of a word or sentence 大寫字母〔尤指詞首、句首字母〕

★**capital**² *adj* **1** [only before a noun 只用於名詞前] punishable by death 可處死刑的: *Murder can be a capital offence.* 謀殺可判死刑。**2** [only before a noun 只用於名詞前] concerned with wealth in the form of money or property 資金的; 資本的: *We need a big programme of capital investment to modernize the railways.* 我們需要一項大規模的投資方案使鐵路現代化。**3** *old fash* excellent 《老式》極好的: *What a capital idea!* 真是個好主意!

cap·i·tal·is·m /ˈkæpətļˌɪzəm; ˈkæpˌtl-ɪzəm/ *n* [U] a political system in which trade and industry belong mostly to private people rather than to the government 資本主義 –compare 比較 **COMMUNISM**

cap·i·tal·ist /ˈkæpətļɪst; ˈkæpˌtl-ˌst/ *n* a person or country that supports capitalism 資本家; 資本主義國家 –**capitalist** *adj*: *the capitalist countries of the West* 西方資本主義國家

cap·i·tal·ize /ˈkæpətļˌaɪz; ˈkæpˌtl-aɪz/ *v* **capitalized, capitalizing, capitalize on** something to use something in order to gain an advantage 利用〔某物〕: *She capitalized on his mistake and won the game.* 她利用他的失誤贏得了比賽。

capital pun·ish·ment /ˌ···ˈ···/ *n* [U] a legal punishment which says that a person who is guilty of a serious crime, such as a murder, should be put to death 死刑

ca·pit·u·late /kəˈpɪtʃəˌlet; kəˈpɪtʃʊleɪt/ *v* **capitulated, capitulating** [I] **1** to stop fighting the enemy and agree to their conditions 投降 **2** to accept someone else's demands unwillingly 屈服: *The hijackers capitulated to the government's threat.* 劫持者屈服於政府的威脅。 –**capitulation** /kəˌpɪtʃəˈleʃən; kəˌpɪtʃʊˈleɪʃən/ *n* [C;U]

ca·price /kəˈpris; kəˈpriːs/ *n* [C;U] a sudden often foolish change of mind or behaviour without any real cause 多變; 反覆無常

ca·pri·cious /kə'prɪʃəs; kə'prɪʃəs/ *adj* often changing without warning 反覆無常的; 多變的: *We can't go camping while the weather is so capricious.* 天氣如此變化莫測，我們無法去露營了。

Cap·ri·corn /'kæprɪ,kɔrn; 'kæprɪkɔːn/ *n* one of the signs of the ZODIAC 摩羯宮

cap·size /kæp'saɪz; kæp'saɪz/ *v* [I;T] **capsized, capsizing** [I;T] to turn upside down in the water, or to make a boat turn upside down in the water (使)傾覆: *The yacht capsized in the storm, but luckily it didn't sink.* 遊艇在風暴中傾覆，但幸好未沉沒。 | *a capsized boat* 傾覆的小船

cap·sule /'kæpsl; 'kæpsjuːl/ *n* **1** a very small object containing medicine which you swallow 藥丸; 膠囊 **2** the part of a space vehicle in which the people live and work 太空艙

★**cap·tain¹** /'kæptɪn; 'kæptɪn/ *n* **1** the leader of a team or group 隊長; 組長: *the captain of the football team* 足球隊長 **2** the person in command of a ship or aircraft 船長, 機長: *Are we ready to sail, Captain?* 我們準備開船了嗎？ **3** an officer of middle rank in the armed forces 〔軍隊的〕上尉, 上校

captain² *v* [T] to be the leader or commander of a group of people 當…的隊長; 領導: *When I was at school I captained the hockey team.* 在校時，我是曲棍球隊的隊長。

cap·tion /'kæpʃən; 'kæpʃən/ *n* words written above or below a picture to say what it is about 〔圖片的〕說明文字: *I didn't understand the drawing until I read the caption.* 我看了說明文字後才看得懂那幅畫。

cap·ti·vate /'kæptə,vet; 'kæptɪveɪt/ *v* **captivated, captivating** [T] to charm and excite someone so that it is difficult for them to think of anything else 迷住; 迷惑: *I was captivated by the city's beauty.* 我被這座城市的美景迷住了。 –**captivating** *adj*

cap·tive¹ /'kæptɪv; 'kæptɪv/ *adj* **1** kept as a prisoner 被關押的: *captive animals* 被關在籠子裡的動物 | *We were held captive for three months.* 我們被拘押了三個月。 **2 a captive audience** a person or people who cannot easily leave and must therefore listen 被動的聽者: *Lying in my hospital bed, I was a captive audience for her boring stories.* 我躺在醫院裡的牀上，於是就成了不得不聽她講那些乏味故事的聽者。

captive² *n* **1** a person kept as a prisoner especially in war 戰俘; 俘虜 **2 take someone captive** to take someone as a prisoner 囚禁某人

cap·tiv·i·ty /kæp'tɪvətɪ; kæp'tɪvəti/ *n* [U] the state of being kept as a prisoner 囚禁; 關押: *Many animals do not breed in captivity.* 許多動物在被關在籠裡的時候就不繁殖。

cap·tor /'kæptər; 'kæptər/ *n fml* a person who keeps someone as a prisoner 〔正式〕俘虜者; 捕捉者: *I soon escaped from my* captors. 我很快就從捉我的人手上逃掉了。

★**cap·ture¹** /'kæptʃər; 'kæptʃər/ *v* **captured, capturing** [T] **1** to take a person or animal as a prisoner 俘虜〔人〕; 捕獲〔動物〕: *He was captured as he tried to escape from the country.* 他在試圖逃出國的時候被捕了。 **2** to take control of something often by force 〔常用武力〕佔領: *They've captured a large share of the market.* 他們佔有很大的市場份額。 | *The speech captured our attention.* 演講吸引了我們的注意力。 **3** to preserve something through pictures or words 〔以圖片、文字〕保存〔某物〕; 留存: *The photographs captured the evening sunlight.* 這些照片拍下了夕陽的餘暉。 **4** *tech* to put something into a form that can be used by a computer 〔術語〕〔用電腦〕記錄〔某物〕

capture² *n* [U] the act of taking or being taken by force 捕獲; (被)擄奪: *He was released six months after his capture.* 他被俘六個月後獲得釋放。

★★**car** /kɑr; kɑːʳ/ *n* **1** a road vehicle with wheels and an engine which is used as a means of travel for a small number of people (小)汽車: *You can't park your car here.* 你不可將車子停在這裡。 **2 by car** travelling in a car 坐汽車: *Shall we go by car?* 我們坐車去好嗎？ **3** a carriage or vehicle used on railways (火車)車廂: *Does this train have a restaurant car?* 這列火車有餐車嗎？ | *a sleeping car* 臥鋪車廂

ca·rafe /kə'ræf; kə'ræf/ *n* a bottle with a wide neck for serving wine or water at a meal 〔餐桌上斟水或酒的〕寬頸玻璃瓶

car·a·mel /'kærəml; 'kærəməl/ *n* **1** [U] burnt sugar used for giving food a special taste and colour 焦糖 **2** [C] a sticky sweet made with sugar, butter, and milk 〔含有焦糖的〕奶油糖塊

car·at /'kærət; 'kærət/ *n* (also 又作 **karat** *AmE* 〔美式〕) a unit which measures the purity of gold or the weight of a jewel 開〔黃金純度單位〕; 克拉〔寶石重量單位〕: *a 22-carat gold ring* 一枚二十二開的金戒指

car·a·van /'kærə,væn; 'kærəvæn/ *n* **1** a vehicle with wheels which can be pulled by a car, and which people can cook and sleep in on holiday 〔有食宿設備的〕旅行拖車 **2** a covered horse-drawn cart in which people such as gipsies (GIPSY) live or travel 〔吉卜賽人等居住或旅行用〕有篷馬車, 大篷車 **3** a group of people with animals travelling together for protection through desert areas 〔穿過沙漠地帶的〕車馬隊: *a caravan of merchants* 商隊

car·a·van·ning /'kærə,vænɪŋ; 'kærəvænɪŋ/ *v* **go caravanning** to go on holiday taking a caravan to cook and sleep in 乘坐〔有食宿設備的〕旅行拖車度假: *My parents always go caravanning in September.* 我的父母總是在九月份乘旅行拖車去度假。 –**caravanning** *n* [U]

car·bo·hy·drate /ˌkɑrboˈhaɪdreɪt; ˌkɑːbəʊ-ˈhaɪdreɪt/ n [C;U] a substance found in food that provides the body with heat and strength 碳水化合物: *Bread is full of carbohydrate.* 麵包含豐富的碳水化合物。

car·bon /ˈkɑrbən; ˈkɑːbən/ n [U] **1** a chemical substance found in a pure form as diamonds or GRAPHITE or in an impure form as coal or petrol 碳〔在鑽石、石墨中以純碳形式存在，在煤、汽油中以非純碳形式存在〕 **2** (also 又作 **carbon paper**) a sheet of thin paper coloured on one side which is used between sheets of typing to make copies 複寫紙

carbon di·ox·ide /ˌ·· ·'··/ n [U] the gas produced when humans and animals breathe out, or when carbon is burned in air 二氧化碳

carbon mo·nox·ide /ˌ·· ·'··/ n [U] a poisonous gas produced when carbon, such as petrol, is burnt in air 一氧化碳

car·bun·cle /ˈkɑrbʌŋkl; ˈkɑːbʌŋkəl/ n a large painful infected swelling under the skin〔生於皮膚下〕癰

car·bu·ret·tor /ˈkɑrbəˌretər; ˌkɑːbjʊˈretəʳ/ n (**carburetor** AmE 《美式》) the part in a car engine where air and petrol mix and produce an explosive gas which provides the power 汽化器；化油器

car·cass /ˈkɑrkəs; ˈkɑːkəs/ n (also 又作 **car-case** BrE 《英式》) the body of a dead animal, especially one which is ready to be cut up as meat 動物屍體〔尤指為切開供食用的〕

★**card** /kɑrd; kɑːd/ n **1** [C] (also 又作 **playing card**) one of a set of 52 small pieces of stiff paper with pictures or numbers on them used for various games 紙牌；撲克牌: *It's my turn to deal the cards.* 輪到我來發牌了。| *a pack of cards* 一副撲克牌 **2 cards** [pl] games played with cards 紙牌遊戲: *Let's play cards.* 我們來玩牌吧。| *I hate people who cheat at cards.* 我討厭那些玩牌時作弊的人。**3** [C] a piece of stiff paper, usually with a picture on the front and a message inside, sent or given to a person on special occasions〔特殊場合用的〕賀卡；慰問卡: *a birthday card* 生日賀卡 | *a Christmas card* 聖誕卡 | *I sent her a getwell card when she was in hospital.* 她住院時，我給她送上一張慰問卡。**4** [C] a POSTCARD 明信片 **5** [C] a small sheet of stiff paper or plastic with information printed on it and having various uses 卡片: *a credit card* 信用卡 | *a business card* 名片 | *an identity card* 身分證 | *a cheque card* 支票保付卡 **6** [U] strong, stiff paper 硬紙 **7 have a card up your sleeve** infml to have a secret, usually effective plan 《非正式》有王牌，有妙計 **8 lay/put your cards on the table** to be completely open and honest about your position or plans 攤牌；把自己的態度或計劃

和盤托出 **9 on the cards** (**in the cards** AmE 《美式》) infml probable 《非正式》很可能的: *They say another price rise for petrol is on the cards.* 據說汽油很可能再次漲價。

card·board /ˈkɑrdˌbord; ˈkɑːdbɔːd/ n [U] a sort of thick, stiff paper often used for making boxes 硬紙板

car·di·ac /ˈkɑrdɪˌæk; ˈkɑːdi-æk/ adj [only before a noun 只用於名詞前] tech connected with the heart or with heart disease 《術語》心臟的；心臟病的: *a cardiac patient* 心臟病人 | *a cardiac arrest* 心跳停止

car·di·gan /ˈkɑrdɪgən; ˈkɑːdɪgən/ n a woollen piece of clothing which is fastened at the front with buttons and worn on the top half of your body〔開襟〕羊毛衫 –see picture on page 210 見 210 頁彩圖

car·di·nal¹ /ˈkɑrdnəl; ˈkɑːdənəl/ n a ROMAN CATHOLIC priest of high rank〔羅馬天主教的〕紅衣主教

cardinal² adj fml most important 《正式》首要的；最主要的: *a cardinal sin* 重大的失誤；主罪

cardinal num·ber /ˌ···'··/ n any of the numbers 1, 2, 3, etc., that show quantity rather than order〔用以表示數量而非次序的 1、2、3等〕基數 –compare 比較 ORDINAL

card in·dex /'·ˌ·'··/ n a number of cards each with a particular piece of information and arranged in a special order, usually alphabetical〔通常按字母順序排列的〕卡片索引

card·phone /ˈkɑrdˌfon; ˈkɑːdfəʊn/ n a public telephone where you pay for your call with a telephone card and not money 磁卡電話

★**care¹** /kɛr; keəʳ/ n **1** [U] the process of looking after someone or something that needs attention 照料；照顧: *The clinic provides a high standard of medical care.* 這家診所提供高水準的醫療服務。| *The children are disabled and need special care.* 這些孩童身有殘疾，需要特殊照顧。| *advice on hair care* 頭髮護理的建議 **2** [U] the responsibility for looking after someone or dealing with something 責任；照管: *We left the baby in the care of our neighbour.* 我們把孩子交給鄰居照看。**3** [U] serious attention and effort 用心；努力: *Try to do your work with a bit more care.* 你工作要更加認真一點。**4** [U] paying attention that you do not damage or hurt someone or something 小心；謹慎: *Glass: handle with care!* 玻璃：小心輕放！**5** [C;U] a feeling of worry, concern, or unhappiness 憂慮；焦慮；哀傷: *freedom from care* 無憂無慮 | *without a care in the world* 無牽無掛 **6 care of** (also 又作 **c/o**) at the address of a particular person〔信封上所寫〕由〔某人〕轉交 **7 take care** be careful 小心；當心: *Take care not to drop that vase.* 小心不要把那隻花瓶砸了。**8 take care of** to be responsible for someone or deal with something 照顧〔某人〕；處理〔某事〕: *I'll take care* *of the baby while you're out.* 你出去的時候，我來照顧孩子。| *Don't worry about your ticket — it's all been taken care of.* 不用擔心票子的事——已經有人處理了。**9 take someone into care** to take a young person into a home run by the government or a local council 把〔青少年〕送進〔國家或地方政府開設的〕收養所照料

■ USAGE 用法: **1** If you want to talk about being responsible for someone or something, use **take care of** or **look after** ☆如要表示對某人或某事負責，用 **take care of** 或 **look after**: *She asked me to* **take care of**/**look after** *her cat while she was away.* 她請我在她外出的時候照看她的貓。| *Who will* **take care of**/**look after** *the children when I'm at work?* 我上班時，誰來照顧孩子？| *My secretary will* **take care of**/**look after** *the travel arrangements.* 我的祕書將負責料理行程的安排。**2** If you are talking about somebody who is ill, you can also use **care for** but this is a rather literary use ☆如要表示照顧病人，也可用 **care for**，但這是比較文雅的用法: *She devoted 20 years of her life to* **caring for** *her elderly parents.* 她照顧年長的父母達二十年之久。(It would be more usual to use **take care of** or **look after** here too. 在這裡，**take care of** 或 **look after** 更為常用。) **3** If you want to tell someone to be careful, use **take care (of)** ☆如要叫某人小心或當心一些，用 **take care (of)**: **Take care of** *that money I gave you! Don't leave it lying around.* 把我給你的錢好好保管！別隨便亂放。| **Take care** *of yourself!* 你自己多保重！| *Bye!* **Take care!** 再見！保重！**4** If you want to talk about something being important (or not important) use **care (about)** ☆如要表示(不)重要，用 **care (about)**: *He cares too much* **about** *other people's opinions.* 他過於在意別人的意見。| *I don't care* **about** *him — what about me?* 我並不在乎他——我怎麼樣？| *I don't care what you think.* 我不在乎你怎麼想。| *"You'll get into trouble." "***I don't care!***"* "你會惹下麻煩的。" "我不在乎！"

---

care² *v* **cared, caring 1** [I;T] to be worried, concerned about, or interested in someone or something 憂慮；關心；操心: *When his dog died Alan didn't seem to care at all.* 艾倫的狗死的時候，他似乎一點也不在乎。| *The only thing she cares* **about** *is money.* 她唯一關心的只是金錢。| *"We'll be late." "I don't care."* "我們要遲到了。" "我無所謂。" | *He doesn't care if he puts on weight.* 他對於體重增加並不在意。| *He doesn't seem to care where he works.* 對於在哪裡上班，他似乎無

所謂。

□ USEFUL PATTERNS 有用句型
to care; to care about something; to care if...; to care where, why, who...

2 care to do something to choose to do something 選擇做某事: *It was a failure, whichever way you care to look at it.* 無論你選擇從哪個角度來看，這件事情都算是失敗了。**3 would you care to** *fml* 〔正式〕= would you like to 你願意...: *Would you care to wait here a moment, sir?* 先生，請稍等片刻，您不介意吧？

care for sbdy/sthg ↔ *phr v* [T] **1** to nurse or look after someone or something 照顧〔某人〕；照料〔某事〕: *He's very good at caring for sick animals.* 他很善於照料有病的動物。**2** [usually used in negatives and questions 通常用於否定句和疑問句] to like something 要；喜歡: *Would you care for a drink?* 你要喝點甚麼嗎？| *I don't much care for coffee.* 我不太喜歡喝咖啡。

★**ca·reer¹** /kə'rɪr; kə'rɪəʳ/ *n* **1** a job or profession in a particular area of work for which you are trained and in which you get more responsibility and earn more money as time goes on 職業；事業: *a career* **in** *law* 律師生涯 | *From this point his career really took off.* 他的事業從這裡開始有了真正的起色。| *She has good career prospects.* 她的職業很有前途。**2** the part of your life when you are working 職業生涯；工作經歷: *She spent most of her career as a teacher in London.* 她工作經歷中的大部分時間是在倫敦當教員。

career² *adj* [only before a noun 只用於名詞前] regarding your job as a career for a long time 職業的: *a career woman* 職業婦女 | *a career diplomat* 職業外交家

career³ *v* [I + adv/prep] to go at full speed as if out of control 〔失控般〕全速行駛: *The car careered down the hill and nearly hit an old lady.* 車子飛速開下山去，險些撞到一位老太太。

care·free /'kɛr,fri; 'keəfri:/ *adj* happy and without worry 無憂無慮的: *The long summer days ahead made her feel quite carefree.* 行將到來的悠長暑期令她很快活。

★**care·ful** /'kɛrfəl; 'keəfəl/ *adj* **1** taking care 小心的: *We were careful not to mention it to his wife.* 我們很小心，避免向他妻子提及此事。| *You should be more careful* **with** *your money.* 你花錢的時候應更加謹慎一些。| *a careful driver* 小心翼翼的駕駛員 | *Be careful crossing the road.* 過馬路要當心。| *Do be careful how you carry those eggs!* 搬運那些雞蛋時千萬要當心！**2 Be careful!** a phrase used when the person you are speaking to faces a possible danger 小心〔用於提醒某人注意危險〕: *Be careful you don't fall off that ladder.* 小心不要從梯子上摔下來。**3** showing concern and giving attention to details 關心的; 仔細的: *The doctor made a careful examination.* 醫生作了一次詳細的檢查。 – **carefully** *adv*: *Drive carefully!* 開車小心! – **carefulness** *n* [U]

□ USEFUL PATTERNS 有用句型
to be careful (not) to do something; to be careful with something; to be careful doing something...; to be careful where/who/what/how...

care·less /'kɛrlɪs; 'keələs/ *adj* **1** not taking enough care 不小心的: *He's a very careless driver.* 他是個粗心大意的司機。 | *It was very careless of you to lose her books.* 你把她的書弄丟了，真太不小心了。 **2** not showing enough concern about detail 草率的; 馬虎的: *This is careless work. Do it again!* 這工作做得很馬虎。再做一遍! –**carelessly** *adv* – **carelessness** *n* [U]

car·er /'kɛrə; 'keərə/ *n* someone who has to stay at home to look after an old or sick person, usually for several years, but who is not paid any money 照料者〔在家照料老人或病人的人，常達數年之久，而無任何報酬〕

ca·ress[1] /kə'rɛs; kə'res/ *n* a loving touch or kiss 愛撫; 親吻

caress[2] *v* [T] to touch or kiss someone lovingly 愛撫; 親吻: *He caressed her long black hair.* 他輕撫她黑色的長髮。

care·tak·er /'kɛr,tekə; 'keə,teɪkər/ *n* a person employed to look after a large public building, such as a school, and to be responsible for small repairs and cleaning 〔學校等公共建築物的〕管理員，看門人

caretaker gov·ern·ment /'···,···/ *n* a government which is in control for a usually short period between the end of one government and the appointment of a new government 〔新舊政府之間的〕看守政府

car·go /'kɑrgo; 'kɑːgəʊ/ *n* **cargoes** *or* **cargos** [C;U] the things which are taken from one place to another in a ship, plane, or other vehicle 〔船、飛機或其他車輛所載運的〕貨物: *We sailed from Newcastle with a cargo of coal.* 我們滿載一船煤從紐卡斯爾啟航。

Car·ib·be·an /,kærə'biən; ,kærɪ'biːən/ *adj* from or connected with a country in the West Indies 加勒比海的

car·i·ca·ture /'kærɪkətʃɚ; 'kærɪkətʃʊər/ *n* [C; U] a drawing or description of a person which is made so that the appearance or character seem more odd or amusing than they really are 諷刺的描寫; 諷刺畫: *Have you seen the caricature of the Prime Minister in the paper today?* 你看到了今天報紙上首相的漫畫像嗎? –**caricature** *v* **caricatured, caricaturing** [T]

car·ing /'kɛrɪŋ; 'keərɪŋ/ *adj* providing care and support 關心照顧人的: *the caring professions, such as nursing* 照料他人的職業，如醫療護理

car·nage /'kɑrnɪdʒ; 'kɑːnɪdʒ/ *n* [U] *fml* the killing and wounding of large numbers of people, especially in war 〔正式〕〔尤指戰爭中〕屠殺, 殘殺: *The battlefield was a scene of terrible carnage.* 戰場上是一片可怕的大屠殺景象。

car·nal /'kɑrnəl; 'kɑːnl/ *adj* [only before a noun 只用於名詞前] *fml* relating to sexual desires and feelings (a word used to express disapproval) 〔正式〕肉體的; 性慾的〔含貶義〕: *carnal pleasures* 淫樂

car·na·tion /kɑr'neʃən; kɑː'neɪʃən/ *n* a sweet-smelling white, pink, or red flower 康乃馨

car·ni·val /'kɑrnəvl; 'kɑːnɪvəl/ *n* [C;U] a public entertainment with processions and dancing on a special occasion, or a period of time when this takes place 狂歡節; 嘉年華會: *carnival time in Rio de Janeiro* 里約熱內盧的嘉年華會

car·ni·vore /'kɑrnə,vor; 'kɑːnɪvɔːr/ *n* an animal that eats meat 肉食動物: *Lions are carnivores; rabbits are not.* 獅子是肉食動物, 兔子則不是。–**carnivorous** /kɑr'nɪvərəs; kɑː'nɪvərəs/ *adj*

car·ol /'kærəl; 'kærəl/ *n* a religious song of joy and praise sung at Christmas 聖誕頌歌

ca·rouse /kə'rauz; kə'raʊz/ *v* **caroused, carousing** [I] *lit* to have some noisy fun after drinking a lot of alcohol 〔文〕狂飲尋樂

car·ou·sel /'kæru,zɛl; ,kærə'sel/ *n* (also 又作 **carrousel**) a moving belt at an airport from which passengers collect their bags and cases 〔機場的〕行李傳送帶

carp[1] /kɑrp; kɑːp/ *v* [I] *infml* to find faults and complain continuously about things that are not important 〔非正式〕挑剔; 吹毛求疵: *I wish you'd stop carping about the way I dress.* 我希望你不要再挑剔我的衣着。

carp[2] *n* a large fish that lives in lakes, pools, and slow-moving rivers 鯉魚

car park /'· ·/ *n* a place where you can leave your car sometimes for a small payment 〔收費〕停車場: *I managed to park in a multistorey car park.* 我設法把車停在多層停車場裡。

car·pen·ter /'kɑrpəntə; 'kɑːpɪntər/ *n* a person who is skilled at making and repairing wooden objects 木匠

car·pen·try /'kɑrpəntri; 'kɑːpɪntri/ *n* [U] the art or work of a carpenter 木匠業; 木工手藝

*★**car·pet[1]** /'kɑrpɪt; 'kɑːpɪt/ *n* **1** [C;U] thick, heavy floor covering for floors or stairs, usually made of wool 〔通常為羊毛製的〕地毯: *a lovely Persian carpet* 漂亮的波斯地毯 | *We'll put carpet down in the hall.* 我們準備在大廳裡鋪上地毯。 –see picture on page 730 見 730 頁彩圖 **2** [C] anything which covers a large area of ground 像地毯一樣的東西: *a carpet of flowers* 遍地鮮花

carpet² *v* [T] to cover something with a carpet 用地毯覆蓋〔某物〕

car phone /'··/ *n* a private telephone in someone's car〔汽車裡的〕私人電話機

car·riage /'kærɪdʒ; 'kærɪdʒ/ *n* **1** *BrE* [C] one of the parts of a train where passengers sit〖英式〗火車(乘客)車廂: *I'll be sitting in the third carriage from the front of the train.* 我將坐在火車前部的第三節車廂裡。–see picture on page 991 見 991 頁彩圖 **2** [C] a wheeled vehicle which is pulled by a horse 馬車 **3** [U] the cost of moving goods from one place to another 運費: *The price includes carriage.* 這價錢包括運費。 **4** [C] a movable part of a machine (機器的)活動部分: *the carriage of a typewriter which holds and moves the paper* 打字機上放置和移動紙張的滑架 **5** [sing;U] *fml* the way a person holds their head and body when standing or walking〖正式〗〔站立或行走時的〕姿態, 姿勢

carried a·way /,···'·/ *adj* [never before a noun 不能用於名詞前] filled with strong feelings or excitement, especially so that you behave unreasonably 過於激動的: *I'm afraid my husband got rather carried away; he's very sorry.* 恐怕我丈夫有點過於激動了, 他十分抱歉。

car·ri·er /'kærɪə; 'kærɪər/ *n* **1** a person or thing that carries goods or passengers from one place to another 貨[客]運商; 貨[客]運交通工具 **2** a person or thing that does not suffer any of the effects of a disease but carries it and passes it to other people 帶菌者〔傳染疾病但本身不受感染的人或物〕

carrier bag /'··· ·/ (**shopping bag** *AmE*〖美式〗) *n* a cheap strong paper or plastic bag with handles, for carrying away from a shop 手提〔紙或塑料製的〕購物袋

car·rot /'kærət; 'kærət/ *n* **1** [C;U] a long, thin, orange vegetable 胡蘿蔔: *Have some more carrots.* 再吃點胡蘿蔔吧。 | *carrot juice* 胡蘿蔔汁 –see picture on page 504 見 504 頁彩圖 **2** [C] *infml* a reward that you are promised for doing something〖非正式〗〔許諾做某事之後可得的〕報酬: *My boss dangled a carrot by saying he'd give me a pay rise if I helped him over the weekend.* 老闆許下諾言, 說如果我在週末幫他一把, 他就給我加薪。

car·ry /'kærɪ; 'kærɪ/ *v* **carried, carried, carrying 1** [T] to hold something and take it with you 攜帶, 輸送〔某物〕: *I had to carry my suitcases all the way to the hotel.* 我不得不一路拎着手提箱去旅館。 | *The police don't usually carry guns.* 警察通常不帶槍。 | *These pipes carry the oil across the desert.* 這些輸油管穿過沙漠把石油輸送出去。–see picture on page 992 見 992 頁彩圖 **2** [T] to have a disease and spread it to other people 傳染〔疾病〕: *Some mosquitoes carry malaria.* 有些蚊子傳染瘧疾。 | *Rats*

are dirty and can carry diseases. 老鼠很髒, 會傳播疾病。 **3** [T] (of a newspaper or magazine) to contain a particular picture or article〔報紙或雜誌〕刊載〔圖片或文章〕: *Several newspapers carried pictures of the scene of the accident.* 有幾家報紙刊登了這起事故現場的照片。 | *The paper carries an article about the dangers of smoking.* 這張報紙上刊載了一篇有關吸煙有害的文章。 **4** [T] to have something as a usual or necessary result 招致; 導致: *The crime of murder carries the death penalty in many countries.* 在許多國家裡, 謀殺罪可判死刑。 | *The job carries certain risks.* 這項工作有些風險。 **5** [I] (of a sound) to be able to reach a certain distance〔聲音〕能傳到(…遠): *Her voice didn't carry to the back of the hall.* 她的聲音傳不到大廳的後部。 | *The sound carried for miles.* 這聲音能傳到數哩以外。 **6 be carried** to be approved 被同意: *The motion was carried by 310 votes to 306.* 這項提議以 310 票對 306 票獲得通過。 **7 be carrying a child** *lit* to be PREGNANT〖文〗懷孕 **8 carry weight** to be respected and believed by people 被人尊重; 被人相信: *His opinions carry a lot of weight.* 他的意見很受重視。 **9 be/get carried away** to be too excited 過於激動: *I got carried away and bought three pairs of shoes instead of one.* 我太忘形了, 買下了三雙鞋子而不是一雙。 **10 carry something too far** to do something too much or for too long 把事情做得過分: *It was funny at first, but she carried the joke too far.* 起初是很有趣的, 不過她的玩笑開得過火了。

carry sthg ↔ **forward** *phr v* [T] to move a number from the bottom of one row of figures to the top of the next row, in order to add it to the next row 將〔數目〕轉入次頁

carry sthg ↔ **off** *phr v* [T] **1** to succeed in doing something 完成〔某事〕: *It's a risky venture, and I'm not sure they'll be able to carry it off.* 這是件要冒風險的事, 我不敢肯定他們能否成功。 **2** to win a prize 贏得〔獎賞、獎品〕: *Jean carried off all the prizes.* 瓊囊括了所有的獎品。

carry on *phr v* **carry on with something, carry on doing something** to continue doing something 繼續做某事: *We carried on with our discussion.* 我們繼續討論。 | *He carried on talking in spite of the noise.* 儘管有噪音, 他仍然說個不停。

carry sthg ↔ **out** *phr v* [T] to complete a job or put into practice a plan or order 實現; 完成; 執行: *This research has been carried out at the University of Leeds.* 這項研究已在利茲大學進行。 | *Our planes carried out a bombing raid on enemy targets.* 我們的飛機執行了一項轟炸敵方目標的任務。 | *He never carried out his threat to resign.* 他威脅要辭職, 但從來沒有那樣做。 | *They were only carrying out their orders.* 他們只不過在執行命令而已。

---

carry through *phr v* **1** [T **carry** sthg ↔ **through**] to put into practice a plan or order 執行〔命令〕；實施〔計劃〕: *The government managed to carry through the reforms despite fierce opposition.* 儘管遭到強烈的反對，政府還是設法進行了改革。 **2** [T **carry** sbdy **through** sthg] to help someone to manage when they are ill or having difficulties 幫助〔某人〕度過難關: *Her great courage carried her through the illness.* 她的勇氣使她度過了生病的難關。

car·ry·cot /ˈkærɪˌkɒt; ˈkærɪkɒt/ *n* an object shaped like a box in which a baby sleeps and can be carried about 手提式箱形嬰兒牀

cart[1] /kɑrt; kɑːt/ *n* **1** a vehicle made of wood and pulled by hand or by animals, used for example on a farm to carry heavy things 〔木製〕手推車；馬車〔如農場的運貨馬車〕 **2 put the cart before the horse** to do unimportant things before the really important ones 本末倒置

cart[2] *v* [T; +adv/prep] *infml* 【非正式】 **1** to carry something heavy 攜帶〔重物〕: *I've been carting this suitcase around the town all afternoon.* 整個下午我都拖着這個手提箱在鎮裡跑來跑去。 **2** to take or remove someone, often disrespectfully, carelessly, or using force 強行帶走；押走: *They carted him off to the police station.* 他們押着他去警察局。 | *She carts the kids around with her wherever she goes.* 她無論去哪兒都把孩子帶在身邊。

carte blanche /ˈkɑrt ˈblɑnʃ; ˌkɑːt ˈblɑːnʃ/ *n* [U] freedom to do exactly what you want to 全權〔處理〕: *My parents gave me carte blanche to organize the party.* 我的父母讓我全權組織聚會。

car·tel /kɑrˈtɛl; kɑːˈtel/ *n* a combination of companies, often international ones, intended to limit fair competition and increase their profits 卡特爾〔公司為減少競爭、增加利潤而組成的國際聯盟〕

cart·horse /ˈkɑrthɔrs; ˈkɑːthɔːs/ *n* a powerful horse used for heavy work on farms 〔農場用以幹重活的〕壯馬

car·ti·lage /ˈkɑrtlɪdʒ; ˈkɑːtəlɪdʒ/ *n* [C;U] a strong elastic substance found round your joints 軟骨〔組織〕

car·tog·ra·phy /kɑrˈtɒgrəfɪ; kɑːˈtɒgrəfɪ/ *n* [U] the science or art of making maps 製圖學；地圖製作法

car·ton /ˈkɑrtn; ˈkɑːtn/ *n* a box made from stiff paper, usually used for holding food or drink 硬紙盒〔常用來裝食品或飲料〕: *a carton of milk* 一盒牛奶 –see picture on page 244 見 244 頁彩圖

car·toon /kɑrˈtun; kɑːˈtuːn/ *n* **1** a humorous drawing, often dealing with something of interest in the news in an amusing way 漫畫；諷刺畫 **2** a set of drawings in a newspaper or magazine telling the story of particular characters 連環畫 **3** a film made by

photographing drawings 卡通片；動畫片: *a Mickey Mouse cartoon* 一部米奇老鼠的動畫片 –**cartoonist** *n*

car·tridge /ˈkɑrtrɪdʒ; ˈkɑːtrɪdʒ/ *n* **1** a tube containing explosive and shot for a gun 彈藥筒；子彈 **2** a small case in a record player containing the needle that picks up sound signals from a record 〔唱機的〕唱頭 **3** a thin tube with ink in it which you put inside a pen 〔鋼筆的〕儲墨管

cart·wheel /ˈkɑrtˌwhil; ˈkɑːtwiːl/ *n* a movement in which a person turns over by putting their hands on the ground and moving their legs sideways in the air 側手翻 –**cartwheel** *v* [I]

carve /kɑrv; kɑːv/ *v* **carved, carving** **1** [T] to cut a special shape out of wood or stone 雕刻〔木、石〕: *The sculptor carved a bird from the block of stone.* 雕塑家把那塊石頭雕成了一隻鳥。 | *They carved their initials on the tree.* 他們把自己名字的首字母刻在樹上。 **2** [I; T] to cut cooked meat 切〔熟肉〕: *Shall I carve you another slice of chicken?* 我再給你切一片雞肉好嗎？ **3 carve something out for yourself** to make or get something by working hard 經過艱苦努力獲得某物: *She has managed to carve out a career for herself as a comic actress.* 她努力為自己開創了一個做喜劇演員的前程。

carve sthg ↔ **up** *phr v* [T] to divide something into smaller pieces 把〔某物〕分成小塊；瓜分: *They carved up the profits between them.* 他們瓜分了利潤。

carv·ing /ˈkɑrvɪŋ; ˈkɑːvɪŋ/ *n* **1** [C] something made by carving 雕刻品 **2** [U] the work, art, or skill of a person who carves 雕刻；雕刻術

carving knife /ˈ·· ˌ·/ *n* a long sharp knife used for cutting large pieces of meat 切肉刀

cas·cade[1] /kæsˈked; kæˈskeɪd/ *n* **1** a small waterfall falling through rocks 小瀑布 **2** *lit* anything that seems to flow downwards in a mass 【文】瀑布般下垂之物: *Her hair fell over her shoulders in a cascade of curls.* 她的卷髮垂落在肩上。

cascade[2] *v* [I +adv/prep] to fall fast and in great quantities 瀑布似地落下: *I watched the rainwater cascading down the window.* 我看着雨水順着窗戶傾瀉而下。

★case /kes; keɪs/ *n* **1** [C] a single example of something 事例；實例: *Doctors have reported several cases of malaria.* 據醫生報告已發現了幾宗瘧疾病例。 | *We are seeing more and more cases of children being neglected and abused.* 我們發現孩子被忽視、被虐待的事例越來越多。 | *This is a typical case of the government's stupidity and lack of understanding.* 這是政府愚蠢和無同情心的一個典型事例。 **2** [C] a set of events that needs to be studied and understood by someone, for example by the police or in a court of law 案件; 案例: *Hundreds of police are working on this case.* 數百名警察在調查此案。| *a very difficult murder case* 很棘手的謀殺案 | *The case will be heard in court next week.* 這案子將於下週審理。**3** [C] the facts and arguments that support what someone is saying 論據; 事實: *There is a very good case* **for** *reducing taxes immediately.* 有一個應當立即減稅的很好的理由。| *For years he has argued the case* **against** *government control.* 數年來他一直在據理反對政府的控制。| *The police have a very good case against her.* 警方掌握了對她極為不利的罪證。**4** [C;U] the form of a word, usually a noun, which shows its relationship with the other words in a sentence; for example, "me" is the object case of "I" 格〔顯示某詞與句中其他詞之間的相互關係; 例如, I 的賓格是 me〕**5** [C] a large box in which goods can be stored or moved〔儲藏貨物的〕大箱子: *a case of wine* 一箱酒 **6** [C] a large bag for carrying your clothes and other things in, for example when you go on holiday〔度假時用作裝衣物及其他物品的〕箱子: *He offered to carry my case to my room.* 他主動幫我把箱子拿到我的房間裡去。**7 a case in point** a good example of something that you are saying〔當前所説事情的〕很好的例子: *More and more children are suffering the effects of divorce. Sarah is a case in point; her parents split up when she was three and she has lived with her grandmother since then.* 越來越多的孩子在遭受父母離婚所帶來的痛苦。薩拉就是一個明顯的例子: 她三歲時父母便離了婚, 從那時起, 她就一直與祖母住在一起。**8 in any case** a phrase you use when you are stating forcefully that something is true 無論如何: *The cost might turn out to be lower than we thought, but in any case it will still be a substantial amount of money.* 實際開支也許會比我們所預料的要低, 但不管怎麼, 那仍會是一筆可觀的數目。| *Tim's not coming to the concert. He says he's too busy. He hasn't got any money, in any case.* 添不來聽音樂會。他說他太忙了。實際上, 他是沒有錢。—see Study Note on page 1325 見 1325 頁學習提示 **9 in that case, in which case** as this is true 既然如此; 那樣的話: *"I'm afraid I won't be able to give you a lift after all." "Well in that case I'll just have to walk."* "對不起, 我還是不能讓你搭我的車。""那麼, 我只好走路去了。" **10 in case, just in case** because something might happen 以防萬一: *I've brought some sandwiches in case we get hungry.* 我帶了些三明治, 以防我們肚子餓。| *I brought my key just in case you forgot yours.* 我帶了我的鑰匙, 以防你忘記帶。**11 in case of** if or when something happens 若〔某事〕發生, 要是…: *In case of fire, sound the alarm and leave the building immediately.* 如發生火災, 按響警鐘, 然後立刻離開大樓。

■ USAGE 用法: Note the tenses of the verbs following **in case** in these sentences ☆注意在這些句子中, 跟在 **in case** 後面動詞的時態: *Take your umbrella* **in case** *it rains.* 帶上你的傘吧, 以防下雨。| *I'll give you the front door key* **in case** *I am out.* 我會把前門的鑰匙給你, 以防萬一我外出。| *She took lots of warm clothes* **in case** *the weather turned cold.* 她帶了許多保暖的衣服, 以防天氣轉冷。

12 the case true or correct 事實: *It is the case that fewer crimes are committed by women than by men.* 婦女犯罪比男子犯罪少, 這是事實。**13 lower case** small letters of the alphabet 小寫字母: *The computer commands should all be written in lower case.* 電腦的指令應當全部用小寫字母寫。| *a lower case "e"* 小寫字母"e" **14 upper case** the CAPITAL letters of the alphabet 大寫字母: *an upper case "E"* 大寫字母"E"

case·ment win·dow /ˌkesmənt'windo; ˌkeɪsmənt 'wɪndəʊ/ *n* (also 又作 **casement**) a window that opens like a door 門式窗

✲cash¹ /kæʃ; kæʃ/ *n* [U] **1** money in coins and notes 現金, 現款: *I haven't got any cash on me – can I pay by cheque?* 我身上沒帶現金——能用支票付款嗎? **2** *infml* money in any form《非正式》錢: *Denis is always short of cash.* 丹尼斯總是手頭緊的。**3 cash on delivery** see 見 C.O.D.

cash² *v* [T] to exchange something such as a cheque for cash 把〔支票等〕兑現: *Can you cash these traveller's cheques for me?* 你能把這些旅行支票給我兑成現金嗎?

cash in on sthg *phr v* [T] to take full advantage of a situation 充分利用: *The company cashed in on the difficulties of its rivals.* 公司充分利用其競爭對手的種種困難。

cash card /'··/ *n* a special plastic card used for obtaining money from a machine at a bank〔用於自動提款機的〕自動提款卡

cash crop /'··/ *n* a crop produced for sale rather than for use by the grower 商品農作物〔為出售而非自用的農作物〕

cash desk /'··/ *n* the desk in a shop where payments are made〔商店的〕付款處, 收款台

ca·shew /'kæʃu; 'kæʃuː/ *n* a small curved nut 腰果

cash flow /'··/ *n* [sing;U] the movement of money into and out of a company 現金流轉: *We've got serious cash flow problems.* 我們在現金流轉方面存在很大的困難。

cash·ier /kæ'ʃɪr; kæ'ʃɪər/ *n* a person that people pay in places like shops, banks, or hotels 出納員

cash·mere /'kæʃmɪr; 'kæʃmɪər/ *n* [U] a kind of fine soft wool 開士米〔一種細軟羊毛〕

cash reg·is·ter /'· ˌ···/ *n* a machine used in places like shops to show how much people have to pay〔商店等處〕收銀機

cas·ing /ˈkeɪsɪŋ; ˈkeɪsɪŋ/ n a protective covering〔起保護作用的〕套，殼: *This wire has a rubber casing.* 這電線外面包有一層橡膠。

ca·si·no /kəˈsino; kəˈsiːnəʊ/ n **casinos** a place where people play cards or other games for money 賭場

cask /kæsk; kɑːsk/ n a barrel-shaped container for holding and storing liquids〔盛液體的〕桶

cas·ket /ˈkæskɪt; ˈkɑːskɪt/ n **1** a small container for holding valuable things like letters or jewellery〔收藏信件珠寶等貴重物品的〕小箱 **2** the usual American word for 〖美式〗= COFFIN

cas·se·role /ˈkæsəˌrol; ˈkæsərəʊl/ n **1** [C] a deep dish with a cover in which food can be cooked and served〔深底有蓋的〕焙盤，砂鍋 –see picture on page 244 見 244 頁彩圖 **2** [C;U] the food cooked in a casserole, usually a mixture of meat and vegetables 砂鍋菜餚〔常為肉、蔬菜的混合菜〕: *a beef casserole* 砂鍋牛肉

cas·sette /kæˈset; kəˈset/ n **1** a small flat container with TAPE inside it, used to record or play sounds 錄音帶匣 **2** a container of photographic film which can be put complete into a camera〔相機的〕軟片匣，膠片匣 **3 cassette recorder** a machine containing a cassette that records and plays back sounds 盒式錄音機

cast¹ /kæst; kɑːst/ v **cast, cast [T] **1** to give a part in a play or a film to an actor 分派〔某人〕扮演角色: *She was cast in the role of Ophelia.* 她被指派扮演奧菲利婭。 **2** to throw something 投；拋；擲: *fishermen casting their nets into the sea* 把網撒入大海的漁民 **3** *lit* to throw light or shadows 〖文〗投下〔光、影〕: *The trees cast a shadow across the lawn.* 樹木在草坪上投下了影子。 **4** to make an object by pouring metal or plastic into a shaped container 鑄造: *a bell cast in bronze* 用青銅鑄成的鐘 **5** be cast away to be left somewhere after your ship has sunk〔沉船後〕在某地漂流 **6 cast an eye over something** to look at something, especially quickly〔尤指迅速地〕看某物一眼 **7 cast a spell** to say magic words in order to make something happen 念咒語〔以使某事發生〕 **8 cast a vote** to express your choice in an election usually by marking a piece of paper or raising your hand 投票 **9 cast light on something** to help to explain something 幫助解釋某事: *You know her better than I do; can you cast any light on her behaviour?* 你比我更了解她；能給我解釋一下她的行為嗎？

   cast about/around for sthg *phr v* [T] to look for something in all directions 到處尋找〔某物〕

   cast off *phr v* [I;T **cast** sthg ↔ **off**] to untie a boat or a ship 解開船纜: *We're ready —*

cast off! 我們準備好了 —— 解纜！

cast² n **1** [+ sing/pl verb] the actors in a play or film 演員陣容: *The cast is ready to start.* 演員們已準備好拍攝。 **2** a hard protective covering for holding a broken bone in place while it gets better〔固定骨折用的〕石膏

cas·ta·nets /ˌkæstəˈnets; ˌkæstəˈnets/ n [pl] a musical instrument made of two pieces of wood which you hold in your hand and strike against each other 響板〔用手握住兩片木板，使其互相敲擊發聲的樂器〕

cast·a·way /ˈkæstəˌwe; ˈkɑːstəweɪ/ n a person who escapes when their ship is sunk and reaches the shore of a strange country or lonely island 逃離沉船後漂流至異鄉或孤島的人

caste /kæst; kɑːst/ n [C;U] the Hindu system of dividing people into different classes of society according to their birth or their job〔印度〕種姓制度，等級制度

cast·er /ˈkæstə; ˈkɑːstə/ n (also 又作 **cast·or**) a wheel fixed to the base of a piece of furniture so that it can be easily moved〔家具的〕腳輪

caster sug·ar /ˈ‥ ‚‥ˈ/ n (also 又作 **castor sugar**) [U] very fine white sugar often used in cooking 細白砂糖

cast·i·gate /ˈkæstəˌget; ˈkæstɪˌɡeɪt/ v **castigated, castigating** [T] *fml* to express strong disapproval of someone 〖正式〗強烈反對〔某人〕

cast·ing /ˈkæstɪŋ; ˈkɑːstɪŋ/ n [U] the choosing of actors for a play or film 挑選演員，分派角色

casting vote /ˌ‥ ˈ‥/ n a deciding vote used by a chairman when both sides have an equal number of votes〔當雙方票數相同時，主席所投的〕決定性一票

cast i·ron /ˌ‥ ˈ‥/ n [U] a hard but easily breakable type of iron 生鐵；鑄鐵

cast-iron /ˌ‥ ˈ‥◄/ adj **1** made of cast iron 生鐵製成的 **2** hard and strong 堅硬的；強壯的: *a cast-iron stomach* 強健的胃 **3** impossible to doubt 不容置疑的: *a cast-iron alibi* 案發時不在現場的鐵證

cas·tle /ˈkæsl; ˈkɑːsəl/ n **1** a large strongly-built building or set of buildings made in the past to give protection from attack〔昔時的〕城堡 **2** one of the powerful pieces in the game of CHESS〔國際象棋中的〕車

cast-off /ˈkæstˌɔf; ˈkɑːstɒf/ n *infml* an unwanted article of clothing 〖非正式〗廢棄的衣服: *She gave her castoffs to her younger sister.* 她把她不要的舊衣服送給了妹妹。

cast·or /ˈkæstə; ˈkɑːstə/ n see 見 CASTER

castor oil /ˌ‥ ˈ‥◄/ n [U] a thick yellow oil taken for medical reasons 蓖麻油

castor sug·ar n [U] see 見 CASTER SUGAR

cas·trate /ˈkæstret; kæˈstreɪt/ v **castrated, castrating** [T] to remove all or part of the sex organs of a male animal or person 閹

割〔動物、人〕 –**castration** /kæsˈtreɪʃən; kæ-ˈstreɪʃən/ *n* [C;U]

cas·u·al /ˈkæʒuəl; ˈkæʒuəl/ *adj* **1** not showing much interest 漫不經心的; 不感興趣的: *His casual manner annoyed her.* 他漫不經心的態度令她惱火。 **2** informal (used of clothes) 隨意的, 非正式的〔指服飾〕: *casual wear* 便服 **3** [only before a noun 只用於名詞前] not serious or thorough 不認真的; 不徹底的: *The casual newspaper reader doesn't read articles on politics every day.* 隨便翻翻報紙的讀者不是每天都看政論文章的。 **4** employed only to do a job lasting a short time 短期受雇的: *casual labour* 臨時工 **5** resulting from chance 偶然的; 碰巧的: *a casual meeting* 巧遇 –**casually** *adv*: *casually dressed* 穿着隨便的

cas·u·al·ty /ˈkæʒuəltɪ; ˈkæʒuəlti/ *n* **casualties 1** [C] a person hurt in an accident or killed in battle 〔事故中的〕受傷者;〔戰鬥中的〕喪生者: *Two buses collided outside the British Museum today. There were no casualties.* 兩輛公共汽車在大英博物館前相撞, 並無傷亡。| *Their army suffered heavy casualties.* 他們的軍隊傷亡慘重。 **2** [U] (also 又作 **casualty department**) a place in a hospital where people hurt in accidents are taken 急救室; 急診室: *They rushed her to casualty.* 他們火速地把她送往急救室。 **3** [C] a person or thing that suffers as a result of an action 受害者; 犧牲品: *The new school was never finished; it was a casualty of the recent spending cuts.* 新學校始終沒有竣工; 它是最近壓縮開支的犧牲品。

★★ **cat** /kæt; kæt/ *n* **1** a small animal with soft fur often kept as a pet or in buildings to catch mice and rats 貓 **2** any animal related to the cat, for example a lion or a tiger 貓科動物〔如獅、虎等〕 **3** let the cat out of the bag *infml* to tell a secret, usually unintentionally 《非正式》〔常指無意中〕泄漏祕密

cat·a·clysm /ˈkætəˌklɪzəm; ˈkætəklɪzəm/ *n fml* a sudden and violent event or change 《正式》突然而劇烈的事件或變動 –**cataclysmic** /ˌkætəˈklɪzmɪk; ˌkætəˈklɪzmɪk/ *adj*

cat·a·comb /ˈkætəˌkom; ˈkætəkuːm/ *n* an underground burial place made up of many passages and rooms 地下墓穴

★ **cat·a·logue**[1] /ˈkætəlɔg; ˈkætəlɒg/ *n* (**catalog** *AmE* 《美式》) **1** a book containing information about goods that may be bought in a shop or sent by post 商品目錄 **2** a book with a list of all the objects in a place, for example a MUSEUM 目錄冊

catalogue[2] *v* **catalogued**, or **cataloged**, **cataloguing** or **cataloging** (**catalog** *AmE* 《美式》) [T] **1** to make a list for a special purpose 編目錄; 分類: *You need to catalogue all the items in the house for valuation purposes.* 你需要把房子中所有東西編個目錄以便估價。 **2** to put information into a cata-

logue 把…編入目錄

cat·a·lyst /ˈkætlɪst; ˈkætl-l̩st/ *n* **1** a substance which, without itself changing, causes chemical activity to go faster 催化劑 **2** something that causes something important to happen 促進因素: *The First World War served as a catalyst for major social changes in Europe.* 第一次世界大戰促成了歐洲的重大社會變革。

cat·a·pult[1] /ˈkætəˌpʌlt; ˈkætəpʌlt/ *n* **1** a small Y-shaped stick with a rubber band fastened between the forks, used by children to shoot small stones 〔兒童玩的〕彈弓 **2** a machine for throwing heavy stones or balls, used as a weapon in the past 〔昔時的〕弩砲, 石弩

catapult[2] *v* [T; + adv/prep] to throw something suddenly 突然扔出; 彈出: *A car crashed into the pram and the baby was catapulted into the road.* 汽車撞上了嬰兒車, 車裡的嬰兒被彈到了馬路上。

cat·a·ract /ˈkætəˌrækt; ˈkætərækt/ *n* **1** a growth on a person's eye causing a slow loss of sight 白內障 **2** a large waterfall 大瀑布

ca·tarrh /kəˈtɑr; kəˈtɑːʳ/ *n* [U] a condition causing a flow of thick liquid in your nose and throat when you have a cold 〔感冒時〕鼻、喉的〕黏膜炎

ca·tas·tro·phe /kəˈtæstrəfɪ; kəˈtæstrəfi/ *n* a sudden, unexpected event that causes great suffering, misfortune, or ruin 巨大的災難: *The flood was a terrible catastrophe in which many people died.* 那次洪水是場大災難, 有許多人喪生。 –**catastrophic** /ˌkætəˈstrɒfɪk; ˌkætəˈstrɒfɪk/ *adj*

★★ **catch**[1] /kætʃ; kætʃ/ *v* **caught** /kɔt; kɔːt/, **caught 1** [T] to hold and stop something that is moving in the air 接住, 抓住〔在空中飛行之物〕: *The dog caught the ball in its mouth.* 狗用嘴巴接住了球。| *Here, I've found your key. Catch!* 在這兒呢, 我找到你的鑰匙了。接住! –see picture on page 992 見 992 頁彩圖 **2** [T] to trap something, especially after chasing or hunting it 建捉〔某物〕; 抓住: *Cats like to catch mice.* 貓喜歡抓老鼠。| *The police are sure they will catch the thief.* 警察有把握抓住那個小偷。 **3** catch someone in the act of, catch someone redhanded to suddenly find someone doing something that they should not be doing 當場發現某人在做〔不應做的事〕: *The thieves were caught redhanded.* 那些小偷在作案時被當場捉住。 **4** [T] to discover something 發現〔某事物〕: *The chances of a cure are very good, if the disease is caught early.* 如果這病發現得早, 治癒的機會就很大。 **5** [T] to be in time for something 趕上: *If we go home now, we'll just catch the 10 o'clock news.* 如果我們現在回家, 那剛巧能趕上十點鐘的新聞。| *Hurry up — we've got a train to catch!* 快點 —— 我們還要趕火車呢! **6** [T] to get an illness 患〔病〕: *Put your coat on, or you'll catch a cold.* 穿上外套, 否則你會染上感冒的。 **7** [I;T] to become or to cause something to be accidentally held, fastened, or stuck 卡住; 鈎住; 纏住; 夾住: *My coat caught in the door.* 我的外衣被門夾住了。 | *I caught my dress on a nail.* 我的衣服被釘子鈎住了。 **8 catch someone's attention** to make someone notice something suddenly 突然引起某人注意 **9 catch someone's imagination** to interest someone so that they start thinking about an idea 促發某人的想像力 **10 catch sight of** to notice someone or something 看見: *I caught sight of my old friend in town today.* 我今天在城裡看見了老朋友。 **11 not catch something** to not hear something clearly 未聽清楚某事: *I didn't quite catch what you said.* 你說的話我聽得不太清楚。 **12** [I;T] (also 又作 **catch fire**) to start to burn 開始燃燒: *The leaves caught quickly.* 樹葉很快便燒着了。 | *The house caught fire.* 房子着火了。 **13 catch someone's eye** to make someone notice you 引起某人注意: *See if you can catch the waiter's eye.* 看你能否引起侍應生的注意。

catch on *phr v* [I] **1** to become popular 風行; 流行: *The new fashion really caught on.* 這種裝束非常流行。 **2** to understand something 理解〔某事〕: *He finally caught on to what they were doing.* 他終於明白了他們在幹甚麼。

catch sbdy ↔ out *phr v* [T] to show that someone is wrong or is doing something wrong 指出〔某人〕的錯誤

catch up *phr v* **1** [I;T **catch** sbdy/sthg **up**] to come up from behind and reach the same point as someone 趕上〔某人〕: *She's slower than her sister, but catching up.* 她比姐姐慢, 但正在迅速趕上。 | *We are catching up with Japan in industrial production.* 我們在追趕日本的工業生產力。 | *You carry on walking and I'll catch you up in a minute.* 你繼續走, 我很快就會趕上來。 **2** [I] to bring or come up to date 趕上〔進度〕: *I have to catch up on writing letters tonight so I can't come out.* 今晚我必須把信趕出來, 所以不能出去。 **3 be caught up in** included in something, often against your wishes 捲入; 介入: *The government seems to have got caught up in the argument between Russia and America.* 政府似乎捲入了俄美之間的爭端。

catch² *n* **1** the action of seizing and holding a ball 接球: *That was a good catch!* 那球接得好! **2** something that has been caught, usually a quantity of fish 捕獲物〔通常指魚〕: *The fishermen got a good catch last night.* 漁民昨夜捕到了很多魚。 **3** a hook or other apparatus for fastening something or holding it shut 掛鈎; 鎖鈎: *The catch on this door is broken.* 這扇門的掛鈎壞了。 **4** *infml* a hidden difficulty 〔非正式〕潛在的困難; 蹊蹺: *That*

house is very cheap; there must be a catch in it somewhere! 那所房子非常便宜, 當中一定有些古怪。

catch-22 /ˌ··ˈ··/ *n* [U] a situation that you cannot escape from because of something that is part of the situation itself 無法擺脫的困境, 讓人左右為難的情況: *The report complained of the catch-22 situation facing homeless people — that to register for a council house they must first have an address.* 報告申訴了無家可歸者尷尬的處境——要申請政府住房, 他們首先必須要有住址。

catch·ing /ˈkætʃɪŋ/ [never before a noun 不能用於名詞前] *infml* infectious (used of a disease) 〔非正式〕傳染性的〔指疾病〕

catch·ment ar·e·a /ˈkætʃmənt ˌɛrɪə; ˈkætʃmənt ˌeərɪə/ *n* the area from which a school gets its pupils, or from which people go to a particular hospital, etc. 服務對象集中區〔該區居民被指定在某一學校入學, 在某醫院就診〕

catch-phrase /ˈ··/ *n* a phrase, often with little meaning, which becomes fashionable and widely used for a time 〔流行一時但往往意義浮淺的〕時髦話

catch·word /ˈkætʃˌwɜːd; ˈkætʃwɜːd/ *n* a word or phrase repeated regularly by a particular person or political party 標語; 口號

catch·y /ˈkætʃɪ; ˈkætʃi/ *adj* easy to remember 容易記住的: *a catchy song* 容易記住的歌曲

cat·e·gor·i·cal /ˌkætəˈɡɒrɪkl; ˌkætəˈɡɒrɪkəl/ *adj* completely certain (used of a statement) 絕對肯定的〔指陳述〕: *a categorical denial* 斷然的否定 **–categorically** /-klɪ; -kli/ *adv*: *I asked her several times to come, but she categorically refused.* 我數次請她來, 但她都斷然拒絕了。

cat·e·go·rize /ˈkætəɡəˌraɪz; ˈkætəɡəraɪz/ *v* **categorized, categorizing** (also 又作 **categorise** *BrE* 〔英式〕) [T] to put someone or something in a group with similar people or things 把〔某人, 某物〕分類, 歸類: *He was categorized as a trouble-maker.* 他屬於愛惹麻煩的那一類人。

*cat·e·go·ry /ˈkætəɡɒrɪ; ˈkætəɡəri/ *n* **categories** a group of similar people or things 類別; 類型

ca·ter /ˈkeɪtə; ˈkeɪtər/ *v* **1** [I] to provide and serve food and drinks for a large group of people 承包伙食; 承辦酒席: *Who's catering at your daughter's wedding?* 誰來承辦你女兒的婚宴? **2 cater for someone** to provide what is wanted or needed by someone 為某人提供服務: *a holiday company that caters mainly for older people* 一家主要為老年人提供假日活動的公司 **3 cater to** to try to please someone's desires or needs, usually of a bad kind 滿足, 迎合〔通常為不良的需要〕: *a paper that caters to the lowest tastes of the* *reading public* 迎合讀者低級趣味的報刊

cat·er·pil·lar /ˈkætəˌpɪlə; ˈkætəˌpɪləʳ/ *n* a small wormlike creature with many legs that feeds on the leaves of plants 毛蟲

ca·the·dral /kəˈθiːdrəl; kəˈθiːdrəl/ *n* an important large church 大教堂

cath·o·lic /ˈkæθəlɪk; ˈkæθəlɪk/ *adj* **1** *fml* including many different things (used to describe interests) 〔正式〕廣泛的〔指興趣〕: *catholic opinions* 廣泛的意見 **2 Catholic** relating to the Roman Catholic Church 天主教的: *Catholic children* 天主教的兒童 | *Catholic schools* 天主教的學校

Catholic *n* someone who follows the Roman Catholic religion 天主教徒: *She's a practising Catholic.* 她是個虔誠的天主教徒。–**Catholicism** /kəˈθɑləˌsɪzəm; kəˈθɒlɪˌsɪzəm/ *n* [U]

cat·nap /ˈkætnæp; ˈkætnæp/ *n infml* a very short light sleep 〔非正式〕小睡; 瞌睡

cat's eye /ˈ· ·/ *n* a small object fixed in the middle of a road which shines when lights shine on it 貓眼石〔裝於道路中央, 車燈照耀時會發光的小型反光裝置〕

cat·tle /ˈkætl; ˈkætl/ *n* [pl] male and female cows kept on a farm 牛

cat·ty /ˈkætɪ; ˈkætɪ/ *adj infml* unpleasant and unkind 〔非正式〕令人不快的; 惡毒的: *a catty remark* 惡毒的話

caught /kɔt; kɔːt/ *v* the past tense and past participle of CATCH ☆ CATCH 的過去式和過去分詞

caul·dron /ˈkɔldrən; ˈkɔːldrən/ *n* (**caldron** *AmE* 〔美式〕) a large round metal pot for boiling liquids over a fire 大鍋

cau·li·flow·er /ˈkɔləˌflaʊə; ˈkɒlɪˌflaʊəʳ/ *n* [C;U] a garden vegetable with green leaves around a large white head of undeveloped flowers 花(椰)菜 –see picture on page 504 見 504 頁彩圖

★★**cause¹** /kɔz; kɔːz/ *n* **1** [C] a person or thing that makes something happen 原因; 起因 –see 見 REASON (USAGE 用法) **2** [U] reason 理由: *Don't give him any cause for complaint.* 不要讓他有任何抱怨的理由。 **3** [C] a principle or movement which people fight for 原則目標; 事業: *She's committed to the cause of nuclear disarmament.* 她獻身於廢除核武器的事業。

★★**cause²** *v* **caused, causing** [T] to make something happen 引起, 導致〔某事物〕: *What caused the accident?* 是甚麼引起了那次事故? | *His illness caused him to miss the game.* 他的病使他錯過了那場比賽。 | *This car has caused me a lot of trouble.* 這輛

□ USEFUL PATTERNS 有用句型
to cause something; to cause someone to do something; to cause someone something

車給我帶來了許多麻煩。 | *The disaster was caused by poor planning.* 這場災害是由於計劃不周所造成的。

cause·way /ˈkɔz,we; ˈkɔːzweɪ/ *n* a raised road or path across wet ground or water 〔濕地或水中的〕堤道

caus·tic /ˈkɔstɪk; ˈkɔːstɪk/ *adj* **1** able to burn by chemical action 腐蝕性的; 苛性的: *caustic soda* 苛性鈉 **2** very unpleasant (used of remarks) 令人不快的; 刻薄的〔指話語〕: *his caustic comments* 他那刻薄的評論

cau·tion¹ /ˈkɔʃən; ˈkɔːʃən/ *n* **1** [U] care taken to avoid danger 謹慎: *You must exercise great caution when operating the machine.* 操作那台機器時, 你必須十分小心才行。 **2** [C] a spoken warning given by a policeman 〔警察的〕口頭警告

caution² *v* [T] to warn someone 告誡, 警告〔某人〕: *The policeman said, "I must caution you that anything you say may be used against you."* 警察說: "我要提醒你, 你說的每一句話都可能成為不利於你的證據。"

cau·tion·ar·y /ˈkɔʃənˌɛrɪ; ˈkɔːʃənəri/ *adj fml* giving advice or a warning 〔正式〕忠告的; 勸告的

cau·tious /ˈkɔʃəs; ˈkɔːʃəs/ *adj* taking care to avoid danger 小心翼翼的; 謹慎的: *a very cautious driver* 十分謹慎的司機 –**cautiously** *adv*: *I opened the door cautiously.* 我小心翼翼地把門打開。 –**cautiousness** *n* [U]

cav·al·cade /ˌkævlˈked; ˌkævəlˈkeɪd/ *n* a procession of people, riders, or vehicles 遊行隊伍; 騎兵隊; 車隊

cav·a·lier /ˌkævəˈlɪr; ˌkævəˈlɪəʳ/ *adj* showing no consideration for the feelings of other people 〔態度〕輕慢的; 傲慢的: *I'm annoyed at your cavalier treatment of him.* 你如此怠慢他, 我很惱火。

cav·al·ry /ˈkævlrɪ; ˈkævəlri/ *n* [U + sing/pl verb] **1** soldiers trained to fight using horses 騎兵 **2** part of the army that uses vehicles 裝甲部隊

cave¹ /kev; keɪv/ *n* a large natural hole below ground or in the side of a cliff or hill 洞穴; 洞窟

cave² *v* **caved, caving**
    cave in *phr v* [I] **1** to fall inwards 坍塌, 陷下: *The roof of the old house caved in.* 屋頂坍塌了下來。 **2** to suddenly stop opposing something 屈服於〔某事物〕

cave·man /ˈkev,mæn; ˈkeɪvmæn/ *n* **cavemen** /-mɛn; -men/ a person who lived in a cave in very ancient times 〔遠古時的〕穴居人

cav·ern /ˈkævən; ˈkævən/ *n* a large deep cave 大洞穴 –**cavernous** *adj*: *the lion's cavernous mouth* 獅子的血盆大口

cav·i·ar /ˌkævɪˈar; ˈkævɪɑːʳ/ *n* (also 又作 **caviare**) [U] the salted eggs of fish, eaten as food 魚子醬

cav·i·ty /ˈkævətɪ; ˈkævɪti/ *n* **cavities** a hole or hollow space in a solid mass 洞; 腔: *a* *cavity in a tooth* 牙洞

ca·vort /kə'vɔrt; kə'vɔːt/ *v* [I] *infml* to jump or dance about noisily〖非正式〗亂跳亂蹦; 狂舞

caw /kɔ; kɔː/ *n* the loud rough cry of various large birds〔烏鴉等〕粗糙的叫聲 –**caw** *v* [I]

cc /ˌsi 'si; ˌsiː 'siː/ a unit used for measuring how much something can contain; an abbreviation for **cubic centimetre**〖縮〗立方厘米〔測量容積的單位〕: *a 250cc engine* 250 立方厘米的發動機

CD /ˌsi 'di; ˌsiː 'diː/ *n* an abbreviation for〖縮〗= COMPACT DISC

*★**cease** /sis; siːs/ *v* **ceased, ceasing** [I;T] *fml* to stop〖正式〗停止: *Disputes with the management must cease immediately.* 與資方的爭論須立即停止。| *The law will cease to be valid from midnight tonight.* 該法律從今天午夜起失效。| *They have ceased trading in that part of the world.* 他們已終止在世界那個地區的貿易活動。

□ USEFUL PATTERNS 有用句型
to cease; to cease to do something; to cease doing something

cease-fire /'··/ *n* a formal agreement between both sides to stop fighting〔交戰雙方的〕停火協定

cease·less /'sislɪs; 'siːsləs/ *adj* going on without stopping for a long time 持續很長時間的; 無休止的: *I'm fed up with all this ceaseless arguing.* 我對這無休止的爭論感到厭倦。–**ceaselessly** *adv*

ce·dar /'sidə; 'siːdəʳ/ *n* [C;U] a tall tree that does not lose its leaves in winter 雪松

cede /sid; siːd/ *v* **ceded, ceding** [T] *fml* to give something, usually land, to another country or person, often after losing a war〖正式〗〔通常在戰敗後〕割讓〔土地等〕: *In 1871 France ceded Alsace-Lorraine to Germany.* 在1871 年, 法國把阿爾薩斯-洛林割讓給德國。

*★**cei·ling** /'silɪŋ; 'siːlɪŋ/ *n* **1** the inner surface of the top of a room 天花板 –compare 比較 ROOF[1] (1) **2** an official upper limit on things like wages or rents〔工資、房租等的〕上限, 最高限度

*★**cel·e·brate** /'selə,bret; 'selɪˌbreɪt/ *v* **celebrated, celebrating 1** [I;T] to do something special because of a particular event or special occasion 慶祝; 歡慶: *You got the job! Let's celebrate.* 你找到了工作! 我們慶祝一下吧。| *We celebrated the New Year with a party.* 我們開了個晚會慶祝新年。**2** [T] *fml* to praise someone in speech or writing〖正式〗讚揚, 頌揚〔某人〕**3** [T] (of a priest) to perform a religious ceremony〔神父〕主持〔宗教儀式〕

cel·e·brat·ed /'seləbretɪd; 'selɪˌbreɪtɪd/ *adj* famous 著名的: *a celebrated painter* 著名畫家 | *Venice is celebrated for its beautiful*

buildings. 威尼斯以其美麗的建築而聞名。

cel·e·bra·tion /ˌselə'breʃən; ˌselɪ'breɪʃən/ *n* **1** [C] a special occasion because something good has happened or because it is an occasion like a birthday 慶祝; 慶賀: *We enjoyed a quiet celebration on our own.* 我們自己安安靜靜地慶祝了一番。**2** [U] *fml* the showing of praise and pleasure〖正式〗頌揚; 歌頌: *in celebration of his magnificent achievement* 頌揚他的偉大成就

ce·leb·ri·ty /sə'lebrətɪ; sɪ'lebrɪti/ *n* **celebrities** a famous person 名人

cel·e·ry /'selərɪ; 'seləri/ *n* [U] a vegetable with greenish-white stems 芹菜: *I only had a stick of celery for lunch.* 午餐我只吃了一根芹菜梗。–see picture on page 504 見 504 頁彩圖

ce·les·ti·al /sə'lestʃəl; sɪ'lestiəl/ *adj fml* relating to the sky or heaven〖正式〗天的, 天上的

cel·i·bate /'seləbɪt; 'selɪbət/ *adj* never taking part in sexual activity, especially for religious reasons〔尤指由於宗教原因而〕禁慾的 –**celibacy** /-bəsɪ; -bəsi/ *n* [U]

*★**cell** /sel; sel/ *n* **1** a small room in a prison or police station where prisoners are kept〔監獄或警察局中的〕小牢房, 小囚室 **2** the smallest part of an animal or plant that can exist on its own 細胞: *Plant cells reproduce by dividing.* 植物細胞以分裂來進行繁殖。**3** a small room with little furniture where a member of a religious organization lives〔修道院中的〕單人小房間

cel·lar /'selə; 'seləʳ/ *n* an underground room, often used for storing things〔常用來儲藏的〕地下室, 地窖: *a wine cellar* 酒窖

cel·list /'tʃelɪst; 'tʃelɪst/ *n* a person who plays the cello 大提琴演奏者

cel·lo /'tʃelo; 'tʃeləʊ/ *n* **cellos** (also 又作 **violincello** *fml*〖正式〗) a musical instrument with four strings, like the VIOLIN but larger and producing a deeper sound; you hold it between your knees 大提琴

cel·lo·phane /'selə,fen; 'seləfeɪn/ *n* [U] *tdmk* thin transparent material used for wrapping up food〖商標〗〔包裝食品用的〕玻璃紙

cel·lu·lar /'seljələ; 'seljʊləʳ/ *adj* relating to the cells in a plant or an animal 細胞的

cel·lu·loid /'seljə,lɔɪd; 'seljʊlɔɪd/ *n* [U] *tdmk* a plastic substance made mainly from cellulose, used in the past to make film〖商標〗賽璐珞〔舊時用以製作攝影膠片的材料〕

cel·lu·lose /'seljə,los; 'seljʊləʊs/ *n* [U] the material from which the cell walls of plants are made, used in making paper, plastic, and many man-made materials 纖維素〔用以製造紙、塑料及許多人造材料〕

Cel·si·us /'selsɪəs; 'selsiəs/ *n* a scale of temperature at which water freezes at 0° and boils at 100° 攝氏: *a temperature of 10° Celsius* 攝氏十度

Cel·tic /ˈsɛltɪk; ˈkeltɪk/ *adj* connected with the people, culture, or language of the Celts, an ancient European people whose descendants live in Wales, Scotland, Ireland, and Britanny 凱爾特人[文化、語]的

ce·ment¹ /səˈmɛnt; sɪˈment/ *n* [U] **1** a grey powder used in building, which becomes hard like stone when mixed with water and allowed to dry 水泥 **2** a type of glue 膠接劑

cement² *v* [T] **1** to strengthen a relationship 加強，鞏固[關係]: *Our holiday together cemented our friendship.* 共度假日使我們的友誼更加牢固。 **2** to cover something with cement 用水泥塗抹於[某物]

cem·e·tery /ˈsɛməˌtɛri; ˈsemɪtri/ *n* a place where dead people are buried 墓地；公墓

cen·sor /ˈsɛnsə; ˈsensər/ *n* an official who examines books, plays, or films and has the power to remove anything offensive 〔書報、戲劇、電影的〕檢查員 –**censor** *v* [T]: *Prisoners' letters are usually censored.* 犯人的信件通常受到檢查。–**censorship** *n* [U]

cen·sure /ˈsɛnʃə; ˈsenʃər/ *n fml* [U] the expressing of strong disapproval 〔正式〕指責，譴責: *The opposition passed a vote of censure on the government.* 反對派通過了一項對政府的不信任動議。 –**censure** *v* **censured, censuring** [T] *fml*〔正式〕

cen·sus /ˈsɛnsəs; ˈsensəs/ *n* an official count of all the people in a country, including details of where they live and the jobs they do 人口普查

cent /sɛnt; sent/ *n* a unit of money used in the US; there are 100 cents in a dollar 美分〔一美元為 100 美分〕

cen·te·na·ry /ˈsɛntəˌnɛri; senˈtiːnəri/ *n* the day or year exactly 100 years after a particular event 一百周年〔紀念〕

cen·ten·ni·al /sɛnˈtɛnɪəl; senˈteniəl/ *n* the usual American word for 〔美式〕= CENTENARY

cen·ter /ˈsɛntə; ˈsentər/ *n,v* see 見 CENTRE

Cen·ti·grade /ˈsɛntəˌgred; ˈsentɪgreɪd/ *n* a scale of temperature at which water freezes at 0° and boils at 100° 攝氏(度)

cen·ti·me·tre /ˈsɛntəˌmitə; ˈsentɪˌmiːtər/ (**centimeter** *AmE*〔美式〕) a unit for measuring length, equal to 0.01 metres or about 0.4 INCHES〔長度計量單位〕厘米〔一厘米約合 0.4 吋〕

cen·tral /ˈsɛntrəl; ˈsentrəl/ *adj* **1** [only before a noun 只用於名詞前] at or forming the centre of a place, object, or system 中心的；中央的: *the mountains of central Europe* 中歐地區的墓山 | *computers linked to a central database* 與中央數據庫連接的電腦 **2** [never before a noun 不能用於名詞前] convenient because of being near the centre 因靠近中心而便利的: *Our house is very central for the shops and theatres.* 我們的房子靠近市中心，到商店和戲院去都很方便。 **3** [only before a noun 只用於名詞前]

the most important 最重要的: *The central aim of this government is social equality.* 本屆政府的首要目標是爭取社會平等。

central heat·ing /ˌ···ˈ···/ *n* [U] a system of heating buildings in which heat is produced at a single point and carried to parts of the building by pipes 中央暖氣系統

cen·tral·ize /ˈsɛntrəˌlaɪz; ˈsentrəlaɪz/ *v* (**centralized, centralizing** (also 又作 **centralise** *BrE*〔英式〕) [T] to place something under central control 置〔某物〕於中央控制之下: *Some countries are really too big for centralized government.* 有些國家實在太大了，無法實行中央集權管理。 –**centralization** /ˌsɛntrələˈzeʃən; ˌsentrəlaɪˈzeɪʃən/ *n* [U]

cen·tre¹ /ˈsɛntə; ˈsentər/ *n* (**center** *AmE*〔美式〕) **1** the exact middle part or point 中心；正中央: *Although London is Britain's capital it is not at the centre of the country.* 倫敦雖然是英國的首都，卻不在全國的正中央。 | *chocolates with soft centres* 軟心的巧克力糖 **2** a place or building used for a particular activity 〔活動的〕中心: *a shopping centre* 購物中心 | *a leisure centre* 娛樂中心 **3** a place where something is very important or very active 中心；中樞: *He likes to be the centre of attention.* 他喜歡引人注目。 | *the centre of the nation's shipbuilding industry* 全國造船業中心 **4 the centre** a position that is not extreme in politics〔政治上的〕中間派；中間立場: *the parties of the centre* 奉行中間路線的黨派 –see 見 MIDDLE² (USAGE 用法)

centre² *v* **centred, centring** (**center** *AmE*〔美式〕) **1** [T] to place something in or at the centre 將〔某物〕置於中心位置: *The picture would look better if you centred it between the two other pictures.* 如果你把這幅畫放在另外兩幅中間，那它看上去會更好些。 **2 centre on something, centre around something** to have something as the most important subject 集中於某事物: *Our thoughts centred on the girl who had died.* 我們的心思全都集中到那個死去的女孩身上。

centre of grav·i·ty /ˌ···ˈ···/ *n* the point in an object on which it will balance 〔物體的〕重心

cen·tu·ri·on /sɛnˈtjurɪən; senˈtʃʊərɪən/ *n* an army officer of ancient Rome, commanding about 100 men 〔古羅馬軍團的〕百人隊隊長，百夫長

cen·tu·ry /ˈsɛntʃəri; ˈsentʃəri/ *n* **centuries 1** a period of 100 years 一百年 **2** (also 又作 **Century**) one of the 100-year periods used in giving dates 一世紀: *the twentieth century* 二十世紀

ce·ram·ics /səˈræmɪks; sɪˈræmɪks/ *n* [pl] objects produced by shaping bits of clay and baking them until they are hard 陶器 –**ceramic** *adj*

ce·re·al /ˈsɪrɪəl; ˈsɪərɪəl/ *n* **1** [C] a plant such as wheat grown to produce grain 穀類植物:

cereal crops 穀類作物 **2** [C;U] food made from grain, eaten at breakfast in some countries〔在一些國家作為早餐的〕穀類食品

cer·e·bral /ˈsɛrəbrəl; ˈserˌbrəl/ *adj tech* connected with the brain《術語》大腦的

cer·e·mo·ni·al /ˌsɛrəˈmonɪəl; ˌserˌˈməʊ-nɪəl◂/ *adj* belonging to a ceremony 禮儀的；儀式的 **–ceremonially** *adv*

cer·e·mo·ni·ous /ˌsɛrəˈmonɪəs; ˌserˌˈməʊ-nɪəs/ *adj* very formal and polite 講究禮儀的；客套的；有禮貌的 **–opposite** 反義 **uncer-emonious –ceremoniously** *adv*

cer·e·mo·ny /ˈsɛrəˌmonɪ; ˈserˌməni/ *n* **cer-emonies 1** [C] a formal, solemn, and well-established action or set of actions used for marking an important public, social, or religious event 典禮；大典；儀式：*the wedding ceremony* 結婚典禮 **2** [U] the special order and formal behaviour demanded by custom on particular occasions 禮儀；禮節：*The queen was crowned with proper ceremony.* 女王在隆重的儀式中接受加冕。 **3 without ceremony** without waiting or treating something as very important 不等待；不重視

★ **cer·tain**[1] /ˈsɜːtn; ˈsɜːtn/ *adj* **1** having no doubts about something 確定的；肯定的：*I'm absolutely certain that it was him I saw.* 我絕對肯定見到的就是他。| *She felt certain that she would get the job.* 她可以肯定自己能得到那份工作。| *I'm not certain where he lives.* 我不敢肯定他住在哪裡。| *We'll win the competition — I'm certain* **of** *that.* 我們將贏得這比賽——我可以肯定。

> □ USEFUL PATTERNS 有用句型
> be certain of something; be certain that…; be certain how, why, when, etc.

2 clearly proved to exist or to be true 有把握的；可靠的：*There is no certain cure for this illness.* 這種疾病目前還沒有可靠的治療方法。 **3** sure to happen 必定發生的：*It is almost certain that the government will lose the next election.* 幾乎可以肯定政府將在下屆大選中失敗。| *The army claim that they are heading for certain victory.* 軍隊稱他們將必勝無疑。– see 見 SURE[1] (USAGE 用法) **4 be certain to do something** to be sure or very likely to do something 肯定會做某事；很可能做某事：*She's certain to pass her exams.* 她肯定會考試合格。| *Whatever I do, he's certain to criticize it.* 不論我做甚麼，他都會批評的。 **5 make certain** to do something in order to be sure about something 弄清楚；確保：*We need to make certain that these policies are implemented.* 我們要確保這些政策得到執行。 **6 know something for certain** to know something without any doubt 確切地知道某事：*I don't know for certain how old she is.* 我不敢肯定她究竟年紀有多大。 **7** [only before a noun 只用於名詞前] quite small in amount or degree 一點；一些：*He makes a*

certain amount of profit from the business, but he'll never be rich. 他從這筆生意中賺了些錢，但他永遠也發不了財。| *I agree with you to a certain extent.* 你說的話有些我是同意的。 **8** [only before a noun 只用於名詞前] present and noticeable, but difficult to describe in detail 某種；某些：*He has a certain charm.* 他另有一種魅力。 **9 a certain** used before someone's name when you do not know the person 某某〔用於不認識的人的名字前〕：*A certain Mr Robinson phoned you today.* 有位名叫羅賓遜先生的人今天打電話給你。

certain[2] *determiner, pron* a word you use to talk about one or more people or things, without saying exactly which ones they are 某，某一；某種，某些：*There are certain reasons why this information cannot be made public.* 由於某些原因，這消息不能公開。| *When the water reaches a certain level, the pump switches itself off.* 當水漲到一定高度，水泵便會自動關掉。| *Certain coastal areas are most at risk from flooding.* 沿海某些地區受到的最大威脅是洪水。| *Certain of these questions have never been answered.* 這當中的某些問題一直沒有得到解答。

★ **cer·tain·ly** /ˈsɜːtnlɪ; ˈsɜːtnli/ *adv* **1** without doubt 肯定地；無疑地；當然：*"I read a lot." "You've certainly got a lot of books!"* "我看很多書。" "你肯定有很多書了！" | *Inflation will almost certainly rise this year.* 今年通貨膨脹幾乎肯定會加劇。 **2** a word used when you are agreeing with something or when you want to make your answer seem strong 當然〔表示同意或加強語氣〕：*"Will you help me?" "Certainly I will."* "你會幫我忙嗎？" "當然(會)。" | *"Can I use your phone?" "Certainly. Go ahead."* "我能用一下你的電話嗎？" "當然可以。請用吧。" **3 certainly not** a strong way of answering a question in the negative 當然不〔強調的回答法〕：*"Will you lend me your comb?" "Certainly not!"* "你能不能把你的梳子借我用一下？" "當然不行！"

cer·tain·ty /ˈsɜːtntɪ; ˈsɜːtnti/ *n* **certainties 1** [U] the quality of being sure 確定性；無疑：*I can't say with certainty what my plans are.* 我無法肯定地說我的計劃是甚麼。 **2** [C] a clearly established fact 不容置疑的事實：*It's an absolute certainty that this horse will win.* 毫無疑問，這匹馬將會獲勝。 **–opposite** 反義 **uncertainty**

★ **cer·tif·i·cate** /səˈtɪfəkɪt; səˈtɪfɪkət/ *n* an important paper containing information that an official person says is true 證書；證明：*a birth certificate* 出生證明書

cer·ti·fy /ˈsɜːtəˌfaɪ; ˈsɜːtˌfaɪ/ *v* **certified, certifying** [T] **1** to declare that something is correct or true 證明〔某事物〕正確無誤：*The bank certified my accounts.* 銀行證明我的賬目無誤。 **2** to provide someone with an official paper to show they have completed a course of training for a particular profession 給〔某人〕頒發畢業證書: *a certified teacher* 有合格證書的教師 **3** to declare someone mad 證明〔某人〕精神失常: *His parents had tried to get him certified insane.* 他的父母試圖證明他精神失常。

cer·ti·tude /'sɜːtə,tjud, 'sɜːtiː,tjuːd/ *n fml* [U] the quality of being sure 〔正式〕確信

cer·vix /'sɜːvɪks; 'sɜːvɪks/ *n tech* the narrow opening into a woman's WOMB 〔術語〕子宮頸 **–cervical** /'sɜːvɪkl; 'sɜːvɪkəl/ *adj*

ce·sar·e·an /sɪ'zɛrɪən; sɪ̩'zeərɪən/ *n* see 見 CAESAREAN

ces·sa·tion /sɛ'seʃən; se'seɪʃən/ *n fml* stopping 〔正式〕停止, 中斷: *a cessation of hostilities* 休戰

cess·pit /'sɛs,pɪt; 'ses,pɪt/ *n* (also 又作 **cesspool** /-pul; -puːl/) an underground container or hole where household waste water is collected, especially SEWAGE 污水坑; 化糞池

cf a word used in writing which tells the reader to compare something else; an abbreviation for the Latin word **confer "compare"** 〔縮〕〔拉丁語、書面用語〕比較

chafe /tʃef; tʃeɪf/ *v* **chafed, chafing 1** [I;T] to make or become sore, painful, or uncomfortable by rubbing (使)擦傷, (使)擦痛: *Her skin chafes easily.* 她的皮膚很容易擦痛。| *Her shoes chafed the skin on her feet.* 她的鞋子擦痛了她腳上的皮膚。**2** [I] to become impatient or annoyed 焦躁; 惱怒: *He chafed* **at** *the delay.* 他因被耽擱而感到惱火。

chaff /tʃæf; tʃɑːf/ *n* [U] the outer part of a seed of grain 穀殼; 糠

★**chain¹** /tʃen; tʃeɪn/ *n* **1** [C;U] rings of metal fitted together 鏈; 鏈條: *The bridge was supported by heavy iron chains hanging from the two towers.* 這座橋是由從兩座橋塔上懸下的粗鐵鏈支撐着的。| *She had a gold chain round her neck.* 她的頸上戴着一條金項鏈。| *Have you got any chain?* 你有項鏈〔手鏈、腳鏈〕嗎? **2** [C] a number of things connected in some way 一連串事物: *Mr Patel runs a chain* **of** *launderettes.* 帕特爾先生經營洗衣連鎖店。| *an unfortunate chain of events* 一連串不幸事件 **3 in chains** kept in prison or as a slave 被囚禁; 被奴役

chain² *v* [T; + adv/prep] to limit the freedom of someone or something with a chain 〔用鏈條〕束縛〔人或物〕: *It's time the dogs were chained up for the night.* 是時候把狗拴起來過夜了。| *The protesters chained themselves to the gate of the nuclear power plant.* 抗議者用鏈條把自己綁在核電廠的大門上。

chain mail /'··/ *n* [U] a type of armour made by joining small metal rings together 鎖子甲〔鐵環製成的盔甲〕

chain re·ac·tion /,···'··/ *n* a number of events or chemical changes related to each other in such a way that each causes the next 連鎖反應

chain-smoke /'· ·/ *v* **chain-smoked, chain-smoking** [I;T] to smoke cigarettes continually 一支接一支地抽煙 **–chain-smoker** *n*

chain store /'··/ *n* one of a group of similar shops owned by one person or organization 聯號; 連鎖店

★**chair¹** /tʃɛr; tʃeəʳ/ *n* **1** a piece of furniture on which one person can sit, which usually has a back, a seat, and four legs 椅子 **2** the person in charge of a meeting 〔會議〕主席; 主席: *Please address your remarks to the chair.* 請把你的意見跟主席說。**3** the position of PROFESSOR 教授的職位: *She holds the chair of chemistry in that university.* 她是那所大學的化學教授。**4 the chair** *infml* the ELECTRIC CHAIR 〔非正式〕電椅

chair² *v* [T] to be the chairman of a meeting 擔任〔會議〕主席; 主持〔會議〕

★**chair·man** /'tʃɛrmən; 'tʃeəmən/ *n* **chairmen** /-mən; -mən/ **1** a person who is in charge of a meeting or who directs the work of a committee or organization 主持人; 主席: *one of our most experienced chairmen* 我們之中最富經驗的主席之一 **2** the person in charge of a large organization or company 董事長; 會長: *the chairman of IBM* 國際商用機器公司董事長

chair·man·ship /'tʃɛrmən,ʃɪp; 'tʃeəmən,ʃɪp/ *n* the rank, position, or period in office of chairman 主席之職〔任期〕

chair·per·son /'tʃɛr,pɜːsn̩; 'tʃeə,pɜːsən/ *n* **chairpersons** someone who is in charge of a meeting or a committee 主席; 主持人; 議長

chair·wom·an /'tʃɛr,wumən; 'tʃeə,wumən/ *n* **chairwomen** /-,wɪmɪn; -,wɪmɪn/ a woman who is in charge of a meeting or a committee 女主席; 女主持人; 女議長

chal·et /ʃæ'le; 'ʃæleɪ/ *n* a small house, usually made of wood and with a steep roof 〔通常有斜頂的〕小木屋

chal·ice /'tʃælɪs; 'tʃælɪs/ *n* a gold or silver decorated cup, used to hold wine in Christian religious services 聖餐杯

chalk¹ /tʃɔk; tʃɔːk/ *n* **1** [U] a soft white rock 白堊: *chalk hills* 白堊山 **2** [C;U] chalk that has been made into sticks and used for writing or drawing 粉筆 **3 as different as chalk and cheese** *infml* completely unlike each other 〔非正式〕完全不同; 毫無相同之處 **–chalky** *adj*

chalk² *v* [I;T] to write, mark, or draw with chalk 用粉筆書寫〔作畫〕

chalk *sthg* ↔ **up** *phr v* [T] *infml* to succeed in getting something, especially points in a competition 〔非正式〕贏得〔尤指比賽得分〕: *Our team has chalked up another victory.* 我隊又獲得了一場勝利。

★**chal·lenge¹** /'tʃælɪndʒ; 'tʃælɪndʒ/ *v* **challenged, challenging** [T] **1** to invite someone to compete against you or to test their abilities 向〔某人〕挑戰: *I challenged him to a game of tennis.* 我邀他與我賽一場網球。| *I challenge you to climb that rock!* 我跟你比賽爬那塊岩石!

□ USEFUL PATTERNS 有用句型
to challenge someone to something; to challenge someone to do something

2 to question whether something is right 質詢〔某事是否正確〕: *She challenged the justice of the new law.* 她質疑新法例的公正性。–**challenger** *n*

*

challenge² *n* **1** [C] an invitation to compete in a fight or match 挑戰: *He accepted his friend's challenge to swim across the river.* 他接受朋友的挑戰, 比賽游泳過河。**2** [C;U] something difficult or exciting that needs a great effort 具有挑戰性的事物: *To build a bridge in a month was a real challenge.* 一個月之內造一座橋委實是個挑戰。–**challenging** *adj*: *a challenging job* 具有挑戰性的工作

***cham·ber** /ˈtʃembə; ˈtʃembəˈ/ *n* **1** a room used for a special purpose like a formal meeting 〔作特殊用途的〕房間, 室〔如會議室〕: *Everyone wanted to hear the new Chairman speak and the Council chamber was full.* 人人都想聽一聽新主席的講話, 所以會議室裡擠滿了人。**2** a group of people elected or appointed to make laws or govern a country 立法機關; 議會: *The upper chamber votes on the proposals put forward in the lower chamber.* 上議院對下議院所提的議案進行表決。**3** an enclosed space, in the body or in a machine 〔機器的〕室; 〔身體內的〕腔: *The gun has six chambers for bullets.* 這把槍有六個槍膛。**4** *old fash* a room, especially a bedroom 〔老式〕房間〔尤指臥室〕**5 chambers** [pl] offices used by lawyers who work at court 律師事務所

cham·ber·maid /ˈtʃembəˌmed; ˈtʃembə-meɪd/ *n* a woman employed to clean and tidy bedrooms, especially in a hotel 〔尤指旅館中的〕女服務員; 女清潔工

chamber mu·sic /ˈ··ˌ··/ *n* music written for a small group of instruments and suitable for performance in a private home or small hall 室內樂〔在私宅或小廳內由小型樂隊演奏的音樂〕

cha·me·le·on /kəˈmiliən; kəˈmiːliən/ *n* a small animal with a long tail, which can change its colour to match its surroundings 變色蜥蜴, 變色龍

champ¹ /tʃæmp; tʃæmp/ *v* [I] to bite noisily 大聲咀嚼

champ² *n infml* 〔非正式〕see 見 CHAMPION

cham·pagne /ʃæmˈpen; ʃæmˈpeɪn/ *n* [U] a French white wine containing a lot of bubbles, often drunk on special occasions 〔法國〕香檳酒

*

cham·pi·on¹ /ˈtʃæmpiən; ˈtʃæmpiən/ *n* **1** (also 又作 **champ** *infml* 〔非正式〕) a person or animal that has won competitions of courage, strength, or skill 冠軍, 優勝者: *a tennis champion* 網球冠軍 **2** a person who fights for a special cause 〔某項運動的〕鬥士, 捍衛者: *a champion of women's rights* 女權運動的捍衛者

champion² *v* [T] to fight for or defend a principle, a movement, or a person 捍衛〔某項運動〕; 擁護〔某項主義或某人〕

***cham·pi·on·ship** /ˈtʃæmpiənˌʃip; ˈtʃæmpiən-ʃip/ *n* **1** a competition held to find the champion 錦標賽, 冠軍賽 **2** the position, title, rank, or period of being the champion 冠軍地位、稱號或等級: *Do you think anyone can take the championship from him?* 你認為有沒有人能從他手裡奪走冠軍的稱號?

***chance¹** /tʃæns; tʃɑːns/ *n* **1** [U] the force that seems to make things happen without cause or reason, and that cannot be controlled by humans 偶然; 機緣; 運氣: *Chance plays an important part in many card games.* 在許多紙牌遊戲中, 運氣很重要。| *It happened quite by chance.* 事情的發生十分偶然。**2** [C;U] a possibility 可能性: *You'd have more chance of catching the train if you got a bus to the station.* 如果你乘公共汽車去火車站, 就更有可能趕上火車。| *Is there any chance that he'll be coming to Paris this week?* 他這星期有沒有可能來巴黎? | *She doesn't stand a chance of winning.* 她沒可能獲勝。| *"What are the chances of seeing the director today?" "No chance!"* "今天見到董事的可能性有多大?" "根本不可能!" **3 a chance in a million** *infml* extremely lucky, or extremely unlucky 〔非正式〕極其(不)走運: *I never thought I'd find it again; it was a chance in a million!* 我從未指望還能再找到它, 真是幸運極了! **4 be in with a chance** to have a slight chance of doing or getting something desirable 沒有多大希望〔做成某事或獲得某物〕**5** [C] a situation that is good for something 機會: *I never miss a chance of playing football.* 我從不錯過踢足球的機會。| *I haven't had a chance to sit down all day!* 整整一天我連一次坐下來的機會也沒有! | *You'd better do it now — you may not get a second chance.* 你最好是現在就做, 你可能不會有另一次機會了。**6** [C] a risk 冒險: *The rope might break, but that's a chance I'll have to take!* 繩子也許會斷, 但我不得不冒那個風險! **7 by any chance** a very polite phrase used in a question in which the answer will be "no" 可能, 或許〔在問句當中作禮貌用語〕: *You haven't got a spare stamp by any chance?* 你也許碰巧有張多餘的郵票吧? **8 on the off chance** in the slight hope that something might happen 抱着不大的希望: *We heard the theatre was full, but we went on the off chance of getting seats.* 我們聽說戲院已滿座, 但仍抱着一線希望去買票。

■ USAGE 用法: Compare 比較 **chance, opportunity, occasion. 1** You can use **chance** or **opportunity** when by good luck you have time to do something ☆當表示由於運氣好而有機會做某事時, 可以使用 **chance** 或者 **opportunity**: *I'll speak to Professor Smith at the conference, if I get the* **chance**/*the* **opportunity**. 有機會的話, 我會在會議上跟史密斯教授談一下。**2** When you are talking about possibility alone, use **chance**, not **opportunity** ☆如僅僅表示可能性, 用 **chance**, 不用 **opportunity**: *There's a slight* **chance** (= possibility) *that this plane will crash.* 這架飛機墜毀的可能性很小。**3** We usually use **occasion** to refer to a time when something happens ☆表示某事發生的某一時間通常用 **occasion**: *He met the president on several* **occasions**. 他好幾次遇見了總統。

chance² v **chanced, chancing** [not in progressive forms 不用於進行式] **1** [T] to take a chance with something 冒險; 碰運氣: *You shouldn't* **chance** *all your money at once.* 你不應一下子拿所有的錢去冒險。**2** [I] *fml* to happen without being planned 〖正式〗偶然發生; 碰巧: *She* **chanced** *to be in the park when I was there.* 我在公園時, 她恰巧也在那裡。**3 chance it** *infml* to take a risk 〖非正式〗試試看, 碰碰運氣

  chance on sbdy/sthg *phr v* [T] *old fash* to meet someone or find something by chance 〖老式〗偶然遇見〔某人〕; 偶然找到〔某物〕

chance³ adj [only before a noun 只用於名詞前] unplanned 偶然的: *a* **chance** *meeting* 偶然的相遇

*★**chan·cel·lor** /'tʃɑːnsələr, 'tʃɑːnsələr/ n (also 又作 **Chancellor**) **1** the head of government, in some countries 〔某些國家的〕總理, 首相: *the West German* **chancellor** 西德總理 **2** the head of a university 大學校長 **3 the Chancellor of the Exchequer** the government minister who deals with taxes and government spending in Britain 〔英國〕財政大臣

chan·cy /'tʃɑːnsi/ adj *infml* risky or uncertain 〖非正式〗冒險的; 沒把握的: *That was a* **chancy** *thing to do. You could have been killed.* 那樣做很危險, 當時你可能會送命的。

chan·de·lier /ˌʃændlˈɪr, ˌʃændəˈlɪər/ n a large decorative holder for lights or candles, hanging from the CEILING 枝形吊燈

★★**change¹** /tʃeɪndʒ, tʃeɪndʒ/ v **changed, changing 1** [I] to become different 改變; (使)變化: *In autumn the leaves* **change** *from green to brown.* 秋天樹葉由綠色變成黃褐色。| *He's* **changed** *a lot since I last saw him.* 自從我上次見他之後, 他變了很多。**2** to make something or someone different 使〔某事或某人〕不同: *The discovery of oil there has* **changed** *the whole character of the area.* 由於發現了石油, 那個地區的整個特色都給改變了。**3** [T] to put something in place of something else 更換; 取代: *Can I* **change** *this red jumper for a blue one?* 這件紅色毛衣能給我換一件藍色的嗎? | *She* **changed** *her books at the library.* 她在圖書館換了幾本書。| *She's* **changed** *her job — she's a hairdresser now.* 她換了工作——現在她是個理髮師。| *He* **changed** *trains in Paris.* 他在巴黎換了火車。| *I don't like talking about the divorce. Let's* **change** *the subject.* 我不喜歡談離婚的事。我們換個話題吧。**4** [I;T] to put on different clothes 換衣服: *She* **changed out of** *her new dress and* **into** *something more comfortable.* 她脫掉新衣服, 換上更舒服的衣服。| *I must* **change** *these shoes before we go out.* 我們出去前, 我必須換穿這雙鞋。| *I'll be ready in five minutes. I've just got to* **change**. 我五分鐘後就準備好。我得去換換衣服。**5 change a baby, change a baby's nappy** to put a new NAPPY on a baby 給嬰兒換尿布 **6 change a bed, change the sheets** to put new coverings on a bed 換牀單 **7** [T] to give money in exchange for money of a different type 兌換〔鈔票〕: *Where can I* **change** *my English money* **for** *dollars?* 我在哪裡能把英國錢換成美元? | *Can you* **change** *a pound* **into** *tenpenny pieces?* 你能幫我把一英鎊換成十便士一個的硬幣嗎? **8 change hands** to become someone else's property 〔某物〕易手; 易主: *This house has* **changed hands** *three times in the last two years.* 這所房子在過去兩年三易其主。**9 change your mind** to form a new opinion or wish 改變主意〔想法〕: *We were going to go to Paris this weekend, but we've* **changed our minds**. 我們本來打算這個週末去巴黎, 但現在已經改變了主意。**10 change your tune** to act in a different way because you have discovered something new 改變行為方式: *He said he didn't like black-haired women, but when he saw my friend Debbie he soon* **changed his tune**! 他說他不喜歡黑髮女郎, 但當他遇到我的朋友黛比時, 他的態度就全變了!

  change into *phr v* **1** [T **change into** sbdy/sthg] to become something different 變成〔某物〕: *The next morning, the water had* **changed into** *ice.* 次日早上, 水結成了冰。**2** [T **change** sbdy/sthg **into** sbdy/sthg] to cause to become something different 使〔某物〕變成: *You can't* **change** *iron* **into** *gold.* 你不可能把鐵變成金子。

  change over *phr v* [I] to make a complete change 徹底轉變; 徹底改變: *In 1971 Britain* **changed over from** *pounds, shillings, and pence* **to** *the new decimal money system.* 1971 年, 英國將英鎊、先令和便士制度改為十進幣制。

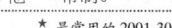

change² *n* **1** [C;U] the act or result of changing 改變; 變化: *We need a change of leadership.* 我們需要更換領導。| *There was little change in his condition.* 他的境況未有甚麼改變。 **2 make a change** to be something different from usual and for that reason enjoyable 作些〔令人愉快的〕改變: *We eat a lot of potatoes, so rice makes a nice change.* 馬鈴薯我們吃得多，所以吃點米飯換換口味倒不錯。 **3 for a change** as something different from usual 為改變一下; 為換換口味: *We always go to French restaurants. Let's go to an Italian restaurant for a change.* 我們老是去法國式餐館。這次立意去意大利式餐館換換口味吧。 **4** [C] something different 改變; 不同的事物: *She's on holiday; she needed a change.* 她在度假; 她需要改變一下生活方式。 **5** [C] something new and fresh used in place of something else 替換物: *He took a change of clothes with him.* 他帶了一些替換的衣服。| *Your car needs an oil change.* 你的車子需要換油。 **6** [U] the money returned to you in a shop when you have paid more than the price of something 〔找回的〕零錢: *Don't forget your change!* 不要忘了找回給你的錢! **7** [U] small coins, rather than notes 零錢; 硬幣: *Can you give me change for a pound?* 你能幫我把一英鎊換成零錢嗎?

> ■ USAGE 用法: **1** If you want to say that one thing is put in the place of another, use **change of** ☆如要表示"替換、更迭", 用 **change of**: *There'll be a change of government at the next election.* 下次選舉時, 政府將會有更迭。| *I need a change of job.* 我需要換個工作。 **2** If you are talking about changes which happen to something or somebody, use **change(s) in** ☆如要表示"變化、改變", 用 **change(s) in**: *There's been a subtle change in his attitude to women.* 他對於女人的態度起了很微妙的變化。| *some interesting changes in the structure of society* 社會結構中一些有趣的變化 | *recent changes in government policy* 政府政策最近所發生的變化 | *a change in the weather* 天氣的轉變

change·a·ble /ˈtʃeɪndʒəbl; ˈtʃeɪndʒəbəl/ *adj* likely to change (used especially of the weather 多變的〔尤指天氣〕 **–changeability** /ˌtʃeɪndʒəˈbɪlətɪ; ˌtʃeɪndʒəˈbɪlɪˌti/ *n* [U]

change·o·ver /ˈtʃeɪndʒˌovər; ˈtʃeɪndʒˌəʊvəʳ/ *n* a change from one activity or system to another 〔制度的〕轉變

chang·ing room /ˈ···/ *n* a room in a clothes shop, swimming pool, or sports centre where you change your clothes 更衣室

chan·nel¹ /ˈtʃænl; ˈtʃænl/ *n* **1** a particular television station 電視頻道; 電視台: *It's on channel 10.* 這節目在第十頻道播放。| *What's on the other channel?* 另外一個台在放甚麼節目? **2** a narrow sea passage 海峽: *The English Channel separates England and France.* 英吉利海峽將英法兩國分隔開來。 **3** a way or passage along which liquid flows 水道; 溝槽: *There's a channel in the middle of the old street to help rainwater flow away.* 這條舊馬路的中央有條用以排雨水的水溝。 **4** a part of a river which is safe for ships travelling along it 〔河流中的〕航道 **5** the line of travel which ships travelling across the sea should use 〔海洋中輪船的〕航線 **6 channels** a way to arrange for something to be done 〔辦事的〕渠道, 途徑: *I'm afraid I can't help you — you'll have to go through the official channels.* 我恐怕幫不了你——你必須依照官方規定的手續去辦理。

channel² *v* **-ll-** (also 又作 **-l-** *AmE* 【美式】) [T] **1** to direct something in a particular way 引導; 導向: *I decided to channel my energies into something useful.* 我決定把精力花在有用的事情上。 **2** to form a channel in something, or to take something such as water somewhere by means of a channel 挖水道; 用渠道引〔水等〕

chant /tʃænt; tʃɑːnt/ *n* **1** a religious song with words sung on very few notes 聖歌 **2** a group of words repeated many times 不斷重複的字句: *a football chant* 足球比賽時的口號 **–chant** *v* [I;T]

cha·os /ˈkeɑs; ˈkeɪ-ɒs/ *n* [U] a state of complete disorder and confusion 混亂: *After the earthquake the city was in chaos.* 地震過後, 城市裡一片混亂。

cha·ot·ic /keˈɑtɪk; keɪˈɒtɪk/ *adj* in a state of complete disorder and confusion 混亂的: *a chaotic muddle* 一片混亂 **–chaotically** /-klɪ; -kli/ *adv*

chap /tʃæp; tʃæp/ *n infml* a man or boy 〖非正式〗傢伙; 小伙子

chap·el /ˈtʃæpl; ˈtʃæpəl/ *n* **1** a part of a church, prison, hospital, college, or school where people pray and where small services can be held 〔教堂、監獄、醫院、學校等中的〕附屬禮拜堂; 小教堂 **2** a church used by nonconformists (NONCONFORMIST), people who do not belong to the Church of England or the Roman Catholic church 〔不屬於英國國教或天主教的〕禮拜堂

chap·er·one¹ /ˈʃæpəˌron; ˈʃæpərəʊn/ *n* an older woman who goes with a young unmarried woman to social events and is responsible for her behaviour 〔陪未婚少女參加社交活動並對其行為負責的年長的〕女監護人

chaperone² *v* **chaperoned, chaperoning** [I;T] to act as a chaperone to someone 監護

chap·lain /ˈtʃæplɪn; ˈtʃæplɪ̩n/ *n* a religious minister who works for a club, a college, part of the armed forces 〔團體、大學、軍隊中的〕牧師

---

chapped /tʃæpt; tʃæpt/ *adj* sore and cracked (used of your skin) 疼痛的; 乾裂的 〔指皮膚〕: *chapped lips* 乾裂的嘴唇

chap·ter /'tʃæptə; 'tʃæptəʳ/ *n* **1** one of the main divisions of a book or long article 〔書或文章的〕章: *Please turn to Chapter Five.* 請翻至第五章。**2** a particular period in someone's life or in history 〔人生或歷史之中的〕時期: *the finest chapter in American history* 美國歷史中最光輝的時期 **3 chapter and verse** giving all the exact details 提供詳情細節

char /tʃɑr; tʃɑːʳ/ *n old fash* 〔老式〕see 見 CHARWOMAN

char·ac·ter /'kærɪktə; 'kærɪktəʳ/ *n* **1** [C;U] the qualities which make a person or place different from another 特點; 個性; 性格: *I know what he looks like, but what about his character?* 我清楚他的相貌, 但他的性格如何? **2** [U] qualities which make someone or something attractively different 特質; 特色: *a woman of great character* 品格高尚的女人 | *The old house had a lot of character.* 這所舊房子很具特色。**3** [C] a person in a book or play 〔書或戲劇中的〕人物: *The main character is a young student.* 主角是個青年學生。**4** [C] *infml* a person who has a particular quality which is described 〔非正式〕〔具有某種特點的〕人: *He's a strange character.* 他是個怪人。**5** [C] *infml* an unusual or humorous person 〔非正式〕不尋常的人; 幽默的人: *He's a real character.* 他真是個滑稽的人。**6** [C] a letter or written sign 字; 字符: *The characters in Chinese writing look like small pictures.* 中國字看上去像是一幅幅小小的圖畫。**7 be out of character** to be unlike someone's usual nature 不符合〔某人〕平時的性格 [RELATED PHRASE 相關詞組 **be in character**]

char·ac·ter·is·tic¹ /ˌkærɪktə'rɪstɪk; ˌkærɪktə'rɪstɪk/ *adj* typical of a person's character 表現某人特性的; 典型的: *With characteristic generosity, she gave them £100.* 她素來慷慨, 給了他們一百英鎊。–**characteristically** /-klɪ; -kli/ *adv*

characteristic² *n* a special and easily recognized quality of someone or something 特點; 特性: *A characteristic of the camel is its ability to live for a long time without water.* 駱駝的特點是不喝水也能生存很長時間。

char·ac·ter·ize /'kærɪktəˌraɪz; 'kærɪktəraɪz/ *v* **characterized, characterizing** (also 又作 **characterise** *BrE* 〔英式〕) [T] **1** to be typical of someone or something 顯示出...特點; 以...為特徵: *His books are characterized by long and detailed descriptions of the countryside.* 他所著的書的特點是對鄉間有詳盡細緻的描寫。**2** to describe the character of a person or thing 把〔某人或某物〕描述為: *She characterized him as lazy and selfish.* 她

把他的性格描述為又懶惰又自私。–**characterization** /ˌkærɪktərə'zeʃən; ˌkærɪktəraɪ'zeɪʃən/ *n* [C;U]

cha·rade /ʃə'red; ʃə'rɑːd/ *n* **1** a false or foolish activity which pretends to be serious 裝模作樣的行為: *The management went through a charade of negotiating with the union leaders.* 資方假惺惺地與工會領導進行了談判。**2 charades** [pl] a game in which people have to guess the word that is being acted out 〔用動作表演的〕字謎遊戲

char·coal /'tʃɑrˌkol; 'tʃɑːkəʊl/ *n* [U] black material used for burning and drawing 〔供燃燒或作畫用的〕木炭; 炭筆

charge¹ /tʃɑrdʒ; tʃɑːdʒ/ *v* **charged, charging 1** [I;T] to ask for an amount of money in payment 索價〔金額〕; 要價; 收費: *How much do you charge for your eggs?* 你的雞蛋賣多少錢? | *The hotel charged me £50 for the room.* 這家旅館要我付五十英鎊的房租。**2** [T] to add the cost of something to someone's bill 記賬: *Charge the drinks to my account.* 把飲料的錢記在我的賬上。**3** [I] to run very fast, often in order to attack someone 猛衝; 進攻: *The children charged out of school.* 孩子們衝出了學校。| *The elephant suddenly charged.* 大象突然向前猛衝。**4** [T] to say officially to someone they have done something against the law 指控; 控告: *He was charged with stealing the jewels.* 他被控偷竊珠寶。**5** [T] *fml* to give someone the responsibility for doing something 〔正式〕指定〔某人〕負責: *The chief engineer is charged with maintaining safety throughout the railway system.* 總工程師要負責維護整個鐵路系統的安全。**6** [T] to pass an electric current through something so that it stores electricity 給〔某物〕充電: *I need to charge my car battery.* 我需要給我車上的電池充電。

charge² *n* **1** [C] the price asked for something 價格; 費用: *The charge for cleaning the curtains was £13.* 清洗窗簾的收費為十三英鎊。| *What are the charges like in that hotel?* 那家旅館的住宿費用是多少? **2 free of charge** costing nothing 免費: *Delivery is free of charge.* 運送服務是不收費的。**3 in charge** in a position of responsibility 負責: *I don't know. Ask Mr Davis — he's in charge.* 我不知道。問問戴維斯先生——他是負責人。**4 take charge** to take control 接管: *She took charge of the business when her father died.* 她父親去世後, 她接管了業務。**5 have charge of** be responsible for 對...負責: *He has charge of the children while his wife is at work.* 太太工作時, 他負責照料孩子。**6** [C] a statement accusing a person of a crime or an offence 控告; 指控: *He was arrested on a charge of murder.* 他被控以謀殺罪而遭逮捕。| *He faces a charge of murder.* 他面臨一項謀殺罪的指控。| *The President's policy leaves him open to charges of favouring the rich.* 總

C

統的政策給別人留下了把柄, 指責他偏袒有錢人。**7 bring a charge against someone** to say formally to someone that someone has done something wrong 指控某人 **8** [C] a rushing forceful attack 猛衝; 攻擊 **9** [C] an explosive put into a gun or weapon 彈藥 **10** [C] electricity put into an electrical apparatus 〔充進電器中的〕電 **11** [C] *fml* a person or thing for which someone is responsible 〔正式〕受照管的人; 由…負責的事

> ■ USAGE 用法: Compare 比較 **charge** and 和 **cost. Cost** is the more general word for the amount of money you need to pay in order to do something or to have something done ☆ 表示做某事所需的費用時, **cost** 更為常用: *The government claim the* **cost** *of providing an adequate health service has greatly increased.* 政府聲稱已大大增加了醫療服務方面的開支。| *What would be the* **cost** *of a week in a London hotel?* 在倫敦的旅館裡住一星期要多少錢? | *The company has agreed to pay the* **cost** *of my trip to Paris.* 公司已同意支付我去巴黎的旅費。**Charge** is the word for the amount of money you are asked to pay for a particular service ☆ **charge** 表示要求某項服務所需支付的錢: *A 10% service* **charge** *is included.* 這裡面包括了百分之十的服務費。| *The hotel provides breakfast free of* **charge**. 旅館免費供應早餐。| *There will be a small* **charge** *for the use of the telephone.* 使用電話要花點費用。

charged /tʃɑrdʒd; tʃɑːdʒd/ *adj* causing strong feelings or argument 引起強烈感情〔激烈爭論〕的: *an emotionally charged atmosphere* 令情緒激動的氣氛

char·i·ot /'tʃærɪət; 'tʃæriət/ *n* a horse-drawn vehicle with 2 wheels, used in ancient times in battles and races 〔古時戰爭或比賽用的〕雙輪馬車 **—charioteer** /,tʃæriə'tɪr; ,tʃæriə'tiə/ *n*

cha·ris·ma /kə'rɪzmə; kə'rizmə/ *n* [U] the special ability to charm or attract other people 特殊的魅力 **—charismatic** /,kærɪz'mætɪk; ,kærizˌmætɪk◂/ *adj*

★**char·i·ty** /'tʃærəti; 'tʃærɪti/ *n* **charities 1** [C] an organization that gives money and help to people who are poor, sick, or in difficulty 慈善機構: *The Red Cross is an international charity.* 紅十字會是國際性的慈善機構。**2** [U] money or help given to people in need 救濟金; 施捨物: *too proud to accept charity* 高傲得不願意接受施捨 | *They make regular donations to charity.* 他們作定期的慈善捐款。**3** [U] sympathy and kindness 同情心; 仁慈 **— charitable** *adj*: *a charitable act* 慈善之舉 **— charitably** *adv*

char·la·tan /'ʃɑrlətn; 'ʃɑːlətən/ *n* a person who pretends to have a special knowledge or skill (a word used to express disapproval) 〔冒充內行的〕騙子〔含貶義〕: *I'm not going to that doctor again — the man's a complete charlatan!* 我不會再去找那個醫生了——他是個十足的騙子!

charm[1] /tʃɑrm; tʃɑːm/ *n* **1** [C;U] the ability to please or delight other people 魅力: *You'll have to use all your charm to talk him into it.* 你必須施展渾身解數, 才能説服他去做這事。| *This town has a charm you couldn't find in a big city.* 這小鎮有種你無法在大城市裡找得到的魅力。**2** [C] an object worn as a decoration or to bring good luck 護身符; 小飾物: *a charm bracelet* 會帶來好運的手鐲 | *a lucky charm* 護身符

charm[2] *v* [T] **1** to please or delight other people 使歡悦; 使陶醉: *She can charm everyone with her smiles.* 她能夠用微笑迷住每一個人。**2** to control something as if by magic 〔彷彿〕以魔法控制〔某物〕: *He charmed the snake with his music.* 他用音樂指揮那條蛇。**—charmer** *n*

charm·ing /'tʃɑrmɪŋ; 'tʃɑːmɪŋ/ *adj* very pleasing and delightful 迷人的; 令人陶醉的: *What a charming young man!* 多有魅力的年輕人啊!**—charmingly** *adv*

charred /tʃɑrd; tʃɑːd/ *adj* black from having been burned 燒黑的: *There was nothing left but a few charred remains.* 除了一些燒黑的殘餘外, 沒有留下任何東西。

★**chart**[1] /tʃɑrt; tʃɑːt/ *n* **1** a table showing information in the form of a picture 表格; 圖表: *a weather chart* 天氣圖 **2** a detailed map of the sea or stars 海圖; 星圖 **3 the charts** a list of the most popular records 暢銷唱片排行榜: *It's gone straight into the charts.* 這張唱片直接打入了排行榜。

chart[2] *v* [T] to show or record something on a chart 用圖表顯示〔記錄〕

★**char·ter**[1] /'tʃɑrtɚ; 'tʃɑːtə/ *n* **1** [C] a statement by the government or ruler which gives rights and freedoms to the people 特許證; 憲章: *a charter of human rights* 人權憲章 **2** [U] the practice of hiring buses or planes for private use 包租〔汽車或飛機〕〔以供私人用〕: *charter flights* 包機

charter[2] *v* [T] to hire a bus or plane for private use 包租〔汽車或飛機〕

chartered ac·coun·tant /,···'···/ *n* an ACCOUNTANT who has completed training 特許會計師

char·wom·an /'tʃɑr,wʊmən; 'tʃɑːˌwʊmən/ *n* **charwomen** /-ˌwɪmɪn; -ˌwɪmɪn/ *old fash* 〔老式〕(also 又作 **char**) a woman who works as a cleaner in a house or office 〔家庭或辦公室的〕清潔女工

char·y /'tʃɛri; 'tʃɛəri/ *adj fml* 〔正式〕 **be chary of** to be careful about what you do or believe 小心的; 謹慎的: *He's chary of spending too much on transport.* 他小心翼翼, 不在交通方面花費太多。**—charily** *adv*

chase¹ /tʃes; tʃeɪs/ v **chased, chasing 1** [I;T] to follow someone or something rapidly in order to catch them 追捕; 追趕: *a cat chasing a mouse* 一隻追捕老鼠的貓 | *Chase after them and remind them about the party.* 追上去提醒他們晚會的事情。 **2** [I;T] to try very hard to get something 努力獲得: *We had a hundred people chasing only three jobs!* 我們有一百個人在爭奪僅有的三份工作! **3** [T + adv/prep] to make someone or something leave or run away 使〔某人或某物〕離開〔跑開〕: *They chased the dog out of the kitchen.* 他們把狗趕出廚房。 | *people chased from their homelands* 被驅逐出家園的人們 **4** [I + adv/prep] to run about in a hurry 匆忙地奔跑: *The children are always chasing in and out.* 孩子們老是在跑進跑出。 | *I've been chasing all over town to buy his present.* 為了給他買禮物, 我跑遍了整個城鎮。

chase² n **1** an act of chasing something 追逐: *an exciting car chase in the film* 電影中那激烈的汽車追逐場面 **2** **give chase** to run after someone in order to catch them 追趕: *She saw the thief and gave chase.* 她看見了那個賊, 便去追趕。

chas·m /'kæzəm; 'kæzəm/ n **1** a deep crack in the surface of the earth or ice 〔地表、冰上的〕深隙 **2** a big difference between two ideas or groups of people 〔思想、派別的〕很大差異: *a political chasm* **between** *the two countries* 兩國之間的政治裂痕

chas·sis /'ʃæsɪ; 'ʃæsi/ n [plural is 複數為 **chassis** /'ʃæsɪ; 'ʃæsiz/] the framework on which the body of a vehicle is built 〔車輛的〕底盤

chaste /tʃest; tʃeɪst/ adj old fash not having sex with anyone, or not having sex with anyone except your husband or wife (a word used to express approval) 〔老式〕貞潔的, 忠貞的〔含褒意〕 **–chastely** adv

chas·ten /'tʃesn; 'tʃeɪsən/ v [T] fml to make someone feel sorry about their bad or foolish behaviour 〔正式〕使〔某人〕自責: *He was chastened by the accident.* 他對這起事故感到十分不安。

chas·tise /tʃæ'staɪz; tʃæ'staɪz/ v **chastised, chastising** [T] fml to punish or blame someone severely 〔正式〕嚴懲, 責罵〔某人〕

chas·ti·ty /'tʃæstəti; 'tʃæstɪti/ n [U] the state of not having sex with anyone, or not having sex with anyone except your husband or wife (a word used to express approval) 貞潔; 忠貞不渝〔含褒意〕: *Chastity before marriage is still demanded in some societies.* 在有些社會中仍然要求婚前的貞潔。

chat /tʃæt; tʃæt/ v **-tt-** [I] to talk in a friendly and informal way 閒談; 聊天: *They like to get together and chat about the old days.* 他們喜歡聚在一起談談過去的日子。 **–chat** n: *I had a chat with Mrs Bennett about her son's problems.* 我與本尼特夫人談過她兒子的一些問題。

chat sbdy ↔ **up** phr v [T] infml to talk to someone with the idea of attracting them and perhaps having sex with them 〔非正式〕與〔某人〕搭訕; 與〔某人〕調情

chât·eau /'ʃæto; 'ʃætəʊ/ n **chateaus** or **chateaux** /ʃæ'toz; 'ʃætəʊz/ a castle or large country house in France 〔法國的〕城堡, 大別墅

chat·line /'tʃæt,laɪn; 'tʃætlaɪn/ n a way of talking to people by telephone; you ring a number and can have a conversation with several different people at the same time 〔能同時與數人通話的〕電話聯絡

chat show /'·· ·/ n a television or radio show in which well-known people talk to each other and are asked questions 〔電視或無線電廣播的〕清談節目

chat·ter¹ /'tʃætə; 'tʃætəʳ/ v [I] **1** to talk rapidly, usually about something unimportant 喋喋不休; 嘮叨: *The children were chattering happily.* 孩子們在高興地說個不停。 **2** **my teeth chattered** = my teeth knocked together because of cold or fear 我的牙齒〔冷得或嚇得〕直打顫

chatter² n [U] **1** informal and unimportant conversation 嘮叨; 閒聊 **2** a rapid knocking sound made by teeth or machines 〔牙齒的〕打顫聲; 〔機器的〕咯咯聲: *the chatter of machine-gun fire* 機關槍的嗒嗒聲

chat·ter·box /'tʃætə,bɑks; 'tʃætəbɒks/ n infml a person who talks a lot 〔非正式〕喋喋不休的人

chat·ty /'tʃætɪ; 'tʃæti/ adj **chattier, chattiest** infml friendly and fond of talking 〔非正式〕和善而愛說話的

chauf·feur /'ʃofə; 'ʃəʊfəʳ/ n a person employed to drive someone's car 〔私人的〕汽車司機 **–chauffeur** v [I;T]

chau·vin·ist /'ʃovɪnɪst; 'ʃəʊvɪnɪst/ n **1** a person who believes that their country is always right and better than all others 沙文主義者; 盲目愛國主義者 **2** a man who believes that men are better than women and who treats women badly 男性至上論者; 歧視女性者 **–chauvinism** n [U]: *his appalling chauvinism* 他那令人可畏的大男子主義 **–chauvinist, chauvinistic** /,ʃovɪ'nɪstɪk; ,ʃəʊvɪ'nɪstɪk/ adj

★ **cheap** /tʃip; tʃip/ adj, adv **1** low in price and good value for money 價廉物美的: *Fresh vegetables are very cheap in the summer.* 在夏天新鮮蔬菜很便宜。 **2** low in price and of poor quality 價廉質劣的: *a cheap-looking suit* 看上去蹩腳的服裝 **3** not valuable 不值錢的: *Five hundred years ago human life was considered very cheap.* 五百年前人的生命被認為是毫無價值的。 **4** unfair and unkind 低級的; 粗卑的: *a cheap victory* 不光彩的勝利 | *a cheap joke* 粗俗的玩笑 **5** **get something cheap** to buy something for less money than it is worth 買到便宜貨 **6** **on the cheap** cheaply and, for that reason, not very well

便宜的; 不好的 **–cheaply** *adv*: *a cheaply-furnished room* 備有便宜家具的(出租)房間

cheap·en /'tʃipən; 'tʃiːpən/ *v* [T] **1** to make someone, especially yourself, less good or honourable 降低〔尤指自己的〕身分: *Don't cheapen yourself by bothering to reply to his insults.* 不要理睬他的侮辱，那樣會使〔自己〕貶身分。 **2** to make something cheaper 使〔某物〕變得便宜: *The dollar's increase in value has cheapened imports.* 美元升值使進口貨物變得更加便宜。

cheat¹ /tʃit; tʃiːt/ *v* **1** [I] to act dishonestly in order to win or gain something 欺詐; 欺騙: *He always cheats at cards.* 他玩牌時總是作弊。 | *They were caught cheating in the exam.* 他們考試時作弊，當場被抓。 **2** [T] to take something unfairly or dishonestly from someone 騙取〔某物〕: *He cheated the old woman out of her money.* 他騙取了那位老婦人的錢。 | *They were cheated of victory.* 他們因受騙而得不到勝利。 **3** [I] to do something in a way which is not the way it should be done, but which is easier 以非正常手段做〔某事〕; 投機取巧

cheat² *n* **1** a person who cheats 騙子 **2** a person who is lazy and does something an easy way instead of the proper way 投機取巧者

★check¹ /tʃɛk; tʃɛk/ *v* **1** [I;T; +(that)] to examine something, or make sure that everything is correct or as you expect it to be 檢查; 檢驗: *I'm just going to check this money.* 我正準備查一查這筆錢。 | *We need to check on the quality.* 我們需要去檢驗一下質量。 | *I don't think she's in the office today. I'll just go and check.* 我想她今天不在辦公室裡。我這就過去看看。 | *Please check that he's done it properly before he leaves.* 請去檢查一下，看他是否在離開之前把事情辦妥。 | *Can you check with the police that we're allowed to enter the area?* 你能否到警方那裡核查一下，以確認我們可以進入該地區? **2** [T] to find out 查; 查出: *He checked the temperature every morning.* 他每天早上都要查看一下氣溫。 | *Check whether the papers have come.* 去看看報紙來了沒有。 **3** [T] to control or hold back 阻止; 抑制: *The illness checked her progress.* 那場病阻礙了她的進步。

check in *phr v* [I] to report your arrival at a hotel desk, an airport, etc. 〔在旅館、機場等〕登記，報到: *You must check in an hour before your plane leaves.* 你必須在飛機起飛前一小時辦理登機手續。

check out *phr v* **1** [I] to pay the bill and leave a hotel 〔在旅館〕結賬; 退房: *We checked out of the Hilton at 10 o'clock.* 我們十點鐘在希爾頓飯店結賬退房。 **2** [T check sthg ↔ out] *infml* to inquire about something to find out whether it is true or correct 〔非正式〕查證; 證實: *The police checked out his story.* 警方核實了他交待的情況。

check up on sbdy/sthg *phr v* [T] to make thorough inquiries about someone or something 追查; 調查: *She heard the police were checking up on her.* 她聽說警方在調查她。

★check² *n* **1** [C] an examination to make sure that something is correct or as you want it to be 檢查; 核查: *a security check at the airport* 機場安全檢查 | *a check on the quality of factory goods* 出廠貨物的質量檢查 | *I'll just have a quick check to see if he's asleep.* 我就去很快的看一下他是不是已經睡着了。 **2 in check** under control 控制住: *We've kept smallpox in check for ten years now.* 我們到目前為止已把天花控制了十年。 **3** [C] the usual American word for a RECEIPT 〔美式〕發票; 收據: *I've lost the check for my coat.* 我把我的外衣發票丟了。 **4** [C] the usual American word for a bill at a restaurant 〔美式〕餐館賬單 **5** [C] the usual American word for 〔美式〕= CHEQUE **6** [C;U] a pattern of coloured squares 方格; 格子: *a blue and white check shirt* 一件藍白格子的襯衫 **7** [U] a situation in a game of CHESS when one player's king is under direct attack 〔國際象棋中〕被「將軍」的局面; 將軍

checked /tʃɛkt; tʃɛkt/ *adj* having a pattern of coloured squares 有格子圖案的: *a checked tablecloth* 有格子花紋的桌布 –see picture on page 243 見 243 頁彩圖

check·er·ed /'tʃɛkəd; 'tʃɛkəd/ *adj* see 見 CHEQUERED

check·ers /'tʃɛkəz; 'tʃɛkəz/ *n* [sing] the usual American word for 〔美式〕= DRAUGHTS

check-in /'··/ *n* the place where you report your arrival at a hotel, an airport, etc. 〔旅館、機場等的〕登記處

checking ac·count /'···,·/ *n* the usual American word for 〔美式〕= a CURRENT ACCOUNT

check·list /'tʃɛk,lɪst; 'tʃɛk,lɪst/ *n* a complete list of things that you must get or do or check, which you use to make sure you do not forget anything 清單; 檢查單

check·mate¹ /'tʃɛk,meɪt; 'tʃɛkmeɪt/ *n* [C;U] the attack and defeat of a king in CHESS 〔國際象棋中的〕將死

checkmate² *v* **checkmated, checkmating** [T] **1** to win a CHESS game with a checkmate 〔國際象棋〕將死 **2** to stop or completely defeat someone 阻止〔某人〕; 徹底擊敗〔某人〕

check·out /'tʃɛk,aʊt; 'tʃɛk-aʊt/ *n* a desk in a self-service shop where you pay for goods 〔超級市場的〕付款台

check·point /'tʃɛk,pɔɪnt; 'tʃɛkpɔɪnt/ *n* a place where an examination is made of people, traffic, or goods 〔人、車輛、貨物的〕檢查站, 關卡: *You have to go through checkpoints on the border.* 你必須經過邊境的檢查站。

check·up /'tʃɛk,ʌp; 'tʃɛk-ʌp/ *n* a medical examination 體格檢查: *I've got to have a checkup for my new job.* 我的新工作需要我

做一次體格檢查。

ched·dar /'tʃɛdə; 'tʃɛdəʳ/ *n* (also 又作 **Cheddar**) [U] a hard smooth yellowish cheese 黃色乾奶酪, 切達乾酪

***cheek¹** /tʃik; tʃiːk/ *n* **1** [C] the fleshy part of your face below your eyes 臉頰: *plump red cheeks* 飽滿紅潤的雙頰 **2** [U] *infml* disrespectful rude behaviour 〔非正式〕粗魯無禮的行為: *She had the cheek to tell me to mind my own business.* 她居然厚着臉皮來叫我別管閒事。

cheek² *v* [T] to behave disrespectfully or rudely towards someone 對〔某人〕粗魯無禮

cheek·bone /'tʃik,bon; 'tʃiːkbəʊn/ *n* the bone just below your eye 顴骨

cheek·y /'tʃik; tʃiːki/ *adj* **cheekier, cheekiest** *infml* disrespectful, though sometimes in an attractive way 〔非正式〕無禮的; 莽撞的; 厚臉皮的: *Don't be so cheeky!* 不許這樣無禮! | *a cheeky smile* 不識羞的笑容 – **cheekiness** *n* [U]

cheep /tʃip; tʃiːp/ *v* [I] (of birds) to make a weak high noise 〔鳥〕輕聲尖叫 – **cheep** *n*

cheer¹ /tʃir; tʃiəʳ/ *n* **1** [C] a shout of approval and encouragement 喝采; 歡呼: *the cheers of the crowd* 觀眾的歡呼 **2** [U] *old fash* happiness and good spirits 〔老式〕高興; 振奮: *Christmas, the season of good cheer* 聖誕, 令人高興的時節

cheer² *v* [I] to shout in approval and support 喝采; 歡呼: *Every time a goal was scored the crowd cheered wildly.* 每進一球, 觀眾便狂熱地歡呼起來。

cheer sbdy ↔ **on** *phr v* [T] to encourage someone by shouting approval 〔用歡呼聲〕鼓勵: *The crowd cheered the home team on.* 觀眾給主隊喝采加油。

cheer up *phr v* **1** [I] to become happier 振作起來; 高興起來: *Cheer up! The news isn't too bad.* 振作起來! 消息還不算太壞。 **2** [T **cheer** sbdy ↔ **up**] to make someone happier 使〔某人〕振作起來: *His friends tried to cheer him up.* 他的朋友設法使他振作起來。

cheer·ful /'tʃirfəl; 'tʃiəfəl/ *adj* **1** tending to laugh and smile and be full of life 愉快的; 高興的: *Despite all her problems, she's always cheerful.* 儘管面臨着許多問題, 她總是很樂觀的。 **2** likely to cause happy feelings 令人愉快的: *cheerful music* 令人愉快的音樂 – **cheerfully** *adv*: *"It doesn't matter," he said cheerfully.* "這沒關係," 他愉快地說。 – **cheerfulness** *n* [U]

Cheer·i·o /'tʃiri,o; ,tʃiəri'əʊ/ *interj infml* a word used when you leave someone or someone leaves you 〔非正式〕再見

cheer·less /'tʃirlis; 'tʃiələs/ *adj* dull and sad 無趣味的; 悲傷的: *a cheerless rainy day* 沉悶的雨天

cheers /tʃirz; tʃiəz/ *interj infml* 〔非正式〕 **1** a word used to express good wishes just before people drink alcohol 乾杯〔用於祝酒〕 **2** thank you 謝謝: *"Here's that £5 I owe*

you." "Oh, cheers." "這是我欠你的五英鎊。" "哦, 謝謝。" **3** a word used when you leave someone or someone leaves you 再見

cheer·y /'tʃiri; 'tʃiəri/ *adj* **cheerier, cheeriest** smiling and cheerful 微笑的; 高興的: *a cheery greeting* 令人愉快的問候 – **cheerily** *adv* – **cheeriness** *n* [U]

***cheese** /tʃiz; tʃiːz/ *n* [C;U] solid food made from milk 乾酪; 乳酪: *We need some cheese for the sandwiches.* 我們需要些乳酪來做三明治。 | *They sell a good range of French cheeses.* 他們出售各式法國乳酪。 – see picture on page 504 見 504 頁彩圖

cheese·cake /'tʃiz,kek; 'tʃiːzkeɪk/ *n* [C;U] cake made with creamy cheese, and sometimes fruit on top 乳酪蛋糕

chee·tah /'tʃita; 'tʃiːtə/ *n* a large animal of the cat family, able to run very fast 獵豹

chef /ʃɛf; ʃef/ *n* the chief cook in a restaurant 〔餐館的〕廚師長, 主廚

***chem·i·cal¹** /'kɛmɪkl; 'kemɪkəl/ *adj* relating to chemistry or made by chemistry 化學的: *A chemical change takes place when the acid is added.* 當加入這種酸時, 便會發生化學變化。 – **chemically** /-klɪ; -kli/ *adv*

***chemical²** *n* any substance used in or produced by chemistry 化學品

chem·ist /'kɛmɪst; 'kemɪst/ *n* **1** a scientist specializing in chemistry who works in industry or at a university 化學家: *a research chemist* 化學研究專家 **2** a person who makes up drugs and medicines in a shop 藥劑師 **3 chemist's** (also 又作 **drugstore** *AmE* 〔美式〕) a shop where medicines and other goods are sold 藥房; 藥店: *I got some skin cream at the chemist's.* 我在藥房買了些護膚霜。

chem·is·try /'kɛmɪstrɪ; 'kemɪstri/ *n* [U] the study of the substances which make up the universe and the way in which they change and combine with each other 化學: *She's got a degree in chemistry.* 她有化學專業的大學學位。

cheque /tʃɛk; tʃek/ *n* (**check** *AmE* 〔美式〕) a form instructing a bank to pay money to someone 支票: *I'd like to pay by cheque, please.* 我想用支票付款。 | *He wrote out the cheque.* 他開出了那張支票。

cheque card /'··/ *n* a plastic card given to people by a bank, promising that the bank will pay out the money written on their cheques up to a certain amount 〔銀行〕支票保付卡: *I'm afraid we can't accept cheques without a cheque card.* 沒有銀行保付卡, 恐怕我們不能收支票。

chequ·er·ed /'tʃɛkəd; 'tʃekəd/ *adj* (**checkered** *AmE* 〔美式〕) **1** covered with a pattern of different coloured squares 有格子圖案的: *a chequered flag* 格子旗 **2** varied, with good and bad parts 斑駁的; 好壞不一的: *He'd had a chequered past.* 他過去飽經滄桑。

cher·ish /'tʃɛrɪʃ; 'tʃerɪʃ/ *v* [T] *fml* to care for

something or someone in a tender, loving way 〖正式〗珍愛; 珍惜: *He cherished the memory of his dead wife.* 他很懷念已故的妻子。

cher·ry /'tʃɛrɪ; 'tʃeri/ *n* **cherries** a small round fruit with red or black skin 櫻桃 – see picture on page 504 見 504 頁彩圖

cher·ub /'tʃɛrəb; 'tʃerəb/ *n* **1** [plural 複數為 **cherubs** *or* **cherubim**] an ANGEL shown in a painting as a young child with wings 〔圖畫中生有翅膀的〕小天使 **2** a sweet and pretty child 天真可愛的小孩 –**cherubic** /tʃə-'rubɪk; tʃə'ruːbɪk/ *adj*

chess /tʃɛs; tʃes/ *n* [U] a game for two players, played on a board of black and white squares, in which each player tries to move his or her pieces to trap the other player's king 國際象棋

*★***chest** /tʃɛst; tʃest/ *n* **1** the upper front part of your body 胸部; 胸膛: *He was suffering from chest pains.* 他的胸部疼痛。 –see 見 PAIN (USAGE 用法) **2** a large strong box with a lid 〔有蓋的〕大箱子: *an old oak chest* 一隻舊橡木箱 **3** get something off your chest to talk about something you are worrying about so that you feel better 說出心裡的煩惱: *It's obvious something's bothering you. Come on, get it off your chest!* 你顯然是有心事。來, 把它說出來吧!

chest·nut¹ /'tʃɛsnət; 'tʃesnʌt/ *n* **1** a tree which produces smooth brown nuts in prickly cases 栗樹 **2** a smooth brown nut in a prickly case 栗子

chestnut² *adj,n* [U] reddish-brown (usually used of hair and horses) 栗色(的); 棕紅色(的)〔通常指毛髮和馬鬃〕

chest of drawers /ˌ··'·/ *n* **chests of drawers** a piece of furniture with several drawers 五斗櫥

chest·y /'tʃɛstɪ; 'tʃesti/ *adj* suffering from a disease of the chest 胸部患有疾病的

chew¹ /tʃu; tʃuː/ *v* [I;T] to crush food with your teeth before swallowing it 咀嚼

  chew sth ↔ **over** *phr v* [T] *infml* to think about a question or a problem 〖非正式〗考慮〔問題〗: *Let me chew it over for a few days and let you know.* 讓我考慮幾天, 然後告訴你。

chew² *n* [sing] the act of chewing 咀嚼

chewing gum /'··· ·/ *n* [U] (also 又作 **gum**) a type of sweet made to be chewed but not swallowed 口香糖

chew·y /'tʃuɪ; 'tʃuːi/ *adj* needing to be chewed 需要咀嚼的: *a chewy toffee* 一塊需要咀嚼的太妃糖

chic /ʃik; ʃiːk/ *adj* fashionable and having a good idea of style 流行的; 時髦的: *I think your hat is rather chic.* 我覺得你的帽子相當時髦。 –**chic** *n* [U]

chick /tʃɪk; tʃɪk/ *n* a young chicken or other bird 小雞; 小鳥

chick·en¹ /'tʃɪkɪn; 'tʃɪkᵊn/ *n* **1** [C] a bird kept

for its meat and eggs 雞: *a huge shed for 2000 chickens.* 能容約二千隻雞的大雞棚 | *He keeps chickens in his garden.* 他在花園裡養雞。 **2** [U] the meat of this bird 雞肉: *chicken pie* 雞肉餡餅 –see 見 MEAT (USAGE 用法) –see picture on page 504 見 504 頁彩圖

chicken² *v*

  chicken out *phr v* [I] *infml* to decide not to do something because you are afraid 〖非正式〗因害怕而放棄〔做某事〕: *I chickened out of telling him at the last minute.* 我在最後一刻還是不敢告訴他。

chick·en·feed /'tʃɪkɪn،fid; 'tʃɪkᵊnfiːd/ *n* [U] *infml* a small unimportant amount of money 〖非正式〗一筆小數額的錢

chicken pox /'··· ·/ *n* [U] a disease which causes fever and spots on the skin 水痘

chic·o·ry /'tʃɪkərɪ; 'tʃɪkəri/ *n* [U] a plant with bitter-tasting leaves 菊苣

chide /tʃaɪd; tʃaɪd/ *v* **chided, chiding** [I;T] *lit* to speak angrily to someone who has done something wrong 〖文〗責備; 責怪

*★***chief¹** /tʃif; tʃiːf/ *n* a leader of a group or organization 領導人; 負責人: *The president is chief of the armed forces.* 總統是武裝部隊的統帥。

*★***chief²** *adj* [only before a noun 只用於名詞前] **1** highest in rank 最高級別的: *the chief clerk* 書記長 **2** most important 最重要的: *Rice is the chief crop in this area.* 大米是該地區的主要農作物。

chief·ly /'tʃiflɪ; 'tʃiːfli/ *adv* mainly 主要地: *The accident happened chiefly because you were careless.* 事故主要是由於你不小心才發生的。

chief·tain /'tʃiftɪn; 'tʃiːftᵊn/ *n* the leader of a tribe 部落首領; 族長

chif·fon /ʃɪ'fɑn; 'ʃɪfɒn/ *n* [U] a soft transparent silky material used for scarves (SCARF) and evening dresses 薄綢〔作圍巾和晚禮服用〕

chil·blain /'tʃɪl،blen; 'tʃɪlbleɪn/ *n* a red painful swelling on your hand or foot, caused by being cold 凍瘡

*★***child** /tʃaɪld; tʃaɪld/ *n* **children** /'tʃɪldrən; 'tʃɪldrən/ **1** a young person, not yet fully grown 小孩; 兒童: *We've known each other since we were children.* 我們從兒時起便互相認識。 **2** a son or daughter 兒子; 女兒; 孩子: *We have five children but they're all grown-up now.* 我們有五個孩子, 不過他們現都已長大成人。 **3** child's play something that is very easy to do 輕而易舉的事: *Riding a bicycle will be child's play when you've had some practice.* 只要多點練習, 騎腳踏車簡直是輕而易舉的事。

  ■ USAGE 用法: Compare 比較 **child** with 和 **baby, infant, toddler, teenager, adolescent, youth, kid.** A very young child is a **baby**, or an **infant** (rather formal). A child who has just learned to walk is a **toddler**. People aged 13 to 19 are **teenagers**. A younger teenager may be called an **adolescent**. This word is rather formal, or it may show disapproval ☆ 年幼的孩子叫 **baby** 或 **infant**（後者比較正式）。剛會走路的小孩叫 **toddler**。十三至十九歲的人叫 **teenagers**。年紀較小的 **teenager** 可以叫做 **adolescent**，這個詞較正式，並含有貶義：*Some adolescents were telling silly jokes.* 有些青少年在開無聊的玩笑。A **youth** is an older teenager, usually male. This word may also show disapproval ☆**youth** 通常指男性青年，也會含有貶義：*The police arrested several youths.* 警察逮捕了幾個青年。British people use **kids** as an informal word for **children** ☆英國人在非正式場合用 **kids** 來代替 **children** 一詞：*Let's take the kids to the park.* 我們帶孩子們去公園吧。Americans use **kids** as an informal word for all young people ☆美國人在非正式場合用 **kids** 來指所有的年輕人：*We met a group of college kids.* 我們遇到了一羣大學生。

child·a·buse /'··,·/ *n* [U] the physical or sexual mistreatment of children 對兒童的（性）虐待

child·bear·ing /'tʃaɪld,berɪŋ; 'tʃaɪld,beərɪŋ/ *n* [U] the process of giving birth to children 生孩子: *worn out with childbearing* 由於生育而疲憊不堪 | *a woman of childbearing age* 育齡婦女

child·birth /'tʃaɪld,bɜːθ; 'tʃaɪldbɜːθ/ *n* [U] the act of giving birth to a child 生產; 分娩

***child·hood** /'tʃaɪld,hʊd; 'tʃaɪldhʊd/ *n* [C;U] the time when you are a child 童年; 兒童時代: *He had a very happy childhood.* 他的童年很快樂。

child·ish /'tʃaɪldɪʃ; 'tʃaɪldɪʃ/ *adj* **1** of or for a child 孩子的: *The girl spoke in a high childish voice.* 小女孩用尖尖的童聲講話。**2** in a silly manner unsuitable for someone who is not a child 孩子氣的; 幼稚的: *a childish remark* 幼稚的意見 –compare 比較 CHILDLIKE –**childishly** *adv* –**childishness** *n* [U]

child·less /'tʃaɪldlɪs; 'tʃaɪldləs/ *adj* not having any children 無子女的: *a childless couple* 一對沒有孩子的夫婦

child·like /'tʃaɪld,laɪk; 'tʃaɪldlaɪk/ *adj* having the natural lovable quality of a child 如孩子般的; 天真無邪的: *She looked at me with childlike trust.* 她像孩子一樣很信任地看着我。–compare 比較 CHILDISH (2)

child·min·der /'tʃaɪld,maɪndɚ; 'tʃaɪldmaɪndəʳ/ *n* someone who looks after other people's children, for example when the parents are at work〔孩子父母外出工作時〕

照顧小孩的人 –**childminding** *n* [U]

chil·dren /'tʃɪldrən; 'tʃɪldrən/ *n* the plural of CHILD ☆ CHILD 的複數 –see picture on page 503 見 503 頁彩圖

chill[1] /tʃɪl; tʃɪl/ *v* [I;T] to make or become cold, but not freezing (使)變冷: *This wine needs to be chilled. I'll pop it in the fridge.* 這葡萄酒需要冰一下。我去把它放在冰箱裏。| *After ten minutes in that cold wind I felt thoroughly chilled.* 在那冷風中待了十分鐘後, 我感覺渾身冰涼。

chill[2] *n* **1** a cold with a fever〔會發熱的〕感冒; 着涼: *I think I've caught a chill.* 我想我是着涼了。**2** [sing] a feeling of coldness 寒冷的感覺; 寒氣: *There was a chill in the air this morning.* 今天早晨很寒冷。

chill[3] *adj* unpleasantly cold (used of weather) 寒冷的〔指天氣〕: *a chill wind* 寒風

chil·li /'tʃɪli; 'tʃɪli/ *n* chillis or chillies **1** [C;U] a small red or green vegetable, used to give a very hot taste to food 辣椒: *red chillies* 紅辣椒 | *chilli sauce* 辣椒醬 **2 chilli con carne** a dish in which small pieces of meat are cooked with beans in a liquid with chillis in it 辣味肉末豆子 **3 chilli powder** a powder made from chillis and used to give a very hot taste to food 辣椒粉

chil·ling /'tʃɪlɪŋ; 'tʃɪlɪŋ/ *adj* making you feel very frightened or worried 令人膽寒的: *a chilling murder story* 令人毛骨悚然的兇殺故事

chill·y /'tʃɪli; 'tʃɪli/ *adj* **chillier, chilliest 1** quite cold 寒冷的: *a chilly morning* 寒冷的早晨 | *I feel chilly without a coat.* 我沒穿外套覺得有些冷。**2** unfriendly 冷淡的; 不友好的: *She gave me a chilly stare.* 她冷冷地看着我。–**chilliness** *n* [sing; U]

chime[1] /tʃaɪm; tʃaɪm/ *n* a clear ringing sound of a bell or of a clock 鐘聲: *the chime of wedding bells* 婚禮的鐘聲 | *the chimes of Big Ben* 大本鐘〔大笨鐘〕的鐘聲

chime[2] *v* **chimed, chiming 1** [I;T] to make musical bell-like sounds 發出鐘聲: *The church bells were chiming.* 教堂的鐘在敲響。**2** [T] to show the time by the sound of bells 以鐘聲報（時）: *The clock chimed one o'clock.* 時鐘鳴報一點鐘了。

chime in *phr v* [I] *infml* to interrupt or join in a conversation suddenly〔非正式〕插話: *"I want to come too," Sally chimed in.* "我也想來。"莎莉插嘴道。

chim·ney /'tʃɪmni; 'tʃɪmni/ *n* a hollow pipe which allows smoke and gases from a fire to go up and out of a building 煙囱: *The factory chimneys poured smoke into the air.* 工廠的煙囱把煙排到空中。–see picture on page 729 見 729 頁彩圖

chim·ney·pot /'tʃɪmni,pat; 'tʃɪmnipɒt/ *n* a pipe at the top of a chimney 煙囱頂管 –see picture on page 729 見 729 頁彩圖

chim·ney·sweep /'tʃɪmni,swip; 'tʃɪmni-swiːp/ *n* (also 又作 **sweep** *infml*〔非正式〕) a person whose job is cleaning the insides of chimneys 煙囪清潔工

chim·pan·zee /ˌtʃɪmpænˈziː; ˌtʃɪmpænˈziː◂/ n (also 又作 **chimp** /tʃɪmp; tʃɪmp/ infml 《非正式》) an African APE with dark hair 〔非洲產的〕黑猩猩

chin /tʃɪn; tʃɪn/ n **1** the front part of your face below your mouth 頦, 下巴 **2 Chin up!, Keep your chin up!** infml a phrase used to someone in a difficult situation to encourage them to be cheerful 《非正式》振作一點!

chi·na /ˈtʃaɪnə; ˈtʃaɪnə/ n [U] **1** a hard white substance made by baking fine clay 瓷; 瓷料 **2** plates, cups, and dishes made from very fine clay 瓷器: She always puts out the best china for visitors. 她總是拿出最好的瓷器給來訪者看。

Chinese¹ /tʃaɪˈniːz; ˌtʃaɪˈniːz◂/ adj from or connected with China 中國的; 中國來的: a Chinese restaurant 中國餐館

Chinese² n **1 the Chinese** the people of China 〔全體〕中國人 **2** [U] the language of China 漢語, 中文

chink /tʃɪŋk; tʃɪŋk/ n **1** a narrow crack or opening 縫隙: He watched the meeting secretly, through a chink in the wall. 他偷偷地從牆上的縫隙中偷看那會議。 **2 chink of light** a narrow beam of light shining through a crack 〔從縫隙中射入的〕一道光 **3** a short ringing sound 叮噹聲: the chink of coins in his pocket 他口袋中硬幣的碰撞聲

chintz /tʃɪnts; tʃɪnts/ n [U] cotton cloth with brightly coloured patterns and a shiny surface 印花棉布: chintz curtains 印花棉布窗簾

★**chip¹** /tʃɪp; tʃɪp/ n **1 chips** long thin pieces of potato cooked in deep fat 油炸馬鈴薯[土豆]條: fish and chips 炸魚和炸馬鈴薯[土豆]條 **2** (also 又作 **microchip, silicon chip**) a very small piece of SILICON containing a set of ELECTRONIC parts and their connections, used especially in computers 〔尤用於電腦〕集成電路片; 矽片 **3** a small piece broken off an object 碎片: a chip of wood 木屑 **4** a crack or mark left when a small piece is broken off an object 缺口: This cup's got a chip in it. 這隻杯子上有個缺口。 **5** the usual American word for 《美式》= CRISP³ **6** a flat plastic object used for representing money in certain games 〔某些遊戲中的〕籌碼 **7 a chip off the old block** infml a person very like one of their parents in character (a phrase used to express approval) 《非正式》性格酷似父親[母親]的人〔含褒意〕 **8 have a chip on your shoulder** infml to be angry because you feel unfairly treated 《非正式》因受到不公正待遇而憤怒: He's got a chip on his shoulder about not having gone to university. 他為沒能上大學而忿忿不平。 **9 when the chips are down** infml when there is a serious situation 《非正式》在緊要關頭

chip² v **-pp-** [I;T] to cause something to lose a small piece from its surface or edge 使〔某物〕掉碎片: This rock chips easily. 這塊石塊易掉碎石。 | Oh dear! Someone's chipped one of the cups. 我的天吶! 有人把其中一隻杯子弄了個缺口。 | a chipped cup 有缺口的杯子 | I've chipped a piece off my tooth! 我的牙齒弄掉了一塊!

chip sthg ↔ **away** phr v [T] to remove or destroy something by gradually breaking small pieces off it 〔敲掉碎片來〕除, 拆毀〔某物〕

chip away at sthg phr v [T] to break small pieces off something 〔從某物上〕把碎片敲下來: He was chipping away at the rock with a hammer. 他在用錘子把石頭一小塊一小塊地敲下來。

chip in phr v infml 《非正式》 **1** [I] to interrupt or join in a conversation suddenly 插嘴; 插話: Of course John had to chip in and upset everybody. 約翰當然不得不插嘴, 這把大家弄得很心煩。 | Sheila chipped in with a few sensible comments. 希拉忽然插進來說了幾句中肯的評語。 **2** [I;T **chip in** sthg] to add your share of money, goods, or activity 捐獻; 捐助: If we all chip in a few pounds we can get her something really nice. 如果我們每人都湊上幾個英鎊, 就可以給她買點好東西。 | Brian chipped in with a couple of bottles of wine. 布萊恩拿了幾瓶葡萄酒來。

chi·rop·o·dist /kaɪˈrɒpədɪst; kɪˈrɒpədɪst/ n a person who looks after people's feet 足科醫生 **–chiropody** n [U]

chirp /tʃɜːp; tʃɜːp/ n the short high sound of small birds or some insects 〔小鳥或某些昆蟲的〕啾啾聲 **–chirp** v [I]

chirp·y /ˈtʃɜːpɪ; ˈtʃɜːpɪ/ adj **chirpier, chirpiest** infml cheerful and happy 《非正式》高興的; 愉快的: You seem very chirpy today. 你今天心情似乎挺高興的。 **–chirpily** adv **–chirpiness** n [U]

chis·el¹ /ˈtʃɪzl; ˈtʃɪzəl/ n a metal tool with a sharp edge at the end of a blade, used for cutting into or shaping wood, stone, or metal 鑿子 –see picture on page 958 見 958 頁彩圖

chisel² v **-ll-** (-l- AmE 《美式》) [I;T] to cut or shape something with a chisel 用鑿子刻: He chiselled a hole in the door. 他用鑿子在門上刻了個洞。

chit /tʃɪt; tʃɪt/ n a short note showing a sum of money that someone owes or has paid 欠款單; 收款單

chit-chat /ˈtʃɪt tʃæt; ˈtʃɪt tʃæt/ n [U] infml informal conversation 《非正式》閒聊

chiv·al·rous /ˈʃɪvlrəs; ˈʃɪvəlrəs/ adj fml showing polite behaviour and good manners towards women (used of men) 《正式》對女士彬彬有禮的 (用於指男人) **–chivalrously** adv **–chivalry** n [U]: "The age of chivalry is not dead," he said, opening the door for her. "騎士的時代還未消失," 他邊說

邊替她把門打開。

chives /tʃaɪvz; tʃaɪvz/ *n* [pl] a plant related to the onion, often eaten uncooked in salads 香葱

chlo·ri·nate /ˈklɔrɪˌnet; ˈklɔːrⅰˌneɪt/ *v* **chlorinated, chlorinating** [T] to disinfect water by putting chlorine in it〔水〕用氯氣消毒 – **chlorination** /ˌklɔrɪˈneʃən; ˌklɔːrⅰˈneɪʃən/ *n* [U]

chlo·rine /ˈklorin; ˈklɔːriːn/ *n* [U] a greenish-yellow gas that has a strong smell and is used to disinfect water 氯, 氯氣

chlor·o·form /ˈklorəˌfɔrm; ˈklɒrəfɔːm/ *n* [U] a poisonous liquid that has a strong smell, formerly used in medicine to make people unable to feel anything 氯仿, 三氯甲烷〔昔時用作麻醉劑〕

chlo·ro·phyll /ˈklorəˌfɪl; ˈklɔːrəfil/ *n* [U] the green substance in the stems and leaves of plants 葉綠素

chock /tʃɑk; tʃɒk/ *n* a shaped piece of wood placed under something to prevent it from moving〔防止物體移動的〕墊木: *Put some chocks behind the wheels or it will roll back.* 在輪子後面放幾塊墊木, 不然它會向後滑的。

chock-a-block /ˈtʃɑk ə ˈblɑk; ˌtʃɒk ə ˈblɒk◂/ *adj* (also 又作 **choc-a-bloc**) [never before a noun 不能用於名詞前] *infml* very crowded and completely full《非正式》非常擁擠的; 擠滿的: *The road was chock-a-block with cars again today.* 今天路上又擠滿了車。

chock-full /ˌ· ·ˈ·/ *adj infml* completely full《非正式》擠滿的; 塞滿的

choco·late /ˈtʃɔkəlɪt; ˈtʃɒklɪt/ *n* **1** [U] a sweet, hard, brown food made from crushed COCOA beans 巧克力, 朱古力: *Would you like a piece of chocolate?* 你要來塊巧克力嗎? | *a bar of chocolate* 一條巧克力 **2** [C] a small sweet covered with chocolate 巧克力糖: *a box of chocolates* 一盒巧克力糖 **3** [C;U] a drink made from hot milk, and sometimes water, mixed with powdered chocolate〔加熱牛奶(和水)的〕巧克力飲料: *A hot chocolate, please.* 請來杯熱巧克力飲料。 | *a tin of drinking chocolate* 一罐巧克力飲料

choice¹ /tʃɔɪs; tʃɔɪs/ *n* **1** [C] the act or result of choosing 選擇; 選擇結果: *I'm sure he's made the right choice.* 我敢肯定他作出了正確的選擇。 | *the people's choice for president* 人民在選舉總統時所做出的選擇 **2** [C;U] the power or chance of choosing 選擇權; 選擇機會: *She gave me a choice between looking after the baby or cleaning the kitchen.* 她給我兩種選擇: 要麼照看孩子, 要麼打掃廚房。 | *I have no choice but to do as he tells me.* 除了照他告訴我的去做以外, 我沒有其他選擇。 **3** [C] a variety of different things from which you can choose 可供選擇的品種: *There's a wide choice of apples in the shops these days.* 這陣子商店裡有許多種蘋果可供挑選。 **4** of your

choice that you prefer 選中的: *the dish of your choice* 你選中的菜餚 **5 from choice, by choice** if you had the power to choose 如果有權作選擇的話: *I wouldn't drive at night from choice.* 如果我有權選擇的話, 我不會在夜裡開車。

choice² *adj* high quality (used of food and drink) 品質優良的〔指食物和飲料〕: *choice apples* 上等蘋果

choir /kwaɪr; kwaɪəʳ/ *n* [+sing/pl verb] a group of people who sing together especially during religious services 歌唱隊; 詩班: *The church choir is singing tonight.* 教堂唱詩班今晚有演唱活動。

choke¹ /tʃok; tʃəuk/ *v* **choked, choking 1** [I] to struggle to breathe or stop breathing because your breathing passages are blocked (使)窒息; (使)呼吸困難: *Water went down his throat and he started to choke.* 水嗆入他的咽喉, 他開始透不過氣來。 **2** [T] to make someone choke 使〔某人〕窒息: *She choked him to death.* 她令他嗆死。 **3** [T] to fill something up completely and block it 塞住; 堵住: *The pipe was choked with leaves.* 管道被樹葉堵住了。

choke sthg ↔ **back** *phr v* [T] to control a strong feeling and not show it more than you can help 強忍住, 抑制住〔感情的流露〕: *They choked back the tears.* 他們忍住了眼淚。

choke² *n* **1** the act or sound of choking 窒息(聲) **2** an apparatus that controls the amount of air going into a car engine; you switch the choke on when the engine is cold〔發動機內的〕阻氣門

chol·e·ra /ˈkɑlərə; ˈkɒlərə/ *n* [U] a dangerous infectious disease which attacks the stomach and bowels 霍亂

cho·les·te·rol /kəˈlɛstəˌrol; kəˈlestərɒl/ *n* [U] a substance which helps to carry fats in the body, too much of which is thought to be bad for the arteries (ARTERY) 膽固醇

choose /tʃuz; tʃuːz/ *v* **chose** /tʃoz; tʃəuz/, **chosen** /ˈtʃozn; ˈtʃəuzən/, **choosing** [I;T] **1** to pick out one thing from a greater number of things 挑選; 選擇: *Would you like to choose the wine?* 你要挑葡萄酒嗎? | *The cakes all looked so good, I didn't know which to choose.* 所有的蛋糕看上去都很好, 我不知道該選哪一個。 | *Choose a cake for me.* 給我挑塊蛋糕。 | *They chose her as their leader.* 他們選她為領導。 | *They chose her to represent them.* 他們選她為代表。 | *Have you chosen where we should go to eat?* 你選好了我們吃飯的地方嗎? | *There are ten to choose from.* 有十個可供挑選。 | *I had to choose between staying with my parents and going abroad.* 是留在父母身邊還是出國, 我必須作出選擇。 | *"Which one shall we buy?" "You choose."* "我們該買哪一個?" "你選吧。" **2 choose to do something** to decide to do something 決定做某事: *Many women choose* to go on working after the birth of their first child. 許多婦女在生下第一個小孩以後決定繼續工作。 | He chose not to go home until later. 他決定晚一點才回家。 **3 there's not much to choose between them, there's little to choose between them** = they are very much alike 他們很相像〔差不多〕，難分上下

choos·y /'tʃuːzi; 'tʃuːzi/ adj **choosier, choosiest** difficult to please 挑剔的: Jean's very choosy **about** what she eats. 瓊對吃的東西很挑剔。

chop[1] /tʃɒp; tʃɒp/ v **-pp-** [T] **1** (also 又作 **chop** sth ↔ **up**) to cut something into very small pieces 把〔某物〕切成小塊〔碎片〕: Chop the onions. 把洋蔥切碎。 | They chopped the branches up. 他們把樹枝砍掉了。 **2** to cut something by repeatedly hitting with a sharp tool, such as an AXE 砍; 切: She chopped the block of wood in two. 她把那塊木頭一砍為二。 | We tried to chop a path through the thick forest. 我們盡力在茂密的樹林裡砍出一條路來。 **3 chop and change** to keep changing your opinion 不斷改變主意: Make your mind up — don't keep chopping and changing! 拿定主意——不要朝三暮四!

chop sth ↔ **down** phr v [T] to chop at a tree near the bottom until it falls 伐倒〔樹木〕

chop[2] n **1** a quick short cutting blow 砍 **2** a small piece of meat, usually containing a bone 排骨; 肋條肉: pork chops 豬排 —see picture on page 504 見 504 頁彩圖 **3 for the chop** infml soon going to be stopped 〔非正式〕將被停止: It looks as if the scheme is for the chop. 這計劃看樣子要放棄了。 **4 get the chop** infml to be dismissed from work 〔非正式〕被解雇

chop·per /'tʃɒpə; 'tʃɒpəʳ/ n **1** a heavy sharpended tool for cutting wood or meat 砍刀; 斧頭 **2** infml a HELICOPTER 〔非正式〕直升機

chop·py /'tʃɒpi; 'tʃɒpi/ adj **choppier, choppiest** covered with many small waves (used of water) 波濤洶湧的〔指水〕: a choppy sea 波濤洶湧的大海

chop·sticks /'tʃɒp,stɪks; 'tʃɒp-stɪks/ n a pair of narrow sticks used in East Asian countries for eating food; you hold them between your thumb and fingers 筷子

cho·ral /'kɔːrəl; 'kɔːrəl/ adj related to or sung by a CHOIR or CHORUS 合唱隊的; 唱詩班的: a choral society 合唱團 | choral music 合唱樂曲

chord /kɔːd; kɔːd/ n **1** a combination of several musical notes sounded at the same time 〔音樂的〕和弦, 和音 **2** tech a straight line joining two points on a curve 〔術語〕弦

chore /tʃɔː; tʃɔːʳ/ n **1** a small regular job in the house, for example the washing-up 雜

事; 雜務〔如洗碗碟〕: I spent the morning doing household chores. 我整個上午都在做家務。 **2** an unpleasant and uninteresting job 令人厭煩的事

chor·e·og·ra·phy /,kɒriˈɒgrəfi; ˌkɔriˈɒgrəfi/ n [U] the art of dancing or the organization of dance steps to be performed on the stage 舞蹈設計; 舞蹈編排 —**choreographer** n

chor·is·ter /'kɒristə; 'kɔristəʳ/ n a member of a CHOIR, especially a boy 唱詩班成員〔尤指男孩〕

chor·tle /'tʃɔːtl; 'tʃɔːtl/ n a laugh of pleasure or satisfaction 開心地笑; 咯咯地笑 —**chortle** v **chortled, chortling** [I]

cho·rus[1] /'kɔːrəs; 'kɔːrəs/ n **1** [C+sing/pl verb] a group of people who sing together 合唱隊: The chorus was very good today. 合唱隊今天唱得很好。 **2** [C] a piece of music for a chorus 合唱曲 **3** [C] a piece of music played or sung after each part of a song 〔歌曲中的〕合唱部分 **4** [sing] something said by a lot of people at the same time 異口同聲的話: His announcement was greeted by a chorus **of** disapproval. 他的聲明遭到了異口同聲的反對。

chorus[2] v [T] to say something together at the same time 異口同聲地說〔某事〕

chose /tʃəʊz; tʃoʊz/ the past tense of CHOOSE ☆ CHOOSE 的過去式

chosen /'tʃəʊzən; 'tʃoʊzən/ the past participle of CHOOSE ☆ CHOOSE 的過去分詞

Christ /kraɪst; kraɪst/ n (also 又作 **Jesus Christ, Jesus**) the man who established Christianity 基督, 耶穌基督

chris·ten /'krɪsən; 'krɪsən/ v [T] **1** a Christian ceremony which makes someone a member of the church by giving them a name 為〔某人〕施洗禮, 〔施洗禮時〕把...命名為: The baby was christened by the priest. 牧師為嬰孩施了洗禮。 | We christened our baby John. 我們給嬰兒施洗禮並取名為約翰。 **2** to name an object officially 正式命名: The ship was christened the Queen Mary. 這艘船被命名為瑪麗皇后號。

chris·ten·ing /'krɪsnɪŋ; 'krɪsənɪŋ/ n the Christian ceremony for naming a person, usually a baby 〔常指嬰兒的〕洗禮

Chris·tian[1] /'krɪstʃən; 'krɪstʃən/ n a person who believes in the religious teachings of Jesus Christ 基督徒

Christian[2] adj **1** relating to Christianity 基督教的: a Christian nation 基督教國家 | the Christian philosophy 基督教的哲學思想 **2** kind and forgiving 仁慈的; 寬容的 **3 Christian name** a person's first name 教名; 名字: What's his Christian name? 他叫甚麼名字? —see 見 FIRST NAME (USAGE 用法)

Chris·ti·an·i·ty /,krɪstʃiˈænəti; ˌkristiˈænəti/ n [U] the religion based on the life and teachings of Jesus Christ 基督教: Do you believe in Christianity? 你信基督教嗎?

Christ·mas /'krɪsməs; 'krɪsməs/ n [C;U] the

period of time around the Christian holy day on December 25th 聖誕節節期: *Christmas cards* 聖誕卡 | *Happy Christmas!* 聖誕快樂! | *Did you have a nice Christmas?* 你聖誕過得愉快嗎?

Christmas Day /ˌ·· '·/ *n* [C;U] the Christian holy day on December 25th in honour of the birth of Jesus Christ 聖誕節〔12月25日〕

Christmas Eve /ˌ·· '·/ *n* the day before Christmas Day 聖誕前夕, 平安夜: *We sing carols on Christmas Eve.* 我們在聖誕前夕唱聖歌。

Christmas tree /'·· ·/ *n* a real or plastic FIR tree with lights and decorations on it, used to decorate people's homes at Christmas 聖誕樹

chrome /krom; krəʊm/ *n* [U] (also 又作 **chromium** /-ɪəm; -ɪəm/) a hard, shiny, silver-coloured metal 鉻: *There's less chrome and more plastic on modern cars.* 現代汽車上的塑料比鉻用得少。

chro·mo·some /'kroməˌsom; 'krəʊmə-səʊm/ *n tech* a very small part of a cell in a plant, animal, or human that controls its nature〔術語〕染色體

chron·ic /'krɑnɪk; 'krɒnɪk/ *adj* **1** lasting a very long time (used of an illness) 慢性的〔指疾病〕: *a chronic cough* 慢性咳嗽 **2** [only before a noun 只用於名詞前] suffering from an illness or other problem over a long period 長期患病的: *a chronic alcoholic* 長期酗酒的酒徒 | *a chronic invalid* 長期患者 **3** *infml* very bad〔非正式〕非常糟糕的; 極壞的: *a chronic example of bad management* 劣質管理的糟透例子 –**chronically** /-klɪ; -klɪ/ *adv*: *chronically depressed* 長期精神不振

chron·i·cle /'krɑnɪkl; 'krɒnɪkəl/ *n* a record of historical events, which are arranged in order of time 編年史, 年代記 –**chronicle** *v* **chronicled, chronicling** [T]: *a book which chronicles the nation's history* 一部按年月順序記載國家歷史的書

chron·o·log·i·cal /ˌkrɑnə'lɑdʒɪkl; ˌkrɒnə-'lɒdʒɪkəl◂/ *adj* arranged according to the order of time 按年月次序排列的: *a list of World Cup winners in chronological order* 按年月順序所排列的世界杯冠軍名單 –**chronologically** /-klɪ; -klɪ/ *adv*

chrys·a·lis /'krɪslɪs; 'krɪsəlɪs/ *n* **chrysalises** /-sɪz; -siːz/ an insect at an early stage of its development, before it can fly 蛹

chry·san·the·mum /krɪ'sænθəməm; krɪ-'sænθɪməm/ *n* a garden plant with large brightly-coloured flowers in autumn 菊花

chub·by /'tʃʌbɪ; 'tʃʌbi/ *adj* **chubbier, chubbiest** pleasantly fat (used especially of children) 圓圓胖胖的〔尤指兒童〕–see picture on page 469 見 469 頁彩圖 –**chubbiness** *n* [U]

chuck /tʃʌk; tʃʌk/ *v* [T] *infml* to throw something with a short, quick movement〔非正

式〕扔; 抛: *Chuck me an apple, will you?* 把蘋果扔給我, 好嗎?

chuck sthg ↔ **away** *phr v* [T] *infml* to get rid of something〔非正式〕扔掉〔某物〕: *"Do you want this polythene bag?" "No, chuck it away."* "你要這個塑料袋嗎?" "不要了, 把它扔了吧。"

chuck sthg ↔ **in** *phr v* [T] *infml* to leave a job, often because you are unhappy with it〔非正式〕〔由於不喜歡而〕放棄〔職業〕: *She hated her boss so much that she chucked in her job.* 她非常討厭她的老闆, 所以便辭了職。

chuck out *phr v infml*〔非正式〕**1** [T **chuck** sbdy ↔ **out**] to force a person to leave a place 驅逐, 趕走〔某人〕: *The barman threatened to chuck us out of the pub if we got drunk.* 酒吧服務員威脅說, 如果我們喝醉就把我們趕出去。**2** [T **chuck** sthg ↔ **out**] to throw something away 扔掉〔某物〕: *I'll chuck out all my old school books and make some more room.* 我會把舊課本全都扔掉, 以便騰出更多的地方。

chuck·le /'tʃʌkl; 'tʃʌkəl/ *v* **chuckled, chuckling** [I] to laugh quietly 輕聲地笑: *I could hear him chuckling to himself as he read his book.* 他看書的時候, 我可以聽見他在輕聲發笑。–**chuckle** *n*: *He gave a quiet chuckle.* 他輕聲笑一笑。

chug /tʃʌg; tʃʌg/ *v* **-gg-** [I+adv/prep] (of an engine or vehicle) to make a heavy beating noise while moving slowly along〔馬達或車輛〕發嘎嘎聲: *The little boat chugged along the river.* 小船沿着河突突地行駛着。| *The old steam engine chugged slowly up the hill.* 那輛舊蒸汽機車突突地慢慢爬上了山坡。–**chug** *n*: *the chug of the engine* 馬達的突突聲

chum /tʃʌm; tʃʌm/ *n old fash infml* a good friend〔老式, 非正式〕好友: *They are old school chums.* 他們是要好的老同學。

chum·my /'tʃʌmɪ; 'tʃʌmi/ *adj old fash infml* friendly〔老式, 非正式〕友好的; 關係好的

chump /tʃʌmp; tʃʌmp/ *n infml* a fool〔非正式〕笨蛋, 傻瓜

chunk /tʃʌŋk; tʃʌŋk/ *n* a solid piece or lump 大塊: *a chunk of cheese* 一大塊乳酪

chunk·y /'tʃʌŋkɪ; 'tʃʌŋki/ *adj* **1** thick and heavy 又厚又重的: *chunky jewellery* 大塊的珠寶 | *a chunky sweater* 又厚又重的毛衣 **2** attractive to women because big, with a broad chest and strong appearance (used of men) 壯實的〔指男人〕

church /tʃɜtʃ; tʃɜːtʃ/ *n* **1** [C;U] a building for public Christian worship 教堂: *the church on the hill* 山上的教堂 **2** [U] the religious services held in a church 禮拜儀式: *I'm going to church today.* 我今天去做禮拜。| *I'll see you after church.* 我做完禮拜後去看你。**3** [C] any of the separate religious groups within the Christian religion〔基督教的〕派別: *She was a loyal member of the Catholic Church.* 她是個虔誠的天主教徒。

C

church·go·er /ˈ·ˌ·ˈ/ *n* a person who goes to church regularly 常去教堂做禮拜的人

Church of Eng·land /ˌ·· ˈ·/ *n* **the Church of England** the state religion in England, with the King or Queen as its head 英國國教會，聖公會

church·yard /ˈtʃɜːtʃˌjɑːd; ˈtʃɜːtʃjɑːd/ *n* an open space around a church in which dead people are buried 〔在教堂周圍的〕教堂墓地

churl·ish /ˈtʃɜːlɪʃ; ˈtʃɜːlɪʃ/ *adj* rude because you do not admit the generosity of other people 粗魯的；無禮的 –**churlishness** *n* [U]

churn¹ /tʃɜːn; tʃɜːn/ *n* **1** a container in which milk is shaken until it becomes butter 〔製黃油用的〕攪乳器 **2** *BrE* a metal container like a very large bottle in which milk is stored or carried from the farm 牛奶桶 – see picture on page 244 見 244 頁彩圖

churn² *v* [T] **1** to make butter using a churn 用攪乳器製〔黃油〕 **2** (*also* 又作 **churn** sthg ↔ **up**) to move about violently 劇烈翻騰：*The ship churned up the water as it passed.* 船駛過時，水面浪花翻騰。 **3** **make your stomach churn** *infml* to make you so nervous or excited that you feel sick 〔非正式〕使人非常緊張或激動〔以致不舒服〕：*The thought of my driving test made my stomach churn.* 一想到駕駛考試，我就覺得胃裡翻騰。

churn sthg ↔ **out** *phr v* [T] *infml* to produce something in large numbers without caring about the quality 〔非正式〕〔不顧及質量地〕大量生產〔某物〕，粗製濫造：*She churns out about three new books every year.* 她每年大約要粗製濫造地出版三本新書。

chute /ʃuːt; ʃuːt/ *n* a long, narrow, steep slope, used for getting things to a lower level 斜槽；滑道：*an emergency chute* 緊急滑梯 | *a rubbish chute* 垃圾斜槽

chut·ney /ˈtʃʌtni; ˈtʃʌtni/ *n* [U] a strong-tasting sweet and sour mixture of fruit or vegetables which is eaten with cheese or meat 〔用水果、蔬菜調製成與乳酪或肉一起食用的〕酸辣醬

CIA /ˌsiː aɪ ˈeɪ; ˌsiː aɪ ˈeɪ/ *n* a government body in the US which gathers secret information about other countries; an abbreviation for **Central Intelligence Agency** 〔縮〕〔美國〕中央情報局：*a member of the CIA* 中央情報局成員

CID /ˌsiː aɪ ˈdiː; ˌsiː aɪ ˈdiː/ *n* a special branch of the UK police force; an abbreviation for **Criminal Investigation Department** 〔縮〕〔英國警察的〕刑事偵組部

ci·der /ˈsaɪdə; ˈsaɪdə/ *n* [C;U] an alcoholic drink made from apple juice 蘋果酒：*Two ciders and a beer, please.* 請來兩杯蘋果酒和一杯啤酒。

ci·gar /sɪˈɡɑː; sɪˈɡɑːr/ *n* a brown tube-shaped roll of uncut tobacco leaves for smoking 雪茄煙

cig·a·rette /ˌsɪɡəˈret; ˌsɪɡəˈret/ *n* a thin white paper tube of finely cut tobacco for smoking 香煙：*She lit a cigarette but stubbed it out immediately.* 她點起一支煙，但又立即把它掐滅了。

cinch /sɪntʃ; sɪntʃ/ *n infml* 〔非正式〕**a cinch** something that you can do very easily 容易做的事：*My exam was a cinch. I passed with top marks.* 我考試很容易。我考了很高分。

cin·der /ˈsɪndə; ˈsɪndə/ *n* all that is left of a piece of coal or other material after it has been burnt 〔煤或其他物質的〕餘燼；煤渣：*All that was left of the fire was the grey cinders.* 那場大火燒過之後，剩下的只有灰色的餘燼。 | *The toast was burnt to a cinder.* 吐司烤焦了。

cin·e·ma /ˈsɪnəmə; ˈsɪnˌmə/ *n BrE* 〔英式〕**1** a theatre in which films are shown for entertainment 電影院：*Which cinema is it at?* 電影在哪家影院上映？ **2 the cinema** the art or industry of making films 電影藝術；電影業：*She's worked in the cinema all her life.* 她畢生從事電影事業。**3 go to the cinema** to go to see a film 去看電影

cin·na·mon /ˈsɪnəmən; ˈsɪnəmən/ *n* [U] a sweet-smelling light brown powder used for giving a special taste to food such as fruit or cakes 肉桂(粉)

ci·pher /ˈsaɪfə; ˈsaɪfə/ *n* (*also* 又作 **cypher**) **1** a secret system of writing 密碼；暗號：*The government uses a secret cipher for its official messages.* 政府用密碼傳遞官方消息。 **2** a person of no importance 無足輕重的人物

cir·ca /ˈsɜːkə; ˈsɜːkə/ *prep fml* (*also* 又作 **c**) a word you use to say that something happened in about the year stated 〔正式〕大約在〔表示年代日期〕：*born circa 50 BC* 生於公元前五十年左右

cir·cle¹ /ˈsɜːkl; ˈsɜːkəl/ *n* **1** a flat, round area enclosed by a curved line, so that everywhere is equally distant from the centre 圓；圓周 **2** an object or area which has the general shape of a circle 圓形物；圈：*Let's sit in a circle.* 我們圍個圈子坐下來吧。 | *a circle of chairs* 排成一圈的椅子 **3** a group of people who meet regularly because they share a common interest 〔具有共同興趣的人形成的〕圈子，…界：*a large circle of friends* 一大羣朋友 | *I belong to the Literary Circle.* 我是文學界的一份子。 **4** an upper floor in a theatre 〔戲院中的〕樓座：*Are we going to sit in the circle or in the stalls?* 我們是坐在樓座還是坐在堂座的座位？ **5 come full circle** to go through several changes or developments and end up back at the starting point 兜個圈子回到原處：*I tried everything I could think of, but ended up coming full circle.* 凡是想到的我都試過了，但仍然是徒勞無功。 **6 go round in circles** to make no progress 沒有取得任何進展 **7 run round in circles** to be very busy without making much progress 瞎忙；空忙

circle² *v* **circled, circling 1** [T] to draw a circle around something 在〔某物〕上劃圈：

The teacher circled their spelling mistakes in red ink. 老師用紅墨水把他們拼寫錯誤的地方圈出來。**2** [I;U] to move in a circle around something 圍繞〔某物〕盤旋: *The plane circled the airport before landing.* 飛機着陸前在機場上空盤旋。

***cir·cuit** /'sɜːkɪt; 'sɜːkɪt/ *n* **1** the closed path of an electric current 電路: *The lights went out because of a sudden break in the circuit.* 由於電路突然中斷, 燈光全部熄滅了。**2** a path in the shape of a ring 環行路線: *We made a circuit of the old city walls.* 我們繞着舊城牆兜了一圈。| *a racing circuit* 環形跑道 **3** a regular journey from place to place for a particular event or purpose 〔為特定目的而進行的〕巡迴旅行: *the tennis circuit* 網球巡迴賽

cir·cu·i·tous /səˈkjuːtəs; sɜːˈkjuːtəs/ *adj fml* going a long and difficult way round 〔正式〕迂迴的; 繞道的: *the river's circuitous course* 迂迴的河道 | *a circuitous route* 迂迴的路線 **–circuitously** *adv*

cir·cu·lar¹ /'sɜːkjələ; 'sɜːkjələr/ *adj* **1** shaped like a circle 圓形的: *a circular area* 圓形地塊 **2** moving in a direction which leads you back to where you started 兜圈子後回到原處的; 循環的: *a circular journey* 循環的旅程 | *a circular argument* 循環論證 **–circularity** /ˌsɜːkjəˈlærəti; ˌsɜːkjʊˈlærˌti/ *n* [U]: *She seemed unaware of the circularity of her argument.* 她似乎不知道自己的論證是在兜圈子。

circular² *n* a printed advertisement, paper, or notice sent to a large number of people 廣告; 傳單; 公告: *Did you see that circular from the new theatre?* 你看到那家新戲院的廣告沒有?

cir·cu·late /'sɜːkjəˌleɪt; 'sɜːkjʊleɪt/ *v* **circulated, circulating 1** [I;T] to move in a circular direction within a closed space 循環: *Blood circulates* **round** *the body.* 血液在體內循環。| *The heart circulates blood round the body.* 心臟使血液在體內循環。**2** [I] *infml* to move about freely and without difficulty 〔非正式〕到處隨意走動: *He circulated at the party, talking to lots of people.* 他在晚會上來回周旋, 與許多人交談過。| *The new roundabout has helped the traffic to circulate better.* 新建的環形路使交通大為改善。**3** [I;T] to spread information to a large group of people 〔向許多人〕傳播信息: *I'll circulate the report at the meeting.* 我準備在會議上向大家傳閱這份報告。| *Jokes were circulating about him.* 外面在流傳有關他的笑話。**–circulatory** /'sɜːkjələˌtɔːri; ˌsɜːkjʊˈleɪtəri/ *adj*

cir·cu·la·tion /ˌsɜːkjəˈleɪʃən; ˌsɜːkjʊˈleɪʃən/ *n* **1** [C;U] the movement of blood through your body 血液循環: *Bad circulation can cause tiredness.* 血液循環不佳可導致身體疲乏。**2** [C] the number of copies of a newspaper, magazine, or book that are sold over a period of time 報紙〔雜誌、書〕的銷售量: *This magazine has a circulation of 400,000.* 這本雜誌的銷量為四十萬份。**3** in circulation: **a** in use in a society and passing from one person to another 在流通之中: *The government has reduced the number of £5 notes in circulation.* 政府已減少了面額五英鎊紙幣的流通量。**b** enjoying an active social life 積極從事社交活動: *He was soon back in circulation after his spell in hospital.* 他在醫院裡住了一段時間後, 很快地又投身到社交活動中去了。[RELATED PHRASE 相關詞組 **out of circulation**]

cir·cum·cise /'sɜːkəmˌsaɪz; 'sɜːkəmsaɪz/ *v* **circumcised, circumcising** [T] to cut off the skin at the end of a man's PENIS or a woman's CLITORIS in a religious ceremony 〔在宗教儀式上〕割除包皮, 割除陰蒂 **–circumcision** /ˌsɜːkəmˈsɪʒən; ˌsɜːkəmˈsɪʒən/ *n* [C; U]

cir·cum·fer·ence /səˈkʌmfərəns; səˈkʌmfərəns/ *n* [C;U] the length around the outside edge of a round object 周長; 圓周: *The Earth's circumference is more than 40,000 kilometres.* 地球的圓周長度超過四萬公里。| *The tower is 20 metres in circumference.* 這座塔周長二十米。

cir·cum·scribe /ˌsɜːkəmˈskraɪb; 'sɜːkəmskraɪb/ *v* **circumscribed, circumscribing** [T] to keep something within narrow limits 限制〔某事物〕: *His activities have been severely circumscribed since his illness.* 自患病後, 他的活動受到了嚴格的限制。

cir·cum·spect /'sɜːkəmˌspekt; 'sɜːkəmspekt/ *adj* careful and avoiding risk 謹慎的; 小心的: *You won't catch Kidd making a rash statement. He's always very circumspect.* 你不會聽見凱德說魯莽的話。他向來非常謹慎。**–circumspection** /ˌsɜːkəmˈspekʃən; ˌsɜːkəmˈspekʃən/ *n* [U]

☆**cir·cum·stance** /'sɜːkəmˌstæns; 'sɜːkəmstæns/ *n* **1** a fact or condition which influences a situation 情形; 情況: *We can't judge what he did till we know all the circumstances.* 直到了解了全部情況, 我們才能判斷他的所作所為。| *Circumstances forced me to accept a very low price.* 當時的情況迫使我不得不接受很低的價錢。**2 circumstances** *fml* the amount of money you have 〔正式〕所擁有〔攜帶〕的錢 **3 in no circumstances, under no circumstances, not under any circumstances** never 決不: *I will not vote for him under any circumstances.* 我決不會投他的票。**4 in the circumstances, under the circumstances** as a result of a particular situation 在這種情況下: *The weather was terrible. In the circumstances, I decided to postpone my journey.* 天氣很糟。在這種情況下, 我決定把旅行推遲。

cir·cum·stan·tial /ˌsɜːkəmˈstænʃəl; ˌsɜːkəmˈstænʃəl/ *adj* indirect, and not proving that something is true (used of evidence) 間接

推測的〔指證據〕: *We've only got circum-stantial evidence.* 我們只有間接推測的證據。

cir·cum·vent /ˌsɜːkəmˈvɛnt; ˌsɜːkəmˈvɛnt/ v [T] *fml* to avoid a rule or law 〔正式〕規避〔法律、規定〕: *The company has opened an office abroad in order to circumvent British tax laws.* 公司在海外開設了一個辦事處，以避開英國的稅法。 **–circumvention** /-ˈvɛnʃən; -ˈvɛnʃən/ n [U]

cir·cus /ˈsɜːkəs; ˈsɜːkəs/ n 1 a group of travelling entertainers and animals who perform various acts of skill and daring 馬戲團 2 a performance by these people 馬戲表演 3 a round open area where a number of streets join together 〔數條街道會聚的〕圓形廣場: *Oxford Circus* 牛津廣場

cis·sy /ˈsɪsɪ; ˈsɪsɪ/ n **cissies** see 見 SISSY

cis·tern /ˈsɪstən; ˈsɪstən/ n a container for storing water, especially for a TOILET 貯水槽；〔尤指抽水馬桶的〕水箱

cit·a·del /ˈsɪtədl; ˈsɪtədəl/ n a castle or fort built to be a place of safety and defence in time of war 〔戰時所用的〕城堡；堡壘

ci·ta·tion /saɪˈteɪʃən; saɪˈteɪʃən/ n 1 a short passage taken from something written or spoken 引文；引句；引證 2 an official statement that someone has been very brave 〔對英勇事跡的〕嘉獎令

cite /saɪt; saɪt/ v **cited, citing** [T] *fml* 〔正式〕 1 to mention something as an example or proof in a formal way 引用；引證: *The minister supported his argument by citing the latest crime figures.* 部長引用了最新的犯罪數字來證明他的論點。 2 to call someone to appear before a court of law 〔法庭〕傳訊: *He was cited in a divorce case.* 他在一場離婚案中被法庭傳訊。

cit·i·zen /ˈsɪtɪzn; ˈsɪtɪzən/ n 1 a person who lives in a particular city or town and can vote there 市民: *the citizens of Rome* 羅馬市民 2 a person who belongs to a particular country by birth or NATURALIZATION, and who expects protection from it 公民；國民: *She's a British citizen but lives in India.* 她是英國公民，但住在印度。

cit·i·zen·ship /ˈsɪtɪznˌʃɪp; ˈsɪtɪzənʃɪp/ n [U] having the official rights and duties of a citizen 公民權；公民身分: *After eight years in the country he obtained American citizenship.* 他在美國待了八年之後，獲得了公民資格。

cit·rus /ˈsɪtrəs; ˈsɪtrəs/ n any of the trees of the orange family grown in warm countries for their juicy fruit 柑橘屬果樹

cit·y /ˈsɪtɪ; ˈsɪtɪ/ n **cities** 1 a place which is more important than a town and has a larger population 城市: *Many industrial cities are experiencing serious unemployment.* 許多工業城市正陷於嚴重的失業問題之中。 2 **the City** the centre of business and money matters in London 倫敦商業區

civ·ic /ˈsɪvɪk; ˈsɪvɪk/ adj relating to a city or its citizens 城市的；市民的；公民的: *the civic centre* 市中心 | *civic duties* 公民的責任

civ·il /ˈsɪvl; ˈsɪvəl/ adj 1 concerning the state as opposed to the army or the church 民間的；國民的〔與軍隊或教會相對〕: *a civil marriage* 公證結婚 | *civil defence* 民防 2 dealing with the legal rights of private citizens 公民權的；民事的: *Civil law is different from criminal law.* 民法與刑法不同。 3 polite enough, without being friendly 有禮貌的；文明的: *Try to be civil to him, even if you don't like him.* 即使你不喜歡他，也要盡量對他客氣些。 **–civilly** /ˈsɪvəlɪ/ adv

ci·vil·ian /səˈvɪljən; sɪˈvɪljən/ n a person who is not a member of the armed forces 平民: *Innocent civilians suffered in the attack.* 進攻使無辜的百姓遭殃。

ci·vil·i·ty /səˈvɪlətɪ; sɪˈvɪlɪtɪ/ n **civilities** 1 [U] behaviour which is polite but not friendly 禮貌；彬彬有禮的行為 2 **civilities** [pl] expressions which are polite but not very friendly 有禮貌的言辭

civ·i·li·za·tion /ˌsɪvɪlaɪˈzeɪʃən; ˌsɪvələˈzeɪʃən/ n (also 又作 **civilisation** *BrE* 〔英式〕) 1 [U] a high level of social organization with developed systems of art, science, religion, and government 文明: *The survival of civilization as we know it depends on many environmental factors.* 正如我們所知道的那樣，文明的生存取決於許多環境因素。 2 [C] a civilized society of a particular time or place 文明社會: *Compare the civilizations of ancient China and Japan.* 把古代中國和日本的文明比較一下。

civ·i·lize /ˈsɪvl͟aɪz; ˈsɪvəlaɪz/ v **civilized, civilizing** (also 又作 **civilise** *BrE* 〔英式〕) [T] to educate and improve a society or nation 教化〔社會或民族〕；使文明: *The Romans hoped to civilize all the tribes of Europe.* 羅馬人希望教化歐洲所有的部落。

civ·i·lized /ˈsɪvl͟aɪzd; ˈsɪvəlaɪzd/ adj (also 又作 **civilised** *BrE* 〔英式〕) 1 having a high level of social organization 文明的；開化的: *a very civilized part of the world* 一個文明發達的地區 2 pleasant, charming, and without roughness of manner or style 有教養的；文雅的: *a very civilized person* 一個很有教養的人 | *This place looks more civilized now than we've painted it.* 現在這個地方要比我們所畫的更加文明。

civil rights /ˌ·· ˈ·/ n [pl] rights such as freedom and equality which belong to all citizens without regard to their race, religion, colour, or sex 公民權: *the civil rights movement* 民權運動

civil ser·vant /ˌ·· ˈ··/ n a person employed in the civil service 〔政府中的〕公務員，文職人員

Civil Ser·vice /ˌ·· ˈ··/ n **the Civil Service** all the various national government departments 〔政府中的〕文職部門: *She is a member of the civil service.* 她是個公務員。 | *The Civil Ser-*

vice has a great deal of power. 政府機構的權
限很大。–see 見 OFFICER (USAGE 用法)

civil war /ˌ·· ·'·/ *n* [C;U] a war between opposing groups of people who live in the
same country 內戰: *the American Civil War*
美國內戰

clad /klæd; klæd/ *adj* [never before a noun
不能用於名詞前] *lit*〖文〗**clad in** wearing or
covered 穿着; 覆蓋: *The old lady was clad in
a fur coat.* 那位老婦人穿着毛皮外套。| *The
mountain was clad in mist.* 山被一片薄霧籠
罩。

★★claim¹ /klem; kleɪm/ *v* **1** [I;T] to say
that something belongs to you
as a right 聲稱〔某物〕為自己所有: *Old people
are able to claim a special heating allowance
from the government.* 老年人可以向政府索取
一筆特別的暖氣津貼。| *Did you claim on
the insurance after your car accident?* 車禍
之後你向保險公司索賠了嗎? | *You are
entitled to claim for your travelling expenses.*
你有權報銷你的差旅費。**2** [+(that)] to say
that something is true, even if there is no
proof 聲稱〔某事〕為真: *He claims to be rich.*
他自稱很富有。| *She claimed that she was
the true Queen.* 她自稱是真正的女王。

> □ USEFUL PATTERNS 有用句型
> to claim to be something; to claim to
> have done something; to claim that…

3 claim lives (of a natural event such as a
flood) to kill people〔洪水等自然災害〕奪去
人的生命: *The earthquake claimed hundreds
of lives.* 地震奪去了數以百計的人的生命。

★★claim² *n* **1** a demand for something as
a right 要求: *The government
would not even consider his claim for
money.* 政府甚至不考慮他索款的要求。| *She
put in a claim for her travelling expenses.* 她
申請出差費。**2** a right to something 權利:
*He has a rightful claim to the property — it
was his mother's.* 他對那筆財產有合法的所有
權——那是他母親留下的。**3** a statement that
something is true, especially one that
other people disagree with〔尤指他人持有
異議的〕主張; 聲稱: *His claim about the
number of people killed in the war was
clearly mistaken.* 他對戰爭死亡人數的聲明顯
然有誤。| *His claim to be the richest man in
England has been disputed.* 他自稱是英國最
富有的人, 但這受到了大家的質疑。**4 claim to
fame** a reason for being famous 成名的原
因: *The town's only claim to fame is that it
has the biggest car park in the country.* 這座
城鎮出名的唯一原因是它擁有國內最大的停車
場。**5 lay claim to something** to say that
something belongs to you as a right 聲稱某
物為己所有 –**claimant** *n*

clair·voy·ant /kleɪˈvɔɪənt; kleəˈvɔɪənt/ *n* a
person who says that they are able to see
what will happen in the future 自稱可預見

未來的人 –**clairvoyant** *adj*: *clairvoyant
powers* 預見未來的能力 –**clairvoyance** *n* [U]

clam¹ /klæm; klæm/ *n* a kind of SHELLFISH
蛤; 蚌

clam² *v* -mm-

clam up *phr v* [I] *infml* to become silent,
especially because of fear or unwillingness
to give information〖非正式〗〔尤因恐懼或不
情願而〕沉默不語

clam·ber /ˈklæmbə; ˈklæmbər/ *v* [I + adv/
prep] to climb over something with difficulty, using both your hands and your feet
〔費力地〕攀爬: *Their wretched children
wouldn't stop clambering over my furniture.*
他們那幾個討厭的孩子在我的家具上不停地爬
來爬去。

clam·my /ˈklæmi; ˈklæmi/ *adj* unpleasantly
warm and sticky 黏乎乎: *clammy hands* 黏濕
的手 | *clammy weather* 潮濕的天氣

clam·our¹ /ˈklæmə; ˈklæmər/ *n* (**clamor**
AmE〖美式〗) **1** [sing] a loud confused
noise or shouting 吵鬧聲; 喧嚷聲: *a clamour
of voices* 鼎沸的人聲 **2** [U] a continuous
strong demand or complaint made by a
large number of people〔許多人連續不斷
的〕強烈要求[抱怨]聲: *ignoring the public
clamour for lower taxes* 對公眾強烈要求降低
稅收的呼聲置之不理

clamour² *v* (**clamor** *AmE*〖美式〗) [I;T] to
express a strong demand for something,
often noisily〔通常是大聲地〕強烈要求: *The
children were clamouring to be fed.* 孩子們吵
着要東西吃。| *They are clamouring for rad-
ical changes in the organization.* 他們強烈要
求對機構進行徹底的改革。

clamp¹ /klæmp; klæmp/ *n* an apparatus for
fastening or holding things firmly together
鉗子; 夾子: *The police are using wheel
clamps to stop cars from parking here.* 警方
使用輪胎夾來防止有人把車停在此處。

clamp² *v* [T] to fasten something with a
clamp 用鉗子夾住〔某物〕: *He clamped the
two pieces of wood together.* 他把兩塊木頭用
鉗子夾緊。

clamp down *phr v* [I] to become firmer
in order to control a situation 嚴格管理:
*The police are going to clamp down on
parking in this area.* 警方準備對該地區的車
輛停放實行嚴格管理。

clamp-down /ˈklæmp.daʊn; ˈklæmpdaʊn/
n infml a sudden official effort to control a
particular activity〖非正式〗打擊; 嚴禁: *The
Government has decided to have a
clampdown on drunken driving.* 政府已決定
嚴禁酒後駕車。

clan /klæn; klæn/ *n* **1** especially in Scotland,
a large group of families all related to one
another and having the same name〔尤指
在蘇格蘭〕宗族; 大家族 **2** a large group of
people related in some way (a word which
is often used in a humorous way) 幫派〔常
含幽默〕

clan·des·tine /klæn'dɛstɪn; klæn'dɛstɨn/ *adj fml* existing or done secretly, and often illegal 〔正式〕〔通常非法而〕祕密的: *a clandestine organization* 一個地下組織

clang /klæŋ; klæŋ/ *v* [I;T] to make a loud, metallic ringing noise 發出叮噹聲: *The prison gate clanged shut.* 監獄大門噹啷一聲關上了。 –**clang** *n* [sing]: *The iron gate shut with a heavy clang.* 鐵門重重地砰的一聲關上了。

clang·er /'klæŋə; 'klæŋɚ/ *n infml* 〔非正式〕 **drop a clanger** to make a very noticeable mistake or an unfortunate remark 犯明顯的錯誤; 說了不適當的話: *She dropped a clanger when she mentioned his ex-wife.* 她說了句不該說的話, 提及到他的前妻。

clank /klæŋk; klæŋk/ *v* [I;T] to make a loud metallic sound 發出噹啷聲: *The prisoner's chains clanked as he walked.* 囚犯走路時, 腳鏈發出了噹啷聲。

clap[1] /klæp; klæp/ *v* **-pp- 1** [I;T] to bring your open hands together with a quick movement and loud sound, especially to show approval or excitement 〔尤指表示贊同或激動時〕拍手: *The teacher clapped her hands to attract the class's attention.* 老師拍拍手以吸引全班同學的注意力。 | *The audience had enjoyed the play, and clapped loudly.* 觀眾非常欣賞這齣戲, 並大聲鼓掌。 **2 clap someone on the back** to hit someone lightly on the back with your open hand in a friendly manner because you are pleased 〔表示高興而友好地〕拍拍某人的背部 **3 not clap eyes on someone** *infml* not to see someone at all for a period 〔非正式〕一段時間內一直未見某人: *She went off with my money, and I haven't clapped eyes on her since.* 她拿走了我的錢, 自那以後我再也沒有見到她。 **4** [T + adv/prep] to put or place something into a particular place or position 把〔某物〕置於: *She immediately realised she had said the wrong thing and clapped her hand over her mouth.* 她馬上意識到自己講錯了話, 用手捂住了嘴。 **5 clap someone in prison** to put someone in prison 把某人關進監獄

clap[2] *n* **1** a sudden loud explosive sound 突然的轟聲: *a clap of thunder* 一聲雷鳴 **2 clap on the back** a light friendly hit on the back with an open hand 〔友善地〕輕拍〔某人〕背部: *He gave me a clap on the back.* 他輕輕地在我背上拍了一下。 **3 give someone a clap** to clap someone's performance 為某人的演出鼓掌: *Come on, everyone, give him a clap!* 大家來給他鼓鼓掌! **4 the clap** *slang* the disease GONORRHEA 〔俚〕淋病

clap·per /'klæpə; 'klæpɚ/ *n* the small metal object hung inside a bell which strikes it to make it ring 鐘錘; 鈴的擊錘

clap·trap /'klæptræp; 'klæptræp/ *n* [U] *infml* silly or insincere remarks that should not be believed 〔非正式〕不可信的蠢話; 胡說: *What a load of claptrap!* 真是一派胡言!

clar·i·fy /'klærəfaɪ; 'klærɨfaɪ/ *v* **clarified, clarifying** [T] to make something easier to understand by explaining it more fully 澄清〔某事〕; 講清楚: *When will the government clarify its position on equal pay for women?* 政府會在甚麼時候對婦女同工同酬問題闡明立場?– **clarification** /ˌklærəfə'keɪʃən; ˌklærɨfɨ'keɪʃən/ *n* [C;U]: *He asked for clarification of the government's position.* 他要求政府澄清立場。

clar·i·net /ˌklærə'nɛt; ˌklærɨ'nɛt/ *n* a tube-like musical instrument made of wood that you play by blowing 單簧管; 豎笛

clar·i·ty /'klærətɪ; 'klærɨtɪ/ *n* [U] **1** the quality of speaking or thinking clearly 〔講話或思路的〕清晰: *He possesses great clarity of mind.* 他思路很清晰。 | *She put forward her argument with great clarity.* 她很清楚地提出了論據。 **2** the ability to be seen or heard clearly 清楚; 明確: *the clarity of the painter's brush-strokes* 畫家繪畫筆觸的明確清晰 | *the clarity of her voice* 她清脆的嗓音

clash[1] /klæʃ; klæʃ/ *v* **1** [I] to come into opposition with someone or something 與〔某人或某物〕衝突: *The violent mob clashed with the police.* 暴民與警察發生了衝突。 | *Our suggestions tend to clash.* 我們的建議有所衝突。 **2** [I] (of two colours or styles) not to look nice together 〔兩種顏色或風格〕不相配, 不協調: *Her orange blouse clashes with her pink lipstick.* 她那橘黃色的襯衫與粉紅色的唇膏不相配。 **3** [I] (of two or more events) to happen, inconveniently, at the same time 〔事件〕同時發生: *I couldn't go to their wedding as it clashed with my holiday.* 我不能參加他們的婚禮, 因為這與我的休假撞了期。 **4** [I;T] to make a loud noise by hitting metal objects against each other 使〔金屬碰撞〕發出撞擊聲

clash[2] *n* **1** a fight or struggle 戰鬥; 衝突: *The government has reported clashes on its border.* 政府報道說在邊境上發生了衝突。 **2** an argument or disagreement 爭論; 衝突: *a clash of interests* 利益上的衝突 **3** a loud metallic noise 〔金屬的〕撞擊聲: *a clash of cymbals* 鐃鈸的撞擊聲

clasp[1] /klæsp; klɑːsp/ *n* **1** a small metal fastener for holding two things together or for shutting something 扣子; 鈎: *the clasp on a belt* 皮帶上的扣子 **2** a tight firm hold, by the hand or in your arms 緊握; 緊抱

clasp[2] *v* [T] **1** to hold something firmly 緊握〔某物〕: *He clasped the money in his hands.* 他把錢緊緊地抓在手裡。 **2** to fasten something with a clasp 扣住, 鈎住〔某物〕

☆class[1] /klæs; klɑːs/ *n* **classes 1** [C+sing/pl verb] a group of pupils or students who are taught together 班級: *a class of 30 children* 有三十個學生的一個班 | *Our class is reading "Macbeth" at the moment.* 我們班現正在讀《麥克白》這篇劇作。 **2** [C;U] a period of time during which pupils or students are taught (一節)課: *What time does the next class begin?* 下一節課甚麼時候開始? | *Don't talk in class!* 課堂上不要講話! **3** [U] the way that a society is divided into different social groups 社會等級: *Class differences can divide a nation.* 社會等級差異會使國家分裂。| *Is education class-based?* 教育是不是以階級為基礎的? **4** [C] (also 又作 **classes** [pl]) a group of people whose members are similar socially and politically 〔社會〕階層; 〔政治〕階級: *Most of the middle class now take their holidays abroad.* 大部分中產階級現在國外度假。| *the working class* 工人階級 | *the upper class* 上層階級 | *the ruling classes* 統治階級 **5** [C] a group of things which have similar characteristics 類別; 種類: *four main word-classes: nouns, verbs, adjectives, and adverbs* 四大詞類: 名詞、動詞、形容詞和副詞 **6** [C] a level of quality for people and things 〔人或物的〕等級: *"What class is your degree?" "I got a third."* 你得的是幾等學位? 「我得了三等。」| *A first-class ticket to Birmingham, please.* 請給我一張去伯明翰的頭等票。**7 be in a class of your own** to be special and different 與眾不同 **8 have class** to have a stylish quality that attracts admiration 具有吸引人的特質: *She dresses beautifully. She's got real class.* 她穿戴得很美, 很是優雅。

class² *v* [T] to state that someone or something belongs in a particular group or type 把〔某人或某物〕歸類: *British women are classed as senior citizens when they are sixty.* 英國婦女到六十歲時, 便被列為老年人。

class-con·scious /ˈ· ˌ··/ *adj* **1** conscious of the importance of social class 有階級覺悟的 **2** very conscious of your own position in society and, usually, thinking that the upper classes are better than the lower classes 有社會等級意識的〔通常認為上等階級優於下等階級〕

*★***clas·sic¹** /ˈklæsɪk; ˈklæsɪk/ *adj* **1** having the highest quality and being of lasting importance 第一流的; 最好的; 不朽的: *It's a classic film — I can't wait to see it again.* 這是部經典影片 — 我真想再看一遍。**2** belonging to a simple and formal style 式樣簡樸的; 傳統式樣的: *a classic dress* 素雅的服裝 | *a classic building* 傳統建築 **3** of a very typical and well-known kind 典型的; 模範的: *She is a classic example of a good teacher.* 她是一個優秀教師的典範。

classic² *n* **1** a highly-praised work of literature of lasting importance 經典文學作品; 傑作: *That book is one of the classics of English literature.* 那部書是英國文學中的經典作品之一。| *a modern classic* 現代佳作 **2** *infml* the best example of something 〔非正式〕典範; 模範: *That joke's a classic. It really is funny!* 那則笑話真是經典。實在是太有趣了! **3 classics** [pl] the languages, literature,

and history of ancient Greece and Rome 古希臘和古羅馬的語言、文學和歷史

*★***clas·si·cal** /ˈklæsɪk̩l; ˈklæsɪkəl/ *adj* **1** (also 又作 **Classical**) in the style of ancient Greek or Roman models in literature or art 〔文學或藝術〕古希臘羅馬風格的: *classical literature* 古典文學 **2** written with serious artistic intentions and having lasting value (used of music) 古典的, 經典的〔指音樂〕: *I prefer pop music to classical music.* 我比較喜歡流行音樂, 不大喜愛古典音樂。**3** based on an old or established system of principles and methods 傳統的; 古典的: *Galileo challenged the classical views on the solar system.* 伽利略挑戰關於太陽系的傳統觀點。

clas·si·fi·ca·tion /ˌklæsəfəˈkeʃən; ˌklæsḷfḷˈkeɪʃən/ *n* **1** [U] the act of classifying people or things into groups 〔把人或物〕分類: *The classification of all the library books took longer than we'd expected.* 把圖書館裡所有的書分類所花的時間比我們預料的要長。**2** [C] a division within a group 類別; 種類

clas·si·fied /ˈklæsᵻˌfaɪd; ˈklæsḷfaɪd/ *adj* **1** officially secret (used of government, especially military, information) 機密的〔指政府情報, 尤指軍事情報〕**2** divided or arranged in classes 分門別類的 **3 classified ad** a small advertisement placed in a newspaper by a person wishing to sell or buy something 分類廣告

*★***clas·si·fy** /ˈklæsəˌfaɪ; ˈklæsḷfaɪ/ *v* **classified, classifying** [T] to arrange or place people or things into groups or types 把〔人或物〕分類: *Whales are classified as mammals, not fish.* 鯨魚被劃分為哺乳動物, 而不是魚類。

*★***class·room** /ˈklæsˌrum; ˈklɑːsrʊm/ *n* a room in a school or college in which a class meets for a lesson 教室; 課堂

class·y /ˈklæsɪ; ˈklɑːsɪ/ *adj* **classier, classiest** *infml* stylish and fashionable, especially in an upper-class way 〔非正式〕時髦的; 高級的

clat·ter /ˈklætə; ˈklætər/ *v* [I;T] to make a number of short, loud sounds by knocking things against each other 發出撞擊聲: *The metal dish clattered down the stone stairs.* 金屬盤子嘩啦嘩啦地沿着石階滾了下去。**–clatter** *n* [sing;U]: *the clatter of the printing machines* 印刷機的嘎嘎聲 | *a clatter of pots and pans* 鍋和盤的碰撞聲

*★***clause** /klɔz; klɔːz/ *n* **1** in grammar, a group of words containing a subject and a FINITE verb, usually forming only part of a sentence. In "She came home when she was tired," "She came home" and "when she was tired" are two separate clauses. 〔文法中的〕子句, 從句〔如在 "She came home when she was tired." 一句中, "She came home" 和 "when she was tired" 是兩個子句〕 **–compare** 比較 PHRASE, SENTENCE **2** a separate part or division of a written legal agreement 〔合約的〕條款

claus·tro·pho·bi·a /ˌklɔstrə'fəʊbɪə; ˌklɔ:strə-
'fəʊbiə/ n [U] fear of being enclosed in a
small closed space 幽閉恐怖症: I suffer from
claustrophobia. 我患有幽閉恐怖症。 **–claus-
trophobic** adj

claw¹ /klɔ; klɔ:/ n **1** a sharp curved nail on
the foot of an animal or bird 〔動物或鳥類
的〕爪 **2** a limb of certain insects and
sea animals such as CRABS, used for attacking
and holding objects 〔某些昆蟲和蟹等海生動
物的〕鉗, 螯

claw² v [I;T] to tear, seize, or pull with a
sharp movement 撕; 奪; 拉: The cat clawed
at the leg of the table. 貓用爪子在桌腿上抓
撓。 | He clawed a hole in my tights. 他在我
的緊身衣上撕開了一個洞。

claw sthg ↔ **back** phr v [T] to get something back with great difficulty or effort 奪
回〔某物〕

clay /kle; kleɪ/ n [U] heavy grey or red earth
which becomes hard when baked at a high
temperature and is used for making pots 黏
土

☆clean¹ /klin; kli:n/ adj **1** free from dirt 乾淨
的; 清潔的: Are your hands clean? 你的雙手
乾淨嗎? | clean clothes 乾淨的衣服 **2** not
yet used 未用過的: a clean piece of paper 一
張還沒有用過的紙 **3** morally or sexually
pure 〔道德或性方面〕純潔的: He led a clean
life. 他過着清白的生活。 | a clean joke 正經
的笑話 **4** not disobeying rules or laws 守規
則的; 合法的: a clean fight 守規則的拳擊比
賽 | a clean driving licence 無違章記錄的駕
駛執照 **5** having a smooth even edge or
surface 邊緣〔表面〕光滑的: a clean cut 乾淨
利落的切割 | the aircraft's clean lines 飛機
平滑均稱的線條 **6 clean sweep: a** a complete removal or change 徹底去除; 徹底改
變: He was anxious to make a clean sweep
of all the old ideas. 他急於將所有舊觀念徹底
改變。 **b** a complete victory in which the
winner wins every part of a competition 勝
利; 大獲全勝: Germany has made a clean
sweep of the swimming events. 德國在游泳項
目上大獲全勝。 **7 come clean** infml to admit
your guilt and tell the unpleasant truth 〔非
正式〕承認罪行; 說出真相: Why don't you
come clean and tell us your real plans? 你為
什麼不坦白說出你真正的計劃?

☆clean² v [I;T] to make something free from
dirt 打掃乾淨; 清潔: I shall have to clean the
windows. I can hardly see out! 我得把窗子擦
一擦。我幾乎看不到外面的東西了! **–clean** n
[sing]: I must give the windows a good
clean. 我必須好好擦一擦下玻璃窗。 **–cleaning**
n [U]: We have a lady to do the cleaning for
us. 我們雇了位女士給我們做清潔工作。

clean out phr v **1** [T clean sthg ↔ out] to
make something thoroughly clean and tidy
把〔某物〕徹底打掃乾淨 **2** [T clean sbdy ↔
out] infml to take all the money belonging
to a person 〔非正式〕耗盡〔某人〕的錢財 **3** [T

clean sthg ↔ **out**] to steal everything from
a place 把〔某處〕盜竊一空: The thieves
cleaned out the store. 那些小偷把商店洗劫一
空。

clean up phr v **1** [I;T **clean** sthg ↔ **up**] to
make something clean or tidy 把〔某物〕打掃
乾淨; 清理: It's your turn to clean up. 輪到你
來做清潔工作了。 | Can you clean up those
pieces of broken bottle? 你能把那些瓶子碎片
清理掉嗎? **2** [T **clean** sthg ↔ **up**] to make a
place free from crime 掃蕩罪惡: The police
have begun a campaign to clean up the inner cities. 警方發動了一場整頓市中心的滅罪
運動。

clean up after sbdy phr v [T] to clean and
put away things that someone else has
made dirty or untidy 把〔別人弄髒或弄亂的
的物品〕收拾乾淨: If you're a housewife, you
seem to spend your whole life cleaning up
after other people. 你如果是個家庭主婦的話,
你好像終身都要替別人收拾東西。

clean³ adv infml completely 〔非正式〕徹底
地; 完全地: The bullet went clean through his
arm. 子彈直穿過他的手臂。 | I clean forgot
his birthday. 我把他的生日忘記得一乾二淨。

clean-cut /ˌ·'·◄/ adj neat and clean in appearance 〔外表〕整潔的

clean·er /'klinə; 'kli:nər/ n **1** a person
whose job is to clean the inside of a building 〔大樓裡的〕清潔工人 **2** a person whose
job is to clean a particular thing 清潔工人:
a window cleaner 窗戶清潔工 **3** a machine
or substance used for cleaning 清潔器; 清潔
劑: a vacuum cleaner 真空吸塵器 **4 cleaner's**
a shop where you can have clothes or material cleaned with chemicals instead of
water 乾洗店 **5 take someone to the
cleaner's** infml to make someone lose all
their money, especially by dishonesty 〔非正
式〕騙光某人的錢

clean·li·ness /'klɛnlɪnəs; 'klenlinəs/ n [U]
the habit of keeping clean 愛清潔的習慣)

clean·ly /'klinlɪ; 'kli:nli/ adv in a neat way,
without making any mess 整齊地: The knife
cut cleanly through the cake. 小刀俐落地把
蛋糕切開。

cleanse /klɛnz; klenz/ v cleansed, cleansing
[T] fml to make a cut or wound free from
dirt 〔正式〕清洗〔傷口〕

cleans·er /'klɛnzə; 'klenzər/ n [C;U] a substance used for cleaning your skin 〔皮膚〕清
潔劑

clean-shav·en /ˌ·'··◄/ adj having no hair on
the lower part of your face 鬍鬚刮得乾淨的

☆☆clear¹ /klɪr; klɪər/ adj **1** easy to see
through 透明的: clear glass 透明的
玻璃 **2** free from anything that marks or
darkens 清澈的; 潔淨的: a clear sky 晴朗的天
空 | clear skin 潔淨的皮膚 **3** free from any-
thing that blocks or prevents 無障礙的; 無覆蓋
的: a clear view 開闊的視野 | The road's
clear of snow now. 道路上現在沒有積雪。 **4**

free from other planned activity 無其他活動安排的: *I see that next week is clear. Let's meet then.* 我看下個星期有空。我們那時候會面吧。 **5** easy to hear, read, or understand 容易聽清〔讀懂、理解〕的: *a clear speaker* 説話清楚的人 | *a clear style of writing* 淺白易懂的寫作風格 | *The instructions aren't very clear.* 説明書不太容易看懂。 **6 get something clear** to come to understand something 弄明白某事物: *I'll go on to the second point if everybody's got the first point clear.* 如果大家都已聽懂第一點，那我就接着講第二點了。 **7 make something clear** to tell someone something or explain it to them so that they understand it 使〔某人〕理解某事物 **8** able to think and understand quickly and well 思維清楚的; 清醒的: *a clear thinker* 頭腦敏鋭的思想家 | *Don't drink too much. You want to keep a clear head for your interview.* 別喝太多酒了。你要保持清醒的頭腦去參加面試。 **9** impossible to doubt, question, or be mistaken about 明白無誤的; 明顯的: *a clear case of murder* 一椿無可置疑的謀殺案 | *She's made her feelings quite clear.* 她已表明了她的感情。 | *It's becoming clear to most people that the Government was wrong.* 對大多數人來説，政府(的政策)有錯這一點是越來越清楚了。 | *It isn't yet clear whether these changes have had any effect.* 目前還不清楚這些變化有甚麼影響。 **10** [never before a noun 不能用於名詞前] feeling certain 肯定的; 有把握的: *She seems quite clear* **about** *her plans.* 她似乎對她的計劃相當有把握。 | *I'm still not clear how it works.* 我還是弄不清楚這東西是怎樣操作的。 **11** free from guilt or blame 清白的; 無內疚的: *a clear conscience* 問心無愧 **12 do I make myself clear?** = do you understand? (a phrase you use when you are annoyed with someone) 你明白我的話嗎?〔用於表示對某人不滿〕 **–clearness** *n* [U]

clear² *adv* **1** out of the way, so as to be no longer inside or near 不接觸; 不靠近; 躲開: *She jumped clear* **of** *the train.* 她縱身一跳，避開了火車。 **2** completely 徹底地; 完全地: *The prisoner got clear away.* 囚犯逃得無影無蹤。

★clear³ *v* **1** [I] to become clear 變清澈; 變清潔: *After the storm the sky cleared.* 暴風雨後，天空晴朗了。 **2** [T] to make something clear 使〔某物〕變得清潔: *This soap should help clear your skin.* 這肥皂應該有助於使你的皮膚變得光潔。 **3** [T + adv/prep] to remove something that is not wanted 把〔不需要的東西〕拿走〔移走〕: *Will you clear the plates away?* 你能把盤子收起來嗎? | *Whose job is it to clear snow* **from** *the road?* 誰負責掃清路上的雪? | *I'll just clear all these papers* **off** *the table.* 我馬上就把所有這些報紙從桌上拿走。 **4** [T] to declare someone to be free from blame 宣告〔某人〕無罪: *He was cleared* **of** *murder, but found guilty of dangerous driving.* 他被證明沒有犯謀殺罪，但被判犯有危險駕駛罪。 **5** [T] to give someone official

permission for something 批准〔某事物〕: *The plans for the new school have not yet been cleared by the council.* 建造新學校的計劃還未得到市政委員會的批准。 **6 clear something with someone** to get official permission for something from someone 使某事物得到某人正式許可: *You can't begin until you've cleared it with the headmaster.* 得不到校長的許可，你不能開始做這件事。 **7** [T] to pass by or over something without touching it 越過〔某物〕: *The horse easily cleared every fence.* 馬輕易地越過每一道柵欄。 **8** [T] to repay a debt in full 還清〔債務〕: *You ought to clear your debts before thinking about another holiday.* 你應該把債還清後才考慮再去度假。 **9 clear the air** to remove doubt and bad feeling by honest explanation 〔以誠實的解釋〕消除疑慮 **10 clear your throat** to cough, often in order to get attention〔通常為引起注意而〕清清嗓子

clear away *phr v* [I;T **clear** sthg ↔ **away**] to make an area tidy by removing things to their proper places 清除; 收拾: *Has everybody finished eating? Can I clear away?* 大家都吃完了嗎? 我能收拾碗筷了吧?

clear off *phr v* [I] *infml* to leave a place, often quickly《非正式》迅速離開〔某地〕: *Clear off, you boys!* 你們這些男孩快走開!

clear out *phr v* **1** [I] *infml* to leave a place《非正式》離開〔某地〕: *cleared out* **of** *the house* 離開房子 **2** [T **clear** sthg ↔ **out**] to collect and throw away unwanted objects 清理掉〔不需要的東西〕: *I decided to clear out all the old clothes that we never wear.* 我決定把我們不穿的舊衣服全部清理掉。 **3** [T **clear** sthg ↔ **out**] to empty something of unwanted objects 把〔某物〕收拾乾淨: *I'm going to clear out my desk.* 我準備把我的書桌整理乾淨。

clear up *phr v* **1** [I;T **clear** sthg ↔ **up**] to tidy up or put things in order 整理; 收拾: *Can you clear up before he arrives please?* 在他到達之前，你能收拾一下嗎? | *I've lots of work to clear up by the weekend.* 週末以前我有許多事情要辦。 **2** [T **clear** sthg ↔ **up**] to find an answer to something 找出答案: *to clear up the mystery* 揭開奧祕 | *Let's try and clear up the misunderstanding.* 我們來試試消除誤會吧。 **3** [I] (of a situation) to get better〔情形〕好轉: *I hope the weather clears up before Sunday.* 我希望天氣能在星期天以前轉晴。 | *My cold has cleared up at last.* 我的感冒終於好了。

clear⁴ *n* in the clear *infml*《非正式》**a** not in danger 沒有危險 **b** not to be blamed or thought guilty 無罪的: *He's got an alibi, so he's in the clear.* 他有不在現場的證明，所以他無罪。

clear·ance /ˈklɪrəns; ˈklɪrərəns/ *n* **1** [U] the removal of things that are not wanted 清理，清除: *a programme of slum clearance* 拆除貧民窟的計劃 **2** [C;U] the act or result of

getting permission or approval 同意; 獲准:
*The ship sailed as soon as it got clearance
from the port authority.* 這艘船一向港口當局
辦好離港手續便起航了。**3** [C;U] the distance between one object and another one
passing beneath or beside it 間隔; 距離: *The
clearance between the bridge and the top of
the bus was only ten centimetres.* 橋與公共汽
車車頂之間的距離只有十公分。**4** [C;U] a
sale of goods at lower prices 清倉大甩賣: *a
shop clearance* 商店清倉大甩賣

clear-cut /ˌ· ˈ·◂/ *adj* **1** clear in meaning〔意
思〕清楚的; 明白的: *We now have clear-cut
plans for future action.* 我們現在對將來的行
動有了明確的計劃。**2** having a smooth and
regular shape 外形光滑勻稱的

clear-head-ed /ˌ· ˈ··◂/ *adj* able to think
clearly and sensibly 頭腦清醒的

clear-ing /ˈklɪrɪŋ; ˈklɪərɪŋ/ *n* a small area of
land that has been cleared of trees inside a
larger area of trees〔森林中樹木砍伐後的〕
空地

clear·ly /ˈklɪrlɪ; ˈklɪəli/ *adv* **1** in a clear
manner 清楚地; 清晰地: *He
spoke very clearly. I could hear every word.* 他講
話很清楚。每一個字我都聽得見。| *The bottle
was clearly labelled.* 瓶子上的標籤貼得很清楚。
2 without any doubt 確定無疑地; 顯然地:
That's clearly a mistake. 那顯然是個錯誤。|
Clearly, he's getting too old for this job. 顯然, 他
做這項工作年紀太大了。

clear-sight-ed /ˌ· ˈ··◂/ *adj* able to make
good judgments 有眼光的

cleav·age /ˈklɪvɪdʒ; ˈkliːvɪdʒ/ *n* **1** the space
between a woman's breasts, especially that
which can be seen when she is wearing a
low-cut dress〔婦女的〕乳溝 **2** *fml* a division
or disagreement between people〔正式〕分
歧; 分裂: *a sharp cleavage in society* **between**
rich and poor 社會上貧富的懸殊差別

cleave /kliv; kliːv/ *v* **cleaved** or **cleft** /klɛft;
klɛft/ or **clove** /klov; kləʊv/, **cleaved** or **cleft**
or **cloven** /ˈklovən; ˈkləʊvən/, **cleaving** [T]
lit to divide or separate something by a
cutting blow〔文〕劈開; 砍開

cleav·er /ˈklɪvə; ˈkliːvəʳ/ *n* an tool like an
AXE, used especially for cutting up large
pieces of meat 剁肉刀

clef /klɛf; klef/ *n* a special sign put at the
beginning of a line of written music to
show how high or low the notes should be
played〔音樂〕譜號

cleft /klɛft; kleft/ the past tense and past
participle of CLEAVE ☆ CLEAVE 的過去式
和過去分詞

clem·en·cy /ˈklɛmənsɪ; ˈklemənsi/ *n fml* [U]
mercy, especially when shown in making
punishment less severe〔正式〕仁慈; 寬容
〔尤指在量刑時〕

clench /klɛntʃ; klentʃ/ *v* [T] to close or hold
tightly 緊合; 緊握: *She clenched her teeth.* 她
咬緊牙關。| *He clenched his money in his*
hand. 他把錢緊緊握在手裡。| *a clenched
fist* 握緊的拳頭

cler·gy /ˈklɜdʒɪ; ˈklɜːdʒi/ *n* [pl] priests, especially in the Christian church, who are
allowed to perform religious services 神職
人員,〔尤指基督教的〕牧師: *the power of the
clergy* 牧師的權力

cler·gy·man /ˈklɜdʒɪmən; ˈklɜːdʒimən/ *n*
clergymen /-mən; -mən/ a member of the
clergy 教士; 牧師 –see 見 PRIEST (USAGE
用法)

cler·i·cal /ˈklɛrɪkl; ˈklerɪkəl/ *adj* **1** relating to
the work of an office clerk 職員工作的; 文
書的: *We're looking for a new clerical assistant.* 我們正在物色一個新的文書助理。**2** relating to or concerning the clergy 神職人員
的; 教士的; 牧師的

clerk /klɑk; klɑːk/ *n* **1** a person employed to
keep records and accounts, and to do general office work 職員; 文書 **2** an official in
charge of the records of a court, town
council, etc.〔法庭、議會中的〕書記員

clev·er /ˈklɛvə; ˈklevəʳ/ *adj* **1** having a quick
and able mind 聰明的: *a clever student* 聰明
的學生 | *a clever worker* 聰明的工人 **2**
showing that someone has a quick and
able mind 顯示出〔某人〕聰明的: *a clever idea*
巧妙的主意 **3** showing ability or skill with
your hands or body 熟練的; 靈巧的: *He's
very clever with his hands.* 他的雙手很靈
巧。–**cleverly** *adv* –**cleverness** *n* [U]

cli·ché /ˈkliːʃe; ˈkliːʃeɪ/ *n* an idea or expression used so commonly that it has lost
much of its meaning and effectiveness (a
word used to express disapproval) 老生常
談; 陳詞濫調〔含貶義〕

click¹ /klɪk; klɪk/ *n* a short sharp sound, such
as the noise of a key turning in a lock 喀嚓
聲; 卡嗒聲

click² *v* **1** [I;T] to make a short sharp sound
發出喀嚓聲: *The door clicked shut.* 門卡嗒一
聲關上了。| *She clicked her fingers to get
the waiter's attention.* 她打了個響指以引起侍
應生的注意。**2** [I] *infml* suddenly to become
clear to someone〔非正式〕恍然大悟: *Her
joke suddenly clicked and we all laughed.* 我
們突然明白了她笑話的含意而大笑起來。**3** [I]
infml to find that you like someone〔非正
式〕發覺喜歡某人: *They clicked immediately.*
他們一見鍾情。

cli·ent /ˈklaɪənt; ˈklaɪənt/ *n* a person
who pays a professional person
or organization for help and advice 委託人;
當事人 –see 見 CUSTOMER (USAGE 用法)

cliff /klɪf; klɪf/ *n* a high very steep face of
rock on a coast〔海岸的〕懸崖: *the white
cliffs of Dover* 多佛爾海邊的白色懸崖

cliff-hang-er /ˈklɪfˌhæŋə; ˈklɪfˌhæŋəʳ/ *n*
infml a story or competition which is exciting because the result is in doubt until the
very end〔非正式〕〔直到最後結果才見分曉
的〕扣人心弦的故事[競賽]: *The game was a*

real cliffhanger. 這是一場真正扣人心弦的比賽。

cli·mac·tic /klaɪˈmæktɪk; klaɪˈmæktɪk/ *adj* forming the most exciting part of something 高潮的; 頂點的

★**cli·mate** /ˈklaɪmɪt; ˈklaɪmɪt/ *n* **1** the average weather conditions at a particular place 氣候: *a tropical climate* 熱帶性氣候 **2** the state of affairs or general feeling at a particular time 氣氛; 風氣: *The present political climate makes an election unlikely.* 在當前的政治氣候下, 進行大選的可能性不大。| *They live in a climate of fear.* 他們生活在恐懼的氣氛裡。

cli·mat·ic /klaɪˈmætɪk; klaɪˈmætɪk/ *adj* relating to the climate of a place 氣候的: *The climatic conditions were good.* 氣候情況很好。

cli·max¹ /ˈklaɪmæks; ˈklaɪmæks/ *n* **1** the most exciting or important part of a story or some action, usually happening near the end 頂點; 巔峰; 高潮: *the climax of the film* 電影的高潮 | *the climax of her career* 她職業生涯的巔峰 **2** the highest point of sexual pleasure 性高潮

climax² *v* [I] to reach the most exciting or important part 達到高潮: *a life of service to the nation, climaxing in her appointment as President* 她為國家服務的一生, 以當上總統而達到了巔峰

★**climb¹** /klaɪm; klaɪm/ *v* **1** [I;T] to move towards the top of something such as a hill or tree 爬; 攀登: *Do you think you can climb that tree?* 你認為你能爬上那棵樹嗎? | *He climbed up the ladder.* 他爬上了梯子。—see picture on page 992 見 992 頁彩圖 **2** [I] to rise 上升: *The plane climbed quickly.* 飛機迅速上升。| *The road climbed steeply up the hill.* 這條路陡峭地通向山上。**3** [I; +adv/prep] to move with difficulty, especially into or out of a small space 費力地爬〔尤指爬過小的空間〕: *She climbed into the car.* 她鑽進汽車裡。| *He climbed out of the window.* 他爬出了窗外。| *We managed to climb down the cliff.* 我們設法從懸崖爬下來。

　climb down *phr v* [I] *infml* to admit that you were wrong about something 〔非正式〕承認做錯某事

climb² *n* **1** a journey upwards made by climbing 攀爬; 爬升: *It was a two-hour climb to the top.* 爬到頂需要兩小時。**2** a steep slope 陡坡: *There was a steep climb on the road out of town.* 鎮外的公路上有一處很陡的坡。

climb·er /ˈklaɪmə; ˈklaɪməʳ/ *n* **1** a person who climbs mountains 爬山者: *a famous mountain climber* 著名的登山運動員 **2** a plant that climbs 攀緣植物

clinch /klɪntʃ; klɪntʃ/ *v* [T] **1** *infml* to settle an agreement 〔非正式〕達成〔協議〕: *The two businessmen clinched the deal quickly.* 兩位生意人很快便達成了交易。**2** to cause some-

one to reach a clear decision 使〔某人〕下定決心: *That clinches it — I'm not going.* 那件事使我打定了主意——我不去。

cling /klɪŋ; klɪŋ/ *v* **clung** /klʌŋ; klʌŋ/, **clung** [I] **1** to hold tightly to something or someone 緊握〔某物〕; 緊抱〔某人〕: *The child was clinging to its mother.* 那孩子緊緊抱着母親不放。**2** to stick firmly to something 緊緊黏住: *The wet shirt clung to his body.* 濕襯衫緊緊黏在他的身上。**3 cling to something** to continue to believe that something is true or right because you want to believe it 堅信某事: *She still clings to the belief that her son is alive.* 她仍堅信她的兒子還活着。

cling·film /ˈklɪŋfɪlm; ˈklɪŋfɪlm/ *n* [U] thin transparent plastic put round food to keep it fresh 〔食物的〕保鮮塑料薄膜

cling·ing /ˈklɪŋɪŋ; ˈklɪŋɪŋ/ *adj* **1** fitting or sticking tightly to your body (used of clothes) 緊身的, 貼身的〔指衣服〕: *a clinging shirt* 緊身的襯衣 **2** too dependent upon the presence of another person 過於依賴他人的: *a clinging child* 依賴性過強的孩子

clin·ic /ˈklɪnɪk; ˈklɪnɪk/ *n* **1** a building or part of a hospital where specialized medical treatment and advice is given 診所; 門診部: *The clinic is near the station.* 診所在車站附近。| *the ear, nose, and throat clinic* 耳鼻喉科診所 **2** a regular period of time when you can go to a hospital for a particular kind of treatment or advice 門診時間: *The antenatal clinics are held on Tuesdays and Thursdays* 產前檢查的門診時間是週二和週四。

clin·i·cal /ˈklɪnɪkl; ˈklɪnɪkəl/ *adj* **1** connected with practical medical treatment rather than medical ideas 臨牀的: *clinical analysis* 臨牀分析 **2** showing little or no personal feeling 冷靜的; 客觀的: *He seemed to have a rather clinical view of the breakup of his marriage.* 他對自己婚姻破裂的態度似乎相當冷靜。–**clinically** /-klɪ; -kli/ *adv*

clink /klɪŋk; klɪŋk/ *v* [I;T] to make a sound like the sound of pieces of glass or metal lightly hitting each other 發出叮噹聲 –**clink** *n* [sing]

clip¹ /klɪp; klɪp/ *n* **1** a small object, usually made of plastic or metal, for holding things tightly together or in place 小夾子; 迴形針: *a paper clip* 紙夾子 | *a hair clip* 髮夾 **2** a short quick blow 猛擊: *She gave him a clip around the ears.* 她給了他一記耳光。**3** the act of cutting something, especially to make it neater 修剪 **4** a short piece of a film or television show, shown separately 〔電影或電視節目的〕片段

clip² *v* -**pp**- **1** [I;T] to put a clip on things to hold them firmly together or to keep them in place 夾住: *Clip these sheets of paper together please.* 請把這些紙夾在一起。| *The lamp clips on to the front of the bicycle.* 燈牢牢地夾在腳踏車的前部。**2** [T] to cut some-

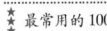

thing, especially in order to cut some parts off or to make it neater 修剪〔某物〕: *I think I'd better clip the hedge.* 我想我最好把樹籬籬修剪一下。 **3** to hit someone with a short quick blow 猛擊〔某人〕

clip clop /ˈklɪpˌklɑp; ˌklɪpˈklɒp/ *n* the sound made by a horse walking on hard ground 得得的馬蹄聲

clip·pers /ˈklɪpəz; ˈklɪpəz/ *n* [pl] a sharp instrument, often like scissors, used for clipping things 剪子: *nail clippers* 指甲剪 | *hedge clippers* 修枝剪 –see 見 PAIR (USAGE 用法)

clip·ping /ˈklɪpɪŋ; ˈklɪpɪŋ/ *n* **1 clippings** [pl] pieces cut off or out of something 剪下的東西: *nail clippings* 指甲屑 **2** a piece of writing that has been cut out of a newspaper or magazine 剪報: *Have you saved that newspaper clipping about my friend?* 你有沒有把報上刊登有關我朋友的消息剪下來保存好?

clique /klik; kliːk/ *n* a small closely united group of people who are part of a larger group and who are often unfriendly to other groups (a word used to express disapproval) 派系，小集團〔含貶義〕 –**cliquey** *adj*

clit·o·ris /ˈklaɪtərɪs; ˈklɪtərɪ̯s/ *n* a small front part of the female sex organ which is a centre of sexual excitement 陰蒂；陰核

cloak¹ /klok; kləʊk/ *n* **1** a loose outer garment worn like a coat but which has no separate coverings for your arms 斗篷；披風 **2** something used to hide the truth 掩飾；偽裝: *a cloak of secrecy* 對於祕密的掩飾

cloak² *v* [T] *lit* to cover something or hide it 〔文〕掩蓋；掩飾；覆蓋: *The hills were cloaked in mist.* 羣山為薄霧所籠罩。

cloak-and-dag·ger /ˌ·· ˈ··/ *adj* [only before a noun 只用於名詞前] full of violence and mystery (used especially of plays, films, and stories) 充滿暴力和陰謀的〔尤指戲劇、電影、故事〕

cloak·room /ˈklokˌrum; ˈkləʊkrum, -ruːm/ *n* **1** a room in a public building where hats, coats and bags may be left for a short time 衣帽間；衣帽寄存處 **2** *BrE* a LAVATORY especially in a public building 〔英式〕〔公共場所的〕廁所

clob·ber /ˈklɑbə; ˈklɒbəʳ/ *v* [T] *infml* 〔非正式〕 **1** to hit someone hard 毆打〔某人〕: *I'll clobber you if you don't do what you're told.* 如果你不照着我所説的去做，我會狠狠地揍你一頓。 **2** to defeat someone easily 輕而易舉地擊敗〔某人〕: *The socialists were clobbered in the last election.* 社會黨黨員在上次大選中遭到慘敗。

★clock¹ /klɑk; klɒk/ *n* **1** an instrument for measuring or showing time, not worn like a watch (時)鐘: *According to the station clock, the train's late.* 按車站大鐘上的時間來説，火車晚點了。 –see picture on page 730 見 730 頁彩圖 **2** an instrument in a car which tells you how many miles or

kilometres a car has travelled 〔汽車的〕里程表 **3 around/round the clock** all day and night, without stopping 日夜不停地: *We worked around the clock to finish the job.* 我們為了完成任務，日夜不停地工作。 **4 put the clock back** to move the hands of a clock to show an earlier time 把鐘撥慢: *In Italy they put the clock back two hours every October.* 在意大利，每年十月他們都把鐘往後撥慢兩小時。 **5 put the clock forward** to move the hands of a clock to show a later time 把鐘撥快 **6 put the clock back, turn the clock back** to return to older ideas or methods 倒行逆施〔即利用舊觀念；使用舊方法〕

clock² *v* [T] to measure how long something takes 計時: *I clocked his progress for the first mile.* 我用秒錶計出他跑第一英里所花的時間。

clock off *phr v* [I] to record the time at which you leave work, especially in a factory 〔尤指在工廠〕記錄下班時間

clock on *phr v* [I] to record the time at which you arrive at work, especially in a factory 〔尤指在工廠〕記錄上班時間

clock sthg ↔ **up** *phr v* [T] to record the number of miles or kilometres travelled, the number of points won, etc. 記錄〔里程數〕: *It's a new car, but we've already clocked up 1000 miles.* 這是一輛新車，但里程表顯示它已跑了一千英里。

clock·wise /ˈklɑkˌwaɪz; ˈklɒk-waɪz/ *adj,adv* in the direction in which the hands of a clock move 順時針方向的〔地〕: *Turn the handle clockwise to lock the door.* 順時針方向轉動把手就可把門鎖上。 –opposite 反義 **anticlockwise**

clock·work /ˈklɑkˌwɜk; ˈklɒk-wɜːk/ *n* [U] **1** machinery that can be wound up with a key, and that is used especially in clocks and toys 〔鐘錶、玩具內的〕發條裝置: *clockwork toys* 用發條開動的玩具 **2 like clockwork** *infml* easily and without problems 〔非正式〕容易地；順利地: *The whole conference ran like clockwork.* 整個會議進行得很順利。

clod /klɑd; klɒd/ *n* a lump of clay or earth 土塊；泥塊

clog /klɑg; klɒg/ *v* -**gg-** [I;T] (also 又作 **clog up, clog** sthg ↔ **up**) to block something or to become blocked (使)塞住；阻塞: *You've clogged the sink* **with** *those cabbage leaves.* 你的那些白菜葉子把洗滌槽塞住了。 | *These roads clog up* **with** *heavy lorries.* 這幾條馬路被重型卡車阻塞了。

clogs /klɑgz; klɒgz/ *n* shoes made of wood or with wooden SOLES 木屐；木底鞋

clois·ter /ˈklɔɪstə; ˈklɔɪstəʳ/ *n* a covered passage in a religious building, which has open archways on one side 〔宗教場所的〕迴廊

clois·tered /ˈklɔɪstəd; klɔɪstəd/ *adj* living apart from the life of others that surrounds you 隱居的; 與世隔絕的: *a cloistered university life* 與外界隔絕的大學生活

clone¹ /klon; kləʊn/ *n tech* the descendant of a single plant or animal, produced scientifically to have exactly the same form as the parent 〖術語〗克隆; 〔與母體完全相同的〕無性繁殖系的細胞

clone² *v* **cloned, cloning** [T] to produce a plant or an animal that is a clone 使無性繁殖

⋆close¹ /kloz; kləʊz/ *v* **closed, closing 1** [T] to shut something 關閉〔某物〕: *She closed the door quietly.* 她輕輕地關上了門。| *The company has decided to close its London branch.* 公司已決定關閉設在倫敦的分行。**2** [I] to shut 關閉: *What time does the library close this evening?* 圖書館今晚甚麼時候關門? **3** [T] to bring something to an end 使結束: *This conversation is now closed.* 這次談話現已結束。

close down *phr v* **1** [T **close** sthg ↔ **down**] to stop all work at a factory or business 使〔工廠〕停產; 使〔商店〕停業: *The steelworks will be closed down next month.* 鋼鐵廠下月停產。**2** [I] (of a factory or business) to stop working 〔工廠〕停產; 〔商店〕停業: *The toy factory closed down last year.* 玩具廠去年停產了。

close in *phr v* [I] **1** to surround someone and gradually move nearer to them 逐漸包圍: *His enemies were gradually closing in on him.* 敵人漸漸地把他包圍了。**2 the days are closing in** = the days are becoming shorter because winter is coming 白天〔由於冬季來臨而〕變短

⋆close² *n* **1** the end of something 結束: *The long strike has finally drawn to a close.* 長時間的罷工終於結束了。| *At the close of play, the score was three all.* 比賽結束時, 得分為3比3。**2** the area around a large important church 〔大教堂的〕圍地; 院子

⋆close³ /klos; kləʊs/ *adj* **1** [never before a noun 不能用於名詞前] near 靠近的; 附近的: *The shops are quite close.* 商店相當靠近。| *Our house is quite close to the town centre.* 我們的房子離市中心相當近。**2** [only before a noun 只用於名詞前] near in relationship 近親的; 關係密切的: *I haven't got many close relatives.* 我的近親不太多。**3** [only before a noun 只用於名詞前] thorough or careful 徹底的; 仔細的: *We kept a close watch on the children.* 我們很留心的看管孩子。**4** too warm and with no wind 悶熱的; 沉悶的: *The weather was close and humid.* 天氣又悶熱又潮濕。**5** decided by only a very small difference 接近的; 不相上下的: *We won, but the game was very close.* 我們贏了, 但比賽非常勢均力敵。**6 close at hand** near 附近的: *The shops are quite close at hand.* 商店離這兒相當近。**7 close call, close shave, close thing** something bad that nearly happened but

did not happen 僥倖的脫險: *That was a close shave.* 那次可真是死裡逃生。–see 見 NEAR (USAGE 用法)

close⁴ *adv* **1** near 接近地; 緊密地: *They were sitting very close together.* 他們緊靠着坐在一起。| *Don't come too close!* 不要靠得太近! **2 close on** *infml* almost 〖非正式〗幾乎: *It happened close on 50 years ago.* 這發生在大約五十年前。

closed /klozd; kləʊzd/ *adj* **1** shut 關閉的: *The door is closed.* 門關了。**2** not open to the public 不對公眾開放的: *The shop is closed on Thursdays.* 這家商店每星期四都不營業。| *The Post Office is closed for lunch.* 郵局在午飯時間不開門。**3** not open to everyone 不對所有人開放的: *a club with a closed membership* 只限於少數人參加的俱樂部 **4** not allowing outside influence 杜絕外界影響的; 封閉的: *a closed prison* 封閉的監獄 **5 closed book** something which you know nothing about 一無所知的事: *Fishing is a closed book to me.* 我對釣魚一竅不通。**6 closed shop** a factory or other establishment in which the workers must belong to one particular trade union 只雇用工會成員的工廠〔商號〕 **7 closed circuit television** a television system used inside a building 閉路電視: *We used closed circuit television at the shop to prevent shoplifting.* 我們在商店使用了閉路電視來防止盜竊。

close-knit /ˌklosˈnɪt; ˌkləʊsˈnɪt⋆/ *adj* (also 又作 **closely-knit**) closely bound together by sharing similar beliefs and activities 緊密結合在一起的: *a close-knit community* 緊密團結的社團

close sea·son /ˈklos ˌsizn̩; ˈkləʊs ˌsiːzən/ *n* (also 又作 **closed season**) the period of each year when certain animals, birds, or fish may not be killed for sport by law 禁獵期; 禁漁期

close-set /ˌklosˈsɛt; ˌkləʊsˈsɛt⋆/ *adj* placed very near to each other (used of eyes) 靠在一起的, 相距很近的〔指眼睛〕

clos·et¹ /ˈklazɪt; ˈklɒzɪt/ *n AmE* a tall cupboard built into the wall of a room 〖美式〗壁櫥

closet² *v* **be closeted with** someone to be talking privately to someone 私下對某人說

closet³ *adj* [only before a noun 只用於名詞前] not shown or admitted openly 私下的; 隱密的; 不公開承認的: *a closet alcoholic* 一個偷偷酗酒的人

close-up /ˈklos ˌʌp; ˈkləʊs ˌʌp/ *n* a photograph or film showing a lot of detail taken very near to the subject 〔照片、電影的〕特寫; 近鏡頭

clo·sure /ˈkloʒɚ; ˈkləʊʒəʳ/ *n* [C;U] the closing of something such as a factory or business 〔工廠、商號等的〕關閉; 歇業; 停工: *The present economic situation has led to the closure of a lot of companies.* 目前的經

濟狀況已使得許多公司結業。| *campaigning against hospital closures* 開展反對關閉醫院的運動

clot¹ /klɑt; klɒt/ *n* **1** a thickened mass or sticky lump, formed when blood dries up 血塊: *a blood clot* 血的凝塊 **2** *BrE infml* a stupid person〔英式，非正式〕笨蛋；傻瓜

clot² *v* **-tt-** [I] to become thick and form lumps 結塊: *clotted cream* 結塊的奶油

cloth /klɔθ; klɒθ/ *n* **1** [U] material made from wool, nylon, or cotton, and used for making things such as clothes and coverings 布料: *I'll need 3 metres of cloth for that dress.* 我需要三米長的布料做那件新衣服。 **2** [C] a piece of material used for a particular purpose〔作特殊用途的〕一塊布: *a cloth for cleaning the windows* 擦窗布 | *two new dish cloths* 兩塊洗碗布

> ■ USAGE 用法: Do not use **cloth** (klɔθ; klɒθ) or **cloths** (klɔθs; klɒθs) to mean "the things that people wear". Instead use **clothes** (kloz; kləʊðz) ☆指 "衣服"時，不用 **cloth** 或 **cloths**；應該用 **clothes** 一詞: *a clothes shop* 服裝店 | *The guests all wore casual clothes.* 客人們均穿着便服。

clothe /kloð; kləʊð/ *v* **clothed, clothing** [T] **1** to provide clothes for someone 為〔某人〕提供衣服: *They have to work hard to feed and clothe their family.* 他們為了養家餬口不得不努力工作。 **2** **clothed in** *fml* dressed in〔正式〕穿着…的: *She was clothed in green.* 她穿着綠色的衣服。

clothes /kloz; kləʊðz/ *n* [pl] garments, such as trousers, dresses, or shirts, that you wear 衣服: *I need some new clothes.* 我需要些新衣服。

> ■ USAGE 用法: Note that **clothes** is a plural noun and cannot be used in the singular. Use it to talk in general about the things that people wear ☆ **clothes** 是複數名詞，不能用作單數，它用來泛指人們一般所穿的衣服: *He bought a lot of new clothes.* 他買了許多新衣服。 | *I need some smart clothes for the wedding.* 我需要些漂亮的衣服來參加婚禮。 If you need to talk about a single article of clothing you can use the rather formal word **garment** ☆如要指單件的衣服，可用 **garment** 一詞，這個詞較為正式: *Customers are allowed to take a maximum of three garments into our fitting rooms.* 顧客最多可拿三件衣服進試衣室。 Usually, however, you will be able to use a more exact word ☆不過通常可以用更為精確的詞來指"衣服": *She bought three sweaters and a pair of trousers.* 她買了三件毛衣和一條褲子。

clothes·horse /'kloz,hɔrs; 'kləʊðzhɔːs/ *n* *BrE* a framework on which clothes are hung to dry indoors〔英式〕晾衣架

clothes peg /'··/ *n* a small wooden or plastic instrument for holding washing on a line to dry〔用於晾衣繩的〕衣夾

cloth·ing /'kloðɪŋ; 'kləʊðɪŋ/ *n* [U] clothes that people wear 衣服: *warm winter clothing* 保暖的冬衣 | *These people need food, clothing, and shelter.* 這些人需要食物、衣服和棲身之所。

***cloud¹** /klaʊd; klaʊd/ *n* **1** [C;U] a white or grey mass of very small drops of water floating in the sky 雲: *Black rain-clouds are gathering.* 烏雲正越聚越多。 | *There's a lot of cloud today.* 今天多雲。 **2** [C] a mass of smoke or dust 煙霧；塵土: *They drove off in a cloud of dust.* 他們在一片飛揚的塵土中駕車走了。 **3** **a cloud of** a large number of small things moving in a mass 一大羣: *a cloud of mosquitos* 一大羣蚊子 **4** [C] something that causes unhappiness or fear〔引起不快或恐懼的〕陰影；烏雲: *The clouds of war were gathering.* 戰爭的烏雲正在不斷結集。 **5** **under a cloud** not approved of or trusted 不獲贊成的；不被信任的: *He left his job under a cloud.* 他由於得不到信任而離職。 **6** **on cloud nine** *infml* extremely happy〔非正式〕極其高興: *He was on cloud nine when he heard he'd got the job.* 當他聽說已得到了那份工作時，他萬分高興。

cloud² *v* **1** [I;T] to make something less easy to see through, or to become less easy to see through (使)混濁; (使)朦朧: *The glass was dirty and clouded.* 玻璃杯又髒又模糊不清。 **2** [T] to make something unclear 使不清楚: *The explanations given seem to cloud the issues even more.* 這些解釋似乎把問題弄得更加令人不解。 **3** [T] to make a situation unhappy or unpleasant 使〔情況〕變得令人不快: *His suspicions clouded their relationship.* 他的懷疑令他們的關係罩上了一層陰影。

cloud over *phr v* [I] **1** (of someone's face) to begin to look unhappy or angry〔臉色〕沉下來: *His face clouded over when I told him the news.* 當我把消息告訴他時，他的臉色沉了下來。

cloud·burst /'klaʊd,bɜrst; 'klaʊdbɜːst/ *n* a sudden very heavy fall of rain 大暴雨

cloud·y /'klaʊdi; 'klaʊdi/ *adj* **cloudier, cloudiest** **1** full of clouds 多雲的: *a cloudy day* 陰天 | *a cloudy sky* 多雲的天空 **2** not transparent 不透明的: *This beer looks cloudy to me.* 我看這啤酒不大清澈。 **3** unclear 不清楚的: *a cloudy memory of what happened* 對發生的事記憶模糊

clout¹ /klaʊt; klaʊt/ *n* *infml*〔非正式〕 **1** [C] a blow or knock given with your hand〔用手〕敲，打 **2** [U] influence 影響

clout² *v* [T] *infml* to hit someone with your hand〔非正式〕〔用手〕敲打〔某人〕

clove¹ /klov; kləʊv/ *n* **1** the dried flower of a

tropical Asian plant, used in cooking 乾丁香花苞〔用作調料〕 **2** a small piece of the GARLIC root 蒜瓣: *a clove of garlic* 一瓣大蒜

clove² the past tense of CLEAVE ☆ CLEAVE 的過去式

clo·ven¹ /'kləvən; 'kləuvən/ the past participle of CLEAVE ☆ CLEAVE 的過去分詞

cloven² *adj* **cloven hoof** a foot divided into two parts, like that of a sheep or goat 〔羊等的〕偶蹄

clo·ver /'kləvə; 'kləuvəʳ/ *n* [U] **1** a small plant with pink, purple, or white flowers 三葉草; 苜蓿 **2 in clover** *infml* living in comfort 〔非正式〕生活舒適

clown¹ /klaun; klaun/ *n* **1** a performer who wears funny clothes and tries to make people laugh by jokes, tricks, or doing silly things 小丑; 丑角 **2** someone who tries to make people laugh by saying or doing silly things 愛開玩笑的人

clown² *v* [I] to behave stupidly or foolishly in order to make people laugh 裝傻〔以逗別人笑〕: *Stop clowning around!* 別再裝傻胡鬧了!

★club¹ /klʌb; klʌb/ *n* **1** a society of people who join together for a certain purpose, for example sport or amusement 俱樂部: *We belong to the golf club.* 我們是高爾夫球會的會員。**2** the building where they meet 俱樂部會所: *The Cricket Club is closed.* 板球俱樂部關門了。**3** a group of people who pay a regular sum of money for something 〔為做某事而定期納費的〕一羣人; 會社: *a book club* 讀書會 **4** a heavy stick, suitable for use as a weapon 〔作武器用的〕棍棒 **5** a specially shaped stick for hitting the ball in a game of GOLF 高爾夫球棒 **6 clubs** a set of playing cards with one or more three-leafed figures printed in black 〔紙牌的〕梅花(圖案)

club² *v* **-bb-** [T] to beat or hit someone with a heavy stick 用棍擊打〔某人〕: *He was clubbed to death.* 他是被人用棍子打死的。

club together *phr v* [I] to share the cost of something with others 分擔費用: *We clubbed together to buy her a present.* 我們湊錢給她買了件禮物。

cluck /klʌk; klʌk/ *n* the noise that a hen makes 〔母雞的〕咯咯叫聲 **–cluck** *v* [I]

clue /klu; kluː/ *n* **1** something that helps you to find an answer to a problem 線索; 提示: *a clue to his disappearance* 有關他失蹤的線索 | *I don't know the answer. Give me a clue.* 我不知道答案。給我一個提示吧。**2 not have a clue** *infml* not to have any idea 〔非正式〕一無所知: *I haven't a clue what time it starts.* 我一點也不知道那是何時開始的。

clued up /ˌ·ˈ·/ *adj infml* very well-informed 〔非正式〕見多識廣的: *He's quite clued up about music.* 他對音樂所知甚多。

clump¹ /klʌmp; klʌmp/ *n* **1** a group of trees,

bushes, or plants growing together 樹叢; 草叢 **2** a heavy solid lump or mass of dirt, soil, or mud 土塊; 泥塊

clump² *v* [I + adv/prep] to walk with slow heavy noisy footsteps 以緩慢而沉重的腳步行走: *Listen to him clumping around upstairs.* 聽他在樓上踱來踱去。

clum·sy /'klʌmzɪ; 'klʌmzi/ *adj* **clumsier, clumsiest 1** awkward and ungraceful in movement 笨拙的; 笨手笨腳的: *Look where you're going, you clumsy boy!* 走路時看看前面呀, 你這笨孩子! **2** awkward, careless or insensitive in the things that you say or do 不得體的; 不知趣的: *a clumsy remark* 一句不得體的話 | *a clumsy attempt to deal with the situation* 為應付局勢所採取的不合時宜的努力 **3** difficult to use or control 難以使用〔駕馭〕的: *Those boots are too clumsy for long walks.* 那雙靴子不適合在長途旅行時穿。**–clumsily** *adv* **–clumsiness** *n* [U]

clung /klʌŋ; klʌŋ/ the past tense and past participle of CLING ☆ CLING 的過去式和過去分詞

clus·ter¹ /'klʌstə; 'klʌstəʳ/ *n* a number of things of the same kind close together in a group 羣; 束; 團: *a cluster of stars* 星團 | *The men were standing in a cluster at the back.* 那些男人在後面站成一堆。

cluster² *v* [I;T] to gather or grow in a group 聚成羣; 成羣地生長: *The boys clustered together round the fire and sang songs.* 男孩子們圍聚在火堆旁唱歌。

clutch¹ /klʌtʃ; klʌtʃ/ *v* **1** [T] to hold something tightly 緊緊抓住〔某物〕; 緊握: *The mother clutched her baby in her arms.* 母親緊緊地把嬰兒抱在懷裡。**2 clutch at** to try to take hold of something 試圖抓住〔某物〕: *She clutched at the bannister as she began to fall.* 她摔下去的時候, 試圖抓住樓梯扶手。**3 clutch at straws** to try anything to help you to get out of a difficult situation 抓住救命稻草; 抓住一切可擺脫困境的機會

clutch² *n* **1** a tight hold on something usually because you are afraid 〔由於害怕而〕緊抓: *His clutch was not tight enough and he fell from the branch.* 他抓得不夠緊, 從樹枝上掉了下來。**2** an apparatus in a car which allows working parts of an engine to be connected or disconnected 〔汽車的〕離合器: *Press the clutch and change gear.* 踩離合器, 然後換檔。–see picture on page 209 見 209 頁彩圖 **3 in the clutches of** in the control or possession of someone 在〔某人〕控制下; 被〔某人〕佔有: *Once he was in the clutches of the enemy he knew he'd never escape.* 他一被敵人抓到, 便知道再也逃不掉了。

clut·ter¹ /'klʌtə; 'klʌtəʳ/ *v* [T] (also 又作 **clutter** sthg ↔ **up**) to make something untidy or fill it with unnecessary objects 使雜亂; 使凌亂: *Don't clutter up your room.* 別把你的房間弄亂。| *The room was cluttered* *with furniture.* 房間裡亂七八糟地放着家具。

clutter² *n* [U] a lot of things scattered about in a disorderly manner 凌亂的東西: *a room full of clutter* 亂七八糟的房間

cm a written abbreviation for 〖縮〗= CENTIMETRE(S)

c/o used when you are sending a letter to someone by sending it to another person who will keep it for them; an abbreviation for *care of* 〖縮〗〔用於信件〕由…轉交: *Send it to John Smith c/o The Post Office, Cambridge.* 請劍橋郵局轉交約翰·史密斯收。

Co.¹ a written abbreviation for 〖縮〗= COUNTY 郡; 縣: *Sunderland, Co. Durham* 達勒姆郡的桑德蘭市

Co.² /ko; kəʊ/ an abbreviation for 〖縮〗= COMPANY 公司: *James Smith & Co.* 詹姆斯·史密斯公司

*★**coach¹** /kotʃ; kəʊtʃ/ *n* **1** *BrE* a bus used for long-distance travel or touring 〖英式〗長途公共汽車 **2** **by coach** travelling in a coach 坐長途車: *We're going by coach.* 我們準備坐長途車去。 **3** a railway passenger carriage 火車的客車廂 **4** a person who trains sportsmen and sportswomen 教練: *a football coach* 足球教練 **5** a large enclosed carriage with four wheels pulled by horses 四輪大馬車

coach² *v* [I;T] to train or teach a person or a group of people 訓練; 指導: *I coach people for English examinations.* 我為準備英語考試的人作輔導。 | *He's being coached for the Olympic Games.* 他正在為奧運會進行訓練。

co·ag·u·late /koˈægjə,let; kəʊˈægjᵿleɪt/ *v* **coagulated, coagulating** [I;T] to change from a liquid into a solid or very thick mass (使)凝結; (使)凝固: *Blood coagulates when it meets air.* 血液遇到空氣便會凝結。 — **coagulation** /ko,ægjəˈleʃən; kəʊ,ægjᵿˈleɪʃən/ *n* [U]

*★**coal** /kol; kəʊl/ *n* **1** [U] a black mineral which is dug from the earth and which can be burned to give heat 煤: *Put some more coal on the fire, please.* 請給火再添些煤。 | *a coal miner* 煤礦工人 **2** [C] *pl* burning pieces of coal 燃燒的煤塊 **3** **haul someone over the coals** *infml* to speak very angrily to someone who has done something wrong 〖非正式〗怒斥某人

co·a·lesce /,koəˈlɛs; ,kəʊəˈles/ *v* **coalesced, coalescing** [I] *fml* to grow together or unite so as to form one group or system 〖正式〗聯合; 合併 — **coalescence** *n* [U]

*★**co·a·li·tion** /,koəˈlɪʃən; ,kəʊəˈlɪʃən/ *n* a union of separate political parties or people for a special purpose, usually for a limited period of time 〔通常只持續一段時期的政黨或個人的〕聯盟, 聯合: *The three parties joined together to form a coalition.* 三個政黨聯合起來結成了同盟。 | *a coalition government* 聯合政府

coal·mine /ˈkol,maɪn; ˈkəʊlmaɪn/ *n* a mine from which coal is dug 煤礦

coarse /kors; kɔːs/ *adj* **1** not fine or smooth 粗的; 粗糙的: *a coarse woollen garment* 粗糙的羊毛外衣 | *coarse grains of sand* 粗砂粒 **2** rough and rather rude in manner 粗魯的; 粗俗的: *coarse behaviour* 粗魯的行為 | *a coarse joke* 粗俗的笑話 — **coarsely** *adv* — **coarseness** *n* [U]

coars·en /ˈkorsn̩; ˈkɔːsən/ *v* **1** [T] to make something coarse 使〔某物〕變粗糙: *The wrong kind of soap can coarsen the skin.* 使用不合適的肥皂會使皮膚粗糙。 **2** [I;T] to make or become rude and rough in manner (使)變粗魯: *She had coarsened since leaving home.* 自離家之後, 她變得很粗魯。 | *The army had coarsened him.* 軍隊生涯使他變得很粗魯。

*★**coast¹** /kost; kəʊst/ *n* **1** the land next to the sea 海岸: *a trip to the coast* 去海岸邊的旅行 | *the north coast of Scotland* 蘇格蘭的北部海岸 | *the Pacific coast* 太平洋海岸 —see 見 SHORE¹ (USAGE 用法) **2** **the coast is clear** *infml* all danger has gone 〖非正式〗危險已經過去: *Leave now, while the coast is clear!* 趁現在沒危險, 快離開!

coast² *v* [I] to keep moving without additional power 滑行: *She switched off the car engine and coasted down the hill.* 她關掉汽車發動機, 滑下了山坡。

coast·guard /ˈkost,gard; ˈkəʊstgɑːd/ *n* **1** **the coastguard** a naval or police organization intended to watch for ships in danger and prevent unlawful activity at sea 〔擔任救生和緝私的〕海岸警衛隊 **2** [C] a member of this organization 海岸警衛隊隊員

coast·line /ˈkost,laɪn; ˈkəʊstlaɪn/ *n* the edge of a coast, as seen from the sea or on a map 海岸線

*★**coat¹** /kot; kəʊt/ *n* **1** a piece of clothing with long sleeves (SLEEVE) that you wear over your other clothes to keep you warm outdoors 外衣; 外套 —see picture on page 210 見 210 頁彩圖 **2** an animal's fur, wool, or hair 〔動物的〕皮毛 **3** a covering of something spread over a surface 塗層: *a coat of paint* 一層油漆

coat² *v* [T] to put a thin covering of something on the surface 給〔某物〕塗上一層; 覆蓋: *The table was coated with dust.* 桌子表面蒙了一層灰塵。

coat hang·er /ˈ· ,··/ *n* —see 見 HANGER

coat of arms /,·· ˈ·/ *n* **coats of arms** a set of patterns or pictures, used by a person or an organization as their special sign 〔某人或某組織用作標誌的〕盾形徽章

coax /koks; kəʊks/ *v* **1** to persuade someone by kind or patient words 哄勸; 勸誘: *I coaxed him into going to school.* 我哄他上學去了。 **2** to obtain something by gentle persuasion 用哄騙得到〔某物〕: *I coaxed a kiss from the little girl.* 我哄得小女孩給我一個吻。 **3** to use patience to make something work 耐心地撥弄: *She coaxed the machine into action.* 她耐心地把機器發動起來。

cob /kab; kɒb/ *n* the long hard central part of an ear of MAIZE, which can be cooked and eaten 玉米穗軸: *corn on the cob* 玉米棒子

cob·bled /ˈkabld; ˈkɒbəld/ *adj* covered with cobble-stones (used of roads) 鋪有鵝卵石的〔指道路〕: *old cobbled streets* 鋪有鵝卵石的古老街道

cob·bler /ˈkablə; ˈkɒbləʳ/ *n old fash* a person who repairs shoes〔老式〕補鞋匠

cob·ble·stones /ˈkabl,stonz; ˈkɒbəlstəʊnz/ *n* (also 又作 **cobbles**) [pl] stones with a rounded upper surface used for covering the surface of roads in former times〔舊時用來鋪路的〕鵝卵石

co·bra /ˈkobrə; ˈkəʊbrə/ *n* an African or Asian poisonous snake 眼鏡蛇

cob·web /ˈkab,web; ˈkɒbweb/ (also 又作 **spiderweb** *AmE*〔美式〕, **web**) *n* a very fine network of sticky threads made by a SPIDER to catch insects 蜘蛛網

Co·ca-Co·la /ˈkokəˈkolə; ˌkəʊkə ˈkəʊlə/ *n tdmk*〔商標〕(also 又作 **Coke** /kok; kəʊk/) **1** [U] a FIZZY non-alcoholic dark-coloured drink 可口可樂(飲料) **2** [C] a bottle or glass of Coca-Cola 一瓶〔杯〕可口可樂: *Two Cokes, please.* 請來兩杯可口可樂。

co·caine /koˈken; kəʊˈkeɪn/ *n* (also 又作 **coke** /kok; kəʊk/ *infml*〔非正式〕) [U] a drug used for preventing pain, or taken illegally for pleasure 可卡因: *Police have seized cocaine with a street value of £8m.* 警方沒收了在街上可賣八百萬英鎊的可卡因。

cock /kak; kɒk/ *n* **1** a fully-grown male bird 雄鳥 **2** a fully-grown male chicken 公雞

cock·a·too /ˌkakəˈtu; ˌkɒkəˈtuː/ *n* an Australian bird with large feathers on the top of its head〔澳大利亞〕葵花鸚鵡; 鳳頭鸚鵡

cock·crow /ˈkak,kro; ˈkɒk-krəʊ/ *n* [U] *lit* the time of day when light first appears〔文〕拂曉; 黎明

cock·e·rel /ˈkakərəl; ˈkɒkərəl/ *n* a young male chicken 小公雞

cock·eyed /ˈkak,aɪd; ˌkɒkˈaɪd◂/ *adj infml*〔非正式〕**1** stupid and not likely to succeed 愚笨的; 愚昧的: *a cockeyed idea* 荒謬的主意 **2** not straight 歪的; 斜的: *That picture's all cockeyed.* 那幅畫全歪了。

cock·le /ˈkakl; ˈkɒkəl/ *n* a small SHELLFISH 鳥蛤

Cock·ney /ˈkakni; ˈkɒkni/ *n* **1** a person born and living in the poorer parts of London especially one from the East End 倫敦人〔尤指住在貧困的東區的人〕 **2** the speech of people who live in the East End of London 倫敦東區腔

cock·pit /ˈkak,pɪt; ˈkɒk,pɪt/ *n* the part of a plane or a racing car in which the pilot or driver sits〔飛機、賽車的〕駕駛艙

cock·roach /ˈkak,rotʃ; ˈkɒk-rəʊtʃ/ *n* (**roach** *AmE*〔美式〕) a large black insect which lives especially in old or dirty houses 蟑螂

cock·sure /ˈkakˈʃur; ˌkɒkˈʃʊəʳ/ *adj* too sure of yourself (a word used to express disapproval) 過於自信的; 自負的〔含貶義〕

cock·tail /ˈkak,tel; ˈkɒkteɪl/ *n* **1** a mixed alcoholic drink 雞尾酒 **2** a small dish of mixed food eaten at the start of a meal 餐前開胃小吃: *a prawn cocktail* 涼拌蝦

cock-up /ˈ·ˌ·/ *n BrE slang* a mistake that prevents something from being done successfully (a rude word)〔英式, 俚〕使某事不能成功的錯誤〔粗魯的詞〕; 一團糟

cock·y /ˈkakɪ; ˈkɒki/ *adj* **cockier, cockiest** *infml* too sure of yourself (a word to express disapproval)〔非正式〕自負的〔含貶義〕: *I don't like him. He's far too cocky.* 我不喜歡他。他實在太自負了。 **–cockiness** *n* [U]

co·coa /ˈkoko; ˈkəʊkəʊ/ *n* **1** [U] a dark brown powder used to make chocolate 可可粉〔用以製巧克力〕 **2** [C;U] a hot drink made from this powder and milk or water〔熱的〕可可飲料: *a cup of cocoa* 一杯可可飲料

co·co·nut /ˈkokənət; ˈkəʊkənʌt/ *n* **1** [C] a very large nut with hard white flesh and a centre filled with a milky juice 椰子 **2** [U] the flesh of this nut eaten raw or used in cooking 椰子肉

co·coon /kəˈkun; kəˈkuːn/ *n* a protective case of silky threads round an insect at the PUPA stage 繭

co·cooned /kəˈkund; kəˈkuːnd/ *adj* **1** wrapped up warmly or tightly〔溫暖地或緊緊地〕包裹起來的: *He was cocooned in his sleeping bag.* 他很舒適地躺在睡袋之中。 **2** protected and cut off from problems in life 不受〔生活中的難題〕困擾的: *He accused them of being cocooned by the welfare state.* 他指責他們在福利國家養尊處優。

cod /kad; kɒd/ *n* [plural is 複數為 **cod**] [C; U] a large sea fish 鱈魚

C.O.D. /ˌsi oˈdi; ˌsiː əʊ ˈdiː/ *a* system where you pay for something when it is delivered; an abbreviation for **cash on delivery**〔縮〕貨到付款(制): *You can order the goods C.O.D.* 你可以用貨到付款的方式訂購商品。

★code¹ /kod; kəʊd/ *n* **1** [C;U] a system of words, letters, or numbers used instead of ordinary writing, to send secret messages 密碼; 暗號: *The message was in code.* 這訊息是用密碼寫的。 **2** [C;U] a system of signals used instead of letters and numbers in a message that is broadcast 代碼: *a telegraphic code* 電報電碼 **3** [C] a part of a telephone number, for a village, town or country〔電話的〕區號: *The code for Nottingham is 0602.* 諾丁漢的電話區號是0602。| *local dialling codes* 本地電話區號 **4** [C] a system of laws or rules 法規; 法典: *the*

Napoleonic code 拿破崙法典 | *the highway code* 公路法 **5** [C] a set of ideas which a society shares〔社會的〕規範: *the accepted code of behaviour* 被社會接受的行為規範 **6 code of practice** the formal rules of correct behaviour for a profession 職業法; 職業道德規範: *The Solicitors' Association has recently drawn up a new code of practice.* 律師協會最近草擬了一項新的律師職業規範。

code² *v* **coded, coding** [T] to translate a message into a code 把〔消息〕譯成密碼

co-ed¹ /ˈkoʊɛd; ˌkəʊˈedˑ/ *adj BrE infml*〔英式, 非正式〕an abbreviation for〔縮〕= CO-EDUCATIONAL

coed² /ˈkoʊɛd; ˈkəʊed/ *n AmE infml* a female student in a college or university open to both sexes〔美式, 非正式〕〔男女同校的〕女大學生

co-ed-u-ca-tion-al /ˌkoʊedʒəˈkeɪʃənl; ˌkəʊedjʊˈkeɪʃənəl/ *adj* educating boys and girls together 男女同校的: *a co-educational school* 男女同校的學校 **–co-education** *n* [U]

co-erce /koʊˈɜːs; kəʊˈɜːs/ *v* **coerced, coercing** [T] *fml* to force someone to do something〔正式〕強迫〔某人做某事〕: *The defendant claimed that he had been coerced* **into** *making a confession.* 被告聲稱他是被迫招供的。 **–coercion** /koʊˈɜːʃən; kəʊˈɜːʃən/ *n* [U]

co-ex-ist /ˌkoʊɪɡˈzɪst; ˌkəʊɪɡˈzɪst/ *v* [I] **1** to exist together peacefully in spite of having different opinions or different political systems〔意見或政治制度不同而〕和平共處: *Now the war has ended, the two countries will have to learn to coexist.* 戰爭現已結束, 兩個國家將要學習和平共處。 **–coexistence** *n* [U]: *peaceful coexistence* 和平共處

C of E /ˌsiː əv ˈiː; ˌsiː əv ˈiː/ an abbreviation for〔縮〕= CHURCH OF ENGLAND

⭐**cof·fee** /ˈkɔːfi; ˈkɒfi/ *n* **1** [U] a brown powder made by crushing the beans of the coffee tree 咖啡(粉) **2** [U] a hot brown drink made from this powder 咖啡: *Would you like a cup of coffee?* 你要來杯咖啡嗎? **3** [C] a cup of coffee 一杯咖啡: *Two coffees, please!* 請來兩杯咖啡!

coffee bar /ˈ··· ·/ *n BrE* a place where light meals, cakes, and non-alcoholic drinks are served〔英式〕咖啡館

coffee ta·ble /ˈ·· ˌ··/ *n* a small low table 咖啡桌 –see picture on page 730 見 730 頁彩圖

cof·fer /ˈkɔːfə; ˈkɒfər/ *n* a large strong box for holding money, jewels, or other valuable objects 保險箱; 保險櫃

cof·fin /ˈkɔːfɪn; ˈkɒfɪn/ *n* the box in which a dead person is buried 棺材

cog /kɑːɡ; kɒɡ/ *n* **1** a tooth round the edge of a wheel that causes it to move or be moved by another wheel in a machine 輪齒 **2 a cog in the machine** an unimportant person in a large organization〔大機構中的〕小人物

co·gent /ˈkoʊdʒənt; ˈkəʊdʒənt/ *adj* having the power to make someone believe a reason or argument 有説服力的 **–cogently** *adv* **–cogency** *n* [U]

cog·i·tate /ˈkɑːdʒəˌteɪt; ˈkɒdʒɪˌteɪt/ *v* **cogitated, cogitating** [I] *fml* to think carefully and seriously about something〔正式〕仔細考慮; 認真思索

co·gnac /ˈkoʊnjæk; ˈkɒnjæk/ *n* [C;U] a strong alcoholic drink made in France 法國白蘭地

co·hab·it /koʊˈhæbɪt; ˌkəʊˈhæb‿t/ *v* [I] *fml* (of two unmarried people) to live together as though married〔正式〕〔未婚者〕同居 **–cohabitation** /koʊˌhæbəˈteɪʃən; kəʊˌhæb‿ˈteɪʃən/ *n* [U]

co·her·ent /koʊˈhɪrənt; kəʊˈhɪərənt/ *adj* **1** clear and easy to understand 清楚易懂的: *a coherent argument* 前後一致的論點 **2** able to put ideas or words together clearly 能清楚表達思想的: *As he recovered from the shock, he gradually became more coherent.* 當他從這一打擊中恢復過來後, 他的思路才逐漸變得清晰起來。 **–coherently** *adv* **–coherence** *n* [U]

co·he·sion /koʊˈhiːʒən; kəʊˈhiːʒən/ *n* [U] **1** the act or state of sticking together tightly 附着; 黏着; 團結: *We need greater cohesion in the party if we want to win the election.* 我們如果想贏得大選, 就需要加強黨內的團結。 **2** *tech* connection in ideas between different parts of a sentence or between one sentence and another〔術語〕〔句子內部或句與句之間的〕連貫性 **–cohesive** /-ˈhɪsɪv; -ˈhiːsɪv/ *adj*

coif·fure /kwɑːˈfjʊr; kwɒˈfjʊər/ *n fml* a style of arranging or cutting a woman's hair〔正式〕〔婦女的〕髮式, 髮型

coil¹ /kɔɪl; kɔɪl/ *v* [I;T] to wind or twist into a continuous circular shape 盤繞; 盤起來: *The snake coiled itself round the tree.* 蛇盤繞在樹上。

coil sthg ↔ **up** *phr v* [T] to wind something into a continuous circular shape 把〔某物〕盤起來: *Now coil up the rope.* 現在把繩子盤起來。 | *The snake coiled itself up again.* 蛇又一次盤起一團。

coil² *n* **1** one of a connected set of rings or twists into which something such as a rope or wire can be wound 卷; 盤: *a coil of rope* 一卷繩子 | *a loose coil of hair* 一團蓬鬆的頭髮 **2** *tech* an apparatus made by coiling a length of wire, used for carrying an electric current〔術語〕〔傳導電流的〕線圈 **3 the coil** a small metal or plastic object fitted inside a woman's body to prevent her having a baby 避孕環

⭐**coin¹** /kɔɪn; kɔɪn/ *n* a piece of money made of metal 硬幣: *I changed £5 at the bank, because I needed some coins for the ticket machine.* 我在銀行換了五英鎊, 因為我在自動售票機買票需要硬幣。

coin² v [T] **1** to make coins from metal 〔用金屬〕製造硬幣: *The government has decided to coin more 50-pence pieces.* 政府已決定製造更多的五十便士硬幣。**2** to invent a new word 創造〔新詞〕: *Who coined the word "nuke"?* "nuke" 這個詞是誰造出來的? **3 to coin a phrase** a phrase used for excusing yourself when you have just used an expression which is used far too much 用句老話語; 俗語說: *"Do you come here often? ...to coin a phrase!"* 常語說: "你常來這兒嗎?"

coin·age /ˈkɔɪnɪdʒ; ˈkɔɪnɪdʒ/ n [U] the system of coins used in a country 〔一個國家的〕硬幣制制: *decimal coinage* 十進位幣制

co·in·cide /ˌkoɪnˈsaɪd; ˌkəʊɪnˈsaɪd/ v **coincided, coinciding** [I] **1** to happen at the same time or in the same place 同時〔同地〕*Unfortunately, our holidays don't coincide this year.* 很遺憾, 我們今年不能在同一時候休假。| *Her eighteenth birthday is going to coincide* **with** *the final exam.* 她的十八歲生日與期末考試是在同一天。**2** (of ideas or opinions) to be in agreement 〔想法、意見〕一致

co·in·ci·dence /koˈɪnsədəns; kəʊˈɪnsɪdəns/ n [C;U] a combination of events, happening by chance which are often surprising 巧合: *What a coincidence that I was in London at the same time as you!* 當時我和你竟然同在倫敦, 真巧! –**coincidental** /koˌɪnsəˈdɛntl; kəʊˌɪnsɪˈdentl/ adj –**coincidentally** adv

coke /kok; kəʊk/ n **1** [U] the solid substance that remains after gas has been removed from coal by heating, used for producing heat by burning 焦炭 **2 Coke** see 見 COCA-COLA **3** [U] see 見 COCAINE

col·an·der /ˈkʌləndə; ˈkʌləndəʳ/ n a bowl-shaped pan with holes in it, used for separating food from liquid 〔食品的〕濾鍋

★★**cold¹** /kold; kəʊld/ adj **1** having a low temperature or one that is lower than it should be 寒冷的: *a cold wind* 冷風 | *It's a cold day for July, isn't it?* 在七月份裡這天氣可夠涼的, 是不是? | *I'm cold.* 我覺得冷。| *My coffee's gone cold.* 我的咖啡涼了。**2** showing a lack of friendly feelings 冷淡的: *a cold smile* 冷冷的笑 | *She seemed cold and uncaring.* 她看上去一副漠不關心的樣子。**3** cooked but not eaten hot (used of food) 冷的〔指食物〕: *cold meats* 冷肉 **4 out cold** unconscious, especially as the result of a severe blow to the head 〔尤指頭部遭重擊後〕昏厥的 **5 cold comfort** little or no help in a bad situation 在困境中〕無助, 沒有多大幫助 **6 cold sweat** a condition of great fear or nervousness 〔因恐懼或緊張而出的〕冷汗: *I broke out in a cold sweat.* 我直冒冷汗。**7 cold turkey** the unpleasant sick feeling caused by the sudden stopping of the use of a drug 〔突然停止服用毒品時產生的〕噁心的感覺 **8 cold war** a state of severe political struggle, but without actual fighting, between countries with opposed political systems 冷戰 **9 get cold feet, have cold feet** to become worried about doing something as the time to do it comes near 〔由於即將去做某事而〕膽怯, 害怕: *She told me she was getting cold feet about getting married.* 她告訴我說她對結婚感到心慌。**10 in cold blood** in a planned and heartless way 蓄意地; 殘忍地: *They killed the old man in cold blood!* 他們殘酷地殺害了那位老人!

cold² n **1** an illness of the nose or throat, which is common in winter and may cause headaches, coughing, and slight fever 感冒; 着涼: *He's got a bad cold.* 他患了重感冒。| *Be careful you don't catch a cold.* 小心一些, 不要着涼。| *She's had two or three colds this winter.* 今年冬天她得過兩三次感冒。**2 the cold** a low temperature or cold weather 低溫; 寒冷: *Don't go out into the cold without a coat!* 不要不穿外衣就到冷的地方去! **3 out in the cold** infml unwanted or not considered 《非正式》受冷落: *He was left out in the cold at school because he didn't like sports.* 他不喜歡體育運動, 因此在學校受冷落。

cold-blood·ed /ˌ·ˈ···◂/ adj **1** having a body temperature that changes according to the temperature of the surroundings 〔動物〕冷血的: *Snakes are cold-blooded.* 蛇是冷血動物。**2** cruel and showing complete lack of feeling 殘忍的: *a cold-blooded murder* 殘酷的謀殺

cold-heart·ed /ˌ·ˈ···◂/ adj lacking sympathy 無同情心的: *a cold-hearted refusal to help* 無情地拒絕施以援手 –**cold-heartedly** adv – **cold-heartedness** n [U]

cold·ly /ˈkoldlɪ; ˈkəʊldli/ adv without friendly feelings 冷淡地; 冷漠地: *He looked at me coldly without a smile.* 他笑也不笑, 冷冷地看着我。

cold·ness /ˈkoldnɪs; ˈkəʊldnɪs/ n [U] **1** the state of being cold 寒冷 **2** lack of friendly feelings 冷淡

col·ic /ˈkɑlɪk; ˈkɒlɪk/ n [U] a severe pain in the stomach and bowels of babies 〔嬰兒的〕腹絞痛

col·lab·o·rate /kəˈlæbəˌret; kəˈlæbəreɪt/ v **collaborated, collaborating** [I] **1** to work together for a special purpose 合作; 協作: *Turner collaborated* **with** *Leech on the marine biology project.* 特納與里奇在海洋生物項目上進行合作。**2** to help an enemy country which has taken control of your own country (a word used to express disapproval) 通敵〔含貶義〕: *He was accused of collaborating with the enemy.* 他被指控與敵勾結。–**collaborator** n –**collaboration** /kəˌlæbəˈreʃən; kəˌlæbəˈreɪʃən/ n [U]: *The two companies are working in close collaboration.* 兩家公司正在緊密合作。

col·lage /kəˈlɑʒ; ˈkɒlɑːʒ/ n **1** [U] the art of

making pictures by sticking various materials onto a surface 拼貼藝術 **2** [C] a picture made in this way 拼貼畫

col·lapse¹ /kə'læps; kə'læps/ *v* **collapsed, collapsing 1** [I] to fall down or inwards suddenly 倒塌; 坍塌: *The bridge collapsed under the weight of the train.* 橋在火車的重壓下塌了。**2** [I] to fall down in a helpless or unconscious condition 昏倒: *This man's collapsed. Please can you get a doctor?* 這個人昏倒了。請你找個醫生來好嗎? **3** [I] to fail suddenly and completely 崩潰; 瓦解; 潰敗: *All opposition to the government collapsed because of the war.* 由於戰爭, 反對政府的勢力全部瓦解。**4** [I;T] to fold into a shape that takes up less space 摺疊: *This table collapses, so I can store it easily when I'm not using it.* 這張桌子可以摺疊, 所以不用的時候, 我可以很容易地把它收起來。

collapse² *n* **1** [U] the act of falling down or inwards 倒塌; 坍塌: *The storm caused the collapse of the entire building.* 暴風雨使大樓整座坍塌。**2** [U] a failure 失敗: *The peace talks were on the verge of collapse.* 和談瀕於失敗。**3** [C;U] the sudden and complete loss of strength or will 〔體力、精力的〕垮掉; 衰竭: *a state of near collapse* 幾乎衰竭的境地 | *He suffered a nervous collapse.* 他患了精神崩潰症。

col·lap·si·ble /kə'læpsəbḷ; kə'læps̩bəl/ *adj* able to be folded up for easy storing 可摺疊的: *a collapsible bicycle* 摺疊式腳踏車

col·lar¹ /'kɑlə; 'kɒlər/ *n* **1** the part of a shirt, dress, or coat that fits round your neck 衣領 –see picture on page 210 見 210 頁彩圖 **2** a band put round an animal's neck 〔套於動物頸上的〕項圈

collar² *v* [T] *infml* to catch and hold someone 〔非正式〕抓住〔某人〕: *The police collared him as he was getting on the boat.* 他在上船時被警方抓住。

col·lar·bone /'kɑlə'bon; 'kɒləbəʊn/ *n* either of a pair of bones going from the base of your neck to your shoulders 鎖骨

col·lat·e·ral /kɑ'lætərəl; kə'lætərəl/ *n* [U] *fml* property or money that you promise to a person in case you cannot pay back a debt 〔正式〕抵押品; 擔保物: *He offered his house as collateral for the loan.* 他把房子作為這筆借款的抵押。

✲col·league /'kɑlig; 'kɒliːg/ *n* a person who works with you, especially in a profession 同事; 同僚

✲col·lect /kə'lɛkt; kə'lekt/ *v* **1** [I;T] to gather together 收集; 集中: *Collect the books and put them on my desk.* 把書收起來放在我的書桌上。| *A crowd of people had collected at the scene of the accident.* 一大羣人眾集在事故現場。| *The government could save money by improving the way it collects taxes.* 政府可改善收稅方式以節約開支。| *"Has she got a hobby?" "Yes, she collects foreign*

coins." "她有沒有甚麼業餘愛好?" "有的, 她搜集外國硬幣。" | *They are collecting data on family size.* 他們在收集家庭規模方面的數據。**2** [T] to come to take someone or something away 接走〔某人或某物〕: *He collected the children from school.* 他從學校把孩子們接走。**3** [I;T] to get money from people to help others 〔為幫助別人〕募集, 集資: *I'm collecting for the blind.* 我正在為盲人募捐。| *How much did you collect?* 你募集了多少錢? **4 collect your thoughts** to try to order your ideas and feel calm before you do something 〔做某事前〕盡力鎮定下來

col·lect·ed /kə'lɛktɪd; kə'lektɪd/ *adj* **1** put together in one book or as a collection 收集成〔一本書〕的: *the collected works of Shakespeare* 莎士比亞全集 **2** cool, calm, and collected in full control of yourself 鎮靜的; 泰然自若的

✲col·lec·tion /kə'lɛkʃən; kə'lekʃən/ *n* **1** [U] the act of collecting something 收集; 收取: *What time is the next collection from this post box?* 這個郵箱下一次收信是甚麼時候? | *Your shoes are ready for collection.* 你的鞋準備好了, 你可以來拿了。**2** [C] a group of things that has gathered together, or has been gathered together 收集物; 聚集: *an odd collection of people* 一羣古怪的人 | *a new collection of poems* 一本新詩集 | *She has a very good collection of foreign stamps.* 她收集了許多非常漂亮的外國郵票。

✲col·lec·tive¹ /kə'lɛktɪv; kə'lektɪv/ *adj* [only before a noun 只用於名詞前] shared by all the members of a group together 集體的; 共同擁有的: *the collective opinion of the governments of Western Europe* 西歐各國政府的共同觀點 | *collective ownership* 集體所有制 –**collectively** *adv*

collective² *n* a business or farm owned and controlled by the people who work in it 集體所有制企業〔農場〕

col·lec·tor /kə'lɛktə; kə'lektər/ *n* **1** a person employed to collect things 〔受雇的〕收集者: *a ticket collector* 收票員 | *a rent collector* 收房租的人 **2** a person who collects things such as stamps or coins for pleasure 〔郵票或硬幣等的〕收集者, 收藏家

✲col·lege /'kɑlɪdʒ; 'kɒlɪdʒ/ *n* **1** [C;U] a place, sometimes part of a university, for education after leaving school or for preparing for a particular type of job 〔大學內的〕學院; 職業學校: *The art college is next to the station.* 藝術學院在火車站旁邊。| *He starts college in January.* 他在一月份開始上大學。**2** [C] a body of teachers and students considered as a whole 學院的全體師生: *The college proposes certain changes of policy.* 學院師生建議在政策上做一些變動。

col·lide /kə'laɪd; kə'laɪd/ *v* **collided, colliding** [I] **1** to crash violently into something 撞; 撞擊: *Two buses have collided in the* *town centre.* 兩輛公共汽車在鎮中心相撞。| *His car collided with a lorry.* 他的汽車與一輛卡車相撞。**2** to come into strong opposition with someone 衝突; 抵觸: *The President collided with Congress over his budget plans.* 總統與國會在財政算上發生了衝突。

col·lie·ry /ˈkɑljərɪ; ˈkɒljəri/ *n* **collieries** *BrE* a mine for coal and the buildings and machinery connected with it〖英式〗煤礦區〔包括建築物和機器設備等〕

col·li·sion /kəˈlɪʒən; kəˈlɪʒn/ *n* **1** a violent crash 猛撞; 撞擊: *Many people were hurt in the collision between a bus and a car.* 有很多人在一輛公共汽車和汽車相撞的事故中受傷。| *a head-on collision* 迎頭相撞 **2** a strong disagreement 抵觸; 衝突: *a collision of interests* 利益衝突 **3 a collision course** a path or course of action likely to result in problems 導致衝突的趨勢[行動路線]: *The government and the trades unions are on a collision course.* 政府和工會發生衝突的趨勢。

col·lo·qui·al /kəˈloʊkwɪəl; kəˈləʊkwiəl/ *adj* used in ordinary informal conversation 口語的, 會話的: *Don't put these colloquial expressions in your examination essay.* 在考試的作文裡不要用這些口語表達方式。**—colloquially** *adv*

col·lo·qui·al·ism /kəˈloʊkwɪəl,ɪzəm; kəˈləʊkwiəlɪzəm/ *n* an expression used in ordinary informal conversation 口語體, 會話體

col·lu·sion /kəˈluʒən; kəˈluːʒn/ *n* [U] *fml* secret agreement between two or more people with the intention of cheating or deceiving others〖正式〗勾結, 串通〔以欺騙他人〕

co·lon /ˈkoʊlən; ˈkəʊlən/ *n* **1** the mark (:) used in writing to introduce a list, examples, or an explanation 冒號 **2** part of the large tube which takes waste matter down from your stomach 結腸

colo·nel /ˈkɜːnl; ˈkɜːnl/ *n* an officer of middle rank in an army or air force〔陸軍或空軍的〕上校

co·lo·ni·al /kəˈloʊnɪəl; kəˈləʊniəl/ *adj* related to countries ruled by a more powerful, distant country 殖民地的: *The African people have successfully fought against colonial rule.* 非洲人民成功地進行了反對殖民統治的鬥爭。

co·lo·ni·al·is·m /kəˈloʊnɪəl,ɪzəm; kəˈləʊniəlɪzəm/ *n* [U] the system of colonizing other countries 殖民主義: *British colonialism led to the establishment of a large empire.* 英國的殖民政策使該國成為一個龐大的帝國。**— colonialist** *adj, n*

col·o·nize /ˈkɑlə,naɪz; ˈkɒlənaɪz/ *v* **colonized, colonizing** (also 又作 **colonise** *BrE*〖英式〗) [I;T] to make a country or area into a colony 把〔一個國家或地區〕變成殖民地: *The British first colonized Australia in the 18th century.* 英國首先在十八世紀把澳大

利亞開拓為殖民地。**—colonization** /,kɑlənəˈzeʃən; ,kɒlənaɪˈzeɪʃən/ *n* [U]

col·on·nade /,kɑləˈned; ,kɒləˈneɪd/ *n* a row of upright stone posts supporting a roof or a row of arches 柱廊

col·o·ny /ˈkɑlənɪ; ˈkɒləni/ *n* **colonies 1** a country or area under the control of a more powerful distant country and often settled by people from that country 殖民地 **2** a group of people from the same country or with the same interests, living together 聚居海外的僑民; 一羣志趣相投而聚居在一起的人: *a nudist colony* 一羣聚居在一起的裸體主義者 **3** a group of the same kind of animals or plants living or growing together〔同類動植物的〕羣, 羣體: *a colony of ants* 一個螞蟻羣

col·or /ˈkʌlɚ; ˈkʌləʳ/ *n* —see 見 COLOUR

col·ored /ˈkʌlɚd; ˈkʌləd/ *adj, n* —see 見 COLOURED

col·or·ful /ˈkʌlɚfəl; ˈkʌləfəl/ *adj* —see 見 COLOURFUL

col·or·ing /ˈkʌlərɪŋ; ˈkʌlərɪŋ/ *n* —see 見 COLOURING

col·or·less /ˈkʌlɚlɪs; ˈkʌlələs/ *adj* —see 見 COLOURLESS

co·los·sal /kəˈlɑsl; kəˈlɒsəl/ *adj* extremely large 龐大的; 巨大的: *a colossal building* 巨大的建築物 | *spending on a colossal scale* 巨額開支

co·los·sus /kəˈlɑsəs; kəˈlɒsəs/ *n* **colossuses** or **colossi** /-saɪ; -saɪ/ a person or thing of very great size, importance, or ability 巨人; 巨物; 重大的事情[人物]: *China is a colossus compared to Hong Kong.* 與香港相比, 中國是個龐然大物。

★**col·our¹** /ˈkʌlɚ; ˈkʌləʳ/ *n* (**color** *AmE*〖美式〗) **1** [U] the quality which allows you to see the difference between, for example, a red flower and a blue flower when they are both the same size and shape 彩色; 色彩: *an insect that can change colour* 會變色的昆蟲 | *colour television* 彩色電視 | *a colour film* 彩色膠卷 **2** [C] red, blue, green, black, brown, yellow, white, etc. 顏色: *What colour is your car?* 你的車是甚麼顏色的? | *They come in different colours.* 它們有各種各樣的顏色。| *a sort of reddish colour* 一種淡紅色 **3** [C;U] a paint or a coloured pencil 顏料; 彩筆: *His paintbox only holds six colours.* 他的顏料盒裡只有六種顏色。| *I must sharpen my colours.* 我必須削尖我的彩筆。**4** [U] the general appearance of someone's skin, especially when related to how healthy they look 氣色; 臉色: *The cold wind brought colour to her cheeks.* 寒風吹得她雙頰通紅。**5** [U] details or behaviour of a place, thing, or person, that are interesting and excite the imagination 特色; 氣質: *She loved the life, noise, and colour of the market.* 她很喜歡市場的活力、熙攘和姿彩。**6 in colour** printed or shown in all colours not just black and white 彩色的: *I thought the film would be in colour but it was an old black and white one.* 我本以為是部彩色影片，但實際上是部黑白的。 **7 off colour** *infml* a little ill〔非正式〕有點不適

■ USAGE 用法: Notice how we use **is** in this question and answer ☆注意 **is** 在此問答中的運用: *"What* **colour** **is** *it?" "It's red."* 「這是甚麼顏色？」「是紅色。」

colour² *v* (**color** *AmE*〖美式〗)**1** [T] to cause something to have colour, especially a picture or something in a picture 為〔某物〕着色〔尤指畫或畫中的物體〕: *His younger sister was colouring a picture.* 他的妹妹正在給一幅畫塗上顏色。 | *Why don't you colour the dog brown?* 你為何不把狗塗成褐色呢？ **2** [I] to gain or change colour 產生顏色；變色: *He coloured with embarrassment.* 他不好意思，臉也紅了。 **3** [T] to influence your opinion about something 影響〔對某事物的〕意見；粉飾，渲染: *Personal feelings coloured his judgment.* 他的判斷力帶有個人感情的色彩。

colour sthg ↔ **in** *phr v* [T] to colour a drawing using coloured pencils〔用彩筆〕給〔畫〕上色: *You haven't coloured the dog in.* 你還未給這條狗上顏色。

colour bar /'··/ *n* the set of laws or customs in some places which prevent black people from mixing freely with white people 膚色障礙〔即黑人與白人的種族隔離〕

colour-blind /'··/ *adj* unable to see the difference between certain colours 色盲的 **–colour blindness** *n* [U]

col·oured¹ /'kʌləd; 'kʌləd/ *adj* (**colored** *AmE*〖美式〗) **1** having colour, used to mean not black or white 彩色的: *coloured sheets* 彩色牀單 | *The sea was green-coloured.* 大海呈現出綠色。 **2** belonging to a race that does not have a white skin or, especially in South Africa, of mixed race (a word that is considered offensive by many people)〔人種〕有色的，混血的〔常認為使用該詞是對人的侮辱〕 **3** full of unfair opinion and not completely honest 帶有偏見的；不夠誠實的

coloured² *n* (**colored** *AmE*〖美式〗) a person in South Africa who is of mixed race〔南非的〕白人與有色人種所生的混血兒

col·our·ful /'kʌləfəl; 'kʌləfəl/ *adj* (**colorful** *AmE*〖美式〗) **1** having bright colours 顏色鮮艷的: *a bird with colourful wings* 翅膀色彩鮮艷的鳥 **2** full of interest, often because of a lot of variety or detail 豐富多彩的；生動活潑的: *a colourful period of history* 歷史上豐富多彩的時期 | *He's a colourful character.* 他是個性格活潑的人。

col·our·ing /'kʌlərɪŋ; 'kʌlərɪŋ/ *n* (**coloring** *AmE*〖美式〗) **1** [C;U] a substance used for giving a colour to food 食用色素: *This prod-*

uct contains no artificial colouring. 這種產品不含人造色素。 **2** [U] the colour of your hair and skin〔毛髮與皮膚的〕顏色: *People with fair colouring should cover up in the sun.* 皮膚白皙的人應該遮避太陽的照射。

col·our·less /'kʌləlɪs; 'kʌlələs/ *adj* (**colorless** *AmE*〖美式〗) **1** without colour 無色的: *Water is a colourless liquid.* 水是一種無色的液體。 **2** lacking interest 無趣的；乏味的: *a colourless existence* 呆板無趣的生活

colour prej·u·dice /'·· ,···/ *n* unreasonable dislike of people of other colours 種族偏見

colour sup·ple·ment /'·· ,···/ *n* a free colour magazine often given with British Sunday newspapers〔英國的一種通常與週日的報紙一起發放的〕彩色增刊

colt /kolt; kəʊlt/ *n* a young male horse 小公馬

★col·umn /'kɑləm; 'kɒləm/ *n* **1** a tall solid stone post, used in a building as a support or decoration 柱，圓柱 **2** anything tall and narrow 柱狀物: *a column of smoke* 煙柱 | *Add up that column of figures, will you?* 把那列數字全部加起來，好嗎？ **3** a group of people moving in a long line 一隊，一列〔行進的人〕: *a column of soldiers* 一隊士兵 **4** one of the long narrow divisions into which print is arranged in a book or on a newspaper page〔書報上的〕一欄: *This page is arranged in two columns.* 這一頁分成兩欄。 **5** an article by a particular writer, that regularly appears in a newspaper or magazine〔報刊的〕專欄(文章): *his weekly column in the local paper* 他每週在當地報紙上發表的專欄

col·umn·ist /'kɑləmɪst; 'kɒləm‚ɪst/ *n* a person who writes a regular article for a newspaper or magazine 專欄作家

co·ma /'kəmə; 'kəʊmə/ *n* a state like sleep, of long unnatural deep unconsciousness, from which it is difficult to wake up 昏迷: *After the accident she went into a coma.* 事故發生之後，她昏迷過去了。

co·ma·tose /'kəmə‚tos; 'kəʊmətəʊs/ *adj* **1** *tech* deeply unconscious〖術語〗昏迷的，不省人事的 **2** sleepy and slow to do anything (a word which is often used in a humorous way) 昏昏欲睡的，反應遲鈍的〔常作幽默用法〕

comb¹ /kom; kəʊm/ *n* **1** a flat piece of plastic or metal with a row of thin teeth, which you use to tidy your hair 梳子 **2** a decoration used in a woman's hair〔女子的〕頭飾 **3** the red fleshy growth on the head of a male chicken〔公雞的〕雞冠

comb² *v* [T] **1** to tidy your hair with a comb 梳〔頭髮〕: *Comb your hair before you go out.* 你出去前把頭髮梳一下。 **2** to search a place thoroughly 徹底搜查: *The police combed the woods for the missing boy.* 警察為尋找失踪的男孩搜遍了樹林。

com·bat¹ /'kɑmbæt; 'kɒmbæt/ *n* [C;U] a fight or struggle between two people, groups, armies, or ideas 戰鬥; 鬥爭: *These troops have very little experience of actual combat.* 這些部隊沒有多少實戰經驗。| *killed in combat* 陣亡

com·bat² /'kɒmbæt; 'kɑmbæt/ *v* **-tt-** (also 又作 **-t-** *AmE* 〖美式〗) [T] *fml* to fight or struggle against something 〖正式〗與…戰鬥; 與…鬥爭: *As a doctor, he spent his life combatting disease.* 他作為醫生，一生都在與疾病作鬥爭。| *The police are now using computers to help combat crime.* 警方正在使用電腦與犯罪活動作鬥爭。

com·ba·tant /'kɒmbətənt; 'kɑmbətənt/ *n* a person who takes part in fighting in a war 參戰者; 戰士

★**com·bi·na·tion** /ˌkɒmbə'neʃən; ˌkɑmbə'neʃən/ *n* **1** [C] a mixture of separate people or things that are joined together to make a single unit 聯合; 結合; 混合: *A combination of parties formed the new government.* 幾個黨派聯合組成了新政府。| *I felt a strange combination of shock and amusement.* 我有種既吃驚又好笑的奇怪感覺。**2** [U] **in combination** being joined together 聯合起來: *The dancers and singers worked well in combination.* 跳舞的人和唱歌的人配合得很好。**3** [C] a set of special numbers or letters needed to open a special lock 〖開密碼鎖的〗號碼組合

★**com·bine¹** /kəm'baɪn; kəm'baɪn/ *v* **combined, combining** [I;T] to join two or more things together (使)聯合[結合]起來: *The two parties have combined to form a government.* 兩黨已聯合起來組成政府。| *We'll have our meeting over dinner and combine business with pleasure.* 我們在吃飯時見面，寓工作於娛樂之中。

com·bine² /'kɒmbaɪn; 'kɑmbaɪn/ *n* **1** a group of businesses joined together 聯合企業 **2** (also 又作 **combine harvester**) a large machine which cuts corn and separates and cleans the grain 聯合收割機

com·bus·ti·ble /kəm'bʌstəbl; kəm'bʌstəbl/ *adj* able to catch fire and burn easily 易燃的: *Petrol is highly combustible.* 汽油極易燃燒。**–combustible** *n*

com·bus·tion /kəm'bʌstʃən; kəm'bʌstʃən/ *n* [U] *fml* the act of catching fire and burning 〖正式〗燃燒

★**come** /kʌm; kʌm/ *v* **came** /keɪm; keɪm/, **come, coming** [I] **1** to move towards a place, especially the place where the speaker is 來: *He got up and came towards me.* 他起身朝我走來。| *The train came into the station.* 火車駛進了車站。| *She came running into the room.* 她跑進了房間來。| *I'm afraid I won't be able to come to the party.* 我恐怕不能來參加晚會。| *You must come and visit us some time.* 你有空一定要來我們這裡坐坐。| *He came over to see what was going on.* 他過來看看發生了甚麼事。**2** to arrive 到達: *Everyone else is here*

but we're still waiting for John to come. 其他人都已在這裡了，但我們仍在等約翰來。| *Spring has come at last!* 春天終於來了！| *I think the time has come to abolish this law.* 我覺得廢除這條法律的時候到了。**3** to reach a place 抵達; 到達: *We walked on until we came to a village.* 我們一直走，直至來到一個村莊。| *They came to a little bridge over a stream.* 他們來到溪流上的一座小橋。| *The water came to my waist.* 水深及我的腰部。| *Her hair comes down to her waist.* 她的頭髮垂及腰間。| *The thick mud came up to my ankles.* 厚厚的爛泥沒到了我的腳踝處。**4** to be in a particular place or position 在〖某一個〗位置: *I came last in the race.* 我在跑步比賽中落在最後。| *What letter comes after "p"?* "p"後面是哪一個字母？**5** to become 變成: *My shoelaces have come undone.* 我的鞋帶鬆開了。| *The label's come off, so I don't know what's inside.* 標籤掉了，所以我不知道裡面裝的是甚麼。| *One of the wheels had come loose.* 有一隻輪子鬆了。**6** to be produced or offered in a particular way 〖以某種方式〗生產，提供: *The bag comes in three different colours, red, blue, or yellow.* 提包有三種顏色: 紅的、藍的和黃的。| *Cars come in all shapes and sizes these days.* 現在生產的汽車有各種形狀和尺寸。**7 come and go** to change often and quickly 變化無常: *These fashions and crazes come and go very rapidly.* 這些流行服飾變化得非常快。**8 come to do something: a** to happen to do something 恰巧做某事: *How did you come to be invited to the party?* 你怎麼會恰巧被邀請去參加晚會的？**b** to begin to do something 開始做某事: *I came to enjoy our little chats.* 我開始喜歡我們的閒聊。| *I'm sure you'll come to enjoy the work in time.* 我肯定你到時會喜歡那項工作的。**9 come to think of it** a phrase you use when you have just remembered something 想起來〖用於剛剛記起某事〗: *Come to think of it she still owes me £20.* 說起來，她還欠我二十英鎊呢。**10 come unstuck** to meet with difficulties and failure 遇到困難和失敗: *I think the government might finally come unstuck over the economy.* 我認為政府最終會在經濟上遭到失敗。**11 how come?** *infml* a phrase you use when you are asking how something happened 〖非正式〗怎麼會?〔用於詢問某事是如何發生的〕: *How come she got that job so easily, when she hasn't got any qualifications?* 她甚麼資格證明也沒有，怎麼會那樣容易就得到了那份工作？**12 to come** in the future 在將來; 在將來: *I'm afraid we might see unemployment rise even further in the weeks and months to come.* 恐怕在未來的幾個星期、幾個月裡，我們會看到失業率進一步上升。

come about *phr v* [I] to happen 發生: *How did this crisis come about?* 這場危機是如何發生的？| *This situation should never have come about.* 這種情況本來不應該發生。

come across phr v **1** [T **come across** sthg/sbdy] to meet someone or discover something by chance 偶然遇見〔某人〕; 偶然發現〔某物〕: *I came across an old friend I hadn't seen for years.* 我偶然遇到了一位多年沒見的老朋友。| *I came across some old books in the attic.* 我在閣樓上發現了一些舊書。**2** [I] to have a particular effect on the people listening〔對聽者〕產生某種效果: *His speech came across very well.* 他的演說很受歡迎。| *She came across as being vain and silly.* 她給人的印象是又虛榮又愚蠢。

come along phr v [I] **1** to advance or improve 進行; 進展: *How's your work coming along?* 你的工作進展得怎麼樣了? **2** to happen or arrive by chance 偶然發生〔出現〕: *I got the job because I came along at just the right time.* 我得到這份工作是因為碰巧遇上了好機會。**3 Come along!** a phrase you use to tell someone to hurry up or make an effort to do something 快點兒!〔用於催促某人〕; 加把勁! *Come along, or we'll be late.* 快點兒, 不然我們要遲到了。

come apart phr v [I] to break into pieces 裂碎; 破裂: *I picked up the book and it just came apart in my hands.* 我拿起書, 它就在我手裡散開了。

come at sbdy phr v [T] to move towards someone in a threatening way〔威脅着〕逼近〔某人〕: *She came at me with a knife.* 她手裡握着刀向我撲過來。

come away phr v [I] to become loose or disconnected from something 脫落; 斷開: *The handle came away in my hands.* 把手脫落在我手裡。

come back phr v [I] **1** to return 回來: *I'm sure she'll come back home eventually.* 我敢肯定她最終會回家來的。**2** to become fashionable or popular again 再次流行: *Bright colours are coming back this year.* 鮮艷的顏色今年再度流行。**3 come back to** something to talk about something again later 過一會兒再談某事: *I'll come back to that question later.* 我過一會再談那個問題。**4 come back to** sbdy to return into your mind 回想起: *I can't think of his name, but it'll probably come back to me in a minute.* 我想不起他的名字, 不過很快就會想起來的。

come between phr v **come between** people to cause trouble between people 在人與人之間〔引起麻煩〕: *We tried not to let our financial difficulties come between us.* 我們盡力不讓經濟困難在我們之間引起甚麼麻煩。

come by sthg phr v [T] to obtain something 得到〔某物〕: *How did you come by all that furniture?* 你是怎麼得到那所有家具的? | *Jobs are hard to come by at the moment.* 目前要找個工作很困難。

come down phr v [I] **1** to fall down 倒下: *Several trees came down in the storm.* 有幾棵樹在暴風雨中被颳倒。**2** to become less 變

少; 下降: *Hopefully, inflation will start to come down now.* 通貨膨脹現在有希望下降。**3 come down in favour of someone, come down on someone's side** to decide to support someone 決定支持某人: *The industrial court came down on the side of the unions.* 工業法庭決定支持工會。

come down on sbdy phr v [T] to punish someone severely, or show strong disapproval of them 嚴懲〔某人〕; 斥責〔某人〕: *The courts are going to come down heavily on young offenders.* 法庭將對年青的罪犯進行嚴懲。

come down to sthg phr v [T] to have something as the most important fact 歸結為〔某事物〕: *What it comes down to is a choice between cutting wages or reducing staff.* 這件事結果只能在減薪或裁員中做出選擇。

come down with sthg phr v [T] infml to catch an illness〔非正式〕患…病: *He came down with flu.* 他患了流感。

come forward phr v [I] to offer to help in some way 主動提供幫助; 自告奮勇: *No one has come forward with information about the murder.* 沒有人來提供有關謀殺案的資料。

come from sthg phr v [T] to have something as a place of origin 從〔某地〕來; 源於: *Milk comes from cows.* 牛奶是從乳牛身上擠出來的。| *Where do you come from?* 你是哪裡來的人? | *I come from Newcastle but I've spent most of my life in London.* 我是紐卡斯爾人, 但大半生是在倫敦度過的。

come in phr v [I] **1** (of information) to be received〔消息〕被收到: *Reports are just coming in of a train crash in the South East.* 關於東南部發生火車相撞事故的報道正不斷傳來。**2** to be elected 當選: *The Socialists came in three years ago.* 社會黨黨員在三年前當選。**3** to become fashionable or popular 流行起來; 時髦: *Ethnic clothes started coming in the early sixties.* 民族服裝在六十年代初期開始流行。**4 have money coming in** to be earning money 正在掙錢: *We haven't got much money coming in at the moment.* 我們目前掙的錢不多。**5 come in handy, come in useful** to be useful 有用: *Don't throw those bottles away — they might come in handy one day.* 別把那些瓶子扔掉 — 有朝一日它們也許會派上用場。

come in for sthg phr v [T] to receive blame or disapproval 受到〔指責〕: *The committee has come in for a lot of criticism recently.* 委員會近來受到許多指責。

come in on sthg phr v [T] to take part in something 參加〔某事物〕: *They were very keen to come in on the plan.* 他們對加入此計劃很熱心。

come into sthg phr v [T] **1** to gain money because someone has left it to you when they died 繼承〔錢財〕: *She came into a lot of money when her mother died.* 她母親死後, 她

繼承了一大筆錢。**2 come into your own** to show your abilities fully 充分施展才能: *He came into his own when he was put in charge of the department.* 他被任命主管這部門後，他的才能得到了充分的發揮。

come of sthg *phr v* [T] **1** to result from something 由〔某事〕引起: *I don't think that any good will come of all this.* 我認為所有這些都不會帶來任何的好處。**2 come of age** to reach the age of 18 or 21, when you are considered to be an adult 成年〔18歲或21歲〕

come off *phr v* **1** [I;T **come off** sthg] to become unfastened or disconnected 脫落; 鬆開: *A button's come off my coat.* 我的大衣掉了一顆鈕扣。| *The door handle came off in my hand.* 門的把手脫落在我的手裡。**2** [I] to happen successfully 成功地舉行: *The wedding came off as planned.* 婚禮按計劃順利舉行。| *I hope the deal comes off.* 我希望能做成這筆生意。**3 come off well** to be in a good position as the result of something 〔由於某事物而〕處於有利地位: *Most schools should come off well from the reorganization.* 大部分學校應當會從這次重組中受益。[RE-LATED PHRASE 相關詞組 **come off badly**] **4 Come off it!** a phrase you use when you do not believe what someone is saying 別胡說了!〔用於表示不相信某人所說的話〕: *Come off it! They must have known what was going on!* 別胡說了! 他們肯定知道是怎麼一回事了!

come on *phr v* [I] **1 be coming on** *infml* to be starting 〔非正式〕開始: *I could feel a headache coming on.* 我覺得頭開始痛了。**2** to advance or improve 進步; 進展: *His French has come on very nicely this term.* 本學期他的法語進步很大。**3 Come on!** a phrase you use to tell someone to hurry up or make an effort to do something 快點!〔用於催促某人動作快些或努力做某事〕: *Come on, let's get going.* 快點, 我們走吧。

come on to sthg *phr v* [T] to begin to talk about something 談及〔某事〕: *I'll come on to the question of money a bit later.* 我稍後再談資金問題。

come out *phr v* [I] **1** to appear in the sky 〔在天空中〕出現: *It was getting dark and the stars were coming out.* 天色逐漸昏暗, 星星開始出現。**2** to be produced and become available for people to buy 上市; 出版: *When's your new book coming out?* 你的新書何時出版? **3** (of information) to become known 〔消息〕傳開; 為人知曉: *It has now come out that many people suffered severe side effects from the drug.* 這種藥對許多人產生了嚴重的副作用, 這事現已暴露了。| *The truth will come out one day.* 真相終有一天會大白。**4** (of a photograph) to be produced successfully 〔照片〕沖洗: *I took a lot of photos on holiday but only a few came out.* 我在度假時拍了很多照片, 可是只沖洗出幾張來。**5** (of a mark) to disappear 〔痕跡〕消失:

I've washed this shirt three times but the stain still hasn't come out. 這件襯衫我洗了三次, 但污跡仍沒洗掉。**6** to declare your opinion publicly 公開表明觀點: *The American government has come out* **against** *the plan.* 美國政府已公開表示反對該計劃。| *Many leading politicians have come out in favour of the war.* 許多主要的政治家都已公開表示支持這場戰爭。

come out in sthg *phr v* [T] to become covered in marks or spots 佈滿〔標記或斑點〕: *He came out in a rash.* 他身上出了疹子。

come out with sthg *phr v* [T] to say something suddenly or unexpectedly 突然說出〔某事〕: *He came out with some ridiculous ideas.* 他突然說了幾個很荒謬的想法。

come over *phr v* **1** [I] to come to a place 來到〔某地〕: *When did you first come over to England?* 你第一次來英格蘭是甚麼時候? | *You must come over and see us some time.* 你有空一定要來看看我們。**2** [I] to have a particular effect on the people listening 〔對聽眾〕產生某種影響: *His speech came over very well.* 他的演說很受歡迎。**3** [T **come over** sbdy] (of a strong feeling) to suddenly have an effect on someone 突然感到: *A feeling of dizziness came over me.* 我突然感到一陣頭暈。| *I don't know what came over him.* 我不知道他怎麼了。

come round *phr v* [I] **1** to become conscious again 甦醒: *He came round after a few minutes.* 他幾分鐘後甦醒過來。**2** to change your mind and accept an idea 改變主意: *He'll come round to our way of thinking sooner or later.* 他遲早會改變態度, 接受我們的想法。**3** to happen as a regular event 〔事件〕定期發生: *Christmas will soon be coming round again.* 聖誕節很快就要來臨。**4** to visit someone 拜訪; 造訪: *You must come round for a drink one evening.* 找天晚上有空你一定要過來坐坐喝一杯。

come through *phr v* **1** [I] (of official information or an official document) to arrive 〔官方消息或正式文件〕抵達: *Have your exam results come through yet?* 你們的考試結果公佈了沒有? | *I'm still waiting for my visa to come through.* 我仍在等我的簽證。**2** [T **come through** sthg] to successfully come to the end of something difficult or unpleasant 渡過困境〔難關〕: *Only a few companies have managed to come through the recession.* 只有幾家公司設法渡過了經濟衰退期。| *We don't know whether he'll come through the operation.* 我們不知道他能否熬過這次手術。

come to *phr v* **1** [**come to** sthg] to reach something 到達: *It has come to my notice that some money is missing.* 我已注意到有些錢不見了。| *The present government came to power in 1990.* 現政府於1990年開始執政。**2** [**come to** sthg] to make a particular amount as a total 總計: *The bill came to*

£15. 賬款共計十五英鎊。 | *Our total savings now come to over £7000.* 我們現在的存款共有七千英鎊。 **3 [come to** sbdy**]** to come into your mind 想起；想到：*Suddenly the words of the song came to me.* 我突然想起了這首歌的歌詞。 | *When did the idea for this book first come to you?* 你最初是在甚麼時候想到要寫這本書的？ **4 [I]** to become conscious again 甦醒，恢復知覺：*I wanted to be there when he came to after the operation.* 我想在他手術後甦醒過來的時候到他那裡去。 **5 when it comes to...** = as far as a particular thing is concerned 關於；談到：*When it comes to politics I know very little.* 談到政治，我所知甚少。 **6 come to pass** *fml* to happen〖正式〗發生

come under sthg *phr v* **[T] 1** to be governed or controlled by someone 受…統轄；受…控制：*This committee will come under the Education Department.* 這個委員會將受教育部管轄。 **2** to receive something unpleasant 遭到：*We came under heavy gunfire.* 我們遭到猛烈的砲擊。 | *The government has come under severe criticism for these policies.* 政府由於這些政策而受到了強烈批評。 **3** to be found in a particular place in a system for storing information 列於〔某一部分〕：*What section does this come under?* 這列在哪一部分？

come up *phr v* **[I] 1** to be talked about or discussed 被討論：*Your question came up at the meeting.* 你的問題在會上給提出來討論了。 **2** to happen 發生：*I'll let you know if anything comes up.* 如果有事發生，我會告訴你的。 | *Something's come up — I'll have to go home.* 出了點事——我得回家了。 | *Her wedding's coming up soon.* 她的婚禮即將舉行。 **3** to come near to someone 走近〔某人〕：*He came up and asked me the time.* 他走過來問我時間。 | *A woman came up to me in the street.* 一個女子在街上向我走過來。 **4** to appear in the sky〔在天空中〕出現：*The snow started to melt as the sun came up.* 太陽出來時，雪便開始融化。

come up against sthg *phr v* **[T]** to meet a problem or difficulty 遇到〔問題或困難〕：*We've come up against a serious problem.* 我們碰到了一個嚴重的問題。

come upon sbdy/sthg *phr v* **[T]** to meet someone or something by chance 偶然遇到〔某人、某事〕：*A bit later I came upon a group hikers out for a walk.* 過了不久，我遇到了一羣遠足者出來旅行。

come up to sthg *phr v* **[T] be coming up to** be getting near to a time 接近〔某一時間〕：*The time is now coming up to six o'clock.* 現在離六點鐘越來越近。

come up with sthg *phr v* **[T]** to think of or suggest an idea 想出〔辦法〕；提出〔建議〕：*He couldn't come up with an answer.* 他想不出答案來。 | *No one has come up with an alternative.* 沒有人想出可供選擇的辦法來。

come·back /ˈkʌmˌbæk; ˈkʌmbæk/ *n* a return to a former position of strength or importance〔實力、地位的〕恢復，復原：*We just managed to make a comeback in the second half of the match.* 我們設法在下半場恢復了原來的水準。 | *Mini-skirts are making a comeback.* 迷你裙正再度流行。

co·me·di·an /kəˈmiːdiən; kəˈmiːdiən/ *n* a person whose job is telling jokes or making people laugh 喜劇演員

co·me·di·enne /kəˌmiːdiˈɛn; kəˌmiːdiˈen/ *n* a female comedian 女喜劇演員

come·down /ˈkʌmˌdaʊn; ˈkʌmdaʊn/ *n infml* a fall in importance〖非正式〗敗落；落泊：*It's a bit of a comedown to get a good pass in the exams and then not get a job.* 考試取得好成績卻找不到工作，這真令人有點失落。

com·e·dy /ˈkʌmədi; ˈkɒmɪdi/ *n* **comedies 1** [C] a funny play, film, or other work 喜劇；喜劇作品 –compare 比較 TRAGEDY：*Her last three films have been comedies.* 她最近拍的三部電影都是喜劇。 | *One of Shakespeare's most famous comedies* 莎士比亞最著名的喜劇之一 **2** [U] the humorous quality of something, either in a play or film or in real life 喜劇性：*We all laughed at the comedy of the situation.* 那情形很滑稽，我們都笑了。 | *an actor with a real flair for comedy* 一個具有真正喜劇天才的演員

come·ly /ˈkʌmli; ˈkʌmli/ *adj lit* attractive (used of women)〖文〗有吸引力的〔指女人〕 **–comeliness** *n* [U]

com·et /ˈkʌmɪt; ˈkɒmɪt/ *n* a very bright object like a star with a long tail, that moves round the sun 彗星

*★**com·fort**[1] /ˈkʌmfət; ˈkʌmfət/ *n* **1** [U] the state of being free from anxiety, pain, or unhappiness 舒適；安逸：*This car is built for comfort.* 這輛車是供休閒用的。 | *They live a life of great comfort.* 他們過着非常安逸的生活。 | *His words gave me some comfort.* 他的話給了我一點安慰。 **2 a comfort** someone or something that gives you encouragement or strength 安慰者；慰藉物：*My husband was a great comfort to me when I was ill.* 我生病時，我丈夫給了我很大的慰藉。 **3** [C] something which makes life easier and more enjoyable 令生活更加安逸〔舒適〕的東西：*the comforts of modern civilization* 現代文明帶來的舒適條件

comfort[2] *v* [T] to make someone feel less worried or unhappy 安慰〔某人〕：*I tried to comfort Jean after her mother's death.* 瓊的母親去世後，我盡量安慰她。 **–comforter** *n*

com·for·ta·ble /ˈkʌmfətəbl; ˈkʌmftəbəl/ *adj* (also 又作 **comfy** /ˈkʌmfi; ˈkʌmfi/ *infml*〖非正式〗) **1** providing physical comfort 舒服的，舒適的：*a comfortable chair* 舒適的椅子 | *I love these shoes — they're so comfortable!* 我喜歡這雙鞋——穿起來非常舒服呢! **2** not experiencing too much physical pain 舒服

的; 不受痛苦的: *I'm quite comfortable in this chair.* 我坐在這椅子上感覺很舒服。**3** feeling happy and confident, with no worries 感到快樂而自信的; 無憂無慮的: *I never feel comfortable when he's around.* 他在我旁邊我就覺得不自在。**4** providing a pleasant way of life without worries about money 〔生活〕充裕的; 小康的: *a comfortable income* 豐厚的收入 | *We're not rich but we're fairly comfortable.* 我們不富裕, 但生活還是蠻不錯的。–**comfortably** *adv*

com·ic¹ /'kɑmɪk; 'kɒmɪk/ *adj* funny or humorous 滑稽的; 好笑的: *a comic performance* 滑稽的表演 | *a comic actress* 喜劇女演員

comic² *n* **1** (also 又作 **comic book** /'··/ *AmE* 〖美式〗) a magazine for children containing pictures which tell a story 〔兒童的〕連環漫畫雜誌 **2** *infml* a person who is funny or amusing, especially a person who entertains people by making them laugh 〖非正式〗喜劇演員; 滑稽的人

com·i·cal /'kɑmɪkl; 'kɒmɪkəl/ *adj* odd or strange in a way that is amusing 古怪而可笑的: *She looked so comical with the bucket on her head.* 她把水桶頂在頭上, 樣子看起來很滑稽。

comic strip /'·· ·/ *n* a set of drawings telling a short story 連環漫畫

com·ing¹ /'kʌmɪŋ; 'kʌmɪŋ/ *n* **1** [sing] *fml* arrival 〖正式〗抵達; 到來: *With the coming of winter, days get shorter.* 隨着冬天的來臨, 白晝越來越短。**2 comings and goings** acts of arriving and leaving 來來往往: *We saw the comings and goings of the visitors from our bedroom window.* 我們從臥室窗口看着客人來來往往。

coming² *adj* [only before a noun 只用於名詞前] going to come or happen soon 即將發生的: *The coming months are going to be hard.* 未來幾個月的日子不會好過。

com·ma /'kɑmə; 'kɒmə/ *n* the mark (,) used in writing for separating different parts of a sentence or things in a list 逗號

★**com·mand¹** /kə'mænd; kə'mɑːnd/ *v* [T] **1** to order someone to do something 命令〔某人〕: *She commanded us to leave the city.* 她命令我們離開城市。| *"Don't move," she commanded.* "不許動", 她下命令說。

□ USEFUL PATTERN 有用句型
to command someone to do something

2 to have control over armed forces 指揮〔部隊〕: *General Carter commands this regiment.* 卡特將軍指揮這個軍團。**3** to deserve and get 贏得; 應得: *He commands a lot of respect.* 他贏得大家的尊敬。–see 見 OR·DER² (USAGE 用法)

command² *n* **1** [C] an order 命令: *All his commands were quickly obeyed.* 大家迅速執行他所有的命令。**2** [U] control 控制; 指揮:

The army is under the king's direct command. 軍隊由國王直接指揮。| *She took command when her husband died.* 丈夫死後, 她掌管一切。**3 in command** having power or control over someone or something 對〔某人或某物〕擁有控制權 **4 command of something** knowledge of something or ability to use it 〔對某方面知識的〕掌握; 運用能力: *He has good command of spoken French.* 他的法語說得很好。| *His command of advanced mathematics is very impressive.* 他對於高等數學的掌握令人讚嘆。

com·man·dant /,kɑmən'dænt; ,kɒmən'dænt/ *n* the chief officer in charge of a military organization 〔軍隊的〕指揮官

com·man·deer /,kɑmən'dɪr; ,kɒmən'dɪəʳ/ *v* [T] **1** to seize private property for military use without asking permission or giving payment 強佔〔私產作軍事用途〕; 徵用 **2** to take something from someone less important or powerful 強佔: *The boss has commandeered my desk again.* 老闆又一次強佔了我的書桌。

com·mand·er /kə'mændɚ; kə'mɑːndəʳ/ *n* an officer in charge of a military or police organization 指揮官; 隊長 **2** *BrE* an officer in the Royal Navy 〖英式〗〔皇家〕海軍中校

com·mand·ing /kə'mændɪŋ; kə'mɑːndɪŋ/ *adj* **1 commanding officer** the officer who is in charge 指揮官 **2** deserving or expecting respect and obedience 有權威的; 支配的: *She spoke in a loud, commanding voice.* 她威嚴地大聲說。| *We've lost our commanding position in the business world.* 我們已失去了在商界的支配地位。

Com·mand·ment /kə'mændmənt; kə'mɑːndmənt/ *n* any of the ten laws in the Bible which God says that people should obey 〔聖經十誡中的〕誡律

com·man·do /kə'mændo; kə'mɑːndəu/ *n* **commandos** *or* **commandoes** a member of a small military unit specially trained for making surprise attacks in enemy areas 突擊隊隊員

com·mem·o·rate /kə'mɛmə,ret; kə'memə,reɪt/ *v* **commemorated, commemorating** [T] to exist in order to make people remember an important person or event 紀念; 緬懷: *This statue commemorates those who died in the war.* 這座塑像是紀念戰爭死難者的。–**commemoration** /kə,mɛmə'reʃən; kə,memə'reɪʃən/ *n* [U]

com·mence /kə'mɛns; kə'mens/ *v* **commenced, commencing** [I;T] *fml* to begin or start 〖正式〗開始: *As it's already two o'clock shall we commence?* 已經兩點鐘了, 我們開始好嗎? | *Should we commence the attack?*

□ USEFUL PATTERNS 有用句型
to commence; to commence something;
to commence doing something

C

我們應該開始進攻了嗎? **–commencement** n

com·mend /kəˈmɛnd; kəˈmɛnd/ v [T] fml
〖正式〗 **1** to praise someone formally 讚揚
〔某人〕: *She was highly commended for her
efficiency.* 她由於效率高而大受讚揚。**2** to tell
someone that something is very good 推薦;
推崇: *This restaurant was commended to
me.* 有人向我推薦這家餐館。

com·men·da·ble /kəˈmɛndəbl; kəˈmendəbəl/
adj worthy of praise 值得讚揚的: *commen-
dable efforts* 值得稱讚的努力 **–commendably**
adv

com·men·da·tion /ˌkɑmənˈdeʃən; ˌkɔmən-
ˈdeɪʃən/ n an official prize or honour given
to someone because they have done something very good 嘉獎; 獎狀: *She was given a
commendation for bravery.* 她由於表現英勇
而受到嘉獎。

com·men·su·rate /kəˈmɛnʃərɪt; kəˈmenʃə-
rɪt/ adj fml equal to something or suitable
for it 〖正式〗相等的; 合適的: *He was given a
job commensurate with his age and experience.* 他得到一份與他年齡和經歷相稱的工作。

✱com·ment¹ /ˈkɑmɛnt; ˈkɔment/ n [C;U] **1**
an opinion about something or a judgment
about it 評論; 評價: *I asked the minister if
she had any comments about the election.*
我問部長, 她對選舉有甚麼評論。| *He was
making rude comments about the other
people in the room.* 他很不禮貌地對房間裡的
其他人評頭論足。| *The director was not
available for comment.* 董事對此事不予評
論。| *a fair comment* 公正的評論 **2 no com-
ment** a phrase used by people in public life
when they do not want to give an opinion
or explanation about something 無可奉告
〔在公眾場合人們不願發表意見或作出解釋時
使用〕

✱comment² v [I; + that] to make a remark or
give an opinion 評論; 發表意見: *The teacher
refused to comment on the examination
results.* 老師拒絕對考試結果發表意見。| *Jean
commented that she thought it was time for a
new government.* 瓊發表意見, 認為是成立新一
屆政府的時候了。

com·men·ta·ry /ˈkɑmənˌtɛrɪ; ˈkɔməntəri/ n
commentaries 1 [C] a description of an
event which is broadcast on radio or television usually while the event is happening
〔電台、電視的〕實況報道: *His spirited commentary makes a match very interesting even
on the radio.* 他生動的報道令即使是收聽比賽
也很有趣。| *a football commentary* 足球現
場評述 **2** [C;U] a written collection of
opinions, explanations or judgments, on a
book, event, or situation 〔書面的〕評論; 評
語; 述評: *political commentaries* 政治評論

com·men·tate /ˈkɑmənˌtet; ˈkɔmənteɪt/ v
commentated, commentating [I] to describe and talk about an event while it is
being broadcast on radio or television 〔電
台、電視〕實況報導 **–commentator** n

com·merce /ˈkɑmɝs; ˈkɔmɜːs/ n [U] the
buying and selling of goods 貿易; 商業: *Our
country has grown rich because of its commerce with other nations.* 我們的國家和其他
國家有貿易往來, 因而變得富裕起來。| *The
recession will hit both industry and commerce.* 經濟衰退對工業和商業會產生不良影
響。

✱com·mer·cial¹ /kəˈmɝʃəl; kəˈmɜːʃəl/ adj **1** related to or used in the buying and selling of
goods 商業的; 貿易的: *Our commercial laws
changed when we joined the EEC.* 我們在加
入歐共體時修改了貿易法。**2** [only before a
noun 只用於名詞前] producing or likely to
produce profit 有利可圖的; 獲利的: *The film
was a commercial success.* 這部電影很賣座。|
a commercial radio station 商業性〔營利性〕
廣播電台 **–commercially** adv

commercial² n an advertisement on television or radio 電視〔電台〕廣告

com·mer·cial·ized /kəˈmɝʃəlˌaɪzd; kəˈmɜː-
ʃəlaɪzd/ adj (also 又作 **commercialised** BrE
〖英式〗) too concerned with making profits
過於注重營利的; 商業化的: *I find Christmas
too commercialized these days.* 我覺得現在
的聖誕節太商業化了。

commercial ve·hi·cle /·ˈ·,·· ·ˈ··/ n a vehicle
used for carrying goods from place to
place along roads 商用運貨車

com·mis·e·rate /kəˈmɪzəˌret; kəˈmɪzəreɪt/ v
commiserated, commiserating [I] to express sympathy or pity for someone after
something unpleasant has happened to
them 同情; 憐憫: *I commiserated with her
over her failure.* 對於她的失敗, 我很同情。

com·mis·e·ra·tion /kəˌmɪzəˈreʃən; kəˌmɪzə-
ˈreɪʃən/ n [U] an expression of sympathy or
pity for someone 同情; 憐憫

✱com·mis·sion¹ /kəˈmɪʃən; kəˈmɪʃən/
n **1** [C;U] an amount
of money that is paid to a salesman when
he or she sells something 佣金: *His salary is
quite small, but he earns a lot on com-
mission.* 他的薪水很少, 不過他賺得不少佣金。|
My commission on this sale should be £100.
我在這筆買賣中可以賺取的佣金應為一百英
鎊。**2** [C] a particular job or duty given to a
person, usually to build something or produce a work of art 工作, 任務〔通常為建築或
製作藝術品方面的工作〕: *He was glad to be
given the commission for the design of a new
theatre.* 他得到設計新劇院這項工作, 感到非常
高興。**3** [C + sing/pl verb] a group of
people specially appointed to perform certain duties 委員會: *She established a commission to suggest improvements in the educational system.* 她成立了一個委員會來提出
改進教育制度的建議。| *The Commission
meet twice a week.* 委員會每週開兩次會。**4**
[C] an official paper appointing someone
to a high rank in the armed forces 〔軍官〕
委任狀

---

commission² *v* [T] **1** to officially ask someone to do something, especially to produce a work of art 委任，委派〔某人做某事，尤指製作一件藝術品〕: *He was commissioned to paint portraits of the royal family.* 他受託為皇室成員畫肖像。| *The Government has commissioned a report on the Health Service.* 政府已要求起草一份有關社會保健服務的報告。**2** to give someone a commission in the armed forces〔軍隊中〕任命，委任

com·mis·sion·aire /kəˌmɪʃənˈɛr; kəˌmɪʃə-ˈneər/ *n BrE* an attendant at the door of a cinema, theatre, or hotel《英式》〔電影院、劇院或旅館的〕看門人

com·mis·sion·er /kəˈmɪʃənər; kəˈmɪʃənər/ *n* an official in charge of a certain government department or other organization〔政府部門或其他組織的〕長官: *the Church commissioners* 教會負責人 | *the British High Commissioner* 英國高級專員

★com·mit /kəˈmɪt; kəˈmɪt/ *v* **-tt-** [T] **1** to do something wrong, bad, or unlawful 犯〔錯誤、壞事或非法的事〕: *There has been a rise in the amount of crime committed.* 犯罪數字已有所上升。| *She committed suicide.* 她自殺了。| *He denied that he had committed the murder.* 他否認自己犯有謀殺罪。**2** to order someone to be placed in a prison or in a MENTAL hospital 把〔某人〕關進〔監獄或精神病院〕: *He was found guilty and committed to prison.* 他被判有罪，被關進了監獄。**3** to set money or time apart for something 撥出〔時間或金錢〕: *They committed all their resources to the project.* 他們把全部的資源都投入該項目中。**4 commit yourself to something** to promise to do or support something 承諾做〔支持〕某事: *The government has committed itself to improving the National Health Service.* 政府已承諾改善國民保健制度。**5 not commit yourself** to not give your true opinion about something 不肯表明自己的意見: *He won't commit himself on the issue of women's rights.* 他不肯說出對於女權問題的看法。**6 commit something to memory** to learn something so that you can remember it 記住某事物: *He committed the address to memory.* 他把地址記住了。

★com·mit·ment /kəˈmɪtmənt; kəˈmɪtmənt/ *n* **1** [C] a responsibility which takes a lot of your time regularly 責任；義務: *We must honour our commitments to smaller nations.* 我們必須兌現對小國所作的承諾。| *family commitments* 對家庭所承擔的責任 **2** [U] a deep belief in a system or idea 效忠；虔誠: *I've never doubted her commitment to feminism.* 我從未懷疑過她對於女權運動的誠心。

com·mit·tal /kəˈmɪtl; kəˈmɪtl/ *n* [C;U] the act of sending a person to prison or to a MENTAL hospital 入獄；入(精神病)院

com·mit·ted /kəˈmɪtɪd; kəˈmɪtɪd/ *adj* very loyal to a particular aim, job, or way of life 虔誠的；忠誠的: *Jean's a very committed teacher.* 瓊是一位十分盡責的教師。| *We are very committed* **to** *equal rights for women.* 我們堅信婦女擁有同等的權力。

★★com·mit·tee /kəˈmɪti; kəˈmɪti/ *n* [+ sing/pl verb] a group of people chosen to study a particular problem or take particular decisions 委員會: *He's on a lot of committees.* 他在許多委員會裡任委員。| *The committee believe that the hospital must be improved.* 委員會認為醫院的條件必須改善。

com·mod·i·ty /kəˈmadəti; kəˈmɒdɪti/ *n* **commodities** a product, especially a mineral or farm product, that is bought and sold 商品〔尤指農、礦產品〕: *agricultural commodities* 農產品

com·mo·dore /ˈkamədɔr; ˈkɒmədɔːr/ *n* an officer of middle rank in the navy 海軍准將

★★com·mon¹ /ˈkamən; ˈkɒmən/ *adj* **1** usual or frequent 普通的；常見的: *Rabbits and foxes are common in Britain.* 兔子和狐狸在英國很常見。| *It is now quite common for women to become managers.* 現在婦女當上經理相當普遍。**2** [only before a noun 只用於名詞前] ordinary and not special 平常的；無特別之處的: *the common people* 老百姓 | *Common salt is very cheap.* 食鹽很便宜。| *There is no cure for the common cold.* 現在沒有醫治一般感冒的辦法。**3** belonging to or shared by two or more people or things 共有的；共享的: *We share a common language.* 我們說同一種語言。| *This feature is common to all the new machinery.* 所有的新機器都有這個特點。**4** having a coarse, rough way of speaking or behaving 粗鄙的，低俗的〔講話或行為〕**5 the Commons** the HOUSE OF COMMONS 下議院 **6 for the common good** in order to help or be to the advantage of people in general 為了幫助大家；為了眾人的利益 **7 common ground** a subject about which people agree 共同的話題: *When it comes to politics, we are on common ground.* 談到政治，我們有着相同的見解。**8 common knowledge** something known by most people 眾所周知的事 **9 common law** the unwritten law of England, based on custom and court decisions rather than on laws made by Parliament〔英國〕普通法〔基於習俗和法院決定而非由議會制定的不成文法〕**10 common-law husband/wife** a man or woman you have lived with for some time without having married, and who is considered to be your husband or wife 同居〔事實〕婚姻中的丈夫〔妻子〕**11 the Common Market** the EEC 歐洲經濟共同體；共同市場 **12 common noun** a noun that is not the name of a particular person, place, or thing; "book" and "sugar" are common nouns 普通名詞〔如"book"和"sugar"〕**13 common sense** practical good sense and judgment 常識: *He's* *got no common sense!* 他連一點常識也沒有! **14 have something in common** to share the same quality, or interest 有共同之處: *John and I have nothing in common.* 約翰和我毫無共同之處。

common² *n* an area of grassland which all people are free to use 公用草地

com·mon·er /'kɒmənə; 'kɑmənəʳ/ *n* a person who is not a member of a noble family or does not have a title 平民

***com·mon·ly** /'kɒmənlɪ; 'kɑmənlɪ/ *adj* usually or generally 通常地; 一般地: *He's commonly known as "Joe".* 人們通常都叫他 "喬"。

common-or·gar·den /,·· ·'···◂/ *adj* [only before a noun 只用於名詞前] *BrE infml* ordinary 〖英式, 非正式〗普通的; 平常的: *They've got a common-or-garden house just like anyone else.* 他們的房子很普通, 和其他人的一樣。

com·mon·place /'kɒmən,pleɪs; ,kɑmən-'pleɪs◂/ *adj* very common or ordinary and so not very interesting 普通的; 平凡的: *Soon it will be commonplace for people to travel to the moon.* 不久, 人們去月球旅行將變得很平常。

Com·mon·wealth /'kɒmən,wɛlθ; 'kɑmən-wɛlθ/ *n* **the Commonwealth** an organization of independent states which were formerly parts of the British Empire, established to encourage trade and friendly relations among its members 英聯邦

com·mo·tion /kə'məʃən; kə'məʊʃən/ *n* [sing; U] noisy confusion or excitement 騷動; 騷亂: *The imprisonment of the union leaders caused a commotion in Parliament.* 工會領導人入獄一事在國會裡引起一陣騷亂。| *What's all the commotion about?* 這場騷亂是怎麼一回事?

com·mu·nal /'kɒmjʊnl; 'kɒmj३nəl/ *adj* shared by or used by all the members of a group 共有的; 公共的: *communal land* 公有土地 | *communal ownership of property* 財產的公有

com·mune¹ /kə'mjuːn; kə'mjuːn/ *v* **communed, communing** *lit* 〖文〗**commune with** to have a close relationship with 與…關係密切: *I often walk by the sea to commune with nature.* 我常漫步海濱, 沉醉於大自然中。

com·mune² /'kɒmjuːn; 'kɒmjuːn/ *n* a group of people who live and work as a team for the general good 公社: *He's joined a commune.* 他參加了公社。

com·mu·ni·ca·ble /kə'mjuːnɪkəbl; kə'mjuː-nɪkəbəl/ *adj fml* able to be passed easily from one person to another (used of ideas and diseases) 〖正式〗可傳達的, 會傳染的〔指思想和疾病〕

***com·mu·ni·cate** /kə'mjuːnə,keɪt; kə'mjuːn३-keɪt/ *v* **communicated, communicating 1** [I] to share or exchange ideas or information with someone by speaking, writing, or using other means 〔通過交談、寫信或其他方式〕與〔某人〕交換信息, 交流思想: *We managed to communicate with each other*

CAR 汽車

Exercise 1 練習一
*There are 10 mistakes in this passage. Change the words in **bold** type to correct the mistakes.* 下面這段文字中有十個錯誤, 改寫黑體字部分來改正錯誤。

Mr Sampson opened the **bonnet** and put his briefcase on the back seat of the car. Then he got in, put his key in the **glove compartment** and started the engine. He put his foot on the **brake pedal** and moved the gear lever into first gear. Before driving off, he adjusted the **heater** so that he could see the traffic behind him. It was still dark so Mr Sampson switched on his **reversing light** so that he could see the road in front of him.

As he approached the town he looked at the **mileometer** and noticed that he was running out of petrol. There was a filling station on the left so Mr Sampson switched on his **windscreen wipers** to show that he was going to turn left. Then he put his foot on the **accelerator** because

he wanted to slow down.

He stopped beside a petrol pump and took off the **hub cap** so that the attendant could fill the petrol tank. "Perhaps I need some oil as well," thought Mr Sampson "I'd better check." So he opened the boot and looked inside. "That's strange," he thought "I'm sure I had an engine when I left home!"

What mistake has Mr Sampson made? 桑普森先生犯了甚麼錯誤?

Exercise 2 練習二
Think of your own car or a car you know well. How many of these things has it got? 想想自己的汽車或者你所了解的汽車, 看看下面這些部件中它佔了幾樣?

wheels	windscreen wipers
steering wheel	indicator lights
aerial	rear view mirror
door mirrors	seat belts
wings	gears

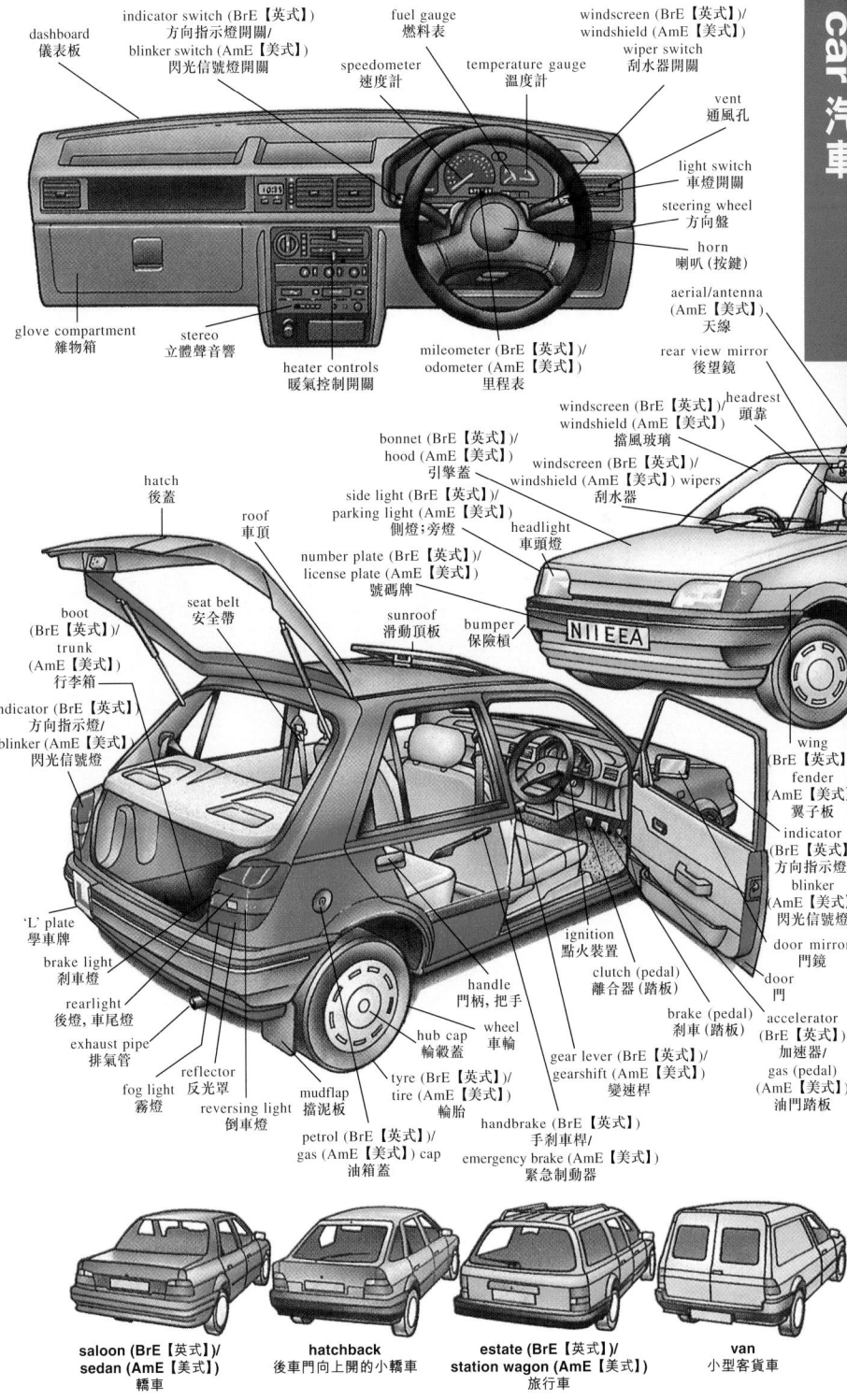

dashboard
儀表板

indicator switch (BrE【英式】)
方向指示燈開關
blinker switch (AmE【美式】)
閃光信號燈開關

fuel gauge
燃料表

windscreen (BrE【英式】)/
windshield (AmE【美式】)
wiper switch
刮水器開關

speedometer
速度計

temperature gauge
溫度計

vent
通風孔

light switch
車燈開關

steering wheel
方向盤

horn
喇叭 (按鍵)

aerial/antenna
(AmE【美式】)
天線

glove compartment
雜物箱

stereo
立體聲音響

heater controls
暖氣控制開關

mileometer (BrE【英式】)/
odometer (AmE【美式】)
里程表

rear view mirror
後望鏡

hatch
後蓋

bonnet (BrE【英式】)/
hood (AmE【美式】)
引擎蓋

roof
車頂

side light (BrE【英式】)/
parking light (AmE【美式】)
側燈;旁燈

number plate (BrE【英式】)/
license plate (AmE【美式】)
號碼牌

windscreen (BrE【英式】)/
windshield (AmE【美式】)
擋風玻璃

windscreen (BrE【英式】)/
windshield (AmE【美式】) wipers
刮水器

headlight
車頭燈

headrest
頭靠

seat belt
安全帶

boot
(BrE【英式】)/
trunk
(AmE【美式】)
行李箱

sunroof
滑動頂板

bumper
保險槓

indicator (BrE【英式】)
方向指示燈/
blinker (AmE【美式】)
閃光信號燈

wing
(BrE【英式】)
fender
(AmE【美式】)
翼子板

indicator
(BrE【英式】)
方向指示燈/
blinker
(AmE【美式】)
閃光信號燈

'L' plate
學車牌

brake light
剎車燈

rearlight
後燈,車尾燈

exhaust pipe
排氣管

fog light
霧燈

reflector
反光罩

reversing light
倒車燈

mudflap
擋泥板

handle
門柄,把手

hub cap
輪轂蓋

wheel
車輪

tyre (BrE【英式】)/
tire (AmE【美式】)
輪胎

petrol (BrE【英式】)/
gas (AmE【美式】) cap
油箱蓋

ignition
點火裝置

clutch (pedal)
離合器 (踏板)

gear lever (BrE【英式】)/
gearshift (AmE【美式】)
變速桿

handbrake (BrE【英式】)
手剎車桿/
emergency brake (AmE【美式】)
緊急制動器

brake (pedal)
剎車 (踏板)

door mirror
門鏡

door
門

accelerator
(BrE【英式】)
加速器/
gas (pedal)
(AmE【美式】)
油門踏板

saloon (BrE【英式】)/
sedan (AmE【美式】)
轎車

hatchback
後車門向上開的小轎車

estate (BrE【英式】)/
station wagon (AmE【美式】)
旅行車

van
小型客貨車

waistcoat (BrE【英式】)/ vest (AmE【美式】) 西裝背心;馬甲

shorts 短褲

vest (BrE【英式】)/ undershirt (AmE【美式】) 背心;汗衫

nightdress/night gown 女裝睡袍

bra 乳罩

knickers (BrE【英式】)/ underpants (AmE【美式】) 女裝內褲;女用短褲襯

underpa 男裝內褲 短褲襯

turban 頭巾

zip (BrE【英式】)/ zipper (AmE【美式】) 拉鏈

tights 女用褲襪

cuff 袖口

t-shirt T 恤衫

jumper (BrE【英式】)/ sweater (AmE【美式】) 套頭毛衣

jean 牛仔

sweatshirt 圓領長袖運動衫

collar 衣領

lapel 翻領

tie 領帶

braces (BrE【英式】)/ suspenders (AmE【美式】) (男褲的)吊帶

shirt 襯衫

sari (印度婦女裹身用的)莎麗

anorak (BrE【英式】)/ parka (AmE【美式】) 帶風帽的外套

jacket 束克

glove 手套

pyjamas (BrE【英式】)/ pajamas (AmE【美式】) 睡衣褲

slipper 拖鞋

boots 長統靴

button 鈕扣

socks 短襪

suit 套裝

scarf 圍巾

leggings 綁腿;護腿

raincoat 雨衣

sleeve 袖子

plimsoll (BrE【英式】)/ tennis shoe (AmE【美式】) 橡皮底帆布鞋;膠底運動鞋

coat 外衣

pocket 衣袋;口袋

skirt 裙子

cardigan 開襟羊毛衫

dress 連衣裙

tracksuit (BrE【英式】)/ sweats (AmE【美式】) 運動服

belt 腰帶

trousers 褲子

ring 戒指

watch 手錶

hat 帽子

brim 帽檐

heel 鞋跟

shoes 鞋

woolly hat (BrE【英式】)/ stocking cap (AmE【美式】) 羊毛帽/絨線帽

mitten 連指手套

buckle (帶子的)搭扣

earring 耳環

(shoe) lace 鞋帶

necklace 項鏈

trainers (BrE【英式】) 運動鞋/ running shoes (AmE【美式】) 跑鞋

bracelet 手鐲

brooch 胸針;飾針

by using sign language. 我們設法用手語來溝通。| *The two ships communicated by radio.* 兩艘船用無線電聯絡。**2** [T] to make an idea or piece of information known and understood 傳達, 傳遞〔意見或信息〕: *Radio and television were widely used to communicate government policy.* 電台和電視被廣泛地用來宣傳政府的政策。| *He doesn't communicate his ideas very clearly to the students.* 他沒有把自己的想法很清楚地告訴學生。

com·mu·ni·ca·ting /kəˈmjunəˌketɪŋ; kəˈmjuːnɪ̩ˈkeɪtɪŋ/ *adj* joined together by a door 相連的: *communicating bedrooms* 相通的臥室

✲com·mu·ni·ca·tion /kəˌmjunəˈkeʃən; kəˌmjuːnɪ̩ˈkeɪʃən/ *n* **1** [U] the act of communicating 傳達; 交換; 交流: *Communication with France was difficult during the telephone and postal strike.* 電信和郵政部門罷工期間, 與法國通訊聯繫很困難。| *Radio and television are im-* *portant means of communication.* 無線電與電視是重要的傳播工具。**2** [C] *fml* a letter or message 〖正式〗書信; 訊息: *This communication is secret; no one but you must see it.* 這封信是機密的, 除了你以外任何人都不准看。**3 communications** [pl] the various ways of communicating, and sending information between places by means of roads, railways, radio, telephone, or television 〔各種〕交通; 通訊方式: *Moscow has excellent communications with all parts of the Soviet Union.* 莫斯科與蘇聯境內各地之間的交通很便捷。| *communications networks* 通訊網絡

com·mu·ni·ca·tive /kəˈmjunəˌketɪv; kəˈmjuːnɪ̩ˈkətɪv/ *adj* very willing to talk or give information 愛説話的; 健談的

com·mu·nion /kəˈmjunjən; kəˈmjuːnjən/ *n* **1** [U] the sharing or exchange of feelings, beliefs or ideas 〔感情、信仰或想法的〕共享, 交流: *communion with nature* 與大自然的交融 | *communion between man and God* 人與上帝之間的交流 **2 Communion** [C;U] the

---

CLOTHES 衣服

Exercise 1 練習一

We wear different clothes for different activities. These people have each made one mistake. What is it? 我們穿不同的衣服參加不同的活動。下面這些人所穿的都有一處出錯, 那是甚麼?

1 Mr Collins is in a business meeting. He is wearing a dark suit, a red t-shirt, black socks and black shoes.
2 Mrs Stanford is climbing a mountain. She is wearing blue jeans, a red sweatshirt, a blue scarf, a red anorak, black socks and green slippers.

3 Sandra is dancing with her boyfriend in a disco. She is wearing a red sweater, a white blouse, a brown skirt, brown tights, red shoes and a blue raincoat.
4 Mandy is jogging in the park. She is wearing a yellow track suit, blue trainers, a red dressing gown and a blue hat.
5 Frank is getting ready to go to bed. He is wearing red and white striped pyjamas, a red tie, a brown dressing gown and brown slippers.

Exercise 2 練習二

How often do these clothes have these things? Put a tick (✓) for always, a cross (✗) for never, and a question mark (?) for sometimes. 下面這些衣服是否常帶有所列的內容? 用(✓)表示" 總是 ", 用(✗)表示" 從不 ", 用(?)表示" 有時 "。

	belt	collar	sleeves	pockets	lapels	buttons
jeans	?	✗	✗	✓	✗	✓
raincoat						
nightdress						
tracksuit						
waistcoat						
gloves						
sandals						
scarf						

---

religious service in churches in which bread and wine are shared in a solemn ceremony 聖餐儀式

com·mu·ni·qué /kə,mjunə'ke; kə'mjuːnʃ-keɪ/ n an official report or declaration to the public or newspapers 公報: *In its latest communiqué the government suggests that both sides will soon reach an agreement.* 在最新發表的公報中，政府暗示雙方不久將達成協議。

com·mu·nis·m /'kɑmju,nɪzəm; 'kɒmjʊ̩nɪzəm/ n [U] the political system in which the state controls the means of production and there is no private property 共產主義 – compare 比較 SOCIALISM

com·mu·nist /'kɑmju,nɪst; 'kɒmjʊ̩nɪst/ n a person who believes in communism 共產主義者

✿com·mu·ni·ty /kə'mjunəti; kə'mjuːnʃti/ n communities [+ sing/pl verb] a group of people who live in the same area or who have the same interests, religion, or nationality 社區; 社團; 社會: *The job of a politician is to serve the community.* 政治家的職責是為大眾服務。 | *They have done a lot for the local community.* 他們為當地的社區做了許多工作。 | *The black community are very worried by these recent events.* 最近的這些事件令黑人社區憂心忡忡。

com·mute /kə'mjut; kə'mjuːt/ v commuted, commuting 1 [I] to travel regularly a long distance between your home and work 返於兩地(上下班); 通勤: *She commutes from Cambridge to London every day.* 她每天來往於劍橋和倫敦之間。 2 [T] *fml* to make a punishment less severe 《正式》減輕〔刑罰〕: *His punishment was commuted from death to life imprisonment.* 他的刑罰由死刑減為無期徒刑。

com·mut·er /kə'mjutɚ; kə'mjuːtəʳ/ n a person who regularly travels a long distance to work 乘車上下班的人, 通勤者

com·pact¹ /kəm'pækt; kəm'pækt/ adj 1 firmly and closely packed together 緊密的: *The trees grew in a compact mass.* 樹木長得很茂密。 2 taking up very little space 佔地小的; 緊湊的: *The flat was tidy and compact.* 這所公寓整潔而且井井有條。 | *This computer is more compact than most.* 這台電腦要比大部分電腦更加小巧玲瓏。

com·pact² /'kɑmpækt; 'kɒmpækt/ n a small flat container for a woman's face powder and a mirror 〔婦女用的〕帶鏡小粉盒

compact disc /,·· '·/ n a type of record with very high quality sound played on a special machine 鐳射唱片 –see picture on page 730 見 730 頁彩圖

com·pact·ed /kəm'pæktɪd; kəm'pæktʃd/ adj pressed together firmly and closely 壓緊的; 結實的: *a compacted mass* 壓得很結實的一團

✿com·pan·ion /kəm'pænjən; kəm'pænjən/ n someone who you spend time with, either as a friend or because you are travelling with them 同伴; 伴侶: *He was my only companion during the war.* 他是我在戰爭期間唯一的夥伴。 | *My fellow travellers were good companions.* 和我同行的人都是好旅伴。

com·pan·io·na·ble /kəm'pænjənəbl; kəm'pænjənəbəl/ adj friendly and likely to be a good companion 友善的; 表示友好的

com·pan·ion·ship /kəm'pænjənʃɪp; kəm'pænjənʃɪp/ n [U] friendly company 交情; 友情: *He missed the companionship he'd enjoyed in the navy.* 他很懷念在海軍服役時的那份戰友間的情誼。

✿com·pa·ny /'kʌmpəni; 'kʌmpəni/ n companies 1 [C + sing/pl verb] an organization of people who work together in business or trade 公司; 商行: *a bus company* 公共汽車[巴士]公司 | *Which company do you work for?* 你在哪家公司工作? | *Robinson and Company* 羅賓遜公司 | *My company sell computers.* 我的公司出售電腦。 2 [C + sing/pl verb] a group of entertainers who work together 文藝團體: *The theatre company tour the country every summer.* 劇團每年夏天在全國各地巡迴演出。 3 [U] friendship from people with whom you spend time 交情; 友情; 陪伴: *I was grateful for Jean's company on the train.* 我很感謝瓊在火車上陪伴我。 4 [U] one or more guests 客人: *No, you can't go out tonight, we're expecting company.* 不行, 你今晚不能出去; 我們有客人來。 5 [C] a group of about 120 soldiers 〔軍隊的〕連〔約一百二十人〕 6 keep someone company to spend time with someone so that they are not alone 陪伴某人: *If you're going for a walk, I'll come too to keep you company.* 你要是出去散步, 那我陪你一起去。 7 in company in the presence of a group of people 當著眾人面前: *Don't swear in company!* 不要當眾罵人! 8 part company to go your own separate ways 分開, 分離

com·pa·ra·ble /'kɑmpərəbl; 'kɒmpərəbəl/ adj *fml* similar and of equal size or quality, and so able to be compared 《正式》〔大小或特性〕相近的; 可比較的: *A comparable car would cost far more abroad.* 類似的汽車在國外要貴得多。 | *This job is not comparable to any other.* 這個工作不同於其他任何工作。 | *His poetry is hardly comparable with Shakespeare's!* 他的詩與莎士比亞的詩根本不能相提並論! –**comparably** adv

com·par·a·tive¹ /kəm'pærətɪv; kəm'pærə-tɪv/ adj 1 showing the differences and similarities between things of the same kind 比較的〔以顯示出同類事物的不同與相同之處〕: *a comparative study of European languages* 歐洲語言的比較研究 2 measured or judged when compared with something of the same kind 相比而言的; 相對的: *the* *comparative wealth of the south of England* 英格蘭南部相對而言較為富裕 **3** related to the form of adjectives or adverbs expressing an increase in quality, quantity, or degree; for example, "bigger" is the comparative form of "big" 比較級的〔如 bigger 是 big 的比較級〕

comparative² *n tech* 《術語》 **the comparative** the comparative form of an adjective or adverb 〔形容詞或副詞的〕比較級(形式) – see Study Note on page 1311 見 1311 頁學習提示

com·par·a·tive·ly /kəmˈpærətɪvlɪ; kəmˈpærətʃvli/ *adv* compared with others 比較地; 相對地: *Man is a comparatively new creature on the face of the earth.* 人類是地球上出現得較晚的生物。

com·pare /kəmˈpɛr; kəmˈpeəʳ/ *v* **compared, comparing** [T] **1** to examine or judge one thing against another in order to show how they are the same or how they are different 比較: *If you compare the two cars you'll find that yours is better designed.* 如果你把兩部車比較一下，你就會發現你的那一部設計得好一些。| *Researchers compared living conditions in London* **with** *those in other cities.* 研究人員把倫敦的生活條件與其他城市的做了比較。| *We've been comparing notes on our trips to India.* 我們一直在談我們印度之行的見聞感想。**2** to say that two things are similar in some way 比較〔兩者的〕相似之處: *She has often been compared to her mother.* 人們常說她像她的母親。**3 compared with, compared to** a phrase used when you are saying how things are different 與…相比〔用以比較不同事物〕: *Their prices are low compared to those in other shops.* 與其他商店相比，他們的價格算是比較低的。**4 cannot compare with, does not compare with** = is not as good as 不如…好: *Living in a town can't compare with living in the country.* 鄉村的生活比城鎮的生活好得多。

com·pa·ri·son /kəmˈpærəsən; kəmˈpærəsən/ *n* **1** [C;U] the act of judging two things and saying whether they are similar or different 比較; 對照: *He made a comparison of housing conditions in different parts of the country.* 他把全國各地的住房狀況做了比較。| *We looked at the prices of goods in one shop, then looked in other shops for comparison.* 我們在一家商店裡看了看商品價格，然後又去跟其他商店的比較一下。**2 in comparison, by comparison** a phrase used when you are comparing things 相比之下: *The driver's injuries were trivial in comparison* **with** *those of the passengers.* 司機所受的傷與乘客相比算是微不足道了。**3 there is no comparison** a phrase used when you are saying that one thing is very much better than another 無法相比〔用於表示一物遠較另一物為好〕: *There is no comparison* **between**

frozen and fresh food. 冷凍食品與新鮮食品根本沒法比。

com·part·ment /kəmˈpɑːtmənt; kəmˈpɑːtmənt/ *n* **1** one of the small rooms in a railway carriage 列車車廂: *We sat in a second-class compartment.* 我們坐在二等車廂。**2** a special part of a container used for keeping certain things in 〔存放物品的〕分隔間: *This fridge hasn't got a compartment for frozen foods.* 這台冰箱沒有存放冷凍食品的分隔間。

com·part·men·tal·ize /ˌkəmpɑːtˈmɛntlaɪz, ˌkɒmpɑːtˈmɛntl-aɪz/ *v* **compartmentalized, compartmentalizing** (also 又作 **compartmentalise** *BrE* 《英式》) [T] to divide something into separate parts 把〔某物〕分成幾部分

com·pass /ˈkʌmpəs; ˈkʌmpəs/ *n* **1** an instrument for showing direction, usually consisting of a freely-moving MAGNETIC needle which always points to the north 指南針; 羅盤 **2 compasses** [pl] a V-shaped instrument used for drawing circles or measuring distances on maps 圓規 **3 the compass of something** *fml* the range of something 《正式》界限[範圍]: *To help the old is well within the compass of the government's social responsibility.* 幫助老人當然是政府的一項社會責任。

com·pas·sion /kəmˈpæʃən; kəmˈpæʃən/ *n* [U] pity or sympathy for people who are suffering 同情; 憐憫: *The world's main religions all teach us to have compassion* **for** *the poor and hungry.* 世界上幾個主要的宗教都勸戒我們對貧窮和飢餓的人要有同情心。

com·pas·sion·ate /kəmˈpæʃənɪt; kəmˈpæʃə-nɪt/ *adj* showing pity or sympathy for other people 富有同情心的 **–compassionately** *adv*

com·pat·i·ble /kəmˈpætəbəl; kəmˈpætʃbəl/ *adj* able to live, exist, or be used together without difficulty or danger 能共處的; 相容的: *Is your computer compatible* **with** *this equipment?* 你的電腦與這台設備兼容嗎? | *Do you think that religion is compatible with science?* 你認為宗教能與科學並存嗎? | *Their marriage ended because they were simply not compatible.* 他們由於完全合不來，終於離婚了。**–opposite** 反義 **incompatible** **–compatibly** *adv*

com·pat·ri·ot /kəmˈpetrɪət; kəmˈpætrɪət/ *n* a person from the same country as another person 同胞; 同國人

com·pel /kəmˈpɛl; kəmˈpɛl/ *v* **-ll-** [T] **1** to make someone do something by force 強迫〔某人做某事〕: *My father compelled us to stay indoors.* 父親強迫我們留在家裡。**2** *fml* to make someone feel something through persuasion 《正式》令〔某人〕感到: *His great skill compels our admiration.* 他嫻熟的技巧令我們不得不欽佩。

com·pel·ling /kəmˈpɛlɪŋ; kəmˈpɛlɪŋ/ *adj* **1**

making you believe something 令人信服的:
This is a very compelling argument. 這是個
非常有説服力的論據。 **2** very exciting and
interesting 激動人心的: *a very compelling
book* 一本引人入勝的書

com·pen·di·um /kəmˈpɛndɪəm; kəmˈpɛn-
dɪəm/ *n* compendiums *or* compendia *fml* a
book containing a short but detailed account of facts or information 〖正式〗概要;
綱要

com·pen·sate /ˈkɑmpən,set; ˈkɔmpənseɪt/
v compensated, compensating **1** [T] to give
someone money for a loss, damage, or
inconvenience 補償; 賠償: *He was compensated* **for** *his loss of earnings.* 他由於喪失收
入而得到補償。 **2** compensate for something
to remove the bad effects of something 彌補
某物: *Her intelligence more than compensates
for her lack of experience.* 以她的智慧彌補她的
經驗不足是綽綽有餘的。

*★ **com·pen·sa·tion** /ˌkɑmpənˈseʃən; ˌkɔmpən-
ˈseɪʃən/ *n* **1** [U] money paid to
pay for loss or damage 補償[賠償]金: *He
lost his job, but got no compensation.* 他失業
了，卻沒有得到任何補償。 **2** [C] something
which makes a situation seem less bad 彌
補[補償]物: *There are some compensations
for the power cuts.* 有一些補償作為對供電中
斷(帶來的損失)的彌補。

com·pen·sa·to·ry /kəmˈpɛnsə,tɔri; ˌkɔm-
pənˈseɪtəri/ *adj* **1** compensatory payment a
payment of money made to compensate
someone 賠款 **2** made to help people with
special needs or problems 補償的〖指用以幫
助有特殊需要與困難的人的〗: *compensatory
education* 補償教育

com·pere /ˈkɑmpɛr; ˈkɔmpeəʳ/ *n BrE* a
person whose job is to introduce acts in
a stage or television show 〖英式〗節目主持
人 **–compere** *v* compered, compering [T]:
Who compered last night's show? 昨晚的節
目是由誰主持的?

*★ **com·pete** /kəmˈpit; kəmˈpiːt/ *v* competed,
competing [I] to try to win or gain something in competition with someone else 競
爭: *John competed* **for** *a place at the school,
but didn't get in.* 約翰想在學校爭取一個名額，
但沒有成功。 | *Although there were only
four horses competing it was an exciting
race.* 儘管只有四匹馬參賽，但仍然非常精彩。 |
The two companies have to compete **against**
each other for customers. 這兩家公司不得不
互相爭取顧客。 | *I don't want to compete*
with *you.* 我不想和你競爭。

com·pe·tent /ˈkɑmpətənt; ˈkɔmpɪtənt/ *adj*
1 having the ability or skill to do something
effectively 能勝任的; 稱職的: *He's a very
competent driver.* 他是個非常稱職的司機。 –
opposite 反義 INCOMPETENT **2** satisfactory and showing ability or skill 令人滿意
的; 表現出能力與技術的: *She did a competent job.* 她的工作表現令人滿意。 **–com-
petence** *n* [U] **–competently** *adv*

*★ **com·pe·ti·tion** /ˌkɑmpəˈtɪʃən; ˌkɔm-
pɪˈtɪʃən/ *n* **1** [U] a
situation in which two or more people are
trying to win or gain the same thing 競爭:
There was keen competition **between** *the
journalists to get the story first.* 記者為了搶先獲
得消息，展開了激烈的競爭。 | *The two firms
were in competition* **with** *each other.* 那兩家公
司在相互競爭。 | *There was a lot of compe-
tition* **for** *the job.* 許多人為了得到這份工作而
展開了競爭。 **2** [C] an event in which many
people try to do the same thing, to find out
who is the best 比賽; 競賽: *a dancing competition* 舞蹈比賽

*★ **com·pet·i·tive** /kəmˈpɛtətɪv; kəmˈpetɪtɪv/ *adj*
1 related to or decided by competition 競爭
的; 以競爭來決定的: *the competitive nature of
British society* 英國社會的競爭性 | *competi-
tive sports* 競技性體育項目 **2** eager to appear
better or more successful than other people
好強的; 有競爭心的: *He's extremely competitive.* 他極其好強。 **3** able to sell or be sold successfully because the price charged is
reasonable 〔由於價格合理而〕易於銷售的:
British industry is not competitive enough. 英國
工業的競爭能力不夠強。 | *Their prices are very
competitive.* 他們的價格很有競爭力。 **–com-
petitively** *adv* **–competitiveness** *n* [U]

com·pet·i·tor /kəmˈpɛtətəʳ; kəmˈpetɪtəʳ/ *n* a
person, team, or firm competing with
another or others 競爭者; 參賽者: *There were
10 competitors in the race.* 有十位選手參加賽
跑。 | *Last year our company sold many more
computers than our competitors.* 去年我們公司
銷售的電腦比競爭對手所銷售的要多得多。

com·pi·la·tion /ˌkɑmplˈeʃən; ˌkɔmpɪˈleɪʃən/
n **1** [C] a book or other work that contains
a collection of smaller works 匯編; 輯錄 **2**
[U] the act of compiling something 編輯,
編寫

com·pile /kəmˈpaɪl; kəmˈpaɪl/ *v* compiled,
compiling [T] to make a report or book
from facts and information found in various places 編寫; 匯編: *It takes years of hard
work to compile a good dictionary.* 編一本好
辭典要花好幾年的功夫。 | *The programme
was compiled by members of the medical research team.* 該計劃是由醫學研究小組的成員
編寫出來的。 **–compiler** *n*

com·pla·cent /kəmˈplesn̩t; kəmˈpleɪsənt/ *adj*
too pleased or satisfied with yourself, and
feeling that you do not need to worry about
something 過於自滿的; 得意洋洋的: *After
winning six times we became complacent and
thought we'd never lose.* 贏了六場比賽以後，我
們得意忘形，以為永遠也不會輸。 **–com-
placency** *n* [U]: *I see no reason for the
government's complacency.* 我認為政府沒有
任何自滿的理由。 **–complacently** *adv*

*★ **com·plain** /kəmˈplen; kəmˈpleɪn/ *v* [I;T +
that] **1** to express feelings of annoyance or

unhappiness about something 抱怨; 埋怨: *Mary is always complaining* **about** *something.* 瑪麗總是牢騷滿腹。| *He complained that he couldn't find a job anywhere.* 他抱怨說自己到處都找不到工作。| *Our neighbour said he'd complain* **to** *the police if we made any more noise.* 我們的鄰居說, 如果我們再吵鬧, 他就要向警方投訴。

□ USEFUL PATTERNS 有用句型
to complain; to complain about something to someone; to complain that…

2 complain of something to say that you have a pain or illness 訴說病痛; 主訴: *He had been complaining of a pain in his chest.* 他一直說胸口疼痛。

com·plaint /kəm'pleɪnt; kəm'pleɪnt/ n **1** [C] a statement expressing annoyance or unhappiness about something 怨言; 牢騷: *The police received several complaints* **about** *the noise from our party.* 警方收到了幾個不滿投訴, 說我們的舞會太吵了。| *I'm really tired of his endless complaints!* 對於他無休止的怨言, 我實在是聽夠了! | *He made a complaint* **against** *his former employers.* 他對以前的雇員提出了控訴。| *We handed in a list of our complaints.* 我們把不滿的事項列出來提交。**2** [C] an illness in one part of your body 〔身體某部位的〕病; 疾病: *a serious liver complaint* 嚴重的肝病 **3** [U] the act of complaining 抱怨; 投訴: *I'm going to write a letter of complaint.* 我打算寫封投訴信。| *You have no cause for complaint.* 你沒有理由發牢騷。

com·ple·ment¹ /'kɒmpləmənt; 'kɒmplɪ-mənt/ n 1 something that completes something else by adding what is lacking 補足物; 補充物: *A fine wine is a complement to a good meal.* 美食加美酒才算是完備。**2 a full complement** the total quantity needed to make something complete 滿額: *The school's English department has its full complement of teachers.* 學校英語系的教師編制已滿額。**3** a word or a phrase, especially a noun or adjective, that follows a verb and describes the subject of the verb; for example, in "She is American", "American" is the complement. 〔文法〕補語〔跟在動詞之後並描述動詞之對象的詞或詞組, 如 "She is American" 中的 "American" 是補語。〕

com·ple·ment² /'kɒmplə,mɛnt; 'kɒmplɪ-mɛnt/ v [T] to make something better or nicer by adding something that was lacking 補充; 補足: *This wine complements the food perfectly.* 用這種酒配這種菜餚可算是完美無缺了。| *The bus and train services complement each other very well.* 公共汽車與火車互相補足, 使交通極為便利。

com·ple·men·tary /,kɒmplə'mɛntərɪ; ,kɒm-plɪ'mɛntərɪ/ adj making something better

or nicer by adding something that was lacking 補充的; 補足的

*★**com·plete¹ /kəm'plit; kəm'pliːt/ adj* **1** having all the parts or people that are necessary or usual 完整的: *John's birthday did not seem complete without his father there.* 沒有他父親在場, 約翰的生日似乎不夠完美。| *a complete set of the works of Shakespeare* 莎士比亞全集 –opposite 反義 **incomplete 2** finished or ended 完成的; 結束的: *When will work on the new railway be complete?* 新鐵路工程何時完工? **3** [only before a noun 只用於名詞前] a word used to add force to what you are saying 絕對的; 十足的〔表示強調〕: *It was a complete surprise to see you on the bus yesterday.* 昨天在公共汽車上遇見你真是意外。| *He's a complete idiot!* 他是個十足的蠢才! **4 complete with** including or containing something additional 齊備的; 備有〔額外的東西〕: *We bought the house complete with furniture.* 我們買了一棟備有全部家具的房子。–**completeness** *n* [U] –**completion /kəm'pliː-ʃən; kəm'pliːʃən/ n** [U]

complete² v completed, completing [T] **1** to add what is missing or needed to something to form a finished whole 使完整: *I need one more stamp before my collection is completed.* 我還需一枚郵票才能湊成完整的一套。| *Seeing her parents again completed her happiness.* 再次見到父母令她心滿意足。**2** to finish something or bring it to an end 完成; 結束: *When will work on the new road be completed?* 新鐵路工程何時完工?

*★**com·plete·ly /kəm'plitlɪ; kəm'pliːtlɪ/ adv** totally 完全地, 十分地: *The army made a completely successful attack on the enemy capital.* 軍隊攻擊敵方首都的行動十分成功。| *I completely forgot about it.* 我完全把這件事忘了。

*★**com·plex¹ /kəm'plɛks; 'kɒmplɛks/ adj** difficult to understand, explain, or deal with 令人費解的; 棘手的: *Her political ideas were too complex to get support from ordinary people.* 她的政治觀點過於令人費解, 所以她得不到普羅大眾的支持。| *This is a very complex problem.* 這是個很棘手的問題。**2** consisting of many closely connected parts 錯綜複雜的: *There is a complex network of roads connecting Glasgow and Edinburgh.* 格拉斯哥與愛丁堡之間有個錯綜複雜的公路網。–**complexity /kəm'plɛksɪtɪ; kəm'plɛks-tɪ/ n complexities** [C;U]

com·plex² /'kɒmplɛks; 'kɒmplɛks/ n 1 a group of buildings or one large building used for a particular purpose 〔為某一目的而建的〕綜合建築: *a sports complex* 綜合性體育館 | *a shopping complex* 綜合性商場 **2** a group of unconscious fears or feelings which influence someone's behaviour and cause problems for them 情結: *He's got a terrible guilt complex.* 他有嚴重的犯罪情結。| *He's got a complex* **about** *his success.*

C

他始終擔心自己不能成功。

com·plex·ion /kəmˈplɛkʃən; kəmˈplekʃən/ n
1 the natural colour and appearance of someone's skin, especially on their face 膚色〔尤指臉色〕: *a pale complexion* 蒼白的面色
2 the complexion of something the general character or nature of something 某事物的複雜性: *The dismissal of the Minister for Foreign Affairs has changed the whole complexion of the government.* 外交部長被革職後，政府的整個複雜形勢為之一改變。

com·pli·ance /kəmˈplaɪəns; kəmˈplaɪəns/ n
[U] *fml* obedience to a rule or law 〔正式〕〔規定或法律的〕遵守: *Compliance with the law is expected of all citizens.* 所有公民都應遵守法律。**2** willingness to agree too easily with the wishes and demands of other people 順從: *I was surprised at her compliance with all our suggestions.* 她對我們所有的建議都很順從，這令我感到意外。

com·pli·ant /kəmˈplaɪənt; kəmˈplaɪənt/ adj
very willing to do what people ask you to do 順從的；服從的: *I don't respect people who are too compliant.* 我看不起那些唯命是從的人。

com·pli·cate /ˈkɒmpləˌket; ˈkɒmpləˌkeɪt/ v
complicated, complicating [T] to make something difficult to understand or deal with 使〔某事物〕複雜化: *It is a serious problem, complicated by the fact that we have no experience in this area.* 這是個嚴重的問題，而更糟糕的是我們在這方面沒有任何經驗。| *Do you always have to complicate matters by forgetting to bring something?* 你是不是總要忘記帶東西來使事情複雜化呢？

com·pli·cat·ed /ˈkɒmpləˌketɪd; ˈkɒmpləˌkeɪtɪd/ adj
very difficult to understand or deal with 複雜的；難以理解的；難以應付的: *Don't ask me such complicated questions.* 別來問我這麼複雜的問題。| *a complicated machine* 結構複雜的機器

com·pli·ca·tion /ˌkɒmpləˈkeʃən; ˌkɒmpləˈkeɪʃən/ n **1** something that adds new difficulties 使複雜化的事物: *The union's demand for higher wages was a complication that the government had not expected.* 工會要求提高工資是政府始料未及的一個難題。**2 complications** [pl] a new illness that happens during the course of another illness 併發症: *He seemed to be getting better, but I'm afraid there are now complications.* 他的病情似乎在好轉，不過我擔心有併發症。

com·plic·i·ty /kəmˈplɪsəti; kəmˈplɪsˌti/ n [U] the act of taking part with another person in something wrong or illegal 合謀；串通

com·pli·ment¹ /ˈkɒmpləmənt; ˈkɒmpləmənt/ n **1** an expression of praise, admiration, or respect 稱讚；讚嘆；恭維: *"You look lovely." "Oh, thanks for the compliment."* "您看上去真漂亮。" "哦，謝謝您的誇獎。" | *Her boss paid her the compliment of*

promoting her. 她老闆提升了她以表示對她的讚賞。**2 compliments** a word used to express respect or good wishes 問候；感謝〔用於稱讚〕: *My compliments to the chef!* 請向廚師致意!

com·pli·ment² /ˈkɒmpləˌment; ˈkɒmpləˌment/ v [T] to say something to someone expressing praise, admiration, or respect 稱讚；讚嘆；恭維: *John complimented Jean on her latest novel.* 約翰讚揚了瓊新寫的一部小說。

com·pli·men·ta·ry /ˌkɒmpləˈmentəri; ˌkɒmpləˈmentəri◂/ adj **1** expressing admiration, praise, or respect 稱讚的；恭維的 **2** given free 免費的: *He gave me some complimentary tickets for the theatre.* 他給了我幾張贈送的戲票。

com·ply /kəmˈplaɪ; kəmˈplaɪ/ v **complied, complying** [I] *fml* to do what is demanded by an order, a rule, or a person with power 〔正式〕服從；遵從；遵守: *People who refuse to comply with the law will be punished.* 不遵守法律的人將受到懲罰。

★**com·po·nent** /kəmˈponənt; kəmˈpəʊnənt/ n any of the parts that make up a whole machine or system 成分；組成部分；零部件

com·pose /kəmˈpoz; kəmˈpəʊz/ v **composed, composing 1** [I;T] to write something, especially a piece of music or poetry 譜寫；寫作〔尤指音樂或詩歌〕: *He plays the piano beautifully, and he composes his own music.* 他彈得一手好鋼琴，還自己譜曲。| *I'm trying to compose a letter to the newspaper.* 我正在試圖給報社寫封信。**2 compose yourself** to make yourself calm and quiet after being angry or upset 鎮定下來: *Please try to compose yourself!* 請盡量鎮定下來! **3 be composed of** to be formed from different parts 由〔不同的幾個部分〕組成: *Water is composed of hydrogen and oxygen.* 水是由氫和氧化合而成的。

com·pos·er /kəmˈpozə; kəmˈpəʊzəʳ/ n a person who writes music 作曲家

com·pos·ite /kəmˈpozɪt; ˈkɒmpəzˌɪt/ adj *fml* made up of a number of different parts or substances 〔正式〕〔由幾個不同部分或材料〕構成的；混合的 −**composite** n

★**com·po·si·tion** /ˌkɒmpəˈzɪʃən; ˌkɒmpəˈzɪʃən/ n **1** [C;U] a piece of music or poetry that you have written 作品〔譜寫的樂曲或創作的詩歌〕: *a piece of music of her own composition* 她自己作的樂曲 | *one of Mozart's last compositions* 莫扎特晚期的作品之一 **2** [C;U] the different parts of which something is made up 組成部分；成分: *Who decided the composition of the committee?* 委員會的成員是誰選定的? | *the chemical composition of plants* 植物的化學成分 **3** [C] a short piece of writing done as an educational exercise 寫作練習；作文: *We had to do a composition on the problem of crime.* 我們要以犯罪問題寫一篇文章。**4** [C] a mixture of various substances 混合物: *a composition* **of** *different chemicals* 化學混合物

com·post /ˈkɑmpost; ˈkɒmpɒst/ *n* [U] a mixture of decayed plant matter, such as cut grass or leaves, used for making the soil richer 堆肥; 混合肥料

com·po·sure /kəmˈpoʒɚ; kəmˈpəʊʒəʳ/ *n* [U] calmness and complete control over your feelings 鎮定; 沉着: *Keep calm: don't lose your composure.* 保持鎮定，不要慌張。

com·pound¹ /kəmˈpaʊnd; kəmˈpaʊnd/ *v fml* 【正式】[T] **1** to add to or increase a problem or difficulty 使嚴重; 增加困難: *His lack of confidence was compounded by losing his job.* 他本來就缺乏信心，現在又失業了，這使他的處境更加艱難。**2 be compounded of** to be formed by mixing different things together 由〔幾種不同物質〕混合而成

com·pound² /ˈkɑmpaʊnd; ˈkɒmpaʊnd/ *n* **1** something consisting of a combination of two or more parts 混合物; 複合物: *a chemical compound* 化合物 **2** an area enclosed by a wall or fence which contains a group of buildings 〔由圍牆或籬笆圍起來的內有建築物的〕場地: *the prison compound* 監獄大院

compound³ *adj* consisting of a combination of two or more parts 複合的; 混合的: *a compound leaf* 複葉

com·pre·hend /ˌkɑmprɪˈhɛnd; ˌkɒmprɪˈhend/ *v* [I;T;+that] *fml* to understand something 【正式】理解〔某事物〕: *The judge said that it was difficult to comprehend the actions of the police in this matter.* 法官説警方在這件事中所採取的行動令人費解。

com·pre·hen·si·ble /ˌkɑmprɪˈhɛnsəbl; ˌkɒmprɪˈhensəbl/ *adj* easily understood 容易理解的: *You often find a writer's books more comprehensible if you know about his life.* 如果了解一個作家的生平，那就更容易看懂他的書。 **−comprehensibly** *adv* **−comprehensibility** /ˌkɑmprɪˌhɛnsəˈbɪləti; ˌkɒmprɪhensəˈbɪlɪti/ *n* [U]

com·pre·hen·sion /ˌkɑmprɪˈhɛnʃən; ˌkɒmprɪˈhenʃən/ *n* **1** [U] the act of understanding or the ability to understand 理解; 理解力 **−opposite** 反義 **incomprehension 2** [C;U] a reading or listening exercise to test how well a student understands written or spoken language 閲讀能力測驗; 聽力測驗

★**com·pre·hen·sive¹** /ˌkɑmprɪˈhɛnsɪv; ˌkɒmprɪˈhensɪv/ *adj* including everything that is necessary 全面的; 綜合的: *The government gave a comprehensive explanation of its plans for industrial development.* 政府就其工業發展計劃作了全面的解釋。 **−comprehensively** *adv*

comprehensive² *n BrE* 【英式】(also 又作 **comprehensive school** /ˌ···ˈ····/) a SECONDARY school where pupils of all abilities are taught 〔招收各種資質學生的〕綜合中學

com·press /kəmˈprɛs; kəmˈpres/ *v* [T] **1** to force a substance into a smaller space 壓縮; 擠壓 **2** to express thoughts, ideas, or information in fewer words 使〔思想、觀點或消息〕變簡練: *The report's been compressed into three pages.* 該報告已被壓縮成三頁。 **−compressed** *adj*: *compressed air* 壓縮空氣 **−compression** /-ˈprɛʃən; -ˈpreʃən/ *n* [U]

★**com·prise** /kəmˈpraɪz; kəmˈpraɪz/ *v* **comprised, comprising** [T] **1** to include or be made up of 包括; 由…組成: *The school staff comprises ten teachers.* 該校的教職員由十位教師組成。 | *The United Kingdom comprises England, Wales, Scotland and Northern Ireland.* 聯合王國包括英格蘭、威爾士、蘇格蘭和北愛爾蘭。 **2** to form a part of a larger group 組成: *Women teachers comprise 15% of the teaching staff.* 女教師佔教師總數的百分之十五。

com·pro·mise¹ /ˈkɑmprəˌmaɪz; ˈkɒmprəmaɪz/ *n* [C;U] an agreement in which both sides accept that they cannot have exactly what they want 妥協; 折衷: *It is better to settle arguments by compromise, not with threats.* 用讓步的辦法來解決紛爭，要比用威脅的辦法好。 | *We eventually reached a compromise.* 我們最終達成了妥協。

compromise² *v* **compromised, compromising 1** [I] to settle an argument by reaching an agreement in which both sides accept that they cannot have exactly what they want 妥協; 折衷: *We couldn't agree whether to go to a restaurant or a café, so we compromised and went to the pub.* 去餐館還是去咖啡館，我們的意見不一致，所以就來個折衷，去了酒吧。 **2 compromise yourself** to do something which shows that you are not completely honest or sincere 使自己有失體面: *She claimed the politician had compromised himself in his private life.* 她聲稱那位政界要人的私生活不夠檢點，這使他聲譽受損。 **−compromising** *adj*

com·pul·sion /kəmˈpʌlʃən; kəmˈpʌlʃən/ *n* **1** [U] force or strong influence that makes a person do something 強迫力; 強制力: *I will pay nothing under compulsion.* 在強迫之下，我一分錢也不會付的。 **2** [C] a strong unreasonable desire to do something 強烈慾望: *Her compulsion to drink is causing serious problems.* 她的酒癮給她帶來嚴重的問題。

com·pul·sive /kəmˈpʌlsɪv; kəmˈpʌlsɪv/ *adj* [only before a noun 只用於名詞前] very difficult to stop or control 難以抑制的: *compulsive gambling* 不可自拔的賭博 | *a compulsive desire to eat all day long* 整天不斷無節制的暴飲暴食 **−compulsively** *adv*

com·pul·so·ry /kəmˈpʌlsəri; kəmˈpʌlsəri/ *adj* which must be done by law 強制性的; 義務的: *Is military service compulsory in your country?* 在你們國家服兵役是不是要義務服兵役？ **−compare** 比較 VOLUNTARY **−compulsorily** *adv*

com·punc·tion /kəmˈpʌŋkʃən; kəmˈpʌŋkʃən/ *n fml* [U] an awkward feeling of guilt that stops you doing something 〖正式〗懊悔; 慚愧: *That woman had no compunction about telling me a lie.* 那個女人對我説謊卻一點也不感到羞愧。

com·pute /kəmˈpjut; kəmˈpjuːt/ *v* **computed, computing** *fml* [T] to calculate a result or answer 〖正式〗計算

✦com·put·er /kəmˈpjutə; kəmˈpjuːtəʳ/ *n* a machine that can store and recall information and make calculations at very high speeds 計算機; 電腦: *a personal computer* 個人電腦 | *computer software* 電腦軟件

com·put·er·ize /kəmˈpjutəˌraɪz; kəmˈpjuːtəraɪz/ *v* **computerized, computerizing** (also 又作 **computerise** *BrE* 〖英式〗) [T] **1** to arrange for a computer to do a lot of the work 用電腦作業; 使電腦化: *The firm has decided to computerize its wages department.* 公司已決定用電腦來管理工資發放部門的工作。 **2** to store information in a computer 將〔信息〕儲存入電腦: *They have computerized their criminal records.* 他們已把犯罪記錄存入電腦。 –**computerized** *adj* –**computerization** /kəmˌpjutəraɪˈzeʃən; kəmˌpjuːtəraɪˈzeɪʃən/ *n* [U]

com·put·ing /kəmˈpjutɪŋ; kəmˈpjuːtɪŋ/ *n* [U] the activity or skill of using a computer 電腦的使用(技術)

com·rade /ˈkɑmræd; ˈkɒmrɪd/ *n* **1** *fml* a close companion 〖正式〗親密的夥伴 **2** someone who belongs to the same union or left wing group 〔同屬一個工會或左翼派別的〕同志: *Comrades, please support this motion.* 同志們, 請支持這項動議。

com·rade·ship /ˈkɑmrædˌʃɪp; ˈkɒmrɪdʃɪp/ *n* [U] *fml* friendship 〖正式〗友誼夥伴關係

con /kɑn; kɒn/ *v* **-nn-** *infml* [T] to trick someone by telling them things that are not true 〔非正式〕欺騙〔某人〕; 哄騙: *They've conned me out of £5.* 他們騙了我五英鎊。 | *He conned me into doing all his work for him.* 他哄騙我代他做了所有的工作。

con·cave /kɑnˈkev; kɒnˈkeɪv◂/ *adj* curved inward, like the inside surface of a hollow ball 凹的, 凹面的: *a concave mirror* 凹鏡 – opposite 反義 **convex**

con·ceal /kənˈsil; kənˈsiːl/ *v* [T] *fml* to hide something 〖正式〗隱藏〔某物〕: *She concealed her feelings.* 她隱藏了自己的感情。 | *He concealed his debts from his wife.* 他對妻子隱瞞了自己的債務。 | *She tried to conceal how she felt.* 她力圖隱藏自己的感受。

con·cede /kənˈsid; kənˈsiːd/ *v* **1** [T; + that] to admit unwillingly that something is true or correct 〔不情願地〕承認〔某事物〕: *I'll concede that particular point, but I still think your basic argument is wrong.* 我承認那一點是對的, 但我還是認為你的基本論據是錯誤的。 | *The bank conceded that they had made a mistake.* 銀行方面承認他們犯了一個

錯誤。 **2** [T] to allow someone to have something 允許〔某人〕得到〔某物〕: *After the First World War, Germany conceded a lot of land to her neighbours.* 第一次世界大戰以後, 德國把大片土地割讓給了鄰國。 | *As there was no chance of winning he conceded the match.* 既然沒有一點取勝的機會, 他就在比賽中讓別人佔先。 **3** **concede defeat** to accept and state that you have lost 承認失敗: *The government conceded defeat as soon as the election results were known.* 選舉結果一公佈, 政府就承認了失敗。

con·ceit /kənˈsit; kənˈsiːt/ *n* (also 又作 **conceitedness** /kənˈsitɪdnɪs; kənˈsiːtɪdnɪs/) [U] too high an opinion of your own abilities and importance 自負, 自大: *showing signs of conceit and selfishness* 表現出自負與自私的跡象

con·ceit·ed /kənˈsitɪd; kənˈsiːtɪd/ *adj* too proud of your abilities or the things that you have done 自負的, 自大的: *He was an arrogant, conceited man.* 他是個傲慢而又自負的人。

con·cei·va·ble /kənˈsivəbl; kənˈsiːvəbəl/ *adj* able to be believed or imagined 可以相信的; 能夠想像的: *It is just conceivable that he'll win, but not really very likely.* 他會贏只不過是想像一下而已, 但實際上極不可能。 –**conceivably** *adv*

con·ceive /kənˈsiv; kənˈsiːv/ *v* **1** [T] to form an idea of something or imagine it 想出〔主意〕; 想像出: *Scientists first conceived the idea of the atomic bomb in the 1930s.* 科學家在三十年代首次有了原子彈的構想。 | *It's difficult to conceive of living without electricity.* 很難想像生活中沒有電會是甚麼樣子。 **2** [I;T] to become PREGNANT with a child 懷孕: *The baby was conceived in March and born in December.* 孩子是三月懷的, 十二月出生。 | *My wife was unable to conceive.* 我的太太不能懷孕。

✦con·cen·trate¹ /ˈkɑnsnˌtret; ˈkɒnsəntreɪt/ *v* **concentrated, concentrating** [I;T] **1** to direct all your thoughts, efforts, or attention towards something 集中〔思想、注意力等〕: *I can't concentrate on anything when I'm hungry.* 我餓了就無法集中精力。 | *He concentrated on finding somewhere to live.* 他集中精力找住處。 | *Be quiet. I'm trying to concentrate.* 安靜點。我在試圖集中精力。 **2** to come or bring together in or around one place 〔使〕集中於〔某處〕: *Industrial development is being concentrated in the south of the country.* 工業發展目前正集中在這個國家的南部。 | *The crowds concentrated round the palace.* 人羣聚集在宮殿周圍。

concentrate² *n* [C;U] a substance which has been made stronger by having liquid removed from it 濃縮物: *orange juice concentrate* 濃縮橙汁

con·cen·trat·ed /ˈkɑnsnˌtretɪd; ˈkɒnsəntreɪtɪd/ *adj* **1** increased in strength by removing some of the liquid 濃縮的 **2** [only before a noun 只用於名詞前] using a lot of attention or effort 全神貫注的; 全力以赴的: *He has made a concentrated effort to improve his work.* 他全力以赴改進自己的工作。

⋆**con·cen·tra·tion** /ˌkɑnsn̩'treʃn̩; ˌkɒnsən'treɪʃən/ *n* **1** [U] direction of attention and hard thought 專心; 專注: *This book will need all your concentration.* 這本書你們要專心去讀。 **2** [C] a large amount of something at a particular place 集中; 匯集: *There is a concentration of industry in the south of the country.* 工業集中在這個國家的南部。 **3 the concentration** *tech* the amount of a substance contained in a liquid 《術語》《液體的》濃度

concentration camp /ˌ··'·· ·/ *n* a prison camp where people are kept during a war 〔戰時的〕集中營

con·cen·tric /kən'sɛntrɪk; kən'sentrɪk/ *adj tech* having the same centre 《術語》同心的: *concentric circles* 同心圓

⋆**con·cept** /'kɑnsɛpt; 'kɒnsept/ *n* a general idea or principle 概念; 原則: *It's difficult to grasp the concept of infinite space.* 掌握無限空間的概念是很難的。

con·cep·tion /kən'sɛpʃən; kən'sepʃən/ *n* **1** [C] a general understanding or idea 概念; 觀念: *You've no conception of what it was like to be there.* 你根本不知道在那兒是甚麼滋味。 **2** [U] the act of forming an idea or plan 構思; 構想: *The robbery was very imaginative in conception.* 那場劫案的構思很新穎。 **3** [U] the process by which a woman becomes PREGNANT 懷孕: *There are nine months between conception and birth.* 婦女從懷孕到生產共需九個月。

con·cep·tu·al /kən'sɛptʃuəl; kən'septʃuəl/ *adj fml* connected with the forming of ideas in your mind 《正式》概念的; 構思的 – **conceptually** *adv*

⋆**con·cern**[1] /kən'sɝn; kən'sɜːn/ *v* [T] **1** to be about 關於: *This story concerns a person who lived in Russia a long time ago.* 這則故事講述的是一個很久以前住在俄國的人。 **2** to be of importance or interest to someone 對〔某人〕重要; 關係到: *The marriage of a queen concerns all the people who live in her country.* 女王的婚姻關係到國內所有的百姓。 | *This concerns all of you.* 這與你們所有人都有關係。 **3** to worry you 使…擔心: *This is a problem which concerns all parents.* 這是個令所有家長都擔心的問題。 **4 concern yourself with something** to take an interest in something 關心某事: *She concerned herself with looking after the old people in her area.* 她為照顧她區內的老人而操心。 **5 to whom it may concern** a phrase used at the beginning of a letter which anyone may read 敬啟者〔一封任何人都有可能閱讀的信的開頭語〕

⋆**concern**[2] *n* **1** [C] a matter that is of interest

or importance to someone 對〔某人〕有利害關係的事: *It's your work I want to talk about. Your private life isn't my concern.* 我想和你談談你的工作情況。你的私生活與我無關。 | *the concerns of ethnic minorities* 各少數民族所關心的事情 **2** [U] worry or anxiety 擔心; 擔憂: *There is no cause for concern.* 不必擔心。 | *There is some concern about his health.* 有人擔心他的健康。 **3 of concern to** important to 對…重要: *The problem of unemployment is of great concern to everyone.* 失業問題對每個人來講都事關重大。 **4** [C] a business or firm 商號; 公司: *The restaurant is a family concern.* 這家飯店是由一家人經營的。 **5 a going concern** a business which is making a profit 贏利的企業

⋆**con·cerned** /kən'sɝnd; kən'sɜːnd/ *adj* **1** anxious or worried 擔心的; 憂慮的: *I was very concerned about my mother's illness.* 我很擔心母親的病。 | *She was concerned for their safety.* 她為他們的安全擔心。 **2** having an active personal interest 感興趣的; 關心的: *I am concerned for their happiness.* 我很關心他們是否幸福。 | *He's very concerned to help.* 他很樂意幫忙。 **3** [only after a noun 只用於名詞後] having something to do with an event or activity 有關的: *I'll pass on your comments to the people concerned.* 我會把你的意見轉達給有關人員。 **4 as far as I'm concerned** = in my opinion 在我看來; 就我而言 **5 be concerned with** to be about 與…有關; 關於: *This story is concerned with a Russian family in the nineteenth century.* 這個故事講的是十九世紀一個俄國家庭的事情。 **6 where something is concerned, as far as something is concerned** in matters that have an effect on something 就某事而言: *Where work is concerned, I always try to do my best.* 就工作而言,我一向盡力而為。

⋆**con·cern·ing** /kən'sɝnɪŋ; kən'sɜːnɪŋ/ *prep fml* in connection with 《正式》關於; 有關: *Concerning your letter, I am pleased to inform you that your plans are quite acceptable to us.* 關於你的來信,我很高興地告訴你,我們覺得你的計劃很可行。 | *a story concerning a beaver and an otter* 一則關於河狸和水獺的故事

⋆**con·cert** /'kɑnsɝt; 'kɒnsət/ *n* **1** a performance given by a number of musicians 音樂會 **2 in concert** *fml* working together 《正式》一致; 合作: *The various governments decided to act in concert over this matter.* 各國政府決定對此事採取一致行動。

con·cert·ed /kən'sɝtɪd; kən'sɜːtɪd/ *adj* [only before a noun 只用於名詞前] **1** planned or done together by agreement 商定的; 協同完成的: *a concerted attempt by all governments to stop crime* 各國政府齊心協力遏制罪案 **2 concerted effort** a very big attempt 巨大的努力: *She has made a concerted effort to improve her work.* 她為改進

工作而作出了很大的努力。–**concertedly** *adv*

con·cer·ti·na /ˌkɒnsəˈtinə; ˌkɒnsəˈtiːnə/ *n* a small musical instrument that you hold in your hands and play by pressing in from each side 六角形手風琴

con·cer·to /kənˈtʃɛrto; kənˈtʃɜːtəʊ/ *n* a piece of music for one or more instruments playing with an ORCHESTRA 協奏曲

con·ces·sion /kənˈsɛʃən; kənˈseʃən/ *n* **1** something allowed unwillingly or after an argument 讓步; 妥協: *The firm's promise to increase our pay was a concession to union demands.* 公司答應給我們增加工資, 是對工會所提要求的讓步。 **2** a right given by a government or owner of land to do something special 特許權: *oil concessions in the North Sea* 北海石油開採特許權

con·cil·i·ate /kənˈsɪlɪˌet; kənˈsɪlieɪt/ *v* **conciliated, conciliating** [T] to reach an agreement with someone after an argument or disagreement 〖正式〗調解; 和解 – **conciliation** /kənˌsɪlɪˈeʃən; kənˌsɪliˈeɪʃən/ *n* [U]: *The government ignored the union's attempts at conciliation.* 政府對於工會尋求和解的努力置若罔聞。

con·cil·i·a·to·ry /kənˈsɪlɪəˌtɔri; kənˈsɪliətəri/ *adj* trying to end a disagreement 和解的; 調解的: *a conciliatory gesture* 和解的姿態 | *a conciliatory tone* 和解的口吻

con·cise /kənˈsaɪs; kənˈsaɪs/ *adj* expressing a lot in a few clear words 簡明的; 簡潔的: *a concise speech* 簡明的演講 | *a concise dictionary* 簡明詞典 –**concisely** *adv* –**conciseness** /kənˈsaɪsnɪs; -s/ *n* [U]

★**con·clude** /kənˈklud; kənˈkluːd/ *v* **1** [I;T] *fml* to come or bring to an end 〖正式〗(使) 結束: *We concluded the meeting at eight o'clock.* 我們在八點鐘結束了會議。 | *"So I had to walk," he concluded.* 最後他說:"那麼我只好步行了了。" | *We concluded by giving him a vote of thanks.* 結束時, 我們向他表示感謝。 **2** [+ (that)] to decide that something is true or reach a decision based on known facts 推斷出; 作出結論: *The judge concluded that the prisoner was guilty.* 法官作出的結論是那囚犯有罪。 **3** [T] *fml* to arrange or settle something after a lot of talking 〖正式〗議定; 締結

★**con·clu·sion** /kənˈkluʒən; kənˈkluːʒən/ *n* **1** a judgment or decision that you reach after some thought 結論; 決定: *What conclusions did you draw from his behaviour?* 從他的舉動你得出了甚麼結論? | *I came to the conclusion that I should accept the job.* 我決定接受這個工作。 **2** the end 結局; 結尾: *I found the conclusion of her book rather difficult to understand.* 我覺得她那本書的結尾很難看懂。 **3** the settling of something like a business deal 商定; 締結: *the conclusion of a peace treaty* 和平條約的締結 **4 in conclusion** a phrase used when you are ending a speech or piece of writing 最後, 總之〔用於結束演講

或文章〕: *In conclusion, I'd just like to thank you all for coming.* 最後, 我對諸位的光臨表示感謝。

con·clu·sive /kənˈklusɪv; kənˈkluːsɪv/ *adj* proving that something is true 確定的; 確實的: *The police have conclusive proof of his guilt.* 警方擁有他罪行的確鑿證據。–opposite 反義 **inconclusive** –**conclusively** *adv*

con·coct /kənˈkɑkt; kənˈkɒkt/ *v* [T] **1** to make something by combining things which are not usually put together 調製; 配製: *Jean concocted a splendid meal from the leftovers.* 瓊用殘羹剩菜做了一頓很可口的飯。 **2** to invent something false 捏造; 編造: *He always manages to concoct some new excuse for being late.* 他總是為自己遲到編造新的藉口。–**concoction** /-ˈkɑkʃən; -ˈkɒkʃən/ *n*

con·com·i·tant /kənˈkɑmətənt; kənˈkɒmɪtənt/ *n fml* something that often goes or happens with something else 〖正式〗伴隨而來之物: *Deafness is a frequent concomitant of old age.* 耳聾常常是伴隨老年而出現的現象。–**concomitant** *adj*: *We lived through the war with all its concomitant sufferings.* 在經歷了戰爭以及隨之而來的種種苦難之後, 我們還是活了下來。

con·cord /ˈkɑnkərd; ˈkɒnkɔːd/ *n* [U] *fml* peaceful and friendly relations 〖正式〗和睦, 和諧: *The two tribes had lived in concord for many centuries.* 這兩個部落已和睦共處了好幾百年了。

con·course /ˈkɑnkors; ˈkɒŋkɔːs/ *n* a large hall or open place where crowds of people can gather 大廳; 廣場: *the airport concourse* 機場大廳

con·crete¹ /ˈkɑnkrit; ˈkɒŋkriːt/ *adj fml* 〖正式〗 **1** existing as something real or solid rather than something in the mind 實在的; 實體的: *I prefer paintings of concrete objects that I can recognize.* 我偏愛那些我能夠辨認出實物的畫像。 **2** clear 清晰的; 具體的: *Have you got any concrete thoughts on what we should do next?* 我們下一步該做些甚麼, 你有甚麼具體的想法? –**concretely** *adv*

con·crete² /ˈkɑnkrit; ˈkɒŋkriːt/ *n* [U] a building material made by mixing sand, very small stones, cement, and water 混凝土: *a concrete floor* 混凝土地板 –**concrete** *v* **concreted, concreting**: *The path has been concreted.* 這條路已鋪上了混凝土。

con·cur /kənˈkɝ; kənˈkɜː/ *v* **-rr-** *fml* [I; +that] to agree 〖正式〗同意; 一致: *The two judges concurred with one another.* 兩位法官的意見一致。 | *We have studied your proposal and we all concur.* 我們研究了你的提議, 大家都表示同意。

con·cur·rent /kənˈkɝənt; kənˈkʌrənt/ *adj* **1** existing or happening at the same time 並存的; 同時發生的: *He is serving two concurrent prison sentences.* 他在服合併執行的兩個徒刑。 **2** *fml* in agreement 〖正式〗一致的: *My opinions are concurrent with yours in this* *matter.* 在此事上我與你的觀點一致。**–concurrently** *adv* **–concurrence** *n* [C;U]

con·cus·sion /kənˈkʌʃən; kənˈkʌʃən/ *n* [U] a medical condition in which you become unconscious or feel confused after a heavy blow to your head 腦震盪: *He's suffering from concussion after falling off his bicycle.* 他從自行車上摔下來以後，給撞成了腦震盪。 **– concuss** *v* [T]: *Don't worry; she's only concussed.* 別擔心，她這只是腦震盪。

con·demn /kənˈdɛm; kənˈdem/ *v* [T] **1** to express strong disapproval of someone or something 斥責，譴責〔某人或某物〕: *Most people are willing to condemn violence of any sort.* 大多數人都樂意譴責任何形式的暴力行為。 **2** to give a serious punishment to someone who is guilty in a court of law 判刑; 宣判: *He was condemned to death.* 他被判處死刑。 **3** to force someone into an unpleasant situation 迫使〔某人〕處於不愉快的境地: *His bad leg has condemned him to a wheelchair.* 他的殘腿使他不得不坐在輪椅上。 **4** to declare a building officially unfit for use 宣告〔建築物〕不適用: *The house has been condemned by the Council.* 市政廳宣佈那所房子已不能住人了。 **–condemnation** /ˌkɑndɛmˈneʃən; ˌkɑndəmˈneɪʃən/ *n* [C;U]

con·den·sa·tion /ˌkɑndɛnˈseʃən; ˌkɑndənˈseɪʃən/ *n* [U] **1** drops of liquid formed when steam or hot air touches a cold surface 〔蒸汽遇冷凝結而成的〕水珠: *There was condensation on the windows.* 窗戶上有凝結的水珠。 **2** the reduction of an account of something into a shorter form 摘要; 節本

con·dense /kənˈdɛns; kənˈdens/ *v* **1** [T] to make an account of something shorter while still including all the important parts 簡縮; 節略: *a condensed report* 簡縮的報告 **2** [I;T] to cool something so that it becomes liquid or solid 使〔某物〕冷卻凝結 **3** [T] to make a liquid thicker by removing some of the water 使濃縮: *cans of condensed soup* 濃縮湯罐頭

con·de·scend /ˌkɑndɪˈsɛnd; ˌkɒndɪˈsend/ *v* **1 condescend to do something** to agree to do something although you think that you are too important to do it 屈尊〔俯就〕做某事: *Do you think the directors will actually condescend to have lunch with us in the canteen?* 你認為董事們真的會屈尊與我們一起在食堂裡吃午飯嗎？ **2** [I] to behave as though you are better or more important than other people 自以為高人一等 **–condescending** *adj*: *Don't be so condescending!* 別那麼盛氣凌人！ **–condescension** *n* [U]

con·di·ment /ˈkɑndəmənt; ˈkɒndɪ̩mənt/ *n fml* a powder or liquid used for giving a special taste to food; for example, salt and pepper are condiments 〔正式〕調味品; 佐料

★★con·di·tion¹ /kənˈdɪʃən; kənˈdɪʃən/ *n* **1** [U] the state that something is in 情況; 狀態: *The car is in ex-*

cellent condition. 這輛車各方面狀況極佳。 **2** [U] someone's state of health 健康狀況: *Her condition is improving.* 她的身體狀況在好轉。 **3 out of condition** not very fit and healthy 不太健康; 身體不適: *I'm a bit out of condition at the moment.* 我現在身體有點不大舒服。 **4** [C] an illness of a part of your body, which continues for a long time 〔慢性的〕疾病: *She has a heart condition.* 她有心臟病。 **5** [C] something that is needed to make something else possible 條件: *We had to satisfy several conditions before we were allowed to join the club.* 我們在加入俱樂部以前要先滿足幾項條件。 **6 on one condition, on condition that** phrases used when you are saying that something will only happen if something else happens 條件是; 如果〔用於表示先決條件〕: *She'll join us on one condition: that we don't discuss divorce.* 她願意參加我們的討論，但條件是我們不談有關離婚的問題。 | *I'll come on condition that John is invited too.* 要是約翰也接到邀請，我就來。 **7 conditions** [pl] the general situation or state of affairs at a particular time or place 環境; 情形: *Their working conditions were terrible.* 他們的工作環境很糟糕。 | *Housing conditions have improved in this area.* 該地區的住房狀況已有改善。 | *Even under the best conditions, we couldn't get there in less than three days.* 即使一切順利，我們也不可能在三天內趕到那裡。

condition² *v* [T] **1** to train someone to behave in a certain way or to have certain beliefs 使適應; 使習慣於: *Most people are conditioned to believe what they read in newspapers.* 大多數人習慣於相信他們在報上讀到的東西。 **2 be conditioned by** to be controlled by something else 為〔其他事物〕所制約; 取決於: *The amount of money I spend is conditioned by the amount I earn.* 我花多少錢取決於我掙多少錢。

con·di·tion·al /kənˈdɪʃənl; kənˈdɪʃənəl/ *adj* depending on something else happening 有條件的; 取決於〔其他事物〕的: *His agreement to buy our house was conditional on us leaving all the furniture in it.* 他同意買我們的房子，但條件是我們得留下所有的家具。 **–conditionally** *adv*

con·di·tion·er /kənˈdɪʃənɚ; kənˈdɪʃənər/ *n* a substance which you put on your hair after you have washed it, to help it remain in good condition 護髮劑

con·di·tion·ing /kənˈdɪʃənɪŋ; kənˈdɪʃənɪŋ/ *n* [U] the process by which someone is trained to behave in certain ways or to hold certain beliefs 形成條件反射的過程; 熏陶

con·do·lence /kənˈdoləns; kənˈdəʊləns/ *n* [U;pl] an expression of sympathy for someone when one of their friends or relatives has died 弔唁; 哀悼: *Please accept my condolences.* 請接受我的弔慰之意。 | *a* *letter of condolence* 弔唁信

con·dom /ˈkɒndəm; ˈkɒndəm/ *n* a rubber covering which a man wears over his PENIS when he is having sex; it is used as a means of birth control or for protection against disease 〔男用〕避孕套; 保險套

con·do·min·i·um /ˌkɒndəˈmɪnɪəm; ˌkɒndə-ˈmɪnɪəm/ *n AmE* 〔美式〕(also 又作 **condo** *infml* 〔非正式〕) **1** a block of flats, each of which is owned by the people who live in it 由許多私人擁有的公寓住宅單位組成的公寓大樓 **2** a single flat in one of these blocks 私人擁有的一套公寓單位

con·done /kənˈdon; kənˈdəun/ *v* **condoned, condoning** [T] to regard bad behaviour as acceptable 寬恕; 原諒: *We would never condone the use of violence.* 我們決不寬恕使用暴力的行為。

con·du·cive /kənˈdjusɪv; kənˈdjuːsɪv/ *adj fml* 〔正式〕 **conducive to** likely to result in something or to make something possible 有助於…的: *Smoking a whole packet of cigarettes a day is not exactly conducive to good health.* 一天抽一包香煙對健康絕對沒有好處。

✱con·duct¹ /kənˈdʌkt; kənˈdʌkt/ *v* **1** [T] to take someone somewhere, often as a guide 帶領〔某人去某地〕; 導遊: *He conducted us on a tour of the castle.* 他領著我們參觀了城堡。 **2 conducted tour** a visit to a place in which a guide goes with you and shows you all the interesting things 有導遊陪同的遊覽 **3** [T] to carry something out 進行; 實施: *British Rail is conducting an enquiry on safety standards on trains.* 英國鐵路正在進行火車安全標準的調查。 **4 conduct yourself** *fml* to behave in a certain way 〔正式〕舉止; 表現: *Servants were expected to conduct themselves in a decorous manner.* 僕人應該舉止得體。 **5** [I;T] to stand in front of musicians and direct their music 指揮〔樂隊〕: *Who's conducting tonight?* 今晚由誰指揮? | *Lyons will be conducting the symphony orchestra.* 萊昂將指揮交響樂隊演出。 **6** [T] to act as a path for electricity or heat 傳導〔電、熱〕: *Rubber won't conduct electricity.* 橡膠不導電。

✱con·duct² /ˈkɒndʌkt; ˈkɒndʌkt/ *n* [U] **1** *fml* behaviour 〔正式〕舉止; 行為: *I'm glad to see your conduct at school has improved.* 我很高興看到你在學校的行為有了進步。 **2** the direction of the course of a business or similar activity 〔企業、活動等的〕發展方向; 進展: *We are not satisfied with the conduct of the negotiations.* 我們對談判的進展感到不滿。

con·duc·tor /kənˈdʌktər; kənˈdʌktər/ *n* **1** a person who directs the playing of a group of musicians while standing in front of them 〔樂隊的〕指揮 **2** a person employed to collect payments from passengers on a bus or train 〔公共汽車或火車的〕售票員 **3** something that acts as a path for electricity or

heat 導體: *Wood is a poor conductor of heat.* 木的導熱性很差。

cone /kon; kəun/ *n* **1** a hollow or solid object with a round base and a point at the top 圓錐體 **2** something you can eat which is shaped like a cone and which has ice-cream inside 圓錐形冰淇淋蛋卷筒: *an ice-cream cone* 蛋卷冰淇淋 **3** the fruit of a PINE or FIR tree 〔松樹或杉樹的〕球果

con·fec·tion·e·ry /kənˈfɛkʃənˌɛrɪ; kənˈfɛk-ʃənərɪ/ *n* [U] sweet cakes, ice-cream, or sweets 糖果; 甜食 **–confectioner** *n*

con·fed·e·ra·cy /kənˈfɛdərəsɪ; kənˈfɛdərəsɪ/ *n* **confederacies** *fml* a union of people, parties, or states for political purposes or trade 〔正式〕聯邦; 同盟

con·fed·e·rate /kənˈfɛdərɪt; kənˈfɛdərˌ‍t/ *n* **1** a member of a confederacy 聯邦的成員 **2** a person who helps you with something secret or dishonest 同謀者; 同夥

con·fed·e·ra·tion /kənˌfɛdəˈreʃən; kənˌfɛdə-ˈreɪʃən/ *n* an organization of groups or firms for political or business purposes 〔政治或商業的〕聯盟, 同盟

con·fer /kənˈfɜː; kənˈfɜːr/ *v* **-rr-** *fml* 〔正式〕 **1** [I] to talk about opinions or views 商討: *The ministers are still conferring on this matter.* 部長們仍在商討此事。 | *The Prime Minister is conferring with her advisors.* 首相在與她的顧問進行商討。 **2** [T] to give a title or honour to someone 授予〔頭銜或榮譽〕: *An honorary degree was conferred on him by the university.* 這所大學授予他榮譽學位。

✱con·fe·rence /ˈkɒnfərəns; ˈkɒnfərəns/ *n* **1** a meeting held so that opinions and ideas on a subject can be exchanged 會議; 協商會: *a conference of European states* 歐洲各國的會議 | *a conference on environmental issues* 有關環境問題的會議 **2 in conference** having a meeting with someone 在開會: *I'm afraid Mrs Pike is in conference until three o'clock.* 派克夫人的會議恐怕要開到三點鐘。

con·fess /kənˈfɛs; kənˈfɛs/ *v* **1** [I;T;+(that)] to admit to a fault or crime 承認〔錯誤或罪行〕; 坦白: *It's time to confess.* 該是坦白的時候了。 | *He has confessed to the murder.* 他承認犯了謀殺罪。 | *She confessed all her crimes.* 她供認了全部罪行。 | *Jean confessed that she'd eaten all the cakes.* 瓊承認她把所有的蛋糕吃掉了。

□ USEFUL PATTERNS 有用句型

to confess; to confess something; to confess to something; to confess to doing something; to confess that…

---

2 I must confess a phrase used when you are being honest and admitting something 老實說〔用於表示坦白承認某事〕: *I must confess I've never liked him very much.* 說句實話, 我一直都不太喜歡他。 **3** [I;T] *tech* to admit your faults to a priest or to God 〔術語〕〔向神父或上帝〕

懺悔

con·fessed /kənˈfɛst; kənˈfɛst/ *adj* admitted by the person concerned to be true 自己承認的的: *Mrs Jones is a confessed alcoholic.* 瓊斯太太自己承認是個酒徒。

con·fes·sion /kənˈfɛʃən; kənˈfeʃən/ *n* **1** [C; U] a statement admitting your crime or faults 供狀; 招供; 坦白: *I'd like to make a confession.* 我願意坦白。 **2** [U] *tech* a meeting with a priest at which you tell him what you have done wrong〔術語〕向神父的懺悔: *Are you going to confession?* 你打算去懺悔嗎？

con·fet·ti /kənˈfɛti; kənˈfeti/ *n* [U] small pieces of coloured paper thrown about at weddings〔婚禮時拋撒的〕五彩紙屑

con·fi·dant /ˌkɒnfiˈdænt; ˈkɒnfiˌdænt; ˌkɒnfiˈdænt/ *n fml* someone you talk to about your secrets or personal matters; a woman who you talk to in this way is called a **confidante**〔正式〕知己; 密友〔其女性知己稱為 **confidante**〕

con·fide /kənˈfaɪd; kənˈfaɪd/ *v* [T; +that] to tell your secrets to someone you trust not to tell anyone else 吐露〔祕密〕: *He confided to me that he had once been in prison.* 他私下告訴我他曾經坐過牢。 | *She confided that her illness was getting worse.* 她吐露說她的病情在惡化。 | *She confided her worries to me.* 她向我吐露了她的煩惱。

> □ USEFUL PATTERNS 有用句型
> to confide something to someone; to
> confide that...; to confide to someone
> that...

confide in sbdy *phr v* [T] to talk freely to someone about your secrets 向〔某人〕吐露祕密: *John felt he could confide in his brother.* 約翰覺得可以對自己的兄弟無話不談。

✲con·fi·dence /ˈkɒnfɪdəns; ˈkɒnfɪdəns/ *n* **1** [U] belief that a person or thing will perform as you hope and expect 信心; 把握: *We have complete confidence in you.* 我們對你充滿信心。 **2** [U] a calm, unworried feeling, based on a strong belief in yourself 自信: *She's a good musician, but she lacks confidence.* 她是個出色的音樂家，但缺乏自信。 **3** [U] trust 信任: *How can I win his confidence?* 我如何才能贏得他的信任呢？ **4 in confidence, in strict confidence** trusting the person being told to keep the matter a secret 相信某人會保守祕密: *I'm telling you all this in confidence.* 我是信得過你才把這一切說給你聽。 **5 take someone into your confidence** to tell someone something secret or private because you trust them 出於信任而把祕密告訴某人 **6** [C] *old fash* a secret〔老式〕祕密: *They exchanged confidences about their boyfriends.* 她們相互吐露有關她們男友的祕密。

✲con·fi·dent /ˈkɒnfɪdənt; ˈkɒnfɪˌdənt/ *adj* **1** certain that things will happen as you want them to 有把握的; 有信心的: *The government is confident of winning the next election.* 政府有把握贏得下屆大選。 | *He is confident that he'll pass the exam.* 他有信心通過考試。 **2** feeling or expressing a strong belief in yourself 有自信心的: *a calm and confident young man* 一個沉着而自信的年輕人 | *a confident smile* 自信的微笑

con·fi·den·tial /ˌkɒnfiˈdɛnʃəl; ˌkɒnfiˈdɛnʃəl/ *adj* intended to be kept secret and not talked about openly 機密的; 祕密的: *This report is still confidential.* 這份報告仍屬機密文件。 | *I think he's been passing confidential information to our competitors.* 我覺得他一直在把祕密情報透露給我們的競爭對手。 – **confidentially** *adv*

con·fid·ing /kənˈfaɪdɪŋ; kənˈfaɪdɪŋ/ *adj* trusting other people with your own private affairs 信任別人的: *her confiding nature* 她那相信他人的天性 –**confidingly** *adv*

✲con·fine /kənˈfaɪn; kənˈfaɪn/ *v* **confined, confining** [T] **1** to keep a person or thing in a small, enclosed space 把...限制於〔小空間〕: *The animal was confined in a very small cage.* 那隻動物被關在一個很小的籠子裡。 | *A bad cold confined John to bed for a week.* 約翰由於重感冒而臥牀一週。 **2** to keep something within limits 限制〔某事物〕: *Please confine your remarks to the subject under discussion.* 請把你的話限於我們討論的題目範圍之內。 **3 confine yourself to** to limit yourself to something 把自己限制在〔某事，某內〕: *I'll confine myself to talking about this one project.* 我只會在這個項目上講述一下。 – **confinement** *n*: *They were kept in confinement for a year, until their trial.* 受審之前，他們被監禁了一年。

con·fines /ˈkɒnfaɪnz; ˈkɒnfaɪnz/ *n* [pl] limits or borders 範圍; 界限: *This is outside the confines of human knowledge.* 這超出了人類知識的範圍。 | *You may not leave the confines of the university.* 你不可走出這所大學的範圍。

✲con·firm /kənˈfɜːm; kənˈfɝːm/ *v* [T; +that] **1** to show or state that something is certainly true or will definitely happen 證實: *The extra evidence confirmed our suspicions.* 額外的證據證實了我們的懷疑。 | *The Prime Minister confirmed that the election would be on June 20th.* 首相證實大選將於6月20日舉行。 **2 be confirmed** *tech* to be admitted to full membership of a Christian church〔術語〕〔教會〕給〔某人〕施堅信禮

con·fir·ma·tion /ˌkɒnfəˈmeɪʃən; ˌkɒnfəˈmeɪʃən/ *n* **1** [U] something that shows other things to be true 證明; 證實: *There has still been no official confirmation of the number of deaths.* 死亡人數還未得到官方證實。 **2** [C; U] *tech* a religious service in which a person is made a full member of a Christian church〖術語〗(基督教的)堅信禮

con·firmed /kənˈfɜːmd; kənˈfɝːmd/ *adj* [only before a noun 只用於名詞前] unwilling to change a habit or way of life 不願改變習慣〔生活方式〕的；根深蒂固的: *He's a confirmed bachelor.* 他是個抱定獨身主義的人。

con·fis·cate /ˈkɒnfɪsˌkeɪt; ˈkɒnfɪskeɪt/ *v* **confiscated, confiscating** [T] to take private property away from someone when you have the right to do so and wish to punish them 沒收〔私人財物〕: *I had my radio confiscated by our chemistry teacher today.* 今天化學老師把我的收音機沒收了。 –**confiscation** /ˌkɒnfɪsˈkeɪʃən; ˌkɒnfɪˈskeɪʃən/ *n* [U]

con·fla·gra·tion /ˌkɒnfləˈɡreɪʃən; ˌkɒnfləˈɡreɪʃən/ *n fml* a large fire that destroys buildings or forests〖正式〗(毀壞建築物或樹林的)大火

★**con·flict¹** /ˈkɒnflɪkt; ˈkɒnflɪkt/ *n* [C;U] **1** a serious disagreement between different people or principles 爭執；衝突: *It will lead to conflict* **between** *Unions and Management.* 這將導致工會與資方的衝突。| *Personal and political conflicts among ministers are increasingly common.* 部長之間的個人衝突和政治衝突突現在愈來愈普遍。**2 come into conflict** to argue or disagree 爭吵；爭論: *We came into conflict over money.* 我們開始為了錢而爭吵。| *Town planners are coming into conflict* **with** *farmers as cities expand.* 隨着城市面積的擴大，負責城市規劃的人與農民正爭論不休。[RELATED PHRASES 相關詞組 **be in conflict; bring people into conflict**] **3** war or fighting 戰爭；戰鬥: *Armed conflict is now unavoidable.* 武裝衝突突現在不可避免。

con·flict² /kənˈflɪkt; kənˈflɪkt/ *v* [I] to disagree 衝突；爭執: *Do British laws conflict* **with** *any international laws?* 英國法律與國際法律有衝突嗎？| *Our job is to make sense of all this conflicting evidence.* 我們的工作就是去理解這些相互矛盾的證據。

con·flu·ence /ˈkɒnfluəns; ˈkɒnfluəns/ *n fml* the place where two or more rivers flow together〖正式〗(河流的)匯合處

con·form /kənˈfɔːm; kənˈfɔːrm/ *v* [I] *fml*〖正式〗**1** to follow established rules or patterns 遵守，符合〔規定或模式〕: *This piece of equipment does not conform* **to** *the official safety standards.* 這台設備不符合官方的安全標準。**2** to behave like most other people 像大多數人一樣行事: *There is great pressure on school-children to conform.* 學生面臨着巨大壓力要他們隨順習俗。–**conformity** *n* [U]

con·form·ist /kənˈfɔːmɪst; kənˈfɔːrmɪst/ *adj, n* a person who follows the established rules, values, and customs of a group or of society (a word often used to express disapproval) 遵奉傳統的人〔常含貶義〕；墨守成規的人

con·found /kənˈfaʊnd; kənˈfaʊnd/ *v* [T] to confuse and surprise someone by being unexpected 使〔某人〕疑惑〔驚訝〕: *The results confounded all our expectations.* 結果與預想相去甚遠，這令我們大感意外。

con·front /kənˈfrʌnt; kənˈfrʌnt/ *v* [T] **1** to face someone boldly or threateningly 勇敢面對；對抗: *I was confronted by two men demanding money.* 兩個男人攔住我，要我把錢交出來。**2 confront someone with something** to show someone something in order to say with reason that they are guilty 當面對證: *When she was confronted with video recordings, she had to admit she was involved.* 面對錄像帶，她不得不承認自己也參與了那起事件。**3** to try to deal with something that you cannot avoid 對付〔無法避免的事情〕；面臨: *You'll have to confront the problem sometime.* 你總會碰到那個問題的。**4** to cause problems for someone 給〔某人〕帶來麻煩: *A number of difficulties now confronted me.* 我現在面臨着許多困難。

con·fron·ta·tion /ˌkɒnfrʌnˈteɪʃən; ˌkɒnfrənˈteɪʃən/ *n* [C;U] a situation of open disagreement 對抗；對峙: *We must avoid confrontation* **with** *the government.* 我們必須避免與政府當局對抗。

con·fuse /kənˈfjuːz; kənˈfjuːz/ *v* **confused, confusing** [T] **1** to make someone feel uncertain about what to think or do 使〔某人〕困惑: *John's account is just confusing me.* 約翰的話真是把我弄糊塗了。**2** to make a situation harder to understand 令〔局勢〕難以理解；搞亂: *Stop trying to confuse matters and listen!* 別把事情弄亂，好好聽着！**3** to find it difficult to tell the difference between people or things 搞不清兩人〔物〕之間的區別；混淆: *I'm always confusing John* **with** *his twin brother.* 我總是分不清約翰和他的孿生兄弟。–**confused** *adj*: *I thought I knew what to do, but now I'm confused.* 我原以為我知道該做甚麼，可是現在我被搞糊塗了。–**confusedly** /kənˈfjuːzdlɪ; kənˈfjuːzɪdli/ *adv* –**confusing** *adj*: *His explanation was really confusing.* 他的解釋真讓人費解。

★**con·fu·sion** /kənˈfjuːʒən; kənˈfjuːʒən/ *n* [U] **1** a situation in which people are uncertain about what to think or do 混亂；紊亂: *There was some confusion as to whether we had won.* 我們到底贏了沒有，人們眾說紛紜。**2** a situation in which it is difficult to tell the difference between two people or things 混淆: *To avoid confusion, the teams wore different colours.* 為避免混淆，各隊穿了不同顏色的衣服。**3** a state of great disorder 騷亂；雜亂: *The announcement caused panic and confusion.* 這項宣佈引起了人們的驚慌與騷亂。

con·geal /kənˈdʒiːl; kənˈdʒiːl/ *v* [I;T] to become thick or solid (使)凝結；(使)凝固: *The liquid congealed.* 液體凝固了。| *congealed*

blood 凝結的血

con·ge·ni·al /kən'dʒinjəl; kən'dʒiːniəl/ *adj fml* pleasing or interesting to you〖正式〗令人愉快的; 有趣味的: *I find both the work and the people congenial.* 我覺得這工作很舒適, 和同事們也很合得來。—**congenially** *adv*

con·gen·i·tal /kən'dʒɛnətl; kən'dʒɛnɪtl/ *adj tech* existing at or from your birth (used of diseases)〖術語〗天生的〔指疾病〕: *congenital deafness* 先天性耳聾 —**congenitally** *adv*

con·ges·ted /kən'dʒɛstɪd; kən'dʒɛstɪd/ *adj* **1** blocked by heavy traffic 交通阻塞的: *The streets of London are increasingly congested.* 倫敦大街上的堵車現象日益嚴重。 **2** blocked with liquid (used of parts of the body) 充血的〔指身體部位〕: *My head hurts and my nose is congested.* 我的頭很疼, 鼻子也塞住了。—**congestion** /-'dʒɛstʃən; -'dʒɛstʃən/ *n* [U]: *traffic congestion* 交通阻塞 | *congestion of the lungs* 肺部充血

con·glom·e·rate /kən'ɡlamərɪt; kən'ɡlɒmərɪt/ *n* a large business firm producing goods of very different kinds〔多種經營的〕聯合大企業; 企業集團

con·glom·e·ra·tion /kən,ɡlamə'reʃən; kən,ɡlɒmə'reɪʃn/ *n* a collection of many different things gathered together 聚集物; 集合物: *It was a strange conglomeration of shops, flats, and government offices.* 形形色色的商店、公寓單位和政府機關擠在一起, 令人感到很奇怪。

con·grat·u·late /kən'ɡrætʃəˌlet; kən'ɡrætʃʊleɪt/ *v* congratulated, congratulating [T] to express your pleasure or admiration for a happy event or success 祝賀: *I was just phoning to congratulate you on your exam results.* 我現在打電話給你, 是對你的考試成績表示祝賀。—**congratulation** /kən,ɡrætʃə'leʃən; kən,ɡrætʃʊ'leɪʃn/ *n* [U] —**congratulatory** /kən'ɡrætʃələˌtori; kən,ɡrætʃʊ'leɪtəri/ *adj: a congratulatory telegram* 賀電

con·grat·u·la·tions /kən'ɡrætʃəˌleʃənz; kən'ɡrætʃʊ'leɪʃnz/ *interj, n* [pl] an expression of pleasure or admiration for someone's success or good fortune 恭喜; 祝賀: *You got the job? Congratulations!* 你得到了那份工作? 恭喜你呀! | *Congratulations on your engagement.* 恭喜你訂婚了!

con·gre·gate /'kaŋɡrɪˌɡet; 'kɒŋɡrɪɡeɪt/ *v* congregated, congregating [I] to come together in a large group 聚集; 集合: *Crowds congregated in the town square to hear the President.* 人們聚集在市鎮廣場上聽總統講話。

con·gre·ga·tion /ˌkaŋɡrɪ'ɡeʃən; ˌkɒŋɡrɪ'ɡeɪʃn/ *n* a group of people gathered together in a church for religious worship〔教堂內做禮拜的〕會眾

con·gress /'kaŋɡrəs; 'kɒŋɡres/ *n* **1** Congress the highest law-making body of the US, consisting of the SENATE and the House of Representatives 美國國會〔由參

院和眾議院組成〕: *Congress has approved the new education budget.* 國會通過了新的教育預算。 **2** (also 又作 **Congress**) a formal meeting of representatives of organizations or countries to exchange information and opinions 代表大會; (正式)會議: *We're attending a medical congress.* 我們在開一個醫學會議。 | *the Congress of Vienna* 維也納會議 —**congressional** /kən'ɡreʃənl; kən'ɡreʃənl/ *adj: congressional elections* 國會選舉

con·i·cal /'kanɪkl; 'kɒnɪkəl/ *adj* shaped like a CONE (1) 圓錐形的: *a conical hat* 圓錐形帽子 | *huts with conical roofs* 有圓錐形屋頂的小屋

co·ni·fer /'konəfɚ; 'kəʊnɪfə(r)/ *n* a tree on which brown cones (CONE (3)) grow and which usually keeps its leaves in winter 針葉樹〔一種結球果的常青樹〕—**coniferous** /ko'nɪfərəs; kə'nɪfərəs/ *adj*

con·jec·ture[1] /kən'dʒɛktʃɚ; kən'dʒektʃə(r)/ *n* [C;U] a guess based on the little information that you have 猜想; 推測: *Whether or not the President knew will always be a matter for conjecture.* 總統是否知曉, 人們有自己去猜了。

conjecture[2] *v* **conjectured, conjecturing** [I; +that] to guess 猜想

con·ju·gal /'kandʒuɡl; 'kɒndʒʊɡəl/ *adj* [only before a noun 只用於名詞前] *fml* concerning the relationship between husband and wife〖正式〗夫妻間的: *the conjugal bed* 夫妻睡的牀

con·ju·gate /'kandʒəˌɡet; 'kɒndʒʊɡeɪt/ *v* **conjugated, conjugating** [T] *tech* to give in a particular order the various forms of a verb that show number, person, and time〖術語〗列出動詞的詞形變化〔單複數、人稱、時態〕: *All I remember from my schooldays is how to conjugate Latin verbs.* 在學校裡所學的我只記得有拉丁文動詞的各種變化了。—**conjugation** /ˌkandʒə'ɡeʃən; ˌkɒndʒʊ'ɡeɪʃn/ *n*

con·junc·tion /kən'dʒʌŋkʃən; kən'dʒʌŋkʃn/ *n* **1** a word such as "but" or "and" that connects words, phrases, or parts of sentences 連(接)詞 –see Study Note on page 1330 見1330頁學習提示 **2 in conjunction with** together with 一起; 共同: *The army is acting in conjunction with the police in the hunt for terrorists.* 軍隊正與警方協同追捕恐怖分子。

con·jure /'kandʒɚ; 'kʌndʒə(r)/ *v* **conjured, conjuring** [I;T] to make something appear as if by magic 如用魔術般變出〔某物〕: *The magician conjured a rabbit out of his hat.* 魔術師從帽子裡變出一隻兔子。 | *Paul's very good at conjuring.* 保羅很會變戲法。

conjure sthg ↔ **up** *phr v* [T] **1** to give an image or idea of something 想像出〔情形〕 **2** to make something appear as if by magic 如用魔術般變出〔某物〕

con·jur·er /'kandʒərɚ; 'kʌndʒərə(r)/ *n* (also

又作 **conjuror**) a professional entertainer who does conjuring tricks to amuse others 魔術師

★con·nect /kəˈnɛkt; kəˈnɛkt/ v **1** [T] (also 又作 **connect** sthg ↔ **up**) to join two or more places or things 連結; 結: *The railway line connects London and Edinburgh.* 這條鐵路線連接倫敦與愛丁堡。| *The plumber connected up all the pipes and turned on the water.* 管道工接通所有的管道，然後打開了水龍頭。| *The tape recorder is connected to a loudspeaker.* 錄音機與揚聲器相連接。 **2** [T] to suggest that two or more things are related 證明…的聯繫: *There is no evidence to connect her with the crime.* 沒有證據證明她與這宗罪案有關。 **3** [T] to join two people by telephone 給〔兩個人〕接通電話: *Could you connect me with a number in Indonesia, please?* 請你幫我把電話接往印尼好嗎? **4** [T] to join something to an electricity supply 將〔某物〕接通電源: *Make sure the machine's connected properly.* 要確保接好機器的電源。 **5** [I] to be planned so that passengers arrive in time to catch another train, bus, or plane and continue on their journey 〔交通〕銜接; 聯運: *The ten o'clock plane connects with a flight to Paris.* 十點鐘的飛機與去巴黎的班機銜接。 –opposite 反義 **disconnect** (for senses 3, 4 僅第三、第四個義項)

con·nect·ed /kəˈnɛktɪd; kəˈnɛktɪd/ adj related to someone or something else 有關係的; 有聯繫的: *Is your decision to leave connected with anything I said?* 你決定要走，是不是與我所説過的甚麼話有關? –opposite 反義 **unconnected**

★con·nec·tion /kəˈnɛkʃən; kəˈnɛkʃən/ n (also 又作 **con·nex·ion** BrE 〔英式〕) **1** [U] the joining of two or more things 連接: *I'm waiting for the connection of the new pipes to the water supply.* 我在等着把新的供水管道連接起來。 –opposite 反義 **disconnection 2** [C] a relationship between things 聯繫; 關係: *Do you know that there's a connection between smoking and heart disease?* 你知不知道心臟病與吸煙有關? **3** [C] a plane, train or bus arranged for a time which allows passengers to continue on the next part of their journey 轉運乘客的交通工具〔如飛機、火車或公共汽車〕: *There are connections in Paris for all European capitals.* 巴黎有前往歐洲各國首都的接駁交通工具。 **4** [C] something that joins two places or things 聯繫物; 連接物: *There are excellent road and railway connections between major cities.* 主要城市之間有着極為便利的公路和鐵路連接。| *The machine won't work because of a faulty connection.* 由於線路接錯，機器無法運轉。 **5** **connections** [pl] people known to someone through their family or through business 〔生意上的〕關係戶; 親屬: *She's English but has Irish connections.* 她是英格蘭人，但有愛

爾蘭親屬。| *We have connections with a firm in Zurich.* 我們與蘇黎世的一家公司有聯繫。 **6 in connection with** fml concerning 〔正式〕關於: *I am writing in connection with your recent request for information about the department.* 此信是有關你最近要求獲得該部門資料的。

con·nive /kəˈnaɪv; kəˈnaɪv/ v **conniving** [I] **1** fml to work secretly for some wrong or illegal purpose 〔正式〕同謀; 串通: *She connived with her friend to cheat in the examination.* 她與朋友串通好在考試中作弊。 **2 connive at something** to make no attempt to stop something that you know is wrong 縱容; 放任: *I believe you connived at the man's escape because you felt sorry for him.* 我知道你縱容那個人逃掉，因為你同情他。

con·nois·seur /ˌkɑnəˈsɜˌ; ˌkɒnəˈsɜːr/ n someone who has a good knowledge and understanding of subjects such as art or music, and whose judgments are respected 鑒賞家; 鑒定家; 行家: *a connoisseur of fine wines* 好酒鑒賞家

con·no·ta·tion /ˌkɑnəˈteʃən; ˌkɒnəˈteɪʃən/ n an idea suggested by a word rather than the actual meaning of the word 隱含意義: *The word "peasant" has negative connotations in English.* "peasant"一詞在英語中含貶義。

con·quer /ˈkɑŋkɚ; ˈkɒŋkər/ v **1** [I;T] to win land or defeat an enemy by fighting 佔領; 擊敗: *The Normans conquered England in 1066.* 諾曼人於1066年佔領了英格蘭。| *a conquering army* 佔領軍 **2** [T] to gain control over something difficult 克服; 征服: *The mountain was finally conquered by climbers in 1982.* 這座山終於在1982年被登山運動員征服。 –**conqueror** n

con·quest /ˈkɑŋkwɛst; ˈkɒŋkwest/ n **1** [U] the defeat or control of something 擊敗; 征服: *the conquest of Britain by invading armies* 入侵軍隊佔領英國 | *The conquest of this rare disease has always been her aim.* 克服這種罕見的疾病一直是她的目標。 **2** [C] land won as a result of fighting 攻佔的土地: *French conquests in Asia* 法國在亞洲佔領的土地 **3** [C] a person of the opposite sex whose admiration or love has been won (a word which is often used in a humorous way) 愛情的俘虜〔常為幽默用法〕: *She's coming to dinner with her latest conquest. (I think his name's Pete.)* 她準備與剛被她征服的男友一起來赴宴。(我記得他的名字好像叫皮特。)

con·science /ˈkɑnʃəns; ˈkɒnʃəns/ n **1** an inner sense that tells you whether you are doing something right or wrong 良心: *Vote according to your conscience.* 憑良心去投票。| *He's behaving like a man with a guilty conscience.* 他一舉一動都顯示出他很內疚。 **2 have a clear conscience** to know that you have done nothing wrong 問心無愧 **3 con-**

science-stricken feeling very guilty about something you have or have not done〔由於做了或未做某事而〕於心不安的 **4 have something on your conscience** to feel guilty about something that you have or have not done 於心不安 **5 in all conscience** doing what you know is right 憑良心〔做事〕: *I couldn't in all conscience stop him seeing his father.* 我不能昧着良心阻止他去探望父親。

con·sci·en·tious /ˌkɑnʃɪˈɛnʃəs; ˌkɒnʃiˈenʃəs/ *adj* careful to do everything very carefully and well 認真的; 謹慎的; 盡責的: *a conscientious worker* 盡責的工人 | *a conscientious piece of work* 苦心做成的活計 –see 見 CONSCIOUS (USAGE 用法) –**conscientiously** *adv* –**conscientiousness** *n* [U]

***con·scious** /ˈkɑnʃəs; ˈkɒnʃəs/ *adj* **1** [never before a noun 不能用於名詞前] awake and able to think 神志清醒的: *He is badly hurt but still conscious.* 他受了重傷, 但神志仍清醒。–opposite 反義 **unconscious 2** [never before a noun 不能用於名詞前] knowing and understanding 知道的; 意識的: *Peter isn't conscious of his bad manners.* 彼得沒有意識到他很無禮。 | *I was conscious that he was ill at ease.* 我感覺到他局促不安。**3** [only before a noun 只用於名詞前] intentional 故意的; 有意的: *a conscious decision* 有意做出的決定 | *a conscious effort* 有目的的努力 –**consciously** *adv*

> ■ USAGE 用法: **1** The usual opposite of **conscious** is **unconscious** ☆ **conscious** 的反義詞通常為 **unconscious**: *He's still **unconscious** after the accident.* 事故發生之後, 他仍神志不清。But in psychology, both **unconscious** and **subconscious** are used ☆然而在心理學中, **unconscious** 和 **subconscious** 都可以用: *the **unconscious/subconscious** mind* 無意識; 下意識 **2** Do not confuse **conscious** with **conscientious** which means "very careful in the way you do your job". ☆不要混淆 **conscious** 與 **conscientious,** 後者的意思是"盡職盡責的"。

***con·scious·ness** /ˈkɑnʃəsnɪs; ˈkɒnʃəsnᵻs/ *n* [sing; U] **1** all the ideas and opinions held by a person or a group of people about a particular subject 意識; 觀念: *You can see his political consciousness developing.* 你會看到他的政治意識變得越來越强。**2** feeling or understanding 覺察; 感覺: *a consciousness that someone else was in the room* 覺得還有其他人在屋裏 **3 lose consciousness** to fall into a state like sleep so that you cannot think or understand what is happening 失去知覺 [RELATED PHRASE 相關詞組 **regain consciousness**]

cons·cript /kənˈskrɪpt; kənˈskrɪpt/ *v* [T] to make someone serve in one of the armed forces 徵〔某人〕入伍: *My son was conscripted into the navy during the war.* 我兒子在戰爭中被徵召入海軍。–**conscript** /ˈkɑnskrɪpt; ˈkɒnskrɪpt/ *n: He's a conscript.* 他是個應徵入伍的士兵。–**conscription** /kənˈskrɪpʃən; kənˈskrɪpʃən/ *n* [U]

con·se·crate /ˈkɑnsɪˌkret; ˈkɒnsᵻkreɪt/ *v* **consecrated, consecrating** [T] to declare something to be holy in a special ceremony 〔通過特殊儀式〕將〔某物〕奉為神聖; 給〔某物〕祝聖: *The church will be consecrated by the bishop.* 主教將為該教堂祝聖。–**consecration** /ˌkɑnsɪˈkreʃən; ˌkɒnsᵻˈkreɪʃən/ *n* [U]

con·sec·u·tive /kənˈsɛkjətɪv; kənˈsekjʊtɪv/ *adj* following one after the other 連續的; 一個接一個的: *I saw him on three consecutive days.* 我一連三天都看見了他。–**consecutively** *adv*

con·sen·sus /kənˈsɛnsəs; kənˈsensəs/ *n* [sing; U] general agreement 一致的意見: *What is the consensus of opinion?* 大多數人的意見是甚麼? | *We must come to a consensus quickly.* 我們必須很快把意見統一起來。

***con·sent**[1] /kənˈsɛnt; kənˈsent/ *v* [I] to agree to something 同意: *Her father reluctantly consented to her marriage.* 她父親勉強同意了她的婚事。–compare 比較 DISSENT[1]

consent[2] *n* [U] **1** agreement or permission 同意; 准許: *We need your parents' written consent.* 我們需要取得你父母的書面同意。**2 by common consent, by general consent** by the agreement of most people 經大多數人同意

***con·se·quence** /ˈkɑnsəˌkwɛns; ˈkɒnsᵻkwəns/ *n* **1** the result of an action or situation 後果; 結果: *Teacher shortages are a consequence of low pay.* 教師短缺是工資太低的結果。 | *If you get caught, you'll have to face the consequences.* 你一旦被抓住, 就得承擔後果。**2 of little/no consequence** not important 不重要

***con·se·quent·ly** /ˈkɑnsəˌkwɛntlɪ; ˈkɒnsᵻkwəntli/ *adv fml* therefore 〔正式〕所以; 因此: *No candidate succeeded in obtaining a majority of the votes. Consequently new elections were held.* 沒有一位候選人得票過半數, 所以舉行了新的選舉。

***con·ser·va·tion** /ˌkɑnsɚˈveʃən; ˌkɒnsəˈveɪʃən/ *n* [U] **1** protection from damage or destruction 保存; 保護〔以免遭破壞或毀滅〕: *the conservation of our limited supplies of water* 對我們有限的水源的保護 **2** the protection of natural things 〔自然資源的〕保護: *I am involved in wild life conservation.* 我參加了保護野生動植物的活動。–**conservationist** *n: Conservationists are protesting about plans for a new motorway.* 生態環境保護主義者正在對新高速公路計劃提出抗議。

con·ser·va·tis·m /kənˈsɝvətɪzəm; kənˈsɜ:-

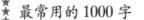

vətɪzəm/ *n* [U] **1** dislike of change, especially sudden change 保守; 守舊: *We are seeing a new conservatism among young people.* 我們在年輕人身上看到了一種新的保守思想。 **2** (also 又作 **Conservatism**) the political beliefs of the Conservative Party, which say that any change to the established order of society should be slow and carefully considered 保守主義〔保守黨的主張〕

con·ser·va·tive¹ /kən'sɜːvətɪv; kən'sɜːvətɪv/ *adj* **1** unwilling to change your ideas about things 守舊的: *He is very conservative in his views of women.* 他對婦女的看法非常保守。 **2** not very modern in style, taste, or manners 〔風格、品味、方式上〕舊式的; 不趨時髦的: *She dresses in a rather conservative way.* 她的衣着相當保守。 **3** careful, and probably less than the true amount 〔數量的估計〕謹慎的; 保守的: *The figure of three million unemployed is a conservative estimate based on government statistics.* 失業人數達三百萬是根據官方統計數據作出的一個保守估計。 **4 Conservative** concerned with or belonging to the Conservative Party 保守黨的: *Conservative voters* 投保守黨票的選民 –**conservatively** *adv*

conservative² *n* **1 Conservative** a member of the Conservative Party 保守黨黨員 **2** someone who does not like change 不喜歡變動的人; 守舊的人

Conservative Party /·ˈ···· ˌ··/ *n* the political party in Britain which tends to be against sudden changes in the way that society is organized, and is against state control of industry 〔英國的〕保守黨

con·ser·va·to·ry /kən'sɜːvətri; kən'sɜːvətɔːri/ *n* **1** a room, mainly of glass, which is joined to a house and where plants are often grown 〔種植植物的〕玻璃暖房 **2** a school where people are trained in music 音樂學校

con·serve /kən'sɜːv; kən'sɜːv/ *v* **conserved, conserving** [T] to keep something from being damaged, wasted, or destroyed 保存; 保護〔某物〕: *Conserve your energy!* 保存你的精力! | *methods of conserving electricity* 節約用電的方法

★★**con·sid·er** /kən'sɪdə; kən'sɪdər/ *v* **1** [I;T] to think about something carefully 認真考慮〔某事〕: *I'm considering changing my job.* 我正在考慮轉換工作。 | *We need some time to consider.* 我們需要一些時間來考慮。

□ USEFUL PATTERNS 有用句型
to consider; to consider something; to consider doing something

2 [T; +(that)] to think of someone or something in a particular way 認為: *I consider him to be a good musician.* 我認為他是

個不錯的音樂家。

□ USEFUL PATTERNS 有用句型
to consider someone to be something; to consider that…

3 [T; +(that)] to take something into account 考慮到〔某事物〕: *If you consider that she's only been studying English a year, she speaks it very well.* 你如果考慮到她只學了一年英語, 那麼她的英語算是説得很不錯了。 | *All things considered, it would be better to resign.* 全盤考慮下來, 還是辭職的好。

★★**con·sid·er·a·ble** /kən'sɪdərəbl; kən'sɪdərəbl/ *adj* fairly large (used of the amount of something) 相當大的〔指數量〕: *a considerable length of time* 相當長的一段時間 | *a considerable number of people* 相當多的人 –**considerably** *adv*: *Our house is considerably smaller than theirs.* 我們的房子比他們的要小得多。

con·sid·er·ate /kən'sɪdərɪt; kən'sɪdərɪt/ *adj* thoughtful about other people's rights or feelings 想得周到的; 體貼的: *It was very considerate of you to tell us you would be late.* 你事先就告訴我們你會晚到, 想得真是周到。 –opposite 反義 –**inconsiderate** –**considerately** *adv*

★**con·sid·er·a·tion** /kən,sɪdə'reʃən; kən,sɪdə'reɪʃən/ *n* **1** [U] thought for other people's feelings 體諒; 體貼: *You show no consideration for anyone but yourself!* 你一點都不為別人考慮, 只想到你自己! **2** [U] careful thought and attention 深思熟慮; 認真考慮: *We shall give your request careful consideration.* 我們會認真考慮你的要求的。 **3** [C] a fact that needs to be considered when making a decision 要考慮的事: *Local facilities are an important consideration when you buy a house.* 買房子時, 考慮一下當地的公共設施是很重要的。 **4 take something into consideration** to consider something when making a judgment 考慮到某事: *Your illness will be taken into consideration by the examiners.* 考官會考慮你的病情。

con·sid·ered /kən'sɪdəd; kən'sɪdəd/ *adj* **1** [only before a noun 只用於名詞前] reached after careful thought 經過考慮的: *It is my considered opinion that you are wrong.* 我經過考慮後認為你是錯的。 **2 all things considered** when you consider everything 從各方面考慮: *All things considered, I think we did very well.* 考慮了各種因素, 我覺得我們做得非常好。

con·sid·er·ing /kən'sɪdərɪŋ; kən'sɪdərɪŋ/ *prep,conj* taking into account 考慮到: *He did very well in his examinations, considering how little work he had done.* 考慮到他未下過多少功夫, 他的考試成績已算相當好了。

con·sign /kən'saɪn; kən'saɪn/ *v* [T] *fml* 〔正式〕 **1** to send something to a person or place for sale 寄售, 託運〔貨物〕: *The goods* *were consigned* **to** *you by rail.* 貨物已由鐵路託運給你。**2** to put a person or thing into a particular place or situation 把〔某人或某物〕交付給: *My mother consigned me* **to** *my uncle's care.* 媽媽把我交給舅舅看管。| *All those papers have been consigned to the dustbin.* 所有的那些報紙都已扔到垃圾箱裡去了。

con·sign·ment /kən'saɪnmənt; kən'saɪnmənt/ *n* **1** [C] a number of goods sent together 託寄貨物: *The whole consignment of bananas was rotten.* 整批託寄的香蕉都腐爛了。**2** [U] the act of sending someone or something to another place 託運; 交付

*★***con·sist** /kən'sɪst; kən'sɪst/ *v* **1 consist of something** to be made up of a number of things 由某物組成: *The city of New York consists of five boroughs.* 紐約由五個行政區組成。| *a delivery of supplies, consisting mainly of food and medicines* 一批主要包括食物和藥品的貨物 **2 consist in something** to be really 〔實際〕在於某物: *For me, the pleasure of the meal consisted entirely in the conversation — the food was terrible.* 對我來說, 那頓飯的樂趣完全在於席間的談話——飯菜本身糟糕透了。

con·sis·ten·cy /kən'sɪstənsɪ; kən'sɪstənsɪ/ *n* **consistencies 1** [U] behaviour which always follows the same principles or pattern 一貫性; 一致性: *We need greater consistency in the advice we give to the public.* 我們應該給公眾提供更加一致的意見。**2** [C;U] the degree of thickness 稠度; 濃度: *Mix the butter and sugar to the consistency of thick cream.* 把黃油和糖混合到稠奶油的程度。

*★***con·sis·tent** /kən'sɪstənt; kən'sɪstənt/ *adj* **1** always following the same principles or patterns of behaviour 一貫的; 始終如一的: *He's been a consistent supporter of women's rights.* 他一貫支持婦女擁有同等的權力。**2 consistent with** in agreement with 與⋯一致; 符合: *That statement is not consistent with what you said earlier.* 那項聲明與你早先所說的話不符。**–consistently** *adv*

con·so·la·tion /ˌkɑnsə'leɪʃən; ˌkɒnsə'leɪʃən/ *n* [C;U] a person or thing that gives comfort during a time of sadness or disappointment 安慰; 慰藉: *The only consolation was that I hadn't spent any money.* 唯一令我欣慰的是我不曾花過錢。

con·sole¹ /kən'sol; kən'səʊl/ *v* **consoled, consoling** [T] **1** to give comfort or sympathy to someone in times of disappointment or sadness 安慰〔某人〕: *Nothing will console her* **for** *the loss of her dog.* 她的狗死了, 沒有甚麼事情能安慰得了她。| *She tried to console me* **with** *a cup of tea.* 她給我一杯茶, 試圖來安慰我一下。**2 console yourself** to make yourself feel better 安慰自己; 想開一些: *Console yourself* **with** *the thought that he didn't get the job either!* 想開些吧, 想想他也沒有得到那份工作呀! **–consolatory** /kən'sɑ-

lə,tɔri; kən'sɒlətəri/ *adj*

con·sole² /'kɑnsol; 'kɒnsəʊl/ *n* a flat surface containing the controls for a machine 〔儀器的〕控制台

con·sol·i·date /kən'sɑlə,det; kən'sɒlɪ̩deɪt/ *v* **consolidated, consolidating** [I;T] **1** to increase in strength or effectiveness 強化; 鞏固: *Britain is trying to consolidate her position in Europe.* 英國正在努力鞏固其在歐洲的地位。**2** to join together 統一; 合併: *Several small businesses have recently consolidated to form a single large company.* 最近數家小企業已合併組成一家大公司。**–consolidation** /kən-ˌsɑlə'deʃən; kən,sɒlɪ̩'deɪʃən/ *n* [C;U]

con·som·mé /ˌkɑnsə'me; kən'sɒmeɪ/ *n* [U] thin, clear soup 清燉湯: *chicken consommé* 燉雞湯

con·so·nant /'kɑnsənənt; 'kɒnsənənt/ *n* **1** a speech sound made by partly or completely stopping the flow of air as it goes through your mouth 輔音, 子音 **2** any of the letters of the English alphabet except a, e, i, o, u 輔音〔子音〕字母

con·sort¹ /'kɑnsɔrt; 'kɒnsɔ:t/ *n fml* the wife or husband of a ruler《正式》〔君王的〕配偶 •

con·sort² /kən'sɔrt; kən'sɔ:t/ *v* **consort with somebody** to spend time in the company of someone who is disapproved of 與壞人結交: *He is said to consort with known criminals.* 據說他跟幾個臭名昭著的罪犯有來往。

con·sor·ti·um /kən'sɔrʃəm; kən'sɔ:tiəm/ *n* **consortiums** *or* **consortia** a number of companies or businesses working together 財團: *The banks have formed a consortium.* 這幾家銀行組成了一個財團。

con·spic·u·ous /kən'spɪkjuəs; kən'spɪkjuəs/ *adj* easily noticed 明顯的; 顯而易見的: *She felt very conspicuous in a men's club.* 她覺得自己在男子俱樂部裡很惹人注目。| *That hat makes him even more conspicuous than usual.* 戴上那頂帽子使他比平常更加引人注目。**–conspicuously** *adv*

con·spir·a·cy /kən'spɪrəsɪ; kən'spɪrəsɪ/ *n* **conspiracies** [C;U] the secret planning of an illegal act by a number of people 陰謀: *She was found guilty of conspiracy to murder.* 她被裁決犯有陰謀殺人罪。| *Details of the conspiracy have just been made public.* 那場陰謀的細節剛剛被公諸於眾。

con·spir·a·tor /kən'spɪrətɚ; kən'spɪrətə[r]/ *n* a member of a group who make a secret plan to do something illegal 參與陰謀者 **–conspiratorial** /kən,spɪrə'tɔrɪəl; kən,spɪrə-'tɔ:riəl/ *adj* : *a conspiratorial whisper* 詭詐的竊竊私語 **–conspiratorially** *adv*

con·spire /kən'spaɪr; kən'spaɪə[r]/ *v* **conspired, conspiring** [I] **1** to plan together secretly to do something illegal 密謀; 共謀: *The four men conspired to rob a bank.* 這四個男人密謀搶劫一家銀行。**2** *fml* to happen at the same time, leading to a particular bad result 〖正式〗同時發生〔而導致不良後果〕: *Events conspired to make the policies impossible to carry out.* 種種事件一齊發生, 使得政策無法執行。| *I felt as though everything was conspiring against me.* 我覺得好像甚麼事都在跟我過不去。

con·sta·ble /ˈkʌnstəbl; ˈkʌnstəbəl/ *n* a British police officer of the lowest rank〔英國的〕警察

con·stab·u·la·ry /kənˈstæbjəˌlɛri; kənˈstæbjʊ̩ləri/ *n* **constabularies** the police force of a particular area or country〔某地區或國家的〕警察部隊

✲**con·stant** /ˈkʌnstənt; ˈkɒnstənt/ *adj* **1** fixed or unchanging 固定不變的: *a constant speed* 穩定的速度 **2** happening all the time 一再發生的: *I dislike these constant arguments.* 我討厭這些接連不斷的爭吵。**3** loyal to a person or idea 忠誠的; 忠實的: *my constant companion* 我忠實的夥伴 **–constantly** *adv*

con·stel·la·tion /ˌkʌnstəˈleʃən; ˌkɒnstɪˈleɪʃən/ *n* a group of stars in a fixed pattern 星座

con·ster·na·tion /ˌkʌnstəˈneʃən; ˌkɒnstəˈneɪʃən/ *n* [U] great shock and worry 驚恐; 驚駭: *He looked at me in consternation.* 他驚恐地看着我。

con·sti·pa·tion /ˌkʌnstəˈpeʃən; ˌkɒnstɪˈpeɪʃən/ *n* [U] inability to empty your bowels for a period of time 便祕 **–constipated** /ˈkʌnstəˌpetɪd; ˈkɒnstɪˈpeɪtɪd/ *adj*

✲**con·sti·tu·en·cy** /kənˈstɪtʃʊənsɪ; kənˈstɪtʃuənsi/ *n* **constituencies** an area of a country, represented in the government by a Member of Parliament 選區

con·sti·tu·ent /kənˈstɪtʃʊənt; kənˈstɪtʃuənt/ *n* **1** a voter in a particular area of a country〔選區的〕選民: *Constituents can see their MP by appointment.* 選民可以通過預約與國會議員會面。**2** any of the parts that make up a whole 構成部分; 成分: *the constituents of an atom* 原子的組成部分 **–constituent** *adj*

✲**con·sti·tute** /ˈkʌnstəˌtjut; ˈkɒnstɪˈtjuːt/ *v* **constituted, constituting** *fml*〖正式〗[+ complement; not in progressive forms 不用於進行式] **1** to form something 組成; 構成: *the 50 states that constitute the USA* 組成美國的五十個州 **2** to be considered the same as something 被認為是: *This constitutes an important breakthrough in medical knowledge.* 這被認為是醫學知識的一項重大突破。

✲**con·sti·tu·tion** /ˌkʌnstəˈtjuʃən; ˌkɒnstɪˈtjuːʃən/ *n* **1** the system of laws and principles according to which a country is governed 憲法: *Are you reading about the American constitution?* 你在看美國憲法嗎? **2** the general condition of a person's body 身體狀況; 體質: *He's always had a weak constitution.* 他體質一直很弱。**3** the way in which something is put together 構造; 組成方式: *I'm concerned about the constitution of the new committee.* 我很關注新委員會的組成人選。

✲**con·sti·tu·tion·al** /ˌkʌnstəˈtjuʃənl; ˌkɒnstɪˈtjuːʃənəl/ *adj* **1** allowed or limited by a political constitution 憲法允許的; 受憲法限制的: *There are severe constitutional limits on the queen's power.* 憲法對女王的權力有嚴格的限制。**2** related to a political constitution 有關憲法的: *a constitutional crisis* 憲法危機 **3** related to a person's general physical condition 體質的 **–constitutionally** *adv*

con·strain /kənˈstren; kənˈstreɪn/ *v* [T] *fml* to make someone behave in a certain way by limiting their freedom to decide〖正式〗約束; 迫使: *I am constrained by the need to care for my mother.* 由於需要, 我不得不照顧母親。

con·strained /kənˈstrend; kənˈstreɪnd/ *adj* **1** awkward and unnatural 拘謹的; 不自然的: *a constrained manner* 拘謹的舉止 **2** feel constrained to do something to feel that you have to do something 覺得必須做某事

✲**con·straint** /kənˈstrent; kənˈstreɪnt/ *n* [C; U] something that limits your freedom of action, often by the use of threat or force〔常通過威脅或武力而對行動自由所做出的〕約束, 束縛: *Teachers have to work within the constraints of the system.* 老師的工作得受到制度的制約。| *We acted under constraint.* 我們的行動受到限制。

con·strict /kənˈstrɪkt; kənˈstrɪkt/ *v* [T] **1** to make something narrower 使〔某物〕更狹窄 **2** to limit someone's freedom of action 限制〔某人的行動〕 **–constricting** *adj* **–constriction** /-ˈstrɪkʃən; -ˈstrɪkʃən/ *n* [U]

✲**con·struct** /kənˈstrʌkt; kənˈstrʌkt/ *v* [T] to build or make something 建造; 建築: *a bridge constructed of metal and concrete* 由金屬和混凝土建造而成的大橋

✲**con·struc·tion** /kənˈstrʌkʃən; kənˈstrʌkʃən/ *n* **1** [U] the business or work of building 建造; 建築業: *I work in the construction industry.* 我從事建築業。**2** [C] something that is built 建築物: *The conference centre is an enormous construction in the city centre.* 會議中心是座落在市中心的一座巨大的建築物。**3** under construction being built 正在建造: *Five new hotels are under construction.* 有五座新的賓館正在興建。

con·struc·tive /kənˈstrʌktɪv; kənˈstrʌktɪv/ *adj* helping to improve or develop something 建設性的; 有利於發展的: *She has a very constructive attitude to local problems.* 她對於當地存在的問題持一種非常積極的態度。**–constructively** *adv*

con·strue /kənˈstru; kənˈstruː/ *v* **construed, construing** *fml* [T] to understand something in a certain way〖正式〗理解〔某事物〕: *My comments were construed as criticism.* 我的評論被人理解為批評。

con·sul /ˈkʌnsl̩; ˈkɒnsəl/ *n* an official who lives in a foreign city and works to help citizens of his or her own country there 領事 **–consular** /-slɚ; -sjʊ̩lər/ *adj*

---

con·su·late /'kɑnslɪt; 'kɒnsjɔ̈lɪ̩t/ *n* the official building in which a consul lives or works 領事館

****con·sult** /kən'sʌlt; kən'sʌlt/ *v* [T] **1** to go to a person or book for information or advice 請教〔某人〕; 查閱〔某書〕: *Have you consulted a doctor about your illness?* 你找醫生看過你的病沒有? | *We need to consult a map.* 我們需要查一下地圖。**2 consult with someone** to exchange opinions or information with someone 與某人交流意見〔商討〕: *I'll need to consult with my partner before making a decision.* 在做決定以前, 我需要跟我的合夥人商量一下。

****con·sul·tant** /kən'sʌltənt; kən'sʌltənt/ *n* **1** an important hospital doctor who gives specialist advice 會診醫師 **2** a person who gives specialist professional advice to others 顧問: *an industrial relations consultant* 勞資關係顧問 **–consultancy** *n* **consultancies** [C;U]: *He runs a computer consultancy firm.* 他經營一家電腦諮詢公司。

****con·sul·ta·tion** /,kɑnsəl'teɪʃən; ˌkɒnsəl'teɪʃən/ *n* **1** [C] a meeting held to exchange opinions and ideas 協商會: *We held a hurried consultation in the corridor.* 我們在走廊裡進行了緊急磋商。**2** [U] an exchange of opinions or ideas 商議; 磋商: *The decision was made in consultation with the local police.* 該決定是在與當地警方商議之後做出的。**3** [U] a search for information, usually in a book 參閱; 查閱: *Dictionaries are available for consultation.* 辭典可供查閱。

con·sume /kən'sum; kən'sjuːm/ *v* **consumed, consuming** [T] *fml*〖正式〗**1** to eat or drink something 吃; 喝 **2** to use something that cannot then be used again 消耗; 消費: *Arguing consumed too many hours of the committee's time.* 爭論花去了委員會太多的時間。| *The country produces far less than it consumes.* 該國的生產量遠遠小於其消費量。**3** (of a fire) to destroy something 〔火〕毀壞, 燒毀: *The buildings were consumed by flames.* 一座座建築物被大火所吞噬。**4** to fill the thoughts or feelings of someone continuously, especially in a damaging way 為某種思想〔感情〕而不斷受折磨: *She was consumed by guilt.* 她深感內疚。

****con·sum·er** /kən'sumɚ; kən'sjuːmə[r]/ *n* a person who buys goods and uses services 消費者: *More laws are needed to protect consumers.* 需要有更多的法規來保障消費者。

con·sum·ing /kən'sumɪŋ; kən'sjuːmɪŋ/ *adj* [only before a noun 只用於名詞前] so strong that nothing else has the same importance 強烈的; 使人全神貫注的: *Her consuming ambition is to be an opera singer.* 她的強烈願望是成為一位歌劇演員。

con·sum·mate¹ /kən'sʌmɪt; kən'sʌmɪ̩t/ *adj fml* extremely skilful〖正式〗技藝高超的: *He won the race with consummate ease.* 他技藝高超, 輕而易舉地贏得了比賽。| *a consum-*

mate liar 撒謊大王

con·sum·mate² /'kɑnsəˌmet; 'kɒnsəmeɪt/ *v* **consummated, consummating** [T] *fml*〖正式〗**1** to make a marriage or relationship complete by having sex〔經同房而〕完〔婚〕**2** to make something complete 使〔事物〕完成: *to consummate a business deal* 完成一筆交易 **–consummation** /,kɑnsə'meʃən; ˌkɒnsə'meɪʃən/ *n* [C;U]

****con·sump·tion** /kən'sʌmpʃən; kən'sʌmpʃən/ *n* [U] **1** the act of eating or drinking something 吃; 喝: *The food was declared unfit for human consumption.* 這食物被宣佈不適宜食用。**2** the use of something 消耗; 消費: *The nation's consumption of coal increased again last year.* 該國煤的消耗量去年再度上升。**3** TUBERCULOSIS (a word no longer used in modern English) 肺病〔現代英語裡已不再使用〕

cont. a word written at the bottom of a page to show that something continues on the next page; an abbreviation for **continued**〖縮〗接下頁〔寫在一頁的下方, 表示在下一頁繼續〕

****con·tact¹** /'kɑntækt; 'kɒntækt/ *n* **1** [U] the state of touching or being close to a person or thing 接觸: *Have the other children been in contact with the disease?* 其餘的孩子與這種病有接觸嗎? | *The fire started when two wires came into contact.* 兩條電線一接觸便著火了。**2** [U] the state of giving a message to someone or exchanging information and ideas 聯繫; 聯絡: *The desert people have little contact with the outside world.* 沙漠居民與外界沒有甚麼聯繫。| *Have you been in contact with your lawyer recently?* 你近來與你的律師有聯繫嗎? | *He's trying to make contact with the ship by radio.* 他在通過無線電努力與那艘船聯絡。**3** [C] *infml* a person you know who can help you in some way〖非正式〗〔可幫忙的〕熟人: *I've got a contact in the tax office who I can phone.* 我在稅務局有個熟人, 我可以打電話給他。**4** [C] a part that completes an electrical CIRCUIT when it touches another part〔電路的〕接觸點

****contact²** *v* [T] to get a message to someone 聯繫, 聯絡〔某人〕: *Do you know where I can contact him?* 你知道我在哪裡可與他聯繫上嗎?

contact lens /'· ··/ *n* a very small plastic LENS which you put on your eye instead of wearing glasses 隱形眼鏡片

con·ta·gious /kən'tedʒəs; kən'teɪdʒəs/ *adj* **1** spread by touch (used of a disease) 接觸傳染的〔指疾病〕**2** spread quickly among people〔在人羣中〕迅速傳染的: *Her laughter was contagious.* 她的笑富有感染力。

****con·tain** /kən'ten; kən'teɪn/ *v* [T] **1** to have something inside that may or may not be a part of it 包含, 含有〔某物〕: *This bottle contains enough water*

for all of us. 這瓶子裡有足夠的水給我們大家喝。 | *a book containing all the information I needed* 一部包含我所需的全部資料的書 | *fertilizers containing nitrogen* 含氮化肥 **2** to keep something under control 控制住〔某物〕: *I tried to contain my anger.* 我盡力控制住自己的怒氣。 | *Drastic measures are required to contain the disease.* 需要採取嚴厲措施來控制住這種疾病。

con·tain·er /kən'teɪnə; kən'teɪnəʳ/ *n* **1** a box, bottle, barrel, or any other object used for holding something 容器〔箱子、瓶子、桶等〕 **2** an extremely large metal box used for carrying goods by road, by sea, or on the railway 集裝箱

con·tam·i·nate /kən'tæmə,neɪt; kən'tæmɪ,neɪt/ *v* **contaminated, contaminating** [T] to make something impure by mixing it with an unclean substance 污染〔某物〕: *All our drinking water has been contaminated.* 我們所有的飲用水都被污染了。 –**contamination** /kən,tæmə'neɪʃən; kən,tæmɪ'neɪʃən/ *n* [U]: *radioactive contamination* 放射性污染

contd. a word written at the bottom of a page to show that something continues on the next page; an abbreviation for **continued** 〔縮〕接下頁〔寫在一頁的下方，表示在下一頁繼續〕

con·tem·plate /'kɑntəm,pleɪt; 'kɒntəmpleɪt/ *v* **contemplated, contemplating 1** [I;T] to consider something carefully for a long time 〔長時間〕認真思考〔某事〕: *He's contemplating his next move.* 他在仔細考慮他的下一步行動。 **2** [T] to consider doing something 考慮〔做某事〕: *Have you ever contemplated leaving him?* 你有沒有想過要離開他?

□ USEFUL PATTERNS 有用句型
to contemplate something; to contemplate doing something

3 [T] *fml* to look thoughtfully at a person or thing 〔正式〕凝視〔人或物〕
con·tem·pla·tion /,kɑntəm'pleɪʃən; ,kɒntəm'pleɪʃən/ *n* [U] deep thought 沉思: *She spent an hour in quiet contemplation.* 她靜靜地沉思了一小時。 –**contemplative** /'kɑntəm,pletɪv; kən'templətɪv, 'kɒntəmpleɪtɪv/ *adj*: *He has a quiet, contemplative nature.* 他性格文靜，喜歡沉思。

★**con·tem·po·ra·ry¹** /kən'tɛmpə,rɛri; kən'tempərəri/ *adj* **1** happening at the present time 當代的: *contemporary art* 當代藝術 **2** belonging to the same time as something else that is mentioned 〔與提到的其他事情〕同時代的: *I'm reading contemporary accounts of the war.* 我正在看有關那場戰爭的當時的報導。

contemporary² *n* **contemporaries** a person living or working at the same time as someone else 同時代的人: *Susan was a contemporary of mine at college.* 蘇珊與我是同

一屆的大學生。

con·tempt /kən'tɛmpt; kən'tempt/ *n* [U] **1** total lack of respect for someone or something 鄙視；輕視: *She gave me a look of utter contempt.* 她極為鄙視地看了我一眼。 **2** beneath contempt too unimportant or unworthy to think about at all 不齒；不屑一顧: *Don't worry about what those boys say to you; they are completely beneath contempt.* 別為那些男孩對你所說的話而擔心，根本不值得去理睬他們。

con·temp·ti·ble /kən'tɛmptəbl; kən'temptɪbəl/ *adj* deserving a total lack of respect 可鄙的: *That was a contemptible trick to play on a friend!* 用那種手段欺騙朋友真卑鄙! –**contemptibly** *adv*

con·temp·tu·ous /kən'tɛmptʃuəs; kən'temptʃuəs/ *adj* feeling or expressing a total lack of respect for a person or thing 鄙視的；輕蔑的: *She gave a contemptuous laugh.* 她輕蔑地笑了笑。 –**contemptuously** *adv*

con·tend /kən'tɛnd; kən'tend/ *v* **1** [T; + that] to claim that something is true 聲稱〔某物為真〕: *The lawyer contended that she had not returned home until 11.00.* 律師稱她十一點鐘才回家。 **2** contend with something to deal with a problem 解決難題: *I felt I had enough difficulties to contend with, without taking on someone else's problems.* 別人的問題暫先不論，我覺得自己就有很多困難有待解決。 **3** [I] to compete for something 爭奪〔某物〕: *They are contending with each other for the party leadership.* 他們在相互爭奪黨的領導權。

con·tend·er /kən'tɛndə; kən'tendəʳ/ *n* a person who takes part in a competition 競爭者

★**con·tent¹** /kən'tɛnt; kən'tent/ *adj* [never before a noun 不能用於名詞前] satisfied and happy 心滿意足的: *Dad seems really content since he retired.* 爸爸自退休以後，似乎很是滿足。 | *She was content to let him deal with all the arrangements.* 她很願意讓他去做一切安排。 | *I'm very content with what I've got.* 我對於自己所擁有的一切感到非常滿足。

★**content²** *v* [T] **1** to make someone feel happy or satisfied 使〔某人〕心滿意足 **2** content yourself with something to limit yourself to something and be satisfied with it 使自己滿足於某物: *John contented himself with one glass of wine.* 約翰喝了杯酒就算了。

con·tent³ /'kɑntɛnt; 'kɒntent/ *n* **1** [U] the subject matter of something 內容: *It's not the style of the book I object to; it's the content.* 我反對的不是那本書的風格，而是內容。 **2** [sing] the amount of a substance contained in something 含量: *Oranges have a high water content.* 橘子的水分含量很高。 **3** contents [pl] the things that are contained in something 內含物；內容: *The police emptied her bag and examined the contents.* 警察把

她的包倒空, 檢查了裡面的東西。| *He drank the entire contents of the bottle.* 他把瓶裡的東西喝光了。| *Check the chapter headings on the contents page.* 在目錄頁上查一下各章的標題。

con·tent·ed /kən'tɛntɪd; kən'tɛntl̩d/ *adj* satisfied and happy 心滿意足的: *My father seems contented at last.* 我父親最終似乎是滿意了。 –**contentedly** *adv* –**contentment** *n* [U]

con·ten·tion /kən'tɛnʃən; kən'tɛnʃən/ *n* **1** [U] argument and lack of agreement about something 爭論: *This is no time for contention.* 現在根本不是爭論的時候。 **2** [C] a claim or opinion 主張; 觀點: *It is my contention that the plan will never succeed.* 我的觀點是該計劃決不會成功。 **3 in contention** competing to win 在競爭

con·ten·tious /kən'tɛnʃəs; kən'tɛnʃəs/ *adj fml* likely to cause argument 〖正式〗會引起爭論的: *His proposal is rather contentious.* 他的建議很容易引起爭論。

con·test¹ /'kɑntɛst; 'kɒntest/ *n* **1** a competition or game 比賽; 競賽: *a contest of skill* 技能比賽 | *a beauty contest* 選美比賽 **2** a struggle or fight 競爭; 爭奪: *the contest **for** leadership of the party* 對該黨領導權的爭奪

con·test² /kən'tɛst; kən'test/ *v* [T] **1** to compete for something 競爭, 爭奪〔某事物〕: *How many people are contesting this seat on the council?* 有多少人在爭奪市議會中這個席位? **2** to argue about a decision 對〔某一決定〕進行辯駁: *I intend to contest the judge's decision in another court.* 我打算到另外一個法院抗辯法官的裁決。

con·tes·tant /kən'tɛstənt; kən'testənt/ *n* someone who is competing 競爭者: *There are 50 contestants in the next race.* 下次比賽有五十個參賽選手。

★★con·text /'kɑntɛkst; 'kɒntekst/ *n* **1** the words before and after a word or phrase 上下文, 語境: *You should be able to tell the meaning of this word from its context.* 你從該詞的上下文中應該能猜出它的含義。 **2** the situation in which something happens 〔某事發生的〕背景; 環境: *You need to see the dispute in its political context.* 你應該結合政治背景來看待這場爭論。 **3 in context** in relation to the whole situation 聯繫全局來看 [RELATED PHRASE 相關詞組 **out of context**: *My words were quoted out of context.* 我的話被斷章取義地拿來引用。] – **contextual** /kən'tɛkstʃuəl; kən'tekstʃuəl/ *adj*

con·ti·nent /'kɑntənənt; 'kɒntɪnənt/ *n* **1** any of the main large land masses on the earth 大陸; 洲: *the continent of Africa* 非洲大陸 **2 the Continent** *BrE* Europe without the British Isles 〖英式〗〔英倫三島除外的〕歐洲大陸: *You can't buy these on the Continent.* 在歐洲大陸上, 你買不到這些東西。 – **continental** /ˌkɑntə'nɛntl; ˌkɒntɪ'nentl◂/ *adj*

con·tin·gen·cy /kən'tɪndʒənsɪ; kən'tɪndʒən-** si/ *n* **contingencies** a possibility that might cause problems in the future 不測事件: *We must be prepared for all contingencies.* 我們必須做好準備以防任何不測。 | *contingency plans* 應急計劃

con·tin·gent¹ /kən'tɪndʒənt; kən'tɪndʒənt/ *n* [+ sing/pl verb] **1** a group of soldiers or police gathered together to help a larger force 〔支援大部隊的〕分遣隊, 警察小隊 **2** a group of people who represent a country or organization 〔代表一個國家或組織的〕代表團: *Has the Scottish contingent arrived yet?* 蘇格蘭代表團到了沒有?

contingent² *adj fml* 〖正式〗 **contingent on** dependent on something uncertain 因〔情況〕而變的: *Our arrival time is contingent on the weather.* 我們的抵達時間要視乎天氣而定。

con·tin·u·al /kən'tɪnjuəl; kən'tɪnjuəl/ *adj* repeated and frequent 反覆的; 頻繁的: *He has continual arguments with his father.* 他常和父親發生爭論。 –**continually** *adv*

> ■ USAGE 用法: Compare 比較 **continual** and 和 **continuous**. **Continual** usually describes repeated actions. These may be annoying actions ☆ **continual** 通常形容 "反覆的、重複的" 事情。這類事情可能會令人惱火: *Stop that continual hammering!* 別沒完沒了地敲打了! | *I'm tired of your continual complaints.* 你總是在發牢騷, 我已聽夠了。 **Continuous** describes things that continue without a break ☆ **continuous** 指 "一刻不停地在進行的" 事情: *I was exhausted after six hours of continuous driving.* 我連續駕車六小時後精疲力竭。

con·tin·u·a·tion /kənˌtɪnju'eʃən; kənˌtɪnju-** 'eɪʃən/ *n* **1** [U] the act of continuing something 繼續; 持續: *They voted against the continuation of this tax system.* 他們投票反對繼續維持這種稅收制度。 **2** [C] something which follows something else and seems a part of it 延續部分: *Her second book is a continuation of her autobiography.* 她第二本書是她自傳的延續。

★★con·tin·ue /kən'tɪnju; kən'tɪnjuː/ *v* **continued, continuing** [I;T] **1** to go on over a long period, without stopping (使)繼續; (使)持續; 連續: *The fighting continued for two days.* 戰鬥持續了兩天。 | *The company is hoping sales will continue at their present rate.* 公司希望銷量能保持目前的水平。 | *He continued **with** his painting.* 他繼續畫他的畫。 | *She continued to look at them in silence.* 她繼續一聲不響地看着他們。 |

> □ USEFUL PATTERNS 有用句型
> to continue something; to continue with something; to continue to do something; to continue doing something

We continued washing the car. 我們繼續在洗車。**2** to start again after an interruption 〔中斷後〕(使)繼續: *The play will continue in 15 minutes.* 這齣戲十五分鐘後接着演下去。| *Are you going to continue gardening after dinner?* 晚飯後你還繼續整理花園嗎?

□ USEFUL PATTERNS 有用句型
to continue something; to continue to do something; to continue doing something

3 to go further in the same direction 〔朝同一方向〕延伸: *This road continues on down the valley.* 這條路順着山谷一直向下延伸。

*con·tin·u·ous /kən'tɪnjʊəs; kən'tɪnjuəs/ *adj* continuing without stopping 連續不斷的: *The brain needs a continuous supply of blood.* 大腦需要不斷地供血。–see 見 CONTINUAL (USAGE 用法) –**continuously** *adv*: *It rained continuously.* 雨一刻不停地下。–**continuity** /ˌkɑntə'nuətɪ; ˌkɒntɪ'njuːɪtɪ/ *n* [U]

con·tort /kən'tɔrt; kən'tɔːt/ *v* [I;T] to twist violently out of shape 使…扭曲: *Her face was contorted with anger.* 她的臉因生氣而扭曲。–**contortion** /-'tɔrʃən; -'tɔːʃən/ *n* [C;U]

con·tour /'kɑntur; 'kɒntʊəʳ/ *n* **1** (also 又作 **contours** [pl]) the shape of an area 〔一個地區的〕輪廓: *the contours of the British coast* 英國海岸線的輪廓 **2** (also 又作 **contour line**) a line drawn on a map joining points of equal height 〔地圖上的〕等高線

con·tra·band /'kɑntrə,bænd; 'kɒntrəbænd/ *n* [U] goods brought into or out of a country illegally 走私貨; 禁運品: *to trade in contraband* 買賣走私物品

con·tra·cep·tion /ˌkɑntrə'sɛpʃən; ˌkɒntrə'sepʃən/ *n* [U] the practice of preventing sex from resulting in the woman becoming PREGNANT, and the methods for doing this 避孕: *Which method of contraception do you use?* 你用哪種避孕方法?

con·tra·cep·tive /ˌkɑntrə'sɛptɪv; ˌkɒntrə'septɪv/ *n* a drug or object used as a means of preventing an act of sex from resulting in the woman becoming PREGNANT 避孕藥; 避孕用具 –**contraceptive** *adj*

*con·tract[1] /'kɑntrækt; 'kɒntrækt/ *n* a formal legal agreement between people, usually in writing 合同; 契約: *My lawyer is drawing up a contract which we should both sign.* 我的律師正在起草一份我們雙方都得簽字的契約。–**contractual** /kən'træktʃuəl; kən'træktʃuəl/ *adj*: *You have a contractual obligation to finish the building this month.* 依據合同, 你必須在本月完成該建築物的施工。–**contractually** *adv*

con·tract[2] /kən'trækt; kən'trækt/ *v* **1** [I;T] to make or become smaller or shorter (使)縮小; (使)縮短: *Metal contracts as it becomes cool.* 金屬冷卻時收縮。| *In conversational English*

"is not" often contracts to "isn't". 在英語口語中, "is not"常被縮寫為"isn't"。**2** [I;T] to arrange something by formal agreement 訂契約; 立合同: *They have contracted to build the new tunnel by 1997.* 他們已訂了合同, 在1997年前建成那條新隧道。| *Have you contracted with a local builder?* 你與本地建築商訂合同了嗎? | *I've been contracted to do the job.* 我已簽訂了做這項工作的合同。**3** [T] to get a serious illness 感染〔嚴重疾病〕: *My son's contracted malaria.* 我兒子得了瘧疾。

contract sthg ↔ out *phr v* [T] to employ another person or firm to do a job 把〔公司〕承包出去: *The work has been contracted out to a private company.* 這項工作已被一家私營公司承包。

con·trac·tion /kən'trækʃən; kən'trækʃən/ *n* **1** [U] the process of getting smaller or shorter 縮小; 縮短 **2** [U] the act of making something smaller or shorter 收縮 **3** [C] the shortened form of a word or words; for example, "won't" is a contraction of "will not". 縮約形式〔如"won't"是"will not"的縮約形式〕

con·trac·tor /'kɑntræktəʳ; kən'træktəʳ/ *n* a person or business that works for other people or businesses 承包人; 承包商: *a building contractor* 建築承包商

con·tra·dict /ˌkɑntrə'dɪkt; ˌkɒntrə'dɪkt/ *v* **1** [I;T] to correct something that someone has said which you believe is wrong 糾正〔某人所說的話〕; 反駁: *Don't contradict me!* 不要頂嘴! **2** [T] to be in opposition or disagreement with something else so that one of the two must be false 與〔其他事物〕相矛盾: *This report contradicts everything we've been told.* 這篇報告與別人所告訴我們的處處都相矛盾。–**contradictory** *adj*

con·tra·dic·tion /ˌkɑntrə'dɪkʃən; ˌkɒntrə'dɪkʃən/ *n* **1** [C;U] a difference between two facts, opinions, or qualities which means that they cannot both be true 矛盾; 抵觸: *There is no contradiction between the Prime Minister's views and my own.* 首相與我的觀點之間沒有矛盾。**2** [U] the act of saying that something is wrong or that the opposite is the truth 否認; 反駁: *I think I can say, without fear of contradiction, that this is of vital importance to all of us.* 我覺得我可以說句不怕被人反駁的話, 那就是這件事對我們大家至關重要。**3 a contradiction in terms** an impossible combination of words 用詞上的自相矛盾: *To say that he is an evil benefactor is a contradiction in terms.* 說他是個惡毒的慈善家是用詞上的自相矛盾。

con·tral·to /kən'trælto; kən'træltəu/ *n* **contraltos** the lowest female singing voice 女低音(歌手)

con·trap·tion /kən'træpʃən; kən'træpʃən/ *n* a strange machine or piece of apparatus 〔新奇的〕機器[器械]: *I don't understand how this contraption works.* 我不明白這種新機器

是如何運轉的。

con·tra·ry[1] /'kɑntrɛri; 'kɒntrəri/ n **1 the contrary** fml the opposite 〖正式〗相反: They say he is guilty, but I believe the contrary. 他們說他有罪, 但我相信他是無辜的。**2 on the contrary** a phrase used to express a strong opposite to what has just been said 恰恰相反〔用於表示事情完全相反〕: "I hear you like your new job." "On the contrary, it's rather boring." "聽說你很喜歡你的新工作。" "恰恰相反, 這工作很枯燥。" **3 to the contrary** that something else is true 其他事情是對的: You may be right; there's no evidence to the contrary. 也許你是對的; 沒有相反的證據證明你不對。

■ USAGE 用法: Compare 比較 **on the contrary**, **on the other hand**, **in contrast**. We use **on the contrary** to show that an idea which came before is completely wrong ☆ **on the contrary** 用來表示前面的觀點完全錯誤: "Tom is a good student, isn't he?" "On the contrary, he's lazy and stupid." "湯姆是個好學生, 是嗎?" "恰恰相反, 他又懶又笨。" We use **on the other hand** to add an idea which is different but is part of a single general picture ☆ **on the other hand** 用以補充不同的觀點, 但仍與前一觀點組成一體: "Dick did badly in the examination. **On the other hand,** his classwork is excellent." "迪克上次的考試成績很糟。但是另一方面, 他的課堂作業倒是非常好。" We use **in contrast** to show that two people or things are completely, and surprisingly, different ☆ **in contrast** 表示兩人或兩物完全相反同: "Harry's work is poor, but in contrast, his sister's work is excellent." "哈里的功課很差, 但與他相反的是, 他妹妹的功課很出色。"

contrary[2] adj **1** opposing 相反的: contrary opinions 相反的意見 **2 contrary to** a phrase used to state that something is not true before expressing an opposite view which is true 與...相反〔用於表示相反但卻是正確的觀點〕: Contrary to popular belief, the sun does sometimes shine in Britain. 與人們通常所認為的相反, 英國有時也有陽光燦爛的日子。

con·trar·y[3] /kən'trɛɪri; kən'treəri/ adj unreasonable (used of a person) 不講理的〔指人〕: Don't be so contrary! 別這麼不講道理!

con·trast[1] /'kɑntræst; 'kɒntrɑːst/ n **1** [C;U] difference between people or things that are compared 差異; 差別: I've never seen such a contrast **between** brother and sister. 我從未見過兄妹間會有這樣大的差別。**2 by contrast, in contrast** when compared with something else in order to show the difference 相形之下: The Labour Party supports state control of key services. The Conserva-

tive Party, by contrast, has decided to privatize them. 工黨支持對重要部門實行國家控制。然而, 保守黨卻已決定將這些部門私有化。–see 見 CONTRARY[1] (USAGE 用法)

con·trast[2] /kən'træst; kən'trɑːst/ v **1** [T] to compare two people or things so that differences are made clear 對比〔以顯出兩人或兩事物的差別〕; 使成對照: In this book the writer contrasts two views of management. 作者在本書中將兩種管理觀點作了對比。| Compare and contrast Mrs Thatcher's policies **with** those of Mr Major. 把戴卓爾夫人和梅杰先生的政策進行比較和對照。**2** [I] to show a difference when compared 〔通過對比〕顯出差別; 形成對照: His attitudes contrast sharply **with** my own. 他的態度與我的態度有鮮明的差別。

con·tra·vene /,kɑntrə'vin; ,kɒntrə'viːn/ v **contravened, contravening** [T] to break a law or a rule 違反〔法律或規定〕: Your behaviour contravened the laws of the country. 你的所作所為違反了國家的法律。–**contravention** /-'vɛnʃən; -'venʃən/ n [C;U]

con·trib·ute /kən'trɪbjut; kən'trɪbjuːt/ v **contributed, contributing 1** [I;T] to join with others in giving money for a person or cause 為〔某人或某事業〕捐助〔錢〕: Everybody contributed a pound towards Jane's present. 每個人都出了一英鎊給簡買禮物。| Would you like to contribute? 你願意捐錢嗎? **2** [I] to help cause something 促成: Luck and a good family background contributed **to** his success. 運氣和良好的家庭背景促使他成功。**3** [I;T] to write something for a magazine or newspaper 〔給雜誌或報紙〕投稿 –**contribution** /,kɑntrə'bjuʃən; ,kɒntrɪ'bjuːʃən/ n [C;U]: Would you like to make a contribution **to** our funds? 你願意給我們的基金捐些錢嗎? | Everyone acknowledges his contribution to Russian literature. 每個人都承認他對俄國文學所做的貢獻。–**contributor** /kən'trɪbjə,tɚ; kən'trɪbjʊtə[r]/ n: a regular contributor to our magazine 一位定期給我們雜誌投稿的人

con·trib·u·to·ry /kən'trɪbjə,tori; kən'trɪbjʊtəri/ adj **1** [only before a noun 只用於名詞前] helping to bring about a result 起促成作用的: a contributory factor in his downfall 促成他垮台的因素 **2** paid for by the workers as well as by the employer (used of a PENSION or insurance plan) 由職工和僱主共同出錢的〔指養老金或保險計劃〕

con·trite /'kɑntraɪt; 'kɒntraɪt/ adj old fashioned or lit showing guilt or sorrow for your actions 〖老式或文〗後悔的, 悔恨的: a contrite apology 深表懊悔的道歉 –**contritely** adv –**contrition** /kən'trɪʃən; kən'trɪʃən/ n [U]

con·trive /kən'traɪv; kən'traɪv/ v **contrived, contriving 1 contrive to do something** to succeed in doing something in spite of difficulty 〔設法〕做成某事: She finally contrived to escape. 她最終還是逃掉了。**2** [T] to succeed in making something happen in spite of difficulty 籌劃〔某事〕: *He actually contrived a meeting with the Queen!* 他總算設法見到了女王!

con·trived /kən'traɪvd; kən'traɪvd/ *adj* unnatural and forced 不自然的; 勉強的: *Her smile was polite, but rather contrived.* 她的笑容很禮貌, 但有點兒不自然.

★★**con·trol**[1] /kən'trol; kən'trəul/ *v* **-ll-** [T] to have direct influence or power over something 控制; 支配; 管理: *The pressure of steam in the engine is controlled by this button.* 引擎的蒸汽壓力是由這個按鈕控制的. | *He wasn't a bad teacher, but he couldn't control his class.* 他是個不錯的老師, 只是管束不了自己班上的學生. | *I realize that you are angry, but please try to control yourself.* 我知道你很生氣, 但是請盡力克制住自己.

★★**control**[2] *n* **1** [U] the power to command or influence 控制力; 支配權: *Which party has control of the town council?* 哪一個黨控制着市議會? | *Don't worry; I am in full control of the situation.* 別擔心, 局勢完全在我控制之下. | *He lost control of the steering and his car ran into a tree.* 他控制不了車子的方向而撞在樹上. | *George took control of the business when his father died.* 喬治在父親死後接管了生意. **2** [C;U] a method or system used to direct or influence something in a particular way 控制辦法; 控制系統: *Where's the volume control on this radio?* 這台收音機的音量調節器在哪裡? | *government control over industry* 政府對工業的控制 | *price controls* 物價控制 **3** [C] the place from which a machine or system is controlled 控制機器[系統]的地方: *Passport control is to your left.* 護照檢查站在你的左面. **4 in control** in command 掌管; 操縱: *Who's in control here?* 這裡是誰負責? **5 out of control** in a state in which no proper direction is possible 失去控制: *The car went out of control and crashed.* 汽車失控後撞毀了. **6 under control** made to behave properly after being in a dangerous or confused state 〔危險或混亂狀態後〕處於控制之下: *The firemen finally got the fire under control.* 消防隊員終於控制了火勢. | *It took the teacher months to bring her class under control.* 老師花了數月時間才把她班上的學生管服. **7** [C] a standard against which scientific results are compared〔與科學實驗結果進行對照的〕標準 **–controller** *n*

con·tro·ver·sial /,kɑntrə'vɜ·ʃəl; ,kɔntrə'vɜːʃəl/ *adj* causing a lot of argument or disagreement 引起爭論的; 有爭議的: *a controversial decision* 有爭議的決定 **–controversially** *adv*

con·tro·ver·sy /'kɑntrə,vɜ·sɪ; 'kɔntrəvɜːsɪ/ *n* **controversies** [C;U] a lot of argument and disagreement about something 爭論; 爭議: *The new proposal has caused an enormous amount of controversy.* 新的提議引起了很多

的爭論. | *I am referring to recent controversies over the tax system.* 我所指的是近來有關稅收制度的那些爭論.

co·nun·drum /kə'nʌndrəm; kə'nʌndrəm/ *n* a confusing and difficult problem 難題; 複雜問題

con·ur·ba·tion /,kɑnɝ'beʃən; ,kɔnɜː'beɪʃən/ *n* a number of towns that have spread and joined together into one area, often with a large city as its centre〔由中心大城市及衛星城鎮構成的〕集合城市

con·va·lesce /,kɑnvə'lɛs; ,kɔnvə'les/ *v* **convalesced, convalescing** [I] to spend time getting well after an illness 病後療養; 康復: *We're sending Nan to the seaside to convalesce.* 我們準備把南送到海邊去療養.

con·va·les·cence /,kɑnvə'lɛsɳs; ,kɔnvə'lesəns/ *n* [sing;U] the period of time you spend getting well again after an illness〔病後的〕康復期

con·va·les·cent /,kɑnvə'lɛsɳt; ,kɔnvə'lesənt/ *n* a person spending time getting well again after an illness 康復期的病人 **–convalescent** *adj*: *a convalescent nursing home* 療養院

con·vec·tion /kən'vɛkʃən; kən'vekʃən/ *n* [U] the movement caused by warm gas or liquid rising, and cold gas or liquid sinking〔氣體、液體的〕對流: *a convection heater* 對流加熱器 | *Warm air rises by convection.* 熱氣因對流作用上升.

con·vene /kən'vin; kən'viːn/ *v* **convened, convening** *fml* 〔正式〕 **1** [I] to meet 開會: *The ministers convened for an emergency session.* 部長們召開了緊急會議. **2** [T] to call a group or committee to a meeting 召集〔人或委員會〕開會: *The chairman has convened a meeting for next Wednesday.* 主席已定於下週三召開會議.

con·ve·ni·ence /kən'vinjəns; kən'viːnɪəns/ *n* **1** [U] qualities which make something right for a particular purpose 方便; 便利: *We bought this house for its convenience.* 我們買這所房子是取其方便. **2** [C] something which makes things easy or comfortable for the user 便利設施: *This kitchen has every modern convenience.* 這個廚房裡有一切現代化設施. **3** [U] personal comfort or advantage〔個人的〕舒適, 方便: *He thinks only of his own convenience.* 他只考慮到自己的方便. **4 at your convenience** at a time which is suitable for you 在您方便的時候

convenience food /·'··· ,·/ *n* [C;U] food which is very easy to prepare and can be used at any time, like a whole meal in one packet 方便食品〔如盒飯〕

con·ve·ni·ent /kən'vinjənt; kən'viːnɪənt/ *adj* **1** suited to your needs or to the situation 方便的, 便利的; 合宜的: *What's a convenient time for you?* 你甚麼時間比較方便呢? **2** usefully near 近便的: *Our house is very convenient for the shops.* 我們家離商店

C

很近。–opposite 反義 **inconvenient** –**conveniently** adv

con·vent /'kɑnvɛnt; 'kɒnvənt/ n a place where religious women called nuns (NUN) live or teach 女修道院

*★***con·ven·tion** /kən'vɛnʃən; kən'venʃən/ n **1** [C;U] the generally accepted way of doing things, especially with regard to social behaviour 習俗; 習慣: *It is a matter of convention rather than a strict rule.* 這是風俗習慣, 而 不 是 嚴格 規定。| *He ignores stylistic conventions when he writes.* 他寫作時總不注重語體習慣。–see 見 HABIT (USAGE 用法) **2** [C] a meeting of people with a shared purpose 會議; 大會: *a teachers' convention* 教師大會 **3** [C] a formal agreement between countries 〔兩國間的〕公約: *Britain has agreed to sign the convention.* 英國已答應簽署該公約。

*★***con·ven·tion·al** /kən'vɛnʃənl; kən'venʃənəl/ adj **1** following accepted customs and standards, sometimes too closely 傳統的; 習慣的; 保守的: *He's an old-fashioned man with conventional ideas.* 他是個守舊的人, 觀念很保守。| *conventional Western medicine* 傳統的西藥 –opposite 反義 **unconventional** **2** not NUCLEAR (used of weapons) 常規的, 非核子的〔指武器〕–**conventionally** adv

con·verge /kən'vɝdʒ; kən'vɜːdʒ/ v **converged, converging** [I] to come together towards the same point 集中; 會聚: *The roads converge just before the station.* 幾條馬路剛好在火車站前匯合了。| *Crowds are converging on the stadium.* 人羣聚集在體育場內。–**convergent** adj –**convergence** n [C;U]

con·ver·sant /kən'vɝsnt; kən'vɜːsənt/ adj fml 〔正式〕**conversant with** familiar with 對...熟悉: *I'm not conversant with the rules yet.* 我還不熟悉這些規則。

*★***con·ver·sa·tion** /ˌkɑnvɚ'seʃən; ˌkɒnvə'seɪʃən/ n [C;U] **1** an informal talk in which people exchange news, feelings, and thoughts 〔非正式的〕談話; 交談: *a private conversation* 私人談話 | *a telephone conversation* 電話交談 | *How can I make polite conversation with someone I dislike?* 我如何才能和我不喜歡的人很有禮貌地進行交談呢? **2 in conversation with** fml talking to someone 〔正式〕與〔某人〕交談 –**conversational** adj: *conversational English* 英語口語 –**conversationally** adv

con·verse /kən'vɝs; kən'vɜːs/ v **conversed, conversing** [I] fml to talk informally〔正式〕談話; 交談

con·ver·sion /kən'vɝʒən; kən'vɜːʃən/ n [C; U] **1** a change from one purpose or system to another 轉變; 轉換: *the conversion of a house into flats* 把一所房子改建成公寓 | *He did a quick conversion from yards into metres.* 他很快把碼換算成米。**2** a change in which a person accepts a new religion or belief completely 宗教[信仰]的改變; 皈

依: *His conversion to Islam was unexpected.* 他改信伊斯蘭教令人意外。

*★***con·vert¹** /kən'vɝt; kən'vɜːt/ v [I;T] **1** to change into another form, state or system (使)轉變; (使)轉化; (使)轉換: *Coal can be converted to gas.* 煤可以轉化為煤氣。| *This seat converts into a bed.* 這個座位可以變成一張牀。| *I want to convert some dollars into pounds.* 我想把一些美元兌換成英鎊。| *They are living in a converted barn.* 他們現在住在一個經過改建的穀倉裡。**2** to accept, or persuade another person to accept, a particular religion, belief, or opinion (使)改變信仰[觀念]: *Anne has converted to Christianity.* 安妮已改信了基督教。| *John was converted to Buddhism by a Thai priest.* 約翰被一位泰國僧人説服, 皈依了佛教。| *My son has finally converted me to pop music.* 我兒子最終使我轉而喜歡了流行音樂。

con·vert² /'kɑnvɝt; 'kɒnvɜːt/ n a person who has been persuaded to accept a particular religion or belief 改變宗教[信仰]的人

con·vert·i·ble¹ /kən'vɝtəbl; kən'vɜːtɪbəl/ adj **1** able to be changed into another form 能轉換形式的: *This bed is easily convertible into a sofa.* 這張牀可以很容易變為沙發用。**2** able to be freely exchanged (used of types of money) 可自由兌換的〔指貨幣〕: *The local currency is not convertible, so you'd better take some dollars.* 當地貨幣不能自由兌換, 所以你最好帶些美元。

convertible² n a car with a roof that can be folded back 摺篷汽車

con·vex /kɑn'vɛks; ˌkɒn'veks◂/ adj tech curved outwards 〔術語〕凸面的: *a convex mirror* 凸鏡 –opposite 反義 **concave**

con·vey /kən've; kən'veɪ/ v [T] **1** fml to take or carry something from one place to another 〔正式〕傳送; 運送〔某物〕: *We were conveyed to the palace in a fleet of Jaguars.* 我們由一隊積架牌汽車接送至宮殿。**2** to make your feelings, ideas or thoughts known to other people 傳達; 表達〔感情、觀點、思想〕: *I can't convey how angry I feel.* 我説不出有多憤怒。

con·vey·er belt /·'··· ·/ n (also 又作 **conveyor belt**) an endless moving belt that carries objects from one place to another 傳送帶

con·vict¹ /kən'vɪkt; kən'vɪkt/ v [T] to declare that someone is guilty of a crime after a trial in a court 宣判〔某人〕有罪: *They were convicted of murder.* 他們被判犯有謀殺罪。| *He's a convicted criminal.* 他是個被判了刑的罪犯。

con·vict² /'kɑnvɪkt; 'kɒnvɪkt/ n a person who has been declared guilty of a crime and sent to prison, especially for a long time 已決犯; 囚犯〔尤指長期監禁者〕: *an escaped convict* 越獄的囚犯

*con·vic·tion /kənˈvɪkʃən; kənˈvɪkʃən/ *n* [C; U] **1** the act of finding someone guilty of a crime after a trial in a court 判罪; 定罪: *After conviction, he appealed to a higher court.* 他被判有罪之後，就上訴高級法院。 | *This was her third conviction for stealing.* 這是她第三次被判犯了偷竊罪。 **2** very firm and sincere belief 堅信; 深信: *a man of strong convictions* 信念堅定的人 | *She was speaking from conviction.* 她說話的語氣很堅定。

*con·vince /kənˈvɪns; kənˈvɪns/ *v* **convinced, convincing** [T] **1** to make someone believe something 使〔某人〕相信〔某事〕: *It took them hours to convince me of his guilt.* 他們花了數小時才令我相信他有罪。 | *It was hard to convince the children that we couldn't afford to keep a pet.* 要讓孩子們明白我們養不起寵物是件困難的事。

□ USEFUL PATTERNS 有用句型
to convince someone of something; to convince someone that…

2 be convinced that to be completely certain about something 堅信; 深信: *I was absolutely convinced he was telling the truth.* 我完全相信他講的是事實。

■ USAGE 用法: Compare 比較 **convince** and 和 **persuade.** These are normally used in different ways. **Convince** means "make someone believe something" and it does not have **to** after it ☆ 這兩個詞的用法通常不一樣。**convince** 指"令某人相信某事"，後面不接 **to**: *The politician* **convinced** *me that his party was the best.* 那位政治家令我相信他的政黨是最優秀的。**Persuade** means "make someone willing to do something" and it often has **to** after it ☆ **persuade** 指"令某人願意去做某事"，後面經常接帶**to**不定式: *The politician* **persuaded** *me to join his party.* 那位政治家說服我加入了他的政黨。**Convince** is sometimes used in a similar way to **persuade,** though some people consider that this is incorrect ☆ 有時 **convince** 的用法與 **persuade** 的用法很接近，但有人認為 **convince** 的這一用法不正確: *They finally* **convinced** *me to leave my job.* 他們最終說服我放棄了工作。

con·vinc·ing /kənˈvɪnsɪŋ; kənˈvɪnsɪŋ/ *adj* so good that you feel something must be true 令人信服的; 有說服力的: *a convincing explanation* 令人信服的解釋 –opposite 反義 **unconvincing –convincingly** *adv*

con·viv·i·al /kənˈvɪvɪəl; kənˈvɪvɪəl/ *adj fml* pleasantly merry and friendly 〔正式〕歡樂的; 歡樂的夜晚: *a very convivial evening* 一個非常歡樂的夜晚 **–conviviality** /kənˌvɪvɪˈælətɪ; kənˌvɪviˈælⱡˌti/ *n* [U]

con·vo·lut·ed /ˈkɒnvəˌlutɪd; ˈkɒnvəluːtⱡd/ *adj fml* difficult to understand 〔正式〕難以理解的: *convoluted arguments* 令人費解的爭論

con·voy /ˈkɒnvɔɪ; ˈkɒnvɔɪ/ *n* [+ sing/pl verb] **1** a group of ships or vehicles travelling together 艦隊; 車隊: *The convoy was attacked by rebels.* 艦隊受到了叛軍的襲擊。 **2 in convoy** travelling together 結隊同行: *They were travelling in convoy.* 他們結伴一同旅遊。

con·vulse /kənˈvʌls; kənˈvʌls/ *v* **convulsed, convulsing** [I;T] to shake violently 〔正式〕(使)劇烈震動: *We were convulsed with laughter.* 我們笑得前仰後合。

con·vul·sion /kənˈvʌlʃən; kənˈvʌlʃən/ *n* an unnaturally violent and sudden movement caused by illness 驚厥; 抽搐: *She occasionally has terrible convulsions.* 她有時會犯嚴重的驚厥。 **–convulsive** /-sɪv; -sɪv/ *adj*

coo /ku; kuː/ *v* [I] **1** to make a sound like the low soft cry of a DOVE or PIGEON〔鴿子等〕發出咕咕聲 **2** to make soft, loving noises 輕柔低語: *She cooed over the new baby.* 她對着嬰兒喁喁細語。

cook¹ /kʊk; kʊk/ *v* **1** [I;T] to prepare food for eating by using heat 烹調; 燒〔飯菜〕: *I enjoy cooking.* 我喜歡烹調。 | *He's cooking dinner for me tonight.* 今晚他來給我做飯。 | *Shall we cook the vegetables or eat them raw?* 我們把蔬菜煮熟吃還是生吃? **2** [I] to be prepared by using heat (used of food) 煮; 燒〔指食物〕: *Make sure this meat cooks for at least an hour.* 記住這肉最起碼要煮一個小時。 **3 be cooking** *infml* to be being planned without your knowledge 〔非正式〕偷偷策劃 **–cooking** *n* [U]: *Do you like English cooking?* 你喜歡英國式的烹調法嗎?

■ USAGE 用法: We can **cook** food in several different ways. We can **bake** bread using dry heat in an **oven.** We can **roast** meat in an oven or over an open fire. We can **grill** pieces of meat, or **toast** thin, flat pieces of bread under direct heat (from a **grill**). We can **boil** potatoes or **stew** meat using a pot filled with water. If the food boils very slowly it **simmers.** We can **braise** meat and vegetables by cooking them slowly in a covered pot with fat and water. We can **steam** vegetables by cooking them over water in a raised container so that the water does not touch them directly. We can **fry** eggs, meat and potatoes by cooking them in hot fat or oil. ☆我們可用數種不同方法來做菜。在烤爐內烤 (bake) 麵包; 在爐子或火上烤 (roast) 肉。通過〔放在烤架上〕直接加熱的辦法烤 (grill) 肉片或烤 (toast) 麵包片。在水中煮 (boil) 馬鈴薯

C

[土豆]或燉 (stew) 肉。如果煮得很慢，就是煨 (simmer)。在鍋內放上油與水，慢慢地燜 (braise) 肉和蔬菜。把蔬菜用另外一個容器與水隔開，可以將其蒸 (steam) 熟。我們可以用滾燙的油炒 (fry) 雞蛋、肉和馬鈴薯[土豆]。

cook sthg ↔ **up** *phr v* [T] *infml*《非正式》**1** to invent something that is not true 捏造，編造〔某事物〕: *She cooked up an excuse about her parents being ill.* 她佯稱父母親生病作為藉口。**2** to plan something which is often secret and not completely honest 偷偷策劃〔不誠實的事〕: *He's cooked up a scheme to get rich quickly.* 他暗地裡制訂了一個能迅速發財的計劃。

cook² *n* a person who prepares and cooks food 廚師: *My mother's a wonderful cook.* 我母親是個非常出色的廚師。

cook-chill /ˌ·ˈ·◂/ *adj* cook-chill food food which is prepared in advance; it is cooked, made cool very quickly, and then warmed up when you want to eat it〔先做熟，然後迅速冷卻，等要食用時再加熱的〕方便食品

cook·er /ˈkʊkə; ˈkʊkɚ/ *n BrE* an apparatus on which food is cooked《英式》炊具

cook·er·y /ˈkʊkərɪ; ˈkʊkəri/ *n* [U] the art or activity of preparing food 烹調，烹飪術: *cookery lessons* 烹飪課 | *a cookery book* 烹飪書；食譜

cook·ie /ˈkʊkɪ; ˈkʊki/ *n* (also 又作 **cooky**) **1** the usual American word for《美式》= BISCUIT **2** *AmE infml* a person of a particular type《美式，非正式》特殊類型的人: *a clever cookie* 精明的人

*★***cool¹** /kul; kuːl/ *adj* **1** slightly cold 微冷的；涼爽的: *a cool day* 涼爽的一天 **2** pleasantly cold 涼快的: *a cool drink* 冷飲 | *It was lovely and cool in the shade.* 在蔭涼處又舒服又涼快。**3** calm and unexcited 冷靜的；不激動的: *Keep cool and do your best.* 保持鎮靜，盡力而為。**4** not as friendly as usual 冷淡的；冷漠的: *Charles has been very cool towards me recently.* 查爾斯近來對我很冷淡。**5 keep a cool head** to stay calm so that you can think clearly 保持鎮靜〔以便能清醒地思考問題〕 –**coolly** /ˈkʊllɪ; ˈkuːl-li/ *adv* –**coolness** *n* [U]

cool² *v* [I;T] **1** to become or to make something slightly colder (使)變涼: *Leave the mixture to cool.* 讓混合物冷卻一下。| *Cool your forehead with a damp cloth.* 用濕布給你的額頭冷敷一下。**2 cool it** *infml* keep calm《非正式》保持鎮定

cool down *phr v* [I;T **cool** sbdy/sthg ↔ **down**] to become calmer, or to make someone calmer (使)鎮定下來: *Cool down and we'll discuss it later.* 先鎮定下來，我們回頭再討論。| *Try and cool her down before she does anything stupid.* 盡量讓她鎮定下來，免得她做出甚麼蠢事。

cool off *phr v* [I] to become less hot 變得涼快一些: *I need to cool off in the shade.* 我需要在蔭涼處涼快一下。

coop¹ /kup; kuːp/ *n* a cage for hens 養雞的籠子: *a chicken coop* 雞籠

coop² *v*

coop sbdy/sthg ↔ **up** *phr v* [T] to shut into a small space 把...關入: *We were cooped up in that tiny room for days.* 我們被關在那間小屋子裡好幾天了。

co·op·e·rate /koˈɑpəˌret; kəʊˈɒpəreɪt/ *v* **cooperated, cooperating** (also 又作 **co-op-erate**) [I] **1** to work or act together for a shared purpose 合作；協作: *The British cooperated **with** the French in building the tunnel.* 英國與法國合作建造那條隧道。**2** to do what someone wants you to do 配合；協助: *I needed help, but he simply wouldn't co-operate.* 我需要人幫忙，但他就是不肯協助。

*★***co·op·e·ra·tion** /koˌɑpəˈreʃən; kəʊˌɒpəˈreɪʃən/ *n* (also 又作 **co-operation**) [U] **1** the act of working together for a shared purpose 合作；協作: *The film was produced in cooperation **with** the BBC.* 這部電影是與英國廣播公司合作製作的。**2** willingness to work together 樂於合作[協助]: *Thank you for your cooperation.* 謝謝你的協助。

co·op·e·ra·tive¹ /koˈɑpəˌretɪv; kəʊˈɒpərətɪv/ *adj* (also 又作 **co-operative**) **1** willing to help 樂於協助的: *The teacher thanked them for being so cooperative.* 老師感謝他們的通力合作。–opposite 反義 **uncooperative 2** done or owned by people working together 合作進行的: *a cooperative farm* 合作農場 –**cooperatively** *adv*

cooperative² *n* a firm, farm, or shop owned and operated by people working together 合作社: *The business has become a cooperative.* 這家企業已變成了一家合作社。

co-opt /ko ˈɑpt; ˌkəʊ ˈɒpt/ *v* [T] to choose someone to join a committee by the votes of existing members〔由現任委員〕推舉而進入委員會: *I've been co-opted **onto** the board of governors.* 我被董事會增選為新董事。

co·or·di·nate¹ /koˈɔrdṇˌet; kəʊˈɔːdɪneɪt/ *v* **coordinated, coordinating** [T] to organize people or things so that they work together effectively 使協調: *We need to co-ordinate our efforts.* 我們需要協調一下我們的努力。

co·or·di·nate² /koˈɔrdṇɪt; kəʊˈɔːdɪṇt/ *n tech* one of a set of numbers or letters that give the exact position of a point on a map《術語》座標

co·or·di·na·tion /koˌɔrdṇˈeʃən; kəʊˌɔːdɪˈneɪʃən/ *n* [U] **1** the organization of people or things so that they work together effectively 協調 **2** the way in which muscles work together when performing a movement〔動作的〕協調: *Dancers need good coordination.* 舞蹈演員需要良好的動作協調。

coot /kut; kuːt/ *n* a small black water bird

with a white spot on its forehead 白骨頂〔一種水鳥〕

cop¹ /kʌp; kɒp/ *n infml* a police officer 〖非正式〗警察

cop² *v* **-pp-**

cop out *phr v* [I] *infml* to avoid doing something that you should do 〖非正式〗逃避; 變卦: *He promised to help and now he's trying to cop out of it!* 他答應幫忙的, 可現在他卻在推卸! **-cop-out** /'··/ *n*: *Writing instead of phoning is a real cop-out!* 不打電話而寫信去, 這是在逃避責任!

★**cope** /kop; kəʊp/ *v* **coped, coping** [I] to deal successfully with something 應付; 對付: *Can you cope* **with** *all this work?* 你應付得了所有這些工作嗎? | *She has so many problems, it's no wonder she can't cope.* 她有這麼多的難題, 難怪她應付不了。

co·pi·ous /'kopiəs; 'kəʊpiəs/ *adj* a lot of something 許多的: *He takes copious notes.* 他記了很多筆記。 **–copiously** *adv*

cop·per /'kʌpə; 'kɒpər/ *n* **1** [U] a soft reddish metal 銅 **2** [U] a reddish-brown colour 紅棕色 **3** [C] *BrE infml* a coin of low value made of brown metal 〖英式, 非正式〗銅幣; 銅板: *Can you lend me a few coppers?* 你能借幾個銅板給我嗎? **4** [C] *infml* a police officer 〖非正式〗警察

copse /kʌps; kɒps/ *n* a small wood of trees or bushes 小樹叢; 灌木林

cop·u·late /'kʌpjə,let; 'kɒpjʊleɪt/ *v* **copulated, copulating** [I] *fml* to have sex 〖正式〗交配 **–copulation** /,kʌpjə'leʃən; ,kɒpjʊ'leɪʃən/ *n* [U]

★**cop·y¹** /'kʌpi; 'kɒpi/ *n* **copies 1** [C] something that is made to look exactly like something else 複製品; 複印件: *I need four copies of this letter.* 這封信我需要四份複印件。 | *That's a good copy of a Picasso.* 那是一幅很不錯的畢加索的臨摹畫。 **2** [C] a single example of a magazine, book, or newspaper 〔雜誌、書籍、報紙〕一份; 一冊: *Have you seen my copy of "The Times"?* 你看見我的那一份《泰晤士報》了嗎? **3** [U] *tech* written material to be printed 〖術語〗準備付印的書面材料: *All copy must reach the editor by tomorrow at the latest.* 所有付印稿最遲須在明天送交編輯。 | *advertising copy* 廣告文稿 | *a copy editor* 文字編輯

copy² *v* **copied, copying 1** [T] to make something that looks exactly like something else 複印; 複製: *Could you copy these documents?* 你能把這些文件複印一下嗎? **2** [T] to do something or behave like someone else 模仿: *Jean always copies the way I dress.* 瓊老是學着我的樣子穿衣服。 **3** [I;T] to cheat by writing exactly the same thing as someone else 抄襲: *He was caught copying in the maths test.* 他在數學考試中抄襲作弊當場被抓。

copy sthg ↔ **down** *phr v* [T] to write down exactly what someone has said 把〔某

人所說的話〕寫下

copy sthg ↔ **out** *phr v* [T] to write something out as it is written elsewhere 抄寫〔文字〕: *I want you to copy out the graph in your exercise books.* 我要你在練習簿上把這段文章抄下來。

copy·right /'kʌpi,raɪt; 'kɒpiraɪt/ *n* [C;U] the right in law to produce or sell a book, play, film, or record for a fixed period of time 版權: *Who owns the copyright* **on** *your book?* 你這本書的版權是誰的?

cor·al /'kʌrəl; 'kɒrəl/ *n* [U] a white, pink, or reddish substance formed from the bones of very small sea animals, often used for making jewellery 珊瑚

cord /kɔrd; kɔ:d/ *n* **1** [C;U] a piece of thick string or thin rope 粗線; 細繩 **2** [C;U] a piece of wire with a protective covering, for connecting electrical apparatus to the electricity supply 電線 **3** [C] a part of the body which looks like a piece of string 〔人體內〕索狀組織: *the spinal cord* 脊髓 | *her vocal cords* 她的聲帶 **4 cords** [pl] *infml* trousers made from corduroy 〖非正式〗燈芯絨褲子

cor·di·al¹ /'kɔrdʒəl; 'kɔ:diəl/ *adj fml* friendly 〖正式〗友善的: *a cordial welcome* 熱烈的歡迎 | *a cordial invitation* 熱誠的邀請 **–cordiality** /,kɔr'dʒælətɪ; ,kɔ:di'æl‿ti/ *n* [U] **–cordially** *adv*

cordial² *n* [C;U] fruit juice to which water is added before drinking 〔加水後作飲料的〕果汁飲料: *lime cordial* 酸橙飲料

cor·don /'kɔrdn; 'kɔ:dn/ *n* a line or ring of police, soldiers, or military vehicles placed around an area to protect or enclose it 警戒線

cordon sthg ↔ **off** *phr v* [T] to enclose an area with a line or ring of police, soldiers, or military vehicles 以警戒線包圍: *The whole area has been cordoned off.* 整個地區已被封鎖。

cor·du·roy /,kɔrdə'rɔɪ; 'kɔ:dʒʊrɔɪ/ *n* [U] thick, strong cotton cloth with raised lines on one side 燈芯絨: *a corduroy jacket* 燈芯絨夾克 | *a pair of corduroy trousers* 一條燈芯絨褲子

★**core¹** /kor; kɔ:ʳ/ *n* **1** the hard central part of certain fruits, which contains the seeds 〔水果的〕果心; 核: *Throw away that old apple core.* 把那個老蘋果核扔了吧。 **2** the central part of something 核心; 中心: *the earth's core* 地心 **3 to the core** completely 完全地: *She's American to the core.* 她是個地地道道的美國人。 **4** the most important part of something 最重要的部分: *the core of the problem* 問題的核心

core² *v* **cored, coring** [T] to remove the hard central part from a fruit 去掉〔水果的〕果心

cork¹ /kɔrk; kɔ:k/ *n* **1** [U] a light material which forms the outer skin of a particular tree trunk and is used for making things like table mats 軟木樹皮〔用來製桌墊等物〕 **2** [C] a round piece of this material which is put into the neck of a bottle, especially one containing wine, to close it tightly 軟木(瓶)塞

cork² *v* [T] to close a bottle tightly by putting a cork in the top of it 以軟木塞塞住〔瓶口〕 –opposite 反義 **uncork**

cork·screw /ˈkɔrkskru; ˈkɔːkskruː/ *n* a tool made of twisted metal with a handle, used for pulling corks out of bottles〔拔軟木塞用的〕螺絲起子; 瓶塞鑽 –see picture on page 958 見 958 頁彩圖

corn /kɔrn; kɔːn/ *n* **1** [U] *BrE* the seed of any of various types of grain plants, especially wheat〔英式〕穀物〔尤指小麥〕 **2** [U] *AmE*〔美式〕(also 又作 **maize, sweet corn** *BrE*〔英式〕) the seed of a tall plant grown, especially in America and Australia, for its ears of yellow seeds 玉米 –see picture on page 504 見 504 頁彩圖 **3** [C] a painful area of hard, thick skin on your foot, usually on or near a toe 雞眼

★**cor·ner¹** /ˈkɔrnɚ; ˈkɔːnəʳ/ *n* **1** the point at which two lines, surfaces, or edges meet 角; 角落: *in the corner of the room* 在房間的角落裡 | *in the bottom left-hand corner of the page* 在該頁左下角 | *He fell and banged his head on the corner of the table.* 他跌倒時頭撞到了桌子角上。| *How many corners does a hexagon have?* 六邊形有幾個角? **2** the place where two roads, paths, or streets meet 街角; 拐角處: *I'll meet you on the corner of Smith Street and Beach Road.* 我將在史密斯街與海濱路的拐角處等你。| *She waited for him on the corner.* 她在街道拐角處等他。**3** a distant part of the world 遠方; 天涯海角: *People came from all corners of the earth to hear her sing.* 人們從世界各地前來聽她演唱。**4** (also 又作 **corner kick** /ˈ·· ·/) a kick taken from the corner of the field in football〔足球的〕角球 **5 in a tight corner** in a difficult or threatening situation from which it is hard to escape 處於困境

corner² *v* **1** [T] to force a person or animal into a difficult situation from which it is hard to escape 把〔人或動物〕逼入困境: *He was cornered behind the bicycle shed.* 他被困在自行車棚的後面。**2 corner the market** to gain control of the buying, selling, or production of goods 壟斷市場: *They have now cornered the market in leather goods.* 他們現已壟斷了皮革商品的市場。**3** [I] (of a vehicle or driver) to turn a corner〔車輛或司機〕轉彎: *My car corners well, even on wet roads.* 即使在濕滑的路面上, 我的車子轉彎也轉得很好。

cor·ner·stone /ˈkɔrnɚˌston; ˈkɔːnəstəun/ *n* **1** a stone set at one of the bottom corners of a building, often as part of a special cer-

emony 基石 **2** something important on which something else depends 基礎; 基本: *Free speech is the cornerstone of democracy.* 言論自由是民主的基礎。

cor·net /ˈkɔrnɪt; ˈkɔːnɪt/ *n* **1** a small, brass, musical instrument like a TRUMPET 短號 **2** *BrE*〔英式〕(also 又作 **cone**) a thin container for ICE-CREAM which is pointed at one end and is eaten with its contents〔裝冰淇淋的〕圓錐形蛋卷

corn·flakes /ˈkɔrnˌfleks; ˈkɔːnfleɪks/ *n* [pl] breakfast food made from crushed corn and usually eaten with milk and sugar 玉米片〔加入牛奶和白糖作早餐用〕

corn·flour /ˈkɔrnflaʊɚ; ˈkɔːnflaʊəʳ/ *n* [U] a fine flour made from crushed corn or other grain and used in cooking to thicken liquids 玉米麵; 穀粉

cor·nice /ˈkɔrnɪs; ˈkɔːnɪs/ *n* a decorative border along the top edge of the front of a building or PILLAR or round the top of the walls in a room 飛簷〔牆或柱頂部突出的裝飾〕; 上楣

corn·y /ˈkɔrni; ˈkɔːni/ *adj* **cornier, corniest** *infml* too familiar, simple, or old-fashioned to be interesting〔非正式〕司空見慣的; 平淡的; 陳舊的: *a corny joke* 老掉牙的笑話 | *a corny film* 平淡的電影

co·rol·la·ry /ˈkɔrəˌlɛri; kəˈrɒləri/ *n* **corollaries** *fml* a statement or course of action that is a direct result of another one〔正式〕推論; 必然的結果

cor·o·na·ry¹ /ˈkɔrəˌnɛri; ˈkɒrənəri/ *adj* [always before a noun 只能用於名詞前] *tech* related to the heart〔術語〕心臟的

coronary² *n* **coronaries** (also 又作 **coronary thrombosis** *fml*〔正式〕) a HEART ATTACK caused when the blood supply to your heart is blocked 冠狀動脈血栓症

cor·o·na·tion /ˌkɔrəˈneʃən; ˌkɒrəˈneɪʃən/ *n* the ceremony at which a person officially becomes king or queen 加冕典禮

cor·o·ner /ˈkɔrənɚ; ˈkɒrənəʳ/ *n* an official who inquires into the causes of an accidental or unexpected death 驗屍官

cor·o·net /ˈkɔrənɪt; ˈkɒrənɪt/ *n* a small decorative covering worn on the heads of princes or members of noble families〔王子或貴族所戴的〕小冠冕

cor·po·ral /ˈkɔrpərəl; ˈkɔːpərəl/ *n* a person of low rank in the army or airforce〔陸軍或空軍的〕下士

corporal pun·ish·ment /ˈ··· ˈ···/ *n* physical punishment, usually hitting someone 體罰: *Corporal punishment is no longer permitted in schools.* 學校裡不再允許對學生進行體罰。

★**cor·po·rate** /ˈkɔrpərɪt; ˈkɔːpərɪt/ *adj* **1** belonging to or shared by all the members of a group 團體的; 全體的: *corporate responsibility* 集體責任 | *a corporate effort* 共同的努力 **2** belonging to or related to a corporation 法人的; 公司的 –**corporately** *adv*

cor·po·ra·tion /ˌkɔːpəˈreɪʃən; ˌkɔːrpəˈreɪʃn/ *n* **1** a large business organization 公司: *John works for a large American chemical corporation.* 約翰在一家很大的美國化學公司工作。| *the British Broadcasting Corporation* 英國廣播公司 **2** [+ sing/pl verb] *BrE* a group of people elected to govern a town 〔英式〕市政當局: *The corporation is in financial trouble.* 市政府遇到了財政困難。

corps /kɔː; kɔːr/ *n* [plural is 複數為 **corps** /kɔːz; kɔːrz/ **1** (also 又作 **Corps**) a trained army group with special duties 特種部隊: *the medical corps* 醫療部隊 **2** a group of people united in the same activity 參與同一項活動的一羣人: *the president's press corps* 總統的記者團 | *the diplomatic corps* 外交使團

corpse /kɔːps; kɔːps/ *n* a dead body 死屍

cor·pu·lent /ˈkɔːpjələnt; ˈkɔːpjǝlənt/ *adj fml* very fat〔正式〕肥胖的 –**corpulence** *n* [U]

cor·pus /ˈkɔːpəs; ˈkɔːpəs/ *n* **corpora** /ˈkɔːpərə; ˈkɔːpərə/ or **corpuses** a collection of all the writings of a special kind 全集: *the corpus of Shakespeare's works* 莎士比亞全集

cor·pus·cle /ˈkɔːpəsl; ˈkɔːpəsəl/ *n* any of the red or white cells in your blood 血球

cor·ral /kəˈræl; kɒˈrɑːl, kə-/ *n* an enclosed area where cattle or horses are kept, es-

pecially in the US〔尤指在美國關牛馬的〕畜欄

cor·rect¹ /kəˈrekt; kəˈrekt/ *adj* **1** without mistakes 無誤的; 正確的: *a correct answer* 正確的答案 | *correct spelling* 正確的拼寫 **2** following proper standards of manners 合乎禮節的; 得體的: *correct behaviour* 得體的舉止 –opposite 反義 **incorrect** –**correctly** *adv* –**correctness** *n* [U]

correct² *v* [T] to make something right or better 改正, 糾正〔某事物〕: *Correct my spelling if it's wrong.* 如果我的拼寫錯了, 請予以糾正。| *She'll need glasses to correct her eyesight.* 她需要戴眼鏡來矯正視力。

cor·rec·tion /kəˈrekʃən; kəˈrekʃn/ *n* **1** [C] a change that makes something right or better 改進; 改進: *I'll show you the mistakes, but I want you to make the corrections.* 我會把錯誤指給你看, 但我要你來改正。 **2** [U] the activity of making something right or better 改正; 糾正: *speech correction* 言語矯正 **3** [U] *old fash* punishment〔老式〕懲罰 –**corrective** /-tɪv; -tɪv/ *adj*: *corrective surgery* 矯正手術

cor·re·la·tion /ˌkɔrəˈleɪʃən; ˌkɒrɪˈleɪʃn/ *n* a relationship in which two things happen together and may have an effect on each other〔兩事物的〕相互關係: *a high correlation* **between** *unemployment and crime* 失

COLOURS 顏色

Colours are often associated with particular things or ideas. Read the dictionary entries for the colours in the box. Also read the entries for words associated with the colour (red carpet, blue collar etc.). Now look at the eight lists of words below. Which colour is connected with the ideas in each list?
顏色常常與特定的一些事物或概念聯繫在一起。請在本詞典中查出下表中所列的表示顏色的單詞, 同時也查出與顏色相關的單詞〔如red carpet, blue collar 等〕。現在請看下列八組詞, 請說出每個詞與哪一種顏色有關聯。

| black |
| green |
| pink |
| white |
| blue |
| grey |
| red |
| yellow |

[1]	[2]	[3]	[4]
shame	butter	dull	good health
anger	gold	fear	
debt	age	worry	
unnecessary rules		heavy	
communist		lack of knowledge	
danger			

[5]	[6]	[7]	[8]
sky	nature	night	with milk or cream
sea	environment	very bad	official
cold	jealous	angry	very hot
nobility	young	having money	
manual	inexperienced	refuse to work with	
sudden and unexpected	permission	evil	
		unlawful	

Do these colours have different meanings in your own language? Which ideas are associated with these colours?
在你的母語中, 這些表示顏色的詞有沒有甚麼不同的含義? 它們常常與哪些概念聯繫在一起?

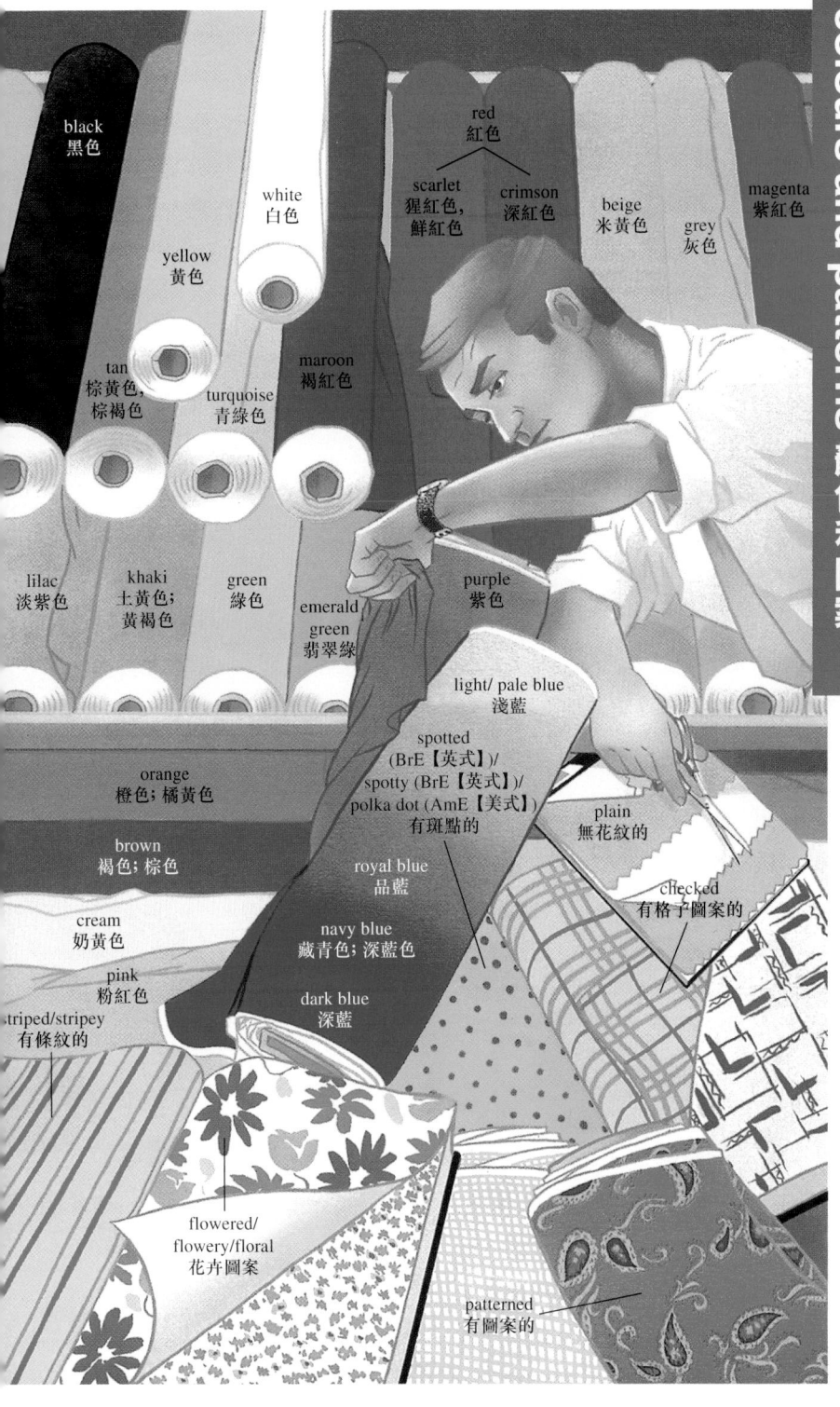

black
黑色

red
紅色

scarlet
猩紅色,
鮮紅色

crimson
深紅色

beige
米黃色

grey
灰色

magenta
紫紅色

white
白色

yellow
黃色

tan
棕黃色,
棕褐色

turquoise
青綠色

maroon
褐紅色

lilac
淡紫色

khaki
土黃色;
黃褐色

green
綠色

emerald
green
翡翠綠

purple
紫色

light/ pale blue
淺藍

spotted
(BrE【英式】)/
spotty (BrE【英式】)/
polka dot (AmE【美式】)
有斑點的

plain
無花紋的

orange
橙色;橘黃色

brown
褐色;棕色

royal blue
品藍

checked
有格子圖案的

cream
奶黃色

navy blue
藏青色;深藍色

pink
粉紅色

dark blue
深藍

striped/stripey
有條紋的

flowered/
flowery/floral
花卉圖案

patterned
有圖案的

barrel
圓木桶

crate
木箱；木格

bucket
水桶

flask (BrE【英式】)/
thermos (AmE【美式】)
保溫瓶

BISCU

churn (BrE【英式】)/
pail (AmE【美式】)
牛奶桶

drum
圓桶

bottle
瓶子

box
盒子

carton
紙盒

can
罐

Cola

bag
包；袋

packet (BrE【英式】)/
package (AmE【美式】)/
box
包；盒

tub
盆；鉢

tin/can
罐

jar
廣口

plant pot (BrE【英式】)/
flower pot (AmE【美式】)
花盆

jug (BrE【英式】)/
pitcher (AmE【美式】)
(有柄帶嘴的) 水壺

saucepan
(有柄和蓋的)
深平底鍋

casserole
砂鍋

frying pan
長柄平底煎鍋

vase
花瓶

kettle
〔燒水用的〕水壺

pot
(陶) 罐

cup & saucer
杯子和茶碟

mug
有柄大杯

glass
玻璃杯

dish
盤子

bowl
碗

teapot
茶壺

sachet (BrE【英式】)/
packet (AmE【美式】)
〔供一次使用的〕小紙袋

tube
一管[枝] (牙膏)

waste bin (BrE【英式】)/
waste paper basket
廢紙簍

beaker
(BrE【英式】)/
glass
大杯子

basket
籃

業與犯罪之間的密切關係 **–correlate** /ˈkɔrə-ˌlet; ˈkɒrəleɪt/ v **correlated, correlating** [I; T]

cor·re·spond /ˌkɔrəˈspɑnd; ˌkɒrɪˈspɒnd/ v [I] **1** to be in agreement with something 與〔某物〕一致; 符合: *These goods don't correspond with the list of the ones I ordered.* 這些商品與我的訂貨單不一致。| *These two lists don't correspond.* 這兩張名單不一致。**2** to be equal to something 等於〔某物〕: *An M.A. in Scotland corresponds to a B.A. from an English university.* 蘇格蘭文學碩士學位相當於英格蘭的大學所頒發的文學學士學位。**3** to exchange letters regularly 〔定期〕通信: *Janet and Bob corresponded for many years.* 珍妮特和鮑勃通信多年。| *I haven't corresponded with any of my old school friends for years.* 我多年未與我的老校友通信了。

cor·re·spon·dence /ˌkɔrəˈspɑndəns; ˌkɒrɪˈspɒndəns/ n [sing;U] **1** the activity of writing or exchanging letters 寫信; 通信: *I need a secretary to help with my correspondence.* 我需要一個祕書來幫我處理信件。**2** the letters exchanged between people 〔往來的〕信件: *The library bought all the correspondence between Queen Victoria and her daughters.* 圖書館買下了維多利亞女王與她的幾個女兒的所有往來信件。**3** agreement or similarity between particular things 符合; 相似: *There is little correspondence between her public statements and reality.* 她的公開聲明與實際情況不相符。**4 correspondence course** a course of lessons that you receive by post and do at home 函授課程

cor·re·spon·dent /ˌkɔrəˈspɑndənt; ˌkɒrɪˈspɒndənt/ n **1** a person with whom another person exchanges letters regularly 通信者 **2** someone employed by a newspaper or by television to report news from a distant area or on a particular subject 新聞記者: *a war correspondent* 戰地通訊記者 | *our correspondent in Rome* 我台駐羅馬記者

cor·re·spon·ding /ˌkɔrəˈspɑndɪŋ; ˌkɒrɪ-

CONTAINERS 容器

Exercise 1 練習一
Complete this passage by filling in the blanks. There is one dash for each missing letter. 填空以完成下列一段文字。每條橫線上填上一個字母。

From cow to cup of tea

　　Farmer Brown milked his cows at four o'clock this morning. He collected the milk in a ²b _ _ _ _ _. Then he poured it into a ²c _ _ _ _ and sent it to the dairy. The people at the dairy put the milk into ³b _ _ _ _ _ s which they then put into ⁴c _ _ _ _ s. The milkman collected the milk from the dairy and delivered it to the houses in the town.

　　Mrs Savage wanted two pints of milk today because her friend, Mrs Rolls, was coming to tea. Mrs Savage boiled some water in the ⁵k _ _ _ _ _ and poured it over the tea leaves which she had put in her best silver ⁶t _ _ _ _ _. Then she put two ⁷c _ _ _ s and two ⁸s _ _ _ _ _ s on a tray. After that, she poured some milk into a small ⁹j _ _ and put it on the tray.

　　"Would you like some milk in your tea?" she asked Mrs Rolls.

　　"No thank you" Mrs Rolls replied "Have you got any lemon?"

Exercise 2 練習二
What are these containers made of? Put a tick (✓) for often, a cross (✗) for never and a question mark (?) for sometimes. 下列容器是由甚麼材料製成的? 請在常用的材料上加上(✓), 在從不使用的材料上加上(✗), 在有時會使用的材料上加上(?)。

	wood	plastic	glass	china	paper	metal
bag	✗	✓	✗	✗	✓	✗
bottle						
crate						
cup						
saucepan						
box						
jug						
vase						
tube						

'spɒndɪŋ/ adj [only before a noun 只用於名詞前] similar or related 相似的; 相關的: *Profits for the first three months are 50% higher than in the corresponding period last year.* 今年頭三個月的利潤比去年同期增加了百分之五十。 –**correspondingly** adv

★**cor·ri·dor** /ˈkɒrədə; ˈkɔrˌdɔːˈ/ n **1** a passage between two rows of rooms 通道, 走廊: *Room 101 is at the end of the corridor.* 101號房間在走廊盡頭。 **2** a narrow piece of land that passes through a foreign country 〔經過他國的〕地帶, 走廊

cor·rob·o·rate /kəˈrɒbəˌret; kəˈrɒbəreɪt/ v **corroborated, corroborating** [T] to support an opinion or claim with additional information or proof 〔用其他資料或證據〕支持〔某一觀點或要求〕: *Several people who saw the accident corroborated the driver's statement.* 有幾位目擊車禍的人證實了司機的陳述。 –**corroborative** adj: *corroborative evidence* 助證 –**corroboration** /kəˌrɒbəˈreɪʃən; kəˌrɒbəˈreɪʃən/ n [U]

cor·rode /kəˈrod; kəˈrəʊd/ v **corroded, corroding** [I;T] to destroy or be destroyed slowly, especially by chemicals 〔尤指被化學品〕腐蝕: *Acid causes metal to corrode.* 酸能使金屬受到腐蝕。 | *Acid corrodes metal.* 酸腐蝕金屬。 –**corrosive** /-sɪv; -sɪv/ adj

cor·ro·sion /kəˈroʒən; kəˈrəʊʒən/ n [U] **1** the process of becoming slowly destroyed by chemicals 腐蝕 **2** a substance, such as RUST, which is produced as a result of this process 腐蝕而成之物〔如鏽〕: *corrosion on the body of a car* 車身上的鐵鏽

cor·ru·ga·ted /ˈkɒrəˌgetɪd; ˈkɒrəgeɪtɪd/ adj formed in rows of folds that look like waves 波紋狀的: *a corrugated iron roof* 瓦楞鐵的屋頂

cor·rupt¹ /kəˈrʌpt; kəˈrʌpt/ adj **1** dishonest and prepared to receive money to do things that are wrong or illegal 貪污的; 腐敗的: *a corrupt judge* 貪污受賄的法官 **2** immoral or bad 有傷風化的; 腐化的: *a corrupt political system* 腐敗的政治制度 **3** containing mistakes and having less value than the original 有錯誤的; 〔與原物比較〕不標準的: *They spoke a corrupt form of French.* 他們說的法語不標準。 | *a corrupt computer disk* 劣質計算機磁盤 –**corruptly** adv –**corruptness** n [U]

corrupt² v [T] **1** to cause a person to become dishonest or immoral 使〔某人〕腐化: *He has been corrupted by power.* 他由於權力在手而變得敗壞。 **2** to change the original form of something so that it has less value 破壞〔某物〕的本來面目: *Our language has been corrupted by the introduction of foreign words.* 我們的語言被外來詞語破壞得面目全非。 –**corruptible** adj –**corruptibility** /kəˌrʌptəˈbɪlətɪ; kəˌrʌptˌbɪlˌti/ n [U]

cor·rup·tion /kəˈrʌpʃən; kəˈrʌpʃən/ n [U] **1** the act or process of making someone dishonest or immoral 道德敗壞 **2** dishonest or immoral behaviour 腐化的行為: *the corruption of the ancient Roman court* 古羅馬宮廷的腐敗

cor·set /ˈkɔrsɪt; ˈkɔːsˌt/ n a very tight-fitting undergarment worn by women to give shape to their body 〔婦女為保持體形而穿的〕緊身胸衣 –**corseted** adj

cor·tege cortège /kɔrˈteʒ; kɔːˈteɪʒ/ n fml a procession of attendants, especially at a funeral 《正式》送葬行列

cosh /kɒʃ; kɒʃ/ n BrE infml a short hard stick which is used as a weapon 〔英式, 非正式〕〔用作武器的〕短棍

cos·met·ic¹ /kɒzˈmetɪk; kɒzˈmetɪk/ n a substance such as a cream or powder, which is intended to make a woman's skin more beautiful 化妝品: *They sell lipsticks, eye shadow, and a whole range of other cosmetics.* 他們經銷唇膏、眼影和一系列其他化妝品。

cosmetic² adj **1** intended to make your skin or body more beautiful 化妝用的; 美容的: *a cosmetic cream* 美容霜 | *cosmetic surgery* 美容手術 **2** dealing only with the appearance of something rather than what is really important 裝門面的: *cosmetic changes to the law* 對法律所進行的表面上的修改

cos·mic /ˈkɒzmɪk; ˈkɒzmɪk/ adj belonging or related to the whole universe 宇宙的 – **cosmically** /-klɪ; -kli/ adv

cos·mo·naut /ˈkɒzməˌnɔt; ˈkɒzmənɔːt/ n a Soviet ASTRONAUT 〔蘇聯的〕宇航員, 太空人

cos·mo·pol·i·tan /ˌkɒzməˈpɒlətn; ˌkɒzmə-ˈpɒlˌtən/ adj **1** consisting of people from many different parts of the world 由來自世界各地的人組成的; 世界性的: *London is a very cosmopolitan city.* 倫敦是個非常國際化的城市。 **2** showing wide experience of different people and places 見識廣的: *a cosmopolitan outlook on life* 對生活的宏達的世界觀

cos·mos /ˈkɒzməs; ˈkɒzmɒs/ n **the cosmos** the universe considered as an ordered system 宇宙

cos·set /ˈkɒsɪt; ˈkɒsˌt/ v [T] to pay a great deal of attention, sometimes too much, to making a person comfortable and contented 寵愛; 縱容〔某人〕

★★**cost¹** /kɒst; kɒst/ n **1** [C] the amount of money paid or needed to buy, do, or produce something 費用; 成本: *Think about the cost of bringing up a child!* 想想看養大一個孩子得花費多少錢! | *The students are given £100 a year to cover the cost of books and stationery.* 學生每年可獲一百英鎊作為支付書籍和文具用品的費用。 | *Our production costs are rising faster than we can increase prices.* 我們的生產成本上升得比我們提高產品價格還要快。 **2** [sing] something needed, given, or lost in order to obtain something 代價; 損失; 犧牲: *War is never* worth the terrible cost in human life. 戰爭根本不能彌補它給人類生活所帶來的巨大損失。 **3 at all costs, at any cost** no matter what the cost or result might be 不管多大代價; 無論如何: *We must avoid war at all costs.* 我們無論如何也要避免戰爭。 **4 to someone's cost** from your own unpleasant experience 從自己不愉快的經歷得知: *Drinking dirty water can be very dangerous, as I found out to my cost.* 喝不清潔的水是很危險的, 我吃過這苦頭。

■ USAGE 用法: Compare 比較 **cost** and 和 **price. Cost** often means the money you pay for a service ☆ **cost** 常指服務費用: *the* **cost** *of having a car repaired* 修車的費用 but we can also use it for very general things ☆但我們也可用它來泛指一般的事物: *the* **cost** *of living* 生活費用。 **Price** usually means the money you pay for a particular object ☆ **price** 通常指買一件物品所付的錢: *What is the* **price** *of this watch?* 這隻錶多少錢?

‡cost² *v* **cost, cost, costing 1** [T no passive 無被動態] to be able to be bought or made at a certain price 花費: *These shoes cost £25.* 這雙鞋要二十五英鎊。| *How much does that dress cost?* 那條連衣裙多少錢? | *This jacket cost me £100.* 這件夾克花了我一百英鎊。

□ USEFUL PATTERNS 有用句型
to cost something; to cost someone something

2 It'll cost you! *infml* 《非正式》= It'll be expensive for you 這要花你許多錢: *You can go by air, but it'll cost you.* 你可以坐飛機去, 但你要花不少錢。 **3** [T] to result in the loss of something 使付出; 使喪失: *The expedition cost him his life.* 他在那次探險中喪生。 | *Her marriage cost her her career.* 她的婚姻使她放棄了職業。 **4** [T past tense and past participle 過去式和過去分詞為 **costed**] to calculate the price to be charged for a job or service 估算〔工作或服務的〕價格〔成本〕: *The builder costed the job at £450.* 建築商估計這項工作得花450英鎊。 **5 cost an arm and a leg, cost the earth, cost a bomb** *infml* to be extremely expensive 《非正式》極為昂貴

co-star /ˈkoˌstɑr; ˈkəʊ stɑːʳ/ *n* a famous actor or actress who appears with another famous actor or actress in a film or play 聯袂主演的明星

cost-ef·fec·tive /ˈ··ˌ··/ *adj* bringing the best possible profits or advantages at the lowest possible cost 低成本高利潤的: *They discovered it was more cost-effective to change from electricity to gas.* 他們發現不用電而改用煤氣更合算。

cost·ly /ˈkɒstlɪ; ˈkɒstli/ *adj* **costlier, costliest 1** costing a lot of money 昂貴的 **2** using a lot of important things which are then lost 代價高昂的: *The war was costly in terms of both human lives and national pride.* 這場戰爭在傷亡及民族自尊心方面所付出的代價是很大的。

cost of liv·ing /ˌ·· ˈ···/ *n* **the cost of living** the cost of buying the goods and services you need to live at an average standard of comfort 生活費用

cos·tume /ˈkɑstjum; ˈkɒstjum/ *n* [C;U] **1** clothes or a garment typical of a certain period, country, activity, or profession 〔某時期、某國家、某活動或某職業的〕衣服; 服飾: *dancers in national costume* 身穿民族服飾的舞蹈員 | *actors in 18th century costume* 身穿十八世紀服裝的演員 | *a swimming costume* 泳裝 | *a costume drama* 古裝劇

co·sy¹ /ˈkozɪ; ˈkəʊzi/ *adj* **cosier, cosiest** (also 又作 **cozy** *AmE* 《美式》) warm and comfortable 溫暖舒適的: *a cosy little house* 舒適的小屋 | *a cosy evening by the fire* 坐在火邊的舒適的夜晚 **–cosily** *adv* **–cosiness** *n* [U]

cosy² *n* **cosies** a covering put over a boiled egg or teapot to keep the contents warm 〔熟雞蛋或茶壺的〕保暖罩子: *a tea cosy* 茶壺保暖套

cot /kɑt; kɒt/ *n* *BrE* a small bed with high, movable sides, for a young child 《英式》〔有活動欄杆的〕幼兒牀

‡cot·tage /ˈkɑtɪdʒ; ˈkɒtɪdʒ/ *n* a small house, especially in the country 小屋; 村舍 **–see** 見 HOUSE (USAGE 用法) **–see picture on page 729** 見 729 頁彩圖

cottage cheese /ˌ··ˈ·/ *n* [U] soft, lumpy, white cheese made from sour milk 〔酸奶製成的〕農家鮮乳酪

cot·ton¹ /ˈkɑtn̩; ˈkɒtn̩/ *n* [U] **1** a tall plant which produces soft white hair used for making thread or cloth 棉株 **2** thread or cloth made from the cotton plant 棉線; 棉布: *a cotton dress* 棉布衣服 | *a reel of blue cotton* 一團藍棉線

cotton² *v*
cotton on *phr v* [I] *infml* to understand something 《非正式》理解〔某事〕: *It was a long time before I cottoned on to what he meant.* 我過了很久才明白他的意思。

cotton wool /ˌ··ˈ·/ *n* [U] *BrE* a soft mass of cotton, used especially for cleaning your skin or wounds 《英式》藥棉

couch¹ /kautʃ; kaʊtʃ/ *n* a long piece of furniture, usually with a back and arms, on which more than one person can sit or lie 長沙發

couch² *v* **be couched in** to be expressed in a certain way 以〔某種方式〕表達: *The government's refusal was couched in friendly terms.* 政府友善地表示拒絕。

cough¹ /kɔf; kɒf/ *v* **1** [I] to push air out from your throat with a sudden rough sound, especially because of discomfort in your lungs or throat as a result of a cold or other infection 咳嗽: *She was coughing and sneezing all day.* 她一整天都在咳嗽打噴嚏。**2** [T] (also 又作 **cough** sth ↔ **up**) to clear something from your throat by coughing 咳出〔某物〕: *I knew she was seriously ill when she began to cough blood.* 她開始咳血時，我就知道她病得很重。**3** [I] to make a sound like a cough 發出咳嗽般的聲音: *The engine coughed once or twice, but would not start.* 引擎喀喀地響了一兩聲，但發動不起來。

cough up *phr v* [I;T **cough up** sth] *infml* to produce money or information unwillingly 〔非正式〕勉強提供〔錢或情報〕

cough² *n* **1** a sudden rough noise caused by someone pushing air out of their throat 咳嗽(聲): *She gave a nervous cough.* 她緊張地咳了一聲。**2** a medical condition marked by frequent coughing 咳嗽(病): *John had a bad cough all last week.* 約翰上星期一直咳得很厲害。

could /kəd; kəd, *strong* 強讀 kʊd; kʊd/ *v negative short form* 否定縮約式 **couldn't** [modal verb 情態動詞] **1** the past tense of CAN ☆ CAN 的過去式: *I can't sing now, but I could when I was young.* 我現在不會唱歌了，但年輕時會唱。| *They asked me if I could dance.* 他們問我會不會跳舞。| *She said that she couldn't come to the party.* 她說無法來參加聚會。| *He asked if he could smoke.* 他問是不是可以抽煙。| *I said that he could borrow my car.* 我說他可以借用我的汽車。**2** used to show that something might be possible 〔表示可能性〕: *He could lose his job if he's not careful.* 他如不小心，可能會失去那份工作。| *I could come tomorrow if you like.* 如果你願意，我可以明天來。| *That could be my handbag over there.* 那邊那隻手提包有可能是我的。| *If we could leave by six o'clock, we'd be in London by eight.* 我們如果在六點以前能出發，八點就可以到倫敦了。| *He was lucky — he could have been killed.* 他算是運了——本來他也許會喪命的。–see Study Note on page 1318 見 1318 頁學習提示 **3 could you** a polite way of asking someone to do something 您能〔表示有禮貌地請求某人做某事〕: *Could you help me lift this box, please?* 請幫我抬一下這隻箱子好嗎？| *Could you just move your chair out of the way, please?* 請你把椅子移開，不要擋着路行嗎？**4 could I, could we, etc.** a polite way of asking someone if they will let you do something 我能；我們能〔表示有禮貌地詢問是否能允許自己做某事〕: *Could I use your telephone, please?* 我能借用一下你的電話嗎？| *Could we leave our bags here, please?* 我們能把袋子放在這兒嗎？**5 I could** *infml* 〔非正式〕= I would like to 我願意；我想: *I could just eat bacon and eggs now!* 我想現在就吃點熏肉和雞蛋！**6 you could** *infml* 〔非正式〕= you should 你應該: *You could tell me when*

you're going to be late home! 你要晚回家！| *You could have washed up your plate!* 你本來可以把自己的盤子洗好的! **7 couldn't you** *infml* a way of trying to persuade someone to do something that they do not want to do 〔非正式〕你難道就不能〔勸別人去做他們不想做的事〕: *Couldn't you just spare five minutes to look at this for me?* 你就不能花五分鐘時間替我看一下這個嗎？

couldn't /'kʊdnt; 'kʊdnt/ *v* short for 縮約式 = "could not": *"Couldn't you see anything?" "No, I couldn't."* "你難道甚麼也看不見嗎?" "是的，甚麼也看不見。"

could've /'kʊdəv; 'kʊdəv/ *v* an abbreviation for 〔縮〕= **could have**: *"I could've gone with you."* "我本來可以跟你一起去的。"

coun·cil¹ /'kaʊnsl; 'kaʊnsəl/ *n* [+ sing/pl verb] a group of people appointed or elected at a local or organizational level to make laws or decisions or to give advice 委員會；議會；理事會: *the Security Council of the United Nations* 聯合國安全理事會 | *We applied to the town council for permission to build a hotel.* 我們向市議會申請批准建造一座旅館。

council² *adj* [only before a noun 只用於名詞前] *BrE* owned and controlled by the local council (used of houses or flats) 〔英式〕郡政府擁有的；郡政府管轄的〔指住房或公寓〕: *We live in a council house in East London.* 我們住在倫敦東區的一所郡政府建的房子裡。

coun·cil·lor /'kaʊnslə; 'kaʊnsələr/ *n* a member of a council 市政委員；議員: *What do you think, Councillor Evans?* 您看怎麼樣，伊萬斯議員？| *I've been a city councillor for years.* 我任市議員已有多年了。

coun·sel¹ /'kaʊnsl; 'kaʊnsəl/ *n* **1** [C;U] *law* the lawyer speaking for someone in a court of law 〔律〕辯護律師: *counsel for the defence* 被告方律師 | *the counsel for the prosecution* 原告方律師 **2** [U] *old fash* advice 〔老式〕意見；忠告

counsel² *v* -**ll**- *BrE* 〔英式〕(-**l**- *AmE* 〔美式〕) [T] *fml* to advise someone 〔正式〕勸告〔某人〕；建議: *We were counselled against travelling at night.* 有人建議我們不要在夜間旅行。| *the counselling service for new students* 為新生提供輔導的服務

coun·sel·lor /'kaʊnslər; 'kaʊnsələr/ *n* (**counselor** *AmE* 〔美式〕) **1** an adviser 顧問: *a marriage guidance counsellor* 婚姻指引顧問 **2** *AmE* a lawyer 〔美式〕律師

count¹ /kaʊnt; kaʊnt/ *v* **1** [I;T] to say the numbers in order, one by one or by groups 〔按順序〕數: *I can count up to 20 in Arabic.* 我能用阿拉伯語數到20。| *Count from one to ten and then open your eyes.* 從一數到十，然後睜開眼睛。**2** [T] to calculate the total number of things in a group 計算〔某物〕的總數: *We counted the paintings and found that one was missing.* 我們點了一下畫的數量，

發現少了一張。| *Have the votes been counted yet?* 選票點完了嗎？ **3** [T] to include someone or something 包括〔某人或某物〕: *There are six people in my family, counting my parents.* 我家有六口人，包括我的父母在內。 **4** [I;T] to consider a person or thing or to be considered of a particular type or quality 認為；算作: *It doesn't count as a crime.* 這不能算作犯罪。| *I count you as one of my best friends.* 我視你為最要好的朋友之一。 **5 count yourself** to consider yourself 認為自己…: *Count yourself lucky to have escaped!* 讓你逃脫了，算你走運！ **6** [I not in progressive forms 不用於進行式] to have value or importance 有價值；有重要性: *It is not how much you read but what you read that counts.* 重要的不是你看了多少書，而是你看了甚麼樣的書。| *He has no experience in this field, so his opinion doesn't count.* 他在這一領域沒有經驗，所以他的看法無足輕重。 **7 count against someone** to help cause someone to lose or fail in something 對某人不利: *Jeans will count against you at the interview.* 穿牛仔服對你的面試很不利。 **8 count the cost** to calculate or suffer the bad effects of something you have done 估計〔承擔〕〔所做之事的〕不利後果 **9 count your blessings** think of all the things you have that make you happy 回想所有令自己開心的事: *Stop complaining and count your blessings.* 別發牢騷，想想讓你自己開心的事吧。 **10 don't count your chickens before they are hatched** don't think that it is certain that you will get something, or that things will happen in the way you hope they will 蛋尚未孵先數小雞；打如意算盤

count down *phr v* [I] to count backwards in seconds to zero, especially before sending a spacecraft into space 倒數〔尤指在發射宇宙飛船前〕

count in *phr v* [T **count** sbdy **in**] *infml* to include someone 《非正式》包括〔某人〕: *If you're planning a trip to London, count me in.* 如果你作計劃去倫敦旅行，把我也算在內。

count on sbdy/sthg *phr v* [T] **1** to depend on someone or something 依靠〔某人或某事物〕: *She can always be counted on for support.* 找她支持，她總是靠得住的。| *You can't count on the weather being fine.* 你不能指望天氣會好轉。| *We can count on him to come.* 我們可以指望他會來的。 **2** to expect someone to do something or something to happen 期望；指望: *I didn't count on John arriving so early.* 我沒料到約翰會到得這麼早。

count out *phr v* **1** [T **count** sthg ↔ **out**] to put things down in turn while counting them 逐一數出: *He counted out ten £5 notes.* 他數出了十張五英鎊的鈔票。 **2** [T **count** sbdy ↔ **out**] to declare a BOXER who fails to rise from the floor after ten seconds to be the loser of a fight 〔由於倒地十秒鐘後仍未爬起而〕判〔被擊倒者〕失敗 **3** [T

count sbdy **out**] *infml* to leave someone out 《非正式》不包括〔某人〕: *If you're playing football in this weather you can count me out!* 如果你們要在這種天氣踢足球，就不要把我算在內!

*count² *n* **1** an act of counting or the total reached by counting 計算；總數: *At the last count, I'd visited 15 countries.* 最後計算下來，我遊覽過十五個國家。 **2 lose count** to fail to know the exact number 不知道確切數字: *I've lost count of how many times he's said he's leaving her.* 他說他要離開她的話，我已記不清他說過多少回了。[RELATED PHRASE 相關詞組 **keep count**] **3** (also 又作 **Count**) the title of a European nobleman with a rank of a British EARL 伯爵〔歐洲貴族的封號〕 **4 be out for the count** to be unconscious for a period of ten seconds during a BOXING match 〔拳手在比賽中昏迷達十秒鐘而〕被判失敗

count·a·ble /ˈkaʊntəbl; ˈkaʊntəbəl/ *adj* **1** able to be counted 可數的 **2 countable noun** *tech* a noun that has both singular and plural forms and that can be used with numbers and with words such as **many,** or **few,** or with **a** or **an**; in this dictionary, countable nouns are often marked [C] 《術語》可數名詞〔有單複數形式，前面也可加上數字及 **many, few, a** 或 **an** 等詞。在本辭典內，該類詞常用 [C] 來表示〕 –opposite 反義 **uncountable** –see Study Note on page 1313 見 1313 頁學習提示

count·down /ˈkaʊnt,daʊn; ˈkaʊntdaʊn/ *n* [C;U] an act of counting backwards in seconds to zero, especially before sending a spacecraft into space 倒數〔尤指在發射宇宙飛船前〕: *Prepare for countdown: ten, nine, eight, seven...* 準備好倒數: 十、九、八、七…

coun·te·nance¹ /ˈkaʊntənəns; ˈkaʊntਂnəns/ *n fml* the appearance of your face or its expression 《正式》面容; 面部表情: *an angry countenance* 怒容

countenance² *v* [T] *fml* to allow something or to approve of it 《正式》同意，贊成〔某事〕: *We will never countenance violence.* 我們絕不贊成使用暴力。

coun·ter¹ /ˈkaʊntə; ˈkaʊntər/ *n* **1** a narrow table or flat surface in a shop or bank where you go to be served 〔商店或銀行的〕櫃台 **2 over the counter** obtainable directly from a shop 可直接從店裡買到的: *Those pills are available over the counter now.* 那些藥丸現在可以在店裡直接買到。 **3 under the counter** secretly, and often not legally 祕密地〔常為非法地〕: *During the war you could only get cigarettes under the counter.* 戰爭期間，你只能在暗地裡才能買到香煙。 **4** a small object used to show a player's position on the board in some games; it is often made of plastic and looks like a coin 〔常為塑料製成的〕籌碼

counter² *v* [I;T] to do or say something

which opposes a person or an idea 反對; 反駁: *My employer countered my request for more money by threatening to dismiss me.* 我的老闆以辭退為恫嚇, 拒絕我的加薪要求。 | *I countered by pointing out that statistics are often unreliable.* 我反駁說統計數字常常靠不住。

counter³ *adv* **run counter to something** to be opposed to something 與某物相反: *ideas that ran counter to everything I believed was right* 與一切我所認為正確無誤的東西背道而馳的觀點

coun·ter·act /ˌkaʊntəˈækt; ˌkaʊntərˈækt/ *v* [T] to reduce or change the effect of something by doing something that has the opposite effect 抵消; 消除: *This drug should counteract the poison.* 這種藥可以解毒。

coun·ter·at·tack /ˈkaʊntərəˌtæk; ˈkaʊntərətæk/ *n* an attack on an enemy who has attacked you 反攻; 反擊 –**counterattack** *v* [I;T]

coun·ter·bal·ance /ˈkaʊntəˌbæləns; ˈkaʊntəˌbæləns/ *n* a weight or force that acts as a balance for another weight or force 平衡; 平衡力 –**counterbalance** /ˌkaʊntəˈbæləns; ˌkaʊntəˈbæləns/ *v* **counterbalanced, counterbalancing** [T]: *He used his weight to counterbalance the load.* 他利用體重來平衡負荷的重物。

coun·ter·clock·wise /ˌkaʊntəˈklɒkˌwaɪz; ˌkaʊntəˈklɒkwaɪz/ *adj, adv* –see 見 ANTI-CLOCKWISE

coun·ter·feit /ˈkaʊntəˌfɪt; ˈkaʊntəfɪt/ *v* [T] to make a copy of something so that people will think it is the real thing 仿造; 偽造: *It is against the law to counterfeit money.* 偽造鈔票是非法的。 –**counterfeit** *adj*: *a counterfeit coin* 偽幣 –**counterfeiter** *n*

coun·ter·foil /ˈkaʊntəˌfɔɪl; ˈkaʊntəfɔɪl/ *n* a part of a cheque that you keep to show what the cheque was for 〔支票的〕存根

coun·ter·mand /ˌkaʊntəˈmænd; ˌkaʊntəˈmɑːnd/ *v* [T] to give an order which means that one given earlier must not be carried out 撤回〔命令等〕

coun·ter·part /ˈkaʊntəˌpɑrt; ˈkaʊntəpɑːt/ *n* a person or thing that serves the same purpose or has the same position as another 地位相對應的人或物: *British police officers are working with their French counterparts to catch the terrorists.* 英國警察正在與他們的法國同行一起追捕恐怖主義分子。

coun·ter·sign /ˈkaʊntəˌsaɪn; ˈkaʊntəsaɪn/ *v* [T] to sign something that someone else has signed 連署; 副署: *I can sign cheques, but my boss has to countersign them.* 我可以在這些支票上簽名, 但須由我的老闆連署。

coun·tess /ˈkaʊntɪs; ˈkaʊntᵻs/ *n* the title of the wife of an EARL or COUNT, or a woman of the same rank 伯爵夫人; 女伯爵

count·less /ˈkaʊntlɪs; ˈkaʊntləs/ *adj* [only before a noun 只用於名詞前] very many 無

數的; 數不盡的: *She succeeded only after countless failures.* 經過無數次失敗後, 她才取得成功。

coun·try¹ /ˈkʌntrɪ; ˈkʌntri/ *n* **countries** **1** [C] a nation or state with its land or population 國家: *Have you visited this country before?* 你以前到過這個國家嗎? **2** [C] the people of a nation or state 全國人民: *Our country has always been peace-loving.* 我國人民向來愛好和平。 –see 見 FOLK¹ (USAGE 用法) **3 the country** the land outside cities or towns 農村; 鄉下: *We're going to spend a few days in the country.* 我們打算到鄉下住幾天。 **4** [U] land with a special nature or character 〔具有某種特性的〕土地: *good farming country* 適宜耕種的土地

country² *adj* [only before a noun 只用於名詞前] in or related to the land outside cities or towns 農村的; 鄉下的: *country life* 農村生活 | *a country house* 村舍

country and west·ern /ˌ··· ·ˈ··/ *n* (also 又作 **country music** /ˌ·· ·ˈ··/) [U] popular music in the style of the southern and western US 〔美國的〕鄉村與西部音樂

coun·try·man /ˈkʌntrɪmən; ˈkʌntrimən/ *n* **countrymen** /-mən; -mən/ a person from your own country 同胞

coun·try·side /ˈkʌntrɪˌsaɪd; ˈkʌntrisaɪd/ *n* [U] land outside the cities and towns, used for farming or left unused 農村; 鄉間

coun·ty /ˈkaʊntɪ; ˈkaʊnti/ *n* **counties** a large area of land in Britain, Ireland, and the US which has its own government to deal with local matters 〔英國、愛爾蘭、美國等國的〕郡, 縣

coup /ku; kuː/ *n* **coups** /kuz; kuːz/ **1** a coup d'état 政變 **2** a clever and successful action 明智而成功的行動: *Getting the contract was quite a coup.* 得到那份合同是相當明智之舉。

coup d'é·tat /ˈku deˈtɑ; ˌkuː deɪˈtɑː/ *n* **coups d'état** (*same pronunciation* 發音相同) (also 又作 **coup**) the sudden or violent seizing of power in a state by a small group of people who have not been elected 政變

cou·pé /ˈkuˈpe; ˈkuːpeɪ/ *n* (also 又作 **coupe** /kup; kuːp/) a car with two doors and a sloping back 雙門小轎車

cou·ple¹ /ˈkʌpl̩; ˈkʌpəl/ *n* **1** two things considered together 一對; 一雙: *I've got a couple of steaks for lunch.* 我有兩塊牛排午餐時吃。 **2** two people, usually a man and a woman, who are married, live together, or have a very close relationship 夫妻; 〔同居或關係密切的〕一對男女: *We've invited three other couples to dinner.* 我們邀請了另外三對夫婦來吃晚飯。 **3** *infml* a small number 〔非正式〕幾個, 幾個: *I'll just have a couple of drinks.* 我就喝上幾杯吧。

couple² *v* **coupled, coupling 1** [T] to join two vehicles together, especially parts of a train 連接〔尤指火車車廂〕: *The engine was coupled to the carriages, and the train pulled out.* 車頭連接上車廂後，火車就開出了車站。**2 coupled with** together with 與...一起: *Low salaries, coupled with a shortage of cheap housing, make it difficult for young people to leave home.* 工資低，再加上便宜的住處又很少，這使得年輕人難以離家搬同。

cou·pon /ˈkupɑn; ˈkuːpɒn/ *n* **1** a piece of paper giving you the right to obtain something free or more cheaply than usual 招待券; 優待券: *a coupon for ten pence off a packet of soap* 買一包肥皂可便宜十便士的優待券 | *Collect six coupons for a free bracelet.* 收集六張優惠券，可免費換一隻手鐲。**2** a printed form, for example in a newspaper, on which you can order goods, ask for information, or enter a competition 〔報紙等上面的〕訂貨單; 查詢單; 參賽券

cour·age /ˈkɜːrɪdʒ; ˈkʌrɪdʒ/ *n* [U] **1** the quality that makes you able to control your fear and do something dangerous or difficult 勇氣; 膽量: *It took courage to stand up to him like that.* 要那樣面對他需要勇氣。*I couldn't be a soldier, I haven't got the courage.* 我不可能當兵，我沒有那份勇氣。**2 have the courage of your convictions** to be brave enough to do or say what you think is right 敢做〔敢說〕自己認為正確的事

cou·ra·geous /kəˈreɪdʒəs; kəˈreɪdʒəs/ *adj* brave 勇敢的: *a courageous action* 勇敢的舉動 | *a courageous person* 勇敢的人 **–courageously** *adv*

cour·gette /kurˈʒɛt; kʊəˈʒet/ *n* a small green MARROW cooked and eaten as a vegetable 小胡瓜

cou·ri·er /ˈkʊriɚ; ˈkʊriəʳ/ *n* **1** a tourist guide who stays with and looks after groups of travellers 旅遊團的導遊 **2** someone who carries important or urgent papers, parcels, or messages 〔傳送緊急文件、包裹、信息的〕信使; 通訊員

★★course¹ /kɔrs; kɔːs/ *n* **1** a movement from one point to another in space or time 過程; 進程: *During the course of the flight we shall be serving drinks.* 飛行途中我們將提供飲料。**2** the direction of movement taken by someone or something 行動方向: *Our course is directly south.* 我們的行進方向是正南方。| *the course of a stream* 河的流向 **3** a set of lessons or studies 課程: *a French course* 法語課程 | *an evening course* 夜校的課程 | *a four-year history course* 四年的歷史課程 **4** *BrE* a plan, especially for medical treatment, with a number of steps 〔英式〕〔由幾個步驟組成的〕計劃〔尤指療程〕: *a course of exercises* 身體鍛鍊計劃 | *You must finish the whole course of tablets, even if your symptoms have gone.* 即使你的症狀都已消除，你還是必須把整個療程的藥片全部服下去。**5** one of the parts of a meal 一道菜: *We had a three-course dinner.* 我們的晚餐是

三道菜。| *The first course was soup.* 第一道菜是湯。**6** an area of land or water on which a race is held or certain types of sport played 〔比賽或運動的〕場地: *a golf course* 高爾夫球場 **7** action you can take in a particular situation 〔在某特定情況下所能採取的〕行動: *There are several courses of action we could take.* 我們可以採取好幾種行動。| *Your best course would be to own up before they find out.* 你最明智的做法就是在他們發現以前老實交待。**8 of course** certainly 當然: *Of course I'll still love you when you're old.* 毫無疑問，你老了我還是會愛你的。| *"Were you glad to leave there?" – "Of course not!"* "你願意離開那裏嗎?" "當然不願意!" **9 on course** going the right way 在正確的方向上: *The ship is on course.* 這艘船航向正確無誤。| *She's on course for a gold medal.* 她已踏上了奪取金牌之路。[RELATED PHRASE 相關詞組 **off course**]

course² *v* **coursed, coursing** [I] *lit* (of liquid) to flow or move rapidly 〖文〗〔液體〕奔流: *Tears coursed down his cheeks.* 眼淚順着他的臉頰流下來。

★★court¹ /kort; kɔːt/ *n* **1** [C;U] a room or building in which law cases can be heard and judged 法庭; 法院: *He appeared in court today charged with attempted murder.* 他因被控企圖謀殺而於今天出庭受審。| *The court was full of people interested in the case.* 法庭上擠滿了對這案子感興趣的人。| *Silence in court!* 法庭上請肅靜! **2 the court** the people gathered together to hear and judge a law case 全體出庭人員; 全體審判員: *The court stood when the judge entered.* 法官進場時，法庭內所有人都站了起來。**3** [C;U] a specially prepared and marked area in which certain ball games, such as tennis, are played 球場: *Are the players on court yet?* 球員都上場了嗎? | *She knocked the ball right out of the court.* 她把球打出了球場。**4** [C] used as the name of a large building, especially a block of flats 一棟公寓〔用作大樓名稱〕: *They lived in Westbury Court.* 他們住在威斯特伯利公寓裏。**5** [C;U] the place where the king or queen lives and carries out his or her formal duties, or the people who spend time in this place 宮廷; 皇宮: *The British court is in London.* 英國的王宮在倫敦。**6 take someone to court** to start an action in law against someone 對某人採取法律行動

court² *v* **1** [T] to pay attention to an important person so that they will like you or help you in someway 對〔重要人物〕獻殷勤; 討好 **2 court disaster** to risk danger or failure by behaving foolishly or without thinking 〔由於盲目行動而〕招致災禍 **3** [I] *old fash* to spend time together with the intention of marrying 〖老式〗求愛; 求婚: *when your mother and I were courting* 當你母親與我談戀愛時

cour·te·ous /ˈkɜːtɪəs; ˈkɝːtɪəs/ *adj fml* polite and respectful to others 〖正式〗有禮貌的; 尊敬的 –opposite 反義 **discourteous** –**courteously** *adv*

cour·te·sy /ˈkɜːtəsɪ; ˈkɝːtḷsi/ *n fml* [U] polite behaviour 〖正式〗禮貌; 彬彬有禮 –opposite 反義 **discourtesy**

court·i·er /ˈkɔːtɪə; ˈkɔːtɪəʳ/ *n* a noble who spent time at the court of a king or other ruler in former times 〖昔時宮廷上的〗朝臣

court-mar·tial[1] /ˌ·'··/ *n* **courts-martial** *or* **court martials 1** a military court that tries people for offences against military law 軍事法庭 **2** a trial by a military court 軍法審判

court-martial[2] *v* **-ll-** (also 又作 **-l-** *AmE* 〖美式〗) [T] to try someone in a military court for an offence against military law 以軍法審判〔某人〕

court·ship /ˈkɔːt·ʃɪp; ˈkɔːt-ʃɪp/ *n lit* [U] the process of courting, or the time during which a man and a woman are courting (COURT[2]) 〖文〗戀愛; 求愛期

court·yard /ˈkɔːtjɑːd; ˈkɔːtjɑːd/ *n* a flat space enclosed by walls or buildings, next to or within a castle, large house, or other large building 庭院; 院子

cous·in /ˈkʌzn; ˈkʌzən/ *n* the child of your uncle or aunt 堂〔表〕兄弟; 堂〔表〕姐妹 –see picture on page 503 見 503 頁彩圖

cove /kəv; kəʊv/ *n* a small sheltered opening in the coastline 小海灣

cov·en /ˈkʌvn; ˈkʌvən/ *n* a group or gathering of witches (WITCH) 巫婆的聚會

cov·e·nant /ˈkʌvənənt; ˈkʌvənənt/ *n* **1** a formal solemn agreement between two or more people or groups 契約; 盟約 **2** a written promise to pay a certain amount of money to someone regularly for a certain number of years 〖定期付錢給某人的〗契約書

Cov·en·try /ˈkʌvəntrɪ; ˈkʌvəntri/ *n* **send someone to Coventry** to refuse to speak to someone as a sign of disapproval or as a punishment 拒絕與某人交談〔表示不贊同或作為處罰〕: *His mates sent him to Coventry for working during the strikes.* 由於他在罷工期間繼續上班, 他的同事都拒絕和他講話。

cov·er[1] /ˈkʌvə; ˈkʌvəʳ/ *v* [T] **1** to place or spread something over something else to protect it or hide it 覆蓋, 遮蔽〔某物〕: *She covered her ears to shut out the noise.* 她雙手捂住耳朵, 不讓聲音吵到她。| *Cover the table* **with** *a cloth.* 用布把桌子鋪起來。–opposite **uncover 2** to lie over a particular surface or area 覆蓋於〔某一表面或地區〕: *furniture covered in dust* 滿是灰塵的家具 | *The town covers five square miles.* 這座小鎮佔地五平方英里。**3** to include or deal with something 包括, 涉及〔某物〕: *His talk covered British history between the wars.* 他的講話涉及到兩次戰爭之間的那段英國歷史。**4** to travel a certain distance 走〔一段距離〕: *I want to cover 100 miles before it gets dark.*

我想在天黑以前走完一百英里。**5** to report the details of an event for a newspaper 報道〔某一事件〕: *Our best reporter covered the trial.* 我們最優秀的記者報道了這次審判。**6** to be enough money to pay for something 〔錢〕夠付…: *Will £10 cover the cost of a new skirt?* 十英鎊夠買件新裙子嗎? **7** to protect someone from loss, especially through insurance 保險: *I'm covered against all accidents.* 我已買了各種事故的保險。**8** to aim a gun at a person or a place in order to protect someone from attack or to prevent someone from escaping 〔用槍〕掩護 **9** to watch and stay close to an opponent or an area in a game such as football 盯防〔對方隊員〕; 看守〔某一區域〕〔如在足球比賽中〕**10 cover for someone** to act in place of someone who is absent 代替某人: *John's ill today so will you cover for him, Jean?* 瓊, 約翰今天病了, 你替他一下好嗎?

cover sthg ↔ **up** *phr v* [T] **1** to place something over something else to protect it or hide it 覆蓋, 遮蓋〔某物〕: *Cover the furniture up before you start painting.* 開始油漆之前, 把家具遮蓋起來。**2** to prevent something from being noticed 掩飾〔某物〕: *She tried to cover up her nervousness.* 她盡力掩飾她的緊張情緒。

cover up for sbdy *phr v* [T] *infml* to hide something wrong or shameful to save someone else from punishment or blame 〖非正式〗掩飾〔別人的錯誤〕; 包庇: *He says he did it, but I think he's trying to cover up for a friend.* 他說是他做的, 但我認為他在為他的朋友開脫。

cover[2] *n* **1** [C] anything that protects something by covering it, especially a piece of material, lid, or top 遮蓋物; 覆蓋物〔尤指蓋子、蓋子〕: *Put a cover on the chair before the cat sits on it.* 在椅子上放好座套才能讓貓坐上去。| *a cushion cover* 墊子套 **2** [C] the outside of a magazine or book 封面; 封底: *the photograph on the front cover* 封面上的照片 **3** [U] shelter or protection 隱蔽處; 掩護: *The flat land gave the soldiers no cover from enemy fire.* 那地方很平坦, 士兵們無處躲避敵人的砲火。**4** [U] insurance against loss or damage 保險: *Make sure you have adequate insurance cover.* 你一定要有適當的保險。**5** [C] something that hides something or keeps it secret 掩飾; 掩護: *This business is a cover* **for** *drug-dealing.* 這生意是用來掩飾販毒活動的。**6 break cover** to come out of hiding 從藏匿處出來 **7 take cover** to shelter or hide from something 躲避〔某事物〕**8 under cover of darkness** while it is dark and no one can see you 趁着天黑〔沒人能看見你〕**9 under separate cover** in a separate envelope or parcel 〔用信件、包裹〕另寄: *This is a receipt. The goods will be sent later under separate cover.* 這是收據。貨物將於晚些時候用包裹另寄。

---

cov·er·age /ˈkʌvərɪdʒ; ˈkʌvərɪdʒ/ *n* [U] the amount of time and space given by television or a newspaper to report a particular piece of news or an event〔電視或報紙對新聞或事件的〕報道量;篇幅

cov·er·ing /ˈkʌvərɪŋ; ˈkʌvərɪŋ/ *n* something that covers or hides something else 覆蓋物;遮蓋物: *Put a covering over the hole.* 用東西把這個洞蓋上。

covering let·ter /ˌ···ˈ··/ *n* a letter or note containing an explanation or more information, sent with a parcel or another letter〔附於包裹或另一信函中的〕説明信;附函

cov·ert /ˈkʌvət; ˈkʌvət/ *adj* secret, hidden, or not openly shown 祕密的;隱藏的;不公開的: *covert political activities* 祕密的政治活動 –opposite 反義 **overt** –**covertly** *adv*

cov·er-up /ˈ··· ·/ *n* an attempt to prevent people knowing about something shameful or criminal 掩飾;掩蓋

cov·et /ˈkʌvɪt; ˈkʌvɪt/ *v* [T] *lit* to have a strong desire to possess something (a word used to express disapproval)〔文〕貪求;垂涎〔含貶義〕–**covetous** *adj*

cow¹ /kaʊ; kaʊ/ *n* **1** a large female animal kept on farms to provide milk 母牛;奶牛 **2** a male or female animal of this kind 牛: *a field full of cows* 田裡到處都是牛 **3** the female form of the elephant and certain other large sea and land animals〔大象及其他海生或陸生的〕雌性動物: *a cow elephant* 母象 **4** an unpleasant woman 令人不快的女人: *She's a real cow.* 她真是個討厭的女人。–see 見 MEAT (USAGE 用法)

cow² *v* [T] to make someone afraid or control them by violence or threats 威脅,恫嚇〔某人〕: *The people were cowed into submission.* 這些人被嚇得屈服貼服。

cow·ard /ˈkaʊəd; ˈkaʊəd/ *n* a person who is not brave (a word used to express disapproval) 膽小鬼〔含貶義〕: *Jump, you coward; you won't hurt yourself!* 跳呀,你這膽小鬼,又不會傷到你自己的! | *I'm such a coward about injections.* 我特別害怕打針。–**cowardly** *adj*

cow·ard·ice /ˈkaʊədɪs; ˈkaʊədəs/ *n* [U] lack of courage 膽小;懦弱

cow·boy /ˈkaʊ,bɔɪ; ˈkaʊbɔɪ/ *n* **1** a man employed to look after cattle, especially in North America〔尤指北美的〕牛仔;牧童 **2** a person who is careless or dishonest in their work or business 工作馬虎的人;不誠實的商人: *cowboy builders* 不誠實的建築商

cow·er /ˈkaʊə; ˈkaʊər/ *v* [I] to bend low and move back because you feel afraid〔由於畏懼而〕蜷縮,退縮: *The children were cowering in a corner.* 孩子們嚇得縮在角落裡。

cow·pat /ˈkaʊ,pæt; ˈkaʊpæt/ *n* a lump of cow DUNG (一堆)牛糞

cow·slip /ˈkaʊ,slɪp; ˈkaʊslɪp/ *n* a wild plant with small yellow flowers 黃花九輪草

cox /kɒks; kɒks/ *n* a person who controls the direction and speed of a rowing boat, especially in races〔賽艇〕舵手 –**cox** *v* [T]: *She'll cox the Oxford boat again next season.* 下一賽季她又將擔任牛津隊的賽艇舵手。

coy /kɔɪ; kɔɪ/ *adj* pretending to be quiet and modest in order to attract attention〔為引起注意而〕裝作覥腆的: *She gave a coy little smile and looked away.* 她忸怩地微微一笑,然後把視線移開了。 | *We all know how well you did. There's no need to be coy about it.* 我們都知道你幹得很好,這一點你不用不好意思。–**coyly** *adv*

coy·ote /ˈkaɪˈotɪ; ˈkɔɪˈaʊt/ *n* a wild dog that looks like a large fox; coyotes live in North America 郊狼〔北美的一種貌似狐狸的野狗〕

coy·pu /ˈkɔɪpu; ˈkɔɪpuː/ *n* **coypus** a large water rat from South America; it is kept for its valuable fur〔產於南美的〕河狸鼠〔其皮毛很貴重〕

co·zy /ˈkozɪ; ˈkəʊzi/ *adj,n* see 見 COSY

crab /kræb; kræb/ *n* **1** [C] a sea animal with a broad flat shell and five pairs of legs 蟹 **2** [U] the flesh of a crab cooked as food 蟹肉 –see picture on page 504 見 504 頁彩圖

crab·by /ˈkræbɪ; ˈkræbi/ *adj infml* bad-tempered〔非正式〕脾氣壞的

crack¹ /kræk; kræk/ *v* **1** [I] to break so that lines appear on the surface 破裂;裂開: *Don't pour hot water into the glass or it will crack.* 別把熱水倒進玻璃杯裡,不然它會裂開的。–see 見 BREAK (USAGE 用法) **2** [T] to break something so that lines appear on its surface〔某物〕裂開〔破裂〕: *I dropped a plate and cracked it.* 我不小心把盤子掉到地上摔裂了。 **3** [I;T] to make a sudden explosive sound or to cause something to make such a sound (使)〔某物〕發出爆裂聲: *He cracked his whip and rode off.* 他用鞭子啪地抽了一下,騎着馬走了。 | *Thunder cracked and rumbled.* 一聲霹靂之後雷聲隆隆。 **4** [T] to hit a part of your body against something and hurt it 使〔身體某一部分〕撞上〔某物而導致受傷〕: *The boy fell and cracked his head against the wall.* 男孩跌倒了,頭撞到了牆上。 **5** [I] to lose control under pressure〔在壓力下〕失去控制: *His voice cracked with emotion.* 他的聲音由於激動而失常。 | *He'd been overworking for weeks when he cracked.* 他好幾週工作過度,身體終於垮掉了。 **6** **crack a joke** *infml* to tell people a joke〔非正式〕講笑話 **7** [T] to succeed in dealing with a problem 解決〔問題〕: *We must crack this problem.* 我們必須解決這個問題。 **8** **crack open a bottle** *infml* to open a bottle of wine, beer, etc.〔非正式〕打開〔酒、啤酒等的〕瓶子

crack down *phr v adv* [I] to become more severe 變得更加嚴厲: *The military government decided to crack down on all political activity.* 軍政府決定對一切政治活動採取嚴厲措施。

crack up *phr v adv* **1** [I] to lose control and be unable to deal with things under pressure〔由於壓力而〕失去控制並垮掉 **2 not all it's cracked up to be** *infml* not as good as people say it is〔非正式〕沒有人說的那樣好

crack² n 1 a thin line or narrow split on the surface of something or between two things 裂縫; 縫隙: *a crack in the window* 窗戶上的裂縫 | *a crack in the floorboards* 地板裂縫 **2** an explosive sound 爆裂聲: *a crack of thunder* 一聲霹靂 | *the crack of the guns* 槍砲聲 **3** a sudden sharp blow 重擊: *a crack on the head* 頭部的重擊 **4 have a crack at something** *infml* to attempt to do something〔非正式〕試著做某事 **5** a joke or funny remark 笑話; 可笑的話語: *He's always making cracks about my big feet.* 他總是拿我的一雙大腳開玩笑。 **6 the crack of dawn** the first light of day 黎明; 晨曦

crack³ adj [only before a noun 只用於名詞前] of high quality or very good ability 高質量的; 技能高超的: *a crack commando unit* 一支精銳的突擊隊 **2 a crack shot** someone who is very good at shooting 神槍手

crack·down /ˈkrækˌdaʊn; ˈkrækdaʊn/ *n* action taken to stop or discourage bad behaviour 取締; 禁止: *a crackdown on drunken driving* 對酒後開車的取締

crack·er /ˈkrækə; ˈkrækəʳ/ *n* **1** a thin unsweetened BISCUIT〔無甜味的〕薄餅乾: *cheese and crackers* 奶酪加餅乾 **2** a small cardboard tube covered with coloured paper and containing a small present; crackers are often pulled open at CHRISTMAS〔常在聖誕節時打開的〕彩包爆竹

crack·le /ˈkrækl; ˈkrækəl/ *v* **crackled, crackling** [I] to make small sharp sounds 發嗶啪聲: *The fire crackled.* 火嗶啪作響。 **–crackle** *n* : *the crackle of burning logs* 木頭燃燒時所發出的嗶啪聲 | *a loud crackle* 爆裂聲

crack·ling /ˈkræklɪŋ; ˈkræklɪŋ/ *n* [U] **1** the hard brown skin of cooked PORK〔烤豬肉的〕脆皮 **2** the sound of something that crackles 嗶啪聲: *the crackling of the fire* 火的嗶啪聲

crack·pot /ˈkrækˌpɒt; ˈkrækpɒt/ *n infml* a person with very strange, foolish, or mad ideas〔非正式〕怪人 **–crackpot** *adj* : *a crackpot scientist* 想法怪異的科學家

cra·dle¹ /ˈkredl; ˈkreɪdl/ *n* **1** a small bed for a baby, especially one that can be moved gently from side to side 搖籃 **2** the place where something began 發源地: *Greece was the cradle of Western civilization.* 希臘是西方文明的發源地。 **3** a framework used for supporting something being built or repaired, or for doing certain jobs 吊架; 支架; 吊籃: *Window cleaners are pulled up and down tall buildings on cradles.* 窗戶清潔工乘坐能升降的吊籃清洗高層建築的窗子。

cra·dle² *v* **cradled, cradling** [T] to hold and support someone gently 輕輕地抱着: *John cradled the baby in his arms.* 約翰把孩子輕輕抱在懷裡。

craft /kræft; krɑːft/ *n* **1** a job or trade needing skill, especially with your hands 技藝; 工藝〔尤指手藝〕: *the jeweller's craft* 珠寶匠的手藝 **2** [plural is 複數為 **craft**] a boat, especially a small one 船舶〔尤指小船〕: *The harbour was full of sailing craft.* 港口裡滿是帆船。

crafts·man /ˈkræftsmən; ˈkrɑːftsmən/ *n* **craftsmen** /-mən; -mən/ a highly skilled worker, especially one who works with their hands 工匠〔尤指手藝人〕: *furniture made by the finest craftsmen* 由一流工匠製成的家具 **–craftsmanship** *n* [U]

craft·y /ˈkræftɪ; ˈkrɑːftɪ/ *adj* cleverly deceitful 狡詐的: *The politician was too crafty.* 那位政客過於狡詐。 **–craftily** *adv* **–craftiness** *n* [U]

crag /kræg; kræg/ *n* a high steep rough rock or mass of rocks 懸崖; 峭壁

crag·gy /ˈkrægɪ; ˈkrægɪ/ *adj* **1** steep and rocky 陡峭的; 多岩石的 **2** rough, with deep lines 粗糙而有皺紋的: *his craggy features* 他那粗獷的容貌

cram /kræm; kræm/ *v* **-mm-** **1** [T] to force people or things into a small space 把〔人或物〕塞入〔很小的空間內〕: *We were all crammed in with hardly room to breathe.* 我們全擠在裡面, 幾乎連透氣的地方都沒有了。 **2 be crammed with, be crammed full of** to be very full of things 塞滿〔某物〕: *a bag crammed with clothes* 一個塞滿衣服的袋子 **3** [I] to prepare for an examination by working very hard for a short time〔為應考而在短期內〕拚命用功: *He sat up all night cramming.* 他為準備考試而開夜車。

cramp¹ /kræmp; kræmp/ *n* [C;U] severe pain from the sudden tightening of a muscle, which makes it difficult to move 抽筋; 痙攣: *stomach cramps* 胃痙攣 | *I've got cramp in my leg.* 我的腿抽筋了。

cramp² *v* **1** [T] to prevent the natural growth or development of something 阻礙〔某物發展〕 **2 cramp someone's style** *infml* to prevent someone from behaving in the way in which they would like to behave〔非正式〕使某人不能發揮才能

cramped /kræmpt; kræmpt/ *adj* **1** limited in space 狹小的: *a cramped little flat* 狹窄的小公寓 **2 cramped handwriting** writing with the letters too closely together 擠在一起的文字

cran·ber·ry /ˈkrænˌbɛrɪ; ˈkrænbərɪ/ *n* **cranberries** a small red sour-tasting berry 越橘

crane¹ /kren; kreɪn/ *n* a machine for lifting heavy objects by means of a very strong rope or wire fastened to a movable arm 起重機; 吊車

crane² *v* **craned, craning** [I;T] to stretch out your neck in order to see something〔為看

清某物而)伸長〔脖子〕: *Jane craned her neck to look for her friend in the crowd.* 簡伸長脖子去人羣中找她的朋友。

cra·ni·um /'kreɪnɪəm; 'kreɪnɪəm/ *n* **craniums** *or* **crania** /-nɪə; -nɪə/ *tech* the part of your SKULL that covers your brain 〔術語〕頭蓋 – **cranial** *adj*

crank /kræŋk; kræŋk/ *n* **1** an apparatus, such as a handle fixed at right angles to a rod, which changes movement in a straight line into circular movement 曲柄; 曲軸 **2** *infml* a person with very peculiar ideas 〔非正式〕有古怪念頭的人: *a religious crank* 宗教信仰古怪的人

craps /kræps; kræps/ *n* [U] **1** an American game played with two DICE for money 〔美國的〕雙骰子賭博遊戲 **2 shoot craps** to play this game 玩擲雙骰子賭博遊戲

crash¹ /kræʃ; kræʃ/ *v* **1** [I;T] to have an accident in a vehicle, or to cause a vehicle to have an accident (使)撞車: *The car crashed into a tree.* 汽車撞在一棵樹上。| *He crashed my car.* 他撞壞了我的車。 **2** [I; + adv/prep] to fall or move noisily 嘩啦一聲掉下; 嘩啦啦地移動: *The plates crashed to the floor.* 盤子嘩啦啦地落到了地上。 **3** [I] to make a sudden loud noise 發出巨響: *The lightning flashed and thunder crashed.* 電光一閃, 雷聲隆隆。 **4** [I] (of a business or an organization concerned with money) to fail suddenly 〔企業等〕倒閉: *The New York stock exchange crashed in 1929.* 紐約股票交易所於 1929 年倒閉。 **5** (of a computer system) to stop working suddenly 〔計算機系統〕突然停止運行

crash² *n* **1** a sudden loud noise 突然的巨響: *a crash of thunder* 雷聲隆隆 | *the crash of breaking glass* 玻璃撞碎聲 **2** a violent accident involving vehicles 撞車事故; 〔飛機〕失事: *All the passengers were killed in the plane crash.* 所有的乘客都在這場空難中喪生。 **3** a sudden severe business failure 〔企業〕倒閉: *the crash of the Metropolitan Bank* 都市銀行的倒閉

crash³ *adj* **1 crash course** a course of study in which you try to learn things very quickly 速成課程 **2 crash diet** a diet intended to help you lose weight very quickly 速效減肥飲食(療法)

crash bar·ri·er /'· ··/ *n* a strong fence built to prevent accidents 〔防止交通事故的〕防撞欄

crash hel·met /'· ··/ *n* a strong HELMET worn by racing car drivers and motorcycle riders to protect their heads in an accident 〔摩托車手等所戴的〕防撞頭盔

crash-land /'· ·/ *v* [I] to land a plane in dangerous conditions so that as little damage as possible is done 〔飛機〕緊急着陸 – **crash landing** /ˌ· '··/ *n* [C;U]

crass /kræs; kræs/ *adj* **1** stupid, unfeeling, or coarse 愚笨的; 愚鈍的; 粗魯的: *cross be-*

haviour 粗魯的行為 | *a crass remark* 粗話 **2** very great (used of stupidity or foolishness) 極度的〔指愚蠢〕: *crass stupidity* 極度的愚蠢 | *crass ignorance* 極度的無知 –**crassly** *adv* –**crassness** *n* [U]

crate /kret; kreɪt/ *n* a large wooden box for carrying or storing things 大木箱: *a milk crate* 牛奶箱 | *a crate of apples* 一大箱蘋果 –see picture on page 244 見 244 頁彩圖

cra·ter /'kretə; 'kreɪtə/ *n* **1** the round bowl-shaped mouth of a VOLCANO 火山口 **2** a rough round hole in the ground 坑: *a bomb crater* 彈坑 | *craters on the moon's surface* 月球表面的環形山

cra·vat /krə'væt; krə'væt/ *n* BrE a wide piece of material that men wear tied round their neck inside their shirt collar 〔英式〕〔男用〕領巾

crave /krev; kreɪv/ *v* **craved, craving** [I;T] to have a very strong desire for something 渴望〔某物〕: *Sometimes I crave for a piece of chocolate.* 有的時候我非常想吃巧克力。| *She craves admiration.* 她渴望得到別人的讚賞。

cra·ven /'krevən; 'kreɪvən/ *adj* completely lacking courage 懦弱的; 膽小

crav·ing /'krevɪŋ; 'kreɪvɪŋ/ *n* a very strong desire 強烈的慾望: *a craving for drugs* 吸毒的強烈慾望 –see 見 DESIRE² (USAGE 用法)

crawl¹ /krɔl; krɔːl/ *v* **1** [I] to move slowly on your hands and knees or with your body close to the ground or other surface 爬; 爬行: *The baby crawled across the room.* 嬰兒從房間這邊爬到那邊。| *There's an insect crawling up your back!* 有隻蟲子在順着你的背往上爬! –see picture on page 992 見 992 頁彩圖 **2** to move slowly and with difficulty 緩慢行進: *The traffic was crawling through the centre of town.* 車輛緩緩地駛過城中心。 **3 be crawling with** to be full of people or insects 滿是〔人或昆蟲〕: *The room was crawling with flies.* 房間裡滿是蒼蠅。| *The town was crawling with soldiers.* 城裡到處是士兵。 **4** *infml* to be very nice to someone in order to get something for yourself (a word used to express disapproval) 〔非正式〕巴結, 奉承〔含貶義〕: *She got her promotion by crawling to the boss.* 她由於巴結老闆才獲得提升。 **5 make your skin crawl** to cause a very unpleasant feeling often of terror 使…毛骨悚然: *Snakes make my skin crawl.* 蛇令我毛骨悚然。

crawl² *n* [sing] **1** a very slow movement or the action of crawling 爬行 **2** a rapid way of swimming on your stomach, moving first one arm and then the other over your head, and kicking your feet up and down 自由式游泳; 爬泳: *I can do the crawl now.* 我現在會做自由式游泳。

cray·fish /'kreɪˌfɪʃ; 'kreɪˌfɪʃ/ *n* **crayfish** *or* **crayfishes** a small animal with a shell, which lives in rivers and streams and can be eaten 淡水螯蝦

cray·on /'kreən; 'kreɪən/ n a stick of coloured WAX, or a pencil containing coloured wax, used for writing or drawing on paper 彩色蠟筆或粉筆 –**crayon** v [I;T]

craze /krez; kreɪz/ n a very popular fashion for a very short time 時尚; 時髦的東西: *This diet is the latest craze in America.* 這種飲食在美國是最新時尚。

crazed /krezd; kreɪzd/ adj very angry or mad 非常生氣的; 發瘋的

★**cra·zy** /'krezi; 'kreɪzi/ adj **1** mad or foolish 發瘋的; 愚蠢的: *He's crazy to go out in this weather!* 這種天氣還要出去, 他真是瘋了! | *a crazy idea* 瘋狂的想法 | *a crazy old man* 一個瘋老頭兒 **2 be crazy about** infml to be very keen on something or someone 〖非正式〗對〔某物或某人〕熱衷的; 狂熱的: *She's crazy about dancing.* 她對跳舞很熱衷。| *He's crazy about her.* 他對她很着迷。**3 drive someone crazy** infml to make someone angry 〖非正式〗令某人生氣: *This noise is driving me crazy.* 這吵鬧聲吵得我快瘋了。**4 like crazy** infml very actively 〖非正式〗賣力地: *You'll have to work like crazy to get this finished.* 你必須拼命工作才能把這事幹完。– **crazily** adv –**craziness** n [U]

creak /krik; kri:k/ v [I] to make a sound like that of a badly-oiled door opening 〔門〕嘎吱作響: *The stairs creaked under his weight.* 樓梯由於他的體重而吱吱作響。–**creak** n

creak·y /'kriki; 'kri:ki/ adj making a creaking sound 嘎吱作響的: *a creaky door* 一扇嘎吱作響的門 –**creakily** adv –**creakiness** n [U]

cream¹ /krim; kri:m/ n **1** [U] the thick fatty yellowish liquid taken from milk, which is eaten or drunk with other foods 奶油: *Have some cream in your coffee.* 給你的咖啡加些奶油吧。| *a cream cake* 奶油蛋糕 | *whipped cream* 攪打的奶油 | *sour cream* 酸奶油 **2** [C;U] something similar to cream or containing cream 奶油狀物; 含奶油物: *a chocolate cream* 巧克力奶油 | *cream of chicken soup* 奶油雞湯 **3** [C;U] a thick substance that you put on your skin 乳霜; 乳膏: *face cream* 面霜 | *Put some of this cream on that burn.* 在燒傷處擦點藥膏。**4 the cream of** the best part of a group 精髓; 精華: *the cream of society* 社會的精英 **5** [U] a yellowish white colour 奶黃色: *You look nice in cream.* 你穿奶黃色衣服很好看。

cream² adj a yellowish-white colour 奶黃色的: *She wore a cream dress.* 她穿一件奶黃色的裙子。–see picture on page 243 見 243 頁彩圖

cream³ v [T] to mix or beat butter and sugar together until the mixture is thick and soft 攪成奶油狀

cream sbdy/sthg ↔ **off** phr v [T] to remove the best 提取〔精華〕: *We cream off the*

cleverest pupils and send them to a special school. 我們把最聰明的學生挑出來送到特別學校去。

cream·y /'krimi; 'kri:mi/ adj **creamier, creamiest 1** containing cream or like cream in taste or feel 含奶油的; 奶油狀的: *creamy coffee* 含奶油的咖啡 | *creamy soap* 柔滑的肥皂 **2** yellowish-white 奶黃色的 –**creaminess** n [U]

crease¹ /kris; kri:s/ n **1** a line made intentionally or accidentally on cloth or paper by folding, ironing, or crushing it 〔布或紙上的〕皺紋, 摺痕: *You've got a crease in your dress where you've been sitting.* 你的衣服坐過的地方起皺了。| *Be careful when you iron your trousers to get the creases straight.* 熨褲子時要注意把摺痕熨直。**2** a line marked on a cricket ground to show where a player should stand to hit the ball 〔板球賽場上的〕擊球區域線

crease² v **creased, creasing** [I;T] to put or get creases in something (使)〔某物〕變皺; (使)〔某物〕有摺痕: *She wanted to wear her black dress but it was too creased.* 她本想穿她的黑裙子, 但是太皺了。| *cloth that creases easily* 容易起皺的布料

crease up phr v [I] infml to begin to laugh a lot 〖非正式〗放聲大笑

★**cre·ate** /kri'et; kri'eɪt/ v **created, creating** [T] **1** to cause something to exist 創立; 創建; 創造: *God created the world.* 上帝創造了世界。| *The new road will create a lot of traffic.* 這條新建的路將引來許多車輛。| *Her bad behaviour is creating a lot of problems.* 她的惡劣行為正在引起許多麻煩。**2** to produce or invent something new 創作; 發明: *creating paintings and sculptures* 作畫和雕塑 | *The designers and technicians together created a new computer system.* 設計人員和技術人員一起設計了新的計算機系統。**3** to appoint someone to a special rank or position 封爵; 授予〔頭銜或職位〕: *The Queen's son was created Prince of Wales.* 女王的兒子被封為威爾士親王。

★**cre·a·tion** /kri'eʃən; kri'eɪʃən/ n **1** [U] the act of creating something 創造; 建立: *the creation of jobs by the government* 政府創造的就業機會 **2** [C] something produced by invention or imagination 創造物; 作品: *an artist's creation* 藝術家的作品 **3** [U] the universe, world, and all living things 宇宙; 世界; 萬物: *Man is the lord of creation.* 人類是萬物的主宰。| *God's creation* 上帝創造的世界

★**cre·a·tive** /kri'etɪv; kri'eɪtɪv/ adj **1** producing new and original ideas and things 有創造力的; 創造性的: *creative thinking* 創造性的思維 | *creative writing* 創造性的寫作 | *They're a creative couple; she paints and he writes novels.* 他們是一對富有創造力的夫婦; 她作畫, 他寫小說。**2** producing results based on newness of thought or imagination 獨創的; 原創的:

useful and creative work 實用而又富有創造性的作品 **–creatively** *adv* **–creativity** /ˌkrie-ˈtɪvəti, ˌkriːeɪˈtɪvⱥti/ (also 又作 **creativeness** /kriˈeɪtɪvnɪs; kriˈeɪtɪvnⱥs/) *n* [U]: *Someone with creativity is needed for this job.* 這個工作需要有創造力的人來做。

cre·a·tor /krɪˈeɪtə; krɪˈeɪtər/ *n* **1** a person who creates 創造者; 創立者: *Unusually, small businesses are the creators of much of this country's wealth.* 與別不同的是, 小型企業是這個國家大部分財富的創造者。 **2 the Creator** God 上帝: *She gave thanks to her Creator.* 她向上帝感恩。

***crea·ture** /ˈkriːtʃə; ˈkriːtʃər/ *n* **1** an animal or being of some kind 動物; 生物: *all God's creatures* 上帝創造的生靈 | *creatures from outer space* 外星生物 | *The crocodile is a strange-looking creature.* 鱷魚是一種模樣古怪的動物。 **2** a person of a particular kind (a word often used to express disapproval, pity, or some other feeling) 某一類人〔常含貶義、憐憫等情感〕: *You stupid creature! You've spoilt all my plans.* 你這笨傢伙! 你把我所有的計劃都破壞了。 | *The poor creature had no family at all.* 這個可憐的人連一個親人都沒有。 **3 a creature of habit** a person who always does things in the same way or at a regular time 墨守成規的人

crèche /kreʃ; kreʃ/ *n BrE* a place where babies and young children are cared for while their parents work 〔英式〕托兒所

cre·dence /ˈkriːdn̩s; ˈkriːdəns/ *n fml*〔正式〕**give credence to something** to show that you believe that something is true 相信〔某事物〕: *The newspapers are giving no credence to his latest statements.* 各家報紙均不相信他最近的聲明。

cre·den·tials /krɪˈdenʃəlz; krɪˈdenʃəlz/ *n* [pl] **1** a letter or other written proof of a person's official position or good character 資格證書 **2** anything that proves a person's abilities or their suitability for something〔證明某人有能力或適合做某事的〕證件; 證明書: *His credentials are excellent. He has all the qualifications and experience we need.* 他的證明材料極佳。他具備我們需要的所有資歷。

cred·i·bil·i·ty /ˌkredəˈbɪləti; ˌkredⱥˈbɪlⱥti/ *n* [U] the quality that something has which makes people trust it or believe it 可信性; 可靠性: *The Chernobyl accident has undermined the credibility of the nuclear power industry.* 切爾諾貝利事故損壞了核能工業的可信性。

cred·i·ble /ˈkredəbl̩; ˈkredⱥbəl/ *adj* deserving to be believed, trusted, or taken seriously 可信的; 可靠的: *This news hardly seems credible.* 這則消息似乎不太可靠。 | *a credible defence policy* 可靠的防禦政策 **–credibly** *adv*

***cred·it¹** /ˈkredɪt; ˈkredⱥt/ *n* **1** [U] the system of buying things and paying for them later 賒購(制度): *You can buy the furniture on credit.* 你可以賒購傢具。 **2** [U] money you are allowed to owe, or the period of time you are allowed to pay, for things you have bought 允許賒賬的數額; 賒賬期: *up to £50 credit* 最多可允許賒賬五十英鎊 | *six months' credit* 六個月的賒賬期 **3** [C] an amount of money in or put into someone's account, for example at a bank〔銀行的〕存款數額: *Last month's credits exceeded debits by £5.* 上月存款比借款多五英鎊。 **4** [U] the quality of being likely to repay debts 信用; 信譽: *His credit is good. You can trust him.* 他的信譽很好。你可以相信他。 **5** [U] public approval or praise for doing something good 名譽; 讚揚: *I got no credit* **for** *my invention.* 我沒有因為我的發明而得到榮譽。 | *Her boss claimed all the credit for her hard work.* 她的老闆把她用辛勤勞動換來的榮譽說成是自己的功勞。 **6** [sing;U] someone who brings honour or respect 增光的人: *You're a real credit* **to** *your team.* 你確實為你們隊增了光。 | *Those children are a credit to their parents.* 那些孩子為他們的父母增了光。 **7** [U] belief or trust 相信; 信任: *This theory is gaining credit among scientists.* 這一理論正在為越來越多的科學家所接受。 **8** [C] a part of a course completed by a student, especially at a university in the US〔尤指美國大學的〕學分 **9 do someone credit** to bring someone honour or respect 為某人贏得榮譽〔尊敬〕: *Our army does us credit.* 我們的軍隊為我們贏得了榮譽。 **10 in credit** containing money (used of a bank account) 有存款的〔指賬戶上〕**11 to someone's credit: a** in someone's favour 為某人增光: *It is to the workers' credit that they opposed the establishment of a military government.* 工人由於反對建立軍政府而贏得了榮譽。 **b** successfully finished 勝利完成: *She's not yet 30, and already she has five books to her credit!* 她還不到三十歲, 卻已經寫了五本書!

credit² *v* [T] **1** to believe something 相信〔某事物〕: *Do you really credit the government's statement?* 你真的相信政府的聲明嗎? **2** to put an amount of money in an account 把〔錢〕存入〔賬戶〕: *Please credit £10* **to** *my account.* 請把十英鎊存入我的賬戶。 | *Credit my account* **with** *£10.* 在我的賬上存入十英鎊。

credit sbdy with sth *phr v* [T] to believe that somebody has a particular good quality 相信〔某人〕有〔某一良好品質〕: *Please credit me with some sense!* 請相信我是有頭腦的!

cred·it·a·ble /ˈkredɪtəbl̩; ˈkredⱥtəbəl/ *adj* deserving praise, honour, or approval 值得讚揚的; 光榮的: *a creditable effort to establish peace* 為締造和平所做的值得稱道的努力 **–creditably** *adv*

credit card /ˈ· · ·/ *n* a card which allows you to obtain goods and services without using coins or notes; the cost is added to your account and you pay it later 信用卡

cred·i·tor /ˈkrɛdɪtə; ˈkrɛdʒˌtər/ *n* a person or firm that someone owes money to 債權人; 債主

cred·u·lous /ˈkrɛdʒələs; ˈkredjʊ̯ləs/ *adj* too willing to believe things, especially without real proof 輕信的; 易信的 –**credulously** *adv* –**credulity** /krəˈdulətɪ; krɪˈdjuːlˌti/ *n* [U]

creed /krid; kriːd/ *n* a system of beliefs or principles, especially religious ones 〔尤指宗教的〕教義; 信條

creek /krik; kriːk/ *n* AmE a small narrow stream or river 〔美式〕小溪; 小河

creep /krip; kriːp/ *v* **crept** /krɛpt; krept/, **crept** [I] **1** to move carefully and quietly, so that no one will notice you 小心翼翼地悄悄的移動〔以免引起別人的注意〕: *The cat crept silently towards the mouse.* 貓悄悄地向老鼠爬過去。| *We crept upstairs because we didn't want to wake the baby.* 我們躡手躡腳地上樓梯，因為我們不想吵醒嬰兒。**2** to move with your body close to the ground 爬行; 匍匐: *The dog crept under the bed.* 狗在牀下爬來爬去。**3** to try to win someone's favour by being too nice to them (a word used to express disapproval) 拍馬; 獻媚〔含貶義〕**4** to move very slowly 緩緩地移動: *The tide crept up the beach.* 海潮緩緩地淹上了海岸。| *cars creeping along the icy roads* 在結冰的馬路上緩緩前行的汽車

  creep in *phr v* [I] to begin to appear 開始出現: *Mistakes are creeping in which could have been avoided.* 本可以避免的錯誤都開始出現。| *More and more foreign words are creeping into the language.* 越來越多的外來詞出現在這種語言中。

  creep up on sbdy/sthg *phr v* [T] to gradually get nearer to someone or something, without being noticed 悄悄靠近某人〔某物〕: *They crept up on the sentry and overpowered him.* 他們偷偷靠近哨兵，然後一舉將其制服。| *Old age is creeping up on me.* 我在不知不覺中變老了。

creep·er /ˈkripə; ˈkriːpər/ *n* a plant which climbs up trees and walls or grows along the ground 匍匐〔攀緣〕植物

creeps /krips; kriːps/ *n infml* 〔非正式〕**give someone the creeps** to make someone feel fear or strong dislike 令某人感到害怕〔厭惡〕: *The old castle gives me the creeps.* 這座古老的城堡令我毛骨悚然。

creep·y /ˈkripi; ˈkriːpi/ *adj* **creepier, creepiest** *infml* creating an unpleasant feeling of fear 〔非正式〕令人感到害怕的: *a creepy old house* 一座陰森森的舊房子 –**creepily** *adv* –**creepiness** *n* [U]

cre·mate /ˈkrimet; krɪˈmeɪt/ *v* **cremated, cremating** [T] to burn a dead person at a funeral ceremony 火化〔屍體〕; 火葬 –**cremation** /krɪˈmeʃən; krɪˈmeɪʃən/ *n* [C;U]

crem·a·to·ri·um /ˌkriməˈtorɪəm; ˌkreməˈtɔːriəm/ *n* **crematoriums** or **crematoria** /-rɪə; -riə/ (also 又作 **crematory** /ˈkriməˌtorɪ; ˈkremətəri/) a building in which dead people are cremated 火葬場

cre·ole /ˈkriol; ˈkriːəʊl/ *n* (also 又作 **Creole**) **1** [C;U] a language which is formed by the combination of a European language with one or more others and is the native language of its speakers; creole languages are common in the Caribbean 克里奧爾語〔由一種歐洲語言和一種或幾種其他語言混合而成的某一民族的母語; 這種語言在加勒比海地區很普遍〕**2** [C] a person of mixed European and African race who comes from the West Indies 克里奧爾人〔住在西印度羣島的歐洲人和非洲人的混血兒〕–**creole** *adj*

cre·o·sote /ˈkriəˌsot; ˈkriːəsəʊt/ *n* [U] thick brown oily liquid used for preserving wood 雜酚油〔木材防腐劑〕

crepe /krep; kreɪp/ *n* (also 又作 **crêpe**) **1** [U] a light cloth with a slightly rough surface made from cotton, silk, or wool 縐綢; 縐布; 縐呢 **2** [U] (also 又作 **crepe rubber** /ˌ· ˈ··/) tightly pressed rubber used especially for the bottoms of shoes 〔用以製鞋底的〕縐膠 **3** [C] a very thin PANCAKE 薄煎餅

crept /krɛpt; krept/ the past tense and past participle of CREEP ☆ CREEP 的過去式和過去分詞

cre·scen·do /krəˈʃɛndo; krɪˈʃendəʊ/ *n* **crescendos** or **crescendoes** **1** a gradual increase in the loudness of a piece of music 〔音樂的〕漸強 **2** a point of greatest excitement or urgency 〔興奮或緊急程度的〕頂點; 高潮: *The demands for an election rose to a crescendo.* 要求舉行大選的呼聲達到了高潮。

cres·cent /ˈkrɛsn̩t; ˈkresənt/ *n* **1** a curved shape like the moon during its first and last quarters, when it forms less than half a circle 新月; 上〔下〕弦月: *a crescent-shaped sword* 弦月狀的劍 | *a crescent moon* 新月〔蛾眉月〕**2** a curved row of houses or a curved street 半圓形的一排房屋; 一條弧形街道: *48 Woodside Crescent* 伍塞街48號 **3** (also 又作 **Crescent**) the sign of the Muslim religion 伊斯蘭教的象徵: *a war between Cross and Crescent* 一場基督教與伊斯蘭教之間的戰爭

cress /krɛs; kres/ *n* [U] a very small plant whose stems and leaves are eaten raw 水芹

crest /krɛst; krest/ *n* **1** a growth of feathers on top of a bird's head 鳥冠; 羽冠 **2** the top of a hill or wave 山頂; 浪尖 **3** a special picture used as a sign of a family or organization 〔家族或組織所用的〕飾章

crest·fal·len /ˈkrɛstˌfɔlən; ˈkrestˌfɔːlən/ *adj* disappointed or sad 失望的; 悲哀的

cret·in /ˈkritn; ˈkretn̩/ *n* **1** *infml* a very stupid person 〔非正式〕傻瓜; 白痴: *You silly cretin!* 你這大傻瓜! **2** a person whose development of mind and body has stopped in early childhood 呆小病患者

cre·vasse /krə'væs; krə̆'væs/ *n* a deep open crack, especially in thick ice〔尤指冰層上的〕裂隙

crev·ice /'krɛvɪs; 'krɛvɪ̆s/ *n* a narrow crack or opening, especially in rock〔尤指岩石的〕縫隙

*****crew** /kru; kruː/ *n* [+ sing/pl verb] **1** all the people working on a ship, plane, or space vehicle〔輪船、飛機或太空船的〕全體工作人員: *The crew is waiting for the captain's instructions.* 全體船員在等船長的指令。| *The crew have gone ashore.* 船員們上岸去了。**2** a group of people working together for a particular purpose〔為某一目的〕一起工作的一羣人: *a television crew* 電視台工作人員 | *the repair crew* 修理人員

crib¹ /krɪb; krɪb/ *n AmE*〖美式〗**1** a bed with movable sides for a baby or small child〔有活動欄杆的〕小兒牀 **2** an open box or wooden framework holding food for animals 飼料槽; 秣槽

crib² *v* **-bb-** [I;T] *infml* to copy something dishonestly from someone else〖非正式〗抄襲; 剽竊: *I didn't know the answers so I cribbed them off John.* 我不知道答案, 所以就抄了約翰的。

crick /krɪk; krɪk/ *n* a painful stiffening of the muscles, especially in your back or neck, making movement difficult〔尤指背部或頸部的〕痛性痙攣 **—crick** *v* [T]: *I cricked my neck playing tennis.* 我打網球時引起頸部痛性痙攣。

*****crick·et** /'krɪkɪt; 'krɪkɪ̆t/ *n* **1** an outdoor game popular in Britain, played with a ball, BAT, and wickets (WICKET) by two teams of 11 players each 板球〔英國流行的一種戶外體育運動〕—see picture on page 957 見 957 頁彩圖 **2** a small brown insect which jumps; the male makes loud noises by rubbing its wings together 蟋蟀

cried /kraɪd; kraɪd/ *v* the past tense and past participle of CRY¹ ☆ CRY¹ 的過去式和過去分詞

cries /kraɪz; kraɪz/ *v* the 3rd person singular present tense of CRY¹ ☆ CRY¹ 的第三人稱單數形式

*****crime** /kraɪm; kraɪm/ *n* **1** [C] an action which is punishable by law 罪; 罪行: *Drug-smuggling is a serious crime.* 毒品走私是嚴重的罪行。| *She had committed a terrible crime.* 她犯了可怕的罪行。**2** [U] illegal activity in general 不法行為; 犯罪活動: *It is the job of the police to prevent crime.* 警察的工作是防止犯罪。| *the crime rate* 犯罪率 | *crime statistics* 犯罪統計數字 **3** [C] a pity or shame 可惜的事; 可恥的事: *It's a crime to waste all this food.* 把所有這些食物都浪費掉, 實在是罪過。

*****crim·i·nal¹** /'krɪmənəl; 'krɪmļnəl/ *adj* **1** [only before a noun 只用於名詞前] related to

crime or its punishment 犯罪的; 刑事的: *a specialist in criminal law* 刑法專家 | *a criminal offence* 刑事犯罪 **2** wrong, but not illegal 錯誤的; 罪過的: *a criminal waste of money* 揮霍金錢的罪過 **—criminally** *adv*

criminal² *n* a person who is guilty of crime 罪犯: *These men are criminals and must be punished!* 這些人是罪犯, 必須受到懲治!

crim·son /'krɪmzn; 'krɪmzən/ *n* [U] a deep purplish red colour 深紅色 **—crimson** *adj* — see picture on page 243 見 243 頁彩圖

cringe /krɪndʒ; krɪndʒ/ *v* **cringed, cringing** [I] **1** to bend and move back especially because of fear 退縮〔尤指由於害怕〕: *She cringed when he came in.* 他一進門, 她就退縮了。**2** to have an uncomfortable feeling of shame 憎惡: *I cringed with embarrassment when she was rude to my teacher.* 她對我老師的態度很粗魯, 我感到又厭惡又難堪。

crin·kle /'krɪŋkl; 'krɪŋkəl/ *v* **crinkled, crinkling** [I;T] to make many fine lines or folds in something 使〔某物〕起皺痕: *My clothes were all crinkled from being in the suitcase.* 我的衣服由於裝在手提箱裡而起皺了。| *His face crinkled, and then he laughed out loud.* 他臉上綻露出笑紋, 隨即放聲大笑。**—crinkle** *n* **—crinkly** *adj* : *chocolates in crinkly paper cases* 裝於皺紋紙盒中的巧克力

crip·ple¹ /'krɪpl; 'krɪpəl/ *n* a person who is unable to use their body properly, especially their legs, because of illness or accident (an old fashioned word which many people consider to be offensive) 身體〔尤指腿腳〕有殘疾的人〔許多人認為使用這個過時的詞沒有禮貌〕

cripple² *v* **crippled, crippling** [T] **1** to hurt or wound a person or an animal so that they cannot move properly 使〔人或動物〕受傷或殘廢 **2** to weaken or damage a system or organization 削弱, 破壞〔系統或組織〕: *The economy was crippled by the war.* 戰爭使經濟受到破壞。| *crippling debts* 極為沉重的債務

*****cri·sis** /'kraɪsɪs; 'kraɪsɪ̆s/ *n* **crises** /-siz; -siːz/ **1** a situation of great danger, difficulty, or uncertainty, often resulting from political disagreements〔常由於政治衝突而出現的〕危機: *a governmental crisis* 政府危機 | *the crisis in Southern Africa* 南非所存在的危機 **2** a situation where people lack what they need〔人們所需物品的〕缺乏: *a housing crisis* 住房緊缺 **3** a feeling of great suffering about a problem in your life〔由於生活中的難題而受到的〕巨大的折磨〔痛苦〕: *His doctor gave him some pills after his last emotional crisis.* 他上次情緒出現巨大波動後, 醫生給了他一些藥片。

crisp¹ /krɪsp; krɪsp/ *adj* **1** hard and dry (used of food) 乾而硬的〔指食物〕: 脆的: *crisp bacon* 發脆的醃燻豬肉 | *Keep the biscuits in a tin so they stay crisp.* 把餅乾放在罐子裡使其保持鬆脆。**2** firm, fresh, or stiff 堅實的; 新

鮮的; 僵硬的: *a crisp apple* 鮮脆的蘋果 | *crisp vegetables* 新鮮蔬菜 | *a crisp new bank note* 新發行的鈔票 | *crisp white sheets* 挺括的白紙 **3** quick and clear (used of speech or writing) 爽快的, 乾脆的〔指講話或寫作〕: *a crisp reply* 乾脆的回答 **4** cold, dry, and fresh (used of weather or air) 乾冷的, 清新的〔指天氣或空氣〕: *a crisp winter's day* 乾冷的冬日 | *the crisp autumn wind* 清爽的秋風 **–crisply** *adv* **–crispness** *n* [U]

crisp² *n* (also 又作 **potato crisp** *BrE*〖英式〗) a thin piece of potato cooked in very hot fat, dried, and usually sold in packets 油炸馬鈴薯[土豆]片

criss·cross¹ /ˈkrɪs,krɔs; ˈkrɪskrɒs/ *adj* having a number of crossing straight lines 縱橫交錯的; 有十字形圖案的: *a crisscross design* 十字形圖案設計

crisscross² *v* [I;T] to form a crisscross pattern on something〔在某物上〕形成交叉狀圖案: *Train tracks crisscross the country.* 鐵軌縱橫交錯遍及全國。

*☆**cri·te·ri·on¹** /kraɪˈtɪrɪən; kraɪˈtɪərɪən/ *n* **criteria** /-rɪə; -rɪə/ *or* **criterions** an established standard or principle on which a judgment is based〔評判的〕標準: *What criteria do you use when judging a student's work?* 你用甚麼標準評定學生功課?

*☆**crit·ic** /ˈkrɪtɪk; ˈkrɪtɪk/ *n* **1** a person who makes judgments about works of art, music, or literature, and writes about them, especially as a job〔尤指評述藝術、音樂或文學等作品的〕評論家 **2** a person who dislikes and expresses strong disapproval of someone or something 吹毛求疵的人, 愛挑剔者: *He's one of her strongest critics.* 他是她最強烈的批評者之一。

*☆**crit·i·cal** /ˈkrɪtɪkl; ˈkrɪtɪkəl/ *adj* **1** judging someone or something severely 嚴厲批評的: *Why are you so critical of the government?* 你為何這樣嚴厲批評政府? **2** very serious, important, or dangerous 非常嚴重的; 至關重要的; 危急的: *a critical stage of the illness* 病情的危險期 | *The elections will be critical for the country's future.* 選舉對該國的未來至關重要。 **3** [only before a noun 只用於名詞前] providing careful judgment of the good or bad qualities of something 評判的; 評定的: *critical writings on art* 對藝術的評述文章 | *a critical analysis of the education system* 對教育體制的批判性評估分析 **–critically** /-klɪ; -kli/ *adv*

*☆**crit·i·cis·m** /ˈkrɪtə,sɪzəm; ˈkrɪt⅟sɪzəm/ *n* [C; U] **1** the act of forming judgments about the good or bad qualities of anything, especially artistic work 評判; 評定 **2** unfavourable judgment or disapproval 批評; 指責: *Your criticisms seem to have offended him.* 你的批評似乎觸怒了他。 | *Everything the government does seems to attract criticism.* 政府所做的每一件事似乎都遭到了批評。

*☆**crit·i·cize** /ˈkrɪtə,saɪz; ˈkrɪt⅟saɪz/ *v* (also 又作

criticise *BrE*〖英式〗) [I;T] **1** to judge someone or something severely 批評; 批判: *The minister criticized my decision.* 部長對我的決定提出了批評。 | *The workers were strongly criticized for going on strike.* 工人們由於罷工而受到了強烈的批評。 **2** to make careful judgments about the good and bad qualities of someone or something 評判, 評定〔某人或某物〕

cri·tique /krɪˈtik; krɪˈtiːk/ *n* an article or book which examines and makes careful judgment of a situation or someone's work 評論性的文章或書籍: *a critique of Marx's writings* 對馬克思著作的評論文章

croak /krok; krəʊk/ *v* [I] **1** to make a deep low noise like a FROG makes 作蛙叫聲 **2** to speak with a rough voice as if you have a sore throat 用沙啞聲說話 **–croak** *n*: *the croak of a frog* 蛙叫聲

cro·chet /kroˈʃe; ˈkrəʊʃeɪ/ *n* [U] **1** a way of making clothes or tablecloths by using wool and a special hooked needle 鈎針編織法 **2** things made by using crochet 鈎針編織品 **3 crochet hook** the needle used in crochet 鈎針 **–crochet** *v* [I;T]: *I'll crochet a dress for a baby.* 我準備用鈎針給嬰兒織件衣服。

crock·e·ry /ˈkrɑkərɪ; ˈkrɒkəri/ *n* [U] cups, plates, and dishes that you eat or drink from 杯子; 盤子; 碟子: *The sink was full of dirty crockery.* 洗滌槽裡滿是用髒的杯盤等物。

croc·o·dile /ˈkrɑkə,daɪl; ˈkrɒkədaɪl/ *n* **1** [C] a large meat-eating animal with a long body, a hard skin, and sharp teeth, which lives in or near rivers in hot countries 鱷魚 **2** [U] the skin of this animal used as leather 鱷魚皮

cro·cus /ˈkrokəs; ˈkrəʊkəs/ *n* **crocuses** a small plant with purple, yellow, or white flowers which open in early spring 番紅花

crois·sant /krwɑˈsɑŋ; ˈkrwɑːsɒŋ/ *n* a piece of light buttery pastry, shaped in a curve and often eaten for breakfast〔常作早餐用的〕新月形麵包

cro·ny /ˈkronɪ; ˈkrəʊni/ *n* **cronies** a friend or companion (a word often used to express disapproval) 朋友, 夥伴〔含貶義〕: *The minister's always doing favours for his cronies.* 部長總是幫他朋友的忙。

crook¹ /kruk; krʊk/ *n* **1** *infml* a dishonest person, often a thief〖非正式〗騙子〔常指賊〕 **2 the crook of your arm** the inside part of your elbow where it bends 臂彎

crook² *v* [T] to bend your arm or finger 彎曲〔胳膊或手指〕: *crooking her finger to beckon us* 她彎一彎手指向我們示意

crook·ed /ˈkrukɪd; ˈkrʊk⅟d/ *adj* **1** twisted or bent 彎曲的: *a crooked street* 彎曲的街道 | *a crooked back* 駝背 **2** *infml* dishonest〖非正式〗不誠實的 **–crookedness** *n* [U]

croon /krun; kruːn/ *v* [I;T] to sing gently in a low soft voice 低聲哼唱

***crop¹** /krɑp; krɒp/ *n* **1** a plant or plant product such as grain, fruit, or vegetables grown by a farmer 農作物; 莊稼: *Wheat is a widely grown crop in Britain.* 在英國，小麥是廣泛種植的農作物。| *The crops were badly damaged in the storm.* 農作物受到了暴風雨的嚴重破壞。**2** the amount of such a product produced and collected in a single season or place〔一個季節或地區的〕收獲量; 收成: *India had the biggest cotton crop ever this year.* 印度今年的棉花收獲量是有史以來最高的。**3** a group of similar things or people that appear at the same time 同時出現的一羣人或一批事物: *a whole new crop of students* 新一批學生

crop² v **-pp- 1** [T] (of an animal) to eat the tops of grass or plants〔動物〕啃吃〔草或植物〕: *The sheep cropped the grass short.* 羊把草啃短了。**2** [T] to cut a person's hair short 剪短〔頭髮〕: *She looks like a prisoner with her cropped hair.* 她剪短了頭髮，看上去像個囚犯。**3** [I] (of a plant) to produce a crop〔植物的〕收獲; 收成: *Pears are cropping well this year.* 今年梨子豐收。

crop up *phr* v [I] *infml* to happen or appear unexpectedly〔非正式〕意外發生〔出現〕: *A problem has cropped up at work so I'll be late home tonight.* 工作中突然出現了問題，所以我今天會晚點回家。

cro·quet /krəˈke; ˈkrəʊkeɪ/ n [U] a game played on grass in which players knock balls through small metal arches with a hammer 槌球遊戲

⋆cross¹ /krɒs; krɒs/ n **1** a shape (x or +) with four equal arms that meet in the centre 交叉形; 十字形 **2** a mark often used as a sign of where something is or should be, for example on a map, or as a sign that something is incorrect, for example in a pupil's work〔表示錯誤或標記的〕叉號, 十字形符號 **3** (also 又作 **Cross**) a shape like an upright post with a bar across it near the top which is a sign of the Christian religion〔代表基督教的〕十字形: *the sign of the Cross* 十字聖號 **4** an object or picture in the shape of a cross which is used for decoration or as a sign of the Christian religion, or worn as an honour for bravery〔用作裝飾或代表基督教的〕十字形物體〔圖案〕;〔因勇敢而獲得的〕金十字架: *She wore a gold cross.* 她戴着一個金十字架。| *The graves were marked by wooden crosses.* 墳墓上豎着木製的十字架。| *He won the George Cross during the war.* 戰爭期間他獲得了喬治十字勳章。**5** a person or situation which causes sorrow or suffering and tests your patience or goodness 帶來苦難的人或環境: *Everyone has his own cross to bear in this life.* 每個人在其一生中都要忍受苦難。**6** a combination of two different things 混合物: *The drink tasted like a cross between coffee and hot chocolate.* 這種飲料的味道像咖啡和熱巧克力的混合味。| *a cross between a horse and a donkey* 馬和驢的混種

⋆cross² v **1** [T] to go, pass, or travel from one side of something to another 越過; 橫過: *The soldiers took three days to cross the desert.* 士兵們用了三天時間穿過沙漠。| *Be careful when you're crossing the road.* 過馬路時要小心。| *We crossed the border at dawn.* 拂曉時分我們越過了邊境。| *The railway line crosses the country from coast to coast.* 鐵路線橫跨全國，從這邊的海岸直抵那邊的海岸。**2** [I;T] to pass across each other 交叉; 相交: *I'll meet you where the paths cross.* 我在兩條路相交的地方與你會面。**3** [T] to make someone angry because you oppose their plans or wishes 與〔某人〕作對: *Anne hates being crossed so don't argue with her.* 安妮討厭別人跟她作對，所以不要和她爭論。**4 cross yourself** to move your hand in the shape of a cross and on the top part of your body as a sign of the Christian religion 在自己胸前劃十字: *She crossed herself as she left the church.* 她在離開教堂時，在自己胸前劃了個十字。**5** [T] to cause an animal or plant to breed with one of another kind 使〔動物或植物〕雜交: *Is it possible to cross a tiger with a lion?* 老虎和獅子進行雜交可能嗎? **6** [T] to put one leg or arm on top of the other 交叉〔腿或胳膊〕: *Jean crossed her legs.* 瓊盤腿而坐。**7 cross swords** to be opposed to someone, especially in an argument 反對〔某人〕〔尤指爭論當中〕: *The management crossed swords with the union over the pay formula.* 資方就工資支付形式與工會發生了爭執。

cross sbdy/sthg ↔ **off** *phr* v [T] to remove something from a list by drawing a line through it〔在清單或名單上〕刪掉: *If you don't want to come, cross your name off.* 你如果不想來，就把自己的名字刪掉。

cross sthg ↔ **out** *phr* v [T] to draw a line through written words, because they are wrong or not to be read〔由於錯誤等〕劃掉: *Cross it out and write it again correctly.* 把它劃掉，然後把正確的再寫上去。

cross³ *adj* angry or bad-tempered 生氣的; 脾氣壞的: *The old man was really cross when Jane broke his window.* 簡妮打破玻璃窗，那位老人真是氣壞了。**–crossly** *adv* **–crossness** n [U]

cross·bar /ˈkrɒs,bɑr; ˈkrɒsbɑːʳ/ n **1** a bar joining two upright posts〔兩根柱子之間的〕橫木: *He almost scored a goal, but the ball hit the crossbar.* 他差點進球，但球擊中了門楣。**2** the top bar of the frame of a man's bicycle〔腳踏車車架的〕橫樑

cross·bow /ˈkrɒs,bo; ˈkrɒsbəʊ/ n a powerful type of BOW³ that is fired like a gun 弩

cross·breed /ˈkrɒs,brid; ˈkrɒsbriːd/ n an animal or plant which is a mixture of breeds〔動植物的〕雜交種 **–crossbred** /-brɛd; -bred/ *adj*: *a crossbred horse* 雜交馬

cross·check /ˈkrɒs,tʃɛk; ˌkrɒsˈtʃek/ v [T] to make certain that a calculation or answer is right by using a different method〔用不同方法〕核對〔計算結果或答案〕

cross-coun·try /ˌ·'···◄/ adj,adv across the fields or open country 越野的: a cross-country race 越野賽跑 | cross-country skiing 越野滑雪

cross-ex·am·ine /ˌ· '···/ v **cross-examined, cross-examining** [I;T] to question somebody, especially a witness, very carefully, usually in order to compare the answers with other answers they have given before 盤詰〔證人〕; 盤詰 –**cross-examination** /ˌ· ···'··/ n [C;U]

cross-eyed /ˌ·'·◄/ adj having eyes which look in towards your nose 內斜視的; 鬥雞眼的

cross·fire /'krɒs,faɪr; 'krɒsfaɪəʳ/ n [U] one or more lines of gunfire coming from different places, but directed at the same point 交叉火力

cross·ing /'krɒsɪŋ; 'krɒsɪŋ/ n 1 a journey across the sea 橫渡大海的旅程 2 a place where two railway lines or tracks cross or where a road crosses the railway〔鐵路的〕交叉道口;〔公路的〕相交處 3 a place at which a road, river, or railway line may be crossed safely〔道路或鐵路的〕人行橫道;〔河流的〕渡口

cross-legged /'krɒs 'lɛgɪd; ˌkrɒs 'legd◄/ adj, adv sitting with your knees wide apart and your ankles crossed 盤腿而坐的〔地〕

cross·piece /'krɒs,pis; 'krɒspiːs/ n a piece of anything lying across something else 橫放物; 橫檔

cross-pur·pos·es /ˌ· '···/ n at cross-purposes talking about different things without being conscious of it, and so not understanding each other 互相誤解: I think we're talking at cross-purposes. 我覺得我們在各說各的, 彼此誤會了。

cross-re·fer /ˌ· ··'·/ v -rr- [I;T] to direct the reader from one place in a book to another place in the same book 參照〔同一本書的另一處〕; 互見: In this dictionary CAPITAL letters are used to cross-refer from one word to another. 在本辭典中, 大寫字體的詞表示這一詞與另一詞相互參照。

cross-ref·erence /ˌ· '···/ n a note in a book telling the reader to look at another place in the same book in order to find more information 參照〔註釋〕; 互見

cross·roads /'krɒs,rodz; 'krɒsrəʊdz/ n [plural is 複數為 **crossroads**] 1 a place where two or more roads cross each other 十字路口 –see picture on page 991 見 991 頁彩圖 2 an important point, especially one where you have to take an important decision 重要時刻〔尤指面臨重大抉擇〕

cross-sec·tion /ˌ·'··,·/ n 1 a drawing of something showing what you would see if you cut across it, especially at right angles to its length 截面圖; 剖面圖: a cross-section of a plant stem 植物莖幹的截面 2 a number

of different people who, together, seem to be typical of society 具代表性的一些人: A cross-section of the public were interviewed by market researchers. 市場調查員採訪了公眾中有代表性的一羣人。

cross·word /'krɒs,wɜd; 'krɒs,wɜːd/ n (also 又作 **crossword puzzle** /'·· ,··/) a printed word game which you do by fitting words guessed from questions and information (called CLUES) into a pattern of numbered squares going down and across 縱橫字謎遊戲

crotch /krɑtʃ; krɒtʃ/ n (also 又作 **crutch**) the part of your body between the tops of your legs, or the part of a pair of trousers that covers this 胯部; 褲襠

crotch·et·y /'krɑtʃətɪ; 'krɒtʃɪti/ adj infml bad-tempered and hard to please〔非正式〕脾氣壞的

crouch /krautʃ; krautʃ/ v [I] to lower your body close to the ground by bending your knees and back 蹲伏; 蹲下: We crouched down behind the wall to shelter from the wind. 我們蹲在牆的後面避風。 | The tiger crouched, ready to spring. 老虎往下一蹲, 準備起跳。 –see picture on page 992 見 992 頁彩圖

crou·pi·er /'krupɪə; 'kruːpɪəʳ/ n a person who collects the money lost and pays out the money won at a table where games such as ROULETTE are played〔在賭台上的〕賭資收付人

crow [1] v /kro; krəʊ/ n 1 a large shiny black bird with a loud cry 烏鴉 2 as the crow flies measuring a distance in a straight line from one point to another 成直線地; 筆直地: We're twenty kilometres from town as the crow flies, but nearly thirty by road. 我們距市鎮的直線距離是二十公里, 但要從公路走, 卻有近三十公里。 3 the loud high cry of a fully-grown male chicken 公雞的叫聲

crow [2] v [I] 1 to make the loud high cry of a fully-grown male chicken〔公雞〕啼叫 2 infml to speak proudly (a word used to express disapproval)〔非正式〕得意地說〔含貶義〕: I wish John would stop crowing about his examination results. 我希望約翰不要再吹噓他的考試成績。

crow·bar /'kro,bɑr; 'krəʊbɑːʳ/ n an iron bar used to force something open or to force two things apart 鐵撬棍

★**crowd** [1] v 1 [I; + adv/prep] to gather together and in large numbers〔大量〕聚集: People crowded round the scene of the accident. 人們聚集在事故現場周圍。 | Screaming fans crowded around the film star. 大喊大叫的影迷圍着那位影星。 2 [T] to fill a place so that it is not easy to move 擠滿〔一地〕: Shoppers crowded the streets. 馬路上擠滿了購物的人。 3 [I;T; + adv/prep] to press tightly into a small place 擠進〔一個小地方〕: They all crowded into the taxi. 他們全都擠進

了計程車。| *There were six of us, all crowded* **into** *a tiny flat.* 我們一共六個人，全部擠進了那間小小的公寓。

crowd² /kraʊd; kraʊd/ *n* **1** a large number of people gathered together for a particular purpose 人羣: *a crowd gathered to watch the parade* 聚在一起看閱兵儀式的人羣 | *There were crowds* **of** *people at the theatre.* 劇院裡聚着一羣一羣的人。| *a football crowd* 一羣看足球賽的人 | *They vanished into the crowd.* 他們消失在人羣之中。**2** *infml* a particular group of friends or a social group 〖非正式〗一羣朋友；某一社會羣體: *I don't like the college crowd.* 我不喜歡大學生。**3** **follow the crowd, go with the crowd** *infml* to be easily influenced and to do what most people do in a particular situation 〖非正式〗附和羣眾；隨大流: *He does what he wants — he doesn't just follow the crowd.* 他想甚麼就做甚麼——而不是隨大流的。

crowd·ed /ˈkraʊdɪd; ˈkraʊdɪd/ *adj* completely full or filled with people 擠滿人的: *a crowded room* 擁擠的房間 | *The beach gets so crowded in August.* 八月份的海灘變得非常擁擠。

crown¹ /kraʊn; kraʊn/ *n* **1** a circular decoration usually made of gold with jewels in it, which a king or queen wears on their head as a sign of royal power 王冠，冕 **2** something which looks like or represents this, often given to someone as a prize 王冠狀物；〔作為獎品的〕桂冠: *a crown of flowers for the Carnival Queen* 海濱狂歡節皇后的花冠 **3** the top or highest part of your head, a hat, or a hill 〔頭、帽或山的〕頂部 **4** **the Crown** the governing power of a kingdom 王權: *land belonging to the Crown* 王室的領地

*****crown²** *v* [T] **1** to place a crown solemnly on the head of a person as a sign of royal power or victory 為〔某人〕加冕；〔為表示勝利而〕給〔某人〕戴桂冠 **2** *lit* to cover the top of something 〖文〗覆蓋於〔某物的〕頂部: *Trees crowned the hill.* 樹木覆蓋了山頂。**3** to complete something in the most perfect way 圓滿地完成〔某事〕: *The government's record was crowned by its success in the peace talks.* 和談的成功為政府的執政記錄圓滿地劃上了句號。**4** **to crown it all** a phrase used when you want to show that the last thing or event in a list is the best or worst thing to happen 更有甚者；更妙〔糟〕的是: *His house burnt down, his car was stolen, and to crown it all he lost his job.* 他的房子燒了，汽車被偷了，更糟糕的是，他失業了。

crown jew·els /ˌ···'·/ *n* [pl] the crown and jewels which belong to the Crown and are worn or used on great state occasions 〔國家慶典時國王或女王所戴的〕王冠和珠寶

crown prince /ˌ· '·/ *n* the man who has the lawful right to be king after the death of the present king or ruling queen; if this person is a woman she is called the **crown princess** 皇太子；皇儲〔如果是女子，則被稱為 **crown princess** 女皇儲〕

*****cru·cial** /ˈkruʃəl; ˈkruːʃəl/ *adj* of the greatest importance 決定性的，極其重要的: *at a crucial moment* 在關鍵時刻 | *Speed is crucial* **to** *our success.* 速度對於我們的成功至關重要。–**crucially** *adv*

cru·ci·fix /ˈkruːsə،fɪks; ˈkruːsɪˌfɪks/ *n* a cross with a figure of Christ on it 有耶穌像的十字架

cru·ci·fix·ion /ˌkruːsəˈfɪkʃən; ˌkruːsɪˈfɪkʃən/ *n* [C;U] the act of crucifying someone 〔某人〕釘死在十字架上 **2** **the Crucifixion** the death of Christ on the Cross, or a picture or other representation of it 耶穌受難；耶穌受難像

cru·ci·fy /ˈkruːsə،faɪ; ˈkruːsɪˌfaɪ/ *v* **crucified, crucifying** [T] **1** to kill someone by nailing them to a cross and leaving them to die 把〔某人〕釘死在十字架上 **2** to be cruel or unpleasant to someone, especially publicly 〔尤指當眾〕虐待，折磨: *He was crucified by public opinion because his book offended so many people.* 他的書激怒了許多人，所以他受到了輿論的嚴屬批評。

crude /kruːd; kruːd/ *adj* **1** in a natural state or untreated 天然的；未經加工的: *crude oil* 原油 | *crude rubber* 生橡膠 **2** rude or lacking sensitive feeling 粗魯的；粗野的: *Do you have to be so crude?* 你難道非得如此粗魯嗎？**3** too simply or unskilfully made, expressed, or calculated 粗糙的；粗略的: *a crude shelter in the forest* 樹林中粗陋的棲身之所 | *crude ideas* 不成熟的想法 | *crude statistics* 粗略的統計數字 –**crudely** *adv*

cru·di·ty /ˈkruːdəti; ˈkruːdɪti/ *n* **crudities** (also 又作 **crudeness** /ˈkruːdnɪs; ˈkruːdnɪs/) [C;U] the quality of being crude, or an example of crude language or behaviour 粗魯的言行

cru·el /ˈkruːəl; ˈkruːəl/ *adj* **crueller, cruellest** **1** without pity; and enjoying causing pain and suffering 殘忍的；殘酷的: *The soldiers were very cruel* **to** *their prisoners.* 士兵們對待囚犯非常殘忍。**2** causing suffering, pain, or hardship 引起痛苦的: *a cruel punishment* 嚴屬的懲罰 | *a cruel remark* 尖刻的話語 | *Dog-fighting is cruel.* 鬥狗很殘酷。–**cruelly** *adv*

cru·el·ty /ˈkruːəlti; ˈkruːəlti/ *n* **cruelties** **1** [U] the quality of being cruel 殘忍；殘酷: *cruelty to animals* 對動物的殘酷虐待 **2** [C] an example of cruel behaviour 殘酷的行徑

cru·el·ty-free /ˌ··· '·•/ *adj* made without being tested on animals (used of products such as soaps) 不做動物試驗的〔如肥皂等產品〕

cru·et /ˈkruːɪt; ˈkruːɪt/ *n* a set of containers for pepper, salt, and other substances to add to your food, put on the table at meals

〔擺在餐桌上的〕一套調味品小瓶

cruise¹ /kruz; kru:z/ *v* [I] **1** to sail for pleasure in an unhurried way 乘船巡遊 **2** (of a car or plane) to move at a steady, unhurried speed, especially on a long journey 〔汽車或飛機〕巡航: *a cruising speed of 60 miles an hour* 每小時 60 英里的巡航速度

cruise² *n* a sea voyage for pleasure 海上遊覽

cruise con·trol /'··,·/ *n* a special part in a car which allows you to use less petrol when you are travelling steadily at high speed 車速控制裝置〔能使汽車高速行駛, 同時又節省燃料〕

cruis·er /'kruzɚ; 'kru:zəʳ/ *n* **1** a boat with places to sleep and eat 〔有食宿場所的〕遊艇 **2** a large fast warship 巡洋艦

crumb /krʌm; krʌm/ *n* **1** a very small piece of dry food, especially bread or cake 〔尤指麵包或糕餅的〕碎屑: *Sweep up the crumbs from under the table.* 把桌子底下的碎屑掃掉。 **2** a very small amount 少許; 一點兒: *We managed to pick up a few crumbs of knowledge.* 我們努力學了一點東西。

crum·ble /'krʌmbl̩; 'krʌmbəl/ *v* **crumbled, crumbling 1** [T] to make something break into very small pieces 把〔某物〕弄成碎片: *He crumbled the bread in his fingers.* 他用手指把麵包捻碎。 **2** [I] to break into small pieces, often because of age 〔常因年久而〕裂成碎片: *As the years passed, the old church crumbled.* 隨着歲月的流逝, 那所教堂倒塌了。 **3** [I] to end or fail 結束; 崩潰: *After centuries the Roman Empire crumbled.* 幾個世紀之後, 羅馬帝國崩潰了。

crum·bly /'krʌmbli; 'krʌmbli/ *adj* easily crumbled 易碎的

crum·pet /'krʌmpɪt; 'krʌmpɪt/ *n* a small round breadlike cake with holes in one side usually eaten hot and spread with butter 〔常塗上黃油熱吃, 一端有孔的〕小圓烤餅

crum·ple /'krʌmpl̩; 'krʌmpəl/ *v* **crumpled, crumpling** [I;T] to make something become full of irregular folds by pressing or crushing it 使〔某物〕起皺: *Don't sit on that shirt — you'll crumple it!* 別坐在那件襯衫上 —— 你會把它弄皺的! | *The front of the car crumpled as it crashed into the wall.* 汽車前部撞在牆上, 車頭撞癟了。

crunch¹ /krʌntʃ; krʌntʃ/ *v* **1** [I;T] to crush food noisily with your teeth 嘎吱嘎吱地咬嚼: *The dog was crunching on a bone.* 狗正嘎吱嘎吱地嚼骨頭。 **2** [I] to make noise like something being crushed 嘎吱作響: *Our feet crunched on the snow.* 我們的腳踩在雪上嘎吱作響。 | *The stones crunched under the car tyres.* 石塊被汽車輪胎壓得嘎吱嘎吱地響。 **–crunchy** *adj* **crunchier, crunchiest**

crunch² *n* **1** a crunching sound 嘎吱的聲音 **2** **the crunch** *infml* a difficult moment at which an important decision must be made 〔非正式〕必須作出重大決定的困難時刻 **if/when it comes to the crunch**, when the crunch comes if you reach the point where you have to act or decide 到了緊要關頭

cru·sade¹ /kru'sed; kru:'seɪd/ *n* **1** **the Crusades** any of the Christian wars to win back Palestine from the Muslims 800 years ago 〔800年以前為奪回巴勒斯坦所進行的〕十字軍東征 **2** a set of activities to support or fight against something that you feel strongly about 〔為支持或反對某物所進行的〕運動: *a crusade* **against** *crime* 遏制犯罪的運動 | *a crusade* **for** *better prison conditions* 爭取改善監獄情況的運動

crusade² *v* **crusaded, crusading** [I] to take part in a crusade 參加運動: *She's always crusading* **for** *women's rights.* 她總是在為女權運動不懈地奮鬥。 **–crusader** *n*

crush¹ /krʌʃ; krʌʃ/ *v* **1** [T] to press something with great force so as to break or destroy its natural shape 壓破; 壓壞: *The tree fell on top of the car and crushed it.* 樹倒在車頂上, 把車壓壞了。 | *Wheat is crushed to make flour.* 小麥被磨成麵粉。 **2** [I; + adv/prep] (of people) to press tightly and uncomfortably into a place 〔人〕擠入: *The crowd crushed through the gates.* 人羣從大門處一擁而入。 **3** [T] to destroy an army or an organization 鎮壓〔軍隊〕; 破壞〔組織〕: *The revolt was crushed by the army.* 那場起義被軍隊鎮壓下去了。

crush² *n* **1** [*sing*] uncomfortable pressure caused by a great crowd of people 擁擠: *There was such a crush on the train!* 火車上竟如此擁擠! **2** [U] a drink made by crushing fruit 果汁: *orange crush* 橘子汁 **3** **have a crush on someone** *infml* to have a strong, foolish, and short-lived love for someone, often an older person 〔非正式〕短暫地迷戀某人: *I had a terrible crush on my teacher.* 我曾經非常迷戀我的老師。

crust /krʌst; krʌst/ *n* [C;U] **1** the hard outer surface of baked bread 麵包皮 **2** baked pastry 油酥皮 **3** a hard outer covering 硬的外殼: *the earth's crust* 地殼 | *a thin crust of ice* 一層薄冰

crus·ta·cean /krʌs'teʃən; krʌ'steɪʃən/ *n* any of a group of animals, mostly sea animals, with several pairs of legs and a hard outer shell; a CRAB is a crustacean 甲殼綱動物〔如蟹等〕

crust·y /'krʌsti; 'krʌsti/ *adj* **1** having a hard well-baked crust 有脆皮的: *a crusty loaf* 脆皮麵包 **2** bad-tempered and impatient 脾氣壞的; 不耐煩的: *a crusty old man* 脾氣粗暴的老人

crutch /krʌtʃ; krʌtʃ/ *n* **1** a stick with a piece that fits under your arm, for supporting a person who has difficulty in walking 拐杖: *When he broke his leg he had to walk on crutches.* 他把腿摔斷了以後, 不得不靠拐杖走路。 **2** –see 見 CROTCH

crux /krʌks; krʌks/ *n* **the crux** the central part of a problem 問題的核心: *The crux of the matter is…* 這件事的關鍵在於…

★cry¹ /kraɪ; kraɪ/ *v* **cried, cried, crying 1** [I] to produce tears from your eyes usually, as a sign of sadness 哭; 哭泣: *She cried when she heard of her friend's death.* 她聽到朋友的死訊時哭了。| *The children cried for their father.* 孩子們哭着要找爸爸。**2** [I] to speak loudly or shout, usually with fear or excitement 〔常因害怕或興奮而〕大聲喊叫: *"Run, run!" he cried.* "快跑, 快跑!" 他喊道。| *"That's wonderful!" she cried.* "那太棒了!" 她叫道。**3** [I] to make the natural sound of certain animals and birds 〔鳥、獸〕鳴, 叫: *Listen to the seabirds crying.* 聽海鳥在叫。**4 cry your eyes out, cry your heart out** to cry a lot for a long time 痛哭: *When her dog died my daughter cried her eyes out.* 狗死的時候, 我女兒痛哭了一場。**5 cry over spilt milk** to waste time feeling sorry about something that cannot be changed for the better 為無可挽回的事而悔恨

cry off *phr v* [I] *infml* to fail to fulfil a promise or agreement 〔非正式〕食言; 毀約: *He said he'd help, but then he cried off.* 他說好幫忙的, 可是卻打了退堂鼓。

cry out *phr v* [I] to shout loudly, usually with fear or pain 〔常因害怕或疼痛而〕大聲喊叫: *He cried out in pain.* 他痛得大喊大叫。

cry out against sthg *phr v* [T] to complain or express your disapproval of something very strongly 強烈反對〔某事物〕

cry out for sthg *phr v* [T] to be in great need of something 迫切需要〔某物〕: *The garden is crying out for rain.* 花園正迫切需要雨水。

★cry² *n* **cries 1** any loud sound expressing a strong feeling like fear or pleasure 〔表示害怕或高興等強烈情感的〕叫喊聲: *a cry of anger* 一聲怒吼 **2** a loud shout, often to attract attention 呼喊聲〔常為了引人注意〕: *a cry of "Stop, thief!"* "站住, 小偷!"的呼喊聲 **3** [sing] a period of crying 哭泣: *You'll be better after you've had a good cry.* 你好好地哭一場會覺舒好一些的。**4** the natural sound of certain animals or birds 〔動物或鳥的〕叫聲 **5** a general public demand 公眾的要求: *a national cry for lower taxes* 全國要求降低稅收的呼聲

crying /ˈkraɪɪŋ; ˈkraɪ-ɪŋ/ *adj infml* 〔非正式〕**1 a crying need** an urgent need 迫切的需要 **2 a crying shame** a very great shame 奇恥大辱: *It's a crying shame, the way she hits that child.* 她那樣打那個孩子, 實在太丟人了。

crypt /krɪpt; krɪpt/ *n* an underground room beneath a church 〔教堂的〕地下室

cryp·tic /ˈkrɪptɪk; ˈkrɪptɪk/ *adj* mysterious or with hidden meaning 神祕的; 晦澀的: *a cryptic message* 密碼電文 | *a cryptic remark* 有言外之意的話 –**cryptically** /-klɪ; -kli/ *adv*

crys·tal /ˈkrɪstl; ˈkrɪstl/ *n* **1** [U] a transparent natural mineral that looks like ice 水晶 **2** [U] colourless glass of very high quality 水晶玻璃: *a crystal wine glass* 水晶玻

璃酒杯 **3** [C] a small regular shape formed naturally by a chemical substance when it becomes solid 結晶體: *sugar and salt crystals* 糖與鹽的結晶體

crys·tal·lize /ˈkrɪstlˌaɪz; ˈkrɪstəlaɪz/ *v* (also 又作 **crystallise** *BrE* 〔英式〕) [I;T] **1** to make a substance form crystals 使〔一種物質〕結晶: *At what temperature does sugar crystallize?* 糖在甚麼溫度下結晶? **2** (of thoughts or opinions) to become clear or fixed 〔思想或觀點〕變明朗或具體: *She's trying to crystallize her ideas into a practical plan.* 她正在設法把她的構想變成一個切實的計劃。| *Their attitude has crystallized.* 他們的態度明朗化了。–**crystallization** /ˌkrɪstləˈzeɪʃən; ˌkrɪstəlaɪˈzeɪʃən/ *n* [U]

cu. an abbreviation for 〔縮〕= CUBIC

cub /kʌb; kʌb/ *n* **1** a young bear, lion, tiger, or fox 〔熊、獅、虎、狐等的〕幼獸 **2 the cubs** (also 又作 **Cub Scouts**) a division of the SCOUTS for younger boys 童子軍

cube¹ /kjub; kjuːb/ *n* **1** a solid object with six equal square sides 立方體 **2** the number made by multiplying a number by itself twice 立方〔乘積〕: *The cube of 3 is 27.* ($3 \times 3 \times 3 = 27$) 3的立方等於27。

cube² *v* **cubed, cubing** [T] **1** to cut something into cubes 把〔某物〕切割成立方體 **2** to multiply a number by itself twice 〔一個數〕自乘兩次: *3 cubed* (written 3^3) *is 27.* 3的立方是27。

cu·bic /ˈkjubɪk; ˈkjuːbɪk/ *adj* related to a way of measuring space when the length of something is multiplied by the width and height of it 立方的; 立方體的: *a cubic centimetre* 一立方厘米 | *cubic capacity* 立體容積

cu·bi·cle /ˈkjubɪkl; ˈkjuːbɪkəl/ *n* a very small enclosed division of a larger room, such as one used for undressing at a swimming pool 〔由大房間分隔而成的〕小室〔如游泳池內的更衣室〕

cuck·oo /ˈkʊku; ˈkʊkuː/ *n* a bird that lays its eggs in another bird's nest; it has a call that sounds like its name 杜鵑; 布穀鳥

cu·cum·ber /ˈkjukʌmbə; ˈkjuːkʌmbəʳ/ *n* [C; U] a long, thin, round vegetable with a dark green skin and light green watery flesh, which is eaten raw 黃瓜 –see picture on page 504 見 504 頁彩圖

cud·dle¹ /ˈkʌdl; ˈkʌdl/ *v* **cuddled, cuddling** [I;T] to put your arms around someone or something lovingly 摟抱; 擁抱: *He was sitting cuddling the baby.* 他抱着嬰兒坐在那裡。

cuddle up *phr v* [I] to lie close and comfortably with someone 依偎着〔某人〕躺着: *The children cuddled up to each other in the dark.* 孩子們在黑暗中互相依偎在一起。

cuddle² *n* [sing] an act of cuddling someone 擁抱: *My daughter came to me for a cuddle.* 我的女兒走過來和我擁抱了一下。

cud·dly /ˈkʌdlɪ; ˈkʌdli/ *adj* lovable, soft, and

C

slightly fat 可愛的; 胖乎乎的: *a cuddly baby* 胖乎乎的嬰兒

cud·gel /ˈkʌdʒəl; ˈkʌdʒəl/ *n* a short thick heavy stick used as a weapon〔用作武器的〕短棍

cue /kjuː; kjuː/ *n* **1** a signal for the next person to speak or act in a play〔戲劇中暗示下一位演員說話或出場的〕尾白, 提示: *The actor missed his cue and came onto the stage late.* 那位演員錯過了提示, 上台晚了。 **2 on cue** exactly when expected 如預料的那樣: *And right on cue he walked through the front door.* 正如預料的那樣, 他穿過了前門。 **3** a long straight wooden rod used for pushing the ball in BILLIARDS or SNOOKER〔枱球等的〕球桿

cuff¹ /kʌf; kʌf/ *n* **1** the end of a shirt SLEEVE〔襯衫的〕袖口 −see picture on page 210 見 210 頁彩圖 **2** *AmE* the TURN-UP of a pair of trousers〔美式〕〔褲腳的〕翻邊 **3 off the cuff** without preparation 未經準備的; 當場: *I'm afraid I can't answer your question off the cuff.* 我恐怕當場回答不出你的問題。 **4** an act of hitting someone lightly with your open hand〔用掌的〕輕拍

cuff² *v* [T] to hit someone lightly with your open hand 用掌輕拍〔某人〕

cui·sine /kwɪˈziːn; kwɪˈziːn/ *n* [U] a style of cooking 烹飪; 烹調

cul-de-sac /ˈkʌldəˈsæk; ˈkʌldəˌsæk/ *n* **cul-de-sacs** *or* **culs-de-sac** a street which is closed at one end 死巷; 死胡同

cul·i·na·ry /ˈkjuləˌnerɪ; ˈkʌlʃəneri/ *adj fml* related to the kitchen or cooking〔正式〕廚房的; 烹飪的: *culinary delights* 燒菜的樂趣 | *culinary skills* 烹飪技術

cull /kʌl; kʌl/ *v* [T] to kill the weakest of a group of animals 將〔一羣動物中最弱的〕殺掉 −**cull** *n* : *a seal cull* 剔出海豹予以殺戮

cul·mi·nate /ˈkʌlməˌnet; ˈkʌlmənet/ *v fml*〔正式〕**culminate in something** to end in something 結束某事物: *minor clashes culminating in a full-scale war* 終於導致全面戰爭的小衝突

cul·mi·na·tion /ˌkʌlməˈneʃən; ˌkʌlməˈneɪʃən/ *n* [U] the last and highest point of something, especially after a long period of development 終點; 頂點: *The discovery was the culmination of his life's work.* 這項發現是他一生工作的頂點。

cu·lottes /kjuˈlɒts; kjuːˈlɒts/ *n* [pl] women's trousers, reaching below the knee, which are cut to look like a skirt〔婦女的〕裙褲

cul·pa·ble /ˈkʌlpəbl; ˈkʌlpəbəl/ *adj fml* deserving blame〔正式〕該受譴責的 −**culpability** /ˌkʌlpəˈbɪlətɪ; ˌkʌlpəˈbɪləti/ *n* [U]

cul·prit /ˈkʌlprɪt; ˈkʌlprʃt/ *n* the person guilty of a crime or offence 罪犯; 犯過者

cult /kʌlt; kʌlt/ *n* **1** a religious group with beliefs considered unusual 宗教教派: *The Moonies' cult is widespread in America.* 統一教教派在美國分佈很廣泛。 | *an ancient tribal cult* 古代的部落宗教 **2** a particular

fashion or style, especially among a small number of people〔尤指一小羣人之中的〕時尚, 風格: *Her books have a certain cult following.* 她的書有一定的崇拜者。

cul·ti·vate /ˈkʌltəˌvet; ˈkʌltʃveɪt/ *v* **cultivated, cultivating** [T] **1** to prepare land to grow crops on 耕作〔土地〕 **2** to plant, grow, and raise a crop 種植〔農作物〕 **3** to develop your mind through study 培養, 陶冶〔心性〕; 修習: *to cultivate a knowledge of art* 修習藝術知識 **4** to encourage the friendship of someone you regard as useful to know 結交〔朋友〕: *John always tries to cultivate people who might be able to help his career.* 約翰一直想結交能在事業上對他有所幫助的人。

cul·ti·vat·ed /ˈkʌltəˌvetɪd; ˈkʌltʃveɪtʃd/ *adj* **1** used for growing plants or crops 耕種的; 耕作的 **2** showing good education and manners 有教養的; 有禮貌的: *He's an extremely cultivated man.* 他是個極有教養的人。

cul·ti·va·tion /ˌkʌltəˈveʃən; ˌkʌltʃˈveɪʃən/ *n* [U] the growing of plants or crops 耕作; 栽培: *to bring new land under cultivation* 耕作新土地

cul·tu·ral /ˈkʌltʃərəl; ˈkʌltʃərəl/ *adj* **1** relating to the art, beliefs, and customs of a particular society 文化的 **2** relating to things like art, music, and theatre 文化(藝術)的: *The city is trying to promote cultural activities.* 這座城市正在努力促進文化活動。 −**culturally** *adv*

cul·ture /ˈkʌltʃə; ˈkʌltʃəʳ/ *n* **1** [C;U] the art, beliefs, and customs of a particular society 文化: *ancient Greek culture* 古希臘文化 | *a tribal culture* 部落文化 **2** [U] things like art, music, and theatre 文化(藝術): *Paris is a good city for anyone who is interested in culture.* 對於文化藝術感興趣的人來講, 巴黎是個好城市。 | *a man of little culture* 沒有甚麼文化的人 **3** [C;U] the growing of bacteria for scientific use 細菌培養 **4** [U] *tech* the practice of raising animals and growing plants〔術語〕養植〔動物〕; 培植〔植物〕: *bee culture* 養蜂

cul·tured /ˈkʌltʃəd; ˈkʌltʃəd/ *adj* **1** showing good education, good manners, and an interest in art and music 有教養的; 有文化修養的: *a cultured mind* 有文化修養的人 −opposite 反義 **uncultured 2** grown or produced by people 人工培養的; 人工種植的: *a cultured pearl* 人工培養的珍珠

cum·ber·some /ˈkʌmbəsəm; ˈkʌmbəsəm/ *adj* **1** heavy and awkward to carry or wear 笨重的: *I hate wearing this cumbersome diving gear.* 我討厭穿這種笨重的潛水服。 **2** lengthy and difficult 繁瑣的: *Getting a passport can be a cumbersome process.* 要取得護照可能需要辦許多繁瑣的手續。

cu·mu·la·tive /ˈkjumjəˌletɪv; ˈkjuːmjʃlətɪv/ *adj* increasing steadily in quantity〔數量〕漸增的; 累積的: *Interest on that loan will be* *cumulative.* 那筆借款的利息是累積增加的。| *the cumulative effect of air pollution* 空氣污染日積月累的後果 –**cumulatively** *adv*: *At first, the drug does no harm, but cumulatively its effects are bad.* 這種藥起初無害，但長期服用便有害處。

cun·ning /ˈkʌnɪŋ; ˈkʌnɪŋ/ *adj* clever at deceiving people 奸詐的；狡猾的: *I knew I would have to be cunning if I wanted to get my own way.* 我知道如果我想照着自己的想法去做，就必須狡猾一些才行。 –**cunning** *n* [U]: *He showed great cunning when he was planning his escape.* 他打算逃跑時，顯得非常狡猾。 –**cunningly** *adv*

★**cup¹** /kʌp; kʌp/ *n* **1** a small round container, usually with a handle, from which hot liquids are drunk 杯子: *a cup and saucer* 一副杯碟 –see picture on page 244 見 244 頁彩圖 **2** the contents of a cup 杯子之物: *a cup of tea* 一杯茶 | *Add one cup of flour to half a cup of sugar.* 把一杯麵粉加入半杯糖中。 **3** a prize in a competition which is often a silver cup on a flat base 獎杯: *Which team do you think will win the cup this year?* 你認為今年哪支隊伍將贏得獎杯？ **4** something shaped like a cup 杯狀物: *the cup of a flower* 花萼 **5 someone's cup of tea** *infml* the sort of thing that someone likes〔非正式〕某人所喜歡的東西: *Football's not really my cup of tea.* 足球不是我真正喜歡的運動。

cup² *v* -**pp**- **cup your hands** to form your hands into the shape of a cup 雙手合成杯狀: *She cupped her cold hands round the mug of hot tea.* 她把冰冷的雙手捂在熱咖啡杯的周圍。

cup·board /ˈkʌbəd; ˈkʌbəd/ *n* a piece of furniture with shelves and a door where clothes, plates, or food may be stored 衣櫥；碗櫥

cup·ful /ˈkʌp.fʊl; ˈkʌpfʊl/ *n* **cupfuls** as much of a substance as a cup will hold 一杯之量: *a cupful of sugar* 一杯糖 | *Add two cupfuls of milk.* 加兩杯牛奶。

cu·rate /ˈkjʊrɪt; ˈkjʊərɪt/ *n* a priest who helps the main priest in a PARISH 助理牧師

cu·ra·tor /kjʊˈreɪtə; kjʊˈreɪtər/ *n* the person in charge of an important collection of books, paintings, or other objects〔圖書館、博物館等的〕館長: *chief curator of the British Museum* 大英博物館館長

curb¹ /kɜːb; kɜːb/ *n* **1** a tight control 緊緊的控制，約束，抑制: *Keep a curb on your anger.* 克制住你的怒火。 **2**–see 見 KERB

curb² *v* [T] to control something undesirable like bad temper 克制，控制〔壞脾氣等〕

curds /kɜːdz; kɜːdz/ *n* [U] the thick soft substance that separates from milk when it becomes sour 凝乳

cur·dle /ˈkɜːdl; ˈkɜːdl/ *v* **curdled, curdling** [I;T] to turn sour and thick 變酸；變稠: *The milk has curdled in the coffee.* 牛奶在咖啡中變稠了。

cure¹ /kjʊr; kjʊər/ *v* **cured, curing** [T] **1** to bring health to someone who is ill 治癒〔病人〕: *This medicine cured me of my cold.* 這種藥治好了我的感冒。 **2** to get rid of an illness or a problem 治好〔疾病〕；解決〔問題〕: *The only way to cure backache is to rest.* 治療背痛的唯一辦法是休息。| *government action to cure unemployment* 政府為解決失業問題而採取的行動 **3** to preserve food, tobacco, or skin by drying it, hanging it in smoke, or covering it with salt〔用曬、熏、醃等方法〕保存〔食物、煙草或獸皮〕

cure² *n* **1** a medicine that cures an illness or disease 藥物: *There is still no cure for the common cold.* 目前仍沒有治療感冒的藥物。 **2** a return to health after illness 治癒: *This drug should bring about a cure.* 這種藥應該產生療效。 **3** something that ends a problem 解決〔問題的〕辦法: *There is no easy cure for high inflation.* 目前沒有解決高通貨膨脹的良策。

cur·few /ˈkɜːfju; ˈkɜːfjuː/ *n* a time during which everyone must stay indoors 宵禁: *The government imposed a curfew from sunset to sunrise.* 政府在日落到日出這段時間內實行了宵禁。

cu·ri·o /ˈkjʊrɪ.o; ˈkjʊərɪəʊ/ *n* a small object, valuable because it is rare, old, or beautiful 古董；珍品

cu·ri·os·i·ty /ˌkjʊrɪˈɒsəti; ˌkjʊərɪˈɒsɪti/ *n* **curiosities 1** [sing;U] the desire to know something or learn about something 好奇心: *There was intense curiosity about their wedding plans.* 不少人對於他們的結婚計劃都有很大的好奇心。 **2** [C] something that is strange, interesting, or rare 奇品，珍品: *My great-aunt's cottage is full of curiosities.* 我姑婆的小屋裡到處都是新奇的東西。

cu·ri·ous /ˈkjʊrɪəs; ˈkjʊərɪəs/ *adj* **1** [never before a noun 不能用於名詞前] eager to know something or to learn about something 好奇的: *We were curious to know where she'd gone.* 我們好奇地想知道她去了哪兒。| *I'm very curious about our new neighbours.* 我對於我們的各位新鄰居感到很好奇。 **2** odd or strange 奇怪的: *We heard a curious noise upstairs.* 我們聽到樓上有奇怪的聲響。 –**curiously** *adv*: *Curiously enough, we had met before.* 真巧，我們以前曾見過面。

curl¹ /kɜːl; kɜːl/ *n* **1** a piece of hair that curves round 鬈髮: *a mass of blonde curls* 一團金黃色的鬈髮 **2** something with the shape of a curl 卷曲物: *a curl of smoke* 一縷青煙

curl² *v* [I;T] **1** to form a curl or curls (使)彎曲: *I don't like my hair straight so I'm having it curled.* 我不喜歡直髮，所以我準備去燙髮。 **2** to move round and round 盤繞: *The ivy curled itself round the branches of the tree.* 常春藤繞在樹枝上。| *The smoke curled upwards.* 煙氣裊裊上升。

curl up *phr v* [I] **1** to lie comfortably with your arms and legs pulled up close to your body 蜷曲; 蜷臥: *She curled up in front of the fire with a good book.* 她捧着一部好書蜷曲在火爐前。 **2** to bend at the edges with age 邊緣卷曲: *The leaves became brown and curled up.* 葉子變黃後卷曲了起來。

curl·y /ˈkɜːli; ˈkɝːli/ *adj* having curls 卷曲的: *curly hair* 鬈髮 –see picture on page 469 見 469 頁彩圖 –**curliness** *n* [U]

cur·rant /ˈkɜːənt; ˈkʌrənt/ *n* **1** a small dried seedless GRAPE, sometimes used in cakes 無核葡萄乾 **2** a small black, red, or white juicy fruit that grows in bunches on certain bushes 醋栗

cur·ren·cy /ˈkɜːənsi; ˈkʌrənsi/ *n* **currencies 1** [C;U] the particular type of money in use in a country 貨幣: *the different currencies of Europe* 歐洲的各種貨幣 | *the need to earn foreign currency to pay for imports* 掙外匯以支付進口物品的需要 | *changing traveller's cheques for the local currency* 將旅行支票兑換成當地貨幣 **2 gain currency** (of an idea) to become accepted 〔觀念〕被人接受

cur·rent¹ /ˈkɜːənt; ˈkʌrənt/ *adj* **1** belonging to the present time 當前的; 現在的: *The work would cost £2000 at current prices.* 按現在的價格, 這項工作需花費二千英鎊。 **2** in general use 通用的: *That word is no longer in current use.* 那個詞如今已不通用了。 –**currently** *adv*

current² *n* **1** [C] a continuously moving mass of liquid or gas, especially one flowing through a slower-moving liquid or gas 水流; 氣流: *The current is strongest in the middle of the river.* 河中央的水流最急。 | *hot air currents* 熱氣流 **2** [C;U] a flow of electricity 電流: *Turn off the current before you change the bulb.* 換燈泡前把電流切斷。 **3** [C] a general movement towards a particular opinion 〔意見的〕趨向: *The current of public opinion is against the government.* 公眾普遍持有反對政府的意見。

current ac·count /ˌ·· ·ˌ·/ *n* a bank account from which money can be taken out by cheque or by using a card; it is meant for ordinary spending money, not for the money you want to save 往來賬戶; 活期賬戶

cur·ric·u·lum /kəˈrɪkjʊləm; kəˈrɪkjʊləm/ *n* **curricula** /-lə; -lə/ *or* **curriculums** all the courses of study offered in a school, college, or university 〔學校的〕全部課程: *Computer studies is now on the curriculum.* 計算機學習現已列入學校課程。

curriculum vi·tae /kəˌrɪkjələm ˈvaɪtiː; kəˌrɪkjʊləm ˈviːtaɪ/ *n BrE fml* a short written account of your education and past employment, used especially when you are looking for a new job 〔英式, 正式〕簡歷; 個人履歷

cur·ry /ˈkɜːri; ˈkʌri/ *n* **curries** [C;U] an Indian dish of meat, vegetables, or fish, cooked in a thick hot-tasting liquid and usually eaten with rice 〔印度的〕咖喱食品: *I like vegetable curry.* 我愛吃咖喱蔬菜。 | *I have a chicken curry.* 我要吃塊咖喱雞。 –**curry** *v* **curried, currying** [T]: *curried chicken* 咖喱雞

curse¹ /kɜːs; kɝːs/ *n* **1** something said which expresses anger or hate, or which uses swear words 咒罵; 咒語 **2 put a curse on someone** to make a solemn wish that with the help of God or some magical power, something unpleasant will happen to someone 詛咒某人 **3** a cause of trouble and harm 禍根; 禍因: *Foxes can be a curse to farmers.* 狐狸會成為農民的大禍害。

curse² *v* **cursed, cursing 1** [T] to wish that something unpleasant will happen to someone 詛咒〔某人〕: *She cursed him for ruining her life.* 她詛咒他, 説他毁了她的一生。 **2** [I;T] to swear at someone or something 咒罵〔某人或某物〕: *cursing the car because it wouldn't start* 由於車子開不動而破口大罵 | *He hit his thumb with the hammer and cursed loudly.* 他把錘子砸在大拇指上, 就大聲地叫罵。 **3 be cursed with** to have something bad that you can't get rid of 因…而受苦: *She was cursed with a stammer all her life.* 她一生飽受口吃之苦。

cur·so·ry /ˈkɜːsəri; ˈkɝːsəri/ *adj* done quickly without attention to details 粗略的; 馬虎的: *Even a cursory glance at the report showed that our situation was serious.* 那篇報告只要粗略一看, 也能發現我們的形勢嚴峻。 –**cursorily** *adv*

curt /kɜːt; kɝːt/ *adj* saying very little and therefore appearing rude 粗率無禮的: *a curt reply* 唐突無禮的回答 | *a curt manner* 粗率的態度 –**curtly** *adv* –**curtness** *n* [U]

cur·tail /kɜːˈteɪl; kɝːˈteɪl/ *v* [T] *fml* to reduce or limit something 〔正式〕削減; 限制〔某物〕: *The government hopes to curtail public spending.* 政府希望減少公共開支。 –**curtailment** *n* [C;U]

cur·tain¹ /ˈkɜːtn; ˈkɝːtn/ *n* **1** a piece of hanging cloth that can be pulled across to cover a window or door 窗簾; 門簾: *I'll draw the curtain as it's getting dark.* 天黑了, 我去把窗簾拉上。 | *a shower curtain* 浴簾 | *a pair of curtains* 一副窗簾 –see picture on page 730 見 730 頁彩圖 **2** a piece of heavy material that can be lowered across the front of the stage in a theatre 〔舞台的〕幕

curtain² *v* [T] to provide a room with a curtain 給〔房間〕裝上窗簾〔門簾〕

curtain sth ↔ off *phr v* [T] to separate something from the rest of the room with a curtain 用簾子把…隔開: *a bedroom with a wash-basin curtained off in one corner* 用簾子把洗臉盆隔開在一角的房間

curt·sy /ˈkɜːtsi; ˈkɝːtsi/ *n* **curtsies** (also 又作 **curtsey**) a woman's act of respect to someone of higher rank, done by bending her knees and lowering her head and shoulders 〔女人行的〕屈膝禮 –**curtsy** v **curtsied, curtsying** [I]

cur·va·ture /ˈkɜːvətʃəʳ; ˈkɜːvətʃɚ/ n [C;U] the degree to which something is curved 彎曲度: *the curvature of the earth's surface* 地球表面的彎曲度

★**curve¹** /kɜːv; kɝːv/ v **curved, curving** [I;T] to bend in the shape of a curve (使)彎曲: *The road curved to the right.* 那條道路向右彎曲。

curve² n a line of which no part is straight and which contains no angles 曲線; 弧線: *a curve in the road* 路的轉彎處

cush·ion¹ /ˈkʊʃən; ˈkʊʃən/ n **1** a bag filled with a soft substance on which you can lie, sit, or rest comfortably 坐墊; 靠墊; 墊子: *He lay on the floor with a cushion under his head.* 他頭枕着墊子躺在地上。–see picture on page 730 見 730 頁彩圖 **2** something like this in shape or purpose 形狀或功用如墊子的東西: *A hovercraft rides on a cushion of air.* 氣墊船靠氣墊行駛。

cushion² v [T] to reduce the force or unpleasant effects of something 減輕〔某事物的力量〕; 減少〔某事物的不良後果〕: *When his wife died nothing could cushion the blow.* 他的妻子去世時, 沒有甚麼事能使他減輕一打擊。| *His savings should cushion him against the problems of old age.* 他的存款應能幫助他解決由年老而帶來的問題。

cush·y /ˈkʊʃi; ˈkʊʃi/ adj **cushier, cushiest** infml easy in a way that makes other people jealous (used of a job or style of life) 〔非正式〕容易的, 舒適的, 輕鬆的〔指工作或生活方式〕–**cushiness** n [U]

cus·tard /ˈkʌstəd; ˈkʌstəd/ n [U] BrE a thick sweet yellow liquid made of milk, eggs, and flour, and poured over sweet foods 〔英式〕牛奶蛋糊, 蛋奶甜羹

cus·to·di·an /kʌˈstəʊdiən; kʌˈstoʊdiən/ n a person who takes care of someone or something officially 監護人; 管理員: *the custodian of the royal library* 皇家圖書館管理員 | *custodians of public morality* 公共道德監護者

cus·to·dy /ˈkʌstədi; ˈkʌstədi/ n [U] **1** the right given in a court of law to look after someone 〔法院賦予的〕監護權: *After the divorce the mother was given custody of the children.* 離婚後, 母親獲得了對孩子們的監護權。**2 in custody** guarded by the police 被拘留〔扣押〕: *The stolen car is now in police custody.* 那輛失竊的汽車現由警方保管。| *The criminal was taken into custody.* 罪犯已被監禁。

★**cus·tom** /ˈkʌstəm; ˈkʌstəm/ n **1** [C;U] an activity or ceremony that is part of the way of life of a particular group of people 習俗; 風俗: *Social customs vary greatly from country to country.* 各國的社會習俗有很大的差異。| *an ancient tribal custom* 古代部落的習俗 **2** [C] something you usually do〔個人

的〕習慣: *It was his custom to shout at lazy pupils.* 他的習慣是對懶惰的學生大聲吼叫。– see 見 HABIT (USAGE 用法) **3** [U] fml regular support given to a shop by those who buy things from it 〔正式〕〔顧客對商店經常性的〕惠顧: *We lost a great deal of custom when that new shop opened.* 那家新的商店開張後, 我們少了許多顧客。

cus·tom·a·ry /ˈkʌstəmˌɛri; ˈkʌstəməri/ adj usual 通常的, 習慣上的: *It is customary to give people gifts on their birthdays.* 習慣上人們過生日是要送禮的。–**customarily** /-mɛrɪli; -məri/ adv

custom-built /ˌ··ˈ·◂/ adj (also 又作 **custom-made**) made specially for a particular person 〔為某人〕定做的

★**cus·tom·er** /ˈkʌstəmə; ˈkʌstəməʳ/ n someone who buys goods or services from a shop or business regularly 顧客: *The new shop across the road has taken away most of my customers.* 馬路對面那家新開的商店把我的大部分顧客都搶走了。

> ■ USAGE 用法: Compare 比較 **customer, shopper, client, patient, guest.** When you buy goods from a particular shop you are a **customer** of that shop ☆ 當你在某個商店購物時, 你就是那家商店的 **customer** (顧客): *Mrs Low can't come to the telephone — she's serving a customer.* 洛太太不能來接電話 — 她正在接待顧客。When you go out to buy goods from shops you are a **shopper** ☆ 當你出去購物時, 你就是 **shopper** (購物者): *a busy street full of shoppers* 擠滿購物者的繁忙街道。When you pay for a service from a professional person such as a lawyer you are a **client**, but when you go to a doctor you are a **patient**. When you pay for a room in a hotel you are a **guest**. ☆當你接受律師等職業人士的付費服務時, 你就是 **client** (委託人, 主顧), 但當你去看醫生時, 你便是 **patient** (病人)。當你住旅館時, 你就是 **guest** (客人, 旅客)。

Cus·toms /ˈkʌstəmz; ˈkʌstəmz/ n [pl] (also 又作 **customs**) a place where your belongings are searched when you leave or enter a country, and where you have to pay tax on certain goods 海關: *As soon as I'd got through customs I jumped into a taxi.* 我一出海關便跳上一輛計程車。

★**cut¹** /kʌt; kʌt/ v **cut, cut, cutting 1** [I;T] to press a sharp object such as a knife into something, with the result that a part of it is removed or it is damaged 切; 削; 割: *She cut the meat into small pieces.* 她把肉切成小塊。| *I cut my finger on a piece of broken glass.* 我的手指被一塊碎玻璃割破了。| *Be careful you don't cut yourself with* *that knife*. 小心別讓那把刀割傷你自己。| *He cut the cake into slices*. 他把蛋糕切成片。| *These scissors don't cut very well*. 這把剪刀不太鋒利。| *He cut a hole in the wood*. 他在木頭上挖了個洞。–see 見 BREAK (USAGE 用法) **2** [T] to make someone's hair or nails shorter by using scissors 剪短〔頭髮或指甲〕: *You ought to cut your fingernails*. 你應該剪一下指甲了。| *I must get my hair cut*. 我得去理髮了。**3** [T] to remove a part of a film, a television broadcast, or a piece of writing 刪節〔電影、電視或文字〕: *Some of the most violent scenes were cut from the film*. 電影中一些最激烈的暴力鏡頭被刪掉了。**4** [T] to reduce something 減少〔某物〕: *Government spending will have to be cut next year*. 明年政府的開支將會減少。| *Bus services in the area have been cut*. 當地的公共汽車車次已經減少了。**5 cut a tooth** to grow a tooth 長牙齒: *Most babies cut their first tooth at about six months old*. 大部分嬰兒在大約六個月大時長出第一顆牙。**6 cut the cards** to divide a pile of playing cards in two before giving them out to the players 〔紙牌遊戲中發牌前〕簽牌 **7 cut corners** to do something in a less than perfect way in order to save time or money 節約、減少費用、省力 **8 cut it fine** to leave yourself very little time or money to do something 〔使用時間或金錢時〕幾乎不留餘地；扣得很緊 **9 cut your losses** to stop taking part in a business that is failing, before you lose too much money 及時放棄無利可圖的事

cut across sthg *phr v* [T] **1** to go across something in order to arrive somewhere more quickly 抄近路穿過: *Go down to the stream, then cut across the field to the main road*. 順着河下去，然後抄近路穿過那片田園就到了大路。**2** to go across the limits of a group or subject, and so include or have an effect on more than one group or subject 超越〔團體或科目的〕界限: *This is an important moral issue which cuts across party lines*. 這是超越黨派界限的一個重要的道德問題。

cut back *phr v* **1** [T cut sthg ↔ back] to cut a plant close to its stem so that it will grow better next year 修剪〔植物〕**2** [I;T cut sthg ↔ back] to reduce something 減少〔某物〕: *All local services will have to be cut back*. 所有市內通訊服務都會受到削減。| *We need to cut back on our expenditure*. 我們需要減少開支。

cut down *phr v* **1** [T cut sthg ↔ down] to make something fall to the ground by cutting it 砍倒〔某物〕: *Hundreds of trees have been cut down*. 數以百計的樹木被砍倒了。**2** [I;T cut sthg ↔ down] to reduce something 減少〔某物〕: *You smoke too much — you ought to cut down*. 你抽煙太多了——你應該少抽些。| *I'm trying to cut down my drinking down*. 我在盡量少喝酒。| *We'll have to cut down on our spending*. 我們將不得不減少

開支。

cut in *phr v* [I] to interrupt someone when they are talking 打斷〔某人的談話〕: *Mr Davies cut in to ask if anyone would like a drink*. 戴維斯先生插嘴問有沒有人想喝杯飲料。| *I continued with my story, but she cut in on me again*. 我繼續講故事，可是她又一次打斷了我。

cut off *phr v* **1** [cut sthg ↔ off] to remove something by cutting it 砍掉〔某物〕: *She cut off a few of the branches*. 她砍掉了幾枝樹枝。**2** [cut sthg ↔ off] to disconnect a supply of something 切斷〔某物的供應〕: *The gas has been cut off*. 煤氣供應已被切斷。**3** [T cut sbdy ↔ off] to disconnect a telephone line while people are talking 〔在別人通話時〕切斷電話線: *We were cut off half way through the conversation*. 我們正談到一半，電話線路中斷了。**4** [T cut sbdy/sthg ↔ off] to separate a person or place from the other people or places around 把〔某人或某地〕隔開: *Several villages have been cut off by the snow*. 數個村莊同外界的聯絡由於大雪而中斷。| *I felt terribly isolated and cut off when we moved to a new town*. 我們剛移居到一個新城鎮時，我感到格外的孤獨。

cut out *phr v* **1** [T cut sthg ↔ out] to remove something by cutting it 割下；剪下: *She cut the advertisement out of the newspaper*. 她從報紙上剪下廣告。**2** [T cut sthg ↔ out] to stop doing something 停止做〔某事〕: *I'm trying to cut out smoking altogether*. 我正在努力徹底戒煙。**3** [I] (of an engine) to stop suddenly 〔引擎〕突然熄火: *Every time I slowed down the engine cut out*. 我每次一減速，引擎就會熄火。**4 cut it out** *infml* a phrase you use to tell someone to stop doing something 〔非正式〕住手〔用於讓某人停止做某事〕**5 not cut out for something, not cut out to do something** not well-suited for something 不適合〔做〕某物: *I'm not cut out for acting*. 我不適合演戲。| *She's not cut out to teach*. 她不合適教書。

cut sthg ↔ **short** *phr v* [T] to bring something to an end before the proper time 縮短〔某事物〕: *Our holiday had to be cut short because the weather was so bad*. 由於天氣十分惡劣，我們不得不縮短了假期。

cut up *phr v* **1** [T cut sthg ↔ up] to cut something into pieces 把〔某物〕切成碎片: *Cut the meat and vegetables up into small pieces*. 把肉和蔬菜切碎。**2 be cut up** to feel very upset 傷心；難過: *He was really cut up when his wife died*. 妻子逝世時，他的確很難過。

cut² *n* **1** an opening or wound caused by cutting 切口；傷口: *There were several small cuts in the cloth*. 這塊布上有幾個小口子。| *How did you get that cut on your hand?* 你手上的那個傷口是怎麼弄的？**2** a piece of meat to be cooked in one piece 切下的一塊肉: *A leg of lamb is one of the most expen-*

sive cuts you can buy. 羊腿是你所能買到的最貴的一塊肉。 **3** a reduction 減少; 削減: *We are all hoping for tax cuts.* 我們都希望能夠減稅。| *There have been massive cuts in government spending.* 政府的開支已經被大量削減。 **4** *infml* a share in something 〖非正式〗份額: *I had been promised my cut of the profits.* 我獲答應利潤當中有我的一份。 **5 a cut above** *infml* of better quality than most other things or people 〖非正式〗比〔其餘的物或人〕質量[品質]好; 略勝一籌: *She thinks she's a cut above the rest of us.* 她認為自己比我們略勝一籌。

cut-and-dried /ˌ··ˈ·◂/ *adj* already decided 已經決定的, 已成定局的: *cut-and-dried opinions* 已決定了的意見

cut·back /ˈkʌt,bæk; ˈkʌtbæk/ *n* a planned decrease 〔計劃中的〕削減: *The government is planning more cutbacks in public expenditure.* 政府正打算進一步削減公共開支。

cute /kjut; kjuːt/ *adj* delightfully pretty and often small 嬌小可愛的: *What a cute little baby!* 多可愛的小寶寶! **–cutely** *adv* **–cuteness** *n* [U]

cut glass /ˌ· ˈ·◂/ *n* [U] glass with patterns cut on it 雕花玻璃: *a cut-glass bowl* 雕花玻璃碗

cu·ti·cle /ˈkjutɪkl̩; ˈkjuːtɪkəl/ *n* an outer covering of hard skin round the lower edges of the nails on your toes and fingers 〔指甲根部的〕硬皮; 角皮

cut·lass /ˈkʌtləs; ˈkʌtləs/ *n* a short sword with a slightly curved blade 短彎刀

cut·le·ry /ˈkʌtlərɪ; ˈkʌtləri/ *n* [U] knives, forks, and spoons used for eating 刀叉餐具

cut·let /ˈkʌtlɪt; ˈkʌtl̩ət/ *n* a small piece of meat with a bone 肉排: *lamb cutlets* 小羊排

cut·out /ˈkʌt,aʊt; ˈkʌtaʊt/ *n* **1** something that disconnects a motor or an electrical CIRCUIT, especially if there is too much load on it 〔馬達等的〕斷流器, 保險裝置 **2** a figure cut out of paper, wood, or cardboard 紙剪[木頭刻]的圖形

cut-price /ˌ· ˈ·◂/ *adj* [only before a noun 只用於名詞前] sold at reduced prices 減價出售的: *cut-price petrol* 減價出售的汽油

cut·ter /ˈkʌtə; ˈkʌtər/ *n* **1** a small fast boat 小快艇 **2** an instrument used for cutting 切割工具: *a hedge-cutter* 樹籬剪 | *a pair of wire-cutters* 鋼絲鉗

cut·ting¹ /ˈkʌtɪŋ; ˈkʌtɪŋ/ *n* **1** a stem or leaf cut from a plant and put in soil or water to form roots and grow into a new plant 插枝; 插條〔從植物上剪下的莖或葉, 放在泥土或水中供分栽用〕 **2** *BrE* an article cut out from a newspaper or magazine 〖英式〗剪報〔報紙或雜誌上剪下的文章〕 **3** a passage cut through a hill for a road or railway 在山中為公路或鐵路開拓出來的通道

cutting² *adj* **1** unkind (used of something that someone says) 不友好的〔指話語〕: *The teacher was unpopular because he was*

always making cutting remarks. 這位老師不受歡迎, 因為他說的話總是很尖刻。 **2** uncomfortably strong and cold (used of the wind) 刺骨的〔指風〕 **–cuttingly** *adv*

CV /ˌsi ˈvi; ˌsiː ˈviː/ *n* an abbreviation for 〖縮〗= CURRICULUM VITAE

cwt *n* **cwts** a written abbreviation for 〖縮〗= HUNDREDWEIGHT

cy·a·nide /ˈsaɪə,naɪd; ˈsaɪənaɪd/ *n* [U] a very strong poison 氰化物

cyc·la·men /ˈsɪkləmən; ˈsɪkləmən/ *n* a plant with white, purple, pink, or red flowers 仙客來〔花呈白色、紫色或(粉)紅色的植物〕

*cy·cle¹ /ˈsaɪkl̩; ˈsaɪkəl/ *n* **1** a number of related events happening in a regularly repeated order 循環; 周而復始: *the cycle of the seasons* 四季的循環 | *the cycle of boom and slump* 盛與衰的反覆交替 **2** the period of time needed for this to be completed 循環期; 週期: *a 50-second cycle* 五十秒的週期 **3** a number of connected poems or songs written about someone or something 〔圍繞某人或某事所寫的一系列互有關聯的〕組歌, 組詩 **4** a bicycle 自行車〔腳踏車〕: *a cycle shop* 自行車商店 | *cycle racing* 自行車賽

cycle² *v* **cycled, cycling** [I] to ride a bicycle 騎自行車〔腳踏車〕**–see picture on page 957** 見 957 頁彩圖

cy·clic /ˈsaɪklɪk; ˈsaɪklɪk/ *adj* (also 又作 **cyclical** /ˈsaɪklɪkl̩; ˈsaɪklɪkəl/) happening again and again in a regular pattern 週期性的; 循環的

cy·clist /ˈsaɪklɪst; ˈsaɪkl̩əst/ *n* someone who rides a bicycle 騎自行車〔腳踏車〕的人

cy·clone /ˈsaɪklon; ˈsaɪkləʊn/ *n* a very violent tropical wind moving rapidly in a circle round a calm central area 旋風

cyg·net /ˈsɪgnɪt; ˈsɪgn̩ət/ *n* a young SWAN 小天鵝

cyl·in·der /ˈsɪlɪndə; ˈsɪlɪndər/ *n* **1** a hollow or solid shape with a circular base and straight sides 圓柱體 **2** the tube within which a PISTON moves backwards and forwards in an engine 〔引擎的〕汽缸

cy·lin·dri·cal /sɪˈlɪndrɪkl̩; s̩ˈlɪndrɪkəl/ *adj* in the shape of a cylinder 圓柱狀的

cym·bal /ˈsɪmbl̩; ˈsɪmbəl/ *n* a musical instrument which is like a round thin metal plate; it is struck, sometimes against another, to make a loud ringing noise 鐃, 鈸〔一種打擊樂器〕**–cymbalist** *n*

cyn·ic /ˈsɪnɪk; ˈsɪnɪk/ *n* someone who thinks that people only do things which will help them in some way 慣世嫉俗的人 **–cynical** *adj* : *She was very cynical about his reason for coming to see her.* 她認為他來看她, 純粹是因為想利用她。**–cynically** /-klɪ; -kli/ *adv* **–cynicism** /-nəsɪzəm; -n̩sɪzəm/ *n* [U]: *There was a mood of general cynicism in the country about the forthcoming elections.* 公眾對於即將進行的選舉普遍持悲觀的態度。

cy·press /ˈsaɪprəs; ˈsaɪpr̩əs/ *n* a tree with

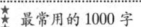

dark green leaves and hard wood, that does not lose its leaves in winter 柏樹

cyst /sɪst; sɪst/ *n* an enclosed hollow growth in or on your body, containing liquid 囊; 囊腫

czar /zɑr; zɑːᵏ/ *n* –see 見 TSAR

Czech¹ /tʃɛk; tʃek/ *adj* of or connected with Czechoslovakia 捷克斯洛伐克的

Czech² *n* **1** [C] a person from Czechoslovakia 捷克斯洛伐克人 **2** [U] a language spoken in Czechoslovakia 捷克斯洛伐克語

D, d

D, d /diː; diː/ **D's, d's** or **Ds, ds** the 4th letter of the English alphabet 英語的第四個字母

-'d 1 short for 〔縮〕= WOULD: *I asked if he'd go.* 我問他去不去。**2** short for 〔縮〕= HAD: *I asked if he'd gone.* 我問他去了沒有。–see 見 **'S** (USAGE 用法)

d an abbreviation for 〔縮〕= **died**: *d 1937* 死於1937年

d' short for 〔縮〕= DO: *D'you like it?* 你喜歡它嗎?

dab¹ /dæb; dæb/ *n* **1** a quick or light touch 輕拍; 輕塗: *He made a few dabs at the fence with the paintbrush, but that was all.* 他用油漆刷子在圍牆上輕輕刷了幾下, 但僅此而已。**2** a small amount of a substance 少量〔物質〕: *a dab of paint* 一點點油漆

dab² *v* **-bb-** [I;T] to touch something lightly and quickly, usually several times 輕撫; 輕拭: *She dabbed her eyes with her handkerchief.* 她用手帕輕拭眼睛。| *He dabbed at the wound with a wet cloth.* 他用濕布輕拭傷口。

dab·ble /'dæbl; 'dæbəl/ *v* **dabbled, dabbling 1** [I] to work at or study something without serious intentions 淺嘗; 涉足: *He likes dabbling in politics.* 他喜歡涉足政治。**2** [T] to move your hands or feet playfully about in water 〔用手、腳〕玩水: *She dabbled her toes in the river.* 她把腳趾浸到河中嬉水。– **dabbler** *n*

dab hand /ˌ· '·/ *n* someone who is very good at something 能手; 內行; 高手: *She's a dab hand at cards.* 她是玩牌高手。

dachs·hund /'dɑks,hund; 'dækshund/ *n* a small dog with short legs and a long body 達克斯獵狗; 獵腸狗〔一種身材長腿短的小獵狗〕

⭐**dad** /'dæd; dæd/ *n infml* father 〔非正式〕爸爸; 爹爹: *Can we go now, Dad?* 我們可以走了嗎, 爸爸? | *Is your dad at home?* 你爹在家嗎?

dad·dy /'dædi; 'dædi/ *n* father (used by and to small children) 爸爸, 爹爹〔用於兒語〕

daf·fo·dil /'dæfədil; 'dæfədil/ *n* a yellow flower seen in early spring 水仙花〔初春常見〕

daft /dæft; dɑːft/ *adj infml* silly or foolish 〔非正式〕傻的; 笨的: *That was a daft thing to do.* 那是件蠢事。| *Don't be so daft!* 別那麼傻乎乎的!

dag·ger /'dægə; 'dægər/ *n* **1** a short pointed knife used in the past as a weapon 短劍; 匕首 **2 at daggers drawn** angry, and ready to fight 劍拔弩張: *They've been at daggers drawn ever since her promotion was announced.* 自從她的晉升宣佈後, 他們一直憤憤不平。**3 look daggers at someone** to look very angrily at someone 對某人怒目而視: *She looked daggers at me as I spoke.* 我發言時, 她對我怒目而視。

⭐**dai·ly¹** /'deɪli; 'deɪli/ *adj, adv* every day, or every working day 每日的[地]; 每個工作日的[地]: *daily meetings* 日常會議 | *The mail is delivered twice daily.* 郵件每天送遞兩次。

daily² *n* **dailies 1** (also 又作 **daily newspaper** /ˌ·· '···/) a newspaper printed and sold every day except Sunday 日報〔除星期日外〕每天出版發行的報紙 **2** (also 又作 **daily help** /ˌ·· '·/) *infml* a woman who comes to your house every day to do housework 〔非正式〕鐘點保姆, 每天來做家務的(女)傭人

dain·ty¹ /'deɪntɪ; 'deɪnti/ *adj* **daintier, daintiest** small, pretty, and delicate 小巧玲瓏的; 秀麗的; 優雅的: *a dainty child* 嬌小可愛的小孩 | *dainty movements* 優雅的動作 – **daintily** *adv* – **daintiness** *n* [U]

dainty² *n* **dainties** a nice piece of food, especially a small cake 精美食品〔尤指小糕餅〕

dair·y /'deəri; 'deəri/ *n* **dairies 1** a place on a farm where milk is kept and butter and cheese are made 乳品場; 牛奶場 **2** a shop where milk, butter, cheese and eggs are sold, or a place from which these products are sent to shops 乳品蛋類商店; 乳品公司 – **dairy** *adj*: *dairy products* 乳製品

dairy cat·tle /'··· ,··/ *n* [pl] cattle kept for milk rather than for meat 乳牛, 奶牛

da·is /'deɪs; 'deɪəs/ *n* a raised part of the floor at one end of a hall, for speakers to stand on 講台

dai·sy /'deɪzɪ; 'deɪzi/ *n* **daisies** a very common small flower, white around a yellow centre 雛菊

dale /deɪl; deɪl/ *n dialect* a valley 〔方言〕山谷

dal·ly /'dælɪ; 'dæli/ *v* **1** [I] to be slow or waste time 拖延; 延誤; 浪費時間: *Don't dally over your food.* 別磨磨蹭蹭地吃東西。**2 dally with** to think about something, but not very seriously 〔不認真地〕考慮〔某事〕: *They dallied with the idea of buying a larger house.* 他們有個不大認真的想法: 不如買間大屋。

dal·ma·tian /dæl'meʃɪən; dæl'meɪʃən/ *n* a large white dog with black spots 達爾馬提亞狗, 斑點狗

dam¹ /dæm; dæm/ *n* a wall or bank built across a river to keep back water 壩; 堤: *The dam burst after weeks of heavy rain.* 下了幾星期的暴雨之後, 水壩決堤了。

---

dam² *v* **-mm-** [T] to build a dam across a river to block it〔在河上〕築水壩: *They're damming the river.* 他們在河上築水壩。

dam up *phr v* [T **dam** sthg ↔ **up**] **1** to build a dam across a river to block it〔在河上〕築水壩 **2** to control a feeling so that it does not show 抑制〔情感〕: *Don't dam up your anger — tell him how you feel.* 別忍氣吞聲——把你的感覺告訴他。

★**dam·age¹** /'dæmɪdʒ; 'dæmɪdʒ/ *n* [U] **1** harm done to something 損害; 損失; 毀壞; 破壞: *The storm caused extensive damage.* 暴風雨造成了巨大的損害。| *This new law has done a lot of damage to the government's popularity.* 這項新法律大大損害了政府的聲望。 **2** **damages** [pl] *law* money that someone must pay to another person for hurting them, or causing harm, or loss〔律〕損害賠償金: *The court ordered the newspaper to pay me £500 in damages.* 法庭責令該報社付給我五百英鎊損害賠償金。

★**damage²** *v* **damaged, damaging** [T] to harm something 損害; (使)損失; 毀壞; 破壞

dam·ask /'dæməsk; 'dæməsk/ *n* [U] a heavy cloth with a pattern woven into it 錦緞; 花緞

dame /dem; deɪm/ *n* **1** *AmE slang* a woman〔美俚〕婦女: *What a dame!* 一個了不起的女人! **2** **Dame** a British title given to a woman to honour her work 女爵士, 貴夫人〔在英國對有地位、有才華女子的尊稱〕: *Dame Ellen Terry was a famous actress.* 艾倫·特里(女)爵士是一位知名的女演員。

damn¹ /dæm; dæm/ *v* [T] **1** (of God) to send someone to HELL after their death〔上帝〕罰〔某人〕入地獄 **2** **damn it, damn you** an expression of anger or disappointment 該死的!〔他媽的!〕〔表示憤怒或失望〕

damn² *adj infml* [only before a noun 只用於名詞前] a word used for giving force to an expression, good or bad (a word which some people consider not to be polite)〔非正式〕完全的; 完全的〔用於加強語氣, 褒貶均可; 但一般認為不夠禮貌〕: *He's a damn fool.* 他是個十足的笨蛋。

damn³ *adv infml*〔非正式〕**1** a word used for giving force to an expression, good or bad (a word which some people consider not to be polite) 十足; 完全〔用於加強語氣, 褒貶均可; 但一般認為不夠禮貌〕: *Don't be so damn foolish.* 別那麼愚蠢透頂。| *He ran damn fast.* 他跑得快極了。 **2** **damn well** a phrase used for giving force to a verb, usually about something bad 無疑地, 肯定地〔用於加強動詞的語氣, 通常指壞事〕: *Don't lie to me — you knew damn well what was happening!* 別對我撒謊——你肯定知道事情的真相!

damn⁴ *interj infml* an expression of anger or disappointment〔非正式〕混蛋! 該死!〔表示憤怒或失望〕

damn⁵ *n infml* **I don't care/give a damn** = I don't care at all〔非正式〕我毫不在乎: *I don't care a damn what you do.* 你幹甚麼我毫不在乎。

dam·na·tion /dæm'neʃən; dæm'neɪʃən/ *n* [U] **1** an expression of anger or disappointment 到底, 究竟〔表示憤怒或失望〕 **2** the state of being sent to HELL after death 罰入地獄

damned /dæmd; dæmd/ *adj* **1** a word used for giving force to a statement 非常〔用於加強語氣〕: *I'm damned sure I gave him the money.* 我非常肯定我把錢給了他。 **2** **well I'm damned, I'll be damned** = I'm very surprised 我十分震驚 **3** **be damned if** to refuse to do something because you think it is unreasonable 決不: *I'm damned if I'm going to give up my one free day of the week to help him.* 我決不會犧牲任何一天去幫助他。

damn·ing /'dæmɪŋ; 'dæmɪŋ/ *adj* strongly suggesting guilt 足以定罪的; 使負罪的: *Some damning information against them was discovered.* 有人發現了足以對他們定罪的材料。

damp¹ /dæmp; dæmp/ *adj* rather wet, often in an unpleasant way 潮濕的: *The room felt cold and damp.* 房間裡又冷又濕。 **–damp, dampness** *n* [U] **–damply** *adv*

damp² *v*

damp sthg ↔ **down** *phr v* [I] to make a fire burn more slowly 減弱火勢, 封(火)〔使火燃燒緩慢〕: *Damp down the fire before you go to bed.* 你睡覺前要把火封起來。

damp·en /'dæmpən; 'dæmpən/ *v* [T] **1** to make something damp 弄濕, 使〔某物〕潮濕: *The rain hardly dampened the ground.* 那場雨連地面也沒有打濕。 **2** to make feelings of happiness or excitement less strong 抑制; 減輕; 減弱〔高興或興奮的情感〕: *Nothing can dampen my spirits on such a nice day.* 在這樣晴朗的日子裡, 甚麼也無法減弱我的興緻!

dam·sel /'dæmzl; 'dæmzəl/ *n lit* a young unmarried woman, especially of noble birth〔文〕閨秀; 少女

dam·son /'dæmzn; 'dæmzən/ *n* a type of PLUM tree, or its purple fruit 西洋李子(樹)

★**dance¹** /dæns; dɑːns/ *v* **danced, dancing** **1** [I] to move your body, especially your feet and hands, at the speed of the music 跳舞: *She loves dancing.* 她很喜歡跳舞。| *I can't dance to this music.* 我不會跳這種節拍的舞。| *Will you dance with me?* 你和我跳個舞好嗎? **2** [T] to perform a dance 跳〔某種〕舞: *Can you dance the quickstep?* 你會跳快步舞曲嗎? **3** [I;T] to move quickly up and down or around 跳躍; 搖擺: *The words on the page were dancing in front of my eyes.* 紙頁上的字在我眼前跳個不停。| *He danced round the room.* 他繞着房間又蹦又跳。| *She danced her little sister in her lap.* 她把小妹妹放在大腿上顛着玩。

dance² *n* **1** [C] an act of dancing 舞蹈; 跳舞: *Let's just have one more dance.* 我們再跳個

舞吧。**2** [C] a particular set of movements, usually performed to music 舞步〔通常按音樂節拍跳〕: *The waltz is a beautiful dance.* 華爾茲是一種優美的舞蹈。**3** [C] a social meeting for dancing 社交舞會: *My parents are going to a dance tonight.* 我的父母今晚要去參加舞會。**4** [U] the art of dancing 舞蹈藝術: *I'm not very keen on modern dance.* 我不太喜歡現代舞蹈。–**dancer** *n*

dan·de·li·on /'dændɪˌlaɪən; 'dænd1ˌlaɪən/ *n* a wild bright yellow flower 蒲公英

dan·druff /'dændrəf; 'dændrəf/ *n* [U] small pieces of dead, white skin that can sometimes be seen in a person's hair 頭皮(屑)

★**dan·ger** /'deɪndʒə; 'deɪndʒɚ/ *n* **1** [U] the possibility of harm 危險: *"Danger! Falling rocks".* "危險! 石塊落下!" | *a danger signal* 一個危險的信號 | *a place where children can play without danger* 孩子們可以安全玩耍的地方 | *She's been very ill, but now she's out of danger.* 她一直病情嚴重, 但現已脫離危險。 | *I think his life's in danger.* 我覺得他有生命危險。**2** in danger of doing something likely to do something 有做某事的危險[可能]: *He's in danger of losing his job.* 他有失業的危險。**3** [C] a possible cause of harm 危險的起因; 危害: *the dangers of smoking* 吸煙的危害

★**dan·ger·ous** /'deɪndʒərəs; 'deɪndʒərəs/ *adj* able or likely to harm people 危險的: *a dangerous criminal* 危險的罪犯 | *a dangerous drug* 有毒的藥 | *The situation is potentially dangerous.* 形勢有潛在的危險。–**dangerously** *adv*: *He's driving very dangerously.* 他駕車駕得很危險。

dan·gle /'dæŋgl; 'dæŋgəl/ *v* **dangled, dangling 1** [I;T] to hang or swing loosely (使)吊着; (使)懸垂: *keys dangling from a chain* 吊在鏈條上的一串鑰匙 | *He sat on the edge of the table dangling his legs.* 他坐在桌沿上, 懸垂着雙腿。**2** dangle something in front of someone to offer something as an attraction, usually because you want someone to do something 以某事物招引某人〔通常指求人幫忙〕

dank /dæŋk; dæŋk/ *adj* unpleasantly wet and cold (used of buildings or parts of buildings) 潮濕的; 陰冷的〔用於指建築物〕: *a dank cellar* 陰冷潮濕的地窖 | *the dank stone walls of his prison cell* 他牢房裡潮濕陰冷的石壁

dap·per /'dæpə; 'dæpɚ/ *adj* small and with a neat appearance (used especially of men) 衣冠楚楚的〔尤指男子〕

dap·pled /'dæpld; 'dæpəld/ *adj* marked with spots of colour, or of sun and shadow 有斑紋的; 陽光斑駁的: *a dappled horse* 花斑馬

★**dare¹** /dɛr; dɛər/ *v negative short form* 否定縮約式 **daren't 1** dare to do something, dare do something to be brave enough to do something 敢做某事: *I daren't tell you any*

more. 我再也不敢告訴你了。 | *We all knew she was wrong, but none of us, dared to tell her.* 我們都知道她錯了, 但我們沒有一個人敢跟她說。 | *I want to ask for a pay rise, but I daren't.* 我想要求加薪, 但我不敢。 | *I dare not be late home again.* 我再也不敢晚回家了。 | *If you dare tell anyone about this, I'll never speak to you again!* 如果你敢向別人談到此事, 我就不會再跟你說話! –see Study Note on page 1318 見 1318 頁學習提示 **2** dare someone to do something to try to persuade someone to do something dangerous so that they can show how brave they are 慫慂某人做某事〔做危險的事以顯示勇敢〕: *He dared me to jump.* 他慫慂我跳。**3** don't you dare a phrase you use to tell someone angrily not to do something 難道你敢〔用於氣憤地阻止某人做某事〕: *Don't you dare talk to me like that!* 難道你敢那樣跟我說話! **4** how dare you a phrase you use when you are very angry about something that someone has done 你怎麼敢…〔用於氣憤地指責某人做了某事〕: *How dare you take my car without asking me?* 你怎麼竟敢不問我就用我的車?

dare² *n* an invitation to someone to do something dangerous in order to show how brave they are 挑戰; 激將

daren't /dɛrnt; dɛənt/ *short for* 縮約式 **dare not**: *I daren't ask him.* 我不敢問他。

dare·say /'dɛr'se; ˌdɛə'seɪ/ *v* **I daresay** = I suppose 我想; 也許: *I daresay you're right.* 我想你是對的。 | *It will come, I daresay.* 我想它會來的。

dar·ing /'dɛrɪŋ; 'dɛərɪŋ/ *adj* very brave 勇敢的; 大膽的: *a daring attempt to save the children from the fire* 從火災中搶救兒童的勇敢嘗試 | *a daring crime* 無法無天的罪行 –**daring** *n* [U] 勇敢: *He showed great daring.* 他表現得十分勇敢。

★**dark¹** /dɑrk; dɑːk/ *adj* **1** without enough light to see clearly 昏暗的: *It's too dark to read.* 這兒暗得不能看書。 | *In winter it gets dark here early.* 冬天這裡天黑得早。**2** black or nearly black in colour 黑色的; 深色的: *dark hair* 深色的頭髮 | *a dark blue shirt* 深藍色的襯衫 | *a man wearing a dark suit* 一位穿着深色西裝的男子 –see picture on page 243 頁 243 頁彩圖 **3** sad and without hope 悲觀的; 憂鬱的: *dark thoughts* 悲觀的想法 | *You always look on the dark side of things.* 你總是從壞的方面看事物。**4** unpleasant and frightening 邪惡的; 陰險的: *There's a dark side to his character.* 他性格中有邪惡的一面。 | *He gave me a dark look.* 他懷有惡意地看了我一眼。**5** keep something dark to keep something secret 保守祕密 –**darkly** *adv*: *He spoke darkly of trouble to come.* 他悲觀地說麻煩將來臨。–**darkness** *n* [U]

dark² *n* **1** the dark the absence of light 黑暗; 無光: *Can cats see in the dark?* 貓在黑暗中看

得見東西嗎？ | *Some children are afraid of the dark.* 有些小孩怕黑。 **2 before dark** before night has begun 在天黑以前: *Make sure you get home before dark.* 天黑前你務必要回家。 [RELATED PHRASE 相關詞組 **after dark** 在天黑以後: *We're not allowed out after dark.* 我們天黑以後不准出門。 **3 keep someone in the dark** to keep something a secret from someone 瞞住某人: *The public were kept in the dark about the government's plans.* 有關政府的計劃，公眾蒙在鼓裡。

dark·en /'dɑrkən; 'dɑːkən/ *v* **1** [I;T] to make or become dark (使)變暗: *The sky darkened and the rain began to fall.* 天空變得黑沉沉，並下起雨來。 **2** [I] (of someone's face) to show anger 〔指臉色〕陰沉: *His face darkened with anger.* 他氣得臉色發紫〔陰沉起來〕。

dark glas·ses /,· '··/ *n* [pl] glasses with dark glass in them to protect your eyes from the sun 墨鏡

dark horse /,· '·/ *n* someone who tends to keep their activities, feelings, or intentions secret, and who may have unexpected qualities or abilities 黑馬〔指實力不為人所知但意外獲勝的賽員或參賽人〕

dar·ling¹ /'dɑrlɪŋ; 'dɑːlɪŋ/ *n* a word used when you speak to or about someone you like or love 心愛的人〔常用於稱呼〕: *Hurry up, darling!* 快點兒，親愛的! | *My granddaughter is a little darling.* 我的孫女是個小寶貝。

darling² *adj* [only before a noun 只用於名詞前] dearly loved 親愛的; 心愛的: *my darling child* 我親愛的孩子

darn¹ /dɑrn; dɑːn/ *v* [I;T] to repair a hole in cloth or a garment by weaving threads across the hole 織補〔布或衣物上的破洞〕: *Can you darn socks?* 你會補襪子嗎? | *I hate darning.* 我不喜歡縫縫補補。 –**darn** *n*

darn² *adj, adv* (also 又作 **darned**) a word used to express anger or disappointment 〔表示憤怒或失望的用語〕: *It's a darn nuisance!* 真是討厭透頂!

dart¹ /dɑrt; dɑːt/ *n* **1** [C] a small object with a sharp point which can be thrown or shot 標槍; 鏢: *a poisoned dart* 塗有毒藥的鏢 **2** [C] a quick sudden movement 急衝; 突進: *He made a dart for the door.* 他朝門口急衝過去。 **3** [C] a fold sewn into a garment, to make it fit better 〔衣服的〕縫褶 **4 darts** [U] a game in which people throw darts at a special circular board called a **dartboard** 擲鏢遊戲

dart² *v* **1** [I + adv/prep] to move suddenly and quickly 急衝; 突進: *He darted towards the door.* 他衝向門口。 | *She darted across the street.* 她飛奔着穿越馬路。 **2 dart a look at someone** to look at someone suddenly and quickly 向某人投目光〔瞥某人一眼〕: *She darted an angry look at her husband.* 她狠狠地瞥了丈夫一眼。

dash¹ /dæʃ; dæʃ/ *v* **1** [I] to move with sudden speed 猛衝; 突進: *I'm late – I must dash!* 我要遲到了——我必須趕快跑。 | *He dashed across the road.* 他衝過馬路。 **2** [I + adv/prep; T+adv/prep] to throw or hit something with great force 衝撞; 撞擊: *The waves dashed against the rocks.* 海浪撞擊着礁石。 | *She dashed the books to the ground.* 她把書狠狠摔在地上。 **3 dash someone's hopes** to destroy someone's hopes completely 使某人希望落空〔破滅〕: *The accident dashed John's hopes of playing in the football team.* 這次事故使約翰參加足球隊的希望破滅了。

dash² *n* **1 make a dash for** to run a short distance very quickly 猛衝; 突進: *I made a dash for the door.* 我朝門口急衝過去。 **2** [C] a small amount of something 少量; 少許: *a dash of pepper* 少量胡椒 | *a dash of colour* 少量顏料 **3** [C] a mark (–) used in writing and printing 破折號 **4** [U] a combination of bravery and a stylish manner 銳氣; 闖勁: *a man of great dash and spirit* 一個智勇雙全的人

dash·board /'dæʃ,bord; 'dæʃbɔːd/ *n* the instrument board in a car, where many of the controls are 〔汽車的〕儀表板 –see picture on page 209 見 209 頁彩圖

dash·ing /'dæʃɪŋ; 'dæʃɪŋ/ *adj* attractive and stylish 有闖勁的: *a dashing young officer* 一位闖勁十足的年輕軍官

da·ta /'detə; 'deɪtə/ *n* [pl;U] facts or information 資料; 材料: *What does the data tell us?* 我們從資料中得到甚麼? | *We can't give you the results until we've looked at all the data.* 我們看了所有材料之後才能給你結果。

■ USAGE 用法: Although plural in its Latin form, **data** is now often used as an uncountable [U] noun. data 一詞雖是拉丁語的複數形式，但現在常用作不可數名詞。

da·ta·base /'detə,bes; 'deɪtə,beɪs/ *n* a large collection of information that is stored in a computer system in such a way that it can easily be found by a computer user 〔電腦系統的〕數據庫; 資料庫

date¹ /det; deɪt/ *n* **1** a particular time that can be shown by a number, for example the number of a day or the number of a year 日期; 月份; 年代: *What's the date today? It's the third of August.* 今天是幾月幾號? 今天是八月三日。 | *The date on the coin is 1921.* 這枚硬幣上的年份是1921年。 **2** an arrangement to meet at a particular time and place 約會: *They made a date to meet soon.* 他們不久就相約會面。 **3** *infml* an arrangement to meet a girlfriend or boyfriend 〔非正式〕〔男女間的〕約會; 幽會: *I've got a date with Jane this evening.* 我今晚和簡有個約會。 **4** *AmE infml* girlfriend or boyfriend 【美式,非正式】約會的對象〔指異性〕: *Of course you can bring your date to my party.* 你當然可以帶你的女〔男〕朋友來參加我的聚會。**5** a small brown sweet fruit with a long stone, which grows on trees in hot countries 棗 **6 out of date** no longer fashionable, or no longer able to be used 過時的; 過期的: *Her clothes are about 20 years out of date.* 她的衣服過時了二十年。| *This ticket is out of date.* 這張票過期了。**7 to date** until now 至今; 到目前為止: *We've had few responses to date.* 我們至今只得到幾個答覆。**8 up to date** modern, well informed, or at the point where you should be 現代的; 新式的: *The equipment here is really up to date.* 這裡的設備確實很新式。| *Keep me up to date with the news, will you?* 讓我了解最新消息,行嗎? | *I'm up to date with my homework now.* 我現在已按時做完了功課。

*date² *v* dated, dating **1** [T] to guess or show the age of something 斷定或表明〔某物〕的日期〔年代〕: *Archeologists can't date this pot exactly.* 考古學家無法精確鑑定這個罐子的年代。| *This dress dates me, doesn't it!* 穿這衣服顯出了我的年齡,是嗎! **2** [T] to write the date on something 在〔某物〕上寫明日期: *a letter dated 15th June* 一封註明六月十五日寫的信 **3** [I] to seem no longer fashionable 顯得過時: *This type of music is beginning to date.* 這類樂曲已逐漸過時。**4** [I;T] *AmE infml* to have or meet a girlfriend or boyfriend 【美式,非正式】〔與男、女朋友〕約會: *They've been dating for months.* 他們〔彼此〕約會已有好幾個月了。| *He's dating Susan.* 他正與蘇珊約會。**5 date back to something, date from something** to have begun or been made at a particular time or time 自某時代存在至今, 回溯至〔建成或源起日期〕: *This church dates back to 1173.* 這座教堂是遠在 1173 年建的。| *The building dates from 1626.* 這大樓建於 1626 年。

dat·ed /ˈdeɪtɪd; ˈdeɪtɪd/ *adj* no longer fashionable 過時的: *These ideas seem rather dated now.* 這些想法現在似乎早已過時。

date of birth /ˌ··ˈ·/ *n* the exact date on which you were born 出生日期: *"What's your date of birth?" "10th May 1960."* "你的生日是幾月幾號?" "1960年5月10日。"

daub /dɔːb; dɔːb/ *v* [T] to put a substance onto a surface carelessly 塗; 塗抹: *His clothes were daubed with mud.* 他的衣服沾上了泥土。| *He daubed paint on the wall.* 他把油漆塗到牆上。

**daugh·ter /ˈdɔːtə; ˈdɔːtər/ *n* someone's female child 女兒: *Mr and Mrs Jones have three daughters.* 瓊斯夫婦有三個女兒。–see picture on page 503 見 503 頁彩圖

daughter-in-law /ˈ···ˌ·/ *n* daughters-in-law the wife of your son 兒媳婦 –see picture on page 503 見 503 頁彩圖

daunt /dɔːnt; dɔːnt/ *v* [T] to make someone afraid that they will not be able to do something 恐嚇〔某人〕; 使氣餒: *We were daunted by the amount of work we had to do.* 我們被一大堆要幹的工作嚇倒了。–**daunting** *adj*: *a daunting task* 一項令人望而生畏的任務

daunt·less /ˈdɔːntlɪs; ˈdɔːntləs/ *adj* brave 無畏的; 不屈不撓的; 勇敢的: –**dauntlessly** *adv*

daw·dle /ˈdɔːdl; ˈdɔːdl/ *n* dawdled, dawdling *infml* [I] to waste time by acting or moving slowly 【非正式】游手好閒; 磨蹭: *Stop dawdling or we'll be late.* 別磨磨蹭蹭的, 否則我們要遲到了。–**dawdler** *n*

dawn¹ /dɔːn; dɔːn/ *n* **1** [C;U] the time of day when light first appears 黎明; 拂曉: *We got up at dawn.* 我們黎明時分起牀。| *the stillness of a summer dawn* 夏日黎明時分的寧靜 **2 dawn is breaking** = light is just beginning to appear 曙光初露 **3 the dawn of** the time when something is just beginning to develop 開端; 開始: *the dawn of civilization* 文明的開端

dawn² *v* **1 the day dawned, the morning dawned** = it began to grow light 破曉: *The morning dawned fresh and clear after the storm.* 暴風雨之後的清晨, 天一破曉便晴空萬里, 空氣新鮮。**2 dawn on, upon somebody** to become clear to someone 逐漸明白; 醒悟: *It suddenly dawned on me that I had caught the wrong train.* 我突然發覺我乘錯了火車。

day /deɪ; deɪ/ *n* **1 [C] a period of 24 hours 一日, 一天: *There are seven days in a week.* 一個星期有七天。| *Christmas Day* 聖誕節 –see 見 USAGE 用法 **2** [C;U] the time between sunrise and sunset 白天, 日間: *I'm usually out during the day.* 白天我通常不在家。| *It rained all day.* 雨下了一整天。**3** [C] a period of work within a 24-hour period 工作的一天: *She works an eight-hour day.* 她每天工作八小時。| *They're demanding a four-day week.* 他們在要求每星期工作四天。**4 days** [pl] a period in history or someone's life 時代; 時期: *in the days before the revolution* 革命前那個時期 | *He began his days in a village.* 他早年生活在鄉村。**5 in my day** = when I was young 小時候; 年輕時: *Things were different in my day.* 我小時候的東西完全不同了。**6 these days, in this day and age** now, as opposed to the past 如今; 當今: *People don't seem so polite these days.* 人們如今似乎不夠禮貌。**7 one day, some day** at some time in the future 總有一天〔= 將來某個時候〕**8 to this day** until now 至今: *To this day we haven't heard the whole story.* 至今我們對事情的了解還不全面。**9 have had your day** not to be popular or successful any longer 不再受歡迎〔順利〕: *Trade Unions have had their day.* 工會不再受人歡迎。**10 call it a day** *infml* to finish working for the day 【非正式】當天工作到此為止 **11 make someone's day** to make someone very pleased or happy 使某人十分得意或高興 **12 the other day** recently 前幾天: *I saw Geoff the other day.* 前幾天我見到傑弗。

day·break /'deɪ,breɪk; 'deɪbreɪk/ *n* [U] the time of day when light first appears 破曉; 黎明

day·dream /'deɪ,drim; 'deɪdriːm/ *n* a lot of pleasant thoughts, especially about things that you would like to happen 白日夢; 幻想 –**daydream** *v* [I]: *She's always daydreaming.* 她總愛做白日夢。–**daydreamer** *n*

day·light /'deɪ,laɪt; 'deɪlaɪt/ *n* [U] **1** the light of day 白晝; 日光: *There's more daylight in summer.* 夏天白晝較長。| *The house was burgled in broad daylight.* 那房子在光天化日之下被盜。**2** the time of day when it begins to get light 黎明, 拂曉

day off /ˌ· '·/ *n* a day when you do not have to go to work 休息日

day re·turn /ˌ·· '·/ *n* a ticket for a bus or train journey when you want to go and come back on the same day 即日來回票

day·time /'deɪ,taɪm; 'deɪtaɪm/ *n* [sing; U] the time between sunrise and sunset 白天; 日間: *I can't sleep in the daytime.* 我在白天睡不着覺。| *Daytime flights are always more expensive.* 坐白天班機總是貴一點。

day-to-day /ˌ·· '·/ *adj* [only before a noun 只用於名詞前] happening every day as a regular part of life 日常的; 每天的: *life's day-to-day routine* 日常生活事務

daze /dez; deɪz/ *n* **in a daze** unable to think or feel clearly 茫然, 迷亂

dazed /dezd; deɪzd/ *adj* unable to think or feel clearly, for example because of a blow or shock 〔由於受到打擊或震驚而〕茫然的: *She was dazed after the accident.* 事故發生後, 她神志不清。| *The news left him dazed.* 這消息使他不知所措。

daz·zle /'dæzl̩; 'dæzəl/ *v* **dazzled, dazzling** [T] **1** to make someone unable to see by throwing a strong light in their eyes 使眼花; 使目眩: *The lights of the car dazzled me.* 汽車的燈光照得我眼花。**2** to fill someone with admiration 使〔某人〕讚許; 稱奇: *The whole family was dazzled by her success.* 她的成功使全家人讚嘆不已。–**dazzle** *n* [sing]: *the dazzle of the bright lights* 亮光的閃爍 | *the dazzle of her smile* 她那微笑的魅力

DC /ˌdi 'si; ˌdi: 'si:/ a flow of electricity that moves in one direction only 直流電: an abbreviation for 〔縮〕= **direct current** –compare 比較 **AC**

DDT /ˌdi di 'ti; ˌdi: di: 'ti:/ *n* [U] a chemical used to kill insects 滴滴涕〔一種殺蟲劑〕

dea·con /'dikən; 'di:kən/ *n* a religious official in various Christian churches; a woman deacon is called a **deaconess** 〔各基督教會中的〕執事; 助祭〔女性稱為 **deaconess**〕

dead¹ /dɛd; ded/ *adj* **1** no longer alive 已死的; 死亡的: *a dead man* 死人 | *a dead body* 屍體 | *That plant is dead.* 那棵植物死了。–

see 見 USAGE 用法 **2** without the necessary power to work properly 無正常功能的: *The phone went dead.* 這電話壞了。**3** without life, movement, or activity 無生氣的; 無活動的: *The whole place seems dead.* 整個地方顯得死氣沉沉。**4** no longer in use 不再使用的: *a dead language* 不再通用的語言 | *dead issues* 不再談論的問題 **5** *infml* very tired 〔非正式〕疲憊的: *I'm absolutely dead.* 我確實累極了。**6** complete or exact (a word used before a noun for emphasis) 完全的; 徹底的〔用於名詞前作強調〕: *We came to a dead stop.* 我們猛然停住了。| *dead silence* 死一般的寂靜 **7 dead to the world** very deeply asleep 熟睡的 **8 wouldn't be seen dead** *infml* = would refuse to do something or go somewhere 〔非正式〕拒絕〔做某事或去某處〕: *I wouldn't be seen dead wearing that hat.* 我寧死也不戴那頂帽子。| *She wouldn't be seen dead at any event organized by Bob.* 她就是不願參加鮑勃組織的活動。

■ USAGE 用法: If you are thinking about the fact that somebody is no longer alive, use the adjective **dead** ☆ 如要表示某人已不在世上, 用形容詞 **dead**: *My grandfather has been dead for several years.* 我的祖父已去世好幾年了。| *When I approached the bed, I realised the patient was dead.* 我走近病牀時, 發現病人已去世。| *Shakespeare and Dickens are dead, but we still read their works.* 雖然莎士比亞和狄更斯不在人世, 但我們還在看他們寫的書。If you are thinking about the moment or the action of dying, use the verb **die** ☆ 如要表示死亡的時刻或動作, 則用動詞 **die**: *My grandfather died in 1985.* 我的祖父於1985年去世。| *I realised the patient had died in the night.* 我發現病人在夜裡去世了。| *When did Dickens die?* 狄更斯是何時去世的?

dead² *n* **1 in the dead of winter, at dead of night** in the middle of winter or in the middle of the night when everything is quiet and still 在隆冬; 在夜闌人靜時 **2 the dead** a person who has died or people who have died 死者

dead³ *adv* **1** *infml* completely or extremely 〔非正式〕全然地; 極其地: *I'm dead tired.* 我累極了。**2** *infml* exactly 〔非正式〕確切地; 恰好: *The police station is dead ahead.* 警察局就在前面。**3 stop dead** to stop suddenly and completely 突然完全停止

dead·en /'dɛdn̩; 'dedn/ *v* [T] to make a sound or feeling less strong 減低〔聲音或感覺〕的強度; 減弱: *The drugs deadened the pain.* 那藥物可以鎮痛。| *Thick walls deaden noise.* 厚牆可以隔音。

dead end /ˌ· '·◂/ *n* **1** a street with no way out at one end 死巷; 死胡同 **2** a situation or position which cannot change or develop any more 絕境; 僵局: *It's a dead end job.* 這項工作沒有出路。

dead·line /ˈdɛd,laɪn; ˈdɛdlaɪn/ *n* a date or time before which something must be done 截止日期; 最後限期: *Next Friday's the deadline for this report.* 下星期五是交這份報告的最後期限。

dead·lock /ˈdɛd,lɒk; ˈdɛdlɒk/ *n* [C;U] a situation in which a disagreement cannot be settled 僵局: *The talks ended in deadlock.* 談判陷入了僵局。

dead·ly¹ /ˈdɛdlɪ; ˈdɛdlɪ/ *adj* **deadlier, deadliest 1** very dangerous and likely to cause death 危險的; 致命的: *a deadly disease* 致命的疾病 | *deadly weapons* 致命的武器 **2** very effective in hurting someone 〔對人〕極厲害的: *a deadly remark* 中傷的言詞 | *a deadly insult* 極力的污辱 **3** complete and total in an unpleasant way 不共戴天的; 滿懷仇恨的: *They are deadly enemies.* 他們是不共戴天的仇敵。 | *There was a deadly silence.* 那裡一片死寂。 **4** *infml* very dull 〔非正式〕枯燥乏味的: *The party was deadly.* 那聚會枯燥乏味。 – **deadliness** *n* [U]

deadly² *adv* very 很; 非常: *He was being deadly serious.* 他總是非常嚴肅認真。

dead·pan /ˈdɛd,pæn; ˈdɛdpæn/ *adj* showing no feeling and appearing to be serious even when you are joking 無表情的〔甚至在說笑話時〕一本正經的: *deadpan humour* 無表情的幽默; 冷面幽默 | *a deadpan expression* 不帶感情的措詞

dead weight /ˈdɛd,wet; ˈdɛd,weɪt/ *n* [sing] something that is very heavy and difficult to lift 重負; 沉重的物體

*⋆**deaf** /dɛf; def/ *adj* **1** unable to hear 聾的; 聽力差的: *a special school for deaf children* 為失聰兒童而設的特殊學校 | *Speak up, I'm a bit deaf.* 說大聲點; 我有點兒耳聾。 **2** **be deaf to something, turn a deaf ear to something** to refuse to listen to something 對某事物充耳不聞: *She was deaf to all my requests.* 她對我的一切要求置之不理〔置若罔聞〕。 **3** **fall on deaf ears** not to be listened to 無人理睬: *His warnings fell on deaf ears.* 他的告誡無人理睬。 – **deafness** *n* [U]

deaf·en /ˈdɛfən; ˈdefən/ *v* [T] to make it difficult for you to hear anything 使聾; 震聾: *We were deafened by the noise.* 我們被噪音震聾了耳朵。 – **deafening** *adj*: *a deafening noise* 震耳欲聾的噪音

⋆⋆**deal¹** /dil; diːl/ *v* **dealt** /dɛlt; delt/, **dealt 1** [I;T] (also 又作 **deal out; deal sthg ↔ out**) to give out playing cards to players in a card game 〔紙牌遊戲中的〕發牌: *It's my turn to deal.* 輪到我發牌了。 | *He dealt out the cards.* 他給大家發牌。 | *I dealt three cards to each player.* 我給每個玩牌的人發了三張牌。 | *I dealt them four cards each.* 我給他們每人發四張牌。 **2** **deal someone a blow** to hit someone hard, or to do some-

one or something sudden harm 打某人一下; 給某人以沉重打擊: *She dealt him a blow on the side of his face.* 她打了他一記耳光。 | *This policy dealt a severe blow to British industry.* 這個政策是對英國工業的沉重打擊。

deal in sthg *phr v* [T] to buy and sell things 買賣; 經營: *This shop deals in men's clothing.* 這家商店經營男士服裝。

deal with sbdy/sthg *phr v* [T] **1** to take the necessary action to find an answer to a problem 對付; 對待; 處理: *How would you deal with this situation?* 你會怎樣對付這種局面? **2** to be about 關於; 涉及; 論述: *This book deals with the troubles in Ireland.* 這本新書論述愛爾蘭的糾紛。 **3** to do business with a company or person 〔與公司或個人〕做生意: *I've dealt with Jones and Taylor for 20 years.* 我與瓊斯和泰勒做生意已有二十年。

⋆⋆**deal²** *n* **1** an arrangement or agreement, especially in business 交易; 買賣: *We did quite well out of the deal.* 我們的生意很興隆。 | *Perhaps we can do a deal with our competitors.* 也許我們能與對方做一筆買賣。 | *It's a deal!* 這生意就這樣定了! **2** **a great deal, a good deal** a lot 大量: *A great deal of money has been spent on the new hospital.* 在這家新醫院上面已經花了一大筆錢。 | *You'll have to work a good deal faster.* 你必須大大加快工作進度。 **3** [C] someone's turn to give out cards to players in a card game 〔紙牌遊戲中輪到某人〕發牌: *Is it my deal?* 該輪到我發牌了嗎? **4** **a bad deal, a raw deal** *infml* unfair or unpleasant treatment 〔非正式〕不公平的待遇: *Working nights again! I always get a raw deal from this company.* 又要做夜班了! 這家公司待我總是不公平。

> ■ USAGE 用法: Remember that **a great deal of** is usually used with uncountable [U] nouns ☆ 切記 **a great deal of** 通常與不可數名詞連用: **a great deal of** *effort/money/kindness* 大量的努力〔金錢、仁慈〕 Do NOT use it with countable [C] nouns. Instead you can say ☆ 不要與可數名詞連用, 但可以說: **a great many** *people/countries/activities* or, more informally, 或者在非正式文體中用 **a lot of** *people/countries/activities*. 許多人〔國家、活動〕或者在非正式文體中用 **a lot of**。

⋆**deal·er** /ˈdilɚ; ˈdiːlə(r)/ *n* **1** a person who buys and sells a particular type of thing 商人: *a used-car dealer* 買賣舊汽車的商人 | *a dealer in stolen goods* 經營偷盜物品的商人 **2** a person who is dealing in a game of cards 發牌人

deal·ing /ˈdilɪŋ; ˈdiːlɪŋ/ *n* **1** [U] the buying and selling of things 買賣; 交易: *There's a lot of drug dealing in this area.* 這個地區有許多人販賣毒品。 **2** [U] a way of behaving towards other people 經營作風: *I'm in* *favour of plain honest dealing.* 我贊同誠實的經營作風. **3 dealings** [pl] personal or business relations with someone 來往; 交易: *I've never had any dealings with him.* 我從來沒和他做過生意.

dealt /dɛlt; dɛlt/ the past tense and past participle of DEAL ☆ DEAL的過去式和過去分詞

dean /diːn; diːn/ n **1** a priest of high rank in some Christian churches, who is in charge of a large church 〔某些基督教會中的〕教長; 主任牧師 **2** an official of high rank in some universities 〔某些大學裡的〕學院院長; 教務長; 系主任

dear¹ /dɪr; dɪəʳ/ adj **1** much loved, or very important to you 親愛的; 寶貴的: *He's a dear friend of mine.* 他是我的一位摯友. | *The house is very dear to her.* 她對這房子有很深的感情. **2** a word used before a name or title at the beginning of a letter 〔用於信首〕親愛的: *Dear Jane* 親愛的簡 | *Dear Sir* 尊敬的先生 | *Dear Mrs Jones* 瓊斯夫人大鑒 **3** expensive 昂貴的: *That coat's too dear, I'm afraid.* 我恐怕那件衣服太貴了.

dear² n a word used when talking to or about someone you like or love 親愛的人; 可愛的人: *Did you have a good day at work, dear?* 親愛的, 你今天工作順利嗎? | *She's a real dear.* 她的確很可愛.

★**dear³** interj a word used for expressing surprise, disappointment, or slight anger 〔表示驚奇、失望、微怒〕哎呀; 唉: *Oh dear! I've lost my pen.* 哎呀! 我把鋼筆丟了. | *Dear! dear! What will he do next?* 唉! 唉! 下一步他該如何是好? 〔接下去他該怎麼辦?〕

dear·ly /dɪrli; 'dɪəli/ adv **1** love someone dearly to love someone very much 深情地愛著某人: *He loves his wife dearly.* 他深愛妻子. **2** would dearly like, would dearly love = would very much like 非常地想〔做某事〕: *I'd dearly love to see what he keeps in that box.* 我很想知道他在那盒子裡藏了些甚麼. **3** pay dearly to suffer a lot as the result of something that you have done 付出巨大代價: *He paid dearly for his mistake.* 他為自己的錯誤付出了巨大的代價.

dearth /dɜːθ; dɜːθ/ n a lack 缺乏; 稀少: *There's a dearth of good secretaries in the firm.* 該公司缺乏稱職的祕書.

★**death** /dɛθ; deθ/ n **1** [C;U] the end of life 死亡: *His mother's death was a great shock to him.* 他母親的死對他是很大的打擊. | *Car accidents cause many deaths.* 車禍造成很多人死亡. **2** [U] the end of something 〔事物的〕破滅; 滅絕: *a defeat that meant the death of all my hopes* 一次意味着我全部希望破滅的失敗 **3** to death until no longer alive 以致死亡〔斷氣〕: *He was beaten to death.* 他被活活打死. **4** put to death to kill someone, especially with official permission 殺死; 〔尤指〕處死: *The prisoners were all put to death.* 囚犯們都被處死. **5 at**

death's door infml extremely ill 〔非正式〕病危; 行將就木 **6 catch your death of cold** infml to become very ill with a cold 〔非正式〕得重感冒: *If you go out dressed like that, you'll catch your death of cold.* 如果你就穿那麼一點衣服外出, 會得重感冒的. **7 frightened to death, worried to death** very frightened or worried 嚇得要命; 擔心得要死

death·blow /'dɛθ.bləʊ; 'deθbləʊ/ n an act or event that destroys or ends something 沉重〔致命〕的打擊: *His refusal to help us dealt a deathblow to our plan.* 他拒絕給我們提供幫助, 這對我們的計劃是個沉重的打擊.

death·ly /'dɛθli; 'deθli/ adj, adv as quiet, as cold, or as pale as someone who is dead 死一般的〔地〕; 非常: *a deathly silence* 死一般的寂靜 | *She looked deathly pale.* 她的面色看上去極為蒼白.

death trap /'· ·/ n something, usually a building or vehicle, which is very dangerous and could cause the death of people in it 死亡陷阱: *That old car is a real death trap.* 那輛破舊的汽車實在是不安全的東西.

death war·rant /'· ·,··/ n a written official order to kill someone 死刑執行令

de·bar /dɪ'bɑːr; dɪ'bɑːʳ/ -rr- v [T] fml debar someone from something to officially prevent someone from doing something 〔正式〕禁止某人做某事: *He's been debarred from using the library.* 他被禁止使用圖書館.

de·base /dɪ'beɪs; dɪ'beɪs/ v debased, debasing **1** [T] to reduce the quality or value of something 貶低品格; 降低品質: **2 debase yourself** to behave in such a way that people have less respect for you 降低自己的身分 **–debasement** n [C;U]

de·ba·ta·ble /dɪ'beɪtəbl; dɪ'beɪtəbəl/ adj perhaps not true 可爭辯的; 未必正確的: *They say their policies have not caused unemployment, but I think that's debatable.* 他們說, 他們的政策並未引起失業, 但我認為這話未必正確.

de·bate¹ /dɪ'beɪt; dɪ'beɪt/ n **1** [C] a formal and often public meeting in which speakers express different arguments in relation to the same subject 辯論; 爭論: *a long debate in Parliament* 國會中的一場長時間辯論 **2** [C;U] the process of talking about a question 討論: *After much debate, the committee decided to close the school.* 經過長時間討論, 委員會決定停辦這所學校. **3 open to debate** perhaps not true 尚可爭論〔或許不夠正確〕

debate² v debated, debating **1** [I;T] to talk about something quite formally with another person or other people, usually in an effort to persuade them 爭論; 辯論: *Ministers are debating the future of the health service today.* 部長們在辯論目前公共醫療衛生服務的發展前景. **2** [T] to consider possibilities 考慮〔可能性〕: *I'm seriously debating whether to change jobs next year.* 我在

認真考慮明年是否要換個工作。

de·bauched /dɪˈbɔtʃt; dɪˈbɔːtʃt/ *adj* behaving badly, especially in relation to sex and alcohol 墮落的; 淫蕩的; 酗酒的: *His behaviour was thoroughly debauched.* 他的行為墮落透頂。

de·bauch·e·ry /dɪˈbɔtʃərɪ; dɪˈbɔːtʃəri/ *n* [U] behaviour which is not socially acceptable, especially in relation to sex and alcohol 墮落; 淫蕩; 酗酒

de·bil·i·tate /dɪˈbɪlə.tet; dɪˈbɪlˌteɪt/ *v* **debilitated, debilitating** [T] to make someone or something weak 使虛弱; 使衰弱: *This heat debilitates most Europeans.* 這場高溫[炎熱]把許多歐洲人的身體都弄得很虛弱。| *a debilitating disease* 使人虛弱的疾病

de·bil·i·ty /dɪˈbɪlətɪ; dɪˈbɪlˌti/ *n* [U] *fml* weakness, especially as the result of illness 〖正式〗衰弱〖尤指病後的虛弱〗

deb·it¹ /ˈdɛbɪt; ˈdebˌt/ *n* a record in your bank account of money that you have spent or that you owe 〔賬簿的〕借項, 借方 –compare 比較 CREDIT

debit² *v* [T] to take money from someone's bank account 〔從某人賬戶內〕提款: *Would you just debit my account, please.* 請你在我的賬戶內提款。–compare 比較 CREDIT

deb·o·nair /ˌdɛbəˈnɛr; ˌdebəˈneər/ *adj old fash* charming, well-dressed, and confident (used of men) 〖老式〗溫文爾雅的; 衣冠楚楚的; 自信的〔指男人〕: *a debonair young man* 溫文有禮、衣着入時的青年人

de·brief /diˈbrif; ˌdiːˈbriːf/ *v* [T] to obtain information from someone who has just done something which is important to you, by asking very detailed questions 詢問執行任務的情況: *All returning diplomats are debriefed.* 所有歸國大使都要作詳細匯報。

deb·ris /dəˈbri; ˈdebri/ *n* [U] the remains of something broken to pieces or destroyed 碎片; 殘骸; 瓦礫: *A lot of debris has been lying around since the war.* 戰爭爆發以來, 到處是一片瓦礫。

‡debt /dɛt; det/ *n* **1** [C;U] something that you owe to someone else 債務; 欠款: *If I win, I'll pay all my debts.* 如果我贏了, 我會還清所有債務。| *I owe you a real debt of gratitude for everything you've done.* 對你為我所作的一切, 我真是感激不盡。**2 a bad debt** money which is owed but which will probably never be repaid 壞賬; 倒賬〔一筆可能永遠不會被償還的債務〕**3 in debt** owing money to someone 欠債: *She's always in debt.* 她總是負債纍纍。| *I'm worried that we're running into debt.* 我擔心我們要開始欠債了。[RELATED PHRASE 相關詞組 **out of debt**] **4 in someone's debt** grateful to someone 欠某人之情: *After all the help you've given me, I'm forever in your debt.* 你給了我那麼多幫助, 我永遠感恩不盡。

debt·or /ˈdɛtɚ; ˈdetər/ *n* a person who owes money 債務人

de·bunk /diˈbʌŋk; ˌdiːˈbʌŋk/ *v infml* [T] to point out the truth about a wrong idea, or make it seem less important 〖非正式〗揭穿; 暴露〔真相〕

de·but /dɪˈbju; ˈdeɪbjuː/ *n* a person's first public appearance 初進社交界; 初次登台: *The singer made his debut as Mozart's Don Giovanni* 這位歌唱家初次登台是表演莫扎特的唐·喬凡尼。

deb·u·tante /ˌdɛbjuˈtɑnt; ˈdebjʊtɑːnt/ *n* a girl who has just formally entered upper-class society 初進社交界的女郎

Dec. *n* a written abbreviation for 〖縮寫〗= DECEMBER

dec·ade /ˈdɛked; ˈdekeɪd/ *n* a period of 10 years 十年: *Prices have risen steadily during the past decade.* 在過去的十年間, 物價一直在上漲。

dec·a·dent /ˈdɛkədnt; ˈdekədənt/ *adj* having falling standards, especially moral standards 墮落的, 頹廢的 –**decadence** *n* [U]

de·caf·fein·at·ed /diˈkæfə.netɪd; diːˈkæfˌneɪtɪd/ *adj* having had the CAFFEINE removed from it (used of tea or coffee) 除去咖啡因的〔指茶或咖啡〕

de·cant /dɪˈkænt; dɪˈkænt/ *v* [T] to pour liquid, especially wine, carefully from one container into another 移注〔尤指將酒從一個容器倒入另一個容器〕

de·cant·er /dɪˈkæntɚ; dɪˈkæntər/ *n* a container, usually a glass bottle, from which you serve wine or certain other drinks 〔通常為玻璃瓶的〕盛酒器

de·cap·i·tate /dɪˈkæpə.tet; dɪˈkæpˌteɪt/ *v* **decapitated, decapitating** [T] to cut off someone's head 把〔某人〕斬首 –**decapitation** /dɪˌkæpəˈteʃən; dɪˌkæpˌˈteɪʃən/ *n* [C; U]

de·cay¹ /dɪˈke; dɪˈkeɪ/ *v* **1** [I;T] to destroy something or be destroyed very slowly through chemical and other changes 腐蝕; 使朽壞: *Sugar can decay your teeth.* 糖會蛀蝕牙齒。| *a decayed body* 腐爛的屍體 **2** [I] to become weaker and less influential, while social standards probably also fall 衰弱; 衰敗: *It seems that all great civilizations decay in time.* 似乎所有偉大的文明都會衰落。

decay² *n* [U] the process, state, or result of decaying 衰敗; 衰弱; 腐朽: *dental decay* 蛀牙 | *This material is tough, and resistant to decay.* 這種物質很堅硬, 能防蛀防腐。

de·ceased /dɪˈsist; dɪˈsiːst/ *n law* **the deceased** a person who has died or people who have died 〖律〗死者: *The deceased left a large sum of money to his wife.* 死者給妻子遺留下一大筆錢。–**deceased** *adj*: *the deceased woman* 那已故的女人

de·ceit /dɪˈsit; dɪˈsiːt/ *n* [U] speech or action which is intended to make someone believe something that is not true for a dishonest purpose 詭計, 欺騙手段

de·ceit·ful /dɪˈsitfəl; dɪˈsiːtfəl/ *adj* intending

to make someone believe something that is not true 欺騙; 不老實的 –**deceitfully** *adv* –**deceitfulness** *n* [U]

de·ceive /dɪˈsɪv; dɪˈsiːv/ *v* **deceived, deceiving 1** [T] to make someone believe something that is not true for a dishonest purpose 欺騙; 哄瞞; 蒙蔽: *He deceived her from their first meeting, when he told her he was single.* 他自第一次見面就欺騙了她, 他說他是單身漢。 **2 deceive yourself** not to allow yourself to think that something is true, although you know really that it is true 自欺欺人〔欺騙自己〕: *When are you going to stop deceiving yourself and face up to reality?* 你甚麼時候才能不自欺欺人, 才肯面對現實呢? –**deceiver** *n*

De·cem·ber /dɪˈsɛmbə; dɪˈsembəʳ/ *n* (also 又作 **Dec.**) the 12th and last month of the year 十二月

de·cen·cy /ˈdiːsn̩si; ˈdiːsənsi/ *n* [U] **1** socially acceptable behaviour 正派; 端莊; 體面 **2 have the decency to do something** to have the good manners to do something 體面行事: *Her work was terrible, but at least she had the decency not to ask for payment.* 她的工作做得很糟糕, 但她至少沒要要報酬, 還算體面。

de·cent /ˈdiːsn̩t; ˈdiːsənt/ *adj* **1** socially acceptable 體面的; 莊重的; 大方的: *Surely that skirt's too short to be decent!* 那條裙子確實太短, 不太雅觀。 **2** acceptable or good 相當不錯的, 像樣的: *You can get quite a decent meal there.* 你能在那裡吃上一頓相當不錯的飯。 | *a decent salary* 可觀的薪水 **3** honest and good (used of people) 誠實正派的〔指人〕: *Decent people just can't feel safe around here any more.* 作風正派的人在這裡再也沒有安全感。 **4** kind 和善的; 好心的: *It's very decent of you to drive me to the station.* 你開車送我到火車站, 你真是太好了。 –**decently** *adv*

de·cen·tral·ize /diˈsɛntrəlaɪz; ˌdiːˈsentrəlaɪz/ *v* **decentralized, decentralizing** (also 又作 **decentralise** *BrE*〔英式〕) [I;T] (of a company or a government department) to move from one big place to several smaller places 〔公司或政府部門〕權力下放; 分權 –**decentralization** /ˌdiːsɛntrəlaɪˈzeɪʃən; ˌdiːˌsentrəlaɪˈzeɪʃən/ *n* [U]

de·cep·tion /dɪˈsɛpʃən; dɪˈsepʃən/ *n* [C;U] an action or behaviour which is intended to make someone believe something that is not true 欺騙; 欺詐; 蒙蔽

de·cep·tive /dɪˈsɛptɪv; dɪˈseptɪv/ *adj* making you believe something that is not true 欺騙的; 欺詐的: *Appearances can be deceptive.* 外表往往是靠不住的。 –**deceptively** *adv* –**deceptiveness** *n* [U]

dec·i·bel /ˈdɛsəˌbɛl; ˈdesɪbel/ *n* *tech* a measure of the loudness of sound 〔術語〕分貝〔音量單位〕

de·cide /dɪˈsaɪd; dɪˈsaɪd/ *v* **1** [I;T; + (that)] to make a choice or

judgment 決定; 決心; 判斷: *I don't know which one to take – I'll let you decide.* 我不知道該取哪一個 — 還是由你來決定吧。 | *I've decided to resign.* 我已決定辭職。 | *Let's decide where to go!* 讓我們決定一下去哪兒! | *They decided on Spain.* 他們決定去西班牙。 | *The court decided in his favour.* 法院判決他勝訴。 | *I decided that it would cost too much.* 我估計要花很多錢。

> □ USEFUL PATTERNS 有用句型
> to decide where, when, how, whether…;
> to decide on something; to decide to do something; to decide that…

2 [T] to make someone arrive at a choice or judgment 使（某人）作出決定［判斷］: *His illness finally decided me, I could not leave.* 他的病最後使我作出抉擇, 我不能走。 **3** [T] to bring something to a clear or certain end 裁決（某事物）; 解決: *A goal in the last minute decided the match.* 最後一分鐘的進球決定了比賽的勝負。

de·cid·ed /dɪˈsaɪdɪd; dɪˈsaɪdɪd/ *adj* very clear or definite 顯然的; 明確的: *a decided change for the better* 明顯的好轉 –**decidedly** *adv*

de·cid·u·ous /dɪˈsɪdʒʊəs; dɪˈsɪdʒuəs/ *adj* having leaves that fall off in autumn 〔秋季〕落葉的: *deciduous trees* 落葉的樹 –compare 比較 EVERGREEN

dec·i·mal¹ /ˈdɛsəml; ˈdesɪməl/ *adj* based on the number 10 以十作基礎的; 十進位的: *decimal currency* 十進制貨幣

dec·i·mal² *n* (also 又作 **decimal fraction**) a number such as .5, .375, or .06 小數〔如.5, .375, .06〕

dec·i·mal·ize /ˈdɛsəmlˌaɪz; ˈdesɪməlaɪz/ *v* **decimalized, decimalizing** (also 又作 **decimalise** *BrE*〔英式〕) [I;T] to change to a decimal system of money, or counting (使)變成十進制 –**decimalization** /ˌdɛsəməlɪˈzeɪʃən; ˌdesɪməlaɪˈzeɪʃən/ *n* [U]

decimal point /ˌ···ˈ·/ *n* the dot at the left of a decimal fraction 小數點

dec·i·mate /ˈdɛsəˌmeɪt; ˈdesɪmeɪt/ *v* **decimated, decimating** [T] *fml* to destroy a large part or a large number of something 〔正式〕毀滅（某物）的大部分: *Disease decimated the population.* 疾病使大批的人死亡。 –**decimation** /ˌdɛsəˈmeɪʃən; ˌdesɪˈmeɪʃən/ *n* [U]

de·ci·pher /dɪˈsaɪfə; dɪˈsaɪfəʳ/ *v* [T] to find meaning in something that is difficult to read or understand 譯解〔難懂的東西〕: *Your writing is almost impossible to decipher.* 你寫的字簡直難以辨認。

de·ci·sion /dɪˈsɪʒən; dɪˈsɪʒən/ *n* **1** [C;U] a choice of one out of a number of possibilities 決定; 決心; 判斷: *Who made the decision to go there?* 是誰決定到那兒去的? | *Whose decision was it?* 那是誰作出的

決定? | *They expect to reach a decision soon.* 他們預期不久就可以作出決定。 | *The moment of decision had arrived.* 是時候作出決定了。 **2** [U] the quality of being able to make choices quickly 果斷; 堅定

de·ci·sive /dɪˈsaɪsɪv; dɪˈsaɪsɪv/ *adj* **1** having or showing the ability to make decisions quickly 果斷的; 決斷的: *We need a strong, decisive leader.* 我們需要既堅強又果斷的領導。 **2** leading to a certain result 決定性的: *a decisive battle* 決定性的戰役 **–decisively** *adv* **–decisiveness** *n* [U]

deck¹ /dɛk; dek/ *n* **1** a level of a ship or bus 〔輪船的〕甲板; 〔公共汽車的〕一層: *Smoking is only allowed on the top deck.* 只准在頂層甲板吸煙。 **2 on deck** on the place around the top of a ship in the open air 在甲板上: *Shall we go up on deck?* 我們到甲板上去, 好嗎? **3** the usual American word for a PACK¹ (4) of playing cards 一副紙牌

deck² *v*

   deck sbdy/sthg ↔ **out** *phr v* [T] to make something or someone more attractive 裝飾〔某人或某物〕: *The street was decked out with flags.* 街上掛滿了旗幟。

deck·chair /ˈdɛk.tʃɛər; ˈdɛktʃeər/ *n* a folding chair usually used outdoors 〔戶外用的〕帆布躺椅

de·claim /dɪˈklem; dɪˈkleɪm/ *v fml* [I;T] to speak loudly and clearly like an actor 〔正式〕慷慨陳詞; 演講 **–declamatory** /dɪˈklæmə.tərɪ; dɪˈklæmətɔːrɪ/ *adj*

★**dec·la·ra·tion** /ˌdɛkləˈreʃən; ˌdɛkləˈreɪʃən/ *n* a written or spoken statement, giving information in an official manner 宣言; 公告; 宣佈: *Please make a written declaration of all the goods you bought abroad.* 請書面申報你在國外購買的全部物品。 | *a declaration of war* 戰爭宣言

★**de·clare** /dɪˈklɛr; dɪˈkleər/ *v* **1** [T; +(that)] to make something public or official, according to rules or custom 宣告; 宣佈: *Our government has declared war on Ruritania.* 我們政府已向魯里坦尼亞宣戰。 | *Jones was declared the winner.* 瓊斯被宣佈為勝利者。 | *I declare Mr B. Schiff elected!* 我宣佈比·希夫先生當選! **2** [T; +(that)] to state something clearly and forcefully 聲明; 斷言: *He declared his support for the terrorists.* 他聲稱支持恐怖分子。 | *She declared that she knew nothing about the robbery.* 她聲稱對那次搶劫一無所知。

□ USEFUL PATTERNS 有用句型
to declare something; to declare that…; to declare yourself to be…

3 [T] to state the value of goods which you have bought abroad and on which you may have to pay tax 申報〔徵稅物品〕: *Have you anything to declare?* 你有甚麼東西要申報嗎?

★**de·cline¹** /dɪˈklaɪn; dɪˈklaɪn/ *v* **declined, declining 1** [I] to move from a better to a worse position, or from higher to lower 衰落; 下降: *As his health has declined, so has his influence.* 隨着他體力的衰退, 他的影響力也在降低。 **2** [I;T] *fml* to refuse something, usually politely 〔正式〕謝絕: *We invited them, but they declined.* 我們邀請他們, 但他們謝絕了。 | *They declined our invitation.* 他們謝絕了我們的邀請。 | *The minister declined to make a statement.* 部長拒絕發表聲明。 **–see** 見 REFUSE (USAGE 用法)

□ USEFUL PATTERNS 有用句型
to decline something, to decline to do something

★**decline²** *n* **1** [C;U] a change to something worse, smaller, or lower 下降; 變小; 變弱: *There has been a sharp decline in interest in farming.* (人們)對農業的關注已急劇下降。 | *The government's popularity is in decline.* 政府的聲望正在降低。 **2 on the decline, falling into decline** becoming weaker or less important 變弱; 失去影響: *The car industry in Britain is falling into decline.* 英國的汽車工業每況愈下。

de·code /ˌdiˈkod; ˌdiːˈkəʊd/ *v* [T] **decoded, decoding** to discover the meaning of something expressed in a CODE¹ (1) 譯〔碼〕; 解〔碼〕

de·com·pose /ˌdikəmˈpoz; ˌdiːkəmˈpəʊz/ *v* **decomposed, decomposing** [I;T] to decay (使)腐爛; 分解 **–decomposition** /ˌdikɑmpəˈzɪʃən; ˌdiːkɒmpəˈzɪʃən/ *n* [U]

dé·cor /ˈdeˈkɔr; ˈdeɪkɔːr/ *n* [U] the decoration and furnishing of a place, house, or stage 裝飾; 佈置〔房屋或舞台〕: *The food at the restaurant is good but the décor is awful.* 那家餐館的飯菜做得不錯, 但佈置得很糟糕。

dec·o·rate /ˈdɛkə.ret; ˈdekəreɪt/ *v* **decorated, decorating 1** [I;T] to make something more attractive by adding something beautiful or by putting paint or paper on the walls of a house 裝飾; 裝修: *The streets were decorated with flags.* 各街道都用旗幟裝飾起來。 | *We spent the weekend decorating.* 我們利用週末來裝修房子。 **2** [T] to give someone an official mark of honour, such as a MEDAL 授予〔某人〕榮譽標誌〔如獎章〕: *He was decorated for outstanding bravery in the last war.* 他因在上次戰爭中英勇無比而獲授獎章。

dec·o·ra·tion /ˌdɛkəˈreʃən; ˌdekəˈreɪʃən/ *n* **1** [U] the act or art of decorating, or the process of being decorated 裝飾; 裝飾藝術; 裝潢 **2** [C;U] something that is added to make something more attractive 裝飾品; 裝潢品: *Christmas decorations* 聖誕節的裝飾品 | *simple architectural designs with no decoration* 沒有裝潢的簡單建築設計 **3** [C] something, such as a MEDAL, which is given as a sign of honour 授予的榮譽標誌〔如獎章〕

dec·o·ra·tive /'dɛkə,retɪv; 'dekərətɪv/ *adj* attractive, or used to make something else more attractive 裝飾的; 作裝飾用的: *a decorative gold table* 作裝飾用的金桌子 —**decoratively** *adv*

dec·o·ra·tor /'dɛkə,retə·; 'dekəreɪtər/ *n* a person who paints houses inside and out 房屋油漆工

dec·o·rous /'dɛkərəs, 'dekərəs/ *adj fml* correct and respectful (used of behaviour or appearance) 〔正式〕正派的; 有禮貌的〔指行為或外表〕—**decorously** *adv*

de·co·rum /dɪ'korəm; dɪ'kɔːrəm/ *n* [U] correct and respectful behaviour or appearance 正派得體; 端莊穩重

de·coy /dɪ'kɔɪ; 'diːkɔɪ/ *n* something which is used for leading a person or bird into a trap 〔引人或鳥入圈套的〕引誘物; 誘餌 —**decoy** *v* [T]

de·crease /dɪ'kris; dɪ'kriːs/ *v* **decreased, decreasing 1** [I] to become less or to make something less in size, number, strength, or quality 減小; 減少; 降低: *Our sales have been decreasing.* 我們的銷售量一直在減少。**2** [T] to make something less in size, number, strength, or quality 使減小; 使減少; 使降低: *The company may need to decrease its workforce.* 公司可能需要減少勞動力。— opposite 反義 **increase** —**decrease** /'dikris; 'diːkriːs/ *n* [C;U]: *a decrease in sales* 銷售量的減少

de·cree¹ /dɪ'kri; dɪ'kriː/ *n* an official command or decision 法令; 政令

decree² *v* [T;+that] to state or order something officially 命令; 頒佈〔法令、政令〕: *The new governor has decreed that all this fighting should end.* 新政府已發佈命令全面結束這場戰爭。

de·crep·it /dɪ'krɛpɪt; dɪ'krepɪt/ *adj* old and in bad condition 老弱的; 破舊的

de·cry /dɪ'kraɪ; dɪ'kraɪ/ *v* [T] *fml* to say that you do not approve of something 〔正式〕反對〔某事物〕; 詆毀

ded·i·cate /'dɛdə,ket; 'dedɪkeɪt/ *v* **dedicated, dedicating** [T] to declare that a place is holy, often with a solemn ceremony 〔以莊嚴的儀式〕供奉, 奉獻: *The new church will be dedicated on Sunday.* 新教堂將於星期日舉行奉獻儀式。

dedicate sthg to sbdy/sthg *phr v* [T] **1** to declare a book or performance to be in honour of someone 將〔書或演出〕獻給〔某人〕: *Tonight's performance is dedicated to the memory of Lord Olivier.* 今晚的演出是為紀念奧利維爾勳爵舉辦的。**2** to give time to a particular purpose 致力於; 獻身於: *She dedicated herself to the fight for equal rights.* 她一心一意為爭取平等權利而鬥爭。| *He dedicated his life to the needs of his country.* 他為國家的需要奉獻了他的一生。**3** to declare a formal association between something and a particular person or people

以…奉獻; 以…供奉: *This monument is dedicated to the earthquake victims.* 這座紀念碑是為地震遇難者而建的。

ded·i·cat·ed /'dɛdə,ketɪd; 'dedɪkeɪtɪd/ *adj* working very hard for a particular purpose, or being very interested in something 忠誠的; 專心致志的: *She's very dedicated to her work.* 她對自己的工作專心致志。| *a dedicated doctor* 一位敬業樂業的醫生

ded·i·ca·tion /,dɛdə'keʃən; ,dedɪ'keɪʃən/ *n* **1** [C;U] the giving of something to a particular purpose 奉獻; 獻身 **2** [U] the quality of being very interested in or working very hard and unselfishly for something 專心致志; 忘我精神: *She worked with great dedication to find a cure for the disease.* 她以忘我精神工作, 以尋找這種疾病的療法。**3** [C] the words at the beginning of a book or a piece of music where writers express their love, respect, or thanks to people 〔書或樂曲前的〕獻辭, 題辭

de·duce /dɪ'djus; dɪ'djuːs/ *v* **deduced, deducing** [T; +that] to decide that something must be true by using information that you already know is true 演繹; 推斷: *...and from this I deduce that he was killed by his exwife.* …由此我推斷他是被他前妻所殺的。—**deducible** *adj*

de·duct /dɪ'dʌkt; dɪ'dʌkt/ *v* [T] to take away an amount or a part from a total 扣除; 減去: *Don't forget to deduct travel expenses from your earnings.* 別忘了從你的工資中扣除旅費。—**deductible** *adj*

de·duc·tion /dɪ'dʌkʃən; dɪ'dʌkʃən/ *n* **1** [C;U] an idea which you reach about the truth of something by using information that you already know is true, or the process of reaching that idea 演繹; 推論; 推斷: *Her deduction that he was now dead was correct.* 她認為他當時已經死亡的推論是正確的。| *His powers of deduction are impressive.* 他的推斷力令人欽佩。**2** [C] an amount which is taken away from a total, or the act of taking it away 扣除額; 扣除: *After deductions, she earns £180 a week.* 扣除各項應扣款之後, 她每週只掙一百八十英鎊。

deed /did; diːd/ *n* **1** *lit* an action 〔文〕行為; 行動: *a good deed* 好事 | *evil deeds* 醜事 **2** *law* a written paper that is an official record of an agreement 〔律〕證書; 契約

deem /dim; diːm/ *v* [T] *fml* to consider 〔正式〕視為, 認為: *I would deem it an honour if you would accompany me.* 你若能奉陪, 我將不勝榮幸。

★★**deep** /dip; diːp/ *adj, adv* **1** going far down from a surface 深的: *The river is very deep here.* 這條河在這地方的水很深。| *a deep wound* 很深的傷口 **2** used in giving measurements to show how far from the outside edge something is 深處的; 縱深的: *a shelf 30 cm deep and 120 cm long* 一個三十厘米深、一百二十厘米寬的架子 | *a* *mine two kilometres deep* 二千米深的礦井 | *How deep is the river here?* 這兒的河有多深? **3** strong and dark (used of colour) 濃重的; 深色的〔指顏色〕: *The sky was deep blue.* 天空是深藍色的。 **4** strongly felt 〔感受〕強烈的: *I have a deep suspicion that he's not telling us the truth.* 我極之懷疑他並沒有我們說實話。 | *deep feelings of hatred* 深惡痛絕 **5** difficult to understand 深奧的: *deep scientific principles* 深奧的科學原理 **6** **deep sleep** a sleep from which it is difficult to wake up 酣睡 **7** **deep thinker** someone who thinks about things in a very serious way 深刻的思想家 **8** **go off the deep end** *slang* to lose your temper suddenly or violently 〔俚〕大發脾氣; 暴跳如雷 **9** **in deep trouble, in deep water** in serious trouble 煩惱不堪; 陷入困境 **10** **thrown in at the deep end** having to begin with the most difficult part of something 不得不從一份工作的最難部分做起 – **deeply** *adv* – **deepness** *n* [U]

deep·en /'diːpən; 'diːpən/ *v* [I;T] to make or become deeper 變深; 加深: *We'll have to deepen the well if we want more water.* 如果我們想要更多的水, 就得加深這口井。 | *The colour of the sky deepened as the sun went down.* 太陽落山時, 天空的顏色變得很深。

deep freeze /ˌ·'·/ *n* a container for keeping food at very low temperatures 深凍冰箱, 冷藏庫

deep-seat·ed /ˌ·'··◂/ *adj* strong and established some time ago 根深蒂固的; 深層的: *a deep-seated dislike of foreigners* 對外國人難以消除的反感

deer /dɪr; dɪə[r]/ *n* [plural is 複數為 **deer**] a large grass-eating animal which can run fast; the males usually have wide branching horns 鹿 –see 見 MEAT (USAGE用法)

de·face /dɪ'feɪs; dɪ'feɪs/ *v* defaced, defacing [T] to spoil the appearance of something, for example by writing or making marks on it 損毀〔某物〕的外觀; 塗污 –**defacement** *n* [U]

de·fame /dɪ'feɪm; dɪ'feɪm/ *v* defamed, defaming [T] *fml* to damage the good opinion held about someone by saying something bad about them 〔正式〕誹謗; 中傷; 破壞⋯的名譽 –**defamatory** /dɪ'fæmə,tɔrɪ; dɪ'fæmətərɪ/ *adj* –**defamation** /ˌdɛfə'meɪʃən; ˌdefə'meɪʃən/ *n* [U]

de·fault[1] /dɪ'fɔlt; dɪ'fɔːlt/ *v* [I] to fail to fulfil an agreement, contract, or duty 違約; 不履行〔條約或義務〕: *He defaulted on his payments for support of the child.* 他不盡義務, 拖欠給孩子的撫養費。

default[2] *n* **1** [U] failure to fulfil an agreement or legal duty 違約; 未履行 **2** **by default** because something that might have made the situation different did not happen 因可能改變局面的事沒有發生: *Her opponent was ill, so she won by default.* 她的對手因病棄權, 所以她不戰而勝。

de·feat[1] /dɪ'fit; dɪ'fiːt/ *v* [T] **1** to win a victory over someone 戰勝; 擊敗: *Scotland defeated Wales by three goals to one.* 蘇格蘭隊以三比一擊敗威爾斯隊。 | *The British army was finally defeated in 1783.* 英國軍隊最終於1783年被戰敗。 **2** to make something fail 挫敗; 使落空: *It was lack of money that defeated their plan.* 他們的計劃因為缺乏資金而落空。 **3** to be too difficult to do successfully 難倒: *This task defeats me!* 這任務把我難倒了!

de·feat[2] *n* **1** [U] victory over someone or something 戰勝; 擊敗: *Superior air defence contributed to their defeat of the enemy.* 優秀的空防為擊敗敵人作出了貢獻。 **2** [C;U] failure to win or to succeed 失敗; 敗北: *The team has suffered several defeats recently.* 球隊最近連遭敗北。 | *He'll never admit defeat.* 他決不肯認輸。

de·feat·is·m /dɪ'fitɪzəm; dɪ'fiːtɪzəm/ *n* [U] expectation of failure 失敗主義 –**defeatist** *n*

def·e·cate /'dɛfə,ket; 'defɪˌkeɪt/ *v* defecated, defecating *fml* [I] to send waste matter out of your bowels 〔正式〕排氣, 大便 –**defecation** /ˌdɛfə'keʃən; ˌdefɪ'keɪʃən/ *n* [U]

de·fect[1] /'difɛkt; 'diːfekt, dɪ'fekt/ *n* something which is lacking or not right 缺乏; 缺點; 缺陷: *There's a defect in each of those machines.* 那些機器每一台都有毛病。 | *Your plan has one serious defect.* 你的計劃有個嚴重缺陷。

de·fect[2] /dɪ'fɛkt; dɪ'fekt/ *v* [I] to leave a group or your country, especially for political reasons, and go to an opposing one 叛變; 背叛〔尤指政治原因〕 –**defector** *n* –**defection** /-'fɛkʃən; -'fekʃən/ *n* [C;U]

de·fec·tive /dɪ'fɛktɪv; dɪ'fektɪv/ *adj* lacking something necessary and so not working well 有缺點的; 有缺陷的: *defective machinery* 有缺陷的機器 –**defectively** *adv* –**defectiveness** *n* [U]

de·fence /dɪ'fɛns; dɪ'fens/ *n* (also 又作 **defense** *AmE* 〔美式〕) **1** [U] the act of protecting someone or something from attack 保衛; 保護; 維護: *the defence of one's country* 保衛自己的國家 | *He spoke in defence of justice.* 他發言維護正義。 **2** [C;U] something that is used for protection 防禦物: *Trees are a defence against the wind.* 樹是防風的屏障。 **3** [U] the weapons and armed forces that a country has to protect itself from attack 防禦裝備: *The government has increased its spending on defence.* 政府增加了國防經費。 **4** [sing] arguments that you use to defend yourself in court 〔在法庭上的〕辯護: *She said in her defence that she had not seen the "No Parking" sign.* 她為自己辯護說, 她沒有看見 "不准停(泊)車" 的標誌。 **5** **the defence** someone who has been charged with a crime, together with their lawyers, in court 被告方; 辯方 –**defenceless** *adj*

★de·fend /dɪˈfɛnd; dɪˈfɛnd/ v **1** [T] to protect someone or something from attack 保衛; 防禦: *We can't defend the port from attack by land and sea.* 我們無法確保港口不受海軍、陸軍的襲擊。| *I don't like having to defend my beliefs.* 我不喜歡要去維護自己的信仰。 **2** [I;T] to protect a position in sports so as to stop an opponent advancing, gaining points, or winning 防護; 防守〔指體育運動〕: *Tonight he will be defending his light-weight boxing title.* 今晚他要保住他的輕量級拳擊頭銜。| *He defended with skill.* 他運用技巧進行防守。 **3** [T] to act as a lawyer for someone who has been charged with a crime 〔為被告〕當辯護律師 **–defensible** adj

★de·fen·dant /dɪˈfɛndənt; dɪˈfendənt/ n *law* a person who has been charged with a crime in a court case〖律〗被告

de·fen·sive /dɪˈfɛnsɪv; dɪˈfensɪv/ adj **1** used or intended for protection 防禦的; 保衛的; 保護的: *defensive weapons* 防禦性武器 | *a defensive position* 防守性陣地 **2** seeming to expect disapproval or attack (used of a person or behaviour) 防備的〔指人或行為〕; 戒備的: *She became very defensive when I asked her how much the car had cost.* 我問她她輛汽車花了多少錢時，她變得十分警覺。 **– defensively** adv **–defensiveness** n [U]

de·fer /dɪˈfɜ˞; dɪˈfɜːʳ/ v **-rr- 1** [T] to delay something until a later date 推遲; 拖延: *Let's defer any action for a few weeks.* 我們推遲幾個星期再行動吧。| *His military service was deferred until he finished college.* 他一直拖到大學畢業才去服役。 **2** *defer to someone* to accept the wishes or opinions of another person, usually because you respect them 遵從; 聽從; 服從: *I shall, of course, defer to your better judgment.* 我當然會聽從你更好的判斷。

def·er·ence /ˈdɛfərəns; ˈdefərəns/ n [U] *fml* respect that you show to someone because of their higher position or greater power 〖正式〗遵從; 依從; 敬重 **–deferential** /ˌdɛfəˈrɛnʃəl; ˌdefəˈrenʃl◂/ adj

de·fi·ant /dɪˈfaɪənt; dɪˈfaɪənt/ adj showing lack of respect or a refusal to obey someone 蔑視的; 違抗的 **–defiance** n [U] **–defiantly** adv

de·fi·cien·cy /dɪˈfɪʃənsɪ; dɪˈfɪʃənsi/ n **deficiencies** [C;U] a condition in which something is lacking or not good enough 缺乏; 缺陷: *Can't you see the deficiencies in this plan?* 難道你看不出這項計劃的缺陷嗎？| *vitamin deficiency* 維生素缺乏症

de·fi·cient /dɪˈfɪʃənt; dɪˈfɪʃənt/ adj not having any or enough of something which is necessary 不足的; 缺乏的: *They tend to eat food deficient in iron.* 他們往往吃些缺乏鐵質的食物。

def·i·cit /ˈdɛfəsɪt; ˈdefɪsɪt/ n an amount, especially of money, which is the difference between what you have and what you need or expected to have 赤字; 逆差; 虧損額: *The directors have reported a deficit of £2.5 million.* 董事們報告虧損額為二百五十萬英鎊。

de·file /dɪˈfaɪl; dɪˈfaɪl/ v **defiled, defiling** [T] to make something less clean or pure 弄髒; 污損: *The animals defiled the water.* 動物把水弄髒了。 **–defilement** n [U]

★de·fine /dɪˈfaɪn; dɪˈfaɪn/ v **defined, defining** [T] to show or explain what something is or means, or what its limits are 給〔某物〕下定義; 表明〔某物〕的界線: *"Hope" is a hard word to define.* "Hope" 是個很難下定義的詞。| *This book defines the position of the national government in city affairs.* 這本書表明了國民政府在處理城市事務中的立場。| *The issue hasn't been clearly defined.* 這問題還未解釋清楚。

def·i·nite /ˈdɛfənɪt; ˈdefn̩ɪt/ adj clear and certain 清楚的; 明確的: *We demand a definite answer.* 我們要求有個明確的答覆。| *a definite success* 確確實實的成功

definite ar·ti·cle /ˌ··· ˈ···/ n in English the word THE〔英語中的〕定冠詞〔即 THE〕

def·i·nite·ly /ˈdɛfənɪtlɪ; ˈdefn̩ɪtli/ adv certainly or clearly 明確地; 確切地; 清楚地: *That answer is definitely true.* 那答案正確無誤。| *That was definitely the best play I've seen all year.* 那無疑是我全年看過的最好的一齣戲。| *He is definitely coming.* 他肯定會來。| *"Will you be inviting Sarah?" "No, definitely not!"* "你會邀請薩拉嗎？" "肯定不會!"

★def·i·ni·tion /ˌdɛfəˈnɪʃən; ˌdefn̩ˈnɪʃən/ n **1** [C] a statement which explains the exact meaning of a word or phrase 定義; 釋義 **2** [U] clearness of shape, colour, or sound〔形狀、色彩、聲音的〕清晰度, 鮮明度: *This photograph lacks definition.* 這張照片不夠清晰。

de·fin·i·tive /dɪˈfɪnətɪv; dɪˈfɪnɪtɪv/ adj **1** providing a firm decision that cannot be questioned 決定性的; 無可置疑的: *a definitive answer* 明確的答覆 **2** showing the highest standard as compared with other similar things 最高水準的; 權威性的: *She's written the definitive history of Vienna.* 她寫下了權威性的維也納歷史。

de·flate /dɪˈflet; ˌdiːˈfleɪt/ v **deflated, deflating** [I;T] **1** to become smaller or make something smaller through loss of air or gas（使）放氣;（使）漏氣;（使）癟下去: *The tyre deflated.* 輪胎漏氣了。| *After the party they deflated the balloons.* 晚會之後, 他們把氣球的氣放掉。 **2** to make someone lose confidence（使）泄氣: *I felt utterly deflated by her laughter.* 我被她笑得完全泄了氣。 **3** to reduce a country's supply of money, leading to less demand for goods and less industrial activity and usually resulting in lower prices 緊縮〔通貨以降低物價〕 **–deflation** /-ˈfleʃən; -ˈfleɪʃən/ n [C;U]

de·flect /dɪˈflɛkt; dɪˈflekt/ v 1 [I;T] to cause something to change direction (使)偏離; (使)轉向: One of their players deflected the ball into his own goal. 他們其中一個球員改變了球的方向，把它弄進了自家的球門。 2 [T] to turn an attack away from yourself 轉移; 引開: I tried to deflect his criticism by changing my account of the incident. 我試圖改變話題來轉移[引開]他的批評。

de·form /dɪˈfɔrm; dɪˈfɔːm/ v [T] to spoil the form or appearance of someone or something 毀壞[某人或某物]的外形[外貌]: a face deformed by disease 因疾病而變形的臉

de·fraud /dɪˈfrɔd; dɪˈfrɔːd/ v [T] to get something from someone by unfair means 騙取; 詐取: They have been charged with intent to defraud their employers. 他們已被指控故意詐騙老闆。

de·frost /diˈfrɔst; ˌdiːˈfrɔst/ v [I;T] to remove ice from something that has been frozen (使)除霜; (使)解凍: I should really defrost the refrigerator. 我真應該給冰箱除霜了。 | Don't let the meat defrost too quickly. 不要讓肉解凍得太快。

deft /dɛft; deft/ adj quick and skilful 靈巧的; 熟練的: a deft catch 熟練的接球動作 –**deftly** adv –**deftness** n [U]

de·funct /dɪˈfʌŋkt; dɪˈfʌŋkt/ adj no longer in existence or working 不存在的; 失效的

de·fuse /diˈfjuz; ˌdiːˈfjuːz/ v defused, defusing [T] 1 to remove the FUSE from something explosive so as to prevent an explosion 拆除[爆炸物的]引信: The expert defused the bomb just in time. 專家及時把炸彈的引信拆除了。 2 defuse a situation to remove the nervousness or possible harm from a situation 緩和局勢

de·fy /dɪˈfaɪ; dɪˈfaɪ/ v defied, defying [T] 1 to refuse to obey someone or something 藐視; 無視; [公然]違抗: In not paying this tax, they are defying the law. 他們不納這種稅是無視法紀的表現。 2 defy someone to do something to ask someone to do something which is considered impossible 向某人挑戰; 激[惹]某人: I defy you to give me one good reason for believing you. 我倒要看看你能否給我一條充分理由讓我相信你。 3 to make something impossible 使[某事物]不可能: The untidiness of his room defies description. 他的房間亂得簡直無法形容。

de·gen·er·ate¹ /dɪˈdʒɛnəˌret; dɪˈdʒenəreɪt/ v degenerated, degenerating [I] to become worse in character, quality, or appearance 衰退; 墮落; 惡化: a fine young man who has degenerated under the influence of alcohol 一個大好青年因酗酒而墮落 | The wide road degenerated into a narrow bumpy track. 寬闊的大路變成了一條崎嶇狹窄的小徑。 –**degeneration** /dɪˌdʒɛnəˈreʃən; dɪˌdʒenəˈreɪʃən/ n [U]

de·gen·er·ate² /dɪˈdʒɛnərɪt; dɪˈdʒenərət/ adj showing a low standard of morals or behaviour 墮落的; 退化的; 頹廢的: a group of degenerate young men 一羣墮落的年輕人

de·grade /dɪˈgred; dɪˈgreɪd/ v degraded, degrading [T] to reduce respect for someone 降低[某人]的身分; 使[某人]丟臉: It was very degrading to be punished in front of the whole class. 在全班同學面前受罰是十分丟臉的。 | Pornography degrades women. 色情作品貶低女性的身分。 –**degradation** /ˌdɛgrəˈdeʃən; ˌdegrəˈdeɪʃən/ n [U]

★**de·gree** /dɪˈgri; dɪˈgriː/ n 1 [C] tech a unit of measurement 《術語》度; 度數: an angle of 90 degrees (90°) 一個90度的(直)角 | It's 84 degrees in the shade. 在陰暗處測量的溫度為84度。 | a temperature of 21 degrees Celsius 攝氏21度的溫度 2 [C;U] level or amount, especially of ability or progress 程度(尤指能力或進展): The students have different degrees of ability. 學生的能力高低各不相同。 | To what degree can he be trusted? 對他能信任到甚麼程度? | He can be trusted to some degree. 對他可信任到某種程度。 | He is getting better by degrees. 他正在逐漸好轉。 3 [C] a course of study at a university or POLYTECHNIC, or the title you get if you complete this 學位; 學銜: To do the job, you must have a degree in history. 從事這項工作必須具有歷史學的大學學位。 | a chemistry degree 化學學位

de·hy·drate /diˈhaɪdret; ˌdiːˈhaɪdreɪt/ v dehydrated, dehydrating 1 [T] to remove all the water from something, often in order to preserve it 使[某物]脫水 2 [I] to lose water from the body [人體]失水 –**dehydration** /ˌdihaɪˈdreʃən; ˌdiːhaɪˈdreɪʃən/ n [U]: He was suffering from dehydration. 脫水使他苦不堪言。

de·i·fy /ˈdiəˌfaɪ; ˈdiːɪˌfaɪ/ v deified, deifying [T] fml to consider something or someone as a god to be worshipped 《正式》把[某人或某物]神化[奉若神明] –**deification** /ˌdiəfəˈkeʃən; ˌdiːɪfɪˈkeɪʃən/ n [U]

deign /den; deɪn/ v deign to do something to lower yourself to do something you consider unimportant 屈尊; 俯就做某事: They wrote to their headmaster, but he didn't even deign to reply. 他們給校長寫了信，但他甚至不屑作答。

de·i·ty /ˈdiəti; ˈdiːɪti/ n deities a god or goddess 神; 女神

dé·jà vu /ˌdeʒɑ ˈvju; ˌdeɪʒɑ ˈvjuː/ n [U] the feeling that you have already experienced in the past what is actually happening at the present moment 似曾經歷的錯覺

de·jec·ted /dɪˈdʒɛktɪd; dɪˈdʒektɪd/ adj sad and disappointed 沮喪的; 失望的: a dejected look 垂頭喪氣的神色 –**dejectedly** adv –**dejection** /dɪˈdʒɛkʃən; dɪˈdʒekʃən/ n [U]

★**de·lay¹** /dɪˈle; dɪˈleɪ/ v 1 [T] to do something later than planned 使延期; 推遲: We decided to delay our holiday until next month. 我們決定把休假推遲到下個月。 | Could you delay giving her the news until we've seen her?

你能否等到我們見到她之後再把消息告訴她?

2 [I;T] to slow something down or cause it to be late 耽擱; 延誤: *They're trying to delay until help arrives.* 他們有意拖延到有人來幫忙。 | *My train was delayed for an hour.* 我的火車誤點一小時。

delay² *n* [C;U] a period of time during which an action or event does not happen as it is supposed to 耽擱; 延誤; 延遲: *Delays of two hours or more were reported on the roads this morning.* 據悉, 今天早晨道路阻塞了兩個多小時。 | *Do it without delay!* 立即動手!

de·lec·ta·ble /dɪˈlɛktəbl; dɪˈlɛktəbəl/ *adj* very pleasing 令人愉快的

del·e·gate¹ /ˈdɛlə،get; ˈdɛlɪgỉt/ *n* a person chosen to represent a group of people 代表

del·e·gate² /ˈdɛlə،get; ˈdɛlɪ،geɪt/ *v* **delegated, delegating 1** [I;T] to give someone part or all of your power, rights, or duties for a certain time 將〔權利、職責〕委託給〔某人〕; 授權給: *Part of the art of management is knowing when to delegate.* 管理的藝術之一是適時用人。 | *I have delegated my command to Captain Roberts.* 我已經把指揮權委託給羅伯茨船長。 **2** [T] to appoint someone to do a particular job 指派, 選派〔某人〕: *I've been delegated to organize the weekly meetings.* 我被指派組織每週舉行的例會。

del·e·ga·tion /،dɛləˈgeʃən; ،dɛlỉˈgeɪʃən/ *n* **1** [U] the giving to someone of part or all of your power, rights, or duties 授權; 委託 **2** [C +sing/pl verb] a group of people chosen to represent others 代表團: *A delegation from the United Nations has just arrived.* 一個美國代表團剛剛抵達。

de·lete /dɪˈlit; dɪˈliːt/ *v* **deleted, deleting** [T] to cross out and remove something that has been written down 刪去〔文字〕: *Delete his name from the list.* 把他的名字從名單上刪去。 **—deletion** /dɪˈliʃən; dɪˈliːʃən/ *n* [C;U]

de·lib·e·rate¹ /dɪˈlɪbərɪt; dɪˈlɪbərỉt/ *adj* **1** intentional 蓄意的; 故意的: *The car crash wasn't an accident – it was a deliberate attempt to kill him!* 那次撞車事故並非意外事故, 而是有人蓄意要謀害他! **2** slow and careful (used of speech, thought, or movement) 不慌不忙的; 從容不迫的〔指言談、思想、動作〕: *He stood up in a very deliberate way and left the room.* 他從容不迫地站起身來, 然後離開了房間。 **—deliberately** *adv*

de·lib·e·rate² /dɪˈlɪbə،ret; dɪˈlɪbəreɪt/ *v* **deliberated, deliberating** [I;T] *fml* to consider something carefully before making a decision 〚正式〛仔細考慮〔再作決定〕: *The judges are deliberating.* 法官們正在仔細研究(案情)。 | *They are deliberating what to do.* 他們在仔細考慮要做的事情。

de·lib·e·ra·tion /dɪ،lɪbəˈreʃən; dɪ،lɪbəˈreɪʃən/ *n* **1** [U] careful consideration 仔細的考慮 **2 deliberations** [pl] careful consideration or discussions about something 仔細考慮的事情 **3** [U] the quality of being slow and unhurried in speech, thought, or movement 〔言語、思想、動作〕緩慢; 從容; 審慎

del·i·ca·cy /ˈdɛləkəsɪ; ˈdɛlɪkəsɪ/ *n* **delicacies 1** [U] the quality of being delicate 精美; 精致; 雅緻; 嬌嫩; 微妙: *She admired the delicacy of the lace table-cloth.* 她欣賞花邊枱布的精緻工藝。 | *a matter of some delicacy* 一件微妙的事情 **2** [C] something good to eat that is considered rare or costly 精美的食品: *Caviar is a great delicacy.* 魚子醬是很名貴的美味食品。

del·i·cate /ˈdɛləkɪt; ˈdɛlɪkỉt/ *adj* **1** easy to damage and therefore needing to be handled carefully 精美的; 精緻的; 嬌嫩的; 脆弱的: *Be careful with those wine glasses – they're very delicate.* 小心那些玻璃酒具——它們很容易破碎。 **2** needing careful consideration in order to avoid failure or trouble 微妙的; 棘手的; 需要小心處理的: *Don't mention his divorce — it's rather a delicate subject.* 別提他離婚的事, 這是個相當尷尬的話題。 | *The negotiations are at a delicate stage.* 談判處於微妙階段。 **3** pleasant though not very noticeable 微弱的; 淡的; 柔和的: *a delicate taste* 清淡的滋味 | *a delicate smell* 幽香 | *a delicate shade of pink* 淡粉紅色 **4** sensitive 靈敏的; 精密的: *A delicate instrument can record even very slight changes in temperature.* 精密的儀器甚至能記錄十分細微的溫度變化。 **5** small, careful, and controlled 靈巧的: *a delicate movement* 靈巧的動作 **6** often ill 纖弱的; 嬌弱的: *a very delicate child* 一個非常弱小的孩子 **—delicately** *adv*

del·i·ca·tes·sen /،dɛləkəˈtɛsn̩; ،dɛlɪkəˈtesn̩/ *n* a shop that sells unusual and often expensive foods, for example cheeses and cold meats from foreign countries 〔出售昂貴外國食品的〕食品店〔如奶酪和冷凍肉類〕

de·li·cious /dɪˈlɪʃəs; dɪˈlɪʃəs/ *adj* tasting or smelling very pleasant 美味的; 可口的; 芬芳的: *Thank you for the delicious meal.* 謝謝你這頓美味可口的飯。 **—deliciously** *adv*

de·light¹ /dɪˈlaɪt; dɪˈlaɪt/ *v* [I;T] to give a great feeling of pleasure 使高興; 使愉快: *a book that is certain to delight* 一本肯定會令人喜愛的書 | *He delighted them with his witty performance.* 他妙趣橫生的表演使他們很開心。

delight in sthg *phr v* [T] to get great pleasure from something 以〔某事物〕為樂; 非常喜歡〔某事物〕: *She delights in making me look stupid.* 她以令我出醜為樂。

delight² *n* [C;U] great pleasure or satisfaction 快樂; 高興; 樂趣: *the delights of London's night life* 倫敦夜生活的樂趣 | *a* *shriek of delight* 興奮的尖叫聲 **2 take delight in something** to enjoy something 以某事物為樂

de·light·ed /dɪˈlaɪtɪd; dɪˈlaɪtɪd/ *adj* very pleased or satisfied 高興的; 愉快的; 快樂的: *Thank you for your invitation – I'd be delighted to come.* 謝謝你的邀請——我很樂意來。| *We were absolutely delighted with his progress.* 我們看到他的進步格外高興。

> □ USEFUL PATTERNS 有用句型
> be delighted with something; be delighted to do something

de·light·ful /dɪˈlaɪtfəl; dɪˈlaɪtfəl/ *adj* very pleasing and attractive 令人高興的; 使人快樂的; 可愛的: *a delightful little girl* 討人喜歡的小女孩 **–delightfully** *adv*

de·lin·quen·cy /dɪˈlɪŋkwənsɪ; dɪˈlɪŋkwənsɪ/ *n* [U] behaviour which is neither socially nor legally acceptable 過失; 違法行為: *the problem of juvenile delinquency* 少年犯罪問題

de·lin·quent /dɪˈlɪŋkwənt; dɪˈlɪŋkwənt/ *n* a young person who does socially unacceptable things or who breaks the law 少年罪犯 **–delinquent** *adj*: *delinquent behaviour* 違法行為

de·lir·i·ous /dɪˈlɪrɪəs; dɪˈlɪərɪəs/ *adj* in an excited dreamy state in which you cannot think clearly, for example because of a fever 神志昏亂的; 譫妄的; 極度亢奮的: *He was so ill he became delirious.* 他病得神志不清。| *delirious with joy* 欣喜若狂 **–deliriously** *adv*: *deliriously happy* 興奮異常 **–delirium** /-rɪəm; -rɪəm/ *n* [U]

★**de·liv·er** /dɪˈlɪvər; dɪˈlɪvə/ *v* [T] **1** to take things to people's houses or places of work 遞送; 傳送: *Letters are delivered every day.* 信件是每天遞送的。| *Yes, we deliver newspapers.* 是的, 我們發送報紙。| *The parcel was delivered to my door.* 包裹送到我家門口。**2** to give something that has been promised or is hoped for 履行〔諾言〕; 實現〔希望〕: *Do you think the government will deliver the promised tax cuts?* 你認為政府會履行減稅的諾言嗎? **3 deliver a baby** to help in the birth of a baby 接生; 助產 **4** to speak or read aloud in public 發表; 表達: *He delivered his speech effectively.* 他深刻有力地發表了演說。**5** *fml* to set someone free from something unpleasant〔正式〕釋放〔某人〕**6 deliver a blow** to hit someone hard 給〔某人〕一擊

de·liv·er·ance /dɪˈlɪvərəns; dɪˈlɪvərəns/ *n* [U] *fml* the act of saving someone from harm or danger or the state of being saved from danger〔正式〕解救; 被拯救

★**de·liv·er·y** /dɪˈlɪvərɪ; dɪˈlɪvərɪ/ *n* **deliveries 1** [C;U] the act of taking something to someone 投遞; 傳送; 交付: *The next postal delivery is at 2 o'clock.* 下一次郵遞時間是兩點鐘。**2** [C;U] the things that are taken to some-

one 遞送的東西: *I signed for a large delivery of coal.* 我簽收了大批訂購的煤。**3** [C] the birth of a child 分娩: *The mother had an easy delivery.* 那位母親順產[分娩順利]。**4** [C;U] the act or style of speaking in public 演講; 演講的風格 **5** [C;U] the act or style of throwing a ball in a game 投球(法): *a good delivery* 一個好的擲球法

del·ta /ˈdɛltə; ˈdɛltə/ *n* **1** the fourth letter of the Greek alphabet (△ δ) 希臘字母表的第四個字母 **2** an area of low land shaped like a △ where a river divides into branches before entering the sea, especially the Nile Delta in Egypt〔河流的〕三角洲〔尤指埃及的尼羅河三角洲〕

de·lude /dɪˈlud; dɪˈluːd/ *v* **deluded, deluding** [T] to make someone believe in something that is not true 欺騙〔某人〕; 哄騙〔某人〕: *Don't delude yourself about her ability to do the job.* 別自欺欺人, 以為她能勝任這工作。| *They were deluded into thinking that their investment would be safe.* 他們給人蒙騙, 以為自己的投資不會有風險。

del·uge¹ /ˈdɛljudʒ; ˈdɛljuːdʒ/ *n* **1** a great flood 洪水 **2** very heavy rain 大雨; 暴雨 **3** a very large number of things which happen at the same time 大量同時發生的事物: *a deluge of questions* 層出不窮的問題

deluge² *v* **deluged, deluging** [T] to have to deal with a large number of things happening at the same time 窮於應付: *The minister was deluged with questions.* 部長窮於應付連珠砲似的問題。

de·lu·sion /dɪˈluʒən; dɪˈluːʒən/ *n* a false belief which is usually strongly held 欺騙; 錯覺; 謬見: *She was under the delusion that he would marry her.* 她患了妄想症, 自以為他會娶她為妻。| *She's suffering from delusions of grandeur.* 她患有誇大妄想症。

de luxe /dɪˈluks; dɪ ˈlʌks/ *adj* of especially good quality and more expensive than other similar products 優質的; 豪華的: *I bought the deluxe model.* 我買的是豪華型號。

delve /dɛlv; delv/ *v* **delved, delving** [I] to search thoroughly in order to find something 搜索; 翻查: *She delved into her handbag for her keys.* 她翻遍了手提包去找鑰匙。

dem·a·gogue /ˈdɛməˌgɒg; ˈdeməgɒg/ *n* a political leader who has gained power by exciting people's feelings rather than by reasoned argument (a word used to express disapproval) 煽動者; 蠱惑民心的政客〔含貶義〕

★★**de·mand**¹ /dɪˈmænd; dɪˈmɑːnd/ *v* [T;+that] to ask for something firmly and not be willing to accept a refusal 要求; 請求: *The workers are demanding more money.* 工人在要求加工資。| *I demanded to know the truth.* 我要求了解事實真相。| *They demanded that he should be dismissed.* 他們要求免他的職。**2** [T] to ask someone firmly to tell you something

盤問; 查問: *"Where have you been all night?"* *she demanded.* "你一整晚到了哪兒去了？" 她盤問道。

> □ USEFUL PATTERNS 有用句型
> to demand something; to demand to do something; to demand that…

3 [T] to need attention, effort, or hard work 需要〔專心、努力或吃苦耐勞〕: *Work of this kind demands total commitment.* 從事這種工作需要全心全意的投入。

demand² *n* **1** [C] an extremely firm request or claim 要求, 請求: *The government had to give in to the terrorists' demands.* 政府不得不對恐怖分子的要求讓步。| *the workers' demand for a 10% pay rise* 工人要求提高工資10% **2 on demand** able to be obtained as soon as it is wanted 一經要求〔即付〕: *machines which dispense cash on demand* 可即時提款的機器 **3** [U] a need or wish of people generally for particular goods or services 需要; 需求: *There's not much demand for hats these days.* 最近對帽子的需求量不大。 **4 in demand, in great demand** wanted by a lot of people 非常需要的; 受歡迎的: *You seem to be in great demand today!* 你如今似乎很受歡迎! **5 make demands on someone** to take up a lot of someone's time and effort 對某人有要求〔花費大量時間和精力〕: *The school makes heavy demands on its teachers.* 學校對教師提出了很高的要求。

de·mand·ing /dɪ'mændɪŋ; dɪ'mɑːndɪŋ/ *adj* needing a lot of effort or attention 很費心的; 很費力的: *a very demanding baby* 一個需要費心費力照顧的嬰孩

de·mar·ca·tion /ˌdimɑr'keʃən; ˌdiːmɑː'keɪʃən/ *n* [sing;U] an imaginary line which separates two areas or activities 分界; 定界; 界限: *There is a clear demarcation between the jobs of editor and sub-editor.* 編輯和副編輯的工作有明確的界限。

de·mean /dɪ'min; dɪ'miːn/ *v* **demean yourself** *fml* to make people have less respect for you 〔正式〕降低自己的身分; 失去別人的尊重: *Don't demean yourself by taking such a badly paid job.* 不要為了做這份收入微薄的工作而降低身分。

de·mea·nour /dɪ'minə; dɪ'miːnər/ *n fml* (**demeanor** *AmE* 〔美式〕) someone's manner and behaviour towards other people 〔正式〕行為; 舉止

de·ment·ed /dɪ'mɛntɪd; dɪ'mentɪd/ *adj* mad or showing an unbalanced mind 發狂的; 精神錯亂的 **–dementedly** *adv*

de·mise /dɪ'maɪz; dɪ'maɪz/ *n* [U] **1** the failure of something or someone that used to be successful 〔人的〕失敗; 〔物的〕壞死: *the demise of the record player* 錄音機失靈 **2** *law* the death of a person 〔律〕死亡

de·mo·bi·lize /di'mobl̩aɪz; diː'məʊbl̩aɪz/ *n*

demobilized, demobilizing *fml* (also 又作 **demobilise** *BrE* 〔英式〕) [T] to let someone leave the armed forces 〔正式〕使〔某人〕復員 **–demobilization** /di,mobl̩ə'zeʃən; dɪˌməʊbəlaɪ'zeɪʃən/ *n* [U]

de·moc·ra·cy /də'mɑkrəsɪ; dɪ'mɒkrəsɪ/ *n* **democracies** **1** [U] a system of government which is made up of representatives who have been elected by the people 民主; 民主政體; 民主制度 **2** [C] a country which has this system of government 民主國家: *Britain is an example of a parliamentary democracy.* 英國是典型的議會民主制國家。

dem·o·crat /'dɛmə,kræt; 'deməkræt/ *n* **1** a person who believes in the principles of democracy 民主主義者 **2 Democrat** a member or supporter of a particular political party 民主黨黨員; 民主黨的支持者: *a Liberal Democrat* 一個自由民主黨黨員 **3 the Democrats** one of the two largest political parties of the US 民主黨〔美國兩大政黨之一〕

dem·o·crat·ic /ˌdɛmə'krætɪk; ˌdemə'krætɪk◂/ *adj* **1** favouring and practising democracy 民主的; 民主主義的: *a democratic system of government* 民主制政府 **2** being fair to different sides 民主作風的; 平等的: *Let's be democratic about this and take a vote.* 我們要公平對待這事, 用投票來決定吧。 **–democratically** /-klɪ; -klɪ/ *adv*

de·mol·ish /dɪ'mɑlɪʃ; dɪ'mɒlɪʃ/ *v* [T] **1** to knock something down or destroy it 拆毀; 拆除: *They're finally going to demolish that old building.* 他們最終將拆毀那座舊建築物。 **2** to prove that an idea or an argument is wrong 推翻, 駁倒〔觀點或論點〕: *We've demolished all her objections to the plan.* 我們全部推翻了她對計劃的反對意見。

dem·o·li·tion /ˌdɛmə'lɪʃən; ˌdemə'lɪʃən/ *n* [C;U] the action of knocking something down or destroying it 拆毀; 摧毀

de·mon /'dimən; 'diːmən/ *n* an evil spirit 惡魔; 魔鬼 **–demonic** /dɪ'mɑnɪk; dɪ'mɒnɪk/ *adj*

de·mon·stra·ble /'dɛmənstrəbl; dɪ'mɒnstrəbl/ *adj fml* able to be shown or proved to be true 〔正式〕可論證的; 可證明的: *a demonstrable fact* 可證明的事實 **–demonstrably** *adv*

dem·on·strate /'dɛmən,stret; 'demənstreɪt/ *v* **demonstrated, demonstrating 1** [T;+that] to prove something by reasoning 論證; 證明; 證實: *Galileo demonstrated that objects of different weight fall at the same speed.* 伽利略證實了不同重量的物體落下時速度是一樣的。 **2** [T;+that] to explain something by showing clearly 示範; 演示: *Please demonstrate how the machine works.* 請示範一下這台機器如何操作。| *She demonstrated the correct way to put a bandage on.* 她示範了紮繃帶的正確方法。 **3** [T] to show a particular skill or quality 顯示; 表露〔技能、品質〕: *He demonstrated extraordinary courage.* 他顯示

了非凡的勇氣。**4** [I] to take part in a public
show of opposition or support for something 示威遊行: *They demonstrated* **against**
the new law. 他們舉行示威反對新法律。–
demonstrator *n*

****dem·on·stra·tion** /ˌdɛmənˈstreʃən; ˌdemən-
ˈstreɪʃən/ *n* **1** [C;U] the act of showing how
something works 示範；解釋: *Can you give*
us a demonstration? 你能給我們作個示範嗎?
2 [C;U] the act of proving something 論證；
證實；證明 **3** [C] a public show of opposition or support for something, often with
marching 示威遊行: *Some students are hold-*
ing a demonstration against nuclear weap-
ons. 有些學生在進行反核武器的示威遊行。

de·mon·stra·tive /dɪˈmɒnstrətɪv; dɪˈmɒn-
strətɪv/ *adj* showing your feelings openly 感
情外露的: *a demonstrative person* 感情外露
的人

de·mor·al·ize /dɪˈmɒrəlˌaɪz; dɪˈmɒrəlaɪz/ *v*
demoralized, demoralizing (also 又作 **de-**
moralise *BrE* 〖英式〗) [T] to make someone lose confidence or courage 使士氣低
落；使泄氣: *The army was demoralized by de-*
feat. 軍隊因戰敗而失去了鬥志。–**demoral-**
ization /dɪˌmɒrələˈzeʃən; dɪˌmɒrəlaɪˈzeɪʃən/
n [U]

de·mote /dɪˈmot; dɪˈməʊt/ *v* **demoted,**
demoting [T] to lower someone in rank or
position, often as a punishment 使降級；使
降職〔常作為懲罰〕–**demotion** /dɪˈmoʃən;
dɪˈməʊʃən/ *n* [C;U]

de·mur /dɪˈmɜ; dɪˈmɜːʳ/ *v* **-rr-** [I] *fml* to
show a lack of eagerness for a plan or a
suggestion 〔正式〕〔對計劃或建議〕表示猶豫；
不願；遲疑: *I demurred* **at** *the prospect of a*
whole evening alone with him. 我不願意和他
單獨度過整個夜晚。

de·mure /dɪˈmjʊr; dɪˈmjʊəʳ/ *adj* quiet and
polite (used especially of women and children) 嫻靜的〔尤指婦女和兒童〕: *a demure*
young lady 嫻靜的少婦 –**demurely** *adv*

den /dɛn; den/ *n* **1** the home of a wild animal, such as a lion or a fox 獸穴；獸窩 **2** a
place where people are busy with a secret
activity 進行祕密活動的場所: *a den of thieves*
賊窩

de·ni·al /dɪˈnaɪəl; dɪˈnaɪəl/ *n* [C;U] **1** the act
of saying that something is not true 否定；
否認: *He has made a public denial of the*
story in the newspapers. 他對報紙上的那篇新
聞報道作了公開否認。**2** a refusal to give
something which people feel is deserved
拒絕；拒絕給予: *a denial* **of** *justice* 漠視公正

den·im /ˈdɛnəm; ˈdenɪm/ *n* **1** [U] a strong
cotton cloth which is often blue, used to
make clothes 〔藍色〕斜紋粗棉布〔用於製衣
服〕; 勞動布: *denim jeans* 斜紋布牛仔褲 **2**
denims [pl] trousers made of denim 斜紋粗
棉布褲 –see 見 PAIR (USAGE用法)

de·nom·i·na·tion /dɪˌnɒməˈneʃən; dɪˌnɒmɪ-
ˈneɪʃən/ *n* a particular religious group

which has slight differences in belief from
other similar groups 宗教派別 –**denom-**
inational *adj*

de·note /dɪˈnot; dɪˈnəʊt/ *v* **denoted, denot-**
ing [T; +that] to be a sign for something 表
示；作為〔某事物〕的符號: *A smile usually*
denotes pleasure. 微笑通常表示高興。| *The*
sign "=" *denotes that two things are equal.*
等號"="表示兩者相等。

de·nounce /dɪˈnauns; dɪˈnaʊns/ *v* **de-**
nounced, denouncing [T] to make a
spoken or written attack against someone
in public 譴責；指責；告發: *The minister's ac-*
tion was denounced in the newspapers. 部長
的行為在報上受到了譴責。| *They denounced*
him to the police as a criminal. 他們向警方告
發他是罪犯。

dense /dɛns; dens/ *adj* **1** closely packed or
crowded together 密集的; 稠密的: *a dense*
crowd 密集的人羣 | *dense traffic* 交通擁擠 **2**
difficult to see through 不易看透的; 濃的: *a*
dense fog 濃霧 **3** *infml* slow to understand
things 〔非正式〕遲鈍的: *He's really dense!* 他
的確很笨! –**densely** *adv*: *a densely populated*
area 人口稠密的地區

den·si·ty /ˈdɛnsəti; ˈdensᵻti/ *n* **densities 1**
[U] the amount to which an area is filled
with people or things 密集; 稠密: *This area*
has a very high population density. 這個地區
的人口密度很高。**2** [C;U] *tech* the relationship of the amount of matter in something
to the space into which the matter is
packed 〔術語〕濃度; 密度: *the density of a*
gas 氣體的密度

dent /dɛnt; dent/ *n* **1** a small hollow in the
surface of something as a result of being
hit 〔因擊、撞、壓而產生的〕凹部, 凹痕: *a bad*
dent in the side of my car 我的汽車側面的大
凹痕 **2 a dent in, a dent to** a reduction in
or to something 減少; 削減; 削弱: *Only get-*
ting third prize was a terrible dent to her
pride. 她只獲得三等獎, 這使她的自尊心大大
受挫。| *The holiday has made a big dent in*
our savings. 這個假日花去了我們一大筆積
蓄。–**dent** *v* [T]: *I'm afraid I've dented the*
car. 我怕我已把汽車撞凹了。

den·tal /ˈdɛntl; ˈdentl/ *adj* related to your
teeth 牙齒的; 牙科的: *dental decay* 蛀牙 | *in*
need of dental treatment 牙齒需要治療

den·tist /ˈdɛntɪst; ˈdentɪst/ *n* **1** a person
professionally trained to examine and treat
people's teeth 牙科醫生 **2 go to the den-**
tist's the place where you go to have your
teeth looked after by the dentist 去看牙醫:
I can't come to the meeting; I've got to go to
the dentist's this afternoon. 我不能來開會了;
我下午得去看牙醫。–**dentistry** *n* [U]

den·tures /ˈdɛntʃəz; ˈdentʃəz/ *n* [pl] a set of
specially made teeth worn by someone
who has lost all or most of their natural
teeth 假牙; 托牙

de·nude /dɪˈnjud; dɪˈnjuːd/ *v* **denuded,**

denuding *fml* [T] to remove the covering from something 〖正式〗使〔某物〕裸露; 去掉遮掩; 使光禿: *Rain has denuded the mountainside of soil.* 雨水剝蝕了山坡上的泥土。

de·nun·ci·a·tion /dɪ,nʌnsɪ'eʃən; dɪ,nʌnsi'eɪ-ʃən/ *n* [C;U] the act of making a spoken or written attack against someone in public 譴責; 告發

✲✲de·ny /dɪ'naɪ; dɪ'naɪ/ *v* **denied, denying 1** [T; +(that)] to say that something is untrue 否定, 否認〔某事〕: *He has denied all the stories in the newspapers.* 他否認了報上所有的新聞報道。| *She denied that she had ever agreed to marry him.* 她否認她曾經答應過嫁給他。| *They denied telling his mother.* 他們否認曾告訴過他母親。

□ USEFUL PATTERNS 有用句型
to deny something; to deny doing something; to deny that…

2 [T] to refuse to accept something 拒絕接受[相信]〔某事〕: *Can you deny the truth of his statement?* 你能否定他講的是事實嗎? **3** [T] to refuse to allow someone to have or do something 不准〔某人獲得某物或做某事〕: *I was denied the chance of going to university.* 我被剝奪了上大學的機會。

□ USEFUL PATTERNS 有用句型
to deny something to someone; to deny someone something

4 *fml* to say that you have no connection with someone or something 〖正式〗否認與〔某人或某事〕有關係; 拋棄: *He has denied his country and his principles!* 他已拋棄了自己的國家和原則!

de·o·do·rant /di'odərənt; diː'əʊdərənt/ *n* [C;U] a chemical substance that is used to prevent unpleasant body smells 〔去除體臭的〕除臭劑

de·part /dɪ'pɑːrt; dɪ'pɑːt/ *v* **1** *fml* [I] to go away from somewhere, especially when starting a journey 〖正式〗離開〔尤指起程〕: *The 9.30 train to Leeds will depart from platform 6.* 開往利茲的火車將於九時三十分在六號站台開出。**2 depart from something** *fml* to turn away from a previous course of action or way of thinking 〖正式〗離開; 背離先前的行為或思路: *I'd like to depart from the main subject of my speech for a few moments.* 我想暫時擱一下我的主要話題。

de·part·ed /dɪ'pɑːrtɪd; dɪ'pɑːtɪd/ *adj* **1** gone for ever 過去的; 往昔的: *her departed youth* 她已逝的青春年華 **2** *fml* dead 〖正式〗已去世的; 已故的

✲✲de·part·ment /dɪ'pɑːrtmənt; dɪ'pɑːt-mənt/ *n* a division in an organization, such as a hospital, university, large shop, or business 部; 科; 系; 局; 處; 部門: *the History Department* 歷史系 | *the toy department* 玩具部 | *the casualty department of the local hospital* 地方醫院的急救室 –**departmental** /,dɪpɑːt'mentl; ,diːpɑːt-'mentl/ *adj*: *a departmental meeting* 部門會議

department store /·'·· ·/ *n* a large shop divided into departments which sell different types of goods 百貨公司[商店]

✲de·par·ture /dɪ'pɑːrtʃər; dɪ'pɑːtʃəʳ/ *n* **1** [C;U] the act of going away from somewhere 離開; 離去: *What is the departure time of the flight to New York?* 飛往紐約的班機甚麼時候起飛? **2** [C] the act of doing something which is different from usual 背離; 違背: *The new system is a radical departure from our old methods.* 這套新的體制完全不同於我們過去的那套。

✲de·pend /dɪ'pend; dɪ'pend/ *v* **that depends, it depends** = I am not completely sure 那得看情況: *"How much do you want to spend?" "I don't know. It depends. I'd like to see what the choice is first."* "你想花多少錢?" "我不知道, 那要看情況。我想先看看選甚麼。"

depend on sbdy/sthg *phr v* [T] **1** to need someone a great deal for help or support 依靠, 依賴〔某人〕: *His family depend on him.* 他的一家人全靠他養活。**2** to trust that someone will help you when you need them to 信賴; 信任: *We're depending on you to finish the job by Friday.* 我們相信你在星期五前能完成這項工作。| *You can depend on me.* 你可以信賴我。**3** to be decided by someone or something 取決於〔某人或某事〕: *The amount you pay depends on where you live.* 你付錢多少取決於你住在哪裡。

de·pen·da·ble /dɪ'pendəbl; dɪ'pendəbəl/ *adj* able to be trusted 可靠的; 可信賴的 –**dependability** /dɪ,pendə'bɪlətɪ; dɪ,pendə'bɪlɪ-tɪ/ *n* [U]

de·pen·dant /dɪ'pendənt; dɪ'pendənt/ *n* (also 又作 **dependent**) a person who depends on someone else for money 受扶養者: *Please state on the document whether you have any dependants.* 請在文件上說明你是否有家屬需要供養。

de·pen·dence /dɪ'pendəns; dɪ'pendəns/ *n* [U] **1** the regular need for someone else's help or support 〔對某人的〕依靠; 依賴: *his dependence on his mother* 他對母親的依賴 **2** the regular need for something 〔對某物的〕依賴: *our increasing dependence on oil* 我們對石油的日益加重的依賴 | *drug dependence* 藥癮; 毒癮

✲de·pen·dent /dɪ'pendənt; dɪ'pendənt/ *adj* **1** in need of someone or something 依靠的; 依賴的: *a dependent child* 受扶養的孩子 | *a country heavily dependent on foreign aid* 一個十分依賴外國援助的國家 **2** decided by a particular thing or fact 取決於〔某事物〕: *The success of the show is always*

dependent on the weather. 演出〔展出〕能否成功總是取決於天氣的情況。

de·pict /dɪˈpɪkt; dɪˈpɪkt/ *v fml* [T] 〔正式〕**1** to represent something in a picture 描繪; 描畫: *This painting depicts the Battle of Waterloo.* 這幅畫描繪的是滑鐵盧戰役。**2** to describe someone as a certain kind of person 描述; 描寫: *The author depicts her as a mean old woman.* 作者把她描述成一個吝嗇的老太太。–**depiction** /dɪˈpɪkʃən; dɪˈpɪkʃən/ *n* [C;U]

de·plete /dɪˈplit; dɪˈpliːt/ *v* depleted, depleting *fml* [T] to reduce the amount of something 〔正式〕消耗〔某物〕: *Unexpected expenses have left us with severely depleted savings.* 意想不到的花費已使我們的積蓄所剩無幾。–**depletion** /dɪˈpliʃən; dɪˈpliːʃən/ *n* [U]

de·plore /dɪˈplor; dɪˈplɔː/ *v* deplored, deploring *fml* [T] to express feelings of extreme disappointment or shock at something 〔正式〕哀嘆; 悲嘆; 為〔某事物〕而震驚: *The teacher deplored the appalling behaviour of her pupils.* 老師對她學生的惡劣行為感到震驚。–**deplorable** *adj: a deplorable waste of money* 可鄙的浪費金錢行為 –**deplorably** *adv: She behaved deplorably.* 她的行為十分可鄙。

de·ploy /dɪˈplɔɪ; dɪˈplɔɪ/ *v* [T] to organize things so that they can be used without delay, especially for military action 部署; 調動〔尤指軍事行動〕: *They deployed all the light aircraft that were available.* 他們調動了所有現存的輕型飛機。–**deployment** *n* [U]

de·port /dɪˈport; dɪˈpɔːt/ *v* [T] to send a foreigner out of a country because they do not have a legal right to be there 把〔沒有合法身分的外國人〕驅逐出境 –**deportation** /ˌdiporˈteʃən; ˌdiːpɔːˈteɪʃən/ *n* [C;U]

de·port·ment /dɪˈportmənt; dɪˈpɔːtmənt/ *n old fash* [U] the way a young lady behaves, especially the way she stands and walks 〔老式〕舉止; 風度; 儀態〔尤指少婦的站立及行走方式〕

de·pose /dɪˈpoz; dɪˈpəʊz/ *v* deposed, deposing [T] to remove someone from a high official position 廢黜; 罷〔某人〕的官; 免〔某人〕的職: *The head of state was deposed by the army.* 國家元首被軍隊廢黜了。

***de·pos·it¹** /dɪˈpazɪt; dɪˈpɒzɪt/ *v* [T] **1** to leave something or to put something down 放下, 放置〔某物〕: *The truck deposited its load of sand.* 貨車卸下了運載的沙子。**2** (of a natural process) to leave something in a place 〔自然過程〕使沉積; 使沉澱: *Every surface was covered in dust deposited by desert winds.* 每一樣東西上面都蓋滿了由沙漠風吹積起的塵土。**3** to officially put money or valuable articles in a safe place, especially a bank 〔在銀行〕存儲〔錢或貴重物品〕: *He's deposited quite a lot of money recently.* 最近他在銀行裡存了不少錢。

deposit² *n* **1** something left in a place by a

natural process 沉積物; 礦藏: *There are rich deposits of gold in those hills.* 那些小山裡埋藏著豐富的金礦。**2** a payment of part of the money owed for something, made so that the seller will not sell the goods to anyone else 訂金, 定金: *We put down a deposit on a new car today.* 我們今天付了買新車的定金。**3** an act of officially putting money or valuable articles in a safe place 〔錢或貴重物品的〕存儲: *I'd like to make a deposit please.* 請給我存一筆錢。**4** money which you pay when you hire or rent something and which you get back if you do not damage what you have rented 押金; 保證金

deposit ac·count /·ˈ···· ·ˌ·/ *n* a bank account which earns interest; you have to tell the bank in advance if you want to take money out 定期存款賬戶

dep·ot /ˈdipo; ˈdepəʊ/ *n* **1** a place where goods are stored 倉庫; 儲藏處 **2** a large area where buses or trains are kept when they are not being used 〔汽車或火車停放的〕車庫 **3** *AmE* a bus or railway station 〔美式〕公共汽車站; 火車站

de·praved /dɪˈprevd; dɪˈpreɪvd/ *adj* evil 墮落的; 腐化的: *The judge described the murderer as a depraved and vicious man.* 法官形容那個殺人犯是個墮落、兇險的人。

de·prav·i·ty /dɪˈprævɪtɪ; dɪˈprævɪti/ *n* depravities [C;U] an evil state or action 墮落〔行為〕

de·pre·ci·ate /dɪˈpriʃɪˌet; dɪˈpriːʃieɪt/ *v* depreciated, depreciating [I] to fall in value 貶值 –**depreciation** /dɪˌpriʃɪˈeʃən; dɪˌpriːʃiˈeɪʃən/ *n* [U]

de·press /dɪˈprɛs; dɪˈpres/ *v* [T] **1** to make you feel very sad 使沮喪; 使憂愁: *The bad news depressed me.* 這壞消息使我很難過。**2** to reduce the amount or value of something 減少〔數量〕; 降低〔價值〕: *The threat of war has depressed business activity.* 戰爭的威脅使經濟蕭條。

de·pressed /dɪˈprɛst; dɪˈprest/ *adj* **1** very sad 沮喪的; 憂愁的 **2** suffering from low levels of business activity 經濟蕭條的〔不景氣的〕: *depressed areas of the country* 國內經濟不景氣的地區

de·press·ing /dɪˈprɛsɪŋ; dɪˈpresɪŋ/ *adj* making you feel very sad 令人憂愁的; 令人沮喪的: *a depressing piece of news* 一則令人沮喪的消息 –**depressingly** *adv*

***de·pres·sion** /dɪˈprɛʃən; dɪˈpreʃən/ *n* **1** [C;U] a feeling of sadness and hopelessness 沮喪; 憂愁; 消沉: *He's suffering from depression.* 他心情憂鬱。**2** [C] a period of reduced business activity and high unemployment 經濟蕭條期: *the great depression of the 1930s* 三十年代的經濟大蕭條 **3** [C] a part of a surface lower than the other parts 窪地; 凹地: *The rain collected in depressions on the ground.* 雨水積聚在地上的低窪處。

de·prive /dɪˈpraɪv; dɪˈpraɪv/ *v* deprived, de-

priving; deprive someone of something to take something away from someone 剝奪某人的某物: *They deprived their prisoner of his rights.* 他們剝奪了囚犯的權利。 —**deprivation** /ˌdɛprɪ'veʃən; ˌdeprɪ'veɪʃən/ *n* [C;U]

de·prived /dɪ'praɪvd; dɪ'praɪvd/ *adj* without food, money, or good living conditions 貧困的; 窮苦的: *a deprived childhood* 貧苦的童年

dept. *n* a written abbreviation for 《縮寫》= DEPARTMENT

*★**depth** /dɛpθ; depθ/ *n* [C;U] **1** the distance from the surface to the bottom of something or from the front to the back 深(度); 縱深: *What is the depth of the shelves?* 架子有多深? | *They dived to a depth of 30 feet.* 他們潛入水中三十英尺的深度。 **2** The amount that someone knows, feels, or understands 〔學識、感情、理解的〕深度: *I was surprised by the depth of his feelings.* 他感情的真摯令我大吃一驚。 **3** the seriousness of a situation 〔形勢的〕嚴峻; 嚴重(性): *the depth of the crisis* 嚴重的危機 **4** in depth in detail 徹底地; 深入地: *We'll have to examine the problem in depth.* 我們必須徹底調查這個問題。 | *an in-depth study* 深入的研究 **5** out of your depth: **a** in water deeper than your height 在水深沒頂的地方 **b** unable to understand something 不能理解某事物: *I'm completely out of my depth in this argument.* 我完全不能理解這場爭論。 **6** the depths the deepest, most central, or worst part of something 最深處; 正中部分; 最壞的情況: *She lives in the depths of the country.* 她住在這個國家的中部地區。 | *the depths of depression* 極度消沉

dep·u·ta·tion /ˌdɛpjə'teʃən; ˌdepjʊ'teɪʃən/ *n* a group of people who are sent somewhere as representatives of a larger group 代表團: *The minister agreed to receive a deputation from the railwaymen's union.* 部長同意接見鐵路工會代表團。

dep·u·tize /'dɛpjəˌtaɪz; 'depjʊtaɪz/ *v* **deputized, deputizing** (also 又作 **deputise** *BrE* 《英式》) [I] to act as a deputy 擔任代表

*★**dep·u·ty** /'dɛpjətɪ; 'depjʊtɪ/ *n* **deputies 1** the person in the second most powerful position in an organization 〔組織機構的〕副手: *the deputy leader of the party* 政黨的副領袖 **2** a person given the power to act for someone else 代表; 代理人: *Jean will be my deputy while I am away.* 我不在的時候, 瓊將作為我的代理人。 **3** a member of the lower house of parliament in certain countries 〔某些國家的〕下院議員, 眾議員

de·rail /di'rel; ˌdiː'reɪl/ *v* [T] to make a train come off the railway line 使〔火車〕出軌 — **derailment** *n* [C;U]

de·ranged /dɪ'rendʒd; dɪ'reɪndʒd/ *adj* seriously ill in the mind 精神錯亂的; 有精神病的: *That poor woman is completely deranged.* 那個可憐的女人精神完全失常。 —**derangement** *n* [U]

der·e·lict /'dɛrəˌlɪkt; 'derʊlɪkt/ *adj* not used

and falling into decay (used of buildings) 廢棄的; 破舊的〔指建築物〕: *a derelict old house* 一幢被廢棄的舊房子

de·ride /dɪ'raɪd; dɪ'raɪd/ *v* **derided, deriding** [T] *fml* to laugh at something you consider to be worthless 《正式》嘲笑; 嘲弄

de·ri·sion /dɪ'rɪʒən; dɪ'rɪʒən/ *n* [U] the action of laughing unkindly at something considered worthless 嘲笑; 嘲弄: *They greeted his suggestion with shouts of derision.* 他們對他的建議大聲嘲笑。 —**derisive** /dɪ'raɪsɪv; dɪ'raɪsɪv/ *adj*: *derisive laughter* 嘲弄的笑聲 —**derisively** *adv*

de·ri·so·ry /dɪ'raɪsərɪ; dɪ'raɪsərɪ/ *adj* **1** very small and so not worth considering seriously 〔由於數量太小而〕招人嘲笑的; 可笑的: *a derisory offer of £10 for something worth £100* 想出價十英鎊購買價值一百英鎊的東西, 真的是很可笑 **2** showing a total lack of respect 目中無人的, 不屑一顧的

der·i·va·tion /ˌdɛrə'veʃən; ˌderʊ'veɪʃən/ *n* the origin from which something comes 起源; 派生〔指詞語〕: *What is the derivation of the word "television"?* "television" 這個詞是怎麼派生而來的?

de·riv·a·tive¹ /də'rɪvətɪv; dɪ'rɪvətɪv/ *n* something coming from something else 派生詞; 衍生物: *French is a derivative of Latin.* 法語是由拉丁語派生出來的。

derivative² *adj* not original or new 非獨創的; 無新意的: *a rather derivative piece of music* 一首蹈襲前人的樂曲

de·rive /də'raɪv; dɪ'raɪv/ *v* **derived, deriving 1** [T] *fml* to get something from someone or from something else 《正式》從〔某人或他物〕取得〔某物〕: *Maria derives great pleasure from playing the piano.* 瑪麗亞從彈鋼琴中得到極大樂趣。 **2** [I;T] to come from 派生; 源於: *The word "television" derives from both Greek and Latin.* "television" 一詞是從希臘語和拉丁語派生而來的。 | *This word is derived from Latin.* 這個詞是從拉丁語派生而來的。

der·ma·ti·tis /ˌdɜːmə'taɪtɪs; ˌdɜːmə'taɪtɪs/ *n* [U] a disease of your skin, marked by redness, swelling, and pain 皮〔膚〕炎

de·rog·a·to·ry /dɪ'rɑgəˌtorɪ; dɪ'rɒgətərɪ/ *adj* *fml* showing lack of respect for someone 《正式》貶低的; 毀損的; 誹謗的: *derogatory remarks about the government* 貶低政府的言論

der·rick /'dɛrɪk; 'derɪk/ *n* a CRANE¹ for lifting and moving heavy weights, for example into or out of a ship 桅桿起重機; 轉臂起重機

de·scend /dɪ'sɛnd; dɪ'send/ *v* *fml* 《正式》 [I;T] to go down 下來; 下降: *The sun descended behind the hills.* 太陽下山了。 | *The Queen descended the stairs.* 女王走下樓梯。 **2** **descend on/upon someone** to arrive suddenly to visit or stay with someone 突然來訪或看望某人: *The whole family descended* *on us at Christmas.* 他們全家突然在聖誕節來我家作客。 **3 descend to something** to behave in a way that is below your usual standards 降低身分做某事: *He eventually descended to cheating.* 他最終墮落到對別人進行詐騙。

de·scen·dant /dɪˈsɛndənt; dɪˈsendənt/ *n* a person or animal that has the stated person or animal as their grandfather or grandmother, great-grandfather, etc. 子孫; 後代; 後裔: *He is a descendant of Queen Victoria.* 他是維多利亞女王的後裔。 –compare 比較 ANCESTOR

de·scend·ed /dɪˈsɛndɪd; dɪˈsend ̩d/ *adj* **descended from someone** having the stated person or animal as their grandfather or grandmother, great-grandfather, etc. 為某人的後裔的: *She claims to be descended from George Washington.* 她聲稱自己是喬治·華盛頓的後裔。

de·scent /dɪˈsɛnt; dɪˈsent/ *n* **1** [C;U] the process of going or coming down 下降; 降下: *The road makes a sharp descent just past the lake.* 那條路剛過湖畔就陡然下傾。 | *his descent into a life of crime* 他沉淪於罪惡的生活 **2** [U] your family origins 血統; 祖籍: *She is of German descent.* 她祖籍是德國。

✱✱de·scribe /dɪˈskraɪb; dɪˈskraɪb/ *v* **described, describing** [T] to say what something is like 描述; 敘述; 描繪: *The police asked me to describe the man.* 警方叫我描述一下那名男子的容貌。 | *Try to describe exactly what happened.* 要盡量準確地描述所發生的事情。 | *Would you describe your mother as a nervous woman?* 你會把你母親描繪成一個神經質的女人嗎?

□ USEFUL PATTERNS 有用句型
to describe something; to describe what/how/where...; to describe someone or something as...

✱de·scrip·tion /dɪˈskrɪpʃən; dɪˈskrɪpʃən/ *n* **1** [C;U] an account of what someone or something is like or how something happened 描述; 敘述; 形容: *Terry gave a detailed description of everything that had taken place.* 黛麗詳細描述了所發生的一切。 | *I recognized the man from the description in the newspaper.* 我根據報上的描述認出了那人。 **2** [C] a sort or kind 種類; 類型: *The hall was packed with people of every description.* 大廳裡擠滿了各種各樣的人。 –**descriptive** /-tɪv, -tɪv/ *adj*: *descriptive writing* 描寫 –**descriptively** *adv*

des·e·crate /ˈdɛsɪˌkret; ˈdesɪkreɪt/ *v* **desecrated, desecrating** [T] to spoil something holy, or to use it for purposes which are not holy 褻瀆; 把〔聖物〕供俗用 –**desecration** /ˌdɛsɪˈkreʃən; ˌdesɪˈkreɪʃən/ *n* [U]

des·ert¹ /ˈdɛzət; ˈdezət/ *n* a large area of land, often covered with sand, where there is very little rain and so very few plants 沙漠; 荒原: *the Sahara Desert* 撒哈拉沙漠 | *a hot desert wind* 沙漠熱風

de·sert² /dɪˈzɜt; dɪˈzɜːt/ *v* **1** [T] to leave a place so that it becomes empty 離棄〔某一地方〕; 放棄: *The weather changed and the holidaymakers deserted the beach.* 天氣發生變化, 度假者離開了海濱。 **2** [T] to leave someone completely or for the last time 拋棄, 遺棄〔某人〕: *John's friends deserted him when he was accused of murder.* 當約翰被指控犯有謀殺罪時, 他的朋友都離他而去。 **3** [I; T] (of someone in the armed forces) to leave a place without permission 〔軍人〕當逃兵; 開小差: *The soldier deserted his post.* 那士兵擅離職守。

de·sert·ed /dɪˈzɜtɪd; dɪˈzɜːt ̩d/ *adj* with no people present 無人的: *a deserted village* 空無一人的村莊

de·sert·er /dɪˈzɜtə; dɪˈzɜːtəʳ/ *n* a person who leaves military service without permission 開小差的人; 逃兵

de·ser·tion /dɪˈzɜʃən; dɪˈzɜːʃən/ *n* [C;U] the act of leaving, especially with the intention of never returning 離棄; 遺棄

✱de·serve /dɪˈzɜv; dɪˈzɜːv/ *v* **deserved, serving** [T not in progressive forms 不用於進行式] to be worthy of a particular thing 應受; 應得; 值得: *You've been working all morning — you deserve a rest.* 你已幹了整整一個上午——你應該休息一下。 | *She deserved to win.* 她是理應獲勝的。

□ USEFUL PATTERNS 有用句型
to deserve something; to deserve to do something

de·serv·ed·ly /dɪˈzɜvɪdlɪ; dɪˈzɜːv ̩dli/ *adv* rightly, because someone is worthy of something 理所當然地; 應得地: *He's made a lot of money, and deservedly so.* 他賺了很多錢, 也是理應所得的。

de·serv·ing /dɪˈzɜvɪŋ; dɪˈzɜːvɪŋ/ *adj* **1** worthy of support and help 值得幫助的〔贊助的〕: *We should give the money to a deserving cause.* 我們應該把錢捐給值得贊助的事業。 **2 deserving of** *fml* worthy of 〔正式〕值得的: *deserving of the highest praise* 值得高度讚揚

des·ic·cate /ˈdɛsəˌket; ˈdes ̩keɪt/ *v* **desiccated, desiccating** [I;T] to make or become dried up (使)乾燥; (使)脫水

✱✱de·sign¹ /dɪˈzaɪn; dɪˈzaɪn/ *v* [T] **1** to make a drawing or plan so that someone can make or build something 設計; 構思: *Who designed the Sydney Opera House?* 悉尼歌劇院是誰設計的? **2** to develop something for a certain purpose or use 設置; 計劃: *a book designed mainly for use in colleges* 一本主要供大學使用的書 | *These coins were designed to help blind people identify their money.* 這些硬幣是為了

D

幫助盲人辨認錢幣而設計的。 –**designer** *n*:
She's a dress designer. 她是一位服裝設計師。|
an aircraft designer 飛機設計師

✭design² *n* **1** [C] a drawing showing
how something is to be made
圖樣; 圖紙 **2** [U] the art of making drawings
or patterns showing how something is to
be made 設計術; 圖案: *a school of dress de-
sign* 服裝設計學校 | *the importance of good
design* 優秀設計的重要性 **3** [C] a decorative
pattern, especially one that is not repeated
裝飾圖案: *a carpet with a floral design in the
centre* 中央有花卉裝飾圖案的地毯 **4** [C] a
plan in your mind 計劃; 方案 **5 have
designs on something** to have the intention of getting something, especially cleverly or dishonestly 企圖將某物佔為己有:
*Watch out for Ted — I think he has designs
on your job.* 對泰德要有所提防——我覺得他
在打你這份工作的主意。

des·ig·nate /ˈdɛzɪɡ.net; ˈdɛzɪɡneɪt/ *v* **designated, designating** [T] **1** to call something
by a particular name because it fulfils a
special purpose 把〔某物〕定名為; 把〔某物〕叫
做: *The wood was designated an area of
special scientific interest.* 該森林被定為特殊科
研林區。| *designated* **as** *a conservation zone*
命名為保護區 **2** to appoint someone formally
to do a particular job 委任〔某人〕; 指派: *She
was designated* **as** *the Minister of Education.*
她獲委任為教育部長。| *designated to take
over the position of Chairman* 被指派去接任主
席的職務 –**designation** /ˌdɛzɪɡˈneʃən; ˌdɛzɪɡ-
ˈneʃən/ *n* [C;U]

des·ig·nate² /ˈdɛzɪɡnɪt; ˈdɛzɪɡnɪt/ *adj* [only
after a noun 只用於名詞後] a person
appointed to a job who has not yet started
work 已委任而尚未上任的: *The Director
designate was invited to attend the meeting.*
候任的主任被邀請列席會議。

de·sir·a·ble /dɪˈzaɪrəbl; dɪˈzaɪərəbəl/ *adj*
worth having, doing, or wanting 稱心的; 合
意的: *a desirable job* 稱心如意的工作 –compare 比較 UNDESIRABLE –**desirability** /dɪ-
ˌzaɪrəˈbɪlətɪ; dɪˌzaɪərəˈbɪlɪtɪ/ *n* [U]

de·sire¹ /dɪˈzaɪr; dɪˈzaɪər/ *v* **desired, desiring**
[T not in progressive forms 不用於進行式] **1**
fml to wish or want something very much
〔正式〕渴望〔某事物〕; 慾望: *We all desire
happiness.* 我們都渴望幸福。 **2** to be sexually
attracted to someone 〔對某人〕產生情慾 **3
leave a lot to be desired** to be not very satisfactory 令人很不滿意: *The standard of
cooking here leaves a lot to be desired.* 這裡
的烹調水平還有許多有待提高之處。

✭desire² *n* [C;U] **1** a strong wish 願望; 心願;
慾望: *filled with a sudden desire for fame* 突
然產生強烈的成名慾 | *I haven't the slightest
desire to see my family again.* 我一點兒也不
想與家人團聚。 **2** a strong wish for sexual
relations with someone 情慾: *Antony's desire for Cleopatra* 安東尼對克婁巴特拉的情慾

■ USAGE 用法: Compare 比較 **desire,
appetite, craving, lust.** You can have
a **desire** for anything ☆ **desire** 是對一
切事物而言的: *a* **desire** *for success* 對(取
得)成功的熱望 | *a* **desire** *to help some-
one* 幫助別人的心願。 **Appetite** is most
often used for things of the body, especially food ☆**appetite** 大多指和身體
有關的事物〔尤指食物〕: *The body has a
good* **appetite.** 嬰兒的胃口很好。 A
craving is a strong desire, especially
for things that people think are bad ☆
craving 則是一種渴望〔尤指渴望得到人
們認為是不好的東西〕: *a* **craving** *for
cigarettes* 煙癮。 **Lust** is a very strong
and usually derogatory word ☆**lust** 是
個語氣很強而且常含貶義的詞: *the* **lust**
for power/sex 權力慾; 淫慾

de·sir·ous /dɪˈzaɪrəs; dɪˈzaɪərəs/ *adj fml*
[never before a noun 不能用於名詞前]
having a strong wish 〔正式〕渴望的, 想得
到...的: *people desirous of fame* 渴望成名的
人

de·sist /dɪˈzɪst; dɪˈzɪst/ *v fml* [I] to stop doing 〔正式〕停止; 斷念: *The judge told the
man to desist* **from** *threatening his wife.* 法官
叫那個男人不得再對妻子進行威脅。

✭desk /dɛsk; dɛsk/ *n* **1** a table, often with
drawers, at which you read, write, or work
書桌; 辦公桌; 寫字枱 –see picture on page
763 見 763 頁彩圖 **2** an area where particular work is done 工作台; 服務台: *I left a
message at the reception desk* 我在服務台留
了言。

des·o·late /ˈdɛslɪt; ˈdɛsələt/ *adj* sad and
lonely 荒涼的; 荒蕪的; 淒涼的: *the desolate
Arctic wastes* 無人居住的北極荒地 –**desolation** /ˌdɛslˈeʃən; ˌdɛsəˈleɪʃən/ *n* [U]: *a
sense of utter desolation* 極度悲傷感

de·spair¹ /dɪˈspɛr; dɪˈspɛər/ *v* [I] to lose all
hope 絕望; 喪失希望: *Don't despair: things
will get better soon!* 不要喪失信心, 情況很快
就會好轉的! | *Sometimes I despair of ever
passing my driving test!* 有時候我對通過駕駛
考試不抱任何希望! –**despairingly** *adv*

despair² *n* [U] complete loss of hope 絕望:
Defeat after defeat filled us with despair. 一
次又一次的失敗使我們完全絕望了。

de·spatch /dɪˈspætʃ; dɪˈspætʃ/ *n,v* –see 見
DISPATCH

✭des·per·ate /ˈdɛspərɪt; ˈdɛspərɪt/ *adj* **1** wanting or needing something very much 極想
望的; 極需要的: *He's desperate* **for** *work.* 他
很想找到工作。 | *They're desperate to es-
cape.* 他們極想逃走。

□ USEFUL PATTERNS 有用句型
be desperate for something; be desperate to do something

2 violent and not caring about danger, especially because you have lost hope〔因絕望而〕不顧一切的; 拼死的: *a desperate criminal* 亡命之徒 **3** dangerous, and done when everything else has failed 鋌而走險的; 孤注一擲的: *a last desperate effort to win* 為取勝而孤注一擲 **4** very difficult and dangerous (used of a situation) 艱難的; 危急的〔指事態〕: *The country is in a desperate state.* 國家處於危急狀態。 –**desperately** *adv*

des·per·a·tion /ˌdɛspə'reʃən; ˌdɛspəˈreɪʃən/ *n* [U] the state of being desperate 絕望; 拼命; 鋌而走險: *He kicked at the locked door in desperation.* 他拼命踢那扇鎖住的門。

des·pic·a·ble /'dɛspɪkəbḷ; dɪ'spɪkəbəl/ *adj* deserving to be despised 可鄙的; 卑鄙的: *That was a despicable thing to do!* 幹那件事真卑鄙! –**despicably** *adv*: *You behaved despicably!* 你的行為真卑鄙!

de·spise /dɪ'spaɪz; dɪ'spaɪz/ *v* **despised, despising** [T not in progressive forms 不用於進行式] to consider something to be worthless or extremely bad 鄙視; 藐視

de·spite /dɪ'spaɪt; dɪ'spaɪt/ *prep* **1** in spite of 儘管; 不管: *Despite the bad weather we had a lovely time.* 儘管天氣不好, 我們還是過得很愉快。 **2** **despite yourself** in spite of the fact that you did not really want to do something 儘管自己不願〔做某事〕: *I found myself apologizing despite myself.* 儘管我不願道歉, 但我發現自己還是這樣做了。

de·spon·dent /dɪ'spɒndənt; dɪ'spɑndənt/ *adj* feeling very unhappy and without hope 沮喪的; 泄氣的; 失望的 –**despondently** *adv* – **despondency** *n* [U]

des·pot /'dɛspɒt; 'dɛspɒt/ *n* a person who has great power and uses it unjustly or cruelly 專制君主; 暴君 –**despotic** /dɪ'spɒtɪk; dɪ'spɑtɪk/ *adj* –**despotism** /'dɛspə,tɪzəm; 'dɛspətɪzəm/ *n* [U]

des·sert /dɪ'zɜ·t; dɪ'zɜːt/ *n* [C;U] sweet food served at the end of a meal〔正餐最後的〕甜食; 甜點心: *We had cake for dessert.* 我們以蛋糕作為甜點心。

des·sert·spoon /dɪ'zɜ·t,spun; dɪ'zɜːtspuːn/ *n* **1** a spoon between a TEASPOON and a TABLESPOON in size 點心匙; 中匙 **2** (also 又作 **dessertspoonful**) as much as a dessertspoon will hold 一點心匙的量

des·ti·na·tion /ˌdɛstə'neʃən; ˌdɛstɪ'neɪʃən/ *n* a place where you are going or where something is sent 目的地; 送達地點: *The parcel was sent to the wrong destination.* 包裹送錯了地方

des·tined /'dɛstɪnd; 'dɛstɪnd/ *adj* **1** intended by fate for some special purpose 命中注定的: *Robert is destined for a career in the army.* 羅伯特的戎馬生涯是命中注定的。 | *The plan was destined not to succeed.* 計劃注定是不會成功的。 **2** **destined for** going to a particular place 去, 到, 往, 赴〔某地〕: *a ship*

destined for Bombay 開往孟買的輪船

□ USEFUL PATTERNS 有用句型
be destined for something; be destined to do something

---

des·ti·ny /'dɛstənɪ; 'dɛstḷni/ *n* **destinies 1** [C] something which must happen 命運: *It would be her destiny to lead her country.* 她命中注定要領導她的國家。 **2** [U] (also 又作 **Destiny**) the force which, some people believe, decides what will happen to us 天數; 天命

des·ti·tute /'dɛstə,tjut; 'dɛstḷtjuːt/ *adj* without things like food and clothing, or the money to buy them 貧困的; 赤貧的: *jobless and destitute, sleeping in doorways and begging for food* 既沒工作又沒錢, 只得於飯餐睡在街頭 –**destitution** /ˌdɛstə'tjuʃən; ˌdɛstḷ'tjuːʃən/ *n* [U]

de·stroy /dɪ'strɔɪ; dɪ'strɔɪ/ *v* [T] **1** to ruin something 摧毀〔某物〕; 毀滅: *The fire destroyed most of the building.* 大火把那座建築物幾乎燒毀了。 | *All hopes of a peaceful settlement were destroyed by his violent speech.* 和解的所有希望都被他激烈的講話打破了。 **2** to kill an animal because it is unwanted or in pain 殺死; 消滅: *The horse broke its leg and had to be destroyed.* 馬摔斷了腿, 不得不把它宰了。

de·stroy·er /dɪ'strɔɪɚ; dɪ'strɔɪər/ *n* **1** a person or thing that destroys something 破壞者; 消滅者 **2** a small fast warship 驅逐艦

de·struc·tion /dɪ'strʌkʃən; dɪ'strʌkʃən/ *n* [U] destroying something or being destroyed 毀滅; 消滅: *The enemy bombs caused widespread destruction.* 敵人的炸彈造成廣泛的破壞。 | *the destruction of the forest by fire* 大火對森林的破壞

de·struc·tive /dɪ'strʌktɪv; dɪ'strʌktɪv/ *adj* causing great damage 破壞(性)的; 毀滅(性)的: *a destructive storm* 摧毀性的風暴 | *These emotional scenes are very destructive.* 這樣令人激動的場面具有很大的破壞性。 –**destructiveness** *n* [U]

de·sul·to·ry /'dɛsḷ,torɪ; 'dɛsəltərɪ/ *adj fml* lacking organization and purpose〔正式〕雜亂的; 無條理的; 隨意的

de·tach /dɪ'tætʃ; dɪ'tætʃ/ *v* [T] to separate something from another thing 拆開; 分離; 分開 –**detachable** *adj*: *a detachable shoulder-strap* 可拆卸的肩帶

de·tached /dɪ'tætʃt; dɪ'tætʃt/ *adj* **1** not connected on any side with any other building (used of a house) 獨立式的; 不連接的〔指房屋〕 –see picture on page 729 見 729 頁彩圖 **2** not influenced by personal feelings (used of a person or an opinion) 不帶個人感情的〔指人或意見〕

de·tach·ment /dɪ'tætʃmənt; dɪ'tætʃmənt/ *n* **1** [U] a state where personal feelings have no influence 超脫; 客觀; 獨立: *The journalist* *viewed the situation with total detachment.* 新聞記者以完全獨立客觀的眼光看待形勢。**2** [C] a group of soldiers, sent from the main group on special duty 分遣隊; 支隊〔獨立小分隊〕

★★de·tail /'ditel; 'di:teɪl/ n **1** [C;U] a small point or fact 細節; 詳情: *Everything in her story is correct, down to the smallest detail.* 她所講述的一切都正確無誤, 連最小的細節也是如此。| *He has a good eye for detail — he notices everything.* 他能明察秋毫——他注意到一切事情。**2 in detail** thoroughly 詳細地: *I haven't read the report in detail yet.* 我還未詳細看過這篇報道。**3 go into detail** to give all the information 詳細敍述 **4 details** [pl] information or the facts about something 詳細資料; 細目: *Send for details of our range of sportswear.* 去把我們的系列運動服的詳細資料弄來。**–detailed** adj: *a detailed account* 詳細的敍述

de·tain /dɪ'ten; dɪ'teɪn/ v [T] fml to make someone stay somewhere 〔正式〕拘留; 扣押; 耽擱: *The police have detained two men for questioning.* 警察拘留了兩個男子進行審問。| *I mustn't detain you, I know you're very busy.* 我不該耽擱你, 我知道你很忙。

★de·tect /dɪ'tɛkt; dɪ'tekt/ v [T] to find or notice something 發覺; 察覺; 發現: *Small quantities of poison were detected in the dead man's stomach.* 在死者胃中發現了少量毒藥。

de·tec·tion /dɪ'tɛkʃən; dɪ'tekʃən/ n [U] **1** the work of finding out all the information about a crime, especially who was responsible 偵查; 偵察: *the art of detection* 偵察術 | *His crime escaped detection for many years.* 他的罪行多年來未被偵察到。**2** noticing or being noticed 發現; 發覺: *The plane penetrated enemy airspace without detection.* 飛機神不知鬼不覺地進入了敵人上空。

★de·tec·tive /dɪ'tɛktɪv; dɪ'tektɪv/ n a person, often a member of the police force, whose special job is to find out information about criminals 偵探

de·tec·tor /dɪ'tɛktɚ; dɪ'tektər/ n any instrument for finding out if something is present 探測器: *a metal detector* 金屬探測器

dé·tente /de'tãt; deɪ'tɒnt/ n (also 又作 **detente**) [U] calmer political relations between countries 〔國際間緊張關係的〕緩和

de·ten·tion /dɪ'tɛnʃən; dɪ'tenʃən/ n [U] the act of preventing a person from leaving a place like a school, police station, or prison, or the state of being prevented from leaving 拘留; 扣押; 監禁; 禁閉: *Political opponents were subject to detention without trial.* 政敵可以未經審判而被關押。| *I'm in detention tomorrow for not doing my homework.* 我因沒做家課, 明天將受到課後留校的懲罰。

de·ter /dɪ'tɝ; dɪ'tɜ:r/ v -rr- [T] fml to discourage someone from doing something 〔正式〕

阻嚇〔某人做某事〕; 阻止: *new airport security measures to deter drug smugglers* 阻嚇毒販的新機場安全措施 | *High fares and poor service deter people* **from** *travelling by train.* 昂貴的車票和差勁的服務使人們不敢乘火車了。

de·ter·gent /dɪ'tɝdʒənt; dɪ'tɜ:dʒənt/ n [C; U] a chemical product used for cleaning things like clothes and dishes 洗滌劑; 洗潔精

de·te·ri·o·rate /dɪ'tɪrɪə͵ret; dɪ'tɪəriəreɪt/ v deteriorated, deteriorating [I] to become worse 惡化; 變壞; 衰退: *His deteriorating health forced him to retire.* 他那不斷惡化的健康狀況迫使他退休。**–deterioration** /dɪ͵tɪrɪə'reʃən; dɪ͵tɪəriə'reɪʃən/ n [U]

★de·ter·mi·na·tion /dɪ͵tɝmə'neʃən; dɪ͵tɜ:mɪ'neɪʃən/ n [U] **1** a firm intention to succeed in doing something 決心; 決意: *The police chief spoke of his determination to catch the killers.* 警長談到他要抓獲兇手的決心。**2** the act of deciding what something is or will be 確定; 測定

★★de·ter·mine /dɪ'tɝmɪn; dɪ'tɜ:mɪn/ v determined, determining [T] fml 〔正式〕**1** to find something out 確定; 查明〔某事物〕: *to determine the rights and wrongs of the case* 判別案情的是非曲直 **2** to decide 決定: *He determined to go at once.* 他決定立刻動身。| *an event which determined his future* 決定他未來的大事

★de·ter·mined /dɪ'tɝmɪnd; dɪ'tɜ:mɪnd/ adj having a strong will; or a strong intention to do something 堅決的; 決意的: *a very determined woman* 很有決心的女子 | *I am absolutely determined to go.* 我極堅決要去。

□ **USEFUL PATTERN** 有用句型
be determined to do something

---

de·ter·min·er /dɪ'tɝmɪnɚ; dɪ'tɜ:mɪnər/ n a word that limits the meaning of a noun and comes before adjectives that describe the same noun 〔用於形容詞前以限定名詞的〕限定詞: *In the phrase "his new car", the word "his" is a determiner.* 在短語"his new car"中, "his" 是個限定詞。

de·ter·rent /dɪ'tɝənt; dɪ'terənt/ n something which stops people doing something because they are afraid of what might happen 威懾物; 制止物: *Do you think the death penalty acts as a deterrent to murderers?* 你認為死刑能對謀殺犯起威懾作用嗎? | *the nuclear deterrent* 核威懾力量 **–deterrent** adj

de·test /dɪ'tɛst; dɪ'test/ v [T not in progressive forms 不用於進行式] to hate someone or something 憎惡; 嫌惡; 痛恨〔某人或某物〕: *I detest people who tell lies.* 我痛恨那些撒謊的人。**–detestable** adj: *a detestable child* 令人討厭的孩子

det·o·nate /'dɛtə͵net; 'detəneɪt/ v detonated, detonating [I;T] to explode or make something explode (使)爆炸; 引爆〔某物〕:

Land-mines can be detonated by vehicles driving over them. 車子從地雷上面開過能引爆地雷。 **–detonation** /ˌdɛtəˈneʃən; ˌdeтəˈneɪʃən/ *n* [U]

de·tour /ˈditur; ˈdiːtʊəʳ/ *n* a longer journey than necessary 繞行的路; 迂迴路: *a detour to avoid the town centre* 避開市中心繞道而行的路

de·tract /dɪˈtrækt; dɪˈtrækt/ *v* **detract from something** to make something seem less good 貶低某物; 使事物受損: *His later work was poor, and this detracted from his reputation.* 他後來的工作幹得很差, 這使他的名譽受損。

det·ri·ment /ˈdɛtrəmənt; ˈdetrɪmənt/ *n fml* 〖正式〗 **1 to the detriment of** causing damage to something 對〔某物〕有害; 有損於〔某物〕: *actions that may be to the detriment of the company's reputation* 會有損於公司聲譽的行為 **2 without detriment to** without damaging something 對〔某物〕無害; 無損於〔某物〕 **–detrimental** /ˌdɛtrəˈmentl; ˌdetrɪˈmentl◂/ *adj*

deuce /djus; djuːs/ *n* [U] 40 points to each player in a game of tennis 〔網球等的〕局末平分, 平手

de·val·u·a·tion /ˌdivæljuˈeʃən; diːˌvæljuˈeɪʃən/ *n* [U] a reduction in the value of something, especially the exchange value of money 降低價值〔尤指貨幣貶值〕

de·val·ue /diˈvælju; diːˈvæljuː/ *v* **devalued, devaluing** [T] to reduce the value of something, especially the exchange value of money 降低〔某物〕的價值〔尤指使貨幣貶值〕: *The currency was devalued by ten per cent.* 貨幣貶值百分之十。

dev·a·state /ˈdɛvəsˌtet; ˈdevəsteɪt/ *v* **devastated, devastating** [T] to damage something so badly that very little is left 徹底摧毀〔某事物〕; 破壞; 蹂躪; 使荒蕪 **–devastation** /ˌdɛvəsˈteʃən; ˌdevəˈsteɪʃən/ *n* [U]

dev·a·stat·ed /ˈdɛvəsˌtetɪd; ˈdevəsteɪtɪd/ *adj* shocked and sorrowful 震驚的; 悲傷的: *When our son was killed, we were devastated.* 我們的兒子被害時, 我們都驚呆了。

dev·a·stat·ing /ˈdɛvəsˌtetɪŋ; ˈdevəsteɪtɪŋ/ *adj* **1** damaging something so badly that very little is left 毀滅性的: *a devastating storm* 破壞力極強的風暴 **2** *infml* 〖非正式〗 making you feel very upset 令人震驚的: *The news was devastating.* 這消息令人震驚。 **– devastatingly** *adv*

de·vel·op /dɪˈvɛləp; dɪˈveləp/ *v* **1** [I] to grow 發展; 發育, 成長: *The fighting could easily develop into a full-scale war.* 這場戰事容易演變成為全面戰爭。 | *This flower developed from a tiny seed.* 這枝花是從一粒小小的種子長出來的。 **2** [T] to improve something or make it grow 改善〔某事物〕; 使發展: *a campaign to develop the local economy* 一場發展當地經濟的運動 **3** [T] to get an illness, a fault, or a characteristic

患〔疾病〕; 出〔故障〕; 出現〔特徵〕: *She developed cancer at the age of 30.* 她三十歲時得了癌症。 | *The machine developed a fault.* 機器出了故障。 | *He had developed a taste for fast food.* 吃快餐變成了他的愛好。 **4** [T] to invent or produce a new product or idea 發明; 開發: *The Romans developed the technique of glass-blowing.* 羅馬人發明了玻璃吹製術。 | *Several companies are currently developing AIDS drugs.* 好幾家公司目前正在開發用於治療愛滋病的藥物。 **5** [T] to build houses and factories on a piece of land 在〔土地〕上建造〔房屋、工廠〕: *Much of the land in the south-east of the county has now been developed.* 該縣東南部的大片土地現在已被開發利用。 **6** [I] (of a country) to start to have modern industries 〔國家〕發展〔現代工業〕: *The government agreed to spend more on helping developing countries.* 政府決定增加開支, 用以幫助發展中國家。 **7** [T] to produce pictures from a photographic film 使〔膠卷〕顯影, 沖印: *I must get my holiday photos developed.* 我得把在假期裡拍的照片沖印出來。

de·vel·op·er /dɪˈvɛləpə; dɪˈveləpəʳ/ *n* a person who makes money by buying land and building houses or factories on it 〔房地產的〕開發者, 發展商

de·vel·op·ment /dɪˈvɛləpmənt; dɪˈveləpmənt/ *n* **1** [C] a new event 新事態; 新情況: *There has been an important new development in the political situation.* 政治形勢已有新的重大發展。 **2** [C] a new invention, or an improvement to an existing machine or process 〔現有設備或過程的〕新發明, 改進: *recent development in the treatment of cancer* 癌症治療的最新成果 **3** [U] the growth or improvement of something 發展; 進展: *the rapid development of the oil industry* 石油工業的迅速發展 | *the country's economic development programme* 國家的經濟發展項目 **4** [U] the building of houses and factories on land 〔房地產和工廠的〕開發: *Plans were being submitted for the development of this site.* 開發這塊地方的計劃已遞交上去。 **5** [C] a group of new buildings 新建住宅區: *a new housing development on the edge of town* 城市外圍的新建住宅區 **6** [U] the invention or production of new products and ideas 新發明; 新產品: *the development of two experimental aircraft* 兩架實驗飛機的發明 | *We should encourage companies to spend more on research and development.* 我們應該鼓勵公司在研究與發展上多作投資。 **7** [U] the process by which a poor country starts to have modern industries 發展過程〔指經濟落後國家的現代工業的發展〕: *The government has given 32 million pounds in food and development aid.* 政府已在食品和發展項目的援助方面投入三千二百萬英鎊。 | *the minister for overseas development* 負責海外發展的部長

de·vi·ant /ˈdiviənt; ˈdiːviənt/ *adj* different

from what is accepted (a word used to express disapproval) 不正常的; 越軌的〔含貶義〕 *deviant* n: *criminals and other deviants* 罪犯和其他離經叛道的人

de·vi·ate /'diːvɪ‚eɪt; 'diːvɪeɪt/ v **deviated, deviating** [I] **deviate from something** to be or become different from what is normal or acceptable 背離, 偏離〔某事〕

de·vi·a·tion /‚diːvɪ'eɪʃən; ‚diːvɪ'eɪʃən/ n [C;U] a noticeable difference from what is expected, particularly from accepted standards of behaviour 背離; 偏離: *sexual deviation* 性變態 | *a deviation from the norm* 標準的偏差

de·vice /dɪ'vaɪs; dɪ'vaɪs/ n **1** a thing invented to fulfil a special purpose 設備; 裝置; 儀器: *a device for measuring stress* 測量壓力的儀器 –see 見 MACHINE (USAGE 用法) **2** a way of achieving a particular purpose 手段; 策略; 詭計: *a device for avoiding income tax* 一種逃避所得稅的手段 **3 leave someone to their own devices** to leave someone to do something alone, and not give them any help or advice 讓某人獨立做某事〔不提供任何幫助或建議〕

dev·il /'dɛvl; 'dɛvəl/ n **1 the Devil** the most powerful evil spirit 魔鬼; 魔王 **2** an evil spirit 惡魔 **3** a high-spirited or troublesome person, especially a child 調皮鬼; 淘氣鬼: *He's good at school, but he's a little devil at home.* 他在學校表現不錯, 但在家裡是個調皮鬼。 **4** infml a word used for a person〔非正式〕傢伙; 人: *You lucky devil!* 你這幸運的傢伙! | *The poor devils lost everything in the floods.* 那些可憐的傢伙被洪水害得傾家蕩產。

dev·il·ish /'dɛvlɪʃ; 'dɛvəlɪʃ/ adj evil and cruel 邪惡的; 兇暴的

de·vi·ous /'diːvɪəs; 'diːvɪəs/ adj **1** not going in the straightest or most direct way 迂迴的; 曲折的: *a devious route* 迂迴的路線 **2** not direct or honest 不直率的, 不誠實的: *a devious plan* 刁滑的方案 | *He's very devious.* 他很狡猾。 –**deviously** adv

de·vise /dɪ'vaɪz; dɪ'vaɪz/ v **devised, devising** [T] to plan or invent something 策劃; 設計; 發明〔某物〕: *He devised a plan for winning the game.* 他想出了一種贏得比賽的辦法。

de·void /dɪ'vɔɪd; dɪ'vɔɪd/ adj fml **devoid of something** completely without something, especially a quality〔正式〕毫無…的; 沒有…的〔尤指品質〕: *He is devoid of human feeling!* 他毫無人性!

de·vo·lu·tion /‚diːvə'luːʃən; ‚diːvə'luːʃən/ n [U] the giving of governmental power to a smaller group 〔政府權力的〕下放; 分權

de·volve /dɪ'vɒlv; dɪ'vɒlv/ v **devolved, devolving, devolve on someone** (of power or work) to be passed to another person or group〔把權力或工作〕移交給某人

de·vote /dɪ'vəʊt; dɪ'vəʊt/ v **devoted, devoting, devote yourself to something, devote your time to something** to give your time

and effort to something 獻身於〔某事物〕; 專心致力於: *He has devoted his life to helping blind people.* 他為幫助盲人而獻出一生。 | *We shouldn't devote any more time to this question.* 我們不應該在此問題上多費時間。

de·vot·ed /dɪ'vəʊtɪd; dɪ'vəʊt‚ɪd/ adj loving someone or something very much and giving them time and attention 熱愛的; 非常忠實的; 全心全意的: *a devoted father* 慈愛的父親 | *He is devoted to his wife.* 他對妻子十分忠實。 –**devotedly** adv

dev·o·tee /‚dɛvə'tiː; ‚dɛvə'tiː/ n a person who admires someone or something 信徒; 愛好者: *a devotee of everything Italian* 一個對意大利的東西樣樣都迷戀的人

de·vo·tion /dɪ'vəʊʃən; dɪ'vəʊʃən/ n [U] **1** the act of giving a lot of attention to something 奉獻 **2** great fondness for someone 熱愛 **3** strong religious feeling 宗教熱情; 虔誠

de·vour /dɪ'vaʊr; dɪ'vaʊər/ v [T] to eat something quickly and hungrily 狼吞虎嚥地吃〔某物〕

de·vout /dɪ'vaʊt; dɪ'vaʊt/ adj having strong religious beliefs 篤信宗教的; 虔誠的: *a devout Hindu* 虔誠的印度教徒 –**devoutly** adv

dew /djuː; djuː/ n [U] the small drops of water which form on cold surfaces during the night 露水; 露珠

dew·y /'djuː; 'djuːɪ/ adj wet with dew 帶露水的

dex·ter·i·ty /dɛks'tɛrətɪ; dɛk'stɛr‚tɪ/ n [U] the quality of cleverness and skill, for example in the use of your hands〔尤指手的〕靈巧; 敏捷

dex·ter·ous /'dɛkstərəs; 'dɛkstərəs/ adj (also 又作 **dextrous**) clever and skilful with your hands 善於用手的; 巧手的

di·a·be·tes /‚daɪə'biːtɪs; ‚daɪə'biːtiːz/ n [U] a disease in which a person cannot control the level of sugar in their blood 糖尿病

di·a·bet·ic /‚daɪə'bɛtɪk; ‚daɪə'bɛtɪk•/ n a person suffering from diabetes 糖尿病患者 –**diabetic** adj: *She became diabetic at the age of 25.* 她二十五歲那年得了糖尿病。 | *diabetic foods* 糖尿病患者適用的食物

di·a·bol·i·cal /‚daɪə'bɒlɪkl; ‚daɪə'bɒlɪkəl/ adj infml very unpleasant and annoying〔非正式〕非常可憎的; 糟透的: *What diabolical weather!* 多麼令人討厭的天氣! –**diabolically** /-klɪ; -klɪ/ adv

di·ag·nose /'daɪəgˌnəʊs; 'daɪəgnəʊz/ v **diagnosed, diagnosing** [T] to discover the nature of a disease or problem 診斷〔疾病〕; 判斷〔問題的性質〕: *The doctor diagnosed my illness as a rare bone disease.* 醫生診斷出我的病是一種罕見的骨病。

di·ag·no·sis /‚daɪəg'nəʊsɪs; ‚daɪəg'nəʊs‚ɪs/ n **diagnoses** /-siz; -siːz/ [C;U] the act of finding out what is wrong and describing it 診斷; 判斷: *What's your diagnosis of the situation?* 你對形勢有甚麼判斷? | *a diagnosis* *of rheumatism* 風濕病的診斷 **–diagnostic** /-'nɑstɪk; -'nɒstɪk/ *adj*: *modern diagnostic techniques* 現代診斷術

di·ag·o·nal /daɪ'ægənl; daɪ'ægənəl/ *adj* **1** running in a sloping direction (used of straight lines) 斜線的; 斜紋的 **2** joining opposite corners of a square 〔正方形的〕對角線的 **–diagonal** *n* **–diagonally** *adv*

di·a·gram /'daɪə,græm; 'daɪəgræm/ *n* a simple drawing which shows how something works 圖解; 圖表 **–diagrammatic** /,daɪəgrə'mætɪk; ,daɪəgrə'mætɪk/ *adj* **–diagrammatically** /-klɪ; -kli/ *adv*

dial[1] /'daɪəl; daɪəl/ *n* **1** the face of an instrument, such as a clock, which shows information by means of a pointer or figures 鐘面, 錶面; 刻度盤 **2** the wheel on a telephone with numbered holes for the fingers, which you move round when you make a telephone call 〔電話機的〕撥號盤

dial[2] *v* **-ll- (-l-** *AmE* 〔美式〕**)** [I;T] to press the buttons or move the dial on a telephone in order to make a telephone call 打電話; 撥〔電話號碼〕: *How do I dial Paris?* 怎樣打電話去巴黎？ | *Put in the money before dialling.* 先投錢幣再撥號。 **–see** 見 TELEPHONE (USAGE 用法)

di·a·lect /'daɪəlɛkt; 'daɪəlekt/ *n* [C;U] a variety of a language spoken in one part of a country 地方話; 方言; 土話: *the Yorkshire and Lancashire dialects* 約克郡和蘭開夏郡的方言 | *a poem written in Scottish dialect* 用蘇格蘭方言寫的一首詩 **–dialectal** /,daɪə'lɛktl; ,daɪə'lektl/ *adj*

di·a·lec·tic /,daɪə'lɛktɪk; ,daɪə'lektɪk/ *n* (also 又作 **dialectics** /,daɪə'lɛktɪks; ,daɪə'lektɪks/) [U] *tech* the art or method of arguing according to certain rules of question and answer 〔術語〕辯證法 **–dialectical** *adj*

di·a·logue /'daɪə,lɒg; 'daɪəlɒg/ *n* (**dialog** *AmE* 〔美式〕) [C;U] **1** a written conversation in a book or play 〔書或劇本中的〕對白; 對話: *a short dialogue* **between** *Hamlet and his mother* 哈姆雷特與他母親的一段簡短對白 | *She's good at writing dialogue.* 她擅長寫對白。 **2** a conversation which examines differences of opinion between leaders or groups of people 對話; 意見交換; 磋商: *At last there is hope of dialogue* **between** *the two sides.* 雙方終於有希望進行對話。

di·am·e·ter /daɪ'æmətə; daɪ'æmˌtə'/ *n* a straight line from one side of a circle to the other side, passing through the centre of the circle 直徑

di·a·met·ri·cal·ly /,daɪə'mɛtrɪklɪ; ,daɪə'metrɪkli/ *adv* **be diametrically opposed** to be completely different 完全相反: *The two ideas are diametrically opposed.* 那兩種觀點截然相反。

di·a·mond /'daɪəmənd; 'daɪəmənd/ *n* **1** [C] a hard, bright precious stone used for jewellery and industrial purposes 金剛石;

金剛鑽; 鑽石: *a diamond ring* 鑽石戒指 **2** [C] a figure with four straight sides of equal length that stands on one of its points 菱形 **3 diamonds** a set of playing cards with one or more diamonds in red 〔紙牌的〕方塊: *the four of diamonds* 方塊四

di·a·per /'daɪəpə; 'daɪəpə'/ *n* the usual American word for 〔美式〕= NAPPY

di·a·phragm /'daɪə,fræm; 'daɪəfræm/ *n* **1** the muscle that separates your lungs from your stomach 橫隔膜 **2** a round rubber object that a woman puts inside her VAGINA to allow her to have sex without having children 〔避孕用的〕子宮帽

di·ar·rhoea /,daɪə'rɪə; ,daɪə'rɪə/ *n* (also 又作 **diarrhea**) [U] an illness in which a person empties their bowels too often and in a very liquid form 腹瀉

di·a·ry /'daɪərɪ; 'daɪəri/ *n* **diaries 1** a daily record of the events in a person's life, often contained in a book 日記: *He recorded all the day's events in his diary.* 他在日記中記下了當天發生的一切事情。 | *Nowadays many people don't bother to keep a diary.* 如今許多人都不記日記了。 **2** *BrE* a book in which you keep a record of things to be done in the future 〔英式〕記事簿: *"Can you come on Wednesday?" "I'll just look in my diary to see if I'm free."* "你星期三能來嗎？" "我要先看一下記事簿才知道是否有空。" **–see picture on page 763** 見 763 頁彩圖

dice[1] /daɪs; daɪs/ *n* [plural is 複數為 **dice**] a small block of wood or plastic, with six sides and a different number of spots from one to six on the various sides, used in games of chance 骰子; 色子

dice[2] *v* **diced, dicing 1** [T] to cut food into small square pieces 將〔食物〕切成小方塊: *The meat should be finely diced.* 這塊肉應切成細丁。 **2 dice with death** to take a great risk 冒巨大危險

dic·ey /'daɪsɪ; 'daɪsi/ *adj* **dicier, diciest** *infml* risky and uncertain 〔非正式〕冒險的; 靠不住的

di·chot·o·my /daɪ'kɒtəmɪ; daɪ'kɒtəmi/ *n* **dichotomies** *fml* a division into two parts or groups which are very different or have very different opinions 〔正式〕一分為二; 分成〔相對的〕兩部分: *the dichotomy* **between** *opponents and supporters of nuclear weapons* 核武器的反對者和支持者之間的分化

dic·tate /'dɪktet; dɪk'teɪt/ *v* **dictated, dictating** [I;T] **1** to say words for someone else to write down or for a machine to record 口述; 使聽寫: *She was dictating a letter to her secretary.* 她在向祕書口授一封信。 | *Don't interrupt me while I'm dictating.* 我在聽寫時別打攪我。 **2** to state conditions that you have the power to force people to accept 發號施令; 命令; 支配: *We're now in a position to dictate terms to our employers.* 我們現在能夠向雇主強硬地提出我們的條件了。

dic·ta·tion /dɪkˈteʃən; dɪkˈteɪʃn/ *n* **1** [U] the act of dictating or writing down what is dictated 口述; 聽寫, 筆錄: *a secretary taking dictation* 按口述作筆錄的祕書 **2** [C] something dictated to test your ability to hear and write a language correctly 聽寫測驗: *The teacher gave us two French dictations today.* 老師今天給我們做了兩次法文聽寫測驗。

dic·ta·tor /dɪkˈteɪtə; dɪkˈteɪtə^r/ *n* a ruler who has complete power over a country especially after gaining power by force 獨裁者

dic·ta·to·ri·al /ˌdɪktəˈtɔrɪəl; ˌdɪktəˈtɔːrɪəl/ *adj* **1** relating to a dictator or like a dictator 獨裁的; 專制的 **2** behaving or giving orders in a forceful way, without regard for people's feelings 喜歡發號施令的; 專橫的: *He's very dictatorial and won't listen to anyone else's opinion.* 他非常專橫, 聽不進別人的意見。–**dictatorially** *adv*

dic·ta·tor·ship /dɪkˈteɪtəˌʃɪp; dɪkˈteɪtəʃɪp/ *n* **1** [C;U] government by a dictator 獨裁統治 **2** [C] a country ruled by a dictator 獨裁者統治的國家

dic·tion /ˈdɪkʃən; ˈdɪkʃən/ *n* [U] the way in which a person pronounces words 發音法: *Actors need training in diction.* 演員需要進行發音法的訓練。

dic·tion·a·ry /ˈdɪkʃənˌɛrɪ; ˈdɪkʃənəri/ *n* **dictionaries** a book that gives a list of words in alphabetical order, with their meanings in the same or another language 詞典; 字典

did /dɪd; dɪd/ the past tense of DO ☆ DO 的過去式

di·dac·tic /daɪˈdæktɪk; daɪˈdæktɪk/ *adj fml* meant to teach, especially to teach a moral lesson 〖正式〗說教的〔尤指道德方面〕; 教誨的

did·n't /ˈdɪdnt; ˈdɪdnt/ short for 〖縮〗= "did not": *You saw him, didn't you?* 你見到他了, 不是嗎?

★ **die¹** /daɪ; daɪ/ *v* **died, died, dying** /ˈdaɪɪŋ; ˈdaɪ-ɪŋ/ [I] **1** to stop living 死; 死亡; 死去: *He died at the age of 102.* 他102歲時去世。| *Her mother was dying of cancer.* 她母親死於癌症。**2** **die a … death** to die in a particular way 以〔某種方式〕死去: *She died a natural death.* 她死得很自然。**3** **be dying for something** to want something very much 極想〔某事物〕: *I was dying for something to eat.* 我極想吃點東西。[RELATED PHRASE 相關詞組 **be dying to do something**]

die away *phr v* [I] (of sound, wind, or light) to become less and less and then stop〔聲音、風、光線〕變弱; 逐漸消失

die down *phr v* [I] to become less strong or violent 變弱; 逐漸平息: *The fire is dying down.* 火勢正漸漸減弱。| *The excitement died down.* 激情逐漸消失了。

die off *phr v* [I] to die one by one 相繼去世: *As she got older and older, her relatives all died off.* 當她越來越年邁時, 她的親屬都相繼去世了。

die out *phr v* [I] to disappear completely and so no longer exist 完全消失; 滅絕: *Most of the old customs have now died out.* 大部分古老的風俗習慣現已消失了。| *Several species have died out already.* 好幾個物種已不復存在。

die² *n* a metal block used for shaping metal or plastic 金屬模子; 印模; 沖模

die·sel en·gine /ˈdɪzl ˌɛndʒən; ˈdiːzəl ˌen-dʒɪn/ *n* (also 又作 **diesel**) a type of oil-burning engine often used for buses and trains 柴油機

★ **di·et¹** /ˈdaɪət; ˈdaɪət/ *n* **1** [C;U] a person's usual food or drink 日常飲食: *Proper diet and exercise are both important for health.* 適當的飲食和運動對於健康都是很重要的。| *living on a diet of fast food* 靠吃快餐度日 **2** [C] a limited list of food and drink that one is allowed 規定的飲食: *This diet only allows you to eat fresh fruit.* 按照這份指定食譜, 你只可以吃新鮮水果。| *a high-fibre diet* 含高纖維質的飲食 **3** **be on a diet, go on a diet** to be trying to lose weight by eating a limited amount of food〔為減輕體重的〕節食, 飲食限制

diet² *v* [I] to try to lose weight by eating a limited amount of food〔為減輕體重〕節食; 控制飲食: *No sugar in my coffee, please – I'm dieting.* 請不要給我的咖啡放糖; 我在節食。

★ **dif·fer** /ˈdɪfə; ˈdɪfə^r/ *v* [I] **1** to be different 不同於; 與…相異; 有區別: *Nylon differs from silk in origin and cost.* 尼龍的來源和成本都不同於絲綢。**2** to have different opinions 意見分歧: *The two brothers often differ.* 這兄弟倆常常意見分歧。| *He differed with his brother on how to look after their parents.* 他和他的兄弟在照顧父母親的問題上看法不一。

★ **dif·fe·rence** /ˈdɪfərəns; ˈdɪfərəns/ *n* **1** [C;U] a way in which things are unlike each other 差異; 差別; 不同之處: *There are many differences between living in a city and living in the country.* 住在城市裡和住在鄉村裡有許多不同之處。| *There is not much difference in size between them.* 兩者的尺寸差別不大。**2** [C] the amount by which two numbers or quantities are different 差額; 差數: *The difference between 5 and 11 is 6.* 11 和 5 的差是 6。**3** **make no difference, not make any difference** to have no effect on a situation 沒有作用或影響 **4** **make all the difference** to be very important and help you in some way 非常重要; 作用很大 **5** **have your differences** to have a slight disagreement with someone 意見略有分歧: *We've had our differences, but we're still good friends.* 雖然我們意見有些分歧, 但我們還是好朋友。

★ **dif·fe·rent** /ˈdɪfərənt; ˈdɪfərənt/ *adj* not the same 差異的; 不同的; 有區別的: *The two sisters are quite dif-*

ferent. 這姐妹倆很不一樣。| *This new drug is quite different* **from** *all the others available.* 這種新藥與所有現在使用的藥有很大區別。| *My opinions are very different* **to** *yours.* 我的觀點與你的很不一致。| *We met a lot of different people at the party.* 我們在聚會上遇到各種各樣的人。–**differently** *adv*

> ■ USAGE 用法: Some people consider that **different from** is the only correct form, and so you will always be right if you use it. Note, however, that **different to** is also very common in British English. **Different than** is also used in American English. ☆有些人認為**different from** 是唯一正確的形式, 因此, 使用它總不會出錯。但要注意: **different to** 在英式英語中十分常見, 而在美式英語中也會用到 **different than**。

dif·fe·ren·tial /ˌdɪfəˈrɛnʃəl/ *n* the amount of difference between things, especially difference in wages between workers at different levels in the same industry 差別; 差異〔尤指同一行業中的〕工資級差

dif·fe·ren·ti·ate /ˌdɪfəˈrɛnʃɪˌet/ *v* **differentiated, differentiating** [I;T] to see, express, or make a difference 區分; 區別: *This company does not differentiate* **between** *men and women — it employs both on equal terms.* 這家公司對男女職工一視同仁——兩者的聘用條件相同。–**differentiation** /ˌdɪfəˌrɛnʃɪˈeʃən/ *n* [C;U]

⋆⋆⋆**dif·fi·cult** /ˈdɪfɪˌkʌlt/ *adj* **1** not easy to do or understand 難的; 艱難的: *The exam questions were all very difficult.* 試題都很難。| *It's difficult to understand her ideas.* 她的想法難以理解。| *It's quite difficult for me to get to your house.* 對我來説, 到你家去很困難。

> □ USEFUL PATTERNS 有用句型
> be difficult to do something, be difficult for someone to do something

2 not helpful and not easy to please (used of people) 難弄的, 難對付的〔指人〕: *a difficult child* 難管的小孩 | *She's being very difficult at the moment.* 她現在很難相處。

⋆⋆⋆**dif·fi·cul·ty** /ˈdɪfɪˌkʌltɪ/ *n* **difficulties 1** something which causes a problem 困難; 難事; 難題; 難點: *Our main difficulty is lack of money.* 我們的主要難題是缺少資金。| *There were some difficulties in reaching an agreement.* 要達成協議有些困難。**2 have difficulty doing something, have difficulty in doing something** to be unable to do something easily 做某事有困難: *I had difficulty hearing the speaker.* 我難以聽見發言者説的話。| *He had no difficulty in understanding her.* 他毫

無困難就明白了她的意思。**3 with difficulty** not easily 困難地: *His English was very bad and he spoke with difficulty.* 他的英語很糟糕, 因此説話很吃力。[RELATED PHRASE 相關詞組 **without difficulty**] **4 be in difficulties, be in difficulty** to have problems 有困難; 有麻煩: *A lot of people are in difficulties with their mortgage repayments.* 許多人對償還抵押借款有困難。| *He went to help her with her car as she was obviously in difficulty.* 她的車顯然出了問題, 所以他就上前幫她一把。[RELATED PHRASE 相關詞組 **get into difficulty**]

dif·fi·dent /ˈdɪfədənt; ˈdɪfḷdənt/ *adj* unable to speak or act with confidence 缺乏自信的; 膽怯的: *He is diffident about expressing his opinions.* 他不好意思表達自己的意見。–opposite 反義 **confident** –**diffidently** *adv* –**diffidence** *n* [U]

dif·fuse¹ /dɪˈfjus; dɪˈfjuːs/ *adj fml*【正式】**1** widely spread 瀰漫的; 散開的: *a diffuse population scattered about the island* 分散在島上不集中的人口 **2** using too many words and not expressing ideas clearly〔文章〕冗長的; 不簡潔的 –**diffusely** *adv*

dif·fuse² /dɪˈfjuz; dɪˈfjuːz/ *v* **diffused, diffusing** [I;T] *fml* to spread something out or become spread out in a lot of different directions or to a lot of different people【正式】(使)傳播; (使)擴散; (使)漫射: *to diffuse knowledge* 傳播知識 | *diffused light* 漫射的光 –**diffusion** /-ˈfjuʒən; -ˈfjuːʒən/ [U]

dig¹ /dɪg; dɪg/ *v* **dug** /dʌg; dʌg/, **dug, digging** [I;T] **1** to break up and move earth 挖掘; 掘地: *I spent two hours digging the vegetable garden.* 我花了兩小時把菜園子挖掘了一遍。| *The dog has been digging in that corner for half an hour.* 狗已在角落裡扒了半小時。| *They dug a tunnel through the mountain.* 他們挖了一條穿山隧道。**2** to push or be pushed into something 戳進; 刺入: *A nail from my shoe was digging* **into** *my foot.* 我鞋裡的一根釘子刺入了我的腳。| *The cat dug its claws into the mouse.* 貓把利爪刺到老鼠身上。

dig at sbdy *phr v* [T] to make unpleasant remarks about someone 諷刺, 挖苦〔某人〕: *The teacher is always digging at me.* 老師總是挖苦我。

dig sthg ↔ **out** *phr v* [T] **1** to find something that has been hidden for a long time 找出〔某物〕; 發現〔某物〕: *Look at those red trousers that I dug out from the back of the cupboard.* 瞧瞧那些從廚櫃後面翻出來的紅褲子。**2** to get something out after it has been buried 挖掘出〔某物〕: *It snowed last night and we had to dig the car out.* 昨夜下雪了, 我們要(從雪裡)挖出那輛車子。

dig sthg ↔ **up** *phr v* [T] **1** to make a hole by taking away earth 挖掘〔泥土〕: *They are digging up the road outside the house.* 他們正在挖掘屋外的那條路。**2** to take something out of the ground 〔從地裡〕挖出〔某物〕: *My neighbour dug up some gold coins in the garden.* 我的鄰居在花園裡掘出一些金幣。**3** to discover facts that had been hidden 發現〔祕密〕; 找到: *Journalists managed to dig up some surprising facts about the minister's past.* 新聞記者們設法揭露那位部長過去一些令人震驚的事實真相。

dig² *n* **1** *infml* a quick push 〔非正式〕推; 戳: *John's falling asleep, just give him a dig.* 約翰睡著了，推他一下吧。**2** an unpleasant remark 挖苦; 嘲諷: *Sally keeps making digs about my work.* 莎莉老是挖苦我的工作。**3** a place where ARCHAELOGISTS are digging to find information about the past which is buried in the ground 考古發掘地 **4 digs** [pl] *BrE infml* lodgings 〔英式，非正式〕寄宿處: *When his family left London, Tom moved into digs.* 湯姆全家離開倫敦時，他便搬進宿舍寄宿。

di·gest¹ /daɪˈdʒɛst; daɪˈdʒɛst/ *v* **1** [T] to change food in the stomach into a form that the body can use 消化〔食物〕: *Babies can't digest cow's milk.* 嬰兒不能消化牛奶。**2** [T] to think about something carefully and understand it 領會; 領悟: *I heard her speech, but I haven't digested it yet.* 我聽了她的演講，但還沒有領會過來。–**digestible** *adj*

di·gest² /ˈdaɪdʒɛst; ˈdaɪdʒɛst/ *n* a short account of a piece of writing which gives the most important facts 摘要; 概要; 文摘: *a digest of Roman laws* 羅馬法匯編

di·ges·tion /dəˈdʒɛstʃən; daɪˈdʒɛstʃən/ *n* [C; U] the act of digesting or the ability to digest food 消化; 消化力: *Digestion is more difficult for old people.* 對老年人來說，消化是較為困難的。| *I've always had a good digestion.* 我的消化力一直很強。

di·ges·tive /dəˈdʒɛstɪv; daɪˈdʒɛstɪv/ *adj* **1** relating to the digestion of food 消化〔食物〕的: *digestive juices* 幫助消化的果汁 **2 digestive biscuit** *tdmk* a type of sweet biscuit 〔商標〕消化餅〔一種圓形的甜餅乾〕

di·git /ˈdɪdʒɪt; ˈdɪdʒɪt/ *n* **1** any of the numbers from 0 to 9 〔從0到9的任何一個〕數字: *The number 2001 contains four digits.* 2001 是個四位數。**2** *fml* a finger or toe 〔正式〕手指; 腳趾

di·gi·tal /ˈdɪdʒətl; ˈdɪdʒətl/ *adj* **digital watch, digital clock** a watch or clock that has no hands and shows the time by means of numbers 數字式手錶〔時鐘〕

dig·ni·fied /ˈdɪgnəˌfaɪd; ˈdɪgnəˌfaɪd/ *adj* proud, calm, and making people feel respect for you 有尊嚴的; 高貴的: *a dignified old man* 有尊嚴的老人 –opposite 反義 **undignified**

dig·ni·ta·ry /ˈdɪgnəˌtɛrɪ; ˈdɪgnəˌtɛri/ *n* **dignitaries** *fml* a person who has an important position in public life 〔正式〕職位高的人; 顯要人物: *Many of the local dignitaries attended the mayor's funeral.* 當地的許多顯要人物都參加了市長的葬禮。

dig·ni·ty /ˈdɪgnɪtɪ; ˈdɪgnɪti/ *n* [U] **1** qualities of character or appearance which make people feel respect 尊貴; 高貴; 高尚; 體面: *He always acted with great dignity.* 他的舉止一向十分端莊體面。**2** formal and grand behaviour 〔舉止〕莊嚴; 端莊; 尊嚴: *The dignity of the occasion was lost when he fell down the steps.* 他跌倒在台階上，破壞了那場合的莊嚴氣氛。

di·gress /dəˈgrɛs; daɪˈgrɛs/ *v* [I] *fml* to stop what you are saying and begin to talk about something else 〔正式〕〔作者，講話者〕扯開話題; 離題: *I'll tell you a funny story, if I may digress for a moment.* 如果我可以暫時離開主題的話，我給你們講一個有趣的故事。– **digression** /-ˈgrɛʃən; -ˈgrɛʃən/ *n* [C;U]

dike /daɪk; daɪk/ *n* –see 見 DYKE

di·lap·i·dat·ed /dəˈlæpəˌdetɪd; dɪˈlæpɪˌdeɪtɪd/ *adj* old, broken, and falling to pieces 破舊的; 破爛的: *a dilapidated old car* 破舊不堪的汽車 | *The house looked a bit dilapidated.* 這房子看上去有點兒破爛。–**dilapidation** /dəˌlæpəˈdeʃən; dɪˌlæpɪˈdeɪʃən/ [U]

di·late /daɪˈlet; daɪˈleɪt/ *v* **dilated, dilating** *fml* [I] (of your eyes) to become bigger 〔正式〕〔眼睛〕瞪大: *Her eyes dilated with terror.* 她嚇得瞪大了雙眼。–**dilation** /-ˈleʃən; -ˈleɪʃən/ *n* [U]

di·lem·ma /dəˈlɛmə; dɪˈlɛmə/ *n* a difficult situation in which you have to choose between two possible actions 困境; 進退兩難的窘境: *She was in a dilemma as to whether to stay at school or get a job.* 她進退兩難，不知該留在學校還是找工作。

dil·i·gent /ˈdɪlədʒənt; ˈdɪlɪdʒənt/ *adj* showing steady, careful effort 勤勉的; 勤奮的: *Though he's not clever he's a dilligent worker and should do well in the exams.* 他並不聰明，卻很勤奮，考試準會取得好成績。– **diligently** *adv* –**diligence** *n* [U]

di·lute /dɪˈlut; daɪˈluːt/ *v* **diluted, diluting** [T] to make a liquid weaker or thinner by mixing another liquid with it 沖淡, 稀釋〔液體〕: *He diluted the paint with water.* 他用水稀釋顏料。–**dilute** /dɪˈlut; ˌdaɪˈluːt◂/ *adj*: *dilute acid* 稀釋酸 –**dilution** /-ˈluʃən; -ˈluːʃən/ *n* [C;U]

dim¹ /dɪm; dɪm/ *adj* **-mm- 1** not bright or clear 不明亮的; 暗淡的; 不清晰的: *The light is too dim for me to read easily.* 光線太暗，我很難閱讀。| *the dim shape of an animal in the mist* 霧中隱約可見的動物的外形 **2** *infml* stupid and foolish 〔非正式〕遲鈍的; 愚蠢的 – **dimly** *adv*

dim² *v* **-mm-** [I;T] to make or become less bright (使)變暗淡; (使)變模糊: *The lights in the theatre began to dim.* 戲院裡的燈光開始暗下來。| *You can use this switch to dim the lights.* 你可以用這個開關使燈光轉暗。

dime /daɪm; daɪm/ *n* a coin of the US and

Canada, worth ten cents〔美國和加拿大的〕十分鎳幣

★di·men·sion /dəˈmenʃən; daɪˈmenʃən/ *n* **1** a measurement in any one direction 任何一種度量〔長度、寬度、厚度等〕: *Length is one dimension, and width is another.* 長是一種度量, 寬又是另一種度量。**2** one side of a problem or subject〔問題或題目的〕方面; 部分: *There is another dimension to this problem which you haven't mentioned.* 這問題還有你尚未提到的另一個方面。**3 dimensions** [pl] the measurements or size of something 大小; 體積; 容積; 程度: *What are the dimensions of the room?* 這房間的空間有多大? | *The true dimensions of the problem have only just been recognized.* 這個問題的嚴重程度剛剛才被人們所認識。**4 dimensional** having the stated number of dimensions 有…維的; (…度)空間的: *A three-dimensional object has length, depth, and height.* 立體的物體有長、寬、高三個度量。

di·min·ish /dəˈmɪnɪʃ; dʒˈmɪnɪʃ/ *v* [I;T] *fml* to become or make something smaller or less important〔正式〕(使)減少; (使)減小; 降低; 削弱: *Children's enthusiasm for noisy games never seems to diminish.* 兒童對喧鬧遊戲的熱情似乎永遠也不會消退。| *The government's diminishing popularity is worrying for the Prime Minister.* 政府日趨低落的聲望使首相憂心忡忡。

di·mi·nu·tion /ˌdɪməˈnjuːʃən; ˌdɪmɪˈnjuːʃən/ *n* [C;U] the condition of diminishing or being diminished 減少; 減小; 降低; 削弱

di·min·u·tive /dəˈmɪnjʊtɪv; dʒˈmɪnjʊtɪv/ *adj fml* extremely small〔正式〕極小的

dim·ple /ˈdɪmpl; ˈdɪmpəl/ *n* a little hollow place especially one that forms in your cheek when you smile 酒窩; 笑靨

din /dɪn; dɪn/ *n* a loud, continuous, confused, and unpleasant noise〔不停的〕喧鬧聲;〔持續的〕嘈雜聲

dine /daɪn; daɪn/ *v fml* **dined, dining** [I] to eat dinner〔正式〕就餐; 進餐: *We dined at the Ritz last night.* 我們昨晚在里茨大酒店吃了一頓飯。| *They dined on lobster and champagne.* 他們吃龍蝦和香檳酒作正餐。

dine out *phr v* [I] to eat dinner in a restaurant or at a friend's home 在外吃飯〔在飯館或朋友家〕

din·er /ˈdaɪnə; ˈdaɪnər/ *n* **1** someone who is having a meal in a restaurant〔餐館的〕就餐者 **2** *AmE* a small restaurant beside the road〔美式〕路旁小餐館 **3** *AmE* a carriage on a train where food is served〔美式〕〔火車的〕餐車

ding-dong /ˈdɪŋdɒŋ; ˌdɪŋˈdɒŋ◂/ *n* **1** [U] the noise made by a bell 鈴聲; 叮噹聲 **2** [sing] *infml* a noisy argument〔非正式〕激烈的爭論; 爭吵: *I had a bit of a ding-dong with my mother last night.* 昨晚我跟母親爭辯了幾句。

din·ghy /ˈdɪŋgɪ; ˈdɪŋgi/ *n* **dinghies 1** a small open boat carried on a larger boat to take passengers to the shore 無篷小船; 救生艇 **2** a small sailing or rowing boat 小遊艇; 小帆船

din·gy /ˈdɪndʒɪ; ˈdɪndʒi/ *adj* **dingier, dingiest** dirty and dull in colour (used of things and places) 骯髒的; 昏暗的〔指物、地方〕: *a dingy little room* 又髒又暗的小房間 – **dingily** *adv* –**dinginess** *n* [U]

dining room /ˈ·· ·/ *n* a room where meals are eaten in a house or hotel〔家裡的〕飯廳;〔旅館的〕餐廳

★din·ner /ˈdɪnə; ˈdɪnər/ *n* **1** [C;U] the main meal of the day, eaten either at midday or in the evening〔中午或晚上吃的〕正餐; 主餐: *What time do you usually have dinner?* 你通常幾點鐘吃飯? | *It's dinner time.* 是吃飯的時候了。| *We're having fish for dinner.* 我們的正餐吃魚。| *My husband's cooking dinner tonight.* 今晚我丈夫在做飯。**2** [C] a formal occasion in the evening when this meal is eaten 晚宴: *The firm are giving a dinner in honour of her retirement.* 公司在為她的退休舉行晚宴。

■ **USAGE** 用法: If *dinner* is at midday, the evening meal is usually called **tea** or (especially later in the evening) **supper**. If *dinner* is in the evening, the midday meal is usually called **lunch**. ☆如果**dinner** 放在中午進行, 晚上這頓飯通常稱為 **tea**〔茶點〕或〔晚些時候進行的〕**supper**〔晚餐〕。如果 **dinner** 在晚上進行, 中午這頓飯通常稱為 **lunch**〔午餐〕。

dinner jack·et /ˈ·· ˌ··/ *n* a man's JACKET which is usually black and worn with a white shirt, black BOW TIE, and trousers on formal occasions〔男用〕晚禮服

di·no·saur /ˈdaɪnəsɔː; ˈdaɪnəsɔːr/ *n* a very large animal that lived in very ancient times and which no longer exists〔古生物〕恐龍

di·o·cese /ˈdaɪəsɪs; ˈdaɪəsɪs/ *n* the area of a country which a BISHOP is responsible for〔由主教管轄的〕教區

dip¹ /dɪp; dɪp/ *v* **-pp- 1** [T] to put something into a liquid for a moment 浸; 泡; 蘸: *I dipped my pen in the ink.* 我把鋼筆在墨水中蘸一蘸。**2** [I;T] to move downwards (使)下沉; 下降: *The sun dipped below the horizon.* 太陽落到地平線下了。| *I wish people would dip their headlights when they meet another car at night.* 我真希望在夜間行車遇到交匯車輛時, 司機能把車前燈的亮度減弱。| *The road dips just around the corner.* 這條路過了拐角處便微微向下斜。

dip into sthg *phr v* [T] **1** to read or study something for a short time 翻閱; 瀏覽: *I haven't read that book properly - I've only dipped into it.* 我還未仔細閱讀那本書——我只是翻閱了一下。**2** to use up money that

D

D

has been saved 動用〔存款〕: *I've had to dip into my savings quite a lot recently.* 最近我需要動用我大量的存款。

dip² *n* **1** a slope down or slight drop in height 傾斜; 斜度: *a dip in the road* 一段下坡路 **2** *infml* a quick swim 〔非正式〕〔為時不長的〕游泳 **3** a thick liquid food into which vegetable pieces can be dipped 〔用來蘸食物吃的〕調味醬〔汁〕: *a cheese dip* 乳酪醬 | *an avocado dip* 鱷梨醬

diph·ther·i·a /dɪf'θɪrɪə; dɪf'θɪərɪə/ *n* [U] a serious infectious disease of the throat which makes breathing difficult 白喉

diph·thong /'dɪfθɔŋ; 'dɪfθɒŋ/ *n tech* a vowel sound made by pronouncing two vowels quickly one after the other 〔術語〕二合元音; 雙元音

di·plo·ma /dɪ'ploʊmə; dɪ'pləʊmə/ *n* a course of study or examination at a particular level and the official piece of paper to show that you have been successful in it 畢業文憑; 畢業證書: *She got her teaching diploma last year.* 她去年取得了教師資格文憑。| *I'm doing a diploma in engineering.* 我在攻讀工程學文憑。

di·plo·ma·cy /dɪ'ploʊməsɪ; dɪ'pləʊməsɪ/ *n* [U] **1** the management of good relations between countries and government 外交; 外交手腕 **2** skill at dealing with people and difficult situations successfully 交際手段; 處世之道: *The lawyers handled the divorce with great diplomacy.* 律師們非常圓滿地處理了這起離婚案。

dip·lo·mat /'dɪpləˌmæt; 'dɪpləmæt/ *n* someone employed by their government to represent their country in another country, for example an AMBASSADOR 外交家; 外交官〔如大使〕

dip·lo·mat·ic /ˌdɪplə'mætɪk; ˌdɪplə'mætɪk◂/ *adj* **1** [only before a noun 只用於名詞前] related to the management of good relations between countries 外交的; 從事外交的: *Nigel joined the diplomatic service.* 奈傑爾加入外交部門工作。 **2** good at dealing with people in a way which causes no bad feeling 有手腕的; 策略的; 圓滑的; 婉轉的: *Try to be diplomatic when you refuse her invitation.* 你拒絕她的邀請時, 要盡可能婉轉些。– **diplomatically** /-klɪ; -kli/ *adv*

dire /daɪr; daɪə/ *adj* **1** very great or terrible 極端的; 非常的; 可怕的: *in dire need of food* 迫切需要食物 | *a dire warning* 可怕的警告 **2 in dire straits** in a seriously difficult position 陷入可怕的困境

★★ **di·rect¹** /də'rɛkt; dɪ'rekt/ *v* **1** [T+adv/prep] to send or aim something at a particular person or thing 把〔某物〕對準〔某人或某事物〕: *Most of the money will be directed towards medical research.* 大部分資金將用於醫學研究。| *civil unrest directed against the white community* 矛頭指向白人的平民騷亂 | *Please direct your*

complaints to the manager. 請你向經理投訴。 **2** [T] *fml* to tell someone the way to a place 〔正式〕給〔某人〕指路: *Can you direct me to the station?* 你能告訴我去火車站怎麼走嗎? **3** [T] to control the way something is done 指揮; 指導; 導演: *He directed the building of the new bridge.* 他指揮那座新橋梁的建造工程。| *Who directed that play on television last night?* 昨晚那個電視劇是誰導演的? **4** [T] *fml* to order 〔正式〕命令; 指示: *The policeman directed the crowd to move back.* 警察命令人羣往後退。–see 見 LEAD (USAGE用法)

★ **di·rect²** *adj* **1** going from one point to another without stopping or turning aside 筆直的; 徑直的: *Which is the most direct way to London?* 去倫敦哪條路線最近? | *a direct flight from London to Los Angeles* 從倫敦直達洛杉磯的航班 | *She scored a direct hit.* 她直接命中而得分。**2** with no other person or thing being included 直接的; 親自的: *He was asked to leave school as a direct result of his behaviour.* 他被勒令退學, 直接原因是他行為不檢。| *We need the chairman's direct intervention.* 我們需要主席親自過問。**3** honest and easily understood 直率的; 坦率的; 直接了當的: *He refused to give a direct answer to my question.* 他拒絕直截了當地回答我的問題。| *I've always found her direct and open.* 我總覺得她很坦誠直爽。**4** [only before a noun 只用於名詞前] exact 正好的; 截然的: *He's the direct opposite of his brother.* 他與他的兄弟截然相反。–**direct** *adv*: *The next flight goes direct to Rome.* 下一班飛機直達羅馬。

di·rec·tion /də'rɛkʃən; dɪ'rekʃən/ *n* **1** [C] the place or point towards which a person or thing moves, faces or is aimed 方向; 方位: *Which direction does the house face?* 這座房子面向哪個方向? | *We travelled in an easterly direction for some time.* 我們朝東方旅行了一段時間。| *When the first shot was fired, the protesters ran off in all directions.* 槍一打響, 抗議的人羣就向四面八方奔逃。**2 in the direction of** towards 往⋯方向: *They drove off in the direction of London.* 他們驅車往倫敦方向駛去。**3** [U] control, guidance, or advice 指揮; 指導; 管理: *The choir is under the direction of Mr Butler.* 合唱團是由巴特勒先生指揮的。| *That boy needs firmer direction from his parents.* 那孩子需要父母嚴加管教。**4 directions** [pl] instructions on how to get somewhere or how to do something 指示; 使用說明: *She gave me directions to the station.* 她告訴我去火車站怎麼走。| *Just follow the directions on the packet.* 就照包裝上的使用說明去做。

di·rec·tive /də'rɛktɪv; dɪ'rektɪv/ *n fml* an official order 〔正式〕指示; 命令

★ **di·rect·ly¹** /də'rɛktlɪ; dɪ'rektli/ *adv* **1** exactly 正好地; 截然: *He lives directly opposite the church.* 他住在教堂的正對面。| *in the flat* *directly above ours* 在我們正上方的公寓裡 **2** honestly and openly 直截了當地; 坦率地: *She answered me very directly.* 她十分坦率地回答了我。 **3** at once or very soon 立即; 馬上: *He should be here directly.* 他應該馬上就到。

directly² *conj* as soon as …就…: *I came directly I got your message.* 我一收到你的消息就來了。

★★**di·rec·tor** /dəˈrɛktə; d｣ˈrɛktər/ *n* **1** a person who controls or manages an organization or company 主管; 董事; 署長; 局長; 處長; 院長; 校長; 所長; 主任 **2** someone who directs a play or film, deciding how it is performed and filmed 〔戲劇、電影等的〕導演

di·rec·to·ry /dəˈrɛktəri; d｣ˈrɛktəri/ *n* **directories** a book or list of names, numbers or other facts, arranged in alphabetical order 〔按字母順序排列的〕姓名地址錄; 號碼簿

dirge /dɜdʒ; dɜːdʒ/ *n* a slow sad song sung at a funeral 輓歌

dirt /dɜt; dɜːt/ *n* [U] **1** an unclean substance, such as mud or dust 污垢; 灰塵; 塵垢: *Wash the dirt off your hands.* 把你手上的污垢洗掉。 | *The floor is covered with dirt.* 地板上布滿灰塵。 **2** soil or loose earth 泥土; 鬆土: *The children were outside playing happily in the dirt.* 孩子們在外面的泥地上玩得正高興。

★**dirt·y¹** /ˈdɜti; ˈdɜːti/ *adj* **dirtier, dirtiest 1** not clean 骯髒的; 污穢的: *dirty hands* 髒手 | *Repairing cars is a dirty job.* 修理汽車是髒活。 **2** concerned with or thinking about sex in rather an unacceptable way 下流的; 色情的; 黃色的: *a dirty joke* 下流的笑話 | *You've got a dirty mind.* 你滿腦子下流事。 | *a dirty old man* 下流的老頭 **3** unpleasant or dishonest 令人不快的; 卑鄙的: *a dirty trick* 卑鄙伎倆 **4** disapproving or unacceptable 惡意的; 令人生厭的: *He gave me a dirty look.* 他惡狠狠地瞪了我一眼。 | *"Empire" is a dirty word these days.* "帝國"這個詞如今令人厭惡。

dirty² *v* **dirtied, dirtying** [T] to make something unclean 弄髒〔某物〕: *Don't dirty your hands.* 別弄髒了你的手。

dis·a·bil·i·ty /ˌdɪsəˈbɪlətɪ; ˌdɪsəˈbɪlｊtɪ/ *n* **disabilities 1** [U] the state in which you cannot use your body properly 無能力; 無力: *She gets a disability pension from the government.* 她領取政府發的傷殘撫恤金。 **2** [C] something that makes you unable to use your body properly 殘疾; 傷殘: *Blindness is a very serious disability.* 雙目失明是十分嚴重的殘疾。

★**dis·a·bled** /dɪsˈebld; dɪsˈeɪbəld/ *adj* **1** unable to use your body properly 喪失能力的; 有殘疾的: *He's been disabled since the war, when he lost his arm.* 他在戰爭中失去一條胳膊, 以後就殘廢了。 **2** **the disabled** people who have a physical problem or illness of the mind which influences the way they live 傷殘人; 殘疾人

dis·ad·van·tage /ˌdɪsədˈvæntɪdʒ; ˌdɪsədˈvɑːntɪdʒ/ *n* something that makes progress or success difficult 不利; 不利條件: *The main disadvantage of the project is the cost.* 這個項目主要的不利條件是資金問題。 | *Not being able to speak Spanish could put you at a disadvantage.* 不會說西班牙語會使你很吃虧。 | *The lack of good training facilities will be to your disadvantage.* 缺乏良好的訓練設備將對你們十分不利。 –opposite 反義 **advantage** –**disadvantageous** /dɪsˌædvənˈtedʒəs; ˌdɪsˌædvənˈteɪdʒəs/ *adj*

dis·ad·van·taged /ˌdɪsədˈvæntɪdʒd; ˌdɪsədˈvɑːntɪdʒd/ *adj* coming from a poor social background 下層社會的; 處於困境的: *More financial help is needed for the disadvantaged sections of the community.* 社區的貧困階層需要得到更多資助。

dis·a·gree /ˌdɪsəˈgri; ˌdɪsəˈgriː/ *v* **disagreed, disagreeing** [I] **1** to have or express different opinions or to quarrel 意見不合; 不同意; 有分歧; 爭執: *We always disagree about everything.* 我們總是樣樣都不同意。 | *They disagreed over who should drive.* 他們為了該由誰開車而爭執不下。 | *I'm afraid I disagree with you.* 恐怕我的看法與你不同。 **2** to be different from each other 不一致; 不符: *These reports disagree on many important points.* 這些報導在許多重要問題上看法不一。 **3 disagree with you** *infml* to make you feel ill 〔非正式〕使某人不舒服: *Onions always disagree with me.* 我吃了洋蔥會感到不舒服。

dis·a·gree·a·ble /ˌdɪsəˈgriəbl; ˌdɪsəˈgriːəbəl/ *adj* unpleasant 令人不快的; 討厭的; 不合意的: *a disagreeable job* 不合意的工作 | *a disagreeable person* 令人討厭的人 –opposite 反義 **agreeable** –**disagreeably** *adv*

dis·a·gree·ment /ˌdɪsəˈgrimənt; ˌdɪsəˈgriːmənt/ *n* [C;U] the action or the state of having a different opinion about something from someone else 意見不一; 分歧: *We have been having a few disagreements lately.* 我們近來一直有些意見分歧。 | *I am in total disagreement with you over this.* 對此我和你的意見完全不一致。

dis·al·low /ˌdɪsəˈlau; ˌdɪsəˈlaʊ/ *v* [T] *fml* to refuse officially to accept something 〔正式〕不准許, 禁止; 不接受: *The referee has disallowed that goal.* 裁判不承認這個進球。

★**dis·ap·pear** /ˌdɪsəˈpɪr; ˌdɪsəˈpɪər/ *v* [I] **1** to move so that you cannot see or find it 消失; 不見: *Several top-secret files have mysteriously disappeared.* 幾份絕密文件神祕地丟失了。 | *By the time the police arrived the rioters had disappeared.* 警察到達時, 鬧事者已經不見了。 **2** to stop existing 不復存在; 滅絕: *Dinosaurs disappeared millions of years ago.* 恐龍在幾百萬年前就滅絕了。 **3 disappear into thin air** to go out of sight suddenly and with no explanation 完全消失 –**disappearance** *n* [C;U] : *Her disappearance*

was very worrying. 她的失蹤令人非常擔憂。

dis·ap·point /ˌdɪsəˈpɔɪnt; ˌdɪsəˈpɔɪnt/ *v* [T] to cause someone to feel disappointed 使〔某人〕失望: *I'm sorry to disappoint you, but I can't come after all.* 讓你失望我很抱歉, 不過我實在是不能來。

dis·ap·point·ed /ˌdɪsəˈpɔɪntɪd; ˌdɪsəˈpɔɪntɪd/ *adj* unhappy because something or someone is not as good as you hoped they would be, or something has not happened as you hoped it would 失望的; 沮喪的: *I'm very disappointed in him.* 他讓我非常失望。 | *Are you disappointed at losing the race?* 輸掉了比賽你很失望嗎? | *I was disappointed to hear you'd failed your driving test.* 聽説你沒有通過駕駛測試, 我很失望。–**disappointedly** *adv*

dis·ap·point·ing /ˌdɪsəˈpɔɪntɪŋ; ˌdɪsəˈpɔɪntɪŋ/ *adj* making you unhappy because something is not as good as you hoped it would be 令人失望[沮喪]的: *Your examination marks are rather disappointing.* 你的考試成績相當令人失望。 | *disappointing news* 令人沮喪的消息 –**disappointingly** *adv*

dis·ap·point·ment /ˌdɪsəˈpɔɪntmənt; ˌdɪsəˈpɔɪntmənt/ *n* **1** [U] the state of being disappointed 失望; 沮喪; 掃興: *To his great disappointment, she wasn't on the train.* 她不在那列火車上, 令他大失所望。**2** [C] someone or something which is not as good as you hoped it would be 令人失望的人或事: *Our son has been a disappointment to us.* 我們的兒子一直使我們失望。 | *The film was a bit of a disappointment – we expected it to be much better.* 那部電影有點兒令人失望, 我們原先把它想得好多了。

dis·ap·prov·al /ˌdɪsəˈpruːvl; ˌdɪsəˈpruːvəl/ *n* [U] a feeling or opinion that someone else is behaving badly 不贊成; 反對: *He spoke with disapproval of your behaviour.* 他談到你的行為時很不以為然。 | *She shook her head in disapproval.* 她搖搖頭表示反對。 –opposite 反義 **approval**

dis·ap·prove /ˌdɪsəˈpruːv; ˌdɪsəˈpruːv/ *v* **disapproved, disapproving** [I] to think that something is wrong or immoral 不贊成; 不同意: *We strongly disapprove of the firm's new policy.* 我們強烈反對公司的新政策。 – opposite 反義 **approve** –**disapprovingly** *adv*

dis·arm /dɪsˈɑːm; dɪsˈɑːm/ *v* **1** [T] to take weapons away from someone 繳〔某人〕的械; 解除〔某人〕的武器: *The police disarmed the criminal.* 警察繳了那罪犯的槍械。**2** [I] to reduce the size and strength of the armed forces in a country 裁軍; 削減軍備: *Unless both sides disarm, neither will feel safe.* 如果雙方不裁軍, 誰都不得安寧。**3** [T] to make someone less angry and more friendly 消除〔某人〕的怒氣[敵意]: *I didn't trust him at first but his smile completely disarmed me.* 我開始時對他不信任, 但他的微笑徹底消除了我的疑慮。

dis·ar·ma·ment /dɪsˈɑːməmənt; dɪsˈɑːməmənt/ *n* [U] the act of reducing a country's weapons or armed forces 裁軍; 削減軍備: *new plans for nuclear disarmament* 核裁軍的新方案

dis·ar·range /ˌdɪsəˈrendʒ; ˌdɪsəˈreɪndʒ/ *v* **disarranged, disarranging** [T] to make something untidy 使〔某物〕不整齊; 弄亂〔某物〕

dis·ar·ray /ˌdɪsəˈre; ˌdɪsəˈreɪ/ *n fml* **in disarray** very untidy or not organized 〔正式〕紊亂; 混亂: *After the fighting, the army was in disarray.* 戰鬥結束之後, 部隊陷入一片混亂。

dis·as·so·ci·ate /ˌdɪsəˈsoʃɪˌət; ˌdɪsəˈsoʊʃɪeɪt/ *v* **disassociated, disassociating** –see 見 DISSOCIATE

***di·sas·ter** /dɪzˈæstə; dɪˈzɑːstər/ *n* [C;U] **1** a sudden event which causes great loss or harm 災難; 大禍: *The earthquake was one of the worst natural disasters the country has ever suffered.* 那場地震是該國所經受的最嚴重的一次自然災害。**2** *infml* a failure 〔非正式〕失敗: *The party was a disaster.* 那次聚會辦得一塌糊塗。

di·sas·trous /dɪzˈæstrəs; dɪˈzɑːstrəs/ *adj* very bad or ending in failure 災難性的; 很糟糕的: *a disastrous mistake* 造成大禍的錯誤 | *The results were disastrous.* 結果是很慘重的。–**disastrously** *adv*

dis·band /dɪsˈbænd; dɪsˈbænd/ *v* [I;T] stop existing as an organisation 〔組織、機構〕解散; 遣散: *The club has disbanded.* 俱樂部已經解散。

dis·be·lief /ˌdɪsbəˈlif; ˌdɪsbəˈliːf/ *n* [U] a feeling that something is not true or doesn't exist 不信; 懷疑: *He shook his head in disbelief.* 他搖搖頭表示懷疑。

dis·be·lieve /ˌdɪsbəˈliv; ˌdɪsbəˈliːv/ *v* **disbelieved, disbelieving** [T] to think that someone is not telling the truth 不信; 懷疑: *I see no reason to disbelieve his story.* 我看沒有甚麼理由不信他所講的事。

■ USAGE 用法: **disbelieve** is a strong and formal word which suggests there are good reasons for not accepting that a story or statement is true. It is not the usual opposite of **believe** especially when **believe** means "approve of". Instead say: *I don't believe you.* | *I don't believe in letting children do what they want.* ☆**disbelieve** 是個語氣相當正式的詞; 它暗示有充分的理由不相信所説的事情。特別是當 **believe** 意為"贊同"時, 其反義詞通常不用 **disbelieve**, 而應該説 *I don't believe you.* (我不贊同你的看法)。*I don't believe in letting children do what they want.* (我不贊成讓孩子為所欲為)。

disc /dɪsk; dɪsk/ *n* (**disk** *AmE* 〔美式〕) **1**

something round and flat 圓盤; 圓板; 圓面: *a metal disc* 金屬圓盤 **2** a record for playing on a RECORD PLAYER 唱片 **3** a flat piece of CARTILAGE between the bones of your back (腰)椎間盤: *The pain was caused by a slipped disc.* 疼痛是因(腰)椎間盤突出而引起的。

dis·card /dɪsˈkɑrd; dɪsˈkɑːd/ *v* [T] to get rid of something as being useless 丟棄; 拋棄: *Discard the outside leaves of the lettuce.* 把萵苣的外層葉子扔掉。| *He discarded his old friends when he got rich.* 他有了錢就把他的老朋友拋棄了。

di·scern /dɪˈzɜrn; dɪˈsɜːn/ *v* [T] *fml* to see, notice, or understand something by looking or thinking about it carefully 〔正式〕看出; 覺察出; 識別: *He was just able to discern the road in the dark.* 他在黑暗中勉強能辨出道路。 —**discernible** *adj* —**discernibly** *adv*

di·scern·ing /dɪˈzɜrnɪŋ; dɪˈsɜːnɪŋ/ *adj* able to make good judgments in matters of style, fashion, or beauty 有識別力的; 有眼力的: *The paper has a discerning readership.* 這份報紙擁有一批精明的讀者。

dis·charge¹ /dɪsˈtʃɑrdʒ; dɪsˈtʃɑːdʒ/ *v* **discharged, discharging** [T] **1** to allow a person to go or send them away 允許〔某人〕離開; 釋放: *She's been discharged from hospital.* 她已獲允許出院。 **2** to send, pour, or let out liquid or gas 排出〔液體或氣體〕: *The wound discharged pus.* 傷口排出了膿水。 | *Smoke was discharged into the atmosphere.* 煙被排入空氣中。 **3** to perform a duty or promise 履行〔義務或諾言〕 **4** to pay a debt completely 清償〔債務〕 **5** to unload something 卸下〔某物〕: *The ship discharged its cargo onto the dock.* 輪船在碼頭上卸下貨物。 **6** to fire a gun 開槍

dis·charge² /dɪsˈtʃɑrdʒ; dɪsˈtʃɑːdʒ/ *n* **1** [U] the action of sending someone or something away 解除; 釋放; 退役: *After my discharge from the army I went into business.* 我退伍後從商。 **2** [C;U] a substance that comes out of something else 排出物: *There's still some discharge from the wound.* 傷口還有些分泌物流出。

di·sci·ple /dɪˈsaɪpl; dɪˈsaɪpəl/ *n* **1** a follower of a religious teacher, especially one of the 12 first followers of Christ 〔宗教〕信徒〔尤指耶穌十二門徒之一〕 **2** a follower of any great leader or teacher 追隨者; 門徒; 崇奉者

dis·ci·pli·nar·i·an /ˌdɪsəplɪˈnɛrɪən; ˌdɪsɪpliˈneəriən/ *n* someone who believes people should obey rules and who makes them do this 執行紀律者; 嚴格紀律信奉者

★**dis·ci·pline¹** /ˈdɪsəplɪn; ˈdɪsɪplɪn/ *n* **1** [C;U] the training of someone's mind and body to produce obedience and self-control 訓練; 訓導; 鍛鍊: *military discipline* 軍事訓練 | *Learning poetry is a good discipline for the memory.* 背詩是訓練記憶的好方法。 **2** [U] control gained as a result of this training

紀律; 風紀: *Good discipline in the classroom makes it easier to work.* 良好的課堂紀律有利於教學。 **3** [U] punishment or firm control intended to produce obedience 懲罰; 處罰; 處分: *That child needs discipline.* 那個孩子需要受處罰。 —**disciplinary** /ˈdɪsəplɪnˌɛrɪ; ˈdɪsɪplɪnəri/ *adj*: *Those who break the rules will face disciplinary action.* 誰要違反規定, 誰就要受到紀律處分。

discipline² *v* **disciplined, disciplining** [T] **1** to train someone to behave or act in a certain way 訓練, 訓導〔某人〕: *You must learn to discipline yourself at university.* 你在大學讀書時, 必須嚴格要求自己。 | *They never discipline their children.* 他們從不管教自己的子女。 **2** to punish someone 懲罰〔某人〕; 處罰〔某人〕: *Offenders will be severely disciplined.* 違法者將受嚴懲。

disc jock·ey /ˈ· ˌ··/ *n* —see 見 DJ

dis·claim /dɪsˈkleɪm; dɪsˈkleɪm/ *v* [T] **disclaim responsibility** to say that you are not responsible for something that has happened 推卸責任: *He disclaimed all responsibility for the accident.* 他否認自己對那次事故有任何責任。

dis·close /dɪsˈkloz; dɪsˈkləʊz/ *v* **disclosed, disclosing** [T] to show or tell someone something 向〔某人〕透露〔某事〕; 泄露: *He refused to disclose his name and address to the police.* 他拒絕向警方透露自己的姓名和地址。

dis·clo·sure /dɪsˈkloʒɚ; dɪsˈkləʊʒəʳ/ *n* [C;U] a fact which is no longer kept secret or the act of telling people this fact 暴露的事實; 透露; 泄露: *She made several surprising disclosures about her past life.* 她透露了自己過去生活中幾件令人吃驚的事情。

dis·co /ˈdɪsko; ˈdɪskəʊ/ *n* **discos** (also 又作 **discotheque** *fml* 〔正式〕) a place or party where people dance to records 迪斯科[的士高]舞廳; 迪斯科[的士高]舞會

dis·col·our /dɪsˈkʌlɚ; dɪsˈkʌləʳ/ *v* (also 又作 **discolor** *AmE* 〔美式〕) [I;T] to change and spoil the colour of something (使)〔某物〕變色; 損壞〔某物〕的色彩: *His teeth were discoloured from smoking.* 他的牙齒由於吸煙而變色。 —**discolouration** /dɪsˌkʌləˈreɪʃən; dɪsˌkʌləˈreɪʃən/ *n* [C;U]

dis·com·fort /dɪsˈkʌmfɚt; dɪsˈkʌmfət/ *n* **1** [U] slight pain or an unpleasant feeling 不舒服; 不適; 不安: *Your injury isn't serious, but may cause some discomfort.* 你的傷並不嚴重, 但可能會引起一些不適。 | *His ex-wife's presence caused him a lot of discomfort.* 他的前妻在場, 使他感到非常不自在。 **2** [C] something that makes you uncomfortable 使人不舒服[不安]的事物: *the discomforts of travel* 旅行的種種不便

dis·con·cert /ˌdɪskənˈsɜrt; ˌdɪskənˈsɜːt/ *v* [T] to make someone feel doubt and anxiety 使〔某人〕疑慮不安; 使窘迫: *She was disconcerted to see that she was being watched.* 她發現有人在

監視她，這使她驚惶失措。–**disconcertingly** *adv*

dis·con·nect /ˌdɪskəˈnɛkt; ˌdɪskəˈnekt/ *v* [T] to break the connection of something, for example, a telephone line or electricity supply 使〔某物〕不連接; 使〔某物〕分離〔如電話線或電源〕: *My phone's been disconnected because I didn't pay the bill.* 我因為沒付電話費而被切斷了電話線路。–opposite 反義 **connect** –**disconnection** /-ˈnɛkʃən; -ˈnekʃən/ *n* [C;U]

dis·con·nect·ed /ˌdɪskəˈnɛktɪd; ˌdɪskəˈnektɪd/ *adj* not well planned or put together (used of thoughts and ideas) 不連貫的; 無條理的〔指思路、想法〕: *a few disconnected remarks* 幾句東拉西扯的話

dis·con·so·late /dɪsˈkɒnslɪt; dɪsˈkɒnsəlɪt/ *adj fml* very unhappy or disappointed 〔正式〕憂傷的; 憂鬱的–**disconsolately** *adv*

dis·con·tent /ˌdɪskənˈtɛnt; ˌdɪskənˈtent/ *n* (also 又作 **discontentment** /-mənt; -mənt/) [U] the feeling of not being happy or satisfied 不滿; 不滿足–**discontented** *adj*

dis·con·tin·ue /ˌdɪskənˈtɪnju; ˌdɪskənˈtɪnjuː/ *v* **discontinued, discontinuing** [T] to stop or end something 停止, 中斷〔某事〕: *That bus service has been discontinued.* 那項公共汽車服務已經停止。| *We can't replace those cups; the pattern's been discontinued.* 我們無法更換那些杯子, 那種款式已停止生產。

dis·cord /ˈdɪskɔrd; ˈdɪskɔːd/ *n* **1** [U] *fml* disagreement between people 〔正式〕不和; 爭論 **2** [C] a lack of agreement heard when musical notes are played which do not sound pleasant together 〔音樂的〕不諧和 –**discordant** /dɪsˈkɔrdnt; dɪsˈkɔːdənt/ *adj*

dis·co·theque /ˌdɪskəˈtek; ˈdɪskətek/ *n fml* 〔正式〕–see 見 DISCO

dis·count¹ /ˈdɪskaʊnt; ˈdɪskaʊnt/ *n* **1** a reduction made to the usual price of something 折扣: *a ten percent discount for cash* 用現金付款的九折優惠 **2 at a discount** below the usual price 打折扣; 減價

dis·count² /ˈdɪskaʊnt; dɪsˈkaʊnt/ *v* [T] to regard something as unlikely to be true or important 不理會〔某事〕; 漠視; 不信: *Experts have discounted the possibility of a second earthquake in the area.* 專家都不大相信該地區可能發生第二次地震。

dis·cour·age /dɪsˈkɜɪdʒ; dɪsˈkʌrɪdʒ/ *v* **discouraged, discouraging** [T] **1** to make someone less confident about something or less willing to do something 使〔某人〕泄氣; 使〔某人〕灰心; 阻止〔某人〕做〔某事〕: *Don't be discouraged by your results.* 不要因你的成績而灰心喪氣。| *The bad weather discouraged people from attending the parade.* 惡劣

□ USEFUL PATTERNS 有用句型
to discourage someone; to discourage someone from doing something

的天氣使人們不能參加遊行。 **2** to persuade someone not to do something 勸阻〔某人做某事〕: *His mother tried to discourage him from joining the navy.* 他母親勸他不要參加海軍。

□ USEFUL PATTERNS 有用句型
to discourage someone; to discourage someone from doing something

–opposite 反義 **encourage** –**discouragingly** *adv* **discouragement** *n* [C;U]

dis·cour·te·ous /dɪsˈkɜːtɪəs; dɪsˈkɜːtiəs/ *adj fml* showing bad manners 〔正式〕失禮的; 粗魯的 –opposite 反義 –**courteous** –**discourteously** *adv*

✫dis·cov·er /dɪˈskʌvə; dɪsˈkʌvəʳ/ *v* **1** [T] to find or learn about something for the first time 發現; 發覺: *Columbus discovered America in 1492.* 哥倫布在1492年發現美洲。| *The stolen goods were discovered in their garage.* 在他們的車庫裡發現了被盜物品。 **2** [T; +(that)] to find out a fact, or the answer to a question 找到〔事實或答案〕: *Did you ever discover who sent you the flowers?* 你到底有沒有找到是誰送花給你? | *Scientists have discovered that this disease is carried by rats.* 科學家已查明這種病是由老鼠傳播的。–see 見 INVENT (USAGE 用法) –**discoverer** *n*

□ USEFUL PATTERNS 有用句型
to discover something; to discover who, why, where, etc.; to discover that…

dis·cov·er·y /dɪˈskʌvərɪ; dɪsˈkʌvəri/ *n* **discoveries 1** [U] the action of finding something 發現: *The discovery of oil on their land made the family rich.* 他們在自己的土地上發現了石油, 這使他們一家變得富有。 **2** [C] something that is found out 被發現的東西: *He made an important archaeological discovery.* 他作出一項重要的考古發現。

dis·cred·it¹ /dɪsˈkrɛdɪt; dɪsˈkredɪt/ *v* [T] to stop people believing in or having respect for something 敗壞…的名聲; 誹謗: *a deliberate attempt to discredit the government.* 故意敗壞政府名聲的企圖

discredit² *n* **1** [U] loss of belief, trust, or the good opinion of others 名聲的敗壞; 丟臉: *Their disgraceful behaviour has brought discredit* **to** *the school.* 他們不光彩的行為敗壞了學校的聲譽。 **2 to your discredit** making people lose their respect for you 丟自己的臉: *To her discredit, she refused to help.* 她拒絕幫助是丟她自己的臉。

dis·cred·i·ta·ble /dɪsˈkrɛdɪtəbl; dɪsˈkredɪtəbəl/ *adj* shameful 可恥的; 丟臉的

di·screet /dɪˈskrit; dɪˈskriːt/ *adj* careful about what you say and do 〔言行〕謹慎的; 慎重的: *a discreet silence* 審慎的沉默 | *It wasn't very discreet of you to ring me up at*

the office. 你往辦公室給我打電話有點考慮欠周。
–opposite 反義 **indiscreet –discreetly** *adv*

di·screp·an·cy /dɪˈskrɛpənsɪ; dɪˈskrɛpənsɪ/ *n* **discrepancies** [C;U] difference between things that should be the same 差異; 不符合; 不一致: *There is some discrepancy between their two descriptions.* 他們兩人的描述有些出入。| *How do you explain the discrepancies in the accounts?* 你怎樣解釋賬目中的差異?

dis·crete /dɪˈskrit/ *adj fml* separate 〔正式〕分離的; 互不連接的: *The examination tests discrete items of language.* 這次考試是測試語言的各個項目。

di·scre·tion /dɪˈskrɛʃən; dɪˈskrɛʃən/ *n* [U] **1** the quality of being careful about what you say and do 謹慎; 慎重 –opposite 反義 **indiscretion 2** the ability to decide what is the best thing to do 判斷力; 決定(能力): *I can't tell you how long to stay. I'll leave that to your discretion.* 我不能告訴你要逗留多久。我會讓你自己來決定。 **3 at someone's discretion** according to someone's judgment 依據某人的見解: *Promotion is at the manager's discretion.* 晉升問題由經理酌情處理。 –**discretionary** *adj*

di·scrim·i·nate /dɪˈskrɪmə‚net; dɪˈskrɪmᵻˌnet/ *v* **discriminated, discriminating** [I] **1** to see or make a difference between things or people 區別; 辨別; 區分: *You must try to discriminate* **between** *facts and opinions.* 你必須設法把事實和看法區別開來。 **2** to treat a person or group differently, usually worse 不公平地對待; 歧視: *That law discriminates* **against** *immigrants.* 那法律歧視(外來)移民。| *Many employers still discriminate* **in favour of** *men.* 許多雇主仍然優待男性。

di·scrim·i·na·tion /dɪ‚skrɪməˈneʃən; dɪ‚skrɪmᵻˈneʃən/ *n* [U] **1** the treating of one group of people differently from another 差別對待; 歧視: *racial discrimination* 種族歧視 | *sex discrimination* 性別歧視 **2** the ability to see small differences between things, usually showing good taste and judgment 鑑賞力; 識別力 –**discriminating** /dɪˈskrɪmə‚netɪŋ; dɪˈskrɪmᵻˌnetɪŋ/ *adj*

dis·cus /ˈdɪskəs; ˈdɪskəs/ *n* a heavy object shaped like a plate which is thrown as far as possible as a sport 鐵餅

di·scuss /dɪˈskʌs; dɪˈskʌs/ *v* [T] to talk about the details of something with someone else 討論; 談論; 商議: *We discussed what to do and where we should go.* 我們討論了該做甚麼和該去哪兒的問題。| *I wanted to discuss my plans with my father.* 我想和父親討論一下我的計劃。

■ USAGE 用法: Remember that the verb **discuss** is transitive and is NOT, therefore, followed by a preposition. (The noun **discussion** may sometimes be followed by the preposition **about**).
☆ 請記住: **discuss** 是及物動詞, 因此, 後面不跟介詞。(名詞 **discussion** 後面有時可以跟介詞 **about**)。Compare 比較: *We were discussing our holiday plans.* 我們當時在討論我們的度假計劃。| *We were having a* **discussion about** *our holiday plans.* 我們當時在討論我們的度假計劃。

di·scus·sion /dɪˈskʌʃən; dɪˈskʌʃən/ *n* **1** [C] a talk about the details of something with someone else 討論; 談論; 商議: *The chairman wants to have a discussion* **about** *training with us.* 主席想和我們討論一下有關訓練的問題。 **2** [U] the act of talking about the details of something 〔對事情的〕討論: *After much discussion the matter was settled.* 經過反覆討論, 問題終於得到解決。 **3 under discussion** being talked about 在討論之中

dis·dain¹ /dɪsˈden; dɪsˈdeɪn/ *n* [U] *fml* the feeling that someone or something is worthless or not important enough to deserve your attention 〔正式〕鄙視; 蔑視; 鄙棄 –**disdainful** *adj*

disdain² *v* [T not in progressive forms 不用於進行式] *fml* 〔正式〕**1** to regard something as worthless 鄙視; 蔑視; 鄙棄: *Why do you disdain my offer of friendship?* 我向你表示友好, 你為何不領情呢? **2 disdain to do something** to refuse to do something because you think it is not worth your attention 不屑做某事: *She disdained to answer.* 她不屑作出回答。

dis·ease /dɪˈziz; dɪˈziːz/ *n* [C;U] an illness caused by infection or a disorder in the body or mind, not by an accident 病; 疾病: *Insects can cause disease.* 昆蟲會引起疾病。| *an infectious disease* 傳染病 | *a rare plant disease* 罕見的植物病 –**diseased** *adj*: *a diseased bone* 有病的骨骼 | *a diseased plant* 有病害的植物

■ USAGE 用法: Compare 比較 **disease** and 和 **illness**. A **disease** is a particular medical condition with a particular cause. It is often serious and long-lasting ☆ **disease** 是指由某一具體病因引起的特定的病症, 病情通常較重, 而且持續時間長: *AIDS is one of the most alarming diseases of modern times.* 愛滋病是一種當代最令人驚恐的疾病。 **Illness** is a more general word for the state of being unwell, and an **illness** is not always serious ☆ **illness** 是表示身體不適的一般用詞, 病情並不一定嚴重: *At this time of year some children are always absent from school because of illness.* 每年這個時候, 有些孩子總要因生病而缺課。

dis·em·bark /ˌdɪsɪmˈbɑrk; ˌdɪsₐmˈbɑːk/ v [I; T] to put or go on shore from a ship, or land from an aircraft (使)上岸; (使)登陸 – **disembarkation** /ˌdɪsɛmbɑrˈkeɪʃən; ˌdɪsəm-ˌbɑːˈkeɪʃən/ n [U]

dis·em·bod·ied /ˌdɪsɪmˈbɑdɪd; ˌdɪsₐmˈbɒd-dɪd/ adj [only before a noun 只用於名詞前] **1** existing without a body 脫離肉體的: *disembodied spirits of the dead* 死者的遊魂 **2** coming from someone who cannot be seen 看不見的人發出的: *disembodied voices in the darkness* 黑暗中那不見其人的說話聲

dis·en·chant·ed /ˌdɪsɪnˈtʃæntɪd; ˌdɪsɪnˈtʃɑːn-tɪd/ adj no longer liking or believing in the value of something 不再着迷的; 不再幻想的: *I'm disenchanted* **with** *my job.* 我對我的工作不再那麼眷戀了。– **disenchantment** n [U]

dis·en·gage /ˌdɪsɪnˈgedʒ; ˌdɪsɪnˈgeɪdʒ/ v **disengaged, disengaging** [I;T] fml 《正式》**1** to disconnect or separate (使) 脫離 (使) 鬆開: *Disengage the gears when you park the car.* 停車時應該把排擋鬆開。**2** (of military or naval forces) to stop fighting〔軍隊、海軍〕脫離接觸, 中止戰鬥

dis·en·tan·gle /ˌdɪsɪnˈtæŋgl; ˌdɪsɪnˈtæŋgəl/ v **disentangled, disentangling** [T] **1** to free something which is knotted or mixed up 解開〔結〕; 理順: *Can you disentangle this piece of string for me?* 你能幫我解開這根繩子 (的結) 嗎? **2** to free from a position it is difficult to escape from 使擺脫: *I finally managed to disentangle myself from the barbed wire.* 我終於從鐵絲網中掙脫出來。

dis·fa·vour (**disfavor** AmE《美式》) /ˌdɪsˈfe-vəʳ; dɪsˈfeɪvəʳ/ n [U] fml v《正式》**1** dislike or disapproval 不喜歡; 不贊成: *His behaviour was viewed with great disfavour.* 他的行為極不受人讚賞。**2** the state of being disliked 受冷遇; 失寵: *John seems to have fallen into disfavour with his boss.* 約翰似乎受到了老闆的冷遇。

dis·fig·ure /dɪsˈfɪgjə; dɪsˈfɪgəʳ/ v **disfigured, disfiguring** [T] to spoil the appearance of 毀損…的外貌; 使變醜: *The disease left his face disfigured.* 疾病使他的臉變得很難看。– **disfigurement** n [C;U]

dis·grace¹ /dɪsˈgres; dɪsˈgreɪs/ n **1** [sing; U] a cause of shame or loss of honour and respect 丟臉; 恥辱; 不光彩: *Being poor is no disgrace.* 貧窮並不是丟臉的事。| *Doctors like that are a disgrace* **to** *our hospitals.* 那樣的醫生是我們醫院的一種恥辱。| *That old suit of yours is a disgrace.* 你那套舊衣服真叫人丟臉。**2 be in disgrace** to be regarded with disapproval because of something you have done wrong 很不討人喜歡; 令人不喜愛

disgrace² v **disgraced, disgracing** [T] **1** to behave badly and so cause shame to someone 使丟臉; 使受恥辱: *He disgraced himself last night by drinking too much.* 昨天夜裡他因喝酒過量而出醜。**2 be disgraced** to be

disapproved of and to lose respect because of something you have done wrong 使〔某人〕失寵; 使失去地位: *Most corrupt leaders are publicly disgraced in the end.* 大部分營私舞弊的領導人最終在公眾心目中威望掃地。

dis·grace·ful /dɪsˈgresfəl; dɪsˈgreɪsfəl/ adj completely unacceptable 可恥的; 丟臉的: *His behaviour was disgraceful!* 他的行為真丟人!

dis·grun·tled /dɪsˈgrʌntld; dɪsˈgrʌntld/ adj annoyed and disappointed 不滿的; 不高興的: *When Mr Simpson was promoted the other supervisors were very disgruntled.* 辛普森先生得到晉升時, 別的管理人員都非常不滿。

dis·guise¹ /dɪsˈgaɪz; dɪsˈgaɪz/ v **disguised, disguising** [T] **1** to change the usual appearance of someone or something in order to hide who they are 假扮; 裝扮成: *She disguised herself* **as** *a man.* 她把自己扮成男裝。| *He was disguised as a football supporter.* 他裝扮成足球支持者。**2** to hide the real situation 掩蓋; 掩飾; 隱瞞: *We cannot disguise the fact that business is bad.* 我們不能掩蓋生意不景氣的事實

disguise² n [C;U] something that you wear to hide who you really are 化裝用具〔服飾〕: *He wore a false beard and thick glasses as a disguise.* 他戴了假鬍鬚和厚眼鏡把自己偽裝起來。| *They crossed the border in disguise.* 他們化了裝越過邊境。

dis·gust¹ /dɪsˈgʌst; dɪsˈgʌst/ n [U] a strong feeling of dislike and disapproval, sometimes making you feel sick 厭惡; 憎惡; 反感: *His dirty habits filled her with disgust.* 她那不講衛生的習慣使她感到厭惡。| *After waiting for their food for an hour they left the restaurant in disgust.* 他們等食物等了一小時之後, 就氣憤地離開了餐館。

disgust² v [T] to make you feel strong dislike and disapproval, and sometimes physically ill 使〔某人〕作嘔; 使厭惡: *We're all disgusted at the way his wife has treated him.* 他的妻子那樣對待他, 使我們都反感了。| *What a disgusting smell!* 多麼令人作嘔的氣味!

dish¹ /dɪʃ; dɪʃ/ n **1** a large container, not very deep, from which food is put onto people's plates 盤; 碟: *a vegetable dish* 菜盤 | *a serving dish*〔上菜用的〕大盤子 –see picture on page 244 見 244 頁彩圖 **2** cooked food of a particular kind 一盤菜; 菜餚; 食品: *a wonderful dish of salmon baked in the oven* 一盤用烤爐烤出來的美味三文魚 **3 dishes** [pl] all the plates, cups, knives, and forks that have been used for a meal〔就餐時用過的〕餐具: *Let's wash the dishes.* 我們來洗碗碟吧。| *We'll do the dishes.* 我們會洗一下餐具。**4** –see SATELLITE DISH

dish² v

dish something ↔ **out** phr v [T] infml to give something out to people《非正式》分發〔某物〕: *to dish out the soup* 把湯舀給大家 |

He's always dishing out advice. 他總是向別人提忠告。

dish up *phr v* [I;T **dish** sthg ↔ **up**] to put the food for a meal onto plates 把〔食物〕盛到盤裡: *Help me dish up the dinner, will you?* 幫我把飯菜盛到盤子裡，行嗎? | *Wash your hands quickly, I'm just about to dish up.* 快洗手，我就要上菜了。

dis·heart·en /dɪsˈhɑːtn; dɪsˈhɑːtn/ *v* [T] to make someone lose hope and confidence 使沮喪; 使失去希望〔信心〕; 使灰心: *She was disheartened by her lack of progress.* 她因沒得到進步而灰心喪氣。

di·shev·elled /dɪˈʃevld; dɪˈʃevəld/ *adj* very untidy (used of a person or their clothes or hair) 衣冠不整的; 不修邊幅的〔指人、衣服或頭髮〕

dis·hon·est /dɪsˈɒnɪst; dɪsˈɒnɪst/ *adj* not honest or truthful 不誠實的; 不老實的: *a dishonest politician* 不誠實的政客 | *to get money by dishonest means* 用不正當的手段弄錢 –**dishonestly** *adv* –**dishonesty** *n* [U]

dis·hon·our /dɪsˈɒnəʳ; dɪsˈɒnəʳ/ *n fml* (**dishonor** *AmE* 〔美式〕) [sing;U] something or someone that brings shame and loss of respect 〔正式〕恥辱; 不名譽; 丟臉的事〔人〕: *His desertion from the army brought dishonour on his family.* 他從部隊開小差，使他的家庭蒙受恥辱。 –**dishonour** *v* [T] –**dishonourable** *adj*

dish·y /ˈdɪʃi; ˈdɪʃi/ *adj* **dishier, dishiest** *infml* having sexual charm 〔非正式〕有性感魅力的; 漂亮誘人的: *I agree, he is rather dishy!* 我也認為他相當有吸引力。

dis·il·lu·sion /ˌdɪsɪˈluːʒən; ˌdɪsɪˈluːʒən/ *v* [T] to correct a belief that someone has that is wrong 使醒悟; 使不再抱幻想: *I hate to disillusion you but we're not going to get a pay rise this year.* 我真不想把實情告訴你，但事實是我們今年將不會加薪。 –**disillusionment** *n* [U]

dis·il·lu·sioned /ˌdɪsɪˈluːʒənd; ˌdɪsɪˈluːʒənd/ *adj* feeling bitter and unhappy because you have learnt the truth about someone or something that you formerly admired 大失所望的; 幻想破滅的: *He's very disillusioned with the present government.* 他對現政府完全失望。

dis·in·clined /ˌdɪsɪnˈklaɪnd; ˌdɪsɪnˈklaɪnd/ *adj* [never before a noun 不能用於名詞前] unwilling 不願意的; 不喜歡的: *I feel disinclined to go out in this weather.* 我不願意在這種天氣出門。 –**disinclination** /ˌdɪsɪnkləˈneɪʃən; ˌdɪsɪnkləˈneɪʃən/ *n* [sing;U] *fml* 〔正式〕

dis·in·fect /ˌdɪsɪnˈfekt; ˌdɪsɪnˈfekt/ *v* [T] to clean something with a chemical that can destroy bacteria 給〔某物〕消毒〔殺菌〕 –**disinfection** /-ˈfekʃən/ *n* [U]

dis·in·fec·tant /ˌdɪsɪnˈfektənt; ˌdɪsɪnˈfektənt/ *n* [C;U] a chemical used to destroy bacteria 消毒劑; 殺菌劑

dis·in·her·it /ˌdɪsɪnˈherɪt; ˌdɪsɪnˈherɪt/ *v* [T] to stop someone from receiving your money and property after your death by changing your WILL³ 剝奪〔某人〕的繼承權

dis·in·te·grate /dɪsˈɪntəˌgret; dɪsˈɪntəgreɪt/ *v* **disintegrated, disintegrating** [I] **1** to break up into small pieces 碎裂; 崩裂: *The box was so old it just disintegrated when he picked it up.* 箱子太破舊了，他一提就散了。 **2** (of an arrangement or organization) to come to an unsuccessful end 〔安排、組織〕瓦解; 崩潰: *The project disintegrated owing to lack of support in the community.* 該項目由於缺乏公眾的支持而告吹了。 –**disintegration** /dɪsˌɪntəˈgreʃən; dɪsˌɪntəˈgreɪʃən/ *n* [U]

dis·in·terest·ed /dɪsˈɪntərəstɪd; dɪsˈɪntrəstɪd/ *adj* able to judge a situation fairly because you will not get an advantage from it 無私的; 公正的; 無偏見的: *As a disinterested observer, who do you think is right?* 作為一個無偏見的旁觀者，你認為誰是對的? –**disinterestedly** *adv*

■ **USAGE** 用法: **1** Compare 比較 **disinterested** and 和 **uninterested.** You are **disinterested** if you have nothing to gain personally from agreeing with one side or another in an argument ☆如果你在爭論中贊同其中一方而不謀私利，你就是 **disinterested** (公正的): *We must get someone who is disinterested to decide which of us is right.* 我們必須請無偏見的人來決定我們當中誰是正確的。 You are **uninterested** in something if you find it boring or if you do not usually give it your attention ☆如果你覺得某事單調乏味或者不常引起你的注意，你就是對其 **uninterested** (不感興趣): *I'm afraid I'm completely uninterested in football.* 我恐怕對足球毫無興趣。 **2** Although **disinterested** is sometimes used to mean "not interested" many people feel that this is not correct. ☆雖然 **disinterested** 有時被用來表示 "not interested"，但許多人覺得這種用法不正確。

---

dis·joint·ed /dɪsˈdʒɔɪntɪd; dɪsˈdʒɔɪntɪd/ *adj* not following naturally (used of words or ideas) 不連貫的; 支離破碎的〔指言語或思想〕: *He gave a rather disjointed account of his holiday.* 他對自己假期生活的敍述很不連貫。 –**disjointedly** *adv*

***disk** /dɪsk; dɪsk/ *n* **1** the usual American spelling of DISC ☆ DISC 的美式常用拼寫 **2** a flat circular piece of plastic used for storing computer information 磁盤

disk drive /ˈ· ·/ *n* a piece of electrical equipment used for passing information to and from a computer disk 磁盤驅動器, 磁碟機 –see picture on page 763 見 763 頁彩圖

dis·like¹ /dɪsˈlaɪk; dɪsˈlaɪk/ *v* **disliked, disliking** [T] to think that something is unpleasant 不喜愛; 厭惡: *I dislike big cities.* 我不喜歡大城市。| *I dislike being spoken to like that.* 我不喜歡別人那樣對我說話。

dis·like² /dɪsˈlaɪk; ˌdɪsˈlaɪk/ *n* [C;U] **1** a feeling that someone or something is unpleasant 不喜愛; 厭惡: *He has a strong dislike for anything to do with politics.* 他對任何與政治有關的事特別厭惡。**2 take a dislike to** to begin to dislike 開始討厭: *She took an instant dislike to him.* 她一下子就對他產生了反感。

dis·lo·cate /ˈdɪsloˌket; ˈdɪsləkeɪt/ *v* **dislocated, dislocating** [T] to put a bone out of its usual place 使骨頭〔關節〕脫位; 脫臼: *He dislocated his shoulder while playing rugby.* 他打橄欖球時肩膀脫臼了。| *a dislocated ankle* 脫臼的腳踝 —**dislocation** /ˌdɪsloˈkeʃən; ˌdɪslə'keɪʃən/ *n* [C;U]

dis·lodge /dɪsˈlɑdʒ; dɪsˈlɒdʒ/ *v* **dislodged, dislodging** [T] to force or knock out of position (使) 強行離開原位; 強行去除: *I managed to dislodge the fishbone from my throat by coughing.* 我設法咳出卡在喉嚨裡的魚骨頭。

dis·loy·al /dɪsˈlɔɪəl; dɪsˈlɔɪəl/ *adj* not loyal 不忠實的; 不忠誠的: *You don't expect a diplomat ever to be disloyal to his country.* 你不會預料外交官會對祖國不忠。 —**disloyally** *adv* —**disloyalty** *n* [C;U]

dis·mal /ˈdɪzml; ˈdɪzməl/ *adj* lacking hope or happiness 悲慘的; 沮喪的; 陰沉的: *a dismal failure* 令人沮喪的失敗 | *dismal weather* 陰沉的天氣 —**dismally** *adv*

dis·man·tle /dɪsˈmæntl; dɪsˈmæntl/ *v* **dismantled, dismantling** [I;T] to come to pieces or to take something to pieces 拆開〔某物〕; 拆卸; 拆除: *This tent dismantles easily.* 這個帳篷很容易拆除。| *I'll have to dismantle the engine.* 我得把引擎拆下來。

dis·may¹ /dɪsˈme; dɪsˈmeɪ/ *n* [U] a strong feeling of fear, anxiety, and hopelessness 驚愕; 驚惶; 失望; 灰心: *They were filled with dismay by the news.* 這消息使他們震驚。| *To their dismay the door was locked.* 令他們驚愕的是門被鎖上了。

dismay² *v* [T] to make someone feel afraid, worried, or disappointed 使驚惶; 使灰心; 使沮喪

dis·mem·ber /dɪsˈmɛmbə; dɪsˈmembə̆r/ *v* [T] to cut or tear the arms and legs from a body 分割...的肢體; 肢解: *The young man's dismembered body was found in the car boot.* 那個年輕人遭肢解的屍體在汽車後部的行李箱裡被發現了。

***dis·miss** /dɪsˈmɪs; dɪsˈmɪs/ *v* [T] **1** to refuse to consider something 拒絕考慮〔某事物〕; 不接受: *He dismissed the idea as impossible.* 他認為那個主意根本不可行而不予考慮。**2** *fml* to remove someone from a job 〔正式〕解雇〔某人〕; 免〔某人〕的職; 開除: *If you're late*

again you'll be dismissed. 如果你再遲到, 就要被解雇。**3** to send someone away 讓〔某人〕離開; 把〔某人〕打發走; 解散: *The teacher dismissed the class early.* 老師提早下課了。 —**dismissal** *n* [C;U]

dis·mis·sive /dɪsˈmɪsɪv; dɪsˈmɪsɪv/ *adj* considering something to be not worthy of attention or respect 輕蔑的; 鄙視的: *He was too dismissive of the problems, in my opinion.* 我認為他太小看這些問題了。

dis·mount /dɪsˈmaʊnt; dɪsˈmaʊnt/ *v* [I] to get off a horse or bicycle 〔從馬背或腳踏車上〕下來 —see 見 TRANSPORT (USAGE 用法)

dis·o·be·di·ent /ˌdɪsəˈbidɪənt; ˌdɪsə'biːdiənt/ *adj* not doing what you are told to do 不服從的; 不順從的: *a disobedient child* 不聽話的孩子 —opposite 反義 **obedient** —**disobediently** *adv* —**disobedience** *n* [U]

dis·o·bey /ˌdɪsəˈbe; ˌdɪsə'beɪ/ *v* [I; T] to choose not to do what you are told to do 不服從, 不順從; 違抗; 違反: *He disobeyed his mother and went to the party.* 他不聽母親的話, 參加了那次聚會。| *to disobey the rules* 違反規則

***dis·or·der** /dɪsˈɔrdə; dɪsˈɔːdə̆r/ *n* **1** [U] untidiness 雜亂; 凌亂: *The house was in a state of complete disorder.* 屋子裡凌亂不堪。**2** [U] noisy and violent behaviour by the public, usually showing great political dissatisfaction 騷亂; 動亂: *Increased taxation gave rise to widespread public disorder.* 增稅引發了大規模的社會騷亂。**3** [C;U] a disease or illness that is not very serious 不適; 小病: *suffering from a stomach disorder* 患胃病

dis·or·der·ly /dɪsˈɔrdəlɪ; dɪsˈɔːdəli/ *adj* **1** (also 又作 **disordered**) untidy 雜亂的; 混亂的; 凌亂的; 無秩序的: *a disorderly room* 亂七八糟的房間 **2** noisy or violent in public 騷亂的; 製造混亂的: *disorderly behaviour* 擾亂社會秩序的行為

dis·or·gan·ized /dɪsˈɔrgəˌnaɪzd; dɪsˈɔːgənaɪzd/ *adj* (also 又作 **disorganised** *BrE* 〔英式〕) showing no order or planning 缺乏組織的; 計劃不周的: *She's so disorganized I'll be surprised if she ever finds herself a job.* 她那麼缺乏條理, 如果她能找到工作, 我會感到很意外。 —**disorganization** /dɪsˌɔrgənəˈzeʃən; dɪsˌɔːgənaɪ'zeɪʃən/ *n* [U]

dis·or·i·en·tate /dɪsˈɔrɪɛnˌtet; dɪsˈɔːrɪənteɪt/ *v* **disorientated, disorientating** (also **disorient** /-rɪˌɛnt; -rɪənt/) [T] **1** to make someone lose their sense of direction 使〔某人〕迷失方向: *I'm completely disorientated. Which direction are we heading in?* 我完全迷失了方向。我們在朝哪個方向走? **2** to make someone feel confused 使〔某人〕迷惘; 使不知所措: *When I retired I felt quite disorientated for a while.* 我退休的時候曾一度十分迷惘。 —**disorientation** /dɪsˌɔrɪɛnˈteʃən; dɪsˌɔːrɪən'teɪʃən/ *n* [U]

dis·own /dɪsˈon; dɪsˈəʊn/ *v* [T] to say that

you have no connection with someone or something 否認〔某物〕是自己的; 聲明與〔某人〕沒有關係: *Peter's father disowned him when he was caught taking drugs.* 彼得被發現吸毒後, 他父親聲明與他脫離父子關係。

di·spar·age /dɪˈspærɪdʒ; dɪˈspærɪdʒ/ *v* **disparaged, disparaging** [T] to make someone or something require of little value or importance 貶低; 輕視: *In spite of your disparaging remarks, I think he did well.* 雖然你說了那些貶低他的話, 我還是認為他幹得不錯。 **–disparagingly** *adv* **–disparagement** *n* [C;U]

di·spar·i·ty /dɪˈspærətɪ; dɪˈspærɪti/ *n* **disparities** [C;U] *fml* the state of being different or unequal 〔正式〕不同; 不等; 差異: *There is a great disparity **in** age between him and his wife.* 他和妻子的年齡相差懸殊。| *Disparity of pay **between** men and women is a serious concern.* 男女之間的工資差異是個嚴重的問題。

dis·pas·sion·ate /dɪsˈpæʃənɪt; dɪsˈpæʃənt/ *adj* calm, fair, and not easily influenced by personal feelings 不動感情的; 冷靜的; 不帶偏見的 **–dispassionately** *adv*

di·spatch¹ /dɪˈspætʃ; dɪˈspætʃ/ *v* (also 又作 **despatch**) [T] to send something away 發送〔某物〕: *The parcels were dispatched yesterday.* 包裹昨天都已發送出去了。

dispatch² *n* (also 又作 **despatch**) a message carried by a government official, or sent to a newspaper by one of its writers 〔由政府官員專遞的〕公文, 急件; 〔記者發給報社的〕新聞專電: *to send a dispatch from Rome to London* 把急件從羅馬發往倫敦

di·spel /dɪˈspel; dɪˈspel/ *v* **-ll-** [T] to get rid of or drive away 驅散; 消除: *His calm words dispelled our fears.* 他那鎮定自若的話消除了我們的憂慮。

di·spen·sa·ble /dɪˈspensəbl; dɪˈspensəbəl/ *adj* not necessary 非必要的; 可有可無的 – opposite 反義 **indispensable**

di·spen·sa·ry /dɪˈspensərɪ; dɪˈspensəri/ *n* **dispensaries** a place where medicines are prepared and given out in a hospital 〔醫院的〕藥房

dis·pen·sa·tion /ˌdɪspənˈseʃən; ˌdɪspənˈseɪʃən/ *n* [C;U] permission to do something not usually allowed 特許; 豁免: *We normally have to be in by 10.30, but we've got a special dispensation for Cup Final night.* 我們通常在十時三十分才能入場, 但優勝杯決賽那一晚我們有特別豁免。

di·spense /dɪˈspens; dɪˈspens/ *v* **dispensed, dispensing** [T] **1** to give out to a number of people 分發; 分配; 施行: *A judge dispenses justice.* 法官主持公正。| *This machine dispenses coffee.* 這台機器發售咖啡。**2** to mix and give out medicines 配藥; 發藥

dispense with sbdy/sthg *phr v* [T] to get rid of and manage without 省掉; 用不着〔某人、某事〕: *I think we can safely dispense with*

his services now. 我想我們現在沒有他的幫忙也行。| *This new computer system dispenses with the need for keeping files.* 新的計算機系統使保存檔案變得沒有必要。

di·spens·er /dɪˈspensə; dɪˈspensər/ *n* a machine from which you can get something, for example by pressing a button 分發器; 自動售貨機: *a cash dispenser* 自動提款機

di·sperse /dɪˈspɜːs; dɪˈspɜːs/ *v* **dispersed, dispersing** [I;T] to scatter in different directions (使)分散; (使)散開; (使)消散; 驅散: *The wind dispersed the smoke.* 風把煙吹散了。| *Slowly, the crowds began to disperse.* 人羣開始緩緩散開。

di·spir·it·ed /dɪˈspɪrɪtɪd; dɪˈspɪrᵻtᵻd/ *adj lit* sad and without hope 〔文〕氣餒的; 垂頭喪氣的

di·splace /dɪsˈples; dɪsˈpleɪs/ *v* **displaced, displacing** [T] **1** to force something out of its usual place 移動〔某物〕的位置: *He displaced a bone in his knee while playing rugby.* 他打橄欖球時, 膝關節弄裂臼了。**2** to take the place of someone or something 取代〔某人或某物〕的位置; 替代; 置換: *The indigenous population were displaced by the settlers.* 外來移民把當地人趕出了家園。**3 displaced person** someone who has been forced to leave their country 被迫流落異國者; 難民; 流亡者 **–displacement** *n* [U]

di·splay¹ /dɪˈsple; dɪˈspleɪ/ *v* [T] **1** to put things where they can be easily seen 陳列; 展出: *to display goods in a shop window* 在櫥窗裡陳列商品 **2** to show something 顯示; 顯露: *He displayed no emotion when he failed his exam.* 他考試不及格卻沒有顯出激動的情緒。| *The computer screen was displaying the figures for last year.* 計算機螢光幕顯示出去年的統計數字。

di·splay² *n* **1** the showing of something in public or in a clear way 陳列; 展覽; 表現: *a fine display of fruit* 水果的精緻陳列 | *a display of skill* 技藝表演 **2 on display** being displayed 被展示; 被陳列: *The goods were on display in the shop window.* 商品陳列在櫥窗裡。

dis·please /dɪsˈpliz; dɪsˈpliːz/ *v* **displeased, displeasing** [T] *fml* to annoy someone or make them angry 〔正式〕使不愉快; 使生氣: *The headmaster and I are very displeased with your general behaviour.* 我和校長對你平時的行為很不滿意。**–displeasure** /dɪsˈpleʒə; dɪsˈpleʒər/ *n* [U]

dis·po·sa·ble /dɪˈspozəbl; dɪˈspəuzəbəl/ *adj* intended to be thrown away after use 用後即丟棄的; 一次性的: *disposable paper plates* 用後即棄的紙盤

dis·pos·al /dɪˈspozl; dɪˈspəuzəl/ *n* [U] **1** the removal of something that is not wanted 丟掉; 清除; 處理: *waste disposal* 廢物處理 **2** *fml* the way that people or things are arranged 〔正式〕佈置; 配置: *the disposal of troops along the frontier* 沿邊界的軍隊部署 **3**

at your disposal free for you to use 供任意使用; 可自行支配: *During his visit I put my car at his disposal.* 在他來訪期間, 我把車交給他隨意使用。

dis·pose /dɪˈspoz; dɪˈspəʊz/ v **disposed, disposing, dispose of something** to get rid of something 去除[處理]某物: *Let's dispose of these old papers.* 我們把這些舊報紙處理掉吧。| *She disposed of my arguments quite easily.* 她輕而易舉地駁倒了我的論點。

dis·posed /dɪˈspozd; dɪˈspəʊzd/ adj fml 《正式》**1 be disposed** to tending to have 有…傾向的: *She's rather disposed to fits of temper.* 她動不動就發脾氣。**2 be disposed to do something** to be willing to do something 願意做某事: *I don't feel disposed to help you.* 我不想幫你的忙。

dis·po·si·tion /ˌdɪspəˈzɪʃən; ˌdɪspəˈzɪʃən/ n fml 《正式》**1** the way you usually behave 性情; 性格: *He has a cheerful disposition.* 他性情開朗。| *a nervous disposition* 易緊張的性格 **2 a disposition to do something** a willingness to do something 做某事的意向: *He showed no disposition to help.* 他不想幫忙。

dis·pos·sess /ˌdɪspəˈzɛs; ˌdɪspəˈzes/ v [T] fml to take someone's land and house away from them 《正式》剝奪[某人財產]

dis·pro·por·tion·ate /ˌdɪsprəˈpɔrʃənɪt; ˌdɪsprəˈpɔːʃənət/ adj too much or too little relative to something else 不成比例的; 不相稱的: *We spend a disproportionate amount of our money on rent.* 我們的錢花在房租上的比例太大。–**disproportionately** adv

dis·prove /dɪsˈpruv; dɪsˈpruːv/ v **disproved, disproving** [T] to show something to be false 證明[某事]有誤或有假

★di·spute¹ /dɪˈspjut; dɪˈspjuːt/ v **disputed, disputing 1** [T] to argue about something angrily and for a long time 爭論; 辯論: *The question was hotly disputed in the Senate.* 該問題在參議院引起激烈的爭論。**2** [T; +that] to question the correctness of something 對[某事的正確性]表示異議: *"It's a very common attitude among the upper classes." "I would dispute that."* "這種看法在上層階級中非常普遍。" "我對此表示懷疑。"

di·spute² /dɪˈspjut; dɪˈspjuːt/ n **1** an argument or quarrel, especially an official one 爭論; 辯論; 糾紛: *a pay dispute* 工資問題的糾紛 **2 in dispute** having an argument or quarrel 在爭論之中; 在爭吵之中: *The men are still in dispute with their employers.* 那些男的還在跟老闆爭執不休。**3 in dispute, under dispute** being talked or argued about 處於爭議之中: *The question is still under dispute.* 該問題處於爭議之中。**4 open to dispute** able to be questioned 可以提出質疑

dis·qual·i·fy /dɪsˈkwɑləˌfaɪ; dɪsˈkwɒlɪˌfaɪ/ v **disqualified, disqualifying** [T] to say that someone cannot take part in an activity usually because they have done something

wrong 取消[某人]的資格; 使不合格: *She's been disqualified from driving.* 她已被取消駕駛資格。| *The winner was disqualified for cheating, and the prize given to the runner-up.* 獲勝者因作弊而被取消資格, 獎品給了第二名。–**disqualification** /ˌdɪskwɑləfəˈkeɪʃən; dɪsˌkwɒlɪfɪˈkeɪʃən/ n [C;U]

dis·quiet /dɪsˈkwaɪət; dɪsˈkwaɪət/ v [T] fml to make someone feel anxious 《正式》使[某人]不安; 使憂慮: *disquieted by his long silences* 他那長時間的沉默令人不安 | *a disquieting remark* 令人不安的話語 –**disquiet** n [U]

dis·re·gard /ˌdɪsrɪˈgɑrd; ˌdɪsrɪˈgɑːd/ v [T] to pay no attention to something 不理會[某事]; 忽視: *The "No Smoking" sign was being completely disregarded.* "禁止吸煙"的牌子竟完全無人理會。–**disregard** n [U]: *She showed a total disregard for my feelings.* 她全然不顧我的感受。| *his reckless disregard for his passengers' safety.* 他對乘客的安全問題置若罔聞。

dis·re·pair /ˌdɪsrɪˈpɛr; ˌdɪsrɪˈpeə/ n [U] a bad condition, needing repair 失修; 破損: *The old houses had fallen into disrepair.* 那些舊房屋經年失修, 破敗不堪。

dis·rep·u·ta·ble /dɪsˈrɛpjətəbl; dɪsˈrepjʊtəbl/ adj thought to have poor standards and probably not to be trusted 名聲不好的; 不光彩的: *his disreputable friends* 他那些聲名狼藉的朋友 | *a disreputable gambling club* 聲名狼藉的賭館 –opposite 反義 **reputable** – **disreputably** adv

dis·re·pute /ˌdɪsrɪˈpjut; ˌdɪsrɪˈpjuːt/ n **bring something into disrepute** to cause something to lose people's respect 使…喪失名譽: *These strikes only bring the nursing profession into disrepute.* 這些罷工事件只會敗壞護理職業的名聲。[RELATED PHRASE 相關詞組 **fall into disrepute**]

dis·re·spect /ˌdɪsrɪˈspɛkt; ˌdɪsrɪˈspekt/ n [U] lack of respect or politeness 不尊敬; 無禮 – **disrespectful** adj –**disrespectfully** adv

dis·rupt /dɪsˈrʌpt; dɪsˈrʌpt/ v [T] to stop something from continuing as expected 使[某事]中斷; 擾亂: *A crowd of protesters disrupted the meeting.* 一羣抗議者擾亂了會議。–**disruption** /-ˈrʌpʃən; -ˈrʌpʃən/ n [C; U]: *The accident has caused widespread disruption to railway services in the south of the city.* (交通)事故使城市南部的鐵路服務廣泛中斷。–**disruptive** /-ˈrʌptɪv; -ˈrʌptɪv/ adj: *He has a disruptive influence on the other children.* 他對別的孩子有一種擾亂性的影響。

dis·sat·is·fac·tion /ˌdɪssætɪsˈfækʃən; dɪˌsætɪsˈfækʃən/ n [U] the state of not being pleased 不滿(意): *There is widespread dissatisfaction in the coal industry.* 煤炭行業的不滿情緒到處可見。

dis·sat·is·fied /dɪsˈsætɪsˌfaɪd; dɪˈsætɪsˌfaɪd/ adj not pleased, especially because you expect more of something or a better standard 不滿(意)的: *I have been very dissatis-fied* **with** *your work this year.* 我對你今年的工作很不滿意。| *dissatisfied customers* 不滿意的顧客

dis·sect /dɪˈsɛkt; dɪˈsɛkt/ *v* [T] **1** to cut up a plant or animal into small pieces for detailed study 解剖〔動植物〕 **2** to look very carefully at all the details of something 剖析; 仔細分析: *to dissect the witnesses' accounts to find the truth* 剖析目擊者的描述以查明真相 **–dissection** /-ˈsɛkʃən; -ˈsɛkʃən/ *n* [C;U]

dis·sem·i·nate /dɪˈsɛmə،net; dɪˈsɛmˌneɪt/ *v* **disseminated, disseminating** [T] *fml* to spread news or ideas widely 〔正式〕散佈; 廣為傳播〔消息或思想〕 **–dissemination** /dɪˌsɛmə'neʃən; dɪˌsɛmɪ'neɪʃən/ *n* [U]: *the dis-semination of their views* 散佈他們的觀點

dis·sen·sion /dɪˈsɛnʃən; dɪˈsɛnʃən/ *n* [U] dis-agreement, often leading to argument 意見分歧〔常導致爭論〕: *His comments caused a great deal of dissension among his followers.* 他的評論在他的追隨者中引起許多爭論。

dis·sent /dɪˈsɛnt; dɪˈsɛnt/ *n* [U] disagreement with the opinion that is held by most people 〔與多數人的〕意見分歧; 異議: *Voices of dis-sent are not tolerated in some countries.* 有些國家不能容忍不同的觀點存在。**–dissent** *v* [I] **–dissenter** *n*

dis·ser·ta·tion /ˌdɪsə'teʃən; ˌdɪsə'teɪʃən/ *n* a long piece of writing done after studying a subject, especially at university 〔尤指大學的〕專題論文, 學位論文

dis·ser·vice /dɪsˈsɝvɪs; dɪˈsɜːvɪs/ *n* [sing] harm or a harmful action 損害; 危害: *You have done a serious disservice* **to** *your country by selling these papers to our enemies.* 你把這些文件出賣給敵人, 對國家造成了嚴重的損害。

dis·si·dent /ˈdɪsədənt; ˈdɪsɪdənt/ *n* some-one who openly and often strongly dis-agrees with an opinion, a group, or a government 持異議者; 持不同政見者: *political dissidents* 持不同政見者 **–dissident** *adj* **–dissidence** *n* [U]

dis·sim·i·lar /dɪsˈsɪmələ; dɪˈsɪmɪlər/ *adj* un-like 不相同的; 不相似的: *The two girls are not dissimilar in appearance; they both take after their mother.* 這兩個女孩長得差不多, 都像她們的母親。

dis·si·pate /ˈdɪsə،pet; ˈdɪsɪpeɪt/ *v* **dissi-pated, dissipating** *fml* 〔正式〕**1** [I;T] to dis-appear or make something disappear (使)消散; 驅散〔某物〕: *The morning mist began to dissipate as the sun rose in the sky.* 太陽當空升起時, 晨霧開始消散。| *Her encourage-ment gradually dissipated his fears.* 她的鼓勵逐漸消除了他的恐懼感。**2** [T] to spend or waste something foolishly 浪費; 揮霍: *He dissipated his large fortune in a few years.* 他在幾年間就把自己的大筆財產揮霍殆盡。

dis·so·ci·ate /dɪˈsoʃɪ،et; dɪˈsəʊʃɪeɪt/ *v* **dis-sociated, dissociating** (also 又作 **disas-**

sociate) [T] to believe or claim that one thing or person has no connection with another 聲稱與…沒有關係: *He dissociated himself* **from** *the decision to close the school.* 他聲稱自己與關閉學校的決定無關。**–dissociation** /dɪˌsosɪ'eʃən; dɪˌsəʊsɪ'eɪʃən/ *n* [U]

dis·so·lute /ˈdɪsə،lut; ˈdɪsəluːt/ *adj fml* with bad or immoral habits 〔正式〕放縱的; 放蕩的: *He had led a dissolute life.* 他那時過着放蕩的生活。**–dissolutely** *adv*

dis·so·lu·tion /ˌdɪsə'luʃən; ˌdɪsə'luːʃən/ *n* [U] *fml* the ending or breaking up of an association, group, or marriage 〔正式〕解散; 解除: *the dissolution of Parliament before a general election* 大選前議會的解散

dis·solve /dɪˈzɑlv; dɪˈzɒlv/ *v* **dissolved, dis-solving 1** [I;T] to make or become liquid when put into a liquid (使)溶解; (使)液化: *Sugar dissolves in water.* 糖溶於水。| *Dis-solve the tablets in warm water.* 把藥片溶化於溫水中。**2** [T] to end or break up a group or a formal relationship 使解散; 使解除; 終止: *The military government dissolved the parliament and suspended all political ac-tivity.* 軍政府解散了議會, 並中止一切政治活動。| *She left him, and their marriage was later dissolved.* 她離他而去; 他們的婚姻關係後來也解除了。**3** [I] to disappear 消散; 消失: *His fears gradually dissolved.* 他的恐懼感逐漸消失。**4 dissolve in** to start showing your feelings in some way because you are un-able to control them any longer 情不自禁: *She suddenly dissolved in tears.* 她突然禁不住淚流滿面。| *We all dissolved into laugh-ter.* 我們都不禁哈哈大笑。

dis·suade /dɪˈswed; dɪˈsweɪd/ *v* **dissuaded, dissuading** [T] to persuade someone not to do something 勸〔某人〕不要做〔某事〕: *I tried to dissuade her* **from** *joining the club.* 我曾設法勸她不要參加那個俱樂部。

dis·tance[1] /ˈdɪstəns; ˈdɪstəns/ *n* **1** [C;U] the amount of space or time between two points 距離; 間距: *What is the distance from London to Glasgow?* 從倫敦到格拉斯哥有多遠? | *We were within easy walking distance of home.* 我們離家很近, 走幾步路就到了。| *You can't expect me to remember at this dis-tance in time!* 你可不能指望我隔了這麼長時間還想得起來! **2** [sing] a point or place that is far away 遠處; 遠方: *The ruins look very impressive from a distance.* 從遠處望去, 那些遺跡令人難忘。| *The pyramids are visible at a distance of several kilometres.* 一座座的金字塔在幾公里以外都能看到。**3 in the dis-tance** far away 在遠處: *We could just see the spire of the cathedral in the distance.* 我們在遠處只能看到大教堂的尖塔。**4 keep your distance** to stay away 保持距離; 保持疏遠: *It's not a very friendly area. The neighbours keep their distance.* 這個地區的人不太友好; 左鄰右里都很疏遠。

distance² v [T] to cause someone to feel or want less connection with someone or something 使遠離; 使疏遠: *She tried to distance herself* **from** *the actions of her government.* 她試圖置身於政府的所作所為之外。 | *a parental attitude which tends to distance young Indian girls from their culture* 父母們傾向於使印度女孩疏遠本國文化的態度

dis·tant /'dɪstənt; 'dɪstənt/ adj **1** far away in space or time 〔空間或時間〕遙遠的; 久遠的: *distant lands* 遙遠的國度 | *the distant sound of a bell* 遠處的鐘聲 | *events in the distant past* 遠古時發生的事情 **2** [only before a noun 只用於名詞前] not very closely connected 〔關係〕遠的; 不緊密的: *Those two boys are distant relations.* 那兩個男孩是遠房親戚。 **3** showing a lack of friendliness or attention 冷淡的; 不友好的: *Jeremy and Susan are distantly related.* 傑里米和蘇珊是遠親。 | *"Very likely," he said distantly.* "很有可能," 他冷漠地說。

dis·taste /dɪs'test; dɪs'teɪst/ *n* [sing;U] a feeling of dislike or disapproval 不喜歡; 厭惡: *She looked at him with distaste.* 她厭惡地望着他。 | *a distaste* **for** *town life* 對都市生活的反感

dis·taste·ful /dɪs'testfəl; dɪs'teɪstfəl/ *adj* unpleasant 使人不愉快的; 令人反感的; 討厭的: *a rather distasteful duty* 相當令人討厭的責任

dis·tend /dɪ'stɛnd; dɪ'stɛnd/ *v* [T] *fml* to make something swell because of pressure from inside 〔正式〕〔因內部壓力〕使〔某物〕膨脹; 使腫脹: *The children's stomachs were distended because of lack of food.* 孩子們的肚子因缺少食物而膨脹。

dis·til /dɪ'stɪl; dɪ'stɪl/ *v* **-ll-** (distill *AmE* 〔美式〕) [T] **1** to turn a liquid into gas and then turn the gas into liquid to make it pure or to obtain alcoholic spirit from it 蒸餾〔液體〕; 用蒸餾法製〔酒〕: *distilled water* 蒸餾水 | *Brandy is distilled from wine.* 白蘭地是由果酒蒸餾製成的。 **2** to express something clearly in a shorter form 用精練〔濃縮〕形式表達: *a distilled account of his travels* 他對旅行的見聞簡明扼要的描述 **–distillation** /ˌdɪstl'eʃən; ˌdɪstl'eɪʃən/ *n* [C;U]

dis·til·le·ry /dɪ'stɪləri; dɪ'stɪləri/ *n* **distilleries** a factory where strong alcoholic drinks are distilled 釀酒廠: *a whisky distillery* 釀製威士忌的酒廠

dis·tinct /dɪ'stɪŋkt; dɪ'stɪŋkt/ adj **1** clearly different or separate 截然不同的; 獨立的: *The party split into two distinct groups.* 該政黨分裂成兩個獨立的團體。 **2 as distinct from** a phrase used to make it very clear that two things or situations are different 有別於〔用來區別兩樣東西或兩種情況〕: *That rule only applies to locally recruited teachers, as distinct from those recruited elsewhere.* 那條規則僅適用於當地招聘的教師, 以便與從別地招聘的教師有所區別。 **3** clearly seen, heard, or understood 明顯的; 清楚的; 清晰的: *a dis-*

tinct smell of burning 明顯的焚燒氣味 | *There's a distinct possibility that we'll all lose our jobs.* 我們顯然都有失業的可能。 **–distinctly** *adv* **–distinctness** *n* [U]

dis·tinc·tion /dɪ'stɪŋkʃən; dɪ'stɪŋkʃən/ n **1** [C; U] a clear difference 區別; 差別: *It's important to draw a distinction* **between** *those under 30 and those over 30.* 把三十歲以下的人和三十歲以上的人區別開來是十分重要的。 | *Why are you making a distinction* **between** *men and women?* 你現在為甚麼要把男女區別開? **2** [U] the quality of being unusually good 優秀品質; 傑出; 卓越: *a writer of distinction* 傑出的作家 **3** [C] a special mark of honour 殊勳; 榮譽(稱號): *This is one of the highest distinctions awarded by the Queen.* 這是女王授予的最高榮譽稱號之一。

dis·tinc·tive /dɪ'stɪŋktɪv; dɪ'stɪŋktɪv/ *adj* clearly marking a person or thing as different from others 與眾不同的; 有特色的: *a distinctive way of walking* 走路的樣子與眾不同 **–distinctively** *adv* **–distinctiveness** *n* [U]

dis·tin·guish /dɪ'stɪŋgwɪʃ; dɪ'stɪŋgwɪʃ/ v **1** [I; T] to recognize the differences between things 區別; 辨別: *to distinguish right* **from** *wrong* 分辨是非 | *I think you have to distinguish* **between** *the women who want to have children and those that don't.* 我認為你得把想要孩子和不想要孩子的婦女加以區別。 **2** [T] to hear, see, or recognize something, often with difficulty 聽出; 看清; 認出: *We could just distinguish the buildings on the horizon.* 我們勉強能看清地平線上的建築物。 **3** [T] to mark something as different 使〔某物〕有別於...: *Elephants are distinguished by their long trunks.* 大象因其長鼻子而有別於其他動物。 **4 distinguish yourself** to behave or perform something so well that people praise you 表現突出; 使傑出: *He distinguished himself in his final examination.* 他在期終考試中脫穎而出。

dis·tin·gui·sha·ble /dɪ'stɪŋgwɪʃəbl; dɪ'stɪŋgwɪʃəbl/ *adj* able to be clearly or easily distinguished 區別得出的; 可以辨明的: *The twins were not easily distinguishable* **from** *each other.* 那對雙胞胎不易區分。 | *A black cat is not easily distinguishable on a dark night.* 在漆黑的夜裡, 黑貓是不易辨別的。 **–** opposite **indistinguishable**

dis·tin·guished /dɪ'stɪŋgwɪʃt; dɪ'stɪŋgwɪʃt/ *adj* **1** of excellent quality or deserving respect 卓越的; 傑出的; 受人尊敬的: *a distinguished performance* 出色的表演 | *a distinguished writer* 傑出的作家 **2 look distinguished** to have a noble appearance which you admire or respect 顯得高貴; 有尊嚴: *Grey hair can look very distinguished.* 灰白的頭髮顯得有尊嚴。

dis·tort /dɪs'tɔrt; dɪ'stɔːt/ *v* [T] **1** to twist out of the usual shape, appearance, or sound 扭歪; 扭曲; 使變形: *trees distorted by the* *wind* 被風吹歪的樹木 | *Her voice sounded distorted on the phone.* 她的嗓音在電話裡聽來有點失真。**2** to twist the meaning of something so that it is untrue 歪曲; 曲解: *He gave a very distorted account of what happened.* 他顛三倒四地描述了所發生的事情。**–distortion** /-ˈtɔːʃən; -ˈtɔːʃən/ *n* [C;U]

dis·tract /dɪˈstrækt; dɪˈstrækt/ *v* [T] **1** to take someone's mind away from what they are doing 使〔某人〕分心; 分散〔某人的〕注意力: *Don't distract me.* 別分散我的注意力。| *She was distracted* **from** *her work by the noise outside.* 外面的喧鬧聲使她不能專注工作。| *It's very distracting having children in the office.* 把孩子放在辦公室會使人分心。**2** to take someone's mind off their troubles 讓〔某人〕散散心; 使〔某人〕快樂: *We took the children out for the day to distract them.* 我們帶孩子們出去消遣了一天。

dis·tract·ed /dɪˈstræktɪd; dɪˈstræktɪd/ *adj* anxious or troubled about many things 心煩意亂的; 困惑的 **–distractedly** *adv*

dis·trac·tion /dɪˈstrækʃən; dɪˈstrækʃən/ *n* **1** something that takes your mind away from what you are doing 使人分心的事物: *There are too many distractions here for me to work properly.* 這裡使人分心的事太多, 使我無法好好工作。**2** something that entertains you or takes your mind off your troubles 娛樂; 消遣: *games, concerts, television — all the usual distractions* 遊戲、音樂會、電視 — 所有這些平常的娛樂 **3 drive someone to distraction** to make someone almost mad by continually annoying them 逼得某人忍無可忍; 逼得某人幾乎到了瘋狂地步: *The child's crying drove him to distraction.* 孩子的哭聲逼得他幾乎發瘋。

dis·traught /dɪˈstrɔːt; dɪˈstrɔːt/ *adj* very anxious and troubled 心煩意亂的: *She was clearly distraught.* 她顯然十分煩惱。

dis·tress¹ /dɪˈstrɛs; dɪˈstres/ *n* [U] **1** great suffering, pain, or discomfort 苦惱; 痛苦; 不適; 疼痛: *The sick man showed signs of distress.* 病人顯出十分痛苦的樣子。| *people in distress because of lack of money* 因沒有錢而受苦受難的人們 **2** a state of danger or great difficulty 危難; 困境: *a ship in distress* 遇險的船 | *a distress signal* 遇難(呼救)信號

distress² *v* [T] to cause someone great pain, unhappiness, or anxiety 使〔某人〕痛苦; 使苦惱; 使憂愁: *He was very distressed about the situation.* 他對形勢極為憂慮。

dis·tress·ing /dɪˈstrɛsɪŋ; dɪˈstresɪŋ/ *adj* causing great unhappiness or anxiety 使人痛苦的; 令人苦惱的: *His parents' divorce was a distressing experience.* 他父母親的離婚是一次令人痛苦的經歷。

*dis·trib·ute /dɪˈstrɪbjuːt; dɪˈstrɪbjuːt/ *v* **distributed, distributing** [T] **1** to give out or divide things among several people 分發; 分配: *He was asked to distribute the prizes.* 他被請來頒發獎品。| *Food is being distributed to*

the refugees. 食物正在分配給難民。**2** to spread things out 使分佈, 使散開: *This new machine distributes seed evenly and quickly over the whole field.* 這台新機器把種子又快又均勻地播撒在整塊田裡。**3** to deliver goods to shops or businesses 把〔貨物〕送到〔商店或商行〕: *Newspapers are distributed by road, not rail.* 報紙是用汽車而不是用火車運送的。

*dis·tri·bu·tion /ˌdɪstrəˈbjuːʃən; ˌdɪstrɪˈbjuːʃən/ *n* [C;U] an act of distributing things or the state of being distributed 分發; 分配; 分送: *the distribution of prizes* 獎品的分發 | *food distribution centres* 食品分配中心 | *The distribution of wealth among the population is very unequal.* 財富在人口中的分配很不平均。

*dis·trict /ˈdɪstrɪkt; ˈdɪstrɪkt/ *n* an area of a country or city, especially one made officially for a particular purpose 區; 管區; 行政區: *a postal district* 郵政區 | *a district council* 區議會 | *a poor district of the city* 城市中的貧民區

dis·trust¹ /dɪsˈtrʌst; dɪsˈtrʌst/ *v* [T] to have no trust in someone 不信任〔某人〕; 懷疑〔某人〕: *He distrusts banks so he keeps his money at home.* 他信不過銀行, 因此把錢放在家裡。

distrust² *n* [sing;U] lack of trust 不信任; 懷疑: *He regards banks with distrust.* 他認為銀行靠不住。| *his distrust of anyone in authority* 他對當官的誰都信不過 **–distrustful** *adj*

dis·turb /dɪˈstɜːb; dɪˈstɜːb/ *v* [T] **1** to interrupt someone, especially a person who is working or sleeping 打擾; 干擾〔尤指對正在工作或睡覺的人〕: *I'm sorry to disturb you, but...* 對不起, 打擾你了, 不過... | *Did the storm disturb you in the night?* 夜裡的暴風雨有沒有把你吵醒? **2** to upset someone 使〔某人〕心神不安或煩惱: *We were very disturbed by the government announcement.* 政府的通告令我們十分不安。| *This is very disturbing news.* 這是令人很煩惱的消息。**3** to change the usual or natural condition of something 擾亂; 激盪: *A light wind disturbed the surface of the water.* 微風使水面泛起漣漪。

dis·turb·ance /dɪˈstɜːbəns; dɪˈstɜːbəns/ *n* **1** [C] a situation in which there is public disorder 騷動; 動亂: *They were charged by the police with causing a disturbance.* 他們被警方指控為擾亂治安。**2** [C;U] something that interrupts you or makes you unable to think clearly about what you are doing 打擾; 干擾: *The noise of traffic is a continual disturbance.* 車輛的噪音是一種持續性的干擾。**3** [C;U] a change in a usual condition 〔心理〕不正常; 精神紊亂: *signs of serious mental disturbance* 精神極不正常的樣子

dis·turbed /dɪˈstɜːbd; dɪˈstɜːbd/ *adj* having or showing signs of an illness of the mind or the feelings 精神紊亂的; 心理不正常的: *She is emotionally disturbed.* 她情緒不正常。

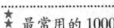 最常用的 1000 字　　★ 最常用的 1001-2000 字　　★ 最常用的 2001-3000 字

dis·use /dɪsˈjus; dɪsˈjuːs/ *n* **fall into disuse** to stop being used 不用; 廢棄: *an old law that had fallen into disuse* 已廢棄法令

dis·used /dɪsˈjuzd; dɪsˈjuːzd◂/ *adj* no longer used 不再使用的: *a disused mine* 廢棄的礦井

ditch¹ /dɪtʃ; dɪtʃ/ *n* a narrow passage cut into the ground for water to flow through 水溝; 渠道: *The water drains into the ditch at the edge of the field.* 水緩緩流入田邊的溝裡。

ditch² *v* [T] *infml* to get rid of someone or something 〔非正式〕拋棄〔某人〕; 丟棄〔某物〕: *She got bored with her boyfriend and ditched him.* 她對她男友感到厭倦, 於是把他甩掉了。| *He took the money and ditched the wallet in a rubbish bin.* 他拿了錢就把錢包扔進垃圾箱。

dith·er /ˈdɪðə; ˈdɪðəʳ/ *v* [I] *infml* to act nervously because you are unable to decide 〔非正式〕躊躇; 猶豫不定

dit·to /ˈdɪto; ˈdɪtəʊ/ *n* a mark (··) meaning the same as the word above 表示"同上"的符號 (··)

   one black pencil at 27p 黑鉛筆27便士一支
   ·· *blue* ·· *at 32p* 藍鉛筆32便士一支

di·van /dɪˈvæn; dɪˈvæn/ *n* a bed which has a base and the part you sleep on, but no frame 〔無靠背或扶手的〕沙發牀

dive¹ /daɪv; daɪv/ *v* **dived** (also 又作 **dove** /dov; dəʊv/ *AmE* 〔美式〕) **diving** [I] **1** to jump head first into water 〔頭先入水〕跳入: *The boy dived into the swimming poll from the diving board.* 那個男孩從跳板一頭跳入游泳池中。**2** to go under the surface of the water 潛水: *They are diving for gold from the Spanish wreck.* 他們正潛水尋找失事的西班牙船隻上的黃金。**3** to go down quickly 俯衝: *The plane dived towards the sea.* 飛機朝海面俯衝下去。**4** to move quickly, especially downwards or out of sight 猛衝〔尤指撲向〕: *The goalkeeper dived for the ball.* 守門員向球撲去。

dive² *n* **1** an act of jumping head first into water 跳水: *a graceful dive into the pool* 優美的跳水動作 **2** a sudden rapid movement, especially downwards or out of sight 突然撲向; 衝向: *When the shots sounded, we made a dive for the nearest doorway.* 槍聲響時, 我們迅速躲進最靠近的一個門廊裡。

div·er /ˈdaɪvə; ˈdaɪvəʳ/ *n* a person who dives, especially one who works at the bottom of the sea in a diving suit with a supply of air 跳水者;〔尤指〕潛水員

di·verge /daɪˈvɜdʒ; daɪˈvɜːdʒ/ *v* **diverged, diverging** [I] *fml* to separate and go on in different directions 〔正式〕分叉; 叉開; 分歧: *That's where the two systems diverged.* 那就是兩種體系的分歧。| *That's where the new system diverges from the old one.* 那就是新體系與舊體系的分歧所在。–**divergence** *n* [C; U]: *a divergence of opinion* 意見的分歧 –**divergent** *adj*

di·verse /daɪˈvɜs; daɪˈvɜːs/ *adj fml* very dif-

ferent 〔正式〕各不相同的; 各種各樣的: *many diverse interests* 多種不同的興趣

di·ver·si·fy /daɪˈvɜsəˌfaɪ; daɪˈvɜːsɪˌfaɪ/ *v* **diversified, diversifying** [I;T] to start to make different sorts of product (使)〔產品〕多樣化: *Some major tobacco companies diversified into food in the late sixties.* 一些大煙草公司在六十年代後期開始兼營食品生產。| *The company needs to diversify its products.* 公司需要使自己的產品多樣化。–**diversification** /daɪˌvɜsəfəˈkeɪʃən; daɪˌvɜːsɪfɪˈkeɪʃən/ *n* [U]

di·ver·sion /daɪˈvɜʒən; daɪˈvɜːʃən/ *n* **1** [C;U] a turning aside from a course, activity, or use 偏離; 轉向; 轉移: *the diversion of a river to supply water to the farms* 河流改道以灌溉農田 | *The traffic had to follow a diversion because of an accident on the main road.* 因主要道路發生車禍, 車輛只好改道行駛。**2** [C] something that a person uses on purpose to turn your attention away from something they do not want you to notice 用以轉移注意力〔視線〕的事物: *All those statistics were just a diversion.* 所有那些統計只是一種用來轉移目標的假象。**3** [C] an entertaining thing to do 消遣; 娛樂: *Big cities have lots of cinemas and other diversions.* 大城市裡有許多電影院和其他娛樂場所。

di·ver·si·ty /daɪˈvɜsətɪ; daɪˈvɜːsɪtɪ/ *n* [U] variety 變化多端; 多樣性: *The plants of Asia show great diversity of form.* 亞洲的植物形態多種多樣。

di·vert /daɪˈvɜt; daɪˈvɜːt/ *v* [T] **1** to turn something aside or from one use or direction to another 使轉移; 使轉向: *They diverted the river to supply water to the town.* 他們使河流改道以便向城市供水。| *diverted traffic* 改道行駛的車輛 | *Money was diverted from scientific research into marketing.* 用於科研的錢撥給了市場銷售。**2** *fml* to amuse 〔正式〕使消遣; 使娛樂: *a game to divert the children* 一種供孩子娛樂的遊戲 **3 divert someone's attention** to turn someone's attention away from something 轉移某人的注意力: *A loud noise diverted my attention.* 一陣喧鬧聲分散了我的注意力。

di·vest /daɪˈvest; daɪˈvest/ *v fml* 〔正式〕**1 divest someone of something** to take away the position, rights, or property of someone 解除〔某人的職務〕; 剝奪〔某人的權利或財產〕: *The disgraced leader was divested of all his power.* 那個失勢的領導失去了一切權力。**2 divest yourself of** to get rid of something 使自己擺脫〔某事〕: *The brewing company Eastern Ales have divested themselves of their interest in Allied Whisky.* 愛爾斯東部釀酒公司已經失去對威士忌聯營公司的興趣。

★**di·vide¹** /dɪˈvaɪd; dɪˈvaɪd/ *v* **divided, dividing 1** [I;T] to separate into parts 分; 分開: *Divide the cake into twelve.* 把蛋糕切成十二塊。| *He divides his time between working and looking after the children.* 他把時間分別

用在工作和照料孩子上。| *This class is too large. We shall have to divide it.* 這個班級太大; 我們得把它分開來。| *The class divided into groups.* 全班分成了幾個小組。**2** [T] to give part of something to each of several people 分配〔某物〕; 分享: *He divided the money equally* **between** *his children.* 他把錢平均分給孩子們。| *They divided the food* **among** *themselves.* 他們一起分享食物。**3** [T] to cause people to disagree or quarrel 使產生分歧〔爭吵〕: *an issue which has divided the country* 一個引起國民意見分歧的問題 **4** [T] to calculate how many times a small number will go into a larger number 除; 除以: *120 divided* **by** *3 is 40.* 120除以3等於40。| *You can't divide 7* **into** *53.* 你無法用7除53。

divide sthg ↔ **up** *phr v* [T] to separate something into parts or share it between several people 分開, 分享〔某物〕: *The land was divided up* **among** *the sons.* 那塊土地被幾個兒子分了。

divide² *n* a difference between two systems or groups〔兩種體制或兩個羣體的〕差異: *the North-South divide* 南北之間的差異

div·i·ded high·way /dəˈvaɪdɪd ˌhaɪweɪ; dʒˈvaɪdʒd ˌhaɪweɪ/ *n* the usual American word for〔美式〕= DUAL CARRIAGEWAY

*****div·i·dend** /ˈdɪvəˌdɛnd; ˈdɪvˌdənd/ *n* **1** the part of the money made by a business which is divided among the people who own shares in the business〔分給股東的〕紅利, 股息: *The company declared a large dividend at the end of the year.* 公司在年底宣佈發放豐厚的紅利。**2** **pay dividends** to produce an advantage, especially as the result of earlier action 產生效益; 得到好處〔尤指回報〕: *Their decision five years ago to computerize the company is now paying handsome dividends.* 他們五年前決定將公司電腦化, 如今正在產生可觀的效益。

di·vid·ers /dəˈvaɪdəz; dʒˈvaɪdəz/ *n* [pl] a V-shaped instrument for measuring distances on paper 分線規; 兩腳規

di·vine¹ /dəˈvaɪn; dʒˈvaɪn/ *adj* **1** connected with a god 神的; 上帝的: *divine inspiration* 神感感應 **2** *old-fash infml* extremely good〔老式, 非正式〕極好的: *That meal was simply divine!* 那頓飯簡直棒極了! –**divinely** *adv*

divine² *v* **divined, divining** [T; + that] *fml* to discover or guess something correctly〔正式〕發現, 猜到〔某物〕: *Although Churchill knew of their agreement, he was unable to divine its exact nature.* 雖然邱吉爾聽說他們達成了協議, 但他無法猜準其本意。

di·ving·board /ˈdaɪvɪŋˌbɔːd; ˈdaɪvɪŋbɔːd/ *n* a board off which people jump head first into water〔跳水用的〕跳板

di·vin·i·ty /dəˈvɪnəti; dʒˈvɪnəti/ *n* **divinities** **1** [U] the quality or state of being a god or connected with a god 神性; 神力; 神威 **2** [C] (also 又作 **Divinity**) a god or goddess 神; 女神 **3** [U] *old-fash* the study of religion〔老

式〕神學

di·vis·i·ble /dəˈvɪzəbl; dʒˈvɪzˌbəl/ *adj* able to be divided 可分的; 可除(盡)的: *15 is divisible by 3.* 15能被3除盡。

*****di·vi·sion** /dəˈvɪʒən; dʒˈvɪʒən/ *n* **1** [U] the act of separating things into parts 分; 分開; 分割: *the division of Germany* 德國的分裂 **2** [U] sharing things among a number of people 分享; 分擔: *the division of responsibility among the teachers* 教師中的責任分工 **3** [C] something that divides or separates 分隔物; 分界線: *The river forms the division between the old and new parts of the city.* 這條河形成了老城區和新城區的分界線。**4** [C] a part of a large organization〔組織或機構的〕部門: *He works in the foreign division of the company.* 他在公司的外事處工作。**5** [C] a deep and painful disagreement between different groups in a society〔社會團體之間的〕分歧; 分裂: *Now that the war is over, attempts must be made to heal the divisions in our society.* 戰爭既然已結束, 社會各團體間的思想分歧應努力加以消除。**6** [U] a MATHEMATICAL operation in which you decide how many times one number will go into another, for example 15 ÷ 3 = 5 除(法)〔如: 15除以3等於5〕

di·vi·sive /dəˈvaɪsɪv; dʒˈvaɪsɪv/ *adj* tending to cause people to disagree or quarrel 造成不和的; 引起分裂的: *He is a divisive influence at meetings.* 他在會議上總會造成不和。

di·vorce¹ /dəˈvɔːs; dʒˈvɔːs/ *n* [C;U] the ending of a marriage as declared by a court of law 離婚: *Is divorce allowed in your country?* 你們國家准許離婚嗎? | *She got a divorce after years of unhappiness.* 她經過幾年不愉快的婚姻生活之後, 終於離了婚。

divorce² *v* **divorced, divorcing** **1** [I;T] to end a marriage legally (使)離婚: *They divorced in 1989.* 他們在1989年離婚。| *He divorced his first wife.* 他和他第一任妻子離了婚。**2** **get divorced** to end a marriage legally 離婚: *My parents got divorced last year.* 我的父母去年離婚了。**3** [T] *fml* to separate〔正式〕使分離; 使脫離: *She finds it hard to divorce fact* **from** *fantasy.* 她發覺現實和幻想很難分開。–**divorced** *adj*: *Is he single, married, or divorced?* 他是單身、已婚還是離了婚?

di·vor·cée /dəˌvɔːˈseɪ; dʒˌvɔːˈsiː/ *n* a divorced woman 離了婚的女人

di·vulge /dəˈvʌldʒ; daɪˈvʌldʒ/ *v* **divulged, divulging** [T; +that] *fml* to tell something that has been secret〔正式〕泄露〔祕密〕: *His doctor divulged that the President had been ill for some time before he died.* 醫生透露說, 總統去世前已經病了一段時間。

DIY /ˌdiː aɪ ˈwaɪ; ˌdiː aɪ ˈwaɪ/ *n* [U] building, repairing, or decorating your house yourself and not paying a workman to do it; an abbreviation for DO-IT-YOURSELF〖縮〗自己動手(做)〔指建造、修理或裝飾不用花錢雇專人〕

diz·zy /ˈdɪzɪ; ˈdɪzɪ/ adj **dizzier, dizziest** having an unpleasant feeling of losing your balance, as if things are going round and round 頭暈目眩的: *The room was so hot that she felt dizzy.* 房間裡熱得她頭暈目眩。– **dizziness** n [U]

DJ /ˌdiˈdʒe; ˌdiˈdʒeɪ/ n a broadcaster who introduces records of popular music on a radio or television show; an abbreviation for DISC JOCKEY〖縮〗〖廣播或電視台的〗流行音樂唱片節目播音員[主持人], 唱片騎師

DNA /ˌdi ɛn ˈe; ˌdi ɛn ˈeɪ/ n tech [U] the acid which carries GENETIC information; an abbreviation for **deoxyribonucleic acid** 〖縮, 術語〗脫氧核糖核酸〔基因訊息的載體〕

★★do –see boxes on pages 323 and 324 見 323 頁和 324 頁方框

do·cile /ˈdɑsl; ˈdəʊsaɪl/ adj quiet and easily controlled 易控制的; 馴服的: *a docile animal* 溫順的動物 –**docility** /dɑˈsɪlətɪ; dəʊˈsɪlɪti/ n [U]

dock¹ /dɑk; dɒk/ n **1** a place where ships are loaded and unloaded, or repaired 碼頭; 船埠; 船塢: *The ship moved away from the dock.* 輪船駛出了碼頭。| *Liverpool docks* 利物浦港區 –see picture on page 991 見 991 頁彩圖 **2 the dock** the place in a court of law where the prisoner stands 〔法庭上的〕被告席; 犯人欄

dock² v **1** [I;T] to sail into a dock 進港; 駛入船塢: *The ship docked at Portsmouth.* 輪船駛入樸次茅斯港。| *We'll be docking in about half an hour.* 我們大約在半小時後靠碼頭。**2 dock someone's wages** to reduce the amount of money that someone is paid 扣除某人的工資: *They docked his wages by £5 last week because one day he was late.* 由於他上星期有一天遲到, 他們從他的工資中扣去五英鎊。

dock·er /ˈdɑkɚ; ˈdɒkəʳ/ n a person who works at a dock, loading and unloading ships 碼頭工人

★★doc·tor¹ /ˈdɑktɚ; ˈdɒktəʳ/ n **1** a person whose profession is to treat sick people 醫生; 大夫: *If you feel so ill, you should go and see a doctor.* 如果你感到病得厲害, 就應該去看醫生。**2 the doctor's** the place where you go to be treated by a doctor 診所; 醫院: *I went to the doctor's this morning.* 今天早上我去診所看病。**3** a person holding one of the highest degrees given by a university, such as a PhD 博士

doctor² v [T] infml 〖非正式〗 **1** to change something, especially in a dishonest way 竄改〔某物〕; 偽造〔某物〕: *The report had been doctored.* 那報告已被人竄改。**2** to make an animal unable to breed by removing its sexual organs 閹割〔牲畜〕

doc·tor·ate /ˈdɑktərɪt; ˈdɒktərɪt/ n the highest degree given by a university 博士學位

doc·tri·naire /ˌdɑktrɪˈnɛr; ˌdɒktrɪˈneəʳ/ adj believing in or acting on a system of ideas without allowing it to be questioned or considering the practical difficulties 空談理論的; 教條主義的

doc·trine /ˈdɑktrɪn; ˈdɒktrɪn/ n [C;U] a religious or political belief, or set of beliefs 教義; 教條; 主義; 信條: *the doctrines of the Catholic church* 天主教會的教義 –**doctrinal** /ˈdɑktrɪnl; dɒkˈtraɪnəl/ adj

★doc·u·ment¹ /ˈdɑkjəmənt; ˈdɒkjʊmənt/ n a paper that gives information about something or proof of something 公文; 文件; 文獻: *Let me see all the official documents concerning the sale of this land.* 讓我看一看有關出售這塊土地的所有正式文件。

doc·u·ment² /ˈdɑkjəˌmɛnt; ˈdɒkjʊˌment/ v [T] to prove or support something with documents 用文件證明〔某事〕; 為〔某事〕提供文件: *The history of this area is very well documented.* 這個地區的歷史有充分的文獻可作依據。–**documentation** /ˌdɑkjəmənˈteʃən; ˌdɒkjʊmənˈteɪʃən/ n [U]

doc·u·men·ta·ry¹ /ˌdɑkjəˈmɛntərɪ; ˌdɒkjʊˈmentəri/ n **documentaries** a film, television, or radio broadcast that presents facts 記錄影片; 記實性電視[廣播]節目: *We saw a documentary about Yorkshire coal miners.* 我們看了一部有關約克郡煤礦工人的記錄片。| *a documentary film* 記錄片 –compare 比較 FEATURE

documentary² adj consisting of or related to documents 文件的; 文獻的; 書面的: *documentary evidence* 書面證據

dod·der·ing /ˈdɑdərɪŋ; ˈdɒdərɪŋ/ adj infml (also 又作 **doddery** /-dərɪ; -dəri/) weak, shaky, and slow, usually from age 〖非正式〗〔常因年老而〕虛弱的; 顫抖的; 遲緩的: *a doddering old man* 蹣跚而行的老頭

dod·dle /ˈdɑdl; ˈdɒdl/ n BrE infml something that is very easy 〖英式, 非正式〗輕而易舉的事: *The last test was a real doddle!* 上次的測試真是易如反掌。

dodge /dɑdʒ; dɒdʒ/ v **dodged, dodging 1** [I;T] to avoid something by suddenly moving aside 閃開; 躲開: *He dodged the falling rock and escaped unhurt.* 他閃身躲過落下來的岩石, 安然脫險了。| *He dodged past me.* 他從我身邊躲閃過去。**2** [T] infml to avoid something in a dishonest way 〖非正式〗施計逃避〔某事〕: *He tried to dodge the tax.* 他企圖逃稅。

dodg·y /ˈdɑdʒɪ; ˈdɒdʒi/ adj **dodgier, dodgiest** BrE infml 〖英式, 非正式〗 **1** not safe 不安全的; 危險的: *Don't sit on that chair. The leg's a bit dodgy.* 別坐在那把椅子上; 椅子腿有點兒靠不住。**2** dishonest and unable to be trusted 狡詐的; 不可靠的: *a dodgy business* 靠不住的事

does /dəz; dəz, *strong* 強讀 dʌz; dʌz/ the 3rd

⁑do¹ /du; du:/ v

present tense 現在式	past tense 過去式	*past participle* 過去分詞
I **do**	I **did**	**done**
You **do**	You **did**	*present participle* 現在分詞
He / she / it **does**	He / she / it **did**	**doing**
We **do**	We **did**	*negative short forms* 否定縮略式
You **do**	You **did**	**don't doesn't didn't**
They **do**	They **did**	

For the pronunciation of these forms look up at their own place in the dictionary. 上述各種形式的發音,可參閱本詞典各自的詞條。

D

1 [auxiliary verb] used with other verbs to form negatives (NEGATIVE) and questions, and sometimes to replace the main verb 與其他動詞連用, 以構成否定句和疑問句; 有時可代替主要動詞:
Don't touch that. 別碰那個。| *She doesn't work here any more.* 她已不在這裡工作。| *I didn't go to the party.* 我沒去參加聚會。| *Do you like fish?* 你喜歡吃魚嗎? | *What did he say?* 他說了些甚麼? | *They live in London, don't they? You saw Jane on Friday, didn't you?* 他們住在倫敦, 是嗎? 你星期五見到簡了, 對嗎? | *She eats a lot more than I do.* 她吃得比我多很多。| *Michael didn't enjoy the holiday, but I did.* 邁克爾假日過得不愉快, 但我卻過得很好。| *"Her parents live in London." "No they don't, they live in Birmingham."* "她父母親住在倫敦。" "不, 他們住在伯明翰。" | *"Why didn't you tell me?" "I did tell you!"* "你怎麼沒告訴我?" "我告訴你了!"

2 [T] to perform an action or take action in some way 做某個動作或採取某個行動:
I must do the ironing this afternoon. 今天下午我必須熨燙衣服。| *What are you doing?* 你在幹甚麼? | *Have you done your homework?* 你做家庭作業了嗎? | *He did a little dance to celebrate.* 他跳了幾個舞以示慶祝。| *He's doing some repairs to the car.* 他在修理汽車。| *Don't forget to do your teeth.* 別忘了刷牙。| *He does the garden for us.* 他幫我們照料花園。| *One drink won't do any harm.* 喝一杯酒不會有害處。| *I'm hoping to do biology at university.* 我希望到大學攻讀生物。| *Our old car can only do about 40 miles per hour.* 我們的舊車每小時只能跑四十英里。

3 **do as you're told** a phrase used to tell a child that they must do something that you are telling them to do 叫你怎麼做, 你就怎麼做〔對孩子的用語〕:
Don't argue with me — just do as you're told! 別跟我爭辯了 — 就照我說的去做!

4 **do something** to take action to solve a problem 採取〔解決問題的〕行動:
The government must do something about the rising levels of unemployment. 政府必須想辦法解決呈上升趨勢的失業率問題。| *Don't just stand there — do something!* 別光在那兒站着 — 想辦法吧!

5 **do someone good** to improve someone's health or make them feel better 促進某人健康; 對某人有好處:
A holiday would do her good. 度假對她的健康有好處。

6 **do well** to be successful 成功; 順利:
He did very well in the exams. 他的考試成績很好。| *You did very well to get all the work finished on time.* 你按時完成了全部工作, 幹得很出色。

7 **do your best** to try as much as you can to do something 盡自己最大努力:
We'll do our best to be there on time. 我們將盡量準時到那裡。

8 **how do you do** a polite greeting that you say to someone when you meet them for the first time 你好!〔初次見面時的禮貌問候語〕

9 **what do you do?** = what is your job? 你幹甚麼工作?
"What does your wife do?" "She's a designer." "你妻子幹甚麼工作?" "她是設計師。"

10 **would do well to do something** a phrase used when you are advising someone to do something 以做某事為明智; 以做某事為好〔用於向別人提出忠告〕:
You'd do well to keep quiet about this. 你對此還是保持沉默為好。

do away with sth *phr v*
[T]
to end something or get rid of it 廢除; 除去; 撤銷:
The government are planning to do away with this tax altogether. 政府正打算完全廢除這項稅收。

do sbdy ↔ **down** *phr v*
　[T]
　to say unpleasant things about someone 説〔某人〕的壞話:
　He's always doing her down. 他老是説她的壞話。

do sbdy **in** *phr v*
　[T]
　infml to kill someone 〔非正式〕殺死〔某人〕
　They've threatened to do him in if he tells the police anything. 他們威脅説，如果他報警就殺了他。

do sbdy **out of** sthg *phr v*
　[T]
　infml to cause someone to lose something by cheating them 〔非正式〕向〔某人〕騙取〔某物〕:
　old people being done out of their savings 被人騙走存款的老人

do sthg ↔ **up** *phr v*
　[T]
　1 to fasten something 扣好〔鈕扣〕; 繫上〔鞋帶〕; 拉上〔拉鏈〕:
　Do your buttons up. 把你的鈕扣扣好。 | *I can't do up my shoelaces.* 我無法繫上鞋帶。
　2 to repair and improve an old building 修理; 整修:
　They've done their house up beautifully. 他們把他們的房子裝修得很漂亮。 | *old barns that have been done up and sold as houses* 經過整修並作為住宅出售的舊穀倉
　3 to wrap something 包紮, 包裹, 捆紮:
　The present was done up in yellow wrapping paper. 禮物用黃色包裝紙包好。

do with *phr v*
　[T]
　1 could do with to need or want something 需要; 想要:
　I could do with a drink. 我想喝杯飲料。 | *That car could do with a good wash!* 那輛車需要好好洗一洗!
　2 what have you done with…? = where have you put…? 你把…放到哪兒去了?
　"What have you done with the scissors?" "I've put them in the drawer." "你把剪刀弄到哪兒去了?" "我把它放在抽屜裡了。" | *What did Mark do with the shopping?* 馬克把買來的東西放在哪兒了?
　3 to do with concerned with something or someone 與〔某人或某物〕有關:
　I don't know exactly what his job is, but it's something to do with computers. 我並不確切地知道他幹甚麼工作，但那工作與電腦有關。 | *Keep out of this dispute. It's nothing to do with you.* 別捲入這場爭論，這與你無關。

do without sthg *phr v*
　[T]
　to continue to live or do something without having a particular thing 沒有…也行; 無需:
　I couldn't do without my car. 我沒有自己的車子不行。 | *If there are no biscuits in the house, you'll just have to do without.* 如果家裡沒有餅乾，你就只好將就了。

do² *n*

dos or do's
　infml 〔非正式〕
　1 a big party 聚會; 宴會:
　They're having a big do at a hotel in town. 他們在城裡的一家旅館舉行盛大宴會。
　2 dos and don'ts things that you must do and things that you must not do 該做的事和不該做的事; 規定; 注意事項:
　Doctors are giving out lists of dos and don'ts for people wanting to lose weight. 醫生在為想減肥的人開飲食單，規定哪些該吃、哪些不該吃。

person singular present tense of DO ☆ DO 的第三人稱單數現在式

doesn't /'dʌznt; 'dʌzənt/ short for 縮約式 = "does not": *He doesn't know why.* 他不知道為甚麼。 | *She likes it, doesn't she?* 她喜歡它，不是嗎？ | *Doesn't he know the way?* 他不知道那種方法嗎？

⋆**dog¹** /dɔg; dɒg/ *n* **1** an animal kept as a pet in some countries, and sometimes used for hunting or for guarding houses 狗; 犬; 獵狗: *He's taken the dog for a walk.* 他在帶狗散步。 **2** a male dog or fox 公狗; 雄狐 **3 a dog in a manger** a person who does not want something but still stops others from having or enjoying it 不願讓別人享用自己並不需要的東西的人，佔着茅坑不拉屎的人 **4 a dog's life** a very unhappy life 痛苦不堪的生活 **5 go to the dogs** to become ruined 毀滅; 垮台; 完蛋: *"This country's going to the dogs!" said the old man.* "這個國家快完蛋了！" 那老頭說道。 **6 not have a dog's chance** *infml* to have no chance at all 〔非正式〕一點機會也沒有; 毫無希望

dog² *v* **-gg-** [T] **1** to follow someone closely 尾隨, 跟蹤〔某人〕 **2** to affect someone continuously 困擾, 折磨〔某人〕: *We were dogged by bad luck.* 倒霉的事屢纏着我們。

dog col·lar /'· ·/ *n* a priest's round white collar 〔非正式〕〔牧師穿的〕白色圓領

dog-eared /'··/ *adj* looking old and much used (used of books and papers) 折角的, 翻舊了的〔指書和文件〕

dog·ged /'dɔgid; 'dɒgɪd/ *adj* refusing to give up in spite of difficulty or opposition 頑強的; 頑固的; 固執的 **–doggedly** *adv*

dog·ge·rel /'dɔgərəl; 'dɒgərəl/ *n* [U] poetry not usually intended to be serious 打油詩

dog·gy /'dɔgi; 'dɒgi/ *n* **doggies** (also 又作 **doggie**) a dog (used by and to small children) 小狗〔用作兒語〕

dog·house /'dɔg,haʊs; 'dɒghaʊs/ *n* **in the doghouse** *infml* being disapproved of because you have done something wrong 〔非正式〕失寵; 丟臉

dog·ma /'dɔgmə; 'dɒgmə/ *n* [C;U] an important belief or set of beliefs that people are often expected to accept without questioning 教義; 教理; 信條; 教條: *church dogma* 宗教教義 | *Marxist dogma* 馬克思主義的信條

dog·mat·ic /dɔg'mætik; dɒg'mætɪk/ *adj* holding or expressing your beliefs very strongly and expecting other people to accept them without question 固執己見的; 武斷的: *He had a very dogmatic manner.* 他的態度非常武斷。 **–dogmatically** /-kli; -kli/ *adv*

dogs·bod·y /'dɔgz,bɑdi; 'dɒgz,bɒdi/ *n* **dogsbodies** *BrE infml* a person in a low position who has to do the least interesting work 〔英式, 非正式〕勤雜工: *I'm just the dogsbody in this office.* 我在這個辦公室裡不過是個打雜的。

do·ing¹ /'duɪŋ; 'duːɪŋ/ the present participle of DO ☆ DO 的現在分詞

doing² *n* **1** [U] something that a person has done 所做的事: *This must be your doing.* 這一定是你幹的事。 **2 doings** [pl] *infml* activities 〔非正式〕活動: *It's a programme about the daily doings of a vet and his family.* 這是關於一個老兽和他家人日常活動的節目。

do-it-your·self /,· ··'·/ *n* see 見 DIY

dol·drums /'dɑldrəmz; 'dɒldrəmz/ *n* **in the doldrums** *infml* 〔非正式〕 **a** quiet, with not much happening (used of business) 蕭條時期; 停滯〔指工商業〕 **b** in a sad state of mind 憂悶; 消沉

dole¹ /dol; dəʊl/ *n* **1 the dole** *BrE infml* money that you receive from the government because you are unemployed 〔英式, 非正式〕〔政府的〕失業救濟金 **2 on the dole** receiving money from the government because you are unemployed 領取〔政府的〕失業救濟金: *I've been on the dole for six months.* 我領失業救濟金已有六個月了。

dole² *v* **doled, doling**

dole sthg ↔ **out** *phr v infml* [T] to give something out in small shares, especially money or food 〔非正式〕少量發放〔尤指金錢或食物〕: *Shall I dole the soup out?* 我來把湯分給大家好嗎？

dole·ful /'dolfəl; 'dəʊlfəl/ *adj* unhappy or in low spirits 令人苦惱的; 令人沮喪的: *She gave me a doleful look.* 她向我苦惱地望了一眼。 **– dolefully** *adv*

doll¹ /dɑl; dɒl/ *n* a small figure of a person, for a child to play with 玩偶; 玩具娃娃

doll² *v*

doll sbdy ↔ **up** *phr v* [T] to make your own or someone else's appearance attractive, perhaps too much or in a way that is not honest 把〔自己或別人〕打扮得花枝招展〔漂漂亮亮〕: *She was all dolled up to go to a party.* 她打扮得花枝招展去參加聚會。

⋆**dol·lar** /'dɑlə; 'dɒlər/ *n* **1** a standard of money, as used in the US, and some other countries; the sign for it is $ and it is worth 100 cents. 元〔美國和其他一些國家的貨幣單位; 符號為$, 幣值相當於一百分〕 **2** a piece of paper or a coin of this value 一元紙幣; 一元硬幣

dol·lop /'dɑləp; 'dɒləp/ *n infml* a large spoonful of sticky food 〔非正式〕一大匙〔黏性食物〕; 一團, 一塊: *a dollop of mashed potato* 一份馬鈴薯〔土豆〕泥

dol·ly /'dɑli; 'dɒli/ *n* **dollies** a DOLL (used by and to small children) 洋娃娃〔用作兒語〕

dol·phin /'dɑlfin; 'dɒlfɪn/ *n* an intelligent sea-animal two to three metres long, which swims about in a group with others 海豚

do·main /do'men; də'meɪn/ *n* **1** an area of activity, interest, or knowledge 〔活動、興趣或知識的〕領域, 範圍: *This problem lies outside the domain of medical science.* 這個問題超出了醫學領域。 **2** *old fash* the land

D

owned or controlled by one person or a government 《老式》領土; 領地

dome /dom; dom/ n a rounded roof on a building or room 圓屋頂, 穹頂

domed /domd; dəomd/ adj having a rounded roof 有穹頂的

★**do·mes·tic¹** /də'mestɪk; də'mɛstɪk/ adj relating to the house, home, or family 家的; 家庭的; 家務的: *Don't neglect your domestic responsibilities.* 不要忽略你的家庭責任。 **2** skilled at housework or taking pleasure in home life 善於做家務的; 喜愛家庭生活的: *I'm afraid I'm not very domestic.* 我恐怕我不太會料理家務。 **3** not wild (used of animals) 非野生的, 馴養的(指動物): *The sheep is a domestic animal.* 羊是一種家畜。 **4** relating to your own country or some particular country 本國的, 國內的: *the government's domestic policies* 政府的國內政策 | *the domestic news followed by the foreign news* 國際新聞之後的國內新聞 –**domestically** /-klɪ; -kli/ adv

domestic² n a servant who works in a house 家僕; 傭人

do·mes·ti·cate /də'mestə,ket; də'mɛstɪ,keɪt/ v **domesticated, domesticating** [T] **1** to make an animal able to live with people and serve them, especially on a farm 馴養〔動物〕 **2 be domesticated** to enjoy and be interested in home life and duties 使喜歡家庭生活; 使關心家務 –**domestication** /də,mestə'keʃən; də,mɛstɪ'keɪʃən/ n [U]

do·mes·tic·i·ty /,domes'tɪsɪtɪ; ,doumɛs'tɪsəti/ n [U] home or family life 家庭生活

dom·i·cile /'daməsl; 'dɒmɪsaɪl/ n fml the place where a person lives or is considered to live for official purposes 《正式》住處; 住所

dom·i·nance /'damənəns; 'dɒmɪnəns/ n [U] importance, power, or controlling influence 優勢; 支配(地位); 控制力: *Their dominance of the market is challenged by these new products.* 他們的市場優勢受到這些新產品的挑戰。

★**dom·i·nant** /'damənənt; 'dɒmɪnənt/ adj most important 最重要的: *The United States is the dominant partner in the alliance.* 美國是聯盟中最重要的夥伴。 **2** very noticeable, often because of being high 高聳的; 居高臨下的: *The castle was in a dominant position overlooking a bend in the river.* 城堡居高臨下, 俯視河流的彎道。 **3** liking to control other people 喜歡支配〔別人〕的: *My sister had a very dominant nature.* 我姐姐生性喜歡支配別人。

★**dom·i·nate** /'damə,net; 'dɒmɪneɪt/ v **dominated, dominating 1** [I;T] to have controlling power over someone or something 支配; 統治; 控制: *The big banks dominate industry.* 這幾家大銀行控制着工業。 | *a dominating personality* 喜歡支配別人的性格 **2** [T] to have the most important place or posi-

tion in something 處於支配地位; 佔首要位置: *The earthquake dominated the news for several days.* 好幾天的新聞都是地震的消息。 **3** [T] to look over something from a high position 聳立於; 俯瞰: *The castle dominated the whole town.* 城堡俯瞰全城。 –**domination** /,damə'neʃən; ,dɒmɪ'neɪʃən/ n [U]

dom·i·neer·ing /,damə'nɪrɪŋ; ,dɒmɪ'nɪərɪŋ/ adj showing a desire to control others, usually without any consideration of their feelings or wishes 盛氣凌人的; 專橫跋扈的

do·min·ion /də'mɪnjən; də'mɪnjən/ n **1** [U] fml the power or right to rule 《正式》統治權; 管轄權: *Alexander the Great held dominion over a large area.* 亞歷山大大帝統治過遼闊的地域。 **2** [C] the land held in complete control by one person, ruler, or government 領土; 版圖: *the King's dominions* 國王的版圖 **3** [C] a self-governing nation of the British COMMONWEALTH 英聯邦自治領: *the dominion of Canada* 加拿大自治領

dom·i·no /'damə,no; 'dɒmɪ,nəʊ/ n **dominoes** one of a set of small flat pieces of wood or plastic with a different number of spots on each, used for playing a game called **dominoes** 西洋骨牌; 多米諾骨牌

don¹ /dan; dɒn/ v **-nn-** old fash [T] to put on a piece of clothing 《老式》穿上〔衣服〕

don² n a teacher at a university, especially at Oxford or Cambridge 〔尤指牛津大學或劍橋大學的〕大學教師

do·nate /'donet; dəʊ'neɪt/ v **donated, donating** [I;T] to make a gift of something to someone for a good purpose 捐贈; 贈送: *The school donated £500 to a local charity.* 學校向當地慈善機構捐了五百英鎊。

do·na·tion /do'neʃən; dəʊ'neɪʃən/ n [C;U] a gift made for a good purpose 捐贈物; 贈品: *She made a generous donation of £1000 to the Children's Hospital.* 她向兒童醫院慷慨捐款一千英鎊。

done¹ /dan; dʌn/ the past participle of DO ☆ DO 的過去分詞

done² adj **1** [never before a noun 不能用於名詞前] finished 完成的; 結束的: *The job's nearly done.* 這項工作快完成了。 **2 Done!** = I accept 行! 好!: *"I'll give you £5 for it." "Done!"* "我願出五英鎊把它買下。" "一言為定!" **3 done for** /'··/ (also 又作 **done in** /,·'·/) infml very tired 《非正式》累壞的; 疲力竭的: *I feel completely done in!* 我感到累極了! **4 done for** dead or about to die 不中用的; 完蛋的: *The prisoner is done for.* 那囚犯快斷氣了。 **5 not done** not socially acceptable 不合乎規矩的; 不得體的: *It isn't done to call your teachers by their first names.* 對老師直呼其名是不禮貌的。

don·key /'daŋkɪ; 'dɒŋki/ n **1** a grey or brown animal like a horse, but smaller and with longer ears 驢 **2 donkey's years** a very long time 很久; 多年: *I've known her for* *donkey's years.* 我認識她已有多年了。

don·key·work /'dɑŋkɪwɜ˞k; 'dɔŋkiwɜːk/ *n* [U] *BrE infml* the hard uninteresting part of a piece of work〔英式, 非正式〕單調乏味的苦差事: *Why do I always have to do the donkeywork?* 為甚麼總讓我做那種單調乏味的苦差事?

do·nor /'donə˞; 'dəunə⁽ʳ⁾/ *n* **1** a person who makes a gift of something to someone for a good purpose 贈送人; 捐贈者 **2** a person who allows some of their blood or a part of their body to be used for medical purposes 供血者; 捐獻器官者: *a blood donor* 捐血者 | *a kidney donor* 腎臟捐獻者

don't /dont; dəunt/ *short for* 縮約式 = "do not": *You know him, don't you?* 你認識他, 是嗎?

doo·dle /'dudl; 'duːdl/ *v* **doodled, doodling** [I] to draw things like lines or figures while you are thinking about something else〔心不在焉地〕亂塗; 亂畫 **–doodle** *n*

doom /dum; duːm/ *n* [C;U] a terrible fate which you cannot avoid 厄運: *A sense of doom overwhelmed me.* 一種厄運感使我不知所措。

doomed /dumd; duːmd/ *adj* unable to avoid a terrible fate 難逃厄運的; 命中注定的: *The plan was doomed to failure.* 那個計劃注定要失敗。 | *the doomed ship* 難逃厄運的船舶

★**door** /dor; dɔː⁽ʳ⁾/ *n* **1** a movable flat surface that opens and closes the entrance to a building, room, piece of furniture, or vehicle 門: *the kitchen door* 廚房門 | *Close the door to the kitchen, will you?* 把廚房門關上, 好嗎? | *There's someone at the front door; can you answer it please.* 有人敲前門, 請你去開門吧。 | *Have you locked the back door?* 你把後門鎖上了嗎? | *He slammed the car door angrily.* 他氣得砰地一聲關上了車門。 | *Thank you for coming, Mr Jackson. My secretary will show you to the door.* 感謝您的光臨, 傑克遜先生。我的祕書會送您到門口的。 –see pictures on pages 209 and 729 見 209 和 729 頁彩圖 **2** an opening for a door 出入口; 門口: *She stepped through the door.* 她從那門口進來。 **3 be on the door** *infml* to have a duty at the entrance to a theatre or event such as collecting tickets〔非正式〕在門口值勤〔如收戲票〕 **4 door to door: a** from the starting point to the finishing point of a journey 從〔旅途的〕起點到終點: *It's 110 kilometres door to door.* 全程有一百一十公里。 **b** from one building to the next building 挨家挨戶地: *We went from door to door collecting money for charity.* 我們挨家挨戶地募集慈善捐款。 | *a door-to-door salesman* 挨戶推銷的售貨員 **5 next door to** in the building or room next to something 在…隔壁: *His office is next door to his secretary's.* 他的辦公室在祕書那間的隔壁。

door·bell /'dor,bɛl; 'dɔːbel/ *n* a bell at the front door of a house which you ring when you go to visit someone 門鈴

door·knob /'dor,nɑb; 'dɔːnob/ *n* a round handle on a door to open it with 球形門把手

door·mat /'dor,mæt; 'dɔːmæt/ *n* a mat placed in front of or inside a door for cleaning your shoes on〔擦蹭鞋底的〕門口地墊; 擦鞋墊

door·step /'dor,stɛp; 'dɔːstep/ *n* **1** a step in front of an outer door 門前的台階 –see picture on page 729 見 729 頁彩圖 **2 on your doorstep** very close to where you live or are staying 在某人住所〔逗留處〕近旁

door·way /'dor,we; 'dɔːwei/ *n* an opening at the door into a building or room 門口; 出入口: *She stood in the doorway, unable to decide whether or not to go in.* 她站在門口, 拿不定主意是否進去。

dope¹ /dop; dəup/ *n infml*〔非正式〕 **1** [U] an illegal drug, especially MARIJUANA 毒品〔尤指大麻〕; 麻醉劑 **2** [C] a stupid person 笨蛋; 蠢貨

dope² *v* **doped, doping** [T] *infml* to give a drug to a person or an animal to change their behaviour〔非正式〕給〔人或動物〕服麻醉劑〔興奮劑〕: *The horse won the race but it had been doped.* 雖然那匹馬贏得了比賽, 但是牠服用過興奮劑。

dop·ey /'dopi; 'dəupi/ *adj* **dopier, dopiest** *infml*〔非正式〕(also 又作 **dopy**) **1** slow, sleepy, and unable to think clearly 昏昏欲睡的: *I'm always a bit dopey before breakfast.* 我早餐前總是感到昏昏沉沉的。 **2** rather stupid 愚蠢的

dorm /dɔrm; dɔːm/ *n* see 見 DORMITORY

dor·mant /'dɔrmənt; 'dɔːmənt/ *adj* **1** not active or growing 不活動的; 休眠的: *a dormant volcano* 休眠火山 | *Most plants lie dormant in winter.* 大多數植物在冬天呈休眠狀態。 **2** not producing any effects 不起作用的: *Opposition to the new motorway remained dormant because there was no organized campaign against it.* 由於沒有有組織的運動起來抗議, 新建高速公路的反對意見仍然不起作用。

dor·mi·to·ry /'dɔrmə,tori; 'dɔːmᵻtəri/ *n* **dormitories** (also 又作 **dorm** *infml*〔非正式〕) **1** a large room for sleeping in, containing a number of beds 大寢室; 宿舍: *a school dormitory* 學校宿舍 **2** *AmE* a building in a college or university where students live and sleep〔美式〕〔學院的或大學的〕學生宿舍樓

dor·mouse /'dɔr,maus; 'dɔːmaus/ *n* **dormice** /-mais; -mais/ a small field mouse which sleeps through the winter 榛睡鼠

dor·sal /'dɔrsl; 'dɔːsəl/ *adj* [only before a noun 只用於名詞前] *tech* of the back part of a fish or animal〔術語〕〔魚或動物〕背部的; 背面的: *That fish has a large dorsal fin.* 那魚有一個大背鰭。

dos·age /ˈdosɪdʒ; ˈdəʊsɪdʒ/ *n* an amount of medicine to be taken over a period of time 〔藥物的〕劑量: *The required dosage is two tablets daily.* 規定劑量為每天兩片(藥)。

dose¹ /dos; dəʊs/ *n* **1** an amount of medicine to be taken at one time 〔藥物的〕一次劑量；一服: *Take one dose, three times a day.* 日服三次，每次服一劑。**2** a period of experiencing something unpleasant 〔不愉快經歷的〕一場；一次: *Your son needs a dose of hard work, if you ask me!* 如果你問我的話，我覺得你兒子需要找份苦差來做!

dose² *v* **dosed, dosing** [T] (also 又作 **dose** sbdy ↔ **up**) to give an amount of medicine to someone 給〔某人〕服(一定劑量的)藥

doss /dɑs; dɒs/

doss down *phr v* [I] *BrE infml* to sleep in a place which is convenient but uncomfortable 〔英式，非正式〕〔在方便但不舒適的地方〕睡覺: *It was too late to go home so he dossed down on the floor.* 要回家已太晚，所以他就在地板上睡了一夜。

dos·si·er /ˈdɑsɪˌe; ˈdɒsɪeɪ/ *n* a set of papers containing detailed information 全套檔案: *The secret police keep dossiers on all foreign journalists.* 祕密警察對所有外國記者都存有檔案。

dot¹ /dɑt; dɒt/ *n* **1** a small round mark 小圓點: *a dot on the letter i* 字母"i"上的小圓點 **2 on the dot** *infml* at the exact point in time 〔非正式〕準時: *The three o'clock train arrived on the dot.* 三點鐘那班火車準時到達。

dot² *v* **-tt-** [T] **1** to mark something with a dot 以小圓點標出〔某物〕 **2 be dotted with** to have things scattered over an area 佈滿；點綴: *a lake dotted with boats* 密佈着小船的湖面

do·tage /ˈdotɪdʒ; ˈdəʊtɪdʒ/ *n* **in your dotage** weak in your mind because of old age 年邁昏瞶: *Don't keep on telling me the same thing — I'm not in my dotage yet, you know!* 別老是跟我嘮叨同一件事 —— 你知道我還沒有年老糊塗!

dote /dot; dəʊt/ *v* **doted, doting, dote on someone** to love and care for someone very much, especially in a way that seems foolish to other people 溺愛[寵愛]某人: *He absolutely dotes on his youngest son.* 他特別溺愛他的小兒子。

dot·ing /ˈdotɪŋ; ˈdəʊtɪŋ/ *adj* [only before a noun 只能用於名詞前] showing great love and care for someone 溺愛的；寵愛的: *a doting husband* 寵愛妻子的丈夫 **–dotingly** *adv*

dot·ty /ˈdɑti; ˈdɒti/ *adj* **dottier, dottiest** *infml* behaving in a strange way 〔非正式〕〔行為〕古怪的

★**doub·le¹** /ˈdʌbl; ˈdʌbəl/ *adj* **1** twice the usual size 兩倍的；加倍的: *He asked for a double whisky.* 他要了一杯雙份的威士忌酒。**2** made up of two things or two parts 由兩樣東西或兩個部分組成的；雙的: *We put a double lock*

on the door. 我們給門上了雙重鎖。**3** made for two people 供兩人用的；雙人的: *a double bed* 雙人牀 | *We booked a double room at the hotel.* 我們在旅館訂了一個雙人房間。**4 see double** to see two things instead of one 把一樣東西看成了兩樣

double² *n* **1** [U] something that is twice as large as something else 兩倍；雙倍(的量、數): *Normally it only costs £3 to get in, but because it was a Sunday I had to pay double.* 平時只花三英鎊即可入場，但由於是星期日，我得付兩倍的錢。**2** [C] a drink of something such as WHISKY which is twice as large as a normal drink 一杯雙份的酒〔如威士忌〕: *I'll have a brandy — a double, please.* 我想喝白蘭地，請來一杯雙份的。**3** [C] someone who looks very much like another person 極相似的人: *I was sure it was Jane I saw in the pub last night, but perhaps it was her double.* 我肯定昨晚在酒店裡看到的人是簡，但也許是個和她長得極為相似的人。**4 doubles** [pl] a game of something such as tennis in which two pairs of players play against each other 雙打〔如網球〕**5 at the double, on the double** very fast 快速地；趕緊地: *Now go and tidy your room at the double!* 現在趕緊去把你的房間整理一下!

double³ *predeterminer* twice as much 雙倍: *The recipe said two cupfuls of milk, but I used double that amount.* 按照烹飪法的說明是用兩杯牛奶，但我用了雙倍份量。| *His weight is double what it was.* 他現在的體重是過去的兩倍。

double⁴ *v* **doubled, doubling 1** [I] to become twice as large as before 變成兩倍；增一倍: *The price of coal has doubled over the last ten years.* 煤的價格在過去的十年內增加了一倍。**2** [T] to make something twice as large as before 使〔某物〕加倍；把〔某物〕增一倍: *The company has managed to double its profits this year.* 公司設法使今年的利潤提高一倍。

double as sthg *phr v* [T] to have something as a second job or a second use 兼任；兼作: *She's the secretary really, but she doubles as the receptionist.* 她確實是祕書，但還兼任接待員。| *The sofa doubles as a bed.* 這沙發還可當牀用。

double back *phr v* [I] to return along the path or road that you have just come along 循原路折回: *He must have set off along this path and then doubled back to confuse us.* 他一定是出發沿着這條路走，然後又循原路折回，把我們弄糊塗了。

double up *phr v* **1** [I] to bend at the waist, usually because you are in pain or laughing a lot 〔常因疼痛或大笑而〕躬身；彎腰: *We all doubled up with laughter.* 我們都笑得直不起腰來。**2 be doubled up** to be bent at the waist, usually because you are in pain or laughing a lot 〔因疼痛或大笑而〕使彎着身子: *He was doubled up with the pain.* 他痛得

彎下了身子。

double-bar·relled /ˌ··'···◂/ *adj* (**double-barreled** *AmE*〘美式〙) **1** having two barrels fixed side by side (used of a gun) 雙管的〔指槍〕 **2** *BrE* having two parts which are joined by a HYPHEN (used of family names)〘英式〙由連字號相連的兩部分組成的; 複姓的〔指姓氏〕

double-breast·ed /ˌ·· '···◂/ *adj* having two wide parts at the front that cross over each other, and a double row of buttons (used of a coat or JACKET) 有雙排鈕扣的〔指大衣或茄克衫〕

double-check /ˌ·· '·/ *v* [I;T; + that] to examine something twice for exactness, safety, or quality 複查〔某事〕; 複核: *She went back to the house to double-check that the front door had been locked.* 她回到屋子去再查看一下前門是否已鎖上了。

double-cross /ˌ·· '·/ *v* [T] *infml* to cheat a person even though you have encouraged them to trust you 〘非正式〙欺騙; 出賣 – **double cross** *n*

double-deck·er /ˌ·· '···◂/ *n* having two levels 雙層〔結構〕: *a double-decker bus* 雙層公共汽車 | *a double-decker sandwich* 雙層三明治

double-dutch /ˌ·· '·/ *n* [U] *BrE* speech or writing that you cannot understand at all (a word which is often used in a humorous way) 〘英式〙難以理解的言語〔文字〕〔幽默用詞〕: *All this jargon is double-dutch to me!* 我一點兒也聽不懂這些行話!

double-glaze /ˌ·· '·/ *v* **double-glazed, double-glazing** [T] to fit a window with an additional sheet of glass in order to keep a building warmer or quieter〔為房子的保暖或隔音〕給〔窗子〕安裝雙層玻璃 –**double-glaz-ing** *n*

double-joint·ed /ˌ·· '···◂/ *adj* having body joints which allow you to bend easily either backwards or forwards 有雙關節的; 關節能前後彎的

double-quick /ˌ·· '·◂/ *adj, adv infml* very quick〘非正式〙急速的: *Get the doctor double-quick!* 趕快去請醫生!

doub·let /ˈdʌblɪt; 'dʌblɪ̩t/ *n* a short tight-fitting piece of clothing that men used to wear in former times〔舊時〕男用緊身上衣

doub·ly /ˈdʌbli; 'dʌbli/ *adv* **1** to twice the degree 加倍地: *You've got to be doubly careful when you're driving in fog.* 你在霧中開車一定要加倍小心。 **2** in two ways 兩方面地; 雙重地

doubt¹ /daʊt; daʊt/ *v* **1** [T; +(that)] not in progressive forms 不能用於進行式] to consider something to be unlikely 認為〔某事〕不大可能: *She may have remembered, but I rather doubt it.* 她或許還記在心上, 但我認為可能性不大。| *I doubt that John will come.* 我不大相信約翰會來。 **2** [T not in progressive forms 不能用於進行式] not to have confidence in 懷疑; 不信任: *I doubt his honesty.* 我對他的誠實表示懷疑。| *How could you ever doubt me?* 怎麼你從來不信任我? –**doubter** *n*

doubt² *n* **1** [C;U] a feeling of uncertainty of belief or opinion 懷疑; 疑惑; 疑問: *There is some doubt whether John will come.* 約翰是否會來還很難說。| *I've no doubt at all who did it.* 這事是誰幹的, 我心裡有數。| *There's no doubt that the plan will succeed.* 毫無疑問這計劃一定會實現。| *He says he can cure me, but I still have my doubts* **about** *it.* 他說他能治好我的病, 但我還是對此表示懷疑。 **2 be in doubt; be open to doubt** (used of a situation) to be in a condition of uncertainty 〔指形勢〕不能肯定的; 不確定的: *The whole matter is still in doubt.* 整個事件的發展仍未見分曉。 **3 no doubt** almost certainly 無疑地; 很可能: *No doubt he'll resign.* 他必定會辭職。| *"I expect Sally will tell him." "No doubt."* "我想賽莉會告訴他的。" "毫無疑問。" **4 without doubt** certainly 無疑地; 確實地: *That was without doubt the worst movie I've ever seen!* 那無疑是我看過的最糟糕的一部電影!

■ **USAGE** 用法: **1** Note that in the following positive sentences **doubt** is followed by **whether** or **as to whether** ☆ 在下列肯定句中, **doubt** 後面跟 **whether** 或者 **as to whether**: *There is some doubt (as to) whether he'll come.* 他是否會來還很難說。| *I have a small doubt as to whether he is suitable for the job.* 他是否適合做這份工作我有點懷疑。 But in the following negative sentences **no doubt** is followed by **that** ☆ 但在下列否定句中, **no doubt** 後面要跟 **that**: *There is no doubt that he'll come.* 他肯定會來的。| *I have no doubt that he is the best person for the job.* 我敢肯定他做這份工作最合適。 **2 No doubt** means only "I think" or "I expect" ☆ **No doubt** 只表示"我認為"或者"我想": **No doubt** (= I expect) *we'll meet again some day.* 我想我們總有一天會再見面的。 **Undoubtedly** is a much stronger expression ☆**Undoubtedly** 的語氣要重得多: **Undoubtedly** (= I'm certain) *the government has made a serious error of judgement.* 毫無疑問, 政府犯了嚴重的判斷錯誤。

---

doubt·ful /ˈdaʊtfəl; 'daʊtfəl/ *adj* **1** uncertain 懷疑的; 疑惑的; 不肯定的: *She's very keen on the idea, but I feel very doubtful* **about** *it.* 她對這個想法特別感興趣, 可是我卻疑慮重重。| *I'm doubtful whether they'll agree to this.* 我不能肯定他們是否會對此表示同意。 **2** unlikely 不大可能的; 未必的: *It's doubtful that we'll be home before midnight.* 我們未必能在午夜回到家裡。 **3** probably worthless or dishonest 不中用的; 靠不住的: *a doubtful character* 靠不住的人 **-doubtfully** *adv*

doubt·less /ˈdautlɪs; ˈdautlɪs/ *adv* certainly 無疑地; 肯定地: *John will doubtless say something to make everyone feel welcome.* 約翰肯定會說一些使大家感到愉快的話。

dough /do; dəu/ *n* [U] **1** flour mixed with water ready for baking 〔製麵包、糕點的〕生麵團 **2** *infml AmE* money 〔非正式，美式〕錢

dough·nut /ˈdonət; ˈdəunʌt/ *n* a small round cake fried in fat and covered with sugar 油炸麵圈餅

dour /dur; duər/ *adj* cold and unfriendly 冷酷的; 嚴厲的: *a dour look* 冷酷的表情 – **dourly** *adv*

douse /daus; daus/ *v* **doused, dousing** (also 又作 **dowse**) [T] to pour water over something 往…上潑水

dove[1] /dʌv; dʌv/ *n* a bird of the PIGEON family, often used as a sign of peace 鴿子 〔常作為和平的象徵〕

dove[2] /dov; dəuv/ *AmE* the past tense of DIVE 〔美式〕DIVE 的過去式

dow·dy /ˈdaudi; ˈdaudi/ *adj* **dowdier, dowdiest 1** dull and unfashionable (used of clothes) 單調的; 過時的〔指衣服〕 **2** dull and uninteresting (used of people) 無生氣的; 令人厭煩的〔指人〕 **-dowdily** *adv* **-dowdiness** *n* [U]

down[1] /daun; daun/ *adv, prep* **1** *adv, prep* in or towards a lower place or position, for example towards the floor or the ground 向下; 向地面: *She bent down to kiss the child.* 她彎下腰去吻那小孩。| *She came running down the hill towards us.* 她從小山上向我們跑來。| *Please sit down.* 請坐下。| *I put the parcel down on the table.* 我把包裹放到桌子上。| *Several trees were blown down in the storm.* 好幾棵樹在暴風雨中被吹倒了。| *He's down in the cellar.* 他在下面的地窖裡。–see picture on page 764 見 764 頁彩圖 **2** *adv* in or towards the South 在南方; 向南方: *We're driving down to London tomorrow.* 我們明天開車南下去倫敦。| *She lives down in the South of France.* 她住在法國南部。**3** *adv* written on paper 寫下; 記下: *Did you write down her name?* 你把她的名字寫下了沒有? | *Make sure you get everything down in writing.* 你要確保把一切都記下了。| *Your name's not down on the list.* 你的名字沒有列入名單。**4** *adv* showing decrease 下降; 下跌: *Production has gone down this year.* 今年的產量下降了。| *Can you please turn the radio down a bit?* 請你把收音機的音量調低一點，好嗎? **5** *adv* from the past towards the present 〔從過去〕傳下來: *The title is passed down from father to son.* 頭銜可以父子相傳。**6** **down the road, down the street** further along or at the far end of the road or street 沿着路; 街〔路〕的盡頭: *people walking down the street* 沿街走的人們 | *He lives just*

down the road. 他就住在街的那一頭。**7** **down a river** along a river in the same direction as the current 往河的下游 **8 down to something** even including something which seems small and unimportant 包括一切地; 徹底地: *The event had been very carefully planned, down to the last detail.* 這項活動經過了精心的策劃，連每一個細節都沒漏掉。**9 down to someone** someone's choice or responsibility 某人的選擇〔責任〕: *It's down to you to do it yourself.* 這得靠你自己動手做了。| *It's down to him to decide whether or not to accept the job.* 是否接受這份工作全由他自己決定。**10 down under** in or to Australia or New Zealand 〔非正式〕在〔往〕澳大利亞或新西蘭 **11 down with something** ill with something 有病; 患病: *She's gone down with flu.* 她得了感冒。| *He's down with bronchitis at the moment.* 他現在患有支氣管炎。**12 Down with ...** a phrase used to show that you do not like a person or group of people in power 打倒〔用於表示對某人或當局的憎恨〕: *Down with the Government!* 打倒政府!

down[2] *adj* [never before a noun 不能用於名詞前] **1** sad 沮喪的; 情緒低落的: *I'm feeling a bit down today.* 我今天有點悶悶不樂。**2** showing decrease 下降的; 下跌的: *Our profits are down by 20%.* 我們的利潤下降了百分之二十。

down[3] *v* [T] **1** to drink something quickly 很快喝下〔飲料〕: *She downed her drink and left.* 她匆匆喝下飲料便離開。**2 down tools** *infml* to stop working as a way of showing that you are angry about something 〔非正式〕停工; 罷工: *After the pay negotiations had broken down, many workers simply downed tools and went home.* 工資問題的談判破裂後，許多工人便毫不猶豫地停工回家了。

down[4] *n* [U] fine soft feathers or hair 絨毛; 羽絨 **-downy** *adj*

down-and-out /ˌ···ˈ···◂/ *n* a person who sleeps on the streets because they have no home or money 窮困潦倒的人; 無家可歸的人

down·cast /ˈdaunkæst; ˈdaunkɑːst/ *adj* sad and discouraged 沮喪的; 悲哀的

down·fall /ˈdaunfɔl; ˈdaunfɔːl/ *n* something that causes a successful person to be ruined 衰落; 垮台: *Greed led to his downfall.* 貪婪導致他身敗名裂。

down·grade /ˌdaunˈgred; ˈdaungreɪd/ *v* **downgraded, downgrading** [T] to give a lower position to an employed person or a lower level to a job or plan 使降職; 使降級: *He was downgraded from sergeant to private.* 他從中士降為士兵。

down·heart·ed /ˌdaunˈhartɪd; ˌdaunˈhɑːtɪd◂/ *adj* sad and discouraged 沮喪的; 消沉的

down·hill /ˌdaunˈhɪl; ˌdaunˈhɪl◂/ *adj, adv* **1** sloping or going towards the bottom of a hill 下山的; 下坡的; 向山下: *The road runs*

downhill. 道路向山下伸展。| *downhill skiing* 滑降滑雪 **2** *infml* becoming easier 〔非正式〕容易的; *We've done the hardest part of the job — it's all downhill from now on.* 我們完成了工作最艱巨的部分——從現在起餘下的工作就好做了。**3 go downhill** to become less acceptable or pleasant 走下坡路; 每況愈下: *His work has been going downhill recently.* 近來他的工作越來越差。

Dow·ning Street /ˈdaʊnɪŋ ˌstriːt; ˈdaʊnɪŋ ˌstriːt/ *n* [U + sing/pl verb] the government of Great Britain 英國政府: *talks between Dublin and Downing Street* 愛爾蘭政府和英國政府之間的談判

down·pour /ˈdaʊnpɔː; ˈdaʊnpɔːr/ *n* a heavy fall of rain 傾盆大雨

down·right /ˈdaʊnraɪt; ˈdaʊnraɪt/ *adv infml* thoroughly or completely (used of a bad quality) 〔非正式〕徹頭徹尾的; 完全的; 十足的〔指素質差〕: *She was worse than unfriendly — she was downright rude!* 她豈止不友好——簡直是粗魯透頂!

down·stairs /ˌdaʊnˈsteəz; ˌdaʊnˈsteəz/ *adj, adv* situated on or going towards the ground floor of a house 在樓下; 往樓下: *She carried her suitcase downstairs.* 她提着手提箱下樓去。| *a downstairs bedroom* 樓下的臥室

down·stream /ˌdaʊnˈstriːm; ˌdaʊnˈstriːm/ *adv* moving with the current of a river or stream 順流而下地: *They travelled downstream.* 他們的旅行順流而下。

down-to-earth /ˌ···◂/ *adj* practical and honest 實際的; 務實的; 誠實的: *a very down-to-earth person* 非常務實的人

down·town /ˌdaʊnˈtaʊn; ˌdaʊnˈtaʊn◂/ *adj, adv* to or in the business centre of a town or city 往[在]城鎮商業中心區: *Let's go downtown.* 我們到市中心去吧。| *downtown offices* 鬧市區的辦公室

down·trod·den /ˈdaʊnˌtrɒdn; ˈdaʊnˌtrɒdn/ *adj lit* treated badly or without respect by people in positions of power 〔文〕被蹂躪的, 被壓迫的

down·turn /ˈdaʊntɜːn; ˈdaʊntɜːrn/ *n* a lessening of business activity or production 〔商業或生產的〕衰退; 下降: *the recent unfortunate downturn in car production* 汽車生產最近令人遺憾的下降

down·ward /ˈdaʊnwəd; ˈdaʊnwəd/ *adj* going down 向下的; 下降的; 降低的: *a downward movement of the head* 垂頭的動作 | *the downward movement of prices* 價格下降

down·wards /ˈdaʊnwədz; ˈdaʊnwədz/ *adv* (also 又作 **downward** *AmE* 〔美式〕) going, looking, or facing down 向下地: *The plane moved gently downwards towards the runway.* 飛機緩緩地向跑道降落。| *He lay on the floor face downwards.* 他臉朝下俯臥在地上。| *Inflation seems to be moving downwards.* 通貨膨脹似乎正在回落。

down·wind /ˈdaʊnˈwɪnd; ˌdaʊnˈwɪnd/ *adj, adv* in the same direction as the wind is moving 順風地[的]

down·y /ˈdaʊni; ˈdaʊni/ *adj* **downier, downiest** covered in fine soft feathers or hair 被羽絨覆蓋的; 長着絨毛的

dow·ry /ˈdaʊri; ˈdaʊəri/ *n* **dowries** money or property that a woman brings to her future husband as a gift from her own family 嫁妝

dowse /daʊs; daʊs/ *v* **dowsed, dowsing** –see 見 DOUSE

doze /dəʊz; dəʊz/ *v* **dozed, dozing** [I] to sleep lightly or for a short period of time 打瞌睡; 打盹兒 –**doze** *n*: *I'll just have a little doze.* 我只想小睡一會兒。

doze off *phr v* [I] to go to sleep unintentionally 打盹兒: *I just dozed off for a moment.* 我剛才打了個瞌睡。

*****doz·en** /ˈdʌzn; ˈdʌzn/ *det, n* **dozen** or **dozens** **1** a group of 12 (一)打; 十二個: *a dozen eggs* 一打雞蛋 **2 dozens** *infml* very many 〔非正式〕許多, 很多: *I've been there dozens of times.* 我去過那兒好多次了。

doz·y /ˈdəʊzi; ˈdəʊzi/ *adj* **dozier, doziest 1** sleepy 想睡的; 令人睏倦的: *The heat made me feel dozy.* 那高溫使我昏昏欲睡。**2** *BrE infml* stupid 〔英式〕笨的; 愚蠢的: *a dozy person* 一個愚蠢的人 –**dozily** *adv*

Dr an abbreviation for 〔縮〕= DOCTOR

drab /dræb; dræb/ *adj* dull and uninteresting 單調的; 乏味的: *a drab colour* 暗無光彩的顏色 –**drabness** *n* [U]

*****draft¹** /drɑːft; dræft/ *n* **1** the first rough written form of a plan, letter, speech, or book 草稿; 草案: *I've made a first draft of my speech for Friday.* 我已經為星期五的演講寫了一份初稿。| *a plan still in draft form* 仍是草案形式的計劃 **2** a written order for money to be paid by a bank, especially from one bank to another 〔尤指銀行之間的〕匯票 **3 the draft** *AmE* the act of making people serve in one of the armed forces 〔美式〕徵兵; 服役

draft² *v* [T] **1** to make the first rough written form of a plan, letter, speech, or book 起草; 草擬 **2** *AmE* to make someone serve in one of the armed forces 〔美式〕徵募; 徵召〔某人〕入伍

drafts·man /ˈdrɑːftsmən; ˈdræftsmən/ *n* **draftsmen** /-mən; -mən/ –see 見 DRAUGHTSMAN

draft·y /ˈdrɑːfti; ˈdræfti/ *adj* **draftier, draftiest** –see 見 DRAUGHTY

*****drag¹** /dræg; dræg/ *v* **-gg- 1** [T] to pull a heavy object along a surface slowly and with difficulty 拖, 拉〔重物〕: *He dragged his suitcase along the platform.* 他拖着手提箱沿着月台走。–see picture on page 992 見992頁彩圖 **2** [T; + adv/prep] to pull someone with force 〔使勁地〕拉, 拖: *He dragged her to her feet.* 他使勁把她拉了起來。**3** [I + adv/prep] to move along while touching the ground 在地上拖着行進: *Her long dress dragged in the dust.* 她的長裙在塵土上拖着走。 **4** [I + adv/prep] to move along more slowly than necessary 落後; 拖在後面: *He dragged behind the others.* 他拖在別人後面慢吞吞地走。 **5** [T + adv/prep] *infml* to make someone go somewhere they do not want to 〖非正式〗硬拉〔某人〗; 硬拖: *Why must you drag me out to a concert on a cold night like this?* 你為甚麼一定要在這麼冷的夜晚硬拉我去聽音樂會?

drag on *phr v* [I] to continue for an unreasonably long time 拖延(過久): *The meeting seemed to drag on for hours.* 會議拖得很長, 好像開了好幾個小時。

drag out *phr v* **1** [drag sthg ↔ out] to make something last an unnecessarily long time 使〔某事〕持續過久; 拖延 **2 drag something out of someone** to force someone to say something 強迫某人說出某事: *The police finally dragged the truth out of her.* 警方終於迫使她說出真相。

drag sthg ↔ up *phr v* [T] *infml* to raise a subject unnecessarily 〖非正式〗不必要地提起〔某事〕: *The newspapers keep dragging up the mistakes he made ten years ago.* 報紙不斷提到他十年前犯的錯誤。

drag² *n* **1** [C;U] a heavy, pulling action 拖; 拉: *the drag of the waves* 波浪的拉力〔即阻力〕 **2** [C] something or someone that makes it harder to do something 障礙物; 累贅的人; 阻力: *He felt that his family was a drag on his career.* 他覺得家庭是他事業成功的障礙。 **3** [C] *infml* something dull and uninteresting 〖非正式〗單調乏味的事物: *The party was a drag, so we left early.* 那次聚會很單調乏味, 所以我們很早就走了。 **4** [C] *infml* an act of breathing in cigarette smoke 〖非正式〗吸入一口煙: *He took a quick drag on his cigarette.* 他迅速吸了一口香煙。 **5** *infml* **in drag** wearing a woman's clothing (used of a man) 〖非正式〗穿着女人的衣服〔指男子〕

drag·on /'drægən; 'drægən/ *n* **1** an imaginary fire-breathing animal with wings 龍 **2** *infml* a bad-tempered old woman 〖非正式〗性格暴烈的老婦人

drag·on·fly /'drægən,flar; 'drægənflar/ *n* **dragonflies** a long thin brightly-coloured flying insect 蜻蜓

drain¹ /dren; dren/ *v* **1** [I;T] to make a liquid flow out until there is none left (使)排光; (使)流光: *Drain the water off the vegetables.* 把蔬菜中的水分排去。 | *The rainwater had all drained away.* 雨水都流掉了。 **2** [I;T] to make something gradually become dry as the liquid in it or on it flows away (使)變乾: *They intend to drain the land to make their crops grow better.* 為使莊稼長得更好, 他們打算把那塊地的水排乾。 **3** [I;T] to use up or remove all of something 消耗; 耗盡: *What strength she had left suddenly drained away.* 她剩下的最後一點體力突然耗

盡了。 | *The country is being drained of its best doctors.* 這個國家最優秀的醫生在不斷外流。 **4** [T] to finish drinking something completely 喝乾; 喝光: *She drained the very last drop of her wine.* 她把酒喝得一乾二淨。 | *He drained his glass and left.* 他喝完杯中的酒就走了。 **5 be drained** to be extremely tired or weak 使精疲力竭: *She felt completely drained of all emotion.* 她感到自己的感情都枯竭了。 | *looking tired and drained* 看上去精疲力竭

drain² *n* **1** a pipe which carries water or waste away from a place 排水管; 下水道; 陰溝: *Make sure the drains don't get blocked.* 要確保下水道沒有堵塞。 **2** a metal cover with openings, found in a street, which carries rainwater away 〔帶小孔的金屬〕下水道蓋〔位於街道邊上〕 –see picture on page 729 見 729 頁彩圖 **3** something that empties or uses up something 消耗; 耗竭: *All this spending is a drain on the money I have saved.* 這一切開銷成了耗盡我積蓄的無底洞。 **4 down the drain** *infml* wasted 〖非正式〗揮霍掉; 浪費掉: *He's failed his driving test again — all that money down the drain!* 他又沒有通過駕駛考試——所花的錢都白費了!

drain·age /'drenidʒ; 'drenidʒ/ *n* [U] a system of pipes or ditches used for draining water or other liquids 排水系統; 排水溝: *The crops suffered damage as a result of poor drainage.* 由於排水設施差, 農作物遭受損害。

drain·ing board /'·· ·/ *n* a board next to a SINK in the kitchen where the wet dishes are left to dry 〔洗滌槽邊上的〕滴水板

drainpipe /'dren,parp; 'drempaip/ *n* a pipe which carries waste, usually water, away from buildings, or from the roof of a building into a DRAIN² 排水管; 水落管 –see picture on page 729 見 729 頁彩圖

drake /drek; dreik/ *n* a male duck 雄鴨

dram /dræm; dræm/ *n* a small amount of alcohol 微量的酒

dra·ma /'dramə; 'dramə/ *n* **1** [C] a serious work of literature for the theatre, radio, or television that can be acted or read 戲; 劇; 劇本 **2** [U] the study of plays 戲劇研究: *Do you prefer music or drama?* 你喜歡音樂還是戲劇? **3** [U] a situation which is made up of exciting events 〔由一系列激烈的事件構成的〕戲劇性場面: *the drama of international politics* 國際政治活動的戲劇性場面 | *Their holidays are always full of drama.* 他們的假期總是充滿戲劇性的場面。

dra·mat·ic /drə'mætɪk; drə'mætɪk/ *adj* **1** related to the theatre or to plays 戲劇的; 劇本的: *I'd like to read more of Ibsen's dramatic works.* 我想多看一些易卜生的戲劇作品。 **2** exciting and unusual, like something that could happen in a drama 戲劇性的; 激動人心的: *a dramatic moment* 激動人心的時刻 | *She made a dramatic entrance.* 她的出場富

有感染力。–**dramatically** /-klɪ; klɪ/ adv

dra·mat·ics /drə'mætɪks; drə'mætɪks/ n **1** [U] activities connected with the theatre 戲劇表演[活動]: *He's taken up amateur dramatics.* 他對業餘戲劇活動產生興趣。**2** [pl] behaviour that shows too much feeling 戲劇性行為[指舉止誇張]: *All your dramatics aren't going to make me change my mind.* 你那所有裝腔作勢的舉動改變不了我的主意。

dram·a·tist /'dræmətɪst; 'dræmətɪst/ n a writer of plays 劇作家; 編劇

dram·a·tize /'dræmə,taɪz; 'dræmətaɪz/ v **dramatized, dramatizing** (also 又作 **dramatise** BrE 〖英式〗) **1** [T] to change a book into a play so that it can be acted 把〔書〕改編成戲劇: *His novel has been dramatized for television.* 他的小說已改編成電視劇。**2** [I;T] to present something in a dramatic manner 戲劇性地描述; 把…戲劇化: *Don't dramatize so much — just give us the facts!* 不要渲染誇張, 就把事實告訴我們吧! – **dramatization** /,dræmətə'zeʃən; ,dræmətaɪ'zeɪʃən/ n [C;U]

drank /dræŋk; dræŋk/ the past tense of DRINK ☆ DRINK 的過去式

drape /dreɪp; dreɪp/ v **draped, draping** [T] **1** to cover or decorate something with cloth 〔用布〕披蓋; 裝飾: *a picture of their leader draped with the national flag* 他們領袖的相片上覆蓋着國旗 | *Drape the flag over the picture.* 把旗子覆蓋在畫像上。**2** to make something hang loosely or carelessly 使隨便地懸掛; 使鬆弛地垂下: *He draped his legs over the arm of the chair.* 他懶洋洋地把兩腿搭在椅子的扶手上。

drap·er·y /'dreɪpərɪ; 'dreɪpəri/ n **draperies 1** [C;U] cloth or clothing arranged in folds 打摺的織物[服裝] **2** [U] BrE cloth sold in a shop 〖英式〗布料; 布匹: *the drapery department* 紡織品部

drapes /dreɪps; dreɪps/ n [pl] the usual American word for 〖美式〗= CURTAINS

dras·tic /'dræstɪk; 'dræstɪk/ adj strong, sudden, and extreme 激烈的; 猛烈的; 極端的: *Drastic changes are needed to improve our sales figures.* 為提高我們的銷售額, 有必要進行重大改革。–**drastically** /-klɪ; klɪ/ adv: *His work has changed drastically since his illness.* 自他生病以來, 他的工作表現有了很大的變化。

draught /dræft; drɑːft/ n (**draft** AmE 〖美式〗) **1** [C] a current of air blowing through a room 通風; 氣流: *You may catch cold if you sit in a draught.* 你坐在通風的位置會着涼的。**2** [C] an amount of water or air swallowed or breathed in at one time 一飲的量; 一口吸入的空氣 **3 on draught** kept in a barrel (used of beer) 桶裝的〔指啤酒〕**4 draughts** [U] BrE a game played by two people, each with 12 round pieces, on a board of 64 squares 〖英式〗國際跳棋〔兩人對下, 每一方有十二枚圓形棋子, 在有六十四個

方格的棋盤上進行〕

draughts·man /'drɑːftsmən; 'drɑːftsmən/ n **draughtsmen** /-mɛn; -mən/ (**draftsman** AmE 〖美式〗) **1** a person whose job is to make detailed drawings of all the parts of a new building or machine 〔建築物或機器的〕製圖員 **2** fml a person who draws well 〖正式〗善於繪畫的人

draught·y /'drɑːftɪ; 'drɑːfti/ adj **draughtier, draughtiest** with cold air currents blowing 有穿堂風的; 通風的: *a draughty room* 有穿堂風的房間

★★ **draw¹** /drɔː; drɔː/ v **drew** /druː; druː/, **drawn** /drɔːn; drɔːn/ **1** [I;T] to make pictures using a pencil or pen 〔用鉛筆或鋼筆〕畫; 描繪: *He drew a plan of the building.* 他畫了一幅大樓的平面圖。| *Lines had been drawn all over the photograph.* 照片上畫滿了線條。| *I can't draw very well.* 我不擅長繪畫。**2** [T] to pull something along 拉; 拖: *a cart drawn by a horse* 馬拉的大車 **3** [T] to remove something from a place 取出, 拔出, 抽出〔某物〕: *He drew a wallet from his pocket.* 他從口袋裡取出錢包。| *Suddenly she drew a knife out of her bag.* 她突然從袋子裡拔出一把刀。| *I drew some money out of the bank.* 我從銀行提取了一些存款。**4** [I] fml to move slowly or gradually 〖正式〗緩慢、持續地〕移動; 行進: *The train drew into the station.* 火車徐徐駛入車站。| *The people drew nearer to watch.* 人們漸漸走上前去觀望。| *She drew away from the fire.* 她從大火中退到了一邊。| *Winter was drawing near.* 冬天漸漸降臨。**5** [T] to attract someone 吸引〔某人〕: *The match is expected to draw a very large crowd.* 比賽預計會吸引一大批人。| *I was somehow drawn to her.* 她對我具有某種吸引力。**6** [I;T] to end a game or match with neither side winning 以平局結束比賽: *We drew the game three all.* 我們以三平結束比賽。**7 be drawn into something** to become concerned in something even though you did not want to be 與某事有牽連; 使參與某事〔但並不情願〕: *I was trying not to get drawn into the conflict.* 我盡量不被捲入到那場衝突中去。**8 draw blood** to make someone bleed 使〔某人〕流血: *The dog bit me but didn't draw blood.* 那狗咬了我一口, 但沒出血。**9 draw a conclusion** to come to an idea after consideration 作出結論: *We can all draw our own conclusions from these statistics.* 我們都能從這些統計數字中得出自己的結論。**10 draw breath** fml to breathe 〖正式〗吸氣 **11 draw lots** to decide who should do something by each choosing one from a group of objects; one object is marked in some way and the person who chooses this one will do the thing that is being decided on 抽籤〔以決定誰來做某事〕**12 draw someone's attention to something** to show something to someone, or tell them about it, so that they notice it 令某人

D

注意某事物: *I'd like to draw your attention to the latest unemployment figures.* 我想引起各位對最新失業人數的注意。**13 draw the curtains** to move curtains so that they are open or shut 拉開〔拉上〕窗簾〔門簾〕: *It was getting dark so I drew the curtains.* 天要黑了，所以我拉上了窗簾。**14 draw the line** to state that something is a limit for you 限制; 劃出界限: *I draw the line at stealing.* 偷東西我是不會去幹的。

draw back *phr v* [I] to move away from someone or something 後退; 退開: *The crowd drew back in terror as the building crashed to the ground.* 樓房倒塌時，人羣都驚恐得往後退。

draw in *phr v* [I] **1** to move to one side of the road and stop 開到路邊停下來: *The bus drew in to let the cars pass.* 公共汽車到路邊，讓那汽車通過。**2 the evenings/nights are drawing in** = it is getting darker earlier in the evenings because winter is coming〔因冬天來臨〕天黑得越來越早

draw on sthg *phr v* [T] to use something 憑藉〔某物〕; 依靠; 利用: *Writers have to draw on their imagination and experience.* 作家必須依賴自己的想像力和生活經歷〔來創作〕。

draw out *phr v* **1** [T draw sthg ↔ out] to take money out of a bank account 取出〔存款〕: *I need to draw out £50.* 我需要提取五十英鎊。**2 the days are drawing out** = the days are becoming longer because spring is coming〔因春天來臨〕白晝越來越長

draw up *phr v* **1** [T draw sthg ↔ up] to form and write a plan or an agreement 起草; 擬訂〔計劃或協議〕: *Your solicitor will draw up a contract for you to sign.* 你的律師會起草一份合同讓你簽署。**2** [I] (of a vehicle) to stop〔交通工具〕停下: *A car drew up outside the bank and three men got out.* 一輛汽車在銀行外面停下，三個男人從車裡走出來。**3 draw yourself up** *lit* to stand up straight《文》使自己站直

draw upon sthg *phr v* [T] to use something 憑藉〔某物〕; 依靠; 利用: *We have a large pool of talent that we can draw upon.* 我們有一大批人才可以利用。

draw² *n* **1** a game in which people buy tickets with numbers on; some numbers are then chosen by chance, and the people with those numbers win a prize 抽彩; 抽獎 **2** a result in a game or match in which neither side has won 不分勝負; 平局: *The match ended in a draw.* 比賽以平局結束。

draw·back /ˈdrɔ,bæk; ˈdrɔːbæk/ *n* something which causes a difficulty 缺點; 弊端; 障礙: *The only drawback of the plan is its cost.* 這項計劃的唯一缺點是耗資太大。

drawer /drɔr; drɔːʳ/ *n* a part of a table or desk which slides out so you can put things in or take them out 抽屜: *Put your things away in the drawer.* 把你的東西存放在抽屜裡。

★draw·ing /ˈdrɔɪŋ; ˈdrɔːɪŋ/ *n* **1** [U] the skill of making pictures with a pen or pencil 繪畫〔技巧〕: *She's very good at drawing.* 她擅長繪畫。**2** [C] a picture made with a pen or pencil 圖畫; 素描: *He made a detailed drawing of the scene.* 他畫了一幅精細的風景畫。**3 go back to the drawing board** *infml* to try and think of another and better idea because something has been unsuccessful《非正式》失敗後從頭做起

drawing pin /ˈ·· ,·/ *n* a short pin with a broad flat head, used especially for putting notices on boards or walls 圖釘

drawing room /ˈ·· ·/ *n* *fml* a room where people sit or entertain other people《正式》客廳; 起居室

drawl /drɔl; drɔːl/ *v* [I;T] to speak slowly and unclearly with the vowel sounds lengthened 慢吞吞地說; 拉長腔調講〔話〕 – **drawl**: *a southern drawl* 一種南方人拉長腔調的說話方式

drawn¹ /drɔn; drɔːn/ the past participle of DRAW ☆ DRAW 的過去分詞

drawn² *adj* **1** pulled across 拉上的: *All the curtains were drawn.* 所有的窗簾都拉上了。**2** tired and worried 疲憊的; 憔悴的; 緊張的: *She looked tired and drawn.* 她看上去臉色憔悴、神情緊張。**3** ended with neither side winning (used of games or competitions) 不分勝負的; 成平局的〔指比賽或競賽〕

dread /dred; dred/ *v* **1** [T; + that] to feel great fear or anxiety about something 懼怕〔某事〕; 畏懼; 擔心: *I'm dreading my driving test.* 我在為駕駛考試發愁。| *We all dreaded having to go to the headmaster's office.* 我們都怕去校長辦公室。| *He dreaded that she would find out.* 他很怕她會發現。

□ **USEFUL PATTERNS** 有用句型
to dread something; to dread doing something; to dread that…

2 I dread to think… = it worries me very much when I think about… 我怕去想…; 我想到…就膽顫心驚: *I dread to think what will happen if they ever meet each other again.* 我不敢去想他們一旦重逢會出甚麼事。–**dread** *n*: *her dread of being caught* 她怕被抓住

dread·ful /ˈdredfəl; ˈdredfəl/ *adj* very bad or unpleasant 糟透了的; 極不合意的; 非常討厭的: *What a dreadful noise!* 多討厭的噪音! | *The play last night was absolutely dreadful!* 昨晚的戲實在是糟糕透頂! | *This is dreadful news!* 這消息真令人討厭!

dread·ful·ly /ˈdredfəlɪ; ˈdredfəlɪ/ *adv* extremely 非常; 極其: *I'm dreadfully sorry.* 我感到非常抱歉。

★dream¹ /drim; driːm/ *n* **1** a set of events and feelings that you experience when you are asleep 夢: *She woke up in the middle of a frightening dream.* 她從惡夢中醒來。**2** something that you think about and hope for 理

想; 願望; 夙願: *It was his dream to play football for his country.* 為國家踢足球是他的夙願。| *The huge number of people at the concert was beyond their wildest dreams.* 他們連做夢也沒有想到會有那麼多人來聽音樂會。**3 in a dream** in a state of mind in which you do not pay much attention to the real world 在夢想〔幻想〕中: *John lives in a dream.* 約翰生活在夢幻中。**4 go like a dream** *infml* to work well 〔非正式〕進展順利; 性能極佳: *My new car goes like a dream.* 我的新汽車開起來得心應手。

dream² *v* **dreamed** /drimd; dri:md/ *or* **dreamt** /drɛmt; drɛmt/, **dreaming** [I; + (that)] **1** to have a dream 做夢; 夢見: *I dreamt that I was back at school.* 我夢見自己回到學校讀書。| *What did you dream about last night?* 你昨夜夢見了甚麼? **2** to imagine something 想像〔某事物〕; 幻想: *I never said that! You must have been dreaming.* 我從來沒有說過那種話! 一定是你自己想像出來的。| *I never dreamed I would get the job.* 我從沒幻想過能得到那份工作。**3 wouldn't dream of** = would never do something because you think it is wrong 決不會做〔錯事〕; 做夢也沒有想到會…: *I wouldn't dream of hurting the child.* 我無論如何也不會傷害那孩子。

■ USAGE 用法: For the past tense and the past participle, **dreamed** and **dreamt** are both used in British English, but Americans more often use **dreamed**. ☆ 在英式英語中, **dreamed** 和 **dreamt** 都可用作過去式和過去分詞; 但 **dreamed** 在美式英語中更為常用。

dream sthg ↔ **up** *phr v* [T] *infml* to think of or imagine something surprising or which is not true 〔非正式〕憑空想出〔某事物〕; 虛構出: *My parents are always dreaming up some reason why I can't stay out late.* 我的父母老是憑空想出一些理由, 不讓我夜裡外出。

dream·er /'drimɚ; 'dri:məʳ/ *n* **1** a person who dreams 做夢的人 **2** a person who has impractical ideas or plans 夢想家; 空想家

dreamt /drɛmt; drɛmt/ past tense and past participle of DREAM ☆ DREAM 的過去式和過去分詞

dream·y /'drimi; 'dri:mi/ *adj* **dreamier, dreamiest 1** living more in the imagination than in the real world 整天做白日夢的; 愛空想的 **2** gentle and beautiful 輕柔的; 美妙: *soft dreamy music* 輕柔美妙的音樂 **–dreamily** *adv*

drear·y /'drɪri; 'drɪəri/ *adj* dull and uninteresting 沉悶的; 陰沉的; 乏味的: *Addressing envelopes all the time is dreary work.* 整天要在信封上寫姓名地址是枯燥無味的工作。| *this awful dreary weather* 這陰沉沉的鬼天

氣 **–drearily** *adv* **–dreariness** *n* [U]

dredge /drɛdʒ; drɛdʒ/ *v* **dredged, dredging** [I;T] to use a dredger 挖泥; 〔捕撈船〕撈: *They dredged the lake in their search for the missing child.* 他們在湖中打撈失蹤的孩子。

dredge sthg ↔ **up** *phr v* [T] **1** to find something by using a dredger 〔用捕撈船〕打撈〔某物〕 **2** to talk about something unpleasant that has been forgotten 提起, 翻出〔不愉快的往事〕: *He dredged up all our old quarrels.* 他重新提起了我們過去的那些爭吵。

dredg·er /'drɛdʒɚ; 'drɛdʒəʳ/ *n* (also 又作 **dredge**) a ship used for digging up mud from the bottom of a river 挖泥船

dregs /drɛgz; drɛgz/ *n* [pl] **1** little bits of solid in a liquid that sink to the bottom and are thrown away 沉澱物; 殘渣: *coffee dregs* 咖啡渣 **2** the worst and most useless parts of something 渣滓: *the dregs of society* 社會的渣滓

drench /drɛntʃ; drɛntʃ/ *v* [T] to make something throughly wet 使〔某物〕濕透: *He went out in the storm and got drenched to the skin.* 他出門遇上暴雨, 被淋得渾身濕透。

dress¹ /drɛs; drɛs/ *v* **1** [I] (also 又作 **get dressed**) to put on clothes 穿衣服: *It only took me ten minutes to wash and dress.* 我僅用了十分鐘來洗漱和穿衣。| *I dressed quickly.* 我很快穿好衣服。| *I'm just getting dressed.* 我剛剛在穿衣服。**2 be dressed** to be wearing clothes, often of a particular type 穿着〔某種衣服〕: *I'm not dressed yet.* 我還沒穿好衣服。| *She was dressed in black.* 她穿着黑色衣服。| *He arrived dressed in a suit and tie.* 他身穿西裝和領帶到場。**3** [I] to wear clothes of a particular type 穿特別的衣服: *He dresses to attract attention.* 他穿着特別, 以引起別人注意。| *She dresses well.* 她穿着講究。**4** [I] to put on formal clothes for the evening 穿晚禮服: *We normally dress for dinner.* 我們通常穿禮服赴宴。**5** [T] to put clothes on someone else, especially a child 給〔別人〕穿衣〔尤指孩子〕: *He was busy dressing the baby.* 他忙着給小孩穿衣服。**6** [T] to clean and put a protective covering on a wound 包紮〔傷口〕 **7** [T] to prepare meat or fish for cooking or eating by removing the parts not usually eaten 〔烹調或食用前〕把〔食物〕處理好 **8** [T] to put a mixture of oil and other things over food to improve its taste 在〔食物〕中加作料: *a salad dressed with oil and vinegar* 拌有油和醋的沙拉

■ USAGE 用法: Compare 比較 **dress, get dressed, put on, wear.** We can use **dress, get dressed,** or **put your clothes on** to talk about the action of getting into clothes. ☆ 我們可以用 **dress, get dressed,** 或者 **put your clothes on** 來表示"穿衣"這個動作。**Dress** is the most formal and **put your clothes on** the most informal ☆**dress** 這個詞最正式, **put your clothes on** 最不正式: *I got up and dressed.* | *I got up and got dressed.* | *I got up and put my clothes on.* (我起牀並穿上了衣服。) We use **wear** to talk about the state of having clothes on ☆我們用 **wear** 表示"穿衣"的狀態: *You're wearing a nice tie today.* 你今天戴了一條漂亮的領帶。

dress up *phr v* **1** [I] (usually of children) to wear someone else's clothes for fun 〔常指孩子〕穿別人的衣服鬧着玩, 裝扮 **2** [I] to put on formal clothes 穿上盛裝; 穿上禮服: *Don't bother to dress up.* 不必穿上禮服。**3** [T **dress** sth ↔ **up**] to make something seem different or more attractive 掩飾, 修飾〔某事物〕: *The report was rather short so he dressed it up with some additional details.* 報告很短, 所以他添枝加葉地增加了一些細節。

☆**dress²** *n* **1** [C] a piece of clothing worn by a woman or girl; it covers her body from her shoulder to her knee 連衣裙; 套裙 –see picture on page 210 見 210 頁彩圖 **2** [U] clothing of a certain type 〔某種特定的〕服裝: *Do we have to wear evening dress for this party?* 我們要穿晚禮服參加這次聚會嗎?

dress³ *adj* [only before a noun 只用於名詞前] **1** used for a dress 女服的; 用以做女服的: *dress material* 女服衣料 **2** suitable for a formal occasion (used of clothes) 適於正式場合的〔指衣物〕: *a dress shirt* 禮用內襯衫

dress cir·cle /ˈ· ͵·· / *n* the upper floor in a theatre 〔戲院中〕二樓樓廳的前排座位

dress·er /ˈdrɛsə; ˈdresər/ *n* **1** *BrE* a piece of furniture for holding dishes, with open shelves above and cupboards below 〔英式〕餐具櫃; 碗櫥 **2** *AmE* a chest of drawers, often with a mirror on top 〔美式〕梳妝枱

dress·ing /ˈdrɛsɪŋ; ˈdresɪŋ/ *n* **1** [C;U] a mixture of oil and other things which can be added to food, often SALADS 〔食物〕調料〔常用於拌沙拉〕: *salad dressing* 沙拉調料 | *French dressing* 法式沙拉調料 **2** [C] a covering for a cut or wound 〔用於包紮傷口的〕敷料, 繃帶 **3** [U] the action of putting on your clothes 穿衣, 穿戴; 打扮, 裝束: *She finds dressing difficult since her accident.* 自她出了事故以來, 穿戴也覺得困難。

dressing down /͵·· ˈ·/ *n* angry words spoken when someone has done something wrong 〔因某人做錯事而遭到的〕訓斥: *The children got a good dressing down.* 孩子們被狠狠地訓斥了一頓。

dressing gown /ˈ·· ͵·/ *n* a garment rather like a long loose coat, that you wear before you get dressed 晨衣, 睡袍

dressing ta·ble /ˈ·· ͵··/ *n* a low table with a mirror, usually in a bedroom 梳妝枱

dress·y /ˈdrɛsɪ; ˈdresi/ *adj* **dressier, dress-**

iest suitable for wearing on formal occasions (used of clothes) 適於正式場合穿的〔指衣服〕

drew /druː; druː/ the past tense of DRAW ☆ DRAW 的過去式

drib·ble /ˈdrɪbl; ˈdrɪbəl/ *v* **dribbled, dribbling 1** [I;T] to flow in drops or a thin stream, or to make a liquid flow in this way (使)滴下; (使)細流: *The water dribbled from the tap.* 水從龍頭裡滴下來。| *She dribbled the oil into the mayonnaise.* 她把油滴入蛋黃醬裡。**2** [I] to let SALIVA flow slowly out of your mouth 流口水: *The baby has just dribbled down my blouse.* 孩子剛才淌口水, 弄濕了我的襯衫。**3** [T] to move a ball forward by a number of short kicks or hits 〔向前〕運球; 帶球 **–dribble** *n* [C;U]

dribs /drɪbz; drɪbz/ *n* **dribs and drabs** *infml* small and unimportant amounts 〔非正式〕少量; 點滴: *He's paying me back in dribs and drabs.* 他一點一點地把錢還給我。

dried /draɪd; draɪd/ the past tense and past participle of DRY ☆ DRY 的過去式和過去分詞

dri·er /ˈdraɪə; ˈdraɪər/ *n* –see 見 DRYER

drift¹ /drɪft; drɪft/ *n* **1** [C;U] a general tendency or movement 傾向; 動向; 趨勢: *the drift of young people from the country to the city* 年輕人從鄉下湧向城市的趨勢 **2** [C] a lot of snow or sand blown into a pile by the wind 〔風吹成的〕雪堆, 沙堆: *deep drifts of snow* 厚厚的積雪 **3** a drifting movement 漂動; 漂流: *the drift of the tide* 潮汐 | *the drift of the current* 水流 **4 the drift** the general meaning of something 主旨; 大意: *"Did you understand what he was talking about?" "Well I got the general drift."* "你理解他在説甚麼嗎?" "嗯, 明白大概的意思。"

drift² *v* [I] **1** to float or be moved gently by wind, waves, or currents 漂流; 飄: *They drifted out to sea.* 他們漂往海上去。**2** to pile up under the force of the wind 吹積; 堆積: *The snow was drifting badly and several roads were closed.* 雪堆積得很厲害, 好幾條路被封堵住了。**3** to live without any real aim or purpose 〔無目標或目的地〕活着; 隨波逐流: *She drifts through life taking one job after another.* 她一生渾渾度日, 始終無固定職業。

drift off *phr v* [I] *infml* to go to sleep 去睡覺

drift·er /ˈdrɪftə; ˈdrɪftər/ *n* **1** a person who travels about without any purpose (a word used to express disapproval) 漂流者, 流浪者〔含貶義〕**2** a fishing boat that uses a floating net 漂網漁船

drill¹ /drɪl; drɪl/ *v* **1** [I;T] to make a hole with a drill 打眼, 鑽孔: *to drill for oil* 鑽井勘探石油 | *I drilled a hole in the wood.* 我在木頭上鑽了一個孔。**2** [T] to train people by making them do the same thing many times 操練, 訓練: *The soldiers were thoroughly drilled in how to respond to attack.* 戰士們接受如何

應付對方攻擊的徹底訓練。

drill² n **1** [C] a tool or machine for making holes 鑽頭, 鑽機: a pneumatic drill 風鑽 | a dentist's drill 牙鑽 –see picture on page 958 見 958 頁彩圖 **2** [U] military training and exercises 〔軍事〕操練; 訓練 **3** [C;U] training and instruction in a subject 〔課程的〕訓練; 練習 **4** [C] practice in what to do in a particular situation 演習: a fire drill 消防演習

dri·ly /ˈdraɪlɪ; ˈdraɪlɪ/ adv **dryly** in a way that is amusing, but you do not notice this at first 〔幽默但〕不形於色地

★**drink¹** /drɪŋk; drɪŋk/ v **drank** /dræŋk; dræŋk/, **drunk** /drʌŋk; drʌŋk/, **drinking 1** [I;T] to take a liquid into your mouth and swallow it 喝; 飲: She gave me some water and I drank. 她給我一些水, 我把它喝了。 | She was drinking a cup of tea. 她在喝一杯茶。 **2** [I] to take in alcohol, either regularly or too much 喝酒; 酗酒: He doesn't smoke or drink. 他既不抽煙也不喝酒。 **3 drink to someone, drink a toast to someone** to have an alcoholic drink to wish someone success or happiness 為〔某人的成功或愉快事情〕祝酒: We drank a toast to the bride and groom. 我們為新郎新娘祝酒乾杯。

drink sth ↔ in phr v [T] to listen, see, or smell something with great enjoyment 被〔某物〕迷住; 陶醉於: They drank in the sights and sounds of the city. 他們被城市的景色和喧鬧聲所迷住。

drink up phr v [I;T **drink** sth ↔ **up**] to finish a drink 把...喝完: Drink up. It's time to go home. 喝完吧, 該回家了。 | Drink up your tea before it gets cold. 趁熱把茶喝完。

★**drink²** n **1** [C] a liquid suitable for swallowing 飲料: Can I have a drink of water, please? 請給我來杯水。 **2** [C;U] an alcoholic drink 酒: Would you like another drink? 你要再來一杯酒嗎? | There's no drink in the house. 家裡沒有酒了。 **3** [C] a small quantity of a drink 少量的酒: He took a drink of his beer and thought about what she had said. 他喝了一點啤酒, 思考她說過的話。

drink·er /ˈdrɪŋkə; ˈdrɪŋkə²/ n a person who drinks alcohol, especially too much 飲酒者〔尤指酒徒〕: Her father was a heavy drinker. 她父親是個酒鬼。

drip¹ /drɪp; drɪp/ v **-pp- 1** (of a liquid) to fall in drops 〔液體〕滴下: Water was dripping from the tap. 水從龍頭裡滴下。 **2** to let liquid fall in drops 滴出液體; 滴水: The tap was still dripping. 龍頭還在滴水。

drip² n **1** the action or sound falling in drops 滴落; 滴水聲: All night I heard the drip drip drip of the water. 我徹夜聽到滴滴答答的滴水聲。 **2** an apparatus for putting drops of a liquid directly through a tube into a blood vessel 靜脈輸液my的滴注器 **3** slang a dull person 〖俚〗平庸乏味的人

drip-dry /ˌ· ˈ·◄/ adj drying smooth and needing no ironing (used of clothing) 滴乾

免燙的; 不燙自平的〔指衣服〕: a drip-dry shirt 滴乾免燙的襯衫

drip·ping¹ /ˈdrɪpɪŋ; ˈdrɪpɪŋ/ n [U] fat and juices that have come from meat during cooking 〔炙肉時滴下的〕油滴

dripping² adj (also 又作 **dripping wet**) very wet 濕淋淋的

★**drive¹** /draɪv; draɪv/ v **drove** /droʊv; drəʊv/, **driven** /ˈdrɪvən; ˈdrɪvən/, **driving 1** [I;T] to guide and control a vehicle 駕駛〔車輛〕: She drives well. 她車開得不錯。 | I never learnt to drive a car. 我從未學會過開汽車。 **2** [T; + adv/prep] to take someone somewhere in a vehicle 用車把〔某人〕送到〔某處〕: Can you drive me to the station? 你能開車送我到火車站嗎? **3** [T; + adv/prep] to force animals to move in a particular direction 驅趕〔動物〕: The farmer was driving his cattle along the road. 農夫沿著大路驅趕牛羣。 **4** [T] to provide the power for something 驅動〔某物〕: The engines drive the ship. 引擎驅動輪船。 **5** [T+adv/prep] to force someone into a particular situation, usually unpleasant 驅進, 迫使〔某人處於某種狀態〕: That noise is driving me out of my mind. 那喧鬧聲吵得我心煩意亂。 | It was her pride that drove her to do it. 她是受自尊心的驅使才這樣做的。 | He's driving me mad. 他逼得我發狂。 **6** [T + adv/prep] to hit something very hard so that it moves in a particular direction 打; 敲; 擊: He drove the nail into the wood. 他把釘子釘入木頭。 | She drove the ball 150 metres. 她把球擊出一百五十米。 **7 drive something home** to make something unmistakably clear 使〔正確無誤地〕理解〔某事物〕: He tried to drive it home to her that they had no money. 他盡力使她明白他們身無分文。 **8 what are you driving at?** = what do you mean? 你是甚麼意思? **9 drive someone up the wall/round the bend** to make someone lose their patience and become angry 逼得某人失去耐心; 逼得某人發瘋

drive off phr v **1** [T **drive** sbdy/sthg ↔ **off**] to force someone or something away or back 擊退; 趕跑: He drove off his attackers. 他把攻擊他的人打退了。 **2** [I] to start moving away in a car 驅車離去: He got into the car and drove off. 他坐入汽車便開走了。

★**drive²** n **1** [C] a journey in a vehicle, especially for pleasure 〔尤指為取樂而進行的〕驅車旅行: Let's go for a drive in the country. 我們開車到郊野去兜兜風吧。 **2** [C] (also 又作 **driveway**) a road from a private house to the street 〔從私人住宅通往大街的〕車道: She parks her car in the drive. 她把車停在私人車道上。 –see picture on page 729 見 729 頁彩圖 **3** [C] an act of hitting a ball forcefully in GOLF or tennis so that it covers a long distance 〔高爾夫球或網球的〕擊球 **4** [C] a strong well-planned effort by a group for a particular purpose 有計劃的努力: The club *is having a membership drive.* 俱樂部正在大力發展新會員。 **5** [C] an important natural need which must be fulfilled 本能的需求; 慾望: *People of that age have a strong sex drive.* 那個年齡的人性慾強烈。 **6** [U] a forceful quality of mind that gets things done 魄力; 動力; 積極性: *He lacks the drive to succeed.* 他缺乏辦大事的魄力。 **7** [C;U] the power from the engine of a vehicle to particular wheels to make it move 傳動; 驅使: *This car has front-wheel drive.* 這輛汽車有前輪驅動裝置。

drive-in /'··/ *n* a place that people can use while remaining in their cars 可坐在車上享用的場所 **–drive-in** *adj* [only before a noun 只用於名詞前]: *a drive-in restaurant* 免下車的餐館

driv·el /'drɪvl; 'drɪvəl/ *v* **-ll-** *BrE* 〖英式〗(**-l-** *AmE* 〖美式〗) [I] to talk nonsense 胡説; 説廢話: *What's he drivelling on about?* 你在喋喋不休地胡謅些甚麼? **–driveller** *n* [U]

driv·en /'drɪvn; 'drɪvən/ the past participle of DRIVE ☆ DRIVE 的過去分詞

⁎**driv·er** /'draɪvə; 'draɪvɚ/ *n* a person who drives 司機; 駕駛員: *a bus driver* 公共汽車司機

drive·way /'draɪv,weɪ; 'draɪvweɪ/ *n* the usual American word for the DRIVE in front of a house 〖美式〗〔住宅前的〕私用車道

driv·ing¹ /'draɪvɪŋ; 'draɪvɪŋ/ *n* [U] **1** the action of operating a vehicle 駕駛: *He enjoys driving fast cars.* 他愛開高速汽車。 **2** the way a person drives 駕駛的方法: *She was warned about dangerous driving.* 她因危險駕駛而被警告。

driving² *adj* [only before a noun 只用於名詞前] **1** very strong and powerful 猛烈的; 強有力的: *driving rain* 暴雨 | *driving ambition* 雄心壯志 **2 in the driving seat** in charge 處於主管〔控制〕地位

driving li·cence /'···,··/ *n* (also 又作 **driver's licence/driver's license** *AmE* 〖美式〗) an official form that shows you are allowed to drive 駕駛執照

driving school /'···,·/ *n* a place where people learn how to drive 〔汽車〕駕駛學校

driz·zle /'drɪzl; 'drɪzəl/ *v* **drizzled, drizzling** [I] to rain very lightly 下濛濛細雨: *It started to drizzle.* 開始下起了毛毛雨。 **–drizzle** *n* [U]

droll /drol; droʊl/ *adj old-fash* odd and amusing 〖老式〗古怪有趣的; 離奇可笑的; 滑稽的: *a droll expression* 滑稽可笑的表情

drom·e·da·ry /'drʌmə,deɪrɪ; 'drɒmədəri/ *n* **dromedaries** a camel with one HUMP¹ (2) 單峯駱駝

drone¹ /dron; droʊn/ *v* **droned, droning** [I] to make a continuous low sound like that of bees 發出〔低沉的〕嗡嗡聲

drone on *phr v* [I] to talk for a long time in an uninteresting way 單調地長談: *The teacher droned on and on.* 老師單調乏味地講個沒完。

drone² *n* **1** a continuous low dull like that of bees 嗡嗡聲: *the distant drone of traffic* 遠處傳來車輛發出的嗡嗡聲 **2** a male bee 雄蜂

drool /drul; druːl/ *v* [I] **1** to let liquid flow from your mouth, especially because you can see or smell something pleasant 〔因看到或聞到好吃東西而〕流口水; 垂涎 **2 drool over something** to admire something in a slightly silly way 癡迷於〔某物〕: *The boys were all drooling over a picture of a girl in a bikini.* 男孩子們都神魂顛倒地望着一張身穿比基尼泳裝女孩的照片。

droop /drup; druːp/ *v* [I] **1** to hang or bend downwards 低垂; 下垂: *His shoulders drooped with tiredness.* 他累得垂下了雙肩。 | *The flowers drooped in the vase.* 那些花在花瓶中低垂着。 **2** to become sad or weakened 變得沮喪, 消沉: *Our spirits drooped.* 我們的情緒低落了。 **–droop** *n*

⁎**drop¹** /drɑp; drɒp/ *n* **1** a small amount of liquid in the shape of a ball 〔液體的〕滴; 珠: *a drop of oil* 一滴油 | *a tear drop* 一滴眼淚 | *Drops of rain fell on the window.* 雨點落在窗子上。 **2** *infml* a small amount of liquid 〖非正式〗少量液體; 點滴: *"Would you like some more tea?" "Just a drop please."* "你要再來點茶嗎?" "一點點就行了。" **3** a small round sweet 小粒糖果: *fruit drops* 水果糖 | *chocolate drops* 巧克力球糖 **4** a distance or movement straight down 落下; 下降: *a long drop to the bottom of the cliff* 掉到很深的山崖底下 | *a drop in temperature* 溫度下降 | *a drop of 10 metres* 往下降了十米 **5** something that is dropped, especially from a plane 空投物: *an air drop of medical supplies* 空投醫療物品 **6 drops** [pl] a liquid medicine that is taken in very small amounts 滴劑: *Add four drops to a glass of water and stir.* 一杯水中加四滴, 然後攪拌。 **7 a drop in the ocean** a small unimportant quantity 滄海一粟 **8 at the drop of a hat** suddenly 立即; 馬上

⁎**drop²** *v* **-pp- 1** [T] to let something fall unintentionally, unexpectedly, or suddenly 〔無意地、意外地或突然地〕使降下; 使落下: *He dropped the bag and ran.* 他扔下袋子就跑了。 –see picture on page 992 見 992 頁彩圖 **2** [I] to fall 落下; 掉下: *The leaves were starting to drop from the trees.* 葉子開始從樹上落下來。 **3** [I;T] to fall or let something fall to a lower level or amount (使)下降; (使)降低: *The price of oil has dropped sharply.* 石油的價格急劇下降。 | *He dropped his voice to a whisper.* 他把説話聲壓低到耳語的程度。 | *The temperature has dropped.* 溫度已經下降。 **4** [T; + adv/prep] *infml* to let someone travelling in your car, taxi, or bus get out at a particular place 〖非正式〗讓〔某人在某處〕下車: *Could you drop me at the station please?* 你可以讓我在火車站下車嗎? **5** [T] to stop doing or considering something 停止, 丟開〔某事〕: *Let's drop the subject.* 我們別談這個話題了。| *When the baby cries her mother drops everything to go and attend to her.* 小孩哭鬧時, 她媽媽丟開一切去照料她。 **6** [T] to leave someone out 開除〔某人〕; 把〔某人〕除名: *George has been dropped from the football team.* 喬治已被足球隊除名。 **7** [I] *infml* to fall down because you are tired or ill 〔非正式〕累倒; 病倒: *We worked until we dropped.* 我們一直幹到累垮為止。 **8 drop a hint** to give a small piece of advice or warning 露口風; 暗示 **9 drop dead** to die suddenly 猝死; 暴死 **10 drop someone a line** to write a short letter to someone 給某人寫封短信

drop in *phr v* [I] to visit someone unexpectedly or informally 順便拜訪〔某人〕: *I'll drop in some time next week.* 我下星期找個時間來看你。

drop off *phr v* **1** [I] to lessen 減少; 減弱: *Interest in the game has dropped off.* 對這種比賽的興趣已經減低。 **2** [I] *infml* to go to sleep often without intending to 〔非正式〕打瞌睡, 打盹兒 **3** [T **drop** sbdy ↔ **off**] to let someone get out of your car at a particular place 讓〔某人在某處〕下車: *Can you drop me off in town?* 讓我在城裡下車, 好嗎?

drop out *phr v* [I] to stop attending or taking part 退出; 退學: *He dropped out of college after only two weeks.* 他在學院裡只上了兩週便退學了。

drop round *phr v* [I] to visit someone unexpectedly or informally 順便拜訪〔某人〕; 〔未事先通知而〕造訪

drop-out /'drɑp.aʊt; 'drɒp-aʊt/ *n* **1** a person who leaves school or college without completing the course 退學者 **2** someone who leaves ordinary society because they do not agree with the accepted ways of living 逃避現實社會的人

drop-per /'drɑpɚ; 'drɒpəʳ/ *n* a short glass tube with a rubber part at one end used for measuring out liquids in drops 滴管

drop-pings /'drɑpɪŋz; 'drɒpɪŋz/ *n* [pl] waste matter from the bowels of animals and birds 〔鳥獸的〕排泄物〔糞便〕

dross /drɔs; drɒs/ *n* [U] something that is useless or not needed 廢料; 渣滓

drought /draʊt; draʊt/ *n* [C;U] a long period of dry weather, when there is not enough water 〔長期〕乾旱; 旱災: *The drought continued for two years.* 旱災延續了兩年之久。 | *in times of drought* 乾旱時期

drove¹ /drov; drəʊv/ *n* **1** a large group of animals being driven together 〔被驅趕着的〕畜羣 **2 droves** [pl] large crowds of people 大批的人羣: *The tourists came in droves.* 旅遊者成羣結隊地來。

drove² past tense of DRIVE ☆ DRIVE 的過去式

drown /draʊn; draʊn/ *v* **1** [I;T] to die or make someone die under water because it is impossible to breathe (使)淹死; 溺死: *All the passengers drowned in the shipwreck.* 所有乘客都在海難中淹死了。 | *He drowned her in the lake.* 他把她溺死在湖裡。 **2** [T] to cover something completely with water 淹沒; 浸沒〔某物〕: *Villages were drowned when the reservoir was constructed.* 修建水庫時, 村莊被水淹沒了。 **3** [T] (also 又作 **drown** sthg ↔ **out**) (of a noise) to be so loud that other sounds cannot be heard 〔聲音〕淹沒; 蓋過〔另一聲音〕: *The music was drowned out by the noise of the traffic.* 音樂被車輛的噪聲淹沒了。 **4 drown your sorrows** to drink alcohol in an attempt to forget your troubles 借酒消愁

drowse /draʊz; draʊz/ *v* **drowsed, drowsing** [I] to be almost asleep or in a light sleep 打瞌睡; 假寐

drow-sy /'draʊzɪ; 'draʊzɪ/ *adj* **drowsier, drowsiest 1** sleepy 睏倦的; 昏昏欲睡的: *These tablets may make you feel drowsy.* 這些藥片會使你昏昏欲睡。 **2** peaceful, and making you feel sleepy 寧靜的; 催眠的: *a drowsy summer afternoon* 令人睏倦的夏日午後 **–drowsily** *adv* **–drowsiness** *n* [U]

drudge /drʌdʒ; drʌdʒ/ *n* a person who does hard, uninteresting work 做苦工〔乏味工作〕的人

drudg-e-ry /'drʌdʒərɪ; drʌdʒəri/ *n* [U] hard, uninteresting work 苦工, 乏味的工作

drug¹ /drʌg; drʌg/ *n* **1** a medicine or something used for making medicines 藥; 藥物; 藥材: *a drug used to treat cancer* 用於治療癌病的藥 **2** a substance which some people take for pleasure or excitement; drugs are often illegal and can make you dependent on them 麻醉品; 〔使人成癮的〕毒品: *Tobacco and alcohol can be dangerous drugs.* 煙和酒都是會對人體極其有害的麻醉品。 | *A growing number of young people are addicted to drugs.* 越來越多年輕人吸毒成癮。

drug² *v* **-gg-** [T] **1** to add drugs to something to make someone unconscious 在〔某物〕中投放麻醉藥: *The coffee was drugged.* 那咖啡攙了麻醉藥。 **2** to give a person or animal a drug to hide pain or make them sleepy 給〔人或動物〕服用麻醉藥: *He had been heavily drugged.* 他服用了大量麻醉藥。

drug-gist /'drʌgɪst; 'drʌgɪst/ *n AmE* someone who prepares and sells medicines and drugs 〔美式〕藥劑師; 藥商

drug-store /'drʌg.stor; 'drʌgstɔːʳ/ *n AmE* a shop which sells medicine and beauty products and also simple meals 〔美式〕藥房; 〔兼營化妝品和便餐的〕雜貨店

dru-id /'druɪd; 'druː.ɪd/ *n* a member of the ancient CELTIC priesthood of Britain, Ireland, and France, before the Christian religion 〔在基督教存在之前, 古代不列顛、愛爾蘭和法蘭西等境內克爾特人信仰的〕德魯伊特的祭司

drum¹ /drʌm; drʌm/ *n* **1** a musical instrument consisting of a skin stretched tight over one or both sides of a hollow circular frame; you hit it with your hand or with a stick 鼓 **2** a large, round container 鼓狀物; 圓桶: *an oil drum* 油桶 –see picture on page 244 見 244 頁彩圖

drum² *v* -mm- **1** [I] to beat or play a drum 打鼓; 擊鼓 **2** [I + adv/prep] to make drum-like noises by continuous beating or striking 不停地敲打〔使其發出打鼓似的聲音〕: *He drummed on the table with his fingers.* 他用手指咚咚地敲打着桌子。| *the sound of rain drumming against the window* 打在窗上的滴滴答答的雨聲 **3** **drum something into someone** to say something to someone so often that they will remember and learn it 向某人灌輸: *She drummed it into the children that they must not cross the road alone.* 她反覆向孩子們強調，他們不可以單獨過馬路。

drum up sthg *phr v* [T] to attract something through hard work and advertising 竭力爭取〔某物〕;〔用廣告〕兜攬: *Let's try to drum up some more business.* 我們要想辦法兜攬多些生意。| *to drum up support* 竭力爭取支持

drum·mer /ˈdrʌmə; ˈdrʌmər/ *n* someone who plays a drum 鼓手

drum·stick /ˈdrʌmˌstɪk; ˈdrʌmˌstɪk/ *n* **1** a stick for beating a drum 鼓槌 **2** the lower part of the leg of a bird, eaten when cooked 家禽的腿下段

drunk¹ /drʌŋk; drʌŋk/ the past participle of DRINK ☆ DRINK 的過去分詞

drunk² *adj* [never before a noun 不能用於名詞前] suffering from the effects of too much alcohol (酒)醉的: *He gets drunk on only two glasses of wine!* 他只喝了兩杯酒就醉了!

drunk³ *n* (also 又作 **drunkard** /ˈdrʌŋkəd; ˈdrʌŋkəd/) a person who is drunk, especially often or continually (a word used to show disapproval) 醉酒者; 酒鬼〔含貶義〕

drunk·en /ˈdrʌŋkən; ˈdrʌŋkən/ *adj* [only before a noun 只用於名詞前] **1** drunk (酒)醉的: *a drunken sailor* 喝醉酒的水手 **2** resulting from or connected with too much drinking of alcohol 醉酒引起的: *a drunken sleep* 酒醉後的酣睡 | *a drunken party* 酗酒者的聚會 –**drunkenly** *adv* –**drunkenness** *n* [U]

dry¹ /draɪ; draɪ/ *adj* **drier, driest** **1** having no water or other liquid inside or on the surface 乾的; 乾涸的: *The wood won't burn unless it's dry.* 木頭如果不乾就燒不着。| *Be careful! The paint isn't dry yet.* 當心! 油漆未乾。 **2** without rain or wetness 乾燥的; 乾旱的: *dry weather* 乾燥的天氣 | *a dry month* 乾旱的月份 | *dry heat* 乾熱 **3** feeling thirsty, or making you feel thirsty (令人)口渴的: *It's dry work digging in the sun.* 在烈日挖土使人感到口渴。 **4** not sweet (used of wine) 不甜

的〔指酒〕 **5** amusing without appearing to be so at first〔幽默但〕不形於色的: *I like his dry sense of humour.* 我喜歡他那種冷面幽默感。 **6** **as dry as a bone** *infml* very dry〔非正式〕乾透的; 十分乾燥的 **7** **as dry as dust** very uninteresting 枯燥乏味的 **8** **dry dock** a place in which a ship is held in position while the water around it is pumped out, leaving the ship dry for repairs 乾船塢 **9** **dry ice** CARBON DIOXIDE in a solid state, used mainly to keep food and other things cold 乾冰〔即固態二氧化碳，用於冷卻〕 **10** **dry rot** a serious disease of wood that makes it decay〔木材的〕乾腐; 乾朽: *They didn't buy the house because it had terrible dry rot.* 他們沒有買那棟房子，因為其木料已嚴重乾朽。–**dryness** *n* [U]

☆dry² *v* **dried, drying** **1** [I] to become dry 變乾: *They laid the clothes out to dry in the sun.* 他們把衣服放到太陽底下曬乾。 **2** [T] to make something dry 使(某物)乾燥; 弄乾: *I need a towel to dry my hair.* 我需要一塊毛巾把頭髮擦乾。| *Shall I dry the dishes?* 我把盆子擦乾好嗎?

dry out *phr v* [I;T **dry** sbdy/sthg ↔ **out**] **1** to make or become completely dry (使)乾透: *Hang your clothes up and they'll soon dry out.* 把你的衣服掛起來，它們馬上就會乾透。 **2** to cure someone from depending on alcohol, or to be cured from this 使(某人)戒酒: *He's gone into hospital to dry out.* 他進了醫院去戒酒。

dry up *phr v* **1** [I;T **dry** sthg ↔ **up**] to make or become completely dry (使)乾透; 乾涸: *The river dries up in the hot season.* 這條河在炎熱的季節乾涸。 **2** [I] to come to an end 停止; 枯竭: *Sources of ivory have dried up following the international ban on the trade.* 國際禁商令頒佈以後，象牙的來源就斷了。

dry-clean /ˌ· ·ˈ·/ *v* [T] to clean clothes with chemicals instead of water 乾洗〔衣服〕

dry-clean·er's /ˌ· ·ˈ··/ *n* a place where clothes can be taken to be dry-cleaned 乾洗店

dry·er /ˈdraɪə; ˈdraɪər/ *n* (also 又作 **drier**) a machine that dries something 烘乾機; 乾燥機: *a hair dryer*〔吹乾頭髮用的〕吹風機

dry·ly /ˈdraɪli; ˈdraɪli/ *adv* see 見 DRILY

du·al /ˈdjuəl; ˈdjuːəl/ *adj* [only before a noun 只用於名詞前] **1** having two parts 雙的; 雙重的: *He has a dual interest in the football team; he's the trainer and his son plays for them.* 他跟該足球隊有雙重關係; 他是足球隊教練，他的兒子則是隊員。| *a dual-purpose instrument* 兩用儀器 **2** **dual carriageway** *BrE* a main road on which the traffic travelling in opposite directions is kept apart by a bar or a narrow piece of land〔英式〕(來往車輛由欄板或狹窄地皮隔開的)雙向公路 –see picture on page 991 見 991 頁彩圖

dub /dʌb; dʌb/ v **-bb-** [T] **1** to name someone or something humorously or descriptively 給〔某人〕起綽號；把〔某物〕戲稱為: *They immediately dubbed him Fatty.* 他們馬上給他取了個綽號叫胖子。 **2** to change the original language of a film or television broadcast so that it is spoken by actors using a foreign language 為〔電影或電視節目〕配音: *an English film dubbed into Spanish* 用西班牙語配音的英國電影 | *Is the film dubbed or does it have subtitles?* 這部影片是配音的還是配上字幕的?

du·bi·ous /'djubɪəs; 'djuːbiəs/ adj **1** feeling doubt 懷疑的；猶豫不決的: *I'm still rather dubious about that plan.* 我對那個計劃仍然有懷疑。 **2** of uncertain value 無把握的；含糊的: *a dubious suggestion* 含糊的建議 **3** probably not completely honest 靠不住的: *a rather dubious character* 相當可疑的人物 – **dubiously** adv –**dubiousness** n [U]

duch·ess /'dʌtʃɪs; 'dʌtʃʃɪs/ n (also 又作 **Duchess**) the title of a woman equal in rank to a DUKE 女公爵

duck¹ /dʌk; dʌk/ n **1** a common water bird with a wide beak, sometimes kept for its meat, eggs, and soft feathers 鴨；野鴨 –see 見 MEAT (USAGE 用法) **2** take to something like a duck to water *infml* to learn or get used to something naturally and very easily 〔非正式〕很自然地；如魚得水地

duck² v **1** [I] to lower your head or body quickly, especially to avoid being hit or seen 迅速低下頭〔彎下身〕〔尤指以免被打中或看見〕: *She had to duck to get through the doorway.* 她要低下頭才能走過門道。 | *He saw a policeman coming, and ducked behind a car.* 他看到一個警察走來，便閃身躲在一輛汽車後面。 **2** [T] *infml* to try to avoid a difficulty or unpleasant responsibility 〔非正式〕逃避；回避〔困難或不快的責任〕: *a speech that ducked all the real issues* 回避實質性問題的發言 **3** duck out of something to escape your responsibility for something 逃避責任: *Don't try to duck out of cleaning up the kitchen!* 別想逃避打掃廚房的責任!

duck·ling /'dʌklɪŋ; 'dʌklɪŋ/ n a young duck 小鴨；幼鴨

duct /dʌkt; dʌkt/ n **1** a thin, narrow tube in your body or in plants which carries liquids or air 〔人體或植物中輸送液體或氣體的〕管；導管: *tearducts* 淚腺管 **2** any kind of pipe or tube for carrying things like liquids, air, or electric power lines 〔輸送液體、氣體或電的〕管道；渠道

dud /dʌd; dʌd/ n *infml* a person or thing that is worthless or useless 〔非正式〕無用的人[物]；廢物假貨: *a dud cheque* 作廢的支票 | *This new battery is a complete dud.* 這節新電池已經報廢。

due¹ /dju; djuː/ adj **1** [never before a noun 不能用於名詞前] expected to happen at a particular time 預期的；預定應

到的: *The next train to London is due at 4 o'clock.* 下一班開往倫敦的火車應在四點鐘到達。 | *The plane is due to arrive at 11.30.* 飛機預定十一點三十分到達。 **2** be due to do something to be going to do something because it has been planned 約定，預定做某事: *I'm due to meet him this afternoon.* 我約定今天下午去接他。 **3** be due for something to be expecting to receive something 應得到某物: *I'm due for a pay rise soon.* 不久就該輪到給我加薪了。 **4** [never before a noun 不能用於名詞前] payable 應付的；到期的: *a bill due today* 今天到期的賬單 **5** [never before a noun 不能用於名詞前] *fml* owed or owing as a debt or right 〔正式〕應支付的；欠款的: *We have discovered that a great deal of money is due to you.* 我們發現欠你許多錢。 | *Our grateful thanks are due to this young man for his prompt action.* 我們衷心感謝這位年青人給予我們及時的幫助。 **6** [only before a noun 只用於名詞前] *fml* suitable 〔正式〕適當的；合適的: *driving without due care and attention* 沒有人應有的謹慎態度開車 **7** due to because of 由於；因為: *Her success is entirely due to hard work.* 她的成功完全是努力工作的結果。 | *The dollar is weak at the moment, due partly to distrust of the new government.* 目前美元疲軟，部分原因是人民對新政府不信任。 **8** in due course in the future, before too long 在不久的將來: *We will be writing to you in due course.* 我們很快就會寫信給你。

■ USAGE 用法: Compare 比較 **due to** and 和 **owing to**. **1** Both expressions are similar in meaning, but **due to** is used after the verb *to be* ☆兩者所表達的意思相近，但 **due to** 用於動詞 to be 後面: *His absence was due to the storm.* (You should not use **owing to** in this sentence.) 他由於暴風雨而未能出席。(本句不能用 **owing to**。) **2** Some people consider it wrong to use **due to** except after the verb *to be*, but many speakers use it after other verbs, in the same way as **owing to** ☆有人認為除了在動詞 to be 後面才可接 **due to** 之外，在其他場合使用都是不規範的，但很多人在說話時把它用於其他動詞的後面，其方法與 **owing to** 相同: *He arrived late due to/owing to the storm.* 由於暴風雨，他來遲了。

due² n **1** give someone their due to admit the good things about someone 承認某人的優點；給某人應有的評價: *I don't like the man, but to give him his due, he's good at his job.* 我不喜歡那人，但說句公道話，他工作幹得不錯。 **2** dues [pl] official charges or payments 應繳費用: *union dues* 工會會費

due³ adv exactly (used before 用於 **north**, **south**, **east**, and 和 **west** 之前) 正對着: *It's* *due north.* 這是正北面。

du·el[1] /'djuəl; 'djuːəl/ *n* a fight between two people with guns or swords to settle a quarrel 〔用槍或劍進行的〕（雙人）決鬥

duel[2] *v* **-ll-** *BrE*〔英式〕**(-l-** *AmE*〔美式〕**)** [I] to fight a duel (進行)決鬥

du·et /dju'ɛt; djuː'et/ *n* a piece of music for two performers 二重奏曲；二重唱曲

duf·fel coat /'dʌfl ˌkot; 'dʌfl ˌkəʊt/ *n* (also 又作 **duffle coat**) a coat made of heavy woollen cloth, fastened with long tubelike buttons and often with a covering for your head〔有棒形鈕扣的〕連帽粗厚呢大衣

dug /dʌg; dʌg/ the past tense and past participle of DIG ☆ DIG 的過去式和過去分詞

dug·out /'dʌgˌaʊt; 'dʌgaʊt/ *n* **1** a small light boat made by cutting out a deep hollow space in a log 獨木舟 **2** a shelter dug in the ground with an earth roof 地下掩體；防空洞

duke /djuk; djuːk/ *n* (also 又作 **Duke**) the title of a nobleman of the highest rank 公爵: *the Duke of Norfolk* 諾福克公爵 | *He became a duke on the death of his father.* 他在父親死後成了公爵。

dul·cet /'dʌlsɪt; 'dʌlsət/ *adj lit* sweet and pleasant (used of sounds)〔文〕動聽的；悅耳的〔指聲音〕

dull[1] /dʌl; dʌl/ *adj* **1** not bright 暗淡的: *a dull grey day* 暗灰的一天 **2** not clear or sharp 不清晰的；隱約的: *a dull banging sound somewhere in the house* 屋子裡某處隱約傳來的砰擊聲 | *a dull ache* 隱痛 **3** uninteresting 乏味的；單調的: *The party was very dull.* 那聚會沉悶乏味。 **4** slow in thinking and understanding things 遲鈍的；呆笨的 **–dully** /'dʌlɪ; 'dʌli/ *adv* **–dullness** *n* [U]

dull[2] *v* [T] to make something dull 使〔某物〕遲鈍；使減輕: *eyes and ears dulled by age* 因年邁而變得不靈的耳目 | *Give me something to dull the pain.* 給我一些可減輕疼痛的藥吧。

du·ly /'djuli; 'djuːli/ *adv fml* at the correct time or in the correct way〔正式〕按時地；恰當地: *The taxi that we had ordered duly arrived, and we drove off.* 我們叫的計程車按時到達，於是我們登車而去。 | *Your suggestion has been duly noted.* 你的建議已得到適當的注意。

dumb /dʌm; dʌm/ *adj* **1** unable to speak 啞的；不會說話的: *dumb animals* 不會說話的動物 | *Children who are deaf and dumb go to a special school.* 聾啞兒童上專門為他們開辦的學校讀書。 **2** *infml* stupid〔非正式〕愚蠢的 **–dumbly** *adv* **–dumbness** *n* [U]

dumb·bell /'dʌmˌbɛl; 'dʌmbel/ *n* a weight consisting of two large metal balls connected by a short bar, often used for exercises 啞鈴

dumb·found·ed /ˌdʌm'faʊndɪd; dʌm'faʊndɪd/ *adj* so surprised that you cannot speak 令人驚呆的: *He just stood there, dumbfounded by the news.* 他被那消息嚇呆了，只懂得站在那裡。

dum·my[1] /'dʌmɪ; 'dʌmi/ *n* **dummies 1** an object made to make people believe it is the real thing 仿製品；仿造物: *The guns the robbers carried were just dummies.* 那些強盜拿的槍都是假的。 **2** something like a human figure made of wood or plastic and used to make or show clothes〔陳列服裝用的〕人像模型: *a dressmaker's dummy* 裁縫店裡的模型人 **3** *BrE* a rubber object for sucking, put in a baby's mouth to keep it quiet〔英式〕〔哄嬰兒用的〕橡皮奶頭 **4** *infml AmE* a stupid fool〔非正式，美式〕笨蛋；蠢貨 **5** a **dummy run** a test to see if a plan works properly before it is actually needed 演習；預演

dum·my[2] *adj* something that is made to seem real but is not 仿造的；假的: *a dummy computer* 計算機模型

dump[1] /dʌmp; dʌmp/ *v* [T] **1** to drop or unload something, especially heavily or carelessly, in a rough pile〔尤指隨便地〕堆放，傾倒: *Don't dump that sand in the middle of the path!* 別把那些沙子倒在路中央! | *They dumped their bags on my floor and left!* 他們把袋子胡亂放在我的地板上就走了! **2** to throw something away irresponsibly〔不負責任地〕倒掉，丟棄〔某物〕: *They dumped their rubbish in the sea.* 他們把垃圾倒在海裡。 **3** to get rid of unwanted goods by selling them to another country at a very low price (a word used to show disapproval)〔向國外廉價〕傾銷〔貶義詞〕

dump[2] *n* **1** a place for dumping something such as waste material 垃圾場: *a rubbish dump* 垃圾堆放處 **2** *infml* an uninteresting, dirty, or untidy place〔非正式〕髒亂的地方: *This town's a real dump.* 這個城鎮簡直是個垃圾堆。 **3** be **down in the dumps** to be feeling sad 鬱鬱的；沮喪的

dump·ling /'dʌmplɪŋ; 'dʌmplɪŋ/ *n* **1** a lump of boiled flour and water, often served with meat or with meat inside it〔水煮的〕肉餡麵團子；餃子 **2** a sweet food made of pastry with fruit inside it 水果布丁: *apple dumplings* 蘋果布丁

dump·y /'dʌmpɪ; 'dʌmpi/ *adj* **dumpier, dumpiest** *infml* short and fat〔非正式〕矮胖的: *a dumpy little man* 矮胖的小個子男人

dunce /dʌns; dʌns/ *n* a person who is slow at learning 蠢才，笨蛋

dune /djun; djuːn/ *n* (also 又作 **sand dune**) a hill of sand made by the wind on the seashore or in a desert〔風吹積成的〕沙丘

dung /dʌŋ; dʌŋ/ *n* [U] solid waste material from the bowels of large animals〔牲畜的〕糞便

dun·ga·rees /ˌdʌŋgə'riz; ˌdʌŋgə'riːz/ *n* [pl] trousers with an additional part covering the top of your body, usually made of heavy cotton cloth 粗棉布工裝褲[工作服]

dun·geon /'dʌndʒən; 'dʌndʒən/ *n* a dark underground prison, especially beneath a

D

castle 土牢;〔尤指古城堡下的〕地牢

dunk /dʌŋk; dʌŋk/ v [T] infml to dip something into liquid 〖非正式〗把〔某物〕浸入〔液體〕: He enjoyed dunking his biscuits in his tea. 他喜歡把餅乾放在茶裡浸一下再吃。

du·o /ˈduːəʊ; ˈdjuːəʊ/ n **duos** two musicians who play or sing together 二重奏; 二重唱

dupe /djuːp; djuːp/ v **duped, duping** [T] to trick or deceive someone 哄騙, 欺騙〔某人〕: The salesman duped me **into** buying a faulty washing machine. 售貨員哄騙我買了一台有毛病的洗衣機。–**dupe** n

du·pli·cate¹ /ˈdjuːplɪkət; ˈdjuːpləˌkeɪt/ n something that is exactly like something else in its appearance, pattern, or contents 複製品; 副本, 抄件: If you've lost your key, I can give you a duplicate. 如果你遺失了鑰匙, 我可以把另外一把給你。–**duplicate** adj [only before a noun 只用於名詞前]: a duplicate key 一把複製的鑰匙

du·pli·cate² /ˈdjuːpləˌket; ˈdjuːpləˌkeɪt/ v **duplicated, duplicating** [T] to copy something exactly 複製; 複寫; 複印: The information was duplicated. 那資料只被複印下來。| I'll get these notes typed up and duplicated. 我要把這些筆記打出來, 並複印一份。–**duplication** /ˌdjuːpləˈkeɪʃən, ˌdjuːplɪˈkeɪʃən; n [U]

du·plic·i·ty /djuːˈplɪsətɪ; duːˈplɪsɪti/ n [U] fml trying by words or actions to make someone believe something that is not true 〖正式〗欺騙, 虛偽

dur·a·ble /ˈdjuːrəbḷ; ˈdjuərəbəl/ adj lasting for a long time 持久的; 耐用的: durable clothing 耐穿的衣服 –**durability** /ˌdjuːrəˈbɪlətɪ; ˌdjuərəˈbɪlɪti/ n [U]

du·ra·tion /djuˈreɪʃən; djuˈreɪʃən/ n [U] the time during which something exists or lasts 持續時間; 期間: He will be in hospital for the duration of the school year. 整個學年他都要住院。

du·ress /ˈdjuːrɪs; djuˈres/ n [U] under duress as a result of illegal or unfair pressure 在脅迫之下: His promise was made under duress. 他的承諾是在脅迫之下作出的。

⋆**during** /ˈdjuːrɪŋ; ˈdjuərɪŋ/ prep **1** all through a period of time 在…期間: We go swimming every day during the summer. 整個夏季我們每天都去游泳。| They lived abroad during the war. 戰爭期間他們一直住在國外。**2** at one moment in a period of time 在…的時候: He died during the night. 他是在夜裡去世的。

dusk /dʌsk; dʌsk/ n [U] the time when daylight changes to darkness 黃昏; 薄暮: The street lights go on at dusk. 路燈在黃昏時分亮起。

dusk·y /ˈdʌskɪ; ˈdʌski/ adj **duskier, duskiest** quite dark in colour 顏色深的; 顏色暗的: her dusky complexion 黝黑的面色

⋆**dust¹** /dʌst; dʌst/ n [U] **1** dry powder made up of extremely small pieces of dirt or

another substance which is stated 灰塵; 塵埃: There was a thick layer of dust on the books. 那些書上積了厚厚的一層灰塵。| gold dust 金粉 | coal dust 煤粉 **2** finely powdered earth 塵土: The car raised a cloud of dust as it went down the dirt road. 汽車駛過那條泥路時捲起了一片塵土。

dust² v **1** [I;T] to clean the dust from something 清除〔某物〕的灰塵: Please dust all the books. 請把所有這些書的灰塵撣掉。| She just hates dusting. 她就是不喜歡撣灰塵。**2** [T] to cover something with a fine powder 〔把粉末〕撒在〔某物〕上: The crops were dusted **with** insecticide. 莊稼上撒上殺蟲劑。

dust·bin /ˈdʌstˌbɪn; ˈdʌstbɪn/ n a container with a lid, for holding waste material such as empty tins and bottles until they can be taken away 垃圾箱

dust·cart /ˈdʌstˌkɑːt; ˈdʌstkɑːt/ n a large motor vehicle which goes from house to house in a town to collect the contents of dustbins 垃圾車

dust·er /ˈdʌstə; ˈdʌstər/ n a cloth for dusting furniture 抹布

dust jack·et /ˈ· ˌ··/ n (also 又作 **dust cover**) a paper cover put as a protection round the cover of a book, often with writing or pictures describing the book 〔書籍的〕護封; 書套

dust·man /ˈdʌstmən; ˈdʌstmən/ n **dustmen** /-mən; -mən/ someone employed to remove waste material from DUSTBINS 清除垃圾的人; 垃圾工

dust·pan /ˈdʌstˌpæn; ˈdʌstpæn/ n a flat container with a handle into which household dust and other waste materials can be brushed 畚箕

dust-up /ˈdʌstˌʌp; ˈdʌstˌʌp/ n BrE infml a quarrel or fight 〖英式, 非正式〗爭吵; 打架

dust·y /ˈdʌstɪ; ˈdʌsti/ adj **dustier, dustiest** covered or filled with dust 滿是灰塵的: a dusty room 佈滿灰塵的房間

Dutch¹ /dʌtʃ; dʌtʃ/ adj of or connected with Holland 荷蘭的; 荷蘭人的; 荷蘭語的

Dutch² n **1** the Dutch the people of Holland 荷蘭人 **2** the language of Holland 荷蘭語

Dutch cour·age /ˌ· ˈ··/ n [U] infml the courage that comes from drinking alcohol 〖非正式〗酒後之勇

du·ti·ful /ˈdjuːtɪfəl; ˈdjuːtɪfəl/ adj having or showing proper respect and obedience 恭敬的; 恭順的 –**dutifully** adv

⋆**du·ty** /ˈdjuːtɪ; ˈdjuːti/ n **duties 1** [C;U] what you must do either because of your job or because you think it is right 責任; 職責; 本分: His duties include taking the letters to the post and arranging meetings. 他的職責包括寄信和安排會議。| I feel it's my duty to help you. 我覺得我有責任幫助你。| Please report for duty tomorrow morning. 請明天早上報到上班。**2 duties** [pl]

taxes 稅: *Customs duties are paid on goods entering the country.* 進口的貨物要徵收關稅。
3 off duty not working (used of people like policemen, soldiers, or nurses) 不上班; 不值班〔指警察、士兵、護士等〕: *When I'm off duty I like to play tennis.* 我下班後喜歡打網球。**4 on duty** working at that particular time (used of people like policemen, soldiers, or nurses) 上班; 值班〔指警察、士兵、護士等〕: *When does he come on duty?* 他甚麼時候來值班?

duty·bound /ˌ‥ ˈ‥/ *adj* [never before a noun 不能用於名詞前] having to do a particular thing because it is right 責無旁貸的; 義不容辭的: *As her parents we are dutybound to help her.* 作為她的父母, 我們有義務去幫助她。

duty-free /ˌ‥ ˈ‥◂/ *adj, adv* allowed to come into the country without tax 免稅的(地): *We bought some duty-free whisky at the airport.* 我們在機場買了些免稅威士忌酒。

du·vet /ˈdjuːve; ˈduːvei/ *n* a large bag filled with feathers or man-made material, used on a bed instead of other coverings 羽絨被

dwarf¹ /dwɔːf; dwɔːf/ *n* **dwarfs** *or* **dwarves** /dwɔːvz; dwɔːvz/ **1** a person, animal, or plant of much less than the usual size 矮子; 侏儒; 矮小的動物或植物: *Without the correct treatment, the child will remain a dwarf.* 不作適當的治療, 這孩子會長不高。| *a dwarf apple tree* 一棵矮蘋果樹 **2** a small imaginary manlike creature in fairy stories 童話中的小矮人: *Snow White and the Seven Dwarfs* 白雪公主和七個小矮人

dwarf² *v* [T] to make something appear small by comparison 使〔某物〕相比之下顯得矮小; 使相形見絀: *That new skyscraper dwarfs all the surrounding buildings.* 那座新建的摩天大樓使周圍的建築物都顯得很矮小。

dwell /dwɛl; dwel/ *v* **dwelt** /dwɛlt; dwelt/ *or* **dwelled 1** [I + adv/prep] *lit* to live in a particular place 〔文〕居住: *They dwelt in a forest.* 他們居住在森林裡。**2 dwell on/upon something** to think, speak, or write too much about something 細想; 詳述: *You shouldn't dwell on the past.* 你不要老是想着過去。**3 -dweller** a person or animal that lives in the stated place 居住在某處的人〔動物〕: *cave-dwellers* 穴居者 | *city-dwellers* 城市居民

dwel·ling /ˈdwɛlɪŋ; ˈdwelɪŋ/ *n fml* the building where people live 〔正式〕住處; 住宅; 寓所: *Welcome to my humble dwelling!* 歡迎光臨寒舍!

dwelt /dwɛlt; dwelt/ the past tense and past participle of DWELL ☆ DWELL 的過去式和過去分詞

dwin·dle /ˈdwɪndl; ˈdwɪndl/ *v* **dwindled, dwindling** [I] to become gradually fewer or smaller 逐漸減少〔變小〕: *The number of people who live on the island is dwindling.* 島上居民的人數正在減少。| *Her money*

gradually dwindled away. 她的錢逐漸耗盡。

dye¹ /daɪ; daɪ/ *n* [C;U] a vegetable or chemical substance, usually liquid, used to change the colour of things 染料

dye² *v* **dyes, dyed, dyeing** [T] to make something a particular colour by means of dye 給〔某物〕染色: *She dyes her hair.* 她染頭髮。| *She dyed the dress red.* 她把連衣裙染成紅色。

dyed-in-the-wool /ˌ‥ ‥ ˈ‥◂/ *adj* [only before a noun 只用於名詞前] impossible to change (a word used to express disapproval) 徹頭徹尾的; 頑固不化的〔含貶義〕: *Charles is a dyed-in-the-wool Republican.* 查爾斯是個徹頭徹尾的共和黨人。

dy·ing /ˈdaɪɪŋ; ˈdaɪɪŋ/ the present participle of DIE ☆ DIE 的現在分詞

dyke /daɪk; daɪk/ *n* (also 又作 **dike**) **1** a thick bank or wall built to control water and prevent flooding 堤; 壩 **2** a narrow passage dug to carry water away 溝; 渠

dy·nam·ic /daɪˈnæmɪk; daɪˈnæmɪk/ *adj* **1** interesting, exciting, and full of activity 有活力的; 精力充沛的: *a dynamic executive* 精力充沛的行政人員 | *a dynamic period in history* 歷史上很有生氣的一個時代 **2** *tech* relating to a force or power that causes movement or change 〔術語〕動力的; 動態的: *dynamic energy* 動能 **–dynamically** /-klɪ; -klɪ/ *adv*

dy·nam·ics /daɪˈnæmɪks; daɪˈnæmɪks/ *n* [U] the science that deals with movement 力學; 動力學

dy·na·mis·m /ˈdaɪnəˌmɪzəm; ˈdaɪnəmɪzəm/ *n* [U] the quality of being dynamic 精力; 活力: *The job requires someone with energy and dynamism.* 做這份工作的人需要精力和幹勁。

dy·na·mite¹ /ˈdaɪnəˌmaɪt; ˈdaɪnəmaɪt/ *n* [U] **1** a powerful explosive used in MINING 達納炸藥; 甘油炸藥 **2** *infml* something or someone that will cause great shock, surprise, admiration 〔非正式〕會引起轟動的人〔事物〕: *That news story is really dynamite!* 那篇新聞報道真的是很轟動!

dynamite² *v* **dynamited, dynamiting** [T] to blow something up with dynamite 〔用炸藥〕炸毀〔某物〕

dy·na·mo /ˈdaɪnəˌmo; ˈdaɪnəməu/ *n* **dynamos** a machine which turns some other kind of power into electricity 發電機

dyn·as·ty /ˈdaɪnəstɪ; ˈdɪnəstɪ/ *n* **dynasties** a line of rulers all of the same family 王朝; 朝代: *a dynasty of Scottish kings* 蘇格蘭王朝 **–dynastic** /daɪˈnæstɪk; dɪˈnæstɪk/ *adj*

dys·en·te·ry /ˈdɪsn̩ˌtɛrɪ; ˈdɪsəntərɪ/ *n* [U] a painful disease of the bowels that causes them to be emptied more often than usual and to produce blood and MUCUS 痢疾

dys·lex·i·a /dɪsˈlɛksɪə; dɪsˈleksɪə/ *n* [U] a problem in reading caused by difficulty in seeing letter shapes 〔因辨不清字形而造成的〕閱讀困難症, 閱讀能力部分喪失 **–dyslexic** *adj*

E, e

E, e /i; iː/ **E's, e's** or **Es, es** the 5th letter of the English alphabet 英語的第五個字母

E a written abbreviation for 〖縮〗= EAST or 或 EASTERN

★★each[1] /iːtʃ; iːtʃ/ *det,pron* every single one of two or more things or people 〔兩個或兩個以上人、物中的〕每一, 每個: *Each speaker will talk for ten minutes.* 每位演講者將發言十分鐘。| *She tried to spend a few minutes with each of her guests.* 她盡量和每位客人都聊上幾分鐘。| *They each want to do something different.* 他們每人都想做一點不同的事情。

each[2] *adv* for or to every thing or every person 每; 各: *The tickets are £1 each.* 票子每張一英鎊。| *She picked up the books and gave the children one each.* 她拿起書, 給孩子們每人一本。

★★each oth·er /ˌ· ˈ··/ *pron* used to show that two or more people do something to the others 彼此; 互相: *Susan and Robert kissed each other.* 蘇珊和羅伯特互相親吻。| *We all cried and hugged each other.* 我們都哭著互相擁抱。

ea·ger /ˈiːgə; ˈiːgər/ *adj* having a strong desire to do something or a strong interest in something 渴望的; 熱衷的: *I was very eager to meet him.* 我渴望和他見面。| *He's eager for success.* 他渴望成功。| *crowds of eager tourists* 一羣羣熱切的遊客 –**eagerly** *adv* –**eagerness** *n* [U]

> □ USEFUL PATTERNS 有用句型
> be eager to do something; be eager for something

ea·gle /ˈiːgl; ˈiːgəl/ *n* a large bird which eats small animals and birds 鷹

eagle-eyed /ˌ·· ˈ·◂/ *adj* noticing every small detail or mistake 注意到細枝末節的; 目光敏銳的

★ear[1] /ɪr; ɪər/ *n* **1** part of your body used for hearing 耳朵: *Rabbits have long ears.* 兔子有對長耳朵。| *an ear infection* 耳朵感染 **2** the head of a grain-producing plant, used for food 〔穀物的〕穗: *an ear of wheat* 小麥穗 **3** be all ears to be listening eagerly to someone 洗耳恭聽 **4** be up to your ears in something to be very busy with something 在⋯忙得不可開交: *I'm up to my ears in work.* 我工作忙得不可開交。 **5** by ear without needing written musical notes 不看樂譜地: *Peter can play almost anything by ear.* 彼得

幾乎全能不看樂譜演奏任何曲子。**6** go in one ear and out the other (of information) to be listened to but not understood or remembered 〔消息〕左耳進右耳出; 當耳邊風 **7** have an ear for to have good recognition of sounds in music or languages 〔對音樂或語言〕有靈敏的聽力: *I've got no ear for music.* 我沒有欣賞音樂的能力。

ear·ache /ˈɪr,ek; ˈɪəreɪk/ *n* [U] a pain inside your ear 耳痛

ear·drum /ˈɪr,drʌm; ˈɪədrʌm/ *n* a tight thin skin inside your ear, which allows you to hear sound 耳膜; 鼓膜

earl /ɜːl; ɜːl/ *n* the title of a British nobleman of high rank 〔英國的〕伯爵: *the Earl of Warwick* 沃里克伯爵 –compare 比較 COUNTESS

ear·lobe /ˈɪrlob; ˈɪələʊb/ *n* the fleshy bottom part of your ear 耳垂

★early /ˈɜːli; ˈɜːli/ *adj, adv* **earlier, earliest 1** before the usual or expected time 早的; 提早: *He always arrives early.* 他總是早到。| *The train was 10 minutes early.* 火車早到了十分鐘。**2** near the beginning of the day or a period of time 清早; 在早期的): *She returned in the early morning.* 她一大清早就回來了。| *I've got to get up early tomorrow.* 明天我得早起。| *We always go on holiday early in the season.* 我們總在季初去度假。| *a man in his early twenties* 二十出頭的小伙子 | *We didn't need to put the chairs out because Mary had done it earlier.* 我們不必把椅子搬出去了, 因為瑪麗早已搬好。**3** at the earliest but not before that time; a phrase used when you are saying that a particular date or time is the soonest that something can happen 最早; 作為最早日期: *The letter will reach him on Monday at the earliest.* 這封信最早也要星期一才能寄到他那裡。**4** it's early days = it is too soon to know something for certain 現在還言之過早 **5** have an early night to go to bed before your usual bedtime 〔比平時〕早睡: *I think I'll have an early night tonight.* 我想我今晚會早睡。

ear·mark /ˈɪr,mɑrk; ˈɪəmɑːk/ *v* [T] to set something aside for a particular purpose 撥出〔某物〕作特定用途: *This money has been earmarked for a new project.* 這筆錢被撥給了新的項目。

★earn /ɜːn; ɜːn/ *v* [T] **1** to get money by working 掙得; 賺得: *He earns a lot of money.* 他掙很多錢。**2** to get something that you deserve because of your qualities or actions 博得; 贏得: *She earned her place in the team by train-*

ing hard. 她經過刻苦的訓練, 在隊裡取得了地位。–see 見 WIN (USAGE 用法)

ear·nest¹ /ˈɝːnɪst; ˈɜːnⅼst/ *adj* serious and sincere (a word often used to express disapproval) 認真的; 一本正經的: *a rather earnest young man* 一本正經的年輕人 **–earnestly** *adv*

earnest² *n* **1 be in earnest** to be serious about something 認真的: *Is he in earnest about his intention to retire?* 他打算退休, 是認真的嗎? **2 begin in earnest, start in earnest** to begin happening seriously 認真開始: *I began working in earnest.* 我開始認真工作。

earn·ings /ˈɝːnɪŋz; ˈɜːnɪŋz/ *n* [pl] money which is earned by working 工資; 薪水

ear·phones /ˈɪrˌfonz; ˈɪəfəʊnz/ *n* [pl] two pieces of a WALKMAN that you fit over your ears so that you can listen to music in private 耳機

ear·plug /ˈɪrˌplʌg; ˈɪəplʌg/ *n* a piece of soft material which you put in your ear to keep out water or noise〔防水或擋噪音的〕耳塞

ear·ring /ˈɪrˌrɪŋ; ˈɪəˌrɪŋ/ *n* a piece of jewellery that you wear on your ear 耳環; 耳飾 –see picture on page 210 見 210 頁彩圖

ear·shot /ˈɪrˌʃɑt; ˈɪəʃɒt/ *n* **within earshot** within the distance at which a sound can be heard 在聽得到的距離之內 [RELATED PHRASE 相關詞組 **out of earshot**]

earth¹ /ɝːθ; ɜːθ/ *n* [U] (also 又作 **the earth**) the world in which we live 地球: *They returned from the moon to the earth.* 他們從月球返回到地球。 | *Earth is the third planet from the sun.* 地球是距離太陽第三位遠的行星。 | *the most beautiful woman on earth* 世上最美的女子 –see 見 LAND (USAGE 用法) **2** [U] soil in which plants grow 土壤: *He planted the seeds in damp earth.* 他把種子種在濕潤的泥土裡。 –see 見 LAND (USAGE 用法) **3** [C] *BrE* An additional safety wire which makes a connection between an electrical apparatus and the ground〔英式〕接地線 **4 what on earth, how on earth, who on earth, etc.** phrases used to express surprise or disapproval 究竟; 到底〔表示驚奇或不贊成〕: *What on earth have you done to your hair?* 你的頭髮到底是怎麼弄的?

■ USAGE 用法: If you are using **earth** with the meaning "the world", remember to use the preposition on ☆ 用 **earth** 表示"地球"時, 要使用介詞 on: *It's the biggest lake on earth.* 這是地球上最大的湖泊。 | *We all live on the same earth.* 我們都住在同一個地球上。 If you are using **world**, remember to use the preposition in ☆用 **world** 時, 要使用介詞 in: *It's the biggest lake in the world.* 這是世界上最大的湖泊。 | *We all live in the same world.* 我們都住在同一個世界上。

earth² *v* [T] to make an electrical apparatus

safer by connecting it to the ground with a wire 把〔電氣裝置〕接地

earth·en·ware /ˈɝːθənˌwɛr; ˈɜːθənweəʳ/ *adj* made of baked clay 陶製的: *an earthenware pot* 陶罐 **–earthenware** *n* [U]: *bowls and plates made of earthenware* 陶製的碗碟

earth·ly /ˈɝːθli; ˈɜːθli/ *adj* [only before a noun 只用於名詞前] **1** belonging to this world as opposed to heaven 塵世的; 世俗的: *earthly possessions* 世間的財物 **2** *infml* a word used in questions and negatives to give force to what we are saying〔非正式〕可能的〔用於問句、否定句以加強語氣〕: *There's no earthly reason for me to go.* 我根本沒有理由去。

earth·quake /ˈɝːθˌkwek; ˈɜːθkweɪk/ *n* (also 又作 **quake**) a sudden violent shaking of the earth's surface 地震: *The town was destroyed by the earthquake.* 這個城鎮毀於地震。

earth·worm /ˈɝːθˌwɝːm; ˈɜːθwɜːm/ *n* a worm 蚯蚓

earth·y /ˈɝːθi; ˈɜːθi/ *adj* **1** often talking about things such as sex, which other people consider rude 粗俗的: *Peter has an earthy sense of humour.* 彼得有一種粗俗的幽默感。 **2** of or like earth 泥土的; 泥土似的: *an earthy taste* 泥土味 **–earthiness** *n* [U]

ear·wig /ˈɪrˌwɪg; ˈɪəˌwɪg/ *n* a kind of insect 蠼螋; 地蜈蚣

ease¹ /iz; iːz/ *n* [U] **1** lack of difficulty 容易; 不費力: *He jumped the wall with ease.* 他輕易地跳過了牆。 **2 a life of ease** a life in which you have plenty of money and no worries 安閒舒適的生活 **3 at ease** feeling comfortable and confident 安適; 自在: *He seemed totally at ease in the new surroundings.* 他在新的環境中顯得十分舒適自在。 **4 ill at ease** worried and nervous 焦慮緊張的

ease² *v* **eased, easing 1** [I;T] to make or become less severe or difficult 緩解; 減輕: *I gave him some medicine to ease the pain.* 我給他一些藥來減輕他的疼痛。 | *The pain has eased.* 疼痛已減輕了。 | *Tensions in the region have eased slightly.* 這個地區的緊張局勢稍有緩和。 **2** [T] to move something carefully, slowly, and gently 小心翼翼地移動〔某物〕: *He eased the window open.* 他小心翼翼地打開窗。

ease off *phr v* [I] to become less severe 減輕; 減弱: *The rain was beginning to ease off.* 雨開始下得小些了。

ease up *phr v* [I] *infml* to do less of something〔非正式〕少做〔某事〕: *I think it's time you eased up on the cigarettes.* 我想你該少抽點煙了。

ea·sel /ˈizl; ˈiːzəl/ *n* a wooden frame to hold a BLACKBOARD or a picture that is being painted 黑板架; 畫架

eas·i·ly /ˈizlⅼi; ˈiːzⅼli/ *adv* **1** without difficulty 容易地: *I can easily finish it today.* 我今天能很容易地就把這件事幹

完。**2** without doubt 無疑地: *She is easily the cleverest girl in the class.* 她無疑是班上最聰明的女生。

☆east¹ /ist; iːst/ *n* **1** [sing;U] the direction in which the sun rises 東方 **2 the east** the eastern part of a country 〔國家的〕東部: *Rain will spread to the east later today.* 今天晚些時候雨將蔓延到東部地區。 **3 the East** the countries of Asia, especially India, China, and Japan 東方〔尤指印度、中國和日本等亞洲國家〕: *the mysteries of the East* 東方之謎 **4 the East** the countries in the eastern part of Europe, especially the ones that had Communist governments 東歐國家〔尤指有共產主義政府的國家〕: *relations between East and West* 東西方關係

east² *adj* **1** (also 又作 **East**) in the east or facing east 在東方的; 向東方的: *the east coast* 東海岸 **2 east wind** a wind coming from the east 東風

east³ *adv* (also 又作 **East**) **1** towards the east 向東, 朝東: *The room faces east.* 這房間是朝東的。 | *We travelled East.* 我們往東旅行。 **2** from the east (used of wind) 從東方來〔指風〕

east·bound /ˈist,baund; ˈiːstbaund/ *adj* travelling towards the east 向東行的: *eastbound traffic* 向東行駛的車輛

Eas·ter /ˈistəʳ; ˈiːstə/ *n* [U] a special Sunday in March or April when Christians remember Christ's death and his return to life; and when people give chocolate eggs as presents 復活節〔紀念耶穌復活的節日, 在三月或四月的一個星期天, 人們互贈巧克力蛋為禮物〕

Easter egg /ˈ··· ·/ *n* a chocolate egg eaten at Easter 〔用巧克力製的〕復活節彩蛋

eas·ter·ly /ˈistəlɪ; ˈiːstəli/ *adj* **1** towards the east 向東的: *in an easterly direction* 向東 **2** coming from the east (used of a wind) 從東來的〔指風〕

☆east·ern /ˈistən; ˈiːstən/ *adj* (also 又作 **Eastern**) **1** belonging to the east part of a country or area 〔國家或地區〕東部的: *a village in Eastern England* 英格蘭東部的一個村莊 **2** belonging to the countries of Asia, especially India, China, and Japan 東方的〔尤指印度、中國和日本等亞洲國家的〕: *Eastern religions* 東方的宗教 **3** belonging to the countries in the east of Europe 東歐國家的

east·ward /ˈistwəd; ˈiːstwəd/ *adj* going towards the east 向東的: *We set off in an eastward direction.* 我們啟程向東出發。 – **eastwards** (also 又作 **eastward** *AmE*〔美式〕) *adv*: *We sailed eastwards.* 我們向東航行。

☆eas·y¹ /ˈizɪ; ˈiːzi/ *adj* **easier, easiest 1** not difficult 容易的: *an easy book* 淺易的書 | *It's easy for us to get to London.* 我們去倫敦是很容易的。 | *This machine is very easy to use.* 這種機器很容易使用。

□ **USEFUL PATTERNS** 有用句型
it is easy for someone to do something; something is easy to do

2 comfortable and without worry or anxiety 舒適的; 安逸的: *He has stopped working now, and leads a very easy life.* 他現在已經不工作了, 過着輕鬆、舒適的生活。 | *with an easy mind* 心情輕鬆地 **3 I'm easy** *infml* = I don't mind at all 〔非正式〕我毫不介意 –**easiness** *n* [U]

☆eas·y² *adv* **easier, easiest 1 easier said than done** easy to talk about doing, but difficult to actually do 說來容易做來難: *Passing exams is much easier said than done.* 要通過考試, 說來容易做來難。 **2 go easy on someone** to be kinder and less severe to someone 對某人寬容 **3 go easy on something** to not use too much of something 節省着用某物 **4 take it easy, take things easy** not to work too hard 不要太拼命工作; 不要太辛苦

easy chair /ˈ·· ·/ *n* a big comfortable chair with arms 〔帶扶手的〕安樂椅

eas·y·go·ing /ˈizɪˈɡoɪŋ, ˌiːziˈɡəʊɪŋ◂/ *adj* not easily worried or annoyed 脾氣隨和的: *He's an easygoing sort of person.* 他是個隨和的人。

☆eat /it; iːt/ *v* **ate** /et; eɪt/, **eaten** /ˈitn; ˈiːtn/ **1** [T] to take food into your mouth and swallow it 吃; 喝: *Eat your dinner!* 吃飯吧! | *Tigers eat meat.* 老虎是吃肉的。 **2** [I] to have a meal 吃飯: *What time do we eat?* 我們甚麼時候吃飯? **3 be eaten up with** to be completely and violently full of feeling such as jealousy or desire 滿懷〔妒忌、慾望〕 **4 eat into something** to damage something by chemical action 腐蝕某物: *The acid had eaten into the metal.* 酸已腐蝕了這塊金屬。 **5 have someone eating out of your hand** to have someone in your power so that they will always do what you tell them to 使某人完全聽命於

eat sthg ↔ **away** *phr v* [T] to destroy something by chemical action 腐蝕〔某物〕

eat up *phr v* [I;T **eat** sthg ↔ **up**] to eat all your food 吃完, 吃光: *She ate up what was left of the pie.* 她吃光了剩下來的餡餅。

ea·ta·ble /ˈitəbl; ˈiːtəbəl/ *adj* fresh enough and pleasant enough to eat 〔食物新鮮〕可吃的

eat·en /ˈitn; ˈiːtn/ the past participle of EAT ☆ EAT 的過去分詞

eat·er /ˈitə; ˈiːtəʳ/ *n* a person who eats in a certain way 食者: *He's a fussy eater.* 他吃東西很挑剔。

eau de co·logne /ˌo də kəˈlon; ˌəʊ də kəˈləʊn/ *n* [U] a kind of perfume that does not have a very strong smell 科隆香水, 古龍香水

eaves /ivz; iːvz/ *n* [pl] the edges of a roof which come out beyond the walls 屋簷: *birds nesting under the eaves* 棲居簷下的鳥兒

E

eaves·drop /ˈivzˌdrɒp; ˈiːvzdrɒp/ *v* **-pp-** [I] to listen secretly to other people's conversation 偷聽〔他人談話〕: *He had eavesdropped on our conversation.* 他偷聽了我們的談話。–**eavesdropper** *n*

ebb¹ /ɛb; eb/ *n* [U] **1** the flow of the sea away from the shore 落潮; 退潮: *The tide is on the ebb.* 潮水正在退落。**2 at a low ebb** not very happy or successful at the moment 處於低潮; 處於衰退狀態: *Fred seems to be at rather a low ebb.* 弗萊德好像情緒很低落。

ebb² *v* [I] **1** (of the sea) to flow away from the shore 〔潮水〕落; 退 **2** *lit* to become gradually weaker 《文》漸漸衰退: *His courage slowly ebbed away.* 他的勇氣慢慢消退了。

eb·o·ny /ˈɛbəni; ˈebəni/ *n* [U] a hard black wood 烏木; 黑檀

e·bul·li·ence /ɪˈbʌljəns; ɪˈbʌliəns/ *n* [U] *fml or lit* the quality of being full of happiness and excitement《正式或文》興高采烈; 歡天喜地 –**ebullient** *adj*: *He arrived at the party in a happy, ebullient mood.* 他快快活活、興高采烈地來參加聚會。

EC /ˌiˈsi; ˌiː ˈsiː/ *n* –see 見 EEC

ec·cen·tric¹ /ɪkˈsɛntrɪk; ɪkˈsentrɪk/ *adj* unusual and rather strange (used of a person or their behaviour) 不尋常的; 古怪的〔指人或行為〕: *The old lady has some eccentric habits.* 這老婦人有些稀奇古怪的習慣。– **eccentrically** /-klɪ; -kli/ *adv* –**eccentricity** /ˌɛksənˈtrɪsɪtɪ; ˌeksenˈtrɪsˌti/, **eccentricities** [C;U]: *his little eccentricities* 他的小怪癖

eccentric² *n* an unusual and rather strange person 行為古怪的人

ec·cle·si·as·tic /ɪˌkliziˈæstɪk; ɪˌkliːziˈæstɪk/ *n* a Christian priest〔基督教的〕傳教士; 牧師

ec·cle·si·as·ti·cal /ɪˌkliziˈæstɪkl; ɪˌkliːziˈæstɪkl/ *adj* (also 又作 **ecclesiastic**) connected with the Christian church 基督教會的: *ecclesiastical history* 教會歷史

ech·o¹ /ˈɛko; ˈekəʊ/ *n* **echoes** a sound sent back or repeated, for example from a wall or inside a cave 回聲; 回音

echo² *v* **echoed, echoing 1** [I] to come back as an echo 產生回聲: *Their voices echoed round the cave.* 他們的聲音在洞內激起回響。**2** [T] to repeat what someone else has said 重複〔他人的話〕; 附和: *His laughter was echoed by the others in the room.* 他一笑, 引得房間裡其他人也笑起來。**3 echo with** to be full of a sound 充滿〔回聲〕: *The room echoed with the sound of music.* 房間裡迴蕩着音樂聲。

é·clair /eˈklɛr; ɪˈkleəʳ/ *n* a finger-shaped pastry with a cream filling inside〔以奶油為餡心的〕手指形鬆餅

e·clipse¹ /ɪˈklɪps; ɪˈklɪps/ *n* **1** [C] the disappearance of the sun's light when the moon passes between it and the earth 日蝕; 月蝕 **2** [C;U] the loss of fame, power, or success〔聲譽、權力、成就等的〕喪失; 黯然失色

eclipse² *v* **eclipsed, eclipsing** [T] **1** to cause an eclipse of the sun or moon 形成日蝕或月蝕: *The moon is partly eclipsed.* 月偏蝕了。**2** to be much better than someone else, with the result that they seem unimportant 勝過〔他人〕; 使〔他人〕黯然失色

e·col·o·gy /ɪˈkɑlədʒi; ɪˈkɒlədʒi/ *n* [U] **1** the pattern of the natural relations of plants, animals, and people to each other and to their surroundings 生態: *the ecology of the rainforest* 雨林生態 **2** the study of ecology 生態學 –**ecologist** *n*

e·co·log·i·cal /ˌikəˈlɑdʒɪkl; ˌiːkəˈlɒdʒɪkəl/ *adj* relating to the ecology of a place and the protection of the plants and animals that are there 生態的; 生態保護的: *the ecological balance of the rainforests* 雨林生態平衡 | *Experts have described the oil slick as an ecological disaster.* 專家們把浮油形容為生態災害。–**ecologically** /-klɪ; -kli/ *adv*

★ec·o·nom·ic /ˌikəˈnɑmɪk; ˌekəˈnɒmɪk◂/ *adj* **1** [only before a noun 只用於名詞前] connected with trade, industry, and wealth 經濟的; 經濟學的: *The country is heading for economic disaster.* 這個國家正面臨一場經濟災難。**2** likely to bring a profit 有經濟效益的, 有利可圖的: *It's no longer economic to run trains to the village.* 這村莊再通火車已無利可圖。

e·co·nom·i·cal /ˌikəˈnɑmɪkl; ˌekəˈnɒmɪkəl/ *adj* **1** not costing a lot of money to use 經濟的; 省錢的: *A small car is more economical than a large one.* 小型汽車比大型的省錢。**2** using only the amount that is necessary, without waste 節儉的: *an economical use of time* 時間的節約使用

e·co·nom·i·cal·ly /ˌikəˈnɑmɪklɪ; ˌekəˈnɒmɪkli/ *adv* **1** not wastefully 不浪費地; 節儉地: *She cooks very economically.* 她做菜很節省。**2** in a way which produces a profit 有利潤地: *Is the company economically viable?* 這公司有利可圖嗎?

★ec·o·nom·ics /ˌikəˈnɑmɪks; ˌekəˈnɒmɪks/ *n* [pl;U] the science or principles of the way in which industry and trade produce and use wealth 經濟學: *The economics of national growth are of great importance to all governments.* 國家的經濟增長對所有的政府而言都是十分重要的。| *He has a degree in economics.* 他有經濟學學位。–**economist** /ɪˈkɑnəmɪst; ɪˈkɒnəmˌst/ *n*

e·con·o·mize /ɪˈkɑnəˌmaɪz; ɪˈkɒnəmaɪz/ *v* (also 又作 **economise** *BrE*〔英式〕) [I] to save money, time, or goods by using them sensibly 節省〔錢、時間或商品〕: *We could economize on petrol by all going in one car.* 我們都坐一輛汽車, 這樣可以節省汽油。

★e·con·o·my¹ /ɪˈkɑnəmɪ; ɪˈkɒnəmi/ *n* **economies 1** [C] the system by which a country's money supply, industry, and trade are organized 經濟體制: *A new government might improve the state* *of the economy.* 一個新政府也許可以改善經濟狀況。**2** [C;U] the careful use of money, time, or goods 節約; 節省: *economy of effort* 精力的節省 | *We will have to make some economies.* 我們得採取一些節約措施。

economy² *adj* [only before a noun 只用於名詞前] cheap or intended to save money 便宜的; 經濟的: *an economy class air ticket* 經濟艙的機票

ec·sta·sy /ˈɛkstəsɪ; ˈɛkstəsi/ *n* **ecstasies 1** [U] a feeling of very great happiness 狂喜: *an expression of ecstasy* 狂喜之態 **2 go into ecstasies** to show that you are very pleased about something 〔對某事物〕十分喜愛; 入迷

ec·stat·ic /ɪkˈstætɪk; ɪkˈstætɪk/ *adj* feeling very happy 狂喜的: *She was ecstatic when I told her the news.* 我告訴她這個消息時，她欣喜若狂。**—ecstatically** /-klɪ; -kli/ *adv*

e·cu·men·i·cal /ˌɛkjuˈmɛnɪkl; ˌiːkjʊˈmɛnɪkəl/ *adj* favouring unity between the different branches of the Christian religion 贊成〔基督教〕不同教派聯合的

ec·ze·ma /ˈɛksɪmə; ˈɛksɪmə/ *n* [U] a medical condition in which your skin is red and swollen 濕疹

ed·dy /ˈɛdɪ; ˈedi/ *n* **eddies** a circular movement of water, wind, smoke, dust, or air 〔水、風、煙、塵土或空氣的〕旋渦; 渦流

edge¹ /ɛdʒ; edʒ/ *n* **1** the part along the outside of something 邊; 邊緣: *the edge of a plate* 碟子的邊 | *the water's edge* 水邊 **2** the point at which something begins to happen 〔某事開始發生的〕邊緣: *This brought us to the edge of disaster.* 這把我們帶到了災難的邊緣。**3** the thin sharp cutting part of a blade or tool 刀口; 刃 **4 have the edge on** to be better than someone or have an advantage over them 勝過〔某人〕; 比〔某人〕優越: *He has the edge on the other students because he works harder.* 他學習刻苦, 所以比其他學生優秀。**5 on edge** nervous and worried 神經質的; 緊張的 **6 -edged** having a certain kind or number of edges 有…邊的; 有…刀口的: *a two-edged sword* 雙刃劍

edge² *v* **edged, edging 1** [T] to place an edge or border on something 給〔某物〕加邊: *a white handkerchief edged with blue* 鑲藍邊的白手絹 **2** [I+adv/prep; T+adv/prep] to move very slowly 徐徐移動: *He edged away.* 他慢慢挪開了。| *She edged her chair closer to mine.* 她把椅子挪近我的椅子。

edge·ways /ˈɛdʒwez; ˈedʒweɪz/ *adv* **1** sideways 從旁邊; 斜着 **2 I couldn't get a word in edgeways** = I couldn't say anything because someone else was talking all the time 我插不上嘴

edg·ing /ˈɛdʒɪŋ; ˈedʒɪŋ/ *n* something that forms an edge or border 邊緣; 飾邊: *a white handkerchief with a blue edging* 鑲藍邊的白手絹

edg·y /ˈɛdʒɪ; ˈedʒi/ *adj infml* nervous 〔非正式〕緊張不安的: *She's been a bit edgy lately,*

waiting for the examination results. 她近來一直有點兒緊張, 正在等待考試成績公佈。

ed·i·ble /ˈɛdəbl; ˈedɪbəl/ *adj* able to be eaten safely 可以食用的: *Can you tell the difference between edible and poisonous berries?* 你能區別出可吃的和有毒的草莓嗎? **—opposite** 反義 **inedible**

e·dict /ˈidɪkt; ˈiːdɪkt/ *n fml* an official public order made by a person in power 〔正式〕佈告; 法令

ed·i·fice /ˈɛdəfɪs; ˈedɪfɪs/ *n fml* a large fine building 〔正式〕宏偉的建築物

ed·i·fy /ˈɛdəfaɪ; ˈedɪfaɪ/ *v* **edified, edifying** [T] *fml* to improve someone's mind or character 〔正式〕開導; 啟發: *He always reads edifying books.* 他總是讀些有啟發性的書籍。**—edification** /ˌɛdəfəˈkeʃən; ˌedɪfɪˈkeɪʃən/ *n* [U]

ed·it /ˈɛdɪt; ˈedɪt/ *v* [T] to prepare a book, newspaper, or film for printing or showing by removing mistakes and deciding what parts should be included or left out 編輯〔書籍、報紙等〕

★**e·di·tion** /ɪˈdɪʃən; ɪˈdɪʃən/ *n* one printing of a book, newspaper, or magazine 〔書、報紙或雜誌的〕版(次); 版本: *a new edition of the dictionary* 詞典的新版本

★**ed·i·tor** /ˈɛdɪtɚ; ˈedɪtə/ *n* **1** a person who edits something such as a book, newspaper article, or film before it is printed or shown 〔書籍、報刊文章的〕編輯; 〔電影的〕剪輯者 **2** a person in charge of a newspaper or magazine 〔報刊、雜誌的〕主編: *the editor of the Daily Mail* 《每日電郵報》的主編

ed·i·to·ri·al¹ /ˌɛdəˈtorɪəl; ˌedɪˈtɔːrɪəl/ *adj* belonging to or done by an editor 編輯的; 編者的: *an editorial office* 編輯室 **—editorially** *adv*

editorial² *n* a part of newspaper giving the editor's opinion on a problem or event 〔報刊的〕社論

ed·u·cate /ˈɛdʒəket; ˈedjʊkeɪt/ *v* **educated, educating** [T] to teach someone, especially in a school or college 〔尤指在學校中〕教育: *He was educated at a very good school.* 他在一所很好的學校受過教育。| *We need to educate the public about the dangers of smoking.* 我們需要教育公眾吸煙是有害的。**—educated** *adj*: *an educated man* 受過教育的人 | *educated tastes in art and literature* 受過訓練的文學及藝術鑑賞力

★★**ed·u·ca·tion** /ˌɛdʒəˈkeʃən; ˌedjʊˈkeɪʃən/ *n* [U] the process of teaching people, especially in a school or college 〔尤指在學校進行的〕教育: *She has had a good education.* 她曾受過良好的教育。| *This government believes in the importance of education.* 這government相信教育的重要性。

★**ed·u·ca·tion·al** /ˌɛdʒəˈkeʃənl; ˌedjʊˈkeɪʃənəl/ *adj* **1** of or about education 教育的: *an educational establishment* 教育機構 **2** providing information or teaching you something 教

育性的; 起教育作用的: *an educational film* 教育電影〔有教育意義的電影〕 **-educationally** *adv*

ed·u·ca·tion·ist /ˌɛdʒəˈkeɪʃənɪst; ˌedʒʒˈkeɪʃənɪst/ *n* (also 又作 **educationalist**) a specialist in education 教育家

EEC /ˌi i ˈsi; ˌiː iː ˈsiː/ *n* (also 又作 **EC**) a European organization established to encourage trade and friendly relations between its members; an abbreviation for European Economic Community 〔縮〕歐洲經濟共同體〔歐洲旨在促進各成員國之間貿易和友好關係的組織〕

eel /il; iːl/ *n* a long snake-like fish 鰻; 鱔

ee·rie /ˈɪri; ˈɪəri/ *adj* strange and frightening 古怪而可怕的: *walking through the dark, eerie woods* 穿過陰森可怕的樹林 **-eerily** *adv* **-eeriness** *n* [U]

ef·face /ɪˈfes; ɪˈfeɪs/ *v* **effaced, effacing** [T] *fml* to rub something out or remove it 〔正式〕擦去, 抹去, 消除: *Someone has effaced part of the address on this letter.* 有人把這封信上的地址擦掉了一部分。

ef·fect[1] /ɪˈfɛkt; ɪˈfekt/ *n* **1** [C;U] a result 結果; 影響: *the effects of an illness* 疾病的後果 | *The advertising campaign didn't have much effect on sales.* 廣告活動並未對銷售額產生很大作用。 **2 effects** *fml* belongings 〔正式〕財物: *No personal effects are to be left here overnight.* 私人財物不能在這兒放過夜。 **3 in effect: a** in operation 在實施; 有效: *The rules will remain in effect until October.* 這些規章到十月份為止仍然有效。 **b** in fact 實際上: *Although she's his assistant, she has, in effect, full control.* 雖然她是他的助手, 但實際上她完全控制一切。 **4 come into effect** to come into operation 開始實行; 生效: *The rule will come into effect on Monday.* 這條規定將在星期一開始生效。 [RELATED PHRASES 相關詞組 **be brought into effect; be put into effect; go into effect**] **5 take effect** to come into operation or start to have results 實施; 奏效: *The new tax system will take effect next May.* 新稅制自明年五月起生效。 | *The medicine quickly took effect.* 藥很快就見效了。 **6 to this effect, to that effect, to the effect that...** with this meaning 意思是: *He called me a fool or words to that effect.* 他用傻瓜等一類的詞語罵我。

effect[2] *v* [T] *fml* to cause something to happen 〔正式〕使...發生, 產生: *I want to effect changes in the management structure of the company.* 我要促成公司管理結構的改革。 —see 見 AFFECT (USAGE用法)

ef·fec·tive /əˈfɛktɪv; ɪˈfektɪv/ *adj* **1** producing the desired result 產生預期結果的; 有效的: *His efforts to improve the school have been very effective.* 他為改進這所學校作出的努力是卓有成效的。 **-opposite 反義 ineffective 2** actual or real 實際的; 真正的: *Although there is a parliament,*

the army is in effective control of the country. 雖然有國會, 但實際控制着國家的是軍隊。 **-effectively** *adv* **-effectiveness** *n* [U]

ef·fec·tu·al /əˈfɛktʃʊəl; ɪˈfektʃʊəl/ *adj fml* producing the results intended 〔正式〕奏效的; 收效的: *Measures to combat unemployment have not been very effectual.* 對抗失業問題的措施不太有效。 **-opposite 反義 ineffectual**

ef·fem·i·nate /əˈfɛmənɪt; ˌfemɪnɪt/ *adj* looking or behaving like a woman (used of men, usually to express disapproval) 女人似的〔指男人, 常含貶義〕 **-effeminacy** *n* [U]

ef·fer·vesc·ent /ˌɛfəˈvɛsnt; ˌefəˈvesənt/ *adj fml* 〔正式〕 **1** forming BUBBLES inside (used of liquids) 冒氣泡的; 起泡沫的〔指液體〕 **2** full of life and excitement (used of people) 興高采烈的; 歡騰的〔指人〕 **-effervescence** *n* [U]

ef·fi·ca·cious /ˌɛfəˈkeʃəs; ˌefɪˈkeɪʃəs/ *adj fml* producing the desired effect (used especially of medicines) 〔正式〕奏效的; 見效的〔尤指藥物〕 **-efficacy** /ˈɛfəkəsɪ; ˈefɪkəsɪ/ *n* [U]

ef·fi·cient /əˈfɪʃənt; ɪˈfɪʃənt/ *adj* working well, quickly, and without waste 有效的; 效率高的: *She is a quick, efficient worker.* 她是一個勤快、效率高的工作人員。 | *This new machine is more efficient than the old one.* 這部新機器比那部舊的效率高。 **-opposite 反義 inefficient -efficiently** *adv* **-efficiency** *n* [U]: *attempts to improve efficiency* 改進效率的嘗試

ef·fi·gy /ˈɛfədʒɪ; ˈefɪdʒɪ/ *n* **effigies** *fml* the face or head and body of someone, usually cut out of wood or stone 〔正式〕〔木或石的〕雕像; 肖像: *an effigy of Christ* 耶穌像

ef·flu·ent /ˈɛflʊənt; ˈeflʊənt/ *n* [C;U] *tech* chemical waste or SEWAGE that flows out from a factory or similar place 〔術語〕〔工廠等地方流出的〕廢水; 污水: *Dangerous effluent is being poured into our rivers.* 有害的廢水正流入我們的江河裡。 —see picture on page 470 見 470 頁彩圖

ef·fort /ˈɛfət; ˈefət/ *n* **1** [U] the use of strength or determination 力氣; 努力: *It took a lot of effort to lift the boxes.* 抬起那些箱子要花很大的力氣。 | *We managed to do it without much effort.* 我們沒費多大力氣就設法辦成了。 **2 an effort** something which needs strength or determination to do 費力的事情: *It was an effort to get up this morning.* 今早晨起床很是費勁。 **3** [C] an attempt to do something, especially one done with a lot of determination 〔尤指勉力的〕嘗試: *Despite all our efforts, we failed.* 儘管我們盡了全力, 我們還是失敗了。 **4 make an effort to do something** to try very hard to do something 勉力想做某事: *He made an effort to arrive on time.* 他盡力準時到達。

ef·fort·less /ˈɛfətlɪs; ˈefətlɪs/ *adj* seeming

to need very little effort 不需費力的; 容易
的: *She skis with such effortless ease.* 她滑起
雪來輕鬆自如。—**effortlessly** *adv*

ef·fron·te·ry /əˈfrʌntərɪ; ɪˈfrʌntəri/ *n* [U]
bold or rude behaviour 厚顏無恥的行為

ef·fu·sive /ɛˈfjusɪv; ɪˈfjuːsɪv/ *adj* showing too
much pleasure or thanks 過分熱情的: *I was
taken aback by her effusive welcome.* 她過分
熱情的歡迎使我大吃一驚。

EFL /ˌi ɛf ˈɛl; ˌiː ef ˈel/ *n* relating to the
teaching of English to people whose first
language is not English; an abbreviation
for **English as a foreign language** 〖縮〗〔對
母語不是英語的人進行的英語教學〕非母語英
語課程

e.g. /ˌi ˈdʒi; ˌiː ˈdʒi/ for example; an abbreviation for the Latin words **exempli gratia**
〖縮〗例如〖源於拉丁文 exempli gratia〗: *sweet
foods, e.g. cake, chocolate, sugar, and ice
cream* 甜食, 例如蛋糕、巧克力、糖和冰淇淋

e·gal·i·tar·i·an /ɪˌgælɪˈtɛrɪən; ɪˌɡælɪˈteəriən/
adj fml having the belief that all people
are equal and should have equal rights 〖正
式〗平等主義的; 主張平等的

★**egg**[1] /ɛg; eɡ/ *n* **1** [C;U] a rounded object
with a hard shell, which can contain a baby
bird, insect, or snake; eggs are often eaten
as food 〔雞、鳥、蛇等的〕蛋; 〔昆蟲等的〕卵:
Each female lays five or six eggs. 每隻雌鳥下
五、六個蛋。| *I never eat bacon and egg.* 我
從不吃煙肉和蛋。| *A dozen eggs, please.* 請
給我一打蛋。—see picture on page 504 見
504 頁彩圖 **2** [C] a cell produced inside a
female that can develop into a baby if it
joins with the male SPERM 卵; 卵細胞 **3 put
all your eggs in one basket** *infml* to risk
everything you have on the success of one
thing 〖非正式〗孤注一擲

egg[2] *v*

egg sbdy ↔ **on** *phr v* [T] to give someone
encouragement to do something foolish or
daring 慫恿〔某人做愚蠢或魯莽的事〕: *I didn't
mean to do it. The others just egged me on.*
我本不打算幹的, 其他人偏慫恿我。

egg·beat·er /ˈɛg,bitə; ˈeɡbiːtə/ *n* a kitchen
tool with a turning handle, used for mixing
打蛋器 —see picture on page 958 見 958 頁
彩圖

egg·cup /ˈɛg,kʌp; ˈeg-kʌp/ *n* a small container which you put a boiled egg in so
that you can eat it easily 〔盛放帶殼煮熟的蛋
的〕蛋杯

egg·head /ˈɛg,hɛd; ˈeɡhed/ *n* a person who
is very highly educated but not very good
at practical things 學者; 學究〔學歷高而不太
懂實際問題的人〕

egg·plant /ˈɛg,plænt; ˈeɡplɑːnt/ *n AmE* [C;
U] a plant that has a large purple fruit
which is eaten as a vegetable 〖美式〗茄子

egg·shell /ˈɛg,ʃɛl; ˈeɡʃel/ *n* the thin hard
part around the outside of an egg 蛋殼

e·go /ˈigo; ˈiːɡəʊ/ *n* your opinion of your
own importance 自我; 自尊: *It was quite a
blow to her ego when she failed her driving
test.* 她沒通過駕駛考試對她的自尊是一大打擊。

e·go·cen·tric /ˌigoˈsɛntrɪk; ˌiːɡəʊˈsentrɪk/
adj thinking only about yourself and what
you want (a word used to express disapproval) 自私自利的; 自我中心的〔含貶義〕

e·go·is·m /ˈigo,ɪzəm; ˈiːɡəʊɪzəm/ *n* [U] behaviour that shows that you are always
thinking about yourself and not other
people (a word used to express disapproval) 利己心; 自私〖含貶義〗 –**egoist** *n* –
egoistic /ˌigoˈɪstɪk; ˌiːɡəʊˈɪstɪk/ *adj*

e·go·tis·m /ˈigə,tɪzəm; ˈeɡətɪzəm/ *n* [U] the
tendency to talk too much about yourself
and to believe that you are better and
more important than other people (a word
used to express disapproval) 自誇; 自負; 自
大〖含貶義〗 –**egotist** *n* –**egotistic** /ˌiɡəˈtɪstɪk;
ˌiːɡəˈtɪstɪk/ *adj*

ei·der·down /ˈaɪdə,daʊn; ˈaɪdədaʊn/ *n* a
thick warm bed covering filled with feathers or soft material 羽絨被

eight /et; eɪt/ *det, n, pron* the number 8 〔數
字〕八

eigh·teen /eˈtin; ˌeɪˈtiːn◂/ *det, n, pron* the
number 18 〔數字〕十八 –**eighteenth** *det, n,
pron, adv*

eighth /etθ; eɪtθ/ **1** *det, pron, adv* 8th 第八 **2**
n one of eight equal parts 八分之一

eigh·ty /ˈetɪ; ˈeɪti/ *det, n, pron* **eighties 1** the
number 80 〔數字〕八十 **2 the Eighties, the
eighties** the years 1980-1989 二十世紀八十年
代 **3 in his eighties, in her eighties,** etc.
aged between 80 and 89 在八十歲到八十九
歲之間 –**eightieth** /ˈetɪɪθ; ˈeɪtiɪθ/ *det, n,
pron, adv*

★**ei·ther**[1] /ˈiðə; ˈaɪðə/ *det, pron* **1** one or
the other of two people or
things 兩者中的任何一個; 兩者之一: *There's
coffee or tea – you can have either.* 咖啡或茶
都有, 你可以任選一種。| *Is either of the boys
coming?* 這兩個男孩中有哪個要來嗎? **2** both
of two things 〔兩者中的〕每一個: *He sat in
the car with a policeman on either side of
him.* 他坐在汽車裡, 兩旁各坐着一名警察。

■ USAGE 用法: In the sentence *Is
either of you ready?* the pronoun
either is used with the singular verb *is*.
This is the usual pattern in formal
writing, but in speech and informal
writing many people use a plural verb
☆ 在 "*Is either of you ready?*" (你們倆有
誰準備好了嗎) 這個句子中, 代名詞
either 後面用單數動詞 *is*, 在正式文字中
這是常用句型, 但在口語和非正式文字中,
很多人用複數動詞: *Are* **either** *of you
ready?* 你們倆有誰準備好了嗎? (The
same is true for **neither** and **none.** ☆
neither 和 **none** 也是同樣情況。)

☆☆either² *conj* used at the beginning or a list of possibilities; the other possibilities are introduced by "or" 不是… 就是…; 或是…或是…〔用於引出由"or"連接的一系列可能性〕: *The baby will be born either at home or in the local hospital.* 這嬰兒不是在家裡出生, 就是在當地醫院出生。| *Either say you're sorry or get out!* 你要麼道歉, 要麼就滾! | *It was either in 1964, 1965, or 1966 – I can't remember.* 不是在 1964 年、1965 年, 就是在 1966 年──我記不起了。

> ■ USAGE 用法: **Either...or** and **neither...nor** are usually followed by a plural verb and a plural pronoun, except in formal English **either...or** 和 **neither...nor** 後面通常用複數動詞和複數代名詞, 但正式英語中除外: *If either John or Mary are here, they will get the message.* 如果約翰或瑪麗在這兒, 他們便會得到這個消息。In formal English this would be *If either John or Mary is here, he or she will get the message.* 在正式英語中是 *If either John or Mary is here, he or she will get the message.* 如果約翰或瑪麗在這兒, 他或她就會得到這個消息。(The same is true for **neither... nor. neither...nor** 也是同樣情況。)

either³ *adv* [used with negatives 與否定式連用] also; you use "either" when you add another negative idea 也(不…)〔用於補充另一否定說法〕: *I haven't read this book, and none of the other students has either.* 我沒讀過這本書, 其他學生也沒讀過。| *"I can't swim." "I can't either."* "我不會游泳。""我也不會。"

e·jac·u·late /ɪˈdʒækjəˌleɪt; ɪˈdʒækjʊ̩leɪt/ *v* **ejaculated, ejaculating** [I;T] **1** *fml* to say or shout something suddenly 〔正式〕突然說(出); 突然喊(出) **2** to let out SEMEN suddenly and with force through the PENIS 射精 **–ejaculation** /ɪˌdʒækjəˈleɪʃən; ɪˌdʒækjʊ̩ˈleɪʃən/ *n* [C;U]

e·ject /ɪˈdʒɛkt; ɪˈdʒɛkt/ *v* [T] *fml* to push or throw someone or something out with force 〔正式〕投出; 噴出; 逐出: *Two boys were ejected from the cinema by the police last night.* 昨晚兩個男孩被警察趕出了電影院。**– ejection** /ɪˈdʒɛkʃən; ɪˈdʒɛkʃən/ *n* [C;U]

eke /ik; iːk/ *v* **eked, eking**

   eke sthg ↔ **out** *phr v* [T] to make a small supply last as long as possible 盡量維持: *During the war we had to eke out our food rations.* 戰爭期間我們不得不盡量節省食物給, 才可多吃上些日子。

e·lab·o·rate¹ /ɪˈlæbərɪt; ɪˈlæbərət/ *adj* full of detail with a large number of parts or very carefully planned 詳盡的; 精心製作的: *She wore an elaborate costume.* 她穿了一件做工精細的衣服。| *Elaborate precautions were taken to ensure her safety.* 為保證她的安全,

已採取了周詳的預防措施。**–elaborately** *adv*

e·lab·o·rate² /ɪˈlæbəˌret; ɪˈlæbəreɪt/ *v* **elaborated, elaborating** [I;T] *fml* to add more detail to something so that it is easier to understand 〔正式〕詳細說明: *Would you care to elaborate a little on what you have already said?* 你能對剛才所說的詳細地說明一下嗎?

e·lapse /ɪˈlæps; ɪˈlæps/ *v* **elapsed, elapsing** [I] *fml* (of time) to pass 〔正式〕〔時間〕逝去; 流逝: *A month elapsed before they could make a final decision.* 過了一個月他們才做出最後決定。

e·las·tic¹ /ɪˈlæstɪk; ɪˈlæstɪk/ *n* [U] a long thin piece of rubber material which springs back into shape after being stretched; elastic is often used in clothing, for example round the waist 有彈性的材料; 橡皮筋; 鬆緊帶〔常用於衣服上, 如圍在腰部〕

elastic² *adj* **1** able to spring back into shape after being stretched 有彈力的; 有彈性的: *The skirt had an elastic waistband.* 那條裙子有鬆緊腰帶。**2** able to change if the situation changes 靈活的; 可順應(變化)的: *The rules are elastic.* 這些規則很有彈性的。**–elasticity** /ɪˌlæsˈtɪsətɪ; ˌiːlæsˈtɪsɪ̩ti/ *n* [U]

elastic band /·ˌ·· ˈ·/ *n* a thin piece of elastic which is used to hold things together 橡皮筋; 橡皮圈

e·lat·ed /ɪˈletɪd; ɪˈleɪtɪ̩d/ *adj* very happy and excited 興高采烈的: *The crowds were elated by the appearance of the new president.* 新任總統的露面使羣眾歡欣鼓舞。**–elation** /ɪˈleʃən; ɪˈleɪʃən/ *n* [U]

el·bow¹ /ˈɛlˌbo; ˈelbəʊ/ *n* **1** the joint in the middle of your arm where it bends 肘 **2** the part of a shirt, or coat which covers the middle part of your arm 〔衣服的〕肘部

elbow² *v* [T+adv/prep] to push someone away with the middle part of your arm bent in front of you 用肘推; 用肘擠: *He elbowed his way through the crowd.* 他用肘推着, 從人羣中擠過去。

el·bow-room /ˈɛlboˌrum; ˈelbəʊrʊm/ *n* [U] freedom to move or do as you want to 可自由活動的空間

el·der¹ /ˈɛldə; ˈeldəʳ/ *adj* [only before a noun 只用於名詞前] the older of two people in a family 〔家庭中的兩個人〕年齡較大的: *My elder brother is a nurse.* 我的哥哥是護士。| *My elder daughter is married.* 我的大女兒結婚了。

> ■ USAGE 用法: Compare 比較 **elder** and 和 **older**. We use **elder** only to talk about people in families and we do not use it in comparisons. We use **older** to make comparisons between all kinds of people and things ☆ **elder** 只用於談論家庭中的成員, 而不用於比較; **older** 用於各種人或物的比較: *Mary is*

> *Tom's* **elder** *sister.* 瑪麗是湯姆的姐姐。| *Mary is* **older** *than Tom.* 瑪麗比湯姆年長。

elder² *n* **1** the older of two people〔兩人中〕年齡較大者: *Which is the elder of the two sisters?* 兩姐妹中誰年紀較大? **2** older people 長者; 長輩: *As children, we were taught to respect our elders.* 我們小時候就教育要尊敬長者。**3** someone holding a respected official position 高官; 首長: *a Church elder* 教會長老 **4** a small tree with white flowers and red or black berries 接骨木〔一種長有白花, 結紅色或黑色漿果的小樹〕

★el·der·ly /ˈɛldəlɪ; ˈeldəli/ *adj euph*【委婉】**1** old (a more polite word for **old**) 年老的〔**old** 更禮貌的説法〕: *My father is getting rather elderly.* 我父親已上了年紀。**2** **the elderly** old people in general (a more polite expression than "old people"〔總稱〕老年人〔比 "old people" 更禮貌〕

el·dest /ˈɛldɪst; ˈeldₔst/ *n* the person in a family who is the oldest of three or more〔家庭中三人或三人以上〕最年長的: *She has three children, and her eldest has just started school.* 她有三個孩子, 最大的一個剛開始上學。—**eldest** *adj*

★e·lect¹ /ɪˈlɛkt; ɪˈlekt/ *v* [T] **1** to choose someone for an official position by voting 選舉; 推選: *She was elected treasurer.* 她被選為財務主管。| *John Major has been elected* **as** *leader of the Conservative Party.* 約翰·梅傑被選為保守黨領袖。| *They elected her to represent them on the committee.* 他們推選她在委員會作他們的代表。

> □ USEFUL PATTERNS 有用句型
> to elect someone; to elect someone as something; to elect someone to do something

2 **elect to do something** *fml* to decide to do something 【正式】決定(做…), 選擇(做…): *She elected to return to work after her baby was born.* 她決定孩子出生後再回去上班。

elect² *adj* [only after a noun 只用於名詞後] *fml*【正式】chosen for a position, but not yet officially in it 當選而尚未就職的, 候任的: *the president elect* 候任總統

★★e·lec·tion /ɪˈlɛkʃən; ɪˈlekʃən/ *n* [C;U] a process in which you choose someone to represent you, or for an official position by voting for them 選舉; 推選: *Have you heard the election results?* 你聽到選舉結果了嗎? | *Representatives are chosen by election.* 代表們是由選舉產生的。| *She's standing for election.* 她在參加競選。| *Labour did badly in the last election.* 工黨在上屆選舉中表現糟糕。

elec·tor /ɪˈlɛktə; ɪˈlektəʳ/ *n* someone who has the right to vote in an election 有選舉

權的人, 選民 —**electoral** *adj*: *Have you checked that your name is on the electoral roll?* 你有沒有核查過你的名字是否在選民名冊上?

e·lec·to·rate /ɪˈlɛktərɪt; ɪˈlektərₔt/ *n* [+sing/pl verb] all the people in a country or an area who have the right to vote in an election 全體選民

★e·lec·tric /ɪˈlɛktrɪk; ɪˈlektrɪk/ *adj* **1** worked by electricity 用電的; 電動的: *an electric cooker* 電爐 | *an electric razor* 電動剃鬚刀 **2** producing, produced by, or carrying electricity 發電的; 電力產生的; 導電的: *an electric plug* 電插頭 | *an electric generator* 發電機 **3** very exciting 令人興奮的: *The atmosphere at the concert was electric.* 音樂會的氣氛令人興奮。

> ■ USAGE 用法: Compare 比較 **electric** and 和 **electrical**. **Electric** has a more direct association with electricity. We use **electric** for things that produce electricity ☆ **electric** 和電有着更為直接的聯繫; 我們用 **electric** 來指產生電的東西: *an electric generator* 發電機, things directly produced by electricity ☆由電直接產生的東西也用 **electric**: *an electric shock* 觸電 | *an electric spark* 電火花, and particular types of machines worked by electricity ☆用電操作的某些機器也用 **electric**: *an electric clock* 電鐘 | *an electric light* 電燈。We use **electrical** for people ☆ **electrical** 用於指人: *an electrical engineer* 電機工程師 or things associated with electricity in a general way ☆通常與電有關係的東西也用 **electrical**: *electrical apparatus* 電器設備 | *an electrical fault in the system* 系統中的電力故障

e·lec·tri·cal /ɪˈlɛktrɪkl; ɪˈlektrɪkəl/ *adj* concerned with or using electricity 與電有關的; 用電的: *an electrical engineer* 電機工程師 | *an electrical fault* 電力故障 —compare 比較 ELECTRIC —see 見 ELECTRIC (USAGE用法) —**electrically** /-klɪ; -kli/ *adv*: *an electrically powered motor* 電動馬達

electric chair /·ˌ·· ˈ·/ *n* (also 又作 **the chair** *infml* 【非正式】) a punishment of death, used in some states of the US, in which a person is tied to a chair and is killed by a powerful electric current 電椅〔美國某些州使用的一種處以死刑的刑具〕

el·ec·tri·cian /ɪˌlɛkˈtrɪʃən; ɪˌlekˈtrɪʃən/ *n* someone whose job is to fit and repair electrical machinery 電器技師; 電工

★e·lec·tri·ci·ty /ɪˌlɛkˈtrɪsətɪ; ɪˌlekˈtrɪsₔti/ *n* [U] the power which is used for heating, lighting, and making some machines work 電

electric shock /·ˌ·· ˈ·/ *n* a sudden feeling of pain caused by touching something which has electricity flowing through it 觸電

e·lec·tri·fy /ɪˈlɛktrəˌfaɪ; ɪˈlektr̩faɪ/ v **electrified, electrifying** [T] **1** to change something to a system using electric power 使電氣化: *The national railways have now been electrified.* 全國鐵路現已實現了電氣化。**2** to excite or surprise someone very much 使極其激動; 使興奮: *The band gave an electrifying performance.* 樂隊的演奏激動人心。 **-electrification** /ɪˌlɛktrəfəˈkeʃən; ɪˌlektr̩fɪˈkeɪʃən/ n [U]

e·lec·tro·cute /ɪˈlɛktrəˌkjut; ɪˈlektrəkjuːt/ v **electrocuted, electrocuting** [T] to kill someone by passing an electric current through their body 以電刑處死〔某人〕 **-electrocution** /ɪˌlɛktrəˈkjuʃən; ɪˌlektrəˈkjuːʃən/ n [C;U]

e·lec·trode /ɪˈlɛktrod; ɪˈlektrəʊd/ n tech a small piece of metal that carries an electric current to or from electrical apparatus〔術語〕電極

e·lec·tron /ɪˈlɛktrɑn; ɪˈlektrɒn/ n tech one of the parts of an atom that has a NEGATIVE electric charge〔術語〕電子

***e·lec·tron·ic** /ɪˌlɛkˈtrɑnɪk; ɪˌlekˈtrɒnɪk/ adj relating to machinery such as radios, television, and computers, which work by means of an electric current passing through different parts of them 電子的; 用電子操作的; 電子器件的 **-electronically** /-klɪ; -klɪ/ adv

e·lec·tron·ics /ɪˌlɛkˈtrɑnɪks; ɪˌlekˈtrɒnɪks/ n [U] the study or making of machinery that works electronically 電子學; 電子器件(的製造): *the electronics industry* 電子工業

el·e·gant /ˈɛləɡənt; ˈelɪɡənt/ adj with a pleasing and stylish appearance〔外表〕高雅的; 優美的; 漂亮的: *an elegant woman* 高雅的女人 | *an elegant piece of furniture* 一件精美的家具 **-opposite** 反義 **inelegant** **-elegantly** adv **-elegance** n [U]

el·e·gy /ˈɛlədʒɪ; ˈelɪdʒɪ/ n **elegies** a sad poem or song for someone who has died 哀歌; 輓詩; 輓歌

★★ **el·e·ment** /ˈɛləmənt; ˈelɪmənt/ n **1** tech a substance that consists of only one type of atom〔術語〕元素 **2 an element of** a small amount of something 少量; 少許: *There is an element of truth in what you say.* 你說的有些道理。**3** a part of a whole 組成部分; 部件: *Publicizing the company is an important element of the job.* 為公司做宣傳是工作的一個重要部分。**4** the metal part of a piece of electrical apparatus which changes the electric current into heat 電熱元件 **5 the elements** the weather, especially bad conditions〔尤指惡劣的〕天氣: *Shall we brave the elements and go for a walk?* 我們別管這壞天氣, 出去散步好嗎? **6** a group of people with similar aims or beliefs〔有相似目標或信仰的〕一羣人: *The rowdy element in the class spoils things for the rest.* 班裡那些

搗亂分子把其他人的事情都弄糟了。**7 in your element** doing what you are happiest doing 為個人所樂而為; 適得其所

el·e·men·tal /ˌɛləˈmɛntl; ˌelɪˈmentl⁄ adj like the powerful forces of nature (像)自然力的

el·e·men·ta·ry /ˌɛləˈmɛntərɪ; ˌelɪˈmentərɪ⁄ adj **1** simple and easy 簡單的; 容易的 **2** concerned with the most simple rules and methods 基礎的, 基本的: *some elementary exercises for the piano* 一些基礎鋼琴練習

el·e·phant /ˈɛləfənt; ˈelɪfənt/ n a very large grey animal, with a long nose called a TRUNK 象

el·e·vate /ˈɛləˌvet; ˈelɪveɪt/ v **elevated, elevating** [T] **1** to make your mind or soul better or more educated 使〔思想、心靈〕更高尚; 使更有教養: *an elevating experience* 陶冶心靈的經歷 | *Can't you read something more elevating than those silly romantic novels?* 你就不能讀點比那些傻乎乎的浪漫小說更有益心靈的東西嗎? **2** fml to raise something or someone to a higher position〔正式〕提高〔某物〕; 提升〔某人〕: *He was elevated to the rank of captain.* 他被提升為上尉〔船長〕。

el·e·va·ted /ˈɛləˌvetɪd; ˈelɪveɪtɪd/ adj in a high position 抬高的; 架高的

el·e·va·tion /ˌɛləˈveʃən; ˌelɪˈveɪʃən/ n **1** [sing] a particular height above sea-level 海拔: *The ski resort is at an elevation of 3000 metres.* 這個滑雪勝地在海拔三千米的高度。**2** [C] tech a drawing of the front, back, or side of a building〔術語〕〔建築物〕立視圖: *the front elevation of a house* 房子的正面立視圖 **3** [U] fml the act of raising someone to a higher position〔正式〕提升; 晉級: *His elevation to First Secretary was announced yesterday.* 昨天宣佈了他被提升為一等祕書。

***el·e·va·tor** /ˈɛləˌvetə; ˈelɪveɪtə/ n the usual American word for〔美式〕= LIFT

e·lev·en /ɪˈlɛvən; ɪˈlevən/ det, n, pron the number 11〔數字〕十一 **-eleventh** det, n, pron, adv

eleventh hour /·,·· ˈ·/ n **the eleventh hour** the very last moment 最後一刻: *War, which had seemed certain, was averted at the eleventh hour.* 原本看來必定發生的戰爭在最後一刻得以避免。

elf /ɛlf; elf/ n **elves** /ɛlvz; elvz/ a small fairy with pointed ears〔雙耳尖尖的〕小精靈 **-elfin** /ˈɛlfɪn; ˈelfɪn/ adj

e·li·cit /ɪˈlɪsɪt; ɪˈlɪsɪt/ v [T] fml to get information from someone by asking questions〔正式〕〔詢問〕得出; 探出

el·i·gi·ble /ˈɛlɪdʒəbl; ˈelɪdʒɪbəl/ adj **1** [never before a noun 不能用於名詞前] legally allowed to do or receive something〔法律上〕允許做或接受〔某物〕的; 有資格…的: *He will become eligible to vote on his next birthday.* 他過了下個生日時就有資格投票了。| *Is she eligible for sickness pay?* 她有資格獲

得病假工資嗎? **2** suitable as a marriage partner 適合(作為婚姻對象)的; 合意的: *The hostess introduced me to an extremely eligible bachelor.* 女主人把我介紹給一位十分合適的單身漢。 –**eligibility** /ˌelədʒəˈbɪlɪti; ˌelɪ̯dʒɪ̯ˈbɪlɪ̯ti/ *n* [U]

e·lim·i·nate /ɪˈlɪmənet; ɪˈlɪmɪ̯neɪt/ *v* **eliminated, eliminating** [T] **1** to get rid of something 排除, 消除, 根除(某物): *Waste matter is regularly eliminated from the body.* 廢物定期從體內排出。 **2** to lose a round in a competition and stop taking part (比賽中)淘汰: *He was eliminated in the quarter-finals.* 他在半準決賽中被淘汰了。 –**elimination** /ɪˌlɪməˈneʃən; ɪˌlɪmɪ̯ˈneɪʃən/ *n* [U]

e·lite /ɪˈlit; eɪˈliːt/ *n* [+sing/pl verb] a small group of people considered the most important because they are very rich, powerful, or clever (由於有錢、有勢或聰明而被視為)傑出人物; 精英: *the aristocratic elite* 貴族精英

e·lit·is·m /ɪˈlitɪzəm; eɪˈliːtɪzəm/ *n* [U] belief in a system that gives advantages to an elite social group 傑出人物統治論; 精英統治論 –**elitist** *adj*

e·lix·ir /ɪˈlɪksɚ; ɪˈlɪksəʳ/ *n lit* an imaginary liquid having the power to change ordinary metals into gold, or make a person live for ever 《文》靈丹妙藥

elk /ɛlk; elk/ *n* a very large deer, with big flat branching horns called ANTLERS 麋; 駝鹿

el·lip·tical /ɪˈlɪptɪkl̩; ɪˈlɪptɪkəl/ *adj* (also 又作 **elliptic**) **1** having the curved shape of a circle when you look at it sideways 橢圓的: *The Earth's path round the sun is elliptical.* 地球繞太陽的軌道是橢圓形的。 **2** a style of writing or speaking that leaves out some words or meaning (文字或語言)隱晦的 –**elliptically** /-klɪ; -klɪ/ *adv*

elm /ɛlm; elm/ *n* [C;U] a tall broad-leaved tree which produces hard heavy wood 榆樹

el·o·cu·tion /ˌɛləˈkjuʃən; ˌeləˈkjuːʃən/ *n* [U] the art of speaking well and clearly in public 演講技巧; 演說術

e·lon·gat·ed /ɪˈlɔŋgetɪd; ˈiːlɒŋɡeɪtɪ̯d/ *adj* long and thin 細長的

e·lope /ɪˈlop; ɪˈləʊp/ *v* **eloped, eloping** [I] to run away secretly with a lover and get married 私奔: *She eloped with her tutor.* 她和她的家庭教師私奔了。 –**elopement** *n* [C;U]

el·o·quent /ˈɛləkwənt; ˈeləkwənt/ *adj fml* able to express ideas and opinions well, so that the hearers are influenced (正式)雄辯的; 有口才的: *He's an eloquent speaker.* 他是位能言善辯的演說者。 –**eloquently** *adv* –**eloquence** *n* [U]

else /ɛls; els/ *adv* **1** a word you use to refer to people or things besides the ones that have already been mentioned 另外; 其他: *Who else would like a drink?* 還有其他人要喝酒嗎? | *If you don't like it here,*

you'd better go somewhere else. 如果你不喜歡這兒, 你最好去別的地方。 | *Apart from John, there was nobody else there that I knew.* 除了約翰以外, 我不認識那兒的其他人。 | *I'm afraid there's nothing else to eat.* 我恐怕沒別的可吃了。 | *She looked odd, as if she was wearing someone else's clothes.* 她模樣古怪, 好像是穿了別人的衣服。 **2 or else:** **a** a phrase you use when you are saying what might happen if someone does not do what you suggest 否則; 不然(用於某人如不照建議的去做, 將會發生某事): *You'd better leave now, or else you'll miss your train.* 你最好現在就走, 否則你會趕不上火車的。 | *Pay me now, or else there'll be trouble!* 現在就付錢給我, 否則你就麻煩了! **b** a phrase you use when you are giving a second possibility 也可能(用於表示第二種可能性): *Perhaps he's still at work, or else in a pub somewhere.* 他可能還在工作, 也可能在某處酒吧裡。

★**else·where** /ˈɛls,hwɛr; els'weəʳ/ *adv* in or to another place 在(去)別處; *The effects of the war will be felt in this country and elsewhere.* 這個國家和其他一些地方將遭受戰爭的影響。 | *If you don't like my food, you can go elsewhere to eat!* 要是你不喜歡我煮的東西, 你可以到別處去吃!

ELT /ˌi el ˈti; ˌiː el ˈtiː/ *n* the principles and practice of teaching English to speakers of other languages; an abbreviation for **English Language Teaching** 《縮》(對母語不是英語者進行的)英語教學

e·lu·ci·date /ɪˈlusə,det; ɪˈluːsɪ̯deɪt/ *v* **elucidated, elucidating** [T] *fml* to make something clear by explaining it fully 《正式》解釋(某事物); 闡明

e·lude /ɪˈlud; ɪˈluːd/ *v* **eluded, eluding** [T] **1** it eludes me = I cannot remember or understand it 我記不起來; 這難倒我了: *The meaning of his speech eludes me.* 他演說的意思我不大明白。 | *His name eludes me for the moment.* 他的名字我一時想不起來了。 **2** to avoid or escape from someone, especially by means of a trick (尤指機敏地)避開(某人); 逃避: *The fox eluded the hunters.* 狐狸擺脫了獵人。

e·lu·sive /ɪˈlusɪv; ɪˈluːsɪv/ *adj* difficult to find or remember 難以找到的; 難以記住的: *I've been trying to get him on the phone, but he's very elusive.* 我一直在打電話找他, 但他很難找。 –**elusively** *adv* –**elusiveness** *n* [U]

elves /ɛlvz; elvz/ the plural of ELF ☆ ELF 的複數形式

'em /əm; əm/ *pron infml* short for 《非正式》縮約式 = THEM

e·ma·ci·at·ed /ɪˈmeʃɪ,etɪd; ɪˈmeɪʃieɪtɪ̯d/ *adj* very thin and weak because of illness or lack of food (因疾病或缺少食物而變得)消瘦的; 憔悴的 –see 見 THIN[1] (USAGE 用法) –**emaciation** /ɪˌmeʃɪˈeʃən; ɪˌmeɪsɪˈeɪʃən/ *n* [U]

em·a·nate /ˈɛmə,net; ˈeməneɪt/ *v* **emanated, emanating emanate from** to come from 發源於; 從…散發出: *Do you know where these rumours emanate from?* 你知道這些謠言出自何處嗎？

e·man·ci·pate /ɪˈmænsəˌpet; ɪˈmænsɪˌpeɪt/ *v fml* **emancipated, emancipating** [T] to make someone free socially, politically, or legally 〖正式〗使〔某人〕不受〔社會習俗、政治或法律等的〕束縛; 解放 **—emancipation** /ɪˌmænsəˈpeʃən; ɪˌmænsɪˈpeɪʃən/ *n* [U]: *the emancipation of women* 婦女的解放 | *emancipation from slavery* 從奴役中解放出來

em·balm /ɪmˈbɑm; ɪmˈbɑːm/ *v* [T] to put chemicals and oils on a dead body to prevent its decay 〔用藥物、油〕對〔屍體〕進行防腐處理

em·bank·ment /ɪmˈbæŋkmənt; ɪmˈbæŋkmənt/ *n* a wide wall which is built to keep water back or to carry a road or railway over low ground 堤岸; 路堤: *The Thames Embankment* 泰晤士河河堤

em·bar·go¹ /ɪmˈbɑrgo; ɪmˈbɑːgəʊ/ *n* **embargoes** an official order to stop trade with another country 〔與另一國家的〕禁止貿易令; 禁運: *an oil embargo* 石油禁運 | *They've decided to lift the embargo on meat imports from Europe.* 他們決定對歐洲進口的肉類實行禁運。

em·bar·go² *v* **embargoed, embargoing** [T] to officially stop trade with another country 禁止貿易; 禁運

em·bark /ɪmˈbɑrk; ɪmˈbɑːk/ *v* [I] **1** to get on a ship before the start of its voyage 上船: *We embarked at Southampton, and disembarked in New York a week later.* 我們在南安普敦上船，一星期後在紐約下船。**2 embark on something** to start something new, difficult, or exciting 開始, 從事〔指新的、難的或令人激動的事物〕: *Haven't you left it rather late to embark on a new career?* 你開始一份新的職業是不是已經晚了? **–embarkation** /ˌɛmbɑrˈkeʃən; ˌembɑːˈkeɪʃən/ *n* [C;U]: *the port of embarkation* 登船港

em·bar·rass /ɪmˈbærəs; ɪmˈbærəs/ *v* [T] to make someone feel ashamed or uncomfortable in front of other people 使窘迫 **– embarrassment** *n* [C;U]: *He could not hide his embarrassment.* 他沒法掩蓋自己的窘態。

em·bar·rassed /ɪmˈbærəst; ɪmˈbærəst/ *adj* ashamed, nervous, or uncomfortable in front of other people 窘迫的; 尷尬的; 侷促不安的: *I feel so embarrassed when I think of how I behaved.* 一想到自己的表現, 我就覺得十分尷尬。 | *He was too embarrassed to ask her to the cinema.* 他窘迫得沒有請她去看電影。

em·bar·rass·ing /ɪmˈbærəsɪŋ; ɪmˈbærəsɪŋ/ *adj* making you feel ashamed 令人窘迫的: *It was a very embarrassing incident.* 這是件非常難堪的事情。

em·bas·sy /ˈɛmbəsɪ; ˈembəsi/ *n* **embassies** a group of officials living in a foreign country and led by an AMBASSADOR, who represent their government and try to keep good relations between the two countries; **embassy** can also be used for the building where these officials work 大使館全體官員; 大使館

em·bat·tled /ɛmˈbætld; ɪmˈbætld/ *adj* continually troubled by problems 受困擾的: *He's leading an increasingly embattled Labour Party.* 他在領導一個麻煩不斷增加的工黨。

em·bed·ded /ɪmˈbɛdɪd; ɪmˈbedɪd/ *adj* fixed firmly and deeply 牢牢[深深]地嵌入的: *He found his bucket firmly embedded in the new concrete.* 他發現自己的水桶牢牢地嵌在新澆的混凝土裡了。

em·bel·lish /ɪmˈbɛlɪʃ; ɪmˈbelɪʃ/ *v* [T] **1** to add decorations in order to make something more beautiful 美化; 裝飾; 修飾: *a white hat embellished with pink roses* 一頂用粉紅色玫瑰裝飾的白帽子 **2** to add details which may not be true to a story to make it more interesting 給〔敘述〕添加細節; 潤飾; 對…加以渲染 **–embellishment** *n* [C;U]

em·ber /ˈɛmbɚ; ˈembəʳ/ *n* **embers** red-hot pieces of wood or coal that remain in a fire when there are no more flames 〔煤塊或木塊的〕餘燼; 餘火

em·bez·zle /ɪmˈbɛzl; ɪmˈbezəl/ *v* **embezzled, embezzling** [T] to steal money that has been put into your care when it really belongs to the company or organization that you work for 侵吞(財物); 盜用[挪用]〔公款〕 **–embezzlement** *n* [U]

em·bit·tered /ɪmˈbɪtɚd; ɪmˈbɪtəʳd/ *adj* feeling angry, sad, or bitter about what has happened to you 感到憤怒的; 難過的; 痛苦的: *a lonely and embittered man* 孤獨而又痛苦的男子

em·bla·zon /ɛmˈblezn; ɪmˈbleɪzən/ *v* [T] to decorate a shield or flag with a COAT OF ARMS 用紋章裝飾〔盾或旗幟〕

em·blem /ˈɛmbləm; ˈembləm/ *n* an object which is the sign of something 徽章; 象徵; 標誌: *The national emblem of England is a rose.* 英格蘭的標誌是一朵玫瑰花。 **–emblematic** /ˌɛmbləˈmætɪk; ˌembləˈmætɪk◂/ *adj*

em·bod·y /ɪmˈbɑdɪ; ɪmˈbɒdi/ *v* **embodied, embodying** [T] **1** *fml* to contain or include something 〖正式〗包含; 包括〔某物〕**2** to express an idea or quality in something physical 體現; 具體表達: *The ideals of freedom and equality are embodied in the constitution.* 自由平等的理想在憲法中體現出來。**–embodiment** *n*: *He was regarded by his enemies as the embodiment of evil.* 他被敵人視為邪惡的化身。

em·boss /ɪmˈbɔs; ɪmˈbɒs/ *v* [T] to decorate something with a raised pattern 用浮雕圖案裝飾〔某物〕: *The name and address of the firm are embossed on its paper.* 商號的名稱和地址凸印在信箋上。

em·brace¹ /ɪmˈbres; ɪmˈbreɪs/ *v* **embraced,**

embracing 1 [I;T] to take and hold someone as a sign of love 擁抱: *The two sisters embraced.* 兩姐妹互相擁抱。| *She embraced her son tenderly.* 她溫柔地擁抱兒子。 **2** [T] *fml* to include something 〖正式〗包括; 牽涉: *This course of study embraces every aspect of the subject.* 本課程涉及這門學科的各個方面。**3** [T] *fml* to become a believer in a religion or political system 〖正式〗信仰; 信奉

embrace² *n* the holding of someone close to you as a sign of love 擁抱

em·broi·der /ɪmˈbrɔɪdə; ɪmˈbrɔɪdɚ/ *v* [T] **1** to do decorative work with a needle on cloth 在〔織物〕上繡花; 刺繡: *a dress embroidered with flowers* 繡花衣服 **2** to add imaginary details to a story to make it more exciting 對〔敍述〕添枝加葉; 渲染: *Don't embroider the truth!* 別對事實加以渲染!

em·broi·der·y /ɪmˈbrɔɪdəri; ɪmˈbrɔɪdɚi/ *n* [C;U] decorative work done with a needle on cloth or the action of doing this 刺繡(品); 繡花

em·broiled /ɛmˈbrɔɪld; ɪmˈbrɔɪld/ *adj* **get/become embroiled in something** to become part of a difficult situation 捲入糾紛: *I refused to get embroiled in their quarrel.* 我不願捲入他們的爭執之中。

em·bry·o /ˈɛmbrɪ,o; ˈembriəʊ/ *n* **1** the young of any creature in its first state before it is born 胚; 胚胎 **2 in embryo** still being developed 仍在發展中的, 未成熟的 —**embryonic** /ˌɛmbrɪˈɒnɪk; ˌembriˈɒnɪk/ *adj*

em·e·rald /ˈɛmərəld; ˈemərəld/ *n* a bright green precious stone 翡翠; 綠寶石 —**emerald** *adj*

✦**e·merge** /ɪˈmɝdʒ; ɪˈmɜːdʒ/ *v* **emerged, emerging** [I] **1** to come or appear from out of somewhere hidden 出現; 浮現: *The sun emerged from behind the clouds.* 太陽從雲層後面露了出來。**2** to become known 暴露; 被知曉: *The facts began to emerge.* 事實開始為人所知了。**3 it emerged that** = it became known as the result of an enquiry 〔調查後〕露出真相: *It emerged that the driver of the car had been drunk.* 情況明朗了, 汽車司機原來是喝醉了酒。**4** to come out from a difficult situation 〔從困境中〕脫身; 擺脫出來: *The President has emerged from the incident with his reputation intact.* 總統已從事件中脫身, 名譽絲毫未損。—**emergence** *n* [U] *fml* 〖正式〗

✦**e·mer·gen·cy** /ɪˈmɝdʒənsɪ; ɪˈmɜːdʒənsi/ *n* **emergencies** an unexpected and dangerous situation which must be dealt with quickly 緊急情況; 不測事件: *Ring the bell in an emergency.* 情況緊急時請按鈴。| *an emergency exit* 太平門

e·mer·gent /ɪˈmɝdʒənt; ɪˈmɜːdʒənt/ *adj* [only before a noun 只用於名詞前] in the early stages of existence or development

剛出現的; 新興的: *the emergent countries of Africa* 非洲的新興國家

em·i·grate /ˈɛmə,gret; ˈemɪˌɡreɪt/ *v* **emigrated, emigrating** [I] to leave your own country in order to go and live in another country 移居外國: *They emigrated to Australia in 1960.* 他們是在 1960 年移居澳大利亞的。—**emigrant** *n* —**emigration** /ˌɛməˈgreʃən; ˌemɪˈɡreɪʃən/ *n*

> ■ USAGE 用法: Compare 比較 **emigrate** and 和 **immigrate**. People **emigrate** if they leave their own country and go to live in another ☆ 從自己的國家移居他國是 **emigrate**: *He couldn't find work in his own country so he decided to emigrate.* 他在本國找不到工作, 所以決定移居外國。*These people are emigrants and their action is emigration.* ☆ 這些人是 **emigrants**, 這種行為是 **emigration**。People **immigrate** if they come to live in a country from another. The verb **immigrate** is rare, but the nouns **immigrant** and **immigration** are common. ☆ 如果從他國遷來某國居住則是 **immigrate**。動詞 **immigrate** 比較少用, 但名詞 **immigrant** 和 **immigration** 則很常用: *an illegal immigrant* 非法移民 | *The government is trying to reduce immigration from countries outside Europe.* 政府正試圖減少來自歐洲以外國家的移民。

ém·i·gré /ˈɛmə,gre; ˈemɪˌɡreɪ/ *n* someone who leaves their own country for political reasons 〔因政治原因而〕移居外國者; 流亡者

em·i·nent /ˈɛmənənt; ˈemɪnənt/ *adj* famous and admired (used of people) 知名的; 受人尊崇的〔指人〕: *an eminent doctor* 名醫 —**eminence** *n* [U]

em·i·nent·ly /ˈɛmənəntlɪ; ˈemɪnəntli/ *adv fml* very 〖正式〗非常: *Your decision was eminently fair.* 你的裁決非常公正。

em·is·sa·ry /ˈɛmə,sɛrɪ; ˈemɪˌsəri/ *n* **emissaries** *fml* a person who is sent from one government to another with an official message 〖正式〗特使; 密使

e·mit /ɪˈmɪt; ɪˈmɪt/ *v* **-tt-** [T] *fml* to send out heat, light, smell, or sound 〖正式〗散發〔熱、光、煙或聲音〕: *The chimney emitted smoke.* 煙囪冒出煙來。—**emission** /ɪˈmɪʃən; ɪˈmɪʃən/ *n* [C;U]: *We must try to reduce emissions from power stations.* 我們必須盡量減少發電廠排出的物質。

e·mol·u·ments /ɪˈmaljəmənts; ɪˈmɒljʊˈmənts/ *n fml* [pl] money received for work 〖正式〗酬金; 報酬; 薪水

✦**e·mo·tion** /ɪˈmoʃən; ɪˈməʊʃən/ *n* [C;U] a strong feeling 激情; 情感; 情緒: *Love and hatred are basic emotions.* 愛和恨都是基本的情感。| *His voice was shaking with emotion.* 他的聲音激動得發抖。—**emotionless** *adj*

E

*e·mo·tion·al /ɪˈmoʃənl; ɪˈməʊʃnəl/ *adj* **1** having strong feelings and showing them, often by crying 易動感情的; 情緒激動的: *He became very emotional when she said she would leave.* 她說她要離開時, 他變得非常激動。–opposite 反義 **unemotional 2** causing you to cry 催人淚下的; 令人感動的: *an emotional film* 催人淚下的影片 **3** relating to a person's emotions 感情(上)的; 情緒(上)的: *The child's bad behaviour is a result of emotional problems.* 這孩子的不良行為是情緒問題導致的結果。–**emotionally** *adv*

e·mo·tive /ɪˈmotɪv; ɪˈməʊtɪv/ *adj* causing strong feeling 激起強烈感情的: *Capital punishment is a very emotive issue.* 死刑是一個非常容易引起強烈感情的問題。

em·pa·thy /ˈɛmpəθɪ; ˈempəθi/ *n* [U] the ability to imagine and experience someone else's feelings 同感; 移情; 共鳴

em·pe·ror /ˈɛmpərər; ˈempərəʳ/ *n* the ruler of an empire 皇帝

*em·pha·sis /ˈɛmfəsɪs; ˈemfəsɪs/ *n* **emphases** /-siz; -siːz/ [C;U] special force given to something to show that it is particularly important 強調; 重點: *The boss lays great emphasis on politeness and punctuality.* 老闆非常強調禮貌和準時。–see 見 EMPHASIZE (USAGE 用法)

*em·pha·size /ˈɛmfəˌsaɪz; ˈemfəsaɪz/ *v* **emphasized, emphasizing** (also 又作 **emphasise** *BrE* 〔英式〕) [T;+that] to put special force or importance on something 強調; 着重: *I must emphasize the fact that they are only children.* 我必須強調這個事實, 就是他們只是孩子。

> ■ USAGE 用法: Remember that the verb **emphasize** is transitive and is NOT, therefore, followed by a preposition. ☆記住動詞 **emphasize** 是及物動詞, 所以後面不能跟介詞。(The noun **emphasis** is followed by the preposition **on** in the phrase **to put/place emphasis on something**. ☆在詞組 **to put/place emphasis on something** 中, 名詞 **emphasis** 後面跟介詞 **on**) Compare 比較: *In her speech she emphasized the importance of hard work.* 她在演講中強調了努力工作的重要性。| *The company puts a lot of emphasis on hard work.* 公司十分強調努力工作。

em·phat·ic /ɪmˈfætɪk; ɪmˈfætɪk/ *adj* speaking or spoken forcefully to show that something is very important 強調的, 着重的: *He answered with an emphatic "No".* 他以斷然的"不"字作了回答。–**emphatically** /-klɪ; -kli/ *adv*

*em·pire /ˈɛmpaɪr; ˈempaɪəʳ/ *n* **1** a group of countries under one government 帝國: *the former British Empire* 以前的大英帝國 **2** a large group of business organisations 大企業集團: *the industrial empire of Standard Oil* 標準石油公司的工業集團

em·pir·i·cal /ɛmˈpɪrɪkl; ɪmˈpɪrɪkəl/ *adj* coming from practical experience of the world not from ideas out of books 憑經驗的; 實證的 –**empirically** /-klɪ; -kli/ *adv* –**empiricism** /ɛmˈpɪrəˌsɪzəm; ɪmˈpɪrɪˌsɪzəm/ *n* [U]

*em·ploy /ɪmˈplɔɪ; ɪmˈplɔɪ/ *v* [T] **1** to give someone a job 雇用〔某人〕: *We employ her as an adviser.* 我們聘她擔任顧問。| *He's now employed as a teacher.* 他現在受雇擔任教師一職。 **2** *fml* to use something 〔正式〕使用〔某物〕: *This bird employs its beak as a weapon.* 這種鳥用嘴作為武器。

*em·ploy·ee /ˌɪmplɔɪˈiː; ɪmˈplɔɪ-iː/ *n* a person who works for someone else 受雇者; 雇員: *a Government employee* 政府的雇員

*em·ploy·er /ɪmˈplɔɪər; ɪmˈplɔɪəʳ/ *n* a person or group that pays people to work for them 雇用者; 雇主: *The car factory is a big employer in the area.* 汽車工廠是這個地區最大的雇主。

*em·ploy·ment /ɪmˈplɔɪmənt; ɪmˈplɔɪmənt/ *n* [U] **1** the state of having paid work 雇用; 受雇: *The number of people in regular employment has fallen.* 常規就業人數減少了。| *He's looking for employment.* 他在找工作。–opposite 反義 **unemployment 2** the act of using something 使用; 運用: *Do you think the employment of force was justified?* 你認為使用武力是正當的嗎?

em·pow·er /ɪmˈpaʊər; ɪmˈpaʊəʳ/ *v fml* 〔正式〕 empower someone to do something to give someone the power or legal right to do something 授權給〔某人做某事〕; 給〔某人〕做…的權力: *The police are now empowered to search private houses.* 警察現在有搜查私人住宅的權力。

em·press /ˈɛmprɪs; ˈemprɪs/ *n* a woman who is an EMPEROR or the wife of an EMPEROR 女皇; 皇后

emp·ty¹ /ˈɛmptɪ; ˈempti/ *adj* **1** containing nothing or nobody 空的; 無人的: *an empty cup* 空杯子 | *There are three empty houses in our street.* 我們這條街上有三幢空房子。 **2** empty of without 沒有: *streets empty of traffic* 沒有來往車輛的街道 **3** without sense, meaning, or importance 無意義的; 不重要的: *empty promises* 兌現不了的諾言 | *Her life seemed empty now.* 她的生活現在顯得空虛。–**emptiness** *n* [U]

empty² *v* **emptied, emptying 1** [T] to remove the contents of a container 使…成為空的, 把…弄空: *They emptied the bottle of wine.* 他們喝乾了瓶中的酒。 **2** [T+adv/prep] to take the contents out of something and put them somewhere else 倒空; 掏光: *He emptied the biscuits onto the plate.* 他把餅乾都倒出來放到盤子裡。 **3** [I] to become empty 成為空的: *The room emptied very quickly.* 房間很快就騰空了。

empty-hand·ed /ˌ·· '··/ adj bringing nothing with you because you have not got what you hoped to get 空手的; 一無所獲的

e·mu /ˈimju; ˈiːmjuː/ n a large Australian bird with a long neck which cannot fly〔澳洲產的體大頸長而不會飛的〕鴯鶓

em·u·late /ˈɛmjəˌlet; ˈemjʊ̩leɪt/ v emulated, emulating [T] fml《正式》to copy someone's good behaviour or success《正式》仿效〔某人的良好行為或成功之處〕–emulation /ˌɛmjə-ˈleʃən; ˌemjʊ̩ˈleɪʃən/ n [U]

e·mul·sion /ɪˈmʌlʃən; ɪˈmʌlʃən/ n [C;U] 1 tech a creamy mixture of liquids which do not mix together completely《術語》乳劑; 乳化液 2 a type of paint used especially for painting walls 乳化漆

★★**en·a·ble** /ɪnˈebl; ɪˈneɪbəl/ v enabled, enabling fml《正式》enable someone to do something to make someone able to do something 使...能夠: The fall in the value of the pound will enable us to export more goods. 英鎊幣值下降使我們能出口更多的貨物。

en·act /ɪnˈækt; ɪˈnækt/ v [T] fml《正式》1 to make something a law 制訂〔法律〕: Several bills were enacted at the end of this session of Parliament. 這屆國會結束時，好幾項議案（被通過而）制定成為法律。 2 to perform a story as a play 演出; 上演 –enactment n [C; U]

e·nam·el /ɪˈnæml; ɪˈnæməl/ n [U] 1 a glassy substance used as decoration or protection on metal, glass, or clay objects 搪瓷; 琺瑯 2 a very shiny kind of paint 瓷釉; 瓷漆 3 the hard, smooth, white surface of your teeth〔牙齒的〕琺瑯質 –enamel v [-ll-] [T]

en·am·oured /ɪnˈæməd; ɪˈnæməd/ adj fml《正式》(enamored AmE《美式》) be enamoured of something to be very fond of something 十分喜愛某物

en bloc /ɛn ˈblak; ˌɒn ˈblɒk/ adv all together as a single unit 整個; 全部; 一起: The whole department resigned en bloc. 整個部門集體辭職了。

en·camp·ment /ɪnˈkæmpmənt; ɪnˈkæmp-mənt/ n a large military camp 營房; 營地

en·case /ɪnˈkes; ɪnˈkeɪs/ v encased, encasing [T] be encased in something to be completely covered by something 被某物全部覆蓋: His body was encased in armour. 他全身披着鎧甲。

en·chant /ɪnˈtʃænt; ɪnˈtʃɑːnt/ v [T] to fill someone with a feeling of delight 使〔某人〕陶醉; 使欣喜 –enchantment n [C;U]

en·chant·ed /ɪnˈtʃæntɪd; ɪnˈtʃɑːntɪ̩d/ adj 1 filled with delight 陶醉的; 欣喜的: He was enchanted by the idea. 這主意使他欣喜若狂。 2 strange and magical 奇怪的; 奇異的; 有魔力的: an enchanted wood 有魔法的木頭

en·chant·ing /ɪnˈtʃæntɪŋ; ɪnˈtʃɑːntɪŋ/ adj delightful and attractive in appearance or behaviour 迷人的; 可愛的: an enchanting child 可愛的孩子

en·cir·cle /ɪnˈsɝkl; ɪnˈsɜːkəl/ v encircled, encircling [T] to surround something 包圍; 環繞: The army encircled the airport. 軍隊包圍了機場。

en·clave /ˈɛnklev; ˈenkleɪv/ n a place or group of people which is completely surrounded by another place or a different group of people 孤立的小塊地區; 存在於其他團體中的獨立小團體

en·close /ɪnˈkloz; ɪnˈkləʊz/ v enclosed, enclosing [T] to surround something completely 將〔某物〕完全包圍; 圍住: a garden enclosed by a high wall 用高牆圍住的花園 | The key was enclosed in a small wooden box. 鑰匙封在一個小木盒裡。 2 to put something inside an envelope with a letter 把〔某物〕裝入信封: I enclose a cheque for £50. 我隨信附上一張五十英鎊的支票。

en·clo·sure /ɪnˈkloʒɚ; ɪnˈkləʊʒəʳ/ n 1 a piece of land that is surrounded by a fence or wall〔用籬笆或牆〕圈起來的一塊地: There's a special enclosure for the horses. 這裡有一個專用於圈馬的場地。 2 something that is put in with a letter〔信中的〕附件

en·com·pass /ɪnˈkʌmpəs; ɪnˈkʌmpəs/ v [T] 1 to include several things 包括, 包含: The company's activities encompass printing, publishing, and computing. 公司的活動包括印刷、出版和計算。 2 fml to surround a place on all sides《正式》環繞

en·core /ˈaŋkɔr; ˈɒŋkɔːʳ/ interj a call made by listeners at a concert or a theatre to show that they liked a performance and want part of it to be performed again 再來一個; 再演一次 –encore n

★**en·coun·ter** /ɪnˈkaʊntɚ; ɪnˈkaʊntəʳ/ v [T] fml《正式》1 to meet something difficult or dangerous 遇到; 遭遇〔困難或危險〕: He encountered a lot of opposition to his plan. 他遇到了很多反對他計劃的意見。 2 to meet someone unexpectedly 邂逅〔某人〕; 偶遇〔某人〕: She encountered a friend on the plane. 她在飛機上與一位朋友不期而遇。 –encounter n: an unpleasant encounter with a dangerous snake 不幸遇到一條毒蛇

★★**en·cour·age** /ɪnˈkɝɪdʒ; ɪnˈkʌrɪdʒ/ v encouraged, encouraging [T] 1 to try to persuade someone to do something 鼓勵: We encouraged him to go to university. 我們鼓勵他上大學。

□ USEFUL PATTERN 有用句型
encourage someone to do something

2 to make it easier for something to happen 促進; 助長: It's in the company's interest to encourage union membership. 鼓勵〔僱員〕加入工會是符合公司利益的。 –encouragement n [C;U]

en·cour·ag·ing /ɪnˈkɝɪdʒɪŋ; ɪnˈkʌrɪdʒɪŋ/ adj making you feel hopeful and confident 鼓

勵的; 令人鼓舞的: *The latest trade figures are encouraging.* 最新的貿易數字令人鼓舞。

en·croach /ɪnˈkrotʃ; ɪnˈkraʊtʃ/ *v* **encroach on/upon something** to take more of something than is right, usual, or acceptable 侵佔〔某物〕: *His new farm buildings encroach on his neighbour's land.* 他農場新建的房屋侵佔了鄰居的土地。 **–encroachment** *n* [C;U]

en·cum·ber /ɪnˈkʌmbə; ɪnˈkʌmbər/ *v* [T] *fml* to make it difficult for you to move or do something〔正式〕妨礙〔活動或做某事〕; 阻礙: *He is encumbered with debts.* 他為債務所累。 **–encumbrance** *n*

en·cy·clo·pe·di·a /ɪnˌsaɪkləˈpidɪə; ɪnˌsaɪkləˈpiːdɪə/ *n* (also 又作 **encyclopaedia**) a book or set of books dealing with every branch of knowledge, usually in alphabetical order〔常以字母順序排列的〕百科全書 **–encyclopedic** /-ˈpidɪk; -ˈpiːdɪk/ *adj* (also 又作 **encyclopaedic**)

E ✲end[1] /ɛnd; end/ *n* **1** the point where something stops or finishes 末端; 盡頭; 終點: *the ends of a rope* 繩子的兩端 | *He walked to the end of the road.* 他走到了路的盡頭。 | *I start work at the end of August.* 我八月底開始工作。 | *He is killed right at the end of the film.* 他就在電影的結尾處被殺害了。 **2** a little piece of something that is left over 殘片, 剩餘物: *cigarette ends* 煙頭〔煙蒂〕 **3** *fml* an aim or purpose〔正式〕目標; 目的: *He does everything for his own political ends.* 他所做的一切都是為了達到自己的政治目的。 | *He is totally dedicated to this end.* 他全心奉獻以達到這個目標。 **4 at a loose end** having nothing to do 無所事事 **5 at an end** finished 結束: *The strike is finally at an end.* 罷工終於結束了。 **6 at the end of the day** when everything is considered 到頭來; 最終: *At the end of the day it's the government's responsibility to stop this from happening.* 阻止這事的發生終歸是政府的責任。 **7 come to an end** to finish 完成; 結束: *The war has finally come to an end.* 戰爭終於結束了。 **8 end to end** with the narrow sides of two objects touching each other: 首尾相接地: *Place the tables end to end.* 把這些桌子排成一行。 **9 get hold of the wrong end of the stick** to understand something wrongly 誤解 **10 in the end** at last 最後: *He managed to pass his driving test in the end.* 他最後努力通過了駕駛考試。 | *Then he falls in love with a beautiful Spanish dancer and marries her. In the end, they go to Madrid and open a dancing school.* 然後他愛上了一位美麗的西班牙舞蹈員, 並和她結了婚。最後, 他們去了馬德里, 開辦了一家舞蹈學校。 **11 make ends meet** to get just enough money for your needs 使收支相抵 **12** *infml* **no end** of very much or very many 非常; 很多: *You have caused me no end of worry.* 你給我帶來了無窮的煩惱。 **13 hours on end, days on end, weeks on end** happening continuously

for hours, days, or weeks 連續幾小時; 連續幾天; 連續幾星期: *We sat there for hours on end.* 我們在那裡一連坐了幾個小時。 **14 put an end to something** to stop something from happening any more 使結束〔終止〕某事物

> ■ **USAGE** 用法 **1** Note the use of the preposition **at** in phrases such as ☆注意如下詞組中介詞 **at** 的使用: **at the end of** *the lesson* 課堂結束時 | **at the end of** *the summer* 夏天結束時; 夏末 | **at the end of** *the holiday* 假期結束時 | **at the end of** *the dinner* 晚飯結束時 (Do NOT use **in the end** to refer to the end of something particular 不要用 **in the end** 來指某種特別事物的末端) **2 In the end** often suggests that something happens after a lot of time or effort ☆ **in the end** 常表示某事經過很多時間或很多努力才發生: *It was a difficult decision but in the end she decided to take the job.* 這個決定很難做, 但到最後她決心接受這份工作。

✲end[2] *v* [I;T] **1** to stop or finish 終止; 結束: *The party ended at midnight.* 聚會半夜才結束。 | *The war ended in 1975.* 戰爭於 1975 年結束。 | *He ended his letter with good wishes to the family.* 他在信末祝福全家安好。 **2 end in something** to result in something 以某事物為結果: *Her efforts finally ended in success.* 她的努力終於給她帶來了成功。

end up *phr v* [I] to finish in a particular place or way 以…結束; 以…告終: *He ended up in a cell for the night.* 他結果要在小牢房裡過了一晚。 | *We ended up taking the train.* 我們結果趕上了火車。

en·dan·ger /ɪnˈdendʒə; ɪnˈdeɪndʒər/ *v* [T] **1** to cause danger to someone or something 使遭危害, 危及〔某人或某物〕 **2 endangered species** a type of animal that might soon no longer exist 瀕於滅種的生物

en·dear /ɪnˈdɪr; ɪnˈdɪər/ *v* [T] **endear yourself to someone** to make someone feel fond of you 使自己得到某人喜愛 **–endearing** *adj*: *an endearing smile* 惹人喜愛的微笑 **–endearingly** *adv*

en·dear·ment /ɪnˈdɪrmənt; ɪnˈdɪəmənt/ *n* [C;U] an expression of love 喜愛; 鍾愛; 親愛: *He whispered endearments to her.* 他悄悄地向她表示愛意。

en·deav·our /ɪnˈdevə; ɪnˈdevər/ *v* (**endeavor** *AmE*〔美式〕) *fml*〔正式〕**endeavour to do something** to try to do something 努力做某事: *You must endeavour to improve your work.* 你必須努力改進你的工作。 **–endeavour** *n* [C;U]

en·dem·ic /ɛnˈdemɪk; enˈdemɪk/ *adj* found regularly in a particular place (used of diseases) 地方性的〔指疾病〕: *This chest disease is endemic among miners in this area.* 這種

胸部疾病是本地區礦工中常見的地方性疾病。

end·ing /'ɛndɪŋ; 'ɛndɪŋ/ *n* the end of a story, film, play, or word〔故事、電影、戲劇的〕結局; 結尾;〔單詞的〕詞尾: *a happy ending* 快樂的結局

en·dive /'ɛndaɪv; 'ɛndɪv/ *n* [C;U] **1** a plant with curly green leaves which are eaten raw〔可生吃的〕菊苣 **2** the usual American word for《美式》= CHICORY (2)

end·less /'ɛndlɪs; 'ɛndləs/ *adj* unpleasant, and seeming never to end 沒完沒了的; 永無休止的: *The journey seemed endless.* 這段路程沒有盡頭。**–endlessly** *adv*

en·dorse /ɪn'dɔrs; ɪn'dɔːs/ *v* **endorsed, endorsing** [T] **1** to say that you support or approve of something or someone 支持〔某人或某事〕; 贊同: *The President endorsed her candidacy.* 總統贊成她作為候選人。**2** to write your name on the back of a cheque 在票據背面簽字; 背書 **3** *BrE* to show on a driving LICENCE that the driver has broken the law《英式》〔在駕駛執照上〕註明違章記錄 **–endorsement** *n* [C;U]

en·dow /ɪn'dau; ɪn'dau/ *v* [T] **1** to provide a school, hospital, or college with a large amount of money that gives a continuing income 資助; 捐款給〔學校、醫院〕**2 be endowed with something** to have a good quality or ability 使具有某種特質, 使天生賦有〔良好的品質或才能〕**–endowment** *n* [C;U]

en·dur·ance /ɪn'djurəns; ɪn'djuərəns/ *n* [U] the ability to bear pain or suffering for a long time〔對痛苦、苦難的〕忍耐力: *Marathon runners need tremendous endurance.* 馬拉松賽跑者需要很大的耐力。

en·dure /ɪn'djur; ɪn'djuə'/ *v* **endured, enduring** *fml*《正式》**1** [T] to bear pain or suffering for a long time 忍受, 忍耐〔痛苦、苦難〕: *I can't endure that noise a moment longer.* 我一刻也不能再忍受那種喧鬧聲。– see 見 BEAR² (USAGE 用法) **2** [I] to continue to exist 持續; 持久: *his enduring fame* 他那不朽的名聲

★en·e·my /'ɛnəmɪ; 'ɛnəmɪ/ *n* **enemies 1** [C] a person who hates and opposes another person 敵人; 仇敵; 反對者: *He's made a lot of enemies at work.* 他在工作上樹敵很多。**2** [+sing/pl verb] the army that you are fighting against in a war 敵軍: *The enemy are advancing.* 敵軍在前進。

en·er·get·ic /ˌɛnə'dʒɛtɪk; ˌɛnə'dʒɛtɪk/ *adj* very active 非常活躍的; 有活力的: *an energetic tennis player* 精力充沛的網球運動員

★★en·er·gy /'ɛnədʒɪ; 'ɛnədʒɪ/ *n* **1** [U] the ability to be active and do a lot of work or sport without feeling tired 活力; 幹勁; 生氣: *Young people usually have more energy than the old.* 年輕人通常比老年人有活力。**2** [U] the power which can produce heat and drive machines 能源; 能量: *atomic energy* 原子能 | *a cheap source of energy* 一種廉價的能源 **3 energies** [pl] the

ability to spend a lot of time and effort doing something 精力: *We'll now need to direct our energies into the election campaign.* 我們現在要把精力投入競選活動。

en·force /ɪn'fors; ɪn'fɔːs/ *v* **enforced, enforcing** [T] **1** to cause a rule or law to be obeyed 執行〔規則〕; 實施〔法律〕: *The new law about safety belts in the back seats of cars will be difficult to enforce.* 汽車後座繫安全帶的新法規將難以實施。**2** to make something happen, especially by threats or force〔尤指用威脅或武力〕強制; 強迫: *They tried to enforce agreement by torturing the prisoners.* 他們企圖以折磨犯人來強迫達成協議。**–enforceable** *adj* **–enforcement** *n* [U]

★en·gage /ɪn'gedʒ; ɪn'geɪdʒ/ *v* **engaged, engaging** *fml*《正式》**1** [T] to arrange to employ someone〔安排〕雇用〔某人〕: *I've engaged a new secretary.* 我聘請了一位新秘書。| *I've engaged him as my assistant.* 我聘請他做我的助手。**2** [T] to attract someone and keep their interest or attention 吸引〔某人的興趣或注意〕: *The new toy didn't engage the child for long.* 新玩具對孩子的吸引力沒有維持多久。**3** [I;T] to attack someone 攻擊〔某人〕: *They engaged the enemy in battle.* 他們在戰鬥中與敵人交戰。**4 engage in something** *fml* to do or take part in something《正式》從事, 參加: *We are now engaged in a legal battle with our suppliers.* 我們現在和供應商在打官司。**5 engage someone in conversation** to talk to someone, especially because you do not want them to notice something that is happening 和某人談話〔尤因不想對方注意正在發生的事〕

en·gaged /ɪn'gedʒd; ɪn'geɪdʒd/ *adj* [never before a noun 不能用於名詞前] **1** having agreed to marry someone 已訂婚的: *My daughter is engaged to a doctor.* 我女兒和一位醫生訂了婚。| *They're engaged.* 他們訂婚了。| *They got engaged in January.* 他們是一月份訂婚的。**2** *fml* busy (used of people)《正式》忙的〔指人〕: *"Can Mr Jones come to the meeting on Monday?" "No, I'm afraid he's otherwise engaged."* "瓊斯先生星期一能來參加會議嗎?" "不行, 我恐怕他有別的事情要忙。" **3** in use (used of a telephone line) 使用中的〔指電話線〕: *Sorry! The number is engaged.* 對不起! 電話現在佔線。– see 見 TELEPHONE (USAGE 用法) **4** in use (used of a public TOILET) 佔用中的〔指公共廁所〕

en·gage·ment /ɪn'gedʒmənt; ɪn'geɪdʒmənt/ *n* **1** an agreement to marry or the period during which two people are engaged 訂婚, 婚約: *Have you heard that John has broken off his engagement to Mary?* 你聽說約翰已和瑪麗解除婚約了嗎? **2** *fml* an arrangement to meet someone or to do something, especially at a particular time《正式》約會; 約定: *I am unable to attend the meeting because of a previous engagement.* 因為事先有個約會, 所以我不能參加會議。

en·gag·ing /ɪnˈgedʒɪŋ; ɪnˈgeɪdʒɪŋ/ *adj* charming 迷人的, 可愛的: *an engaging smile* 迷人的微笑 **–engagingly** *adv*

en·gen·der /ɪnˈdʒɛndə; ɪnˈdʒɛndəʳ/ *v* [T] *fml* to produce a state or feeling 〖正式〗產生〔狀態或感情〕

★**en·gine** /ˈɛndʒən; ˈɛndʒn̩/ *n* **1** a machine with moving parts which produces power from steam, electricity, or oil and uses it to make something move 發動機; 引擎: *the engine of a car* 汽車的引擎 | *a jet engine* 噴氣發動機 **2** a machine which pulls a railway train 機車; 火車頭

★**en·gi·neer¹** /ˌɛndʒəˈnɪr; ˌɛndʒn̩ˈnɪəʳ/ *n* **1** a person who is professionally trained to build and repair machines, roads, bridges, and harbours 工程師; 技師: *a telephone engineer* 電話工程師 | *a civil engineer* 土木工程師 **2** a skilled person who controls the engine on a ship 輪機手

engineer² *v* [T] to arrange or cause something by clever secret planning 策劃; 操縱: *He had powerful enemies who engineered his ruin.* 他有幾個勢力強大的敵人在密謀令他下台。

★**en·gi·neer·ing** /ˌɛndʒəˈnɪrɪŋ; ˌɛndʒn̩ˈnɪərɪŋ/ *n* [U] the science or profession of an engineer 工程學; 工程師行業

En·glish¹ /ˈɪŋglɪʃ; ˈɪŋglɪʃ/ *adj* from or connected with England 英格蘭的; 英國的: *She's studying English literature.* 她在學習英國文學。

English² *n* **1 the English** the people of England 英格蘭人 **2** [U] the language of the UK, the USA, Australia and many other countries 英語; 英文: *How long have you been learning English?* 你學了英語多久了?

En·glish·man /ˈɪŋglɪʃmən; ˈɪŋglɪʃmən/ **-men** /-mən; -mən/ *n* a man who comes from England or who has English parents 英國男人; 英格蘭男人; 英格蘭裔男人

En·glish·wom·an /ˈɪŋglɪʃˌwʊmən; ˈɪŋglɪʃˌwʊmən/ **-women** /-ˌwɪmɪn; -ˌwɪmɪn/ *n* a woman who comes from England or who has English parents 英國女人; 英格蘭女人; 英格蘭裔女人

en·grave /ɪnˈgrev; ɪnˈgreɪv/ *v* **engraved, engraving** [T] **1** to cut words or pictures on wood, stone, or metal 〔在木、石、金屬上〕雕刻: *His name was engraved on the tombstone.* 他的名字刻在墓碑上。 **2 be engraved on your mind/memory** to be fixed deeply in your mind so that you are unable to forget anything 深深印入心中; 銘記在心: *The terrible scene was engraved on his memory for ever.* 那可怕的情景永遠銘刻在他的記憶中了。 **–engraver** *n* **–engraving** *n* [C;U]

en·gross·ed /ɪnˈgrost; ɪnˈgrəʊst/ *adj* [never before a noun 不能用於名詞前] completely holding your attention so that you do not think of anything else 全神貫注的: *He was*

so engrossed **in** *his work that he forgot to eat.* 他專心致志地工作, 以致忘了吃飯。

en·gulf /ɪnˈgʌlf; ɪnˈgʌlf/ *v* [T] *lit* (of the earth, the sea, fire) to surround something and swallow it up 〖文〗〔陸地、海洋、火〕吞沒; 淹沒: *The stormy sea engulfed the small boat.* 洶湧的大海吞沒了那艘小船。

★**en·hance** /ɪnˈhɑns; ɪnˈhɑːns/ *v* **enhanced, enhancing** [T] to increase the quality, value, or beauty of something 增加, 提高〔品質、價值〕; 美化: *Passing the examination should enhance your chances of getting a job.* 通過考試就會增加你找到工作的機會。

e·nig·ma /ɪˈnɪgmə; ɪˈnɪgmə/ *n* a person, thing, or event that is mysterious and very hard to understand 神祕的人; 不可思議的事物; 謎: *Her disappearance remains an enigma.* 她的失蹤仍是個謎。 **–enigmatic** /ˌɛnɪgˈmætɪk; ˌɛnɪgˈmætɪk/ *adj*: *an enigmatic smile* 神祕莫測的微笑 **–enigmatically** /-klɪ; -kli/ *adv*

★**en·joy** /ɪnˈdʒɔɪ; ɪnˈdʒɔɪ/ *v* [T] **1** to get pleasure from things and experiences 享受…的樂趣; 喜愛: *I enjoyed the film very much.* 我 很 喜 愛 這 部 電 影。 | *He thoroughly enjoyed his day out.* 他在外面痛痛快快地玩了一天。 | *She enjoys listening to music.* 她喜愛聽音樂。

□ **USEFUL PATTERNS** 有用句型
to enjoy something; to enjoy doing something

---

2 *fml* to have something good 〖正式〗享有: *He has always enjoyed very good health.* 他身體一直十分健康。 | *They enjoy a high standard of living.* 他們享有很高的生活水平。 **3 enjoy yourself** to have a good time 過得快活: *Did you enjoy yourself at the party?* 你在聚會上玩得愉快嗎? **–enjoyment** *n* [C;U]: *We hope the interruption didn't spoil your enjoyment of the programme.* 我們希望這次打擾沒有破壞你們欣賞節目的興致。

en·joy·a·ble /ɪnˈdʒɔɪəbl; ɪnˈdʒɔɪəbəl/ *adj* providing pleasure or happiness (used of activities and experiences) 〔指活動或經歷〕使人快樂的: *an enjoyable holiday* 愉快的假期 | *an enjoyable film* 令人愉快的影片 **–enjoyably** *adv*

en·large /ɪnˈlɑrdʒ; ɪnˈlɑːdʒ/ *v* **enlarged, enlarging 1** [I;T] to make something get larger (使)擴大; 擴展: *We're enlarging the vegetable garden to grow more food.* 我們在擴大菜園, 以便種植更多的蔬菜。 | *I'd like to have this photograph enlarged.* 我想放大這張照片。 **2 enlarge on something** to add more length and detail to writing or speech 詳述某事; 細說某事 **–enlargement** *n* [C;U]

en·light·en /ɪnˈlaɪtn; ɪnˈlaɪtn̩/ *v* [T] to make someone understand something or free them from false beliefs 啟發; 開導; 啟迪: *I'm rather confused about what this is for; can you enlighten me?* 我實在弄不清這是為

何目的, 你能開導我嗎?

en·light·ened /ɪnˈlaɪtn̩d; ɪnˈlaɪtənd/ *adj* extremely sensible, especially because of being wiser and more modern 開明的; 有見識的: *the government's enlightened housing policy* 政府開明的房屋政策

en·list /ɪnˈlɪst; ɪnˈlɪst/ *v* **1** [I;T] to join or let someone join the army, navy, or airforce (使)入伍; 從軍: *He enlisted when he was 18.* 他十八歲時入伍。| *We must enlist more men.* 我們必須徵募更多的男子入伍。**2** [T] to get someone's help or support 得到〔某人的〕幫助或支持) –**enlistment** *n* [C;U]

en·liv·en /ɪnˈlaɪvn; ɪnˈlaɪvən/ *v* [T] to make people or events more active, cheerful, or interesting 使有生氣; 使更活躍; 使生動

en masse /en ˈmæs; ˌɒn ˈmæs/ *adv* all together 全體; 一起: *The senior management resigned en masse.* 高級管理人員集體辭職了。

en·mi·ty /ˈenmətɪ; ˈenmɪ̩ti/ *n* [U] a strong feeling of hatred towards another person or group of people 仇恨; 敵意

en·no·ble /ɪˈnobl; ɪˈnəʊbəl/ *v* **ennobled, ennobling** [T] **1** to make someone better and more honourable 使更高尚; 使崇高: *His character has been ennobled by his sufferings.* 他所受的苦難使他的品格顯得更高尚。**2** to make someone a nobleman 封〔某人〕為貴族

e·nor·mi·ty /ɪˈnɔːmətɪ; ɪˈnɔːmɪ̩ti/ *n* the enormity of the size or seriousness of something 〔某事物的〕巨大; 嚴重: *the enormity of the housing problem* 房屋問題的艱巨性 | *He didn't seem to comprehend the enormity of his crime.* 他好像沒有理解到他的罪行的嚴重性。

e·nor·mous /ɪˈnɔːməs; ɪˈnɔːməs/ *adj* extremely large 巨大的; 極大的: *an enormous house* 巨大的房屋 | *an enormous meal* 豐盛的饗飧 | *an enormous amount of money* 巨額金錢 | *The film was an enormous success.* 這部電影取得了巨大的成功。

e·nor·mous·ly /ɪˈnɔːməslɪ; ɪˈnɔːməsli/ *adv* extremely 極大地; 巨大地: *an enormously rich woman* 非常富有的女子 | *He's enormously popular.* 他深受大眾歡迎。

e·nough[1] /əˈnʌf; ɪˈnʌf/ *det, pron* as much or as many as is necessary 足夠的; 充分的: *We should have enough seats for everyone.* 我們該有足夠的座位給每個人坐。| *They didn't have enough money to buy a car.* 他們不夠錢買車。| *Has everyone had enough to eat?* 每個人都夠吃了嗎? | *I've ordered five pints of milk – that should be enough.* 我訂了五品脫牛奶, 應該夠了。

■ USAGE 用法: **1** Enough comes after adjectives ☆ **enough** 置於形容詞後: *Is he old enough?* 他年齡夠大嗎? **2** When we use **enough** with a noun it usually

comes before the noun ☆ **enough** 和名詞連用時, 常置於名詞前: *I haven't got enough money.* 我沒有足夠的錢。Putting **enough** after the noun sounds rather formal or literary ☆ **enough** 放在名詞後聽上去比較正式, 像書面語: *Ah! If only I had money enough to travel there!* 啊! 要是我有足夠的錢去那兒旅遊就好了!

enough[2] *adv* **1** to the necessary extent or degree 足夠地; 充分地: *The water isn't warm enough to swim in.* 要游泳的話, 這水不夠暖和。| *She could have passed the exam, but she didn't work hard enough.* 她本來可以通過考試, 但她不夠用功。**2** not very, but to a certain degree 尚; 相當: *He's nice enough, but I wouldn't want to see too much of him!* 他人還不錯, 但我不想多見他! **3** **strangely enough, oddly enough, interestingly enough,** etc a phrase you use to say that something is quite strange, odd, interesting, etc 說來也奇怪〔用於敍述奇怪、古怪、有趣的事〕: *Strangely enough, I didn't see Jim at the party.* 說也奇怪, 我在聚會上沒見到吉姆。

en·quire /ɪnˈkwaɪr; ɪnˈkwaɪər/ *v* **enquired, enquiring** [I;T] –see 見 INQUIRE

en·qui·ry /ɪnˈkwaɪrɪ; ɪŋˈkwaɪəri/ *n* –see 見 INQUIRY (USAGE 用法)

en·rage /ɪnˈreɪdʒ; ɪnˈreɪdʒ/ *v* **enraged, enraging** [T] to make someone very angry 激怒〔某人〕; 使〔某人〕大發雷霆: *Her behaviour enraged him.* 她的行為激怒了他。| *He was enraged to find she didn't care.* 他發現她並不在意, 這使他大發雷霆。–**enraged** *adj*: *her enraged parents* 她被激怒的父母

en·rich /ɪnˈrɪtʃ; ɪnˈrɪtʃ/ *v* [T] **1** to make someone rich 使〔某人〕富裕: *The discovery of oil will enrich the nation.* 石油的發現將使這個國家富有起來。**2** to improve the quality of something by adding something to it 充實; 使豐富: *Music can enrich your whole life.* 音樂能充實你的人生。–**enrichment** *n* [U]

en·rol /ɪnˈrol; ɪnˈrəʊl/ *v* **-ll-** (also 又作 **enroll**) [I;T] to make yourself or another person officially a member of a course or school (使)註冊; (使)入學 –**enrolment** *n* [C;U]: *Enrolment begins on Tuesday.* 星期二開始註冊。

en route /ˌɒn ˈruːt; ˌɒn ˈruːt/ *adv* on the way 在途中: *I was en route to New York.* 我當時是在去紐約的途中。

en·sconced /ɛnˈskɒnst; ɪnˈskɒnst/ **be ensconced** to be comfortably positioned somewhere 〔舒服地〕安置於: *He was ensconced in a big armchair in front of the fire.* 他舒適地安坐在火爐前的一張大扶手椅上。

en·sem·ble /ɒnˈsɒmbl; ɒnˈsɒmbəl/ *n* **1** a set of things that combine with or match each other to make a whole 全體; 整體; 總體;

Your coat, hat, and shoes make an attractive ensemble. 你的外衣、帽子和鞋配在一起非常漂亮。| **2** a small group of musicians who regularly play together 合奏〔合唱〕組

en·sign /'ɛnsaɪn; 'ensaɪn/ *n* **1** a flag on a ship, especially to show what nation the ship belongs to〔尤指表明國籍的〕船〔艦〕旗 **2** an officer of the lowest rank in the US navy〔美國的〕海軍少尉

en·slave /ɪn'slev; ɪn'sleɪv/ *v* **enslaved, enslaving** [T] **1** to make someone into a slave 使〔某人〕成為奴隸 **2** to put someone in a very difficult situation from which they cannot escape 征服〔某人〕; 控制〔某人〕: *He felt enslaved by his family's demands.* 他覺得自己受制於家庭的需求。**–enslavement** *n* [U]

en·sue /ɛn'su; ɪn'sjuː/ *v* **ensued, ensuing** [I] *fml* to happen afterwards, often as a result 《正式》接着發生; 因而產生: *Terrible fighting ensued.* 接着發生了一場激戰。| *Thousands were killed in the ensuing battle.* 在接下來的戰爭中有數以千計的人被殺。

en·sure /ɪn'ʃʊr; ɪn'ʃʊər/ *v* **ensured, ensuring** [T;that] to make something certain to happen 確保〔某事〕發生; 保證; 擔保: *If you want to ensure that you catch the plane, take a taxi to the airport.* 如果你想確保趕上飛機, 就坐計程車去機場吧。| *We need to change the law to ensure fair treatment for all people.* 我們需要改變法律, 確保所有的人都得到公正的待遇。

en·tail /ɪn'tel; ɪn'teɪl/ *v* [T] to make something necessary, or have something as a necessary part 使〔某事物成為〕必要; 必需: *Writing a history book entails a lot of work.* 編寫一本歷史書需要很大的功夫。

en·tan·gle /ɪn'tæŋgl; ɪn'tæŋgəl/ *v* **entangled, entangling** [T] **1** to cause something to become caught or twisted with something else 使纏住; 使糾纏: *The bird flapped about and entangled itself in the wire.* 鳥兒拍動翅膀, 被纏在鐵絲網裡了。**2 be entangled** to be connected with someone or something bad that it is difficult to escape from 使捲入; 使陷入; 牽連: *He became entangled in dishonest business dealings* 他捲入了不正當的商業交易中。| *She became entangled with a real drunkard.* 她被一個十足的酒鬼纏住了。**–entanglement** *n* [C;U]

en·ter /'ɛntɚ; 'entə/ *v* **1** [I;T] *fml* to come or go into a particular place《正式》進入: *He entered the room cautiously.* 他小心翼翼地走進房間。| *Please knock before entering.* 進來前請先敲門。| *Enter Hamlet, stage left.* 哈姆雷特從舞台左側上場。| *Further west, the river enters the forest.* 這條河一直向西流入森林。**2** [T] to become a member of a profession or organization 成為〔某專業或機構的〕成員: *More and more people want to enter the medical profession.* 越來越多的人想從事醫療

行業。| *He wants to enter Parliament.* 他想成為國會議員。**3** [I;T] to say that you want to take part in something (報名)參加: *Five Germans entered the race.* 五個德國人參加了那比賽。| *He entered himself for the exam.* 他自己報名參加了考試。

□ **USEFUL PATTERNS** 有用句型
to enter something; to enter for something; to enter someone for something

4 [T] to begin a new period of time 開始進入〔新階段〕: *The talks have now entered their third week.* 會談已進入第三個星期。**5** [T] to include in a store of information on a computer 存入〔電腦〕: *Have you entered the new data yet?* 你把新數據存入電腦了嗎? **6** [T] to write down names or amounts in a record book 登記: *Please enter her name on the register.* 請把她的名字登記下來。

enter into sthg *phr v* [T] **1** to share in or take part in 分享; 參與: *She entered into the children's game enthusiastically.* 她興緻勃勃地參與孩子們的遊戲。**2** to be an important part of or influence on something 是〔某事物的〕重要一部分; 產生影響: *Money doesn't enter into it at all — it's the principle that matters to me.* 錢在這件事上根本無關緊要——我考慮的是原則。**3** to start to take part in something formally 開始參加: *They have entered into an agreement with their bankers.* 他們和銀行家達成了協議。

en·ter·prise /'ɛntɚ‚praɪz; 'entəpraɪz/ *n* **1** [C] a company or business 公司; 企業; 事業: *This company's one of the largest enterprises of its kind.* 這家公司是同類企業中最大的一家。**2** [U] a way of organizing business 辦企業的方式; 企業: *Do you believe in private enterprise, or in government ownership of industry?* 你相信私營企業還是國營企業? **3** [C] a plan or action that is daring or difficult〔艱巨的或帶冒險性的〕計劃: *Have you heard about their latest enterprise?* 你有沒有聽說過他們最近的冒險計劃? **4** [U] the courage and ability that is needed to do something daring or difficult 膽量; 冒險精神; 進取心: *I admire their enterprise.* 我佩服他們的冒險精神。

en·ter·pris·ing /'ɛntɚ‚praɪzɪŋ; 'entəpraɪzɪŋ/ *adj* having or showing the willingness to do things that are difficult, new, or daring 有進取心的; 有事業心的; 有魄力的

en·ter·tain /‚ɛntɚ'ten; ‚entə'teɪn/ *v* **1** [T] to amuse and interest someone 給〔某人〕快樂; 使〔某人〕感興趣; 娛樂〔人〕: *She entertained her friends with a description of herself learning to ski.* 她向朋友們描述自己怎麼學滑雪, 引起了他們的興趣。**2** [I;T] to treat someone as a guest by providing food and drink for them 招待; 款待; 請客: *He does most of his entertaining in restaurants.* 他招待客人大都是去餐館。| *We're entertaining Harold's business partners this evening.* 我們今晚要款

待哈羅德生意上的夥伴。**3** [T] *fml* to be ready and willing to think about an idea, doubt, or suggestion〔正式〕考慮, 接受〔主意、疑慮或建議〕

en·ter·tain·er /ˌɛntəˈteɪnə; ˌentəˈteɪnəʳ/ *n* a person who amuses and entertains people professionally, for example by singing or telling jokes 職業演員;〔娛樂節目的〕表演者: *a popular television entertainer* 一個受歡迎的電視演員

en·ter·tain·ing /ˌɛntəˈteɪnɪŋ; ˌentəˈteɪnɪŋ/ *adj* amusing and interesting 使人愉快的; 有趣的: *an entertaining story* 引人入勝的故事 – **entertainingly** *adv*

en·ter·tain·ment /ˌɛntəˈteɪnmənt; ˌentəˈteɪnmənt/ *n* **1** [U] activities which amuse or interest people 娛樂; 招待: *Senior staff get an allowance for the entertainment of foreign visitors.* 高級職員有招待外國賓客的津貼。| *the entertainment industry* 娛樂業 **2** [U] amusement or interest 快樂; 樂趣: *The little girl tried to put on her mother's shoes, much to our entertainment.* 這小女孩試圖穿她媽媽的鞋子, 逗得我們樂不可支。**3** [C] a public performance, for example at a cinema or theatre 文娛表演: *The tourist office will tell you about local entertainments.* 觀光旅遊辦事處會告訴你有關本地文娛表演的情況。

en·thral /ɛnˈθrɔl; ɪnˈθrɔːl/ *v* **-ll-** (also 又作 **enthrall**) [T] to completely hold someone's attention and interest 迷住; 吸引住: *The boy was enthralled by the soldier's stories.* 那個男孩被士兵的故事迷住了。 –**enthralling** *adj*

en·throne /ɪnˈθron; ɪnˈθrəʊn/ *v* **enthroned, enthroning** [T] to mark the official beginning of the period of rule of a king or queen by placing them on an official seat 使〔國王或女王〕登基 –**enthronement** *n* [C; U]

en·thuse /ɪnˈθjuz; ɪnˈθjuːz/ *v* **enthused, enthusing** [I] to say how wonderful you think something is 表示熱心: *He was enthusing about his new radio.* 他對自己的新收音機愛不釋手。

★en·thu·si·as·m /ɪnˈθjuzɪˌæzəm; ɪnˈθjuːzɪæzəm/ *n* [C;U] a strong feeling of interest, admiration, or eagerness 巨大的興趣; 熱情; 熱心: *The new teacher is full of enthusiasm for her work.* 這位新教師對她的工作充滿熱情。

en·thu·si·ast /ɪnˈθjuzɪˌæst; ɪnˈθjuːzɪæst/ *n* someone who is very interested in and keen on something 熱衷於〔某事物的〕人; 熱心者: *a cycling enthusiast* 腳踏車愛好者

en·thu·si·as·tic /ɪnˌθjuzɪˈæstɪk; ɪnˌθjuːzɪˈæstɪk/ *adj* very interested in something or keen on something 很感興趣的; 熱心的; 熱情的: *She seemed enthusiastic about the idea.* 她好像對這主意很感興趣。| *We got an enthusiastic response from our customers.* 我們得到了顧客們的熱情回應。

en·tice /ɪnˈtaɪs; ɪnˈtaɪs/ *v* **enticed, enticing** [T] to persuade someone to do something by offering something pleasant 誘惑; 慫恿: *The good weather enticed me away from doing housework and into the garden.* 晴朗的天氣吸引我放下家務活兒, 走到花園來。–**enticement** *n* [C;U]

★en·tire /ɪnˈtaɪr; ɪnˈtaɪəʳ/ *adj* [only before a noun 只用於名詞前] complete 全部的; 完全的: *She spent the entire day in bed.* 她一整天都躺在牀上。| *I am in entire agreement with you.* 我完全同意你的意見。–**entirely** *adv*: *I'm afraid your work is not entirely satisfactory.* 我恐怕你的工作不能完全令人滿意。

en·tire·ty /ɪnˈtaɪrtɪ; ɪnˈtaɪərᵻtɪ/ *n* **in its entirety** as a complete whole 作為一個整體: *He bought the collection of books in its entirety.* 他把這套書全部買了下來。

★en·ti·tle /ɪnˈtaɪtl̩; ɪnˈtaɪtl̩/ *v* **entitled, entitling** [T] **1** to give someone the right to have or do something 授予〔某人做某事的〕權利: *This ticket entitles you to a first class seat.* 憑這張票, 你可以坐頭等艙。| *I think I'm entitled to know why I wasn't given the job.* 我認為我有權知道為甚麼不給我那份工作。

□ **USEFUL PATTERNS** 有用句型
to entitle someone to something; to entitle someone to do something

2 to give a title to a book, play, film, or painting 給〔書、劇本、電影或畫〕題名〔定名〕 – **entitlement** *n* [U]: *You've used up all your holiday entitlement.* 你已經用完你應享有的假期。

en·ti·ty /ˈɛntətɪ; ˈentᵻtɪ/ *n* **entities** something that has a single separate and independent existence 獨立存在物; 實體: *After the war Germany was divided; it was no longer one political entity.* 戰後德國被一分為二, 不再是一個統一的政治實體。

en·to·mol·o·gy /ˌɛntəˈmɑlədʒɪ; ˌentəˈmɒlədʒɪ/ *n* [U] the scientific study of insects 昆蟲學 –**entomologist** *n*

en·tou·rage /ˌɑntuˈrɑʒ; ˈɒntʊrɑːʒ/ *n* [+sing/pl verb] all the people who look after and travel with an important person〔要人的〕隨行人員; 陪同人員: *The president's entourage occupied six cars.* 總統的隨行人員佔用了六輛汽車。

en·trails /ˈɛntrəlz; ˈentreɪlz/ *n* [pl] the inside parts of a person or animal, especially the bowels〔人或動物的〕內臟〔尤指腸〕

en·trance[1] /ˈɛntrəns; ˈentrəns/ *n* **1** [C] a gate, door, or other opening by which you go into a place 門口; 入口處; 進口: *Excuse me — where is the entrance to the cinema?* 對不起, 請問電影院的入口處在哪裡? **2** [C] someone's arrival in a particular place 進入; 到達: *The minister's entrance was greeted with a loud cheer.* 首相在一片高聲的歡呼中

E

登場。**3** [U] the right to enter a place 進入權; 准許入場: *Known football hooligans will be refused entrance to the match.* 出了名的足球流氓將不准入場觀看比賽。| *We will have to charge an entrance fee.* 我們要入場費。**4 make an entrance** to come into a place, often in a way which makes people notice you〔常以引人注目的方式〕入場: *She made a dramatic entrance leading her two pet lions.* 她領着兩隻寵物獅子引人注目地登場了。

■ USAGE 用法: Compare 比較 **entrance** and 和 **entry**. For the ordinary act of entering, the usual word is **entry** ☆ 表示普通的"進入"動作, 常用 **entry**: *Britain's entry into the EEC* 英國的加入歐洲經濟共同體 | *"No entry"* (road sign) "禁止進入"(路標)。**Entrance** is used especially to talk about a ceremony or performance ☆ **entrance** 尤用於談及儀式或演出等: *to make an entrance onto the stage* 登上舞台, or to talk about the right to enter ☆ 或者可用於談及進入的權利: *a university entrance exam* 大學入學考試 | *an entrance fee* 入場費

---

*en·trance² /ɪnˈtræns; ɪnˈtrɑːns/ v entranced, entrancing [T] to fill someone with great wonder and delight 使〔某人〕出神; 使〔某人〕狂喜: *The children watched entranced as the circus animals performed.* 馬戲團的動物表演時, 孩子們看得出了神。

en·trant /ˈɛntrənt; ˈentrənt/ n a person who enters a profession, race, or competition 加入某行業的人; 參加比賽〔競賽〕者

en·treat /ɪnˈtriːt; ɪnˈtriːt/ v [T] fml to beg someone humbly to do something〔正式〕懇求; 請求: *She entreated him to forgive her.* 她懇求他原諒。**–entreaty** n **–entreaties** [C; U]

en·trenched /ɪnˈtrɛntʃt; ɪnˈtrentʃt/ adj firmly established and difficult to change (used of rights, customs, and beliefs; a word often used to express disapproval)〔權利、習俗、信念〕根深蒂固的〔常含貶義〕: *his entrenched political ideas* 他那根深蒂固的政治觀

en·tre·pre·neur /ˌɑntrəprəˈnɝ; ˌɒntrəprəˈnɜːr/ n a person who starts a business or arranges for a piece of work to be done in the hope of making a profit 企業家; 承包者 **–entrepreneurial** adj

en·trust /ɪnˈtrʌst; ɪnˈtrʌst/ v [T] to give someone something to be responsible for 委託; 託付: *The lawyers entrusted the child to*

□ USEFUL PATTERNS 有用句型
to entrust something to someone; to entrust someone with something

---

his care. 律師把孩子委託給他照顧。| *She was entrusted with the responsibility for organizing the event.* 她受委託負責組織這個項目。

*en·try /ˈɛntrɪ; ˈentrɪ/ n entries 1 [C] a person or thing entered for a race or competition 參加比賽〔競賽〕的人或物: *The winning entry was a portrait of an old man.* 獲獎的參賽作品是一位老人的肖像畫。| *There were 800 entries for the marathon.* 有八百人參加了馬拉松比賽。**2** [C] a piece of information listed in a book or on a computer 項目, 條目: *The next entry in this dictionary is the word "entwine".* 本詞典的下一個詞條是"entwine"一詞。**3** [C;U] the act of joining a group or organization 進入; 加入: *Britain's entry into the European Monetary System* 英國的加入歐洲貨幣體系 **4** [U] the right to enter a building or country 進入權: *The refugees were refused entry to Britain.* 難民被拒絕進入英國。**5** [C] someone's arrival in a room 進入〔房間〕: *She pretended not to notice his entry.* 她假裝沒注意到他進來。**6** [C] a door, gate, or passage by which you enter a place 大門, 入口; 通道 –see 見 ENTRANCE (USAGE 用法) **7 No Entry** words used on a sign to show you cannot go into a place 禁止進入〔用於標牌上〕

en·twine /ɪnˈtwaɪn; ɪnˈtwaɪn/ v entwined, entwining [T] to twist something round something else 使纏繞; 盤繞: *They walked along with their fingers entwined.* 他們手牽着手朝前走。

e·nu·me·rate /ɪˈnjuːməˌret; ɪˈnjuːməreɪt/ v enumerated, enumerating [T] fml to name things on a list one after the other〔正式〕數; 列舉 **–enumeration** /ɪˌnjuːməˈreʃən; ɪˌnjuːməˈreɪʃən/ n [C;U]

e·nun·ci·ate /ɪˈnʌnsɪˌet; ɪˈnʌnsieɪt/ v enunciated, enunciating **1** [I;T] to pronounce words or sounds clearly〔清晰地〕發音; 唸字: *An actor must learn to enunciate properly.* 演員必須學會清晰正確地發音。**2** [T] fml to express ideas or principles clearly and firmly〔正式〕闡明〔觀點或原理〕**–enunciation** /ɪˌnʌnsɪˈeʃən; ɪˌnʌnsiˈeɪʃən/ n [C;U]

en·vel·op /ɪnˈvɛləp; ɪnˈveləp/ v [T] to cover something completely 把〔某物〕包住; 裹住: *The building was soon enveloped in flames.* 那幢房子很快就陷入了火海之中。

en·ve·lope /ˈɛnvəˌlop; ˈenvələup/ n the paper container for a letter or a card 信封; 封套

en·vi·a·ble /ˈɛnvɪəbl; ˈenviəbəl/ adj making you wish you had something or could do something 令人羨慕的: *He has a very enviable position in society.* 他在社會上的地位令人羨慕。| *It's not an enviable task, trying to get the two sides to agree.* 要使雙方達成協議, 這可不是份值得羨慕的工作。**–opposite** 反義 **–unenviable –enviably** adv

en·vi·ous /ˈɛnvɪəs; ˈenviəs/ adj wishing that

you had someone else's qualities or possessions 羨慕的; 妒忌的: *She was envious of her sister's new job.* 她羨慕姐姐的那份新工作。–see 見 JEALOUS (USAGE 用法) –**enviously** *adv*

en·vi·ron·ment /ɪnˈvaɪrənmənt; ɪnˈvaɪərən-mənt/ *n* **1** the physical and social conditions in which people live and which influence their lives 〔社會、生活〕環境: *Children need a happy home environment.* 孩子們需要一個幸福的家庭環境。| *a pleasant working environment* 愉快舒適的工作環境 **2 the environment** the natural world of land, sea, and air in which people, plants, and animals live 自然環境: *the destruction of the environment by pollution* 污染對自然環境的破壞

■ USAGE 用法: Compare 比較 **environment** and 和 **surroundings**. Your **environment** means all the things, people and ideas among which you live and which make you the person you are ☆**environment** 指人周圍所有的事物、人們以及生活其中並受其塑造的觀念: *His political beliefs were influenced by the environment he grew up in.* 他的政治信念受到其成長環境的影響。Your **surroundings** are simply the physical things (such as buildings, hills and trees) that you can see around you ☆ **surroundings** 僅指可以看見的周圍的具體事物〔如建築物、山、樹等〕: *My new house is in pleasant surroundings.* 我的新房子座落在舒適的環境中。

✱**en·vi·ron·men·tal** /ɪnˌvaɪrənˈmɛntl; ɪnˌvaɪərənˈmentl◂/ *adj* **1** relating to the natural world of land, sea and air 自然環境的: *The accident could do a lot of environmental damage.* 這ума事故可給環境造成嚴重損害。| *They are very interested in environmental issues.* 他們對環境問題很感興趣。**2** relating to the physical and social conditions in which people live 有關自然社會環境的 – **environmentally** *adv*: *products which are environmentally friendly* 對環境無害的產品

en·vi·ron·men·tal·ist /ɪnˌvaɪrənˈmɛntlɪst; ɪnˌvaɪərənˈmentəlɪst/ *n* a person who wants and tries to prevent the natural world from being spoilt 環境保護者

en·vi·rons /ɪnˈvaɪrənz; ˈenvɪrənz/ *n* [pl] *fml* the area surrounding a town 〔正式〕城郊; 郊區

en·vis·age /ɛnˈvɪzɪdʒ; ɪnˈvɪzɪdʒ/ *v* **envisaged, envisaging** (also 又作 **envision** /ɛnˈvɪʒən; ɪnˈvɪʒən/ *AmE* 〔美式〕) [T;+that] to think that something is a future possibility 設想; 預見: *When do you envisage being able to pay back the money?* 你設想一下何時能還清這筆錢?

en·voy /ˈɛnvɔɪ; ˈenvɔɪ/ *n* a messenger, es-

pecially one sent to a foreign government 使者; 使節

en·vy¹ /ˈɛnvɪ; ˈenvɪ/ *n* [U] **1** an unpleasant feeling you have towards someone when you wish that you had their qualities or possessions 羨慕; 妒忌: *They were full of envy when they saw his new car.* 他們看見他的新車都羨慕極了。**2 be the envy of** to have something which other people wish they had 〔某事物〕是…羨慕[妒忌]的對象: *Their health service is the envy of the world.* 他們的醫療服務為世人羨慕。

envy² *v* **envied, envying** [T] to wish that you had what someone else has got 羨慕; 妒忌: *I envy your ability to work so fast.* 你能幹得這麼快, 真讓我羨慕。| *I don't envy you your journey in this bad weather.* 我才不羨慕你在這種壞天氣去旅行呢。

□USEFUL PATTERNS 有用句型
to envy someone; to envy something; to envy someone something

ep·au·let /ˈɛpəˌlɛt; ˌɛpəˈlet/ *n* (also 又作 **epaulette**) a shoulder decoration, especially on a military or naval uniform 〔制服的〕肩章, 肩飾

e·phem·e·ral /əˈfɛmərəl; ɪˈfemərəl/ *adj* lasting only for a short time 短暫的: *ephemeral pleasures* 短暫的樂趣 | *ephemeral fashions* 短暫流行的時裝

ep·ic¹ /ˈɛpɪk; ˈepɪk/ *adj* full of brave action and excitement (used of stories or events) 〔指小說或事件〕英雄的; 壯麗的; 史詩般的: *an epic journey to the South Pole* 可歌可泣的南極之行

epic² *n* a long poem, book, or film about the deeds of gods and great men, or the early history of a nation 史詩; 史詩般的書或電影: *a Hollywood epic about the Roman Empire* 好萊塢製作的有關羅馬帝國的史詩般的影片

ep·i·dem·ic /ˌɛpəˈdɛmɪk; ˌepɪˈdemɪk/ *n* **1** a large number of cases of the same infectious disease at the same time 流行病: *an epidemic of cholera* 流行性霍亂 | *a flu epidemic* 流行性感冒 **2** something which develops and spreads quickly 流傳; 盛行: *an epidemic of violent crime* 暴力罪行的盛行 – **epidemic** *adj*

ep·i·gram /ˈɛpəˌgræm; ˈepɪˌgræm/ *n* a short amusing poem or saying which expresses a clever idea 諷刺性短詩; 警句; 雋語 –**epigrammatic** /ˌɛpəgrəˈmætɪk; ˌepɪgrəˈmætɪk/ *adj*

ep·i·lep·sy /ˈɛpəˌlɛpsɪ; ˈepɪˌlepsɪ/ *n* [U] a disease of the brain which causes sudden attacks of uncontrolled violent movement and loss of consciousness 癲癇症; 羊癇瘋

ep·i·lep·tic /ˌɛpəˈlɛptɪk; ˌepɪˈleptɪk◂/ *n* someone who suffers from epilepsy 患癲癇病的人 –**epileptic** *adj*: *an epileptic fit* 癲癇

病發作

ep·i·logue /ˈɛpəˌlɔg; ˈepɪˌlɒg/ *n* (also 又作 **epilog** *AmE* 〖美式〗) something at the end of a piece of literature which finishes it neatly 〔文藝作品的〕尾聲; 後記

ep·i·sode /ˈɛpəˌsod; ˈepɪˌsəʊd/ *n* **1** one part of a book or play which appears on radio, on television, or in a magazine in separate parts which make a story 〔書或戲劇中的〕一節; 一集: *The next episode will be broadcast next week.* 下一集將於下週播出。 **2** one separate event 獨立事件; 插曲: *There was a rather amusing episode in the pub last night.* 昨晚小酒館裡發生了一段相當有趣的插曲。

e·pis·tle /ɪˈpɪsl; ɪˈpɪsəl/ *n* **1** *fml* a letter, especially a long and important one (a word which is often used in a humorous way) 〖正式〗書信〔尤指較長的重要信件〕〔常含幽默〕 **2 Epistle** one of the letters in the Bible written by the first followers of Christ 〔聖經中的〕使徒書信

ep·i·taph /ˈɛpəˌtæf; ˈepɪˌtɑːf/ *n* a description of or thought about a dead person, often written on a stone above their grave 墓誌銘

ep·i·thet /ˈɛpəˌθɛt; ˈepɪˌθet/ *n* an adjective or descriptive phrase, especially of praise or blame, which is used about a person 表述形容詞, 修飾語〔尤用於褒貶人物〕

e·pit·o·me /ɪˈpɪtəmɪ; ɪˈpɪtəmi/ *n* **be the epitome of** to be the perfect or most typical example of something 典型; 縮影: *She's the epitome of good taste in her elegant new coat.* 她穿着優雅的新大衣, 可謂是有品味的典型人物。

e·pit·o·mize /ɪˈpɪtəˌmaɪz; ɪˈpɪtəmaɪz/ *v* **epitomized, epitomizing** (also 又作 **epitomise** *BrE* 〖英式〗) [T] to be very typical of 為...的典型表現: *The conduct of this strike epitomizes what is wrong with industrial relations in this country.* 這次罷工是這個國家在勞資關係方面的問題的縮影。

e·poch /ˈɛpək; ˈiːpɒk/ *n* a period of time in history during which important events or developments happened 〔有重要事件或重大發展的〕時期; 時代, 紀元

e·qual¹ /ˈikwəl; ˈiːkwəl/ *adj* **1** the same in size, number, amount, or value 〔大小、數量、價值等〕相等的; 相同的: *Cut the cake into six equal pieces.* 把蛋糕切成相等的六塊。 | *The two squares are equal in size.* 這兩個正方形大小相等。 | *I owe him £100. That's equal to one week's salary.* 我欠他一百英鎊。這相當於一週的薪水。 **2** the same as something that another more fortunate group of people already has 平等的: *Men can't complain if women want equal pay for equal work.* 如果婦女要求同工同酬, 男人沒甚麼可抱怨的。 | *Black citizens demanded equal rights.* 黑人公民要求得到平等的權利。 **3 equal to something** *fml* having the necessary strength, ability, or courage for some-

thing 〖正式〗能勝任某事: *Is Bill equal to the job of running the office?* 比爾有能力管理該辦事處的工作嗎? **4 on equal terms** without one person or group having any advantage over another one 以平等的條件: *The diplomats chose a neutral country so they could meet on equal terms.* 外交官選擇了一個中立國, 以便他們可以平等的地位會晤。

equal² *n* a person who has the same ability, position, or rights as someone else 同等的人: *He's a popular teacher because he treats the children as equals.* 他是個受歡迎的老師, 因為他平等對待孩子們。

equal³ *v* **-ll- (-l-** *AmE* 〖美式〗) [T] **1** to be the same as something else in number or amount 〔數目或數量〕等於: *"x=y" means that x equals y.* "x=y"意思是 x 等於 y。 **2** to be as good or the same standard as someone or something else 比得上: *Thompson has equalled the world record for the 400 metres.* 湯普森平了四百米賽跑的世界紀錄。

e·qual·i·ty /ɪˈkwɑlətɪ; ɪˈkwɒlɪti/ *n* [U] having the same conditions, possibilities, and rights as everyone else 平等; 相等: *racial equality* 種族平等 –opposite 反義 **inequality**

e·qual·ize /ˈikwəlˌaɪz; ˈiːkwəlaɪz/ *v* **equalized, equalizing** (also 又作 **equalise** *BrE* 〖英式〗) **1** [T] to make things equal in size, numbers, or amount 使相等; 使平等; 使均等: *Our party's policy is to try to equalize the tax burden.* 我們黨的政策是試圖均分稅務負擔。 **2** [I] to reach the same total of points as your opponent in sport 〔在比賽中與對方〕拉平比分: *Scotland equalized a few minutes before the end of the match.* 蘇格蘭隊在比賽結束前幾分鐘與對方拉平了比分。

★**e·qual·ly** /ˈikwəlɪ; ˈiːkwəli/ *adv* **1** to the same degree 相同地; 相等地: *They are both equally qualified for the job.* 他們倆同樣有資格做那份工作。 **2** in parts which are the same size 平均地: *They shared the work equally between them.* 他們把工作平分了。 **3** a word used to compare two ideas which have the same importance 〔用於比較同樣重要的兩個主意〕同樣地: *I think a new road should be built through the city centre, but equally, we shouldn't forget that this will be unpopular with local residents.* 我認為應該修一條直達市中心的新路, 但我們同樣不該忘記當地居民不會歡迎這主意的。

eq·ua·nim·i·ty /ˌikwəˈnɪmətɪ; ˌiːkwəˈnɪmɪti/ *n* [U] *fml* calmness of mind in a difficult situation 〖正式〗〔困境中的〕平靜; 沉着; 鎮定: *He received the bad news with surprising equanimity.* 他聽到那個壞消息時顯得異常鎮定。

e·quate /ɪˈkwet; ɪˈkweɪt/ *v* **equated, equating** [T] to consider something to be the same as something else 同等看待; 使等同: *You can't equate passing examinations with being intelligent.* 你不能把考試及格就當成是

E

聰明。

*e·qua·tion /ɪˈkweɪʒən; ɪˈkweɪʒən/ n tech a statement that two amounts or values are the same〔術語〕等式; 方程式: In the equation x+2y=7, what is x? 在方程式 x+2y=7 中, x 是多少?

E·qua·tor /ɪˈkweɪtəʳ; ɪˈkweɪtəʳ/ n the Equator an imaginary line drawn round the world at an equal distance between its most northern and southern points 赤道

e·qua·to·ri·al /ˌiːkwəˈtɔːrɪəl; ˌekwəˈtɔːrɪəl◂/ adj on or near the Equator and therefore very hot 在赤道上的; 在赤道附近的; 酷熱的: equatorial rainforests 赤道雨林

e·ques·tri·an /ɪˈkwestrɪən; ɪˈkwestrɪən/ adj connected with horse-riding 騎馬的; 騎術的: equestrian sports 馬術運動

e·qui·dis·tant /ˌiːkwɪˈdɪstənt; ˌiːkwɪˈdɪstənt◂/ adj the same distance from two places 等距離的: Rome is about equidistant from Cairo and Oslo. 從羅馬到開羅和到奧斯陸的距離差不多一樣遠。

e·qui·lat·e·ral /ˌiːkwəˈlætərəl; ˌiːkwɪˈlætərəl◂/ adj having all three sides equal〔三角形〕等邊的: an equilateral triangle 等邊三角形

e·qui·lib·ri·um /ˌiːkwəˈlɪbrɪəm; ˌiːkwɪˈlɪbrɪəm/ n [U] fml a balance between different forces or influences so that everything stays calm or at the same level〔正式〕平衡; 均衡: Inflation has been rising during the past few months, but now seems to be in a state of equilibrium. 通貨膨脹在過去幾個月中一直在上升, 但目前好像處於平衡狀態。

eq·uine /ˈiːkwaɪn; ˈekwaɪn/ adj of or like horses 馬的; 似馬的

eq·ui·nox /ˈiːkwənɒks; ˈiːkwɪnɒks/ n one of the two times in the year when day and night are of equal length〔晝夜平分的〕春[秋]分

e·quip /ɪˈkwɪp; ɪˈkwɪp/ v -pp- [T] 1 to supply someone with what is needed for a particular purpose 裝備; 配備: The council can't afford to equip the school properly. 政務委員會無力給學校提供適當的設備。| They equipped themselves with ropes before beginning to climb. 他們開始攀登以前, 給自己配備了繩子。 2 to prepare someone for a particular situation or experience 使〔某人〕有準備: His education hadn't equipped him for life's problems. 他所受的教育還不能使他應付得了生活中的問題。–equipped adj: a well equipped kitchen 設備完善的廚房 | students ill equipped to pass an exam 準備得不充分要去參加考試的學生們

*e·quip·ment /ɪˈkwɪpmənt; ɪˈkwɪpmənt/ n [U] the things which are used for a particular activity 配備; 設備: modern office equipment 現代辦公室設備 | photographic equipment 攝影設備

eq·ui·ta·ble /ˈekwɪtəbəl; ˈekwɪtəbəl/ adj fair and just 公平的; 公正的: an equitable division of the money 金錢的合理分配 –equitably adv

eq·ui·ty /ˈekwətɪ; ˈekwɪtɪ/ n equities 1 [U] the quality of being fair and just 公平; 公正; 公道: the equity of the judgment 公正的裁決 2 equities [pl] the equal parts into which ownership of a company is divided, on which no fixed interest is paid〔無固定利息的〕普通股: the equities market 普通股市場

*e·quiv·a·lent¹ /ɪˈkwɪvələnt; ɪˈkwɪvələnt/ adj having the same number, amount, or value as something else 等值的; 等量的; 等價的: He changed his pounds for the equivalent amount in dollars. 他把英鎊兌換成等值的美元。–equivalence n [U]

equivalent² n something that has the same value, size, or meaning as something else 等價物; 相等物; 對應的詞語: Some American words have no British equivalents. 一些美國英語在英國英語中沒有對應的詞語。

e·quiv·o·cal /ɪˈkwɪvəkəl; ɪˈkwɪvəkəl/ adj 1 having a double or doubtful meaning (used of words) 有歧義的; 模棱兩可的〔指詞語〕 2 difficult to understand or explain 難以理解[解釋]的 –opposite 反義 unequivocal –equivocally /-klɪ; -klɪ/ adv

e·ra /ˈɪərə; ˈɪərə/ n a long period of time begun or marked by an important event or discovery〔以某一重大事件或發現為標誌的〕時代; 時期; 紀元: the post-war era 戰後時期 | With the invention of the computer we moved into a new era. 隨着電腦的發明, 我們進入了一個新紀元。

e·rad·i·cate /ɪˈrædɪkeɪt; ɪˈrædɪkeɪt/ v eradicated, eradicating [T] to completely destroy something 根除; 消滅: Many tropical diseases have still not been successfully eradicated. 許多熱帶疾病還沒有被成功地消滅。–eradication /ɪˌrædɪˈkeɪʃən; ɪˌrædɪˈkeɪʃən/ n

e·rase /ɪˈreɪs; ɪˈreɪz/ v erased, erasing [T] to rub out or remove something completely 擦掉〔某物〕; 抹去

e·ras·er /ɪˈreɪsəʳ; ɪˈreɪzəʳ/ n the usual American word for〔美式〕= RUBBER

e·rect¹ /ɪˈrekt; ɪˈrekt/ adj in an upright position 直立的; 垂直的: With her head erect, she walked slowly down the aisle. 她昂着頭, 沿着通道慢慢地走。

erect² v [T] 1 fml to build something〔正式〕建造; 建立: This monument was erected in honour of Queen Charlotte. 這座紀念碑是為夏洛特女王而建造的。 2 to fit something together and put it in an upright position 使…直立; 豎立: This garden furniture is easy to erect. 這套花園設備很容易架立起來。

e·rec·tion /ɪˈrekʃən; ɪˈrekʃən/ n 1 [U] the building or placing of something in an upright position 建立; 架設: the erection of a new hospital 新醫院的建立 2 [C;U] the hardening and swelling of a man's PENIS in sexual excitement〔陰莖的〕勃起(狀態)

E

e·rode /ɪˈrod; ɪˈrəʊd/ v **eroded, eroding** [I;T] **1** to gradually destroy or be destroyed 逐漸損壞; 逐漸受損: *His authority has been eroded away.* 他的權力已被削弱了。| *Confidence in the new government is eroding.* 對新政府的信心正在減退。 **2** to wear or be worn away gradually by wind, rain, or acid 腐蝕; 被〔風、雨、酸等〕侵蝕: *The coast is slowly being eroded.* 海岸正在慢慢地被沖蝕。| *The cliffs are eroding.* 懸崖正受到侵蝕。 **–erosion** /ɪˈro-ʒən; ɪˈrəʊʒən/ n [U]: *soil erosion* 土壤侵蝕

e·rot·ic /ɪˈrɑtɪk; ɪˈrɒtɪk/ adj relating to sexual love and desire 性愛的; 性慾的; 色情的: *erotic feelings* 性感受 | *an erotic picture* 色情畫 **–erotically** /-klɪ; -kli/ adv **–eroticism** /-təˌsɪzəm; -tɪsɪzəm/ n [U]

err /ɜ; ɜːʳ/ v fml [I] **1** fml to make a mistake 〖正式〗犯錯誤: *I think the government has erred in its decision to abolish this tax.* 我認為政府錯在決定廢除這項稅收。 **2 err on the side of** to show a tendency towards a particular way of behaving 傾向於〔某種行為方式〕

er·rand /ˈɛrənd; ˈerənd/ n a short journey to take a message or to buy something 〔短程的〕差使; 跑腿〔送信或購物〕: *I've got a few errands to do in town.* 我要去城裏辦幾件事。

er·rant /ˈɛrənt; ˈerənt/ adj fml [only before a noun 只用於名詞前] behaving in a bad and irresponsible way 〖正式〗行為不良的; 不負責任的: *She went to London to bring back her errant daughter.* 她去倫敦把誤入歧途的女兒領回來。

er·rat·ic /əˈrætɪk; ɪˈrætɪk/ adj changeable or irregular in movement or behaviour 〔動作、行為〕反覆無常的; 不穩定的: *I'm rather an erratic tennis-player.* 我是個技術相當不穩定的網球手。 **–erratically** /-klɪ; -kli/ adv

er·ro·ne·ous /əˈroniəs; ɪˈrəʊniəs/ adj fml mistaken or incorrect 〖正式〗錯誤的; 不正確的: *erroneous opinions* 不正確的意見 | *erroneous ideas* 錯誤的觀點 **–erroneously** adv

✱er·ror /ˈɛrə; ˈerəʳ/ n [C;U] **1** a mistake 錯誤: *an error of judgment* 判斷錯誤 | *a computer error* 電腦錯誤 | *The accident was caused by human error.* 這次事故是由人為過錯造成的。 **2 in error** by mistake 弄錯: *It was done in error.* 這件事是弄錯的。

> ■ USAGE 用法: Compare 比較 **error** and 和 **mistake**. ☆ **1 Error** is a more formal word than **mistake** and often suggests something more serious ☆ **error** 比 **mistake** 更正式, 常指更嚴重的事物: *Your homework is full of **mistakes**.* 你的作業錯誤百出。 | *a serious political **error*** 嚴重的政治錯誤 **2 Error** sometimes suggests something which is morally wrong ☆ **error** 有時指道德上的過失: *the **errors** of his youth* 他年輕時

> 犯的過失 **3** Notice these fixed phrases ☆ 注意這些固定片語: *an **error** of judgment* 判斷錯誤 | *by **mistake*** 弄錯

er·u·dite /ˈɛrʊˌdaɪt; ˈerʊdaɪt/ adj showing deep knowledge and learning 博學的: *an erudite philosopher* 博學的哲學家

e·rupt /ɪˈrʌpt; ɪˈrʌpt/ v [I] **1** (of a VOLCANO) to explode and throw out fire, ash, and smoke 〔火山〕爆發; 噴發 **2** to suddenly happen or begin in a frightening way 突然發生; 爆發: *Violence erupted after the match.* 比賽後發生了暴力事件。 **3** to suddenly become angry or violent 突然發怒: *The crowd erupted.* 羣眾突然發怒了。 **–eruption** /ɪˈrʌpʃən; ɪˈrʌpʃən/ n [C;U]

es·ca·late /ˈɛskəˌlet; ˈeskəleɪt/ v **escalated, escalating** [I;T] to become more serious, bigger, or more widespread (使)升級; (使)擴大: *Government policies escalated unemployment.* 政府的政策使失業率進一步上升。| *The cost of property is escalating dramatically.* 房產的成本暴漲。 **–escalation** /ˌɛskəˌleʃən; ˌes-kəˈleɪʃən/ n [U]

es·ca·la·tor /ˈɛskəˌletə; ˈeskəleɪtəʳ/ n a set of moving stairs carrying people up or down between different levels 自動扶梯

es·ca·pade /ˈɛskəˌped; ˈeskəpeɪd/ n a wild, exciting, and sometimes dangerous adventure that disobeys rules or causes trouble 〔越軌的〕冒險行為; 惡作劇

✱es·cape¹ /əˈskep; ɪˈskeɪp/ v **escaped, escaping 1** [I] to succeed in getting out of a place where you are kept by force 逃脫; 逃跑: *They escaped **from** prison.* 他們從監獄裏逃走了。 **2** [T] to avoid something difficult or dangerous 逃避, 避開〔困難或危險〕: *She tried to escape her responsibilities.* 她企圖逃避責任。 | *He narrowly escaped being drowned.* 他險些淹死。 **3** [T] to be forgotten or remain unnoticed 被忘掉; 未被注意到: *I'm afraid your name escapes me.* 我恐怕記不起你的名字了。 | *Nothing escapes his attention.* 甚麼事情也逃不過他的注意。 **4** [I] to get out of a hole or crack in a container 漏出; 逸出: *I think gas is escaping from the pipe.* 我想煤氣管正在漏氣。

escape² n **1** [C;U] the getting out or away from somewhere free and alive 逃跑; 逃脫: *The thief jumped into a car and made his escape.* 小偷跳上一輛汽車逃跑了。 | *She had a narrow escape when the wall nearly fell on her.* 牆塌下來, 險些砸着她。 **2** [C;U] something that makes you free from something unpleasant or dull 消遣物; 消遣; 解悶: *He reads thrillers as an escape **from** his boring routine.* 他閱讀驚險小説, 作為在乏味的例行公事之餘的消遣。 **3** [C] an amount of something that gets out of a hole or crack in a container 漏泄; 逸逸: *an escape of gas* 煤氣逸漏

es·cap·is·m /əˈskepɪzəm; ɪˈskeɪpɪzəm/ *n* [U] activity that provides something pleasant and imaginary to think about instead of unpleasant or dull reality 消遣; 逃避現實: *Science-fiction stories are pure escapism!* 科幻小說純粹是逃避現實! –**escapist** *adj,n*

es·carp·ment /ɛˈskɑrpmənt; ɪˈskɑːpmənt/ *n* a long steep slope or cliff on a mountainside 〔山的〕陡坡; 懸崖

es·cort[1] /ˈɛskɔrt; ˈeskɔːt/ *n* **1** a person or vehicle that travels with someone as a guard or an honour 護送者; 護衛隊 **2 under escort** with an escort 在護送下: *The prisoner travelled* **under** *police escort.* 犯人在警察押送下上路。**3** *fml* a person of the opposite sex who goes with someone as a companion to a social event 〔正式〕陪伴某人赴社交活動的異性: *Mary's escort arrived to take her out for the evening.* 瑪麗的男伴來陪她去參加晚會。

e·scort[2] /ɪˈskɔrt; ɪˈskɔːt/ *v* [T] to go with someone 護送〔某人〕: *The politician was escorted by the directors as he toured the factory.* 那位政治家由董事們陪同參觀了工廠。

e·soph·a·gus /iˈsɑfəgəs; ɪˈsɒfəgəs/ *n* –see 見 OESOPHAGUS

es·o·ter·ic /ˌɛsəˈtɛrɪk; ˌesəˈterɪk/ *adj* understood by only a small number of people who have a specialist knowledge 深奧難懂的; 冷僻的: *Some words are really too esoteric for this dictionary.* 有些單詞實在太冷僻了, 沒有收入這本詞典內。

ESP /ˌi ɛs ˈpi; ˌiː es ˈpiː/ **1** the teaching of English to students who need it for a particular job or purpose; an abbreviation for **English for Specific Purposes** 〔縮〕〔針對為找工作或為特殊目的學習英語的學生進行的〕特殊用途英語教學 **2** knowledge which seems to have been gained without the use of sound, touch, taste or smell, or sight; an abbreviation for **extra-sensory perception** 〔縮〕〔五官以外的〕超感知覺

es·pe·cial /əˈspɛʃəl; ɪˈspeʃəl/ *adj* [only before a noun 只用於名詞前] *fml* 〔正式〕not ordinary or usual 特別的; 不平常的

★★ **es·pe·cial·ly** /əˈspɛʃəli; ɪˈspeʃəli/ *adv* (also 又作 **specially**) **1** to a particularly great degree 特別地; 格外: *"Do you like chocolate?" "Not especially."* "你喜歡吃巧克力嗎?" "不特別喜歡。" **2** in particular 特別地; 尤其: *I love Italy, especially in summer.* 我很喜歡意大利, 尤其是在夏天。**3** for a particular person or purpose 專門地: *This crown was made especially for the King.* 這頂王冠是為國王特製的。

es·pi·o·nage /ˈɛspiənɪdʒ; ˈespiənɑːʒ/ *n* [U] the activity of finding out the secret information of a country or company and sending it to enemies or competitors 諜報[間諜]活動

es·pla·nade /ˌɛspləˈned; ˈespləneɪd/ *n* a level open space where people walk for pleasure, often near the sea in seaside towns 〔常指沿海城鎮供人散步的〕(海濱)廣場

Esq. /əˈskwaɪə; ɪˈskwaɪər/ *n* [only after a noun 只用於名詞後] *BrE* a title of politeness after a man's full name; a written abbreviation for **esquire**; not used much now 〔英式, 縮〕= esquire 用作禮儀稱呼, 放在男子全名後的 尊稱)... 先生: *The envelope is addressed to Peter Jones, Esq.* 信封上寫着彼得·瓊斯先生收。

es·say /ˈɛse; ˈeseɪ/ *n* a short piece of writing on a particular subject, written especially as part of a course of study 論說文; 散文; 隨筆: *We've got to write an essay on the war with Napoleon.* 我們得寫一篇關於和拿破崙開戰的文章。

es·sence /ˈɛsns; ˈesəns/ *n* **1** [U] the most important part of something which contains its most typical qualities 本質; 要素; 實質: *The essence of his argument is that we should not destroy the ozone layer.* 他的論點的實質是我們不該破壞臭氧層。**2** [C;U] the best part of a substance that has been taken out and reduced to a liquid 香精: *vanilla essence* 香草香精 **3 in essence** a phrase used when you are talking about the most important part of an idea, situation, or event 本質上; 實質上〔用於談到觀點、形勢或事件的最重要部分〕

★ **es·sen·tial** /əˈsɛnʃəl; ɪˈsenʃəl/ *adj* **1** completely necessary 必不可少的: *Previous experience of this type of job is not essential.* 以前是否做過這種工作並非必需條件。**2** [only before a noun 只用於名詞前] central or most important 根本的; 最重要的: *What is the essential difference between these two political systems?* 這兩種政治制度的主要區別是甚麼? –**essential** *n*: *The room was furnished with the bare essentials: a bed, a chair, and a table.* 房間裡擺設了最簡單的必需品——一張牀、一把椅子和一張桌子。

★ **es·sen·tial·ly** /əˈsɛnʃəli; ɪˈsenʃəli/ *adv* **1** most importantly 非常重要地: *She's essentially a very kind person.* 她本質上是個非常和善的人。| *The problem is essentially one of cost.* 這個問題最重要的就是成本。**2** a word used to show that something is generally true 基本上: *In spite of some silly mistakes, his work is essentially sound.* 儘管有些可笑的錯誤, 他的工作基本上還是幹得不錯的。

★★ **es·tab·lish** /əˈstæblɪʃ; ɪˈstæblɪʃ/ *v* **1** [T] to set up or begin something 建立, 設立〔某事物〕: *This company was established in 1850.* 這家公司成立於1850年。| *The club has established a new rule allowing women to join.* 俱樂部訂定了一條新規例, 允許婦女入會。| *We're trying to establish contact with the crashed plane.* 我們正在設法和墜毀的飛機取得聯繫。**2** [T] to make people recognize your or someone else's position, ability, or claim

使〔地位、能力、聲明等〕被承認, 確立: *He quickly established himself* **as** *a powerful member of the new government.* 他很快使自己在新政府中成為有勢力的人物。| *His next film, "Taxi Driver", established his fame as an actor.* 他的下一部影片《計程車司機》確立了他作為演員的聲譽。**3** [T; +(that)] to find out or prove something 找出; 證實: *His lawyer tried to establish that he had been abroad at the time.* 他的律師試圖證實他當時在國外。| *They couldn't establish the cause of the accident.* 他們無法找出事故的原因。

★es·tab·lish·ment /əˈstæblɪʃmənt; ɪˈstæblɪʃmənt/ *n* **1** [U] the setting up of a system or organization 建立; 設立; 制定: *the establishment of new laws protecting children* 制定保護兒童的新法律 **2** [C] *fml* a place run as a business or for a special purpose 〔正式〕企業; 機構: *This hotel is a very well-run establishment.* 這家旅館是個經營有方的單位。| *a research establishment* 研究機構 **3 the Establishment** the powerful organizations and people who control public life and usually do not like making great changes 社會權力機構; 統治集團

★es·tate /əˈstet; ɪˈsteɪt/ *n* **1** a piece of land on which buildings of a similar type have been built together 有大片同類建築物的土地, 區: *an industrial estate* 工業區 | *a housing estate* 住宅區 **2** an area of land in the country with a large house on it owned by one person or a family 〔鄉村的〕一大片私有土地 **3** *law* all the money and property a person leaves behind them when they die 〔律〕遺產

estate a·gent /·'·· , ··'·/ *n* (**real estate agent** *AmE* 〔美式〕) a person whose job is to buy and sell houses and land for people 房地產經紀人

estate car /·'·· ·/ *n BrE* a car with a door at the back and a lot of room to put bags and cases 客貨兩用車; 旅行車 –see picture on page 209 見 209 頁彩圖

es·teem¹ /əˈstim; ɪˈstiːm/ *n* [U] respect and admiration for another person 尊重, 尊敬〔某人〕: *She is held in high esteem by her male colleagues.* 她受到男性同事的尊敬。

esteem² *v* [T] *fml* 〔正式〕 **1** to respect and admire someone greatly 尊重; 尊敬: *The old teacher was much loved and esteemed.* 這位老教師深受愛戴。 **2** to consider someone to be a particular thing 以為; 認為: *I did not esteem him to be trustworthy.* 我認為他並不值得信任。

es·ti·ma·ble /ˈɛstəməbl; ˈestɪməbəl/ *adj fml* deserving admiration and respect 〔正式〕值得敬重的

★es·ti·mate¹ /ˈɛstə͵met; ˈestɪmeɪt/ *v* **estimated, estimating** [I;T;+(that)] to judge or calculate the value, size or amount of something 估計; 估價: *Can you estimate how far it is?* 你能估計有多遠嗎? | *That film cost an*

estimated £25 million to make. 那部影片的估算成本為二千五百萬英鎊。| *It has been estimated that more and more old people will live to be 100.* 據估計越來越多的老人將能活到一百歲。

★es·ti·mate² /ˈɛstəmɪt; ˈestɪmɪt/ *n* **1** a statement of the probable cost of doing a job 估價: *I got several estimates for having the roof repaired, and accepted the lowest.* 我在修理屋頂前, 收到了好幾家報價, 最後接受了報價最低的一家。 **2** a calculation or judgment of the value, size, or amount of something 判斷; 估計: *I asked him to make an estimate of the painting's value.* 我請他估一下這幅畫的價。| *At a rough estimate I'd say it was 300 years old.* 粗略估計, 我會說它有三百年了。

es·ti·ma·tion /͵ɛstəˈmeʃən; ͵estɪˈmeɪʃən/ *n* [sing] judgment or opinion 判斷; 估計; 評價: *She's really gone down in my estimation since she used all my ideas in her book.* 自從她在書裡用了我所有的觀點以後, 我對她的評價低了很多。

es·tranged /əˈstrendʒd; ɪˈstreɪndʒd/ *adj* **1** no longer living with your husband or wife 〔夫妻〕分居的 **2** no longer speaking to your family 〔和家人〕疏遠的 –**estrangement** *n* [C; U] *fml* 〔正式〕

es·tu·a·ry /ˈɛstʃʊ͵ɛrɪ; ˈestʃʊəri/ *n* **estuaries** the wide part of a river where it joins the sea 〔與海相連的〕河口; 三角灣: *the Thames estuary* 泰晤士河河口

etc. /ɛtˈsɛtərə; ͵etˈsetərə/ *adv* a word used at the end of a list to show that there are other things which you could also include; an abbreviation for the Latin phrase *et cetera* 〔縮〕以及其他, 等等: *They bought tea, coffee, sugar, etc.* 他們買了茶、咖啡、糖等等。

etch /ɛtʃ; etʃ/ *v* [I;T] to draw a picture by cutting lines on a metal plate with a needle and acid 〔用酸在金屬上〕蝕刻; 浸蝕〔圖畫〕 –**etching** *n*

e·ter·nal /ɪˈtɜnl; ɪˈtɜːnl/ *adj* going on for ever or for a very long time 永恆的; 永久的: *Do you believe in eternal life?* 你相信永生嗎? –**eternally** *adv*

e·ter·ni·ty /ɪˈtɜnətɪ; ɪˈtɜːnɪti/ *n* **1** [U] time without end, particularly time after death, which is said to last forever 永恆; 永生; 來世 **2 an eternity** a period of time that seems very long because you are annoyed, anxious, or not interested 〔因煩惱、焦慮、不感興趣等〕顯得漫長的時間: *Every moment seemed an eternity.* 每一刻似乎都很漫長。

e·ther /ˈiθɚ; ˈiːθəʳ/ *n* [U] a light colourless liquid, easily changed into a gas, which was used in the past to put people to sleep before a medical operation 醚; 乙醚

e·the·re·al /ɪˈθɪrɪəl; ɪˈθɪəriəl/ *adj* unnaturally light and delicate 輕飄的; 縹緲的; 精微的

eth·ic /ˈɛθɪk; ˈeθɪk/ *n* **1** an idea that influences people's behaviour and beliefs 道德, 倫理: *the Christian ethic* 基督教的倫理

2 ethics [pl] moral rules or principles of behaviour which you believe in 道德準則; 倫理標準: *Whether you agree or disagree with the death penalty is a question of ethics.* 同意還是反對死刑是一個道德準則問題。

eth·i·cal /ˈɛθɪkl̩; ˈeθɪkəl/ *adj* **1** relating to what you believe is right and wrong 道德的; 倫理的: *The use of animals in scientific tests raises some difficult ethical questions.* 用動物做科學試驗會引起一些棘手的道德問題。**2** morally good or correct 合乎道德的; 規矩的: *The judge said that the doctor's behaviour had not been ethical.* 法官説那位醫生的行為不符合職業道德規範。–opposite 反義 **unethical** –**ethically** /-klɪ; -kli/ *adv*

★**eth·nic** /ˈɛθnɪk; ˈeθnɪk/ *adj* relating to a particular racial, national, or tribal group 種族的; 民族的: *ethnic minorities* 少數民族 | *ethnic food* 具有民族特色的食物

eth·nol·o·gy /ɛθˈnɑlədʒɪ; eθˈnɒlədʒi/ *n* [U] the study and comparison of different races of people 人種學, 民族學

e·thos /ˈiθɑs; ˈiːθɒs/ *n* the typical values, ideas, and beliefs of a certain group of people〔某一羣人的〕精神特質

et·i·quette /ˈɛtɪkɛt; ˈetɪkət/ *n* [U] the formal rules of polite and proper behaviour in society or in a particular profession 禮節; 禮儀

et·y·mol·o·gy /ˌɛtəˈmɑlədʒɪ; ˌetɪˈmɒlədʒi/ *n* [U] the study of the origins, history, and changing meanings of words 詞源學

eu·ca·lyp·tus /ˌjukəˈlɪptəs; juːkəˈlɪptəs/ *n* [C;U] a tall tree that produces an oil used in medicine〔產油的〕桉樹

eu·lo·gize /ˈjulə̩dʒaɪz; ˈjuːlədʒaɪz/ *v* **eulogized, eulogizing** (also 又作 **eulogise** *BrE*〔英式〕) [T] *fml* to praise someone or something very highly〔正式〕頌揚, 讚揚〔某人〕

eu·lo·gy /ˈjulədʒɪ; ˈjuːlədʒi/ *n* **eulogies** [C; U] *fml* a speech or a piece of writing that praises the qualities of a person〔正式〕頌詞; 頌文

eu·nuch /ˈjunək; ˈjuːnək/ *n* a man who has had his sex organs removed 閹人; 太監

eu·phe·mis·m /ˈjufə̩mɪzəm; ˈjuːfɪ̩mɪzəm/ *n* [C;U] a pleasanter or less direct word or phrase used to talk about something that is considered awkward or unpleasant 委婉語 –**euphemistic** /ˌjufəˈmɪstɪk; ˌjuːfɪˈmɪstɪk◂/ *adj*

eu·pho·ri·a /juˈforɪə; juːˈfɔːriə/ *n* [U] a feeling of extreme happiness and excitement 高漲的情緒; 極度興奮的情緒 –**euphoric** *adj*

Eu·ro·pe·an¹ /ˌjurəˈpiən; juərəˈpiən◂/ *adj* from or connected with a country in Europe 歐洲的: *the European Community* 歐洲經濟共同體 | *Eastern European wines* 東歐產的葡萄酒

European² *n* a person from a country in Europe 歐洲人

Eu·ro·pe·an Ec·o·nom·ic Com·mu·ni·ty (also 又作 **European Community** /ˌ····· ·· ·ˈ···/) *n* a European organization established to encourage trade and friendly relations between its member countries 歐洲經濟共同體

eu·tha·na·si·a /ˌjuθəˈneʒə; ˌjuːθəˈneɪziə/ *n* [U] the practice of killing incurably ill or old people in a painless way 安樂死(術)

e·vac·u·ate /ɪˈvækju̩et; ɪˈvækjueɪt/ *v* **evacuated, evacuating** [T] to move people from a dangerous place to a safer place 疏散; 撤離: *During the war, children living in cities were evacuated to the country.* 在戰爭中, 住在城市裡的兒童被疏散到農村。–**evacuation** /ɪˌvækjuˈeʃən; ɪˌvækjuˈeɪʃən/ *n* [C;U]

e·vac·u·ee /ɪˈvækjuˌi; ɪˌvækjuˈiː/ *n* a person who has been sent from a dangerous to a safe place 被疏散者

e·vade /ɪˈved; ɪˈveɪd/ *v* **evaded, evading** [T] **1** to avoid doing something you should do 規避; 逃避〔職責〕: *If you try to evade paying your taxes you risk going to prison.* 如果你企圖逃稅, 你就有坐牢的危險。 | *He evaded the question.* 他廻避了那個問題。**2** to manage to avoid being caught 逃脱〔追捕〕: *After his escape he evaded capture for several days.* 他逃跑後, 躲了好幾天還沒有給人抓到。

e·val·u·ate /ɪˈvælju̩et; ɪˈvæljueɪt/ *v* **evaluated, evaluating** [T] *fml* to judge the importance or value of something after studying its good and bad points〔正式〕評估, 評價〔某事物〕: *The students' work is evaluated regularly.* 學生們的作業定期受到評估。–**evaluation** /ɪˌvæljuˈeʃən; ɪˌvæljuˈeɪʃən/ *n* [C;U]

e·van·gel·i·cal /ˌivænˈdʒɛlɪkl̩; ˌiːvænˈdʒelɪkəl/ *adj* **1** believing in the importance of a personal Christian faith and of studying the Bible, rather than in religious ceremonies 新教會福音派的〔認為信仰和研讀《聖經》比宗教儀式更為重要〕**2** being too eager to spread your own beliefs and ideas 熱衷於傳播自己的信仰的

e·van·ge·list /ɪˈvændʒə̩lɪst; ɪˈvændʒɪ̩lɪst/ *n* someone who travels from place to place in order to tell people about Christianity〔基督教〕福音傳道者 –**evangelism** *n* [U]

e·vap·o·rate /ɪˈvæpə̩ret; ɪˈvæpəreɪt/ *v* **evaporated, evaporating** [I;T] **1** to change into steam and disappear (使)蒸發; 揮發: *The puddle evaporated in the sun.* 水坑裡的水在陽光下蒸發了。**2** to become less and less before disappearing completely 消散: *My anger evaporated when I saw her.* 我一見她怒氣就平息了。–**evaporation** /ɪˌvæpəˈreʃən; ɪˌvæpəˈreɪʃən/ *n* [U]

e·va·sion /ɪˈveʒən; ɪˈveɪʒən/ *n* [C;U] the act of avoiding something by being clever or deceitful 逃避; 躲避: *George is in prison for tax evasion.* 喬治因逃税而入獄。

e·va·sive /ɪˈvesɪv; ɪˈveɪsɪv/ *adj* trying not to talk about something 迴避的；推諉的；閃爍其詞的: *an evasive answer* 閃爍其詞的回答 –**evasively** *adv* –**evasiveness** *n* [U]

eve /iv; iːv/ *n* **1** the night or day before a religious holiday〔宗教節日的〕前夜；前夕: *Christmas Eve* 聖誕節前夕 **2 the eve of** the time just before an important event〔重大事件發生的〕前夕，前一刻: *on the eve of the election* 在選舉前夕

e·ven[1] /ˈivən; ˈiːvən/ *adj* **1** level and smooth 平坦的；平滑的: *You need a nice even surface to work on.* 你需要在一個很平滑的表面上工作。| *The roads were narrow and not very even.* 路又狹窄又不平坦。**2** staying at the same level 穩定的；平均的: *The seeds need an even temperature to germinate.* 種子需要穩定的溫度來發芽。**3** equal 平等的；相等的: *It was quite an even competition.* 那是一場勢均力敵的比賽。| *I won three points in the last game, which means that I'm now even* **with** *the leader.* 我在上一局贏了三分，這意味着現在我跟領先者打成平手。| *We think there should be a more even distribution of wealth in the world.* 我們認為世界上財富的分配應該更加平等。**4 get even with someone** to do something unpleasant to someone in return for something unpleasant that they did to you 和某人算賬；向某人報復 **5 even number** a number that can be divided by 2 偶數: *The answer should always be an even number.* 答案應該總是偶數。**6 an even chance** an equal possibility that something will happen or not happen〔某事發生與否的〕相等的可能性: *He's got an even chance of winning.* 他有一半獲勝的機會。

even[2] *adv* **1** a word you use when you are saying that something is surprising or unusual〔用以說明某事令人驚訝或不尋常〕甚至；連…都: *We went down to the beach, and we even had a quick swim in the sea.* 我們去了海灘，甚至還在海裡游了一下泳呢。| *Even Mary seemed to enjoy herself, and she usually hates parties.* 連瑪麗也顯得很愉快，她平時可是討厭派對的。| *This is a sport that can be enjoyed by everyone, even old people.* 這是一項大家都能享受的運動，甚至對老年人也是如此。**2** a word you use for making comparisons stronger〔用以加強比較〕甚至〔比…〕還；更加: *It was cold yesterday, but it's even colder today.* 昨天很冷，但今天更冷。| *The film was even more boring than I'd expected.* 那部影片甚至比我預料的還要無聊。**3 even if** no matter if 即使；雖然: *Even if we could afford it we wouldn't go abroad for our holidays.* 即使我們有能力，我們也不會出國度假。| *We'll still have the garden party, even if it rains.* 就算下雨，我們也會舉行花園聚會。**4 even though** although 雖然: *He forgot to bring the book with him, even though I reminded him several times.* 雖然我提醒了

他好幾次，他還是忘了帶那本書。**5 even so** in spite of this 儘管這樣: *I know she's not been very well and I know she's had a hard time recently. Even so, you'd think she could do a little bit to help.* 我知道她身體不太好，最近又不太順心。儘管如此，你該料到她還是能幫上點兒忙的。

even[3] *v*

even out *phr v* [I;T **even** sthg ↔ **out**] to make or become more equal (使)均等: *The distribution of wealth within our society is gradually being evened out.* 我們社會的財富分配正在逐漸均等。

eve·ning /ˈivnɪŋ; ˈiːvnɪŋ/ *n* [C;U] the end of the day and early part of the night 傍晚；黃昏，晚上: *Are you planning to go out this evening?* 你今天晚上打算出去嗎？

evening dress /ˈ·· ·/ *n* **1** [U] special clothes worn for formal occasions in the evening 晚禮服 **2** [C] a dress, usually long, worn by women for a formal occasion 女士晚禮服

e·vent /ɪˈvent; ɪˈvent/ *n* **1** something that happens which is important, interesting, or unusual〔指重要、有意思或不尋常的〕事件: *a social event* 社會重大事件 | *The article discusses the course of events leading up to her death.* 那篇文章討論了導致她死亡的一系列事件發展的過程。**2** a race or competition arranged as part of a day's sports〔運動會的〕比賽項目: *The next event will be the 100 metres race.* 下一個項目是一百米賽跑。**3 at all events** at least 至少；不管怎樣: *She lost nearly everything but at all events she's still alive.* 她幾乎失去了一切，但至少她還活着。**4 in any event** whatever happens 無論如何: *I'll probably see you tomorrow, but in any event I'll phone.* 我明天可能會來看你，但無論如何我會打電話的。**5 in the event** when something actually happened 到頭來；結果: *We thought he'd be nervous on stage, but in the event he was fine.* 我們原以為他上台會緊張的，但結果他沒事。**6 in the event of** *fml* if something happens〔正式〕如果〔某事發生〕；萬一: *In the event of rain, the party will be held indoors.* 如果下雨，聚會就在室內舉行。

e·vent·ful /ɪˈventfəl; ɪˈventfəl/ *adj* full of exciting or interesting events 充滿重大事件的；多變故的: *an eventful life* 經歷豐富的一生 | *We've had rather an eventful day.* 我們度過了不平凡的一天。–opposite 反義 **uneventful**

e·ven·tu·al /ɪˈventʃuəl; ɪˈventʃuəl/ *adj* [only before a noun 只用於名詞前] happening in the end as a result 最終的；結局的: *a research programme aimed at the eventual eradication of this disease* 一項旨在最終消滅這種疾病的研究計劃

e·ven·tu·al·i·ty /ɪˌventʃuˈælətɪ; ɪˈventʃuˈæləti/ *n* **eventualities** a possible event or result, especially an unpleasant one 可能發生的事件或結果〔尤指不愉快的〕；不測事件:

We must be prepared for all eventualities. 我們必須作好應付各種意外的準備。

e·ven·tu·al·ly /ɪˈvɛntʃuəlɪ; ɪˈvɛntʃuəlɪ/ *adv* in the end 最終; 終於: *She worked so hard that she eventually made herself ill.* 她工作太辛苦, 終於病倒了。–see Study Note on page 1325 見 1325 頁學習提示

ev·er /ˈɛvɚ; ˈɛvə/ *adv* **1** at any time 在任何時候; 從來: *Nothing ever makes him angry.* 從來沒有任何事會使他生氣。 | *Have you ever met my wife?* 你見過我太太嗎? | *If you ever come to Spain, we must meet.* 如果你甚麼時候來西班牙, 我們一定要見面。 | *It was the best holiday we've ever had.* 那是我們度過的最美好的假期。 | *I don't think I'll ever go back to live in London.* 我想我再也不會回倫敦去住的。 **2 ever since** since a particular time, which is a long time ago 此後一直; 從此: *We've been good friends ever since we were children.* 我們從小就一直是好朋友。 | *This factory closed down two years ago, and it's been empty ever since.* 這家工廠兩年前關閉了, 此後一直空置着。 **3** used in questions to give more force to what you are saying〔用於疑問句中以加強語氣〕究竟, 到底: *"He says he won't be coming to the meeting." "Why ever not?"* "他說他不會來參加會議。" "究竟為甚麼不來?" **4** continuing to happen all the time 一直; 不斷地: *the ever-increasing population* 不斷增長的人口 | *our ever-expanding economy* 我們一直在發展的經濟 **5 ever after** for all time in the future 從此以後一直: *They got married and lived happily ever after.* 他們結了婚, 從此以後一直生活得很幸福。 **6 ever so, ever such** *infml* very; used to add force to what you are saying〔非正式〕很; 非常〔用於加強語氣〕: *She's ever so upset about it.* 她對此很不安。 | *It's ever such a good film.* 這真是一部非常好的影片。 | *They're ever such nice people.* 他們都是非常好的人。

> ■ USAGE 用法: Compare 比較 **whatever** and 和 **what ever**. We usually write **whatever** as one word. ☆ **whatever** 常寫作一個詞。*Do* **whatever** *she tells you.* 她叫你做甚麼你就做甚麼。But we write **what ever** (two separate words) for questions expressing great surprise ☆在疑問句中表示很驚奇的語氣時, **what ever** 分開寫作兩個詞: **What ever** *gave you such a strange idea?* 你怎麼會得出一個這樣奇怪的主意? The same is true of **however** and **how ever**. **however** 和 **how ever** 也是同樣的情況。

ev·er·green /ˈɛvɚˌgrin; ˈevəgriːn/ *n* a tree or bush that does not lose its leaves in winter 常綠樹; 常綠灌木

ev·er·last·ing /ˌɛvɚˈlæstɪŋ; ˌevəˈlɑːstɪŋ◂/ *adj fml* continuing for ever〔正式〕永久的; 永恆的: *God has promised us everlasting life.* 上

帝許諾給予我們永生。 | *By winning so often she has won everlasting fame.* 她因為頻頻獲勝, 贏得了永久的聲譽。

ev·er·more /ˌɛvɚˈmor; ˌevəˈmɔːr/ *adv lit* always〔文〕始終; 永遠: *He swore to love her for evermore.* 他發誓永遠愛她。

ev·ery /ˈɛvrɪ; ˈevrɪ/ *det* **1** all of more than two people or things〔兩among以上的人或東西的〕每一(個): *I believe every word he says.* 我相信他說的每一句話。 | *I enjoyed every minute of the party.* 整個聚會上我都玩得很愉快。 **2** once in each 每; 每隔…的: *He comes to see us every day.* 他每天來看我們一次。 | *We go to Scotland every three months or so.* 我們每三個月左右去一次蘇格蘭。 | *Change the oil in the car every 5000 miles.* 汽車每行駛五千英里要換一次油。 **3** as much as possible, or very much or very many 充分的; 盡一切可能的: *We made every attempt to get there on time.* 我們千方百計要準時到達那裡。 | *There is every chance that we will lose our jobs.* 我們完全有可能失業。 | *We have every reason to believe that we will be successful.* 我們有充分的理由相信我們會成功。 **4 every other day, week, year, etc** each second day, week, year, etc 每隔一天[一週、一年]: *Take the medicine every other day.* 這藥每隔一天服用一次。 | *We go to visit them every other week.* 我們每隔一週去探望他們一次。

> ■ USAGE 用法: Compare 比較 **every one** and 和 **everyone**. **Every one** means "every person or thing already mentioned" and it is often followed by *of* ☆ **every one** 指"提及過的每一個人或每一件事物", 後面常跟 *of*: *There are 16 students in the class and* **every one** *of them passed.* 班裡有十六個學生, 每個人都及格了。**Everyone** (or **everybody**) means "every person" and it is not usually followed by *of* ☆ **everyone** (或 **everybody**) 指"每一個人", 後面不常跟 *of*: **Everyone** *in the class passed the exam.* 班上人人都通過了考試。

ev·ery·bod·y /ˈɛvrɪˌbɑdɪ; ˈevrɪbɒdɪ/ *pron* (also 又作 **everyone**) [used with a singular verb 與單數動詞連用] every person 每個人; 人人: *I hope that everybody enjoys the party.* 我希望每個人都喜歡這次聚會。 | *She gets on well with everyone.* 她和每個人都相處得很好。

> ■ USAGE 用法: **Everybody, somebody, anybody** always take a singular verb ☆ **everybody, somebody, anybody** 的動詞總是用單數形式: *Has* **everybody** *finished?* 大家都完成了嗎? | *Does* **anybody** *want a drink?* 有誰想喝一杯嗎? But they are often followed by a plural pronoun, except in very formal

language ☆但除了在正式的語言中, 後面常跟複數代詞: **Everybody** *understands, don't they?* 每個人都懂了, 是嗎? | **Anybody** *can do that if they try.* 如果大家都肯試試, 人人都能做的。 | **Somebody's** *left their gloves in my office.* 有人把手套留在我的辦公室裡了。 | (**Everyone, someone, anyone** behave in the same way. **everyone, someone, anyone** 也是同樣情況)

***ev·ery·day** /ˈɛvrɪˈde; ˈevrɪdeɪ/ *adj* [only before a noun 只用於名詞前] ordinary, common, and usual 每天的; 日常的; 普通的: *Accidents are an everyday occurrence in our house.* 在我們家裡, 事故是經常發生的事。

***ev·ery·one** /ˈɛvrɪˌwʌn; ˈevrɪwʌn/ *pron* –see 見 EVERYBODY

***ev·ery·thing** /ˈɛvrɪˌθɪŋ; ˈevriθɪŋ/ *pron* [used with a singualr verb 與單數動詞連用] all things 一切事物; 凡事: *Everything was going according to plan.* 一切都在按計劃進行。 | *Is everything ready for the party?* 聚會的一切都準備妥當了嗎? | *I've forgotten everything I learnt at school.* 我把在學校裡所學的東西都忘記了。 | *I was fed up with my job, with my home life, with everything.* 我對我的工作, 對我的家庭, 對所有的事都感到厭煩。

***ev·ery·where** /ˈɛvrɪˌhwɛr; ˈevriweəʳ/ *adv* in or to every place 各處; 到處: *We looked everywhere for her.* 我們到處找她。 | *This situation will affect people everywhere in Britain.* 這種局面將會影響英國各地的人。 | *She follows me everywhere I go.* 我走到哪裡, 她就跟到哪裡。

e·vict /ɪˈvɪkt; ɪˈvɪkt/ *v* [T] to make someone leave a house or land by law 〔依法〕把〔某人〕趕走; 驅逐: *My cousin was evicted from his flat because he hadn't paid the rent all year.* 我表弟因為一年沒付房租而被趕出了公寓。 –**eviction** /ɪˈvɪkʃən; ɪˈvɪkʃən/ *n* [C;U]

***ev·i·dence** /ˈɛvədəns; ˈevɪdəns/ *n* **1** [U] words or objects which prove a statement, support a belief, or make something more clearly true 證明; 證據; 證詞: *There is some evidence to suggest that he was there on the night she was murdered.* 有一些證據證明她被謀殺當晚他在現場。 | *An important piece of evidence has been found.* 發現了一條重要的證據。 | *We saw no evidence of damage to crops.* 我們沒有證據證明農作物受到破壞。 | *He gave evidence for the accused.* 他為被告提供了證據。 **2 in evidence** clearly and easily seen 顯而易見的: *The police were much in evidence whenever the President made a public appearance.* 每當總統在公開場合露面時, 到處都可以看到警察。

***ev·i·dent** /ˈɛvədənt; ˈevɪdənt/ *adj* plain or clear from signs you notice 明顯的; 明白的:

It's evident that you've been drinking. 顯然你一直在喝酒。 | *her evident unhappiness* 她明顯的不快 –**evidently** *adv: He is evidently unwilling to discuss it.* 顯然他不願討論此事。

***e·vil**[1] /ˈivl; ˈiːvəl/ *adj* **1** wicked and harmful, especially in thought or behaviour 〔尤指思想上或行為中〕邪惡的; 有害的: *an evil influence* 極壞的影響 | *an evil regime* 邪惡的政權 **2** *infml* very unpleasant 〔非正式〕討厭的, 使人不舒服的: *What an evil smell!* 多麼難聞的氣味! –**evilly** /ˈivlɪ; ˈiːvəl-li/ *adv*

evil[2] *n* [C;U] *fml* something that is very unpleasant and harmful 〔正式〕邪惡; 不幸: *He gave me a lecture on the evils of drink.* 他就飲酒的危害告誡了我一番。 | *Taxation is a necessary evil.* 稅收雖令人討厭, 但不可或缺。

e·vo·ca·tion /ˌɛvoˈkeʃən; ˌevəˈkeɪʃən/ *n* [C;U] something that makes you remember or think about something else 召喚; 引起: *evocations of her childhood* 喚起她對童年時代的回憶

e·voc·a·tive /ɪˈvɑkətɪv; ɪˈvɒkətɪv/ *adj* producing memories and feelings 引起回憶的; 喚起感情的: *The smell of those flowers is evocative of my childhood in India.* 那些花的氣味喚起了我對於印度的童年時代的回憶。

e·voke /ɪˈvok; ɪˈvəʊk/ *v* **evoked, evoking** *fml* [T] to produce or call up a memory or feeling 〔正式〕引起, 喚起〔回憶、情感〕: *The old film evoked memories of my childhood.* 這部老片子喚起了我對童年的回憶。 | *His comments evoked great anger.* 他的評論引起了很大的憤怒。

***ev·o·lu·tion** /ˌɛvoˈluʃən; ˌiːvəˈluːʃən/ *n* [U] **1** the gradual development of the various types of plants and animals from simpler forms over thousands of years 〔生物〕進化: *Darwin's theory of evolution* 達爾文的進化論 | *In the course of evolution, some birds have lost the power of flight.* 在進化過程中, 一些鳥喪失了飛行的能力。 **2** gradual change and development 演變; 演化; 發展: *the evolution of the motor car* 汽車的發展 –**evolutionary** *adj*

e·volve /ɪˈvɑlv; ɪˈvɒlv/ *v* **evolved, evolving** [I; T] to develop gradually by a long continuous process (使)逐步發展; (使)逐漸演變: *The British political system has evolved over several centuries.* 英國的政治制度是經過幾個世紀逐步發展而成的。 | *Some people believe that we evolved from the apes.* 有些人認為我們是從類人猿進化而來的。

ewe /ju; juː/ *n* a female sheep 母羊

ex·a·cer·bate /ɪgˈzæsəˌbet; ɪgˈzæsəbeɪt/ *v* **exacerbated, exacerbating** [T] *fml* to make something worse 〔正式〕使惡化; 使加劇: *The drugs they gave her only exacerbated the pain.* 他們給她服用的藥只是加重了她的痛楚。

ex·act[1] /ɪgˈzækt; ɪgˈzækt/ *adj* correct in every detail 精確的; 正確的: *an exact amount* 精確的數量 | *It is two minutes and five seconds past twelve, to be exact.* 確切的

時間是十二時兩分五秒。| *You have to be very exact to do this job.* 你做這項工作必須十分嚴謹。–**exactness** *n* [U]

exact² *v* [T] *fml* to demand something, usually forcefully and get it〖正式〗強求; 強要: *I finally managed to exact a promise from them.* 我終於迫使他們許下了諾言。

ex·act·ing /ɪgˈzæktɪŋ/ *adj* demanding a lot of care, effort, and attention 要求嚴格的; 需要極小心[努力]的: *an exacting boss* 要求嚴格的老闆 | *exacting standards of safety* 嚴格的安全標準

★**ex·act·ly** /ɪgˈzæktlɪ; ɪgˈzæktli/ *adv* **1** with complete correctness 確切地; 精確地: *I don't know exactly where she lives, but it's in London somewhere.* 我不知道她的確切地址, 但是在倫敦某處。| *What exactly were you doing here last night?* 昨天晚上你究竟在這裡幹甚麼? **2** a word used for adding force to what you are saying〔用於強調〕正是; 恰好: *Our new house is exactly what we've always wanted.* 我們的新房子正是我們一直所想要的。**3** a word used to agree with someone or with what they are saying〔用於同意某人〕確實如此: *"So you believe, minister, that we must spend more on education?" "Exactly!"* "部長先生, 所以您認為我們必須在教育事業上花多點錢?" "正是!" **4** not exactly: **a** not really 並不, 並非: *He's not exactly stupid, but he's no Einstein either!* 他並不笨, 可是他也不是愛因斯坦! **b** a word used as a reply to show that something is not completely true〔用作回答, 表示某事不完全正確〕不完全是: *"So you missed the meeting." "Not exactly. I got there ten minutes before it ended."* "所以你錯過了這次會議。" "不完全是那樣。我在會議結束前十分鐘到了那裡。"

ex·ag·ge·rate /ɪgˈzædʒə,ret; ɪgˈzædʒəreɪt/ *v* **exaggerated, exaggerating** [I;T] to make something seem larger or more important than it really is 誇大; 誇張; 言過其實: *The seriousness of the situation has been exaggerated in the press.* 局勢的嚴重性被新聞界誇大了。–**exaggerated** *adj*: *walking with an exaggerated limp* 誇張地一瘸一拐地走 –**exaggeration** /ɪg,zædʒəˈreʃən; ɪg,zædʒəˈreɪʃən/ *n* [C;U]: *It's a bit of an exaggeration to call him a millionaire.* 把他稱作百萬富翁, 未免有點誇大其詞。

ex·alt /ɪgˈzɔlt; ɪgˈzɔːlt/ *v* [T] *fml*〖正式〗**1** to praise someone very highly 讚揚〔某人〕; 歌頌 **2** to raise someone to a high rank 提拔; 提升〔某人〕

ex·al·ta·tion /,ɪgzɔlˈteʃən; ,egzɔːlˈteɪʃən/ *n* [U] *fml* great joyfulness〖正式〗興奮

ex·alt·ed /ɪgˈzɔltɪd; ɪgˈzɔːltɪd/ *adj* of high rank〔地位〕崇高的

ex·am /ɪgˈzæm; ɪgˈzæm/ *n* an official test of knowledge or ability in a particular subject 考試; 測驗: *When do we get the exam results?* 我們甚麼時候可以拿到考試成績? | *I've failed my chemistry exam.* 我的化學考試不

及格。

★**ex·am·i·na·tion** /ɪg,zæməˈneʃən; ɪg,zæmɪ-ˈneɪʃən/ *n* **1** [C;U] a detailed consideration of or check on something 檢查; 調查: *Before we can offer you the job, you will have to have a medical examination.* 我們聘用你之前, 你得做一次體格檢查。| *The proposal is still under examination.* 提議仍在審查之中。**2** [C] *fml* an official test of knowledge or ability in a particular subject〖正式〗考試; 測驗: *Did you pass your history examination?* 你歷史考試及格了嗎?

★**ex·am·ine** /ɪgˈzæmɪn; ɪgˈzæmɪn/ *v* **examined, examining** [T] **1** to look at someone or something carefully and closely, in order to find out something 仔細地檢查〔人或物〕: *My luggage was examined when I entered the country.* 我進入這個國家時, 我的行李受到了檢查。| *The doctor examined him thoroughly.* 醫生徹底地檢查他的身體。| *The police examined the room for fingerprints.* 警察為找尋指紋, 檢查了房間。**2** to ask someone questions to get information, for example in a court of law 查問; 訊問: *The witness was examined on her relationship with the accused.* 證人被查問到她和被告的關係。**3** to consider an idea in detail 仔細考慮

ex·am·in·er /ɪgˈzæmɪnɚ; ɪgˈzæmɪnər/ *n* someone who thinks of the questions for an examination, or marks them 出卷人; 閱卷人; 主考官

★**ex·am·ple** /ɪgˈzæmpl; ɪgˈzɑːmpəl/ *n* **1** one of a particular kind of thing which shows the typical qualities of those things 例子; 例證: *This church is a wonderful example of medieval architecture.* 這座教堂是中世紀建築的絕妙典範。**2** a person or behaviour that other people should be encouraged to copy 範例; 榜樣: *Her courage is a shining example to us all.* 她的勇敢行為是我們大家的光輝榜樣。| *Peter, you should try to set a good example to your younger brothers.* 彼得, 你應該給弟弟們做個好榜樣。**3** for example you use this phrase when you are giving an example to support what you are saying and make your meaning clearer 舉例; 例如: *There has been a serious rise in food prices this year. The price of meat, for example, has doubled since March.* 今年的食品價格上漲得很厲害。比如肉類從三月以來已增加了一倍。| *Seeds are naturally protected in various ways. For example, they are usually hard on the outside.* 種子自然地受到各種各樣的保護。例如, 它們的外殼通常是堅硬的。| *I'd really like to go somewhere interesting this summer – Tokyo or Hong Kong, for example.* 我今年夏天真想去有意思的地方 — 例如東京或者香港。–see Study Note on page 1325 見 1325 頁學習提示 **4** make an example of someone to punish someone so that others will be afraid to behave as they did 懲罰某人以儆

戒他人; 懲一儆百

ex·as·pe·rate /ɛg'zæspə,ret; ɪg'zɑːspəreɪt/ v **exasperated, exasperating** [T] to annoy someone or make them extremely angry 激怒〔某人〕: *I was exasperated by all the delays.* 這種種耽擱使我非常惱怒。 —**exasperating** adj: *You are the most exasperating man I have ever known.* 你是我所認識的人中最惹人生氣的一個。—**exasperation** /ɪg,zæspə'reʃən; ɪg,zɑːspə'reɪʃən/ n [U]: *In sheer exasperation, she kicked the photocopying machine.* 她很憤怒, 踢了複印機一腳。

ex·ca·vate /'ɛkskə,vet; 'ekskəveɪt/ v [T] **1** to make a hole by digging 挖〔洞〕; 開鑿: *They plan to excavate a large hole before putting in the foundations.* 他們計劃在打地基前先掘一個大洞。 **2** to remove earth to find remains of the past 發掘〔古物〕: *We have been excavating a Roman house.* 我們在發掘一座羅馬人的房子。 —**excavation** /,ɛkskə'veʃən; ,ekskə'veɪʃən/ n [C;U]: *archaeological excavations* 考古發掘

ex·ca·va·tor /'ɛkskə,vetə; 'ekskəveɪtə/ n a large machine that digs and moves earth 挖土機

ex·ceed /ɪk'sid; ɪk'siːd/ v [T] fml《正式》**1** to be greater than a particular amount〔在數量上〕超過: *The cost will not exceed £50.* 費用不會超過五十英鎊。 **2** to do more than what is lawful or acceptable 超出〔合法的、可接受的範圍〕: *He was fined for exceeding the speed limit.* 他因超速而被罰款。

ex·ceed·ing·ly /ɪk'sidɪŋlɪ; ɪk'siːdɪŋlɪ/ adv old fash 〔老式〕極其, 非常: *They were exceedingly kind to me.* 他們待我極為客氣。

ex·cel /ɪk'sɛl; ɪk'sel/ v -ll- fml《正式》**1** [I] to be extremely good at something 擅長〔某事物〕: *I've never excelled at sports.* 我從不擅長體育運動。 **2 excel yourself** to do even better than usual 比平時做得更好: *What a wonderful meal! You've really excelled yourself, Jim.* 這頓飯好極了! 吉姆, 你真有一手。

ex·cel·lence /'ɛksləns; 'eksələns/ n [U] the quality of being excellent 優秀; 卓越, 傑出: *the excellence of his cooking* 他烹飪技術的高超

Ex·cel·len·cy /'ɛkslənsɪ; 'eksələnsi/ n **Excellencies** a title for certain people of very high rank 閣下〔對身居高位的人的尊稱〕: *The King will see you now, your Excellency.* 閣下, 國王現在要接見你。 | *His Excellency the Spanish ambassador* 西班牙大使閣下

ex·cel·lent /'ɛkslənt; 'eksələnt/ adj extremely good 優秀的; 卓越的: *He's in excellent health.* 他身體極好。 | *Your examination results are excellent.* 你的考試成績優異。 —**excellently** adv

ex·cept¹ /ɪk'sɛpt; ɪk'sept/ prep, conj (also 又作 **except for**) not including a particular person or thing 除...之外: *I answered all the questions except the last one.* 除了最後一題

之外, 我回答了所有的問題。 | *I know nothing about it except what I read in the paper.* 我除了在報上讀到的以外, 甚麼也不知道。 | *We can do nothing except hope that they are all right.* 我們無能為力, 只希望他們平安無事。 | *The bus was empty except for one old lady.* 公共汽車上空蕩蕩的, 只坐了一位老太太。

ex·cept·ed /ɪk'sɛptɪd; ɪk'sept̩d/ adj [only after a noun 只用於名詞後] not included 除...外的: *He's not interested in anything, politics excepted.* 除了政治之外, 他對甚麼都不感興趣。

ex·cept·ing /ɪk'sɛptɪŋ; ɪk'septɪŋ/ prep except 除...之外

ex·cep·tion /ɪk'sɛpʃən; ɪk'sepʃən/ n **1** someone or something that is not included in a general statement 例外: *It's been very cold, but today's an exception.* 天氣一直很冷, 但今天是例外。 **2 make an exception** to treat someone or something differently 破例: *We don't normally accept credit cards, but we'll make an exception in your case.* 我們一般不接受信用卡, 但你這個情況我們準備破例一次。 **3 take exception to** to be offended and made angry by something 因〔某事〕而不悅; 生氣: *I took the greatest exception to his rudeness.* 我對他的粗魯行為極為反感。 **4 without exception** including everyone 全部包括; 沒有例外: *I see him every day, without exception.* 我每天都看見他, 從不例外。 **5 with the exception of** apart from 除了...之外: *Everyone was tired, with the exception of John.* 除了約翰之外, 大家都累了。

ex·cep·tion·al /ɪk'sɛpʃənl; ɪk'sepʃənəl/ adj of unusually high quality or ability 異常的; 傑出的: *All her children are clever, but the youngest boy is really exceptional.* 她的孩子都很聰明, 但最小的男孩尤其突出。 —**exceptionally** adv

ex·cerpt /'ɛksɝpt; 'eksɜːpt/ n a small part of a book, speech, or musical work 摘錄; 節錄

ex·cess¹ /ɪk'sɛs; ɪk'ses/ n **1** [sing] a larger amount than is needed or usual 過量; 過分: *There is an excess of violence in the film.* 這部影片暴力鏡頭過多。 **2 in excess of** more than 超過: *This year's profits were in excess of a million pounds.* 今年的利潤超出了一百萬英鎊。 **3 to excess** too much 過分: *He drinks to excess.* 他飲酒過量。 **4 excesses** [pl] unacceptable, immoral, or cruel actions 過分的行為: *Hitler's excesses in the last war* 希特勒在上一場戰爭中的暴行

ex·cess² /'ɪksɛs; 'ekses/ adj [only before a noun 只用於名詞前] more than is usual or allowed 過多的; 超額的: *She paid excess postal charges on the letter.* 她這封信付了超重費。

ex·ces·sive /ɪk'sɛsɪv; ɪk'sesɪv/ adj too much or too great 過多的; 過分的: *The charge for the room was excessive.* 這房間的收費太高

了。 –**excessively** *adv*

★★**ex·change**[1] /ɪksˈtʃendʒ; ɪksˈtʃeɪndʒ/ *n* **1** the giving of something to someone who gives you something else 交換: *an exchange of political prisoners between the two countries* 兩國政治犯的交換 **2 in exchange** given to someone because they are giving something to you 作為交換: *I gave him my bike in exchange for some records.* 我拿我的腳踏車跟他換了幾張唱片。**3** a short period of fighting or talking between two people or groups 〔短時間的〕交火; 交談: *Two soldiers were wounded in the exchange.* 兩americ士兵在交火中受了傷。| *There were some bitter exchanges of views in Parliament yesterday.* 昨天國會裡進行了幾場激烈的辯論。**4** a period in someone else's house or job while they come to your house or job 〔房屋的〕互換; 〔工作的〕調換: *She's going on an exchange to Munich.* 她要去慕尼黑交流(工作)。**5** (also 又作 **Exchange**) a place where businessmen meet to buy and sell 交易所: *I worked at the Stock Exchange for two years, selling shares in companies.* 我在證券交易所工作了兩年, 從事出售公司股票的工作。**6** a TELEPHONE EXCHANGE 〔電話〕交換台

exchange[2] *v* **exchanged, exchanging** [T] to give something to someone who gives you something else 交換: *The two armies exchanged prisoners.* 兩軍交換戰俘。| *They exchanged glances.* 他們對望了一眼。| *I exchanged the goods **for** cash.* 我拿這些貨換現金。| *This jumper is far too big. Perhaps the shop will exchange it.* 這件套頭毛衣實在太大了。也許商店會給換一件。

exchange rate /·'· ·/ *n* (also 又作 **rate of exchange**) the value of the money of one country compared to that of another country 兌換率; 匯率

Ex·cheq·uer /ɪksˈtʃɛkə; ɪksˈtʃekər/ *n* **the Exchequer** the department of the British government which collects taxes and pays out public money 英國財政部

ex·cise[1] /ˈɪkˈsaɪz; ˈeksaɪz/ *n* [U] the government tax on certain goods produced and used inside a country 消費稅; 國內貨物稅

ex·cise[2] /ɪkˈsaɪz; ɪkˈsaɪz/ *v* **excised, excising** [T] *fml* to remove something completely by cutting it out 〔正式〕切除; 割去: *The tumour was excised.* 腫瘤被切除了。

ex·ci·ta·ble /ɪkˈsaɪtəbl; ɪkˈsaɪtəbəl/ *adj* easily excited 容易興奮的; 容易激動的 –**excitability** /ɪkˌsaɪtəˈbɪlətɪ; ɪkˌsaɪtəˈbɪlᵻtɪ/ *n* [U]

ex·cite /ɪkˈsaɪt; ɪkˈsaɪt/ *v* **excited, exciting** [T] **1** to make someone very happy, eager, or nervous about something 使激動; 使興奮: *The story excited the little boy very much.* 這故事使小男孩興奮不已。| *Don't excite yourself please. Keep calm.* 請別激動, 保持冷靜。**2** *fml* to make people have strong feelings 〔正式〕引起; 激發〔強烈感情〕: *The*

court case has excited a lot of public interest. 法院審判的案件引起許多公眾的關心。

ex·cit·ed /ɪkˈsaɪtɪd; ɪkˈsaɪtᵻd/ *adj* full of strong feelings of expectation or happiness 激動的; 興奮的: *excited children opening their Christmas presents* 興奮的孩子們正在打開他們的聖誕禮物 | *She's very excited about getting the part in the film.* 得以在這部電影裡扮演一個角色, 她興奮不已。| *It's nothing to get excited about.* 沒甚麼值得激動。–**excitedly** *adv*

★**ex·cite·ment** /ɪkˈsaɪtmənt; ɪkˈsaɪtmənt/ *n* **1** [U] the condition of being excited 興奮; 激動: *As the end of the game grew near, the crowd's excitement increased.* 隨着比賽接近尾聲, 羣眾越來越激動。**2** [C] something that makes you excited 令人興奮的事; 刺激物: *Life will seem very quiet after the excitements of the holiday.* 假期一陣興奮之後, 生活將顯得十分平靜。

★**ex·cit·ing** /ɪkˈsaɪtɪŋ; ɪkˈsaɪtɪŋ/ *adj* causing excitement 令人興奮〔激動〕的: *an exciting story* 激動人心的故事 | *an exciting football match* 激動人心的足球比賽 –opposite **unexciting**

ex·claim /ɪkˈsklem; ɪkˈskleɪm/ *v* [I] to speak loudly and suddenly, because of pain, shock, or surprise 〔因痛苦、震驚或驚訝而〕呼喊; 驚叫: *"Good heavens!" he exclaimed. "It's six o'clock already."* 天哪!" 他大聲説, "已經六點鐘了。" | *She exclaimed in delight when she saw the presents.* 她看見禮物, 高興得大叫起來。

ex·cla·ma·tion /ˌɛksklə'meʃən; ˌeksklə'meɪʃən/ *n* a word or words expressing a sudden strong feeling 感歎詞〔語〕

exclamation mark /·'·· ·/ *n* (also 又作 **exclamation point** *AmE* 〔美式〕) a mark(!) which is written after an exclamation, as in the sentence "I'm hungry!" 感歎號〔如"I'm hungry!" 中的(!)〕

★**ex·clude** /ɪkˈsklud; ɪkˈskluːd/ *v* **excluded, excluding** [T] **1** to stop someone entering somewhere or doing something 不讓〔某人〕進入〔某處〕; 不讓〔某人〕做〔某事〕: *Women are excluded **from** the club.* 婦女不得參加該俱樂部。| *I was excluded **from** taking part in the discussions.* 我被拒絕參加討論。**2** to not include something 不包括〔某物〕: *The policy definitely excludes damage by fire.* 這份保險單肯定不包括火災造成的損害。**3** to not accept a reason or possibility 排除〔理由或可能性〕: *We can't exclude the possibility that his wife killed him.* 我們不能排除他妻子殺死他的可能性。–**exclusion** /-ˈskluʒən; -ˈskluːʒən/ *n* [U]

ex·clud·ing /ɪkˈskludɪŋ; ɪkˈskluːdɪŋ/ *prep* not including 不包括; 除…外: *There were 30 people in the hotel, excluding the hotel staff.* 旅館裡除了工作人員之外, 有三十個人。–opposite **including**

ex·clu·sive[1] /ɪkˈsklusɪv; ɪkˈskluːsɪv/ *adj* **1** for people who are wealthy and of a high social class 高級的; 豪華的: *one of London's most exclusive hotels* 倫敦最高級的旅館之一 **2** [only before a noun 只用於名詞前] limited to use by one particular person or group 專用的; 獨家的: *This bathroom is for the President's exclusive use.* 這間浴室是總統專用的。 | *"The Times" got an exclusive interview with Mr Gorbachev.* 《泰晤士報》獨家採訪了戈爾巴喬夫先生。 **3 mutually exclusive** unable to exist together (used of two things) 不能共存的〔指兩件東西〕: *The two plans are mutually exclusive.* 這兩項計劃無法共存。 **4 exclusive of** not including 不包括: *The hotel charges £45 a day, exclusive of meals.* 這旅館一天收費四十五英鎊, 不包括膳食。–**exclusiveness** *n* [U]

**exclusive² ** *n* a newspaper story given to or printed by only one newspaper 獨家新聞〔報道〕

ex·clu·sive·ly /ɪkˈsklusɪvlɪ; ɪkˈskluːsɪvli/ *adv* only 專有地; 單獨地: *This room is exclusively for women.* 這房間是供婦女專用的。

ex·com·mu·ni·cate /ˌɛkskəˈmjunəˌket; ˌekskəˈmjuːnɪˌkeɪt/ *v* **excommunicated, excommunicating** [T] to punish someone by taking away their membership of the church 把〔某人〕逐出教會 –**excommunication** /ˌɛkskəˌmjunəˈkeʃən; ˌekskəmjuːnɪˈkeɪʃən/ *n* [C;U]

ex·cre·ment /ˈɛkskrɪmənt; ˈekskrɪˌmənt/ *n* [U] *fml* the solid waste matter passed out from your body through your bowels 〔正式〕糞便, 排泄物

ex·crete /ɛkˈskrit; ɪkˈskriːt/ *v* **excreted, excreting** [I;T] *fml* to get rid of waste matter from your body, especially from your bowels 〔正式〕排泄 –**excretion** /-ˈskriʃən; -ˈskriːʃən/ *n* [C;U]

ex·cru·ci·at·ing /ɪkˈskruʃɪˌetɪŋ; ɪkˈskruːʃiˌeɪtɪŋ/ *adj* extremely bad (used of pain) 劇烈的〔指疼痛〕: *an excruciating headache* 劇烈的頭痛 –**excruciatingly** *adv*

ex·cur·sion /ɪkˈskɝʒən; ɪkˈskɜːʃən/ *n* a short journey made for pleasure, usually by several people together 遠足; 短途旅行: *We went on a day excursion to Blackpool.* 我們到布萊克浦作了一日遊。

ex·cu·sa·ble /ɪkˈskjuzəbl; ɪkˈskjuːzəbəl/ *adj* that can be forgiven (used of behaviour) 可原諒的; 可寬恕的〔指行為〕–opposite 反義 **inexcusable** –**excusably** *adv*

ex·cuse¹ /ɪkˈskjuz; ɪkˈskjuːz/ *v* **excused, excusing** [T] **1** to forgive someone, often for something not very serious 原諒〔常指不太嚴重的事〕: *Please excuse my bad handwriting.* 請原諒我的字寫得不好。 | *You must excuse my behaving so badly last night.* 你一定要原諒我昨晚表現得那麼糟糕。 | *I can never excuse her for her rudeness.* 我永遠不能原諒她的無禮。 | *She always excuses him for lying to her.* 她總是原諒他對她撒謊。

□ USEFUL PATTERNS 有用句型
to excuse something; to excuse your doing something; to excuse someone for something; to excuse someone for doing something

2 to provide a reason for bad behaviour so that it seems less serious 〔為不良行為〕辯解; 開脫: *He admitted that he hadn't punished her, excusing it as a moment of weakness.* 他承認沒有懲罰她, 辯解說這是一時軟弱。 | *I can't excuse myself; I shouldn't have done it.* 我無法為自己辯解: 我本來不該幹的。 | *Nothing can excuse lying to your parents.* 甚麼都不能成為你向父母撒謊的理由。

□ USEFUL PATTERNS 有用句型
to excuse something; to excuse yourself; to excuse doing something; to excuse your doing something

3 excuse yourself to ask permission to be absent 請求准予缺席: *She excused herself from the meeting.* 她請求不參加這次會議。 **4** to free someone from a duty or give them permission to leave 免除〔某人的〕責任; 准予離開: *He was excused piano practice.* 他可以不參加鋼琴練習。 | *She was excused from going to the school sports day.* 她獲准可以不參加學校的運動日。 | *Would you excuse me for a moment?* 我能離開一會兒嗎?

□ USEFUL PATTERNS 有用句型
to excuse someone (from) something; to excuse someone from doing something

5 excuse me a polite expression used when you want to get someone's attention, when you want to get past someone, when you want to leave a group of people who are talking, when you have done something slightly embarrassing or rude, or, in American English, when you want someone to repeat what they have said 對不起; 請原諒〔客套話, 用於想引起別人注意時, 想從別人身前走過時, 想離開談話的人羣時, 做了某件令人有點尷尬或無禮的事時, 或者在美國英語中, 想要某人重複一遍已講過的話時〕: *Excuse me, but have you got the time, please?* 對不起, 請問現在幾點了? | *She stepped on my foot, and immediately said "Excuse me".* 她踩了我的腳, 馬上說了聲 "對不起"。 | *Excuse me for interrupting, but there's a phone call for you.* 對不起打擾一下, 有電話找你。 –see 見 SORRY¹(USAGE 用法)

ex·cuse² /ɪkˈskjus; ɪkˈskjuːs/ *n* [C;U] **1** the reason given, whether true or not, to explain a mistake, bad behaviour, or absence 〔對錯誤、不良行為或缺席的〕理由; 藉口: *Have you any excuse for coming so late?* 你這麼晚

才來有甚麼理由嗎? | *Stop making excuses!* 別找藉口了! **2** a reason for doing something or for not doing something 理由; 辯解: *She has a party whenever she can find an excuse.* 她總能找到理由舉辦聚會。

■ USAGE 用法: Compare 比較 **excuse, reason, pretext**: *His excuse for being absent was that he was ill.* (= he said he was ill and this may or may not have been true) 他缺席的理由是他病了。(= 他說他病了, 這可能是真的, 也可能是假的) | *His reason for being absent was that he was ill.* (= he really was ill) 他缺席的原因是他病了。(= 他真的病了) | *He took a week off work on the pretext that he was ill.* (= he said he was ill but this was not the real reason) 他藉口生病, 請了一個星期的假。(= 他說他病了, 但這不是真正的原因)

ex·e·cra·ble /'ɛksɪkrəbl; 'eksɪ̥krəbəl/ *adj fml* extremely bad《正式》極壞的: *execrable manners* 惡劣的態度 **–execrably** *adv*

ex·e·cute /'ɛksɪ,kjut; 'eksɪ̥kjuːt/ *v* **executed, executing** [T] **1** to kill someone as a lawful punishment 依法處死《某人》: *She was executed for murder.* 她因殺人而被處決。 **2** *fml* to follow an order, plan, or instruction《正式》執行, 實行《命令、計劃或指令》: *The lawyer duly executed the old lady's will.* 律師忠實地執行了老婦人的遺囑。 **3** *fml* to perform a difficult movement or dance step《正式》表演《有難度的動作或舞步》: *The pilot successfully executed the manoeuvre.* 飛行員成功地表演了這個動作。

ex·e·cu·tion /,ɛksɪ'kjuʃən; ,eksɪ̥'kjuːʃən/ *n* **1** [C;U] a lawful killing as a punishment 依法處決: *Executions used to be held in public.* 過去處決犯人都公開執行。 **2** [U] *fml* the performance or completion of an order, plan, or instructions《正式》《命令、計劃、指令的》執行; 完成; 實施: *It was a good idea but it was never put into execution.* 這是個好主意, 但從未付諸實行。 | *The execution of a will can take a long time.* 執行遺囑要花很長時間。 **3** [U] *fml* skill in performing something difficult《正式》技巧; 手法: *The pianist's execution was brilliant but he played without feelings.* 這位鋼琴家的技巧高超, 但演奏得毫無感情。

ex·e·cu·tion·er /,ɛksɪ'kjuʃənɚ; ,eksɪ̥'kjuːʃənəʳ/ *n* the official who executes someone 死刑執行人, 行刑人

ex·ec·u·tive¹ /ɪg'zɛkjutɪv; ɪg'zekjʊtɪv/ *adj* [only before a noun 只用於名詞前] having the power to make and carry out decisions, especially in business《尤指商業上》有行政權力的; 執行的: *He has been given full executive powers.* 他被授予行政管理的全部權力。 | *the executive branch of government* 政府的行政部門

executive² *n* **1** a person in a company with the power to make decisions《公司的》行政人員; 主管: *a meeting with senior executives* 和高級主管的會晤 **2** the executive [+sing/pl verb] the group in an organization who have the power to make decisions《組織中的》決策層; 執行委員會: *The union executive are opposed to a strike.* 工會執行委員會反對罷工。

ex·ec·u·tor /ɪg'zɛkjətɚ; ɪg'zekjḁtəʳ/ *n* the person who carries out the orders in the will made by someone before they died 遺囑執行人

ex·em·pla·ry /ɪg'zɛmplərɪ; ɪg'zempləri/ *n* [only before a noun 只用於名詞前] suitable as an example or as a warning 典範的; 儆戒性的: *exemplary behaviour* 堪稱典範的行為 | *an exemplary punishment* 儆戒性的懲罰

ex·em·pli·fy /ɪg'zɛmplə,faɪ; ɪg'zemplɪ̥faɪ/ *v* **exemplified, exemplifying** [T] to be or give a typical example of something 例示; 舉例說明: *The recent oil price rises exemplify the difficulties which the motor industry is now facing.* 最近的石油漲價是汽車工業正面臨的困難的一個例子。 **–exemplification** /ɪg,zɛmpləfə'keʃən; ɪg,zempḷf‚'keɪʃən/ *n* [C;U]

ex·empt¹ /ɪg'zɛmpt; ɪg'zempt/ *adj* [never before a noun 不能用於名詞前] officially freed from a duty, service, or payment《責任、服務或付款》被免除的: *He is exempt from military service.* 他被免除兵役。

exempt² *v* [T] to officially free someone from a duty, service, or payment 使《某人》免除; 豁免: *His bad health exempted him from military service.* 他身體不好, 因而免服兵役。 **–exemption** /-'zɛmpʃən; -'zempʃən/ *n* [C;U]

★ex·er·cise¹ /'ɛksɚ,saɪz; 'eksəsaɪz/ *n* **1** [C;U] the use of any part of your body or mind so as to strengthen it or practise a skill 鍛鍊; 訓練; 運動: *If you don't take more exercise you'll get fat.* 你如果不多運動, 就會發胖。 | *She does exercises to strengthen her voice.* 她做發聲練習以加強嗓音。 | *piano exercises* 彈鋼琴的練習 **2** [C] a question or set of questions to be answered by a pupil for practice 練習; 習題: *Look at Exercise 2 on page 3.* 看第三頁的練習二。 **3** [C] a set of actions carried out by soldiers in time of peace to practise fighting 軍事演習: *They're here for a NATO exercise.* 他們在這裡參加北大西洋公約組織的軍事演習。 **4** [U] *fml* the use of a stated power or right《正式》《權力的》行使; 《能力的》運用: *the exercise of one's right to vote* 選舉權的行使

exercise² *v* **exercised, exercising 1** [I] to do physical exercises in order to be healthy 鍛鍊; 運動: *You should exercise more.* 你應該多運動。 **2** [T] *fml* to use a power, quality, or right《正式》運用; 行使: *The police urged the demonstrators to exercise restraint.* 警察力勸示威者克制。

ex·ert /ɪgˈzɜ·t; ɪgˈzɜːt/ *v* [T] **1** to use strength or skill in a determined way for a particular purpose 〔為特定目的〕運用〔力量、技能〕: *My wife's been exerting a lot of pressure on me to change my job.* 我妻子一直在對我施加很大的壓力，要我轉換工作。| *Please exert all your influence on the Company directors.* 請你對公司的董事們施加一切影響力。**2 exert yourself** to make an effort 努力: *He never exerts himself to help anyone.* 他從不積極幫助別人。

ex·er·tion /ɪgˈzɜ·ʃən; ɪgˈzɜːʃən/ *n* [C;U] great effort 費力; 努力: *I was really tired after all my exertions.* 我竭盡全力之後，真是累極了。

ex·hale /eksˈhel; eksˈheɪl/ *v* **exhaled, exhaling** [I;T] to breathe out air 呼出(空氣) –opposite 反義 **inhale** –**exhalation** /ˌɛksəˈleʃən; ˌekshəˈteɪʃən/ *n* [C;U]

ex·haust¹ /ɪgˈzɔst; ɪgˈzɔːst/ *v* [T] **1** to tire someone out 使〔某人〕精疲力竭: *What an exhausting day!* 多麼令人疲倦的一天啊! | *I'm absolutely exhausted!* 我疲倦不堪! | *That child exhausts me.* 那孩子弄得我筋疲力盡。**2** to use something up 用完; 耗光: *The soldiers have nearly exhausted their food supplies.* 士兵們差不多耗盡了食物。**3** to say everything there is to say about something 詳盡無遺地論述: *Well, we've exhausted the subject of work.* 好，我們已詳盡無遺地討論了工作上的問題。

exhaust² *n* **1** [C] (also 又作 **exhaust pipe** /·ˈ· ·/) the pipe which allows unwanted gas or steam to escape from an engine or machine 〔發動機或機器的〕排氣管 –see picture on page 209 見 209 頁彩圖 **2** [U] the gas or steam which escapes through this pipe 〔從排氣管排放出的〕廢氣

ex·haus·tion /ɪgˈzɔstʃən; ɪgˈzɔːstʃən/ *n* [U] extreme tiredness 筋疲力盡: *She's suffering from exhaustion.* 她在受疲憊之苦。

ex·haus·tive /ɪgˈzɔstɪv; ɪgˈzɔːstɪv/ *adj* extremely thorough 徹底的; 完全的: *an exhaustive study of the problem* 對問題的透徹研究 – **exhaustively** *adv*

ex·hib·it¹ /ɪgˈzɪbɪt; ɪgˈzɪbɪt/ *v* [T] **1** to show something in public 展出; 展覽〔某物〕: *Her paintings were exhibited in France.* 她的畫在法國展出。**2** *fml* to show a sign of a feeling or quality 〔正式〕表示; 顯示: *They exhibited no emotion when they heard of her death.* 他們聽到她的死訊後，臉上毫無表情。

exhibit² *n* **1** something that is exhibited, especially in a MUSEUM 〔尤指在博物館裡的〕展品 **2** *AmE* a public show of objects 〔美式〕展覽會

ex·hi·bi·tion /ˌɛksəˈbɪʃən; ˌeksɪˈbɪʃən/ *n* **1** [C;U] a public show of objects 展覽; 展覽會: *an international trade exhibition* 國際貿易展覽會 | *The children's paintings are on exhibition at the school.* 孩子們的畫在學校展出。**2** [C] the act of showing particular behaviour 表現; 顯示: *an exhibition of bad temper* 壞脾氣的表現 **3 make an exhibition of yourself** to behave foolishly 出洋相; 出醜

ex·hi·bi·tion·is·m /ˌɛksəˈbɪʃənˌɪzəm; ˌeksɪ-ˈbɪʃənɪzəm/ *n* [U] the behaviour of a person who wants to get attention from other people all the time (a word used to express disapproval) 表現狂〔癖〕; 風頭主義〔含貶義〕: *I was really embarrassed by his exhibitionism at the party.* 他在聚會上一心要出風頭，弄得我很不自在。–**exhibitionist** *n*

ex·hib·i·tor /ɪgˈzɪbɪtɚ; ɪgˈzɪbɪtə/ *n* someone whose work is shown at an exhibition 參展者

ex·hil·a·rate /ɪgˈzɪləˌret; ɪgˈzɪləreɪt/ *v* **exhilarated, exhilarating** [T] to make someone feel very cheerful and excited 使〔某人〕高興; 使〔某人〕興奮: *We felt very exhilarated after our long walk in the fresh air.* 我們在新鮮的空氣中步行了很長一段時間後，感到精神很振奮。| *an exhilarating ride in his sports car* 乘坐他的跑車很是刺激 –**exhilaration** /ɪgˌzɪləˈreʃən; ɪgˌzɪləˈreɪʃən/ *n* [U]

ex·hort /ɪgˈzɔrt; ɪgˈzɔːt/ *v* [T] *fml* to urge or advise someone strongly to do something 〔正式〕激勵, 規勸〔某人〕: *The general exhorted his men to fight well.* 將軍激勵士兵英勇作戰。–**exhortation** /ˌɛgzɚˈteʃən; ˌek-sɔːˈteɪʃən/ *n* [C;U]

ex·hume /ɪgˈzjum; ɪgˈzjuːm/ *v* **exhumed, exhuming** [T] *fml* to take a dead body out of the grave 〔正式〕〔從墓中〕掘出〔死屍〕–**exhumation** /ˌɛkshjuˈmeʃən; ˌeksjuˈmeɪʃən/ *n* [C;U]

ex·ile¹ /ˈɛgzaɪl; ˈeksaɪl/ *n* **1** [U] forced absence from your own country, often for political reasons 〔常為政治原因的〕流放; 放逐: *Napoleon was sent into exile.* 拿破崙被放逐。| *He died in exile.* 他在流放中死去。**2** [C] someone who has been forced to leave their country, especially for political reasons 〔尤指為政治原因的〕流亡國外者; 流亡分子

exile² *v* **exiled, exiling** [T] to send someone away from their own country 流放〔某人〕; 放逐〔某人〕

ex·ist /ɪgˈzɪst; ɪgˈzɪst/ *v* [I] **1** to be real or present, and not imagined 存在; 生存: *The technology for performing these operations already exists.* 做這種手術的技術早已存在。| *Do you think fairies exist?* 你相信真有神仙嗎? **2** (of a person) to live under difficult conditions, especially with very little money or food 〔人在困境中〕維持生活: *She exists on tea and bread.* 她靠茶和麵包度日。

ex·ist·ence /ɪgˈzɪstəns; ɪgˈzɪstəns/ *n* **1** [U] the state of being alive, real, or present 存在: *This law came into existence in 1918.* 這項法律產生於 1918 年。| *She doesn't believe in the existence of God.* 她不相信上帝的存在。**2** [sing] a way of living 生活方式: *Working as a writer can be a very lonely existence.*

當作家可以是一種很孤單的生活。

★**ex·ist·ing** /ɪgˈzɪstɪŋ; ɪgˈzɪstɪŋ/ *adj* [only before a noun 只用於名詞前] present or being used now 目前的; 現存的: *We'll get new computers to replace the existing ones.* 我們將以新電腦來代替現在用的這些。

ex·it¹ /ˈɛgzɪt; ˈegzɪt/ *n* **1** a door or other way out from a public place 出口 **2** a point where a road leaves a MOTORWAY 快車道的出口 **3 make an exit** *fml* to leave a place often in a way which makes people notice you〖正式〗〔常以引人注目的方式〕離開: *She made a hasty exit.* 她匆匆離去了。

exit² *v* **1** [I] to leave 離開: *She exited pretty quickly when she heard him arriving.* 她聽說他來了,便急急忙忙地離開了。 **2 exit** a word used as an instruction to an actor or actress to leave the stage〔用於指示演員〕退場: 下場: *Exit Hamlet, bearing the body of Polonius.* 哈姆雷特,揹着波洛涅斯的屍體退下。 **3** [I;T] to leave a computer program 退出〔電腦程序〕

ex·o·dus /ˈɛksədəs; ˈeksədəs/ *n* [sing] the movement of a lot of people leaving a place at the same time〔大批人同時的〕外出; 離開: *an exodus of cars from the city every evening* 每天傍晚從城裡開出來的大批汽車

ex·on·e·rate /ɪgˈzɑnə͵ret; ɪgˈzɒnəreɪt/ *v* **exonerated, exonerating** *fml* [T] to show that someone is not guilty〖正式〗表明〔某人〕無罪: *The report on the accident exonerates the company* **from** *any responsibility.* 事故報告表明該公司沒有任何責任。

ex·or·bi·tant /ɪgˈzɔrbətənt; ɪgˈzɔːbɪtənt/ *adj* much greater than is reasonable (used of prices and demands) 過高的; 過度的〔指價錢、要求〕: *That hotel charges exorbitant prices.* 那家旅館收費高得驚人。 **–exorbitantly** *adv*

ex·or·cis·m /ˈɛksɔr͵sɪzm; ˈeksɔː͵sɪzəm/ *n* [C; U] a way of driving an evil spirit away by prayer or command〔用祈禱或咒語的〕驅邪, 驅魔 **–exorcist** *n*

ex·or·cize /ˈɛksɔr͵saɪz; ˈeksɔː͵saɪz/ **exorcised, exorcizing** (also 又作 **exorcise** *BrE*〖英式〗) [T] to free a person or place from an evil spirit in a religious ceremony〔用宗教儀式〕給〔某人、某地〕驅除邪魔

ex·ot·ic /ɪgˈzɑtɪk; ɪgˈzɒtɪk/ *adj* **1** unusual and exciting 不同尋常的; 奇異的: *exotic clothes* 奇裝的異服 **2** from a distant and interesting country 外國來的; 異國情調的: *exotic food* 外來食品 | *exotic smells* 奇異的氣味

★**ex·pand** /ɪkˈspænd; ɪkˈspænd/ *v* [I;T] **1** to increase in size or number 擴大; 擴充; 擴展; 使膨脹: *Iron expands when it is heated.* 鐵受熱時會膨脹。 | *The company has expanded its operations in Scotland.* 這家公司擴大了在蘇格蘭的經營範圍。 **2 expand on something** to give more details about something you have said or written 詳述〔某事物〕: *Could you expand on your last point, please?* 能否

請你詳述一下最後那一點? **–expandable** *adj*

ex·panse /ɪkˈspæns; ɪkˈspæns/ *n* a large area of something 一大片地區: *a vast expanse* **of** *sand* 一大片沙子

★**ex·pan·sion** /ɪkˈspænʃən; ɪkˈspænʃən/ *n* [U] the process of increasing in size 擴大; 擴展; 擴張; 膨脹: *the expansion of metals when heated* 金屬加熱時的膨脹 | *economic expansion* 經濟發展

ex·pan·sive /ɪkˈspænsɪv; ɪkˈspænsɪv/ *adj* friendly and willing to talk 友好的; 健談的: *Later, after dinner, he became quite expansive.* 晚飯過後, 他變得很健談了。 **–expansively** *adv*

ex·pat·ri·ate /ɛksˈpetrɪ͵et; ekˈspætrɪət/ *n* (also 又作 **expat** /ˈɛksˈpæt; eksˈpæt/ *infml*〖非正式〗) someone living in a country which is not their own 移居國外者; 僑民

★**ex·pect** /ɪkˈspɛkt; ɪkˈspekt/ *v* **1** [T;+(that)] to believe that something will happen 預計; 預料 I *expect she'll do well.* 我預料她會做得好。 | *We fully expected it to be a complete disaster.* 我們完全預料到這會搞得一塌糊塗。 | *Do you expect to travel a lot this year?* 你預計今年會去很多地方旅遊嗎? | *The Prime Minister was re-elected, as expected.* 一如所料, 首相再次當選。 | *I had no idea what to expect.* 我預料不到會發生甚麼事。 **–see** 見 WAIT¹ (USAGE 用法)

> □ USEFUL PATTERNS 有用句型
> to expect something; to expect (that) something will happen; to expect something to happen; to expect to do something

2 half expect to believe that something is possible, although in fact it is very unlikely 差一點以為: *Your grandfather looked so much better last night that I half expected him to join in the dancing.* 你祖父昨晚看上去好多了, 我差一點以為他也要來跳舞呢。 **3 I expect...** a phrase used to say that you think something is probably true 我估計〔用於表示認為某事可能如此〕: *"Is she coming?" "I expect so."* "她會來嗎?" "我想會的。" | *I expect you're hungry. Let's have dinner.* 我想你餓了。我們吃飯吧。 **4 be expecting someone or something** to feel sure that someone or something will arrive, often because you have arranged it〔常因已做了安排而〕確信某人或某事物會來: *We're expecting them for lunch.* 我們正等待他們來吃午飯。 | *Are you expecting a parcel?* 你在等一件包裹嗎? **5 be expecting a baby, be expecting** to be going to have a baby 即將分娩; 懷孕 **6** [T] to hope for or demand certain behaviour because you think that this behaviour is desirable or necessary 期望; 要求: *Visitors to the hospital are expected not to smoke.* 醫院的訪客被要求不要抽煙。 | *We expect the highest standards from all our* *employees.* 我們希望所有的雇員都能達到最高標準。| *Her teachers always expected too much of her.* 她的老師總對她期望過高。

□ USEFUL PATTERNS 有用句型
to expect something from/of someone;
to expect someone to do something

---

7 what do you expect? a phrase used to show that you are not surprised by something 你還能指望甚麼？ 你還想怎麼樣？〔用於表示對某事不驚訝〕: *"I feel sick." "Well what do you expect after a six-course meal?"* "我覺得想嘔心。" "你一頓飯吃了六道菜還會舒服嗎？"

ex·pec·tan·cy /ɪkˈspɛktənsɪ; ɪkˈspɛktənsi/ *n* [U] a feeling of excitement about something that is going to happen 期待; 期望

ex·pec·tant /ɪkˈspɛktənt; ɪkˈspɛktənt/ *adj* **1** waiting with excitement 期待的; 期望的: *the expectant crowds outside the palace* 皇宮外面滿懷期待的人羣 **2 expectant mother** a woman whose baby is soon going to be born 孕婦 **–expectantly** *adv*

☆ex·pec·ta·tion /ˌɛkspɛkˈteʃən; ˌɛkspɛkˈteɪʃən/ *n* **1** [U] strong belief that something will happen 期待的事物; 預期: *She has little expectation of getting married now.* 她預計自己現在不大會結婚。| *Contrary to expectation it was John who failed the exam.* 與預期的相反, 約翰沒考及格。 **2** [C] a feeling of hope or confidence that something will happen 期望; 希望: *the high expectations of young people today* 對如今的年輕人的很高期望

ex·pe·di·en·cy /ɪkˈspidɪənsɪ; ɪkˈspiːdiənsi/ *n* [U] convenience rather than what it is morally correct to do (a word used to express disapproval) 方便; 合算; 權宜〔含貶義〕: *All his actions are governed by expediency.* 他所有的行動都是權宜之計。

ex·pe·di·ent¹ /ɪkˈspidɪənt; ɪkˈspiːdiənt/ *adj* [never before a noun 不能用於名詞前] useful or helpful but not necessarily morally correct 有用的; 有幫助的; 合算的: *She thought it expedient not to tell her mother where she had been.* 她認為不告訴母親她去過哪裡是適當的。

expedient² *n* a useful plan, idea, or action which provides an answer for an urgent problem 權宜之計; 應急辦法: *When she forgot her keys she got into the house by the simple expedient of climbing through a window.* 她忘了帶鑰匙, 便以簡單的應急方法, 爬窗進入屋子。

ex·pe·dite /ˈɛkspɪˌdaɪt; ˈɛkspɪˌdaɪt/ *v* **expedited, expediting** *fml* [T] to make something happen more quickly 〔正式〕加快〔進程〕; 促進〔行動〕

ex·pe·di·tion /ˌɛkspɪˈdɪʃən; ˌɛkspɪˈdɪʃən/ *n* a journey, usually long and carefully organized, which is made for a particular pur-pose 〔為特定目的而作的〕旅行; 遠征; 探險: *an expedition to the North Pole* 北極探險 | *a shopping expedition* 上街購物

ex·pel /ɪkˈspɛl; ɪkˈspɛl/ *v* **-ll-** [T] **1** to force someone to leave a country 驅逐〔某人〕出境: *Six American diplomats have already been expelled.* 六個美國外交官已被驅逐出境。 **2** to send someone away officially from a school or club 開除, 趕出〔學校、俱樂部〕: *I was expelled* **from** *school for smoking.* 我因為抽煙被學校開除了。 **3** to force something out from your body or a container 〔從體內或容器中〕排出; 噴出: *The pressure causes air to be expelled from the lungs.* 壓力使得空氣從肺內排出。

ex·pend /ɪkˈspɛnd; ɪkˈspɛnd/ *v* *fml* [T] to spend or use something 〔正式〕花費; 消費: *A great deal of time, money and energy have been expended unnecessarily.* 大量的時間、金錢和精力不必要地花費了。

ex·pen·da·ble /ɪkˈspɛndəbl; ɪkˈspɛndəbəl/ *adj* no longer needed, and so able to be thrown away or destroyed 可消耗的; 可毀掉的

☆ex·pen·di·ture /ɪkˈspɛndɪtʃə; ɪkˈspɛndɪtʃər/ *n* [U] **1** the amount of money that someone spends 支出; 開支: *promises to increase government expenditure* **on** *education* 政府在教育上增加開支的承諾 **2** spending or using of time, money, or effort for a particular purpose 〔為特定目的在時間、金錢、精力上的〕花費, 使用

☆ex·pense /ɪkˈspɛns; ɪkˈspɛns/ *n* [C;U] **1** cost in money 費用; 價錢: *It's quite an expense, having a car.* 擁有一輛汽車的花費很大。| *the expense of private school fees* 花在私立學校學費上的開支 **2 expenses** [pl] the money you use or need for a purpose 〔為某種目的用的或需要的〕開支; 經費: *While she's abroad on business her company pay all her expenses.* 她到海外公幹時, 公司支付她的一切開支。| *travelling expenses* 旅費 **3 great expense, little expense, no expense** by paying a lot of money, a little money only, no money at all 花很多錢; 花一點點錢; 根本不花錢: *They went to great expense to make the party a success.* 他們花了很多錢把聚會辦得很成功。| *She's had her flat redecorated at very little expense to herself.* 她自己只花了一點兒錢就把她的房子重新裝修了一遍。 **4 at the expense of** causing loss or damage to something 在〔某事物〕受損害的情況下: *He finished the job at the expense of his health.* 他以犧牲健康來完成了這項工作。 **5 at someone's expense: a** with someone paying the cost 由某人負擔費用: *He had his book printed at his own expense.* 他自費印書。 **b** as a joke against someone so as to make them seem silly 〔以開玩笑〕捉弄某人: *We had a good laugh at Mike's expense.* 我們大大嘲笑了麥克一番。

☆ex·pen·sive /ɪkˈspɛnsɪv; ɪkˈspɛnsiv/ *adj* cost-

---

ing a lot of money 昂貴的: *It's much too expensive!* 這實在太貴了! | *an expensive new coat* 昂貴的新外套 –opposite 反義 **inexpensive** –**expensively** *adv*

★ex·pe·ri·ence[1] /ɪk'spɪrɪəns; ɪk'spɪərɪəns/ *n* **1** [U] knowledge or skill which comes from doing or feeling something for a long time rather than from books 經驗; 體驗: *a teacher with five years' experience* 有五年教學經驗的老師 | *I know from experience that it won't work.* 我根據經驗知道這不會起作用。 **2** [C] something that happens to you and has an effect on your mind and feelings 經歷; 閱歷: *Our journey by camel was quite an experience.* 我們騎駱駝旅行真是一次難忘的經歷。

★experience[2] *v* **experienced, experiencing** [T] to feel, or to be influenced by something that happens 經歷; 體驗: *The country is experiencing a sharp economic decline.* 這個國家正在經歷一場急劇的經濟衰退。 | *She's experienced a few difficulties at work recently.* 最近她在工作上經歷了一些困難。

ex·pe·ri·enced /ɪk'spɪrɪənst; ɪk'spɪərɪənst/ *adj* good at something because you have spent a lot of time doing it 有經驗的; 老練的: *an experienced doctor* 一位老練的醫生 | *experienced travellers* 見多識廣的旅行者 –opposite 反義 **inexperienced**

★ex·per·i·ment[1] /ɪk'spɛrəmɛnt; ɪk'spɛrɪmənt/ *n* [C;U] **1** a scientific test done in order to learn something or prove the truth of an idea 實驗: *The architect wanted to carry out an experiment in town planning.* 這位建築師要做一個城鎮規劃的實驗。 | *The theory has been proved conclusively by experiment.* 這個理論經由實驗肯定性地證明了。 **2** the trying out of a new idea or process 〔新想法或新方法的〕試驗: *The school is an experiment in bilingual education.* 這所學校用作進行雙語教學的試驗。

ex·per·i·ment[2] /ɪk'spɛrəmɛnt; ɪk'spɛrɪmənt/ *v* [I] **1** to do a scientific test to find out or prove something 進行實驗: *Is it right to experiment* **on** *animals?* 用動物做實驗對嗎? **2** to try out a new idea or process to see what results it has 〔對新想法或新方法〕進行試驗: *She likes experimenting* **with** *different recipes.* 她喜歡嘗試不同的烹飪法。 –**experimentation** /ɪk,spɛrəmɛn'teɪʃən; ɪk,spɛrɪmen'teɪʃən/ *n* [U]

★ex·per·i·men·tal /ɪk,spɛrə'mɛntl; ɪk,sperɪ'mentl/ *adj* using or testing new ideas 實驗(性); 試驗(性)的: *an experimental farm* 實驗農場 –**experimentally** *adv*

★ex·pert /'ɛkspɜt; 'ɛkspɜːt/ *n* a person with special knowledge or skills as a result of experience or study 專家; 能手: *She's an expert* **in** *19th century literature.* 她是十九世紀文學的專家。 –**expert** *adj*: *He's expert at handling teenagers.* 他在處理青少年問題方面經驗豐富。 | *an expert cook* 技術高超的廚師 –**expertly** *adv*

★ex·per·tise /,ɛkspɜ'tiz; ,ekspɜː'tiːz/ *n* [U] a skill or knowledge of something which comes from experience or training 專門技能; 專業知識: *Her technical expertise saved the company.* 她的技術知識拯救了那公司。

ex·pire /ɪk'spaɪr; ɪk'spaɪəʳ/ *v* **expired, expiring** [I] **1** to come to the end of the time that something can be legally used 到期, 期滿; 終止: *My visa expires next month.* 我的簽證下個月到期。 **2** *lit* to die 《文》逝世

ex·pir·y /ɪk'spaɪrɪ; ɪk'spaɪərɪ/ *n* [U] the end of a stated period of time for which a legal DOCUMENT or agreement can be used 〔期限的〕終止; 期滿: *What is the expiry date on your driving licence?* 你的駕駛執照甚麼時候到期? | *the expiry of our lease* 我們的租約期滿

★ex·plain /ɪk'splen; ɪk'splem/ *v* [I;T; +that] **1** to make something clear and easy to understand 解釋; 說明: *I don't understand this but the lawyer will explain.* 我不明白這個, 但律師會解釋的。 | *Can you explain the new policy to us?* 你能把這新的政策向我們解釋一下嗎? | *Could you explain how to turn the heating on?* 你能說明一下怎麼開暖氣嗎? | *She explained that the farm belonged to her brother.* 她解釋說這農場是屬於她哥哥的。

> □ USEFUL PATTERNS 有用句型
> to explain something; to explain something to someone; to explain that..., to explain how, why, etc.

2 to give a reason for something 說明〔某事的〕原因: *Can you explain your stupid behaviour?* 你能為你這種愚蠢的行為辯解嗎? | *That explains why he's not here.* 那解釋了他不在這兒的原因。 | *I explained that I'd missed the bus.* 我解釋說我誤了那班公共汽車。

> □ USEFUL PATTERNS 有用句型
> to explain something; to explain something to someone; to explain that..., to explain how, why, etc.

3 explain yourself to make your meaning clear or give a reason for your behaviour 把自己的意思表達清楚; 解釋自己的行為: *Could you explain yourself please?* 請說明一下你的理由, 好嗎?

explain sthg ↔ **away** *phr v* [T] to make something seem unimportant or not your fault 通過解釋消除, 為…辯解: *Your department will have to explain away the poor sales figures.* 你們部門得為那糟糕的銷售額辯解。

★ex·pla·na·tion /,ɛksplə'neʃən; ,eksplə'neɪʃən/ *n* [C;U] **1** what you say or write to make something easily understood 解釋; 說

明: *First, I'll give you a short explanation of how the machine works.* 首先，我將簡要地說明一下這台機器如何操作。 **2** something that gives a reason for something else 辯解；理由: *Can you think of any explanation for his rudeness?* 你能想出他行為粗魯的理由嗎？

ex·plan·a·to·ry /ɪkˈsplænə,tori; ɪkˈsplænətəri/ *adj* giving more information about something or a reason for something 解釋的；說明的；辯解的

ex·ple·tive /ˈɛksplɪtɪv; ɪkˈspliːtɪv/ *n* a word which is said loudly and suddenly to express anger or annoyance 咒駡語

ex·pli·ca·ble /ˈɛksplɪkəbḷ; ekˈsplɪkəbəl/ *adj* [never before a noun 不用於名詞前] *fml* understandable 〔正式〕可解釋的；可理解的: *Her behaviour is explicable if you consider her age.* 如果你考慮到她的年紀，她的行為就可以理解了。 –opposite 反義 **inexplicable** – **explicably** *adv*

ex·pli·cit /ɪkˈsplɪsɪt; ɪkˈsplɪsḷt/ *adj* clear and fully expressed 明確的；清楚的: *Could you ask her for more explicit instructions?* 你能請她再給些明確的指示嗎？ –compare 比較 IMPLICIT – **explicitly** *adv*

ex·plode /ɪkˈsplod; ɪkˈspləʊd/ *v* **exploded, exploding 1** [I;T] to blow up or burst suddenly with a lot of noise and force (使)爆炸；(使)突然爆裂: *A bomb has exploded in the centre of London.* 一枚炸彈在倫敦市中心爆炸了。 **2** [I] to show very strong feeling suddenly 〔強烈感情〕爆發: *He exploded with anger.* 他勃然大怒。 **3** [T] to prove a general idea or belief to be wrong 推翻，打破(一種普遍的觀點或信念): *These statistics explode the myth that women are worse drivers than men.* 這些統計數字戳穿了婦女駕駛技術比男人差的荒誕說法。 **4** [I] to increase quickly 快速增長: *The population is exploding.* 人口在迅速增長。

★**ex·ploit¹** /ɪkˈsplɔɪt; ɪkˈsplɔɪt/ *v* [T] **1** to use someone unfairly, usually by paying them very little for their hard work 剝削: *Farm workers are being exploited by the big landowners.* 農場工人正受到大地主的剝削。 **2** to use or develop something fully in order to make money from it (充分)利用；開發: *We must exploit the country's mineral resources.* 我們必須開發國家的礦產資源。 –**exploitation** /ˌɛksplɔɪˈteʃən; ˌeksplɔɪˈteɪʃən/ *n* [U]

ex·ploit² /ˈɛksplɔɪt; ˈeksplɔɪt/ *n* an action which is brave, clever, or interesting in some way 英勇行為；功績

★**ex·plore** /ɪkˈsplor; ɪkˈsplɔːʳ/ *v* **explored, exploring** [T] **1** to travel into or through a place to find out about it 勘探；探測；探險: *We spent a week exploring the coast.* 我們花了一週時間在海濱進行探測。 **2** to examine or think about something carefully 仔細檢查；探究: *We must explore all the possibilities.* 我們必須探討所有的可能性。 –**exploration** /ˌɛkspləˈreʃən; ˌekspləˈreɪʃən/ *n* [C;U]: *a journey*

of exploration into China 去中國探險的旅行–**exploratory** /ɪkˈsplorə,tori; ɪkˈsplɒrətəri/ *adj*

ex·plo·rer /ɪkˈsplorə; ɪkˈsplɔːrəʳ/ *n* someone who travels to distant places to find out about them 勘探者；考察者；探險者

ex·plo·sion /ɪkˈsploʒən; ɪkˈspləʊʒən/ *n* **1** a loud noise caused by something bursting 爆炸(聲): *When she lit the gas there was a loud explosion.* 她點燃煤氣時，響起了巨大的爆炸聲。 **2** a sudden increase 激增: *the population explosion* 人口激增 **3** a sudden expression of very strong feeling 〔強烈感情的〕爆發: *an explosion of anger* 大發雷霆

ex·plo·sive¹ /ɪkˈsplosɪv; ɪkˈspləʊsɪv/ *adj* **1** which could blow up 會爆炸的: *It's dangerous to smoke when handling explosive materials.* 在處理爆炸物品時，吸煙很危險。 **2** able to cause very strong feelings or argument 激起強烈感情的；易引起爭議的: *Race relations is an explosive issue.* 種族關係是一個爆炸性的問題。 –**explosively** *adv*

explosive² *n* [C;U] something in a bomb which makes it blow up 爆炸物

ex·po·nent /ɪkˈsponənt; ɪkˈspəʊnənt/ *n* a person who expresses or supports a particular belief or idea 〔理論、觀點的〕倡導者；擁護者: *She's an exponent of Marxism.* 她是馬克思主義的擁護者。

★**ex·port¹** /ɪksˈport; ɪkˈspɔːt/ *v* [I;T] to send things to another country, usually to sell them 出口；輸出: *The country was exporting cigars and revolutionary ideas.* 這個國家輸出雪茄煙和革命觀點。 –compare 比較 IMPORT¹

ex·port² /ˈɛksport; ˈekspɔːt/ *n* **1** [U] the business of sending goods to another country and selling them 出口業；輸出: *the export trade* 出口貿易 | *The export of gold is forbidden.* 出口黃金是禁止的。 **2** [C] something that is sold and sent to another country 出口物；輸出品: *Wool is one of the chief exports of Australia.* 羊毛是澳大利亞的主要出口貨物之一。 –compare 比較 IMPORT²

ex·port·er /ɪkˈsportə; ɪkˈspɔːtəʳ/ *n* a person, company, or country that sells goods to other countries 出口商；輸出國: *Zambia is the world's largest exporter of copper.* 贊比亞是世界上最大的銅輸出國。

★**ex·pose** /ɪkˈspoz; ɪkˈspəʊz/ *v* **exposed, posing** [T] **1** to uncover something 暴露；顯露: *You mustn't expose your skin to the sun.* 你不能在太陽下曝曬皮膚。 **2 be exposed to** be put in a situation where you might be harmed 處於可能受傷害的境遇: *She was exposed to a lot of danger in the war.* 她在戰爭中經歷過許多危險。 **3** to tell people about something bad or someone who has done something bad and kept it secret 揭露〔壞事〕；揭發〔罪行〕: *He was exposed on television as a persistent liar.* 他撒謊成性，終於在電視裡遭人揭發。 **4** to uncover a film to the light, when taking a photograph 使〔膠片〕

曝光 **5 expose yourself** (of a man) to show your sexual parts on purpose in the hope of exciting or shocking people〔男人〕有意地裸露自己的性器官〔以刺激或驚嚇他人〕

ex·po·sé /ˌɛkspo'ze; ek'spɔuzeɪ/ *n* a public statement of the facts about something〔事實的〕公開陳述; 揭露: *The film is an exposé of the President's connections with organized crime.* 這部影片揭露了總統和有組織罪行的關係。

ex·posed /ɪk'spozd; ɪk'spɔuzd/ *adj* not protected from attack or sheltered from bad weather 無保護的; 無遮蔽的

ex·po·si·tion /ˌɛkspə'zɪʃn; ˌekspə'zɪʃən/ *n* 1 [C;U] *fml* a detailed explanation of something〔正式〕闡述; 詳細的解釋: *a full exposition of her political beliefs* 對她的政治信念的闡述 **2** [C] an international show of industrial products 工業產品的國際博覽會

*★**ex·po·sure** /ɪk'spoʒɚ; ɪk'spɔuʒəʳ/ *n* 1 [U] a situation where you are influenced and affected by something 暴露; 顯露: *They risked exposure to harmful radiation.* 他們冒着暴露在有害輻射之下的危險。 **2** [U] the harmful effect on someone's body of being out in cold weather for a long time〔身體長時間〕暴露在室外寒冷的天氣中: *We nearly died of exposure on the cold mountain.* 我們在寒冷的山上差點凍死。 **3** [C;U] a situation where the truth about something shocking is made known 揭露; 揭發: *I threatened him with public exposure.* 我揚言要向公眾揭發他。 **4** [C] the amount of film that must be uncovered to the light to take one photograph〔未拍膠片的〕張數: *I have three exposures left on this film.* 這卷膠片上我還有三張底片(沒拍)。 **5** [U] treatment (形勢)處理; 對待: *The situation received a lot of exposure on television.* 這種形勢在電視中受到大肆宣傳。

ex·pound /ɪk'spaund; ɪk'spaund/ *v* [T] *fml* to give a reasoned and detailed explanation of something〔正式〕闡述, 解釋〔某事物〕: *The priest expounded his beliefs to us.* 牧師向我們闡明自己的宗教思想。

*★★**ex·press**[1] /ɪk'sprɛs; ɪk'spres/ *v* [T] **1** to show a feeling or thought by saying or doing something〔用言詞或行動〕表達, 表露〔感情或思想〕: *I can't express how grateful I am.* 我無法表達我的感激之情。 | *She expressed surprise when I told her you were coming.* 我告訴她你要來時, 她表示驚訝。 **2** to write a price or quantity in a particular way〔用特定方式〕寫出〔價格或數量〕: *The figure is expressed as a percentage.* 這個數字用百分比來表示。 **3 express yourself** to write or say what you think or feel 表達自己的感情〔思想〕: *He expresses himself well in English.* 他能用英語清楚地表達自己的意思。

express[2] *n* **1** [C] (also 又作 **express train** /··'·/) a fast train which stops at only a few stations 快車 **2** [U] a service given by the post office or railways for carrying things faster than usual〔郵局、鐵路的〕速遞; 快件服務: *Send the letter by express.* 把這封信用快郵寄出。

express[3] *adv* by a very quick service 用快遞的方式: *I sent the parcel express.* 我把包裹用快遞方式寄出了。

express[4] *adj* [only before a noun 只用於名詞前] **1** clearly stated or exact 明確的; 明白的: *It was her express wish that you should have her jewels after her death.* 她明確表示, 她去世後你應得到她的珠寶。 | *I came here with the express purpose of seeing you.* 我是特意來這見你的。 **2** going or sent quickly 快速的; 快遞的: *an express train* 快車 | *express delivery* 快遞

*★**ex·pres·sion** /ɪk'sprɛʃn; ɪk'spreʃn/ *n* **1** [C; U] the act of saying or showing what you think or feel 表示; 表露; 表達: *freedom of expression* 自由發表意見 | *the expression of strong beliefs* 強烈信念的表達 **2** [U] the ability to show feeling when you are acting or performing music 表達感情的能力: *She doesn't sing with much expression.* 她唱歌沒有感情。 **3** [C] a word or group of words which has a particular meaning〔有特定意義的〕詞語; 措詞: *"Fly off the handle" is an expression which means "lose your temper".* "Fly off the handle" 是個表示 "大發脾氣" 的詞組。 **4** [C] a look on someone's face 表情: *an angry expression* 怒容

ex·pres·sion·less /ɪk'sprɛʃnlɪs; ɪk'spreʃənləs/ *adj* showing no feeling (used of someone's voice or face) 無感情[表情]的〔指聲音或臉孔〕

ex·pres·sive /ɪk'sprɛsɪv; ɪk'spresɪv/ *adj* showing feelings or meaning 顯示感情的; 意味深長的: *A baby's cry may be expressive of hunger or pain.* 嬰兒的啼哭可能表示飢餓或疼痛。 | *an expressive silence* 意味深長的沉默 – **expressively** *adv*

ex·press·ly /ɪk'sprɛslɪ; ɪk'spresli/ *adv fml* clearly or specially〔正式〕明確地; 特意地: *I told you expressly to lock the door.* 我明確地對你說過要鎖上門。 | *The lift has been put in expressly for the disabled.* 這部電梯是專為殘疾人士建造的。

ex·press·way /ɪk'sprɛsˌwe; ɪk'spresweɪ/ *n* the usual American word for〔美式〕= MOTORWAY

ex·pro·pri·ate /ɛks'proprɪˌet; ɪk'sprəuprɪeɪt/ *v* **expropriated, expropriating** [T] *fml* to take away another person's property, often for public use〔正式〕徵用: *The State expropriated all land owned by foreigners.* 國家徵用了外國人手裡所有的土地。

ex·pul·sion /ɪk'spʌlʃn; ɪk'spʌlʃən/ *n* [C;U] the act of forcing someone to leave a place such as a country, a club, or a school as a result of an official decision 驅逐; 開除: *the child's expulsion from school* 這孩子被開除

出校 | *the expulsion of three diplomats* 三個
外交官被驅逐出境

ex·pur·gate /ˈɛkspɚˌget; ˈekspəgeɪt/ *v* **ex-purgated, expurgating** [T] *fml* to make
something such as a book or a play accep-table by taking out anything which might
shock or offend people〔正式〕刪除〔書籍或
劇本中的〕不當之處

ex·qui·site /ˈɛkskwɪzɪt; ɪkˈskwɪzᵻt/ *adj* **1** ex-tremely beautiful, delicate, or sensitive 優
美的; 精緻的; 敏感的: *exquisite manners* 優美
的儀態 | *an exquisite piece of jewellery* 一件
精緻的首飾 | *He has exquisite taste in music.*
他對音樂有細膩的鑑賞力。 **2** strongly felt or
experienced 感受強烈的: *exquisite pleasure*
極大的樂趣 –**exquisitely** *adv*

ex·tem·po·rize /ɪkˈstɛmpəˌraɪz; ɪkˈstempə-raɪz/ *v* **extemporized, extemporizing** [I] to
speak without time for thought or prep-aration 當場發言; 即興表演: *The actress for-got her lines and had to extemporize.* 女演員
忘了台詞, 只好即興發揮。

★**ex·tend** /ɪkˈstɛnd; ɪkˈstend/ *v* **1** [I+adv/prep]
to reach, stretch, or continue 伸展; 延伸; 延
續: *The hot weather extended into October.*
炎熱的天氣延續到了十月份。 | *His land
extends all the way to the river.* 他的土地一直
延伸到河邊。 **2** [T] to make something
longer or bigger 擴展; 延長: *They are
extending the railway to the next town.* 他們
把鐵路延伸到了下一個市鎮。 **3** [T] to make
something exist over a longer period 使延
期: *I need to extend my visa.* 我需要延長簽證
期。 **4** [T] to stretch out a part of your body
伸出; 展開〔身體的一部分〕: *She extended her
hand and I took hold of it.* 她伸出一隻手, 我
握住了它。 **5** [T] *fml* to give or offer some-thing to someone〔正式〕給予; 提供: *I'd like
to extend a warm welcome to our guests.* 我
謹向來訪者表示熱烈的歡迎。 | *The bank will
extend more credit to you.* 銀行將向你提供更
多的信用貸款。

★**ex·ten·sion** /ɪkˈstɛnʃən; ɪkˈstenʃn/ *n* **1** [C;
U] something which increases what is
already there 延伸; 擴展: *the extension of
the copyright laws to cover recorded material*
版權法延伸到包括音像資料 **2** [C] a part
which is added to make something longer
or bigger 增加的部分: *We plan to build an
extension on the house.* 我們打算擴建房子。
3 [C] a telephone line which leads from
one central point to various rooms or
offices in a large building 電話分機: *Could I
have extension 45, please?* 請給我接四十五號
分機, 好嗎?

★**ex·ten·sive** /ɪkˈstɛnsɪv; ɪkˈstensɪv/ *adj* large
in amount or area 大量的; 廣大的; 廣闊的:
an extensive garden 寬敞的花園 | *extensive
damage* 巨大的破壞 | *extensive knowledge*
廣博的知識 –**extensively** *adv*

★★★**ex·tent** /ɪkˈstɛnt; ɪkˈstent/ *n* **1** [U] the
size or limit of something 面

積; 限度: *The full extent of the Sahara desert
is not known.* 撒哈拉沙漠的全貌是個未知數。 |
I was surprised at the extent of his knowl-edge. 我對他淵博的知識感到驚訝。 **2 to a cer-tain extent, to some extent, to a large ex-tent** partly but not completely 相當程度上;
某種程度上; 很大程度上: *I agree with what
you say to a certain extent.* 我在相當程度上同
意你所說的。 **3 to the extent that, to the ex-tent of, to such an extent that** to a point
where something else happens 到了…程度:
*The temperature rose to such an extent that
the firemen had to leave the burning build-ing.* 溫度驟升, 消防隊員不得不離開那正在燃
燒的建築物。

ex·ten·u·ate /ɪkˈstɛnjuˌet; ɪkˈstenjueɪt/ *v* **ex-tenuated, extenuating** [T] **1** *fml* to make
bad behaviour less serious by finding
excuses for it〔正式〕〔找藉口〕減輕; 掩飾 **2
extenuating circumstances** facts which
help to excuse bad behaviour 情有可原的情
況

ex·te·ri·or¹ /ɪkˈstɪrɪɚ; ɪkˈstɪərɪəʳ/ *adj* on the
outside surface 外部的; 外面的; 外表的: *the
exterior walls* 外牆 –opposite 反義 **interior**

exterior² *n* the outer appearance or surface
of something 外部; 外表; 外面: *the exterior of
the house* 房子的外部 | *Deep unhappiness
was hidden beneath his cheerful exterior.* 他
歡樂的外表下藏着深深的不快。 –opposite 反
義 **interior**

ex·ter·mi·nate /ɪkˈstɝməˌnet; ɪkˈstɜːmᵻ-neɪt/ *v* **exterminated, exterminating** [T] to
kill every member of a group of people or
animals 消滅; 根除 –**extermination** /ɪkˌstɝ-məˈneʃən; ɪkˌstɜːmᵻˈneɪʃən/ *n* [U]

★**ex·ter·nal** /ɪkˈstɝnl; ɪkˈstɜːnəl/ *adj* **1** outside
a place, person, or thing 外面的; 外部的; 在
外的: *external walls* 外牆 | *There are a lot of
external pressures on her.* 她有很多外來的壓
力。 **2** coming to do a job at your organi-zation from another one 外來的: *an exter-nal examiner* 外來的主考官 **3** able to be
seen, but not real or natural 外觀的; 表面
的: *Despite external appearances, she's very
shy.* 她很害羞, 儘管外表並非如此。 **4 for ex-ternal use only** not to be drunk or eaten 只
供外用 –opposite 反義 **internal** –**external-ly** *adv*

ex·tinct /ɪkˈstɪŋkt; ɪkˈstɪŋkt/ *adj* **1** having no
living example 滅絕的; 絕種的: *Every year
several species of bird become extinct.* 每年
都有幾種鳥絕種。 **2** no longer active (used
of VOLCANOS) 不再活動的〔指火山〕

ex·tinc·tion /ɪkˈstɪŋkʃən; ɪkˈstɪŋkʃən/ *n* [U] **1**
the killing or death of the last remaining
animals of a certain kind 滅絕; 絕種: *The
human race is now threatened with complete
extinction.* 人類現在受到完全滅絕的威脅。 **2**
the end or ending of something 破滅; 熄滅:
the extinction of his hopes 他希望的破滅

ex·tin·guish /ɪkˈstɪŋgwɪʃ; ɪkˈstɪŋgwɪʃ/ *v* [T]

fml〖正式〗**1** to put out a light or fire 熄滅〔燈、火〕: *Please extinguish all cigarettes.* 請把所有香煙弄熄。**2** to destroy a feeling or an idea 使〔感情、想法〕破滅; 消滅: *Nothing could extinguish his belief that she would get better.* 他相信她會好起來的, 甚麼都不能使他這個信念破滅。

ex·tol /ɪkˈstɔl; ɪkˈstəul/ *v* **-ll-** [T] *fml* to praise someone or something very highly 〖正式〗頌揚; 讚美: *He extols her virtues and sees none of her faults.* 他對她的優點大加稱讚, 對缺點卻視而不見。

ex·tort /ɪkˈstɔrt; ɪkˈstɔːt/ *v* [T] to obtain something by force or threats 強奪; 敲詐; 勒索: *He's been accused of extorting money* **from** *local shopkeepers.* 他被指控向當地的店主勒索錢財。 **–extortion** /-ˈstɔrʃən; -ˈstɔːʃən/ *n* [U]: *a promise obtained by extortion* 逼出來的承諾

ex·tor·tion·ate /ɪkˈstɔrʃənɪt; ɪkˈstɔːʃən‚t/ *adj* unfairly high or great (used of demands and prices) 太高的; 過度的〔指要求、價格〕 **–extortionately** *adv*

✶ex·tra¹ /ˈɛkstrə; ˈɛkstrə/ *adj, adv* **1** [only before a noun 只用於名詞前] beyond what is usual or necessary 特別的〔地〕; 額外的〔地〕: *an extra loaf of bread* 一個額外的麵包 | *I'll have to work extra hard.* 我必須特別努力地工作。 **2** [never before a noun 不能用於名詞前] as well as the regular charge 外加的: *Dinner costs £8, and wine is extra.* 晚飯的價錢是八英鎊, 酒水另計。 | *They charge extra for a cooked breakfast.* 他們對做好的早餐另外收費。

extra² *n* **1** something that is added and for which you usually have to pay more 額外的東西; 另收費用的項目: *It's £500 a term without any extras such as piano lessons.* 一個學期五百英鎊, 鋼琴課等不再另外收費。 **2** someone who has a very small part in a film, for example in a crowd scene〔拍攝電影羣眾場面時的〕臨時演員

ex·tract¹ /ɪkˈstrækt; ɪkˈstrækt/ *v fml*〖正式〗[T] **1** to pull or take something out, often with difficulty〔費力地〕抽出; 拔出: *She extracted some papers* **from** *the file.* 她用力從文件夾中抽出一些文件。 **2** to remove something from another substance using a machine or some other process〔用機器或其他方法〕提取; 榨取: *They are extracting gold* **from** *those rocks.* 他們正從礦石中提煉出黃金。 | *Oil is extracted from the seeds of certain plants.* 油是從某些植物的種子裡榨取來的。 **3** to obtain something from someone with difficulty 設法得到: *See if you can extract any more information* **from** *him.* 看看你能否從他那裡設法取得更多的情報。 **4** to remove a tooth from someone's mouth 拔〔牙〕: *I had a tooth extracted.* 我拔了一顆牙。

ex·tract² /ˈɛkstrækt; ˈɛkstrækt/ *n* [C] a passage taken from a longer piece of speech or writing, for example to show the

style 摘錄; 引用; 選段: *She read me a few extracts* **from** *his letter.* 她給我唸了幾段他來信的摘錄。 **2** [C;U] a product obtained by removing it from some other substance 提煉物; 濃縮物: *meat extract* 肉汁

ex·trac·tion /ɪkˈstrækʃən; ɪkˈstrækʃən/ *n* **1** [C;U] the removal of something 拔出; 抽出: *Her teeth are so bad that she needs five extractions.* 她的牙齒壞得很厲害, 需要拔掉五顆。 | *the extraction of coal from a mine* 從煤礦中採煤 **2** [U] the origin of a person's family 血統; 祖籍, 世系: *an American of Russian extraction* 俄羅斯血統的美國人

ex·tra·cur·ric·u·lar /‚ɛkstrəkəˈrɪkjələr; ‚ɛkstrəkəˈrɪkjʊlər/ *adj* outside the regular course of work in a school or college 課外的: *extracurricular activities* 課外活動

ex·tra·dite /ˈɛkstrə‚daɪt; ˈɛkstrədaɪt/ *v* **extradited, extraditing** [T] to send someone, who may be guilty of a crime and who has escaped to another country back to their own country for trial 引渡〔逃犯〕 **–extradition** /‚ɛkstrəˈdɪʃən; ‚ɛkstrəˈdɪʃən/ *n* [C;U]

ex·tra·ne·ous /ɪkˈstreniəs; ɪkˈstreɪniəs/ *adj fml* not belonging to or directly connected with the subject 〖正式〗無關的; 沒有直接聯繫的: *His account of the evening includes a lot of extraneous details.* 他對當晚的敍述包括了許多與本題無關的細節。

✶ex·tra·or·di·na·ry /ɪkˈstrɔrdn‚ɛrɪ; ɪkˈstrɔːdə-nəri/ *adj* **1** very strange 非常奇怪的: *What an extraordinary idea!* 多麼奇特的想法! **2** unusual or special 不尋常的; 特別的: *a girl of extraordinary beauty* 異常美麗的女孩 | *An act was passed giving the army extraordinary powers.* 這項法案的通過賦予軍隊特別的權力。 **3 extraordinary meeting** a meeting which is not a regular one but arranged to deal with a particular problem 特別會議 **–extraordinarily** *adv*

ex·trap·o·late /ɪksˈtræpə‚let; ɪkˈstræpəleɪt/ *v* **extrapolated, extrapolating** [I;T] *fml* to use the information you have to decide what might happen in the future 〖正式〗〔從已知信息〕推斷; 推知

ex·trav·a·gant /ɪkˈstrævəgənt; ɪkˈstrævə-gənt/ *adj* **1** spending or costing too much money 奢侈的; 浪費的: *the government's extravagant policies* 政府鋪張浪費的政策 | *When it comes to books, he's always been extravagant.* 書本方面, 他總是花費太多。 **2** beyond what is reasonable 過度的; 過分的: *He makes the most extravagant claims about this new invention of his.* 他對他的這項新發明提出了極其過分的要求。 | *extravagant praise* 過分的讚揚 **–extravagantly** *adv* **–extravagance** *n* [C;U]: *I was shocked at his extravagance.* 他的浪費令我嚇呆了。

✶ex·treme¹ /ɪkˈstrim; ɪkˈstriːm/ *adj* **1** [only before a noun 只用於名詞前] at the far edge or end of something 在盡頭的; 末端的: *in the extreme north* 在最北面 **2** [only before a noun 只用於名詞前] very great 極度的; 極大的: *extreme heat* 酷熱 | *extreme danger* 極度危險 **3** going beyond the usual limits and likely to be disapproved of by most people 極端的; 過度的: *His political ideas are rather extreme.* 他的政治觀點相當極端。| *an extreme right-wing party* 極右翼黨派

extreme² *n* **1** a point beyond what is usual or reasonable 極端; 極度: *He used to be a Communist, but now he's gone to the other extreme and joined the Fascists.* 他過去是個共產主義者, 可是現在走向了另一個極端, 加入了法西斯組織。| *Sometimes he eats enormous amounts and sometimes nothing. He goes from one extreme to the other.* 他有時吃得太多, 有時甚麼也不吃。他從一個極端走到另一個極端。**2 carry something to extremes** to behave in a way which is good in itself, but to do it to an unreasonable degree 把某事引向極端: *That's carrying efficiency to extremes.* 那樣強調效率是過了頭了。[RELATED PHRASES 相關詞組 **go to extremes, take something to extremes**] **3 in the extreme** to a very great degree 極度; 非常: *She was uncooperative in the extreme.* 她非常不合作。

ex·treme·ly /ɪkˈstriːmlɪ; ɪkˈstriːmli/ *adv* very 極端地; 非常地: *I'm extremely sorry.* 我非常難過。

ex·trem·ist /ɪkˈstriːmɪst; ɪkˈstriːml̩st/ *n* a person with strong political opinions which most people consider are beyond the limits of what is reasonable 極端分子: *The laboratory was destroyed by extremists protesting about animal rights.* 實驗室被那些為動物權利而提出抗議的極端分子破壞了。 **–extremist** *adj* **–extremism** *n* [U]

ex·trem·i·ty /ɪkˈstrɛmətɪ; ɪkˈstrɛml̩ti/ *n* **extremities** [sing] the highest degree of suffering and sorrow 〔痛苦和悲傷的〕極度; 極點: *an extremity of pain* 劇痛 **2 extremities** [pl] your hands and feet 〔人的〕手足, 四肢: *The fire will warm our extremities, at least.* 這堆火至少會使我們的手腳暖和起來。 **3** [C] *fml* the furthest point or edge of something 〔正式〕盡頭; 末端: *The huts were situated at the extremity of the field.* 那些小屋在田地的盡頭處。

ex·tri·cate /ˈɛkstrɪˌket; 'ɛkstrl̩keɪt/ *v* **extricated, extricating** [T] to free someone or something from a place or a difficult situation 使解脫; 使擺脫; 解救: *Help me extricate this bird from the fence.* 幫我把這隻鳥從柵欄上救下來。| *It was two hours before he managed to extricate himself from the meeting.* 過了兩小時他才設法從這次會議中脫身。

ex·tro·vert /ˈɛkstroˌvɝt; 'ɛkstrəvɜːt/ *n* a person who likes to be with other people and finds them easy to talk to 性格外向的人

ex·u·be·rant /ɪgˈzjubərənt; ɪgˈzjuːbərənt/ *adj* very happy, excited, and active 興高采烈的; 生氣勃勃的: *an exuberant child* 朝氣蓬勃的孩子 **–exuberantly** *adv* **–exuberance** *n* [U]

ex·ude /ɪgˈzjud; ɪgˈzjuːd/ *v* **exuded, exuding** **1** [I;T] to flow out slowly or cause a liquid to flow out slowly (使)溢出; (使)緩慢流出: *Sweat exuded from every part of his body.* 他渾身冒汗。**2** [T] to show a feeling or quality strongly 充分顯露〔感情或特質〕: *He exuded great charm to those around him.* 他向周圍那些人散發出巨大的魅力。

ex·ult /ɪgˈzʌlt; ɪgˈzʌlt/ *v* *lit* [I] to be very pleased about something that is successful 〔文〕狂喜; 歡欣鼓舞: *The people exulted in the victory.* 人們為取得勝利而歡欣鼓舞。| *They exulted at the enemy's defeat.* 他們因為擊敗敵人而歡躍。**–exultant** *adj* **–exultation** /ˌɛgzʌlˈteʃən; ˌeɡzʌlˈteɪʃən/ [U]: *They heard a cry of exultation as the climber reached the mountain top.* 登山者到達山頂時, 聽到一陣歡呼聲。

★ **eye¹** /aɪ; aɪ/ *n* **1** one of the two organs on your face with which you see 眼睛: *He lost an eye in an accident.* 他在一次事故中失去了一隻眼睛。| *She has beautiful blue eyes.* 她有一雙美麗的藍眼睛。**2** the hole in a needle through which the thread passes 針眼 **3** the dark spot on a potato from which a new plant can grow 〔馬鈴薯的〕芽眼 **4** the calm centre of a storm 〔風暴的〕風眼 **5 an eye for** good judgment about something 鑑賞力: *She's got a good eye for fashion.* 她對時裝很有眼光。**6 have an eye on** to watch and judge someone 觀察評判〔某人〕: *They've got their eyes on you for promotion.* 他們為了晉升的事在密切注意你。**7 have eyes in the back of your head** *infml* to be able to see or notice everything 〔非正式〕能看到一切: *You need eyes in the back of your head with small children.* 你要腦後長眼睛才能看得住小孩子們。**8 in the eyes of, in someone's eyes** in someone's opinion 在某人看來: *In her father's eyes, she can do nothing wrong.* 在她父親的眼裡, 她是不會做錯事的。| *In the eyes of the law, she's a dangerous criminal.* 從法律上看, 她是個危險的罪犯。**9 keep an eye on** *infml* to watch someone or something to check that they are safe 〔非正式〕照看〔某人或某事〕; 對…留神: *Our neighbours keep an eye on the house while we're away.* 我們外出的時候, 鄰居給我們照看房子。**10 keep an eye out for, keep your eyes open for** *infml* to try to notice and remember someone or something 〔非正式〕努力注意並記住; 留心: *The police are keeping an eye out for trouble.* 警察正在密切注意事端的發生。**11 keep your eyes peeled/skinned** *infml* to watch carefully 〔非正式〕密切注意; 留心; 警覺: *The thieves kept their eyes peeled for the police.* 小偷時刻提防着警察。**12 make eyes at someone** *infml* to show that you find someone sexually attractive by looking at them in an inviting way 〔非正

E

式〕向某人送秋波 **13 see eye to eye** to agree with someone completely 完全同意〔某人〕: *He and his brother don't always see eye to eye.* 他和他兄弟的看法並不總是一致。**14 under your very eyes, before your very eyes** in front of you, so that you can see it with no difficulty 在…面前: *They must have stolen the papers under my very eyes.* 他們一定是在我面前偷走了文件。**15 up to your eyes in, up to the eyes in** *infml* having a lot of something to deal with 〔非正式〕非常忙: *I'm up to my eyes in work.* 我工作忙得不可開交。**16 with your eyes open** knowing about the possible problems 明知後果如何: *You married him with your eyes open, so don't complain now!* 你明知和他結婚的結果是怎樣，所以現在不要埋怨了! **17 -eyed** having eyes of a particular type or number 有〔某種類型〕眼睛的: *blue-eyed* 藍眼睛的 | *one-eyed* 獨眼的 | *bright-eyed* 目光明亮的

eye² v eyed, eyeing [T] to look at something carefully with interest or distrust 〔有興趣地或不信任地〕注視, 細看

eye·ball /ˈaɪˌbɔl; ˈaɪbɔːl/ *n* the whole of your eye, including the part hidden inside your head 眼球

eye·brow /ˈaɪˌbraʊ; ˈaɪbraʊ/ *n* **1** the line of hairs above each of your eyes 眉毛 **2 raise your eyebrows** to show surprise, doubt, or disapproval 揚起眉毛〔表示驚奇、懷疑或不贊成〕: *A lot of eyebrows were raised at the news of the minister's dismissal.* 部長被免職的消息令許多人感到驚訝。

eye-catch·ing /ˈ· ˌ··/ *adj* so unusual or at-tractive that you cannot help looking at it 引人注目的: *an eye-catching advertisement* 引人注目的廣告 | *an eye-catching dress* 引人注目的衣服

eye·lash /ˈaɪˌlæʃ; ˈaɪlæʃ/ *n* one of the small hairs which grow from the edge of each eyelid (眼)睫毛

eye·lid /ˈaɪˌlɪd; ˈaɪˌlɪd/ *n* one of the two pieces of skin which can move down to cover your eyes 眼瞼; 眼皮

eye-o·pen·er /ˈ· ˌ···/ *n* [sing] something surprising, from which you learn something for the first time 使人驚奇的事物; 使人大開眼界的事物: *The film about China was a real eye-opener.* 這部關於中國的影片着實令人大開眼界。

eye·sight /ˈaɪˌsaɪt; ˈaɪsaɪt/ *n* [U] the ability to see 視力: *He's got very poor eyesight.* 他視力很差。

eye·sore /ˈaɪˌsor; ˈaɪsɔːʳ/ *n* something ugly which many people have to look at〔許多人不得不看到的〕難看的東西: *That new shopping centre is a real eyesore.* 這座新的購物中心真是難看。

eye·strain /ˈaɪˌstren; ˈaɪstreɪn/ *n* [U] a painful and tired condition of the eyes caused, for example, by reading in bad light 眼睛疲勞

eye·wit·ness /ˈaɪˌwɪtnɪs; ˈaɪˌwɪtnəs/ *n* a person who sees an event and is able to describe it, especially in a court of law 目擊者; 見證人: *Were there any eyewitnesses to the crime?* 這宗案件有任何目擊者嗎?

F, f

F, f /ɛf; ef/ **F's, f's** or **Fs, fs** the 6th letter of the English alphabet 英語的第六個字母

F an abbreviation for 〖縮〗= FAHRENHEIT

fa·ble /'febl; 'feɪbəl/ *n* a short story, often about animals, that teaches a lesson or truth 寓言

★**fab·ric** /'fæbrɪk; 'fæbrɪk/ *n* **1** [C;U] cloth 織物; 布: *a delicate silk fabric* 柔軟的絲織品 **2** [U] the walls and roof of a building 建築物的牆和屋頂 **3 the fabric of society** the way society is organized and the customs of society 社會的結構

fab·ri·cate /'fæbrɪ,ket; 'fæbrɪkeɪt/ *v* **fabricated, fabricating** [T] to invent information in order to deceive people 捏造; 編造: *Later we realized that he'd fabricated the whole story.* 我們後來才明白, 整個故事都是他編造出來的。– **fabrication** /,fæbrɪ'keʃən; ,fæbrɪ'keɪʃən/ *n* [C;U]

fab·u·lous /'fæbjələs; 'fæbjələs/ *adj* **1** *infml* very good or pleasant 〖非正式〗極好的; 令人愉快的: *You look fabulous!* 你的氣色非常好! | *We had a fabulous holiday.* 我們的假期過得很愉快。**2** [only before a noun 只用於名詞前] extremely great (used especially of someone's beauty or wealth) 驚人的; 巨大的〖尤指某人的美貌或財富〗**3** existing only in stories 寓言中的; 傳說中的: *fabulous creatures* 傳說中的生物

fab·u·lous·ly /'fæbjələslɪ; 'fæbjələsli/ *adv* **fabulously rich, fabulously beautiful** extremely rich or beautiful 極其富有; 極其美麗

fa·cade /fə'sad; fə'sɑːd/ *n* (also 又作 **façade**) **1** the front of a building 〖建築物的〗正面 **2** a way of behaving which hides your real feelings or character 〖不露真情或性格的〗外表; 外觀

★**face**[1] /fes; feɪs/ *n* **1** the front part of your head, which has your eyes, nose, and mouth on it 臉; 面孔: *a happy face* 高興的面容 | *She had a surprised expression on her face.* 她臉上流露出驚訝的表情。**2 a long face** an unhappy expression 不高興的表情〖板着臉〗**3 a straight face** a serious expression 嚴肅的表情〖繃着臉〗: *I felt bad about laughing at him but I just* couldn't keep a straight face. 嘲笑他我覺得不快, 但我就是正經不起來。**4 face to face** looking directly at someone 面對面地〖看某人〗: *I'd like to talk to him face to face.* 我想和他當面談一談。**5** the surface of a clock or watch, which has numbers on it to show the time 鐘〖錶〗面 **6** the side of a mountain or wall of rock 山坡; 〖礦石的〗晶面; 採掘面: *the north face of Everest* 珠穆朗瑪峯的北坡 | *workers at the coal face* 在煤層採掘面工作的工人 **7** *fml* the appearance or nature of something 〖正式〗面貌; 本質: *the changing face of capitalism* 資本主義那變化無常的本質 **8 on the face of it** judging by what you already know or can see 從表面判斷; 顯然 **9 take something at face value** to accept or believe something without questioning it 對某事信以為真 **10 come face to face with something** to be forced to deal with something unpleasant 被迫面對某事物: *She came face to face with death.* 她面前只有死路一條。**11 in the face of** in spite of 不顧: *She succeeded in the face of great difficulties.* 儘管困難重重, 她還是完成了任務。**12 lose face** to lose the respect of other people 失面子; 丟臉 **13 save face** to avoid losing the respect of other people 顧全面子; 沒丟臉

★**face**[2] *v* **faced, facing** [T] **1** to be looking towards something 朝〖某物〗看: *She turned to face me.* 她轉過身來看着我。**2** to have the front pointing towards something 面朝; 面向: *The house faces north.* 這房子朝北。**3** to have to deal with something unpleasant 對付〖令人不快的事〗: *There are a lot of problems that we need to face.* 有許多問題需要我們處理。**4 be faced with something** to have to deal with something difficult or unpleasant 面臨某事〖指難題或討厭的事〗: *We were faced with a difficult choice.* 我們面臨的是棘手的抉擇。**5 face the music** to accept punishment for something you have done 因自己的行為受懲罰 **6 can't face** to be unwilling to do something because it is too difficult or unpleasant 不願做〖太難或不愉快的事〗: *I can't face going to the dentist today.* 我不願今天去看牙醫。

face up to sthg *phr v* [T] to accept something difficult or unpleasant 敢於承擔〖難事或不快的事〗: *You'll have to face up to your responsibilities now.* 你現在得勇於承擔自己的責任。

face·cloth /'fes,klɒθ; 'feɪsklɒθ/ *n* a small cloth that you use to wash your body 〖洗臉等用的〗毛巾

face·less /ˈfeɪslɪs; ˈfeɪsləs/ *adj* dull and without human feeling 令人生厭的; 無人情的: *faceless bureaucrats* 無人情味的官僚

face-lift /ˈ· ˌ·/ *n* a medical operation to make your face look younger by tightening the skin〔將面部皮膚拉緊使其看上去年輕的〕整容手術

face-sav·ing /ˈ· ˌ··/ *adj* allowing someone to appear worthy of respect even though they may not be 保全面子的: *The union quickly negotiated a face-saving agreement with the management.* 工會很快與資方達成了一項保全面子的協議。

fac·et /ˈfæsɪt; ˈfæsɪt/ *n* **1** a part of something to be considered〔所consider. 事情的〕一個方面: *That is only one facet of his personality.* 那只是他性格的一個方面。 **2** a flat side of a cut jewel or precious stone〔寶石等的〕平面; 刻面

fa·ce·tious /fəˈsiːʃəs; fəˈsiːʃəs/ *adj* tending to use unsuitable jokes in a serious situation (a word used to express disapproval〔在嚴肅場合〕好開玩笑的〔含貶義〕–**facetiously** *adv* –**facetiousness** *n* [U]

fa·cial[1] /ˈfeɪʃəl; ˈfeɪʃəl/ *adj* relating to or concerning your face 面部的: *facial hair* 面部的汗毛 –**facially** *adv*

facial[2] *n* a beauty treatment for your face 面部按摩; 美容

fa·cile /ˈfæsl; ˈfæsaɪl/ *adj* too simple, and therefore meaningless (a word used to express disapproval) 太容易的; 無意義的〔含貶義〕: *facile remarks* 信口開河的話 | *a facile explanation* 膚淺的解釋

fa·cil·i·tate /fəˈsɪləˌteɪt; fəˈsɪlɪˌteɪt/ *v* **facilitated, facilitating** [T] *fml* to make something easier〔正式〕使〔某事〕變得容易; 使便利: *The new railway line will facilitate north-south communications.* 新建的鐵路幹線將使南北的交往變得便捷。

★**fa·cil·i·ty** /fəˈsɪlətɪ; fəˈsɪlɪtɪ/ *n* **1** [C] an additional useful service or ability 附加功能或能力: *The computerized phone has a call-back facility.* 電腦控制的電話具有回話功能。 **2** [sing] *fml* an ability to do something easily〔正式〕技能; 技巧: *She's got a real facility for languages.* 她確實有學習語言的才能。 **3 facilities** [pl] things which can be used for a particular purpose 設備; 設施: *The college has excellent sports facilities.* 這所學院有良好的體育設施。

fac·ing /ˈfeɪsɪŋ; ˈfeɪsɪŋ/ *n* [U] **1** an outer surface put onto a wall to protect it or make it attractive〔起保護作用的〕面層; 飾面 **2** material sewn into parts of a garment to make those parts thicker〔衣服的〕貼邊; 鑲邊

fac·sim·i·le /fækˈsɪmɪlɪ; fækˈsɪmɪli/ *n* an exact copy of a picture or piece of writing〔字或畫的〕摹本

★**fact** /fækt; fækt/ *n* **1** [C] something that is known for certain to be true or to

have happened 事實: *We must learn all the facts before we make any judgements.* 我們必須了解全部事實後才能作出判斷。 | *The report contains a lot of theories but very few facts.* 這報告包含了許多理論問題, 但缺乏事實。 | *The fact that you haven't got these qualifications doesn't necessarily mean that you can't go to university.* 你沒有這些資歷的事實並不一定意味着你就不能上大學。 | *The fact is that I don't have enough money to go on holiday this year.* 實際情況是我今年沒有足夠的錢去度假。 **2** [U] the truth 真相; 實情: *Often it is difficult to separate fact from fiction.* 把真事和虛構區分開來時常很難。 **3 in fact, in point of fact, in actual fact, as a matter of fact** phrases you use when you are stating that something is true, especially when it is surprising 事實上; 實際上〔尤指意外〕: *I don't mind if you can't give me a lift. In fact, I'd quite like to walk.* 你讓不讓我搭便車我都無所謂; 實際上我很喜歡步行。 | *The government is claiming that inflation is coming down, but in actual fact it is higher than ever before.* 政府宣稱通貨膨脹正在回落, 但事實上現在比以往任何時候都要高。 **4 know something for a fact** to know that something is certainly true 確實地知道某事: *I know for a fact that he intends to hand in his resignation.* 我確實知道他想遞交辭呈。

fac·tion /ˈfækʃən; ˈfækʃən/ *n* **1** [C] a group within a larger group, which has different aims or ideas from the larger group〔持歧見的, 大集團中的〕小派別; 小集團 **2** [U] disagreement between members of a group 派系分歧

★**fac·tor** /ˈfæktə; ˈfæktər/ *n* **1** one of the conditions or influences which has an effect on a situation 因素: *His friendly manner was an important factor in his success.* 他的友好態度是他獲得成功的重要因素。 **2** *tech* a whole number which can be multiplied by another whole number to produce a given number〔術語〕因子; 因數: *2 and 3 are factors of 6.* 2 和 3 是 6 的因數。

★**fac·to·ry** /ˈfæktrɪ; ˈfæktəri/ *n* **factories** a building or group of buildings where goods are made in large quantities 工廠; 製造廠 – see picture on page 470 見 470 頁彩圖

facts of life /ˌ· · ˈ·/ *n* **the facts of life** the details about sex and how babies are born 性知識

fac·tu·al /ˈfæktʃuəl; ˈfæktʃuəl/ *adj* containing facts or based on facts 事實的; 根據事實的: *a factual account of the war* 一篇關於戰爭的真實報導 –**factually** *adv*

fac·ul·ty /ˈfækltɪ; ˈfækəlti/ *n* **faculties 1** a natural ability, for example the ability to see or think 官能; 能力〔如: 視、思考等〕: *The old man was still in command of all his faculties.* 那位老人仍然耳聰目明。 **2** a group of university departments〔由大學的幾個系組

F

成的)院: *the science faculty* 理學院

fad /fæd; fæd/ *n* an interest or fashion that only lasts a short time 一時的興趣[風尚]: *His interest in photography is just a passing fad.* 他對攝影的愛好僅是一時的興致。

fade /feɪd; feɪd/ *v* **faded, fading 1** [I;T] to make or become paler in colour 使(使)褪色: *My T-shirt faded in the sun.* 我的短袖汗衫被太陽曬得褪了色。| *The photographs have been faded by the light.* 照片被光線照得褪了色。**2** [I] to become weaker or not as strong 逐漸變弱[消失]: *Hopes of a peace settlement are now fading.* 和平解決的希望正在逐漸消失。

fade away *phr v* [I] to become gradually weaker and then disappear 逐漸變弱[消失]: *The sound of thunder faded away.* 雷聲漸漸消失了。

fae·ces /'fiːsiz; 'fiːsiːz/ *n* (also 又作 **feces** *AmE*【美式】) [pl] *tech* the solid waste material that you pass from your bowels【術語】糞便

fag /fæg; fæg/ *n infml*【非正式】**1 a fag** an unpleasant and tiring thing to do 吃力的工作; 苦差事: *I find the housework a real fag.* 我覺得家務工作真累人。**2** *BrE* a CIGARETTE【英式】香煙 **3** *AmE* a HOMOSEXUAL (a word used to express disapproval, and which some people find offensive)【美式】同性戀者(含貶義)

fagged /fægd; fægd/ *adj BrE infml*【英式, 非正式】[never before a noun 不能用於名詞前] (also 又作 **fagged out**) very tired 十分疲倦的

fag·got /'fægət; 'fægət/ *n* (also 又作 **fagot** *AmE*【美式】) **1** a ball of cut-up meat which is cooked and eaten 肉丸子 **2** a bunch of small sticks for burning (a word no longer used in modern English) 柴把; 柴綑(在現代英語中已不再使用)

Fah·ren·heit /'færənˌhaɪt; 'færənhaɪt/ *n* a scale of temperature in which water freezes at 32° and boils at 212° 華氏溫度計(冰點為 32 度, 沸點為 212 度)—compare 比較 CENTIGRADE

☆☆fail¹ /feɪl; feɪl/ *v* **1** [I] to be unsuccessful 失敗: *She failed in her attempt to convince him.* 她試圖說服他, 但沒成功。**2 fail to do something** to not do something which was expected or needed 忽視或未能做某事: *He failed to turn up for the meeting.* 他未能出席會議。**3** [I;T] to be unsuccessful in an examination 沒有通過(考試): *I've failed my driving test three times.* 我已三次沒通過駕駛執照考試。| *Oh no, I've failed!* 啊呀不好, 我考試沒有及格! **4** [I] to stop working properly 失靈; 失去作用: *The engine failed just after the plane took off.* 飛機剛起飛引擎就失靈了。**5** [T] *fml* to disappoint someone(正式)使(某人)失望: *I know you won't fail me.* 我知道你不會使我失望。**6** [T] to be not enough 缺乏; 不足: *My courage failed me at*

the last minute. 我終於因缺乏勇氣而退縮。

fail² *n* **1** an unsuccessful result in an examination (考試)不及格 **2 without fail: a** certainly 必定; 一定: *I shall bring you that book without fail.* 我一定把那本書給你帶來。**b** always 總是: *He's there every Friday without fail.* 他每星期五總是在那裡。

fail·ing¹ /'feɪlɪŋ; 'feɪlɪŋ/ *n* a fault or weakness 弱點; 缺點: *His main failing is greed.* 他的主要弱點是貪得無厭。

failing² *prep* in the absence of 如果沒有; 若無…時: *Failing instructions, I did what I thought best.* 如果沒有指示, 我就做自己認為是最適當的事。

☆fail·ure /'feɪljə; 'feɪljə/ *n* **1** [U] lack of success 失敗: *His plans ended in failure.* 他的計劃終告失敗。**2** [C] a person or thing that has not succeeded 失敗的人或事情: *As a writer, he was a failure.* 作為一個作家, 他是失敗了。| *The party was a total failure.* 那次聚會辦得極不成功。**3** [C;U] a situation in which something stops working or does not produce what people expect 衰竭; 失靈; 缺乏; 不足: *He died of heart failure.* 他死於心力衰竭。| *The country has suffered a series of crop failures.* 國家接連遇到農作物歉收。**4 failure to do something** the fact that someone has not done something 不履行某事; 沒做某事: *We were worried about his failure to contact us.* 我們為他沒和我們取得聯繫而感到不安。

faint¹ /feɪnt; feɪnt/ *adj* **1** weak and about to lose consciousness 虛弱的; 快要昏厥的: *I began to feel a little bit faint.* 我開始感到有點兒頭暈。**2** not strong or clear 微弱的; 模糊的; 暗淡的: *a faint sound* 微弱的聲音 | *a faint smell of coffee* 淡淡的咖啡香味 | *a faint possibility* 極小的可能性 **3 not have the faintest idea** to have no idea at all 根本不知道: *I didn't have the faintest idea what he was talking about.* 我根本不明白他在說些甚麼。**–faintly** *adv* **–faintness** *n* [U]

faint² *v* [I] to lose consciousness for a short time (暫時)失去知覺; 暈倒: *Several people fainted in the heat.* 好幾個人被熱得暈倒了。

☆fair¹ /feə; feə/ *adj* **1** just or reasonable 公正的; 公平的: *a fair decision* 公正的裁決 | *That's not fair! It's my turn.* 那樣不公平! 現在該輪到我了。| *We need to find a taxation system that is fair to everyone.* 我們需要一個對人人都公平的課稅制度。**–opposite** 反義 **unfair 2 fair enough** a phrase used to say that something is reasonable, although you have or have had some doubts 說得對; 有道理(雖表示同意, 但並不十分肯定): *I suppose it's fair enough to take time off work for a sick child.* 我認為抽出點工作時間去照料生病的孩子當然是好的。**3 fair play** just and honest treatment of everyone concerned 公平對待(每個人) **4** fairly good or large 相當好(大)的: *She's got a fair command of the language.* 她對這種語言掌握得相當紮實。| *a* *fair-sized garden* 相當大的花園 **5** fine and without clouds (used of the weather) 晴朗的〔指天氣〕 **6** light in colour (used of someone's hair or skin) 白晢的; 淺色的〔指毛髮或皮膚〕 –see picture on page 469 見 469 頁彩圖 **7** with light-coloured hair or skin 帶白膚金髮的: *She's very fair.* 她有一頭金髮, 皮膚白晢。 –**fairness** *n* [U]

*★**fair²** *adv* **play fair** to play or behave honestly and fairly 公平地比賽[行事]

fair³ *n* **1** *BrE* a FUNFAIR〔英式〕遊樂場 **2** a market for farm produce and animals〔買賣農副產品和牲畜的〕集市: *cattle fairs* 買賣牲畜的集市 **3** a very large show of goods or advertising 大型商品展覽會; 博覽會: *a book fair* (大型)書展

fair·ground /ˈfɛrˌɡraʊnd; ˈfeəɡraʊnd/ *n* an open space where a FUNFAIR is held 露天遊樂場

*★**fair·ly** /ˈfɛrlɪ; ˈfeəli/ *adv* **1** in a just and reasonable way 公正地; 公平地: *I felt that I hadn't been treated fairly.* 我覺得自己沒有得到公平的待遇。 **2** quite 相當地: *She speaks English fairly well.* 她英語說得相當好。 –see 見 RATHER (USAGE用法)

fai·ry /ˈfɛrɪ; ˈfeəri/ *n* **fairies** an imaginary figure that looks like a very small human, often with wings, and has magical powers〔常帶翅膀的〕小仙子; 小精靈

fairy tale /ˈ·· ·/ *n* (also 又作 **fairy story** /ˈ·· ·,·/) a story for children about fairies and other imaginary magical people 神話故事; 童話

fait ac·com·pli /ˌfɛt əkōˈpli; ˌfeɪt əˈkɒmpli/ *n* **faits accomplis** /ˌfɛt əkōˈpliz; ˌfeɪt əˈkɒmpliːz/ something that has already happened and cannot be changed 既成事實

*★**faith** /feθ; feɪθ/ *n* **1** [U] trust and confidence 信任; 信心: *I've got great faith in her ability to succeed.* 我對她獲得成功的能力抱有很大信心。 **2 break faith with someone** to fail to keep a promise that you had made to someone 對某人不守信用 **3 keep faith with someone** to keep a promise that you had made to someone 對某人守信用 **4 in good faith** sincerely, believing that what you are doing is right 真誠地〔堅信自己的所作所為是對的〕: *They had acted in good faith.* 他們誠心誠意地辦事。 **5** [C] a religion 宗教: *the Christian faith* 基督教 **6** [U] religious belief 宗教信仰: *a man of great faith* 有強烈宗教信仰的人

faith·ful /ˈfeθfəl; ˈfeɪθfəl/ *adj* **1** loyal to someone, and continuing to support them 忠實的; 不斷給予支持的: *a faithful friend* 忠實的朋友 **2** true to the facts or to the original meaning 如實的; 真實的: *a faithful translation* 忠於原文的譯本 **3** loyal to your partner by not having a sexual relationship with anyone else 忠貞的: *She was always faithful to him.* 她對他一直很忠貞。 –opposite 反義 **unfaithful** (for sense 3) **4 the**

faithful the people who belong to a particular religion〔宗教的〕忠實信徒 –**faithfulness** *n* [U]

faith·ful·ly /ˈfeθfəlɪ; ˈfeɪθfəl-i/ *adv* **1** in a legal or sincere way 忠實地; 真誠地: *I promised you faithfully.* 我真誠地向你承諾。 **2** exactly 準確地: *I copied the letter faithfully.* 我一字不差地把信抄了下來。 **3 Yours faithfully** the usual way of ending a letter that begins "Dear Sir" or "Dear Madam" 您的忠實的〔常用於以"敬愛的先生"或"親愛的夫人"等開頭的信的結尾〕 –compare 比較 SINCERELY

faith·less /ˈfeθlɪs; ˈfeɪθləs/ *adj* disloyal or dishonest 不忠實的; 不忠誠的

fake¹ /fek; feɪk/ *v* **faked, faking** [T] **1** to copy something in order to deceive people〔為了欺騙而〕仿造〔某物〕: *She faked her mother's handwriting.* 她模仿母親的筆跡。 **2** to pretend to experience something 假裝; 偽裝: *He faked illness.* 他裝出生病的樣子。

fake² *n* **1** something that is not real, but only a copy 假貨; 贗品 **2** someone who pretends to be something that they are not really 騙子; 冒充者: *Do you think all astrologers are fakes?* 你認為占星家都是騙子嗎?

fake³ *adj* made to look like something real in order to deceive people 假的; 偽造的: *fake money* 假幣; 偽鈔

fal·con /ˈfɔlkən; ˈfɔːlkən/ *n* a hunting bird that can be trained by people 獵鷹

fal·con·ry /ˈfɔlkənrɪ; ˈfɔːlkənri/ *n* [U] the art of training falcons to hunt 獵鷹訓練術

*★**fall¹** /fɔl; fɔːl/ *v* **fell** /fɛl; fel/, **fallen** /ˈfɔlən; ˈfɔːlən/, **falling** [I] **1** to move downwards towards the ground 落下; 降落; 跌落: *A tile fell off the roof.* 一塊瓦片從屋頂落了下來。 | *The glass fell to the floor and broke.* 玻璃杯掉到地上打碎了。 | *Snow was falling.* 雪下個不停。 **2** to move from being in a standing position to lying on the ground, usually as the result of an accident 跌倒; 摔倒; 倒下: *She tripped and fell.* 她腳一絆就摔倒了。 | *Several trees fell down in the gales.* 好幾棵樹在那場風暴中倒下了。 –see picture on page 992 見 992 頁彩圖 **3** to become lower in level or amount 下降: *The temperature fell to freezing point.* 溫度降到了冰點。 | *Inflation is falling at last.* 通貨膨脹終於出現回落 **4** (of hair) to hang loosely〔頭髮〕下垂; 散落: *Her hair fell over her shoulders.* 她的頭髮垂在肩上。 **5** to be killed in a battle 陣亡; 戰死: *soldiers who had fallen in the war* 陣亡的士兵 **6** to be defeated or lose power 被擊敗; 垮台: *The government may well fall at the next election.* 政府有可能在下屆選舉中垮台。 **7** to happen 降臨; 來臨: *Night fell quickly.* 暮色很快降臨。 | *Christmas falls on a Friday this year.* 今年聖誕逢星期五。 | *A silence fell as he entered the room.* 他一走進房間大家便安靜下來。 **8** to pass into a new state 進入另一

種狀態; 變成: *She fell asleep in her chair.* 她在椅子上睡着了。 | *She fell ill.* 她生病了。 | *He's fallen in love again.* 他又在戀愛了。 | *She fell silent.* 她靜了下來。 **9 his face fell =** he started to look sad or disappointed 他的臉色一沉 **10 fall flat** to fail to produce the desired effect on people 未產生預期的效果: *His jokes all fell flat.* 他講的笑話根本沒有讓人發笑。 **11 fall into place** to become understandable 變得明朗: *Suddenly everything fell into place and I realized what a fool I'd been.* 一切頓時變得明朗, 我發現我是多麼愚蠢。 **12 fall on your feet** to come out of a difficult situation without being harmed 逢凶化吉; 化險為夷; 幸免於難 **13 fall short** to fail to reach a desired result or standard 沒有達到目標[標準]: *The council planned to build 100 houses this year, but they have fallen short of their target.* 市政議會原來計劃今年建造一百棟房子, 但他們沒有達到預期的目標。 **14 fall to bits, fall to pieces** to break into pieces 成為碎片: *I picked the book up and it fell to bits.* 我把書撿了起來, 但已成了碎片。

fall about *phr v* [I] *infml* to laugh a lot 〖非正式〗大笑起來: *They all fell about laughing.* 他們都捧腹大笑。

fall apart *phr v* [I] to break into pieces 破碎; 破裂: *That coat's falling apart!* 那件衣服已開始破裂!

fall back *phr v* [I] to move away from something 後退; 退讓: *The crowd fell back to let the doctor through.* 人羣向後退, 讓醫生過去。

fall back on sthg *phr v* [T] to use something because other things have failed 借助於; 求助於: *You'll always have your training as a teacher to fall back on.* 你受過的師資訓練總有派得上用場的時候。

fall behind *phr v* [I] to fail to make progress as quickly as you should 落後: *I've fallen behind with my work.* 我的工作落後了。

fall for *phr v* **1** [T **fall for** sthg] to be cheated or deceived by something 受...的騙; 上...的當: *I knew it was just a trick, and I wasn't going to fall for it.* 我知道那只是個騙局; 我不會上當。 **2** [T **fall for** sbdy] to start loving someone suddenly and strongly 迷戀〔某人〕

fall in with sbdy/sthg *phr v* [T] to agree with someone or agree to something 贊同〔某人或某物〕: *I'm quite prepared to fall in with this idea.* 我很贊同這個想法。

fall off *phr v* [I] to decrease in quality or amount 〔質量〕下降; 〔數量〕減少: *Membership has fallen off this year.* 會員人數今年減少了。

fall out *phr v* [I] to quarrel 爭吵; 吵架: *I've fallen out with my mother.* 我和媽媽吵了架。 | *We fell out over money.* 我們是為了錢而吵的。

fall over *phr v* [I] to fall to the ground 跌倒; 倒下: *She tripped and fell over.* 她絆了一下就跌倒在地上。

fall through *phr v* [I] to fail to happen or fail to be completed 落空; 不能實現: *We had planned to go on holiday, but it all fell through.* 我們原來打算去度假, 但未能如願。

☀fall² *n* **1** [C] an act of falling 落下; 跌落; 降落: *He had a nasty fall and broke his wrist.* 他重重地跌了一跤, 摔斷了手腕。 | *a fall of 70 metres* 七十米的落差 **2** [C] something that has fallen to the ground 落下的東西: *A fall of rocks blocked the road.* 落下的岩石堵塞了道路。 | *We've had a heavy fall of snow.* 我們這兒下了一場大雪。 **3** [C] a decrease 下降: *a sudden fall in temperature* 氣溫驟降 | *We're hoping for a fall in interest rates.* 我們盼望利率下調。 **4** the fall of the defeat of a person or country 〔人或國家的〕垮台: *This crisis could lead to the fall of the government.* 這場危機會導致政府垮台。 **5 the fall** the usual American word for 〖美式〗 = AUTUMN

fal·la·cious /fəˈleɪʃəs; fəˈleɪʃəs/ *adj fml* based on false reasoning 〖正式〗謬誤的: *a fallacious argument* 錯誤的論點

fal·la·cy /ˈfæləsɪ; ˈfæləsi/ *n* **fallacies** a false idea or argument 謬見; 謬論: *It is a popular fallacy that success always brings happiness.* 認為成功必定帶來幸福是一種普遍的錯誤見解。

fall·en /ˈfɔːlən; ˈfɔːlən/ the past participle of FALL ☆ FALL 的過去分詞

fal·li·ble /ˈfæləbl; ˈfæləbəl/ *adj fml* able to make a mistake 〖正式〗易犯錯誤的: *Everybody is fallible.* 人人都難免犯錯誤。 —opposite 反義 **infallible – fallibility** /ˌfæləˈbɪlətɪ; ˌfæləˈbɪləti/ *n* [U]

falling-off /ˌ·· ·ˈ·/ *n* [sing] a decrease 減少: *a falling-off in the numbers of men reporting for duty.* 報到上班人數的減少。

fall·out /ˈfɔːlaʊt; ˈfɔːlaʊt/ *n* [U] the dangerous RADIOACTIVE dust left in the air after an atomic or NUCLEAR explosion 〔原子彈爆炸後留在空氣中的〕放射性墜塵

fal·low /ˈfæləʊ; ˈfæloʊ/ *adj* dug but left for a while with no crops planted (used of land) 犁過而未播種的〔指耕地〕

☀false /fɔːls; fɔːls/ *adj* **1** not true or correct 錯誤的; 不正確的: *He gave the police false information.* 他向警方提供了不真實的情報。 | *We had given them the false impression that everything was under control.* 我們給他們的假象是: 一切都在控制之下。 **2** not real, or made to look like the real thing 假的; 偽造的: *false teeth* 假牙 | *She was using a false passport.* 她在使用假護照。 **3** not sincere in your behaviour 〔行為〕不誠實的: *Everything about her seemed false.* 她的所作所為都靠不住。 **4 false alarm** a warning of something dangerous, which does not happen 虛假的警報 **5 under false pretences** by deceiving people and hiding the truth 冒充別人行騙: *He had got into the building under false pretences.* 他冒充別人進了大樓. –**falsely** *adv* –**falseness** *n* [U]

false·hood /ˈfɔls·hʊd; ˈfɔːlshʊd/ *n* **1** [C] a statement that is untrue 謊言 **2** [U] the quality of being untrue 虛假: *We must establish the truth or falsehood of these claims.* 我們必須證實這些索賠的真假.

fal·set·to /fɔlˈsɛto; fɔːlˈsetəʊ/ *n* an extremely high male singing voice 假聲男高音

fal·si·fy /ˈfɔlsəˌfaɪ; ˈfɔːlsɪˌfaɪ/ *v* falsified, falsifying [T] to change information and make it untrue 竄改; 偽造: *He was accused of falsifying the facts.* 他被指控捏造事實. – **falsification** /ˌfɔlsəfəˈkeʃən; ˌfɔːlsɪfɪˈkeɪʃən/ *n* [C;U]

fal·si·ty /ˈfɔlsətɪ; ˈfɔːlsɪti/ *n* [U] the quality of being false or untrue 虛假; 不真實

fal·ter /ˈfɔltɚ; ˈfɔːltər/ *v* [I] **1** to become weaker and more unsteady 搖晃; 蹣跚; 顫抖: *Her voice faltered and she began to cry.* 她的聲音發顫, 接着就哭了起來. | *He faltered and almost fell.* 他走路搖搖晃晃, 幾乎要摔倒. **2** to lose confidence in what you are doing 動搖; 猶豫: *He never faltered in his resolve to prove his innocence.* 他要證實自己是清白的決心從不動搖. –**falteringly** *adv*

fame /fem; feɪm/ *n* [U] the condition of being well known and admired 名聲; 名望: *She hoped to find fame as a dancer.* 她希望成為有名氣的舞蹈家.

famed /femd; feɪmd/ *adj* well known and admired 有名的; 著名的: *The mountains are famed for their beauty.* 這些山脈以美麗的景色而聞名.

☆**fa·mil·i·ar** /fəˈmɪljɚ; fəˈmɪliər/ *adj* **1** known, seen, or experienced before 熟悉的; 經歷過的; 常見的: *Your face seems familiar to me.* 你看上去好像很面熟. | *It was a familiar sight.* 那是常見的情景. **2 familiar with something** already knowing something 熟悉某事物: *Are you familiar with Harrison's poetry?* 你熟悉哈里森的詩嗎? –opposite 反義 **unfamiliar** (for senses 1 and 2) **3** too friendly and informal for a particular situation 過分親暱的: *I didn't like his familiar way of talking to me.* 我不喜歡他跟我說話時那種過分親暱的樣子. –**familiarity** /fəˌmɪliˈærətɪ; fəˌmɪliˈærɪti/ *n* [U]

fa·mil·i·ar·ize /fəˈmɪljəˌraɪz; fəˈmɪliəraɪz/ *v* familiarized, familiarizing (also 又作 **familiarise** *BrE* 〔英式〕) **1** [T] to help someone understand something 使〔某人〕熟悉〔某事物〕: *First of all, we'd like to familiarize you with the regulations.* 首先, 我想讓你們熟悉一下規章制度. **2 familiarize yourself with something** to inform yourself about something 使自己熟悉〔通曉〕〔某事物〕: *I need to familiarize myself with the dictionary codes.* 我得熟悉一下詞典中的符號.

fa·mil·i·ar·ly /fəˈmɪljɚlɪ; fəˈmɪliəli/ *adv* in a

way which is too friendly and informal for the situation 親密地; 不拘禮節地: *He slapped me on the back familiarly.* 他隨和地拍拍我的背.

☆**fam·i·ly**[1] /ˈfæməlɪ; ˈfæmili/ *n* families **1** [C+sing/pl verb] a group of people related by blood or marriage, especially a group of two parents and their children 家; 家庭: *Our family has lived in this house for over a hundred years.* 我們家在這座房子裡已住了一百多年. | *the Spanish family next door* 隔壁那一家西班牙人 | *a one-parent family* 單親家庭 | *family photographs* 家人照片 | *Are your family coming?* 你們全家都來嗎? **2** [U] part of someone's family 家屬: *He can come; he's family.* 他能來, 他是家屬. **3** [C] a number of children in one family 子女: *They are both trying to bring up large families on very little money.* 他們倆靠一點點錢在盡力撫養那麼多子女. **4** [C] a group of things related by being similar in some way 〔有相似之處的〕一類東西; 〔動植物的〕科: *tigers and other members of the cat family* 老虎和其他貓科動物

family[2] *adj* suitable for children as well as older people 適合全家大小的; 一家老小咸宜的: *The new Disney film is good family entertainment.* 這部迪士尼新片非常適合全家大小一起觀賞.

family plan·ning /ˌ··· ˈ··/ *n* [U] the controlling of the number of children born in a family by the use of any of various CONTRACEPTIVE methods 計劃生育; 家庭計劃: *family planning clinics* 計劃生育門診部

family tree /ˌ··· ˈ·/ *n* a plan of the relationships between the members of a family 家譜(圖), 家庭譜系

fam·ine /ˈfæmɪn; ˈfæmɪn/ *n* [C;U] very serious lack of food 饑荒: *widespread famine* 遍及各地的饑荒 | *The famine has already caused 300 deaths in rural areas.* 饑荒已經在農村導致了三百人死亡.

fam·ished /ˈfæmɪʃt; ˈfæmɪʃt/ *adj* infml be famished to be extremely hungry 〔非正式〕極其饑餓的

☆**fa·mous** /ˈfeməs; ˈfeɪməs/ *adj* very well known 著名的; 出名的: *a famous actor* 名演員 | *France is famous for its fine food and wine.* 法國以其佳餚和美酒聞名.

■ USAGE 用法: Compare 比較 **famous, well-known, notorious, infamous. Famous** is like **well-known** but is a stronger word and means "known over a wide area" ☆ **Famous** 與 **well-known** 意思相似, 但前者語氣較強, 表示 "廣為人知的": *the doctor, the postman and other* **well-known** *people in our village* 我們村裡的醫生、郵差和其他為人熟知的人士 | *He's a* **famous** *actor – people everywhere in the world recog-*

---

nize his face. 他是著名演員, 世界各地的人都能認出他來。**Notorious** means "famous for something bad" ☆ **notorious** 表示"因壞事而出名": *He was* **notorious** *for his evil deeds.* 他因做了壞事而聲名狼籍。**Infamous** (rather literary) can mean the same as **notorious** when used before a noun ☆ **infamous** (較正式)用於名詞前時其意義與 **notorious** 相同: *an* **infamous** *criminal* 臭名昭著的罪犯, but it can also mean simply wicked or evil (not necessarily **famous**) 但它也可以直接表示"惡毒的", "邪惡的"(不一定臭名遠揚): *Not many people knew about his infamous crimes.* 知道他惡行的人並不太多。

fa·mous·ly /ˈfeɪməslɪ; ˈfeɪməsli/ *adv infml* very well 〔非正式〕非常好地: *I've always got on famously with my mother-in-law.* 我和岳母相處得蠻好。

fan¹ /fæn; fæn/ *n* **1** an instrument used to keep you cool by making a flow of air 扇子: *a paper fan* 紙扇 | *an electric fan* 電風扇 **2** something with the shape of a half circle 扇狀物: *a fan of papers* 扇形文件 **3** a keen supporter 狂熱擁護者; 迷: *football fans* 足球迷 | *I've always been a great fan of the Beatles.* 我一直非常迷戀披頭士樂隊。

fan² *v* **-nn-** [T] **1** to cause air to move onto something 搧; 搧動(空氣): *She fanned her face with a newspaper.* 她用報紙往臉上搧風。 | *Use this to fan the fire.* 用這個搧火。 **2** to cause a feeling to become stronger 煽動〔情緒〕; 激起: *His rudeness fanned her irritation into anger.* 他的粗魯使她的惱怒變成了憤怒。

   fan out *phr v* [I;T **fan** sthg ↔ **out**] to spread out from a central point (使)分散; (使)成扇形散開: *The soldiers fanned out across the hillside.* 戰士們在山腰上成扇形散開。 | *Watch the swans fanning out their wings!* 瞧那些展翅飛翔的天鵝!

fa·nat·ic /fəˈnætɪk; fəˈnætɪk/ *n* a person whose beliefs and behaviour are extreme and often unquestioning, especially in religious or political matters 〔宗教或政治事務方面的〕狂熱者: *a religious fanatic* 狂熱的宗教信徒 | *health food fanatics* 迷信保健食品的人 **—fanatic, fanatical** *adj* **—fanatically** /-klɪ; -kli/ *adv* **—fanaticism** /-tə‚sɪzəm; -t‚sɪzəm/ *n* [U]

fan·ci·er /ˈfænsɪə; ˈfænsɪər/ *n* a person who has a strong interest in a certain type of animal or plant 對某種動、植物有強烈興趣的人: *a pigeon-fancier* 養鴿愛好者

fan·ci·ful /ˈfænsɪfʊl; ˈfænsɪfəl/ *adj* **1** unrelated to reality 脫離現實的; 空想的: *fanciful ideas* 不切實際的想法 **2** showing unusual imagination 富於幻想的: *a fanciful poet* 想像力豐富的詩人 **—fancifully** *adv*

fan·cy¹ /ˈfænsɪ; ˈfænsi/ *n* **fancies 1 take a fancy to** to be attracted to a person or thing 被〔某物〕所吸引; 愛上〔某人〕: *I've taken a sudden fancy to that pink hat.* 我突然被那頂粉紅色帽子吸引住了。 **2 take someone's fancy** to attract someone 吸引某人: *The idea of travelling alone took my fancy.* 獨自一人旅行的想法吸引了我。 **3** an idea with little relation to reality 空想; 幻想: *her strange fancies* 她那奇特的幻想 **4** a liking for something 愛好: *How do I know that your wanting a dog is not just a passing fancy?* 我怎麼知道你想養狗不僅僅是一時的愛好?

fan·cy² *v* **fancied, fancying 1** [T] *infml* to have a desire for something 〔非正式〕想要做〔某事〕: *I fancy a swim.* 我想游一會兒泳。 | *Do you fancy going for a walk?* 你想去散散步嗎? **2** [T] *infml* to be attracted to someone 〔非正式〕喜愛〔某人〕: *I fancy the man with the beard.* 我很喜歡那個留著大鬍子的人。 **3** [+ (that)] *old fash* to believe 〔老式〕以為; 猜想: *He fancied he had met her before.* 他認為他以前見到過她。 **4** a word used to express surprise or disapproval 〔用於表示驚奇、反對等〕: *Fancy him being married to both of them!* 想不到他竟把她們兩個都娶了! | *Fancy that!* 多奇怪呀! **5 fancy yourself** to have too high an opinion of yourself 自命不凡; 自負: *He really fancies himslef as a dancer!* 他確實以為自己是了不起的舞蹈員!

fan·cy³ *adj* not ordinary, but highly decorated, brightly coloured, or unusually expensive 別致的; 裝飾講究的; 色彩鮮艷的; 昂貴的: *fancy cakes* 精美的蛋糕 | *fancy ideas* 不尋常的想法 | *His furnishings are too fancy for my liking.* 他的家具太貴, 不合我意。

fancy dress /,·· '·/ *n* [U] unusual or amusing clothes worn for a special occasion 〔特殊場合穿的〕奇裝異服: *We've got to go in fancy dress, so I'm making a frog costume.* 我們得穿化裝服去, 所以我在做一件蛙式服裝。 | *a fancy dress party* 化裝舞會

fancy-free /,·· '·/ *adj* free to do anything you want, especially because you do not have the responsibilities of a close relationship with someone 無拘束的〔尤指沒有親人需要負擔〕

fan·fare /ˈfænfeə; ˈfænfeər/ *n* a short, loud piece of music played, especially on the TRUMPET, to introduce a person or event 〔在重要人物到場或重大事件開始前用喇叭吹奏的〕嘹亮的短曲

fang /fæŋ; fæŋ/ *n* a long sharp tooth 長而尖的牙

fan·ta·size¹ /ˈfæntə‚saɪz; ˈfæntəsaɪz/ *v* **fantasized, fantasizing** (also 又作 **fantasise** *BrE* 〔英式〕) [I; +(that)] to have strange or wonderful ideas about something 想像, 幻想〔某事物〕: *He fantasized about acting in Hollywood.* 他幻想成為好萊塢演員。 | *We were fantasizing that we would be rich one* *day*. 我們幻想着總有一天會變得很富有。

fan·tas·tic /fæn'tæstɪk; fæn'tæstɪk/ *adj* **1** *infml* extremely good 〔非正式〕極好的: *a fantastic meal* 極豐盛的一餐 | *That's a fantastic idea!* 那主意太棒了! **2** *infml* very large 〔非正式〕巨大的: *She's spent a fantastic amount of money on that house.* 她花了一大筆錢買下那座房子。 **3** very strange and unrelated to reality 奇異的; 不現實的; 荒誕的: *a fantastic dream* 怪誕的夢 | *fantastic fears* 奇異的恐懼 **—fantastically** /-klɪ; -klɪ/

fan·ta·sy /'fæntəsɪ; 'fæntəsɪ/ *n* **fantasies** [C; U] something quite unreal which you imagine 想像[幻想]物: *She's trying to live out one of her fantasies.* 她試圖在她某個幻想中生活一段時間。 | *The story is pure fantasy.* 這故事純屬虛構。 | *He lives in a fantasy world.* 他生活在一個幻想的世界中。

far¹ /'far; faɪʳ/ *adv* **farther** /'farðəʳ; 'faɪðəʳ/ or **further** /'fɜːðəʳ; 'fɜːðəʳ/, **farthest** /'farðɪst; 'faɪðɪst/ or **furthest** /'fɜːðɪst; 'fɜːðɪst/ **1** a long way away 遠; 遙遠: *Is it far to your house?* 去你家遠不遠? | *Shall we walk? It's not very far.* 我們步行去好嗎? 離這兒不遠。 | *How far is the station from here?* 火車站離這兒有多遠? | *We walked quite far into the woods.* 我走到了樹林的深處。 | *We don't see him very often because he lives too far away.* 我們不常見到他, 因為他住得太遠。 | *Christmas is still quite far off.* 聖誕節還很遙遠。 **2** very much 非常; 很: *This essay is far better than your last one.* 這篇文章比你上次寫得好得多。 | *I'm afraid I'm far too busy to stop and chat.* 恐怕我實在太忙了, 沒法停下來和你聊天。 **3** as far as I know = to the degree that I know something, although I do not know for certain 就我所知〔但沒有把握〕: *As far as I know, she's still intending to come.* 就我所知, 她還是想來。 | *As far as we knew, the deal was still on.* 就我們所知, 那筆交易還在進行。 **4** by far, far and away by a large amount 顯然: *This is by far the best machine on the market at the moment.* 這顯然是目前市場上最好的機器。 | *This is far and away the most important medical achievement this century.* 這顯然是本世紀最重大的醫學成就。 **5** far from: **a** not at all 毫不; 一點也不: *She looked far from happy!* 她看上去一點也不高興! **b** instead of 代替; 而不是: *Far from being angry, he was actually quite pleased.* 他根本沒有生氣, 事實上他很高興。 **6** go so far as to do something to do something surprising 做令人吃驚的事: *He even went so far as to say that all money should be abolished.* 他甚至令人吃驚地說, 所有貨幣都應廢除。 **7** go far to be successful and reach a position of power 非常成功; 大有作為: *She's very clever and will go far in this profession.* 她很聰明, 做這個職業前途無量。 **8** not go very far to not be enough 不夠; 不足: *It sounds a lot of money but it won't go very far these days.* 這錢聽起來不少,

但這些日子就是不夠花。 **9** go too far to do something too much, in a way that other people find unacceptable 做得過分〔使別人無法接受〕: *He's often slightly rude to people, but this time he just went too far!* 他待人常有點兒粗魯, 但這次未免太過分了。 **10** how far to what degree 到甚麼程度: *I don't know how far to believe him.* 我不知道該相信他到甚麼程度。 | *I wasn't sure how far I could trust him.* 我不敢確定我對他應信任到多大程度。 **11** not far off, not far out not wrong by a very large amount 大致正確的: *He predicted that inflation would rise to 10%, which was not far off.* 他預測通貨膨脹將上漲至百分之十, 這個數字出入不大。 **12** so far until now 迄今為止: *I've been here for three weeks now, and so far I've enjoyed myself.* 我來這兒已經有三個星期了, 我一直過得很愉快。 | *So far these reports have not been confirmed officially.* 這些報告迄今未獲正式批准。 **13** so far so good a phrase you use to say that until now things have been successful 到目前為止一切都很順利

■ USAGE 用法: You can use **far** to talk about distance in questions and negatives ☆ **far** 可以用在疑問句和否定句中表示距離: *Did you walk* **far**? 你走得遠不遠? | *How* **far** *did you walk?* 你走了多遠? You can also use **far** in statements after *too*, *as* and *so* ☆ **far** 也可用於陳述句中的 *too*, *as* 和 *so* 後面: *It's too* **far** *to reach in one day.* 那兒太遠, 一天之內到不了。 | *I went as* **far** *as I could.* 我盡可能地走得遠一點。 | *The boy walked so* **far** *that he could not find his way back.* 那男孩走得太遠, 結果找不到回來的路了。 Note, however, that you should NOT use **far** in ordinary statements. Instead use **a long way** or **a long distance** ☆但要注意: 在一般陳述句中不可以用 **far**, 而應該用 **a long way** 或 **a long distance**: *He walked* **a long way**. 他走的很遠。 | *It's* **a long way** *from the station to the school.* 從火車站到學校有很長一段路。 | *My house is* **a long way** *from the town centre.* 我家離市中心很遠。

far² *adj* **1** distant (used especially of the more distant of two things) 遠的〔尤指兩者相隔較遠〕: *A few people were fishing on the far bank of the river.* 河對岸有幾個人在釣魚。 | *I could see Jane walking along on the far side of the road.* 我可以看到簡走在路的那一邊。 | *She was sitting at the far end of the room.* 她坐在房間的那一頭。 | *They live in the far South of the country.* 他們住在這個國家的南面。 **2** as/so far as... is concerned you use this expression when you say what subject you are talking or writing about, that is, which particualr part of a situation

or which particular person's opinion 就…
而言〔用於表示談論或論述的話題，即特定的情
況或看法〕: *As far as money is concerned,
things are a bit difficult. But otherwise, I
think they're fine.* 涉及到資金，事情有點難辦；
但在其他方面我認為一切順利。| *As far as
Beryl is concerned, there's no problem, but
of course Alan always finds something to
complain about.* 對貝麗爾來説並沒有甚麼問
題，但是艾倫必定要找碴兒發牢騷。**3 a far cry
from something** very different from something 與某事物大不相同: *It's a lovely house,
and a far cry from that tiny flat they used to
live in.* 這房子蠻漂亮，與他們過去住的那套小
公寓迥然不同。

far·a·way /ˈfɑrəˌwe; ˈfɑːrəweɪ/ *adj* distant
遙遠的; 恍惚的: *a faraway place* 遙遠的地
方 | *She's got that faraway look in her eyes.
I think she's in love.* 她眼中流露出那種恍惚
的神情。我覺得她在戀愛。

farce /fɑrs; fɑːs/ *n* **1** [C;U] a light humorous
play in which a lot of silly things happen 笑
劇; 鬧劇; 滑稽戲 **2** [C] an occasion or set of
events that is silly and pointless 愚蠢可笑的
場合或事情: *The meeting was a complete
farce.* 會議開成了亂哄哄的鬧劇。

far·ci·cal /ˈfɑrsɪkl; ˈfɑːsɪkl̩/ *adj* silly and
pointless 愚蠢可笑的: *a farcical attempt to
reform the tax system* 改革稅收制度的愚蠢可
笑的嘗試 –**farcically** /-klɪ; -kli/ *adv*

fare¹ /fer; feəʳ/ *n* **1** [C] the money that you
pay to travel in a public vehicle〔公共車輛
的〕票價; 車費: *Train fares have gone up
again.* 火車票又漲價了。**2** [U] food, especially as provided at a meal 食品〔尤指伙
食〕: *simple country fare* 農村人吃的粗茶淡飯

fare² *v* **fared, faring** *fml* **fare well** to do well
〖正式〗進展: *The company did not fare very
well under his leadership.* 公司在他的領導下
進展並不順利。[RELATED PHRASE 相關
詞組 **fare badly**]

Far East /ˌ · ˈ·◂/ *n* **the Far East** the countries in Asia that are east of India, such as
China and Japan 遠東〔印度東面的亞洲國家，
如: 中國和日本〕

fare·well /ˌferˈwel; feəˈwel/ *n* GOODBYE 告
別: *a farewell party* 告別宴會 | *Say your
farewells, and we'll go.* 你去告別一下，我們就
走。–**farewell** *interj old fash*〖老式〗: *Farewell, my darling!* 再見，我親愛的!

far·fetched /ˈfɑrˈfetʃt; ˌfɑːˈfetʃt◂/ *adj* difficult to believe 難以置信的; 牽強的: *a far-
fetched excuse* 牽強的藉口

far-flung /ˌ · ˈ·◂/ *adj* **1** spread over a wide
area 廣泛的: *This map shows their far-flung
trade connections.* 這張地圖顯示了他們廣泛
的貿易關係。**2** distant 遙的: *a far-flung corner of the Empire* 英帝國的一個邊遠地區

★**farm¹** /fɑrm; fɑːm/ *n* **1** an area of land and
buildings, where crops are grown or animals raised 農場; 飼養場: *a pig farm* 養豬
場 | *We work on the farm.* 我們在農場工作。|

Do you sell farm produce? 你們出售農產品
嗎? **2** a farmhouse 農舍

farm² *v* [I;T] to use land for growing crops
or raising animals 種田; 飼養動物: *Our family has been farming for generations.* 我們家
祖祖輩輩都是種田的。| *to farm the land* 耕
種土地

farm sbdy/sthg ↔ **out** *phr v* [T] **1** to send
work out to other people to do 把〔工作〕包
給別人做: *We must farm out some of these
projects.* 我們必須把這些項目的一部分承包給
別人。**2** to send a person into the care of
someone else 把〔某人〕寄養出去; 托別人照看
〔某人〕: *As children, we were often farmed
out to friends and relatives.* 我們小時候經常
被寄養在親戚朋友家裡。

farm·er /ˈfɑrmɚ; ˈfɑːmə/ *n* the owner or
manager of a farm 農場主; 牧場主; 農民

farm·hand /ˈfɑrmˌhænd; ˈfɑːmhænd/ *n* a
person who is employed to work on a farm
農場工人

farm·house /ˈfɑrmˌhaus; ˈfɑːmhaus/ *n* (also
又作 **farm**) the main house on a farm,
where the farmer lives 農舍

farm·ing /ˈfɑrmɪŋ; ˈfɑːmɪŋ/ *n* [U] the activity or business of working on a farm 農
業; 耕作; 農事

farm·yard /ˈfɑrmˌjɑrd; ˈfɑːmjɑːd/ *n* a yard
next to or among farm buildings 農家庭院

far-off /ˌ · ˈ·◂/ *adj* distant in space or time
〔空間或時間〕遙遠的

far-reach·ing /ˌ · ˈ··◂/ *adj* having a wide influence 〔影響〕廣泛的: *They're demanding
far-reaching political changes.* 他們在要求進
行廣泛的政治改革。

far·sight·ed /ˈfɑrˈsaɪtɪd; ˌfɑːˈsaɪtɪd◂/ *adj* **1**
able to see clearly the future effects of
present actions 有遠見的 **2** the usual American word for〖美式〗= LONGSIGHTED –
farsightedness *n* [U]

far·ther /ˈfɑrðɚ; ˈfɑːðə/ *adv, adj* the COM-
PARATIVE form of FAR〔FAR 的比較級形
式〕較遠更[的]: *We walked a mile farther
down the road.* 我沿着那條路又走了一英里。

■ USAGE 用法: You can use either
farther or **further** to talk about places
and distances ☆ **farther** 或 **further** 都
可用於談論地點和距離: *further/farther
down the road* 沿着路繼續往前。But
when the meaning is "more" or "extra" use **further** ☆但如表達的意思是
"更多的"或"另外的"，就要用 **further**:
*For further information write to the
above address.* 欲知詳情，請按上述地址
致函詢問。

far·thest /ˈfɑrðɪst; ˈfɑːðɪst/ *adv, adj* the SU-
PERLATIVE form of FAR〔FAR 的最高級形
式〕最遠更[的]: *We wanted to find out who
could swim the farthest.* 我們想了解誰游得最
遠。

far·thing /'fɑːðɪŋ; 'fɑːðɪŋ/ *n* an old British coin of little value 法尋〔英國舊時面值很小的硬幣〕

fas·ci·nate /'fæsᵊnet; 'fæsᵊneɪt/ *v* **fascinated, fascinating** [T] to be extremely interesting or attractive to someone 使〔某人〕極感興趣; 強烈地吸引; 迷住: *Other people's beliefs fascinate me.* 我對別人的信仰特感興趣。 | *I've always been fascinated by astrology.* 我老是被占星術所迷住。–**fascinating** *adj*: *I find his latest theory fascinating.* 我發現他的最新理論很有吸引力。–**fascination** /ˌfæsᵊn'eɪʃən; ˌfæsᵊ-'neɪʃn/ [U]: *Old castles have a certain strange fascination for me.* 古城堡對我具有某種奇特的魅力。

fas·cis·m /'fæʃˌɪzəm; 'fæʃɪzəm/ *n* (also 又作 **Fascism**) [U] an extreme political system which supports nationalism and very strong central government control 法西斯主義

fas·cist /'fæʃɪst; 'fæʃɪst/ *n* **1** (also 又作 **Fascist**) a supporter of fascism 法西斯主義者: *the Fascist Party* 法西斯黨 **2** *infml* a person who acts in a cruel, hard way which allows no opposition 〔非正式〕法西斯分子〔指做事心狠手毒, 不許對方反抗的人〕– **fascist** *adj*

✻**fash·ion¹** /'fæʃən; 'fæʃən/ *n* **1** [C] a way of dressing or behaving that is usual or popular at a certain time 〔服飾的〕流行款式; 〔舉止的〕時尚; 風尚: *Narrow trousers are the latest fashion.* 緊身褲是最新的時裝。 | *It's not the fashion to send children away to school now.* 如今把孩子送到別處去上學已不時髦了。 **2 in fashion** popular now 流行; 入時 **3 out of fashion** no longer popular 不再流行; 過時 **4** [U] changing custom, especially in women's clothing 時尚〔尤指婦女的服飾〕: *the history of fashion* 時裝的發展史 **5** [sing] *fml* a certain way of behaving or doing something 〔正式〕方式; 樣子: *He behaved in a very strange fashion all evening.* 整個晚上他的舉止言行都非常奇怪。 | *She wore her hair schoolgirl-fashion.* 她留着(中、小學)女生樣式的頭髮。**6 after a fashion** not very well 勉強; 不很好: *Well, yes, I do speak Russian, after a fashion.* 噢, 是的, 我會説俄語, 但不太好。

fashion² *v* [T] *fml* to shape or make something, usually with your hands 〔正式〕用手工使〔某物〕成形; 製成〔某物〕: *He fashioned the clay into an elegant pot.* 他把黏土做成了一把精美的壺。

fash·ion·a·ble /'fæʃənəbl; 'fæʃənəbəl/ *adj* usual or popular at a particular time 流行的; 時髦的: *a fashionable dress* 時髦的連衣裙 | *a fashionable restaurant* 時髦人士光顧的餐館 | *Those ideas were fashionable in the '60s.* 那些思想在六十年代很時髦。–opposite 反義 **unfashionable** –**fashionably** *adv*: *fashionably dressed* 衣着時髦的

✻**fast¹** /fæst; fɑːst/ *adj* **1** moving, happening,

or acting quickly 快的; 迅速的; 敏捷的: *a fast car* 跑得很快的汽車 | *fast music* 節奏快的音樂 | *a fast journey* 匆匆之行 **2** firmly fixed 牢固的; 堅固的: *Are the colours in this shirt fast?* 這件襯衫的顏色會褪掉嗎? | *Make the boat fast with that rope.* 用那根繩子把船繫牢。**3** [never before a noun 不能用於名詞前] showing a time that is later than the true time (used of a clock or watch) 偏快的〔指鐘、錶〕: *My watch is fast.* 我的錶快了。 | *The clock's five minutes fast.* 鐘快了五分鐘。

✻**fast²** *adv* **1** quickly 快地; 迅速地: *You're learning very fast.* 你學得很快。 | *He ran faster and faster.* 他越跑越快。**2** firmly 緊緊地; 牢固地: *It's stuck fast in the mud.* 它陷在泥裡動彈不得。 | *Hold fast to that branch!* 緊緊握住那根樹枝! **3 fast asleep** sleeping deeply 酣睡

fast³ *v* [I] to eat no food for a period, especially for religious or health reasons 禁食〔尤指因宗教或健康原因〕; 齋戒: *Muslims fast during Ramadan.* 回教徒在齋月裡齋戒。

fast⁴ *n* an act or period of eating no food 禁食期; 齋戒期: *He broke his fast by drinking a little milk.* 他以喝少量牛奶開齋。

fas·ten /'fæsn; 'fɑːsn/ *v* **1** [I;T] to fix or close firmly 紮牢; 關緊; 繫牢; 扣住: *He fastened his coat.* 他把外衣扣緊。 | *The door fastens with a hook.* 這扇門是用鈎子拴緊的。 | *Can you fasten that board to the wall?* 你能把那塊板固定在牆上嗎? –opposite 反義 **unfasten 2 fasten on/upon something** to take something eagerly and use it 趕緊抓住並利用某物: *The President fastened on the idea at once.* 總統立即採納了這個意見。

fasten sthg ↔ **up** *phr v* [T] to close something 關緊; 拴住; 繫牢: *Fasten that suitcase up.* 把那只手提箱關緊。

fas·ten·er /'fæsnə; 'fɑːsnər/ *n* something that closes something or fixes things together 緊固物; 夾持器; 扣件: *a zip fastener* 拉鏈

fa·sten·ing /'fæsnɪŋ; 'fɑːsnɪŋ/ *n* something that holds things shut, especially doors and windows 扣件〔尤指門、窗的〕扣拴物

fast food /'· ·/ *n* [U] food that is prepared quickly and sold by restaurants to be eaten at once or taken away 快餐食品: *a fast food restaurant selling pizzas and hamburgers* 售賣意大利薄餅和漢堡包的快餐店

fas·tid·i·ous /fæs'tɪdɪəs; fæ'stɪdɪəs/ *adj* **1** worried about quality or cleanliness, and very difficult to satisfy (a word used to express disapproval) 對品質和衛生不放心的; 難以滿足的〔含貶義〕: *a fastidious eater* 吃東西挑剔的人 **2** careful and concerned with detail 仔細認真的: *He was extremely fastidious about all aspects of his work.* 他對自己工作的各方面都特別仔細認真。–**fastidiously** *adv*

fast·ness /'fæstnɪs; 'fɑːstnɪs/ *n* [U] the quality of being firm and fixed (used especially of colours in cloth) 牢固(性); 固定(性)〔尤指

布料的顏色〕

■ **USAGE** 用法: The noun **fastness** has nothing to do with the adjective **fast**, meaning "quick". If we need a noun we have to use **speed** or **quickness**. ☆名詞 **fastness** 與意為"快"的形容詞 **fast** 無關。**fast** 的名詞形式可以用 **speed** 或 **quickness**.

***fat¹** /fæt; fæt/ *adj* **1** having a lot of fat, and especially too much fat, on your body 多脂肪的;〔尤指身體〕肥胖的: *He's got very fat recently.* 他最近變得很胖。| *a fat baby* 胖乎乎的嬰兒 **2** large, wide, or thick 大的; 寬的; 厚的: *a fat salary* 優厚的薪水 | *fat books* 厚厚的書本 | *a fat cucumber* 粗大的黃瓜 **3 a fat lot of** *infml* not any at all〔非正式〕一點也不: *She's a fat lot of help.* 她一點幫助也沒有。–**fatness** *n* [U]

■ **USAGE** 用法: If you want to be polite about someone do not say that they are **fat**. **(Rather) overweight** is a more polite way of saying that you think someone is too big and heavy. **Plump** means "slightly fat" and is often used to show that you think this is quite pleasant. **Chubby** has a similar meaning and is most commonly used of children and babies. If someone is extremely fat and unhealthy they can be described as **obese**. ☆若想對人有禮貌, 就不應說人家 **fat**。用 **(rather) overweight** 表示某人個子太大、身體超重就比較有禮。**Plump** 意為"稍胖", 常用以指胖得很適宜。**Chubby** 的意思相似, 一般用以指兒童和嬰兒。若某人長得特別胖而呈病態, 則可用 **obese** 表示。

---

fat² *n* **1** [U] the substance under the skins of animals and human being which helps to keep them warm〔動植物的〕脂肪 **2** [C;U] an oily substance from animals or vegetables, which is used in cooking〔動植物的〕油: *animal fats* 動物油 | *potatoes fried in deep fat* 油炸馬鈴薯〔土豆〕

fa·tal /ˈfeɪtl; ˈfeɪtl/ *adj* **1** causing or resulting in death 致命的: *a disease which is usually fatal to cows* 常使母牛致死的疾病 | *a fatal accident* 致命的事故 **2** very important and unfortunate 重大的; 不幸的: *She made the fatal decision to marry Henry.* 她作出了嫁給亨利的重大決定。| *a fatal mistake* 不幸的錯誤 –**fatally** *adv: He was shot and fatally wounded.* 他被槍打中而受了重傷。

fa·tal·is·m /ˈfeɪtlˌɪzəm; ˈfeɪtlˌɪzəm/ *n* [U] the belief that events are decided by a power beyond human control 宿命論 –**fatalist** *n* – **fatalistic** /ˌfeɪtlˈɪstɪk; ˌfeɪtlˈɪstɪk/ *adj*

fa·tal·i·ty /fəˈtæləti; fəˈtæləti/ *n* **fatalities** *fml*〔正式〕**1** [C] a death as a result of violence or an accident〔暴力或事故造成的〕死亡: *It was a terrible crash, but there were surprisingly few fatalities.* 那是一宗嚴重的撞車事故, 但沒想到死亡的人很少。**2** [U] the belief that events are decided by a power beyond human control 宿命論

fate /feɪt; feɪt/ *n* **1** [U] (also 又作 **Fate**) a power beyond human control that is believed to decide events 命運; 天命; 運數: *Fate has brought us together.* 命運使我們相聚在一起。**2** [C] an end, especially death 結局〔尤指死亡〕: *They met with a terrible fate.* 他們的結局十分可怕。**3** [sing] what will happen to someone or something〔人或物的〕注定要發生的事; 未來: *I wonder whether the examiners have decided our fate yet.* 我不知道主考官是否已決定我們的命運。| *Now that oil is scarce, the fate of the motor car is uncertain.* 由於石油短缺, 汽車將來會怎樣就難以預料了。**4 a fate worse than death** *infml* a terrible experience〔非正式〕可怕的經歷; 活受罪: *Going out with him would be a fate worse than death!* 跟他一起出去真是活受罪!

fat·ed /ˈfeɪtɪd; ˈfeɪtɪd/ *adj* [never before a noun 不能用於名詞前] caused or decided by a power beyond human control 命中注定的: *It was fated that we should never reach Tokyo.* 我們注定到不了東京。| *We were fated to meet.* 我們注定要相遇。

fate·ful /ˈfeɪtfəl; ˈfeɪtfəl/ *adj* important for the future, especially because of its unpleasant effects 重大的〔尤因有其壞的影響〕: *the fateful decision to start his own company* 他要自己開公司的重大決定

****fa·ther¹** /ˈfɑːðə; ˈfɑːðər/ *n* **1** a male parent 父親: *That's my father.* 那是我父親。| *their adoptive father* 他們的養父 –see picture on page 503 見 503 頁彩圖 **2** *fml* a word used to talk to or about a male parent〔正式〕爸爸: *Father says we can go.* 爸爸說我們可以走了。**3** a man who is respected for having started something 創始人; 先驅: *the father of modern scientific thought* 近代科學思想之父 **4** (also 又作 **Father**) a priest, especially in the Roman Catholic church 神父〔尤指羅馬天主教的〕: *Father Brown* 布朗神父 | *Come in, father.* 請進, 神父。**5 Father** God, in the CHRISTIAN religion 上帝;〔基督教的〕聖父

father² *v* [T] to become a male parent (a formal word which is often used in a humorous way) 成為父親〔常含幽默的正式用詞〕: *his desire to father a child* 他想有個孩子的願望

Father Christ·mas /ˌ·· ˈ··/ *n* an old man dressed in red with a long white beard who, children believe, comes down the chimney to bring them presents at CHRISTMAS 聖誕老人

father fig·ure /ˈ·· ˌ··/ *n* an older man who you depend on for advice and help〔依靠其指點和幫助的〕長者; 父親般的人物

---

fa·ther·hood /ˈfaðəˌhud; ˈfɑːðəhʊd/ *n* [U] the state of being a father 父親的身分: *the pleasures and responsibilities of fatherhood* 做父親的責任和樂趣

father-in-law /ˈ·· ··/ *n* **father-in-law** the father of your wife or husband 岳父; 公公 – see picture on page 503 見 503 頁彩圖

fa·ther·less /ˈfaðəlɪs; ˈfɑːðəlɪs/ *adj* without a father who is alive or who you see regularly 父親不在世的; 沒有父親似的

fa·ther·ly /ˈfaðəlɪ; ˈfɑːðəli/ *adj* typical of a kind or concerned father 父親般的; 慈父般的: *Mr Smith was just trying to give you some fatherly advice.* 史密斯先生正想給你一些慈父般的忠告。

fath·om¹ /ˈfæðəm; ˈfæðəm/ *n* a measure of the depth of water; a fathom is equal to 6 feet or 1.8 metres 英噚〔測水深的量度單位, 一英噚等於 6 英尺或 1.8 米〕

fathom² *v* [T] (also 又作 **fathom** sbdy/sthg ↔ **out**) to understand the meaning of something or the reason for it 理解〔某事物〕; 找出〔某事物〕的原因: *I can't quite fathom your last remark.* 我聽不懂你最後那句話。| *Nobody could fathom out why he had been invited.* 無人能知道他被邀請的原因。

fa·tigue¹ /fəˈtiːg; fəˈtiːg/ *n* **1** [U] great tiredness 疲勞; 疲乏: *He was pale with fatigue.* 他累得臉色蒼白。 **2** [U] *tech* weakness in a substance such as metal which may cause it to break 〔術語〕〔金屬材料的〕疲勞 **3 fatigues** [pl] clothes worn by soldiers for certain duties 〔士兵做某些雜務時穿的〕工作服

fatigue² *v* **fatigued, fatiguing** [T] *fml* to make someone very tired 〔正式〕使〔某人〕非常疲勞: *a fatiguing job* 累人的工作

fat·ten /ˈfætn; ˈfætn/ *v* [T] (also 又作 **fatten** sbdy/sthg ↔ **up**) to make a person or animal fatter 使〔人〕變胖; 使〔動物〕變肥: *Those chickens are being fattened for market.* 那些雞正養得肥肥的以供應市場。| *We must fatten you up a bit, now that you're feeling better.* 既然你感到好多了, 我們就要把你養得胖一點。–**fattening** *adj*: *Stop eating fattening foods like chocolate and cakes.* 別吃那些諸如巧克力和蛋糕之類的會使人發胖的食品。

fat·ty /ˈfætɪ; ˈfæti/ *adj* **fattier, fattiest** containing or consisting of a lot of fat (used especially of food) 含脂肪多的; 脂肪多的〔尤指食物〕 –**fattiness** *n* [U]

fat·u·ous /ˈfætʃuəs; ˈfætʃuəs/ *adj* without any sensible or intelligent meaning or purpose 愚昧的; 蠢的: *What a fatuous remark!* 多麼愚蠢的話呀! –**fatuously** *adv*

fau·cet /ˈfɔsɪt; ˈfɔːsɪt/ *n* the usual American word for 〔美式〕 = a TAP¹ (1)

★fault¹ /fɔlt; fɔːlt/ *n* **1** [C] a problem with something which stops it working properly 毛病; 故障: *a small electrical fault in the motor* 馬達中電路上的小故障 **2** [C] a weak-ness in someone 〔人的〕缺點; 弱點: *His only fault is that he has no sense of humour.* 他的唯一弱點是缺乏幽默感。 **3** [sing] responsibility for a bad situation 〔對壞事的〕責任; 過錯; 過失: *"It's not our fault that we're late."* *"Whose fault is it, then?"* "這次遲到不是我們的過錯。" "那麼又是誰的錯呢?" –see 另見 BLAME² (USAGE用法) **4 at fault** wrong or mistaken 有錯; 有責任: *I admit that I was at fault.* 我承認我有過錯。 **5** [C] *tech* a crack in the Earth's surface 〔術語〕〔地球表層的〕斷層: *the San Andreas fault* 聖安德里亞斯斷層 **6** [C] a SERVICE¹ in tennis which is not allowed by the rules 〔網球的〕發球失誤: *a double fault* 兩次發球失誤 **7 find fault** to complain about something, especially too much 抱怨; 找碴兒: *She's always finding fault with the way I dress.* 她對我的穿着打扮老是要挑剔。 **8 to a fault** to an extreme degree 過分地; 過度地: *She's generous to a fault.* 她過於慷慨。

fault² *v* [T usually used in negatives and questions 常用於否定句和疑問句] to find things that are wrong with someone or something 找〔某人或某物的〕錯; 挑毛病: *We couldn't fault her performance.* 她的演出我們無懈可擊。

fault·less /ˈfɔltlɪs; ˈfɔːltləs/ *adj* perfect 完美無缺的: *a faultless display of gymnastics* 完美無缺的體操表演 –**faultlessly** *adv*

fault·y /ˈfɔltɪ; ˈfɔːlti/ *adj* **1** not working properly 有故障的: *a faulty wire in the electrical system* 電路系統中有一根線出現故障 **2** not correct 有錯誤的: *faulty reasoning* 錯誤的推論

fau·na /ˈfɔnə; ˈfɔːnə/ *n* [U] *tech* animals, especially all those living in a particular place at a particular time 〔術語〕〔某一時期某一地區的〕所有動物: *the fauna of the Brazilian rainforests* 巴西雨林的動物羣 | *interesting flora and fauna* 令人感興趣的植物羣和動物羣

faux pas /ˌfəʊ ˈpɑ; ˌfəʊ ˈpɑː/ *n* **faux pas** /ˌfəʊ ˈpɑz; ˌfəʊ ˈpɑːz/ something you do or say which, unknown to you, is not socially acceptable 有失檢點的行為或語言

★fa·vour¹ /ˈfeivə; ˈfeivər/ *n* (**favor** AmE 〔美式〕) **1** [C] something you do from kindness, and not becuase you have to 恩惠; 善行: *As a special favour, I'll let you boys stay up late tonight.* 作為特殊恩惠, 我答應你們男孩子今晚遲睡。| *Can I ask a favour of you? Will you lend me your car?* 請你幫個忙行嗎? 把你的汽車借我用一下, 可以嗎? **2 do someone a favour** to help someone by doing something they ask you to do 幫某人忙; 勞某人的駕: *Can you do me a favour and look after the children for an hour?* 勞你的駕, 這些孩子請你照料一個小時, 行嗎? **3** [U] active approval 贊同; 讚許: *How do you think I can win her favour?* 你認為我怎樣才能博得他的嘉許? | *He has never looked on any of* *my ideas with favour.* 他從來就沒有支持過我的看法。**4 in favour** *fml* popular 〖正式〗受歡迎的: *His political ideas seem to come very much in favour at the moment.* 他的政治觀點現在似乎深受歡迎。[RELATED PHRASE 相關詞組 **out of favour**] **5 in favour of something: a** in support of something 支持某事物: *Are you in favour of making divorce more difficult?* 你是否支持使離婚變得更困難？ **b** in order to do something else 為做別的事而…, 寧願選擇: *He refused a job in industry in favour of a university appointment.* 他為了一份大學的教職而拒絕從事工業界的工作。**6** [U] unfairly kind treatment of one person, to the disadvantage of others 偏愛; 偏袒: *I try not to show favour to my own child above the others in the class.* 我盡量在班裡其他同學面前不偏祖自己的孩子。**7 in someone's favour: a** to a person's advantage 對某人有利: *At least the bank's mistakes are always in our favour!* 至少, 銀行的差錯總會對我們有利。**b** deciding that someone is right 判決某人是對的〖無罪〗: *The tribunal decided in his favour.* 法庭判他無罪。

*favour² *v* (**favor** *AmE* 〖美式〗) [T] **1** to like something more than the other possibilities 贊同〖某事物〗: *The president is believed to favour further tax cuts.* 人們認為總統會贊同進一步減稅。**2** to treat someone with unfair kindness, to the disadvantage of other people 偏愛〖某人〗; 偏袒: *It's clear she favours Jack more than her other children.* 顯然, 她對傑克的偏愛超過她對另外幾個孩子。**3** to give someone an advantage 有利於〖某人〗: *The position of the sun favoured the visiting team.* 太陽的位置對客隊有利。**4 favour someone with something** *fml* to give someone something that you think they will like 〖正式〗向某人惠贈〖惠賜〗某物: *She favoured him with a charming smile.* 她對他賜以迷人的一笑。

fa·vou·ra·ble /ˈfeɪvərəbl; ˈfeɪvərəbəl/ *adj fml* 〖正式〗(**favorable** *AmE* 〖美式〗) **1** pleasing 令人高興的: *Try and make a favourable impression on my mother.* 要盡量給我母親留下良好的印象。**2** approving 稱讚的; 贊同的: *I hear favourable accounts of your work.* 我聽到一些對你的工作的好評。**3** helpful or useful 有幫助的; 有用的: *The company will lend you money on very favourable terms.* 公司將以非常優惠的條件貸款給你。–opposite 反義 **unfavourable** –**favourably** *adv*

*fa·vou·rite¹ /ˈfeɪvərɪt; ˈfeɪvərɪt/ *n* (**favorite** *AmE* 〖美式〗) **1** a person or thing that you like more than any other one of its kind 最受喜愛的人或物: *This book is one of my favourites.* 這是我最喜愛的一本書。**2** someone who receives more attention and approval than is right and fair 受寵的人: *Teachers should not have favourites.* 教師不應該有受寵的學生。**3** the competitor in

each race that is expected to win 〖比賽中〗最有希望獲勝的競爭者: *The favourite came in second.* 最有希望獲勝的結果得了第二名。

favourite² *adj* (**favorite** *AmE* 〖美式〗) liked more than all other ones of its kind 最喜愛的: *What's your favourite television programme?* 你最喜歡看的電視節目是甚麼？

fa·vou·ri·tis·m /ˈfeɪvərɪˌɪzəm; ˈfeɪvərɪˌtɪzəm/ *n* (**favoritism** *AmE* 〖美式〗) [U] the giving of unfair approval or advantage to one person or group of people out of many 偏愛; 偏袒

fawn¹ /fɔn; fɔːn/ *n* **1** [C] a young deer 幼鹿 **2** [U] a light yellowish-brown colour 淺黃褐色

fawn² *v* **fawn on someone** to try very hard to win someone's approval by paying them a lot of attention and praising them a lot, without being sincere 奉承; 討好; 巴結: *They were fawning on their rich uncle.* 他們在巴結那個有錢的叔叔。

fax /fæks; fæks/ *v* [T] to send copies of writing or pictures along a telephone line using special machines 用傳真機〖透過電話線路〗傳送〖圖文〗: *Could you fax the information to me?* 你能把資料用傳真機傳送給我嗎？ | *I'll fax you a copy of the letter.* 我會把信傳真一份給你。

□ USEFUL PATTERNS 有用句型
to fax something to someone; to fax someone something

–**fax** *n*: *I'll send a fax.* 我會傳真給你的。–see picture on page 763 見 763 頁彩圖

FBI /ˌɛf biː ˈaɪ; ˌɛf biː ˈaɪ/ *n* a US government department concerned with crime and the protection of national secrets; an abbreviation for **Federal Bureau of Investigation** 〖縮〗〖美國的〗聯邦調查局: *an FBI agent* 聯邦調查局的調查員

****fear¹** /fɪr; fɪəʳ/ *n* **1** [C;U] the feeling that you have when danger is near or something unpleasant is likely to happen 害怕; 恐懼; 擔心: *She has a great fear of fire.* 她非常怕火。 | *The government's fear that the unemployment figures would rise again was today proved correct.* 政府擔心失業人數可能再次上升, 今天已得到證實。 | *We live in fear of an enemy attack.* 我們的日子過得提心吊膽, 生怕敵人進攻。**2** [U] the possibility that something will happen, usually something undesirable 可能性〖常指不受歡迎的事物〗: *There's not much fear of snow at this time of year.* 每年的這個時候, 下雪的可能性就不大了。 | *Is there any fear of him arriving early?* 他會不會提前到達？ **3 for fear of** because of anxiety about 生怕; 以免: *I couldn't move for fear of falling.* 我不能動, 生怕掉下去。**4 no fear!** *infml* a phrase used in answer to a question or suggestion to say that you certainly will not do something

〔非正式〕當然不! 絕不!〔用於回答別人的問題或建議〕

★**fear²** v [not in progressive forms 不用於進行式] fml〔正式〕**1** [T; +(that)] to be afraid of something or someone 害怕、懼怕〔某事或某物〕: *They feared being attacked on the road.* 他們生怕在路上遭到襲擊。| *She has always feared old age.* 她總是害怕年老。| *Experts fear that there will be a new outbreak of the disease.* 專家們擔心這種疾病會再一次爆發。**2** **fear for** to be afraid for the safety of someone or something〔為某人或某物的安全〕擔憂: *She feared for the lost child.* 她為丟失的孩子而擔憂。**3** **I fear** fml a phrase used when the news you are telling someone is bad〔正式〕恐怕〔用於敍述壞消息〕: *"Is there enough money?" "I fear not."* "錢夠不夠?""恐怕不夠。"| *I fear we've missed our chance.* 恐怕我們已經錯過機會。

fear·ful /ˈfɪrfəl; ˈfɪəfəl/ adj fml〔正式〕**1** afraid 害怕的; 懼怕的: *He was fearful of her anger.* 他害怕他生氣。**2** terrible 可怕的; 嚇人的: *a fearful storm* 可怕的風暴 –**fearfully** adv

fear·less /ˈfɪrlɪs; ˈfɪələs/ adj unafraid 不怕的; 無畏的: *a fearless climber* 無畏的登山者 – **fearlessly** adv –**fearlessness** n [U]

fear·some /ˈfɪrsəm; ˈfɪəsəm/ adj fml frightening〔正式〕可怕的; 嚇人的: *a fearsome sight* 嚇人的景象

fea·si·ble /ˈfizəbl; ˈfiːzɪbəl/ adj possible to do 可行的; 可做的: *Your plan sounds quite feasible.* 你的計劃聽起來相當可行。–**feasibly** adv –**feasibility** /ˌfizəˈbɪlətɪ; ˌfiːzɪˈbɪlɪti/ n [U]: *We're doing a feasibility study of the scheme.* 我們正在對計劃進行可行性研究。

feast¹ /fist; fiːst/ n **1** an unusually large and often public meal for a special occasion 盛宴; 宴會: *The king held a feast.* 國王舉行了一次盛大的宴會。| *What a feast!* 多麼盛大的宴會! **2** a day when a particular religious event is remembered 宗教節日: *Christmas is an important feast for Christians.* 聖誕節是基督教徒的重大節日。

feast² v **1** [I] to eat a large, special meal 參加宴會 **2** **feast your eyes on something** to look at something for a long time because you like it 盡情欣賞某物; 飽眼福

feat /fit; fiːt/ n a clever action, showing strength, skill, or courage 武藝; 技藝: *It was quite a feat to move that piano by yourself.* 你真有能耐, 一個人就搬動了那架鋼琴。

fea·ther¹ /ˈfɛðɚ; ˈfeðə/ n one of the light, soft things which cover a bird's body 羽毛

feather² v **feather your nest** to make yourself rich, especially dishonestly 使自己變得富有〔尤指以不誠實的手段致富〕; 中飽私囊

★★★**fea·ture¹** /ˈfitʃɚ; ˈfiːtʃə/ n **1** a typical part of something, or a quality that something has 特點; 特徵; 特色: *Wet weather is a feature of life in Scotland.* 陰雨天氣是蘇格蘭生活的一個特色。| *The car has a lot of new features.* 這輛汽車有許多新特點。**2** **features** [pl] a person's eyes, nose, and mouth 面貌; 容貌 **3** a special long newspaper article or a special treatment of a subject on radio or television〔報紙的〕特寫;〔廣播或電視的〕專題節目: *a feature on personal computers* 關於個人電腦的特寫 **4** (also 又作 **feature film**) a full-length cinema film which tells a story〔電影的〕正片; 故事片

feature² v **featured, featuring 1** [T] to include someone special as a performer 由〔某人〕主演: *a new film featuring Jack Nicholson* 由傑克·尼科爾森主演的新片 **2** **feature in something** to be present as an important part of something 在某事物中起重要作用: *Art doesn't feature at all in their lives.* 藝術在他們生活中不起任何作用。**3** [T] to advertise something more than usual 為〔某物〕大做廣告〔宣傳〕: *We're featuring bedroom furniture this month.* 我們這個月月在為臥室家具大做廣告。

Feb·ru·a·ry /ˈfɛbru˛ɛrɪ; ˈfebruəri/ n (also 又作 **Feb.**) the 2nd month of the year 二月

feces /ˈfisiz; ˈfiːsiːz/ n see 見 FAECES

feck·less /ˈfɛklɪs; ˈfekləs/ adj unable to plan and manage your life properly 無能的; 無效率的

fed /fɛd; fed/ the past tense and past participle of FEED ☆ FEED 的過去式和過去分詞

★**fed·e·ral** /ˈfɛdərəl; ˈfedərəl/ adj [only before a noun 只用於名詞前] **1** formed of states which decide their own affairs, but are controlled by a central government 聯邦〔制〕的: *Switzerland is a federal republic.* 瑞士是一個聯邦制的共和國。**2** relating to the central government of a country as opposed to the states that form it 聯邦政府的〔與組成聯邦的各州相對〕: *Americans pay both federal taxes and state taxes.* 美國人既付聯邦稅又付州稅。

fed·e·ra·tion /ˌfɛdəˈreʃən; ˌfedəˈreɪʃən/ n **1** a group of states which each decide their own affairs, but are controlled by a central government 聯邦 **2** a group of societies or organizations that have come together to form a larger organization 聯合會: *the Federation of British Industry* 英國工業聯合會

fed up /ˌ· ˈ·/ adj [never before a noun 不能用於名詞前] infml unhappy, tired, and uninterested〔非正式〕不愉快的; 厭煩的; 無興趣的: *I'm really fed up with my job!* 我對自己這份工作真的是厭倦了!

★**fee** /fi; fiː/ n a sum of money that you pay for professional services, for example to a doctor, lawyer, or private school〔付給醫生、律師等的〕服務費;〔私立學校的〕學費 –see 見 PAY² (USAGE用法)

fee·ble /ˈfibl; ˈfiːbəl/ adj extremely weak 虛弱的; 無力的: *He became very feeble after the operation.* 手術後他變得非常虛弱。| *a feeble joke* 不高明的笑話 –**feebly** adv –**feebleness** n [U]

☆**feed¹** /fid; fiːd/ *v* **fed** /fɛd; fed/, **fed 1** [T] to give food to someone 給〔人或動物〕食物; 餵（養）; 飼（養）: *He doesn't even earn enough to feed his family.* 他賺的錢甚至不足以養家餬口。 | *Have you fed the dog?* 你餵過狗沒有? **2** [I] (of animals and babies) to eat 〔動物和嬰兒〕吃: *Birds feed on seeds and berries.* 鳥吃種子和漿果。 **3** [T + adv/prep] to put something slowly and continuously into something esle 把〔一樣東西〕緩慢地、不斷地供給或輸入〔另一樣東西〕: *The information is fed into the computer.* 資料被輸入電腦。 | *Keep feeding the wire through the hole.* 不停地往洞裡插電線。 **4** [T] to make something grow bigger or stronger 使〔某物〕變大〔增強〕: *This kind of book only serves to feed people's prejudices.* 這種書只能有助於加重人們的偏見。 | *The lake is fed by several streams.* 這湖是由幾條溪流的水匯聚而成的。

feed² *n* **1** [C] a meal taken by an animal or baby 〔動物或嬰兒的〕一頓; 一餐 **2** [U] food for animals 飼料

feed·back /'fid,bæk; 'fiːdbæk/ *n* [U] **1** information about how good or how successful something is, which is given to the person who did or made the thing 反饋的信息: *The company welcomes feedback from customers.* 公司歡迎來自顧客的反饋意見。 **2** uncontrolled noise from an AMPLIFIER 〔擴音器的失控〕噪聲

☆**feel¹** /fil; fiːl/ *v* **felt** /fɛlt; felt/, **felt 1** [+complement; T] to experience a sensation 感到; 覺得: *I felt very happy.* 我感到很快活。 | *She felt ill.* 她覺得不舒服。 | *We were all feeling tired and hungry.* 我們都感到又累又餓。 | *How do you feel today?* 你今天感覺怎麼樣? | *She felt as if she was going to faint.* 她覺得自己好像要暈過去了。 | *He felt a sudden desire to laugh.* 他感到突然要笑出聲來。 | *I have never felt pain like that before.* 我覺得以前從來沒有這樣痛過。 **2** [+complement] to make you experience a sensation 使人感覺到: *It feels strange being back here after all these years.* 闊別多年之後回到這裡，一切都感到陌生。 | *I have often wondered what it would feel like to be rich and famous.* 我時常在琢磨，人出了名有了錢之後不知會有甚麼感受。 **3** [T] to touch something with your fingers in order to find out what it is like 摸; 觸〔某物〕: *He felt my arm to see if it was broken.* 他摸摸我的手臂，看看是否骨折。 **4** [T] to experience something touching you 感覺到; 感受到: *I felt something crawling up my leg.* 我覺得有東西順着我的腿往上爬。 | *I could feel the warm sun on my arms and legs.* 我可以感受到照在我手臂和腿上的太陽的溫暖。 **5** [+complement] to seem to have a particular quality which you experience by touching 〔摸上去〕給人某種手感: *Your feet feel cold.* 你的雙腳摸上去很冷。 | *The sheet feels wet.* 牀單摸上去很潮濕。 | *It looked and felt*

like glue. 它的外觀和手感都似膠水。 **6** [T; +complement] to believe something, or have it as an idea or opinion 以為; 認為: *I feel that something must be done to help these people.* 我認為有必要做些事情來幫助這些人。 | *I felt certain that something terrible was going to happen.* 我敢肯定可怕的事將要來臨。 | *You know how I feel about violence on television.* 你知道我對電視中出現的暴力所持的態度。 | *What do you feel about this idea?* 你認為這個主意怎麼樣? | *I felt that I had to talk to him.* 我覺得我得找他談一談。 | *I felt it necessary to apologize.* 我認為有必要道歉。 | *She felt tempted to shut the door in his face.* 她真想當着他的面砰地把門關上。 **7** **feel for something** to try to find something by searching with your fingers 〔用手〕尋找; 摸索: *She felt in her bag for a pencil.* 她在手提包裡摸着，想找一枝鉛筆。 **8** **feel for someone** to be sorry because someone is suffering 同情某人: *Poor child! I really feel for her!* 可憐的孩子! 我確實很同情她! **9** **feel like** to want to do or have something 想要〔某物、做某事〕: *Do you feel like a drink?* 你想喝杯飲料嗎? | *I don't feel like dancing today.* 我今天不想去跳舞。 **10** **feel your way** to move slowly and carefully because it is dark and you have to use your hands to find out where you are going 〔因天黑而用手〕摸索着走

feel² *n* [sing] **1** the sensation that you experience when you touch and feel something 觸覺; 手感: *The skin has a rough feel.* 皮膚摸上去很粗糙。 **2** **have a feel** to feel something 感受; 體驗: *Can I have a feel of it?* 可以讓我感受一下嗎? **3** **get the feel of something** to become used to something 習慣於〔某事〕: *The car seemed strange at first, but I soon got the feel of it.* 這輛汽車初用起來好像有點彆扭，但我馬上就習慣了。

feel·ers /'filəz; 'fiːləz/ *n* [pl] **1** the thread-like parts on the front of an insect's head, with which it touches things 〔昆蟲的〕觸鬚; 觸角 **2** **put out feelers** to make informal suggestions in order to find out what other people will think of them 試探別人的反應

☆**feel·ing** /'filɪŋ; 'fiːlɪŋ/ *n* **1** [C] a sensation that you experience, either in your body or in your mind 感覺; 感受: *The fever was accompanied by feelings of tiredness and nausea.* 那次發燒伴有疲乏和噁心的感覺。 | *feelings of shame* 恥辱的感覺 | *You shouldn't try to hide your feelings.* 你不應該隱藏你的感受。 **2** [C] a belief or opinion 想法; 看法: *I have a feeling we're being followed.* 我覺得有人在跟蹤我們。 | *My feeling is that we should go ahead and publish the book.* 我的看法是我們應該繼續做下去，把書出版。 **3** [U] the ability to notice physical sensations 知覺: *He lost all feeling in his legs.* 他的雙腿完全失去了知覺。 **4** [U] sympathy and understanding 〔同情、理解等〕感

受力; 感情: *She plays the piano with great feeling.* 她彈鋼琴很有感情。 **5 bad feelings** feelings of anger between people 反感; 不滿: *The new working hours caused a lot of bad feeling at the factory.* 新的工作時間在廠裡激起了許多人的不滿。 **6 hurt someone's feelings** to make someone feel upset 傷了某人的感情 **7 no hard feelings** no feelings of anger between people who have quarrelled 〔爭吵後〕不生氣; 不記仇: *He apologized, and there are no hard feelings.* 他作了道歉, 這樣雙方的氣就消了。

feet /fit/ the plural of FOOT ☆ FOOT 的複數形式

feign /fen; feɪn/ *v* [T] *lit* to pretend 〔文〕假裝; 佯作: *She feigned death.* 她裝死。

feint /fent; feɪnt/ *n fml* a false attack or blow made to deceive your opponent 〔正式〕佯攻; 虛擊

fe·line /ˈfilam; ˈfiːlaɪn/ *adj* like a cat, or relating to a cat or a member of the cat family 貓的; 貓科的

fell[1] /fɛl; fel/ the past tense of FALL[1] ☆ FALL[1] 的過去式

fell[2] *v* [T] **1** to cut down a tree 砍伐〔樹木〕 **2** *lit* to knock someone down 〔文〕擊倒; 打倒〔某人〕

fell[3] *n BrE* high, wild, rocky country 〔英式〕荒野丘陵地

fel·low[1] /ˈfɛlo; ˈfeləʊ/ *n* **1** *infml old fash* a man 〔非正式, 老式〕男人; 小伙子 **2** (also 又作 **Fellow**) a member of a society connected with a branch of learning or of some universities 〔學術團體的〕會員; 〔大學的〕研究員: *She's now a Fellow of the Royal Society.* 她現在是(英國)皇家學會會員。

*fellow[2] *adj* [only before a noun 只用於名詞前] **1** being in the same situation as you are 同伴的; 同類的: *You'll soon get to know your fellow students.* 你很快就會認識你的同學。 **2 fellow feeling** a feeling of sympathy and understanding for other people 同情; 相互了解

fel·low·ship /ˈfɛloʃɪp; ˈfeləʊʃɪp/ *n* **1** [C] a group of people who have come together because they have a shared interest 〔由志趣愛好相同的人組成的〕團體; 協會; 聯誼會 **2** [C] the job of a FELLOW[1] (2) at a university 〔大學中〕研究員的職位; 董事的職位 **3** [U] the condition of being friends through sharing or doing something together 夥伴關係; 交情; 友誼: *There was a strong feeling of fellowship among the team members.* 隊員之間有着深厚的友情。

fel·o·ny /ˈfɛləni; ˈfeləni/ *n* **felonies** *law* a serious crime such as murder 〔律〕重罪〔如謀殺〕

felt[1] /fɛlt; felt/ the past tense and past participle of FEEL ☆ FEEL 的過去式和過去分詞

felt[2] *n* [U] firm thick cloth made of wool or other material pressed flat 毛氈: *a felt hat* 氈帽

felt-tip /ˈ · ˌ ·/ *n* (also 又作 **felt-tip pen**) a coloured pen with a small piece of felt for a NIB 氈頭筆

*fe·male[1] /ˈfimel; ˈfiːmeɪl/ *n* **1** any animal of the sex that can give birth to young 雌性動物 **2** a woman (a word which is usually used by men to express disapproval, and which is considered offensive in this use) 女人〔男子常用該詞表示貶義, 用它被看作是無禮和冒犯〕

*female[2] *adj* **1** relating to or belonging to the sex that gives birth to young 母的; 雌性的: *a female elephant* 母象 **2** *tech* producing fruit (used of plants or parts of plants) 〔術語〕結果實的; 有雌蕊的〔指植物、樹枝〕 **3** concerning or relating to women 婦女的; 女性的: *We only employ female workers.* 我們只雇用女工。

■ USAGE 用法: **Female** and **male** are used to show what sex a creature is ☆ **Female** 和 **male** 用來表示生物的性別: *a female gorilla* 母猩猩 They are also used when talking about things which relate to one sex or the other ☆他們也可用來談論與男、女兩性有關的事物: *The male body is usually heavier than the female body.* 男的體重一般都超過女的。 **Feminine** and **masculine** are used to describe qualities that are supposed to be typical of one sex or the other ☆ **Feminine** 和 **masculine** 則是用來描述男女兩性的典型特質: *delicate feminine hands* 女子嬌嫩的手 | *She wears rather masculine clothes.* 她的衣着打扮富有男子氣。

---

fem·i·nine /ˈfɛmənɪn; ˈfemᵻnᵻn/ *adj* **1** having qualities that are considered typical of women 女性的; 女子氣的; 女性化的: *She always wears very feminine clothes.* 她總是穿典型的女子服裝。– see 見 FEMALE (USAGE 用法) **2** *tech* relating to a certain class of words in some languages 〔術語〕〔某些語言〕陰性的

fem·i·nin·i·ty /ˌfɛməˈnɪnəti; ˌfemᵻˈnɪnᵻti/ *n* [U] the quality of being feminine 女子的氣質

fem·i·nis·m /ˈfɛmənɪzəm; ˈfemᵻnɪzəm/ *n* [U] the belief that women should have the same rights and chances as men 女權主義; 男女平等主義 **–feminist** *n, adj*

fe·mur /ˈfimə; ˈfiːməʳ/ *n tech* the long bone in the upper part of your leg 〔術語〕股骨

fen /fɛn; fen/ *n* an area of low, wet land, especially in the east of England 〔尤指英格蘭東部的〕沼澤地帶

fence[1] /fɛns; fens/ *n* **1** something upright like a wall, but made of wood or wire, dividing two areas of land 柵欄; 籬笆; 圍欄 –see picture on page 729 見 729 頁彩圖 **2** *infml* someone who buys and sells stolen

---

F

goods 〔非正式〕買賣贓物的人 **3 sit on the fence** to avoid taking sides in an argument (a phrase which is usually used to express disapproval) 抱騎牆態度; 保持中立〔常含貶義〕

fence² *v* **fenced, fencing 1** [I] to fight with a long thin pointed sword as a sport 擊劍 **2** [T] to put a fence round something 把〔某物〕用籬笆〔柵欄〕圍起

fence sthg ↔ **in** *phr v* [T] to keep something in a place by putting a fence round it 用籬笆〔柵欄〕圍起〔某物〕

fence sthg ↔ **off** *phr v* [T] to separate an area by putting a fence round it 用籬笆〔柵欄〕將〔某處〕隔開: *We've fenced off part of the garden.* 我們已把部分圍地用籬笆隔開了。

fenc·ing /'fɛnsɪŋ; 'fɛnsɪŋ/ *n* [U] **1** the sport of fencing 擊劍運動 **2** material for making fences 築籬笆〔柵欄〕的材料

fend /fɛnd; fɛnd/ *v* **fend for yourself** to look after yourself 照料自己; 獨立生活: *I've had to fend for myself since I was 14.* 我從十四歲起就自己謀生了。

fend sbdy/sthg ↔ **off** *phr v* [T] **1** to defend yourself against attack 擋開: *He struggled to fend her off.* 他掙扎着把她擋開了。 **2** to avoid a person or thing 避開: *He spent the meeting trying to fend off difficult questions.* 他在會上消磨時間, 想避開難題。

fend·er /'fɛndə; 'fɛndəʳ/ *n* **1** a low metal wall round an open fireplace, to stop the coal from falling out 火爐的圍欄 **2** *AmE* the WING of a car 〔美式〕〔汽車輪胎的〕擋泥板

fer·ment¹ /fə'mɛnt; fə'ment/ *v* [I;T] to change chemically by the action of a living substance such as YEAST (使)發酵: *The wine is beginning to ferment.* 酒開始發酵了。 **–fermentation** /,fɜ:mɛn'teʃən; ,fɜ:men'teʃən/ *n* [U]

fer·ment² /'fɜ:mɛnt; 'fɜ:ment/ *n* [U] political trouble and excitement caused by change 騷動; 動亂: *Eastern Europe was in ferment.* 東歐處於動蕩之中。

fern /fɜn; fɜ:n/ *n* a green plant with leaves shaped like feathers, and no flowers 蕨; 蕨類植物

fe·ro·cious /fə'rəʃəs; fə'rəʊʃəs/ *adj* fierce and violent 殘忍的; 兇猛的; 兇惡的: *a ferocious animal* 兇猛的動物 | *ferocious punishments* 殘酷的懲罰 **–ferociously** *adv* **–ferocity** /fə'rɑsəti; fə'rɒsɪti/ *n* (also 又作 **ferociousness** /fə'rəʃəsnəs; fə'rəʊʃəsnəs/) [U]

ferret /'fɛrɪt; 'ferɪt/ *v*

ferret sthg ↔ **out** *phr v infml* [T] to discover information by searching for it carefully〔通過仔細搜查〕發現情報: *She managed to ferret out the truth.* 她設法查明了真相。

fer·ry¹ /'fɛri; 'feri/ *n* **ferries** (also 又作 **ferry-boat** /'fɛri,bot; 'feribəʊt/) **1** a boat that carries people and things across a narrow stretch of water 渡船: *cross-Channel ferries* 跨越英吉利海峽的渡船 **2 by ferry** travelling

in a ferry 乘渡船: *You can cross the river by ferry.* 你可以乘渡船過河。

ferry² *v* **ferried, ferrying** [T+adv/prep] to carry people or goods from one place to another, usually regularly 〔定期地〕運送〔人或貨物〕: *I spend the day ferrying the children to and from their various activities.* 我整天都花在接送孩子們參加各項活動上了。

fer·tile /'fɜ:tl; 'fɜ:taɪl/ *adj* **1** able to produce or grow many fruits or seeds 能結果實的; 肥沃的; 富饒的: *The agricultural land is very fertile round here.* 這一帶的農田非常肥沃。 **2** able to have babies or young 能生育的; 可繁殖的 **3 fertile imagination** a mind that can easily imagine things, or think of new and original ideas 豐富的想象力 **–opposite** 反義 **infertile –fertility** /fɜ'tɪləti; fɜ:'tɪlɪti/ *n* [U]

fer·ti·lize /'fɜ:tl,aɪz; 'fɜ:tl̩laɪz/ *v* **fertilized, fertilizing** (also 又作 **fertilise** *BrE* 〔英式〕) [T] **1** to start the development of young in a female creature or plant; in animals, the male's SPERM fertilizes the female's egg 使〔雌性的動植物〕受精〔受胎〕 **2** to put fertilizer on land 施肥於〔土地〕 **–fertilization** /,fɜ:tl ə'zeʃən; ,fɜ:tl̩laɪ'zeɪʃən/ *n* [U]

fer·ti·liz·er /'fɜ:tl,aɪzə; 'fɜ:tl̩laɪzəʳ/ *n* [C;U] a chemical or natural substance that you put on the land to make crops grow better 肥料; 化肥

fer·vent /'fɜ:vənt; 'fɜ:vənt/ *adj* feeling or showing strong and sincere feelings 熱情的; 熱誠的; 強烈的: *a fervent desire to win* 強烈的求勝慾望 | *He's a fervent believer in free speech.* 他是強烈主張言論自由的人。 **–fervently** *adv*

fer·vour /'fɜ:və; 'fɜ:vəʳ/ *n* (**fervor** *AmE* 〔美式〕) [U] strong and sincere feeling 熱烈; 熱誠; 熱情

fes·ter /'fɛstə; 'festəʳ/ *v* [I] **1** (of a wound) to become infected 〔傷口〕感染; 化膿 **2** to become increasingly unpleasant 逐漸惡化: *Don't let these feelings of resentment fester!* 別讓這些怨恨情緒繼續加重!

*****fes·ti·val** /'fɛstəvl; 'festɪvəl/ *n* **1** an occasion when people come together to enjoy themselves, especially to mark a special religious event 節日; 喜慶日〔尤指宗教的〕: *Christmas is one of the festivals of the Christian church.* 聖誕節是基督教的一個節日。 **2** an event consisting of many artistic, musical, or theatrical performances 〔藝術、音樂或戲劇的〕會演期; the *Edinburgh Festival* 愛丁堡藝術節 | *the Cannes Film Festival* 康城電影節

fes·tive /'fɛstɪv; 'festɪv/ *adj* full of happiness because people have come together to enjoy themselves 歡樂的; 節日似的: *We were all in a festive mood.* 我們都沉浸在歡樂的氣氛之中。

fes·tiv·i·ty /fɛ'stɪvəti; fe'stɪvɪti/ *n* **festivities 1 festivities** [pl] a happy event when people come together to enjoy themselves 慶典; 慶祝活動: *the wedding festivities* 結婚慶典 **2** [U] happiness because people have come together to enjoy themselves 歡樂; 歡慶: *There was a feeling of festivity in the town.* 城裡一片歡樂氣氛。

fes·toon /fɛsˈtuːn; feˈstuːn/ *v fml* festooned with decorated with attractive things〔正式〕給…飾花彩

fe·tal /ˈfiːtl; ˈfiːtl/ *adj* see 見 FOETAL

fetch /fɛtʃ; fɛtʃ/ *v* [T] **1** to go and get a person or thing and bring them back 接來〔某人〕; 取來〔某物〕: *Run and fetch the doctor!* 跑去把醫生請來! | *Quick! Fetch me a cloth!* 快! 去給我拿塊布來!

> □ USEFUL PATTERNS 有用句型
> to fetch something; to fetch something for someone; to fetch someone something

2 *infml* to be sold for a particular amount 〔非正式〕賣得〔某價錢〕: *The house should fetch at least £80,000.* 這房子至少能賣八萬英鎊。

fetch·ing /ˈfɛtʃɪŋ; ˈfɛtʃɪŋ/ *adj* attractive 迷人的; 吸引人的: *That's a very fetching blouse.* 那件女裝襯衫十分迷人

fete¹ /fet; fet/ *n* an outdoor event with games, competitions, and things for sale, to collect money for a special purpose〔室外舉行的〕園遊會; 義賣會

fete² *v* **feted, feting** *fml* [T] to welcome someone and do honour to them with public parties and ceremonies〔正式〕盛宴招待; 隆重歡迎: *The Queen was feted everywhere she went.* 女王不論走到哪裡都受到盛情款待。

fet·id /ˈfɛtɪd; ˈfiːtɪd/ *adj* smelling very unpleasant 惡臭的: *fetid air* 臭氣

fet·ish /ˈfiːtɪʃ; ˈfɛtɪʃ/ *n* **1** an object that is worshipped and thought to have magic power〔被認為賦有神力而加以崇拜的〕物神 **2** something to which a person pays an unreasonable amount of attention 盲目崇拜物; 迷戀物 –**fetishism** *n* [U]

fet·ter /ˈfɛtə; ˈfɛtər/ *v* [T] *fml*〔正式〕**1** to tie someone up with chains around their ankles 給〔某人〕戴上腳鐐 **2** to prevent someone from behaving freely 束縛〔某人〕

fet·ters /ˈfɛtəz; ˈfɛtəz/ *n* [pl] **1** chains fixed around a prisoner's ankles 腳鐐 **2** things that prevent you from behaving freely 桎梏; 束縛

fet·tle /ˈfɛtl; ˈfɛtl/ *n* in fine fettle *infml* in good health〔非正式〕身體健壯

fe·tus /ˈfiːtəs; ˈfiːtəs/ *n* see 見 FOETUS

feud /fjuːd; fjuːd/ *n* a strong and long-lasting quarrel between two people or groups of people〔兩人或兩個家族之間的〕世仇; 長期不和: *The two families were engaged in a bitter feud.* 那兩個家族進行的是一場沒完沒了的爭鬥。

feud·al /ˈfjuːdl; ˈfjuːdl/ *adj* relating to the system common in the past by which people held land and received protection from land owners in return for doing work for them 封建的; 封建制度的 –**feudalism** *n* [U]

fe·ver /ˈfiːvə; ˈfiːvər/ *n* **1** [C;U] an illness in which you develop a very high temperature 發燒; 發熱: *Has she got a fever?* 她有沒有發燒? | *a yellow fever epidemic* 黃熱流行病 **2** [sing] a very excited state 激動不安; 高度興奮: *She was in a fever of impatience.* 她極不耐煩。

fe·ver·ish /ˈfiːvərɪʃ; ˈfiːvərɪʃ/ *adj* **1** suffering from a very high temperature 發燒的; 發熱的: *She looked hot and feverish.* 她看上去在發高燒。 **2** extremely active or excited 極度興奮的; 狂熱的 –**feverishly** *adv: They were working feverishly.* 他們在狂熱地工作。

★★few /fjuː; fjuː/ *det, pron, n* [used with a plural verb 與動詞複數形式連用] **1** not very many 很少; 不多: *She has very few friends.* 她沒有幾個朋友。 | *The few people who came were all members of the family.* 到場的那幾個人都是家庭成員。 | *The pilots are all highly trained, and they make few mistakes.* 飛行員都經過高水準的訓練, 他們很少出現失誤。 **2** a small number 少數; 幾個: *Let's stay a few days longer.* 讓我們再多留幾天吧。 | *I need to buy a few things.* 我需要去買幾樣東西。 | *Why not invite a few of your friends?* 為甚麼不邀請你的幾位朋友來? | *We printed 200 leaflets, but there are only a few left now.* 我們印了二百張傳單, 但現在只剩下幾張而已。 **3** few and far between not happening or found very often 不常發生的; 稀少的: *Our holidays are few and far between.* 我們的假期很少。 **4** quite a few, a good few quite a lot 相當多; 不少: *Quite a few people came out to watch.* 有不少人出來觀望。 | *Quite a few of us were beginning to get worried.* 我們中間有不少人開始擔憂了。

fez /fɛz; fɛz/ *n* fezzes a kind of round red hat with a flat top, worn by some Muslim men〔回教男子戴的〕平頂無邊圓筒帽

fi·an·cé /ˌfiɑ̃nˈseɪ; fiˈɒnseɪ/ *n* a man to whom a woman is ENGAGED to be married; a woman who is ENGAGED to a man is called his **fiancée** 未婚夫〔**fiancée** 為未婚妻〕: *This is my fiancé, George.* 這位是我的未婚夫, 喬治。

fi·as·co /fiˈæskəʊ; fiˈæskəʊ/ *n* fiascos (also 又作 **fiascoes** *AmE*〔美式〕) an event which is a complete failure 徹底的失敗; 慘敗: *The meeting was a total fiasco.* 會議開得極不成功。

fib¹ /fɪb; fɪb/ *n infml* a small unimportant lie〔非正式〕小謊言: *Don't tell fibs!* 別撒謊!

fib² *v* **-bb-** [I] to tell fibs 撒小謊 –**fibber** *n: You fibber!* 你這個小騙子!

fi·bre /ˈfaɪbə; ˈfaɪbər/ *n* (**fiber** *AmE*〔美式〕) **1** [C] one of the thin thread-like parts that form many natural substances such as wool, wood, or muscle and some substances made by humans 〔天然或人造的〕纖維 **2** [C;U] a thread used for making things such as cloth or rope 〔用於製布或繩的〕纖維: *natural cotton fibre* 天然棉纖維 | *man-made fibres such as nylon* 像尼龍那樣的人造纖維 **3** [U] strength of character 品質; 氣質: *He lacks moral fibre.* 他缺乏道德品質。**4** [U] a part of plants that can be eaten but is passed through the body; fibre is supposed to be good for your health 〔對健康有益的〕纖維質: *Some breakfast cereals are high in fibre.* 有些早餐用的穀類食品中, 纖維素的含量很高。

fi·bre·glass /ˈfaɪbəˌglɑːs; ˈfaɪbəglæs/ *n* (**fiberglass** *AmE* 〔美式〕) [U] a material made from glass fibres and plastic, used for making things such as small boats 玻璃纖維

fi·brous /ˈfaɪbrəs; ˈfaɪbrəs/ *adj* like or made of fibres 纖維狀的; 纖維製成的

fick·le /ˈfɪkl; ˈfɪkəl/ *adj* changing your mind often about what you want or what you like 〔對所喜愛的東西〕易變的; 無常的 — **fickleness** *n* [U]

fic·tion /ˈfɪkʃən; ˈfɪkʃən/ *n* **1** [U] stories or books about imaginary things and events 小説: *a writer of popular fiction* 通俗小説作家 **2** [C;U] something that you pretend is true although it is not 虛構的事; 捏造的事: *The newspaper report was a complete fiction.* 那篇報導純屬捏造。

fic·tion·al /ˈfɪkʃənl; ˈfɪkʃənəl/ *adj* happening or told in a story 小説的; 虛構的: *a fictional account of a journey to the moon* 虛構的月球旅行記

fic·ti·tious /fɪkˈtɪʃəs; fɪkˈtɪʃəs/ *adj* **1** false or untrue 假的; 不真實的: *His account of what happened was completely fictitious.* 他對所發生事情的敍述全都是瞎編。**2** existing only in a story 虛構的: *The characters in this film are purely fictitious.* 電影中的人物純屬虛構。

fid·dle¹ /ˈfɪdl; ˈfɪdl/ *n infml* 〔非正式〕**1** a VIOLIN 小提琴 **2** a dishonest action in which someone gets money for themselves 欺詐; 欺騙行為; 騙局: *He was involved in an insurance fiddle.* 他與一宗保險金詐騙案有牽連。

fid·dle² *v* **fiddled, fiddling** *infml* 〔非正式〕**1 fiddle with something, fiddle about/around with something** to move something around or play with it with no particular purpose 〔無目的地〕撥弄; 胡亂擺弄: *Stop fiddling with your pencil and pay attention!* 別撥弄你的鉛筆了, 要集中精神! **2** [T] *BrE* to prepare something dishonestly for your own advantage 〔英式〕偽造; 竄改: *He had been fiddling his income tax for years.* 他多年來一直瞞報他的所得稅。

fid·dler /ˈfɪdlə; ˈfɪdlə/ *n infml* someone who plays the VIOLIN 〔非正式〕小提琴手

fid·dly /ˈfɪdlɪ; ˈfɪdli/ *adj infml* needing delicate movements of your fingers 〔非正式〕

需要手巧的: *a very fiddly job* 巧手才能做得了的事

fi·del·i·ty /faɪˈdeləti; fɪˈdeləti/ *n* [U] **1** *fml* faithfulness 〔正式〕忠實; 忠誠; 忠貞: *He spoke on the theme of fidelity in marriage.* 他講話的主題是婚姻的忠貞問題。 –opposite 反義 **infidelity** (2) **2** the exactness of something that has been copied or recorded 〔複製或錄製物的〕精確; 保真度

fid·get¹ /ˈfɪdʒɪt; ˈfɪdʒət/ *v* [I] to move your body around in a restless, impatient way 坐立不安; 煩躁: *Stop fidgeting, children, and listen!* 孩子們, 別坐立不安的, 要專心聽講! – **fidgety** *adj*

fidget² *n infml* a person who fidgets 〔非正式〕坐立不安的人

★**field¹** /fild; fiːld/ *n* **1** an enclosed area of land on a farm, used for animals or crops 田; 地; 牧場: *fields of corn* 玉米地 **2** an open area where sport is played 運動場: *a football field* 足球場 **3** an area where there are mines 礦區: *coal and oil fields* 煤田和油田 **4** a branch of knowledge or activity 〔學術或活動的〕領域; 範圍: *There have been exciting new developments in the field of cancer research.* 在癌症研究領域取得了一些令人振奮的新進展。 | *a man famous in his own field* 在自己專業領域有名氣的人 **5 the field: a** the place where battles take place in a war 戰場; 戰地 **b** *tech* all the horses in a race 〔術語〕〔賽馬中的〕全部馬匹 **6 in the field** in the place or conditions in which events really happen 在實地; 在現場: *We haven't yet tested the new equipment in the field.* 我們還沒有對這套新設備進行實地測試。**7** the area in which a certain force is felt 〔可感知某種力的〕場: *the moon's gravitational field* 月球的引力場 | *a magnetic field* 磁場 **8 field of vision** the area that you can see 視野: *I looked through the hole in the fence, but he was outside my field of vision.* 我透過籬笆上的孔往裡看, 但他不在我的視野裡。**9 have a field day** to enjoy yourself very much by doing something which you do not often get the chance to do 〔因做不常有機會做的事而〕過得特別痛快: *If the newspapers hear about this, they'll have a field day!* 報界若聞及此事會忙得不亦樂乎!

field² *v* [I;T] to try to catch or stop the ball in a game of cricket or BASEBALL, so that the other team does not get any points 〔板球和棒球〕接球; 截球 〔以阻止對方隊得分〕 – **fielder** *n*

field e·vent /ˈ· ·ˌ·/ *n* a sports event in ATHLETICS which does not take place on the running track; the high jump is one field event 田賽項目〔如跳高〕

field hock·ey /ˈ· ˌ·/ *n* the usual American expression for 〔美式〕= HOCKEY

field mar·shal /ˈ· ˌ·/ *n* (also 又作 **Field Marshal**) the officer of highest rank in the British army 〔英軍的〕陸軍元帥: *Field Mar-*

shal Montgomery 陸軍元帥蒙哥馬利

field trip /'· ·/ *n* a trip to a place in order to study something which is found or happens in that place 實地調查[考察]旅行

field·work /'fild,wɜk; 'fiːldwɜːk/ *n* [U] scientific or social study done in the place where things are found or happen naturally [科研或社會的]實地調查[考察]: *Most of the anthropologists I know have done fieldwork in West Africa.* 我所知道的考古學家大部分都在非洲西部作實地考察。

fiend /find; fiːnd/ *n* **1** a very cruel and wicked person 殘暴的人; 惡魔般的人 **2** *infml* a person who is very keen on a particular thing [非正式] 耽迷於某一事物的人: *a fresh air fiend* 注重於呼吸新鮮空氣的人

fiend·ish /'findɪʃ; 'fiːndɪʃ/ *adj* **1** fierce and cruel 兇猛的; 殘酷的: *a fiendish temper* 殘暴的脾氣 **2** *infml* very clever and full of imagination [非正式] 非常聰明的; 想像力豐富的: *a fiendish plan* 巧妙而又複雜的計劃 – **fiendishly** *adv*: *a fiendishly difficult question* 非常刁鑽的問題

fierce /firs; fiəs/ *adj* **1** angry, violent, and likely to attack 憤怒的; 兇猛的; 好鬥的: *a fierce guard dog* 兇猛的看家狗 | *He had a fierce look on his face.* 他臉上一副兇相。 **2** very great or strong 強烈的; 激烈的: *the fierce heat of the sun* 太陽的酷熱 | *Competition for jobs is very fierce.* 求職的競爭十分激烈。 –**fiercely** *adv* –**fierceness** *n* [U]

fi·er·y /'faɪri; 'faɪəri/ *adj* **1** the colour of fire 似火的; 火紅的: *fiery red hair* 火紅的頭髮 | *a fiery sunset* 火紅色的日落 **2** full of violent feeling 暴躁的: *He has a fiery temper.* 他的脾氣暴躁。

fi·es·ta /fi'estə; fi'estə/ *n* a religious holiday in Spain or Latin America, at which people come together to enjoy themselves [西班牙或拉丁美洲的]宗教狂歡節日; 喜慶日

fif·teen /fɪf'tin; ˌfɪf'tiːn◂/ *det, n, pron* the number 15 [數字]十五 –**fifteenth** *det, n, pron, adv*

fifth /fɪfθ; fɪfθ/ *det,n,pron,adv* **1** 5th 第五(個) **2** one of five equal parts 五分之一

fif·ty /'fɪfti; 'fɪfti/ *det, n, pron* **fifties 1** the number 50 [數字]五十 **2 the Fifties,** the fifties the years 1950-1959 五十年代[指從一九五〇年到一九五九年] **3** in her fifties, in their fifties, etc. aged between 50 and 59 在五十歲到五十九歲之間 –**fiftieth** *det, n, pron, adv*

fifty-fifty /ˌ·· '··◂/ *adj,adv* **1** divided equally between two people 對半的[地]; 平分的[地]: *Let's split the bill fifty-fifty.* 我們把賬單平攤了吧。 **2 a fifty-fifty chance** an equal chance that something will happen or not happen [某事發生的]可能性參半: *He's got a fifty-fifty chance of survival.* 他的生死可能性參半。

fig /fɪg; fɪg/ *n* a soft sweet fruit with many small seeds, often eaten dried 無花果

fig. a written abbreviation for [縮]= FIGURE¹ (6)

fight¹ /faɪt; faɪt/ *v* **fought** /fɔt; fɔːt/, **fought 1** [I;T] to use violence against other people in an attempt to hurt or kill them 與[某人]戰鬥; 搏鬥; 打架; 打仗: *Did your father fight in the war?* 你父親參加了那場戰爭嗎? | *They fought to the death.* 他們戰鬥到生命的終止。 | *The two boys fought each other.* 那兩個男孩打了架。 | *Many battles have been fought here.* 在這兒進行了許多戰役。 **2** [I] to quarrel 吵架: *Let's try not to fight about money.* 讓我們盡量別為錢而爭吵。 **3** [I;T] to try very hard to prevent or stop something 爭取防止或制止[某事物]: *This government is determined to fight crime.* 該政府決心打擊犯罪行為。 | *We must fight against injustice.* 我們必須與不公正現象作戰。 **4** [I] to try very hard to do or obtain something 爭取做或獲得[某事物]: *We've been fighting for equal rights for nearly 100 years.* 我們為爭取平等權利而戰鬥了將近一百年。 | *Car workers are fighting to keep their jobs.* 汽車工人在極力爭取保住自己的飯碗。

☐ **USEFUL PATTERNS** 有用句型
to fight for something; to fight to do something

5 fight an election to try to win an election and be elected 設法在選舉中獲勝 **6 fight your way** to move along by pushing past other people 從人羣中擠出: *He had to fight his way through the crowd.* 他只好奮力從人羣中擠出來。 **7 be fighting a losing battle** to be trying to do or prevent something without being successful 在努力從事或抵抗無成功希望的事情: *She's fighting a losing battle against cancer.* 她正在進行一場成功希望渺茫的抵抗癌病的鬥爭。

fight back *phr v* **1** [I] to protect yourself by fighting someone who is attacking you 抵抗; 還擊 **2** [T **fight back** sthg] to try not to show a particular feeling 克制; 抑制[感情]: *He was fighting back tears.* 他強忍住眼淚。

fight off *phr v* **1** [T **fight** sthg ↔ **off**] to succeed in making something unpleasant go away 成功地驅除[壞事]: *A good diet should help you to fight off infections.* 合適的飲食有助於治癒你的感染。 **2** [T **fight** sbdy ↔ **off**] to make someone who is attacking you go away by fighting them 擊敗; 擊退: *They managed to fight off their attackers.* 他們設法擊退了進攻者。

fight out *phr v* **fight it out** to settle a disagreement by fighting or arguing [透過爭鬥或爭論]解決[分歧]

fight² *n* **1** [C] an attempt by two or more people to hurt or kill each other 戰鬥; 搏鬥; 打架: *The police were called to stop a fight outside the pub.* 警察被召去制止酒店外的一

場打鬥。**2** [C] a determined attempt to prevent something or obtain something 〔為制止或得到某物的〕鬥爭: *the fight* **against** *inflation* 抑制通貨膨脹的爭鬥 | *our fight* **for** *equality* 我們為爭取平等權利而戰 **3** [U] the desire or strength to fight 鬥志; 戰鬥力: *There's not much fight left in the old man now.* 這位老人現在已經沒剩下多少鬥志了。**4** **put up a good fight** to fight well against someone stronger than yourself 〔與強者〕英勇搏鬥

fight·er /ˈfaɪtər; ˈfaɪtər/ *n* **1** someone who fights 戰士; 戰鬥者 **2** someone who continues trying to do something although it is very difficult 鬥士; 奮鬥者 **3** (also 又作 **fighter plane**) an aircraft used for fighting battles 戰鬥機; 殲擊機

fig·ment /ˈfɪgmənt; ˈfɪgmənt/ *n* **a figment of someone's imagination** something imagined and not real 想像的事物; 虛構的事物

fig·u·ra·tive /ˈfɪgjərətɪv; ˈfɪgjɔrətɪv/ *adj* using a word in a way which develops its main or usual meaning in an imaginative way 〔詞語〕比喻的: *a figurative use of the word* 該詞的比喻用法 —compare 比較 LITERAL (3) —**figuratively** *adv: I was using the word figuratively.* 我比喻性地用了那個詞。

★fig·ure¹ /ˈfɪgjər; ˈfɪgər/ *n* **1** a written sign used to represent a number 數字: *Write the amount in words and in figures.* 把這個總額用文字和阿拉伯數字寫出來。| *a four-figure number* 四位數的數字 **2** an amount of something expressed as a number 數額; 數目: *The Government has not yet published this year's export figures.* 政府尚未公布今年的出口數額。| *Recent figures indicate that inflation is rising.* 最近的數字表明通貨膨脹在繼續上升。**3** a person, seen in a picture or from a distance 〔繪畫中或從遠處看到的〕人像; 人影: *a group of figures on the left of the picture* 照片左邊的一羣人 | *I could see a figure in the distance.* 我能看到遠處有一個人影。**4** your shape, considered from the point of view of how attractive it is 體形; 風姿; 身材: *She's got a lovely figure.* 她的身材很動人。**5** an important person 要人; 名人: *He is one of the senior figures in the government.* 他是政府機構中的元老。| *leading literary figures* 文學界的要人 **6** a numbered drawing used in a book to explain something 圖表; 圖解

★figure² *v* **figured, figuring** **1** [I] to be included in something 成為〔某物〕的一部分; 出現於〔某物〕: *He figured prominently in a recent magazine story.* 他在最近一期雜誌文章上的出現引人注目。| *Both men figure in the list.* 那兩位男子的名字都出現在名單上。**2** [+ (that)] *AmE* to believe that something is the case or that something should be done 〔美式〕認為; 估計: *We figured we'd better get a new car.* 我們認為我們最好買輛新汽車。**3** **that figures** *infml* that is what I would ex-

pect 〔非正式〕不出我所料

figure sthg/sbdy ↔ **out** *phr v* [T] to understand someone or something 理解〔某人或某事物〕: *I was trying to figure out what was happening.* 我試圖弄明白出了甚麼事。

fig·ure·head /ˈfɪgjərˌhɛd; ˈfɪgəhɛd/ *n* **1** a leader who has no real power 有名無實的首腦; 傀儡 **2** an ornament on the front of a sailing ship, often in the shape of a person 船頭雕飾〔常雕成人像〕

figure of eight /ˌ··· ˈ·/ *n* anything of the shape of the number 8, such as a knot or pattern 8字形〔如繩結或圖案〕

figure of speech /ˌ·· · ˈ·/ *n* a word or phrase used with a FIGURATIVE meaning 比喻: *I didn't really mean you're wicked; it was just a figure of speech.* 我並不是說你真的很缺德, 這只是一個比喻。

fil·a·ment /ˈfɪləmənt; ˈfɪləmənt/ *n* a thin thread, such as the wire producing light inside an electric light BULB 細絲; 細線〔如電燈泡內的燈絲〕

filch /fɪltʃ; fɪltʃ/ *v* [T] *infml* to steal something of small value secretly 〔非正式〕偷〔不貴重的東西〕

★file¹ /faɪl; faɪl/ *n* **1** a box or other container for storing important papers 〔存放重要文件的〕箱子或其他櫃子 –see picture on page 763 見 763 頁彩圖 **2** a collection of papers stored together 檔案; 案卷; 卷宗: *Here's our file on the Middle East.* 這是我們關於中東的文件檔案。| *We keep a file on each student's progress.* 我們把每個學生的進展都存檔。**3** a collection of information stored in a computer under one name 〔電腦〕文件: *a data file* 數據文件 | *Open a new file for this project.* 為這個研究項目另開一個檔案。**4** a tool used for making hard or rough surfaces smooth 銼; 銼刀: *Use a file for these rough edges.* 用銼刀把這些粗糙的邊緣銼一下。| *a nail file* 指甲銼 –see picture on page 958 見 958 頁彩圖 **5** **in single file** one behind the other in a line 成單行; 成一列縱隊: *We walked along in single file.* 我們排成一列縱隊往前走。

file² *v* **filed, filing** **1** [T] to put something in a file with other papers 把〔某物〕歸檔〔存檔〕: *File this under "Accounts".* 把這個歸入"賬目"一欄檔案裡。**2** [I;T] *law* to make an official request or complaint 〔律〕提出〔申請〕; 提出〔訴訟〕: *He has filed an application for planning permission.* 他提交了建築許可證的申請書。| *She is filing for divorce.* 她在正式申請離婚。**3** [I;T] to make something smoother by using a file 用銼把〔某物〕銼平: *She was filing her nails.* 她在銼指甲。**4** [I+adv/prep] to walk on behind the other 排成單行縱隊行進: *They filed slowly past the president's grave.* 他們排成單行縱隊慢慢地從總統墓前走過。

fil·et /fɪˈle; fɪˈlɛt/ *n* see 見 FILLET

fi·li·al /ˈfɪlɪəl; ˈfɪlɪəl/ *adj fml* expected of a

son or daughter〖正式〗子女的; 孝順的: *filial respect* 子女對父母的敬重

fil·i·gree /ˈfɪləˌgri; ˈfɪl⟩ˌgriː/ *n* [U] delicate decorative work in gold or silver wire〔用金絲或銀絲製成的〕精工飾品

fil·ing cab·i·net /ˈ·· ˌ··/ *n* a set of drawers in an office, used for storing important papers –see picture on page 763 見 763 頁彩圖

fil·ings /ˈfaɪlɪŋz; ˈfaɪlɪŋz/ *n* [pl] very small sharp bits of metal 銼屑: *iron filings* 鐵銼屑

★**fill**¹ /fɪl; fɪl/ *v* **1** [I] to become full 充滿; 擠滿. *The room soon filled with people.* 房間裡不久就擠滿了人。| *His eyes filled with tears.* 他的眼睛充滿了淚水。**2** [T] to make something full 裝滿; 填滿; 擠滿: *Fill the bucket with water.* 往桶裡裝滿水。| *Crowds of people filled the streets.* 成羣結隊的人擠滿了街道。**3** [T] to cause strong feelings in someone 使〔某人〕充滿〔強烈感情〕: *The news has filled my colleagues with anxiety.* 那消息使我的同事們憂心忡忡。| *She was filled with anger.* 她滿腔怒火。**4** [T] to have or perform a particular job or position 充任〔某職〕: *The White House didn't have anyone who could fill the role of negotiator.* 白宮派不出能充當談判者這一角色的人物。| *There are not enough young people available to fill the job vacancies.* 可以填補這些工作空缺的年輕人不夠。**5** [T] to satisfy a need or demand 滿足〔需要或要求〕: *This larger vehicle more closely fills their needs.* 這輛大車更進一步地滿足了他們的需要。

fill in *phr v* **1** [T fill sthg ↔ in] to put something into a space so that the space is filled 填滿〔某物〕: *I filled in all the cracks.* 我填滿了所有的裂縫。**2** [T fill sthg ↔ in] to complete a form by writing information on it 填寫〔表格〕: *I haven't filled in my application form yet.* 我還沒有填寫申請表格。**3** [T fill sbdy in] to give someone information about something 向〔某人〕提供〔關於某事的〕消息 **4** [I] to do someone's job or take their place 接替〔某人的工作〕; 代替: *Can you fill in for Steve tonight as he's ill?* 史蒂夫病了, 今晚你能代他一下嗎? | *If Jane can't come, I'll fill in* 如果簡來不了, 我會代替她的。

fill out *phr v* **1** [T fill sthg ↔ out] to complete a form by writing information on it 填寫〔表格〕**2** [I] to get fatter 變胖: *Her face is beginning to fill out.* 她的臉開始發胖。

fill up *phr v* [I;T fill sbdy/sthg ↔ up] to become or make something completely full (使)裝滿: *Could you fill the kettle up with water, please?* 請把這壺裝滿水, 行嗎? | *The room soon filled up with people.* 房間很快就擠滿了人。

fill² *n* **1** your fill as much as you need or want 充分滿足; 足夠: *He had drunk his fill.* 他喝了個夠。**2** have had your fill of something to have had enough of something and not want any more of it 對某物忍受夠

了: *I've had my fill of arguments.* 我已經受夠了爭爭吵吵。

fil·let¹ /ˈfɪlɪt; ˈfɪl⟩t/ *n* (also 又作 **filet** *AmE* 〖美式〗) a piece of fish or meat with no bones in it 無骨的魚片或肉片: *a fillet steak* 牛柳排 | *fillets of sole* 鰈魚片 –see picture on page 504 見 504 頁彩圖

fillet² *v* (also 又作 **filet** *AmE* 〖美式〗) [T] to prepare a piece of fish or meat by taking out the bones 把〔魚或肉〕去骨切片

fill·ing¹ /ˈfɪlɪŋ; ˈfɪlɪŋ/ *n* **1** [C] a small amount of a special substance put into a hole in a tooth to preserve the tooth〔補牙用的〕填補物: *You've got a lot of fillings.* 你的牙補了好多處。**2** [C;U] something put inside a cake or chocolate, or between two pieces of bread〔糕餅、巧克力或麵包夾層中的〕餡子: *a delicious chocolate cream filling* 美味的巧克力奶油餡

filling² *adj* making you feel full quickly (used of food) 一吃就飽的〔指食物〕: *This pudding is very filling.* 這個布丁一吃就飽。

filling sta·tion /ˈ·· ˌ··/ *n* a place that sells petrol and oil for cars and other vehicles 汽車加油站

fil·ly /ˈfɪlɪ; ˈfili/ *n* **fillies** a young female horse 小母馬

★**film**¹ /fɪlm; fɪlm/ *n* **1** [C;U] a roll of plastic substance which you put inside a camera and on which photographs are taken 膠片; 軟片; 膠卷: *I used three whole films while I was on holiday.* 我在假期裡用了三卷膠卷。| *My camera's run out of film.* 我相機裡的膠卷已經拍完了。**2** [C] a story or play recorded on film and shown in a cinema or on television 影片; 電影: *Have you seen any good films lately?* 你最近看過甚麼好片子嗎? **3** [C] a small amount of a substance spread over a surface〔物體表面的〕薄層: *Everything was covered with a thin film of dust.* 到處都是薄薄的一層灰。**4** [U] a very thin sheet of plastic used for covering or wrapping things〔用於遮蓋或包紮物品的〕塑料薄膜

film² *v* [I;T] to make a film of something for the cinema or television 拍攝電影或電視: *We'll be filming all day tomorrow.* 明天我們要整天拍電影。| *They filmed the Queen's arrival in Paris.* 他們拍攝了女王抵達巴黎的場面。

film star /ˈ· ·/ *n* a well-known actor or actress who acts in films 電影明星

film·strip /ˈfɪlmˌstrɪp; ˈfɪlmˌstrɪp/ *n* [C;U] a length of photographic film used to show photographs or drawings one after the other as still pictures 幻燈片

film·y /ˈfɪlmɪ; ˈfɪlmi/ *adj* fine and almost transparent 輕薄透明的: *a filmy silk dress* 輕薄透明的綢衣

fil·ter¹ /ˈfɪltə; ˈfɪltəʳ/ *n* **1** an apparatus used to keep a substance clean; filters work by allowing only the substance itself to pass

F

through, but not unwanted substances such as dirt or chemicals 過濾器: *a water filter* 淨水過濾器 **2** a coloured glass that changes the light which passes through it into a camera 濾色鏡; 濾光鏡

filter² *v* [I;T] **1** to pass a substance through a filter 過濾: *We always filter our drinking water.* 我們總要把飲用水過濾一下。**2** [I+adv/prep] to reach people or a place gradually 〔消息〕慢慢傳開; 〔人流〕緩緩進入: *The visitors are filtering into the dining-room.* 來訪者緩緩走進餐廳。| *The news slowly filtered through to everyone in the office.* 消息慢慢走漏出去, 結果辦公室裡的人全都知道了。

filter sbdy/sthg ↔ **out** *phr v* [T] to remove by means of a filter or a system for choosing between people 濾除〔某物〕; 淘汰〔某人〕: *We managed to filter out the dirt.* 我們設法濾掉了污物。| *Try and filter out unsuitable applicants before the interviews.* 要盡量在面試以前把不合適的申請人淘汰掉。

filth¹ /fɪlθ/ *n* [U] **1** very nasty dirt 骯髒; 污物: *Go and wash that filth off your hands.* 去把你手上的髒物洗掉。**2** language or pictures which people find rude or offensive, especially because they are connected with sex 下流的文字或圖片: *I don't know how you can read such filth.* 我不知道你怎麼會去看這種猥褻的讀物。

filth·y /ˈfɪlθi; ˈfɪlθi/ *adj* **filthier, filthiest 1** very dirty 骯髒的; 污穢的: *Your hands are filthy!* 你的手太髒了! **2** rude or offensive, especially concerning sex 淫穢的: *filthy language* 淫穢的語言 –**filthiness** *n* [U]

fin /fɪn; fɪn/ *n* a part of a fish's body shaped like a small wing, which helps it to swim 魚鰭

fi·nal¹ /ˈfaɪnl; ˈfaɪnl/ *adj* **1** [only before a noun 只用於名詞前] coming last or at the end of something 最後的; 最終的: *the final episode of the TV series* 電視連續劇的最後一集 | *the final stages of the game* 比賽的最後階段 | *We had a final cup of coffee before we left.* 我們離開之前喝了最後一杯咖啡。**2** unable to be changed or questioned (used of a decision or an offer) 不能改變的; 確定的〔指決定或提議〕: *I won't go, and that's final!* 我不去, 就這樣定了! | *Is that your final offer?* 那是貴方的最後報價嗎?

final² *n* **1** [C] the last and most important game in a competition 決賽: *the World Cup Final* 世界杯決賽 | *She got through to the finals.* 她進入決賽。**2 finals** [pl] the last and most important set of examinations in a college course 〔大學課程的〕期末考試: *How did you get on in your finals?* 你的期末考試考得怎麼樣?

fi·na·le /fɪˈnɑli; fɪˈnɑːli/ *n* the last part of a piece of music or a musical show 終曲; 末樂章: *a spectacular grand finale* 壯觀的大結局

fi·nal·ist /ˈfaɪnlɪst; ˈfaɪnl-ɪst/ *n* one of the people or teams who have reached the final in a competition 參加決賽的選手〔運動隊〕

fi·nal·i·ty /faɪˈnælətɪ; faɪˈnælɪti, fɪ-/ *n* [U] the quality of being certain and unchangeable 決定性; 不可改變性: *"No!" he said with finality.* "不!" 他斬釘截鐵地說。

fi·nal·ize /ˈfaɪnlˌaɪz; ˈfaɪnl-aɪz/ *v* **finalized, finalizing** (also 又作 **finalise** *BrE* 【英式】) [T] to complete an arrangement 完成〔安排〕: *It's time to finalize our plans for the concert.* 我們該把舉辦音樂會的計劃確定下來。

fi·nal·ly /ˈfaɪnlɪ; ˈfaɪnl-i/ *adv* **1** after a long delay 拖延很久以後; 最終; 終於: *We finally set off after lunch.* 我們吃完午飯終於出發了。**2** a word used when you have several points to make and you come to the last one 最後〔用於講到最後一個要點〕: *We've seen how different soils suit different plants, and how rainfall affects their growth. Finally, I'd like to look at the significance of light.* 我們已經看到, 不同的土壤是怎樣適合種植不同的植物; 雨水又是如何影響它們的生長。最後, 我想來看看光的重要性。| *And finally, I'd like to thank you all for coming tonight.* 最後, 我要感謝你們諸位今晚的光臨。**3** a word used when you are describing a number of events that happen one after the other, and you come to the last one 〔用於講到幾個依次發生的事情的最後一件事時〕: *We had a week at the seaside in Holland. Then we spent a couple of days in Antwerp. Finally, we went to Bruges.* 我們在荷蘭的海濱度過一星期; 接着在安特衛普逗留了幾天。最後, 我們去了布魯日。**4** a word used when you come to the last of a number of instructions 〔用於幾條文字說明的最後一條〕: *Make a cheese sauce. Boil the pasta in salted water until it is just soft. Mix the pasta with the sauce. Finally, put the dish into a hot oven for 20 minutes to brown it.* 準備好乳酪調味汁; 把意大利麵食放入鹽水煮軟; 在煮好的麵中拌入乳酪調味汁。最後, 裝盤放入烤爐烘烤二十分鐘使其變成褐色。**5** in a way that does not allow further change 決定性地; 徹底地: *It's not finally settled yet.* 此事尚未徹底解決。

fi·nance¹ /fəˈnæns; ˈfaɪnæns/ *n* **1** [U] the management of money, especially for a company or a government 財務的管理; 財政: *He's an accountant in the Finance Department.* 他是財務部的會計。**2** [U] money provided by a bank or other organization to help run a business 〔銀行或其他機構提供的〕資金: *Unless we get more finance, we'll have to close the school down.* 除非我們能得到更多的資金, 否則我們只好關閉學校。**3 finances** [pl] the amount of money that a person or an organization has 〔個人或機構的〕財源; 財力: *We'd better review our*

F

finances before we buy a new car. 我們購買新車以前最好打財務狀況檢查一下。

⭐**finance**² *v* **financed, financing** [T] to provide money for something 供資金給〔某事〕; 為〔某事〕提供款項: *The repairs will be financed by the local council.* 裝修工作將由地方政務委員會提供經費。

⭐**fi·nan·cial** /fə'nænʃəl; fɔ'nænʃəl/ *adj* connected with money 金融的; 財政的: *The City of London is a great financial centre.* 倫敦市是個很大的金融中心。 | *He works as a financial adviser.* 他的職業是財務顧問。 | *The project was a financial success.* 那個研究項目獲利巨大。 – **financially** *adv*

fi·nan·cier /ˌfɪnən'sɪr; fɔ'nænsɪər/ *n* someone who controls or lends large sums of money 財政家; 金融家

finch /fɪntʃ; fɪntʃ/ *n* a small bird 雀科鳴鳥

⭐**find**¹ /faɪnd; faɪnd/ *v* **found** /faʊnd; faʊnd/, **found 1** [T] to discover or obtain something, usually when you have been looking for it or when you need it 發現, 找到〔尋找或需要之物〕: *I can't find my boots!* 我找不到我的靴子! | *Did you find what you were looking for?* 你找到了你在找的東西嗎? | *Oil has been found in the North Sea.* 北海已發現石油。 | *I found a Roman coin in the garden.* 我在花園裡找到了一枚羅馬硬幣。 | *We need to find a solution to this problem.* 我們需要找到解決這個問題的辦法。 | *There are many people who cannot find a place to live.* 有許多人找不到住處。 **2** [+that] to learn or discover a fact 了解到, 發現〔事實〕: *Scientists have found that this disease will respond to treatment by drugs.* 科學家已經發現這種疾病用藥物治療會有起色。 | *We went to her house, but found that she was out.* 我們去了她家, 但發現她不在。 | *I'm finding that the job is not as easy as I thought it would be.* 我發覺這份工作並不是像我所預料的那麼輕鬆。 **3** [T] to have a particular feeling about something or someone 〔對某人或某物〕產生某種感覺: *I find him boring!* 我發覺他很討厭! | *I found the film very interesting.* 我覺得這部片子很有趣。 **4** [T] to have enough of something to be able to do something that you want to do 擁有〔足夠的〕某物去做想做的事情〕: *I can never find the time to read novels.* 我從來都擠不出時間看小說。 | *We couldn't find enough money to pay for the holiday.* 我們賺不到足夠的錢去度假。 | *I couldn't find the courage to tell him the bad news.* 我鼓不起勇氣把壞消息告訴他。 **5 find fault with someone/something** to complain about someone or something 埋怨某人或某事物: *She's always finding fault with my work!* 她老是埋怨我的工作! **6 find someone guilty** to declare that someone is guilty of a crime 宣判某人有罪: *The jury found him guilty.* 陪審團判他有罪。 [RELATED PHRASE 相關詞組 **find someone**

not guilty] **7 find yourself somewhere** to become conscious that you are in a particular place or doing a particular thing, but without having planned it 發現自己處於某種狀態、〔不知不覺中〕發現自己在做某事: *When I woke up I found myself in hospital.* 當我甦醒過來時, 發現自己躺在醫院裡。 | *I found myself shouting and swearing at him.* 我發現自己對他又喊又罵。 **8 find your feet** to become used to new or strange surroundings 習慣〔適應〕新的或陌生的環境 **9 find your way** to reach a place by discovering the way to get there 發現〔到某處的〕路線: *I managed to find my way back to the station.* 我設法找到了回火車站的路。

find out *phr v* **1** [I;T **find** sthg ↔ **out**] to learn or discover a fact 了解〔事實〕: *Did you ever find out who got the job?* 你知道誰得到了那份工作嗎? | *I found out that he'd been stealing things from the company.* 我發現他一直在偷公司的東西。 | *We never found out his name.* 我們從來不知道他的名字。 **2** [T **find** sbdy **out**] to discover that someone has been doing something dishonest 發現, 查出〔某人的不誠實行為〕: *He'd been fiddling the books for years before he was found out.* 在被人識破之前的幾年裡, 他一直在騙寫書籍。

find² *n* something good that you find 〔有價值的〕發現物: *That Greek restaurant is a real find!* 找到那家希臘餐館真是個了不起的發現!

⭐**find·ing** /'faɪndɪŋ; 'faɪndɪŋ/ *n* something learnt or decided as the result of an official enquiry 官方調查的結果: *The committee on child care will publish its findings next week.* 兒童保育委員會將於下週發表調查結果。

⭐**fine**¹ /faɪn; faɪn/ *n* an amount of money paid as a punishment 罰金; 罰款: *a parking fine* 違規停車罰款

fine² *v* **fined, fining** [T] to make someone pay a sum of money as a punishment 處〔某人〕以罰款: *He was fined £200.* 他被罰款二百英鎊。

fine³ *adj* **1** of very good quality 美好的; 完美的; 優秀的: *She's a fine musician.* 她是位出色的音樂家。 | *one of the finest buildings in Europe* 歐洲最完美的建築物之一 **2** [not used in questions or negatives 不用於疑問句或否定句] acceptable 可接受的: *"I'll be there at two o'clock." "Yes, that's fine."* "我要兩點鐘到那裡。" "好的, 那就這樣。" | *"What's your new flat like?" "It's fine."* "你的新公寓怎麼樣?" "不錯。" **3** very thin 纖細的; 尖細的: *a pencil with a fine point* 筆頭尖細的鉛筆 | *I've got very fine hair.* 我的頭髮很纖細。–see 見 THIN¹ (USAGE用法) **4** in very small grains or bits 顆粒微小的: *a fine powdery dust* 一種粉末狀微塵 **5** bright and sunny 晴朗的: *a fine summer morning* 晴朗的夏日早晨 **6** [not used in questions or negatives 不用於疑問句或否定句] reasonably healthy and happy 健康愉快的: *"How are you?"* *"I'm fine."* "你好嗎?" "很好。" **7** delicate and careful 精巧的; 精確的: *He made a few fine adjustments to the engine.* 他對引擎作了一些精確調整。 | *I missed some of the finer points in the argument.* 我在辯論中遺漏了一些細節。 **8 fine art** beautiful paintings and other works of art 美術品: *She's doing a course in fine art.* 她在攻讀美術課程。 **9 the fine arts** activities such as painting and music, which are concerned with producing beautiful things 美藝術〔如繪畫, 音樂等〕

fine⁴ *adv* well 好: *That suits me fine.* 那對我很合適。 | *We get on fine.* 我們相處得不錯。

fine·ly /'faɪnlɪ; 'faɪnli/ *adv* **1** carefully and delicately 仔細地; 精確地: *These instruments are very finely tuned.* 這些儀器都作過精確調整。 **2** until very thin or in very small bits 微小地; 細小地: *finely cut vegetables* 切得很碎的蔬菜

fi·ne·ry /'faɪnərɪ; 'faɪnəri/ *n* [U] beautiful clothes and jewellery worn on special occasions 〔特殊場合穿戴的〕華麗的服飾: *the guests in all their wedding finery* 穿着華麗衣服參加婚禮的客人

fi·nesse /fɪ'nɛs; fɪ'nes/ *n* [U] a clever way of dealing with people and situations 手腕; 手段; 策略: *Paul handled the meeting with great finesse.* 保羅用非常靈活的方式掌握會議。

fin·ger¹ /'fɪŋɡə; 'fɪŋɡəʳ/ *n* **1** one of the movable parts, with joints, at the end of each of your hands 手指 **2** the part of a GLOVE that covers a finger 〔手套的〕套手指部分 **3 cross your fingers, keep your fingers crossed** *infml* to hope for the best 〔非正式〕祈求好運: *I hope the weather stays fine for tomorrow's game. We must just keep our fingers crossed.* 我希望明天比賽時天氣能保持晴朗。我們只得祈求好運了。 **4 have a finger in every pie** *infml* to be connected with everything that is happening 〔非正式〕插手一切事情 **5 lift a finger, raise a finger** to make any effort to help 出力幫助: *No one lifted a finger to save the prisoners.* 沒有人出力去救救那些囚犯。 **6 pull your finger out, get your finger out** *infml* to start working hard 〔非正式〕開始努力工作 **7 put your finger on something** to recognize the truth of something 認清某事的實情: *I can't quite put my finger on what's wrong.* 我看不出問題出在哪裡。

finger² *v* [T] to feel or touch something with your fingers 用手指觸摸: *She fingered the fine silk.* 她用手摸了摸那塊細綢。

fin·ger·nail /'fɪŋɡə,nel; 'fɪŋɡəneɪl/ *n* one of the hard flat pieces at the end of each finger 手指甲: *The baby's fingernails need cutting.* 嬰兒的指甲要剪一剪了。

fin·ger·print /'fɪŋɡə,prɪnt; 'fɪŋɡə,prɪnt/ *n* a mark made of the lines on the end of your finger 指紋(印); 手印: *The police interviewed*

him and took his fingerprints. 警方和他進行面談並取了他的指紋。 | *The burglars left their fingerprints all over the house.* 那些竊賊在屋內到處都留下了他們的指紋。

fin·ger·tip /'fɪŋɡə,tɪp; 'fɪŋɡə,tɪp/ *n* **1** the end of a finger 指尖 **2 have something at your fingertips** to know something well and be able to find or remember it easily 對某事物瞭如指掌: *You'd better ask David — he has all the information at his fingertips.* 你最好去問大衛, 他對所有情況都瞭如指掌。

fin·i·cky /'fɪnɪkɪ; 'fɪnɪki/ *adj infml* 〔非正式〕 **1** disliking many things 愛挑剔的: *Eat up your fish and don't be so finicky.* 把你的魚吃完, 別太挑剔了。 **2** needing great attention to detail 需要特別注意細節的: *It's a very finicky job being a typesetter.* 排字工人做的工作需要非常細緻。

fin·ish¹ /'fɪnɪʃ; 'fɪnɪʃ/ *v* **1** [I;T] to come to an end or complete something 結束; 完成〔某事〕: *What time does the concert finish?* 音樂會甚麼時候結束? | *When do you finish your college course?* 你甚麼時候大學畢業? | *I haven't finished reading that book yet.* 我還沒有看完那本書。

□ **USEFUL PATTERNS** 有用句型
to finish something; to finish doing something

2 [I;T] to stop work 停止; 做完工作: *What time do you finish on Friday?* 你星期五幾點鐘做完工作? **3** [T] to eat, drink, or use the rest of something 吃完; 喝光; 耗盡: *The cat will finish the fish.* 貓會把魚吃光的。 | *Let's finish the wine.* 讓我們把酒喝完。 | *Have you finished the blue paint?* 你把藍漆用完了嗎? **4** [T] *infml* to make someone extremely tired 〔非正式〕使〔某人〕累垮: *Climbing all those stairs has really finished me.* 爬了那麼多樓梯可真把我給累壞了。

finish off *phr v* **1** [T **finish** sbdy/sthg ↔ **off**] to kill a person or animal that is hurt 殺死〔受傷的人或動物〕 **2** [I;T **finish** sthg ↔ **off**] to complete something 完成〔某事〕: *I'm just finishing off the report.* 我剛寫完報告。 | *I'm just finishing off here.* 我現在剛剛做完〔這事〕。 **3** [T **finish** sthg ↔ **off**] to eat, drink, or use the rest of something 吃完; 喝光; 耗盡

finish up *phr v* **1** [I] to be in a particular situation or do something at the end of something 最後處於某種狀況; 以〔做某事〕結尾: *We finished up with a brandy.* 我們在最後喝了白蘭地。 | *They finished up at a disco.* 他們最後去了迪斯科舞廳。 **2** [T **finish** sthg ↔ **up**] to eat, drink, or use the rest of something 吃完; 喝光; 耗盡

finish with sbdy/sthg *phr v* [T] **1** to have no more use for a person or thing 不再使用〔某物〕; 不再為〔某人〕幫忙: *I'll borrow the scissors if you've finished with them.* 要是你

已用完剪刀的話，我想借一下。| *Have you finished with the typist?* 你為那個打字員忙完了沒有? **2** to end a relationship 斷絕關係: *He's finished with Mary at last!* 他終於和瑪麗斷絕關係!

fin·ished /ˈfɪnɪʃt; ˈfɪnɪʃt/ *adj* **1** at the end of an activity or relationship 〔活動或關係〕結束了的: *I'll be finished in about an hour.* 我大約還要一個小時才能做完。**2** [never before a noun 不能用於名詞前] without hope of continuing 完結了的; 完蛋了的: *If the bank refuses to lend us the money, we're finished.* 如果銀行拒絕給我們貸款，我們就完蛋了。**3** [only before a noun 只用於名詞前] completed 完成的: *the finished product* 製成品 | *a beautifully finished old table* 製作精美的老式桌子

finishing school /ˈ··· ·/ *n* a private school where rich girls learn social behaviour and other useful skills 精修學校〔有錢女子學習社交禮儀和其他技能的私立學校〕

fi·nite /ˈfaɪnaɪt; ˈfaɪnaɪt/ *adj* limited 有限制的: *a finite number of possibilities* 有限的幾種可能性 –opposite 反義 **infinite**

fi·ord /fjɔːd; ˈfiːɔːd/ *n* see 見 FJORD

fir /fɜː; fɜːʳ/ *n* (also 又作 **firtree** /ˈfɜːtriː; ˈfɜː-triː/) a tree that keeps its thin sharp leaves in winter, forms seeds in a CONE, and grows mainly in cold countries 冷杉; 樅

★**fire**¹ /faɪr; faɪəʳ/ *n* **1** [U] flames, light, and great heat 火: *People discovered fire thousands of years ago.* 人類在幾千年以前發現了火。**2** [C;U] flames which are out of control and destroying things 火災; 失火: *a forest fire* 森林火災 | *The hotel was seriously damaged by fire.* 旅館被火嚴重毀壞了。| *Is the cottage insured against fire?* 這小屋有保火險嗎? **3** [C] a pile of burning coal or wood used to heat room or to cook food over 爐火; 火堆: *We sat in front of the roaring fire and chatted.* 我們坐在熊熊的爐火前聊天。| *The campers lit a fire to boil some water.* 露營者點起了一堆火燒水。**4** [C] a gas or electrical apparatus with red-hot wires or flames, used to heat a room 煤氣取暖器; 電爐: *Could you switch the fire on?* 你能不能把暖爐打開? **5 on fire** burning and being damaged by fire 着火; 起火: *The house is on fire!* 房子着火啦! **6 under fire** being shot at 遭到砲火射擊: *The regiment was under fire from all sides.* 團隊遭到來自四面八方的射擊。**7 -fired** operated by a particular substance which is burnt 使用某種燃

料的: *oil-fired central heating* 燃油的中央暖氣系統 | *a coal-fired power station* 燃煤發電站

★**fire**² *v* **fired, firing 1** [I;T] to shoot with a gun 開槍射擊: *He's firing at us!* 他正朝着我們開槍! | *The German guns were firing all night.* 德國兵的槍聲通宵不斷。| *He ran into the bank and fired his gun into the air.* 他衝進銀行並朝天鳴槍。| *Gunmen fired five shots at the President.* 持槍歹徒朝着總統射了五槍。**2** [T] *infml* to dismiss someone from a job 〔非正式〕解雇, 開除〔某人〕: *Get out! You're fired!* 你被解雇了! **3** [T] to say things very quickly one after the other 急速地連續説(話): *The journalists fired questions at the Prime Minister.* 新聞記者們對首相提出了連珠砲似的問題。**4** [T] to produce strong feelings in someone 激起〔某人的強烈感情〕: *The speech fired the crowd's imagination.* 演講激發起聽眾的想像力。**5** [I] (of an engine) to make the petrol burn and the engine work 〔引擎〕點火; 發動: *The engine is only firing on three cylinders.* 這引擎只有三個汽缸工作。**6** [T] to bake clay objects 燒製〔陶瓷製品〕

fire away *phr v* [I] to begin to speak or ask questions 開始説話; 開始提問: *If anyone has any questions, fire away!* 誰有問題就請提出叻!

fire a·larm /ˈ· ·,·/ *n* a signal, such as a ringing bell, to warn people of fire 火警警報

fire·arm /ˈfaɪr,ɑːm; ˈfaɪərɑːm/ *n* a gun 槍枝; 火器: *Do I need a licence to carry firearms?* 我攜帶槍枝需要許可證嗎?

fire bri·gade /ˈ· ·,·/ *n* (**fire department** /ˈ· ·,·/ *AmE*〔美式〕) [sing/pl verb] an organization of people who are trained to put out fires 消防隊: *Phone for the fire brigade!* 打電話叫消防隊來!

fire en·gine /ˈ· ·,·/ *n* a special vehicle that carries firemen and apparatus to put out fires 救火車; 消防車

fire es·cape /ˈ· ·,·/ *n* a set of metal stairs leading down outside a building to the ground, by which people can escape from a fire 〔可藉以逃離火災的〕太平梯 –see picture on page 729 見 729 頁彩圖

fire ex·tin·guish·er /ˈ· ·,··/ *n* a metal container with water or chemicals inside for putting out a fire 滅火器

fire·guard /ˈfaɪr,ɡɑːd; ˈfaɪəɡɑːd/ *n* a protective metal framework put round a fireplace 壁爐欄

fire·man /ˈfaɪr,mən; ˈfaɪəmən/ *n* **firemen** /-mən; -mən/ a person whose job is to put out fires 消防員

fire·place /ˈfaɪr,pleɪs; ˈfaɪəpleɪs/ *n* an opening for a fire in the wall of a room 壁爐; 火爐 –see picture on page 730 見 730 頁彩圖

fire·proof /ˈfaɪr'pruːf; ˈfaɪəpruːf/ *adj* protected so that it cannot be changed by fire 防火的; 耐火的 –**fireproof** *v* [T]

fire-rais·ing /ˈ· ˌ··/ n [U] the crime of starting fires on purpose 縱火罪

fire·side /ˈfaɪr̩ˌsaɪd/ ˈfaɪəsaɪd/ n the area around the fireplace 壁爐旁: *Let's sit and read by the fireside.* 我們坐在壁爐旁看書吧。

fire sta·tion /ˈ· ˌ··/ n a building for firemen (FIREMAN) and their apparatus and vehicles 消防站

fire·wood /ˈfaɪr̩ˌwʊd/ ˈfaɪəwʊd/ n [U] wood that has been cut for use on fires 木柴

fire·work /ˈfaɪr̩ˌwɜːk/ ˈfaɪəwɜːk/ n a small container filled with an explosive powder that is burnt to produce a show of light, noise, and smoke 煙火, 煙花: *a firework display* 煙花表演 | *Shall we let off some fireworks?* 我們放些煙花, 好嗎?

fir·ing squad /ˈ· ˌ·/ n a group of soldiers ordered to shoot and kill a prisoner 行刑隊〔奉命處死囚犯的一隊士兵〕

★**firm¹** /fɜːm; fɜːm/ adj **1** not soft and not moving much when pressed 堅硬的; 結實的: *a firm bed* 結實的牀 | *Choose firm tomatoes.* 挑些硬的番茄。 **2** with no uncertainty 堅定的; 肯定的: *a firm belief in God* 對上帝的堅定信仰 | *a firm date for the wedding* 確定的結婚日期 | *firm evidence* 可靠的證據 **3** solidly fixed 穩固的; 牢固的: *I don't think that chair is firm enough to stand on.* 我認為那把椅子不穩固, 不能往上站人。 | *firm foundations* 堅固的基礎 **4** strong 有力的: *a firm handshake* 有力的握手 **5** using strong control 嚴管的; 堅決的: *If parents were firmer with their children, there would be fewer discipline problems.* 如果家長對自己的孩子管得更嚴一些, 紀律問題就會少得多。 **6** not decreasing in value 堅挺的; 穩定的: *The pound remained firm against the dollar yesterday.* 昨天英鎊對美元的匯價仍然堅挺。

★**firm²** n a business company 商行; 公司

fir·ma·ment /ˈfɜːməmənt; ˈfɜːməmənt/ n **the firmament** *lit* the sky〔文〕天空; 蒼穹

first¹ /fɜːst; fɜːst/ n,pron **1 the first** the person or thing that comes before all others 第一個〔人或事〕: *Jim was the first to arrive.* 吉姆是第一個到的人。 **2** [C] the highest class of degree that you can get from a British university〔英國大學畢業生的〕最高成績; 優等 **3 a first** something that has never happened before 創舉〔指以前從未發生過的事物〕 **4 at first** in the beginning 最初; 開始時: *At first I didn't believe him but then I realized that he was telling the truth.* 開始時我不相信他, 但後來我意識到他說的是實話。—see 見 BEGINNING (USAGE用法) **5 from the first, from the very first** from the beginning 從一開始: *I knew from the first that I wasn't going to like the job.* 我從一開始就知道我不會喜歡這份工作。

★**first²** det,adv **1** before anything or anyone else 首先; 在首位; 第一: *George arrived first.* 喬治第一個到達。 | *I want to go into town, but first I must finish writing this letter.* 我想到城裡去, 但我得先把這封信寫完。 | *She came first in the competition.* 她在比賽中得了第一名。 **2 for the first time** 首次: *Is this your first visit to London?* 這是你第一次訪問倫敦嗎? | *We first met back in 1967.* 我們首次見面是早在一九六七年。 **3** when you have several points you want to make, you can order them and number them "First,…", "Second,…", etc〔當有幾個要點要講述時, 可用 "First,…", "Second,…" 等加以羅列〕: *There are several reasons why the plan will not work. First, there has not been enough preparation. Second, there is not enough money.* 該計劃行不通的原因有那麼幾個: 第一, 準備工作不夠充分; 第二, 資金不足。 **4** you can use "first" when you are going to mention the first of several events〔"first" 可用於提到幾件事情中的第一件事〕: *We had soup first. Then we had a lovely piece of beef. And then for pudding we had lemon mousse.* 我們首先喝湯; 接着吃一塊可口的牛肉; 然後吃的甜點是檸檬奶油凍。 | *First we cleared the ground. Then we built a low platform.* 首先我們清理場地。然後搭了一個不高的平台。 **5** you can use "first" when you are going to give the first of a number of instructions〔"first" 可用於幾條說明的第一條〕: *First, put one spoonful of coffee per person into the righthand compartment. Then put one cup of water per person into the lefthand compartment.* 首先, 給每人一匙咖啡放入右邊這一格; 然後再給每人一杯水放入左邊那一格。 **6 first of all: a** before anything else 首先 **b** firstly and most importantly; when you have several points you want to make, you can use this expression to introduce the first〔如要表述幾個要點, 可用該詞組引出第一要點〕: *First of all, I am so glad I am to be here.* 首先, 我要說的是我能光臨此地是多麼的高興。 **c** you can use this expression when you are talking about the first of several events〔可用於所談論的幾件事情的第一件〕: *First of all, we had something to eat. Then we went to see one of the famous temples.* 首先, 我們吃了點東西。接着我們去參觀一個著名的廟宇。 | *Let's, first of all, try and decide about holiday dates.* 讓我們首先設法定下度假日期。 | *"Have you fixed the holiday dates?" "Yes, we did that first of all."* "你們定了度假日期沒有?" "定了, 我們一開始就定了。" **d** you can use this expression when you are giving the first of a number of instructions〔可用於幾條說明的第一條〕: *First of all, make sure that the two pieces of wood are thoroughly clean. Then put a thin layer of glue on each piece.* 首先, 檢查一下兩塊木頭是否非常乾淨。然後在每塊木頭上塗一層薄薄的膠水。 **7 at first** at the beginning of a period, as opposed to later on in the same period 起初〔與同一時期的後階段作對照〕: *At first I* *didn't like him, but now I do.* 起初我不喜歡他，但現在我喜歡他了。**8 in the first place: a** when you have several points you want to make, you can use this expression to introduce the first one 第一; 首先〔用於引出幾個要點中的第一個〕: *They won't be interested in that house. In the first place, it's too far from where they work. And in the second place, it's more than they are prepared to pay.* 他們對那座房子不會感興趣。首先，離工作地點太遠。 其次是要價太高，超過他們的承受能力。**b** to start with; you use this expression when you are finding fault with someone and saying that you have no sympathy with them 原先; 作為根本緣由〔用於批評某人並且不表示同情〕: *It's no use complaining about getting hurt. You shouldn't have been riding on the roof in the first place.* 受了傷再抱怨有甚麼用。你一開始就不該騎在車頂上。**9 first thing** at the beginning of the day 在大清早: *I'll phone you first thing tomorrow morning.* 我明天一大清早就給你打電話。

first aid /ˌ · ˈ · / *n* [U] treatment you could give someone hurt in an accident or suddenly taken ill before the doctor arrives 急救: *Get me the first-aid box, quickly!* 急救箱給我拿來，快!

first class /ˌ · ˈ · ◂/ *adv* **1** in the most comfortable and most expensive part of the train, plane, or ship 乘坐頭等車廂或艙位: *There's a lot more space if you travel first class.* 乘坐頭等車廂[艙位]旅行特別寬敞。**2** by a class of mail delivered as quickly as possible and costing more money 用第一類郵件〔快件〕: *You'll have to send it first class to get it there on Saturday.* 你得用第一類郵件投寄，才能使它在星期六到達那裡。

first-class /ˌ · ˈ · ◂/ *adj* **1** of the highest or best quality 最好的; 第一流的: *a first-class piece of work* 傑出的工作 | *Her cooking is absolutely first-class.* 她的烹飪技術絕對是一流的。**2** for travel in the most comfortable and most expensive part of a train, plane, or ship 〔車廂或艙位〕頭等的: *a first-class ticket* 頭等(車、船或機)票 | *a first-class compartment* 頭等車廂

first floor /ˌ · ˈ · ◂/ *n* **1** *BrE* the first floor of a building above ground level 〔英式〕二樓 **2** *AmE* the floor of a building at ground level 〔美式〕底層, 一樓 –compare 比較 GROUND FLOOR (1)

first·hand /ˌfɜːstˈhænd/ *adj, adv* learnt directly and not from other people 第一手的; 原始的; 直接的: *It's not firsthand information, so I don't know if we should believe it.* 這不是第一手資料，因此我不知道我們該不該相信。

first la·dy /ˌ · ˈ · · / *n* **the First Lady** the wife of the President of the USA 〔美國〕總統夫人

first·ly /ˈfɜːstli/ *adv* when you have

several points you want to make, you can order them and number them "Firstly,…", "Secondly,…", etc. 首先〔當有幾個要點要表述時，可用 "Firstly,…", "Secondly,…" 等加以羅列〕: *There are several reasons why the plan will not work. Firstly, there has not been enough preparation. Secondly, there is not enough money.* 該計劃行不通的原因有幾個: 首先，準備工作不夠充分; 其次是資金不足。

first name /ˈ · · / *n* the name or names that come before your family name 〔位於姓氏前的〕名字: *Mr Smith's first name is Peter.* 史密斯先生的名字是彼得。| *His first names are Peter George.* 他的名字是彼得·喬治。–compare 比較 SURNAME

> ■ **USAGE** 用法: In English-speaking countries your **first name** usually means the first of the names which your parents give you at birth, but it can also mean *all* the names your parents give you. In Christian countries people sometimes use **Christian name** in the same way. People also use **given name** and (less commonly) **forename** in the same way, especially on official forms. ☆在說英語的國家裡，**first name** 通常指出生時父母第一次取的名字，但也可以指父母給取的全部名字。在基督教國家裡，人們有時以同樣的方式使用教名。人們還同樣使用 **given name** 和 **forename**〔不太常見〕，尤其用於填寫正式表格。

first per·son /ˌ · ˈ · · ◂/ *n* [sing] **1** a form of verb which you use with "I" or "we" 第一人稱(形式)〔如 "I" 或 "we"〕**2** a way of telling a story in which the teller uses the first person〔敘述中的〕第一人稱: *The story was written in the first person. It began "I was born in…".* 這篇故事是用第一人稱寫的，以 "我生於…"開始。

first-rate /ˌ · ˈ · ◂/ *adj* of the highest quality 第一流的; 第一流的: *to use first-rate materials* 使用最好的材料 | *This beer is first-rate!* 這種啤酒是第一流的!

fis·cal /ˈfɪskl̩; ˈfɪskəl/ *adj* of or related to public money, taxes, or debts 財政的; 公款

fish¹ /fɪʃ; fɪʃ/ *n* **fish** or **fishes 1** [C] a creature which lives in water and uses its fins (FIN) and tail to swim 魚: *We only caught three fish all day.* 我們一整天只捉了三條魚。**2** [U] the flesh of a fish when used as food 魚肉: *We had fish and chips for dinner.* 我們晚餐時吃了魚加炸馬鈴薯條。–see picture on page 504 見 504 頁彩圖

fish² *v* **1** [I] to try to catch fish 捕魚; 釣魚: *He's fishing* **for** *trout.* 他在釣鱒魚。| *Dad's taken John fishing.* 爸爸帶約翰去釣魚了。**2** **go fishing** to go to a suitable place and fish 去釣魚: *"Where are Sandy and Les?"*

"They've gone fishing." 桑迪和雷斯在哪兒?" "他們去釣魚了。" **3** [T+adv/prep] to search 摸索; 搜尋: *She fished around in her handbag for her purse.* 她在手提包裡摸索着找錢包。 **4 fish for** to try to get something in an indirect way 設法用間接手段得到〔某物〕: *She's always fishing for compliments.* 她總是拐彎抹角討別人的恭維。

fish sthg ↔ **out** *phr v* [T] to bring something out after searching for it 〔經搜尋後〕掏出; 摸出: *She fished out a small red box from the bottom of her handbag.* 她從手提包的底部掏出一個紅色小盒子。

fish·er·man /ˈfɪʃəmən; ˈfɪʃəmən/ *n* **fishermen** /-mən; -mən/ someone who catches fish, for sport or as a job 漁民; 釣魚者

fish·ing /ˈfɪʃɪŋ; ˈfɪʃɪŋ/ *n* [U] the sport or job of catching fish 捕魚; 釣魚〔作為娛樂運動或職業〕: *Fishing is a very popular pastime in Ireland.* 釣魚是愛爾蘭十分普遍的消遣活動。 | *Can we do some fishing on holiday?* 我們能在假期裡去釣魚嗎?

fishing rod /ˈ·· ˌ·/ *n* a long thin stick with a string with a hook, used for catching fish 釣竿

fish·mon·ger /ˈfɪʃˌmʌŋɡɚ; ˈfɪʃˌmʌŋɡəˈ/ *n* **1** someone who works in a shop that sells fish 〔商店的〕魚販; 魚商 **2 fishmonger's** a shop where you buy fish 魚店; 魚鋪: *I'm going to the fishmonger's.* 我要去魚鋪(買魚)。 | *I got it at the fishmonger's.* 我是從魚販那裡買的。

fish slice /ˈ· ·/ *n BrE* a kitchen tool used for lifting and turning foods 〔英式〕鍋鏟; 炒勺 –see picture on page 958 見 958 頁彩圖

fish·y /ˈfɪʃi; ˈfɪʃi/ *adj* **fishier, fishiest 1** tasting or smelling of fish 魚味的; 魚腥味的 **2** seeming false 可疑的; 靠不住的: *That story sounds very fishy to me.* 那件事我聽起來覺得靠不住。

fis·sion /ˈfɪʃən; ˈfɪʃən/ *n* [U] *tech* the splitting into parts of certain atoms to produce a powerful force 〔術語〕(原子的)裂變

fist /fɪst; fɪst/ *n* a hand with the fingers tightly curled up 拳; 拳頭: *She shook her fist angrily.* 她憤怒地揮着拳頭。

★fit¹ /fɪt; fɪt/ *v* **-tt- 1** [I;T] to be the right size or shape (使)適合; 合身: *This door fits very badly.* 這扇門的尺寸很不合適。 | *This dress doesn't fit me.* 這件衣服我穿着不合身。 **2** [T+adv/prep] to find enough space for something 〔騰出足夠的地方〕容納〔某物〕: *I can't fit any more books onto this shelf.* 我沒法往這個架子上放多點書了。 | *We should be able to fit some more desks into this room.* 我們應該可以在這個房間裡多放幾張書桌。 **3** [T] to put something correctly into place 安裝〔某物〕: *We're having new locks fitted on all the doors.* 我們正在所有的門上安裝新鎖。 **4** [T] to be suitable for something 與〔某事物〕相符; 相稱: *to make the punishment fit the crime* 按罪量刑 **5 fit the bill** to be just

what is needed 符合需要: *We needed a journalist who spoke French and Arabic, and she fitted the bill.* 我們需要一位會說法語和阿拉伯語的記者, 她正合適。 **6 fit like a glove** to fit very well and closely 非常合身

> ■ USAGE 用法: The usual past form of **fit** is **fitted**. But when talking about size and shape, Americans sometimes use **fit** as a past form ☆ **fit** 的過去式常為 **fitted**, 但當談到大小尺寸和形狀時, 美國人有時把 **fit** 用作過去式: *He said that the suit fit him perfectly.* 他説他穿那套西裝非常合身。

fit in *phr v* **1** [I] to have a friendly, easy relationship with other people in a group because you are similar to them 與〔別人〕合得來; 和睦相處: *He fitted in very well with the group.* 他與組裡的其他成員相處得很好。 **2** [I] to happen or do things at a time that is suitable and does not affect other arrangements 與〔某事物〕相適應; 相協調: *The trouble with this job is that the hours don't fit in with the school day.* 這份工作的難處在於上班時間和上課時間不協調。 | *Don't change your arrangements. I'll fit in with you.* 別改變你的計劃了, 我會配合你的。 **3** [T **fit** sbdy/sthg ↔ **in**] to find a time to see someone or do something 安排時間〔見某人或做某事〕: *Doctor Jones can fit you in on Thursday afternoon.* 鍾斯醫生可以安排在星期四下午給你看病。

fit sthg ↔ **out** *phr v* [T] to fit something with all the things necessary for a particular purpose 〔為某一目的〕供給〔某事物〕必要的設備; 裝備: *The old warehouse has been fitted out as a car showroom.* 這個舊倉庫已經裝備齊全, 成了汽車陳列室。

★fit² *n* **1** the way in which something fits 合適; 合身: *This coat's a beautiful fit.* 這件外衣非常合身。 | *I'll try to climb through, but it's a tight fit.* 我要盡量爬過去, 但得貼緊身子。 **2** a loss of consciousness, with strange uncontrolled movements of the body 昏厥; 痙攣: *He suffers from epileptic fits.* 他患有癲癇病。 **3** a short attack of a slight illness or violent feeling 〔輕微疾病或強烈感情的〕發作; 陣發: *a fit of coughing* 一陣咳嗽 | *I hit her in a fit of anger.* 我一氣之下打了她。 **4 have a fit** *infml* to get very angry 〔非正式〕發怒: *Mum will have a fit when she sees what you've done.* 媽媽要是看到你所做的事, 會非常生氣。 **5** a sudden need to laugh or do something particular 〔大笑或活動的〕一陣突發: *The children burst into fits of laughter.* 孩子們突然發出陣陣笑聲。 | *I had a fit of letter writing yesterday.* 我昨天猛然寫了一陣子信。 **6 in fits and starts** continually starting and stopping 一陣一陣地; 間歇地

fit³ *adj* **1** [never before a noun 不能用於名詞前] right and suitable 適合的: *She's not fit to* *be in charge of small children.* 她不適宜照顧幼兒。| *a meal fit for a king* 一頓美餐

2 physically healthy and strong, often as a result of regular exercise 健康的; 強健的〔常指定期鍛鍊的結果〕: *He runs three miles every morning. That's why he's so fit.* 他每天早晨跑步三英里; 所以身體很結實。| *She goes to keep-fit classes and does exercises every day.* 她每天都去健身班進行鍛鍊。–opposite 反義 **unfit 3 fit to do something** almost ready to do something 幾乎要做某事: *He looked fit to burst.* 他看上去就要發火了。| *We worked until we were fit to drop.* 我們一直工作到累得幾乎要趴下。**4 as fit as a fiddle** very healthy 非常健康 **5 see fit to, think fit to** consider it right to do something 認為〔做某事〕恰當; 決定: *He saw fit to phone me up in the middle of the night!* 他決定在半夜給我打電話! | *You must do as you see fit.* 你必須做你認為該做的事。

fit·ful /ˈfɪtfəl; ˈfɪtfəl/ *adj* happening in many short periods and not continuous 斷斷續續的; 一陣陣的 –**fitfully** *adv: She slept fitfully.* 她的睡眠時斷時續。

fit·ment /ˈfɪtmənt; ˈfɪtmənt/ *n* a piece of fitted furniture〔安裝好了的〕設備; 家具: *bathroom fitments* 浴室設備

fit·ness /ˈfɪtnəs; ˈfɪtnᵻs/ *n* [U] **1** the condition of being physically fit 健康: *doing exercises to improve their fitness* 做體操以增強體質 **2** the quality of being suitable 適合; 合格: *his fitness to command the army* 他適合指揮軍隊 | *her fitness for the job* 她能勝任這做這份工作

fit·ted /ˈfɪtɪd; ˈfɪtᵻd/ *adj* **1** [never before a noun 不能用於名詞前] having a part or piece of apparatus 配有…部件的: *Is the car fitted with a C.D. player?* 這輛汽車裝有雷射唱機嗎? | *It's got a CD player fitted.* 它配有雷射唱機。**2** fixed in place 固定的: *a fitted carpet* 固定的地毯

fit·ter /ˈfɪtə; ˈfɪtər/ *n* someone who puts together machines or electrical parts 裝配工

fit·ting¹ /ˈfɪtɪŋ; ˈfɪtɪŋ/ *adj fml* right or suitable〔正式〕恰當的; 適合的: *It is fitting that we should remember those who have given their lives for freedom.* 我們紀念那些為爭取自由而捐軀的人們是合宜的。–opposite 反義 **unfitting**

fitting² *n* **1** an occasion when you put on clothes that are being made for you, to see if they fit 試衣; 試樣: *I'm going for a fitting on Tuesday.* 我打算星期二去試衣。**2 fittings** [pl] things that are fixed into a building but can be moved if necessary〔建築物中的〕固定裝置; 設備: *electric light fittings* 電

燈裝置

five /faɪv; faɪv/ *det,n,pron* the number 5〔數字〕五(個)

fiv·er /ˈfaɪvə; ˈfaɪvər/ *n infml* £5 or a five-pound note〔非正式〕五英鎊(鈔票): *It costs a fiver.* 它的價格是五英鎊。| *I've only got fivers.* 我只有面額五英鎊的鈔票。

★fix¹ /fɪks; fɪks/ *v* [T+adv/prep] to fasten something firmly 使〔某物〕固定: *She fixed the mirror onto the wall.* 她把鏡子固定在牆上。**2** [T] to arrange and establish an exact time, price, or place 安排, 確定〔時間、價格或地點〕: *Let's fix a time for the meeting.* 讓我們確定一下開會時間。| *The rent was fixed at £100.* 租金定為一百英鎊。| *If you want to meet them I can fix it.* 要是你想見他們, 我可以作出安排。**3** [T] to arrange the result of something unfairly 不公正地操縱〔某事〕: *The election was fixed.* 選舉被人操縱了。**4** [T] to repair something or make small changes to it 修理〔某物〕; 修整: *I must get the car fixed.* 我必須請人把汽車修理一下。| *She's in the Ladies fixing her make up.* 她在女廁所裡化妝打扮。**5** [T] to remember something because it is important or unusual 牢記〔重要的事情〕: *Let me fix the address in my mind.* 讓我把地址牢記在心上。**6** [T+adv/prep] to direct your attention steadily at something 盯住〔某物〕; 凝視〔某物〕: *She fixed her eyes on the clock.* 她凝視著那個鐘。| *He fixed me with his intense gaze.* 他以熱切的目光凝視著我。**7** [T] *AmE* to prepare food or drink for someone〔美式〕為〔某人〕準備〔食物或飲料〕: *Let me fix you a drink.* 我來給你弄點喝的。**8** [T] *infml* to punish someone〔非正式〕懲罰〔某人〕: *I'll fix him for calling me a liar!* 他罵我是說謊的人, 我要收拾他一下! **9 fix the blame on someone** to decide that someone is guilty 歸咎於某人

fix on sbdy/sthg *phr v* [T] to decide on someone or something 確定〔某事〕; 選定〔某人〕: *We've fixed on 14th April for the wedding.* 我們已經決定在四月十四日舉行婚禮。

fix up *phr v* **1** [I;T **fix** sthg ↔ **up**] to arrange something 安排〔某事〕: *I've fixed up another meeting.* 我安排了另一個會議。| *We'd already fixed up to go to Majorca.* 我們已經安排好去馬約卡島。| *I've fixed up for you to see the doctor.* 我為你去看醫生作了安排。**2** [T **fix** sthg ↔ **up**] to put something in place, often something that is only wanted for a short period 安裝〔某物〕〔常指只因一時需要的東西〕: *Doug's going to fix up some lights for the party.* 道格將為聚會安裝一些燈。| *Daisy fixed me up some shelves above the worktop.* 黛西給我在工作枱上面安裝了一些架子。**3 fix someone up with something** to provide someone with something they need 為某人提供所需之物: *Can you fix me up with a bed for the night?* 你能安排我過夜嗎? | *He fixed him up with a holiday job.* 他

為他安排了一份假期裡做的工作。**4** [T **fix** sthg ↔ **up**] to repair something or make it suitable for new needs 修理〔某物〕使其能派新的用場: *We'll have to fix up the attic as a bedroom.* 我們將要把閣樓裝修成臥室。**5 get fixed up: a** to find somewhere to live 尋找住處 **b** to succeed in making suitable arrangements 成功地作了合適的安排: *He was hoping to go to university, but I don't know whether he's got fixed up yet.* 他希望上大學，但我不知道他是否已作了適當的安排。

fix² *n infml*〔非正式〕**1** an awkward or difficult position 窘境; 困境: *We're in a real fix. We can't get any spare parts for the car before Monday.* 我們真的沒法子; 星期一之前無法弄到汽車備件。**2** *infml* something that has been dishonestly arranged〔非正式〕受操縱的事情: *It was a fix, that election!* 有人操縱了那次選舉! **3** an INJECTION of a drug like HEROIN 毒品注射〔如海洛因〕: *They looked as if they needed a fix of something.* 他們看上去好像需要來一針毒品。

fix·a·tion /fɪksˈeɪʃən; fɪkˈseɪʃən/ *n* a strong unhealthy feeling about or love for 固結; 固戀: *He has a fixation about* cleanliness. 他有潔淨癖。| *a mother fixation* 戀母情結

*fixed /fɪkst; fɪkst/ *adj* **1** not movable or changeable 固定的; 不能動的: *The tables are firmly fixed to the floor.* 桌子都牢牢地固定在地板上。| *The date is fixed now.* 日期現已確定。**2** held firmly and unchangingly 堅定不移的; 固執的: *He has very fixed ideas on this subject.* 他對這個問題的看法十分固執。**3 how are you fixed...?** = are you free...? 你〔甚麼時候〕有空嗎?: *I think we need another meeting. How are you fixed for Thursday morning?* 我認為我們需要再開一個會。你星期四上午有空嗎?

fix·ed·ly /ˈfɪksɪdlɪ; ˈfɪksɪdli/ *adv* unchangingly 不變地; 不動地: *Harry stared fixedly at the ground and looked embarrassed.* 哈里一動不動地凝視着地面，臉上顯出窘態。

fix·ture /ˈfɪkstʃə; ˈfɪkstʃəʳ/ *n* **1** something that is fixed into a building and sold with it〔房屋內的〕固定附屬裝置: *bathroom fixtures* 浴室附屬裝置 **2** a match or sports competition taking place on an agreed date 預定的比賽或體育競賽

fizz¹ /fɪz; fɪz/ *v* [I] (of a liquid) to produce bubbles (BUBBLE), or make the sound of very small bubbles bursting〔液體〕起泡; 發嘶嘶聲

fizz² *n* **1** the bubbles (BUBBLE) of gas in a liquid〔液體的〕氣泡: *This champagne has lost all its fizz!* 這瓶香檳酒已經沒有一點兒汽泡! **2** the sound of fizzing 嘶嘶聲 **–fizzy** *adj* **fizzier, fizziest:** *fizzy drinks like Coca-cola* 像可口可樂那樣的有氣飲料

fiz·zle /ˈfɪzl; ˈfɪzəl/ *v*

fizzle out *phr v* [I] to end in nothing after a good start〔開始不錯的事情〕終於失敗: *The party fizzled out before midnight.* 聚會在午夜前虎頭蛇尾地結束了。

fjord /fjɔrd; ˈfiːɔːd/ *n* (also 又作 **fiord**) a narrow bit of the sea between cliffs or steep slopes, especially in Norway〔尤指挪威的〕峽灣

flab·ber·gast·ed /ˈflæbəˌgæstɪd; ˈflæbəgɑːstɪd/ *adj infml* extremely surprised〔非正式〕目瞪口呆的; 大吃一驚的: *I was flabbergasted when he told me how much it had cost.* 當他把那價錢告訴我時，我大吃一驚。

flab·by /ˈflæbɪ; ˈflæbi/ *adj* **flabbier, flabbiest** having soft, loose flesh and muscles〔肌肉〕鬆弛的; 不結實的: *I'm getting very flabby. I suppose I ought to take more exercise.* 我的肌肉越來越鬆弛。我想我應該多參加鍛鍊。**–flabbiness** *n* [U]

flag¹ /flæg; flæg/ *n* **1** a square or OBLONG piece of cloth with a pattern in certain colours, used as a sign of a country or organization, or as a signal 旗: *The Egyptian flag was fluttering in the breeze.* 埃及國旗在微風中飄揚。| *The ship was flying the national flag of Japan.* 那艘輪船掛着日本國旗。**2** a small piece of paper joined to a pin given out by people collecting money for the poor or sick〔為窮人或病人募資金的人們分發的〕小紙旗 **3** a big square piece of stone for a floor or path〔鋪地或路的〕石板

flag² *v* **-gg-** [I] to become tired or less interested 變得疲倦或乏味: *After walking for three hours, we began to flag.* 走了三小時之後，我們開始感到疲乏無力。| *I tried to revive his flagging interest in the subject.* 我設法使他重新恢復對這個問題逐漸衰退的興趣。

flag sbdy/sthg ↔ **down** *phr v* [T] to signal to a vehicle to stop by waving at the driver〔揮手向司機〕發出停車信號: *They flagged down a lorry, which took them to a garage.* 他們揮手攔截了一輛卡車，把他們帶到一個加油站。

flag·pole /ˈflægˌpol; ˈflægpəʊl/ *n* a tall pole for a flag 旗桿

fla·grant /ˈfleɡrənt; ˈfleɪɡrənt/ *adj* open and showing no sign of guilt 公然的; 明目張膽的: *a flagrant abuse of taxpayers' money* 公然濫用納稅人繳的稅款 | *a flagrant liar* 當面說謊的人 **–flagrantly** *adv*

flag·stone /ˈflæɡˌston; ˈflæɡstəʊn/ *n* a hard, smooth, flat piece of stone for a floor or path〔鋪地面或路的〕石板

flail /fleɪl; fleɪl/ *v* [I;T] to wave violently but aimlessly about〔使勁地〕胡亂揮動; 擺動: *Her legs flailed in the water.* 她的雙腿在水中使勁地擺動。

flair /flɛr; fleəʳ/ *n* [sing;U] the natural ability to do something well 天賦; 天資: *She's got a real flair for making people feel at home.* 她真有本事，能使人感到無拘無束。

flake¹ /fleɪk; fleɪk/ *n* a small, thin piece of something 小薄片: *soap flakes* 肥皂片 | *snowflakes* 雪花 | *Flakes of plaster had fallen from the ceiling.* 薄薄的泥灰片從天花

板上脫落下來。**–flaky** *adj: flaky pastry* 酥餅

flake² *v* **flaked, flaking** [I] to fall off in flakes 成薄片狀剝落: *The paint's beginning to flake off.* 油漆開始成片狀剝落。

flake out *phr v* [I] *infml* to fall asleep or become unconscious because of great tiredness〖非正式〗〔累得〕睡着或昏倒

flaked out /ˌ · ˈ·/ *adj infml* extremely tired because of what you have been doing〖非正式〗〔因勞累而〕精疲力竭的: *After one game of tennis I was absolutely flaked out.* 我打完一局網球就徹底累垮了。

flam·boy·ant /flæmˈbɔɪənt; flæmˈbɔɪənt/ *adj* **1** showy and confident 愛炫耀的; 自信的: *With a flamboyant gesture he threw off the cover to reveal the statue.* 他以炫耀的姿態揭掉罩子, 露出了雕像。**2** brightly coloured and noticeable 豔麗的; 顯眼的: *a flamboyant orange shirt* 豔麗的橘紅色襯衫 – **flamboyantly** *adv* –**flamboyance** *n* [U]

flame¹ /flem; fleɪm/ *n* **1** [C;U] red or yellow burning gas seen when something is on fire 火焰; 火舌: *The dry sticks burst into flames.* 枯枝燃燒起來。| *Suddenly the car disappeared in a sheet of flame.* 汽車突然消失在一片大火中。**2 in flames** burning 着火 **3 naked flame** a flame which is not covered or protected 露天大火

flame² *v* **flamed, flaming** to become red or bright by or as if by burning 成火紅色; 發光: *The evening sky flamed red and gold.* 傍晚的天空閃耀着火紅色的亮光。

fla·men·co /fləˈmɛŋko; fləˈmeŋkəʊ/ *n* a form of very fast and exciting Spanish dancing and music 佛拉明柯舞〔一種快速、充滿激情的西班牙舞曲〕

flam·ing /ˈflemɪŋ; ˈfleɪmɪŋ/ *adj* **flaming row** a very angry quarrel 氣呼呼的爭吵: *I've just had a flaming row with my mother.* 我剛和媽媽氣呼呼地吵了一架。

fla·min·go /fləˈmɪŋgo; fləˈmɪŋgəʊ/ *n* **flamingos** *or* **flamingoes** a tall tropical water bird with long thin legs and pink and red feathers 紅鶴; 火烈鳥〔羽色粉紅或深紅的熱帶大涉禽〕

flam·ma·ble /ˈflæməbl; ˈflæməbəl/ *adj* easily set on fire 易燃的 –opposite 反義 **nonflammable**

> ■ USAGE 用法: **Flammable** is not the opposite of **inflammable**. The two words have the same meaning, but **flammable** is the usual form in American English and is also the technical word in British English. ☆ **Flammable** 並非是 **inflammable** 的反義詞。這兩個詞的意義相同, 但 **flammable** 是美式英語的常用形式, 而在英式英語中則用作專業術語。

flan /flæn; flæn/ *n* a round open case made of pastry or cake, with a filling such as fruit or cheese 果醬餅; 果餡餅

flange /flændʒ; flændʒ/ *n* the flat edge that stands out from the main surface of an object such as a railway wheel, to keep it in position〔火車的〕輪緣; 凸緣

flank¹ /flæŋk; flæŋk/ *n* **1** the fleshy side of an animal between its RIBS and its HIP 脅, 側腹 **2** the side of an army in battle〔作戰軍隊的〕側翼: *The enemy attacked us on the left flank.* 敵人進攻我方的左翼。

flank² *v* [T] **be flanked with** to have things on one or both sides 位於…的側面: *a road flanked with tall buildings* 兩側高樓林立的道路

flan·nel /ˈflænl; ˈflænl/ *n* **1** [U] soft light woollen cloth 法蘭絨: *flannel trousers* 法蘭絨褲 **2** [C] a piece of cloth used for washing yourself〔洗澡用的〕法蘭絨布塊

flap¹ /flæp; flæp/ *n* **1** [C] a wide flat part of anything that hangs down often to cover an opening 片狀垂懸物〔常可蓋住開口部分〕: *a cap with flaps to cover my ears* 帶護耳的帽子 | *They crept under the flap of the tent.* 他們在帳篷的布簾下爬行。| *the flap on an envelope* 信封口蓋 **2** [sing] the sound of flapping 輕拍聲: *the slow flap of the sails* 船帆緩慢的拍擊聲 **3 in a flap** *infml* in a state of excited anxiety〖非正式〗惴惴不安; 慌亂: *Don't get in a flap – we'll soon find it.* 別慌亂, 我們很快就會找到它的。

flap² *v* **-pp- 1** [I;T] to move something flat and large up and down or backwards and forwards making a noise 拍打; 拍動; 飄動: *The large bird flapped its wings.* 那只大鳥拍打着翅膀。| *The sails flapped in the wind.* 船帆在風中飄動。**2** [I] *infml* to become very excited and anxious〖非正式〗惴惴不安; 激動; 憂慮

flap·jack /ˈflæpˌdʒæk; ˈflæpdʒæk/ *n* a small flat cake 小煎餅

flare¹ /flɛr; fleəʳ/ *v* **flared, flaring** (also 又作 **flare up) 1** [I] to burn suddenly with a bright flame 突然燒旺: *The fire suddenly flared up.* 火突然燒得很旺。**2** (also 又作 **flare up**) to become suddenly very bad after being quiet for a period〔平靜一段時間後〕突然惡化: *Fighting in the area has flared up again.* 該地區的戰爭又爆發了。

flare² *n* **1** an object which sends out a bright light; it is shot into the air as a signal that someone needs help〔作為信號發出的〕閃光〔之物〕 **2** a sudden bright flame 突然的火苗: *There was a sudden flare as she lit the gas.* 她點煤氣時, 突然閃出了火苗。**3 flares** [pl] trousers which become wider from the knee down 喇叭褲

flared /flɛrd; fleəd/ *adj* shaped so as to get wider towards the bottom (used of trousers or skirts) 喇叭狀的〔指褲或裙〕

flare-up /ˈ· ·/ *n* a sudden burst of activity in the opposition between two groups〔兩個羣體之間對立行動的〕突然爆發: *a sudden* *flare-up of the fighting* 戰爭突然爆發

flash¹ /flæʃ; flæʃ/ v **1** [I] (of a light) to appear or shine for a moment 〔光〕閃爍: *The lightning flashed.* 閃電一掠而過。| *the flashing light on top of the police car* 警車頂部的閃光燈 **2** [T] to make a light shine for a moment 使〔燈〕閃光: *Why is that driver flashing his lights at me?* 那位司機幹嗎朝着我閃車燈? | *Stop flashing that light in my eyes.* 別把燈朝着我的臉打。

　flash back *phr v* [I] to return suddenly to an earlier time 忽然回想起〔過去時光〕; 閃現: *My mind flashed back to last Christmas.* 我忽然回想起去年聖誕節的情景。

flash² *n* **1** [C] sudden quick bright light 閃光; 閃爍: *flashes of lightning* 一道道閃電 **2** **flash of inspiration** a sudden good idea 靈感的閃現[突發] **3** [C;U] the method or apparatus for taking photographs in the dark 閃光攝影術; 閃光燈: *Did you use a flash?* 你用了閃光燈嗎? **4** **flash in the pan** a sudden success that will not be repeated 曇花一現: *This book was just a flash in the pan. I don't think he'll ever write another one as good.* 這本書只是一時的成功, 我認為他再也寫不出這樣的好書。 **5** **in a flash, like a flash** very quickly 瞬間; 即刻

flash·back /ˈflæʃˌbæk; ˈflæʃbæk/ *n* part of a film or book that goes back in time to show what happened earlier in the story 〔電影或書的〕倒敍(情節): *Then there's a flashback to his childhood.* 接着就是他童年故事的一段倒敍。

flash·light /ˈflæʃˌlaɪt; ˈflæʃlaɪt/ *n* the usual American word for 〔美式〕= TORCH

flash·y /ˈflæʃɪ; ˈflæʃɪ/ *adj* **flashier, flashiest** bright and expensive-looking in a way which you find unpleasant 俗麗的; 浮華的; 華而不實的: *a large flashy car* 華而不實的大轎車 | *cheap flashy clothes* 俗麗的廉價服裝 —**flashily** *adv*: *flashily dressed* 穿得顯眼而俗氣

flask /flæsk; flɑ:sk/ *n* **1** a bottle which is specially made for keeping liquids either hot or cold 〔可存放冷、熱液體的特製〕保溫瓶 —see picture on page 244 見 244 頁彩圖 **2** a narrow-necked glass bottle used by scientists 〔科學家使用的〕長頸瓶; 燒瓶 **3** a flat bottle for carrying alcohol or other drinks in your pocket 〔可放在衣袋中的〕扁酒瓶

*★**flat¹** /flæt; flæt/ *adj* **flatter, flattest 1** smooth and level without any raised parts, and not curved, pointed, or sloping 平的: *I need a flat surface to write on.* 我需要一個可寫字的平面。| *He's got quite a flat nose.* 他長着一個扁平的鼻子。| *a flat roof* 平屋頂 **2** not hilly or mountainous 平坦的: *Western Holland is very flat.* 荷蘭西部十分平坦。 **3** without enough air inside (used of tyres) 癟的〔指輪胎〕: *I've got a flat tyre.* 我有個輪胎漏了氣。 **4** no longer fresh because the gas has been lost (used of beer and other gassy

drinks) 〔啤酒或其他有氣飲料〕走了氣的 **5** having no more electric current left inside (used of batteries (BATTERY)) 電用完了的〔指蓄電池〕: *The car won't start. I left my lights on, so I expect the battery's flat.* 汽車起動不了。車一直開着, 所以我猜蓄電池沒電了。 **6** dull and uninteresting 單調乏味的: *Life seems very flat since you left.* 你走以後生活似乎非常單調沉悶。 **7** [only after a noun 只用於名詞後] *tech* lower than the main note (used of musical notes) 〔術語〕降音的; 降半音的〔指音符〕: *a piano concerto in E flat* 降 E 調鋼琴協奏曲 **8** slightly too low (used of musical notes) 偏低的〔指音符〕 **9** not having a high heel (used of shoes) 低跟的〔指鞋子〕 **10** **flat rate, flat fee** a fixed amount paid for something 固定收費 **11** **flat refusal** a complete and firm refusal 斷然的拒絕 **12** **and that's flat** *infml* 〔非正式〕= that is my decision and I won't change it 斷然無疑: *I won't go, and that's flat!* 我不去, 那是斷然無疑的!

*★**flat²** *n* **1** a set of rooms on one floor which are a home in a building or block 〔在同一層樓上的〕一套房間: *The house is divided into flats.* 這房子分成幾套房間。| *the people in the top flat* 住在頂層套房裡的人 –see picture on page 729 見 729 頁彩圖 –see 見 HOUSE (USAGE用法) **2** **flats** [pl] low level plains especially near water 低漥沼澤地: *mud flats* 泥沼地 **3** the flat part or side of something 〔某物的〕扁平部分; 平面: *I hit him with the flat of my hand.* 我用手掌打了他。 **4** a flat note in music 降半音 **5** the sign for a flat note in music 降半音符號 **6** *infml* a flat tyre 〔非正式〕漏氣輪胎

flat³ *adv* **1** lower than the note you are trying to sing or play 以降調〔演唱或演奏〕 **2** exactly, and not more than a certain period of time 恰恰; 正好: *I got dressed in three minutes flat!* 我穿衣正好花了三分鐘。 **3** **flat broke** completely without money 身無分文 **4** **flat out** at full speed 用全速: *I've been working flat out for two weeks now.* 我現已竭盡全力工作了兩個星期。

flat·ly /ˈflætlɪ; ˈflætli/ *adv* **1** spoken in a dull way with no feeling 麻木地〔說〕: *"It's hopeless," he said flatly.* "沒指望了," 他淡淡地說。 **2** **flatly refuse, flatly deny** to say very strongly that you will not do something or did not do something 斷然拒絕〔做某事〕; 完全否認〔做了某事〕

flat rac·ing /ˈ·　·ˌ·/ *n* [U] the sport of horseracing on flat ground 〔無障礙的〕平地賽馬

flat·ten /ˈflætn; ˈflætn/ *v* [T] to make something flat 把〔某物〕弄平; 使平貼: *Their crops had been flattened by the rain.* 他們的農作物被雨打得倒在地上了。| *I flattened myself against the wall.* 我把身子緊貼在牆上。

flat·ter /ˈflætə; ˈflætər/ *v* **1** [T] to praise someone too much or insincerely in order to please them 向〔某人〕諂媚; 奉承: *He flattered her on her cooking.* 他對她的烹調阿諛奉承。 **2 be flattered** to feel pleased that someone has shown that they think well of you 使滿意; 使感到榮幸: *She was flattered at the invitation.* 承蒙邀請, 她感到不勝榮幸。 **3 flatter yourself: a** to claim reasonably that something good is the case 自信: *I flatter myself that I know a good wine when I taste one.* 我自信好酒我一品嘗就知道。 **b** to believe unreasonably that something good is the case 自以為: *He is flattering himself if he thinks he can cook better than Sandy.* 如果他認為自己燒菜的水準比珊蒂高的話, 那是自以為是了。

flat·ter·ing /ˈflætərɪŋ; ˈflætərɪŋ/ *adj* making someone look attractive 令人喜愛的; 悅人的: *That dress is very flattering.* 那件連衣裙非常悅人。

flat·ter·y /ˈflætəri; ˈflætəri/ *n* [U] praising someone too much or insincerely in order to please them 諂媚; 奉承

flat·u·lence /ˈflætʃələns; ˈflætʃjələns/ *n* [U] *fml* the condition of having too much gas in your stomach 〔正式〕腸胃氣脹

flaunt /flɔnt; flɔːnt/ *v* [T] to show something to people so that they will admire it (a word used showing disapproval) 炫耀; 誇示〔含貶義〕: *She came into school flaunting her new gold watch.* 她走進學校, 一路炫耀她新買的金錶。

flau·tist /ˈflɔtɪst; ˈflɔːtɪst/ *n* (**flutist** *AmE* 【美式】) someone who plays she FLUTE 吹長笛者

fla·vour¹ /ˈfleivə; ˈfleɪvər/ *n* (**flavor** *AmE* 【美式】) [C;U] **1** a taste that you experience when you eat or drink something 味; 滋味; 味道: *a strong flavour of cheese* 一股濃重的乳酪味 | *Choose from six popular flavours of ice cream!* 請在受歡迎的六種味道的冰淇淋中挑選! | *This bread has plenty of flavour.* 這種麵包很有滋味。 **2 -flavoured** having a particular flavour 有...味道的: *strawberry-flavoured ice cream* 草莓味冰淇淋 **–flavourless** *adj*

flavour² *v* (**flavor** *AmE* 【美式】) [T] to give food a particular taste 給〔食物〕調味; 加味於...: *I flavoured the cake with chocolate.* 我用了巧克力給蛋糕調味。

fla·vour·ing /ˈfleivərɪŋ; ˈfleɪvərɪŋ/ *n* (**flavoring** *AmE* 【美式】) [U] something added to food to improve the taste 調味品; 調料: *Add a spoonful of banana flavouring.* 加一些香蕉調料。

flaw /flɔ; flɔː/ *n* a small mistake or weakness that makes something not perfect 缺點; 瑕疵: *a flaw in the material* 該材料的缺點 | *the flaws in a contract* 合約中的缺陷

flawed /flɔd; flɔːd/ *adj* [T] not perfect 不完美的; 有缺陷的: *a flawed argument* 有謬誤的論點

flaw·less /ˈflɔlɪs; ˈflɔːləs/ *adj* without any mistake or weakness 無缺點的; 無瑕的: *flawless beauty* 無可挑剔的美 | *a flawless performance* 無懈可擊的演出

flax /flæks; flæks/ *n* [U] the thread made from the stem of a plant with blue flowers, used for making LINEN 亞麻纖維

flax·en /ˈflæksn; ˈflæksən/ *adj esp.lit* pale yellow (used of hair) 【尤文】淡黃色的〔指頭髮〕

flea /fli; fliː/ *n* a small jumping insect without wings, that feeds on human or animal blood 跳蚤

flea mar·ket /ˈ· ·ˌ··/ *n* a street market where you can buy old or used goods 〔經營舊貨的〕露天市場; 跳蚤市場

fleck /flɛk; flɛk/ *n* a small coloured mark or spot on something 〔物體上的〕色斑; 小點: *brown cloth with flecks of red* 帶紅色斑點的棕色布料

flecked /flɛkt; flɛkt/ *adj* **flecked with** marked or covered with small marks or spots 帶有〔某種〕斑點的

flee /fli; fliː/ *v* **fled** /flɛd; flɛd/, **fled** [I;T] to escape by hurrying away 逃走; 逃掉: *They all fled **from** the burning building.* 他們都從着火的大樓裡逃了出來。 | *thousands of refugees fleeing from the civil war* 成千上萬逃離內戰的難民 | *Once the police were on their trail, they fled the country.* 他們一被警察追蹤就逃離本國。

fleece¹ /flis; fliːs/ *n* a sheep's woolly coat 〔未剪的〕羊毛

fleece² *v* **fleeced, fleecing** [T] *infml* to rob someone by tricking them or by charging too much money 【非正式】敲詐〔某人〕; 向〔某人〕漫天索價: *They really fleeced us at that hotel!* 那家旅館對我們真的可以說是敲詐勒索!

fleec·y /ˈflisi; ˈfliːsi/ *adj* soft and woolly 柔軟的; 羊毛狀的

fleet /flit; fliːt/ *n* **1** a group of ships, especially warships in the navy working together 〔行動統一的〕艦隊 **2** a group of vehicles belonging to one company 〔某一公司的〕車隊

fleet·ing /ˈflitɪŋ; ˈfliːtɪŋ/ *adj* short and passing or happening quickly 短暫的; 飛逝的: *fleeting smile* 一閃而過的笑容

★flesh¹ /flɛʃ; flɛʃ/ *n* [U] **1** the soft substance including fat and muscle, that covers bones and lies under your skin 肉〔包括骨頭和皮膚之間的脂肪和肌肉〕 **2** your skin 皮膚: *her soft, white flesh* 她那柔軟白皙的皮膚 **3** the soft part of a fruit or vegetable, which can be eaten 果肉; 蔬菜的可食部分 **4 the pleasures of the flesh** sexual pleasures 肉慾; 情慾 **5 your own flesh and blood** your own family or relations 親骨肉; 親人 **6 in the flesh** in real life, as opposed to on television or in a picture 本人〔與電視或相片中的人作對比〕: *He's more handsome in the flesh than in his photographs.* 他本人比照片上英俊。

flesh·y /'flɛʃɪ; 'fleʃi/ *adj* **fleshier, fleshiest 1** like flesh 似肉的 **2** fat 肥胖的: *his round, fleshy face* 他又圓又胖的臉

flew /fluː; fluː/ the past tense of FLY ☆ FLY 的過去式

flex¹ /flɛks; fleks/ *v* [T] to bend and move your limbs or muscles so as to stretch and loosen them 屈曲〔四肢或肌肉〕〔使其放鬆〕: *The runners flexed their muscles as they waited for the race to begin.* 賽跑選手在等候比賽開始時, 伸屈四肢, 放鬆肌肉。

flex² *n BrE* [C;U] electric wire in a protective covering, which connects an electrical machine to a supply of electricity 〔英式〕〔電器的〕花線; 皮線 –see picture on page 958 見 958 頁彩圖

flex·i·ble /'flɛksəbl; 'fleksḷbəl/ *adj* **1** easily bent 易彎曲的; 柔韌的 **2** able to change to suit different needs or situations 可適應不同需要或情況的; 可變通的; 靈活的: *flexible working hours* 彈性工作時間 –opposite 反義 **inflexible** –**flexibility** /ˌflɛksə'bɪlətɪ; ˌfleksḷ-'bɪlˌti/ *n* [U]

flick /flɪk; flɪk/ *v* **1** [I;T] to move or hit something quickly and lightly 輕快地動、打、拍、彈等: *He flicked ash into the ashtray.* 他把灰輕輕彈入煙灰缸。| *The snake's tongue flicked in and out of its mouth.* 蛇的舌頭在嘴裡輕快地伸進伸出。 **2** [T] to move something such as a piece of string quickly at one end so that the other end moves quickly and suddenly 彈去; 拂去〔某物〕: *Taking a tea towel, he flicked the crumbs off the table.* 他拿了一塊擦餐具的抹布, 拂去桌上的麵包屑。 **3 flick a switch** to move a button or control on a machine so that it is on or off 輕按開關: *Could you just flick that switch off?* 就把那個開關關掉, 行嗎? **4 flick through something** to turn the pages of something such as a book or a newspaper quickly in order to find a particular thing or to get an idea of what is in it 飛快地翻閱〔書或報紙〕; 瀏覽: *She flicked through the paper until she found the TV times.* 她快速地翻閱着報紙, 直至找到電視節目的播出時間。 –**flick** *n: Isn't it marvellous to have the house warm at the flick of a switch?* 一按開關房子就會暖和, 那不是太奇妙了嗎?

flick·er¹ /'flɪkə; 'flɪkəʳ/ *v* [I] to burn or move unsteadily 閃爍; 搖曳: *The wind blew the flickering candle out.* 風把閃爍不定的蠟燭吹滅了。| *Shadows flickered on the wall.* 影子在牆上晃動。

flicker² *n* [sing] **1** an unsteady movement from a light or a fire 閃爍; 搖曳 **2** a slight feeling that lasts only a very short time 一閃而過的情緒: *a flicker of interest* 一時的興趣

flick knife /'··/ *n* a knife with a blade that springs out from inside the handle when a button is pressed 彈簧刀

★**flight** /flaɪt; flaɪt/ *n* **1** [C;U] the act of flying 飛翔; 飛行: *a bird in flight* 飛翔的鳥 | *a bird's first flight from the nest* 鳥兒離窠的第一次飛翔 **2** [C] a trip by plane 班機; 空中旅行: *"Did you have a good flight?" "No, it was the worst flight I've ever been on."* "你的空中旅行順利嗎?" "不順利, 這是我所乘坐過的最糟糕的一次航班。" | *Flight 705 to Paris* 去巴黎的705號班機 **3** [C] a set of stairs between different floors 一段樓梯: *She fell down a flight of stairs.* 她從一段樓梯上跌了下來。 **4** [sing] the act of running away or escaping 逃走; 逃跑: *the flight of refugees from the war zone* 難民從戰區逃走 **5 take flight** to run away from something in a hurry 逃走; 逃跑: *When the police arrived the thieves took flight.* 警察趕到時, 小偷便逃跑了。

flight·less /'flaɪtlɪs; 'flaɪtləs/ *adj* unable to fly 不會飛的: *The penguin is a flightless bird.* 企鵝是一種不會飛的鳥。

flight·y /'flaɪtɪ; 'flaɪti/ *adj* **flightier, flightiest** not serious enough and often changing from one man to another, or from one idea to another (used of women and their behaviour) 輕浮的; 朝三暮四的; 反覆無常的〔指女子及其行為〕 –**flightiness** *n* [U]

flim·sy /'flɪmzɪ; 'flɪmzi/ *adj* **flimsier, flimsiest** light, thin and not strong 輕而薄的; 軟弱的; 脆弱的: *flimsy cloth* 輕薄的布 | *a flimsy argument* 站不住腳的論點 –**flimsiness** *n* [U]

flinch /flɪntʃ; flɪntʃ/ *v* [I] **1** to move back in fear when shocked or in pain 〔因吃驚、害怕或疼痛〕畏縮; 退縮: *He didn't flinch once when the doctor was cleaning the wound.* 醫生清洗他的傷口時, 他毫不畏懼。 **2 flinch from something** to feel unwilling to do something unpleasant 不願做某種不愉快的事: *She's not the sort to flinch from an argument, however fierce.* 無論辯論有多麼激烈, 她都不會退縮。

fling¹ /flɪŋ; flɪŋ/ *v* **flung** /flʌŋ; flʌŋ/, **flung** [T] to throw something violently or with force 〔用力地〕扔; 擲; 拋〔某物〕: *She always flings her coat on the floor when she comes home.* 她回到家裡總是把衣服扔在地板上。| *The military government flung its opponents into prison.* 軍人政府把反對派投入監獄。| *She flung her arms around him.* 她猛地伸出雙臂把他抱住。

fling² *n* **1** a short time when you really enjoy yourself, especially if it is your last chance to do it 一時的放縱〔尤指最後的行樂〕 **2** a short love affair 短暫的做愛

flint /flɪnt; flɪnt/ *n* **1** [C;U] a type of very hard grey stone that makes very small flames when struck with steel 燧石; 火石 **2** [C] a small piece of metal used in cigarette lighters to light the petrol or gas 〔打火機用的〕打火石

flip /flɪp; flɪp/ *v* **-pp- 1 flip through something** to turn the pages of something such as a book or a newspaper quickly in order to find a particular thing or to get an idea of what is in it 草草翻閱書報等: *Hang on. I just want to flip through Radio Times.* 等一會兒, 我只想草草翻閱一下廣播電視週刊。**2** [T+adv/prep] to change the position of something by a quick light movement 〔輕快地〕改變、移動〔某物〕: *Could you just flip up the lid of the bin for me?* 你能不能就幫我把箱子蓋打開? | *She flipped the eggs over and cooked the other side.* 她很快地把(雞)蛋翻過來燒另一面。**3 flip a coin** to use your finger and thumb to send a coin spinning into the air in order to make a decision according to which way up it lands 〔為作出抉擇而向空中〕拋擲硬幣 **4** [I] *infml* to become suddenly very angry or upset 〔非正式〕發怒 **–flip** *n*

flip·pant /'flɪpənt; 'flɪpənt/ *adj* disrespectful about serious subjects 輕率的: *flippant remarks* 輕率的言語 **–flippantly** *adv* **–flippancy** *n* [U]

flip·per /'flɪpə; 'flɪpəʳ/ *n* a limb of certain larger sea animals which has a flat edge and is used for swimming 〔某些海生大動物的〕鰭(狀)肢

flirt[1] /flɜːt; flɜːt/ *v* [I] to behave with a member of the opposite sex in a way that attracts his or her attention 調情; 賣俏: *He's always flirting* **with** *the women in the office.* 他老是與辦公室的女職員調情。 **–flirtation** /flɜː'teɪʃən; flɜː'teɪʃən/ *n* [C;U]

flirt[2] *n* a person who often flirts with members of the opposite sex 調情的人; 賣俏的人

flir·ta·tious /flɜː'teɪʃəs; flɜː'teɪʃəs/ *adj* behaving in a way which attracts the attention of someone of the opposite sex 調情的; 賣俏的

flit /flɪt; flɪt/ *v* **-tt-** [I+adv/prep] to fly or move from one place to another with quick light movements 輕快地飛動: *The birds flitted from branch to branch.* 鳥兒在樹林間飛來飛去。

float[1] /fləʊt; fləʊt/ *v* **1** [I] to stay at the top of liquid 浮; 漂: *Wood floats on water.* 木頭漂浮在水上。**2** [T] to make something float 使〔某物〕漂浮 **3** [I+adv/prep] to travel on the surface of water as it travels along, or with a current of air 漂流; 漂動: *The logs float down the river.* 圓木順着河流漂下。**4** [I+adv/prep] to move easily and lightly 漂然走動 **5** [T] to allow the exchange value of money to vary freely in value against other countries' money from day to day 使〔貨幣匯率〕浮動: *After the pound was floated, its value went down.* 英鎊對外匯率浮動後出現了貶值。**6** [T] to start to sell shares in a company to the public 〔公開〕發行〔公司股票〕

float[2] *n* **1** a light flat object that helps someone or something float 漂浮物 **2** a small object that floats on a fishing line or net 浮標; 浮子 **3** a large vehicle which is specially decorated for processions 〔遊行時用的〕大花車 **4** a small amount of coins which a

salesperson has before they start to sell so that they will be able to give change 〔商店的〕日常備用零錢

float·ing /'fləʊtɪŋ; 'fləʊtɪŋ/ *adj* **1** not fixed or settled 浮動的; 流動的: *London has a large floating population.* 倫敦有大批流動人口。**2 floating voter** a person who does not always vote for the same political party 浮動選民〔未必總投同一政黨選票的人〕

flock[1] /flɒk; flɔk/ *n* **1** a group of sheep, goats, or birds 羊羣; 鳥羣 **2** a large crowd of people 一大羣人

flock[2] *v* [I+adv/prep] to go somewhere in large crowds 羣集; 蜂擁: *People flocked to the cinema to see the new film.* 人們蜂擁到電影院去看那部新影片。

flog /flɒg; flɔg/ *v* **-gg-** [T] **1** to beat someone severely with a whip or stick, as a punishment 〔作為懲罰〕鞭打; 棒打〔某人〕**2** *infml* to sell something 〔非正式〕出售〔某物〕**3 flog a dead horse** *infml* to waste your time with useless efforts 〔非正式〕徒勞無益; 白費勁

flog·ging /'flɒgɪŋ; 'flɔgɪŋ/ *n* [C;U] a severe beating with a whip or stick, as punishment 〔作為懲罰的〕鞭打; 棒打

flood[1] /flʌd; flʌd/ *n* **1** a great overflow of water on to a place that is usually dry 洪水; 水災: *The town was destroyed by the floods.* 這個鎮被洪水沖毀了。 | *The river rose to flood level.* 河水漲到了泛濫點。**2** a large number of things that arrive together 大量; 大批(的東西): *There was a flood* **of** *complaints about the bad language used in the show.* 人們對節目裡的粗言穢語大為不滿。

flood[2] *v* **1** [I;T] to fill or cover with water (使)淹沒: *Every spring the river floods the valley.* 每年春天河水都會淹沒山谷。 | *Our street floods whenever we have rain.* 我們這條街下雨就淹水。**2** [I+adv/prep] to come or go to a place in large numbers 大量湧到: *Requests for information flooded in after the advertisement.* 廣告登出之後, 索取資料的信件潮湧般寄來。 | *Settlers flooded from Europe to America in the 19th century.* 十九世紀, 歐洲移民紛紛湧到了美國。**3** [T] to fill a place with things 使〔某物〕充斥〔某處〕: *The market has been flooded* **with** *cheap imitations.* 廉價贋品已經充斥了市場。**–flooding** *n* [U]: *When the snow melted, there was widescale flooding.* 雪溶化時, 洪水到處泛濫。

flood·gate /'flʌd,geɪt; 'flʌdgeɪt/ *n* **1** a gate used for controlling the flow from a large body of water 防洪閘門 **2 open the floodgates** to make it possible for a lot of people to do something 打開閘門〔使許多人做某事成為可能〕: *The new freedom of the press has opened the floodgates to the democracy movement.* 新的出版自由為民主運動打開了閘門。

flood·light /'flʌd,laɪt; 'flʌdlaɪt/ *n* a large electric light used for lighting sports grounds, or the outside of buildings at night 〔運動場或建築物外的〕泛光燈; (泛光)探照燈

flood·light² v **-lighted** or **-lit** /lɪt; lɪt/, **-lighted** or **-lit** [T] to light a place by using floodlights 用泛光燈照明: *Buckingham Palace is floodlit at night.* 白金漢宮在夜晚被泛光燈照得通亮。

★floor¹ /flɔr; flɔːʳ/ n **1** the surface on which you stand indoors 〔室內的〕地面; 地板: *He threw the book onto the floor.* 他把書扔到了地上。 **2** a level of a building 〔樓房的〕層: *I live on the ground floor of a block of flats.* 我住在公寓大樓的底樓。| *Our office is on the sixth floor.* 我們的辦公室在七樓。–see picture on page 729 見 729 頁彩圖 **3 the floor** the part of a parliament or council building where members sit and speak 議員就坐和發言的席位

■ USAGE 用法: In British English the bottom floor of a building (at ground level) is called the **ground floor.** In American English this is called the **first floor.** In British English the next level up is called the **first floor.** In American English it is called the **second floor.** ☆在英式英語中, 樓房的底層〔地面層〕叫作 **ground floor,** 而在美式英語中則叫 **first floor.** 在英式英語中, 地面的上一層叫 **first floor,** 而在美式英語中則叫 **second floor.**

floor² v [T] **1** to knock someone down 把〔某人〕打倒在地: *He floored his attacker with one heavy blow.* 他重重一拳就把攻擊他的人打倒在地。 **2** to ask someone a question or put them in a situation to which they have no answer 問倒; 難倒〔某人〕: *The teacher seemed completely floored by my question.* 老師似乎完全被我的問題難住了。

floor·board /ˈflɔr,bɔrd; ˈflɔːbɔːd/ n a board in a wooden floor 一塊木頭地板

flop¹ /flɑp; flɒp/ v **-pp- 1** [I+adv/prep] to move or fall heavily or awkwardly 〔沉重地或笨重地〕移動, 倒下: *He can't swim much. He just flops about in the water.* 他不大會游泳, 只能在水中瞎撲騰。| *She flopped into an armchair.* 她驀地倒在扶手椅上。 **2** [I] *infml* to be very unsuccessful 〔非正式〕失敗: *The new play flopped after only two weeks.* 這齣新戲僅上演了兩個星期就失敗了。

flop² n **1** a heavy, falling movement 重墜 **2** an event that is very unsuccessful 失敗的事情

flop·py /ˈflɑpɪ; ˈflɒpi/ adj **floppier, floppiest** soft and not at all stiff 鬆軟: *a floppy hat* 鬆軟下垂的帽子

floppy disk /ˌ·· ˈ·/ n a specially treated piece of plastic on which information for a computer is stored 〔電腦的〕軟磁盤 –see picture on page 763 見 763 頁彩圖

flo·ra /ˈflɔrə; ˈflɔːrə/ n [U] *tech* all the plants growing wild in a particular place 〔術語〕〔生長在某一地區的〕植物羣

flo·ral /ˈflɔrəl; ˈflɔːrəl/ adj made of flowers or containing flowers 用花做的; 含花的: *floral patterns* 花卉圖案 –see picture on page 243 見 243 頁彩圖

flor·id /ˈflɔrɪd; ˈflɒrɪd/ adj fml 〔正式〕 **1** having too much decoration 過分裝飾的; 華麗的: *florid language* 華麗的言詞 **2** having a red face 臉色紅潤的

flor·ist /ˈflɔrɪst; ˈflɒrɪst/ n **1** a person who sells flowers 花商 **2 florist's** a shop which sells flowers 花店: *Did you get the daffodils at the florist's?* 你在花店買到水仙花了嗎?

flo·til·la /floˈtɪlə; fləˈtɪlə/ n a group of small ships, especially warships 小船隊〔尤指小艦隊〕

flounce /flaʊns; flaʊns/ v **flounced, flouncing** [I+adv/prep] to walk showing you are angry 氣呼呼地走動: *She refused my advice and flounced out of the house.* 她拒絕接受我的忠告, 氣呼呼地離開了屋子。

floun·der /ˈflaʊndə; ˈflaʊndə/ v [I] **1** to move wildly about in the water when you are trying to save yourself from drowning 〔在水中〕掙扎〔以免淹死〕 **2** to continue to act but without producing good results because you do not really know what to do 笨拙而錯亂地行事

flour /flaʊr; flaʊə/ n [U] powder made from wheat and used for making bread, pastry, or cakes 麵粉

flour·ish¹ /ˈflɝɪʃ; ˈflʌrɪʃ/ v **1** [I] to grow healthily or successfully 茂盛; 繁榮: *Plants like that will not flourish in the shade.* 那種植物在陰涼處不會長得茂盛。| *The company has really flourished since we moved our factory to Scotland.* 自從我們把工廠遷移到蘇格蘭以後, 公司確實興旺發達了。 **2** [T] to wave something in your hand and so draw attention to it 揮舞〔以引起注意〕: *"I've passed my examination!" shouted Jane, flourishing a letter.* "我通過考試了!" 簡揮舞着一封信嚷道。

flourish² n a special showy movement to do honour to someone or to draw attention to yourself 顯眼的動作〔用以向某人致意或引起注意〕: *He opened the door with a flourish.* 他以一個誇張的動作打開了門。

flour·ish·ing /ˈflɝɪʃɪŋ; ˈflʌrɪʃɪŋ/ adj happy and successful 欣欣向榮的; 成功的: *a flourishing market town of about 12,000 people* 一個大約有一萬二千人的欣欣向榮的集鎮 | *"How's David?" "Oh, he's flourishing. Everything's going very well."* "大衛好嗎?" "噢, 他幹得相當不錯。一切都很順利。"

flout /flaʊt; flaʊt/ v [T] to disobey a rule or law 藐視〔法規〕: *He had flouted all the rules.* 他藐視所有的規章制度。

★flow¹ /flo; fləʊ/ v [I] **1** (of liquid) to move or pour smoothly 〔液體〕流動; 湧出: *The river's flowing quite fast here.* 這兒的河水流得很

快。| *Her tears flowed fast.* 她的眼淚一湧而出。**2** to move forward steadily or smoothly 川流不息；暢通無阻: *The traffic never flows freely in the town centre.* 市中心的交通從來都不會暢通無阻。**3** (of hair and clothes) to hang loosely〔頭髮、衣服〕飄垂；飄拂: *Her hair flowed over her shoulders.* 她的頭髮飄垂在肩上。| *long flowing robes* 寬鬆飄灑的長袍

flow² *n* [U] a smooth steady movement 流動: *the gentle flow of the river* 緩緩流動的河水 | *the flow of electricity to our homes* 接通我們家的電流

☆**flow·er¹** /ˈflaʊə; ˈflaʊəʳ/ *n* **1** the part of a plant, often beautiful and coloured, that produces seeds or fruit 花 **2** a plant that is grown for the beauty of its flowers 開花植物: *I think I'll plant some flowers under the windows.* 我想要在窗下種些花草。**3 in flower** having flowers on 在開花(期): *The roses are in flower.* 這些玫瑰花正在盛開。

flower² *v* [I] (of a plant) to produce flowers〔植物〕開花: *This bush flowers in the spring.* 這叢矮樹春天開花。

flow·er·bed /ˈflaʊə‚bɛd; ˈflaʊəbed/ *n* a piece of ground in a garden or park, in which flowers are grown 花壇 –see picture on page 729 見 729 頁彩圖

flow·ered /ˈflaʊəd; ˈflaʊəd/ *adj* decorated with flower patterns 用花卉圖案裝飾的: *flowered dress material* 有花卉圖案的衣料 – see picture on page 243 見 243 頁彩圖

flow·er·pot /ˈflaʊ‚pɑt; ˈflaʊəpɒt/ *n* a pot in which a plant can be grown 花盆

flow·er·y /ˈflaʊrɪ; ˈflaʊəri/ *adj* **1** decorated with flowers 用花裝飾的: *a flowery pattern* 花卉圖案 –see picture on page 243 見 243 頁彩圖 **2** containing fancy language (used of speech or writing) 詞藻華麗的〔指演講或文章〕

flown /floʊn; fləʊn/ the past participle of FLY ☆ FLY 的過去分詞

flu /flu; fluː/ *n* [U] a disease which is like a bad cold but more serious 流行性感冒

fluc·tu·ate /ˈflʌktʃʊ‚et; ˈflʌktʃʊeɪt/ *v* **fluctuated, fluctuating** [I] to change often 波動；漲落；起伏: *The price of vegetables fluctuates according to the season.* 蔬菜的價格隨季節而波動。| *His feelings fluctuated between excitement and fear.* 他的情緒起伏不定，時而激動，時而恐懼。–**fluctuation** /‚flʌktʃʊˈeʃən; ‚flʌktʃʊˈeɪʃən/ *n* [C;U]

flue /flu; fluː/ *n* a pipe in a chimney up which smoke or heat passes 煙道；暖氣管

flu·en·cy /ˈfluənsɪ; ˈfluːənsi/ *n* [U] the ability to speak a language easily and without thinking〔說話〕流利；流暢

flu·ent /ˈfluənt; ˈfluːənt/ *adj* **1** able to speak or write a language easily and well〔說話或寫作〕流利的；流暢的: *She is fluent in English.* 她的英語很流利。**2** very good (used of languages) 流利的〔指語言〕: *Her English is fluent.* 她的英語很流利。| *She speaks flu-*

ent English. 她會講一口流利的英語。–**fluently** *adv*

fluff¹ /flʌf; flʌf/ *n* [U] **1** soft loose waste from woollen or other materials〔織物的〕絨毛；蓬鬆毛: *The carpet needs cleaning — it's covered in fluff.* 地毯需要清潔一下，上面滿是絨毛。**2** very soft fur or hair on a young animal or bird〔禽獸的〕軟毛

fluff² *v*

fluff sthg ↔ **out** *phr v* [T] (also 又作 **fluff** sthg ↔ **up**) to make something soft appear larger by getting lots of air into it 抖鬆、拍鬆〔某物〕: *The bird fluffed out its feathers in the sun.* 鳥在陽光下抖鬆羽毛。| *She fluffed up the pillows.* 她把枕頭拍鬆。

fluff·y /ˈflʌfɪ; ˈflʌfi/ *adj* **fluffier, fluffiest** soft and light, like hair or fur〔像絨毛那樣〕輕軟的；鬆軟的: *a fluffy jumper* 輕軟的無袖連衣裙–**fluffiness** *n* [U]

flu·id¹ /ˈfluɪd; ˈfluː‚ɪd/ *adj* **1** having a moving, flowing quality, like liquids, air, or gas 流動的；流體的 **2** not fixed or settled 不固定的；不穩定的: *Our ideas on the subject are still fluid.* 我們對這個問題的想法還未確定。–**fluidity** /fluˈɪdətɪ; fluːˈɪdʌti/ *n* [U]

fluid² *n* [C;U] a liquid 液體；流體

fluid ounce /‚·· ˈ·/ *n* a measure of liquid equal to one 20th of a PINT or 0.0284 of a litre 液量盎司〔等於二十分之一品脫，或 0.0284 升〕

fluke /fluk; fluːk/ *n infml* something lucky that happens by chance〔非正式〕僥倖發生的事: *She isn't usually good at tennis. That winning stroke was a fluke.* 她平時網球打得並不好，那致勝的一擊不過是僥倖而已。

flum·mox /ˈflʌməks; ˈflʌməks/ *v* [T] *infml* to confuse someone and make them uncertain what to say or do〔非正式〕使〔某人〕困惑；使慌亂

flung /flʌŋ; flʌŋ/ the past tense and past participle of FLING ☆ FLING 的過去式和過去分詞

flu·o·res·cent /‚fluəˈrɛsnt; fluəˈresənt/ *adj* **1** fluorescent light a very bright light in the form of a tube 螢光 **2** seeming to shine very brightly when lit up 發螢光的

flu·o·ride /ˈfluə‚raɪd; ˈflʊəraɪd/ *n* [U] a chemical substance that helps protect teeth against decay 氟化物〔可預防齲齒〕

flur·ry /ˈflɝɪ; ˈflʌri/ *n* **flurries 1** a sudden sharp rush of wind, rain, snow 陣風；陣雨；陣雪 **2** a sudden short and very active period 一陣〔混亂、忙亂、激動〕: *His arrival produced a flurry of excitement.* 他的抵達引起了一陣騷動。

flush¹ /flʌʃ; flʌʃ/ *v* **1** [T] to clean a TOILET or pipe with a sudden flow of water 沖洗〔廁所或管道〕: *Remember to flush the toilet.* 別忘了沖洗廁所。**2** [I] to be cleaned by means of a flow of water 被沖洗: *The lavatory won't flush.* 抽水馬桶沖不下去了〔堵塞了〕。**3** [I] to become red in the face because you feel ashamed 〔因感到慚愧而〕臉發紅: *She flushed when she couldn't answer the question.* 她因回答不出問題而臉紅。

flush out *phr v* **1** [T **flush** sthg ↔ **out**] to clean something or to remove something blocking a pipe by running water through it 〔用水〕沖洗; 清除〔堵塞物〕 **2** [T **flush** sbdy ↔ **out**] to force someone to leave a hiding place 把〔某人〕趕出〔隱蔽處〕

flush² *n* **1** a sudden flow of water that cleans a TOILET or pipe 〔馬桶或管道的〕沖洗 **2** redness of your face caused by being hot, ill, or ashamed 〔因炎熱、疾病或羞愧引起的〕臉紅; 漲紅; 紅暈 **3 in the first flush of** in the first part of something pleasant 令人愉快之事的初始: *In the first flush of success he ordered drinks for everybody.* 他初次成功十分喜悦, 為大家要了些飲料。

flush³ *adj* **1** flat and level with a surface 齊平的; 同平面的: *These cupboards aren't flush with the wall.* 這些櫥櫃與牆不在同一平面上。 **2** [never before a noun 不能用於名詞前] *infml* having plenty of money 〔非正式〕很有錢的: *I've just been paid, so I'm feeling quite flush.* 我剛領到工資, 所以覺得很富裕。

flushed /flʌʃt; flʌʃt/ *adj* **1** red in the face 臉紅的: *Louisa's looking rather flushed. I hope she isn't sickening for anything.* 露伊莎的臉色很發紅。希望她別得甚麼病。 **2** very excited or pleased about something 〔因某事〕非常激動的; 高興的: *He arrived late, flushed with excitement.* 他來遲了, 激動得滿臉通紅。

flus·ter /ˈflʌstə; ˈflʌstər/ *n* **in a fluster** feeling hot, nervous, and confused 緊張的; 慌亂的

flus·tered /ˈflʌstəd; ˈflʌstəd/ *adj* made to feel nervous and confused, and perhaps hot and uncomfortable 使緊張的; 使慌亂的

flute /fluːt; fluːt/ *n* a musical instrument like a pipe, which you play by blowing across a hole in the side 長笛

flut·ist /ˈfluːtɪst; ˈfluːtɪst/ *n see 見* FLAUTIST

flut·ter¹ /ˈflʌtə; ˈflʌtər/ *v* **1** [I] to fly or move through the air with light quick movements in different directions 〔在空中輕快地〕飛動; 飛舞: *There were moths fluttering round the light.* 有一些蛾繞着燈飛來飛去。 | *The dead leaves fluttered to the ground.* 枯葉飄到地上。 **2** [I;T] to wave or move quickly up and down or backwards and forwards 飄揚; 抖動: *The flag fluttered in the wind.* 旗幟迎風飄揚。 | *The geese stood up and fluttered their wings.* 鵝站立着抖動翅膀。 **3 her heart fluttered** = she felt excited and nervous 她的心怦怦直跳〔她覺得既興奮又緊張〕

flutter² *n* [sing] **1** a light, quick movement in different directions 拍翅; 飄動: *There was a flutter of wings among the trees.* 林間鳥兒在拍打翅膀。 **2 in a flutter** feeling nervous and excited 緊張的; 激動的

flux /flʌks; flʌks/ *n* [U] *fml* a state of continual change 〔正式〕不斷變化的狀態: *Our future plans are unsettled. Everything is in a state of flux.* 我們有關將來的計劃尚未定了, 一切都在不斷變化之中。

*fly¹ /flaɪ; flaɪ/ *v* **flew** /fluː; fluː/, **flown** /fləʊn; fləʊn/ **1** [I] to move through the air 飛; 飛行: *A small bird flew up into the tree.* 一隻小鳥飛到了樹上。 | *This plane is due to fly to New York this evening.* 這架飛機預定今晚飛往紐約。 **2** [I;T] to travel by plane, or take a person or thing somewhere by plane 乘飛機旅行; 空運〔人或物〕: *She flew to London yesterday.* 昨天她乘飛機前往倫敦。 | *I hate flying.* 我不喜歡乘坐飛機。 | *Our goods are flown all over the world.* 我們的貨物被空運到世界各地。 **3** [T] to be the pilot of a plane 駕駛〔飛機〕: *I've always wanted to fly an aeroplane.* 我老是想開飛機。 **4** [I;T] to move about in the wind, or hold or fix something so that it moves about in the wind 飄揚; 使〔某物〕飛揚: *A flag was flying on top of the building.* 旗子在大樓頂上隨風飄揚。 | *We're going off to fly our kite.* 我們要去放風箏。 **5** [I+adv/prep] to move quickly or suddenly 疾行; 疾跑: *The train flew past the station.* 火車從站前疾駛而過。 | *She flew up the stairs.* 她奔上樓去。 **6** [I] to pass quickly 〔時間〕飛逝: *Our holiday has just flown!* 我們的假期一晃就過去了! | *Doesn't time fly?* 時間過得真快呀! **7 fly at someone, let fly at someone** to attack someone, physically or with words 〔用拳或言語〕攻擊某人 **8 fly into a temper, fly into a rage** to become very angry 勃然大怒 **9 fly off the handle** to become very angry 狂怒 **10 I must fly** = I must leave quickly 我必須趕快走

fly² *n* **flies** /flaɪz; flaɪz/ **1** a small flying insect with two wings 蒼蠅 **2 flies** [pl] the front opening of a pair of trousers 褲子前面的開口: *Your flies are open!* 你的褲子拉鏈開了! **3 fly in the ointment** a small unwanted thing that spoils the pleasure of something 掃興的事物

fly·ing /ˈflaɪɪŋ; ˈflaɪɪŋ/ *adj* **1** [only before a noun 只用於名詞前] able to fly 能飛的 **2 flying jump, flying leap** a long or high jump 急行起跳: *He took a flying leap and jumped across the stream.* 他急行幾步, 然後縱身跳過溪流。 **3 flying visit** a very short visit 短暫的訪問 **4 get off to a flying start** to make a very good beginning 開端很好 **5 pass with flying colours** to succeed very well in an examination or a test 以優異成績通過考試 **6 send/knock something flying** to knock something over by pushing or hitting it violently 把〔某物〕撞倒[擊倒]

flying sau·cer /ˌ·· ˈ···/ *n* a plate-shaped vehicle which is believed to come from another world 飛碟; 不明飛行物

fly·o·ver /ˈflaɪˌəʊvə; ˈflaɪˌəʊvər/ *n* a kind of bridge where one road crosses another 立交橋; 高架公路

FM /ˌef ˈem; ˌef ˈem◂/ a system of broadcasting by radio in which the signal comes at a varying number of times per second; an abbreviation for **frequency modulation** 〔縮〕調頻

foal /fol; fəʊl/ *n* a young horse 駒; 小馬

foam¹ /fom; fəʊm/ *n* [U] **1** a mass of small bubbles (BUBBLE) formed when air is mixed with a liquid 泡沫: *The breaking waves had edges of foam.* 波浪邊上帶着泡沫。 **2** soft rubber or a man-made material full of small bubbles (BUBBLE) of air 泡沫橡膠;〔人造〕泡沫材料 –**foamy** *adj*

foam² *v* [I] **1** to be full of small bubbles (BUBBLE) 充滿泡沫: *a glass of foaming beer* 一杯注滿泡沫的啤酒 | *He looked as if he was foaming at the mouth.* 他看上去在口吐白沫。 **2** to have foam coming out 起泡沫; 吐白沫: *It was foaming at the mouth.* 牠在口吐白沫。

fob /fab; fɒb/ *v*

fob sbdy ↔ **off** *phr v* [T] to give someone something unsatisfactory as a way of making them go away or keep quiet 〔用低劣的東西〕哄騙或搪塞〔某人〕: *She just fobbed me off* **with** *a stupid excuse.* 她用愚蠢的藉口勉強地把我搪塞過去。

fo·cal point /ˈfokl ˌpɔɪnt; ˈfəʊkəl ˌpɔɪnt/ *n* [sing] the centre of interest 感興趣的中心: *Television is now the focal point of family life in many British homes.* 看電視現在是許多英國人家庭生活中的主要消遣。

fo·cus¹ /ˈfokəs; ˈfəʊkəs/ *n* **1** the point at which beams of light or heat, or waves of sound meet after their direction has been changed〔光線或聲波的〕焦點 **2** a centre of attention, activity, or interest〔注意、活動或興趣的〕中心: *He immediately became the focus of attention.* 他很快成了眾人注意的中心人物。 **3** *in focus* giving a clear picture 焦距對準的; 清晰的: *That photograph's not quite in focus.* 那張照片拍得不太清晰。 | *Those trees aren't in focus.* 那些樹拍得不清楚。 [RELATED PHRASE 相關詞組 **out of focus**]

focus² *v* **-s-** *or* **-ss-** [I;T] **1** to bring something into focus, or come into focus (使)聚焦; 調節焦距: *I think I must have forgotten to focus the camera.* 我想我必然是忘了調整照相機的焦距。 | *I'll focus* **on** *the main group of people over there.* 我要把鏡頭對準那兒一羣重要人物。 | *The beams of light moved across the sky and focused on the aircraft.* 探照燈的光束劃過天空, 對準了飛機。 **2** to make something or someone the central point of interest 使〔某物或某人〕成為人感興趣的焦點: *All eyes were focused* **on** *him.* 所有的目光都集中到他身上。 | *Attention focused on the new Prime Minister.* 注意力集中到了新首相身上。

fod·der /ˈfadə; ˈfɒdə(r)/ *n* [U] food for horses and farm animals 飼料; 秣

foe /fo; fəʊ/ *n* *lit* an enemy 〔文〕敵人

foe·tus /ˈfitəs; ˈfiːtəs/ *n* (also 又作 **fetus**) a young human or animal that is still developing inside its mother 胎兒; 胚胎 – **foetal** *adj*

fog /fag; fɒg/ *n* [C;U] very thick mist which makes it difficult to see 霧

fog·bound /ˈfag,baund; ˈfɒgbaʊnd/ *adj* unable to travel or operate because of fog 因霧而不能旅行或運作的; 被霧困住的: *Heathrow Airport is fogbound.* 希思羅機場因霧而關閉。

fog·gy /ˈfagɪ; ˈfɒgi/ *adj* **foggier, foggiest 1** very misty 多霧的: *Foggy weather has made driving conditions very dangerous.* 霧天開車很危險。 **2** *not have the foggiest idea* *infml* to not know at all 〔非正式〕根本不知道: *"What time is it?" "I haven't the foggiest idea."* "幾點鐘了?" "我一點也不知道。"

foi·ble /ˈfɔɪbl; ˈfɔɪbəl/ *n* *fml* a rather strange or foolish personal habit 〔正式〕怪癖; 怪習性

foil¹ /fɔɪl; fɔɪl/ *v* [T] *fml* to prevent someone from doing something successfully 〔正式〕挫敗; 使受挫折: *The attempted robbery was foiled by security guards.* 那次有預謀的搶劫被保安人員挫敗了。

foil² *n* **1** [U] metal beaten into very thin sheets like paper and used to wrap food 箔; 金屬薄片〔用於包裝食品〕: *Our food is wrapped in foil to keep it fresh.* 我們的食品用箔紙包裝可以保持新鮮。 **2** [C] a person or thing that makes the good qualities of another person or thing more noticeable 襯托物; 陪襯者

foist /fɔɪst; fɔɪst/ *v* *foist something on someone* to force someone to accept something that they do not want 把某事物強加於某人: *I wish he wouldn't try to foist his political ideas on other people.* 但願他別把自己的政治觀點強加於人。

fold¹ /fold; fəʊld/ *v* **1** [T] to bend or press back one part of something onto the remaining part 摺疊: *She folded the letter in half.* 她把信對摺起來。 | *Her clothes had all been neatly folded and put in a drawer.* 她的衣服都摺疊得整整齊齊, 放到了抽屜裡。 **2** [I] to be able to be folded 能夠摺疊: *a folding chair* 能摺疊的椅子 | *Does this bed fold?* 這張牀可以摺疊嗎? **3** [T+adv/prep] to wrap something 包、裹〔某物〕: *He folded the seeds in a piece of paper.* 他用紙把種子包起來。 **4** *fold your arms* to cross your arms in two places over your chest 雙臂交叉放在胸前 **5** [I] (of a business) to fail 〔企業〕倒閉: *The company folded and she lost her job.* 公司倒閉, 她就失業了。

fold up *phr v* **1** [T **fold** sthg ↔ **up**] to fold something several times so that it becomes smaller 摺疊: *Could you fold your clothes up, please?* 請你把衣服摺疊起來, 好嗎? **2** [I] (of a business) to fail 〔企業〕倒閉

fold² *n* a folded part or place 摺疊的部分;

褶: *The curtain hung in heavy folds.* 窗簾以厚厚的褶懸掛著。

fold·er /'fəʊldə; 'fəʊldə^r/ *n* a folded piece of cardboard used for holding loose papers 文件夾

fo·li·age /'fəʊlɪdʒ; 'fəʊlɪ-ɪdʒ/ *n* [U] *fml* leaves 〔正式〕葉; 葉子

folk¹ /fəʊk; fəʊk/ *n infml* [pl] people 〔非正式〕人們: *He's gone into an old folk's home.* 他已住進了養老院。

folk² *adj* [always before a noun 只能用於名詞前] belonging to or typical of the people of a particular country or area or of ordinary people who have no special knowledge 民間的: *folk music* 民間音樂 | *folk songs* 民歌 | *folk art* 民間藝術

folk·lore /'fəʊk,lɔː; 'fəʊklɔː^r/ *n* [U] all the ancient knowledge, beliefs, and stories of a racial or national group 民俗(學); 民間信仰; 民間傳說

☆☆fol·low /'fɒləʊ; 'fɒləʊ/ *v* **1** [I;T] to go after someone 跟隨; 隨後: *She followed me into the kitchen.* 她跟著我進了廚房。 | *You go first and I'll follow later.* 你先去, 我隨後就到。 | *I think we're being followed!* 我覺得有人在跟蹤我們! **2** [I;T] to come after something 接在〔某事物〕之後: *Disease often follows war.* 戰爭之後常常是疫症流行。 | *We expect even greater successes to follow.* 我們期待往後取得更大的成就。 | *The lightning was followed by a loud crash of thunder.* 閃電過後緊接著就是一陣響雷。 **3** [T] to go in the same direction as a road, path, or river 沿著〔路或河〕行進: *Follow the road until you come to the hotel.* 沿著這條路你就可到達那家旅館。 **4** [T] to pay attention to something and take an interest in it as it develops 傾聽; 關注: *I followed her speech with great attention.* 我全神貫注地聽她的演說。 | *This particular murder case was followed with interest by hundreds of people.* 這宗特殊的謀殺案受到了數百人的關注。 **5** [I;T] to understand something clearly 聽懂; 領會: *I didn't quite follow what you said.* 我不太明白你說的話。 **6** [T] to accept someone's instructions, advice, or example, and act according to it 遵照; 聽從: *Did you follow the instructions on the packet?* 你是否按照包裝上的說明去做了? | *If you follow my advice, you'll sell the house immediately.* 要是你聽從我的勸告, 你馬上就會賣掉房子。 **7** [I; + that] to be true because something else is true 結果必然是: *Just because you are rich, it doesn't follow that you are happy.* 僅僅因為你有錢, 並不能說你就一定幸福。 **8 as follows** as comes after this 如下 **9 follow in someone's footsteps** to do the same as someone else did in the past 效法他人 **10 follow suit** to do what someone else has just done 學樣; 跟著做: *Mr Higgs stood up to leave. Mr and Mrs White followed suit.* 希格斯先生站起身就走。懷特先生及夫人也照樣離去。 **11**

follow your nose to do what you naturally feel you should do, as opposed to following rules 憑本能或直覺行事〔而不循規蹈矩〕

follow sthg ↔ **through** *phr v* [T] to complete something or carry it out to the end 完成〔某事〕; 堅持到底: *We intend to follow through this line of enquiry.* 我們想把這項調查工作進行到底。

follow sthg ↔ **up** *phr v* [T] **1** to act further on something or find out more about it 繼續做〔某事〕; 追究: *That's an interesting suggestion, and I'll certainly follow it up.* 那是個有意思的建議, 我定會進一步加以落實。 **2** to do something else after you have done a first thing 對〔某事〕採取進一步行動: *I wrote to them, and then followed up my letter with a visit.* 我先給他們寫了一封信, 接著又登門拜訪。

fol·low·er /'fɒləʊə; 'fɒləʊə^r/ *n* an admirer or supporter of a person, belief, or cause 追隨者; 擁護者; 信徒: *the followers of Marx* 馬克思的擁護者 | *a follower of fashion* 趕時髦者

☆☆fol·low·ing¹ /'fɒləʊɪŋ; 'fɒləʊɪŋ/ *adj* **1 the following day, week, year, etc.** the next day, week, year, etc. 第二天; 第二週; 第二年: *I arranged to meet her on the following day.* 我安排第二天與她見面。 | *We went to Spain again the following year.* 我們第二年又去了西班牙。 **2 the following** going to be mentioned next 下述的; 下列的: *Please bring with you the following things: a change of clothes, shoes, a towel, and some food.* 請你隨身攜帶下列物品: 替換衣服, 鞋子, 毛巾和食品。

following² *n* **1 the following** the people or things that are going to be mentioned next 下列, 下述的人或物: *The following have been chosen to play in tomorrow's match: Duncan Ferguson, Hugh Williams, Robin Sinclair...* 現已選定下列人員參加明天的比賽: 鄧肯·弗格森, 休·威廉斯, 羅賓·辛克萊... **2** [sing] a group of supporters or admirers 一羣支持者或擁護者: *She has quite a large following in the North.* 她在北方有一大批擁護者。

following³ *prep* after 在…之後: *Following the speech, there will be a few minutes for questions.* 演說之後將有幾分鐘時間用於提問。

follow-up /'·· ·/ *adj* done as the continuation of something started earlier 後續的; 跟進的: *a follow-up visit from the doctor* 醫生(對病人的)後續檢查 **–follow-up** *n*: *This meeting was a follow-up to the one held last year.* 這次會議是去年那次會議的繼續。

fol·ly /'fɒlɪ; 'fɒli/ *n* **follies** [C;U] *fml* a very foolish action 〔正式〕愚蠢的行為: *He remembered the follies of his own youth.* 他想起了年輕時做過的蠢事。 | *To reduce public spending on health would be an act of the greatest folly.* 削減公共醫療開支將是極其愚蠢的行為。

fond /fɑnd; fɒnd/ *adj* **1 fond of** liking someone or something 喜愛〔某人或某事〕: *I'm very fond of her.* 我非常喜歡她。| *I'm not particularly fond of spicy food.* 我不是特別喜歡吃辣的食物。| *We're all quite fond of sightseeing.* 我們都非常喜歡遊覽。

□ USEFUL PATTERNS 有用句型
be fond of someone/something; be fond of doing something

2 [only before a noun 只用於名詞前] having or showing loving feelings 溺愛的；深情的: *Her fond parents were there to watch her perform.* 疼愛她的父母親到場觀看了她的演出。| *I got on the boat after a fond farewell from friends.* 和朋友熱情告別之後我就上了船。**3** [only before a noun 只用於名詞前] foolishly hopeful 盲目輕信的: *He's still waiting, in the fond belief that she'll come back to him.* 他還在等着，盲目相信她會回到他身邊來。–**fondness** *n* [U]

fon·dle /ˈfɑndl/ *v* **fondled, fondling** [T] to touch or stroke someone or something gently and lovingly 愛撫；撫摸〔某人或某物〕: *A cat sat on her knee, and she was fondling it gently.* 一隻貓蹲在她膝蓋上，她輕輕地撫摸着牠。

fond·ly /ˈfɑndlɪ; ˈfɒndlɪ/ *adv* **1** in a loving way 親愛的；深情地: *He was smiling at me fondly.* 他深情地向我微笑。**2** in a foolishly hopeful way 天真地；盲目輕信地: *She fondly imagined that she could pass her examination without working.* 她天真地以為自己無須用功也能通過考試。

font /fɑnt; fɒnt/ *n* a large vessel in a church, that contains water for baptizing (BAPTIZE) people 〔教堂中的〕洗禮盆；聖水盆

✭✭food /fud; fuːd/ *n* [C;U] **1** anything that people or animals eat 食物；養料: *Milk is the natural food for young babies.* 奶是嬰兒的天然食物。| *They gave us plenty of food and drink.* 他們給了我們大量食物和飲料。**2 food for thought** something which makes you think carefully 令人深思的事

food pro·ces·sor /ˈ· · ,··· / *n* an electric apparatus used for mixing and cutting up food 食品研磨器 –see picture on page 958 見 958 頁彩圖

fool¹ /ful; fuːl/ *n* **1** a silly person 蠢人；傻瓜: *You silly fool! What did you leave the bag there for?* 你這人真傻！你幹嘛把手提包留在那兒？| *I felt such a fool when I realized I'd got on the wrong bus.* 我發現我搭錯了公共汽車時，覺得自己真是個糊塗蟲。**2 make a fool of yourself** to do something silly 使自己出醜 **3 make a fool of someone** to make someone seem silly 使某人出醜 **4 fool's paradise** a happy situation which is not going to last, but the people in the situation do not know that 虛幻的樂境

fool² *v* [T] to deceive or trick someone 欺騙，

愚弄〔某人〕: *You can't fool him. He's much too clever for that.* 你愚弄不了他；他非常精明，不會上你的當。

fool about/around *phr v* [I] to behave in a silly way 胡鬧；瞎弄: *You shouldn't fool around with dangerous chemicals.* 你不應該瞎弄危險的化學品。

fool·har·dy /ˈfulˌhɑrdɪ; ˈfuːlˌhɑːdi/ *adj* taking unwise risks 魯莽的: *It would be foolhardy to borrow any more money.* 再借錢可真是太魯莽了。–**foolhardiness** *n* [U]

fool·ish /ˈfulɪʃ; ˈfuːlɪʃ/ *adj* **1** not sensible 不明智的: *It was very foolish of you to park the car in the middle of the road.* 你把車停在馬路中間真是太傻了。**2** stupid and silly 愚蠢的；傻的: *I felt very foolish when I realized what I'd done.* 當我明白自己的作為時，覺得十分愚蠢。–**foolishly** *adv* –**foolishness** *n* [U]

fool·proof /ˈfulˌpruf; ˈfuːlˌpruːf/ *adj* **1** that cannot go wrong 不會出錯的；可靠的: *I've found a foolproof way of doing it.* 我找到了萬無一失的方法去做這件事。| *Our plan is completely foolproof.* 我們的計劃已萬無一失。**2** *infml* very simple to understand or use 〔非正式〕十分簡單明瞭的；容易使用的: *The new machines are foolproof.* 新機器操作很簡單。

fools·cap /ˈfulzˌkæp; ˈfuːlsˌkæp/ *n* [U] a large size of writing paper 大頁書寫紙

✭foot¹ /fut; fʊt/ *n* **feet** /fit; fiːt/ **1** [C] the part of your body at the end of your leg, on which you stand 腳；足: *My feet hurt!* 我的腳真痛！**2** [sing] the bottom or lower part of something 〔某物的〕底部；最下部: *He stood at the foot of the stairs.* 他站在樓梯底部。| *She sat at the foot of the bed.* 她坐在牀腳處。**3** [C] [plural is 複數形式為 **foot** or 或 **feet**] a measure of length equal to 12 inches or about 0.305 metres 英尺〔12 英寸或約 0.305 公尺〕: *"How tall are you?" "Five foot six inches."* "你身高多少？" "五英尺六英寸。"| *He's at least six feet tall.* 他身高至少有六英尺。**4 leap to your feet** to stand up 站起來: *He leapt to his feet as I walked in.* 我走進去時，他站起身來。**5 not put a foot wrong** to not say or do anything wrong 不講錯話；不做錯事 **6 on foot** walking 步行: *We'll have to go on foot.* 我們只好步行去。**7 on your feet: a** standing up 站着: *I've been on my feet all day!* 我已整整站了一天了！**b** in good health 康復: *I should be back on my feet again by next week.* 到下星期我就可以康復了。| *We must get the economy back on its feet.* 我們一定要振興經濟。**8 put your feet up** to rest by lying or sitting with your feet supported on something 躺下休息；將雙腳平放着休息: *I think I'll put my feet up for half an hour.* 我想我要躺下來休息半小時。**9 put your foot down** to forbid something by saying very firmly that it must not happen 堅決反對〔禁止〕〔某事〕**10 put your foot in it** to say something unsuitable and so cause an awkward situation 説話不得體而造成尷尬局面 **11 set foot in a place** to go into a place 進入〔某地〕: *I hope he never sets foot in this house again!* 我希望他再也不要踏進這個家! **12 -footed** having a particular number of feet or a particular type of feet 有〔一定數量或某一種類的〕腳的: *four-footed animals* 四足動物 | *Ducks are web-footed.* 鴨子是蹼足的。

foot² v foot the bill *infml* to pay for something 〔非正式〕支付〔某物〕: *Hopefully, the insurance company will foot the bill for the damage.* 保險公司有望賠償損失。

★**foot·ball** /ˈfʊtbɔl; ˈfʊtbɔːl/ *n* **1** [U] a game for two teams in which a ball is kicked about a field and the players try to get goals (GOAL) 足球比賽: *They play football at school.* 他們在學校踢足球。 | *Where are my football boots?* 我的足球鞋在哪裡? **2** [C] a large ball filled with air, used for playing football 足球 **3** see 見 AMERICAN FOOTBALL –**footballer** *n*

football pools /ˈ··· ·/ *n* **the football pools** a game in which people risk small amounts of money on the results of football matches 足球賽賭博

foot·bridge /ˈfʊtbrɪdʒ; ˈfʊtbrɪdʒ/ *n* a narrow bridge for people who are walking 人行橋; 步行橋 –see picture on page 991 見 991 頁彩圖

foot·hills /ˈfʊthɪlz; ˈfʊthɪlz/ *n* [pl] low hills at the bottom of a mountain or chain of mountains 山麓小丘: *the foothills of the Himalayas* 喜馬拉雅山脈的山麓丘陵

foot·hold /ˈfʊthold; ˈfʊthəʊld/ *n* **1** a space where you can put your foot to help you to climb up or down a rock or mountain 立腳處〔攀登時可踩腳的地方〕 **2** a job or position from which you can advance 〔有發展前途的〕地位或工作: *I need to get a foothold in the profession.* 我需要在職業上打下穩固的基礎。

foot·ing /ˈfʊtɪŋ; ˈfʊtɪŋ/ *n* [sing] **1** a firm hold with your feet on a surface 站穩: *She lost her footing and fell.* 她沒站穩, 跌倒了。 **2** a particular way of working or operating 工作或運作的特殊方法: *The army was put on a war footing.* 軍隊處於戰爭狀態。 **3** a relationship 關係: *I was on a very good footing with the director.* 我和董事的關係十分融洽。

foot·lights /ˈfʊtlaɪts; ˈfʊtlaɪts/ *n* [pl] a row of lights along the front edge of the stage in a theatre 〔舞台前面的〕腳燈

foot·loose /ˈfʊtlus; ˈfʊtluːs/ *adj* not liking to settle down in one place and accept the usual responsibilities of work or family 自由自在的; 無拘無束的

foot·man /ˈfʊtmən; ˈfʊtmən/ *n* **footmen** /-mən; -mən/ a male servant in the past 〔舊時的〕男僕

foot·note /ˈfʊtnot; ˈfʊtnəʊt/ *n* a note at the bottom of a page in a book, to explain

something or add more information 腳註

foot·path /ˈfʊtpæθ; ˈfʊtpɑːθ/ *n* a narrow path or track for people to walk on 小徑; 小路

foot·print /ˈfʊtprɪnt; ˈfʊtprɪnt/ *n* a mark shaped like a foot, which you make when you walk on a surface 腳印; 足跡: *Who left these muddy footprints on the kitchen floor?* 誰在廚房的地板上留下了這些泥腳印?

foot·sore /ˈfʊtsor; ˈfʊtsɔːr/ *adj* having painful or swollen feet because you have been walking a lot 〔因走路過多而〕腳痛的; 腳酸的

foot·step /ˈfʊtstep; ˈfʊtstep/ *n* the sound or sound of a person's step 腳印; 腳步聲: *Her footsteps were clearly marked in the snow.* 她的腳印清晰地印在雪地上。 | *He heard soft footsteps coming up the stairs.* 他聽到有人輕輕走上樓的腳步聲。

foot·wear /ˈfʊtwer; ˈfʊtweər/ *n* [U] *fml* shoes and boots 〔正式〕鞋類〔鞋、靴等〕

★**for¹** /fə; fər, *strong* 強讀 fɔr; fɔːr/ *prep* **1** meant to be given to someone or used by someone or something 〔表示對象、用途等〕給; 為; 供: *I've got a present for you.* 我有件禮物要送給你。 | *He offered to buy a drink for me.* 他主動為我買了一杯飲料。 | *I've bought some new chairs for the office.* 我給辦公室買了幾把新椅子。 **2** used to show who is helped or supported by something 〔表示受益、受幫助的對象〕為了…: *Shall I carry your case for you?* 我幫你搬箱子, 好嗎? | *Is there anything I can do for you?* 我能為你做些甚麼嗎? | *She works for a local manufacturing company.* 她在當地一家製造公司工作。 | *I'd love to play football for England.* 我很想為英格蘭隊踢足球。 **3** used to show who a feeling is directed towards 〔表示某種情感的對象〕: *I feel very happy for you.* 我很替你開心。 | *She felt nothing but contempt for him.* 她對他的感受只有鄙視。 **4** used to show the purpose of something 〔表示目的〕用於; 適合於: *These scissors are very good for cutting carpet.* 這把剪刀剪地毯非常合適。 | *It's very nice, but what's it for?* 這東西相當精緻, 但能派甚麼用場? **5** used to show the reason for something or the cause of something 〔表示原因、理由〕因為; 由於: *They were punished for talking in class.* 他們因上課講話而受罰。 | *He got twenty years in prison for robbery with violence.* 他因暴力搶劫罪而被判了二十年監禁。 **6** towards a particular place 向; 往〔某地〕: *We set off for France.* 我們動身去法國。 | *Is that the boat for Ireland?* 那是去愛爾蘭的船嗎? **7** with a particular meaning 意為; 表示: *What's the French word for "dog"?* "狗"的法語怎麼說? **8** used to show how much you have to pay in order to get something 〔表示某物的價錢〕花費: *You can get a room in a hotel for £40 a night.* 你花四十英鎊就可以在旅館租一個房間過夜。 **9** used to show a length of time or distance 〔表示時間或距離的長度〕達;

計: *We've lived here for ten years.* 我們已在這兒住了十年。| *They walked for twenty miles before they found a village.* 他們走了二十英里才找到一個村莊。**10** by or at a particular time 在〔某一特定時間〕; 在…時節: *They asked us to be there for six o'clock.* 他們叫我們六點鐘到那裡。| *Are you coming home for Christmas?* 你回家來過聖誕節嗎? | *We must get there for the start of the play.* 我們必須在演出開始前趕到那裡。| *What did you get for your birthday?* 你過生日時收到些甚麼禮物? **11** in favour of someone or something 贊成, 支持〔某人或某事物〕: *24 people voted for the proposal and 16 voted against.* 二十四人投票贊成該建議, 十六人投了反對票。**12** when considering a particular fact 考慮到…; 就…而言: *She's very tall for her age.* 就她的年齡而言, 她長得很高。

for² *conj fml* because 〔正式〕因為; 由於: *He was surprised that she was late, for she was usually very punctual.* 他對她的遲到感到意外, 因為她一般都很準時。

for·age /ˈfɒrɪdʒ; ˈfɔrɪdʒ/ *v* **foraged, foraging** **1** [I] (of animals) to wander about looking for food 〔動物〕尋找食物 **2 forage for something, forage around for something** to look for something busily 搜尋某物

foray /ˈfɒre; ˈforeɪ/ *n* **1** a sudden rush into enemy country by a small number of soldiers 突襲 **2** a short attempt at doing something 短暫〔初步〕嘗試: *his unsuccessful foray into politics* 他那初次涉足政治而不成功的嘗試

for·bade /fəˈbed; fəˈbeɪd/ **forbad** /-ˈbæd; -ˈbæd/ the past tense of FORBID ☆ FORBID 的過去式

for·bear /fɔrˈbɛr; fɔːˈbeəʳ/ *v* **forbore** /-ˈbor; -ˈbɔːʳ/, **forborne** /-ˈborn; -ˈbɔːn/ [I] *fml* not to do something that you could do because you think that it is wiser not to do it 〔正式〕克制; 自制

for·bear·ance /fɔrˈbɛrəns; fɔːˈbeərəns/ *n* [U] *fml* patience and forgiveness 〔正式〕克制; 寬容

for·bear·ing /fɔrˈbɛrɪŋ; fɔːˈbeərɪŋ/ *adj fml* gentle, patient, and forgiving 〔正式〕寬容的; 有耐心的

for·bid /fəˈbɪd; fəˈbɪd/ *v* **forbade** /-ˈbed; -ˈbeɪd/, **forbidden** /-ˈbɪdn; -ˈbɪdn/, **forbidding** [T] to order someone not to do something 禁止, 不准〔某人做某事〕: *Smoking is strictly forbidden.* 嚴禁吸煙。| *The law forbids the use of chemical fertilizers.* 法律禁止使用化學肥料。| *He forbade her to tell anyone about it.* 他不准她把這事告訴任何人。

□ USEFUL PATTERNS 有用句型
to forbid something; to forbid someone to do something

for·bid·ding /fəˈbɪdɪŋ; fəˈbɪdɪŋ/ *adj* looking fierce, unfriendly, or dangerous 樣子可怕的; 令人生畏的: *The mountains looked dark and forbidding.* 那些山脈看上去一片漆黑, 令人望而生畏。–**forbiddingly** *adv*

force¹ /fors; fɔːs/ *n* **1** [U] power or strength 力; 力量: *The force of the explosion destroyed the building completely.* 爆炸力徹底摧毀了大樓。**2** [U] physical strength 力氣; 體力: *She had lost her key, so we had to open the door by force.* 她丟了鑰匙, 所以我們不得不強行把門打開。**3** [U] violence 暴力; 武力: *The regime was removed by force.* 該政權被暴力推翻。| *The police have said that they will use force if necessary to remove the demonstrators.* 警方表示, 若有必要他們將使用武力把示威者趕走。**4** [C] someone or something that has a strong influence or a lot of power 有重要影響(力)的人或事: *She is a powerful force in world politics.* 她是對世界政治有重大影響的人物。| *the forces of evil* 惡勢力 **5** [C;U] a natural power that has a strong physical effect on things 〔自然界的〕力: *the force of gravity* 地心引力 | *a magnetic force* 磁力 **6** [C] a group of people who are trained to fight together 軍事力量; 武裝力量; 部隊: *Both land and sea forces were used in the attack.* 在進攻中使用了陸軍和海軍部隊。| *the police force* 警察部隊 **7 force of habit** the fact that you have done something many times before, which makes you do it again without thinking about it 由於習慣: *I locked the door from force of habit.* 我習慣性地鎖上了門。**8 in force: a** in effect or in operation (used of a law or a system) 有效的; 現行的〔指法律或制度〕: *The law has been in force for six months now.* 法律生效至今已有六個月了。| *The new arrangements will come into force next week.* 新的安排將從下星期開始實施。**b** in large numbers 大量的; 大批的: *The police were out in force to prevent any trouble.* 出動了大批警察來制止騷亂。**9 join forces** to work together to do something 聯合〔做某事〕: *Scientists have joined forces with environmentalists to find a solution to the problem.* 科學家已經和研究環境污染的專家聯合起來, 共同尋找解決問題的辦法。

force² *v* **forced, forcing** [T] **1** to make someone do something that they do not want to do 強迫, 迫使〔某人做某事〕: *He forced her to give him the key.* 他強迫她交出鑰匙。| *They may agree to help me, but I can't force them to.* 他們也許肯幫我的忙, 但我不能強迫他們。

□ USEFUL PATTERN 有用句型
to force someone to do something

2 to use physical effort to make an object do what you want it to do 用力使〔某物〕移動、打開等: *She tried to force her suitcase through the tiny hole in the fence.* 她使勁要

把手提箱從籬笆的小洞中塞過去。| *The burglars had forced the window open.* 竊賊強行打開了窗戶。 **3** to produce something with difficulty or by unwilling effort 勉強作出: *She managed to force a smile.* 她盡量強作笑臉。 **4 force something on someone** to make someone accept something that they do not want 勉強某人接受某事物: *He didn't want any reward, and we had to force the money on him.* 他不要任何報酬，我們只好硬要他把錢收下。 **5 force a lock** to break a lock open 把鎖砸開 **6 force your way** to go into or through somewhere by using physical strength 使勁擠過: *He forced his way through the crowd.* 他使勁擠過人羣。

forced /forst; fɔːst/ *adj* [only before a noun 只用於名詞前] **1** done or made because it is necessary to act without delay 強迫的; 不得已的: *The aircraft had to make a forced landing.* 飛機不得不迫降。 **2** done with unwilling and unnatural effort 勉強的; 不自然的: *forced laughter* 勉強的歡笑

force·ful /forsfəl; 'fɔːsfəl/ *adj* powerful and confident 強有力的; 有説服力的: *a forceful speech* 有説服力的講話 | *She made a forceful impression on the girls.* 她給那些女孩子留下了深刻的印象。 **–forcefully** *adv* – **forcefulness** *n* [U]

for·ceps /'fɔrsəps; 'fɔːseps/ *n* [pl] a medical instrument used for holding objects firmly 〔醫用的〕鑷子; 鉗子

for·ci·ble /'fɔrsəbl; 'fɔːsɪbəl/ *adj* [only before a noun 只用於名詞前] **1** using physical force 用體力的; 強行的: *The police had to make a forcible entry.* 警察必須強行進入。 **2** having power to influence the minds of others 強有力的; 有説服力的: *His death was a forcible reminder of the dangers around us.* 他的死充分提醒我們周圍有危險。 **–forcibly** *adv*

ford[1] /ford; fɔːd/ *n* a place in a river where the water is not very deep and it is possible to cross without using a bridge 河中可涉水而過的淺處; 淺灘

ford[2] *v* [T] to cross a river or stream on foot or in a vehicle 〔步行或開車〕涉水而過

fore /for; fɔːr/ *n* **come to the fore** to become popular and well-known 走紅; 出名: *He came to the fore in the early '80s.* 他在八十年代初曾非常顯赫。

fore·arm /'for,arm; 'fɔːrɑːm/ *n* the lower part of your arm, between your hand and elbow 前臂

fore·bear /'for,bɛr; 'fɔːbeər/ *n* your fore-bears people who were members of your family, usually a long time ago 祖宗; 祖先

fore·bod·ing /for'bodɪŋ; fɔː'bəʊdɪŋ/ *n* [U] *fml* a feeling that something bad or evil is going to happen 〔正式〕〔對不祥之事的〕預感: *I waited for the phone call with foreboding.* 我懷着不祥的預感等電話。

fore·cast[1] /for'kæst; 'fɔːkɑːst/ *v* **forecast,**

forecast [T] to say what will probably happen in the future 預測; 預報: *Heavy rain has been forecast for tomorrow.* 天氣預報説明天有暴雨。 | *Their political opponents are forecasting a huge rise in unemployment.* 他們的政敵在預測，失業率將大幅上升。

forecast[2] *n* a statement of what is expected to happen in the future 預報; 預測: *The weather forecast said it would rain.* 天氣預報説會下雨。 | *forecasts of impending financial disaster* 對即將到來的金融危機的預測

fore·court /'for,kort; 'fɔːkɔːt/ *n* an open space in front of a large building 前院; 前庭: *the car park in the station forecourt* 火車站前院的停車場

fore·fa·ther /'for,faðɚ; 'fɔː,fɑːðər/ *n* your forefathers people who were members of your family a long time ago 祖先; 祖宗: *their custom since the days of their forefathers* 祖傳習俗

fore·fin·ger /'for,fɪŋgɚ; 'fɔː,fɪŋgər/ *n* the finger next to your thumb 食指

fore·front /'for,frʌnt; 'fɔːfrʌnt/ *n* the fore-front the leading position 最前列; 最重要的位置: *She's been at the forefront of the struggle for equal rights.* 她一直站在為爭取平等權利而鬥爭的最前列。

fore·go /for'go; fɔː'gəʊ/ *v* **forewent** /-'wɛnt; 'wɛnt/, **foregone** /-'gɒn; -'gɒn/ (also 又作 **forgo**) [T] *fml* to choose not to have something pleasant 〔正式〕放棄，拋棄〔好事〕: *You shouldn't forego this opportunity to visit New York.* 你不該放棄這次訪問紐約的機會。

fore·gone /'for,gɒn; 'fɔːgɒn/ *adj* **foregone conclusion** a result that is certain 必然結果

fore·ground /'for,graʊnd; 'fɔːgraʊnd/ *n* the foreground the nearest part of a scene 前景〔景物的前部〕: *This is a photograph of our new house, with my parents in the fore-ground.* 這是我們新住宅的照片，靠前的是我的父母。

fore·hand /'for,hænd; 'fɔːhænd/ *n* a tennis stroke played with the inner part of your hand and arm facing forward 〔網球的〕正手擊球 **–compare** 比較 BACKHAND **–forehand** *adj*

fore·head /'forɪd; 'fɒrɪd/ *n* the part of your face above your eyes and below your hair 額; 前額

★**for·eign** /'fɔrɪn; 'fɒrɪn/ *adj* **1** coming from a country or nation that is not your own 外國的; 從外國來的: *Do you speak any foreign languages?* 你會説外語嗎？ | *I collect foreign coins.* 我收集外國硬幣。 **2** **foreign to** unfamiliar to someone 對某人陌生的: *He's a very good person. Unkindness is foreign to his nature.* 他為人厚道; 兇狠不是他的本性。 **3 foreign body** something that is in the wrong place and likely to cause harm 〔易引起損傷的〕異物 **4 foreign affairs** matters concerning relationships with other countries 外交事務: *the Ministry of*

Foreign Affairs 外交部 **5 foreign exchange** the practice of buying and selling foreign money 外匯; 國際匯兌

for·eign·er /ˈfɔrɪnə; ˈfɒrɪnəʳ/ *n* a person belonging to a race or country other than your own 外國人

fore·leg /ˈfɔr,lɛg; ˈfɔːleg/ *n* either of the two front legs of an animal〔動物的〕前腿

fore·man /ˈfɔrmən; ˈfɔːmən/ *n* **foremen** /-mən; -mən/ an experienced worker who is put in charge of a group of workers 領班; 工頭

fore·most¹ /ˈfɔr,most; ˈfɔːməʊst/ *adj* [only before a noun 只用於名詞前] **the foremost** the most important or best of a group of things 最重要的; 最佳的: *Shakespeare is said to be the foremost writer in the English language.* 莎士比亞被認為是最傑出的英語作家。

foremost² *adv* **first and foremost** you use this phrase when you have several points you want to make and you are going to talk about the most important one first 首要的是〔用於首先談論幾個要點中最重要的一個〕

fore·name /ˈfɔr,nem; ˈfɔːneɪm/ *n fml* the name that your parents give you, in addition to your family name〔正式〕〔除姓之外的〕名(字) –see 見 FIRST NAME (USAGE 用法)

fo·ren·sic /fəˈrɛnsɪk; fəˈrensɪk/ *adj* [only before a noun 只用於名詞前] *tech* related to the scientific examination of a crime〔術語〕法庭的; 法醫的: *A specialist in forensic medicine was called as a witness.* 一名法醫專家被召來作證。

fore·run·ner /ˈfɔr,rʌnə; ˈfɔːˌrʌnəʳ/ *n* a person or thing that prepares the way for someone or something that follows 先驅; 先兆; 先導: *Mrs Pankhurst, who fought for votes for women, was a forerunner of modern feminists.* 為婦女選舉權而奮鬥的潘克赫斯特夫人, 是現代婦女運動的先驅。

fore·see /fɔrˈsi; fɔːˈsiː/ *v* **foresaw** /-ˈsɔ; -ˈsɔː/, **foreseen** /-ˈsin; -ˈsiːn/ [T] to form an idea or judgment about what is going to happen in the future 預見; 預知: *Who could have foreseen such problems in 1938?* 誰能在一九三八年就預料到這樣的問題?

fore·see·a·ble /fɔrˈsiəbl; fɔːˈsiːəbəl/ *adj* **1** which can be expected to happen 可預見到的: *a foreseeable accident* 可預見的事故 **2 in the foreseeable future** as far ahead in time as we can see 在可預見的將來

fore·shad·ow /fɔrˈʃædo; fɔːˈʃædəʊ/ *v* [T] *lit* to be a sign of what is to come〔文〕預示; 預兆

fore·sight /ˈfɔr,saɪt; ˈfɔːsaɪt/ *n* [U] the ability to imagine what will probably happen in the future 預見; 先見之明: *He had the foresight to invest his money outside the oil industry.* 他很有遠見, 沒在石油工業上投資。

fore·skin /ˈfɔr,skɪn; ˈfɔːˌskɪn/ *n* a loose fold of skin covering the end of a man's PENIS〔陰莖頭部的〕包皮

★for·est /ˈfɔrɪst; ˈfɒrɪst/ *n* [C;U] a large area of land with many trees growing close together 森林; 林區: *A large part of Africa is made up of thick forest.* 非洲的大部分地區都是茂密的森林。| *Most of the ancient forests of England have been cut down.* 英國的原始森林大多已被砍伐。

fore·stall /fɔrˈstɔl; fɔːˈstɔːl/ *v* [T] *fml* to defeat someone, or someone's plan, by acting first〔正式〕〔用先發制人的手段〕挫敗〔某人或某人的計劃〕: *We forestalled his attempt to steal the map back by handing it over to the police first.* 我們搶先一步把地圖交給了警方, 使他們偷回來的企圖落空。

for·est·ry /ˈfɔrɪstrɪ; ˈfɒrɪstrɪ/ *n* [U] the science of planting and caring for large areas of trees 林學; 造林學 **–forester** *n*

fore·taste /ˈfɔr,test; ˈfɔːteɪst/ *n* [sing] a small early experience of something that will come later 預先的體驗; 淺嘗

fore·tell /fɔrˈtɛl; fɔːˈtel/ *v* **foretold** /-ˈtold; -ˈtəʊld/, **foretold** [T; +that] to say what will happen in the future 預言; 預示: *Who can foretell what will happen in the year 2030?* 誰能預料在 2030 年會發生甚麼?

fore·thought /ˈfɔr,θɔt; ˈfɔːθɔːt/ *n* [U] wise planning for the future 深謀遠慮: *With a little forethought, you wouldn't have got yourself into such a mess.* 你當初若是稍微考慮一下, 便不會陷入這麼狼狽的境地。

fore·told /fɔrˈtold; fɔːˈtəʊld/ the past tense and past participle of FORETELL ☆ FORETELL 的過去式和過去分詞

for·ev·er /fəˈɛvə; fərˈevəʳ/ *adv* **1** for all future time 永遠: *I want to stay here forever.* 我想永遠待在這裡。| *This way of life has now gone forever.* 這種生活方式現已一去不復返了。**2 be forever doing something** to do something very often in an annoying way 老是做某事: *He's forever asking silly questions.* 他老是問些愚蠢的問題。

fore·warn /fɔrˈwɔrn; fɔːˈwɔːn/ *v* [T;+that] to warn someone of something dangerous or unpleasant which will happen 預先警告〔告誡〕〔某人〕: *We had been forewarned about his terrible temper.* 對於他那可怕的脾氣, 我們已經事先得到警告。

fore·word /ˈfɔr,wɜd; ˈfɔːwɜːd/ *n* a short introduction at the beginning of a book 前言; 序言: *a book on architecture with a foreword by Prince Charles* 一本由查理斯王子作序的建築學論著

for·feit¹ /ˈfɔrfɪt; ˈfɔːfɪt/ *v* [T] to have something taken away from you, for example as a punishment〔作為懲罰而〕喪失, 失去〔某物〕: *Because he's complained about the goods so late, he's forfeited his right to exchange them.* 因為他對那些貨物的投訴太晚, 所以失去了退換的權利。

forfeit² *n* something that you have taken

F

away from you 喪失的東西: *If you guess wrongly, you have to pay a forfeit.* 如果你猜錯了，就得受罰。

for·gave /fə'ɡev; fə'ɡeɪv/ the past tense of FORGIVE ☆ FORGIVE 的過去式

forge[1] /fɔrdʒ; fɔ:dʒ/ v **forged, forging 1** [T] to make a copy of something in order to deceive people 偽造〔某物〕; 假冒: *He got the money by forging his brother's signature on a cheque.* 他在支票上假冒他哥哥的簽字，從而得到了那筆錢。 | *She was sent to prison for forging a passport.* 她因偽造護照而入獄。 **2** [T] to form objects by heating metal and beating it with a hammer 鍛造; 打鐵 **3** [T] to succeed in making a good relationship with someone 〔與某人〕建立〔良好關係〕: *They have forged an alliance with the French Socialists.* 他們與法國社會黨人建立了聯盟。 **4** [I+adv/prep] to move with a sudden increase of speed and power 突然加速前進: *She forged into the lead just before the end of the race.* 就在賽跑接近終點時，她突然加速跑到最前面。 | *He didn't do very well at school, but he's forged ahead in the last two years.* 他過去在校時成績不佳，但最近兩年卻迎頭趕了上來。

forge[2] n **1** a place with a fire used for heating and shaping metal objects 鍛造車間; 鐵匠鋪; 鐵匠工場: *a working village forge* 正在運作的鄉辦鐵匠工場 **2** a large apparatus that produces great heat inside itself, used for melting metal and making iron 鍛鐵爐

forg·er /'fɔrdʒɚ; 'fɔ:dʒər/ n a person who makes copies of things in order to deceive people 偽造者

for·ge·ry /'fɔrdʒərɪ; 'fɔ:dʒəri/ n **forgeries 1** [U] the act of making a copy of something in order to deceive people 偽造行為; 偽造罪: *He was sent to prison for forgery.* 他因偽造罪入獄。 **2** [C] something that has been copied in order to deceive people 偽造品; 贗品: *The bank manager told me the notes were all forgeries.* 銀行經理告訴我，鈔票都是偽造的。

⋆**for·get** /fə'ɡɛt; fə'ɡet/ v **forgot** /-'ɡɑt; -'ɡɒt/, **forgotten** /-'ɡɑtn; -'ɡɒtn/, **forgetting 1** [I;T;+(that)] to fail to remember something 忘記〔某事物〕: *She asked me to post some letters, but I forgot.* 她叫我寄幾封信，但我給忘了。 | *I've forgotten his name.* 我把他的名字忘了。 | *Don't forget to bring something to drink.* 別忘了帶點飲料回來。 | *I forget who said it.* 我忘記了那是誰說的。 | *They'd forgotten that we were coming.* 他們忘了我們要來。

□ USEFUL PATTERNS 有用句型
to forget something; to forget to do something; to forget that…

2 [I;T] to stop thinking about someone or

something 把〔某人或某事物〕忘掉: *Let's forget the arguments and be friends again.* 讓我們忘掉過去那些爭爭吵吵，重新和好吧。 | *"I'm sorry I broke your teapot." "Forget it."* "對不起，我把你的茶壺打碎了。" "沒關係。" **3** [T] to fail to give attention to someone 忽略; 忽視〔某人〕: *Don't forget your friends when you are rich!* 別有了錢就忘了朋友! **4 forget yourself** to lose your temper or self-control and act in an unacceptable way 失去自制; 忘形

■ USAGE 用法: If you want to mention the place where something has been left, do NOT use **forget.** Use the verb **leave** instead. ☆若要提到東西遺忘在某處，不能用 **forget**，而要用 **leave**。 Compare 比較: *I'm sorry, I've forgotten my book.* 對不起，我忘了帶書。 | *I'm sorry, I've left my book at home.* 對不起，我把書遺忘在家裡了。 | *I parked the car and forgot to take my keys with me.* 我停放好車子，忘了隨手把鑰匙拿下。 | *I parked the car and left my keys inside.* 我停放好車子，把鑰匙遺忘在車內了。 | *She's forgotten her passport!* 她忘記了帶護照! | *She's left her passport behind.* 她把護照遺忘了沒帶走。

for·get·ful /fə'ɡɛtfəl; fə'ɡetfəl/ adj **1** having the habit of forgetting things 健忘的: *My old aunt has become rather forgetful.* 我那年老的姑媽已變得很健忘。 **2 forgetful of** not thinking about something 不考慮，想不到〔某事物〕 –**forgetfully** adv –**forgetfulness** n [U]

for·give /fə'ɡɪv; fə'ɡɪv/ v **forgave** /-'ɡev; -'ɡeɪv/, **forgiven** /-'ɡɪvən; -'ɡɪvən/, **forgiving** [I;T] to say or feel that you are no longer angry with someone about something 原諒; 寬恕; 饒恕: *I'll never forgive you for what you said to me last night.* 我永遠不會原諒你昨晚對我說的那些話。 | *He forgave her the awful things she said about him.* 他原諒她說了他的壞話。 | *Do you think he'll forgive me for scratching his car?* 我刮破了他的車子，你認為他會寬恕我嗎?

□ USEFUL PATTERNS 有用句型
to forgive someone for something;
to forgive someone for doing something

for·give·ness /fə'ɡɪvnɪs; fə'ɡɪvnʲs/ n [U] the act of forgiving someone 原諒; 饒恕; 寬恕: *He begged his victim for forgiveness.* 他懇求受害者寬恕。

for·giv·ing /fə'ɡɪvɪŋ; fə'ɡɪvɪŋ/ adj willing to forgive people 寬容的: *She has a gentle, forgiving nature.* 她生性溫柔寬容。

for·go /fɔr'ɡo; fɔ:'ɡəʊ/ v see 見 FOREGO

for·got /fə'ɡɑt; fə'ɡɒt/ the past tense of FORGET ☆ FORGET 的過去式

for·got·ten /fəˈgɒtn; fəˈgɒtn/ the past participle of FORGET ☆ FORGET 的過去分詞

fork¹ /fɔrk; fɔːk/ *n* **1** an instrument for eating food which has a handle at one end with two or more points at the other end 餐叉; 叉子 **2** a farm or gardening tool which has a wooden handle with two or more metal points at the end 草叉; 耙 –see picture on page 958 見 958 頁彩圖 **3** a place where something such as a road or a river divides 〔路的〕分岔; 〔河的〕分流處: *We came to a fork in the road.* 我們來到岔路口。

fork² *v* **1** [I] to divide like the shape of the letter Y 分為字母 Y 的形狀; 分岔: *You'll see our house on the left, just before the road forks.* 就在路分岔前的左邊, 你會看見我們的房子。 **2 fork left, fork right** to take either the left or the right road at a place where the road divides 走左岔路; 走右岔路: *Fork left at the bus station.* 到了公共汽車站走左岔路。

　　fork out *phr v* [I;T **fork** sthg ↔ **out**] *infml* to pay money unwillingly 〔非正式〕〔不情願地〕付錢: *I had to fork out another £10 for the school fund.* 我勉強為學校基金再付了十英鎊。

forked /fɔrkt; fɔːkt/ *adj* dividing into two or more parts at a point 分岔的; 叉狀的: *a forked road* 分岔的道路 | *a snake's forked tongue* 蛇的叉狀舌

fork·lift truck /ˈfɔrk ˌlɪft ˈtrʌk; ˌfɔːklɪft ˈtrʌk/ *n* a small vehicle for lifting and carrying heavy goods, for example inside a factory; it has a fork on the front which goes underneath the goods 叉車; 鏟車

for·lorn /fəˈlɔrn; fəˈlɔːn/ *adj* **1** left alone and unhappy 孤獨淒涼的; 孤苦伶仃的 **2 forlorn hope** a plan or attempt that is very unlikely to succeed 難以實現的計劃; 渺茫的希望 – **forlornly** *adv*

⋆form¹ /fɔrm; fɔːm/ *n* **1** [C;U] a shape 形狀; 體型: *The tall graceful form of a woman appeared at the top of the stairs.* 一位體型修長優雅的女士出現在樓梯的頂端。 | *a church built in the form of a cross* 按十字架形狀建造的教堂 **2** [C] a kind or sort 類型; 種類: *different forms of government* 不同類型的政體 | *I dislike any form of exercise.* 我不喜歡任何一種運動。 **3** [C] an official printed paper with spaces in which to answer questions and give other information 表格: *Please fill in this form, giving your name, age, and address.* 請填寫這份表格; 填明姓名、年齡和地址。 | *an application form* 申請表 **4 on form** working well, either at your job or at a sport 〔工作或運動〕狀態良好 [RELATED PHRASE 相關詞組 **off form**] **5 in fine form, on good form, on great form** in good spirits, and especially good at entertaining other people 情緒良好〔尤指待人接物〕 **6** [C] a class in a school 年級: *Her*

older brother is in the sixth form. 她哥哥上六年級。 **7** [C] a long low wooden seat without a back 長櫈

⋆form² *v* **1** [I] to come gradually into existence 形成; 產生: *A cloud of smoke formed over the burning city.* 燃燒着的城市上空形成了一片煙霧。 | *A plan began to form in his mind.* 一項計劃開始在他的腦海中形成。 **2** [T] to gradually get an idea 形成〔想法〕: *I formed the impression that she was not being completely honest.* 我有這樣的印象, 那就是她不太誠實。 **3** [T] to make or produce something 構成, 形成〔某物〕: *The past tense of "help" is formed by adding "-ed".* help 的過去式是加 -ed 構成的。 | *We need to form a new committee.* 我們需要成立一個新的委員會。 **4** [T] to make a particular shape 成特定形狀: *She tied the two sticks together to form a cross.* 她把兩根短棒紮在一起, 做成一個十字架。 | *The men formed a chain to pass the goods from the carts to the boats.* 那些人排成一行, 把貨物從車子上挪到船上去。 **5** [+ complement] to be 是; 為: *Flour, eggs, fat, and sugar form the main contents of a cake.* 麵粉、蛋、脂肪和糖是做蛋糕的主要原料。

⋆form·al /ˈfɔrml; ˈfɔːməl/ *adj* **1** based or done according to accepted rules or customs 正式的; 正規的; 合乎傳統習俗的: *a formal dinner party* 正式晚宴 | *Formal dress must be worn.* 必須穿上禮服。 **2** suitable for official occasions or serious writing, but not usually used in ordinary conversation 〔文體〕正式的; 莊重的: *The letter was very formal.* 那是封非常正式的信件。 – **formally** *adv*

for·mal·i·ty /fɔrˈmælətɪ; fɔːˈmælɜˌtɪ/ *n* **formalities 1** [C] something done according to laws or customs 正式手續: *There are a few formalities to settle before you become the legal owner of the car.* 你在成為合法車主之前, 要先辦理幾項正式手續。 **2** [C] an act which has lost its real meaning 形式: *The written part of the examination is just a formality – no one ever fails it.* 筆試部分只是一種形式而已; 沒有人不及格。 **3** [U] careful attention to rules and behaviour 講究禮節; 拘泥形式: *There's no time for formality in everyday life.* 日常生活中沒有時間講究禮節。

for·mal·ize /ˈfɔrmlˌaɪz; ˈfɔːməlaɪz/ *v* **formalized, formalizing** (also 又作 **formalise** *BrE* 〔英式〕) [T] to put an agreement or plan into a clear form and make it official 使〔協議或計劃〕成為正式〔文字〕形式: *The agreement must be formalized before it can have the force of law.* 該協議必須寫成文字才有法律效力。

⋆for·mat /ˈfɔrmæt; ˈfɔːmæt/ *n* the way in which something is arranged or produced 〔事物的〕安排方式; 生產方式: *We're trying a new format for our television show this year.* 我們正在嘗試為今年的電視節目作新的編排。 | *Official reports are usually written to* *a set format.* 正式報告通常要按固定格式寫成。

★for·ma·tion /fɔrˈmeʃən; fɔːˈmeɪʃən/ *n* **1** [U] the shaping or developing of something 組成; 形成; 養成: *the formation of a child's character* 兒童個性的形成 **2** [C;U] an arrangement of people, ships, or aircraft 〔人、船或飛機的〕排列; 隊形: *drawn up in battle formation* 排成戰鬥隊形 | *formation dancing* 編隊跳舞 **3** [C] the shape of something which is formed by a natural process 〔自然〕形成物; 結構: *There are several kinds of cloud formation.* 雲層的構成形式有好幾種。| *volcanic rock formations* 火山巖層

for·ma·tive /ˈfɔrmətɪv; ˈfɔːmətɪv/ *adj* **1** having an influence on your development 影響發展的 **2 the formative years** the time when a child's character is formed and developed 兒童性格的形成時期

★for·mer[1] /ˈfɔrmɚ; ˈfɔːməʳ/ *adj* [only before a noun 只用於名詞前] *fml* of an earlier time 〔正式〕以前的; 從前的: *a former President of the United States* 美國的前任總統 | *In former times the building was a prison, but it is currently in use as a government office.* 這建築物從前是監獄, 但現在已作政府辦公大樓。

former[2] *n* [plural is 複數為 **former**] *fml* the first of two people or things just mentioned 〔正式〕前者: *Germany and the United States are Britain's two most important trading partners, the former being the major supplier of goods, the latter being Britain's main export market.* 德國和美國是英國的兩個最重要的貿易夥伴; 前者是貨物的主要提供者, 後者是英國的主要出口市場。| *Will they negotiate or will they go to war? At present the former seems more likely.* 他們願意談判還是開戰? 現在前者的可能性似乎更大一些。

for·mer·ly /ˈfɔrmɚlɪ; ˈfɔːməli/ *adv* in the past 以前; 從前: *Peru was formerly ruled by the Spanish.* 祕魯從前受西班牙人的統治。

for·mi·da·ble /ˈfɔrmɪdəbḷ; ˈfɔːmᵻdəbəl/ *adj fml* **1** very great or powerful so that you feel respect or fear 〔正式〕令人畏懼的; 令人敬畏的: *a formidable voice* 可怕的聲音 | *a formidable old lady* 令人欽佩的老太太 **2** hard to defeat or deal with 難以克服的; 難以應付的: *They faced formidable difficulties in their attempt to reach the South Pole.* 他們在到達南極的嘗試中遇到了難以克服的困難。| *formidable weather conditions* 惡劣的天氣情況 –**formidably** *adv*

★for·mu·la /ˈfɔrmjələ; ˈfɔːmjʊlə/ *n* **formulas** or **formulae** /-liː, -liː/ **1** a group of letters, signs, or numbers expressing a general scientific law or rule 公式; 方程式; 分子式: *The chemical formula for water is H_2O.* 水的化學分子式是H_2O。**2** a list of instructions for making something 配方; 製法: *Someone has stolen the secret formula for the new drink.* 有人偷了這種新飲料的祕密配方。**3** a

plan for dealing with a difficult problem 〔對付難題的〕方案; 計劃: *to draw up a formula for a lasting peace* 制定一個長久和平的方案

for·mu·late /ˈfɔrmjəˌlet; ˈfɔːmjᵿleɪt/ *v* **formulated, formulating** [T] **1** to express something in a short clear form 用簡明的形式表達〔某事〕: *He took care to formulate his reply very clearly.* 他小心謹慎地作了確切的回答。**2** to invent and prepare a plan or suggestion 構想, 準備〔計劃或建議〕: *They are currently formulating a new policy on Northern Ireland.* 他們目前在制定一項對北愛爾蘭的新政策。–**formulation** /ˌfɔrmjəˈleʃən; ˌfɔːmjᵿˈleɪʃən/ *n* [C;U]

for·ni·cate /ˈfɔrnəˌket; ˈfɔːnᵻkeɪt/ *v* **fornicated, fornicating** [I] *biblical* to have sexual relations with someone without being married to them 《聖經》私通; 通姦 –**fornication** /ˌfɔrnᵻˈkeʃən; ˌfɔːnᵻˈkeɪʃən/ *n* [U]

for·sake /fəˈsek; fəˈseɪk/ *v* **forsook** /-ˈsʊk; -ˈsʊk/, **forsaken** /-ˈsekən; -ˈseɪkən/, **forsaking** [T] *fml* to leave someone or something completely 〔正式〕離棄〔某人〕; 放棄〔某物〕: *They felt that their leader had forsaken them in their hour of need.* 他們感覺到領導人在他們需要之時不顧而去。

fort /fɔrt; fɔːt/ *n* **1** a strongly made building used for defence 堡壘; 要塞 **2 hold the fort** *infml* to manage affairs for someone while they are away 〔非正式〕代人處理事務: *I have to make a phone call. Can you hold the fort for ten minutes please?* 我得去打個電話; 請你照料十分鐘, 好嗎?

for·te /ˈfɔrteɪ; ˈfɔːteɪ/ *n* [sing] a strong point in a person's character or abilities 長處; 特長: *Games are not my forte.* 球類運動不是我的特長。

forth /fɔrθ; fɔːθ/ *adv* **1** *lit* out from a place 〔文〕向前(方): *He went forth into the desert to pray.* 他前往沙漠中去祈禱。**2 and so forth** used to say that there are lots of other things that you could add to a list 等等〔用於表示列舉未盡〕: *The place was full of junk – old furniture, paintings, and so forth.* 那地方全是破爛貨: 有舊家具、繪畫等等。**3 back and forth** first in one direction and then in the other 來回地; 往返

forth·com·ing /ˈfɔrθˌkʌmɪŋ; ˌfɔːθˈkʌmɪŋ◂/ *adj fml* 〔正式〕**1** happening or appearing very soon 即將發生[出現]的: *a list of forthcoming events* 即將舉行的活動表 **2** [never before a noun 不能用於名詞前] given or offered 可得到的: *Funds will soon be forthcoming.* 資金很快就要兌現。**3** [never before a noun 不能用於名詞前] ready to be helpful and give information 樂意幫助並提供信息的: *I asked several villagers, but none of them was very forthcoming.* 我問了好幾個村民, 但他們都不熱心相助。

forth·right /ˈfɔrθˌraɪt; ˈfɔːθraɪt/ *adj* very direct and honest in manner and speech 〔言

行〕直率的; 坦誠的: *She made the point in her usual forthright manner.* 她像往常那樣直言不諱地談了看法。–**forthrightness** *n* [U]

forth·with /fɔrθ'wɪθ; fɔ:θ'wɪð/ *adv fml* without delay〔正式〕即刻; 立即

for·ti·fi·ca·tion /ˌfɔrtəfə'keʃən; ˌfɔ:tﬁf̩'keɪʃən/ *n* **1 fortifications** [pl] towers and walls set up as a means of defence〔塔樓、城牆等〕防禦工事 **2** [U] the act of making something stronger or more effective 加強; 強化

for·ti·fy /'fɔrtəˌfaɪ; 'fɔ:tﬁfaɪ/ *v* **fortified** [T] **1** to strengthen something against attack 加強防禦; 設防: *a fortified city* 設防的城市 | *They had only two weeks in which to fortify the coastal areas against the enemy.* 他們只有兩個星期時間來加強海岸區的防禦, 以阻止敵人的進攻。**2** to make something stronger or more effective 強化〔某物〕; 使〔某物〕更有效: *a breakfast cereal fortified with vitamins* 用於早餐的維生素強化麥片

for·ti·tude /'fɔrtəˌtjud; 'fɔ:tﬁtju:d/ *n* [U] *fml* firm and lasting courage in bearing trouble or pain, without complaining〔正式〕堅韌; 剛毅

fort·night /'fɔrtnaɪt; 'fɔ:tnaɪt/ *n* a period of two weeks 兩星期: *I'm going away for a fortnight.* 我要外出兩週。 | *He's coming in a fortnight's time.* 他兩週後要來這裡。

fort·night·ly /'fɔrtˌnaɪtlɪ; 'fɔ:tnaɪtli/ *adv* happening or appearing every two weeks 每兩週地; 兩週一次地 –**fortnightly** *adj*: *a fortnightly visit* 兩週一次的拜訪

for·tress /'fɔrtrɪs; 'fɔ:trﬁs/ *n* a castle or other very large strongly made building used for defence 城堡; 堡壘; 要塞

for·tu·i·tous /fɔr'tjuətəs; fɔ:'tju:ﬁtəs/ *adj fml* lucky and happening by chance〔正式〕偶然的; 意外的: *a fortuitous meeting* 偶然相遇 –**fortuitously** *adv*

for·tu·nate /'fɔrtʃənɪt; 'fɔ:tʃənət/ *adj* lucky 幸運的; 吉利的; 僥倖的: *He's fortunate in having a good job.* 他很幸運, 有份好工作。 | *She's fortunate to have very good health.* 她身體很健康, 真是好福氣。 | *It was fortunate for her that she had enough money to get the car repaired.* 她很僥倖, 有足夠的錢把汽車修好。–opposite 反義 **unfortunate**

for·tu·nate·ly /'fɔrtʃənɪtlɪ; 'fɔ:tʃənətli/ *adv* luckily 幸運地; 幸虧: *I was late in getting to the station, but fortunately for me, the train was late too.* 我到火車站已經遲了, 但幸好火車也誤了點。 | *Fortunately, the wind dropped and the fire died down.* 幸虧風力減弱, 火才得以熄滅。–opposite 反義 **unfortunately**

for·tune /'fɔrtʃən; 'fɔ:tʃən/ *n* **1** [C] a large amount of money 大筆錢財; 巨款: *His house must be worth a fortune by now.* 他的房子如今一定很值錢。 | *He made a fortune on the stock exchange.* 他在股票交易中賺了一大錢。**2** [U] luck 運氣; 好運: *She had the good fortune to be free from illness all her life.* 她運氣好, 一生中沒有病痛。**3** [C] whatever

happens by chance to a person, good or bad 命運; 人生遭遇: *Through all his changing fortunes, he never lost courage.* 他一生坎坷, 卻從未喪失勇氣。**4 tell someone's fortune** to tell someone what will happen to them in the future 給某人算命 **5 make your fortune** to become very rich 發財: *He made his fortune by getting into the market at the right time.* 他適時經商發了財。**6 a small fortune** *infml* a large amount of money〔非正式〕很多錢: *That new car must have cost you a small fortune.* 買那輛新車一定花了你很多錢。

fortune-tell·er /'···ˌ··/ *n* a person who tells you what is going to happen in the future 算命者; 看相者

for·ty /'fɔrtɪ; 'fɔ:ti/ *det,n,pron* **forties 1** the number 40〔數字〕四十 **2 the Forties, the forties** the years 1940-1949 四十年代〔1940年到1949年〕: *He went to school in the Forties, just after the war.* 他是四十年代上的學, 那時戰爭剛結束。**3 in her forties, in their forties, etc.** aged between 40 and 49 在四十歲到四十九歲之間: *I first got reading glasses when I was in my forties.* 我在四十多歲便開始用放大鏡閱讀。**4 forty winks** a short sleep 打盹; 小睡 –**fortieth** *det, n, pron, adv*

for·um /'forəm; 'fɔ:rəm/ *n* a place or meeting where people talk about public matters 論壇; 討論會: *The letters page of this newspaper is a forum for public argument.* 這份報紙的讀者來信欄是大眾論壇。

for·ward[1] /'fɔrwəd; 'fɔ:wəd/ *adj* **1** in the direction that is in front of you 向前的: *a forward movement* 向前的移動 **2** quick to learn things (used of babies)〔智力〕發育早的; 早熟的〔指兒童〕**3** too bold and too sure of yourself 魯莽的; 冒失的

forward[2] *v* [T] **1** to send letters and parcels to someone's new address 轉遞〔信件、包裹〕; 轉交: *Could you forward our mail to us?* 你能否把我們的郵件轉寄給我們? **2 forwarding address** someone's new address, to which letters and parcels should be sent〔郵件轉遞的〕新地址

for·wards /'fɔrwədz; 'fɔ:wədz/ *adv* (also 又作 **forward**) **1** in the direction that is in front of you 向前: *They crept forwards.* 他們匍匐前進。**2** towards the future 向將來: *We must look forwards, not backwards.* 我們應該面向未來, 不走回頭路。 | *He described the change in the law as a big step forwards.* 他把法律的改動視為一大進步。

fos·sil /'fasl; 'fɒsəl/ *n* the hardened remains of an animal or plant of long ago, or the print in the rock that shows where it has been 化石

fossil fuel /'·· ˌ·/ *n* [U] a substance such as coal or oil which has been formed from things that were living a long time ago; fossil fuels are burnt to produce heat 礦物

燃料

fos·sil·ize /'fɒslˌaɪz; 'fɒsḻlaɪz/ v **fossilized, fossilizing** (also 又作 **fossilise** BrE 《英式》) [I;T] to make or become a fossil 〔使〕成化石: *the fossilized remains of a prehistoric bird* 史前鳥的化石殘骸

fos·ter /'fɒstə; 'fɒstəʳ/ v [T] **1** to care for someone else's child for a period of time in return for payment; the child lives with you, but you do not have the legal rights or responsibilities of the parent 養育; 收養; 照顧 –compare 比較 ADOPT (1) **2** fml to encourage something to grow or develop 《正式》培養; 助長: *We hope these meetings will foster friendly relations between our two countries.* 我們希望這些會晤將有助於發展我們兩國之間的友好關係。

foster child /'·· ,·/ n **foster children** a child who is fostered 收養的孩子

foster par·ent /'·· ,··/ n an adult who fosters a child 養父; 養母

fought /fɔt; fɔːt/ the past tense and past participle of FIGHT ☆ FIGHT 的過去式和過去分詞

foul¹ /faul; faʊl/ adj **1** very dirty, or with a very unpleasant smell 惡臭的; 污穢的: *The air in the cellar was damp and foul.* 地下室的空氣既潮濕又污濁。 **2** very unpleasant 惡劣的; 極壞的: *What foul weather!* 天氣真是糟糕透了! | *She's got a foul temper.* 她的脾氣壞透了。 **3** foul language rude and unpleasant language 粗魯的髒話 **4** foul play: a play which is against the rules in a sport 〔運動中的〕犯規行為 **b** tech criminal violence which causes death 〔術語〕〔導致死亡的〕暴行; 謀殺: *He is thought to have died of natural causes, and foul play is not suspected.* 他被認為是自然死亡, 沒有懷疑是謀殺。

foul² n an act that is against the rules in a sport 〔運動中的〕犯規行為

foul³ v **1** [T] fml to make something dirty in a very unpleasant way 《正式》弄髒; 弄污; 污染: *Dogs must not foul the pavement.* 禁止狗在人行道上便溺。 **2** [I] to do something which is against the rules of a sport, especially football 〔在運動中〕犯規〔尤指足球〕

foul sthg ↔ up phr v [T] infml to spoil something 《非正式》弄亂, 搞糟〔某事物〕

found¹ /faund; faʊnd/ the past tense and past participle of FIND ☆ FIND 的過去式和過去分詞

*★**found²** v [T] **1** to start to build a town or a building, or establish an organization 建造〔城市或大樓〕; 創建〔機構〕: *The Romans founded a great city here.* 羅馬人在這裡建了一座大城市。 | *The company was founded in 1724.* 這家公司創辦於 1724 年。 **2** be founded on to be based on 基於; 以…為根據: *The story is not founded on facts.* 這個故事不是根據真人真事寫成的。

*★**foun·da·tion** /faun'deʃən; faʊn'deɪʃən/ n **1** [sing] the act of starting to build a town or building, or establishing an organization 建立; 創立; 創辦 **2** [C] an organization that gives out money for certain special purposes 基金會: *The Gulbenkian Foundation gives money to help artists.* 古爾本基安基金會捐款資助藝術家。 **3** [C] the belief or idea on which a belief or way of life is based 基礎; 基本信仰或思想: *built on the foundation of Christian beliefs* 建立在基督教信念的基礎上 **4** [U] facts that prove that something is true 〔事實〕根據: *The allegations are completely without foundation.* 這些指控毫無根據。 **5** foundations [pl] a solid base deep in the earth on which something is supported or built 地基

found·er¹ /'faundə; 'faʊndəʳ/ n **1** a person who founds something 創始人; 創建者: *Mohammed was the founder of the Muslim religion.* 穆罕默德是伊斯蘭教的創始人。 **2 a founder member** a member of a club or an organization from its beginning 〔俱樂部或組織的〕發起人之一

found·er² v [I] **1** (of a ship) to fill with water and sink 〔船〕沉沒 **2** to fail 失敗: *The plan foundered for lack of support.* 該計劃因缺乏支持而告吹。

foun·dry /'faundri; 'faʊndri/ n **foundries** a place where metal or glass is melted down and formed into shapes or parts of machinery 鑄造廠; 玻璃廠

foun·tain /'fauntn; 'faʊntḻn/ n **1** a decorative structure that pumps a stream of water up into the air 〔裝飾用的〕噴泉; 噴水池 **2** a strong flow of liquid that goes straight up into the air 噴水: *A fountain of water was shooting up from the burst pipe.* 一股水從破裂的水管中噴出來。

fountain pen /'·· ·/ n a pen which you fill with ink and which has a metal point for writing with 自來水筆

four /fɔ; fɔːʳ/ det,n,pron **1** the number 4 〔數字〕四 **2** on all fours on your hands and knees 用雙手和雙膝; 爬着: *He was crawling about on all fours.* 他在地上到處爬。

four·teen /'fɔ'tin; ˌfɔː'tiːn◂/ det,n,pron the number 14 〔數字〕十四 –**fourteenth** det, n, pron, adv

fourth /fɔθ; fɔːθ/ det,pron,adv,n **1** 4th 第四〔個〕 **2** one of four equal parts 四分之一

fowl /faul; faʊl/ n fowl or fowls a bird such as a hen which is kept and eaten 家禽

fox¹ /faks; fɒks/ n a doglike wild animal with reddish fur 狐狸

fox² v [T] to tell or ask someone something they cannot understand or find an answer to 使〔某人〕難以理解; 把〔某人〕難住

fox·trot /'faks,trat; 'fɒkstrɒt/ n a formal dance with short quick steps 狐步舞

foy·er /'fɔɪə; 'fɔɪeɪ/ n an entrance hall of a theatre or hotel 〔劇院或旅館的〕門廳, 門廊

frac·as /'frekas; 'frækɑː/ n [sing] a noisy

quarrel or fight in which a lot of people take part 吵架; 打鬧

frac·tion /ˈfrækʃən; ˈfrækʃən/ n **1** a division or part of a whole number; ⅓ and ½ are fractions 分數; 小數〔如⅓和½都是分數〕 **2** a very small piece or amount 小部分; 一點兒: *We're selling it at a fraction of the original price.* 我們以原價的一小部分錢把它賣掉。

frac·tion·al /ˈfrækʃənl; ˈfrækʃənəl/ adj very small or to a very small degree 少許的; 少量的 **–fractionally** adv

frac·tious /ˈfrækʃəs; ˈfrækʃəs/ adj fml bad-tempered about small things and ready to quarrel (used especially of a child) 〔正式〕暴躁的; 易怒的〔尤指兒童〕

frac·ture[1] /ˈfræktʃə; ˈfræktʃɚ/ n tech a break or crack in something, especially a bone 〔術語〕折斷; 斷裂〔尤指骨折〕: *a fracture of the hip* 股骨部骨折

fracture[2] v **fractured, fracturing** [I;T] to break or crack (使)折斷; 斷裂: *He fell and fractured his leg.* 他跌了一跤, 造成腿部骨折。| *a fractured rib* 肋骨骨折

fra·gile /ˈfrædʒəl; ˈfrædʒaɪl/ adj **1** easily broken or damaged 易碎的; 易損壞的: *Things made of glass are always fragile.* 玻璃製品總是很容易打碎。| *a fragile relationship* 脆弱的關係 **2** weak in health 虛弱的: *a fragile old lady* 身體虛弱的老婦人 **–fragility** /frəˈdʒɪlətɪ; frəˈdʒɪləti/ n [U]

*frag·ment[1] /ˈfrægmənt; ˈfrægmənt/ n a small piece or part of something 片斷; 碎片: *I overheard a fragment of their conversation.* 我無意中聽到他們談話的隻言片語。| *tiny fragments of glass* 微小的玻璃碎片

frag·ment[2] /frægˈmɛnt; fræɡˈmɛnt/ v [I] to break into small pieces 成為碎片 **–fragment·ation** /ˌfrægmənˈteʃən; ˌfrægmənˈteɪʃən/ n [U]

frag·men·tary /ˈfrægmən,tɛrɪ; ˈfrægməntəri/ adj made up of only a few pieces of information, which do not seem to be connected 由零碎的、無聯繫的信息組成的: *There was only fragmentary evidence linking him to the bombings.* 只有些支離破碎的證據來證明他與爆炸事件有牽連。

frag·men·ted /ˈfrægmɛntɪd; fræɡˈmɛntɪd/ adj made up of different pieces of information which are not connected very well 〔信息〕不完整的; 無條理的: *We received only a fragmented account of the incident.* 我們只聽到這個事件的一些斷續不全的敘述。

fra·grance /ˈfregrəns; ˈfreɪgrəns/ n [C;U] a sweet or pleasant smell 芳香; 芬芳; 香味: *a light, flowery fragrance* 一股淡淡的花香 | *The fragrance of the roses filled the room.* 房間裡充滿了玫瑰花的芳香。

fra·grant /ˈfregrənt; ˈfreɪgrənt/ adj having a sweet or pleasant smell 有香味的; 芬芳的: *The air in the garden was warm and fragrant.* 花園裡的空氣又暖和又芬芳。

frail /frel; freɪl/ adj weak and in poor health

體弱的: *a frail old woman* 體弱的老婦人

frail·ty /ˈfreltɪ; ˈfreɪlti/ n **frailties 1** [U] the state of being weak 虛弱; 脆弱: *an old man of increasing age and frailty* 年邁體弱的老頭 **2** [C] a weakness 弱點; 缺點: *We all have our little frailties.* 我們自身都有小小的弱點。

*frame[1] /frem; freɪm/ v **framed, framing** [T] **1** to fix a firm border or case round a picture or photograph 給〔圖畫或相片〕裝框: *I'm having her photo professionally framed.* 我正請專人給她的照片鑲鏡框。**2** fml to express something in a particular way 〔正式〕〔以特定方法〕表達〔某事〕: *An examiner must frame his questions clearly.* 主考人必須把試題表達清楚。**3** infml to make someone appear guilty of a crime by giving false statements or producing false proofs 〔非正式〕誣告; 陷害

frame[2] n **1** the main supports over and around which something is built 支架; 構架; 骨架: *Their boats are made of skins stretched over a wooden frame.* 他們的小船是用獸皮繃在木架上製成的。| *a bicycle frame* 腳踏車車架 **2** lit the body of a person or an animal 〔文〕〔人或動物的〕身軀: *a man with a powerful frame* 體格魁梧的男子 **3** a firm border or case into which something is fixed 框; 框架: *a window frame* 窗框 | *sunglasses with pink plastic frames* 帶粉紅色塑膠框架的墨鏡 **4** one of the many separate photographs which make a cinema film 〔影片的〕一個畫面〔鏡頭〕 **5 frame of mind** the state of your mind or feelings at a particular time 心境; 心情; 情緒: *I'm in the wrong frame of mind to make a decision now.* 我現在沒有心思來作決定。

frame·work /ˈfrem,wɜk; ˈfreɪmwɜːk/ n **1** a supporting frame or structure 構架; 骨架; 結構: *This building has a steel framework.* 這座大樓是鋼鐵結構。**2** a general set of rules or beliefs within which a society or an organization works 〔社會或組織的〕準則; 信仰

franc /fræŋk; fræŋk/ n the standard coin of France, Switzerland, Belgium, and some other countries 法郎〔法國、瑞士、比利時等國家的貨幣〕

fran·chise /ˈfræntʃaɪz; ˈfræntʃaɪz/ n **1** [sing] the right to vote in a public election 選舉權 **2** [C] a right given by a company to someone, allowing them to sell the company's goods or services 〔公司授予個人售賣該公司產品或經營某業務的〕特許權

frank /fræŋk; fræŋk/ adj direct and honest in the way that you speak to people (a word usually used to show approval) 坦誠的; 直率的: *To be perfectly frank, I don't like her.* 說實在的, 我並不喜歡她。| *He was quite frank with me about my chances of getting the job.* 關於我有沒有希望得到那份工作, 他對我坦誠相告。

frank·ly /ˈfræŋklɪ; ˈfræŋkli/ adv **1** you say

F

this when you are going to give an honest opinion which is not favourable 坦率地說〔用於表達否定的看法〕: *Frankly, I think he's useless.* 老實説，我覺得他很不中用。**2** in an honest and open way 坦率地; 真誠地: *She spoke frankly about her fears for the future.* 她坦率地道出了自己對將來的恐懼感。

fran·tic /ˈfræntɪk; ˈfræntɪk/ *adj* **1** very worried and frightened 〔因焦急和擔心而〕發狂似的: *We were frantic* **with** *worry about you.* 我們對你可真是擔心得要命。**2** very hurried 匆忙的; 慌亂的: *It was a frantic rush to get everything ready.* 為把一切準備就緒，大家都忙得不可開交。–**frantically** /-klɪ, -kli/ *adv*

fra·ter·nal /frəˈtɜːnl; frəˈtɜːnl/ *adj fml* 〖正式〗**1** relating to brothers 兄弟的; 兄弟般的 **2** friendly 友善的; 友好的 –**fraternally** *adv*

fra·ter·ni·ty /frəˈtɜːnəti; frəˈtɜːnˌti/ *n* **fraternities 1** [C] people who do the same job or have the same interests 〔職業或興趣相同的〕羣體: *members of the medical fraternity* 醫務界的同行 **2** [U] *fml* the state of showing friendship or support to other people 〖正式〗友愛; 博愛

frat·er·nize /ˈfrætəˌnaɪz; ˈfrætənaɪz/ *v* **fraternized, fraternizing** (also 又作 **fraternise** *BrE* 〖英式〗) [I] *fml* to meet people and talk to them in a friendly way 〖正式〗友善交往: *The university lecturers tend not to fraternize* **with** *their students.* 大學講師往往不跟學生親近往來。

fraud /frɔːd; frɔːd/ *n* **1** [C;U] dishonest behaviour which is intended to deceive people, often in order to gain money 欺騙(行為); 詐騙: *He was found guilty of fraud.* 他被判定犯了詐騙罪。| *The whole thing had been an elaborate fraud.* 那是件精心策劃的詐騙案。**2** [C] a person who is not what they claim to be 騙子

fraud·u·lent /ˈfrɔːdʒələnt; ˈfrɔːdjˌlənt/ *adj fml* deceitful or dishonest, often in order to gain money 〖正式〗欺騙的; 欺詐的: *He obtained the money by fraudulent means.* 他用欺騙手段弄到了錢。–**fraudulently** *adv*

fraught /frɔːt; frɔːt/ *adj* **1** **fraught with danger, problems, etc.** full of danger, full of problems, etc. 充滿危險; 充滿困難: *The long journey was fraught with danger.* 那次長途旅行充滿了危險。**2** *infml* very worried and anxious 〖非正式〗憂慮的; 焦慮的

fray¹ /freɪ; freɪ/ *v* **1** [I] to develop loose threads round the edges, sometimes when thin and worn 〔布邊〕被磨損; 破損: *This material frays when you cut it. It's a real nuisance.* 這種布料裁剪時容易破損，真是討厭。**2** **my temper frayed** = I started to feel very angry 我的脾氣煩躁

fray² *n* **the fray** busy and tiring action or a fight or argument (a word which is often used in a humorous way) 吵架; 打架; 戰鬥; 爭辯〔常含幽默〕: *Are you ready for the fray?*

(這次爭鬥)你準備好了嗎?

frayed /freɪd; freɪd/ *adj* thin and worn with loose threads round the edges 〔織物邊緣〕磨破的

freak¹ /friːk; friːk/ *n* **1** a person or an animal that is unnatural or unusual in some way 畸形或不正常的人或動物 **2** a strange, unexpected happening 怪事; 反常現象: *By some strange freak, a little snow fell in Egypt a few years ago.* 真是稀奇，埃及幾年前也下了一點雪。**3** *infml* a person who takes a special interest in something 〖非正式〗對某物有特別興趣的人: *a film freak* 影迷

freak² *adj* [only before a noun 只用於名詞前] very unusual and unlikely to happen 反常的: *a freak storm* 反常的暴風雨

freak³ *v*

freak out *phr v* [I] *infml* to become very excited, upset, or angry 〖非正式〗極度興奮、不安或憤怒

freak·ish /ˈfriːkɪʃ; ˈfriːkɪʃ/ *adj* very unusual and strange 反常的; 奇特的: *rather mad, freakish behaviour* 瘋狂古怪的行為

freck·le /ˈfrekl; ˈfrekəl/ *n* a small brown spot on a person's skin, especially on their face 雀斑〔尤指臉部的〕–**freckled** *adj*: *a freckled face* 長有雀斑的臉

★free¹ /friː; friː/ *adj* **1** able to act as you wish, and not limited or controlled 自由的; 不受約束的: *People are demanding the right to free speech and a free press.* 人們要求得到言論自由和新聞自由的權利。| *You are free to come and go as you want.* 你來去自由，不受約束。**2** not a prisoner 不受監禁的: *He walked from the police station a free man.* 他從警察局走出來，成了自由的人。| *All political prisoners will be set free next week.* 所有的政治犯都將於下週釋放。**3** costing nothing 免費的: *All the drinks are free.* 所有的飲料都是免費的。| *I've got a couple of free tickets for tonight's concert.* 我有幾張今晚音樂會的免費門票。**4** **do/get something for free** to do or get something without paying for it 無償做某事; 免費得到某物 **5** **free of charge** without asking for any payment 免費: *Meals will be provided free of charge.* 伙食將免費提供。**6** without work or duty 空閒的: *I'm free all afternoon.* 我整個下午都有空。| *She doesn't get much free time.* 她的空餘時間不多。**7** not being used 未被佔用的: *Is this seat free?* 這座位有人嗎? **8** **free from something, free of something** not having or suffering from something unpleasant 沒有或不受某(不愉快)事物影響: *She is never free from pain.* 她從未擺脱過病痛。| *Keep all parts of the machine free of dust and dirt.* 把所有這些機器零件存放在沒有灰塵的地方。**9** **free with something** very willing to give something 對某物出手大方: *She's very free with her money.* 她花錢很大方。**10** **free and easy** not taking things too seriously 隨便的; 不拘禮節的 **11** a

free kick in football, the chance for a player on one side to kick the ball freely from the place where a player on the other side has broken the rules〔足球〕罰自由球 **12 a free agent** someone who can act as they choose 有自主權的人

*free[2] *adv* **1** in an uncontrolled manner 自由地; 無約束的: *Don't let the dog run free on the main road.* 別讓狗在大街上隨便亂跑。**2** without payment 免費的: *Babies are allowed to travel free on buses.* 嬰兒可免費乘公共汽車。**3** so as to become loose or disconnected 鬆開地; 脫開地: *I pushed the gate hard and at last it swung free.* 我使勁一推大門, 結果終於鬆開了。

free[3] *v* **freed** /frid; friːd/, **freeing** [T] **1** to let someone leave a place so that they are free 使〔某人〕自由; 釋放: *All the political prisoners have now been freed.* 政治犯現已全部釋放。**2** to move or loosen someone or something that is stuck or trapped 使〔卡住的人或物〕鬆動: *He managed to free his hands.* 他設法鬆動自己的雙手。**3** to take away something unpleasant from someone 使〔某人〕擺脫〔不快之事〕: *We must try to free the world from hunger.* 我們一定要讓世界擺脫飢餓。| *He had been freed of all his responsibilities.* 他解脫了身上的一切責任。**4** to make it possible for someone or something to be used 使〔某人或某物〕用於〔某一方面〕: *The Government is being asked to free money for new housing.* 人們在要求政府把錢用於建造新的住宅。

*free·dom /ˈfridəm; ˈfriːdəm/ *n* **1** [C;U] the power to do, say, think, or write what you want 行動、言論、思想、寫作等的〕自由權: *They are calling for freedom of speech and freedom of religion.* 他們在要求得到言論自由和宗教信仰自由。| *We must defend our fundamental freedoms.* 我們必須捍衛我們基本自由的權利。| *Women are demanding the freedom to choose when they have children.* 婦女要求對何時生兒育女有自由選擇的權利。**2** [U] the state of being free, and not a prisoner or under anyone's control 自由; 釋放: *He just stood there, enjoying his first moments of freedom.* 他只是站在那兒, 享受着剛獲釋的片刻樂趣。**3 freedom from something** the state of not being hurt by something unpleasant 擺脫某事物: *freedom from hunger* 擺脫飢餓 **4 freedom fighters** someone who fights in a war against a bad government or army〔與腐敗政府或軍隊作戰的〕自由戰士

free en·ter·prise /ˌ· ˈ····/ *n* [U] a social system in which trade and business are carried on without much government control〔政府很少干預商業活動的〕自由企業制

free-for-all /ˌ· · ˈ·/ *n infml* a fight or noisy argument in which a lot of people take part《非正式》有很多人參加的爭吵或辯論

free·hand /ˈfriˌhænd; ˈfriːhænd/ *adj, adv* drawn by hand, without the use of a ruler or other instrument〔不用儀器〕徒手畫的

free·lance /ˈfriˈlæns; ˈfriːlɑːns/ *adj, adv* not employed by anyone else, but selling your work to an organization or organizations 自由作家的〔地〕; 自由職業的〔地〕: *a freelance journalist* 自由撰稿記者 | *He works freelance.* 他是一位自由職業者。–**freelance, freelancer** *n*: *Most of the work is done by freelances.* 大部分工作都由自由作家承擔。

free·ly /ˈfrili; ˈfriːli/ *adv* **1** of your own will, without being forced 自願地; 主動地: *I freely admit that what I said was wrong.* 我主動承認我說的話錯了。**2** in an open and honest way, without being limited by fear of what will happen as a result 直爽地; 坦率地: *You can speak freely in front of us.* 你可以在我們面前直言不諱。**3** without any difficulty or any limitation on movement 自由地: *Oil the wheel. Then it will turn more freely.* 給輪子上點油, 這樣它就會運轉自如。**4 freely available** easily obtainable 容易弄到 **5** in large amounts 大量地: *He gives his time freely to help the party.* 他為幫着舉辦這次聚會花了大量時間。| *The wound bled freely.* 傷口流了大量的血。

free·ma·son /ˈfriˌmesn̩; ˈfriːˌmeɪsən/ *n* (also 又作 **Freemason, Mason**) a man belonging to an ancient and widespread secret society whose members treat each other as brothers and have certain special signs and words by which they recognize each other 共濟會會員〔古代分布很廣的祕密會社的成員, 其成員視彼此如兄弟般相處, 並用某些特殊記號和文字作為識別的手段〕

free·ma·son·ry /ˈfriˌmesn̩ri; ˈfriːˌmeɪsənri/ *n* [U] **1** (also 又作 **Freemasonry, Masonry**) the organization and practices of the freemasons 共濟會的組織和活動 **2** a natural feeling of friendliness between people who are alike 意氣相投; 默契

free·think·er /ˈfriˈθɪŋkə; ˌfriːˈθɪŋkər/ *n* someone who forms their opinions according to reason and does not accept official teachings, especially about religion 自由思想者〔尤指宗教上的〕

free·way /ˈfriˌwe; ˈfriːweɪ/ *n* the usual American word for《美式》= a MOTORWAY

free·wheel /ˈfriˈhwil; ˌfriːˈwiːl/ *v* [I] to move forward on a bicycle or in a vehicle without using any power〔行車時〕靠慣性滑行

free will /ˌ· ˈ·/ *n* [U] **1** the belief that people are able to choose what they will do, and are not controlled by God or NECESSITY〔不受上帝或自然規律支配的〕自由意志; 自由選擇 **2 of your own free will** by choice 出於自願: *She left of her own free will.* 她是自願離開的。

freeze[1] /friz; friːz/ *v* **froze** /froz; frəʊz/, **frozen** /ˈfrozn̩; ˈfrəʊzən/, **freezing 1** [I;T] to make or become hard because of extreme cold (使)結冰; (使)凍住: *The milk has frozen* *solid.* 牛奶已經凍住了。| *The cold weather might freeze the water in the pipes.* 寒冷的天氣會把管子裡的水凍住。**2** [I] (of the weather) to be at or below the temperature at which water becomes ice〔天氣〕冷得使水結冰; 嚴寒: *It's freezing tonight.* 今晚有結冰。**3** [I] *infml* to feel very cold〔非正式〕覺得很冷: *I'm freezing!* 我冷極了! **4** [T] **a** to preserve food by means of very low temperatures 冷凍〔食物〕; 冷藏: *I'll freeze the rest of these beans.* 我要把剩下的豆子冷凍起來。[I] **b** (of food) to be preserved in this way〔食物〕冷凍; 冷藏: *Not all fruit freezes well.* 並不是所有水果都能冷藏。**5** [I] to stop suddenly and become still, usually with fear 驚呆; 嚇呆: *He froze at the sight of the snake.* 他一看到蛇就嚇呆了。**6** to officially fix something such as prices or wages at a certain level for a period of time 凍結〔物價或工資等〕

freeze² *n* **1** a fixing of something such as prices or wages at a certain level〔物價或工資等的〕凍結: *a wage freeze* 工資凍結 **2** a period of very cold icy weather 冰凍期; 嚴寒期

freez·er /ˈfriːzə; ˈfriːzəʳ/ *n* a large container like a cupboard in which food can be stored for a long time because the temperature is below zero 冰櫃; 冷藏箱

freezing point /ˈ·· ‚·/ *n* **1** [U] (aslo 又作 **freezing**) the temperature at which water becomes ice (0 degrees CENTIGRADE) 冰點〔攝氏零度〕: *The temperature has dropped to freezing point.* 氣溫已降至冰點。**2** [C] the temperature at which a liquid freezes〔液體的〕結冰點: *The freezing point of alcohol is much lower than that of water.* 酒精的結冰點比水的結冰點要低得多。

freight /fret; freɪt/ *n* [U] goods carried by ship, train, or plane〔水運、陸運或空運的〕貨物: *This aircraft company deals with freight only. It has no passenger service.* 這家航空公司只經營貨運, 沒有客運業務。

freight·er /ˈfretə; ˈfreɪtəʳ/ *n* a ship or aircraft for carrying goods 貨船; 運貨飛機

French¹ /frentʃ; frentʃ/ *adj* from or connected with France 法國的; 法國人的; 法語的: *French wine* 法國酒 | *Her husband's French.* 她丈夫是法國人。

French² *n* **1** the French the people of France 法國人 **2** [U] the language of France 法語: *She speaks fluent French.* 她會說一口流利的法語。

French fries /‚· ·/ *n* [pl] thin pieces of potato fried in oil (法式)炸薯條

French loaf /‚· ·/ *n* a long thin loaf of white bread 法式長條狀麵包

French·man /ˈfrentʃmən; ˈfrentʃmən/ *n* **Frenchmen** /-mən; -mən/ a man who is a French citizen 法國男子

French stick /‚· ·/ *n* a long thin loaf of white bread (法式)長條麵包

French win·dows /‚· ‴··/ *n* [pl] glass doors opening out onto the garden of a house〔通向院內花園的〕落地玻璃門

French·wo·man /ˈfrentʃˌwumən; ˈfrentʃˌwumən/ *n* **Frenchwomen** /-ˌwɪmɪn; -ˌwɪmɪn/ a woman who is a French citizen 法國女子

fre·net·ic /frəˈnetɪk; frɛˈnetɪk/ *adj* very fast, excited, and wild (used of actions) 極度激動的〔指行動〕; 狂亂的〔指行動〕 **–frenetically** /-klɪ; -klɪ/ *adv*

fren·zied /ˈfrenzɪd; ˈfrenzid/ *adj* too excited and wild or very busy (used of actions) 極其激動的; 狂亂的〔指行動〕: *The place was full of frenzied activity.* 那地方到處都是一片忙亂。**–frenziedly** *adv*

fren·zy /ˈfrenzi; ˈfrenzi/ *n* [sing;U] a state of mind in which you are very excited, worried, or angry 極度激動; 狂亂; 狂怒: *He worked himself up into a frenzy before his exams.* 考試前夕他緊張得幾乎瘋了。| *The atmosphere was one of panic and frenzy.* 那是一種既恐慌又狂熱的氣氛。

*fre·quen·cy /ˈfriːkwənsɪ; ˈfriːkwənsi/ *n* **frequencies 1** [U] the number of times that something happens〔某事發生的〕頻率: *This type of accident appears to be happening with increasing frequency.* 這類事故的發生似乎越來越頻繁。**2** [C] the number of radio waves per second at which a radio signal is broadcast〔無線電的〕周率: *We broadcast on three different frequencies.* 我們用三種不同的周率進行廣播。

fre·quent¹ /ˈfriːkwənt; ˈfriːkwənt/ *adj* happening often 時常發生的: *Sudden rainstorms are frequent on this coast.* 這一帶海岸經常突然發生暴風雨。| *He's a frequent visitor.* 他是一位常客。–opposite 反義 **infrequent** –**frequently** *adv*

fre·quent² /frɪˈkwent; frɪˈkwent/ *v* [T] *fml* to go to a place often〔正式〕常去〔一地方〕: *He frequents the best clubs in town.* 他常去城裡最豪華的夜總會。

*fresh¹ /freʃ; freʃ/ *adj* **1** [only before a noun 只用於名詞前] new and different 新的; 不同的: *There has been no fresh news since yesterday.* 從昨天起一直沒有新消息。| *It's time to take a fresh look at this problem.* 現在應重新考慮一下這個問題了。| *I'll make a fresh pot of tea.* 我重新給你沖一壺茶。**2** recently picked, caught, or produced and therefore in good condition (used of food) 新鮮的, 新採的, 新產的〔指食物〕: *fresh bread* 新烤的麵包 | *This milk doesn't smell very fresh.* 這牛奶聞上去不是很新鮮。**3** clean, cool, and pleasant 清新的; 清潔的: *I must go outside for a breath of fresh air.* 我得出去吸點新鮮空氣。| *The sheets smelled clean and fresh.* 這些牀單聞上去很清新。**4** clear and healthy (used of someone's skin) 白淨健康的〔指皮膚〕: *a young man with a fresh complexion* 一位氣色好的年輕男子 **5 fresh water** water that is not salty and can be drunk

〔可飲用的〕淡水 **6** cool and windy (used of the weather) 涼爽的; 有風的〔指天氣〕 **7** **fresh from, fresh out of** having recently left a place 剛離開〔某處〕: *a new teacher fresh from university* 大學剛畢業的新教師 – **freshness** *n* [U]

fresh·en /ˈfrɛʃən; ˈfreʃən/ *v* **1** [T] to make something cleaner, fresher, and more pleasant 使〔某物〕新鮮 **2** [I] (of the wind) to become stronger 〔風〕變強

　freshen up *phr v* **1** [I] to wash yourself〔為自己〕梳洗: *I'll just go and freshen up.* 我這就去梳洗扮一下。**2** [T **freshen** sbdy/sthg ↔ **up**] to make someone or something cleaner, fresher, and more pleasant 使〔某人或某物〕變清新; 清潔

fresh·er /ˈfrɛʃə; ˈfreʃəʳ/ *n infml* a first year student at university〔非正式〕大學一年級學生

fresh·ly /ˈfrɛʃlɪ; ˈfreʃli/ *adv* [only before a past participle 只用於過去分詞前] recently 剛才; 最近: *a wonderful smell of freshly baked bread* 新烤麵包的誘人香味 | *a freshly mown lawn* 剛修剪過的草坪

fresh·wa·ter /ˈfrɛʃˌwɔtə; ˈfreʃˌwɔːtəʳ/ *adj* [only before a noun 只用於名詞前] living in or belonging to rivers or lakes, not the sea 生活於淡水的; 淡水的: *freshwater fish* 淡水魚

fret /frɛt; fret/ *v* **-tt-** to be worried 發愁; 擔心: *Don't fret. Everything will be all right.* 別發愁, 一切都會好起來的。 | *She's still fretting* **about** *getting there late.* 她還在為晚到那兒擔心。

fret·ful /ˈfrɛtfəl; ˈfretfəl/ *adj* tending to complain a lot because of unhappiness 煩躁的; 〔因不快而〕發牢騷的: *The child was tired and fretful.* 那孩子又疲倦又煩躁。–**fretfully** *adv*

fri·ar /ˈfraɪə; ˈfraɪəʳ/ *n* a man belonging to a Christian religious group; in the Middle Ages friars travelled around teaching people about the Christian religion〔中世紀基督教的〕雲遊傳道男修士; 托鉢修士

fri·a·ry /ˈfraɪərɪ; ˈfraɪəri/ *n* **friaries** a building in which friars live 男修道院

fric·tion /ˈfrɪkʃən; ˈfrɪkʃən/ *n* [U] **1** the natural force which prevents one surface from sliding easily over another 摩擦力 **2** the repeated rubbing of two surfaces together 摩擦 **3** unfriendliness and disagreement between people 不和; 衝突: *There's been a lot of friction in the office recently.* 最近辦公室裡出現不少矛盾。

Fri·day /ˈfraɪdɪ; ˈfraɪdi/ *n* [C;U] the last day of the working week, the day before the weekend 星期五

fridge /frɪdʒ; frɪdʒ/ *n* a large metal container which food or drink can be stored to keep it cold for a short time 冰箱

✶friend /frɛnd; frend/ *n* **1** a person you know well and like 朋友: *She's a close friend* **of** *mine.* 她是我的一個知心朋友。 | *my best friend* 我最好的朋友 | *He's an old*

friend of the family. 他是這家人的老朋友。**2** **be friends with someone** to have a close relationship with someone 與某人關係密切: *I've been friends with her for years.* 我和她多年來關係很好。**3** **make friends** to form a close relationship with people 交朋友; 建立友誼: *He has a pleasant manner, and makes friends very easily.* 他態度隨和, 很容易結交朋友。 | *Have you made friends* **with** *your new neighbours yet?* 你和新來的鄰居交上朋友了嗎? **4** a helper or supporter of something 贊助者; 支持者: *the friends* **of** *Norwich Cathedral* 諾里奇大教堂的贊助人

> ■ USAGE 用法: Remember to use a possessive noun or pronoun in phrases such as ☆在下列這樣的詞組中要使用所有格名詞或代名詞: *He's a friend* **of mine.** 他是我的一個朋友。 | *A friend* **of ours** *told us...* 我們的一位朋友告訴我們... | *some friends* **of Peter's** 彼得的一些朋友 | *a great friend* **of hers/his** 她的[他的]一個偉大的朋友

✶friend·ly¹ /ˈfrɛndlɪ; ˈfrendli/ *adj* **friendlier, friendliest 1** acting in a kind and pleasant way, like a friend 友好的; 友誼的: *He's not very friendly* **to** *newcomers.* 他對新來的人不太友好。 | *a friendly nation* 友好國家 –opposite 反義 **unfriendly 2 be friendly with someone** to have someone as your friend 與某人很友好: *She's quite friendly with the manager.* 她和經理很友好。**3** not causing unpleasant feelings 不傷感情的; 友善的: *We've been having a friendly argument on politics.* 我們一直在友好地爭論政治問題。**4** done just for pleasure, and not part of a competition〔競賽〕增進友誼的: *It's only a friendly game.* 這只是一場友誼賽。–**friendliness** *n* [U]

friendly² *n* **friendlies** a game played for pleasure or practice and not as part of a competition 友誼賽

✶friend·ship /ˈfrɛndʃɪp; ˈfrendʃɪp/ *n* [C;U] a relationship between friends 友誼; 友情; 友愛: *True friendship is worth more than money.* 真正的友情比金錢更珍貴。 | *His friendships never last very long.* 他與朋友的友誼從來不會持久。

frieze /friz; friːz/ *n* a decorative border along the top of a wall〔牆上沿的〕裝飾橫條; 雕帶

frig·ate /ˈfrɪgɪt; ˈfrɪgət/ *n* a small fast warship〔小型〕護衛艦

fright /fraɪt; fraɪt/ *n* **1** [U] a feeling of fear 驚嚇: *I was shaking with fright.* 我嚇得渾身發抖。**2** **get a fright** to feel suddenly frightened by something 嚇了一跳; 吃驚: *I got a terrible fright when I saw your face at the window.* 看到你的臉突然出現在窗口, 可把我嚇了一大跳。**3** **give someone a fright** to make someone feel frightened suddenly 使

F

某人大吃一驚 **4 take fright** to become frightened suddenly 受驚嚇

fright·en /ˈfraɪtn; ˈfraɪtn̩/ *v* [T] **1** to make someone feel afraid 使〔某人〕害怕; 驚嚇: *The thought of losing my job frightened me.* 我一想到要失去工作就感到害怕。| *The horse was frightened by the sudden noise.* 那匹馬被突如其來的噪音嚇壞了。**2 frighten someone into doing something** to make someone do something by frightening them 恐嚇某人使做某事 **3 frighten someone out of their wits** to frighten someone very much 使某人嚇得不知所措

    frighten sbdy ↔ **away** *phr v* [T] to make someone go away by frightening them 把〔某人〕嚇跑

    frighten sbdy ↔ **off** *phr v* [T] to make someone stop doing something by frightening them 嚇走〔某人〕: *He managed to frighten off his attackers.* 他設法嚇走了攻擊他的人。

fright·ened /ˈfraɪtnd; ˈfraɪtnd/ *adj* afraid or worried 受驚的; 擔驚受怕的: *a crowd of frightened children* 一羣受驚的孩子 | *A lot of people are frightened of snakes.* 許多人怕蛇。| *I was frightened to look at him.* 我看到他就害怕。| *I was frightened that I'd upset you.* 我當時生怕使你煩惱。| *It had grown dark and he felt very frightened.* 天黑了, 他感到非常害怕。

> □ USEFUL PATTERNS 有用句型
> be frightened of something; be frightened to do something; be frightened that...

fright·en·ing /ˈfraɪtnɪŋ; ˈfraɪtnɪŋ/ *adj* making you feel afraid or worried 令人驚恐的; 駭人的: *That was a very frightening experience.* 那是令人害怕的經歷。| *It's frightening how quickly a child can drown.* 可怕的是孩子可以很快就給淹死了。–**frighteningly** *adv*

fright·ful /ˈfraɪtfəl; ˈfraɪtfəl/ *adj* terrible 可怕的; 驚人的: *The battlefield was a frightful scene.* 那戰場的景象很可怕。| *The place was in a frightful mess.* 那地方亂七八糟的。

fright·ful·ly /ˈfraɪtfəli; ˈfraɪtfəli/ *adj old fash infml* extremely 〔老式, 非正式〕極端地: *I'm afraid I'm frightfully late.* 恐怕我來得太遲了。

fri·gid /ˈfrɪdʒɪd; ˈfrɪdʒɪd/ *adj* **1** having an unnatural dislike of sexual activity (used of a woman) 性慾冷淡的; 性冷感的〔指婦女〕**2** formal and unfriendly 鄭重而冷淡的: *a frigid smile* 冷淡的微笑 **3** *tech* very cold 〔術語〕寒冷的; 嚴寒的: *a frigid zone* 嚴寒地帶 – **frigidly** *adv* –**frigidity** /frɪˈdʒɪdəti; frɪˈdʒɪdəti/ *n* [U]

frill /frɪl; frɪl/ *n* **1** a decorative edge on a piece of material made of a band of cloth 〔布製的〕飾邊; 褶邊 **2 frills** [pl] attractive but unnecessary additions 〔華而不實的〕附加物; 虛飾: *I just want an ordinary car, with-*

out the frills. 我只要一輛沒有多餘裝飾的普通汽車。

frill·y /ˈfrɪli; ˈfrɪli/ *adj* **frillier, frilliest** decorated with frills 有飾邊的: *The little girl wore a frilly party dress.* 小女孩穿着一件有飾邊的禮服。

fringe¹ /frɪndʒ; frɪndʒ/ *n* **1** a short border of hair hanging over a person's forehead 〔額前〕劉海: *Her fringe isn't straight because she tried to cut it herself.* 她的劉海不直, 因為她曾自己試着剪過。–see picture on page 469 見 469 頁彩圖 **2** a decorative edge of hanging threads on a curtain, tablecloth, or piece of clothing 〔窗簾, 桌布或衣服的〕飾邊; 流蘇 **3** the edge, or the part farthest from the centre 邊緣: *It was easier to move about on the fringe of the crowd.* 在人羣外圍走動比較容易。**4** the most extreme part of an organization 〔組織的〕最極端部分; 一羣見解偏激的人: *a policy supported only by a fringe element in the party* 一項只受到黨內意見偏激分子支持的政策 | *fringe theatre* 〔上演實驗性劇本的〕末流劇院

fringe² *v* **fringed, fringing** [T] to act as a border to something 作為〔某物的〕邊緣; 圍繞: *A line of trees fringed the river.* 一排樹木種在河邊。| *a pool fringed with trees* 四周種着樹木的水池

fringe ben·e·fit /ˈ· ,···/ *n* something received from an employer in addition to wages, for example a car or house 〔除工資之外的〕附加福利〔如汽車或房子〕: *The pay's awful but there are a lot of fringe benefits.* 工資雖然很低, 但附加福利卻不少。

frisk /frɪsk; frɪsk/ *v* **1** [I] (of an animal or child) to run and jump about playfully 〔動物或孩子〕歡快地蹦跳: *new lambs frisking in the fields* 在田野裡蹦跳的羔羊 **2** [T] *infml* to search someone for hidden weapons or goods by passing your hands over their body 〔非正式〕搜〔某人〕的身〔以尋找暗藏的武器或物品〕: *All the passengers were frisked before being allowed onto the plane.* 所有的乘客都要經過搜身才准登上飛機。

frisk·y /ˈfrɪski; ˈfrɪski/ *adj* **friskier, friskiest** full of life and joyful activity 活潑的; 快活的: *frisky lambs* 活蹦亂跳的羔羊 –**friskily** *adv*

frit·ter /ˈfrɪtə; ˈfrɪtər/ *v*

    fritter sthg ↔ **away** *phr v* [T] to waste your time or money on small unimportant things 浪費〔時間或金錢〕: *He fritters away his time doing crossword puzzles.* 他把時間耗費在填碎橫字謎上。

fri·vol·i·ty /frɪˈvɒləti; frɪˈvɒlʲti/ *n* **frivolities** **1** [U] failure to be properly serious about things 輕浮: *We feel that his frivolity makes him unsuited to a position of trust.* 我們覺得他的輕浮使他不適宜擔當重任。**2** [C] an act or remark which is silly, when it should be serious 輕浮的言行: *A political speech should not be full of frivolities.* 政治演說不應

該充滿輕浮的言詞。

friv·o·lous /ˈfrɪvələs; ˈfrɪvələs/ *adj* **1** silly or not giving serious attention to important matters 愚蠢的; 輕浮的: *When he tried to make a little joke, the judge warned him not to give frivolous replies to the lawyer's questions.* 當他試圖開個小小的玩笑時, 法官警告他不要對律師的提問作輕率的回答。| *a frivolous empty-headed young man who thought about nothing except clothes and parties* 一個只圖穿著打扮和參加派對, 輕率浮躁的年輕人 **2** amusing and light and not at all useful 輕鬆無聊的: *I feel like doing something frivolous. Let's go and have an ice cream in Harrod's.* 我真想輕鬆一下, 我們去哈羅德飲食店吃杯冰淇淋吧。

frizz /frɪz; frɪz/ *v* [T] *infml* to force hair into short tight curls 《非正式》使〔頭髮〕鬈曲

frizz·y /ˈfrɪzɪ; ˈfrɪzi/ *adj* **frizzier**, **frizziest** *infml* with a lot of small, tight curls (used of hair)《非正式》鬈曲的〔指頭髮〕: *Some people have naturally frizzy hair.* 有些人的頭髮天生是鬈曲的。

fro /frəʊ; frəʊ/ *adv* **to and fro** from one place to another and back again 來回的; 往復的: *While she waited, she paced anxiously to and fro.* 她邊等邊焦急不安地來回踱步。

frock /frɒk; frɒk/ *n old fash* a dress worn by a woman or girl《老式》長裙

frog /frɒg; frɒg/ *n* **1** a small hairless animal with long legs, usually brownish-green in colour, that lives in water and on land, and makes a deep rough sound 蛙 **2 a frog in your throat** *infml* difficulty in speaking because of roughness in your throat《非正式》〔因咽喉不適而〕嗓音嘶啞

frog·man /ˈfrɒgmən; ˈfrɒgmən/ *n* **frogmen** /-mən; -mən/ a skilled underwater swimmer who wears a rubber suit with large flat shoes and a special apparatus for breathing 蛙人〔穿戴蛙式潛水裝備的潛水員〕

frog·march /ˈfrɒgmɑːtʃ; ˈfrɒgmɑːtʃ/ *v* [T+adv/prep] to force a person to move forward with their arms held tightly firmly from behind 迫使〔某人〕〔反剪雙臂〕前行; 蛙式押送

frol·ic /ˈfrɒlɪk; ˈfrɒlɪk/ *v* **frolicked**, **frolicked**, **frolicking** [I] to play and jump about gaily 嬉戲; 嬉鬧: *The young lambs were frolicking about in the field.* 小羔羊在田野裡嬉戲。 — **frolic** *n*: *The children are having a frolic before bedtime.* 孩子們就寢前正在歡快的玩耍。

from /frəm; frəm, *strong* 強讀 frʌm; frʌm/ *prep* **1** used to show where or when something started, or where something or someone used to be 從…; 自…; 由…〔表示空間或時間的起點〕: *Is this the train from London?* 這是從倫敦開來的火車嗎? | *They stayed from Monday till Friday.* 他們從星期一住到星期五。| *I'm from Leeds originally.* 我的老家在里茲。| *I'll get a book from the library.* 我要從圖書館借一本書。| *The new*

motorway will go from London to Plymouth. 新建的高速公路將從倫敦通到普里茅斯。 **2** sent or given by a particular person 由〔某人〕寄來或送來: *I've had a letter from my mother.* 我收到了媽媽的來信。| *I didn't get a present from John.* 我沒有拿到約翰的禮物。| *I didn't expect to get any sympathy from her.* 我並不指望得到她的同情。 **3** out of 自…; 從…〔表示狀態的改變〕: *Bread is made from flour and water.* 麵包是用麵粉和水做的。| *Can you translate this from German into English for me?* 你能幫我把這個從德語譯成英語嗎? **4** used to show distance or separation〔表示距離或分開〕: *The village is five miles from the coast.* 這個村莊離海岸五英里。 **5** used to show removal〔表示拿走〕: *Everything valuable had been taken from the house.* 所有值錢的東西都從家裡拿走了。 **6** used to show subtraction〔表示減去〕: *Take 24 from the total.* 從總數中減去二十四。 **7** because of 因為; 由於: *He's suffering from depression.* 他患有抑鬱症。

frond /frɒnd; frɒnd/ *n* a leaf of a FERN or of a PALM〔蕨類或棕櫚類的〕葉子

★**front**¹ /frʌnt; frʌnt/ *n* **1** the most forward part of something, or the part that you usually see 前面; 前部: *The teacher called him out to the front of the class.* 老師把他叫出來, 站到全班面前。| *There were roses growing up the front of the house.* 房子正面種了些玫瑰。| *He was sitting in the front of the car.* 他坐在車子的前排。| *It's a blue jacket with gold buttons down the front.* 這是件胸前帶金鈕扣的藍色夾克。 **2 a front** a way of behaving which is intended to give people a particular idea about you 態度; 舉止; 模樣: *She was very upset but she put on a brave front.* 她內心很不安, 但卻裝出不怕的樣子。| *We must show a united front.* 我們一定要表現出團結一致的姿態。 **3 the front** the line along which fighting takes place in a war〔戰爭的〕前線; 前方 **4** *tech* a line of separation between two masses of air of different temperatures〔術語〕〔氣〕鋒〔冷熱空氣團的分界處〕: *A cold front is moving across the country.* 一股冷鋒正橫掃全國。 **5** a person or place used for hiding an illegal activity 非法活動的掩護者或隱蔽處: *The drug dealers used a travel company as a front for their operations.* 販毒分子用一家旅遊公司為他們的活動作掩護。 **6 in front: a** ahead 在前面: *John walked in front and the others followed behind.* 約翰走在前面, 其他人緊隨其後。 **b** winning in a game or competition〔比賽〕獲勝: *We were in front at half time.* 我們在上半場結束時就獲勝了。 **7 in front of: a** at the front of something or someone 在〔某人或某物〕的前面: *There was a car parked in front of the house.* 有一輛汽車停在房子前面。| *She was standing right in front of me.* 她就站在我的面前。 –see picture on page 764 見 764 頁彩圖

b with a particular person present 當着〔某人〕的面: *Don't swear in front of the children.* 不要在孩子們面前罵人。

> ■ USAGE 用法: Use **in front of** when one thing is separate from the other ☆當一樣東西和另一樣東西分開時，可使用 **in front of**: *A child ran into the road in front of the bus, so the driver had to stop.* 一個小孩跑到馬路上一輛公共汽車的前面，因此司機必須把車停下。| *We had our photo taken on the lawn in front of the school.* 我們在學校前面的草坪上拍照留念。 Use **at/in the front of** when one thing is inside or part of the other ☆當一樣東西是另一樣東西的組成部分時，要用 **at/in the front of**: *The no-smoking seats are at/in the front of the plane.* 不准吸煙的座位在飛機的前部。| *We were right at the front of the theatre so we had a good view of the stage.* 我們正好坐在劇院的前排，因此舞台看得一清二楚。

★**front²** *v* [T] (of a building) to have something at the front 〔建築物〕面對; 面向: *The hotel fronts the beach.* 那家旅館面對着海濱。

front³ *adj* [only before a noun 只用於名詞前] at the front of something 前面的; 前部的: *His name was written on the front cover of the book.* 他的名字寫在書的封面上。| *She was sitting in the front seat of the car.* 她坐在汽車的前排座位上。| *The house has no front garden.* 這房子沒有前花園。

front·age /ˈfrʌntɪdʒ; ˈfrʌntɪdʒ/ *n* a part of a building or of a piece of land that stretches along a road or river 〔建築物的〕正面; 前方; 沿街或河的空地: *The shop has frontages on two busy streets.* 這家商店的門面對着兩條熱鬧的街道。| *a restaurant with a river frontage* 帶有一片臨河空地的餐廳

front·al /ˈfrʌntl; ˈfrʌntl/ *adj* [always before a noun 只能用於名詞前] **1** direct 直接的: *The Opposition have launched a frontal attack on the Government's economic policies.* 反對黨對政府的經濟政策發起了正面攻擊。 **2** of, at, or to the front 前面的; 正面的

front door /ˌ· ˈ·/ *n* the main entrance door to a house, usually at the front 正門; 前門 – see picture on page 729 見 729 頁彩圖

fron·tier /frʌnˈtɪr; ˈfrʌntɪər/ *n* **1** a border, especially where the land of two countries meets 邊境; 邊界; 邊疆: *They were shot trying to cross the frontier.* 他們在企圖越過邊境時被擊斃了。| *Sweden has frontiers with Norway and Finland.* 瑞典與挪威和芬蘭接壤。 **2** **the frontiers of something** the limits of knowledge about something 某物的邊緣〔指知識〕: *to advance the frontiers of science* 拓展科學的領域 | *the frontiers of medical knowledge* 醫學知識的新領域

frost¹ /frɒst; frɒst/ *n* **1** [U] a white powdery substance formed on outside surfaces from very small drops of water when the temperature of the air is below freezing point 霜: *The car windows were covered with frost.* 汽車的窗上結滿了霜。 **2** [C;U] the weather condition when frost forms 嚴寒天氣; 冰凍(期): *Frost has killed several of our new young plants.* 嚴寒天氣把我們幾株新栽的幼苗凍死了。| *There was a hard frost last night.* 昨夜有嚴重霜凍。

frost² *v* **1** **be frosted, get frosted** (of plants) to be damaged or killed by frost 〔植物〕被霜凍死, 凍壞 **2** [T] to make something become covered with frost 使〔某物〕結霜: *The cold has frosted the windows.* 寒冷的天氣使窗子上結了霜。

frost over *phr v* [I] to become covered with frost 結霜: *The fields have frosted over.* 田野裡結滿了霜。

frost up *phr v* [I] to become covered in frost and unable to be used 結滿了霜〔因而不能使用〕: *My windscreen's frosted up.* 我車上那擋風玻璃結滿了霜。

frost·bite /ˈfrɒst.baɪt; ˈfrɒstbaɪt/ *n* [U] swelling and discoloration of a person's body, especially of their fingers, toes, or ears, caused by great cold 凍傷; 凍瘡: *The climbers were suffering from frostbite.* 登山者全都凍傷了。 **–frostbitten** *adj*

fros·ted glass /ˌ·· ˈ·/ *n* glass which has a pattern in it, so that it is not possible to see through it 磨砂玻璃; 毛玻璃: *a frosted glass door* 毛玻璃門

frost·y /ˈfrɒsti; ˈfrɒsti/ *adj* **frostier, frostiest** **1** very cold 嚴寒的: *It was a frosty morning.* 那是個嚴寒的早晨。 **2** covered with frost 結霜的 **3** not friendly 不友好的; 冷淡的: *a frosty greeting* 冷冰冰的問候 **–frostily** *adv*: *"Good morning," he said frostily.* "早安," 他冷淡地說。 **–frostiness** *n* [U]

froth¹ /frɒθ; frɒθ/ *n* [sing;U] a white mass of bubbles (BUBBLE) formed on top of or in a liquid, or in your mouth 泡; 泡沫

froth² *v* to make or produce froth 起泡沫: *The beer frothed as it was poured out.* 啤酒倒出時泛起泡沫。| *The sick animal was frothing at the mouth.* 那隻患病的動物正口吐白沫。

froth·y /ˈfrɒθi; ˈfrɒθi/ *adj* **frothier, frothiest** full of or covered with froth 多泡沫的; 蓋滿泡沫的: *frothy beer* 充滿泡沫的啤酒 **–frothily** *adv* **–frothiness** *n* [U]

frown /fraʊn; fraʊn/ *v* [I] to bring your eyebrows (EYEBROW) together, especially in anger or effort, or to show displeasure, so that lines appear on your forehead 皺眉; 蹙額〔表示生氣、不贊同等〕: *The teacher frowned angrily at them.* 老師生氣地對他們皺起眉頭。 **–frown** *n*: *She looked at her examination paper with a worried frown.* 她擔心地皺着眉頭看試卷。

frown on sthg *phr v* [T] to disapprove of

something 不贊成〔某事〕: *She wanted to go to France by herself, but her parents frowned on the idea.* 她想自己單獨去法國，但她父母不贊成這個主意。

froze /froz; frəʊz/ the past tense of FREEZE ☆ FREEZE 的過去式

fro·zen[1] /'frozn; 'frəʊzən/ the past participle of FREEZE ☆ FREEZE 的過去分詞

frozen[2] *adj* **1** *infml* very cold 【非正式】嚴寒的; 寒冷的: *I'm absolutely frozen. Do you mind if I put the heating on?* 我可真凍壞了; 我把暖氣打開，行嗎? **2** turned to ice because of the cold 結冰的; 冰凍的: *the frozen river* 結了冰的河 **3** preserved by being kept at a temperature below zero 冷凍的: *frozen food* 冷凍食品 | *frozen peas* 冷凍豌豆 | *You can use fresh or frozen raspberries.* 你可以用新鮮懸鈎子或者是冷凍的。 **4 frozen with fear** unable to move because you are frightened 因恐懼而嚇呆

fru·gal /'frugl; 'fruːgəl/ *adj* **1** careful in your use of money or food 節約的; 節儉的: *Although he's become rich, he's kept his frugal habits.* 他雖然已經富有起來，但仍保持節儉的習慣。 **2** small in quantity and cost 少量的; 花錢少的: *a frugal supper of bread and cheese* 只有麵包和乳酪的簡便晚餐 **–frugally** *adv* **–frugality** /fru'gælɪti; fruː'gælɪ˷ti/ *n* [U]

＊fruit /frut; fruːt/ *n* **1** [C;U] the part of a tree or bush that contains seeds and is often eaten as food 水果: *We need some more fruit. We haven't got any bananas or oranges.* 我們需要多備些水果，香蕉和桔子還沒有買來。 | *fruit and vegetables* 水果和蔬菜 | *There was a bowl of fruit on the table.* 桌上放着一盤水果。 | *a fruit bowl* 果盤 **2 the fruits of** the result of something, especially when gained through hard work 〔某事物〕的成果; 結果〔尤指透過辛勤勞動獲得的〕: *The old man was enjoying the fruits of his life's work.* 那老人在享受他一生工作換來的成果。

fruit·ful /'frutfəl; 'fruːtfəl/ *adj* successful and producing good results 成功的; 富有成效的: *a fruitful meeting* 卓有成效的會議 **– fruitfully** *adv* **–fruitfulness** *n* [U]

fru·i·tion /fru'ɪʃn; fruː'ɪʃən/ *n* [U] *fml* fulfillment of plans or aims 【正式】〔計劃或目標的〕實現; 完成: *After much delay, the plan to build the new hospital came to fruition.* 經過不少耽擱之後，建造新醫院的計劃終於實現了。

fruit·less /'frutlɪs; 'fruːtləs/ *adj* unsuccessful or not bringing the desired result (used of an effort) 不成功的; 無收益的; 徒勞的〔指努力〕: *So far the search for the missing boy has been fruitless.* 到目前為止，尋找失蹤男孩的工作還是沒有結果。 **–fruitlessly** *adv* **– fruitlessness** *n* [U]

fruit ma·chine /' · · ,·/ *n* a machine which you put money in for amusement; if certain combinations of pictures of fruit appear, you win money back 吃角子老虎〔一種以出現某些水果組合圖形贏錢的賭具〕

fruit·y /'fruti; 'fruːti/ *adj* **fruitier, fruitiest 1** tasting or smelling of fruit 有水果味的: *This red wine is lovely and fruity.* 這種紅葡萄酒質優味濃。 **2** *infml* rich and deep (used of a person's voice) 【非正式】圓潤的; 深沉的〔指嗓音〕: *a fruity laugh* 洪亮的笑聲

frus·trate /'frʌstreɪt; frʌ'streɪt/ *v* **frustrated, frustrating** [T] to prevent something that someone planned or intended to happen from happening 挫敗〔某人的計劃或意圖〕; 阻止: *The prisoner's attempt at escape was frustrated by a watchful guard.* 囚犯企圖逃跑，結果被一名警覺的守衛阻止了。 **–frustration** /frʌs'treɪʃən; frʌ'streɪʃən/ *n* [U]

frus·trat·ed /'frʌstretɪd; frʌ'streɪ˷tɪd/ *adj* dissatisfied because you are unable to do something〔因做不成某事而〕失意的; 泄氣的: *She feels very frustrated now that she can't see well enough to read.* 她因看不清字而非常泄氣。

frus·trat·ing /'frʌstretɪŋ; frʌ'streɪtɪŋ/ *adj* making you feel dissatisfied because you are unable to do something〔因做不成某事而〕令人泄氣的; 使人沮喪的: *It's very frustrating not being able to read.* 無法看書真使人掃興。

fry /fraɪ; fraɪ/ *v* **fried, fried** [I;T] to cook in hot fat or oil 油煎; 油炸; 油炒: *Shall I fry the fish for dinner?* 晚飯要不要我炸魚? | *The eggs were frying in the pan.* 蛋在平底鍋裡煎。 | *fried rice* 炒飯 **–see** COOK[1] (USAGE 用法)

fry·ing pan /' · · ,·/ *n* **1** a flat pan with a long handle, used for cooking food in oil or fat 長柄平底煎鍋 **–see picture on page 244** 見 244 頁彩圖 **2 out of the frying pan into the fire** out of a bad situation and into a worse one 跳出油鍋又落火炕; 愈弄愈糟

ft a written abbreviation for 〔縮〕= FOOT or 或 FEET, in measurements 英尺

fudge /fʌdʒ; fʌdʒ/ *n* [U] a soft creamy sugary sweet 乳脂軟糖: *chocolate fudge* 巧克力軟糖 | *Do you want a piece of fudge?* 你要吃一塊軟糖嗎?

＊fuel[1] /'fjuəl; fjuəl/ *n* [C;U] **1** material which is burned to produce heat or power, for example wood, coal, oil, and gas 燃料〔如木頭，煤，石油和煤氣〕: *Of course, all public buildings use more fuel in the winter.* 當然，所有公共大樓在冬天要消耗更多的燃料。 | *fuel bills* 燃料賬單 | *a car with high fuel consumption* 燃料高消耗的汽車 **2 add fuel to something** to make a situation worse 在某事物上加燃料〔指使事情搞得更糟〕

fuel[2] *v* **-ll- (-l- AmE** 【美式】) **1** be fuelled by to work using a particular fuel 用〔某種燃料〕運作: *cars fuelled by electricity* 用電開動的汽車 **2** [T] to make a feeling or situation worse 使情緒或事情更糟

＊fu·gi·tive /'fjudʒətɪv; 'fjuːdʒɪ˷tɪv/ *n* *fml* a person escaping from danger or punish-

F

ment 〖正式〗逃亡者; 逃跑者: *a fugitive* **from** *justice* 逃犯

ful·crum /ˈfʌlkrəm; ˈfʊlkrəm/ *n* the point on which a bar that is being used for lifting something turns or is supported 〔槓桿的〕支點: *the fulcrum of a pair of scales* 天平的支點

***ful·fil** /fʊlˈfɪl; fʊlˈfɪl/ *v* -**ll**- (also 又作 **fulfill** *AmE* 〖美式〗) [T] **1** to perform or carry out an order, duty, or promise 履行〔職責、諾言〕; 執行〔命令〕: *He always fulfils his obligations.* 他總是能履行自己的義務。| *You have not fulfilled the conditions of the contract.* 你尚未履行合約所規定的條件。**2** to supply or satisfy a need, demand, or purpose 滿足〔需要、要求或目的〕: *Do you know anyone who can fulfil our requirements?* 你認識一些能夠滿足我們要求的人嗎? **3** to make something true or cause something to happen 實現; 使應驗: *If he's lazy, he'll never fulfil his ambition to be a doctor.* 如果他懶惰, 就永遠無法實現當醫生的抱負。| *to fulfil a prophecy* 預言應驗 **4 fulfil yourself** to develop your character and abilities fully 充分發揮自己的能力和特點: *She fulfilled herself both as a mother and as a writer.* 她作為一個母親和作家, 都是十分出色的。–**fulfilling** *adj*: *a very fulfilling job* 令人滿意的工作

ful·fil·ment /fʊlˈfɪlmənt; fʊlˈfɪlmənt/ *n* (also 又作 **fulfillment** *AmE* 〖美式〗) [U] **1** the act of fulfilling or state of being fulfilled 履行; 實現: *After many years, his plans have come to fulfilment.* 他的計劃多年之後終於實現了。**2** satisfaction after successful effort 〔成功後的〕滿意; 滿足: *a sense of fulfilment* 滿足感

****full**¹ /fʊl; fʊl/ *adj* **1** holding or containing as much or as many as possible (used of a space or container) 滿的; 裝滿的〔指空間或容器〕: *This car park's full. You'll have to find somewhere else to park.* 這個停車場已經滿了; 你得另找地方停車。| *a full glass of wine* 滿滿一杯酒 | *This bottle's only half full.* 這個瓶子只裝了一半。| *Your bag's too full. Take out some of the fruit or it'll fall out.* 你的袋子裝得太滿了。拿出一些水果, 否則就要撐破了。| *The lecture hall is full to overflowing.* 演講大廳全部座滿, 人都擠到了門外。**2 be full up: a** to be completely full 全滿的: *The bus is full up. We'll have to wait for the next one.* 公共汽車擠滿了乘客, 我們只好等下一輛了。**b** *infml* (also 又作 **be full**) to have had enough to eat 〔非正式〕吃飽的: *"Do you want any more?" "No, thanks. I'm full up."* "你想再來點兒嗎?" "不要了, 謝謝, 我已經吃飽了。" **3 be full of: a** to contain or have a lot of 有很多的; 充滿的: *The field was full of sheep.* 田野裡到處是羊。| *This work's full of mistakes.* 這部作品錯誤百出。| *He was full of enthusiasm.* 他滿懷熱情。**b** to think and talk about only one subject which you are very interested in 專心的; 專

注的: *She's full of this trip to America.* 她心裡只想着這次訪美旅行。**4** complete or whole 完整的; 完全的: *Please write down your full name and address.* 請寫下你的全名和詳細地址。| *I want a full account of what happened.* 我想了解所發生事情的完整的敍述。| *The roses are in full bloom.* 玫瑰花在盛開。| *The course lasts a full year.* 該課程要上整整一年。| *A full moon shone brightly.* 滿月當空, 銀光閃閃。**5** [only before a noun 只用於名詞前] the highest or greatest possible 最高或最大程度的: *He drove the car at full speed through the town.* 他全速開車駛過市鎮。| *She got full marks in all the tests.* 她所有的考試都得了滿分。**6** very busy, often in a satisfying way 忙碌〔常含充實感〕: *He has led a full life.* 他一生都忙忙碌碌。| *The doctor has a very full day today.* 醫生今天忙了一整天。**7** fitting loosely and made with plenty of material (used of clothes) 寬鬆的〔指衣服〕: *a full skirt* 寬下擺女裙 | *full sleeves* 寬鬆的袖子 **8** fleshy (used of someone's body or of a part of it) 豐滿的: *She's rather full in the face.* 她的臉圓圓的。| *a full figure* 豐滿的體形 | *full lips* 飽滿的嘴唇 **9** deep, strong, and powerful (a word used of colour, smell, sound, or taste which expresses approval) 〔顏色〕深濃的; 〔氣味〕強烈的; 〔聲音〕圓潤的; 〔味道〕濃郁的〔含褒義〕: *This cheese has a good full flavour.* 這種乳酪具有濃郁的味道。**10** full frontal showing people with no clothes on from the front 正面全裸: *two full frontal shots in the film* 電影中的兩個正面全裸鏡頭 **11** full of beans *infml* feeling cheerful and ready for action 〔非正式〕精力充沛的 **12 on a full stomach** as soon as you have eaten 一吃完飯: *You shouldn't go swimming on a full stomach.* 你不應該剛吃完飯就去游泳。**13 in full swing** at the most active part 正在非常熱烈地進行中: *By the time we arrived, the party was in full swing.* 我們趕到時, 聚會正在熱烈地進行。**14 be full of yourself** to think you are better than other people (an expression used to express disapproval) 自以為是〔含貶義〕

full² *adv* **1** straight or directly 直接地: *The sun shone full on her face.* 太陽光直照在她臉上。**2 full on** working at the greatest speed or power possible (used of a machine) 以最快的速度或最大的功率運轉〔指機器〕: *The fire was full on.* 電爐已經開到了最大功率。**3 full well** with complete certainty 確切地; 完全有把握地: *They knew full well that he wouldn't keep his promise.* 他們清楚地知道他不會遵守諾言。

full³ *n* **1 in full** completely 完全地; 全部地: *The debt must be paid in full.* 債務必須全部償還。**2 to the full** as much as it is possible to 充分地; 盡情地: *We enjoyed our holiday to the full.* 我們的假日過得痛快極了。

full-blown /ˌ·ˈ·◂/ *adj* **1** [only before a noun 只用於名詞前] fully developed 充分發展的:

We're afraid that the fighting may develop into a full-blown war. 我們擔心戰鬥會演變成一場全面戰爭。**2** *lit* completely open (used of a flower) 〔文〕盛開的〔指花〕

full board /ˌ· ·/ *adj* with all meals provided 全食宿: *Is your holiday full or half board?* 你的度假生活是全食宿還是半食宿?

full-grown /ˌ· '·◂/ *adj* (also 又作 **fully-grown**) completely developed (used of an animal, plant, or person) 成熟的; 完全發育的〔指動物, 植物或人〕: *A full-grown elephant can weigh over 6000 kilograms.* 成年大象的體重可超過六千公斤。

full-length /ˌ·'·◂/ *adj,adv* **1** showing all of a person, from their head to their feet (used of a painting, photograph, or mirror) 全身的〔地〕〔指畫像、相片或鏡子〕 **2** reaching to the ground (used of a piece of clothing) 長及地面的〔地〕〔指衣服〕: *a full-length evening dress* 拖地晚禮服 **3** of the usual length (used of a play or book) 正常長度的; 未經刪節的〔指劇本或書〕: *a full-length feature* 正常長度的故事片 **4** completely flat on the ground (used of a person) 平躺在地的〔地〕〔指人〕: *She fell full-length.* 她橫倒在地上。

full·ness /ˈfʊlnɪs; ˈfʊlnɪs/ *n* (also 又作 **fulness**) [U] **1** the condition of being full or busy 滿; 充滿; 豐滿; 忙碌 **2** **in the fullness of time** *fml* at last, though probably after a long time 〔正式〕終於

full-scale /ˌ·'·◂/ *adj* **1** [only before a noun 只用於名詞前] using all possible powers or forces 全力的; 全面的: *a full-scale attack on an enemy position* 對敵軍陣地的全面進攻 **2** of the same size as the object represented (of a model, drawing, or copy) 照原尺寸的〔指模型、圖樣或複本〕: *a full-scale model of an elephant at the museum* 博物館裡一具跟大象大小一樣的模型

full stop /ˌ· '·/ *n* a written point (.) marking the end of a sentence or a shortened form of a word 句點; 句號: *Put in a full stop after "now".* 在"now"後面加上句點。

full-time /ˌ· '·◂/ *adj, adv* working for the usual number of hours or days in a job or course of study 專職的; 全日制的: *a full-time student* 全日制學生 | *full-time employment* 全天工作〔專職工作〕 | *He used to work full-time, but now he only works three days a week.* 他做過全日工作, 但現在每週只工作三天。–compare 比較 PART-TIME

ful·ly /ˈfʊlɪ; ˈfʊlɪ/ *adv* completely or thoroughly 完全地; 徹底地; 充分地: *I don't fully understand his reasons for leaving.* 我不完全理解他離開的原因。 | *a fully trained nurse* 受過充分訓練的護士

fully-fledged /ˌ···◂/ *adj* completely trained 受過充分訓練的: *a fully-fledged doctor* 受過充分訓練的醫生

fully-grown /ˌ···◂/ *adj* see 見 FULL-GROWN

fum·ble /ˈfʌmbl; ˈfʌmbəl/ *v* **fumbled, fumbling 1** [I] to move your fingers or hands

awkwardly when you are looking for something or trying to do something 亂摸; 摸索: *She fumbled about in her handbag for a pen.* 她在手提包裡摸索着找尋鋼筆。 | *He fumbled for the light switch in the dark.* 他在黑暗中摸索着找尋電燈開關。 **2** [I] to search with some difficulty for a word or expression 苦苦思索措詞: *He's not a very good speaker. He often has to fumble for the right word.* 他是個不善於演講的人, 他得苦思冥想找個適當的措詞。 **3** [I;T] to handle something, usually a ball, without skill 笨拙地處理〔某事〕〔常指漏接球、失球〕

fume /fjuːm; fjuːm/ *v* **fumed, fuming** [I] to show signs of great anger and impatience 發怒; 發火: *"Was he angry?" "Yes, he was really fuming."* "他生氣了嗎?" "是的, 他確實是怒氣沖沖。"

fumes /fjuːmz; fjuːmz/ *n* [pl] heavy strong-smelling air given off from things such as smoke, gas, or fresh paint 〔煙、煤氣、新的油漆等發出的〕難聞的氣味: *The air was thick with tobacco fumes.* 空氣裡充滿了香煙氣味。 | *petrol fumes* 汽油油煙

fu·mi·gate /ˈfjuːmɪˌgeɪt; ˈfjuːmɪˌgeɪt/ *v* **fumigated, fumigating** [T] to clear something of disease, bacteria, or harmful insects by means of chemical smoke or gas 以煙熏消毒: *The man was found to have an infectious disease, so all his clothes had to be fumigated.* 那位男子被發現患有傳染病, 因此他所有的衣服都得用煙熏來消毒。 –**fumigation** /ˌfjuːmɪˈgeɪʃən; ˌfjuːmɪˈgeɪʃən/ *n* [U]

*fun /fʌn; fʌn/ *n* [U] **1** amusement, enjoyment, or pleasure, or something that causes these 娛樂; 樂趣: *Have fun at the party tonight.* 在今天的晚會上好好玩吧。 | *It's no fun playing football in the rain.* 下雨天踢足球一點也不好玩。 | *Going to the fair is good fun.* 到遊樂場去很開心。 **2** **have fun** enjoy yourself 玩得高興: *We had some good fun when we all worked together.* 我們在一起共事時時候過得很愉快。 **3** **for fun, for the fun of** it just for pleasure, and not for a serious purpose 開玩笑地; 非認真地: *He's learning French just for fun.* 他學法語只是為了消遣。 **4** playfulness 頑皮; 嬉戲: *She's very cheerful and full of fun.* 她非常高興, 又很頑皮。 **5** **in fun** as a joke, without any serious or harmful intention 開玩笑地; 非故意地: *I only threw it at you in fun. I didn't mean to hurt you.* 我朝你扔過去只是開個玩笑, 並沒有傷害你的意思。 **6** **make fun of someone, poke fun at someone** to laugh, or cause other people to laugh, unkindly at someone 嘲笑〔某人〕; 拿〔某人〕開玩笑: *People make fun of her because she wears such strange clothes.* 大家嘲笑她, 因為她穿着這麼古怪的衣服。 –see 見 FUNNY (USAGE 用法)

*func·tion[1] /ˈfʌŋkʃən; ˈfʌŋkʃən/ *n* **1** the natural or usual purpose of a thing or duty of a person 功能; 作用; 職責: *The function of an adjective is to describe a noun.* 形容詞的作用就是修飾名詞。 | *The function of a chairman is to lead and control meetings.* 主席的職責是主持會議。**2 a** large or important gathering of people for pleasure or on some special occasion 重大聚會; 集會: *This room may be hired for weddings and other functions.* 這房間可租來舉行婚禮以及其他重大聚會。 | *The minister has to attend all kinds of official functions.* 部長得參加各種官方的盛大聚會。

function² /v/ [I] (especially of a thing) to work or be in action 〔尤指事物〕運轉; 活動; 起作用: *The machine won't function properly if you don't oil it.* 你若不給機器加油, 它就不能正常運轉。

func·tion·al /ˈfʌŋkʃənl; ˈfʌŋkʃənəl/ *adj* **1** made for or concerned with practical use only, without decoration 為實用而設計的; 實用的; 不加裝飾的: *functional furniture* 實用家具 **2** working properly 正常運行的 – **functionally** *adv*

★**fund¹** /fʌnd; fʌnd/ *n* **1** [C] a supply or sum of money set apart for a special purpose 基金; 專款: *the school sports fund* 學校的體育運動基金 **2 funds** [pl] money for a special purpose 資金: *We're having a dance to raise funds for the new swimming-pool.* 我們在為新建游泳池的集資而表演舞蹈。

★**fund²** /v/ [T] to provide money for an activity or organization 為〔活動或組織〕提供資金; 撥款: *The search for a cure for this disease is being funded by the government.* 政府正提供資金以探索這種疾病的治療方法。

★**fun·da·men·tal** /ˌfʌndəˈmentl; ˌfʌndəˈmentl/ *adj* relating to the most important parts of something, which other parts depend on 根本的; 基本的: *Our sales campaign is failing badly and we will have to make some fundamental changes to it.* 我們的銷售活動很差勁, 我們要對此作些根本的變化。 | *a fundamental difference of opinion* 根本的意見分歧 | *This agreement is of fundamental importance for world trade.* 這項協定對世界貿易具有重大意義。 –**fundamentally** *adv*: *She is fundamentally unsuited to office work.* 她根本就不適合做辦公室工作。

fun·da·men·tal·is·m /ˌfʌndəˈmentlˌɪzəm; ˌfʌndəˈmentəlɪzəm/ *n* [U] the practice of following the rules of a religion, such as Christianity or Islam, very exactly 〔不折不扣地信奉宗教原則的〕原教旨主義: *the rise of Islamic fundamentalism* 伊斯蘭原教旨主義的興起 –**fundamentalist** *n, adj*

fun·da·men·tals /ˌfʌndəˈmentlz; ˌfʌndəˈmentlz/ *n* [pl] the most important or necessary parts or rules 基本原則〔原理〕; 基本規則: *If the boys are going to camp for ten days, they'll need to know the fundamentals of cooking.* 這些男孩子如果要去露營十天, 便

須懂得做飯的基本知識。

fu·ne·ral /ˈfjunərəl; ˈfjuːnərəl/ *n* a ceremony, usually religious, in which a dead person is buried or burned 〔常指宗教的〕葬禮; 喪禮: *a funeral service* 喪葬儀式 | *a funeral procession* 送葬的隊伍

fu·ne·re·al /fjuˈnɪriəl; fjʊˈnɪəriəl/ *adj* heavy and sad and suitable for a funeral 悲哀而莊嚴的; 適於葬禮的: *There was a funereal silence.* 當時一片悲哀肅穆的寂靜。

fun·fair /ˈfʌn.feə; ˈfʌnfeər/ *n* (also 又作 **fair**) a noisy brightly-lit show at which you can ride on machines and play games for small prizes 遊樂園; 遊樂場

fun·gus /ˈfʌŋɡəs; ˈfʌŋɡəs/ *n* **fungi** /-dʒaɪ; -dʒaɪ, -ɡaɪ/ *or* **funguses** a plant without flowers, leaves, or green colouring matter; it is usually a fleshy stem supporting a broad rounded top, or in a very small form that looks like powder 真菌: *Mushrooms and mould are both types of fungi.* 蘑菇和霉菌是兩種真菌。

funk /fʌŋk; fʌŋk/ *n* [U] a type of modern popular music with a heavy regular beat used for dancing 鄉土爵士樂〔一種強節奏的現代流行音樂〕

funk·y /ˈfʌŋki; ˈfʌŋki/ *adj* **funkier, funkiest** *infml* 〔非正式〕 **1** having a simple direct style and feeling (used of JAZZ or similar music) 樸實無華的; 充滿感情的〔指爵士樂等〕 **2** good, attractive, or fashionable 美好的; 時髦的; 新型的: *a funky party* 新式派對

fun·nel¹ /ˈfʌnl; ˈfʌnl/ *n* **1** an object used for pouring liquids or powders into a container; it has a wide, round top and a narrow tube coming out at the bottom 漏斗 – see picture on page 958 見 958 頁彩圖 **2** a metal chimney for letting out smoke from a steam engine or steamship 〔蒸汽機或輪船的〕煙囪

funnel² /v/ **-ll-** (**-l-** *AmE* 〔美式〕) **1** [I;T] to pass through a funnel or a narrow space like a funnel 通過漏斗或漏斗狀的狹窄空間: *The wind is funnelled between the skyscrapers.* 風穿流於摩天大樓之間的空曠處。 **2** [T] to send things which have come from different places to a single place 把〔匯集的東西〕送到〔某處〕: *We will funnel the money collected to the famine areas.* 我們要把募集的錢送到遭受饑荒的地區。

fun·ni·ly /ˈfʌnɪli; ˈfʌnɪli/ *adv* **1** in a strange or unusual way 奇怪地; 古怪地; 反常地: *She's been acting rather funnily just recently.* 她最近的行動相當古怪。 **2** in an amusing way 滑稽地; 有趣的 **3 funnily enough** strangely 說來奇怪: *There were black clouds and loud thunder, but funnily enough it didn't rain.* 天上烏雲密佈, 雷聲隆隆, 然而奇怪的是沒有下雨。

★**fun·ny** /ˈfʌni; ˈfʌni/ *adj* **funnier, funniest 1** amusing and causing laughter 有趣的; 可笑的: *a funny story* 好笑的故事 | *a funny joke*

風趣的笑話 | *I don't think that's at all funny.* 我覺得那件事一點也不可笑。**2** strange, unexpected, or hard to explain 稀奇古怪的; 意想不到的; 難以解釋的: *What's that funny noise?* 那是甚麼怪聲音? | *That's funny! I'm sure I parked the car here, but now it's gone!* 那可真是怪了!我肯定把車停在這兒, 但現在卻不見了! | *A funny thing happened to me at work today.* 今天我在工作中發生了一件怪事。**3** [never before a noun 不能用於名詞前] *infml* slightly ill 〖非正式〗不大舒服的: *She always feels a bit funny if she looks down from a high place.* 她從高處往下看時, 總感到有點難受。

■ USAGE 用法: If you want to say that you enjoy something use **fun** but NOT **funny** ☆若要表示"從某事物獲得樂趣"可用 **fun**, 而不是 **funny**: *Skiing is* **fun**. 滑雪運動很有樂趣。| *We all went to the coast on Sunday. It was* **fun**. 我們星期日都去了海濱, 玩得很痛快。| *It's great* **fun** *trying out new recipes.* 試着用新的烹飪法做菜是一大樂趣。

funny-look·ing /ˈ·· ˌ·ˈ·/ *adj* having a strange appearance 容貌古怪的: *He's a funny-looking boy. He's got a very long neck.* 他是個長相古怪的男孩, 他的脖子非常長。

fur /fɜː; fɜːr/ *n* **1** [U] the soft thin hair that grows thickly over the bodies of some types of animal, for example bears, rabbits, and cats 〔熊、兔、貓等獸類的〕濃密的軟毛 **2** [C] a hair-covered skin of certain animals, such as foxes or rabbits 〔狐或兔等動物的〕毛皮: *Several valuable furs were stolen from the shop.* 好幾塊昂貴的毛皮料子被人從商店偷走了。**3** [C] a coat made of fur, or a piece of fur that a woman wears round her shoulders 毛皮衣服; 〔婦女的〕毛皮披肩 **4** [U] a hard covering on the inside of pots, or hot-water pipes, which comes out of the water 〔鍋、熱水管中的〕水垢; 水鏽

fu·ri·ous /ˈfjʊərɪəs; ˈfjʊrɪəs/ *adj* **1** very angry 憤怒的: *He'll be furious* **with** *us if we're late.* 如果我們遲到, 他會對我們大發雷霆。| *He'll be absolutely furious* **at** *being kept waiting.* 讓他久等, 他定會勃然大怒。**2** [always before a noun 只能用於名詞前] wild or uncontrolled 狂亂的; 猛烈的; 極度的: *a furious temper* 暴躁的脾氣 | *There was a furious knocking at the door.* 有人在猛烈地敲門。— **furiously** *adv*

fur·long /ˈfɜːlɒŋ; ˈfɜːlɒŋ/ *n* a unit for measuring length, equal to 220 yards or 201 metres, used mainly in horseracing 弗隆〔長度單位, 等於220碼或201米; 主要用於賽馬〕

fur·nace /ˈfɜːnɪs; ˈfɜːn⅟s/ *n* an enclosed space where metals or other materials are heated to very high temperatures, or where certain materials are burned to pro-

duce steam 火爐; 熔爐

fur·nish /ˈfɜːnɪʃ; ˈfɜːnɪʃ/ *v* [T] **1** to put furniture in a room or building 為〔房間或樓房〕配備家具: *They furnished the house in traditional style.* 他們以傳統風格為房子配備了家具。**2** *fml* to supply what is necessary for a special purpose 〖正式〗〔為某一特殊用途〕供應, 提供〔必需品〕

fur·nished /ˈfɜːnɪʃt; ˈfɜːnɪʃt/ *adj* containing furniture 配有家具的: *We're renting a furnished flat.* 我們租用配有家具的公寓。

fur·nish·ings /ˈfɜːnɪʃɪŋz; ˈfɜːnɪʃɪŋz/ *n* [pl] articles of furniture or other articles fixed in a room, such as a bath, curtains, etc. 家具; 室內陳設〔如浴缸、窗簾等〕

★**fur·ni·ture** /ˈfɜːnɪtʃə; ˈfɜːnɪtʃər/ *n* [U] large objects that are used in houses, like beds, tables, or chairs 家具: *The house was full of heavy, old-fashioned furniture.* 屋裡擺滿了笨重的老式家具。| *garden furniture* 庭院家具

fu·ro·re /fjʊəˈrɔːri; fjʊˈrɔːri/ *n* (also 又作 **furor**) [sing] a sudden burst of angry or excited interest among a large group of people 狂怒; 轟動: *His news caused quite a furore.* 他的消息引起了一陣轟動。

fur·row /ˈfɜːrəʊ; ˈfʌrəʊ/ *n* **1** one of the long deep lines made across a field when a farmer turns the earth over 犁溝; 壟溝: *The deep furrows made it difficult to walk across the field.* 深深的犁溝使人難以穿過那塊田地。**2** any long deep cut or fold 溝渠; 皺紋

fur·rowed /ˈfɜːrəʊd; ˈfʌrəʊd/ *adj* **1** having furrows 有犁溝的; 有皺紋的 **2 a furrowed brow** a forehead with lines in it because of worry or deep thought 〔因憂慮而引起的〕有皺紋的前額

fur·ry /ˈfɜːri; ˈfɜːri/ *adj* furrier, furriest of, like, or covered with fur 毛皮的; 似毛皮的; 毛皮覆蓋的: *furry material* 毛皮衣料 | *a furry little rabbit* 毛茸茸的小兔子

★**fur·ther**[1] /ˈfɜːðə; ˈfɜːðər/ *adv* **1** the COMPARATIVE form of FAR ☆ FAR 的比較級形式: *She can swim much further than I can.* 她游泳游得比我遠得多。| *I can't remember any further back than 1980.* 比 1980 年更遠的事我已記不起來了。**2** more 更多: *I have nothing further to say.* 我沒有別的話要說了。—see 見 FAR-THER (USAGE用法)

further[2] *adj* [only before a noun 只用於名詞前] additional 附加的: *I have one further question for you.* 我還有一個問題要問你。

further[3] *v fml* [T] to help something to advance or succeed 〖正式〗促進, 推進〔某事〕: *They hope that the strike will further the cause of women's rights.* 他們希望罷工能推動爭取女權的事業。

fur·ther·ance /ˈfɜːðərəns; ˈfɜːðərəns/ *n fml* [U] action to help something succeed 〖正式〗促進; 推進

further ed·u·ca·tion /ˌ·· ···ˈ··/ *n* [U] edu-

F

cation after leaving school, but not at a university〔辦在大學以外的〕繼續教育; 進修

*fur·ther·more /ˈfɝðɚˌmor; ˌfɜːðəˈmɔːʳ/ *adv fml* in addition to what has been said; you use "furthermore" to say that you are going to make an additional point《正式》此外; 而且〔用於表示附加的説明〕: *The development of this land as an industrial estate will destroy an area of outstanding natural beauty. Furthermore, it will make quite unreasonable demands on the scarce local water supply.* 把這塊土地開發成工業區會使優美的自然環境遭到破壞。此外, 這將對當地本來就不足的飲水供應提出相當不合理的要求。

fur·ther·most /ˈfɝðɚˌmost; ˈfɜːðəməust/ *adj lit* most distant《文》最遠的: *the furthermost station on the railway line* 該鐵路線上最遠的車站

fur·thest /ˈfɝðɪst; ˈfɜːðɪst/ *adj,adv* the SUPERLATIVE of FAR ☆ FAR 的最高級形式: *Let's see who can swim the furthest.* 讓我們看看誰游得最遠。| *He walked off into the furthest field.* 他走到了最遠的那塊田裡。

fur·tive /ˈfɝtɪv; ˈfɜːtɪv/ *adj* acting as if you want to keep something secret 偷偷摸摸的; 鬼鬼祟祟的: *The man's furtive manner made the policeman suspicious.* 那個男人鬼鬼祟祟的樣子引起了警察的懷疑。**–furtively** *adv* **– furtiveness** *n* [U]

fu·ry /ˈfjʊrɪ; ˈfjʊəri/ *n* **furies 1** [C;U] very great anger 狂怒; 暴怒: *She was filled with fury.* 她怒火滿腔。| *He stormed out of the meeting in a fury.* 他怒氣沖沖地退出會議。**2** [sing] wild force or activity 猛烈; 狂暴: *At last the fury of the storm lessened.* 暴風雨的勢頭終於減弱了。

fuse¹ /fjuz; fjuːz/ *n* **1** a thin piece of wire in a PLUG or electric system that prevents damage by melting if there is too much power〔電路的〕保險絲 **2** this wire and its container 熔斷器: *She had to change the fuse before the hair-dryer would work.* 她得更換熔斷器才會使吹風機正常運轉。**3** a string or narrow pipe connected to a bomb or FIREWORK which allows you to light it and move away before it explodes 導火線; 導火索

fuse² *v* **fused, fusing** [I;T] **1** to stop working, or make something stop working, because a fuse has melted〔因保險絲熔斷而〕中斷工作: *All the lights fused.* 保險絲熔斷使電燈全部熄滅。| *You'll fuse the system if you aren't careful.* 你若不小心會把該系統的保險絲燒斷。**2** to melt together because of heat and become or make into one thing 熔化; 熔合: *The old coins had fused together in the fire.* 舊硬幣在火裡熔化在一起。**3** to join together and become one thing 混合; 結合: *In this work, the writer successfully fuses past and present.* 在這部作品中, 作者成功地把過去和現在融為一體。

fu·se·lage /ˈfjuzlɪdʒ; ˈfjuːzəlɑːʒ/ *n* the main

body of an aircraft, in which travellers and goods are carried〔飛機〕機身

fu·sion /ˈfjuʒən; ˈfjuːʒən/ *n* [C;U] melting, or joining together by melting 熔化; 熔合: *This metal is formed by the fusion of two other types of metal.* 這種金屬是由其他兩種金屬熔合而成的。| *nuclear fusion* 核聚變

fuss¹ /fʌs; fʌs/ *n* [sing;U] **1** unnecessary or unwelcome excitement, anger, or impatience 大驚小怪; 小題大作: *What a fuss about nothing!* 真是大驚小怪, 自尋煩惱! | *You can't believe anyone would make so much fuss over losing a penny.* 你難以相信會有人對丟失一便士是那樣的大驚小怪。| *There's sure to be a fuss when they find the window's broken.* 他們發現窗子被人打破時準會大吵大鬧。**2 kick up a fuss, make a fuss** to cause trouble, especially by complaining loudly or angrily 挑起事端〔尤指大吵大鬧〕**3 make a fuss of someone** to pay a lot of attention to someone 對某人特別注意; 過分關懷〔體貼〕某人

fuss² *v* [I] to act or behave in a nervous, restless, and anxious way over small matters 小題大作; 大驚小怪: *Don't fuss. We're sure to catch our train.* 別緊張, 我們一定能趕上火車。| *She fusses too much about her health. She's always going to the doctor.* 她過於擔心自己的身體, 老是去看醫生。| *You fuss over me as if I were a child.* 你對我過於操心, 把我當小孩子看待。

fuss·y /ˈfʌsɪ; ˈfʌsi/ *adj* **fussier, fussiest 1** too concerned about details 過分注意細節的; 挑剔的: *He's fussy about his food. If it isn't cooked just right, he won't eat it.* 他吃東西很挑剔, 如果燒得不恰到好處, 他就不吃。**2** nervous and excitable (used especially of a person's actions) 易激動的; 神經質的〔尤指某人的行為〕: *small fussy movements of her hands* 她雙手神經質的小動作 **3** having too much detailed decoration 過分裝飾的: *a fussy hat* 過分裝飾的帽子 **–fussily** *adv* **– fussiness** *n* [U]

fus·ty /ˈfʌstɪ; ˈfʌsti/ *adj* **fustier, fustiest** having an unpleasant smell as a result of having been shut up for a long time, especially when not quite dry (used of a room, a box, or clothes) 發霉味的; 霉臭的〔指房間、箱子、衣服等〕**–fustiness** *n* [U]

fu·tile /ˈfjutl; ˈfjuːtaɪl/ *adj* useless or unsuccessful 無用的; 無效的: *She threw away her purse, in a futile attempt to shake off her pursuers.* 她扔掉錢包, 試圖甩掉跟蹤她的人, 但沒有奏效。| *Don't waste my time with such futile questions!* 別把我的時間浪費在這麼無聊的問題上! | *It's futile to complain.* 發牢騷是無濟於事的。**–futility** /fjuˈtɪlətɪ; fjuːˈtɪləti/ *n* [U]: *the futility of war* 戰爭的無謂

*fu·ture /ˈfjutʃɚ; ˈfjuːtʃəʳ/ *n* **1 the future** the time that has not yet come 將來; 未來: *You should start saving money for the future.* 為了將來, 你應該開始儲錢。|

At some time in the future, we will all eat pills instead of food. 在未來的某個時候, 我們都會以吃藥丸代替吃飯。 | *What will the future bring?* 未來會給我們帶來些甚麼? **2 in future** from now on 從今以後; 今後: *In future, you'll have to be more careful.* 今後, 你得更加小心。 **3** [sing] what will happen to a person or thing〔人或事物的〕前途; 前景: *It is impossible to predict the future of the company.* 不可能預測到公司的前景。 | *I'm thinking about your future.* 我在考慮你的前途。 **4** [C;U] likelihood of success, especially in your job 成功的可能性〔尤指工作〕: *There's no future in teaching these days.* 如今教書沒有前途。 | *There's quite a future in computing.* 電腦的運用大有前途。 **5 the future** *tech* in grammer, the tense of the verb that expresses what will happen at a later time〔術語〕〔文法中的〕將來式: *In the sentence, "I will leave tomorrow", the verb is in the future.* 在 "I will leave tomorrow" 這個句子中, 動詞用了將來式。 –**future** *adj:*

future generations 子孫後代 | *the future tense* 將來時態

fu·tur·is·tic /ˌfjutʃɚˈɪstɪk; ˌfjuːtʃəˈrɪstɪk◂/ *adj* of strange modern appearance 未來派的; 標新立異的: *a futuristic building* 新潮式樣的大樓 –**futuristically** /-klɪ; -klɪ/ *adv*

fuzz /fʌz; fʌz/ *n* [U] **1** *infml* soft light loose waste that rubs off a woollen article〔非正式〕絨毛; 細毛 **2** *infml* short hairs on your face or arms, or other parts of your body〔非正式〕毛髮 **3 the fuzz** *slang* the police〔俚〕警察

fuzz·y /ˈfʌzɪ; ˈfʌzɪ/ *adj* **fuzzier, fuzziest** *infml*〔非正式〕 **1** standing up in a light short mass (used of hair) 毛茸茸的〔指毛髮〕 **2** not clear in shape or sound〔輪廓、聲音〕模糊的; 不清楚的: *The television picture is rather fuzzy tonight.* 今晚的電視影像很模糊。 **3** having a raised soft hairy surface (used of clothes or material) 表面毛茸茸的〔指衣物或材料〕 –**fuzzily** *adv* –**fuzziness** *n* [U]

G, g

G, g /dʒi; dʒiː/ **G's, g's** or **Gs, gs** the 7th letter of the English alphabet 英語的第七個字母

g tech 〔術語〕 a written abbreviation for 〔縮〕 = GRAM(s) or 或 GRAVITY

gab·ble /ˈgæbl̩; ˈgæbəl/ v gabbled, gabbling [I;T] to say words so quickly that they cannot be heard clearly 急促而含糊地說話: *Stop gabbling!* 別在那裡喋喋不休了! | *What on earth are you gabbling about?* 你到底在嘮叨些甚麼呀?

ga·ble /ˈgebl̩; ˈgeɪbəl/ n the three-cornered upper end of the wall of a building where it meets the roof 山形牆; 三角牆

gad /gæd; gæd/ v -dd-
  gad about phr v [I;T **gad about** sthg] infml to travel round a place to enjoy yourself 〔非正式〕遊蕩; 閒逛: *He's always gadding about.* 他總是在到處遊蕩。 | *She's away, gadding about Europe.* 他人不在, 現正在歐洲到處遊蕩。

gad·get /ˈgædʒɪt; ˈgædʒɪt/ n a small machine or useful apparatus 小機械; 小裝置: *a clever little gadget for opening tins* 設計巧妙的小開罐器 –see 見 MACHINE¹ (USAGE 用法)

gag¹ /gæg; gæg/ n a piece of cloth put over or into someone's mouth to prevent them from talking or shouting 〔防止人講話或喊叫的〕綁在嘴上或塞在嘴裡的布

gag² v -gg- **1** [T] to prevent someone from speaking by using a gag 將布塞入嘴中〔綁在嘴上〕〔以防止某人講話〕 **2** [I] to nearly throw food up after you have taken it into your mouth and it has gone down your throat 嘔住; 作嘔

ga·ga /ˈgɑgɑ; ˈgɑːgɑː/ adj infml 〔非正式〕**1** having a weak mind, especially in old age 〔尤指年老時〕心智衰弱的 **2 go gaga** to lose your powers of mind, especially in old age 〔尤指年老時〕心智衰弱 **3 be gaga about someone, be gaga over someone** to love someone so much that you seem silly 對某人很癡情

gage /gedʒ; geɪdʒ/ n,v **gaged, gaging** –see 見 GAUGE

gag·gle /ˈgægl̩; ˈgægəl/ n [sing] a group, usually of geese (GOOSE) or of people who make a lot of noise 一羣鵝; 一羣吵鬧的人

gai·e·ty /ˈgeətɪ; ˈgeɪ,tɪ/ n [U] a feeling of fun and enjoyment 歡樂; 快活

gai·ly /ˈgelɪ; ˈgeɪli/ adv in a cheerful way 歡樂地; 快活地

*★**gain¹** /gen; geɪn/ v [I;T] **1** to have an increase in something 增加; 增添: *I'm sure he's gaining weight.* 我敢肯定他的體重正在增加。 | *The train gained speed.* 火車的速度越來越快。 | *Surprisingly, the government gained in popularity.* 令人驚訝的是, 政府竟然會越來越受歡迎。 **2** to get something useful or wanted 獲得〔有用或想要的東西〕: *It's not an interesting job but at least I'm gaining experience.* 這個工作沒有意思, 但起碼我是在積累經驗。 | *Who stands to gain from the contract?* 誰將從這份合約中受益? –see 見 WIN¹ (USAGE用法) **3** (of a watch or clock) to work too fast 〔錶或鐘〕走得太快: *My watch is gaining five minutes a week.* 我的手錶每週快五分鐘。 **4 gain ground** to become stronger or more popular 變得更加強健〔更受歡迎〕

  gain on sbdy/sthg phr v [T] to reduce the distance between yourself and someone else you are following and trying to catch up with 接近〔在你前面的或你在追趕的人〕; 趕上

*★**gain²** n **1** an increase, often in weight or wealth 〔常指重量或財富的〕增加: *The baby showed a considerable gain in weight.* 這個嬰兒的體重增加了許多。 **2** an advantage or improvement 利益; 改善: *The workforce secured considerable gains in their conditions of employment.* 工人的工作條件得到了很大的改善。 **3 do something for gain** to do something for your own advantage and especially for money 為自己的利益而做某事〔尤指為錢〕

gait /get; geɪt/ n fml someone's way of walking 〔正式〕步法; 步態

ga·la /ˈgelə; ˈɡɑːlə/ n an occasion or performance for public enjoyment 公眾娛樂表演; 盛會: *a swimming gala* 游泳運動會

gal·ax·y /ˈgæləksɪ; ˈɡæləksi/ n galaxies any of the large groups of stars which make up the universe 星系 –**galactic** /gəˈlæktɪk; gəˈlæktɪk/ adj

gale /gel; geɪl/ n a strong wind 大風: *The old tree was blown down in the gale.* 那棵老樹在大風中被吹倒了。 –see 見 WIND (USAGE 用法)

gall /gɔl; gɔːl/ n **have the gall to do something** to have the boldness and rudeness to do something without being at all ashamed 竟然有臉做某事: *They had the gall to call me lazy, after all the work I'd done.* 我幹完了那麼多的活兒, 他們竟然還有臉說我懶!

gal·lant /ˈgælənt; ˈɡælənt/ adj **1** courageous

勇敢的; 英勇的: *a gallant soldier* 英勇的戰士 **2** *lit* attentive and polite to women (used of men) 〖文〗對女士殷勤有禮的〔指男士〕 –
gallantly *adv* –**gallantry** *n* [U]

gal·le·on /'gælɪən; 'gæliən/ *n* a large sailing ship, used in the past 〔昔時〕大帆船

*★**gal·le·ry** /'gælərɪ; 'gæləri/ *n* **galleries 1** a room, hall, or building where paintings or other works of art are shown, and sometimes offered for sale 畫廊; 藝術品陳列室 **2** an upper floor built out from an inner wall of a hall, from which activities in the hall, may be watched 廊台〔可居高臨下看大堂內的活動〕; 樓座 **3** a long narrow room, such as one used for shooting practice 狹長的房間〔如射擊訓練室〕 **4** a level underground passage in a mine 〔礦區的〕地下坑道 **5** the highest upper floor in a theatre 〔戲院的〕頂層樓座

gal·ley /'gælɪ; 'gæli/ *n* **1** a ship which was rowed by slaves, especially an ancient Greek or Roman warship 〔由奴隸划的〕船〔尤指古希臘或古羅馬的戰艦〕 **2** a ship's kitchen 船上的廚房

gal·lon /'gælən; 'gælən/ *n* a unit for measuring liquids equal to 8 pints (PINT); a British gallon equals 4.54 litres (LITRE) and an American gallon equals 3.78 litres 加侖 [液體計量單位, 一加侖等於八品脫; 英國的一加侖等於4.54升, 美國的一加侖等於3.78升]

gal·lop¹ /'gæləp; 'gæləp/ *v* **1** [I] (of a horse, or a person riding a horse) to go at the fastest speed 〔馬或騎者馬〕飛奔: *The horse galloped down the hill.* 馬飛奔下山。| *The riders galloped off.* 他們騎着馬飛奔而去。**2** [I + adv/prep] *infml* (of a person) to run very fast 〖非正式〗〔人〕飛快地跑

gal·lop² *n* **1** [sing] the movement of a horse at its fastest speed 〔馬的〕飛奔 **2** [C] a ride at this speed 騎馬飛奔: *a long gallop before breakfast* 早餐前騎着馬長時間的飛奔 **3 at a gallop** very fast 飛快地

gal·lop·ing /'gæləpɪŋ; 'gæləpɪŋ/ *adj* [always before a noun 只能用於名詞前] increasing very quickly 迅速增加的: *galloping inflation* 急劇惡化的通貨膨脹

gal·lows /'gæləʊz; 'gæləʊz/ *n* [plural is 複數為 **gallows**] the wooden frame on which murderers used to be killed by being hanged with a rope 絞架

ga·lore /gə'lɔːr; gə'lɔːr/ *adj* [only after a noun 只用於名詞後] in large amounts or numbers 多的; 大量的: *He's got money galore.* 他很有錢。| *friends galore* 許多朋友

ga·losh·es /gə'lɒʃɪz; gə'lɒʃɪz/ *n* [pl] rubber shoes worn over ordinary shoes when it rains or snows 〔雨、雪天穿的〕橡膠套鞋

gal·va·nize /'gælvə‚naɪz; 'gælvənaɪz/ *v* **galvanized, galvanizing** (also 又作 **galvanise** *BrE* 〖英式〗) [T] **1** to put a covering of metal over a sheet of another metal using

electricity 電鍍: *galvanized iron* 鍍鋅鐵(皮) **2** to shock someone so much that they take action without delay 刺激〔某人〕〔立刻採取行動〕: *The fear of losing his life galvanized him* **into** *action.* 喪命的恐懼促使他立刻採取行動。

gam·bit /'gæmbɪt; 'gæmbɪt/ *n* **1** a set of opening moves in the game of CHESS in which a piece is risked to gain an advantage later 〔國際象棋開局時冒犧牲一子的危險以期後來取得優勢的〕開局讓棋法 **2** an action made to produce a future effect, especially an opening move in an argument or conversation 〔辯論或談話中的〕有預謀的行動

gam·ble¹ /'gæmbl; 'gæmbəl/ *v* **gambled, gambling** [I] **1** to risk your money or property on horse races, in card games, or in business 賭馬; 賭博; 投機: *He lost a fortune gambling at the casino.* 他在賭場裡輸掉了一大筆錢。**2** to take a risk in the hope of gaining something 冒險〔希望能獲得某物〕: *We're having the party outside. Of course, we're gambling* **on** *the weather.* 我們準備在戶外聚會。當然, 我們這是把賭注押在了天氣上。–**gambler** *n*

gamble sthg ↔ **away** *phr v* [T] to lose money by gambling 賭掉, 輸光〔錢〕: *He's gambled away all his money.* 他把所有的錢都輸光了。

gamble² *n* [sing] an act in which you take a risk in the hope of success 賭博; 冒險: *The operation may not succeed. It's a bit of a gamble.* 手術可能不成功。這有點冒險。

gam·bol /'gæmbl; 'gæmbəl/ *v* **-ll-** (**-l-** *AmE* 〖美式〗) *lit* [I] to jump about playfully, like lambs or children 〖文〗〔如小羊或孩子般〕雀躍; 嬉戲

*★**game¹** /geɪm; geɪm/ *n* **1** [C] a form of play or sport 遊戲; 運動: *Football is a game which doesn't interest me.* 足球是一項我不感興趣的運動。| *He's very good at ball games.* 他對球類運動非常在行。**2** [C] a particular occasion when you play a game 一場遊戲: *Let's have another game of cards.* 我們再來打一局牌吧。| *a game of football* 一場足球賽 **3** [C] a part of a competition with a fixed number of points, as in tennis 〔如網球中的〕局; 盤: *She won the first three games but lost the set 3-6.* 她贏了前三局, 但整場比賽卻以三比六敗北。**4 games: a** [pl] a particular set of sports competitions 運動會: *The Olympic Games are held every four years.* 奧林匹克運動會每四年舉行一次。**b** [U] the playing of team games and other forms of physical exercise out of doors at school 〔學校的〕戶外體育活動 –see 見 SPORT (USAGE 用法) **5** [U] wild animals, birds, and fish which are hunted for food and as a sport 獵物; 野味: *Pheasants are the commonest game birds in Britain.* 野雞是英國最常見的獵禽。| *big game hunting in Africa* 在非洲的大規模狩獵

G

6 [C] *infml* a secret intention or plan, usually dishonest 〔非正式〕詭計；計謀: *What's your little game, then?* 那麼你的鬼點子是甚麼？ **7 give the game away** *infml* to tell people something which is intended to be kept secret 〔非正式〕泄露祕密 **8 the game is up** = you've been caught 你被抓住〔事情已經敗露〕

game² *adj* **1** willing to try something 願意試試〔某事〕的: *"Shall we try and climb up to the ridge?" "Yes, I'm game."* 「我們要不要試着爬到山脊上去？」「好，我願意試試看。」 **2** brave and determined 勇敢的；堅定的: *The little boy fell and hurt himself, but he was game enough to get up and try again.* 小男孩倒在地上受了傷，但他很勇敢，爬起來以後又試了一次。 **–gamely** *adv*

game·keep·er /ˈgemˌkipə; ˈgeɪmˌkiːpəʳ/ *n* a man employed to raise and protect the wild animals and birds kept for hunting on private land (私人)獵場看守員

gam·mon /ˈgæmən; ˈgæmən/ *n* [U] meat from a pig, when it has been preserved by smoke or salt 熏肉；醃肉

gam·ut /ˈgæmət; ˈgæmət/ *n* **1 the gamut of something** the complete range of a subject 整個領域；全部範圍 **2 run the whole gamut of** to experience everything connected with a subject 經歷〔某一領域內的〕全部過程

gan·der /ˈgændə; ˈgændəʳ/ *n* a male GOOSE 雄鵝

gang¹ /gæŋ; gæŋ/ *n* [+ sing/pl verb] **1** a group of people working together, especially criminals, prisoners, or building workers 〔尤指罪犯，囚犯或建築工人的〕一羣；一幫；一隊: *The gang was planning a robbery.* 這幫傢伙在計劃進行一次搶劫。 **2** a group of young people, mostly young men, who cause trouble or fill other people with fear 〔鬧事青少年的〕一夥: *a gang fight in downtown New York* 紐約市區裡的一起青少年鬥毆事件 **3 the gang, our gang** *infml* our group of friends 〔非正式〕我們的一羣朋友〔夥伴〕: *Have you seen any of the gang lately?* 最近你見過我們的任何夥伴嗎？

gang² *v*

gang up *phr v* [I] to work together as a close group against someone 結成一夥〔對付某人〕: *She feels that everyone's ganging up on her.* 她覺得人人都在合夥對付她。

gang·ling /ˈgæŋglɪŋ; ˈgæŋglɪŋ/ *adj* unusually tall and thin, and so appearing awkward in movement 瘦長而舉止笨拙的

gan·grene /ˈgæŋgrin; ˈgæŋgriːn/ *n* [U] the decay of the flesh of part of a person's body, caused when blood has stopped flowing there 壞疽 **–gangrenous** /-grɪnəs; -grɪnəs/ *adj*

gang·ster /ˈgæŋstə; ˈgæŋstəʳ/ *n* a member of a group of armed criminals 歹徒；匪徒

gang·way /ˈgæŋˌwe; ˈgæŋweɪ/ *n* **1** *BrE* a clear space between two rows of seats in a cinema, theatre, bus or train 〔英式〕〔電影院，戲院，公共汽車，或火車上兩排座位之間的〕通道；過道 **2** a bridge by which people get onto or off a ship 〔供人們上下船用的〕舷梯；跳板

gan·try /ˈgæntrɪ; ˈgæntrɪ/ *n* **gantries** a structure like a bridge used to support things such as railway signals and signs on large roads 〔鐵路或馬路的〕跨線信號架

gaol /dʒel; dʒeɪl/ *n*, *v* see 見 JAIL

gaol·er /ˈdʒelə; ˈdʒeɪləʳ/ *n* see 見 JAILER

★**gap** /gæp; gæp/ *n* **1** an empty space between two objects or two parts of an object 裂縫；缺口: *The gate was locked but we went through a gap in the fence.* 門鎖住了，但我們從籬笆的一處缺口中鑽了過去。 **2** a time which is not filled by the usual or wanted activity 〔時間上的〕間隔；間隙: *uncomfortable gaps in the conversation* 談話中令人感到不自在的間隙 **3** an absence of something which prevents something from being complete 〔某物的〕缺乏: *There are wide gaps in my knowledge of history.* 我的歷史知識有許多空白。 | *a gap in the market* 市場的缺口 **4** a difference between two things or groups of people 〔兩種事物或兩羣人之間的〕差別；差距: *the gap between management and unions* 資方與工會之間的分歧

gape /gep; geɪp/ *v* **gaped, gaping** [I] **1** to look hard in surprise, with your mouth open 目瞪口呆地凝視: *"What are you gaping at?" "Look, over there, it's the President!"* 「你愣在那裡看甚麼？」「瞧，那是總統呀！」 **2** to come apart or open widely 裂開；敞開: *a gaping hole* 裂開的洞

gar·age /ˈgəˈrɑʒ; ˈgærɑːʒ/ *n* **1** a building in which cars and other vehicles can be kept 汽車庫 –see picture on page 729 見 729 頁彩圖 **2** a place where petrol can be bought and cars can be repaired 〔兼汽車修理的〕加油站

garb /garb; gɑːb/ *n* [U] *lit* clothing of a particular style 〔文〕〔特種〕服裝

gar·bage /ˈgarbɪdʒ; ˈgɑːbɪdʒ/ *n* [U] **1** *AmE* things that have been thrown away because they are no longer needed 〔美式〕垃圾；廢物 **2** stupid and worthless ideas or words 愚蠢或無價值的想法或話語

garbage can /ˈ··ˌ·/ *n* the usual American word for 〔美式〕= DUSTBIN

garbage col·lec·tor /ˈ··ˌ··/ *n* the usual American word for 〔美式〕= DUSTMAN

garbage truck /ˈ···ˌ·/ *n* the usual American word for 〔美式〕= DUSTCART

gar·bled /ˈgarbld; ˈgɑːbəld/ *adj* confused and giving a false idea of the facts 混亂不清的；混淆事實的: *The newspaper gave a garbled account of the meeting.* 報紙對會議作了歪曲的報導。

★**gar·den¹** /ˈgardn; ˈgɑːdn/ *n* **1** a piece of land, usually near a house, on which grass, flowers, and vegetables can be grown 花園; 菜圃: *She's in the front garden.* 她在屋子前面的花園裡。– see picture on page 729 見 729 頁彩圖 **2** (also 又作 **gardens**) a public park with flowers, grass, paths, and seats 公園

garden² *v* [I] to work in a garden, making plants grow 從事園藝; 種植花木 –**gardener** *n* –**gardening** *n* [U] : *My mother's very keen on gardening.* 我的母親對園藝非常熱心。

gar·gan·tu·an /gɑrˈgæntʃuən; gɑːˈgæntʃu-ən/ *adj* extremely big 極大的: *a gargantuan meal* 極為豐盛的一餐

gar·gle /ˈgɑrgl; ˈgɑːgəl/ *v* **gargled, gargling** [I] to treat a bad throat medically by blowing air through a special liquid held at the back of your mouth 〔用藥水〕漱喉 – **gargle** *n*

gar·goyle /ˈgɑrgɔil; ˈgɑːgɔil/ *n* a hollow figure of a person or animal, especially on the roof of a church, through whose mouth rainwater is carried away 〔尤指教堂屋頂上呈人或動物狀的〕滴水嘴

gar·ish /ˈgɛrɪʃ; ˈgeərɪʃ/ *adj* unpleasantly bright 俗麗的; 過於豔麗的: *garish colours* 過於豔麗的色彩 –**garishly** *adv* –**garishness** *n* [U]

gar·land /ˈgɑrlənd; ˈgɑːlənd/ *n* **1** a circle of flowers or leaves placed round your neck for decoration or as a sign of victory 〔作為裝飾或紀念勝利的套在頸間的〕花環; 花冠; 花圈 **2** a long line of decorations used to decorate a house at special times such as Christmas 〔如在聖誕節等節日期間所用的〕華飾; 燈彩

gar·lic /ˈgɑrlɪk; ˈgɑːlɪk/ *n* [U] a plant rather like an onion, which is used in cooking to give a strong taste 蒜; 大蒜: *a clove of garlic* 一瓣蒜

gar·ment /ˈgɑrmənt; ˈgɑːmənt/ *n fml or tech* a piece of clothing 〔正式或術語〕(一件)衣服: *This garment should be hand-washed.* 這件衣服應當手洗。

gar·ner /ˈgɑrnɚ; ˈgɑːnəʳ/ *v* [T] *fml* to collect something, for example information, usually with difficulty 〔正式〕〔帶有難度的〕收集〔如資料〕; 貯藏

gar·nish /ˈgɑrnɪʃ; ˈgɑːnɪʃ/ *n* something that is used to improve the appearance of food, such as small pieces of fruit or vegetable 食物上的裝飾〔如小片的水果或蔬菜〕–**garnish** *v* [T]

gar·ret /ˈgɛrɪt; ˈgærɪt/ *n* a small usually unpleasant room at the top of a house 閣樓

gar·ri·son /ˈgɛrəsn; ˈgærɪsən/ *n* a group of soldiers living in a town and defending it 衛戍部隊; 駐軍

gar·ru·lous /ˈgærələs; ˈgærələs/ *adj* habitually talking too much, especially about unimportant things 嘮叨的; 喋喋不休的 – **garrulously** *adv*

gar·ter /ˈgɑrtɚ; ˈgɑːtəʳ/ *n* a band of elastic material worn round your leg to keep a

sock or STOCKING up 〔吊〕襪帶

☆**gas¹** /gæs; gæs/ *n* **gases** (also 又作 **gasses** *AmE* 〔美式〕) **1** [C;U] a substance like air, which is not solid or liquid 氣體: *Three of the main greenhouse gases are carbon dioxide, methane, and nitrous oxide.* 溫室裡的三種主要氣體是二氧化碳、甲烷和二氧化氮。 **2** [U] a substance of this type which is burnt in the home for heating and cooking 煤氣 **3** [U] *AmE infml* PETROL 〔美式，非正式〕汽油

gas² *v* **-ss-** [T] to poison or kill a person or animal with gas 用氣體使〔人或動物〕中毒或喪生

gas cham·ber /ˈ· ˌ··/ *n* a room which can be filled with gas so that people or animals can be killed 毒氣室〔用以毒死人或動物〕

gas·e·ous /ˈgæsɪəs; ˈgæsɪəs/ *adj* of or like gas 氣體的

gash /gæʃ; gæʃ/ *v* [T] to make a deep cut in something 〔在某物上〕割出深的切口 –**gash** *n*

gas·ket /ˈgæskɪt; ˈgæskɪt/ *n* a flat piece of soft material which is placed between two surfaces so that steam, oil, or gas cannot escape 墊片〔用於接頭處以免漏氣或漏油〕

gas mask /ˈ· ·/ *n* a breathing apparatus worn over your face to protect you against poisonous gases 防毒面具

gas·o·line /ˈgæsl̩ˌin; ˈgæsəliːn/ *n* (also 又作 **gasolene, gas** *infml* 〔非正式〕) [U] the usual American word for 〔美式〕= PETROL

gas·o·me·ter /gæsˈɑmətɚ; gæˈsɒmɪtəʳ/ *n* a round metal container, bigger than most buildings, in which gas is stored 大型儲煤氣罐; 儲煤氣槽

gasp /gæsp; gɑːsp/ *v* [I] **1** to take a quick short breath or breaths, making a sudden noise 急促地喘氣: *As her head came above the water she gasped for breath.* 她頭浮出水面的時候就大口地吸氣。 **2** to take in your breath suddenly, especially because of surprise, or shock 猛地吸口氣〔尤指因驚訝或震驚〕: *The audience gasped in amazement as she put her head in the lion's mouth.* 她把頭伸入獅子的嘴裡時，觀眾都倒吸了一口涼氣。 –**gasp** *n*: *He gave a gasp of surprise.* 他吃驚地倒吸了一口涼氣。

gasp·ing /ˈgæspɪŋ; ˈgɑːspɪŋ/ *adj* [never before a noun 不能用於名詞前] *infml* very thirsty 〔非正式〕非常渴的: *Is there any orange juice? I'm absolutely gasping.* 有沒有橘子汁? 我真渴死了。| *gasping for a drink* 想喝些飲料

gas sta·tion /ˈ· ˌ··/ *n* the usual American word for 〔美式〕= FILLING STATION

gas·sy /ˈgæsi; ˈgæsi/ *adj* **gassier, gassiest** full of gas 充滿氣體的: *a gassy drink* 氣很足的飲料

gas·tric /ˈgæstrɪk; ˈgæstrɪk/ *adj* [only before a noun 只用於名詞前] *tech* relating to or belonging to your stomach 〔術語〕胃的; 屬於胃的: *the gastric juices* 胃液

G

gas·tro·en·te·ri·tis /ˌgæstrəʊˌentəˈraɪtɪs; ˌgæs-trəʊ-entəˈraɪtɪs/ n [U] an illness in which your food passages, including your stomach and intestines (INTESTINE), are swollen 腸胃炎

gas·tron·o·my /gæsˈtrɒnəmi; gæˈstrɒnəmi/ n [U] the art and science of cooking and eating good food 美食學；烹調法 **–gastronomic** /ˌgæstrəˈnɒmɪk; ˌgæstrəˈnɒmɪk◂/ adj: The dinner was a great gastronomic success. 這頓飯從烹飪角度來說極為成功。 **– gastronomically** /-klɪ; -klɪ/ adv

gas·works /ˈgæsˌwɜːks; ˈgæswɜːks/ n [plural is 複數為 **gasworks**] a place where gas for use in the home and industry is made from coal 煤氣廠

☆**gate** /geɪt; geɪt/ n **1** an object like a low or wide door that is used outside to close an opening in a fence or wall 門；圍牆門；籬笆門: chatting over the garden gate 隔着一道籬笆門在閒聊 | park gates 公園大門 –see picture on page 729 見 729 頁彩圖 **2** an entrance or way out, especially in an airport 〔尤指機場的〕出入口

ga·teau /ˈgætəʊ; ˈgætəʊ/ n **gateaux** /-təz; -təʊz/ [C;U] a special large cake that looks very decorative and has cream and often fruit in it 奶油[水果]大蛋糕

gate·crash /ˈgeɪtˌkræʃ; ˈgeɪtkræʃ/ v [I;T] to go to a party or official occasion without having been invited 〔未受邀請而〕擅自參加〔宴會等〕；闖入 **–gatecrasher** n

gate·post /ˈgeɪtˌpəʊst; ˈgeɪtpəʊst/ n a post from which a gate is hung or to which it fastens (大門)門柱 –see picture on page 729 見 729 頁彩圖

gate·way /ˈgeɪtˌweɪ; ˈgeɪtweɪ/ n **1** an opening in a fence or wall across which a gate may be put 〔籬笆或牆上的〕出入口 **2** a way of reaching something desirable 途徑；方法: Higher education can be the gateway to a worthwhile career. 接受高等教育可能是你獲得一個有價值的工作的途徑。 **3** a place which leads you somewhere else 門徑: Come to Singapore — gateway to the East. 請到新加坡來——這裡是通往東方的門戶。

☆**gath·er** /ˈgæðə; ˈgæðər/ v **1** [I;T] to come together in a group 聚集: A crowd soon gathered to see what had happened. 很快就有一羣人聚攏過來看看發生了甚麼事情。 | you can just gather round, I'll explain what I want you to do. 如果你們站到我周圍，我就告訴你們我要你們做甚麼事情。 | The sheep had gathered together in a corner of the field. 綿羊已聚在田地的一個角落裡。 **2** [T] to collect flowers, crops, or several objects 收集〔物品〕；採集〔花、農作物等〕: I gathered a few roses. 我採了幾朵玫瑰。 **3** [T] to obtain something gradually from different places 〔從不同的地方〕收集〔某物〕: Scientists have been gathering information about the disease. 科學家一直在收集有關這種疾病的資料。 **4** [T] to slowly increase force or speed 逐漸

增加〔力量或速度〕: As the bus came onto the open road it gathered speed. 公共汽車開上開闊的馬路之後便逐漸加快了速度。 **5** [T; + (that)] to understand from something said or done 推測；了解: I gather she's ill, and that's why she hasn't come. 我想她是病了，所以沒有來。 | "She's ill." "So I gather." "她病了。" "我也這麼想。" **6** [T] to pull material into small folds by using a long thread 打摺；襇: a skirt gathered at the waist 腰部打褶的裙子

gath·er·ing /ˈgæðərɪŋ; ˈgæðərɪŋ/ n a meeting or coming together of a group of people 會議；集會: It was not a happy gathering. 這次聚會並不太愉快。

gauche /gəʊʃ; gəʊʃ/ adj awkward in social behaviour 不善交際的

gau·dy /ˈgɔːdi; ˈgɔːdi/ adj **gaudier, gaudiest** too bright in colour 俗麗的 **–gaudily** adv

gauge¹ /geɪdʒ; geɪdʒ/ n (also 又作 **gage** AmE 【美式】) **1** an instrument for measuring the quantity or amount of something 測量儀器: the fuel gauge 燃料表 **2** a fact you can use to judge a person or situation 〔用以對人或局勢作出判斷的〕事實: Is the number of people passing exams a reliable gauge of educational success? 考試及格的人數能準確地反映出教育是否成功嗎？

gauge² v **gauged, gauging** (also 又作 **gage** AmE 【美式】) [T] **1** to measure something by using a gauge 用儀器測量 **2** to judge the value or meaning of something or of someone's actions 評判；判斷〔某物或某人行動的價值或意義〕: It's difficult to gauge his reaction. 還很難判斷出他的反應。

gaunt /gɔːnt; gɔːnt/ adj **1** very thin, as if ill 憔悴的 **2** bare or severe in appearance 荒涼的；蕭穆的

gaunt·let /ˈgɔːntlɪt; ˈgɔːntlɪt/ n **gauntlets** [pl] long thick gloves (GLOVE) which protect your hand; people on motorbicycles wear gauntlets 〔摩托車手所戴之〕長而厚的手套

gauze /gɔːz; gɔːz/ n [U] soft net-like material 紗布；薄紗: cotton gauze 棉紗布 | gauze curtains 薄紗窗簾 | Dress the wound with gauze. 用紗布把傷口包起來。

gave /geɪv; geɪv/ the past tense of GIVE ☆ GIVE的過去式

gaw·ky /ˈgɔːki; ˈgɔːki/ adj **gawkier, gawkiest** awkward in movement, especially because of having long thin limbs 〔尤指由於四肢瘦長而〕行動笨拙的

gawp /gɔːp; gɔːp/ v [I] to look at something in a rude and foolish way 不禮貌地傻看

gay¹ /geɪ; geɪ/ adj **1** infml HOMOSEXUAL 【非正式】同性戀的: gay rights 同性戀者的權利 **2** bright or attractive 鮮豔而吸引人的: gay colours 繽紛的色彩 **3** old fash cheerful and happy 【老式】愉快的；高興的

gay² n a HOMOSEXUAL person, especially a man 〔尤指男子〕同性戀者: a more liberal at-

G

titude to gays and lesbians 對男、女同性戀者所採取的更為寬容的態度

gaze /geɪz/ v **gazed, gazing** [I; + adv/prep] to look steadily at someone or something for a long time 凝視〔某人或某物〕: *He gazed fondly at his children.* 他愛意盈盈地凝視着自己的兒女。| *She sat gazing into the distance.* 她坐在那裡, 凝視遠方。–**gaze** n [sing] a steady fixed look 凝視; 注視: *her worried gaze* 憂鬱的凝視

ga·zelle /gəˈzɛl; gəˈzɛl/ n a graceful animal like a small deer 瞪羚

ga·zumped /gəˈzʌmpt; gəˈzʌmpt/ v be gazumped *infml* to be unable to buy a house that the owner agreed to sell you because they have decided to sell it instead to someone who has offered more money〔非正式〕〔價錢談妥後屋主將房屋〕抬價改售〔他人〕

GB /ˌdʒiː ˈbiː; ˌdʒiː ˈbiː/ an abbreviation for〔縮〕= **Great Britain** 英國

GCSE /ˌdʒiː siː ɛs ˈiː; ˌdʒiː siː es ˈiː/ an examination in any of a range of subjects, taken in British schools by pupils aged 15 or 16: an abbreviation for **General Certificate of Secondary Education**〔縮〕〔英國十五或十六歲的學生參加的〕普通中等教育證書考試

gear¹ /gɪr; gɪəʳ/ n **1** [C;U] an apparatus, especially one consisting of a set of toothed wheels, that allows power to be passed from one part of a machine to another so as to control its power, speed, and direction of movement 齒輪傳動裝置; 排檔: *Most cars have four forward gears.* 大多數汽車有四個前進排檔。| *The hill was so steep I had to go into second gear.* 山很陡, 我不得不換成了二檔。| *She changed gear as she approached the bend.* 開近轉彎處時地換了檔。**2 in gear** having the engine directly connected to the wheels (used of a car or other vehicle) 掛上檔〔指汽車或其他交通工具〕: *Don't leave it in gear. Put it into neutral.* 別掛排檔。放在空檔上好了。**3** [U] the special clothes or objects you need for a particular activity, especially a sport〔為某一活動, 尤指某一項運動而準備的〕衣服或用具: *climbing gear* 登山用具

gear² v **1 gear something to something** to make one thing be in accordance with another thing 使一物與另一物一致; 使適應: *Education should be geared to the children's needs and abilities.* 教育應適應兒童的需要和能力。**2 be geared up to do something** to be prepared to do something, and, often, nervous about doing it〔通常是緊張地〕準備好做某事

gear·box /ˈgɪrˌbaks; ˈgɪəbɒks/ n a metal case containing the gears of a vehicle 變速箱

gear le·ver /ˈ· ˌ··/ n (also 又作 **gearshift** /ˈgɪrʃɪft; ˈgɪəʃɪft/ AmE 〔美式〕) a metal rod which controls the gears of vehicle 變速

桿 –see picture on page 209 見 209 頁彩圖

gee /dʒiː; dʒiː/ *interj AmE infml* people sometimes say this when they are surprised or they are enjoying themselves〔美式, 非正式〕〔表示驚訝或高興〕哎呀; 哇: *Gee, honey. That sure is a nice dress.* 哎呀, 親愛的, 那真是件漂亮的裙子。

geese /giːs; giːs/ the plural of GOOSE ☆ GOOSE 的複數形式

gel¹ /dʒɛl; dʒɛl/ n [C;U] a substance in a state between solid and liquid 凝膠; 凍膠: *hair gel* 髮膠

gel² v **-ll-** [I] **1** (of a liquid) to become firmer and like a jelly〔液體〕變為膠狀 **2** (of ideas) to take a clear shape〔想法〕變得清晰; 成形 **3** (of a group of people) to become united〔一羣人〕聯合起來

gel·a·tine /ˈdʒɛlətɪn; ˈdʒɛlətiːn/ n (also 又作 **gelatin** /ˈdʒɛlətɪn; ˈdʒɛlətˌn̩/ AmE 〔美式〕) [U] a clear substance used for making jellies 明膠

ge·lat·i·nous /dʒəˈlætənəs; dʒˌˈlætˌnəs/ adj tech in a state between solid and liquid like jelly〔術語〕膠狀的

gel·ig·nite /ˈdʒɛlɪgˌnaɪt; ˈdʒɛlɪgnaɪt/ n [U] a very powerful explosive 葛裡炸藥

gem /dʒɛm; dʒem/ n **1** a precious stone, especially when cut into a regular shape〔尤指經琢磨的〕寶石 **2** a thing or person of special value 具有特殊價值的物或人; 精華; 精品

Gem·i·ni /ˈdʒɛməˌnaɪ; ˈdʒemˌnaɪ/ n one of the signs of the ZODIAC 雙子星座; 雙子宮

gen /dʒɛn; dʒen/ n [U] *infml* the correct or complete information〔非正式〕正確的〔完整的〕消息〔情報〕: *He gave me all the gen on the new office arrangements.* 他把關於辦公室新安排的全部情況告訴了我。

gen·der /ˈdʒɛndə; ˈdʒendəʳ/ n [C;U] *tech* 〔術語〕**1** the sexual division into male and female 性別: *There must be no discrimination according to race or gender.* 不應該有種族或性別歧視的存在。**2** in grammar, the division of nouns, adjectives, etc., into MASCULINE, FEMININE, or NEUTER〔文法〕性〔分為陽性、陰性、中性〕: *German has three genders.* 德語中有三種性。| *Differences of gender in French are shown in the different endings of adjectives.* 法語在性上面的差別顯現於形容詞詞尾的變化。

‑gene /dʒiːn; dʒiːn/ n the part of a cell which controls the development of all the qualities in a living thing which have been passed on from its parents 遺傳基因

ge·ne·al·o·gy /ˌdʒiːnɪˈælədʒɪ; ˌdʒiːniˈælədʒi/ n **genealogies 1** [U] the study of the history of the members of a family 家譜學; 宗譜學 **2** [C] an account of the history of a particular family 家譜; 宗譜 –**genealogist** n – **genealogical** /ˌdʒiːnɪəˈlɒdʒɪkl; ˌdʒiːniːˈlɒdʒɪkəl/ adj

gen·e·ra /ˈdʒɛnərə; ˈdʒenərə/ the plural of

GENUS ☆GENUS 的複數形式

gen·e·ral¹ /ˈdʒɛnərəl; ˈdʒɛnərəl/ *adj* **1** concerning most people or places 大眾的; 普遍的: *The general feeling is that it's wrong.* 普遍的感覺是這件事錯了。 | *Concern about pollution is now very general.* 現在人們普遍關注污染問題。 **2** concerning the whole of something, rather than its parts 總體的; 全面的: *a general increase in prices* 價格的普遍上漲 | *The general condition of the car is good, although the battery needs replacing.* 儘管需要更換電池, 但這輛車的總體情況還不錯。 | *the general manager* 總經理 **3** not limited to one subject only 不限於某一門學科的: *a general university degree* 大學的普通學位 | *general education* 普通教育 **4** not limited to providing only one service or product 不限於提供只一種服務的; 不限於生產一種產品的: *a general hospital* 綜合性醫院 | *the general store* 雜貨店 **5** describing the main points, but not the details 概略的; 籠統的: *Give me a general idea of what the job involves.* 把這項工作的大致情況跟我說說。 **6** true or usual in most cases 普遍適用的; 通用的: *As a general rule, patients must make an appointment to see the doctor.* 一般而言, 病人看醫生需要預約。 **7 in general** mainly or in most cases 通常; 一般而言; 大體上: *In general, my colleagues are very hardworking.* 總的說來, 我的同事工作都很勤奮。 | *People in general are fed up with the present government.* 大多數人已對現在的政府感到厭倦了。

general² *n* (also 又作 **General**) an officer of very high rank in the armed forces, especially the army 〔尤指陸軍〕將軍: *General De Gaulle* 戴高樂將軍 | *Yes, General.* 是的, 將軍。

general an·aes·thet·ic /ˌ··· ··ˈ··/ *n* [C;U] a substance used in hospitals to make someone unconscious while an operation is performed on them 全身麻醉劑

general e·lec·tion /ˌ··· ·ˈ··/ *n* an election in which all the voters in a country choose the members of the government 大選; 普選

gen·e·ral·i·ty /ˈdʒɛnəˈrælətɪ; ˌdʒɛnəˈrælˌtɪ/ *n* **generalities** a general statement which is not at all detailed 概論; 概述: *The President's speech was full of vague generalities.* 總統的演講通篇都是非常籠統的話。

gen·e·ral·i·za·tion /ˌdʒɛnərələˈzeɪʃən; ˌdʒɛnərəlaɪˈzeɪʃən/ *n* **1** [C] a statement made about a group as a whole; it may not be true in every case 推論 **2** [U] the act of generalizing 歸納

gen·e·ral·ize /ˈdʒɛnərəlˌaɪz; ˈdʒɛnərəlaɪz/ *v* **generalized, generalizing** (also 又作 **generalise** *BrE* 〔英式〕) to make a general statement or form a general principle by looking at particular examples 總結; 歸納: *I don't think it's fair to generalize from only two examples.* 我認為單單看兩個例子就作出

gen·e·ral·ized /ˈdʒɛnərəl,aɪzd; ˈdʒɛnərəlaɪzd/ *adj* concerning or having an effect on a large number of people or things 普遍的; 廣泛的: *Use of this equipment in hospital is now fairly generalized.* 醫院裡現在廣泛使用了這種設備。

general know·ledge /ˌ··· ·ˈ··/ *n* [U] knowledge about many different subjects 〔關於不同學科的〕普遍知識: *For a child, his general knowledge is excellent.* 作為一個孩子, 他在各個學科上的知識是非常豐富的。 **2** knowledge shared by most people, such as the names of important cities 常識〔如重要城市的名字〕

gen·er·al·ly /ˈdʒɛnərəlɪ; ˈdʒɛnərəli/ *adv* **1** usually 通常; 一般: *We generally go to the seaside for our holidays.* 我們通常去海邊度假。 **2** by most people 大多數人; *It was generally agreed that the plan was a good one.* 一般人都認為這個計劃很好。 **3** considering something as a whole 總體上: *Her work is generally of a high standard.* 總體上講, 她的作品具有很高的水準。

general prac·ti·tion·er /ˌ··· ·ˈ···/ *n* see 見 GP

general pub·lic /ˌ··· ·ˈ··/ *n* [+sing/pl verb] ordinary people, who have no special part in an event or organization 一般公眾; 普通百姓: *The general public were not allowed into the courtroom.* 普通的百姓不允許進入法庭。

general strike /ˌ··· ·ˈ·/ *n* the stopping of work by most of the workers in a country at the same time 全國總罷工: *The unions have called for a general strike next Friday.* 工會已號召下週五舉行全國總罷工。

gen·e·rate /ˈdʒɛnə,reɪt; ˈdʒɛnəreɪt/ *v* **generated, generating** [T] **1** *tech* to produce heat, power, or electricity 〔術語〕產生〔熱量、能量或電力〕: *Our electricity comes from the new generating station.* 我們用的電來自那座新建的發電站。 **2** to cause something to exist 使〔某物〕產生: *Our discussion generated a lot of new ideas.* 我們的討論產生了許多新的想法。

gen·e·ra·tion /ˌdʒɛnəˈreʃən; ˌdʒɛnəˈreɪʃən/ *n* **1** [C] the group of people in a family at the same stage in its development; for example you and your aunt's children belong to the same generation 〔家族中的〕一代 **2** [C] all people of about the same age 同年齡的人: *the younger generation* 年輕的一代 | *Most people of my father's generation can remember the hardship of war.* 我父親那一代的大部分人都能記得戰爭的艱苦。 **3 generation gap** the difference in ideas between one generation and another 代溝〔兩代人之間的隔閡〕 **4** [C] the average period of time that it takes for children to become adults, about 25 to 30 years 兒童成長

G

為成人所需的平均時間〔約二十五年到三十年〕; 一代: *It will take at least another generation to solve this country's problems.* 最起碼還要有一代人的時間才能解決這個國家的問題。**5** [C] all the members of a particular class of things at a stage of their development 同一發展階段的產物: *the new generation of word processors* 新一代文字處理機 **6** [U] the production of heat, power, or electricity〔熱量、能量、電力的〕產生: *Solar energy may soon be used for the generation of all our electricity.* 太陽能也許不久就可以生產我們所需要的全部電力。

gen·e·ra·tor /ˈdʒɛnəˌretɚ; ˈdʒenəreɪtə/ *n* a machine which produces electricity 發電機

ge·ner·ic /dʒəˈnɛrɪk; dʒɪˈnerɪk/ *adj* shared by or typical of a whole class of things 共有的; 普通的

gen·e·rous /ˈdʒɛnərəs; ˈdʒenərəs/ *adj* **1** willing to give money, help, and kindness 慷慨的; 大方的: *It was very generous of you to lend them your new car to go on holiday.* 你肯把你的新車借給他們去度假用, 真是慷慨。**2** larger in amount than usual 大量的; 豐富的: *a generous meal* 豐盛的一餐 | *a generous gift* 一份厚禮 –**generously** *adv* – **generosity** /ˌdʒɛnəˈrɑsəti; ˌdʒenəˈrɒsɪti/ *n* [U] : *a letter thanking her for her generosity* 一封對她的慷慨表示感謝的信

gen·e·sis /ˈdʒɛnəsɪs; ˈdʒenɪsɪs/ *n fml* the beginning of something〔正式〕開端; 起源

ge·net·ic /dʒəˈnɛtɪk; dʒɪˈnetɪk/ *adj* **1** of or concerning genes (GENE) or genetics 遺傳基因的; 遺傳學的 **2 the genetic code** *tech* the arrangement of genes which gives a living thing the qualities of its parents〔術語〕遺傳密碼〔使生物體具有其母體的性質的基因排列方式〕**3 genetic engineering** *tech* the changing of the nature of a living thing by changing its genes〔術語〕遺傳工程學〔透過改變基因來改變生物體的性質〕–**genetically** /-klɪ; -kli/ *adv*

ge·net·ics /dʒəˈnɛtɪks; dʒɪˈnetɪks/ *n* [U] the study of how living things develop particular qualities according to the influence of those substances in their cells which are passed on from their parents 遺傳學

ge·ni·al /ˈdʒinjəl; ˈdʒiːniəl/ *adj* cheerful, friendly, and good-tempered 愉快的; 友好的; 脾氣好的: *"See you," he said with a genial wave.* "再見", 他邊説邊親切地揮揮手。– **genially** *adv* –**geniality** /ˌdʒiniˈælətɪ; ˌdʒiːniˈælɪti/ *n* [U]

gen·i·tals /ˈdʒɛnətəlz; ˈdʒenɪtlz/ *n* (also 又作 **genitalia** /ˌdʒɛnəˈteljə; ˌdʒenɪˈteɪliə/ *fml*〔正式〕) [pl] the outer sex organs 外生殖器 –**genital** *adj*

gen·i·tive /ˈdʒɛnətɪv; ˈdʒenɪtɪv/ *n tech* the special form of a noun or adjective which is used in some languages to show possession〔術語〕〔文法〕所有格 –**genitive** *adj*

ge·ni·us /ˈdʒinjəs; ˈdʒiːniəs/ *n* **1** [U] great

and rare powers of thought and imagination 非凡的思辯與想像力; 天才: *Her latest book is a work of sheer genius.* 她最新的一部書絕對是天才之作。**2** [C] a person of very great ability 天才人物: *Einstein was a true genius.* 愛因斯坦的確是個天才。| *That's it! You're an absolute genius!* 這就對啦! 你真是個不折不扣的天才! **3** [sing] a special ability 特殊的才能; 天賦: *She has a genius for making people feel at home.* 她有讓人感覺賓至如歸的才能。

gen·o·cide /ˈdʒɛnəˌsaɪd; ˈdʒenəsaɪd/ *n* [U] the killing of a whole race or nation 種族滅絕; 滅絕種族的大屠殺

gen·re /ˈʒɑnrə; ˈʒɒnrə/ *n* a class of literature, music, paintings, or SCULPTURE that shares a particular style or subject〔文學、音樂、繪畫、雕塑的〕種類; 類型: *the genre of horror fiction* 恐怖小説類

gen·teel /dʒɛnˈtil; dʒenˈtiːl/ *adj* trying to be unnaturally polite or respected 假裝彬彬有禮的: *a genteel old lady* 故作高雅的老婦人 – **genteelly** /-ˈtillɪ; -ˈtiːl-li/ *adv* –**gentility** /-ˈtɪlətɪ; -ˈtɪlɪti/ *n* [U]

gen·tile /ˈdʒɛntaɪl; ˈdʒentaɪl/ *n* (also 又作 **Gentile**) a person who is not Jewish 非猶太人 –**gentile, Gentile** *adj*

★gen·tle /ˈdʒɛntl̩; ˈdʒentl̩/ *adj* **1** not rough or violent in manner or movement〔態度、行動〕溫和的; 溫馴的: *Be gentle when you brush the baby's hair.* 給嬰兒梳頭髮時要輕些。| *a gentle wind* 和風 **2** kind and calm 親切的; 平靜的: *a gentle voice* 親切的聲音 | *gentle brown eyes* 顯得很平靜的褐色的眼睛 **3** not steep or sharp 不陡峭的: *a gentle slope* 平緩的斜坡 –**gentleness** *n* [U] –**gently** *adv*: *"Don't cry," he said gently.* "別哭", 他溫柔地説。| *She rocked the baby gently in her arms.* 她把嬰兒抱在懷裡輕輕地搖。

★gen·tle·man /ˈdʒɛntl̩mən; ˈdʒentlmən/ *n* **gentlemen** /-mən; -mən/ **1** a man who behaves well towards other people and who can always be trusted to act honourably 先生; 紳士; 君子 **2** *fml* a man〔正式〕男人

■ USAGE 用法: We often use **gentleman** and **lady** as a respectful way of speaking about a man or woman, especially when the person is present ☆當我們有禮貌地提及一個男人或女人時, 尤其當被提及的人在場時, 常用 **gentleman** 和 **lady**: *It isn't my turn — this gentleman/lady was here before me.* 還沒輪到我——這位先生/女士排在我前面。We also use the phrase **ladies and gentlemen** at the beginning of a speech ☆我們也用 **ladies** 和 **gentlemen** 來作為演講的開始: **Ladies and gentlemen,** *I'd like to introduce our speaker for this evening.* 女士們, 先生們, 我來介紹一下今晚為大家作演講的嘉賓。

G

In other cases **man** and **woman** are the usual words. ☆ 在其他的情況下, **man** 和 **woman** 是較為常用的詞。

gen·tri·fy /'dʒɛntrɪ,faɪ; 'dʒentrɪfaɪ/ v **gentrified, gentrified: be gentrified** (of an area) to become more typical of an area where rich people live by the process of richer people gradually moving there〔地區〕(由於富人逐漸的遷入而)顯示出富人居住區的特徵—**gentrification** /,dʒɛntrɪfɪ'keʃən; ,dʒentr½fɪ'keɪʃən/ n [U]

gen·try /'dʒɛntri; 'dʒentri/ n [pl] **the gentry** formerly, people born of high, but not the highest, social class〔昔時〕上流社會人士; 紳士

gents /dʒɛnts; dʒents/ n [plural is 複數為 **gents**] BrE infml a public TOILET for men〔英式, 非正式〕男廁所

*****gen·u·ine** /'dʒɛnjʊɪn; 'dʒenjuᵻn/ adj **1** real 真的: a genuine leather handbag 真皮手提包 | There's no doubt this Picasso is genuine. 這肯定是幅畢加索的真跡。**2** sincere and honest 誠摯的; 誠實的: a very genuine person 非常真誠的人 —**genuinely** adv —**genuineness** n [U]

ge·nus /'dʒiːnəs; 'dʒiːnəs/ n **genera** /'dʒɛnərə; 'dʒenərə/ tech a group of closely related kinds of animal or plant〔術語〕〔動植物的〕屬

ge·og·ra·phy /dʒɪ'ɑgrəfɪ; dʒiːˈɒɡrəfɪ/ n [U] **1** the study of the countries of the world, including such things as seas, rivers, mountains, population and weather 地理學 **2** infml the arrangement of the parts of a particular place〔非正式〕地形: I can't show you the way, because I don't know the geography of the neighbourhood. 我無法給你帶路, 因為我不清楚本地的地形。 —**geographer** n —**geographic** /,dʒɪə'græfɪk; ,dʒɪə'græfɪk/, **geographical** /-fɪkl; -fɪkəl/ adj —**geographically** /-klɪ; -klɪ/ adv

ge·ol·o·gy /dʒɪ'ɑlədʒɪ; dʒiːˈɒlədʒɪ/ n [U] the study of the structure of materials like rocks and soil and their changes during the history of the Earth 地質學 —**geologist** n —**geological** /,dʒɪə'lɑdʒɪkl; ,dʒɪə'lɒdʒɪkəl/ adj —**geologically** /-klɪ; -klɪ/ adv

ge·o·met·ric /,dʒɪə'mɛtrɪk; ,dʒɪə'metrɪk/ adj (also 又作 **geometrical** /-trɪkl; -trɪkəl/) **1** concerning geometry 幾何的 **2** involving repeated angles and shapes formed by lines 幾何圖形的: the abstract geometric patterns of Islamic art 伊斯蘭教藝術中抽象的幾何圖形 —**geometrically** /-klɪ; -klɪ/ adv

ge·om·e·try /dʒɪ'ɑmətrɪ; dʒiːˈɒmᵻtri/ n [U] the study in MATHEMATICS of shape and form, using angles and lines 幾何學

Geor·gian /'dʒɔrdʒən; 'dʒɔːdʒən/ adj of the period of rule of the first four British kings named George (1711-1830) (英國)喬治王朝時代的〔1771-1830〕: Georgian architecture 喬治王朝時代的建築 | a beautiful Georgian house 一所漂亮的喬治王朝時代建造的房子

ge·ra·ni·um /dʒə'renɪəm; dʒəˈreɪnɪəm/ n a plant with red, pink, or white flowers 天竺葵

ge·ri·at·rics /,dʒɛrɪ'ætrɪks; ,dʒerɪˈætrɪks/ n [U] the branch of medicine concerning the illnesses, treatment, and care of old people 老年醫學; 老年病學 —**geriatric** adj: a geriatric hospital 老年病科醫院

germ /dʒɝm; dʒɜːm/ n **1** a very small living thing which causes illness 病菌 **2 the germ of an idea** the beginning of an idea which may develop further〔想法的〕起源; 萌芽

Ger·man¹ /'dʒɝmən; 'dʒɜːmən/ adj from or connected with Germany 德國的

German² n **1** [C] a person from Germany 德國人 **2** [U] the language of Germany, Switzerland, and Austria 德語〔德國、瑞士和奧地利使用的語言〕: In this part of the country we speak a dialect of German. 在這個國家的該地區我們說一種德語的方言。

German mea·sles /,·· '··/ n [U] an infectious illness in which red spots appear on your body 德國麻疹; 風疹

ger·mi·nate /'dʒɝmə,net; 'dʒɜːmᵻneɪt/ v **germinated, germinating 1** [I] (of a seed) to start growing〔種子〕發芽 **2** [T] to make a seed start growing 使〔種子〕發芽 —**germination** /,dʒɝmə'neʃən; ,dʒɜːmᵻˈneɪʃən/ n [U]

ger·und /'dʒɛrənd; 'dʒerənd/ n in grammar, a noun made from a verb; in the sentence "I like swimming", "swimming" is a gerund; in English gerunds end in -ing〔文法〕動名詞〔由動詞轉化而成的名詞; 如在句子 "I like swimming" 中, "swimming" 便是動名詞; 英語中的動名詞均以 "ing" 結尾〕

ges·ta·tion /dʒɛs'teʃən; dʒeˈsteɪʃən/ n tech [U] **1** the carrying of a child or young animal inside its mother's body before birth〔術語〕懷孕; 妊娠 **2** the beginning and development of an idea or plan〔思想或計劃〕醞釀, 孕育

ges·tic·u·late /dʒɛs'tɪkjə,let; dʒeˈstɪkjᵿleɪt/ v **gesticulated, gesticulating** [I] to move your hands and arms, often while you are speaking, to express something urgency or excitement〔說話時〕做手勢〔以表達緊迫或激動〕 —**gesticulation** /,dʒɛstɪkjə'leʃən; dʒe,stɪkjᵿˈleɪʃən/ n [C;U]

*****ges·ture¹** /'dʒɛstʃɚ; 'dʒestʃə/ n **1** [C;U] movement, usually with your hands or head, to express a certain meaning 手勢; 示意動作: He made an angry gesture. 他作了個憤怒的手勢。 | He didn't speak a word of English, so we communicated entirely by gesture. 他一個英語單詞也不會講, 所以我們完全靠打手勢進行溝通。**2** [C] an action which is done to show your feelings or intentions〔示意情感或意圖的〕姿態: "We've invited our new *neighbours to dinner." "That's a nice gesture."* "我們已請了新鄰居來吃飯。" "這可是個友好的表示。" | *a gesture of friendship* 一種友好的表示

gesture² *v* **gestured, gesturing** [I;+that] to tell someone something by moving your hands or head 作手勢〔把某事告訴某人〕: *She gestured that it was time to leave.* 她打了個手勢, 示意該走了。 | *They gestured to us to go away.* 他們作手勢叫我們走。 | *He gestured in the direction of the station.* 他用手勢指了指車站的那個方向。

☆☆**get** see box on pages 473 to 479 見 473 頁至 479 頁之方框

get·a·way /ˈgetəˌweɪ; ˈgetəweɪ/ *n* **1** [sing] an escape 逃跑; 逃脱: *the getaway car* 藉以逃脱的汽車 **2 make a getaway** to leave a place quickly, especially after doing something criminal 迅速離開〔某地〕〔尤指做了違法的事情以後〕: *The thieves made a quick getaway.* 竊賊們很快逃掉了。

get-to-geth-er /ˈ·· ··/ *n* a friendly informal meeting or party 非正式的聚會: *a get-together of old school friends* 老校友的聚會

get·up /ˈgetˌʌp; ˈgetʌp/ *n infml* an unusual set of clothes 〔非正式〕一套不同尋常的衣服

gey·ser /ˈgizə; ˈgiːzər/ *n* **1** a natural spring of hot water and steam which can rise suddenly into the air from the earth 天然噴泉 **2** an apparatus for heating water by gas, used in a kitchen or bathroom 〔廚房或浴室中的〕煤氣熱水器

ghast·ly /ˈgæstli; ˈgɑːstli/ *adj* **ghastlier, ghastliest 1** *infml* extremely bad or unpleasant 〔非正式〕極壞的; 令人極為不快的: *a really ghastly man* 特別令人討厭的人 | *ghastly food* 很糟糕的食物 | *I felt ghastly after drinking that wine.* 喝了那酒以後, 我很不舒服。 | *ghastly news* 極壞的消息 | *the most ghastly crime* 令人髮指的罪行 **2** very pale and ill-looking (used of a person) 面色蒼白的〔指人〕

gher·kin /ˈgɜːkɪn; ˈgɜːkɪn/ *n* a small green vegetable usually eaten after being kept in VINEGAR〔醋醃的〕小黃瓜

ghet·to /ˈgetəʊ; ˈgetəʊ/ *n* **ghettos** or **ghettoes** a part of a city in which a group of people of similar race or nationality live, usually because they are poor or not accepted as full citizens〔城市中的〕貧民區或未取得正式國籍者聚居的區域

ghetto blast·er /ˈ·· ··/ *n infml* a large CASSETTE RECORDER that can be carried around〔非正式〕一種可隨身攜帶的大型錄音機

ghost /gost; gəʊst/ *n* **1** the spirit of a dead person who appears again 鬼魂: *Do you believe in ghosts?* 你相信有鬼魂嗎? | *The ghost of Lady Margaret is said to haunt the castle.* 據說馬格麗特太太的鬼魂常在那座城堡出沒。 **2 give up the ghost: a** *infml* to die〔非正式〕死 **b** to stop working because

something has gone wrong that cannot be repaired (used especially of machines)〔由於某物壞了無法修復而〕停止工作〔尤指機器〕 **3 the ghost of a** *infml* the slightest〔非正式〕一點; 絲毫: *You haven't got the ghost of a chance of getting the job.* 你得到這份工作的希望十分渺茫。

ghost·ly /ˈgostli; ˈgəʊstli/ *adj* having the unnatural and frightening qualities of a ghost 鬼魂似的; 可怕的: *I saw a ghostly light ahead of me in the darkness.* 我看見前面的黑暗處有一道像鬼火一樣的亮光。

ghost town /ˈ· ·/ *n* a town which is now empty because all the people have left 被廢棄的城鎮

ghoul /gul; guːl/ *n* **1** a spirit in stories which takes bodies from graves to eat them〔神話中的〕食屍鬼 **2** a person who is unnaturally interested in death and dead bodies 對死亡和死屍極感興趣的人 –**ghoulish** *adj*

GI /ˌdʒiː ˈaɪ, ˌdʒiː ˈaɪ/ *n* **GI's** or **GIs** a soldier in the US army, especially during World War Two〔尤指二次世界大戰時的〕美國兵

gi·ant¹ /ˈdʒaɪənt; ˈdʒaɪənt/ *n* **1** an extremely big strong man in fairy stories, who is often unfriendly or cruel〔神話中常為不友好或冷酷的〕巨人 **2** a large business organization 大企業: *The company he works for is one of the giants of the pharmaceutical industry.* 他所在的公司是藥品工業中的一家大企業。 **3** something which is a much larger size than usual 巨物

giant² *adj* [only before a noun 只用於名詞前] extremely large 極大的: *a giant cucumber* 特大的黃瓜 | *It's better value to get the giant-size packet.* 買特大包裝更划算。

gib·ber·ish /ˈdʒɪbərɪʃ; ˈdʒɪbərɪʃ/ *n* [U] meaningless sounds, talk, or ideas 無意義的聲音、話語或主意

gib·bet /ˈdʒɪbɪt; ˈdʒɪbɪt/ *n* the wooden post from which criminals were hanged 絞刑架

gib·bon /ˈgɪbən; ˈgɪbən/ *n* an animal like a monkey with long arms and no tail 長臂猿

gibe /dʒaɪb; dʒaɪb/ *n* (also 又作 **jibe**) a remark which makes someone look foolish 譏笑; 嘲弄

gib·lets /ˈdʒɪblɪts; ˈdʒɪbləts/ *n* [pl] the parts of a bird, such as the heart and LIVER, which are taken out before it is cooked〔禽類可食用的〕內臟, 雜碎

gid·dy /ˈgɪdi; ˈgɪdi/ *adj* **giddier, giddiest 1** feeling as though everything is moving round you and that you are going to fall 眩暈的: *I felt giddy just watching the children jumping up and down.* 我單單是看着孩子們跳上跳下就感到頭暈。 **2** [only before a noun 只用於名詞前] causing a feeling of unsteady movement or falling 令人眩暈的: *We looked down from a giddy height.* 我們從一個令人眩暈的高度朝下看。 –**giddily** *adv* –**giddiness** *n* [U]

☆**gift** /gɪft; gɪft/ *n* **1** something which you give

or receive as a present 禮物; 贈品: *a free gift* 免費的禮物 | *a gift shop* 禮品商店 **2** a natural ability to do something 天賦: *He has a gift* **for** *music.* 他有音樂天賦。 | *a gift* **for** *learning languages* 學習語言的天賦 **3** *infml* something very easy or very cheap 〖非正式〗輕而易舉的事; 便宜貨: *That last exam question was a gift!* 上次那道試題真簡單! | *At that price it's a gift!* 只賣這個價, 真太便宜了!

gift·ed /ˈgɪftɪd; 'gɪftᵻd/ *adj* **1** naturally very good at something 有天賦的: *a gifted painter* 有天賦的畫家 **2** unusually clever 極為聰明的: *Their daughter is very gifted.* 他們的女兒非常聰明。

gig /gɪg; gɪg/ *n infml* a performance of popular music or JAZZ 〖非正式〗(流行音樂或爵士音樂的)演奏會: *They're doing a gig in Glasgow next month.* 他們下個月在格拉斯哥開一場流行音樂會。

gi·gan·tic /dʒaɪˈɡæntɪk; dʒaɪ'gæntɪk/ *adj* unusually large in amount or size 巨大的; 龐大的: *a gigantic appetite* 特大的胃口 | *a gigantic waste of money* 對金錢的大量浪費 – **gigantically** /-kli; -kli/ *adv*

gig·gle /ˈgɪgl; 'gɪgəl/ *v* **giggled; giggling** [I] to laugh in a silly childish way 咯咯地傻笑

giggle *n*

gild /gɪld; gɪld/ *v* [T] to cover something with a thin coat of gold or gold paint 給〔某物〕鍍金[塗以金色]

gill¹ /gɪl; gɪl/ *n* an opening through which a fish breathes 鰓

gill² /dʒɪl; dʒɪl/ *n* a unit for measuring liquids equal to ¼ PINT or 0.142 of a LITRE 吉耳〔液量單位; 等於十分之一品脫或0.142升〕

gilt /gɪlt; gɪlt/ *n* [U] a thin covering of gold or gold paint 金(色)塗層: *All the paintings had elaborate gilt frames.* 所有的畫都有非常精巧的鍍金畫框。

gim·mick /ˈgɪmɪk; 'gɪmɪk/ *n infml* something unusual or clever, used to attract people 〖非正式〗(用以吸引人的)非同尋常的或設計巧妙的東西; 花招: *The picture of the pretty girl on the cover of the book is just a sales gimmick.* 封面上印的美女畫不過是個促銷的噱頭。 –**gimmicky** *adj*

gin /dʒɪn; dʒɪn/ *n* [C;U] a strong colourless alcoholic drink made from grain and certain berries 杜松子酒

gin·ger¹ /ˈdʒɪndʒə; 'dʒɪndʒɚ/ *n* [U] **1** a plant with a root which can be used in cooking to give a hot strong taste 薑 **2** an orange brown colour 紅褐色, 薑黃色: *ginger*

DESCRIBING PEOPLE 人的描述

Exercise 1 練習一

How would you describe yourself? Using words you know and words from the illustration, complete the table below. 你會怎樣描述你自己? 用你知道的詞彙和彩圖中的詞彙完成以下表格。

Hairstyle
Colour of hair
Body shape (build)
Colour of eyes
Complexion
Other details (beard, glasses etc.)

Can you fill in a similar table for someone you know well? It should be someone who you can't see at the moment. See how well you can describe the person. 你能為你熟悉的人填一張相似的表格嗎? 這個人應屬眼前你看不見的人。 看看你能描述得多好。

Hairstyle
Colour of hair
Body shape (build)
Colour of eyes
Complexion
Other details (beard, glasses etc.)

Exercise 2 練習二

Read this description of Mr Sampson 閱讀一下對桑普森先生的描述:

Mr Sampson is small and stout. He has short brown hair. He has bright blue eyes and a fair complexion. He has a brown moustache and he wears glasses.

Now write a description of the person you described in Exercise 1 in the same way. 現在用同樣的方法來描寫一下你在練習一中描述過的那個人。

Would you prefer to be taller, shorter, thinner, fatter? Would you prefer to have curlier/straighter hair? Write a description of the way you would like to look. 你喜歡更高些還是更矮些, 更瘦些還是更胖些? 你喜歡頭髮更卷些或更直些? 描寫一下你想讓自己變成的樣子。

---

fringe
【BrE 英式】/
bangs
【AmE 美式】
劉海

short hair
短髮

shoulder length hair
齊肩髮

parting (BrE【英式】)/
part (AmE【美式】)
(頭髮的)分縫

auburn hair
赤褐色的頭髮

sunglasses/dark glasses
太陽眼鏡;墨鏡

ginger (BrE【英式】)/
red (AmE【美式】) hair
紅褐色的頭髮

straight hair
直髮

fair
白皙的(皮膚)

blond hair
淡黃色的頭髮

long hair
長髮

brunette
深褐色
的頭髮

stocky
矮胖的;
粗壯的

petite
嬌小
玲瓏的

ponytail
馬尾辮

tanned
曬成棕褐色的

blonde hair
金色的頭髮

pale
臉色蒼白

slim
苗條的

brown hair
棕色的頭髮

receding hair
往後禿的頭髮

greying (BrE【英式】)/
graying (AmE【美式】) hair
花白的頭髮

grey
【英式】/
gray
【美式】
hair
白的頭髮

curly hair
鬈髮

bald
禿的

moustache
小鬍子

glasses
眼鏡

mousey hair
灰黃色的頭髮

white hair
白髮

black hair
黑髮

beard
鬍子
mp
髻

stout
肥胖的

stout
肥胖的

well built
體格健壯的

short
矮的

tall thin
高瘦的

plait (BrE【英式】)/
braid (AmE【美式】)
辮子

small
(年紀)小的

global warming
Heat from the sun reaches the earth, but pollution in the atmosphere prevents it escaping back into space, and the temperature of the atmosphere rises. This is also called 'The Greenhouse Effect'.

全球氣候變暖現象
太陽釋放出來的熱量到達地球，但大氣污染阻礙了熱量散發到太空，氣溫便隨之而升高。這也稱作"溫室效應"。

air pollution
Cars, factories, power stations and rubbish dumps all emit gases which add to air pollution.

空氣污染
汽車、工廠、發電站和垃圾堆都會釋放出一些污染空氣的氣體。

deforestation
Cutting down and burning trees destroys wildlife habitats and adds to air pollution.

濫伐森林
砍伐和焚燒森林破壞了野生物的生存環境，造成了空氣污染。

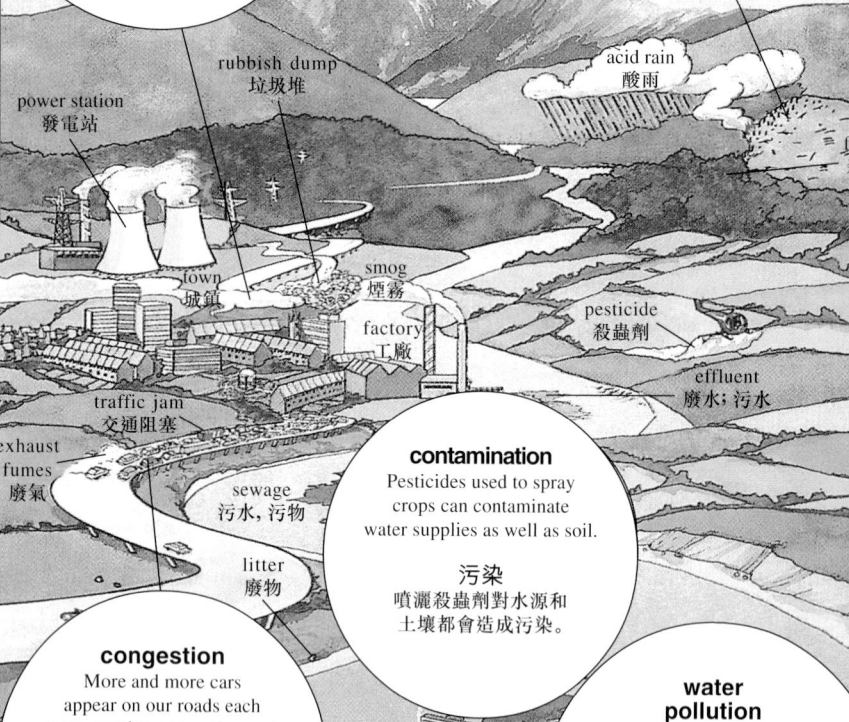

ozone lay
臭氧層

rubbish dump
垃圾堆

acid rain
酸雨

fo
森

power station
發電站

smog
煙霧

pesticide
殺蟲劑

factory
工廠

town
城鎮

effluent
廢水；污水

traffic jam
交通阻塞

exhaust fumes
廢氣

contamination
Pesticides used to spray crops can contaminate water supplies as well as soil.

污染
噴灑殺蟲劑對水源和土壤都會造成污染。

sewage
污水，污物

litter
廢物

congestion
More and more cars appear on our roads each year, causing congestion and pollution.

交通阻塞
每年都有越來越多的汽車駛到街上，造成道路擁塞和污染。

oil slick
浮油

oil tanker
運油船

water pollution
Oil spills, effluent from factories and sewage all add to pollution in our rivers and seas.

水污染
船隻漏出的油污、工廠排放的廢水和其他污水污物也會加劇河流和海洋的污染。

hair 紅褐色的頭髮 | *a ginger cat* 薑黃色的貓 –see picture on page 469 見 469 頁彩圖

ginger² *v*

ginger sth ↔ **up** *phr v* [T] to make something more exciting or active 使〔某事物〕更加振奮或活躍: *We need some more youngsters to ginger up the group.* 我們需要更多的年輕人來活躍這個集體的氣氛。

ginger ale /ˌ··'·/ *n* [U] a gassy non-alcoholic drink made with ginger and often mixed with other drinks 薑味汽水

ginger beer /ˌ··'·/ *n* [U] a gassy non-alcoholic drink with a strong taste, made with ginger 薑啤〔薑味較濃的汽水〕

gin·ger·ly /ˈdʒɪndʒəˈli; ˈdʒɪndʒəli/ *adv* carefully, slowly, and gently 小心地; 緩緩的; 輕輕地: *I reached out gingerly to touch the snake.* 我小心翼翼地伸出手去摸那條蛇。

ging·ham /ˈɡɪŋəm; ˈɡɪŋəm/ *n* [U] white and coloured cotton cloth which has a pattern of small squares 方格子棉布

gip·sy /ˈdʒɪpsɪ; ˈdʒɪpsi/ *n* **gipsies** (also 又作 **gypsy**) a member of a race of people who travel about in covered carts, and who earn money by telling the future, selling flowers, singing, etc. 吉卜賽人

gi·raffe /dʒəˈræf; dʒɪˈrɑːf/ *n* an African animal with a very long neck and legs, and yellow skin with brown spots 長頸鹿

gir·der /ˈɡɜːdə; ˈɡɜːdəʳ/ *n* a long strong thick piece of iron or steel, which supports a floor, roof, or part of a bridge 大樑

gir·dle /ˈɡɜːdl; ˈɡɜːdl/ *n* a tight undergarment for women, worn to make them look thinner 〔婦女的〕緊身褡

★★**girl** /ɡɜːl; ɡɜːl/ *n* **1** a female child 女孩; 姑娘: *There are more girls than boys in this school.* 這所學校的女生比男生多。 **2** a daughter 女兒: *I've got two boys and a girl.* 我有兩個兒子和一個女兒。 **3** a woman 女士: *I'm going out with the girls from work.* 我準備下班後和幾位女士一起出去。 | *We girls must stick together.* 我們婦女必須團結起來。 | *the girls in the office* 辦公室裡的女職員 **4** old fash **girlfriend** 〔老式〕女友: *He's got a new girl.* 他找了個新的女友。

> ■ **USAGE** 用法: Although the word **girl** is sometimes used to refer to an adult woman, some people find this offensive, especially if the speaker is a man. ☆儘管 **girl** 一詞有時用來指成年婦女, 但有人認為這種用法不禮貌; 尤其當講話人為男子的時候。

girl·friend /ˈɡɜːlˌfrɛnd; ˈɡɜːlfrɛnd/ *n* **1** a special

ENVIRONMENTAL PROBLEMS 環境問題

Use the words in the box to complete these two newspaper articles about en-vironmental problems. Write the number of the space beside each word. 用方框中的單詞完成以下兩篇有關環境問題的報刊文章。把空格處的數字寫在每個單詞旁邊。

pesticides	spray	chemicals
rain	mixture	smog
chimneys	power	clouds
forests	blood	

TALL CHIMNEYS CAUSE ACID RAIN

In December 1952, nearly four thousand people died in London. They died because they breathed a terrible ¹____ of smoke and fog which the Londoners called ²____. Scientists discovered that most of the smoke came from factories and ³____ stations. The government told them to build tall ⁴____ so the smoke would blow away. This solved the problem in London but it caused more problems elsewhere. The smoke went high up into the ⁵____ where the chemicals in the smoke mixed with water to make acid ⁶____. These blew across the English Channel and caused acid rain to fall in Scandinavia and Northern Europe. This acid rain destroyed buildings, ⁷____ and lakes in those countries.

CHEMICALS MAKE BLOOD-RED SEA

The valley of the River Po in Northern Italy is an important agricultural area. The farmers in this region produce a lot of very good food but they use a lot of chemicals to help them. They ⁸____ the fields with fertilisers and ⁹____ to feed and protect the crops. Unfortunately, when it rains, a lot of these ¹⁰____ are washed away from the earth into streams and eventually into the River Po. This river carries the chemicals into the Adriatic sea. In 1989, parts of the Adriatic sea became as red as ¹¹____. An algae, a type of sea weed, was growing in the rich mixture of chemicals in the water. Tourists didn't want to swim in red sea water and they cancelled their holidays.

G

★★ 最常用的 1000 字 ★ 最常用的 1001-2000 字 ★ 最常用的 2001-3000 字

female friend of a boy or man 女朋友: *He seems to have a new girlfriend every week.* 他似乎每個星期都有一個新的女朋友。**2** a woman's female friend 〔女子的〕女伴: *She's going out with some girlfriends tonight.* 她今晚和她的幾個女伴一起出去。

girl guide /ˌ·'·/ *n* (also 又作 **girl scout** /'··/ *AmE* 【美式】) a member of an association for girls, the **Girl Guides**, who take part in activities like camping, and learn to be practical and helpful 女童子軍 −compare 比較 SCOUT[1](2)

girl·hood /'ɡɜ·lhʊd; 'ɡɜːlhʊd/ *n* [C;U] the state or time of being a young girl 少女時代

girl·ish /'ɡɜ·lɪʃ; 'ɡɜːlɪʃ/ *adj* like a young girl 女孩子似的: *sounds of girlish laughter* 女孩子一樣的笑聲 −**girlishly** *adv* −**girlishness** *n* [U]

gi·ro /'dʒaɪro; 'dʒaɪərəʊ/ *n* [U] a system of banking run by a bank or post office, where payments can be made from one account to another 銀行〔郵局〕轉賬制度: *I'll pay by giro.* 我用銀行轉賬方式付款。

girth /ɡɜ·θ; ɡɜːθ/ *n fml* **1** [C;U] the distance around something round 圍長; 周長: *the girth of a tree* 樹幹的周長 **2** [C] a long piece of leather which is fastened tightly round a horse to keep the SADDLE on 〔馬的〕肚帶

gist /dʒɪst; dʒɪst/ *n* **the gist** the main points or general meaning 要點; 主旨: *I didn't understand everything, but I got the gist.* 我並不是處處都懂了, 而是明白了大意。

give[1] /ɡɪv; ɡɪv/ *v* **gave** /ɡev; ɡeɪv/, **given** /'ɡɪvn; 'ɡɪvn/, **giving 1** [T] to hand or pass something to someone, either for them to look at or use, or as a present 給; 交給; 遞給; 送給: *He picked up the book and gave it to me.* 他撿起書就交給了我。| *She gave me a gold bracelet for my birthday.* 她送我一個金手鐲作為生日禮物。

□ USEFUL PATTERNS 有用句型
to give something to someone; to give someone something

2 [T] to allow or cause someone to have something 允許〔使〕〔某人〕擁有〔某物〕: *Give me a chance to try the job.* 給我一次機會試試那份工作。| *This is a great opportunity that has been given to me.* 這是給我的一次非常好的機會。| *The news gave us a terrible shock.* 這消息令我們極為震驚。| *That child has given us a lot of trouble.* 那個孩子給我們帶來了許多麻煩。| *The noise gave me a headache.* 這噪音讓我頭疼。| *Give me a few more days, and I'll get the work finished.* 再多給我幾天, 我就能把工作做完。| *Can you give me some more information?* 你能給我再多提供些訊息嗎? | *Don't forget to give the message to John.* 別忘了把這口信帶給約翰。| *Let me give you a piece of advice.* 我來給你提個意見。

□ USEFUL PATTERNS 有用句型
to give someone something; to give something to someone

3 [T] to perform an action 做〔某一動作〕: *She gave a sudden cry of delight.* 她突然高興地叫了起來。| *She gave the child a smack.* 她給了那個孩子一巴掌。| *He gave me a long disapproving look.* 他不以為然地盯着我看了許久。| *He gave the door a push.* 他推了一下門。| *They gave an excellent performance.* 他們進行了一次出色的表演。| *He's giving us a talk about bee-keeping.* 他在給我們作關於養蜂的講話。| *She's giving a lecture to first-year students this evening.* 她今晚要給一年級學生講課。

□ USEFUL PATTERNS 有用句型
to give something; to give someone something; to give something to someone

4 [I] to bend, stretch, or break under the weight or pressure of something 〔在重量或壓力下〕彎曲; 伸長; 折斷; 坍塌: *The branch he was sitting on began to give.* 他坐着的那根樹枝開始彎曲。| *The leather will give a little bit as you wear the shoes.* 你穿着鞋子的時候, 鞋子的皮會被拉長一點。**5 give something some thought, give something your attention** to think about something or pay attention to it 考慮某事; 注意某事: *I'd like to give the matter a bit more thought.* 這件事情我想再考慮一下。| *I haven't been able to give my attention to the problem yet.* 到現在為止我還沒有注意過這個問題。**6 give a party** to have a party 舉行宴會〔聚會〕: *We're giving a big party on Saturday — would you like to come?* 星期六我們有個很大的聚會——你願意來嗎? **7 be given to understand/believe** to think that something is true because someone has told you that it is true 〔因有人告知某事而〕使相信: *I was given to understand that the job would involve a lot of travelling.* 我聽說做這個工作要常在外面跑。**8 give or take a certain amount** perhaps a certain amount more or less than the amount you have mentioned 〔比提到的數目〕可能多些, 也可能少些; 或多或少: *The test takes an hour, give or take a few minutes.* 考試要進行一個小時左右的時間。| *She must be sixty, give or take a few years.* 她肯定有六十歲左右了。**9 I give you that, I'll give you that** = I admit what you say 我承認你所說的話: *The hotel's not cheap, I give you that, but it's really good.* 這家旅館不便宜, 這我承認, 不過它確實是個好旅館。**10 give way: a** to yield in an argument 〔在爭論中〕讓步: *In the end my mother gave way and said that I could go to the concert.* 最終母親還是讓步了, 同意我去聽音樂會。| *He refused*

get /gɛt; get/ *v*

got /gɑt; gɒt/ (also 又作 **gotten** /'gɑtṇ; 'gɒtṇ/ *AmE*〖美式〗), **getting**

1 [T] to obtain something 得到; 獲得:
I must get a new car. 我得去買部新車。 | *Where did you get those shoes?* 你在哪裡買到那雙鞋的? | *I must get a birthday present for my mother.* 我必須給我母親買份生日禮物。 | *Shall I get you a drink?* 我給你拿杯飲料好不好?

> □ USEFUL PATTERNS 有用句型
> to get something for someone; to get someone something

2 [T] to receive or have something 收到; 擁有:
Did you get my letter? 你收到了我的信嗎? | *I got loads of presents for my birthday.* 我收到了許多生日禮物。 | *I don't get much time for reading.* 我沒有多少時間看書。 | *I can't remember when I first got the idea for the story.* 我記不起第一次想到要寫這個故事是甚麼時候了。 | *I don't want her to get the wrong impression.* 我不想讓她得到一個錯誤的印象。

3 [+ complement] to become 變成; 變得:
The food's getting cold. 食物變冷了。 | *She must have got lost.* 她必定是迷路了。 | *The economic situation seems to be getting worse.* 經濟形勢似乎變得越來越糟。 | *I started to get angry with him.* 我開始生他的氣。

4 [I; + adv/prep] to move somewhere or arrive somewhere 移動; 抵達〔某地〕:
She got onto the train. 她上了火車。 | *Hundreds of people were trying to get into the building.* 數以百計的人在試圖闖進那幢樓。 | *We finally got to London at eleven o'clock.* 我們終於在十一點抵達倫敦。 | *I'll have to leave early in the morning, and I won't get back until late at night.* 我一大早就要離開,而且要到深夜才能回來。 | *He was looking forward to getting home.* 他在盼望着回家。

5 [T; + adv/prep] to move something somewhere 把〔某物〕移至〔某處〕:
We couldn't get the table through the door. 我們無法把桌子從這扇門裡搬進去。

6 [T] to cause something to happen or be done 使〔某事〕發生; 做好〔某事〕:
She couldn't get the car started. 她無法把汽車發動起來。 | *We must get this job finished.* 我們必須做完這項工作。 | *I must get hair cut.* 我得去理髮。 | *Why don't you get those shoes mended?* 你為何不去修補一下那雙鞋?

7 [T] to suffer something unpleasant that happens to you 遭受:
She got her fingers caught in the door. 她的手指卡在門上。

8 [+ complement] to be the person that something happens to 受到; 為某事所發生的對象:
He got run over by a car. 他被車撞倒了。 | *She was hoping she might get promoted.* 她希望獲得提升。 | *Let's hope that nobody gets killed.* 我們希望不要出人命吧。

9 [T] to prepare a meal 準備〔飯菜〕:
Dad's just getting the dinner. 爸爸剛在準備晚餐。

10 [T] to catch an illness 患〔疾病〕:
I think I'm getting flu. 我想我患了流行性感冒。 | *She got some rare tropical disease.* 她得了某種罕見的熱帶地區的疾病。

11 [T] to go on a bus, train, or plane 登上〔公共汽車、火車或飛機〕:
Shall we walk or get the bus? 我們走路還是乘公共汽車去? | *I got a taxi to the station.* 我叫了輛計程車去火車站。

12 [T] to catch a person 抓住〔某人〕:
The police haven't managed to get the man who committed these murders. 警方仍未抓到這幾宗謀殺案的兇手。

13 [T] *infml* to understand something〖非正式〗理解; 明白:
Nobody got the joke. 沒有人明白那個笑話的含義。

G

14 [T] *infml* to annoy you 〔非正式〕使自己惱怒:
What gets me is the fact that he's so incompetent! 令我生氣的是他竟如此不稱職!
15 **get to do something** to succeed in doing something, or be allowed to do something 做成某事; 被允許做某事:
I hope I'll get to know him better in time. 我希望我到時能更加了解他。| *I never got to see the original documents.* 我一直沒有機會看到文件的原稿。
16 **get someone to do something** to ask or tell someone to do something 讓某人做某事:
If I can't manage to move it on my own, I'll get Sam to help me. 如果我自己搬不動, 我會讓山姆來幫我的。
17 **get doing something** to start doing something 開始做某事:
We'd better get walking if we want to make it by lunch time. 如果想在午飯時間趕到, 我們最好現在就走。| *Let's get going with the cleaning.* 我們開始打掃吧。
18 **be getting somewhere** to be making progress 取得進步:
I think we're finally getting somewhere with this project. 我覺得我們終於在這個項目上有了進展。| *I've spent a lot of time on this essay, but I don't seem to be getting anywhere.* 我在這篇論文上花了許多時間, 但似乎沒有甚麼進展。
19 **it's getting to me** = it is making me tired or annoyed 令我疲倦; 令我生氣:
At first all the teasing was a joke, but now it's really getting to me. 起初, 一切嘲弄不過是開個玩笑, 但現在卻真的要讓我生氣了。

get about *phr v*
[I]
1 to move or travel around 到處走動; 到處旅行:
I don't get about much these days. 這些日子我不大到處走動了。
2 (of news) to spread 〔消息〕傳播:
News of the affair soon got about. 關於這件事的消息很快就傳開了。

get sthg ↔**across** *phr v*
[T]
to explain something in a way that people can understand 使理解〔某事〕:
He's not very good at getting his ideas across to people. 他不善於把自己的觀點向別人講清楚。

get ahead *phr v*
[I]
to be successful in your job and so reach a high position 〔在工作上〕成功:
She's clever and ambitious, and determined to get ahead. 她聰明伶俐, 雄心勃勃, 決心在事業上獲得成功。

get along *phr v*
[I]
1 to advance or make progress with a job that you are doing 〔工作上〕取得進展; 進步:
How are you getting along with the decorating? 裝修的事情進展如何了?
2 to have a friendly relationship with someone 與〔某人〕保持良好的關係:
*I get along quite well **with** my family.* 我和家人的關係相當好。| *We don't get along very well.* 我們不大合得來。
3 **I must be getting along** = I must leave now 我現在必須走了

get around *phr v*
1 [I] to move or travel around 到處走動; 到處旅行:
I don't get around much these days. 這些日子我不大到處走動了。
2 [I] (of news) to spread 〔消息〕傳播:
News of the affair soon got around. 關於這件事的消息很快就傳開了。
3 [T **get around** sthg] to avoid or manage to deal with a difficulty 避免〔困難〕; 設法解決〔困難〕:

I'm sure we can get around this problem somehow. 我相信我們總有辦法解決這問題。

get around to sthg *phr v*
[T]
to find the time to do something 找時間來做〔某事〕:
I finally got around to writing to her. 我終於抽出時間給她寫了封信。

get at *phr v*
1 [T **get at** sthg] to manage to reach something 設法觸及〔某物〕:
Put the tools up on that shelf where the children can't get at them. 把工具放到架子上孩子們觸不着的地方。
2 [T **get at** sbdy] to say unkind things to someone 挖苦, 中傷:
Stop getting at me! 不要老是挖苦我!
3 what are getting at? = what do you mean? 你指的是甚麼?

get away *phr v*
[I]
to escape from a place or manage to leave it 逃離〔某地〕; 設法離開〔某地〕:
In the confusion one of the prisoners managed to get away. 混亂之中有個囚犯設法逃走了。 | *I'm sorry I'm late. I was in a meeting and couldn't get away.* 對不起我遲到了。我剛才在開會, 脫不開身。 | *We're hoping to get away on holiday this year.* 今年我們希望到外地去度假。 | *I didn't get away* **from** *the office until eight o'clock.* 我直到八點鐘才離開辦公室。

get away from sthg *phr v*
[T]
you can't get away from this fact = you must admit that this fact is true 你不得不承認這是事實。
The government can't get away from the fact that the Health Service needs more money. 政府不得不承認這一事實: 社會保健服務需要更多資金。

get away with sthg *phr v*
[T]
to do something bad and escape being punished for it 做壞事之後逃脫懲罰:
He stole thousands of pounds from the company — and got away with it! 他從公司裡偷走了數以千計的英鎊, 還居然蒙混過了關!

get back *phr v*
1 [I] to return, usually to your home 回來〔通常指回家〕:
I heard you were on holiday. When did you get back? 我聽說你去度假了。是甚麼時候回來的?
2 [I] to return to a state or a situation that you were in before 恢復到原來的狀態或形勢:
Labour are hoping to get back into power at the next election. 工黨正希望在下屆大選中重新執政。 | *I hope that things will soon get back to normal.* 我希望事情能很快恢復正常。
3 [I] to move away from something 離開〔某物〕:
The police shouted to the crowd to get back. 警察大聲喊着叫羣眾離開。
4 [T **get** sthg ↔ **back**] to have or be given something that you used to have 重新得到〔曾經擁有的某物〕:
I lent Jane one of my records and I haven't got it back yet. 我把我的一張唱片借給了珍, 到現在還沒有取回。
5 get back to someone to speak or write to someone later, especially in order to give them some information or tell them your decision about something 以後再答覆某人〔尤指把信息或決定告訴對方〕:

I'll think about the offer and get back to you this afternoon. 這個提議我考慮一下，下午給你回音。

get behind *phr v*
[I]
to fail to do your work on time 拖欠, 脫期
*I've got a bit behind **with** my work.* 我有些工作還未按時做完。

get by *phr v*
[I]
to manage to continue your way of life 勉強度日:
We don't have much money but we get by. 我們的錢不多，但仍可勉強過活。

get down *phr v*
1 [T **get** sthg ↔ **down**] to manage to swallow something 設法吞下, 咽下〔某物〕:
Try to get a bit of food down if you can. 如果可以的話，盡量吃點東西下去吧。
2 [T **get** sthg ↔ **down**] to record something in writing 寫下, 記下〔某物〕:
It's no use just coming to an informal agreement — you've got to get it down in writing. 只達成非正式的協議是沒有用的——你必須把它寫下來。
3 [T **get** sbdy ↔ **down**] to make you feel sad 使沮喪:
This dreadful weather's really getting me down. 這種討厭的天氣真使我受不了。

get down to sthg *phr v*
[T]
to begin doing something seriously 開始認真做〔某事〕:
Right, let's get down to work. 好, 我們開始認真投入工作吧。

get in *phr v*
1 [T] (of a bus, train, or plane) to arrive at a place 〔公共汽車、火車或飛機〕抵達〔某地〕:
The plane got in late. 飛機晚點到達。
2 [I] to arrive home 到家:
What time did you get in last night? 你昨晚是甚麼時候到家的?
3 [I] to be elected 當選:
I hope the Conservatives don't get in again at the next election. 我希望保守黨在下屆大選中不要再當選。
4 [T **get** sbdy ↔ **in**] to ask someone to come and help you do something in your home 請〔某人〕上門做某事:
I'll have to get a plumber in to look at the tap. 我得請個管子工來看一下那水龍頭。
5 [T **get** sthg ↔ **in**] to manage to say something during a discussion 在討論中插話:
I couldn't get a single word in at the meeting. 開會時我一句話也插不上。

get in on sthg *phr v*
[T]
to take part in something 參加〔某事〕:
It sounds like a very interesting project; I'd like to get in on it. 這聽起來倒是個很有意思的項目, 我願意加入。

get into *phr v*
1 [T **get into** sthg] to start doing something or experiencing something 開始做; 使經歷; 使陷入〔某事〕:
She wants to get into teaching. 她想去教書。 | *I don't want to get into trouble with the police.* 我不想在警察那裡惹麻煩。 | *We got into a conversation about gardening.* 我們開始談起了園藝。
2 [T **get** sbdy **into** sthg] to cause someone else to start doing something or experiencing something 使〔某人〕開始; 使〔某人〕陷入〔某事〕:
I hope I didn't make you late and get you into trouble. 我希望我沒有令你遲到而給

你添了麻煩。

3 what has got into you? = why are you behaving in such a strange way? 你怎麼會一反常態?
He used to be very friendly, but I don't know what's got into him recently. 他以前一直很友善, 但我不知道為甚麼他近來一反常態。

get off *phr v*
1 [I;T **get off** sthg] to climb down from something that you were on, such as a bus, train, bicycle, or horse 從〔公共汽車、火車、腳踏車或馬上〕下來:
The bus stopped and several people got off. 公共汽車停了, 有幾個人下車。| *I got off the train at Leeds.* 我在里茲下了火車。
2 [I;T **get off**] *infml* to leave work〔非正式〕下班:
I should be able to get off by five o'clock. 我應該能在五點鐘以前下班。| *When do you get off work today?* 你今天甚麼時候下班?
3 [T **get** sthg ↔ **off**] to remove a piece of clothing 脫掉〔衣服〕:
Give me time to get my coat off! 給我點時間, 讓我把外衣脫掉!
4 [I] to escape punishment for something bad that you have done〔做壞事後〕逃脫懲罰:
The boys got off with just a warning. 那些男孩只受警告沒受處罰。
5 [T **get** sbdy **off**] to help someone to escape punishment for something bad that they have done 使〔某人〕〔在做壞事後〕逃脫懲罰:
I had a good lawyer who managed to get me off with just a fine. 我有個好律師, 他讓我只是交了些罰款便沒事了。
6 get off! a phrase you use when you are telling someone not to touch something〔警告某人不要碰某物時所用的短語〕不要碰!

get off with sbdy *phr v*
[T]
to start a sexual relationship with someone 與〔某人〕發生性關係:
She got off with him at Julie's party. 她在朱莉的派對上搭上了他。

get on *phr v*
1 [I;T **get on** sthg] to climb onto something such as a bus, train, bicycle or horse 登上〔公共汽車、火車〕; 騎上〔腳踏車、馬〕:
The bus stopped and I got on. 公共汽車停了, 我上了車。| *She got on the bus.* 她上了公共汽車。
2 [I] to have a friendly relationship with someone 與〔某人〕保持友好的關係:
*Do you get on well **with** your parents?* 你與父母相處得好嗎? | *We've always got on very well.* 我們一直相處得很好。
3 [I] to continue doing something seriously〔認真地〕繼續做〔某事〕:
We'll have a quick break for lunch, then we'll get on. 我們會在午飯時稍稍休息, 然後繼續工作。| *I must get on **with** the cooking.* 我必須趕快去做菜。
4 [I] to succeed and reach a high position in your job 在工作上取得成功:
You'll have to work harder than this if you want to get on. 如果想要在工作上獲得成功, 你得比現在更加勤勉才行。
5 [T **get** sthg **on**] to put on a piece of clothing 穿上〔衣服〕:
Ask the children to get their shoes on. 叫孩子們把鞋穿上。
6 be getting on:
a to be getting quite old 上年紀:
She's getting on a bit now — she must be nearly seventy. 她現在年紀越來越大了——必定將近七十歲了。
b to be getting quite late 時間晚了:
Time's getting on, so we'd better hurry up. 時間已越來越晚了, 所以我們最好快一點。

get on for *phr v*
getting on for nearly a particular age, time, or amount 接近〔某一年紀、時間或數量〕:
She must be getting on for fifty now. 她現在必定快五十歲了。| *It was getting on for lunch time.* 快到午飯時間了。| *There were getting on for two hundred people there.*

那裡有近二百人。

get onto *phr v*

1 [T **get onto** sbdy] to speak or write to someone 與〔某人〕接觸:
I'll get onto our solicitor as soon as possible. 我準備盡快找我們的律師談一下。
2 [T **get onto** sthg] to begin to talk about something 開始談論〔某事〕:
I'll talk about the theory first, and then get onto the practical details. 我首先講一下理論,隨後再談實際的細節問題。
3 [T **get onto** sthg] to climb onto something such as a bus, train, bicycle, or horse 登上〔公共汽車、火車〕; 騎上〔腳踏車、馬〕:
I got onto the train and sat down. 我上了火車便坐了下來。

get out *phr v*

1 [T **get** sthg ↔ **out**] to take something from the container that it was in 從...拿出〔某物〕:
She opened her bag and got out a handkerchief. 她打開手提包,拿出了一條手帕。
2 [I;T **get** sbdy ↔ **out**] to leave a place or make someone else leave a place 離開〔某地〕; 使〔某人〕離開〔某地〕:
She told me to get out. 她叫我離開。 | *Hundreds of people are still stranded in the country, and we must get them out.* 這個國家有數以百計的人仍處在困境之中,我們必須把他們解脫出來。
3 [T **get** sthg ↔ **out**] to produce something 生產; 發表, 出版:
We've got to get that report out by next week. 下星期以前我們必須公佈那份報告。
4 [I] (of news) to become known 〔消息〕泄露:
This story mustn't get out. 這件事不得泄露出去。

get out of *phr v*

1 [T **get out of** sthg] to avoid doing something 避免〔做某事〕:
I'm supposed to be going to a meeting later, but I'm hoping to get out of it. 稍後我應該要去參加一個會議,但我希望不用去。
2 [T **get out of** sthg] to be able to leave something or stop doing something 能夠離開〔某事物〕; 能夠停止〔做某事〕:
I hope we'll be able to get out of this mess. 我希望我們能擺脫這種困境。 | *You must get out of the habit of calling me "darling" at work.* 你必須戒除在上班時叫我"親愛的"這個習慣。
3 [T **get** sthg **out of** sbdy] force someone to tell you something 強迫〔某人〕說出〔某事〕:
I couldn't get the man's name out of her. 我無法使她把那個男人的名字告訴我。
4 **get a lot out of something** to learn a lot from something, or enjoy it a lot 從...學到許多東西; 從...得到很大的享受:
I got a lot out of the course. 我從這課程中學到了很多東西。

get over *phr v*

1 [T **get over** sthg] to recover from something unpleasant such as an illness or a disappointment 從〔疾病或失望中〕恢復過來:
She still hasn't got over the shock of her mother's death. 她尚未從母親去世對她的打擊中恢復過來。
2 **can't get over something** to find something very surprising 覺得某事很令人吃驚:
I can't get over how rude he was to you. 他對你如此無禮,我感到十分吃驚。

get sthg **over with** *phr v*

[T]
to do something that is unpleasant because you want it to be done and finished 〔想〕把〔令人不快的事〕做完:
I want to get the operation over with as soon as possible. 我想盡快做完手術。

get round *phr v*

1 [T **get round** sthg] to avoid or manage to deal with a difficulty 避免〔困難〕; 設法

解決〔困難〕:
We should be able to get round this problem. 我們應該可以避免這個問題。
2 [T **get round** sbdy] to persuade someone to do what you want them to do 説服〔某人〕去做〔你希望他去做的事〕:
My father doesn't want to let us go but I'm sure I can get round him. 我父親不想讓我們去, 不過我有把握説服他。
3 [I] (of news) to spread 〔消息〕傳播:
News of the affair soon got round. 關於這件事的消息很快就傳開了。

get round to sthg *phr v*
[T]
to find the time to do something 找時間做〔某事〕:
I must get round to writing some letters. 我必須抽出時間來寫幾封信。

get through *phr v*
1 [I] to reach someone by telephone 打通電話:
I can't get through **to** *my office.* 我打不通辦公室的電話。
2 **get through to someone** to make someone understand what you are saying 使某人理解; 把...(向某人) 講清楚:
Whatever I say, I can't seem to get through to him. 不論我説甚麼, 我似乎都無法使他明白。
3 [T **get through** sthg] to do or finish something successfully 完成〔某事〕:
Of course you'll get through the exam! 你當然會順利通過考試的!
4 [T **get** sbdy **through** sthg] to help someone to do or finish something successfully 幫助〔某人〕完成〔某事〕:
good friends who got me through a difficult time 幫我渡過艱難時期的好朋友
5 [T **get through** sthg] to use a large amount of something 大量使用〔某物〕:
We got through loads of money on holiday. 度假時我們花了許多錢。

get together *phr v*
[I] to meet with people in order to discuss something for a social event 聚會, 相聚:
Let's get together for a drink one evening. 我們找天晚上聚在一起喝一杯。| *I got together* **with** *a few friends to plan the trip.* 我與幾個朋友聚在一起計劃這次旅行。

get up *phr v*
1 [I] to rise from a sitting or lying position, especially to rise from your bed after sleeping 坐起來; 站起來;〔尤指睡覺之後〕起牀:
What time do you usually get up in the morning? 你早上一般幾點起牀? | *He got up from his chair and walked to the window.* 他從椅子上站起身來走到窗前。
2 [T **get** sbdy **up**] to make someone rise from their bed 使〔某人〕起牀:
Can you go and get the children up? 你能去把孩子們叫起來嗎?
3 [I] (of the wind) to become stronger 〔風〕變得猛烈, 增強

get up to sthg *phr v*
1 to reach a particular place in a story or a piece of writing 讀到〔故事或文章的某處〕:
Have you got up to chapter five yet? 你讀到第五章了沒有?
2 to do something bad 做壞事:
She'd be furious if she knew what her children got up to. 如果她知道她的孩子做了甚麼壞事, 她必定會火冒三丈的。

to give way and admit that he was wrong. 他不肯讓步，堅決不認錯。**b** to break 破裂；折斷；坍塌: *The floor gave way under the weight.* 地板受重壓而裂開了。**c** to allow other vehicles to go before you when you are driving〔開車時〕讓路: *You have to give way to traffic coming from the left.* 你得給從左面開過來的車讓路。**d** to become less important or less useful than something else〔比起其他事物〕重要性減低；效用減低: *Steam trains gave way to electric ones.* 蒸汽火車被電氣火車所取代。**e** to allow yourself to show a feeling 流露〔感情〕: *He gave way to his grief.* 他顯出悲傷的樣子。

give away *phr v* **1** [T **give** sthg ↔ **away**] to give something to someone as a present, usually because you do not want it any more〔常因不再想要了而〕把〔某物〕贈送給〔某人〕: *I've given away most of the children's toys, now that they've grown up.* 孩子們都已長大，我就把他們大部分的玩具都送人了。**2** [T **give** sbdy ↔ **away**] to hand a woman to her husband at a wedding〔在婚禮中〕將新娘交給新郎: *She was given away by her father.* 她的父親把她交給了新郎。**3** [T **give** sthg ↔ **away**] to make known something that was secret 泄露〔祕密〕: *They were determined not to give their names away.* 他們決心不暴露自己的名字。**4 give the game away** to make known something that was secret 泄露祕密: *It was the fact that you laughed that gave the game away.* 你笑了出來，所以泄露了祕密。

give sthg ↔ **back** *phr v* [T] to return something to its owner 把〔某物〕還給〔其主人〕: *I'll give you your book back next week.* 我下星期把書還給你。| *Give me my pen back.* 把我的鋼筆還給我。| *I gave the records back to Julie.* 我把唱片還給了朱莉。

□ USEFUL PATTERNS 有用句型
to give something back to someone; to give someone something back; to give someone back something

give in *phr v* **1** [I] to yield in an argument or fight〔爭論或戰鬥中〕讓步；屈服: *We will not give in to threats or intimidation.* 我們決不屈服於威脅或恫嚇。**2** [T **give** sthg ↔ **in**] to hand something in to someone who has authority 把〔某物〕交給〔具有權威的人〕: *Give your examination papers in to the teacher at the front of the class.* 把你們的試卷交給在教室前面的那位老師。

give sthg ↔ **off** *phr v* [T] to send out a liquid, gas, or smell 流出〔液體〕；散發出〔氣體〕；發出〔氣味〕: *The dustbin was giving off a horrible smell.* 垃圾箱發出難聞的味道。

give out *phr v* **1** [T **give** sthg ↔ **out**] to give something to each of several people 分發: *She gave the books out to the children.* 她把書發給孩子們。**2** [I] to no longer

work properly 不再正常地工作: *The power's given out.* 斷電了。| *His strength gave out.* 他的力氣用盡了。

give over *phr v* [I;T **give over** doing sthg] *infml* to stop doing something〔非正式〕停止〔做某事〕: *Will you give over nagging me! 你別老是對着我嘮叨個沒完好不好？*

give up *phr v* **1** [T **give up** sthg] to stop having something or doing something 放棄〔某物〕；停止〔做某事〕: *I'm trying to give up smoking.* 我正在盡力戒煙。| *I gave up that idea a long time ago.* 很久以前我就放棄了那個念頭。| *They refused to give up hope.* 他們不肯放棄希望。| *He'll probably have to give up his job.* 他可能不得不放棄這個工作。**2** [T **give** sthg ↔ **up**] to allow someone else to have or use something 讓〔別人〕擁有〔使用〕〔某物〕: *Very few people will give their seat up to an elderly person.* 很少有人願意給老人讓座。**3** [I] to admit that you cannot do something and so stop trying to do it〔承認做不了某事而〕放棄努力: *She was determined to finish the task, and refused to give up.* 她決心完成這項任務，所以不肯放棄努力。**4** [T **give** sbdy ↔ **up**] to tell the police where someone is〔向警方〕告發〔某人〕: *His brother gave him up to the police.* 他的哥哥向警方告發了他。**5 give someone up for dead** to start believing that someone is dead 開始相信某人已死亡: *The search has been abandoned and the children have been given up for dead.* 人們放棄了搜索，認為孩子們已經死了。

give² *n* [U] the quality that something has of moving, bending, or stretching 彈力；彈性；伸展性: *Make sure that the shoes have enough give to allow your feet to move about comfortably.* 注意鞋一定要有足夠的伸展性，這樣你的腳走起路來才感覺舒服。

give-and-take /ˌ·· '·/ *n* [U] willingness of people involved in an argument to listen to each other and accept some of the other person's wishes〔爭執中的〕互相謙讓: *We can only settle this argument if there is a bit of give-and-take on both sides.* 只有我們雙方都作些讓步才能解決這一爭端。

give-a·way /ˈgɪvə,weɪ; ˈgɪvəweɪ/ *n* [sing] a remark, look, or object that tells people what was being hidden from them 泄露祕密的話語、表情或物品: *She tried to hide her feelings, but the tears in her eyes were a giveaway.* 她試圖掩飾自己的感情，但眼中的淚水表露出了她的真情。| *The packet of cigarettes on the table was a dead give-away.* 桌上的那包香煙把事情徹底暴露了。

giv·en¹ /ˈgɪvən; ˈgɪvn/ the past participle of GIVE ☆ GIVE 的過去分詞

given² *adj* **1** [only before a noun 只用於名詞前] decided on and stated 決定好的；規定的: *The work must be done within the given time.* 這工作必須在規定的時間內完成。**2** particular 某一；某個: *The problems of any* given society are unique. 任何一個社會的問題都是獨一無二的。**3 be given to** to be in the habit of 有...的習慣: *He's given to heavy drinking.* 他有酗酒的習慣。

given³ *prep* if you consider 如果考慮到: *Given that they're inexperienced, they've done a good job.* 在缺乏經驗的情況下，他們的這個工作已經算做得不錯了。

given name /'·· ·/ *n* the usual American word for〖美式〗= FIRST NAME

giz·zard /'gɪzəd; 'gɪzəd/ *n* the second stomach of a bird〖鳥的〗砂囊, 胗

gla·cial /'gleʃəl; 'gleɪʃəl/ *adj* **1** of ice or glaciers 冰的; 冰川〖河〗的: *glacial deposits* 冰川沉積 **2** relating to an ICE AGE 冰川時期的 **3** very unfriendly 很不友好的; 冷淡的: *He gave me a glacial smile.* 他對我冷冷地笑了一下。

gla·ci·er /'gleʃə; 'glæsɪər/ *n* a mass of ice which moves very slowly down a mountain valley 冰川; 冰河

*★**glad** /glæd; glæd/ *adj* **gladder, gladdest 1** [never before a noun 不能用於名詞前] pleased and happy 愉快的; 高興的: *I'm glad he's got the job.* 我很高興他找到了這份工作。| *I'm glad about her promotion.* 我很高興她得到了晉升。| *We were so glad to hear that your daughter's recovering from her illness.* 聽說你女兒的病好了，我們非常高興。**2 glad of** grateful for 對...感激: *I'd be glad of some help with the luggage.* 如能幫忙提一下行李，我將非常感謝。**3 be glad to do something** to be very willing to do something 很願意做某事 **4** [only before a noun 只用於名詞前] *old fash* bringing happiness〖老式〗令人高興的: *Have you heard the glad tidings?* 你聽到那個令人高興的消息了嗎？ —**gladness** *n* [U]

glad·den /'glædn; 'glædn/ *v* [T] to make someone happy 使〖某人〗高興: *The sight of his son running about after his long illness gladdened his father's heart.* 父親看見久病後的孩子在到處奔跑，心中非常高興。

glade /gled; gleɪd/ *n lit* an open space without trees in a wood or forest〖文〗林中的空地

glad·i·a·tor /'glædi,etə; 'glædɪeɪtər/ *n* an armed man who fought against men or wild animals in a public place to entertain people 鬥士; 鬥獸士〖在公共場合與人或野獸角鬥, 以供人娛樂〗

glad·ly /'glædlɪ; 'glædli/ *adv* very willingly or eagerly 高興地; 急切地: *I'll gladly come and help you.* 我很樂意來幫助你。

glam·o·rize /'glæməraɪz; 'glæməraɪz/ *v* **glamorized, glamorizing** (also 亦作 **glamorise** *BrE*〖英式〗) [T] to make something appear more attractive than it really is 使〖某物〗更吸引人

glam·o·rous /'glæmərəs; 'glæmərəs/ *adj* (also 又作 **glamourous**) having glamour 富有魅力的: *a glamorous job* 吸引人的工作 | *a glam-*

orous girl 富有魅力的姑娘 –**glamorously** *adv*

glam·our /'glæmə; 'glæmər/ *n* (**glamor** *AmE*〖美式〗) [U] a special quality of charm, beauty, and excitement 魅力: *the glamour of foreign countries* 異國的魅力 | *the glamour of a job in pop music* 流行音樂行業工作的魅力

*★**glance¹** /glæns; glɑːns/ *v* **glanced; glancing** [I; + adv/prep] to look for a very short time 瞥一眼: *He glanced at his watch.* 他看了一下手錶。| *I glanced round the room before I left.* 我略略環視了一下房間才離開。| *She glanced down the list of names.* 她大致看了一下名單。

glance off *phr v* [I;T **glance off** sthg] to hit lightly and move quickly off at an angle 擦過〖某物〗: *The ball glanced off his racket into the corner.* 球擦過他的拍子, 飛到角落裡去了。

> ■ USAGE 用法: Compare 比較 **glance** and 和 **glimpse**. The verb **glance** means "to look at something quickly" ☆ **glance** 指"迅速地看某物一眼": *As he spoke he glanced at his watch.* 他發言時, 看了一下手錶。**Glimpse** (or more commonly **catch a glimpse of**) means "to see by chance just for a moment" ☆ **glimpse**〔**catch a glimpse of** 更為常用〕指"偶然瞥見": *I glimpsed/caught a glimpse of his face as he disappeared round the corner.* 他消失在拐角處時, 我無意中瞥見了他的臉。

*★**glance²** *n* **1** a quick short look 一瞥: *One glance at his face told me he was ill.* 我只看了一眼他的臉, 就知道他病了。| *She cast a quick glance at her notes and began to speak.* 她瞥了一眼筆記, 然後開始發言。| *At first glance the essay looked quite good, but actually it was full of mistakes.* 乍一看, 這篇散文似乎不錯, 但實際上文章裡錯誤百出。**2 at a glance** at once 立刻: *She saw at a glance that he'd been crying.* 她一看就知道他哭過了。

glanc·ing /'glænsɪŋ; 'glɑːnsɪŋ/ *adj* [only before a noun 只用於名詞前] **glancing blow** a hit which slips to one side 偏斜的一擊: *He caught me with a glancing blow on the chin.* 他一拳斜着打中了我的下巴。

gland /glænd; glænd/ *n* an organ of your body which produces a liquid substance, either to be passed out of your body or into your blood 腺: *a sweat gland* 汗腺 – **glandular** /'glændʒələ; 'glændʒələr/ *adj*: *glandular fever* 腺熱

glare¹ /glɛr; gleər/ *v* **glared, glaring** [I] **1** to look at someone in an angry way 怒目而視: *They didn't fight, but stood there glaring at one another.* 他們沒有打起來, 只是站在那裡怒目相視。**2** to shine with a strong light, usually in a way that hurts your eyes 發出

G

強光〔通常是刺眼的光〕: *The sun glared down on them out of a cloudless sky.* 碧空萬里，耀眼的陽光直照在他們身上。| *The headlights glared through the darkness.* 車燈發出的強光穿過了黑暗。

glare² *n* **1** an angry unfriendly look 怒視: *I started to offer help, but he gave me a fierce glare so I stopped.* 我正要給他幫忙，但是他惡狠狠地瞪了我一眼，所以我也就算了。**2 the glare** a hard unpleasant effect given by a strong light 強光的不良刺激: *She put on her dark glasses to reduce the glare of the sun.* 她戴上了墨鏡，以減少太陽光對眼睛的刺激。**3 the glare of publicity** continuous attention from newspapers and television 報紙和電視所不斷給予的關注

glar·ing /'glɛrɪŋ; 'glɛərɪŋ/ *adj* **1** too bright 耀眼的; 刺目的: *glaring stage lights* 刺眼的舞台燈光 | *a glaring red* 耀眼的紅色 **2** very noticeable (used of something bad) 明顯的〔指壞事物〕: *The report is full of glaring errors.* 這份報告滿是明顯的錯誤。| *a glaring omission* 明顯的疏漏 –**glaringly** *adv*

★★**glass** /glæs; glɑːs/ *n* **1** [U] a hard easily-broken substance that lets light through and is used for windows and bottles 玻璃: *We'll have to get a new pane of glass for the window.* 我們得去買一塊新的窗玻璃。| *I've cut my hand on some broken glass.* 我的手被幾塊碎玻璃割破了。**2** [U] (also 又作 **glassware**) a collection of objects made of this 玻璃製品: *She collects china and glass.* 她收集瓷器和玻璃製品。**3** [C] a small glass container with no handle which you drink from 玻璃杯: *a whisky glass* 威士忌酒杯 | *He asked the waiter for a clean glass.* 他問侍應生要了一隻乾淨的酒杯。–see picture on page 244 見 244 頁彩圖 **4** [C] the drink in a glass container 玻璃杯裡的飲料: *I'd like a glass of wine, please.* 請給我來杯葡萄酒。| *Have one more glass before you go.* 你走之前再喝一杯。**5 the glass** *BrE* the measurement shown on a BAROMETER, an apparatus with a pointer which moves downwards when bad weather is coming 〔英式〕晴雨表的讀數: *The glass is falling; it's going to rain.* 晴雨表的水銀柱在下降; 天要下雨了。**6 glasses** [pl] two pieces of specially cut glass in a frame worn in front of your eyes to help you to see better 眼鏡: *I have to wear glasses for reading.* 看書時我必須戴眼鏡。| *I need a new pair of glasses.* 我需要一副新眼鏡。| *That man in the dark glasses is a film star.* 那個戴墨鏡的人是電影明星。–see picture on page 469 見 469 頁彩圖

glass fi·bre /ˌ· '···◄/ *n* (also 又作 **fibre glass**) [U] a substance made from very thin pieces of glass, used to keep out the cold or for making things like boats 玻璃纖維

glass·house /'glæs,haus; 'glɑːshaus/ *n BrE* a glass building used for growing plants in

〔英式〕溫室; 暖房

glass·ware /'glæs,wɛr; 'glɑːsweər/ *n* (also 又作 **glass**) [U] glass objects such as dishes and drinking glasses 玻璃製品〔器皿〕

glass·y /'glæsɪ; 'glɑːsi/ *adj* **glassier, glassiest 1** smooth and shining, like glass 〔如玻璃般〕光滑而明亮的 **2** with no expression or sign of life in the eyes 〔眼中〕無表情的; 無生氣的: *a glassy stare* 呆滯的凝視

glaze¹ /glez; gleɪz/ *v* **glazed, glazing** [T] **1** to fit glass into a frame 把玻璃裝入框架中: *a glazed door* 裝有玻璃的門 **2** to put a shiny surface on pots and bricks 給〔陶器或瓷磚〕上釉 **3** to put a little beaten egg or milk onto food to make it shine 將打過的雞蛋或牛奶加到食物上以增加色澤

glaze over *phr v* [I] (of eyes) to become dull and lifeless 〔眼神〕變呆滯: *His eyes glazed over and he fell back unconscious.* 他的目光變得呆滯，接着身體往後倒下便不省人事。

glaze² *n* a shiny surface on pots or food 釉; 食物上有光澤的表面

gla·zi·er /'glezɚ; 'gleɪziər/ *n* someone whose job is to fit glass into window frames 裝玻璃的工人

gleam¹ /glim; gliːm/ *n* **1** a small amount of gentle light 微光: *The gleam of the camp fire was a welcome sight.* 營火發出微光，一幅令人愉快的景象。**2** an expression on someone's face which you see only for a short time 〔表情的〕閃現: *a gleam of interest* 一絲感興趣的神情 | *a gleam of hope* 一線希望

gleam² *v* **1** to shine 閃光: *The river gleamed softly in the moonlight.* 河水在月光下閃着柔和的光。| *I polished the furniture until it gleamed.* 我把家具擦得錚亮。**2** to show an expression or feeling 閃現出〔神情或情感〕: *Her eyes gleamed with excitement.* 她的雙眼閃現出興奮之情。

glean /glin; gliːn/ *v* [T] *fml* to get information in small amounts and with difficulty 〔正式〕一點點地搜集〔信息〕: *She wasn't giving much away, but I managed to glean a few interesting facts.* 她沒有透露多少東西，但是我還是想辦法搜集到了一些令人感興趣的事實。

glee /gli; gliː/ *n* [U] joy and delight 歡喜; 高興: *The children laughed with glee.* 孩子們高興地笑了起來。–**gleeful** *adj* –**gleefully** *adv*

glen /glɛn; glen/ *n* a narrow mountain valley in Scotland 〔蘇格蘭的〕狹谷

glib /glɪb; glɪb/ *adj* **glibber, glibbest 1** good at speaking quickly so that you persuade other people, whether persuading the truth or not 能說會道的; 口齒伶俐的: *a glib salesman* 能說會道的推銷員 **2** spoken too easily to be true 油嘴滑舌的: *He's always ready with a glib excuse.* 他隨時都能編出好聽的藉口。–**glibly** *adv*

glide /glaɪd; glaɪd/ *v* **glided, gliding** [I + adv/prep] **1** to move forward noiselessly in a smooth, effortless way 滑行: *The boat glided over the river.* 船在河上滑行。| *The dancers glided across the floor.* 跳舞的人在地板上輕輕滑過。**2** to fly smoothly following air currents 滑翔 –**glide** *n*

glid·er /'glaɪdə; 'glaɪdəʳ/ *n* a plane without an engine 滑翔機

glid·ing /'glaɪdɪŋ; 'glaɪdɪŋ/ *n* [U] the sport of flying gliders 滑翔運動 –**gliding** *v* [only in progressive forms 只用於進行式]: *Have you ever been gliding?* 你參加過滑翔運動嗎？

glim·mer[1] /'glɪmə; 'glɪməʳ/ *v* [I] to give a very faint unsteady light 發出搖曳的微光: *The lights glimmered in the valley below.* 山谷底下的燈光閃閃爍爍，搖曳不定。

glimmer[2] *n* **1** a faint unsteady light 閃爍的微光 **2** a small uncertain sign 微弱的跡象[微兆]: *a glimmer of hope* 一線希望

glimpse[1] /glɪmps; glɪmps/ *v* **glimpsed, glimpsing** [T] to get a quick incomplete look at something or someone 瞥見〔某物或某人〕: *I just glimpsed her in the crowd and then she was gone.* 我在人羣中剛好瞥見了她，然後她就不見了。

glimpse[2] *n* a quick look at or incomplete view of something 一瞥; 瞥見: *I only caught a fleeting glimpse of the thief, so I can't describe him very well, I'm afraid.* 我只是瞥見過那個賊一眼，所以恐怕沒法把他詳細地描述出來。–see 見 GLANCE (USAGE用法)

glint[1] /glɪnt; glɪnt/ *v* [I] **1** to give out small flashes of light, like those from a metal surface 〔金屬表面般〕閃亮; 閃光: *The car park was full of shiny new cars glinting in the sun.* 停車場裡停滿了新車，在陽光下閃閃發光。**2** (of eyes) to show a particular feeling 〔眼睛〕閃現某種神情: *His bright blue eyes glinted with fury.* 他明亮的藍眼睛閃着怒火。

glint[2] *n* **1** a flash of light, like that from a hard shiny surface 〔金屬表面般的〕閃光: *I could see the glint of coins in her hand.* 我能看見她手裡的硬幣在閃閃發光。**2** a feeling clearly seen in someone's eyes 〔眼中某種神情的〕閃現: *There was a wicked glint in his eyes.* 他的眼中閃現出調皮的神情。

glis·ten /'glɪsn; 'glɪsən/ *v* [I] to shine with a lot of very small flashes as if from a wet surface 〔潮濕的表面般〕閃亮; 閃光: *Her eyes were glistening with tears.* 她的眼閃着淚光。| *The grass glistened with dew in the early morning sun.* 晨曦中，小草閃着晶瑩的露珠。

glit·ter[1] /'glɪtə; 'glɪtəʳ/ *v* [I] to shine brightly with flashes of light 閃耀; 閃亮: *Her diamond earrings glittered in the candlelight.* 她的鑽石耳環在燭光下閃閃發光。

glitter[2] *n* **1** [sing] a bright light, which seems to flash 閃爍的光輝; 閃亮: *the glitter of the sun on the waves* 浪花反射出的燦爛陽光 **2** [U] attractiveness and excitement 魅力; 興奮: *Beneath all the glitter, the fashion industry is a tough place to work in.* 時裝業表面上光彩迷人，但其實是個工作艱苦的行業。

glit·ter·ing /'glɪtərɪŋ; 'glɪtərɪŋ/ *adj* [only before a noun 只用於名詞前] **1** splendid or excellent 動人的; 華麗的; 優秀的: *a glittering performance* 動人的表演 | *a glittering career* 光輝的生涯 **2** shining 閃亮的: *a glittering diamond* 閃閃發亮的鑽石

gloat /gləʊt; gləʊt/ *v* [I] to be extremely pleased with your own success or someone else's bad luck 〔對自己成功〕得意揚揚; 〔對別人倒楣〕幸災樂禍: *He gloated over the failure of his competitors.* 他對競爭對手的失敗幸災樂禍。–**gloatingly** *adv*

***glo·bal** /'gləʊbl; 'gləʊbəl/ *adj* **1** of or concerning the whole world 全世界的; 全球的: *global warming* 全球變暖現象 | *events of global importance* 世界性重大的事件 **2** taking account of all possible considerations 全面的; 全盤考慮的: *The report takes a global view of the company's problems.* 該報告對公司的問題作了全面的論述。–**globally** *adv*

globe /gləʊb; gləʊb/ *n* **1** the Earth 地球: *She has travelled all over the globe.* 她周遊過全世界。**2** an object in the shape of a round ball 球體 **3** a round object with a map of the world on it which can be turned around on its base 地球儀

globe·trot·ter /'gləʊbˌtrɒtə; 'gləʊbtrɒtəʳ/ *n* someone who travels to a lot of different countries 周遊世界者

glob·u·lar /'glɒbjʊlə; 'glɒbjʊləʳ/ *adj* round like a ball 球形的

glob·ule /'glɒbjuːl; 'glɒbjuːl/ *n* a small drop of a liquid or something that has melted 一小滴〔液體或熔化物〕: *Wax fell from the candle in small globules.* 一滴滴的蠟從蠟燭上淌下來。

gloom /gluːm; gluːm/ *n* **1** a feeling of deep sadness or hopelessness 憂愁; 憂鬱: *The Stock Market crash filled them all with gloom.* 股票市場的暴跌令他們都憂心忡忡。| *She goes around spreading gloom and doom wherever she goes.* 她走到哪裡，就把悲觀和絕望的情緒傳到哪裡。**2** darkness that is not quite complete 昏暗; 陰暗: *We peered through the gloom, trying to see the road ahead.* 我們在昏暗之中試圖看清前面的路。

gloom·y /'gluːmɪ; 'gluːmi/ *adj* **gloomier, gloomiest 1** rather dark and unpleasant 陰暗的; 令人不快的: *a gloomy day* 陰暗的日子 | *a gloomy house* 陰暗的房子 **2** having or giving little hope or cheerfulness 沒有希望的; 抑鬱的: *Our future now seems gloomy.* 我們的未來現在看起來沒有甚麼希望。| *Cheer up – there's no need to look so gloomy.* 振作起來 — 沒必要看上去一副鬱鬱不樂的樣子。– **gloomily** *adv*

glo·ri·fy /'glɔːrəˌfaɪ; 'glɔːrɪˌfaɪ/ *v* **glorified, glorifying** [T] **1** to give glory or fame to something 頌揚〔某物〕; 給〔某物〕以光榮〔榮耀〕**2** to make something appear more important than it really is 使〔某物〕顯得更重要: *She was glorified in the press for her*

G

work with the poor. 新聞界美化了她為窮人所做的工作。 **–glorification** /ˌglɔːrəfəˈkeɪʃən; ˌglɔːrɪ̥fɪˈkeɪʃən/ *n* [U]

glo·ri·ous /ˈglɔːrɪəs; ˈglɔːriəs/ *adj* **1** having, or deserving, great fame and honour 光榮的; 榮耀的: *a glorious victory* 光榮的勝利 **2** beautiful and splendid 美麗的; 華麗的; 燦爛的: *glorious colours* 絢麗的色彩 | *a glorious day* 美好的一天 **3** *infml* very enjoyable 〔非正式〕宜人的; 愉快的: *We had a glorious time at the beach.* 我們在海濱玩得很愉快。 **– gloriously** *adv*

glo·ry¹ /ˈglɔːrɪ; ˈglɔːri/ *n* **glories 1** [U] great fame, honour, and admiration 光榮; 榮譽; 榮耀: *The soldiers died bravely on the battlefield, earning themselves everlasting glory.* 戰士們在戰場上英勇犧牲，為自己贏得了不朽的榮譽。 **2** [U] beautiful and splendid appearance 美麗的外表; 壯觀: *The bright moonlight lit up the castle in all its glory.* 明亮的月光使城堡顯得很壯觀。 **3 the glory of, the glories of** the thing or things that are especially beautiful or give cause for pride 特別美麗的事物; 引以自豪的事物: *Receiving a knighthood from the Queen was the crowning glory of his career.* 被女王授予騎士頭銜是他一生中的無上光榮。 | *the glories of Paris* 巴黎的驕傲 **4** [U] *fml* praise, honour, and thanks 〔正式〕讚頌; 榮耀; 感謝: *Glory be to God!* 榮耀歸於上帝!

glo·ry² *v* **gloried, glorying**

glory in sthg *phr v* [T] to enjoy something very much 因〔某事〕而喜悅: *They gloried in their new freedom.* 他們為自己獲得新的自由而喜悅。

gloss¹ /glɒs; glɒs/ *n* **1** [sing;U] a bright shine on a smooth surface 〔光滑平面上的〕光澤; 光亮: *gloss paint* 光漆 | *the gloss on her hair* 她頭髮的光澤 **2** [sing;U] a pleasant appearance which hides the truth 虛飾; 假象: *What is there beneath the gloss?* 假象後隱藏的是甚麼? **3** [C] an explanation of a written word or idea 詞語或觀點的解釋; 註釋

gloss² *v* [T] to provide an explanation of a difficult word or idea 解釋〔詞語或難懂的觀點〕: *Textbooks sometimes gloss difficult expressions.* 課本有時對難以理解的辭句進行註解。

gloss over sthg *phr v* [T] to write or talk of something favourably or quickly to hide its faults 〔書寫或講話時〕辯解; 掩飾: *The company has tried to gloss over its recent losses in its annual report.* 公司企圖在年報裡掩飾其最近的虧損。

glos·sa·ry /ˈglɒsərɪ; ˈglɒsəri/ *n* **glossaries** a list of explanations of words, especially unusual ones, at the end of a book 〔尤指書尾的〕詞彙表; 難字匯編

gloss·y /ˈglɒsɪ; ˈglɒsi/ *adj* **glossier, glossiest 1** shiny and smooth 有光澤的; 光滑的: *Our cat has glossy black fur.* 我們的貓長着光滑的黑毛。 **2 glossy magazine** a magazine

printed on good quality shiny paper with coloured pictures 用有光紙印刷的雜誌

glove /glʌv; glʌv/ *n* a piece of clothing worn on your hand, with separate parts for the thumb and each finger 〔分指的〕手套 –see picture on page 210 見 210 頁彩圖

glow¹ /gloʊ; gləʊ/ *v* [I] **1** to shine with a dull steady light 發光; 發紅: *The blacksmith heated the iron bar till it glowed.* 鐵匠把鐵棒一直燒到發紅。 | *Their cigarettes glowed in the darkness.* 他們的香煙在黑暗中發光。 **2** to look warm or red in the face, because of hard work or strong feelings 〔由於用力或激動而〕臉色發紅〔發熱〕: *She was glowing with embarrassment.* 她的臉變得通紅。 | *Her cheeks glowed.* 她的臉頰紅了。 **3** to look bright and colourful 光彩奪目: *The hills glowed in the evening sunlight.* 羣山在落日餘暉中蕩漾着光輝。

glow² *n* [sing] **1** a soft warm light 光亮; 光輝: *There was a dull red glow in the night sky showing us where the city lay.* 夜色中隱約的亮光給我們展示了城市的方位。 **2** a red colour on someone's face after exercise or because of good health 〔運動後或由於健康而出現的〕滿面的紅光: *the rosy glow of health* 容光煥發 **3** a strong good feeling 強烈的感情: *a glow of satisfaction* 心滿意足 | *I felt a glow of happiness at the news.* 聽到這消息我感到特別高興。

glow·er /ˈglaʊə; ˈglaʊəʳ/ *v* [I] to look at someone with an angry expression 怒視〔某人〕: *He just glowered at me and went on eating.* 他只是瞪了我一眼，然後接着吃飯。

glow·ing /ˈgloʊɪŋ; ˈgləʊɪŋ/ *adj* very favourable 非常有利的: *We have always received glowing reports from his teachers.* 我們一直從他的諸位老師那裡收到對他很有利的報告。

glow·worm /ˈ· ·/ *n* an insect which gives out a greenish light from the end of its tail 螢火蟲

glu·cose /ˈglukoʊs; ˈgluːkəʊs/ *n* [U] a natural form of sugar found in fruit 葡萄糖

glue¹ /glu; gluː/ *n* [U] a sticky substance used for joining things together 膠; 膠水 **– gluey** *adj*

glue² *v* **glued, gluing** *or* **glueing** [T] **1** to join things together with glue 用膠水黏合: *She glued the two pieces together again.* 她把那兩片東西重新黏合起來。 **2 glued to something** watching something with such interest and attention that you are unwilling to stop 集中精力注視某事物: *He sat glued to the television all afternoon.* 他整個下午都坐着看電視。

glue-snif·fing /ˈ· ˈ·/ *n* [U] the harmful breathing in of fumes (FUME) of glue to produce a state of changed consciousness 〔使產生迷幻效果的〕吸膠毒

glum /glʌm; glʌm/ *adj* **-mm-** sad 悶悶不樂的: *Why are you looking so glum?* 你為甚麼看上

G

去如此悶悶不樂?–**glumly** *adv*

glut /glʌt; glʌt/ *n* [sing] a larger supply than is necessary 供應過剩: *a glut of eggs on the market* 市場上雞蛋供應過剩

glu·ti·nous /'glutɪnəs; 'gluːtɬnəs/ *adj* sticky 黏的: *a bowl of glutinous rice* 一碗糯米

glut·ton /'glʌtn; 'glʌtn/ *n* **1** a person who frequently eats too much 經常暴食者 **2 a glutton for punishment** *infml* a person who is always ready to do or accept more of something hard or unpleasant 〔非正式〕能吃苦耐勞和任勞任怨的人

glut·ton·y /'glʌtni; 'glʌtəni/ *n* [U] the habit of eating too much 貪食; 暴食 –**gluttonous** *adj*

gly·ce·rine /'glɪsrɪn; 'glɪsərɪn/ *n* (also 又作 **glycerin** *AmE* 【美式】) [U] a sticky colourless liquid used in making soap, medicines, and explosives 甘油; 丙三醇

gm *n* an abbreviation for 〔縮〕= GRAMS 克

GMT /,dʒi ɛm 'ti; ,dʒiː em 'tiː/ *n* [U] an abbreviation for 〔縮〕= **Greenwich Mean Time**

gnarled /nɑrld; nɑːld/ *adj* rough and twisted, with hard lumps, especially as a result of old age or hard work 粗糙而有硬節的〔尤指由於年老或幹粗活所致〕: *a gnarled tree trunk* 瘤子瘤的樹幹 | *the old man's gnarled hands* 那個老人粗糙的雙手

gnash /næʃ; næʃ/ *v* [T] **gnash your teeth** to make a noise with your teeth by biting hard, especially because you are angry or in pain 咬牙切齒〔尤指由於憤怒或疼痛〕

gnat /næt; næt/ *n* a small flying insect that bites 蚋; 蚊; 蠓

gnaw /nɔ; nɔː/ *v* **1** [I;T] to keep biting on something, often until you make a hole 咬; 啃: *The bones are for the dog to gnaw on.* 這些骨頭是給狗啃的。| *Rats have gnawed their way through the wall.* 老鼠咬穿了牆壁。**2 gnaw (away) at someone** to worry someone over a period of time 〔在一段時間內〕令某人憂心忡忡

gnaw·ing /'nɔɪŋ; 'nɔːɪŋ/ *adj* [only before a noun 只用於名詞前] worrying you over a period of time 令人苦惱的: *gnawing hunger* 令人痛苦的饑餓

gnome /nom; nəʊm/ *n* **1** a little old man in children's stories who lives under the ground and often guards stores of gold 〔童話中在地下守護黃金的〕土地神 **2** a decorative figure of one of these 守護神塑像: *a garden gnome.* 花園裡的地神像

go[1] /go; gəʊ/ *v* **went** /wɛnt; went/, **gone** /gɔn; gɒn/, **going 1** [I + adv/prep] to move towards a place, usually away from the place where the speaker is 去〔尤指離開說話者所在之處〕: *We went to France for our holidays.* 我們去法國度假了。| *She went into the kitchen.* 她走進廚房。| *We went by bus.* 我們坐公共汽車去的。| *This car's going too fast.* 這輛車開得太快了。| *His hand went to*

his pocket. 他的手伸進了口袋。**2** [I] to leave a place 離開〔某地〕: *It's late; I must be going.* 時間不早了, 我必須走了。| *The train goes in 15 minutes.* 火車十五分鐘後開。**3** [I] to travel somewhere in order to do something 去〔某地〕做某事: *They've gone shopping.* 他們購物去了。| *Let's go fishing.* 我們去釣魚吧。| *He had gone to buy a newspaper.* 他去買了張報紙。| *She's gone for a walk.* 她出去散步了。**4** [I + adv/prep] to reach as far as a particular place, or lead to a particular place 通到〔某地〕; 延伸到〔某地〕: *Does this road go to the station?* 這條路通到車站嗎? | *The valley goes from east to west.* 這個山谷從東向西延伸。| *Some trees have roots that go very deep.* 有些樹木的根紮得很深。| *Where does this path go?* 這條路通往哪裡? **5** [I + adv/prep] to be placed somewhere, or fit there 放於〔某處〕; 適合於〔某處〕: *"Where do the knives go?" "In this drawer."* "這些小刀放在哪裡?" "放在這個抽雁裡。" | *The bottles won't all go in the box.* 這個箱子裝不下所有的瓶子。**6** [+ complement] to become 變得: *Her hair's going grey.* 她的頭髮正在變白。| *She went red in the face and ran out of the room.* 她臉一紅, 跑出了房間。| *He's gone blind.* 他變瞎了。| *I think I'm going mad.* 我覺得我快要發瘋了。–see 見 BECOME (USAGE用法) **7** [+ complement] to be or remain in a particular state 處於〔保持〕某種狀態〕: *When the crops fail, the people go hungry.* 莊稼欠收, 大家就要挨餓。| *Her complaints went unnoticed.* 她的抱怨未被人注意。| *The murderer went unpunished.* 兇手未受到懲罰。**8** [I] (of a machine) to work properly 〔機器〕正常運轉: *The car won't go.* 汽車開不動了。| *The clock's stopped and I can't get it to go again.* 鐘停了, 我沒法讓它再走。**9** [I] to be sold 售出: *In the end, the painting went for £2000.* 最後, 這幅畫賣了二千英鎊。**10** [I] to become weakened and not work properly any more. 變得虛弱而無法正常運轉〔工作〕: *I had a bad cold and my voice went.* 我患了重感冒, 嗓子啞了。| *These shoes are very old and the soles are going.* 這雙鞋很舊, 鞋底快掉了。| *Her sight is going.* 她的視力越來越差。**11** [T] to make a particular sound or have particular words 發出某種聲音; 具有某種字眼: *Ducks go "quack".* 鴨子"嘎嘎"叫。| *How does that song go?* 那首歌怎麼唱? **12** [I] to look or taste nice together 〔外觀或味道〕相配: *Those colours don't go together very well.* 那些顏色不十分相配。| *Do you think this hat will go with my red dress?* 你覺得這頂帽子和我的紅裙子配在一起協調嗎? | *Does red wine go with chicken?* 吃雞的時候, 喝紅葡萄酒是否合適? **13 be going to** a phrase you use to say that something will happen in the future 將要〔表示在將來會發生某事〕: *I think it's going to rain.* 我覺得天快要下雨了。| *She's going to have a baby.* 她

要生孩子了。│ *I'm going to apply for a new job.* 我準備去申請一個新的工作。**14 get going** to start doing something 開始〔做某事〕: *Come on, let's get going.* 快點，我們開始吧。**15 keep going** to keep doing something although it is difficult〔儘管很困難，仍然〕繼續〔做某事〕: *I was determined to keep going and finish the race.* 我決心堅持跑完比賽全程。**16 be gone** to have left or disappeared 離開了；消失了: *When I turned round she was gone.* 我轉過身發覺她不見了。│ *Those days are gone now.* 那些日子一去不復返了。**17 go and** to go somewhere in order to do something 到〔某處〕去做〔某事〕: *Go and see if there's anyone at the door.* 去看看門口是否有人。**18 go to someone** to be given to someone 給某人: *The first prize went to the team from Manchester.* 曼徹斯特隊獲得了頭獎。│ *The job went to a local woman.* 這個工作給了當地的一位女士。**19 go well** to be successful 成功: *Business is going very well at the moment.* 現在的生意很興隆。│ *My talk went very well.* 我的講話很成功。[RELATED PHRASE 相關詞組 **go badly**] **20 to go** remaining 剩下；餘下: *There are just three weeks to go until Christmas.* 只有三個星期就到聖誕節了。

go about *phr v* **1** [I] to spend a lot of time with someone, often going to a lot of different places with them 常與某人一起出去: *She goes about **with** a group of school friends.* 她常與一羣校友一起出去。**2** [I] (of a disease) to spread〔疾病〕傳播；蔓延: *Chicken pox seems to be going about at the moment.* 目前水痘似乎在到處蔓延。**3 go about doing something** to begin working at something 開始做某事: *I'm not quite sure how to go about mending a clock.* 我對修理鐘沒有多大的把握。

go after sthg *phr v* [T] to try to get something 盡力得到〔某物〕: *He's gone after a job in the civil service.* 他爭取在政府部門謀個職位。

go against *phr v* **1** [T **go against** sthg] to be in opposition to something, or do something that is in opposition to something 與〔某物〕相反；違背〔某物〕: *I couldn't work for that company – it would go against all my principles.* 我不能為那家公司做事，因為這違背我所有的原則。│ *She went against her mother's wishes and became a dancer.* 她違背母親的意願，當了舞蹈員。**2** [T **go against** sbdy] to be unfavourable to someone 對〔某人〕不利: *Public opinion is going against us.* 輿論將對我們不利。│ *The case may go against you.* 這個案子可能對你不利。

go ahead *phr v* [I] **1** to do something that you had planned to do 做計劃中的事情: *We decided to go ahead **with** our building plans.* 我們決定實施我們的建築計劃。**2** to take place as planned〔按計劃〕發生: *We all hope that the carnival will go ahead.* 我們都希望狂

歡節能如期舉行。

go along with sbdy/sthg *phr v* [T] to agree with someone or something 同意〔某人或某事〕: *They were quite happy to go along with our suggestion.* 他們欣然同意我們的建議。│ *I'll go along with you.* 我同意你的意見。

go around *phr v* **1** [I;T **go around** sthg] to spread or be told to a lot of people 流傳；傳播: *There are a lot of colds going around at the moment.* 現在感冒正到處流行。│ *There's a really funny joke going around the office.* 辦公室裡在傳一個非常滑稽的笑話。**2** [I] to spend a lot of time with someone, often going to a lot of different places with them 常跟某人一起出去: *Why do you go around **with** such strange people?* 你為甚麼和這些怪人混在一起？│ *Those two always go around together.* 他們兩個總是形影不離。**3** [I] to be enough for everyone 足夠分配給每個人: *Are there enough chairs to go around?* 有沒有足夠的椅子給大家坐？

go back *phr v* [I] **1** to return 回去: *I left Scotland fifty years ago and I don't think I'll ever go back.* 我五十年前離開了蘇格蘭，我想我以後不會再回去了。│ *I'd like to go back to what the chairman said earlier.* 我想再回到主席先前所說的話題。**2 go back to something** to start doing something again 重新開始做某事: *She went back to her work.* 她重新去上班。│ *He went back to cleaning the window.* 他再一次去擦窗子。**3** to reach backwards in time 追溯: *My family goes back to the 18th century.* 我的家史可追溯到十八世紀。

go back on sthg *phr v* [T] to fail to keep a promise or an agreement 違背〔諾言或協議〕: *I won't go back on my promise.* 我決不違背諾言。

go by *phr v* **1** [I] to move past someone or something 經過〔某人或某物〕: *A car went by.* 一輛汽車從旁邊開過。**2** [I] (of time) to pass〔時間〕逝去: *Two years went by before he got another letter from her.* 兩年過去了他才收到她的另外一封信。**3** [T **go by** sthg] to act or make a judgement according to a particular thing 依照〔某物〕行動；依照〔某物〕作出判斷: *He always goes by the rules.* 他向來按規定行事。│ *You can't go by what he says.* 你不能按他說的去做。

go down *phr v* [T] **1** to decrease 減少: *The standard of work has gone down.* 工作標準降低了。│ *Inflation seems to be going down.* 通貨膨脹似乎在下降。**2** to become less swollen 消腫: *That tyre's going down.* 那隻輪胎癟了下去。**3 a ship/boat goes down** = a ship or boat sinks 輪船或小艇沉沒: *Three boats went down in the Channel last night.* 昨夜有三艘船在英吉利海峽沉沒。**4 the sun goes down** = the sun disappears from the sky at the end of the day 太陽落山 **5 go down well** to be accepted 被接受: *His* *speech went down very well.* 他的演講很受歡迎。[RELATED PHRASE 相關詞組 **go down badly**] **6 go down in history** to be recorded as being very important〔作為重要事件〕載入史冊: *This day will go down in history.* 這一天將載入史冊。

go down with sthg *phr v* [T] to catch an illness 患〔病〕: *He's gone down with flu.* 他得了流感。

go for *phr v* **1** [T **go for** sbdy] to attack someone 攻擊〔某人〕: *She went for him with a knife.* 她手持小刀向他衝了上去。**2** [T **go for** sthg] to try to get something 試圖得到〔某物〕: *I've decided to go for the job at the BBC.* 我已決定在英國廣播公司裡謀某個職位。**3** [T **go for** sbdy/sthg] to like or be attracted to someone or something 喜歡〔某物或某人〕; 為〔某物或某人〕所吸引: *I don't really go for modern music.* 我不太喜歡現代音樂。| *I don't go for men like him.* 我不喜歡他那樣的男人。**4** [T **go for** sthg] to choose something 選擇〔某物〕: *She always tends to go for brightly-coloured clothes.* 她總是喜歡挑選顏色鮮豔的衣服。**5** [T **go for** sbdy/sthg] to be true for a particular person or thing as well as for other people or things 通用於〔某人或某物〕: *I think this report is very badly done, and that goes for all the other work done in this office.* 我認為這份報告寫得很差，這個辦公室裡的所有其他工作也一樣。

go in for sthg *phr v* [T] **1** to take part in something 參與〔某事〕: *I didn't go in for the crossword competition this year.* 今年我沒有參加縱橫字謎比賽。**2** to make a habit of doing something 愛好〔某事〕: *I don't go in for sport very much.* 我不太喜歡運動。| *I've never really gone in for dancing.* 我從來沒有真正喜歡過跳舞。

go into sthg *phr v* [T] **1** to start doing something as your job 從事〔某職業〕: *She decided to go into politics.* 她決定從政。| *I'd like to go into journalism.* 我想從事新聞工作。**2** to examine or describe something in detail 仔細檢查〔某物〕; 詳細描述〔某物〕: *I don't want to go into all the details of this case.* 此案的細節問題我不打算全部都談。| *The book goes into all the complexities of English grammar.* 本書論述了英語文法中的所有複雜問題。

go off *phr v* **1** [I] to explode 爆炸: *A bomb went off in central London this morning.* 一枚炸彈今晨在倫敦市中心爆炸。**2** [I] to ring or sound loudly〔鈴〕大聲響: *The fire alarm went off.* 火警大聲響了起來。**3** [I] (of food) to go bad〔食物〕變壞: *The milk's gone off.* 牛奶變壞了。**4** [I] to stop operating 中斷; 停止運行: *The heating goes off at night.* 夜裡暖氣停了。**5** [T **go off** sbdy/sthg] to stop liking someone or something 不再喜歡〔某人或某物〕: *I've gone off coffee.* 我不再喜歡喝咖啡了。| *I've gone off the idea of sharing a house with friends.* 我不再想和朋友們共住一

間房了。**6 go off well** (of an event) to be successful〔事情〕成功: *The conference went off very well.* 會議非常成功。[RELATED PHRASE 相關詞組 **go off badly**]

go off with sthg *phr v* [T] to take away something that belongs to someone else 拿走〔別人的東西〕: *Someone's gone off with my pen.* 有人把我的鋼筆拿走了。

go on *phr v* **1** [I] to take place or happen 發生: *What's going on here?* 這裡出甚麼事了? | *There was a party going on next door.* 隔壁房間在舉行宴會。**2 go on with something, go on doing something** to continue doing something 繼續做某事: *He went on talking even though no one was listening.* 儘管沒人在聽，他還是繼續說着。| *She went on with her work.* 她繼續做她的工作。**3 go on to do something** to do something later 接着做某事: *She did her degree and went on to become a university lecturer.* 她得到了學位，然後當了一名大學講師。**4** [I] (of time) to pass〔時間〕過去: *As the day went on, it became hotter.* 那天的天氣越來越熱。**5** [I] to come into operation and start working 開始運轉〔運行〕: *The lights went on at six o'clock.* 六點鐘的時候燈亮了。**6** [I] to keep talking or complaining about the same thing 反覆談論〔抱怨〕〔一件事〕: *He keeps going on about his diet.* 他一直在談論他的飲食問題。| *She's been going on at me all morning!* 她整個上午都和我嘮叨個沒完! **7** [T **go on** sthg] to use a piece of information in order to understand something or prove something 利用某一情報理解或證明〔某事〕: *As yet, the police have very little to go on.* 到目前為止，警方所得到的消息很少，無法進一步證實。**8 Go on!** a phrase you use when you want to encourage someone to do something 來吧!〔用於鼓勵某人做某事〕: *Go on, try it.* 來吧，試試看。**9 to be going on with, to go on with** for the moment 目前; 暫時: *Here's £10. That should be enough to be going on with.* 這裡有十英鎊。這些錢應該暫時夠用了。

go out *phr v* [I] **1** to leave a house or other building 離開〔房間或建築物〕: *She's gone out for a walk.* 她出去散步了。| *We don't go out very much in the evenings.* 晚間我們不大外出。**2** to spend time regularly with someone of the opposite sex 與異性常在一起: *Are you still going out* **with** *Graham?* 你還和格雷姆交往嗎? | *They've been going out* **together** *for years.* 他們談情說愛已有多年了。**3** (of a fire) to stop burning〔火〕熄滅: *The fire's gone out again.* 火又滅了。**4** (of a light) to stop shining〔燈〕熄滅: *Suddenly the kitchen light went out.* 廚房燈突然熄滅了。**5** to be no longer fashionable or popular 不再流行: *Clogs went out years ago!* 木屐在許多年前就不流行了!

go over sthg *phr v* [T] to look at something or examine it in detail 仔細查看〔某物〕: *I need to go over the accounts again to*

G

see if they're accurate. 我需要仔細檢查一下賬目看看它們是否準確。 **2** to explain something in detail 詳細解釋〔某物〕: *I'll go over this point again later.* 我過會兒再來解釋這一點。

go over to sthg *phr v* [T] to change your mind and join a new religion or political party 改變〔宗教信仰、政治派別〕: *She went over to the Republicans after their election victory.* 共和黨選舉獲勝後, 她加入了該黨。

go round *phr v* **1** [I;T **go round** sthg] to spread or be told to a lot of people 流傳; 蔓延: *There are a lot of colds going round at the moment.* 現在感冒正到處流行。 | *There's a really funny joke going round the office.* 辦公室裡在傳一個非常滑稽的笑話。 **2** [I] to spend a lot of time with someone, often going to a lot of different places with them 常跟某人一起出去: *Who does she usually go round* **with**? 她通常和誰一起外出? | *Those two always go round* **together.** 他們兩個總是形影不離。 **3** [I] to be enough for everyone 足夠分配給每個人: *There wasn't enough wine to go round.* 沒有足夠的酒給大家喝。

go through *phr v* **1** [T **go through** sthg] to suffer or experience something unpleasant 經歷〔不愉快的事〕: *I couldn't go through another experience like that.* 那樣的事再經歷一次我可受不了。 | *Let's hope we never have to go through another war.* 但願我們千萬不要再經歷一次戰爭。 **2** [I;T **go through** sthg] to be accepted and approved 被接受; 被通過: *The government proposed a change to the tax law, but it never went through.* 政府建議修改稅法, 但從未通過。 | *The Bill has now gone through Parliament.* 該提案現已在國會獲得通過。 **3** [T **go through** sthg] to read, look at, or explain something carefully 仔細閱讀〔檢查、解釋〕: *I went through the article again.* 我又把文章認真看了一遍。 | *I went through the whole house looking for my purse.* 我為找我的錢包翻遍了整個房間。 | *Could you go through that last point again?* 你能把最後一點再解釋一遍嗎?

go through with sthg *phr v* [T] to complete something that you had planned or agreed to do 完成〔計劃或同意做的事〕: *At the last minute she realized that she couldn't go through with the murder.* 最後一刻她才意識到她完成不了那個謀殺計劃。

go towards sthg *phr v* [T] to help with the cost of something 有助於解決〔某事〕的費用: *This money will go towards a deposit for a house.* 這些錢有助於解決房子的押金問題。

go under *phr v* [I] **1** (of a ship or boat) to sink〔輪船或小艇〕沉沒 **2** (of a business) to fail〔企業〕倒閉: *The firm finally went under last year.* 公司去年年終倒閉。

go up *phr v* [I] **1** to increase 增加: *Prices have gone up sharply this year.* 今年物價大幅度上漲。 **2** to be built 興建; 建立: *A lot of*

new houses are going up round here. 這附近將建許多新的房子。 **3 go up in flames** to burn 燃燒: *The whole house went up in flames.* 整所房子被火焰吞沒。

go with sthg *phr v* [T] to be found or given with something 伴隨〔某物〕; 附帶得到〔某物〕: *the responsibilities that go with owning your own home* 自己擁有住房而需承擔的責任 | *There are quite a lot of perks that go with the job.* 做那個工作可獲得許多福利。

go without *phr v* **1** [I;T **go without** sthg] to manage without something 沒有〔某事物〕而將就對付: *We had to go without a lot of things when I was a child.* 我小時候的生活經常缺吃少穿。 | *If there's no coffee, you'll just have to go without.* 如果沒有咖啡, 你也只好將就一下了。 **2 it goes without saying** = it is clear, without needing to be stated 不言自明; 不言而喻: *It goes without saying that water is critical to our survival.* 水對我們的生存至關重要, 這一點不言而喻。

go² *n* **goes** *infml*〔非正式〕 **1** [U] the quality of being full of life and very active 生氣; 活力: *The children are full of go.* 孩子們充滿了活力。 **2** [C] an attempt to do something 嘗試; 企圖: *I'd like to have a go at mending the roof myself.* 我想試著自己來修屋頂。 | *He's had three goes at his driving test now.* 駕駛考試他現已試過三次了。 **3 your go** your turn in a game〔遊戲、比賽中〕輪到自己: *It's my go now!* 現在該我了! **4 on the go** busy all the time 一直很忙: *Those children are always on the go!* 那些孩子一直忙忙碌碌!

goad /gəud; gəʊd/ *v* [T] to annoy or encourage someone continually, causing them to do something 刺激; 鼓勵: *The journalists goaded him until he lost his temper completely.* 記者們一直在刺激他, 直到他大發雷霆為止。 | *She was goaded* **into** *action by the fear of losing her job.* 對失業的懼怕促使她採取了行動。

go·a·head¹ /ˈ· ·ˌ·/ *n* **the go-ahead** permission to act 同意; 贊成: *We can't start building until we get the go-ahead from the council.* 我們要得到市議會的允許後才能開始興建房屋。

go·a·head² *adj* [only before a noun 只用於名詞前] active in using new methods for better results (used especially of people and companies)〔為獲得更好的效果而〕積極嘗試新辦法的〔尤指人和公司〕

★★★ goal /gol; gəʊl/ *n* **1** the space, usually between two posts, where you must put the ball in games such as football in order to win a point〔足球等的〕球門: *Jones will be in goal for tomorrow's match.* 明天的比賽由瓊斯來守門。 **2** the point which you win when you do this 進球得的分: *We won by three goals to one.* 我們以三比一獲勝。 **3 an own goal** a point which you give to the other team when you accidentally put the ball into your own goal 誤將球踢入自家球門

4 your aim or purpose 目標; 目的: *Set yourself new goals, and try to achieve them!* 給自己訂些新的目標, 然後力圖實現。

goal·keep·er /ˈgol,kipɚ; ˈɡəʊl,kiːpəʳ/ *n* (also 又作 **goalie** /ˈgolɪ; ˈɡəʊli/ *infml* 〔非正式〕) the player who is responsible for stopping the ball before it goes into the goal, in games such as football 〔足球比賽等的〕守門員

goat /ˈgot; ɡəʊt/ *n* an animal with a beard and horns which gives milk and a rough wool 山羊

gob·ble /ˈgabl̩; ˈɡɒbəl/ *v* **gobbled, gobbling 1** [I;T] to eat very quickly, and sometimes noisily 狼吞虎嚥地吃: *The children gobbled up their food and rushed out to play.* 孩子們急急忙忙吞下食物, 便跑出去玩了。| *They gobbled it down.* 他們把它大口吞了下去。**2** [I] to make the sound a TURKEY makes 〔火雞〕咯咯地叫

gob·ble·dy·gook /ˈgabldɪ,guk; ˈɡɒbəldiguːk/ *n* (also 又作 **gobbledegook**) [U] important-sounding but meaningless official language 聽似重要而實際毫無意義的官話: *This form is a load of gobbledygook!* 這張表上全是廢話!

go-be·tween /ˈ· ·,·/ *n* a person who takes messages from one person or side to another, because they are unwilling or unable to meet each other 中間人; 掮客; 媒人

gob·let /ˈgablɪt; ˈɡɒbl̩t/ *n* a special cup, usually made of glass or metal, used for drinking wine 〔玻璃或金屬的〕高腳(酒)杯

gob·lin /ˈgablɪn; ˈɡɒblɪn/ *n* a small ugly fairy in children's stories that enjoys playing tricks on people 〔愛惡作劇的〕小妖精

god /gad; ɡɒd/ *n* **1** one of the beings or spirits which are worshipped because of the power they are believed to have over nature and the lives of human beings 神 **2** the being who, especially in the Christian, Jewish, and Muslim religions, is worshipped as maker and ruler of the world 〔尤指基督教、猶太教和伊斯蘭教中的〕上帝; 造物主; 真主: *to ask God for forgiveness* 祈求上帝原諒 **3 for God's sake** an expression which is used to show that you are annoyed or impatient about something 看在上帝面上; 天哪〔表示惱怒或不耐煩〕 **4 God forbid** = I hope it does not happen 我希望不要發生這種事情: *God forbid that my parents should find out about this!* 但願不要讓我父母發現此事! **5 God knows, God alone knows** *infml* I really do not know 〔非正式〕我實在不知道: *God knows where he's gone!* 天知道他去哪裡了! **6 God willing** *old fash* if God allows it to happen, or if all goes well 〔老式〕如上帝允許; 如一切順利: *She'll be married soon, God willing.* 如無意外, 她很快就要結婚。**7 Oh God, My God, Good God** phrases which are used to express strong feelings such as surprise or fear 天哪〔用於表示吃驚或恐懼等〕: *Oh God, I'm in real trouble now!* 天哪, 這下我可真的遭殃了! **8 Thank God** a phrase which you use to express your happiness that trouble has passed 謝天謝地〔用於表示麻煩已經過去〕: *Thank God you're safe!* 謝天謝地, 你沒有出事!

■ USAGE 用法: Many expressions with the word **God** are commonly used in a non-religious way to show surprise, anger, fear, etc. Note, however, that some people might find these offensive. ☆ 許多含有 **God** 一詞的短語沒有宗教方面的含義, 只是表示驚奇、憤怒、恐懼等情感。但是請注意, 有些人可能會認為這些短語不禮貌。

god·child /ˈgad,tʃaɪld; ˈɡɒdtʃaɪld/ *n* a person, usually a child, whose religious education you have promised at a Christian ceremony to be responsible for 〔基督教的〕教子; 教女

god·daugh·ter /ˈgad,dɔtɚ; ˈɡɒd,dɔːtəʳ/ *n* a female godchild 教女

god·dess /ˈgadɪs; ˈɡɒdɪs/ *n* a female being or spirit worshipped because of the power she is believed to have over nature and the lives of human beings 女神

god·fa·ther /ˈgad,faðɚ; ˈɡɒd,faːðəʳ/ *n* a man who has promised to be responsible for someone's religious education 教父

god-fear·ing /ˈ· ,··/ *adj fml* good and well-behaved according to the rules of religion 〔正式〕虔誠的

god·for·sak·en /ˈgadfɚ,sekən; ˈɡɒdfəseɪkən/ *adj* having no pleasant or desirable qualities (used of a place) 沒有令人愉快或吸引人的特點的〔指地方〕

god·less /ˈgadlɪs; ˈɡɒdləs/ *adj fml* showing no respect towards or belief in God 〔正式〕不信神的; 不敬神的

god·ly /ˈgadlɪ; ˈɡɒdli/ *adj* **godlier, godliest** *fml* showing obedience to God by behaving according to the rules and standards of your religion 〔正式〕虔誠的; 敬神的

god·moth·er /ˈgad,mʌðɚ; ˈɡɒd,mʌðəʳ/ *n* a woman who has promised to be responsible for someone's religious education 教母

god·pa·rent /ˈgad,pɛrənt; ˈɡɒd,peərənt/ *n* the person who promises at a Christian ceremony to help a person with their religious education 教父; 教母

god·send /ˈgad,sɛnd; ˈɡɒdsend/ *n* something which is unexpected and very fortunate 天賜之物; 意外的好運

god·son /ˈgad,sʌn; ˈɡɒd,sʌn/ *n* a male GODCHILD 教子

goes /goz; ɡəʊz/ **1** the 3rd person singular present of GO[1] ☆ GO[1] 的第三人稱單數現在式形式 **2** the plural of GO[2] ☆ GO[2] 的複數形式

gog·gle /ˈɡɒɡl; ˈɡɒɡəl/ v **goggled, goggling** [I] to look hard at something with your eyes wide open, especially because you are surprised 瞪大眼睛瞪視〔尤指因吃驚〕: *They all goggled in astonishment* **at** *my uniform.* 他們全都睜大眼睛吃驚地看着我的制服。

gog·gles /ˈɡɒɡlz; ˈɡɒɡəlz/ n [pl] large round glasses with an edge which fits against your skin, used to protect your eyes 護目鏡: *skiing goggles* 滑雪護目鏡

going¹ /ˈɡəʊɪŋ; ˈɡəʊɪŋ/ adj **1** [never before a noun 不能用於名詞前] infml able to be obtained〔非正式〕能夠得到的: *There's plenty of work going in the shipyard.* 船廠裡有許多工作職位。**2** [only before a noun 只用於名詞前] as paid at present〔報酬〕現行的: *The going rate for the job is £4 per hour.* 這工作目前的工資是每小時四英鎊。**3 a going concern** an active profitable business 盈利的商行 **4 have a lot going for it, have a lot going for you** to have a lot of advantages or good qualities 有許多有利條件〔優點〕

going² n **1** [U] the act of someone's leaving〔某人的〕離開; 離去: *Her going will be a great loss to the company.* 她的離去對公司是一大損失。**2** the rate of travel or progress 行進[進展]的速度: *We climbed the mountain in three hours, which was pretty good going.* 我們用了三個小時爬上那座山, 這速度是相當快的。**3** the condition or possibility of travel or progress 行進[進展]的狀況[可能性]: *The mud made it heavy going for the car.* 泥濘使汽車難以行駛。**4 while the going is good** while it is still easy or possible to leave 趁情況有利時離開; 及時脫身

going-o·ver /ˌ··ˈ··/ n [sing] infml〔非正式〕**1** an examination of something, and treatment of problems that are found〔對某物的〕檢查;〔對所發現問題的〕處理: *The car needs a good going-over before we take it on a long journey.* 在我們作長途旅行之前, 汽車需要好好地檢修一次。**2** a beating 痛打; 鞭笞

goings-on /ˌ··ˈ·/ n [pl] activities, usually of an unusual or undesirable kind〔反常的或不正當的〕活動: *You wouldn't believe the goings-on at the party last night!* 你不會相信昨夜的聚會上搞了哪些活動!

★gold¹ /ɡəʊld; ɡəʊld/ adj **1** made of gold 金子製成的: *a gold coin* 金幣 **2 gold medal** a piece of gold that you win when you come first in a race or competition 金牌 **3** the colour of gold 金色的: *gold paint* 金色顏料

gold² n **1** [U] a valuable yellow metal 金子; 黃金: *a gold mine* 金礦 | *gold dust* 金粉 **2** [C] a gold medal 金牌

★gold·en /ˈɡəʊldn̩; ˈɡəʊldən/ adj **1** made of gold or looking like gold 金子製成的; 似金子的: *a golden crown* 金皇冠 | *golden hair* 金髮 **2** [only before a noun 只用於名詞前] wonderful or valuable 極好的: *a golden opportunity* 良機 **3 golden handshake** a large amount of money given to someone when they leave a job (大筆的)退休金 **4 golden rule** a very important way of behaving, that you must remember 非常重要的原則; 金科玉律 **5 golden wedding** the date that is exactly 50 years after the date of a wedding 金婚紀念日〔結婚五十週年紀念日〕

gold·fish /ˈɡəʊldˌfɪʃ; ˈɡəʊldˌfɪʃ/ n [plural is 複數為 **goldfish**] a small orange fish which is usually kept in glass bowls or in garden pools 金魚

gold·mine /ˈɡəʊldˌmaɪn; ˈɡəʊldmaɪn/ n **1** a place where gold is taken out of the ground 金礦 **2** a successful business or activity which makes large profits 成功的企業; 贏得巨利的活動 **3 be sitting on a goldmine** to possess something extremely valuable 擁有極為值錢的東西

★golf /ɡɒlf; ɡɒlf/ n [U] a game in which people hit small hard balls into holes, using a special set of sticks 高爾夫球(運動): *golf balls* 高爾夫球 | *a golf course* 高爾夫球場 | *Let's play a round of golf before tea.* 喝茶前我們來打一場高爾夫球吧。–see picture on page 957 見 957 頁彩圖 –**golfer** n: *He's a professional golfer.* 他是個職業高爾夫球選手。

golf club /ˈ··/ n **1** an association of people who play golf 高爾夫球俱樂部 **2** the buildings and land they use 高爾夫球會所及場地 **3** (also 又作 **club**) a wooden or metal stick used for hitting the ball in a game of golf 高爾夫球棒

gone¹ /ɡɒn; ɡɒn/ the past participle of GO ☆GO 的過去分詞

gone² prep later or older than 晚於; 比…老: *It's gone midnight.* 已過了午夜。| *He's gone seventy.* 他已七十多歲了。

gong /ɡɒŋ; ɡɒŋ/ n a round piece of metal hanging from a frame, which makes a deep ringing sound when it is hit 鑼

gon·na /ˈɡɒnə; ˈɡɒnə, ˈɡənə/ going to 打算; 將要

> ■ USAGE 用法: People sometimes write **gonna** to suggest an American or nonstandard British English pronunciation of **going to**. But before a verb, to show the future ☆人們有時在寫內唸時 用 **gonna** 來表示 **going to** 的美式或非標準的英式發音。但若用在動詞前, 則表示將來時態: *"I'm gonna find her,"* he said. "我打算去找她," 他說。They do not write or say **gonna** to talk about movement, as in *I'm going to Canada.* ☆但表示行動時, 人們不用 **gonna**。如 *I'm going to Canada.* (我將要去加拿大。)

gon·or·rhe·a /ˌɡɒnəˈriːə; ˌɡɒnəˈrɪə/ n (also 又作 **gonorrhoea**) [U] a disease of the sex organs, passed on during sexual activity 淋病

★★**good**[1] /gʊd; gʊd/ *adj* **better, best 1** of a high standard 高水準的: *a good book* 好書 | *a very good memory* 好記性 | *good reading skills* 良好的閱讀技巧 **2** skilful or successful at something 有技巧的; 成功的: *a good cook* 好廚師 | *She's good at languages.* 她擅長學習語言。 | *He's always been good with children.* 他一直很會教育孩子。 **3** useful or suitable for particular purpose 〔對某一目的〕有用的; 適合的: *It's a good day for painting the windows.* 今天給窗戶上油漆很合適。 | *That's a good idea.* 那是個好主意。 | *good advice* 有益的忠告 **4 it's a good thing, it's a good job** it is fortunate 算是走運: *He would have been furious — it's a good job you didn't tell him!* 他本來會火冒三丈的——還好你沒有告訴他! **5 no good, not much good, not any good** useless or bad 無用的; 不好的: *It's no good trying to explain it to her; she's too young.* 解釋給她聽沒有用, 她年紀太小。 | *Is that book any good?* 那本書有用嗎? | *A car's not much good to me, since I can't drive!* 汽車對我沒甚麼用, 因為我不會開! **6** pleasant or favourable 令人愉快的; 有利的: *good weather* 好天氣 | *Have a good time!* 好好玩! | *You stand a good chance of getting the job.* 你很可能得到那份工作。 | *That's very good news.* 那是非常好的消息。 **7** useful to your health or character 有益於身心健康的: *Milk is good for you.* 喝牛奶對你的健康有益。 | *It's actually good for a child to eat chips occasionally.* 孩子偶爾吃點薯條實際上有好處。 **8** healthy 健康的: *Sit here so that you can talk into her good ear.* 坐在這裡, 這樣你就可以對着她那隻正常的耳朵講話。 **9** morally right 有道德的: *St Francis led a good life and did many good deeds.* 聖法蘭西斯過着高尚的生活, 他做了許多善事。 **10** kind 友善的; 友好的: *She's always been very good to me.* 她待我一直很好。 | *It's good of you to help.* 承蒙幫助, 真太好了。 **11** well-behaved (used especially of children) 規矩的〔尤指孩子〕; 聽話的: *Be good when we visit your aunt.* 去阿姨家的時候要聽話。 **12** [only before a noun 只用於名詞前] a word used to show that something is great in degree, amount, or size 〔程度、數量、尺寸〕很大〔多〕的: *Have a good look.* (你)仔細看。 | *Their team gave us a good beating.* 他們隊把我們打得落花流水。 | *It's a good five kilometres away.* 那裡足有五公里遠。 **13 a good deal** quite a lot 許多; 相當多: *We're expecting a good deal of support for our new movement.* 我們正期待着我們的新運動能得到廣泛的支持。 **14 a good many, a good few** quite a large number of 許多 **15 as good as** almost (the same thing as) 幾乎一樣: *He as good as refused.* 他事實上等於拒絕了。 | *We're as good as ruined.* 我們幾乎破產了。 **16 as good as gold** very well behaved 表現很好的 **17** a word you use to show that you are pleased about something; or that you agree with someone 好; 行〔表示滿意或同意〕: *"I've finished." "Good."* "我做完了。" "好!" **18 good for you!** a phrase used to express approval and pleasure at someone's success 幹得好! 〔用於對某人的成功表示贊成或高興〕: *"I've passed all my exams." "Good for you!"* "我考試全通過了。" "不錯啊!" **19 good gracious, good grief, good heavens, good Lord, good God** phrases used as an expression of surprise, shock, anger, or another strong feeling 老天哪〔用於表示驚奇、震驚、憤怒或其他強烈的感受〕: *Good heavens! Is that the time? I must be going.* 天哪! 到時間了嗎? 我得走了。 **20 in good time** early, or early enough for something 很早: *We got to the airport in good time.* 我們很早便到了機場。 **21 make good** to become successful and wealthy 取得成功; 變得富有 **22 make good something** to pay for something that has been lost or damaged 彌補〔賠償〕損失: *The loss to the company was made good by the other directors.* 公司的損失由其他的董事作出賠償。

good[2] *n* **1** [U] advantage 利益; 好處: *It's no good crying now!* 現在哭也沒有用! | *What's the good of having a car if you can't drive?* 如果你不會開車, 有輛車有甚麼用? **2 do you good** to help you in some way 〔在某方面〕對你有利: *A holiday would do you good.* 休假對你會有好處。 **3 for the good of something or someone** to be helpful to someone or something 對某人或某事有利: *We must do it, for the good of the company.* 為了公司利益, 我們必須做此事。 | *I'm punishing you for your own good.* 為了你好我這才懲罰你。 **4** [U] action or behaviour which is morally right, worthy of praise, and in accordance with religious beliefs and principles 善事; 善行: *the battle between good and evil* 善與惡的鬥爭 **5 be up to no good** to be doing, or intending to do, something wrong or bad 為非作歹; (想)做壞事 **6 for good** for ever 永遠: *They've decided to move up north for good now.* 他們現已決定搬到北方去住, 永遠不回來了。 **7 goods** [pl] **a** things such as clothes, food, or kitchen materials that can be owned, bought, or sold 〔衣服、食物或廚房用品等〕商品; 物品: *The shop sells a variety of goods.* 這家商店出售各種各樣的商品。 | *all my worldly goods* 我的全部財物 **b** BrE heavy articles to be moved from one place to another 〔英式〕〔從一地運往另一地的〕貨物: *a goods train* 貨物列車 **8 deliver the goods, come up with the goods** *infml* to do what is needed or expected 〔非正式〕做需要做的事; 做預料中的事

good af·ter·noon /ˌ·ˌ···/ *interj* a phrase used to greet someone in the afternoon 午安; 下午好〔用於午後與別人打招呼〕: *"Good afternoon, Mr Davis." "Hello, Jack."* "午安, 戴維斯先生。" "你好, 傑克。"

good·bye /ɡʊdˈbaɪ; ɡʊdˈbaɪ/ *interj* (also 又作 **bye** *infml* 〔非正式〕) a word that you use when you leave someone or someone leaves you 再見; 再會〔用於離別時〕: *"Goodbye, Mrs Jackson." "Goodbye."* "再見, 傑克遜夫人。""再見。" **–goodbye** *n*: *They said their goodbyes and left.* 他們説聲再見就走了。

good eve·ning /ˌ·'··/ *interj* a phrase used to greet someone in the evening 晚上好〔用於晚上與別人打招呼〕

good-for-noth·ing /ˈ··ˌ··/ *n* a useless and worthless person 沒用的人 **–good-for-nothing** *adj* [only before a noun 只用於名詞前]

Good Fri·day /ˌ· '··/ *n* the Friday before EASTER, a Christian religious holiday 耶穌受難日〔復活節前的星期五〕

good-hu·moured /ˌ· '···◂/ *n* (**good-humored** *AmE* 〖美式〗) cheerful and pleasant in a difficult situation 〔在困境中〕心情愉快的: *He was very good-humoured about the mess the children made in his kitchen.* 孩子們把他的廚房弄得一塌糊塗, 但他還是和和氣氣的。 **–good-humouredly** *adv*

good·ies /ˈɡʊdɪz; ˈɡʊdiz/ *n* [pl] *infml* something particularly attractive or pleasant, especially something good to eat 〖非正式〗吸引人或令人愉快的東西〔尤指好吃的東西〕: *a bag full of all sorts of goodies* 裝滿了各種好吃東西的袋

good-look·ing /ˌ·'··◂/ *adj* attractive (used of a person) 吸引人的〔指人〕: *He's very good-looking.* 他非常帥。 **–see** 見 BEAUTIFUL (USAGE 用法)

good mor·ning /ˌ·'··/ *interj* a greeting used in the morning 早安; 早上好〔用於上午與別人打招呼〕: *Good morning, Mrs Brown. How are you today?* 早安, 布朗太太。你今天好嗎?

good-na·tured /ˌ·'··◂/ *adj* friendly, pleasant, and rarely angry 友善的; 愉快的; 不易動怒的 **–good-naturedly** *adv*

good·ness /ˈɡʊdnɪs; ˈɡʊdnɪs/ *n* [U] **1** a word used in expressions of surprise and annoyance 天哪; 哎呀〔用於表示吃驚或惱怒〕: *Goodness me!* 我的天哪! | *For goodness' sake, stop making such a noise!* 看在老天爺的份上, 別再吵了! **2** the quality of being kind 善良; 友善 **3** the part of food which is good for your health 〔食物〕對健康有益的部分: *All the goodness has been boiled out of the vegetables.* 蔬菜的養分都被煮掉了。

good·night /ˌɡʊd'naɪt; ˌɡʊd'naɪt/ *interj* an expression used when you are going home at night or before you go to bed or to sleep 晚安〔用於晚上分別或就寢前〕: *"Goodnight Jimmy." "Goodnight, Mum."* "晚安, 吉米。""晚安, 媽媽。"

good·will /ˌɡʊd'wɪl; ˌɡʊd'wɪl/ *n* [U] kind feelings towards people 善意; 好意: *The agreement will need a certain amount of goodwill on both sides if it is to succeed.* 該協議若要順利實施, 雙方都需要一定的善意。

good·y /ˈɡʊdɪ; ˈɡʊdi/ *interj* an expression of pleasure, used especially by children 好啊〔尤指孩子們用以表示高興的用語〕: *Oh goody!*

We're going to have ice cream. 哦, 太棒啦! 我們有冰淇淋吃啦。

goody-good·y /ˌ··'··, ˌ··'··/ *n* **goody-goodies** a person who tries too hard to be good and please others (a word which shows disapproval, used especially by children) 裝得非常聽話的人〔含貶義, 尤用於孩子們中間〕; 賣乖的人: *Why did you tell the teacher, you goody-goody?* 你為甚麼去告訴老師, 你這喜歡賣乖的傢伙?

goo·ey /ˈɡuɪ; ˈɡuːi/ *adj* **gooier, gooiest** *infml* 〖非正式〗 **1** sticky and usually sweet 黏而甜的: *gooey cream cakes* 黏性的奶油蛋糕 **2** showing too much tenderness 過於多情的: *I hate gooey romantic films!* 我討厭傷感的愛情影片!

goof /ɡuf; ɡuːf/ *v* [I] *infml* to make a silly mistake 〖非正式〗犯愚蠢的錯誤 **–goof** *n*

goof·y /ˈɡufi; ˈɡuːfi/ *adj* **goofier, goofiest** silly and slightly mad 愚蠢的; 神經質的

goon /ɡun; ɡuːn/ *n* *infml* a foolish person 〖非正式〗笨蛋

goose /ɡus; ɡuːs/ *n* **geese** /ɡis; ɡiːs/ a large white bird similar to a duck, kept for its meat and eggs 鵝

goose·ber·ry /ˈɡusˌbɛri; ˈɡʊzbəri/ *n* **gooseberries 1** a small, round green fruit used in cooking 醋栗: *a gooseberry bush* 醋栗叢 | *a gooseberry pie* 醋栗餅 **2** play gooseberry *BrE* to be present as a third person in the company of two lovers who want to be alone 〖英式〗不知趣地和一對情侶在一起

goose·flesh /ˈɡusˌflɛʃ; ˈɡuːsfleʃ/ *n* [U] (also 又作 **goose pimples** /ˈ·ˌ··/ [pl]) a condition in which the hair on your skin is raised because you are cold or frightened 〔因寒冷或恐懼而起的〕雞皮疙瘩

gore¹ /ɡor; ɡɔːr/ *v* **gored, goring** [T] (of an animal) to wound with the horns 〔動物〕用角頂傷: *He was attacked by the bull and severely gored.* 那頭公牛向他衝了過去, 他被嚴重牴傷了。

gore² *n* [U] thick blood from a wound 傷口的凝血

gorge¹ /ɡordʒ; ɡɔːdʒ/ *n* a deep narrow valley 峽谷

gorge² *v* **gorged, gorging: gorge yourself on something** to fill yourself with food 塞飽食物: *She gorged herself all day on cream cakes.* 她一整天都在拚命吃奶油蛋糕。

gor·geous /ˈɡordʒəs; ˈɡɔːdʒəs/ *adj* *infml* very beautiful and nice 〖非正式〗非常美麗的; 非常好的: *What a gorgeous, sunny day!* 多麼晴朗的好天氣呀! | *She was wearing an absolutely gorgeous dress.* 她穿了件極為漂亮的裙子。

go·ril·la /ɡəˈrɪlə; ɡəˈrɪlə/ *n* a very large strong animal similar to a monkey, with dark fur 大猩猩

gorse /ɡors; ɡɔːs/ *n* [U] a wild bush with prickles and bright yellow flowers 荊豆

gor·y /ˈɡori; ˈɡɔːri/ *adj* **gorier, goriest** full of

violence and blood 充滿暴力和血腥的: *a gory film* 一部充滿暴力的影片 | *There had been a murder. He told them all the gory details.* 發生了一起謀殺案。他把所有駭人聽聞的細節告訴了他們。

gosh /gɑʃ; gɒʃ/ *interj* an expression of surprise 哎呀；天哪〔表示驚訝〕: *Gosh! What a coincidence!* 天哪! 真是巧合!

gos·ling /ˈgɑzlɪŋ; ˈgɒzlɪŋ/ *n* a young GOOSE 小鵝，幼鵝

go-slow /ˌ·ˈ·◂/ *n BrE* a period of working as slowly as possible because of a disagreement with your employer〔英式〕〔由於與雇主有分歧而引起的〕怠工

gos·pel /ˈgɑspḷ; ˈgɒspəl/ *n* **1 the Gospels** the four books in the Bible about the life and teachings of Christ 福音書 **2** [U] (also 又作 **gospel truth**) something which is completely true 絕對真理；真事: *What I'm telling you is gospel.* 我現在告訴你的絕對沒錯。| *No, honestly, it's the gospel truth.* 不，說句實話，這事情千真萬確。**3** [C] *infml* a set of ideas that someone believes in strongly〔非正式〕信奉的一整套觀點: *spreading the feminist gospel* 傳播女權主義 **4** [U] (also 又作 **gospel music**) a style of music popular in America with black Christians 福音音樂〔美國黑人的一種宗教音樂〕

gos·sa·mer /ˈgɑsəmə; ˈgɒsəməʳ/ *n* [U] **1** light silky thread made by spiders (SPIDER) 蛛絲 **2** a very light thin material 薄紗

gos·sip[1] /ˈgɑsəp; ˈgɒsɨp/ *n* **1** [C;U] informal talk or writing about other people's actions and private lives 閒話；流言蜚語: *I don't approve of gossip.* 我不贊成背後議論別人。| *two neighbours having a gossip in the street* 兩位在街上說長道短的鄰居 **2** [C] a person who likes talking about other people's private lives (a word used to show disapproval) 喜歡談論別人私生活的人〔含貶義〕: *a nosey old gossip* 愛到處打聽的老饒舌者

gossip[2] *v* [T] to talk or write gossip about someone or something 說長道短；傳播流言蜚語

gossip col·umn /ˈ·· ˌ··/ *n* part of a newspaper where the private lives of famous people are written about〔報紙上有關名人私生活的〕閒話專欄

got /gɑt; gɒt/ **1** the past tense and past participle of GET ☆ GET 的過去式和過去分詞 **2 have got, have got to** –see 見 HAVE

Goth·ic /ˈgɑθɪk; ˈgɒθɪk/ *adj* **1** of a style of building common in Western Europe between the 12th and 16th centuries, with pointed arches〔建築〕哥德式的〔盛行於十二至十六世紀的西歐，以尖頂為其特徵〕: *a Gothic cathedral* 一座哥德式大教堂 **2** with a lot of detailed decoration (used of printing) 裝飾考究的〔指印刷〕: *Gothic script* 哥德式字體 **3** happening in dark strange places (used of stories) 發生在黑暗而陌生之處的〔指故事〕

got·ta /ˈgɑtə; ˈgɒtə/ **1** have/has got to 必須 **2** have/has got a 有；具有

> ■ **USAGE** 用法: People only write **gotta** when they want to suggest a very informal or nonstandard pronunciation of **have got to** and **have got a** ☆ 只有當人們要表示出一種很不正式的或不標準的英語發音時，才在書寫中用 **gotta** 來表示 **have got to** 和 **have got a**: *I gotta go* (= I must go) 我必須走了。| **Gotta** *match?* (= Have you got a match?) 有火柴嗎? But this pronunciation is quite common in ordinary speech. ☆ 但在口語中，這種發音很常見。

got·ten /ˈgɑtṇ; ˈgɒtṇ/ the usual American past participle of GET ☆ GET 的美式過去分詞

gouge /gaʊdʒ; gaʊdʒ/ *v* **gouged, gouging**
  gouge sthg ↔ **out** *phr v* [T] to dig a hole in something or get something out, with a pointed tool〔用尖的工具〕在〔某物上〕挖一個洞；把〔某物〕挖出來

gourd /gord; gʊəd/ *n* a fruit with a hard shell which is often used as a drinking vessel or dish 葫蘆

gour·met /ˈgʊrme; ˈgʊəmeɪ/ *n* a person who knows a lot about food and drink and enjoys eating good food 美食家

gout /gaʊt; gaʊt/ *n* [U] a disease which makes your toes, knees, and fingers hurt and swell 痛風

*　**gov·ern** /ˈgʌvən; ˈgʌvən/ *v* **1** [I;T] to control and direct the affairs of a country and its people 統治；治理〔國家和人民〕: *a state governed by the top army officers* 被高層軍人統治的國家 | *Is this man fit to govern?* 這個人來管理國家合適嗎? **2** [T] to control or fix something 控制〔某物〕；固定〔某物〕: *The price of coffee is governed by the quantity which has been produced.* 咖啡的價格視其產量的多少而定。

gov·ern·ess /ˈgʌvənɪs; ˈgʌvənɨs/ *n* a woman who lives with a family and teaches the children at home 家庭女教師

**　**gov·ern·ment** /ˈgʌvənmənt; ˈgʌvənmənt/ *n* **1** [C + sing/ pl verb] (also 又作 **the Government**) the people who rule a country 政府: *The Government is planning new tax increases.* 政府正在計劃新的增稅。| *the French government* 法國政府 **2** [U] the action, form, or method of ruling 管轄；治理；統治: *a government of the people by the people* 民治 | *The country has not always had fair government.* 該國並非一直治理得很好。

*　**gov·er·nor** /ˈgʌvənə; ˈgʌvənəʳ/ *n* (also 又作 **Governor**) a person who controls an organization or place 統治者；管轄者: *the Governor of the prison* 典獄長 | *the Governor of California* 加利福尼亞州州長 |

She's one of the school governors. 她是學校的理事之一。

gown /gaʊn; gaʊn/ *n* **1** a woman's dress, especially one worn on formal occasions〔尤指正式場合穿的〕女服: *a beautiful evening gown* 漂亮的女裝晚禮服 **2** a special long loose piece of clothing worn by a judge, lawyer, teacher, or doctor〔法官、律師、教師或醫生所穿的〕寬鬆長袍

GP /ˌdʒiːˈpiː; ˌdʒiːˈpiː/ *n* a doctor who is trained in ordinary medicine and works in a particular area of a town 普通醫生; an abbreviation for GENERAL PRACTITIONER【縮】普通〔全科〕醫生: *Who's your GP?* 你們這裡普通醫生是誰?

*★***grab**[1] /græb; græb/ *v* **-bb-** [T] **1** to seize something with a sudden rough movement, especially for a selfish reason〔尤指出於自私〕突然抓住〔某物〕: *He grabbed the money and ran off.* 他一把搶過錢就逃之夭夭。 **2 grab at something** to try to take something or pick something up 試圖抓住某物: *She grabbed at the key, but he drew his hand back.* 她想抓到那把鑰匙, 但他把手縮了回去。 **3** to eat some food or get some sleep quickly 迅速吃點東西; 迅速睡一覺: *I have to work through lunch; I'll just pop out and grab a sandwich.* 我一中午都必須工作; 所以準備把握時間出去吃個三明治。 **4 grab at a chance/opportunity** to take a chance eagerly 抓住機會: *She grabbed at the opportunity to travel.* 她抓住機會去旅遊。 **5 how does it grab you?** *infml*〔非正式〕= what do you feel about it? 你覺得這怎麼樣?: *How does the idea of a trip to Zambia grab you?* 你覺得去贊比亞旅遊這個主意怎麼樣?

grab[2] *n* a sudden attempt to seize something 抓取; 試圖抓住: *The thief made a grab at my bag.* 那個小偷想搶我的手提包。

grace[1] /greɪs; greɪs/ *n* [U] **1** the quality of being effortless and attractive in movement〔動作的〕優美; 優雅: *She dances with tremendous grace.* 她舞跳得極為優美。 **2 have the grace to do something** to say or do something that shows you know you have been wrong or deserve blame〔知道自己錯了或應受責備而〕通情達理地去做某事: *She had the grace to admit that he had been right after all.* 她很有雅量, 終於承認他是對的。 **3 with good grace, with a good grace** willingly 樂意地: *He admitted defeat with a good grace.* 他坦然地承認失敗。 [RELATED PHRASE 相關詞組 **with bad grace**] **4 the grace of God** the favour or mercy of God 上帝的恩惠〔仁慈〕: *By the grace of God the ship came safely home through the storm.* 承蒙上帝保祐, 這艘船在暴風雨中安然返航。 **5 fall from grace** to fall from a position of favour 失寵 **6** a delay allowed as a favour 寬限: *I can't pay by Friday, but luckily they're giving me a week's grace.* 我星期五以前付不出錢, 但幸運的是他們給了我一星期的寬限。 **7** a prayer

said before a meal〔飯前的〕祈禱 **8 Your Grace** a way of speaking to a DUKE, DUCHESS, or ARCHBISHOP 閣下〔對公爵, 公爵夫人和大主教的尊稱〕: *Yes, Your Grace.* 是的, 閣下。

grace[2] *v* **graced, gracing** [T] *fml* (of important people) to agree to be present at an event (a word which is often used in a humorous way)〔正式〕〔重要人物〕答應到場〔常含幽默〕: *The chairman graced us with his presence.* 主席答應我們來參加。

grace·ful /ˈgreɪsfəl; ˈgreɪsfəl/ *adj* **1** attractively and effortlessly smooth in movement〔動作〕優美的; 優雅的: *a graceful dancer* 動作優美的舞蹈員 **2** showing fair and honourable behaviour 得體的: *a graceful apology* 得體的道歉 **–gracefully** *adv*

■ USAGE 用法: Compare 比較 **graceful** and 和 **gracious**. **Graceful** means attractive or pleasant. We use it especially to describe the shape or movements of a person or animal ☆ **Graceful** 意為吸引人的或令人愉快的。我們尤用其來形容人或動物的體型或動作: *a graceful dancer* 動作優美的舞蹈員 | *the graceful movement of a deer* 鹿的敏捷動作。But we can also use it to describe people when they are sorry for something or are accepting defeat ☆ 但我們也可用其來形容人們對某事表示歉意或承認失敗: *He made a graceful apology.* 他體面地道了歉。| *The defeated candidate accepted the result of the election gracefully.* 落選的候選人很坦然地對待選舉結果。We use **gracious** to describe people's manners. It suggests an important person being polite to someone less important ☆ 我們用 **gracious** 來形容人們的態度。這詞表示地位高的人對地位低的人彬彬有禮, 和藹可親: *The Queen thanked them graciously.* 女王很有禮貌地向他們致謝。

grace·less /ˈgreɪsləs; ˈgreɪsləs/ *adj* **1** awkward and unattractive in movement or form 不優雅的; 不優美的 **2** lacking in good manners 無禮的 **–gracelessly** *adv*

gra·cious /ˈgreɪʃəs; ˈgreɪʃəs/ *adj fml*〔正式〕**1** polite, kind, and pleasant, especially in a generous way 有禮貌的; 和善的: *Lord Watchet was gracious enough to show us around his beautiful home.* 瓦奇勛爵親切地帶着我們參觀了他漂亮的房子。–see 見 GRACEFUL (USAGE 用法) **2** [only before a noun 只用於名詞前] having qualities such as comfort and beauty made possible by wealth 優裕的; 舒適的: *gracious living* 舒適的生活 **3 Gracious, Good gracious!** *old fash* an expression of surprise〔老式〕天哪〔表示驚訝〕**–graciously** *adv*

gra·da·tion /grəˈdeɪʃən; grəˈdeɪʃən/ *n* a stage

in a set of changes or degrees of development 等級; 階段; 層次: *expressing every gradation of feeling from joy to grief* 把從高興到悲哀的每種情感都表現出來 | *gradations of colour* 色彩的不同層次

***grade**[1] /greɪd; greɪd/ *n* **1** a particular level of rank or quality 階級; 等級: *This grade of wool can be sold at a lower price.* 這種等級的羊毛可以用較低價格出售。| *These teachers are only on the second grade of the pay scale.* 按工資級差表, 這些老師只排在第二等。**2** *AmE* a class of a particular year group at school 〔美式〕年級: *She's in the fifth grade.* 她五年級了。**3** a mark for an examination or a piece of schoolwork 分數; 成績: *Did you get a good grade for your essay?* 你的文章有沒有得到好分數? **4 make the grade** to reach the necessary standard 達到必要的標準

grade[2] *v* **graded, grading** [T] to separate things into levels of rank or quality 把〔東西〕分等[分級]: *These potatoes have been graded according to size.* 這些馬鈴薯已按大小分出了等級。

grade cross·ing /'·, ··/ *n* the usual American word for 〔美式〕= LEVEL CROSSING

gra·di·ent /'greɪdɪənt; 'greɪdɪənt/ *n* the degree of steepness of a slope 傾斜度; 坡度: *a steep hill with a gradient of 1 in 8* 坡度為1:8 的陡峭的小山

grad·u·al /'grædʒuəl; 'grædʒuəl/ *adj* happening slowly and by degrees 逐漸的: *a gradual increase in the number of home owners* 有房者數目在逐漸增加 –**gradually** *adv*: *He gradually began to understand.* 他漸漸開始明白了。

grad·u·ate[1] /'grædʒuɪt; 'grædʒuᵻt/ *n* **1** a person who has completed a university first degree course 大學畢業生: *a graduate of Oxford University* 牛津大學的畢業生 **2** *AmE* a person who has completed a course at a college, school, etc. 〔美式〕〔學院、學校等的〕畢業生: *a high school graduate* 高中畢業生 **3** the usual American word for 〔美式〕= POSTGRADUATE 研究生: *graduate school* 研究所; 研究院 | *a graduate student* 研究生

grad·u·ate[2] /'grædʒu,eɪt; 'grædʒueɪt/ *v* **graduated, graduating 1** [I] to obtain a degree at a university 獲得學位; 大學畢業 **2** [I] *AmE* to complete an educational course 〔美式〕畢業 **3** [T] to divide something into levels 把〔某物〕分等級: *a graduated pay scale* 分等級的工資級別 **4 graduate to something** to move on to something that is more important or more difficult 繼續去做更重要或更困難的事情

grad·u·a·tion /,grædʒu'eɪʃən; ,grædʒu'eɪʃən/ *n* **1** [U] the act of graduating with a university degree or American high school DIPLOMA 大學畢業; 〔美國的〕高中畢業: *graduation with honours* 作為優等生畢業 **2** [C] the ceremony at which you receive a degree or diploma 畢業典禮: *Are your parents coming to your graduation?* 你的父母來參加你的畢業典禮嗎?

graf·fi·ti /græ'fiːtɪ; græ'fiːti/ *n* [U] drawings or writing on a wall, often of a humorous, rude, or political nature 〔牆上的〕亂塗亂畫〔通常含有幽默的、粗魯的或政治的色彩〕: *The walls of the subway are covered in graffiti.* 地鐵牆上到處是亂塗亂畫的東西。

graft[1] /græft; græft/ *v* [T] **1** to add something to part of a damaged human body 〔人體器官〕移植: *The doctors grafted some skin from her thigh onto her face.* 醫生從她的大腿上切下一點皮膚移植到她的臉上。**2** to add something to something else 加上; 增加: *The last part of the report had just been grafted on as an afterthought.* 報告的最後部分只是事後想起給加上去的。**3** to join one plant to another in order to make a new one 〔植物的〕嫁接: *The rose had been grafted onto strong root stock.* 玫瑰已被嫁接到強健的根狀莖上了。

graft[2] *n* **1** [C] a piece cut from one plant and joined to another one so that it grows there 嫁接枝條 **2** [C] a piece of healthy living skin or bone put onto or into a part of your body which has been damaged 〔皮膚或骨頭等〕移植物: *She's badly burnt and will need a lot of skin grafts.* 她被嚴重燒傷, 需要大面積的植皮。**3** [U] *AmE* the practice of gaining money dishonestly by the use of political influence 〔美式〕貪污; 受賄 **4** [U] *infml* hard work 〔非正式〕勞累的工作

grain /greɪn; greɪn/ *n* **1** [C] a single seed of rice, wheat, or other food plants 穀粒: *He lived on a few grains of rice a day.* 那時他每天靠幾顆米粒餬口。**2** [U] crops from plants which produce such seeds, especially wheat 穀物〔尤指小麥〕: *a cargo of grain* 一批需要運送的糧食 **3** [C] a single very small piece of a hard substance 粒; 顆粒: *a grain of sand* 一粒沙子 | *grains of salt* 鹽粒 **4 there's not a grain of truth in it** there is no truth at all in it 這事無絲毫真實性 **5 the grain** the natural arrangement of the threads or fibres (FIBRE) in wood, rock, and cloth 〔木頭、石頭或布料的〕紋理: *You need to cut wood in the direction of the grain.* 你必須順着木紋劈木頭。**6 it goes against the grain** = I am not used to doing this and I do not really approve of it 我不習慣做此事, 故而不贊成

gram /græm; græm/ *n* (also 又作 **gramme**) a unit for measuring weight equal to 1/1000 of a kilogram 克〔重量單位, 等於千分之一公斤〕

***gram·mar** /'græmə; 'græməʳ/ *n* **1** [U] the rules of a language by which words change their forms and are combined into sentences 語法; 文法: *I find German grammar very difficult.* 我覺得德語的文法很難。| *She*

G

keeps correcting my grammar. 她不斷地糾正我的語法。**2** [C] *a book which teaches these rules* 文法書: *This is the best Italian grammar I've seen.* 這是我所見過的最好的意大利語文法書。

grammar school /'·· ·/ *n a school in Britain, especially in the past, for children over the age of 11 who are considered to be of high ability*〔尤指昔時英國的〕文法學校〔能力較強的11歲以上兒童所上的學校〕—compare 比較 COMPREHENSIVE[2]

gram·mat·i·cal /grə'mætɪkl; grə'mætɪkəl/ *adj* **1** [only before a noun 只用於名詞前] *concerning grammar* 文法的: *grammatical rules* 文法規則 **2** *correct according to the rules of grammar* 符合文法規則的: *That is not a grammatical sentence.* 那句話不符合文法規則。—**grammatically** /-klɪ; -klɪ/ *adv: Is this grammatically correct?* 這從文法角度來說對不對?

gramme /græm; græm/ *n see* 見 GRAM

gram·o·phone /'græməfon; 'græməfəun/ *n old fash a* RECORD PLAYER〔老式〕唱機; 留聲機

gran /græn; græn/ *n BrE infml grandmother*〔英式, 非正式〕祖母; 外祖母

gra·na·ry /'grænərɪ; 'grænəri/ *n* **granaries** *a building in which grain, especially wheat, is stored* 穀倉〔尤指麥倉〕; 糧庫

★**grand**[1] /grænd; grænd/ *adj* **1** *splendid in appearance* 壯麗的; 宏偉的: *a grand occasion* 莊嚴的場合 | *a millionaire who entertained his guests on a grand scale* 以盛大的場面招待賓客的百萬富翁 **2** *important but perhaps too proud (used of a person)* 高傲的; 自負的〔指人〕: *He's too grand to associate with people from the village.* 他過於自負, 不願跟村裡來的人交往。**3** *old fash infml very pleasant*〔老式, 非正式〕愉悅的: *That was a grand party.* 那是一次歡樂的聚會。—**grandly** *adv* —**grandness** *n* [U]

grand[2] *n* **1** [plural is 複數為 **grand**] *infml 1000 dollars or pounds*〔非正式〕一千元[鎊]: *He paid fifteen grand for that car.* 他買那輛車花了一萬五千元。**2** (also 又作 **grand piano**) *a large flat piano, usually played at concerts*〔常在音樂會上使用的〕大鋼琴; 平台鋼琴

gran·dad /'græn,dæd; 'grændæd/ *n* (also 又作 **granddad**) *infml a grandfather*〔非正式〕爺爺; 外公

grand·child /'grænd,tʃaɪld; 'græntʃaɪld/ *n* **grandchildren** /-,tʃɪldrən; -,tʃɪldrən/ *the child of your son or daughter* 孫子; 外孫; 孫女; 外孫女 —see picture on page 503 見 503 頁彩圖

grand·daugh·ter /'græn,dɔtɚ; 'græn,dɔːtəʳ/ *n the daughter of your son or daughter* 孫女; 外孫女 —see picture on page 503 見 503 頁彩圖

gran·deur /'grændʒɚ; 'grændʒəʳ/ *n* [U] *fml*〔非正式〕**1** *great beauty, power, and size* 壯

麗; 莊嚴; 宏大: *the grandeur of nature* 大自然的壯麗景象 **2** *great personal importance* 偉大

grand·fa·ther /'grænd,fɑðɚ; 'grænd,fɑːðəʳ/ *n the father of your father or mother* 祖父; 外祖父 —see picture on page 503 見 503 頁彩圖

grandfather clock /'··· ·, ,···'·/ *n a tall clock in a wooden case which stands on the floor*〔有木製外殼的〕落地式大擺鐘

gran·di·ose /'grændɪ,os; 'grændiəus/ *adj intended to be important and splendid but seeming useless* 浮誇的; 鋪張的: *He's always producing grandiose schemes for making money.* 他總是不斷制定出野心勃勃的賺錢計劃。

grand·ma /'grændmɑ; 'grænmɑː/ *n infml grandmother*〔非正式〕奶奶; 外婆

grand·moth·er /'grænd,mʌðɚ; 'græn,mʌðəʳ/ *n the mother of your father or mother* 祖母; 外祖母 —see picture on pate 503 見 503 頁彩圖

grand·pa /'grændpɑ; 'grænpɑː/ *n infml grandfather*〔非正式〕爺爺; 外公

grand·par·ent /'grænd,pɛrənt; 'græn,peərənt/ *n the parent of your father or mother* 祖父; 外祖父; 祖母; 外祖母 —see picture on page 503 見 503 頁彩圖

grand·son /'grænd,sʌn; 'grænsʌn/ *n the son of your son or daughter* 孫子; 外孫 —see picture on page 503 見 503 頁彩圖

grand·stand /'grænd,stænd; 'grændstænd/ *n a structure, with a roof and seats, from which people watch sports matches and races*〔比賽場地的〕大看台

grange /grendʒ; greɪndʒ/ *n a large country house with farm buildings* 農莊; 莊園

gran·ite /'grænɪt; 'grænɪt/ *n* [U] *a very hard rock often used for building* 花崗岩[石]

gran·ny /'grænɪ; 'græni/ *n* **grannies** *infml grandmother*〔非正式〕奶奶; 外婆

★**grant**[1] /grænt; grɑːnt/ *n money given by the state or local council for a particular purpose*〔國家或地方政府的〕撥款: *student grants* 學生助學金 | *a house improvement grant* 房屋裝修補助金

★**grant**[2] *v* [T] **1** *fml to give someone something that they want or ask for, especially officially*〔正式〕給予〔某人所求之物〕: *They granted her request.* 他們答應了她的請求。| *The country was granted its independence in 1968.* 該國於 1968 年獲准獨立。| *They have been granted permission to build a garage.* 他們已獲准建造一個車庫。

> □ USEFUL PATTERNS 有用句型
> to grant something; to grant someone something; to grant something to someone

2 I grant you that *a phrase you use to say*

that another person's statement is true in an exact sense, but you think that the main idea that you are expressing is still correct 這我承認〔用於表示贊同別人的話，但堅持認為自己的話也是正確的〕: *"The Prime Minister doesn't support the strikers." "I grant you that, but it's obvious they have his sympathy."* "首相不支持罷工工人。" "這我承認，但很明顯他是同情他們的。" **3 granted** that is true 那是真的: *"We've been very successful this year." "Granted. But can we do it again next year?"* "今年我們非常成功。" "不錯。但是明年我們還能保持下去嗎？" **4 take something for granted** to believe a fact or action, without questioning 想當然; 把某物認為當然: *I just took it for granted that you were married.* 我只是想當然地認為你結婚了。 **5 take someone for granted** to treat someone with no thought and not be conscious of their true value〔認識不到某人的價值而〕不認真對待某人; 不關心某人: *He's so busy with his job that he takes his family completely for granted.* 他工作太忙，所以根本沒有把家人放在心上。

gran·u·lat·ed /ˈɡrænjə,leɪtɪd; ˈɡrænjᵿˌleɪtᵻd/ *adj* **granulated sugar** sugar consisting of very small bits of 砂糖

gran·ule /ˈɡrænjul; ˈɡrænjuːl/ *n* a small round piece 小顆粒: *instant coffee granules* 速溶咖啡(晶) —**granular** /-njələˈ, -njᵿləˈ/ *adj*

grape /ɡreɪp; ɡreɪp/ *n* a small green or dark purple juicy fruit which grows on a VINE, used to make wine 葡萄: *a bunch of seedless grapes* 一串無籽葡萄 −see picture on page 504 見 504 頁彩圖

grape·fruit /ˈɡreɪp,frut; ˈɡreɪpfruːt/ *n* **grapefruit** *or* **grapefruits** a large round yellow fruit with a thick skin, similar to an orange but with a more acid taste 葡萄柚; 西柚 −see picture on page 504 見 504 頁彩圖

grape·vine /ˈɡreɪp,vaɪn; ˈɡreɪpvaɪn/ *n* **on the grapevine, through the grapevine** because of people talking informally 道聽途說: *News of how she felt about it finally reached him through the office grapevine.* 他在辦公室裡聽人閒談，終於知道了她的感受。

graph /ɡræf; ɡræf, ɡrɑːf/ *n* a drawing showing how two different values are related to each other〔表示兩個不同值之間關係的〕圖表: *Plot a graph showing the average temperature for each month.* 畫一張顯示每月平均溫度的圖表。 | *a piece of graph paper* 一張標繪紙

graph·ic /ˈɡræfɪk; ˈɡræfɪk/ *adj* **1** giving a clear and detailed description in words〔文字〕生動的; 詳細的: *a graphic account of the operation on his stomach* 關於他胃部手術的詳細報告 **2** concerned with drawing, letters, or signs 圖畫的; 字母的; 符號的: *the graphic arts* 書畫藝術

graph·ics /ˈɡræfɪks; ˈɡræfɪks/ *n* [pl] drawings or representations of an object 繪圖;

圖表: *Computer graphics are used in many areas of industrial design.* 電腦製圖現在被用於工業設計的許多領域。

graph·i·cally /ˈɡræfɪklɪ; ˈɡræfɪkli/ *adv* in a very clear and detailed manner 生動地; 詳細地: *She described the events so graphically that I could almost see them.* 她把那些事件描述得如此生動，我像是親眼目睹似的。

grap·ple /ˈɡræpl; ˈɡræpəl/ *v* **grappled, grappling**

grapple with *phr v* **1** [T **grapple with** sbdy] to seize someone and struggle with them 與〔某人〕扭打〔格鬥〕: *He grappled with the thief.* 他與小偷扭打在一起。 **2** [T **grapple with** sthg] to try hard to deal with a difficult problem 盡力解決〔難題〕: *grappling with my physics homework* 絞盡腦汁做我的物理作業

grasp¹ /ɡræsp; ɡrɑːsp/ *v* [T] **1** to take or keep a firm hold of something with one or both of your hands 抓牢, 抓緊〔某物〕: *She suddenly grasped my arm.* 她突然緊抓住我的胳膊。 | *He grasped the rope with both hands.* 她用雙手緊緊抓住繩子。 **2** to succeed in understanding 理解; 領會: *The speech was in French, but I managed to grasp the main ideas.* 演講用的是法語，但我還是設法聽懂了大意。 **3 grasp at something** to try to take, hold, or use 力圖抓住〔握住、使用〕某物: *He grasped at the first excuse that came to mind.* 他想到一個理由便立刻將它拿來作為藉口。 **4 grasp the nettle** to deal firmly with an unpleasant job or subject 果敢地做令人不快的工作

grasp² *n* [sing] **1** a firm hold 緊抓; 緊握: *The kitten wriggled out of my grasp.* 小貓從我緊抱着的手中掙脫。 **2** the ability to reach something 拿到某物的能力: *The prize was suddenly within her grasp.* 她一下子獲獎有望。 **3** understanding 理解: *This work is beyond my grasp.* 這部作品我看不懂。 | *She has a good grasp of the English language.* 她對英語有很強的理解力。

grasp·ing /ˈɡræspɪŋ; ˈɡrɑːspɪŋ/ *adj* eager for more money (a word used to express disapproval) 貪財的〔含貶義〕: *Most landlords are mean and grasping.* 大部分的房東又吝嗇又貪財。

☆grass /ɡræs; ɡrɑːs/ *n* **1** [U] a common low-growing green plant that covers wide areas of ground on hills and in fields, gardens, parks, etc. 草; 青草: *Sheep were grazing on the rich green grass.* 綿羊在吃繁茂的青草。 | *The sign said 'Keep off the grass'.* 牌子上寫着 "請勿踐踏草地"。 **2** [C;U] a green or brown plant with tall straight stems and flat blades 禾本科植物: *He hid behind some tall grasses.* 他躲在很高的草叢後面。 **3** [U] MARIJUANA 大麻

grass·hop·per /ˈɡræs,hɑpəˈ; ˈɡrɑːs,hɔpəˈ/ *n* an insect which makes a loud noise and can jump high in the air 蚱蜢

G

grass·land /'græs,lænd; 'grɑːslænd/ n [C; U] land covered mainly with grass, used especially for cattle to feed on 草地; 草原

grass roots /ˌ· '·/ n [pl] the ordinary people in an organization or political party, not the leaders 基層民眾: *the views of the grass roots.* 基層羣眾的看法。| *at the grass roots level* 在基層

gras·sy /'græsɪ; 'grɑːsi/ adj **grassier, grassiest** covered with growing grass 長滿草的

grate¹ /gret; greɪt/ n the metal bars and frame which hold the coal and wood in a fireplace〔火爐上的〕爐架

grate² v **grated, grating 1** [T] to rub food against a hard rough surface so as to break it into small pieces 磨碎〔食物〕: *grated cheese* 磨碎的乾酪 **2** [I] to make a sharp unpleasant sound 發出刺耳的聲音: *The chalk grated on the blackboard.* 粉筆寫在黑板上吱吱作響。 **3 grate on someone's nerves** (of a noise or behaviour) to make someone annoyed〔聲音或行為〕令某人惱怒: *His whistling grated on her nerves.* 他的口哨聲令她很惱火。

*★**grate·ful** /'gretfəl; 'greɪtfəl/ adj feeling or showing thanks to another person 感激的; 感謝的: *I'd be grateful if you could let me know by Friday.* 如果你能在星期五以前通知我, 我將非常感謝。| *I'll always be grateful to Joe for not telling my father about it.* 喬未把此事告訴我父親, 我對他將一直非常感激。 – **gratefully** adv: *She gratefully accepted their offer of help.* 她很感激地接受了他們來幫忙的提議。 – **gratefulness** n [U]

grat·er /'gretə; 'greɪtəʳ/ n an instrument for grating things into small pieces 磨碎東西的工具 –see picture on page 958 見 958 頁彩圖

grat·i·fy /'grætə,faɪ; 'grætɪfaɪ/ v **gratified, gratifying** [T] fml〔正式〕**1** to give pleasure and satisfaction to someone 使〔某人〕高興和滿足: *I was gratified to hear that he had taken my advice.* 聽說他採納了我的建議, 我感到很高興。 **2** to fulfil a need or desire 滿足〔需要或慾望〕: *Just gratify our curiosity and tell us how he reacted.* 你就滿足一下我們的好奇心, 把他的反應告訴我們吧。 – **gratifying** adj: *an immensely gratifying response to our appeal* 對我們的請求所作出的極令人滿意的反應 – **gratification** /ˌgrætəfə'keʃən; ˌgrætɪfɪ'keɪʃən/ n [C;U]

grat·ing¹ /'gretɪŋ; 'greɪtɪŋ/ n a frame or network of metal bars, often used to protect a hole or window〔保護洞口或窗口的〕柵欄: *The coin fell through a grating at the side of the road.* 硬幣從路邊的柵欄裡掉了進去。

grating² adj sharp, hard, and unpleasant (used of a sound) 尖銳刺耳的〔指聲音〕: *a grating voice* 尖銳的嗓音 –**gratingly** adv

grat·i·tude /'grætə,tjud; 'grætɪtjuːd/ n [U] the feeling of being grateful 感激之情; 謝意: *I'd like to express my gratitude to everyone involved.* 我想對參與此事的所有的人表示感謝。

gra·tu·i·tous /grə'tjuətəs; grə'tjuːɪtəs/ adj unnecessary or undeserved 不必要的; 不值得的: *films full of gratuitous violence* 充斥着不必要的暴力鏡頭的電影 | *a gratuitous insult* 無端的侮辱 –**gratuitously** adv

gra·tu·i·ty /grə'tjuətɪ; grə'tjuːɪti/ n **gratuities** fml a gift of money for a service〔正式〕小費; 賞錢: *Gratuities are not accepted in the hotel.* 這家旅館裡不收小費。

grave¹ /grev; greɪv/ n the place where a dead person is buried 墳墓: *a simple grave with a wooden cross* 一座有木製十字架的樸素的墳墓

grave² adj **graver, gravest 1** giving cause for worry, and often needing urgent attention 令人憂慮的; 嚴重的: *The growth in the world's population is a matter of grave concern to us all.* 世界人口的增長對我們所有人來說都是一個令人擔憂的問題。 | *"I'm afraid his condition is grave," said the doctor.* "他的情況恐怕很嚴重," 醫生說。 **2** serious or solemn 嚴肅的; 莊嚴的: *His face was grave as he told them about the accident.* 他把事故經過告訴他們的時候, 臉上的神情很嚴肅。 – **gravely** adv

grav·el /'grævl; 'grævəl/ n [U] a mixture of small stones with sand, used on the surface of roads or paths 碎石: *footsteps crunching on the gravel* 踩在碎石上嘎吱嘎吱的腳步聲

grav·el·ly /'grævəlɪ; 'grævəli/ adj **1** (also 又作 **gravelled** /'grævld; 'grævəld/) made of or covered with gravel 由碎石製成的; 鋪有碎石的 **2** having a low rough sound〔聲音〕低沉而沙啞的: *a gravelly voice* 沙啞的嗓音

grave·stone /'grev,ston; 'greɪvstəʊn/ n a stone put up over a grave with the name and dates of birth and death of the dead person on it 墓碑: *a white marble gravestone* 白色大理石墓碑

grave·yard /'grev,jard; 'greɪvjɑːd/ n a piece of ground, often near a church, where people are buried〔教堂附近的〕墓地

grav·i·tate /'grævə,tet; 'grævɪteɪt/ v **gravitated, gravitating gravitate towards** to be attracted by and move gradually towards a place, an idea, etc 被〔某一地方或主意等〕吸引: *She gravitated towards her boss's point of view.* 她被老闆的觀點所吸引。

grav·i·ta·tion /ˌgrævə'teʃən; ˌgrævɪ'teɪʃən/ n[U] **1** the act of moving gradually towards something 吸引力 **2** see 見 GRAVITY (1) – **gravitational** adj

grav·i·ty /'grævətɪ; 'grævɪti/ n [U] **1** (also 又作 **gravitaion**) the natural force which makes objects fall when they are dropped 地心吸力; 重力 **2** seriousness 嚴重; 嚴肅: *You must understand the gravity of the situation.* 你必須認識到局勢的嚴重性。

gra·vy /'grevɪ; 'greɪvi/ v [U] liquid made with the juice which comes out of meat as

G

it cooks, and served with the meat 肉汁

gray /gre; greɪ/ *adj,n,v AmE*〖美式〗see 見
GREY

graze¹ /grez; greɪz/ *v* **grazed, grazing 1** [I;T]
(of animals) to feed on grass〔動物〕吃草:
There were cattle grazing in the field. 有牛在
田野裡吃草。**2** [T] to break the surface of
your skin by rubbing it against something
擦傷〔皮膚〕: *She fell down and grazed her
knee.* 她跌倒時把膝蓋擦傷了。**3** [T] to touch
something lightly while passing it〔經過時〕
輕輕擦過[觸及]〔某物〕: *The bullet just grazed
his hand.* 子彈僅僅擦過他的手。

graze² *n* a small wound on your skin 皮膚上
的擦傷: *It's nothing serious — just a graze.*
沒甚麼要緊──只是擦傷了。

grease¹ /gris; griːs/ *n* [U] **1** melted animal
fat 動物油脂: *Strain the grease off the gravy.*
把肉汁的油脂濾掉。**2** a thick oily substance
油膏; 潤滑油: *The valves need a bit more
grease on them.* 閥門上需要再多加點潤滑油。

grease² /griz; griːs, griːz/ *v* **greased, greas-
ing** [T] to put grease on something 給〔某
物〕塗油: *If you grease the lock it will turn
more easily.* 你如果給鎖塗點油, 它開起來會更
容易。

grease·proof pa·per /ˈgris,pruf ˌpepɚ; ˌgriːs-
pruːf ˈpeɪpə/ *n* [U] paper which does not
let grease pass through it 防[耐]油紙; 蠟紙

greas·y /ˈgrisɪ; ˈgriːsi/ *adj* **greasier, greasiest**
slippery and covered with grease 滑的; 覆有
油的: *I can't bear greasy food.* 我受不了油膩
的食物。–**greasily** *adv* –**greasiness** *n* [U]

★★**great** /gret; greɪt/ *adj* **1** large in size,
amount, or degree:〔尺寸〕大的;
〔數量〕多的;〔程度〕高的: *The great ship
sailed away.* 巨輪開走了。| *a great big fish*
一條巨大的魚 | *It was a great loss to us all.*
這對我們所有人都是個巨大的損失。| *These
peace talks are of the greatest importance.* 這
些和平談判極為重要。| *The great majority
of people are in favour of this change.* 絕大
多數人贊成這一變化。| *She's a great friend
of mine.* 她是我的一個密友。**2** very important 非常重要的: *the great civilizations of the
past* 具有重要意義的古代文明 | *one of our
greatest living poets* 最偉大的當代詩人之一 |
great works of art 重要的藝術作品 | *This is
a great occasion.* 這是個重要的場合。**3** *infml*
very good〖非正式〗非常好的: *What a great
idea!* 真是個好主意! | *I feel great today.* 今
天我感覺很好。| *I think she's great!* 我覺得
她很了不起。**4** [only before a noun 只用於名
詞前] a word used to say that someone
does something a lot〔用於表示某人常做某
事〕: *He's a great talker.* 他很健談。| *She's a
great one for saying what she thinks.* 她想到
甚麼就說甚麼。–**greatness** *n* [U]

★**great·ly** /ˈgretlɪ; ˈgreɪtli/ *adv fml* 〖正式〗[used
before past participles 用於過去分詞前]
very much 很; 非常: *I was greatly moved by
his kindness.* 他的善意令我大為感動。| *He*

was greatly influenced by his father. 他受父
親的影響很大。

greed /grid; griːd/ *n* [U] a strong desire to
obtain too much food, money, or power 貪
心; 貪婪: *He asked for more out of sheer
greed.* 純粹出於貪心, 他又多要了一些。|
their greed for gold 他們對於黃金的貪慾

greed·y /ˈgridɪ; ˈgriːdi/ *adj* **greedier, greed-
iest** wanting too much of something, especially food or power 貪婪的; 貪心的; 貪吃
的: *It's greedy to take so many biscuits.* 拿這
麼多的餅乾太貪心了。| *greedy for power* 貪
圖權力 –**greedily** *adv* –**greediness** *n* [U]

Greek¹ /grik; griːk/ *adj* from or connected
with Greece 希臘來的; 與希臘有關的

Greek² *n* **1** [C] a person from Greece 希臘
人 **2** [U] the language of Greece 希臘語

★**green¹** /grin; griːn/ *adj* **1** the colour of leaves
and grass 綠色的: *She was wearing a green
dress.* 她穿了條綠裙子。–see picture on
page 243 見 243 頁彩圖 **2** covered with
grass and trees rather than buildings 覆蓋
有草木的: *We must preserve the green areas
in our cities.* 我們必須保存我們城市的綠
地。**3** connected with the protection of the
natural world 與保護自然界有關的: *More
and more people are becoming interested in
green issues.* 越來越多的人開始對保護自然界
的問題感興趣。| *the Green party* 綠黨 | *We
should look for green alternatives to harmful
chemicals.* 我們應該去尋找綠色產品來代替有
害的化學產品。**4** a green salad a salad
made with green vegetables such as LET-
TUCE 綠色蔬菜沙拉 **5** have green fingers
BrE〖英式〗, **have a green thumb** *AmE*〖美
式〗to have natural skill in making plants
grow well 有園藝技能 **6** young and inexperienced 年輕的; 無經驗的: *He's still a bit green.*
他經驗仍有些欠缺。**7** be green with envy to
be very jealous because you want something that someone else has〔由於想要別人
所有的東西而〕十分嫉妒 **8** the green light
permission to begin doing something 允許
開始做某事[開綠燈] –**greenness** *n* [U]

★**green²** *n* **1** [U] the colour of leaves and
grass 綠色: *She was dressed in green.* 她穿着
綠色衣服。**2** [C] an area of grass for the
general use of the people of a town〔供城
鎮居民使用的〕草地; 綠地: *playing cricket on
the village green* 在村裡草地上打板球 **3** [C] a
smooth flat area of grass used for playing
a game 用於某種運動的草地: *a bowling green*
草地滾球場 **4** greens [pl] green vegetables
whose leaves are cooked and eaten 綠色蔬
菜 **5** the Greens [pl] members of political
parties concerned with the protection of
the natural world〔關注自然界的保護問題
的〕綠黨成員

green belt /ˈ· ·/ *n* [C;U] a stretch of land
round a town, where building is not allowed and fields and woods remain 綠化地
帶〔城鎮周圍不允許建造建築物的地帶〕

green·e·ry /'griːnəri; 'griːnəri/ n [U] attractive green leaves and plants 吸引人的綠葉和綠色植物

green·gage /'griːngeɪdʒ; 'griːngeɪdʒ/ n a soft juicy greenish-yellow fruit like a PLUM 青梅子；青李子

green·gro·cer /'griːngrəʊsə; 'griːngrəʊsəʳ/ n BrE【英式】1 a person who has a shop selling vegetables and fruit 蔬菜水果商：I bought some oranges from the greengrocer. 我在蔬菜水果店買了些橘子。2 greengrocer's a shop selling vegetables and fruit 蔬菜水果店：The greengrocer's didn't have any carrots this morning. 今天上午蔬菜水果店裡沒有胡蘿蔔。| I got the onions at the greengrocer's on the corner. 我的洋葱是在轉角處那間蔬菜水果店裡買的。

green·house /'griːnhaʊs; 'griːnhaʊs/ n a glass building used for growing plants which need heat, light, and protection from winds 玻璃暖房；溫室

greenhouse ef·fect /'···,·/ n the greenhouse effect the gradual warming of the air around the Earth, thought to be caused by the increased level of gases such as CARBON DIOXIDE in the air; the gases which are thought to cause the greenhouse effect are called greenhouse gases 溫室效應〔地球大氣層逐漸變暖，據認為是由二氧化碳等氣體的含量上升所引起的，產生溫室效應的氣體被稱為 greenhouse gases〕

Green·wich Mean Time /ˌgrɪnɪdʒ 'miːn ˌtaɪm, ˌgrenɪtʃ 'miːn taɪm/ n (also 又作 GMT) the time at Greenwich, in London, which is on an imaginary line dividing east from west; times in the rest of the world are fixed in relation to this 格林尼治〔格林威治〕時間

greet /griːt; griːt/ v [T] 1 to welcome someone when you meet them 與〔某人〕打招呼；問候；致意：She greeted us by shouting a friendly "Hello!" 她見到我們時，友善地叫了聲"你們好!" 2 to receive something in a particular way〔以某種方式〕對待〔某物〕：His ideas were greeted with scorn. 他的觀點被人瞧不起。

greet·ing /'griːtɪŋ; 'griːtɪŋ/ n [C;U] words produced when you meet someone or send them good wishes 招呼；問候："Good morning," I said, but she didn't discuss the greeting. "早安," 我說。但是她沒有理睬我的招呼。| Christmas greetings 聖誕賀辭

gre·gar·i·ous /grɪˈgɛərɪəs; grɪˈgeərɪəs/ adj fml enjoying being with other people【正式】喜歡與別人在一起的；愛交際的

gre·nade /grɪˈned; grəˈneɪd/ n a small bomb which can be thrown by hand or fired from a gun 手榴彈；槍榴彈

grew /gruː; gruː/ the past tense of GROW ☆ GROW 的過去式

★**grey¹** /gre; greɪ/ adj greyer, greyest (also 又作 gray AmE【美式】) 1 the colour like black mixed with white 灰色的；灰白的：

heavy, grey rain clouds 陰沉的烏雲 –see picture on page 243 見 243 頁彩圖 2 go grey to start to have grey hair 開始長灰白頭髮：She's starting to go grey. 她的頭髮開始變白了。–see picture on page 469 見 469 頁彩圖 3 dull and cloudy (used of the weather) 陰暗多雲的〔指天氣〕4 pale in colour because of fear or worry (used of someone's face)〔臉色由於恐懼或憂慮而〕蒼白的 –greyness n [U]

grey² n (also 又作 gray AmE【美式】) [C;U] a grey colour 灰色：She was dressed in grey. 她身穿灰色衣服。| dull greys and browns 暗灰色與棕色

grey³ v (also 又作 gray AmE【美式】) [I] be greying to be turning grey; you say that a person's hair is greying or that a person is greying 變成灰色；頭髮開始變白：He's greying a bit on top. 他頭頂上的頭髮開始有點變白了。–see picture on page 243 見 243 頁彩圖

grey ar·e·a /'· ,···/ n an area of knowledge that is not clear or fully understood〔知識領域內不十分清楚或沒有充分理解的〕灰色地區

grey·hound /'greˌhaʊnd; 'greɪhaʊnd/ n a thin dog with long legs that can run very fast 靈緹〔一種獵犬〕

grid /grɪd; grɪd/ n 1 a set of straight lines that cross each other to form a lot of small squares (方)格子 2 a network of wires supplying electricity 輸電網：the national grid 全國輸電網 3 a system of numbered squares printed on a map so that you can describe the exact position of something〔地圖上的〕座標方格

grid·dle /'grɪdl; 'grɪdl/ n an iron plate used for baking flat cakes over a fire〔烤糕餅用的〕烤盤

grief /griːf; griːf/ n [U] 1 great sorrow caused especially by the death of someone you love〔尤指因所愛之人的去世而引起的〕憂傷；悲痛：She went nearly mad with grief. 她悲痛欲絕，幾乎發瘋。2 come to grief to fail or be hurt 失敗；受傷：All my schemes came to grief. 我所有的計劃都失敗了。3 good grief! an expression of surprise〔表示驚奇的短語〕

griev·ance /'griːvəns; 'griːvəns/ n a reason for complaint 委曲；抱怨；不滿：We have called a meeting with the unions to discuss their grievances. 我們已與工會方面開了個會，討論他們不滿的問題。

grieve /griːv; griːv/ v grieved, grieving 1 [I] to feel very sad, especially because someone you love has died〔尤指因所愛之人的去世而〕感到悲痛：She is still grieving for her dead husband. 她仍在為她死去的丈夫悲傷不已。2 [T] fml to make you very unhappy【正式】令人傷心

griev·ous /'griːvəs; 'griːvəs/ adj fml very harmful【正式】非常有害的：a grievous mistake 嚴重的錯誤 –grievously adv

grill¹ /grɪl; grɪl/ v [T] 1 to cook food under

direct heat 烤; 燒; 焙: *We grilled the sausages and potatoes.* 我們在火上烤香腸和馬鈴薯。–see 見 COOK² (USAGE用法) **2** *infml* to question someone severely and continuously〔非正式〕嚴厲盤問〔某人〕: *He was grilled for two hours before the police let him go.* 警方盤問了他兩個小時才放他走。

grill² *n* **1** an open metal shelf under direct heat in a cooker, where food can be cooked quickly〔爐灶下面烤食物的〕烤器; 烤架: *Put the meat under the grill.* 把肉放在烤架下面。 **2** a set of bars which can be put over a fire to cook food on〔置於火上的〕柵狀烤架

grille /grɪl; grɪl/ *n* a metal framework of bars over a door or window used for protection〔門或窗上防護用的〕鐵柵欄

grim /grɪm; grɪm/ *adj* **1** very unpleasant or sad 不快的; 難過的: *the grim news of his death* 他的死訊令人難過 | *The future looks grim.* 前景看上去不容樂觀。 **2** determined and serious 堅定的; 嚴肅的: *He gave a grim smile.* 他堅定地笑了笑。–**grimly** *adv*

gri·mace /grɪˈmes; grɪˈmeɪs/ *v* **grimaced, grimacing** [I] to make an expression of pain or anger which makes your face look twisted and unattractive 作怪相〔表示痛苦或憤怒〕: *He grimaced with pain.* 他痛得臉都變形了。–**grimace** *n*: *She gave a grimace at the mention of his name.* 聽到他的名字, 她作了個鬼臉。

grime /graɪm; graɪm/ *n* [U] thick black dirt 污垢; 污物: *His face and hands were covered with grime.* 他的臉和手上沾滿了污垢。

grim·y /ˈgraɪmɪ; ˈgraɪmɪ/ *adj* **grimier, grimiest** covered with thick dirt 覆有污垢的

grin¹ /grɪn; grɪn/ *v* **-nn-** [I] **1** to give a very wide smile 咧着嘴笑: *He grinned at me.* 他對我咧着嘴笑。 **2** **grin and bear it** *infml* to suffer an unpleasant situation without complaining〔非正式〕毫無怨言地忍受

grin² *n* a very wide smile 咧嘴的笑: *She had a big grin on her face.* 她咧開嘴大笑。

grind¹ /graɪnd; graɪnd/ *v* **ground** /graʊnd; graʊnd/, **ground** [T] **1** (also 又作 **grind** sthg ↔ **up**) to crush something into small pieces or a powder 把〔某物〕碾成碎片或粉末: *new machines to grind wheat* 磨小麥的新機器 | *freshly-ground coffee* 新磨成的咖啡 **2** to sharpen something such as a knife by rubbing it on a hard surface 磨尖〔刀具〕 **3** to press something with a lot of force against something else 擠壓〔某物〕: *The dirt was deeply ground into the carpet.* 污垢被深深地踩到地毯裡去了。 **4** **grind to a halt** to come slowly to a stop 逐漸停止

grind sbdy ↔ **down** *phr v* [T] to keep someone in a state of suffering and hopelessness 使〔某人〕受折磨; 使〔某人〕毫無希望

grind² *n* [sing] uninteresting work 枯燥乏味的工作: *He finds any kind of study a real grind.* 他認為任何一種研究工作都枯燥無味。

grind·er /ˈgraɪndɚ; ˈgraɪndə(r)/ *n* a machine that grinds something 研磨機: *a coffee grinder* 咖啡研磨器

grind·ing /ˈgraɪndɪŋ; ˈgraɪndɪŋ/ *adj* **grinding poverty** extreme POVERTY 極端貧窮

grip¹ /grɪp; grɪp/ *v* **-pp-** [T] **1** to hold something very tightly 緊緊握住〔某物〕: *He gripped my hand in fear.* 他害怕地緊緊握着我的手。 **2** to hold your attention completely 緊緊吸引住注意力: *The audience was gripped by the young actor's performance.* 觀眾被這位年輕演員的表演緊緊吸引住了。

grip² *n* **1** a very tight forceful hold 緊握: *He kept a tight grip on the handle.* 他緊緊抓住把手。 **2** **be losing your grip** *infml* to be becoming less able to do or understand something〔非正式〕做或理解某事的能力降低 **3** *AmE* a bag for carrying your belongings when you are travelling〔美式〕旅行袋 **4** **come/get to grips with something** to start dealing seriously with something difficult 開始認真應付難題

gripe¹ /graɪp; graɪp/ *v* **griped, griping** [I] *infml* to complain continually〔非正式〕不斷抱怨; 發牢騷: *He's always griping.* 他老是發牢騷。

gripe² *n* *infml* a complaint〔非正式〕抱怨; 牢騷: *My main gripe is that there's no hot water.* 我主要的不滿是沒有熱水。

grip·ping /ˈgrɪpɪŋ; ˈgrɪpɪŋ/ *adj* holding your attention completely 吸引注意力的: *I found the film really gripping.* 我覺得這部電影確實扣人心弦。

gris·ly /ˈgrɪzlɪ; ˈgrɪzlɪ/ *adj* **grislier, grisliest** very unpleasant and nasty 令人不快的; 討厭的: *the grisly remains of the bodies* 可怕的殘骸 | *the grisly details of the murder* 令人厭惡的兇殺細節

gris·tle /ˈgrɪsl; ˈgrɪsəl/ *n* [U] the part of meat which is not soft enough to eat 軟骨

grit¹ /grɪt; grɪt/ *n* [U] **1** very small pieces of stone 砂粒; 砂礫: *There was a piece of grit in the rice.* 米飯裡有粒沙子。 **2** *infml* determination and courage〔非正式〕決心; 勇氣 –**gritty** *adj*

grit² *v* **-tt-** [T] **1** to put grit on top of ice or snow on the surface of a road in order to stop cars slipping 在〔冰上或雪上〕撒砂子〔防止汽車打滑〕 **2** **grit your teeth** to become determined and continue when you are in a difficult situation〔在困境中〕下定決心堅持下去; 咬緊牙關: *She just had to grit her teeth and carry on.* 她不得不咬緊牙關堅持下去。

groan¹ /grosn; grəʊn/ *v* [I] to make a loud, low sound of pain, worry, or disapproval 呻吟〔表示痛苦和憂慮〕; 嘆息〔表示不贊成〕: *She groaned in agony.* 她痛苦地呻吟着。 | *"Not another test!" groaned the students.* "別再考試了!" 學生們低聲地叫。

groan² *n* a loud, low sound of pain, worry, or disapproval 呻吟; 抱怨; 嘆息: *There were*

G

loud groans when he asked them to work late. 當他要求他們晚上班時, 他們便抱怨起來。

gro·cer /ˈgrəʊsə; ˈgrəʊsər/ *n* a shopkeeper who sells many kinds of food and goods for the house 食品雜貨商

gro·cer·ies /ˈgrəʊsərɪz; ˈgrəʊsəriz/ *n* [pl] foods such as flour, coffee, and rice which you buy from a grocer's shop 食品雜貨〔如麵粉、咖啡、大米〕

grog·gy /ˈgrɒgɪ; ˈgrɒgi/ *adj* **groggier, groggiest** *infml* feeling weak and ill 〔非正式〕感覺虛弱〔生病〕: *I always feel a bit groggy in the mornings.* 早上我總感到身體有些發虛。

groin /grɔɪn; grɔɪn/ *n* the part of your body where your legs meet 腹股溝

groom¹ /grum; gruːm/ *n* **1** a person who looks after horses 馬伕 **2** (also 又作 **bride-groom** *fml* 〔正式〕) a man who is getting married 新郎

groom² *v* [T] **1** to clean horses by rubbing and brushing them 刷洗〔馬匹〕 **2** to prepare someone for a special position or occasion 培養〔某人〕; 使作好準備: *He's being groomed for the star role.* 他正在為當明星作準備。

groomed /grumd; gruːmd/ *adj* well **groomed** having a neat, tidy appearance 外表整潔的

groove /gruːv; gruːv/ *n* a narrow track cut in a surface of something 凹槽; 紋: *The needle moves along the groove on a record.* 唱針在唱片的紋路裡滑動。| *The cupboard door slides open along a groove.* 碗廚的門是順着凹槽滑開的。

grope /grop; grəʊp/ *v* **groped, groping** [I + adv/prep] **1** to search for something that you cannot see, using your hands 〔用手〕摸索: *He groped in his pocket for his ticket.* 他在口袋裡摸索着尋找那張票子。**2** **grope your way somewhere** to move towards a place by feeling with your hands because you cannot see 〔由於看不見而〕摸索着到某處: *I groped my way back to my seat.* 我摸索着回到了自己的座位上。**3** **grope for something** to try to find or discover something such as the answer to a problem 探索某物〔如問題的答案〕

gross¹ /gros; grəʊs/ *adj* **1** unpleasantly fat 過於肥胖的: **2** very rude and offensive 粗魯的; 冒犯的: *We were all shocked by his gross behaviour.* 我們大家對他的粗魯行為感到震驚。**3** [only before a noun 只用於名詞前] very bad and unacceptable 非常糟糕的; 無法接受的: *the gross inequalities in our society* 我們社會中所存在的嚴重的不平等 **4** total 總共的: *The gross weight of the product is 250g.* 該產品總重量為250克。**5** calculated before you have paid any taxes 納稅前的: *What's your gross annual income?* 你的稅前年收入是多少? –compare 比較 NET³ –**grossly** *adv* –**grossness** *n* [U]

FAMILY TREE 家庭譜系

***Exercise 1* 練習一** *Complete these sentences about the illustration.* 根據彩圖填空。

1 Ted is Bill's _____ .
2 Ted is Pat's _____ .
3 Ruth is Geoff's _____ .
4 Joe is Cathy's _____ .
5 Dawn is Eric's _____ .
6 Karen is Anne's _____ .
7 Jean is Jane's _____ .
8 Helen and John are Eric's _____ .

Puzzle 難題
A man is standing in front of a picture of a boy. He says:
   Brothers and sisters have I none
   But this boy's father
   Is my father's son.
Who can the man see in the picture?

***Exercise 2* 練習二** *Match the two parts of these sentences.* 將左右兩欄對應的句子連接起來。

1 My father's mother
2 My mother's sister's daughter
3 My son's wife
4 My father's brother
5 My mother's father
6 My uncle's wife
7 My husband's father
8 My daughter's husband
9 My husband's mother
10 My sister's husband

A is my brother-in-law.
B is my uncle.
C is my son-in-law.
D is my grandfather.
E is my father-in-law.
F is my aunt.
G is my mother-in-law.
H is my grandmother.
I is my cousin.
J is my daughter-in-law.

Can you make a family tree of your family, or a family you know well, like the one in the illustration? 你能像彩圖一樣, 畫一張自己的家庭或你所熟知的家庭的家譜嗎?

The people shown here are all related to ANNE.
這些人都和安有親戚關係。

grandparents
祖父母

grandfather
祖父

grandmother
祖母

Ted 特德　Mary 瑪麗

parents
父母

| uncle 姑丈 | aunt 姑母 | father 爸爸 | mother 媽媽 | father-in-law 公公[家翁] | mother-in-law 婆婆[家姑] |

Joe 喬　Cathy 凱茜　　Bill 比爾　Pat 帕特　　John 約翰　Helen 海倫

| cousin 表兄弟 | cousin 表姐妹 | brother-in-law 姐[妹]夫 | sister 姐[妹] | | husband 丈夫 | brother-in-law 大伯子[小叔子] | sister-in-law 妯娌 |

Ian 伊恩　Liz 莉茲　Mike 邁克　Jean 瓊　ANNE 安　Eric 埃里克　Geoff 傑弗　Ruth 露絲

| nephew 侄 | niece 侄女 | son-in-law 女婿 | daughter 女兒 | son 兒子 | daughter-in-law 媳婦 |

children
子女

Phil 菲爾　Sue 蘇　Steve 史蒂夫　Jane 簡　Frank 弗蘭克　Karen 凱倫

grandchildren
孫輩

grandson
外孫

granddaughter
外孫女

Chris 克里斯　Dawn 道恩

food 食物

bananas
香蕉

oranges
橙子;橘子

apples
蘋果

bread
麵包

milk
牛奶

cheese
乾酪

eggs
蛋

butter
牛油[黃油]

grapefruit
葡萄柚; 西柚

peaches
桃

lemons
檸檬

plums
李子, 梅

cabbage
椰菜[包心菜]

potatoes
馬鈴薯[土豆]

pears
梨

beans
豆

cauliflower
花椰菜

turnips
蘿蔔; 蕪菁

carrots
胡蘿蔔

strawberries
草莓

onions
洋蔥

Brussels sprouts
球芽甘藍

peas
豌豆

leeks
韮蔥

sausage
香腸

beetroot
(BrE 【英式】)/
beets
(AmE 【美式】)
甜菜根

chicken
雞肉

bacon
鹹豬肉, 燻豬肉

sweetcorn
(BrE 【英式】)/
corn
(AmE 【美式】)
甜玉米

chop
排骨

mushrooms
蘑菇

minced
(BrE 【英式】)/
ground
(AmE 【美式】)
beef
剁碎的牛肉

radishes
小蘿蔔

celery
芹菜

fillet
去骨切成片的魚、肉

peppers
辣椒

cucumbers
黃瓜

lobster
龍蝦

raspberries 山莓

tomatoes
蕃茄[西紅柿]

crab
蟹

mussels
淡菜

lettuce
生菜

blackberries 黑莓

grapes
葡萄

cherries
櫻桃

gross² *v* [T] to earn as a total amount 總共賺得: *The company grossed £2,000,000 last year.* 公司去年的總收入為二百萬英鎊。

gross³ *n* [plural is 複數為 **gross**] a group of 144 things 籮〔144個〕: *three gross of eggs* 三籮雞蛋

gro·tesque /grəˈtesk; grəʊˈtesk/ *adj* very ugly or nasty 極醜陋的; 極討厭的: *people wearing grotesque masks* 帶着醜陋面具的人 | *The very idea is grotesque!* 就是這個主意令人討厭! –**grotesquely** *adv*

grot·to /ˈgratə; ˈgrɒtəʊ/ *n* **grottoes** *or* **grottos** a small attractive cave 〔吸引人的〕小洞穴

grot·ty /ˈgrati; ˈgrɒti/ *adj* **grottier, grottiest** *slang* unpleasant and of bad quality 〔俚〕令人不快的; 品質惡劣的: *She lives in a grotty little room with nowhere to cook.* 她住在一間條件惡劣的小房間裡, 連燒飯的地方都沒有。–**grottiness** *n* [U]

grouch¹ /graʊtʃ; graʊtʃ/ *n infml* 〔非正式〕 **1** a small complaint 小的牢騷 **2** a person who keeps complaining 不斷抱怨的人

grouch² *v* [I] *infml* to complain in a bad-tempered way 〔非正式〕抱怨; 發牢騷

grouchy /ˈgraʊtʃɪ; ˈgraʊtʃi/ *adv* **grouchier, grouchiest** *infml* often complaining in a bad-tempered way 〔非正式〕愛發牢騷的

★★**ground¹** /graʊnd; graʊnd/ *n* **1 the ground** the surface of the earth 地面: *The branch broke and fell to the ground.* 樹枝斷了, 落到地上。**2 below ground** below the surface of the earth 在地下 **3 above ground** on or above the surface of the earth 在地上 **4** [U] land 土地: *The ground is too dry for planting seeds.* 這土地太乾, 不適宜播種。**5** [C] a piece of land used for a particular purpose 〔作某一用途的〕場地: *a football ground* 足球場 | *a burial ground* 墓地 **6 grounds** [pl] land belonging to a large building 建築物周圍的場地; 庭園: *Let's take a walk through the grounds.* 我們在庭園裡散步吧。**7** [U] a subject or an area of knowledge 科目; 知識領域: *I think that the book tries to cover too much ground.* 我覺得這本書力圖涉及的知識領域太廣了。 | *We spent hours going over the same old ground.* 我們花了數小時複習同一個老課題。**8 grounds** [pl] a reason why you do something 〔做某事的〕理由: *We have good grounds for thinking that she was involved in the affair.* 我們有充分的理由認為她參與了此事。 | *You have no grounds for complaint.* 你沒有任何理由抱怨。**9 on grounds of…, on**

FOOD 食物

Exercise 1 練習一
Look at this list of different kinds of fruit. Which ones grow in your country? Do you know where the other fruits grow?
請看下表中列出的表中各種水果的名稱。哪幾種水果生長於你們的國家? 你知道其餘的水果生長在何處嗎?

apples	bananas	blackberries
cherries	grapefruit	grapes
lemons	oranges	peaches
pears	plums	raspberries
strawberries		

Exercise 2 練習二
Do you like these vegetables? Mark the list like this. 你喜歡這些蔬菜嗎? 請在各種蔬菜名稱旁作下列標記:
√ √ = *I like this vegetable very much*
√ = *I like this vegetable*
✕ = *I don't like this vegetable*
? = *I don't know this vegetable*

beans	beetroot	cabbage
carrots	cauliflower	celery
cucumber	leeks	lettuce
mushrooms	onions	peas
peppers	potatoes	radishes
sprouts	sweetcorn	tomatoes
turnips		

Exercise 3 練習三
Use the words in the box to complete this passage. 選用方框中的詞語填入下文中。

bananas	mushrooms	ham
butter	milk	eggs
cheese	onions	

It is quite easy to make an omelette. First, break three ¹e_____ into a bowl. Add some ²m_____, season the mixture with salt and pepper and use a whisk to beat. Melt some ³b_____ in a frying pan and pour in the mixture. Cook for a few minutes until it begins to set. You can then add ⁴m_____ or other savoury fillings such as ⁵c_____, ⁶h_____ or ⁷o_____. Omelettes can sometimes also be made with sweet foods like ⁸b_____.

---

the grounds of... because of 因為...; 由
於...: *She divorced him on the grounds of
his adultery.* 由於他與人通姦, 她和他離了婚。
10 on the grounds that... because 因為...:
*He resigned on the grounds that he needed
to spend more time with his family.* 由於需要
和家人有更多時間在一起, 他辭了職。 **11 gain
ground** to become more popular 變得更加
流行: *These ideas seem to be gaining ground.*
這些觀念似乎愈來愈流行。 [RELATED
PHRASE 相關詞組 **lose ground**: *The
government have lost a lot of ground over
this issue.* 政府在這個問題上失去了許多公眾
的支持。] **12 get something off the ground**
to start something successfully 順利地開始
做某事 –see 見 LAND (USAGE 用法)

> ■ USAGE 用法: Compare 比較 **ground**
> and 和 **floor**. Both words can mean
> "the surface that we walk on", but
> **floor** is most commonly used when
> the surface is indoors ☆ 這兩個詞都指
> "我們所走的地面", 但是 **floor** 主要用來
> 指室內的地面: *The branch fell to the
> **ground**.* 樹枝落到了地上。 | *The cup
> fell to the **floor**.* 杯子掉到了地上。 | *The
> **ground** was covered with dead leaves.*
> 地上蓋滿了枯樹葉。 | *The **floor** was
> covered with thick carpet.* 地板上鋪著厚
> 厚的地毯。

ground² *v* **1** [I] (of a boat) to hit the bottom
of a sea or lake and be unable to move
〔船〕擱淺 **2** [T] to cause a boat to hit the
bottom of a sea or lake 使〔船〕擱淺 **3** [T] to
prevent a person or plane from flying 禁止
〔人或飛機〕起飛: *All planes have been
grounded because of thick fog.* 由於有大霧,
所有的飛機都停飛了。 **4 be grounded on/in
something** to be based on something 基於
某物; 以某物為根據: *an argument grounded
on personal experience* 以親身經歷為根據的
論點

ground³ the past tense and past participle
of GRIND ☆ GRIND 的過去式和過去分詞

ground floor /ˌ· ˈ·◂/ *n* (**first floor** *AmE* 〖美
式〗) the part of a building at ground level
〔樓房的〕底層: *I live on the ground floor.* 我
住在一樓。

ground·ing /ˈɡraʊndɪŋ; ˈɡraʊndɪŋ/ *n* [sing] a
complete training in the main points of a
skill or subject 〔某一技能或學科的〕基礎; 根
基: *a good grounding in the basic skills of
reading and writing* 閱讀與寫作等基本技能方
面的良好基礎

ground·less /ˈɡraʊndlɪs; ˈɡraʊndləs/ *adj* not
based on reason or on facts (used of
feelings or ideas) 無根據的; 無理由的〔指感
情或觀念〕: *groundless fears* 莫名的恐懼 |
*Fortunately, my suspicions proved ground-
less.* 幸運的是, 我的懷疑〔疑慮〕被證明是沒有
根據的。

grounds·man /ˈɡraʊndzmən; ˈɡraʊndzmən/
n **groundsmen** /-mən; -mən/ a man employed to look after a sports field or park
運動場〔公園〕管理員

ground·swell /ˈɡraʊndswɛl; ˈɡraʊndswel/ *n*
[sing] a sudden increase in the number of
people who think or feel something (某種)
突然高漲的情緒; 呼聲: *a groundswell of opinion* 越來越高的呼聲

ground·work /ˈɡraʊndˌwɜːk; ˈɡraʊndwɜːk/
n [U] the work which forms the base for
some kind of study or skill 基礎工作: *We'll
have to do most of the groundwork early in
1993.* 1993 年年初, 我們將須把大部分基礎工
作做完。

group¹ /ɡruːp; ɡruːp/ *n* [+ sing/pl verb]
1 a number of people or things
that are together, or that are connected in
some way 羣; 組; 類; 簇: *a family group* 一家
人 | *a group of tall trees* 高大的樹叢 |
*Schoolchildren are taught according to age
groups.* 學童按年齡分組教學。 **2** a small
number of people who sing and play popular music together 演唱團: *My favourite
group are playing here tonight.* 我最喜愛的演
唱團今晚在此演出。

group² *v* [I;T] to form into one or more
groups 組合; 集合; 把...分成若干類〔組〕: *People
can be grouped into several types.* 可以分
成數種類型。 | *We must group together to
fight this proposal.* 我們必須團結一致反對這
項提議。

group·ie /ˈɡruːpɪ; ˈɡruːpi/ *n infml* a young
girl who follows the members of a POP
group, especially to have sex with them 〖非
正式〗〔尤指為與其發生性關係而〕追隨歌星的
年輕女孩

group·ing /ˈɡruːpɪŋ; ˈɡruːpɪŋ/ *n* a number
of people or things that form a group 形成一
組〔羣〕的人或物: *We are now seeing
several new political groupings in Parliament.* 我們
現在可以發現議會裡正在出現幾個新的政治團
體。

grouse¹ /ɡraʊs; ɡraʊs/ *n* [plural is 複數為
grouse] [C;U] a smallish fat bird which is
shot for food and sport, or its flesh as food
松雞; 松雞肉

grouse² *v* **groused, grousing** [I] *infml* to
complain 〖非正式〗抱怨; 發牢騷: *You're
always grousing and grumbling about something!* 你總是沒完沒了的抱怨這個, 抱怨那個!

grove /ɡrəʊv; ɡrəʊv/ *n* **1** *lit* a small group of
trees 〖文〗小樹林 **2** an area planted with
certain types of trees 〔種植某種樹木的〕園
地: *an orange grove* 柑橘園 | *olive groves* 橄
欖樹林 **3 Grove** part of the name of a
road ...路, ...街〔路名的一部分〕

grov·el /ˈɡrɒvl; ˈɡrɒvəl/ *v* **-ll-** (**-l-** *AmE* 〖美
式〗) [I] **1** to show extreme respect for
someone because they are important or
powerful and you are frightened of them
極為敬重〔某人〕; 俯首貼耳 **2** to lie or move

flat on the ground, especially because you are afraid of someone〔由於害怕而在某人面前〕趴在地上; 匍匐前進 **–groveller** *n*

★★grow /gro; grəʊ/ *v* **grew** /gru; gruː/ **grown** /gron; grəʊn/, **growing** **1** [I] to get bigger by natural development〔自然地〕長大: *A lot of weeds grow very quickly.* 許多雜草長得非常快。| *A lamb grows into a sheep.* 小綿羊長成大羊。| *The population is growing too quickly.* 人口增長過快。**2** [I] (of plants) to be alive in a particular place〔植物〕生長: *Cotton grows wild here.* 這裡棉花蔓生。| *trees growing beside the river* 生長在河邊的樹木 **3** [T] to care for plants and help them to grow 種植〔植物〕; 栽培: *We're not growing potatoes this year.* 今年我們沒種馬鈴薯。**4** [T] to allow your hair to grow 讓〔毛髮〕生長: *He's grown a beard.* 他已留起了鬍鬚。**5** [+ complement] to gradually become 逐漸變成: *She's growing old.* 她漸漸老了。| *The noise grew louder.* 聲音越來越響。| *It's growing dark; we must go home soon.* 天越來越暗, 我們必須快些回家。**6 grow to do something** to start gradually to do something 逐漸開始做某事: *After a while I grew to like him.* 過了一段時間, 我就開始漸漸喜歡他了。**7** [I] to become larger or more important 變得更大〔更重要〕: *The problem of homelessness is growing all the time.* 人們無家可歸的問題在日益嚴重。

grow away from sbdy *phr v* [T] to have a less close relationship with someone 與〔某人〕日漸疏遠: *Since she went to university she's grown away from the family.* 自從上大學之後, 她與家人的關係便日益疏遠。

grow into sthg *phr v* [T] **1** to become something 變成: *She's grown into a fine young woman.* 她已出落成一位漂亮的姑娘。**2** to become big enough for clothes or shoes 長得適合於〔穿衣服或鞋子〕: *The coat is too long, but she'll grow into it.* 這件外衣太長, 不過等她再長大些就會合身的。

grow on sbdy *phr v* [T] to become gradually more pleasant or enjoyable to you 漸漸被〔自己〕所喜愛: *I didn't like this house at first, but it's grown on me.* 起先我不喜歡這所房子, 但現在已開始喜歡它了。

grow out of sthg *phr v* [T] **1** to become too big or too old for something 長得太高或太大而不適於〔某事物〕: *She's grown out of all her clothes.* 她長大了, 所有的衣服都穿不下。| *Most children grow out of wetting the bed.* 大部分孩子長大了就不會再尿床。**2** to develop as a result of something 由〔某物〕而產生: *Her political beliefs grew out of her hatred of injustice.* 她的政治觀點源於她對於不公平現象的憎惡。

grow up *phr v* [I] **1** (of people) to develop from a child into a man or woman〔人〕長大; 成人 **2** to begin or develop 開始; 形成: *The custom grew up of dividing the father's land between the sons.* 把父親的地產

分給兒子們的習俗漸漸形成了。

grow·er /ˈgroɚ; ˈgrəʊəʳ/ *n* a person who grows plants or fruit for sale〔產品供出售的〕種植者

growl /graʊl; graʊl/ *v* [I] **1** (of a dog) to make a deep, unfriendly sound〔狗〕狂吠: *The dog looked up and growled at me.* 那隻狗抬起頭對著我吼叫。**2** to say something in a rough, angry voice 咆哮著說 **–growl** *n*

grown¹ /gron; grəʊn/ the past participle of GROW ☆GROW 的過去分詞

grown² *adj* [only before a noun 只用於名詞前] adult 成年的: *A grown man like you shouldn't act like that.* 一個像你這樣的人不應該有這種舉動。

grown-up¹ /ˌ· ·◂/ *adj* adult 成年的: *She has a grown-up daughter who lives abroad.* 她有個成年的女兒住在國外。| *He's very grown-up for his age.* 就他的年齡而言, 他已很老成了。

grown-up² /ˈ· ·/ *n* an adult (a word used by children) 大人〔孩子間的用語〕: *Quick! The grown-ups are coming!* 快點兒! 大人們來啦!

★growth /groθ; grəʊθ/ *n* **1** [U] the act or rate of growing and developing 成長(速度); 發展(速度): *the slow growth* **of** *world literacy* 世界掃盲工作的進展緩慢 | *The animals are fed on hormones to stimulate growth.* 人們餵動物吃荷爾蒙以刺激其生長。**2** [sing] increase in numbers or amount〔數量的〕增加: *a sudden growth* **in** *the membership of the club* 俱樂部會員人數的突然增加 **3** [C] an unnatural lump that has grown in a part of someone's body 腫瘤

grub¹ /grʌb; grʌb/ *n* **1** [C] a young insect that has just come out of the egg and looks like a small worm 蠐螬; 蛆 **2** [U] *infml* food〔非正式〕食物

grub² *v* **-bb-**

grub about/around *phr v* [I] to dig with your hands, often in order to find something 用手挖掘〔通常為了尋找某物〕

grub·by /ˈgrʌbɪ; ˈgrʌbi/ *adj* **grubbier, grubbiest** *infml* dirty〔非正式〕骯髒的

grudge¹ /grʌdʒ; grʌdʒ/ *v* **grudged, grudging** [T] to allow someone to have something unwillingly, or feel annoyed that they have it 勉強地給; 嫉妒: *I don't grudge him his success.* 我並不嫉妒他的成功。

□ USEFUL PATTERNS 有用句型
to grudge something to someone; to grudge someone something

grudge² *n* **1** a cause for disliking or hating another person 反感; 怨恨: *I always feel he has a grudge* **against** *me.* 我總感覺他對我很反感。**2 bear a grudge** to continue to have feelings of anger about someone's past actions〔對某人過去的行為〕耿耿於懷: *Don't worry — I'm not the sort to bear grudges.* 別擔心 — 我可不是那種記仇的人。

grudg·ing /ˈɡrʌdʒɪŋ; ˈɡrʌdʒɪŋ/ *adj* given unwillingly 勉強給予的: *her grudging praise* 她勉強說出來的讚揚話 —**grudgingly** *adv*

gru·el /ˈɡruəl; ˈɡruːəl/ *n* [U] a thin liquid food used especially for sick people〔尤指給病人吃的〕粥

gru·el·ling /ˈɡruəlɪŋ; ˈɡruːəlɪŋ/ *adj* (**grueling** *AmE*〖美式〗) very difficult and tiring 非常困難的; 非常累人的

grue·some /ˈɡrusəm; ˈɡruːsəm/ *adj* connected with death in a way which is shocking and which makes you feel sick 令人毛骨悚然的: *a gruesome murder* 令人膽寒的兇殺案

gruff /ɡrʌf; ɡrʌf/ *adj* rough and unfriendly 粗魯的; 不友好的: *In spite of his gruff manner, he is really very kind.* 他儘管舉止粗魯, 但實際上心地十分善良。 —**gruffly** *adv* – **gruffness** *n* [U]

grum·ble¹ /ˈɡrʌmbl̩; ˈɡrʌmbəl/ *v* **grumbled, grumbling** [I] to complain in a quiet but bad-tempered way 輕聲抱怨: *He keeps grumbling* **about** *his neighbours.* 他一直在輕聲抱怨他的左鄰右舍。

grumble² *n* a complaint or expression of dissatisfaction 抱怨; 牢騷

grump·y /ˈɡrʌmpi; ˈɡrʌmpi/ *adj* **grumpier, grumpiest** bad-tempered 脾氣壞的: *You're very grumpy today — what's the matter?* 你今天的脾氣很壞——是怎麼回事?

grunt /ɡrʌnt; ɡrʌnt/ *v* [I] **1** to make the low rough sound that pigs make 發出豬叫聲 **2** to make a short deep rough sound in the throat, often when dissatisfied or unwilling to talk〔通常在不滿或不願講話時〕發出哼聲: *He didn't say anything, just grunted from behind his newspaper.* 他沒說甚麼, 只是在報紙後面嘟噥了一聲。 —**grunt** *n*

★**guar·an·tee¹** /ˌɡærənˈti; ˌɡærənˈtiː/ *n* **1** an agreement by the maker of an article to repair it or give you another one if it goes wrong within a certain period of time 保證書〔一段時間內產品若是出現問題, 製造商負責修理或調換〕: *The radio has a two-year guarantee.* 這台收音機有兩年保用期。 **2** a formal declaration that something will happen or be done〔做某事的〕正式聲明; 保證: *There's no guarantee she will accept the offer.* 她沒有保證接受這提議。 | *Can you give me a guarantee that the goods will be delivered this week?* 你能向我保證在本星期交貨嗎? **3** an agreement to be responsible for the fulfilment of someone else's promise, for example paying a debt〔實現承諾的〕擔保書 **4** **under guarantee** (of an article) covered by a maker's guarantee〔商品〕有保用的

guarantee² *v* **guaranteed, guaranteeing 1** [T; + that] to give a promise of quality, or that faults will be repaired 保證〔品質或負責修理〕: *All our food is guaranteed free of artificial preservatives.* 我們所有的食品保證不含

人工防腐劑。 | *The manufacturers guarantee the watch for three years.* 製造廠商對這種手錶保用三年。 | *They have guaranteed that any faulty parts will be replaced free of charge.* 他們已保證有毛病的零件都可免費更換。 | *Our products are guaranteed to last for years.* 我們的產品保證可使用多年。 **2** [+ (that)] to promise or make sure that something will certainly happen 允諾; 保證: *I guarantee that you'll enjoy yourself.* 我保證你會玩得很高興。 | *I can't guarantee this will work.* 我不敢保證這會起作用。

guar·an·tor /ˈɡærəntɔ; ˌɡærənˈtɔːr/ *n* a person who agrees to be responsible for the fulfilment of someone else's promise, for example paying a debt 保證人; 擔保人

★**guard¹** /ɡɑrd; ɡɑːd/ *n* **1** someone like a soldier, policeman, or prison officer, who watches over someone or something to prevent escape, danger, or attack 衛兵; 守衛; 獄吏: *security guards* 保安人員 **2** a group of people, especially soldiers, whose duty is to guard someone or something 警衛隊: *They all went to watch the changing of the guard.* 他們都去看警衛隊換崗了。 **3** a railway official in charge of a train〔火車的〕列車長 **4** something which covers and protects 遮蓋或保護裝置: *Football players sometimes wear shin guards.* 足球運動員有時穿着護脛。 **5** **be on guard, stand guard** to be in a state of watchful readiness to protect or defend something 處於警戒狀態; 守衛: *There's a policeman on guard at the entrance.* 有警察守衛在入口處。 | *They are standing guard over the house.* 他們在看守那所房子。 **6** **on your guard** ready to deal with a sudden trick or attack 提防突然的〔奸計或進攻〕: *Be on your guard against pickpockets.* 注意提防扒手。 [RELATED PHRASE 相關詞組 **off your guard**] **7** **under guard** being guarded 被守衛: *The prisoner was brought in under guard.* 囚犯在看守之下給抓進來了。

guard² *v* [T] **1** to keep something safe by watching for danger 防衛; 守護: *The dog guarded the house.* 狗看守着房子。 | *The soldiers were guarding the bridge against attack.* 士兵守護着橋, 以免遭到襲擊。 **2** to watch a prisoner so that they do not escape 看管〔囚犯〕

guard against sthg *phr v* [T] to try to prevent something by taking special care 預防; 防止〔某事〕: *You should wash your hands when preparing food, to guard against spreading infection.* 你做飯時應洗手, 以防傳播疾病。

guard·ed /ˈɡɑrdɪd; ˈɡɑːdɪd/ *adj* careful; not to say too much (used of speech) 小心的; 謹慎的〔指言語〕 —**guardedly** *adv*

guard·i·an /ˈɡɑrdiən; ˈɡɑːdiən/ *n* **1** a person or place that guards or protects 保護人; 保護所: *The Bank of England is the guardian of our wealth.* 英國銀行是我們財富的保護所。 **2** someone who is legally responsible for

G

looking after a child whose parents have died 〔兒童的〕監護人 **3 guardian angel** a good spirit believed by some people to protect them 守護天使

guard of hon·our /'· ·'··/ *n* a group of people, usually soldiers, who act as a ceremonial guard to an important person on a special occasion 儀仗隊

gua·va /'gwɑːvə; 'gwɑːvə/ *n* the round fruit of a small tropical tree with pink or white flesh and seeds in the centre 番石榴

guer·ril·la /gə'rɪlə; gə'rɪlə/ *n* (also 又作 **guerilla**) a member of an independent military group, often fighting for political reasons, which fights larger forces by making surprise attacks or by planting explosives 游擊隊員: *guerrilla warfare* 游擊戰

***guess**[1] /gɛs; ges/ *v* **1** [I;T; +(that)] to give an opinion without knowing or considering all the facts 猜測; 猜想: *Can you guess my age?* 你猜得出我的年齡嗎? | *I guessed I'd find you in here.* 我猜我能在這裡找到你。 | *Guess where I've been.* 猜猜我去過哪裡。 | *I guessed it to be about £300.* 我猜它大約要三百英鎊。 | *I had no idea so I guessed.* 我一無所知，所以就猜了猜。

□ USEFUL PATTERNS 有用句型
to guess something; to guess (that); to guess something to be…; to guess who/where/what/how…

2 [T + (that)] to know or learn something by using all the facts that you know 推測; 估計: *I guessed from the look on her face that he had died.* 從她臉上的表情，我估計他已死去。 **3** [+ (that)] *infml AmE* to think that something is true or likely 〔非正式, 美式〕認為〔某事〕真實或可能: *I guess you don't have time to go out now you have young children.* 我想你現在有了小孩子，恐怕就沒有時間出去了。 **4 keep someone guessing** to keep someone uninformed and uncertain about what will happen next 不讓某人知道接下去會發生甚麼事情

guess[2] *n* **1** an attempt at working out the correct answer 猜測: *She made a wild guess but it was completely wrong.* 她胡亂猜測，但根本不對。 **2** a judgment made without knowing all the facts 估計; 推測: *My guess is that he didn't come because his parents wouldn't let him.* 我猜想他沒來是因為他父母不讓他來。 | *At a guess, I'd say she was 35.* 讓我猜，我說她當時有三十五歲了。

***guest** /gɛst; gest/ *n* **1** a person who is in someone's home by invitation to stay for a short time or for a meal 客人; 賓客: *I'll phone you when our guests have left.* 我們的客人離開後，我就打電話給你。 **2** a person who is invited out and paid for at a theatre or restaurant 〔被邀請上戲院或餐館〕來賓; 佳賓: *They are coming to the concert as my*

guests. 他們將作為我的佳賓來參加音樂會。 **3** a person who is staying in a hotel or guesthouse 〔住旅館或賓館的〕旅客: *Guests are requested not to remove the coathangers.* 旅館請住宿的客人不要拿走衣帽架。 –see 見 CUSTOMER (USAGE 用法) **4 be my guest!** *infml* 〔非正式〕= please feel free to do so 請便: *"May I borrow your pen?" "Be my guest!"* "我能借你的鋼筆用一用嗎?" "請便!"

guest·house /'gɛst,haʊs; 'gesthaʊs/ *n* **guesthouses** /-,haʊzɪz; -haʊz z/ a private house where visitors may stay and have meals for payment 賓館; 小旅館

guest of hon·our /'· · ·'··/ *n* the most important person who has been invited to a party or meal 聚會或宴會上最重要的人物; 貴賓

guest·room /'gɛst,rʊm; 'gest-rʊm/ *n* a bedroom in a private house which is kept for visitors to sleep in 〔私人住宅的〕留給賓客用的寢室; 客房

guf·faw /gʌ'fɔ; gə'fɔː/ *n* a loud and perhaps rude laugh 大笑; 哄笑 –**guffaw** *v* [I]

***guid·ance** /'gaɪdns; 'gaɪdəns/ *n* [U] helpful advice 有益的建議; 指導

***guide**[1] /gaɪd; gaɪd/ *n* **1** someone who takes you round a place of interest explaining things to you, or someone who helps you travel in a dangerous area 嚮導; 導遊: *You need a guide to show you the city.* 你需要一個導遊帶你遊覽這個城市。 | *a mountain guide* 在山裡領路的嚮導 **2** something which provides a model on which opinions or behaviour can be based 準則; 依據: *As a rough guide you should cover one question an hour.* 作為一個大約的依據，你應該一個小時做一道題。 **3** a book which teaches the way to do something or provides information about something 手冊; 指南: *a parents' guide to childhood diseases* 父母使用的兒童疾病手冊 **4** see 見 GIRL GUIDE

guide[2] *v* **guided, guiding** [T + adv/prep] **1** to show someone where to go 引導; 指引: *She guides people around the city.* 她帶領人們參觀城市。 | *The light guided them back to harbour.* 燈光指引他們返回港口。 **2** to control the movement of something 控制〔某物的運動〕; 領導; 操縱: *The pilot guided the plane onto the runway.* 飛行員把飛機開上了跑道。 | *The government will guide the country through the difficulties ahead.* 政府將領導國家渡過面臨的困難。 –see 見 LEAD[1] (USAGE 用法)

guide book /'· ·/ *n* (also 又作 **guide**) a book which gives tourists information about a place 旅遊指南

guide·lines /'gaɪd,laɪnz; 'gaɪdlaɪnz/ *n* [pl] rules or instructions about how something should be done 指導方針; 準則

guild /gɪld; gɪld/ *n* an association of people who share the same interests or the same skills or profession 同業公會; 協會: *the guild*

G

guile /gaɪl; gaɪl/ n [U] deceit of a clever, indirect kind 奸詐

guile·less /ˈgaɪlɪs; ˈgaɪl-ləs/ adj simple and sincere 單純的; 誠摯的

guil·lo·tine[1] /ˈgɪlə,tin; ˈgɪləti:n/ n 1 a machine used in France for cutting off the heads of criminals, which worked by means of a heavy blade sliding down between two posts 〔法國使用的〕斷頭台 2 a machine for cutting paper 切紙機

guillotine[2] v **guillotined, guillotining** [T] to cut off someone's head with a guillotine 用斷頭台將〔某人〕斬首

guilt /gɪlt; gɪlt/ n [U] 1 the fact of having broken a law 違法; 罪行: *The jury acquitted him because his guilt could not be proved.* 因為無法證實罪行, 陪審團將他無罪釋放。 2 responsibility for something wrong 罪過; 責任: *When children behave badly the guilt sometimes lies with the parents.* 孩子行為不端, 有時責任在父母身上。 3 the unhappy feelings produced by knowledge or belief that you have done something wrong 內疚; 不安: *She was tortured by guilt.* 她被內疚的心情所折磨。 –**guiltless** adj

*★**guilt·y** /ˈgɪltɪ; ˈgɪlti/ adj **guiltier, guiltiest** 1 having broken a law or disobeyed a moral or social rule 違法的; 有罪的: *He was guilty of murder.* 他犯有謀殺罪。 | *He was found guilty.* 他被判定有罪。 2 showing or feeling unhappiness because you have done something wrong 內疚的; 不安的: *a guilty look* 內疚的神情 | *a guilty conscience* 內疚 –**guiltily** adv

guinea pig /ˈgɪnɪ pɪg; ˈgɪni pɪg/ n 1 a small furry animal rather like a rat without a tail, which is often kept by children as a pet 天竺鼠, 豚鼠 2 a person or animal used in some kind of test 用於試驗的人或動物: *They want us to be their guinea pigs and try out their new soap.* 他們想把我們當作試驗對象, 試試他們的新型肥皂。

guise /gaɪz; gaɪz/ n fml the outward appearance of something, which hides the truth 〔正式〕〔掩蓋實情的〕外表; 偽裝: *In his new film he appears in various guises: as a lawyer, a soldier, and a window cleaner.* 在他的新影片中, 他扮演了各式各樣的人物: 律師、士兵和窗戶清潔工。

*★**gui·tar** /gɪˈtɑr; gɪˈtɑ:ʳ/ n a musical instrument with six strings which are plucked (PLUCK), a long neck and a wooden or plastic body 吉他

*★**gulf** /gʌlf; gʌlf/ n 1 a large deep stretch of sea partly enclosed by land 海灣: *the Gulf of Mexico* 墨西哥灣 2 a serious difference or separation between people and their understanding of each other 〔人們之間的〕鴻溝; 隔閡; 分歧: *a huge gulf between the bosses and their employees* 老闆與雇員之間的巨大分歧 3 a deep hollow place in the

earth's surface 深淵; 深坑

gull /gʌl; gʌl/ n see 見 SEAGULL

gul·let /ˈgʌlɪt; ˈgʌl̩t/ n infml the foodpipe from your mouth to your stomach 〔非正式〕食道

gul·li·ble /ˈgʌləbl̩; ˈgʌl̩bəl/ adj easily tricked or persuaded to believe something 易受騙的; 輕信的: *He's so gullible you could sell him anything.* 他常容易上當, 你騙他甚麼他都相信。

gul·ly /ˈgʌlɪ; ˈgʌli/ n **gullies** also 又作 **gulley** 1 a small narrow valley cut into a hillside by heavy rain 隘谷; 沖溝 2 a deep ditch made to take water away 溝渠; 水渠

gulp[1] /gʌlp; gʌlp/ v 1 [T] to swallow food or drink quickly 大口吞下; 大口喝: *She gulped down her coffee and rushed out.* 她大口喝完咖啡後跑了出去。 2 [I] to make a sudden swallowing movement as if you are surprised or nervous 〔如同吃驚或緊張時〕倒吸氣

gulp sthg ↔ **back** phr v [T] to prevent the expression of feeling by swallowing 強抑〔感情時〕忍住: *She gulped back her tears.* 她強忍住眼淚。

gulp[2] n 1 a large mouthful 一大口: *He took a few gulps of water and felt much better.* 他喝了幾大口水, 感覺好多了。 2 an act of swallowing quickly 吞咽: *He gave a nervous gulp.* 他緊張地一口吞下。

gum[1] /gʌm; gʌm/ n 1 see 見 CHEWING GUM 2 [U] a sticky substance used for sticking things together 黏膠 3 **gums** the areas in your mouth where your teeth are fixed 齒齦 4 [C] a hard jelly-like sweet 橡皮軟糖: *a fruit gum* 水果味的橡皮軟糖

gum[2] v -mm- [T] to stick something in position with glue 〔用黏膠〕黏住: *He gummed the labels onto the parcels.* 他把標籤黏貼在包裹上。

gum sthg ↔ **up** phr v [T] infml to prevent something from working or moving properly because a sticky substance has been produced and dried up 〔非正式〕〔由於產生的黏性物質變乾而〕使〔某物〕無法正常運轉或活動: *The baby's eyes were all gummed up.* 嬰孩的眼睛都被黏住了。

gum·boot /ˈgʌm,but; ˈgʌmbu:t/ n a long rubber boot that you wear to keep your feet dry 〔防水的〕高統膠靴

gump·tion /ˈgʌmpʃən; ˈgʌmpʃən/ n [U] infml the ability to think or act in a sensible or courageous way 〔非正式〕精明; 果敢

*★**gun**[1] /gʌn; gʌn/ n a weapon from which bullets or larger metal objects are fired through a metal tube 槍; 砲

gun[2] v

gun sbdy ↔ **down** phr v [T] to shoot someone and kill or wound them without pity 槍殺〔某人〕; 開槍打傷

gun·boat /ˈgʌn,bot; ˈgʌnbəʊt/ n a small but heavily armed warship 砲艇

gun·fire /'gʌn,faɪr; 'gʌnfaɪər/ n [U] the repeated firing of guns 砲火

gunge /gʌndʒ; gʌndʒ/ n BrE infml [U] an unpleasant, dirty, and sticky substance〔英式, 非正式〕骯髒討厭的黏性物質: *What's this horrible gunge in the bottom of the bucket?* 桶底裡可怕的黏糊糊的是甚麼東西?

gun·man /'gʌn,mæn; 'gʌnmən/ n **gunmen** /-mən; -mən/ a criminal armed with a gun 持槍歹徒

gun·ner /'gʌnər; 'gʌnər/ n a soldier in a part of the British Army which uses heavy guns〔英國陸軍的〕砲兵

gun·point /'gʌn,pɔɪnt; 'gʌnpɔɪnt/ n **at gunpoint** while pointing a gun or having a gun pointed at you 用槍指着; 被人用槍指着: *They were forced at gunpoint to hand over the money.* 他們在槍口之下被迫交出了錢。

gun·pow·der /'gʌn,paʊdər; 'gʌn,paʊdər/ n [U] an explosive material in the form of a powder 火藥

gun·run·ner /'gʌn,rʌnər; 'gʌn,rʌnər/ n a person who illegally and secretly brings guns into a country, especially for the use of those who wish to fight against the government〔尤指反對政府的〕軍火走私者 **–gun·running** n [U]

gun·shot /'gʌn,ʃɑt; 'gʌnʃɔt/ n the act or sound of firing a gun 槍砲射擊; 槍砲聲

gur·gle /'gɜ·gl; 'gɜ:gəl/ v **gurgled, gurgling** [I] **1** to make a sound like water flowing unevenly, for example out of a bottle or over stones 作汨汨聲〔如水從瓶中倒出或在石頭上流淌之聲〕 **2** (of a baby) to make sounds of delight in the throat〔嬰兒〕發出高興的咯咯聲: *The baby gurgled contentedly.* 嬰兒滿意地咯咯笑起來。**–gurgle** n

gu·ru /'guru; 'gʊru:/ n **1** an Indian priest or teacher of religion 古魯〔印度的祭司或宗教導師〕 **2** a greatly respected person whose ideas are followed〔受人崇敬的〕權威; 精神領袖: *He has become the great guru of modern technology.* 他已成為現代技術之父。

gush¹ /gʌʃ; gʌʃ/ v **1** [I + adv/prep] to flow or pour out quickly in large quantities 湧出; 大量流出: *Oil gushed out of the broken pipe.* 油從斷裂的管道中湧出。| *Blood gushed from his wound.* 血從他的傷口湧出。**2** [I] to express admiration or pleasure too strongly and perhaps without true feeling 表達過於強烈的讚嘆或高興之情; 裝腔作勢 **–gushing** adj : *gushing praise* 滔滔不絕的讚揚

gush² n a sudden flow of something 湧出: *There was a gush of blood as the wound reopened.* 傷口再次裂開時, 血湧了出來。| *a gush of enthusiasm* 一腔熱誠

gust /gʌst; gʌst/ n a sudden strong rush of wind 一陣強風〔狂風〕: *A gust of wind blew the door shut.* 一陣強風吹得把門關了起來。**–see 見 WIND (USAGE 方法) –gust** v [I]

gus·to /'gʌsto; 'gʌstəʊ/ n with gusto with eager enjoyment 興致勃勃地: *He started painting with great gusto.* 他興致勃勃地開始作畫。

gust·y /'gʌsti; 'gʌsti/ adj with strong gusts of wind 有強風的: *a gusty day* 颳風的日子

gut¹ /gʌt; gʌt/ n **1** [C] the foodpipe which passes through your body 腸子 **2** [U] strong thread made from this part of animals 腸線: *The fishing line is made of gut.* 這根釣絲是用腸線做成的。**3 guts** [pl] the inner organs of your stomach 內臟 **4 guts** [U] courage 勇氣: *We all knew the boss was making a terrible mistake, but no one had the guts to tell him.* 我們都知道老闆在犯嚴重錯誤, 但沒有人有膽量告訴他。

gut² v **-tt-** [T] **1** to take out the inner organs of a dead animal 取出〔動物屍體〕的內臟 **2** to destroy the inside of a building completely 徹底毀壞〔建築物〕的內部: *The huge factory was gutted by the fire in minutes.* 幾分鐘之內這家大工廠就被大火毀掉了。

gut³ adj infml〔非正式〕[only before a noun 只用於名詞前] coming from natural feelings rather than from careful thought 發自內心的; 直覺的: *I had a gut feeling that something terrible would happen.* 我有一種直覺, 要發生甚麼可怕的事情。| *a gut reaction* 本能的反應

gut·ter /'gʌtər; 'gʌtər/ n **1** a narrow ditch at the side of a road, or an open pipe fixed to a roof, to collect and carry away rainwater 路旁排水溝; 屋簷簷槽 **–see picture on page 729** 見 729 頁彩圖 **2 the gutter** the extremely poor social conditions of a big dirty city 大城市的極為貧困的社會狀況

gutter press /'·· ,·/ n **the gutter press** newspapers which are full of shocking stories about people's private lives〔專登聳人聽聞的個人私生活新聞的〕低級趣味報紙

gut·tur·al /'gʌtərəl; 'gʌtərəl/ adj sounding as though it is produced deep in the throat 似喉嚨裡發出的: *a guttural voice* 喉音

***guy** /gaɪ; gaɪ/ n infml a man〔非正式〕男人; 傢伙: *a nice guy* 一個不錯的傢伙

guz·zle /'gʌzl; 'gʌzəl/ v **guzzled, guzzling** [I; T] to eat or drink eagerly, quickly, and often continuously 大吃大喝; 狂飲; 濫吃: *He's been guzzling beer all evening.* 他整個晚上都在猛飲啤酒。

gym /dʒɪm; dʒɪm/ n **1** [C] see 見 GYMNASIUM **2** [U] for the teaching of GYMNASTICS 體育館; 體育的: *a gym class* 體育課

gym·kha·na /dʒɪm'kɑnə; dʒɪm'kɑ:nə/ n BrE an event with competitions for horses and their riders〔英式〕賽馬會

gym·na·si·um /dʒɪm'neɪzɪəm; dʒɪm'neɪzɪəm/ n (also 又作 **gym**) a hall with apparatus for physical exercise 健身房; 體育館

gym·nast /'dʒɪmnæst; 'dʒɪmnæst/ n a person who trains and is skilled in particular physical exercises 體育家; 體操運動員

gym·nas·tics /dʒɪm'næstɪks; dʒɪm'næstɪks/ n [U] exercises to develop your physical

G

strength and ability to move quickly and easily 體操; 體育 –**gymnastic** *adj* [only before a noun 只用於名詞前]

gy·nae·col·o·gy /ˌdʒaɪnɪˈkɒlədʒɪ; ˌgaɪnɪˈkɒl- ədʒi/ *n* (**gynecology** *AmE* 〖美式〗) [U] the branch of medicine which deals with women's illnesses and the female sex organs 婦科(學) –**gynaecological** /-kəˈlɒ- dʒɪkl; -kəˈlɒdʒɪkəl/ *adj* (**gynecological** *AmE* 〖美式〗) –**gynaecologist** /ˌdʒaɪnɪˈkɒlədʒɪst; ˌgaɪnɪˈkɒlədʒɪ̦st/ *n* (**gynecologist** *AmE* 〖美式〗)

gyp·sy /ˈdʒɪpsɪ; ˈdʒɪpsi/ *n* **gypsies** see 見 GIPSY

gy·rate /ˈdʒaɪret; dʒaɪˈreɪt/ *v* **gyrated, gyrating** [I] to swing round and round a fixed point, in one direction or with changes of direction 旋轉; 迴旋: *The dancers gyrated wildly to the strong beat of the music.* 跳舞者隨着強烈的音樂節奏大幅度地旋轉。 –**gyration** /dʒaɪˈreʃən; dʒaɪˈreɪʃən/ *n* [C;U]

gy·ro·scope /ˈdʒaɪrəˌskop; ˈdʒaɪrəskəʊp/ *n* (also 又作 **gyro** /ˈdʒaɪro; ˈdʒaɪrəʊ/ *infml* 〖非正式〗) a heavy wheel which spins inside a frame, used for keeping ships and aircraft steady, and also as a children's toy 陀螺儀; 迴轉儀 –**gyroscopic** /ˌdʒaɪrəˈskɒpɪk; ˌdʒaɪrə- ˈskɒpɪk/ *adj*

H, h

H, h /etʃ; eɪtʃ/ **H's, h's** or **Hs, hs** the 8th letter of the English alphabet 英語的第八個字母

ha /hɑ; hɑː/ *interj* a shout of surprise 哈〔表示驚奇〕

hab·er·dash·er /ˈhæbə,dæʃə; ˈhæbədæʃəʳ/ *n* **1** *BrE* a shopkeeper who sells pins, sewing thread, and other small things used in dressmaking 〔英式〕縫紉用品經銷商 **2** *AmE* a shopkeeper who sells men's clothing 〔美式〕男子服飾用品商

hab·er·dash·er·y /ˈhæbə,dæʃəri; ˈhæbədæʃəri/ *n* [U] pins, thread, and other things used in dressmaking 縫紉用品

*★**hab·it** /ˈhæbɪt; ˈhæbɪt/ *n* **1** [C;U] something you do regularly, often without thinking 習慣: *She has the annoying habit* **of** *biting her fingernails.* 她有咬指甲的惡習。| *He smokes only out of habit.* 他吸煙只是一種習慣。| *I can't get him to break the habit.* 我無法令他改掉這個習慣。**2** [C] a special set of clothes worn by members of some religious groups 法衣 **3** **be in the habit of doing something** to do something regularly 定期做某事: *We're in the habit of meeting for lunch on Fridays.* 我們總是在星期五見面吃午飯。[RELATED PHRASES 相關詞組 **get into the habit of; make a habit of:** *Make a habit of cleaning your teeth after meals.* 要養成飯後刷牙的習慣。]

> ■ USAGE 用法: Compare 比較 **habit, custom, practice, convention.** A **habit** is something which one person does regularly ☆ **habit** 是指一個人經常做的事情: *He has an annoying habit of biting his nails.* 他有咬指甲的惡習。A **custom** usually means something a whole society has done for a long time ☆ **custom** 通常指一個社會在長時期內一直做的事情: *the custom of giving presents at Christmas* 聖誕節時送禮物的習慣。**Practice** can mean the same as **custom,** but it often has a derogatory meaning ☆ **practice** 的含義可與 **custom** 相同，但該詞常含貶義: *Many people condemn the practice of shooting animals for sport.* 許多人譴責把獵殺動物作為體育運動的習俗。It can also mean the usual way of doing things in a business or organization ☆也可以指企業或機構通常辦事情的方式: *The normal practice in this company is to send the bill as soon as the job is done.* 這家公司的常規做法是工作一做完就寄出賬單。The **conventions** of a society are the rules of behaviour that it expects people to follow ☆ 一個社會的 **conventions** 指的是人們應當遵守的行為規範: *It is a* **convention** *in Britain that people attending funerals should wear dark clothes.* 按照英國風俗，人們在出席葬禮時應穿深色衣服。

hab·i·ta·ble /ˈhæbɪtəbl; ˈhæbɪtəbəl/ *adj* good enough to live in 適於居住的 −opposite 反義 **uninhabitable**

hab·i·tat /ˈhæbə,tæt; ˈhæbɪtæt/ *n* the place where a plant or animal usually lives 〔動植物的〕產地；棲息地: *plants in their natural habitat* 原產地的植物

hab·i·ta·tion /,hæbəˈteʃən; ,hæbɪˈteɪʃən/ *n fml* 〔正式〕**1** [U] the activity of people living in a place 居住: *a house unfit for human habitation* 不適宜人住的房子 **2** [C] a place to live in 住房；住處

ha·bit·u·al /həˈbɪtʃʊəl; həˈbɪtʃuəl/ *adj* [only before a noun 只用於名詞前] **1** usual 通常的: *her habitual rudeness* 她那習慣性的粗魯 **2** done as a habit, or doing something as a habit 習慣的；習慣性的: *He's a habitual cigar smoker.* 他是個抽雪茄成癮的人。−**habitually** *adv*: *She's habitually late.* 她經常遲到。

hack¹ /hæk; hæk/ *v* [I + adv/prep;T] to cut roughly, violently, or in uneven pieces 砍；劈: *They hacked a path through the forest.* 他們在森林中砍出了一條路。| *They hacked away at the brambles.* 他們在砍有刺灌木。| *The victim was hacked to death.* 受害人被砍死了。

hack² *n* **1** a horse kept for riding 供騎用的馬 **2** a ride on a horse, often in the countryside 〔通常在鄉間的〕騎馬 **3** a writer who does a lot of poor quality work 蹩腳文人

hack·er /ˈhækə; ˈhækəʳ/ *n* a person who spends a lot of time using a computer, especially one who secretly tries to use or change the information in someone else's computer 黑客〔尤指偷偷使用或改變他人電腦內信息的人〕

hack·ing cough /,··· ·/ *n* a cough with a rough unpleasant sound 乾咳

hack·neyed /ˈhæknɪd; ˈhæknɪd/ *adj* meaningless because used and repeated too often 陳腐的；老生常談的

hack·saw /ˈhæk,sɔ; ˈhæksɔː/ *n* a tool that

has a fine-toothed blade and is used for cutting metal 鋼鋸; 弓鋸

had /əd, həd; d, əd, həd, *strong* 強讀 hæd; hæd/ the past tense and past participle of HAVE ☆ HAVE 的過去式和過去分詞

had·dock /ˈhædək; ˈhædək/ *n* [plural is 複數為 **haddock**] [C;U] a common fish found in northern seas, or its flesh as food 黑線鱈 〔產於北大西洋的一種食用魚〕

had·n't /ˈhædnt; ˈhædnt/ *v* short for 縮約式 = "had not": They'd arrived, hadn't they? 他們已經到了, 是嗎?

hae·mo·glo·bin /ˌhiːməˈgləʊbɪn; ˌhiːməˈgloʊbn/ *n* (**hemoglobin** *AmE* 〔美式〕) [U] a red colouring matter in the blood which contains iron and carries oxygen 血紅蛋白

hae·mo·phil·i·a /ˌhiːməˈfɪliːə; ˌhiːməˈfɪliə/ *n* (**hemophilia** *AmE* 〔美式〕) [U] an illness in which the sufferer bleeds for a long time after they are cut or injured; the mother or the father may pass it to the children, but only males show the effects of it 血友病

hae·mo·phil·i·ac /ˌhiːməˈfɪliːæk; ˌhiːməˈfɪliæk/ *n* (**hemophiliac** *AmE* 〔美式〕) a person who suffers from haemophilia 血友病患者

haem·or·rhage¹ /ˈhemərɪdʒ; ˈhemərɪdʒ/ *n tech* 〔術語〕 (**hemorrhage** *AmE* 〔美式〕) [C; U] a flow of blood, especially a long, large, or unexpected one 出血〔尤指持續大量出血〕

haemorrhage² *v tech* 〔術語〕 (**hemorrhage** *AmE* 〔美式〕) [I] to have a haemorrhage 大量出血

haem·or·rhoid /ˈheməˌrɔɪd; ˈhemərɔɪd/ *n* (**hemorrhoid** *AmE* 〔美式〕) **haemorrhoids** blocked and swollen blood-carrying tubes at the opening of the lower end of a person's bowel 痔瘡

hag /hæg; hæg/ *n* an ugly old woman, who might also be evil 醜老太婆; 巫婆

hag·gard /ˈhægəd; ˈhægəd/ *adj* showing tiredness or anxiety in the lines on your face and around your eyes 〔面容〕憔悴的

hag·gle /ˈhægl; ˈhægəl/ *v* **haggled, haggling** [I] to argue over the price of something 討價還價: He haggled *over* the price of the horse *with* the dealer. 他與賣主就那匹馬討價還價. | The British are not used to haggling. 英國人不習慣討價還價.

ha-ha /ˌ·ˈ·/ *interj* a shout of laughter 哈哈 〔笑聲〕

hail¹ /heɪl; heɪl/ *n* **1** [U] small drops of ice which fall from the sky 冰雹 **2** [C] a lot of things which strike suddenly and violently 突如其來的許多東西: a hail of bullets 一陣彈雨

hail² *v* **1** [I] to fall as very small drops of ice 下冰雹: It's hailing. 正在下冰雹. **2** [T] to call out to someone in greeting or to gain attention 呼喚; 招呼: I hailed a taxi. 我叫了輛計程車.

hail sbdy/sthg ↔ **as** sthg *phr v* [T] to praise something publicly as being a par-

ticular thing 把〔某物〕譽為: They hailed the statue as an important work of art. 他們把這座塑像譽為一件重要藝術作品.

hail from somewhere *phr v* [T] to come from a place 從〔某地〕來: She hails from Liverpool. 她來自利物浦.

hail·stone /ˈheɪlstəʊn; ˈheɪlstoʊn/ *n* a small ball of ice 雹粒

hail·storm /ˈheɪlstɔːm; ˈheɪlstɔːrm/ *n* a storm when small balls of ice fall heavily 雹暴

★**hair** /heə; heər/ *n* **1** [C] a fine threadlike thing which grows from the skin of a person or animal 〔人或動物的〕毛, 汗毛: The cat has left her loose hairs all over my clothes. 貓掉下的毛黏得我衣服上到處都是. **2** [U] a lot of these threadlike things together, for example on your head 頭髮: I must get my hair cut. 我必須去理髮. **3 let your hair down** *infml* to behave freely and perhaps wildly, especially after acting formally 〔非正式〕〔尤指正式場面結束後〕隨便一些; 無拘無束 **4 make someone's hair stand on end** to make someone feel very afraid 使某人毛骨悚然 **5 not turn a hair** *infml* to show no fear or worry 〔非正式〕不害怕; 不擔心 **6 -haired** *adj* having a certain kind of hair 有某種頭髮的: long-haired 長髮的 | fair-haired 金髮的

hair·brush /ˈheəbrʌʃ; ˈheəbrʌʃ/ *n* a brush you use on your hair 髮刷; 毛刷

hair·cut /ˈheəkʌt; ˈheəkʌt/ *n* **1** having your hair cut 理髮: I need a haircut. 我需要理髮. **2** the style your hair is cut in 髮型; 髮式: soldiers with short haircuts 頭髮剪得很短的士兵

hair·do /ˈheəduː; ˈheəduː/ *n infml* the style a woman's hair is shaped into 〔非正式〕女髮式; 女髮型

hair·dress·er /ˈheəˌdresə; ˈheəˌdresər/ *n* **1** a person who cuts, washes, and arranges people's hair 理髮師; 美髮師 **2 hairdresser's** a shop where you go to get your hair cut and washed 理髮店: I'm going to the hairdresser's on Monday. 我打算星期一去理髮店理髮. | The hairdresser's is next to the Post Office. 理髮店在郵局隔壁. –**hairdressing** *n* [U]

hair·dry·er /ˈheəˌdraɪə; ˈheəˌdraɪər/ *n* a machine that dries your hair by blowing hot air onto it 〔吹乾頭髮用的〕吹風機

hair·grip /ˈheəgrɪp; ˈheəgrɪp/ *n* a flat pin with two sides used to hold women's hair in place 〔婦女用的〕髮夾

hair·line /ˈheəlaɪn; ˈheəlaɪn/ *n* **1** the place above your forehead where your hair starts growing 前額髮際線 **2** [only before another noun 只用於另一名詞前] a very thin line or crack 非常細的線或縫: a hairline fracture of the arm 胳臂上細小的骨裂

hair·net /ˈheənet; ˈheənet/ *n* a net worn by women over their hair to keep it in place 〔婦女用的〕髮網

hair·piece /'hɛr,pis; 'heəpiːs/ n a piece of false hair used to make your own hair seem thicker 假髮

hair·pin /'hɛr,pɪn; 'heə,pɪn/ n a pin made of wire bent into a U-shape to hold your hair in position 〔U形〕髮卡; 髮針

hairpin bend /,·· '·/ n a narrow U-shaped curve on a road 〔道路的〕U型急轉彎處

hair·rais·ing /'· ,··/ adj that makes one very afraid 令人非常害怕的: a hair-raising experience 令人毛骨悚然的經歷

hair's breadth /'·· /· [sing] a very short distance 非常短的距離〔一髮之差〕: We missed the other car by a hair's breadth. 我們差一點碰到那輛車。

hair slide /'·· /· n a small decorative fastener to keep your hair in place 〔裝飾性的〕小髮夾

hair·split·ting /'· ,··/ n [U] too much interest in unimportant differences and points of detail 吹毛求疵的

hair·style /'hɛr,staɪl; 'heəstaɪl/ n the style your hair is shaped into 髮型; 髮式

hair·y /'hɛrɪ; 'heərɪ/ adj 1 having a lot of hair on your body or limbs 〔身體或四肢〕多毛的: hairy legs 多毛的腿 | a hairy chest 多毛的胸脯 2 infml exciting and rather dangerous 〔非正式〕驚險的: It was rather hairy driving down through the mountains in the dark. 在黑暗中開車下山真是驚險。 – **hairiness** n [U]

hal·cy·on days /'hælsɪən'dez; ,hælsɪən 'deɪz/ n [pl] lit a time of peace and happiness 〔文〕太平時期; 美好時光

hale /hel; heɪl/ adj **hale and hearty** /,···'··/ very healthy 非常健康的

☆☆ **half¹** /hæf; hɑːf/ n **halves** /hævz; hɑːvz/ 1 one of two equal parts of something 半; 一半: the first half of the football match 足球賽的上半場 2 **in half** into two equal parts 分成相等的兩部分: Cut it in half. 把它切成兩半。 | We split the profits in half. 我們平分了利潤。 3 half a pint of beer 半品脫〔啤酒〕: Two halves please. 請來兩杯半品脫啤酒。 4 a ticket that costs only half the amount of an ordinary ticket, for example because it is for a child 〔兒童的〕半價票: One and two halves to Oxford Circus, please. 請給我去牛津廣場的一張全票和兩張半票。 5 **by half** by half of the full amount 用一半: We've had to reduce our workforce by half. 我們已把工人數目減半。 6 **go halves** to share the cost of something 均攤某物的費用: Why don't you buy it, and I'll go halves with you? 我願意和你分攤費用, 你為甚麼還不買呢?

☆ **half²** predeterminer, pron half in amount 一半: Half of the guests are already here. 半數客人已到。 | Of the people who work here, about half are women. 在這裡工作的人之中, 約有一半是婦女。 | She lives about half a mile from here. 她住的地方離這兒約半英里。 |

Three and a half months have passed since he died. 他去世已三個半月了。 | Half the people here are strangers to me. 這裡有一半的人我不認識。

half³ adj not complete, but only a half of something 不完整的; 僅一半的: I've ordered a half portion because I'm not very hungry. 我不是很餓, 所以就要了半份。 | a half mile 半英里 | She gave me a half smile. 她衝着我微微一笑。

half⁴ adv 1 only partly, but not completely 部分地; 不完全地: She's half French and half English. 她有一半法國血統, 一半英國血統。 | I half thought that you might come and join us. 我有點希望你能來加入我們的行列。 2 **half and half** made or done with two equal parts of two things 各一半: "Do you use milk or water?" "Half and half." "你用牛奶還是用水?" "各用一半。"

half·back /'hæf,bæk; 'hɑːfbæk/ n a football player who plays in the middle of the field 〔足球的〕中(前)衛

half-baked /,· '··/ adj infml not properly planned or thought about 〔非正式〕未經詳細計劃或考慮的

half board /,· '·/ adj with bed, breakfast, and an evening meal provided 半食宿的〔指提供住宿及早、晚餐的〕: Half-board accommodation is enough for us — we don't eat lunch. 我們要半住宿就夠了——我們不吃午餐。

half-broth·er /'· ,··/ n a brother related to you through only one of your parents 同父異母[同母異父]兄弟

half-caste /'·· /· n a person whose parents are of different races (a word which some people consider to be offensive) 混血兒〔有些人認為該詞不禮貌〕 – **half-caste** adj

half-heart·ed /,· '··◁/ adj showing little effort and no real interest 不盡力的; 不熱心的: a half-hearted attempt 隨便的試試 – **half-heartedly** adv

half-life /'·· /· n the time it takes for half the atoms in a RADIOACTIVE substance to decay 〔放射性物質中原子的〕半衰期

half-mast /,· '·/ n **at half-mast** a phrase used to describe a flag placed half-way down the flagpole as a sign of sorrow 下半旗〔以示哀悼〕

half·pen·ny /'hepnɪ; 'heɪpnɪ/ n a very small old British coin, two of which were equal to a penny 半便士硬幣

half-sis·ter /'· ,··/ n a sister related to you through only one of your parents 同父異母[同母異父]姐妹

half term /,· '·◁/ n a short holiday in the middle of a school TERM 〔學校的〕期中假

half-tim·bered /,· '··◁/ adj having the wooden frame of an old building showing in the outer walls 〔老式房屋〕露明木架的

half time /,· '·◁/ n [U] the period of rest between two parts of a sports match 〔比賽的〕

中場休息

half·way /ˈhæfˌwe; ˌhɑːfˈweɪ◂/ *adj,adv* at the middle point between two things 中途 的; 中途: *We live half-way between London and Oxford.* 我們住在倫敦和牛津中間。| *the halfway mark in a race* 賽跑比賽的半程指示 標記

half-wit /ˈ··/ *n* a stupid person 愚蠢的人 – **half-witted** /ˌ·ˈ··◂/ *adj*

half year·ly /ˌ· ˈ··◂/ *adj* happening twice a year 半年發生一次的

hal·i·but /ˈhæləbət; ˈhæl¦bət/ *n* [C;U] a very large flat sea fish used as food 大比目 魚〔食用海魚〕

⁎**hall** /hɔl; hɔːl/ *n* **1** the passage just inside the front door of a house, from which the other rooms are reached 門廳; 正門走廊 **2** a large room in which meetings, dances, dinners, or concerts can be held 〔可舉行會 議, 舞會, 晚宴和音樂會的〕大廳 **3** see 見 HALL OF RESIDENCE

hal·le·lu·ja /ˌhælɪˈluːjə; ˌhæl¦ˈluːjə/ *interj, n* (also 又作 **alleluia**) an expression of praise, joy, and thanks to God 哈利路亞〔表示讚美, 高興和對上帝的感謝〕

hall·mark /ˈhɔlˌmɑrk; ˈhɔːlmɑːk/ *n* **1** the mark made on objects of precious metal to prove that they are silver or gold 〔金銀製品 上的〕純度印記 **2** a particular quality or way of behaving that is very typical of a certain person or thing 特徵; 特點: *Clear expression is the hallmark of a good writer.* 表達清楚是 一個優秀作家的特點。– **hallmark** *v*: *hallmarked silver* 有純度印記的銀器

hal·lo /həˈlo; həˈləʊ/ *interj,n* see 見 HELLO

hall of res·i·dence /ˌ·· ˈ···/ *n* (also 又作 **hall**) a building belonging to a college or university where students live 大學生宿舍樓

hal·lowed /ˈhæləd; ˈhæləʊd/ *adj lit* honoured and respected 〔文〕受崇敬的: *the hallowed memories of great people* 對於偉人 的追思

Hal·low·e'en /ˌhæloˈin; ˌhæləʊˈiːn/ *n* the night of October 31, when children play tricks and dress up in strange clothes 萬聖 節前夕〔10月31日夜〕

hal·lu·ci·nate /həˈlusnˌet; həˈluːs¦neɪt/ *v* **hallucinated, hallucinating** [I] to see things which are not there 產生幻覺: *Some drugs cause people to hallucinate.* 有些藥會 使人產生幻覺。

hal·lu·ci·na·tion /həˌlusnˈeʃən; həˌluːs¦ˈneɪ ʃən/ *n* [C;U] seeing something that is imagined, often as the result of a drug or an illness of the mind 幻覺

hall·way /ˈhɔlˌwe; ˈhɔːlweɪ/ *n* the passage just inside the front door of a house 門廳

ha·lo /ˈhelo; ˈheɪləʊ/ *n* a golden circle representing light around the heads of holy people in religious paintings 〔宗教畫 像中聖人頭部的〕光輪

halt¹ /hɔlt; hɔːlt/ *v* [I;T] *fml* to stop or make

something stop 〔正式〕停止; 使〔某事物〕停 止: *The train was halted by work on the line ahead.* 火車由於前面路軌施工而停了下來。

halt² *n* a stop or pause 停止; 暫停: *The train came to a sudden halt just before the station.* 就在要進站時, 火車突然停了下來。

hal·ter /ˈhɔltɚ; ˈhɔːltɚ/ *n* a rope or leather band fastened round a horse's head to lead it 〔馬的〕籠頭; 韁繩

halt·ing /ˈhɔltɪŋ; ˈhɔːltɪŋ/ *adj* stopping and starting as if uncertain 猶豫不決的; 躊躇的 – **haltingly** *adv*

halve /hæv; hɑːv/ *v* **halved, halving** [T] **1** to divide something into two equal parts 把 〔某物〕對半分 **2** to reduce something to half the amount that it was before 把〔某物〕減 半: *By introducing computers we should be able to halve the time we spend in administration.* 使用電腦可以把花在管理上的時 間減少一半。

halves /hævz; hɑːvz/ the plural of HALF ☆ HALF 的複數形式

ham /hæm; hæm/ *n* **1** [C;U] preserved meat from the upper part of a pig's leg 火腿: *a ham sandwich* 火腿三明治 –see 見 MEAT (USAGE 用法) **2** [C] an actor whose act- ing is unnatural with too much movement and expression 表演過火的演員: *a ham ac- tor* 表演過火的演員

ham *v* **-mm-** **ham it up** to act in an unnatu- ral, artificial way with too much movement and expression 表演過火: *Stop hamming it up!* 別再表演得太過火!

ham·burg·er /ˈhæmbɝgɚ; ˈhæmbɜːgɚ/ *n* small pieces of meat made into a flat cir- cular shape, cooked and eaten between pieces of bread 漢堡包

ham-fist·ed /ˌ· ˈ··◂/ *adj* (also 又作 **ham- handed**) awkward when using your hands, so that you knock things over easily 笨手笨 腳的

ham·let /ˈhæmlɪt; ˈhæml¦t/ *n* a small village 小村莊

ham·mer¹ /ˈhæmɚ; ˈhæmɚ/ *n* **1** a tool with a heavy metal head on a wooden handle used for hitting nails or breaking things 錘 子; 榔頭 –see picture on page 958 見 958 頁 彩圖 **2** something made to hit something else, for example in a piano, or a part of a gun 當作錘子使用之物〔如鋼琴的音錘, 槍的擊 鐵〕 **3** **be/go at it hammer and tongs** to fight or argue violently 激烈地爭鬥〔爭吵〕

ham·mer² *v* **1** [I;T] to hit something with a hammer 用錘子敲〔某物〕: *Hammer the nails in to the wall.* 把釘子錘進牆裡。| *They've been hammering away all day next door.* 他 們在隔壁用錘子敲了一整天。 **2** [I;T] to hit something repeatedly 反覆敲打〔某物〕: *The police hammered at the door.* 警察反覆敲門。 **3** [T] *infml* to defeat someone beyond any doubt by fighting, or in a game 〔非正式〕 〔在比賽或戰鬥中〕徹底擊敗〔某人〕: *We* *hammered the other team.* 我們徹底擊敗了另一隊。

hammer away at sthg *phr v* [T] to keep working hard on something 一直努力做〔某事〕: *We've been hammering away at the problem for ages.* 我們很長時間一直在想辦法解決這個問題。

hammer sthg ↔ **in** *phr v* [T] to force someone to understand something by repeating it often 向〔某人〕反覆灌輸〔某事物〕: *I've been trying to hammer into them the importance of writing clearly.* 我一直在對他們強調寫寫清楚的重要性。

hammer sthg ↔ **out** *phr v* [T] to talk about something in detail and come to a decision about it 詳細討論〔某事〕後作出決定: *We've got to get together and try to hammer out a solution.* 我們得在一起議一議，盡力想出個解決辦法。

ham·mock /ˈhæmək; ˈhæmək/ *n* a long piece of cloth or net which can be hung up by its ends and used for sleeping in 吊牀

ham·per¹ /ˈhæmpə; ˈhæmpəʳ/ *v* [T] to make someone's movement or activity difficult 妨礙〔某人的行動或活動〕: *The snow hampered our efforts.* 大雪妨礙了我們所作的努力。| *Business is often hampered by bureaucracy.* 官僚作風常阻礙商業的發展。

hamper² *n* a large basket with a lid, often used for carrying food 〔裝食品的〕有蓋大籃子

ham·ster /ˈhæmstə; ˈhæmstəʳ/ *n* a small mouse-like animal which is kept as a pet and which stores food in its cheeks 倉鼠〔一種寵物，其頰囊能儲食物〕

ham·string¹ /ˈhæm.strɪŋ; ˈhæm.strɪŋ/ *n* one of the strong cords in the back of your leg, which join the muscles to the bones 膕繩肌腱; 腿腱

hamstring² *v* **hamstrung** /-.strʌŋ/; -strʌŋ/, **hamstrung** [T] to make it difficult for someone to do something 使〔某人〕做〔某事〕很困難: *The social services are hamstrung by lack of funds.* 社會福利事業由於缺乏資金而陷入癱瘓。

★★★**hand¹** /hænd; hænd/ *n* **1** one of the parts of your body that are at the ends of your arms and that you use for picking things up 手: *She had a book in her hand.* 她手裡拿着一本書。**2** a pointer on a clock that shows you what the time is 〔鐘錶的〕指針: *The minute hand's broken on my watch.* 我手錶的分針斷了。**3** a set of playing cards that one person holds in a game 一手牌: *I've got a really good hand.* 我拿的這手牌真不錯。**4** a worker who works using his or her hands 用手工作的人: *The farm hands were coming in from the fields.* 農場工人正從地裡回來。| *All hands on deck!* 全體船員到甲板上集合! **5 a hand** some help 一些幫助: *Could you give me a hand with this suitcase?* 你能幫我提一下這個手提箱嗎? | *I*

could do with a hand in the garden. 如有人幫忙，我就能照料花園。**6 a big hand** a lot of clapping (CLAP) to show support or enjoyment 鼓掌〔表示支持或高興〕: *Let's have a big hand for our next guest singer!* 讓我們大家熱烈鼓掌歡迎下一位客串歌手! **7 an old hand** someone who has a lot of experience at something 老手; 經驗豐富的人: *She's an old hand at this sort of work.* 做這種工作她是老手了。**8 at first hand** by your own direct experience 從自身的直接經驗; 第一手的: *I found out about it at first hand.* 我是自己直接發現的。**9 at hand** *fml* near in time or place 〔正式〕〔時間或地點〕臨近: *The great day is at hand.* 這個重要的日子即將到來。**10 by hand: a** made by someone using their hands rather than a machine 手工製成的: *All the stitching has been done by hand.* 所有的線都是用手縫的。**b** written, not printed 手寫的: *Our essays all had to be written by hand.* 我們所有的文章都必須用手寫。**11 have your hands full** to be very busy 非常忙碌: *With three young children I should think you've got your hands full!* 有三個小孩子要帶，我想你一定很忙! **12 get/lay your hands on something** to get or obtain something 得到某物; 獲得某物: *If only I could get my hands on a bit of extra money!* 但願我能再有點額外的收入! **13 get out of hand** to become difficult to control 變得難以控制: *The party seemed to be getting out of hand.* 晚會的場面似乎有點失控。**14 hand in hand: a** holding each other's hand 手拉手: *They walked down the road hand in hand.* 他們手拉着手走在馬路上。**b** always happening together 總是同時發生的: *Dirt and disease go hand in hand.* 骯髒與疾病關係密切。**15 Hands off!** a phrase you use when you are telling someone not to touch something 不許碰!〔用於告訴某人不要用手觸及某物〕**16 have a hand in something** to be partly responsible for something 對某事負有部分責任: *I had no hand in organizing the trip.* 我沒有參與組織此次旅行。**17 in hand** being dealt with 在辦理中: *I have the matter well in hand.* 這件事我幹得很順手。**18 in good hands** being well cared for 受到很好的照顧: *At least I know that the children are in good hands.* 最起碼我知道孩子們正受到很好的照顧。**19 in your hands** in your possession 在你手中; 被你擁有: *The painting is no longer in my hands.* 這幅畫已不在我這裡了。| *An interesting book has come into my hands.* 有本很有意思的書到了我手裡。**20 off your hands** no longer your responsibility 不再負責: *I shall be glad when the children are finally off my hands.* 孩子們最終不用我照顧，那我會很高興。**21 on hand** ready to help or ready to be used 準備幫忙; 隨時可用: *The emergency services are on hand in case there was any trouble.* 應急服務部門作好了準備，如有事故隨時可以協助。**22 on the one**

hand, on the other hand phrases that you use when you are comparing different ideas 一方面，另一方面〔用於比較兩個不同的觀點〕: *On the one hand the job isn't very well paid, but on the other hand I enjoy it.* 這個工作雖然報酬不高，但我喜歡做。–see 見 CONTRARY² (USAGE 用法) **23 to hand** near to you and ready to be used 在附近; 隨時可用: *I haven't got a pen to hand.* 我沒有帶筆。

★**hand²** v [T] **1** to pass something to someone 把〔某物〕遞給〔交給〕〔某人〕: *She handed the letter to John.* 她把信交給約翰。| *He handed the book back to me.* 他把書遞給我。| *Could you hand me that cup please?* 能麻煩你把那隻杯子遞給我嗎？

> □ USEFUL PATTERNS 有用句型
> to hand something to someone; to hand someone something

2 have to hand it to someone to have to admit that someone is very good at something or has done something very well 不得不承認某人擅長做某事或做某事十分成功: *You have to hand it to her, she gives very good speeches.* 你得承認，她演講十分到家。

hand sthg ↔ **down** *phr v* [T] to give or leave something to people who are younger than you or come after you 把〔某事〕傳給後人: *This ring was handed down from my aunt.* 這隻戒指是我阿姨傳下來的。

hand sthg ↔ **in** *phr v* [T] to give something to someone in a position of authority 上交; 提交; 呈交: *Please hand in your books at the end of the lesson.* 下課時請把書交上來。

hand sthg ↔ **on** *phr v* [T] to give something to someone else after you have used it 〔用過以後〕把〔某物〕傳給別人: *Please read this notice and hand it on.* 請看一下這則通知，然後再傳給別人看。

hand sthg ↔ **out** *phr v* [T] to give things to each member of a group of people 分發〔某物〕: *Hand out the pencils.* 把鉛筆發給大家。

hand over *phr v* **1** [T **hand** sbdy/sthg ↔ **over**] to give someone or something to a person 把〔某人或某物〕交給〔某人〕: *Come on, hand over the money.* 快，把錢交出來。| *He was handed over to the police.* 把他交給了警方。**2** [I;T **hand** sthg ↔ **over**] to give power or responsibility to someone else 移交〔權力、責任〕: *The old government will hand over to the new one next week.* 舊政府將於下週把權力移交給新政府。| *The captain refused to hand over command of his ship to anyone else.* 船長拒絕把船的指揮權交給其他人。

hand·bag /'hænd,bæg; 'hændbæg/ *n* a small bag for a person, usually a woman, to carry money and personal things in 〔通常指婦女用的〕手提包

hand baggage /'· ,··/ *n* see 見 HAND LUGGAGE

hand·book /'hænd,bʊk; 'hændbʊk/ *n* a short book giving instructions and information about something 手冊

hand·brake /'hænd,brek; 'hændbreɪk/ *n BrE* an apparatus in a vehicle which you work with your hand and which prevents the vehicle from moving 手刹車; 手閘 –see picture on page 209 見 209 頁彩圖

hand·cuff /'hænd,kʌf; 'hændkʌf/ *v* [T] to put handcuffs around someone's wrists 給〔某人〕戴上手銬

hand·cuffs /'hænd,kʌfs; 'hændkʌfs/ *n* [pl] two metal rings joined together which can be locked around the wrists of a prisoner 手銬

hand·ful /'hænd,fʊl; 'hændfʊl/ *n* **1** the quantity of something which can easily be held in the hand 一把: *She picked up a handful of pebbles and threw them into the sea.* 她撿起一把石子，把它們扔進了海裡。**2** a small number of people 少數人: *We invited thirty people, but only a handful of them came.* 我們邀請了三十位客人，但只來了幾個人。**3** a child or animal which is difficult to control 難以控制的小孩或動物: *That child is quite a handful.* 那個孩子很難管。

hand·i·cap¹ /'hændɪ,kæp; 'hændɪkæp/ *n* **1** a disability or disadvantage 殘疾; 不利: *Blindness is a great handicap.* 失明是一大殘疾。| *Being small is a handicap in a crowd like this.* 在這樣一羣人中，個子小很不利。**2** a disadvantage given to the stronger competitors in a race or other sport, such as making them carry more weight or run further than others 〔比賽中的〕讓步; 讓賽

handicap² *v* **-pp-** [T] to disadvantage someone or make it difficult for them to do something 對〔某人〕不利; 妨礙: *We were handicapped by lack of money.* 我們因缺錢而吃虧。

hand·i·capped /'hændɪ,kæpt; 'hændɪkæpt/ *adj* suffering from a disability of your mind or body, which prevents you from living a normal life 〔智力或身體上〕有殘疾的: *He's both mentally and physically handicapped.* 他在智力上和身體上都有殘疾。

hand·i·craft /'hændɪ,kræft; 'hændɪkrɑːft/ *n* **1** a skill such as sewing or weaving in which you use your hands carefully to make something 手工藝 **2 handicrafts** [pl] objects which you make by careful use of your hands 手工藝品

hand·i·work /'hændɪ,wɜːk; 'hændɪwɜːk/ *n* [U] **1** work which demands skilful use of your hands 手工 **2** something which is done or made by someone 手工製成的物品: *The extension to the house is his handiwork.* 他自己動手把房子擴建了。

hand·ker·chief /'hæŋkɚtʃɪf; 'hæŋkətʃiːf/ *n* a

piece of cloth or thin soft paper used for wiping your nose 手帕; 紙巾

✻**han·dle¹** /'hændl; 'hændl/ *n* a part of an object which is specially made for holding it or for moving it 柄; 把手

handle² *v* **handled, handling** [T] **1** to hold or move something with your hands 握住〔某物〕; 移動〔某物〕: *She handled the pieces of glass carefully.* 她小心翼翼地處理玻璃碎片。 **2** to deal with someone or something 對付〔某人或某物〕: *He handled a difficult argument skilfully.* 他巧妙地應付了一場困難重重的辯論。| *Ms Brown handles the company's accounts.* 布朗女士管理公司的賬目。| *He has no idea how to handle children.* 他不懂如何照顧孩子。

han·dle·bars /'hændlbɑrz; 'hændlbɑːz/ *n* [pl] a long piece of metal above the front wheel of a bicycle or motorcycle, which you move with your hands to control the direction it goes in 〔腳踏車或摩托車的〕把手

han·dler /'hændlə; 'hændlər/ *n* **1** a person who is responsible for the control of an animal (動物)訓練員 **2** a person whose job is to deal with a particular type of object 〔某種物品的〕處理者: *baggage handler* 行李搬運者

hand lug·gage /'·‚··/ *n* (also 又作 **hand baggage** *AmE* 〖美式〗) [U] the small bags of a traveller, which can easily be carried by hand 手提行李

hand·made /'hænd‚med; ‚hænd'meɪd◂/ *adj* made by hand, not by machine 手工製的

hand·out /'hænd‚aʊt; 'hændaʊt/ *n* **1** something, such as food or clothes, which is given free to someone who is poor 施捨物; 救濟品〔如食品或衣物〕 **2** information which is given out, especially on a printed sheet 講義; 印刷品: *Handouts will be distributed at the end of the lecture.* 講課完了會把講義發給大家。

hand·picked /'hænd'pɪkt; ‚hænd'pɪkt◂/ *adj* chosen with great care 精心挑選的

hand·shake /'hænd‚ʃek; 'hænd‚ʃeɪk/ *n* an act in which two people take each other's right hand when they meet or leave each other 握手

hand·some /'hænsəm; 'hænsəm/ *adj* **1** physically attractive (used especially of men) 英俊的; 有魅力的〔尤指男子〕 –see 見 BEAUTIFUL (USAGE 用法) **2** generous 慷慨的; 大方的: *a handsome reward* 可觀的回報 | *a handsome offer* 慷慨的提議 –**handsomely** *adv*

hand·stand /'hænd‚stænd; 'hændstænd/ *n* a movement in which you kick your legs into the air so that your body is upside down and supported on your hands 倒立

hand-to-mouth /‚·‚·'·◂/ *adj* **hand-to-mouth existence** a way of life in which you have very little money 拮据的生活 –**hand-to-mouth** *adv*

hand·writ·ing /'hænd‚raɪtɪŋ; 'hænd‚raɪtɪŋ/ *n* [U] writing done by hand with a pen or pencil, or a particular person's style of writing 書寫; 筆跡; 筆風: *She has very clear handwriting.* 她的筆跡很清晰。

hand·y /'hændɪ; 'hændi/ *adj* **handier, handiest 1** useful and simple to use 有用的; 方便使用的: *This is a handy little box.* 這是隻輕巧的小箱子。| *An answer-phone to take calls while I'm out would be very handy.* 我外出時有應答電話就會很方便。 **2 handy with something** clever at using something with your hands 使用某事雙手靈巧的: *He's very handy with a needle.* 他很會做針線活兒。 **3** *infml* conveniently near 〖非正式〗附近的; 近便的: *The shops are quite handy.* 商店就在附近, 很方便。| *Keep the pills handy!* 把藥片放在近旁! **come in handy** to be useful 會有用的: *A few more traveller's cheques may come in handy on holiday.* 度假時多帶幾張旅行支票會有用的。–**handily** *adv*

hand·y·man /'hændɪ‚mæn; 'hændimæn/ *n* **handymen** /-‚mɛn; -men/ -men/ a person who is good at doing repairs and practical jobs in the house 擅長在家裡做修修補補等雜活的人

✻**hang¹** /hæŋ; hæŋ/ *v* **hung** /hʌŋ; hʌŋ/, **hung 1** [T] to fix something somewhere by its top part, so that the lower part is free 懸掛; 吊: *You can hang your coat on the hook over there.* 你可以把外衣掛在那邊的鉤子上。 **2** [I] to be fixed somewhere by the top part, with the lower part free 懸掛著; 吊著: *Her coat was hanging on the door.* 她的外衣掛在門上。 **3** [T] to fix wallpaper onto a wall 貼〔牆紙〕 **4** [T] [past tense is 過去時為 **hanged**] to kill someone, usually as a punishment, by putting a rope around their neck and dropping them so that all their weight is taken by it 吊死〔某人〕; 絞死〔某人〕: *He was hanged for murder.* 他因謀殺而被絞死。

hang about/around *phr v* [I;T **hang about** sthg] to wait near a place without any clear purpose 在〔附近〕閒逛: *There were a lot of people hanging about near the entrance.* 有許多人在入口處附近閒逛。| *I hung around the station for nearly an hour.* 我在車站附近閒逛了近一個小時。

hang back *phr v* [I] to be unwilling to do something 不願做〔某事〕

hang on *phr v infml* 〖非正式〗**1** [I] to keep hold of something 握住〔某物〕 **2** [I] to wait 等; 等待: *Hang on a minute: I'm just coming.* 等一下, 我馬上就來。 **3** [T **hang on** sthg] to depend on something 取決於〔某事物〕: *A lot hangs on his success tomorrow.* 許多事情都取決於他明天能否成功。

hang onto sthg *phr v* [T] **1** to keep hold of something 握住〔某物〕: *We had to hang onto the sides of the boat.* 我們必須抓住船的兩邊。 **2** to keep something 保留〔某物〕: *We decided to hang onto the house until prices*

H

were higher. 我們決定把房屋保留到價格上漲後再出售。

hang up *phr v* **1** [I] to finish a telephone conversation by putting the telephone down 掛斷電話: *I said goodbye and hung up.* 我道聲再見便掛斷了電話。–see 見 TELE-PHONE¹ (USAGE 用法) **2** [I;T **hang** sthg ↔ **up**] to fix something or be fixed by the top part, with the lower part free 懸掛; 掛着: *Hang your coat up.* 把你的外衣掛起來。| *Your dress is hanging up in the wardrobe.* 你的衣服掛在大衣櫃裡。

hang up on sbdy *phr v* [T] to finish a telephone conversation with someone by putting the telephone down before they have finished speaking 在某人講完話前掛斷電話: *I was trying to explain, but he hung up on me.* 我正要解釋, 他卻掛斷了電話。

hang² *n* **get the hang of something** *infml* to develop the skill of doing something, or an understanding of how something works 〔非正式〕掌握做某事的竅門; 理解某物的運行方式: *Typing is difficult at first, but you'll soon get the hang of it.* 打字一開始很難, 但你很快就能掌握竅門。

han·gar /'hæŋə; 'hæŋəʳ/ *n* a big building where aircraft are kept 飛機庫 –see picture on page 991 見 991 頁彩圖

hang·er /'hæŋə; 'hæŋəʳ/ *n* (also 又作 **coat hanger**) a piece of wood, metal, or plastic with a hook on top, which you use to hang up a piece of clothing 衣架

hanger-on /ˌ··'·/ *n* **hangers-on** a person who tries to be friendly with another person or group, for their own advantage 食客; 奉承者

hang-glid·er /'hæŋˌglaɪdə; 'hæŋˌglaɪdəʳ/ *n* a type of large KITE which you hang from and use to fly through the air 懸掛式滑翔機

hang-glid·ing /'·ˌ··/ *n* [U] a sport of flying using a hang-glider 懸掛式滑翔運動: *Hang-gliding is very popular.* 懸掛式滑翔運動十分流行。–**hang-gliding** *v* [only in progressive forms 只用於進行式]: *They've gone hang-gliding.* 他們滑翔去了。

hang·ing /'hæŋɪŋ; 'hæŋɪŋ/ *n* [C;U] death caused by putting a rope around someone's neck and dropping them so that all their weight is taken by it 絞刑; 絞死: *Are you in favour of hanging?* 你贊成絞刑嗎?

hang·man /'hæŋmən; 'hæŋmən/ *n* **hang-men** /-mən; -mən/ a person whose work is hanging criminals 絞刑吏

hang·o·ver /'hæŋˌovə; 'hæŋəʊvəʳ/ *n* **1** the feeling of sickness and headache which you have the day after drinking too much alcohol 宿醉〔指喝酒過多之後第二日的頭痛及不適〕 **2** something that results or remains from an earlier event or state 遺留物; 後遺症: *That rule is a hangover from the days when all doctors were men.* 那條規定是所有醫生都是男的那個時期留下來的。

hang-up /'hæŋˌʌp; 'hæŋʌp/ *n infml* something which a person gets unusually worried about 〔非正式〕令人非常擔憂的事情; 苦惱: *He's got a real hang-up about his appearance.* 他為自己的外貌而苦惱。

han·ker /'hæŋkə; 'hæŋkəʳ/ *v* **hanker after something, hanker for something** to have a great desire for something 渴望得到某物 –**hankering** *n* : *a hankering after fame and wealth* 追名逐利

han·kie /'hæŋki; 'hæŋki/ *n* **hankies** (also 又作 **hanky**) *infml* a handkerchief 〔非正式〕手帕

hap·haz·ard /ˌhæp'hæzəd; ˌhæp'hæzəd◄/ *adj* unplanned or disorderly 隨意的, 無秩序的: *It's a very haphazard system.* 這是套非常混亂的制度。–**haphazardly** *adv*

✭hap·pen /'hæpən; 'hæpən/ *v* **1** [I] to take place 發生: *A funny thing happened yesterday.* 昨天發生了一件滑稽的事情。| *What will happen if your parents find out?* 如果你父母發現, 會發生甚麼事情呢? **2** **happen to: a** to do or to be something by chance 恰巧; 偶然: *I happened to see him yesterday.* 昨天我偶然遇到了他。| *She happened to be at the gate when I went by.* 我經過的時候, 她恰巧在大門口。**b** a phrase used to give force to what you are saying, when you are angry 恰恰〔憤怒時表示強調〕: *That happens to be my bike you just knocked over!* 你剛碰倒的就是我的自行車! **3** **happen to someone/something** to take place and have an effect on somebody or something 發生在某人身上; 發生在某事上: *She's very late — I hope nothing's happened to her.* 她遲到了——我希望她沒出甚麼事情。**4** **as it happens, it so happens that** a phrase used when what you are saying is slightly surprising, or when the thing mentioned is so by chance 恰巧; 碰巧〔表示所說的事有些令人吃驚, 或所說的事出於偶然〕: *As it happens, I still have the money.* 我正好身上還帶着錢。| *It so happened that we moved away from that area.* 我們恰巧已從那個地方搬走了。**5** **happen on something** to find something by chance 偶然發現某事

■ USAGE 用法: **1** Compare 比較 **happen, occur, take place.** Events usually **happen** or (more formal) **occur** by accident ☆偶然發生的事情用 **happen** 或用 **occur** 〔較以正式〕: *When did the explosion* **happen/occur**? 甚麼時候發生的爆炸? Events usually **take place** by arrangement ☆事先安排好的事常用 **take place**: *When will the wedding* **take place**? 何時舉行婚禮? **2** If you want to ask about a problem which someone has at the present moment, it is usually better not to use the word

happen. Instead, ask ☆如詢問某人此刻是否遇到了問題，通常最好不要用 **happen,** 而應該這樣問: **What's the matter?** 出甚麼事了? | **What's wrong?** 怎麼了? | **Is anything the matter?** 有甚麼事嗎?

hap·pen·ing /ˈhæpənɪŋ; ˈhæpənɪŋ/ n an event, especially a strange one 事情〔尤指奇怪的事情〕

hap·pi·ly /ˈhæpɪlɪ; ˈhæpɪˌli/ adv **1** in a happy manner 高興地: *laughing happily* 笑得很開心 | **2** willingly 樂意地; 欣然地: *I'll happily go to the shops for you.* 我很樂意替你去商店。**3** fortunately 幸運地: *Happily, the accident was prevented.* 幸運的是，終於避免了那起事故。

hap·pi·ness /ˈhæpɪnɪs; ˈhæpinɪs/ n [U] the state of being pleased or satisfied 幸福; 高興; 滿意

★**hap·py** /ˈhæpɪ; ˈhæpi/ adj **happier, happiest** **1** feeling, expressing, or giving pleasure and satisfaction 高興的, 愉快的; 幸福的; 滿意的: *a happy child* 快樂的孩子 | *You look very happy.* 你看上去很高興。| *a happy marriage* 美滿的婚姻 | *I'm not very happy about their decision.* 我對他們的決定不太滿意。–opposite 反義 **unhappy 2 be happy to do something** to be willing to do something 願意做某事: *I'll be happy to meet him when I have time.* 有時間的話，我很願意見見他。**3** a word which you use in greetings to express your good wishes for a particular occasion 祝…愉快〔用於特殊場合表示問候或祝願〕: *Happy New Year!* 新年快樂! | *Happy Birthday!* 生日快樂!

happy-go-lucky /ˌ···ˈ··◂/ adj showing a cheerful lack of concern for the need to think or plan carefully 無憂無慮的

ha·rangue /həˈræŋ; həˈræŋ/ v **harangued, haranguing** [T] to try to persuade someone that you are right with a long, loud angry speech 用沒完沒了的大聲訓斥來試圖說服〔某人〕–**harangue** n

har·ass /ˈhærəs; ˈhærəs/ v [T] to annoy or worry someone by causing trouble for them on repeated occasions 煩擾〔某人〕: *Please stop harassing me!* 請別來煩我! –**harassment** n [U]

har·bour¹ /ˈhɑːbə; ˈhɑːbə/ n (also 又作 **harbor** *AmE* 【美式】) [C;U] an area of water where ships can shelter from the rough waters of the open sea 港口; 港灣 – see picture on page 991 見 991 頁彩圖

harbour² v (also 又作 **harbor** *AmE* 【美式】) [T] **1** to give protection and shelter to someone who is hiding from the police 庇護; 藏匿; 窩藏: *He was arrested on suspicion of harbouring terrorists.* 他因被懷疑庇護恐怖分子而遭逮捕。**2** to keep a thought or feeling in your mind for a long time 〔長時間〕懷有〔某種想法或感情〕: *She harbours a secret*

desire to be a film star. 她暗懷成為電影明星的願望。

★★★**hard¹** /hɑːd; hɑːd/ adj **1** firm and stiff 堅實的; 堅硬的: *This cheese is as hard as rock!* 這塊奶酪硬得像石頭! **2** difficult to do or understand 難做的; 難懂的: *That's a very hard question.* 那是個很難回答的問題。| *It's hard to know what he's really thinking.* 很難了解他到底在想些甚麼。

□ USEFUL PATTERNS 有用句型
be hard to do something; be hard for someone to do something

3 needing a lot of force or effort 用力的; 費勁的: *It was hard work moving those logs.* 移動那些木頭是很費力氣的工作。| *Give it a good hard push.* 使勁推它。**4** unpleasant and full of difficulties 不愉快的; 困難重重的: *The police gave him a hard time.* 警察給他吃了苦頭。| *Their life had always been hard.* 他們的日子一直很艱難。**5** showing no kindness 冷酷的; 無情的: *He's a very hard man.* 他是個冷酷無情的人。**6 be hard on someone** to treat someone severely and unkindly 嚴厲地對待某人: *Don't be too hard on him; he didn't mean to do it.* 不要對他過於嚴厲，他不是故意這樣做的。**7** containing a lot of LIME, that prevents soap from mixing properly (used of water) 含無機鹽的〔指水〕**8** certain (used of facts) 肯定的〔指事實〕: *We need some hard evidence.* 我們需要些確鑿的證據。| *These are the hard facts of the situation.* 局勢確實就是這樣。**9** pronounced as /k/ rather than /s/ (used of the letter **c**) or pronounced as /g/ rather than /dʒ/ (used of the letter **g**) 〔字母 **c**〕發作/k/ 而不發作/s/ 的;〔字母 **g**〕發作/g/ 而不發作 /dʒ/ 的 **10 hard as nails: a** physically strong and very fit 身體強健的 **b** showing no tenderness 冷酷無情的 **11 hard drugs** strong illegal drugs 烈性毒品 **12 a hard winter** a very cold winter 非常寒冷的冬天 –**hardness** n [U]

★**hard²** adv **1** making a great effort 努力地: *Push hard!* 用力推! | *She's working hard.* 她工作很努力。| *I had to think long and hard before I could find the answer.* 我努力思考良久才想出了答案。| *However hard he listened, he could hear nothing.* 不論他如何用力去聽，他還是甚麼也聽不見。**2** strongly or heavily 強烈地; 厲害地: *It's raining harder than ever.* 雨下得比任何時候都大。| *She laughed so hard that she fell off her chair.* 她大笑不止，以至於從椅子上跌了下來。**3 be hard hit** to suffer because of something that has happened 〔由於發生了某事而〕遭受打擊: *Farmers have been hard hit by the bad weather.* 農民由於惡劣的天氣而損失慘重。**4 be hard pushed, be hard put** to have great difficulty doing something 〔做某事〕遇到很大的困難: *I was hard pushed to hand in my essay on time.* 我很難按時把文章交上去。**5**

H

hard done by unfairly treated 受到不公正的待遇: *She's beginning to feel very hard done by.* 她開始感到自己受到了很不公正的待遇。**6 hard at it** *infml* working with great effort 〖非正式〗努力工作: *She's been hard at it since six this morning.* 她從今晨六時起就一直在努力工作。

hard-and-fast /ˌ··'··◂/ *adj* **hard-and-fast rules** rules which are fixed and unchangeable 不容改變的規定

hard·back /'hɑrdbæk; 'hɑːdbæk/ *n* a book with a strong stiff cover 硬封面的書; 精裝本

hard·board /'hɑrdbord; 'hɑːdbɔːd/ *n* [U] a kind of wood made out of small pieces of wood which have been pressed into sheets 硬質纖維板

hard-boiled /ˌ·'·◂/ *adj* boiled until the yellow part is hard (used of eggs) 煮得老的〔指雞蛋〕

hard cash /ˌ·'·/ *n* [U] coins and notes, not a cheque 現鈔; 現金: *He will only accept hard cash.* 他只肯收現金。

hard core /ˌ·'·/ *n* the people most concerned at the centre of a group or activity, or the most determined in following its aims 〔團體或活動的〕中堅分子; 堅持追求目標的人: *The hard core in the party make all the decisions.* 該黨的中堅分子作出所有的決定。| *Now only the hard core remains.* 現在, 只有鐵桿分子留了下來。 –**hard-core** *adj* [only before a noun 只用於名詞前]: *hard-core opposition to the government's plans* 對政府計劃的堅決反對

hard currency /ˌ·'····/ *n* money from particular countries which can be exchanged freely 硬通貨幣; 可自由兌換的貨幣

hard disk /ˌ·'·/ *n* a part of a computer on which you can store information, and which you cannot remove from the computer 硬碟磁盤〔固定於計算機內儲存信息的部分〕 –see picture on page 763 見 763 頁彩圖

hard·en /'hɑrdn; 'hɑːdn/ *v* **1** [I;T] to make or become firm and stiff (使)變硬: *The cement was beginning to harden.* 水泥開始變硬。| *The pottery is then baked to harden it.* 陶器隨後被烘烤, 使它變硬。**2** [I;T] to make or become stronger and more determined (使)變得更強硬; (使)變得更堅定: *Opposition to the government hardened after the crisis.* 危機之後, 反對政府的力量變得更加強硬。| *The government has hardened its attitude to trade unions.* 政府對工會的態度已變得更強硬。**3** [T] to make someone more severe, and less kind and sensitive 使〔某人〕更嚴厲; 使〔某人〕更冷酷無情; 使〔某人〕更麻木: *I'm becoming hardened to criticism.* 我對批評正變得越來越無所謂。| *a hardened criminal* 冷酷的罪犯

hard·head·ed /ˈhɑrdˈhɛdɪd; ˌhɑːdˈhedｊd/ *adj* able to make decisions based only on reason and not feelings 頭腦冷靜的; 精明的: *a hardheaded businesswoman* 精明的女商人

hard-heart·ed /ˌ·'···◂/ *adj* having no kind feelings or sympathy for people 冷酷無情的–**hard-heartedness** *n* [U]

hard·line /'hɑrd,laɪn; ˌhɑːd'laɪn◂/ *adj infml* unwilling to change your strong and fixed beliefs 〖非正式〗不願改變固有信念的; 立場堅定的: *hardline supporters of the government's policies* 政府政策的堅定支持者 – **hardliner** *n*

hard luck /ˌ·'·◂/ *interj,n infml* 〖非正式〗[U] **1** bad luck 不幸; 倒霉: *Failing the test was really hard luck.* 測驗不及格實在倒霉。**2 hard luck!** a phrase used to show that you are sorry about something unpleasant that has happened to someone 真不幸!〔用於對某人遇到了令人不快的事表示難過〕

*★**hard·ly** /'hɑrdlɪ; 'hɑːdli/ *adv* **1 can hardly, could hardly** able to do something only with difficulty 幾乎不能; 勉強才能: *I can hardly see.* 我幾乎看不見。| *She could hardly speak.* 她幾乎説不出話來。**2 hardly ever, hardly any** almost never or almost none 幾乎從不; 幾乎沒有: *We hardly ever go out.* 我們幾乎從不外出。| *I've got hardly any money.* 我幾乎沒錢了。| *You've eaten hardly anything.* 你幾乎甚麼東西也沒吃。**3** only just 僅; 剛才: *I hardly know the people I work with.* 我不大認識跟我一起工作的人。| *We had hardly started our journey when the car broke down.* 我們剛起程, 車就壞了。**4** not at all 一點不; 絲毫不: *It's hardly surprising that he got annoyed!* 他發火, 這絲毫也不令人感到奇怪! | *This is hardly the time for making jokes!* 這根本不是開玩笑的時候!

■ USAGE 用法: Compare 比較 **hardly, scarcely, barely, no sooner. 1 Hardly, scarcely,** and **barely** are followed by **when,** but **no sooner** are followed by *than* in sentences like these ☆ **hardly, scarcely** 和 **barely** 後接 **when,** 但 **no sooner** 後接 *than,* 如在下列句子中: *The game had* **hardly/scarcely/barely** *begun when it started raining.* 比賽剛開始就下起雨來了。| *The game had* **no sooner** *begun than it started raining.* 比賽剛開始就下起雨來了。**2** All of these expressions change the usual word order of the sentence when they come at the beginning ☆當這些詞被置於句首時, 整個句子的語序都要改變: **Hardly/scarcely/barely** *had the game begun when it started raining.* 比賽剛開始就下起雨來了。| **No sooner** *had the game begun than it started raining.* 比賽剛開始就下起雨來了。**3 Hardly** and **scarcely** can come before *any, ever* and *at all* to mean "almost no", "almost never", "almost not" ☆ **hardly** 和 **scarcely** 可置於 *any, ever* 和 *at all* 前面, 意為"幾乎沒有"、"幾乎從不"、"幾乎不": *We've*

hardly/scarcely *any money left.* 我們幾乎沒剩下甚麼錢。 | *He's* **hardly/scarcely** *ever late.* 他幾乎從不遲到。 | *We* **hardly/scarcely** *got wet at all.* 我們身上幾乎一點沒濕。 (**Barely** can also take this pattern but is less common. **barely** 也可用於該句型，但較少見。)

hard of hear·ing /ˌ·····/ *adj* unable to hear properly 聽力不佳的

hard·ship /ˈhɑrdʃɪp; ˈhɑːdʃɪp/ *n* [C;U] a difficult situation, such as lack of money or food, which causes great suffering 艱苦；困苦；貧困: *The new tax laws are causing the poor a lot of hardship.* 新稅法正給窮人帶來許多困難。 | *They suffered many hardships.* 他們遭受了許多苦難。

hard up /ˌ·'·◂/ *adj* not having enough money 拮据的: *We were very hard up after I lost my job.* 我失業後，我們的手頭很拮据。

hard·ware /ˈhɑrd,wɛr; ˈhɑːdweəʳ/ *n* [U] **1** metal tools and other goods for use in the home and garden 〔家庭和花園用的〕金屬器具；五金製品 **2** machinery which makes up a computer system 〔計算機〕硬件 **3** military machinery and weapons 武器裝備

hard·wear·ing /ˌhɑrdˈwɛrɪŋ; ˌhɑːdˈweərɪŋ◂/ *adj* strong, and lasting for a long time (used especially of clothes and shoes) 耐穿的〔尤指衣物和鞋〕

hard·wood /ˈhɑrd,wʊd; ˈhɑːdwʊd/ *n* [C;U] strong heavy wood from certain types of tree, used to make good furniture 〔製家具用的〕硬木

har·dy /ˈhɑrdi; ˈhɑːdi/ *adj* **hardier, hardiest** **1** strong and able to bear difficult conditions 強壯的；能吃苦的: *You have to be really hardy to live in such a cold climate.* 生活在如此寒冷的氣候裡，你必須要非常能吃得起苦才行。 **2** able to live through the winter above ground (used of plants) 耐寒的〔指植物〕 **hardiness** *n* [U]

hare[1] /hɛr; heəʳ/ *n* an animal like a rabbit, but larger, with long ears, a short tail, and long back legs which allow it to run fast 野兔

hare[2] *v* **hared, haring** [I +adv/prep] *infml* to run very fast 〔非正式〕飛奔: *He hared off down the road.* 他沿着大路飛奔。

hare·brained /ˈhɛr,brend; ˈheəbreɪnd/ *adj* impractical and foolish (used of people or ideas) 不切實際的〔指人或觀點〕；愚蠢的: *a harebrained scheme* 不切實際的計劃

hare·lip /ˈhɛr,lɪp; ˌheəˈlɪp/ *n* a top lip which is divided into two parts because it did not develop properly before birth 唇裂；兔唇

har·em /ˈhɛrəm; ˈheərəm/ *n* **1** the place in a Muslim house where the women live 〔伊斯蘭教徒的〕閨房 **2** the group of women who live in this place 伊斯蘭教閨房中的女眷

hark /hɑrk; hɑːk/ *v*

hark back to sthg *phr v* [T] to mention things which happened in the past 提及〔往事〕: *You're always harking back to how things were when you were young.* 你總是重提你年輕時的境況。

harm[1] /hɑrm; hɑːm/ *n* [U] **1** damage 破壞: *The whole incident did his reputation a lot of harm.* 整個事件嚴重地損害了他的聲譽。 | *Speeches like this do more harm than good.* 這種言辭弊大於利。 **2** **come to no harm** to not be hurt or damaged 沒有受到損害: *We got caught in the storm, but luckily the ship came to no harm.* 我們遇上了風暴，但幸運的是船並未受損。 **3** **out of harm's way: a** safe from danger 沒有危險: *At last he was home, and out of harm's way.* 他終於到家，脫離了危險。 **b** unable to cause hurt or damage 不會引起傷害或破壞: *Put the knife in the drawer, out of harm's way.* 把小刀放在抽屜裡，以免傷着人。 **4** **there's no harm** there is nothing to lose by doing something 〔做某事〕不會有甚麼損害: *There's no harm in finding out how much it would cost.* 算出成本沒有甚麼不好。 **5** **do no harm, not do any harm** to not do any damage, and probably do some good 沒有甚麼壞處〔也許會有點好處〕: *She might refuse, but it would do no harm to ask her.* 她也許會拒絕，但問問她總是不要緊吧。 | *It wouldn't do you any harm to go to bed early.* 早睡覺對你不會有壞處的。

harm[2] *v* [T] to hurt or damage someone or something 傷害，損害〔某人、某物〕: *Our house wasn't harmed at all in the storms.* 我們的房子在暴風雪中安然無恙。

harm·ful /ˈhɑrmfəl; ˈhɑːmfəl/ *adj* causing someone to be hurt or causing something to be damaged 〔對某人〕有害的: *the harmful effects of smoking* 吸煙的害處

harm·less /ˈhɑrmləs; ˈhɑːmləs/ *adj* not likely to hurt or offend people, or damage things 無害的；無惡意的；不致傷的: *The dog is completely harmless.* 這條狗根本不會傷人。 | *a harmless question* 無惡意的問題 **–harmlessly** *adv*

har·mon·i·ca /hɑrˈmɑnɪkə; hɑːˈmɒnɪkə/ *n* a musical instrument that you play by holding it to your mouth, moving it from side to side, and blowing or sucking 口琴

har·mo·nize /ˈhɑrmə,naɪz; ˈhɑːmənaɪz/ *v* **harmonized, harmonizing** (also 又作 **harmonise** *BrE* 〔英式〕) [I] **1** to sing or play a piece of music so that the notes combine with the main tune in a pleasant way 用和聲歌唱或演奏 **2** to go together well 協調；和諧: *The design for the house harmonized well with the surrounding buildings.* 這座房屋的式樣與周圍的建築很協調。

har·mo·ny /ˈhɑrmənɪ; ˈhɑːmənɪ/ *n* **harmonies** **1** [C;U] notes of music combined together in a way which sounds pleasant 和聲；和弦 **2** [U] a state of peaceful agreement 協調；和諧: *We lived together in perfect* *harmony until the baby was born.* 嬰兒出生前，我們的生活一直非常和諧。 –**harmonious** /hɑrˈmoʊnɪəs; hɑːˈməʊnɪəs/ *adj*

har·ness¹ /ˈhɑrnɪs; ˈhɑːnɪ‚s/ *n* **1** the bands which are used to control a horse or small child 〔馬的〕挽具; 〔嬰兒的〕繫帶 **2 in harness** wearing a harness (used of a horse) 套着挽具〔指馬〕

harness² *v* [T] **1** to put a harness on a working animal such as a horse 給〔馬等〕套上挽具 **2** to use a natural force to produce useful power 用〔自然力〕產生能量: *River water is harnessed to produce electricity.* 河水被用來發電。

harp¹ /hɑrp; hɑːp/ *n* a large musical instrument with strings running from top to bottom of an open three-cornered frame; you play the harp by stroking (STROKE¹) or pulling the strings with your fingers 豎琴 –**harpist** *n*

harp² *v* **harp on something, harp on about something** to talk a lot about something even when other people are not interested in it 嘮叨某事

har·poon /hɑrˈpun; hɑːˈpuːn/ *n* a spear at the end of a long rope, which is used for hunting large sea animals 魚叉 –**harpoon** *v* [T]

harp·si·chord /ˈhɑrpsɪˌkɔrd; ˈhɑːpsɪkɔːd/ *n* a musical instrument like a small piano, used especially in former times 撥弦古鋼琴

har·row·ing /ˈhærəwɪŋ; ˈhærəʊɪŋ/ *adj* very upsetting 令人傷心的; 令人難過的: *a harrowing experience* 令人傷心的經歷

harsh /hɑrʃ; hɑːʃ/ *adj* **1** unpleasantly bright, loud, or rough 刺眼的; 刺耳的: *The colours are too harsh.* 顏色太刺眼了。 | *a harsh voice* 刺耳的聲音 **2** very severe, cruel, or unkind 嚴厲的; 冷酷無情的: *a harsh punishment* 嚴厲的懲罰 | *harsh words* 嚴厲的措詞 | *It was a very harsh winter.* 那是個極為寒冷的冬天。 –**harshly** *adv* –**harshness** *n* [U]

har·vest¹ /ˈhɑrvɪst; ˈhɑːvɪst/ *n* **1** the act or period of gathering the crops 收獲; 收獲季節: *We all helped with the harvest.* 我們都幫忙收割。 | *It's harvest time again.* 又是收獲的時節了。 **2** the crops that are gathered 收成; 收獲物: *We've got a good harvest this year.* 今年我們獲得了豐收。

harvest² *v* [T] to gather a crop 收割〔糧食〕

has /əz, həz; z, əz, həz, *strong* 強讀 hæz; hæz/ the 3rd person singular present tense of HAVE ☆ HAVE 的一般現在時第三人稱單數形式 –see **'S** (USAGE 用法)

has-been /ˈ· ·/ *n infml* a person who is no longer important or successful 〔非正式〕過時的人

hash /hæʃ; hæʃ/ *n* **1** [C;U] a meal containing meat which has been cut up in small pieces and re-cooked 回鍋肉丁便餐 **2 make a hash of something** to do something badly 把某事弄得亂七八糟: *She made a*

complete hash of her report. 她這份報告寫得亂七八糟。 **3** [U] see 見 HASHISH

hash·ish /ˈhæʃiʃ; ˈhæʃiːʃ/ *n* (also 又作 **hash** *infml* 〔非正式〕) [U] a drug which is made from the dried leaves or hardened juice of the CANNABIS plant and which is often rolled into cigarettes for smoking 大麻麻醉劑

has·n't /ˈhæznt; ˈhæzənt/ *v* short for 縮約式 = "has not": *Hasn't he finished yet?* 他還沒做完嗎?

has·sle /ˈhæsl; ˈhæsəl/ *n infml* 〔非正式〕 [C;U] **1** an annoying difficulty 令人惱怒的困難 〔麻煩〕: *It's a real hassle to get this child to eat.* 讓這個孩子吃飯實在是困難。 | *the hassle of using public transport* 使用公共交通設施所帶來的麻煩 **2** an annoying argument 令人惱怒的爭論: *It's bad enough at work — I don't need any hassle from you too!* 工作情況已經夠糟糕了——我不需要你再來爭論不休!

hassle² *v* **hassled, hassling** [T] *infml* to cause someone continuing annoyance 〔非正式〕不斷煩擾〔某人〕: *Don't keep hassling me about the washing-up!* 不要老是來找我洗碗筷! | *He was hassling her for money.* 他纏着她要錢。

haste /heɪst; heɪst/ *n* [U] the act of doing things too quickly 急忙; 匆忙: *In his haste, he forgot to put on his coat.* 匆忙之間, 他忘記了穿上外套。

has·ten /ˈheɪsn; ˈheɪsən/ *v* **1** [I] to hurry, or be quick to do something 急忙; 趕快: *She hastened home.* 她匆匆回家。 | *She hastened to add that she had never taken drugs herself.* 她趕緊補充說她自己從未吸過毒。 **2** [T] to make something happen more quickly 使〔某事〕盡快發生: *His progress to high office was hastened by his family connections.* 他的家庭關係使他迅速得到提升。

hast·y /ˈheɪsti; ˈheɪsti/ *adj* **hastier, hastiest 1** hurried 匆忙的: *a hasty meal* 匆忙的一餐 **2** acting or deciding something too quickly, without thinking about it carefully 草率的; 倉促的: *Let's not be hasty.* 我們不要草率行事。 | *We don't want to make a hasty decision.* 我們不想倉促地做出決定。 –**hastily** *adv*

*****hat** /hæt; hæt/ *n* a piece of clothing which you wear on top of your head to cover it, often for protection against the weather 帽子 –see picture on page 210 見 210 頁彩圖

hatch¹ /hætʃ; hætʃ/ *v* **1** [I;T] to break open, or to cause an egg to break open, letting a young bird out of an egg 〔蛋〕孵化; 使〔蛋〕孵化: *Three eggs have already hatched.* 三隻蛋已經孵化。 | *We hatch the eggs by keeping them in a warm place.* 我們把蛋放在溫暖的地方使其孵化。 **2** [I] (of a young bird or animal) to break through an eggshell and be born 〔鳥或動物〕破殼而出; 孵出 **3 hatch a plot, hatch a plan** to plan something secretly, usually something bad 祕密策劃〔尤指壞事〕: *They hatched a plan to murder the king.* 他們密謀殺害國王。

hatch² *n* **1** the cover or door of an opening on a ship or plane through which people and things can pass 〔船或飛機的〕艙口 **2** an opening in a wall, for passing food from a kitchen to the room where people eat 〔廚房向餐廳傳遞菜肴的〕窗口

hatch·back /ˈhætʃbæk; ˈhætʃbæk/ *n* a car with a door at the back which opens upwards 後車門向上開的小轎車 —see picture on page 209 見 209 頁彩圖

hatch·et /ˈhætʃɪt; ˈhætʃɪt/ *n* a small axe with a short handle 短柄小斧

*hate¹ /het; heɪt/ *n* [U] a strong feeling of dislike 憎恨; 憎惡: *She looked at me with hate in her eyes.* 她用憎恨的目光看着我。

hate² *v* **hated, hating** [T] **1** to have a great dislike of someone or something 憎恨, 憎惡〔某人或某物〕: *I hate violence.* 我憎恨暴力行徑。| *They really hate each other.* 他們十分憎恨對方。**2** *infml* to dislike something or not enjoy it〔非正式〕討厭; 不喜歡: *I hate tomatoes.* 我不喜歡西紅柿。| *I hate using the telephone.* 我討厭打電話。

□ USEFUL PATTERNS 有用句型
to hate something; to hate doing something

3 I would hate to = I would not enjoy 我不喜歡: *I would hate to live in London.* 我不喜歡住在倫敦。**4 I hate to tell you** a phrase used when you are telling someone some bad news 我本不想把這事告訴你〔用於把壞消息告訴某人時〕

hate·ful /ˈhetfəl; ˈheɪtfəl/ *adj* very unpleasant and unkind 可惡的; 不友好的: *That was a hateful thing to say.* 説那樣的話很不客氣。—**hatefully** *adv*

ha·tred /ˈhetrɪd; ˈheɪtrɪd/ *n* [U] a very strong feeling of dislike 憎恨; 仇恨: *She is full of hatred for the driver who killed her dog.* 她對開車壓死她的狗的那位司機充滿了仇恨。| *a hatred* **of** *computers* 討厭電腦

hat·ter /ˈhætə; ˈhætər/ *n* a person who makes or sells hats 製帽人; 帽商

hat trick /ˈ··/ *n* three successes coming one after the other especially in sports such as football or cricket〔足球或板球運動中〕連續三勝: *He scored a brilliant hat trick!* 他出色地連中三元!

haugh·ty /ˈhɔtɪ; ˈhɔːti/ *adj* **haughtier, haughtiest** *fml* appearing proud and showing that you think other people are less important than yourself (a word used to express disapproval)〔正式〕傲慢的; 自負的〔含貶義〕—**haughtily** *adv* —**haughtiness** *n* [U]

haul¹ /hɔl; hɔːl/ *v* [I;T] to pull hard using a lot of effort 用力拉[拖]: *The logs had to be*

hauled along the ground. 不得不在地上用力拖這些木頭。| *They hauled away on the ropes.* 他們用力拉繩子。

haul up *phr v* **be hauled up in court** to be made to appear before a court 被押解上法庭

haul² *n* **1** an act of pulling hard 拖; 拉 **2** a **long haul** a long and difficult journey or job 長途跋涉; 困難而費時的工作: *It was a long haul home.* 要經過長途跋涉才能到家。**3** the amount of fish caught at one time with a net〔魚〕一網的捕獲量 **4** an amount of stolen or forbidden goods 一次偷得的物品〔禁品〕: *The thieves got away with a valuable haul of jewellery.* 賊人偷走了一批珍貴的珠寶。

haul·age /ˈhɔlɪdʒ; ˈhɔːlɪdʒ/ *n* [U] **1** the business of carrying goods by road 公路貨運（業）**2** the amount of money charged for carrying goods by road 公路貨運費

haunch /hɔntʃ; hɔːntʃ/ *n* part of your body which includes your bottom and the tops of your legs 腰臀部: *They were squatting on their haunches.* 他們蹲在那裡。

haunt¹ /hɔnt; hɔːnt/ *v* [T] **1** (of the spirit of a dead person) to visit someone or appear in a place〔鬼魂〕拜訪〔某人〕;〔鬼魂〕出現於〔某地〕: *A headless man haunts the castle.* 一個無頭男鬼常在那座城堡中出沒。**2** (of something unpleasant) to keep coming into someone's thoughts〔令人不快的事〕縈繞在〔某人〕心裡: *His words will haunt me for the rest of my life.* 他的話將永遠縈繞在我心頭。

haunt² *n* *infml* a place where someone goes regularly〔非正式〕〔某人〕常去的地方: *This pub is one of my favourite haunts.* 這家酒館是我最喜歡去的一個地方。

haunt·ed /ˈhɔntɪd; ˈhɔːntɪd/ *adj* **1** lived in or visited by the spirits of dead people 鬼魂出沒的: *a haunted house* 一所鬧鬼的房屋 | *That castle is thought to be haunted.* 據説那座城堡裡有鬼魂出沒。**2** looking very worried 看上去焦慮不安的: *She had a haunted look on her face.* 她臉上有種焦慮的神情。

haunt·ing /ˈhɔntɪŋ; ˈhɔːntɪŋ/ *adj* strange in a sad or pleasant way and remaining in your thoughts for a long time 不易忘記的: *a haunting memory* 不易忘卻的記憶 | *a haunting melody* 不易忘記的旋律 —**hauntingly** *adv*

*have —see box on pages 526 and 527 見 526 頁和 527 頁方框

ha·ven /ˈhevən; ˈheɪvən/ *n* *lit* a place of calm and safety〔文〕安全的地方; 避難所

have·n't /ˈhævnt; ˈhævənt/ *v* short for 縮約式 = "have not": *You've been here before, haven't you?* 你以前來過這裡, 是嗎? | *I haven't got any money.* 我一點錢都沒有。

hav·oc /ˈhævək; ˈhævək/ *n* [U] **1** widespread damage or confusion 大範圍的破壞; 大混亂: *The storm last night caused havoc*

H

☆☆have /həv, həv; strong 強讀 hæv; hæv/ *v*

present tense 現在式	past tense 過去式	past participle 過去分詞
I **have,** I**'ve**	I **had,** I**'d**	**had**
You **have**	You **had,** you**'d**	
He/she/it **has,** he**'s,**	He/she/it **had,** he**'d,**	present participle 現在分詞
she**'s,** it**'s**	she**'d,** it**'d**	**having**
We **have,** we**'ve**	We **had,** we**'d**	negative short forms 否定縮略式
You **have,** you**'ve**	You **had,** you**'d**	**haven't hasn't hadn't**
They **have,** they**'ve**	They **had,** they**'d**	

For the pronunciation of these forms look them up at their own place in the dictionary. 上述各種形式的發音，可參閱本詞典內各自的詞條。

1 [auxiliary verb] used to form the perfect tenses of verbs 用於形成動詞的完成式:
I've written a letter to him. 我給他寫了封信。 | *He's gone home.* 他已回家了。 | *Have you finished?* 你做完了嗎？ | *She had already spent the money.* 她已把那筆錢花掉了。 | *I've lived here for ten years.* 我在這裡已住了十年了。 | *Have you ever been to Spain?* 你去過西班牙嗎？

2 have to, have got to an expression you use to say that someone must do something or something must happen 必須; 不得不〔表示某人必須做某事或某事一定會發生〕:
You have to press that switch to turn the machine on. 你必須按那個開關才能開動機器。 | *I'm sorry I've got to go now.* 對不起我得告辭了。 | *Have we got to show our passports on the boat?* 我們在船上要出示護照嗎？ | *Did you have to queue for long?* 你是不是要排很長時間的隊？ | *I'll have to phone him later.* 我得在晚些時候打電話給他。 | *We signed the agreement, but we didn't have to pay any money immediately.* 我們簽了協議，但不必立刻付款。

3 [T] (also 又作 **have got** BrE〔英式〕) to own or possess something 擁有; 佔有:
Most people have a washing machine now. 現在大部分人都有洗衣機。 | *Have you got a pencil?* 你有鉛筆嗎？ | *I haven't got any money.* 我沒有錢。 | *Do you have many friends?* 你的朋友多不多？ | *They've got three children.* 他們有三個孩子。 | *She has a very good job.* 她有一份理想的工作。

4 [T] to receive something 接到; 收到:
I had a letter from Jane today. 今天我收到簡的來信。 | *Have you had any news from Steve yet?* 你有沒有史蒂夫的消息？

5 [T] to experience, enjoy, or do something 經歷; 享受; 做:
Let's have a swim. 我們去游泳吧。 | *I had breakfast at eight o'clock.* 我八點鐘吃早餐。 | *Have a look at this.* 看看這個。 | *We're having a meeting this afternoon.* 我們今天下午要開會。 | *This policy will have a serious effect on young people.* 這政策將對青年人產生嚴重的影響。 | *I had my watch stolen yesterday.* 我的手錶昨天被偷了。

6 have something done to cause something to be done 使〔某事〕完成:
I need to have my hair cut. 我需要去理髮。 | *I must have this tap mended.* 我必須把這水龍頭修理一下。

7 have a baby to give birth to a baby 生孩子:
She had her first baby last year. 她去年生下了第一個孩子。

8 have done with something to finish something 結束某事:
I decided to tell him immediately and have done with it. 我決定馬上告訴他, 然後結束此事。

9 have had it to be too old and no longer useful 因為太陳舊而不再用了:
That old car's had it. 那輛舊車不能用了。

10 have it in for someone *infml* to behave in an unpleasant way towards someone because you do not like them 〔非正式〕〔由於不喜歡而〕和某人過不去

11 have it off, have it away *BrE infml* to have sex 〔英式, 非正式〕與…發生性關係

12 have to do with to have a connection with something 與〔某物〕有關:
Her job has something to do with banking. 她的工作和銀行業有關。 | *This problem has nothing to do with you!* 這個問題與你無關!

13 I won't have = I will not allow 我不會允許:
I won't have behaviour like this in my house! 我不允許在我的屋子裡有這種行為!

have on *phr v*
1 [T **have** sthg ↔ **on, have got** sthg ↔ **on**]
to be wearing something 穿着:
What did she have on? 她穿了甚麼衣服? | *He had nothing on except a pair of shorts.* 他只穿了一條短褲。 | *It was cold, so I'd got my coat on.* 天氣很冷, 所以我穿了大衣。
2 [T **have** sthg **on, have got** sthg **on**] to have arranged to do something 安排〔做某事〕:
Do you have anything on tonight? 你今晚有甚麼安排嗎? | *I've got nothing on all this week.* 我這個星期都沒有甚麼安排。
3 be having someone on *infml* to be tricking someone, by telling them something that is not true 〔非正式〕欺騙某人; 愚弄某人

have out *phr v*
1 [T **have** sthg ↔ **out**]
to get something removed from inside your body 〔從體內〕去除; 切除:
I had three teeth out last week. 上週我拔了三顆牙。 | *She had her appendix out.* 她切除了盲腸。
2 have it out with someone
to settle an argument with someone by talking freely and angrily to them 〔通過與某人暢談或爭吵來〕解決與某人的爭端

have up *phr v*
be had up to be taken to court for doing something illegal 〔由於做非法的事〕被法庭傳訊:
He was had up for dangerous driving. 他因危險駕駛而被法庭傳訊。

everywhere. 昨夜的暴風雨到處都造成了破壞。 **2** **play havoc with something, wreak havoc on something** to confuse something or cause serious damage to it 使某物混亂; 嚴重破壞某物: *The delay played havoc with our plans.* 這一耽擱打亂了我們的計劃。| *The floods wreaked havoc on the city.* 洪水破壞了這座城市。

hawk¹ /hɔk; hɔːk/ *n* a large bird with very good eyesight which catches other birds and small animals for food 鷹

hawk² *v* [T] **1** to sell goods on the street or at the doors of houses, especially while travelling from place to place (沿街)叫賣: *He's hawking his paintings from door to door.* 他挨家挨戶地賣他的畫。 **2** to try to sell your ideas by taking them from place to place 傳播〔觀點〕: *He's been hawking his ideas around from publisher to publisher.* 他在一個個出版商那裡傳播他的觀點。 **–hawker** *n*

haw·thorn /ˈhɔːθɔrn; ˈhɔːθɔːn/ *n* a tree which has white or red flowers, and red berries in autumn 山楂樹

hay /he; heɪ/ *n* [U] grass which has been cut and dried, especially for cattle food 乾草〔尤指用作牛的飼料〕

hay fe·ver /ˈ·ˌ··/ *n* [U] an illness like a bad cold, caused by breathing in POLLEN dust from plants 枯草熱, 花粉病

hay·stack /ˈheˌstæk; ˈheɪstæk/ *n* a large pile of dried grass built for storing 乾草堆

hay·wire /ˈheˌwaɪr; ˈheɪwaɪər/ *adj* **go haywire** to become confused and out of control 變得混亂; 失去控制: *My plans have all gone haywire since they changed the times of our holidays.* 由於他們改變了我們的假期時間, 我的計劃全被打亂了。| *The computer's gone haywire after the power cut.* 斷電之後, 電腦失控了。

haz·ard¹ /ˈhæzərd; ˈhæzəd/ *n* a danger 危險: *Drinking too much alcohol can be a real health hazard.* 酒精飲料喝得過多確實會危害健康。| *hazard warning lights* 危險信號燈

hazard² *v* [T] *fml*〖正式〗**1** to risk something or put it in danger 冒...的危險: *He hazarded all his money in the attempt to save the business.* 他孤注一擲, 拿出了所有的錢來挽救企業。 **2** **hazard a guess** to make a guess which may be wrong 試著猜一猜〔可能會猜錯〕

haz·ard·ous /ˈhæzədəs; ˈhæzədəs/ *adj* likely to harm people 〔對人〕有危害的: *hazardous chemicals* 有害的化學品

haze /hez; heɪz/ *n* [U] a light mist or smoke 薄霧; 輕煙: *a haze of cigarette smoke* 香煙的煙霧 | *a heat haze* 熱蒸汽

ha·zel¹ /ˈhezl; ˈheɪzəl/ *n* a tree which bears nuts that can be eaten 榛樹

hazel² *adj* having a light greenish brown colour 淡褐色的: *She has hazel eyes.* 她有一雙淡褐色的眼睛。

haz·y /ˈhezɪ; ˈheɪzi/ *adj* **hazier, haziest 1** misty or rather cloudy 有薄霧的; 多雲的: *The mountains were hazy in the distance.* 遠方的羣山籠罩在薄霧之中。 **2** uncertain or confused 不肯定的; 不清楚的: *I'm rather hazy about the details of their plans.* 我對他們的計劃的細節不甚清楚。

H-bomb /ˈetʃˌbam; ˈetʃ bɒm/ *n* see 見 HYDROGEN BOMB

★he /ɪ, hɪ; i, hi, *strong* 強讀 hi; hiː/ *pron* [used as the subject of a verb 用作動詞的主語] **1** the male person or animal who has already been mentioned 他; 牠〔雄性動物〕: *"Where's John?" "He's gone to the cinema."* "約翰在哪裡?" "他去看電影了。" **2** the person who has already been mentioned, when it has not been stated whether they are male or female 他〔已經提及的人, 不論男女〕: *Every doctor should do what he thinks best.* 每位醫生都應該做他認為最為合適的事情。

★head¹ /hɛd; hed/ *n* **1** the part of your body which contains your brain, and where your eyes, ears, nose, and mouth are 頭; 頭部: *He nodded his head.* 他點點頭。 **2** your mind 頭腦: *His head's full of silly ideas!* 他腦子裡全是愚蠢的想法! **3** the part at the top or front of something 物品的頂端〔前端〕: *He sat at the head of the table.* 他坐在桌子的上首。| *Move to the head of the queue.* 到隊列的最前面去。 **4** a person who is in charge of a group or an organization 負責人; 領導人: *She's the head of a large computer firm.* 她是一家電腦大公司的負責人。 **5** (also 又作 **head teacher**) the teacher in charge of a school 校長 **6 heads** the front side of a coin, which often has a picture of a person's head on it〔硬幣的〕正面〔常印有頭像〕: *Let's toss a coin; you call, heads or tails?* 我們來投幣決定; 你說, 要正面還是反面? **7** a word used for counting farm animals 頭〔牲畜的計量單位〕: *They've got 40 head of cattle.* 他們有四十頭牛。 **8 a head, per head** for each person 每人: *They do set meals at £8 a head.* 他們把價格定為每人八英鎊一餐。 **9 above your head** too difficult for you to understand 難以理解 **10 bang your head against a brick wall** to waste your efforts by trying to do something impossible 徒勞; 枉費心機 **11 bite someone's head off, snap someone's head off** to speak very angrily to someone 生氣地斥責某人 **12 bring something to a head** to make a situation reach a point where something must be done or decided 使局勢發展到必須做出決定的境地 [RELATED PHRASE 相關詞組 **come to a head**] **13 go to your head: a** to make you drunk 使醉倒: *The wine's gone straight to my head.* 我喝的酒衝上來了。 **b** to make you too proud 使過於自負: *His success has gone to his head.* 他被成功衝昏了頭腦。 **14 head over heels** turning right

H

over in the air 頭朝下摔倒: *She tripped and fell head over heels.* 她絆了一下，栽倒了。**15 head over heels in love** completely in love 在熱戀中 **16 keep your head** to remain calm 保持鎮靜 **17 keep your head above water** to keep out of difficulties, especially out of debt 未陷入困境〔尤指不負債〕 **18 lose your head** to act wildly or without reason because you are afraid or angry〔由於恐懼或憤怒〕舉止粗野; 失去理智 **19 I can't make head nor tail of this** = I can't understand this 我不明白 **20 off your head** *infml* mad 〔非正式〕發瘋的 **21 off the top of your head** without thinking very carefully about something 未認真考慮: *I can't give you any more details off the top of my head.* 不經認真考慮，我不能告訴你更多的細節問題。**22 on your own head be it** = you will be responsible for any bad results of your actions 你必須對後果負責 **23 put your heads together** to talk about something together 一起商討〔某事〕: *We'll have to put our heads together to find an answer.* 我們必須一起討論一下以找出答案。**24 shout your head off, scream your head off** to shout very loudly 高聲叫喊 **25 take it into your head to do something** to suddenly decide to do something 突然決定做某事: *He took it into his head to learn Russian.* 他突然決定去學俄語。

★head² v 1 [T] to be at the front or top of something 在〔某物〕的前端〔頂端〕: *The car headed the procession.* 這輛車行駛在隊伍的最前面。**2** [T] to be in charge of a group or an organization 負責; 領導: *Who heads the government?* 誰是政府的首腦? **3** [T] to hit a ball with your head 用頭頂〔球〕: *He headed it into the goal.* 他把球頂進了球門。**4** [I +adv/prep; T+adv/prep] to move or make something move in a certain direction〔使〕朝某方向移動: *We're heading home.* 我們正朝着家走。| *We were heading for the coast.* 當時我們正往海邊走。| *We headed him towards the house.* 我們指引他向那所屋子走。| *You're heading for trouble.* 你在自找麻煩。**5 be headed** to have a particular title 有標題的: *The letter was headed 'Confidential'.* 這封信頭上寫着"機密"的字樣。

head sbdy ↔ **off** *phr v* [T] to make somebody move in a different direction by moving in front of them 把〔某人〕引向別的方向: *They were running towards the house, but we headed them off at the gate.* 他們正朝那所屋子跑去，但我們在大門口把他們引開了。

head·ache /ˈhɛd.ek; ˈhɛdeɪk/ *n* **1** a pain in your head 頭疼: *I've got a headache again.* 我的頭又疼了。–see 見 ACHE² (USAGE 用法) **2** something that causes problems or worry 產生麻煩或令人憂慮的事情: *The problem of unemployment is a big headache for the government.* 失業問題令政府大為頭痛。

head·band /ˈhɛd.bænd; ˈhɛdbænd/ *n* a band that you wear on your head usually

to keep hair back from your face 束髮帶〔防止頭髮垂在臉上〕

head·dress /ˈhɛd.drɛs; ˈhɛd-drɛs/ *n* an ornamental covering for the head 頭飾; 頭巾

head·first /ˈhɛdˈfɜst; ˌhɛdˈfɜːst◂/ *adv* with your head first and the rest of your body following 頭先向前地: *He fell headfirst into the lake.* 他頭向下落入湖中。

head·gear /ˈhɛd.gɪr; ˈhɛdɡɪəʳ/ *n* [U] hats or anything that you wear on your head 帽子; 頭盔; 頭飾

head·ing /ˈhɛdɪŋ; ˈhɛdɪŋ/ *n* the words written as a title at the top of a piece of writing 標題; 題目

head·lamp /ˈhɛd.læmp; ˈhɛdlæmp/ *n* a HEADLIGHT 車頭燈

head·land /ˈhɛdlənd; ˈhɛdlənd/ *n* a narrow piece of land running out into the sea 岬; 海岬

head·light /ˈhɛd.laɪt; ˈhɛdlaɪt/ *n* a powerful light at the front of a vehicle 車頭燈: *Switch your headlights on!* 把車頭燈打開! – see picture on page 209 見 209 頁彩圖

head·line /ˈhɛd.laɪn; ˈhɛdlaɪn/ *n* **1** the title printed in large letters above a story in a newspaper〔報紙的〕大標題 **2 the headlines** the main points of the news read on radio or television〔廣播、電視的〕新聞提要

head·long /ˈhɛd.lɔŋ; ˈhɛdlɒŋ/ *adv,adj* **1** done very quickly 迅速地〔的〕: *a headlong descent into anarchy and disorder* 頃刻間演變成一種混亂的無政府狀態 **2 rush headlong into something** to do something without stopping to think about it carefully 倉促地做某事: *They rushed headlong into marriage.* 他們倉促地結了婚。

head·mas·ter /ˈhɛdˈmæstɚ; ˈhɛdˈmɑːstəʳ/ *n* the male teacher in charge of a school 校長

head·mis·tress /ˈhɛdˈmɪstrɪs; ˌhɛdˈmɪstrɪs/ *n* the female teacher in charge of a school 女校長

head-on /ˌ· ˈ·◂/ *adv,adj* with the heads or front parts hitting each other 迎面地〔的〕: *a head-on collision* 迎面相撞 | *We hit the bus head-on.* 我們迎面撞上了公共汽車。

head·phones /ˈhɛd.fonz; ˈhɛdfəʊnz/ *n* [pl] an apparatus which fits over your ears and is used to receive radio messages or listen to records or tapes 頭戴式受話機; 耳機

★head·quar·ters /ˈhɛdˈkwɔrtɚz; ˈhɛdˌkwɔːtəz/ *n* (also 又作 **HQ**) [+ sing/pl verb] the office or place where the people work, controlling a large organization, such as the police or army〔一個大規模機構，如警署或軍隊的〕總部: *Our firm's headquarters are in Geneva.* 我們公司的總部在日內瓦。

head·room /ˈhɛd.rum; ˈhɛdrʊm/ *n* [U] space above a vehicle passing under a bridge or through a TUNNEL〔車輛通過橋下或穿越隧道時的〕淨空高度

head·set /ˈhɛd.sɛt; ˈhɛdsɛt/ *n* a set of headphones 一副耳機

H

head·stand /ˈhɛdˌstænd; 'hɛdstænd/ *n* a position with your head and hands on the ground and your legs in the air 倒立: *Can you do a headstand?* 你會倒立嗎?

head start /ˌ· ˈ·/ *n* have a head start to have an advantage over other people〔與他人相比〕具有優勢: *He had a head start over the other players as he was so much stronger.* 他身體強健得多, 故比其他運動員佔優。

head·stone /ˈhɛdˌston; 'hɛdstəun/ *n* a stone which marks the top end of a grave, and which usually has the dead person's name on it 墓碑

head·strong /ˈhɛdˌstrɔŋ; 'hɛdstrɔŋ/ *adj* determined to do what you want against all other advice 頑固的; 任性的

head·way /ˈhɛdˌwe; 'hɛdweɪ/ *n* make headway to get good results when dealing with a difficulty〔在困難中〕獲得滿意的結果

head·wind /ˈhɛdˌwɪnd; 'hɛdˌwɪnd/ *n* a wind blowing directly against you 逆風; 頂頭風

head·y /ˈhɛdi; 'hɛdi/ *adj* **headier, headiest 1** making you feel drunk 易使人醉的: *a heady wine* 醉人的酒 **2** with a feeling of lightness and excitement 飄飄然的; 興奮的: *We were all heady with success.* 我們所有的人都因成功而有些飄飄然。

heal /hil; hiːl/ *v* [I;T] to make or become healthy again 治癒; 病癒: *His wounds are healing nicely.* 他的傷口癒合得很好。| *This cream should help to heal the cuts.* 這種軟膏應有助於刀傷癒合。 **–healer** *n*

heal up *phr v* [I] to become healthy again 病癒

★★ **health** /hɛlθ; helθ/ *n* [U] **1** the state of being well and without illness or disease 健康: *Health is more important to me than money.* 對我來說健康比金錢更重要。 **2** the general condition of your body 健康狀況: *She's in very good health.* 她的身體非常健康。| *Smoking is very bad for your health.* 吸煙對你的健康非常有害。

health food /ˈ··/ *n* food that is natural and without added chemicals, and believed to be better for your health〔天然的、不含化學物質的〕保健食品

★ **health·y** /ˈhɛlθi; 'helθi/ *adj* **healthier, healthiest 1** strong and usually in good health 強健的; 健康的: *healthy children* 健康的孩子 | *a healthy plant* 健壯的植物 **2** likely to improve your health 可能對健康有益的: *healthy seaside air* 有益健康的海邊空氣 | *healthy food* 有益健康的食品 **3** showing that your health is good 顯示健康狀況良好的: *a clear healthy skin* 光滑而健康的皮膚 | *a healthy appetite* 好胃口 **–healthily** *adv* – **healthiness** *n* [U]

heap[1] /hip; hiːp/ *n* a pile or mass of things one on top of the other 堆: *The books lay in a heap on the floor.* 書堆放在地板上。– **heaped** *adj*: *a heaped teaspoon of sugar* 滿

一茶匙糖

heap[2] *v* [T] **1** to pile something up in large amounts 堆積〔某物〕: *He heaped the plate with food.* 他在盤子裡盛滿食物。| *He heaped food on the plate.* 他把食物裝滿盤子。 **2 heap praise/criticism on someone** to give a lot of praise or criticism to someone 極力讚揚〔批評〕某人

★★ **hear** /hɪr; hɪəʳ/ *v* **heard** /hɝd; hɜːd/, **hearing 1** [I;T not in progressive forms 不用於進行式] to be conscious of a sound through your ears 聽見: *I can't hear very well.* 我聽不太清楚。| *I can hear someone knocking.* 我能聽見有人在敲門。 **2** [T; + (that) not in progressive forms 不用於進行式] to be told or informed about something 被告知; 聽說: *I heard that he was ill.* 我聽說他病了。| *I've heard a lot about him, but I've never met him.* 我聽說過許多關於他的事情, 但從未見過他。 **3** [T] to listen with attention especially to a case in court 聽取; 審理〔案件〕: *The judge heard the case.* 法官審理了這起案件。| *She heard what he had to say.* 她聽了他要說的話。 **4 won't hear of something** = refuse to allow something 不允許某事: *I won't hear of you walking home; I'll pick you up at the station.* 我不許你們走著回家, 我會開車到車站來接你們的。 **5 hear from someone** to receive news from someone, usually by letter 獲悉某人的消息〔通常通過信函〕: *I heard from her last week.* 上週我收到她的一封信。 **6 have heard of someone/something** to know about someone or something 聽說過某人〔某事〕: *Who's he? — I've never heard of him.* 他是誰? — 我從未聽說過他。 **7 Hear! Hear!** a shout of agreement 對! 對!〔表示同意的叫喊聲〕

■ **USAGE** 用法: Compare 比較 **hear** and 和 **listen to**. If you **hear** something you take in sound with your ears, whether you want to or not. If you **listen to** something you pay attention in order to hear ☆ **hear** 表示不論你是否願意, 你"聽見"了某種聲音。而 **listen to** 則表示你"注意聽", 目的是要聽見: *I wasn't listening to the conversation, but I heard my name mentioned.* 我沒有去聽他們的對話, 但我聽見他們提到了我的名字。

hear sbdy ↔ **out** *phr v* [T] to listen to someone who is speaking until that person has finished 聽〔某人〕說完: *Don't interrupt, just hear me out before you start talking.* 別插嘴, 你聽我說完再說。

★ **hear·ing** /ˈhɪrɪŋ; 'hɪərɪŋ/ *n* **1** [U] the sense by which you hear sound 聽覺: *Her hearing is getting worse.* 她的聽覺愈來愈差。 **2** [C] *law* a trial of a case before a judge〔律〕〔案件的〕審理 **3 get a hearing** to be given the chance to explain something 得到解釋〔某

事)的機會: *It's a good idea, so try to get a hearing for it.* 這是個好主意，所以要想辦法講給別人聽。[RELATED PHRASE 相關詞組 **give someone a hearing**] **4 hard of hearing** not able to hear very well 聽力不佳 **5 hearing aid** a small machine which makes sounds louder, used by people who cannot hear well 助聽器 **6 in someone's hearing, within someone's hearing** within the distance at which someone can hear what is being said 在某人聽得見的距離內: *Don't talk about it in his hearing.* 不要在他聽得到的地方討論此事。

hear·say /'hɪr,se; 'hɪəseɪ/ *n* [U] things which are said rather than proved 謠傳；傳聞: *I don't know if he's really leaving his job; it may only be hearsay.* 我不知道他是否真的要辭職；這有可能只是謠傳而已。

hearse /hɜ˞s; hɜːs/ *n* a car which is used to carry a dead body to the funeral 靈車

★★**heart** /hart; haːt/ *n* **1** the organ inside your chest which controls the flow of blood by pushing it round your body 心；心臟 **2** this organ when thought of as the centre of your feelings, especially love 心地；內心: *He seems rather fierce, but has a kind heart.* 他看上去很兇，但卻心地善良。 **3** the centre of something or the most important part of it 中心；核心；實質: *the heart of a cabbage* 白菜菜心 | *the heart of the city* 市中心 | *Let's get to the heart of the matter.* 我們來討論一下事情的實質吧。 **4** a shape which is supposed to be like the shape of a heart 心形 **5 hearts** a set of playing-cards with one or more heart-shaped figures printed on it in red 〔牌〕紅心；紅桃 **6 a person after your own heart** a person who is like you in some way and who you like 合自己心意的人: *He's a man after my own heart.* 他正是我中意的人。 **7 at heart** a phrase used when saying what someone is really like 在內心裡；實際上〔用於表示某人實際是何種人〕: *He's very kind at heart.* 他實際上非常善良。 **8 break someone's heart** to make someone very unhappy 使某人非常傷心 **9 from the heart, from the bottom of your heart** said sincerely or with deep feeling 由衷地說；深情地說 **10 my heart leapt** = I felt very happy 我感到非常高興 **11 my heart sank** = I felt very unhappy or disappointed 我感到非常難過〔失望〕 **12 know/learn something by heart** to know or learn something so that you can remember it perfectly 記住某事；背出某事: *We had to learn the speech by heart for homework.* 作為家庭作業，我們必須把這篇演講背出來。 **13 lose heart** to no longer have the courage or will to do something 失去勇氣〔做某事〕；喪失意志〔做某事〕 **14 not have the heart to do something** to be unable to do something because it seems too unkind 不忍心做某事: *I didn't have the heart*

to tell her the bad news. 我不忍心把這壞消息告訴她。 **15 set your heart on something** to want something very much 非常想要某物: *She has set her heart on going to university.* 她渴望上大學。 **16 take heart** to feel encouraged and so able to do something difficult 鼓起勇氣〔做困難的事〕 **17 take something to heart** to feel very sad or upset by something 對某事感到難過或憂慮: *Don't take it to heart! I was only joking.* 別擔心！我不過是開個玩笑。 **18 with all your heart** said sincerely or with deep feeling 由衷地說；深情地說 **19 -hearted** having a certain type of character 有某種心腸的: *She's very kind-hearted.* 她心地善良。 | *a cold-hearted business man* 冷酷無情的商人

heart·ache /'hart,ek; 'haːteɪk/ *n* lit [U] deep feelings of sorrow and pain 〔文〕傷心；痛心

heart at·tack /'··,·/ *n* a very dangerous medical condition in which a person's heart suddenly stops working properly 心臟病發作: *He died of a heart attack.* 他死於心臟病。

heart·beat /'hart,bit; 'haːtbiːt/ *n* [C;U] the regular movement of someone's heart 心跳: *The doctor listened to the rapid heartbeat of the sick child.* 醫生聽了聽那位病孩的急促的心跳。

heart·break /'hart,brek; 'haːtbreɪk/ *n* [C;U] lit deep sorrow and disappointment 〔文〕心碎；傷心；絕望

heart·break·ing /'hart,brekɪŋ; 'haːt,breɪkɪŋ/ *adj* making you feel very sad 令人心碎的: *heartbreaking photos of the refugees* 令人心碎的難民照片

heart·brok·en /'hart,brokən; 'haːt,brəʊkən/ *adj* (also 又作 **broken-hearted**) feeling very upset 感到悲痛的；感到難過的

heart·burn /'hart,bɜ˞n; 'haːtbɜːn/ *n* [U] a condition in which you feel an unpleasant burning in your chest, caused by INDIGESTION 〔由於消化不良而引起的〕胃灼熱

heart·en /'hartn̩; 'haːtn̩/ *v* [T] to encourage someone and make them more cheerful 鼓舞〔某人〕；令〔某人〕振奮: *He was heartened by her kindness.* 她的好意使他感到鼓舞。

heart·felt /'hart,felt; 'haːtfelt/ *adj* deeply felt and sincere 衷心的；摯誠的: *She gave him her heartfelt thanks.* 她表示衷心感謝他。

hearth /harθ; haːθ/ *n* the floor of a fire-place in a house 壁爐前的地板 –see picture on page 730 見 730 頁彩圖

heart·i·ly /'hartlɪ; 'haːtɪli/ *adv* **1** done strongly and cheerfully 熱忱地；熱心地: *She laughed heartily.* 她開懷大笑。 | *They ate heartily.* 他們大吃一頓。 **2** very or completely 非常地；完全地: *I'm heartily sick of your questions.* 我對你的問題感到極為煩厭。

heart·less /'hartlɪs; 'haːtlɪs/ *adj* cruel and showing no pity 冷酷的；殘忍的

heart·rend·ing /'hart,rɛndɪŋ; 'haːt,rendɪŋ/

adj causing a feeling of deep sorrow or pity 令人心碎的: *the heartrending cries of the wounded* 傷者發出的叫聲令人心碎

heart·strings /ˈhɑrtˌstrɪŋz; ˈhɑːtˌstrɪŋz/ [pl] **play on someone's heartstrings** to cause someone to feel deep love or pity 引發某人的愛慕或憐憫之心

heart-to-heart /ˌ···◂/ *n* an open and honest talk, usually in private, and mentioning personal details 〔通常在私下的〕坦誠的談話

heart·y /ˈhɑrti; ˈhɑːti/ *adj* **heartier, heartiest 1** very friendly 友善的; 親切的: *a hearty greeting* 親切的問候 | *a hearty welcome* 熱烈的歡迎 **2 hale and hearty** strong and healthy 強健的 **3** large (used of meals) 豐盛的〔指飯菜〕: *a hearty breakfast* 豐盛的早餐 – **heartiness** *n* [U]

☆**heat¹** /hit; hiːt/ *n* **1** [U] the temperature of something, especially when it is warm or being made hot 溫度〔尤指物體在熱的時候或加熱時的溫度〕: *Test the heat of the water before you get in the bath.* 進浴缸前先試試水溫。 **2** [U] a feeling of warmth 溫暖; 溫熱: *This radiator doesn't give off much heat.* 暖氣管沒有散發出多少熱量。 | *Can you feel the heat of the sun's rays?* 你感覺到太陽光的溫暖嗎? | *Does this metal react to heat?* 這種金屬遇熱起反應嗎? **3** [sing] hot weather or the hottest part of the day 熱天; 酷暑: *I can't stand this heat.* 我受不了這麼熱的天。 | *I really suffer from the heat.* 這麼熱的天讓我着實吃了不少苦。 | *He went out in the heat and got sunstroke.* 他頂着酷熱外出, 中了暑。 **4** [U] **the heat of** a time of great anger or excitement 特別生氣[興奮]的時候: *In the heat of the argument I called him an idiot.* 在激烈的爭吵中, 我罵他是傻瓜。 | *In the heat of the moment I forgot to thank them properly.* 當時我非常激動, 竟忘記向他們道謝了。 **5 be on heat** (of certain female animals, usually dogs) to be in a state of sexual excitement during the breeding season 〔雌性動物, 尤指狗〕發情 **6** [C] a part of a race or competition where the winners compete against other winners to decide the end result 〔比賽的〕預賽: *She was knocked out in the qualifying heats.* 她在資格預選賽中被淘汰。

heat² *v* [T] to make something warm or hot 把〔某物〕加熱: *I'll heat some milk for the coffee.* 我去熱點牛奶沖咖啡喝。 | *It's expensive to heat these big rooms.* 給這些大房間供應暖氣費用很高。

heat up *phr v* [I;T **heat** sthg ↔ **up**] to make or become warm or hot (使)變暖; (使)變熱: *I'll heat up the soup.* 我來把湯熱一下。

heat·ed /ˈhitɪd; ˈhiːtˌɪd/ *adj* angry and excited 憤怒的; 激烈的: *a heated argument* 激烈的爭論 | *She got very heated about it.* 她對此非常憤怒。 –**heatedly** *adv*

heat·er /ˈhitɚ; ˈhiːtəʳ/ *n* a machine for heating air or water 暖氣機; 熱水器: *a fan heater* 風扇取暖器 | *Please would you switch off the heater?* 請把暖氣關掉好嗎?

heath /hiθ; hiːθ/ *n* an open piece of wild land without any farms 荒地; 荒野

hea·then /ˈhiðən; ˈhiːðən/ *n old fash* a person who does not belong to one of the large established religions 《老式》異教徒 – **heathen** *adj*

heath·er /ˈhɛðɚ; ˈheðəʳ/ *n* [U] a plant with small pink or purple flowers which grows wild on open windy land 石南屬植物

heat·ing /ˈhitɪŋ; ˈhiːtɪŋ/ *n* [U] a system for keeping rooms and buildings warm 暖氣系統

heat·stroke /ˈhitˌstrok; ˈhiːtstrəʊk/ *n* [U] a condition of fever and weakness caused by too much heat 中暑

heat wave /ˈ··/ *n* a period of unusually hot weather 熱浪; 酷暑時期

heave¹ /hiv; hiːv/ *v* **heaved, heaving 1** [I;T] to pull and lift something with effort 〔用力〕拉起, 舉起〔某物〕: *We heaved him to his feet.* 我們拉他站了起來。 | *They all heaved on the rope, and at last the rock moved.* 所有人都用力拉繩子, 終於拉動了那塊石頭。 **2** [I] to move up and down regularly 有規律地起伏: *Her chest heaved as she breathed with difficulty.* 她呼吸困難, 胸膛一起一伏。 **3** [I] to feel sick or VOMIT 感到噁心; 嘔吐: *The sight of so much blood made my stomach heave.* 看到這麼多血, 我感到很噁心。 **4 heave a sigh** to let out a deep breath with a sound expressing emotion 長吁一口氣: *We all heaved a sigh of relief when we heard the plane had landed safely.* 聽説飛機已安全着陸, 我們都寬慰地舒了一口氣。

heave² *n* a pull or throw 拉; 擲: *Just one more heave, and the stone will be in the right place.* 只要再拉一下, 就可以把石頭拉到要放的地方。

heav·en /ˈhɛvən; ˈhevən/ *n* **1** [U] a place of complete happiness, where God or the gods are supposed to live and where the souls of good people go after they die 天堂 –compare 比較 HELL **2 the heavens** *lit* the sky 《文》天空 **3 for heaven's sake** a phrase used to show anger or impatience 看在老天的份上〔表示憤怒或不耐煩〕: *For heaven's sake hurry up!* 看在老天的份上你快點兒吧! **4 good heavens, heavens** a phrase used to show surprise 天哪〔表示驚訝〕: *Good heavens! Have you finished already?* 我的天哪! 你已做完了嗎? | *Heavens, no!* 天哪, 不! **5 heaven knows** a phrase used to say that you do not know something 天知道〔表示你不知道某事〕: *Heaven knows why he's taking so long!* 天知道他怎麼花這麼長時間!

heav·en·ly /ˈhɛvənli; ˈhevənli/ *adj* **1** [only before a noun 只用於名詞前] of or from heaven 天堂的; 從天堂來的: *a heavenly vision* 天堂的幻像 | *a heavenly angel* 天上的天使 **2** *infml* wonderful〔非正式〕極好的: *What heavenly weather!* 多好的天氣啊!

heav·en·wards /ˈhɛvənwɚdz; ˈhɛvənwədz/ *adv* (also 又作 **heavenward** /ˈhɛvənwɚd; ˈhɛvənwəd/ *AmE*〔美式〕) towards the sky or heaven 朝天空; 向天堂

★★ **heav·y** /ˈhɛvɪ; ˈhɛvɪ/ *adj* **heavier, heaviest 1** weighing a lot 沉重的: *The bag is too heavy for me to carry.* 這隻包太重, 我拎不動。**2** used when asking the weight of something〔用於詢問重量〕: *How heavy are you?* 你的體重是多少? **3** great in amount 數量大的: *heavy rain* 大雨 | *heavy traffic* 擁擠的交通 | *There were heavy casualties.* 傷亡的人很多。**4** using a lot of force 力量大的: *a heavy blow to the head* 對頭部的重擊 **5** slow and ungraceful 緩慢的; 笨拙的: *his heavy movements* 他緩慢的行動 **6** difficult and full of hard work (used of a period of time) 困難的; 工作繁忙的〔指一段時間〕: *I've had a heavy day at the office.* 我在辦公室裡忙了一天。**7** serious and difficult to understand (used of a piece of writing) 沉悶的; 難以理解的〔指文章〕**8** solid and difficult for your stomach to deal with (used of food)〔指食物〕硬的; 不易消化的〔指食物〕**9** hot and without wind (used of the weather) 悶熱的〔指天氣〕**10 heavy breathing** loud, deep breathing 沉重的呼吸 **11 heavy drinker** someone who drinks a lot of alcohol 酒癮大的人 **12 heavy industry** organizations that produce goods such as coal, steel, and chemicals that are used in the production of other goods 重工業 **13 heavy metal** a style of rock music played loudly on electric musical instruments and drums 重金屬搖滾樂 **14 heavy sleeper** someone who sleeps deeply and is not easily woken 睡得沉而不易喚醒的人 **15 heavy smoker** someone who smokes a lot 煙癮大的人 **16 heavy work** work which needs a lot of physical strength 重體力的工作 **17 make heavy weather of something** to make something more difficult than it really is 把某事弄得比實際困難 –**heavily** *adv* –**heaviness** *n* [U]

heavy-du·ty /ˌ‥ ‥◂/ *adj* made to be used a lot or for rough treatment (used of clothes and machines) 耐穿的〔指衣服〕; 耐用的〔指機器〕

heavy-hand·ed /ˌ‥ ‥◂/ *adj* unkind or unfair in the way you treat other people 粗魯的; 粗暴的

heav·y·weight /ˈhɛvɪˌwet; ˈhɛvɪweɪt/ *n* **1** a BOXER in the heaviest class 重量級拳擊運動員 **2** a person of great importance or influence 重要人物; 有影響的人物

He·brew /ˈhibru; ˈhiːbruː/ *n* [U] the language used by the Jews, in ancient times and at present 希伯來語 –**Hebrew** *adj*

heck·le /ˈhɛkl; ˈhekəl/ *v* **heckled, heckling** [I;T] to interrupt a speaker or speech with confusing or unfriendly remarks, especially a political meeting〔尤指在政治會議上〕質問; 詰問 –**heckler** *n* : *a crowd of hecklers* 一羣質問者 –**heckling** *n* [U]

hec·tare /ˈhɛktɛr; ˈhektɑːʳ/ *n* a unit for measuring areas of land, which equals 10,000 square metres 公頃〔面積單位, 等於一萬平方米〕

hec·tic /ˈhɛktɪk; ˈhektɪk/ *adj* very busy or full of excitement 非常繁忙的; 興奮的: *a hectic day* 繁亂的一天 –**hectically** /-klɪ; -klɪ/ *adv*

he'd /ɪd, hɪd; id, hid, *strong* 強讀 hid; hiːd/ **1** short for 縮約式 = "he would": *He'd go there now if he could afford it.* 如果有錢, 他現在就會去。**2** short for 縮約式 = "he had": *He'd gone.* 他已走了。| *He'd got a few minutes to spend with her.* 他有幾分鐘時間和她在一起。

hedge¹ /hɛdʒ; hedʒ/ *n* **1** a row of bushes round the edge of a garden or field 樹籬 – see picture on page 729 見 729 頁彩圖 **2 hedge against inflation** protection against money losing its value 防止貨幣貶值

hedge² *v* **hedged, hedging 1** [T] to make a hedge round something 用樹籬圍起〔某物〕**2** [I] to avoid answering a question directly 避免正面回答問題: *You're hedging again — have you or haven't you got the money?* 你又在閃爍其詞了——你究竟有沒有錢? **3 hedge your bets** to protect yourself by supporting more than one side in a competition or struggle〔競賽或爭鬥中〕支持雙方以便保護自己; 兩邊下注; 一腳踏兩船

hedge·hog /ˈhɛdʒˌhɑɡ; ˈhedʒhɒɡ/ *n* a small animal which has a prickly back 刺猬

hedge·row /ˈhɛdʒˌro; ˈhedʒrəʊ/ *n* a row of bushes along a country road or separating fields〔鄉間道路上或把田地分隔開的〕灌木樹籬

he·don·is·m /ˈhidn̩ˌɪzəm; ˈhiːdənɪzəm/ *n* [U] the idea that pleasure is the most important thing in life 享樂主義 –**hedonist** *n* –**hedonistic** /ˌhidəˈnɪstɪk; ˌhiːdəˈnɪstɪk/ *adj*

heed¹ /hid; hiːd/ *v* [T] *fml* to take notice of a warning or piece of advice〔正式〕注意〔警告或忠告〕: *The Government did not heed earlier warnings about hijacking.* 政府對於早先有關劫機的警告並未加以注意。

heed² *n* [U] *fml*〔正式〕**take heed of, pay heed to** to take notice of something 注意〔某物〕: *The Minister must take heed of public demand for better food safety.* 部長必須注意公眾對於提高食品安全的要求。

heed·less /ˈhidlɪs; ˈhiːdləs/ *adj fml*〔正式〕**heedless of** without taking any notice of something or someone 不注意〔某事或某人〕

heel¹ /hil; hiːl/ *n* **1** the back part of your foot 腳後跟 **2** the part of a shoe or sock under your heel 鞋跟; 襪後跟: *I've got a hole* *in the heel of my sock.* 我的襪後跟上有個洞。| *boots with high heels* 高跟靴 –see picture on page 210 見 210 頁彩圖 **3 on your heels, at your heels** very closely behind you 緊跟在後面: *He was right on my heels.* 他緊跟在我身後。

heel² *v* [T] to put a heel on a shoe or boot 給〔鞋或靴〕上後跟

hef·ty /'hɛfti; 'hefti/ *adj* **heftier, heftiest** big or strong 大的; 強壯的: *a hefty blow to the jaw* 對下顎的一記重拳 | *a hefty price increase* 價格大幅上漲

★**height** /haɪt; haɪt/ *n* **1** [C;U] the measurement from the bottom to the top of something 高度: *a woman of medium height* 一位身材中等的女士 | *the height of the building* 建築物的高度 **2** [C] a particular distance above the ground 〔離地面的〕高度: *The plane reached a height of 60,000 feet.* 飛機的飛行高度達到了六萬英尺。| *The river rose to the height of the road.* 河水漲到了與馬路齊平的高度。| *The shelf needs fixing at waist height.* 架子的齊腰處需要修理。–compare 比較 DEPTH **3** [C;U] the quality of being tall or high 高: *His height makes him stand out in a crowd.* 他高大的身材令他在人羣中很突出。**4** [C] a high position or place 高處; 高地: *We looked down from a great height to the town below.* 我們從很高的地方俯視下面的城鎮。**5 the height of: a** the most powerful part of 最有力的部分: *at the height of the storm* 在暴風雨最猛烈的時候 **b** the greatest possible kind of 極度; 極點: *It's the height of stupidity to go sailing when you can't swim.* 不會游泳就去駕駛帆船是愚蠢透頂的事情。

height·en /'haɪtn̩; 'haɪtn̩/ *v* [I;T] to make or become greater in degree (使)在程度上變大 [強]: *As she waited, her excitement heightened.* 她越等心裡就越激動。| *Tension heightened in the run-up to the election.* 選舉醞釀期間, 氣氛越來越緊張。

hei·nous /'henəs; 'heɪnəs/ *adj fml* very evil 〔正式〕非常邪惡的: *heinous crimes* 令人髮指的罪行

heir /ɛr; eəʳ/ *n* the person who will have the money, property, or title of someone who dies 〔錢財, 財產或頭銜的〕繼承人: *The Prince of Wales is the heir **to** the throne.* 威爾士王子是王位繼承人。

heir·ess /'ɛrɪs; 'eərɪs/ *n* a woman or girl who will receive great wealth when someone dies 女繼承人

heir·loom /'ɛr'lum; 'eəluːm/ *n* a valuable object given by older members of a family to younger ones over many years 祖傳寶物; 傳家寶: *a family heirloom* 傳家寶

held /hɛld; held/ the past tense and past participle of HOLD ☆ HOLD 的過去式和過去分詞

hel·i·cop·ter /'hɛlɪˌkɑptɚ; 'helɪˌkɒptəʳ/ *n* an aircraft which is made to fly by a set of large fast-turning metal blades fixed on top of it 直升飛機 –see picture on page 991 見 991 頁彩圖

hel·i·port /'hɛləˌpɔrt; 'helɪˌpɔːt/ *n* a helicopter airport 直升飛機機場

he·li·um /'hiliəm; 'hiːliəm/ *n* [U] a gas that is lighter than air, will not burn, and is used in hot air balloons (BALLON¹) 氦氣〔不會燃燒, 用於熱氣球中〕

hell¹ /hɛl; hel/ *n* **1** [U] in the Christian and Muslim religions, a place where the souls of bad people are said to be punished after death 地獄 –compare 比較 HEAVEN **2** [U] a very unpleasant situation 令人極之不快的境況: *Driving a car in a snowstorm is real hell!* 暴風雪裡開車真是討厭! **3 what the hell, who the hell, etc.** *infml* expressions used in anger or to give strength to what you are saying 〔非正式〕到底〔表示憤怒或強調〕: *What the hell's that thing on your head?* 你頭上那個東西到底是甚麼? **4 a hell of a lot** *infml* a lot 〔非正式〕許多: *He must earn a hell of a lot of money.* 他肯定掙很多錢。**5 for the hell of it** *infml* for fun 〔非正式〕好玩; 找樂趣: *Then we decided to go swimming at midnight just for the hell of it.* 為了好玩, 我們於是決定在半夜裡去游泳。**6 give someone hell** *infml* 〔非正式〕: **a** to make life very unhappy for someone 令某人的日子過得很不愉快 **b** to speak very angrily to someone who has done something wrong 〔由於做錯事而〕斥責某人: *My father was in bed when I got in, but he gave me hell the next morning.* 我回到家的時候父親已睡下了, 但第二天早晨他斥責了我一頓。**7 go to hell** *infml* an expression which someone uses to tell someone very rudely to go away 〔非正式〕滾開〔非常無禮地叫人走開〕**8 like hell** *infml* very much 〔非正式〕非常: *We had to run like hell to catch the bus.* 為趕公共汽車, 我們拼命地跑。**9 play hell with** *infml* to really spoil something 〔非正式〕破壞: *The snow played hell with the weekend sports programme.* 大雪使週末的體育安排成為泡影。**10 to hell with** *infml* an expression some people use when they decide to forget about something they should do 〔非正式〕讓... 見鬼去吧〔表示準備把應該做的事情忘掉〕: *To hell with the washing up! Let's watch the film.* 讓洗碗的事情見鬼去吧! 我們去看電影。

hell² *interj infml* a swear word which some people use to express annoyance 〔非正式〕見鬼〔表示惱怒時所用的罵人的話〕: *Oh, hell! I've missed the last train.* 哦, 見鬼! 我誤了最後一班火車。

■ USAGE 用法: The word **hell** is commonly used in spoken English to show anger or to add strength to an expression. Although it is not generally considered to be very strong, some

☆ **hell** 一詞在口語中常用來表示憤怒或加強語氣。儘管一般認為該詞語氣不十分強烈，但有些人仍認為用該詞不夠禮貌。

he'll /ɪl, hɪl; il, hil, *strong* 強讀 hil; hiːl/ **1** short for 縮約式＝"he will" **2** short for 縮約式＝"he shall"

hell·ish /ˈhelɪʃ; ˈhelɪʃ/ *adj infml* very unpleasant 〔非正式〕很討厭的: *The weather's been hellish recently.* 最近的天氣很糟糕。– compare 比較 HEAVENLY –**hellishly** *adv*

hel·lo /həˈlo; həˈləʊ/ *interj, n* hellos (also 又作 **hallo, hullo** *BrE* 〔英式〕) **1** the usual word of greeting 喂; 你好〔常用的問候語〕: *Hello, John! How are you?* 喂, 約翰! 你好嗎? **2** the word used for starting a telephone conversation 喂〔打電話用的招呼語〕: *Hello, who's speaking, please?* 喂, 請問是哪一位? **3** *BrE* an expression of surprise 〔英式〕喲〔表示驚訝〕: *Hello! Somebody's left their hat behind.* 喲! 有人把帽子留在這裡忘記帶走了。**4** a word used to attract someone's attention 喂〔用以引起別人的注意〕: *Hello! Is anybody there?* 喂! 那兒有人嗎?

■ USAGE 用法: When you are speaking on the telephone use the phrase **this is…** to say who you are ☆打電話時, 用 **this is** 來說明自己的身分: *Hello, this is Jane Jones. May I speak to Jim?* 喂, 我是簡·瓊斯。請問吉姆在嗎? | *Hello Jim. This is Jane.* 喂, 吉姆。我是簡。If you know the other person quite well then you may use the less formal phrase **it's** ☆如果與對方熟識, 可用比較隨便一些的 **it's** 來說明自己的身分: *Hello Penny. It's Sue.* 喂, 佩妮。我是蘇。

helm /helm; helm/ *n* at the helm in control of a group or organization 負責; 領導

hel·met /ˈhelmɪt; ˈhelmɪt/ *n* a hard hat that you wear to protect your head; motorcyclists, policemen, and miners wear helmets 頭盔; 防護帽

help¹ /help; help/ *v* **1** [I;T] to make things easier for someone, especially by doing part of their work 幫助; 幫忙: *Could you help me move this cupboard?* 你能幫我移一下這個碗櫃嗎? | *We helped him to decorate the sitting-room.* 我們幫他裝飾了客廳。| *Is there anything I can do to help?* 有沒有甚麼事要我幫忙? | *"Can I help you?" "Yes, I'd like some information, please."* "您要甚麼?" "我想要些資料。" | *He helped his mother into the car.* 他幫助母親坐進汽車。| *Can you help me with my homework?* 你能幫幫我做家庭作業嗎? **2** [I;T] to make something better 促進; 緩和: *Crying won't help.* 哭是沒有用的。| *Have you got anything to help a cold?* 你有沒有治療感冒的藥? | *The fall in the dollar will help the pound.* 美元下跌對英鎊有利。

□ USEFUL PATTERNS 有用句型
to help someone; to help someone with something; to help someone (to) do something

3 [I;T] to share in producing a result 促成: *The cold winter has helped to keep oil prices high.* 寒冷的冬天使油的價格居高不下。**4** [T] to give food to someone during a meal 〔席間〕給〔某人〕食物: *Can I help you to some potatoes?* 我給你夾些馬鈴薯好嗎? **5** can't help *infml* can't avoid, prevent, or have control over 〔非正式〕無法避免〔防止、控制〕: *I couldn't help laughing when I saw his haircut.* 我看見他的髮型時忍不住笑了。| *She can't help her big feet.* 她天生腳大, 對此她一點辦法都沒有。**6** I can't help it *infml* 〔非正式〕＝it's not my fault 這不是我的過錯: *I can't help it if all the trains are cancelled.* 如果所有的火車班次都取消的話, 那就不能怪我了。**7** help yourself *infml* 〔非正式〕: **a** to take something for yourself 自己拿〔某物〕: *"Can I have a drink?" "Help yourself."* "我可以喝杯飲料嗎?" "你自己拿吧!" | *Help yourself to a drink.* 你自己拿杯飲料喝吧。**b** to take something without permission 未經允許擅自拿〔某物〕: *He just helped himself to the money when no one was looking.* 沒人注意時, 他就擅自把錢拿走了。

help out *phr v* [I;T help sbdy ↔ out] to help when there is a special need 〔有特殊需要時〕幫助: *The cook's ill, so I'm helping out this week.* 廚師病了, 所以這星期我來幫忙。| *Can I help you out?* 我可以幫你解決問題嗎? –**helper** *n*

■ USAGE 用法: Compare 比較 **help, assist, aid. 1** Assist is more formal than **help**, and **aid** is even more formal. ☆ **assist** 比 **help** 正式; **aid** 一詞更加正式。**2** Notice the forms which can come after **help** ☆注意 **help** 後的幾種形式: *He helped me to improve.* 他幫我取得進步。| *He helped me improve.* 他幫我取得進步。Notice the forms which come after **assist** and **aid** ☆注意 **assist** 和 **aid** 後面的形式: *These loans will assist/aid our country in improving its economy.* 這些貸款將幫助我們的國家改善經濟狀況。**3** Assist always suggests that the person being assisted is doing part of the work. ☆ **assist** 通常暗示接受幫助的人也一起參與工作。Compare 比較: *The police are asking the public to assist them.* 警方要求公眾協助他們。| *If you are ill, this medicine will help you.* 你如果病了, 這種藥對你會有用的。

help² *n* **1** [U] the act of helping someone 幫助; 幫忙: *If you want any help, just ask me.* 你如果需要幫忙, 儘管叫我好了。 **2 a help** something or someone that helps you 有幫助的物或人: *This machine is a great help in making cakes more quickly.* 這台機器對於加快蛋糕的製作非常有用。 **3 be of help** to help someone 幫助〔某人〕: *Can I be of any help?* 有甚麼我可以幫忙的嗎？ **4 Help!** a word that you shout if you need help, especially if you are in danger 救命啊！

help·ful /ˈhelpfəl; ˈhelpfəl/ *adj* **1** providing help or willing to help 提供幫助的; 樂於幫忙的: *She's so kind and helpful.* 她態度和善, 又樂於助人。 **2** useful 有用的: *Thanks for your helpful suggestions.* 謝謝你提出有益的建議。 **–helpfully** *adv* **–helpfulness** *n* [U]

help·ing /ˈhelpɪŋ; ˈhelpɪŋ/ *n* a serving of food 〔食物的〕一份: *I'd like a second helping, I'm still hungry!* 我想再要一份, 我還是很餓！

help·less /ˈhelplɪs; ˈhelpləs/ *adj* unable to look after yourself or to do things without help 不能自立的; 無助的: *a helpless child* 不能自立的孩子 | *They were helpless against another enemy attack.* 他們無法抵禦敵人再次進攻。 **–helplessly** *adv* **–helplessness** *n* [U]

he-man /ˈ··/ *n* **he-men** *infml* a strong man, proud of his powerful muscles 〔非正式〕對自己發達的肌肉感到自豪的強健男子

hem¹ /hem; hem/ *n* the lower edge of a piece of cloth when turned under and sewn down, for example on a skirt or dress 〔衣服或裙子下擺的〕摺邊

hem² *v* **-mm-** [T] to put a hem on a piece of clothing 給〔一塊布料〕縫上摺邊

hem sbdy ↔ in *phr v* [T] to surround someone tightly, with the result that they cannot move or escape 緊緊包圍〔某人〕〔使其無法活動或逃跑〕: *The whole army was hemmed in by the enemy, and there was no hope of escape.* 軍隊全部被敵人包圍, 絲毫沒有逃脫的希望。

hem·i·sphere /ˈhemɪsfɪr; ˈheməˌsfɪə/ *n* **1** half of a SPHERE, an object like a ball 半球 **2** a half of the earth, especially the northern or southern half, or the eastern or western half 〔地球的〕半球

hem·line /ˈhemlaɪn; ˈhemlaɪn/ *n* length of a dress or skirt 衣裙的長度

hem·lock /ˈhemlɑk; ˈhemlɒk/ *n* [U] a poisonous drug 由毒芹提取的毒藥

he·mo·glo·bin /ˌhiməˈgloubɪn; ˌhiːməˈgləʊbɪn/ *n* see 見 HAEMOGLOBIN

he·mo·phil·i·a /ˌhiməˈfɪliə; ˌhiːməˈfɪliə/ *n* see 見 HAEMOPHILIA

he·mo·phil·i·ac /ˌhiməˈfɪliæk; ˌhiːməˈfɪliæk/ *n* see 見 HAEMOPHILIAC

hem·or·rhage /ˈheməridʒ; ˈhemərɪdʒ/ *n, v* see 見 HAEMORRHAGE

hem·or·rhoid /ˈheməˌrɔɪd; ˈhemərɔɪd/ *n* see 見 HAEMORRHOID

hemp /hemp; hemp/ *n* [U] a plant used for making strong rope, a rough cloth, and the drug CANNABIS 大麻

hen /hen; hen/ *n* **1** a female chicken 母雞 **2** a female bird 雌鳥: *a hen pheasant* 雌雉

hence /hens; hens/ *adv fml* 〔正式〕 **1** for this reason 因此: *The town was built near a bridge on the River Cam: hence the name Cambridge.* 這座城鎮建在康姆河上一座橋的附近, 因此而得名為康橋〔現譯劍橋〕。 **2** from this time onward 從這時起: *three days hence* 從今天起三天以後

hence·forth /ˌhensˈfɔrθ; ˌhensˈfɔːθ/ *adv fml* 〔正式〕 (also 又作 **henceforward** /ˌhensˈfɔrwəd; ˌhensˈfɔːwəd/) from now on 從今以後: *The company will henceforth be known as Johnson and Brown Inc.* 公司從今以後稱為約翰遜和布朗公司。

hench·man /ˈhentʃmən; ˈhentʃmən/ *n* **henchmen** /-mən; -mən/ a faithful supporter, especially of a political leader, who obeys without question and does violent and dishonest acts 〔尤指追隨政治領袖的〕忠實的支持者; 黨羽

hen·na /ˈhenə; ˈhenə/ *n* [U] a reddish-brown substance used to colour people's hair 散沫花染劑〔棕紅色的染劑, 用於染髮〕

hen·pecked /ˈhenˌpekt; ˈhenpekt/ *adj* **henpecked husband** a husband whose wife continually finds fault with him and tells him what to do 懼內的丈夫, 怕老婆的男人

hep·a·ti·tis /ˌhepəˈtaɪtɪs; ˌhepəˈtaɪtɪs/ *n* [U] a LIVER disease which causes your skin to go yellow and which makes you feel very weak 肝炎

her¹ /ɚ, hɚ; ə, hə, strong 強讀 hɝ; hɜː/ *det* relating to or belonging to the female person or animal who has already been mentioned 她的: *My mother came in and sat down in her chair.* 我母親走進來, 坐在她的椅子上。 | *She was sitting drinking her coffee.* 她坐在那裡喝她的咖啡。

her² *pron* [used as the object of a verb 用作動詞的賓語] the female person or animal who has already been mentioned 她: *"Do you like Mary?" "No, I can't stand her!"* "你喜歡瑪麗嗎？" "不, 我受不了她那一套!"—see 見 ME (USAGE 用法)

her·ald¹ /ˈherəld; ˈherəld/ *n* **1** a person who carried messages for a ruler in the past 〔昔時的〕傳令官 **2** *lit* a sign that something is going to come soon 〔文〕預兆: *a herald of a new age* 一個新時代的預兆

herald² *v* [T] **1** to be a sign that something is going to come soon 預示〔某事物的〕來臨; 預兆: *This reform heralds the birth of a new era.* 這場改革預示着一個新紀元的誕生。 **2** to say publicly that something is going to happen so that people are expecting to happen 預言; 預告: *the much heralded edu-*

cation reforms 廣為人所預言要進行的教育改革

her·ald·ry /ˈhɛrəldrɪ; ˈherəldri/ *n* [U] the study and use of COATS OF ARMS 紋章學 – **heraldic** /hɛˈrældɪk; heˈrældɪk/ *adj*

herb /hɝb; hɜːb/ *n* a plant used to improve the taste of food, or as a medicine 香草; 藥草 –compare 比較 SPICE –**herbal** *adj : a herbal remedy* 藥草治療法

her·ba·ceous /hɝˈbeɪʃəs; həˈbeɪʃəs/ *adj* having a stem that is soft and not woody (used of plants) 草本的〔指植物〕

herb·al·ist /ˈhɝbəlɪst; ˈhɜːbəlɪst/ *n* a person who treats diseases with herbs 草藥醫生

her·bi·vore /ˈhɝbɪˌvɔr; ˈhɜːbɪ͵vɔːʳ/ *n* an animal which only eats grass and plants 食草動物 –**herbivorous** /hɝˈbɪvərəs; hɜːˈbɪvərəs/ *adj*

herd[1] /hɝd; hɜːd/ *n* **1** a group of animals of one kind which live and feed together 獸羣: *a herd of elephants* 一羣大象 **2 the herd** people generally thought of as acting or thinking all alike 大眾; 民眾: *Don't just follow the herd — do what you really want to!* 不要只是隨大流 — 做你自己真正想做的事!

herd[2] *v* [T +adv/prep] to make people or animals move together in a herd or like a herd 使〔人或動物〕成羣地移動: *The farmer herded the cows into the field.* 農民把牛羣趕到地裡。| *We were herded into the room.* 我們被領入一間房間。

herds·man /ˈhɝdzmən; ˈhɜːdzmən/ *n* **herdsmen** /-mən; -mən/ a man who looks after a herd of animals 牧人

★★**here** /hɪr; hɪəʳ/ *adv* **1** in or to this place 在這裡; 到這裡: *I've lived here for ten years.* 我在這裡住了十年。| *Come over here.* 到這邊來。| *It's two miles from here.* 那裡距此有兩英里遠。| *Could you sign here, please?* 請在這裡簽個字好嗎? | *My friend here will help you.* 我在這裡的朋友會幫你忙的。**2** at this point 在這點上: *I think I agree with you here.* 我覺得在這點上我同意你的意見。**3 here is, here are** a phrase used for drawing attention to someone or something 在這裡〔用於請別人注意某人或某物〕: *Here's the money.* 錢在這裡。| *Here they are.* 他們在這裡。**4 here and there** in several places 在幾個地方: *The landscape was empty except for odd houses here and there.* 這一帶除了零星有幾所房屋外, 空空如也。**5 here's to** a phrase you use when you are having a drink and wishing someone good luck 祝…〔用於喝酒時祝某人好運〕: *Here's to your new job.* 為你新的工作乾杯。**6 here you are** a phrase you use when you are giving someone something that they want 給你〔用於把某人所需的東西給他〕

here·af·ter /hɪrˈæftɚ; ͵hɪərˈɑːftəʳ/ *adv fml* after this time 〔正式〕從今以後

here·by /hɪrˈbaɪ; ͵hɪəˈbaɪ/ *adv fml* or *law* by doing or saying this 〔正式或律〕以此方式; 特

此: *I hereby declare her elected.* 我特此宣佈她已經當選。

he·red·i·ta·ry /həˈrɛdəˌtɛrɪ; hɪˈredɪtəri/ *adj* able to be passed down from parent to child 遺傳的: *a hereditary disease* 遺傳病

he·red·i·ty /həˈrɛdətɪ; hɪˈredəti/ *n* [U] the passing on of qualities from parent to child in the cells of the body 遺傳: *According to the laws of heredity, tall parents tend to have tall children.* 根據遺傳規律, 個子高的父母所生的孩子個子也往往比較高。

here·in /hɪrˈɪn; ͵hɪərˈɪn/ *adv fml* or *law* in this piece of writing 〔正式或律〕在此文中; 於此處

her·e·sy /ˈhɛrəsɪ; ˈherəsi/ *n* **heresies** [C;U] belief, especially religious or political, opposed to the official or generally accepted one 異教; 異端邪説

her·e·tic /ˈhɛrətɪk; ˈherətɪk/ *n* a person who holds a religious or political belief opposed to the official or generally accepted one 持異端邪説者; 異端教徒 –**heretical** /həˈrɛtɪk; həˈretɪkl/ *adj*

here·with /hɪrˈwɪθ; ͵hɪəˈwɪð/ *adv fml* or *law* with this piece of writing 〔正式或律〕與此文一起; (隨函)附上: *I send you herewith two copies of the contract.* 我隨函寄上合同副本兩份。

her·i·tage /ˈhɛrətɪdʒ; ˈherɪtɪdʒ/ *n* [sing] objects and customs which are passed down over many years within a family or nation 遺產; 傳統: *Much of our country's artistic heritage was destroyed during the war.* 我國許多藝術方面的遺產毀於這場戰爭。

her·met·ic /hɝˈmɛtɪk; hɜːˈmetɪk/ *adj* very tightly closed so that no air can get in or out 密封的; 不透氣的 –**hermetically** /-klɪ; -kli/ *adv*

her·mit /ˈhɝmɪt; ˈhɜːmɪt/ *n* a person who lives away from other people in order to think and pray 隱士; 獨居修道士

her·mit·age /ˈhɝmɪtɪdʒ; ˈhɜːmɪtɪdʒ/ *n* a place where a hermit lives 隱居處; 修道院

her·ni·a /ˈhɝnɪə; ˈhɜːniə/ *n* [C;U] the medical condition in which an organ pushes through its covering wall, usually the bowel through the stomach wall 脱出; 疝(氣)

★**he·ro** /ˈhɪro; ˈhɪərəʊ/ *n* **heroes 1** a person respected or admired for bravery or goodness 英雄 **2** the most important male character in a play, film, or story 〔戲劇、電影或故事中的〕男主角; 男主人公

he·ro·ic /hɪˈroɪk; hɪˈrəʊɪk/ *adj* **1** showing bravery, strength, and goodness 英勇的: *heroic deeds* 英勇事跡 **2** needing great effort and determination 需要很大的努力與決心的: *her heroic attempt to succeed* 她追求成功的不懈努力 –**heroically** /-klɪ; -kli/ *adv*

he·ro·ics /hɪˈroɪks; hɪˈrəʊɪks/ *n* [pl] speech or actions which are meant to appear grand, though they mean nothing 裝腔作勢

的言行

her·o·in /ˈhɛro·ɪn; ˈhɛrəʊɪn/ *n* [U] a drug which some people take illegally for pleasure, and which the user can become dependent on; doctors sometimes give heroin to lessen pain 海洛因〔一種會上癮的毒品, 醫生有時用其來止痛〕

her·o·ine /ˈhɛro·ɪn; ˈhɛrəʊɪn/ *n* **1** a woman remembered or admired for bravery or goodness 女英雄 **2** the most important female character in a play, film, or story〔戲劇, 電影或故事中的〕女主角

her·o·is·m /ˈhɛro,ɪzəm; ˈhɛrəʊɪzəm/ *n* [U] very great courage 英勇; 極大的勇氣: *an act of great heroism* 大無畏的舉動

her·on /ˈhɛrən; ˈhɛrən/ *n* a bird with long legs which lives near water (蒼)鷺

her·ring /ˈhɛrɪŋ; ˈhɛrɪŋ/ *n* a silver-coloured fish which lives in the sea 鯡(魚)

hers /hɝz; hɜːz/ *pron* something relating to or belonging to the female person or animal who has already been mentioned 她的 (所有物): *When we went to collect our coats, my mother realized that she had left hers in the car.* 我們去拿外衣時, 母親才發覺她的外衣留在車裡了。| *My hand touched hers.* 我的手碰到了她的手。

★★**herself** /hɚˈsɛlf; əˈself/ *pron* **1** used as the object of a verb or a PREPOSITION when the subject of a verb is female and the action is done to the same person〔反身代詞〕她自己: *She washed herself and got dressed.* 她洗了個澡, 穿上了衣服。| *Mary looked at herself in the mirror.* 瑪麗看着鏡中的自己。| *She had scratched herself on a rusty nail.* 她被一枚生鏽的鐵釘劃傷了。| *Sarah decided to buy herself some new clothes.* 薩拉決定給自己買幾件新衣服。**2** used to add force to the word "she", or to the name of a female person or animal 自己〔強調"她"〕: *She herself admitted that it wasn't her best painting.* 她自己承認那不是她最好的一幅畫。| *I'd like to speak to the doctor herself, please.* 我希望跟醫生本人談一談。| *She had done all the decorating herself.* 她一個人做完了全部的裝飾工作。**3 by herself** alone, with no one with her or helping her (她)單獨地; 獨力地: *Mary had spent the day by herself.* 瑪麗獨自一人過了一天。| *She had managed to mend the roof by herself.* 她終於獨自修好了屋頂。

he's /ɪz; hɪz; iz, hiz, *strong* 強讀 hiz; hiːz/ **1** short for 縮約式 = "he is": *He's a writer.* 他是個作家。| *He's coming.* 他來了。**2** short for 縮約式 = "he has": *He's got two cars.* 他有兩部汽車。| *He's had a cold.* 他得了感冒。

hes·i·tant /ˈhɛzətənt; ˈhezɪtənt/ *adj* unwilling or being slow to do something because you are worried or uncertain about it〔由於擔心或無把握而〕不願意的; 猶豫不決的: *She's hesitant **about** making new friends.* 她不願結交新朋友。**–hesitantly** *adv*

hes·i·tate /ˈhɛzə,tet; ˈhezɪteɪt/ *v* **hesitated, hesitating 1** [I] to pause or wait for a while before you do something because you are worried or uncertain about it〔做事前由於擔心或沒有把握而〕猶豫; 躊躇: *He hesitated before entering the room.* 他進屋子之前猶豫了。| *I'm hesitating about this new job offer I've had.* 我對於別人提供給我的這個新工作正在猶豫之中。**2 hesitate to do something** to be unwilling to do something because you think that it might not be the right thing to do〔由於認為某事可能不合適而〕不願意做某事: *I hesitate to ask him to lend me some money.* 我不願去向他借錢。**3 don't hesitate** a phrase used when you are saying that someone should do something which they might feel worried or uncertain about 不要不好意思…〔用於勸某人做某事不要有顧慮〕: *Don't hesitate to ask me if you need any help.* 如果需要我幫忙, 請儘管告訴我, 不要不好意思。

hes·i·ta·tion /ˌhɛzəˈteʃən; ˌhezɪˈteɪʃən/ *n* **1** [C;U] a pause or wait before you do something because you feel worried or uncertain about it〔做事前由於擔心或沒有把握而引起的〕猶豫; 躊躇: *Without a moment's hesitation she jumped into the river.* 她毫不猶豫地跳進河裡。| *After some hesitation he agreed to do what we asked.* 他猶豫了一會兒便同意去做我們要求他做的事情。**2 have no hesitation** to feel certain that what you are saying or doing is right 肯定自己所說或所做的事情是正確的: *I have no hesitation in saying that the government is doing everything possible to solve our economic problems.* 我可以肯定地說, 政府正在盡一切力量解決我們的經濟問題。

het·e·ro·ge·ne·ous /ˌhɛtərəˈdʒiniəs; ˌhetərəʊˈdʒiːniəs/ *adj fml* of many different kinds 〔正式〕許多不同種類的: *a heterogeneous mix of nationalities* 多民族的混合體

het·e·ro·sex·u·al /ˌhɛtərəˈsɛkʃuəl; ˌhetərəʊˈsekʃuəl/ *adj* attracted by people of the opposite sex 異性戀的 比較 –compare HOMOSEXUAL, BISEXUAL **–heterosexual** *n*

het up /ˌhɛt ˈʌp; ˌhet ˈʌp/ *adj* [never before a noun 不能用於名詞前] *infml* anxious and worried 〔非正式〕焦慮的; 緊張的: *He's all het up **about** tomorrow's examination.* 他對於明日的考試很擔心。

hew /hju; hjuː/ *v* **hewed, hewed** *or* **hewn** /hjun; hjuːn/ [T] *fml or lit* to cut something heavy or hard with an axe or other tool〔正式或文〕砍; 劈

hex·a·gon /ˈhɛksə,ɡɑn; ˈheksəɡən/ *n* a figure with six sides 六邊[角]形 **–hexagonal** /hɛkˈsæɡənəl; hekˈsæɡənəl/ *adj*

hey /he; heɪ/ *interj infml* a shout used to call attention or to express surprise or interest 〔非正式〕喂; 嘿〔用於引起注意、表示驚奇或感興趣的叫喊〕: *Hey! Where are you going?* 喂! 你去哪兒?

hey·day /'he,de; 'heɪdeɪ/ n [sing] the period of greatest power or success 全盛時期: *In the heyday of their empire, the Romans controlled most of the western world.* 羅馬帝國在全盛時期控制了西方世界的大部分地區。| *In his heyday, he was one of the best footballers in the world.* 他在全盛時期是全世界最好的足球運動員之一。

hi /haɪ; haɪ/ interj infml HELLO 〔非正式〕嗨;你好〔用作問候語〕

hi·a·tus /haɪ'etəs; haɪ'eɪtəs/ n [sing] fml a pause when nothing happens 〔正式〕間斷;停頓

hi·ber·nate /'haɪbə,net; 'haɪbəneɪt/ v **hibernated, hibernating** [I] (of animals) to be in or go into a sleep-like state during the winter 〔動物〕冬眠 –**hibernation** /,haɪbə'neʃən; ,haɪbə'neɪʃən/ n [U]

hic·cup /'hɪkʌp; 'hɪkʌp/ n (also 又作 **hiccough**) **1** hiccups [pl] repeated sharp sounds in your throat which you sometimes get after eating or drinking 打嗝; 呃逆: *"I've got hiccups again." "You shouldn't eat so fast."* "我又在打嗝了。""你不該吃得這麼快。" **2** a small problem 小問題: *"How's the new system working?" "Well, we had a few hiccups at the beginning, but nothing major."* "新的系統運轉如何?" "哦,我們在一開始碰上了一些小麻煩,但問題不大。" –**hiccup** v **-pp-** [I]

hid·den /'hɪdn; 'hɪdn/ adj difficult to see, find, or notice 不易被看見〔發現、注意到〕的: *a hidden danger* 潛在的危險 | *a hidden meaning* 暗含的意思

★**hide¹** /haɪd; haɪd/ v **hid** /hɪd; hɪd/, **hidden** /'hɪdn; 'hɪdn/, **hiding 1** [T] to put something in a place where no one can see it or find it 隱藏〔某物〕: *He hid the letter inside his jacket.* 他把信藏在茄克衫裡。| *Where have you hidden the presents?* 你把禮物藏到哪裡去啦? **2** [T] to keep something secret 隱瞞〔某事物〕: *She seems to be hiding information from them.* 她似乎在隱瞞消息, 沒有告訴他們。| *Don't hide your feelings. Say what you think.* 不要隱瞞你的感情。你怎麼想就怎麼說。 **3** [I] to go to a place where no one can see you or find you 躲藏; 隱匿: *I'll hide behind the door.* 我去躲在門後面。

hide² n [C;U] the skin of a large animal used for leather 〔用於製皮革的〕獸皮

hide·bound /'haɪd,baʊnd; 'haɪdbaʊnd/ adj having fixed, unchangeable opinions (a word used to express disapproval) 思想偏狹頑固的〔含貶義〕

hid·e·ous /'hɪdɪəs; 'hɪdɪəs/ adj extremely ugly or shocking to see, hear, or experience 極其醜陋的; 令人驚駭的: *a hideous wound* 可怕的傷口 | *a hideous scream* 嚇人的尖叫聲 –**hideously** adv : *the hideously mutilated body of a young woman* 一具殘缺不全的駭人的少婦屍體

hid·ing /'haɪdɪŋ; 'haɪdɪŋ/ n **1** give someone a **good hiding** infml to beat someone as a punishment 〔非正式〕〔作為懲罰〕痛打某人: *I'll give you a good hiding when we get home!* 回到家以後我要好好地揍你一頓! **2** **go into hiding** to hide yourself 把自己隱藏起來: *The escaped prisoner went into hiding in the mountains.* 越獄的囚犯逃到山裡躲了起來。[RELATED PHRASE 相關詞組 **be in hiding**]

hi·er·ar·chy /'haɪə,rɑrkɪ; 'haɪərɑːki/ n **hierarchies 1** [C;U] a system of organization in which the members are arranged into higher and lower ranks 等級制度: *There's a very rigid hierarchy in the civil service.* 政府文職部門有一套十分嚴格的等級制度。**2** [C + sing/pl verb] the most powerful members of an organization 〔一個組織中〕最高層; 領導層: *The party hierarchy will never accept him as leader.* 該黨的最高層決不會同意後也來作領袖。–**hierarchical** /,haɪə'rɑrkɪk; haɪə-'rɑːkɪkəl/ adj

hi·e·ro·glyph /'haɪərə,glɪf; 'haɪərəglɪf/ n a picture-like sign which represents a word in ancient Egyptian writing 〔古埃及的〕象形字

hi·e·ro·glyph·ics /,haɪərə'glɪfɪks; ,haɪərə-'glɪfɪks/ n [pl] the ancient Egyptian system of writing which uses picture-like signs to represent words 〔古埃及的〕象形文字

hi-fi /'haɪ,faɪ; 'haɪ faɪ/ n [C;U] high quality apparatus for reproducing recorded sound 〔高保真度的〕音響設備: *Modern hi-fi is so good that it's just like sitting in the concert hall!* 現代的高保真音響設備質量上乘, 給人一種坐在音樂廳裡的感覺! | *a hi-fi shop* 高保真音響店 –see picture on page 730 見 730 頁彩圖

hig·gle·dy-pig·gle·dy /'hɪgldɪ'pɪgldɪ; ,hɪgəl-di 'pɪgəldi/ adj,adv infml in disorder 〔非正式〕混亂的〔地〕

★**high¹** /haɪ; haɪ/ adj **1** having a top that is a large distance above the ground or above the bottom (not usually used of living things) 高的〔不常用於有生命的東西〕: *It's a very high building.* 這是座很高的樓。| *a high mountain* 高山 –compare 比較 TALL **2** used in giving measurements …高〔用於測量〕: *How high is it?* 它有多高? | *four metres high* 四米高 **3** at a point a large distance above the ground 〔比地面〕高的: *That shelf's too high for me. I can't reach it.* 那塊擱板太高了, 我拿不到上面的東西。| *the highest town in England* 英國地勢最高的城鎮 **4** above or greater than what is usual 高於通常水平的: *the high cost of food* 昂貴的食品價格 | *travelling at high speed* 高速行駛 **5** near the top in rank 〔職位〕高的: *She held high office in the last government.* 她在上屆政府裡擔任高級職位。| *high social status* 很高的社會地位 **6** very good 非常好的: *I have a very high opinion of his work.* 我對他的工作評價很高。| *a very high standard* 很高的

標準 | *high principles* 崇高的原則 **7** excited by alcohol or drugs 〔由於酒精或毒品作用而〕非常興奮的: *She was high on drugs.* 她吸毒之後感覺飄然欲仙。 **8** near the top of the set of sounds which the ear can hear 〔聲音,音調〕高的: *a high voice* 很高的嗓音 | *a high note* 很高的樂音 **9 the High Court** the most important court for non-criminal cases 〔審理非刑事案件的〕高等法院 **10 higher education** education at university or college 高等教育 **11 high explosive** a very powerful explosive 高爆炸藥; 烈性炸藥 **12 high fidelity** very good quality (used of apparatus for playing COMPACT DISCS, tapes (TAPE¹), and records) 高保真度〔指播放激光唱片、磁帶和唱片的設備〕 **13 high heels** women's shoes with high heels 〔婦女的〕高跟鞋 **14 high jump** a sport in which people jump over a bar which is gradually raised higher and higher 〔運動〕跳高 **15 be for the high jump** *BrE infml* to be about to be told by a person in a position of responsibility that you should not have done something 〘英式, 非正式〙將受到警告 **16 the high life** the enjoyable life of rich and fashionable people 〔上層社會的〕豪華生活 **17 high profile** the state of attracting a lot of attention to yourself or your actions 引人注目的狀態; 高姿態: *The company has a high profile in the area of personal computers.* 該公司在個人電腦領域裡有着引人注目的形象。 **18 high school** a school for children aged 11-18 中學〔供十一至十八歲孩童上的學校〕 **19 the high season** the time when the largest number of people are on holiday 旅遊旺季; 度假旺季 **20 high spirits** great cheerfulness or readiness to have rather wild fun 興高采烈: *He was in great high spirits after the match.* 比賽之後他極為興奮。 **21 the High Street** the main street of a town 大街〔市鎮的主要街道〕: *I bought it in the High Street.* 我在大街上買的。 | *Camden High Street* 坎登大街 **22 high tea** *BrE* a large early-evening meal 〘英式〙傍晚茶點 **23 high tide** the point at which the sea is highest up the shore or river 〔海水〕高〔滿〕潮時: *It's a dangerous place at high tide.* 高潮時此地很危險。 **24 It's high time** a phrase you use when you think someone should do something that has been delayed too long 早說該...〔表示某人早就應該做某事〕: *It's high time you bought a new car.* 你早就該買部新車了。

■ **USAGE** 用法: **1** Note that we use **high** to describe measurements even if these measurements are not very big ☆我們用 **high** 來表示測量所得的高度, 即便這一高度並不很高: *The wall was only three feet high.* 這堵牆僅三英尺高。 **2** Compare 比較 **high** and 和 **tall**. We use **high** (opposite **low**) for most

things, but **tall** (opposite **short**) for people ☆**high** 〔反義詞為 **low**〕主要用於物, 但是 **tall** 〔反義詞為 **short**〕則用於人: *The building was more than 30 storeys high.* 這座樓有三十幾層高。 | *She was well over six feet tall.* 她身高超過六英尺。 | *a high mountain* 高山 | *a high shelf* 很高的架子 | *a tall man/woman* 高個子男人/女人。 We can also use **tall** for things when the height is very much greater than the width ☆我們也可用 **tall** 來描述高度比寬度大得多的物體: *a tall pine tree* 高大的松樹 | *the tall skyscrapers of Hong Kong* 香港的摩天大樓

high² *adv* **1** to or at a high level or position 到達高處; 在很高的位置上: *They climbed high.* 他們爬得很高。 | *The plane flew high above.* 飛機高高地飛在天上。 | *He's high up in the civil service now.* 他在政府部門裡擔任很高的職位。 | *He's risen high in the world.* 他是個舉世知名的人。 **2 high and low** everywhere 到處: *I searched high and low for it.* 為了它, 我到處都找遍了。

high³ *n* **1** the highest level 最高水平: *The price of food reached a new high this week.* 本週食品價格升到了一個新的高點。 **2** *infml* a state of great excitement and happiness, sometimes produced by a drug 〘非正式〙〔常由毒品產生的〕極度興奮和快樂

high·brow /'haɪ,braʊ; 'haɪbraʊ/ *adj* connected with art, music, or books and often difficult to understand 品味高的: *high-brow classical music* 高品味的古典音樂

high-class /ˌ·'·◂/ *adj* **1** of good quality 高質量的 **2** of high social position 社會地位高的

high-flown /ˌ·'·◂/ *adj* sounding very grand but having very little meaning (used of language) 誇張的; 誇大的〔指語言〕

high-hand·ed /ˌ·'·◂/ *adj* making decisions or acting without talking to other people first (a word used to express disapproval) 專橫的; 專制的〔含貶義〕: *a high-handed decision* 武斷的決定 –**high-handedness** *n* [U]

high·land /'haɪlənd; 'haɪlənd/ *adj* coming from or relating to a mountainous area 〔來自〕高地的: *highland cattle* 高地的牛

Highland fling /ˌ··'·/ *n* a fast Scottish country dance 蘇格蘭高地舞

High·lands /'haɪləndz; 'haɪləndz/ *n* [pl] **the Highlands** mountainous areas 高地: *the Scottish Highlands* (蘇格蘭)高地

high-lev·el /ˌ·'··◂/ *adj* [only before a noun 只用於名詞前] concerning people at the top of an organization 高層次的; 高級別的: *high-level peace talks* 高級和談

high·light¹ /'haɪ,laɪt; 'haɪlaɪt/ *n* **1** an important detail which stands out from the rest because it is the best or most interesting part 最精彩〔最突出〕的部分: *a film of the*

highlights of *the competition* 一部回顧比賽精彩場面的影片 **2 highlights** [pl] small light-coloured areas in someone's hair, produced by colouring the hair artificially 〔頭髮〕染過色的淺色部分

highlight[2] *v* [T] to pick out something as an important part 突出〔某事物〕; 強調: *The report highlights the problems of the unemployed.* 報告強調了失業者的問題。

high·ly /'haɪlɪ; 'haɪlɪ/ *adv* **1** to a high or great degree 非常地; 很: *highly skilled* 技巧很高的 | *highly enjoyable* 很有趣的 | *He's very highly paid.* 他報酬很高。**2 speak highly of someone** to praise someone's qualities or abilities 讚揚某人的人品或能力

highly-strung /ˌ··'·◂/ *adj* nervous and excitable 緊張的; 易激動的

high-mind·ed /ˌ·'·◂/ *adj* having high principles or moral standards (sometimes used to express disapproval) 品格高尚的〔有時含貶義〕 **–high-mindedness** *n* [U]

High·ness /'haɪnɪs; 'haɪnɪs/ *n* a title used of or to certain royal people 〔對某些皇族的尊稱〕閣下; 殿下: *Your Highness* 殿下 | *His Highness Prince Leopold* 利奧波德親王殿下

high-pow·ered /ˌ·'·◂/ *adj* **1** very powerful 強有力的: *a high-powered car* 馬力強勁的車 **2** very successful 非常成功的: *high-powered businessmen* 非常成功的商人

high-pres·sure /ˌ·'·◂/ *adj* [only before a noun 只用於名詞前] **1** having or using high pressure (used of a machine or substance) 高壓的〔指機器或物質〕: *a high-pressure hosepipe* 高壓軟水管 **2** carried out or working with great speed and force (used of an action, job, or person) 速度很快的; 強行的〔指行動、工作或人〕: *A high-pressure salesman may make you buy something you don't want.* 強行推銷的推銷員可能會使你買些不需要的東西。

high-rise /'· ·◂/ *adj* [only before a noun 只用於名詞前] very tall, with many floors (used of buildings) 高層的〔指建築物〕: *She lives in a high-rise flat.* 她住在一幢高層公寓裡。

high-spir·it·ed /ˌ·'··◂/ *adj* full of fun 歡樂的

high-tech /ˌ·'·◂/ *n* [U] the use of the most modern and advanced machines, processes, and methods in business and industry 高技術 **–high-tech** *adj* : *a new high-tech washing machine* 新推出的高技術洗衣機

high tech·nol·o·gy /ˌ····'···◂/ *n* [U] the use of the most modern and advanced machines, processes, and methods in business and industry 高技術: *the age of high technology* 高技術時代

high·way /'haɪweɪ; 'haɪweɪ/ *n AmE* or *law* 【美式或律】**1** a broad main road, especially one going from one town to another 公路〔尤指兩座城鎮之間的〕**2 the Highway Code** the official list of rules for vehicle drivers in Britain 〔英國的〕公路法規

high·way·man /'haɪˌweɪmən; 'haɪweɪmən/ *n* **highwaymen** /-mən; -mən/ a man who used to stop travellers on the roads and rob them of their money in the past 〔昔時的〕攔路搶劫者; 強盜

hi·jack /'haɪˌdʒæk; 'haɪdʒæk/ *v* [T] to take control of a vehicle or aircraft illegally, often for political aims 〔常出於政治目的而〕劫持〔車輛或飛機〕**–hijacker** *n* **–hijacking** *n* [C;U]

hike[1] /haɪk; haɪk/ *n* a long walk in the country 〔在鄉間的〕徒步旅行, 遠足

hike[2] *v* **hiked, hiking** [I] to go on a long walk in the country 作徒步旅行, 去遠足 **–hiker** *n* **–hiking** *n* [U]

hi·lar·i·ous /hə'lerɪəs; hɪ'leərɪəs/ *adj* very funny and making you laugh a lot 非常滑稽的; 令人捧腹的: *The party got quite hilarious after they'd had a few glasses.* 他們喝下幾杯酒之後, 宴會變得相當熱鬧。| *a hilarious film* 令人捧腹的電影 **–hilariously** *adv*

hi·lar·i·ty /hə'lærətɪ; hɪ'lærᵻti/ *n* [U] cheerfulness and laughter 歡樂; 歡笑

hill /hɪl; hɪl/ *n* a raised area of land not as high as a mountain 小山; 山岡

hill·ock /'hɪlək; 'hɪlək/ *n* a little hill 小丘

hill·side /'hɪlˌsaɪd; 'hɪlsaɪd/ *n* the side of a hill 小山坡

hill·y /'hɪlɪ; 'hɪlɪ/ *adj* having many hills 多山丘的; 多小山的: *hilly countryside* 多山的鄉間

hilt /hɪlt; hɪlt/ *n* **1** the handle of a sword, or of a knife which is used as a weapon 〔刀或劍的〕柄 **2 to the hilt** completely 完全地: *I'll support you to the hilt.* 我完全支持你。| *We're up to the hilt in debt.* 我們負債累累。

★★ him /hɪm; ɪm, *strong* 強讀 hɪm; hɪm/ *pron* [used as the object of a verb 用作動詞的賓語] the male person or animal who has already been mentioned 他; 牠〔雄性動物〕: *"Where's John?" "I think I saw him in town."* "約翰在哪裡?" "我好像在城裡看見過他。"–see 見 ME (USAGE 用法)

★★ himself /hɪm'sɛlf; ɪm'sɛlf, *strong* 強讀 hɪm-; hɪm-/ *pron* **1** used as the object of a verb or a PREPOSITION when the subject of a verb is male and the action is done to the same person 〔反身代詞〕他自己: *He washed himself and got dressed.* 他洗了個澡, 穿上了衣服。| *John looked at himself in the mirror.* 約翰看着鏡中的自己。| *He had scratched himself on a rusty nail.* 他被一枚生鏽的鐵釘劃傷了。| *Peter decided to buy himself some new clothes.* 彼得決定給自己買幾件新衣服。**2** used to add force to the word "he", or to the name of a male person or animal 自己〔強調"他"〕: *He himself admitted that it wasn't his best painting.* 他自己承認那不是他最好的一幅畫。| *I'd like to speak to the doctor himself, please.* 我希望跟醫生本人談一談。| *He had done all the decorating himself.* 他一個人做完了全部的裝飾工作。**3**

by **himself** alone, with no one with him or helping him (他)單獨地; 獨力地: *John had spent the day by himself.* 約翰獨自一人過了一天。| *He had managed to mend the roof by himself.* 他終於獨自修好了屋頂。

hind /haɪnd; haɪnd/ *adj* **hind legs** the back legs of an animal 動物的後腿

hin·der /ˈhɪndə; ˈhɪndər/ *v* [T] to prevent from doing something 阻止; 阻礙: *The bomb attack may hinder the progress of the peace talks.* 轟炸可能會阻礙和談進展。

hind·quar·ters /ˈhaɪndˈkwɔrtəz; ˈhaɪnd-ˌkwɔːtəz/ *n* [pl] the back part of an animal including its legs 〔動物的〕後臀及後腿

hin·drance /ˈhɪndrəns; ˈhɪndrəns/ *n* something or somebody that prevents you from doing something 阻礙做某事的物或人: *He said he'd help me do the job, but he was more of a hindrance than a help.* 他說可以幫我幹活, 但與其說是幫忙, 倒不如說是添麻煩。

hind·sight /ˈhaɪndˌsaɪt; ˈhaɪndsaɪt/ *n* [U] understanding why and how something happened, but only after it has happened 事後的理解[聰明]: *With the benefit of hindsight I can see it was a mistake to buy that car.* 我事後才看出買那輛汽車是錯誤的。

Hin·du /ˈhɪndu; ˈhɪnduː/ *n* a person whose religion is Hinduism 印度教徒 –**Hindu** *adj*

Hin·du·is·m /ˈhɪnduˌɪzəm; ˈhɪnduːizəm/ *n* [U] the chief religion of India, notable especially for its belief in many gods and that people return after death in another form 印度教

hinge[1] /hɪndʒ; hɪndʒ/ *n* a metal part which joins two things together so that one of them can swing freely; a hinge joins a door to a frame, or a lid to a box 〔門、箱等上的〕鉸鏈; 合葉: *I must oil the hinges to stop the gate creaking.* 我必須給鉸鏈上些油以免大門嘎吱作響。

hinge[2] *v* **hinged, hinging** [T] to join things together with a hinge 用鉸鏈連接: *The fridge door is hinged on the right.* 冰箱門的鉸鏈裝在右邊。

hinge on/upon sthg *phr v* [T] to depend on something 取決於〔某事物〕: *The success of the plan hinges on local support.* 該計劃能否成功取決於地方上的支持。

hint[1] /hɪnt; hɪnt/ *n* **1** an indirect suggestion 暗示: *I wish you would give us a hint about the winner.* 我希望你能給我們一些有關獲勝者的暗示。 **2 a hint of** a small sign or amount of something 一點跡象; 少量東西: *There's a hint of summer in the air, although it's only April.* 儘管才四月, 外面已有夏天的氣息。| *a sauce with a hint of garlic* 略帶蒜味的醬 **3** useful advice 有用的忠告: *helpful hints for removing stains* 有關除污方法的實用指示 **4 drop a hint** to suggest something to someone in an indirect way 給〔某人〕以提示 **5 take a hint** to understand someone's indirect suggestion 理解某一暗

示: *They took the hint and left immediately.* 他們領會了暗示, 立即離開。

hint[2] *v* [I;T; +(that)] to suggest or mention something indirectly 暗示: *I hinted to him that I was dissatisfied with his work.* 我向他暗示我對他的工作不滿意。| *The minister hinted at an early election.* 部長暗示要早日舉行選舉。

> □ USEFUL PATTERNS 有用句型
> to hint at something; to hint that...; to hint to someone that...

hin·ter·land /ˈhɪntəˌlænd; ˈhɪntəlænd/ *n* **the hinterland** the inner part of a country, beyond the coast or the banks of an important river 內地; 腹地

hip /hɪp; hɪp/ *n* the fleshy part on either side of your body above your legs and below your waist 臀部: *He stood with his hands on his hips.* 他雙手叉在臀部上站立着。

hip·pie /ˈhɪpɪ; ˈhɪpɪ/ *n* **hippies** (also 又作 **hippy**) a person who is against the standards of ordinary society, believes in love and peace and dresses in a colourful way; hippies were common in the 1960s 〔反對一般社會的準則, 相信愛情與和平, 穿着色彩豔麗的服裝, 常見於60年代的〕嬉皮士

hip·po·pot·a·mus /ˌhɪpəˈpɑtəməs; ˌhɪpə-ˈpɔtəməs/ *n* **hippopotamuses** or **hippopotami** /-maɪ; -maɪ/ (also 又作 **hippo** /ˈhɪpəʊ; ˈhɪpəʊ/ *infml* 〔非正式〕) a large African animal with short legs and thick hairless skin, which lives near rivers 〔產於非洲的〕河馬

hire[1] /haɪr; haɪər/ *v* **hired, hiring** **1** *BrE* to get the use of something for a short time by paying a certain amount of money 〔英式〕租用〔某物〕: *I'm going to hire an evening dress for the dance.* 我準備租件晚禮服去參加舞會。 **2** to employ someone to work for you for a short time 雇用〔某人〕: *The fruit is picked by hired labourers.* 水果由雇來的工人去採摘。

> ■ USAGE 用法: Compare 比較 **hire** and 和 **rent**. In British English you **hire** things for just a short time ☆在英式英語中, **hire** 表示租用很短一段時間: *Let's hire a car for the weekend.* 我們週末去租輛汽車吧。| *I'll have to hire a suit for the wedding.* 我得為婚禮租一套禮服。 If you are talking about a longer period, use the word **rent** ☆如果租用時間較長, 用 **rent** 一詞: *Is that your own television or do you rent it?* 那台電視是你自己的還是租來的? Always use the word **rent** when talking about houses or flats ☆談到租房子或公寓時, 要用 **rent** 一詞: *They live in a rented flat in the city centre.* 他們住在市中心一套租來的公寓裡。 (In American English the

H

word **rent** is used for all these things. 在美式英語中，**rent** 一詞可用於上述所有的句子。)

hire sbdy/sthg ↔ **out** *phr v* [T] to give your services or the use of something for payment 出租〔某物〕; 受雇用: *Why don't you hire out your car to your neighbours while you're away?* 你不在家時，何不將汽車出租給鄰居呢? | *Farm labourers used to hire themselves out for the summer.* 過去農業勞力常在夏天受人雇用。

hire² *n* [U] the use of something on payment of some money 出租; 租用; 雇用: *Boats for hire.* 出租小艇。 | *We'll have to pay for the hire of a room.* 我們得付房間的租金。

hire pur·chase /ˌ·ˈ··/ *n* [U] (also 又作 **HP**) a system of payment for goods by which you pay small regular sums of money until you have paid the full price 分期付款購買法: *I bought the stereo system on hire purchase.* 我用分期付款方式購買了這套立體聲音響。

★★his¹ /ɪz; ɪz, *strong* 強讀 hɪz; hɪz/ *det* **1** relating to or belonging to the male person or animal who has already been mentioned 他的: *My father came in and sat down in his chair.* 我父親走進來，坐在他的椅子上。 | *He was sitting drinking his coffee.* 他坐在那裡喝他的咖啡。 **2** relating to or belonging to the person who has already been mentioned, when it has not been stated whether they are male or female 〔泛指上文已經提到過的人; 不論男女〕他的: *Everyone should do his best.* 每個人都應盡力而為。

★his² *pron* something relating to or belonging to the male person or animal who has already been mentioned 他的(東西): *When we went to collect our coats, my father realized that he had left his in the car.* 我們去拿外衣時，父親才發覺他把外衣留在車裡了。 | *My hand touched his.* 我的手碰到了他的手。

hiss /hɪs; hɪs/ *v* **1** [I] to make a sound like a continuous "s" 發出"嘶嘶"的聲音: *Gas escaped with a hissing noise from the broken pipe.* 煤氣嘶嘶地從破裂的管子中逸出。 **2** [I; T] to say in a sharp whisper 發噓聲: *The boy hissed a warning to be quiet.* 男孩用噓聲警告別人保持安靜。 **3** to make this sound in order to show anger or disapproval 發出噓聲以表示憤怒或反對: *She was hissed off the stage.* 她被噓聲轟下了台。–**hiss** *n*: *The snake gave an angry hiss.* 蛇發出憤怒的嘶嘶聲。

his·to·ri·an /hɪsˈtorɪən; hɪˈstɔːrɪən/ *n* a person who studies or writes about history 歷史學家; 史學工作者

his·tor·ic /hɪsˈtɔrɪk; hɪˈstɒrɪk/ *adj* important in history 具有歷史意義的: *a historic occasion* 具有歷史意義的場合 | *historic buildings* 具有歷史意義的建築物

his·tor·i·cal /hɪsˈtɔrɪkl; hɪˈstɒrɪkəl/ *adj* **1** concerning events that really happened or people that really existed in the past 歷史的; 歷史上的: *We cannot be sure whether King Arthur was a historical figure.* 我們不敢肯定亞瑟王是否一個歷史人物。 | *a historical novel* 歷史小說 **2** connected with the study of history 有關歷史學的: *an institute for historical research* 歷史研究所 –**historically** /-klɪ; -klɪ/ *adv*

★★his·to·ry /ˈhɪstrɪ; ˈhɪstəri/ *n* **histories 1** [U] events in the past, especially when seen as a whole 歷史: *a significant moment in South African history* 南非歷史上的一個重要時刻 **2** [U] the study of events in the past, especially those concerned with politics or social conditions 歷史學: *History is my favourite subject at school.* 歷史是我在校時最喜歡的一門課程。 **3** [C] a description of the development of something during the period in which it has existed 發展史: *the history of the computer* 電腦發展史 **4** [C] a set of facts relating to the past of a person 個人過去的歷史: *the patient's medical history* 病人的病歷 **5** **have a history of** to have a record of illness, social difficulties, or criminal activities in the past 具有〔疾病、社會困難或犯罪活動〕的歷史: *She has a history of back trouble.* 她有背部疼痛的病史。 | *The accused has a history of shoplifting.* 被告有在商店偷竊的歷史。 **6** **make history, go down in history** to do something important which will be remembered 做出載於史冊的重大事情

his·tri·on·ic /ˌhɪstrɪˈɒnɪk; ˌhɪstrɪˈɒnɪk/ *adj* showing strong feelings which are too theatrical to be sincere (a word used to express disapproval) 演戲般的; 做作的〔含貶義〕–**histrionically** /-klɪ; -klɪ/ *adv*

his·tri·on·ics /ˌhɪstrɪˈɒnɪks; ˌhɪstrɪˈɒnɪks/ *n* [pl] behaviour which is insincere and like a theatrical performance (a word used to express disapproval) 矯揉做作; 裝腔作勢〔含貶義〕

★hit¹ /hɪt; hɪt/ *v* **hit, hit, hitting** [T] **1** to bring your hand, or something held in your hand, forcefully against someone or something 重擊，打擊〔某人或某物〕: *She hit the burglar on the head.* 她用力打了小偷的頭。 | *He hit the ball over the net.* 他把球打過網。 | *The demonstrator was hit by a rubber bullet.* 示威者被一顆橡皮子彈擊中。–see picture on page 992 見 992 頁彩圖 **2** to come up against something forcefully and suddenly 碰撞: *She hit her head on the low ceiling.* 她的頭撞到了低矮的天花板上。 | *The dog was hit by a truck.* 狗被卡車撞了。 **3** to have a bad effect on someone 對〔某人〕有不良影響: *Inflation has hit poor people the hardest.* 通貨膨脹對窮人打擊最大。

H

通貨膨脹對窮人的打擊最大。**4 to arrive at a place or position** 到達〔某地或某個位置〕: *We hit the main road two miles further on.* 我們到達了兩英里以外的大路上。| *The dollar hit an all time low today on the money markets.* 今天美元在貨幣市場上跌到了有史以來的最低點。**5 hit it off with** *infml* **to have a good relationship with** 〔非正式〕與…關係良好: *I'm glad to see the two girls hitting it off so well.* 很高興看到兩個女孩子相處得這麼融洽。**6 hit the jackpot** *infml* **to have a big success** 〔非正式〕非常成功 **7 hit the nail on the head** to be exactly correct in what you have said 所說的完全正確; 正中要害 **8 hit the road** *infml* to start on a journey 〔非正式〕上路; 出發 **9 hit the roof** (also 又作 **hit the ceiling** *AmE* 〔美式〕) *infml* to show great anger 〔非正式〕大發雷霆 **10 hit the sack** *infml* to go to bed 〔非正式〕上牀睡覺

hit back *phr v* [I] to reply forcefully to an attack on yourself 反擊; 回擊: *The Prime Minister has hit back angrily* **at** *these criticisms.* 首相憤然駁斥了這些批評。

hit on/upon sthg *phr v* [T] to have a good idea about something by chance 偶然想到〔好主意〕: *Peter has hit upon an idea that will get us out of our difficulty.* 彼得無意中想出了一個能讓我們擺脫困境的好主意。

hit out at sbdy/sthg (also 又作 **hit out against** sbdy/sthg) *phr v* [T] to disagree violently with someone or something 猛烈抨擊: *The newspapers are hitting out at the government's latest decision.* 各家報紙對政府最近作出的決定進行猛烈的抨擊。

hit² *n* **1 a blow with your hand or something held in your hand** 〔用手或手中之物的〕擊; 打: *He aimed a wild hit at his attacker.* 他拼命朝對手打去。| *That was a good hit. It almost saved the game.* 那一擊很不錯。幾乎挽救了比賽局勢。**2** the act of successfully striking something aimed at 擊中: *I scored a direct hit with my first shot.* 我第一槍就命中目標。**3 something, especially a film, song, or play, that is very successful** 十分成功的事物〔尤指電影、歌曲或戲劇〕: *Her first record was a big hit.* 她的首張唱片十分暢銷。**4 make a hit with someone** to make someone have a good opinion of you 使某人對你具有好印象: *You've made a real hit with my parents!* 你給我父母留下了非常好的印象!

hit-and-miss /ˌ·ˈ·/ *adj* unplanned and depending on chance 無計劃的; 靠運氣的

hit-and-run /ˌ·ˈ·◂/ *adj* **1 hit-and-run accident** a road accident in which the person who causes the accident drives away quickly 駕車失事後不顧而去的交通事故 **2 hit-and-run driver** a driver who causes an accident but does not stop to help 駕車失事後不顧而去的汽車司機

hitch¹ /hɪtʃ; hɪtʃ/ *v* **1** [T] to fasten by hooking something over something else 鈎住; 拴住: *Another railway carriage has been hitched*

on. 另外一節車廂已經掛上鈎了。| *Hitch your horse to the gate.* 把你的馬拴在大門上。**2** [I;T] *infml* to travel by getting free rides in other people's cars 〔非正式〕搭便車: *He hitched across Europe.* 他搭便車橫跨歐洲。| *Let's hitch a ride.* 我們搭一次便車吧。

hitch sthg ↔ **up** *phr v* [T] to pull a piece of clothing upwards into the proper position 向上拉〔衣物〕: *John hitched up his trousers.* 約翰提了提他的褲子。

hitch² *n* a slight difficulty which delays something for a while 小故障; 障礙: *a technical hitch* 小的技術故障 | *The first performance went off without a hitch.* 首演一帆風順。

hitch·hike /ˈhɪtʃˌhaɪk; ˈhɪtʃhaɪk/ *v* **hitch·hiked, hitchhiking** [I] to travel by getting free rides in other people's cars by standing at the side of the road and signalling to drivers 沿途搭便車旅行 **–hitch-hiker** *n*

hith·er /ˈhɪðə; ˈhɪðə/ *adv* **1** *old fash* to this place 〔老式〕到此處: *Come hither!* 到這裡來! **2 hither and thither** *lit* in all directions 〔文〕到處; 四面八方

hith·er·to /ˌhɪðəˈtu; ˌhɪðəˈtuː◂/ *adv fml* up until now 〔正式〕迄今; 到現在為止: *Hitherto we have always paid the rent on Mondays.* 到目前為止我們一直是在星期一付租金。

hit-list /ˈhɪtˌlɪst; ˈhɪtlɪst/ *n* a list of people against whom something bad is planned 預謀打擊〔殺害〕的名單

hive /haɪv; haɪv/ *n* **1** (also 又作 **beehive**) a small container or hut in which bees are kept 蜂房 **2** a very busy place 繁忙的地方: *The classroom was* **a hive of** *activity.* 教室裡大家都在忙忙碌碌。

h'm /həm; m, hm/ *interj* (also 又作 **hm**) a sound made with your lips closed to express doubt or disagreement; or to give yourself time to think before speaking 哼; 呣〔表示懷疑、不贊同或遲疑〕

HMS /ˌeɪtʃ em ɛs; ˌeɪtʃ em es/ title for a ship in the British Royal Navy; an abbreviation for *His/Her Majesty's Ship* 〔縮〕英國皇家海軍艦艇: *HMS Belfast* 皇家海軍艦艇貝爾法斯特號

hoard¹ /hord; hɔːd/ *n* a store of things which someone has collected very carefully and often secretly 貯藏

hoard² *v* [T] to store things secretly in large amounts 大量貯藏〔物品〕, 囤積 **–hoarder** *n*

hoard·ing /ˈhordɪŋ; ˈhɔːdɪŋ/ *n BrE* 〔英式〕**1** a fence put round a piece of land when building is going on 〔修築工地的〕圍籬 **2** a high fence or board on which large advertisements are stuck 廣告招貼板

hoar·frost /ˈhor.frɒst; ˈhɔːfrɒst/ *n* [U] white frozen drops of water, seen on grass and plants after a cold night 〔寒夜後見於草木上的〕白霜

hoarse /hors; hɔːs/ *adj* sounding rough and hard, for example when you have a cold (used of a person or voice) 沙啞的, 嘶啞的〔指人的嗓音〕: *We shouted ourselves hoarse at the football match.* 我們在足球賽中喊啞了嗓子。 –**hoarsely** *adv* –**hoarseness** *n* [U]

hoar·y /'hɔrɪ; 'hɔːri/ *adj lit* grey or white with age (used of hair)〔文〕灰白的〔指頭髮〕

hoax /hoks; həʊks/ *n* a trick which makes someone believe something which is not true 騙局; 惡作劇: *We all left the building after a telephone caller said there was a bomb, but it was just a hoax.* 有人打電話來說樓內有炸彈, 我們便全部撤離, 但那只是個惡作劇。 –**hoax** *v* [T]

hob /hab; hɒb/ *n* the flat top of a gas or electric cooker on which pans are placed 〔煤氣爐或電爐上放平底鍋的〕擱架; 爐盤

hob·ble /'habl; 'hɒbəl/ *v* **hobbled, hobbling** **1** [I] to walk with difficulty, taking small steps 跛行; 蹣跚: *She hobbled home, clutching her stick.* 她拄着拐杖, 一瘸一拐地回家。 **2** [T] to tie two legs of an animal together so that it cannot run away 捆縛〔動物的雙腿〕〔使其無法逃跑〕

hob·by /'habɪ; 'hɒbi/ *n* **hobbies** an activity which you enjoy doing in your free time 業餘愛好: *Do you have a hobby?* 你有沒有甚麼業餘愛好? –see 見 RECREATION (USAGE 用法)

hob·by·horse /'habɪˌhɔrs; 'hɒbihɔːs/ *n* **1** a child's toy like a horse's head on a stick 馬頭桿〔玩具〕; 竹馬 **2** a subject which someone has strong opinions about and likes to talk about 喜歡反覆談的話題

hob·nob /'habˌnab; 'hɒbnɒb/ *v* -**bb**- [I] to have a social relationship, often with someone in a higher position 與〔某人, 尤指地位較高的人〕親近: *I've been hobnobbing with the directors at the office party.* 我在公司宴會上一直在與各位董事應酬。

ho·bo /'hobo; 'həʊbəʊ/ *n* **hoboes** or **hobos** *AmE infml* a person with no home or regular work〔美式, 非正式〕流浪漢; 無業游民

hock /hak; hɒk/ *n* [C;U] a type of German white wine 霍克酒〔德國產的一種白葡萄酒〕

hock·ey /'hakɪ; 'hɒki/ *n* (**field hockey** *AmE*〔美式〕) a game for two teams of 11 players, who use special sticks to hit a ball around a field 曲棍球

hod /had; hɒd/ *n* a container with a long handle, used by builders' workmen for carrying bricks〔建築工人用以運磚的〕磚斗

hodge·podge /'hadʒˌpadʒ; 'hɒdʒpɒdʒ/ *n* – see 見 HOTCHPOTCH

hoe¹ /ho; həʊ/ *n* a long-handled garden tool used for removing wild plants and making the soil loose 鋤頭 –see picture on page 958 見 958 頁彩圖

hoe² *v* **hoed, hoeing** [I;T] to use a hoe 用鋤頭鋤地

hog¹ /hag; hɒg/ *n* **1** *AmE* a pig, especially a fat male one for eating〔美式〕豬〔尤指供食用的肥豬〕 **2** *infml* a rude person who eats too much〔非正式〕貪吃而粗魯的人 **3 go the whole hog** *infml* to do something thoroughly or completely〔非正式〕徹底地做某事; 全力以赴 **4 road hog** a person who drives in a rude manner 駕車粗野的人

hog² *v* -**gg**- [T] *infml* to take or use all of something so that no one else can use it〔非正式〕把〔某物〕全部佔為己有; 獨佔: *I can't overtake because the car in front is hogging the middle of the road.* 我無法超車, 因為前面那輛車開在馬路的正中央。

hoist¹ /hɔɪst; hɔɪst/ *v* [T] **1** to lift up something heavy 舉起〔重物〕: *He hoisted the bag over his shoulder.* 他把包扛上肩膀。 **2** to raise something using ropes or a special machine〔用繩索或特殊的機器〕升起; 吊起: *The sailors hoisted the flag.* 水手們升起了旗幟。 | *The cargo was hoisted onto the ship.* 貨物被吊到了船上。

hoist² *n* a machine for lifting heavy goods 起重機

hold¹ /hold; həʊld/ *v* **held** /hɛld; held/, **held, holding 1** [T] to keep something in your hands, arms, or mouth 拿住; 握住; 咬住: *She was holding a book.* 她拿着一本書。 | *He held her in his arms.* 他把她擁在懷裡。 | *The dog was holding a newspaper in its mouth.* 那條狗嘴裡叼了張報紙。 –see picture on page 992 見 992 頁彩圖 **2** [T] to move a part of your body into a particular position, or keep it there 使〔身體某一部分〕保持某種姿勢: *She held her hand up.* 她舉着手。 | *They held their heads up.* 他們昂起頭。 **3** [T] to keep someone somewhere as a prisoner 看管住〔囚犯〕: *He is being held in police custody.* 他被警方拘留。 **4** [T] to keep something in a particular position 使〔某物〕保持在某個位置上: *The roof is held up by four enormous pillars.* 屋頂由四根巨大的柱子支撐着。 | *The picture is held in place by a hook.* 這幅畫用鈎子掛着。 **5** [T] to be able to contain a particular amount 能夠容納〔某一數量〕: *The pan holds about one litre.* 這隻平底鍋可以裝下約一公升液體。 | *The cinema holds 500 people.* 該電影院可容納五百人。 **6** [T] to have something 擁有; 有: *Who holds the keys to the church?* 誰有教堂的鑰匙? | *He held the office of prime minister for four years.* 他擔任了四年的首相。 | *Do you hold a current driving licence?* 你有有效的駕駛執照嗎? **7** [T+that] to have a particular opinion 持〔某種觀點〕: *A lot of people hold the view that criminals are not punished severely enough.* 許多人認為對於罪犯的懲罰還不夠嚴峻。 | *She holds that the government's policy is mistaken.* 她認為政府的政策錯了。 | *I hold you personally responsible for this tragedy.* 我認為你要對這起悲劇負責。 **8** [T] to cause an event to take place 使〔事情〕發生: *We're holding a party next week.* 我們下週舉行宴會。 | *The meeting was held at the company's headquarters.* 會

議是在公司總部舉行的。 **9** [I] to remain good or true 保持良好狀態; 保持正確: *The invitation still holds.* 邀請仍然有效。 | *Let's hope the good weather holds.* 但願這好天氣能持續下去。 | *What I said before still holds.* 我以前所說的仍然沒錯。 **10 hold a conversation** to have a conversation 進行談話: *It was impossible to hold a conversation with all that noise going on.* 在那樣嘈雜的情況下無法進行談話。 **11 hold your breath** to stop breathing for a short while 屏住呼吸: *Don't forget to hold your breath when you dive into the water!* 跳入水中時，不要忘記屏住呼吸! **12 Hold it!** a phrase you use when you are telling someone to stop doing something 停下! 住手!〔用於要某人停止做某事〕 **13 hold still** to remain still and not move 保持靜止不動: *Hold still while I take a photo.* 我拍照時不要動。 **14 hold the line** to wait for a short time when you are talking on the telephone, for example so that someone can find the person that you want to talk to 不掛斷電話: *If you'll just hold the line for a minute I'll put you through to Mr Atkins.* 請您別掛斷電話，稍等片刻，我給您接到亞特金斯先生那裡。 **15 hold your own** to do as well as other people 與別人做得一樣好: *Although he was by far the youngest competitor he certainly held his own.* 儘管他是最年輕的參賽選手，但他確實與別人做得一樣好。

hold sthg **against** sbdy *phr v* [T] to continue to feel angry with someone or dislike them because of something bad that they did in the past 〔因某人的錯事而〕繼續生〔某人〕的氣; 繼續討厭〔某人〕: *The fact that someone has been in prison should not be held against them.* 不應該因為有人曾經入獄而歧視他們。

hold back *phr v* **1** [T **hold** sbdy/sthg ↔ **back**] to prevent someone or something from moving forwards 阻止〔某人或某物〕向前移動: *Police held the crowd back.* 警方阻止人羣向前走。 | *People built banks of earth to hold back the flood waters.* 人們築堤以阻擋上漲的河水。 **2** [I] to be unwilling to do something because you are not sure that it is the right thing to do 〔由於不知這樣做是否正確而〕不願做某事; 猶豫: *She held back for a long time before she finally went to the police.* 她猶豫許久才去找警方。 **3** [T **hold** sbdy ↔ **back**] to prevent someone from developing properly 阻礙〔某人的正常發育〕: *Illness can hold a child back quite significantly.* 疾病會嚴重影響孩子的發育。 **4** [T **hold** sthg ↔ **back**] to keep something secret 保密, 隱瞞〔某物〕: *I knew that he was holding something back.* 我知道他隱瞞了一些事情。

hold sthg **down** *phr v* [T] **1** to keep a job 保住〔工作〕: *He seems to be unable to hold down a job for more than a few weeks.* 他做工作似乎都沒有超過幾個星期。 **2** to keep

something at a low level 把〔某物〕保持在低水平上; 抑制: *the government's determination to hold down prices* 政府控制物價上漲的決心

hold forth *phr v* [T] *fml* to talk for a long time about something 〔正式〕長時間談論〔某物〕

hold sbdy/sthg ↔ **off** *phr v* [T] to cause someone or something to remain at a distance 使同〔某人或某物〕保持一定距離; 擋住: *They managed to hold off the enemy's attack.* 他們設法擋住了敵人的進攻。

hold on *phr v* [I] *infml* to wait for a short time 〔非正式〕稍等; 別掛斷: *Could you hold on? I'll just see if he's in.* 您稍等一下好嗎? 我去看看他在不在。

hold onto sthg *phr v* [T] **1** to hold something with your hand 用手抓住〔某物〕: *She held onto the side of the boat.* 她用手抓住小船的邊。 **2** to manage to keep something 設法保住〔某物〕: *He held onto his job.* 他設法保住自己的工作。

hold out *phr v* **1** [T **hold** sthg ↔ **out**] to offer something to someone by moving it towards them 把〔某物〕提供給〔某人〕: *He held out his hand to her.* 他向她伸出了手。 **2** [I] to manage to last in spite of difficulties 〔在困境中〕堅持: *The people held out until help arrived.* 那些人一直堅持到有人來救援。 **3 hold out hope** to remain hopeful 抱着希望: *I don't hold out much hope that the weather will improve.* 我對天氣會轉好不抱多大希望。

hold out for sthg *phr v* [T] to demand something firmly and wait until you get it 堅持要求得到〔某物〕: *The men are still holding out for more pay.* 這些人堅持要求增加工資。

hold sthg **over** *phr v* [T] to move something to a later date 推遲〔某事物〕, 使延期: *We may have to hold the meeting over until next week.* 我們有可能要把會議推遲到下週。

hold sbdy **to** sthg *phr v* [T] to make someone do what they said that they would do 使〔某人〕遵守〔諾言〕: *I shall hold him to his promise.* 我一定讓他遵守諾言。

hold up *phr v* **1** [T **hold** sbdy/sthg ↔ **up**] to delay someone or something 延誤〔某人或某事物〕: *The building work was held up by the bad weather.* 建造工程由於惡劣的天氣而耽擱了。 **2** [T **hold** sbdy ↔ **up**] to stop someone in order to rob them 攔路搶劫〔某人〕: *He was held up at gunpoint and robbed.* 他遭到持槍歹徒搶劫。 **3** [**hold** sbdy/sthg ↔ **up**] to give someone or something as an example of something 提出〔某人或某物〕作為榜樣: *He always held up his youngest son as a model of hard work.* 他總是舉出他的小兒子作為勤奮工作的典範。

hold with sthg *phr v* [T] not hold with something to not agree with something 不贊成某事: *I don't hold with these modern* *teaching methods.* 我不贊成這些現代的教學方法。

*hold² n 1 the part of a ship where goods are stored 〔船的〕貨艙 **2** the act of holding something 握住: *I seemed to be losing my hold of the rope.* 我似乎漸漸握不住繩子了。**3** something that you can hold when you are climbing 〔攀登時〕可以握住的東西: *I couldn't find a hold for my hands.* 我找不到抓手的地方。**4 a hold over someone** power or control over someone 左右某人的力量; 對某人的控制: *Religion has a strong hold over these people.* 宗教對這些人具有很強的控制力。| *His hold over her seemed to be weakening.* 他對她的控制似乎越來越弱。**5 get hold of something: a** to take something in your hand and hold it 抓住, 握住某物: *I got hold of the sack and lifted it up.* 我抓住包, 把它舉了起來。**b** to find someone or obtain something 找到某人; 獲得某物: *I need to get hold of some money quickly.* 我需要馬上弄到些錢。**6 take hold of something** to take something in your hand and hold it 抓住, 握住某物: *He took hold of the rope and pulled.* 他抓住繩子用力拉。

hold·all /ˈhɔːldɔːl; ˈhəʊldɔːl/ n a large bag or small case used when travelling 旅行包

*hold·er /ˈhəʊldə; ˈhəʊldəʳ/ n **1** a person who has control of or owns a place, a position, or a thing 〔地方, 位置或物品〕持有人; 擁有者: *the holder of the office of chairman* 擔任主席職務的人 | *Only ticket-holders will be admitted to the show.* 只有持票者才能進去參觀。**2** something which contains or supports something else 夾具; 支撐物: *a cigarette holder* 煙嘴 | *a candle holder* 燭台

*hold·ing /ˈhəʊldɪŋ; ˈhəʊldɪŋ/ n **1** a piece of land which you own or rent 〔擁有或租用的〕土地 **2** shares in a company 公司股票

hold·up /ˈhəʊldʌp; ˈhəʊldʌp/ n **1** a delay, for example one caused by traffic 耽擱〔如交通阻塞〕: *Sorry I'm late, there was a holdup down by the bridge.* 對不起, 我遲到了, 因為在那橋的附近遇到了塞車。**2** a robbery in which people are threatened with a gun 持槍搶劫: *a masked holdup at the bank* 蒙面匪徒持槍搶劫銀行

*hole¹ /həʊl; həʊl/ n **1** an empty space or opening in or through something solid 洞; 孔: *The men have dug a hole in the road.* 那些人在路上挖了個洞。| *There's a hole in my sock.* 我的襪子上有個洞。**2** the home of a small animal 〔小動物的〕洞穴: *a rabbit hole* 兔子的洞穴 **3** a hollow place into which the ball must be hit in the game of GOLF 〔高爾夫球的〕球洞: *an 18-hole golf course* 有十八個洞的高爾夫球場 **4** *infml* a small unpleasant place 〔非正式〕令人不快的小地方: *His flat's a bit of a hole.* 他的公寓小得像個窩。**5 pick holes in something** to find the weak points in something such as an argument or idea 在論點或觀點中尋找弱點〔漏洞〕

hole² v holed, holing [T] **1** to make a hole in something 打洞於〔某物〕: *Our ship was holed and began to sink.* 我們的船被撞了個洞, 開始下沉。**2** to hit a ball into a hole when playing GOLF 〔高爾夫球〕把球打進洞

*hol·i·day /ˈhɒlədeɪ; ˈhɒlɪdi/ n **1** a day of rest from work; often of religious or political importance 假日〔常指具有宗教或政治意義的假日〕: *The Fourth of July is a national holiday in the United States.* 七月四日是美國的國慶節。| *Next Friday is a holiday.* 下週五是假日。**2** a period of time when you do not go to work, school, or university, but have a rest or go away somewhere 假期: *the school holidays* 學校的假期 | *We spent the Easter holidays in Crete.* 我們在克里特過復活節。| *a skiing holiday* 滑雪的假期 | *According to the contract you get 25 days paid holiday a year.* 按合同, 你一年有二十五天的帶薪假日。| *a holiday resort* 度假勝地 | *Where did Mary go for her holiday?* 瑪麗到哪裡度假? **3 on holiday, on your holidays** having a holiday 在度假: *I'm afraid Mr Jones is away on holiday.* 恐怕瓊斯先生外出度假了。| *When you go on holiday don't forget to write to me!* 你去度假時, 別忘了給我寫信! —**holiday** v [I]

hol·i·day·mak·er /ˈhɒlədeɪˌmeɪkə; ˈhɒlɪdiˌmeɪkəʳ/ n a person on holiday 度假者

hol·i·ness /ˈhəʊlɪnɪs; ˈhəʊlɪnɪs/ n **1** [U] the state or quality of being holy 神聖 **2 Holiness** a title of the POPE 陛下, 聖座〔對教皇的尊稱〕: *Your Holiness* 陛下 | *His Holiness Pope John Paul* 若望·保祿教皇陛下

hol·ler /ˈhɒlə; ˈhɒləʳ/ v [I;T] *infml AmE* to shout out 〔非正式, 美式〕喊叫: *"Let go," she hollered.* "我們走," 她叫道。—**holler** n

hol·low¹ /ˈhɒləʊ; ˈhɒləʊ/ adj **1** having an empty space or hole inside 中空的; 空心的: *The pillars look solid, but in fact they're hollow.* 這些柱子看上去是實心的, 實際上是空心的。**2** sunken inwards (used of parts of a person's face) 〔指臉〕凹陷的: *hollow cheeks* 凹陷的臉頰 **3** having a ringing sound which goes on for some time 〔聲音〕空洞的; 低沉的: *the hollow sound of a large bell* 低沉的大鐘聲 **4** not sincere, or without real value 虛偽的; 無價值的: *the hollow promises of politicians* 政客虛偽的諾言 —**hollowness** n [U]

hollow² n a space or hole in the surface of something, often the ground 洞; 坑

hollow³ v

hollow sthg ↔ out *phr v* [T] to remove the inside of something 挖空〔某物〕: *He hollowed out a log.* 他把一根木頭挖空了。

hol·ly /ˈhɒli; ˈhɒli/ n **hollies** [C;U] a small tree with dark green prickly leaves and red berries 冬青(樹)

hol·o·caust /ˈhɒləˌkɔːst; ˈhɒləkɔːst/ n great destruction and the loss of many lives by fire or war 大屠殺, 毀滅: *fear of a nuclear holocaust* 對核毀滅的恐懼

H

hol·o·gram /ˈhɑləgræm; ˈhɒləgræm/ *n* a picture of something made with LASER beams which makes it look solid, not flat 〔用激光製成的〕全息圖

hol·ster /ˈholstɚ; ˈhəʊlstə^r/ *n* a leather holder for a gun, usually worn on a belt around the waist 手槍皮套〔通常繫於腰際〕

*★**ho·ly** /ˈholi; ˈhəʊli/ *adj* **holier, holiest 1** connected with God and religion 上帝的; 宗教的: *the Holy Bible* 聖經 | *the holy city of Mecca* 麥加聖城 **2** morally pure and giving yourself to God 聖潔的; 獻身上帝的: *a holy man* 獻身上帝的人 | *She led a holy life.* 她過着聖潔的生活。 **3 take holy orders** to become a priest 成為牧師

hom·age /ˈhɑmɪdʒ; ˈhɒmɪdʒ/ *n* [U] things said or done as signs of great respect 表示崇敬的話語或事情: *They paid homage to the king.* 他們向國王致敬。

*★★**home**¹ /hom; həʊm/ *n* **1** [C;U] place where you usually live especially with your family 家; 家庭: *"Where do you live?" "Well, Nigeria is my home, but I'm living in London just now."* "你住在哪裡?" "哦, 我家在尼日利亞, 但我眼下住在倫敦。" | *Buckingham Palace is the home of the Queen and her family.* 白金漢宮是女王及其家屬的住所。 | *He's not at home now; he should be back at seven.* 他現時不在家, 他應當在七點鐘回來。 **2** [sing] a place where a thing usually lives or comes from 棲息地; 產地: *India is the home of elephants and tigers.* 印度是大象和老虎的棲息地。 | *America is the home of baseball.* 美國是棒球的發源地。 **3** [C] a place for the care of a group of people or animals of the same type, who do not live with a family 收容所: *a children's home* 兒童之家 | *an old people's home* 老年人之家 | *Battersea Dog's Home* 貝特西狗之家 **4 be/feel at home** not to feel worried, especially about your skills or experience 不擔心〔尤指對於自己的技術或經驗〕: *He's completely at home working with children.* 他善於帶孩子。 **5 make yourself at home** a phrase used to invite someone to behave as they like in your home 請隨便些〔用於請某人不用拘謹〕

┌─────────────────────────────────┐
│ ■ USAGE 用法: **1** There is no **to** in │
│ these sentences ☆這些句子中沒有 **to**: │
│ *I'm coming* **home**. 我馬上回家。 **2** │
│ British people use **at home** in sen- │
│ tences like these ☆英國人在這些句子中 │
│ use **at home**: *Let's stay at home tonight.* │
│ 今晚我們就呆在家裡吧。 | *Is John* **at** │
│ **home**? 約翰在家嗎? Americans often │
│ miss out **at** ☆美國人常省略 **at**: *Let's* │
│ *stay* **home** *tonight*. 今晚我們就呆在家裡 │
│ 吧。 | *Is John* **home**? 約翰在家嗎? │
└─────────────────────────────────┘

*★★★**home**² *adv* **1** to or at your home 到家; 在家: *Is she home yet?* 她到家了

嗎? | *I must be getting home.* 我必須回家了。 | *We're home at last.* 我們終於到家了。 **2** to the right place 到達合適的位置: *He struck the nail home.* 他把釘子敲到頭。 **3 come home to someone** to be fully understood by someone 為某人所充分理解: *At last it's come home to me how much I owe to my parents.* 我終於明白了父母給與我的恩惠有多麼大。 [RELATED PHRASE 相關詞組 **bring something home to someone**]

home³ *v*

home in on sthg *phr v* [T] to aim or move exactly towards something 對準〔某物〕; 朝〔某物〕移動

home⁴ *adj* [only before a noun 只用於名詞前] **1** related to or being a home, place of origin, or base 家的; 原產地的; 基地的: *the home office of an international firm* 一家國際公司的本部 | *Birmingham is my home town.* 伯明翰是我的故鄉。 **2** not foreign 非外國的; 本國的: *the home country* 祖國 | *home affairs* 國內事務 **3** playing on your own sports field rather than that of an opponent 〔比賽〕在主場進行的: *We've watched all the home matches.* 我們看了所有的主場比賽。 | *the home team* 主隊

home-brew /ˌ·ˈ·/ *n* [U] beer made at home 家釀的啤酒

home·com·ing /ˈhom,kʌmɪŋ; ˈhəʊm,kʌmɪŋ/ *n* an arrival home, especially after a long absence 〔尤指長期離開以後的〕回家; 回國

home ec·o·nom·ics /ˌ· ··ˈ··/ *n* a school subject dealing with cooking and learning to manage a home 家政學

home help /ˌ·ˈ·/ *n BrE* a person who is sent in by the local council to help clean and cook for someone who is ill or very old 〔英式〕〔地方當局派到病人或老人家裡幫助做清潔工作及做飯的〕家庭幫工

home·land /ˈhom,lænd; ˈhəʊmlænd/ *n* the country where you were born 祖國; 家鄉

home·ly /ˈhomli; ˈhəʊmli/ *adj* **1** simple and ordinary 簡單的; 普通的: *a homely meal of bread and cheese* 有麵包和奶酪的家庭便餐 **2** *AmE* ordinary and not good-looking (used of a person) 〔美式〕平常的, 不漂亮的〔指人〕–**homeliness** *n* [U]

Home Of·fice /ˈ· ,··/ *n* [+ sing/pl verb] **the Home Office** the British government department which deals with keeping order inside the country and controlling who comes into it 〔英國的〕內政部: *The Home Office is considering your request.* 內政部正在考慮你的請求。 –compare 比較 FOREIGN OFFICE

home·less /ˈhomlɪs; ˈhəʊmləs/ *adj* **1** having nowhere to live 無家可歸的: *So now he's unemployed and homeless.* 所以現在他失業了, 無家可歸。 **2 the homeless** people who have nowhere to live 無家可歸者 –**homelessness** *n* [U]

home-made /ˌ·ˈ·◂/ *adj* made in someone's

home rather than in a factory or a shop 家裡做的; 自製的: *delicious home-made cakes* 自製的美味蛋糕

ho·me·op·athy /ˌhoʊmiˈɑpəθi; ˌhəʊmiˈɒpəθi/ *n* see 見 HOMOEOPATHY

home·sick /ˈhoʊmˌsɪk; ˈhəʊmˌsɪk/ *adj* sad because you are away from home 想家的; 思鄉的: *I was homesick for the old farm and for my friends.* 我非常想念那座舊農場，想念朋友們。| *He says he never feels homesick.* 他說他從不想家。 **–homesickness** *n* [U]

home·spun /ˈhoʊmˌspʌn; ˈhəʊmspʌn/ *adj* containing only a few simple ideas 僅僅包含幾個簡單觀點的; 樸素的: *a homespun philosophy* 樸素的哲學

home·stead /ˈhoʊmˌstɛd; ˈhəʊmsted/ *n* a farm with its buildings and land 〔包括建築物及土地的〕農莊

home truth /ˌ·ˈ·/ *n* something unpleasant but true about yourself which you learn from someone else 逆耳的忠言

home·ward /ˈhoʊmwəd; ˈhəʊmwəd/ *adj* [always before a noun 只能用於名詞前] going towards home 回家的: *the homeward journey* 回家的旅程 **–homewards** *adv* (also 又作 **homeward** *AmE* 〖美式〗): *hurrying homewards after work* 下班後匆匆回家

home·work /ˈhoʊmˌwɜrk; ˈhəʊmwɜːk/ *n* [U] **1** work which teachers give students to do at home 〔老師佈置的〕家庭作業: *We've got loads of homework tonight.* 今晚我們有許多家庭作業。 **2** preparation for a meeting or speech 〔為會議或演講所做的〕準備工作: *The politicians had obviously done their homework well and knew the problems.* 顯然，政客們做了充分的準備，他們知道問題所在。

hom·i·cid·al /ˌhɑməˈsaɪdl; ˌhɒmɪˈsaɪdl◂/ *adj* likely to murder someone 有殺人傾向的: *a homicidal maniac* 殺人狂

hom·i·cide /ˈhɑməˌsaɪd; ˈhɒmɪsaɪd/ *n fml or law* 〖正式或律〗 **1** [C;U] the crime of murder 殺人罪 **2** [C] a murderer 兇手; 殺人犯

hom·i·ly /ˈhɑmɪli; ˈhɒmɪli/ *n* homilies *fml* a long and dull talk giving advice on how to behave 〖正式〗(長篇)說教

hom·ing /ˈhoʊmɪŋ; ˈhəʊmɪŋ/ *adj* [only before a noun 只用於名詞前] **1** having the ability, which is found in certain birds and animals, to find the way home 〔某些鳥和動物〕有歸家能力的: *a homing pigeon* 能回家的鴿子 **2** able to guide itself to something it is aimed at (of a modern weapon of war) 自動導引的〔指現代武器〕

ho·moe·op·athy /ˌhoʊmiˈɑpəθi; ˌhəʊmiˈɒpəθi/ *n* (also 又作 **homeopathy**) [U] a way of treating a disease by giving small amounts of a drug which, in larger amounts, would produce an illness like the disease 順勢療法〔給與病人少量藥物，此藥物如果大量服用，將引起類似的疾病〕 **–homoeopath** /ˈhoʊmiəˌpæθ; ˈhəʊmiəpæθ/ *n* **–ho-**

moeopathic /ˌhoʊmiəˈpæθɪk; ˌhəʊmiəˈpæθɪk◂/ *adj*

ho·mo·ge·ne·ous /ˌhoʊməˈdʒiniəs; ˌhəʊməˈdʒiːniəs/ *adj* (also 又作 **ho·mog·enous**) formed of parts which are all the same 由類似成分組成的 **–homogeneity** /ˌhoʊmədʒəˈniəti; ˌhɒmədʒəˈniːɪti/ *n* [U]

ho·mo·ge·nized /həˈmɑdʒəˌnaɪzd; həˈmɒdʒənaɪzd/ *adj* (also 又作 **homogenised** *BrE* 〖英式〗) **homogenized milk** milk without any cream on top because the fat is broken up and mixed with the milk 均質牛奶

ho·mo·sex·u·al /ˌhoʊməˈsɛkʃʊəl; ˌhəʊməˈsekʃʊəl/ *n* someone who is sexually attracted to members of the same sex 同性戀者 **–homosexual** *adj*: *a homosexual relationship* 同性戀關係 **–compare** 比較 BISEXUAL, HETEROSEXUAL, LESBIAN

hone /hoʊn; həʊn/ *v* **honed, honing** [T] *fml* to sharpen a tool 〖正式〗把〔工具〕磨利

***hon·est** /ˈɑnɪst; ˈɒnɪst/ *adj* **1** open and direct 坦誠的; 直率的: *To be quite honest with you, I don't think you'll pass.* 坦率地說，我認為你會不及格。 **2** not likely to lie, steal, or cheat 誠實的; 老實的: *An honest employee is a rare thing.* 誠實的雇員實在難求。 **3** truthful and sincere 真心的; 誠懇的: *an honest face* 誠懇的面孔 | *an honest opinion* 真誠的觀點 **–opposite** 反義 **dishonest**

hon·est·ly /ˈɑnɪstli; ˈɒnɪstli/ *adv* **1** without lying, stealing, or cheating 誠實地; 老實地: *And if I can't get the money honestly, I'll have to think of something else.* 如果我不能用誠實的方式弄到那筆錢的話，我將不得不想想別的辦法。 **2** speaking truthfully 老實說: *I honestly don't mind working late tonight.* 坦白說，我並不在意今晚工作到很晚。 **3 Honestly!** a word used to express annoyance 真是! 〔用於表示惱怒〕: *Honestly! What a stupid thing to do!* 真是的! 做這種事該有多蠢啊!

hon·es·ty /ˈɑnɪsti; ˈɒnɪsti/ *n* [U] **1** the quality of being honest 誠實; 誠懇; 坦率: *We've never doubted your honesty.* 我們從未懷疑過你的誠實。 **2 in all honesty** being open and truthful 坦率地, 坦白地: *In all honesty, the chances of getting the money back are slim.* 說實話，討回那筆錢的希望很渺茫。

hon·ey /ˈhʌni; ˈhʌni/ *n* **1** [U] the sweet sticky golden-brown substance produced by bees, which can be eaten on bread 蜂蜜 **2** [C] *AmE* a word used when speaking to someone you love 〖美式〗親愛的〔對所愛的人的稱呼〕: *Hurry up, honey, we're going to be late.* 快一點，親愛的，我們要遲到了。

hon·ey·comb /ˈhʌniˌkoʊm; ˈhʌnikəʊm/ *n* a wax container made by bees and consisting of six-sided cells in which honey is stored 蜂房; 蜂巢

hon·ey·moon /ˈhʌniˌmun; ˈhʌnimuːn/ *n* **1** the holiday taken by a man and woman who have just got married 蜜月: *Where are they going for their honeymoon?* 他們準備去

哪裡度蜜月? **2** a short period at the beginning of a new job or government when everyone is happy with the people concerned〔新工作剛開始或新政府剛上台時人際關係〕短暫的和諧時期: *The honeymoon's over for the new President.* 新總統上台後的"蜜月時期"已結束. –**honeymoon** *v* [I]

hon·ey·suck·le /ˈhʌnɪˌsʌkl̩; ˈhʌnɪˌsʌkəl/ *n* [C;U] a climbing plant with sweet-smelling flowers 忍冬〔一種攀緣植物, 其開出的花氣味芳香〕

honk /hɔŋk; hɒŋk/ *v* [I;T] to make the sound like a GOOSE or a car horn 發出鵝叫聲; 發出汽車喇叭聲: *As she drove past, she honked the horn.* 她開車經過時, 按了按喇叭. –**honk** *n*

hon·or·ar·y /ˈɑnəˌrɛrɪ; ˈɒnərərɪ/ *adj* **1** given as an honour without the usual work necessary 榮譽的: *an honorary degree* 榮譽學位 | *an honorary title* 榮譽稱號 **2** without payment 無報酬的; 名譽的: *the honorary chairman* 名譽主席 | *the honorary treasurer* 義務財務主管

*****hon·our**[1] *v* /ˈɑnə; ˈɒnər/ *n* (**honor** *AmE*〔美式〕) **1** [U] great respect and admiration 榮譽; 尊敬; 敬重: *They fought for the honour of their country.* 他們為國家的榮譽而戰. | *We award you this trophy as a mark of honour.* 作為表彰, 我們將這獎品發給你. **2** [sing] something that brings great respect and pride 引起人們尊敬的事物; 令人引以為豪的事物: *It is a great honour to have the Duke here today.* 今天公爵能夠光臨此地令大家倍感榮幸. | *She's an honour to the profession.* 她是這個行業的驕傲. | *Will you do me the honour of accepting my invitation?* 你能賞光接受我的邀請嗎? **3** [U] high principles and standards of behaviour 名譽; 信譽: *a man of honour* 有信譽的人 | *It's a matter of honour.* 這是件關係到名譽的事情. **4** in honour of someone, in someone's honour to show respect for someone 為表示對某人的敬意: *A rose bush was planted in honour of the Queen Mother's birthday.* 為慶祝皇太后的生日, 人們種了一株玫瑰. **5** Honour a respectful title for a judge 閣下; 大人〔對法官的尊稱〕: *Good morning, your Honour.* 您早, 法官大人. | *His Honour Judge Thompson* 湯普遜法官大人

honour[2] *v* (**honor** *AmE*〔美式〕) [T] **1** to show respect to someone or to praise them publicly 向〔某人〕致敬; 表揚: *Today the Queen is honouring us with her presence.* 今日女王駕臨, 我們不勝榮幸. | *The villagers came to honour their chief.* 村民前來對他們的首領表示敬意. **2** to keep an agreement 承兌: *The bank has refused to honour his cheque.* 銀行拒絕兌現他的支票. | *You must honour your commitments to the firm.* 你必須兌現對公司所做的承諾.

hon·our·a·ble /ˈɑnərəbl̩; ˈɒnərəbəl/ *adj* (**honorable** *AmE*〔美式〕) **1** showing or deserving respect and admiration 光榮的; 值得尊敬的: *an honourable settlement to the strike* 罷工問題的體面解決 **2** showing high principles 高尚的; 正直的: *The honourable thing to do would be to marry her.* 應該做的光明正大的事情便是同她結婚. **3** [only before a noun 只用於名詞前] a title given to the children of certain British noblemen, and various official people, including Members of Parliament 尊敬的〔對某些英國貴族子弟及官員包括國會議員的稱號〕: *Will the Honourable member please answer the question?* 請尊敬的議員先生回答該問題。| *the Honourable Miss Fortescue* 尊敬的福特斯丘小姐 –**honourably** *adv*

hon·ours /ˈɑnəz; ˈɒnəz/ *n* (**honors** *AmE*〔美式〕) [pl] **1** (also 又作 **Hons**) a university UNDERGRADUATE degree of a higher standard than an Ordinary degree〔大學的〕榮譽學位: *James Brown BA (Hons)* 文學學士詹姆斯·布朗(優等) | *a first class honours degree in History* 歷史學一等榮譽學位 **2** do the honours *infml* to act as the host or hostess by offering drinks or food〔非正式〕盡主人之誼〔提供飲料及食物〕

hood /hud; hud/ *n* **1** part of a coat which can be pulled up to cover your head in bad weather〔外衣上的〕兜帽, 風帽 **2** a movable cover over a car or PRAM〔汽車或嬰兒車的〕折疊式車篷 **3** *AmE* the BONNET covering the engine of a car〔美式〕汽車引擎罩

hood·ed /ˈhudɪd; ˈhudʒd/ *adj* **1** (of a garment) with a hood 有兜帽的: *a hooded raincoat* 有兜帽的雨衣 **2** half closed (used of eyelids) 半閉的〔指眼皮〕

hood·wink /ˈhudˌwɪŋk; ˈhudˌwɪŋk/ *v* [T] to trick or deceive someone 欺騙〔某人〕

hoof /huf; huːf/ *n* **hoofs** or **hooves** /huvz; huːvz/ the hard foot of certain animals like the horse〔馬、牛等動物的〕蹄

hook[1] /huk; huk/ *n* **1** a curved piece of metal, plastic, or wood for hanging things on 掛鉤; 吊鉤: *She hung up her coat on the hook behind the door.* 她把外衣掛在門背後的掛鉤上. | *curtain hooks* 窗簾鉤 **2** a curved piece of metal 鉤子; 鉤: *a fish hook* 魚鉤 | *a crochet hook* 鉤針 | *a picture hook* 掛畫鉤 **3** hook and eye a small metal hook and bar used for fastening clothes〔衣服上的〕扣和環 **4** a hit given in BOXING with the elbow bent〔拳擊中的〕鉤拳 **5** get off the hook to get out of a difficult situation 擺脫困境 **6** off the hook having the telephone receiver lifted off so that the telephone will not ring〔電話聽筒〕未掛上

hook[2] *v* [T] **1** to catch or fasten something with a hook (用鉤)鉤住〔某物〕: *Those two bits hook together.* 那兩塊東西鉤在一起。| *We've hooked a fish!* 我們釣到一條魚! **2** to place something in a position like a hook 把〔某物〕置於鉤狀: *He hooked his leg over the arm of the chair.* 他把一條腿蹺在椅背上. |

Hook the rope over that nail. 把繩子掛在那個釘子上。**3** to hit a ball in GOLF or cricket so that it does not go in a straight line〔高爾夫球或板球〕打鈎球; 打曲線球: *Oh no! I've hooked it!* 哦不! 我的球打偏啦!

hook sthg ↔ **up** [T] *infml* to connect something 《非正式》聯接〔某物〕: *Can you hook up this computer to the mainframe?* 你能把這台電腦接到主機上去嗎?

hooked /hʊkt; hʊkt/ *adj* **1** shaped like a hook 鈎狀的: *a hooked nose* 鷹鈎鼻 **2** [never before a noun 不能用於名詞前] *infml* dependent on drugs 《非正式》吸毒成癮的: *She's hooked on crack.* 她有吸可卡因的毒癮。**3** having a great liking for 非常喜歡的; 着迷的: *I'm absolutely hooked on that new television soap opera.* 我對那部新的電視肥皂劇十分着迷。| *She's really hooked on him.* 她真的很迷戀他。

hoo·li·gan /ˈhuːlɪgən; ˈhuːlɪˌgən/ *n* a noisy, violent, young person who causes trouble by fighting and breaking things 流氓; 不良分子 **–hooliganism** *n* [U]

hoop /huːp; huːp/ *n* a circular band of wood or metal round a barrel or used as a child's toy〔桶的〕箍;〔作為玩具的〕環 **–hooped** *adj*

hoo·ray /huːˈreɪ; huˈreɪ/ *interj* a shout of joy or approval 好哇! 萬歲!〔表示高興或贊成〕: *Hooray! We've won!* 好哇! 我們贏啦!

hoot¹ /huːt; huːt/ *v* **1** [I;T] to make a loud noise 發出很大的響聲: *I hooted my horn at the children playing in the road.* 我對着在路上玩耍的孩童大聲按汽車喇叭。| *Did you hear the owl hooting last night?* 你昨夜聽到貓頭鷹叫嗎? **2** [I] to laugh loudly, often unkindly 大聲地笑〔通常是不友好地〕: *The children hooted with delight.* 孩子們快活地哈哈大笑。

hoot² *n* **1** the sound made by an OWL or by a car or ship's horn 貓頭鷹的叫聲; 汽車的喇叭聲; 輪船的汽笛聲 **2** a shout of laughter, often unkind 大笑〔通常是不友好的〕: *His speech was greeted with hoots of laughter.* 他講話時大家發出陣陣的哄笑。**3** *infml* something very amusing 《非正式》非常好笑的事: *That play was a real hoot!* 那齣戲實在是滑稽! **4** I don't give two hoots, I don't care a hoot *infml* I don't care at all 《非正式》我根本不在乎: *He doesn't care two hoots whether he passes his examination or not.* 他根本不在乎自己考試是否及格。

hoot·er /ˈhuːtə; ˈhuːtər/ *n* **1** a car horn 汽車喇叭 **2** a whistle which signals the beginning or end of work〔鳴響上下班信號的〕汽笛 **3** *slang* a nose 《俚》鼻子

hoo·ver /ˈhuːvə; ˈhuːvər/ *n tdmk* (also 又作 **Hoover**) a machine you use to clean a carpet《商標》吸塵器 **–hoover** *v* [I;T]: *Jim hoovered the flat before the guests arrived.* 客人來之前, 吉姆用吸塵器打掃了一下公寓。

hooves /huːvz; huːvz/ the plural of HOOF ☆ HOOF 的複數形式

hop¹ /hɒp; hɒp/ *v* **-pp-** **1** [I] (of people) to jump on one leg〔人〕單腳跳 –see picture on page 992 見本彩圖 **2** [I] (of small creatures) to jump with the legs together〔小動物〕跳躍: *The bird hopped onto my finger.* 小鳥跳到我的手指上。**3** [I +adv/prep] *infml* to get quickly onto, into, or out of something 《非正式》迅疾跳上〔跳進、跳出〕: *She hopped on her bicycle and rushed off.* 她跳上自行車, 飛快地騎走了。| *Hop in and I'll give you a lift to the station.* 快上車, 我送你去車站。**4** Hop it! *infml* Go away!《非正式》滾開! **5** hopping mad very angry 非常生氣; 狂怒

hop² *n* **1** a small jump 跳躍 **2** *infml* a short aircraft flight 《非正式》短程飛行: *We'll do the final hop from Cairo to Luxor the following day.* 最後, 我們將於第二天由開羅飛至盧克索。**3** on the hop *infml* unprepared or very busy 《非正式》未經準備的; 非常忙碌: *Their sudden arrival caught me on the hop.* 他們突然到來令我措手不及。**4** a tall climbing plant with flowers 忽布, 啤酒花 **5** hops the dried seed-cases of a plant, used for giving taste to beer 啤酒花種皮〔用以使啤酒具有苦味〕

★ **hope¹** /həʊp; həʊp/ *v* **hoped, hoping 1** [I; +(that)] to want something to happen and have some confidence that it probably will happen 希望; 期望: *I hope he comes tomorrow.* 我希望他明天來。| *She hopes to go to college next year.* 她盼望明年上大學。| *We're hoping for a big order from the Middle East.* 我們正希望能從中東獲得一份大的訂單。| *"Is she coming?" "I hope so."* "她會來嗎?" "希望如此。" | *I hope not.* 我不希望這樣。

□ USEFUL PATTERNS 有用句型
to hope that...; to hope to do something; to hope for something

2 hope for the best to hope that everything will work out satisfactorily 希望一切都能如願

■ USAGE 用法: Hope and wish can both be used to give people good wishes for the future. I hope (that) is commonly used in this way ☆ hope 和 wish 都可用來對別人表示良好的祝願。I hope (that) 通常用法如下: *I hope that you have a good journey.* 我希望你旅途順利。| *I hope you get better soon.* 我希望你的病情能很快好轉。| *I hope your exam goes well.* 我希望你考試一帆風順。I wish you + noun is a much more formal expression ☆ I wish you + noun 是一個正式得多的表達法: *May I wish you a pleasant journey, Sir?* 先生, 請允許我祝願您旅途順利。| *We*

wish you *a speedy recovery.* 我們希望您能早日康復。

hope² *n* **1** [C;U] the expectation of something happening as you want it to 希望; 期望: *Hopes* **of** *reaching a peace settlement are now fading.* 達成和平協議的希望愈來愈小。| *Don't give up hope. He may still come.* 不要放棄希望。他可能還會來。| *I have high hopes of passing the exam.* 我考試及格的希望很大。| *The doctors don't hold out much hope for her.* 醫生們對她不抱太大的希望。**2** [C] someone or something that could bring success 可能會帶來成功的人或物: *Please help me — you're my last hope.* 請幫我一把——你是我最後的希望。| *The only hope we have of a settlement is for both sides to compromise.* 我們對於解決爭端所抱的唯一希望便是雙方都能讓步。

hope·ful /'hopfəl; 'həʊpfəl/ *adj* **1** feeling quite confident 抱有信心的: *I'm hopeful that he'll arrive early.* 我相信他會早到。**2** giving reason to think success is possible 有成功希望的: *hopeful signs of economic recovery* 經濟有望復甦的跡象 –**hopefulness** *n* [U]

hope·ful·ly /'hopfəlɪ; 'həʊpfəlɪ/ *adv* **1** in a hopeful way 有希望地 **2** if everything goes well 如果一切順利: *Hopefully we'll be there by dinnertime.* 如果一切順利，我們能在晚餐時到達那裡。

■ USAGE 用法: This second meaning of **hopefully** is now very common, especially in speech, but some people still consider that it is incorrect. ☆ **hopefully** 的第二種用法現在非常普遍，尤其是在口語中，但有些人仍認為這種用法不正確。

hope·less /'hoplɪs; 'həʊpləs/ *adj* **1** having or giving no signs of hope 沒有希望的: *tears of hopeless despair* 絕望的眼淚 | *a hopeless situation* 陷於絕望的境況 **2** *infml* very bad or unskilled 〖非正式〗非常糟糕的; 無技能的: *I'm hopeless at maths.* 我在數學上是沒指望了。–**hopelessly** *adv* –**hopelessness** *n* [U]

hop·scotch /'hɒpskɒtʃ; 'hɒpskɒtʃ/ *n* [U] a children's game in which a stone is thrown onto numbered squares and each child hops (HOP) from one to another 跳房子〔一種兒童遊戲〕

horde /hord; hɔːd/ *n* a large crowd of people 一大羣(人): *There were hordes of tourists at the castle.* 城堡那裡有大羣大羣的遊客。

ho·ri·zon /hə'raɪzn; hə'raɪzən/ *n* **1 the horizon** the line in the distance where the sky seems to meet the earth or sea 地平線 **2 horizons** [pl] the limit of your ideas, knowledge, or experience 〔思想, 知識或經驗的〕界限, 範圍; 眼界

hor·i·zon·tal /,hɒrə'zɒntl; ,hɒrɪ'zɒntl◂/ *adj* in a flat position, along or parallel to the ground 水平的: *Stand the table on its legs, so that the top is horizontal.* 把桌子放好, 讓桌面保持水平。–compare 比較 VERTICAL – **horizontally** *adv*

hor·mone /'hɔrmon; 'hɔːməʊn/ *n* a substance produced by your body and passed into your blood to encourage growth 荷爾蒙〔體內產生的並進入血液刺激身體發育的物質〕, 激素

horn /hɔrn; hɔːn/ *n* **1** [C] a hard pointed growth on the heads of some cattle, sheep, and wild animals 〔牛、羊和野獸等頭上的〕角 **2** [U] the substance that horns are made of 角質: *The knife has a horn handle.* 這把刀有個角質的柄。**3** [C] something which gives a short loud sound as a warning 喇叭: *a car horn* 汽車喇叭 | *He sounded his horn as he approached the bend in the road.* 他開近轉彎處時按響了喇叭。**4** [C] a musical instrument consisting of a long metal tube, usually bent several times and played by blowing 〔樂器〕號(角): *the French horn* 法國號 | *a hunting horn* 獵號

hor·net /'hɔrnɪt; 'hɔːnɪt/ *n* a large insect which can sting, related to the WASP 大黃蜂

horn·pipe /'hɔrnpaɪp; 'hɔːnpaɪp/ *n* a dance performed by sailors, or the music for a hornpipe 〔水手跳的〕角笛舞; 角笛舞曲

horn·y /'hɔrnɪ; 'hɔːnɪ/ *adj* **hornier, horniest** hard and rough 堅硬而粗糙的: *The old gardener had horny hands.* 老園丁有雙粗糙的手。

hor·o·scope /'hɔrəˌskop; 'hɒrəskəʊp/ *n* a statement about someone's character, life, and future, based on the positions of the stars or planets (PLANET) at the time of their birth 占星術算命〔即根據人們出生的時間及出生時星座的位置而對其性格, 生活和未來所做的預言〕

hor·ren·dous /hɒ'rɛndəs; hɒ'rendəs/ *adj* extremely unpleasant 極其討厭的: *What horrendous weather!* 多可惡的天氣呵! –**horrendously** *adv*

hor·ri·ble /'hɒrəbl; 'hɒrɪbəl/ *adj* **1** causing shock and dislike 可怕的; 令人厭惡的: *a horrible accident* 可怕的事故 **2** *infml* very unpleasant 〖非正式〗很討厭的: *What a horrible dress!* 多討厭的衣服呵! | *I have a horrible feeling we're going to miss the train.* 我有種不妙的感覺, 我們會趕不上火車。–**horribly** *adv*

hor·rid /'hɒrɪd; 'hɒrɪd/ *adj* very unpleasant or unkind 很討厭的; 很不友善的: *Don't be so horrid to your little sister.* 不要對你的小妹妹這麼兇。–**horridly** *adv*

hor·rif·ic /hɒ'rɪfɪk; hɒ'rɪfɪk/ *adj* very shocking and unpleasant 很可怕的; 很討厭的: *The film showed the most horrific murder scenes.* 這部電影有極其恐怖的兇殺場面。–**horrif-**

ically /-klɪ; -kli/ *adv*

hor·ri·fy /ˈhɔrəˌfaɪ; ˈhɒrɨˌfaɪ/ *v* **horrified, horrifying** [T] to shock someone greatly 使〔某人〕感到恐怖; 使〔某人〕感到震驚: *I was horrified by the news of her murder.* 我對她被人殺害的消息感到震驚. | *a horrifying story* 恐怖故事 –**horrifyingly** *adv*

*hor·ror /ˈhɔrɚ; ˈhɒrə[r]/ *n* **1** [U] a feeling of great shock, anxiety, and fear 驚恐; 恐懼; 恐怖: *Seeing the children playing on the cliff filled me with horror.* 看見孩子們在懸崖上玩耍, 我害怕極了. | *I watched in horror as the cars crashed into each other.* 我看見汽車相撞, 驚恐萬狀. **2 the horror of, the horrors of** the unpleasantness of something that is shocking and frightening 驚恐; 恐怖: *the horrors of war* 戰爭的恐怖 | *The full horror of the accident only hit me later.* 我後來才感覺到了那起事故的可怕. **3 have a horror of** to hate something and be afraid of it 憎恨; 害怕: *I have a horror of snakes.* 我怕蛇. **4** [C] *infml* an unpleasant child 〔非正式〕令人討厭的小孩: *The little horror never stops playing tricks on his parents.* 那個小淘氣不斷地捉弄他的父母.

horror film /ˈ·· ·/ *n* a film in which strange and frightening things happen 恐怖影片

hors d'oeu·vre /ɔrˈdœvrə; ˌɔː ˈdɜːv/ *n* **hors d'oeuvres** small amounts of cold meat and vegetables served at the beginning of a meal 〔餐前的〕冷盆, 小吃

★★horse /hɔrs; hɔːs/ *n* **1** a large four-legged animal which people ride on and use for pulling heavy things 馬 –see 見 TRANSPORT (USAGE 用法) **2** an exercise apparatus for jumping over 跳馬; 鞍馬 **3 straight from the horse's mouth** *infml* told to you directly from the person concerned 〔非正式〕從當事人那裡直接獲悉: *"Who told you she was leaving?" "I heard it straight from the horse's mouth."* "誰告訴你她要走了?" "她自己直接告訴我的."

horse·back /ˈhɔrsˌbæk; ˈhɔːsbæk/ *n* **on horseback** riding on a horse 騎在馬上

horse·box /ˈhɔrsˌbɑks; ˈhɔːsbɒks/ *n* a large enclosed container pulled by another vehicle and used for carrying horses 運馬棚車

horse chest·nut /ˌ· ˈ···/ *n* **1** a large tree with white or pink flowers 七葉樹 **2** a shiny brown nut from this tree 七葉樹的堅果

horse·play /ˈhɔrsˌple; ˈhɔːspleɪ/ *n* [U] rough noisy behaviour by young people for fun 〔年輕人的〕喧鬧; 胡鬧

horse·pow·er /ˈhɔrsˌpaʊɚ; ˈhɔːsˌpaʊə[r]/ *n* [U] (also 又作 **HP**) a measure of the power of an engine 馬力〔引擎的功率單位〕

horse·rac·ing /ˈhɔrsˌresɪŋ; ˈhɔːsˌreɪsɪŋ/ *n* [U] the sport of racing horses 賽馬 –see picture on page 957 見 957 頁彩圖

horse·rad·ish /ˈhɔrsˌrædɪʃ; ˈhɔːsˌrædɪʃ/ *n* a plant whose root is used to make a strong-tasting SAUCE usually eaten with meat 辣

根〔其根可製成醬汁與肉類一起食用〕

horse·shoe /ˈhɔrsˌʃu; ˈhɔːs-ʃuː/ *n* **1** a curved piece of iron nailed to the bottom of a horse's foot 馬蹄鐵; 馬掌 **2** something with this shape, often believed to bring good luck 馬蹄形物〔常被認為會帶來好運〕

hors·y /ˈhɔrsi; ˈhɔːsi/ *adj* (also 又作 **horsey**) **1** very interested in horses and riding 喜歡馬[騎馬]的 **2** looking like a horse 似馬的 – **horsiness** *n* [U]

hor·ti·cul·ture /ˈhɔrtɪˌkʌltʃɚ; ˈhɔːtɨˌkʌltʃə[r]/ *n* [U] the practice of growing fruit, flowers, and vegetables 園藝 –**horticultural** /ˌhɔrtɪˈkʌltʃərəl; ˌhɔːtɨˈkʌltʃərəl◂/ *adj* –**horticulturalist** *n*

hose[1] /hoz; həʊz/ *n* **1** [C;U] (also 又作 **hosepipe**) a piece of rubber or plastic tube used to direct water onto fires, a garden, or a car 橡皮軟管; 塑料軟管〔用於滅火, 澆灌或洗車〕–see picture on page 958 見 958 頁彩圖 **2** *old fash* TIGHTS, STOCKINGS, or socks 〔老式〕連褲襪; 長統襪; 短統襪

hose[2] *v* **hosed, hosing** [T] (also 又作 **hose** sthg ↔ **down**) to water or wash something using a hose 用軟管澆洗〔某物〕: *I'll just hose the car down.* 我馬上去用軟管沖洗汽車. | *We'll have to hose the garden soon.* 我們必須快些給花園澆水.

ho·sie·ry /ˈhoʒəri; ˈhəʊʒəri/ *n* [U] *fml* the word used in a shop for socks, STOCKINGS, and TIGHTS 〔正式〕襪類; 內衣類

hos·pice /ˈhɑspɪs; ˈhɒspɨs/ *n* a hospital where people who are dying of incurable illnesses are cared for 〔晚期病人的〕安養院

hos·pi·ta·ble /ˈhɑspɪtəbḷ; ˈhɒspɪtəbəl/ *adj* being welcoming to guests or visitors, asking them into your home and feeding them 殷勤待客的; 好客的 –opposite 反義 **inhospitable** –**hospitably** *adv*

hos·pi·tal /ˈhɑspɪtḷ; ˈhɒspɪtḷ/ *n* [C;U] a place where people who are hurt or ill have medical treatment 醫院: *Did you know that Jane's in hospital?* 簡住院了, 你知道嗎?

hos·pi·tal·i·ty /ˌhɑspɪˈtæləti; ˌhɒspɨˈtælɨti/ *n* [U] **1** welcoming behaviour towards guests 殷勤; 好客 **2** food and a place to sleep given to guests 供給客人的食宿

hos·pi·tal·ize /ˈhɑspɪtḷˌaɪz; ˈhɒspɪtl-aɪz/ *v* (also 又作 **hospitalise** *BrE* 〔英式〕) **hospitalized, hospitalizing** [T] to send someone into hospital 送〔某人〕住院: *He broke a leg and was hospitalized for a month.* 他的一條腿斷了, 住院一個月. –**hospitalization** /ˌhɑspɪtḷɪˈzeʃən; ˌhɒspɪtəl-aɪˈzeɪʃən/ *n* [U]

*host[1] /host; həʊst/ *n* **1** someone who invites guests 〔款待客人的〕主人: *We thanked our host and left the party.* 宴會上我們謝過主人之後告退了. **2** a country or organization which provides the space and equipment for a special event 東道國; 主辦機構: *the host nation for the next Olympics* 下屆奧運

會的東道國 **3** [+sing/pl verb] a large number 大量: *A whole host* **of** *difficulties have arisen.* 出現了一大堆難題。 **4** someone who introduces other performers, such as those on a TV show〔電視等的〕節目主持人

host² *v* [T] to act as a host for a special event 主持, 主辦〔某特別活動〕: *Which country is hosting the next Commonwealth Games?* 下一屆的英聯邦運動會由哪國主辦?

hos·tage /ˈhɒstɪdʒ; ˈhɒstɪdʒ/ *n* **1** someone kept as a prisoner by a group of people who threaten to hurt them if certain things are not done 人質: *He has been held hostage now for three years.* 他被扣作人質已有三年。 **2 take/hold someone hostage** to keep someone as a hostage 把某人扣作人質: *Three children have been taken hostage.* 三個孩子被扣作人質。

hos·tel /ˈhɒstl; ˈhɒstl/ *n* a building in which students, or young people working or travelling away from home, can eat and sleep cheaply 〔為學生或年輕人提供廉價食宿的〕旅舍, 招待所: *a youth hostel* 青年招待所

hos·tel·ry /ˈhɒstlrɪ; ˈhɒstəlri/ *n old fash* a place where alcoholic drinks may be bought and drunk《老式》酒店

host·ess /ˈhɒstɪs; ˈhəʊstɪs/ *n* **1** a woman who invites guests〔款待客人的〕女主人 **2** (also 又作 **airhostess**) a woman who looks after the passengers on an aeroplane 空中小姐 **3** a woman who is paid by a man to be his companion for the evening 陪酒女郎; 舞女

hos·tile /ˈhɒstl; ˈhɒstaɪl/ *adj* **1** unfriendly 不友善的: *The Prime Minister was greeted by a hostile crowd.* 首相遇到了一幕反對他的人。 **2** belonging to an enemy 敵方的: *hostile territory* 敵方領土

hos·til·i·ties /hɒsˈtɪlətɪz; hɒˈstɪlɪˌtiz/ *n* [pl] *fml* war-like fighting《正式》戰鬥: *Hostilities have broken out between the two countries.* 兩國間爆發了戰鬥。

hos·til·i·ty /hɒsˈtɪlətɪ; hɒˈstɪlɪti/ *n* [U] strong dislike or disapproval 反對; 敵意

hot¹ /hɒt; hɒt/ *adj* **hotter, hottest 1** having a high temperature 熱的; 燙的: *It's very hot in here — can I open a window?* 這裡很熱 — 我能開窗嗎? | *The water isn't hot yet.* 水還沒熱。 | *Bake the pie in a hot oven for half an hour.* 把餡放在熱烤爐裡烤半個小時。 | *If you're hot, take your pullover off.* 如果你覺得熱, 就把毛衣脫掉。 **2** causing a burning taste in the mouth 辣的: *a hot curry* 辛辣的咖喱 **3** very excitable or exciting 易激動的; 令人激動的: *a hot temper* 火爆脾氣 | *The battle for the presidency is likely to grow hotter in the next few weeks.* 對於總統寶座的爭奪在接下去的幾週內可能會更加激烈。 **4** very recent and interesting (used of news) 最新的; 有趣的〔指新聞〕 **5 hot air** meaningless talk or ideas 空話; 空想 **6 hot and bothered** so worried about something that

you do not think clearly 慌亂的; 心急火燎的 **7 hot on someone's trail/track** chasing and ready to catch someone 追捕某人 **8 hot on something** skilled in and knowledgeable about something 擅長於某些事物: *I'm not very hot on mental arithmetic.* 我不擅長心算。 **9 hot on the heels of** following or happening just after someone or something 緊跟着〔某人〕,〔某事物〕接踵而來 **10 hot under the collar** angry or excited and ready to argue 憤怒的; 激動的; 準備爭辯的

★**hot²** *v* **-tt-**

hot up *phr v* [I] *infml* to become more exciting or active《非正式》變得更為激動〔活躍〕: *The election campaign is hotting up.* 競選活動日漸升溫。

hot·bed /ˈhɒtbed; ˈhɒtbed/ *n* a place where a lot of something undesirable develops 〔壞事物滋長的〕溫牀: *The city is a hotbed* **of** *crime.* 這個城市是犯罪的溫牀。

hot-blood·ed /ˌ·ˈ···◂/ *adj* showing strong feelings of anger or love 怒火中燒的; 熱烈的

hotch·potch /ˈhɒtʃpɒtʃ; ˈhɒtʃpɒtʃ/ *n* (also 又作 **hodgepodge** *AmE*《美式》) [sing] a number of things mixed up without any sensible order or arrangement 混雜物; 大雜燴

hot dog /ˌ·ˈ·/ *n* a special sort of long red SAUSAGE in a bread ROLL 熱狗〔夾香腸的麵包〕

★**ho·tel** /hoˈtel; həʊˈtel/ *n* a building where people can stay by paying for their rooms and meals 旅館; 旅社

ho·tel·i·er /ˌhoˈtelɪr; həʊˈteliər/ *n* a person who owns or manages a hotel 旅館老闆〔經理〕

hot·foot¹ /ˈhɒtfʊt; ˈhɒtfʊt/ *adv* moving quickly and eagerly 火速地; 急匆匆地

hotfoot² *v* *hotfoot* it *infml* to move fast《非正式》急行: *We hotfooted it down the street.* 我們順着大街快步走。

hot·head /ˈhɒthed; ˈhɒthed/ *n* someone who does things too quickly, without thinking 魯莽而衝動的人; 急性子 **–hotheaded** /ˈhɒtˈhedɪd◂/ *adj*

hot·house /ˈhɒthaʊs; ˈhɒthaʊs/ *n* a warm glass building where flowers and delicate plants can grow 溫室; 暖房

hot·line /ˈhɒtlaɪn; ˈhɒtlaɪn/ *n* a direct telephone line between heads of government 熱線〔政府首腦之間的直線電話〕

hot·ly /ˈhɒtlɪ; ˈhɒtli/ *adv* **1** in anger and with force 憤怒地; 有力地: *The rumour was hotly denied.* 這一流言被斷然否定。 **2** closely and eagerly 密切地; 熱切地: *He was hotly pursued by his dog.* 他的狗對他緊追不捨。

hot·plate /ˈhɒtpleɪt; ˈhɒtpleɪt/ *n* a flat metal surface, usually on an electric cooker, which is used to heat food in pans or keep food warm〔電爐竈上的〕加熱板

hot-water bot·tle /ˌ·ˈ·· ˌ··/ *n* a rubber container which is filled with hot water and is placed inside a bed to warm it〔放上取暖用的〕熱水袋

hound¹ /haʊnd; haʊnd/ *n* a dog used for hunting or racing 獵狗

hound² *v* [T] to follow someone continually usually trying to get them to do or say something 不斷地追逐〔以使某人說出某事或做某事〕: *I'm fed up being hounded by the press.* 對於記者的糾纏，我煩透了。

★★hour /aʊr; aʊəʳ/ *n* **1** a period of 60 minutes 小時: *There are 24 hours in a day.* 一天有二十四個小時。| *It takes five hours to get to Glasgow by train.* 坐火車去格拉斯哥要花五個小時。| *a two-hour journey* 兩小時的行程 **2** a time when a new hour starts 鐘點；點鐘: *The clock struck the hour.* 鐘在正點報時。| *The attack began at 1600 hours.* 進攻是在十六點準時開始的。**3** (also 又作 **hours**) a period of time set aside for a particular purpose or activity〔用於某一目的或活動的〕一段時間: *I'll meet you in my lunch hour.* 我在午飯時與你見面。| *During office hours I can be contacted at this number.* 辦公時間，你可用這個號碼打電話找我。| *the hospital's visiting hours* 醫院的探望時間 **4** a particular time of day or night 某一時刻: *The trains don't run at this hour of the night.* 深夜這個時候火車不開。| *She arrived at the appointed hour.* 她在約定的時間抵達。**5** an important moment or period 重要時刻〔時期〕: *He supported me in my hour of need.* 在我需要的時候，他給了我支持。| *It was our country's finest hour.* 這是我們國家最輝煌的時期。**6 after hours** after work has normally finished 下班之後 **7 for hours** for a long time 很長時間: *I've been waiting here for hours.* 我已等了很久了。**8 in an hour** after one hour has passed 一小時後: *I'll be back in an hour.* 我一小時後回來。**9 on the hour** at one o'clock, two o'clock, etc. 在每小時的正點: *The trains leave on the hour and twenty five minutes past the hour.* 火車每小時正點及每小時過二十五分開出一列。**10 at all hours** at any time during the whole day or night 在任何時候 **11 keep late/regular hours** to go to bed late or at regular hours 晚睡晚起〔定時作息〕 **12 out of hours** before or after the usual times of work 工作時間以外 **13 by the hour** for each hour that passes 按小時: *We're paid by the hour.* 我們的報酬按小時計算。

hour hand /'· ·/ *n* the small pointer on a clock which shows the time in hours 時針

hour·ly /'aʊrli; 'aʊəli/ *adj, adv* **1** every hour or once an hour 每一小時(的)；每小時一次的〔地〕: *Take one tablet hourly.* 這藥一小時吃一片。| *There's an hourly train to Oxford.* 每小時有一班火車去牛津。**2** at any time soon 隨時；無時無刻: *We're expecting him hourly.* 我們時刻在盼望他來。**3** for each hour 每小時: *hourly-paid workers* 按小時付酬的工人

★house¹ /haʊs; haʊs/ *n* **houses** /'haʊzɪz; 'haʊzɪz/ **1** a building of one or more levels where people, often one family, live 房屋；住宅: *Do you live in a house or a flat?* 你住的是一幢房子還是一套公寓？**2** [+sing/pl verb] the people living in this type of building 住在一幢房子內的人；家人: *Be quiet or you'll wake the whole house!* 輕一點，否則會把屋內所有的人都給吵醒的! **3** a building used for a particular thing 用於某一目的的建築物: *a hen-house* 雞舍 | *the opera-house* 歌劇院 **4** a business firm 商行；公司: *a publishing house* 出版社 | *He works for a Paris fashion house.* 他在一家巴黎時裝公司工作。**5** one of several divisions of a school, each with its own name, whose pupils compete against each other〔在校學生為競賽而分成〕組 **6 House** a group of people who can make laws 立法院；議院: *the House of Commons* 下議院 | *the House of Representatives* 眾議院 **7** an important noble or royal family 名門；皇室: *The House of Windsor is the British royal family.* 溫莎家族是英國皇室。**8** the people watching a performance in a theatre or concert hall〔劇場或音樂廳的〕觀眾: *They played to a packed house.* 他們為滿場觀眾演出。**9** the people at a DEBATE 辯論者: *The motion to be debated today is "This house believes that nuclear power has a future".* 今日辯論的議題是"本方相信核能具有光明的未來"。**10 bring the house down** to make the people watching a play laugh or CLAP very loudly in admiration 博得觀眾滿堂喝采 **11 get on like a house on fire** to be or become very good friends with someone very quickly 很快與某人成為好友；一見如故 **12 on the house** paid for by the management, not by you 由老闆付錢 **13 put/set your house in order** to sort out your affairs and problems 整理自己的事情；解決自己的問題

■ **USAGE 用法: A house** is a building for people to live in, and usually has more than one level (storey). A **cottage** is usually a small, old house, especially in the country. A **bungalow** is a fairly modern house built on only one level. A set of rooms (including a kitchen and a bathroom) inside a larger building is called a **flat** in British English and an **apartment** in American English. A small one-room flat is sometimes called a **bedsitter** or **bedsit** in British English. ☆ **house** 是住宅，通常不止一層。**cottage** 通常是一座小而舊的住宅，尤指在鄉間的住宅。**bungalow** 是比較現代化的一層樓的住宅。一幢大樓中的一套住房〔包括廚房和浴室〕，在英式英語中稱為 **flat**，在美式英語中稱為 **apartment**。一個房間的小公寓

H

在英式英語中有時稱為 **bedsitter** 或 **bedsit**.

house² /haʊz; haʊz/ *v* **housed, housing** [T] **1** to provide someone with a place to live 給〔某人〕提供住處: *The refugees have been housed in an old warehouse.* 難民給安排住在一座舊倉庫裡. **2** to provide space for something 給〔某物〕提供空間: *That new building will house the Smith collection of painting.* 將在那座新樓中放置史密斯的繪畫作品.

house ar·rest /ˈ··,·/ *n* **under house arrest** forbidden to leave your house because the government thinks you are dangerous 〔由於政府認為是危險分子而〕被軟禁在家

house·boat /ˈhaʊs,bot; ˈhaʊsbəʊt/ *n* a boat which people live in, and which is not usually moved 用於居住的船; 船屋

house·bound /ˈhaʊs,baʊnd; ˈhaʊsbaʊnd/ *adj* not able to move out of the house, because of illness or old age 〔因生病或年老而〕不能外出的

house·break·er /ˈhaʊs,brekə; ˈhaʊs,breɪkəʳ/ *n* a thief who enters a house by force in order to steal things 〔闖入住宅的〕盜賊

★**house·hold¹** /ˈhaʊs,hold; ˈhaʊshəʊld/ *n* [+ sing/pl verb] all the people living together in a house 一家人; 同住一所房子的人: *The whole household was up early.* 一家人很早便起牀了.

household² *adj* [only before a noun 只用於名詞前] **1** concerned with the management of a house 家庭的: *household expenses* 家裡的開支 | *household chores* 家裡的雜活兒 **2** (also 又作 **Household**) concerned with the protection of the royal family 保衞皇室的: *the household cavalry* 皇家騎兵

house·hold·er /ˈhaʊs,holdə; ˈhaʊs,həʊldəʳ/ *n* someone who owns or is in charge of a house 房主; 戶主; 家長

household name /ˌ···ˈ·/ *n* (also 又作 **household word**) someone or something very well-known and talked about a lot 家喻戶曉的人〔事〕

house·keep·er /ˈhaʊs,kipə; ˈhaʊs,kiːpəʳ/ *n* someone who is paid to clean and organize your house and to cook for you 管家

house·keep·ing /ˈhaʊs,kipɪŋ; ˈhaʊs,kiːpɪŋ/ *n* [U] **1** the cleaning and management of a house, and the cooking for the people who live in it 持家; 料理家務 **2** (also 又作 **housekeeping money**) the money provided for food and other things needed in the home 用於家庭開支的錢

house-to-house /ˌ···ˈ·◂/ *adj* going to every house in an area 挨家挨戶的: *a house-to-house search* 挨家挨戶的搜查

house·man /ˈhaʊs,mæn; ˈhaʊsmən/ *n* **housemen** /-mən; -mən/ a JUNIOR doctor who is completing hospital training and often living in the hospital 駐院實習醫生

house·mas·ter /ˈhaʊs,mæstə; ˈhaʊs,mɑːstəʳ/ *n* a teacher who is in charge of one of the houses in a school; a woman housemaster is called a **housemistress** 〔寄宿學校的〕舍監〔女舍監稱作 **housemistress**〕

house-proud /ˈ··/ *adj* spending a lot of time keeping your house clean and in perfect order 熱衷於美化家庭的

house-trained /ˈ··/ *adj* (**housebroken** /ˈhaʊs,brokən; ˈhaʊs,brəʊkən/ *AmE* 〖美式〗) trained to go out of the house to empty the bowels or BLADDER (used of house pets) 訓練成到房外去便溺的〔指家養寵物〕

house-warm·ing /ˈhaʊs,wɔrmɪŋ; ˈhaʊs,wɔːmɪŋ/ *n* a party given when you have moved into a new house 慶祝喬遷的宴會

house·wife /ˈhaʊs,waɪf; ˈhaʊs-waɪf/ *n* **housewives** /-waɪvz; -waɪvz/ a married woman who does not usually work outside the home 家庭主婦; 家庭婦女

house·work /ˈhaʊs,wɜk; ˈhaʊswɜːk/ *n* [U] work done in a house, such as cooking, washing, and cleaning 家務〔如做飯, 洗衣, 打掃〕

★**hous·ing** /ˈhaʊzɪŋ; ˈhaʊzɪŋ/ *n* **1** [U] buildings to live in 住房: *The number of people in poor housing is increasing.* 住在破舊房子裡的人數在不斷增加. | *Housing conditions in inner London must be improved.* 倫敦市區的住房條件必須改善. **2** [C] protective covering for machinery 〔機器的〕防護罩: *the engine housing* 引擎外罩

housing es·tate /ˈ···,·/ *n* a group of houses or flats built in one place at the same time 住宅區

hove /hov; həʊv/ the past tense and past participle of HEAVE ☆ HEAVE 的過去式和過去分詞

hov·el /ˈhʌvl; ˈhɒvəl/ *n* a small dirty house 又小又髒的屋子

hov·er /ˈhʌvə; ˈhɒvəʳ/ *v* [I] **1** to stay in the air in one place 〔在空中〕懸停: *A helicopter was hovering above the crowd.* 有架直升機懸停在人羣頭頂上. **2** to wait around one place 徘徊; 逗留: *He was hovering by the door, waiting to talk to me.* 他在門口徘徊, 等着與我談話.

hov·er·craft /ˈhʌvə,kræft; ˈhɒvəkrɑːft/ *n* a boat which flies over the water, lifted up on a bed of air 氣墊船 –see picture on page 991 見 991 頁彩圖

★**how¹** /haʊ; haʊ/ *adv* **1** used in questions when you are asking in what way something is done 怎樣; 如何〔用於詢問用某種方式做某事〕: *How do you spell it?* 那個單詞怎樣拼? | *How did you find out about this?* 這情況你是如何發現的? **2** used in questions about amount or number 多少〔用於詢問數量〕: *How old are you?* 你多大了? | *How many people were there?* 當時有多少人? | *How tall is he?* 他個子有多高? **3**

how is, how are used to ask about a person's health 如何; 怎樣〔用於詢問健康狀況〕: *How is your mother?* 你的母親身體好嗎? | *How are you?* 你好嗎? **4** *lit* used to make a statement stronger《文》多麼〔用於強調〕: *How kind she is!* 她多麼親切啊! | *How I hate that man!* 我多恨那個人啊!

how² *conj* used when you are stating the way in which something happens 怎樣; 如何〔用於説明某事是如何發生的〕: *I can't remember how I did it now.* 我現在記不起當初是怎麼做的。

★how·ev·er /hauˈɛvə; hauˈevərˈ/ *adv* **1** in spite of this; used when you are adding a fact or statement that is surprising or is not what people expect from the last thing you said 儘管如此〔用於補充令人吃驚的事實或話語, 或者補充人們無法從你剛才所説的話中所能猜想到的事實或話語〕: *The company's profits have fallen slightly this year. However, a spokesman for the company said that he expected the situation to improve very soon.* 今年公司利潤略有下降。儘管如此, 公司一位發言人説他預計這一情況將很快好轉。 | *She failed to win the gold in the European Championships last week. This does not, however, mean that she has no chance in the Olympics.* 她沒能在上週的歐洲錦標賽中獲得金牌。儘管如此, 這並不意味着在奧運會上她就沒有機會奪魁。 | *The room was very small. It was very comfortable, however.* 房間很小, 但十分舒適。–see Study Note on page 1325 見 1325 頁學習提示 –see 見 EVER (USAGE 用法) **2** no matter how 不論如何: *She always goes swimming, however cold it is.* 她不論天氣多麼寒冷, 都堅持去游泳。 **3** (also 又作 **how ever**) used when you are surprised and are asking how something happened 到底; 究竟〔用於吃驚地詢問某事是如何發生的〕: *However did you get here?* 你究竟是怎樣到這裡來的?

howl¹ /haul; haul/ *v* [I] **1** to make a long loud crying sound 嗥叫; 咆哮: *The dogs howled all night.* 那幾隻狗整夜嗥叫。 | *The wind howled in the trees.* 風在樹林裡怒號。 **2** to cry loudly 大聲哭: *The baby's howling.* 嬰兒在哇哇大哭。 **3 howl with laughter** to laugh loudly 大聲哄笑
howl sbdy ↔ down *phr v* [T] to make a loud noise so that someone who is speaking cannot be heard by other people 大吵大鬧以壓倒〔某人〕説話的聲音

howl² *n* a long loud cry 嗥叫; 咆哮

HP /ˌetʃ ˈpi; ˌeɪtʃ ˈpiː/ **1** an abbreviation for 〔縮〕= HIRE PURCHASE **2** an abbreviation for 〔縮〕= HORSEPOWER

HQ /ˌetʃ ˈkju; ˌeɪtʃ ˈkjuː/ an abbreviation for 〔縮〕= HEADQUARTERS: *See you back at HQ.* 我們回到總部再見。

hr, hrs a written abbreviation for 〔縮〕= HOUR or 或 HOURS

HRH part of the title of a prince or princess; an abbreviation for **His Royal Highness** or **Her Royal Highness**〔縮〕殿下〔王子或公主的頭銜的一部分〕

hub /hʌb; hʌb/ *n* **1** the central part of a wheel 輪轂 **2** the place which is most important, or where most things happen (活動)中心區

hub·bub /ˈhʌbʌb; ˈhʌbʌb/ *n* [sing] a loud noise made by lots of people talking at the same time 喧嘩; 吵鬧聲

hud·dle¹ /ˈhʌdl; ˈhʌdl/ *v* **huddled, huddling** [I + adv/prep] to crowd closely together in a group 擠成一堆: *We huddled round the fire to keep warm.* 我們擠在火堆四周取暖。

huddle² *n* a group of people or things very close together 一堆人或物

hue /hju; hjuː/ *n fml* a colour or shade of a colour《正式》色彩; 色度

huff¹ /hʌf; hʌf/ *n* **in a huff** in a bad temper 怒氣沖沖: *He left the party in a huff.* 他怒氣沖沖地離開了宴會。

huff² *v* [I] **huff and puff** to breathe noisily because you are doing something difficult and tiring〔由於在做困難或累人的事情而〕氣喘吁吁

hug /hʌg; hʌg/ *v* **-gg-** [T] **1** to hold someone tightly in your arms because you love them 擁抱〔某人〕 **2** to stay close to something 緊挨着〔某物〕: *The boat hugged the coast.* 船緊靠海岸行駛。 –**hug** *n*: *He gave me a quick hug.* 他匆匆抱了我一下。

★huge /hjudʒ; hjuːdʒ/ *adj* very big 非常大的; 巨大的: *a huge house* 巨大的房子 | *The film was a huge success.* 這部電影取得了巨大的成功。 –**hugely** *adv*: *a hugely successful film* 取得巨大成功的電影

huh /hʌ; hʌh/ *interj* a word used for asking a question or for expressing surprise or disapproval 嘿; 嗯哈〔用來發問, 表示驚奇或異議〕

hulk /hʌlk; hʌlk/ *n* **1** the body of an old broken ship〔廢舊船的〕船體 **2** a person or thing that looks very large and heavy 笨重的人或物

hulk·ing /ˈhʌlkɪŋ; ˈhʌlkɪŋ/ *adj* [always before a noun 只能用於名詞前] very large and heavy 龐大笨重的: *a hulking great man* 體格龐大的人

hull¹ /hʌl; hʌl/ *n* the main body of a ship 船身; 船體

hull² *v* [T] to take the outer covering off some grains, seeds, or vegetables, or to take the group of leaves off the top of some fruits such as strawberries (STRAWBERRY) 除去…的外皮〔英、穀、葉〕

hul·la·ba·loo /ˈhʌləbəˌlu; ˌhʌləbəˈluː/ *n* [sing] a lot of noise made by people shouting 喧嘩

hul·lo /həˈlo; hʌˈləʊ/ *interj,n* see 見 HELLO

hum /hʌm; hʌm/ *v* **-mm-** **1** [I] to make a continuous low noise like the noise that bees make 發嗡嗡聲〔如蜜蜂的聲音〕 **2** [I;T] to sing a piece of music by making a continuous sound with your lips closed 哼唱: *Hum the tune if you don't know the words.* 如果你不知道歌詞, 就哼調子吧。 **3** [I] (of a place) to be full of activity 充滿活力: *The office was humming.* 辦公室裡人們忙忙碌碌。– **hum** n : *the hum of traffic outside* 外面汽車的嗡嗡聲

★hu·man¹ /'hjumən; 'hju:mən/ adj **1** of or concerning people 人的: *the human voice* 人聲 **2** typical of people, especially when showing feelings or weaknesses 具有人的特點的〔尤指在表現出情感或弱點方面〕: *You can never eliminate the possibility of human error.* 你決不能排除人為錯誤的可能。 | *Of course I make mistakes — I'm only human.* 我當然會出錯——我只是個人。 –opposite 反義 **inhuman**

★human² n (also 又作 **human being**) a man, woman, or child, not an animal 人; 人類: *Human beings have only been on the Earth for a relatively short time.* 人類在地球上只生存了相對較短的一段時間。

hu·mane /hju'men; hju:'meɪn/ adj showing kindness and sympathy 人道的; 仁慈的; 富有同情心的 –opposite 反義 **inhumane –humanely** adv : *Animals should be killed as humanely as possible.* 應當盡可能用人道的方法屠宰動物。

hu·man·is·m /'hjumən,ɪzəm; 'hju:mənɪzəm/ n [U] a system of beliefs concerned with the needs of people, and with finding answers to human problems by people themselves rather than by a God or a religion 人道主義; 人本主義 **–humanist** n

hu·man·i·tar·i·an /hju,mænə'terɪən; hju:-,mæn ɪ'teəriən/ n a person who works to improve people's lives and reduce people's suffering 人道主義者 **–humanitarian** adj

hu·man·i·ty /hju'mænətɪ; hju:'mæn ɪti/ n **humanities 1** [U] sympathy and kindness 人道; 仁慈: *a man of great humanity* 非常仁慈的人 **2** [U] people of the world in general 人類: *The regime stands accused of crimes against humanity.* 該政權被控對人類犯有罪行。 **3** [U] fml the state or fact of being a human being 《正式》人性; 人的屬性 **4 humanities** [pl] studies such as literature, languages, and history, which are concerned with people rather than with science 人文學科〔如藝術, 語言和歷史〕

hu·man·ize /'hjumə,naɪz; 'hju:mənaɪz/ v **humanized, humanizing** (also 又作 **humanise** BrE 《英式》) [T] to make something more pleasant for people 使〔某物〕變得更令人舒適

hu·man·ly /'hjumənlɪ; 'hju:mənli/ adv **humanly possible** possible for any person 對任何人來說是可能的: *It's not humanly possible to complete all the work in such a short time.* 在如此短的時間內完成所有的工作非人力所及。

human na·ture /,·· '··/ n [U] the behaviour, qualities, and desires of a typical ordinary person 人的天性; 普通人的行為, 特點和慾望: *It's only human nature to want a comfortable life.* 想過舒適的生活不過是人的天性。

human race /,·· '·/ n **the human race** all people in the world thought of as a group 人類

human rights /,·· '·/ n [pl] the rights such as freedom, equality, and justice which every person should have 人權〔如自由, 平等和公正〕

hum·ble¹ /'hʌmbl; 'hʌmbəl/ adj **1** believing that you are not any better or more important than other people 謙虛的; 謙恭的 **2** unimportant, and having a low social position 地位卑微的: *He was only a humble bank clerk.* 他不過是個小小的銀行職員。 **3 in my humble opinion** a phrase used when you are giving your opinion quite strongly, but do not want to offend other people 愚以為〔用於以比較強的語氣提出自己觀點而不希望觸怒他人〕

humble² v **humbled, humbling** [T] to make someone feel less proud and less important 使〔某人〕謙恭; 使〔某人〕卑微: *I felt humbled by the experience.* 此經歷使我感到恥辱。

hum·bug /'hʌm,bʌg; 'hʌmbʌg/ n **1** [U] old fash nonsense 《老式》胡說 **2** [C] a hard sweet which tastes of MINT 薄荷硬糖

hum·drum /'hʌm,drʌm; 'hʌmdrʌm/ adj ordinary and dull, without any variety 單調乏味的: *We lead a humdrum life.* 我們過著單調乏味的生活。

hu·mer·us /'hjumərəs; 'hju:mərəs/ n the bone in the top half of your arm 肱骨

hu·mid /'hjumɪd; 'hju:m ɪd/ adj having a lot of wetness in the air, and usually very hot (used of the weather) 濕熱的〔指天氣〕: *The afternoon was hot and humid.* 下午天氣又熱又潮。

hu·mid·i·fy /hju'mɪdə,faɪ; hju:'mɪd ɪfaɪ/ v **humidified, humidifying** [T] to make the air less dry 使空氣潮濕

hu·mid·i·ty /hju'mɪdətɪ; hju:'mɪd ɪti/ n [U] the wetness that is in the air 潮濕; 濕氣: *It's uncomfortable working outside in this humidity.* 在外面這種潮濕的空氣裡工作很不舒服。

hu·mil·i·ate /hju'mɪlɪ,et; hju:'mɪlieɪt/ v **humiliated, humiliating** [T] to make someone feel ashamed and lose other people's respect 羞辱〔某人〕: *She could not forgive him for humiliating her in front of her friend.* 她無法原諒他當着朋友的面羞辱她。 **–humiliation** /hju,mɪlɪ'eʃən; hju:,mɪli'eɪʃən/ n [C;U]

hu·mil·i·ty /hju'mɪlətɪ; hju:'mɪl ɪti/ n [U] the quality of being humble 謙恭; 卑微

hu·mor·ist /ˈhjumərɪst; ˈhjuːmərˌɪst/ *n* a person who makes jokes or writes amusing things 逗笑的人; 幽默作家

hu·mor·ous /ˈhjumərəs; ˈhjuːmərəs/ *adj* funny and amusing in a clever way 滑稽的; 幽默的; 詼諧的: *She kept making humorous remarks.* 她一直在說幽默的話。–**humorously** *adv*

hu·mour¹ /ˈhjumɚ; ˈhjuːməʳ/ *n* (**humor** *AmE* 【美式】) [U] **1** the ability to laugh and find things funny 對滑稽事物的感受能力: *She doesn't have a sense of humour.* 她沒有幽默感。 **2** the quality of being funny and making people laugh 幽默; 滑稽: *I'm afraid I couldn't see the humour in the situation.* 對不起, 我看不出這情形有甚麼可笑之處。 **3 in a good humour** happy and behaving pleasantly 情緒良好的: *He seems to be in a good humour today.* 他今天看上去心情很好。 [RELATED PHRASE 相關詞組 **in a bad humour**]

humour² *v* (also 又作 **humor** *AmE* 【美式】) [T] to accept someone's unreasonable behaviour or wishes to keep them happy 遷就, 迎合〔某人〕: *Don't argue, just humour him and he'll stop.* 不要爭辯, 你就遷就他一下, 他會停下來的。

hump¹ /hʌmp; hʌmp/ *n* **1** a large lump on the back of a person or camel 〔人的〕駝背; 〔駱駝的〕駝峯 **2** a small hill or raised part in a road 小圓丘; 〔路面上的〕小凸面

hump² *v* [T +adv/prep] *infml* to carry something heavy 【非正式】提〔重物〕: *I humped the case upstairs.* 我把箱子拎到樓上。

hu·mus /ˈhjuməs; ˈhjuːməs/ *n* [U] rich soil made of decayed plants and leaves 腐殖土

hunch¹ /hʌntʃ; hʌntʃ/ *n* an idea based on feeling rather than on facts or proof 直覺; 預感: *I had a hunch we would find him at the airport.* 當時我有種預感: 我們會在機場找到他。

hunch² *v* [T] to pull your back or shoulders into a rounded shape 使〔背或肩膀〕隆起: *He was sitting hunched in a corner.* 他躬着身體坐在角落裡。

hunch·back /ˈhʌntʃˌbæk; ˈhʌntʃbæk/ *n* a person with a large lump on the back 駝背的人

hun·dred /ˈhʌndrəd; ˈhʌndrɪd/ *det, n, pron* **hundred** *or* **hundreds 1** the number 100 〔數字〕一百 **2 hundreds** a very large number of people or things 許許多多〔人或物〕: *We received hundreds of letters.* 我們收到了數以百計的來信。–**hundredth** *det, n, pron, adv*

■ USAGE 用法: **1** British people say **hundred and** in numbers, like this ☆ 英國人讀數字時, 在 **hundred** 後要加上 **and**, 如下例: *326 = three* **hundred and twenty six**. Americans usually miss out **and** ☆美國人通常不加 **and**: *326 = three*

hundred *twenty six* **2** We can use plural forms like **hundreds** and **thousands** when they are not part of another number ☆ 當 **hundreds** 和 **thousands** 不是另外一個數字的一部分時, 我們可以用其複數形式: **Hundreds** *of people attended the concert.* 數以百計的人參加了音樂會。 | **Thousands** *of pounds have been spent on the new hospital.* 為建造新醫院, 已花了數千英鎊。

hun·dred·weight /ˈhʌndrəd,wet; ˈhʌndrɪˌdweɪt/ [plural is 複數為 **hundred weight**] a measure of weight equal to 112 pounds in Britain, and 100 pounds in America 英擔〔重量單位, 等於英國的112磅, 美國的100磅〕

hung /hʌŋ; hʌŋ/ the past tense and past participle of HANG ☆ HANG 的過去式和過去分詞

Hung·ar·i·an¹ /hʌŋˈgɛriən; hʌŋˈgeəriən/ *adj* from or connected with Hungary 匈牙利來的; 匈牙利的

Hungarian² *n* **1** [C] a person from Hungary 匈牙利人 **2** [U] the language of Hungary 匈牙利語

hun·ger¹ /ˈhʌŋgɚ; ˈhʌŋgəʳ/ *n* [U] **1** the feeling that you want or need to eat 飢餓: *He could feel pangs of hunger in his stomach.* 他感到腹中陣陣的飢餓。 **2** lack of food 食物的缺乏: *people dying of hunger* 餓死的人們

hunger² *v* **hunger for something, hunger after something** to want something very much 渴望得到某物

hunger strike /ˈ··ˌ·/ *n* a refusal to eat, especially by prisoners, as a sign of strong dissatisfaction 〔尤指囚犯的〕絕食抗議

hun·gry /ˈhʌŋgri; ˈhʌŋgri/ *adj* **hungrier, hungriest 1** wanting or needing food 飢餓的 **2 go hungry** to have no food or not enough food 沒有食物; 挨餓: *We often went hungry.* 我們經常挨餓。 **3 hungry work** work that makes you feel hungry 使人飢餓的繁重工作 **4 hungry for something** wanting or needing something very much 渴望得到某物–**hungrily** *adv*

hunk /hʌŋk; hʌŋk/ *n* a thick piece of something, for example bread or meat 大塊〔如麵包或肉〕

hunt¹ /hʌnt; hʌnt/ *v* **1** [I;T] to chase animals in order to catch and kill them, either for food or for sport 打獵; 獵殺〔動物〕: *Owls prefer to hunt at night.* 貓頭鷹喜歡在夜間獵食。 | *They hunt small birds and animals.* 他們獵捕小鳥和動物。 | *The men were out hunting.* 那些人出去打獵了。 **2** [T] to try to find and catch someone 追捕〔某人〕: *Police hunting the murderer have appealed for help from the public.* 追捕兇手的警察呼籲市民協助。 **3 hunt for something** to search carefully for something 仔細搜尋某物: *I spent* *the morning hunting for my passport.* 我整個上午都在找護照。

hunt sbdy/sthg ↔ **down** *phr v* [T] to succeed in finding someone or something after a lot of effort 〔經過許多努力後〕找到〔某人或某物〕

hunt² *n* **1** the chasing and sometimes killing of animals 打獵; 狩獵: *an elephant hunt* 獵捕大象 **2** a careful search for someone or something 仔細尋找: *The police hunt for the missing child continued today.* 警方今天繼續尋找失蹤的孩子。 **3** a group of people who regularly hunt foxes together or the place where they do this 定期在一起獵狐的人; 獵狐區

hunt·er /'hʌntə; 'hʌntər/ *n* **1** a person or animal that hunts wild animals 獵人; 〔獵捕其他動物的〕獵獸 **2** a person who searches for something with a lot of interest 熱切的追尋者: *The auction was full of bargain hunters.* 拍賣會場上到處都是來撿便宜貨的人。

hur·dle¹ /'hɜ·dl; 'hɜːdl/ *n* **1** a frame for jumping over in a race 〔跨欄賽跑時用的〕欄架 **2** a difficulty which must be dealt with before you can do something else 障礙; 難關

hurdle² *v* **hurdled, hurdling** [T] to jump over something 跳過〔某物〕

hurl /hɜ·l; hɜːl/ *v* [T] **1** to throw something with force 用力扔〔某物〕: *He hurled a brick through the window.* 他把一塊磚扔進窗裡。 **2** hurl abuse, hurl insults to shout unpleasant things at someone 辱罵〔某人〕

hur·ly-bur·ly /'hɜ·lɪ,bɜ·lɪ; 'hɜːlɪ ,bɜːlɪ/ *n* [sing] noisy activity 喧鬧: *the hurly-burly of city life* 城市生活的喧鬧

hur·ray /hə'reɪ; huˈreɪ/ *interj* (also 又作 **hooray** /hu'reɪ; huˈreɪ/, **hurrah** /hə'rɑː; huˈrɑː/) a shout of joy, excitement, or approval 好哇; 萬歲〔表示高興、激動或贊成的叫喊〕: *We've done it! Hurray!* 我們做完啦! 萬歲!

hur·ri·cane /'hɜ·ɪ,ken; 'hʌrɪ̩kən/ *n* a storm with a very strong fast wind 颶風

hurricane lamp /'··· ·/ *n* a lamp which has a strong cover to protect the flame inside from wind 防風燈

hur·ried /'hɜ·ɪd; 'hʌrɪd/ *adj* done very quickly because there is not much time 匆忙做成的: *a hurried meeting* 匆匆的會晤 – **hurriedly** *adv*

hur·ry¹ /'hɜ·ɪ; 'hʌrɪ/ *v* **hurried, hurrying 1** [I] to go somewhere quickly 匆忙去〔某地〕: *He hurried across the road.* 他快速走過馬路。 | *We hurried home.* 我們匆忙回家。 | *We're late. We'd better hurry.* 我們已遲了。我們應該快點走。 **2** [T] to send or bring someone somewhere quickly or make them do something quickly 送〔某人〕迅速到達〔某地〕; 使〔某人〕迅速做〔某事〕: *She hurried us to the airport.* 她把我們急送到機場。 | *Don't hurry me. I'm working as fast as I can.* 別再催我了。我已經

在用最快的速度做了。

hurry up *phr v* [I;T **hurry** sbdy/sthg ↔ **up**] to do something more quickly, or make something happen more quickly 更快地做〔某事〕; 使〔某事〕更快地發生: *I wish you'd hurry up!* 我希望你能再快些! | *I tried to hurry them up.* 我盡力催他們再快些。 | *Can you hurry the work up a bit?* 你做這工作能再快點嗎?

hurry² *n* [U] **1** be in a hurry to be trying to do something quickly, or eager to do something quickly 在盡快地做某事; 急着趕做某事: *I can't stop and talk.* 我不能停下來講話。 | *I'm busy.* 我正忙着呢。 | *She seems in a hurry to leave.* 她似乎急着要走。 | *I'm in no hurry to change my job.* 我並不急着換工作。 | *There's no need to rush. I'm not in any hurry.* 沒必要急。我並不匆忙。 **2** do something in a hurry to do something quickly because you do not have much time 〔由於時間不多而〕匆忙做某事: *I always make mistakes if I try to do things in a hurry.* 我如果匆匆忙忙做事情, 就老是出錯。 **3** there's no hurry = there is no need to do things quickly because there is plenty of time 〔由於有充裕的時間而〕不必匆忙 **4** what's the hurry? = why are you doing things so quickly? 你為甚麼這麼匆忙? **5** I won't do this again in a hurry = I won't be very eager to do this again because it was unpleasant in someway 〔由於不太喜歡〕我不會再輕易做這事了

★hurt¹ /hɜ·t; hɜːt/ *v* **hurt, hurting 1** [T] to cause pain or damage to your own body or someone else's body 使疼痛; 使受傷: *I fell over and hurt myself.* 我跌倒時摔傷了。 | *She hurt her leg when she fell.* 她跌倒時傷了腿。 | *Sorry. Did I hurt you?* 對不起。我傷着你了嗎? | *The light was hurting my eyes.* 這光刺得我眼睛疼。 **2** [I] to cause you pain 引起疼痛: *My feet are hurting.* 我的腳在痛。 | *My back hurts.* 我的背痛。 | *Does this hurt?* 這裡疼嗎? **3** [T] to upset someone and make them unhappy 使〔某人〕難過; 令〔某人〕不快: *She knew that she had hurt him very badly.* 她知道她深深地傷了他的心。 | *I tried not to hurt her feelings.* 我盡量不傷她的感情。 **4** it won't hurt = it will do no harm 沒有壞處: *It won't hurt her to do a bit of hard work for a change!* 讓她換些重活做做不會有甚麼壞處! | *It won't hurt if we're a few minutes late.* 我們就是遲到幾分鐘也不會有甚麼問題。 –**hurt** *n* [U]

> ■ **USAGE** 用法: When **hurt** is used in the sense of bodily damage, you may be *slightly/badly/seriously* **hurt** but do not use these adverbs when speaking of unhappiness caused by someone's behaviour. Compare ☆如果 **hurt** 用來指身體上的傷害, 可以用 *slightly, badly,*

seriously 來修飾；但用來指由於某人的行為而引起的不快時，不要用上述副詞來修飾。試比較: *She was badly/slightly* **hurt** *when she fell off the ladder* 她從梯子上摔下來時，受了重/輕傷; and 和 *She was very deeply/rather* **hurt** *by his unkind words.* 他刻薄的話令她十分/相當傷心。– see 見 WOUND (USAGE 用法)

hurt² *adj* **1** [never before a noun 不能用於名詞前] suffering pain, for example after an accident 受傷的; 疼痛的〔如在事故之後〕: *He was obviously badly hurt.* 他顯然是受了重傷。**2** unhappy and offended 不高興的; 傷心的: *I was very hurt when they didn't turn up.* 他們沒有來, 我感到很傷心。

hurt·ful /ˈhɜːtfəl; ˈhɜːtfəl/ *adj* making you feel offended and unhappy 傷感情的; 令人傷心的: *What he said was very hurtful.* 他說的話很令人傷心。

hur·tle /ˈhɜːtl; ˈhɜːtl/ *v* **hurtled, hurtling** [I + adv/prep] to move very fast 快速移動: *A car came hurtling round the corner.* 一輛汽車飛速開過拐角。

⋆⋆**hus·band** /ˈhʌzbənd; ˈhʌzbənd/ *n* the man a woman is married to 丈夫 –see picture on page 503 見 503 頁彩圖

hus·band·ry /ˈhʌzbəndrɪ; ˈhʌzbəndri/ *n fml* [U] farming 〔正式〕農(牧)業

hush¹ /hʌʃ; hʌʃ/ *v* **Hush!** a word used to ask someone to be quiet 噓!〔用於讓人安靜下來〕

hush sthg ↔ **up** *phr v* [T] to keep something secret that should be public knowledge 隱瞞〔應該讓公眾知道的事情〕; 不讓張揚: *The whole affair had been hushed up.* 整個事情已被隱瞞起來。

hush² *n* [sing] a peaceful silence 寂靜: *A hush fell over the room.* 室內一片寂靜。

hushed /hʌʃt; hʌʃt/ *adj* quiet 安靜的: *talking in hushed voices* 輕聲地說話

hush-hush /ˌ·ˈ·/ *adj infml* secret (used especially of official plans) 〔非正式〕祕密的〔尤指官方計劃〕

husk /hʌsk; hʌsk/ *n* the outer covering of some grains and seeds 〔某些穀類和種子〕外殼; 皮

hus·ky¹ /ˈhʌskɪ; ˈhʌski/ *adj* **huskier, huskiest** having a pleasant rough sound (used of someone's voice) 沙啞的〔指人的嗓音〕– **huskily** *adv* –**huskiness** *n* [U]

husky² *n* **huskies** a working dog with thick hair, used to pull SLEDGES over the snow 愛斯基摩狗〔用來拉雪橇〕

hus·sy /ˈhʌsɪ; ˈhʌsi/ *n* **hussies** *old fash* a young woman who behaves in a sexually improper way 〔老式〕蕩婦

hus·tings /ˈhʌstɪŋz; ˈhʌstɪŋz/ *n* **the hustings** [pl] speeches and other political activities which go on just before an election, when

the political parties are trying to win votes 競選演說〔活動〕

hus·tle¹ /ˈhʌsl; ˈhʌsəl/ *v* **hustled, hustling** [T + adv/prep] to make someone move fast by pushing them 推搡〔某人〕; 驅趕: *He was hustled into the car.* 他被推進了汽車。

hustle² *n* **hustle and bustle** activity in which a lot of people are busy doing things and moving about 忙碌; 繁忙: *the hustle and bustle of city life* 城市生活的繁忙

hus·tler /ˈhʌslə; ˈhʌslər/ *n AmE* someone who tries to earn money in any way that they can, often in an illegal or deceitful way 〔美式〕騙子

hut /hʌt; hʌt/ *n* a small house or shelter, often made of wood 小木屋; 棚屋

hutch /hʌtʃ; hʌtʃ/ *n* a small cage for keeping rabbits in 小兔籠

hy·a·cinth /ˈhaɪəˌsɪnθ; ˈhaɪəsน̩θ/ *n* a plant with bell-shaped flowers, which grows in winter and spring 風信子〔一種植物〕

hy·ae·na /haɪˈiːnə; haɪˈiːnə/ *n* see 見 HYENA

hy·brid /ˈhaɪbrɪd; ˈhaɪbrด̩d/ *n* an animal or plant that is produced from parents of different breeds 〔動物或植物的〕雜交種: *A mule is a hybrid of a donkey and a horse.* 騾子是驢和馬的雜交種。

hy·drant /ˈhaɪdrənt; ˈhaɪdrənt/ *n* a water pipe in the street from which water can be taken to put out fires 〔街道旁的〕消防龍頭

hy·drau·lic /haɪˈdrɒlɪk; haɪˈdrɒlɪk/ *adj* concerning or moved by the pressure of water or other liquids 水壓的: *hydraulic power* 水力

hy·drau·lics /haɪˈdrɒlɪks; haɪˈdrɒlɪks/ *n* [U] the science which studies the use of water to produce power 水力學

hy·dro·e·lec·tric /ˌhaɪdrəʊ·ɪˈlektrɪk; ˌhaɪdrəʊ·ɪˈlektrɪk◂/ *adj* related to producing electricity by the power of moving water, for example the water in a river 水力發電的

hy·dro·foil /ˈhaɪdrəˌfɔɪl; ˈhaɪdrəfɔɪl/ *n* a large motorboat with special parts fitted on the bottom, so that it moves along the surface of the water 水翼船

hy·dro·gen /ˈhaɪdrədʒən; ˈhaɪdrədʒən/ *n* [U] a gas that has no colour or smell, that is lighter than air, and that burns very easily 氫

hydrogen bomb /ˈ··· ·/ *n* (also 又作 **H-bomb**) a very powerful type of ATOM BOMB 氫彈

hy·e·na /haɪˈiːnə; haɪˈiːnə/ *n* (also 又作 **hyaena**) a wild dog-like animal of Africa and Asia, which has a cry like a laugh 鬣狗

hy·giene /ˈhaɪdʒiːn; ˈhaɪdʒiːn/ *n* [U] the practice of keeping yourself and the things around you clean in order to prevent illnesses from spreading 衛生

hy·gien·ic /ˌhaɪdʒɪˈenɪk; haɪˈdʒiːnɪk/ *adj* clean and not likely to spread illness 衛生的 –opposite 反義 **unhygienic** –**hygienically**

H

/-klɪ; -kli/ *adv*

hymn /hɪm; hɪm/ *n* a religious song of the Christian church which people sing together during a religious service 〔基督教的〕聖歌

hy·per·bo·le /haɪˈpɜ·bə·li; haɪˈpɜːbəli/ *n* [C; U] the use of language which makes something sound bigger, smaller, better, or worse than it really is 誇張(法)

hy·per·mar·ket /ˈhaɪpə·ˌmɑrkɪt; ˈhaɪpəˌmɑː·kɪt/ *n* a very large SUPERMARKET 大型超級市場

hy·phen /ˈhaɪfən; ˈhaɪfən/ *n* a short line (-) which is used to join words or parts of words 連字符, 連(字)號

hy·phen·ate /ˈhaɪfənˌet; ˈhaɪfəneɪt/ *v* **hyphenated, hyphenating** [T] to join words with a hyphen 用連字符〔號〕連接〔單詞〕

hyp·no·sis /hɪpˈnosɪs; hɪpˈnəʊs̩s/ *n* [U] the production of a sleep-like state in someone's mind 催眠(狀態): *She told him all her secrets when she was under hypnosis.* 她在催眠狀態下把所有的祕密都告訴了他。 —**hypnotic** /hɪpˈnɑtɪk; hɪpˈnɒtɪk/ *adj* —**hypnotically** /-klɪ; -kli/ *adv*

hyp·no·tis·m /ˈhɪpnəˌtɪzəm; ˈhɪpnətɪzəm/ *n* [U] the practice of hypnotizing someone 催眠(術) —**hypnotist** *n*

hyp·no·tize /ˈhɪpnəˌtaɪz; ˈhɪpnətaɪz/ *v* **hypnotized, hypnotizing** (also 又作 **hypnotise** *BrE* 《英式》) [T] to put someone into a sleep-like state in order to control them or find out information 使〔某人〕進入催眠狀態〔以便控制或獲取情報〕

hy·po·chon·dri·ac /ˌhaɪpəˈkɑndrɪˌæk; ˌhaɪpəˈkɒndriæk/ *n* a person who worries about their health all the time, although they are usually perfectly healthy 疑病症患者 —**hypochondria** /-drɪə; -driə/ *n* [U]

hy·poc·ri·sy /hɪˈpɑkrəsɪ; hɪˈpɒkr̩si/ *n* [U] pretending to be or believe something different from, and usually better than, what you really are or really believe 偽善; 造作: *The government's claim to be concerned about poverty is sheer hypocrisy.* 政府聲稱關心窮人是純粹的腥腥作態。

hyp·o·crite /ˈhɪpəˌkrɪt; ˈhɪpəkrɪt/ *n* a person who says one thing and does another, usually something worse 偽善者; 偽君子: *What a hypocrite! He should practise what he preaches.* 真是個偽君子! 他應當言行一致。 —**hypocritical** /ˌhɪpəˈkrɪtɪk; ˌhɪpəˈkrɪtɪkəl/ *adj* —**hypocritically** /-klɪ; -kli/ *adv*

hy·po·der·mic /ˌhaɪpəˈdɜ·mɪk; ˌhaɪpəˈdɜː·mɪk/ *n* an instrument for putting drugs directly into a person's body through their skin 皮下注射器 —**hypodermic** *adj* : *a hypodermic syringe* 皮下注射器

hy·po·ther·mi·a /ˌhaɪpəˈθɜ·mɪə; ˌhaɪpəʊˈθɜː·mɪə/ *n* [U] *tech* a condition in which your body temperature falls below the usual level and you are very ill 《術語》體溫過低: *Every winter some old people die from hypothermia.* 每年冬天都有一些老年人死於體溫過低。

hy·poth·e·sis /haɪˈpɑθəˌsɪs; haɪˈpɒθ̩s̩s/ *n* **hypotheses** /-ˌsiz; -siːz/ an explanation which has not yet been proved to be true 假說, 假設: *If we accept this hypothesis, it could explain why our weather is changing so rapidly.* 如果我們接受這一假說, 便能解釋天氣為何會轉變得如此迅速。

hy·po·thet·i·cal /ˌhaɪpəˈθɛtɪkl̩; ˌhaɪpəˈθetɪkəl/ *adj* based on a situation which is either not known to have happened, or has not yet been proved to be true 假設的; 假定的: *Let's imagine a hypothetical situation in which Britain begins to suffer from major earthquakes...* 我們可以想像這樣一種假設的情景, 即英國開始接連遭受到大地震... —**hypothetically** /-klɪ; -kli/ *adv*

hys·ter·ec·to·my /ˌhɪstəˈrɛktəmɪ; ˌhɪstəˈrektəmɪ/ *n* [C;U] the medical operation for removing a woman's WOMB 子宮切除(術)

hys·te·ri·a /hɪsˈtɪrɪə; hɪˈstɪərɪə/ *n* [U] **1** a condition of uncontrollable nervous excitement or anger 歇斯底里, 癔病 **2** mass hysteria wild excitement in a crowd of people 人羣的無比興奮: *News of the victory produced mass hysteria in the streets of the capital.* 勝利的消息令首都大街上的人羣無比興奮。

hys·ter·i·cal /hɪsˈtɛrɪkl̩; hɪˈsterɪkəl/ *adj* **1** in a state of hysteria or as a result of hysteria 處於歇斯底里狀態的: *a hysterical woman* 歇斯底里的女人 | *hysterical crying* 歇斯底里的叫喊 **2** *infml* extremely funny 《非正式》極其滑稽可笑的: *You should go and see the film — it's absolutely hysterical.* 你應該去看這部電影 — 好笑極了。 —**hysterically** /-klɪ; -kli/ *adv*

hys·ter·ics /hɪsˈtɛrɪks; hɪˈsterɪks/ *n* [pl] **1** an attack of uncontrollable nervous excitement or anger 歇斯底里發作: *He always has hysterics at the sight of blood.* 他一見到血就會歇斯底里發作。 **2** **in hysterics** laughing uncontrollably 狂笑不止

H

I, i

I, i /aɪ; aɪ/ **I's, i's** *or* **Is, is** the 9th letter of the English alphabet 英語的第九個字母

★★ **I** /aɪ/ *pron* [used as the subject of a verb 用作動詞的主語] the person who is speaking 我: *I don't like coffee.* 我不喜歡咖啡。| *My brother and I waited outside.* 我和我兄弟在外面等候。

★ **ice¹** /aɪs; aɪs/ *n* **1** [U] water which has frozen so that it is solid 冰: *We get ice on the lake in winter.* 冬天我們這裡的湖結冰。| *Would you like ice in your whisky?* 你的威士忌酒裡要放冰嗎? | *Her hands were as cold as ice.* 她雙手冰冷。**2** [C] *old fash* a serving of ICE CREAM〔老式〕一份冰淇淋: *Two ices, please.* 請給我兩客冰淇淋。**3 keep something on ice** to keep something for later use 把某物留待以後用: *Let's keep that idea on ice for now.* 目前我們把這主意留待以後採用吧。

ice² *v* **iced, icing** [T] **1** to make something very cold by using ice〔用冰〕使〔某物〕冰冷: *iced drinks* 冰凍飲料 **2** to cover a cake with ICING〔在糕餅上〕塗上糖霜

ice over, ice up *phr v* [I] to become covered with ice 被冰覆蓋: *The lake iced over during the night.* 夜裡湖面結冰了。

Ice Age /ˈ· ·/ *n* a time in the past when ice covered many parts of the earth 冰川期; 冰河時代

ice·berg /ˈaɪsˌbɜːg; ˈaɪsbɝg/ *n* a very large piece of ice floating in the sea 冰山; 浮在海洋上的巨大冰塊

ice·box /ˈaɪsˌbɑks; ˈaɪsbɒks/ *n* a box where food is kept cool with blocks of ice〔用冰塊冷凍食物的〕冰櫃

ice cream /ˌ· ˈ·◂/ *n* [C;U] a frozen sweet food 冰淇淋: *Two ice creams, please.* 請給我兩客冰淇淋。| *a bowl of chocolate ice cream* 一碗巧克力冰淇淋

ice cube /ˈ· ·/ *n* a small block of ice that you put in a drink to make it cold〔加入飲料用的〕小方冰塊

ice hock·ey /ˈ· ˌ··/ *n* [U] a game played between two teams on ice; each team tries to hit a hard object into a GOAL with a long stick 冰球運動

ice lol·ly /ˈ· ˌ··/ *n* a piece of sweet-tasting ice on a stick 冰棍; 棒冰; 雪糕

ice skate /ˈ· ·/ *n* a boot with a metal blade on the bottom which you wear to move over ice 冰鞋 **–ice-skate** *v* **ice-skated, ice-skating** [I]

i·ci·cle /ˈaɪsɪkl̩; ˈaɪsɪkəl/ *n* a pointed stick of ice that hangs down from a surface 冰柱; 冰錐: *icicles hanging from the roof* 屋簷上懸垂的冰柱

ic·ing /ˈaɪsɪŋ; ˈaɪsɪŋ/ *n* [U] a mixture of fine powdery sugar and water or butter, used to decorate cakes〔撒在糕餅上的〕糖霜; 糖衣

i·con /ˈaɪkɑn; ˈaɪkɒn/ *n* (also 又作 **ikon**) a picture or figure of a holy person, used in the Eastern branches of Christianity〔東正教的〕聖像

ic·y /ˈaɪsɪ; ˈaɪsɪ/ *adj* **icier, iciest 1** extremely cold 冰冷的: *an icy wind* 冰冷的風 **2** covered with ice 結冰的; 冰封的: *Drive carefully. The roads are icy.* 開車小心, 馬路結冰了。**3** showing annoyance in a quiet, controlled manner 冷冷的; 冷冷的: *She gave me an icy look.* 她冷冰冰地看了我一眼。**–icily** *adv* **–iciness** *n* [U]

I'd /aɪd; aɪd/ **1** short for〔縮〕= "I had": *I'd already left by the time you arrived.* 你到之前我已經離開了。**2** short for〔縮〕= "I would": *I'd love to go but I can't afford it.* 我很想去但我出不起錢。

★★ **i·dea** /aɪˈdɪə; aɪˈdɪə/ *n* **1** [C] a plan or suggestion 計劃; 建議: *What a brilliant idea! Let's do it.* 多好的建議! 我們來幹吧。| *She's full of good ideas.* 她有很多好主意。| *It was Bill's idea to have the race.* 參加比賽是比爾的主意。**2** [C] an opinion or belief 意見; 信念: *He's got some weird religious ideas.* 他有一些稀奇古怪的宗教信念。| *I've an idea that he's on holiday this week.* 我認為這星期他在休假。**3** [C;U] a picture in your mind 思想; 概念: *I've got a good idea of what he wants.* 我清楚地知道他要甚麼。| *Have you any idea of the problems involved?* 你對有關的問題知道些甚麼嗎? **4 get the idea** to begin to believe something, often mistakenly〔常指錯誤地〕開始相信〔某事〕: *He's somehow got the idea that I don't like him.* 他不知怎麼認為我不喜歡他。**5 have no idea** not to know about something at all 毫無所知; 料想不到: *You've no idea how worried I was!* 你一點也想不到我有多擔心! **6 put ideas in someone's head** to make someone hope for things they cannot have 使某人有希望

★ **i·deal¹** /aɪˈdɪəl; aɪˈdɪəl/ *adj* **1** perfect 完美的; 理想的: *an ideal place for a holiday with* *young children* 和小孩一起度假的理想地方 **2** expressing perfection which is unlikely to exist in the real world 想像的; 不切實際的; 空想的: *Plato's ideal system of government* 柏拉圖的空想政體

ideal² *n* **1** a perfect example 完美典型; 典範: *That's my ideal of what a house should be like.* 那就是我理想中的房子的式樣。 **2** a belief in high or perfect standards 理想: *a woman with high ideals* 一位具有崇高理想的女士 | *democratic ideals* 民主理想

i·deal·is·m /aɪ'dɪəl,ɪzəm; aɪ'dɪəlɪzəm/ *n* [U] the belief that you should live according to your ideals 理想主義: *youthful idealism* 年輕人的理想主義 –**idealist** *n* –**idealistic** /,aɪdɪəl-'ɪstɪk; ,aɪdɪə'lɪstɪk/ *adj* –**idealistically** /-klɪ; -kli/ *adv*

i·deal·ize /aɪ'dɪəl,aɪz; aɪ'dɪəlaɪz/ *v* **idealized, idealizing** (also 又作 **idealise** *BrE*【英式】) [T] to imagine something as perfect or better than it really is 使〔某事物〕理想化 –**idealization** /aɪ,dɪələ'zeʃən; aɪ,dɪəlaɪ'zeɪʃən/ *n* [C;U]

i·deal·ly /aɪ'dɪəlɪ; aɪ'dɪəli/ *adv* **1** perfectly 完美地: *She's ideally suited to the job.* 她再稱職不過了。 **2** if conditions were perfect, which they aren't 理想地: *Ideally, I would like to be a teacher, but there are so few jobs now.* 合乎理想地說, 我很想當個教師, 但空缺很少。

i·den·ti·cal /aɪ'dɛntɪkl; aɪ'dentɪkl/ *adj* **1** exactly alike 完全相同的: *We were wearing identical dresses.* 我們穿著一模一樣的衣服。 | *Your voice is identical **to** your sister's.* 你的嗓音和你妹妹的完全相同。 **2** the same 同一的: *This is the identical hotel that we stayed in last year.* 這就是我們去年住過的那家旅館。 –**identically** /-klɪ; -kli/ *adv*

i·den·ti·fi·ca·tion /aɪ,dɛntəfə'keʃən; aɪ,den-tɪfɪ'keɪʃən/ *n* **1** [C;U] the recognizing and naming of someone or something 認出; 識別; 鑑定: *identification of the dead body by the brother* 由兄弟來辨認屍體 **2** [U] an official paper which proves who you are 身分證明(文件): *Let me see your identification.* 讓我看看你的身分證明。 | *His only means of identification was his passport.* 他證明身分的唯一辦法是用他的護照。 **3** [U] the feeling that you share the ideas, feelings, and problems of another person 認同: *He felt a strong sense of identification **with** the hero of the book.* 他覺得和書中的主人公有一種強烈的認同感。

i·den·ti·fy /aɪ'dɛntə,faɪ; aɪ'dentɪfaɪ/ *v* **identified, identifying** [T] to recognize and name someone or something 認出; 識別; 鑑定: *I identified the coat at once — it was my brother's.* 我立即認出了那件外衣——它是我兄弟的。 | *He identified the criminal.* 他認出了罪犯。

identify with *phr v* **1** [T **identify with** sbdy/sthg] to feel sympathy for someone or feel that you share something with some-one 同情〔某人〕; 認同〔某人〕: *Reading this book, we can identify with the main character's struggle.* 讀了這本書, 我們會對主人翁的鬥爭寄予同情。 **2 be identified with something** to be considered to be connected with something 被認為和某事物有關: *We can't use him in our advertisements — he's too closely identified with our competitor's products.* 我們不能在廣告中用他——他被認為和我們對手的產品有極為密切的關係。

i·den·ti·ty /aɪ'dɛntətɪ; aɪ'dentɪti/ *n* **identities** [C;U] **1** who someone is 身分: *The identity of the murdered woman has not yet been established.* 被謀殺的婦女的身分尚未得到確證。 **2** something that makes you feel that you belong to a certain group of people 特性: *our own cultural identity* 咱們自己的文化特性

i·de·ol·o·gy /,aɪdɪ'ɑlədʒɪ; ,aɪdi'ɒlədʒi/ *n* **ideologies** [C;U] a set of ideas typical of a social or political group〔社會團體或政治團體特有的〕思想體系: *Marxist ideology* 馬克思主義的思想體系 –**ideological** /,aɪdɪə'lɑdʒɪkl; ,aɪdɪə'lɒdʒɪkl/ *adj* –**ideologically** *adv*

id·i·o·cy /'ɪdɪəsɪ; 'ɪdɪəsi/ *n* **idiocies** [C;U] great stupidity 極端愚蠢

id·i·om /'ɪdɪəm; 'ɪdɪəm/ *n* **1** a phrase which means something different from the meanings of the separate words 習語; 成語: *To "kick the bucket" is an English idiom meaning "to die".* "kick the bucket" 是英語中的一個習語, 意為"死去"。 **2** a person's typical style of expression in language 個人特有的語言表達方式: *the idiom of the young* 年輕人的用語

id·i·o·mat·ic /,ɪdɪə'mætɪk; ,ɪdɪə'mætɪk/ *adj* natural and informal (used of language) 自然的; 日常談話用的〔指語言〕: *idiomatic English* 地道的英語 –**idiomatically** /-klɪ; -kli/ *adv*

id·i·o·syn·cra·sy /,ɪdɪə'sɪŋkrəsɪ; ,ɪdɪə'sɪŋkrə-si/ *n* **idiosyncrasies** a strange or unusual habit or way of behaving that a person has〔個人的〕癖好: *Keeping pet snakes is an idiosyncrasy of his.* 養蛇玩賞是他的一個癖好。 –**idiosyncratic** /,ɪdɪosɪn'krætɪk; ,ɪdɪəsɪn'kræ-tɪk/ *adj*

id·i·ot /'ɪdɪət; 'ɪdɪət/ *n* a foolish person 白痴; 傻子; 笨蛋: *Idiot! You've dropped my watch!* 笨蛋! 你把我的手錶掉了! | *He's a complete idiot.* 他是個十足的笨蛋。 –**idiotic** /,ɪdɪ'ɑtɪk; ,ɪdɪ'ɒtɪk/ *adj* –**idiotically** /-klɪ; -kli/ *adv*

i·dle¹ /'aɪdl; 'aɪdl/ *adj* **1** lazy 懶惰的 **2** not working 不在工作的; 閒著的: *We can't afford to have all this expensive machinery lying idle.* 讓所有這些昂貴的機械閒置著, 我們可負擔不起損失。 **3** having no useful result 無用的; 無效的: *idle gossip* 閒言碎語 | *His words were just idle threats; he can't harm us.* 他的話只不過是嚇唬人的, 傷害不了我們。 –**idleness** *n* [U] –**idly** *adv*

i·dle² *v* **idled, idling** [I] **1** to waste time doing nothing 虛度時光 **2** to run slowly (used of an engine) 空轉〔指機器〕 **–idler** *n*

idle away sthg *phr v* [T] to waste time doing nothing 虛度〔時光〕: *We idled away a few hours talking.* 我們閒聊浪費了幾個小時。

i·dol /ˈaɪdl; ˈaɪdl/ *n* **1** an image worshipped as a god 偶像 **2** a famous person who is loved and admired 受人崇拜的著名人物

i·dol·a·try /aɪˈdɒlətrɪ; aɪˈdɑlətri/ *n* [U] the worship of idols 偶像崇拜 **–idolatrous** *adj*

i·dol·ize /ˈaɪdl͵aɪz; ˈaɪdəl͵aɪz/ *v* **idolized, idolizing** (also 又作 **idolise** *BrE*〖英式〗) [T] to love or admire someone greatly, perhaps too much 極度熱愛或敬慕〔某人〕; 崇拜: *He idolizes his father.* 他十分崇拜他父親。

id·yll /ˈaɪdl; ˈɪdɪl/ *n* (also 又作 **idyl**) a peaceful happy scene or period of life 和平歡樂的風景或一段生活 **–idyllic** /aɪˈdɪlɪk; ɪˈdɪlɪk/ *adj: an idyllic scene* 田園風光 **–idyllically** /-klɪ; -kli/ *adv*

i.e. /͵aɪ ˈiː; ͵aɪ ˈiː/ a phrase used when you want to give more information about something you have just said; an abbreviation for the Latin words *id est*〖縮〗即; 那就是〔用於對所説的事物給予更多的説明〕: *The cinema is only open to adults, i.e. people over 18.* 這電影院只對成年人開放, 即十八歲以上的人。

★★★**if** /ɪf; ɪf/ *conj* **1** supposing that something happens or is true 假如; 如果; 要是: *If we don't get much rain this summer there could be serious water shortages.* 如果今年夏天雨水不多, 就有可能發生嚴重的水荒。 | *Give me a ring if you need any help.* 如果你需要幫助, 就給我打個電話。 | *If I had enough money I would retire tomorrow.* 假如我有足夠的錢, 我明天就退休。 | *I think I'll be free on Friday night, if not, I can manage Saturday morning.* 我想我星期五晚上有空, 如果不行的話, 我可以安排在星期六早上。 **2** used after verbs like "ask", "know", and "wonder" 是否〔用於動詞 "ask", "know" 和 "wonder" 等後面〕: *Do you know if Jane's coming?* 你知道簡是否會來嗎? | *I wonder if he's all right.* 我不知道他是否還好。 **3** although 雖然: *It was a good film, if a little long.* 雖然長了點兒, 但這是部好電影。 **4 do you mind if?** a polite way of asking someone if you can do something 如果…你介意嗎?〔詢問某人自己是否能做某事的禮貌説法〕: *Do you mind if I smoke?* 我抽煙你介意嗎? **5 if anything** a phrase you use when you are saying something that is the opposite of what you have just said 甚至正相反〔用於表示和剛才所説的正相反〕: *She didn't seem upset about losing her job. If anything she seemed very happy.* 她看上去並不為失掉工作而苦惱; 正相反, 她顯得很高興。 **6 if I were you** a phrase you use when you are giving advice to someone 如果我是你的話〔用於給某人忠告時〕: *If I were you I'd sell that house and buy a smaller one.* 如果我是你的話, 你就把那幢房子賣了再買一幢小的。 **7**

if only a phrase you use to express a strong wish 要是…多好〔用於表示強烈的願望〕: *If only we had a bit more money.* 要是我們的錢再多點有多好。

■ USAGE 用法: Do not use *if* with *will/won't* unless you mean "be willing" ☆除非在表示"願意"時, 否則 *if* 後面不要使用 *will/won't*: *If you'll* (=if you are willing to) *give me a lift I'll be extremely grateful.* 如果你們願意讓我搭車, 我將萬分感激。 | *If you won't* (=if you are willing to) *help me I'll do it myself.* 如果你不願意幫我的忙, 我就自己做。 Compare 比較: *If this car gives me any more trouble I'll be really angry.* 如果這輛汽車再給我添任何麻煩, 我真要發火了。

---

ig·loo /ˈɪglu; ˈɪgluː/ *n* **igloos** a rounded house made of hard icy blocks of snow〔用堅硬的雪塊砌成的〕圓形房子

ig·ne·ous /ˈɪgnɪəs; ˈɪgnɪəs/ *adj tech* formed from hot liquid rock which has become cool and gone hard〖術語〗〔岩石〕火成的

ig·nite /ɪgˈnaɪt; ɪgˈnaɪt/ *v* **ignited, igniting** [I; T] *fml* to start burning, or make something start burning〖正式〗着火; 點燃: *The petrol suddenly ignited and there was a terrific explosion.* 汽油突然着火燒起來, 發生了可怕的爆炸。

ig·ni·tion /ɪgˈnɪʃən; ɪgˈnɪʃən/ *n* **1** [C] the electrical CIRCUIT which starts a car engine〔汽車引擎的〕點火裝置; 點火開關: *Turn on the ignition.* 開點火開關。 **–see picture on page 209** 見 209 頁彩圖 **2** [U] *fml* the process of making something start burning〖正式〗點火; 着火

ig·no·ble /ɪgˈnəbl; ɪgˈnəʊbəl/ *adj lit* not showing high principles or honour〖文〗卑鄙的; 不光彩的

ig·no·min·i·ous /͵ɪgnəˈmɪnɪəs; ͵ɪgnəˈmɪnɪəs/ *adj* bringing shame or strong public disapproval 恥辱的; 丟臉的: *an ignominious defeat* 不光彩的失敗 **–ignominiously** *adv*

ig·no·ra·mus /͵ɪgnəˈreɪməs; ͵ɪgnəˈreɪməs/ *n* someone who does not know about something they should know 無知的人

ig·no·rance /ˈɪgnərəns; ˈɪgnərəns/ *n* [U] lack of knowledge 無知; 不知: *We were kept in complete ignorance of the company takeover.* 我們對公司被接管之事一無所知。

ig·no·rant /ˈɪgnərənt; ˈɪgnərənt/ *adj* **1** lacking knowledge or education (a word often used to show disapproval) 無知的; 愚昧的〔常含貶義〕: *How can he be so ignorant?* 他怎麼能這麼無知? **2** having no information about something 不知道的: *Many people are totally ignorant of their rights.* 很多人對他們的權利一無所知。 **–see** 見 IGNORE (USAGE 用法)

★**ig·nore** /ɪgˈnɔr; ɪgˈnɔː/ *v* **ignored, ignoring** [T] to take no notice of someone or something 忽視; 不顧; 不理: *Ignore those boys and they'll soon stop misbehaving.* 別理會那些男孩, 他們過一會兒就不鬧了。

■ **USAGE** 用法: Compare 比較 **ignore** and 和 **be ignorant of**. If you **ignore** something you know about it but pay no attention ☆**ignore** 表示雖然知道某事, 但卻置之不理: *He knew there was a speed limit but he **ignored** it and drove very fast.* 他知道有車速限制, 但卻置之不理, 把車開得飛快。 If you **are ignorant of** something you don't know about it ☆如果用 **be ignorant of,** 則表示不知道某事: *Most passengers were totally ignorant of the safety procedures.* 大多數旅客根本不知道安全措施。

i·kon /ˈaɪkɑn; ˈaɪkɒn/ *n* see 見 ICON

*ill¹ /ɪl; ɪl/ *adj* **worse** /wɝs; wɜːs/, **worst** /wɝst; wɜːst/ **1** [never before a noun 不能用於名詞前] hurt or not in good health 受傷的; 有病的: *critically ill in hospital with gunshot wounds* 受了槍傷而病情危急 | *mentally ill* 精神病的 **2** [only before a noun 只用於名詞前] bad or harmful 壞的; 有害的: *ill luck* 惡運 | *I'm suffering from the ill effects of having eaten too much over Christmas.* 我聖誕節吃得太多, 現在嘗到了惡果。 | *There's a lot of ill feeling about her being promoted.* 對她得到提升一事, 人們都很反感。

ill² *adv* [no comparative 無比較級] **1** unpleasantly or badly 使人不愉快地; 壞地: *You shouldn't speak ill of your neighbours.* 你不該說鄰居的壞話。 | *She seems ill-suited to this job.* 她看來不適合幹這工作。 **2 can ill afford** cannot very easily afford 難以負擔: *I can ill afford the time.* 我簡直抽不出時間。

ill³ *n* a bad thing, especially a problem or cause of worry 不幸; 問題; 苦惱: *the social ills of unemployment and poverty* 社會的失業和貧窮弊病

I'll /aɪl; aɪl/ **1** short for 〖縮〗= "I will" **2** short for 〖縮〗= "I shall"

ill-ad·vised /ˌ·····◄/ *adj* not wise 不明智的

il·le·gal /ɪˈligl; ɪˈliːgəl/ *adj* against the law 不合法的; 違法的: *It's illegal for people under 17 to drive a car in Britain.* 在英國十七歲以下的人開車是違法的。 **—illegally** *adv*: *illegally parked* 違法停車的 **—illegality** /ˌɪliˈgæləti; ˌɪliˈgælɨti/ *n* [C;U]

il·le·gi·ble /ɪˈlɛdʒəbl; ɪˈledʒɨbəl/ *adj* impossible to read 難以辨認的: *illegible handwriting* 難以辨認的筆跡 **—illegibly** *adv* **—illegibility** /ɪˌlɛdʒəˈbɪləti; ɪˌledʒɨˈbɪlɨti/ *n* [U]

il·le·git·i·mate /ˌɪlɪˈdʒɪtəmɪt; ˌɪlɪˈdʒɪtɨmɨt/ *adj* **1** born to parents who are not married 私生的: *an illegitimate child* 私生子 **2** not allowed by the rules 非法的; 違法的 **—illegitimately** *adv* **—illegitimacy** *n* [U]

ill-e·quipped /ˌ·····◄/ *adj* not having something needed for a particular activity 裝備不良的; 設備缺乏的

ill-fat·ed /ˌ·····◄/ *adj* unlucky 不幸的: *an ill-fated attempt to climb Everest* 攀登珠穆朗瑪峰的倒霉的嘗試

il·li·cit /ɪˈlɪsɪt; ɪˈlɪsɨt/ *adj* not allowed by law or approved of by society 非法的; 違禁的: *illicit trade in drugs* 毒品非法交易 | *an illicit love affair* 私通 **—illicitly** *adv*

ill-in·formed /ˌ·····◄/ *adj* having incorrect or not enough information about something 消息有誤的; 消息不足的

il·lit·e·rate /ɪˈlɪtərɪt; ɪˈlɪtərɨt/ *adj* unable to read and write 不識字的; 文盲的: *About half the population is still illiterate.* 約有一半人口仍是文盲 **—illiteracy** *n* [U]: *the battle against illiteracy* 掃盲運動

*ill·ness /ˈɪlnɪs; ˈɪlnɨs/ *n* **1** [C] a disease 疾病: *It could be one of several illnesses going around at present.* 這可能是目前的幾種流行病之一。 **2** [C;U] a period of being ill 患病期: *We haven't seen her since her illness. How is she now?* 自從她患病以來我們還沒見過她。 她現在怎麼樣? –see 見 DISEASE (USAGE用法)

il·lo·gi·cal /ɪˈlɑdʒɪkl; ɪˈlɒdʒɪkəl/ *adj* not reasonable or sensible 不合邏輯的; 悖理的: *That statement is totally illogical!* 那份陳述完全不合邏輯! **—illogically** /-klɪ; -klɨ/ *adv*

ill-treat /ˌ·····◄/ *v* [T] to be cruel to someone 虐待〔某人〕; 折磨: *an ill-treated child* 受虐待的孩子

il·lu·mi·nate /ɪˈlumə,net; ɪˈluːmɨneɪt/ *v* **illuminated, illuminating** [T] **1** to shine light on something 照亮〔某物〕: *The room was illuminated by candles.* 這間屋子用蠟燭照明。 **2** to make something clearer 闡明〔某事物〕; 解釋: *His article illuminates a much misunderstood area of study.* 他的文章對很多人誤解的一個研究領域進行了闡明。

il·lu·mi·nat·ing /ɪˈlumɪ,netɪŋ; ɪˈluːmɨneɪtɪŋ/ *adj* helping to explain something 有啟發性的: *an illuminating remark that showed her real character* 顯示她真正性格的有啟發性的話

il·lu·mi·na·tion /ɪ,luməˈneʃən; ɪ,luːmɨˈneɪʃən/ *n* [U] **1** lighting 照明; 照亮: *The illumination is too weak to show the detail of the painting.* 照明不夠, 無法顯示畫作的細節。 **2 illuminations** [pl] the show of coloured lights used to make a town bright and colourful for a special occasion 燈彩; 燈飾

il·lu·sion /ɪˈljuʒən; ɪˈluːʒən/ *n* **1** something seen wrongly, not as it really is 錯覺; 幻覺; 假象: *The lake in the desert was just an optical illusion.* 沙漠中的湖泊只是一種視力錯覺。 **2** a false belief or idea 錯誤的信仰或觀念: *He liked having two secretaries; it gave him an illusion of power.* 他喜歡有兩個祕書, 這給他一種權力在握的幻想。 | *I have no illusions about him; I know he's a liar.* 我對他不抱幻想, 我知道他是個慣於撒謊的人。

*il·lus·trate /ˈɪləstret; ˈɪləstreɪt/ *v* **illustrated,**

illustrating [T] **1** to add pictures to a book or magazine 給〔雜誌、書〕加插圖: *a beautifully illustrated history of science* 一本有精美插圖的科學史 **2** to explain something by giving examples 舉例說明〔某事物〕: *"I can illustrate the point with these graphs."* "我可以用這些圖表來說明這個論點"

il·lus·tra·tion /ˌɪləs'treʃən; ˌɪlə'streɪʃən/ *n* **1** [C] a picture in a book or magazine 插圖: *It's not a very good story, but I like the illustrations.* 這故事不是很好，可我喜歡裡面的插圖。 **2** [C] an example which explains something 例證；實例: *That's a typical illustration of his meanness.* 那是說明他為人卑鄙的典型例子。 **3** [U] the drawing of pictures for books or the giving of examples to explain something 圖示；說明 **4 by way of illustration** as an example 作為例證

il·lus·tra·tive /ɪ'lʌstrətɪv; 'ɪləstreɪtɪv/ *adj fml* helping to show or explain something 〔正式〕起說明作用的: *an illustrative example* 說明問題的例子 | *Such situations are illustrative of the need for immediate action.* 這些情況說明了立刻採取行動的必要性。

il·lus·tra·tor /'ɪləsˌtretə; 'ɪləstreɪtəʳ/ *n* a person who draws pictures for books or magazines 插圖畫家

il·lus·tri·ous /ɪ'lʌstrɪəs; ɪ'lʌstriəs/ *adj* extremely famous and widely admired 著名的；受到廣泛崇拜的: *the illustrious name of Shakespeare* 莎士比亞的英名

I'm /aɪm; aɪm/ short for〔縮〕= "I am"

⭐**im·age** /'ɪmɪdʒ; 'ɪmɪdʒ/ *n* **1** a picture of someone or something in your mind〔頭腦中的〕景象: *As she spoke, an image of a country garden came into my mind.* 她在發言時，我腦海裡浮現出一幅鄉村花園的景象。 **2** the opinion which people have of someone or of an organization 形象；概念: *The government will have to improve its image if it wants to win the election.* 政府如果想在大選中獲勝，必須改變自己的形象。 **3 be the image of** to look very like someone else 酷似〔某人〕: *He's the image of his father.* 他酷似他父親。 **4** something in a poem or painting that suggests a particular quality〔詩或圖畫中〕象徵；典型: *The image of the butterfly creates a strong sense of beauty and powerlessness.* 蝴蝶這個象徵創造出了一種強烈的美感和軟弱無力感。 **5** an object representing a god or person to be worshipped 偶像

im·age·ry /'ɪmɪdʒrɪ; 'ɪmɪdʒəri/ *n* [U] the use of phrases in literature which suggest feelings and ideas〔文學的〕形象化描述；比喻

i·ma·gi·na·ble /ɪ'mædʒɪnəbl; ɪ'mædʒɪnəbəl/ *adj* able to be thought of 可以想像的: *every imaginable possibility* 可以想得到的一切可能性

i·ma·gi·na·ry /ɪ'mædʒəˌnɛrɪ; ɪ'mædʒɪnəri/ *adj* not real, but produced from someone's mind 想像的；虛構的: *All the characters in*

this book are imaginary. 這本書中所有的人物都是虛構的。

⭐**i·ma·gi·na·tion** /ɪˌmædʒə'neʃən; ɪˌmædʒə'neɪʃən/ *n* **1** [C;U] the ability to form pictures or ideas in your mind 想像力: *Your story shows plenty of imagination.* 你的故事顯示了充分的想像力。 | *a vivid imagination* 生動的想像力 **2** [C] your mind 頭腦（想像）: *The difficulties are all in your imagination.* 困難全是你頭腦裡想像出來的東西。

i·ma·gi·na·tive /ɪ'mædʒəˌnetɪv; ɪ'mædʒɪnətɪv/ *adj* using or having imagination 運用想像力的；富於想像力的: *imaginative writing* 富於想像力的寫作 | *She is a highly imaginative child.* 她是個想像力極豐富的孩子。 –opposite 反義 **unimaginative –imaginatively** *adv*

⭐**i·ma·gine** /ɪ'mædʒɪn; ɪ'mædʒɪn/ *v* **imagined, imagining 1** [T; +(that)] to form a picture or idea in your mind 想像: *Try to imagine life in a hundred years time.* 試著想像一下一百年後的生活。 | *You can imagine how amazed I was!* 你可以想像我有多驚訝! | *Imagine that you've won a million pounds.* 想像一下你贏了一百萬英鎊。 | *It's hard to imagine living in a palace.* 很難想像宮廷中的生活。 | *I simply can't imagine George helping with the baby!* 我簡直不能想像喬治幫忙照料嬰兒!

> □ USEFUL PATTERNS 有用句型
> to imagine something; to imagine what, how, etc...; to imagine that...; to imagine doing something; to imagine someone doing something

2 [T; +(that)] to believe or have an idea about something, especially mistakenly or without proof〔尤指錯誤地或無根據地〕猜想；設想: *No one's listening to your phone calls — you're just imagining the whole thing!* 沒人在聽你打電話——你只是在設想整件事情! | *She imagined that everyone was talking about her.* 她猜想每個人都在談論她。 **3** [+ (that)] [not in progressive forms 不用於進行式] to consider something to be probable 認為；料想: *I imagine she's exhausted after her journey.* 我想她旅行後累極了。

im·bal·ance /ɪm'bæləns; ɪm'bæləns/ *n* a lack of balance or equality 不平衡；失調: *When more males are born than females, there is a population imbalance.* 當男性出生多於女性時，就會造成人口比例失調。 | *a serious trade imbalance* **between** *the two countries* 兩國間嚴重的貿易不平衡

im·be·cile /'ɪmbəsl; 'ɪmbəsiːl/ *n* an extremely stupid person 低能兒 –**imbecility** /ˌɪmbə'sɪlətɪ; ˌɪmbɪ'sɪlɪti/ *n* [U]

im·bibe /ɪm'baɪb; ɪm'baɪb/ *v* **imbibed, imbibing** [I;T] *fml* to drink, especially alcohol 〔正式〕喝；飲〔尤指含酒精的飲料〕

im·bue /ɪmˈbjuː; ɪmˈbjuː/ v **imbued, imbuing** **imbue sbdy with sthg** *phr v* [T] *fml* to fill someone with a particular quality 〔正式〕 使〔某人〕充滿〔某種品質〕: *A President should be imbued with a sense of responsibility for the nation.* 一位總統應該充滿對國家的責任感。

im·i·tate /ˈɪmətet; ˈɪmɪˌteɪt/ v **imitated, imitating** [T] to copy someone's behaviour, appearance, or speech 模仿〔某人的行為、外表或言語〕: *James can imitate his father perfectly.* 詹姆斯能夠維妙維肖地模仿他的父親。| *imitating American dress and culture* 模仿美國服飾和文化 **–imitator** *n* **–imitative** *adj*: *imitative behaviour* 模仿的行為

im·i·ta·tion /ˌɪməˈteʃən; ˌɪmɪˈteɪʃən/ *n* **1** [C] a copy in appearance or behaviour 〔行為或外表的〕模仿: *He does a good imitation of the President.* 他模仿總統很逼真。| *They're not real diamonds, just imitations.* 這些不是真的鑽石，只是仿製品。**2** [U] the act of copying something 模仿的動作: *They say that imitation is the sincerest form of flattery.* 他們說模仿是恭維的最真誠的形式。

im·mac·u·late /ɪˈmækjəlɪt; ɪˈmækjʊlɪt/ *adj* **1** completely clean and unspoilt 純潔的; 無瑕疵的: *immaculate white shoes* 潔白的鞋子 **2** without fault 無過失的: *immaculate behaviour* 沒有過失的行為 **–immaculately** *adv*: *immaculately dressed* 衣着一塵不染

im·ma·te·ri·al /ˌɪməˈtɪrɪəl; ˌɪməˈtɪərɪəl/ *adj* unimportant 不重要的: *The time is immaterial — it's the place the accident happened that we need to know.* 時間並不重要——我們需要知道事故發生的地點。

im·ma·ture /ˌɪməˈtjʊr; ˌɪməˈtʃʊər/ *adj* **1** not behaving in an adult manner 不成熟的; 舉止不像成人的: *I think he's rather immature for a man of 30.* 我想作為一個三十歲的男人，他還相當幼稚。**2** not fully formed or developed 發育未全的: *an immature salmon* 還沒長大的鮭魚 **–immaturely** *adv* **–immaturity** *n* [U]

im·mea·su·ra·ble /ɪˈmɛʒərəbl; ɪˈmeʒərəbəl/ *adj* too large to be measured 大得無法計量的: *the immeasurable depths of the ocean* 海洋深不可測 | *The storm has done immeasurable damage.* 暴風雨造成了無法估量的損失。

im·me·di·a·cy /ɪˈmidɪəsɪ; ɪˈmiːdɪəsi/ *n* [U] *fml* the closeness of something, which causes it to be noticed or means that it must be dealt with immediately 〔正式〕刻不容緩: *He did not realize the immediacy of the danger.* 他沒意識到危險迫在眉睫。

★im·me·di·ate /ɪˈmidɪt; ɪˈmiːdɪət/ *adj* **1** done or needed at once and without delay 立即的: *an immediate reply* 立即的答覆 | *We must take immediate action.* 我們必須立即採取行動。**2** nearest 最接近的; 貼近的: *in the immediate future* 在最近的將來 | *My immediate family consists of my son and my wife.*

我最親近的家人包括兒子和妻子。

★im·me·di·ate·ly [1] /ɪˈmidɪtlɪ; ɪˈmiːdɪətli/ *adv* **1** without delay 立即; 馬上: *Stop that immediately!* 馬上把它停下來! | *I went immediately after I'd eaten.* 我吃完後馬上去了。**2** directly 直接地: *Everyone who is immediately involved will be informed of developments.* 直接有關的每個人都會得到事態發展的通知。| *I'd parked immediately in front of the theatre.* 我把車直接停在戲院前面了。

> ■ USAGE 用法: **Immediately** is usually too direct to use in polite requests. It is better to use the phrase **as soon as possible** ☆在禮貌的請求中，用 **immediately** 常過於直截了當。最好用詞組 **as soon as possible**: *I would be grateful if you could send me the information* **as soon as possible.** 請你盡快把資料送來，實在非常感激。| *Could you let me know* **as soon as possible?** 你可以盡快讓我知道嗎?

immediately [2] *conj* as soon as 一…就…〔就…〕: *I came immediately I heard the news.* 我一聽到這個消息就來了。

im·me·mo·ri·al /ˌɪməˈmorɪəl; ˌɪmɪˈmɔːrɪəl/ *adj* going back longer than people can remember 無法追憶的

im·mense /ɪˈmɛns; ɪˈmens/ *adj* very large 巨大的: *an immense palace* 巨大的宮殿 | *That's an immense improvement on your first attempt!* 跟第一次做的成績比較，今次有了極大改進! **–immensity** *n* [U]: *the immensity of space* 太空浩瀚無際

im·mense·ly /ɪˈmɛnslɪ; ɪˈmensli/ *adv* very much 非常; 很: *I enjoyed it immensely.* 我很喜愛它。| *an immensely complex situation* 非常複雜的情況

im·merse /ɪˈmɜːs; ɪˈmɜːs/ v **immersed, immersing 1** [T] to cover something completely in a liquid 浸沒: *Immerse the cloth in the dye.* 把布浸泡在染料裡。**2 immerse yourself in something** to direct all your thoughts and attention to something 使自己沉浸於某事物; 使自己專心於某事物: *I immersed myself in my work to try to forget her.* 我埋頭於工作，試圖忘掉她。**–immersion** /ɪˈmɜːʃən; ɪˈmɜːʃən/ *n* [U]

im·mer·sion heat·er /ˈ··· ˌ··/ *n* an electric water heater in a TANK 浸沒式〔電子〕熱水器

im·mi·grant /ˈɪməɡrənt; ˈɪmɪɡrənt/ *n* a person coming into a country from abroad to make their home there 〔外來〕移民; 僑民 – compare 比較 EMIGRANT **–see** 見 EMIGRATE (USAGE用法)

im·mi·gra·tion /ˌɪməˈɡreʃən; ˌɪmɪˈɡreɪʃən/ *n* [U] the process of entering another country to make your life and home there 移居; 移民入境: *the immigration office at the airport* 機場入境移民辦事處 | *There are* *strict controls on immigration into this country.* 移居這個國家有嚴格的控制。—see 見 EMIGRATE (USAGE用法)

im·mi·nence /ˈɪmənəns; ˈɪmˌnəns/ *n* [U] the nearness of something which is going to happen, especially something unpleasant 〔尤指使人不快的事〕逼近; 急迫: *The imminence of the exams made them work harder.* 考試即將來臨, 這迫使他們更加用功。

im·mi·nent /ˈɪmənənt; ˈɪmˌnənt/ *adj* going to happen very soon 逼近的; 急迫的: *A general election is now imminent.* 大選馬上就要來臨。| *in imminent danger of death* 瀕臨死亡的危險

im·mo·bile /ɪˈmobl; ɪˈməʊbaɪl/ *adj* **1** completely still 固定的: *Keep the broken leg immobile.* 把骨折的腿固定好。**2** not able to move 不能移動的 **–immobility** /ˌɪmoˈbɪlətɪ; ˌɪməʊˈbɪlə̩tɪ/ *n* [U]

im·mo·bi·lize /ˈɪmobl̩aɪz; ɪˈməʊbə̩laɪz/ *v* **immobilized, immobilizing** (also 又作 **immobilise** *BrE* 〔英式〕) [T] to make something unable to move 使〔某物〕不能移動: *The fishing boats have been immobilized by the storms.* 漁船因為暴風雨而動彈不得。

im·mod·e·rate /ɪˈmɑdərɪt; ɪˈmɒdər̩ɪt/ *adj* not kept within sensible limits 無節制的: *immoderate wage demands* 對工資的過高要求

im·mod·est /ɪˈmɑdɪst; ɪˈmɒd̩ɪst/ *adj* **1** telling the good things about yourself instead of hiding them 不謙虛的: *He was most immodest about his promotion.* 他對自己的晉升極不謙虛。**2** improper and likely to shock other people 不適當的; 不端莊的: *an immodest dress* 不正派的衣着 **–immodestly** *adv* **–immodesty** *n* [U]

im·mor·al /ɪˈmɔrəl; ɪˈmɒrəl/ *adj* **1** not considered good or right 不道德的: *Using other people for your own profit is immoral.* 為私利而利用別人是不道德的。**2** going against accepted standards of sexual behaviour 放蕩的; 淫蕩的: *A pimp lives off the immoral earnings of a prostitute.* 皮條客靠妓女賣淫所得過日子。**–immorally** *adv* **–immorality** /ˌɪmɔˈrælətɪ; ˌɪməˈræl̩tɪ/ *n* [U]

im·mor·tal /ɪˈmɔrtl; ɪˈmɔːtl/ *adj* **1** that will not die 不死的; 長生的: *Nobody is immortal.* 人都是要死的。**2** remembered for ever 不朽的; 永久的: *Shakespeare's immortal plays* 莎士比亞的不朽劇作 **–immortality** /ˌɪmɔrˈtælətɪ; ˌɪmɔːˈtæl̩tɪ/ *n* [U]

im·mor·tal·ize /ɪˈmɔrtl̩aɪz; ɪˈmɔːtələaɪz/ *v* **immortalized, immortalizing** (also 又作 **immortalise** *BrE* 〔英式〕) [T] to cause someone or something to be remembered for ever 使不朽; 使名垂千古: *Dickens' father was immortalized as Mr Micawber in "David Copperfield".* 狄更斯的父親作為米考伯先生出現在《大衛·科波菲爾》中而名垂於世。

im·mo·va·ble /ɪˈmuvəbl; ɪˈmuːvəbəl/ *adj* impossible to move 不可移動的 **–immova-**

bly *adv*

im·mune /ɪˈmjun; ɪˈmjuːn/ *adj* **1** not harmed by something 不受〔某物〕傷害的; 有免疫力的: *Most of them are immune to hepatitis.* 他們大多數人對肝炎有免疫力。| *The president seems to be immune to criticism.* 總統似乎沒有受到批評的影響。**2 immune from something** specially protected from something 免於某事: *You will probably be immune from punishment if you help the police.* 你如果協助警方就可能免受懲罰。**–immunity** *n* [U]: *diplomatic immunity* 外交豁免權

immune sys·tem /·ˈ·· ,·ˈ·/ *n* **the immune system** a system in your body which produces special substances to fight against disease-causing substances that have entered your body 〔人體〕免疫系統

im·mu·nize /ˈɪmjə̩naɪz; ˈɪmjə̩naɪz/ *v* **immunized, immunizing** (also 又作 **immunise** *BrE* 〔英式〕) [T] to protect someone from disease, usually by putting certain substances into their body with a special needle 〔常以皮下注射法〕使〔某人〕免疫 **–immunization** /ˌɪmjunəˈzeʃən; ˌɪmjə̩naɪˈzeɪʃən/ *n* [C;U]

im·mu·ta·ble /ɪˈmjutəbl; ɪˈmjuːtəbəl/ *adj fml* never changing 〔正式〕永不改變的; 永恆的: *the immutable laws of nature* 永恆的大自然規律

imp /ɪmp; ɪmp/ *n* a playful, troublesome little character in fairy stories 〔神話中的〕小精靈

im·pact /ˈɪmpækt; ˈɪmpækt/ *n* **1** [C] the strong effect that something has on something else 影響; 作用: *That new computer has made quite an impact on our office.* 那台新電腦對我們的辦公室產生了很大影響。**2** [U] the force of one object hitting another 衝[撞]擊力 **3 on impact** at the moment when one object hits another 在〔物體〕相撞的一刻

im·pair /ɪmˈpɛr; ɪmˈpeəʳ/ *v* [T] to damage or weaken something 損害, 削弱〔某物〕: *His hearing was impaired by the explosion.* 爆炸後他的聽力受到了損害。**–impairment** *n* [U]

im·pale /ɪmˈpel; ɪmˈpeɪl/ *v* **impaled, impaling** [T] **be impaled on something** to have something sharp and pointed going through your body 被尖銳的某物刺穿〔身體〕: *He fell out of the window and was impaled on the iron railings.* 他從窗口跌下來, 被鐵欄杆刺傷了。

im·part /ɪmˈpart; ɪmˈpaːt/ *v* [T] *fml* 〔正式〕**1** to pass on qualities or feelings 給予〔品質〕; 傳遞〔感情〕: *The herbs imparted a delicious flavour to the stew.* 這種香草給燉的菜增添了鮮美的味道。**2** to tell or pass on information 告知; 通知; 透露: *I've no news to impart.* 我沒有消息可以透露。

im·par·tial /ɪmˈparʃəl; ɪmˈpaːʃəl/ *adj* fair and not giving special support to one side

公平的; 不偏袒的: *an impartial judge* 公正的法官 | *an impartial news report* 不帶偏見的新聞報導 **–impartially** *adv* **–impartiality** /ˌɪmpɑːˈʃælətɪ; ɪmˌpɑːʃiˈælj^ti/ *n* [U]

im·pass·a·ble /ɪmˈpæsəbḷ; ɪmˈpɑːsəbəl/ *adj* not able to be travelled over 不能通行的; 通不過的: *The snow has made the road impassable.* 雪使道路無法通行。

im·passe /ɪmˈpæs; æmˈpɑːs/ *n* [sing] a difficult situation in which neither side will give way 僵局; 絕境: *Negotiations have reached an impasse.* 談判陷入了僵局。

im·pas·sioned /ɪmˈpæʃənd; ɪmˈpæʃənd/ *adj* filled with deep feelings (used of speech) 充滿激情的〔指講話〕: *an impassioned plea for the prisoners to be freed* 強烈請求釋放犯人

im·pas·sive /ɪmˈpæsɪv; ɪmˈpæsɪv/ *adj* showing no feelings 沒有表情的; 無動於衷的 – **impassively** *adv*: *He watched impassively as his house burned down.* 他毫無表情地看着自己的房子燒毀。

im·pa·tient /ɪmˈpeɪʃənt; ɪmˈpeɪʃənt/ *adj* **1** easily annoyed by delays, or other people's weaknesses 不耐煩的; 急躁的: *The teacher was too impatient with slow learners.* 這老師對遲鈍的學生十分不耐煩。 **2** annoyed and bad-tempered 惱火的、壞脾氣的: *an impatient reply* 惱火的答覆 **3** **impatient for** something eager for something 急於某事: *impatient for his dinner* 急於吃他的晚飯 **4** **impatient to do** something wanting to do something very much 十分想做某事: *I was impatient to leave.* 我迫不急待地要離開。 – **impatience** *n* [U]: *He could barely conceal his impatience.* 他再也按捺不住焦急的心情。 **–impatiently** *adv*

im·peach /ɪmˈpiːtʃ; ɪmˈpiːtʃ/ *v* [T] *law* to say a public official is guilty of a serious crime against the state 〔律〕彈劾〔公職人員〕 – **impeachment** *n* [U]

im·pec·ca·ble /ɪmˈpekəbḷ; ɪmˈpekəbəl/ *adj* without any faults 無任何錯誤的; 無懈可擊的: *impeccable manners* 無懈可擊的舉止 – **impeccably** *adv*

im·pe·cu·ni·ous /ˌɪmpɪˈkjuːnɪəs; ˌɪmpɪˈkjuːnɪəs/ *adj fml* having little or no money, especially continually〔正式〕〔尤指經常〕手頭拮据的; 沒錢的

im·pede /ɪmˈpiːd; ɪmˈpiːd/ *v* **impeded, impeding** [T] to slow down the process of doing something by making it difficult 妨礙, 阻礙〔某事〕: *The attempt to rescue the climbers was impeded by bad weather.* 營救登山者的工作受到了惡劣天氣的妨礙。

im·ped·i·ment /ɪmˈpedəmənt; ɪmˈpedʒ-mənt/ *n* **1** a fact or event which makes action difficult or impossible 妨礙; 阻礙; 障礙: *The country's huge foreign debt will be a major impediment to its development.* 這個國家的巨額外債將成為發展的主要障礙。 **2** **a speech impediment** a physical or nervous difficulty which prevents someone from speaking clearly 口吃; 結巴

im·pel /ɪmˈpel; ɪmˈpel/ *v* **-ll-** [T] *fml* (of an idea or feeling) to drive someone to take action〔正式〕〔思想或感情〕驅使, 激勵〔某人〕: *He felt impelled to write to the paper about it.* 他覺得非給報社寫信反映此事不可。

□ **USEFUL PATTERN** 有用句型
to impel someone to do something

im·pend·ing /ɪmˈpendɪŋ; ɪmˈpendɪŋ/ *adj* going to happen soon (used of something unpleasant) 即將發生的〔指不愉快的事情〕; 迫近的: *We had no warning of the impending disaster.* 對即將發生的災難, 我們並沒得到警告。

im·pen·e·tra·ble /ɪmˈpenətrəbḷ; ɪmˈpen-trəbəl/ *adj* **1** impossible to get through 透不過的; 穿不過的: *the impenetrable forest* 無法通過的森林 | *impenetrable darkness* 一片漆黑 **2** impossible to understand 費解的; 不能理解的: *an impenetrable mystery* 難解之謎

im·per·a·tive[1] /ɪmˈperətɪv; ɪmˈperətɪv/ *adj fml* very urgent and important〔正式〕緊急的; 極重要的: *It's imperative that you go at once.* 你必須馬上就去。

imperative[2] *n* the form of a verb which expresses a command 祈使語氣(動詞): *In "Come here!" the verb "come" is in the imperative.* 在 "Come here!" 中, 動詞 "come" 是祈使語氣。

im·per·cep·ti·ble /ˌɪmpəˈseptəbḷ; ˌɪmpə-ˈseptʒbəl/ *adj* not noticed because of being very small or slight〔由於極微小而〕察覺不到的: *an almost imperceptible movement of her eyelid* 她的眼瞼幾乎察覺不出的跳動 **–imperceptibly** *adv* **–imperceptibility** /ˌɪmpə-ˌseptəˈbɪlətɪ; ˌɪmpəseptʒˈbɪlʒtɪ/ *n* [U]

im·per·fect[1] /ɪmˈpɜːfɪkt; ɪmˈpɜːfɪkt/ *adj* with some fault or problem 有缺點的; 有問題的: *I have only an imperfect knowledge of French.* 我只有一點兒不甚透徹的法語知識。 – **imperfectly** *adv* **–imperfection** /ˌɪmpəˈfek-ʃən; ˌɪmpəˈfekʃən/ *n* [C;U]

imperfect[2] *n* **the imperfect, the imperfect tense** the tense of a verb which shows an incomplete or repeated action in the past〔動詞的〕未完成過去時: *In "we were walking down the road" the verb "were walking" is in the imperfect.* 在"we were walking down the road"中, 動詞"were walking"是過去未完成時。

im·pe·ri·al /ɪmˈpɪrɪəl; ɪmˈpɪərɪəl/ *adj* (also 又作 **Imperial**) **1** relating to an empire or its ruler 帝國的; 皇帝〔或女皇〕的: *the Imperial Palace* 皇宮 **2** relating to the British system of measurement 英制的: *The Imperial gallon is not the same size as the American one.* 英制的加侖和美制的不一致。

im·pe·ri·al·ism /ɪmˈpɪrɪəlˌɪzəm; ɪmˈpɪərɪ-əlɪzəm/ *n* [U] the gaining of political and trade advantages over poorer nations by a powerful country which rules them or helps them〔大國從其統治或資助的窮國中取得的〕政治和貿易優勢 **-imperialist** *n, adj* – **imperialistic** /ɪmˌpɪrɪəlˈɪstɪk; ɪmˌpɪəriəˈlɪstɪk◂/ *adj*

im·per·il /ɪmˈpɛrəl; ɪmˈpɛrɪl/ *v* **-ll-** (also 又作 **-l-** *AmE*〖美式〗) [T] *fml* to put someone in danger〖正式〗使〔某人〕陷於危險

im·pe·ri·ous /ɪmˈpɪrɪəs; ɪmˈpɪəriəs/ *adj fml* proud, and expecting other people to obey you〖正式〗傲慢的；專橫的: *an imperious voice* 傲慢的聲調 **-imperiously** *adv* – **imperiousness** *n* [U]

im·per·son·al /ɪmˈpɜːsn̩l; ɪmˈpɜːsənəl/ *adj* not showing or including personal feelings 與個人感情無關的: *an impersonal letter* 一封非私人信 | *a large impersonal organization* 一個沒有人情味的大機構 **-impersonally** *adv*

im·per·so·nate /ɪmˈpɜːsn̩et; ɪmˈpɜːsəneɪt/ *v* **impersonated, impersonating** [T] to pretend to be another person by copying their appearance and behaviour〔通過模仿外表、舉止〕冒充；扮演: *He impersonates all the well-known politicians.* 他扮演所有著名的政治家。 **-impersonator** *n* **-impersonation** /ɪmˌpɜːsn̩ˈeɪʃən; ɪmˌpɜːsəˈneɪʃən/ *n* [C;U]

im·per·ti·nent /ɪmˈpɜːtn̩ənt; ɪmˈpɜːtn̩nənt/ *adj* rude or not respectful, especially to an older or more important person〔尤指對年長者或位尊者〕粗魯的；失禮的: *I will not tolerate such impertinent remarks.* 我不會容忍這麼無禮的話。 **-impertinence** *n* [U] – **impertinently** *adv*

im·per·tur·ba·ble /ˌɪmpɚˈtɜːbəbl; ˌɪmpəˈtɜːbəbl/ *adj* remaining calm in spite of difficulties 沉着的；冷靜的 **-imperturbably** *adv* **-imperturbability** /ˌɪmpɚˌtɜːbəˈbɪlətɪ; ˌɪmpətɜːbəˈbɪlˌti/ *n* [U]

im·per·vi·ous /ɪmˈpɜːvɪəs; ɪmˈpɜːviəs/ *adj* **1** impervious to not influenced or changed by something 不受〔某事物〕影響的；不因〔某事物〕而改變的: *He seemed totally impervious to reason.* 他似乎無可理喻。 **2** not allowing anything to pass through 不能透過的；不能穿過的: *an impervious rock such as granite* 像花崗岩這種無物可透的岩石

im·pet·u·ous /ɪmˈpɛtʃʊəs; ɪmˈpetʃuəs/ *adj* **1** tending to be quick to act, but without thinking carefully 魯莽的: *an impetuous young man* 魯莽的小伙子 **2** done or made too quickly 過快的；急躁的: *an impetuous decision which she soon regretted* 她作了輕率的決定，不久感到後悔了 **-impetuously** *adv*

im·pe·tus /ˈɪmpətəs; ˈɪmpɪtəs/ *n* **1** [C;U] encouragement 推動；激勵: *The government's plan gave fresh impetus to our industry.* 政府的計劃給工業注入了新的動力。 **2** [U] the force of something moving 推動力；衝力: *The car ran down the hill under its own impetus.* 這輛汽車藉着本身的衝力開下了山。

im·pi·e·ty /ɪmˈpaɪətɪ; ɪmˈpaɪˌti/ *n* [U] lack

of respect for religion〔對宗教〕不敬；不虔誠 **-impious** /ˈɪmpɪəs; ˈɪmpɪəs/ *adj*

im·pinge /ɪmˈpɪndʒ; ɪmˈpɪndʒ/ *v* **impinged, impinging, impinge on/upon** to have an effect on someone or something 對〔某人或某物〕起作用；影響: *The economic crisis is impinging on every aspect of our lives.* 經濟危機正在影響我們生活的各個方面。

imp·ish /ˈɪmpɪʃ; ˈɪmpɪʃ/ *adj* like a little devil 小鬼似的；頑皮的: *an impish smile* 頑皮的笑容 **-impishly** *adv*

im·plac·a·ble /ɪmˈplekəbl; ɪmˈplækəbl/ *adj* impossible to make less angry 無法平息的: *an implacable enemy* 死敵

im·plant /ɪmˈplænt; ɪmˈplɑːnt/ *v* [T] **1** to fix something into someone's body by means of an operation 把〔某物〕嵌入〔體內〕；移植 **2** to make an idea become completely accepted 灌輸〔想法〕: *They were accused of trying to implant their own political values into the students.* 他們被指控試圖向學生灌輸自己的政治上的價值觀。 **-implant** /ˈɪmplænt; ˈɪmplɑːnt/ *n*: *hormone implants* 注射激素

im·plau·si·ble /ɪmˈplɔːzəbl; ɪmˈplɔːzˌbl/ *adj* unlikely to be true 不像真實的: *an implausible explanation* 難以叫人相信的解釋

im·ple·ment¹ /ˈɪmpləmənt; ˈɪmplˌmənt/ *n* a tool 工具；用具: *gardening implements* 園藝工具

im·ple·ment² /ˈɪmpləˌmɛnt; ˈɪmplˌment/ *v* [T] to carry out or put into practice 貫徹；執行: *The committee's suggestions will be implemented immediately.* 委員會的意見將立即執行。 **-implementation** /ˌɪmpləmɛnˈteɪʃən; ˌɪmplˌmenˈteɪʃən/ *n* [U]

im·pli·cate /ˈɪmplɪˌket; ˈɪmplˌket/ *v* **implicated, implicating** [T] *fml* to show that someone is connected with something, especially a crime〖正式〗表明〔某人〕與〔某罪行〕有牽連: *The police found a letter which implicated him in the robbery.* 警察發現了一封信，信中表明他與搶劫案有牽連。

★**im·pli·ca·tion** /ˌɪmplɪˈkeʃən; ˌɪmplˌˈkeɪʃən/ *n* **1** something that is suggested but not expressed directly 含意: *He smiled, but the implication was that he didn't believe me.* 他笑了，但這笑意味着他不相信我的話。 **2** by implication by expressing something indirectly 含蓄地；不直接表示地: *She said very little directly, but a great deal by implication.* 她直接的話説得很少，但言外之意卻很多。 **3** a possible later effect of an action or decision 可能的後果: *The article assesses the wider implications of the nuclear accident.* 這篇文章估計了核事故可能造成的更廣泛的後果。

im·plic·it /ɪmˈplɪsɪt; ɪmˈplɪsˌt/ *adj* **1** suggested or understood though not directly expressed 含蓄的；暗示的: *an implicit threat* 暗示的恫嚇 | *Her opposition was implicit in her failure to support the plan.* 她沒支持這個計劃，這暗示了她是反對的。 **-compare** 比較

EXPLICIT **2** [only before a noun 只用於名詞前] complete and unquestioning 絕對的; 無疑的: *She has implicit trust in her doctor.* 她對自己的醫生絕對信任。 –**implicitly** *adv*

im·plore /ɪm'plɔr; ɪm'plɔːrˈ/ *v* **implored, imploring** [T] *fml* to ask someone for something or to do something with great eagerness and anxiety 〔正式〕懇求; 乞求: *She implored his forgiveness.* 她懇求他原諒。| *I implore you to go now.* 我求求你現在就走吧。 –**imploring** *adj*

im·ply /ɪm'plaɪ; ɪm'plaɪ/ *v* **implied, implying** [T;+(that)] **1** to suggest something in an indirect way 暗示: *He didn't actually say he'd been invited, but he certainly implied that he had.* 他實際上沒有說他受到了邀請, 但他肯定暗示了這個意思。| *Are you implying that we're not telling the truth?* 你是否暗示我們沒說真話? –see 見 INFER (USAGE用法) **2** to suggest that something is necessary or true 意味着: *Taking responsibility for organizing the event implies real commitment.* 負責組織這次活動的人必須要有承擔義務的偉大精神。| *The fact that no one answered the phone implies that they're not at home.* 沒人接電話意味着他們不在家。

im·po·lite /,ɪmpə'laɪt; ,ɪmpə'laɪt/ *adj* slightly rude 不禮貌的: *It was impolite of her not to say goodbye.* 她不告辭是失禮的。 –**impolitely** *adv* –**impoliteness** *n* [U]

im·pol·i·tic /ɪm'pɑlətɪk; ɪm'pɒlɪtɪk/ *adj fml* not wise or well-judged for your purpose 〔正式〕失策的; 不當的: *It's unlike him to make such an impolitic decision.* 他可不像是個做出如此失策的決定的人。

im·pon·de·ra·ble /ɪm'pɑndərəbl; ɪm'pɒndərəbəl/ *adj* impossible to calculate or measure exactly –**imponderables** *n* [pl] 無法確切估量的事物: *You cannot anticipate the effect of imponderables such as power and influence.* 你無法預料像權勢那樣難以精確估量的東西所產生的影響。

im·port[1] /ɪm'pɔrt; ɪm'pɔːt/ *v* [T] to bring goods in from another country 進口: *We import thousands of cars from Japan.* 我們從日本進口數千輛汽車。 –compare 比較 EXPORT –**importer** *n*

im·port[2] /'ɪmpɔrt; 'ɪmpɔːt/ *n* **1** [C] something brought in from another country 進口貨: *Imports rose last month.* 上個月進口(量)增加了。| *flooding the market with cheap imports* 廉價的進口貨充斥着市場 **2** [U] the bringing of something in from another country 進口: *the import of food from abroad* 從國外進口食品 **3** [U] *fml* importance 〔正式〕重要: *a matter of no great import* 無關緊要的事

im·por·tance /ɪm'pɔrtns; ɪm'pɔːtns/ *n* [U] **1** the quality or state of being important 重要(性): *It is a matter of national importance.* 這是國家大事。 –opposite 反義 **unimportance 2** the

reason why something or someone is important 〔某事或某人〕重要的原因: *Explain the importance of North Sea oil to the British economy.* 解釋一下北海石油對英國經濟的重要性。

im·por·tant /ɪm'pɔrtnt; ɪm'pɔːtənt/ *adj* **1** special or particularly useful or valuable 重要的; 重大的: *Don't worry about it; it's not important.* 別擔心; 這不重要。| *a very important meeting* 很重要的會議 | *It is important to get the right qualifications.* 取得合適的資格是很重要的。| *It's important that you get well again quickly.* 你迅速康復才是重要的。| *Privacy is important to her.* 一人獨處對她來說很重要。

□ USEFUL PATTERNS 有用句型
be important to do something; be important that...; be important to someone

2 having influence or power 有勢力的; 有影響的: *an important new writer* 一位有影響的新作家 –opposite 反義 **unimportant** –**importantly** *adv*

im·por·ta·tion /,ɪmpɔr'teɪʃən; ,ɪmpɔː'teɪʃən/ *n* [U] bringing something in from another place 進口; 輸入

im·pose /ɪm'poz; ɪm'pəʊz/ *v* **imposed, imposing 1** [T] to force someone to accept something they do not want 強迫〔某人〕接受〔某事物〕: *Economic sanctions have been imposed on South Africa.* 南非被迫接受經濟制裁。| *The judge imposed a fine of £10,000.* 法官宣判罰款一萬英鎊。 **2** [T] to establish an additional payment officially 徵收〔稅款〕: *A new tax has been imposed on cigarettes.* 對煙類已實施了新稅收。 **3** [I] to expect someone to help you by doing something that they may not really want to do 麻煩〔某人〕: *Thank you for the offer, but I don't want to impose on you.* 感謝你的提議, 但我不想麻煩你。 –**imposition** /,ɪmpə'zɪʃən; ,ɪmpə'zɪʃən/ *n* [C;U]: *protesting against the imposition of a sales tax on books* 抗議徵收書籍銷售稅

im·pos·ing /ɪm'pozɪŋ; ɪm'pəʊzɪŋ/ *adj* large or powerful in appearance 壯觀的; 氣勢雄偉的: *an imposing building* 氣勢宏偉的建築物 –**imposingly** *adv*

im·pos·si·ble /ɪm'pɑsəbl; ɪm'pɒsɪbəl/ *adj* **1** that cannot happen or exist, or that cannot be done 不可能發生的; 不可能存在的; 辦不到的: *I'm afraid that's quite impossible.* 恐怕那實在是不可能的。| *It's impossible to realize how angry I felt.* 不可能說得清我有多憤怒。| *an impossible task* 辦不到的任務 | *It's impossible for me to get there before eight o'clock.* 對我而言, 八點以前到達那裡是不可能的。 **2** very unpleasant or difficult to deal with 難以對付的; 不好對付的: *You're putting me in an impossible position.* 你讓我置身於

一個尷尬的境地。–**impossibly** *adv: imposs-ibly difficult* 極端困難的 –**impossibility** /ɪm-,pɑsə'bɪlətɪ; ɪm,pɒs'bɪlᵻ˥ti/ *n* [U]

> □ USEFUL PATTERNS 有用句型
> be impossible to do something; be im-possible for someone to do something

im·pos·tor /ɪm'pɑstə-; ɪm'pɒstər/ *n* (**impos-ter** *AmE*【美式】) someone who pretends to be someone else in order to get something they want 冒名頂替者: *You're not a doctor! You're an impostor!* 你不是醫生! 你是個冒牌貨!

im·po·tent /'ɪmpətənt; 'ɪmpətənt/ *adj* **1** lacking power to influence people or events 無影響力的; 無能為力的: *a govern-ment which seemed impotent in its last years of office* 在任期最後幾年中似乎無能為力的政府 **2** unable to perform the sex act (used of a man) 無性交能力的〔指男子〕 –**impotence** *n* [U] –**impotently** *adv*

im·pound /ɪm'paʊnd; ɪm'paʊnd/ *v* [T] *fml* to take official possession of something 〔正式〕沒收; 扣押: *If you park your car there, it will be impounded by the police.* 如果你把汽車停放在那兒,它就會被警察扣押。

im·pov·er·ished /ɪm'pɑvərɪʃt; ɪm'pɒvərɪʃt/ *adj* made poor 被弄得窮困的: *an impove-rished African country* 一個貧窮的非洲國家 | *the spiritually impoverished Western lifestyle* 精神上貧困的西方生活方式

im·prac·ti·ca·ble /ɪm'præktɪkəbl; ɪm'præk-tɪkəbəl/ *adj* impossible to do or use 不能做的; 不能用的: *It would be impracticable to stop using insecticides completely.* 完全不再使用殺蟲劑是不太可能的。–**impracticably** *adv* –**impracticability** /ɪm,præktɪkə'bɪlətɪ; ɪm,præktɪkə'bɪlᵻ˥ti/ *n* [U]

im·prac·ti·cal /ɪm'præktɪkl; ɪm'præktɪkəl/ *adj* not good at dealing with ordinary situations and problems in a sensible way 不合情理的; 不切實際的: *an impractical per-son who can't even boil an egg* 一個連煮個雞蛋都不會的毫無實踐能力的人 | *I need help-ful ideas — his are completely impractical.* 我需要能幫上忙的主意 —— 他的主意完全不切實際。–**impractically** *adv*

im·pre·cise /,ɪmprɪ'saɪs; ,ɪmprɪ'saɪs/ *adj* not exact or clear 不精確的; 不清楚的: *Her directions were very imprecise.* 她的指示很不清楚。

im·preg·na·ble /ɪm'prɛgnəbl; ɪm'prɛgnəbəl/ *adj* very strong and unable to be entered or conquered 攻不破的; 不可征服的: *an im-pregnable castle* 堅不可摧的城堡

im·preg·nate /'ɪmprɛgnet; 'ɪmprɛgneɪt/ *v* **impregnated, impregnating** [T] **1** to cause a substance to enter and spread com-pletely through another substance 浸注; 灌透; 使充滿: *a cleaning cloth impregnated with polish* 一種飽含亮漆的清潔布 **2** *fml* to

make a female PREGNANT【正式】使懷孕

im·pre·sa·ri·o /,ɪmprɪ'sɑrɪ,o; ,ɪmprɪ'sɑːrɪ-əʊ/ *n* a person who arranges theatrical or musical performances〔戲劇、音樂演出的〕主辦人, 經理

***im·press** /ɪm'prɛs; ɪm'pres/ *v* **1** [T] to fill someone with admiration or respect 使感動; 使欽佩: *I was very impressed with their new house.* 他們的新房子給我留下了深刻印象。| *The teacher told me he was impressed by your essay.* 老師對我說你的文章令他很感動。**2** impress **something on** someone to make someone understand the importance of something 使〔某人〕了解〔某事的〕重要性: *My father impressed on me the value of hard work.* 我父親對我強調了努力工作的重要意義。

***im·pres·sion** /ɪm'prɛʃən; ɪm'preʃən/ *n* **1** the way something looks or appears to you 印象; 感覺: *If the shop is untidy, it makes a bad impression on the customers.* 如果店面不整潔會給顧客一個壞印象。| *She said she was happy, but I got the impression that something was wrong.* 她說她很快活, 但我有這麼一種印象, 有些事情不對勁兒。**2** make an impression to cause people to remember you, usually favourably 給人留下〔常指好的〕印象 **3** be under the impression that to be-lieve that something is true 認為; 以為: *Oh, is he only the form master? I was under the impression that he was the headmaster.* 噢, 他只是班主任? 我還以為他是校長呢。**4** a mark left by pressure 壓印; 印記: *He took an impression of the key to make a copy.* 他壓取了鑰匙的模子, 以便複製一把。**5** a copy of a person's appearance or behaviour as a funny theatrical performance〔對某人外貌或舉止的〕滑稽模仿: *He did his impression of the president.* 他對總統作了滑稽模仿。

im·pres·sio·na·ble /ɪm'prɛʃənəbl; ɪm'preʃə-nəbəl/ *adj* easy to influence 易受影響的: *My son's at an impressionable age.* 我兒子正處於可塑性強的年齡。

im·pres·sion·is·m /ɪm'prɛʃən,ɪzəm; ɪm'pre-ʃənɪzəm/ *n* [U] a style of painting which produces effects by light and colour rather than by details of form; it was popular in France between 1870 and 1900 印象派〔一種繪畫風格, 用光線和色彩而不是對物體的細部描繪來產生效果; 1870 年至 1900 年間在法國流行〕–**impressionist** *n*

im·pres·sion·is·tic /ɪm,prɛʃən'ɪstɪk; ɪm,preʃə-'nɪstɪk◂/ *adj* based on the way something appears to someone, rather than on know-ledge or facts 憑印象的; 主觀的: *We need facts, not an impressionistic account of what happened.* 我們需要事實, 而不是對發生的事憑印象的描述。–**impressionistically** /-klɪ; -klɪ/ *adv*

***im·pres·sive** /ɪm'prɛsɪv; ɪm'presɪv/ *adj* caus-ing admiration 令人欽佩的: *We've suc-ceeded in collecting an impressive amount*

of money. 我們成功地募集了一筆可觀的款項。| *an impressive stamp collection* 收藏的郵票令人讚嘆 –**impressively** *adv* –**impressiveness** *n* [U]

im·print¹ /ɪm'prɪnt; ɪm'prɪnt/ *v* [T] **1** to print or press a mark on something 在〔某物〕上蓋〔印〕 **2** **be imprinted on your mind/ memory** to leave a clear picture in your mind that you will never forget 牢記, 銘刻在心中〔腦海中〕: *Every detail is imprinted on my mind.* 每個細節都印在我的腦海中。

im·print² /'ɪmprɪnt; 'ɪmprɪnt/ *n* **1** a mark left on or in something 印痕; 痕跡: *An imprint of his thumb was left in the concrete.* 他的大拇指印留在水泥裡。 **2** the clear picture or effect of something in your mind 深刻的印象

im·pris·on /ɪm'prɪzn̩; ɪm'prɪzən/ *v* [T] to keep someone in a place from which they cannot escape, especially in a prison 關押, 監禁〔某人〕: *He's been imprisoned for over 27 years.* 他被監禁了超過二十七年。 –**imprisonment** *n* [U]

im·prob·a·ble /ɪm'prɑbḷ; ɪm'prɔbəbəl/ *adj* not likely to happen or to be true 不太可能發生的; 未必確實的: *It's possible that no one saw him leave, but it seems highly improbable.* 可能沒人看見他離開, 但這似乎很靠不住。

im·promp·tu /ɪm'prɑmptu; ɪm'prɔmptjuː/ *adj fml* done without preparation〔正式〕無準備的; 即興的: *an impromptu speech* 即席演講

im·prop·er /ɪm'prɑpɚ; ɪm'prɔpəʳ/ *adj* **1** not suitable or correct 不合適的; 不正確的: *The director of the charity was accused of improper use of funds.* 這個慈善團體的董事被指控對基金使用不當。 **2** rude or socially unacceptable 粗魯的; 不合禮儀的: *an improper suggestion* 不成體統的建議 –**improperly** *adv* –**impropriety** /,ɪmprə'praɪətɪ; ,ɪmprə'praɪətɪ/ *n* **improprieties** [C;U]

★★ **im·prove** /ɪm'pruv; ɪm'pruːv/ *v* **improved, improving 1** [I] to become better 變得更好: *I think your English is improving.* 我覺得你的英語在進步。 **2** [T] to make something better 改進; 改善: *Security precautions have now been improved.* 保安措施現已改善。 **3 improve yourself** to rise higher in society, especially through education〔尤指通過教育〕求上進 **4 improve on/upon something** to produce something better than something else 生產出比〔其他東西〕更好的東西: *I don't think anyone can improve on her score.* 我認為沒人能超過她的成績。

★★ **im·prove·ment** /ɪm'pruvmənt; ɪm'pruːvmənt/ *n* [C; U] a change which makes something better or shows that something is getting better 改進; 改良; 改善: *His health is showing signs of improvement.* 他的健康狀況顯出好轉

的跡象。| *a considerable improvement* **in** *our exam results* 考試成績有相當大的進步 | *This year's exam results are a vast improvement* **on** *last year's.* 今年的考試成績和去年相比取得了巨大的進步。| *He's talking of making more improvements to the house.* 他在説要對房子進行更多的改進。

> ■ **USAGE** 用法: We speak about an **improvement in** something if it has got better ☆如果某件事物有所改善, 用 an **improvement in** something 來表示: *There has been an* **improvement in** *the weather.* 天氣好轉。| *There has been a definite* **improvement in** *your work recently.* 最近你的工作有了明顯的改進。 We speak about an **improvement on** something if we are comparing two things, and one of them is better than the other ☆如果要對兩件事物進行比較, 其中之一比另一件好, 用 an **improvement on** something 來表示: *Today's weather is an* **improvement on** *yesterday's.* 今天天氣比昨天好。| *Your results this term are a great* **improvement on** *last term's performance.* 你這學期的成績比上學期的好多了。

im·prov·i·dent /ɪm'prɑvədənt; ɪm'prɔvɪdənt/ *adj fml* wasting money and not preparing for the future〔正式〕揮霍的; 無遠見的 –**improvidence** *n* [U]

im·pro·vise /'ɪmprə,vaɪz; 'ɪmprəvaɪz/ *v* **improvised, improvising** [I;T] to do or make something without planning in advance〔事先無計劃地〕臨時做: *I forgot the words of my speech, so I had to improvise.* 我忘了我的演講詞, 只好即席演説。 –**improvisation** /,ɪmprəvaɪ'zeʃən; ,ɪmprəvaɪ'zeɪʃən/ *n* [C;U]

im·pru·dent /ɪm'prudn̩t; ɪm'pruːdənt/ *adj* not wise or thoughtful 不明智的; 輕率的; 魯莽的 –**imprudence** *n* [U] –**imprudently** *adv*

im·pu·dent /'ɪmpjədənt; 'ɪmpjʊdənt/ *adj* rude and not showing any respect 放肆的; 無禮的 –**impudence** *n* [U] –**impudently** *adv*

im·pulse /'ɪmpʌls; 'ɪmpʌls/ *n* **1** a sudden strong wish to do something 衝動: *She had a sudden impulse to hit him.* 她心血來潮想打他。 **2 on impulse** because of a sudden strong wish 因一時衝動: *He bought the bicycle on impulse.* 他一時衝動買了這輛自行車。 **3** *tech* a short electrical signal sent in one direction along a wire or a nerve, or through the air〔術語〕脈衝; 搏動: *an electrical impulse* 電流的脈衝

im·pul·sive /ɪm'pʌlsɪv; ɪm'pʌlsɪv/ *adj* tending to do things suddenly without thinking about the results 衝動的: *Don't be so impulsive, or you'll regret it later!* 別那麼衝動, 否則你以後會後悔的! –**impulsively** *adv* –**impulsiveness** *n* [U]

im·pu·ni·ty /ɪm'pjunətɪ; ɪm'pjuːnɪ̩tɪ/ *n* **with**

impunity without any danger of being punished 免受懲罰: *Students ignored the new regulations with impunity.* 學生們對新規定置之不理。

im·pure /ɪmˈpjur; ɪmˈpjʊəʳ/ *adj* **1** old fash concerned with sex and regarded as bad 《老式》不純潔的; 淫穢的: *impure thoughts* 不純潔的念頭 **2** not pure, but mixed with other substances 不純的; 摻雜的: *The heroin was found to be impure.* 這海洛因被發現不純。 –**impurity** *n* –**impurities** [C;U]: *impurities in the water supply* 供應的水中的雜質

im·pute /ɪmˈpjut; ɪmˈpjuːt/ *v* imputed, imputing, impute something to someone *fml* to claim that someone has something or has done something 《正式》把某事物歸因於某人: *How can they impute such disgraceful motives to the teachers?* 他們怎麼能把這麼可恥的動機歸因於老師呢? –**imputation** /ˌɪmpjuˈteʃən, ˌɪmpjʊˈteɪʃən/ *n* [C;U]

in¹ /ɪn; ɪn/ *adv, prep* **1** *adv, prep* surrounded by something or contained by it 在…裡; 在…之內; 在裡面: *The cups are in the cupboard.* 杯子在碗櫥裡。 | *There was nobody in the house.* 屋子裡沒人。 | *Put the butter in the fridge.* 把黃油放在冰箱裡。 | *people swimming in the sea* 在海裡游泳的人 | *There were sheep in the field.* 田野裡有羊。 | *She lives in London.* 她住在倫敦。 | *By tomorrow we'll be in France.* 到明天我們就在法國了。 | *She's in hospital.* 她在醫院裡(住院)。 | *She opened her bag and put the packet in.* 她打開包把盒子放進去。 | *I knocked on the door and he shouted "come in."* 我敲敲門, 他大聲說"進來"。–see picture on page 764 見 764 頁彩圖 **2** *adv* given or sent to someone who has a position of power 給; 送至〔有權勢者〕: *Applications must be in by next Thursday.* 申請下星期四前必須交來。 | *Letters of support have been flooding in this week.* 支持的信件這星期如潮水般湧來。 **3** *adv* present at your home or your place of work 在家; 在工作的地方: *I'm afraid Mr Jones isn't in at the moment.* 恐怕瓊斯先生現在不在。 **4** *prep* wearing something 穿着: *men in dark suits* 一羣穿深色衣服的男士 | *a woman dressed in a red coat* 穿紅外衣的女子 **5** *prep* during a period of time 在…期間: *I hope we'll see you in the Spring.* 我希望我們在春天會見到你。 | *We had a lot of snow in January.* 我們一月份下雪很多。 | *I haven't seen much of John in the last few weeks.* 最近幾星期我不大看見約翰。 **6** *prep* after a period of time 在〔若干時間〕以後: *I'll be back in an hour.* 我一小時後回來。 | *The train leaves in a few minutes.* 火車幾分鐘以後開。 | *We're going on holiday in two weeks.* 我們兩星期後去度假。 **7** *prep* as a result of a feeling that you have 由於〔某種感情〕: *In my excitement, I knocked the flowers off the table.* 因為激動, 我把桌上的花

碰下來了。 | *She looked round in surprise.* 她驚訝地環顧四周。 **8** *prep* having a particular job 從事〔某種特定工作〕: *She's in politics.* 她是從政的。 | *a job in insurance* 保險業的工作 **9** *prep* using something in order to write or say something 用〔某物說或寫〕: *They were talking in French.* 他們用法語交談。 | *a note written in pencil* 用鉛筆寫的便箋 **10** *prep* used in expressions showing the relation between two amounts〔表示兩個數目間的關係〕每: *a slope of 1 in 3* 傾斜度為一比三 | *a tax of 40p in the pound* 每英鎊徵收四十便士的稅 **11** *adv* batting (BAT) in a game of cricket〔板球賽中的〕擊球: *England are in at the moment.* 英格蘭隊目前擊球。 **12 the tide is in** = the sea is at the point when it is highest and closest to the land 在漲潮 **13 day in day out, week in week out, etc** every day, week etc for a long time without any change 日復一日; 週復一週 **14 in and out of somewhere** sometimes in a place, sometimes out of it over a long period of time 時進時出於某處: *He's been in and out of prison for years.* 他多年來屢次進出監獄。 **15 in all** in total 總計: *There were 20 people there in all.* 那裡總共有二十個人。 **16 in for something** going to have something bad or unpleasant 即將遭受壞事或不愉快的事: *She's in for a nasty surprise!* 她會大大地吃一驚的! | *I think we're in for trouble.* 我想我們要遇到麻煩了。 **17 in on something** concerned with something or sharing in it 和某事有關係的; 參預某事的: *I wanted to be in on the deal.* 我要參預這交易。 **18 in with someone** friendly with someone 和某人友好相處 **19 the ins and outs of something** the various parts of something such as a job, some of which are good and some bad 某事的詳情〔如工作的各方面〕

in² *adj* fashionable 時髦的: *Bright colours are in at the moment.* 現在鮮豔的色彩很時髦。 | *the in place to go* 可去的時髦場所

in³ *n* a written abbreviation for 〔縮〕= INCH(es)

in·a·bil·i·ty /ˌɪnəˈbɪləti, ˌɪnəˈbɪlɪti/ *n* [sing] lack of ability, power, or skill 無能力; 無力量; 無技能: *an inability to work alone* 沒有單獨工作的能力 | *inability to stop smoking* 無力戒煙

in·ac·ces·si·ble /ˌɪnəkˈsɛsəbl, ˌɪnəkˈsesɪbəl/ *adj* very difficult or impossible to reach 很難到達的; 達不到的: *Heavy snow made the village inaccessible to traffic.* 大雪使車輛進不了這個村莊。 | *inaccessible mountain villages* 外人很難進入的山村 –**inaccessibility** /ˌɪnəkˌsɛsəˈbɪləti, ˌɪnəksesɪˈbɪlɪti/ *n* [U]

in·ac·cu·rate /ɪnˈækjərɪt; ɪnˈækjʊrɪt/ *adj* not correct 不準確的 –**inaccurately** *adv* –**inaccuracy** *n* –**inaccuracies** [C;U]

in·ac·tion /ɪnˈækʃən; ɪnˈækʃən/ *n* [U] lack of action 無行動; 不活動

in·ac·tive /ɪnˈæktɪv; ɪnˈæktɪv/ *adj* not active 不活動的; 不活躍的 –**inactivity** /ˌɪnækˈtɪvəti;

ˌɪnæk'tɪvɪti/ *n* [U]

in·ad·e·qua·cy /ɪn'ædəkwəsɪ; ɪn'ædˌkwɔsi/ *n* **inadequacies** [C;U] an example of the state of being inadequate 不夠; 不充足

in·ad·e·quate /ɪn'ædəkwɪt; ɪn'ædˌkwɔt/ *adj* not good enough in quality, ability, or amount 不充足的;〔品質、能力〕不夠好的: *I felt inadequate in my new job, so I left.* 我覺得對於新工作不能勝任, 所以走了。 | *The food was inadequate for 14 people.* 這些食物不夠十四個人吃。 **–inadequately** *adv*

in·ad·ver·tent /ˌɪnəd'vɜtnt; ˌɪnəd'vɜtənt/ *adj* done without thinking or by accident 漫不經心的; 偶然的 **–inadvertently** *adv*: *He inadvertently knocked over his cup of coffee.* 他不留神碰翻了自己那杯咖啡。

in·a·li·en·a·ble /ɪn'eljənəbl; ɪn'eɪliənəbəl/ *adj fml* inalienable right a right which cannot be taken away〔正式〕不可剝奪的權利: *Freedom of speech should be an inalienable right.* 言論自由應是不可剝奪的權利。

i·nane /ɪn'en; ɪ'neɪn/ *adj* stupid and without meaning 愚蠢的; 無意義的: *an inane remark* 空話 | *inane behaviour* 愚蠢的行為 **– inanely** *adv*

in·an·i·mate /ɪn'ænəmɪt; ɪn'ænˌmɪt/ *adj* not living 無生命的: *an inanimate object* 無生命的物體

in·ap·pli·ca·ble /ɪn'æplɪkəbl; ɪn'æplɪkəbəl/ *adj* unrelated to the subject 與主題無關的 **– inapplicability** /ˌɪnæplɪkə'bɪlətɪ; ɪn'æplɪkə-'bɪlˌti/ *n* [U]

in·ap·pro·pri·ate /ˌɪnə'proprɪɪt; ˌɪnə'prəʊpri-ɪt/ *adj* not suitable for a particular event or purpose 不恰當的; 不合適的: *Your short dress is inappropriate for a formal party.* 你穿這條短裙去參加正式聚會是不恰當的。 **–inappropriately** *adv* **–inappropriateness** *n* [U]

in·ar·tic·u·late /ˌɪnɑr'tɪkjəlɪt; ˌɪnɑː'tɪkjʊlɪt/ *adj* **1** unable to express yourself clearly when speaking 口齒不清的; 詞不達意的: *He's very intelligent, but completely inarticulate.* 他極聰明, 但根本無法清晰地表達自己的意思。 **2** not well-formed or not clearly expressed 結構不好的; 表達不清楚的: *an inarticulate speech* 一篇表達得不清楚的演講 **– inarticulately** *adv*

in·as·much as /ˌɪnəz'mʌtʃ əz; ˌɪnəz'mʌtʃ əz/ *conj fml* owing to the fact that〔正式〕由於: *Their father is also guilty, inasmuch as he knew what they were going to do.* 他們的父親也有罪, 因為他知道他們打算幹甚麼。

in·at·ten·tion /ˌɪnə'tɛnʃən; ˌɪnə'tenʃən/ *n* [U] lack of attention 不注意; 漫不經心

in·at·ten·tive /ˌɪnə'tɛntɪv; ˌɪnə'tentɪv/ *adj* not giving attention 不注意的; 漫不經心的: *an inattentive pupil* 不專心的小學生 **– inattentively** *adv* **–inattentiveness** *n* [U]

in·au·di·ble /ɪn'ɔdəbl; ɪn'ɔːdɪbəl/ *adj* too quiet to be heard 輕得聽不見的 **–inaudibly** *adv* **–inaudibility** /ˌɪnɔdə'bɪlətɪ; ɪnˌɔːdɪ'bɪ-

in·au·gu·rate /ɪn'ɔgjəˌret; ɪ'nɔːgjʊˌreɪt/ *v* **inaugurated, inaugurating** [T] **1** to introduce a new leader or official into an important job in an organization by holding a special ceremony 為〔新領導或新官員〕舉行就職典禮: *The president was inaugurated last week.* 總統上週舉行了就職典禮。 **2** to open a new building or start a public event with a special ceremony 為〔新建築物〕舉行落成典禮; 為〔公共事務〕舉行開幕式: *The new school was inaugurated last week.* 這所新學校上週舉行了落成典禮。 **–inaugural** *adj* [only before a noun 只用於名詞前]: *an inaugural ceremony to open the new hospital* 為新建的醫院舉行的開業典禮 **–inauguration** /ɪnˌɔgjə-'reʃən; ɪˌnɔːgjʊ'reɪʃən/ *n* [C;U]

in·aus·pi·cious /ˌɪnɔ'spɪʃəs; ˌɪnɔː'spɪʃəs/ *adj* showing signs that the future will be unlucky 不祥的; 凶兆的: *an inauspicious start to the term* 這學期不祥的開端 **–inauspiciously** *adv* **–inauspiciousness** *n* [U]

in·born /ɪn'bɔrn; ˌɪn'bɔːn◂/ *adj* present from birh as part of a person or animal's nature or behaviour 天生的; 天賦的: *Birds have an inborn ability to fly.* 鳥來來就會飛。

in·bred /ɪn'brɛd; ˌɪn'bred◂/ *adj* **1** having become part of your nature as a result of early training〔由於早期訓練的結果而〕成為天賦的 **2** bred from closely related members of a family 近親交配的

in·breed·ing /'ɪnˌbridɪŋ; 'ɪnbriːdɪŋ/ *n* [U] breeding from closely related members of a family 近親交配

Inc /ɪŋk; ɪŋk/ an abbreviation for〔縮〕= INCORPORATED

in·cal·cu·la·ble /ɪn'kælkjələbl; ɪn'kælkjʊlə-bəl/ *adj* too great to be counted or measured 數不清的; 不可估量的: *an incalculable risk* 極大的的風險 **–incalculably** *adv*

in·can·des·cent /ˌɪnkən'dɛsnt; ˌɪnkæn'de-sənt/ *adj* giving a bright light when heated 熾熱的; 白熾的 **–incandescence** *n* [U]

in·can·ta·tion /ˌɪnkæn'teʃən; ˌɪnkæn'teɪʃən/ *n* the saying or singing of words used in magic 咒語; 符咒

in·ca·pa·ble /ɪn'kepəbl; ɪn'keɪpəbəl/ *adj* not able to do something 無能力的; 不能做〔某事〕的: *He's incapable of deceiving anyone.* 他不會騙人。 | *He seems completely incapable.* 他似乎一點能力也沒有。

> □ **USEFUL PATTERNS** 有用句型
> be incapable of something; be incapable of doing something

in·ca·pa·ci·tate /ˌɪnkə'pæsəˌtet; ˌɪnkə'pæ-sˌteɪt/ *v* **incapacitated, incapacitating** [T] to weaken or harm someone physically so they are not able to do something 使無能力; 使傷殘: *He was incapacitated as a result of the accident.* 他因事故致殘。

in·ca·pa·ci·ty /ˌɪnkəˈpæsəti; ˌɪnkəˈpæsˌti/ *n* [U] lack of ability, strength, or power to do something 無能力；無力量；無權力: *an incapacity to lie* 不會撒謊 | *the country's incapacity to solve its economic problems* 國家對解決經濟問題無能為力

in·car·ce·rate /ɪnˈkɑrsəˌret; ɪnˈkɑːsəreɪt/ *v* **incarcerated, incarcerating** [T] *fml* to imprison someone 《正式》監禁〔某人〕 – **incarceration** /ɪnˌkɑrsəˈreʃən; ɪnˌkɑːsəˈreɪʃən/ *n* [U]

in·car·nate /ɪnˈkɑrnɪt; ɪnˈkɑːnɪt/ *adj* [only after a noun 只用於名詞後] **1** in the form of a physical body 人體化的；化身的: *the devil incarnate* 魔鬼的化身 **2** a word used to show strongly that something or someone has a particular quality 典型的；是〔某種品質〕化身的: *She was happiness incarnate.* 她是幸福的化身。

in·car·na·tion /ˌɪnkɑrˈneʃən; ˌɪnkɑːˈneɪʃən/ *n* **1** the act of putting a spirit into physical form 〔神靈的〕化身: *Local people believe this god has many incarnations.* 當地人相信這個神有很多化身。 **2** a person or thing that is the perfect example of a quality 典型；化身: *She's the very incarnation of generosity.* 她是慷慨的化身。

in·cen·di·a·ry /ɪnˈsɛndɪˌɛri; ɪnˈsendiəri/ *adj* [only before a noun 只用於名詞前] causing fires 引起燃燒的: *an incendiary bomb* 燃燒彈

in·cense¹ /ˈɪnsɛns; ˈɪnsens/ *n* [U] a substance that gives off a sweet smell when burnt, often used in religious services 〔常於宗教祭供時用的〕香

in·cense² /ɪnˈsɛns; ɪnˈsens/ *v* **incensed, incensing** [T] to make someone very angry 使〔某人〕憤怒: *I was incensed at his rudeness.* 我對他的粗魯無禮感到憤怒。

in·cen·tive /ɪnˈsɛntɪv; ɪnˈsentɪv/ *n* [C;U] an encouragement to do something 刺激；動力: *The prospect of being chosen for the team gave me an incentive and I trained twice as hard.* 有望入選該隊給了我動力，我加倍地努力訓練。 | *He's got no incentive to study further.* 他沒有深造的動力。

in·cep·tion /ɪnˈsɛpʃən; ɪnˈsepʃən/ *n* [U] *fml* the beginning of an activity or organization 《正式》〔活動或組織的〕開始；開端: *He's worked for that company since its inception.* 自從那家公司開辦以來，他一直在那兒工作。

in·ces·sant /ɪnˈsɛsnt; ɪnˈsesənt/ *adj* never stopping 不停的；持續不斷的: *incessant noise* 持續不斷的噪音 – **incessantly** *adv*

in·cest /ˈɪnsɛst; ˈɪnsest/ *n* [U] a sexual relationship between close relatives in a family, for example between a brother and sister 亂倫 – **incestuous** /ɪnˈsɛstʃʊəs; ɪnˈsestʃʊəs/ *adj* – **incestuously** *adv*

***inch¹** /ɪntʃ; ɪntʃ/ *n* **1** a unit for measuring length, equal to 1/12 of a foot or about 0.025 metres 英寸〔一英尺的十二分之一，約0.025米〕 **2 inch by inch** very slowly and by a small amount at a time 漸漸地；一點一點地

inch² *v* [I+adv/prep] (also 又作 **inch your way**) to move slowly with care or difficulty 〔小心或艱難地〕緩慢移動: *I inched through the narrow space.* 我在狹縫中緩慢地穿行。

in·ci·dence /ˈɪnsədəns; ˈɪnsɪdəns/ *n* [sing] how often something happens 發生率: *There's a high incidence of disease there.* 那裡的患病率很高。

*‡**in·ci·dent** /ˈɪnsədənt; ˈɪnsɪdənt/ *n* a single event which is usually not very important 小事

in·ci·den·tal /ˌɪnsəˈdɛntl; ˌɪnsɪˈdentl◂/ *adj* happening or existing in connection with something else 附帶的；伴隨的: *incidental details* 附帶的細節 | *an event incidental to the main action* 伴隨主要活動的事情

in·ci·den·tal·ly /ˌɪnsəˈdɛntli; ˌɪnsɪˈdentli/ *adv* you say "incidentally" when you say something you have just thought of; it may be unconnected with the last subject or it may be about another part of it 順便說；順便提一句〔用於說及剛剛想到的某事，可能和最後一個話題無關，或是其中的另一部分〕: *I must go now. Incidentally, if you want that book I'll bring it next time.* 我現在必須走了。順便提一句，如果你要那本書，我下次帶來。 | *I think that's Joan's bag. Incidentally, did you know she was expecting a baby?* 我想那是瓊的包。順便說一句，你知道她懷孕了嗎？

in·cin·e·rate /ɪnˈsɪnəˌret; ɪnˈsɪnəreɪt/ *v* **incinerated, incinerating** [T] *fml* to destroy unwanted things by burning them 《正式》把〔廢物〕燒毀；火化 – **incineration** /ɪnˌsɪnəˈreʃən; ɪnˌsɪnəˈreɪʃən/ *n* [U]

in·cin·e·ra·tor /ɪnˈsɪnəˌretɚ; ɪnˈsɪnəreɪtəʳ/ *n* a machine for burning unwanted things 〔廢物的〕焚化爐

in·cip·i·ent /ɪnˈsɪpɪənt; ɪnˈsɪpiənt/ *adj fml* starting to happen or exist 《正式》開始發生或存在的: *incipient disease* 早期的疾病

in·ci·sion /ɪnˈsɪʒən; ɪnˈsɪʒən/ *n fml* a sharp cut into something made with a special tool, often by a doctor during an operation 《正式》〔常指在手術中的〕切口；切開: *An incision was made into the patient's stomach.* 在病人胃部開了一道切口。

in·ci·sive /ɪnˈsaɪsɪv; ɪnˈsaɪsɪv/ *adj* going clearly and directly to the main point of a subject 深刻的；透徹的: *incisive statements* 透徹的陳述 | *an incisive mind* 敏銳的頭腦 – **incisively** *adv*

in·ci·sor /ɪnˈsaɪzɚ; ɪnˈsaɪzəʳ/ *n* any of your eight front teeth which have a cutting edge 切牙；門齒

in·cite /ɪnˈsaɪt; ɪnˈsaɪt/ *v* **incited, inciting** [T] **1** to cause or encourage someone to do something by making them feel angry or excited 刺激，煽動〔某人做某事〕: *a violent speech inciting the army to rebel* 一篇煽動軍隊反叛、措辭激烈的演講

□ USEFUL PATTERN 有用句型
to incite someone to do something

2 to cause a strong feeling or action 煽動: *He was charged with inciting a riot.* 他被控煽動暴亂。–**incitement** *n* [C;U]

in·clem·ent /ɪnˈklemənt; ɪnˈklemənt/ *adj* *fml* cold or stormy (used of weather) 《正式》寒冷的〔指天氣〕; 狂風暴雨的

in·cli·na·tion /ˌɪnkləˈneɪʃən; ˌɪnklɪˈneɪʃən/ *n* **1** [C;U] a liking or wish to do something 傾向; 愛好; 意向: *You always follow your own inclinations instead of thinking of our feelings.* 你總是隨心所欲, 而不考慮我們的感受。 | *I've no inclination to be a doctor.* 我不想當醫生。 **2** [C] a bending movement of your head or hand 點頭; 搖手: *He gave an inclination of the head.* 他點了點頭。 **3** [sing] a slope 斜坡

in·cline¹ /ɪnˈklaɪn; ɪnˈklaɪn/ *v* **inclined, inclining** **1** [T] to encourage or influence someone to have certain feelings or opinions 使〔某人〕傾向於; 使〔某人〕感到: *The strangeness of her story inclines me to believe she is telling the truth.* 她把她的故事說得那麼奇妙, 使得我以為她講的是事實。 –compare 比較 INCLINED **2** [T] *fml* to make a part of your body bend downward 《正式》使〔身體的一部分〕傾斜: *She inclined her head in greeting.* 她點頭致意。 **3** [I] to slope 傾斜: *The garden inclines towards the street.* 這個花園向街道傾斜。

in·cline² /ˈɪnklaɪn; ˈɪnklaɪn/ *n* a slope 斜坡: *a steep incline* 陡峭的斜坡

in·clined /ɪnˈklaɪnd; ɪnˈklaɪnd/ *adj* [never before a noun 不能用於名詞前] **1** feeling you want to do something or are going to do it 想要〔做某事〕; 打算〔做某事〕的: *The news makes me inclined to change my mind.* 這消息使我想改變主意。

□ USEFUL PATTERN 有用句型
be inclined to do something

–see also 另見 DISINCLINED
2 likely or tending to do something 傾向於〔做某事〕的; 可能〔做某事〕的: *He's inclined to lose his temper.* 他往往容易發脾氣。

□ USEFUL PATTERN 有用句型
be inclined to do something

3 be inclined to think/believe/agree etc used to show you hold an opinion, but not very strongly 傾向於認為/相信/同意〔用於表示持有看法, 但不太強烈〕: *I'm inclined to agree with Jim.* 我傾向於同意吉姆(的見解)。

in·clude /ɪnˈkluːd; ɪnˈkluːd/ *v* **included, including** [T] **1** to have or contain something as a part of a whole 包括; 包含: *The price includes postage charges.* 這價錢包括郵費。 | *Is service included in the bill?* 賬單中包括服務費嗎? | *This fitness programme includes swimming regularly.* 這套健身方案包括定期游泳。 **2** to make something part of a whole or larger set 使〔某物〕成為整體的一部分; 把〔某物〕算入: *I included eggs on the list of things to buy.* 我把雞蛋列入購物單中。

in·clud·ed /ɪnˈkluːdɪd; ɪnˈkluːdɪd/ *adj* [only after a noun 只用於名詞後] including 包括在內的: *all of us, me included* 我們所有的人, 包括我在內

in·clud·ing /ɪnˈkluːdɪŋ; ɪnˈkluːdɪŋ/ *prep* a word used to show that some people or things form part of the larger set or whole that you are talking about 包括〔用於表示一些人或東西組成了所談及整體的一部分〕: *There are six people, including three women.* 共有六個人, 包括三位女士。 | *Your total expenses, including bills, are £200.* 你的總開銷, 包括這些賬單, 是二百英鎊。 –opposite 反義 **excluding**

in·clu·sion /ɪnˈkluːʒən; ɪnˈkluːʒən/ *n* [U] the act of including or state of being included 包括; 包含

in·clu·sive /ɪnˈkluːsɪv; ɪnˈkluːsɪv/ *adj* **1** containing or including everything 包括[包含]一切的: *an inclusive charge* 已包括一切在內的收費 **2** [only after a noun 只用於名詞後] including other costs that are often paid separately (used of a price or charge) 包括〔通常另付的費用〕在內的〔指價格或費用〕: *The rent is £10 inclusive of heating.* 房租十英鎊, 包括暖氣費在內。 **3** [only after a noun 只用於名詞後] including all the numbers or dates 包括所有的數字或日期: *Wednesday to Friday inclusive* 從星期三到星期五, 包括首尾兩日 –**inclusively** *adv*

in·cog·ni·to /ˌɪnkɒɡˈniːtəʊ; ˌɪnkɑɡˈniːtoʊ/ *adj, adv* [never before a noun 不能用於名詞前] hiding who you really are, especially by taking another name when your own is well-known 〔尤指知名人物〕隱瞞身分的[地]: *She was travelling incognito.* 她隱姓埋名地旅行。

in·co·her·ent /ˌɪnkəʊˈhɪərənt; ˌɪnkoʊˈhɪrənt/ *adj* unclear and without connections between ideas or words 〔思想或語言〕不清晰的; 不連貫的; 語無倫次的: *When he got her letter, he became incoherent with rage.* 他收到她的信, 氣得語無倫次。 –**incoherence** *n* [U] –**incoherently** *adv*

in·come /ˈɪnˌkʌm; ˈɪnkʌm/ *n* [C;U] money which you receive, usually payment for work 收入〔常指工資〕: *Half our income goes on rent.* 我們的一半收入用於房租。 | *Low-income families need government help.* 低收入家庭需要政府的幫助。 –see 見 PAY² (USAGE 用法)

in·com·ing /ˈɪnˌkʌmɪŋ; ˈɪnkʌmɪŋ/ *adj* [only before a noun 只用於名詞前] **1** coming towards you 進來的: *an incoming tide* 漲潮

2 moving towards a particular place and about to arrive there 正來臨的; 將到達的: *incoming passengers* 將到達的旅客 | *incoming traffic* 開來的車輛 **3** appointed or elected to a new job 新任命的; 新推選的: *the incoming director* 新任董事 **4** **incoming calls** telephone calls you receive 打進來的電話

in·com·mu·ni·ca·do /ˌɪnkəˌmjunɪˈkado; ˌɪnkəmjuːˈnɪˈkaːdəʊ/ *adv, adj* [never before a noun 不能用於名詞前] kept away from people so that you cannot give or receive messages 不能與他人接觸地[的]

in·com·pa·ra·ble /ɪnˈkɑmpərəbl; ɪnˈkɒmpərəbəl/ *adj* too good or great to be compared with other examples of the same thing (大得)無可比擬的; (好得)與倫比的: *incomparable wealth* 無比富有 | *incomparable beauty* 絕世之美 **–incomparably** *adv: This model is incomparably better than the other.* 這模型比其他的不知好多少。**–incomparability** /ɪnˌkɑmpərəˈbɪlətɪ; ɪnˌkɒmpərəˈbɪlti/ *n* [U]

in·com·pat·i·ble /ˌɪnkəmˈpætəbl; ˌɪnkəmˈpætɭbəl/ *adj* too different from another person or thing to be able to live or exist with them 彼此不相容的; 不能共存的: *Their marriage broke up because they were basically incompatible.* 他們的婚姻破裂了, 因為他們根本合不來。| *His plan is incompatible* **with** *the company's intentions.* 他的計劃和公司的意圖相抵觸。**–incompatibility** /ˌɪnkəmˌpætəˈbɪlətɪ; ˌɪnkəmpætɭˈbɪlti/ *n* **incompatibilities** [C;U]

in·com·pe·tence /ɪnˈkɑmpətəns; ɪnˈkɒmpɪtəns/ *n* [U] lack of ability and skill resulting in useless work 不勝任; 無能力; 不稱職

in·com·pe·tent /ɪnˈkɑmpətənt; ɪnˈkɒmpɪtənt/ *adj* lacking the skill or ability to do something properly 無能力的; 不稱職的; 不勝任的: *an incompetent lawyer* 不合格的律師**–incompetent** *n: He is a total incompetent.* 他是個毫無用處的人。**–incompetently** *adv*

in·com·plete /ˌɪnkəmˈplit; ˌɪnkəmˈpliːt/ *adj* without all its parts or not complete 不完全的; 不完善的

in·com·pre·hen·si·ble /ˌɪnkɑmprɪˈhɛnsəbl; ɪnˌkɒmprɪˈhensɭbəl/ *adj* unable to be understood 不能理解的 **–incomprehensibility** /ˌɪnkɑmprɪˌhɛnsəˈbɪlətɪ; ɪnˌkɒmprɪˈhensɭˈbɪlti/ *n* [U] *adv*

in·com·pre·hen·sion /ˌɪnkɑmprɪˈhɛnʃən; ɪnˌkɒmprɪˈhenʃən/ *n* [U] the state of not understanding 不理解

in·con·cei·va·ble /ˌɪnkənˈsivəbl; ˌɪnkənˈsiːvəbəl/ *adj* difficult or impossible to believe 難以置信的; 不能相信的: *It once seemed inconceivable that men should travel to the moon.* 一度認為人飛上月球是不可想像的。| *He can't go on holiday alone; it's inconcei-*

vable. 他不會一個人去度假; 這是難以置信的。**–inconceivably** *adv*

in·con·clu·sive /ˌɪnkənˈklusɪv; ˌɪnkənˈkluːsɪv/ *adj* **1** not leading to a firm decision or result 非決定性的; 非結論性的; 無結果的: *an inconclusive discussion* 非決定性的討論 **2** which has not proved anything 沒有說服力的: *inconclusive evidence* 無說服力的證據 **–inconclusively** *adv*

in·con·gru·ous /ɪnˈkɑŋgruəs; ɪnˈkɒŋgruəs/ *adj* strange or surprising in relation to the surroundings 不協調的; 不和諧的: *A modern church would look incongruous in that village.* 一座現代化的教堂在那村子裡會看上去不協調。**–incongruously** *adv* **–incongruity** /ˌɪnkɑŋˈgruətɪ; ˌɪnkənˈgruːti/ *n* [U]

in·con·se·quen·tial /ˌɪnkɑnsəˈkwɛnʃəl; ˌɪnkɒnsɭˈkwenʃəl/ *adj* unimportant 不重要的: *an inconsequential idea* 無關緊要的想法 **–inconsequentially** *adv*

in·con·sid·e·ra·ble /ˌɪnkənˈsɪdərəbl; ˌɪnkənˈsɪdərəbəl/ *adj* not considerable large in size or value 〔尺寸或價值〕大的: *The actress paid a not inconsiderable sum of money for the house.* 女演員為那幢房子付了不算小的一筆錢。

in·con·sid·er·ate /ˌɪnkənˈsɪdərɪt; ˌɪnkənˈsɪdərɭt/ *adj* not thinking of other people's feelings or the effect of your behaviour on them 不考慮別人感情的; 不體諒別人的: *It was rather inconsiderate of her to keep us waiting.* 她讓我們一直等著, 太不體諒人了。**–inconsiderately** *adv*

in·con·sis·tent /ˌɪnkənˈsɪstənt; ˌɪnkənˈsɪstənt/ *adj* **1** having different parts that do not agree (used of ideas and opinions) 前後不一致的; 不協調的〔指主意、意見〕: *Those remarks are inconsistent* **with** *what you said yesterday.* 那些話和你昨天說的不一致。| *The two statements are inconsistent.* 兩份陳述不一致。**2** tending to change 易變的: *This weather is so inconsistent — one moment it's raining and the next it's sunny.* 這天氣真反覆無常——一會兒下雨, 一會兒又放晴。| *inconsistent behaviour* 反覆無常的行為 **–inconsistency** *n* **inconsistencies** [C;U]

in·con·so·la·ble /ˌɪnkənˈsoləbl; ˌɪnkənˈsəʊləbəl/ *adj* feeling too full of sorrow to be comforted 〔由於極其悲哀而〕無法安慰的; 傷心欲絕的: *She is inconsolable* **over** *the loss of her dog.* 她因為失去了她的狗而傷心極了。| *inconsolable grief* 無法安慰的悲傷 **–inconsolably** *adv: inconsolably sad* 極度悲哀

in·con·spic·u·ous /ˌɪnkənˈspɪkjuəs; ˌɪnkənˈspɪkjuəs/ *adj* **1** too small or hidden to be easily noticed 〔太小或太隱蔽而〕難以覺察的; 不顯眼的: *an inconspicuous doorway* 不顯眼的出入口 **2** not attracting attention 不引人注目的: *He was a quiet, inconspicuous figure.* 他是個安安靜靜, 不引人注目的人。**–inconspicuously** *adv*

in·con·ti·nent /ɪnˈkɑntənənt; ɪnˈkɒntɭnənt/

adj unable to control your BLADDER or bowels〔大小便〕失禁的: *With old age, he became increasingly incontinent.* 隨着年紀大起來，他變得越來越容易小便失禁。 –**incontinence** *n* [U]

in·con·tro·ver·ti·ble /,ɪnkɒntrə'vɜːtəbl; ɪn-,kɒntrə'vɝːtəbəl/ *adj* which cannot be disproved 無可辯駁的: *incontrovertible evidence* 無可辯駁的證據 –**incontrovertibly** *adv*

in·con·ve·ni·ence¹ /,ɪnkən'vinjəns; ,ɪnkən-'viːnjəns/ *n* [C;U] difficulty or discomfort 不便; 不適: *Commuters suffered great inconvenience because the trains were always late.* 列車經常遲到，這使得乘火車上下班的人極不方便。

inconvenience² *v* **inconvenienced, inconveniencing** [T] to make things difficult or inconvenient for someone 給〔某人〕帶來不便; 麻煩: *I hope it won't inconvenience you to drive me to the station.* 我希望駕車送我到車站不會給你帶來不便。

in·con·ve·ni·ent /,ɪnkən'vinjənt; ,ɪnkən'viːnjənt/ *adj* causing difficulty because something does not suit you 不方便的; 引起困難的: *an inconvenient time* 不適合的時間 – **inconveniently** *adv*

in·cor·po·rate /ɪn'kɔrpə,reɪt; ɪn'kɔːpəreɪt/ *v* **incorporated, incorporating** [T] to include something or make it part of a whole 把〔某事物〕併入; 包含: *They incorporated his suggestions into their plans.* 他們把他的建議納入他們的計劃。 | *The design for the shopping centre incorporates parking facilities.* 購物中心的設計包括停車場所。 –**incorporation** /ɪn,kɔrpə-'reʃən; ɪn,kɔːpə'reɪʃən/ *n* [U]

in·cor·po·rat·ed /ɪn'kɔrpə,retɪd; ɪn'kɔːpə-reɪtɪd/ *adj AmE*〔美式〕(also 又作 **Inc**) [only after a noun 只用於名詞後] formed into a CORPORATION according to law〔根據法律〕組成公司的 –compare 比較 LIMITED

in·cor·rect /,ɪnkə'rɛkt; ,ɪnkə'rɛkt/ *adj* not correct 不正確的 –**incorrectly** *adv* – **incorrectness** *n* [U]

in·cor·ri·gi·ble /ɪn'kɔrɪdʒəbl; ɪn'kɒrɪdʒɪbəl/ *adj* having faults which will never be changed (used of people or behaviour) 不可救藥的; 難以糾正的〔指人或行為〕: *She's an incorrigible liar.* 她是個不可救藥的撒謊者。 – **incorrigibly** *adv*

in·cor·rup·ti·ble /,ɪnkə'rʌptəbl; ,ɪnkə'rʌptɪbəl/ *adj* too honest to be improperly influenced, particularly by being offered money to do something illegal 廉潔的; 不受賄賂的

in·crease¹ /ɪn'kris; ɪn'kriːs/ *v* **increased, increasing** 1 [I] to become larger in amount, number, or degree 增加; 增大; 增長; 增強: *The population of this town has increased dramatically.* 這個城鎮的人口

大幅度地增長。 2 [T] to make something larger in amount, number, or degree 使增加; 使增大; 使增長; 使增強: *They have increased the price of petrol by 3%.* 他們把汽油的價格提高了百分之三。 | *His speech has increased speculation that he will resign soon.* 他的演說增加了有關他不久將辭職的推測。 –opposite 反義 **decrease**

in·crease² /'ɪnkris; 'ɪnkriːs/ *n* [C;U] 1 a rise in amount, number, or degree 增加; 增大; 增長; 增強: *a sharp increase in spending* 消費大增 | *an increase of 10%* 百分之十的增長 –opposite 反義 **decrease** 2 **on the increase** becoming more frequent than in the past 正在增加: *Smoking seems to be on the increase among teenagers.* 青少年中的吸煙率似乎在增加。

in·creas·ing·ly /ɪn'krisɪŋli; ɪn'kriːsɪŋli/ *adv* more and more 越來越多地: *I'm finding it increasingly difficult to live on my wages.* 我發現靠自己的工資生活越來越難了。

in·cred·i·ble /ɪn'krɛdəbl; ɪn'krɛdəbəl/ *adj* 1 difficult or impossible to believe 難以置信的; 不可能相信的: *His story sounded pretty incredible to me.* 對我而言，他的故事聽來太難以置信。 | *an incredible excuse* 難以置信的藉口 2 *infml* extremely good or wonderful〔非正式〕好極了的; 絕妙的: *What an incredible house!* 多棒的房子啊! 3 very large in amount 極多的: *They pay some incredible amount for his school fees.* 他們為他支付了巨額學費。 –**incredibly** *adv*

in·cred·u·lous /ɪn'krɛdʒələs; ɪn'krɛdjʊləs/ *adj* unable to believe something, or showing disbelief 不相信的; 表示懷疑的: *He sounded incredulous when I told him what had happened.* 我告訴他出了甚麼事，但他似乎認為難以置信。 | *an incredulous look* 懷疑的目光 –**incredulously** *adv* –**incredulity** /,ɪnkrə'djuləti; ,ɪkrə'djuːlɪti/ *n* [U]

in·cre·ment /'ɪnkrəmənt; 'ɪnkrəmənt/ *n* a regular increase in the amount of money you earn in your job〔薪水的定期〕增加: *They get annual increments of £400.* 他們每年加薪四百英鎊。 –**incremental** /,ɪnkrɪ'mɛntl; ,ɪnkrə'mentl/ *adj*

in·crim·i·nate /ɪn'krɪmə,net; ɪn'krɪmɪneɪt/ *v* **incriminated, incriminating** [T] to make someone seem guilty of a crime 使〔某人〕顯得有罪: *incriminating evidence* 可顯示有罪的證據 | *She incriminated herself by refusing to answer the police's questions.* 她拒絕回答警方的問題，受到了牽連。 –**incrimination** /ɪn,krɪmə'neʃən; ɪn,krɪmə'neɪʃən/ *n* [U]

in·cu·bate /'ɪnkjə,bet; 'ɪnkjʊbeɪt/ *v* **incubated, incubating** 1 [T] to sit on eggs and keep them warm until the young birds come out 孵〔卵〕 2 [I] (of eggs) to be kept warm until the young birds come out〔卵〕被孵化 –**incubation** /,ɪnkjə'beʃən; ,ɪnkjʊ-'beɪʃən/ *n* [U]

in·cu·ba·tor /'ɪnkjə,betəʳ; 'ɪnkjʊbeɪtəʳ/ *n* 1 a

machine for keeping eggs warm until the young birds come out 孵化器 **2** a place where small weak babies are given help to live〔放置體弱嬰兒的〕恆溫箱

in·cul·cate /ɪnˈkʌlket; ˈɪŋkʌlkeɪt/ v **inculcated, inculcating** [T] *fml* to fix beliefs or principles in someone's mind by repeating them frequently〔正式〕反覆灌輸〔信念或原則〕: *He inculcated his religious beliefs into his children.* 他向兒女反覆灌輸自己的宗教信仰。

in·cum·bent /ɪnˈkʌmbənt; ɪnˈkʌmbənt/ *adj* **1** be incumbent on/upon someone *fml* to have a duty or responsibility to do something〔正式〕某人義不容辭的; 某人有責任的: *It's incumbent on the purchaser to check the contract before buying.* 買主在購買前有責任檢查合同。 **2** [only before a noun 只用於名詞前] holding a particular office 現任的; 在職的: *the incumbent president* 現任總統 –**incumbent** *n*: *the present incumbent* 現任者

in·cur /ɪnˈkɝ; ɪnˈkɜː/ v **-rr-** [T] to receive something unpleasant as a result of certain behaviour or actions〔因為某種行為或舉動〕招致〔不愉快的事〕; 遭受; 引起: *I incurred his dislike from that day on.* 從那天起我招致了他的厭惡。 | *to incur a debt* 招致負債

in·cur·a·ble /ɪnˈkjʊrəbl; ɪnˈkjʊərəbl/ *adj* **1** impossible to cure 無法治癒的: *an incurable disease* 不治之症 **2** impossible to change 不能改變的; 無可救藥的: *incurable optimism* 無可救藥的樂觀 –**incurably** *adv* –**incurability** /ɪnˌkjʊrəˈbɪlətɪ; ɪnˌkjʊərəˈbɪl f ti/ *n* [U]

in·cur·sion /ɪnˈkɝʒən; ɪnˈkɜːʃən/ *n* *fml* a sudden attack on or entrance into a place by a person or thing that should not be there〔正式〕襲擊; 侵入

in·debt·ed /ɪnˈdɛtɪd; ɪnˈdetɪd/ *adj* **indebted to someone** very grateful to someone for help that they have given you 對某人十分感激: *I'm indebted to all the people who have contributed to the success of this party.* 我十分感激所有為使這次聚會成功而出力的人。 –**indebtedness** *n* [U]

in·de·cent /ɪnˈdisnt; ɪnˈdiːsənt/ *adj* offensive to general standards of behaviour 舉止粗鄙的; 下流的; 有傷風化的: *an indecent remark* 下流話 | *That dress is indecent!* 那件連衣裙有傷風化。 –**indecently** *adv*: *indecently dressed* 穿得不體面的 –**indecency** *n* – **indecencies** [C;U]

in·de·ci·sion /ˌɪndɪˈsɪʒən; ˌɪndɪˈsɪʒən/ *n* [U] the inability to decide about what to do 無決斷力; 遲疑不決: *His indecision lost him the chance of a new job.* 他的猶豫不決使他失去了一次得到新工作的機會。

in·de·ci·sive /ˌɪndɪˈsaɪsɪv; ˌɪndɪˈsaɪsɪv/ *adj* **1** unable to make decisions 無決斷力的; 猶豫不決的 **2** giving an uncertain or unsatisfactory result 非決定性的; 非結論性的: *an indecisive answer* 非結論性的答覆 | *an indecisive victory* 非決定性的勝利 –**indecisively**

adv –**indecisiveness** *n* [U]

★★**in·deed** /ɪnˈdid; ɪnˈdiːd/ *adv* **1** used in answers when you want to say "yes" or "no" very strongly 當然〔用於在回答中堅定地說"是"或"不是"〕: *"Did you hear the explosion?" "I did indeed."* 你聽到爆炸聲了嗎? 我當然聽到了。 **2** used with the word "very" when you want to make your meaning stronger 確實; 實在〔和"very"連用以加強語氣〕: *It was very successful indeed.* 確實非常成功。 | *Thank you very much indeed.* 真太感謝你了。 **3** used when you are adding something that gives force to what you have already said 其實; 甚至〔對所說內容進行補充, 表示遞進〕: *These changes will benefit very few people. Indeed, a lot of people will be much worse off.* 這些變革只會使很少一部分人得到好處。 實際上, 許多人將更加貧困。 –see Study Note on page 1325 見 1325 學習提示 **4** used to show surprise or anger 真的嗎; 真是的〔表示驚奇或憤怒〕: *"He left without finishing the job." "Did he indeed!"* "他沒完成工作就離開了。" "他也真是的!"

in·de·fen·si·ble /ˌɪndɪˈfɛnsəbl; ˌɪndɪˈfens f bl/ *adj* impossible to excuse or defend 不可原諒的; 無法辯解的; 無法防禦的: *indefensible behaviour* 不可原諒的行為

in·de·fi·na·ble /ˌɪndɪˈfaɪnəbl; ˌɪndɪˈfaɪnəbl/ *adj* which cannot easily be described or explained 難以描述的; 難以解釋的: *There's an indefinable air of tension in this town.* 這城鎮裡有種難以描述的緊張氣氛。 –**indefinably** *adv*

in·def·i·nite /ɪnˈdɛfənɪt; ɪnˈdefən f t/ *adj* not clear or fixed 不清楚的; 不確定的: *indefinite opinions* 含糊的意見 | *He's gone away for an indefinite period.* 他要離開一段不知多長的時間。

in·def·i·nite·ly /ɪnˈdɛfənɪtlɪ; ɪnˈdefən f tli/ *adv* for a period of time without a fixed limit〔時間〕無限期地: *Books can be borrowed indefinitely unless requested by another reader.* 這些書可以無限期地借閱, 直到其他讀者要借為止。

in·del·i·ble /ɪnˈdɛləbl; ɪnˈdeləbl/ *adj* unable to be rubbed out 擦不掉的: *indelible ink* 擦不掉的墨水 –**indelibly** *adv*: *an experience indelibly printed on my memory* 我記憶中一次難以磨滅的經歷

in·del·i·cate /ɪnˈdɛləkət; ɪnˈdel f k f t/ *adj* slightly impolite or offensive 不文雅的; 無禮的: *an indelicate remark* 粗鄙的話 –**indelicately** *adv* –**indelicacy** *n* –**indelicacies** [C; U]

in·dem·ni·fy /ɪnˈdɛmnə,faɪ; ɪnˈdemn f faɪ/ v **indemnified, indemnifying** [T] to promise to pay someone in case of loss or damage〔遇損失或損壞時〕保證賠償 –**indemnification** /ɪn,dɛmnəfəˈkeʃən; ɪn,demn f f f ˈkeɪʃən/ *n* [C;U]

in·dem·ni·ty /ɪnˈdɛmnətɪ; ɪnˈdemn f ti/ *n*

indemnities 1 [U] protection against loss or damage, especially in the form of a promise to pay〔尤指以保證賠償形式的〕保障 **2** [C] payment for loss or damage 賠償金

in·dent /ɪnˈdɛnt; ɪnˈdɛnt/ v [T] to start one line of writing further from the left of the page than the others〔在書寫或印刷的一行中〕縮格; 縮排: *Don't forget to indent the first line of a new paragraph.* 別忘了新起段落的首行要縮格書寫。

☆in·de·pen·dence /ˌɪndɪˈpɛndəns; ˌɪndɹ̩ˈpɛndəns/ n [U] the quality or state of being independent or free 獨立; 自主; 自立: *This money gives me independence from my family.* 這筆錢使我能離家自立了。| *India gained independence from Britain in 1947.* 印度於 1947 年脫離英國獲得獨立。

☆in·de·pen·dent /ˌɪndɪˈpɛndənt; ˌɪndɹ̩ˈpɛndənt◂/ adj **1** free from government by another country 獨立的; 自治的: *Zimbabwe became independent in 1980.* 津巴布韋於1980 年獨立。**2** not dependent on other people or things for help, money, or support 自立的; 不依賴別人資助的: *She's a very independent person.* 她是個自食其力的人。| *an independent inquiry* 獨立調查 | *an independent school* 私立學校 **–independently** adv

in·de·scri·ba·ble /ˌɪndɪˈskraɪbəbl; ˌɪndɪˈskraɪbəbəl/ adj too extreme to be described 難以形容的: *My feelings were indescribable.* 我的感情難以形容。**–indescribably** adv: *indescribably awful* 可怕得難以形容

in·de·struc·ti·ble /ˌɪndɪˈstrʌktəbl; ˌɪndɪˈstrʌktɹ̩bəl/ adj too strong to be destroyed 破壞不了的; 堅不可摧的 **–indestructibility** /ˌɪndɪˌstrʌktəˈbɪlətɪ; ˌɪndɪstrʌktɹ̩ˈbɪlɹ̩ti/ n [U]

in·de·ter·mi·nate /ˌɪndɪˈtɜ·mənɪt; ˌɪndɪˈtɜːmɹ̩nɪt/ adj not clear or fixed 不清楚的; 不確定的: *a trip of indeterminate length* 旅程長短未定的旅行 | *an indeterminate colour* 模糊的顏色

☆in·dex¹ /ˈɪndɛks; ˈɪndɛks/ n **indexes** or **indices** /-dəˌsiz; -dɹ̩siːz/ **1** an alphabetical list at the back of a book which gives the names and subjects mentioned in it and the pages where these can be found〔書末人名、題目等的〕索引 **–compare** 比較 CONTENTS **2** a system of figures by which prices and costs can be compared with a former level〔用於價格或費用今昔比較的〕指數: *the cost of living index* 生活費用指數 **3** a sign of something that is changing 標誌; 跡象: *The steady fall in share prices is an index of the uncertainty about the government's future.* 股票價格持續下跌標誌着政府前途未卜。

index² v [T] **1** to provide something with an index or include something in an index 做索引; 把〔某物〕編入索引 **2** to connect two things so that they change together 使〔兩

者〕掛鈎: *Pensions should be indexed to inflation.* 養老金應和通脹率掛鈎。

index fin·ger /ˈ·· ˌ·/ n the finger next to your thumb 食指

In·di·an¹ /ˈɪndɪən; ˈɪndɪən/ adj from or connected with India or Indians 印度(人)的; 印第安(人)的: *Do you like Indian food?* 你喜歡印度的食品嗎？

Indian² n **1** a person from India 印度人 **2** (also 又作 **American Indian**) a person descended from any of the original peoples of America 美洲印第安人

☆in·di·cate /ˈɪndəˌket; ˈɪndɹ̩keɪt/ v indi·cated, indicating **1** [T] to point at or show someone something 指點; 指示; 指出: *She indicated the room where he might be.* 她指出可以在哪一個房間找到他。**2** [T;+(that)] to show something in a way that may not be quite clear〔可能不太清楚地〕表明; 表示: *I indicated that his help was not welcome.* 我表示他的幫助不受歡迎。| *All the signs indicate that people will want to buy our product.* 所有的跡象都表明人們會喜歡買我們的產品。**3** [I;T] to show which way you are turning in a vehicle by the use of lights or hand signals〔用燈光或手勢〕指示〔行車方向〕: *He's indicating left.* 他指示車向左拐彎。| *Don't forget to indicate.* 別忘了標示行車方向。

☆in·di·ca·tion /ˌɪndəˈkeʃən; ˌɪndɹ̩ˈkeɪʃən/ n [C; U] something which tells you what may be true or may happen 表示; 跡象: *He has given us no indication of his intentions.* 他沒有向我們表示他的意圖。

in·di·ca·tive /ɪnˈdɪkətɪv; ɪnˈdɪkətɪv/ adj [never before a noun 不能用於名詞前] a sign of something 指示的; 象徵的: *Surely his presence is indicative of his desire to help?* 想必他的到來表示他想來幫忙吧？ **–indicatively** adv

in·di·ca·tor /ˈɪndəˌketə; ˈɪndɹ̩keɪtəʳ/ n **1** BrE a light on certain vehicles like a car which flashes to show which way it is turning〔英式〕〔汽車的〕方向指示燈 **–see picture on page 209** 見 209 頁彩圖 **2** a needle or pointer on a machine showing the measure of something, such as speed 指針

in·di·ces /ˈɪndəˌsiz; ˈɪndɹ̩siːz/ the plural of INDEX ☆ INDEX 的複數

in·dict /ɪnˈdaɪt; ɪnˈdaɪt/ v [T] fml to charge someone formally with a legal offence〔正式〕控告, 起訴〔某人〕 **–indictment** n [C;U] **– indictable** adj: *an indictable offence* 可提起公訴的罪行

in·dif·fer·ent /ɪnˈdɪfərənt; ɪnˈdɪfərənt/ adj **1** not caring about or noticing something 不在乎的; 不關心的; 不注意的: *I was so excited to see snow that I was indifferent to the cold.* 我看到下雪激動得連寒冷也不在乎了。**2** not very good 不大好的: *I must warn you I'm an indifferent cook.* 我得提醒你我是個手藝平平的廚師。**–indifferently** adv **–indifference** n

[U]: *He treats me with indifference.* 他待我冷淡。

in·di·ge·nous /ɪnˈdɪdʒənəs; ɪnˈdɪdʒənəs/ *adj* belonging to a place originally 土生土長的; 本地的: *the indigenous population* 土生土長的人口 | *Rubber is not indigenous* **to** *Malaysia.* 橡膠不是馬來西亞的土產。– **indigenously** *adv*

in·di·ges·ti·ble /ˌɪndəˈdʒɛstəbl̩; ˌɪndɪˈdʒɛst-əbəl/ *adj* **1** not easily broken down in your stomach into substances to be used by your body (used of food) 不易消化的〔指食物〕 **2** difficult to understand 難理解的: *Such a mass of facts and figures made the report indigestible.* 這麼一大堆事實和數字弄得這報告難以理解。–**indigestibility** /ˌɪndə-ˌdʒɛstəˈbɪləti; ˌɪndɪdʒɛstəˈbɪləti/ *n* [U]

in·di·ges·tion /ˌɪndəˈdʒɛstʃən; ˌɪndɪˈdʒɛs-tʃən/ *n* [U] illness or pain which is caused by your stomach being unable to deal with the food that you have eaten 消化不良(症)

in·dig·nant /ɪnˈdɪgnənt; ɪnˈdɪgnənt/ *adj* feeling or expressing surprised anger at something which you think is not right 憤慨的; 義憤的: *He was indignant* **at** *her lack of co-operation.* 他對她缺乏合作精神表示憤慨。– **indignantly** *adv*

in·dig·na·tion /ˌɪndɪgˈneɪʃən; ˌɪndɪgˈneɪʃən/ *n* [U] feelings of surprised anger about something which you think is not right 憤慨; 義憤: *I expressed my indignation* **at** *such rudeness.* 我對如此的粗魯無禮表示了憤慨。

in·dig·ni·ty /ɪnˈdɪgnətɪ; ɪnˈdɪgn̩ti/ *n* **indig-nities** [C;U] something that offends your sense of self-respect 侮辱(言行); 輕蔑: *I suffered the indignity* **of** *having to apologise in front of all those people.* 我得在所有那些人面前道歉, 蒙受了侮辱。

in·di·go /ˈɪndɪˌgo; ˈɪndɪgəʊ/ *adj* dark pur-plish blue 靛藍色的 –**indigo** *n* [U]

in·di·rect /ˌɪndəˈrɛkt; ˌɪndɪˈrɛkt/ *adj* not directly connected to or with something 間接的; 迂迴的: *This is a very indirect route to the station!* 去車站的這條路線繞了大彎子! | *The accident was an indirect result of her carelessness.* 這事故是她不小心的間接後果。| *an indirect answer* 轉彎抹角的回答 – **indirectly** *adv*

in·dis·ci·pline /ɪnˈdɪsəplɪn; ɪnˈdɪsəpl̩ɪn/ *n* [U] state of disorder resulting from lack of control〔由於管理不善造成的〕混亂狀態; 無秩序

in·dis·creet /ˌɪndɪˈskrit; ˌɪndɪˈskriːt/ *adj* say-ing or doing things which you should not say or do 言行失檢的 –**indiscreetly** *adv* – **indiscretion** /-ˈskrɛʃən; -ˈskreʃən/ *n* [C;U]: *Her indiscretion caused a major scandal.* 她的行為有失檢點, 結果變成了一件大醜聞。

in·dis·crim·i·nate /ˌɪndɪˈskrɪmənɪt; ˌɪndɪ-ˈskrɪmɪnət/ *adj* not choosing or chosen carefully 不加〔仔細〕選擇的: *the indiscrimi-nate murder of ordinary people by terrorists* 恐怖主義者對老百姓不分青紅皂白的殺害 – **indiscriminately** *adv*

in·di·spen·sa·ble /ˌɪndɪsˈpɛnsəbl̩; ˌɪndɪ-ˈspɛnsəbəl/ *adj* too important to be without 不可缺少的; 必需的: *She's become quite indispensable* **to** *the company.* 她已成了公司裡少不了的人。–**indispensability** /ˌɪndɪˌspɛn-səˈbɪləti; ˌɪndɪspensəˈbɪlɪti/ *n* [U]

in·dis·posed /ˌɪndɪˈspozd; ˌɪndɪˈspəʊzd/ *adj* [never before a noun 不能用於名詞前] *fml* ill〖正式〗有病的; 不適的: *Mrs Blythe is indis-posed and therefore unable to attend the meeting.* 布萊塞太太病了, 因此不能參加會議。

in·dis·pu·ta·ble /ˌɪndɪˈspjutəbl̩; ˌɪndɪˈspjuː-təbəl/ *adj* too certain to be questioned 不容置疑的 –**indisputably** *adv*: *That is indis-putably true.* 那是千真萬確的。

in·dis·tinct /ˌɪndɪˈstɪŋkt; ˌɪndɪˈstɪŋkt/ *adj* not easily seen, heard, or remembered 不清楚的; 模糊的: *I have only an indistinct mem-ory of my father.* 我對父親只有模糊的印象。– **indistinctly** *adv*

in·dis·tin·guish·a·ble /ˌɪndɪsˈtɪŋgwɪʃəbl̩; ˌɪn-dɪˈstɪŋgwɪʃəbəl/ *adj* which cannot be recog-nized as different from something else 難以區別的: *The material is indistinguishable* **from** *real silk, but much cheaper.* 這料子和真絲難以區別, 但便宜得多。| *The twins are indistinguishable.* 這對雙胞胎難以分辨。– **indistinguishably** *adv*

✲in·di·vid·u·al[1] /ˌɪndəˈvɪdʒʊəl; ˌɪndɪ-ˈvɪdʒʊəl/ *adj* **1** single or separate 個別的; 單獨的: *Each individual leaf on the tree is different.* 樹上每片葉子都不相同。| *Individual attention must be given to every student.* 對每個學生都必須分別加以留意。**2** personal and different 個人的; 不同的: *She wears very individual clothes.* 她的衣着非常獨特。

✲individual[2] *n* **1** a single person or member of a group, treated separately 個人; 個體: *the rights of the individual* 個人權利 | *People want to be treated as individuals.* 人們都想被當作獨立的個體。**2** *infml* a person, especially one who is different in some way〖非正式〗〔尤指有點特別的〕人: *What a bad-tempered individual you are!* 你這傢伙脾氣多壞!

in·di·vid·u·al·i·ty /ˌɪndəˌvɪdʒʊˈælətɪ; ˌɪndɪ-ˌvɪdʒʊˈælɪti/ *n* [U] the quality which makes someone or something different from all others 個性: *Her work shows great individuality.* 她的工作顯示了很強的個性。

in·di·vid·u·al·ly /ˌɪndɪˈvɪdʒʊəlɪ; ˌɪndɪˈvɪdʒʊə-li/ *adv* separately 分別地; 各自地: *Individu-ally I find children easy to deal with.* 我發現孩子單獨地一個個容易應付。

in·di·vis·i·ble /ˌɪndəˈvɪzəbl̩; ˌɪndɪˈvɪzəbəl/ *adj* impossible to divide or to separate into parts 不可分割的

in·doc·tri·nate /ɪnˈdɑktrɪˌet; ɪnˈdɒktrɪ̩neɪt/ *v* **indoctrinated, indoctrinating** [T] to put ideas into someone's mind in such a way that they will not accept other different ideas 向〔某人〕灌輸〔思想〕(使其不再接受其他不同觀念): *They've been indoctrinated from childhood to believe only what the government tells them.* 他們從小就被灌輸這種觀念，只會相信政府對他們所說的。–**indoctrination** /ɪnˌdɒktrɪˈneɪʃən; ɪnˌdɒktrɪˈneɪʃən/ *n* [U]

in·do·lent /ˈɪndələnt; ˈɪndələnt/ *adj fml* lazy 〔正式〕懶惰的: *an indolent student* 懶學生 – **indolently** *adv* –**indolence** *n* [U]

in·dom·i·ta·ble /ɪnˈdɒmətəbḷ; ɪnˈdɒmḷtəbəl/ *adj fml* too strong to be discouraged 〔正式〕不氣餒的; 不屈不撓的: *a man of indomitable spirit* 具有不屈不撓精神的人 – **indomitably** *adv*

in·door /ˈɪnˌdɔr; ˈɪndɔːʳ/ *adj* [only before a noun 只用於名詞前] which is done, used, or belongs inside a building 在室內做的; 在室內使用的; 室內的: *indoor sports* 室內運動 | *indoor clothes* 室內用的衣服 –opposite 反義 **outdoor**

in·doors /ˈɪnˈdɔrz; ˌɪnˈdɔːz◂/ *adv* inside a building 在室內: *We went indoors.* 我們進入屋裡。 | *We spent the afternoon indoors.* 我們在屋子裡過了一個下午。–opposite 反義 **outdoors**

in·du·bi·ta·ble /ɪnˈdjuːbɪtəbḷ; ɪnˈdjuːbɪtəbəl/ *adj fml* certain and unquestionable 〔正式〕不容置疑的 –**indubitably** *adv*

in·duce /ɪnˈdjuːs; ɪnˈdjuːs/ *v* **induced, inducing** [T] *fml* 〔正式〕 **1** to persuade someone to do something, or to make them do it 勸誘，促使〔某人做某事〕: *What induced you to spend so much money on a pair of shoes?* 是甚麼促使你花這麼多錢買一雙鞋? **2** to cause something 導致: *Too much food induces sleepiness.* 吃得過飽會產生睡意。 **3** to make a woman start giving birth by the use of drugs or other medical treatment 〔用藥物或其他醫療手段〕為〔產婦〕引產

in·duce·ment /ɪnˈdjuːsmənt; ɪnˈdjuːsmənt/ *n* [C;U] encouragement to do something 誘因; 引誘物; 鼓勵: *I gave him money as an inducement to leave.* 我給他錢以引誘他離開。

in·duc·tion /ɪnˈdʌkʃən; ɪnˈdʌkʃən/ *n* **1** [C;U] introduction to something like a new job or organization 〔新工作或組織的〕加入: *an induction course* 入門課程 **2** [U] the process of making a woman begin to give birth by the use of drugs or other medical treatment 〔用藥物或其他醫療手段的〕引產 **3** [U] a way of reasoning in which you arrive at general ideas by considering particular examples 歸納（法）

in·dulge /ɪnˈdʌldʒ; ɪnˈdʌldʒ/ *v* **indulged, indulging 1** [T] to allow someone to do or have what they want 放縱〔某人〕; 遷就: *He indulges his children terribly.* 他對孩子百般縱容。 **2** *infml* [I;T] to let yourself have what you want, especially too much of something that is bad for you 〔非正式〕使〔自己〕

縱情享受〔尤指不好的東西〕: *I'm not a big chocolate eater, but I do indulge occasionally.* 我不是個特別愛吃巧克力的人，但有時會盡情地吃。 | *I sometimes indulge in a cigarette.* 我有時喜歡抽一支煙享受一下。

in·dul·gence /ɪnˈdʌldʒəns; ɪnˈdʌldʒəns/ *n* **1** [U] the habit of allowing someone to do or have what they want 縱容; 放任 **2** [C] something which you want and let yourself have, especially too much of something that is bad for you 嗜好: *Sweets are my only indulgence.* 糖果是我唯一的嗜好。 –**indulgent** *adj*: *indulgent parents* 溺愛子女的父母 – **indulgently** *adv*

★**in·dus·tri·al** /ɪnˈdʌstrɪəl; ɪnˈdʌstrɪəl/ *adj* **1** relating to industry and the people who work in it 工業的; 從事工業的: *industrial processes* 工業程序 **2** having highly developed industries 工業高度發達的: *Japan is an industrial nation.* 日本是個工業國。–**industrially** *adv*

in·dus·tri·al·ist /ɪnˈdʌstrɪəlɪst; ɪnˈdʌstrɪəlɪst/ *n* a person who is closely concerned in the system of earning profits in industry, especially a factory owner 工業家; 實業家; 廠主

in·dus·tri·al·ize /ɪnˈdʌstrɪəlˌaɪz; ɪnˈdʌstrɪəlaɪz/ *v* **industrialise** *BrE* 〔英式〕) [I;T] to make or become industrially developed 使工業化; 實現工業化 –**industrialization** /ɪnˌdʌstrɪələˈzeɪʃən; ɪnˌdʌstrɪəlaɪˈzeɪʃən/ *n* [U]

in·dus·tri·ous /ɪnˈdʌstrɪəs; ɪnˈdʌstrɪəs/ *adj* hard-working 勤勞的; 勤奮的: *an industrious student* 勤奮的學生 | *an industrious nation* 勤勞的民族 –**industriously** *adv* –**industriousness** *n* [U]

★**in·dus·try** /ˈɪndəstri; ˈɪndəstri/ *n* **industries 1** [C;U] work, or a particular kind of work, which uses people and machinery to produce goods 工業; 企業: *the clothing industry* 服裝業 | *the development of heavy industry* 重工業的發展 **2** [U] *fml* continual hard work 〔正式〕勤奮; 勤勞

i·ne·bri·at·ed /ɪnˈiːbrɪˌeɪtɪd; ɪˈniːbrɪeɪtḷd/ *adj fml* drunk 〔正式〕喝醉的

in·ed·i·ble /ɪnˈedəbḷ; ɪnˈedəbəl/ *adj* not suitable for eating 不適合食用的

in·ef·fa·ble /ɪnˈefəbḷ; ɪnˈefəbəl/ *adj fml* too great to be described in words 〔正式〕無法形容的; 不可言喻的

in·ef·fec·tive /ˌɪnəˈfektɪv; ˌɪnɪˈfektɪv/ *adj* (also 又作 **ineffectual** /ˌɪnəˈfektʃuəl; ˌɪnɪˈfektʃuəl/) unable to produce the intended result or to do anything well 無效果的; 不起作用的; 無能的: *He's too ineffective to be chairman.* 他太無能，不能當會議主席 | *ineffectual measures* 不奏效的措施 –**ineffectively** *adv*

in·ef·fi·cient /ˌɪnəˈfɪʃənt; ˌɪnɪˈfɪʃənt/ *adj* not

working as well as possible and so not producing good results quickly 效率低的; 不稱職的: *inefficient management* 效率低的管理 | *an inefficient secretary* 不稱職的祕書 –**inefficiently** *adv* –**inefficiency** *n* [U]

in·el·e·gant /ɪn'ɛləgənt; ɪn'ɛlɪgənt/ *adj* without grace or style 不雅的; 不精緻的 –**inelegantly** *adv* –**inelegance** *n* [U]

in·el·i·gi·ble /ɪn'ɛlɪdʒəbḷ; ɪn'ɛlɨdʒɨbəl/ *adj* not permitted to do or have something 不允許做或有〔某事物〕的; 不合格的: *As a foreign national, he is ineligible to vote.* 作為外僑, 他沒有資格投票。| *She is ineligible for legal aid.* 她沒有資格得到法律援助。 –**ineligibility** /ˌɪnɛlɪdʒə'bɪlətɪ; ɪnˌelɨdʒɨ'bɪlɨti/ *n* [U]

in·ept /ɪn'ɛpt; ɪ'nɛpt/ *adj* **1** foolishly unsuitable 不恰當的; 荒謬的: *an inept remark* 不恰當的話 **2** totally unable to do something 無能的: *He's inept at tennis.* 他根本不會打網球。 –**ineptly** *adv* –**ineptitude** *n* [U]

in·e·qual·i·ty /ˌɪnɪ'kwɑlətɪ; ˌɪnɪ'kwɒlɨti/ *n* **inequalities** [C;U] lack of equality 不平等: *social inequality* 社會不平等 | *There are many inequalities in our legal system.* 我們的法律制度中有許多不平等。

in·ert /ɪn'ɝt; ɪ'nɜːt/ *adj* **1** without the power or will to move or act 無活動力的 **2** *tech* not acting chemically with other substances 〔術語〕惰性的; 不起化學作用的

in·er·tia /ɪn'ɝʃə; ɪ'nɜːʃə/ *n* [U] **1** unwillingness to move or to do anything active 不活動: *a feeling of inertia* 懶散的感覺 **2** *tech* a quality in something which causes it to stay where it is or to continue moving in the same direction 〔術語〕慣性; 惰性

in·es·ca·pa·ble /ˌɪnə'skepəbḷ; ˌɪnɪ'skeɪpəbəl/ *adj* impossible to avoid 不可避免的

in·es·sen·tial /ˌɪnə'sɛnʃəl; ˌɪnɨ'senʃəl/ *adj* not necessary 非必要的; 可有可無的

in·es·ti·ma·ble /ɪn'ɛstəməbḷ; ɪn'estɨməbəl/ *adj* too great to be calculated 無法估計的: *a jewel of inestimable value* 無法估計價值的珠寶 –**inestimably** *adv*

⋆**in·ev·i·ta·ble** /ɪn'ɛvətəbḷ; ɪ'nevɨtəbəl/ *adj* **1** impossible to prevent 不可避免的: *She could see that conflict was inevitable.* 她知道衝突不可避免。 **2** [only before a noun 只用於名詞前] *infml* so usual that you expect it 〔非正式〕照例必有的; 老一套的: *We were served the inevitable cucumber sandwiches and tiny cakes.* 侍者照例又給我們端來黃瓜三明治和小蛋糕。 **3 the inevitable** something that is sure to happen 必然會發生的事情: *He was forced to accept the inevitable and resign.* 他被迫接受這不可避免的事實並辭了職。 –**inevitably** *adv* –**inevitability** /ˌɪnɛvətə'bɪlətɪ; ɪˌnevɨtə'bɪlɨti/ *n* [U]

in·ex·act /ˌɪnɪg'zækt; ˌɪnɪg'zækt/ *adj* not exact 不精確的 –**inexactitude** *n*

in·ex·cu·sa·ble /ˌɪnɪk'skjuzəbḷ; ˌɪnɪk'skjuːzəbəl/ *adj* too bad to be excused 不可原諒的; 不能寬恕的: *inexcusable behaviour* 不可寬恕的行為 –**inexcusably** *adv*

in·ex·haus·ti·ble /ˌɪnɪg'zɔstəbḷ; ˌɪnɪg'zɔːstɨbəl/ *adj* so much that it can never all be used 用不完的; 無窮無盡的: *an inexhaustible supply of energy* 取之不竭的能量供應 –**inexhaustibly** *adv*

in·ex·o·ra·ble /ɪn'ɛksərəbḷ; ɪn'eksərəbəl/ *adj fml* impossible to change or stop 〔正式〕不容改變的; 不可阻擋的 –**inexorably** *adv* –**inexorability** /ɪnˌɛksərə'bɪlətɪ; ɪnˌeksərə'bɪlɨti/ *n* [U]

in·ex·pe·di·ent /ˌɪnɪk'spidɪənt; ˌɪnɪk'spiːdɨənt/ *adj* not useful or advisable 沒用的; 不明智的

in·ex·pen·sive /ˌɪnɪk'spɛnsɪv; ˌɪnɪk'spensɪv/ *adj fml* cheap 〔正式〕廉價的 –**inexpensively** *adv*

in·ex·pe·ri·ence /ˌɪnɪk'spɪrɪəns; ˌɪnɪk'spɪərɪəns/ *n* [U] lack of experience 缺乏經驗

in·ex·pe·ri·enced /ˌɪnɪk'spɪrɪənst; ˌɪnɪk'spɪərɪənst/ *adj* without the necessary experience of something 沒有經驗的: *an inexperienced driver* 無經驗的司機

in·ex·plic·a·ble /ɪn'ɛksplɪkəbḷ; ˌɪnɪk'splɪkəbəl/ *adj* impossible to explain or understand 無法說明的; 費解的: *the inexplicable disappearance of the documents* 文件無故失蹤 –**inexplicably** *adv*

in·ex·pres·si·ble /ˌɪnɪk'prɛsəbḷ; ˌɪnɪk'spresɨbəl/ *adj* too great to be expressed in words (used of feelings) 難以言傳的; 無法用言詞表達的〔指感情〕 –**inexpressibly** *adv*

in·ex·tri·ca·ble /ɪn'ɛkstrɪkəbḷ; ɪn'ekstrɪkəbəl/ *adj fml* impossible to separate or to escape from 〔正式〕分不開的; 無法逃離的: *an inextricable connection between smoking and illness* 吸煙和疾病間分不開的關係 –**inextricably** *adv*

in·fal·li·ble /ɪn'fæləbḷ; ɪn'fælɨbəl/ *adj* **1** never wrong (used of people) 永無過失的〔指人〕 **2** unable to fail 不會失敗的: *an infallible plan* 萬無一失的計劃 **3** always having the intended effect 確實有效的: *an infallible cure* 肯定有效的療法 –**infallibility** /ɪnˌfælə'bɪlətɪ; ɪnˌfælɨ'bɪlɨti/ *n* [U]

in·fa·mous /'ɪnfəməs; 'ɪnfəməs/ *adj* well known for something bad 聲名狼藉的; 臭名昭著的: *an infamous criminal* 臭名昭著的罪犯 –see 見 FAMOUS (USAGE用法)

in·fa·my /'ɪnfəmɪ; 'ɪnfəmi/ *n* **infamies** [C;U] the state of being well known for bad behaviour 臭名昭著; 聲名狼藉

in·fan·cy /'ɪnfənsɪ; 'ɪnfənsi/ *n* **1** [U] early childhood 幼兒期; 嬰兒期 **2 in its infancy, in their infancy** at an early stage 在早期; 在初期: *The project is still in its infancy.* 這計劃仍處於初期階段。

⋆**in·fant** /'ɪnfənt; 'ɪnfənt/ *n* a very young child 嬰兒; 幼兒: *He's still an infant.* 他還是個嬰兒。| *an infant school* 幼兒學校 –see 見 CHILD (USAGE用法)

in·fan·tile /ˈɪnfənˌtaɪl; ˈɪnfəntaɪl/ *adj* **1** relating to small children 嬰兒(期)的: *infantile illnesses* 小兒病 **2** like that of a small child 幼稚的; 孩子氣的: *infantile behaviour* 幼稚的行為

in·fan·try /ˈɪnfəntrɪ; ˈɪnfəntri/ *n* [U] soldiers who fight on foot 步兵

in·fat·u·at·ed /ɪnˈfætʃuˌeɪtɪd; ɪnˈfætʃʊeɪtˌɪd/ *adj* filled with a strong unreasonable feeling of love for someone 迷戀着的; 熱戀着的 –**infatuation** /ɪnˌfætʃuˈeɪʃən; ɪnˌfætʃʊˈeɪʃn/ *n* [C;U]

in·fect /ɪnˈfɛkt; ɪnˈfekt/ *v* [T] **1** to give someone or something a disease 傳染〔疾病〕: *She was infected by a dirty needle.* 她因使用了受污染的針頭而受到傳染。| *10% of the town's population was infected at the height of the epidemic.* 流行病高峯時, 鎮上一成的人受到了傳染。| *He was infected with cholera.* 他染上了霍亂。 **2** to make a place or a thing dangerous 使〔地方或東西〕不安全的: *infected food* 受污染的食物 | *an infected area* 受污染的地區 **3** to influence people and make them feel or behave in the same way as you 使〔人〕受影響; 感染: *We were all infected by her enthusiasm.* 我們都被她的熱情感染了。

in·fec·tious /ɪnˈfɛkʃəs; ɪnˈfekʃəs/ *adj* **1** able to be spread and caught, especially through the air (used of diseases) 傳染性的〔指疾病〕: *I know it's serious, but is it infectious?* 我知道這很嚴重, 但會傳染嗎? **2** likely to influence others 有感染力的: *infectious laughter* 有感染力的笑聲 –**infectiously** *adv* –**infectiousness** *n* [U]

in·fer /ɪnˈfɜ˞; ɪnˈfɜːʳ/ *v* **-rr-** [T;+that] to understand a meaning that is not clearly stated 推斷; 推定: *I infer from your letter that you do not wish to see us.* 我從你信中推想, 你不想見我們。–**inference** /ˈɪnfərəns; ˈɪnfərəns/ *n* [C;U]

■ **USAGE** 用法: Compare 比較 **infer** and 和 **imply**. As a listener you **infer** something (=take a certain meaning from) the words of the speaker ☆ 聽者可從說話者的話中 **infer** 某事(=獲得某種意思): *I inferred from his remarks that he hadn't enjoyed his holiday.* 我從他的話中推斷出他假期過得不愉快。As a speaker, your words **imply** something (= suggest a certain meaning indirectly) ☆説話者所説的話可以 **imply** 某事(=間接地暗示某種意思): *His remarks implied that he hadn't enjoyed his holiday.* 他的話暗示他假期過得不愉快。

in·fe·ri·or¹ /ɪnˈfɪrɪə˞; ɪnˈfɪəriəʳ/ *adj* not as good or as important as another person or thing 差的; 次的; 不重要的: *His work is inferior to mine.* 他的工作比我的差。| *He's so clever, he makes me feel inferior.* 他如此

聰明, 使我感到自愧不如。–opposite 反義 **superior** –**inferiority** /ɪnˌfɪriˈɑrətɪ; ɪnˌfɪəriˈɒrᵻti/ *n* [U]

inferior² *n* a person in a lower position, especially at work (a word used to show disapproval) 〔尤指工作中的〕下級; 地位低的人〔含貶義〕

in·fer·nal /ɪnˈfɜ˞nl; ɪnˈfɜːnl/ *adj* **1** *infml* terrible and often very annoying 〔非正式〕討厭的; 惱人的: *Stop that infernal noise!* 別再這麼討厭地吵鬧了! **2** relating to HELL 地獄的: *the infernal powers* 地獄中的惡魔

in·fer·no /ɪnˈfɜ˞no; ɪnˈfɜːnəʊ/ *n* **infernos** a very large fire 熊熊大火: *The burning building became an inferno.* 燃燒着的大樓成了地獄。

in·fer·tile /ɪnˈfɜ˞tl; ɪnˈfɜːtaɪl/ *adj* **1** unable to have babies 不能生育的 **2** unable to grow plants 不能生長植物的; 貧瘠的: *infertile soil* 瘠土 –**infertility** /ˌɪnfɜ˞ˈtɪlətɪ; ˌɪnfɜːˈtɪlᵻti/ [U]

in·fest /ɪnˈfɛst; ɪnˈfest/ *v* [T] to cause trouble to a person or thing by being present in large numbers 成羣侵擾〔人或物〕: *The fields are infested with snakes.* 這田地裡有大批的蛇出沒。–**infestation** /ˌɪnfɛsˈteʃən; ˌɪnfesˈteɪʃn/ *n* [C;U]

in·fi·del /ˈɪnfədl; ˈɪnfᵻdl/ *n* a person with a different religion from your own or with no religion at all (a word no longer used in modern English) 異教徒; 不信宗教者〔現代英語中不再使用〕

in·fi·del·i·ty /ˌɪnfəˈdɛlətɪ; ˌɪnfᵻˈdelᵻti/ *n* **infidelities** [C;U] disloyalty or an act of disloyalty to your marriage partner or the person you live with, which usually includes having sex with someone else 〔夫婦間的〕不忠實; 不貞行為

in·fight·ing /ˈɪnˌfaɪtɪŋ; ˈɪnfaɪtɪŋ/ *n* [U] competition and disagreement between close members of a group, which can become very unpleasant 內訌; 暗鬥

in·fil·trate /ɪnˈfɪltreɪt; ˈɪnfɪltreɪt/ *v* **infiltrated, infiltrating** [T] to go into something, often secretly and with an unfriendly purpose 〔常祕密地、不懷好意地〕滲入; 滲透: *The terrorist organization was infiltrated by police informers.* 恐怖組織中間混進了警方的密探。| *That smell infiltrated every corner of the house.* 那種氣味滲透到了房間的每一個角落。–**infiltrator** *n* –**infiltration** /ˌɪnfɪlˈtreʃən; ˌɪnfɪlˈtreɪʃn/ *n* [U]

in·fi·nite /ˈɪnfənɪt; ˈɪnfᵻnᵻt/ *adj* very great or without limits 極大的; 無限的: *infinite kindness* 無限的仁慈 | *infinite possibilities* 極大的可能性 –**infinitely** *adv*

in·fin·i·tes·i·mal /ˌɪnfɪnəˈtɛsəml; ˌɪnfɪnᵻˈtesᵻml/ *adj* very, very small 極微小的 –**infinitesimally** *adv*

in·fin·i·tive /ɪnˈfɪnətɪv; ɪnˈfɪnᵻtɪv/ *n* *tech* the form of the verb that can be used after other verbs and with *to* before it, such as go in *I can go, I want to go,* and *It is important to go*〖術語〗動詞不定式〔如 go 在 I can go, I want to go, 和 It is important to go 中都是不定式〕–**infinitive** *adj*

in·fin·i·ty /ɪnˈfɪnətɪ; m'fɪnˌti/ *n* [U] **1** limitless time or space〔時空的〕無限 **2 an infinity of** a number of something which is too great to count 多得無法計算的數量: *an infinity of tasks to do* 要做的數不清的工作 **3** a number which is greater than any other 無窮大

in·firm /ɪnˈfɜːm; ɪnˈfɝm/ *adj fml* weak in body or mind, especially because of old age〖正式〗〔尤指因年老而〕身心衰弱的 – **infirmity** *n* [C;U]

in·fir·ma·ry /ɪnˈfɜːmərɪ; ɪnˈfɝməri/ *n* **infirmaries** a hospital or other place where the sick are given care and treatment 醫院; 醫務室

in·flame /ɪnˈfleɪm; ɪnˈfleɪm/ *v* **inflamed, inflaming** [T] to fill someone with strong feelings 使〔某人〕充滿激情: *The speech inflamed his enemies.* 演說激怒了他的敵人。| *inflamed with desire* 慾火中燒

in·flamed /ɪnˈfleɪmd; ɪnˈfleɪmd/ *adj* red and swollen as a result of infection 紅腫的; 發炎的: *The cut has become inflamed.* 傷口發炎了。

in·flam·ma·ble /ɪnˈflæməbl; ɪnˈflæməbəl/ *adj* (also 又作 **flammable** *AmE* or *tech*〖美式或術語〗) which catches fire and burns easily 易燃的: *Be careful! Those gases are highly inflammable.* 小心! 那些氣體是高度易燃的。–opposite 反義 **nonflammable** –see 見 FLAMMABLE (USAGE用法)

in·flam·ma·tion /ˌɪnfləˈmeɪʃən; ˌɪnfləˈmeɪʃən/ *n* [C;U] swelling and soreness as a result of infection 發炎; 炎症

in·flam·ma·to·ry /ɪnˈflæmətərɪ; ɪnˈflæmətɔːri/ *adj* likely to cause strong feelings or violence 使人激憤的; 煽動性的: *an inflammatory speech* 煽動性的演說

in·fla·ta·ble /ɪnˈfleɪtəbl; ɪnˈfleɪtəbəl/ *adj* which you fill with air before use 充氣的: *an inflatable mattress* 充氣牀墊

in·flate /ɪnˈfleɪt; ɪnˈfleɪt/ *v* **inflated, inflating** [I;T] *fml* to fill with air or gas and so make or become bigger〖正式〗(使)充氣; (使)膨脹 –opposite 反義 **deflate**

in·flat·ed /ɪnˈfleɪtɪd; ɪnˈfleɪtɪd/ *adj* **1** filled with air or gas 充了氣的: *an inflated tyre* 充了氣的輪胎 **2** *fml* greater than is reasonable〖正式〗誇張的: *He has an inflated opinion of his own importance.* 他自以為了不起。

in·fla·tion /ɪnˈfleɪʃən; ɪnˈfleɪʃən/ *n* [U] general rise in prices 通貨膨脹: *The government is introducing new measures to control inflation.* 政府正推行新的措施來控制通貨膨脹。– **inflationary** *adj*: *the government's inflationary policies* 政府的通貨膨脹政策

in·flect /ɪnˈflekt; ɪnˈflekt/ *v tech*〖術語〗**1** [I] (of a word) to change the form of its end-ing according to its use〔單詞〕屈折變化 **2** [T] to change the sound of your speech 變〔音〕; 轉〔調〕

in·flex·i·ble /ɪnˈfleksəbl; ɪnˈfleksəbəl/ *adj* **1** hard and impossible to bend 僵硬的; 不能彎曲的 **2** impossible to influence or change 堅定不移的; 不受影響的; 不可改變的: *He's being completely inflexible about this.* 他對此一直堅定不移。| *inflexible rules* 不可改變的規則 – **inflexibly** *adv* – **inflexibility** /ɪnˌfleksəˈbɪlətɪ; ɪnˌfleksəˈbɪlˌti/ *n* [U]

in·flict /ɪnˈflɪkt; ɪnˈflɪkt/ *v* **inflict something on/upon someone** to force something unwanted or unpleasant on someone 把〔不需要、不愉快的〕某事物強加於某人: *Don't inflict your own problems on me.* 別把你自己的問題強加於我。– **infliction** /-ˈflɪkʃən; -ˈflɪkʃən/ *n* [U]

☆in·flu·ence[1] /ˈɪnfluəns; ˈɪnfluəns/ *n* **1** [C;U] an effect that someone or something has on events, behaviour, or opinions 影響; 作用; 影響力: *He used his influence to get his son a job.* 他利用自己的影響給兒子找了個工作。| *My parents have no influence over what I do.* 父母對我的所作所為沒有影響力。**2** a person with the power to have an effect on people or events 有影響的人; 有權勢的人: *She's a good influence on her friends.* 她是個對她朋友起好影響的人。**3 under the influence of** experiencing the effects of a person or thing 在…的影響下: *driving under the influence of alcohol* 酒後駕車

☆influence[2] *v* **influenced, influencing** [T] to have an effect on someone or something 影響〔某人或某事〕; 對〔某人或某事〕起作用: *Don't let me influence your decision.* 別讓我影響你的決定。

in·flu·en·tial /ˌɪnfluˈenʃəl; ˌɪnfluˈenʃəl/ *adj* having or able to have an effect on others 有影響力的; 能影響別人的: *an influential person* 有影響力的人物 | *an influential decision* 有影響力的決定 – **influentially** *adv*

in·flu·en·za /ˌɪnfluˈenzə; ˌɪnfluˈenzə/ *n* [U] (also 又作 **flu**) an illness where you have a cold and a temperature 流行性感冒

in·flux /ˈɪnflʌks; ˈɪnflʌks/ *n* the arrival of large numbers of people or things〔人或物〕大量湧進: *There was a sudden influx of goods from Japan.* 突然湧進了大批日本貨。

☆in·form /ɪnˈfɔːm; ɪnˈfɔːrm/ *v* [T] *fml*〖正式〗**1** to tell someone something 告知, 通知〔某人〕: *I informed him of my decision.* 我把我的決定告訴了他。| *She informed me that she was leaving.* 她告訴了我她要走了。

☐ **USEFUL PATTERNS** 有用句型
to inform someone of something; to inform someone that…

2 inform against someone, inform on someone to tell the police, or someone in charge, about a person who has done something wrong 告發某人; 檢舉某人

***in·for·mal** /ɪnˈfɔːml; ɪnˈfɔːməl/ *adj* **1** not following official rules or methods, and therefore friendly and easy in manner 非正式的; 不拘禮節的: *The new director held an informal party to celebrate his promotion.* 新任董事開了個不拘禮節的晚會來慶祝他得到晉升。| *informal talks between the two presidents* 兩位總統間的非正式會談 **2** suitable for ordinary situations but not for official occasions (used of clothes or behaviour) 日常的; 非正規的〔指衣服或行為〕: *The invitation said "Dress: informal".* 請柬上寫着"請穿便服"。| *an informal wave of his hand* 他的手隨意揮動 **3** used in ordinary conversation or writing, for example between friends, but not when writing or speaking on official occasions (used of speech or words) 非正式的; 日常使用的; 口語體的〔指談話或言辭〕: *'Kid' is an informal word for 'child'.* "kid"是"child"的非正式用語。–**informally** *adv* –**informality** /ˌɪnfɔːˈmælətɪ; ˌɪnfɔːˈmælɪˌti/ *n* [U]

in·for·mant /ɪnˈfɔːmənt; ɪnˈfɔːmənt/ *n* a person who gives information, especially secretly 〔尤指祕密地〕提供消息或情報者: *The journalist would not reveal the identity of his informant.* 這個記者不會透露他的消息提供者的身分。

★★☆**in·for·ma·tion** /ˌɪnfəˈmeʃən; ˌɪnfəˈmeɪʃən/ *n* [U] knowledge about something or someone in the form of facts 消息; 情報; 資料: *Have you got any information* **about** *local events, please?* 請問你知道關於當地發生的事的情況嗎？| *I need some information* **on** *changes in weather patterns.* 我需要一些關於天氣變化模式的資料。| *an interesting piece of information* 一則有趣的消息 | *According to my information, he is now safely in Morocco.* 據我所知, 他已經安抵摩洛哥。

in·for·ma·tive /ɪnˈfɔːmətɪv; ɪnˈfɔːmətɪv/ *adj* giving useful or interesting facts 增進知識的; 提供資料的: *an informative television programme* 增進知識的電視節目 –opposite 反義 **uninformative** –**informatively** *adv*

in·formed /ɪnˈfɔːmd; ɪnˈfɔːmd/ *adj* **1** having or showing knowledge 了解情況的; 有知識的: *well-informed* 消息靈通的 | *badly informed* 消息閉塞的 | *Please keep me informed* **of** *the latest developments in the situation.* 請讓我了解一下形勢的最新發展。**2** using your knowledge of a situation 基於對情況的了解的: *an informed opinion* 有根據的意見

in·form·er /ɪnˈfɔːmə; ɪnˈfɔːməʳ/ *n* a person who gives information about someone else to the police, often in return for money 告密者; 告發者; 檢舉者: *The police informer was found murdered soon after the trial.* 審判後不久, 向警方告發的人就遭人謀殺了。

in·fra·red /ˌɪnfrəˈrɛd; ˌɪnfrəˈrɛd‹/ *adj* using beams of light that cannot be seen 紅外線的: *an infrared lamp* 紅外線燈

in·fra·struc·ture /ˈɪnfrəˌstrʌktʃə; ˈɪnfrəˌstrʌktʃəʳ/ *n* the system which is necessary to support the operation of a country or an organization 基礎; 基礎結構: *More money is needed for roads and railways if the country's transport infrastructure is to be maintained.* 要維持國家的運輸基礎結構, 需要在公路和鐵路建設上投入更多的錢。

in·fre·quent /ɪnˈfrikwənt; ɪnˈfriːkwənt/ *adj* not coming or happening very often 不常發生的; 不常來的: *infrequent visits* 偶爾的訪問 | *infrequent buses* 班次較少的公共汽車 –**infrequently** *adv*

in·fringe /ɪnˈfrɪndʒ; ɪnˈfrɪndʒ/ *v* **infringed, infringing 1** [T] to go against a law 違反〔法律〕: *He infringed the regulations.* 他違反了法規。**2** [I;T] to take away someone's rights 侵犯〔權利〕: *He felt that his liberty had been infringed.* 他覺得自己的自由遭到了侵犯。| *This law infringes* **on** *our basic right to freedom of speech.* 這條法律侵犯我們言論自由的基本權利。–**infringement** *n* [C;U]: *an infringement* **of** *copyright* 侵犯版權

in·fu·ri·ate /ɪnˈfjʊrɪˌet; ɪnˈfjʊəriˌeɪt/ *v* **infuriated, infuriating** [T] to make someone very angry 激怒〔某人〕; 使〔某人〕十分生氣: *Her attitude really infuriates me!* 他的態度令我大為光火! –**infuriating** *adj*: *His silence on the subject is absolutely infuriating.* 他在這個問題上保持沉默實在是令人大為生氣。

in·fuse /ɪnˈfjuz; ɪnˈfjuːz/ *v* **infused, infusing 1** [T] to give hot water a certain taste by putting in a substance such as tea leaves 泡〔茶〕**2 infuse someone with something** to fill someone with a quality 使某人充滿某種品質: *He was infused with enthusiasm for the project.* 他對這項工程滿懷熱情。–**infusion** /ɪnˈfjuːʒən; ɪnˈfjuːʒən/ *n* [C;U]: *an infusion of herbs* 草藥泡劑 | *an infusion of new ideas* 新思想的灌輸

in·ge·ni·ous /ɪnˈdʒinjəs; ɪnˈdʒiːniəs/ *adj* having or showing cleverness at making or inventing things 善於創造發明的; 靈巧的: *What an ingenious gadget!* 多靈巧的小玩意兒呀! | *an ingenious solution to the problem* 解決問題的巧妙辦法 –**ingeniously** *adv*

in·ge·nu·i·ty /ˌɪndʒəˈnuːətɪ; ˌɪndʒɪˈnjuːəˌti/ *n* [U] skill and cleverness in making, inventing, or arranging things 巧妙; 心靈手巧; 足智多謀

in·gen·u·ous /ɪnˈdʒɛnjʊəs; ɪnˈdʒɛnjʊəs/ *adj* honest, trusting, and inexperienced 直率的; 無經驗的; 單純的 –**ingenuously** *adv*

in·got /ˈɪŋgət; ˈɪŋgət/ *n* a lump of metal in a regular shape 錠

in·grained /ɪnˈgreɪnd; ɪnˈgreɪnd/ *adj* fixed firmly and deeply, and so difficult to remove or destroy 根深蒂固的: *ingrained dirt* 積垢 | *ingrained habits* 根深蒂固的習慣

in·gra·ti·ate /ɪnˈgreʃɪˌet; ɪnˈgreɪʃɪeɪt/ v ingratiated, ingratiating. **ingratiate yourself with someone** to gain favour with someone by making yourself pleasant to them and saying things that will please them (used to show disapproval) 討好某人; 使自己得到某人的歡心〔含貶義〕: *I hate the way he tries to ingratiate himself with the boss.* 我討厭他一心討好老闆的樣子。 –**ingratiating** adj: *an ingratiating smile* 討人喜歡的笑容 –**ingratiatingly** adv

in·grat·i·tude /ɪnˈgrætəˌtjud, ˈtjud; ɪnˈgrætɪtjuːd/ n [U] lack of gratefulness 忘恩負義: *Everyone was shocked by her ingratitude.* 大家都對她忘恩負義的行為感到震驚。

in·gre·di·ent /ɪnˈgridɪənt; ɪnˈgriːdiənt/ n one of the things that goes into a mixture when something is made, especially in cooking 〔尤指烹調的〕原料; 〔混合物的〕組成部分: *Flour and eggs are the most important ingredients.* 麵粉和雞蛋是最重要的原料。| *Let me check the ingredients for this recipe.* 讓我核對一下這份菜譜上的原料。

in·hab·it /ɪnˈhæbɪt; ɪnˈhæbɪt/ v [T not in progressive forms 不用於進行式] fml to live in a place 《正式》居住於〔某地〕: *That island is inhabited by dangerous tribes.* 那個島上居有危險的部落居住。

in·hab·i·tant /ɪnˈhæbətənt; ɪnˈhæbɪtənt/ n a person who lives in a particular place 居民: *inhabitants of large cities* 大城市的居民

in·hale /ɪnˈhel; ɪnˈheɪl/ v inhaled, inhaling [I;T] to breathe air or something else into your body 吸入〔氣體〕: *Once outside in the fresh air, he inhaled deeply.* 一到戶外的新鮮空氣中，他就深深地吸了口氣。| *These days none of us can avoid inhaling car exhaust fumes.* 如今我們人人都免不了吸入汽車排出的廢氣。

in·her·ent /ɪnˈhɪrənt; ɪnˈhɪərənt/ adj naturally present in a person or thing, and not able to be thought of as separate 內在的; 固有的: *I'm afraid there's an inherent weakness in the design.* 恐怕這設計有個內在的缺點。| *the problems inherent in this system* 這體制中固有的問題

in·her·ent·ly /ɪnˈhɪrəntlɪ; ɪnˈhɪərəntli/ adv having a certain quality naturally present 內在地; 固有地: *He was misguided on this occasion, but he's not inherently evil.* 他這次是誤入歧途, 他並非生性墮落的人。

in·her·it /ɪnˈhɛrɪt; ɪnˈherɪt/ v [T] **1** to receive something from someone who has died or moved on 繼承〔某物〕: *He's inherited a fortune from his rich uncle.* 他從有錢的叔叔那裡繼承了一大筆錢。| *We have inherited these housing problems from the last government.* 我們從上屆政府手裡接過這些住房問題。 **2** to have the same qualities as your parents 經遺傳而得到〔特質〕: *She inherited her mother's beauty and her father's weak character.* 她繼承了母親的美麗

樣貌和父親的軟弱性格。 –**inheritance** n [C; U]: *the laws of inheritance* 繼承法 | *leaving his successors an appalling inheritance of corruption and poverty* 遺留給他的繼任者驚人的腐敗和貧窮

in·hib·it /ɪnˈhɪbɪt; ɪnˈhɪbɪt/ v [T] **1** to stop something from happening or developing in the usual or expected way 抑制; 阻止: *Recent regulations have inhibited the growth of new businesses.* 最近的規定限制了新辦企業的發展。 **2** to make someone feel unable to express themselves freely 使〔某人〕不能自由表達: *His presence inhibits me from saying what I want to.* 他的在場使我怯於說出我想說的話。| *I find him inhibiting.* 我發現他很拘謹。

in·hib·it·ed /ɪnˈhɪbɪtɪd; ɪnˈhɪbɪtɪd/ adj unable to feel easy and express yourself freely and naturally 拘謹的; 不能自然表達的: *She's far too inhibited to talk frankly about sex.* 她對有關性的事諱莫如深。

in·hi·bi·tion /ˌɪnhɪˈbɪʃən; ˌɪnhɪˈbɪʃən/ n [C; U] a feeling of being inhibited 拘謹; 禁忌: *She soon loses her inhibitions when she's had two or three glasses of wine.* 她喝過兩三杯酒後, 很快變得無所顧忌。

in·hos·pi·ta·ble /ɪnˈhɑspɪtəbl; ˌɪnhɒˈspɪtəbəl/ adj **1** not welcoming guests, especially into your home 不好客的; 不殷勤招待的 **2** not suitable to stay in (used of a place) 不適於居住的〔指地方〕: *inhospitable desert areas* 荒涼的沙漠地帶 –**inhospitably** adv

in·hu·man /ɪnˈhjumən; ɪnˈhjuːmən/ adj **1** too cruel and lacking in feelings to be considered as human 殘酷的; 無人性的: *an inhuman act* 野蠻的行為 **2** not human 非人〔類〕的: *an inhuman scream* 非人的尖叫聲

in·hu·mane /ˌɪnhjuˈmen; ˌɪnhjuːˈmeɪn/ adj not showing ordinary human kindness to living creatures 〔對生物〕不仁慈的; 無人道的: *inhumane treatment of animals* 虐待動物 –**inhumanely** adv

in·hu·man·i·ty /ˌɪnhjuˈmænɪtɪ; ˌɪnhjuːˈmænɪti/ n inhumanities [C;U] the quality of being cruel and harming other human beings 殘酷無情; 不人道; 野蠻: *an example of man's inhumanity to man* 一個人對同類殘忍的例子 | *the inhumanities of war* 戰爭的殘酷

in·im·i·ta·ble /ɪnˈɪmətəbl; ɪˈnɪmɪtəbəl/ adj impossible for anyone else to copy with the same quality 無法模仿的; 無與倫比的

in·iq·ui·tous /ɪˈnɪkwətəs; ɪˈnɪkwɪtəs/ adj fml extremely unjust or wicked 《正式》極不公正的; 邪惡的 –**iniquity** n –**iniquities** [C;U]

i·ni·tial¹ /ɪˈnɪʃəl; ɪˈnɪʃl/ adj [only before a noun 只用於名詞前] at the beginning 最初的; 開始的: *The initial talks formed the basis of the later agreement.* 最初的會談為以後達成的協議奠定了基礎。| *She calmed down after the initial shock.* 她先是大吃一驚, 後來就平靜下來。| *the initial stages of an illness*

疾病的最初階段

initial² *n* the letter at the beginning of a name 姓名的首字母: *The briefcase had the initials S.L. on it.* 這公事包上面有姓名的首字母 S.L.。

initial³ *v* **-ll-** (also 又作 **-l-** *AmE*〖美式〗) [T] to sign a piece of writing with the initials of your name to show approval or agreement 在〔文書〕上簽上姓名的首字母〔表示批准或同意〕: *Could you initial these memos, sir?* 先生, 請在這些備忘錄上簽上名字的首字母, 可以嗎?

***i·ni·tial·ly** /ɪˈnɪʃəlɪ; ɪˈnɪʃəli/ *adv* in the early stages but not the later stages 最初; 開頭: *The project was set up in 1990. Initially, we didn't have a great deal of success, but later on, after J.F. Danby took over as head, a lot of valuable work was done.* 這項計劃是 1990 年提出的。最初, 我們不算很成功, 但後來, 自從 J. F. 丹比接任領導以後, 開展了許多有價值的工作。

i·ni·ti·ate /ɪˈnɪʃɪɪt; ɪˈnɪʃiˌt/ *v* **initiated, initiating 1** [T] to be responsible for starting something 創始, 發起〔某事物〕: *The government has recently initiated a massive new housebuilding programme.* 政府最近開始實施一項新的浩大的建房方案。**2 initiate someone into something** to introduce someone to some secret knowledge or into a club or group, especially with a special ceremony 傳授某人奧祕;〔尤指通過特別儀式〕介紹某人加入〔俱樂部或社團〕 **–initiation** /ɪˌnɪʃɪˈeɪʃən, ɪˌnɪʃiˈeɪʃən/ *n* [C;U]: *initiation into a secret society* 加入一個祕密社團

***i·ni·tia·tive** /ɪˈnɪʃɪˌetɪv; ɪˈnɪʃətɪv/ *n* **1** [C] the first movement or action which starts something happening 發端; 首創: *The government is making some fresh initiatives to try to resolve the dispute.* 政府正提出一些新的倡議, 力圖解決這一爭端。**2 take the initiative** to be the first to do something 首先做某事: *I think you should take the initiative and ask your boss if she'll send you to Paris.* 我想你該先採取行動, 問問你的老闆她會不會派你去巴黎。**3** [U] the ability to make decisions and take action without the help of other people 決斷能力; 主動能力: *I wish you'd show some initiative instead of always asking me what to do.* 我希望你表現得主動一些, 別老是問我該做甚麼。**4 on your own initiative** according to your own plan and without help 主動地; 自己決定地: *Did he do it on his own initiative?* 他是自己做主幹的嗎?

in·ject /ɪnˈdʒɛkt; ɪnˈdʒekt/ *v* [T] **1** to force liquid into someone's body with a special needle 給〔某人〕注射: *The drug can't be swallowed; it has to be injected.* 這種藥不能口服, 只可注射。| *She injected the rat with a new drug.* 她給老鼠注射新藥。**2** to introduce new ideas or feelings 引入〔新想法或感情〕: *I hope the new teacher can inject some*

life into that class! 我希望新教師能給那個班級注入一些活力!

in·jec·tion /ɪnˈdʒɛkʃən; ɪnˈdʒekʃən/ *n* **1** [C; U] the act of forcing a liquid into something with a needle 注射: *The nurse gave him an injection against typhoid.* 護士給他打針治療傷寒。**2** [C] putting more money into a business or government organization or plan〔給企業、政府組織或計劃〕注入資金: *The business was in need of an injection of new capital.* 這企業需要注入新資本。

in·ju·di·cious /ˌɪndʒuˈdɪʃəs; ˌɪndʒuːˈdɪʃəs/ *adj fml* showing poor judgment of a situation (used of an action or statement)〖正式〗判斷不當的〔指行為或陳述〕 **–injudiciously** *adv*

in·junc·tion /ɪnˈdʒʌŋkʃən; ɪnˈdʒʌŋkʃən/ *n law* a command or official order that tells you to do or not to do something〖律〗命令; 指令; 禁令: *The actress took out an injunction against the magazine to prevent it from publishing the article about her.* 女演員拿出一份對該雜誌的禁令, 阻止其刊登有關她的那篇文章。

in·jure /ˈɪndʒə; ˈɪndʒəʳ/ *v* **injured, injuring** [T] to hurt a living thing 傷害〔生物〕: *She was badly injured in the accident.* 她在事故中受重傷。| *He injured his knee during training.* 他訓練時弄傷了膝蓋。| *The injured people were taken to hospital.* 把傷者送往醫院。**–see** 見 WOUND² (USAGE用法) **–injurious** /ɪnˈdʒʊrɪəs; ɪnˈdʒʊəriəs/ *adj*: *Smoking is injurious to health.* 吸煙對健康有害。

***in·ju·ry** /ˈɪndʒərɪ; ˈɪndʒəri/ *n* **injuries** [C;U] harm or damage to a living thing 傷害; 損害: *insurance against injury at work* 工傷保險 | *He suffered serious injuries to the head and neck.* 他的頭部和頸部嚴重受傷。

in·jus·tice /ɪnˈdʒʌstɪs; ɪnˈdʒʌstɪs/ *n* **1** [U] unfairness 不公正; 不公平: *the injustice of the charge* 收費不公平 **2** [C] an unfair act 不公正的行為: *life's little injustices* 生活中的委屈 **3 do someone an injustice** to judge someone in an unfair way and believe something bad about them 冤枉某人; 使某人受屈

ink /ɪŋk; ɪŋk/ *n* [U] coloured liquid used for writing or printing 墨水

ink·ling /ˈɪŋklɪŋ; ˈɪŋklɪŋ/ *n* [sing] a slight idea 略知; 模糊概念: *I had an inkling something like this was going to happen.* 我隱約覺得一定會發生這樣子的事情。

ink·y /ˈɪŋkɪ; ˈɪŋki/ **1** marked with ink 有墨水痕跡的 **2** very dark 墨黑的; 漆黑的

in·laid /ˌɪnˈled; ˌɪnˈleɪd◂/ *adj* with another material set in the surface to form a pattern 鑲嵌的: *wood inlaid with gold* 嵌金的木頭 | *inlaid wood* 鑲嵌花樣的木製品

in·land /ˈɪnlənd; ˈɪnlənd/ *adj* [only before a noun 只用於名詞前] in or towards the centre of the country, not near the coast or near other countries 內地的; 內陸的; 國內的: *an inland sea* 內海 | *inland trade* 國內貿易 **–inland** /ˈɪnˌlænd; ˈɪnˈlænd/ *adv: travelling inland* 在內陸旅行

in-laws /ˈ·ˌ·/ *n* [pl] relatives because of marriage, especially the mother and father of the person you have married 姻親; 親家

in·let /ˈɪnˌlɛt; ˈɪnlɛt/ *n* **1** a narrow stretch of water going from the sea or a lake into the land 水灣〔從海、湖流入陸地的水域〕 **2** a way in for water or another liquid〔水或液體的〕入口

in·mate /ˈɪnmet; ˈɪnmeɪt/ *n* a person who is kept in a place, usually with a lot of other people 被收容者〔常和其他許多人同住〕: *The prison governor talked the inmates into coming down from the roof.* 典獄長說服犯人從屋頂上下來。 | *She's an inmate of the local mental hospital.* 她是當地精神病院的一個病人。

in·most /ˈɪnˌmost; ˈɪnməʊst/ *adj* farthest inside 最內的; 最深處的

inn /ɪn; ɪn/ *n* a small hotel, usually an old one, which also serves food and drink〔常較陳舊的〕小旅店; 客棧

in·nate /ˌɪˈnet; ˌɪˈneɪt◂/ *adj* which someone was born with (used of a quality) 天生的; 天然的〔指品質〕: *She has an innate sense of fun.* 她有一種天生的風趣感。 **–innately** *adv*

★**in·ner** /ˈɪnɚ; ˈɪnəʳ/ *adj* [only before a noun 只用於名詞前] **1** on the inside 內部的; 裡面的: *the inner ear* 內耳 | *an inner room* 內室 **2** not expressed (of feelings) 內心的〔指感情〕: *inner doubts* 內心的疑惑 | *words with an inner meaning* 話裡有話 **3** closest to the centre 靠近中心的: *the inner circle of power* 權力的核心集團 **4** **inner city** the central part of a city, especially an area with a lot of poor people and bad conditions of life 市中心〔尤指居民多, 生活條件差的地區〕: *the problem of inner city decay* 市中心敗落的問題

in·ner·most /ˈɪnɚˌmost; ˈɪnəməʊst/ *adj* farthest inside 最裡面的; 最深處的

in·nings /ˈɪnɪŋz; ˈɪnɪŋz/ *n* (plural is 複數為 **innings**) the period of time during which a team or player has their turn to hit the ball in a sport〔球隊或球員可以擊球的〕局; 回合

inn·keep·er /ˈɪnˌkipɚ; ˈɪnˌkiːpəʳ/ *n* a person in the past who owned and ran an inn〔舊時的〕客棧掌櫃; 旅店老闆

in·no·cent /ˈɪnəsnt; ˈɪnəsənt/ *adj* **1** not guilty of a crime 無罪的; 清白的: *"But I'm innocent!" he protested.* "可我是無罪的!" 他抗議道。 | *He was innocent of the crime.* 他沒犯這個罪。 | *The bomb exploded, injuring dozens of innocent people.* 炸彈爆炸了, 傷及很多無辜者。 **2** harmless in effect or intention (used of a thing) 無害的, 無惡意的〔指事物〕: *innocent pleasures* 無害的娛樂 | *an innocent remark* 無惡意的話 **3** not able to recognize evil or unpleasant intentions 天

真的; 單純的: *a trusting and innocent young child* 天真輕信的小孩 **–innocently** *adv: "Who, me?" she said innocently.* "你說是呀? 是說我嗎?" 她天真地說。 **–innocence** *n* [U]: *determined to prove his innocence* 決心證明他無罪

in·noc·u·ous /ɪˈnɑkjuəs; ɪˈnɒkjuəs/ *adj* not likely to harm or intended to harm or offend people 無害的; 不得罪人的: *It seemed a perfectly innocuous remark to me, but he was very annoyed by it.* 這話我聽來似乎無傷大雅, 但他卻火冒三丈。

★**in·no·va·tion** /ˌɪnəˈveʃən; ˌɪnəˈveɪʃən/ *n* [C; U] the introduction of something new 革新; 創新: *recent innovations in printing methods* 最近在印刷方法上的革新 | *an attempt at innovation* 嘗試創新 **–innovative** /ˈɪnoˌvetɪv; ˈɪnəˌveɪtɪv/ *adj: innovative ideas* 新穎的想法

in·nu·en·do /ˌɪnjuˈɛndo; ˌɪnjuˈendəʊ/ *n* **innuendoes** *or* **innuendos** [C;U] the suggestion of something unpleasant in words, without saying it directly 影射(的話); 暗諷(的話): *her neighbour's innuendoes about her behaviour* 鄰居在背後說話諷刺她的行為

in·nu·me·ra·ble /ɪˈnjumərəbl; ɪˈnjuːmərəbl/ *adj* too many to be counted 無數的; 數不清的

i·noc·u·late /ɪˈnɑkjəˌlet; ɪˈnɒkjʊˌleɪt/ *v* **inoculated, inoculating** [I;T] to introduce a weak form of a disease into a living body as a protection against catching the disease 給…接種; 給…作預防注射 **–inoculation** /ɪˌnɑkjəˈleʃən; ɪˌnɒkjʊˈleɪʃən/ *n* [C; U]: *a government programme of inoculation* 政府的接種計劃

in·of·fen·sive /ˌɪnəˈfɛnsɪv; ˌɪnəˈfensɪv/ *adj* not causing any harm, or not causing dislike in other people 不傷害人的; 不觸犯人的: *an inoffensive manner* 不得罪人的態度 | *Anne is a quiet, inoffensive sort of woman.* 安妮是那種安詳隨和的女性。 **–inoffensively** *adv*

in·op·por·tune /ˌɪnɑpɚˈtjun; ɪnˈɒpətjuːn/ *adj fml* not suitable at the time〔正式〕不合時宜的: *an inopportune remark* 不合時宜的話 | *He called at rather an inopportune moment.* 他在一個很不恰當的時刻打電話。 **–inopportunely** *adv*

in·or·di·nate /ɪnˈɔrdnɪt; ɪˈnɔːdənɪt/ *adj fml* beyond reasonable limits〔正式〕無節制的; 過度的: *an inordinate amount of work to do* 有非常多的工作要做 **–inordinately** *adv*

in·or·gan·ic /ˌɪnɔrˈgænɪk; ˌɪnɔːˈgænɪk◂/ *adj* not made of living material 無機的; 無生物的 **–inorganically** /-klɪ; -klɪ/ *adv*

★**in·put** /ˈɪnˌpʊt; ˈɪnpʊt/ *n* **1** [C;U] something put in or given for use by someone or something 投入(物) **2** [U] information that is put into a computer〔計算機的〕輸入信息 **–input** *v: to input information* 輸入信息

in·quest /ˈɪnkwɛst; ˈɪnkwest/ *n* an official

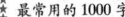

inquiry to find out the cause of a sudden or unexpected death, especially when there is a possibility of crime〔尤指調查猝死原因的〕審問; 審理

in·quire /ɪnˈkwaɪr; ɪnˈkwaɪə^r/ v **inquired**, **inquiring** *fml*【正式】(also 又作 **enquire**) **1** [I;T] to ask for information 打聽; 詢問: *I'll inquire about the trains.* 我將打聽有關火車的情況。| *I inquired what he wanted.* 我問他要甚麼。| *They inquired whether he would attend.* 他們問他是否參加。**2 inquire after someone** to ask about someone's health 問候某人: *She inquired after my mother.* 她問起我母親的健康情況。**3 inquire into** to search for the facts about something 調查; 審查: *The police are inquiring into the matter.* 警方正在調查這件事。–see 見 ASK (USAGE用法)

in·quir·ing /ɪnˈkwaɪrɪŋ; ɪnˈkwaɪərɪŋ/ *adj* (also 又作 **enquiring**) showing an interest in learning about things 好奇的; 愛打聽的; 愛探索的: *a child with an inquiring mind* 富有好奇心的孩子

*★**in·quir·y** /ɪnˈkwaɪrɪ; ɪnˈkwaɪəri/ n **inquiries** (also 又作 **enquiry**) **1** [C;U] a question that tries to find out information 詢問; 打聽: *We've had several hundred inquiries about the new plans.* 關於這些新計劃我們有幾百項問題要查詢。**2** [C] a search for facts 調查: *Two people are helping the police with their inquiries.* 有兩個人正在幫助警方調查。| *The papers are calling for a government inquiry into the incident.* 報界要求政府對這次事件進行調查。**3 make inquiries** to ask for information 詢問: *I'm going to make some inquiries about his previous employers.* 我要詢問有關他以前幾個雇主的一些情況。

■ USAGE 用法: **Enquiry** and **inquiry** are almost the same, but **enquiry** is more often used for a simple request for information, and **inquiry** for a long serious study ☆ **enquiry** 和 **inquiry** 幾乎是相同的, 但 **enquiry** 更常用來表示簡單地打聽消息, **inquiry** 則表示一種長時間的認真的研究: *Thank you for your* **enquiries** *about my health.* 謝謝你問候我的健康情況。| *a government* **inquiry** *into the dangers of smoking* 政府對吸煙危害健康的調查

in·qui·si·tion /ˌɪnkwəˈzɪʃən; ˌɪŋkwɪˈzɪʃən/ n an attempt to find out the facts about something, especially one that is carried out using violent methods〔尤指用暴力方法〕查究; 調查

in·quis·i·tive /ɪnˈkwɪzətɪv; ɪnˈkwɪzɪtɪv/ *adj* trying to find out too many details about things and people 好追根究底的; 過分好奇的: *Don't be so inquisitive!* 別這麼追根究底! | *an inquisitive face at the window* 在窗口好奇張望的一張臉 –**inquisitively** *adv* –

inquisitiveness n [U]

in·roads /ˈɪnˌrodz; ˈɪnrəʊdz/ **make inroads into : a** to take away or use up large amounts of something 佔去; 耗去: *My holiday made terrible inroads into my savings.* 我的假期大大耗去了我的積蓄。**b** to advance into a new area 進展; 進入〔新區域〕: *Their new soft drink is already making inroads into the market.* 他們新推出的汽水已經打入市場。

in·sane /ɪnˈsen; ɪnˈseɪn/ *adj* mad or senseless 發瘋的; 荒唐的: *He suggested what? The man must be totally insane!* 他建議甚麼? 這人一定是徹底瘋了! | *an insane idea* 愚蠢荒唐的主意 –**insanely** *adv*: *insanely jealous* 妒忌得發狂

in·san·i·ta·ry /ɪnˈsænəˌtɛrɪ; ɪnˈsænɪtəri/ *adj* likely to harm people's health by causing disease 有害健康的; 不衛生的: *living in appallingly insanitary conditions* 居住在極其不衛生的環境中

in·san·i·ty /ɪnˈsænətɪ; ɪnˈsænɪti/ n [U] madness 瘋狂; 精神錯亂: *There is a family history of insanity.* 有家族精神病史。

in·sa·tia·ble /ɪnˈseʃɪəbl; ɪnˈseɪʃəbəl/ *adj* that cannot be satisfied 無法滿足的: *an insatiable appetite* 無法滿足的胃口 –**insatiably** *adv*

in·scribe /ɪnˈskraɪb; ɪnˈskraɪb/ v **inscribed**, **inscribing** [T] *fml* to write words on or cut words into the surface of something, especially as a lasting record【正式】〔尤指作為持久的記錄〕題寫; 刻: *The president was presented with a specially inscribed copy of the book.* 贈送給總統一本專門題贈的書。–**inscription** /ɪnˈskrɪpʃən; ɪnˈskrɪpʃən/ n

in·scru·ta·ble /ɪnˈskrutəbl; ɪnˈskruːtəbəl/ *adj* mysterious and not easy to understand 神祕的; 費解的: *"We'll see," he said with an inscrutable smile.* "我們等著瞧," 他神祕地笑著說。–**inscrutably** *adv* –**inscrutability** /ɪnˌskrutəˈbɪlətɪ; ɪnˌskruːtəˈbɪlɪti/ n [U]

in·sect /ˈɪnsɛkt; ˈɪnsekt/ n a small creature with no bones and a hard outer covering, six legs, and a body divided into three parts; ants and flies are insects 昆蟲; 蟲〔如螞蟻或蒼蠅等〕

in·sec·ti·cide /ɪnˈsɛktəˌsaɪd; ɪnˈsektɪsaɪd/ n [C;U] a chemical substance used to kill insects 殺蟲藥; 殺蟲劑

in·se·cure /ˌɪnsɪˈkjʊr; ˌɪnsɪˈkjʊə^r/ *adj* **1** afraid or unsure of yourself 擔憂的; 沒把握的: *She shouts at her staff a lot; I think she's rather insecure.* 她常對職員大喊大叫, 我想她是缺乏信心。**2** not safe, and likely to fall 不牢固的; 不穩定的; 不安全的: *I feel very insecure up this ladder.* 站在這梯子上, 我感到不安全。**3** likely to fail or be lost 可能失敗的: *an insecure investment* 無保障的投資 –**insecurely** *adv* –**insecurity** n [U]

in·sen·si·tive /ɪnˈsɛnsətɪv; ɪnˈsensɪtɪv/ *adj* **1** not kind or helpful to others because you do not understand how they feel 不敏感的; 麻木不仁的: *an insensitive remark* 麻木不仁 的話 **2** not having the feeling which is usual when you have a particular experience 麻木的; 感覺遲鈍的: *insensitive* **to** *pain* 對疼痛感覺遲鈍 **–insensitively** *adv* **– insensitivity** /ɪnˌsɛnsəˈtɪvɪtɪ; ɪnˌsensɪ̩ˈtɪvɪ̩ti/ *n* [U]

in·sep·a·ra·ble /ɪnˈsɛpərəbḷ; ɪnˈsepərəbəl/ *adj* impossible to separate from something else or from one another 分不開的; 不可分 離的: *The government's energy policy is surely inseparable* **from** *its policy on environmental issues.* 政府的能源政策確實和 其環境問題上的政策密不可分。 **– inseparably** *adv*

in·sert /ɪnˈsɝt; ɪnˈsɜːt/ *v* [T] to put something inside something else 插入; 嵌入: *He inserted the key* **in** *the lock.* 他把鑰匙插入鎖 中。**–insertion** /ɪnˈsɝʃən; ɪnˈsɜːʃən/ *n* [U]

in·shore /ˌɪnˈʃor; ˌɪnˈʃɔːr◂/ *adv, adj* near, towards, or to the shore 向海岸(的); 近海岸 (的): *He rowed inshore.* 他划近海岸。| *an inshore lifeboat* 沿岸的救生艇

✲in·side¹ /ɪnˈsaɪd; ɪnˈsaɪd◂/ *n* **1** the part of something that is in the middle of it or within it 裡面; 內部: *The inside of the house needs painting.* 房子的內部需要油漆。**–see** picture on page 764 頁 764 頁彩圖 **2 your insides** [pl] your stomach 肚子; 腸胃: *My insides were hurting.* 我肚子痛。

inside² *adv, prep* **1** in or into something 在 裡面; 向裡面: *I opened the box to see what was inside.* 我打開盒子看看裡面有甚麼。| *There was nobody inside the house.* 房子裡 沒人。**2** *prep* within a particular amount of time 在[一定時間]之內: *They should be here inside an hour.* 他們應在一小時內到這裡。**3 inside out** with the usual inside parts on the outside 裡面朝外地: *You've got your jumper on inside out.* 你把毛衣穿反了。

inside³ *adj* [only before a noun 只用於名詞 前] **1** situated on the inside of something 裡面的; 內部的: *the inside pages of the book* 書的內頁 **2** **inside lane** the part of a MOTORWAY or large road where vehicles drive more slowly 內車道 **3** **inside information** information that is given by someone who knows about something because they are part of it 內部消息

in·sid·er /ɪnˈsaɪdɚ; ɪnˈsaɪdər/ *n* someone in a group who has special knowledge or power 知情人; 權威人士: *Police are investigating recent insider trading on the stock market.* 警方正在對最近的股票內幕交 易進行調查。

in·sid·i·ous /ɪnˈsɪdɪəs; ɪnˈsɪdiəs/ *adj* unnoticed while developing but causing a bad result 暗中為害的; 潛在的: *an insidious trend towards a police state* 變為警察國家的潛在趨 勢 **–insidiously** *adv* **–insidiousness** *n* [U]

in·sight /ˈɪnˌsaɪt; ˈɪnsaɪt/ *n* [C;U] the power of using your mind to understand something deeply 洞察力; 深刻見解: *Visiting the hospital gave me an insight* **into** *the problems of the people who live there.* 去醫 院視察使我對住院者的生活問題有了深刻了 解。| *a writer who shows great insight into human nature* 對人性表現出深刻見解的作家

in·sig·ni·a /ɪnˈsɪɡnɪə; ɪnˈsɪɡniə/ *n* [plural is 複數為 **insignia**] a BADGE or other object which shows the power of an official or important person 〔表示官員或要人權力的〕 徽章; 識別符號: *the insignia of office* 官職的 識別符號 | *I could tell he was an officer by the insignia on his uniform.* 我憑他制服上的 標誌知道他是個軍官。

in·sig·nif·i·cant /ˌɪnsɪɡˈnɪfəkənt; ˌɪnsɪɡˈnɪfɪkənt/ *adj* of little or no value or importance 無價值或價值不大的; 無足輕重的: *The cost will be insignificant compared to the benefits it will bring us.* 跟它要帶來的利潤相 比, 成本可算微不足道。**–insignificance** *n* [U]

in·sin·cere /ˌɪnsɪnˈsɪr; ˌɪnsɪnˈsɪər/ *adj* not sincere 不誠懇的: *an insincere smile* 虛偽的微 笑 **–insincerity** /-ˈsɛrətɪ; -ˈserɪ̩ti/ *n* [U]

in·sin·u·ate /ɪnˈsɪnjuˌet; ɪnˈsɪnjueɪt/ *v* **insinuated, insinuating 1** [+(that)] to suggest something unpleasant indirectly, by behaviour or remarks 含沙射影地說; 旁敲側擊地暗 示: *Are you insinuating that I'm not telling the truth?* 你是不是含沙射影地表示我沒說真 話? **2 insinuate yourself into something** to succeed in becoming part of something or accepted by someone, by using rather unpleasant indirect methods 〔採用討厭的迂 迴手段〕使自己成為某事物的一部; 使自己被接 受: *He gradually insinuated himself into the boss's favour.* 他漸漸取得了老闆的寵信。

in·sin·u·a·tion /ɪnˌsɪnjuˈeʃən; ɪnˌsɪnjuˈeɪʃən/ *n* words or actions which suggest something unpleasant 影射; 暗示: *I object to these malicious insinuations* **about** *my father's honesty!* 我不同意這些說我父親不誠 實的惡意影射!

in·sip·id /ɪnˈsɪpɪd; ɪnˈsɪpɪ̩d/ *adj* lacking a strong character, taste, or effect 枯燥無味 的; 淡而無味的: *This food is quite insipid.* 這 食物淡而無味。| *an insipid smile* 沒有生氣 的微笑

✲in·sist /ɪnˈsɪst; ɪnˈsɪst/ *v* **1** [I; +(that)] to declare firmly and repeatedly, especially when someone else doubts you or opposes you 堅持; 堅決認為: *I insisted that he was mistaken.* 我堅持說他搞錯了。| *She insisted* **on** *her innocence.* 她堅持她是無罪的。

☐ **USEFUL PATTERNS** 有用句型
to insist on something; to insist that...

2 [I;+ (that)] to order or demand that something must happen or be done 堅決主 張; 堅決要求; 一定要: *They are insisting* **on**

immediate repayment. 他們堅決要求立即償還。| *I insisted that he should go.* 我一定要他去。| *You must come to dinner with us — I insist!* 你一定要來和我們一起吃飯——我堅持這一點!

□ USEFUL PATTERNS 有用句型
to insist on something; to insist that…

3 **if you insist** a phrase used when you are agreeing to do something you don't really want to do 如果你一定要〔用於同意做並非真想做的事情〕: *OK, OK, I'll ask my father about it, if you insist.* 好, 好, 如果你一定要我問的話, 那麼我跟父親查詢一下情況吧。

in·sis·tence /ɪnˈsɪstəns; ɪnˈsɪstəns/ *n* [U] the act of stating or demanding something very strongly 堅持要求; 堅決主張: *I did it, but only at your insistence.* 我做了這件事, 只是因為你堅持要求。| *His insistence on a vegetarian diet makes socializing very difficult.* 他堅持素食, 這給社交帶來了很大的困難。

in·sis·tent /ɪnˈsɪstənt; ɪnˈsɪstənt/ *adj* **1** repeatedly stating or demanding something 堅持的; 堅決要求的: *The government is insistent that industry should be more competitive.* 政府堅持工業應該更有競爭力。**2** needing or demanding urgent attention 迫切的; 急切的: *the insistent ringing of the telephone* 急促的電話鈴聲 | *The calls for tax reform are becoming more insistent.* 對稅收改革的要求越來越迫切了。—**insistently** *adv*

in si·tu /ɪn ˈsaɪtjuː; ɪn ˈsɪtjuː/ *adv* in its original place in place 在原地; 就地

insofar as /ˌɪnsəˈfɑːr əz; ˌɪnsəˈfɑːr əz/ *conj* (also 又作 **in as far as, in so far as**) to the degree that 到如此程度: *I'll help you insofar as I can.* 我會盡我所能幫助你。

in·so·lent /ˈɪnsələnt; ˈɪnsələnt/ *adj* rude or disrespectful 無禮的; 傲慢的: *an insolent child* 無禮的孩子 | *an insolent remark* 傲慢無禮的話 | *insolent behaviour* 傲慢無禮的行為 —**insolently** *adv* —**insolence** *n* [U]

in·sol·u·ble /ɪnˈsɒljəbl; ɪnˈsɒljəbl/ *adj* (also 又作 **insolvable** /ɪnˈsɒlvəbl; ɪnˈsɒlvəbl/ *AmE* 【美式】) **1** impossible to explain or to find an answer to 不能解釋的; 不能解決的: *an insoluble problem* 不能解決的問題 **2** which cannot be DISSOLVED in a liquid 不能溶解的 —opposite 反義 **soluble**

in·sol·vent /ɪnˈsɒlvənt; ɪnˈsɒlvənt/ *adj* without enough money to pay what you owe 無償債能力的 —**insolvency** *n* [U]

in·som·ni·a /ɪnˈsɒmnɪə; ɪnˈsɒmnɪə/ *n* [U] an inability to sleep over a period of time 失眠 —**insomniac** /-nɪæk; -nɪæk/ *n*: *all-night television for insomniacs* 為失眠者開設的通宵電視

in·spect /ɪnˈspekt; ɪnˈspekt/ *v* [T] **1** to examine something carefully 仔細檢查〔某事物〕: *The college will need to inspect all previous*

academic records. 這所大學需要檢查以前所有的學業成績。**2** to make an official visit to judge the quality of something such as an organization 視察: *Most schools are inspected at least once a year.* 大多數學校每年至少接受一次視察。—**inspection** /ɪnˈspekʃən; ɪnˈspekʃən/ *n* [C;U]: *We must arrange a thorough inspection of all our equipment.* 我們必須對所有的設備安排一次徹底的檢查。| *Officials came to carry out a safety inspection.* 官方人士到來進行了一次安全檢查。| *On closer inspection, the painting was found to be genuine.* 經進一步仔細檢查, 發現這幅畫是真跡。

in·spec·tor /ɪnˈspektə; ɪnˈspektər/ *n* **1** an official whose job is to establish the quality or legality of something 檢查員; 視察員; 督察員: *a ticket inspector* 檢票員 | *a school inspector* 學校視察員 **2** a police officer of middle rank 〔警察〕巡官: *a police inspector* 警官 | *Inspector Grant* 格蘭特巡官

in·spi·ra·tion /ˌɪnspəˈreɪʃən; ˌɪnspᵻˈreɪʃən/ *n* **1** [C;U] something or someone that encourages you to do or produce something good, especially a work of art 鼓舞人心的人或事物;〔尤指藝術創作的〕靈感: *Dante was the inspiration for my book on Italy.* 但丁是促使我寫有關意大利這本書的靈感。| *Her hard work and imagination are an inspiration to everyone in the company.* 她的勤勉和創造力對公司的每個人都是一種鼓舞。**2** [C] a good idea 妙計; 好主意: *I've had an inspiration — let's paint the doors black!* 我有個好主意——我們把門漆成黑色! —**inspirational** *adj*

in·spire /ɪnˈspaɪr; ɪnˈspaɪər/ *v* **inspired, inspiring** [T] **1** to encourage someone to do something, especially by your own confidence or excitement 鼓舞; 鼓勵: *The trainer inspired the team to even greater efforts.* 教練鼓勵球隊更加努力。| *I was inspired to work harder.* 我得到鼓勵, 更加努力工作。| *an inspiring speech* 激勵人心的講話

□ USEFUL PATTERNS 有用句型
to inspire someone to something; to inspire someone to do something

2 cause someone to feel something 使〔某人〕產生〔某種感情〕: *He inspires confidence in everyone he works with.* 他激起每個同事的信心。

in·spired /ɪnˈspaɪrd; ɪnˈspaɪəd/ *adj* caused by or filled with inspiration 由靈感引起的; 充滿靈感的: *an inspired guess* 憑靈感的猜測 | *She sang as if inspired.* 她好像靈感受到引發而唱起歌來。

in·sta·bil·i·ty /ˌɪnstəˈbɪlətɪ; ˌɪnstəˈbɪlᵻti/ *n* [U] lack of STABILITY 不穩定; 不穩固

✶in·stall /ɪnˈstɔːl; ɪnˈstɔːl/ *v* (also 又作 **instal**) **1** [T] to put something in place ready for use

安裝; 設置: *We're installing a new heating system.* 我們在安裝新的取暖裝置。 **2** [T] to give someone an official position, especially with ceremony 〔尤指通過儀式〕使〔某人〕就職: *The new head of the university is being installed today.* 大學的新校長今天就職。 **3 install yourself** to settle yourself in a particular place 把自己安置於〔某處〕: *I installed myself in front of the fire.* 我在爐火前坐定下來。 **–installation** /ˌɪnstəˈleʃən; ˌɪnstəˈleɪʃən/ *n* [C;U]

in·stal·ment /ɪnˈstɔlmənt; ɪnˈstɔːlmənt/ *n* (also 又作 **installment** *AmE* 〔美式〕) **1** a single payment of a number of payments which will, in time, complete the full payment 分期付款: *I'm paying for the car in instalments.* 我分期付款買這輛車。 **2** a single part of a book, play, or television broadcast which appears in regular parts until the story is completed 〔連載作品或分集戲劇等的〕一部分; 一集: *The final instalment will appear in next month's edition of the magazine.* 最後一部分將在下個月的那期雜誌中刊出。

✱in·stance /ˈɪnstəns; ˈɪnstəns/ *n* **1** a single example or case of something 例子; 實例: *I have noted several instances **of** disrespectful behaviour.* 我已注意到了幾個無禮行為的例子。 **2 for instance** for example; you use this phrase when you are giving an example to support what you are saying, and make your meaning clearer 例如〔用於證實自己所說的內容, 使之更清楚〕: *Roman civilization was very advanced technologically. They had underfloor central heating, for instance.* 羅馬文明在工業技術上已非常先進了。例如, 他們有地下中央供暖設備。 | *Bees are very strong for their size. For instance, they can carry up to a quarter of their own body weight.* 就它們的大小而言, 蜜蜂是很強壯的。例如, 它們能承受自身體重四分之一的重量。 | *Have you considered, for instance, the damage it would do to staff relations?* 你有沒有考慮過, 譬如說, 它會對員工關係造成的損害? –see Study Note on page 1325 見 1325 頁學習提示 **3 in the first instance** first of all 首先

in·stant¹ /ˈɪnstənt; ˈɪnstənt/ *n* **1** a moment 片刻; 瞬息: *Not for an instant did I believe he had lied.* 我絲毫也不相信他撒謊。 | *The instant I saw him I knew he was angry.* 我一見到他就知道他生氣了。 **2 this instant** now, without delay 此刻; 立即: *Do as I say this instant!* 馬上照我說的去辦。

instant² *adj* **1** happening at once 立即的; 即刻的: *The new diet was an instant success.* 新的節食法立竿見影。 **2** very quick to prepare for use 已配製好的; 使用方便的: *instant coffee* 速溶咖啡 | *instant mashed potatoes* 現成的馬鈴薯泥

in·stan·ta·ne·ous /ˌɪnstənˈteɪnɪəs; ˌɪnstən-ˈteɪnɪəs/ *adj* happening at once 即刻的; 瞬間

的; 猝發的 **–instantaneously** *adv*

in·stant·ly /ˈɪnstəntlɪ; ˈɪnstəntlɪ/ *adv* at once 立即; 馬上: *The car hit a tree and the driver was killed instantly.* 汽車撞上了一棵樹, 司機當場死亡。

✱in·stead /ɪnˈsted; ɪnˈsted/ *adv* **1** in place of something else 作為替代; 反而: *There was no chicken left so we had fish instead.* 雞沒有了, 所以我們改吃魚。 | *He didn't go to the library as he had planned. Instead, he met up with some friends and went for a drink.* 他沒照原來的計劃去圖書館, 反而碰上了幾位朋友, 一起去喝了一杯。 **2 instead of** in place of something else 代替; 而不是: *Can we change our meeting to Tuesday instead of Thursday?* 我們能把星期四的會議換到星期二嗎? | *Instead of just complaining all the time, why don't you do something about it!* 別老是光發牢騷, 你幹嘛不做點甚麼!

in·step /ˈɪnˌstep; ˈɪnstep/ *n* the middle part of your foot between your toes and your ankle, or the part of a shoe which covers this 腳背; 鞋面

in·sti·gate /ˈɪnstəˌget; ˈɪnstɪgeɪt/ *v* **instigated, instigating** [T] *fml* to make something begin to happen 〔正式〕使〔某事〕開始發生: *He has instigated legal proceedings against the company.* 他開始起訴公司。 **–instigator** *n* **–instigation** /ˌɪnstəˈgeʃən; ˌɪnstɪˈgeɪʃən/ *n* [U]

in·stil /ɪnˈstɪl; ɪnˈstɪl/ *v* (also 又作 **instill** *AmE* 〔美式〕) **-ll-** [T] *fml* to put something, especially ideas or feelings, into someone's mind, usually by a continuing effort 〔正式〕逐漸灌輸〔尤指思想或感情〕: *I instilled the need for good manners **into** all my children.* 我不斷向孩子們灌輸講禮貌的必要。

in·stinct /ˈɪnstɪŋkt; ˈɪnstɪŋkt/ *n* [C;U] **1** the natural force in people and animals which causes certain behaviour patterns, such as nest-building, and which seems not to be based on learning or thinking 〔人和動物的〕本能: *Some animals hunt by instinct.* 有些動物有捕食的本能。 **2** a feeling about how to act or what is true 直覺: *Trust your instincts and do what you think is right.* 憑你的直覺去幹你認為正確的事。 | *Instinct tells me he'll be back!* 直覺告訴我他會回來的! **–instinctive** /ɪnˈstɪŋktɪv; ɪnˈstɪŋktɪv/ *adj: an instinctive fear of snakes* 天生怕蛇 **–instinctively** *adv: Instinctively, I knew she was ill.* 憑直覺, 我知道她病了。

✱in·sti·tute¹ /ˈɪnstəˌtjut; ˈɪnstɪtjuːt/ *n* an organization formed for a special purpose, or the building in which it carries out its affairs 〔為特定目的組建的〕機構; 學院; 協會; 會址: *a research institute* 研究所

institute² *v* **instituted, instituting** [T] *fml* to introduce or start something 〔正式〕開創; 建立; 實行: *The president agreed to institute reforms.* 總統同意實行改革

☆in·sti·tu·tion /ˌɪnstəˈtjuʃən; ˌɪnstɪˈtjuːʃən/ *n* **1** an established organization which provides people with help, work, medical treatment, or protection, such as a school or hospital 團體; 公共機構(如學校或醫院): *a mental institution* 精神病院 **2** something, such as a custom, which has been in existence for a long time and which is considered important 制度; 習俗: *the institution of marriage* 婚姻制度 **3** the act of introducing or starting something 建立; 設立; 制定: *the institution of a new law* 新法律的制定 —**institutional** *adj*

in·struct /ɪnˈstrʌkt; ɪnˈstrʌkt/ *v* [T] **1** to give someone knowledge or information 教; 教導; 指導: *They instructed me in the best ways of doing the job.* 他們教我用最好的辦法來做這項工作。 **2** to order someone to do something 指示; 命令: *I've been instructed to wait here until the teacher arrives.* 我得到指示在這裡等到老師來。 | *He's instructed his lawyer to proceed with the sale of his house.* 他囑咐律師着手安排出售房子。

> □ USEFUL PATTERN 有用句型
> to instruct someone to do something

☆in·struc·tion /ɪnˈstrʌkʃən; ɪnˈstrʌkʃən/ *n* **1** [U] teaching 教導; 指導: *He's still under instruction, but should finish his training next year.* 他仍在接受指導, 不過明年可以結束培訓。 **2** [C] an order or some advice on how to do something 指示; 命令: *a book of instructions for operating the new washing machine* 使用新洗衣機的説明書 | *an instruction manual* 指導手冊 —**instructional** *adj*

in·struc·tive /ɪnˈstrʌktɪv; ɪnˈstrʌktɪv/ *adj* giving useful information 增進知識的; 有教益的 —**instructively** *adv*

in·struc·tor /ɪnˈstrʌktə; ɪnˈstrʌktər/ *n* a person who teaches an activity 指導者; 教員; 教練: *a driving instructor* 汽車駕駛教練

☆in·stru·ment /ˈɪnstrəmənt; ˈɪnstrəmənt/ *n* **1** an object which you use to help you in your work 工具; 用具; 器具; 器械: *medical instruments* 醫療器械 **2** (also 又作 **musical instrument**) an object, such as a piano, which you play to make musical sounds 樂器 **3** an object which you use to measure something 儀器; 儀表 **4** the means of something happening or being done 手段 —see 見 MACHINE (USAGE用法)

in·stru·men·tal /ˌɪnstrəˈmentl; ˌɪnstrəˈmentl/ *adj* **1** the cause or means of something happening or being done 起作用的; 有幫助的: *I was instrumental in getting the company to change its policy.* 我在促使公司改變政策方面起了推動作用。 **2** played by musical instruments, not voices 用樂器演奏的: *an instrumental piece* 器樂作品

in·sub·or·di·nate /ˌɪnsəˈbɔːdnɪt; ˌɪnsəˈbɔːdn̩t/ *adj* disobedient (used of a person of lower rank or their behaviour) 不順從的; 不服從的〔指地位低的人或他們的行為〕 —**insubordination** /ˌɪnsəˌbɔːdnˈeʃən; ˌɪnsəˌbɔːdəˈneɪʃən/ *n* [U]

in·sub·stan·tial /ˌɪnsəbˈstænʃəl; ˌɪnsəbˈstænʃəl/ *adj* not solid, strong, or satisfying 不堅實的; 不堅固的; 不能使人滿意的: *insubstantial evidence* 不太有力的證據 | *an insubstantial meal* 不足以果腹的一餐

in·suf·fe·ra·ble /ɪnˈsʌfrəbl; ɪnˈsʌfərəbəl/ *adj* unpleasant and too proud in manner or behaviour 難堪的; 傲慢的: *insufferable rudeness* 令人難以忍受的粗魯 | *He's insufferable.* 他過於傲慢。 —**insufferably** *adv*

in·suf·fi·cient /ˌɪnsəˈfɪʃənt; ˌɪnsəˈfɪʃənt/ *adj fml* not enough 〔正式〕不足的; 不夠的: *insufficient evidence* 不足的證據 | *The food was insufficient for our needs.* 食物不夠我們吃。 —**insufficiently** *adv* —**insufficiency** *n* [U]: *an insufficiency of medical facilities* 醫療設施的缺乏

in·su·lar /ˈɪnsələ; ˈɪnsjʊlər/ *adj* **1** not interested in new ideas or experiences, or having no knowledge of them 思想狹隘的; 保守的 **2** of or like an island 島嶼的; 像島嶼的 —**insularity** /ˌɪnsəˈlærəti; ˌɪnsjʊˈlærɪti/ *n* [U]

in·su·late /ˈɪnsəˌleɪt; ˈɪnsjʊleɪt/ *v* **insulated, insulating** [T] **1** to cover something in order to prevent electricity, heat, or sound from passing through it 使絕緣; 使隔熱; 使隔音: *We should insulate the loft.* 我們應該讓閣樓隔熱[隔音]。 | *insulated* **against** *heat loss* 防止熱量散失的設施 **2** to protect someone from ordinary experiences or outside influences 把(某人)隔離; 使隔絕(免受日常瑣事干擾或外界影響): *The royal family is insulated* **from** *many of the difficulties faced by ordinary people.* 皇室成員根本不會遇到平民百姓所面臨的許多困難。

in·su·la·tion /ˌɪnsəˈleɪʃən; ˌɪnsjʊˈleɪʃən/ *n* [U] **1** the action of insulating or the state of being insulated 絕緣; 隔音; 隔熱; 隔離: *Insulation will cut your heating bills.* 隔熱可以減少取暖費。 **2** material which insulates 絕緣[隔音; 隔熱]材料

in·sult¹ /ɪnˈsʌlt; ɪnˈsʌlt/ *v* [T] to offend someone by your speech or behaviour 侮辱; 辱罵(某人): *He felt insulted by her lack of interest in his achievements.* 她對他的成就不感甚麼興趣, 這使他覺得受到了侮辱。 | *an insulting remark* 侮辱性的言語

insult² /ˈɪnsʌlt; ˈɪnsʌlt/ *n* something which someone says or does that offends you 侮辱; 凌辱: *He shouted insults at the other driver.* 他大聲辱罵另一個司機。

in·su·pe·ra·ble /ɪnˈsuːpərəbl; ɪnˈsjuːpərəbəl/ *adj fml* too difficult to deal with 〔正式〕不可逾越的; 不能克服的: *insuperable difficulties* 無法克服的困難 | *an insuperable obstacle* 不可逾越的障礙 —**insuperably** *adv*

★in·sur·ance /ɪn'ʃʊrəns; ɪn'ʃʊərəns/ *n* **1** [U] an agreement by contract to pay money in case of a misfortune such as damage, loss, or accident 保險: *life insurance* 人壽保險 | *car insurance* 汽車保險 | *an insurance policy* 保險單 | *to claim on your insurance* 向你投保的公司提出索賠要求 **2** [U] the business of making and selling such agreements 保險業: *He works in insurance.* 他從事保險業。 **3** [U] money which you pay to an insurance company or which the company pays to you in order to make or keep such a contract 保險費; 保險金額: *The insurance on my house has gone up again.* 我那座房屋的保險費又上漲了。 **4** [sing] protection against something 安全保證; 預防措施: *I bought another lock as an additional insurance against thieves.* 為了防賊, 我又買了一把鎖, 作為雙重保險。

in·sure /ɪn'ʃʊr; ɪn'ʃʊə^r/ *v* **insured, insuring 1** to protect someone or something from the costs of damage, loss, or an accident by making an agreement with a company that will pay those costs 給〔某人或某事物〕保險〔以防損失〕: *My house is insured against fire.* 我的房子保了火險。 | *Are you insured?* 你保了人壽險嗎? **2** the usual American word for 〖美式〗= ENSURE

in·sur·gent /ɪn'sɜ˞dʒənt; ɪn'sɜːdʒənt/ *n* a person who is trying to take power by force from the people who have power in a country 起義者; 造反者; 暴動者; 叛亂者 – **insurgent** *adj* –**insurgency** *n* [C;U]

in·sur·moun·ta·ble /ˌɪnsə'maʊntəbl; ˌɪnsə'maʊntəbl/ *adj* too large or difficult to deal with 不可逾越的; 難以克服的

in·sur·rec·tion /ˌɪnsə'rɛkʃən; ˌɪnsə'rekʃən/ *n* [C;U] action taken to try and remove the people who have power, such as the government 起義; 暴動; 造反

in·tact /ɪn'tækt; ɪn'tækt/ *adj* [never before a noun 不能用於名詞前] whole because no part has been touched or spoilt 完整的; 未經觸動的; 未受損傷的: *the last vase of a set that remained intact* 一套花瓶中剩下的完整無損的最後一隻

in·take /'ɪn,tek; 'ɪnteɪk/ *n* [sing] **1** the process of taking something in 吸入; 納入; 接收: *fuel intake* 燃料的注入 **2** the amount or number of something which is taken in somewhere 吸入數量; 納入數量: *the yearly intake of students* 每年的招生人數

in·tan·gi·ble /ɪn'tændʒəbl; ɪn'tændʒəbl/ *adj* which cannot be clearly understood or known 難以理解的; 不易捉摸的: *an intangible quality* 不可捉摸的性質 | *We felt an intangible presence in the room.* 我們感到房間裡有一種難以捉摸的東西。 –**intangibly** *adv* –**intangibility** /ɪn,tændʒə'bɪlətɪ; ɪn,tændʒɪ'bɪlɪtɪ/ *n* [U]

in·te·gral /'ɪntəgrəl; 'ɪntɪgrəl/ *adj* necessary to complete something 構成整體所必要

的: *an integral part of the argument.* 論據的必要組成部分

in·te·grate /'ɪntə,gret; 'ɪntɪgreɪt/ *v* **integrated, integrating 1** [I;T] to become or to make a person part of a social group 〔使〕成為社會團體的一員: *Some immigrants integrate into the community surprisingly quickly.* 有些移民能極其迅速地適應社會生活。 | *We need to integrate deaf children with hearing children of a similar age.* 我們要讓聾的和有聽力的同齡孩子融為一體。 **2** [T] to put two or more things together 使〔兩件或更多的東西〕結合: *We need to integrate these findings with the results of previous research.* 我們要把這些研究成果和以前的成果結合起來。 –**integration** /ˌɪntə'greʃən; ˌɪntɪ'greɪʃən/ *n* [U]

in·te·grat·ed /'ɪntə,gretɪd; 'ɪntɪgreɪtɪd/ *adj* with a good mixture of qualities and groups 融合的; 綜合的; 互相協調的: *This is an integrated school which children of many different races and social classes attend.* 這是一所兼收許多不同種族和不同社會階層子女的學校。 | *an integrated system* 相互協調的體系

in·teg·ri·ty /ɪn'tɛgrətɪ; ɪn'tegrɪtɪ/ *n* [U] **1** strength and honesty of character or moral principle 正直; 誠實; 廉正: *a man of complete integrity* 剛正不阿的人 **2** *fml* a state of being whole or complete 〖正式〗完整; 完全: *Our national integrity is being threatened.* 我們國家的完整正受到威脅。

in·tel·lect /'ɪntl,ɛkt; 'ɪntɪlekt/ *n* **1** [C;U] the ability to use the power of reason, rather than to feel or act 智力; 思維能力 **2** [U] the quality of being very intelligent 非凡的才智: *His father was also noted for his intellect.* 他的父親還以才智非凡而聞名。

★in·tel·lec·tual¹ /ˌɪntl'ɛktʃʊəl; ˌɪntɪ'lektʃʊəl◂/ *adj* needing, using, or concerning the ability to reason 需智力的; 用腦力的; 智力的: *intellectual subjects* 知識性學科 | *an intellectual argument* 需要智力的辯論 | *intellectual stimulation* 智力刺激 –see 見 INTELLIGENT (USAGE 用法) –**intellectually** *adv*

intellectual² *n* a person who is well educated and interested in activities which demand a lot of thought and understanding 知識分子: *university lecturers and other intellectuals* 大學講師及其他知識分子

★in·tel·li·gence /ɪn'tɛlədʒəns; ɪn'telɪdʒəns/ *n* [U] **1** the ability to learn and understand 智力; 理解力: *an intelligence test* 智力測驗 | *a boy of low intelligence* 智力低的男孩 **2** information gathered about a country's enemies, or the group of people who gather it 情報; 情報人員: *military intelligence* 軍事情報 | *the Central Intelligence Agency of the US* 美國中央情報局

in·tel·li·gent /ɪn'tɛlədʒənt; ɪn'telɪdʒənt/ *adj* having or showing powers of reasoning and understanding 有才智的; 理解力強的: *a*

highly intelligent woman 一位理解力很強的女士 | *an intelligent suggestion* 明智的建議 – opposite 反義 **unintelligent** –**intelligently** *adv*

> ■ USAGE 用法: Compare 比較 **intelligent** and 和 **intellectual**. **Intelligent** is an adjective. An **intelligent** person is someone with a quick and clever mind. **Intellectual** can be an adjective or a noun. An **intellectual** (person) is someone who is well educated and interested in subjects which need long periods of study. A small child, or even a dog, can be **intelligent** but cannot be called an **intellectual**. ☆ **intelligent** 是形容詞。An **intelligent** person 是指頭腦聰明反應快的人。**intellectual** 可以是形容詞或名詞。An **intellectual** (person) 是指受過良好教育，並對需要長期研究的課題感興趣的人。一個小孩或一隻狗都可以用 **intelligent** (聰明的)來形容，但不能稱為 **intellectual** (知識分子)。

in·tel·li·gi·ble /ɪnˈtɛlɪdʒəbḷ; ɪnˈtɛlɪdʒḷbəl/ *adj* that can be understood (used especially of speech or writing) 可理解的〔尤指言語或寫作〕 –**intelligibly** *adv* –**intelligibility** /ɪnˌtɛlɪdʒəˈbɪlətɪ; ɪnˌtɛlɪdʒḷˈbɪlɪti/ *n* [U]

☆**in·tend** /ɪnˈtɛnd; ɪnˈtend/ *v* **1** [I] to have the intention of doing something 想要; 打算; 意欲: *I had to leave sooner than I had intended.* 我得比原來打算的早一些離開。| *I intended to catch the early train, but I didn't get up in time.* 我原打算趕早班火車，但我遲了起牀。| *He didn't intend to cause so much unhappiness.* 他並不想弄得這麼不開心。

> □ USEFUL PATTERN 有用句型
> to intend to do something

2 [T] to mean someone or something to be or do something 打算使…成為; 意思是…: *The flowers were intended for you.* 這些花原是要給你的。| *It was intended as a joke.* 這只是想開個玩笑罷了。| *It was intended to be cooked slowly.* 這東西原打算用慢火煮的。| *He didn't intend them to wait for him.* 他沒打算讓他們等他。

> □ USEFUL PATTERNS 有用句型
> to intend someone to do something; to intend something to happen; to be intended for someone or something; to be intended as something

*☆**in·tense** /ɪnˈtɛns; ɪnˈtens/ *adj* **1** great or strong (used especially of feelings and sensations) 強烈的; 劇烈的〔尤指感情〕: *intense cold* 嚴寒 | *intense sorrow* 極度悲痛

2 having very strong feelings about things (used of people) 熱情的; 熱切的〔指人〕: *I find her a little too intense.* 我發現她有點過於熱情。–**intensely** *adv* –**intensity** *n*: *He was surprised by the intensity of her feelings.* 他對她的強烈感情感到驚訝。

in·ten·si·fy /ɪnˈtɛnsəˌfaɪ; ɪnˈtensḷfaɪ/ *v* **intensified, intensifying** [I;T] to become or to make something stronger 加強; 增強: *Police have intensified their search for the criminal.* 警方加緊搜捕那個罪犯。–**intensified** *adj*

in·ten·sive /ɪnˈtɛnsɪv; ɪnˈtensɪv/ *adj* **1** giving a lot of attention or action to something, often only for a short time 〔常只持續短時間〕精心的; 深入細緻的; 集中的: *intensive farming* 精耕細作 | *a short intensive English course* 短期英語強化課程 **2 intensive care** very special hospital care for people who are dangerously ill or very badly hurt (重病) 深切治療; 特別護理: *the intensive care unit* 特別護理組 | *He's been transferred to intensive care.* 他已改為接受深切治療。–**intensively** *adv*

in·tent[1] /ɪnˈtɛnt; ɪnˈtent/ *n fml*〔正式〕[U] **1** intention 意圖; 目的: *a declaration of intent* 意圖的宣告 | *He entered the building with intent to steal.* 他進入大樓企圖行竊。| *with good intent* 出於好意 **2 to all intents and purposes** in every important way 幾乎在一切方面; 實際上: *His proposal is, to all intents and purposes, exactly what we had in mind.* 他的建議實際上正是我們心裡所想的。

intent[2] *adj* **1** showing or doing something with fixed attention 專心致志的; 一心一意的: *an intent look* 目不轉睛的注視 | *She's intent on her studies.* 她專心致志地學習。**2 intent on doing something** determined to do something 決心做某事: *He's intent on going to France next year.* 他一心想明年去法國。–**intently** *adv* –**intentness** *n* [U]

☆**in·ten·tion** /ɪnˈtɛnʃən; ɪnˈtenʃ*ə*n/ *n* [C;U] a plan or purpose 計劃; 意圖; 目的: *I've got no intention of changing my mind.* 我不打算改變主意。| *It wasn't my intention to make you miss your train.* 我不是故意讓你誤火車的。| *He is full of good intentions, but can do nothing to help.* 他滿懷好意，但愛莫能助。

in·ten·tion·al /ɪnˈtɛnʃənḷ; ɪnˈtenʃənəl/ *adj* intended or done on purpose 有意的; 故意的 –opposite 反義 **unintentional** –**intentionally** *adv*: *I'm sorry if I upset you — I didn't do it intentionally.* 如果打攪了你很抱歉——我不是故意這麼幹的。

in·ter /ɪnˈtɜ; ɪnˈtɝ/ *v* -**rr**- [T] *fml* to bury a dead person〔正式〕埋葬

in·ter·act /ˌɪntəˈækt; ˌɪntɚˈækt/ *v* [I] **1** to have an effect on each other or something else 相互影響; 相互作用: *The two chemicals interact, causing a violent explosion.* 兩種化學品互相作用，引起了一場劇烈爆炸。**2** to talk to other people and form relationships with them 交往; 交流: *When honest discussion is possible, couples interact more effectively.* 夫婦一旦能坦誠相見，相互間就可更好地溝通。 –**interaction** /ˌɪntəˈækʃən; ˌɪntəˈækʃən/ *n* [U]: *There should be more interaction* **between** *doctors and the social services.* 醫生和社會福利機構之間應該加強協作。

in·ter·cede /ˌɪntəˈsid; ˌɪntəˈsiːd/ *v* **interceded, interceding** [I] to speak in favour of someone else in order to help them 代為請求; 說情: *He interceded* **with** *the governor on my behalf.* 他代我向主管說情。 –**intercession** /-ˈsɛʃən; -ˈseʃən/ *n* [C;U]

in·ter·cept /ˌɪntəˈsɛpt; ˌɪntəˈsept/ *v* [T] to stop and often seize a person or thing that is moving from one place to another 攔截; 截住: *The parcel of drugs was intercepted by the police.* 這包毒品被警方截獲了。 | *I think someone in the Ministry is intercepting confidential memos.* 我想部裡有人正在截取機密備忘錄。 | *He was intercepted before he reached the border.* 他在抵達邊境前被截住。 –**interception** /-ˈsɛpʃən; -ˈsepʃən/ *n* [U]

in·ter·change /ˈɪntəˌtʃendʒ; ˈɪntətʃeɪndʒ/ *n* **1** [C;U] exchange 交換; 互換; 交替: *an interchange of ideas* 交換意見 **2** [C] a system of samller roads by which two main roads are connected 〔公路的〕互通式立體交叉: *You leave the motorway at the next interchange.* 你在下一個立體交叉道駛離高速公路。

in·ter·chan·gea·ble /ˌɪntəˈtʃendʒəbl; ˌɪntəˈtʃeɪndʒəbl/ *adj* which can be used in place of each other or something else 互可換的; 可交替的 –**interchangeably** *adv*: *The two words are used interchangeably.* 這兩個單詞可交換使用。

in·ter·com /ˈɪntəˌkʌm; ˈɪntəkɒm/ *n* a system by which you can talk through a machine to people who are in a different room or in different parts of a building 內部通話系統: *There was an announcement on the intercom.* 內部通話系統上有個通知。

in·ter·con·ti·nen·tal /ˌɪntəˌkɑntəˈnɛntəl; ˌɪntəkɒntɪˈnentl/ *adj* between different land masses 洲際的: *intercontinental trade* 洲際貿易 | *Intercontinental flights leave from Terminal 4.* 洲際航班從四號站樓起飛。

in·ter·course /ˈɪntəˌkors; ˈɪntəkɔːs/ *n* [U] **1** see 見 SEXUAL INTERCOURSE **2** a sharing of feelings, ideas, activities, and so on allowing people to know each other better 交流; 交往; 交際: *social intercourse* 社會交往

in·ter·de·pen·dent /ˌɪntədɪˈpɛndənt; ˌɪntədɪˈpendənt/ *adj* depending on each other 互相依賴的; 互相依存的 –**interdependence** *n* [U]

in·terest[1] /ˈɪntərɪst; ˈɪntrɪst/ *n* **1** [C; U] a desire to give your attention to something 興趣: *I have no interest* **in** *politics.* 我對政治沒興趣。 | *He's showing an interest in music.* 他對音樂感興趣。 **2 of interest** able to hold your attention 能引起興趣的: *Is there anything of interest on the news?* 有沒有甚麼令人感興趣的新聞? [RELATED PHRASE 相關詞組 **of no interest**] **3** [C] an activity or subject to which you give time and attention 愛好: *Eating seems to be his only interest in life.* 吃似乎是他生活中唯一的愛好。 **4** [C;U] an advantage 利益: *The child's interest must come first.* 孩子的利益應該放在首位。 | *We have an interest in selling quickly before prices fall.* 我們在價格下跌前迅速賣出，賺了一筆。 **5 in someone's interest** to someone's advantage 為了某人的利益: *It is not in your interest to sell now.* 現在賣出對你不利。 | *I have agreed to this only in the interests of better working relations.* 我只是為了改善工作關係才同意這個的。 **6 have someone's interests at heart** to care about someone being treated fairly 把某人的利益放在心上 **7** [U] money paid for borrowing money 利息: *Interest rates on property loans are now at 15%.* 購房貸款目前的利率是15%。 | *an interest-free loan* 無息貸款 **8** [C] a share in a company 〔公司的〕股份: *She sold her interest* **in** *the company.* 她賣掉了自己在公司的股份。 | *business interests* 企業產權

interest[2] *v* [T] **1** to make you want to know more about something 使感興趣: *Football doesn't interest me at all.* 足球無法引起我的興趣。 **2** to persuade someone to buy or do something 說服某人買或做〔某事物〕: *Can I interest you* **in** *a cup of coffee?* 請你喝杯咖啡好嗎?

in·ter·est·ed /ˈɪntərɪstɪd; ˈɪntrɪstɪd/ *adj* **1** concerned to know more about something, or wanting to take part in something 關心的; 感興趣的: *He was interested in my suggestion for increasing productivity.* 他對提高生產率的建議很感興趣。 | *an interested look on his face* 他臉上表現出感興趣的神色 | *I would be very interested in being involved in the scheme.* 我對能參與這個規劃十分感興趣。 –opposite 反義 **uninterested**

□ USEFUL PATTERNS 有用句型
be interested in something; be interested in doing something

2 [only before a noun 只用於名詞前] personally concerned and therefore possibly unable to make a fair judgment 有利害關係的; 不能做公正判斷的: *We shall be calling a meeting of all interested parties.* 我們要召有關各黨派開個會議。 –opposite 反義 **disinterested** –**interestedly** *adv*

in·terest·ing /ˈɪntərɪstɪŋ; ˈɪntrɪstɪŋ/ *adj* catching and keeping your attention 有趣的; 令人關注的: *an interesting idea* 有趣的念頭 | *That's very interesting!* 那很有趣! –opposite 反義 **uninteresting** –**interestingly** *adv*

in·ter·fere /ˌɪntəˈfɪr; ˌɪntəˈfɪə[r]/ *v* **interfered,**

interfering [I] **1** to concern yourself with other people's affairs 干涉; 干預: *Don't interfere! 別干涉! | You're always interfering in my private life.* 你老是干涉我的私生活。 **2** to get in the way or make something difficult 妨礙; 阻止: *Having to work late interferes with my social life.* 工作到很晚妨礙了我的社交生活。 | *Don't interfere with our affairs and we won't interfere with yours.* 別妨礙我們的事情, 這樣我們也不會來妨礙你們的。

in·ter·fer·ence /ˌɪntəˈfɪrəns; ˌɪntəˈfɪərəns/ *n* [U] **1** the act or action of interfering 干涉; 妨礙; 阻止: *I resent his mother's interference in our relationship.* 我恨他母親妨礙我們的關係。 **2** the confused noises which, for example, make a radio station difficult to listen to 干擾(聲): *"We apologize for the interference, which is due to bad weather conditions."* "因為天氣情況不好, 造成了干擾, 我們向大家致歉。"

in·ter·im[1] /ˈɪntərɪm; ˈɪntərɪm/ *n* **in the interim** in the time between two events 在此期間

interim[2] *adj* useful for a limited time 暫時的; 臨時的: *an interim report* 臨時報告 | *interim measures to control football hooligans* 控制足球流氓的臨時措施

in·te·ri·or[1] /ɪnˈtɪrɪə; ɪnˈtɪərɪə[r]/ *n* **1** the inside part of something 內部: *the palace's restored interior* 宮殿修復的內部 **2 the interior** the part of a country away from the coast 內陸: *journeys into the interior* 去內地的旅行 **3** affairs within a particular country 內政: *the Ministry of the Interior* 內政部

interior[2] *adj* indoors 室內的: *interior design* 室內設計 | *an interior decorator* 室內裝飾設計師 –opposite 反義 **exterior**

in·ter·ject /ˌɪntəˈdʒɛkt; ˌɪntəˈdʒekt/ *v* [I;T] *fml* to interrupt, or to put in a sudden remark when someone is speaking 《正式》 〔突然〕插入〔說話〕

in·ter·jec·tion /ˌɪntəˈdʒɛkʃən; ˌɪntəˈdʒekʃən/ *n fml* 《正式》 **1** [C] a phrase, word, or set of sounds used as a sudden remark 感嘆詞; 感嘆語: *interjections such as "Oh!" or "Well done!"* 如"啊"或"幹得好"等感嘆詞 **2** [U] the act of interrupting someone with a sudden remark 插話

in·ter·lock /ˌɪntəˈlɑk; ˌɪntəˈlɒk/ *v* [I;T] to fasten or be fastened together so as to be firmly joined together (使)連鎖; (使)連結; (使)互相扣住: *to interlock the fingers of two hands* 將雙手手指交叉 | *The gear wheels interlock.* 齒輪互相嚙合。

in·ter·lop·er /ˌɪntəˈlopə; ˈɪntələʊpə[r]/ *n fml* a person who enters a place without any right to be there 《正式》闖入者

in·ter·lude /ˈɪntəˌlud; ˈɪntəluːd/ *n* **1** a period of time between activities or events 間歇 **2** the time between parts of a play, film, or

concert 〔戲劇、影片或音樂會的〕幕間休息

in·ter·mar·ry /ˌɪntəˈmærɪ; ˌɪntəˈmærɪ/ **intermarried, intermarrying** [I] (of different groups of people) to marry each other 〔不同種族間的〕通婚: *The two families have been intermarrying for hundreds of years.* 兩個家族數百年來一直通婚。 –**intermarriage** *n* [U]

in·ter·me·di·a·ry /ˌɪntəˈmidiˌɛrɪ; ˌɪntəˈmiːdiəri/ *n* **intermediaries** a person who comes between two other groups or people so as to bring them into agreement 調解人; 中間人

in·ter·me·di·ate /ˌɪntəˈmidɪt; ˌɪntəˈmiːdiət/ *adj* between two levels or stages 中間的; 中級的: *an intermediate student of English* 英語中級程度的學生 | *an intermediate step towards the final design* 設計定稿前的中間步驟

in·ter·ment /ɪnˈtɜ·mənt; ɪnˈtɜːmənt/ *n* [C;U] *fml* burial 《正式》埋葬; 安葬

in·ter·mi·na·ble /ɪnˈtɜ·mɪnəbl; ɪnˈtɜːmɪnəbl/ *adj* not interesting and seeming endless 無休止的; 沒完沒了的: *an interminable speech* 沒完沒了的講話 | *interminable delays* 無休止的耽擱 –**interminably** *adv*

in·ter·mis·sion /ˌɪntəˈmɪʃən; ˌɪntəˈmɪʃən/ *n* the usual American word for 《美式》 INTERVAL

in·ter·mit·tent /ˌɪntəˈmɪtnt; ˌɪntəˈmɪtənt/ *adj* happening at some times and not other times 間歇的; 斷斷續續的: *an intermittent fault* 斷斷續續的毛病 | *an intermittent noise* 斷斷續續的噪聲 –**intermittently** *adv*

in·tern /ɪnˈtɜ·n; ɪnˈtɜːn/ *v* [T] to put someone in prison or limit their freedom of movement for political reasons 〔為政治原因〕拘留, 扣押〔某人〕

⋆**in·ter·nal** /ɪnˈtɜ·nl; ɪnˈtɜːnl/ *adj* **1** of or in the inside of something such as your body or an organization 內部的; 體內的; 組織內的: *internal damage* 內部損傷 | *an internal report* 內部報告 **2** inside a particular country, or concerning the affairs of that country 國內的; 內政的: *internal trade* 國內貿易 | *internal flights* 國內航班 –opposite 反義 **external** –**internally** *adv*

in·ter·nal-com·bus·tion en·gine /ˌ·ˈ·· ˈ·· ·/ *n* an engine which produces power inside itself by burning a substance such as petrol 內燃機

⋆**in·ter·na·tion·al**[1] /ˌɪntəˈnæʃənl̩; ˌɪntəˈnæʃənəl/ *adj* between nations or concerning more than one nation 國際的; 世界的: *international relations* 國際關係 | *an international organization* 國際組織 | *an international star* 國際明星 –**internationally** *adv*

international[2] *n* **1** an international sports match 國際體育比賽 **2** a player who performs in such a match 參加國際比賽的運動員: *an England international* 參加國際比賽

的英格蘭選手

in·ter·plan·e·ta·ry /ˌɪntɚˈplænəˌtɛrɪ; ˌɪntə-ˈplænɪ͵tərɪ◂/ *adj* [only before a noun 只用於名詞前] happening or done between the PLANETS 行星間的: *interplanetary travel* 星際旅行

in·ter·play /ˈɪntɚˌple; ˈɪntəpleɪ/ *n* [U] the action or effect of two or more things on each other 相互作用; 相互影響: *the interplay of light and sound* 光和聲的相互作用 | *the interplay* **between** *the forces of good and evil* 正邪兩股力量的相互作用

in·ter·pose /ˌɪntɚˈpoz; ˌɪntəˈpəʊz/ *v* **interposed, interposing** *fml* 〖正式〗 **1** [T] to put something between two people or things 插入 **2** [I;T] to interrupt, or to introduce something into a conversation 插(話): *"But we've tried that,"* she interposed. "但我們試過那個," 她插話說。

*⭐**in·ter·pret** /ɪnˈtɝprɪt; ɪnˈtɜːprɪt/ *v* [T] **1** to put language into the words of another language, usually by talking 翻譯〔常指口譯〕: *We need somebody to interpret* **from** *Russian* **into** *English.* 我們需要一個把俄語口譯為英語的人。 **2** to understand the meaning of something 把〔某事物〕理解為; 解釋: *Her silence is being interpreted* **as** *cowardice.* 他的沉默被理解為膽怯。 | *He can interpret your dreams.* 他懂得解釋你的夢。 **3** to perform a work of art in a particular way that shows your own understanding of it〔根據本人對藝術作品的理解〕演繹; 表演; 體現: *He interpreted Hamlet* **as** *a man lost between two social orders.* 他把哈姆雷特演繹成一個迷失在兩個社會階層中的人。

*⭐**in·ter·pre·ta·tion** /ɪn͵tɝprɪˈteʃən; ɪn͵tɜːprɪ-ˈteɪʃən/ *n* [C;U] **1** your own particular understanding 見解: *What's your interpretation of recent political events?* 你對最近的政治事件有甚麼見解? **2** explanation 解釋: *I would put a different interpretation on the murder myself.* 我對謀殺案有不同的見解。 **3** a particular understanding of a work of art, especially as shown in performance 表演; 演繹; 藝術處理: *Schnabel's interpretation* **of** *Beethoven* 施納貝爾對貝多芬(樂曲)的藝術處理

in·ter·pret·er /ɪnˈtɝprɪtɚ; ɪnˈtɜːprɪtə/ *n* a person who interprets from one language into another 傳譯員: *The Russian ambassador answered* **through** *an interpreter.* 俄國大使通過傳譯回答提問。

in·ter·ro·gate /ɪnˈtɛrəˌget; ɪnˈterəgeɪt/ *v* **interrogated, interrogating** [T] to question someone formally for a special purpose especially for a long time and perhaps with threats or violence〔尤指長時間地, 可能用威脅或暴力手段地〕詢問; 審問; 質問: *She was interrogated for several hours by two officers.* 她被兩個軍官審問了幾個小時。 — **interrogator** *n* — **interrogation** /ɪn͵tɛrəˈge-ʃən; ɪn͵terəˈgeɪʃən/ *n* [C;U]

in·ter·rog·a·tive /ˌɪntəˈrɑgətɪv; ˌɪntəˈrɒgə-tɪv/ *n* a sentence, phrase, or word which asks a question 疑問句〔詞〕 — **interrogative** *adj* — **interrogatively** *adv*

in·ter·rupt /ˌɪntəˈrʌpt; ˌɪntəˈrʌpt/ *v* [I;T] **1** to break someone's flow of speech or action by saying or doing something 打斷〔某人的講話或動作〕: *I'm sorry to interrupt, but I'd just like to make a point.* 對不起打擾了, 可我只想陳述一個觀點。 | *Don't interrupt him now.* 現在別打擾他。 **2** to break the flow of something continuous 中斷〔連續的事物〕: *During the strike milk supplies were interrupted.* 罷工期間牛奶供應中斷了。 — **interruption** /-ˈrʌpʃən; -ˈrʌpʃən/ *n* [C;U]

in·ter·sect /ˌɪntɚˈsɛkt; ˌɪntəˈsekt/ *v* [I;T] (of lines and roads) to cross〔線或路〕交叉; 相交

in·ter·sec·tion /ˌɪntɚˈsɛkʃən; ˌɪntəˈsekʃən/ *n* a place where roads or lines cross〔線或路的〕交叉處: *a busy intersection* 交通繁忙的交叉路口

in·ter·spersed /ˌɪntɚˈspɝst; ˌɪntəˈspɜːst/ *adj* **interspersed with** having things mixed in here and there 點綴的: *a field of grass, interspersed with a few flowers* 一片草地, 點綴着些許花兒

*⭐**in·ter·val** /ˈɪntɚvl; ˈɪntəvəl/ *n* **1** a period of time between the parts of a play, concert, or other public performance〔戲劇、音樂會等的〕幕間休息: *We had an ice cream in the interval.* 我們幕間休息時吃了冰淇淋。 **2** a period of time between events 間隔; 間歇: *There was a long interval before he replied.* 隔了好久他才回答。 | *the interval* **between** *the arrest and the trial* 從逮捕到審判之間的間隔 **3 at intervals: a** happening regularly after periods of time 每隔…時間: *The bell rang at 20-minute intervals.* 每隔二十分鐘打一次鈴。 **b** at equal distances 每隔…距離: *The seeds are planted at intervals of six inches.* 這些種子每隔六英寸播栽。

in·ter·vene /ˌɪntɚˈvin; ˌɪntəˈviːn/ *v* **intervened, intervening** [I] **1** to interrupt something, especially to prevent a bad result〔尤指為了防止壞的結果而〕干預; 干涉: *The government refused to intervene* **in** *the dispute between British Coal and the miners.* 政府拒絕調停英國煤礦公司和礦工之間的糾紛。 **2** to happen between events 發生於其間 — **intervention** /-ˈvɛnʃən; -ˈvenʃən/ *n* [C; U]

in·ter·ven·ing /ˌɪntɚˈvinɪŋ; ˌɪntəˈviːnɪŋ/ *adj* **in the intervening years** in the time between two events 在兩件事情之間的時間中: *I hadn't seen him since 1986 and he'd aged a lot in the intervening years.* 我自1986年以來沒見過他, 他在此期間老了很多。

*⭐**in·ter·view**[1] /ˈɪntɚˌvju; ˈɪntəvjuː/ *n* **1** a meeting where a person is asked questions to decide whether they should be given a job or a place on an educational course 面試;

面談: *I didn't even get an interview.* 我還沒經過面試呢。| *She's got an interview for a place at Warwick University.* 她為了得到沃里克大學的職位接受了面試。**2** a meeting where a person is asked questions to find out about their actions or opinions, sometimes broadcast on radio or television or printed in a newspaper or magazine〔記者的〕採訪; 訪談: *The film star agreed to give an interview after the wedding.* 這位影星同意在婚禮後接受採訪。

interview² *v* [T] to ask somebody questions in an interview〔在面談或採訪時向某人〕提問: *She's being interviewed for the job.* 她正在接受求職面試。| *A Dutch reporter interviewed the prime minister.* 一名荷蘭記者訪問首相。**–interviewer** *n*

in·ter·view·ee /ˌɪntəvjuˈiː; ˌɪntəvjuˈiː/ *n* someone who is interviewed 接受訪問者; 接受面試者

in·ter·weave /ˌɪntəˈwiːv; ˌɪntəˈwiːv/ *v* **interwove** /-ˈwəʊv; -ˈwoʊv/, **interwoven** /-ˈwəʊvən; -ˈwoʊvən/, **interweaving** [T] to weave things together 使交織: *curtains made of red cloth interwoven with gold* 交織着金線的紅布窗簾

in·ter·wo·ven /ˌɪntəˈwəʊvən; ˌɪntəˈwoʊvən/ *adj* mixed together 混雜在一起的: *The two ideas are so interwoven you can't really separate them.* 這兩種念頭混在一起，你實在無法把它們分開。

in·tes·tate /ɪnˈtɛstet; ɪnˈtesteɪt/ *adj law* not having made a will giving the names of the people who should have your property after your death〔律〕未留下遺囑的: *He died intestate.* 他未留遺囑就去世了。

in·tes·tine /ɪnˈtɛstɪn; ɪnˈtestɪn/ *n* the tube carrying food from your stomach out of your body 腸 **–intestinal** *adj*

in·ti·ma·cy /ˈɪntəməsɪ; ˈɪntəməsi/ *n* **1** a close, often sexual, relationship 親暱關係〔常指性關係〕**2** pleasant and close familiarity 親密; 密切: *in the intimacy of your home* 在你家庭的親密關係中 **3** physical nearness 貼身

in·ti·mate¹ /ˈɪntəmɪt; ˈɪntəmət/ *adj* **1** having an extremely close relationship 關係密切的; 親密的: *intimate friends* 密友; 至交 | *They had been intimate with the president for some time.* 他們和總統曾一度關係密切。**2** most personal and private 個人的; 私人的: *her intimate beliefs* 她的個人信仰 **3** detailed 詳盡的: *an intimate knowledge of the city* 對這城市的詳盡了解 **4** pleasantly close and informal 怡人的; 不拘禮節的: *an intimate atmosphere* 融洽怡人的氣氛 | *an intimate candlelit dinner for two* 適於兩人世界的燭光晚餐 **5** [never before a noun 不能用於名詞前] *fml* having sex with someone〔正式〕有性關係的 **6 on intimate terms with** having a close relationship with 與…關係密切 **– intimately** *adv*

in·ti·mate² /ˈɪntəˌmet; ˈɪntəˌmeɪt/ *v* [T;+that] **intimated, intimating** *fml* to make something known indirectly〔正式〕暗示: *He intimated that we should leave.* 他暗示我們該走了。| *She intimated her feelings with a look.* 她用眼神暗示感情。**–intimation** /ˌɪntəˈmeɪʃən; ˌɪntəˈmeɪʃən/ *n* [C;U]

in·tim·i·date /ɪnˈtɪməˌdet; ɪnˈtɪməˌdeɪt/ *v* **intimidated, intimidating** [T] to make someone frightened, especially by threatening violence, because you want them to do something 恐嚇, 恫嚇, 威脅〔某人做某事〕: *They tried to intimidate me into getting them the key.* 他們試圖脅迫我給他們鑰匙。**– intimidation** /ɪnˌtɪməˈdeɪʃən; ɪnˌtɪmə'deɪʃən/ [U]

★in·to /ˈɪntə; ˈɪntə, *before vowels* 元音前 ˈɪntu; ˈɪntʊ, *strong* 強讀 ˈɪntu; ˈɪntuː/ *prep* **1** so as to be inside or in something 進入; 到…裡面: *He got into the car and drove off.* 他鑽入汽車, 駕車而去 | *She dived into the water.* 她一頭扎入水中。–see picture on page 764 見 764 頁彩圖 **2** so as to be in a particular state 成為; 轉為: *This government has got the economy into a terrible mess.* 這屆政府把經濟搞得一團糟。| *He had worked himself up into a temper.* 他激動得大發脾氣。**3** so as to be wearing something 穿: *She changed into her jeans.* 她換上牛仔褲。**4** so as to hit something 觸及; 碰撞: *The car crashed into a tree.* 汽車撞在一棵樹上。**5** used when dividing one number by another 除: *Three into six goes twice.* 六除以三等於二。**6** *infml* very interested in something or keen on it〔非正式〕渴望〔某事物〕; 對〔某事物〕很感興趣: *He's really into music at the moment.* 他現在對音樂很感興趣。

in·tol·er·a·ble /ɪnˈtɒlərəbl; ɪnˈtɑlərəbəl/ *adj* **1** completely unacceptable 完全不能接受的: *intolerable behaviour* 不能容忍的行為 | *It's an intolerable situation.* 這是令人無法接受的情況。**2** so bad that you cannot bear it 不能容忍的; 不能忍受的: *intolerable pain* 無法忍受的疼痛 **–intolerably** *adv*

in·tol·er·ant /ɪnˈtɒlərənt; ɪnˈtɑlərənt/ *adj* not willing to accept ways of thinking and behaving which are different from your own 不容異的; 偏狹的: *intolerant of any opposition* 不能容忍反對意見 **–intolerantly** *adv* **–intolerance** *n* [U]: *racial intolerance* 種族偏執

in·to·na·tion /ˌɪntəˈneɪʃən; ˌɪntəˈneɪʃən/ *n* [U] the rise and fall in the level of someone's voice 語調; 音調

in·tox·i·cate /ɪnˈtɒksɪˌket; ɪnˈtɑksɪˌkeɪt/ *v* **intoxicated, intoxicating** *fml*〔正式〕[T] **1** to make someone drunk 使〔某人〕喝醉 **2** to cause strong feelings of wild excitement 使陶醉; 使激動不已 **–intoxication** /ɪnˌtɒksɪˈkeɪʃən; ɪnˌtɑksɪˈkeɪʃən/ *n* [U]

in·tox·i·ca·ted /ɪnˈtɒksɪˌketɪd; ɪnˈtɑksɪˌkeɪtɪd/ *adj* **1** *fml* drunk〔正式〕喝醉的 **2** wildly excited 陶醉的; 極其興奮的: *intoxicated by success* 因成功而狂喜

in·tox·i·cat·ing /ɪnˈtɒksəˌketɪŋ; ɪnˈtɒksɪ̩keɪtɪŋ/ *adj* **1** containing alcohol and likely to make you drunk 含酒精的; 醉人的 **2** causing strong feelings of wild excitement 令人極其興奮的: *the first intoxicating taste of freedom* 初嘗自由的興奮感覺

in·trac·ta·ble /ɪnˈtræktəbḷ; ɪnˈtræktəbəl/ *adj fml* 〖正式〗 **1** difficult to do anything about or change 難對付的; 難改變的: *an intractable problem* 棘手的問題 **2** difficult to control or influence 難駕馭的; 難影響的: *She's such an intractable child!* 她真是個難管教的孩子! **–intractability** /ɪnˌtræktəˈbɪlətɪ; ɪnˌtræktəˈbɪlə̩ti/ *n* [U]

in·tran·si·gent /ɪnˈtrænsɪdʒənt; ɪnˈtrænsḷdʒənt/ *adj fml* unwilling to change your ideas when other people want you to (a word used to express disapproval) 〖正式〗 不讓步的; 不妥協的〔含貶義〕 **–intransigence** *n* [U]

in·tran·si·tive /ɪnˈtrænsətɪv; ɪnˈtrænsḷtɪv/ *adj* having no object (used of verbs) 不及物的〔指動詞〕: *In this dictionary the mark* [I] *shows that a verb is intransitive.* 在本辭典中, [I] 符號表示動詞是不及物的。**–see** Study Note on page 1328 見 1328 頁學習提示

in·tra·u·te·rine de·vice /ˌɪntrəˈjuːtəraɪn dɪˈvaɪs; ˌɪntrəjuːtəraɪn dɪˈvaɪs/ *n* (also 又作 **IUD**) a metal or plastic object in the shape of a spring or ring, which is put into the childbearing organ of a woman to prevent her from having children 子宮避孕器

in·tra·ve·nous /ˌɪntrəˈviːnəs; ˌɪntrəˈviːnəs◂/ *adj* put directly into a VEIN which takes blood back to the heart 進入靜脈的: *an intravenous injection* 靜脈注射 **–intravenously** *adv*

in·trep·id /ɪnˈtrepɪd; ɪnˈtrepḷd/ *adj lit* showing no fear 〖文〗無畏的: *intrepid explorers* 無畏的探險者 **–intrepidly** *adv*

in·tri·ca·cy /ˈɪntrɪkəsɪ; ˈɪntrɪkəsi/ *n* **intricacies 1** [U] the quality of containing many small detailed parts and often being difficult 錯綜複雜: *I don't think you appreciate the intricacy of the problem.* 我想你沒意識到問題的錯綜複雜。**2 intricacies** [pl] many small details which are not at all simple 錯綜複雜的細節: *the intricacies of political behaviour* 政治表現中的錯綜複雜的細節

in·tri·cate /ˈɪntrɪkət; ˈɪntrɪkḷt/ *adj* containing many detailed parts and being difficult to understand or follow 錯綜複雜的; 難以理解的: *an intricate pattern* 複雜的花紋 **– intricately** *adv*

in·trigue¹ /ɪnˈtriːg; ɪnˈtriːg/ *v* **intrigued, intriguing 1** [T] to interest someone greatly 引起〔某人的〕極大興趣: *Your story intrigues me.* 你的故事引起我的極大興趣。| *an intriguing idea* 引人入勝的主意 | *I'm very intrigued by this new idea for saving*

paper. 我對這種節約紙張的新主意很感興趣。**2** [I] to make secret plans or to get an advantage for yourself by indirect and dishonest means 要陰謀; 使詭計

intrigue² /ˈɪntriːg; ˈɪntriːg/ *n* [C;U] the act or practice of making secret plans to get an advantage for yourself by indirect and dishonest means 陰謀; 詭計: *There was talk of political intrigue.* 傳聞有政治陰謀。| *He told me of various financial intrigues in the City.* 他告訴我城中的種種金融陰謀。

in·trin·sic /ɪnˈtrɪnsɪk; ɪnˈtrɪnsɪk/ *adj* being part of the nature of the stated thing 內在的; 固有的; 本質的: *The dirt doesn't affect its intrinsic value.* 那片污垢不影響它的自身價值。**–intrinsically** /-klɪ; -kli/ *adv*

in·tro·duce /ˌɪntrəˈdjuːs; ˌɪntrəˈdjuːs/ *v* **introduced, introducing** [T] **1** to make one person known for the first time to another 介紹; 使相互認識: *John, may I introduce you to Debbie Jones?* 約翰, 讓我介紹你跟德比·瓊斯認識好嗎? | *Let me introduce myself: my name is Simpson.* 讓我自我介紹一下: 我名叫辛普森。| *He introduced himself* **as** *the parish clerk.* 他自我介紹是教區牧師。**2** to bring in or use something for the first time 〔初次〕引進或使用〔某物〕: *Potatoes were introduced* **into** *Europe from South America.* 馬鈴薯是從南美傳入歐洲的。| *A new examination will be introduced next year.* 明年將使用新試題。**3** to produce the first part of something, especially to suggest or explain the main part 作為〔某事物的〕開頭; 引出〔尤指提示或解釋事物的主體〕: *This song introduces the most important part of the play.* 這首歌引出這齣戲最主要的部分。**4** to cause someone to experience or know about something for the first time 使〔某人〕初次經歷〔了解〕: *They introduced me* **to** *the latest methods.* 他們使我了解了最新的方法。

in·tro·duc·tion /ˌɪntrəˈdʌkʃən; ˌɪntrəˈdʌkʃən/ *n* **1** [U] the act of introducing or the state of being introduced 介紹: *the introduction of a new product* 新產品的介紹 **2** [C] the first part of something such as a book, which tells you about the rest 〔書等的〕引言; 導言; 序: *The Active Study Dictionary has a useful introduction.* 進階辭典的引言很有幫助。**3** [C] a first experience 初次經歷: *It was my first real introduction* **to** *flying.* 這是我第一次真正坐飛機。**4 make the introductions** to introduce people to each other 為人互相介紹認識

in·tro·duc·to·ry /ˌɪntrəˈdʌktərɪ; ˌɪntrəˈdʌktəri◂/ *adj* which introduces 引導的; 介紹的: *a few introductory remarks before the main points* 主要觀點前的幾句開場白

in·tro·spec·tion /ˌɪntrəˈspekʃən; ˌɪntrəˈspekʃən/ *n* [U] *fml* the habit of looking into your own thoughts and feelings 〖正式〗 內省; 反省

---

in·tro·vert /ˈɪntrəˌvɜˑt; ˈɪntrəvɜːt/ *n* a person who is inward-looking and does not find it easy to be in other people's company 性格內向的人；內傾者 −compare 比較 EXTRO-VERT

in·tro·vert·ed /ˈɪntrəˈvɜˑtɪd; ˈɪntrəvɜːtɪd/ *adj* concerned with your own thoughts, acts, and personal life, rather than wanting to spend time with others 內向的；內傾的〔關心自己的思想、行為或生活而不願與他人相處〕 −**introversion** /ˌɪntrəˈvɜˑʃən; ˌɪntrəˈvɜː-ʃən/ *n* [U]

in·trude /ɪnˈtrud; ɪnˈtruːd/ *v* **intruded, intruding** [I] to go into a place when you are not wanted 闖入；侵入；打擾：*I don't want to intrude* **on** *them if they're busy.* 如果他們很忙，我就不打擾了。| *I really don't think we should intrude.* 我真的覺得我們不該闖入。

in·trud·er /ɪnˈtrudɚ; ɪnˈtruːdəʳ/ *n* a person who has come in secretly and without permission 侵入者；闖入者

in·tru·sion /ɪnˈtruʒən; ɪnˈtruːʒən/ *n* [C;U] the act of intruding 侵入；闖入；打擾：*This advertising by phone is a real intrusion* **into** *your private life.* 這種電話廣告真是對個人私生活的侵擾。| *intrusions* **on** *my time* 佔用我的時間 −**intrusive** /-sɪv; -sɪv/ *adj*

in·tu·i·tion /ˌɪntjuˈɪʃən; ˌɪntjuːˈɪʃən/ *n* [C;U] the power of understanding something without reasoning or proof 直覺：*You have no evidence, only intuition!* 你沒有證據，只有直覺！| *She had an intuition that her daughter was in trouble.* 她有一種直覺，女兒遇上麻煩了。−**intuitive** /ɪnˈtjuɪtɪv; ɪnˈtjuːɪ-tɪv/ *adj* −**intuitively** *adv*

in·un·date /ˈɪnʌnˌdet; ˈɪnəndeɪt/ *v* **inundated, inundating 1** be inundated with to receive so many of something that it is difficult to manage 收到太多而無法應付：*We were absolutely inundated with requests for advice.* 好多人向我們徵求意見，弄得我們實在無法應付。**2** [T] *fml* to flood a place badly 〔正式〕泛濫；淹沒 −**inundation** /ˌɪnʌnˈdeʃən; ˌɪnənˈdeɪʃən/ *n* [C;U]

in·vade /ɪnˈved; ɪnˈveɪd/ *v* **invaded, invading 1** [I;T] to attack a country with an army and go into it and take control 侵略；侵犯：*Poland was invaded in 1939.* 波蘭於 1939 年遭到入侵。| *He had secret plans to invade France.* 他祕密計劃侵略法國。**2** [I;T] to enter a place in large numbers 大量進入：*Tourists invaded the seaside town in summer months.* 夏季，旅遊者大量湧入那座海濱城鎮。**3** [T] to enter and spoil something 侵害，干擾〔某事物〕：*Don't invade someone's privacy.* 不要侵犯別人的隱私權。 −**invader** *n*

in·va·lid¹ /ˈɪnvəlɪd; ˈɪnvəliːd/ *n* a person made weak by illness 病弱者；傷殘者：*After the accident, my mother spent the rest of her life as an invalid.* 事故之後我母親成了個殘疾者度過餘生。

invalid² /ɪnˈvælɪd; ɪnˈvælɪd/ *adj* no longer correct or fit for use 無效的；作廢的：*an invalid ticket* 廢票

in·val·i·date /ɪnˈvæləˌdet; ɪnˈvælɪdeɪt/ *v* **invalidated, invalidating** [T] *fml* 〔正式〕**1** to make something invalid 使〔某事物〕無效；使作廢 **2** to show that an argument or position is not good 表示〔辯論或職位〕不好 −**invalidity** /ˌɪnvəˈlɪdətɪ; ˌɪnvəˈlɪdɪti/ *n* [U]

in·val·ua·ble /ɪnˈvæljəbl̩; ɪnˈvæljʊbəl/ *adj* so useful that you could not easily manage without it 非常寶貴的：*Thank you for your invaluable help.* 謝謝你非常寶貴的幫助。 −see 見 VALUABLE (USAGE用法)

in·var·i·a·ble /ɪnˈvɛrɪəbl̩; ɪnˈveəriəbəl/ *adj* happening regularly or never changing 恆定的；不變的：*an invariable routine* 不變的慣例

in·var·i·a·bly /ɪnˈvɛrɪəblɪ; ɪnˈveəriəbli/ *adv* *fml* always〔正式〕總是：*The bosses are invariably middle-aged men.* 老闆總是中年男子。

in·va·sion /ɪnˈveʒən; ɪnˈveɪʒən/ *n* **1** [C;U] an action in which an army attacks a country and takes control 侵略；入侵：*the invasion of Italy* 對意大利的入侵 **2** [U] the arrival or spread of something harmful 侵害；侵犯

in·vec·tive /ɪnˈvɛktɪv; ɪnˈvektɪv/ *n* [U] *fml* rude, forceful, attacking speech, used for blaming someone for something〔正式〕猛烈抨擊；痛罵

in·vent /ɪnˈvɛnt; ɪnˈvent/ *v* [T] **1** to make up, think of, or produce something for the first time 發明；創造：*Alexander Graham Bell invented the telephone in 1876.* 1876 年亞歷山大·格雷厄姆·貝爾發明了電話。**2** to make up something unreal or untrue 虛構；捏造：*The whole story was invented.* 整個故事是虛構的。| *I tried to invent an excuse.* 我試圖編造藉口。

■ USAGE 用法: You **discover** something that existed before, such as a place or a fact ☆ **discover** 表示發現過去就存在的事物，如某地方或某事實：*They* **discovered** *oil in the North Sea.* 他們在北海發現了石油。| *Fleming* **discovered** *penicillin.* 弗萊明發現了青黴素。You **invent** something that did not exist before, such as a machine or a method ☆ **invent** 表示發明過去不存在的事物，如機器或方法：*Who first* **invented** *the computer?* 誰首先發明了電腦？

---

in·ven·tion /ɪnˈvɛnʃən; ɪnˈvenʃən/ *n* **1** [U] the act of inventing something 發明；創造：*The invention* **of** *the telephone was the start of modern telecommunications systems.* 電話的發明是現代電信系統的開端。**2** [C] something that has been invented 發明物: *The telephone is a wonderful invention.* 電話是一項了不起的發明。 **3** [U] the ability to invent things 創造力; 發明才能: *a wonderful story, full of invention* 一個妙極了的故事, 富有創造力

in·ven·tive /ɪnˈvɛntɪv; ɪnˈventɪv/ *adj* able to think of good, new ideas 有創造力的; 有發明才能的: *an inventive person* 有發明才能的人 –**inventiveness** *n* [U]

in·ven·tor /ɪnˈvɛntə; ɪnˈventər/ *n* a person who invents something new 發明者; 創造者

in·ven·to·ry /ˈɪnvən,tɔrɪ; ˈɪnvəntri/ *n* **inventories** a list of all the goods in a place 存貨清單: *an inventory of all the office furniture* 所有辦公家具的清單

in·verse /ɪnˈvɜs; ˌɪnˈvɜːs◂/ *n* the inverse of the opposite of 相反; 反面 –**inverse** *adj* – **inversely** *adv*

in·vert /ɪnˈvɜt; ɪnˈvɜːt/ *v* [T] to put something upside down or back to front 使上下或前後顛倒: *She caught the insect by inverting her cup over it.* 她用杯子倒過來捉住了那隻蟲子。 –**inversion** /-ˈvɜʃən; -ˈvɜːʃən/ *n* [C;U]

in·ver·te·brate /ɪnˈvɜtəbrɪt; ɪnˈvɜːtɪbrət/ *n tech* a creature which has no BACKBONE 〖術語〗無脊椎動物

inverted com·mas /·,·· ·ˈ··/ *n* [pl] **1** marks used in writing to show that somebody's real words are being given 引號 **2 in inverted commas** used by the speaker to suggest the opposite of what has just been said 所謂的〔用以表示相反的意思〕: *Her friends, in inverted commas, all disappeared when she was in trouble.* 她那些所謂朋友, 在她遇到麻煩時都無影無蹤了。

in·vest /ɪnˈvɛst; ɪnˈvest/ *v* [I;T] **1** to use money to make a profit out of something that will increase in value 投(資): *She decided to invest £10,000 in the gas industry.* 她決定將一萬英鎊投資於煤氣業。 **2** to put time, effort, or money into something in the hope that later it will be worth it 耗費, 投入〔時間、精力或金錢〕: *I've invested a lot of time and effort in this plan.* 我已在此計劃中投入了大量的時間和精力。

in·ves·ti·gate /ɪnˈvɛstəˌget; ɪnˈvestɪgeɪt/ *v* **investigated, investigating** [I;T] to examine carefully, or inquire about the reasons for something, or the character of someone 調查; 審查: *The police are investigating the incident.* 警方在調查這次事件。 –**investigator** *n* –**investigation** /ɪnˌvɛstəˈgeʃən; ɪnˌvestɪˈgeɪʃən/ *n* [C;U]: *an investigation into corruption in the Civil Service* 對公職部門中貪污受賄的調查

in·ves·ti·ture /ɪnˈvɛstətʃə; ɪnˈvestɪtʃər/ *n* a ceremony giving someone a position of high rank 授職儀式

in·vest·ment /ɪnˈvɛstmənt; ɪnˈvestmənt/ *n* **1** [C;U] the act of putting money into a busi-

ness in order to get a profit 投資: *He regards the house as an investment.* 他把這房子視作一項投資。 **2** [C] an amount of money put into a business so that you get a profit 投資額: *an investment of £1000 in a growing business* 投資一千英鎊於一個越來越興旺的企業 | *I believe he's sold all his South African investments now.* 我認為他現在已出售了他在南非的全部投資項目。

in·vet·e·rate /ɪnˈvɛtərɪt; ɪnˈvetərɪt/ *adj* [only before a noun 只用於名詞前] fixed in a bad habit or way of thinking 積習很深的; 根深蒂固的: *an inveterate liar* 積重難返的説謊者

in·vid·i·ous /ɪnˈvɪdɪəs; ɪnˈvɪdɪəs/ *adj* **1** which will make people unjustly offended or jealous 招致不滿或妒忌的: *They all sing equally well, so I don't want to make invidious distinctions between them.* 他們唱得都一樣好, 所以我不想對他們做招人不滿的區別。 **2** unfair 不公平的: *an invidious comparison* 不公平的比較

in·vi·gi·late /ɪnˈvɪdʒə,let; ɪnˈvɪdʒɪleɪt/ *v* **invigilated, invigilating** [I;T] *BrE* to be in charge of an examination and watch over the people taking it in order to prevent dishonesty 〖英式〗監(考) –**invigilator** *n* –**invigilation** /ɪnˌvɪdʒəˈleʃən; ɪnˌvɪdʒɪˈleɪʃən/ *n* [C;U]

in·vig·o·rating /ɪnˈvɪgə,retɪŋ; ɪnˈvɪgəreɪtɪŋ/ *adj* making you feel strong and healthy 使人精力充沛的: *an invigorating swim in the lake* 令人心曠神怡的湖中暢泳

in·vin·ci·ble /ɪnˈvɪnsəbəl; ɪnˈvɪnsəbəl/ *adj* too strong to be defeated 無敵的; 不能征服的

in·vis·i·ble /ɪnˈvɪzəbəl; ɪnˈvɪzəbəl/ *adj* **1** that cannot be seen 看不見的; 無形的: *Germs are invisible to the naked eye.* 細菌是肉眼看不見的。 | *The magic had made her invisible.* 魔法使得她隱身。 **2** not recorded (usually of profit and loss) 未列在賬目上的〔指損益〕: *invisible earnings* 賬外收入 –**invisibly** *adv* – **invisibility** /ɪnˌvɪzəˈbɪlətɪ; ɪnˌvɪzəˈbɪlɪti/ *n* [U]

in·vi·ta·tion /ˌɪnvəˈteʃən; ˌɪnvɪˈteɪʃən/ *n* a spoken or written offer of a chance to go to something such as a meal or party or to do something 邀請; 請柬: *an invitation to a party* 晚會請帖 | *an invitation to visit our factory in Birmingham* 邀請參觀我們在伯明翰的工廠 | *Did you receive my invitation?* 你收到我的請柬了嗎?

⋆**in·vite** /ɪnˈvaɪt; ɪnˈvaɪt/ *v* **invited, inviting** [T] **1** to ask someone to something such as a meal or a party 邀請(某人): *She invited me to her party.* 她邀請我參加她的晚會。 | *They've invited us to stay for the weekend.* 他們已邀請我們共度週末。

> □ **USEFUL PATTERNS** 有用句型
> to invite someone to something; to
> invite someone to do something

2 to request something formally 請求; 要求: *The television interviewer invited the minister to comment on the recent events.* 電視採訪記者請部長就最近的事件發表意見。| *Questions were invited after the lecture.* 講座結束後歡迎提問。

□ USEFUL PATTERNS 有用句型
to invite something; to invite someone to do something

3 to make it too easy for something to happen 招致; 引起: *Some shops invite crime by making it easy to take things.* 有些商店顧客取貨太方便, 這等於招引犯罪。

■ USAGE 用法: It is not necessary to use the word **invite** when you are actually inviting someone to do something. In fact, it often sounds more natural in informal English to use a different expression ☆當實際上在邀請某人做某事時, 並不需要用 **invite** 這個單詞。其實在非正式英語中, 用別的表達法常常聽來更自然: **Will you** *come to my party?* 你們來參加晚會好嗎? | **Would you like to** *come to the cinema?* 你想來看電影嗎? | **We were wondering if** *you'd like to* come to dinner. 我們不知道你是否願來參加宴會。The verb **invite** is more common, however, in formal invitations ☆但在正式的請柬中, 動詞 **invite** 更常用: *Mr and Mrs Jones invite* **you** *to the wedding of their daughter...* 瓊斯夫婦邀請您參加他們女兒的婚禮... | **We would like to invite you** *to a celebration lunch to launch our new prouduct.* 我們想邀請您參加午宴, 慶祝我們的新產品投放市場。

invite sbdy **in** *phr v* [T] to ask someone who comes to your door to come inside 請〔某人〕進屋: *When I called at the house, she invited me in for a coffee.* 我去看她時, 她請我進去喝了杯咖啡。

invite sbdy **out** *phr v* [T] to ask someone to go to a show, play, or social event with you 邀請〔某人〕外出〔看戲、參加社會活動等〕: *After my husband died, I wasn't invited out for months.* 我丈夫去世後, 我有幾個月沒約會應酬。

invite sbdy **over** *phr v* [T] to ask someone to come and visit you in your home 邀請〔某人〕來家做客: *I've invited four people over for dinner tonight.* 我已邀請了四個人今晚來家吃飯。

in·vit·ing /ɪnˈvaɪtɪŋ; ɪnˈvaɪtɪŋ/ *adj* attractive 誘人的; 吸引人的: *an inviting prospect* 誘人的前景 **–invitingly** *adv*

in·voice[1] /ˈɪnvɔɪs; ˈɪnvɔɪs/ *n* a bill for goods sent or work done 發票; 發貨清單; 完成工作的清單

invoice[2] *v* **invoiced, invoicing** [T] to send someone a bill for work done or goods sent to them 開發票〔清單〕給〔某人〕

in·voke /ɪnˈvok; ɪnˈvəʊk/ *v* **invoked, invoking** [T] *fml* 〖正式〗 **1** to mention something such as a law because it supports your position 求助於〔法律等〕 **2** to call out to a power, especially God, for help 祈求〔尤指上帝〕保佑 **3** to request or beg for something 懇求; 乞求: *She invoked their forgiveness.* 她乞求他們原諒。

in·vol·un·ta·ry /ɪnˈvɒləntəri; ɪnˈvɒləntəri/ *adj* not done from choice or intention 非自願的; 非故意的: *He gave an involuntary smile.* 他勉強笑了一笑。**–involuntarily** *adv*

✲**in·volve** /ɪnˈvɒlv; ɪnˈvɒlv/ *v* **involved, involving** [T] **1** to cause someone to become connected or concerned 使〔某人〕捲入; 牽涉〔某人〕: *It shouldn't be necessary to involve the other departments.* 沒必要把其他部門也牽涉進來。| *Please don't involve me* **in** *your domestic problems.* 請別把我捲進你們的家庭問題中去。| *I wouldn't get involved* **with** *him if I were you.* 如果我是你, 我就不會捲進去。**2** to have something as a necessary part or result 包含; 含有...結果: *Taking the job involves living abroad.* 接受這份工作就一定要住在國外。**–involvement** *n* [U]

□ USEFUL PATTERNS 有用句型
to involve something; to involve doing something

✲**in·volved** /ɪnˈvɒlvd; ɪnˈvɒlvd/ *adj* **1** concerned with an activity 捲入的; 參與的: *He got involved* **in** *smuggling.* 他參與走私。| *She's involved in Red Cross work.* 她參與紅十字會的工作。| *He's involved* **with** *the drama society.* 他參與戲劇團體的活動。**2** closely connected in a relationship, especially a sexual one 有密切關係的〔尤指性關係〕: *He was involved* **with** *another woman.* 他和另一個女子有染。**3** not simple 不簡單的: *a long and involved explanation* 冗長而複雜難懂的解釋

in·ward /ˈɪnwəd; ˈɪnwəd/ *adj* [only before a noun 只用於名詞前] **1** on or towards the inside of something 內部的; 向內的 **2** felt by a person but not shown to other people 內心的; 精神的: *a feeling of inward contentment* 精神上的滿足感

in·wards /ˈɪnwədz; ˈɪnwədz/ *adv* (also 又作 **inward** *AmE* 〖美式〗) towards the inside of something 向內部

i·o·dine /ˈaɪədiːn; ˈaɪədiːn/ *n* [U] a substance used in photography, and on wounds to prevent infection 碘; 碘酒

i·on /ˈaɪən; ˈaɪən/ *n* an electrically charged atom 離子

i·o·ta /aɪˈotə; aɪˈəʊtə/ *n* **not an iota of** not any at all 一點也不: *There's not an iota of* *truth in that.* 那種說法毫無事實根據。

IOU /,aɪ o 'ju; ,aɪ əʊ 'juː/ *n* a piece of paper saying that you owe a certain amount of money to someone else, with your signature at the bottom; an abbreviation for **I owe you**〖縮〗借據: *I can't give you the money now. Can I give you an IOU?* 我現在沒法給你錢。可以給你一張借條嗎?

IPA /,aɪ pi 'e; ,aɪ piː 'eɪ/ a system of signs used for representing speech sounds; an abbreviation for **International Phonetic Alphabet**〖縮〗國際音標: *This dictionary uses the IPA.* 這本辭典使用國際音標。

IQ /,aɪ 'kju; ,aɪ 'kjuː/ a measure of how clever someone is; an abbreviation for **Intelligence Quotient**〖縮〗智商: *a very high IQ* 很高的智商 | *She has an IQ of 127.* 她智商為127。

IRA /,aɪ ɑ 'e; ,aɪ ɑːr 'eɪ/ an illegal organization whose aim is to unite Northern and Southern Ireland by force; an abbreviation for **Irish Republican Army**〖縮〗〔一個非法組織, 目的在於用武力統一南北愛爾蘭的〕愛爾蘭共和軍

i·ras·ci·ble /ɪ'ræsəbl; ɪ'ræs⅃bəl/ *adj fml* tending to get angry easily〖正式〗易怒的; 性情暴燥的 **–irascibly** *adv* **–irascibility** /ɪ,ræsə'bɪlətɪ; ɪ,ræs⅃'bɪl⅃ti/ *n* [U]

i·rate /aɪ'reɪt; aɪ'reɪt◂/ *adj fml* angry〖正式〗憤怒的: *an irate letter to the editor* 寫給編輯的一封憤怒的信 **–irately** *adv*

ir·i·des·cent /,ɪrə'desnt; ,ɪr⅃'desənt/ *adj lit* showing changing colours as light falls on it〖文〗彩虹色的〔燈光照射時會變色〕: *iridescent soap bubbles* 彩虹色的肥皂泡沫 **– iridescence** *n* [U]

i·ris /'aɪrɪs; 'aɪər⅃s/ *n* **1** a tall flower, typically yellow or purple, with long thin leaves 鳶尾花〔為黃色或紫色, 葉細長〕 **2** the round, coloured part of your eye 虹膜

I·rish¹ /'aɪrɪʃ; 'aɪərɪʃ/ *adj* from or connected with Ireland 愛爾蘭的; 愛爾蘭人的: *Irish whiskey* 愛爾蘭威士忌 | *the Irish President* 愛爾蘭總統 | *an Irish accent* 愛爾蘭口音

Irish² *n* **the Irish** the people of Ireland 愛爾蘭人

irk /ɜk; ɜːk/ *v* [T] to annoy someone 惹惱〔某人〕: *It really irks me to have to do his work as well as mine.* 要做他的工作還要做他的工作, 這真叫我氣惱。

irk·some /'ɜksəm; 'ɜːksəm/ *adj* annoying 令人惱怒的: *irksome duties* 令人厭煩的職責

✦i·ron¹ /'aɪən; 'aɪən/ *n* **1** [U] a very common and useful MAGNETIC metal that is used in the making of steel, and is found in very small quantities in certain foods, and in your blood 鐵: *an iron foundry* 鑄鐵廠 | *iron pills* 含鐵質的藥丸 **2** [C] a flat-bottomed object with a handle on top, which is heated and used for making clothing smooth 熨斗: *an electric iron* 電熨斗 | *Use a hot iron on your jeans.* 把你的牛仔褲

熨一熨。**–see picture on page 958** 見 958 頁彩圖

iron² *v* [T] to make clothes smooth with an iron 熨: *I've been doing the ironing all day.* 我整天都在熨燙衣服。 | *Would you like me to iron your shirt for you?* 你要我給你熨襯衫嗎?

iron sthg ↔ **out** *phr v* [T] to remove difficulties or find an answer to problems 消除〔困難〕; 找到〔答案〕: *We need to iron out a few problems.* 我們需要解決幾個問題。

iron³ *adj* **1** made of iron 鐵製的: *iron gates* 鐵門 **2** firm and unchanging (used of people and their way of thinking) 堅強的; 剛強的〔指人和考慮問題的方法〕: *the Iron Lady* 鐵娘子 | *iron discipline* 鐵的紀律

Iron Cur·tain /,·· '··/ *n* the western border between the COMMUNIST countries of Eastern Europe and the rest of the world which in the period after the Second World War could not easily be crossed for purposes of trade, the exchange of information, or travel 鐵幕〔二次大戰後東歐共產黨國家同世界其他國家之間的西部界線, 不易通過這界線進行貿易活動、交流信息、旅遊等〕: *behind the Iron Curtain* 鐵幕背後

i·ron·ic /aɪ'rɒnɪk; aɪ'rɒnɪk/ *adj* (also 又作 **ironical**) **1** using words in a humorous way to mean the opposite of what they usually mean 諷刺的; 冷嘲的 **2** amusing, often in a bitter way, because not what is expected or suitable 具有諷刺意味的; 出乎意料的; 令人啼笑皆非的 **–ironically** /-klɪ; -klɪ/ *adv*

ironing board /'··· ·/ *n* a long narrow table on which clothes are spread to be ironed 燙衣板 **–see picture on page 958** 見 958 頁彩圖

i·ron·mon·ger /'aɪən,mʌŋgə; 'aɪən,mʌŋgər/ *n BrE*〖英式〗**1** a shopkeeper who sells things which you need in your house and garden such as pans and tools 五金商人 **2** **ironmonger's** a shop selling equipment for the house and garden 五金店

i·ron·mon·ger·y /'aɪən,mʌŋgərɪ; 'aɪən,mʌŋgəri/ *n* [U] *BrE* things which you need in your house and garden such as pots and pans, especially those made of metal〖英式〗五金器具

i·ron·y /'aɪrənɪ; 'aɪərəni/ *n* **ironies** **1** [U] the amusing use of words which are clearly opposite to your meaning 反語; 冷嘲: *"Oh, well done!" she said with irony.* "喔, 幹得好!" 她挖苦說。 **2** [C;U] a course of events or a condition which has the opposite result from what is expected, usually a bad result 具有諷刺意味的事; 令人啼笑皆非的局面; 嘲弄: *life's little ironies* 生活的小小嘲弄 | *The irony of it all was that he turned out to be right.* 整件事富有嘲弄意味的是結果他是對的。

ir·ra·tion·al /ɪ'ræʃənl; ɪ'ræʃənəl/ *adj* **1** without reasonable behaviour 〔行為〕沒有理性的: *The drugs made her quite irrational.* 毒品

使她完全失去理性。**2** not supported by reason 不合理的; 荒謬的: *irrational fears* 荒謬的恐懼 **–irrationally** *adv*

ir·rec·on·ci·la·ble /ɪˈrɛkənˌsaɪləbl̩; ˌɪˌrɛkən-ˈsaɪləbl̩/ *adj* which cannot be brought into agreement 不能和解的; 勢不兩立的: *irreconcilable differences of opinion* 不可調節的意見分歧 | *a hobby irreconcilable with his job* 和他的工作互相對立的業餘愛好 **– irreconcilably** *adv*

ir·re·fu·ta·ble /ˌɪrɪˈfjutəbl̩; ˌɪrɪˈfjuːtəbl̩/ *adj* too strong to be disproved 無可辯駁的; 駁不倒的: *an irrefutable argument* 無可辯駁的論證 **–irrefutably** *adv*

ir·reg·u·lar /ɪˈrɛgjəlɚ; ɪˈregjəlɚ/ *adj* **1** not evenly shaped 〔形狀〕不規則的: *an irregular coastline* 曲折的海岸線 | *She has irregular features.* 她臉部兩邊不對稱。**2** happening again and again, but with different lengths of time between the occasions 無規律的; 不等時的: *an irregular heartbeat* 不齊的心律 | *I hate working irregular hours.* 我討厭工作不定時。**3** not according to the usual rules or habits 不合常規的: *"No permit? This is most irregular, Sir."* "沒有通行證? 這樣子不合常規, 先生。" **4** not following the usual pattern in grammar 〔語法〕不規則的: *an irregular verb* 不規則動詞 **–irregularly** *adv* **–irregularity** /ɪˌrɛgjəˈlærətɪ; ɪˌregjəˈlærŭti/ *n* **irregularities** [C;U]

ir·rel·e·vance /ɪˈrɛləvəns; ɪˈrelŭvəns/ *n* [U] the state of not having any real connection or importance 無關; 不相干

ir·rel·e·van·cy /ɪˈrɛləvənsɪ; ɪˈrelŭvənsi/ *n* **irrelevancies** something which has no importance 不要緊的事物: *Don't waste time with irrelevancies like that.* 別在那樣不相干的事上浪費時間。

ir·rel·e·vant /ɪˈrɛləvənt; ɪˈrelŭvənt/ *adj* not having any real connection or importance 不相干的; 不重要的: *If he can do the job well, his age is irrelevant.* 如果他能做好這份工作, 年齡是無關緊要的。 | *His age is irrelevant to the situation.* 他的年齡和這種情況無關。**–irrelevantly** *adv*

ir·rep·a·ra·ble /ɪˈrɛpərəbl̩; ɪˈrepərəbl̩/ *adj* too bad to be repaired or put right 無法修復的; 不可彌補的: *The assassination did irreparable damage to relations between the two countries.* 暗殺事件給兩國關係造成了不可彌補的損失。**–irreparably** *adv*

ir·re·place·a·ble /ˌɪrɪˈpleɪsəbl̩; ˌɪrɪˈpleɪsəbl̩/ *adj* too special or unusual for another one to take its place 無法替代的; 獨一無二的: *Be careful! That antique vase is irreplaceable.* 小心! 那隻古董花瓶可是舉世無雙的。 | *No one's irreplaceable.* 沒有人是不可替代的。

ir·re·pres·si·ble /ˌɪrɪˈprɛsəbl̩; ˌɪrɪˈpresŭbl̩/ *adj* too strong or forceful to be held back 壓抑不住的; 控制不住的: *irrepressible high spirits* 壓抑不住的興奮 **–irrepressibly** *adv*

ir·re·proa·cha·ble /ˌɪrɪˈprotʃəbl̩; ˌɪrɪˈprəʊtʃə-**

bəl/ *adj fml* without blame 〔正式〕無可指責的 **–irreproachably** *adv*

ir·re·sis·ti·ble /ˌɪrɪˈzɪstəbl̩; ˌɪrɪˈzɪstŭbl̩/ *adj* too powerful or pleasant to leave or fight against 不可抵抗的; 不能拒抗的; 富有誘惑力的: *an irresistible argument* 無可辯駁的論據 | *Those chocolates look quite irresistible!* 這些巧克力看上去真誘人! **–irresistibly** *adv*

ir·re·spec·tive /ˌɪrɪˈspɛktɪv; ˌɪrɪˈspektɪv/ *adv* **irrespective of** without being connected to 不考慮…; 不顧…: *a film that can be enjoyed by anyone, irrespective of age* 一部老少皆宜的電影

ir·re·spon·si·ble /ˌɪrɪˈspɑnsəbl̩; ˌɪrɪˈspɒnsŭbl̩/ *adj* showing no ability to think of the effect of your actions 不負責任的: *His behaviour was very irresponsible – he might have hurt somebody.* 他的行為很不負責——他可能已傷害了別人。**–irresponsibly** *adv* **–irresponsibility** /ˌɪrɪˌspɑnsəˈbɪlətɪ; ˌɪrɪˌspɒnsŭˈbɪlŭti/ *n* [U]

ir·rev·e·rent /ɪˈrɛvərənt; ɪˈrevərənt/ *adj* showing lack of respect, especially for religion 不尊敬的; 〔尤指對宗教〕不虔誠的 **– irreverently** *adv* **–irreverence** *n* [U]

ir·rev·o·ca·ble /ɪˈrɛvəkəbl̩; ɪˈrevəkəbl̩/ *adj* that cannot be changed 不可改變的: *an irrevocable decision* 不能改變的決定 **– irrevocably** *adv*

ir·ri·gate /ˈɪrəˌget; ˈɪrɪˌgeɪt/ *v* **irrigated, irrigating** [T] to supply water to dry land to help crops grow 灌溉〔田地〕**–irrigated** *adj* **–irrigation** /ˌɪrəˈgeʃən; ˌɪrɪˈgeɪʃən/ *n* [U]

ir·ri·ta·ble /ˈɪrətəbl̩; ˈɪrɪtəbl̩/ *adj* easily made angry 易怒的; 急躁的: *Don't take any notice, he's always irritable in the mornings.* 別理會, 他早晨總是很急躁。**–irritably** *adv* **– irritability** /ˌɪrətəˈbɪlətɪ; ˌɪrɪtəˈbɪlŭti/ *n* [U]

ir·ri·tant /ˈɪrətənt; ˈɪrɪtənt/ *n* a substance which makes a part of your body painful and sore 刺激性物質: *Wash the irritant out of your eyes immediately.* 馬上把你眼睛裡的刺激性物質洗掉

ir·ri·tate /ˈɪrəˌtet; ˈɪrɪˌteɪt/ *v* **irritated, irritating** [T] **1** to make angry or excite in an unpleasant way 使惱怒; 使煩燥: *The way she bites her nails really irritates me.* 她咬指甲的樣子真叫我惱火。**2** to make a part of your body painful and sore 使〔身體的一部分〕疼痛: *Wool irritates my skin.* 羊毛刺得我皮膚難受。**–irritation** /ˌɪrəˈteʃən; ˌɪrɪˈteɪʃən/ *n* [C; U]

is /s, z; s, z, əz, *strong* 強讀 ɪz; ɪz/ *v* the third person singular of the present tense of BE ☆動詞 BE 的第三人稱單數現在式 **–see** 見 *'S* (USAGE用法)

Is·lam /ˈɪsləm; ˈɪslɑːm/ *n* **1** the MUSLIM religion, started by MOHAMMED 伊斯蘭教 〔由穆罕默德創立〕**2** the people and countries that practise the Muslim religion 伊斯蘭教徒; 伊斯蘭教國家 **–Islamic** /ɪzˈlæmɪk; ɪzˈlæmɪk/ *adj*

---

is·land /ˈaɪlənd; ˈaɪlənd/ *n* **1** a piece of land surrounded by water 島: *Britain is an island.* 英國是個島國。 **2** (also 又作 **traffic island**) a raised place in the middle of the road where people crossing can wait for traffic to pass 安全島〔馬路中央的凸起處，橫穿馬路的行人可以在此等待車輛駛過〕

isle /aɪl; aɪl/ *n lit* an island 〔文〕島

is·n't /ˈɪznt; ˈɪznt/ short for 〔縮〕= "is not": *It's Monday, isn't it?* 今天是星期一，對吧？ | *Isn't she pretty?* 她不是很漂亮嗎？ | *That's strange, isn't it?* 那挺奇怪，是不是？ | *Dinner isn't ready yet.* 晚飯還沒準備好。

i·so·late /ˈaɪsəleɪt; ˈaɪsəleɪt/ *v* isolated, isolating [T] to separate one person or thing from others 使隔離；使孤立: *Several villages have been isolated by the floods.* 洪水使好幾個村莊與外界隔絕了。 | *When you isolate someone from their friends, they soon become depressed.* 如果你把一個人和他的朋友隔開，他很快會變得沮喪消沉。

★i·so·lat·ed /ˈaɪsəleɪtɪd; ˈaɪsəleɪtɪd/ *adj* **1** a long way from other houses 孤零零的: *an isolated farmhouse* 孤零零的一座農舍 **2** lonely and without friends 孤單的；沒有朋友的: *At first, she felt very isolated.* 一開始她感到很孤單。 **3** single, and not part of a general pattern 孤立的: *an isolated incident* 孤立的事件

i·so·la·tion /ˌaɪsəˈleɪʃən; ˌaɪsəˈleɪʃən/ *n* **1** in isolation existing or happening separately from other things 孤立地: *You can't consider one sentence in isolation.* 你不能孤立地考慮一個句子。 **2** [U] loneliness 孤單: *the isolation and poverty of the homeless* 無家可歸者的孤單和窮困

is·sue¹ /ˈɪʃuː; ˈɪʃuː/ *n* **1** [C] a subject which people are talking and arguing about 問題；議題；爭論點: *The economy is no longer the main issue in this election.* 經濟不再是這次選舉的主要問題了。 | *key issues* 關鍵問題 | *a side issue* 附帶問題 **2** [C] something printed in large numbers and sold or given out at one time 發行物；期，號: *the new issue of Radio Times, on sale today* 新的一期《廣播時報》，今天有售 | *a new issue of stamps* 新發行的郵票 **3** [U the act of coming out or being produced 問世；發行 **4** make an issue of something to make something appear more important than it really is, by talking about it a lot 〔通過大量談論〕使某事顯得比實際上重要；小題大作: *She makes such an issue of her divorce.* 她對自己的離婚小題大作。 **5** at issue under consideration 在考慮中的: *Her ability is not at issue; it's her health we're worried about.* 她的能力不必多加考慮，我們擔心的是她的健康。 **6** take issue with someone to disagree with someone 不同意某人

★issue² *v* issued, issuing [T] **1** to bring out something printed or official for the notice of the public 發行；頒布；出版: *"Greek Cookery" was later issued in paperback.* 《希臘烹飪術》後來發行了平裝本。 **2** to supply someone with something officially 分配；撥發: *They issued the soldiers with guns.* 他們把槍發給士兵。

issue from sthg *phr v* [T] to come out of or result from something 由〔某事物〕得出〔產生〕

isth·mus /ˈɪsməs; ˈɪsməs/ *n* a narrow area of land which joins two larger land masses 地峽

★★it /ɪt; ɪt/ *pron* [used as the subject or the object of a verb 用作動詞主語或受詞] **1** the thing that has already been mentioned 它；這；那〔指已提到的事物〕: *"Where's my coat?" "It's in the cupboard."* 我的上衣在哪兒？ "在櫥裡。" | *I picked up the letter and put it in my pocket.* 我撿起信放進口袋裡。 | *The government has become very unpopular since it introduced the new tax.* 政府推行新稅法後變得不受歡迎。 **2** the baby or animal that has already been mentioned〔指已提到的嬰兒或動物〕: *What a beautiful baby — is it a boy?* 多漂亮的嬰孩——是個男孩嗎？ **3** a situation or fact generally 這；那〔指一般情況或事實〕: *It's lovely here.* 這兒很美。 | *It's a pity that you can't come.* 真遺憾你不能來。 | *Sometimes I find it difficult to concentrate on my work.* 有時我覺得專心工作很難。 **4** used when making statements about the weather, time, or date〔用於說明天氣，時間或日期〕: *It's two o'clock.* 現在兩點。 | *Is it raining?* 在下雨嗎？ | *It's the 23rd June.* 今天六月二十三日。 **5** used as the subject of a sentence when you want to make one part of the sentence more important〔用作句子的主語強調句子的某一部分〕: *It was John who told me, not Helen.* 是約翰告訴我的，不是海倫。 | *It's the money that I'm worried about.* 我擔心的是錢。 **6** that's it: **a** a phrase used to say that something is finished 就這些了；完了〔用於表示某事物已結束〕: *We've just got one more wall to paint and then that's it.* 我們只要多油漆一面牆便完成全部工作了。 | *That's it! I'm not working for that company any more!* 我不幹了！我不會再為那公司工作！ **b** a phrase used to agree with someone or say that something is correct 對了〔用於表示同意某人或某事正確〕: *Hold the ladder for me — that's it.* 幫我扶好梯子——對了。

成部分時，**it's** 也是 "it has" 的縮約式: **It's been rainning for hours.** 下了幾個小時的雨了。| "Where's the cat?" "**It's gone next door.**" "貓在哪裡？" "它跑到隔壁去了。" **Its** (with no apostrophe) is the possessive form of "it" ☆ **its** (無撇號)是 it 的所有格形式: The cat licked **its** paws. 貓舔了自己的爪子。| The baby's playing with **its** toys. 嬰兒在玩自己的玩具。

I·tal·i·an¹ /ɪ'tæljən; ɪ'tæliən/ adj from or connected with Italy 意大利(人)的: His wife is Italian. 他妻子是意大利人。

Italian² n 1 [C] a person from Italy 意大利人 2 [U] the language of Italy 意大利語: an opera sung in Italian 用意大利語演唱的歌劇

i·tal·ics /ɪ'tælɪks; ɪ'tælɪks/ n [pl] the style of printing with small letters sloping to the right 斜體字: This example is printed in italics. 這例句是用斜體字排印的。 **–italic** adj

itch¹ /ɪtʃ; ɪtʃ/ v [I] 1 to have a feeling on your skin that makes you want to rub that part with something rough or sharp 發癢: This mosquito bite itches all the time. 這個蚊子塊一直發癢。| I itch all over. 我渾身發癢。 2 **be itching to do something** infml to have a desire to do something soon 〔非正式〕渴望做某事: I'm itching to go. 我渴望去。 3 **be itching for something** to have an urgent desire for something 渴望得到某物: He seems to be itching for a fight. 他似乎特別想打一架。

itch² n 1 a feeling on your skin which makes you want to rub that part with something rough or sharp 癢 2 a strong desire 渴望 – **itchy** adj **–itchiness** n [U]

it'd /'ɪtəd; 'ɪtəd/ 1 short for 〔縮〕= "it would": It'd be all right if I had enough money. 如果我有足夠的錢就好了。 2 short for 〔縮〕= "it had": It'd been raining earlier that morning. 那天上午早些時候一直在下雨。

■ USAGE 用法: Although **it'd** is frequently used as a short form in spoken English, it is not often used in writing. It is more usual to use the full forms, **it would** or **it had**. ☆ **it'd** 在英語口語中經常用作縮約式，但在書面語中不常用。一般更常用完整的形式，**it would** 或 **it had**。

i·tem /'aɪtəm; 'aɪtˌm/ n 1 a single thing among a set or on a list 項目；條款: The police examined several items of clothing. 警察檢查了幾件衣服。 2 **news item** a piece of news on television or in a newspaper 〔電視裡或報紙上的〕一條新聞

i·tem·ize /'aɪtəmaɪz, ˌaɪz; 'aɪtəmaɪz/ v **itemized**, **itemizing** (also 又作 **itemise** BrE 〔英式〕) [T] to write down all the separate parts of something in a list 逐條記載；詳細登錄: an

itemized bill 分列細目的賬單

i·tin·e·rant /aɪ'tɪnərənt; aɪ'tɪnərənt/ adj [only before a noun 只用於名詞前] fml travelling from place to place 〔正式〕巡迴的；流動的: an itinerant worker 流動工人

i·tin·e·ra·ry /aɪ'tɪnə,rɛrɪ; aɪ'tɪnərəri/ n itineraries a plan of a journey 旅行計劃

it'll /'ɪtl; 'ɪtl/ short for 〔縮〕= "it will"

its /ɪts; ɪts/ det connected with or belonging to the thing that has already been mentioned 它的〔指已提到的東西〕: The cat was sitting drinking its milk. 這隻貓坐着喝牛奶。| The committee had its final meeting last night. 委員會昨晚開了最後一次會議。

it's /ɪts; ɪts/ 1 short for 〔縮〕= "it is": It's a lovely day today. 今天天氣真好。 2 short for 〔縮〕= "it has": It's been a long time since we last met. 我們已很久沒見面了。

■ USAGE 用法: Note that "it has" does NOT have a short form if "has" is being used as a full verb ☆ 注意如果"has"用作實義動詞，"it has"沒有縮略形式: I've lost my cat. **It has** a green collar. 我丟了我的貓。它有個綠領子。

it·self /ɪt'self; ɪt'self/ pron 1 used as the object of a verb or a PREPOSITION when the subject of a verb is an animal or a thing and the action is done to the same animal or thing 它自己；它本身〔當某事物或生物作一動作，而其本身又是動作的承受者時，本詞用作動詞或介詞的受詞〕: The cat washed itself in front of the fire. 貓在火爐前給自己洗澡。| The government has made itself unpopular. 政府搞得自己不得人心。 2 used to add force to the word "it", or to the name of a thing or an animal 本身；自身〔用來強調 it 或其他一些名詞〕: There's no point in putting new tyres on, when the car itself is so old. 如果汽車本身已很舊了，換上新輪胎也沒用。 3 **in itself** by its own nature, without considering anything else 本質上；就其本身而言: Do you think that art is important in itself? 你認為藝術本身重要嗎？

ITV /ˌaɪtiː'viː; ˌaɪ tiː 'viː/ a group of British broadcasting companies supported by private money; an abbreviation for **Independent Television** 〔縮〕〔由私人經營的〕獨立電視公司: It was on ITV last Saturday. 上星期六獨立電視公司播出這個了。

IUD /ˌaɪjuː'diː; ˌaɪ juː 'diː/ an abbreviation for 〔縮〕= INTRAUTERINE DEVICE

I've /aɪv; aɪv/ short for 〔縮〕= "I have": I've been here before. 我以前來過這裡。| I've got lots of time. 我有很多時間。| I've no doubt she's forgotten. 我確信她是忘了。

i·vo·ry /'aɪvərɪ; 'aɪvəri/ n [U] 1 hard white bone from which an elephant's tusks are made 象牙: ivory beads 象牙珠子 | piano keys made of ivory 象牙做的鋼琴鍵 2 creamy white 象牙色; 乳白色: *a wedding dress of ivory silk* 乳白色的絲綢結婚禮服

i·vy /ˈaɪvɪ; ˈaɪvi/ *n* [U] a climbing plant with shiny three- or five-pointed leaves 常春藤

J, j

J, j /dʒeɪ; dʒeɪ/ **J's, j's** *or* **Js, js** the 10th letter of the English alphabet 英語的第十個字母

jab¹ /dʒæb; dʒæb/ *v* **-bb-** [T] to push or hit something with quick, forceful movements 刺, 戳, 猛擊〔某物〕: *He jabbed the stick into the ground.* 他把棍子戳在地上。

jab² *n* **1** a sudden forceful push or blow 猛刺; 猛戳 **2** *infml* an INJECTION〔非正式〕打針; 注射: *Have you had your cholera jabs yet?* 你打過霍亂預防針了嗎?

jab·ber /'dʒæbə; 'dʒæbəʳ/ *v* [I] *infml* to talk quickly but not clearly〔非正式〕急促而含糊不清地說話: *I can't understand you if you keep jabbering away like that.* 如果你一直這樣嘰哩咕嚕地說個不停, 我就無法聽懂。

jack¹ /dʒæk; dʒæk/ *n* **1** an apparatus for lifting a heavy weight, such as a car, off the ground 千斤頂, 起重器 **2** a playing card with a picture of a young man on it〔紙牌中的〕"J"牌, 傑克: *the Jack of Hearts* 紅桃傑克

jack² *v*

   jack sthg ↔ **up** *phr v* [T] to lift up a heavy object with a jack 用千斤頂頂起: *You jack the car up and I'll change the wheel.* 你用千斤頂把車托起來, 我來換輪子。

jack·al /'dʒækɔl; 'dʒækɔːl/ *n* a wild animal of the dog family 豺, 胡狼

jack·daw /'dʒækdɔ; 'dʒækdɔː/ *n* a kind of bird which is believed to steal small bright objects 寒鴉〔據說會偷發亮的小東西〕

*★**jack·et** /'dʒækɪt; 'dʒækɪ̩t/ *n* **1** a short coat 短上衣; 夾克(衫) –see picture on page 210 見 210 頁彩圖 **2** the skin of a baked potato〔烤過的〕馬鈴薯皮: *potatoes cooked in their jackets* 連皮一起烤的馬鈴薯 **3** an outer cover for certain machines or engines that get very hot〔溫度很高的機器或引擎的〕外殼 **4** (also 又作 **dust jacket**) a loose paper cover put as protection round the hard cover of a book〔書的〕護封, 書套 **5** *AmE* a stiff envelope for keeping a record in〔美式〕唱片封套

jack-in-the-box /'···,·/ *n* a children's toy which is a box from which an amusing figure jumps when the top is opened〔開盒蓋時有趣的玩偶會跳起的〕玩偶盒

jack knife /'·· ·/ *n* **jack knives** a pocket knife with a blade that folds into the handle 摺刀

jack-knife *v* **jack-knifed, jack-knifing** [I] (of a large vehicle) to bend suddenly in the middle in an uncontrolled way〔大的車輛〕中間突然彎折並失控: *An articulated lorry has jack-knifed on the bend up the hill.* 在上山的彎道處, 一輛絞接卡車突然彎折失控。

jack-of-all-trades /,· · ' · ·/ *n* a person who can do many different kinds of work 能做各種事情的人; 萬能博士

jack·pot /'dʒæk,pɒt; 'dʒækpɒt/ *n* **1** the biggest amount of money to be won in a game of cards or chance〔賭贏的〕最大賭注 **2 hit the jackpot** *infml* to win a large amount of money or have a big success〔非正式〕贏得一大筆錢; 取得很大的成功

jade /dʒeɪd; dʒeɪd/ *n* [U] a precious green stone which is used to make jewellery 翡翠

ja·ded /'dʒeɪdɪd; 'dʒeɪdɪ̩d/ *adj* tired and uninterested because you have had too much of something 疲憊的; 厭倦的: *She seemed jaded and in need of a break.* 她似乎很累了, 需要歇一歇。

jag·ged /'dʒægɪd; 'dʒægɪ̩d/ *adj* having a rough uneven edge with many sharp points 邊緣不整齊的; 尖利的

jag·u·ar /'dʒægwar; 'dʒægjuəʳ/ *n* a large spotted wild cat of Central and South America 美洲豹

jail¹ /dʒeɪl; dʒeɪl/ *n* (also 又作 **gaol** *BrE*〔英式〕) [C;U] a prison 監獄: *He had spent 20 years in jail.* 他在監獄裡度過了二十年。

jail² *v* (also 又作 **gaol** *BrE*〔英式〕) [T] to put someone in jail 把〔某人〕監禁

jail·er /'dʒeɪlə; 'dʒeɪləʳ/ *n old fash* (also 又作 **jailor; gaoler** *BrE*〔英式〕) a person who is in charge of a prison or prisoners〔老式〕獄卒

jam¹ /dʒæm; dʒæm/ *n* [U] **1** a sweet food made by boiling and preserving fruit in sugar; jam is usually spread on bread 果醬: *a little pot of strawberry jam* 一小罐草莓醬 / *jam tarts* 果醬餡餅 **2** a mass of people, vehicles, or things pressed so close together that movement is difficult or impossible〔人、汽車、物等的〕阻塞; 擁擠: *a traffic jam* 交通阻塞 **3 be in a jam** *infml* to be in trouble or difficulty〔非正式〕陷入困境; 遇到困難: *Could you lend me £5? I'm in a bit of a jam.* 你能借給我五英鎊嗎? 我有點小困難。

jam² *v* **-mm-** **1** [T + adv/prep] to pack or press things tightly together in a place 把〔物品〕塞入: *I jammed everything into my* *bag.* 我把所有東西都塞進袋子裡。**2** [I;T] to make or become stuck (使)卡住: *The wheels have jammed.* 輪子卡住了。| *She tried to open the window, but it was jammed.* 她試圖打開窗，但窗被卡住了。**3** [T] to block a road so that no vehicles can move in it 堵塞〔馬路〕: *The roads were all jammed with cars.* 馬路上堵滿了車。**4** [T] to block radio messages by broadcasting noise 干擾〔無線電波〕**5 jam on the brakes** to stop a vehicle by using the BRAKES forcefully and suddenly 猛踩剎車

jamb /dʒæm; dʒæm/ *n* a side post of a door or window〔門、窗的〕側柱

jam·bo·ree /ˌdʒæmbəˈri; ˌdʒæmbəˈriː/ *n old fash* a happy party or gathering〔老式〕快樂的宴會〔聚會〕

jam-packed /ˌ· ˈ·◁/ *adj infml* very full of people or things〔非正式〕擠滿〔人或物〕的: *The town is always jam-packed for the carnival.* 狂歡節時，鎮裡總是擠滿了人。

jan·gle /ˈdʒæŋgl; ˈdʒæŋgəl/ *v* **jangled, jangling** [I;T] to make a sharp sound like metal striking against metal or move something so that it makes such a sound (使)發出〔金屬撞擊般〕尖銳的聲音: *The fire bell jangled.* 火警鐘響了起來。| *She jangled her keys.* 她把鑰匙弄得叮噹作響。

jan·i·tor /ˈdʒænətɚ; ˈdʒænɪtər/ *n* a person who looks after a large public building〔公共大樓的〕管理員；門房

Jan·u·a·ry /ˈdʒænjuˌɛrɪ; ˈdʒænjuəri/ *n* (also 又作 **Jan.**) the 1st month of the year 一月

Jap·a·nese[1] /ˌdʒæpəˈniz; ˌdʒæpəˈniːz◁/ *adj* of or connected with Japan 日本的: *My car is Japanese.* 我的汽車是日本製造的。

Japanese[2] *n* **1 the Japanese** the people of Japan 日本人 **2** [U] the language of Japan 日語

jar[1] /dʒɑr; dʒɑːr/ *n* **1** a wide-mouthed container, usually made of glass, and used for storing food 罐子；壜子；廣口瓶: *a jar of cherry jam* 一瓶櫻桃醬 –see picture on page 244 見 244 頁彩圖 **2** the food or other contents in a jar 廣口瓶內所裝的食品或其他東西: *He was so hungry he ate two jars of fish paste.* 他餓壞了，吃了兩瓶魚醬。**3** an unpleasant shock to the body 身體的震動: *Sudden jars can cause injuries to joggers.* 身體突然的震動可能會使慢跑者受傷。

jar[2] *v* **-rr- 1** [I] to make an unpleasant or annoying sound 發出令人不快或惱怒的聲音: *His voice really jarred on me.* 他的聲音真令我很不舒服。**2** [T] to give you an unpleasant shock〔令人難受地〕震動: *The fall jarred every bone in my body.* 這一跤摔得我渾身骨頭疼。| *He seemed jarred by the news.* 他似乎對此消息大吃一驚。

jar·gon /ˈdʒɑrgən; ˈdʒɑːɡən/ *n* [U] special words that most people find hard to understand, because they are used only by a particular group of people 術語；行話:

computer jargon 計算機術語

jaun·dice /ˈdʒɔndɪs; ˈdʒɔːndɪs/ *n* [U] a disease that makes your eyes and skin turn yellow 黃疸(病)

jaun·diced /ˈdʒɔndɪst; ˈdʒɔːndɪst/ *adj* **1** suffering from jaundice 患黃疸(病)的 **2** tending to judge other people unfavourably 有偏見的: *a jaundiced view of life* 對生活所持的偏見

jaunt /dʒɔnt; dʒɔːnt/ *n* a short journey, usually for pleasure 短途旅遊

jaun·ty /ˈdʒɔntɪ; ˈdʒɔːnti/ *adj* **jauntier, jauntiest** showing that you feel cheerful and confident 愉快的；有信心的: *a jaunty wave of the hand* 得意洋洋的揮手 –**jauntily** *adv*

jav·e·lin /ˈdʒævlɪn; ˈdʒævəlɪn/ *n* a light spear which is thrown as a sport 標槍

jaw /dʒɔ; dʒɔː/ *n* one of the two bony parts of your face in which your teeth are set 頜；顎

jay /dʒe; dʒeɪ/ *n* a noisy brightly-coloured bird 樫鳥

jay·walk /ˈdʒeˌwɔk; ˈdʒeɪwɔːk/ *v* [I] to cross streets in a careless and dangerous way 肆意亂穿越馬路 –**jaywalker** *n*

jazz[1] /dʒæz; dʒæz/ *n* [U] music with a strong beat and some free playing by each musician in the band 爵士樂

jazz[2] *v*

jazz sthg ↔ **up** *phr v* [T] *infml* to make something more interesting, bright, or enjoyable〔非正式〕使〔某物〕更加有趣〔明亮〕: *We need to jazz this room up a bit.* 我們需要把這間屋子裝飾一下使之更有生氣。

jazz·y /ˈdʒæzɪ; ˈdʒæzi/ *adj* **jazzier, jazziest** *infml* attracting attention, for example by using bright loud colours〔非正式〕絢麗的；花哨的: *a very jazzy dress* 一件非常花哨的衣服

jeal·ous /ˈdʒɛləs; ˈdʒeləs/ *adj* **1** feeling bitter, unhappy, and angry towards someone because they have something that you want 嫉妒的: *He's jealous of their success.* 他嫉妒他們的成功。| *She was a jealous child who never got on with her sisters.* 她是個愛嫉妒的孩子，與她的姐妹從來都相處得不好。| *He's just jealous of you!* 他不過是在嫉妒你! **2** feeling fearful and protective because you think someone may try to take something that belongs to you 唯恐失去的；小心守護的: *Pat is very jealous of her possessions.* 珮特非常珍惜她的財物。| *He's insanely jealous of his wife's love.* 他發瘋一樣地唯恐失去妻子對他的愛。–**jealously** *adv*: *a dog jealously guarding its bone* 小心翼翼地看守着骨頭的狗

■ **USAGE** 用法: Compare 比較 **jealous** and 和 **envious**. **Jealous** suggests a stronger and more unpleasant feeling

than **envious.** If you are **jealous** you are angry because of a person's good luck or because a person shows love to someone else. If you are **envious** you would simply like to have what another person has ☆ **jealous** 有一種 比 **envious** 更強烈、更令人不快的意思。 **jealous** 表示由於別人有好運或有人對別 人表現出愛意而惱怒。**envious** 只表示希 望獲得別人擁有的東西: *Tom was so* **jealous** *when Ann got the job that he could hardly speak to her.* 安妮得到那份 工作時，湯姆極為嫉妒，幾乎不肯與她說 話。| *The little boy is* **jealous** *of the new baby.* 這小男孩對新生的嬰兒很是嫉 妒。| *Congratulations on your new job — I'm really* **envious**! 祝賀你得到了 新工作——我可真羨慕!

jeal·ous·y /ˈdʒɛləsɪ; ˈdʒɛləsi/ *n* **jealousies** [C;U] a jealous feeling 嫉妒: *I was trying to hide my jealousy.* 我在盡力掩蓋我的嫉妒。| *petty rivalries and jealousies* 微不足道的競爭 與嫉妒

jeans /dʒiːnz; dʒiːnz/ *n* [pl] trousers made of strong cotton cloth, which are worn informally 牛仔褲: *a pair of blue denim jeans* 一 條藍色斜紋牛仔褲 –see picture on page 210 見 210 頁彩圖

jeep /dʒiːp; dʒiːp/ *n* a small vehicle suitable for travelling over rough ground 吉普車

jeer /dʒɪr; dʒɪr/ *v* [I;T] to laugh rudely at someone 嘲笑(某人): *The crowd jeered at us.* 那羣人嘲笑我們。| *He was jeered by the audience.* 他被觀眾嘲笑了一通。–**jeers** *n* [pl]

jell /dʒɛl; dʒɛl/ *v* [I] **1** (also 又作 **gel**) to become a thicker, firmer substance 凝成膠狀 **2** (of ideas and thoughts) to become clearer and more certain (觀點和思想)更加清晰而肯定

jel·ly /ˈdʒɛlɪ; ˈdʒɛli/ *n* **jellies 1** [C;U] a soft sweet food made with fruit and eaten as part of a meal 果凍; 果膠: *jelly and ice cream* 果凍與冰淇淋 **2** [U] a sweet food made with fruit and sugar and used for spreading on bread 果醬(用於塗麵包): *apple jelly* 蘋果醬 **3** [sing] any material that is between a liquid and a solid state 膠狀物 質: *The juices had solidified into a jelly.* 果汁 凝成了果凍。**4 my legs felt like jelly** = I felt very nervous 我覺得很緊張

jel·ly·fish /ˈdʒɛlɪ,fɪʃ; ˈdʒɛlifɪʃ/ *n* **jellyfishes** or **jellyfish** a sea creature with a body that looks like jelly 水母; 海蜇

jem·my /ˈdʒɛmɪ; ˈdʒɛmi/ *n* **jemmies** (**jimmy** *AmE* 〔美式〕) an iron bar used by thieves to break open locked doors and windows 〔盜賊用來撬門窗的〕撬棍

jeop·ar·dize /ˈdʒɛpəd,aɪz; ˈdʒɛpədaɪz/ *v* **jeopardized, jeopardizing** (also 又作 **jeopardise** *BrE* 〔英式〕) [T] *fml* to put some-thing in danger of being destroyed or harmed 〔正式〕使〔某物〕處於危險之中: *If you are rude to the boss it may jeopardize your chances of success.* 你如果對老闆無禮， 就可能毀掉你成功的機會。

jeop·ar·dy /ˈdʒɛpədɪ; ˈdʒɛpədi/ *n* [U] *fml* 〔正式〕**in jeopardy** in danger of being de-stroyed or harmed 在危險中: *He has put his whole future in jeopardy.* 他已危害了自己的 整個前途。

jerk¹ /dʒɜːk; dʒɜːk/ *v* **1** [T] to pull suddenly and quickly 猛拉: *She jerked the string of the puppet.* 她猛地一拉木偶的繩子。| *He jerked his head forward.* 他把頭突然向前一伸。**2** [I] to move with a sudden quick movement 猛 然一動: *The bus jerked to a stop.* 公共汽車猛 然剎車，就停住了。

jerk² *n* a short quick pull or movement 猛 拉; 猛的一動: *The bus stopped with a jerk.* 公 共汽車猛然停住了。–**jerky** *adj*

jer·kin /ˈdʒɜːkɪn; ˈdʒɜːkɪ̩n/ *n* a short coat with no covering for your arms 無袖短外衣

jer·ry-built /ˈdʒɛrɪ,bɪlt; ˈdʒɛri bɪlt/ *adj* built quickly, cheaply, and badly (used of buildings) 匆促草率建成的〔指建築物〕

jer·sey /ˈdʒɜːzɪ; ˈdʒɜːzi/ *n* **1** [C] a piece of woollen clothing, usually worn over a shirt 毛衣, 羊毛衫〔通常穿在襯衣外面〕**2** [U] a fine, soft woollen cloth used for women's dresses 細毛布料〔做女裝用〕

jest /dʒɛst; dʒɛst/ *n old fash* 〔老式〕**1** a joke 笑話; 玩笑 **2 in jest** in fun 開玩笑地: *He only said it in jest!* 他不過是玩著說這個的! –**jest** *v* [I]

jest·er /ˈdʒɛstə; ˈdʒɛstəʳ/ *n* a man kept in the past by a king or queen to amuse them and tell jokes 弄臣〔昔時為國王或女王說笑逗 樂的人〕

jet¹ /dʒɛt; dʒɛt/ *n* **1** [C] a narrow stream of liquid, gas, or steam which comes force-fully out of a small hole 〔液體、氣體等的〕噴 射流: *A jet of water shot up into the air.* 一道 水柱噴向空中。**2** [C] a hole in a machine through which gas or a flame comes 〔機器 上〕噴氣孔; 噴火孔: *She put a match to the gas jet to light the gas.* 她把火柴放在爐嘴上點 燃煤氣。**3** [C] a powerful, modern aircraft 噴氣式飛機: *a jet fighter* 噴氣式戰鬥機 **4** [U] a hard black substance used for making jewellery 煤玉; 黑玉

jet² *v* **-tt-** [I + adv/prep] *infml* to travel by aircraft 〔非正式〕坐飛機旅行: *She jetted in from Hollywood last week.* 她上週從好萊塢 坐飛機來到這裡。| *jetting around the world* 坐飛機周遊世界

jet-black /ˌ· ˈ· ◂/ *adj* very dark shiny black 烏黑發亮的

jet en·gine /ˌ· ˈ· ·/ *n* an engine that pushes out a stream of hot air and gases behind it, and is used for making aircraft fly 噴氣發動 機

jet-lag /ˈ· ·/ *n* [U] a tired and confused

feeling that you have after a long journey in an aircraft 飛行時差綜合症 **-jetlagged** *adj*

jet-pro·pelled /ˌ· ·'··◁/ *adj* made to fly or given power by a jet engine 噴氣發動機推進的 **-jet propulsion** *n* [U]

jet set /'··/ *n* **the jet set** a group of rich, successful, and fashionable people 成功而時髦的有錢階層: *a member of the international jet set* 一位坐噴氣式飛機環遊世界的闊佬

jet·ti·son /'dʒɛtəsən; 'dʒetˌsən/ *v* [T] *fml* 〔正式〕 **1** to decide not to use an idea, chance, or plan 放棄〔主意、機會或計劃〕: *The company decided to jettison the project.* 公司決定放棄該項目。 **2** to throw something away, especially from a moving vehicle 〔尤指從正在運行的交通工具中〕扔掉: *We had to jettison the cargo to make the ship lighter.* 我們要扔掉貨物, 以減輕船的重量。

jet·ty /'dʒɛtɪ; 'dʒeti/ *n* **jetties** a wall built out into the sea or a river, used for getting on and off ships 碼頭; 突堤, 防波堤 **-see** picture on page 991 見 991 頁彩圖

Jew /dʒu; dʒuː/ *n* a person whose religion is JUDAISM or who is descended from Jews 猶太人 **-Jewish** *adj*: *the Jewish religion* 猶太教 | *My husband is Jewish.* 我丈夫是猶太人。

jew·el /'dʒuəl; 'dʒuːəl/ *n* **1** a precious stone that is worn or used to decorate ornaments 寶石: *the Crown Jewels* 皇冠上的寶石 **2** a person or thing of great value 貴重的人[東西]: *This painting is the jewel of my collection.* 這幅畫是我藏畫中最珍貴的一幅。

jew·elled /'dʒuəld; 'dʒuːəld/ *adj* (**jeweled** *AmE* 〔美式〕) decorated with jewels 鑲有寶石的

jew·el·ler /'dʒuələ; 'dʒuːələʳ/ *n* (**jeweler** *AmE* 〔美式〕) **1** a person who buys, sells, and repairs watches and jewellery 鐘錶商; 珠寶商 **2 jeweller's** a shop selling watches and jewellery 鐘錶店; 珠寶店: *I got my watch repaired at the jeweller's in the High Street.* 我在高街的鐘錶店修理我的錶。

jew·el·lery /'dʒuəlrɪ; 'dʒuːəlri/ *n* (**jewelry** *AmE* 〔美式〕) [U] things such as rings which people wear to make themselves look attractive 珠寶; 首飾: *I've never worn a lot of jewellery.* 我從不佩戴許多首飾。 | *I keep brooches, necklaces, and rings in my jewellery box.* 我把胸針、項鏈和戒指都保存在我的首飾盒裡。

jibe /dʒaɪb; dʒaɪb/ *n* (also 又作 **gibe**) a remark which makes someone else look foolish 嘲諷的話

jif·fy /'dʒɪfɪ; 'dʒɪfi/ *n infml* 〔非正式〕 **a jiffy** a moment 一會兒; 片刻: *I'll be ready in a jiffy.* 我一會兒就準備好。 | *I won't be a jiffy.* 我一會兒就好了。

jig¹ /dʒɪg; dʒɪg/ *n* a quick merry dance, popular in the past 吉格舞〔昔時流行的輕快

舞曲〕

jig² *v* **-gg-**

jig about/around *phr v* [I] to dance or move up and down with quick short movements 跳吉格舞; 蹦跳

jig·gle /'dʒɪgl; 'dʒɪgəl/ *v* **jiggled, jiggling** [T] *infml* to move something from side to side with short quick movements 〔非正式〕使〔某物〕快速左右擺動: *Jiggle the key in the lock — maybe the door will open.* 把鑰匙在鎖裡左右動一動──門可能就會被打開的。

jig·saw /'dʒɪgsɔ; 'dʒɪgsɔː/ *n* (also 又作 **jigsaw puzzle** /'·· ˌ··/) a game consisting of a wooden or cardboard picture cut up into many small irregular shaped pieces which you have to fit together again 拼圖遊戲

jilt /dʒɪlt; dʒɪlt/ *v* [T] to refuse to see a lover any more or refuse to marry someone after you have promised to do so (a word used to express disapproval 拋棄〔情人〕; 毀棄〔婚約〕

jim·my /'dʒɪmɪ; 'dʒɪmi/ *n* **jimmies** *AmE* 〔美式〕**-see** 見 JEMMY

jin·gle¹ /'dʒɪŋgl; 'dʒɪŋgəl/ *v* **jingled, jingling** **1** [T] to move something so that it makes a sound like metal striking gently against metal 使〔某物〕發出叮噹聲: *He jingled the money in his pocket.* 他口袋裡的錢叮噹作響。 **2** [I] to make a soft sound like small bells ringing 叮噹作響: *We could hear their bracelets jingling.* 我們可以聽見他們的手鐲在叮噹作響。

jingle² *n* **1** a soft ringing sound like the sound of small bells or keys being knocked together 〔如鈴或鑰匙撞擊發出的〕叮噹聲 **2** a simple poem or song which is easy to remember and is used in a radio or TV advertisement 〔用於電台或電視中的〕廣告短詩[短歌]

jinx /dʒɪŋks; dʒɪŋks/ *n infml* a person or thing that brings bad luck 〔非正式〕不祥的人; 不祥之物: *There seems to be a jinx on our team.* 我們隊似乎交了惡運。

jinxed /dʒɪŋkst; dʒɪŋkst/ *adj infml* causing or bringing bad luck 〔非正式〕帶來惡運的; 不祥的

jit·ters /'dʒɪtəz; 'dʒɪtəz/ *n infml* 〔非正式〕 **the jitters** feelings of great nervousness 焦慮; 極度緊張: *I always get the jitters before an exam.* 考試前我總是極度緊張。

jit·ter·y /'dʒɪtərɪ; 'dʒɪtəri/ *adj* nervous 緊張的: *I get jittery waiting for the results.* 我焦慮不安地等著結果。

jive¹ /dʒaɪv; dʒaɪv/ *n* [sing] a fast dance done to popular music with a strong regular beat 〔一種快節奏的〕搖擺舞

jive² *v* **jived, jiving** [I] to dance a jive 跳搖擺舞

job /dʒɒb; dʒɒb/ *n* **1** regular work you do to earn money 工作; 職業; 職位: *He has a good job in a bank.* 他在銀行裡有份很好的工作。 | *Many jobs will be lost if the* factory closes down. 這家工廠若是關閉，便會失掉許多就業機會。 | *a part-time job* 兼職工作 **2** a piece of work 一件工作: *The plumber's done a really good job.* 管道工幹了一件非常出色的工作。 | *Here's a nice little job for you — washing up!* 有件不錯的小差事給你 —— 洗碗去吧! | *The nurses have now completed the job of weighing all the children.* 護士們現已完成了給孩子稱體重的工作。 **3** responsibility, duty, or purpose 責任; 職責; 目的: *It's not my job to interfere.* 我沒有責任干預那件事。 | *It's the job of this computer to calculate prices.* 這台計算機用來計算價格。 **4 do the job** *infml* to succeed in doing what is needed or wanted 〔非正式〕成功地幹需要或想要幹的事: *For peeling potatoes this knife does the job nicely.* 要削馬鈴薯皮, 這把小刀很管用。 **5 a good job** an informal phrase you use when you want to say that it was a good thing that something happened 一件好事〔說明一件發生的事是件好事時的非正式的口語表達法〕: *She's lost a lot of weight — and a good job too!* 她體重減輕了許多 —— 這也是件好事! **6 have a job doing something** to find it difficult to do something 發現做某事很困難: *I had a real job finding somewhere to park the car.* 我費了很大工夫找停車的地方。 **7 just the job** *infml* exactly the thing that is wanted or needed 〔非正式〕正是想〔需〕要的東西: *Thanks for that book; it was just the job.* 謝謝你的那本書, 我正好要用到它。 **8 give something up as a bad job** to decide that you will not be concerned with someone or something any more, because they cannot change or improve 〔由於無法改變或改善而〕不再關心: *I'm afraid his teachers have just given him up as a bad job.* 恐怕他的老師都已對他不抱甚麼希望了。 **9 make a good job of something, make a bad job of something** to do something well or badly 把某事做好; 把某事做壞 **10 make the best of a bad job** to do as much or as well as possible in a difficult or unsatisfactory situation 〔在困難或令人不滿的情況下〕盡力而為 **11 a nine-to-five job** a job with regular hours 固定時間的工作, 朝九晚五的工作: *Like most actors, Pete would hate a nine-to-five job.* 像大部分演員一樣, 皮特也不會喜歡朝九晚五的工作。 **12 on the job** while working or at work 工作時; 上班時: *Junior doctors are sometimes so tired they fall asleep on the job.* 資歷較淺的醫生有時會非常疲倦, 以至於會在工作時睡着。 **13 out of a job** unemployed 失業

■ USAGE 用法: Compare 比較 **job**, **work**, **occupation**, **post**, **position**, **trade**, **profession.** Your **job** is what you do to earn a living. **Job** is a countable word. **Work** has the same meaning but is uncountable. **Occu-** **pation** has the same meaning but is more formal ☆ 你的 **job** 就是你藉以謀生的工作。**job** 是個可數名詞。**work** 的意思與之相同, 但是不可數名詞。**occupation** 的意思也相同, 但更為正式: *Please state your occupation on this form.* 請在該表中填上你的職業。**Post** and **position** are formal words for a particular job ☆**post** 和 **position** 是正式的用語, 表示某個專門的職業: *the post/position of lecturer in English at Newcastle University* 紐卡斯爾大學英語講師的職位。A **trade** is a skilled job in which you use your hands ☆**trade** 是指有專門技能的手工行業: *She's an electrician by* **trade**. 她的職業是電工。A **profession** is a job such as that of a doctor or lawyer, for which you need special training and a long education. ☆**profession** 是需要接受過特殊訓練和長期教育的工作, 如醫生或律師的工作。

job lot /ˈ··, ·ˈ·/ *n* a group of different things which are cheap, of poor quality, and bought or sold together 整批買賣的廉價而質劣的雜貨

jock·ey /ˈdʒɑki; ˈdʒɒki/ *n* a person who rides in horse races, especially as a job 賽馬騎師〔尤指職業騎師〕

joc·u·lar /ˈdʒɑkjələ˞; ˈdʒɒkjʊˈlə˞/ *adj fml* cheerful and amusing 〔正式〕高興的; 可笑的: *He was in a jocular mood.* 他心情很輕鬆愉快。 | *a jocular remark* 一句幽默詼諧的話 —**jocularly** *adv*

jodh·purs /ˈdʒɑdpə˞z; ˈdʒɒdpəz/ *n* [pl] special trousers that you wear for horse riding 馬褲

jog¹ /dʒɑg; dʒɒg/ *v* **-gg- 1** [I] to run slowly, usually for exercise 慢跑〔常作為運動〕: *I go jogging in the park before breakfast.* 早餐前我在公園裡慢跑。 | *She jogged off down the road.* 她順着馬路往下慢跑。—see picture on page 992 見 992 頁彩圖 **2** [T] to knock or push something slightly 輕碰, 輕推〔某物〕: *He jogged my elbow and spoiled what I was drawing.* 他輕輕碰了一下我的肘部, 破壞了我正在畫的畫。 **3 jog someone's memory** to make someone remember something 令某人想起某事物

jog² *n* **1** a slight shake, push, or knock 輕搖; 輕推; 輕敲 **2** a slow steady run, usually done for exercise 〔常作為運動的〕慢跑: *Let's go for a jog.* 我們去慢跑吧。

jog·ging /ˈdʒɑgɪŋ; ˈdʒɒgɪŋ/ *n* [U] the activity of running slowly and steadily as a form of exercise 〔作為運動的〕慢跑: *Jogging's the in thing at the moment.* 慢跑是目前最流行的玩意。

joie de viv·re /ˌʒwadə'vivr; ˌʒwɑ: də 'viːvrə/ *n* [U] great enjoyment of life 人生的極大樂趣

---

join¹ /dʒɔɪn; dʒɔɪn/ v **1** [T] to fix or connect two things to each other 連接; 結合: *The plumber joined this pipe to a new one.* 管道工把這根管子連到一根新管子上面。| *Join the two ends of the rope together.* 把這繩子的兩端繫在一起。| *The two villages are joined by a country path.* 那兩個村莊由一條鄉間小路連接起來。**2** [I;T] to come together or be united with someone or something else 與〔某人、某物〕會合〔相聚〕: *Won't you join us for a drink?* 你來和我們一起喝杯酒好嗎？| *I'll be joining my family next week in Paris.* 我下週將在巴黎與家人團聚。| *Where do the roads join?* 道路在哪裡相交？**3** [I;T] to become a member of an organization or start work in an organization 參加〔組織〕: *He joined the Labour Party.* 他加入了工黨。| *I joined the company in 1986.* 我於1986年加盟該公司。| *I went along to the club, but they wouldn't let me join.* 我去了俱樂部，但他們不讓我參加。**4** [T] to take part in an activity 參加〔活動〕: *Come on in and join the fun!* 快進來一起玩吧！**5** join a queue to take your place at the end of a line of people 排隊: *We joined the queue for tickets.* 我們排隊買票。**6** join hands to hold each other's hands 手拉手: *We all joined hands and danced around in a circle.* 我們所有人都手拉手圍成一個圈跳舞。

join in phr v [I;T **join in** sthg] to take part in an activity 參加〔活動〕: *Sarah never joins in, but prefers to play on her own.* 莎拉從不與別人一起玩，她喜歡獨自玩耍。| *We all joined in the singing.* 我們大家一起唱歌。

join up phr v **1** [I] BrE to become a member of the army, navy, or air force 〔英式〕參軍 **2** [I;T **join** sthg ↔ **up**] to come together to form one group or thing 組成一組: *Both classes are joining up for their history lessons.* 兩個班級合起來上歷史課。| *He was trying to join up the pieces of a jigsaw puzzle.* 他正在盡力把拼圖拼起來。| *I've been trying to join the bits up.* 我一直在嘗試把這些小片拼起來。

join² n a place where two things are joined together 〔兩個物體的〕連接處: *It's so well made that you can't see the join.* 這東西做得很好，你看不出其中的接縫。

join·er /'dʒɔɪnə; 'dʒɔɪnɚ/ n BrE a person who makes doors, window frames, and door frames 〔英式〕〔製造門、窗框和門框等的〕細木工人

join·er·y /'dʒɔɪnəri; 'dʒɔɪnəri/ n [U] BrE the trade and work of a joiner 〔英式〕細木工行業〔手藝〕

joint¹ /dʒɔɪnt; dʒɔɪnt/ n **1** a part of your body where two bones meet, for example at your knee 關節: *My hip joints feel very stiff.* 我的髖關節感覺很僵硬。**2** the place where two things are fixed together 接合處: *The pipe was leaking at one of the joints.* 管子的接合處在泄漏。**3** BrE a large piece of meat

for cooking, usually with a bone in it 〔英式〕一大塊肉〔通常帶有骨頭的〕: *a roast Sunday joint* 星期日午餐時吃的烤肉 **4** infml a public place like a club or bar where people go for fun 〔非正式〕公眾娛樂場所 **5** infml a cigarette containing the drug CANNABIS〔非正式〕〔含有大麻的〕香煙

joint² adj [only before a noun 只用於名詞前] shared by or belonging to two or more people 共享的; 共有的: *to take joint action* 採取聯合行動 | *We are joint owners.* 我們是共同擁有者。| *It was a joint effort* 那是共同的努力。**–jointly** adv: *The project will be financed jointly by the government and the company.* 那個項目將由政府和公司共同出資建設。

joint³ v [T] to separate meat into fairly large pieces for cooking 把〔肉〕切成大塊

joint·ed /'dʒɔɪntɪd; 'dʒɔɪntɪ̥d/ adj having joints which can move 有活動關節的: *a jointed doll* 關節能活動的洋娃娃

joist /dʒɔɪst; dʒɔɪst/ n a beam of wood or metal which supports the floor or roof of a building 〔支承地板或屋頂的〕托樑

joke¹ /dʒəʊk; dʒəʊk/ n **1** something such as a funny story which you tell people to make them laugh 笑話: *Have you heard the joke about the doctor and the taxi-driver?* 你聽說過那則關於醫生和計程車司機的笑話嗎？| *He made a joke about politicians.* 他拿政客們開了個玩笑。| *They chatted and cracked jokes until late that night.* 那天他們聊天談笑直到深夜。**2** a joke someone or something which you cannot respect or take seriously 無法令人尊重或認真對待的人或事: *The exam was a complete joke — far too easy!* 這場考試簡直是兒戲——太容易了！**3** beyond a joke serious and worrying 嚴肅的; 令人擔憂的: *The noise made by our neighbour is really getting beyond a joke now.* 我們鄰居發出的吵鬧聲已經不是開玩笑般的小事了。**4** the joke's on him = he looks foolish, instead of the person he tried to play a joke on〔想開別人的玩笑〕自己反倒成為笑料 **5** make a joke of something to be funny or amusing about something serious 拿嚴肅的事情開玩笑 **6** no joke infml very difficult or serious 〔非正式〕非常為難的; 非常嚴肅的: *Looking after four children is no joke!* 照顧四個孩子可不是鬧着玩的！**7** play a joke to do something funny, such as an amusing trick, to make people laugh 開玩笑: *He played a joke on us by pretending to lose the tickets.* 他裝作把票丟了，跟我們開了個玩笑。**8** take a joke to be amused by a joke against yourself 經得起開玩笑: *Can't you take a joke?* 跟你開個玩笑你都受不了嗎？

joke² v joked, joking [I] **1** to tell an amusing story or make a funny remark 說笑話: *You mustn't joke with him about religion.* 你千萬不要和他說有關宗教的玩笑話。**2** to tell someone something which you do not

J

mean seriously 開玩笑: *She smiled when she realized I was only joking.* 當她意識到我不過是在開玩笑時, 她笑了。 **3 you must be joking, you're joking** *infml* a phrase you use when you don't believe something 〔非正式〕你(一定是)在開玩笑〔用於表示不相信某事〕: *"Sue passed the exam!" "You must be joking — she didn't do any work for it."* 蘇考試及格了!"你一定是在開玩笑吧 —— 她可是一點也沒有努力過。" **–jokingly** *adv*: *I'm sure his remarks were meant jokingly.* 我肯定他的話只是在開玩笑。

jok·er /ˈdʒəʊkə; ˈdʒəʊkɚ/ *n* **1** a person who likes to make jokes 愛開玩笑的人 **2** an additional playing card, which may have any value in certain games〔某些紙牌戲中的〕百搭〔可代表任何點數〕

jol·lit·y /ˈdʒɒlɪtɪ; ˈdʒɒləˌti/ *n* [U] *fml* cheerfulness〔正式〕高興; 愉快

jol·ly¹ /ˈdʒɒlɪ; ˈdʒɒli/ *adj* **jollier, jolliest** happy and cheerful 高興的; 愉快的: *She's a very jolly person.* 她是個十分快活的人。| *a jolly laugh* 愉快的笑聲

jolly² *adv old fash, infml*〔老式, 非正式〕**1** very 非常, 很: *You were jolly lucky!* 你真幸運! **2 jolly well** really 無疑地, 真正地: *No, I jolly well won't apologize!* 不, 我的確不會道歉!

jolly³ *v* **jollied, jollying**

  jolly sbdy **along** *phr v* [T] to encourage someone in a friendly or joking way〔以友好或開玩笑的方式〕鼓勵

jolt /dʒɒlt; dʒəʊlt/ *v* **1** [I;T] to make something shake or move suddenly 使〔某物〕突然晃動〔移動〕: *The cart jolted along over the rough road.* 馬車順着崎嶇的道路顛簸而行。**2** [T] to give someone a shock 令〔某人〕震驚: *Her angry words jolted him out of the belief that she loved him.* 她憤怒的說話令他非常震驚, 以至於他認為她已不愛他了。**–jolt** *n*

jos·tle /ˈdʒɒsl; ˈdʒɒsəl/ *v* [I;T] **1** to knock or push against another person 撞, 推〔某人〕: *The players were jostled by an angry crowd as they left the field.* 運動員離開賽場時, 被憤怒的羣眾推搡着。| *Don't jostle!* 別推! **2** to compete for attention or money 爭取獲得〔注意或金錢〕: *film stars jostling for fame and fortune* 爭名奪利的電影明星

jot¹ /dʒɒt; dʒɑt/ *n* **not a jot** not at all or none at all 一點也不; 絲毫也不: *not a jot of truth in it* 當中沒有一點兒是真的

jot² *v* **-tt-** [T] to write something down quickly and without thinking about it very carefully 匆匆記下〔某事〕: *He jotted her address down on his newspaper.* 他在報紙上迅速記下了她的地址。

jot·ter /ˈdʒɒtə; ˈdʒɑtɚ/ *n* a number of pieces of paper joined together, used for writing notes on 便條本, 便箋簿

jour·nal /ˈdʒɜːnl; ˈdʒɜːnl/ *n* **1** a serious newspaper or magazine connected with a particular subject or profession 報紙; 雜誌: *She's reading the British Medical Journal.* 她在看《英國醫學雜誌》。| *a trade journal* 行業雜誌 **2** *lit* a daily record of events or your activities〔文〕日記; 日誌

jour·nal·is·m /ˈdʒɜːnl̩ˌɪzəm; ˈdʒɜːnəl-ˌɪzəm/ *n* [U] the job of collecting information and writing things for newspapers and magazines, radio, and television 新聞工作

★**jour·nal·ist** /ˈdʒɜːnlɪst; ˈdʒɜːnəl-ˌɪst/ *n* a person whose profession is journalism 新聞工作者 **–journalistic** *adj*

★**jour·ney¹** /ˈdʒɜːnɪ; ˈdʒɜːni/ *n* **1** a trip from one place to another, usually by land〔通常為陸上的〕旅行; 旅程: *He made the long journey to Scotland by train.* 他坐火車長途旅行至蘇格蘭。| *a car journey* 坐汽車旅行 | *a three-day journey* 為期三天的旅行 | *They're going on a journey.* 他們打算去旅行。–see 見 TRAVEL (USAGE 用法) **2 break a journey** to interrupt a journey for a short time 途中作短暫停留: *We decided to break our journey in London, and spend the night there.* 我們決定在倫敦作短暫停留, 在那裡過夜。

journey² *v* **journeyed, journeying** [I + adv/prep] *lit* to travel somewhere〔文〕旅行: *She's journeyed all over the world.* 她已周遊了全世界。| *journeying south* 向南旅行

joust /dʒʌst; dʒaʊst/ *v* [I] to fight on horseback with long spears, especially as a sport; men used to joust in the Middle Ages〔尤指中世紀的一項運動〕騎着馬用長矛比武

jo·vi·al /ˈdʒəʊvɪəl; ˈdʒəʊviəl/ *adj* cheerful and friendly 高興的; 友善的: *a jovial old man* 友善的老人 | *a jovial greeting* 友好的問候 **–joviality** /ˌdʒəʊvɪˈælɪtɪ; ˌdʒəʊviˈælɨti/ *n* [U]

jowl /dʒaʊl; dʒaʊl/ *n* the lower part of the side of your face, especially the skin covering your lower jaw 下頜; 下巴

★**joy** /dʒɔɪ; dʒɔɪ/ *n* **1** [U] a feeling of great happiness 高興; 快樂; 喜悅: *He was filled with joy.* 他滿心歡喜。| *To our joy, she won first prize.* 令我們高興的是, 她獲得了一等獎。**2** [C] a person or thing that makes you feel happy or gives you pleasure 令人高興的人〔事物〕: *That dancer's a joy to watch.* 看那位舞蹈演員跳舞是件樂事。| *the joy of skiing* 滑雪的樂趣

joy·ful /ˈdʒɔɪfəl; ˈdʒɔɪfəl/ *adj* extremely happy 令人高興的; 快樂的: *It was a joyful occasion.* 那是一個歡樂的時刻。**–joyfully** *adv* **–joyfulness** *n* [U]

joy·less /ˈdʒɔɪlɪs; ˈdʒɔɪləs/ *adj* unhappy and without pleasure 不快樂的, 不高興的

joy·ous /ˈdʒɔɪəs; ˈdʒɔɪəs/ *adj lit* extremely happy〔文〕令人高興的; 歡樂的 **–joyously** *adv*

joy·ride /ˈdʒɔɪˌraɪd; ˈdʒɔɪraɪd/ *n infml* a ride taken for fun in a stolen vehicle〔非正式〕乘着偷來的車兜風

joy·stick /ˈdʒɔɪˌstɪk; ˈdʒɔɪstɪk/ *n* an upright handle moved to control the operation of something such as an aircraft or a computer game〔如飛機或遊戲機上的〕操縱桿

JP /ˌdʒeɪ ˈpiː; ˌdʒeɪ ˈpiː/ *n* a person who gives judgments in a local court of law in Britain; an abbreviation for JUSTICE OF THE PEACE〔縮〕〔英國的〕治安法官; 地方官

jub·i·lant /ˈdʒuːblənt; ˈdʒuːbḷlənt/ *adj* very happy because you have been successful 〔由於成功而〕歡騰的: *crowds of jubilant football supporters* 雀躍歡呼的足球擁躉 –**jubilation** /ˌdʒuːblˈeɪʃən; ˌdʒuːbḷˈleɪʃən/ *n* [U]

ju·bi·lee /ˈdʒuːbḷˌi; ˈdʒuːbḷˌliː/ *n* a period of great rejoicing to remember an important event, usually after 25 or 50 years 週年紀念〔通常為二十五年或五十年慶典〕: *the Club's silver jubilee party* 俱樂部成立二十五年紀念宴會

Ju·da·is·m /ˈdʒuːdeɪɪzəm; ˈdʒuːdeɪ-ɪzəm/ *n* [U] the religion and civilization of the JEWS, which is based on the OLD TESTAMENT of the Bible and JEWISH books of law 猶太教; 猶太文化

jud·der /ˈdʒʌdə; ˈdʒʌdɚ/ *v* [I] *BrE* (of a machine or a vehicle) to shake violently〔英式〕〔機器或車輛〕劇烈振動

★**judge¹** /dʒʌdʒ; dʒʌdʒ/ *v* **judged, judging 1** [I; T] to decide who or what is the winner in a competition〔在競賽中〕評判, 裁決: *She had been asked to judge an essay-writing competition.* 她獲邀擔任散文寫作比賽的評判。 **2** [T; + that] to form or give an opinion about someone or something after careful thought〔認真考慮後〕認為; 斷定: *The directors judged that the project was too expensive.* 董事都認為該項目花費過大。 | *Schools tend to be judged by their exam results.* 學校的好壞往往由學生的考試成績來評定。 | *Try to judge the distance from here to the car.* 嘗試判斷一下從這裡到那部汽車之間的距離。 | *It's difficult to judge who is responsible for the accident.* 很難判斷誰應對這起事故負責。 **3** [T] to form an opinion of someone after thinking about their behaviour and character 對〔某人〕作出評價: *I could never relax with her, because I felt she was always judging me.* 我跟她在一起從來不能放鬆, 因為我覺得她總在對我品評。 | *The new model was judged a failure.* 新的模型被評是失敗之作。 | *We judged it better to cancel the match.* 我們判斷下來認為取消比賽更為明智。 **4** [T] to make decisions in a law court〔法庭上〕審理; 判決: *Who will judge the next case?* 誰來審理下一個案件? **5 judging by, judging from** a phrase used when you are giving a reason for saying or thinking something 從…來判斷〔用於說出某事或考慮某事的原因〕: *Judging by the look on his face, I'd say he passed!* 從他臉上的表情看, 我敢說他及格了!

★**judge²** *n* **1** a public official who has the power to decide questions brought before a court of law 法官; 審判員: *a high-court*

judge 高等法院法官 | *Judge Anderson* 安德森法官 **2** a person who is appointed to make a decision in a competition〔比賽的〕裁判員; 評判: *The panel of judges included several well-known writers.* 評判小組中包括幾位名作家。 **3** a person who has the knowledge and experience to give an opinion about the value of something 鑑定人; 鑑賞家: *She's a good judge of wine.* 她是個優秀的評酒專家。 | *a poor judge of character* 不善看清別人性格的人

★**judg·ment** /ˈdʒʌdʒmənt; ˈdʒʌdʒmənt/ *n* (also 又作 **judgement**) **1** [C] an official decision given by a judge or a court of law〔法官或法院的〕判決; 裁決: *The judgment was given yesterday.* 法院的判決於昨天宣佈。 **2** [C] an opinion formed after careful thought〔認真思考之後的〕看法; 評價: *In my judgment, the plan is unlikely to succeed.* 依我看, 這個計劃不大會成功。 **3** [U] the ability to make sensible, wise decisions 判斷力: *a man of sound judgment* 判斷力很強的人 | *Her decision shows a lack of political judgment.* 她的決定顯示出她缺乏政治判斷力。 **4 pass judgment: a** to give a decision in a court of law 作出判決 **b** to form an opinion of someone or something, often a bad one 形成對〔某人或某物〕的看法〔通常為不好的看法〕

Judgment Day /ˈ·· ·/ *n* (also 又作 **Judgement Day**) the day when Christians believe God will judge everybody〔上帝的〕最後審判日

ju·di·cial /dʒuːˈdɪʃəl; dʒuːˈdɪʃəl/ *adj* belonging to or concerned with a court of law, a judge, or a judge's decisions 法院的; 法官的; 判決的

ju·di·cia·ry /dʒuːˈdɪʃɪˌeri; dʒuːˈdɪʃəri/ *n* [+ sing/pl verb] *fml*〔正式〕**the judiciary** all the judges in a court of law considered as one group, and forming a branch of government 司法部; 司法系統〔部門〕

ju·di·cious /dʒuːˈdɪʃəs; dʒuːˈdɪʃəs/ *adj* having or showing good judgment or good sense 明智的; 具有良好判斷力的 –**judiciously** *adv*

ju·do /ˈdʒuːdoʊ; ˈdʒuːdəʊ/ *n* [U] a type of self-defence, often practised as a sport, in which you try to throw your opponent to the ground 柔道: *He's got a black belt in judo.* 他有柔道的黑腰帶級。

jug /dʒʌɡ; dʒʌɡ/ *n* *BrE* a container for liquids with a handle and a lip for pouring〔英式〕〔有柄帶嘴的〕壺, 罐 –see picture on page 244 見 244 頁彩圖

jug·ger·naut /ˈdʒʌɡəˌnɔːt; ˈdʒʌɡənɔːt/ *n* *BrE* a very large LORRY〔英式〕重型貨車

jug·gle /ˈdʒʌɡl; ˈdʒʌɡəl/ *v* **juggled, juggling 1** [I;T] to keep several objects in the air at the same time by throwing them up quickly and catching them again 玩雜耍〔同時拋接數件物品〕: *He can juggle with plates.* 他能同時拋接好幾隻盤子。 | *Can you juggle?* 你會玩雜耍嗎? **2** [T] to change numbers or

J

ideas cleverly 巧妙地改變〔數字或主意〕: *I'm just juggling the figures to see if we can afford to buy the house.* 我只是在數字上做做文章，看看我們是否買得起房子。

jug·gler /'dʒʌglə; 'dʒʌglə'/ *n* someone who juggles to entertain people 玩雜耍的人

juice /dʒuːs; dʒuːs/ *n* [C;U] **1** the liquid part of fruit or vegetable, often made into a drink 水果汁; 蔬菜汁〔常製成飲料〕: *orange juice* 橘子〔橙〕汁 **2** the liquid in your stomach, that helps you to DIGEST food 胃液 **3** the liquid from meat that is cooking 肉汁: *Spoon the juices over the meat.* 用匙舀些肉汁澆到肉上。

juic·y /'dʒuːsɪ; 'dʒuːsi/ *adj* **juicier, juiciest 1** having a lot of juice 多汁的: *a juicy orange* 多汁的橙子 **2** interesting, especially because of providing information about bad or improper behaviour 〔尤指由於提供了有關不良行為的消息而覺得〕有趣的, 繪影繪色的: *I want all the juicy details.* 我想知道所有有趣的細節。**3** *infml* desirable 〔非正式〕希望得到的; 理想的: *a fat juicy contract to end all our problems* 能解決我們所有問題的一份條件優厚的合同

juke·box /'dʒuk,bɒks; 'dʒuːkbɒks/ *n* **jukeboxes** a music machine, often found in bars, which plays records when you put a coin into it 〔投幣式〕自動點唱機〔常設在酒吧內〕

Ju·ly /dʒuˈlaɪ; dʒuˈlaɪ/ *n* (also 又作 **Jul.**) the 7th month of the year 七月

jum·ble /'dʒʌmbl; 'dʒʌmbəl/ (also 又作 **jumble sth ↔ up**) *v* **jumbled, jumbling** [T] to mix things in a disordered way 將混亂: *My thoughts were all jumbled up.* 我的思緒全部亂成一團。 | *The clothes lay jumbled on the floor.* 衣物亂七八糟地堆在地板上。– **jumble** *n* [sing]: *a chaotic jumble of toys and books* 一堆雜亂的玩具和書籍

jumble sale /'·· ·/ *BrE n* a sale of used things to collect money for a good purpose 〔英式〕舊雜物的義賣: *The Brownies are holding a jumble sale for the orphans.* 女童子軍在舉行舊雜物義賣。

jum·bo¹ /'dʒʌmbo; 'dʒʌmbəʊ/ *adj* (also 又作 **jumbo-sized** /'·· ·/) [only before a noun 只用於名詞前] extremely large (a word often used in advertisements) 特大的〔常用於廣告中〕: *a jumbo pack of washing powder* 特大包裝的洗衣粉

jumbo² *n* (also 又作 **jumbo jet** /'·· ·/) a very large passenger aircraft 巨型噴氣式客機, 珍寶機

jump¹ /dʒʌmp; dʒʌmp/ *v* **1** [I] to push yourself into the air by using the strength of your legs and feet 跳; 跳躍: *The children were jumping up and down.* 孩子們在跳上跳下。 | *She jumped out of the window.* 她從窗口跳了出去。 | *He jumped over the fence.* 他跳過了籬笆。–see picture on page 992 見 992 頁彩圖 **2 jump up, jump to your feet** to

stand up quickly and suddenly 突然站起來: *I jumped up and ran to the door.* 我突然起身跑向房門。 **3** [T] to cross something by jumping over it 跳過〔某物〕: *He jumped the stream.* 他跳過了小溪。 | *None of the horses managed to jump the fence.* 沒有一匹馬能跳過那道圍欄。**4** [I] to make a quick sudden movement because something has frightened you or surprised you 〔由於受驚〕突然一跳: *The noise made me jump.* 那聲音嚇了我一跳。 | *Oh, you frightened me! I nearly jumped out of my skin!* 哦, 你嚇了我一跳! 我差點兒嚇死了! **5** [I] to increase suddenly and by a large amount 突然上升; 暴漲: *The price of oil jumped sharply in 1973.* 油價於1973年急劇上漲。**6 jump on the bandwagon** to do or say something just because most people are doing it or saying it 人云亦云; 跟著別人做某事 **7 jump to a conclusion** to decide that something is true before you have all the information you need 匆匆作出結論: *Wait a minute! Don't start jumping to conclusions.* 等一下! 別急著開始下結論。**8 jump the gun** to do something before it is the proper time 搶先做某事, 過早地採取行動 **9 jump a queue** to move to the front of a line of people who are all waiting for something (a phrase used to express disapproval) 不按次序排隊; 插隊〔含貶義〕: *I'm really fed up with people jumping the queue.* 我實在討厭那些插隊的人。

jump at sth *phr v* [T] to accept something eagerly 馬上接受〔某事物〕: *I'd jump at the chance of going abroad.* 我欣然接受了這次出國的機會。

jump on sbdy *phr v* [T] to speak sharply to someone, often unfairly 〔常指不公平地〕斥責〔某人〕: *She jumps on me every time I make the slightest mistake.* 每次我犯了一點小錯誤, 她就會對我嚴加斥責。

jump² *n* **1** an act of jumping 跳; 跳躍: *a parachute jump* 跳傘 **2** a sudden large increase in amount 數量的激增: *a huge jump in population* 人口的劇增 **3** a thing to be jumped over 需要跳越的物體: *The horse cleared all the jumps.* 這匹馬跳過了所有的障礙物。**4 be/stay one jump ahead** *infml* to manage to have an advantage over your competitors by knowing what they are doing 〔非正式〕〔由於了解競爭對手所做的事而〕佔有優勢

jump·er /'dʒʌmpə; 'dʒʌmpə'/ *n* **1** *BrE* a piece of woollen clothing for the upper half of your body, which you put on by pulling it over your head 〔英式〕套頭毛衣–see picture on page 210 見 210 頁彩圖 **2** *AmE* a dress that does not cover your arms and is usually worn over a shirt or woollen garment 〔美式〕〔穿在女襯衫外的〕無袖連衣裙

jump·y /'dʒʌmpɪ; 'dʒʌmpi/ *adj* **jumpier, jumpiest** *infml* nervous 〔非正式〕緊張的: *I*

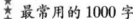
J

was very jumpy about flying. 我非常害怕坐飛機。

junc·tion /'dʒʌŋkʃən; 'dʒʌŋkʃən/ *n* a place where roads or railway lines join〔公路或鐵路的〕聯接點，匯合處

junc·ture /'dʒʌŋktʃə; 'dʒʌŋktʃər/ *n fml*〔正式〕**at this juncture** at this important moment 在這緊要關頭

June /dʒuːn; dʒuːn/ *n* (also 又作 **Jun.**) the 6th month of the year 六月

jun·gle /'dʒʌŋgl; 'dʒʌŋgl/ *n* **1** [C;U] a thick tropical forest 熱帶叢林: *the jungles of South America* 南美的熱帶叢林 **2** [C] a difficult situation in which you have to struggle very hard〔必須努力掙扎的〕困境: *This city is a real jungle.* 這座城市真是一片混亂。| *the jungle of tax laws* 稅法的繁雜

ju·ni·or¹ /'dʒuːnjə; 'dʒuːniər/ *adj* **1** of lower rank or position 職位低的；地位低的: *a junior officer* 級別較低的官員 | *a junior minister* 級別較低的部長 | *He's still very junior within the company.* 他在公司裡的職位仍很低。**2** [never before a noun 不能用於名詞前] younger than somebody else 年紀較輕的，較年幼的: *She is junior to me.* 她比我年輕。| *Bill is three years my junior.* 比爾比我年輕三歲。

junior² *n* **1** [C] someone who has a low rank or position 低級職位的人；地位低的人: *the office junior* 初級職員 **2** [only after a name 只用於名字後] the younger one of two men in the same family who have exactly the same name〔在同一家庭中姓名完全相同的兩個人中的〕較年幼的: *John B. Heathcote Junior* 小約翰·B·西斯科特

junk /dʒʌŋk; dʒʌŋk/ *n* **1** [U] *infml* old useless things〔非正式〕廢舊雜物: *This is just a load of old junk.* 這不過是一堆舊東西。**2** [C] a flat-bottomed Chinese sailing ship 中國（平底）帆船

junk food /'· ·/ *n* [C;U] bad quality food which is not good for you, especially because it contains a lot of chemicals〔尤指因其含有大量化學成分而〕不利健康的劣質食品

junk·ie /'dʒʌŋki; 'dʒʌŋki/ *n infml*〔非正式〕(also 又作 **junky**) a person who takes drugs and is dependent on them, especially HEROIN 有毒癮者〔尤指吸海洛因者〕

jun·ta /'dʒʌntə; 'dʒʌntə/ *n* a military government that has come to power by force, not through elections〔通過武力而非選舉產生的〕軍人政府

Ju·pi·ter /'dʒuːpətə; 'dʒuːpɪtər/ *n* the largest PLANET of the group that includes the Earth 木星

jur·is·dic·tion /,dʒʊrɪs'dɪkʃən; ,dʒʊərɪs'dɪkʃən/ *n* [U] the right of an official person or court of law to carry out the law or make decisions about it 司法權；審判權；管轄權: *This matter is outside the jurisdiction of the health department.* 此事超出了衛生部門的職責範圍。

ju·ris·pru·dence /,dʒʊrɪs'pruːdns; ,dʒʊərɪs'pruːdəns/ *n* [U] *fml* the science or study of the law〔正式〕法學；法律學

ju·rist /'dʒʊrɪst; 'dʒʊərɪst/ *n fml* a person with a thorough knowledge of law〔正式〕法學家；法律學者

ju·ror /'dʒʊrə; 'dʒʊərər/ *n* a member of a jury 陪審員；評判員

ju·ry /'dʒʊri; 'dʒʊəri/ *n* **juries** [+ sing/pl verb] **1** a group of people chosen to hear all the details of a case in a court of law and give their decision on it 陪審團: *The jury found him guilty of murder.* 陪審團裁定他犯有殺人罪。**2** a group of people chosen to decide the winners in a competition〔比賽的〕評判委員會: *And the jury has voted number two a hit!* 評判委員會還投了二號參賽者一票!

★just¹ /dʒʌst; dʒʌst/ *adj* fair and morally right 公正的；正義的: *This is a just punishment.* 這是個公正的懲罰。| *a just war* 一場正義的戰爭

★just² /dʒəst; dʒəst; *strong* 強讀 dʒʌst; dʒʌst/ *adv* **1** exactly at a particular time or place 正好，恰好〔在某時或某地〕: *He was sitting just here.* 那時他就坐在此處。| *He arrived just as I was leaving.* 我剛要走時，他就來了。| *I was just about to phone you.* 我剛才正要打電話給你。**2** exactly 恰恰: *Thank you — it's just what I wanted.* 謝謝——這恰是我所想要的。**3** not by a very great amount 數量不大地；剛剛: *They've been away for just over two weeks.* 他們剛走了兩個星期。| *The skirt came to just below her knees.* 裙子剛過她的膝蓋。**4** (also 又作 **only just**) not very easily 不太容易地；勉強地: *I could just see her in the distance.* 我能勉強看見她在遠處。| *I can only just lift it.* 我勉強能把它舉起來。**5** very recently 最近；剛才: *We've just moved in.* 我們剛搬進來。| *I've just spoken to him on the telephone.* 我剛和他在電話裡通過話。**6** only 僅僅；只: *I don't want anything to eat. Just a coffee, please.* 我甚麼都不想吃。請只給我一杯咖啡。| *He just stood there laughing at us.* 他只是站在那裡笑我們。**7** used to make a command stronger〔用於加強命令的語氣〕: *Just do as you are told!* 告訴你怎麼做就怎麼做! | *Just imagine what it would be like.* 你就想想那將會是甚麼樣子。**8** **just about** almost 幾乎，差不多: *The house is just about ready.* 房子差不多準備好了。**9** **just now: a** at this moment 現在: *We're having dinner just now — can I phone you back later?* 我們現在正在吃飯——過一會兒我再打電話給你行嗎? **b** a moment ago 剛才: *I was talking to her just now so she can't be far away.* 我剛才還在和她說話，所以她走不遠。**10** **just the same** in spite of that 儘管那樣: *I know she's probably fast asleep, but I think I'll pop up and make sure just the same.* 我知道她可能睡着了，儘管如此，我還是打算起來去核實一下。

■ USAGE 用法: British people usually use **just, already** and **yet** with the present perfect tense ☆英國人通常將 **just, already** 和 **yet** 與現在完成式連用: *The bell has **just** rung.* 鈴剛響過。 | *I've **already** seen him.* 我已經見到他了。 | *Have you eaten **yet**?* 你吃過飯了嗎? Americans often use the simple past tense in informal speech and this is becoming more common in British English also ☆ 美國人在非正式談話中常將上述三詞用於過去式當中。這現象現在在英式英語中越來越普遍: *The bell **just** rang.* 鈴剛響過。 | *I **already** saw him.* 我已經見到他了。 | *Did you eat **yet**?* 你吃過飯了嗎? But many people still consider this form incorrect. ☆但是仍有許多人認為這種形式不正確。

jus·tice /ˈdʒʌstɪs; ˈdʒʌstḷs/ *n* **1** [U] treatment of other people which is fair and morally right 公正; 正義: *the struggle for justice* 為正義而進行的鬥爭 | *a strong sense of justice* 強烈的正義感 **2** [U] the system in a country which makes laws and punishes people who break them 司法(制度): *a court of justice* 法院; 法庭 **3** [C] *AmE* a judge in a law court 〔美式〕法官 **4 bring someone to justice** to catch a criminal and bring him before a law court 將罪犯繩之於法 **5 do justice to someone or something** to treat someone or something in a fair and proper way 公平對待: *She's a boring teacher, but to do her justice, fairly thorough.* 雖然她是個乏味的老師, 但說句公道話, 她的課講得相當詳盡。 **6 do yourself justice** to behave in a way which is worthy of your qualities or abilities 發揮自己的才能: *She was so nervous that she really didn't do herself justice in the exam.* 她在考試中太緊張, 沒有發揮出自己的水平。

Justice of the Peace /ˌ· · · ·ˈ·/ *n fml* 〔正式〕 (also 又作 **JP**) a person who gives judgments in a local court of law in Britain 〔英國的〕治安法官

jus·ti·fi·a·ble /ˈdʒʌstəˌfaɪəbl; ˈdʒʌstḷˈfaɪəbəl/ *adj* reasonable, and able to be justified 有道理的; 可證明為正當的 –**opposite** 反義 **unjustifiable** –**justifiably** *adv*: *He was justifiably angry.* 他有理由地生氣。

jus·ti·fied /ˈdʒʌstəˌfaɪd; ˈdʒʌstḷfaɪd/ *adj* **1** having a good and acceptable reason for doing something 有正當理由〔做某事〕的: *I don't think you were justified **in** being so angry with him.* 我認為你沒有理由對他這樣發火。 **2** reasonable and acceptable 有理由的; 可接受的: *I don't think that military intervention is justified.* 我認為軍事干涉是毫無道理的。

*****jus·ti·fy** /ˈdʒʌstəˌfaɪ; ˈdʒʌstḷfaɪ/ *v* **justified, justifying** [T] to show or give a good reason for something 證明〔某事〕有道理: *How can you justify your rude behaviour?* 你怎樣為你的粗魯舉止辯解呢? | *We can't justify spending any more money on this project.* 我們沒有理由再在這個項目上花費更多的錢了。

□ USEFUL PATTERNS 有用句型
to justify something; to justify doing something

–**justification** /ˌdʒʌstəfəˈkeʃən; ˌdʒʌstḷfḷˈkeɪʃən/ [U]

jut /dʒʌt; dʒʌt/ *v* **-tt-**
jut out *phr v* [I] to stick out or up further than other things around it 突出; 伸出: *The wall juts out here to allow room for the chimney.* 牆壁的這個地方向外突出, 給煙囪留了一些空間。

jute /dʒuːt; dʒuːt/ *n* [U] a substance from a plant used for making rope and rough cloth 〔用於製繩子和粗布的〕黃麻纖維

ju·ve·nile¹ /ˈdʒuvənl; ˈdʒuːvənaɪl/ *adj* **1** concerned with young people who are not yet adults 少年的: *a juvenile court* 少年法庭 **2** childish or foolish 幼稚的; 愚蠢的: *a juvenile sense of humour* 帶稚氣的幽默感

juvenile² *n fml or tech* 〔正式或術語〕 **1** a young person 少年 **2 juvenile delinquent** a young person who has been found guilty of a crime 少年罪犯: *Juvenile delinquents vandalized the children's playground.* 少年罪犯蓄意破壞了兒童遊樂場。

jux·ta·pose /ˌdʒʌkstəˈpoz; ˌdʒʌkstəˈpəʊz/ *v* **juxtaposed, juxtaposing** [T] *fml* to put two things close together, often to show how different they are 〔正式〕使〔兩件物品〕並列〔並置〕〔通常為了顯示它們的差別〕 –**juxtaposition** *n* /ˌdʒʌkstəpəˈzɪʃən; ˌdʒʌkstəpəˈzɪʃən/ *n* [U]

K, k

K, k /ke; keɪ/ **K's, k's** or **Ks, ks** the 11th letter of the English alphabet 英語的第十一個字母

kaf·tan /ˈkæftən; ˈkæftæn/ n a long, loose piece of clothing with long sleeves〔束腰帶的〕長袖長袍

ka·lei·do·scope /kəˈlaɪdəˌskɒp; kəˈlaɪdəskəʊp/ n **1** a tube fitted at one end with mirrors and pieces of coloured glass which shows many coloured patterns when you turn it 萬花筒 **2** a pattern of changing colours continuously 千變萬化的圖案: *The sky became a kaleidoscope of colours.* 天空的顏色千變萬化。

kan·ga·roo /ˌkæŋgəˈru; ˌkæŋgəˈruː◂/ n an Australian animal which jumps along on its large back legs and carries its young in a special pocket 袋鼠

kar·at /ˈkærət; ˈkærət/ n see 見 CARAT

ka·ra·te /kəˈrɑte; kəˈrɑːti/ n [U] an Asian sport in which people fight using their hands and feet as weapons 空手道〔一種源自亞洲的徒手搏擊運動〕

K.C. /ˌkeˈsi; ˌkeɪ ˈsiː/ a British lawyer of high rank; an abbreviation for KING'S COUNSEL〖縮〗英國王室法律顧問〔英國高級律師〕– compare 比較 Q.C.

ke·bab /kəˈbæb; kɪˈbæb/ n small pieces of meat cooked on a stick 烤肉串

keel[1] /kil; kiːl/ n **1** a bar along the bottom of a ship from which the whole frame of the boat is built up 船的龍骨 **2** a piece going down into the water from the bottom of a ship to keep it upright 船的龍骨板 **3** **keep on an even keel** to keep going steadily without any sudden changes 平穩前進

keel[2] v

keel over v [I] to fall over sideways 傾覆: *The ship keeled over in the storm.* 這艘船在暴風雨中傾覆。

*★**keen** /kin; kiːn/ adj **1** having a strong and active interest in something 熱心的; 熱切的:

□ **USEFUL PATTERNS** 有用句型
be keen on something; be keen to do something

She was very keen to talk to him. 她非常渴望跟他講話。 | *I'm not very keen* on *football.* 我不大喜愛足球。 | *She's a very keen gardener.* 她很熱衷於園藝。 **2** strong and deep (used of feelings) 強烈的; 深切的〔指感情〕: *a keen sense of failure* 強烈的失敗感 | *a keen desire* 熱望 **3** clever and quick at understanding 聰明的; 聰慧的: *a keen mind* 聰明的頭腦 | *a keen sense of humour* 很強的幽默感 **4** very sensitive (used of the senses) 敏銳的〔指感覺〕: *a keen sense of smell* 靈敏的嗅覺 **5** very hard (used of competitions) 激烈的〔指比賽〕: *a keen contest* 激烈的比賽 | *There has been keen competition for the job.* 對這項工作一直存在着激烈的競爭。 –**keenly** adv –**keenness** n [U]

*★**keep**[1] /kip; kiːp/ v **kept** /kept; kept/, **kept, keeping 1** [T] to continue to have something and not need to return it to anyone else 保存; 保留: *You can keep it; I don't need it any more.* 你留着吧; 我不再需要它了。 | *He gave me £5 and told me to keep the change.* 他給我五英鎊, 告訴我不用找零錢了。 | *There's no point in keeping all those old clothes.* 留着那些舊衣服是毫無意義的。 **2** [T] to have something in a particular place〔在某處〕放置〔某物〕: *Where do you keep the coffee?* 你把咖啡放在哪裡? | *I always keep a spare key in my bag.* 我總是在手袋裡放一把備用的鑰匙。 **3** [T] to look after something for a short time〔暫時〕保管〔某物〕: *Could you keep this for me until I get back?* 你能幫我把這個保管到我回來嗎? **4** [+complement] to remain 保持: *It's difficult to keep warm in this cold weather.* 這麼冷的天氣之下要保持和暖是很困難的。 | *Keep still for a minute while I take a photo.* 我拍照時請暫時保持別動。 **5** [T] to make someone or something remain in a place or state 使〔某人或某物〕保持〔在某處或某種狀態〕: *They kept her in hospital for three weeks.* 他們讓她住院三週。 | *The noise kept me awake.* 這噪音令我無法入睡。 | *She put on her sunglasses to keep the sun out of her eyes.* 她戴上墨鏡, 以免陽光照到她的眼睛。 **6** [T] to make regular written records of things 定期記錄: *Keep an account of what you spend.* 你的花費都要記賬。 | *I've kept a diary for years.* 我已記了好幾年日記。 **7** [T] to provide food, clothes, and other necessary things for someone 供養〔某人〕, 贍養〔某人〕: *What he earns isn't enough to keep him and his family.* 他掙的錢不夠養家餬口。 **8** [T] to have animals and look after them, often for

K

food 飼養〔動物〕: *I'd love to keep chickens.* 我很想養小雞。**9** [I] (of food) to remain fresh and fit to eat 〔食物〕保鮮; 可供食用: *Milk only keeps for a few days.* 牛奶只能保鮮數天。**10** [T] to delay someone 耽擱〔某人〕: *What kept you?* 甚麼事讓你耽擱了? | *I know you're busy so I won't keep you for long.* 我知道你很忙, 所以不會耽誤你許多時間。**11** [T] to fulfil a promise or an agreement 履行〔諾言〕; 執行〔協議〕: *I always keep my promises.* 我總是履行自己的諾言的。 | *He failed to keep his appointment.* 他未能按時赴約。**12 keep doing something** to continue doing something 繼續做某事: *Don't keep interrupting me!* 別老是插嘴! | *Just keep walking in the same direction and you'll get to the village.* 一直朝同一個方向走, 你就能走到那個村莊。**13 keep someone from doing something** to prevent someone from doing something 阻止某人做某事: *She tried to keep me from seeing the letter.* 她試圖不讓我看見那封信。**14 keep something from someone** to fail to tell someone something 未把某事告訴某人: *She knew his name but she kept it from me.* 她知道他的名字, 但沒有告訴我。 | *Details of the plan were kept from the public.* 該計劃的細節未向大眾公開。**15 keep a secret** to not tell people a secret 保守祕密: *Can you keep a secret?* 你能保守祕密嗎? **16 keep someone company** to remain with someone so that they are not alone 陪伴某人: *I stayed with her in the afternoon to keep her company.* 下午我留下來陪她作伴。**17 keep your head** to remain calm 保持頭腦冷靜

keep at sthg *phr v* [T] to continue doing something 繼續做〔某事〕: *I found the work difficult but I kept at it and passed the exam.* 我感到功課很難, 但我仍不懈地努力, 終於通過了考試。

keep sthg ↔ **back** *phr v* [T] to fail to give someone a piece of information 隱瞞〔消息〕: *She told us what happened, but I'm sure she's keeping something back.* 她把所發生的事情告訴我們, 但我肯定她隱瞞了一些東西。

keep down *phr v* **1** [T **keep** sthg ↔ **down**] to prevent something from increasing 阻止〔某物〕增長, 抑制: *The government is determined to keep down inflation.* 政府決心抑制通貨膨脹。**2** [T **keep** sbdy ↔ **down**] to keep people in a state where they are not free 關押〔某人〕

keep off *phr v* **1** [I] to remain off or away from a place 遠離; 離開: *Notices warned us to keep off the grass.* 通告警告我們不要走進草地。**2** [T **keep** sthg ↔ **off** (sthg)] to prevent someone or something from going onto something 擋開〔某人、某物〕: *I put my umbrella up to keep the rain off.* 我撐起傘擋雨。

keep on *phr v* **1 keep on doing something**

to continue doing something 繼續做某事: *Prices keep on increasing.* 物價持續上漲。 | *She keeps on asking me what the time is!* 一直在問我幾點鐘了! **2** [T **keep** sthg ↔ **on**] to continue to have a house or flat 繼續租用〔房子或公寓〕: *I think I'll keep the flat on during the summer.* 我準備在夏天繼續租用這套房子。

keep on about sthg *phr v* [T] to keep talking about something 繼續談論〔某事物〕: *He kept on about the good old days when he was in the army.* 他喋喋不休地談論他在從軍時的美好的往日。

keep on at sbdy *phr v* [T] to keep complaining to someone 一直抱怨〔某人〕

keep out *phr v* **1** [I] to remain outside a place 留在〔某處〕外面: *Notices on the fence warned us to keep out.* 籬笆上的通告警告我們不要進去。**2** [T **keep** sbdy/sthg ↔ **out**] to cause someone or something to remain outside a place 使〔某人或某物〕留在〔某處〕外面: *They had put up barriers to keep people out.* 他們已設下障礙防止人們進來。

keep to *phr v* **1** [T **keep to** sthg] to stay in a place or position 留在〔某處〕: *Traffic must keep to the left.* 車輛必須靠左行駛。 | *He kept to the footpaths.* 他沿着小徑向前走。**2** [T **keep to** sthg] to limit yourself to something 使自己限於〔某物〕: *Please keep to the subject.* 請圍繞這個主題談。 | *You must keep to your budget.* 你的開支不可以超出預算。**3 keep something to yourself** to not tell other people about something 對某事物保守祕密: *He kept the news to himself.* 他不把這消息告訴任何人。**4 keep yourself to yourself** to spend a lot of time by yourself, and not talk to other people very much 不大與別人交往

keep up *phr v* **1** [T **keep** sthg ↔ **up**] to cause something to remain high 使〔某事物〕不掉下來: *She kept her spirits up by singing.* 她以唱歌來保持精神高昂。**2** [T **keep** sbdy **up**] to cause someone to remain awake and out of bed 不讓〔某人〕上牀〔睡覺〕: *I hope I'm not keeping you up.* 我希望我沒有打擾你上牀休息。**3** [**keep** sthg ↔ **up**] to continue to do something 繼續做〔某事〕: *She started screaming with rage, but I knew she wouldn't keep it up for long.* 她火冒三丈, 開始大聲尖叫, 但我知道她叫不了多久。**4** [I] to remain level with someone 同〔某人〕保持同一水平; 跟上〔某人〕: *I ran as fast as I could, but I couldn't keep up* **with** *the others.* 我拼命跑, 卻仍跟不上其他人。**5 keep up with something** to know about things that are happening 知道正在發生的事情: *I like to try and keep up with what's happening in the world.* 我喜歡設法了解世界上發生的事情。**6 keep up with the Joneses** to compete with your neighbours socially, for example by trying to have a nicer house or a better car 與鄰居比闊氣〔例如試圖購買比他

K

們更好的房子或汽車〕

keep² *n* **1** [U] the cost of necessary things such as food and lodgings 生活必需品的費用〔如食宿費用〕: *He gave them £50 a week to pay for his keep.* 他每週給他們五十英鎊作為他的生活費。 **2** [C] a main tower in a castle 城堡的主塔

keep·er /'kipə; 'ki:pər/ *n* **1** a person who looks after the animals in a ZOO〔動物園內的〕飼養員 **2** a person who is responsible for the objects in a MUSEUM 博物館管理員

keep·ing /'kipŋ; 'ki:pɪŋ/ *n* **1 in someone's keeping** in someone's care or charge 讓某人保管: *The money will remain in my keeping.* 這筆錢由我來保管。 **2 in keeping with something** suitable for something 和…一致、與…協調: *a silly joke not quite in keeping with the occasion* 不太合時宜的愚蠢玩笑 [RELATED PHRASE 相關詞組 **out of keeping with something**]

keep·sake /'kip,sek; 'ki:pseɪk/ *n* a small present that someone gives you so that you will remember them 小紀念品

keg /kɛg; keg/ *n* a small barrel 小桶

ken·nel /'kɛnl; 'kenl/ *n* **1** a small hut for a dog to sleep in 狗舍；狗窩 **2 kennels** [pl] a place where dogs are bred or where they are cared for when their owners are away〔寄養狗的〕養狗場

kept /kɛpt; kept/ the past tense and past participle of KEEP ☆ KEEP 的過去式和過去分詞

kerb /kɜ·b; kɜ:b/ *n* (**curb** *AmE*【美式】) a line of raised stones separating the foot-path from the road〔人行道的〕路緣 –see picture on page 729 見 729 頁彩圖

ker·nel /'kɜ·nl; 'kɜ:nl/ *n* **1** the part of a nut, fruit stone, or seed inside its shell〔堅果或果核內的〕仁；〔穀米的〕粒 **2** the most important part of something〔事物的〕核心；要點: *The kernel of his argument is that we need more teachers.* 他的論點的核心是我們需要更多的老師。

ker·o·sene /'kɛrə,sin; 'kerəsi:n/ *n* (also 又作 **kerosine**) [U] the usual American word for【美式】= PARAFFIN (1)

kes·trel /'kɛstrəl; 'kestrəl/ *n* a type of bird that kills and eats animals 茶隼；紅隼

ketch·up /'kɛtʃəp; 'ketʃəp/ *n* [U] a thick liquid made from tomatoes (TOMATO), used for giving a pleasant taste to food 調味番茄醬

ket·tle /'kɛtl; 'ketl/ *n* a covered container for boiling water in; it has a handle and a narrow mouth for pouring〔燒水用的〕水壺 –see picture on page 244 見 244 頁彩圖

ket·tle·drum /'kɛtl,drʌm; 'ketldrʌm/ *n* a large drum with a curved bottom 定音鼓

★★**key¹** /ki; ki:/ *n* **1** a specially shaped piece of metal that you put in a lock to open or close something, to wind a clock, or stop or start an engine 鑰匙: *I've lost the*

car keys. 我把汽車鑰匙弄丟了。 | *the key to the cupboard* 碗櫥鑰匙 **2 keys** the buttons on a computer or TYPEWRITER which you press when you use it〔電腦或打字機的〕鍵 **3 keys** the narrow black and white bars on a musical instrument which you press to make a particular sound〔樂器的〕鍵: *the keys of an organ* 風琴的鍵 **4** a list of the answers to problems or exercises〔問題或練習的〕答案: *the key to the grammar exercises* 語法練習答案 **5** the explanation for, or way to get, a particular result〔對於某一結果的〕解釋；〔得到某一結果的〕方法: *Her unhappy childhood is the key to her character.* 不愉快的童年是形成她性格的關鍵。 | *Diet is the key to good health.* 飲食是健康的關鍵。 **6** a set of musical notes based on a particular note〔音樂的〕調；主音調: *a song in the key of C* 一首 C 調的歌曲

★**key²** *v*

key sthg ↔ in *phr v* [T] to put information into a computer by pressing the keys 用鍵盤輸入

key³ *adj* [only before a noun 只用於名詞前] very important or necessary 非常重要的；關鍵性的: *a key witness* 重要見證人

key·board¹ /'ki,bord; 'ki:bɔ:d/ *n* **1** the set of keys on a machine such as a computer which you press when you use it〔機器上的〕鍵盤: *a typewriter keyboard* 打字機鍵盤 –see picture on page 763 見 763 頁彩圖 **2** a row of keys on a musical instrument〔樂器上的〕鍵盤: *the keyboard of a piano* 鋼琴鍵盤

key·board² *v* [I;T] to make a piece of writing ready to print or to put information into a computer by operating a keyboard 用鍵盤輸入〔操作〕: *Applicants for this post should have good keyboarding skills.* 申請該職位的人應該具有良好的鍵盤操作技能。 –**keyboarder** *n*

keyed up /'kid 'ʌp; ,ki:d 'ʌp/ *adj infml* excited or nervous〔非正式〕激動的；緊張的: *We're all very keyed up about the examination.* 我們對於考試都感到非常緊張。

key·hole /'ki,hol; 'ki:həul/ *n* a hole in a lock, where you put a key 鑰匙孔

key·note /'ki,not; 'ki:nəut/ *n* **1** the particular note on which a musical KEY is based〔音調的〕主音 **2** the central or most important idea in something 要旨；基調: *The keynote of their election campaign has been educational reforms.* 他們競選活動的基調是教育改革。

key ring /'· ·/ *n* a ring on which keys are kept 鑰匙圈

kg a written abbreviation for【縮】= KILO-GRAM(S)

kha·ki /'kɑki; 'kɑ:ki/ *n* [U] **1** a yellow-brown colour 土黃色，黃褐色 –see picture on page 243 見 243 頁彩圖 **2** strong cloth of this colour, often worn by soldiers 卡其布〔常為士兵穿的軍服用料〕–**khaki** *adj*

K

kib·butz /kɪˈbuts; kɪˈbʊts/ *n* **kibbutzim** /-sɪm; -sɪm/ *or* **kibbutzes** a farm or factory in Israel where many people live together and share their work and income 基布兹〔以色列的合作農場或集體工廠〕,集居區

★**kick¹** /kɪk; kɪk/ *v* **1** [T] to hit something forcefully with your foot 踢: *She kicked the pile of books over.* 她把整堆書踢倒了。| *Stop kicking the dog!* 不要再踢那隻狗了! – see picture on page 992 見 992 頁彩圖 **2** [I; T] to move your legs or feet strongly and forcefully 踢蹬: *The baby kicked happily.* 那嬰兒高興地踢踢腳。| *He was lying in the water, kicking his legs.* 他躺在水中, 用腳蹬水。**3** [T] to hit a ball or other object with your foot so that it moves 踢動〔球或其他物體〕: *He kicked the ball over the fence.* 他把球踢過了籬笆。**4 kick a habit** *infml* to stop doing something which you used to do as a habit 〔非正式〕戒除習慣 **5 I could kick myself, I kicked myself** a phrase used when you are cross with yourself for not doing something better or differently 我真該打自己的耳光〔用於因未做好某事而對自己生氣〕: *I could have kicked myself for making such a stupid mistake.* 犯了這樣一個愚蠢的錯誤, 我真該打自己的耳光。

kick about/around *phr v* [I] **be kicking about** to be somewhere in a place, although you do not know exactly where 在某處放着: *There are a couple of old buckets kicking about in the shed.* 棚子裡攔着幾個水桶。

kick off *phr v* **1** [I] to start a football match 〔足球賽〕開球 **2** [I;T **kick sthg ↔ off**] *infml* to start a conversation or a meeting 〔非正式〕開始談話[會見]

kick sbdy ↔ out *phr v* [T] to force someone to leave a place or a job 攆走; 開除

kick up *phr v* [I] **kick up a fuss, kick up a row** *infml* to cause trouble about something, sometimes something unimportant 〔非正式〕惹麻煩〔有時是小麻煩〕: *If they don't empty the dustbin this week, I'm going to kick up a real fuss.* 除垃圾箱內的垃圾, 我就真的要他們好看。

kick² *n* **1** a strong, sometimes violent, movement of your leg or foot 踢; 蹬: *Give the door a kick to open it.* 把門一腳踢開。**2** *infml* a strong feeling of excitement or pleasure 〔非正式〕激動; 快樂: *She drives fast just for kicks.* 她只是為了刺激才開快車。| *He gets a real kick out of skiing.* 他一滑雪便非常興奮。

kick-off /ˈkɪkˌɔf; ˈkɪk-ɒf/ *n* the kick which begins a game of football 〔足球賽的〕開球: *The kickoff is at three o'clock today.* 足球賽今天下午三點鐘開始。

★**kid¹** /kɪd; kɪd/ *n* **1** [C] *infml* a child or young person 〔非正式〕小孩; 年輕人: *My kids are two and six.* 我的兩個孩子是一個兩歲, 一個六歲。| *college kids* 大學生 | *It's immoral*

putting kids in uniform and sending them to fight a war. 讓孩子們穿上軍裝去作戰是不道德的。–see 見 CHILD (USAGE用法) **2 kid sister, kid brother** *AmE infml* a younger sister or brother 〔美式, 非正式〕妹妹; 弟弟 **3** [C] a young goat 小山羊 **4** [U] leather made from the skin of a young goat 小山羊皮

kid² *v* **-dd-** *infml* 〔非正式〕**1** [I;T] to pretend as a joke that something is true 戲弄; 欺騙: *He's not really hurt. He's only kidding.* 他沒有真的受了傷。他不過是開玩笑。| *You can't kid me. I know you're not telling the truth.* 你騙不了我。我知道你沒說實話。**2** [T] to joke playfully with someone 〔某人〕開玩笑: *We kidded him about his new haircut.* 我們拿他的新髮型來開玩笑。**3 kid yourself** to deceive yourself 欺騙自己: *He's been kidding himself that he'll win.* 他一直在騙自己說他會贏。**4 you're kidding, you must be kidding** a phrase used when you don't believe something that someone is telling you 你一定是在開玩笑〔用於表示不相信別人告訴你的事情〕

kid·nap /ˈkɪdnæp; ˈkɪdnæp/ *v* **-pp-** (also 又作 **-p-** *AmE* 〔美式〕) [T] to take someone away by force in order to demand money or something else for their safe return 綁架〔某人〕–**kidnapper** *n*

kid·ney /ˈkɪdni; ˈkɪdni/ *n* **1** either of the pair of organs in your body which separate waste from your blood and produce URINE 腎; 腎臟 **2** an animal's kidney used as food 〔作食物用的動物的〕腰子

kidney ma·chine /ˈ··· ,·/ *n* a machine that can do the work of diseased human kidneys 人工腎; 血液透析器

★**kill¹** /kɪl; kɪl/ *v* **1** [I;T] to make a plant, an animal, or a person die 殺死〔植物, 動物或人〕; 致死: *These chemicals can kill.* 這些化學品能使人致命。| *First she killed her husband, then she killed herself.* 她先殺了丈夫, 然後自殺身亡。| *Some of the plants were killed by the frost.* 一些植物被凍死了。**2 be killing you** *infml* to be causing you great pain 〔非正式〕使自己感到劇痛: *My feet are killing me!* 我的腳痛得要命! **3 kill time** to make time pass by finding something unimportant to do 消磨時間: *I read a book to kill time.* 我以看書消磨時間。**4 kill two birds with one stone** to get two good results from one action 一舉兩得; 一箭雙鵰; 一石二鳥

■ USAGE 用法: Compare 比較 **kill, murder, slaughter, butcher, assassinate, massacre. Kill** is a general word meaning "to cause (anything) to die". **Murder** means "to kill a person on purpose" ☆ **kill** 是個普通的詞, 表示"殺死". **murder** 表示"蓄意殺害某人": *He murdered his wife by putting poison in*

her food. 他在食物中下毒, 謀殺了他的妻子。**Slaughter** means "to kill animals for food", but it can also describe the cruel, or unnecessary killing of humans ☆ **slaughter** 表示"屠宰動物以供食用", 但也可表示對於人類的殘忍或不必要的殺害: *Thousands of people were needlessly slaughtered in a senseless war.* 成千上萬的人在一場毫無意義的戰爭中無謂地喪生。**Butcher** is even stronger ☆ **butcher** 的語義更為強烈: *Our small army was butchered by the much larger enemy forces.* 我們的小部隊遭到了強大得多的敵軍的殘殺。To **assassinate** means "to kill an important political figure" ☆ **assassinate** 表示"刺殺[暗殺]政治要人": *an attempt to assassinate the president* 刺殺總統的企圖。To **massacre** means "to kill large numbers of defenceless people" ☆ **massacre** 表示"大量殺害手無寸鐵的人": *The army entered the town and massacred all the women and children.* 敵軍進城後大肆屠殺所有婦女和兒童。

kill sbdy/sthg ↔ **off** *phr v* [T] to kill or destroy people or things one at a time 一一殺死[人]; 滅絕: *The trees were killed off by the severe winter.* 嚴冬把樹一棵棵地凍死了。

kill² *n* **1** [sing] the bird or animal killed in hunting 獵獲的鳥獸: *They drag their kill to a safe place before eating it.* 他們把獵物拖到一個安全的地方才吃。**2 the kill** the act or moment of killing a hunted bird or animal 宰殺獵物; 捕殺的時刻

kill·er /'kɪlə; 'kɪləʳ/ *n* a person, animal, or thing that kills 殺生的人[動物、事物]; 殺手; 兇手: *This disease is a killer.* 這種疾病是致命的。| *Police are still looking for the killer.* 警方仍在尋找兇手。| *a killer shark* 食人鯊

kill·ing¹ /'kɪlɪŋ; 'kɪlɪŋ/ *n* **1** a murder 謀殺: *a series of brutal killings* 一系列謀殺案 **2 make a killing** to make a large amount of money quickly and easily 發橫財

killing² *adj infml* extremely tiring 【非正式】令人筋疲力盡的: *This work is really killing.* 這工作實在令人疲憊不堪。

kill·joy /'kɪl,dʒɔɪ; 'kɪldʒɔɪ/ *n infml* a person who intentionally spoils other people's enjoyment 【非正式】故意令人掃興的人

kiln /kɪln; kɪln/ *n* a machine for baking pots or bricks or drying wood 窰: *a brick kiln* 磚窰

kil·o·gram /'kɪlə,græm; 'kɪləgræm/ *n* (also 又作 **kilogramme**) a unit for measuring weight, equal to 1,000 grams or 2.205 pounds 千克; 公斤〔重量單位, 等於 1000 克或 2.205磅〕

kil·o·me·tre /'kɪlə,miːtə; 'kɪlə,miːtəʳ/ *n* (**kilometer** *AmE* 【美式】) a unit for measuring length, equal to 1,000 metres or

0.6214 miles 千米; 公里〔長度單位, 等於 1000 米或 0.6214 英里〕

kil·o·watt /'kɪlə,wɑt; 'kɪləwɒt/ *n* 1,000 WATTS 千瓦: *a three-kilowatt electric fire* 一個三千瓦的電爐

kilt /kɪlt; kɪlt/ *n* a short woollen skirt with many pressed folds, worn by women, or by men from Scotland as their national dress 〔蘇格蘭的〕有褶短裙

ki·mo·no /kə'monə; kɪ'məʊnəʊ/ *n* a long loose Japanese garment 日本和服

kin /kɪn; kɪn/ *n* [pl] **1** members of your family (a word no longer used in modern English) 家屬; 親屬〔當代英語中不再使用〕 **2 your next of kin** *fml* your closest relatives 〔正式〕至親

★ **kind¹** /kaɪnd; kaɪnd/ *n* **1** [C] a group with its own character, different from other groups 種; 類: *"She likes to read these big fat books about rich people in America — that kind of thing." "Oh, I don't like that kind of book."* "她喜歡看這些大部頭的書, 都是些有關美國有錢人的事——諸如此類的書。" "哦, 我不喜歡那一類書。" | *different kinds of biscuits — plain ones, chocolate ones, nut ones, spicy ones...* 不同種類的餅乾——淡味的、巧克力味的、堅果味的、辛辣味的... | *"What kind of car has she got?" "Some sort of small hatchback, I think."* "她的車是哪一類?" "我想是那種車尾門向上開的小客車。" | *all kinds of people* 各種各樣的人 | *People of that kind really annoy me.* 那種人真讓我覺得討厭。| *I don't like this one much. Have you got any other kinds?* 我不太喜歡這一種。你還有其他品種的嗎? | *They are different in size, but not in kind.* 他們尺碼不一樣, 但是同一類型。**2 kind of: a** a phrase used when you are describing something not very exactly 有點像〔用於不太精確描述某物〕: *It's a kind of reddish-brown colour.* 那有點像紅褐色。**b** a phrase used in very informal conversation which does not have any exact meaning 有點〔在非正式談話中使用, 沒有確切含義〕: *She kind of hoped to be invited.* 她有點希望得到邀請。**3 in kind** with the same treatment 以同一方式[手段]: *He spoke to her very angrily, and she replied in kind.* 他非常憤怒地對她講話, 她也以同樣的方式回敬。**4 pay someone in kind** to pay someone using goods or services, not money 以貨物或服務代替金錢來支付給某人 **5 of a kind: a** *old fash* of the same sort 【老式】同一種類: *They're all of a kind, politicians. It doesn't matter which party they belong to.* 政客都是同一類人, 不管他們屬於哪個黨派。**b** of a sort which is not very good 不大好的一種: *She gave us coffee of a kind.* 她給我們一些所謂的咖啡。

■ USAGE 用法: If you use **kind** or **sort** in the singular, they should be followed by a singular noun ☆如果 **kind** 或 **sort** 用單數形式, 則它們後面應當跟一個單數名詞: *I don't like that* **kind/sort** *of book.* 我不喜歡那一類書。| *This* **kind/sort** *of question is never easy.* 這類問題從來就不容易回答。| *I've never understood that* **kind/sort** *of thing.* 我從來就不明白那種事情。If you use the plural **kinds** or **sorts**, follow them with a noun in the plural ☆如果 **kinds** 或 **sorts** 用複數形式, 則它們後面應當跟一個複數名詞: *We sell all* **kinds/sorts** *of shoes.* 我們銷售各種各樣的鞋。| *I meet many different* **kinds/sorts** *of people in my work.* 工作上我遇到許多不同類的人。Unless, of course, the noun is uncountable ☆當然, 除非所跟名詞為不可數名詞: *three* **kinds/sorts** *of cheese* 三種乳酪 | *new* **kinds/sorts** *of pollution* 新類型的污染 (You will sometimes hear sentences such as "I hate those kind/sort of questions", but this is considered to be incorrect. ☆你有時會聽到諸如"I hate those kind/sort of questions" 的句子, 但這被認為是不正確的。)

kind² *adj* **1** helpful, caring, and friendly towards other people 樂於助人的; 關心他人的; 親切的: *a kind person* 和善的人 | *a kind voice* 親切的聲音 | *She's very kind to animals.* 她非常愛護動物。| *It was so kind of you to write to me.* 謝謝你寫信給我。**2 would you be so kind as to...?, would you be kind enough to...?** phrases used when you are asking someone politely to do something 請問您能...嗎? 〔用於禮貌地請求別人做某事〕: *Would you be so kind as to help me with my suitcase?* 請問您能幫我提一下箱子嗎? –opposite 反義 **unkind**

kin·der·gar·ten /ˈkɪndəˌgɑrtn; ˈkɪndəgɑːtn/ *n* a school for children under five years old 幼兒園, 幼稚園

kind-heart·ed /ˌ·ˈ···◂/ *adj* caring and sympathetic 善心的; 富有同情心的: *a kindhearted person* 一個好心人 –**kind-heartedly** *adv*

kin·dle /ˈkɪndl; ˈkɪndl/ *v* **kindled, kindling** [T] **1** to make something start to burn 使〔某物〕開始燃燒, 使着火: *We managed to kindle a fire.* 我們設法點起了一堆火。**2** to make someone begin to have a particular feeling 令〔某人〕開始有某種感覺: *The news kindled hopes that he might still be alive.* 這消息燃起了人們的希望, 也許他還活着。

kin·dling /ˈkɪndlɪŋ; ˈkɪndlɪŋ/ *n* [U] things such as dry wood, leaves, and grass which are used for lighting a fire 引火物〔如乾木頭、樹葉或草〕

kind·ly¹ /ˈkaɪndlɪ; ˈkaɪndli/ *adj* **kindlier, kindliest** having a gentle and caring nature 溫柔的; 和善的: *She's the kindliest person I've ever met.* 她是我所遇到的最和善的人。| *He gave me a kindly smile.* 他對我親切地笑了笑。–**kindliness** *n* [U]

kindly² *adv* **1** in a kind manner 親切地; 和善地: *She spoke kindly to him.* 她親切地跟他談話。–opposite 反義 **unkindly 2** a word you use to show you are cross when you want someone to do something 請〔用於表示叫某人做某事時感到生氣〕: *Would you kindly put that book back?* 請你把那本書放回原處好不好? **3** a word you use when you ask someone very politely to do something 請〔用於非常禮貌地請別人做某事〕: *Would you kindly pass me my bag?* 請你把我的袋子遞給我好嗎? **4 not take kindly to something** to not like 不喜歡: *He didn't take kindly to what I said.* 他不喜歡聽我的話。

> ■ USAGE 用法: **1** Remember that **kindly** is not always used in polite requests. On the contrary, it often expresses anger or annoyance ☆記住 **kindly** 並非總是用於禮貌的請求中。恰恰相反, 該詞常表示憤怒或惱怒: *Would you kindly remove your feet from that seat!* 請你把腳從那個位子上放下來好不好! | *Kindly shut up at the back!* 後面的人請不要再說話了! **2** If you want to make a request very polite, one way is to use the phrase **Could you possibly...?** ☆如果想表示禮貌的請求, 一種方法是使用詞組 **Could you possibly...?**: *Could you possibly give me a hand with this?* 麻煩你幫我拎一下這個好嗎? | *Could you possibly spare me a minute?* 你能給我抽出一分鐘的時間嗎?

kind·ness /ˈkaɪndnɪs; ˈkaɪndnɪs/ *n* **1** [U] the quality of being kind 和善; 好意: *kindness to animals* 對動物的愛護 **2** [C] a kind action 仁慈的舉動; 友好的行為: *It would be a kindness to tell him the bad news immediately.* 把壞消息立即告訴他是仁慈之舉。| *their many small kindnesses to us* 他們對我們的許多關照

kin·dred¹ /ˈkɪndrɪd; ˈkɪndrɪd/ *n* [pl] your relatives or family (a word no longer used in modern English) 親屬; 家人〔當代英語中不再使用〕

kindred² *adj* **kindred spirit** a person whose interests, taste, and views are similar to your own 志趣相投的人: *We soon realised that we were kindred spirits.* 我們很快便意識到我們志趣相投。

ki·net·ic /kɪˈnɛtɪk; kɪˈnetɪk/ *adj tech* relating to movement 〔術語〕運動的; 動力的

ki·net·ics /kɪˈnɛtɪks; kɪˈnetɪks/ *n* [U] the science that studies movement 動力學

 ★king /kɪŋ; kɪŋ/ *n* **1** (also 又作 **King**) the male ruler of a country who is not elected but is usually the son of a former

ruler; King is also used as a title 國王〔也用作稱號〕: *the King of Spain* 西班牙國王 | *King Edward* 愛德華國王 **2** the most important or famous male member of a group〔羣體中〕最重要者; 大王: *The lion is the king of the jungle.* 獅子是叢林之王。 | *Ladies and gentlemen — the king of comedy!* 女士們、先生們——向大家介紹喜劇之王! **3** one of the pieces in the game of CHESS〔國際象棋中的〕王 **4** a playing card with a picture of a king on it〔紙牌中的〕K: *the king of diamonds* 方塊K

*king·dom /ˈkɪŋdəm; ˈkɪŋdəm/ *n* **1** a country governed by a king or queen 王國 **2** any of the three great divisions of the natural world 自然三界之一: *the animal kingdom* 動物界 | *the plant kingdom* 植物界

king·fish·er /ˈkɪŋ₊fɪʃə; ˈkɪŋ₊fɪʃəʳ/ *n* a small brightly-coloured bird that feeds on fish in rivers and lakes 翠鳥〔一種食魚鳥〕

king·ly /ˈkɪŋlɪ; ˈkɪŋlɪ/ *adj* belonging to or suitable for a king 國王的; 適合於國王身分的

king·pin /ˈkɪŋ₊pɪn; ˈkɪŋ₊pɪn/ *n* the most important person in a group, upon whom the success of the group depends〔決定成敗的〕關鍵人物

King's Coun·sel /ˌ· ˈ··/ *n fml*〖正式〗—see 見 K.C.

kink /kɪŋk; kɪŋk/ *n* **1** a curve or twist in something such as wire that is usually straight〔如電線等通常為直的東西的〕扭結 **2** *infml* a strangeness of someone's mind or character, especially with regard to sex〖非正式〗〔尤指性方面的〕奇想; 怪癖 **—kinky** *adj*

kins·man /ˈkɪnzmən; ˈkɪnzmən/ *n* **kinsmen** /-mən; -mən/ a relative; a female kinsman is called a **kinswoman** (a word no longer used in modern English) 親戚〔女親戚稱為 **kinswoman**〕〔當代英語中不再使用〕

ki·osk /ˈkiːɒsk; ˈkiːɒsk/ *n* **1** a small shop on the street with an open window through which you buy things such as newspapers and sweets〔出售報紙和糖果等的〕小亭 **2** a public telephone box 公用電話亭

kip /kɪp; kɪp/ *v* **-pp-** *infml*〖非正式〗睡覺 **–kip** *n* [sing; U]: *He's going to have a kip.* 他準備去睡一覺。

kip·per /ˈkɪpə; ˈkɪpəʳ/ *n* a salted and smoked fish 醃燻魚

*kiss¹ /kɪs; kɪs/ *v* [I;T] to touch someone with your lips as a sign of love or fondness or as a greeting 吻: *She kissed him lightly on the forehead.* 她輕輕吻了吻他的額頭。 | *They kissed under the stars.* 他們倆在點點繁星之下接吻。 | *He kissed the children goodnight.* 他吻吻孩子們, 和他們道晚安。 | *The returning exiles kneeled and kissed the ground.* 重返家園的流放犯人跪着親吻大地。

kiss² *n* **1** a touch with your lips 吻: *She gave him a kiss.* 她吻了他一下。 **2 kiss of life** a method of preventing the death of a per-son by breathing into their mouth 口對口的人工呼吸

kissagram /ˈkɪsəgræm; ˈkɪsəgræm/ *n* a person who is paid to visit someone on a special occasion and give them a kiss 受雇在特殊場合拜訪某人並親吻他們的人

kit¹ /kɪt; kɪt/ *n* **1** [U] the special clothes and other articles needed by a soldier or sailor, or used in a particular sport〔士兵、水手的〕隨身攜帶的衣物; 某項體育運動所需的衣物: *I've forgotten my tennis kit.* 我忘記帶打網球用的衣物。 | *There will be a kit inspection at 0800 hrs.* 八點鐘要進行衣物檢查。 **2** [C] a set of articles or tools needed for a particular purpose and usually kept together〔用於某一目的, 通常保存在一起的〕成套物品; 成套工具: *my shaving kit* 我的剃鬚用具 | *a make-up kit* 一套化妝用具 | *a repair kit* 一套修理工具 **3** [C] a set of separate pieces sold ready to be put together 一套待裝配的元件: *a model aircraft kit* 飛機模型全套元件

kit² *v* **-tt-**

kit sbdy ↔ **out** *phr v* [T] to supply someone with everything that they need for a particular purpose 給〔某人〕提供必需品: *She was well kitted out for the trip.* 她配齊了旅行的必需品。

kit bag /ˈ· ·/ *n* a long narrow bag used by soldiers and sailors for carrying their kit〔士兵、水手的〕長型旅行袋; 行李袋

*kitch·en /ˈkɪtʃɪn; ˈkɪtʃ₅n/ *n* a room used for preparing and cooking food 廚房

kitch·en·ette /ˌkɪtʃɪnˈet; ˌkɪtʃ₅ˈnet/ *n* a very small kitchen, or a part of a room used for cooking 小廚房; 房間裡用作廚房的一個角落

kitchen gar·den /ˌ·· ˈ··/ *n* a garden where fruit and vegetables are grown〔種植水果蔬菜的〕家庭菜園

kite /kaɪt; kaɪt/ *n* **1** a light frame, usually made of wood or metal and covered with paper, cloth, or plastic; you hold the kite by a long string and make it fly in the air 風箏 **2** a large bird that eats small birds and animals 鳶〔鷹的一種, 以小鳥和小動物為食〕

kith and kin /ˌkɪθ ən ˈkɪn; ˌkɪθ ən ˈkɪn/ *n old fash*〖老式〗[pl] **1** friends and relatives 親戚朋友: *We may not agree with their politics, but we must remember that they are our kith and kin.* 我們可能會不同意他們的政治觀點, 但我們必須記住他們是我們的親友。 **2** people who share your country's way of life and values because of a shared past〔由於有共同的歷史而〕生活方式及價值觀念都相同的人: *British people's kith and kin in New Zealand* 生活在新西蘭的英國後裔

kit·ten /ˈkɪtn; ˈkɪtn/ *n* a young cat 小貓

kit·ten·ish /ˈkɪtnɪʃ; ˈkɪtn-ɪʃ/ *adj* playful like a kitten 小貓般頑皮的

kit·ty /ˈkɪtɪ; ˈkɪtɪ/ *n* **kitties 1** an amount of money collected by all the players at the beginning of a card game, and taken by the winner 〔紙牌戲中的〕全部賭注 **2** *infml* a sum of money collected by a group of people, and used for an agreed purpose 【非正式】〔為某共同目的〕所湊集的一筆資金 **3** a child's word for a cat 貓咪〔兒童用語〕: *"Here, kitty kitty," called the little girl.* "過來，貓咪，"小女孩叫道。

kiwi fruit /'kiwɪfrut; 'ki:wi: fru:t/ *n* **kiwi fruit** *or* **kiwi fruits** a fruit with brown skin and green flesh 獼猴桃

klep·to·ma·ni·a /ˌklɛptə'menɪə; ˌkleptə-'meɪnɪə/ *n* [U] a disease of the mind that causes a strong and uncontrollable desire to steal 盜竊癖；偷竊狂 **–kleptomaniac** /-nɪ-ˌæk; -nɪæk/ *n*

km a written abbreviation for 【縮】= KILO-METRE(S)

knack /næk; næk/ *n infml* a special skill or clever way of doing something difficult 【非正式】技巧；訣竅: *He has the knack of making friends wherever he goes.* 他有一種到處結交朋友的本事。

knave /nev; neɪv/ *n* **1** a dishonest man (a word no longer used in modern English) 狡詐的人〔當代英語中不再使用〕 **2** the JACK in a game of cards 〔紙牌中的〕傑克 **–knav-ish** *adj*

knead /nid; ni:d/ *v* [T] **1** to press something firmly and repeatedly with your hands to make a smooth paste 揉；捏: *Flour and water are kneaded to make bread.* 把麵粉與水揉捏來製麵包。 **2** to press a muscle or other part of someone's body with your fingers to cure pain or stiffness 按摩，推拿

☆☆knee¹ /ni; ni:/ *n* **1** the middle joint of your leg, where it bends 膝；膝蓋: *He had fallen and hurt his knee.* 他摔了一跤，膝蓋受了傷。 **2** the part of a garment that covers your knee 〔褲子的〕膝部: *He had big holes in the knees of his trousers.* 他的褲子膝部有幾個大洞。 **3** on your knee on the top part of your legs when you are sitting down 在膝上: *Come and sit on my knee.* 來坐在我的膝上。 **4** bring/force someone to their knees to force someone to admit defeat 迫使某人屈服 **5** bring/force something to its knees to nearly destroy something 幾乎毀壞某物

knee² *v* **kneed, kneeing** [T] to hit someone or something with your knee 用膝蓋撞擊〔某人、某物〕

knee·cap /'nikæp; 'ni:kæp/ *n* the bone in front of your knee 髕骨；膝蓋骨

knee-deep /ˌ·'·◄/ *adj* [never before a noun 不能用於名詞前] **1** deep enough to reach your knees 深及膝蓋的: *The water is knee-deep.* 水深及膝蓋。 **2 knee-deep in something: a** standing in something that comes up as far as your knees 站在深及膝蓋的某物中: *We were knee-deep in mud.* 我站在深及膝蓋的泥漿中。 **b** very busy with something 忙於某事: *I'm knee-deep in work.* 我的工作忙得不可開交。

kneel /nil; ni:l/ *v* **knelt** /nɛlt; nelt/, **knelt** [I] (also 又作 **kneel down**) to go down or remain on one or both of your knees 跪下；跪着: *She knelt down to pray.* 她跪下來祈禱。 | *He was kneeling by the fire.* 他跪在火堆旁。 —see picture on page 992 見 992 頁彩圖

knell /nɛl; nel/ *n lit* 【文】 **1** the sound of a bell rung for a death or funeral 喪鐘聲 **2** the sign that something has ended 某事結束的徵兆

knelt /nɛlt; nelt/ the past tense and past participle of KNEEL ☆ KNEEL的過去式和過去分詞

knew /nju; nju:/ the past tense of KNOW ☆ KNOW 的過去式

knick·ers /'nɪkəz; 'nɪkəz/ *n BrE* [pl] a woman's undergarment worn below the waist 【英】女用短襯褲 —see picture on page 210 見 210 頁彩圖

knick-knack /'nɪkˌnæk; 'nɪk næk/ *n infml* 【非正式】(also 又作 **nick-nack**) a small ornament for the house 〔室內的〕小擺設；小玩意兒

☆knife¹ /naif; naɪf/ *n* **knives** /naɪvz; naɪvz/ **1** a sharp blade fixed in a handle and used for cutting or as a weapon 刀: *a table knife* 餐刀 | *sharpen the knife* 把刀磨得鋒利 **2** have/get one's knife in someone *infml* to treat someone as an enemy and always try to harm them 【非正式】敵視某人；欲加害某人

■ USAGE 用法: Note the word order in this fixed phrase ☆注意這個固定片語中的詞序: **knife and fork**

knife² *v* **knifed, knifing** [T] to push a knife into someone so that they are hurt 用小刀刺傷〔某人〕: *He had been attacked and knifed.* 他被人襲擊並被刺了一刀。

knight¹ /nait; naɪt/ *n* **1** a man of noble rank trained to fight on horseback during the Middle Ages 〔中世紀時的〕騎士，武士 **2** a man who has the title SIR given to him by the king or queen for his service to the country 爵士〔其稱號用Sir, 在英國是由國王或女王授予的榮銜〕 **3** a piece with a horse's head used in the game of CHESS 〔國際象棋中的〕馬

knight² *v* [T] to make someone a knight 封〔某人〕為爵士: *He was knighted by the Queen in 1981.* 他在1981年被女王封為爵士。

knight·hood /'naithud; 'naɪthʊd/ *n* [C;U] the rank or title of a knight 爵士的身分；爵士的頭銜

knit /nɪt; nɪt/ *v* **-tt-** **1** [I;T] to make clothes by using wool or other threads and long needles or a special machine 編結，編織〔衣物〕: *I'm knitting a pair of socks.* 我在織一雙襪子。 | *She knitted the baby a jumper.* 她給嬰孩織了件套頭毛衣。 | *He likes to watch TV and knit.* 他喜歡邊看電視邊織毛衣。 |

She does a lot of knitting. 她織很多毛衣。**2** [I] (of broken bones) to grow together properly 〔折斷的骨頭〕癒合 **3 knit your brows** to show that you are angry or worried by making lines appear on your forehead 皺起眉頭〔表示憤怒或憂慮〕

knit·ting /'nɪtɪŋ; 'nɪtɪŋ/ *n* [U] something which is being knitted 編織物: *She keeps her knitting in a bag.* 她把織的東西放在一個袋子裡。

knitting nee·dle /'·· ,··/ *n* a long thin stick that you use when you are knitting 織針

knit·wear /'nɪt,wer; 'nɪtweə⁽ʳ⁾/ *n* [U] knitted clothing 針織品: *I'm afraid we don't sell knitwear.* 對不起,我們不出售針織品。

knives /naɪvz; naɪvz/ the plural of KNIFE ☆ KNIFE 的複數形式

knob /nɑb; nɒb/ *n* **1** a round lump at the end of a stick 〔手杖的〕圓頭 **2** a round handle on a door or drawer 〔門或抽屜的〕球形把手 **3** a round control button on a machine 〔機器的〕旋鈕 **4 a knob of butter** a small amount of butter 一小塊黃油

knob·bly /'nɑbli; 'nɒbli/ *adj* **knobblier**, **knobbliest** having round hard lumps 有球狀硬塊的: *knobbly knees* 呈球狀突起的膝蓋

★**knock¹** /nɑk; nɒk/ *v* **1** [I] to make a noise by hitting something several times with your closed hand in order to attract attention 〔為引起注意〕敲擊: *I knocked* **at** *the door.* 我敲門。| *He knocked* **on** *the window.* 他敲了敲窗。**2** [T] to hit something hard or roughly, often so that it moves or falls 重擊;碰撞〔通常使其移動或落下〕: *She knocked the cup off the table.* 她把桌上的杯子碰落到了地上。| *The doorway was so low that he knocked his head against it.* 門口非常低,他的頭撞了一下。| *He knocked the nails into the wall.* 他把釘子敲進牆裡。**3** [T] to make someone fall in a particular position or become unconscious by hitting them hard 擊倒〔人〕;擊昏〔人〕: *He was knocked unconscious with a hammer.* 他被人用錘子打昏。| *His opponent knocked him flat on his back.* 他的對手把他打得仰面倒在地上。**4** [T] *infml* to say unfavourable things about someone or something 〔非正式〕說⋯的壞話;挑剔: *Stop knocking him — he's a good singer really.* 別這麼挑剔他了 — 他實際上是個不錯的歌手。**5 knock something out of someone** to force someone to stop behaving in a particular way 迫使某人放棄某種行為方式: *We'll soon knock that arrogance out of her!* 我們很快就會讓她丟掉那份自負!

　knock about/around *phr v infml* 〔非正式〕**1** [I] to get a lot of experience in different situations or places 漫遊〔各地〕: *He's been knocking about in different countries for years.* 多年來他一直在各國遊歷。**2** [I] to spend your free time with someone because they are your friend or lover 與〔朋友或情人〕共度閒暇時光: *Sally's been knocking*

about **with** *Jim for years.* 莎莉和吉姆來往已好幾年了。**3** [T **knock** sbdy **about**] to hit someone roughly 虐待;痛打〔某人〕: *She had been quite badly knocked about.* 她被人痛打了一頓。

　knock sthg ↔ **back** *phr v infml* [T] to drink something quickly or in large quantities 〔非正式〕狂飲,痛飲: *She knocked back ten glasses of wine.* 她一連喝了十杯酒。

　knock down *phr v* **1** [T **knock** sthg ↔ **down**] to intentionally destroy and remove a building 拆毀〔建築物〕: *Our house is being knocked down to make way for a new road.* 我們的房子正在被拆毀,以便修築一條新公路。**2** [T **knock** sbdy ↔ **down**] to hit someone with the vehicle you are driving so that they fall to the ground 開車撞倒: *She was knocked down by a bus.* 她被一輛公共汽車撞倒。**3** [T **knock** sthg ↔ **down**] to reduce in price 降低〔價〕: *The price was knocked down to £3.* 價格降到了三英鎊。**4** [T **knock** sbdy ↔ **down**] to persuade someone to reduce a price 說服〔某人〕減價: *I knocked him down to £3.* 我把他的價格壓到三英鎊。

　knock off *phr v* **1** [I] *infml* to stop doing something, especially work 〔非正式〕停止做〔某事,尤指工作〕: *Let's knock off early today.* 我們今天早點下班吧。**2** [T **knock** sthg ↔ **off**] to lower a price by a particular amount 削價: *I'll knock $2 off.* 我準備削價兩塊錢出售。**3** [T **knock** sthg ↔ **off**] *infml* to steal something 〔非正式〕偷竊〔某物〕

　knock out *phr v* **1** [T **knock** sbdy ↔ **out**] to make someone go to sleep or become unconscious 使〔某人〕睡覺〔昏厥〕**2 be knocked out** *infml* to be very surprised or shocked by something 〔非正式〕對〔某事〕感到吃驚〔震驚〕**3** [T **knock** sbdy ↔ **out**] to defeat a person or team so that they do not continue in a competition 淘汰: *Our team was knocked out in the first round.* 我們隊在第一輪便被淘汰了。

　knock sbdy ↔ **over** *phr v* to hit someone with the vehicle you are driving so that they fall to the ground 開車撞倒〔某人〕

　knock sthg ↔ **up** *phr v infml* to make something in a hurry 〔非正式〕匆匆做成〔某物〕: *Can you knock up a meal for us now?* 你現在能馬上給我們燒一頓飯嗎?

knock² *n* **1** the sound made by hitting a surface with your closed hand in order to attract attention 〔為引起注意的〕敲擊聲: *a knock* **at** *the door* 敲門聲 **2** a rough blow 痛擊: *Suddenly he felt a knock on the back of his head.* 他突然感到後腦被人狠狠地打了一下。**3** a piece of bad luck or trouble 不幸;麻煩: *He's taken a few knocks recently.* 他最近碰上好幾件倒霉事。

knock·er /'nɑkɚ; 'nɒkə⁽ʳ⁾/ *n* a piece of metal fixed to a door and used by visitors for knocking at the door 〔裝在門上供來訪者敲門用的〕門環

knock-kneed /ˌ· ˈ·◂/ *adj* having legs that turn inwards so that your knees touch when you are walking 膝外翻的

knock-on ef·fect /ˈ· · ·ˌ·/ *n* **have a knock-on effect** to cause something which causes something else, which causes something else, etc. 連鎖反應: *A rise in the price of petrol will have a knock-on effect right through the economy.* 石油價格的上漲將對經濟帶來連鎖反應。

knock·out /ˈnɑk.aʊt; ˈnɒk-aʊt/ *n* **1** a situation in a fighting match in which one fighter makes the other unconscious〔拳賽中的〕擊倒對手: *He won the fight by a knockout.* 他擊倒對手，贏得了這場拳賽。**2** *infml* someone or something that is very good or very attractive〖非正式〗非常好或非常吸引人的人或物 **3** **knockout competition** a competition in which only the people or teams that win one match continue in the competition and play other matches 淘汰賽

knoll /nol; nəʊl/ *n* a small round hill 土墩; 小圓丘

knot¹ /nɑt; nɒt/ *n* **1** a fastening formed by tying together the ends of pieces of string, rope, or wire〔線、繩、索等的〕結: *She tied her belt with a knot.* 她把腰帶打了個結。**2** a small hard spot in wood where a branch joined a tree 樹木上的節, 節瘤 **3** a small group of people gathered close together 一小羣聚在一起的人 **4** a measure of the speed of a ship, about 1,853 metres per hour 節〔船速測量單位，約為每小時1853米〕**5** **a knot in your stomach** an uncomfortable feeling in your stomach caused by fear or anxiety〔由於恐懼或憂慮〕胃縮成一團的感覺

knot² *v* **-tt-** [T] to fasten something by tying its ends together 把〔某物〕打成結: *Knot the ends of the rope together.* 把這條繩子的兩端打個結。| *I knotted the rope round the branch.* 我把繩子繞在樹枝上打了個結。

knot·ty /ˈnɑti; ˈnɒti/ *adj* **knottier, knottiest** full of difficulties 困難重重的: *a knotty problem* 棘手的問題

know¹ /no; nəʊ/ *v* **knew** /nju; njuː/, **known** /non; nəʊn/ **1** [I;T+**that**] (that) not in progressive forms 不用於進行式] to have information in your mind which you are sure is true 知道; 知曉: *I know that Bill left yesterday.* 我知道比爾是昨天離開的。| *They don't know your telephone number.* 他們不知道你的電話號碼。| *Do you know where she lives?* 你知道她住在哪裡嗎? | "*He's very ill.*" "*Yes, I know.*" "他病得很重。" "是的，我知道。"

> □ USEFUL PATTERNS 有用句型
> to know something; to know that...; to know who, why, where, etc.

2 **know about something, know of something** to have heard about someone or something, although you do not have a lot of information 聽說過: *Did you know about the meeting yesterday?* 你知道昨天有會議嗎? | *I know of only one factory which has closed down.* 我聽說只有一家工廠倒閉了。**3** **know something backwards** to know or understand something perfectly 對某事物瞭如指掌; 精通: *She knows her subject backwards.* 她對自己的學科十分熟悉。**4** **know one thing from another** to understand the difference between two things 能區分兩件事物: *She doesn't know her left from her right.* 她分不清左右。**5** [T] to have learnt and be able to use a language or skill 懂得, 掌握〔語言或技能〕: *Do you know any Spanish?* 你懂西班牙語嗎? | *I don't know how to ski.* 我不會滑雪。

> □ USEFUL PATTERNS 有用句型
> to know something; to know how to do something

6 [T] to have learnt and understood about a subject from studying or personal experience〔通過學習或親身經歷〕學得; 知悉: *The professor knows a lot about architecture.* 該教授懂得許多建築學方面的知識。| *She doesn't know anything about teaching — she's never taught.* 她對教學一無所知——她從來沒有當過老師。**7** [T] to be familiar with a person or place 認識〔某人〕; 熟悉〔某地〕: *He's known Jack for years.* 他認識傑克已有多年了。| *Do you know London?* 你對倫敦熟悉嗎? **8** [T] to be able to recognize someone or something 認出〔某人或某物〕: *She knows a good wine when she tastes it.* 她一嘗就能辨別出酒的好壞。| *You'll know him by his pink jacket!* 你只要看到他的粉紅茄克衫就能認出他! **9** [T] *fml* to experience something deeply and fully〖正式〗切身經歷〔某事〕: *She has known both grief and happiness.* 憂患和喜悅她都經歷過。**10** **I know** a phrase used to show that you agree with what someone says 我知道了〔用於表示同意別人所說的話〕: "*He's a most unpleasant person.*" "*I know.*" "他是個極令人討厭的人。" "我知道。" **11** **you know:** **a** a phrase used in informal conversation when you are explaining something 你知道〔用於在非正式談話中解釋某事〕: *She's an easy child, you know, never seems to get upset.* 你知道, 她是個容易滿足的孩子, 似乎從來沒有不高興過。**b** an informal phrase used when you are trying to explain what you mean more clearly 你看〔用於更加詳細地解釋自己說話的含義〕: *...the building on the left. You know, the black one.* ...左邊那幢大樓。瞧, 就是那幢黑的。**12** **you know something? do you know something? you know what? do you know what?** informal phrases used when you are going to tell someone something you have just understood; you expect that they will agree with you 我來告訴你; 聽我說

〔用於非正式口語中，表示準備把自己剛剛理解的事情告訴某人；你認為他們會同意你所說的話〕: *"Do you know something? We've got this upside down." "I thought it didn't seem right."* 你知道嗎？我們把這東西放顛倒了。"我當時就覺得看上去不對頭。" **13 do you know what?** a phrase used in informal conversation when you want to get attention for a new idea or a surprising piece of information 真想不到〔用於非正式談話中，希望別人注意一個新觀點或令人吃驚的消息〕: *"Do you know what? Fred's bought a dog." "Has he! I thought he said he'd never buy another one."* "真想不到！弗雷德買了一隻狗。" "是嗎！我記得他曾說過他不會再買了。" **14 get to know** to become familiar with a person or a place 開始熟悉〔某人或某地〕: *I got to know Harry when we worked together.* 我是在與哈里共事時認識他的。 | *The best way to get to know the city is to visit it on foot.* 熟悉這座城市的最好辦法就是步行去遊覽。 **15 let someone know** to tell or inform someone about something 把某事告訴〔通知〕某人: *Let me know when you're arriving.* 告訴我你何時到達。 **16 know best** a phrase used about someone when you think they will make the right decision about something because of their experience 最清楚〔表示由於某人的經驗而認為他們會做出最佳決定〕: *Let the teachers decide — they know best.* 讓老師們來決定吧——他們最清楚。 **17 know better** to be sensible or wise enough not to do something 明事理〔而不做某事〕: *She's old enough to know better than to talk to strangers.* 她長大了，知道不要和陌生人講話。 **18 know your own mind** to have firm ideas about what you want or like 有自己的想法；有決斷 **19 you never know** a phrase used to say that it is not certain what is going to happen 很難說〔表示不能肯定將發生甚麼事〕: *You never know, you might get the job.* 很難說，也許你會得到那份工作。 **20 there's no knowing** it is impossible to know 不可能知道: *There's no knowing what he'll do next.* 無法知道他接下去會做甚麼。

■ **USAGE** 用法: Compare 比較 **know** and 和 **learn.** We use **know** especially when a person is conscious of something ☆ **know** 尤用於表示一個人知道某事: *I know you're lying* 我知道你在撒謊, has skill in something ☆或一個人有做某事的技能: *I know how to drive* 我會開汽車, or has met someone before ☆或以前曾遇到過某人: *I know your brother.* 我認識你哥哥。 To **learn** means "to get to know something" ☆ **learn** 表示"開始知道〔學會做〕某事": *I was shocked to learn of his death.* 聽到他的死訊，我很震驚。 | *I'm learning to drive.* 我正在學開車。

---

know² *n* **in the know** knowing about something that other people do not know about, especially something secret 知道別人不知道的東西〔尤指祕密〕

know-all /ˈ · ·/ *n* a person who behaves as if he or she knows everything (a word used to express disapproval) 自以為無所不知的人〔含貶義〕

know-how /ˈ · ·/ *n* [U] *infml* special knowledge in a scientific or industrial field 〔非正式〕〔科學或工業領域的〕專門知識: *These countries rely on Western technology and know-how.* 這些國家依靠西方的技術和知識。

know·ing /ˈnəʊɪŋ; ˈnəʊɪŋ/ *adj* showing that you understand something secret about someone even though you do not express this directly 心照不宣的: *a knowing smile* 心照不宣的一笑

know·ing·ly /ˈnəʊɪŋli; ˈnəʊɪŋli/ *adv* **1** in a way that shows you understand about something even though you do not express this directly 會意地，心照不宣地 **2** intentionally 故意地: *She would never knowingly hurt anyone.* 她絕不會故意傷害任何人。 –opposite 反義 **unknowingly**

⭐**knowl·edge** /ˈnɒlɪdʒ; ˈnɒlɪdʒ/ *n* [U] **1** information and understanding about something, gained through learning and experience 知識；學識；學問: *She has a detailed knowledge* **of** *this period.* 她對這時期的情況了解很詳盡。 | *all branches of scientific knowledge* 科學知識的各門分支學科 | *His knowledge* **of** *Russian is excellent.* 他在俄語方面的知識出類拔萃。 **2 to your knowledge** as far as you know 就自己所知: *To my knowledge, he now lives in Manchester.* 就我所知，他目前住在曼徹斯特。 **3 without someone's knowledge** without informing someone about something 未告知某人: *He called a meeting without the Minister's knowledge.* 他背着部長召開了會議。 [RELATED PHRASE 相關詞組 **with someone's knowledge**]

knowl·edge·a·ble /ˈnɒlɪdʒəbl; ˈnɒlɪdʒəbəl/ *adj* well-informed and showing a good understanding of a subject 〔在某學科上〕有豐富知識的: *He's very knowledgeable* **about** *plants.* 他對植物很在行。 –**knowledgeably** *adv*

known¹ /nəʊn; nəʊn/ *adj* **1** generally recognized as being something or having particular qualities 有名的；出名的: *He's a known criminal.* 他是個出了名的罪犯。 | *a plant known* **for** *it's healing properties* 以療效顯著而出名的植物 **2 known as: a** popular or famous as 以…聞名；公認為: *She's known as a singer.* 她是個知名的歌手。 **b** called publicly 以…知名，通常名叫: *Samuel Clemens, known as Mark Twain, became a famous American writer.* 塞繆爾·克萊門斯以馬克·吐溫的名字成為美國有名的作家。 **3 make it known** *fml* to tell people about something

K

openly and publicly〖正式〗把〔某事〕公佈〔發表〕: *He made it known* **to** *his friends that he did not wish to enter politics.* 他向朋友宣佈，他不想步入政界。

known² the past participle of KNOW ☆ KNOW 的過去分詞

knuck·le¹ /'nʌkl; 'nʌkəl/ *n* a joint in your fingers, especially where they join the wide part of your hand 指關節

knuckle² *v* **knuckled, knuckling**

  knuckle down *phr v* [I] *infml* to start working hard〖非正式〗開始努力工作: *I think I'd better knuckle down to work now.* 我認為我最好現在就開始努力工作。

  knuckle under *phr v* [I] to be forced to accept that you have to do what someone powerful tells you to do 屈服; 唯命是從

knuckle-dust·er /'·· ,··/ *n* a metal covering for your knuckles, that people wear for fighting 指節金屬套〔打鬥時套在手上〕

ko·a·la /kə'ɑlə; kəʊ'ɑːlə/ *n* (also 又作 **koala bear** /·,··'·/) an Australian animal like a small bear 樹袋熊〔產於澳大利亞〕

Ko·ran /ko'rɑn; kɔː'rɑːn/ *n* **the Koran** the holy book of the Muslims〔伊斯蘭教的〕古蘭經〔可蘭經〕

ko·sher /'koʃə·; 'kəʊʃəʳ/ *adj* prepared according to Jewish law (used of food) 按猶太教規準備的〔指食物〕: *kosher meat* (符合猶太教規) 潔淨可食的肉

kow·tow /kaʊ'taʊ; ˌkaʊ'taʊ/ *v* [I] *infml* to behave towards someone in a way which is too humble and too respectful〖非正式〗對〔某人〕唯命是從

Krem·lin /'krɛmlɪn; 'kremlਂn/ *n* [+ sing/pl verb] **the Kremlin** the central government of Russia or the group of buildings which are the central offices of the government 俄羅斯政府; 克里姆林宮: *As yet there has been no response from the Kremlin.* 克里姆林宮對此還沒有作出回應。

ku·dos /'kjudɑs; 'kjuːdɒs/ *n* [U] honour, praise, or fame for doing something〔由於做某事而獲得的〕榮譽; 讚揚; 名聲: *He got a great deal of kudos for his work at the university.* 他由於在大學裡所做的工作而獲得了不少榮譽。

kung fu /ˌkʊŋ 'fu; ˌkʊŋ 'fuː/ *n* [U] a Chinese style of fighting using your hands and feet 功夫; 中國拳術

kw a written abbreviation for〖縮〗= KILOWATT(S)

K

L, l

L, l /ɛl; el/ **L's, l's** or **Ls, ls** the 12th letter of the English alphabet 英語中的第十二個字母

L a sign used on a car to show that the driver is a learner and has not passed the official driving test〔汽車上的標誌, 用於表示該司機為實習駕駛員, 尚未通過駕駛考試〕–see picture on page 209 見 209 頁彩圖

l a written abbreviation for〔縮〕= litre(s)

lab /læb; læb/ n infml〔非正式〕see 見 LA-BORATORY

*★**la·bel**[1] /'lebl; 'leɪbəl/ n a piece of paper or cloth which is fixed to something and gives information about what it is 標籤

label[2] v **-ll- (-l-** AmE〔美式〕) [T] **1** to fix or tie a label on something 貼標籤於〔某物〕: The bottle was labelled "poisonous". 瓶子上的標籤寫着"有毒"。 **2** to describe someone as belonging to a particular type or group 把〔某人〕歸類為: He had been labelled a thief. 他被人稱為小偷。 | I don't want to be labelled as a fool. 我不想被人稱為傻瓜。

la·bor·a·tory /'læbrə,tɔrɪ; lə'bɔrətrɪ/ n **laboratories** (also 又作 **lab** infml〔非正式〕) a building or room which contains scientific apparatus and in which a scientist works 實驗室

la·bo·ri·ous /lə'borɪəs; lə'bɔːrɪəs/ adj needing great effort 需要努力的; 費力的: a laborious task 一項吃力的工作 **–laboriously** adv

*★**la·bour**[1] /'lebə; 'leɪbə[r]/ n (**labor** AmE〔美式〕) **1** [C;U] hard work, especially tiring physical work 勞力; 勞動〔尤指體力勞動〕: The job involves a lot of manual labour. 這份工作需要大量手工作業。 **2** [U] the workers of an industry or country considered as a group or class 工人; 勞工: unskilled labour 非熟練工人 | organized labour 有組織的勞工 **3** [C;U] the act of giving birth to a baby 分娩: She was in labour for three hours. 她分娩長達三小時。 | a difficult labour 難產 **4 labour of love** work that you do because you want to do it or enjoy doing it 喜歡做的工作 **5 Labour** [U + sing/pl verb] the British Labour Party 英國工黨: Do you think Labour will win the next election? 你認為工黨會在下屆大選中獲勝嗎? | Labour intend to renationalize electricity. 工黨準備把電力工業再度國有化。

labour[2] v (**labor** AmE〔美式〕) **1** [I] to work hard using your hands〔用雙手〕勞動, 工作: They saw peasants labouring in the fields. 他們看見農民在田裡勞動。 **2** [I] to do something with great effort or difficulty 吃力

地做〔某事〕: She laboured up the hill with her bags. 她帶着提包吃力地爬上山。 | Jack laboured over the report for hours. 傑克吃力地寫那篇報告, 寫了好幾個小時。 –see 見 WORK (USAGE 用法) **3** [T] **labour the point** to talk about something in too great detail or at unnecessary length 過於詳細〔冗長〕地談論〔某事〕: I understand — there's no need to labour the point! 我懂了! 我沒必要一再解釋! **4 labour under a delusion/ misapprehension** to believe something that is not true 誤以為; 痴心妄想: He laboured under the delusion that she loved him. 他誤以為她愛他。

la·bour·er /'lebərə; 'leɪbərə[r]/ n (**laborer** AmE〔美式〕) a worker whose job needs physical strength rather than skill 體力勞動者; 勞工; 工人

Labour Party /'·· ,··/ n [+ sing/pl verb] **the Labour Party** the political party in Britain and some other countries which represents workers and the less wealthy 工黨: The Labour Party is hoping to win the election. 工黨希望贏得大選。 | I first joined the Labour Party ten years ago. 十年前我先是加入了工黨。

labour-sav·ing /'·· ,··/ adj saving you a lot of hard work, especially physical work 節省勞力的〔尤指節省體力〕: I don't know how our grandmothers managed without all our labour-saving devices. 我不知道在沒有節省勞力的工具的情況下, 祖母那一代是如何熬過來的。

Lab·ra·dor /'læbrə,dɔr; 'læbrədɔː[r]/ n a type of large dog 拉布拉多獵犬

lab·y·rinth /'læbə,rɪnθ; 'læbərɪnθ/ n a network of narrow twisting passages or paths, through which it is difficult to find your way 迷宮; 曲徑: We made our way through the labyrinth of narrow, twisting alleyways in the old city. 我們在那古老的城市中, 穿越了迷宮似的狹窄而曲折的小巷。

lace[1] /les; leɪs/ n **1** [U] a very fine cloth with a lot of holes in it, which is used to decorate clothes and other things 網眼織物; 花邊; 飾帶: lace curtains 網眼紗簾 **2** [C] a string or cord which goes through two holes on the edges of clothes or shoes in order to fasten them together 鞋帶; 繫帶 –see picture on page 210 見 210 頁彩圖

lace[2] v **laced, lacing** [T] **1** (also 又作 **lace sthg ↔ up**) to fasten something with a lace or laces 用帶繫住〔某物〕: He laced up his shoes. 他繫好了鞋帶。 –opposite 反義 **unlace**

2 to add a small amount of something strong to a drink 給〔飲料〕摻酒〔藥物〕: *coffee laced **with** brandy* 加有少許白蘭地酒的咖啡 | *to lace a drink with poison* 在飲料裡下毒

la·ce·rate /'læsə,ret; 'læsəreɪt/ *v* **lacerated, lacerating** [T] *fml* to cut skin very badly 〔正式〕割破〔皮膚〕: *Her face was badly lacerated by the broken glass.* 她的臉被碎玻璃嚴重割傷。 **–laceration** /,læsə'reʃən; ,læsə'reɪʃn/ *n* [C;U]

lace-up /'··/ *n* **lace-ups** (also 又作 **lace-up shoes**) shoes which have pairs of holes on the top that are used for fastening them with a cord 繫帶的鞋

****lack¹** /læk; læk/ *v* [T not in progressive forms 不用於進行式] to be without or not have enough of something you need or want 缺乏〔某物〕, 沒有: *He's talented, but he lacks confidence.* 他有天賦, 但缺乏信心。 | *The company lacks the capital to invest in new projects.* 公司缺乏資金來開發新項目。

****lack²** *n* [sing;U] the state of not having something or not having enough of it 缺乏; 不足: *The plants died through lack of water.* 植物由於缺水而枯死了。 | *There's a certain lack of enthusiasm for the project.* 人們對該項目沒有多大的興趣。

lack·ey /'læki; 'læki/ *n* a person who behaves too much like a servant and obeys other people without question (a word used to express disapproval) 〔如僕人般〕唯命是從者; 卑躬屈膝者〔含貶義〕

lack·ing /'lækɪŋ; 'lækɪŋ/ *adj* [never before a noun 不能用於名詞前] *fml* 〔正式〕 **1** not present when needed 缺乏的;〔需要時〕沒有的: *Accurate information about the accident is lacking so that we do not know what really happened.* 我們缺乏了那起事故的準確消息, 所以不知道到底發生了甚麼事。 **2 be lacking in something** to be without the needed amount of a particular quality 缺少某物: *She's certainly not lacking in courage.* 她當然不是沒有勇氣。

la·con·ic /lə'kɑnɪk; lə'kɒnɪk/ *adj* using few words 〔語言〕簡潔的, 言簡意賅 **–laconically** /-klɪ; -kli/ *adv*

lac·quer /'lækər; 'lækər/ *n* [U] a transparent or coloured substance used for forming a hard shiny surface on metal or wood, or for making hair stay in place 漆; 髮蠟; 噴髮膠 **–lacquer** *v* [T] : *a lacquered table* 上過漆的桌子

la·crosse /lə'krɔs; lə'krɒs/ *n* [U] an outdoor game played by two teams; each player has a long stick with a net at the end to throw and catch the ball 兜網球, 長曲棍球〔用帶網的曲棍來擲球和捕球的一種戶外球類運動〕

lac·tic /'læktɪk; 'læktɪk/ *adj* *tech* relating to or obtained from milk 〔術語〕(取自)乳汁的

lac·y /'lesɪ; 'leɪsi/ *adj* **lacier, laciest** **1** made from lace or decorated with LACE 網眼織物的; 飾有花邊的 **2** looking like LACE 似繫帶的

****lad** /læd; læd/ *n* *infml* a boy or young man 〔非正式〕男孩; 少年; 小伙子

lad·der¹ /'lædər; 'lædər/ *n* **1** a wooden, metal, or rope frame with steps on it, which is used for climbing up and down things 梯子 –see picture on page 958 見 958 頁彩圖 **2** the different stages and levels of an organization 〔組織機構內的〕不同階層; 階梯: *the promotion ladder* 晉升的階梯 **3** the torn part of a woman's STOCKING or TIGHTS 〔婦女長統襪或緊身褲的〕抽絲

ladder² *v* **1** [T] to tear a pair of STOCKINGS or TIGHTS 使〔統襪或緊身褲〕抽絲: *Damn! I've laddered my tights.* 該死! 我的褲襪抽絲了! **2** [I] (of STOCKINGS or TIGHTS) to become torn 〔長統襪或緊身褲〕被抽絲

la·den /'ledn; 'leɪdn/ *adj* heavily loaded 重載的; 滿載的: *The bushes were laden **with** fruit.* 灌木叢果實纍纍。 | *lorries fully laden with vegetables* 滿載蔬菜的貨車

la·dle¹ /'ledl; 'leɪdl/ *n* a large, round, deep spoon with a long handle, used especially for putting soup into bowls 長柄勺〔尤用於舀湯〕 –see picture on page 958 見 958 頁彩圖

ladle² *v* **ladled, ladling** [T] to serve food with a ladle 用(長柄)勺舀〔食物〕

****la·dy** /'ledɪ; 'leɪdi/ *n* **ladies** **1** a polite word for a woman 女士〔禮貌的用語〕: *Ask the lady in the shop to get them.* 請商店裡的那位女士來拿這些東西。 | *Good morning, ladies.* 女士們, 早上好。 | *a lady doctor* 女醫生 **2** a woman of good manners and behaviour 舉止文雅的女子; 淑女: *She's a real lady — never criticizes anyone.* 她是個真正的淑女 —— 她從不批評任何人。 **3** a woman from a good family and of high social rank 貴婦人: *The lords and ladies danced at the ball.* 貴族男女在舞會上跳舞。 **4** *AmE slang* a word used for talking to a woman, or attracting her attention 〔美式, 俚〕太太; 夫人; 小姐〔用於引起注意〕: *You dropped your glove, lady.* 小姐, 你的手套掉了。 –see 見 GENTLEMAN (USAGE 用法) **5 Lady** a title put before the name of a woman of high social rank or position 夫人〔置於婦女名字前表示其較高的社會地位或職位的頭銜〕: *Lady Henrietta Woods* 亨利亞達·伍茲夫人 **6 Ladies** [plural is 複數為 **Ladies**] a public TOILET for women 女廁所: *Can you tell me where the Ladies is?* 你能告訴我女廁所在哪裡嗎?

la·dy·bird /'ledɪ,bɝd; 'leɪdibɜːd/ *n* *BrE* a small round flying insect which is usually red with black dots 〔英式〕瓢蟲

lady-in-wait·ing /,·· · '··/ *n* **ladies-in-waiting** a woman who is the servant of a queen or princess 〔女王或公主的〕侍女; 宮廷侍女

lag /læg; læg/ *v* **-gg-** [T] to cover water pipes and containers with a special ma-

L

terial to prevent loss of heat 給〔水管、容器〕加上外罩保溫

lag behind *phr v* [I] to move or develop more slowly than others 走得慢；落後: *I walked in front with the children lagging behind.* 我走在前面，孩子們落在後面。| *Our car industry is starting to lag behind that in other countries.* 我們的汽車工業開始落後於其他國家。

la·ger /'lagə; 'lɑːgə/ *n* **1** [U] a kind of light beer 淡啤酒 **2** [C] a glass, bottle, or can of light beer 一杯〔一瓶、一罐〕(貯藏)啤酒: *Two lagers, please.* 請拿兩杯啤酒來。

la·ger lout /'·· ,·/ *n* a young man who drinks a lot of lager and behaves in a rough and violent way 酗酒鬧事的年輕人

la·goon /lə'gun; lə'guːn/ *n* a lake of sea water, separated from the sea by banks of sand 潟湖，環礁湖

laid /led; leɪd/ the past tense and past participle of LAY ☆ LAY 的過去式和過去分詞

lain /len; leɪn/ the past participle of LIE ☆ LIE 的過去分詞

lair /lɛr; leəʳ/ *n* **1** a hidden place where a wild animal rests and sleeps 獸穴: *a wolf in its lair* 在穴裡的狼 **2** a place where someone hides 躲藏處: *The robbers were too scared to leave their lair.* 強盜非常害怕，不敢離開他們的巢穴。

*lake /lek; leɪk/ *n* a large mass of fresh water surrounded by land 湖: *We took a boat across the lake.* 我們乘船渡湖。

lamb¹ /læm; læm/ *n* **1** [C] a young sheep 小羊，羔羊 **2** [U] the meat of a young sheep 羔羊肉

lamb² *v* [I] (of sheep) to give birth to lambs 〔羊〕產小羊

lame¹ /lem; leɪm/ *adj* **1** not able to walk properly because one or both your legs are hurt or damaged 跛的；瘸的 **2** weak or not easily believed (used of an excuse or argument) 站不住腳的；不易令人相信的〔指藉口或論點〕: *He came up with a pretty lame excuse.* 他想出了一個十分站不住腳的藉口。 **3** **lame duck** a person or business that does not produce good results or get things done 不中用的人；無能的企業；"跛足鴨" – **lamely** *adv* –**lameness** *n* [U]

lame² *v* [T] **laming, lamed** to make someone lame 使〔某人〕跛〔瘸〕

la·ment¹ /lə'mɛnt; lə'ment/ *v fml* 〖正式〗 [I;T] to feel or express deep sorrow or disappointment 感到悲痛；痛惜；哀悼

lament² *n fml* 〖正式〗 **1** a strong expression of disappointment or sorrow 失望；悲傷 **2** a song or piece of music expressing grief at the death of somebody 哀歌；輓歌

lam·en·ta·ble /'læməntəbl; 'læməntəbəl/ *adj* very bad and disappointing 很不像樣的；令人惋惜的: *Many of our schools are in a lamentable state.* 我們許多學校的情形是令人痛心的。–**lamentably** *adv*

lam·i·nated /'læmə,netɪd; 'læm ˌneɪt ˌd/ *adj* covered with a thin sheet of plastic for protection 覆有塑料保護層的: *a laminated wall chart* 覆有塑料薄膜的掛牆圖表

lamp /læmp; læmp/ *n* an apparatus, usually one that you can move, for giving light; lamps use electricity, gas, or oil 燈 –see picture on page 730 見 730 頁彩圖

lam·poon¹ /læm'pun; læm'puːn/ *n* a piece of humorous writing strongly attacking a person or government 激烈的諷刺文章

lampoon² *v* [T] to attack a person or government by means of a lampoon 用諷刺文抨擊〔個人或政府〕；嘲諷

lamp·post /'læmp,post; 'læmp-pəʊst/ *n* a tall pole with a lamp on top which lights a street or other public area 路燈柱，燈桿 – see picture on page 729 見 729 頁彩圖

lamp·shade /'læmp,ʃed; 'læmpʃeɪd/ *n* a cover placed over a lamp to soften its light or decorate it 燈罩

lance /læns; lɑːns/ *n* a long spear used by soldiers on horseback in the past 〔昔時騎兵用的〕長矛

★land¹ /lænd; lænd/ *n* **1** [U] ground owned as property 地產；地皮: *Who owns this land?* 這塊地皮是誰的？ | *Our garden is very small so we're buying some land from the council.* 我們的花園太小了，所以我們打算從市政廳那裡再買些土地。| *a shortage of building land* 建築用地的短缺 **2** [U] the solid dry part of the earth's surface, compared with the sea or air 陸地: *We decided to travel by land.* 我們決定作陸上旅行。 **3** [U] ground used for farming 田地；農田: *This is excellent land for wheat.* 這是種小麥的極好農田。 **4** **the land: a** the country as opposed to towns and cities 農村；鄉下: *People in cities often dream of returning to the land.* 城裡的人常夢想回到農村去。 **b** the solid dry part of the earth's surface, compared with the sea or air 陸地: *The ship was about two miles from the land.* 那艘船距陸地約兩英里。 **c** farming 耕作 **5** [C] *lit* a country or nation 〖文〗國家；國度: *the special feeling you have for your native land* 你對於祖國所懷有的特殊感情 | *a land of opportunities* 充滿著機遇的國度 **6** **lands** [pl]: **a** a large areas of the earth's surface which are of the same natural type 〔屬同一自然景觀的〕大片地區，地域: *the forest lands of Norway* 挪威的森林地帶 **b** large areas of ground owned as property 大片地產；領地: *the lands of the Duke of Burgundy* 伯根第公爵的領地

■ USAGE 用法: **1** Compare **land** and **earth** as surfaces where people live and work. If we own an area that we can build things on we call it a piece of **land** ☆ 比較 **land** 和 **earth** 用作人們

所居住和工作的地面時的用法。如果我們擁有一片可以建造房屋的土地，我們稱其為 **land**: *the high price of land in London* 倫敦高昂的地價。We also use **land** when we compare the dry surface of the world with the sea ☆當我們拿地球表面乾燥部分與大海相比時，我們也用 **land** 一詞: *After a week at sea, the sailors saw land.* 在海上航行一星期之後，水手們才看見了陸地。But when we compare it with the sky or space we call it **earth** or **the Earth** ☆但當我們拿它與天空或太空相比時，我們稱其為 **earth** 或 **the Earth**: *After a week in space, the spacecraft returned to earth.* 在太空中逗留一星期之後，飛船回到了地球。**2** Compare **land, ground, soil, earth** as places where plants grow. We use **land** when we talk about areas used for farming ☆ 比較 **land, ground, soil, earth** 作種植農作物的地點時的用法。當我們談到用於耕種的土地時，用 **land** 一詞: *good land for growing corn* 適宜種植玉米的好地。For smaller areas we can use **ground** ☆面積較小的土地可稱為 **ground**: *a small piece of ground where I can grow a few potatoes* 我能種植一些馬鈴薯的一小塊地。The substance in which plants grow is **soil** or **earth** ☆植物賴以生長的物質是 **soil** 或 **earth**: *a tub filled with soil/earth* 裝滿土壤的盆

***land²** *v* **1** [I] to arrive somewhere after a journey by air 〔飛行後〕着陸: *We landed at Heathrow at three o'clock in the morning.* 凌晨三點我們的飛機在希思羅機場着陸。**2** [I] to fall or come down to the ground after or moving through the air 降落: *The bird landed on a branch.* 鳥飛落到樹枝上。| *The ball landed in the water.* 球落到了水裡。**3** [T] to bring goods or people onto land after a journey 使〔人〕登陸；卸下〔貨物〕: *The ship landed its cargo at Dover.* 船在多佛港卸貨。**4** [T] to get something that is very difficult to get 獲得〔難以得到的東西〕: *She's just landed a great new job.* 她剛找到一份理想的新工作。**5 land someone in something** to put someone in a difficult situation or an unpleasant place 使某人陷入困境: *She landed us in a real mess!* 她使我們陷入非常狼狽的境地! **6 land someone with something** to cause someone to have something difficult or unpleasant to deal with 讓某人對付困難或討厭的事情: *We were landed with a huge bill at the end of the day.* 到頭來，我們還要應付一張巨額的賬單。**7 land on your feet** to come successfully out of a difficulty 成功地擺脫困境

land up *phr v* [I] to find yourself after a long journey or a number or events in a place or situation that you did not expect 最終；終於落到某種處境: *They landed up in Rio de Janeiro.* 他們到處遊蕩，最終到了里約熱內盧。| *She landed up married to a widower with three children.* 她最終嫁給了一個有三個孩子的鰥夫。

land·ed /ˈlændɪd; ˈlændɦd/ *adj* [only before a noun 只用於名詞前] owning large amounts of land 擁有大量土地的: *a landed family* 擁有大量土地的家族 | *the landed gentry* 擁有大量土地的紳士們

land·ing /ˈlændɪŋ; ˈlændɪŋ/ *n* **1** the space at the top of a set of stairs in a building 樓梯平台；樓梯口: *His bedroom leads off the landing.* 他的臥室在樓梯口。**2** the act of arriving on land or bringing something onto land 登陸；着陸: *The plane's landing was delayed because of fog.* 由於大霧，飛機延遲着陸。**3** (also 又作 **landing stage**) a flat surface where boats stop to let people get on or off 碼頭

land·la·dy /ˈlændˌledɪ; ˈlændˌleɪdɪ/ *n* **landladies 1** a woman from whom you rent a room, building, or piece of land 女房東；女地主: *My landlady keeps complaining about the noise.* 我的女房東一直在抱怨這噪音。**2** a woman who owns or is in charge of a PUB 〔酒館的〕女店主

land·locked /ˈlændˌlɑkt; ˈlændlɒkt/ *adj* surrounded by land, with no coast 內陸的，被陸地包圍的: *Switzerland is a landlocked country.* 瑞士是個內陸國家。

***land·lord** /ˈlændˌlɔrd; ˈlændlɔːd/ *n* **1** a man from whom you rent a room, building, or piece of land 房東；地主 **2** a man who owns or is in charge of a PUB 〔酒館的〕店主

land·mark /ˈlændˌmɑrk; ˈlændmɑːk/ *n* **1** an easily recognizable object, such as a tall tree or building, by which you can tell where you are 陸標，地標 **2** an event, idea, or discovery which marks a very important stage in a process 里程碑；人生轉捩點: *The discovery of penicillin was a landmark in the history of medicine.* 青黴素的發現是醫學史上的里程碑。

***land·scape¹** /ˈlændskep; ˈlændskeɪp/ *n* **1** a view across an area of land (陸上)風景，(陸上)景色: *a gentle landscape of rolling hills* 小山綿延起伏的柔和景象 | *an ugly urban landscape* 醜陋的城市風景 **2** a picture of country scenery 鄉間的風景畫 –see 見 VIEW¹ (USAGE 用法)

landscape² *v* **landscaped, landscaping** [T] to make a piece of land look attractive by planting trees and flowers in a pleasant arrangement 〔通過植樹種花〕美化〔土地〕: *beautiful landscaped gardens* 經過美化的美麗的花園

land·slide /ˈlændˌslaɪd; ˈlændslaɪd/ *n* **1** a sudden large fall of earth or rocks down a mountain, hill, or cliff 山崩；崩塌；滑坡: *The road was blocked by a landslide.* 道路由於山

崩而被堵了。**2** the winning of an election by a person or political party when they get many more votes than their opponents 〔競選中〕一方選票佔壓倒性多數；一面倒的勝利: *a landslide victory* 大獲全勝；壓倒性的勝利

land·slip /ˈlændˌslɪp; ˈlændslɪp/ *n* a small landslide 〔小規模的〕山崩，滑坡，山泥傾瀉

*★**lane** /leɪn; len/ *n* **1** a narrow country road or a narrow street in a town 鄉間小路；〔城鎮中的〕小巷 **2** part of the name of a street 街 〔路名的一部分〕: *205 Cedar Lane* 西達街205號 **3** one of the parts of a main road which are separated by white lines so that fast and slow cars travelling in the same direction and stay apart 車道 –see picture on page 991 見 991 頁彩圖 **4** a fixed path across the sea or through the air used regularly by ships or aircraft 〔輪船或飛機的〕航線，航道

*★**lan·guage** /ˈlæŋgwɪdʒ; ˈlæŋgwɪdʒ/ *n* **1** [U] the ability of human beings to express themselves through a system of sounds, words, and grammar 語言(能力): *Some children acquire language faster than others.* 有些孩子學習語言的速度比其他孩子快。 **2** [C] a system of sounds, words, and grammar used by the people of a particular area or country to express themselves in speech or writing 〔某一地區或國家的〕語言(文字): *People from this region often speak three languages.* 這地區的人常説三種語言。| *foreign languages* 外語 | *the Zulu language* 祖魯語 **3** [U] words or phrases used by a particular group of people, in a particular subject, or in a particular piece of writing 術語；〔某群人或某範疇的〕用語: *the language of anthropology* 人類學用語 | *the language of teenagers* 十幾歲孩童的用語 | *The language in the novel is beautiful.* 這本小説的言詞很優美。 **4** [C;U] any system of signs or movements used to express meanings or feelings 〔用於表達意思或感情的〕一套信號或動作: *the language of music* 音樂語言 | *a computer language* 電腦語言

language la·bor·a·tory /'·· · ,···/ *n* a special room in a school or college in which people can learn other languages using TAPE RECORDERS 語言實驗室

lan·guid /ˈlæŋgwɪd; ˈlæŋgwɪd/ *adj* lacking strength and moving slowly but attractively 懶洋洋的；慢吞吞的 –**languidly** *adv*: *She sipped her wine languidly.* 她懶洋洋地呷着酒。

lan·guish /ˈlæŋgwɪʃ; ˈlæŋgwɪʃ/ *v* [I] *lit* 〖文〗 **1** to be forced to suffer an unpleasant experience for a long time 〔被迫〕長期受苦，受折磨: *The hostages are still languishing in prison.* 那些人質仍在監獄中受折磨。 **2** to or become weak 變得虛弱〔衰弱〕: *The flowers were languishing in the heat.* 花兒在

炎熱的天氣裡漸漸枯萎。

lan·guor /ˈlæŋgə; ˈlæŋgɚ/ *n* [U] *lit* pleasant tiredness or lack of strength 〖文〗懶洋洋，身心倦怠: *the languor of a summer afternoon* 夏季午後的慵懶 –**languorous** *adj*

lank /læŋk; læŋk/ *adj* unattractive, long, and dull (used of hair) 長得難看的〔指頭髮〕

lank·y /ˈlæŋkɪ; ˈlæŋki/ *adj* **lankier, lankiest** very thin, tall, and ungraceful (used of people) 瘦長難看的〔指人〕

lan·tern /ˈlæntən; ˈlæntən/ *n* a lamp used in the past, consisting of a container made of glass and metal, enclosing a candle 燈籠

lap¹ /læp; læp/ *n* **1** the part of your body between your waist and your knees when you are sitting down 〔人坐着時腰以下到膝為止的〕大腿部；膝上: *She was sitting on her mother's lap.* 她坐在母親的膝上。 **2** a single journey round the track in a race 〔跑道的〕一圈 **3** the lap of luxury conditions of very great comfort 優裕的環境

lap² *v* **-pp- 1** [T] (of an animal) to drink by using short, quick movements of the tongue 〔動物〕舔，舔食: *The cat was lapping the milk off the floor.* 貓在舔地上的牛奶。 **2** [I] (of water) to touch something gently while making soft, gentle sounds 〔水〕輕輕拍打: *The sea lapped **against** the rocks.* 海水輕輕拍打着岩石。 **3** [I] to run completely round the track in a race 〔跑道上〕跑完一圈: *Alan Jones lapped in under two minutes.* 亞倫·瓊斯不到兩分鐘就跑完了一圈。 **4** [T] to pass another competitor in a race so that you are one full lap ahead of them 〔跑道上〕領先〔對手〕一圈

lap sth ↔ up *phr v* [T] **1** (of an animal) to drink liquid by using short, quick movements of the tongue 〔動物〕舔: *The dog lapped the water up.* 狗把水舔光了。 **2** to accept something eagerly, although it may be false or insincere 熱切地接受〔某物〕並信以為真: *He lapped up all their praise.* 他欣然接受他們的讚揚。

la·pel /ləˈpel; ləˈpel/ *n* the part of the front of a coat or JACKET that is joined to the collar and folded back on each side of the front opening 〔西服或夾克的〕翻領 –see picture on page 210 見 210 頁彩圖

lapse¹ /læps; læps/ *n* **1** [C] a small example of bad behaviour, especially by someone who usually behaves well 過失；失誤: *After that little lapse, he was his usual charming self.* 那次小失誤以後，他又恢復了往日的魅力。 **2** [C] a moment when you do not pay attention, or when you forget something 疏忽；記錯: *a lapse of memory* 記錯 **3** [sing] the passing away of a period of time 時間的流逝: *After a lapse of several years he came back to see us.* 幾年後，他回來看我們。

lapse² *v* **lapsed, lapsing** [I] **1 lapse into something** to gradually pass into a less desirable or less active state 退步；陷入；倒退:

After a year of fame, the group lapsed back into obscurity. 那個組合紅了一年，之後就漸漸銷聲匿跡了。 | *She lapsed into silence.* 她漸漸安靜下來。 **2** (of a legal right or an agreement) to end 〔法律規定的權利或協議〕終止，使失效: *Their agreement lapsed last year, and neither company renewed it.* 他們的協議去年失效了，雙方公司仍未續簽。 **3** to no longer believe in or practise your religion 不再信仰〔宗教〕; 不按〔宗教規定〕行事: *a lapsed Catholic* 離經叛道的天主教徒

lar·ce·ny /ˈlɑrsn̩ɪ; ˈlɑːsəni/ *n* **larcenies** [C;U] *law* the act of stealing something 〖律〗偷竊〔罪〕

larch /lɑrtʃ; lɑːtʃ/ *n* a tall tree with bright green needles 落葉松

lard /lɑrd; lɑːd/ *n* [U] pig fat used in cooking 豬油

lar·der /ˈlɑrdɚ; ˈlɑːdəʳ/ *n* a cupboard or small room in a house where food is stored 食物櫥; 食品貯藏室

★★**large** /lɑrdʒ; lɑːdʒ/ *adj* **1** greater or bigger than usual in size, number, or amount 巨大的; 大量的: *a large sum of money* 一大筆錢 | *a large house* 大房子 | *a large family* 大家庭 –opposite 反義 **small 2 at large: a** as a whole 整個，全部: *The country at large is hoping for great changes.* 整個國家都盼望有巨大的變革。 **b** free after escaping, and not caught or held 逃脫後自由自在的; 逍遙法外的: *Two of the prisoners are still at large.* 兩名囚犯仍逍遙法外。 **3 as large as life** a phrase used of someone whose presence you find surprising 〔人〕意外出現，確確實實(就在眼前): *And suddenly there he was, as large as life.* 他突然間來了，沒錯，確確實實是他本人。 –**largeness** *n* [U]

★**large·ly** /ˈlɑrdʒlɪ; ˈlɑːdʒli/ *adv* mostly or mainly 主要地; 大部分地: *This country is largely desert.* 這個國家大半都是沙漠。 | *He left his job largely because he was bored.* 他辭職主要是由於感到厭倦了。

large-scale /ˌ··ˈ/ *adj* **1** happening over a large area or with large numbers or quantities 大規模的: *Supplying the troops with food is a very large-scale operation.* 給部隊供應食物是一項規模很大的行動。 | *large-scale migrations of birds* 候鳥的大規模遷徙 **2** showing a small area in great detail (used of maps) 大比例尺的〔指地圖〕: *Large-scale maps, on a scale of 1:1250, are only available for large towns.* 只有大城鎮才會繪成 1:1250 的大比例尺地圖。

lar·gesse /ˈlɑrdʒɪs; lɑːˈʒes/ *n* (also 又作 **largess** *AmE* 〖美式〗) [U] the generous giving of money or gifts to people of a lower social position than yourself 慷慨的施捨[贈與]

lark¹ /lɑrk; lɑːk/ *n infml* 〖非正式〗 **1** something daring done for a bit of fun 嬉戲; 玩樂: *He did it for a lark, he didn't mean any harm.* 他是鬧着玩才做那件事，他並沒有惡意。

2 a small brown singing bird 雲雀, 百靈科鳥

lark² *v*

lark about/around *phr v* [I] to do silly things for fun or amusement 嬉鬧, 鬧着玩

lar·va /ˈlɑrvə; ˈlɑːvə/ *n* **larvae** /-viː; -viː/ the wormlike young of an insect 〔昆蟲的〕幼蟲 –**larval** *adj*

lar·yn·gi·tis /ˌlærɪnˈdʒaɪtɪs; ˌlærɪnˈdʒaɪtɪs/ *n* [U] a painful infection of the larynx, which makes it difficult to speak 喉炎

lar·ynx /ˈlærɪŋks; ˈlærɪŋks/ *n* **larynxes** or **larynges** /ləˈrɪndʒiz; ləˈrɪndʒiːz/ the hollow boxlike part in your throat, in which the sounds of your voice are produced 喉(頭)

las·civ·i·ous /ləˈsɪvɪəs; ləˈsɪviəs/ *adj* feeling or showing very strong sexual desire in a way that you do not like 好色的; 猥褻的 –**lasciviously** *adv*

la·ser /ˈlezɚ; ˈleɪzəʳ/ *n* a very powerful narrow beam of light which is used to cut hard substances and in medical operations; the machine which produces these beams is also called a **laser** 激光, 雷射; 激光器, 雷射裝置

lash¹ /læʃ; læʃ/ *v* **1** [T] to hit someone violently with a whip 〔用鞭子〕抽打, 鞭打 **2** [I;T] to beat against something violently 猛擊〔某物〕: *waves lashing against the shore* 拍打着海岸的波浪 **3** [I;T] to move violently or suddenly 猛烈擺動: *The cat lashed its tail angrily.* 那隻貓生氣地搖動着尾巴。 **4** [T] to tie things firmly together with rope 〔用繩索〕緊緊捆綁: *During the storm all the boxes had to be lashed down.* 在暴風雨中，所有箱子都須綁緊。 | *They lashed the crates together.* 他們把板條箱綁在一起。

lash out *phr v* [I] **1** to hit someone suddenly and violently with your hands, feet, or a weapon 〔用手、腳或武器〕突然猛擊〔某人〕: *He suddenly lashed out at me.* 他突然向我猛烈攻擊。 **2** to speak very angrily to someone 憤怒地對〔某人〕講話, 抨擊: *An opposition spokesman lashed out against government policy.* 一位反對派發言人猛烈地抨擊政府的政策。

lash² *n* **1** the thin leather part of a whip 鞭子的皮條部分 **2** a blow with a whip 鞭打, 抽打 **3 lashes** the hairs that grow round the edges of your eyes 眼睫毛

lass /læs; læs/ *n dialect* 〖方言〗 a young girl or woman 少女; 姑娘

las·so¹ /ˈlæso; ləˈsuː, ˈlæsəʊ/ *n* **lassos** or **lassoes** a rope with one end that can be tightened in a circle, used for catching horses and cattle 〔套馬、牛用的〕套索

lasso² *v* [T] to catch an animal with a lasso 用套索捕捉〔動物〕

★★**last**¹ /læst; lɑːst/ *n, pron* **1** the person or thing after all the others 最後的人或物: *He was the last to arrive.* 他是最後一個到達的。 **2 at last, at long last** in the end, after a long time 最終; 最後: *At last I've* *found a job that I enjoy.* 我最終找到了自己喜愛的工作。**3 to the last** until the end 直到最後; 直到結束

★★last² *det, adv* **1** after everything or everyone else 最後的[地]: *George arrived last.* 喬治最後到達。| *He came last in the competition.* 他在比賽中是最後的一名。| *This was the last thing that he did before he died.* 這是他生前所做的最後一件事。**2** used when talking about the most recent occasion or the most recent period of time mentioned 最近一次; 上一次: *When did you last see him?* 你最近一次是甚麼時候見到他的? | *I didn't go to the class last week.* 我上星期沒有去上課。**3 last but not least** used when you are making your last point and want to say that it is just as important as the others 最後但並非最不重要的(一點) **4 last thing** at the end of the day 一天結束時: *I always try and tidy up the house last thing at night.* 我晚上所做的最後一件事總是收拾屋子。**5 last of all** a phrase you can use when you come to your last point 最後(一點): *Last of all, don't forget to check your spelling.* 最後, 不要忘記檢查拼寫。

■ **USAGE** 用法: **1** When your point of view is in the present, looking back to the past, say **last** *night*, **last** *week*, etc. ☆如果着眼點在目前, 回顧過去時便說 **last** *night* (昨晚), **last** *week* (上星期)等: *I went to bed late* **last** *night.* 昨晚我很晚才睡覺。| *I spoke to Sue* **last** *Monday.* 我上星期一找蘇談過話。But when your point of view is in the past, looking even further back into the past, use expressions like *the* **previous** *night/the* *night* **before**, *the* **previous** *week/the* *week* **before** ☆但當着眼點在過去, 而要回顧更早一些的過去時, 則用 *the* **previous** *night/the* *night* **before** (前一晚), *the* **previous** *week/the* *week* **before** (前一個星期)等表達法: *I told her I had spoken to Sue* **the previous** *Monday.* 我告訴她我前一個星期一就找蘇談過了。**2** Compare 比較 **latest** and 和 **last**. Use **latest** when you mean "new and most recent" ☆當表示"新的、最近的"時, 用 **latest**: *Have you heard the* **latest** *news?* 你聽到了最新的消息嗎? Use **last** when you mean "coming at the end" or "coming before the latest one" ☆當表示"最後的"或"上一次的"時用 **last**: *'The Magic Flute' was Mozart's* **last** *opera.* 《魔笛》是莫扎特的最後一部歌劇。| *Have you read Bigg's* **latest** *novel? It's better than her* **last** *one.* 你看過碧歌的最新小說嗎? 它比她的上一部小說好。

★★last³ *v* [I] **1** to continue to happen for a period of time 持續; 延續: *The hot weather lasted until September.* 炎熱的天氣

一直持續到九月份。| *Each class lasts* **for** *one hour.* 每堂課的時間為一個小時。**2** to remain in good condition 保持良好狀態: *A cheap watch won't last as long as a more expensive one.* 廉價手錶不及貴的手錶經久耐用。

last-ing /ˈlæstɪŋ; ˈlɑːstɪŋ/ *adj* continuing for a long time 持久的; 耐久的: *a lasting sorrow* 長久的悲哀

last-ly /ˈlæstlɪ; ˈlɑːstli/ *adv* **1** a word used when you come to the last of several points you are making 最後(一點): *We've seen how different soils suit different plants, and how rainfall affects their growth. Lastly, I'd like to look at the significance of light.* 我們已經知道了不同的土壤如何適宜種植不同的植物, 也知道了降雨量是如何影響植物生長的。最後, 我想講一下光的重要性。| *I'd like, lastly, to thank my parents for their help.* 最後, 我想感謝父母對我的幫助。**2** a word used when you are describing a number of events that happen one after the other and you come to the last one, or when you come to the last in a list of instructions 最後〔用於提及一連串事物或說明中的最後一點〕: *She closed the windows and turned off the lights. Lastly, she locked the door.* 她關上窗, 熄了燈。最後, 她鎖上房門。| *Leave the cake to cool. Lastly, decorate the top with cherries.* 讓蛋糕冷卻一下。最後, 在上面放上櫻桃作為裝飾。

■ **USAGE** 用法: Do not confuse **lastly** and **at last**. ☆ 不要混淆 **lastly** 和 **at last**。**1** Use **lastly** when you are talking about several things in order and you want to show that you have reached the final stage on the list ☆ 在敘述幾件有順序的事情並說到最後一件時, 用 **lastly**: *...And* **lastly** *I would like to thank everyone for making this such a memorable occasion.* 最後, 我想感謝各位使這次活動成為一個令人難忘的盛會。| *I'll start by asking you about your previous experience, then we can talk about your present employment, and* **lastly** *I'll tell you a bit about the job here.* 首先我會問一下你以前的工作經歷, 然後我們可以談談你現在的工作情況, 最後我會告訴你一些這裡的工作。(Note that you can also use **finally** in the same way. 注意, 在這種情況下, 你也可以用 **finally** 一詞。) **2** Use **at last** when you want to show that something has happened after a long time or after a lot of waiting ☆當你想表示很久以後或等了很長時間以後終於發生了某事, 用 **at last**: *She tried again and again until* **at last** *she succeeded.* 她嘗試了一次又一次, 直到最後取得成功。| *When* **at last** *the rescuers found them, two people* *had already died.* 營救人員最終找到他們的時候，已有兩人死亡。| *"At last!" she exclaimed as she managed to catch the waiter's eye.* "終於等到了！" 當她讓服務員注意到她的時候，她叫了出來。(Note that you can also use **finally** in this way. 注意，在這種情況下，你也可以用 **finally** 一詞。)

latch¹ /lætʃ; lætʃ/ *n* **1** a fastening for a door, gate, or window, which works by putting a metal bar in a space 〔門窗的〕閂 **2** a lock for a house door that can be opened from the inside with a handle but from the outside only with a key 碰鎖; 彈簧鎖 **3 on the latch** fastened only with a latch, but not locked 只閂上但沒有上鎖

latch² *v* [T] to fasten a door, gate, or window with a latch 用碰鎖鎖上〔門、窗〕; 閂上: *She forgot to latch the door.* 她忘了閂上門。–opposite 反義 **unlatch**

latch on *phr v* [I] *infml* to understand something 〔非正式〕理解; 明白

latch onto *phr v infml* 〔非正式〕**1** [T **latch onto** sthg] to gain an understanding of something 理解〔某事〕; 明白〔某事〕: *He soon latched onto how to do it.* 他很快就明白該怎樣做。**2** [T **latch onto** sbdy/sthg] to become very interested in a person or idea, so that you do not let them go 〔由於很感興趣而〕纏住〔某人〕; 不放棄〔某一觀點〕: *She had latched onto me at the conference.* 她在會議上把我纏住了。

late /let; leɪt/ *adj, adv* **1** arriving or happening after the usual, arranged, or expected time 遲〔晚〕到的; 遲(到), 晚(到): *The train was 10 minutes late.* 火車晚點十分鐘。| *She was late for the meeting.* 她開會遲到了。| *We had a late breakfast.* 我們早餐吃得很晚。| *We arrived a few minutes late.* 我們晚到了幾分鐘。**2** towards the end of a period of time 〔一段時間的〕晚期的, 後期的: *She returned in the late afternoon.* 她下午很晚才回來。| *She's in her late thirties.* 她已近四十歲了。| *We always go on holiday late in the summer.* 我們總在夏天快結束時去度假。| *I'll see you later on this evening.* 今晚我稍後再和你見面。–compare 比較 **EARLY²** **3 late night** a night when you stay up late and do not go to bed at your usual time 很晚睡覺的夜晚 **4 too late for something** no longer possible to do something 不可能再做某事了; …已太遲了: *It's too late to apply for this job.* 申請這個工作已太遲了。| *It was too late for the doctors to save him.* 醫生已來不及救他了。**5** [always before a noun 只用於名詞前] who has died 已故的; 逝去的: *her late husband* 她已故的丈夫 **6 of late** *fml* recently 〔正式〕最近以來: *He's been behaving very strangely of late.* 他最近舉止一直很古怪。–**lateness** *n* [U]

late·ly /'letlɪ; 'leɪtli/ *adv* in the recent past 近來; 最近: *I haven't seen her much lately.* 最近我不常見到她。| *He's been doing a lot of gardening lately.* 近來他常在園子裡料理花草。

la·tent /'letnt; 'leɪtənt/ *adj* present but not yet noticeable, active, or fully developed 潛伏的; 潛在的: *the latent tensions between the two countries* 兩國間潛在的緊張關係

lat·er /'letɚ; 'leɪtə^r/ *adv* **1** after some time 較晚地; 後來: *I can't do it now, but I'll do it later.* 我現在不能做，但我稍後會做。| *At first they said 32 people had died, but later they said it was 15.* 起初他們説有三十二人喪命，但後來又説是十五人。| *She had a cup of coffee and read for a while. Later that afternoon she took a walk down to the beach.* 她喝了杯咖啡，看了會兒書。下午晚些時候又散步去了海濱。**2 later on** after some time 過後, 以後: *I can't do it now, but I'll do it later on.* 我現在不能做，但過後我會做。

lat·e·ral /'lætərəl; 'lætərəl/ *adj* [only before a noun 只用於名詞前] *tech* 〔術語〕**1** connected with the side of something 側面的; 橫向的: *a lateral movement* 橫向運動 **2 lateral thinking** a way of thinking about problems in which you use your imagination in order to find new answers 水平思維, 橫向思維〔使用想像力以尋求新答案的思考方式〕

lat·est /'letɪst; 'leɪtৢst/ *adj infml* 〔非正式〕**1** the most recent 最近的; 最新的: *Here's our reporter in New York with the latest news on the crisis.* 現在由我駐紐約記者向大家報導此次危機的最新消息。| *the latest fashions from Paris* 巴黎最新式的時裝 **2 at the latest** a phrase used to give the latest time by which something will happen 至遲, 最晚: *I'll ring you on Friday at the latest.* 我至遲會在星期五打電話給你。

la·tex /'leteks; 'leɪteks/ *n* [U] a whitish substance produced by certain kinds of tree and used to make rubber 膠乳; 橡漿

lathe /leð; leɪð/ *n* a machine for shaping metal or wood by turning it round against a sharp tool 車牀

la·ther¹ /'læðɚ; 'lɑːðə^r/ *n* [sing;U] a white mass produced by mixing soap and water together 〔肥皂水的〕泡沫: *His chin was covered with a thick lather.* 他的下巴上塗滿了厚厚的肥皂泡沫。

lather² *v* **1** [I] (of soap) to produce a lather 〔肥皂〕產生泡沫: *This washing powder doesn't lather very well.* 這種洗衣粉不大起泡沫。**2** [T] to cover something with lather 用泡沫覆蓋

Lat·in¹ /'lætɪn; 'lætɪn/ *n* [U] the language of the ancient Romans 拉丁語; 拉丁系語言

Latin² *adj* **1** written in Latin 拉丁語的; 用拉丁語寫成的: *a Latin inscription* 拉丁碑文 **2** relating to a nation that speaks a language developed from Latin, such as Spanish, Portuguese, Italian, or French 拉丁語系民

族〔如西班牙、葡萄牙、意大利、法國〕的

Latin A·mer·i·can /ˌ· ·ˈ··ˌ·/ *adj* relating to the Spanish or Portuguese speaking countries of South and Central America 拉丁美洲的

lat·i·tude /ˈlætəˌtjud; ˈlætɪ̩tjuːd/ *n* **1** [C;U] the distance north or south of the EQUATOR measured in degrees 緯度: *The latitude of the ship is 20 degrees south.* 該船的緯度是南緯二十度。 –compare 比較 LONGITUDE **2 latitudes** [pl] an area of the world which is at a certain distance from the EQUATOR 緯度地區: *At these latitudes you often get strong winds.* 這一些緯度地區經常有強風。 **3** [U] freedom to do or say what you like 〔言行的〕自由: *That school allows its students a great deal of latitude* **in** deciding which subjects to study. 那所學校在選擇學習科目方面給學生很大的自由。

la·trine /ləˈtrin; ləˈtriːn/ *n* a hole in the ground used as a TOILET, for example in a military camp 茅坑〔如兵營的廁所〕

★**lat·ter¹** /ˈlætə˞; ˈlætə˞/ *adj fml* 〔正式〕 [only before a noun 只用於名詞前] **1** nearer to the end; later 較後的; 較晚的: *the latter years of her life* 她的晚年 **2** the second of two people or things just mentioned 〔剛被提及的兩人或兩物中的〕後者的: *Of the pig and the cow, the latter animal is more valuable.* 那頭豬和那頭牛相比, 後者更有價值。 | *Of pigs and cows, the latter animals are more valuable.* 豬和牛相比, 後者更有價值。

latter² *n* **the latter** the second of two people or things just mentioned 〔剛被提及的兩人或兩物中的〕後者: *Cotton-manufacturing and steel-making are in decline, the former because of cheap imports from the East, the latter because of over-production.* 棉花生產和鋼鐵製造業都在衰退, 前者是由從東方進口廉價物品造成的, 而後者是由過度生產造成的。

lat·ter·ly /ˈlætəlɪ; ˈlætəli/ *adv fml* recently or lately 〔正式〕(較)近期; 後來

lat·tice /ˈlætɪs; ˈlætɪs/ *n* a wooden or metal framework consisting of thin pieces of wood or metal crossed over each other; a lattice is often used as a fence or as a support for climbing flowers 〔作籬笆或爬藤架用的〕格子框架

lau·da·ble /ˈlɔdəbl; ˈlɔːdəbəl/ *adj fml* deserving praise (used of behaviour or actions) 〔正式〕值得讚揚的〔指行為或舉止〕 – **laudably** *adv*

★**laugh¹** /læf; lɑːf/ *v* **1** [I] to make a sound with your voice, usually while smiling, because you find something funny 大笑; 發笑: *It was so funny we couldn't stop laughing.* 這太好笑了, 我們忍不住大笑起來。 | *Nobody laughs* **at** *his jokes.* 沒有人聽了他的笑話而發笑。 | *Ben laughed nervously.* 賓緊張地笑了笑。 **2 laugh your head off** to laugh for a long time very loudly 捧腹大笑; 大笑不止

laugh at sbdy/sthg *phr v* [T] to treat a person or thing as very foolish, or make jokes about them 嘲弄; 嘲笑: *They'll just laugh at you for listening to him.* 如果你聽他的, 他們只會嘲笑你。

laugh sthg ↔ off *phr v* [T] to pretend, by laughing or joking, that something is less serious than it is 用笑掩飾: *She tried to laugh it off, but I could see that she was upset.* 她試圖一笑了之, 但我看得出她心情不好。

laugh² *n* **1** the sound you make when you find something funny 笑, 笑聲: *a hearty laugh* 爽朗的笑聲 | *When I mentioned Jim, he let out a loud laugh.* 我提到吉姆時, 他大笑起來。 **2 do something for a laugh/for laughs** to do something for fun 為取樂而做某事: *We all dressed up in silly hats just for a laugh.* 我們都戴了頂樣子很可笑的帽子來取樂。

laugh·a·ble /ˈlæfəbl; ˈlɑːfəbəl/ *adj* extremely foolish, and not worth taking seriously 荒唐可笑的 – **laughably** *adv*

laugh·ter /ˈlæftə˞; ˈlɑːftə˞/ *n* [U] the act or sound of laughing 笑; 笑聲

★**launch¹** /lɔntʃ; lɔːntʃ/ *v* [T] **1** to make a newly-built boat move into the water for the first time 使〔新船〕首次下水 **2** to send a modern weapon or spacecraft into the sky 發射〔現代化武器或太空船〕: *to launch a missile* 發射導彈 | *The rocket is due to be launched this afternoon.* 火箭預計在今天下午發射。 **3** to start an important activity or plan 開辦; 創辦; 發起: *They might be planning to launch an attack very soon.* 他們可能正在計劃即將發起攻勢。 | *A new campaign has just been launched by the government.* 政府剛發起了一項新的運動。 **4** to let people know about a new product 推出〔新產品〕: *The new chocolate was launched last week.* 這種新的巧克力於上星期推出。

launch² *n* **1** the act of launching something 發射; 下水; 投放市場 **2** a large motor boat used for carrying people on rivers and lakes 〔河或湖上的〕遊艇; 汽艇

laun·der /ˈlɔndə˞; ˈlɔːndə˞/ *v* [T] to wash and iron clothes and sheets 洗燙〔衣物〕

laun·derette /ˌlɔndəˈrɛt; lɔːnˈdret/ *n* a shop where you pay to wash and dry your clothes and sheets in machines 自助洗衣店

laun·dry /ˈlɔndrɪ; ˈlɔːndri/ *n* **laundries 1** [C] a place where clothes and sheets are washed and ironed 洗衣店; 洗衣房 **2** [U] clothes and sheets that need washing or that have just been washed 要洗的或剛洗好的衣服

laur·el /ˈlɔrəl; ˈlɒrəl/ *n* **1** a small tree with shiny leaves that do not fall in winter 月桂樹 **2 laurels** [pl] *fml* honour that you receive for something that you have done 〔正式〕〔表示榮譽的〕桂冠

la·va /ˈlɑvə; ˈlɑːvə/ *n* [U] rock in a very hot liquid state which flows from a VOLCANO;

when this rock becomes cool and solid it is still called lava〔火山噴出的〕熔岩; 火山岩

lav·a·to·ry /ˈlævəˌtɔrɪ; ˈlævətəri/ *n* **lavatories** a TOILET 廁所: *I need to go to the lavatory.* 我需要去廁所。| *a public lavatory* 公共廁所

lav·en·der /ˈlævəndə; ˈlævẟndəʳ/ *n* [U] a plant with sweet-smelling pale purple flowers 薰衣草

lav·ish¹ /ˈlævɪʃ; ˈlævɪʃ/ *adj* **1** very generous 非常慷慨的: *She's very lavish with presents for the children.* 她送禮物給孩子們很是慷慨。**2** given in great quantity 大量給予的: *lavish praise* 大肆吹捧 **–lavishly** *adv*: *We were entertained lavishly by various Hollywood directors.* 我們從不同的荷里活[好萊塢]導演的作品中得到了很多娛樂。

lavish² *v* **lavish something on someone** to give someone a lot of something in a very generous way 慷慨地給予: *He lavished gifts on us.* 他送給我們許多禮物。

★★**law** /lɔ; lɔː/ *n* **1** [C] a rule developed by a society, and supported by the power of the government, to control social and business relationships 法令; 法規: *a law against drinking and driving* 禁止酒後駕車的法令 | *There should be a law against that kind of behaviour.* 應該制定一項法規來禁止那種行為。| *Parliament has passed a new law aimed at reducing the amount of fraud in businesses.* 議會已通過了一項新的法令, 旨在減少商業欺詐活動。| *Under the new law, shops will be able to open all day on Sundays.* 根據新法規, 商店可在星期日全天營業。**2** [U] (also **the law**) the system of rules developed by a government or society to control social and business relationships 法; 法律: *If you break the law, you will be punished.* 你如果違法, 就會受到懲罰。| *tribal law* 部落的法規 | *You are obliged by law to pay taxes.* 按照法律規定, 你必須納稅。**3 against the law** not legal 違法的; 非法的: *Driving without a seat belt is against the law.* 駕車時不繫安全帶是違法的。**4** [U] the system of law, and the way particular laws work, studied as a subject〔作為學科的〕法律; 法學: *She's studying law at university.* 她在大學裡攻讀法律。| *a law degree* 法學學位 **5** [U] a particular group of rules in a system of law 某一方面的法律: *He's been charged under military law.* 他被控違反了軍事法。**6** [C] a statement describing a natural process which, in certain conditions, always has the same effect 定律; 規律: *Boyle's law is a scientific principle.* 玻意耳定律是一項科學原理。| *the law of gravity* (萬有)引力定律 **7 the law** *infml* the police, or a policeman or policewoman 〔非正式〕警方; 警察: *The law was there in force.* 警察在那裡執法。**8 law and order** a situation in which people respect and obey the law 法治, 治安, 法律與秩序: *a breakdown*

in law and order 破壞法治 | *Finally, the army was used to maintain law and order.* 最終, 法律秩序要動用軍隊來維護。

law-a·bid·ing /ˈ··ˌ··/ *adj* obeying the law 守法的; 安分守己的

law court /ˈ··/ *n* a room or building in which law cases are heard and judged 法庭

law·ful /ˈlɔfəl; ˈlɔːfəl/ *adj fml* allowed by law 〔正式〕法律允許的; 合法的: *a lawful marriage* 合法的婚姻 | *I was going about my lawful business.* 我打算做我的合法生意。– see 見 LEGAL (USAGE 用法) –opposite 反義 **unlawful –lawfully** *adv*

law·less /ˈlɔlɪs; ˈlɔːləs/ *adj fml* 〔正式〕 **1** breaking the law in a wild and violent way 失去法律控制的; 無法無天的: *a lawless mob* 無法無天的暴民 **2** not governed by law (used of a country or place) 沒有法律的; 法紀所不及的〔指國家或地方〕: *a lawless frontier town* 沒有法律的邊境城鎮

lawn /lɔn; lɔːn/ *n* a stretch of ground covered with closely cut grass in a garden or park 草坪; 草地 –see picture on page 729 見 729 頁彩圖

lawn-mow·er /ˈ·ˌ··/ *n* a machine that you use to cut the grass in a garden 割草機 – see picture on page 958 見 958 頁彩圖

law·suit /ˈlɔˌsut; ˈlɔːsjuːt/ *n* a case in a court of law concerning a disagreement between two people or companies, rather than a criminal and the police〔解決兩人或兩個公司之間的紛爭的〕訴訟(案)

★**law·yer** /ˈlɔjə; ˈlɔːjəʳ/ *n* a person whose business it is to advise people about laws and to represent them in court; lawyers in Britain are either SOLICITORS or BARRISTERS 律師

lax /læks; læks/ *adj* not obeying the rules, following correct standards, or behaving properly 不嚴格的; 鬆懈的: *lax morals* 放蕩行為 | *Lax security allowed the thieves to enter.* 鬆懈的保安措施使小偷有機可乘。| *Discipline at this school is lax.* 這家學校的紀律並不嚴格。

lax·a·tive /ˈlæksətɪv; ˈlæksətɪv/ *n* a medicine or something you eat that causes your bowels to empty easily 瀉藥, 通便劑

★**lay¹** /le; leɪ/ *v* **laid** /led; leɪd/, **laid 1** [T+adv/prep] to put someone or something in a particular position or on a flat surface 把〔某人或某物〕置放, 平放: *They laid the injured woman down on the grass.* 他們把受傷的女人平放在草地上。| *He laid his coat over a chair.* 他把外衣放在椅子上。**2** [T] to put something in the proper position on the ground or in the ground 把〔某物〕放置於地上的適當位置: *He was learning how to lay bricks so he could build his own house.* 他正在學習砌磚頭, 以便能自建房屋。| *to lay pipes* 鋪設管道 | *to lay a new carpet* 鋪新地毯 **3 lay the table** to arrange knives, forks, plates, and other things on a table ready for a meal 擺好餐具〔準備開飯〕 **4 lay an egg** (of a bird or an insect) to produce an egg 〔鳥或昆蟲〕下蛋; 產卵 **5** [T] *fml* to make a statement, charge, or complaint in an official or public way 〔正式〕發表(聲明); 提出 〔訴訟、指控〕: *The proposal was laid before the committee.* 這項建議已提交委員會(討論)。| *The police have laid a serious charge against you.* 警方已對你提出嚴厲的指控。 **6 lay the blame on someone** to blame someone 責怪 某人 **7 lay the blame for something at someone's door** to blame someone for something 因為某事責怪某人 **8 lay emphasis on something** to say that something is very important 強調某事: *We must lay more emphasis on the protection of the environment.* 我們必須進一步強調環保的重要性。 **9 lay claim to something** *fml* to state that something belongs to you 〔正式〕聲稱擁有 某物 **10 lay your hands on something** to find something 找到某物: *It's here somewhere, but I can't lay my hands on it at the moment.* 它就在這附近, 但目前我找不到。 **11 lay hold of someone/something** to take hold of someone or something very firmly 緊緊抓住某人或某物 **12 be laid low** to be weak with an illness 使病倒: *I was laid low with flu all last week.* 上星期我得了流行性感冒, 病了整個星期。 **13 lay something to rest: a** to bring a feeling such as fear or grief to an end 消除某種感覺〔如恐懼或悲傷〕: *Her fears were soon laid to rest.* 她很快便消除了恐懼。 **b** to show that something is false or not true 〔顯示出某事是錯誤的或不符合事實 的而〕了結: *The report should lay to rest recent allegations of police brutality.* 該報告應 當可以了結最近關於警方野蠻行徑的指控。 **14 lay a trap** to prepare a trap to catch a person or an animal 設下圈套〔以逮捕某人或捕 獲動物〕

> ■ USAGE 用法: Do not confuse the transitive verb **lay (laid, laid)** with the intransitive verb **lie (lay, lain)** ☆不要 把及物動詞 **lay (laid, laid)** 和不及物動 詞 **lie (lay, lain)** 相混淆: *He laid his trousers on the bed.* 他把褲子放在牀上。| *He lay on the bed.* 他躺在牀上。A third verb **lie (lied, lied)** is intransitive and means "to tell a lie." ☆另外一個動詞 **lie (lied, lied)** 是不及物動詞, 表示"說 謊"。

lay sthg ↔ **down** *phr v* [T] **1** to put something down when you have finished using it 放下〔某物〕 **2** to make a firm statement or give a rule 宣稱; 規定: *It's laid down in the regulations.* 這在條例中已有明文規定。 **3 lay down the law** to give other people orders in an unpleasant commanding manner 〔向別人〕發號施令: *I can't stand the way she lays down the law.* 我受不了她那副發號

施令的樣子。

lay sthg ↔ **in** *phr v* [T] to obtain and store a supply of something 儲備, 儲存〔某 物〕: *We've laid in enough food for the winter.* 我們已儲備了足夠的食品過冬。

lay into sbdy *phr v infml* [T] to attack someone physically or with words 〔非正式〕 〔用武力或言辭〕攻擊; 抨擊〔某人〕

lay off *phr v* **1** [T **lay** sbdy ↔ **off**] to stop employing a worker, because there is not enough work 〔由於沒有足夠的工作而〕解僱 〔某人〕: *They laid us off for three months.* 他 們停僱了我們三個月。 **2** [I;T **lay off** sthg] *infml* to stop doing something annoying or harmful 〔非正式〕停止(做)〔討厭或有害的事 情〕: *You'd better lay off smoking!* 你最好別 吸煙!

lay sthg ↔ **on** *phr v* [T] to provide food, entertainment or a service, especially in a generous way 〔尤指慷慨地〕提供〔食物、樂趣 或服務〕: *They laid on a party for all the old people in the village.* 他們為全村的老年人舉 行了一次聚會。

lay sthg ↔ **out** *phr v* [T] **1** to spread out or arrange things 展開; 佈置: *She laid out her new clothes on the bed.* 她把新衣服擺到 了牀上。 **2 be laid out** to be planned and arranged in a particular way 被設計; 被安 排: *The garden is laid out rather formally.* 花 園設計得頗為正規。

lay up *phr v* **be laid up** to be kept indoors or in bed with an illness 因病臥牀: *I was laid up with a cold.* 我因感冒而臥牀。

lay² *adj* [only before a noun 只用於名詞前] **1** of or done by people who are not in official positions within a religion 非神職的: *a lay preacher* 非正式的布道者 **2** not trained in or having knowledge of a particular profession or subject, such as law or medicine 非專業的; 外行的: *No lay person can understand all these technical terms.* 外行人無法理 解所有這些術語。

lay³ the past tense of LIE¹ ☆ LIE¹ 的過去式

lay·a·bout /ˈleəˌbaut; ˈleɪəbaut/ *n infml* a lazy person who avoids work 〔非正式〕躲避 工作的人; 游手好閒的人

lay-by /ˈ··/ *n* a space next to a road where vehicles may stop for a short while 路側停 車處

*lay·er¹ /ˈleə; ˈleɪər/ *n* a piece of some material or a quantity of a substance which is laid flat on a surface or placed between two things 層: *These seeds must be covered with a layer of earth.* 這些種子必須蓋上一層 泥 土。| *She's wearing several layers of clothing to try to stay warm.* 她穿了好幾件衣 服保暖。

layer² *v* [T] to put things down in layers 把...堆積成層: *Layer cheese and potatoes in the dish.* 把乳酪和馬鈴薯一層層地放在碟子 裡。

lay·man /ˈlemən; ˈleɪmən/ *n* **laymen** /-mən;

-mən/ **1** a person who is not trained in a particular profession or subject 外行人; 門外漢 **2** a person who is a member of a religion, but does not have an official position 普通信徒, 平信徒

lay-off /'··/ *n* the stopping of a worker's job at a time when there is little work 〔工作清淡時的〕臨時解僱

lay·out /'le͵aʊt; 'leɪaʊt/ *n* **1** the way in which the parts of something are arranged, especially on a drawing or plan 〔尤指圖畫或方案的〕設計; 佈局: *the layout of the new shopping centre* 新的購物中心的佈局 **2** the way in which printed matter is set out on a page 版面編排〔設計〕

laze /lez; leɪz/ *v* **lazed, lazing** [I] (also 又作 **laze around**) to spend time enjoyably resting and doing nothing 閒散; 混日子: *I spent the morning just lazing around.* 我消磨了一個上午, 甚麼事也沒有做。

la·zy /'lezi; 'leɪzi/ *adj* **lazier, laziest 1** disliking and avoiding activity, effort, or work 懶惰的; 懶散的: *He won't work — he's just too lazy!* 他不肯工作, 實在是太懶了! **2** slow and without much effort (used of an action or movement) 緩慢的; 懶洋洋的〔指舉止或行動〕: *a lazy smile* 慵懶的一笑 **3** spent doing nothing (used of periods of time) 〔指一段時間〕未做事情的; 令人懶洋洋的: *a lazy afternoon* 一個無所事事的下午 **–lazily** *adv* **–laziness** *n* [U]

lb lbs a written abbreviation for POUND, when it is a measure of weight 〔縮〕磅

★★★ **lead¹** /lid; liːd/ *v* **led** /led; led/, **led 1** [T + adv/prep] to show the way somewhere, or take someone there by going in front of them 給〔某人〕指路; 給〔某人〕帶路; 帶領: *The stewardess led them onto the plane.* 空中小姐領着他們上了飛機。| *She led me to her office.* 她帶我進了她的辦公室。| *The horses were led into the yard.* 馬被牽進了園子。**2** [I + adv/prep; T + adv/prep] to go towards a place or be the means of reaching a place 通往; 通向: *a small path leading to the top of the hill* 通往山頂的一條小路 | *This road leads you to the town centre.* 順着這條路, 你可以走到鎮中心。**3** [T] to be responsible for directing a group of people 領導〔一輩人〕; 率領: *He's been chosen to lead the new team.* 經挑選由他帶領新的隊伍。**4** [I] to be winning in a game or race 〔比賽中〕領先: *England were leading 1-0 at half time.* 上半場英國隊以一比零領先。**5 lead to something** to cause something or result in something 引起; 導致: *The strike could lead to a loss of jobs.* 罷工可能會導致失業。**6 lead someone to do something** to persuade someone to do something, or influence them so that they do something 說服某人做某事; 影響某人使其做某事: *What led you to resign?* 甚麼事情使你辭職? | *I was led to believe that you were ill.* 我以為你生病

了。**7 lead the way: a** to show other people where to go by going in front of them 〔給別人〕帶路 **b** to be more advanced than other people 領先〔於別人〕: *This university leads the way in cancer research.* 這所大學在癌症研究方面居於領先地位。**8 lead a ... life** to experience a particular kind of life 過...的生活: *He led a very lonely life.* 他過着很孤單的生活。

■ USAGE 用法: Compare 比較 **lead, guide, direct**. To **lead** is to show the way by going first ☆ **lead** 指走在前面帶路: *You lead and we'll follow.* 你在前面帶路, 我們跟着你走。To **guide** is to go with someone who needs help, in order to show the way and explain things ☆ **guide** 指與需要幫助的人領路, 並作沿途解說: *He guided the tourists round the castle.* 他帶領遊客參觀城堡。To **direct** is to explain to someone how to get to a place ☆ **direct** 指告訴某人如何去某個地方: *Could you direct me to the station, please?* 請問去車站往哪裡走?

---

lead sbdy ↔ **on** *phr v infml* 〔非正式〕[T] to persuade somebody to believe something that is not true 哄騙勸誘, 使...誤信: *I don't believe you — you're just leading me on!* 我不信, 你這不過是在騙我!

lead up to sthg *phr v* [T] **1** to come before and result in something 漸漸引向; 作為...的頭一步: *the events leading up to his arrest* 一步步引向他被捕的事件 **2** to guide a conversation to the point where you can talk about a particular subject or ask for something 把話題引向〔某一點〕: *His flattering remarks were leading up to a request for money.* 他的甜言蜜語是他開口要錢的頭一步。

lead² *n* **1** a more advanced position 領先地位: *Japan has a lead in the industrial use of robots.* 日本在工業上使用機械人方面處於領先地位。**2** [C] a good example for other people to follow 模範; 榜樣: *The Prime Minister always provides a strong lead.* 首相一直是大家的好榜樣。| *the company's lead in helping the community* 在幫助社區方面公司所起的模範作用 **3 take the lead** to be more advanced or more successful than others 帶頭, 領先: *Japan took the lead in car production.* 日本在汽車生產方面居首位。**4 be in the lead** to be winning in a game or competition 〔比賽中〕領先: *England were in the lead at halftime.* 半場時英國隊領先。**5** [sing] the number of points by which one competitor is ahead of another 領先的分數: *England has a lead of ten points to three.* 英國隊以10比3領先。**6** [C] the most important part in a play or film 〔戲劇或電影的〕主角: *A French actress plays the lead in this film.* 一位法國女演員在這部影片中擔任主角。**7** [C] a rope, chain, or narrow piece of leather tied to a dog to control it〔繫狗用的〕繩索, 鏈條, 皮帶 **8** [C] an electric wire which carries power to a machine 電線 –see picture on page 958 見 958 頁彩圖 **9** [C] a piece of information which may lead to a discovery of something not known 線索: *The police have several leads to follow in this case.* 警方已掌握了關於此案的幾條線索。

lead³ /lɛd; lɛd/ *n* **1** [U] a soft heavy grey metal, used for waterpipes and for covering roofs 鉛 **2** [C;U] a thin stick of a black substance used in the centre of pencils 鉛筆心: *a soft lead pencil* 軟鉛心的鉛筆

lead·en /ˈlɛdn; ˈlɛdn/ *adj lit* 〔文〕 **1** dull grey 鉛(灰)色的: *a leaden sky* 灰暗的天空 **2** without cheerfulness or excitement 鬱鬱不樂的; 沉悶的, 沉重的

✶**lead·er** /ˈliːdə; ˈliːdər/ *n* **1** a person who guides or directs a group, team, or organization 領導者, 領袖: *the leader of a political party* 政黨的領袖 | *union leaders* 工會領導人 **2** a person or thing who is winning a race or competition at a particular moment〔比賽中〕領先的人〔物〕 **3** the main article in a newspaper, which gives the newspaper's opinion about something that is happening〔報紙的〕社論

✶**lead·er·ship** /ˈliːdəʃɪp; ˈliːdərʃɪp/ *n* [U] **1** the position of leader 領導(地位); 領導權: *the battle for the leadership of the Labour Party* 為工黨領導權所進行的鬥爭 **2** the qualities necessary in a leader 領導才能

lead·ing /ˈliːdɪŋ; ˈliːdɪŋ/ *adj* [always before a noun 只能用於名詞前] **1** most important or main 最重要的; 主要的: *the leading role in the film* 電影中的主角 | *one of Greece's leading modern composers* 希臘現代最傑出的作曲家之一 **2 leading question** a question formed in such a way that it suggests one particular answer 誘導性問題

✶**leaf¹** /liːf; liːf/ *n* **leaves** /liːvz; liːvz/ **1** [C] one of the flat green parts of a plant that are joined to its stem or branch〔植物的〕葉子 | **be in leaf** to be covered with leaves 長滿葉子: *The poplar trees are in leaf again.* 白楊樹又長滿了葉子。 **3** [C] a thin sheet of paper, especially a page in a book〔尤指書本中的〕一頁 **4** [U] metal, especially gold or silver, in a very thin sheet 薄金屬片;〔尤指金或銀的〕箔: *a book decorated with gold leaf* 一本有金箔作裝飾的書 **5 take a leaf out of someone's book** to behave like someone else because their behaviour has had very good results 仿效某人, 以某人為榜樣 **6 turn over a new leaf** to begin to behave in a better, more responsible way 改過自新; 重新做人

leaf² *v*

  leaf through sthg *phr v* [I;T] to turn the pages of a book or magazine to see if there is anything you are interested in or to find particular information 瀏覽, 匆匆翻

閱〔書籍或雜誌〕

leaf·let /ˈliːflɪt; ˈliːflət/ *n* a printed sheet of paper, given free to the public, which provides information about a particular subject or advertises something〔免費發放給大眾以提供某方面信息或為某物做廣告的〕傳單; 摺疊印刷品

leaf·y /ˈliːfi; ˈliːfi/ *adj* **leafier, leafiest** **1** having a lot of leaves 多葉的: *leafy vegetables* 多葉蔬菜 **2** having a lot of trees (used of a place) 多樹木的〔指地方〕

✶**league** /liːg; liːg/ *n* [sing/pl verb] **1** a group of sports clubs or players that play matches between themselves〔運動〕俱樂部的聯合會: *the Football League* 足球聯合會 | *a league match* 聯賽 **2** a group of people or countries who have joined together to work for a common aim 聯盟; 同盟 **3 in league** working together, often secretly or for a bad purpose 暗中合謀; 私下勾結: *He was accused of being in league* **with** *the terrorists.* 他被控與恐怖主義分子合謀。

leak¹ /liːk; liːk/ *n* **1** a small hole or crack, for example in a container or pipe, through which a gas or liquid escapes or passes 漏洞; 漏隙; 裂縫: *There's a leak* **in** *the flat roof.* 公寓的屋頂有個裂縫。 | *a leak in the tank* 油箱上的漏隙 | *a petrol leak* 汽油滲漏 **2** the telling of news or other information to the public that is supposed to be secret〔新聞或消息的〕泄漏; 透露

leak² *v* **1** [I;T] to let a liquid or gas in or out of a hole or crack 滲漏〔液體或氣體〕: *The bottle leaks.* 這個瓶子漏了。 | *The tank is leaking petrol.* 油箱在漏油。 **2** [I + adv/prep] (of a liquid or gas) to pass through a hole or crack〔液體或氣體〕漏出: *Oil was leaking out of the tank.* 油從油箱中漏出來。 **3** [T] to make information known to the public when it is supposed to be secret 泄漏〔祕密〕; 走漏〔消息〕: *Someone in the ministry leaked the story to the newspapers.* 部裡有人將這件事泄漏給了報界。

  leak out *phr v* [I] (of information that is supposed to be secret) to become known to the public〔祕密〕泄漏

leak·age /ˈliːkɪdʒ; ˈliːkɪdʒ/ *n* [C;U] **1** an act of leaking 泄漏; 滲漏 **2** an amount of liquid or gas which escapes through a hole or crack 漏出來的液體或氣體; 滲漏物

leak·y /ˈliːki; ˈliːki/ *adj* **leakier, leakiest** letting liquid leak in or out 漏的: *a leaky bucket* 漏水的桶

lean¹ /liːn; liːn/ *v* **leant** /lɛnt; lɛnt/ *or* **leaned, leant** *or* **leaned** **1** [I] to slope or bend from an upright position 傾斜; 彎曲: *That wall leans so much it might fall over.* 那堵牆傾斜得很厲害, 可能會倒塌。 | *He leaned forward to hear what she said.* 他俯身向前聽她說甚麼。 **2** [I + adv/prep] to rest or bend against something so that your weight is supported 倚靠: *He leaned on the back of the chair.* 他

靠在椅背上。–see picture on page 992 見 992 頁彩圖 **3** [T + adv/prep] to place something so that its weight is supported on or against something else 把〔某物〕靠置於: *Lean it against the wall.* 把它靠在牆上。 **4 lean on someone** to need someone's help or depend on them 倚賴某人, 依靠某人: *She leans on her family a lot.* 她十分依賴她的家人。

lean² *adj* **1** without much fat (used of meat) 瘦的〔指肉〕 **2** thin but strong and healthy (used of people) 瘦削而強健的〔指人〕–see 見 THIN¹ (USAGE 用法) **3** producing little of value 獲利少的: *This has been a lean year for business.* 這是生意不景氣的一年。 | *a lean harvest* 歉收 **–leanness** *n* [U]

lean·ing /ˈliːnɪŋ; ˈliːnɪŋ/ *n* a tendency to have a particular belief or opinion 傾向; 偏好: *At one time, Jack had a strong leaning* **towards** *socialism.* 傑克曾一度非常傾向社會主義。

leant /lɛnt; lɛnt/ the past tense and past participle of LEAN ☆ LEAN 的過去式和過去分詞

leap¹ /liːp; liːp/ *v* **leapt** /lɛpt; lɛpt/ *or* **leaped** /liːpt; liːpt/, **leapt** *or* **leaped** **1** [I;T] to jump through the air very high or over a distance 跳躍; 跳越: *The horse leapt over the stream.* 那匹馬跳過了小溪。 | *The prisoner leapt the wall and ran away.* 囚犯越牆逃跑了。–see picture on page 992 見 992 頁彩圖 **2** [I + adv/prep] to move or act quickly 快速移動; 迅速行動: *When she heard the knock at the door, she leapt to her feet.* 她一聽到敲門聲, 就立刻站了起來。 | *She leapt to my defence.* 她趕緊為我辯護。 **3** [I + adv/prep] to increase suddenly 突然增加: *Unemployment has leapt up to 10%.* 失業率激增至百分之十。 **4 leap at something** to accept something eagerly 急切地接受某物: *I leapt at the chance to go to Paris.* 我迫不急待地接受了去巴黎的機會。

leap² *n* **1** a sudden jump which is high or over a distance 跳躍: *With a leap she crossed the stream.* 她一躍就跳過了小溪。 **2** a large increase in number or amount 數量的激增: *There has been a sudden leap in oil prices.* 油價大幅度上漲。

leapt /lɛpt/ the past tense and past participle of LEAP ☆ LEAP 的過去式和過去分詞

leap year /ˈ··/ *n* [C] a year in which February has 29 days instead of 28 days 閏年〔二月份有二十九天〕: *There is a leap year every four years.* 每四年便有一個閏年。

★★**learn** /lɜːn; lɜːn/ *v* **learned** *or* **learnt** /lɜːnt; lɜːnt/, **learned** *or* **learnt 1** [I;T] to gain knowledge of something or skill in doing something 學, 學習; 學會〔知識或技術〕: *The child is learning quickly.* 這孩子學得很快。 | *I'm trying to learn French.* 我正在努力學法語。 | *He is learning to write.* 他在

學習寫作。 | *She is learning how to dance.* 她在學跳舞。

> □ USEFUL PATTERNS 有用句型
> to learn something; to learn to do something; to learn how to do something

2 [T] to put and hold something in your memory 記住; 熟記〔某事物〕: *Learn this list of words.* 熟讀這單詞表。 **3** [I;T + (that)] to become informed of something 獲悉; 聽說: *She learnt* **of** *her son's success in the newspapers.* 她從報紙上得知兒子獲得了成功。

> □ USEFUL PATTERNS 有用句型
> to learn something; to learn that...; to learn of/about something

4 [I] to come to understand something, especially that you should behave in a certain way 理解; 領悟; 懂得〔尤指應如何舉止〕: *You must learn not to spend all your money on records.* 你必須明白不能把所有的錢都用來買唱片。–see 見 KNOW (USAGE 用法)

> □ USEFUL PATTERNS 有用句型
> to learn something; to learn to do something

5 learn your lesson, learn the hard way, learn from your mistakes to suffer so much from doing something that you will not do something again 汲取教訓 **6 learn parrot fashion, learn by rote** to learn something by repeating it over and over again, without trying to understand it 死記硬背 **7 learn the ropes** to find out how things are done 懂得事情的做法 [RELATED PHRASE 相關詞組 **show someone the ropes**]

learn·ed /ˈlɜːnɪd; ˈlɜːnɪd/ *adj* respected for having or expressing a lot of knowledge 博學的; 包含廣泛知識的; 學術性的: *a learned man* 博學的人 | *a learned book* 學術著作 **–learnedly** *adv*

learn·er /ˈlɜːnə; ˈlɜːnə/ *n* a person who is learning 學習者: *She's a slow learner.* 她是個遲鈍的學習者。 | *a learner driver* 見習駕駛員

★**learn·ing** /ˈlɜːnɪŋ; ˈlɜːnɪŋ/ *n* [U] great knowledge that you have got by studying 學識; 學問; 知識

learnt /lɜːnt; lɜːnt/ the past tense and past participle of LEARN ☆ LEARN 的過去式和過去分詞

★**lease** /liːs; liːs/ *n* a written agreement by which property is given to someone to use for a certain time in return for rent or a sum of money 〔房地產的〕租約, 租契: *a five-year lease* 為期五年的租約 **–lease** *v* **leased, leasing** [T]: *They've leased the house out while they're abroad.* 他們在出國時, 把房子租

了出去。 | *I've leased a small shop.* 我租了一家小商店。

leash /liːʃ; liːʃ/ *n fml* a length of leather, chain, or rope tied to a dog to control it〖正式〗(繫狗用的)皮帶，鐵鏈，繩子: *Dogs must be kept on a leash.* 狗必須用皮帶繫住。

★★least¹ /liːst; liːst/ *adv* [superlative of LITTLE 的最高級] **1** to the smallest degree 最小; 最少: *The attack happened just when we least expected it.* 進攻發生在我們最料想不到的時候。 | *This is the least friendly place I've ever been to!* 這是我所到過的最不好客的地方! | **2 least of all** especially not〔在許多…之中〕最不〔最少〕: *Nobody was pleased to see him, least of all me.* 沒人願意見他，我就更不用說了。 **3 not least** a phrase used when you are giving an important reason for something, or an important example of something 部分地; 尤其〔用於陳述重要理由或舉出重要例子〕: *Trade has been bad, not least because of the increased cost of raw materials.* 生意一直不好，一個重要原因是原材料漲價了。

least² *det, pron* [superlative of LITTLE 的最高級] **1** the smallest amount 最少的; 最少量: *In the end I chose the one that cost the least.* 最後，我選中了最便宜的一個。 | *I chose the meat that had the least fat on it.* 我選了肥肉最少的一塊肉。 **2 at least: a** used when you are giving the smallest amount of something 至少; 起碼〔用於給出最小數量〕: *There must have been at least 500 people there.* 那裡一定至少有五百人。 | *Shoes like that cost £50 at least!* 買那樣的鞋至少要花五十英鎊! **b** used when you are giving the smallest thing that someone should do 至少; 最起碼〔用於說出別人至少應做的事〕: *She should at least apologize!* 她至少應該道歉! | *They could at least have answered my letter!* 他們最起碼應該給我回封信! **c** used when you are giving one advantage that exists among a lot of disadvantages 至少〔用於指出許多缺點中的一個優點〕: *The hotel was noisy and dirty, but at least it was cheap.* 這家旅館又嘈雜又骯髒，但至少價錢還算便宜。 **d** used when you have made a statement which you are correcting because it was too strong 至少〔用於改正自己所說的語氣過於強烈的句子〕: *She's coming with us. At least, I think she is.* 她要和我們一來來。至少，我認為她是這樣打算的。 **3 not in the least** not at all 一點兒也不，絲毫不: *She's not in the least worried.* 她一點兒也不擔心。

★leath·er /ˈlɛðə; ˈlɛðɚ/ *n* [U] treated animal skin used for making things like shoes and bags 皮革: *a leather coat* 皮外衣

leath·er·y /ˈlɛðəri; ˈlɛðəri/ *adj* hard and stiff like leather 似皮革的; 堅韌的: *leathery meat* 堅韌而嚼不爛的肉

★★leave¹ /liːv; liːv/ *v* **left** /lɛft; lɛft/, **leaving** **1** [I;T] to go away from a person or place 離開: *They're just leaving.* 他們剛巧

了出去。 | *His brother has left home.* 他的哥哥離家了。 | *The ship is leaving for New York soon.* 這艘船將開往紐約。 | *She's left her husband.* 她離開了丈夫。 **2** [T] to allow something to remain, especially after you have gone away〔尤指走後〕使…處於〔某種狀態〕留下: *She's left your dinner in the oven.* 她留了飯菜在爐裡給你。 | *Someone has left the window open.* 有人把窗打開了。 | *Is there any coffee left?* 還有咖啡嗎? | *Why have you left your vegetables?* 你為甚麼剩下了蔬菜(沒吃)? | *I'll leave the rest of the work until tomorrow.* 我打算把餘下的工作留到明天再做。 | *2 from 8 leaves 6.* 8減2等於6。 **3** [T + adv/prep] to forget to take or bring something 忘記拿〔某物〕: *Don't leave your coat behind!* 不要忘了拿外衣! | *I've done my homework, but I've left it at home.* 我做了家庭作業，可是我把它留在家裡了。 –see 見 FORGET (USAGE 用法) **4** [T] to pass on property after your death〔去世後〕遺留: *My father left everything **to** my sister.* 我父親把一切都留給了妹妹。 **5 leave something to someone** to make someone responsible for something 交由某人負責某事: *I don't mind where we go. I'll leave that to you.* 我們去哪裡我無所謂，你來決定吧。 | *He left the accounts to me.* 他把賬目交給我來管理。 **6 leave someone alone** to allow someone to be by themselves 讓某人獨處 **7 leave someone/something alone** not to touch, move, worry, or annoy them 不打擾某人或某物: *Don't tease the dog — leave him alone!* 別逗那隻狗，讓牠獨自呆著吧! | *Leave those cakes alone or there won't be enough for tea.* 別動那些蛋糕，不然吃茶點時東西就不夠吃了。 **8 leave go** to stop holding a person or thing 放開〔某人或某物〕: *Don't leave go **of** the handle.* 別鬆開那個把手。 **9 leave no stone unturned** to try everything possible in order to do something or to find something 千方百計〔做某事或尋找某物〕: *We will leave no stone unturned in our efforts to find an answer.* 我們將不遺餘力地尋找答案。

leave off *phr v* [I;T **leave off** sthg] to stop or give up doing something 停止做〔某事〕; 放棄做〔某事〕: *I wish the rain would leave off.* 我希望雨會停。 | *I didn't leave off work until ten o'clock last night.* 昨天晚上我一直工作到十點鐘。

leave sbdy/sthg ↔ **out** *phr v* [T] to fail to include a person or thing 不包括〔某人或某物〕; 排除; 遺漏: *I left out the important point.* 我漏掉了重要的一點。 | *They left me out **of** the team.* 他們沒有讓我加入他們的隊伍。

★leave² *n* [U] **1** a period of time away from work or duty 休假; 假期: *Those soldiers are on leave.* 那些士兵在休假。 | *I'm spending my next leave in Greece.* 下一次休假我準備去希臘。 | *She's taking three months maternity leave.* 她正在休三個月的產假。 **2** *fml* permission 〖正式〗准許, 許可: *Have you been given leave to swim here?* 你在這裡游泳得到過許可嗎?

leaves /livz; liːvz/ the plural of LEAF ☆ LEAF 的複數

lech·er·ous /ˈlɛtʃərəs; ˈlɛtʃərəs/ *adj* having or showing openly a desire for continual sexual pleasure (a word used to express disapproval) 縱慾的; 好色的〔含貶義〕 – **lecherously** *adv* –**lecher** *n*

lech·er·y /ˈlɛtʃəri; ˈlɛtʃəri/ *n* [U] strong and continual interest in sexual pleasure (a word used to express disapproval) 好色; 色慾〔含貶義〕

*lec·ture** /ˈlɛktʃə; ˈlɛktʃəʳ/ *v* **lectured, lecturing** **1** [I] to give a formal talk or a number of talks to a group of people, especially as a method of teaching in a college 講授; 講課; 演講: *She lectures on English history.* 她講授英國歷史。 **2** [T] to give someone a long solemn scolding or warning 長篇大論地訓誡: *He lectured us on the evils of drink.* 他告誡我們酗酒的壞處。 –**lecture** *n*: *a history lecture* 歷史講座 | *He gave a very good lecture on computer programming.* 他就有關電腦程序設計方面作了一次十分出色的講座。 | *a lecture on good manners* 一次關於良好的行為舉止的演講

lec·tur·er /ˈlɛktʃərə; ˈlɛktʃərəʳ/ *n* a person who teaches at a university or college or who gives formal talks to people interested in a particular subject (大學)講師; 講授者: *a lecturer in economics* 經濟學講師 | *a biology lecturer* 生物學講師 –**lectureship** *n*: *She's got a lectureship at Oxford.* 她獲得了牛津大學的講師職位。

led /lɛd; lɛd/ *v* the past tense and past participle of LEAD¹ ☆ LEAD¹ 的過去式和過去分詞

ledge /lɛdʒ; lɛdʒ/ *n* **1** a flat, narrow shelf 平窄的架子: *There's a bird on the window ledge.* 窗台上有隻小鳥。 **2** a flat shelf on the side of a cliff or rock 岩架; 岩礁

led·ger /ˈlɛdʒə; ˈlɛdʒəʳ/ *n* an account book in which the money going in and out of a company is recorded〔公司的〕賬簿; 分類賬

leech /liːtʃ; liːtʃ/ *n* a small wormlike creature that lives by drinking the blood of living animals 水蛭; 螞蟥

leek /liːk; liːk/ *n* a green and white vegetable with a long stem and a taste similar to that of an onion 韭葱 –see picture on page 504 見 504 頁彩圖

leer /lɪr; lɪəʳ/ *n* an unpleasant smile expressing cruel enjoyment or thoughts of sex 不懷好意的笑; 色迷迷的笑 –**leer** *v* [I]: *He leered at the young girl.* 他色迷迷地瞧着那年輕的女子。–**leeringly** *adv*

lee·way /ˈliːweɪ; ˈliːweɪ/ *n* [C;U] the additional time, space, money and so on that allows you to change or do something if necessary〔時間、空間、金錢上〕隨意處置的

餘地: *We should allow a bit of leeway in case the traffic is bad.* 我們應該留點時間, 以防交通擁擠。

*left¹** /lɛft; lɛft/ *adj* [only before a noun 只用於名詞前] **1** on the side of the body that contains a person's heart〔身體〕左側的: *her left arm* 她的左臂 **2** on your left side 左邊的; 左面的: *the left bank of the stream* 小溪的左岸 –opposite 反義 **right**

left² *n* **1** the left the left side or direction 左邊; 左側; 左方: *Keep to the left.* 靠左邊走。 | *The shop is on the left, past the traffic lights.* 那家商店在過了交通燈之後的靠左邊。 | *The window is to the left of the door.* 窗在門的左側。 **2** [C] a blow with the left hand 左手的一擊 **3** the Left, the left political parties or groups that generally support the workers and work for social change 左派政黨〔組織〕: *supporters of the left* 左派政黨支持者 | *The extreme left are calling for a wealth tax.* 極左分子正在要求徵收財富稅。–opposite 反義 **right**

left³ *adv* towards the left 向左: *Go down to the crossroads and turn left.* 走到十字路口後向左轉。–opposite 反義 **right**

left⁴ the past tense and past participle of LEAVE ☆ LEAVE 的過去式和過去分詞

left-hand /ˌ·ˈ··◂/ *adj* [only before a noun 只用於名詞前] **1** on or going to the left 左邊的; 朝左行的: *the left-hand page* 左邊的一頁 | *a left-hand bend in the road* 路的左轉彎處 | *on the left-hand side* 在左邊 **2** of, for, with, or done by the left hand 左手的; 左手做的

left-hand·ed /ˌ·ˈ···◂/ *adj* **1** using the left hand more easily than the right for certain actions 慣用左手的 **2** made for a left-handed person to use 為慣用左手的人做的: *left-handed scissors* 左手用的剪刀 **3** done with the left hand 用左手做的 –opposite 反義 **right-handed** –**left-handedness** *n* [U]

left lug·gage of·fice /ˌ·ˈ···,··/ *n* a place, especially in a station, where you can leave your bags for a certain period〔尤指車站的〕行李寄存處

left-o·ver /ˈlɛft,ovə; ˈlɛft,əʊvəʳ/ *adj* remaining after you have used what you need 剩下的; 未用完的: *I made the curtains, and there was enough leftover material for some cushion covers.* 我做完窗簾, 剩下的布料還足夠做幾個墊子。

left-o·vers /ˈlɛft,ovəz; ˈlɛft,əʊvəz/ *n* [pl] food which remains uneaten after a meal 剩飯菜

left·wards /ˈlɛftwədz; ˈlɛftwədz/ *adv* (also 又作 **leftward** *AmE*〖美式〗) towards the left 向左邊 –opposite 反義 **rightwards** – **leftward** *adj*

left wing /ˌ·ˈ·◂/ *adj* having certain political ideas which include support for greater social change 左派的; 激進派的; 左翼的: *a left-wing politician* 左翼政客 | *She's very left* *wing.* 她的思想左傾。 –**left wing** *n*: *the left wing of the party* 黨內的激進派 –**opposite** 反義 **right wing** –**left-winger** /ˌ··ˈ··/ *n*

★**leg** /lɛg; lɛg/ *n* **1** one of the limbs on which a person or an animal walks 〔人或動物的〕腿 –see 見 PAIR (USAGE 用法) **2** the part of a pair of trousers that covers your leg 褲腿 **3** one of the long thin supports on which a piece of furniture stands 家具的腿腳，支架 **4** one stage of a journey or competition 〔旅程或賽程的〕一段: *The last leg of the journey always seems the longest.* 最後一段旅程總是顯得最長。 **5 -legged** with legs of a certain number or kind (有)…腿的: *a four-legged animal* 四條腿的動物 | *sitting cross-legged* 盤腿而坐

leg·a·cy /ˈlɛgəsɪ; ˈlɛgəsi/ *n* **legacies 1** money or property that passes to you on the death of the owner, following their official written wishes 遺產；遺贈物: *I got a small legacy* **from** *my aunt.* 我從姑母那裡得到一小筆遺產。 **2** a situation which is passed on or left behind by someone or something that came before 〔某人或某事〕遺留下來的局面: *The legacies* **of** *the war were disease and hunger.* 戰爭所遺留下來的禍害是疾病和飢餓。

★★**le·gal** /ˈligl; ˈliːɡəl/ *adj* **1** allowed by law 法律允許的，法定的，合法的: *Are her business dealings really legal?* 她的買賣真的合法嗎？ –**opposite** 反義 ILLEGAL **2** [only before a noun 只用於名詞前] relating to or using the law 與法律有關的；使用法律的: *the legal system* 法律制度 | *The Council is taking legal action against its accountant.* 理事會正在對其會計師採取法律行動。 –**legally** *adv* –**legality** /lɪˈɡæləti; lɪˈɡælɪ̩ti/ *n* [U]

> ■ USAGE 用法: Compare 比較 **legal, lawful, legitimate. Legal** is the ordinary word for actions allowed by the law, and the general word for things connected with the law ☆ **legal** 為"合法的"的普通詞，也普遍用於與法律有關的事物: *It is* **legal** *for people over 18 to buy alcohol.* 十八歲以上的人買酒是合法的。 | *the* **legal** *profession* 法律專業。 **Lawful** suggests that the law has moral or religious force ☆ **lawful** 暗示該法律有道德或宗教約束力: *a* **lawful** *marriage* 合法婚姻 | *your* **lawful** *king* 你們的合法國王。 **Legitimate** means "accepted by law, custom or common belief" ☆ **legitimate** 指"為法律、習俗及一般信仰所接受的": *the* **legitimate** *government* 合法政府 | *He claimed that bombing the town was a* **legitimate** *act of war.* 他宣稱轟炸這座城鎮是戰爭中的正當行動。 | *Her illness was a* **legitimate** *reason for being absent from work.* 她生病是沒來上班的正當理由。

le·gal·ize /ˈligl̩ˌaɪz; ˈliːɡəlaɪz/ *v* **legalized,**

legalizing (also 又作 **legalise** *BrE* 〔英式〕) [T] to make something legal 使〔某事〕合法化: *The use of certain drugs may be legalized.* 某些藥品的使用可能會合法化。 –**legalization** /ˌliglə'zeʃən; ˌliːɡəlaɪ'zeɪʃən/ *n* [U]

legal ten·der /ˌ·· ˈ··/ *n* any form of money which, by law, must be accepted if it is offered in payment 法定貨幣

le·ga·tion /lɪˈɡeʃən; lɪˈɡeɪʃən/ *n* a group of people who are employed to represent their government in a foreign country 公使館；公使館全體人員

le·gend /ˈlɛdʒənd; ˈlɛdʒənd/ *n* **1** [C] an old story, usually about ancient times, which is probably not true 傳奇故事；傳說: *the legend of King Arthur* 亞瑟王的傳奇 **2** [U] stories of this kind considered together 民間傳說: *a character in Chinese legend* 中國民間傳說中的人物 **3** [C] a person who has become famous in a particular area of activity 〔某一領域中的〕傳奇式人物: *Dylan has become a legend in his own lifetime.* 戴蘭在他那個時代成為了一個傳奇式人物。 **4** [C] words written on something like a map to describe its contents 銘文；圖例；文字說明

le·gen·da·ry /ˈlɛdʒəndˌɛrɪ; ˈlɛdʒəndəri/ *adj* **1** told of in a legend 傳奇的；傳說的: *the legendary kings of Ireland* 傳說中的愛爾蘭王 **2** very famous but perhaps hard to believe 非常著名的，大名鼎鼎的: *His drinking was legendary.* 他喝酒喝得出了名。

leg·gings /ˈlɛgɪŋz; ˈlɛgɪŋz/ *n* [pl] an outer covering which you wear to protect your legs 綁腿，護腿 –see picture on page 210 見 210 頁彩圖

leg·gy /ˈlɛgɪ; ˈlɛgi/ *adj* **leggier, leggiest** with particularly long legs (used especially of women, children, and young animals) 腿修長的〔尤指婦女、兒童和小動物〕 –**legginess** *n* [U]

le·gi·ble /ˈlɛdʒəbl̩; ˈlɛdʒ ̩bəl/ *adj* clear enough to be read, or to be read easily (used of writing or print) 清楚易讀的〔指字跡或印刷〕 –**opposite** 反義 **illegible** –**legibly** *adv*: *Please write legibly.* 請寫得清楚些。 –**legibility** /ˌlɛdʒə'bɪlətɪ; ˌlɛdʒ ̩'bɪlɪ̩ti/ *n* [U]

le·gion /ˈlidʒən; ˈliːdʒən/ *n* **1** a group of soldiers or other armed men 軍團 **2** a large group of people 一大批(人): *A legion of admirers had gathered outside to see the star leave.* 大批仰慕者聚在門外，以目睹這位明星的離去。

le·gis·late /ˈlɛdʒɪsˌlet; ˈlɛdʒ ̩sleɪt/ *v* **legislated, legislating** [I] to make laws 制定法律，立法: *Parliament may legislate against the selling of human organs.* 議會可能會制定法律禁止出售人體器官。 –**legislator** *n*

★**le·gis·la·tion** /ˌlɛdʒɪs'leʃən; ˌlɛdʒ ̩s'leɪʃən/ *n* [U] **1** the act of making laws 立法 **2** a body of laws 法規: *new legislation concerning the employment of children* 有關雇用兒童的新法規

le·gis·la·tive /ˈlɛdʒɪsˌletɪv; ˈledʒɨsslətɪv/ adj [only before a noun 只用於名詞前] **1** concerning the making of laws (有關) 立法的 **2** having the power and duty to make laws 有立法權的: a legislative assembly 立法議會

le·gis·la·ture /ˈledʒɪsˌletʃɚ; ˈledʒɨsleɪtʃɔr/ n the group of people who have the power to make and change laws 立法機關

le·git·i·mate /lɪˈdʒɪtəmɪt; lɨˈdʒɪtɨmɨt/ adj **1** legal or correct 合法的; 正當的: Her demand for compensation is perfectly legitimate. 她要求賠償是完全正當的。–opposite 反義 **illegitimate 2** born of parents who are legally married to each other 婚生的 –opposite 反義 **illegitimate 3** reasonable 合理的: They had a legitimate reason for being late. 他們遲到是有正當理由的。–see 見 LEGAL (USAGE 用法) –**legitimately** adv –**legitimacy** n [U]

*****lei·sure** /ˈliʒɚ; ˈleʒɚr/ n **1** [U] free time 空閒, 閒暇: A wide variety of leisure activities is available to students outside class time. 學生在課餘時可參加各種各樣的消遣活動。 **2 at leisure, at your leisure : a** not working or busy 不在工作; 不忙 **b** without hurrying 不匆忙: You can finish that at your leisure, it's not urgent. 你有空時才做, 這事不急。

lei·sured /ˈliʒɚd; ˈleʒɚd/ adj having plenty of free time 有空閒的: the leisured classes 有閒階層

lei·sure·ly /ˈliʒɚlɪ; ˈleʒɚli/ adj [only before a noun 只用於名詞前] done without hurrying 悠閒的, 不慌不忙的: a leisurely walk 悠閒的散步

lem·on /ˈlɛmən; ˈlemən/ n [C;U] a fruit with a thick yellow skin and a sour taste 檸檬: a lemon drink 檸檬飲料 | mineral water with a slice of lemon 加有一片檸檬的礦泉水 –see picture on page 504 見 504 頁彩圖

lem·on·ade /ˌlɛmənˈed; ˌlemɑˈneɪd/ n [U] **1** a sweet, gassy drink 汽水 **2** a drink made from the juice of fresh lemons with sugar and water 鮮檸檬水

*****lend** /lɛnd; lend/ v **lent** /lɛnt; lent/, **lent** [T] **1** to give someone the use of something for a limited time 借給; 借出〔某物〕: Can you lend me £10? 你能借給我十英鎊嗎？ | I've lent my notes to Bob. 我已把筆記借給鮑勃了。

> □ USEFUL PATTERNS 有用句型
> to lend something to someone; to lend someone something

2 fml to add something to a person, thing or situation〔正式〕為〔人、物或局勢〕增添: The flags lent colour to the streets. 這些旗幟為街道增添了色彩。 | The new evidence lends support to claims that she is innocent. 她是無辜的説法得到了新證據的支持。 **3 lend a hand** to help someone do something 幫助〔某人做某事〕: Could you come and lend a hand in the kitchen? 你來廚房幫幫忙嗎？ **4**

lend an ear to listen sympathetically〔同情地〕傾聽 **5 lend yourself to** to be easily used or thought of in a certain way 適用於…; 對…有用: This hall lends itself to large meetings. 這大廳適合於舉行大型會議。

*****length** /lɛŋθ; lɛŋθ/ n **1** [C;U] the measurement or distance from one end of something to the other along its longest side 長度; 長: The length of the room is 10 metres. 房間長度為十米。 | The garden is 40 metres in length. 花園有四十米長。 | We walked the length of the street. 我們走完了整條街。–compare 比較 BREADTH **2** [C] a piece of something, especially of a certain length or for a particular purpose 一段; 一節〔尤指用於某一目的〕: a length of rope 一段繩子 **3** [C] the amount of something 數量: He judges a book by its length! 他竟然用厚薄來判斷一本書！ **4** [C;U] the amount of time something takes 時間的長短: We are all worried about the length of her visit. 我們都擔心她到訪的時間是否太長。 **5 at length : a** after a long time〔很長時間後〕終於: At length he came back. 他終於回來了。 **b** in detail 詳盡地: They spoke at length about the situation. 他們詳盡地討論了形勢。 **6 go to any lengths, go to considerable lengths, go to great lengths** to be prepared to do anything, or more than is usual〔為取得成功〕不惜一切代價; 不遺餘力; 不擇手段: He would go to any lengths to keep his government in power. 他會不惜一切代價使他的政府能繼續執政。

length·en /ˈlɛŋθən; ˈlɛŋθən/ v [I;T] to become or to make something longer (使)變長 –opposite 反義 **shorten**

length·ways /ˈlɛŋθˌwez; ˈlɛŋθweɪz/ adv (also 又作 **lengthwise** /-ˌwaɪz; -waɪz/, **longways**) in the direction of the length 縱長地: Fold the cloth lengthways. 把這塊布縱向地折疊。

length·y /ˈlɛŋθɪ; ˈlɛŋθi/ adj **lengthier, lengthiest** very long, and sometimes too long 冗長的, 過長的: a lengthy speech 冗長的演講 –**lengthily** adv

le·ni·ent /ˈliniənt; ˈliːniənt/ adj not severe 不嚴厲的; 寬容的: a lenient teacher 寬容的老師 | a lenient view of his behaviour 對他的行為所持的寬容的看法 | a lenient punishment 寬大的處罰 –**lenience** (also 又作 **leniency**) n [U]

lens /lɛnz; lenz/ n **1** a special piece of glass or plastic, curved on one or both sides, which you use to see things more clearly 鏡片; 透鏡: He has changed his glasses for contact lenses. 他已不戴眼鏡, 改戴隱形眼鏡。 | A simple telescope has two lenses. 簡單的望遠鏡有兩塊透鏡。 **2** the part of your eye which collects the light〔眼球的〕晶狀體

lent /lɛnt; lent/ the past tense and past participle of LEND ☆ LEND 的過去式和過去分詞

Lent *n* [U] the 40 days before EASTER, during which many Christians give up certain foods or other pleasures 四旬齋〔復活節前基督徒齋戒禁慾的四十天〕

len·til /'lɛntl; 'lɛntl/ *n* a small round seed which is dried and used for food 小扁豆

Le·o /'lio; 'liːəʊ/ *n* one of the signs of the ZODIAC 獅子宮

leop·ard /'lɛpəd; 'lepəd/ *n* a large, fierce animal belonging to the cat family, which has a yellow coat with black spots; a female leopard is called a **leopardess** 豹〔母豹稱為 **leopardess**〕

le·o·tard /'liətad; 'liːətɑːd/ *n* a tight-fitting garment which covers a person's body from their neck to the top of their legs; it is worn by dancers and by people doing exercises 〔跳舞或參加運動的人所穿的〕緊身連衣褲

lep·er /'lɛpə; 'lepər/ *n* **1** a person who has leprosy 麻瘋病患者: *a leper hospital* 麻瘋病醫院 **2** a person who is avoided by other people, perhaps because of something bad they have done 〔由於做了壞事〕大家避之唯恐不及的人

lep·ro·sy /'lɛprəsɪ; 'leprəsi/ *n* [U] a serious illness in which your skin becomes hard and thick and loses its feeling, and your flesh is badly damaged 麻瘋病 **–leprous** /'lɛprəs; 'leprəs/ *adj*

les·bi·an /'lɛzbɪən; 'lezbiən/ *n* a woman who is sexually attracted to other women 女同性戀者 **–lesbian** *adj* **–lesbianism** *n* [U]

★★less[1] /lɛs; les/ *det, pron, adv* [comparative of LITTLE 的比較級] **1** not as much 較少地; 不如; 不那麼: *The next train should be less crowded than this.* 下一班火車應該沒有這班這麼擁擠。| *I go to London less frequently than before.* 我去倫敦不如以前那麼頻繁了。| *He works less than he used to.* 他工作做得不如過去那麼多了。| *People in this country spend less money on food than people in other European countries.* 該國的人花在食物上的錢比歐洲其他國家的人要少。| *Could you try to make less noise?* 你能盡量輕聲一點嗎? | *Let's have less of that shouting!* 我們少一點那樣叫喊吧! **2 less and less** continuing to become smaller in amount or degree 〔數量或程度〕愈來愈少〔小〕: *I seem to be spending less and less of my time working.* 我花在工作上的時間似乎愈來愈少。| *People are becoming less and less interested in politics.* 人們對政治越來越不感興趣。 **3 no less than** a phrase used to show that you are surprised that a number or amount is so large 竟有…之多〔表示吃驚〕: *There were no less than 2,000 people at the rally.* 集會上竟有二千人之多。

> ■ USAGE 用法: In informal English many people now use **less** and **least**

with plural nouns, but this is still considered to be incorrect. **Fewer** and **fewest** are the generally accepted correct forms ☆在非正式英語中，現在許多人在複數名詞前用 **less** 和 **least**，但這種用法仍然被認為是不正確的。廣為人所接受的正確形式應為 **fewer** 和 **fewest**: *There were fewer people than I expected.* 人數比我預期的要少。| *Who has made the fewest mistakes?* 誰犯的錯誤最少?

★★less[2] *prep* subtracting a particular number or amount 扣除; 減去: *You will be paid £200 a week, less tax.* 你每週的工資為二百英鎊，再要扣除稅款。

less·en /'lɛsn; 'lesən/ *v* [I;T] to become or to make something smaller in size, amount, or importance (使)變小; (使)變少

less·er /'lɛsə; 'lesər/ *adj, adv* [only before a noun 只用於名詞前] not so great or not so much 較次要的(的); 較小(的): *the lesser of two evils* 兩害中的較輕者 | *one of the lesser-known African writers* 其中一位比較鮮為人知的非洲作家

★les·son /'lɛsn; 'lesən/ *n* **1** something which is taught to or learned by a pupil 課; 課程: *a physics lesson* 物理課 | *piano lessons* 鋼琴課 **2** the period of time in which a subject is studied (一節)課; 課時: *The school day is divided into eight forty-minute lessons.* 學校一天有八節四十分鐘的課。 **3** an experience from which you should learn 教訓: *His car accident was a lesson to him.* 那次車禍對他是個教訓。 **4** a passage from the BIBLE which is read to people in church 禮拜儀式中誦讀的一段聖經

lest /lɛst; lest/ *prep* in case something unwanted should happen 以免; 以防: *I wrote down the date lest I should forget it.* 我寫下了日期，以免忘記。

★★let /lɛt; let/ *v* **let, let, letting** [T] **1** to allow someone to do something, or allow something to happen 允許〔某人做某事〕; 讓〔某事發生〕: *My dad wouldn't let me smoke.* 父親不允許我抽煙。| *They let the prisoners go.* 他們放走了囚犯。| *I knocked on the door but they didn't let me in.* 我敲了門，但他們不讓我進去。| *Please let the doctor through.* 請讓醫生過去吧。| *Don't let the paper get wet.* 別把紙弄濕。

> □ USEFUL PATTERNS 有用句型
> to let someone do something; to let something happen; to let someone in, out, through, past, etc.

2 a word you use to say that someone can do something or should do something 讓; 使; 要〔表示某人可以或應該做某事〕: *Let him do what he likes; I don't care.* 讓他去做他想

做的事，我無所謂。| *Let there be no mistake about it.* 要保證不要出錯。**3** to allow someone to use a room, building, or piece of land in return for regular payments 租出，借出〔房間、房屋、土地〕: *We decided to let the house rather than sell it.* 我們決定出租而不是出售我們的房子。**4 let alone** not to mention something which is even less possible 更不用說: *The baby can't even walk, let alone run.* 這嬰兒連走路都不會，更不用說跑了。**5 let someone alone, leave someone alone** to not touch or trouble someone 不管某人；不打擾某人: *Let your sister alone!* 不要打擾你妹妹! | *I wish the press would just let me alone.* 我希望新聞界不要來打擾我。**6 let go of someone/something, let someone/something go** to stop holding someone or something 鬆開〔某人或某物〕; 放開〔某人或某物〕: *Let go of my arm.* 放開我的胳膊。| *Don't let go of the handle.* 抓住把手不要鬆開。| *Let me go!* 放開我! | *The police held him for 24 hours before letting him go.* 警方拘留了他二十四小時後才放他走。**7 let yourself go** to behave more freely and more naturally than you would usually 隨心所欲；盡情地〔做…〕: *She had a few drinks and let herself go a bit.* 她喝了幾杯酒，讓自己放鬆一些。**8 let someone know** to tell someone about something 告訴某人: *Let me know what day you'll be arriving.* 告訴我你哪一天到。**9 let me** a phrase you use when you are going to do something 讓我〔表示準備做某事〕: *Let me just get my coat and we can go.* 讓我去拿一下外衣，我們就可以走了。| *Let me start by talking about pollution in general.* 首先讓我從總體上談談污染問題。**10 let us, let's** a phrase you use when you are suggesting to someone that you should both do something or all do something 讓我們〔表示建議某人一起做某事〕: *Let's meet in town.* 我們在鎮裡見面吧。| *Come on, let's get going.* 來吧，我們走吧。

■ USAGE 用法: **1 Let us** is usually shortened to **let's** when it is used in conversation to make a suggestion which includes the person you are speaking to ☆ 在表示包括你說話的對象時，**let us** 常縮寫成 **let's**: *Come on, Jim, let's go and have lunch!* 來吧，吉姆，我們一起去吃午飯吧! | *Let's have a party at the end of term.* 學期結束時，我們開個派對吧。**2 Let's** can be used by itself to show that you agree with someone else's suggestion ☆ **let's** 可單獨使用，表示同意別人的建議: *"Shall we go to the cinema tonight?" "Oh, yes. Let's!"* "今晚我們去看電影好嗎?" "哦，好的。我們一起去!" **3** The negative of **let's** is **let's not** ☆ **let's** 的否定形式為 **let's not**: *Let's not waste time on this.* 讓我們別

在這上面浪費時間了。(In British English **don't let's** is also possible 英式英語中有時也用 **don't let's**)

let down *phr v* **1** [T **let** sbdy ↔ **down**] to cause someone to be disappointed 使〔某人〕失望: *I'm sorry to let you down, but I really can't come this evening.* 讓你失望我很抱歉，但我今晚實在是不能來了。| *She felt that the education system had let her down.* 她感到教育制度令她很失望。**2** [T **let** sthg ↔ **down**] to make a piece of clothing longer 把〔衣服〕放長，加長

let in for *phr v* **let yourself in for something** to cause yourself to experience something unpleasant or unwanted 使自己陷入[捲入]…; 給〔自己〕招致: *I don't think he realizes what he's letting himself in for.* 我認為他並不知道他在給自己惹甚麼麻煩。

let sbdy **in on** sthg *phr v* [T] to allow someone to know something that was secret 把〔祕密〕告訴〔某人〕: *They refused to let me in on the joke.* 他們不肯把那個笑話告訴我。

let off *phr v* **1** [T **let** sbdy ↔ **off** (sthg)] to allow someone not to do something that it is their duty to do 免除〔某人應盡的職責〕: *They let him off his homework because he was ill.* 他們允許他不做家庭作業，因為他病了。**2** [T **let** sbdy ↔ **off**] to not give someone a punishment when they have done something wrong 免除對〔某人〕的懲罰: *The police let him off with a caution.* 警察警告了他之後便放了他。**3** [T **let** sthg ↔ **off**] to cause something to explode 使〔某物〕爆炸: *people letting off fireworks* 放煙火的人們

let on *phr v* [I] to tell a secret 泄露祕密: *He asked me where John was, but I didn't let on.* 他問我約翰在何處，但我不肯透露。

let sthg ↔ **out** *phr v* [T] **1** to express a sound 發出〔聲響〕: *She let out a sharp cry of pain.* 她發出了痛苦的尖叫。**2** to make clothes bigger 把〔衣服〕加大: *I had to let my skirt out.* 我不得不把我的裙子放長。

let up *phr v* [I] to become less or stop 變小；減弱；停止: *Will this rain ever let up?* 這場雨會停嗎?

let·down /ˈletdaʊn; ˈletdaʊn/ *n infml* a disappointment 〔非正式〕失望; 令人失望的事: *Rain on our wedding day; what a letdown!* 我們結婚的那一天下雨，真叫人掃興!

le·thal /ˈliːθəl; ˈliːθəl/ *adj* able to kill people or destroy things 致命的，殺傷性的: *a lethal dose of a poison* 一種藥劑的致命量 | *His business tactics can be lethal to small companies.* 他做生意的策略對小公司可以具有殺傷性。

leth·ar·gy /ˈleθədʒɪ; ˈleθədʒɪ/ *n* [U] the state of being unwilling or physically unable to make the effort to do anything because you feel lazy, tired, or ill 睏倦; 懶散;

無精打采 **–lethargic** /lɪˈθɑːrdʒɪk; lɪˈθɑːdʒɪk/ *adj*

★let·ter /ˈletə; ˈletəʳ/ *n* **1** a written or printed message which is usually sent to someone in an envelope 信: *Would you post my letter when you go out?* 你外出時幫我把這封信寄了好嗎？| *I must write them a letter.* 我必須給他們寫封信。 **2** one of the signs in writing or printing that represents a speech sound 字母: *Start the sentence with a capital letter.* 句子的第一個字母要大寫。| *How many letters are there in your name?* 你的名字有幾個字母？ **3 the letter of** the exact words of an agreement or law, rather than its real or intended meaning 〔協議或法律的〕字面意義; 措辭 **4 to the letter** exactly as something is written or told to you 嚴格按照文字〔指示〕: *Follow the instructions to the letter.* 嚴格按照指示行事。

let·ter·box /ˈletəˌbɒks; ˈletəbɒks/ *n* **1** a box in a place such as a post office or the street in which letters can be posted 郵筒, 郵箱 **2** *BrE* a hole in the front door or wall of a building into which letters are delivered 〔英式〕信箱 –see picture on page 729 見 729 頁彩圖

let·ter·head /ˈletəˌhed; ˈletəhed/ *n* the name and address of a person or business printed at the top of their writing paper 信箋抬頭, 信頭〔印於信箋上端的名稱、地址〕

let·ter·ing /ˈletərɪŋ; ˈletərɪŋ/ *n* [U] letters or words that are written or drawn in a particular style 〔以某種風格書寫或繪製的〕字體

let·tuce /ˈletɪs; ˈletɪs/ *n* [C;U] a plant with large pale green leaves, which are eaten raw 萵苣, 生菜 –see picture on page 504 見 504 頁彩圖

let·up /ˈletˌʌp; ˈletʌp/ *n* [C;U] an end to or decrease in activity 〔活動的〕中止; 減少

leu·kae·mia /ljəˈkiːmɪə; luːˈkiːmɪə/ *n* (also 又作 **leukemia**) [U] a very serious illness in which the blood has too many white cells 白血病

★lev·el¹ /ˈlevl; ˈlevəl/ *n* **1** [C;U] a position of height in relation to a flat surface 水平面; 層面: *We are now at 5,000 metres above sea level.* 我們現在的高度是海拔五千米。| *The garden is arranged on two levels.* 花園有高低兩個層面。| *an eye-level grill* 與眼睛齊高的烤架 **2** a position in a system of ranks 級別: *pay increases for lower-level managers* 級別較低的經理的加薪 | *talks at ministerial level* 部長級會談 **3** [C] a smooth flat surface, especially a wide area of flat ground 平面〔尤指大塊平地〕: *You should build on the level, not on the slope.* 你應該在平地上而不是斜坡上建造房屋。 **4** [C] the amount, degree, or number of something 水平; 程度: *Workers have been told to increase production levels.* 工人都已經得到指示, 提高生產水平。| *The general level of achievement is satisfactory.* 所取得的成就整

體水平令人滿意。 **5** the usual American word for 〔美式〕= SPIRIT LEVEL **6 on the level** *infml* honest, or honestly 〔非正式〕誠實的; 誠實地

★level² *v* **-ll-** (**-l-** *AmE* 〔美式〕) [T] **1** to make something flat and even 使〔某物〕平坦, 把…弄平: *Level the ground before you plant the seeds.* 播種之前先平整一下土地。 **2** to knock something down to the ground 推倒; 夷平: *They levelled all the old trees to make way for the road.* 他們把所有的老樹都砍光了, 好騰出地方修築公路。 **3 level something at** to aim a weapon at a person or thing 用〔武器〕瞄準〔某人或某物〕 **4 level something at someone, level something against someone** to make a complaint about someone 對某人提出指控: *A serious charge was levelled at the minister.* 〔有人〕對部長提出了嚴厲的指控。 **5 level with someone** *infml* to be honest with someone 〔非正式〕誠懇地對待某人

level off *phr v* [I] (also 又作 **level out**) to become steady or equal 變得穩定〔平穩〕: *Prices have begun to level off now.* 物價現已開始穩定下來。

level³ *adj* **1** flat, with no part higher than the rest 平的; 平坦的: *If the table top isn't level, things will roll off.* 如果桌面不平坦, 東西就會滾下去。| *a level teaspoonful of salt* 一平匙的鹽 **2** at the same height, position, or standard 同等高度〔水準〕的: *The child's head is level **with** his father's knee.* 這孩子長到他父親的膝部那麼高了。| *The horses are level now, but Blue Magic is looking tired.* 這幾匹馬現已齊頭並進, 但"藍魔法"看上去累了。 **3** steady and calm (used of a person's voice or the way they look at something) 堅定的; 平靜的〔指人的聲音或眼神〕 **4 do your level best** *infml* to do all that you can 〔非正式〕盡力而為

level⁴ *adv* so as to be level with or parallel to a flat surface 平齊地; 平行地: *missiles flying level with the ground* 貼着地面飛行的導彈

level cross·ing /ˌ·· ˈ··/ *n BrE* a place where a road and a railway cross each other 〔鐵路和公路的〕平交道口 –see picture on page 991 見 991 頁彩圖

level-head·ed /ˌ·· ˈ··◂/ *adj* calm and sensible in making judgments 頭腦冷靜的; 明智的

le·ver¹ /ˈlevə; ˈliːvəʳ/ *n* **1** a bar which you place under something heavy or stiff and push down on to move the object 槓桿 **2** a handle on a machine which you push or pull to operate it 〔機器的〕控制桿: *a gear lever* 變速桿 **3** something which you can use to influence someone 用來影響某人的事物: *They used the threat of strike action as a lever.* 他們用罷工威脅為手段。

lever² *v* [T + adv/prep] to move a person or thing, using a lever or similar movement 〔用槓桿〕撬動: *They levered the rocks into*

position. 他們用槓桿把石塊撬到位。| *He had to lever open the window.* 他不得不把窗撬開。| *She managed to lever herself up from the sofa.* 她設法從沙發上撐起身子。

le·ver·age /ˈlɛvərɪdʒ; ˈliːvərɪdʒ/ *n* [U] **1** the action, use, or power of a lever 槓桿作用; 槓桿的力量 **2** power, influence, or other means of obtaining a result 力量; 影響; 手段

lev·er·et /ˈlɛvərɪt; ˈlɛvərɪt/ *n* a young HARE 小野兔

lev·i·tate /ˈlɛvə₃tet; ˈlɛvɪteɪt/ *v* **levitated, levitating** [I;T] to rise and float in the air as if by magic, or to make a person or thing do this (使)懸浮空中 –**levitation** /ˌlɛvəˈteʃən; ˌlɛvɪˈteɪʃən/ *n* [U]

lev·i·ty /ˈlɛvətɪ; ˈlɛvɪti/ *n* [U] *fml* lack of seriousness or respect for serious matters 〔正式〕輕浮; 輕率

lev·y /ˈlɛvɪ; ˈlɛvi/ *n* an official demand for a tax or for people to become soldiers 徵稅; 徵兵 –**levy** *v* **levied, levying** [T] : *to levy a tax on tobacco* 徵煙草稅

lewd /lud; luːd/ *adj* dealing with sex, or showing an interest in it, in a way that is not socially acceptable 淫蕩的; 猥褻的: *a lewd gesture* 猥褻的手勢 –**lewdly** *adv* –**lewdness** *n* [U]

lex·i·cal /ˈlɛksɪkl; ˈlɛksɪkəl/ *adj tech* about or relating to words 〔術語〕(有關)詞彙的 – **lexically** /-klɪ; -kli/ *adv*

lex·i·con /ˈlɛksɪkən; ˈlɛksɪkən/ *n* a list of the words of a language or subject, often recorded in a dictionary 〔某種語言或學科的〕詞典; 詞彙表

li·a·bil·i·ty /ˌlaɪəˈbɪlətɪ; ˌlaɪəˈbɪl₃ti/ *n* **liabilities** **1** [C;U] something for which you are legally responsible, or the condition of being responsible for it 〔法律〕責任; 義務: *The firm does not accept liability for the accident.* 該公司不肯對這起事故負責。 **2** [C] *tech* a debt 〔術語〕債務: *Our liabilities exceed our assets.* 我們的債務超過了資產。 **3** [C] a person or thing that makes what you want to do more difficult 累贅: *A small child is a real liability in a restaurant.* 小孩子在餐館裡實在是個累贅。

li·a·ble /ˈlaɪəbl; ˈlaɪəbəl/ *adj* [never before a noun 不能用於名詞前] **1** likely to do something or to happen, especially from habit or a certain tendency 〔尤指由於習慣或趨勢〕易於〔做某事或發生〕: *He is liable to lose his temper in situations like this.* 在這種情況下他很容易發脾氣。 **2** legally responsible for something 對〔某事〕負法律責任的: *I am not liable for my son's debts.* 我沒有義務替兒子還債。

li·aise /liˈez; liˈeɪz/ *v* **liaised, liaising** [I] **1** to work together so that the different people concerned are informed about what is being done 建立聯繫: *We must liaise closely with the government on this.* 為了此事, 我們必須與政府取得密切聯繫。 **2** to keep diffe-

rent groups or people informed about what the others are doing 聯絡; 聯繫: *My main job is to liaise between management and the unions.* 我的主要工作是在資方和工會間進行聯繫。

li·ai·son /ˈliːəˌzɑn; liˈeɪzən/ *n* **1** [sing; U] a working association or connection 聯絡; 聯繫: *There was close liaison between the school and the parents.* 學校與家長之間有密切的聯繫。 **2** [C] a short sexual relationship between a man and a woman who are not married to each other 〔男女間的〕私通

li·ar /ˈlaɪə; ˈlaɪər/ *n* a person who tells lies 說謊者

li·bel /ˈlaɪbl; ˈlaɪbəl/ *n* [C;U] *law* something which is written about someone which is not true or not fair and which makes other people lose respect for them 〔律〕誹謗性文字 –**libel** *v* **-ll-** (**-l-** *AmE* 〔美式〕) [T]

li·bel·lous /ˈlaɪbələs; ˈlaɪbələs/ *adj* (**libelous** *AmE* 〔美式〕) **1** containing a libel against someone 誹謗性的: *a libellous article in a newspaper* 報上的一篇誹謗性文章 **2** in the habit of writing libels 慣於寫誹謗性文章的 – **libellously** *adv*

★**lib·e·ral**¹ /ˈlɪbərəl; ˈlɪbərəl/ *adj* **1** willing to respect the ideas of others 尊重他人意見的: *a liberal attitude to drugs* 對毒品所持的寬容態度 **2** favouring a wide general knowledge and possibilities for self-expression 主張博學多聞和表述自我的: *a liberal education* 通才教育 **3** giving or given freely and generously 慷慨的; 大方的: *a liberal supporter of the hospital* 醫院的慷慨贊助者 | *a liberal supply of food* 供應充足的食品 **4** (also 又作 **Liberal**) supporting gradual social and political change 支持〔社會政治〕變革的 –**liberalism** *n* [U]

liberal² *n* **1** a person who is willing to respect the ideas of others 思想開明的人 **2** a person who is in favour of gradual social change 支持改革者 **3** **Liberal** a person who supports the Liberal Democrats in Britain, or a similar political party in other countries 自由黨黨員

Liberal Dem·o·crats /ˌ··· ˈ···/ *n* the **Liberal Democrats** [pl] a British political party which works for gradual social and political change 〔英國的〕自由民主黨

lib·e·ral·i·ty /ˌlɪbəˈrælətɪ; ˌlɪbəˈræl₃ti/ *n* [U] (also 又作 **liberalness** /ˈlɪbərəlnɪs; ˈlɪbərəln₃s/) **1** generosity 慷慨; 大方 **2** willingness to respect other ideas 寬容; 開明

lib·e·ral·ly /ˈlɪbərəlɪ; ˈlɪbərəli/ *adv* generously, or in large quantities 慷慨地; 大量地

lib·e·rate /ˈlɪbəˌret; ˈlɪbəreɪt/ *v* **liberated, liberating** [T] *fml* to free a person, animal, or a country 〔正式〕解放; 釋放: *The government has promised to liberate all political prisoners.* 政府已保證釋放所有政治犯。 | *The country was liberated after five years of enemy occupation.* 這個國家被敵國佔領了五年

後解放了。**–liberator** *n* **–liberation** /ˌlɪbəˈreɪ-ʃən; ˌlɪbəˈreɪʃən/ *n* [U]

lib·er·at·ed /ˈlɪbəˌretɪd; ˈlɪbəˌreɪtˌd/ *adj* acting according to modern ideas of what is acceptable in social and sexual matters 〔在社交及兩性問題上〕(思想)解放的; 放縱的: *a liberated woman* 生活不檢點的女人

lib·er·ty /ˈlɪbɚtɪ; ˈlɪbəti/ *n* **liberties 1** [U] personal or political freedom from outside control 〔個人或政治的〕自由: *the ideals of liberty and democracy* 自由與民主的理想 **2** **liberties** [pl] personal or political freedoms 〔個人或政治的〕自由(權): *the need to protect our civil liberties* 保護公民自由的需要 **3** [U] the right or permission to do something 〔做某事的〕許可(權) **4** **at liberty: a** free from prison or other control 不受監禁[控制]的 **b** allowed to do something 獲允許〔做某事〕 **5** **take the liberty** to do something without asking permission, because you think you would be allowed to do so 冒昧〔做某事〕: *I took the liberty of helping myself to a drink. Is that all right?* 我冒昧地喝了杯飲料。您不介意吧?

li·bi·do /lɪˈbaɪdo; lɪˈbiːdəʊ/ *n* **libidos** *tech* sexual desire 〔術語〕性慾

Li·bra /ˈlaɪbrə; ˈliːbrə/ *n* one of the signs of the ZODIAC 天秤宮

li·brar·i·an /laɪˈbrɛrɪən; laɪˈbreərɪən/ *n* a person who is in charge of a library or who helps to run one 圖書館館長; 圖書館管理員 **–librarianship** *n* [U]

★★★ **li·bra·ry** /ˈlaɪˌbrɛrɪ; ˈlaɪbrəri/ *n* **libraries 1** a building or room containing books and magazines which the public or members of a special group can look at or borrow 圖書館: *the school library* 學校圖書館 **2** a collection usually of books, but sometimes of other objects, which may be looked at or borrowed 〔書或其他物品的〕庫; 租借館: *a record library* 唱片租借館 | *a toy library* 玩具庫

lice /laɪs; laɪs/ *n* the plural of LOUSE ☆ LOUSE 的複數形式

★ **li·cence** /ˈlaɪsns; ˈlaɪsəns/ *n* (**license** *AmE* 〖美式〗) **1** [U] permission to do something 〔做某事的〕許可 **2** [C] an official paper showing that you have permission to do something 許可證; 執照: *a driving licence* 駕駛執照 | *a licence to sell alcohol* 賣酒的許可證 **3** [U] freedom, or too much freedom, of action or expression 〔行動或言論的〕自由; 放縱

li·cense /ˈlaɪsns; ˈlaɪsəns/ *v* (also 又作 **li·cence**) **licensed, licensing** [T] to give official permission for someone to do something 批准, 許可

li·censed /ˈlaɪsnst; ˈlaɪsənst/ *adj* having a licence, especially to sell alcohol or to practise a certain profession 領有執照的: *a licensed restaurant* 有營業執照的餐館 | *a licensed debt-collector* 有執照的收賬人

license plate /ˈ··· ·/ *n* the usual American word for 〖美式〗 = NUMBERPLATE

li·cen·tious /laɪˈsenʃəs; laɪˈsenʃəs/ *adj fml* behaving in a sexually uncontrolled manner 〖正式〗淫蕩的 **–licentiously** *adv* **–licentiousness** *n* [U]

li·chen /ˈlaɪkɪn; ˈlaɪkən/ *n* [C;U] a flat spreading plant that covers the surfaces of stones and trees 地衣

lick¹ /lɪk; lɪk/ *v* [T] **1** to move your tongue across a surface 舔: *She licked the stamps and stuck them on.* 她舔濕郵票後把它們黏了上去。 | *The dog always licks his dish clean.* 這條狗總是把自己的盤子舔得很乾淨。 **2** *infml* to defeat a person or group of people 〖非正式〗擊敗〔某人或一羣人〕: *Our team was well and truly licked.* 我們的隊被打得落花流水。 **3** **lick your lips** to move your tongue across your lips, showing that you are looking forward to something, or you have enjoyed something 舔嘴唇〔表示期待或滿足〕; 切盼 **4** **lick your wounds** to feel sorry for yourself after a defeat 〔失敗後〕為自己感到難過

lick² *n* **1** a movement of your tongue across a surface 舔 **2** *infml* a small amount of something 〖非正式〗一點點; 少量: *This door needs a lick of paint.* 這扇門需要稍漆一下。

lic·o·rice /ˈlɪkərɪs; ˈlɪkərɪs/ *n* [U] see 見 LIQUORICE

lid /lɪd; lɪd/ *n* **1** the piece that covers the open top of a pot, box, or other container and that you can lift up or remove 蓋子 **2** see 見 EYELID

★★ **lie¹** /laɪ; laɪ/ *v* **lay** /le; leɪ,/ **lain** /len; leɪn/, **lying** /ˈlaɪɪŋ; ˈlaɪ·ɪŋ/ [I + adv/prep] **1** to be in a flat position on a surface 平臥, 躺: *The book is lying on the table.* 書平放在桌上。 | *He lay on the floor, reading a book.* 他躺在地上看書。 **2** to be in a certain place or position 位於, 在: *The town lies to the east of us.* 那城鎮坐落在我們的東面。 **3** to be found 被發現; 存在: *The truth lies somewhere between the statements of the two men.* 真相就在這兩個人所說的話裡。 **4** to remain or be kept in a certain place or condition 留在〔某一地方〕; 保持〔某種狀態〕: *Don't leave your money lying in the bank.* 不要把錢存在銀行裡。 | *The town lay in ruins.* 這城鎮成了一片廢墟。 **5** **lie ahead,** be in store to happen in the future 將要發生: *The situation is fine now, but who knows what lies ahead!* 現在情況是不錯, 但誰知將來會發生些甚麼! **6** **lie behind something** to be the hidden reason for something 是…的潛在原因: *It's not clear what lies behind her decision to leave.* 還不清楚她決定離開的真正原因是甚麼。 **7** **lie in wait** to wait for someone who is not expecting you and usually does not want to see you 等待不想見你的人 **8** **lie low** to stay hidden so that people, especially the police, cannot find you 藏匿

lie about/around *phr v* [I] to spend your time doing nothing because you are lazy 無所事事地混日子; 遊手好閒

lie down *phr v* [I] to put yourself into a flat position on a surface 躺下: *Lie down and sleep for a while.* 躺下來睡一會兒。–see 見 LAY¹ (USAGE 用法)

lie in *phr v* [I] to stay in bed later than usual in the morning 睡懶覺

lie² ** *v* **lied, lied, lying [I] to say something that you know is not true 説謊: *Don't lie to me! I know where you've been.* 別説謊! 我知道你去過哪裡了。| *She lied **about** her age to get the job.* 她為得到那份工作而隱瞞了年齡。

lie³ *n* a statement which you know is not true 謊言: *That child tells lies all the time.* 那個孩子一直在説謊。| *She said she loved me, but it was all a lie.* 她説她愛我, 可全是騙人的鬼話。

lie-down /'··/ *n infml* a short rest, usually on a bed 〖非正式〗(常指在牀上的)小睡; 小憩

lie-in /'··/ *n infml* a longer rest in bed than usual, so that you get up later in the morning 〖非正式〗早上晚起, 睡懶覺: *I really enjoy a lie-in at the weekend.* 我非常喜歡在週末睡懶覺。

lieu /lu; lju:/ *n fml* 〖正式〗**in lieu** instead of something 代替, 作為…的替代: *I'll take your watch in lieu of payment.* 我會拿你的手錶抵債。

lieu·ten·ant /lu'tɛnənt; lɛf'tɛnənt/ *n* an officer of low rank in the armed forces 陸軍中尉; 海軍上尉

★★**life** /laɪf; laɪf/ *n* **lives** /laɪvz; laɪvz/ **1** [U] the quality that allows animals and plants to continue existing 生命, 性命: *He lost his life in an accident.* 他在一起事故中喪命。| *Is there life after death?* 死後還有生命嗎? **2** [U] living things 生物: *There is no life on the moon.* 月球上沒有生物。| *plant life* 植物 **3** [U] human existence 人生; 生活: *Life isn't all fun.* 人生並非皆歡樂。**4** [C] the period during which you are alive, or from your birth until now 一生; 終身: *a long and happy life* 長壽而幸福的一生 | *I have lived in England all my life.* 我這輩子都住在英國。**5** [C;U] the way in which you live 生活方式: *They lead very busy lives.* 他們的生活很忙碌。| *How do you like married life?* 你覺得婚姻生活如何? **6** [C] the period during which something continues to work or to exist 有效期; 生存期: *Many new magazines have a very short life.* 許多新雜誌的壽命很短。**7** [U] activity 活動: *There were signs of life in the forest as the sun rose.* 太陽升起來了, 林中有生命活動的跡象。| *The children are full of life this morning.* 今天早晨孩子們都精神煥發。**8 be the life and soul of something** to amuse and entertain other people in a group 是〔使其他人愉快的〕靈魂, 支柱: *He was the life and soul of the party.* 他是聚會上最活躍的人。**9** [U] (also 又作 **life im-**

prisonment /··'····/) the punishment of being put in prison for the rest of your life, or for a very long time 終生監禁: *sentenced to life for the murder* 因謀殺被判終生監禁 **10** [C] (also 又作 **life story** /'···/) a written, filmed, or other account of a person's existence 〔被寫成書、拍成電影或以其他方式記錄下來的〕生平記載, 傳記: *a short life of Shakespeare* 莎士比亞短暫的生平 **11 Not on your life!** *infml* certainly not! 〖非正式〗當然不!

■ USAGE 用法: Notice that some fixed phrases use **life**, but others use **living**. For example **life** is used in **quality of life**, **way of life**, and **lifestyle** ☆注意, 有些詞組中用 **life**, 而其他的用 **living**。比如 **life**用於 **quality of life**, **way of life** 和 **lifestyle** 等詞組中: *They claim that **quality of life** is more important than a big salary.* 他們聲稱生活素質比豐厚的薪金更重要。| *We soon got used to the American **way of life**.* 我們很快就習慣了美國的生活方式。| *modern diseases caused by poor diet and a hectic **lifestyle*** 由於營養不良和生活忙碌引起的現代疾病。But **living** is used in **cost of living, standard of living**, and **earn/make a living** ☆但是 **living** 用於 **cost of living, standard of living** 和 **earn/make a living** 等詞組中: *The **cost of living** has more than doubled in the last two years.* 過去兩年間, 生活費用上漲了一倍之多。| *industrialized countries enjoying a high **standard of living*** 擁有很高生活水準的工業化國家 | *It's hard to **earn your living** as a poet.* 做詩人很難維持生計。

life belt /'··/ *n* a belt or ring that will float, and that you hold or wear if you fall into water to stop you sinking 救生帶; 救生圈

life·blood /'laɪf,blʌd; 'laɪfblʌd/ *n* [U] something that gives continuing strength and force to a person or thing 生命線; 命脈: *Trade is the lifeblood of most modern states.* 貿易是當代大多數國家的命脈。

life·boat /'laɪf,bot; 'laɪfbəʊt/ *n* a boat used for saving people who are in danger at sea 救生艇[船]

life ex·pec·tan·cy /,·· ·'···/ *n* [C;U] the average number of years that a person can expect to live 平均(預期)壽命: *The life expectancy of people in Britain has increased in this century.* 本世紀英國人的平均壽命增加了。

life·guard /'laɪf,gɑrd; 'laɪfgɑːd/ *n* a person whose job is to help swimmers if they are in danger 救生員

life jack·et /'·, ··/ *n* a garment filled with air that you wear round your chest to support you in water 救生衣

life·less /'laɪflɪs; 'laɪfləs/ *adj* **1** dead or seeming to be dead 死的; 無生命的: *the lifeless body of the victim* 受害者的屍體 **2** without strength, interest, or activity 無生氣的; 單調的; 沉悶的: *a lifeless performance* 沉悶的演出 **–lifelessly** *adv* **–lifelessness** *n* [U]

life·like /'laɪf,laɪk; 'laɪflaɪk/ *adj* very much like real life or a real person 生動的; 逼真的: *a lifelike statue* 栩栩如生的塑像

life·line /'laɪflaɪn; 'laɪflaɪn/ *n* **1** a rope which is used for saving people who are in danger in the water 救生索 **2** something which is very necessary to someone 生命線: *The telephone is my lifeline to the outside world.* 電話是我與外界聯繫的生命之線。

life·long /'laɪf,lɒŋ; 'laɪflɒŋ/ *adj* [only before a noun 只用於名詞前] continuing all your life 終身的: *a lifelong friendship* 一輩子的友誼

life sci·ence /'· ,··/ *n* **the life sciences** [pl] the sciences that study plant, animal, and human life 生命科學

life-size /,· '··◂/ *adj* (also 又作 **life-sized** /,· '··◂/) of the same size as what it represents (used of a work of art) 與實物一樣大小的〔指藝術品〕: *a life-size portrait* 與真人一樣大的肖像畫

life·style /'laɪf,staɪl; 'laɪfstaɪl/ *n* the way you live, including the conditions you live in, the things you own, and the things you do 生活方式: *a healthy lifestyle with a sensible diet and plenty of exercise* 飲食合理、經常運動的健康生活方式

life·time /'laɪf,taɪm; 'laɪftaɪm/ *n* the period of time during which a person is alive or something continues 一生; 終身; 生存期

★**lift¹** /lɪft; lɪft/ *v* **1** [T] to move something to a higher level 舉起, 抬起, 搬起: *I can't lift this suitcase.* 我拿不動這個手提箱。 | *Can you lift the carpet while I sweep under it?* 我掃地毯底下的時候, 你能把地毯抬起來嗎? | *He lifted his head as she entered the room.* 她走進房間的時候, 他抬起了頭。–see picture on page 992 見 992 頁彩圖 **2** [I] to move upwards and often disappear 向上升; 消散: *As the mist lifted, the farmhouse became visible.* 雲霧一散去, 農舍就變得清晰可見。 **3** [T] to remove a limit or rule 撤銷, 取消〔限制或規定〕: *Restrictions on journalists have been lifted by the new government.* 新政府已取消了對記者的種種限制。 **4** [I;T] to make or become happier (使)高興: *My heart lifted at the news.* 這消息令我心裡很高興。 **5** [T] *infml* to steal something〔非正式〕偷竊 **6** [T] *infml* to use other people's ideas without saying that they are not your own〔非正式〕剽竊, 盜用〔他人的觀點〕 **7** [T + adv/ prep] to carry something into or out of a place by plane 用飛機運送〔某物〕 **8** not lift a finger to do nothing to help someone 一點也不幫助〔某人〕: *None of my children lifts a finger at home.* 我的孩子們在家裡一點家務也不做。

lift off *phr v* [I] (of a space vehicle) to rise up into the air〔太空船〕升空: *The rocket lifts off at 12.00.* 火箭於十二點鐘發射。

★**lift²** *n* **1** [C] an apparatus in a building that carries people or goods up and down between floors 升降機 **2** [C] a free ride in a vehicle (免費)搭乘, 搭便車: *Can you give me a lift into town?* 我能搭你的車進城嗎? **3** [sing] *infml* a feeling of new confidence or cheerfulness〔非正式〕振奮; 精神抖擻: *The exam results gave me a real lift.* 考試結果令我確實精神一振。 **4** [C;U] upward pressure of air on the wings of an aircraft〔飛機兩翼所受的〕空氣浮力; 升力

lift-off /'· ·/ *n* the moment when a space vehicle rises up into the air 發射, 起飛

lig·a·ment /'lɪgəmənt; 'lɪgəmənt/ *n* one of the strong bands that join bones or hold some part of your body in position 韌帶: *He tore a ligament playing football.* 他踢足球時撕裂了韌帶。

★**light¹** /laɪt; laɪt/ *n* **1** [U] the natural force that allows us to see things 光; 光線; 光亮: *This light is not good enough to read by.* 這光線不夠亮, 無法看書。 | *She worked by candlelight.* 她借燭光工作。 **2** [U] the light of the sun or the time it lasts 陽光; 陽光持續的時間: *I must finish this painting before the light goes.* 我必須趁天黑前畫完這幅畫。 **3** [C] something that produces light 發光體; 燈; 光源: *Turn off the lights when you go to bed.* 上床睡覺時把燈關掉。 | *a neon light* 霓虹燈 **4** [C] something that is used to start a cigarette burning 引火物: *Have you got a light, please?* 你有火嗎? **5** [sing;U] brightness in your eyes which shows your feelings 眼光; 眼神 **6** [C] the way something or someone appears 理解; 見識: *Workers and employers see the problem in quite a different light.* 工人和雇主對問題的看法大相徑庭。 **7** come to light, be brought to light to become known 顯露, 為人所知: *New information has come to light.* 新的消息已披露了出來。 **8** go out like a light to fall asleep as soon as you get into bed or to become unconscious 沉睡; 昏迷 **9** in the light of taking something into account 考慮到〔某事物〕; 按照: *In the light of your recent behaviour, I'm afraid I must ask you to leave the company.* 考慮到你近來的行為, 很抱歉我不得不要求你離開公司。 **10** see the light to understand or accept something, especially a religious belief 理解; 接受〔尤指宗教信仰〕 **11** throw light on, shed light on, cast light on to make something clearer 使〔某物〕更為清晰: *The report sheds light on the real cause of the problem.* 報告解釋了問題的真正起因。

★**light²** *v* **lit** /lɪt; lɪt/, **lit** **1** [I;T] to start burning, or to start something burning (使)燃燒, 點燃: *He lit a cigarette.* 他點燃了一支香煙。 | *The fire won't light.* 這火

點不着。**2** [T] to give light to something 照亮〔某物〕: *The room is lit by several large lamps.* 該房間被幾盞大燈照亮了。

> ■ USAGE 用法: The usual past participle of **light** is **lit** ☆**light** 的過去分詞通常為 **lit**: *He's lit a match.* 他點着了一根火柴。| *The match is lit.* 火柴點着了。But if the past participle stands as an adjective before the noun we use **lighted** ☆但是如果其過去分詞在名詞前作形容詞用時,我們就用 **lighted**: *a lighted match* 一根點着了的火柴

light up *phr v* **1** [I;T **light** sthg ↔ **up**] to become or to make something bright (使)變得明亮: *Her face lit up with joy.* 她因高興而容光煥發。| *The factory fire lit up the surrounding area.* 工廠裡的大火照亮了周圍地區。**2** [I] to begin to smoke a cigarette 點上香煙: *He borrowed some matches and lit up.* 他借了幾根火柴,點了香煙。

***light³** *adj* **1** weighing little 輕的: *It's so light a child could lift it.* 這東西很輕,連小孩子都拿得動。**2** not heavy, strong, or serious 不重的; 不強烈的; 不嚴重的: *You need a light touch to play the piano quietly.* 你要輕輕地彈鋼琴,就得輕輕地敲打琴鍵。| *a light wind* 微風 | *These stories are just light bedtime reading.* 這些故事不過是供睡覺前看的消遣性讀物。**3** bright 明亮的: *a light room* 明亮的房間 **4** pale 淡的; 淺的: *light blue* 淺藍 –see picture on page 243 見 243 頁彩圖 **5** a light meal 便餐 **6** a light sleeper someone who wakes easily from sleep 睡覺易醒的人 **7** make light of something to treat something as if it were not important 輕視某事 **8** make light work of something to do something as if it were easy 輕易地做某事

light⁴ *adv* travel light to travel without many possessions 輕裝地旅行: *I always travel light.* 我旅行時總是少帶行李的。

light bulb /'··/ *n* the glass part of an electric lamp that gives out light 電燈泡

light·en /'laɪtn̩; 'laɪtn̩/ *v* **1** [T] to make something less heavy 使〔某物〕變輕, 減輕 **2** [I;T] to become or to make something less dark (使)變亮 **3** [I] (of someone's face, voice, or mood) to become more cheerful 〔某人的臉、聲音或心情〕變得愉快

light·er /'laɪtɚ; 'laɪtɚ/ *n* an instrument which produces a flame for lighting things like fires or cigarettes 點火器; 打火機: *a cigarette lighter* 打火機

light-fin·gered /ˌ·'··◂/ *adj infml* in the habit of stealing small things 〔非正式〕有小偷小摸習慣的, 好順手牽羊的

light-head·ed /ˌ·'··◂/ *adj* **1** feeling slightly ill in your head 頭暈的 **2** foolish or irresponsible 愚蠢的; 不負責的; 輕率的

light-heart·ed /ˌ·'··◂/ *adj* cheerful 輕鬆

愉快的

light·house /'laɪt,haʊs; 'laɪthaʊs/ *n* a tall building with a powerful flashing light that guides ships or warns them of dangerous rocks 燈塔 –see picture on page 991 見 991 頁彩圖

light·ing /'laɪtɪŋ; 'laɪtɪŋ/ *n* [U] **1** the system or apparatus that gives light to a place 照明設備: *We need more lighting in this office.* 這辦公室裡我們需要更多的照明設備。**2** the kind of light that this system produces (照明的)光線: *I want stronger lighting above the desks.* 我需要在桌子上有更強的光線。

light·ly /'laɪtli; 'laɪtli/ *adv* **1** with little weight or force 輕輕地: *He pressed lightly on the handle.* 他輕輕捏了捏把手。**2** to a small degree 稍微: *lightly cooked* 稍加烹煮的 | *lightly armed* 稍加武裝的 **3** without thinking carefully about something or knowing its importance 不慎重地, 輕率地: *I didn't start this court action lightly, you know!* 你要知道,我可不是隨隨便便就採取這項法律行動的!

light·ning¹ /'laɪtnɪŋ; 'laɪtnɪŋ/ *n* [U] a flash of bright light in the sky, usually followed by thunder 閃電: *The tower has been struck by lightning.* 那座塔被閃電擊中了。

lightning² *adj* [only before a noun 只用於名詞前] very quick, short, or sudden 很快的; 很短的; 突然的: *a lightning visit* 突然的造訪

lightning con·duc·tor /'·· ·,··/ *n* (**lightning rod** /'·· ·/ *AmE* 【美式】) a piece of metal fixed to the top of a building and leading down to the ground, which prevents the building being damaged if it is struck by lightning 避雷針

light·weight /'laɪt'weɪt; 'laɪt·weɪt/ *adj* **1** of less than average weight or importance 較平均重量為輕的; 次要的: *a lightweight camera* 輕型攝像機 | *His books are lightweight, but quite amusing.* 他的書很淺薄, 但相當有趣。**2** *tech* weighing between 59 and 61 kilos (used of people who fight as a sport) 【術語】〔拳擊運動員〕輕量級的〔體重在59至61公斤之間〕: *a lightweight boxer* 輕量級拳擊選手 –**lightweight** *n*

light year /'··/ *n* the distance that light travels in one year 光年

***like¹** /laɪk; laɪk/ *v* **liked, liking** [T] **1** to find someone or something pleasant 喜歡, 喜愛, 喜好: *Do you like bananas?* 你喜歡吃香蕉嗎? | *I've never liked her brother.* 我從來不喜歡她的弟弟。| *I didn't like the film very much.* 我不太喜歡那部電影。| *I don't like the way this crisis is being handled.* 我不喜歡處理這次危機的方式。| *Do you like reading?* 你喜歡看書嗎?

> □ USEFUL PATTERNS 有用句型
> to like someone/something; to like doing something

2 like to do something to do something if

it is possible because you think that it is a good idea〔由於認為是個好主意，故而只要可能便〕願意做某事: *I like to go to the dentist every six months.* 我願意每半年去看一次牙醫。**3 not like to do something** to be unwilling to do something 不願做某事: *I don't like to interrupt them again.* 我不願再次打斷他們的話。**4 would like something, would like to do something** to choose something or choose to do something 選擇某物; 選擇做某事: *Would you like tea or coffee?* 你要喝茶還是喝咖啡? | *Would you like a biscuit?* 你想吃塊餅乾嗎? | *I'd like to meet him.* 我想見見他。**5 if you like** if you want this 如果你喜歡: *We can go out if you like.* 你要是願意的話，我們可以出去。 | *I'll carry that for you, if you like.* 如果你要的話，我可以替你拿那個東西。

> ■ USAGE 用法: **1 Like** used on its own means "to be fond of or enjoy" ☆**like** 單獨使用時表示"喜歡、喜愛": *I like coffee.* 我喜歡喝咖啡。(= I'm fond of it) **2** When asking for something **I would like/I'd like** is more common and more polite than **I want** ☆如果想要某物，**I would like/I'd like** 比 **I want** 更為常用，也更禮貌: *I'd like a cup of coffee.* 我想要杯咖啡。 | *I'd like to go to the cinema.* 我想去看電影。**3** When offering something to someone use **Would you like**…? ☆徵詢某人是否要某物時，用 **Would you like**…?: *Would you like a cup of coffee?* 你想要杯咖啡嗎?

like² *adj fml* similar〔正式〕相似的; 同類的: *running, swimming, and other like sports* 跑步、游泳及類似的運動

like³ *prep* **1** similar to something or someone in some way 像〔某人或某物〕: *She looks like her mother.* 她很像她的母親。 | *It tastes like chicken.* 這東西味道像雞肉。 | *He was like a son to me.* 在我看來，他就像兒子一樣。 | *Once the car has been painted it'll look like new.* 這部車上了油漆後就會像新的一樣。 | *Like you, I was very disappointed by the announcement.* 和你一樣，我對這項聲明也感到很失望。**2** used when you are asking someone to describe a person or thing or give their opinion 如…一樣〔用於要求別人描述人或某物，或給出他們的意見〕: *What's she like?* 她這個人如何? | *What was the film like?* 那電影怎麼樣? **3** typical of someone or something 〔某人或某物〕符合…的特徵: *It was just like Mary to be late.* 像瑪麗這樣的人才會老是遲到。 | *You're acting like a child!* 你的舉動像個孩子! **4** for example 例如: *I enjoy outdoor sports like tennis and football.* 我喜歡諸如網球和足球等戶外運動。 | *A lot of people are still fit and healthy when they retire, like my parents for example.* 許多人退

休時仍很健壯，比如像我父母。

> ■ USAGE 用法: Note the difference between these uses of **like** and **as** ☆注意 **like** 和 **as** 用法上的差別: *He plays tennis like a professional.* 他打起網球來像個職業運動員。(= He plays as well as a professional 他和職業運動員打得一樣好) | *He plays tennis as a professional.* 他以職業運動員的身分打網球。(= He is a professional 他是個職業運動員)

like⁴ *n* **1 the like** things that are similar 同類的事物: *running, swimming, and the like* 跑步、游泳等等 **2 likes and dislikes** things that you do or do not like 喜歡和不喜歡的事情; 好惡; 愛憎

like·a·ble /ˈlaɪkəbl; ˈlaɪkəbəl/ *adj* (also 又作 **likable**) easy to like (used of a person) 討人喜歡的〔指人〕

like·ly¹ /ˈlaɪklɪ; ˈlaɪkli/ *adj* **likelier, likeliest** **1** probable or expected 可能的: *It seems likely that she'll pass her exams.* 她似乎有可能通過考試。 | *The likeliest result of the match is a draw.* 比賽最可能的結果是平局。–opposite 反義 **unlikely 2 be likely to do something** to be probably going to do something 很有可能做某事: *Inflation is likely to increase again this month.* 本月通貨膨脹率很可能再次上升。 | *Are we likely to arrive on time?* 我們是否可以按時到達? **3** suitable to give results 會有結果的: *a likely plan* 可能成功的計劃 | *a likely candidate for promotion* 可能被提升的人選

likely² *adv* **1 very likely, most likely** probably 很可能地: *They'll very likely come by car.* 他們很可能坐車來。**2 as likely as not** probably 很可能 **3 not likely!** *infml* certainly not!〔非正式〕根本不可能!

lik·en /ˈlaɪkən; ˈlaɪkən/ *v* [T] *fml*〔正式〕 **liken something to** to compare a person or thing with something which is similar 把某物比作: *Our little company can be likened to a big, happy family.* 我們的小公司可以比作一個快樂的大家庭。

like·ness /ˈlaɪknɪs; ˈlaɪknɪs/ *n* [C;U] similarity to something or someone else 相像，相似: *Have you noticed the strong family likeness among the girls?* 你有沒有注意到這一家的女孩子非常相像?

like·wise /ˈlaɪkˌwaɪz; ˈlaɪk-waɪz/ *adv* **1** the same or in the same way 相同地; 同樣地: *John took off his shoes, so Peter did likewise.* 約翰脫了鞋，彼得也脫了。**2** also 又; 也: *For this job you need a lot of patience; likewise a sense of humour.* 做這個工作你需要有很大的耐心，也需要有幽默感。

lik·ing /ˈlaɪkɪŋ; ˈlaɪkɪŋ/ *n* [sing] **1** fondness for something 喜歡: *I have only recently developed a liking for cigars.* 我最近才開始喜歡抽雪茄煙的。**2 to your liking** as you like it 合心意; 對胃口: *Is the food to your liking,* *sir?* 先生, 這菜合您的意思嗎? **3 for your liking** for your taste 對自己的品味來說: *The wallpaper is too bright for my liking.* 這種牆紙在我看來過於鮮艷了。

li·lac /ˈlaɪlək; ˈlaɪlæk/ *n* **1** [C] a tree with pink, purple, or white flowers which smell nice 紫丁香(花) **2** [U] a pale purple colour 淡紫色 –see picture on page 243 見 243 頁彩圖

li·lo /ˈlaɪlo; ˈlaɪləʊ/ *n* lilos a plastic bed filled with air which you can lie on by the sea or floating on the water 〔海濱或水上用的〕氣墊牀

lilt /lɪlt; lɪlt/ *n* [sing] the pleasant rise and fall of a voice or tune 抑揚頓挫的聲音; 輕快的旋律 **–lilt** *v*

lil·y /ˈlɪli; ˈlɪli/ *n* lilies a plant, usually with large white flowers 百合(花)

limb /lɪm; lɪm/ *n* **1** a leg, arm, or wing of an animal 肢, 翼, 翅膀 **2** a large branch of a tree 大樹枝 **3 out on a limb** alone, without support 孤立無援

lim·ber /ˈlɪmbə; ˈlɪmbər/ *v*
　limber up *phr v* [I] to prepare for serious exercise by stretching your muscles 熱身

lim·bo /ˈlɪmbo; ˈlɪmbəʊ/ *n* limbos **1** a state of uncertainty or waiting 不穩定的狀態; 等待的狀態: *I'm in limbo until I start my new job.* 我現在沒有着落, 一直等待開始新工作。**2** a dance from the West Indies in which a dancer leans back and passes under a rope or bar near the floor 林波舞〔西印度羣島的一種舞蹈, 舞蹈者後仰然後接近地面的繩或杆下通過〕

lime /laɪm; laɪm/ *n* **1** [U] a white substance used in making cement or to improve the soil 石灰 **2** [C] a tree with yellow flowers and heart-shaped leaves 椴樹, 菩提樹 **3** [C] a small green fruit which is juicy and tastes sour 酸橙

lime·light /ˈlaɪmlaɪt; ˈlaɪmlaɪt/ *n* **the limelight** attention from the public 公眾注意的中心: *The rich and famous have to get used to being in the limelight.* 富人和名人必須習慣於受到公眾的注意。

lim·e·rick /ˈlɪmərɪk; ˈlɪmərɪk/ *n* a short, usually funny poem with five lines 五行打油詩

lim·it¹ /ˈlɪmɪt; ˈlɪmɪt/ *n* **1** the outside of something 邊界; 界限: *the limits of his kingdom* 他的王國的邊界 **2** the greatest quantity of something that is possible or acceptable 限度; 極限: *My patience has reached its limit.* 我的忍耐已到了極限。 | *Don't break the speed limit.* 別超過速度限制。**3 the limit** something or someone which is very annoying or upsetting 令人非常惱怒或生氣的事或人: *This bus service is the limit. It's never on time.* 這公共汽車服務真叫人受不了, 從來就沒有準時過。**4 off limits** *AmE* where you are not allowed to go 〔美式〕禁止入內: *The air base is off limits to civilians.* 平民百姓禁止進入這個空軍基地。**5 within limits** to a reasonable point 在合理限度內

*limit² *v* [T] to keep something below a certain point or amount 限定; 限制〔某事物〕: *We must limit our spending.* 我們必須限制開銷。 | *We must limit him to an hour's television a night.* 我們必須限制他每晚最多只能看一個小時電視。

*lim·i·ta·tion /ˌlɪməˈteɪʃən; ˌlɪmɪˈteɪʃən/ *n* **1** [C;U] a limit or the fact or condition of limiting or being limited, or the limit imposed 限定; 限制: *There are limitations on what we can spend in this tax year.* 在這個稅收年度裡我們可以開銷的項目有限制。**2 limitations** the limits to what you are able to do 最大的能力; 能力所及的範圍: *I know my limitations, so I'll get someone else to put the new roof on.* 我知道自己能力有限, 所以準備請別人來裝上新的屋頂。

*lim·it·ed /ˈlɪmɪtɪd; ˈlɪmɪtɪd/ *adj* **1** small in amount or degree 有限的: *He has a limited understanding of the facts.* 他對於那些事實的了解很有限。–opposite 反義 **unlimited 2** (also 又作 **Ltd.** after the name of the company 在公司名稱之後) having a reduced duty to pay back debts 負有限責任的: *a limited company* 有限公司 | *Longman Group Ltd.* 朗文集團有限公司

lim·it·ing /ˈlɪmətɪŋ; ˈlɪmɪtɪŋ/ *adj* preventing improvement or increase in something 有限制性的: *One limiting factor in the improvement of health care is the shortage of doctors.* 醫生不足是改善健康保健服務的一個限制性因素。

lim·ou·sine /ˈlɪmə.zin; ˈlɪməzi:n/ *n* a large expensive car, usually with the driver's seat separated from the back by a sheet of glass 大型豪華轎車

limp¹ /lɪmp; lɪmp/ *v* [I] to walk in an uneven way because one leg moves less easily than the other 一瘸一拐地走, 跛行 **–limp** *n*: *He walks with a limp.* 他走起路來一瘸一拐。

limp² *adj* without strength or firmness 無力的; 不堅定的: *She suddenly went limp and fell to the ground.* 她突然癱下來倒在地上。 | *a limp handshake* 無力的握手 **–limply** *adv* **–limpness** *n* [U]

lim·pet /ˈlɪmpɪt; ˈlɪmpɪt/ *n* a small sea animal with a shell, which holds on tightly to rocks 帽貝

lim·pid /ˈlɪmpɪd; ˈlɪmpɪd/ *adj* *lit* clear (used especially of liquid) 〔文〕清澈的〔尤指液體〕

linc·tus /ˈlɪŋktəs; ˈlɪŋktəs/ *n* [U] liquid medicine to cure coughing 止咳糖漿

*line¹ /laɪn; laɪn/ *n* **1** a long, thin mark on a surface 線; 線條: *Can you draw a straight line?* 你能畫條直線嗎? | *a line drawing* 線條畫 | *Deep lines covered my grandfather's face.* 祖父的臉上佈滿了深深的皺紋。**2** something that acts as a limit or border 界限; 邊界: *Jones crossed the finishing line two seconds ahead of the next* *runner.* 瓊斯比第二位選手早兩秒鐘到達終點線。| *There's a very fine line between punishment and cruelty.* 懲罰和殘酷虐待之間有條很微妙的分界線。**3** a row of people or things〔人或物的〕行，排，列: *A line of people queued outside the cinema.* 電影院外排了一行人。| *My word-processor gives me 54 lines of text to each page.* 我的文字處理機每頁有五十四行。**4** a piece of string, wire, or cord 一段繩[線]: *a clothes line* 晾衣繩 | *a washing line* 曬衣繩 | *a fishing line* 釣魚線 **5** a telephone connection or wire 電話線(路): *The lines to Indonesia are terrible.* 到印度尼西亞的電話線路很糟糕。| *Hold the line, please!* 請不要掛斷電話! **6** a railway track 鐵路線; 路軌: *Passengers may not cross the lines.* 乘客不許跨越路軌。**7** a company that provides a system for travelling or for moving goods, especially by sea or air 航線，運輸線; 運輸公司: *an airline* 航空公司 | *a shipping line* 海運公司 **8** an opinion or way of behaving 觀點; 行動方式: *What is the government's line on overcrowding in prisons?* 政府對於監獄過度擁擠這個問題持甚麼觀點? | *The police will take a tough line with hooligans.* 警方準備對流氓採取嚴厲的行動。**9** a job or other activity that you do or that interests you 工作; 行業; 專長: *Her line is selling children's clothes.* 她經營兒童服裝。| *Fishing isn't really my line.* 我實在不擅長釣魚。**10** a type of goods〔貨物的〕類; 種: *Brooks are advertising a new line in hats.* 布魯克斯正在為一種新款帽子做廣告。**11** a number of people who are descended from each other 家系，世系: *He comes from a long line of actors.* 他來自一個演員世家。**12 lines** [pl] the positions or defences of an army 軍隊的位置[防線]: *He disappeared behind enemy lines.* 他在敵軍防線的後面消失了。**13 lines** [pl] the words an actor learns and says in a play 台詞 **14 along the line** at some point 在某一點, 在某方面: *Somewhere along the line I stopped loving him.* 在某方面上, 我不再愛他了。**15 along the lines of** meaning more or less this 大意是說: *He said something along the lines of, "I have no respect for them".* 他的大意是說"我並不敬重他們"。**16 be in line for** being seriously considered for a job 被認真考慮〔做某項工作〕; 很有可能獲得〔某項工作〕: *She's in line for promotion at work.* 她很有可能獲得提升。**17 be in line with: a** to form a straight line with something 與〔某物〕形成一條直線: *Plant the trees in line with the hedge.* 種植樹木時, 使它們和籬笆成一條直線。**b** to fit in with something 符合〔某事〕, 和…一致的: *That isn't in line with my ideas at all.* 那和我的觀點格格不入。**18 be in the firing line** to be where you could be attacked or blamed 處於受攻擊[受責備]的位置 **19 be on the right lines** to be working towards a good result 朝正確的方向工作 **20 be out of line** to be different, or

to behave in a way which is not acceptable 不一致; 舉止出格: *Your comments on the president's decision are out of line.* 你對於總統的決定所發表的評論太過火了。

line² *v* **lined, lining** [T] **1** to draw or mark lines on something 畫線於〔某物〕: *lined paper* 畫了線條的紙 | *Worry lined his forehead.* 他的額頭上出現了憂愁的皺紋。**2** to form rows along something 排列成行: *Crowds lined the streets.* 人羣夾道成行。**3** to put some kind of material closely around the inside of something 給〔某物〕加襯裡: *a coat lined with fur* 以皮毛作襯裡的外衣 **4 line your own pocket, line your pockets** to make money for yourself, perhaps dishonestly〔可能通過不正當手段〕為自己牟利, 中飽私囊

line up *phr v* **1** [I;T **line** sbdy/sthg ↔ **up**] to move into a row 排隊: *He lined up behind the others.* 他排在其他人的後面。| *Line the glasses up and I'll fill them.* 把酒杯排好, 我來把它們倒滿。**2** [T **line** sbdy/sthg ↔ **up**] to arrange something, or to arrange for someone to be present 安排〔某事〕; 安排〔某人〕出席: *I've lined up a famous singer for the school concert.* 我邀請了一位著名歌手來參加學校的音樂會。

lin·e·ar /ˈlɪnɪə; ˈlɪnɪəʳ/ *adj* **1** of or in lines 線(上)的: *a linear diagram* 線性圖表 **2** relating to length 長度的: *linear measurements* 長度測量 **3** in one direction 一個方向的: *linear change* 方向上的改變

lin·en /ˈlɪnɪn; ˈlɪn̩n/ *n* [U] **1** a kind of heavy cloth 亞麻布 **2** things like sheets and tablecloths that are made of cloth 家庭日用織品(如牀單、桌布等): *Is there any clean bed linen?* 有乾淨的牀單嗎?

lin·er /ˈlaɪnə; ˈlaɪnəʳ/ *n* **1** a large passenger ship 大客輪 **2** a piece of material used inside something to protect it 襯墊: *a dustbin liner* 垃圾箱襯墊

lines·man /ˈlaɪnzmən; ˈlaɪnzmən/ *n* **linesmen** /-mən; -mən/ **1** a sports official who stays near the edge of the playing area and decides when the ball has gone outside it 〔運動中的〕巡邊員, 邊線裁判 **2** a person whose job is to take care of electrical or telephone lines 〔電線、電話線的〕線務員

line-up /ˈlaɪnʌp; ˈlaɪnʌp/ *n* **line-ups 1** a row of people, especially one organized by the police so that someone might recognize a person they had seen doing a crime 〔尤指警方為了讓人識別出疑犯的〕一列人 **2** a collection of people or things for a reason 〔由於某種原因而〕集合起來的人; 一系列的事物: *Tonight's line-up on BBC1 includes this week's episode of "Dallas".* 英國廣播公司一台今晚的節目包括本週的一集《達拉斯》。

lin·ger /ˈlɪŋə; ˈlɪŋəʳ/ *v* [I] to continue or wait for a time before going 逗留; 徘徊: *The pain lingered on for weeks.* 疼痛持續了好幾個星期。| *He lingered outside the school*

---

after everybody else had gone home. 在別人都已回家之後, 他仍在學校外徘徊。 | *She was left with the lingering fear that he would not return.* 她心中有種久久不能消除的恐懼, 就是他不會再回來。 –**lingerer** *n*

lin·ge·rie /'læn3ə,ri; 'læn3əri:/ *n* [U] *fml* underclothes and night-clothes for women 〔正式〕女式內衣; 女式睡衣

lin·guist /'lɪŋgwɪst; 'lɪŋgwᵻst/ *n* **1** a person who studies and is good at foreign languages 研究和通曉幾種外語的人 **2** a person who studies human language 語言學家

lin·guis·tics /lɪŋ'gwɪstɪks; lɪŋ'gwɪstɪks/ *n* [U] the study of language in general and of particular languages 語言學 –**linguistic** *adj* –**linguistically** /-klɪ; -klɪ/ *adv*

lin·i·ment /'lɪnəmənt; 'lɪnᵻmənt/ *n* [C;U] an oily liquid that you rub on to your skin, especially to treat pain and stiffness in your joints 皮膚擦劑〔尤指用以消除關節的疼痛和僵硬〕

lin·ing /'laɪnɪŋ; 'laɪnɪŋ/ *n* a piece of material covering the inner surface of something like a drawer or an article of clothing; 襯裡; 裡子

link¹ /lɪŋk; lɪŋk/ *n* **1** something which connects two other things 連接物: *There's a new rail link between the two towns.* 有條新鐵路將兩個城鎮連接起來。 **2** a connection between two things 關連; 聯繫: *a link between smoking and lung diseases* 抽煙與肺病之間的關連 **3** one ring of a chain 〔鏈的〕一環

link² *v* [I;T] (also 又作 **link up; link sthg ↔ up**) to connect 連接; 聯繫: *The road links all the new towns.* 這條路把所有的新城鎮都連在一起。 | *They walked with linked arms.* 他們手挽手地走。 | *She was able to link up all the different pieces of information.* 她能把所有不同的信息聯繫起來。

link·age /'lɪŋkɪdʒ; 'lɪŋkɪdʒ/ *n* [U] the fact or process in which things are connected, or the way in which they are connected 連接; 接合; 關聯

links /lɪŋks; lɪŋks/ *n* [plural is 複數為 **links**] a piece of ground on which GOLF is played 高爾夫球場

link·up /'lɪŋk,ʌp; 'lɪŋk-ʌp/ *n* a connection 連接; 聯繫

li·no·le·um /lɪ'nəʊlɪəm; lᵻ'nəʊlɪəm/ *n* (also 又作 **lino** /'laɪnəʊ; 'laɪnəʊ/ *infml* 〔非正式〕) [U] a floor covering which is made of strong cloth under a hard surface 油地氈

lin·seed oil /'lɪn,sid 'ɔɪl; ,lɪnsiːd 'ɔɪl/ *n* [U] an oil which is used in some paints and inks 亞麻籽油〔用於某些油漆或墨水中〕

lint /lɪnt; lɪnt/ *n* [U] **1** soft material which is used for protecting wounds 〔裹傷口的〕軟麻布 **2** small pieces or threads that come off a piece of cloth 絨毛: *This tea towel leaves lint on the glasses.* 這塊茶巾上掉下來的絨毛留在玻璃杯上了。

lin·tel /'lɪntl; 'lɪntl/ *n* a piece of stone or

wood across the top of a window or door 〔門、窗上的〕過樑

li·on /'laɪən; 'laɪən/ *n* **1** a large yellow animal which belongs to the cat family and lives mainly in Africa; a female lion is called a **lioness** 獅子〔母獅子叫做 **lioness**〕 **2** **the lion's share** the largest part of something 最大的一份

*lip /lɪp; lɪp/ *n* **1** one of the two edges of your mouth 嘴唇: *He kissed her on the lips.* 他吻了她的嘴唇。 **2** the edge of a container or opening 〔容器或洞的〕邊緣, 口: *the lip of the cup* 杯子口 **3** a **stiff upper lip** a lack of expression of feeling 無表情, 面不改色 **4** **-lipped** with lips of a certain kind 有…嘴唇的: *red-lipped* 紅嘴唇的 | *thin-lipped with anger* 氣得雙唇緊閉

lip-read /'lɪp,rid; 'lɪp riːd/ *v* [I] to watch people's lip movements to understand what they are saying because you cannot hear them 唇讀; 觀唇辨意 –**lipreading** *n* [U]

lip·stick /'lɪp,stɪk; 'lɪp,stɪk/ *n* [C;U] colour which women put on their lips to make them brighter 口紅, 唇膏: *I'll just put on some lipstick.* 我只擦點口紅。 | *I bought a new lipstick today.* 我今天買了一支新的口紅。

liq·ue·fy /'lɪkwə,faɪ; 'lɪkwᵻfaɪ/ *v* **liquefied, liquefying** [I;T] to become or make something liquid (使)液化: *Butter liquefies in heat.* 黃油遇熱熔化。

li·queur /lɪ'kɜ·; lɪ'kjʊər/ *n* a strong, usually sweet alcoholic drink which is often drunk after a meal 甜露酒, 利口酒〔通常在餐後飲用〕

liq·uid¹ /'lɪkwɪd; 'lɪkwᵻd/ *n* [C;U] a substance which flows and is not solid or gas 液體: *It is important to drink a lot of liquid in hot climates.* 氣候炎熱時, 多喝水是很重要的。

liquid² *adj* **1** in the form of a liquid (used especially of something which is usually solid or gas) 液體的; 液態的〔尤指通常為固體或氣體的物質〕: *liquid gold* 液態黃金 | *liquid oxygen* 液態氧 **2** clear and flowing, with pure notes (used of sounds) 清脆流暢的〔指聲音〕

liq·ui·date /'lɪkwɪ,det; 'lɪkwᵻdeɪt/ *v* **liquidated, liquidating** [T] **1** to kill or destroy someone 殺死; 摧毀〔某人〕: *The government is suspected of liquidating its political opponents.* 政府被懷疑處決了持不同政見的人。 **2** to close a business, usually because it has too many debts 〔常由於債務過多〕清算〔公司〕 –**liquidation** /,lɪkwɪ'deʃən; ,lɪkwᵻ'deɪʃən/ *n* [U]: *The company has gone into liquidation.* 這家公司已停業清理資產。

liq·uid·ize /'lɪkwə,daɪz; 'lɪkwᵻdaɪz/ *v* **liquidized, liquidizing** [T] to crush food into a liquid 把〔食物〕壓擠成汁 –**liquidizer** *n*: *making soup in the liquidizer* 用榨汁機製湯

liq·uor /'lɪkɚ; 'lɪkəʳ/ *n* [U] **1** *BrE tech* al-

alcoholic drink 〚英式, 術語〛酒精類飲料 **2** *AmE* strong alcoholic drink, such as WHISKY 〚美式〛烈(性)酒〔如威士忌〕

liq·uo·rice /ˈlɪkərɪs; ˈlɪkərɪs/ *n* (also 又作 **licorice**) [U] a sweet black substance used especially in sweets 甘草

lisp /lɪsp; lɪsp/ *v* [I;T] to speak in such a way that you pronounce /s/ sounds as /θ/ 咬舌; 口齒不清地説話〔如把 /s/ 發成 /θ/〕–**lisp** *n* [sing]: *She speaks with a lisp.* 她説話口齒不清。

lis·som /ˈlɪsəm; ˈlɪsəm/ *adj* (also 又作 **lissome**) *lit* graceful in shape and movement (used of a person or their body) 〚文〛姿態優雅的〔指人或身體〕–**lissomly** *adv* – **lissomness** *n* [U]

list[1] /lɪst; lɪst/ *n* **1** [C] a set of names of things that you write one below the other to remember them or keep them in order 清單; 名單: *He checked their names against his list.* 他按名單核對他們的名字。| *We'd better make a shopping list before we go out.* 我們出去之前, 最好先列一張購物清單。**2** [sing] a position leaning to one side 傾斜: *The ship had a list of 30 degrees.* 船傾斜三十度。

list[2] *v* **1** [T] to write things down or mention them one after the other 列出清單[單子]: *He listed all the things he had to do.* 他列出了所有要做的事情。**2** [I] (of a ship) to lean to one side 〔船〕傾斜

lis·ten /ˈlɪsn; ˈlɪsən/ *v* [I] **1** to give attention to a person or sound that you can hear 聽: *She's listening **to** the radio.* 她在聽收音機。| *Listen to me.* 聽我説。–see 見 HEAR (USAGE 用法) **2** to pay attention to what someone says 傾聽; 聽從: *Listen to people who have experience of these problems.* 去聽聽經歷過這些問題的人的意見。| *Listen, I'll tell you a story.* 聽着, 我給你講個故事。**3 listen for, listen out for** to be prepared to hear a certain sound 留心聽〔某種聲音〕: *Can you listen out for the baby crying while I'm upstairs?* 我在樓上時, 你能留神聽着嬰兒的哭聲嗎?

  listen in *phr v* [I] **1** to pay attention to the private conversation of others 偷聽〔私人談話〕**2** to listen to a radio broadcast 收聽〔廣播〕–**listen** *n* [sing] *infml* 〚非正式〛: *Have a listen to this!* 聽聽這個!

list·less /ˈlɪstlɪs; ˈlɪstləs/ *adj* without the strength or the interest to do anything 無精打采的; 不感興趣的–**listlessly** *adv*

lit /lɪt; lɪt/ the past tense and past participle of LIGHT ☆ LIGHT 的過去式和過去分詞

li·ter /ˈlɪtə; ˈliːtəʳ/ *n* see 見 LITRE

lit·e·ra·cy /ˈlɪtərəsɪ; ˈlɪtərəsi/ *n* [U] the ability to read and write 讀寫能力; 識字; 有文化: *The government is funding a new adult literacy campaign.* 政府正在為一項新的成人識字運動提供資金。–opposite 反義 **illiteracy**

lit·e·ral /ˈlɪtərəl; ˈlɪtərəl/ *adj* **1** according to the usual meaning of the words 按字面意思的 –compare 比較 FIGURATIVE **2** exact 精確的: *a literal account of a conversation* 談話的精確記錄 **3** word by word 逐字的: *a literal translation* 逐字翻譯, 直譯 **4** showing little imagination 缺乏想像力的: *a literal approach to a subject* 對某學科的乏味的研究 – **literalness** *n* [U]

lit·e·ral·ly /ˈlɪtərəlɪ; ˈlɪtərəli/ *adv* **1** really (a word used to give force to what you say) 真正地; 確實地〔用於加強語氣〕: *The house is literally 10 metres from the sea.* 這所房子距離大海真的只有十米遠。| *She's done literally nothing to help.* 她實際上根本沒有動手相助。| *He was literally blue with cold.* 他簡直凍得全身青紫。**2** word by word 逐字地: *Can you translate that literally?* 你能把那個逐字翻譯出來嗎? **3** according to the words and not the intention 按字面意思: *I took what he said literally, which may have been a mistake.* 我將他所説的照字面意思來理解, 但可能是錯的。

> ■ USAGE 用法: Although **literally** means "really", it is often used simply to give force to expressions which are not at all "real" ☆儘管 **literally** 表示 "實際上", 但它往往只是被用來強調並不符合 "實際" 的話: *He* **literally** *exploded with anger.* 他快要氣炸了。| *She'll* **literally** *kill me if she finds out.* 她若發現實情, 會把我殺了。Note, however that some people consider this use to be incorrect. ☆請注意, 有些人認為這種用法不正確。

lit·e·ra·ry /ˈlɪtərərɪ; ˈlɪtəreri/ *adj* concerned with or related to literature 文學(上)的: *a literary magazine* 文學雜誌 | *a literary prize* 文學獎

lit·e·rate /ˈlɪtərɪt; ˈlɪtərət/ *adj* **1** able to read and write 有讀寫能力的 **2** well-educated 受過良好教育的–opposite 反義 **illiterate**

lit·e·ra·ture /ˈlɪtərətʃə; ˈlɪtərətʃəʳ/ *n* [U] **1** written works which are of artistic value 文學作品: *English literature* 英國文學 | *modern literature* 現代文學 **2** *infml* printed material on a certain subject or to help sell a product 〚非正式〛〔學科的〕著述; 〔產品的〕宣傳資料: *I've read all the literature **on** plant care.* 我已讀了有關植物種植的所有資料。| *He's sent off for literature **on** different makes of car.* 他被派去撰寫關於不同品牌汽車的宣傳資料。

lit·i·gate /ˈlɪtəgeɪt; ˈlɪtəgeɪt/ *v* **litigated, litigating** [I;T] *tech* to bring or defend a case in a court of law 〚術語〛提出訴訟; 辯解–**litigant** *n* –**litigation** /ˌlɪtəˈgeɪʃən; ˌlɪtəˈgeɪʃən/ *n*

lit·mus /ˈlɪtməs; ˈlɪtməs/ *n* [U] a material which turns red when it is touched by an acid substance and blue when touched by an ALKALI 石蕊: *litmus paper* 石蕊試紙〔遇酸變紅, 遇鹼變藍〕

li·tre /ˈliːtə; ˈliːtəʳ/ *n* (also 又作 **liter** *AmE* 《美式》) a unit for measuring liquid, equal to about 1¾ PINTS 升〔液量單位, 等於 1¾ 品脫〕: *a litre of oil* 一升油

lit·ter¹ /ˈlitə; ˈlitəʳ/ *n* **1** [U] small things which have been thrown away 垃圾; 廢物: *Please place litter in the bin provided.* 請把廢物扔在所提供的垃圾箱裡。 –see picture on page 470 見 470 頁彩圖 **2** [C] a group of young animals born at the same time to one mother 一窩〔動物〕: *a litter of puppies* 一窩小狗 **3** [U] something that farm animals sleep on or that cats use in a box as a TOILET〔供動物睡覺用的〕褥草;〔供貓用的〕便溺用沙

litter² *v* [T] to cover a surface with things untidily 亂扔: *The floor was littered with old newspapers.* 地上扔滿了舊報紙。

lit·tle¹ /ˈlitl; ˈlitl/ *adj* **1** [only before a noun 只用於名詞前] small 小的: *It's only a little house.* 這只是一所小房子。| *a little wooden box* 一個小木箱 **2** [only before a noun 只用於名詞前] short 短暫的: *I had to wait a little while before my name was called.* 我還得等一會兒才叫到我的名字。 **3** young 年紀小的: *a group of little children* 一羣小孩 **4** not important 微不足道的, 不重要的: *These are all little problems.* 這些都是小問題。

> ■ USAGE 用法: **Little** and **small** can both mean "of less than average size", but **little** is often used to suggest the speaker's feelings or opinion as well. It is frequently used to show approval of something which you think is pleasantly small ☆ **little** 和 **small** 都可表示"比普通的要小", 但 **little** 通常還暗示出說話者的感情和觀點, 常用來形容被認為小巧可愛的東西: *a sweet little kitten* 可愛的小貓 | *We're looking for a little cottage in the country.* 我們想在鄉間找一所小木屋。But it can also be used, together with another adjective, to show dislike or disapproval ☆ 但該詞也可以和另外一個形容詞一起使用, 表示不喜歡或厭惡: *a silly little man* 個子矮小的蠢傢伙 | *a classroom full of horrible little boys* 教室內滿是可怕的小男孩 | *Keep your nasty little hands to yourself!* 管好你那雙髒兮兮的小手!

lit·tle² *adv* less /les; les/, least /liːst; liːst/ not much 不大; 不太: *a little known fact* 鮮為人知的事實 | *She goes out very little.* 她很少外出。

lit·tle³ *det, pron* less, least **1** not very much 稍許; 一點點: *I have very little money left.* 我沒剩多少錢了。| *We had little to talk about.* 我們沒有甚麼可談的。| *I*

understood little of his speech. 他的演講我只聽懂一點點。 **2** **a little: a** a small amount 少量; 少許: *Add two eggs and a little milk.* 加入兩個雞蛋和少量牛奶。| *May I have a little of that cake?* 那塊蛋糕我可以吃一點點嗎? **b** quite 有些; 相當: *I was a little annoyed.* 我有些氣惱了。 **3** **little by little** gradually 逐漸地: *Little by little the people came to accept us.* 人們逐漸地接受了我們。

little fin·ger /ˌ·· ˈ··/ *n* the smallest finger on your hand 小指

live¹ /liv; liv/ *v* **lived, living 1** [I] to be or to continue to be alive 活着; 生存: *The rich live while the poor die.* 有錢人活着, 而窮人卻死了。| *He is unlikely to live much longer.* 他多半活不長了。 **2** [I + adv/prep] to have your home in a certain place 居住: *Where do you live?* 你住在哪裡? | *I live in a flat in Liverpool.* 我住在利物浦的一所公寓裡。 –see 見 STAY¹ (USAGE 用法) **3** [I;T] to lead a certain kind of life 過...的生活: *We can't earn enough to live comfortably.* 我們掙的錢不夠舒適地度日。| *She lived a quiet, country life.* 她過着安靜的鄉村生活。 **4** [I] to exist 存在: *He still lives in my imagination.* 他仍存在於我的想像中。 **5** **live and let live** to accept other people's behaviour 接受他人的行為方式; 待人寬容 **6** **live a lie** to lead a life that hides who you really are, or what you are like 隱姓埋名地生活 **7** **live by doing something** to make an income from a certain activity 靠做某事謀生: *He lives by stealing.* 他靠偷竊為生。 **8** **live by something** to behave according to the rules of something 按某事的規定行事: *I live by my own moral code.* 我按自己的道德標準行事。 **9** **live in sin** *old fash* to live with a person of the opposite sex who is not married to you《老式》同居; 姘居 **10** **live it up** to have a very good and active social life 享受多姿多彩的社交生活: *Shall we live it up at the disco tonight?* 今晚我們去跳迪斯科享受一番好嗎?

live sthg ↔ down *phr v* [T] to make people forget something shameful or strange that you have done 使〔人〕遺忘〔自己所做的可恥或奇怪的事情〕: *He arrived as the meeting ended, and he'll never live that down.* 他到達的時候會議已結束了, 這件事別人不會忘記的。

live in *phr v* [I] to sleep and eat in the building where you work or study 住宿在工作或學習地點: *I've decided to live in for my first term at college.* 我決定在第一個學期住在大學裡。

live off *sbdy/sthg phr v* [T] to obtain your food or income from a person or thing 靠〔某人或某物〕過活: *She's still living off her parents.* 她仍靠父母供養過日子。| *I live off the money from my first book.* 我靠我第一本書掙來的錢過日子。

live on *phr v* **1** [I] to continue living 繼續活着: *She lived on for 20 years after her hus-*

L

band's death. 丈夫去世後, 她還活了二十年。
2 [T **live on** sthg] to eat only a certain kind of food 靠〔吃某一種食物〕維生: *She lives on fruit and vegetables.* 她靠吃水果和蔬菜維生。
3 [T **live on** sthg] to get your money from a person or thing 從〔某人或某物〕得到錢: *He lives on the rent from his tenants.* 他靠房客的租金過日子。

  live out *phr v* [I] to eat and sleep in a place away from your place of work or study 不在工作或學習處住宿

  live up to sthg *phr v* [T] to reach someone's high standards 達到…的高標準: *Did the film live up to your expectations?* 這部電影有你期望的那樣好嗎?

  live with sbdy *phr v* [T] **1** to share your home with someone you love but that you are not married to 與〔情人〕同居: *She's living with her boyfriend.* 她與男友同居。 **2** to accept something unpleasant 容忍, 忍受〔令人不快的事物〕: *You learn to live with the pain.* 你要學會忍受這種痛苦。

***live²** /laɪv; laɪv/ *adj* **1** alive 活的: *The cat was playing with a live mouse.* 那貓在玩弄一隻活老鼠。 –opposite 反義 **dead 2** broadcast as it happens 現場直播的: *The programme was live.* 這節目是現場直播的。 **3** connected to the electricity supply and able to shock anyone who touches it 帶電的, 通電的: *a live wire* 帶電的電線 **4** slowly burning 慢慢燃燒的: *live coals* 在慢慢燃燒的煤炭 **5** ready to explode or fire 會爆炸〔起火〕的: *a live bomb* 會爆炸的炸彈

live·li·hood /ˈlaɪvlɪˌhʊd; ˈlaɪvlihʊd/ *n* the way in which you earn your money 謀生手段; 生計: *The oil spill has taken away fishermen's livelihood.* 溢油斷了漁民的生計。

live·ly /ˈlaɪvli; ˈlaɪvli/ *adj* **livelier, liveliest** active or full of life 活潑的; 有活力的: *Both children have very lively minds.* 兩個孩子的思想都很活躍。 | *It was a lively debate.* 那是一次熱烈的辯論。 | *She takes a lively interest in our affairs.* 她對我們的事情非常感興趣。 – **liveliness** *n* [U]

liv·en /ˈlaɪvən; ˈlaɪvən/ **liven up** *phr v* [I;T **liven** sbdy/sthg ↔ **up**] to become or to make a person or thing more active or full of life (使)活潑; (使)有活力: *How can we liven this party up?* 我們如何才能使這個晚會熱鬧起來呢?

liv·er /ˈlɪvɚ; ˈlɪvər/ *n* **1** [C] a large organ in your body which cleans your blood 肝臟 **2** [U] this organ from an animal's body, used as food 動物的肝臟〔供食用〕

lives /laɪvz; laɪvz/ the plural of LIFE ☆ LIFE 的複數

live·stock /ˈlaɪvˌstɑk; ˈlaɪvstɒk/ *n* [U] animals kept on a farm 家畜, 牲畜

liv·id /ˈlɪvɪd; ˈlɪvɪd/ *adj* **1** *infml* very angry 〖非正式〗非常生氣的 **2** blue-grey (used of discoloured skin) 烏青色的〔指變色的皮膚〕: *His legs were covered with livid bruises.* 他的

腿上滿是烏青的瘀傷。 –**lividly** *adv*

liv·ing¹ /ˈlɪvɪŋ; ˈlɪvɪŋ/ *adj* **1** alive now 活的: *She has no living relatives.* 她沒有活着的親人了。 **2** having life 有生命的: *plants, animals, and other living things* 植物、動物及其他生物 **3** used now 使用中的: *a living language* 現在通用的語言

living² *n* **1** [C] the way in which you earn money 謀生手段; 生計: *What does she do for a living?* 她靠甚麼維持生計? | *I'm trying to make a living out of painting.* 我正試圖以畫畫為生。 **2** [U] way of life 生活方式: *Our standard of living has dropped because the cost of living is increasing faster than my salary.* 由於生活費用的上漲速度比我工資的上漲速度快, 所以我們的生活水準已經下降。

living room /ˈ··· ·/ *n* the main room in a house where people usually sit and do things together 客廳, 起居室

liz·ard /ˈlɪzɚd; ˈlɪzəd/ *n* an animal with a rough skin, four legs, and a long tail 蜥蜴

-'ll /əl, l/ short for 〖縮〗WILL or SHALL: *He'll soon be here.* 他很快就到這裡。 –see 見 'S (USAGE 用法)

lla·ma /ˈlɑmə; ˈlɑːmə/ *n* a South American animal with thick woolly hair, often used for carrying goods 美洲駝

***load¹** /lod; ləʊd/ *n* **1** a quantity of something, especially something heavy, that is being carried or to be carried 負荷物; 裝載: *The lorry is transporting a load of furniture.* 這輛貨車正在運送一批家具。 **2** the amount which a certain vehicle or apparatus can carry 〔車輛的〕載運量: *a car load of people* 一車的人 | *two loads of washing* 要分成兩批洗的衣服 **3** the work that must be done by a person or apparatus 工作量: *Increased business has increased the load on our staff.* 業務的增長增加了我們雇員的工作量。 **4** the power of an electricity supply 發電量 **5** something difficult or unpleasant that you have to bear 必須忍受的困難或不快之事: *Knowledge of his crime is a heavy load for her to carry.* 知道他的罪行對她來説是種沉重的負擔。 **6 a load of, loads of** *infml* a lot of something 〖非正式〗許多, 大量: *She's got loads of money.* 她有很多錢。 | *That book is a load of rubbish.* 那本書裡盡是些胡言亂語。

load² *v* **1** [I;T] to put a quantity of things on or into something 裝載; 放入: *Load the suitcases into the car.* 把這些手提箱放進車裡。 **2** [T] to give someone a lot of things 給〔某人〕很多東西: *They loaded me with gifts.* 他們給了我許多禮物。 **3** [T] to put a bullet into a gun or a film into a camera 給〔槍〕上子彈; 給〔相機〕裝入膠卷 **4** [T] to move information into the memory of a computer 把〔信息〕輸入電腦

  load sbdy/sthg ↔ **down** *phr v* [T] to make a person or thing carry a lot of heavy things 使〔人或物〕背負許多重物: *I was loaded down with shopping.* 我提着大包小包

從購物買來的物品。

load up *phr v* [I;T **load** sthg ↔ **up**] to put a quantity of things into or onto something 裝入; 裝上: *Have you loaded the car up yet?* 你把東西裝上車了嗎?

load·ed /'lodɪd; 'ləʊdɪd/ *adj* **1** giving an unfair advantage 偏袒的: *The argument was loaded in his favour.* 這個論點是偏袒他的。| *He's playing with loaded dice.* 他在玩曲過手腳的骰子。**2** containing more meanings than that which appears at first 有暗含的意義的, 暗示性的: *a loaded question* 意味深長的問題 **3** [never before a noun 不能用於名詞前] *infml* having lots of money 〖非正式〗有許多錢的: *Let him pay; he's loaded.* 讓他付款吧, 他有的是錢。

loaf¹ /lof; ləʊf/ *n* **loaves** /lovz; ləʊvz/ bread that has been shaped and baked in one large piece 〔麵包的〕一條: *a loaf of bread* 一條麵包

loaf² *v*

loaf about/around *phr v* [I] *infml* to waste time, especially by not working when you should 〖非正式〗消磨時光; 虛度光陰 – **loafer** *n*

★**loan¹** /lon; ləʊn/ *n* **1** something which is lent, especially money 借出之物, 借〔貸〕款: *We've applied for a £10,000 bank loan.* 我們已向銀行申請一筆一萬英鎊的貸款。**2** the act of lending or the condition of being lent 借出: *She asked for the loan of my car.* 她問我借車。| *The book you want is on loan at the moment.* 你要的書現在借出去了。

loan² *v* [T] to lend something to someone 把〔某物〕借給〔某人〕: *She loaned her pictures to the gallery for a year.* 她把自己作的畫借給畫廊用一年。

□ USEFUL PATTERNS 有用句型
to loan something to someone; to loan someone something

---

loath /loθ; ləʊθ/ *adj* (also 又作 **loth**) be **loath to do something** to be unwilling to do something 不願意做某事: *I am loath to lend you any more money.* 我不願再借錢給你了。

loathe /loð; ləʊð/ *v* **loathed, loathing** [T] to feel great dislike for a person or thing 厭惡, 憎恨〔人或物〕: *I loathed all my teachers.* 我憎恨我所有的老師。| *He loathes getting up so early.* 他厭惡這麼早起牀。–**loathing** *n* [C;U]

loath·some /'loðsəm; 'ləʊðsəm/ *adj* very unpleasant 令人厭惡的。

loaves /lovz; ləʊvz/ the plural of LOAF ☆ LOAF 的複數

lob /lɑb; lɒb/ *v* **-bb-** [T + adv/prep] to throw or hit a ball high in the air in a gentle curve 把〔球〕挑高 –**lob** *n*: *a lob into the back corner of the court* 把球高挑到後場的角落裡

lob·by¹ /'lɑbɪ; 'lɒbi/ *n* **lobbies 1** an entrance hall just inside the main door to a building 門廳; 門廊: *I'll meet you in the hotel lobby.* 我在旅館大堂裡見你。**2** a group of people who try to influence the decisions of those in power in relation to a particular matter 遊說集團: *The clean air lobby is fighting plans for a new chemical factory.* 空氣清潔運動組織正在反對興建新化工廠的計劃。

lobby² *v* [I;T] to meet or try to influence a person in power in relation to a particular matter 遊說: *We're going to lobby our MP to ask him to vote against the proposal.* 我們打算遊說我們的議員投票反對該項提議。

lobe /lob; ləʊb/ *n* **1** (also 又作 **earlobe**) the round fleshy part at the bottom of your ear 耳垂 **2** *tech* any rounded division of a body organ, especially your brain and lungs 〖術語〗〔腦、肺等的〕葉

lob·ster /'lɑbstɚ; 'lɒbstəʳ/ *n* [C;U] a sea animal with a shell, a long body, and eight legs, or its flesh as a food 龍蝦 –see picture on page 504 見 504 頁彩圖

★**lo·cal¹** /'lokl; 'ləʊkəl/ *adj* **1** belonging to or in a certain place, especially the place where you live 當〔本〕地的, 地方性的〔尤指居住地的〕: *There are two local newspapers.* 當地發行了兩份報紙。| *The local council is improving public services.* 當地的議會正在改善公共服務。**2** *tech* having an effect on a particular part of something, especially a part of your body 〖術語〗〔尤指身體上〕局部的: *local anaesthetic* 局部麻醉

local² *n* **1** *infml* a bar near your home, especially one which you often drink at 〖非正式〗住處附近的酒館 **2** a person who lives in a certain place 本地人; 當地居民: *Let's ask one of the locals for directions.* 我們問問本地人該如何走哩。

lo·cal·i·ty /lo'kælətɪ; ləʊ'kælɪti/ *n* **localities** a place or position 地區

lo·cal·ize /'lokl͵aɪz; 'ləʊkəlaɪz/ *v* **localized, localizing** (also 又作 **localise** *BrE* 〖英式〗) [T] to keep something within a small area 使〔某事物〕局部化 –**localization** /͵lokəlaɪ'zeʃən; ͵ləʊkəlaɪ'zeɪʃən/ *n* [U]

lo·cal·ly /'lokl͡ɪ; 'ləʊkəli/ *adv* in the area that you are in or you have mentioned 在本地區: *Do you live locally?* 你住在本地嗎?

★**lo·cate** /'loket; ləʊ'keɪt/ *v* **located, locating** [T] **1** to find the position of something 找到〔某物〕的位置: *We located the nearest schools before we decided to move to this part of town.* 我們找到離家最近的學校後, 才決定搬到城裡的這一地區。**2** be **located** to be placed in a certain position 位於: *The house is located next to the river.* 這所房子位於河邊。| *The offices are conveniently located in the town centre.* 辦公室位於城中心, 非常便利。

★**lo·ca·tion** /lo'keʃən; ləʊ'keɪʃən/ *n* **1** a place or position 地點; 位置: *This is a suitable location for a camp.* 這是個適合露營的地方。**2**

---

in a suitable place, outside the buildings owned by the film company, where part of a film is made 〔電影的〕外景拍攝地: *The desert scenes were shot on location in the Sahara.* 沙漠鏡頭是在撒哈拉的外景地拍攝的。

*lock¹ /lɑk; lɒk/ *n* **1** an apparatus for fastening something, usually with a key 鎖: *He put new locks on the doors.* 他給幾道門裝上了新鎖。 | *I need a lock and chain for my bike.* 我需要給我的腳踏車配上鎖和鏈子。 **2** a stretch of water closed off by gates so that the water level can be raised or lowered to move boats up or down 有水閘的河道; 水閘: *The canal climbs the hill by means of a series of locks.* 運河通過一系列的水閘流向山上。 **3** a small number of hairs that grow together 一綹頭髮 **4** lock, stock, and barrel completely 完全地: *We sold everything, lock, stock and barrel.* 我們把東西統統賣掉了。 **5** under lock and key safely locked away 被安全地鎖了起來

lock² *v* **1** [I;T] to fasten something, usually with a key 鎖; 鎖上: *Lock the door.* 把門鎖上。 | *The door won't lock.* 門鎖不上。 **2** [T + adv/prep] to put something in a place and close it with a key 用鎖鎖住: *I've locked the medicines in the cupboard.* 我把藥鎖在碗櫥裡了。 **3** [I] to become fixed in a certain position 卡住; 固定於某一位置: *I can't move the car; the wheels have locked.* 我無法開動汽車, 車輪給卡住了。

lock sthg/sbdy ↔ away *phr v* [T] to put a thing or person in a safe place which you close with a key 把〔物或人〕鎖藏〔關押〕起來: *Lock your money away.* 把你的錢鎖藏起來。 | *The beautiful princess was locked away in a high tower.* 美麗的公主被關在一座高高的塔裡。

lock in *phr v* **1** [T lock sbdy ↔ in] to keep someone in a place by closing the door with a key 把〔某人〕鎖在裡面: *She heard the key turn; she was locked in.* 她聽見鑰匙的轉動聲, 她被鎖在裡面了。 **2** be locked in something to be unable to get out of a situation 無法擺脫某種情況: *locked in a struggle which neither side can win* 處於雙方均無法取勝的爭鬥中

lock sbdy ↔ out *phr v* [T] to keep someone out of a place by closing the door with a key 把〔某人〕鎖在門外: *Somehow I managed to lock myself out of the house.* 不知怎的, 我把自己鎖在了門外。

lock up *phr v* **1** [I;T lock sthg ↔ up] to make a building safe by closing the doors with keys 鎖好房門: *Don't forget to lock up when you go out.* 出門時別忘記鎖好房門。 | *Have you locked up the garage?* 你把車庫鎖好了嗎? **2** [T lock sbdy/sthg ↔ up] to put someone or something in a safe place which you close with a key 把〔某人或某物〕鎖藏〔關〕起來: *Lock your bike up in the*

shed. 把你的腳踏車鎖在棚子裡。 | *People like him should be locked up!* 像他那種人應當被關起來! –**lockable** *adj*

lock·er /ˈlɑkə; ˈlɒkəʳ/ *n* a small cupboard for keeping things in, for example at a school or in a station, which is closed with a key 〔學校或車站等處的〕寄物櫃

lock·et /ˈlɑkɪt; ˈlɒkət/ *n* a small metal case which you wear on a chain around your neck, and in which you can keep a small picture of someone you love, or a lock of their hair 〔項鏈上的〕紀念品飾盒〔可以存放所愛之人的照片或頭髮〕

lock·out /ˈlɑkaʊt; ˈlɒkaʊt/ *n* the employers' action of not allowing people to go back to work until they accept an agreement 〔雇主在工人未接受協議前的〕閉廠

lo·co·mo·tive¹ /ˌlɑkəˈmoʊtɪv; ˌləʊkəˈməʊtɪv◂/ *adj tech* concerning or causing movement 〔術語〕運動的; 使移動的: *locomotive powers* 運動力 –**locomotion** /-ˈmoʊʃən; -ˈməʊʃən/ *n* [U]

locomotive² *n fml* a railway engine 〔正式〕火車頭; 機車

lo·cum /ˈloʊkəm; ˈləʊkəm/ *n* a doctor or priest who is doing the work of another doctor or priest who is away for a period 〔醫生、牧師等的〕臨時代理人

lo·cust /ˈloʊkəst; ˈləʊkəst/ *n* an insect which flies in large groups, often destroying crops 蝗蟲

lodge¹ /lɑdʒ; lɒdʒ/ *v* **lodged, lodging** **1** [I + adv/prep] to stay in someone's house for payment 寄住; 寄宿: *She's lodging with friends at the moment.* 她目前正寄住在朋友們家裡。 **2** [T + adv/prep] to arrange a place for someone to stay in 安排〔某人〕住宿: *They have been lodged in a guesthouse.* 他們獲安排住進一家賓館。 **3** [I + adv/prep; T + adv/prep] to stick firmly in a certain position 絆住; 卡住: *He got a chicken bone lodged in his throat.* 有根雞骨頭卡在他的喉嚨裡。 **4** [T] to make a statement officially 正式提出〔聲明〕: *You must lodge a complaint with the authorities.* 你必須向當局提出控告。 **5** [T + adv/prep] *fml* to put something in a safe place 〔正式〕存放〔某物〕: *You had better lodge those papers with your lawyer.* 你最好把那些文件存放在你的律師那裡。

lodge² *n* **1** a small house on the land of a great house and usually at the entrance to its park 〔大宅或公園入口處的〕門房, 管理員室 **2** a small house for people to stay in while doing certain activities such as skiing (SKI) 〔供人們參加某些活動, 如滑雪時休息的〕小屋, 小舍

lodg·er /ˈlɑdʒə; ˈlɒdʒəʳ/ *n* a person who pays rent to live in someone's house 寄宿人; 房客

lodg·ing /ˈlɑdʒɪŋ; ˈlɒdʒɪŋ/ *n* **1** [U] a place to stay for payment 寄宿處: *a night's lodging*

夜宿 | *board and lodging* 食宿 **2 lodgings** [pl] a room or rooms in someone's house where you may live for payment 寄宿的房間: *I'm staying in lodgings until I find a flat.* 我在找到公寓前, 寄宿在別人家裡。

loft /lɔft; lɒft/ *n* a room or space under the roof of a building 閣樓; 頂樓

loft·y /'lɔftɪ; 'lɒftɪ/ *adj* **loftier, loftiest 1** showing an unusually high standard of thought or feeling 高尚的; 崇高的: *lofty aims* 崇高的目標 **2** showing that you believe you are better than other people 高傲的; 傲慢的: *a lofty smile* 高傲的微笑 **3** *lit* very high 〔文〕很高的 **–loftily** *adv* **–loftiness** *n* [U]

log¹ /lɔg; lɒg/ *n* **1** a thick piece of wood from a tree 大木頭; 原木 **2** an official written record of the journey of a ship or plane 航海日誌; 飛行日誌; 航行紀錄 **3** see 見 LOGARITHM

log² *v* **-gg-** [T] to record something officially 正式記錄〔某事〕

log in *phr v* [I] (also 又作 **log on**) to enter a computer system 進入電腦系統

log out *phr v* [I] (also 又作 **log off**) to leave a computer system 退出[停止使用]電腦系統

lo·gan·ber·ry /'lɔgən,bɛrɪ; 'ləʊgənbəri/ *n* **loganberries** a small red fruit 羅甘莓, 洛干楊梅

log·a·rith·m /'lɔgə,rɪðəm; 'lɒgərɪðəm/ *n* (also 又作 **log** *infml* 〔非正式〕) a number which represents a value of another number, and which can be added to another logarithm instead of multiplying the original number 〔數學中的〕對數 **–logarithmic** /,lɔgə'rɪðmɪk; ,lɒgə'rɪðmɪk◁/ *adj*

log·ger·heads /'lɔgə,hɛdz; 'lɒgəhedz/ *n* **at loggerheads** in strong disagreement with someone 不和; 相爭

lo·gic /'lɑdʒɪk; 'lɒdʒɪk/ *n* [U] **1** the science of reasoning by formal methods 邏輯學 **2** a way of reasoning 推理方法 **3** *infml* good sense 〔非正式〕良好的辨識力

lo·gic·al /'lɑdʒɪkḷ; 'lɒdʒɪkəl/ *adj* **1** in accordance with the rules of logic 符合邏輯的: *a logical argument* 合乎邏輯的論證 **2** sensible 合理的: *It seems a logical decision.* 這似乎是個合理的決定。 **–opposite** 反義 **illogical** **–logically** /-klɪ; -kli/ *adv*

lo·gis·tics /lo'dʒɪstɪks; lə'dʒɪstɪks/ *n* [pl] the organization of a lot of people or things in a difficult operation 後勤(工作); 統籌安排: *The logistics of distributing so many food parcels are extremely complex.* 分發這麼多食物包的後勤工作是極其困難的。 **–logistic** *adj* **–logistically** /-klɪ; -kli/ *adv*

loins /lɔɪnz; lɔɪnz/ *n* [pl] the part of your body below your waist and above your legs 腰部; 下身

loi·ter /'lɔɪtɚ; 'lɔɪtə'/ *v* [I] **1** to stay in or near a place for no clear reason 閒蕩; 徘徊: *He was caught loitering near the security en-* trance to the bank. 他被人發現在銀行安全入口附近徘徊。 **2** to move slowly, with frequent stops 走走停停: *Don't loiter on your way home!* 別在回家路上走走停停! **–loiterer** *n*

loll /lɑl; lɒl/ *v* [I] **1** (also 又作 **loll about/around**) to sit or lie in a way that looks lazy 懶散地坐[躺] **2** (of your head or tongue) to hang down loosely 〔頭部或舌頭〕〔鬆馳地〕垂下

lol·li·pop /'lɑlɪ,pɑp; 'lɒlipɒp/ *n* **1** a hard sweet made of boiled sugar on the end of a stick 棒棒糖 **2** (also 又作 **lolly** *BrE* 〔英式〕) ice cream or frozen juice on the end of a stick 冰棍, 棒冰

lollipop man /'··· ,·/ *n* *BrE* a person whose job is to stop traffic with a stick shaped like a lollipop so that school children can cross; a woman who does this is called a **lollipop lady** 〔英式〕〔出示車輛停車指示牌讓學生過馬路的〕交通糾察〔做這種工作的女性稱為 **lollipop lady**〕

lol·ly /'lɑlɪ; 'lɒli/ *n* **lollies** see 見 LOLLIPOP

lone /lon; ləʊn/ *adj* [only before a noun 只用於名詞前] without companions 孤獨的; 單獨的: *A lone rider was coming towards me.* 獨行騎士向我走來。

lone·ly /'lɑlɪ; 'ləʊnli/ *adj* **lonelier, loneliest 1** alone and unhappy 孤寂的; 寂寞的: *He was lonely without his wife.* 沒有了妻子, 他很寂寞。 **2** far from where people live, and not often visited 偏僻的: *a lonely country road* 鄉間的一條偏僻的路 **–see** 見 ALONE (USAGE 用法) **–loneliness** *n* [U]

lon·er /'lonɚ; 'ləʊnə'/ *n* a person who seems to like being alone 喜歡獨處的人

lone·some /'lonsəm; 'ləʊnsəm/ *adj* *AmE infml* lonely 〔美式, 非正式〕孤單的, 孤寂的 **–see** 見 ALONE (USAGE 用法)

long¹ /lɔŋ; lɒŋ/ *adj* **1** measuring a large amount in length, distance, or time 長的; 遠的; 長久的: *long hair* 長髮 | *long journey* 長途旅行 | *He took a long time to get here.* 他花了很長時間才到這裡。 **–opposite** 反義 **short 2** covering a certain distance or time 〔距離或時間〕長的; 久的: *How long was her speech?* 她的演講有多長時間? | *It was an hour long.* 這有一個小時之久。 | *The garden is 20 metres long and 15 metres wide.* 花園有二十米長, 十五米寬。 **3** lasting or seeming to last more time than usual or than you want to 冗長的; 過長的: *It's been a long day.* 今天過得很慢。 | *long hours of waiting* 長時間的等待 **4 in the long run** in the end 從長遠的觀點來看, 最終: *Everything should be all right in the long run.* 一切最終都會變好的。 **5 in the long term** in the distant future 就長遠而言: *The company's position in the long term looks very good.* 長遠來說, 公司的境況是很好的。 **6 long in the tooth** old (used of a person or animal) 年紀大的, 老的〔指人或動物〕 **7 not by a long chalk,**

not by a long shot *infml* not at all 〖非正式〗一點也不: *"Is he ready yet?" "No, not by a long chalk."* 〝他準備好了嗎?〞〝沒有, 還差得遠呢。〞

★★ **long²** *adv* **1** a long time or for a long time 長時間地: *Will you be long?* 你要花很長時間嗎? | *I can't wait much longer.* 我不能再等多久了。 **2 as long as, so long as** on condition that 假如; 只要: *We'll go out as long as the weather is fine.* 只要天氣好, 我們就會出去。 **3 long ago** at a distant time in the past 很久以前 **4 no longer, not any longer** not any more 不再: *He no longer lives here.* 他不再住在這裡了。 | *He doesn't work here any longer.* 他不再在這裡工作了。 **5 so long** *infml* you say this when you leave someone or someone leaves you 〖非正式〗再見〔用於告別〕

long³ *n* **1** a long time 長時間: *Were you there for long?* 你在那裡很長時間了嗎? **2 before long** soon 不久, 很快: *I'll be back before long.* 我很快就回來。 **3 the long and the short of it** the general result 總的結果

long⁴ *v* [I;T] to want something very much 渴望: *I'm longing to go.* 我渴望去。 | *I'm longing for him to come home.* 我渴望着他回家。 | *He longed for the end of term.* 他渴望學期的結束。

> □ USEFUL PATTERNS 有用句型
> to long for something; to long to do something; to long for something to happen

long-dis·tance /ˌ· ˈ···◂/ *adj* [only before a noun 只用於名詞前] from one point to a far point 長途的: *He's a long-distance runner.* 他是個長跑運動員。 | *I want to make a long-distance telephone call.* 我想打個長途電話。– **long-distance** *adv*: *to telephone long-distance* 打長途電話

long drink /ˈ··/ *n* a drink which usually contains a little alcohol in a large amount of liquid 只含少量酒精的飲料

lon·gev·i·ty /lɑnˈdʒɛvətɪ; lɒnˈdʒevɪti/ *n* [U] *fml* long life 〖正式〗長壽

long face /ˌ·ˈ·/ *n* a face with a sad expression 不悅的面容: *Don't pull such a long face, it's not that bad!* 別愁眉苦臉的, 事情沒有那麼糟糕!

long·hand /ˈlɔŋˌhænd; ˈlɒŋhænd/ *n* [U] ordinary writing by hand 普通書寫: *Can you write those notes out in longhand?* 你能把這些筆記寫出來嗎?

long·ing /ˈlɔŋɪŋ; ˈlɒŋɪŋ/ *n* [C;U] a strong feeling of wanting something 渴望: *He had a secret longing for the lifestyle of the rich and famous.* 他私下渴望着富人和名人的生活方式。 | *gazing at her with longing* 以渴望的目光注視着她–**longingly** *adv*

lon·gi·tude /ˈlɑndʒəˌtjud; ˈlɒndʒɪˌtjuːd/ *n* [C;U] a position on the Earth measured in degrees east or west of an imaginary line which runs through London 經度

lon·gi·tu·di·nal /ˌlɑndʒəˈtjudn̩l; ˌlɒndʒɪˈtjuːdɪnəl/ *adj* from one end of a line or an object to the other 長度的; 縱長的 – **longitudinally** *adv*

long jump /ˈ··/ *n* [sing] a sport in which people jump as far as possible along the ground 跳遠

long-range /ˌ· ˈ··◂/ *adj* [only before a noun 只用於名詞前] covering a long distance or time 遠距離的; 長期的: *long-range weapons* 遠程武器 | *long-range forecasts* 長期的預報

long-sight·ed /ˌlɔŋˈsaɪtɪd; ˌlɒŋˈsaɪtɪd◂/ *adj* not able to see things clearly when they are very close to your eyes 遠視的 –opposite 反義 **shortsighted**

long·stand·ing /ˌlɔŋˈstændɪŋ; ˌlɒŋˈstændɪŋ◂/ *adj* which has existed for a long time 持久的: *There is a longstanding trade agreement between the two countries.* 兩國之間有一項長期貿易協定。

long-term /ˌ· ˈ·◂/ *adj* for or in the distant future 長期的: *a long-term plan* 長期計劃 | *No one knows what the long-term effects of these drugs will be.* 無人知道這些藥品的長效性。–opposite 反義 **short-term**

long wave /ˌ·ˈ·/ *n* [U] radio broadcasting on waves of 1,000 metres or more 〔無線電的〕長波

long·ways /ˈlɔŋˌwez; ˈlɒŋweiz/ *adv* see 見 LENGTHWAYS

long·wind·ed /ˌlɔŋˈwɪndɪd; ˌlɒŋˈwɪndɪd◂/ *adj* saying or writing too much in a dull way 〔說話〕嘮叨的; 〔寫作〕冗長的: *He made a longwinded speech about social reform.* 他發表了一次關於社會改革的冗長的演講。

loo /lu; luː/ *n BrE infml* a TOILET 〖英式, 非正式〗廁所

★★ **look¹** /lʊk; lʊk/ *v* **1** [I] to turn your eyes towards something so that you can see it 看, 瞧, 望: *She looked at me angrily.* 她生氣地看着我。 | *He was sitting looking out of the window.* 他坐着望向窗外。 | *The scene was so horrible I couldn't bear to look.* 這場面太可怕了, 我不忍看。 | *I called to him but he looked away.* 我叫他, 但他別過臉去了。 **2** [+ complement] to have a particular appearance 看來, 顯得: *You look tired.* 你看上去很累。 | *He looks like my brother.* 他看上去很像我弟弟。 **3** [I+adv/prep] to face in a particular direction 面向, 朝向: *The house looks out onto the river.* 這所房子面向大河。 **4 Look!, Look here!** a word or phrase you use when you want someone to notice something or pay attention to something 瞧〔用於希望某人注意某物〕: *Look where you're going!* 注意你走的方向! | *Look at the time — we're late.* 你瞧瞧時間——我們遲了。 **5 look as if, look like** to seem probable 看起來可能: *It looks as if we're going to miss the plane.* 看來我們可能

趕不上飛機了。| *It looks like it's going to rain.* 看樣子快要下雨了。**6 look on the bright side** to think about the good parts of a situation, not the bad ones 看事情好的方面，對…抱樂觀態度 **7 look someone in the eye** to look directly and boldly at someone 直視某人: *He was too ashamed of himself to look me in the eye.* 他很不好意思，不敢正眼看我。**8 not much to look at** not very attractive 不太吸引人

look after sbdy/sthg *phr v* [T] to take care of someone or something 照顧〔某人或某物〕: *Who will look after the baby?* 誰來照顧嬰兒? | *Are you being well looked after?* 你得到很好的照顧嗎? | *She will look after the business for me while I'm away.* 我不在時她來替我料理生意。

look ahead *phr v* [I] to plan for the future 為將來做打算: *We must look ahead and invest for the future.* 我們必須未雨綢繆，為將來進行投資。

look around *phr v* [I] to search 到處尋找: *I'm looking around* **for** *a new job.* 我正在找一份新的工作。

look at sbdy/sthg *phr v* [T] **1** to watch someone or something 看〔某人或某物〕: *looking at the children playing in the street* 看孩子們在街上玩 **2** to regard or judge someone or something in a particular way 對待，看待〔某人或某物〕: *I look at life differently now, since the accident.* 自那起事故以後，我改變了對生活的態度。**3** to read something 閱讀: *Could you look at this report for me?* 你能幫我看一下這份報告嗎? **4** to consider or examine something 考慮，研究；檢查〔某事物〕: *A committee has been set up to look at the problem of homelessness.* 已經成立了一個委員會來研究無家可歸這個問題。

look back *phr v* [I] **1** to think about or remember things that happened in the past 回顧；回想: *When I look back I realize how happy my childhood was.* 現在回想過去，我才意識到自己的童年是多麼快樂。**2 he never looked back** = he became very successful 他很成功，一路領先: *He won his first game at the age of 18 and then never looked back.* 他十八歲時贏得了首場比賽，然後便一帆風順。

look down on sbdy/sthg *phr v* [T] to have a low opinion of someone or something or think that they are socially inferior 看不起〔某人或某物〕: *She looks down on me because I'm only a secretary.* 她因為我只是個祕書而瞧不起我。

look for sbdy/sthg *phr v* [T] to try to find someone or something 尋找〔某人或某物〕: *I'm looking for Mr Baker.* 我在找貝克先生。| *She's gone to look for a public telephone.* 她去了找公用電話。

look forward to sthg *phr v* [T] to feel happy because you are going to do something that you will enjoy 期望；盼望: *We're looking forward to the party.* 我們盼望着這次聚會。| *I'm looking forward to meeting you.* 我期望着與你見面。

look into sthg *phr v* [T] to examine the facts about something 調查〔某事物〕: *Police are looking into the allegations of corruption.* 警方在調查有關貪污的指控。| *There's a fault in the machine and we're looking into it.* 機器出了問題，我們正在檢查。

look on *phr v* **1** [I] to watch something while other people take part 旁觀: *I looked on in dismay as the fight started.* 鬥毆開始後，我在一旁沮喪地看着。**2** [T **look on** sbdy/sthg] to consider someone or something in a particular way 認為；看作: *I look on him* **as** *a friend.* 我視他為朋友。

look out *phr v* **1 Look out!** a phrase you use to tell someone to be careful 小心! 注意!〔用於告訴別人留神〕: *Look out! There's a car coming!* 小心! 一輛汽車開過來了! **2** [T **look** sthg ↔ **out**] to find something from among your possessions〔從自己的東西中〕找出〔某物〕: *I'll look out some old clothes for the jumble sale.* 我準備挑一些舊衣服用作義賣。

look out for sbdy/sthg *phr v* [T] to make sure that you notice someone or something 注意看着〔某人或某物〕: *Look out for Jane at the conference.* 開會時注意一下簡。

look sthg ↔ **over** *phr v* [T] to examine something quickly 瀏覽，迅速檢查〔某物〕: *Could you look the car over for me before I buy it?* 在我買車前，你能幫我把車很快地檢查一下嗎?

look round *phr v* **1** [I;T **look round** sthg] to look at a lot of things, especially before you buy something〔尤指購買前〕看許多東西: *It's a good idea to look round for a while before buying a car.* 買車前多看一些車是個好主意。| *Let's go and look round the shops.* 我們去逛逛商店吧。**2** [I] to search (到處)尋找: *She looked round* **for** *a piece of paper.* 她到處找一張紙。

look through sthg *phr v* [T] to examine something carefully 認真檢查〔某物〕: *Could you look through this article for me?* 你能幫我仔細看一下這篇文章嗎? | *I looked through the pile of papers.* 我認真審查過這堆文件了。

look up *phr v* **1** [T] to get better 好轉，改善: *Things are looking up at last!* 事情終於開始好轉了! **2** [T **look** sthg ↔ **up**] to find a piece of information in a book〔在書中〕查閱〔資料〕: *Can you look up the word "instigate" for me?* 你能幫我查一下"instigate"這個詞嗎? **3** [T **look** sbdy ↔ **up**] to visit someone when you are in the place where they live 拜訪，看望: *Look me up if you're ever in this part of the country.* 如果你到這地方來，請來看看我。

look upon sbdy/sthg *phr v* [T] to consider someone or something in a particular way

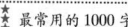

看待〔某人或某物〕: *I look upon him as a friend.* 我視他為朋友。

look up to sbdy *phr v* [T] to respect and admire someone 尊敬, 敬仰: *All his pupils look up to him.* 他所有的學生都很敬重他。

look² *n* **1** an act of looking at something 看; 瞧: *She gave me an angry look.* 她生氣地看了我一眼。 | *Did you have a look at the new computer?* 你看過那部新電腦了嗎? | *Take a look at this huge spider!* 看看這隻大蜘蛛! | *Have you had a look at that newspaper article yet?* 你看過報紙上那篇文章了嗎? | *We need to have another look at the whole question of teachers' pay.* 我們需要從另一個角度看整個有關教師薪水的問題。 **2** a person's appearance, or an expression on their face 外表; 表情: *I knew she didn't like it by the look on her face.* 我從她臉上的表情可以知道她並不喜歡它。 | *He had a frightened look in his eyes.* 他的眼中有種驚恐的神色。 | *She had the look of someone who would succeed in life.* 她有一種在生活中將會成功的表情。 **3 looks** [pl] someone's appearance, especially when it is attractive 〔尤指吸引人的〕外表: *Good looks aren't everything.* 漂亮的外表不是一切。 | *He kept his looks even in old age.* 即使上了年紀, 他仍然保持了他以前的外貌。 **4 by the look of it, by the looks of it** judging by the appearance of something 從外表看, 看樣子: *That car's ready for the scrap heap by the look of it.* 看樣子這座車該扔掉了。 | *We're in for some rain by the looks of it.* 看樣子我們會遇到大雨。 **5 not like the look of something** to feel worried by something 對某事擔憂: *The whole deal sounds dishonest to me — I don't like the look of it.* 整項交易在我聽來似乎不大正當 — 我對此感到很擔心。

look·out /'lʊk,aʊt; 'lʊk-aʊt/ *n* **1** [C] a person whose duty is to watch, usually for danger 監視者; 守望者: *The general posted a lookout on each hill.* 將軍在每座小山上都設立了崗哨。 **2** [C] a place to watch from 瞭望台; 崗哨 **3** [sing] *infml* a future possibility that may be unwelcome 〔非正式〕〔可能令人不快的〕前景: *It's a bad lookout for us if he gets ill now.* 他如果現在生病, 那情況對我們很不妙。 | *It's your lookout if you're caught.* 你如果被抓住, 那你的前景就是這樣了。 **4 be on the lookout for, keep a lookout for** to be watching or searching for a person or thing 尋找〔某人或某物〕: *He's on the lookout for a job.* 他在找工作。

loom¹ /lum; luːm/ *n* a frame or machine for weaving cloth 織布機

loom² *v* [I] **1** to come into sight in a way that seems unfriendly 〔以不友善的方式〕隱約出現: *A figure loomed out of the mist.* 一個人影在霧中隱隱出現。 **2** to cause fear or worry as the time comes closer 逼近: *The exams are looming.* 考試逐漸逼近。

loon·y /'luni; 'luːni/ *adj infml* 〔非正式〕

loonier, looniest mad or strange (used of a person) 瘋狂的; 奇怪的〔指人〕 –**loony** *n*

loop¹ /lup; luːp/ *n* the circular shape made by something like a piece of string when it is bent into a curve 〔繩、線等繞成的〕圈, 環

loop² *v* **1** [I;T] to form a curve with something like a piece of string 使形成圈〔環〕 **2** [T + adv/prep] to fasten with a circular piece of something like a piece of string 〔用繩圈狀物〕扣繫住: *Loop the rope round the gate.* 把繩子套在門上。

loop·hole /'lup,hol; 'luːphəʊl/ *n* a way of avoiding something, especially one provided by faults in a law or agreement 〔法律或協議的〕漏洞: *The company has found a loophole in the tax laws.* 公司發現了稅法中的一個漏洞。

*loose¹ /lus; luːs/ *adj* **1** not fixed or held together by or in anything 未固定的; 散裝的: *They sell chocolates loose or in boxes.* 他們賣的巧克力有散裝, 也有盒裝。 **2** not firmly fixed 不牢的; 鬆動的: *That screw is loose — you'd better tighten it.* 那隻螺絲鬆了, 你最好把它擰緊。 **3** free from control 不受束縛的: *Dogs are not allowed to wander loose in the park.* 在公園裡不得讓狗隻鬆縛亂跑。 **4** not fitting tightly (used of clothes) 寬鬆的〔指衣服〕: *He lost so much weight his trousers were quite loose.* 他體重減輕許多, 褲子顯得很寬鬆。 **5** not exact 不精確的: *a loose translation* 不精確的譯文 **6** without morals (used of people or their behaviour) 放蕩的〔指人或其行為〕 **7 at a loose end** having nothing to do 無所事事 –**loosely** *adv* –**looseness** *n* [U]

loose² *v* **loosed, loosing** [T] *fml* or *lit* 〔正式或文〕 to free a person or animal from control 釋放〔人或動物〕 –compare 比較 LOOSEN

loose³ *n* **on the loose** free from control, especially of the law 自由的〔尤指不受法律束縛〕: *a dangerous criminal on the loose* 逍遙法外的危險罪犯

loos·en /'lusn; 'luːsən/ *v* [I;T] to become or to make something less firm, fixed, or tight (使)變鬆: *He loosened his collar.* 他鬆開了衣領。 –opposite 反義 **tighten**

loosen up *phr v* [I] **1** to exercise your muscles in preparation for physical activity 〔運動前〕做準備活動: *I need time to loosen up before the race.* 比賽前我需要時間做一些準備活動。 **2** to become less tense 放鬆: *A drink will help you to loosen up.* 喝杯飲料會有助於你放鬆。

loot¹ /lut; luːt/ *n* [U] money or goods stolen by soldiers in war time, or by thieves, especially during periods of violence in society 戰利品; 掠奪物; 贓物

loot² *v* [I;T] to steal things from a place, especially in war time or during periods of social unrest 掠奪; 搶劫: *After the riots, crowds of people looted the shops.* 暴亂之後,

大批羣眾搶劫了商店。| *Food and farm animals were looted.* 食品和牲畜橫遭掠奪。– **looter** *n*

lop /lɒp; lɒp/ *v* **-pp-** [T] to cut something off, especially a branch from a tree 砍下〔尤指樹枝〕

lope /ləʊp; ləʊp/ *v* **loped, loping** [I + adv/prep] (especially of animals) to move quite fast with long, easy steps〔尤指動物〕輕快地奔跑

lop-sid-ed /ˌ·'··◂/ *adj infml* uneven because the two sides are different〔非正式〕兩邊不平衡的

loq-ua-cious /lɒˈkweɪʃəs; ləʊˈkweɪʃəs/ *adj fml* tending to talk a lot〔正式〕話多的，饒舌的 –**loquacity** /lɒˈkwæsəti; ləʊˈkwæsჳti/ *n* [U]

★**lord**[1] /lɔːd; lɔːd/ *n* **1** a ruler or master 君主；主人 **2** a nobleman 貴族 **3** Lord a title that you use when you are talking to or about certain official people or noblemen 閣下；勳爵〔與某些官員或貴族説話時所用的稱呼〕: *the Lord Mayor of London* 倫敦市長閣下 | *Lord Grade* 格雷德勳爵 | *Not guilty, my Lord.* 我認為無罪，大人。**4 the Lord** God 上帝 **5 Our Lord** the son of God 耶穌 **6 Lord, Good Lord** words used to express surprise or worry 天哪〔表示驚訝或憂慮〕: *Good Lord!* 天哪! | *Oh Lord, I forgot!* 哦天哪，我竟然忘了!

lord[2] *v* **lord it over someone** to behave towards someone as if you are better and more important than they are 對某人擺架子；發號司令

lord·ly /ˈlɔːdlɪ; ˈlɔːdli/ *adj* showing people that you think you are better and more important than they are 貴族氣的；高傲的

lord·ship /ˈlɔːdʃɪp; ˈlɔːdʃip/ *n* (also 又作 **Lordship**) a title that you use when you are talking to or about certain official people or noblemen 閣下；大人〔與某些官員或貴族説話時所用的稱呼〕: *Good morning, your Lordship.* 大人，早安! | *I've written to their Lordships.* 我已給大人們去信了。

lore /lɔː; lɔː/ *n* [U] knowledge or old beliefs about a certain subject, or held by a particular group〔某一學科的〕知識；〔某一部分人的〕信仰

lor·ry /ˈlɒrɪ; ˈlɒri/ *n BrE* **lorries** a large motor vehicle for carrying heavy goods 貨車 –see picture on page 991 見 991 頁彩圖

★★★**lose** /luːz; luːz/ *v* **lost** /lɒst; lɒst/, **losing 1** [T] to be without something because you cannot find it 遺失，丟失: *I've lost my notes.* 我把筆記弄丟了。**2 lose your way** not to know where you are any longer 迷路 **3** [T] not to have something any longer, or to cause it to be taken away from you 喪失，失去: *I've lost all interest in football.* 我對足球一點興趣也沒有了。| *She lost her parents while she was very young.* 她年紀很小的時候雙親已過世了。| *He lost an eye in the acci-*

dent. 他在事故中失去了一隻眼睛。| *His foolish behaviour lost him his job.* 他的愚蠢行為令他丟了工作。**4 lose touch with someone** not to have contact with a person any longer 與某人失去聯繫 **5 lose track of** not to have knowledge of a person or thing any longer 失去對〔某人或某物〕的了解: *Dinner already? I'd lost track of the time.* 吃晚飯了嗎? 我已經沒有時間概念了。**6 lose face** not to have the respect of other people any longer 丟臉，出醜 **7** [I;T] to fail to win something 未贏得；輸掉: *He lost the argument.* 他輸掉了那場辯論。| *England lost to Australia by 2 goals to 3.* 英格蘭隊以2比3輸給了澳大利亞隊。**8** [T] to have less money than before, or to cause you to have less money (使)虧損；賠錢: *We lost £200 on that job.* 我們在那項工作上賠了二百英鎊。| *His accident cost him a week's wages.* 他那場事故讓他損失了一週的薪水。**9** [T] to have less of something than before 損失，減少: *He's lost a lot of weight recently.* 最近他體重輕了不少。**10 be lost on someone** to have no effect on someone 對某人沒有作用: *His charm is completely lost on me.* 他的魅力對我絲毫不起作用。**11** [T] to waste time or a chance to do something 浪費，損失〔做某事的時間或機會〕: *The doctor lost no time in calling an ambulance.* 醫生毫不浪費一點時間，立即叫了救護車。**12** [I;T] (of a watch or clock) to move too slowly〔錶或鐘〕走慢: *This watch loses 5 minutes a day.* 這錶一天慢五分鐘。–opposite 反義 **gain 13 lose your cool, lose your temper** to become angry 發怒；發脾氣

lose out *phr v* [I] *infml* to make a loss〔非正式〕損失: *The firm lost out on the deal.* 公司在這筆交易中有損失。

los·er /ˈluːzə; ˈluːzər/ *n* **1** a person who has been defeated 輸家，損失者: *Nobody will play with him because he is such a bad loser.* 他輸不起，沒人願意與他比賽。–compare 比較 **WINNER 2** a person who is always unsuccessful 失敗者: *I sometimes think I'm a born loser!* 有時我認為自己是個天生的失敗者!

★★**loss** /lɒs; lɒs/ *n* **1** [U] the act or fact of losing something 遺失，丟失: *Have you reported the loss of your car?* 你有沒有向警方報失你的車? **2** [C] the sadness or disadvantage that you feel when you lose a person or thing 損失所帶來的難過或不利: *His death was a great loss to his friends.* 他的去世對他的朋友來說是個巨大的損失。**3** [C] income which is less than what you have spent 金錢上的損失；虧損: *The company has made a big loss this year.* 公司今年賠了一大筆錢。**4** [C;U] death 死亡；去世: *The enemy suffered heavy losses.* 敵方損失慘重。| *There's a danger of loss of life.* 有失去生命的危險。**5 at a loss** uncertain about what to do or say 不知所措: *I'm at a loss for words.*

L

我不知該説甚麼好。**6 be a dead loss** *infml* to be useless〖非正式〗無價值，不中用: *He's a dead loss as a manager.* 作為經理，他毫無用處。

lost[1] the past tense and past participle of LOSE ☆ LOSE 的過去式和過去分詞

lost[2] /lɒst; lɔst/ *adj* **1** unable to be found 遺失的，丢失的: *lost keys* 丢失的鑰匙 **2** no longer possessed by you 失去的，不復存在的: *I regret the lost opportunity.* 對於那錯失了的機會我感到很遺憾。**3 be lost, get lost** to be unable to find your way 迷路的: *I always get lost in London.* 我在倫敦總是會迷路。**4** killed or destroyed 被殺的；毀滅的: *The fund is for the families of fishermen lost at sea.* 這筆資金用於救濟在大海中喪生的漁民的家庭。

★**lot** /lɒt; lɑt/ *n* **1 a lot, lots** a great number or amount 許多；大量: *A lot of people have applied for the job.* 許多人應徵這份工作。| *She's got lots of money.* 她很有錢。**2 a lot: a** very much 非常: *I like him a lot.* 我很喜歡他。| *She looks a lot older now.* 她現在看起來老多了。**b** often 經常: *I see John quite a lot.* 我常見到約翰。**3 the lot** the whole number or amount 總數；總量: *I'll give you £10 for the lot.* 我準備一共給你十英鎊。**4** [C] a group of people or things 一批人[物]: *Another lot of students will be arriving soon.* 另一批學生很快就要到了。**5** [C] an article or group of articles sold together at an AUCTION sale〖拍賣時的〗一件[一批]物品 **6** *AmE* an area of land used for parking cars on〖美式〗停車場 **7 someone's lot** someone's way of life 某人的命運: *Generally I'm quite happy with my lot.* 總的來説我對自己的命運很滿意。

lo·tion /ˈləʊʃən; ˈloʊʃən/ *n* [C;U] a liquid mixture that you use to make your skin clean or healthy 皮膚清潔液，護膚液

lot·te·ry /ˈlɒtəri; ˈlɑtəri/ *n* **lotteries 1** a competition in which prizes are given to people who have bought the winning numbered tickets which are picked by chance 抽彩票(給獎法) **2** something which is decided by chance 碰運氣的事

lo·tus /ˈləʊtəs; ˈloʊtəs/ *n* a white or pink flower that grows on the surface of lakes, especially in Asia 蓮(花)

loud[1] /laʊd; laʊd/ *adj* **1** making a lot of noise (聲音)響亮的: *loud music* 喧鬧的音樂聲 | *a loud voice* 響亮的嗓音 **2** unpleasantly noisy or colourful 嘈雜的；過分花哨的: *Don't you think that wallpaper is rather loud?* 你難道不覺得那種牆紙有點花哨了嗎? – **loudly** *adv* –**loudness** *n* [U]

loud[2] *adv* **1** in a way that makes a lot of noise 大聲地: *Shout louder and someone might hear.* 再大聲點，有人也許會聽見。**2 out loud** –see ALOUD

loud·speak·er /ˌlaʊdˈspiːkə; ˌlaʊdˈspiːkər/ *n* something which makes what you say seem

louder 揚聲器

lounge[1] /laʊndʒ; laʊndʒ/ *n* **1** a comfortable room for sitting in, in a house or a hotel〔住所或旅館中的〕休息室 **2** a waiting room at an airport〔機場的〕等候室: *the departure lounge* 候機室

lounge[2] *v* **lounged, lounging** [I + adv/prep] (also 又作 **lounge about, lounge around**) to stand, sit or lie somewhere in a lazy way 懶洋洋地站[坐、躺]着: *He just lounges around all day doing nothing.* 他整天無所事事。

lounge bar /ˈ··/ *n* a comfortably furnished room in a PUB or hotel, where drinks cost a little more than in other bars〔酒館或旅館內的〕雅座酒吧

louse[1] /laʊs; laʊs/ *n* **lice** /laɪs; laɪs/ **1** a small insect that lives on the skin and in the hair of people and animals 虱子 **2** *infml* an unpleasant, worthless person〖非正式〗討厭的小人物

louse[2] *v* **loused, lousing**

louse sthg ↔ **up** *phr v* [T] *AmE infml* to deal unsuccessfully with something〖美式，非正式〗搞糟，搞壞〔某事〕

lou·sy /ˈlaʊzi; ˈlaʊzi/ *adj* **lousier, lousiest 1** *infml* terrible〖非正式〗糟糕的: *What lousy weather!* 多糟糕的天氣啊! | *I feel lousy.* 我覺得很不舒服。**2** [never before a noun 不能用於名詞前] covered with lice 佈滿虱子的

lout /laʊt; laʊt/ *n* an unpleasant and often threatening young man with bad manners 討厭而粗暴的年輕人 –**loutish** *adj*

lov·a·ble /ˈlʌvəbl; ˈlʌvəbəl/ *adj* producing feelings of love and liking 討人喜歡的，可愛的: *a lovable child* 可愛的孩子

★**love**[1] /lʌv; lʌv/ *n* **1** [C;U] a strong feeling of warmth for another person or thing 愛；喜愛: *He has a great love of children.* 他非常喜愛孩子。| *Her love for her husband is strong and constant.* 她對丈夫的愛強烈深刻，恒久不變。| *He died for the love of his country.* 出於對祖國的熱愛，他獻出了生命。–opposites 反義 **hate, hatred 2 be in love, fall in love** with someone to feel or to begin to feel great warmth for a person, usually of the opposite sex 戀愛，愛情: *He fell in love with her at their first meeting.* 他對她一見鍾情。**3** [C] a person who you love 所愛之人: *I'll do it, my love.* 親愛的，我來做這件事。**4** [C] something that you like doing very much 喜歡做的事: *Music was the love of his life.* 音樂是他生活中的一大愛好。**5** [U] warm interest and enjoyment of something 強烈興趣；喜好: *Her love of sport leaves little time for meeting friends.* 她十分熱愛運動，使她很少有時間跟朋友見面。**6** [U] no points (used in tennis) 零分〔用於網球比賽〕: *McEnroe leads 15-love.* 麥肯羅以15比0領先。**7 be little love lost between people, be no love lost between people** bad relations between two or more people 人與人之間的關係很壞，相互憎惡: *There's been no love lost*

between the sisters since their mother's death. 自母親去世後，姊妹間關係一直很糟糕。 **8 not for love nor money** not by any means 決不

★★love² *v* **loved, loving 1** [T] to feel love, desire, or strong friendship for someone 愛，熱愛: *I love my mother very much.* 我很愛我的母親。 **2** [I;T] to like or enjoy something very much 喜愛〔某事〕: *He loves singing.* 他喜愛唱歌。 | *I'd love a drink.* 我想要杯飲料。 | *She'd love to see you again.* 她很希望再見你一次。 –opposite 反義 **hate**

□ **USEFUL PATTERNS** 有用句型
to love something, to love doing something; to love to do something

love af·fair /'·· ,·/ *n* an experience of love, and often sexual love, between two people who are not married to each other 風流韻事; 性關係

★love·ly /'lʌvlɪ; 'lʌvli/ *adj* **lovelier, loveliest 1** beautiful 美麗的: *We had a lovely view of the mountains.* 我們可看見秀麗的山色。 **2** *infml* very pleasant 〔非正式〕非常宜人的: *That was a lovely meal.* 那一頓飯令人愉快。 **–loveliness** *n* [U]

★lov·er /'lʌvə; 'lʌvəʳ/ *n* **1** a person who you have sex with outside marriage 情人; 情夫; 情婦: *They were lovers first and then became friends.* 他們起先是情人，後來成了朋友。 **2** a person who enjoys something 〔…的〕愛好者: *an art lover* 藝術愛好者

lov·ing /'lʌvɪŋ; 'lʌvɪŋ/ *adj* showing or feeling love 鍾愛的; 示愛的: *He gave her a loving look.* 他深情地看了她一眼。 | *a loving father* 慈愛的父親 **–lovingly** *adv*

★★low¹ /loʊ; loʊ/ *adj* **1** not high above the ground or from the bottom of something to the top 矮的; 低的: *a low wall* 一堵矮牆 | *We need two low shelves, and then one higher up the wall.* 我們需要兩個較低的架子，然後在牆上再裝一個較高的。 **2** small in size, degree, amount, or value 〔尺寸、程度、數量、價值〕低的; 少的: *Prices in that shop are very low.* 那家商店的價格很低。 | *Temperatures are low for June.* 對於六月份來說，氣溫是很低的。 | *I have a low opinion of his work.* 我對他的作品評價很低。 | *low-fat milk* 低脂肪牛奶 | *a low-paid job* 薪水很低的工作 **3** weak or unhappy 虛弱的; 不高興的: *She's still feeling a bit low after her operation.* 手術後，她仍感到身體有些虛弱。 | *He's been in low spirits since his girlfriend left.* 自女友走後，他情緒一直很低落。 **4** not loud 〔聲音〕輕的: *a low voice* 輕輕的嗓音 **5** deep (used of a musical note) 低的〔指音符〕 **6** near the bottom in position or rank 〔地位或職位〕低的: *a man of low birth* 出身低微的人 **7** not morally acceptable 卑劣的: *Lying to get the job was a very*

low trick. 為得到工作而撒謊是卑劣的手法。 **8 have a low opinion of someone or something** not to respect a person or like a thing 看不上眼的; 貶低的 –opposite 反義 **high** (for 1, 2, 4, 5, 6, 7, 8) **–lowness** *n* [U]

low² *adv* **1** in or to a low position, standard or level 低，向下; 低水準地: *He was bent low over a book.* 他低着頭看書。 **2** quietly 安靜地 **3** (in music) with deep notes 〔音樂〕音調低沉地 –opposite 反義 **high**

low³ *n* a level that is low 低水平，低點: *Profits have reached a new low this month.* 本月的利潤降到了新的低點。 –opposite 反義 **high**

low·down /'loʊdaʊn; 'loʊdaʊn/ *n* **the low-down on** *infml* information about a person or thing 〔非正式〕〔某人或某事的〕真相，內幕

low-down /'··/ *adj* [only before a noun 只用於名詞前] unfair and not worthy of respect 不公平的; 不值得尊重的; 卑劣的

low·er¹ /'loʊə; 'loʊəʳ/ *adj* [only before a noun 只用於名詞前] being the bottom part of something, or the bottom one of two or more things 較低的; 下層的: *The bottle is on the lower shelf.* 瓶子放在下層的架子上。 –opposite 反義 **upper**

lower² *v* [T] **1** to make something smaller in amount or quality 使〔某物〕減少，降低: *Please lower your voice.* 請把你的嗓音壓低一些。 **2** to move something down 降下〔某物〕: *Lower the flags!* 把旗降下來! –opposite 反義 **raise** (for 1, 2) **3 lower yourself** to lose your own or other's respect for you by doing something 降低自己的身分 **4 lower your voice** speak more quietly 壓低嗓音

lower case /,·· '·◂/ *adj* printed as small letters such as a and b, rather than in capital letters such as A and B 用小寫字母印刷的 **–lower case** *n* [U]

low-key /,· '·◂/ *adj* (also 又作 **low-keyed**) quiet and controlled 低調的; 有節制的

low·land /'loʊlənd; 'loʊlənd/ *adj* at about sea level (used of land) 低地的〔指土地〕 **–lowlands** *n* [pl]

low·ly /'loʊlɪ; 'loʊli/ *adj* **lowlier, lowliest** low in rank or position 職位低的; 地位低的: **–lowly** *adv* **–lowliness** *n* [U]

low-ly·ing /,· '··◂/ *adj* at about sea level (used of land) 〔指土地〕約與海面平齊的

loy·al /'lɔɪəl; 'lɔɪəl/ *adj* faithful to people, places, or things 忠實的; 忠誠的: *He's a loyal supporter of the local football club.* 他是當地足球俱樂部的忠實支持者。 **–loyally** *adv*

loy·al·ist /'lɔɪəlɪst; 'lɔɪəl̩ɪst/ *n* a person who remains faithful to an existing ruler or government 〔擁護統治者或現政府的〕忠誠分子

loy·al·ty /'lɔɪəltɪ; 'lɔɪəlti/ *n* **loyalties 1** [U] behaviour in which you remain faithful to someone or something 忠實; 忠誠: *his loyalty to his friends* 他對朋友的忠誠 **2 loyalties**

[pl] feelings of friendship and faithfulness 忠誠的感情: *Work or home — you've got to decide where your loyalties lie.* 要工作還是要家庭——你必須決定你的忠誠繫於哪一方。

loz·enge /ˈlɑzɪndʒ; ˈlɒzɪndʒ/ *n* a small sweet, especially one that you suck to make a sore throat feel better 小塊扁糖〔尤指潤喉糖〕

LP /ˌɛlˈpi; ˌel ˈpiː/ *n* a record which plays for about 20 minutes on each side (雙面)密紋唱片 –compare 比較 SINGLE

L-plate /ˈɛl plet; ˈel pleɪt/ *n* the letter L, put on a vehicle in Britain to show that the driver is a learner L 字牌, 學車牌〔英國的實習駕駛員標牌, 置於機動車輛上〕

LSD /ˌɛl ɛs ˈdi; ˌel es ˈdiː/ *n* [U] a strong drug that makes you see things in a strange and different way 迷幻藥

Ltd a written abbreviation for 〔縮〕= LIMITED: *M.Y. Dixon and Son, Ltd, Booksellers M.Y.*狄克遜父子圖書有限公司

lu·bri·cant /ˈlubrɪkənt; ˈluːbrɪkənt/ *n* [C;U] a substance which helps the parts of something like a machine to move easily 潤滑劑

lu·bri·cate /ˈlubrɪˌket; ˈluːbrɪkeɪt/ *v* **lubricated, lubricating** [T] to make something move easily by adding a substance such as oil 使〔某物〕潤滑 –**lubrication** /ˌlubrɪˈkeʃən; ˌluːbrɪˈkeɪʃən/ *n* [U]

lu·cid /ˈlusɪd; ˈluːsɪd/ *adj* **1** easy to understand 易懂的: *a lucid explanation* 簡單明瞭的解釋 **2** able to express yourself clearly 表達清楚的: *There are lucid moments in her madness.* 她在瘋狂之中也有清醒的時候。–**lucidly** *adv* –**lucidity** /luˈsɪdəti; luːˈsɪdᵻti/ *n* [U]

★**luck** /lʌk; lʌk/ *n* [U] **1** something that brings you good or bad fortune, as if by chance 運氣: *Luck was with us and we won easily.* 我們運氣好, 贏得輕鬆。| *I've had bad luck all week.* 我這個星期一直運氣不好。**2** good fortune 好運, 幸運: *She phoned to wish me luck.* 她打電話來祝我好運。**3 Any luck?** = Were you successful? 你成功了嗎? **4 be in luck** to have good fortune 走運〔RELATED PHRASE 相關詞組 **be out of luck**〕 **5 Bad luck!, Hard luck!** phrases that you use to express sympathy with someone 真倒霉!〔用於對別人表示同情〕 **6 be down on your luck** to be in a period when nothing is going well for you 不走運, 倒霉 **7 the luck of the draw** the result of chance 碰運氣的結果

★**luck·y** /ˈlʌki; ˈlʌki/ *adj* **luckier, luckiest** having, resulting from, or bringing good luck 幸運的; 帶來好運的: *He's a lucky man.* 他是個走運的人。| *That was a lucky find!* 那項發現真要靠運氣! | *I carry a lucky charm to protect me when I travel.* 出門旅行時, 我會帶一個會帶來好運的護身符。–opposite 反義 **unlucky** –**luckily** *adv*: *Luckily, she was in when I called.* 幸運的是, 我打電話時她剛好

在家。

lu·cra·tive /ˈlukrətɪv; ˈluːkrətɪv/ *adj fml* making a lot of money 〔正式〕賺錢的, 獲利多的: *I am working on a very lucrative business deal.* 我正在做一筆很賺錢的生意。–**lucratively** *adv*

lu·di·crous /ˈludɪkrəs; ˈluːdɪkrəs/ *adj* very foolish 非常愚蠢的: *What a ludicrous suggestion!* 多麼荒唐的提議啊!

lug /lʌg; lʌg/ *v* **-gg-** [T + adv/prep] *infml* to pull or carry something with great effort and difficulty 〔非正式〕使勁拖[拉]

lug·gage /ˈlʌgɪdʒ; ˈlʌgɪdʒ/ *n* [U] the bags and cases of a traveller 行李: *I don't want to take too much luggage on this trip.* 這次旅行我不想帶太多行李。

lu·gu·bri·ous /luˈgjubriəs; luːˈguːbriəs/ *adj fml* sad, especially sadder than necessary 〔正式〕悲傷的, 鬱鬱不樂的 –**lugubriously** *adv*

luke·warm /ˈlukˈwɔrm; ˌluːkˈwɔːm◂/ *adj* **1** not very hot (used of liquid) 不太熱的〔指液體〕 **2** showing little interest or pleasure 不感興趣的; 不熱心的

lull¹ /lʌl; lʌl/ *v* [T] to make someone feel sleepy, less active, or safe 使〔某人〕入睡; 使平靜下來: *The movement of the train soon lulled me to sleep.* 火車的晃動很快使我昏昏欲睡。| *We were lulled into a false sense of security.* 我們被哄騙, 產生了一種虛假的安全感。

lull² *n* a period in which there is less activity (暫時)平息期: *During a lull in the fighting he managed to sleep for a while.* 戰鬥間歇期間, 他設法睡了一會兒。

lul·la·by /ˈlʌləˌbaɪ; ˈlʌləbaɪ/ *n* **lullabies** a pleasant song that you sing to help a child fall asleep 催眠曲, 搖籃曲

lum·ba·go /lʌmˈbego; lʌmˈbeɪgəʊ/ *n* [U] pain in the lower part of your back 腰痛

lum·ber¹ /ˈlʌmbɚ; ˈlʌmbə/ *v* [I + adv/prep] to move in a slow, awkward manner 笨拙地移動 **2 lumber someone with something** *BrE infml* to give someone something that they do not want 〔英式, 非正式〕給某人不想要的東西: *I was lumbered with the cooking and cleaning.* 我被迫要負責做飯和做清潔工作。

lumber² *n* [U] *AmE* 〔美式〕TIMBER

lum·ber·jack /ˈlʌmbɚˌdʒæk; ˈlʌmbədʒæk/ *n* a person whose job it is to cut down trees for wood 伐木工人

lu·mi·na·ry /ˈluməˌnɛri; ˈluːmᵻnəri/ *n* **luminaries** *fml* a person whose mind, knowledge, or actions are famous and respected 〔正式〕傑出人物; 名人

lu·mi·nous /ˈlumənəs; ˈluːmᵻnəs/ *adj* shining in the dark 發光的; 夜明的: *luminous paint* 發光漆 –**luminously** *adv*

lump¹ /lʌmp; lʌmp/ *n* **1** a mass of something solid 團; 塊: *He took a simple lump of clay and made a beautiful pot.* 他拿了塊普通的泥

製成了一隻漂亮的罐子。**2** a hard swelling on or in your body〔身體上的〕腫塊: *She found a lump in her left breast.* 她發現左乳上有個腫塊。**3** a small block of sugar 小塊方糖: *How much sugar — one lump or two?* 要放多少糖——一塊還是兩塊? **4 a lump in your throat** a tight sensation in the throat caused by strong feelings such as pity〔由憐憫等強烈情感引起的〕喉嚨哽住; 哽咽

lump² *adj* **lump sum** a single undivided amount of money 一次總付的錢: *I can give you a lump sum or weekly payments.* 我可以把錢一次性地付給你, 也可以每週付你一筆。

lump³ *v* **1 lump it** *infml* to accept a bad situation without complaining《非正式》勉強容忍, 忍受: *That's my decision, and you'll just have to lump it.* 那就是我的決定, 你只能將就一點了。**2 lump people or things together** to put two or more people or things together or treat them in the same way 把〔人或物〕放在一起同等對待: *All these costs can be lumped together as "expenses".* 所有這些費用可放在一起作為「開銷」。

lump·y /ˈlʌmpɪ; ˈlʌmpi/ *adj* **lumpier, lumpiest** having lumps 有塊的: *The sauce was lumpy.* 這種醬汁結塊了。

lu·na·cy /ˈlunəsɪ; ˈluːnəsi/ *n* [U] **1** madness 瘋狂 **2** strange or foolish behaviour 奇怪的行為; 愚蠢的行為

lu·nar /ˈlunə; ˈluːnəʳ/ *adj* concerning or going to the moon 月亮的; 去月球的: *a lunar voyage* 月球旅行

lunar month /ˌ·· ·ˈ·/ *n* a period of about 29 days, which is the time the moon takes to circle the earth 太陰月; 陰曆一個月

lu·na·tic /ˈlunəˌtɪk; ˈluːnətɪk/ *n* a person who is mad, foolish, or strange 瘋子; 怪人: *You can't just go round insulting people, you lunatic!* 你這瘋子, 你不可以到處去侮辱別人! **–lunatic** *adj*

★**lunch¹** /lʌntʃ; lʌntʃ/ *n* (also 又作 **luncheon** /ˈlʌntʃən; ˈlʌntʃən/ *fml*《正式》) [C;U] a meal that you eat in the middle of the day 午餐: *Shall we meet for lunch?* 我們午餐時見面好嗎? | *The lunch hour is from 1 to 2 pm.* 午飯時間是下午一點到兩點。**–see** 見 DINNER (USAGE 用法)

lunch² *v* [I] to eat lunch, especially when it is a formal meal 吃午飯〔尤指正式的午餐〕: *I'm lunching with the directors today.* 今天我要與董事們共進午餐。

lunch·time /ˈlʌntʃˌtaɪm; ˈlʌntʃtaɪm/ *n* [U] the time at which you have lunch 午餐時間

lung /lʌŋ; lʌŋ/ *n* one of the two organs which you use to breathe 肺

lunge /lʌndʒ; lʌndʒ/ *v* **lunged, lunging** [I + adv/prep] to make a sudden forceful movement, especially to attack someone 向前猛衝〔尤指襲擊某人〕: *He lunged at me with a knife.* 他持刀向我衝來。**–lunge** *n*

lurch¹ /lɜːtʃ; lɜːtʃ/ *n* a sudden, uncontrolled movement 突然的失控: *The boat gave a lurch sideways towards the rocks.* 小艇突然向一邊傾斜, 撞向礁石。

lurch² *v* [I + adv/prep] to move with irregular, sudden steps 蹣跚而行: *The drunken man lurched across the road.* 那個醉漢蹣跚地穿過馬路。

lure¹ /lʊr; lʊəʳ/ *n* [C] **1** something that attracts you 誘惑物: *It is the lure of money that brings them to the city.* 是金錢的誘惑使他們來到這城市。**2** something used to attract animals so that they can be caught〔誘捕動物用的〕誘餌

lure² *v* **lured, luring** [T] to attract a person or animal 吸引, 引誘: *She's been lured here by the promise of a high salary.* 她被高工資的許諾吸引到這裡來了。

lu·rid /ˈlʊrɪd; ˈlʊərɪd/ *adj* **1** very brightly coloured (a word used to show disapproval) 色彩絢麗的〔含貶義〕: *It was a lurid picture of a sunset.* 那是一幅火紅的日落圖。**2** very unpleasant (a word used to show disapproval) 可怕的, 駭人聽聞的〔含貶義〕: *The papers gave the lurid details of the murder.* 報紙描述了那起謀殺案聳人聽聞的細節。**–luridly** *adv*

lurk /lɜːk; lɜːk/ *v* **1** [I + adv/prep] to wait in hiding, especially for an evil purpose 埋伏, 潛伏: *A man was seen lurking near the scene of the crime.* 有人看見一個男子埋伏在犯罪現場的附近。**2** [I] to remain, especially in your mind〔尤指在心裡〕潛藏: *He had the lurking suspicion that she might be guilty.* 他一直暗裡懷疑她或許有罪。

lus·cious /ˈlʌʃəs; ˈlʌʃəs/ *adj* pleasant or sweet in taste, smell, or appearance 甘美的; 芬芳的; 悅目的: *luscious fruit* 甘美的水果 **–lusciousness** *n* [U]

lush /lʌʃ; lʌʃ/ *adj* thick, healthy and growing well (used especially of plants) 茂盛的; 蔥翠的〔尤指植物〕

lust¹ /lʌst; lʌst/ *n* [C;U] strong desire for a person or thing, especially sexual desire 強烈的慾望〔尤指性慾〕: *His feelings for her were little more than lust.* 他對她所懷的感情不過是肉慾而已。| *She was driven by a lust for power.* 她受到權力慾的驅使。

lust² *v* **lust after, lust for** to have a strong desire for someone or something 對〔某人或某物〕懷有強烈慾望: *He lusted after wealth.* 他貪求財富。| *She lusts for her tenant.* 她對她的房客垂涎三尺。**–see** 見 DESIRE (USAGE 用法)

lust·ful /ˈlʌstfəl; ˈlʌstfəl/ *adj* feeling or showing strong sexual desire 好色的, 有強烈性慾的 **–lustfully** *adv*

lus·tre /ˈlʌstə; ˈlʌstəʳ/ *n* (also 又作 **luster** *AmE*《美式》) [U] the brightness of a polished surface 光澤 **–lustrous** /ˈlʌstrəs; ˈlʌstrəs/ *adj* **–lustrously** *adv*

lust·y /ˈlʌstɪ; ˈlʌsti/ *adj* **lustier, lustiest** strong and healthy 身體強健的 **–lustiness** *n* [U]

lute /lut; luːt/ *n* an old musical instrument with strings 魯特琴

lux·u·ri·ant /lʌgˈʒʊriənt; lʌgˈzjuəriənt/ *adj* thick, healthy and growing well (used especially of plants) 茂盛的；葱翠的〔尤指植物〕: *The plant was covered in luxuriant foliage.* 那株植物上長滿了葱翠的葉子。 –compare 比較 LUXURIOUS –**luxuriantly** *adv* –**luxuriance** *n* [U]

lux·u·ri·ate /lʌgˈʒʊrɪˌet; lʌgˈzjuəriert/ *v* **luxuriated, luxuriating, luxuriate in something** to enjoy doing something pleasurable in a lazy way 盡情享受某事

lux·u·ri·ous /lʌgˈʒʊriəs; lʌgˈzjuəriəs/ *adj* very comfortable and expensive 極舒適的；豪華的: *Life in prison will be difficult for someone used to such luxurious surroundings.* 對習慣生活在那種舒適環境的人來說，監獄生活是艱苦的。 –**luxuriously** *adv*

lux·u·ry /ˈlʌkʃəri; ˈlʌkʃəri/ *n* **luxuries 1** [U] great comfort, which is provided by wealth 奢侈；豪華: *He leads a life of luxury.* 他過着奢侈的生活。 | *We're moving to a luxury flat in central London.* 我們準備搬入倫敦市中心的一套豪華公寓裡去居住。 **2** [C] something pleasant that you do not need and cannot often afford 奢侈品: *Foreign holidays are a real luxury.* 在國外度假實在是奢侈的事。

ly·chee /ˈliːtʃi; ˈlaɪtʃiː/ *n* an Asian fruit with sweet white flesh 荔枝

ly·ing /ˈlaɪɪŋ; ˈlaɪ-ɪŋ/ the present participle of LIE ☆ LIE 的現在分詞

lynch /lɪntʃ; lɪntʃ/ *v* [T] attack and kill someone thought to be guilty of a crime, without a legal trial and usually by hanging them 以私刑處死〔某人〕: *He was lynched by the angry townspeople.* 他被鎮裡憤怒的羣眾拷打致死

lynx /lɪŋks; lɪŋks/ *n* **lynxes** a wild animal with a short tail that belongs to the cat family 猞猁

lyre /laɪr; laɪər/ *n* an ancient Greek musical instrument with strings stretched on a U-shaped frame 里拉（琴）〔古希臘的一種弦樂器，琴身作U形〕

lyr·ic /ˈlɪrɪk; ˈlɪrɪk/ *n* **1** [C] a poem that expresses strong personal feeling 抒情詩 **2 lyrics** [pl] the words of a song 歌詞

lyr·i·cal /ˈlɪrɪkl; ˈlɪrɪkəl/ *adj* **1** full of pleasure about something 非常愉快的 **2** POETIC 詩的 –**lyrically** /-klɪ; -klɪ/ *adv*

lyr·i·cist /ˈlɪrɪsɪst; ˈlɪrəsɪst/ *n* a person who writes the words for songs 抒情詩人；歌詞作者

M, m

M, m /ɛm; em/ **M's, m's** or **Ms, ms** the 13th letter of the English alphabet 英語的第十三個字母

m a written abbreviation for 〖縮〗= METRE

MA /ˌem ˈe; ˌem ˈeɪ/ **1** a higher university degree; an abbreviation for **Master of Arts** 〖縮〗文學碩士(學位): *He has an MA in English Literature.* 他有英國文學碩士學位。**2** a person who has an MA 文學碩士

ma'am /mæm; mæm/ *n old fash* or *AmE* 〖老式或美式〗a polite way of addressing a woman 夫人; 女士〔對婦女的尊稱〕: *Can I help you, ma'am?* 我能幫您嗎, 夫人?

mac /mæk; mæk/ *n see* 見 MACKINTOSH

ma·ca·bre /məˈkɑbə; məˈkɑːbrə/ *adj* strange, frightening, and often connected with death 奇怪的; 恐怖的; 和死亡有關的: *macabre tales of violent murders* 暴力謀殺的恐怖故事

mac·a·ro·ni /ˌmækəˈroni; ˌmækəˈrəʊni◂/ *n* [U] a food made of short thin tubes of PASTA 通心粉; 通心麵

mace /mes; meɪs/ *n* a decorative rod carried by an official in certain ceremonies as a sign of power 權杖〔在某些典禮中, 官員手持的裝飾性手杖, 作為權力的標誌〕

Mach /mɑk; mæk/ *n* [sing] a unit of measurement for very high speeds 馬赫〔一種極高的速度的計量單位〕: *If a plane is flying at Mach 1, it is flying at the speed of sound.* 假如飛機以一馬赫的速度飛行, 那麼它的速度就是音速。

ma·chet·e /məˈtʃete; məˈʃeti/ *n* a knife with a broad heavy blade 大砍刀

ma·chine¹ /məˈʃin; məˈʃiːn/ *n* **1** a man-made apparatus which uses electricity or other power to perform work 機器; 機械(裝置): *a sewing machine* 縫紉機 | *a washing machine* 洗衣機 **2** by **machine** using a machine 用機器: *The books are all packed by machine.* 這些書都用機器打包。

■ **USAGE** 用法: Compare 比較 **machine, appliance, tool, instrument, device,** and 和 **gadget**. A **machine** usually uses power, and you do not work it directly with your hands ☆**machine** 一般使用動力, 不直接用手操作: *the **machines** in the factory* 工廠裡的機器 | *Tickets are available from the **machine** on the platform.* 可以通過站台上的自動售票機買到票。| *a knitting ma-*

---

chine 編織機。Electrical machines used in the home (such as washing machines) can also be called **appliances** ☆家用電器(如洗衣機)也可稱為 **appliances**: *a shop selling household appliances* 賣家用電器的商店。A **tool** is an object which you hold in your hand and which you use for making things from wood, metal, or other materials ☆**tool** 是拿在手中的工具, 用來把木料、金屬或其他材料做成各種東西: *carpenter's tools such as hammers, drills and saws* 木匠的工具, 如鎚、鑽和鋸。An **instrument** is an object which you use to do very exact or careful work, usually by hand ☆**instrument** 是用來做很精確細緻的工作, 常用手操作: *medical/surgical instruments* 醫療〔外科手術〕器械 | *A thermometer is an **instrument** for measuring temperature.* 溫度計是測量溫度的儀器。**Device** is a general word for any object which has been produced for doing work, and is usually used when there is no suitable particular word ☆**device** 是一個通用詞, 指製造出來供人幹活用的任何一樣東西。當沒有合適的特定用詞時常用這個詞: *an electronic **device** which controlled the opening of the doors* 控制開門的電子儀器 | *I have no idea how this **device** works.* 我不知道這儀器的工作原理。**Gadget** is an informal word for a small and perhaps unusual device for doing a particular job ☆**gadget** 是非正式用詞, 指小的並且可能不平常的器具, 用來做某種特殊工作: *a clever little **gadget** for opening bottles* 一個小巧的開瓶器具

---

machine² *v* **machined, machining** [T] to make something by machine, usually in a factory 〔常在工廠裡〕用機器製造〔某物〕— **machinist** *n*

ma·chine·gun /məˈʃin.gʌn; məˈʃiːngʌn/ *n* a gun which fires bullets very quickly one after another 機(關)槍

ma·chin·e·ry /məˈʃinəri; məˈʃiːnəri/ *n* [U] **1** machines in general 〔總稱〕機械; 機器: *The machinery must be kept in good working order.* 機器必須保持良好的運行狀態。**2** the operation of a system or process 機構: *The machinery of the law works slowly.* 法律機制運作緩慢。

ma·cho /ˈmɑtʃo; ˈmætʃəʊ/ *adj infml* showing

---

very male qualities (a word used to show disapproval)〖非正式〗大男子氣概的〔含貶義〕

mack·e·rel /ˈmækərəl; ˈmækərəl/ n [C;U] a sea fish with a blue and silver skin 鯖(魚)

mack·in·tosh /ˈmækɪnˌtɒʃ; ˈmækɪntɒʃ/ n (also 又作 **mac**) a coat which keeps out water 雨衣

mac·ro·bi·ot·ic /ˌmækrəbaɪˈɒtɪk; ˌmækrəʊbaɪˈɒtɪk◂/ adj concerning food such as vegetables and whole grains which are thought to produce good health〔蔬菜、穀物等〕能促進健康的; 益壽的

***mad** /mæd; mæd/ adj **1** ill in the mind 瘋; 神經錯亂的: He's gone quite mad in his old age. 他上了年紀神經失常。 **2** extremely foolish 極愚蠢的: You're mad to drive so fast! 你開這麼快, 簡直是發瘋了! | What a mad idea! 多蠢的想法! **3** mad about infml filled with strong feeling, interest, or admiration 〖非正式〗狂熱的; 着迷的: He's mad about football. 他對足球着了迷。 | She's mad about him. 她迷戀他。 **4** infml angry 〖非正式〗憤怒的: I got mad with him for being late. 我因為他遲到而大發雷霆。 **5** drive someone mad to annoy someone very much 使人惱怒得發狂 **6** like mad infml very hard or fast 〖非正式〗拼命地; 極快地: If you run like mad you might just catch the train. 如果你拼命地跑, 也許能趕上火車。

mad·am /ˈmædəm; ˈmædəm/ n **1** Madam a formal way of addressing a woman in a business letter 女士〔業務書信中對婦女的正式稱呼〕: Dear Madam ... 尊敬的女士...−compare 比較 SIR **2** a formal way of addressing a female customer 夫人; 女士; 小姐〔對女顧客的正式稱呼〕: Would Madam like to try another size? 夫人要不要試試另一個尺碼?

mad·den /ˈmædn; ˈmædn/ v [T] to make someone very angry or annoyed 激怒〔某人〕; 使惱怒

mad·den·ing /ˈmædnɪŋ; ˈmædənɪŋ/ adj infml very annoying 〖非正式〗使人惱怒的: maddening traffic delays 使人惱火的交通耽擱

made[1] /med; meɪd/ the past tense and past participle of MAKE[1] ☆ MAKE[1] 的過去式和過去分詞

made[2] adj [never before a noun 不能用於名詞前] **1** formed of something 由〔某事物〕做成的: The frame is made of silver. 框架是銀製的。 | Pancakes are made from eggs, flour, and milk. 薄煎餅是雞蛋、麵粉和牛奶做成的。 **2** completely suited for someone 完全適合的: Those two are made for each other. 那兩個完全匹配。 **3** sure of success 肯定會成功的: If you find gold you're made for life. 如果你找到黃金, 這輩子肯定生活無憂。

■ USAGE 用法: **Made of** and **made from** have very similar meanings, but

they are often used in slightly different ways. If the original material has been completely changed, use **made from** ☆ **made of** 和 **made from** 意思很相近, 但在使用中常有細微差別。如果原材料完全改變了, 用 **made from**: Bread is **made from** flour and water. 麵包是麵粉和水做的。 | luxury soap **made from** the finest ingredients 用料最講究的高檔香皂 | some jam **made from** the fruit in our garden 用我們花園裡的水果所製成的一些果醬。 If the original materials can still be recognized, use **made of** ☆ 如果原材料仍可分辨, 用 **made of**: a statue **made of** the finest marble 用最好的大理石做的雕像 | handbags **made of** cheap black plastic 用廉價的黑色塑料做的手提包

mad·ly /ˈmædlɪ; ˈmædlɪ/ adv **1** in a mad, wild way 瘋狂地: He rushed madly out of the room. 他發瘋似地衝出了房間。 **2** love someone madly to love someone very much 深愛某人

mad·man /ˈmædmən; ˈmædmən/ n **madmen** /-mən; -mən/ a man who is mad (男)瘋子: He drives like a madman. 他像個瘋子似地開車。

mad·ness /ˈmædnɪs; ˈmædnɪs/ n [U] **1** the state of being mad 瘋狂 **2** extremely foolish behaviour 極度愚蠢的行為: It would be sheer madness to try to cross the desert on your own. 你試圖獨自穿越沙漠簡直是愚蠢透頂。

mad·wom·an /ˈmædˌwʊmən; ˈmædˌwʊmən/ n **madwomen** /-ˌwɪmɪn; -ˌwɪmɪn/ a woman who is mad 女瘋子; 瘋女

mael·strom /ˈmelstrəm; ˈmeɪlstrəm/ n the uncontrollable violent force of events which may lead to destruction 大動亂: She got sucked into the maelstrom of political controversy. 她捲入了政治爭論的漩渦中。

maes·tro /ˈmaɪstro; ˈmaɪstrəʊ/ n a great or famous musician 音樂大師; 大音樂家

Maf·i·a /ˈmɑfɪˌɑ; ˈmɑːfɪə/ n [+sing/pl verb] **the Mafia** an organization of criminals who control many activities by violent means 黑手黨

***mag·a·zine** /ˌmægəˈzin; ˌmægəˈziːn/ n **1** (also 又作 **mag** /mæg; mæg/ infml 〖非正式〗) a sort of book with large pages and a paper cover, containing writing, photographs, and advertisements, printed every week or month 雜誌: a photography magazine 攝影雜誌 | a woman's weekly magazine 婦女週刊 −see picture on page 730 見 730 頁彩圖 **2** the part of a gun in which bullets are placed before firing 〔槍的〕彈倉; 彈盤 **3** a place in which weapons and bullets are kept 彈藥庫

ma·gen·ta /məˈdʒentə; məˈdʒentə/ n, adj

[U] a dark purplish pink colour 洋紅色 – see picture on page 243 見 243 頁彩圖

mag·got /ˈmægət; ˈmægət/ *n* a creature like a small worm; maggots are the young of flies or other insects 蛆

ma·gic¹ /ˈmædʒɪk; ˈmædʒɪk/ *n* [U] **1** a special power sometimes believed to control events by calling on spirits, or saying special words 魔法；法術；巫術: *They say the old witch practises black magic.* 他們說這老巫婆會施魔法. **2** the art of a CONJURER who entertains by producing unexpected objects and results by tricks 魔術；戲法: *He pulled the rabbit out of the hat by magic.* 他從帽子裡變出一隻兔子來. –**magic** *adj* [only before a noun 只用於名詞前]: *a magic trick* 戲法

ma·gic·al /ˈmædʒɪkl̩; ˈmædʒɪkəl/ *adj* mysterious, strange, and exciting 神祕的；奇異的；令人興奮的: *a magical evening beneath the stars* 星空下迷人的夜晚 –**magically** /-klɪ; -kli/ *adv*

ma·gi·cian /məˈdʒɪʃən; məˈdʒɪʃən/ *n* a person who performs tricks or magic 巫師；魔術師

ma·gis·te·ri·al /ˌmædʒɪsˈtɪrɪəl; ˌmædʒɪˈstɪriəl/ *adj* **1** *fml* having the power of a master or ruler 〖正式〗有權威的；威風的: *a proud magisterial manner* 驕傲威嚴的舉止 **2** [only before a noun 只用於名詞前] relating to a magistrate 地方法官的

ma·gis·trate /ˈmædʒɪs.tret; ˈmædʒɪstreɪt/ *n* an official who judges cases in the lowest law courts 地方法官

mag·nan·i·mous /mægˈnænəməs; mægˈnænɪməs/ *adj* very generous and forgiving towards other people 寬宏大量的；慷慨的 –**magnanimity** /ˌmægnəˈnɪmətɪ; ˌmægnəˈnɪməti/ *n* [U]

mag·nate /ˈmægnet; ˈmægneɪt/ *n* a wealthy and powerful person in business 工商界巨頭；大企業家

mag·ne·si·um /mægˈniːsɪəm; mægˈniːziəm/ *n* [U] a silver-white metal that burns with a bright light 鎂

mag·net /ˈmægnɪt; ˈmægnɪt/ *n* a piece of iron which can make other metal objects come towards it (either naturally or by passing an electric current through it) 磁石；磁鐵

mag·net·ic /mægˈnɛtɪk; mægˈnetɪk/ *adj* **1** having the power of a magnet 有磁力的: *a powerful magnetic force* 強磁力 **2** attracting people easily 有吸引力的；有魅力的: *a magnetic personality* 有魅力的性格 – **magnetically** /-klɪ; -kli/ *adv*

magnetic field /ˌ·· ˈ·/ *n* the space in which the force of a magnet is effective 磁場: *the Earth's magnetic field* 地球的磁場

magnetic pole /ˌ·· ˈ·/ *n* either of two points near the NORTH POLE and the SOUTH POLE of the Earth towards which the compass needle points 磁極

magnetic tape /ˌ·· ˈ·/ *n* [C;U] a TAPE on which sound or other information can be recorded 〔錄音用的〕磁帶

mag·net·is·m /ˈmægnə.tɪzəm; ˈmægnɪtɪzəm/ *n* [U] **1** the qualities of a MAGNET 磁性；磁力 **2** strong personal charm 〔人的〕魅力: *We were overwhelmed by the sheer magnetism of his personality.* 我們完全為他的個性魅力所傾倒.

mag·net·ize /ˈmægnə.taɪz; ˈmægnɪtaɪz/ *v* (also 又作 **magnetise** *BrE* 〖英式〗) [T] to make a piece of iron into a MAGNET 使磁化

mag·nif·i·cent /mægˈnɪfəsnt; mægˈnɪfɪsənt/ *adj* extremely good or beautiful 極好的；極美的: *There were magnificent gold decorations inside the ballroom.* 舞廳裡裝飾得金碧輝煌. –**magnificence** *n* [U] –**magnificently** *adv*

mag·ni·fy /ˈmægnə.faɪ; ˈmægnɪfaɪ/ *v* **magnified, magnifying** [T] **1** to make something appear larger than it is 放大〔某物〕: *If you look through the microscope you will see the specimen magnified clearly.* 通過顯微鏡你可以看到放大得很清晰的標本. **2** to make something seem more important than it really is 誇大〔某事物〕: *You really mustn't magnify these little problems.* 你絕對不該誇大這些細枝末節的問題. –**magnification** /ˌmægnəfəˈkeʃən; ˌmægnɪfɪˈkeɪʃən/ *n* [C;U]

mag·ni·fy·ing glass /ˈ···· ·/ *n* a curved piece of glass with a handle which makes objects appear larger than they really are 放大鏡

mag·ni·tude /ˈmægnə.tjud; ˈmægnɪtjuːd/ *n* [U] *fml* great size or importance 〖正式〗巨大；重要性

mag·no·li·a /mægˈnolɪə; mægˈnəʊliə/ *n* a tree with large white or pink flowers 木蘭

mag·pie /ˈmæg.paɪ; ˈmægpaɪ/ *n* a fairly large black and white bird which has a noisy cry 喜鵲

ma·hog·a·ny /məˈhɒgənɪ; məˈhɒgəni/ *n* [U] **1** a hard dark wood often used for making furniture 〔製作家具的〕桃花心木，紅木 **2** a dark reddish brown colour 紅褐色

maid /med; meɪd/ *n* **1** a female servant 女僕，女傭 **2** *lit* a young unmarried woman 〖文〗少女；未婚的年輕女子

maid·en¹ /ˈmedn; ˈmeɪdn/ *n* *lit* a young unmarried woman 〖文〗少女；未婚的年輕女子

maiden² *adj* [only before a noun 只用於名詞前] **1** first 首次的；初次的: *The ship made its maiden voyage last year.* 這艘船去年首航. **2** **maiden aunt** an old, unmarried aunt 未婚的姑媽

maid·en·ly /ˈmednlɪ; ˈmeɪdnli/ *adj* *lit* gentle and modest 〖文〗溫柔的；謙和的

maiden name /ˈ·· ·/ *n* a woman's family name before marriage 〔女子的〕娘家姓

mail¹ /mel; meɪl/ n [U] **1** the system for sending things by post 郵政(制度): *The bad weather caused a disruption to the mail.* 天氣惡劣給郵遞造成了混亂。 **2** letters and anything else sent by post 郵件; 信件: *She was sitting in the garden opening her mail.* 她坐在花園裡拆開郵件。

mail² v [T] *AmE* to send something to someone by the mail 〖美式〗郵寄〔某物〕: *Can you mail these cards for me, please?* 請你替我把這些卡片寄出去好嗎? | *I'll mail the book to you.* 我會把書寄給你的。

mail·bag /'mel,bæg; 'meɪlbæg/ n a strong bag for carrying letters and parcels 郵袋

mail·box /'mel,baks; 'meɪlbɒks/ n *AmE* **1** a place outside the house where letters are delivered 〖美式〗信箱 **2** an outdoor POSTBOX 郵箱, 郵筒

maim /mem; meɪm/ v [T] to harm someone very badly, so that they are damaged for life 使〔某人〕殘廢

✲main¹ /men; meɪn/ adj [only before a noun 只用於名詞前] most important 最重要的; 主要的: *the main meal of the day* 一天的主餐 | *Here are the main points of the news again.* 現在重播新聞提要。 **–mainly** adv : *We sell mainly children's clothes.* 我們主要出售兒童服裝。 | *I like all music, but I'm mainly interested in jazz.* 甚麼音樂我都喜歡, 但最感興趣的是爵士樂。

main² n **1 in the main** usually 通常; 平常 **2 the mains** large pipes or wires supplying water, gas, or electricity 〔自來水、煤氣的〕總管道; 〔電的〕幹線

main·land /'men,lænd; 'meɪnlənd/ n **the mainland** the main part of a country, without its islands 大陸

main·spring /'men,sprɪŋ; 'meɪnsprɪŋ/ n [sing] *fml* the most important reason for an action 〖正式〗主要原因〔動力〕: *His belief in freedom was the mainspring of his fight against slavery.* 他對自由的信仰是他為反對奴隸制度而鬥爭的動力。

main·stay /'men,ste; 'meɪnsteɪ/ n [sing] the most important part of something 主要依靠; 支柱: *Farming is still the mainstay of this country's economy.* 農業仍是這個國家的經濟支柱。

main·stream /'men,strim; 'meɪnstriːm/ n **the mainstream** the group of people who are considered to behave in a usual way 主流: *Her views are very much those of the mainstream.* 她的觀點大體屬於主流。 **–mainstream** adj: *mainstream education* 主流教育

✲main·tain /men'ten; meɪn'teɪn/ v [T] **1** to continue to have or do something as before 保持; 維持: *He maintained his interest in football all his life.* 他對足球的興趣一生不減。 | *We need to maintain good relations with the suppliers.* 我們要與供應商保持良好關係。 **2** [T] to support someone with money 贍養〔某人〕; 負擔: *He is too poor to maintain a wife and children.* 他窮得連妻兒都養不起。 **3** [T] to keep something in good condition or look after it 保養; 維修: *It costs a lot of money to maintain an old house.* 保養一座老房子很花錢。 **4** [T;+(that)] to argue that something is the case 堅稱; 主張: *Throughout the trial he maintained his innocence.* 他在審判過程中堅持自己無罪。

□ USEFUL PATTERNS 有用句型
to maintain something; to maintain that …

✲main·te·nance /'mentənəns; 'meɪntənəns/ n [U] **1** the act of keeping something in good condition 保養; 維修: *I'm going to classes in car maintenance.* 我要去上汽車維修課。 **2** money that a person sends regularly to someone to provide for things they need 贍養費; 扶養費: *He has to pay maintenance to his ex-wife.* 他得付給前妻贍養費。

mai·son·ette /,mez'ɛt; ,meɪzə'net/ n a flat on two floors, that is part of a larger house 〔佔兩層樓的〕公寓套房

maize /mez; meɪz/ n [U] a tall plant which bears SWEETCORN 玉米

ma·jes·ty /'mædʒɪstɪ; 'mædʒ{sti/ n **1** [U] greatness or power 壯麗; 雄偉: *We admired the majesty of the snow-topped mountains.* 我們欣賞頂峯積雪的壯麗山巒。 **2 your Majesty, his Majesty, their Majesties** a title for a king or queen 陛下〔對帝王或王后、王的尊稱〕: *Her Majesty the Queen* 女王陛下 | *Thank you, your Majesty.* 謝謝, 陛下。 **–majestic** /mə'dʒestɪk; mə'dʒestɪk/ adj **–majestically** /-klɪ; -kli/ adv

✲ma·jor¹ /'medʒɚ; 'meɪdʒər/ adj [only before a noun 只用於名詞前] more important or serious than other things 較重要的; 較嚴重的: *The car needs major repairs.* 這輛汽車需要大修。 | *a major operation* 大手術

major² n **1 Major** an officer of middle rank in an army or air force 〔陸軍或空軍的〕少校 **2** *tech* a person who has, in law, reached the age of being an adult 〖術語〗〔達到法定年齡的〕成年人

major³ v **major in something** to study something as your main subject at university 主修〔大學的〕科目: *He's majoring in physics.* 他主修物理。

✲ma·jor·i·ty¹ /mə'dʒɔrətɪ; mə'dʒɒr{ti/ n **majorities 1** [U + sing/pl verb] more than half of a group of people 大半; 大多數: *The majority of primary school teachers are women.* 小學教師大多數為女性。 | *At the meeting, young people were in the majority.* 會上年輕人佔多數。 **2** [C] the difference between the number of votes gained by the winner and the loser 〔選舉中的〕超過的票數: *She won by a large majority.* 她以很大的多數票取勝。 | *He had a majority of 900 votes.* 他以超過對方九百票取勝。 **3** [C] the age when you become an adult in law 法定成年年齡

★**majority²** *adj* [only before a noun 只用於名詞前] reached by the agreement of most members of a group 多數成員同意後達成的: *a majority decision* 多數派的決定

★**make** –see box on pages 685 to 687 見 685 至 687 頁方框

make-be·lieve /'··,·/ *n* [U] a state of pretending or imagining things which are not real 假裝; 虛幻: *She lives in a world of make-believe.* 她生活在虛幻的世界裡。

mak·er /'meka; 'meɪkər/ *n* a person or company that makes something 製造者; 製造廠商: *If your watch doesn't work properly, it's best to send it back to the makers.* 要是你的錶是壞了不準, 最好把它送回手錶廠去。

make·shift /'mek,ʃɪft; 'meɪkʃɪft/ *adj* [only before a noun 只用於名詞前] used only for a short time because there is nothing better to use 權宜的; 臨時代用的: *They made a makeshift table from some old pieces of wood.* 他們用一些舊木頭做了張臨時用的桌子。

make-up /'·· ·/ *n* 1 [C;U] powder or paint worn on the face 化妝; 化妝品: *Too much make-up looks unnatural.* 濃妝豔抹看上去不自然。| *eye make-up* 眼部化妝品 2 [C] the combination of qualities (in a person's character) 性格; 氣質

mak·ing /'mekɪŋ; 'meɪkɪŋ/ *n* 1 [U] the act or business of making something with your hands 〔手工〕製作; 〔手工〕製造業: *She's really good at dressmaking.* 她很會做女式服裝。 2 **the making of someone** the reason for someone's success 某人的成功因素: *Hard work will be the making of him.* 艱苦的工作會把他造就成材。 3 **in the making** in the process of becoming something 在形成中: *He's a company chairman in the making.* 他正在成為公司的董事長。 4 **the makings of** everything necessary for developing into something 〔發展成某事物的〕一切素質; 必要條件: *He has the makings of a good doctor.* 他具備成為一個優秀醫生的一切素質。

mal·ad·just·ed /,mælə'dʒʌstɪd; ,mælə'dʒʌst‐t‐d‐/ *adj* having problems in your mind which prevent a happy or normal life 〔心理〕調節不良的

mal·a·dy /'mælədɪ; 'mælədi/ *n* **maladies** *fml* something that is wrong with a system or an organization 《正式》〔制度或組織的〕弊病

ma·laise /mæ'lez; mɔ'leɪz/ *n* [C;U] a general feeling of dissatisfaction because something is wrong 〔普遍的〕不滿, 不安: *the underlying social malaise in this country* 這個國家潛在的社會不滿情緒

ma·lar·i·a /mə'lɛrɪə; mə'leəriə/ *n* [U] a common tropical disease caused by the bite of a certain MOSQUITO 瘧疾 –**malarial** *adj* [only before a noun 只用於名詞前]

mal·con·tent /'mælkən,tɛnt; 'mælkəntent/ *n* a dissatisfied person who is likely to make trouble 不滿者; 反叛者

★**male** /mel; meɪl/ *adj* belonging to the sex that does not give birth to young 男性的; 公的; 雄的: *The male bird is very brightly coloured.* 雄鳥毛色鮮豔。| *a male voice* 男聲 –see 見 FEMALE (USAGE 用法) –**male** *n*

male chau·vin·ist /,· '···◂/ *n* a man who believes men are better than women 大男子主義者 –**male chauvinism** *n* [U]

ma·lev·o·lent /mə'lɛvələnt; mə'levələnt/ *adj lit* wishing to do evil to others 《文》惡意的; 惡毒的 –**malevolence** *n* [U] **malevolently** *adv*

mal·for·ma·tion /,mælfɔr'meʃən; ,mælfɔː'meɪʃən/ *n* [C;U] *tech* the condition of being formed or shaped wrongly 《術語》畸形 –**malformed** /mæl'fɔrmd; ,mæl'fɔːmd◂/ *adj*

mal·func·tion /mæl'fʌŋkʃən; mæl'fʌŋkʃən/ *n* a fault in the way a machine works 〔機器的〕故障: *delays owing to malfunctions of the computer* 由於電腦發生故障而造成的耽擱 –**malfunction** *v* [I]

mal·ice /'mælɪs; 'mæl‐s/ *n* [U] the wish to hurt other people 惡意: *He assured us that he bore us no malice, but I still didn't trust him.* 他一口咬定對我們毫無惡意, 但我仍不相信他。

ma·li·cious /mə'lɪʃəs; mə'lɪʃəs/ *adj* intended to hurt people 惡意的; 惡毒的: *malicious gossip* 用意惡毒的流言蜚語 –**maliciously** *adv*

ma·lign /mə'laɪn; mə'laɪn/ *v* [T] to say unpleasant and untrue things about someone 中傷; 誹謗: *a politician who has been much maligned by the newspapers* 被報紙大加誹謗的政客

ma·lig·nant /mə'lɪgnənt; mə'lɪgnənt/ *adj* 1 full of hate and a strong wish to hurt people 惡意的; 惡毒的 2 serious enough to cause death if not stopped 致命的; 惡性的: *a malignant tumour* 惡性腫瘤

ma·lin·ger /mə'lɪŋgə; mə'lɪŋgər/ *v* [I] to avoid work by pretending to be ill 裝病逃避工作: *He says he's got flu, but I think he's malingering.* 他說他得了流感, 可我認為他在裝病(逃避工作)。–**malingerer** *n*

mal·lard /'mæləd; 'mæləd/ *n* a wild duck 綠頭鴨〔一種野鴨〕

mal·le·a·ble /'mælɪəbl; 'mæliəbəl/ *adj* 1 able to be beaten or made into a new shape (used of metals) 可鎚的; 可鍛的〔指金屬〕 2 easily influenced (used of people) 易受影響的〔指人〕

mal·let /'mælɪt; 'mæl‐t/ *n* a wooden hammer 木槌 –see picture on page 958 見 958 頁彩圖

mal·nu·tri·tion /,mælnju'trɪʃən; ,mælnju‐'trɪʃən/ *n* [U] bad health resulting from lack of food or from the wrong sorts of

M

⁺**make¹**/mek; meɪk/ v

made /med; meɪd/, **making**

1 [T] to do something 做〔某事〕:
We need to make a decision. 我們需要做決定。 | *They were making a dreadful noise.* 他們發出討厭的噪音。 | *She made a brilliant speech.* 她做了一次精彩的演講。 | *I need to make a phone call.* 我需要打個電話。 | *He made several mistakes.* 他犯了幾個錯誤。 | *Try not to make a mess.* 盡量別弄亂。

2 [T] to produce something 生產, 製造〔某物〕:
I'm just going to make a cup of coffee. 我正打算煮杯咖啡。 | *She made herself a dress.* 她給自己做了件衣服。 | *We make 2,000 cars a week in this factory.* 我們在這家工廠每週生產二千輛汽車。 | *The film was made on location in Africa.* 這部電影在非洲拍攝外景。

> □ USEFUL PATTERNS 有用句型
> to make something; to make something for someone; to make someone something

3 [T] to earn 賺; 掙:
I don't make enough money to go on expensive holidays! 我的收入有限, 花錢多的假期我負擔不起! | *The company made a huge profit this year.* 這家公司今年賺到了巨額利潤。 | *She makes her living writing children's books.* 她以寫兒童讀物維生。

4 [T; + complement] to cause someone to do something, or cause something to happen 使〔某人〕做〔某事〕; 使〔某事〕發生:
His behaviour made me angry. 他的行為使我生氣。 | *We want to make the kitchen bigger.* 我們想把廚房擴大些。 | *We're going to make the spare bedroom into a study.* 我們打算把備用臥室改成書房。 | *I feel that my experiences have made me a better person.* 我覺得自己的種種經歷使我成為一個更健全的人。 | *She was made a director of the company.* 她被選為公司董事。 | *The army will make a man of you!* 陸軍生涯會使你成為真正的男子漢。

5 [T] to cause someone to do something, or cause something to happen 使〔某人〕做〔某事〕; 使〔某事〕發生:
How do you make this machine work? 你是怎樣使這機器運轉的? | *The smell made me feel ill.* 這氣味使我感到不舒服。 | *You made me jump!* 你嚇了我一跳! | *These people should be made to work!* 應該強迫這些人工作! | *That hairstyle makes you look very young.* 那種髮型使你看上去很年輕。

> □ USEFUL PATTERNS 有用句型
> to make someone do something; to be made to do something

6 [T] to calculate an answer or result 計算; 估計:
"Have you got the answer yet?" "Yes, I make it 425." "你得出答案了嗎?" "嗯, 我算出是425。"

7 [T] to add up to 等於; 總計:
Two and two make four. 二加二等於四。

8 [T] to have the right qualities for something 具有〔合適的品質〕:
This will make a good present for my mother. 這將是一份送給我母親的好禮物。 | *I think she'll make an excellent doctor.* 我認為她會成為一個優秀的醫生。

9 [T] to manage to get to a place or an event 努力到達; 努力做成:
I'm afraid I won't be able to make the party on Friday. 恐怕我無法趕得及星期五的聚會。

10 [T] *infml* to cause something to be good or attractive 〖非正式〗使〔某事物〕令人滿意或吸引人:
That wallpaper really makes the room. 那牆紙真使房間生色不少。| *The trip round the islands really made our holiday.* 環島旅行真使我的假期生色不少。

11 **make a bed** to tidy a bed that someone has slept in by straightening the sheet and pulling up the covers 鋪牀

12 **he made her his wife** *lit* = he married her 〖文〗= 他娶了她

13 **make a friend, make friends** to become friendly with someone 與〔某人〕友好;與〔某人〕交朋友:
I see you've made a friend already. 我看出你已交了個朋友。| *I've made friends* **with** *quite a number of people since we moved here.* 我搬到這裡以後已結交了不少朋友。
[RELATED PHRASE 相關詞組: **make an enemy:** *He's made quite a few enemies.* 他已結下了幾個對頭。]

14 **make someone's day** to make someone feel very happy 使某人非常高興:
It made my day when he told me I was going to get a pay rise. 他告訴我我將獲加薪,這使我非常高興。

15 **make it: a** to arrive in time 準時到達:
If we set off now, we should make it to the station before the train goes. 如果我們現在動身,應該能在火車開走前趕到車站。
b to be able to attend an event 能參加〔活動〕:
I wanted to go to her lecture, but I couldn't make it. 我想去聽她的講座,但沒法參加。
c to succeed 成功:
She feels she's finally made it as a singer. 她覺得自己作為一名歌手,終於成功了。

16 **What time do you make it?** = What time does your watch say? = 你的錶現在幾點?
"What time do you make it?" "I make it four o'clock." "你的錶幾點?" "四點。"

17 **make do** to use something even though it is not very good or is not enough 將就使用;湊合着用:
I haven't got any cream, so we'll have to make do **with** *milk.* 我一點奶油都沒有,我們只好用牛奶吧。

18 **be made of** to be formed of a particular substance 由〔特定材料〕構成:
cups made of plastic 塑料杯 | *a table made of old wooden crates* 用舊木板箱做的桌子

19 **what do you make of this?** a phrase used to ask someone's opinion about something that you think is strange 〔自己認為奇怪的事物,詢問某人的看法〕

20 **make as if to do something** to show that you are about to do something 顯示將要做某事:
She made as if to leave. 她似乎要走。

21 **make your way somewhere** to go somewhere 去某處:
We slowly made our way home. 我們慢慢地回家。

22 **make way** to move so that someone else can go where you were 讓路

make for sthg *phr v*
[T]
1 to move towards something 朝〔某物〕前進; 衝向:
He made for the door. 他衝向門口。
2 to result in something 導致:
The large print makes for easy reading. 用大字體印刷方便閱讀。

make off *phr v*
to leave a place quickly 匆忙離開, 溜掉:
The thieves made off **with** *a considerable amount of money and jewellery.* 小偷帶着大量首飾現鈔匆忙逃走。

make out *phr v*

1 [T **make** sthg ↔ **out**] to see, hear, or understand something with difficulty 勉強看出〔聽出; 理解〕〔某事物〕:
I could just make out the shape of the building. 我只能勉強看出大樓的輪廓。| *I could hear voices, but I couldn't make out what they were saying.* 我能聽到説話聲, 但聽不清楚他們在説甚麼。

2 [T **make** sthg ↔ **out**] to write the necessary information on a cheque 填寫〔支票〕:
The cheque was made out to me. 這張支票是開給我的。

3 make out that... to pretend 假裝:
He makes out that he's a qualified doctor. 他假稱是個夠資格的醫生。

4 make yourself out to be to pretend that you are something 把自己裝作是...:
He makes himself out to be the most important person in the whole company. 他聲稱自己是全公司最重要的人物。

make sthg ↔ **over** *phr v*

[T] *fml*

to pass over money or goods to someone 〖正式〗移交, 轉讓〔財產〕:
*The house was made over **to** his children.* (他把) 這房子轉讓了給他的子女。

make up *phr v*

1 [T **make** sthg ↔ **up**] to invent a story or a piece of information in order to deceive people 虛構, 捏造,〔為了欺騙而〕編造:
We later found out that he'd made the whole thing up. 我們後來發現整件事都是他編造的。

2 [T **make** sthg ↔ **up**] to form something 組成, 構成〔某事物〕:
the members who make up the committee 組成委員會的成員 | *Society is made up of lots of different groups of people.* 社會是由許多各種各樣的人組成的。

3 [I;T **make** sbdy **up**] to put special powder and paints on your face in order to make yourself more attractive 化裝; 化妝:
She made herself up carefully. 她仔細地為自己化妝。

4 [T **make** sthg ↔ **up**] to form or prepare something by putting the different parts together 配製; 拼湊成〔物〕:
I made up a bed on the floor. 我鋪了個地鋪。

5 [T **make** sthg ↔ **up**] to make an amount complete 補足〔數額〕:
The rest of the money will be made up by the government. 其餘的錢將由政府補足。

6 [I] to become friends again after a quarrel 言歸於好,〔爭吵後〕和解

make up for sthg *phr v*

[T] to reduce the bad effect of something 補償, 彌補〔某事物〕:
The long hot summer made up for the miserable spring. 這個悠長的炎夏, 彌補了春天令人苦惱的缺點。

make² *n*

1 a product produced by a particular maker 樣式, 牌子:
"What make is your car?" "It's a Ford." "你的汽車是甚麼牌子?" "是福特。"

2 on the make trying to gain money and power 追名逐利

M

food 營養不良

mal·prac·tice /mæl'præktıs; ˌmæl'prækt ̩s/ *n* [U] a failure to carry out your professional duty properly, often resulting in loss or physical harm to someone 失職〔常給別人帶來損失或肉體傷害〕: *He sued his doctor for malpractice.* 他控告醫生治療失當。

malt /mɔlt; mɔːlt/ *n* [U] grain such as BARLEY, which has been specially treated and is used for making alcoholic drinks〔製造酒類的〕麥芽: *a bottle of malt whisky* 一瓶麥芽威士忌

mal·treat /mæl'trit; mæl'triːt/ *v* [T] *fml* to treat someone cruelly and roughly《正式》粗暴殘酷地對待; 虐待: *The children had been physically maltreated too.* 孩子們肉體上也受到了虐待。**–maltreatment** *n* [U]

mam·mal /'mæml ̩; 'mæməl/ *n* a type of animal born live, not in an egg, which is fed on its mother's milk 哺乳動物

mam·moth¹ /'mæməθ; 'mæməθ/ *n* a very large hairy elephant which used to live on earth 猛獁〔古代的長毛巨象〕

mammoth² *adj* [only before a noun 只用於名詞前] extremely large 龐大的; 巨大的: *a mammoth task* 重大的任務

man¹ /mæn; mæn/ *n* **men** /mɛn; men/ **1** [C] an adult human male (成年)男子; 男人: *men, women, and children* 男人、女人和孩子 | *a Polish man and his German wife* 一個波蘭男子和他的德國太太 **2** [C] a human being, male or female 人: *No man could have survived that.* 沒人能夠幸免。**3** [U] the human race 人類: *Man cannot live by bread alone.* 人不能單靠麵包生活。**4** [C] a male employed by someone 男雇員: *The men are threatening to go on strike.* 雇工們在威脅要罷工。**5** [C] a soldier of low rank 普通士兵 **6** [C] a male member of a team〔球隊的〕男隊員 **7** [C] any of the objects moved by each player in a board game 棋子: *chess men* 國際象棋棋子 **8 as one man** everyone together 全體一致地: *The audience stood up as one man and cheered.* 觀眾全體起立喝采。**9 man and wife** husband and wife 夫婦 **10 the man in the street** the average person, who represents general opinion〔代表一般意見的〕普通人: *This kind of film doesn't appeal to the man in the street.* 這種電影不合一般人的口味。**11 a man of the world** a man with a lot of experience of life 老於世故的人

■ USAGE 用法: Many people do not like the use of **man** to mean human beings (men and women) in general. If you want to avoid this use, you can use other words such as: **humans, human beings, the human race, people.** ☆許多人不喜歡用 **man** 總概人類(男人和女人)。如果要避免這種用法, 可以使用別的詞, 如: **humans, human beings, the human race, people**。

man² *v* **-nn-** [T] to operate or be in charge of equipment 操縱; 配備: *Man the guns!*〔對砲手的口令〕就位! | *the first manned spacecraft* 第一艘載人宇宙飛船

man³ *interj AmE infml* used when speaking to a person, expressing anger or impatience with them《美式, 非正式》嗨, 嘿〔對人說話時表示生氣或不耐煩〕: *For goodness' sake, man, think of others for a change!* 看在老天爺面上, 嗨, 換過來為別人想想!

man·a·cles /'mænəklz; 'mænəkəlz/ *n* [pl] rings or chains on the hands or feet of a prisoner 手銬; 腳鐐

man·age /'mænıdʒ; 'mænıdʒ/ *v* **managed, managing 1** [T] to control or be in charge of a business or activity 控制; 管理〔企業或活動〕: *He managed the company while his father was away.* 他父親不在時由他管理公司。| *She manages the money very well.* 她理財有方。**2** [I;T] to succeed in dealing with something such as a problem 設法做到; 勉力完成: *We don't have much money, but we manage.* 我們錢不多, 但能應付。| *Do you think we'll manage to finish the work by Friday?* 你認為到星期五我們可以完成這項工作嗎?

□ USEFUL PATTERNS 有用句型
to manage something; to manage to do something

man·age·a·ble /'mænıdʒəbl ̩; 'mænıdʒəbəl/ *adj* easy or possible to control or deal with 可控制的; 易管理的: *a manageable hair style* 好做的髮型 | *Our new garden is quite small, and much more manageable than our last one.* 我們的新花園很小, 比過去的那個容易管理得多了。

man·age·ment /'mænıdʒmənt; 'mænıdʒmənt/ *n* **1** [U] the control of something such as a business or money〔企業或錢財的〕管理; 經營 **2** [C;U] the people in charge of a firm or organization〔商行或組織的〕管理人員; 管理部門: *a breakdown in communication between management and the workforce* 資方和工人之間交流的失敗 | *The management is having talks with the workers.* 主管人員正在和工人談判。

man·ag·er /'mænıdʒɚ; 'mænıdʒər/ *n* a person who directs the affairs of a business or team of workers 經理; 管理人: *the manager of a football team* 足球隊的經理 | *My bank manager is extremely helpful.* 我的銀行經理極肯幫忙。| *Why don't you complain to the manager?* 你為甚麼不向經理投訴呢?

man·ag·er·ess /'mænıdʒɚıs; ˌmænıdʒə'res/

n a woman who controls a shop or restaurant〔商店或餐館的〕女經理; 女管理人: *I'd like to see the manageress, please.* 我希望見一下你們的女經理。

man·a·ge·ri·al /ˌmænəˈdʒɪrɪəl; ˌmænɪˈdʒɪəriəl/ *adj* [only before a noun 只用於名詞前] concerned with or belonging to the work of a manager 經理的; 管理上的: *She has excellent managerial skills.* 她有出色的管理技能。

man·date /ˈmændet; ˈmændeɪt/ *n fml*〖正式〗**1** the power given to a government to act according to the wishes of the people of a country〔國民對政府的〕授權: *It is ridiculous for the government to claim it has a mandate from the people for these measures.* 政府聲稱得到人民的授權推行這些措施, 簡直荒唐。**2** a formal command given by a high official〔上級官員下達的〕正式命令

man·da·to·ry /ˈmændəˌtorɪ; ˈmændətəri/ *adj fml* which must be done〖正式〗強制的; 必須履行的

mane /men; meɪn/ *n* the long thick hair growing from the neck of a horse or a lion〔馬或獅子頸部的〕長鬃毛

ma·neu·ver /məˈnuvɚ; məˈnuːvəʳ/ *n* –see 見 MANOEUVRE

man·ger /ˈmendʒɚ; ˈmeɪndʒəʳ/ *n* a long open container used for feeding horses and cattle〔馬、牛的〕食槽

man·gled /ˈmæŋgld; ˈmæŋgəld/ *adj* crushed or cut to pieces 壓碎的; 破碎的: *The mangled wreckage was towed away from the scene of the crash.* 壓得粉碎的殘骸被拖離了撞車事故的現場。

man·go /ˈmæŋgo; ˈmæŋgəʊ/ *n* **mangoes or mangos** a sweet yellow fruit 芒果

man·grove /ˈmæŋgrov; ˈmæŋgrəʊv/ *n* a tropical tree which grows in water or on muddy land 紅樹〔生長在水裡或沼澤地上的熱帶樹〕

mang·y /ˈmendʒɪ; ˈmeɪndʒi/ *adj* **mangier, mangiest** of bad appearance because of loss of hair 患疥癬的: *a mangy old dog* 老癩皮狗

man·han·dle /ˈmænˌhændl; ˈmænhændl/ *v* **manhandled, manhandling** [T] to move someone roughly, using force 用力粗暴地拖[拉]〔某人〕: *She complained that she had been manhandled by the police.* 她抱怨説警察對她連拖帶拉。

man·hole /ˈmænˌhol; ˈmænhəʊl/ *n* a covered opening in a road leading to underground pipes 人孔〔馬路中有蓋的洞口, 通往地下管道〕

man·hood /ˈmænhʊd; ˈmænhʊd/ *n* [U] the state of being a man rather than a boy〔男子的〕成年

ma·ni·a /ˈmenɪə; ˈmeɪniə/ *n* **1** a strong desire or liking for something 癖好; 狂熱: *a mania for driving fast cars* 開快車的癖好 **2** *tech* an illness of the mind〖術語〗躁狂

ma·ni·ac /ˈmenɪˌæk; ˈmeɪniæk/ *n* **1** a person who suffers from a certain illness of the mind 躁狂者: *a sex maniac* 性慾狂者 **2** a wild thoughtless person 瘋子: *You're driving like a maniac.* 你像個瘋子在開車。

man·ic /ˈmænɪk; ˈmænɪk/ *adj* very excited and wild 極度激動的; 瘋狂的: *a manic outburst* 瘋狂的爆發

man·i·cure /ˈmænɪˌkjur; ˈmænɪkjʊəʳ/ *n* a beauty treatment for your hands and fingernails 修指甲 **–manicure** *v* **manicured, manicuring** [T] **–manicurist** *n*

man·i·fest¹ /ˈmænəˌfɛst; ˈmænɪfest/ *adj fml* very easy and clear to see〖正式〗明顯的 **–manifestly** *adv* : *It was manifestly obvious that they were in love.* 這再明白不過了, 他們倆在戀愛。

manifest² *v* [T] *fml*〖正式〗**1** to show something plainly 顯示〔某事物〕; 表明: *Such rash actions manifest a total disregard for personal safety.* 行動如此魯莽表明完全無視人身安全。**2** **manifest itself** to become clear and easy to see 顯現; 顯露: *Her creativity manifests itself in many ways.* 她的創造力顯露在很多方面。

man·i·fes·ta·tion /ˌmænəfɛsˈteʃən; ˌmænɪfeˈsteɪʃən/ *n* [C;U] *fml* a sign showing that something exists or is happening〖正式〗表明; 表露; 顯現: *Riots are a clear manifestation of growing discontent with the government.* 騷亂是對政府日漸增長的不滿情緒的一種清楚表現。

man·i·fes·to /ˌmænəˈfɛsto; ˌmænɪˈfestəʊ/ *n* **manifestos** *or* **manifestoes** a written declaration which states the aims and opinions of a political party〔政黨的〕書面宣言

man·i·fold /ˈmænəˌfold; ˈmænɪfəʊld/ *adj fml* many in number or kind〖正式〗許許多多的; 多種多樣的: *The problems facing the government are manifold.* 政府面臨的問題是多種多樣的。

ma·nil·a /məˈnɪlə; məˈnɪlə/ *adj* (also 又作 **manilla**) [only before a noun 只用於名詞前] made of strong brown paper 馬尼拉紙製的

ma·nip·u·late /məˈnɪpjəˌlet; məˈnɪpjʊleɪt/ *v* **manipulated, manipulating** [T] **1** to control and influence someone or something for a particular purpose〔為某一目的而〕控制, 影響〔某人或某事物〕: *He accused the government of manipulating public opinion.* 他指控政府操縱公眾輿論。**2** to work with skilful use of your hands〔熟練地〕操作: *He manipulated the control buttons and achieved the required result.* 他熟練地操縱控制鈕, 得到了指定的結果。**–manipulative** *adj* **–manipulation** *n* [C;U]

man·kind /mænˈkaɪnd; ˌmænˈkaɪnd/ *n* [U] the human race, both men and women 人類: *the worst war in the history of mankind* 人類歷史上最殘酷的戰爭

M

man·ly /'mænlɪ; 'mænli/ *adj* **manlier, manliest** having qualities typical of a man, especially strength and courage 有男子氣概的; 強壯的: *a manly voice* 有男子氣概的嗓音–**manliness** *n* [U]

man-made /ˌ· ˈ·◂/ *adj* **1** produced by people and not found in nature 人造的; 人工的: *a man-made lake* 人工湖 **2** made from chemical substances 合成的: *Nylon is a man-made material.* 尼龍是一種合成材料。

manned /mænd; mænd/ *adj* controlled by the people inside it (used of a vehicle) 有人控制的〔指車輛〕: *a manned spacecraft* 載人太空船–opposite 反義 **unmanned**

☆**man·ner** /'mænə; 'mænəʳ/ *n* **1** [sing] the way of doing something 方式; 方法: *Let's discuss things in a calm manner.* 讓我們平心靜氣地討論事情。 **2** [sing] the way in which someone talks and behaves towards other people 舉止; 態度: *I don't like his rude manner.* 我不喜歡他的粗魯態度。 **3 manners** [pl] ways of behaving and speaking which are considered to be socially acceptable or socially unacceptable 禮貌; 禮儀; 規矩: *It's bad manners to eat like that!* 那樣吃相很沒禮貌! | *Her manners were perfect.* 她特別有禮貌。 **4 all manner of** many different kinds of 形形色色的; 各種各樣的 **5 in a manner of speaking** a phrase used when you want to say that something is generally true, but not exactly true 不妨説; 可以説〔用於表示認為某事大體如此, 但並非完全確實〕

man·nered /'mænəd; 'mænəd/ *adj fml* having an unnatural way of behaving〔正式〕不自然的; 矯揉造作的: *a mannered way of speaking* 矯揉造作的講話方式

man·ner·is·m /'mænə,rɪzəm; 'mænərɪzəm/ *n* a personal habit of behaviour or speech〔行為、語言的〕習性

ma·noeu·vra·ble /mə'nuːvrəbl; mə'nuːvərəbl/ *adj* (**maneuverable** *AmE*〔美式〕) easily moved or turned 易移動的; 可轉動的: *a very light and manoeuvrable car* 車身輕、易操縱的汽車–**manoeuvrability** /mə,nuːvrə'bɪlətɪ; mə,nuːvərə'bɪləti/ *n* [U]

ma·noeu·vre¹ /mə'nuːvə; mə'nuːvəʳ/ *n* (**maneuver** *AmE*〔美式〕) **1** a set of planned moves for an army or navy for training purposes〔陸軍或海軍的〕調動調遣: *naval manoeuvres* 海軍調動 | *The regiment is abroad on manoeuvres.* 這個團正往海外調動。 **2** a skilful move or clever trick 策略; 花招

manoeuvre² *v* **manoeuvred, manoeuvring** (**maneuver** *AmE*〔美式〕) [T] to move or turn something skilfully 巧妙地移動或調動: *It was difficult to manoeuvre the furniture through the door.* 很難把家具左轉右拐地搬過這道門。

man·or /'mænə; 'mænəʳ/ *n* a large country house with land 莊園

man·pow·er /'mæn,pauə; 'mæn,pauəʳ/ *n*

[U] the number of people needed for a certain type of work 勞動力: *a need for skilled manpower* 對有技術的勞動力的需求

man·sion /'mænʃən; 'mænʃən/ *n* a large house 大廈; 宅第

man·slaugh·ter /'mæn,slɔtə; 'mæn,slɔːtəʳ/ *n* [U] *law* the crime of killing a person unlawfully but not intentionally〔律〕非預謀的殺人罪; 過失殺人

man·tel·piece /'mæntl,pis; 'mæntlpiːs/ *n* the shelf above a fireplace 壁爐架–see picture on page 730 見 730 頁彩圖

man·u·al¹ /'mænjuəl; 'mænjuəl/ *adj* using your hands 手工的; 用手的: *craftwork requiring great manual dexterity* 需要雙手靈巧的手工活兒–**manually** *adv*

manual² *n* a book of information telling you how to do something, or use a machine 手冊; 指南

☆**man·u·fac·ture¹** /ˌmænjə'fæktʃə; ˌmænjə'fæktʃəʳ/ *v* **manufactured, manufacturing** [T] to make or produce something by machinery in a factory〔用機器〕製造; 生產: *We manufacture door knobs.* 我們生產門把手。–**manufacturer** *n*

manufacture² *n* [U] the act of manufacturing something 製造; 生產: *the manufacture of computer parts* 電腦部件的生產

ma·nure /mə'njuə; mə'njuəʳ/ *n* [U] waste matter from animals, which is put on the land to improve the soil〔動物的〕糞便; 肥料

man·u·script /'mænjə,skrɪpt; 'mænjəskrɪpt/ *n* **1** the first copy of a book or piece of writing before it is printed 原稿; 手稿 **2** an old book written by hand before printing was invented 手寫本〔印刷發明前用手寫的書〕: *a medieval manuscript* 中世紀的手寫本

☆**man·y** /'mɛnɪ; 'meni/ *det, pron* **more** /mɔr; mɔːʳ/ **most** /moust; məust/ **1** a large number 多; 許多: *Many people are afraid to go out after dark.* 很多人害怕天黑後外出。 | *Not many of the children can read.* 孩子中不是很多人識字。 | *There are simply too many cars on the roads.* 馬路上汽車實在太多了。 **2** used in questions about the number of people or things that there are 多少〔用於詢問數目〕: *How many people were there?* 那裡有多少人? **3 a good many, a great many** a very large number 很多: *A good many MPs have signed the petition.* 很多國會議員已在請願書上簽了名。 **4 many a** a lot of 許多: *I've been to Paris many a time.* 我去過巴黎多次。

☆**map¹** /mæp; mæp/ *n* a detailed plan of a place or area as it would appear if you saw it from above 地圖: *a map of Europe* 歐洲地圖 | *a street map of Brighton* 布賴頓街道圖

map² *v* **-pp-** [T] to make a map of a place 繪製〔某處的〕地圖

map sth ↔ **out** *phr v* [T] to plan something in detail 詳細計劃〔某事〕: *She felt that her whole life had been mapped out for her.*

她覺得自己整個一生都已籌劃好了。

ma·ple /ˈmepl; ˈmeɪpəl/ n a tree which has leaves with five points 槭樹; 楓樹

mar /mɑr; mɑːʳ/ v **-rr-** [T] to spoil 損壞: *motorways which mar the beauty of the countryside* 破壞農村美景的高速公路

mar·a·thon[1] /ˈmærəˌθɑn; ˈmærəθən/ n a 26-mile running race 馬拉松賽跑〔全長二十六英里〕

marathon[2] adj lasting a long time 馬拉松式的; 漫長的: *a marathon speech* 無休止的演講

ma·raud·ing /məˈrɔdɪŋ; məˈrɔːdɪŋ/ adj [only before a noun 只用於名詞前] searching for something to steal, burn, or destroy 搶劫的; 劫掠的: *They were attacked by marauding soldiers.* 他們遭到劫掠的士兵襲擊。

mar·ble /ˈmɑrbl; ˈmɑːbəl/ n **1** [U] a hard cold stone used for building, which is often polished to show the irregular pattern of colour in it 大理石: *a marble fireplace* 大理石壁爐 | *a gravestone made of marble* 大理石墓碑 **2 marbles** small coloured glass balls which children roll along the ground as a game 〔兒童遊戲用的〕玻璃彈子

march[1] /mɑrtʃ; mɑːtʃ/ v **1** [I;T] to walk with firm regular steps like a soldier 齊步行進; 前進: *The soldiers marched along the road.* 士兵沿着馬路行進。 | *protesters marching through the streets* 反對者在街上遊行 | *We've marched twenty miles today.* 我們今天已行進了二十英里。 –see picture on page 992 見 992 頁彩圖 **2** [I + adv/prep] to walk to a place in a determined manner 堅定地走向〔某處〕: *She slammed the door and marched out of the house.* 她砰的一聲關上門，大步走出屋子。 –see 見 WALK[1] (USAGE 用法) **3** [T + adv/prep] to take someone roughly to a place, by holding them 粗暴地拉〔推/拽〕: *I was marched out of the building.* 我被人從大樓裡推出來。

march[2] n **1** [C;U] the act of marching 行進; 行軍: *The soldiers had a long march ahead of them.* 士兵有很長一段路要行進。 **2** [C] the distance covered while marching for a certain period of time 〔在一定時間內的〕行程: *Our destination is four days' march away.* 到我們的目的地要四天的行程。 **3** [C] a piece of music with a regular beat 進行曲 **4** [C] a large number of people who march from one place to another to show their opinions or dissatisfaction 遊行示威者: *Many bystanders joined in the student march.* 很多旁觀者加入了學生遊行的行列。 **5** [sing] the steady development of something 進展; 進行: *the march of time* 時間的推移 | *the slow march to equality* 邁向平等的緩慢進展

March n (also 又作 **Mar**) the 3rd month of the year 三月

mar·chio·ness /ˈmɑrʃənɪs; ˈmɑːʃənɪs/ n the wife of a MARQUIS, or her title 侯爵夫人; 女候爵

mare /mɛr; meəʳ/ n an adult female horse 牝馬

mar·ga·rine /ˈmɑrdʒəˌrin; ˌmɑːdʒəˈriːn/ n [U] a yellow substance similar to butter made from animal or vegetable fat 人造黃油

***mar·gin** /ˈmɑrdʒɪn; ˈmɑːdʒɪn/ n **1** a space near the edge of a page 〔頁邊的〕空白: *Make notes in the margin of your book.* 在你書頁邊的空白處作批注。 **2** an amount greater than what is necessary 餘地; 餘裕: *In the end, we won by a decisive margin.* 最後我們以決定性的優勢獲勝。 | *Our profit margin is very low this year.* 今年我們利潤很低。

mar·gin·al /ˈmɑrdʒɪnl; ˈmɑːdʒɪnəl/ adj **1** not very important or large 無關緊要的; 不太大的: *The new law will cause only a marginal increase in the cost of living.* 新的法律將導致生活費用輕度上漲。 **2 marginal seat** a place in parliament which can be lost or won by a small number of votes, and so pass from one party's control to that of another 〔競選中雙方票數接近並可能為任何一方爭得的〕邊緣議會席位 – **marginally** adv

mar·i·gold /ˈmærəˌgold; ˈmærɪgəʊld/ n a garden plant with yellow or orange flowers 金盞花; 萬壽菊

mar·i·jua·na /ˌmærəˈwɑnə; ˌmærɪˈwɑːnə, -ˈhwɑːnə/ n (also 又作 **marihuana**) [U] a form of the illegal drug CANNABIS smoked in cigarettes for pleasure 大麻(煙)

ma·ri·na /məˈrinə; məˈriːnə/ n a harbour for pleasure boats 〔停泊遊艇的〕港口

mar·i·nate /ˈmærəˌnet; ˈmærɪneɪt/ v **marinated, marinating** (also 又作 **marinade** /ˈmærəˌned; ˈmærɪneɪd/) [T] to leave meat or fish in a mixture of wine, oil, and SPICES, to give it a special taste before cooking 〔烹飪前〕把(肉、魚)浸於調味汁中

ma·rine[1] /məˈrin; məˈriːn/ adj [only before a noun 只用於名詞前] related to or concerning the sea 海的; 海生的: *Marine life was badly affected by oil pollution.* 海洋生物受到了石油污染的重大影響。 | *a marine biologist* 海洋生物學家

marine[2] n a soldier who serves in the navy 海軍士兵

mar·i·o·nette /ˌmærɪəˈnɛt; ˌmærɪəˈnet/ n a PUPPET worked by strings or wires 牽線木偶

mar·i·tal /ˈmærətl; ˈmærɪtl/ adj **1** concerning marriage 婚姻的: *marital bliss* 婚姻的極大幸福 **2 marital status** your state with regard to marriage, for example whether you are single or married 婚姻狀況

mar·i·time /ˈmærəˌtaɪm; ˈmærɪtaɪm/ adj [only before a noun 只用於名詞前] **1** concerning ships or the sea 海事的; 海軍的; 海的: *maritime law* 海事法 | *a great maritime power* 海上強國 **2** living or existing near the sea 濱海居住的; 生存於沿海的: *the maritime provinces* 沿海諸省

mar·jo·ram /ˈmɑrdʒərəm; ˈmɑːdʒərəm/ *n* [U] a plant with small dark green leaves which are used in cooking 墨角蘭〔葉小, 呈墨綠色, 用於烹調〕

★**mark¹** /mɑrk; mɑːk/ *n* **1** a spot or cut that spoils the natural colour or appearance of something 痕跡; 斑點: *His feet left dirty marks all over the floor.* 他的腳在地板上到處留下了污跡。 | *The table was covered in scratch marks.* 桌子上滿是刮痕。 **2** something printed or written which has a meaning 符號; 記號: *She picked up her pen and made a couple of marks on the page.* 她拾起筆在書頁上作了幾個記號。 **3** a figure or letter given by a teacher to represent how good someone's work is 分數: *The highest mark in the test was nine out of ten.* 這次測驗的最高分是十分制中的九分。 | *Did you get a good mark?* 你有沒有得到高分? **4** a number or point on a scale 刻度: *We must get unemployment down below the two million mark.* 我們必須把失業人數降低到兩百萬以下。 **5 as a mark of** in order to show a particular feeling or quality 以示〔某種感情或品質〕: *We stood up as a mark of respect when he came in.* 他進來時我們起立以示敬意。 **6** a particular type of a machine 〔機器的〕型號; 式樣: *The Mark 4 model is the best we've ever produced.* 四號樣式是我們所生產的最好的一種。 **7** a German coin 馬克〔德國貨幣單位〕 **8 have the marks of, bear the marks of** to be typical of something 是〔某事物的〕典型: *He bore all the marks of a politician.* 他是個典型的政客。 **9 make a mark, leave a mark** to have a lasting effect 留下持久的印象: *His years in prison have left their mark on him.* 多年的監獄生活在他身上留下了烙印。 **10 on your marks, get set, go!** an expression used to tell runners to get ready for a race and then to start 各就各位, 預備, 跑!〔用於賽跑時發令〕

★**mark²** /[T] **1** to make a mark on something in a way that spoils its appearance 留痕跡於〔某物〕: *Water can easily mark a polished wooden surface.* 水很容易在光亮的木製表面上留下痕跡。 **2** to write or print words or signs onto something in order to give information about it 作記號於〔某物〕: *The letter was marked "confidential".* 信上標着"機密"。 **3** to show where something is 標出〔某物〕: *A heap of stones marked his grave.* 他的墳墓用一堆石頭作標記。 **4** to be a sign of something 成為〔某事物的〕標誌: *This new legislation marks the end of the National Health Service as we know it.* 這條新法律標誌着我們所認識的國民保健制度的終結。 | *a concert to mark the 50th anniversary of the composer's death* 紀念這位作曲家逝世五十週年的音樂會 **5** to give a mark to a piece of work to show how good it is 評分數: *I've got*

a pile of exam papers to mark. 我有一堆試卷要批改。 **6 mark my words** = you will see later that I am right 你留心聽着〔以後你會發現我是對的〕。 **7 mark time** to spend time working but not advancing at all 原地踏步〔工作沒有進展〕

mark sthg ↔ **down** *phr v* [T] to lower the price of goods 〔商品〕降價: *These winter coats have been marked down from £45 to £25.* 這些冬季大衣已從四十五英鎊降價到二十五英鎊。

mark out *phr v* **1** [T **mark** sthg ↔ **out**] to draw lines round an area 劃線於〔一個區域〕四周: *They marked out the tennis court with white paint.* 他們用白漆劃出網球場地。 **2 mark someone out for something** to show that someone is suitable for something 表明某人適合於某事物: *Her powerful speeches marked her out for political success.* 她有力的演說表明她必能在政治上取得成就。

★**marked** /mɑrkt; mɑːkt/ *adj* **1** noticeable 顯著的; 明顯的: *He showed a marked lack of interest.* 他用顯縮乏興趣。 **2 a marked man** a man who is in danger and being watched by an enemy 受(敵方)監視的人 –**markedly** /ˈmɑrkɪdli; ˈmɑːkɪdli/ *adv*: *They have markedly different approaches to the problem.* 他們對這個問題的處理辦法截然不同。

mark·er /ˈmɑrkə; ˈmɑːkər/ *n* **1** a large pen 大墨水筆; 記號筆: *a felt-tip marker* 氈頭筆 **2** an object which shows where something is 標識: *a boundary marker* 界標

★★**mar·ket¹** /ˈmɑrkɪt; ˈmɑːkɪt/ *n* **1** a building or open place where people meet to buy and sell goods 市場; 集市: *a cattle market* 牲口市場 | *an antiques market* 古董市場 **2** an area or country where there is a demand for goods 行銷地區〔國家〕: *They sell to new markets in the Far East.* 他們向遠東的新市場銷售。 | *the home market* 國內市場 **3** demand for goods 需求; 銷路: *There's not much of a market for ice cream in the winter.* 冬天對冰淇淋的需求量不大。 **4 on the market** able to be bought 在市場上買賣; 登記出售: *Their house is now on the market.* 他們登記了把房子出售。

market² *v* [T] to offer something for sale and try to encourage people to buy it 銷售; 推銷: *The firm markets many types of goods.* 這家公司銷售許多類型的商品。 –**marketable** *adj*

market gar·den /ˌ··· ˈ··/ *n BrE* an area for growing vegetables and fruit for sale 〔英式〕〔以供應市場為目的的〕商品果〔菜〕圃

★**mar·ket·ing** /ˈmɑrkɪtɪŋ; ˈmɑːkɪtɪŋ/ *n* [U] the business activities concerned with advertising and selling 銷售; 經銷

mar·ket·place /ˈmɑrkɪtˌpleɪs; ˈmɑːkɪtˌpleɪs/ *n* **1** an open area where a market is held 集市; 市場 **2 the marketplace** the business of buying and selling in competition with others 〔競爭性的〕商業買賣: *The marketplace is the real test for a new product.* 市場交易是對新產品的真正考驗。

mark·ings /'markɪŋz; 'maːkɪŋz/ *n* [pl] coloured marks on an animal or bird 〔獸類或鳥類的〕斑點: *The leopard has beautiful markings.* 豹有美麗的斑點。

marks·man /'marksmən; 'maːksmən/ *n* **marksmen** a person who can shoot well with a gun 神槍手

mark·up /'mark,ʌp; 'maːk-ʌp/ *n* the amount by which a price is raised by the seller to allow him to make a profit 標高的價格: *a markup of 20% on cigarettes* 香煙售價標高百分之二十

mar·ma·lade /'marml,ed; 'maːməleɪd/ *n* [U] a kind of JAM, made from oranges or similar fruit 橘子醬; 果醬

ma·roon¹ /mə'run; mə'ruːn/ *v* [T] to leave someone alone in a place where no one lives, with no way of escaping 把〔某人〕放逐到渺無人煙的地方: *The boat sank and we were marooned on a little island.* 船沉沒了, 我們流落到一個小島上。

maroon² *n, adj* [U] dark red-brown colour 褐紫紅色(的) –see picture on page 243 見 243 頁彩圖

mar·quee /mar'ki; maːˈkiː/ *n* a large tent used for outdoor public events 〔用來進行戶外公眾活動的〕大帳篷

mar·quis /'markwɪs; 'maːkwɨs/ *n* (also 又作 **marquess**) the title of a nobleman of high rank 候爵

✦**mar·riage** /'mærɪdʒ; 'mærɪdʒ/ *n* **1** [C] the act of making a man and woman husband and wife by a legal ceremony 結婚; 婚禮: *The marriage took place in church.* 婚禮在教堂舉行。 **2** [C;U] the relationship between a man and wife 婚姻關係: *They have had twenty years of happy marriage together.* 他們在一起已過了二十年快樂的婚姻生活。| *This is his second marriage.* 這是他的第二次婚姻。 **3** [U] the state of being married 婚姻狀況: *I've never seen the advantage of marriage myself.* 我自己是從來沒看到過結婚的好處。

✦**mar·ried** /'mærɪd; 'mærɪd/ *adj* **1** having a husband or wife 已婚的: *a married man* 已婚男子 | *She's much happier single than married.* 她單身比結婚快樂得多。 **2 married to** having someone as a husband or wife 與〔某人〕結為夫妻的: *She's married to my cousin.* 她嫁給了我表兄。 **3 get married** to take a person as your husband or wife 結婚: *I'm getting married next week.* 我下週結婚。

mar·row /'mæro, 'mærəʊ/ *n* **1** [U] the soft fatty substance in the hollow centre of bones 骨髓 **2** [C] a long dark green vegetable 西葫蘆

✦**mar·ry** /'mæri; 'mæri/ *v* **married, marrying** **1** [I;T] to take a person as your husband or

wife in a legal ceremony (和...)結婚: *Will you marry me?* 你會和我結婚嗎? **2** [T] to perform the ceremony of marriage 主持婚禮: *An old priest married them.* 一位年老的牧師為他們主持了婚禮。| *We were married by the ship's captain.* 船長為我們主持了婚禮。

Mars /marz; maːz/ *n* the PLANET nearest to the Earth and fourth away from the sun 火星

marsh /marʃ; maːʃ/ *n* [C;U] an area of soft and wet low land 沼澤(地帶) –**marshy** *adj*

mar·shal¹ /'marʃəl; maːʃəl/ *n* **1** an officer of the highest rank in certain armed forces 陸軍元帥 **2** an official who helps with the organization of a public ceremony or event 司儀官; 典禮官 **3** *AmE* a chief officer of a police or fire-fighting force 〔美式〕警察局長; 消防隊長

marshal² *v* **-ll-** (**-l-** *AmE* 〔美式〕) [T] **1** to arrange facts in good order 整理; 安排: *He gave a good speech, and he marshalled the arguments very clearly.* 他作了一次不錯的演講, 把論點列舉得井井有條。 **2** to lead or show the way to the correct place 引領; 指引: *Police were on duty to marshall the crowds.* 警察值勤引領人羣。

marsh·mal·low /'marʃ,mælo; ,maːʃ'mæləʊ/ *n* a light round soft sweet 軟鬆糖果, 棉花糖

mar·su·pi·al /mar'sjupɪəl; maːˈsjuːpɪəl/ *n tech* a type of animal which carries its young in a pocket of skin on the mother's body 〔術語〕有袋動物

mar·tial /'marʃəl; 'maːʃəl/ *adj* [only before a noun 只用於名詞前] concerning war or soldiers 戰爭的; 軍人的: *martial music* 軍樂 | *The country is now under martial law.* 這個國家現在實行軍事管制。

martial arts /,·· '·/ *n* [pl] sports concerned with fighting skills that come from China or Japan, for examlpe JUDO 〔中國或日本的〕武術〔如柔道〕

Mar·tian /'marʃɪən; 'maːʃən/ *adj, n* an imaginary creature from MARS 〔虛構的〕火星人(的)

mar·tyr¹ /'martɚ; 'maːtə/ *n* **1** a person who is killed or made to suffer for their beliefs 殉難者; 殉道者: *the early Christian martyrs* 早期的基督教殉道者 **2** someone who suffers in the hope of receiving sympathy (a word used to express disapproval) 為博得同情而受苦難者〔含貶義〕: *I think she actually enjoys being a martyr.* 我想她實際上喜歡受苦以博得別人同情。

martyr² *v* [T] to kill someone or make them suffer for their beliefs 對〔堅持某種信仰者〕進行屠殺或加以折磨

mar·tyr·dom /'martɚdəm; 'maːtədəm/ *n* [U] the death or suffering of a martyr 殉難; 殉身; 折磨

mar·vel¹ /'marvl; 'maːvəl/ *n* a wonderful thing or example 令人驚奇的事或事例; 奇蹟: *The operation was a marvel of medical skill.*

M

這手術是醫療技術的傑作。

marvel² v -ll- (-l- AmE 【美式】) [I;T;+that] to wonder or be surprised at something 驚奇; 對⋯⋯感到驚異: *We marvelled **at** their skill.* 對於他們的技術，我們讚嘆不已。| *They marvelled that he was unharmed.* 他們十分驚奇他可以安然無恙。

mar·vel·lous /ˈmɑrvləs; ˈmɑːvələs/ adj (**marvelous** AmE 【美式】) wonderful or surprisingly good 了不起的; 絕妙的; 神奇的: *What marvellous weather!* 天氣真是好極了！| *That's a marvellous idea!* 那主意太妙啦！ **–marvellously** adv

Marx·is·m /ˈmɑrksɪzm; ˈmɑːksɪzəm/ n [U] the teachings of Karl Marx on which COMMUNISM is based 馬克思主義 **–Marxist** n, adj

mar·zi·pan /ˈmɑrzə,pæn; ˈmɑːzɪˌpæn/ n [U] a sweet paste made of almonds (ALMOND), sugar, and egg, used for making sweets and covering cakes〔用來做糖果、澆在糕餅上的〕杏仁蛋白糊

mas·ca·ra /mæsˈkærə; mæˈskɑːrə/ n [U] a substance used for colouring a person's eyelashes (EYELASH) and making them look longer 睫毛膏

mas·cot /ˈmæskət; ˈmæskət/ n something that is thought to bring good luck to a particular person〔被認為會帶來好運的〕吉祥物: *I always carry this keyring; it's my lucky mascot.* 我一直帶着這個鑰匙圈，它是我的幸運吉祥物。

mas·cu·line /ˈmæskjəlɪn; ˈmæskjʊlɪn/ adj 1 having the qualities of a man 有男子特徵的 **–see** 見 FEMALE (USAGE 用法) 2 belonging to the class in grammar that includes words for males〔語法中〕陽性的: *"Drake" is the masculine word for "duck".* drake 是 duck 的陽性詞。 **–masculinity** /ˌmæskjəˈlɪnəti; ˌmæskjʊˈlɪnəti/ n [U]

mash /mæʃ; mæʃ/ v [T] to crush food into a soft substance after cooking 把〔熟食〕搗成泥狀: *Mash the potatoes with a fork.* 用叉子把馬鈴薯搗成泥狀。

mask¹ /mæsk; mɑːsk/ n a covering over all or part of someone's face 面罩; 面具: *bank robbers wearing masks* 戴面具的銀行劫匪 | *a surgeon's mask* 外科醫生用的口罩 **–masked** adj

mask² v [T] to keep something from being noticed 掩飾; 掩蓋〔某事物〕: *His smile masked his anger.* 他的笑容掩蓋了怒氣。| *The sugar masked the bitter taste of the medicine.* 糖蓋住了藥的苦味。

mas·o·chis·m /ˈmæzə,kɪzəm; ˈmæsəkɪzəm/ n [U] the wish to be hurt in order to gain pleasure, especially sexual pleasure〔尤指色情〕受虐狂 **–masochist** n **–masochistic** /-ˈkɪstɪk; -ˈkɪstɪk/ adj: *masochistic tendencies* 受虐狂的傾向

ma·son /ˈmesn; ˈmeɪsən/ n 1 someone who is skilled at making things with stone 石匠

2 **Mason** a FREEMASON 共濟會會員

Ma·son·ic /məˈsɑnɪk; məˈsɒnɪk/ adj connected with Freemasons (FREEMASON) 共濟會(會員)的

ma·son·ry /ˈmesn̩ri; ˈmeɪsənri/ n [U] brick or stone from which a building is made〔建築物的〕磚石部分: *She was hit by a piece of falling masonry.* 她被(建築物上)落下的一塊石頭砸着了。

mas·que·rade /ˌmæskəˈred; ˌmæskəˈreɪd/ v **masqueraded, masquerading** [I] to pretend to be 假冒; 假扮: *He masqueraded **as** her brother.* 他冒充是她的兄弟。

★**mass¹** /mæs; mæs/ n 1 [C] a solid lump 團; 塊; 堆: *a solid mass **of** rock* 一塊大石頭 2 **masses** [pl] infml a large number〔非正式〕大量; 大宗: *Help yourself; I've got masses **of** spare copies.* 你隨便拿; 我有好多多餘的複本。 3 [U] tech the amount of physical material in something〔術語〕質量: *A litre of gas has less mass than a litre of water.* 一升氣體的質量比一升水的質量少。 4 **Mass** a religious service in some Christian churches in which people share bread and wine 彌撒 5 **the masses** ordinary people considered as a group 羣眾; 平民: *entertainment for the masses* 大眾娛樂

★**mass²** v [I;T] to gather together in large numbers 聚集; 聚攏: *Crowds massed at the airport to greet the President.* 人羣聚集在機場歡迎總統。

mass³ adj [only before a noun 只用於名詞前] of or for a large number of people 大眾的; 大量的: *a mass murderer* 殺了很多人的兇手 | *mass unemployment* 大量市民失業

mas·sa·cre /ˈmæsəkər; ˈmæsəkəʳ/ v **massacred, massacring** [T] to kill a large number of people in a violent and cruel manner 大屠殺 **–see** 見 KILL¹ (USAGE用法) **–massacre** n

mas·sage /məˈsɑʒ; ˈmæsɑːʒ/ v **massaged, massaging** [T] to press and rub someone's body with your hands to take away pain or stiffness 按摩; 推拿 **–massage** n [C;U]: *His trainer gave him a massage.* 他的教練給他按摩。

mas·seur /mæˈsɜr; mæˈsɜːʳ/ n a person who gives massages; a woman masseur can be called a **masseuse** 按摩師〔女按摩師叫 **masseuse**〕

★**mas·sive** /ˈmæsɪv; ˈmæsɪv/ adj extremely large, strong, or powerful 極大的; 結實的; 強有力的: *a massive increase in the cost of living* 生活費用大幅上漲 | *massive castle walls* 城堡的高大圍牆 **–massively** adv

mass me·di·a /ˌ· ˈ··/ n [+sing/pl verb] **the mass media** the means of giving information to the general public, through radio, television, and the newspapers 大眾傳播媒介〔如廣播, 電視, 報刊〕

mass-pro·duce /ˌ· ·ˈ·/ v **mass-produced, mass-producing** [U] to make large quan-

M

tities of an object in a factory〔工廠〕大量生產: *cheap mass-produced furniture* 成批生產的廉價家具 –**mass-production** *n* [U]

mast /mæst; mɑːst/ *n* **1** a long upright pole for carrying sails on a ship 桅杆 **2** a pole for radio or television aerials (AERIAL) or for a flag 天線桿; 旗桿

mas·ter¹ /ˈmæstə; ˈmɑːstəʳ/ *n* **1** a man in control of people, animals, or things 主人: *The slaves rebelled against their masters.* 奴隸反抗他們的主人。| *The dog has been trained to carry its master's newspaper.* 這條狗已被訓練到能為主人取報紙。 **2** a male teacher 男教師: *the history master* 歷史教師 **3** a man of great skill in art or in working with his hands 藝術大師; 手藝高超的人: *The painting is the work of a master.* 這幅畫是一位藝術大師的作品。

master² *adj* [only before a noun 只用於名詞前] **1** most important 最重要的: *the master bedroom* 主臥室 **2** having a lot of skill and experience 技術熟練的, 有經驗的: *a master plumber* 身手不凡的管子工 | *a master chef* 手藝高明的廚師。

master³ *v* [T] **1** to learn something thoroughly, or gain a lot of skill in managing something 掌握; 精通: *It takes years to master a new language.* 掌握一門新語言要花好幾年時間。| *Master the art of public speaking in six easy lessons!* 通過六篇易學課程, 掌握當眾演說藝術! **2** to learn to control a bad feeling 學會控制〔壞的感情〕: *I've never been able to master my fear of spiders.* 我從來不能克制自己對蜘蛛的恐懼。

mas·ter·ful /ˈmæstəfəl; ˈmɑːstəfəl/ *adj* showing full control and understanding of people and situations 好支配人的; 專橫的 – **masterfully** *adv*

master key /ˈ·· ·/ *n* a key that will open several different locks 萬能鑰匙

mas·ter·ly /ˈmæstəlɪ; ˈmɑːstəli/ *adj* extremely clever and skilful 巧妙的; 熟練的: *a masterly move* 一着妙棋

mas·ter·mind /ˈmæstəˌmaɪnd; ˈmɑːstəmaɪnd/ *n* a very clever person who is responsible for a plan 智囊; 出謀劃策者: *the mastermind behind the robbery* 搶劫的幕後策劃者 –**mastermind** *v* [T]

Master of Arts /ˌ··· ·ˈ·/ *n* –see 見 MA

Master of Science /ˌ··· ·ˈ·/ *n* –see 見 MSc

mas·ter·piece /ˈmæstəˌpis; ˈmɑːstəpiːs/ *n* an extremely good painting, book, or other work of art which is the best a person has done〔藝術品的〕傑作; 名作

mas·ter·y /ˈmæstərɪ; ˈmɑːstəri/ *n* **1** [U] excellence in skill or art 精通; 熟巧: *He shows complete mastery of the dance routine.* 他顯示出對固定的舞步極為精通。 **2** full control over something 完全控制: *He finally achieved mastery over his fear.* 他終於克制住了自己的恐懼。

mas·tiff /ˈmæstɪf; ˈmæstɪf/ *n* a large powerful guard dog 大馴犬

mat /mæt, mæt/ *n* **1** a small piece of rough strong material used for covering part of a floor 蓆墊; 地蓆 **2** a small piece of material placed on a table to protect its surface when something hot or wet is put on it〔桌上用的〕小墊子

☆**match¹** /mætʃ; mætʃ/ *n* **1** [C] a short thin stick of wood that produces a flame when it is struck against a rough surface 火柴: *a box of matches* 一盒火柴 **2** [C] a game or sports event (體育)比賽: *a football match* 足球賽 | *a chess match* 棋賽 **3** [sing] a thing that is like another thing or is suitable to be put together with another thing 相似〔匹配〕之物: *The hat and shoes are a perfect match.* 這頂帽子和這雙鞋子完全相配。 **4** no **match for someone** not as good as someone in some way 和某人無法匹敵: *He's good, but he's no match for a real professional.* 他不錯, 但還比不過真正的專家。

☆**match²** *v* **1** [I;T] to be like something or suitable for use with something 和〔某事物〕相似〔相配〕: *The curtains don't match the paint.* 窗簾不配油漆的顏色。| *The curtains and paint don't match.* 窗簾和油漆顏色色不協調。| *a brown skirt with a jacket to match* 有夾克衫相配的啡色裙子 **2** [T] to find something like something or suitable for use with something 找與〔某事物〕相像或相配的東西: *I'm trying to match this yellow wool.* 我在找可以和這黃色毛線相配的東西。 **3** [T] to be equal to something or find an equal to something 是〔某事物的〕對手; 可以和〔某事物〕較量: *a book which doesn't match the standard of his earlier ones* 這本書比不上他以往寫的那些書的水準 | *This hotel can't be matched for service and food.* 在服務質量和伙食方面, 這家旅館是無可匹敵的。 **4** well-**matched** suitable for each other or to compete with each other 相配的; 相稱的: *John and his wife are well-matched.* 約翰和他太太是十分匹配的一對。| *The two fighters aren't very well-matched.* 這兩名拳擊手不很相配。

match·box /ˈmætʃˌbɑks; ˈmætʃbɒks/ *n* a small box in which matches are sold 火柴盒

match·ing /ˈmætʃɪŋ; ˈmætʃɪŋ/ *adj* [only before a noun 只用於名詞前] the same or suited 相同的; 協調的: *The twins wore matching T-shirts.* 這對雙胞胎穿着一樣的T恤衫。

match·less /ˈmætʃlɪs; ˈmætʃləs/ *adj fml* so good that nothing can equal it《正式》無敵的; 無比的: *her matchless beauty* 她的美貌絕世無雙

match·mak·er /ˈmætʃˌmekə; ˈmætʃˌmeɪkəʳ/ *n* a person who tries to arrange marriages or relationships 媒人

mate¹ /met; meɪt/ *n* **1** a friend or a person you work with 同事; 夥伴; 朋友: *He's a mate of mine.* 他是我的一個夥伴。| *my old*

M

schoolmates 我的老同學 **2** *BrE infml* a friendly way of addressing a man (used mainly by men)〔英式，非正式〕老兄；老弟；夥計〔主要用於男人間，是對男子的友好稱呼〕: *What time is it, mate?* 老兄，幾點鐘啦？ **3** the rank below a ship's captain〔船上的〕大副: *the first mate* 大副 **4** an animal's sexual partner 動物的配偶: *the search for a mate* 尋找配偶

mate² *v* **mated, mating** [I] to come together sexually for the production of young 成配偶；交配: *Birds mate in the spring.* 鳥在春季交配。

★★ **ma·te·ri·al¹** /məˈtɪrɪəl; məˈtɪriəl/ *n* **1** [C;U] a substance from which something is or can be made 材料；原料: *Building materials are expensive.* 建築材料很昂貴。| *material for floor coverings* 鋪地板的材料 **2** [C;U] cloth 布；衣料: *a few metres of dress material* 幾米長的衣料 **3** [U] information for use in a book, film, or play〔書籍、影片或戲劇的〕素材；資料: *research material* 研究資料 **4 materials** [pl] the things you use for an activity 用具；設備: *writing materials* 文具

*material² adj of or concerning possessions and money, not things of the mind or soul 物質的: material comforts 物質享受 | Our material needs are food and clothing. 我們的物質需要是食品和衣物。–materially adv

ma·te·ri·al·is·m /məˈtɪrɪəlˌɪzəm; məˈtɪriəlɪzəm/ *n* [U] a great interest in and desire for possessions and money (a word used to express disapproval) 實利主義；物質主義〔含貶義〕–**materialistic** /-ˈlɪstɪk; -ˈlɪstɪk/ *adj* –**materialist** *adj, n*

ma·te·ri·al·ize /məˈtɪrɪəlˌaɪz; məˈtɪriəlaɪz/ *v* **materialized, materializing** (also 又作 **materialise** *BrE*〔英式〕) [I] (of something planned or expected) to become real or actual〔計劃或期望的某事〕實現: *His hopes never materialized.* 他的希望從未實現。

ma·ter·nal /məˈtɜːnl; məˈtɜːnl/ *adj* **1** like a mother or received from a mother 母親似的；從母親處得到的: *maternal feelings* 母親般的感情 **2** [only before a noun 只用於名詞前] related through the mother's part of the family 母系的: *my maternal grandfather* 我的外祖父 –**maternally** *adv*

ma·ter·ni·ty /məˈtɜːnəti; məˈtɜːnti/ *adj* [only before a noun 只用於名詞前] concerning or belonging to the mother before the baby is born, and to giving birth 孕婦的；產婦的: *a maternity dress* 孕婦服裝 | *a maternity hospital* 產科醫院 –**maternity** *n* [U]

math·e·ma·ti·cian /ˌmæθəməˈtɪʃən; ˌmæθ‚məˈtɪʃən/ *n* a person who studies or who is skilled in mathematics 數學家

math·e·mat·ics /ˌmæθəˈmætɪks; ˌmæθ‚ˈmætɪks/ *n* [U] (also 又作 **maths** /mæθs; mæθs/, **math** /mæθ; mæθ/ *AmE*〔美式〕) the science of numbers and of the structure and measurement of shapes 數學 –**mathematical** *adj* –**mathematically** /-klɪ; -kli/ *adv*

mat·i·née /ˌmætɪˈneɪ; ˈmæt‚neɪ/ *n* a performance of a play or film given in the afternoon〔戲劇或電影的〕日場；下午場

ma·tric·u·late /məˈtrɪkjəˌlet; məˈtrɪkj‚leɪt/ *v* **matriculated, matriculating** *fml* [I] to pass an examination and gain entrance to a university〔正式〕〔通過考試〕獲大學錄取 –**matriculation** /məˌtrɪkjəˈleʃən; məˌtrɪkj‚ˈleɪʃən/ *n* [U]

mat·ri·mo·ny /ˈmætrəˌmoni; ˈmætr‚məni/ *n* [U] *fml* the state of being married〔正式〕婚姻(生活) –**matrimonial** /ˌmætrəˈmonɪəl; ˌmætr‚ˈməunɪəl◂/ *adj*

ma·trix /ˈmetrɪks; ˈmeɪtrɪks/ *n* **matrices** /-trɪˌsiz; -tr‚siːz/ *or* **matrixes** *tech* a set of numbers, figures, or signs shown in rows in table form〔術語〕矩陣

ma·tron /ˈmetrən; ˈmeɪtrən/ *n* **1** a female nursing officer who has control over the nurses in a hospital 護士長 **2** a woman in a boarding school who looks after the health of the children〔學校的〕女舍監 **3** *lit* an older married woman〔文〕〔年長的〕已婚婦女

matt /mæt; mæt/ *adj* having a surface which is dull rather than shiny 表面無光澤的: *Do you want a gloss or matt finish on these photos?* 這些照片的表面你是要拋光還是不要有光澤？

mat·ted /ˈmætɪd; ˈmæt‚d/ *adj* twisted in a thick untidy mass 纏結在一起的: *matted hair* 亂蓬蓬的頭髮

★★ **mat·ter¹** /ˈmætɚ; ˈmætəʳ/ *n* **1** [C] something you have to deal with or give attention to 事情；問題: *There are several important matters we should discuss.* 我們有幾件重要的事應該討論一下。| *a business matter* 生意上的事 **2 make matters worse** to make a bad situation even more serious 使情況更糟: *I lost my purse and, to make matters worse, my doorkey was in it.* 我丟了錢包，更糟的是，我的房門鑰匙在裡面。 **3 the matter** a trouble or a cause of trouble or illness 麻煩事；麻煩或毛病的起因: *Is something the matter? Are you all right?* 有甚麼麻煩嗎？你沒事兒吧？ | *What's the matter with the radio?* 這收音機出甚麼毛病了？ **4** [U] the physical material which makes up the world and everything which can be seen or touched 物質 **5** [U] things of a particular kind for a particular purpose 材料: *reading matter* 閱讀材料 | *waste matter* 廢料 **6 as a matter of fact a** in fact 實際上；事實上: *"I don't suppose you've got a key." "No, as a matter of fact I haven't."* "我想你沒有鑰匙。" "是的，我確實沒有。" **b** you use this expression when you are saying something unexpected after the last thing 事實上，實際

上: *"Would you like a chocolate?" "As a matter of fact, I don't eat chocolates."* "你要來塊巧克力嗎?" "事實上, 我不吃巧克力。" **7 a matter of: a** a little more or less than …左右; 大約: *We only had to wait a matter of ten minutes.* 我們只要等十分鐘左右。**b** a question of …的問題: *Answering this question is just a matter of using your intelligence.* 回答這個問題只是用你的智力而已。| *a matter of opinion* 看法不同的問題 **8 a matter of course** a usual event 理所當然的事: *When I go out of the house I lock the door as a matter of course.* 當我出時, 鎖門是理所當然的事。**9 a matter of life or death** something very serious and urgent 生死攸關的事情 **10 for that matter** a phrase to show that what you have said about one thing can also be said about another 至於那件事; 說到這一點〔表示所說的一件事與另一件事相同〕: *I've never approved of divorce and nor, for that matter, does your father.* 我從來不贊成離婚, 在這點上你父親也不贊成。**11 no matter** it makes no difference 無論; 不管: *We'll finish the job, no matter how long it takes.* 不管花多少時間, 我們都要完成這項工作。

⋆**matter²** *v* [I] to be important 要緊; 有關係: *It doesn't matter if I miss the train, because there's another one in ten minutes.* 趕不上火車也沒關係, 因為十分鐘後還有一班車。| *I don't think anybody matters to her apart from herself.* 我認為除了她自己以外, 沒有人對她來說是要緊的。

matter-of-fact /ˌ···⋅◂/ *adj* concerned with facts, not imagination or feelings 就事論事的; 並非想像的; 不帶感情的: *She described the attack in a very matter-of-fact manner.* 她就事論事地認真描述了這次進攻。

mat·ting /ˈmætɪŋ; ˈmætɪŋ/ *n* [U] a thick woven material used for floor covering〔編織的〕地蓆

mat·tress /ˈmætrɪs; ˈmætrɪs/ *n* a thick mat filled with feathers or springs, for sleeping on 牀墊

ma·ture /məˈtjuə; məˈtʃʊər/ *adj* **1** fully grown and developed 成熟的 **2** sensible and typical of an adult 明智的; 有成年人特點的: *a mature approach to life* 對待生活的明智態度 **3** ready to be eaten or drunk (used of cheese or wine) 可以吃的; 醸熟的〔指乾酪或酒〕 –opposite 反義 **immature – mature** *v* **matured, maturing** [I;T]: *After six years the wine will have matured.* 這酒六年後就能醸成。**–maturity** *n* [U]

mature stu·dent /ˌ··· ˈ···/ *n BrE* a student at a university or college who begins their course at the age of 25 or over〔英式〕成年大學生〔25 歲或以上開始讀大學的學生〕

maud·lin /ˈmɔːdlɪn; ˈmɔːdlɪn/ *adj* stupidly sad, probably because of drinking too much alcohol〔酒後〕傷感的

maul /mɔːl; mɔːl/ *v* [T] **1** (of animals) to hurt someone badly by tearing their flesh〔動物〕撕破〔某人〕皮肉; 抓破; 打傷: *The hunter was mauled by a lion.* 獵人為獅子所傷。**2** to handle something roughly or in an unwelcome way 粗手粗腳地擺弄〔某物〕

mau·so·le·um /ˌmɔːsəˈliəm; ˌmɔːsəˈlɪəm/ *n* a large and decorative stone building built over a grave or graves 陵墓

mauve /məʊv; məʊv/ *adj, n* [U] pale purple 淡紫色(的)

mav·e·rick /ˈmævrɪk; ˈmævərɪk/ *n* someone, especially a politician, who is determined to be different to the rest of the group (a word used to express disapproval)〔尤指政治家〕持異見者〔含貶義〕

max. *adj* a written abbreviation for〔縮〕= MAXIMUM 最高的; 最大的: *max headroom 4 metres* 淨空最高四米

max·im /ˈmæksɪm; ˈmæksɪm/ *n* a short saying that expresses a general truth 格言; 箴言: *"Waste not, want not" is her favourite maxim.* "不浪費, 不愁缺"是她最喜愛的格言。

max·i·mize /ˈmæksəˌmaɪz; ˈmæksɪˌmaɪz/ *v* **maximized, maximizing** (also 又作 **maximise** *BrE*〔英式〕) [T] to increase something to the greatest possible size 把〔某物〕增加到最大限度: *We must maximize our chances of success.* 我們必須極力增加成功的可能性。

⋆**max·i·mum** /ˈmæksəməm; ˈmæksɪməm/ *adj* [only before a noun 只用於名詞前] the largest, or most that is possible 最大的; 最多的: *Today's maximum temperature will be 17 degrees.* 今天最高溫度十七度。| *driving at maximum speed* 以最高速度行駛 –opposite 反義 **minimum – maximum** *n* : *This lamp will give you the maximum of light.* 這盞燈會提供給你最充足的光線。| *I smoke a maximum of 15 cigarettes a day.* 我一天最多抽十五支煙。

⋆⋆**may** /me; meɪ/ *v* [modal verb 情態動詞] **1** used to show that something is possible 可能; 也許〔表示可能性〕: *He may come or he may not.* 他可能來也可能不來。| *What he says may be true.* 他的話可能是真的。| *There may be a link between this drug and various forms of cancer.* 這種藥可能和多種癌症有關係。| *I don't know where John is. He may have missed his train.* 我不知道約翰在哪兒, 他也許沒趕上火車。**2** *fml* to be allowed to do something〔正式〕可以; 准許〔做某事〕: *You may come in now.* 現在你可以進來了。–see Study Note on page 1318 見 1318 頁學習提示 **3 may I, may we, etc** a very polite way of asking someone if they will let you do something 請問我/我們可以…嗎?〔詢問某人是否讓自己做某事的禮貌表達法〕: *May I use your telephone?* 我可以用一下你的電話嗎? | *May we go home now?* 我們現在可以回家嗎? **4** *fml* used when you are expressing a wish that something will happen〔正式〕祝; 願〔表示願望〕: *May you always be happy together.* 祝你們永遠快樂。**5**

M

may as well a phrase you use to say that you are going to do something because there is nothing else that you really want to do 不妨；還是…的好〔用於因為沒有其他任何事要做而打算做某事〕: *If we're not going out we may as well go to bed.* 如果我們不出去，還是去睡覺為好。

May *n* the 5th month of the year 五月

★**may·be** /ˈmebɪ; ˈmeɪbi/ *adv* perhaps 也許: *"Are you coming tonight?" "Maybe."* "你今天晚上來嗎？" "也許來。" | *Maybe I ought to phone her.* 也許我該給她打個電話。| *There were a lot of people there — maybe a couple of hundred.* 那兒有好多人 —— 也許有幾百個。

> ■ USAGE 用法: **Maybe** and **perhaps** are commonly used in suggestions, requests, and orders to make them sound less forceful and, therefore, more polite ☆ **maybe** 和 **perhaps** 常用於建議，請求和命令中以緩和語氣，顯得更為禮貌些: **Maybe/Perhaps** *we ought to go now.* 也許我們應該現在就走。| **Maybe/Perhaps** *you should phone your mother.* 也許你該打電話給你母親。| *Could you* **maybe/perhaps** *help me carry these boxes to the car?* 也許你能幫我把這些箱子抬到車上？| **Maybe/perhaps** *you'd like to phone me this evening.* 也許你想今晚打電話給我。They can also be used to "soften" criticism ☆ 它們也可用來"緩和"批評: *He's not exactly fat, but he's* **maybe/perhaps** *a bit overweight.* 確切地說他並不肥胖，但也許有點超重。

may·day /ˈme,de; ˈmeɪdeɪ/ *n* **1** a radio signal used as a call for help from a ship or plane〔輪船或飛機的〕無線電求救信號 **2 May Day** 1st May, when public events and processions are held to mark the coming of spring, or by workers' organizations 五一(勞動)節；五朔節

mayn't /ment; meɪənt/ *v* short for 〖縮〗= "may not"

may·on·naise /,meə'nez; ,meɪə'neɪz/ *n* [U] a thick yellow SAUCE eaten with salads (SALAD) and other cold food〔拌色拉和其他冷食的〕蛋黃醬

mayor /ˈmeə; ˈmeəʳ/ *n* a person elected each year to be the head of a city or town council; a woman mayor or the wife of a mayor is called a **mayoress** 市長〔女市長或市長夫人叫 **mayoress**〕

may·pole /ˈme,pol; ˈmeɪpəʊl/ *n* a tall decorated pole round which people dance on MAY DAY 五朔節花柱

maze /mez; meɪz/ *n* a system of twisting passages which it is difficult to find your way through 迷津；迷宮: *lost in the maze* 在迷宮裡迷路 | *a maze* **of** *narrow winding streets* 迷宮似的狹窄而曲折的街道

★**me** /mɪ; mi, *strong* 強讀 mi; miː/ *pron* [used as the object of a verb 用作動詞的受詞] the person who is speaking 我: *Can you see me?* 你看得見我嗎？| *That's me on the left of the photograph.* 照片上左邊那人是我。| *He handed the book to me.* 他把書遞給我。| *She bought me a drink.* 她給我買了杯飲料。

> ■ USAGE 用法: In conversation we usually use **me** after *as*, *than*, and *be* ☆ **me** 在會話中常用於 *as*, *than* 和 *be* 的後面 : *He isn't as thin as* **me.** 他不像我那麼瘦。| *He's fatter than* **me.** 他比我胖。| *It's* **me.** 是我。In formal language we usually try to express the idea in a different way ☆ 在正式語言中，通常盡量用不同的方法表達: *He isn't as thin as* **I** *am.* 他不像我那麼瘦。| *He's fatter than* **I** *am.* 他比我胖。| *I am the one/the person/etc.* 我就是這個人。The same is true of **her, him, us, them.** ☆ **her, him, us, them** 也是同樣情況。

mead·ow /ˈmɛdo; ˈmɛdəʊ/ *n* [C;U] a field with grass and flowers growing on it 草地

mea·gre /ˈmigɚ; ˈmiːɡəʳ/ *adj* very small in amount 極少量的: *He cannot exist on his meagre income.* 他沒法靠自己微薄的收入生存。| *a meagre diet* 粗茶淡飯

★**meal** /mil; miːl/ *n* **1** [C] an amount of food eaten at one time 一餐: *She cooks a hot meal in the evenings.* 晚上她總燒一頓熱飯。| *Breakfast is my favourite meal.* 早飯是我最喜愛的一餐。**2** [C] (also 又作 **mealtime**) the time when you eat a meal 進餐時間: *The whole family meets at meals.* 一家人在一起吃飯。| *When the meal was over, the men went outside.* 吃完飯，男人都走到外面去了。**3 make a meal of something** to give something more effort, consideration, or time than it deserves 對某事做得太過分；小題大作 **4** [U] grain which has been crushed into a powder〔穀類碾成的〕粉

meal·y-mouthed /ˈmilɪˈmaʊðd; ˌmiːli-ˈmaʊðd/ *adj* expressing things indirectly, not plainly, especially when something unpleasant must be said (used of people and speech; a word that expresses disapproval) 不直率的；轉彎抹角的〔指人和話；含貶義〕: *mealy-mouthed politicians* 說話轉彎抹角的政客

★**mean**[1] /min; miːn/ *v* **meant** /mɛnt; ment/ **1** [T; +(that)] not in progressive forms 不用於進行式 to represent or express a meaning 意思是；表示…的意思: *What does this French word mean?* 這個法語單詞是甚麼意思？| *The red light means "Stop".* 紅燈表示"停止"。| *The sign means that vehicles are not allowed in this area.* 這個指示牌表示車輛不能進入該地區。**2** [I;T] plan or intend something 打算；意欲: *Sorry,*

I didn't mean to interrupt. 對不起, 我不是有意打擾的。| *I've been meaning to ask you — how did you get on at the interview?* 我一直想問你——你面試進展如何？| *The flowers were meant for you, not her.* 那些花原打算給你, 不是給她的。| *She said Tuesday, but she meant Thursday.* 她説的是星期二, 但她是指星期四。

□ USEFUL PATTERNS 有用句型
to mean something; to mean something for someone; to mean to do something

3 [T;+(that)] not in progressive forms 不用於進行式] to be a sign of 意味着; 是...的徵兆: *Those clouds mean rain.* 那些雲是下雨的徵兆。| *A red rose means "I love you".* 紅玫瑰表示"我愛你"。**4 I mean** you use "I mean" when you want to explain more clearly or in detail something that you have just said 我的意思是〔用於想把自己剛説過的內容解釋得更清楚、更詳細〕: *I don't think he can really afford it.* *I mean, it's not as if he's a rich man.* 我想事實上他負擔不起。我的意思是, 他不像是個有錢的人。**5 you mean, do you mean...?** you use these expressions when you are making sure that you have understood what someone else has just said 你的意思是...?〔用於確證自己理解了別人剛才所説的內容〕: *"He's got a new job in the City." "You mean he isn't going to go back to Ireland?"* "他在倫敦城得到一份新工作。" "你的意思是他不打算回愛爾蘭了？" **6 mean everything to, mean a lot to** to be very important to 對...很重要: *Her children mean everything to her.* 她的孩子對她來説就是一切。| *His work means a lot to him.* 他的工作對他來説十分重要。[RELATED PHRASES 相關詞組 **mean nothing to, mean very little to**] **7 be meant to do something** to be supposed to do something 應該做某事: *He's meant to be the best plumber in town.* 他應該成為鎮上最出色的管子工。| *Boys are meant to be tough.* 男孩子應該很堅強。| *You're not meant to eat the orange peel!* 你不該吃橘子皮! **8 mean business, mean it** to act with serious intentions 當真: *I'm leaving you — and I really mean it!* 我要離開你——我是當真的! | *Watch out! Your competitors mean business.* 小心! 你的競爭對手是當真的。**9 mean well** to intend to be helpful 懷好意: *She can be rather tactless, but I know she means well.* 她可能不夠圓通, 但我知道她的用意是好的。

mean² *adj* **1** not generous, and unwilling to share 吝嗇的; 小氣的: *He's so mean, he didn't even get his son a birthday present.* 他是如此吝嗇, 甚至不給自己兒子生日禮物。**2** unkind and nasty 苛刻的; 刻薄的: *Don't be mean to your little sister!* 別對你的小妹妹這麼刻薄! **3** *AmE* bad-tempered 〔美式〕壞脾氣的: *That's a mean dog; be careful!* 那是條

惡狗; 小心! **4** *lit* of low social position 〔文〕〔社會地位〕低下的; 卑賤的: *a man of mean birth* 出身低微的人 **5** [only before a noun 只用於名詞前] average (used of measurements) 平均的〔指度量衡〕: *The mean yearly rainfall is 20 inches.* 平均年降雨量是二十英寸。**6** *infml* very good 〔非正式〕出色的: *She plays a mean game of tennis.* 她打了一場很好的網球比賽。**7 no mean** a phrase you use to say that something is very good 〔某事物〕很好的: *She's no mean tennis player.* 她是位很好的網球選手。| *It's no mean achievement, winning the contest at your age.* 以你這個年齡便贏得這項比賽的冠軍是了不起的成績。–**meanly** *adv* –**meanness** *n* [U]

mean³ *n* **1** an average of a set of numbers 平均數: *The mean of 7, 9, and 14 is 10.* 7, 9, 14 的平均數是10。**2** a course of action which is the middle way of doing something and is not extreme 中庸; 中間

me·an·der /mɪˈændə; mɪˈændəʳ/ *v* [I] **1** (of rivers and roads) to have a lot of bends 〔河流、路〕蜿蜒 **2** (of people or talk) to wander slowly without any particular purpose 〔人或談話〕漫步; 閒逛; 閒聊

★mean·ing /ˈmiːnɪŋ; ˈmiːnɪŋ/ *n* [C;U] **1** what you are intended to understand from something spoken or written, from a sign or mark 意思; 意義; 含義: *One word can have several meanings.* 一個單詞可能有好幾個意思。**2 What's the meaning of this?** a phrase used when you are angry and want someone to explain what they are doing, or have done 這是甚麼意思?〔用於生氣時要求某人解釋其作為〕**3** importance or value 重要性; 價值: *He says his life has lost its meaning since his wife died.* 他説自從妻子去世以後, 他的生活已失去意義。

mean·ing·ful /ˈmiːnɪŋfl; ˈmiːnɪŋfəl/ *adj* containing an important meaning 有重要意義的: *He gave her a meaningful look.* 他朝她意味深長地看了一眼。–**meaningfully** *adv*

mean·ing·less /ˈmiːnɪŋlɪs; ˈmiːnɪŋləs/ *adj* without meaning or purpose 無意義的; 無目的的: *meaningless scribble* 無意義的塗鴉

★means /miːnz; miːnz/ *n* [plural is 複數為 **means**] **1** [C] a method 方法: *We now have the means to save most of these children.* 我們現在有拯救大多數孩子的辦法了。| *Use whatever means you think best.* 用你認為最佳的方法。**2** *fml* **a means to an end** a way of getting the result that you want 〔正式〕達到目的的方法 **3** [U] money or wealth 金錢; 財富: *Have you the means to support a family?* 你有錢維持一家生活嗎? | *a man of means* 富有的人 **4 by all means** *fml* a phrase used when you are saying politely that someone may do something 〔正式〕當然可以〔用於婉轉地表示某人可以做某事〕: *"May I borrow your paper?" "By all means".* "借你的報紙給我看可以嗎?" "當然可以。" **5**

M

by means of by using something 用〔某物〕; 借助〔某物〕: *The deaf often communicate by means of signs.* 耳聾者經常借助手勢交流。**6 by no means** *fml* not at all 《正式》一點也不: *It is by no means certain that you will be acquitted.* 很難確定你會獲判無罪。

meant /mɛnt/ ment/ the past tense and past participle of MEAN ☆ MEAN 的過去式和過去分詞

mean·time /ˈmin,taɪm; ˈmiːntaɪm/ *n* **in the meantime** in the time between two events 在兩件事間隔時間裡; 在此期間: *I'll phone for a taxi. In the meantime you must get packed.* 我打電話叫計程車, 在此期間, 你得打點好行李。

★mean·while /ˈmin,hwaɪl; ˈmiːnwaɪl/ *adv* (also 又作 **meantime** *infml* 《非正式》) during the same period of time when something else is happening 同時; 在此期間: *All my friends have been getting on well in their jobs and meanwhile I've been unemployed.* 我所有的朋友在工作上都已幹得不錯, 而我卻失業。| *Add all the ingredients except the spaghetti and cook slowly for half an hour. Meanwhile, cook the spaghetti in boiling salted water until it is just beginning to soften.* 除了意大利麵條以外, 把其他所有原料都加進去, 文火燒半小時。同時, 把意大利麵條放在加了鹽的沸水中煮, 直到剛好開始變軟為止。| *The photocopies won't be ready until half past three, so shall we sort these files out meanwhile?* 影印件要到三點半才能準備好, 在此期間我們整理一下這些文件好嗎?

mea·sles /ˈmizlz; ˈmiːzlz/ *n* [the U] an infectious illness that gives you a fever and small red spots on your skin 麻疹

meas·ly /ˈmizlɪ; ˈmiːzlɪ/ *adj infml* small and not enough 《非正式》很小的; 不充足的: *She gave me a measly little piece of cheese.* 她給了我一片小得可憐的乾酪。

mea·su·ra·ble /ˈmɛʒrəbl; ˈmeʒərəbl/ *adj* large enough to be reasonably measured or noticed 可測量的; 值得注意的: *There was a measurable improvement in productivity this year.* 今年生產率有了顯著的提高。– **measurably** *adv*

★mea·sure¹ /ˈmɛʒɚ; ˈmeʒəʳ/ *v* **measured, measuring 1** [T] to find out the size, length, amount, or degree of something 計量; 測量〔尺寸、長短、數額、程度〕: *He measured the height of the cupboard.* 他量了碗櫥的高度。| *His tailor is measuring him for a new suit.* 他的裁縫在給他量體裁新衣。**2** [T] to show or record the amount or size of something 表示或記錄〔數量或尺寸〕: *A clock measures time.* 鐘用來計時。**3** [+ complement] to have the stated size 有一定的尺寸: *He measures more round the waist than he used to.* 他的腰圍比以前粗了。| *It measures six feet from edge to edge.* 從一邊到另一邊有六英尺。

measure sthg ↔ **out** *phr v* [T] to take a measured quantity from a larger amount 〔從大數量中〕量出〔若干〕: *To make the cake, first measure out 250 grams of flour.* 做蛋糕先要量出 250 克麵粉。

measure up *phr v* [I] to show good enough qualities 符合; 夠得上: *I'm afraid he just didn't measure up* **to** *the job.* 我怕他幹這項工作不夠資格。

★mea·sure² *n* **1** an action taken to bring about a certain result 措施: *The government has promised to take measures to help the unemployed.* 政府已答應採取措施幫助失業者。**2** An amount or unit in a measuring system 計量單位: *An hour is a measure* **of** *time.* 小時是計時的單位。| *He poured himself a large measure of brandy.* 他給自己倒了大量的白蘭地。**3 a measure of, a certain measure of, some measure of** *fml* some amount of 《正式》一定數量的: *I think we can claim some measure of success in persuading young people not to smoke.* 我想我們在勸說年輕人不要吸煙方面可謂取得了一定的成效。**4 be a measure of something** to show how good something is 衡量某事物的尺度: *It's a measure of his skill in business that the firm is doing so well.* 公司辦得這麼好是衡量他經營有方的尺度。**5** an instrument used for calculating amount, length, or weight 量具; 量器: *This glass is a litre measure.* 這玻璃杯是個一公升的量器。**6 for good measure** in addition, to make everything more satisfactory 另外, 作為外加的東西: *After I'd weighed out the apples, I put in another one for good measure.* 我稱過蘋果後, 又添上了一個。

★mea·sure·ment /ˈmɛʒɚmənt; ˈmeʒəmənt/ *n* **1** [U] the act of measuring 測量 **2** [C] a length or height found by measuring 〔量得的〕長度或高度: *What's your measurement?* 你量得的長度[高度]是多少? | *I'll just take your measurements, sir.* 我這就給您量尺寸, 先生。

★meat /mit; miːt/ *n* [U] **1** the flesh of animals that is cooked and eaten 食用肉; *There's not much meat on that bone.* 那塊骨頭上沒有多少肉。**2** valuable ideas or material 有價值的想法或材料: *It was a clever speech, but there was no real meat in it.* 那是一篇巧妙的演講, 但沒有甚麼真正有價值的內容。–**meaty** *adj*

■ USAGE 用法: The meat from some animals has a different name from the name of the animal it comes from. For example, the meat from a **cow** is called **beef**, the meat from a **pig** is **pork** or **ham** or **bacon**, the meat from a **deer** is **venison,** and the meat from a **sheep** is **mutton.** But the meat from a **lamb** is **lamb,** and for birds the same word is used for both the meat and the bird it comes from ☆ 某些動物的肉和動物本身的名稱不同。例如, **cow** (牛)的肉叫**beef**(牛肉), **pig**(豬)的肉叫**pork**(豬肉) 或 **ham** (火腿), **deer** (鹿) 的肉叫**venison**(鹿肉), **sheep**(羊)的肉叫**mutton** (羊肉)。但是**lamb**(羔羊)的肉仍叫**lamb** (羔羊肉), 至於禽類的名稱和肉都是同一個單詞: *Shall we have chicken or duck for dinner?* 晚飯我們吃雞還是吃鴨?

mec·ca /'mɛkə; 'mɛkə/ *n* a place that many people wish to go to 眾人想去的地方; 勝地

me·chan·ic /mə'kænɪk; mɪ'kænɪk/ *n* a person who is skilled in using and repairing machinery 機修工; 技工: *a car mechanic* 汽車機修工

me·chan·i·cal /mə'kænɪkl; mɪ'kænɪkəl/ *adj* **1** moved, worked, or produced by machinery 用機械的; 機械製的: *a mechanical digger* 機械挖掘器 **2** done without thought or feeling 機械的; 呆板的: *She seemed distracted and nodded with a mechanical smile.* 她顯得心煩意亂, 機械地微笑着點頭。– **mechanically** /-klɪ; -klɪ/ *adv*

me·chan·ics /mə'kænɪks; mɪ'kænɪks/ *n* [U] **1** the science of the action of forces on objects 力學 **2 the mechanics of something** the ways in which something works or is carried out 某事物的運作方法, 技巧: *Now we'll have to work out the mechanics of setting up the scheme.* 現在我們得確定製訂該方案的運作方法。

mech·a·nis·m /'mɛkə,nɪzəm; 'mɛkənɪzəm/ *n* **1** the arrangement and action of the parts of a machine 機械裝置; 機件: *The clock doesn't go; there's something wrong with the mechanism.* 鐘不走了; 是機件出了毛病。**2** something which makes it possible to carry out actions 機構; 結構: *the mechanism of the brain* 大腦的結構 | *the mechanism of local government* 地方政府機構

mech·a·nize /'mɛkə,naɪz; 'mɛkənaɪz/ *v* **mechanized, mechanizing** (also 又作 **mechanise** *BrE*〖英式〗) [T] to use machines for doing work 用機器做(工作); 使機械化: *Most of the men lost their jobs when the process was mechanized.* 工序機械化後大多數工人失業了。– **mechanization** /,mɛkənə'zeʃən; ,mɛkənaɪ'zeɪʃən/ [U]

med·al /'mɛdl; 'mɛdl/ *n* a flat piece of metal, usually round or cross-shaped, given as an honour for an act of bravery or skill 獎章; 勳章: *She won a gold medal at the Olympic Games.* 她在奧林匹克運動會上贏得了一枚金牌。| *The old soldier wore his war medals on his jacket.* 這個老兵在夾克衫上佩戴了他的軍功章。

me·dal·li·on /mɪ'dæljən; mɪ̩'dælɪən/ *n* a round medal piece of jewellery worn round the neck, usually by men〔男子掛在頸部作首飾用的〕圓形大獎章; 大獎牌

med·al·list /'mɛdlɪst; 'mɛdəlɪst/ *n* (**medalist** *AmE*〖美式〗) a person who has won a medal, especially in sport〔尤指體育運動中的〕獎牌獲得者: *He was the silver medallist in the 800 metres.* 他是八百米賽跑的銀牌得主。

med·dle /'mɛdl; 'mɛdl/ *v* **meddled, meddling** [I] to interest yourself in something which is not your business 管閒事; 干涉〔他人的事〕: *I dared not meddle with the papers on his desk.* 我不敢亂動他桌上的文件。| *Don't meddle in his affairs.* 別干涉他的事。

★**me·di·a** /'midɪə; 'midɪə/ **1** the plural of MEDIUM 或 MEDIUM 的複數形式 **2 the media** [+ sing/pl verb] the newspapers, television, and radio 大眾傳播媒介: *The media have a lot of power these days.* 大眾傳播媒介現在具有很大的力量。| *Media coverage of the event was very limited.* 傳媒對這次事件的報導篇幅很有限。

med·i·ae·val /,midɪ'ivl; ,medi'iːvəl/ *adj* –see 見 MEDIEVAL

me·di·ate /'midɪ,et; 'miːdɪeɪt/ *v* **mediated, mediating** *fml*〖正式〗 **1** [I] to act as a peacemaker 調解; 斡旋: *The government mediated between the workers and the employers.* 政府在勞資之間進行調解。**2** [T] to produce an agreement by mediating 經調解解決: *The army leaders have mediated a settlement.* 軍隊領導人居中促成了和解。– **mediation** /,midɪ'eʃən; ,miːdi'eɪʃən/ *n* [U] – **mediator** *n*

★**med·i·cal**[1] /'mɛdɪkl; 'medɪkəl/ *adj* **1** concerning medicine and treating the sick 醫學的; 醫療的: *a medical student* 醫科學生 | *It is extremely difficult to get to the top of the medical profession.* 要登上醫學職業的頂峯是極其困難的。| *medical care for the elderly* 對老年人的醫療護理工作 **2** concerning the treatment of disease by medicine rather than by operation 內科的; 藥物治療的: *the hospital's new medical ward* 醫院的新內科病房 –**medically** /-klɪ; -klɪ/ *adv*

medical[2] *n infml* a thorough examination of your body〖非正式〗體格檢查: *I have to have a medical before I can start my new job.* 我得接受體格檢查後才能開始做新的工作。

med·i·cat·ed /'mɛdɪ,ketɪd; 'medɪ̩keɪtɪd/ *adj* mixed with a medical substance 加入藥物的: *medicated shampoo* 藥物洗髮劑

med·i·ca·tion /,mɛdɪ'keʃən; ,medɪ̩'keɪʃən/ *n* [C;U] a drug used to treat an illness 藥物: *It is better to sleep naturally, without taking medication.* 最好是不吃藥而自然入睡。| *She's on medication for her heart.* 她正用藥物治療心臟病。

me·di·ci·nal /mə'dɪsnl; mɪ̩'dɪsənəl/ *adj* **1** used as medicine 藥用的: *medicinal alcohol* 藥用酒精 **2** connected with curing illness 和治療有關的: *for medicinal purposes* 為了治療的目的

★**medi·cine** /'mɛdəsn̩; 'mɛdsən/ *n* **1** [C;U] a substance that you drink or swallow to treat illness 藥; 藥劑: *a bottle of medicine* 一瓶藥水 | *Keep all medicines away from children.* 把所有的藥都放在孩子拿不到的地方。**2** [U] the science of treating illness and damage to the body 醫學

★**med·i·e·val** /,mɛdɪ'iːvl̩; ,mɛdi'iːvəl/ *adj* (also 又作 **mediaeval**) of the period in European history between about AD 1100 and AD 1500, the Middle Ages 中世紀的〔歐洲歷史上約在公元 1100 年到 1500 年之間〕; 中古時代的

me·di·o·cre /'miːdɪ,okə; ,miːdi'əʊkər/ *adj* neither very good nor very bad, but not really good enough 中等的; 平庸的: *He reads a lot of mediocre detective stories.* 他閱讀許多平庸的偵探故事。–**mediocrity** /,miːdɪ'ɑkrətɪ; ,miːdi'ɒkrˌti/ *n* [U]

med·i·tate /'mɛdə,tet; 'mɛdˌteɪt/ *v* **meditated, meditating** [I] **1** to fix your mind on one idea or activity, especially for religious reasons or to gain a calm peaceful mind 〔尤指為宗教原因或為使心情平靜而〕沉思; 冥想 **2** to think seriously or deeply 認真考慮; 深思: *He meditated on the matter for two days before giving his answer.* 他對此事深思了兩天才作出回答。–**meditation** /,mɛdə'teʃən; ,medˌteɪʃən/ *n* [U]: *He was interested in yoga and meditation.* 他對瑜伽和冥想感興趣。

med·i·ta·tive /'mɛdə,tetɪv; 'medˌtətɪv/ *adj* showing deep and careful thought 沉思的; 冥想的 –**meditatively** *adv*

me·di·um¹ /'miːdɪəm; 'miːdiəm/ *adj* [only before a noun 只用於名詞前] of middle size, amount, or quality 中等的: *a medium-sized apple* 中等大小的蘋果 | *He's of medium height.* 他中等身高。

medium² *n* **media** /-dɪə; -diə/ *or* **mediums 1** a method for giving information or expressing yourself in art 傳遞信息的媒介; 藝術表現形式: *He writes books, but the theatre is his favourite medium.* 他寫書, 但他最喜愛的藝術表現形式是戲劇。**2** a substance in which objects or living things exist, or through which a force travels 介質; 媒介物; 〔生物的〕生活環境: *A fish in water is in its natural medium.* 水中的魚是處於其天然的生活環境中。| *Sound travels through the medium of air.* 聲音通過空氣這一媒介傳播。**3** [plural is 複數為 **mediums**] a person who claims to have power to receive messages from the spirits of the dead 靈媒; 巫師 **4** a middle position 中間; 折衷: *There's a happy medium between eating all the time and not eating at all.* 在整天吃和一點也不吃之間存在着一種可行的折衷辦法。

medium wave /'··· '·/ *n* [U] radio receiving or broadcasting on waves of between about 180 and 600 metres in length (無線電) 中波 〔波長在 180 米到 600 米之間〕

meek /mik; miːk/ *adj* gentle and uncomplaining 溫順的; 馴服的 –**meekly** *adv* –**meekness** *n* [U]

★**meet** /mit; miːt/ *v* **met** /mɛt; met/, **met, meeting 1** [I;T] to come together with another person or thing 遇見; 相遇: *Let's meet for dinner.* 我們聚一聚, 一起吃飯吧。| *I met him in the street.* 我在街上遇見了他。| *I'll drive to the station and meet her off the train.* 我將開車去車站, 接她下火車。**2** [I;T] to be introduced to someone 和〔人〕相識: *Come to the party and meet some interesting people.* 請你來參加聚會, 結識一些有趣的人。| *Haven't we met before?* 我們以前見過面嗎? **3** [I;T] to touch or come together 接觸; 相遇: *Their lips met.* 他們的嘴唇碰在一起了。| *The two cars met head-on.* 兩輛汽車迎面相撞。| *His eyes met mine and I knew that he understood.* 他的目光和我相遇, 我知道他理解了。**4** [I] to join 會合: *My trousers won't meet round my waist.* 我的褲子腰部扣不上。| *The two roads meet just north of Birmingham.* 這兩條路就在伯明翰的北面匯合。**5** to experience something unpleasant 經歷; 遭受〔不愉快的事〕: *She met her death in a plane crash.* 她在一次飛機失事中遇難。**6** [T] to answer or greet something in a particular way 〔以某種方式〕回答; 對付: *His speech was met with cries of anger.* 對他的演講, 人們報以怒喊。**7** [T] to satisfy a need, desire, or demand 滿足〔需要、慾望或要求〕: *Does the hotel meet your expectations?* 這家旅館符合你的要求嗎? | *Can you meet your debts?* 你能償還債務嗎? **8 meet someone halfway** to come to an agreement by giving the other person some of what they want 同某人妥協 **9 there's more to something than meets the eye** there are hidden facts, difficulties, or reasons in something 某事中有看不到的事實, 困難或原因: *The job seems easy, but there's more to it than meets the eye.* 這份工作看上去容易, 但有見不到的難處。

meet up *phr v* [I] to meet, by arrangement, to do something together 約會〔一起做某事〕; 碰頭: *Let's meet up after the play.* 散戲後我們碰碰頭。| *I met up with Pete the other day.* 我前幾天和彼得碰過頭。

meet with sbdy/sthg *phr v* [T] **1** to find someone or something by chance 偶然發現〔某人或某事物〕; 遭到: *I met with some difficulties when I tried to enter the country.* 我在設法進入那個國家時遇到一些困難。| *They met with an accident on their way back.* 他們在歸來途中發生了車禍。**2** to have a meeting with 會見; 和…會晤: *The Prince met with several heads of state.* 王子會見了幾位國家元首。

★**meet·ing** /'mitɪŋ; 'miːtɪŋ/ *n* **1** a gathering of people for a purpose 集會; 會議: *The Chairman declared the meeting open.* 主席宣佈會議開始。| *There's a council meeting in the Church*

Hall tonight. 今晚在教會廳有一個市政會議。 **2** the people in such a gathering 與會者: *The meeting voted in favour of the proposal.* 與會者投票贊成這項提議。 **3** the coming together of two or more people, by chance or arrangement 偶遇; 約會: *Our meeting at the station was quite by chance.* 我們在車站相遇純屬偶然。

meg·a·lo·ma·ni·a /ˌmɛɡələˈmeɪnɪə; ˌmegələʊˈmeɪnɪə/ *n* [U] the belief that you are more important or powerful than you really are 夜郎自大; 妄自尊大 **–megalomaniac** /-ˈmenɪˌæk; -ˈmeɪnɪæk/ *n*

meg·a·phone /ˈmɛɡəˌfon; ˈmegəfəʊn/ *n* an instrument shaped like a horn which makes your voice louder when you speak into it 喇叭筒; 擴音器

meg·a·ton /ˈmɛɡəˌtʌn; ˈmegətʌn/ *n* a measure of the explosive power of bombs 百萬噸級〔炸彈爆炸力計算單位〕: *A one megaton bomb has the same power as a million tons of TNT.* 一顆百萬噸級的炸彈威力相當於一百萬噸黃色炸藥。

mel·an·chol·y /ˈmɛlən.kəlɪ; ˈmelənkəlɪ/ *n* [U] lit a feeling of great sadness 〔文〕憂鬱 **–melancholy** *adj* lit 〔文〕: *We found her alone and feeling melancholy.* 我們發現她很孤獨並感到憂鬱。

mel·ee /ˈmeˈle; ˈmeleɪ/ *n* a struggling or disorderly crowd 混亂〔混戰〕的人羣

mel·low /ˈmɛlo; ˈmeləʊ/ *adj* **1** sweet and ripe or fully developed, especially after being kept for a long time (used of fruit and wine) 甜熟的〔指水果、酒〕;〔尤指經過長期存放而〕芳醇的 **2** soft, warm, and smooth (used of colours, light, and sound) 柔和的〔指顏色、光線和聲音〕; 暖色的; 光滑的: *the mellow notes of the saxophone* 薩克斯管的柔和音符 **3** gentle and friendly, because you are quite old or in a pleasant state of mind (used of people)〔人由於年老或心情愉快而〕溫和友善的; 老練的; 成熟的 **–mellow** *v* [I;T]: *The years have mellowed him.* 歲月使他變得老練。

me·lo·di·ous /məˈlodɪəs; mɪˈləʊdɪəs/ *adj* sweet-sounding and tuneful 悅耳的; 旋律優美的

mel·o·dra·ma /ˈmɛlə.drɑmə; ˈmelədrɑːmə/ *n* [C;U] a type of story or play that is full of sudden events and unusually strong feelings 情節劇

mel·o·dra·mat·ic /ˌmɛlədrəˈmætɪk; ˌmelədrəˈmætɪk/ *adj* showing unreasonably strong and excited feelings 表現過分強烈感情的: *He says he's going to kill her, but he's just being melodramatic.* 他說他要殺了她, 但他只不過是在胡鬧而已。

mel·o·dy /ˈmɛlədɪ; ˈmelədɪ/ *n* **melodies 1** a song or tune 歌曲; 曲調 **2** a clearly recognizable tune in a larger musical arrangement of notes (主)旋律

mel·on /ˈmɛlən; ˈmelən/ *n* [C;U] a large juicy fruit with a thick green or yellow skin 瓜; 甜瓜

melt /mɛlt; melt/ *v* **1** [I;T] to become liquid or to cause a substance to become a liquid by heating it (使)融化; (使)熔化: *The ice is melting in the sun.* 冰正在陽光下融化。 | *Melt the chocolate in a saucepan.* 在深平底鍋裡融化巧克力。 **2** [I;T] to become or cause someone to become gentle or sympathetic (使某人)變得溫和或有同情心: *His anger quickly melted.* 他的怒氣很快消失了。 | *My heart melted when I heard her crying.* 我聽見她的哭聲就心軟了。

> ■ USAGE 用法: The adjective **molten** means **melted,** but is used only of things that melt at a very high temperature ☆形容詞 **molten** 的意思是 **melted,** 但只指高溫下熔化的東西: *molten rock/metal* 熔岩/熔化了的金屬 but 但是要用 *melted chocolate/ice* 融化的巧克力/冰

melt away *phr v* [I] to disappear easily 容易消失: *I don't know where my money goes — it just seems to melt away.* 我不知道我的錢都上哪兒去了——它似乎消失了。

melt sthg ↔ **down** *phr v* [T] to make a metal object liquid by heating it, in order to use the metal again 熔化〔金屬物〕; 回爐: *They melted down the silver sixpences to make jewellery.* 他們熔化六便士的銀幣用來打首飾。

★mem·ber /ˈmɛmbə; ˈmembəʳ/ *n* **1** a person belonging to a club, group, or organization〔俱樂部、團體或組織的〕成員, 會員: *a member of the family* 家庭的一員 | *a Member of Parliament* 國會議員 | *She became a member of the Labour party.* 她成了工黨成員。 **2** a member country, a member state a country which has joined an international organization〔國際組織的〕會員國

mem·ber·ship /ˈmɛmbəˌʃɪp; ˈmembəʃɪp/ *n* **1** [U] the state of being a member of a club, group, or organization 會員身分; 會員資格: *Have you applied for membership yet?* 你申請了會員資格嗎? **2** [C + sing/pl verb] all the members of a club, group, or organization 全體會員: *We're trying to increase our membership.* 我們力圖增加會員人數。 | *The membership disagree about the proposed change in the rules.* 全體會員否決了修改規章的動議。

mem·brane /ˈmɛmbren; ˈmembreɪn/ *n* tech a soft thin skin which covers or connects part of your body〔術語〕膜: *A delicate, vibrating membrane in the ear helps to convey sounds to the brain.* 耳朵裡一層柔軟顫動的薄膜幫助把聲音傳送到大腦。

me·men·to /mɪˈmɛnto; mɪˈmentəʊ/ *n* **mementos** a small object which reminds

you of a special occasion or person 紀念物;
紀念品

mem·o /ˈmɛmo; ˈmɛməʊ/ *n* **memos** (also 又
作 **memorandum**) a note from one person
or office to another within the same
organization 備忘錄

mem·oirs /ˈmɛmwɑrz; ˈmɛmwɑːz/ *n* [pl] a
book written by an important person
telling about their experiences〔重要人物
的〕自傳; 回憶錄

mem·o·ra·ble /ˈmɛmərəbl; ˈmɛmərəbəl/ *adj*
special and worth remembering 特殊的; 值
得紀念的: *The film was memorable for its
wonderful photography.* 這部電影因其美妙的
攝影而令人難忘。| *a memorable trip abroad*
難忘的海外旅遊

mem·o·ran·dum /ˌmɛmə'rændəm; ˌmɛmə-
'rændəm/ *n* **memoranda** /-də; -də/ *or* **mem-
orandums** *fml* a memo〔正式〕備忘錄

me·mo·ri·al /məˈmɔrɪəl; mɪˈmɔːrɪəl/ *n* **1** a
stone structure built in a public place in
memory of a person or an important event
紀念碑: *a war memorial* 戰爭紀念碑 **2** something which exists or is done in memory of
someone 紀念物; 紀念儀式: *a memorial
service at the parish church for those killed
in the explosion* 為紀念爆炸(事件)中的死難
者而在教區教堂舉行的儀式 | *the Winston
Churchill Memorial Award for young musicians* 獎勵年輕音樂家的溫斯頓·邱吉爾紀念獎

mem·o·rize /ˈmɛmə,raɪz; ˈmɛməraɪz/ *v*
memorized, memorizing (also 又作 **mem-
orise** *BrE*〔英式〕) [T] to learn and remember something exactly 記住, 熟記〔某事物〕:
He memorized the list of phone numbers. 他
熟記名單上的電話號碼。

mem·o·ry /ˈmɛmərɪ; ˈmɛməri/ *n* **memories 1** [C;U] your ability
to remember events and experience 記憶
力: *She's got a good memory for faces.* 她對
見過面的人都記得住。| *After the accident,
he completely lost his memory.* 事故以後他完
全喪失了記憶力。**2** [C] something that you
remember from the past 記憶的事物; 回憶:
*One of my earliest memories is of playing at
my grandmother's house.* 我記得的其中一件
最早的往事是在我祖母家裡玩。| *The music
brought back vivid memories of happier
days.* 聽到這音樂就令我生動地想起以往的快
樂日子。**3** [C] the part of a computer in
which information is stored〔電腦的〕儲存
器: *The system can't cope if you overload the
memory.* 如果儲存器超負荷, 系統無法應付。**4
within living memory** during the time
which people now alive can remember 在
活着的人們記憶中: *The great storm is well
within living memory.* 對於仍然在世的人們來
說, 那次大風暴記憶猶新。**5 in memory of
someone** as a way of remembering or
reminding others of someone 為紀念某人:
*The gravestone read "In loving memory of a
dear husband and father".* 墓碑上寫着"紀念

親愛的丈夫和父親"。

men /mɛn; mɛn/ *the plural of* MAN ☆MAN
的複數形式

men·ace¹ /ˈmɛnɪs; ˈmenᵻs/ *n* **1** someone or
something which brings danger or
threatens you 帶來危險或有威脅的人或物: *a
busy road which is a menace to the
children's safety* 威脅孩子安全的繁忙道路 **2**
[U] the quality of appearing threatening 威
脅; 恐嚇: *He spoke with menace in his voice.*
他帶着威脅的口吻說。**3** [C] a troublesome
person or thing 討厭的人或物: *That child's
an absolute menace.* 那孩子實在討厭。

men·ace² *v* **menaced, menacing** [T] to be
likely to harm someone or something 威脅,
威嚇〔某人, 某事物〕

me·nac·ing /ˈmɛnɪsɪŋ; ˈmenᵻsɪŋ/ *adj* threatening 恐嚇的; 威脅的: *a menacing look* 威脅
的神情 | *Dark menacing clouds brought a
sudden end to the picnic.* 黑壓壓的烏雲表示
暴風雨快要來臨, 野餐活動唯有即時結束。—
menacingly *adv*

me·na·ge·rie /məˈnædʒərɪ; mɪˈnædʒəri/ *n*
a collection of wild animals in a private
zoo〔私人動物園養的〕一批野生動物

mend¹ /mɛnd; mend/ *v* **1** [T] to repair something 修理〔某物〕: *We ought to mend that
hole in the fence.* 我們應該修補籬笆上的那個
洞。| *I hate mending socks.* 我討厭補襪子。
2 [I] to become well or healthy again 痊癒,
恢復健康: *That leg's mending nicely now.* 那
條腿很快好起來。**3 mend your ways** to improve your behaviour 改過自新: *If you don't
mend your ways, you'll end up in prison.* 如
果你不改過自新, 到頭來會坐牢的。

mend² *n* **be on the mend** to get better after
illness 病後在康復中

me·ni·al /ˈmɪnɪəl; ˈmiːnɪəl/ *adj* not interesting or skilled and not regarded as important (used of work) 乏味的〔指工作〕; 不重要
的: *She was furious at being given such a
menial job.* 給了她這麼一份乏味的工作, 她為
此很惱火。

men·o·pause /ˈmɛnə,pɔz; ˈmenəpɔːz/ *n* **the
menopause** the time when a woman's
periods (PERIOD¹) stop, usually when she
is middle-aged〔中年婦女的〕絕經期; 更年期

men·stru·al /ˈmɛnstruəl; ˈmenstruəl/ *adj*
concerning a woman's monthly PERIOD¹ 月
經的

men·stru·ate /ˈmɛnstru,et; ˈmenstrueɪt/ *v*
menstruated, menstruating [I] to have a
monthly PERIOD¹ 行經; 來月經: –**menstru-
ation** /ˌmɛnstru'eʃən; ˌmenstru'eɪʃən/ *n* [U]

men·tal /ˈmɛntl; ˈmentl/ *adj* **1** concerned
with the brain or thinking 腦力的; 精神的:
her declining mental powers 她正在衰退的腦
力 **2** [only before a noun 只用於名詞前]
done or made only in the mind 只在心裡做
的: *mental arithmetic* 心算 | *He made a
mental note to remember to get the lock
fixed.* 他在心裡記着要請人修鎖。**3** [only

before a noun 只用於名詞前] concerning illness of the mind 精神病的: *a mental hospital* 精神病院 | *a mental patient* 精神病人 **–mentally** *adv: He's mentally ill.* 他精神上有病。

men·tal·i·ty /mɛnˈtælətɪ; menˈtælŝti/ *n* **mentalities** someone's character and ways of thinking 心態; 思維方法: *I can't understand the mentality of anyone who would hurt a child deliberately.* 我無法理解故意傷害孩子的人的心態。

men·tion[1] /ˈmɛnʃən; ˈmenʃən/ *v* **1** [T; +(that)] to say or write about something in a few words 談起, 提到 〔某事物〕: *"We had another meeting last week." "Yes. Jill mentioned it."* "我們上週又開了一次會。" "是呀, 吉爾提起過。" | *We mentioned that we would like to see the match and he arranged it for us immediately.* 我們說起想看比賽, 他馬上為我們作了安排。

□ USEFUL PATTERNS 有用句型
to mention something; to mention something to someone; to mention that...

2 [T] to say the name of someone or something 提出〔某人或某事物的〕名字: *He mentioned a useful contact in London.* 他提及在倫敦一個可以幫忙的人。**3 Don't mention it** a phrase used as a polite reply when someone thanks you 別客氣; 不用謝 **4 not to mention** = and in addition there is... 此外還...: *They have three dogs to look after, not to mention the cat and the parrot.* 他們有三隻狗要照管, 此外還有貓和鸚鵡。

mention[2] *n* [sing] a short remark about something or naming of a person 提及; 簡短的陳述: *I got a mention in the list of helpers.* 在幫助者的名單中有提及我。

men·tor /ˈmɛntɚ; ˈmentɔːr/ *n* someone who regularly gives advice to another person, especially to someone a lot younger than them 顧問; 指導者

men·u /ˈmɛnju; ˈmenjuː/ *n* **1** a list of the foods available in a restaurant 菜單 **2** a list of different choices shown on a computer SCREEN 〔電腦屏幕上的〕項目單; (功能)選擇單

mer·ce·na·ry[1] /ˈmɝsṇ͵ɛrɪ; ˈmɜːsənəri/ *n* **mercenaries** a soldier who fights for a foreign country for money 〔外國的〕雇傭兵

mercenary[2] *adj* having too great an interest in gaining money 唯利是圖的; 貪財的

mer·chan·dise /ˈmɝtʃən͵daɪz; ˈmɜːtʃəndaɪz/ *n* [U] things for sale 商品; 貨物

mer·chant /ˈmɝtʃənt; ˈmɜːtʃənt/ *n* a person who buys and sells goods, usually in large amounts, especially from and to foreign countries 商人; 〔尤指〕外貿批發商

merchant na·vy /͵·· ˈ··/ *n* a nation's ships which are used in trade, not war 〔一國的〕商船

mer·ci·ful /ˈmɝsɪfəl; ˈmɜːsɪfəl/ *adj fml* 〖正式〗 **1** willing to forgive people instead of punishing them 寬大的; 仁慈的: *a merciful king* 仁慈的國王 **2** fortunate and preventing suffering 幸運的; 免受痛苦的: *Death came as a merciful release from all his pain.* 死亡使他終於可以從所有的痛苦中解脫出來。 **–mercifully** *adv*

mer·ci·less /ˈmɝsɪlɪs; ˈmɜːsɪləs/ *adj* showing no mercy to others 無仁慈之心的; 冷酷無情的: *The king was totally merciless and had all the villagers put to death.* 國王冷酷無情, 把所有村民處死。**–mercilessly** *adv*

mer·cu·ry /ˈmɝkjərɪ; ˈmɜːkjʊri/ *n* [U] a silver-coloured metal that is liquid at ordinary temperatures and is used in thermometers (THERMOMETER) 汞; 水銀

mer·cy /ˈmɝsɪ; ˈmɜːsi/ *n* **1** [U] kindness, pity, and willingness to forgive people 慈悲; 憐憫; 寬恕: *The prisoner begged the judge for mercy.* 犯人懇求法官寬恕。**2 a mercy** a fortunate thing 幸運的事: *It was a mercy the fire didn't reach the house.* 火沒燒到房子真是走運。**3 at the mercy of** powerless against someone or something 任憑〔某人或某事物〕擺佈: *They were lost at sea, at the mercy of wind and weather.* 他們在海上迷失了方向, 任憑風吹雨淋。

mere /mɪr; mɪər/ *adj* **1** [only before a noun 只用於名詞前] nothing more than 僅僅的; 只不過的: *He lost the election by a mere 20 votes.* 他僅以二十票之差在競選中失利。 | *She's not ready for marriage; she's a mere child.* 她還沒去結婚做好準備; 她只是個孩子。**2 the merest** the smallest possible 十分微小的; 微不足道的: *The merest little criticism makes him angry.* 微不足道的小小一點批評也會使他生氣。

mere·ly /ˈmɪrlɪ; ˈmɪəli/ *adv* only 只; 僅僅: *Don't blame me for the bad news; I'm merely the messenger.* 別將這壞消息怪罪於我, 我只不過是個報信者。

merge /mɝdʒ; mɜːdʒ/ *v* **merged, merging 1** [I] to disappear into the background or the darkness 消失; 融合: *One colour merged into the other.* 一種顏色和另一種顏色融合在一起。 | *My friends merged into the darkness and were soon out of sight.* 我的朋友們消失在黑暗中, 很快就看不見了。**2** [I] to combine, especially gradually 〔尤指逐漸〕結合; 合併: *The two roads merge a mile ahead.* 這兩條路在前面一英里處會合。 | *The company has recently been merged* **with** *Apex Electronics.* 這家公司最近已和艾帕克斯電子公司合併了。

merg·er /ˈmɝdʒɚ; ˈmɜːdʒər/ *n* a joining together of two or more companies or organizations 〔公司或組織的〕合併

me·rid·i·an /məˈrɪdɪən; məˈrɪdiən/ *n* one of the imaginary lines drawn on a map from

M

the North Pole to the South Pole over the surface of the Earth 子午線; 經線

me·ringue /məˈræŋ; məˈræŋ/ n [U] a light sweet white cake made of sugar and egg whites 蛋白甜糕餅

mer·it¹ /ˈmɛrɪt; ˈmɛrḷt/ n **1** [U] the quality of deserving praise or reward 功勞; 價值; 長處: *This controversial novel is undoubtedly of great literary merit.* 這篇引起爭論的小說在文學上肯定很有價值。 **2** [C] a good quality 優點: *One of his many merits is absolute honesty.* 他的許多優點之一是絕對誠實。 **3 judge something on its merits** to decide about something purely because of its qualities, without letting your feelings affect your decision 根據某事物本身的好壞來判斷

merit² v [T] *fml* to deserve something 〔正式〕值得, 應該得到〔某事物〕: *Your suggestion merits serious consideration.* 你的建議值得認真考慮。

mer·i·to·ri·ous /ˌmɛrəˈtɔrɪəs; ˌmɛrḷˈtɔːrɪəs/ adj fml deserving reward or praise 〔正式〕值得獎勵或表揚的

mer·maid /ˈmɜ·med; ˈmɜːmeɪd/ n an imaginary creature with a woman's body and a fish's tail instead of legs 〔傳說中的〕美人魚

mer·ri·ly /ˈmɛrɪli; ˈmɛrḷli/ adv **1** in a happy way 快樂地; 高興地: *She laughed merrily.* 她快活地大笑。 **2** without proper thought 〔思想〕糊塗地: *You can't just go on merrily ignoring your debts, you know.* 你要知道, 你不能不理會債務, 一味糊裡糊塗地混日子。

mer·ri·ment /ˈmɛrɪmənt; ˈmɛrɪmənt/ n [U] fml laughter and enjoyment 〔正式〕歡笑; 歡樂

mer·ry /ˈmɛri; ˈmɛri/ adj **merrier, merriest 1** happy and cheerful 歡樂的; 愉快的: *a merry laugh* 歡樂的笑聲 **2** infml slightly drunk 〔非正式〕微醉的: *We got a bit merry at the party.* 在宴會上我們有點喝醉了。 **3 Merry Christmas!** = Have a happy time at Christmas 聖誕快樂!

mer·ry·mak·ing /ˈmɛrɪˌmekɪŋ; ˈmerɪˌmeɪkɪŋ/ n [U] lit fun and enjoyment 〔文〕盡情歡樂

mesh¹ /mɛʃ; meʃ/ n **1** [U] material like a net, made from plastic, wire, or thread 網狀物: *We made a fence from some wire mesh.* 我們用一些鐵絲網做了個籬笆。 **2** [C] the spaces of a certain size in such a network 網眼: *Use a net with a large mesh so that smaller fish can escape.* 用一張網眼大的網, 以便較小的魚得以逃走。

mesh² v [I] to fit together closely 〔文〕翏合

mes·mer·ize /ˈmɛsməˌraɪz; ˈmezməraɪz/ v **mesmerized, mesmerizing** (also 又作 **mesmerise** BrE〔英式〕) **be mesmerized** to be so attracted by something that you cannot think about anything else 被迷住: *We stood quite still, mesmerized by the falling snow-*

flakes. 我們靜靜地站着, 被飄落的雪花迷住了。

mess¹ /mɛs; mes/ n **1** [U] a dirty or untidy state 雜亂; 髒亂: *Your bedroom's in a terrible mess.* 你的臥室亂得一塌糊塗。 | *Someone's dropped a plate of cakes. Please would you clean up the mess?* 有人把一盤蛋糕掉到了地上。請你收拾一下好嗎? **2 a mess** a person who looks untidy or dirty 不整潔的人; 骯髒的人: *Sorry I look such a mess. I've been working in the garden.* 真抱歉我看上去一副邋遢相; 我在花園裡收拾呢。 **3** [C] a place in which members of the armed forces eat 軍人食堂: *the officers' mess* 軍官食堂 **4** [C] a situation full of problems and trouble 混亂的局面: *I've made such a mess of my life.* 我的生活一團糟。 | *That's another fine mess you've got me into!* 你又把我搞得處境如此狼狽!

mess² v

mess about/around phr v **1** [I] to spend time doing things slowly and with no particular purpose 磨蹭; 混日子: *We usually spend Sundays messing about in the garden.* 我們常常星期天在花園裡消磨時間。 **2** [I] to behave stupidly 胡鬧: *Oh, stop messing about and be serious for a minute!* 哎, 別胡鬧, 正經一會兒! **3** [T **mess** sbdy **about/around**] to treat a person badly by not being honest or fair to them 粗暴地或不誠實地對待〔某人〕

mess sthg ↔ **up** phr v [T] to spoil something or make it untidy 把〔某事物〕弄糟, 弄亂: *Who messed up all the papers on my desk?* 誰把我桌上的文件弄得亂七八糟? | *The rain has messed up all our plans.* 這場雨把我們所有的計劃都打亂了。

mess with sbdy/sthg phr v [T] infml to become connected with a person or thing that is dangerous in some way 〔非正式〕〔和危險的人或東西〕發生關係: *He told us not to start messing with drugs.* 他告訴我們別嘗試跟毒品打交道。

✲mes·sage /ˈmɛsɪdʒ; ˈmesɪdʒ/ n **1** a spoken or written piece of information passed from one person to another 〔口頭或書面的〕消息; 信息: *There's an important message for you.* 有個重要的信息帶給你。 | *I'm afraid he's out. Can I take a message?* 恐怕他出去了。我可以帶個信嗎? | *We left a message telling her to meet us at the station.* 我們留了個信, 告訴她在車站接我們。 **2** an important or central idea 寓意; 要旨; 中心思想: *a film with a clear message* 寓意清晰的影片 **3 get the message** infml to understand what someone is trying to tell you 〔非正式〕理解意思; 領會; 明白

mes·sen·ger /ˈmɛsndʒɚ; ˈmesndʒə/ n a person who brings a message 送信人; 報信者; 信使

mes·si·ah /məˈsaɪə; mḷˈsaɪə/ n **1** a great religious leader who will save the world 彌賽亞; 救世主 **2 the Messiah** Christ, in the

M

Christian religion〔基督教中的〕基督

Mes·srs /ˈmɛsəz; ˈmɛsəz/ a written abbreviation for the plural of MR, especially in the names of firms〔縮〕先生(尤用於商號的名字, MR 的複數形式): *Messrs Ford and Dobson, solicitors* 福特及多布森先生, 律師

mess·y /ˈmɛsɪ; ˈmɛsi/ *adj* **messier, messiest** **1** untidy or dirty 凌亂的; 骯髒的: *What a messy bedroom!* 臥室真凌亂! **2** unpleasant and causing a lot of trouble (used of a situation) 棘手的; 難辦的〔指局面〕: *She's trying to settle down after a messy divorce.* 經過一場棘手的離婚糾紛後, 她盡力想過安定的生活。**–messily** *adv*

met /mɛt; mɛt/ the past tense and past participle of MEET ☆MEET 的過去式和過去分詞

me·tab·o·lis·m /məˈtæbl͵ɪzəm; mᵊˈtæbə‑lɪzəm/ *n* the chemical processes in your body that use food for growing and for the power you need to do things 新陳代謝

met·al /ˈmɛtl; ˈmɛtl/ *n* [C;U] any of the hard shiny substances which can usually be used for passing an electric current 金屬: *common metals such as lead, copper, and tin* 鉛、銅、錫等普通金屬 | *a metal pipe* 金屬管 | *pouring the molten metal* 倒入熔化的金屬

me·tal·lic /məˈtælɪk; mᵊˈtælɪk/ *adj* made of or like metal 金屬製的; 金屬似的: *shiny metallic colours* 閃亮的金屬似的顏色 | *a metallic sound* 金屬般的聲音

met·a·mor·pho·sis /͵mɛtəˈmɔːfəsɪs; ͵mɛtə‑ˈmɔːfəsᵊs/ *n* **metamorphoses** /‑siːz; ‑siːz/ [C; U] complete change from one form to another 徹底變形: *the metamorphosis of a rather ugly caterpillar into a beautiful butterfly* 由醜陋的毛蟲蛻變成美麗的蝴蝶

met·a·phor /ˈmɛtəfə; ˈmɛtəfᵊr/ *n* [C;U] a way of describing something by saying it has the qualities of something else; it compares things without using the words "as" or "like"; examples are *the sunshine of her smile* and *What a toad that man is!* 隱喻, 暗喻〔即不用"as"或"like"而把一個事物比作另一事物。如"笑容燦爛", "那人真是隻癩蛤蟆!"〕**–compare** 比較 SIMILE **–metaphorical** /͵mɛtəˈfɒrɪkl; ͵mɛtəˈfɒrɪkəl/ *adj* **–metaphorically** /‑klɪ; ‑klɪ/ *adv: When I say he's got green fingers I am, of course, speaking metaphorically.* 我說他有"綠色的手指"當然是暗喻。

mete /miːt; miːt/ *v*

    mete sthg ↔ **out** *phr v* [T] to officially give someone a punishment, or bad treatment of some kind〔官方〕懲罰〔某人〕

me·te·or /ˈmiːtɪə; ˈmiːtɪᵊr/ *n* a small piece of rock or metal that burns brightly when it falls from space into the air around the Earth 流星

me·te·or·ic /͵miːtɪˈɒrɪk; ͵miːtiˈɒrɪk/ *adj* very fast and lasting only a short time 迅疾的; 短

暫的: *a meteoric rise to fame* 迅速成名

me·te·o·rite /ˈmiːtɪə͵raɪt; ˈmiːtɪəraɪt/ *n* a small meteor that has landed on the Earth 隕星; 隕石

me·te·o·rol·og·i·cal /͵miːtɪərəˈlɒdʒɪkl; ͵miː‑tɪərəˈlɒdʒɪkəl/ *adj* relating to the scientific study of weather conditions 氣象學的

me·ter /ˈmiːtə; ˈmiːtᵊr/ *n* **1** a machine which measures the amount of something used 計; 儀; 表: *a gas meter* 煤氣表 **2** the American spelling of METRE ☆METRE 的美式拼法

★**meth·od** /ˈmɛθəd; ˈmɛθəd/ *n* **1** [C] a way of doing something 方法; 方式: *They've developed a new method of testing for the virus.* 他們研究出一種測定這種病毒的新方法。| *old-fashioned teaching methods* 老式教學法 **2** [C; U] an orderly arrangement or plan 條理; 秩序: *There's not much method in the way they do their accounts.* 他們記賬的方法沒有甚麼條理。

me·thod·i·cal /məˈθɒdɪkl; mᵊˈθɒdɪkəl/ *adj* doing things carefully using an ordered system (辦事) 有條理: *He's rather slapdash, but she's very methodical.* 他很草率, 但她卻很有條理。**–methodically** /‑klɪ; ‑klɪ/ *adv*

Meth·o·dist /ˈmɛθədɪst; ˈmɛθədᵊst/ *n* a person from a branch of the Christian Church begun by John Wesley in the 18th century〔基督教的〕循道宗信徒〔該宗派由約翰·威斯利於十八世紀開創〕**–Methodist** *adj* **–Methodism** *n* [U]

meth·o·dol·o·gy /͵mɛθədˈɒlədʒɪ; ͵mɛθəˈdɒ‑lədʒi/ *n* **methodologies** [C;U] *tech* a set of methods or principles for doing something〔術語〕一套方法; 方法學

meth·yl·at·ed spir·its /͵mɛθəˌleɪtɪdˈspɪrɪts; ͵mɛθᵊˌleɪtᵊd ˈspɪrᵊts/ *n* [U] (also 又稱 **meths** /mɛθs; mɛθs/ *BrE infml*〔英式, 非正式〕) alcohol used for cleaning purposes or for burning in lamps or heaters〔用於清潔或燃燒的〕甲基化酒精

me·tic·u·lous /məˈtɪkjələs; mᵊˈtɪkjᵊlᵊs/ *adj* with very careful attention to detail 非常注意細節的: *meticulous drawings* 細緻的素描 | *She dusted the room with meticulous care.* 她非常細心地在房間裡打掃和撣灰。**–meticulously** *adv*

★**me·tre** /ˈmiːtə; ˈmiːtᵊr/ *n* (**meter** *AmE*〔美式〕) **1** a unit for measuring length, equal to 39.37 INCHES〔長度單位〕米; 公尺〔合39.37英寸〕: *It's ten metres long.* 它有十米長。**2** an arrangement of words in poetry into strong and weak beats〔詩的〕韻律; 格律

met·ric /ˈmɛtrɪk; ˈmɛtrɪk/ *adj* concerning the system of measurement based on the metre and kilogram 公制的; 米制的

Met·ro /ˈmɛtrəʊ; ˈmɛtroʊ/ *n* **the Metro** an underground railway system in some cities〔某些城市的〕地下鐵道系統; 地鐵: *Did you go on the Metro in Paris?* 你坐過巴黎的地鐵嗎?

me·trop·o·lis /mə'trɑplɪs; mɪ'trɒpəlɪs/ n fml a very large city, or the capital city of a country 〖正式〗大城市; 首都 —**metropolitan** /,metrə'pɑlətn; ,metrə'pɒlɪtən/ adj

mew /mju; mju:/ v [I] to make the sound a cat makes 咪咪[喵喵]叫 —**mew** n

mg the written abbreviation for 〖縮〗= MILLIGRAM

mi·aow /mɪ'au; mi'au/ v [I] to make the crying sound a cat makes 喵喵叫 —**miaow** n

mice /maɪs; maɪs/ the plural of MOUSE ☆ MOUSE 的複數形式

mick·ey /'mɪki; 'mɪki/ n **take the mickey out of someone** infml to make someone feel or look foolish by copying them or laughing at them 〖非正式〗取笑, 嘲弄某人

mi·cro /'maɪkro; 'maɪkrəʊ/ n **micros** infml a microcomputer 〖非正式〗微型電腦

mi·crobe /'maɪkrob; 'maɪkrəʊb/ n a very small living creature that can only be seen with a microscope 微生物

mi·cro·chip /'maɪkrotʃɪp; 'maɪkrəʊ,tʃɪp/ n see 見 CHIP[1]

mi·cro·com·put·er /,maɪkrokəm'pjutə; ,maɪkrəʊkəm'pju:tə[r]/ n (also 又作 **micro** infml 〖非正式〗) a small computer, for use at home or in schools or offices 微型電腦

mi·cro·cos·m /'maɪkrə,kazəm; 'maɪkrəʊkɒzəm/ n a little world that contains all the qualities and activities of a larger world 微觀世界; 縮影

mi·cro·fiche /'maɪkrofiʃ; 'maɪkrəʊfi:ʃ/ n [C; U] a sheet of microfilm with information printed in very small type 縮微膠片: The entire catalogue is now on microfiche. 完整的目錄現在都在縮微膠片上了。

mi·cro·film /'maɪkrə,fɪlm; 'maɪkrəʊfɪlm/ n [C;U] a film for photographing a printed page reduced to a very small size 縮微膠卷

mi·cro·phone /'maɪkrə,fon; 'maɪkrəfəʊn/ n (also 又作 **mike** infml 〖非正式〗) an instrument for making sounds louder or recording them 麥克風; 擴音器; 話筒: Speak into the microphone, or the people at the back won't be able to hear you. 對着擴音器說, 否則後排的人聽不見你的話。

mi·cro·pro·ces·sor /'maɪkrə'prosesə; ,maɪkrəʊ'prəʊsesə[r]/ n tech the central CHIP in a small computer which controls most of its operations 〖術語〗〔電腦中的〕微處理機

mi·cro·scope /'maɪkrə,skop; 'maɪkrəskəʊp/ n a scientific instrument that makes extremely small objects look larger, and is used for examining them 顯微鏡

mi·cro·scop·ic /,maɪkrə'skapɪk; ,maɪkrə'skɒpɪk/ adj **1** by means of a microscope 用顯微鏡的: The police scientist made a microscopic examination of the dust from the prisoner's clothes. 警方的科學家用顯微鏡對犯人衣服上的塵土進行了檢驗。 **2** very detailed 十分仔細的: a microscopic examination of the house and grounds 對房子和周圍的庭園所作的極為仔細的檢查 **3** infml very small 〖非正式〗極微小的: microscopic organisms 極微小的有機體 | microscopic handwriting 極小的書寫字跡

mi·cro·wave /'maɪkrə,wev; 'maɪkrəweɪv/ n (also 又作 **microwave oven** /,··· '··/) a machine which cooks food very quickly by short wave RADIATION rather than by heat 微波爐

mid·day /'mɪd,de; ,mɪd'deɪ◂/ n [U] at 12 o'clock in the middle of the day 正午; 中午: We had lunch around midday. 我們大約在正午時分吃午餐。

☆**mid·dle[1]** /'mɪdl; 'mɪdl/ adj [only before a noun 只用於名詞前] in or nearly in the centre 中間的; 當中的: He was the middle child of the five. 他是五個孩子中的老三。

☆**middle[2]** n [sing] **1** the central part, point, or position 中部; 中央; 中間: Here's a photo of them — he's the one in the middle. 這是他們的照片——中間的那個就是他。 | Draw a line down the middle of the page. 在這頁的中間往下畫一條線。 **2** infml your waist 〖非正式〗腰部: He's getting fatter round the middle. 他的腰部越來越粗。 **3 in the middle of doing something** busy doing something 正忙於做某事

■ USAGE 用法: **Centre** has a similar meaning to **middle** when used to talk about physical position. **Centre** usually suggests a more exact physical point ☆ 談到具體位置時, **centre** 和 **middle** 意思相似。 **centre** 常指更準確的中心點: the centre of the circle. 圓圈的中心。 Use **middle** when you cannot be so exact ☆ 不能很精確時用 **middle**: the **middle** of the forest. 森林的中部。 **Middle** is more usual when you are thinking of things as lines rather than areas ☆ 當考慮事物的長度而不是面積時常用 **middle**: He was driving down the **middle** of the road. 他沿着馬路的中央開車。 and when talking about rows of objects or people ☆ 談及物體或人的排列時, 也常用 **middle**: Eve was on the left, Tom on the right, and Ted in the **middle**. 伊夫在左邊, 湯姆在右邊, 泰德在中間。

---

middle age /,·· '·◂/ n [U] **1** the time in your life when you are between about 40 and 60 years old 中年〔40歲至60歲之間〕 **2 the Middle Ages** the period in European history between about AD 1100 and AD 1500 中世紀〔歐洲的一個歷史時期, 約從公元1100年至1500年〕

middle-aged /,·· '·◂/ adj between about 40 and 60 years old (used of people) 中年的〔指人〕

middle class /,·· '·◂/ **the middle class, the middle classes** [pl] the social class which is

M

made up of people who are not noble or wealthy, and do not work with their hands, but work in offices or do professional jobs such as teaching 中產階級 –**middle-class** *adj*

Middle East /ˌ· '·◂/ *n* the Middle East part of Asia between the eastern Mediterranean and India 中東〔地中海和印度之間〕 – **Middle Eastern** *adj*

mid·dle·man /ˈmɪdlˌmæn; ˈmɪdlmæn/ *n* **middlemen** /-mɛn; -mɛn/ a person who buys goods and sells them again 經紀人; 中間人; 掮客

middle-of-the-road /ˌ·· · '·◂/ *adj* not extreme (used of ideas, especially political ideas) 不走極端的〔尤指政治思想〕

mid·dling /ˈmɪdlɪŋ; ˈmɪdlɪŋ/ *adj infml* of average quality〔非正式〕中等的; 普通的

midge /mɪdʒ; mɪdʒ/ *n* a very small flying insect that can bite 蠓; 搖蚊

midg·et /ˈmɪdʒɪt; ˈmɪdʒɪt/ *n* a very small person 侏儒; 小矮人 –**midget** *adj*

Mid·lands /ˈmɪdləndz; ˈmɪdləndz/ *n* the Midlands the central parts of England 英格蘭中部

mid·night /ˈmɪdˌnaɪt; ˈmɪdnaɪt/ *n* [U] 12 o'clock at night 午夜; 子夜: *The party finished at midnight.* 聚會在午夜結束。

mid·riff /ˈmɪdrɪf; ˈmɪdrɪf/ *n* the part of your body between your chest and your waist 腹部

midst /mɪdst; mɪdst/ *n* [U] *lit*〔文〕**1** in the midst of in the middle of 在…之中 **2** in their midst = among them 在他們中間

mid·way /ˈmɪdˈweɪ; ˌmɪdˈweɪ◂/ *adv* halfway 中途: *There's a small village midway between these two towns.* 這兩座城鎮的中間有個小村莊。| *I arrived midway through the concert.* 我在音樂會舉行到一半時到達。

mid·week /ˈmɪdˈwiːk; ˌmɪdˈwiːk◂/ *n* [U] the middle days of the week, Tuesday, Wednesday, and Thursday 一週的中間幾天〔週二、週三、週四〕 –**midweek** *adj*: *a midweek match* 週中的比賽

mid·wife /ˈmɪdˌwaɪf; ˈmɪdwaɪf/ *n* **midwives** /-ˌwaɪvz; -waɪvz/ someone who advises and helps women when they give birth to children 助產士; 產婆

mien /miːn; miːn/ *n lit* a person's appearance or expression〔文〕〔人的〕外表; 風度

★★★ **might** [superscript 1] /maɪt; maɪt/ *v negative short form* 否定縮約式為 **mightn't** [modal verb 情態動詞] **1** used to show that something is possible 可能; 也許〔表示可能性〕: *I might come and see you this evening.* 我可能今晚來看你。| *We might not have enough money to go on holiday.* 我們也許沒有足夠的錢去度假。| *I don't know where Jane is — she might have gone into town.* 我不知道簡在哪裡——她也許到城裡去了。| *I think that might be an eagle over there.* 我想那裡可能有一隻鷹。| *We were afraid that it*

might rain. 我們怕天可能會下雨。◦–see Study Note on page 1318 見 1318 頁學習提示 **2 might I, might we, etc.** *fml* a very polite way of asking someone if they will let you do something〔正式〕我(們)可以…嗎〔用於非常有禮貌地詢問某人是否讓自己做某事〕: *Might I borrow your newspaper?* 可以借你的報紙給我看嗎? | *Might we park our car here for a few minutes?* 可否讓我們把汽車停在這兒幾分鐘? **3 you might, you might at least** = you should 你應該: *You might tell me when you're going to be late home!* 你打算晚回家該告訴我一聲! | *You might have phoned to let us know where you were!* 你該打個電話讓我們知道你在哪裡! **4 might well** a phrase you use to say that something is very likely 多半會〔表示可能〕: *He might well lose his job.* 他多半會丟了他的工作。| *I haven't seen my aunt for thirty years. She might well be dead now.* 我已有三十年沒見到我的阿姨。她現在很可能去世了。**5 might as well** a phrase you use to say that you are going to do something because there is nothing else that you really want to do 不妨; 倒不如〔用於因為沒有其他任何事要做而打算做某事〕: *If there's nothing else to do here, we might as well go home.* 如果這兒沒其他事了, 我們還是回家吧。**6 I might have known** a phrase you use to say that you do not find something surprising 我早知道〔用於表示發現某事並不令人驚奇〕: *I might have known she'd refuse.* 我早知道她會拒絕。

might [superscript 2] *n* [U] great power or strength 威力; 力量: *the might of the American army* 美國陸軍的力量 | *I pushed with all my might but the rock wouldn't move.* 我使盡全力推, 可是石頭動也不動。

might·n't /ˈmaɪtnt; ˈmaɪtənt/ *v* short for〔縮〕= "might not": *They mightn't come.* 他們也許不來。

might·y /ˈmaɪtɪ; ˈmaɪti/ *adj* **mightier, mightiest 1** strong and powerful 強大的; 強有力的: *He struck the rock a mighty blow.* 他使勁猛擊了一下那塊巖石。| *Even the mightiest of empires come to an end.* 即使最強大的帝國也要滅亡。**2 high and mighty** too proud of your own importance 趾高氣揚; 神氣活現 –**mightily** *adv*

mi·graine /ˈmaɪgreɪn; ˈmiːgreɪn/ *n* [C;U] a severe headache 偏頭痛

mi·grant /ˈmaɪgrənt; ˈmaɪgrənt/ *n* a person, animal, or bird that moves from one place to another 移居者; 遷移動物; 候鳥: *Migrant workers move from country to country in search of work.* 流動工人為尋找工作從一個國家遷移到另一個國家。

mi·grate /maɪˈgreɪt; maɪˈgreɪt/ *v* **migrated, migrating** [I] **1** (of birds and fish) to travel regularly from one part of the world to another, according to the seasons of the year〔鳥〕遷徙;〔魚〕洄游 **2** to move from one place to another to live or work, often

M

for a limited period 遷移; 〔尤指有限期地〕遷居: *Some tribes migrate with their cattle in search of fresh grass.* 有些部落為了尋找新鮮的牧草而趕着牲畜一起遷移。 –**migratory** /'maɪgrə,tɔrɪ; maɪ'greɪtəri/ *adj*

mi·gra·tion /maɪ'greʃən; maɪ'greɪʃən/ *n* [C; U] moving to another place 遷移; 移居: *Scientists have studied the migration of fish over long distances.* 科學家研究了魚類遠距離洄游的現象。 | *Wars always cause great migrations of people.* 戰爭逼使人民進行大遷移。

mike /maɪk; maɪk/ *n infml* 〔非正式〕 –see 見 MICROPHONE

mild /maɪld; maɪld/ *adj* **1** gentle (used of people) 溫和的〔指人〕: *He has too mild a nature to get angry, even if he has good reason.* 他性情十分溫和, 即使有充分的理由也不發火。 **2** not severe 不嚴重的: *The thief was given a milder punishment than he deserved.* 這小偷受到的懲罰比他應得的輕。 | *It's been a mild winter this year.* 今年冬天不太冷。 **3** not strong, rough, or bitter 味淡的; 不苦的; 不粗糙的: *mild cheese* 味淡的乾酪 | *mild soap* 軟性肥皂 –**mildness** *n* [U]

mil·dew /'mɪl,dju; 'mɪldju/ *n* [U] a growth that forms on food, leather or plants, that have been kept for a long time in warm and wet conditions 霉; 霉菌

mild·ly /'maɪldlɪ; 'maɪldli/ *adv* **1** in a mild way 溫和地: *She complained loudly to the shopkeeper, who answered her mildly.* 她大聲向店主抱怨; 店主卻溫和地回答她。 **2** slightly 輕微地; 稍微: *I was only mildly interested in the story I read in the newspaper.* 在報上看到的那個故事, 我只是略感興趣罷了。 **3** **to put it mildly** using gentle words to describe something you think is bad 〔對自己認為不好的事〕説得婉轉些: *The government's policy has not been a great success, to put it mildly.* 説得婉轉些, 政府的政策不太成功。

mile /maɪl; maɪl/ *n* a unit for measuring length, equal to 1,609 metres or 1,760 yards 英里〔長度單位, 等於1609米或1760碼〕: *He has a 10-mile drive each day to and from his work.* 他每天上下班驅車十英里。 | *He walked for miles without getting tired.* 他走了好幾英里路也不累。

mile·age /'maɪlɪdʒ; 'maɪlɪdʒ/ *n* **1** [C;U] the distance that is travelled, measured in miles 英里數: *What mileage has your car done?* 你的汽車共行走了多少英里? | *What mileage does your car do per gallon?* 你的汽車一加侖汽油可走多少英里? **2** [U] *infml* an amount of use 〔非正式〕好處; 用處: *The newspapers are getting a lot of mileage out of the royal wedding — there's a new story about it every day.* 報界從皇家婚禮中得到不少好處——每天都有新的東西報道。

mile·om·e·ter /maɪ'lɒmətə; maɪ'lɒmɪtər/ *n BrE* (also 又作 **milometer**) an instrument

fitted in a vehicle to record the number of miles it travels 〔車裡的〕計程表: –see picutre on page 209 見 209 頁彩圖

mile·stone /'maɪl,ston; 'maɪlstəʊn/ *n* **1** a stone at the side of a road, on which the number of miles to the next town is marked 里程碑 **2** an important event in a person's life or in history 〔個人生活或歷史上的〕重要事件: *The invention of the wheel was a milestone in the history of the world.* 輪子的發明是世界歷史上的重大事件。

mi·lieu /mi'ljø; 'miːljɜː/ *n* **milieus** or **milieux** /-'ljøz, -ljɜːz/ surroundings, especially a person's social surroundings 環境; 〔尤指人的〕社會環境

mil·i·tant /'mɪlətənt; 'mɪlɪtənt/ *adj* being ready to fight or use force, or saying that you are 好鬥的; 好戰的; 激進的: *A few militant members of the crowd started throwing stones at the police.* 人羣中幾個好鬥的人開始向警察扔石頭。 | *a militant speech* 激進的演説 –**militant** *n*: *The student disorders were blamed on a few militants.* 這次學生鬧事歸咎於幾個激進分子。 –**militancy** *n* [U] **militantly** *adv*

mil·i·ta·ry[1] /'mɪlə,tɛrɪ; 'mɪlɪtəri/ *adj* [only before a noun 只用於名詞前] connected with soldiers, armies, or war 軍人的; 軍隊的; 戰爭的: *In some countries all the young men do a year's military service.* 在某些國家, 所有的男青年都要服一年兵役。 | *combined naval and military operations* 海陸軍聯合的軍事行動 | *a military hospital* 陸軍醫院

military[2] *n* [*pl*] **the military** the army 軍隊: *The military were called in to restore order in the city.* 軍隊奉召到市內維持治安。

mil·i·tate /'mɪlə,tet; 'mɪlɪteɪt/ *v* **militated, militating**

militate against sthg *phr v* [T] to act as a reason against something 對〔某事〕有影響; 妨礙: *The fact that he'd been in prison militated against his chances of getting a job in a bank.* 他曾蹲過監獄, 這件事影響了他在銀行謀職的機會。

mi·li·tia /mə'lɪʃə; mə'lɪʃə/ *n* men trained as soldiers who are not members of the regular army but used only in special situations 民兵: *The militia are sometimes used for dealing with riots.* 民兵有時會負責鎮壓騷亂。

milk[1] /mɪlk; mɪlk/ *n* [U] **1** a white liquid produced by female animals to feed their young; the milk of some animals is drunk by human beings or made into butter or cheese 奶; 牛奶; 羊奶: *a bottle of milk* 一瓶牛奶 –see picture on page 504 見 504 頁彩圖 **2** a whitish liquid or juice obtained from certain plants and trees 〔某些植物和樹木的〕乳液; 汁水: *coconut milk* 椰子汁

milk[2] *v* **1** [I;T] to take milk from a cow, goat, or other animal 擠〔牛、羊等的〕奶;

The farmer milks the cows twice a day. 農夫一天給母牛擠兩次奶。 **2** [T] to get money from someone or something by clever or dishonest means 榨取〔錢財〕: *He lives by milking his parents for all they are worth.* 他靠不斷榨取爹娘的錢財過活。

milk float /'· ·/ *n BrE* a vehicle driven by electricity which is used by a milkman for delivering milk〔英式〕(電動)送奶車

milk·man /'mɪlk,mæn; 'mɪlkmən/ *n* **milk·men** /-mɛn; -mən/ a man who sells milk, especially one who goes from house to house each day to deliver it 賣牛奶的人;〔尤指〕送牛奶的人

milk shake /,· '·/ *n* a drink of milk and ICE CREAM shaken up together and given the taste of fruit, chocolate or other things 奶昔〔牛奶和冰淇淋混在一起的飲料，有水果味、巧克力味或其他味道〕

milk·y /'mɪlkɪ; 'mɪlki/ *adj* **milkier, milkiest 1** containing a lot of milk 含奶的: *I like my coffee milky.* 我喜歡在咖啡中多加些牛奶。 **2** not clear (used of liquids) 混濁的〔指液體〕–**milkiness** *n* [U]

★mill¹ /mɪl; mɪl/ *n* **1** a large machine for crushing corn or grain into flour 碾磨機; 磨粉機 **2** a building where certain goods are produced 工廠; 工場: *Cotton cloth is made in a cotton mill.* 棉布是由棉紡廠生產的。| *The valley was full of disused mills.* 這村子裡到處都是廢棄的工場。 **3** a small machine, used in a kitchen, for crushing certain things into powder 家用粉碎機; 碾磨機: *a coffee mill* 咖啡碾磨機 | *a pepper mill* 胡椒碾磨機

mill² *v* [T] to crush something in a mill and produce it in the form of a powder 碾磨, 碾碎〔某物〕: *The flour was milled only two miles from where the corn had grown.* 磨麵粉的地方離小麥生長處僅兩英里遠。

mill about/around *phr v* [I] to move without purpose in large numbers 成羣無目的地移動: *There were a lot of people milling about in the streets.* 許多人漫無目的地在街上轉來轉去。

mil·len·ni·um /mə'lɛnɪəm; mɪ'lɛnɪəm/ *n* **millennia** /-nɪə; -nɪə/ **1** a period of 1,000 years 一千年; 千年期 **2 the millennium** a future age in which all people will be happy and contented 未來的太平盛世

mil·le·pede /'mɪlə,pid; 'mɪl²pi:d/ *n* –see 見 MILLIPEDE

mill·er /'mɪlə; 'mɪləʳ/ *n* a man who owns or works a mill that produces flour 磨坊主; 磨坊工人

mil·let /'mɪlɪt; 'mɪl²t/ *n* [U] the small seeds of certain grain plants used as food 小米: *millet cakes* 小米餅 | *a bag of millet* 一袋小米

mil·li·gram /'mɪlə,græm; 'mɪl²græm/ *n* (also 又作 **milligramme**) a unit for measuring weight, equal to 1,000th of a gram

mil·li·li·tre /'mɪlə,litə; 'mɪl²,li:təʳ/ *n* (**milliliter** *AmE*〔美式〕) a liquid measure equal to 1,000th of a litre 毫升〔千分之一升〕

mil·li·me·tre /'mɪlə,mitə; 'mɪl²,mi:təʳ/ (**millimeter** *AmE*〔美式〕) *n* a unit for measuring length, equal to 1,000th of a metre 毫米〔千分之一米〕

mil·li·ner /'mɪlənə; 'mɪl²nəʳ/ *n* a person who makes or sells women's hats 女帽製造商或銷售商

mil·li·ne·ry /'mɪlə,nɛrɪ; 'mɪl²nəri/ *n* [U] the goods made or sold by a milliner 女帽: *the millinery department in a large shop* 大商店裡的女帽部

mil·lion /'mɪljən; 'mɪljən/ *det, n, pron* **million** *or* **millions** the number 1,000,000 一百萬

mil·lion·aire /,mɪljən'ɛr; ,mɪljə'neəʳ◂/ *n* a very wealthy person who has at least 1,000,000 pounds or dollars; a woman millionaire is called a **millionairess** 百萬富翁; 巨富〔女百萬富翁叫 **millionairess**〕

mil·li·pede /'mɪlə,pid; 'mɪl²pi:d/ *n* (also 又作 **millepede**) a small creature rather like a worm, but with a lot of legs 馬陸; 千足蟲

mill·stone /'mɪl,ston; 'mɪlstəʊn/ *n* **1** a circular stone used to make flour 磨石; 磨盤 **2** a **millstone round your neck** a person or thing that gives you trouble or worries 帶來麻煩或憂慮的人或物

mil·om·e·ter /maɪ'lɒmətə; maɪ'lɒm²təʳ/ *n* see 見 MILEOMETER

mime¹ /maɪm; maɪm/ *n* **1** [U] the practice of using actions without language to show meaning 做手勢: *I couldn't speak Chinese, but I showed in mime that I wanted a drink.* 我不會講漢語，但我用手勢表示要杯飲料。| *the art of mime* 手勢的藝術 **2** [C] an actor who performs without using words 啞劇演員

mime² *v* **mimed, miming** [I;T] to act something in mime 以啞劇的形式表演; 模仿表演: *The actor was miming the movements of a bird.* 演員在模仿表演鳥的動作。

mim·ic /'mɪmɪk; 'mɪmɪk/ *n* a person who is good at copying someone else's manners or speech especially in a way that causes laughter 善於模仿的人;〔尤指〕逗笑的人 – **mimic** *v* **mimicked, mimicking** [T]: *She made us all laugh by mimicking the teacher.* 她模仿老師，逗得我們大家都笑了。

min.¹ *n* a written abbreviation for〔縮〕= MINUTES: *Boil for 10 min., drain, and serve.* 煮十分鐘，瀝乾，然後端上去。

min.² *adj* a written abbreviation for〔縮〕= MINIMUM: *min. length 30 metres* 最短三十米長

min·a·ret /,mɪnə'rɛt; ,mɪnə'ret/ *n* a tall thin tower on a MOSQUE, from which Muslims are called to prayer〔伊斯蘭教寺院的〕宣禮塔

mince[1] /mɪns; mɪns/ v **minced, mincing 1** [T] to cut meat into very small pieces 將〔肉〕切碎; 剁碎 **2** [I+adv/prep] to walk in an unnatural way, taking short little steps 〔扭扭捏捏地〕用小碎步走路 **3 not mince matters, not mince your words** to speak of something bad or unpleasant using plain direct language 直截了當地說

mince[2] n [U] **1** BrE meat that has been minced 〔英式〕肉末; 肉糜 **2** AmE mincemeat 〔美式〕百果餡

mince·meat /'mɪns‚mit; 'mɪns-miːt/ n [U] **1** a mixture of dried fruit, used as a sweet filling inside pastry 百果餡 **2 make mincemeat of** infml to defeat or destroy a person or thing 〔非正式〕擊敗; 擊潰: *She makes mincemeat of the people she interviews.* 她令接受她採訪的人狼狽不堪。

*★**mind**[1] /maɪnd; maɪnd/ n **1** [C;U] your way of thinking or the thoughts that you have 思維(方法); 想法: *She has a very quick mind.* 她的思維很敏捷。 | *I can't get that picture out of my mind.* 我忘不了那情景。 | *I'm sorry, I wasn't listening — my mind was on other things.* 對不起, 我沒在聽——我在想其他事情。 **2** [C] a person who is able to think well and has good ideas 有才智的人: *She's among the best scientific minds in the country.* 她是這個國家最有科學才智的人物之一。 **3 be in two minds about something** to be unable to make a decision about something 無法對某事做出決定: *I'm still in two minds about whether to accept the job.* 我對於是否接受這份工作仍拿不定主意。 **4 change your mind** to change your opinion 改變主意: *I was going to leave tomorrow, but I've changed my mind.* 我本打算明天走, 但我改變主意了。 **5 come to mind, spring to mind** to come into your mind suddenly 突然出現在腦海中: *One or two ideas sprang to mind.* 一兩個念頭突然浮上腦海。 **6 in your mind's eye** in a picture that you have in your mind 在頭腦想像中: *In my mind's eye I could see him sitting at a desk in a dingy office.* 我可以想像他在一間昏暗的辦公室裡坐在桌子旁的樣子。 **7 it went out of my mind** = I forget about it 我忘了 **8 have a good mind to do something** to feel that you would like to do something 真有點想做某事: *I've got a good mind to leave home!* 我真有點想離家! **9 have something on your mind** to be thinking or worrying about some thing 正在想或擔心某事: *I've had a lot on my mind recently.* 近來我有許多事牽腸掛肚。 **10 keep your mind on something** to continue thinking about something 把注意力集中在某事物上: *Try to keep your mind on your work.* 盡量把注意力集中在你的工作上。 **11 keep something in mind** to remember something 記住某事: *You must keep in mind the fact that most of these women have never worked before.* 你必須記住這些婦

女大多數從未工作過。 **12 make up your mind** to decide 下決心; 決定: *I can't make up my mind whether to accept his offer or not.* 我無法決定是否要接受他的提議。 **13 no one in their right mind** no one who is sensible 所有神志正常的人都不會…: *No one in their right mind would buy that house!* 神志正常的人絕對不會買那幢房子! **14 of one mind, of the same mind** having the same opinion about something 有一致意見的: *We are of the same mind on this matter.* 在這件事上我們意見一致。 **15 out of your mind** infml mad 〔非正式〕發瘋的 **16 put your mind to something** to give your attention to something 注意某事物; 專心於某事物: *She could easily pass the exam if she put her mind to it.* 如果她專心致志, 就能輕易及格。 **17 state of mind** the way that you are feeling, for example how happy or sad you are feeling 心情; 情緒: *At the moment he's in a very unconfident state of mind.* 目前他處於極度缺乏信心的情況。 **18 take your mind off something** to make you stop thinking about something 使不再想某事物: *I need a holiday to take my mind off all my problems.* 我需要休假, 暫時不去想這許多的問題。 **19 to my mind** in my opinion 依我看; 根據我的意見: *To my mind it's the government's responsibility to help these people.* 依我看幫助這些人是政府的責任。 **20 turn your mind to something** to begin to think about something seriously 開始認真考慮某事: *Now let's turn our minds to tomorrow's meeting.* 現在讓我們集中精神安排明天開會的事情。

mind[2] v **1** [I;T] used in commands to tell someone to be careful 注意; 當心〔用於命令句〕: *Mind the step.* 小心那級台階。 | *Mind you don't drop that glass.* 當心別掉了那隻玻璃杯。 | *Mind! You nearly knocked me over.* 小心! 你差點把我撞倒! **2 Mind out!** a phrase you use when you are warning someone that there is danger 當心〔用於警告某人有危險〕: *Mind out! There's a car coming!* 當心! 有輛汽車開過來了! **3** [T] to take care of a child or an animal 照料, 照看〔孩子或動物〕: *I need someone to mind the baby while I'm out.* 我需要找個人在我外出時照看嬰兒。 **4** [I; T] to be annoyed about something or be opposed to it 介意; 反對: *I borrowed your car yesterday — I hope you don't mind.* 我昨天借用了你的汽車——希望你不介意。 | *Would you mind if I opened the window?* 你介意我開窗嗎? | *Do you mind if I use your telephone?* 我借用你的電話行嗎? **5 I don't mind** I would be happy with either thing 無所謂: *"Would you like red or white wine?" "I don't mind."* "你要紅葡萄酒還是白葡萄酒?" "無所謂。" **6 I wouldn't mind** infml a phrase you use to say that you would like something 〔非正式〕〔用於表示想要某物〕: *I wouldn't mind a little rest!* 我覺得歇一會兒也不錯! **7 mind your own business** a phrase

M

you use to tell someone not to be too interested in things that do not concern them 別管閒事; 管好你自己的事 **8 mind you** a phrase you use when you are adding more information to what you have just said 請注意; 告訴你吧〔用於補充所說的內容〕: *He spends a lot of his time in bed now. Mind you, he is 93.* 他現在有很多時間都是在牀上度過的。 告訴你吧, 他九十三歲了。 **9 never mind** it doesn't matter 沒關係; 不要緊: *"I'm afraid I've broken your dish." "Never mind, it was only a cheap one."* "對不起, 我打碎了你的碟子。" "沒關係, 這只是個便宜的碟子。"

mind·er /ˈmaɪndə; ˈmaɪndəʳ/ *n* a person whose job is to look after someone, especially a young child 照料人員;〔尤指〕照看兒童者

mind·less /ˈmaɪndlɪs; ˈmaɪndləs/ *adj* **1** stupid, and done without thought 愚笨的; 不用腦子的: *mindless cruelty* 無意中造成的殘酷行為 **2** so simple that no thought is needed 簡單得毋須動腦筋的: *a mindless task* 不必動腦筋的任務 **–mindlessly** *adv*

mine¹ /maɪn; maɪn/ *pron* something relating to or belonging to the person who is speaking 我的(東西): *His house is very similar to mine.* 他的房子和我的很像。 | *Put that book down — it's mine!* 放下那本書 — 那是我的!

★**mine²** *n* **1** a deep hole or network of holes under the ground from which coal, gold, tin, and other mineral substances are dug 礦; 礦井: *a coal mine* 煤礦 | *There's been an accident at the mine!* 礦上發生意外事故啦! – compare 比較 QUARRY **2** a kind of bomb that is placed just below the ground or in the sea and is exploded electrically from far away or when touched 地雷; 水雷 **3** a **mine of information** a person who knows a lot about a particular subject〔對某一問題〕所知甚多者

mine³ *v* **mined, mining 1** [I;T] to dig substances out of the ground 採礦; 開採: *Coal was mined here for centuries.* 在這裡採煤有數個世紀了。 | *He's interested in a career in mining.* 他對採礦這一職業感興趣。 | *They are mining for diamonds.* 他們在開採鑽石。 **2** [T] to put bombs in the ground or the sea 佈水雷; 埋地雷: *All the roads leading to the city had been mined.* 通往這座城市的所有道路都佈了地雷。

mine·field /ˈmaɪnˌfild; ˈmaɪnfiːld/ *n* a piece of land or water in which mines have been placed 佈雷區

min·er /ˈmaɪnə; ˈmaɪnəʳ/ *n* a person who works underground digging out mineral substances 礦工

min·e·ral /ˈmɪnərəl; ˈmɪnərəl/ *n* any solid substance like salt or coal formed naturally in the earth 礦物

mineral wa·ter /ˈ··· ˌ··/ *n* [C;U] water that comes from a natural spring and contains minerals which are thought to be good for you 礦泉水: *a bottle of mineral water* 一瓶礦泉水 | *I'll have a mineral water, please.* 請給我來一杯礦泉水。

min·gle /ˈmɪŋɡl; ˈmɪŋɡəl/ *v* **mingled, mingling** [I;T] to mix with another thing or with other people (使)混合: *The king often left his palace at night and mingled with the people in the streets.* 國王常在晚上離開王宮和街上的人羣混在一起。 | *mingled joy and sorrow* 悲喜交加

min·i·a·ture /ˈmɪnətʃə; ˈmɪniətʃəʳ/ *n* **1** a very small copy of something that is usually bigger 微型複製品: *The child was playing with his miniature railway.* 這孩子在玩他的微型玩具鐵路。 **2 in miniature** in a much smaller form 微型的 **3** a very small painting of a person 微型人像

min·i·bus /ˈmɪnɪbʌs; ˈmɪnibʌs/ *n* **1** a small bus with seats for between six and twelve people 小型公共汽車〔乘員六至十二人〕: *The children go to school in a minibus.* 孩子們坐小型公共汽車上學。 **2 by minibus** travelling in a small bus 坐小型公共汽車: *We're travelling by minibus.* 我們坐小型公共汽車旅行。

min·i·mal /ˈmɪnɪml; ˈmɪniˌməl/ *adj* the smallest possible amount or size 最低限度的; 最小的; 最少的: *Fortunately, the storm only did minimal damage to the crops.* 幸好, 暴風雨只給莊稼造成了很小的損失。 **–minimally** *adv*

min·i·mize /ˈmɪnɪmaɪz; ˈmɪniˌmaɪz/ *v* **minimized, minimizing** (also 又作 **minimise** BrE《英式》) [T] to reduce something to the smallest possible amount or degree 使〔某事物〕減到最小數量或最低限度: *You can minimize the danger of driving at night by driving slowly and with great care.* 如果你放慢車速, 多加小心, 就能把夜間駕駛的危險性降到最低。 –compare 比較 MAXIMIZE

★**min·i·mum** /ˈmɪnəməm; ˈmɪniˌməm/ *adj* smallest in amount or lowest in price of what is possible or needed 最低的; 最小的: *He does the minimum amount of work and then expects promotion!* 他工作幹得最少卻盼着晉昇! –compare 比較 MAXIMUM – **minimum** *n*: *Let's try and keep the cost to a minimum.* 讓我們嘗試把成本降到最低。

min·ing /ˈmaɪnɪŋ; ˈmaɪnɪŋ/ *n* [U] the action or industry of getting minerals out of the earth by digging 採礦(業): *coalmining* 採煤業 | *a mining company* 採礦公司

★**min·is·ter¹** /ˈmɪnɪstə; ˈmɪnɪstəʳ/ *n* **1** a politician who is a member of the government and is in charge of a particular government department 部長; 大臣: *the Minister of Transport* 運輸部長 | *the Foreign Minister* 外交大臣 **2** a priest in some branches of the Christian church〔基督教某些教派的〕牧師 –see 見 PRIEST (USAGE用法)

M

minister² v [I] *fml* **minister to someone** to help someone and provide what is needed 〔正式〕幫助〔某人〕; 侍候〔某人〕: *We minister to the sick.* 我們照料病人。

min·is·ter·i·al /ˌmɪnəˈstɪrɪəl; ˌmɪnɪˈstɪəriəl/ *adj* connected with a government minister or ministry 部長的; 部的: *As part of her ministerial duties, she often had to travel abroad.* 她得經常出國, 這是身為部長的一部分職責。

★**min·is·try** /ˈmɪnɪstrɪ; ˈmɪnɪstri/ *n* **ministries** **1** (also 又作 **Ministry**) a government department led by a minister 〔政府的〕部: *The army, navy, and airforce are all controlled by the Ministry of Defence.* 海、陸、空軍都受國防部指揮。**2 the ministry** the profession or work of a priest 牧師職位或工作: *Our son wants to enter the ministry.* 我們的兒子想做牧師。

mink /mɪŋk; mɪŋk/ *n* [C;U] a small brown animal which produces valuable fur 水貂: *a mink coat* 貂皮大衣

★**mi·nor¹** /ˈmaɪnə; ˈmaɪnər/ *adj* small in degree, size, or importance, especially in comparison with something else 較輕微的; 較小的; 較次要的: *She has been given a minor part in the new play.* 她在這齣新戲裡分到一個次要角色。| *a very minor illness* 微恙; 小病 –opposite 反義 **major**

minor² *n law* a person below the age at which they are fully responsible in law for their actions; in Britain a minor is a person who is not yet 18 years old 〔律〕未成年人〔在英國指未滿十八歲的人〕

★**mi·nor·i·ty** /məˈnɔrətɪ; maɪˈnɒrɪti/ *n* **minorities** [+ sing/pl verb] **1** the smaller number or part of something 少數: *Only a minority of people want the war to continue.* 只有少數人希望戰爭繼續下去。–compare 比較 MAJORITY **2** a small part of a population which is different from the rest in race or religion 少數民族: *a law to protect religious minorities* 保護少數民族宗教信仰的法律 **3** [only before a noun 只用於名詞前] supported by a small number of people 少數派: *Cricket is a minority sport in the US.* 板球在美國只是少數人喜愛的運動。

min·ster /ˈmɪnstə; ˈmɪnstər/ *n* a large or important church 大教堂

min·strel /ˈmɪnstrəl; ˈmɪnstrəl/ *n* a musician in the Middle Ages who travelled around the country playing and singing songs 〔中世紀的〕遊方音樂家

mint¹ /mɪnt; mɪnt/ *n* **1** [U] a small plant whose leaves have a strong fresh smell and taste and are used in preparing drinks or food 薄荷 **2** [C] a sweet with the taste of PEPPERMINT 薄荷糖: *Have one of these mints!* 請吃塊這種薄荷糖! **3** [C] a place in which coins and banknotes are officially made by the government 鑄幣廠: *the Royal Mint* 皇家鑄幣廠 **4 in mint condition** new or like new and so in perfect condition 嶄新的

mint² v [T] to produce money officially 鑄造〔錢幣〕

min·u·et /ˌmɪnjuˈɛt; ˌmɪnjuˈet/ *n* a type of slow graceful dance or the music for it 小步舞(曲)

mi·nus¹ /ˈmaɪnəs; ˈmaɪnəs/ *prep* **1** less 減去: *17 minus 5 leaves 12.* 十七減五等於十二。**2** below the freezing point of water by the stated number of degrees 零下的: *The temperature was minus 10 degrees.* 氣溫是零下十度。**3** without a person or thing that is missing 缺少: *Now the team is minus a goalkeeper.* 眼下這個隊缺少一個守門員。

minus² *n* (also 又作 **minus sign**) a sign (-) used to show that the stated number is less than zero or that the second number is to be taken away from the first 負號; 減號

minus³ *adj* [only before a noun 只用於名詞前] less than zero 負的; 零下的 –compare 比較 PLUS³

min·us·cule /ˈmɪnʌskjul; ˈmɪnəskjuːl/ *adj* very, very small 極小的

★**min·ute¹** /ˈmɪnɪt; ˈmɪnɪt/ *n* **1** [C] one of the sixty parts into which an hour is divided 分〔一小時的六十分之一〕: *The train arrived at exactly four minutes past eight.* 火車八點零四分正到達。| *It's only a few minutes' walk from here to the station.* 從這兒到火車站只要走幾分鐘。**2** [sing] *infml* a very short space of time 〔非正式〕一會兒; 片刻: *I'll be ready in a minute.* 我馬上就準備好。| *"Are you ready yet?" "No, but I won't be a minute."* "你準備好了嗎?" "還沒有, 不過馬上就好。" | *It'll just take a minute.* 只要花一會兒工夫。**3 at any minute** very soon 隨時; 馬上: *We're expecting him at any minute.* 他隨時會來。**4 the minute** as soon as 一…就: *I recognized him the minute I saw him.* 我一看到他就認出來了。**5 this minute** immediately 立刻; 馬上: *Come here this minute!* 馬上來這裡! **6** [C] a unit of measurement equal to a 60th of a degree 分〔角的度量單位, 一度的六十分之一〕: *The exact measurement of this angle is 80 degrees 30 minutes (80°30').* 這個角的確切度數是 80 度 30 分。**7 minutes** [pl] a written record of business done, suggestions made, and decisions taken at a meeting 會議記錄: *The minutes of the last meeting were read out to the committee.* 向委員會宣讀了上次的會議記錄。

mi·nute² /məˈnjut; maɪˈnjuːt/ *adj* very small indeed 微小的: *I've never seen such minute writing.* 我從未見過這麼小的字體。| *minute details* 細枝末節 –**minutely** *adv*

mir·a·cle /ˈmɪrəkl; ˈmɪrəkəl/ *n* **1** a wonderful happening that cannot be explained by the laws of nature and is said to be the work of God or a holy person 〔神或聖人創造的〕奇蹟: *Christ is supposed to have performed*

M

miracles such as turning water into wine. 一般認為耶穌創造了許多奇蹟，例如把水變成酒。 **2** a surprising and wonderful happening 奇事; 不可思議的事: *It will be a miracle if I pass the examination.* 如果我能通過考試，那將是一個奇蹟。 | *a miracle cure* 特效療法

mi·rac·u·lous /mɪˈrækjələs; mɪˈrækjʊ̩ləs/ *adj* surprising and wonderful 令人驚奇的; 神奇的: *He made a miraculous recovery from his illness.* 他生病後奇蹟般地康復了。 | *miraculous beauty* 超脫的美麗 **–miraculously** *adv: It was a terrible explosion, but miraculously no one was killed.* 這是一次可怕的爆炸，但沒有一個人死亡，真是奇蹟。

mi·rage /məˈrɑːʒ; ˈmɪrɑːʒ/ *n* a strange effect of hot air conditions in a desert, in which objects can be seen which are not really there 海市蜃樓

★**mir·ror**¹ /ˈmɪrə; ˈmɪrəʳ/ *n* a piece of glass, or other shiny or polished surface, which shows images that fall on it 鏡子: *He examined himself carefully in the bathroom mirror.* 他在浴室的鏡子前仔細地打量自己。

mirror² *v* [T] to represent or to be similar to something else 反映〔某事物〕; 與〔某物〕相似

mirth /mɜːθ; mɜːθ/ *n* [U] *fml* joy and laughter 〔正式〕歡樂; 歡笑 **–mirthless** *adj*

mis·ad·ven·ture /ˌmɪsədˈventʃə; ˌmɪsədˈventʃəʳ/ *n* [C;U] *law or lit* bad luck, like an accident 〔律或文〕不幸; 意外事故: *A verdict was recorded of death by misadventure.* 記錄在案的裁決是意外致死。

mis·an·throp·ic /ˌmɪsənˈθrɒpɪk; ˌmɪsənˈθrɑːpɪk/ *adj* a word used to describe someone who hates everybody, trusts no one, and avoids being in the company of others 厭惡人類的; 不與他人交往的

mis·ap·ply /ˌmɪsəˈplaɪ; ˌmɪsəˈplaɪ/ *v* **misapplied, misapplying** [T] *fml* to use something for the wrong purpose 〔正式〕誤用; 濫用 **–misapplication** /ˌmɪsæpləˈkeɪʃən; ˌmɪsæpl̩ˈkeɪʃən/ *n* [C;U]

mis·ap·pre·hend /ˌmɪsæprɪˈhend; ˌmɪsæprɪˈhend/ *v* [T] *fml* to understand something wrongly 〔正式〕誤解〔某事〕: *The accident was caused by one motorist completely misapprehending the intentions of the other.* 事故發生的原因是一個汽車駕駛員完全誤解了另一個駕駛員的意圖。 **–misapprehension** *n* [C;U]

mis·ap·pro·pri·ate /ˌmɪsəˈprəʊprɪˌet; ˌmɪsəˈprəʊprieɪt/ *v* **misappropriated, misappropriating** [T] *fml or law* to take something and use it dishonestly 〔正式或律〕挪用; 盜用; 侵佔; 私吞: *He was sent to prison for misappropriating company money.* 他由於挪用公司的錢而被關進了監獄。 **–misappropriation** /ˌmɪsəprəʊprɪˈeɪʃən; ˌmɪsəprəʊprɪˈeɪʃən/ *n* [C;U]

mis·be·have /ˌmɪsbɪˈhev; ˌmɪsbɪˈheɪv/ *v* **misbehaved, misbehaving** [T] to behave badly 行為不端; 舉止不檢點: *She was punished for misbehaving in class.* 她由於上課不守紀律而受罰。

mis·be·ha·viour /ˌmɪsbɪˈhevjə; ˌmɪsbɪˈheɪvjəʳ/ *n BrE* (**misbehavior** *AmE* 〚美式〛) [U] bad behaviour 〚英式〛不規矩行為; 不正當舉止

mis·cal·cu·late /ˌmɪsˈkælkjəˌlet; ˌmɪsˈkælkjʊ̩leɪt/ *v* **miscalculated, miscalculating** [I; T] to calculate wrongly 算錯: *I miscalculated the time it would take me to reach the station.* 我算錯了到車站所需的時間。 **–miscalculation** /ˌmɪskælkjəˈleɪʃən; mɪsˌkælkjʊ̩ˈleɪʃən/ *n* [C;U]

mis·car·riage /ˌmɪsˈkærɪdʒ; ˌmɪsˈkærɪdʒ/ *n* **1** an act of giving birth too early for the baby to live 小產; 流產: *She's had another miscarriage.* 她又小產了。 **–compare** 比較 ABORTION, STILLBIRTH **2 miscarriage of justice** a wrong decision by the law courts, which results in the punishment of a person who is not guilty 審判不公; 誤判

mis·car·ry /ˌmɪsˈkæri; ˌmɪsˈkæri/ *v* **miscarried, miscarrying** [I] **1** (of a woman) to give birth to a baby too early for it to live 〔孕婦〕小產; 流產 **2** (of an intention or plan) to be unsuccessful 〔意圖、計劃〕失敗; 受挫

mis·cel·la·ne·ous /ˌmɪslˈenɪəs; ˌmɪslˈleɪnɪəs/ *adj* of different kinds 各種各樣的; 不同種類的

mis·chief /ˈmɪstʃɪf; ˈmɪstʃ̩f/ *n* [U] **1** enjoyable behaviour, often by children, which others do not approve of 惡作劇; 胡鬧; 搗蛋: *She's always getting into mischief.* 她老是搗蛋。 | *It's very quiet, so I expect they're up to some mischief.* 真靜，我估計他們在搞甚麼惡作劇。 **2** behaviour which is intended to cause harm 意在引起危害的行為: *Be careful who you tell. There's always someone ready to make mischief.* 不要隨便告訴其他人，小心有人會挑撥離間。

mis·chie·vous /ˈmɪstʃɪvəs; ˈmɪstʃ̩vəs/ *adj* **1** showing enjoyment of things that others do not approve of 惡作劇的; 愛搗蛋的; 淘氣的: *a mischievous smile* 淘氣的笑容 | *mischievous child* 淘氣的孩子 **2** intended to cause trouble 惡意的; 有害的: *a mischievous remark* 惡意中傷的話 **–mischievously** *adv*

mis·con·ceived /ˌmɪskənˈsivd; ˌmɪskənˈsiːvd/ *adj* unsuitable and badly thought out 設想錯誤的: *The government's plan for the railways is wholly misconceived.* 政府的鐵路規劃設想得完全不對頭。

mis·con·cep·tion /ˌmɪskənˈsepʃən; ˌmɪskənˈsepʃən/ *n* a wrong understanding of something 誤解: *Public attitudes to doctors are based on the misconception that they are well-paid.* 公眾對醫生有一種錯誤的印象，認為他們報酬優厚。

mis·con·duct /ˌmɪsˈkɒndʌkt; ˌmɪsˈkɒndʌkt/ *n* [U] *fml* bad behaviour, especially by a professional person 〔正式〕不端行為;〔尤指

職業人士的〕不法行為: *Both lawyers have been accused of misconduct.* 兩名律師都被控行為不法。

mis·con·struc·tion /ˌmɪskən'strʌkʃən; ˌmɪskən'strʌkʃən/ *n* [C;U] *fml* mistaken understanding《正式》曲解; 誤解: *A law must be stated in the clearest language, so that there is no danger of misconstruction.* 法律條文必須用最清楚的語言來陳述, 這樣就無曲解之虞了。

mis·con·strue /ˌmɪskən'stru; ˌmɪskən'struː/ *v* **misconstrued, misconstruing** [T] *fml* to understand something in a way that was not intended《正式》誤解〔某事物〕: *Do you think my behaviour could have been misconstrued?* 你認為我的行為會遭到誤解嗎?

mis·deeds /ˌmɪs'diːdz; ˌmɪs'diːdz/ *n* [pl] *fml* or *lit* wrong or wicked acts《正式或文》不端行為; 惡行; 罪惡: *He was punished at last for his many misdeeds.* 他終於因為種種罪行而受到懲罰。

mis·de·mea·nour /ˌmɪsdɪ'miːnə; ˌmɪsdɪ'miːnəʳ/ *n BrE*《英式》(**misdemeanor** *AmE*《美式》) **1** *fml* an action that is wrong but not very serious《正式》〔情節較輕的〕行為不檢 **2** *law* a crime that is less serious than, for example, stealing or murder《律》輕罪 – compare 比較 FELONY

mis·di·rect /ˌmɪsdə'rɛkt; ˌmɪsdə'rɛkt/ *v* [T] to direct a person wrongly 給(人)指錯方向: *I asked a boy the way to the station, but he misdirected me.* 我問一個男孩去火車站怎麼走, 他卻給我指錯了方向。

mi·ser /'maɪzə; 'maɪzəʳ/ *n derog* a person who hates spending money, and who saves it instead (a word used to express disapproval) 吝嗇鬼; 守財奴〔含貶義〕–**miserly** *adj*

mis·e·ra·ble /'mɪzərəbl; 'mɪzərəbəl/ *adj* **1** very unhappy 很不幸的; 痛苦的: *The child is cold, hungry, and tired, so of course he's feeling miserable.* 這孩子又冷又餓, 疲憊不堪, 他當然感到很痛苦。**2** very poor in quality or amount〔質量〕蹩腳的; 糟糕的;〔數量〕少[小]得可憐的: *What miserable weather!* 多糟糕的天氣! | *Who can live on such a miserable salary?* 誰能靠少得這麼可憐的薪水過活? –**miserably** *adv* : *a miserably cold day* 冷得要命的一天 | *She failed miserably.* 她失敗得很慘。

mis·e·ry /'mɪzəri; 'mɪzəri/ *n* [U] great unhappiness or suffering 痛苦; 不幸; 苦難: *Her baby died and, to add to her misery, she lost her job.* 她的嬰兒夭折了, 使她更為痛苦的是, 她又失了業。

mis·fire /ˌmɪs'faɪə; ˌmɪs'faɪəʳ/ *v* **misfired, misfiring** [I] **1** (of a gun) to fail to send out the bullet when fired〔槍〕不發火; 射不出子彈 **2** (of a plan or joke) to fail to have the desired result〔計劃、笑話〕達不到預期效果

mis·fit /'mɪsˌfɪt; 'mɪsˌfɪt/ *n* a person who

does not fit well and happily into their social or work situation 不適應社會或工作環境的人

mis·for·tune /mɪs'fɔːtʃən; mɪs'fɔːtʃən/ *n* [C; U] bad luck, often of a serious nature 晦氣; 厄運: *His failure in business was due to misfortune, not his own mistakes.* 他生意失敗是由於運氣太壞, 而不是決策失誤造成的。

mis·giv·ing /mɪs'gɪvɪŋ; mɪs'gɪvɪŋ/ *n* [C;U] a feeling of doubt 疑慮; 擔憂: *He looked with misgiving at the strange food on his plate.* 他用疑慮的眼光看他碟子上奇怪的食物。| *I could see he had some misgivings about lending me his car.* 我看得出, 他對於把汽車借給我有點不放心。

mis·guid·ed /mɪs'gaɪdɪd; mɪs'gaɪdɪd/ *adj* wrong, as a result of ideas that are not correct (used of opinions or actions) 被錯誤引導的〔指主意或行動〕: *She has a misguided view of human nature.* 她對人性的看法不對頭。

mis·han·dle /mɪs'hændl; ˌmɪs'hændl/ *v* **mishandled, mishandling** [T] to deal with something in the wrong way 處理〔某事〕不當: *The sale of the house was mishandled by the estate agents.* 房地產經紀人在這幢房子的銷售上處理不當。

mis·hap /'mɪsˌhæp; 'mɪshæp/ *n* something that happens to you which is unpleasant but not very serious 不幸的事; 小事故: *A mishap like losing his coat won't make him less cheerful.* 諸如丟了大衣之類的晦氣事並不會使他降低興致。

mis·in·form /ˌmɪsɪn'fɔːm; ˌmɪsɪn'fɔːm/ *v* [T] to give someone the wrong information 向〔某人〕誤報消息: *I believe that we have been misinformed* **about** *the cost of the new building.* 我認為關於這幢新大樓的成本, 我們得到的消息不正確。

mis·in·ter·pret /ˌmɪsɪn'tɜːprɪt; ˌmɪsɪn'tɜːprɪt/ *v* [T] to understand something wrongly 誤解: *The driver misinterpreted the sign and took the wrong road.* 駕駛員誤解了標誌, 走錯了路。–**misinterpretation** /ˌmɪsɪnˌtɜːprɪ'teɪʃən/ *n* [C;U]

mis·judge /mɪs'dʒʌdʒ; mɪs'dʒʌdʒ/ *v* **misjudged, misjudging** [T] to form a wrong opinion of someone 錯誤地判斷〔某人〕; 錯看〔某人〕: *He's honest, and you misjudge him if you think he isn't.* 他為人誠實, 如果你認為他不是的話, 那你就看錯了人。

mis·lay /mɪs'leɪ; mɪs'leɪ/ *v* **mislaid** /-'leɪd; -'leɪd/, **mislaid** [T] to put something somewhere and then forget where you put it 〔某物〕放在記不起的地方: *She's mislaid her glasses again.* 她又忘記把眼鏡放在甚麼地方了。

mis·lead /mɪs'liːd; mɪs'liːd/ *v* **misled** /-'lɛd; -'lɛd/, **misled** [T] to cause someone to have the wrong idea 使〔某人〕產生錯誤想法: *Don't let his friendly manner mislead you into trusting him.* 不要讓他友好的態度使你誤

M

信他。| *a misleading description* 騙人的描述

mis·man·age /ˌmɪsˈmænɪdʒ; ˌmɪsˈmænɪdʒ/ v **mismanaged, mismanaging** [T] to handle private or public affairs so badly that they are not successful 對〔私事或公事〕管理不善; 處理不當: *The company has been mismanaged for years.* 這家公司數年來經營不善。– **mismanagement** n [U]

mis·no·mer /mɪsˈnomə; mɪsˈnəʊməʳ/ n a wrong or unsuitable name 錯誤或使用不當的名字〔名稱〕: *To call it a hotel is a misnomer – it was more like a prison!* 稱它旅館是用詞不當——它更像一座監獄!

mi·so·gy·nist /mɪˈsɑdʒɜnɪst; mɪˈsɒdʒ ɪ nɪst/ n a person who hates women 厭惡女人者

mis·place /mɪsˈples; ˌmɪsˈpleɪs/ v **misplaced, misplacing** [T] to have good feelings for a person or thing that does not deserve them 把〔感情〕寄託於不值得寄托的對象: *Your trust in that man is misplaced.* 你錯信了那個男人。

mis·print /mɪsˈprɪnt; ˈmɪsˌprɪnt/ n a mistake in printing 印刷錯誤: *This newspaper is full of misprints.* 這張報紙有很多印刷錯誤的地方。

mis·pro·nounce /ˌmɪsprəˈnaʊns; ˌmɪsprəˈnaʊns/ v **mispronounced, mispronouncing** [T] to pronounce a word incorrectly 發錯〔詞的〕音 – **mispronunciation** /ˌmɪsprəˌnʌnsɪˈeɪʃən; ˌmɪsprəˌnʌnsɪˈeɪʃən/ n [C;U]

mis·quote /mɪsˈkwot; mɪsˈkwəʊt/ v **misquoted, misquoting** [T] to make a mistake in reporting words spoken or written by a person 錯誤地引用; 誤引: *The politician complained that the newspapers had misquoted him.* 這位政治家抱怨報紙錯誤引述他的話。– **misquotation** /-kwoˈteʃən; -kwəʊˈteɪʃən/ n [C;U]

mis·read /mɪsˈrid; ˌmɪsˈriːd/ v **misread** /-ˈrɛd; -ˈred/ **misread** /-ˈrɛd; -ˈred/ to read or understand something wrongly 讀錯; 誤解: *Did you misread the date on the letter?* 你有沒有看錯信上的日期? | *The general misread the enemy's intentions.* 將軍誤解了敵軍的意圖。

mis·rep·re·sent /ˌmɪsrɛprɪˈzent; ˌmɪsreprɪˈzent/ v [T] to give an untrue explanation or description of someone, or someone's words or actions, in such a way that unfavourable ideas may be spread 不如實地解釋或敘述; 歪曲: *Our decision to reduce taxes has been misrepresented as an attempt to gain popularity.* 我們決定降低稅收,卻被歪曲成為了贏得人心而推行的措施。

★**miss¹** /mɪs; mɪs/ v **1** [I;T] to fail to do something that was intended or possible, such as hitting or finding a person or thing 未擊中; 未找到; 未趕上: *The falling rock just missed my head.* 掉下來的石頭差一點擊中我的腦袋。| *He arrived too late and missed the train.* 他到得太晚,沒趕上火車。| *He shot at me but missed.* 他向我開槍,但沒有射

中。| *I don't want to miss seeing that play on television tonight.* 我不想錯過今晚電視播放的那齣戲。**2** [T] to feel unhappy because you are not with a certain person, in a certain place, or in possession of something 〔因某人不在或失去某物而〕惦念; 想念: *Her children have gone to Australia and she misses them very much.* 她的孩子都到澳大利亞去了,她很惦念他們。| *I miss living in the country.* 我懷念以前住在鄉村的日子。| *Give the beggar a coin; you won't miss it.* 給那乞丐一枚硬幣吧; 你是不在乎的。**3** [T] to discover that you do not have something 發覺〔某物〕遺失: *I didn't miss the key until I reached the front door.* 我走到了大門口,才發現丟了鑰匙。**4** miss the boat *infml* to lose a good chance, especially because you are too slow 〔非正式〕坐失時機; 錯過機會 **5** miss the point to fail to understand something that has been said 沒理解〔已說過的事情〕

miss out *phr v* **1** [T miss sbdy / sthg ↔ out] to fail to include a person or thing 遺漏; 略去: *You have missed out two important points in your report.* 你在報告中漏掉了重要的兩點。**2** [I] to lose a chance of advantage or enjoyment 失去〔得益或享樂的〕機會: *You're the one who'll miss out if you don't come.* 如果你不來,你就失去很好的機會了。| *I missed out on the Christmas party.* 我失去了參加聖誕節聚會的機會。

miss² n **1** Miss [only before a noun 只用於名詞前] a title used before the name of a girl or an unmarried woman 小姐〔對少女或未婚婦女的稱呼〕: *Miss Brown* 布朗小姐 | *Miss Edna Smith* 埃德娜·史密斯小姐 – compare 比較 MRS, MS **2** (also 又作 **Miss**) a form of address used to women in certain situations, for example by pupils to a female teacher 〔對婦女在某些場合下的一種稱呼,如學生對女教師〕: *Can I go home now, Miss?* 老師,我現在可以回家了嗎? **3 a near miss** something which is almost what is intended, but just fails 幾乎達到預定目標的某物: *There were several near misses before a goal was scored.* 得分之前有幾次差點進球。**4 give something a miss** *BrE infml* to decide not to do something 〔英式,非正式〕決定不做某事: *I think I'll give the film a miss, if you don't mind.* 如果你不介意的話,我想不去看電影了。

mis·shap·en /mɪsˈʃepən; ˌmɪsˈʃeɪpən/ adj shaped in a way that is not natural, normal, or intended 畸形的; 奇形怪狀的

mis·sile /ˈmɪsl; ˈmɪsaɪl/ n **1** an explosive weapon which can fly under its own power and which can be aimed at a distant object 導彈; 飛彈 **2** an object or a weapon thrown by hand or shot from a gun 投擲物; 發射物: *Bottles and other missiles were thrown at the police.* 用瓶子和其他東西投向警察。

miss·ing /ˈmɪsɪŋ; ˈmɪsɪŋ/ adj **1** not in the

M

expected or proper place and so needing to be found 失蹤的; 不見的: *Will the police have a list of missing persons?* 警方可以提供失蹤者名單嗎? | *There are papers missing from the file.* 檔案裡缺少了一些文件。 **2** not included 不包括的: *One important point was missing from his account.* 他的敘述裡漏了一個要點。 **3** not in the expected place 不在的; 缺席的: *Two people were missing, but we started the meeting without them.* 有兩個人沒來, 但我們仍然開始開會。 | *I noticed he had a finger missing from his left hand.* 我看到他的左手缺了一個手指。

★**mis·sion** /'mɪʃən; 'mɪʃən/ *n* **1** a group of people who are sent abroad for a special reason 使團; 代表團: *a British trade mission to Russia* 前赴俄國的英國貿易代表團 **2** the duty or purpose for which these people are sent 使命; 任務: *The soldiers' mission was to blow up the enemy's radio station.* 士兵的任務是炸毀敵人的無線電台。 **3** a place where a particular form of religion is taught and medical services are often given 傳教地; 慈善醫療設施所在地: *A hospital and a school are being built at the mission.* 教區內正在建造一座醫院和一所學校。 **4** the particular work which you believe you should do 職責: *Her mission in life seems to be helping lonely old people.* 她的天職似乎就是幫助孤獨的老人。

mis·sion·ar·y /'mɪʃənˌɛri; 'mɪʃənəri/ *n* **missionaries** a person who is sent to a foreign country to teach and spread religion 〔派往國外的〕傳教士

mis·spell /ˌmɪs'spɛl; ˌmɪs'spel/ *v* **misspelt** /-'spɛlt; -'spelt/ *or* **misspelled, misspelt** *or* **misspelled** [T] to spell a word wrongly 拼錯〔單詞〕—**misspelling** *n* [C;U]

mis·spend /ˌmɪs'spɛnd; ˌmɪs'spend/ *v* **misspent** /-'spɛnt; -'spent/ **misspent** [T] to spend things like time or money wrongly or unwisely 濫用; 亂花; 浪費: *I regret my misspent youth.* 我後悔虛度青春。

mist[1] /mɪst; mɪst/ *n* [C;U] very small drops of water floating in the air making it difficult to see 薄霧: *The mountain top was covered in mist.* 山頂籠罩在薄霧中。

mist[2] *v*

mist over *phr v* [I] to become covered with mist 蒙上薄霧: *The window misted over.* 玻璃窗蒙上了一層薄霧。

mist *sthg* ↔ **up** *phr v* [I;T] to cover or become covered with mist (變得)蒙上薄霧: *The hot air misted up the windows.* 熱空氣使窗子蒙上了一層薄霧。

★**mis·take**[1] /mə'stek; mɪˈsteɪk/ *v* **mistook** /məs'tʊk; mɪˈstʊk/, **mistaken** /mə'stekən; mɪˈsteɪkən/, **mistaking** [T] **1** to have the wrong idea about something 誤解; 弄錯: *He'd mistaken the address, and gone to the wrong house.* 他弄錯了地址, 走到另一家去了。 **2** to confuse one person or thing with

another 把〔某人或某事〕誤認為: *She was a complete stranger who I mistook for my friend's sister.* 她是個我根本不認識的陌生人, 我卻把她誤認為是我朋友的妹妹。

mistake[2] *n* **1** something which is not correct 錯誤: *There were several spelling mistakes in your written work.* 你的書面作業有幾個字拼錯了。 | *There must be some mistake in this bill.* 這份賬單肯定有錯。 | *Tom made a mistake in his calculations.* 湯姆的計算出錯。 – see 見 ERROR (USAGE 用法) **2** by mistake without intending to do something 不是故意地; 錯誤地: *I paid the bill twice by mistake.* 我弄錯了, 付了兩次賬。

mis·tak·en /mə'stekən; mɪˈsteɪkən/ *adj* wrong 錯誤的; 弄錯的: *If you thought she intended to be rude, you were mistaken.* 如果你認為她是故意粗魯無禮, 那你就錯了。 | *I had the mistaken idea that it would be quicker to take the train.* 我誤以為坐火車要快些。 –**mistakenly** *adv*

Mis·ter /'mɪstɚ; 'mɪstər/ *n* [only before a noun 只用於名詞前] see 見 MR

mis·time /mɪs'taɪm; ˌmɪs'taɪm/ *v* **mistimed, mistiming** [T] to do or say something at a wrong or unsuitable time 在不適當的時候做或說〔某事〕: *The general mistimed his attack.* 將軍發動進攻的時間不合適。

mis·tle·toe /'mɪslˌto; 'mɪsəltəʊ/ *n* [U] a plant with small white berries that is often hung in rooms at Christmas time 槲寄生〔常於聖誕節時懸掛室內〕

mis·tress /'mɪstrɪs; 'mɪstrɪs/ *n* **1** a woman who is in control 主婦; 女主人: *She felt she was no longer mistress in her own house when her husband's mother came to stay.* 婆婆在家中暫住, 她感到自己不再是女主人了。 **2** BrE a teacher in a secondary school 〔英式〕(中學)女教師: *Do you like the new English mistress?* 你喜歡新來的英語女教師嗎? –compare 比較 MASTER[1] **3** a woman with whom a man has a sexual relationship but to whom he is not married 情婦: *His wife left him when she discovered he had a mistress.* 他妻子發現他有個情婦後就離開了他。

mis·trust /mɪs'trʌst; mɪs'trʌst/ *v* [T] to be unable to trust someone or their reasons for behaving in a certain way 不信任; 懷疑: *I mistrust his motives.* 我懷疑他的動機。 – **mistrust** *n* [U]: *We both have a great mistrust of politicians.* 我們倆都極不信任政客。–**mistrustful** *adj*

mist·y /'mɪsti; 'mɪsti/ *adj* **mistier, mistiest** covered with mist 籠罩着薄霧的: *a misty morning* 輕霧籠罩的早晨 | *eyes misty with tears* 淚水模糊的眼睛

mis·un·der·stand /ˌmɪsʌndɚ'stænd; ˌmɪsʌndə'stænd/ *v* **misunderstood** /-'stʊd; -'stʊd/ **misunderstanding 1** [I;T] to understand something wrongly 誤解: *I think you misunderstand me.* 我認為你誤解了我的意思。 | *Have I misunderstood?* 是不是我理解

錯了? **2** [T] to fail to recognize the true character or qualities of someone 對〔某人的真實性格或品質〕不能認識; 不了解: *Why am I always misunderstood by people who work for me?* 為甚麼那些為我工作的人總是不了解我?

mis·un·der·stand·ing /ˌmɪsʌndəˈstændɪŋ; ˌmɪsʌndəˈstændɪŋ/ *n* **1** [C;U] confusion 誤解; 曲解: *I think there's been a misunderstanding about the arrangements.* 我想關於這些安排有些誤解。 **2** [C] a disagreement less serious than a quarrel 分歧; 不和; 爭執: *We've had our misunderstandings in the past, but we're the best of friends now.* 我們過去有過爭執, 但現在是最好的朋友。

mis·use¹ /ˌmɪsˈjuːz; ˌmɪsˈjuːz/ *v* **misused, misusing** [T] to use something in the wrong way or for the wrong purpose 誤用; 濫用

mis·use² /ˌmɪsˈjuːs; ˌmɪsˈjuːs/ *n* [C;U] a bad, wrong, or unsuitable use 誤用, 濫用〔某事物〕: *It was an unforgivable misuse of his power.* 他濫用權力, 不可原諒。

mite /maɪt; maɪt/ *n* **1** a very small creature that lives, for example, in the fur of animals 蟎 **2** a small child, especially one you feel sorry for 小孩子; 〔尤指覺得可憐的〕小傢伙: *The poor little mite looked ill and hungry.* 這可憐的小傢伙看來又病又餓。

mit·i·gate /ˈmɪtəˌgeɪt; ˈmɪtɪˌgeɪt/ *v* **mitigated, mitigating** [T] *fml* to make a wrong or harmful action less serious 〔正式〕減輕; 緩和: *Only increased foreign aid can mitigate the terrible effects of the war.* 只有增加外援才能減輕戰爭帶來的嚴重後果。 | *Are there any mitigating circumstances in this case?* 本案中有沒有可使罪行減輕的情節? – **mitigation** /ˌmɪtəˈgeɪʃən; ˌmɪtɪˈgeɪʃən/ *n* [U]

mi·tre /ˈmaɪtə; ˈmaɪtər/ *n* (**miter** *AmE* 〔美式〕) a tall pointed hat worn by priests of high rank 主教冠

mit·ten /ˈmɪtn; ˈmɪtn/ *n* a garment for your hand; one part covers your thumb, and a larger part covers all four fingers 連指手套〔拇指分開, 其他四指連在一起〕–see 見 PAIR (USAGE 用法) –see picture on page 210 見 210 頁彩圖

★**mix¹** /mɪks; mɪks/ *v* **1** [I;T] to combine into a single substance or thing 使〕混合; 攪和: *You can't mix oil and water.* 你無法把油和水混合在一起。 | *Oil and water don't mix.* 油和水不能混合。 | *Oil doesn't mix with water.* 油不可以和水混合。 | *Put the flour, eggs, and milk into a bowl and mix them together.* 把麵粉、蛋和牛奶放進碗裡一起攪和。 | *You can mix blue and yellow to produce green.* 把藍色和黃色加在一起便會變成綠色。 **2** [I] to talk to other people, usually with enjoyment, at social events 交往; 交際: *He's such a friendly person that he mixes well in any company.* 他是個十分友善的人, 和任何人都相處得很好。

mix sbdy/sthg ↔ **up** *phr v* [T] **1** to confuse one person or thing with another 混淆〔人或物〕: *It's easy to mix him up with his brother.* 很容易把他同他的兄弟混淆起來。 | *Do you mix the twins up?* 你把這對雙胞胎混淆起來了嗎? **2** to put into disorder 弄亂: *If you mix up those papers, I'll be angry.* 如果你把那些文件弄亂, 我要生氣的。

mix² *n* **1** [C;U] a combination of different substances, ready to use 混合物: *cake mix* 蛋糕混合料 **2** [sing] a group of different things or people 混雜的東西〔人羣〕: *There was rather a strange mix of people at the party.* 聚會上有形形色色的人。

mixed /mɪkst; mɪkst/ *adj* **1** of different kinds 混合的; 混雜的: *I have mixed feelings about the book.* 我對這本書的看法是褒貶參半。 **2** of or for both sexes 男女混合的: *a mixed school* 男女同校的學校 | *mixed bathing* 男女同浴

mixed up /ˌ·ˈ·◂/ *adj* **1** confused 迷惑的; 糊塗的: *I've had so much conflicting advice that I'm a bit mixed up.* 各方面給我的意見互相矛盾, 頭腦都給弄糊塗了。 | *a mixed up kid* 頭腦混亂的孩子 **2 mixed up in something, mixed up with someone** connected with something or someone bad 與某人〔某事〕有牽連的: *I'm afraid he's mixed up in some dishonest business.* 恐怕他同欺騙勾當有關。 | *Are you mixed up with those troublemakers?* 你和鬧事者有牽連嗎?

mix·er /ˈmɪksə; ˈmɪksər/ *n* **1** a machine in which substances are mixed 攪拌機: *a food mixer* 食品攪拌機 **2** a person who gets on well or badly with other people 〔善於或不善於〕與人相處的人: *To do this job well, you need to be a good mixer.* 要做好這項工作, 你要善於交際。

★**mix·ture** /ˈmɪkstʃə; ˈmɪkstʃər/ *n* **1** [C;U] a number of substances mixed together 混合物: *This tobacco is a mixture of three different sorts.* 這種煙草是由三個品種混合而成的。 | *You need some cough mixture.* 你要服些止咳混合劑。 **2** [sing] a combination of things or people of different types or qualities 混雜的事物; 雜亂的人羣: *I listened to his excuse with a mixture of amusement and disbelief.* 我懷着一種既好笑又難以置信的心情聆聽他作出辯解。 **3** [U] *fml* the action of mixing or state of being mixed 〔正式〕混合; 混合狀態

mix-up /ˈ··/ *n* *infml* a state of disorder caused by bad planning or confusion 〔非正式〕混亂; 雜亂: *There was a mix-up at the station and some of our group got on the wrong train.* 火車站上很混亂, 我們其中的一些人上錯了火車。

mm a written abbreviation for 〔縮〕= MILLIMETRES

moan¹ /mon; məʊn/ *n* **1** a low sound expressing pain or suffering 呻吟聲; 嗚咽聲: *The moans of the patient in the next bed*

M

kept me awake. 隔壁牀上病人的呻吟聲使我無法入睡。**2** a complaint (a word used to express disapproval) 不滿；牢騷〔含貶義〕: *He always has some moan or another about his job.* 他總是對自己的工作抱怨這抱怨那的。

moan² *v* [I] **1** to make a low sound expressing pain or suffering 呻吟；嗚咽: *The sick child moaned a little, and then fell asleep.* 這個生病的孩子稍許呻吟了幾聲，後來睡着了。**2** to complain (a word used to express disapproval) 抱怨；發牢騷〔含貶義〕: *Stop moaning and think about how lucky you are.* 別抱怨了，想想你有多幸運。

moat /mot; məʊt/ *n* a deep ditch that in former times was dug for defence round a castle and was usually filled with water〔古時城堡為了防禦而在四周挖的〕壕溝；護城河

mob¹ /mɑb; mɒb/ *n* a large noisy crowd, especially one which is violent (a word often used to express disapproval) 暴徒；亂民〔含貶義〕: *An angry mob gathered outside the town hall.* 一羣憤怒的暴民聚集在鎮公所外面。 | *mob violence* 暴徒騷亂

mob² *v* **-bb-** [T] to crowd around someone because of interest or admiration〔出於感興趣或敬佩而〕團團圍住〔某人〕: *The party leader was mobbed by his supporters.* 這位政黨領袖被他的支持者團團圍住。

mo·bile¹ /mobl; 'məʊbaɪl/ *adj* able to move, or be moved, quickly and easily 可移動的；流動的；活動的: *She's much more mobile now that she's bought a car.* 自從她買了輛汽車後，活動量就大得多了。 | *Out here in the country, we buy all our food from the mobile shop.* 在鄉下這個地方，我們所有的食品都是從流動商店買來的。 —opposite 反義 **immobile** —**mobility** /moˈbɪləti; məʊˈbɪlˌti/ *n* [U]

mo·bile² /'mobl; 'məʊbaɪl/ *n* an ornament made of small objects tied to wires or string and hung up so that they are moved by currents of air〔小物體製成，懸掛在繩索等上的〕風鈴飾物

mo·bil·ize /mobl,aɪz; 'məʊbˌlaɪz/ *v* **mobilized, mobilizing** (also 又作 **mobilise** BrE 〔英式〕) [I;T] to gather together for a particular service or purpose, especially for war〔為某種服務或目的，尤指為戰爭〕動員: *Our country's in great danger; we must mobilize.* 我國現時情況危急；我們必須動員應付。 | *He's trying to mobilize all the support he can get for his new political party.* 他正在設法動員所有支持者擁護他的新政黨。 —**mobilization** /,mobləˈzeʃən; ,məʊbˌlaɪˈzeɪʃən/ *n* (also 又作 **mobilisation** BrE 〔英式〕) [C;U]

moc·ca·sin /'mɑkəsn; 'mɒkəsɪn/ *n* a low shoe made of soft leather 莫卡辛鞋；無後跟軟皮鞋

mock¹ /mɑk; mɒk/ *v* **1** [I;T] to make fun of a person or thing in an unkind way 嘲笑；嘲弄: *The pupil did his best, and the teacher was wrong to mock his efforts.* 這個學生已盡了全力，老師嘲笑他的努力是不對的。 | *Don't mock — it could happen to anyone!* 別嘲笑 —— 這可能發生在任何人身上！**2** [T] to make fun of someone by copying their behaviour 通過模仿來取笑〔某人〕: *He made them laugh by mocking the way the teacher walked.* 他模仿老師走路的樣子，逗得他們哈哈大笑。 —**mocking** *adj* —**mockingly** *adv*

mock² *adj* [only before a noun 只用於名詞前] like something real but not actually the real thing 假的；仿製的；模擬的: *The army training exercises ended with a mock battle.* 軍隊的訓練演習以一場模擬戰結束。 | *a mock exam* 模擬考試

mock·e·ry /'mɑkəri; 'mɒkəri/ *n* **1** [U] the act of making fun of someone or something 嘲笑；嘲弄 **2** [sing] something that is not what it should be 虛假的東西；冒牌: *The medical examination was a mockery; the doctor hardly looked at the child.* 體格檢查是虛假的；那醫生對孩子幾乎都不看。 **3 make a mockery of** to make something seem stupid 使〔某事物〕顯得荒謬；嘲弄: *If everyone is accepted, it makes a mockery of the entrance exam.* 如果每個人都獲錄取，那就是對入學考試的嘲弄。

mod·al verb /,modl'vɜ:b; ,məʊdl'vɜ:b/ *n* a verb such as "can", "might", or "must", which is used with other verbs 情態動詞〔如"can", "might", "must"〕 —see Study Note on page 1318 見 1318 頁學習提示

mod cons /,mɑd'kɑnz; ,mɒd'kɒnz/ *n* BrE infml [pl] all modern conveniences in a building such as hot water and central heating〔英式，非正式〕〔建築物中的〕一應俱全的現代化生活設備〔如熱水、中央空調〕

*mode /mod; məʊd/ *n* fml a way of doing something〔正式〕方式；方法: *There is no single mode of transport which you can rely on.* 你不能單依靠一種類型交通工具。

*mod·el¹ /'mɑdl; 'mɒdl/ *n* **1** a small copy of something 模型: *a model of the Eiffel Tower* 艾菲爾鐵塔的模型 | *model aircraft* 飛機模型 **2** a person employed to wear clothes and show them to possible buyers in a shop or in photographs 時裝模特兒: *He's a male model.* 他是個男時裝模特兒。 **3** a person employed to be painted, drawn, or photographed by an artist〔供藝術家寫生或攝影的〕模特兒 **4** a person or thing that can serve as a perfect example of something, for others to copy 模範；典範: *This pupil's written work is a model of care and neatness.* 這學生的書面作業是細心和整潔的典範。 | *She's a model student.* 她是個模範學生。 **5** a particular type of object, especially a vehicle or machine, made by a particular company〔尤指汽車或機器的〕型號: *Rolls-Royce have produced two new models this year.* 勞斯·萊斯公司今年已生產了兩種新型號〔汽車〕。

model² *v* **-ll-** (**-l-** *AmE* 〖美式〗) **1** [T] to make a small copy of something 做〔某物的〕模型: *He modelled a ship out of bits of wood.* 他用零碎木料做了一艘船的模型。**2** [I; T] to shape a soft substance, such as clay, into an object 使成型; 做模型: *I model in clay.* 我用黏土做模型。**3** [I] to work as a model, showing clothes or sitting for artists 作藝術家的模特兒 **4** [T] to wear and show a garment to possible buyers 做服裝模特兒: *Angela is modelling an attractive blue silk dress.* 安吉拉在做時裝模特兒, 展示一件漂亮的藍綢連衣裙。**5 model yourself on someone** to copy another person or the way that they do something 模仿某人; 仿效某人: *She has always modelled herself on her mother.* 她總是以自己母親為榜樣。

mod·e·rate¹ /ˈmɑdərɪt; ˈmɔdərɪt/ *adj* **1** not extreme 不過分的; 適度的: *At the time of the accident, the train was travelling at a moderate speed.* 意外發生的時候, 火車正以中速行駛。| *a child of only moderate ability* 只有一般能力的孩子 | *moderate wage demands* 適度的工資要求 **2** supporting political ideas that are not extreme 〔政治觀點〕溫和的; 穩健的: *moderate political opinions* 溫和的政治觀點

mod·e·rate² /ˈmɑdəˌret; ˈmɔdəreɪt/ *v* **moderated, moderating** [I;T] to make or become less strong (使)和緩; 減弱; 節制: *He should moderate his language when children are present.* 孩子們在場時, 他說話應有節制。| *The wind was strong all day, but it moderated in the evening.* 風一整天都刮得很厲害, 但到傍晚時有所減弱。

mod·e·rate³ /ˈmɑdərɪt; ˈmɔdərɪt/ *n* a person whose political opinions are not extreme 溫和派; 穩健派 –compare 比較 EXTREMIST

mod·e·rate·ly /ˈmɑdərɪtlɪ; ˈmɔdərɪtli/ *adv* quite 尚; 相當: *a moderately successful film* 一部還算成功的影片

mod·e·ra·tion /ˌmɑdəˈreʃən; ˌmɔdəˈreɪʃən/ *n* [U] **1** control of your behaviour or remarks to within reasonable limits 適度; 節制; 溫和: *He showed great moderation in his response to his attackers.* 他對攻擊他的人所做的回答表現出了極大的節制。**2 in moderation** within sensible limits 適中地; 有節制地: *I only drink in moderation.* 我只是有節制地飲酒。

⋆⋆mod·ern /ˈmɑdən; ˈmɔdn/ *adj* belonging to the present time 現代的: *In this part of the city, you can see ancient and modern buildings next to each other.* 在城市的這一部分, 你可以看到古舊的建築物和現代建築物相映成趣。| *modern languages* 現代語言 | *modern ideas* 現代觀點 –**modernity** /mɑˈdɜːnətɪ; mɔˈdɜːnɪti/ *n* [U]

mod·ern·ize /ˈmɑdənˌaɪz; ˈmɔdənaɪz/ *v* **modernized, modernizing** (also 又作

modernise *BrE* 〖英式〗) [T] to make something suitable for the needs of the present time 使現代化; 使適應現代需要: *We're modernizing the house, starting with a new bathroom.* 我們要使這幢房子變得現代化, 先從搞一個新浴室着手。–**modernization** /ˌmɑdənəˈzeʃən; ˌmɔdənaɪˈzeɪʃən/ *n* [C;U]

mod·est /ˈmɑdɪst; ˈmɔdɪst/ *adj* **1** having or expressing a lower opinion of your own abilities than you deserve (a word used to express approval) 謙虛的〔含褒義〕: *She's very modest about her success.* 她對自己的成功很謙虛。| *a modest child* 謙虛的孩子 **2** small in quantity, size, or value 不大的; 適度的: *There has been a modest rise in house prices this year.* 房價今年略有上漲。**3** avoiding or not showing anything that might offend (used of people, their behaviour, and their clothing) 端莊的; 得體的; 正派的〔指人, 舉止, 衣飾〕–**modestly** *adv*

mod·es·ty /ˈmɑdəstɪ; ˈmɔdɪsti/ *n* [U] the quality, state, or fact of being modest (a word usually used to express approval) 謙虛〔常含褒義〕: *His natural modesty saved him from being spoilt by fame and success.* 他生來謙虛, 這使他不致被名譽和成功沖昏頭腦。

mod·i·cum /ˈmɑdɪkəm; ˈmɔdɪkəm/ *n* **a modicum of something** a small amount of something 少量; 一點點: *If he had a modicum of sense, he would go to college.* 要是他稍有一點理智, 他就會去上大學。

mod·i·fi·ca·tion /ˌmɑdəfəˈkeʃən; ˌmɔdɪfɪˈkeɪʃən/ *n* [C;U] a slight change made to something 修改; 更改; 改變: *A few simple modifications to this design would greatly improve it.* 這個設計只要作幾處簡單的修改便可大為改善。| *Modification of the plans may be necessary later.* 以後也許需要對這些計劃做修改。

mod·i·fy /ˈmɑdəˌfaɪ; ˈmɔdɪfaɪ/ *v* **modified, modifying** [T] to change something slightly 修改; 更改; 改造: *The car has been modified so that it can be used in the desert.* 這輛汽車已經過改造, 可以在沙漠中使用。

mod·ish /ˈmɑdɪʃ; ˈməʊdɪʃ/ *adj fml* fashionable 〖正式〗時髦的; 流行的

mod·u·late /ˈmɑdʒəˌlet; ˈmɔdjʊleɪt/ *v* **modulated, modulating** *tech* [T] to vary the strength or nature of a sound 〖術語〗改變音量; 使轉調

⋆mod·ule /ˈmɑdʒul; ˈmɔdjuːl/ *n* **1** one of a number of standard parts used to make a building or piece of furniture 建築部件; 傢具組件 **2** a part of a space vehicle that can be used independently of the other parts 〔航天器上各個獨立的〕艙 **3** one of a number of parts that combine to make a full course at some colleges 〔組成一門課程的〕單元

Mo·ham·me·dan /moˈhæmədən; məʊˈhæmɪdən/ *adj, n old fash* 〖老式〗(also 又作

Muhammadan) see 見 MUSLIM

moist /mɔɪst; mɔɪst/ *adj* slightly wet 微濕的; 濕潤的: *Water the plants just enough to keep the earth moist.* 給這些植物澆水, 只要能保持泥土濕潤就夠了。 | *eyes moist with tears* 眼睛噙着淚水

moist·en /ˈmɔɪsn; ˈmɔɪsən/ *v* [I;T] to make or become slightly wet 弄濕; 沾濕; 變(潮)濕

mois·ture /ˈmɔɪstʃə; ˈmɔɪstʃəʳ/ *n* [U] water in small quantities or in the form of steam or mist 潮濕; 濕氣; 水分: *There is little moisture in the desert air.* 沙漠的空氣幾乎不含一點水分。

mo·lar /ˈmolə; ˈməʊləʳ/ *n* one of the large teeth at the side of your mouth used for breaking up food 臼齒; 磨牙

mo·las·ses /məˈlæsɪz; məˈlæsɪz/ *n* [U] **1** a thick, dark, sweet liquid produced from sugar plants 糖蜜; 糖漿 **2** the usual American word for 〖美式〗= TREACLE

mold /mold; məʊld/ *n, v* – see 見 MOULD

mole /mol; məʊl/ *n* **1** a small furry animal that digs passages underground to live in 鼴(鼠) **2** *BrE infml* a person who provides secret information to an enemy or competitor about the organization they work for 〖英式, 非正式〗內奸; 間諜 **3** a small dark brown mark on your skin 痣

mol·e·cule /ˈmoləˌkjul; ˈmɒlɪkjuːl/ *n tech* the smallest part of any substance that can exist without losing its own chemical nature, consisting of one or more atoms 〖術語〗分子 – **molecular** /məˈlɛkjʊlə; məˈlekjʊləʳ/ *adj*

mole·hill /ˈmolˌhɪl; ˈməʊlˌhɪl/ *n* **1** a small heap of earth made by a mole digging underground 〔由鼴鼠打洞扒出的泥土堆成的〕鼴鼠丘 **2 make a mountain out of a molehill** to make an unimportant matter seem more important than it is 小題大作

mo·lest /məˈlɛst; məˈlest/ *v* [T] **1** to annoy or attack someone or something 騷擾; 干擾〔某人或某事〕: *A dog that molests sheep has to be killed.* 必須殺死騷擾羊羣的狗。 **2** to annoy or attack a person sexually 調戲; 猥褻; 對…作性騷擾

mol·li·fy /ˈmoləˌfaɪ; ˈmɒlɪfaɪ/ *v* **mollified, mollifying** [T] to make someone calmer 使〔某人〕平靜; 平息: *She refused to be mollified by a bunch of flowers.* 她不肯為(接受)一束花而就此息怒。

mol·lusc /ˈmoləsk; ˈmɒləsk/ *n* (also 又作 **mollusk** *AmE* 〖美式〗) any of a class of animals with soft bodies and no backbone or limbs, usually covered with a shell 軟體動物

molt /molt; məʊlt/ *v* – see 見 MOULT

mol·ten /ˈmoltn; ˈməʊltən/ *adj* turned to liquid by very great heat (used of metal or rock) 熔化的〔指金屬, 岩石〕

M **mom** /mam; mɒm/ *n* the usual American word for 〖美式〗= MUM

mo·ment[1] /ˈmomənt; ˈməʊmənt/ *n* **1** [C] a very short period of time 片刻; 瞬間: *It will only take a moment.* 這只要片刻時間。 | *I'll be back in a moment.* 我馬上就回來。 | *Just a moment! I want to speak to you.* 請稍等一下! 我想跟你說句話。 **2** [C] a particular point in time 特定時刻: *At that moment, the door opened and the teacher walked in.* 就在那時, 門打開了, 老師走了進來。 **3** [C] the right time for doing something 〔做某事的〕適當時刻: *That is the moment to attack.* 那是出擊的時候。 **4** [U] *fml* importance 〖正式〗重要; 重大: *a matter of the greatest moment* 意義極為重大的事情 **5 at any moment** at an unknown time but very soon 在任何時候; 隨時: *He might come back at any moment.* 他隨時可能回來。 **6 at the moment** at the present time 此刻; 目前: *We have no car at the moment.* 我們此刻沒有汽車。 **7 the moment** at exactly the time when 一…(就)…: *I recognized him the moment I saw him.* 我一眼就認出他了。

mo·men·ta·ry /ˈmomənˌtɛri; ˈməʊməntəri/ *adj* lasting for a very short time 片刻的; 瞬息的; 短暫的: *She experienced a momentary feeling of fear.* 她感到了一陣的恐懼。 – **momentarily** *adv*: *He was so surprised that he was momentarily unable to speak.* 他驚訝得一時說不出話來。

mo·men·tous /moˈmɛntəs; məʊˈmentəs/ *adj* very important 重大的; 重要的: *It was a momentous decision that we have never regretted.* 這是一個重要決定, 我們從不後悔。

mo·men·tum /moˈmɛntəm; məʊˈmentəm/ *n* [U] **1** *tech* the quantity of movement of an object 〖術語〗動量; 衝量: *The rock gained momentum as it rolled down the mountainside.* 石塊滾下山時, 動量越來越大。 **2** the development of a powerful force 衝力; 勢頭: *The struggle for political independence is gathering momentum.* 為政治獨立而鬥爭的力量日漸增長。

mon·arch /ˈmɑnək; ˈmɒnək/ *n* a ruler of a state, such as a king or queen, who has the right to rule by birth 君主; 國王; 女王; 女皇

mon·arch·ist /ˈmɑnəkɪst; ˈmɒnəkɪst/ *n* a person in favour of the idea that members of a royal family should rule rather than elected leaders 君主主義者

mon·ar·chy /ˈmɑnəki; ˈmɒnəki/ *n* **monarchies 1** [U] rule by a king or queen 君主統治; 君主制 **2** [C] a state ruled by a king or queen 君主國

mon·as·tery /ˈmɑnəsˌtɛri; ˈmɒnəstri/ *n* **monasteries** a building in which religious men called monks (MONK) live 隱修院; 寺院

mo·nas·tic /məˈnæstɪk; məˈnæstɪk/ *adj* **1** connected with monasteries 隱修院的; 寺院的 **2 a monastic life** a simple life for which you need little money 簡樸克己的生活

mo·nas·ti·cis·m /məˈnæstəˌsɪzəm; məˈnæs-tḷsɪzəm/ n [U] the way of life of monks (MONK) in a monastery 隱修生活方式

Mon·day /ˈmʌndɪ; ˈmʌndi/ n the day of the week after Sunday and before Tuesday 星期一

*★**mon·e·ta·ry** /ˈmʌnəˌtɛrɪ; ˈmʌnˌtəri/ adj connected with money 金錢的; 貨幣的: the international monetary system 國際貨幣制度

★**mon·ey** /ˈmʌnɪ; ˈmʌni/ n [U] 1 coins or paper notes with their value printed on them, which you use when you buy and sell things 貨幣; 錢: He doesn't usually carry much money on him. 他通常身邊不會帶很多錢。| The repairs will cost a lot of money. 維修要花很多錢。| He earns a lot of money as a TV presenter. 作為一名電視節目主持人, 他錢掙得很多。2 wealth 財富: Money doesn't always bring happiness. 金錢並不一定帶來幸福。| She comes from a family with money. 她出身於富裕的家庭。| Money makes the world go around. 金錢使世界運轉。| He made his money in property. 他搞房地產賺錢。3 be in the money to be rich 發財 4 have money to burn to have more money than you need 有花不完的錢 5 your money's worth full value for the money you have spent 錢花得值得[合算]的: Theatre tickets were expensive, but we felt we got our money's worth. 戲票很貴, 但我們認為值得。

mon·grel /ˈmʌŋgrəl; ˈmʌŋgrəl/ n a dog with parents of different breeds 雜種狗

*★**mon·i·tor**[1] /ˈmɑnətər; ˈmɑnɪtɚ/ n 1 a person or machine that examines or shows what is happening 監聽員; 監聽器; 監視器 2 a pupil chosen to help the teacher in various ways〔學校的〕班長; 級長

monitor[2] v [T] to watch, listen to, or examine what is happening 監視; 監聽; 監控: We have been monitoring the enemy's radio broadcasts. 我們一直在監聽敵方的電台廣播。| Monitor the child's progress and let me know of any problems. 密切注意孩子的進展情況, 有問題請立即通知我。

monk /mʌŋk; mʌŋk/ n a member of an all-male religious group that lives together in a MONASTERY 修道士; 僧侶

mon·key /ˈmʌŋkɪ; ˈmʌŋki/ n monkeys 1 an active tree-climbing animal with a long tail, belonging to the class of animals most like man 猴(子) 2 infml a very active child who enjoys playing〖非正式〗淘氣鬼; 頑童: He's a little monkey. 他是個小淘氣。

monkey wrench /ˈ··· / n a tool used for holding or turning things of different widths 活動扳手

mon·o /ˈmɑno; ˈmɑnəʊ/ adj using a system of sound recording, broadcasting, or receiving in which the sound appears to come from one direction only when played back〔廣播、錄音等〕單聲道的: a mono

record 單聲道唱片 –compare 比較 STEREO

mon·o·chrome /ˈmɑnəˌkrom; ˈmɒnəkrəum/ adj 1 one colour only 單色的: a monochrome painting 單色畫 2 showing black, white, and grey only 黑白的: a monochrome film 黑白影片

mon·o·cle /ˈmɑnəkəl; ˈmɒnəkəl/ n a special piece of glass worn over one eye only, to help you see better with that eye 單片眼鏡

mo·nog·a·my /məˈnɑgəmɪ; məˈnɒgəmi/ n [U] the custom or practice of having only one wife or husband at a time 一夫一妻制 –**monogamous** adj

mon·o·gram /ˈmɑnəˌgræm; ˈmɒnəgræm/ n a sign, usually formed of the first letters of your names, printed on writing paper or marked on other possessions〔常由姓名首字母組成, 印在信紙上或其他所有物上〕交織字母; 花押字 –**monogrammed** adj

mon·o·lith /ˈmɑnlˌɪθ; ˈmɒnəlɪθ/ n a large piece of stone placed so that it stands by itself 獨塊巨石

mon·o·lith·ic /ˌmɑnlˈɪθɪk; ˌmɒnəˈlɪθɪk◂/ adj 1 very large 龐大的: a monolithic building 龐大的建築物 2 forming a system that seems unlikely to change (a word often used to express disapproval) 鐵板一塊的; 一成不變的〔常含貶義〕: a monolithic system of government 一成不變的政治體制

mon·o·logue /ˈmɑnlˌɔg; ˈmɒnəlɒg/ n (also 又作 **monolog** AmE〖美式〗) 1 a long speech in a play or film spoken by one person〔戲劇或影片中的〕獨白 2 a rather long speech by one person, which prevents others from taking part in the conversation (a word often used to express disapproval)〔使別人簡直無法插嘴的〕滔滔不絕的話; 長篇大論〔常含貶義〕

mon·o·plane /ˈmɑnəˌplen; ˈmɒnəupleɪn/ n an aircraft with a single wing on each side 單翼(飛)機

mo·nop·o·lize /məˈnɑplˌaɪz; məˈnɒpəlaɪz/ v **monopolise, monopolizing** (also 又作 **monopolise** BrE〖英式〗) [T] to have complete control of something 壟斷; 獨佔: The cigarette industry is monopolized by a few large companies. 香煙行業由少數幾家大公司壟斷。| She monopolizes the teacher's attention. 她佔去了老師的全部注意力。

mo·nop·o·ly /məˈnɑplɪ; məˈnɒpəli/ n **monopolies** 1 [C] the right or power, shared with no one else, to provide a service or to produce something 壟斷(權); 專利(權): The postal services are a government monopoly. 郵務是政府的專利。2 [sing] possession of something or control over something, which others do not share 獨佔; 完全控制: He seems to think he has a monopoly of brains. 他似乎認為只有他才算聰明。

mon·o·rail /ˈmɑnəˌrel; ˈmɒnəʊreɪl/ n a railway system using a single rail 單軌鐵路

mon·o·syl·lab·ic /ˌmɑnəsɪˈlæbɪk; ˌmɒnəsɪ-

M

'læbɪk/ *adj* **1** having one SYLLABLE (used of a word)〔詞〕單音節的 **2** short and rather rude (used of remarks)〔話〕短而粗魯的: *He gave monosyllabic answers to my questions.* 他簡短而又粗魯地回答了我的問題。

mon·o·syl·la·ble /'mɑnə,sɪləbl; 'mɒnə,sɪləbəl/ *n* a word with only one SYLLABLE 單音節詞

mon·o·tone /'mɑnə,ton; 'mɒnətəʊn/ *n* [sing] a manner of speaking or singing in which the voice continues on the same note 單調的聲音: *He spoke in a monotone.* 他用單調的聲音說話。

mo·not·o·nous /mə'nɑtnəs; mə'nɒtənəs/ *adj* always the same 單調的: *I'm beginning to find my job rather monotonous.* 我開始發現自己的工作相當單調。 **–monotonously** *adv* **–monotony** *n* [U]

mon·soon /mɑn'sun; mɒn'suːn/ *n* [C] **1** the heavy rains which fall in parts of Asia at a particular time of the year〔亞洲某些地方的〕雨季 **2** the wind that brings these rains 季風

mon·ster /'mɑnstə; 'mɒnstəʳ/ *n* **1** a creature, imaginary or real, that causes fear because of its unnatural shape, size, or qualities 怪物; 妖怪: *a sea monster* 海妖; 海怪 | *I'll tell you a story about a terrible monster who lived in the woods.* 我要給你們講一個故事, 是關於住在樹林裡的可怕妖怪的。 **2** a very evil person 壞蛋; 惡人: *The judge told the murderer that he was a monster.* 法官對兇手說他是個窮兇極惡的人。 **3** a very large or strange animal, plant or thing 巨獸; 龐然大物: *That dog's a real monster!* 那條狗真是大得嚇人! | *a monster potato* 特大的馬鈴薯

mon·stros·i·ty /mɑn'strɑsəti; mɒn'strɒsɪti/ *n* monstrosities something made or built in such a way that it is very ugly 醜物: *Have you seen that new office building in the town centre? It's a monstrosity!* 你見過市中心的新辦公大樓嗎? 真是難看極了!

mon·strous /'mɑnstrəs; 'mɒnstrəs/ *adj* **1** very ugly 醜陋的 **2** shocking 駭人聽聞的: *monstrous cruelty* 極為殘酷 | *Your behaviour in class is monstrous!* 你在班裡的行為太不像話了! **–monstrously** *adv*: *monstrously expensive* 貴得不像話

month /mʌnθ; mʌnθ/ *n* **1** any one of the 12 parts into which the year is divided 月; 月份 **2** a period of about four weeks 一個月的時間: *The baby will be exactly six months old tomorrow.* 明天這嬰兒正好六個月大了。

month·ly /'mʌnθlɪ; 'mʌnθli/ *adj, adv* every month or once a month 每月(的); 每月一次(的): *a monthly meeting* 每月一次的例會 | *We meet monthly.* 我們每月見一次面。

mon·u·ment /'mɑnjəmənt; 'mɒnjʊmənt/ *n* **1** a structure that preserves the memory of a person or event 紀念碑; 紀念堂; 紀念塔: *This pillar is a monument to all those who died in the war.* 這座紀念碑是獻給所有那些在戰爭中犧牲的人的。 | *That big empty office building is a monument to bad planning.* 那個空無一人的辦公大樓是設計不當的一個明證。 **2** an old building, or what remains of it, considered worthy of preservation for its historic interest or beauty 遺跡; 遺址: *an ancient monument* 古跡

mon·u·ment·al /,mɑnjə'mɛntl; ,mɒnjʊ'mentl/ *adj* **1** very large, and of great and lasting worth 巨大的; 不朽的: *The artist spent years on one monumental painting.* 那位藝術家用了好幾年時間繪製一幅雄偉的油畫。 **2** very great in degree 非常; 極度的: *monumental stupidity* 極為愚蠢

moo /mu; muː/ *n* the noise that a cow makes 哞〔牛叫聲〕 **–moo** *v* [I]

mood /mud; muːd/ *n* **1** the state of your feelings at a particular time 心境; 情緒: *The beautiful sunny morning put him in a happy mood.* 美好而晴朗的早晨使他心情愉快。 | *His moods change very quickly.* 他情緒變化無常。 | *She's in a bad mood today.* 她今天情緒不好。 **2** a state of mind which makes you bad-tempered 心情不好: *Ignore him when he's in one of his moods.* 他心情不好, 不要跟他爭辯。 **3** the right state of mind for a particular activity〔從事某一活動的〕合適心境; 精神狀態: *She was very tired, and in no mood for dancing.* 她非常疲倦, 沒有心情跳舞。 **4** *tech* any of three groups of forms of a verb; the INDICATIVE expresses a fact, the IMPERATIVE a command or request, and the SUBJUNCTIVE a condition〔術語〕語氣〔陳述、祈使、虛擬〕

mood·y /'mudɪ; 'muːdi/ *adj* **moodier, moodiest** **1** bad-tempered, angry, displeased, or unhappy 脾氣壞的; 悶悶不樂的; 情緒低沉的 **2** having feelings that change often and quickly (a word often used to express disapproval) 心情多變的; 喜怒無常的〔常含貶義〕 **–moodily** *adv* **–moodiness** *n* [U]

moon /mun; muːn/ *n* **1** the moon the object which moves round the earth once every 28 days, and can be seen shining in the sky at night 月球 **2** the shape of this object as it appears at a particular time 月亮: *Last night there was a full moon.* 昨晚是滿月。 **3** a body that turns round a PLANET other than the earth 衛星: *Saturn has several moons.* 土星有好幾顆衛星。 **4** over the moon very happy 很愉快; 很高興: *She's over the moon about her new job.* 她對自己的新工作感到很滿意。 **5** once in a blue moon very rarely 極少: *I see him once in a blue moon.* 我極少看到他。

moon *v*

moon about/around *phr v* [I] to wander about or behave in an unhappy way, often because you are in love 聞蕩;〔常因在戀愛中而〕悶悶不樂

moon·beam /'mun,bim; 'muːnbiːm/ *n* a beam of light from the moon (一道)月光

moon·light /'mun,laɪt; 'muːnlaɪt/ *n* [U] the light of the moon 月光: *The moonlight on the calm sea added to the beauty of the scene.* 月光照在風平浪靜的海面上，更添景色之美。

moon·lit /'mun,lɪt; 'muːn,lɪt/ *adj* [only before a noun 只用於名詞前] given light by the moon 月光照耀下的: *a beautiful moonlit night* 美麗的月夜

moor¹ /mʊr; mʊəʳ/ *n* a wide, open area of land, covered with rough grass or low bushes, not farmed because of its poor soil 曠野; 荒原: *Shall we go for a walk on the moors?* 我們去曠野上散散步好嗎？

moor² *v* [T] to fasten a boat to land, or to an object in the water, by means of ropes or chains 使停泊; 繫泊〔船隻〕

moor·ings /'mʊrɪŋz; 'mʊərɪŋz/ *n* [pl] a place where a boat is moored 停泊處; 泊地: *Several ships broke away from their moorings in the storm.* 有好幾艘船在暴風雨中從停泊處被刮走了。

moose /mus; muːs/ *n* [plural is 複數為 **moose**] a type of large deer that lives in north America 〔北美的〕駝鹿

moot point /,mut 'pɔɪnt; ,muːt 'pɔɪnt/ *n* a point about which there is disagreement or doubt 爭論未決的觀點

mop¹ /map; mɒp/ *n* **1** a tool for washing floors or dishes, made of a stick with soft material fastened to one end 拖把;〔刷碗用的〕小拖把 **2** *infml* a thick untidy mass of hair 〖非正式〗蓬亂的頭髮: *a dark mop of curls* 蓬鬆的黑色卷髮

mop² *v* **-pp-** [T] **1** to clean something with a mop 用拖把洗刷: *I mopped the kitchen floor an hour ago, and look at it now!* 我一小時前拖了廚房間的地板，現在你瞧！ **2** to dry something by rubbing it with a cloth 抹乾; 擦乾: *He mopped his sweaty face with a handkerchief.* 他用手帕擦乾汗淋淋的臉。

mop sthg ↔ **up** *phr v* [T] to remove unwanted liquid or dirt with a mop 用拖把拖洗或擦去〔不想要的液體〕: *Can you mop up the milk you spilt?* 你可以把灑出來的牛奶擦掉嗎？

mope /mop; məʊp/ *v* **moped, moping** [I] to be unhappy, often without trying to become more cheerful 百無聊賴; 悶悶不樂

mope about/around *phr v* [I] to sit or wander around without taking an interest in anything because you are unhappy 沒精打采地坐着或閒蕩

mo·ped /'moped; 'məʊped/ *n* a bicycle which has a small engine 機動腳踏車

★★**mor·al¹** /'mɔrəl; 'mɒrəl/ *adj* **1** [only before a noun 只用於名詞前] concerning or based on what is considered right or wrong 道德

(上)的: *a man of high moral standards* 道德高尚的人 | *She refused to join the army for moral reasons.* 由於道德上的原因，她拒絕參軍。| *What right have you to make moral judgments about my behaviour?* 你有甚麼權利對我的行為做道德評價？ **2** behaving only in a way that is considered by society to be good or acceptable 有道德的; 品行端正的: *My grandfather was a very moral man who never told a lie in his life.* 我的祖父是個品行端正的人，一生從未說過一次謊。–opposite 反義 **immoral 3 moral support** support in the form of encouragement rather than practical help 道義上的支持 **4 moral victory** the result of a contest or argument in which the losing side feels it has proved itself to be right 精神上的勝利

moral² *n* **1** a lesson that can be learnt from a story or event, which shows you the right way to behave 〔由故事或事件引出的〕道德上的教訓; 寓意: *The moral of this story is that crime does not pay.* 這個故事的寓意是，犯罪是不值得的。 **2 morals** [pl] principles which you live by, based on what is considered right and wrong 道德; 倫理: *He has no morals.* 他毫無道德觀念。

mo·rale /mo'ræl; mə'rɑːl/ *n* [U] a confident state of mind, especially in a bad situation 〔尤指在逆境中〕士氣; 精神面貌: *The team's morale is high despite their recent defeat.* 儘管最近失敗了，全隊的士氣仍然很高。

mor·al·ist /'mɔrəlɪst; 'mɒrəlɪst/ *n* a person who tries to make others behave in the way that person strongly believes to be right (a word usually used to express disapproval) 道德家; 說教者〔常含貶義〕 – **moralistic** /,mɔrə'lɪstɪk; ,mɒrə'lɪstɪk◂/ *adj*

mo·ral·i·ty /mɔ'rælətɪ; mə'ræl̩tɪ/ *n* [U] an idea of what is right or acceptable behaviour 道德(性): *One sometimes wonders if there's any morality in politics.* 人們有時懷疑，政治中是否有道德可言。

mor·al·ize /'mɔrəl,aɪz; 'mɒrəlaɪz/ *v* **moralized, moralizing** (also 又作 **moralise** *BrE* 〖英式〗) [I] to express your ideas about what is correct behaviour (a word usually used to express disapproval) 說教〔常含貶義〕–**moralizer** *n*

mor·al·ly /'mɔrəlɪ; 'mɒrəlɪ/ *adv* **1** in a way which is considered right and proper (a word used to express approval) 有道德地; 品行端正地〔含褒義〕–opposite 反義 **immorally 2** with regard to right or good behaviour 道德上; 道義上: *What you did wasn't actually against the law, but it was morally wrong.* 你所做的事並未真正觸犯法律，但從道德上來講是錯誤的。

mo·rass /mo'ræs; mə'ræs/ *n* **1** a confusion which is difficult to make sense of 困境: *The report took a long time to read because of the morass of details.* 由於其中有許多糾纏不清的細節，讀那篇報告花了很長時間。 **2** an

M

area of very wet ground 沼澤; 泥潭

mor·a·to·ri·um /ˌmɒrəˈtɔːrɪəm; ˌmɔːrəˈtɔːrɪəm/ n **moratoria** /-rɪə; -rɪə/ **1** a declaration that a particular activity will be stopped or delayed for a time〔某項活動〕暫停; 中止; 延遲: a moratorium on the building of new houses 宣佈暫停建設新房屋 **2** the length of such a delay 暫停的期限; 推遲的時間

mor·bid /ˈmɔːbɪd; ˈmɔːbḷd/ adj having an unhealthy, unnatural interest in unpleasant subjects, especially death (a word used to express disapproval)（精神、思想方面）病態的; 不健康的〔含貶義〕: a morbid interest in fatal diseases 對致命疾病有病態的興趣 **–morbidly** adv **–morbidity** /mɔːˈbɪdətɪ; mɔːˈbɪdḷti/ n [U]

⋆⋆**more** /mɔːr; mɔːr/ det, pron, adv [comparative of MANY, MUCH 是 MANY, MUCH 的比較級] **1** a greater amount, or to a greater degree 更多的數量; 更多; 更: People tend to sleep more in winter. 人們在冬天往往會睡得較多。| I wanted to discuss the matter more. 我想進一步討論這個問題。| This book is much more interesting than his last one. 這本書比他的上一本書有趣得多。| There were more people at this meeting than there were at the last one. 參加這次會議的人比上次多。| I wish I could spend more time gardening. 我希望能在園藝上花更多的時間。| We seem to spend more of our money on food these days. 我們近來好像在吃上面多花了錢。**2 once more, twice more, etc** happening once again, twice again, etc 再（發生）一次; 兩次地: I wanted to see her once more before she left. 我想在她離開前再見她一次。**3** an additional number or amount 額外的數目; 另外的一些: Have some more tea. 再喝點茶吧! | I've got to write two more letters this morning. 今天早晨我得再寫兩封信。**4 not any more** no longer 不再: They don't live here any more. 他們已經搬走。| After this trip, I won't be going abroad any more. 這次旅行結束後，我不會再出國了。**5 more and more** an increasing amount 越來越…: Our task was becoming more and more difficult. 我們的工作變得越來越難。| We seem to spend more and more each month. 似乎我們每個月月花的錢越來越多。| The children were trampling more and more mud into the house. 孩子們把越來越多的泥踩到房子裡來了。**6 more or less** about or almost 或多或少; 左右; 大約: The building work will cost £300, more or less. 修建工作大約要花三百鎊。| "Have you finished your work yet?" "More or less." "你完成工作了嗎?""差不多吧。"**7 more than** more important than 比…更重要: She was much more than a friend to me. 對我而言，她遠遠不止是個朋友。**8 what's more** a phrase used to introduce an additional point that you are making 而且〔用於引入另

一個觀點〕: The country is in a terrible state. Inflation is high, unemployment is high, and what's more the government doesn't seem able to do anything about it. 國家的情況很糟糕。通脹率高, 失業率高, 而且政府對此似乎無能為力。

more·o·ver /mɔːrˈovə; mɔːˈrəʊvər/ adv fml used when you are saying something which adds to what you have already said or supports it〔正式〕再者; 加之; 此外; 而且〔用於對自己説過的內容進行補充或加以支持〕: The Government should have acted long ago. Moreover, they should not have discouraged private companies from taking action. 政府早就該行動了。而且, 他們不應該勸阻私人公司採取行動。

morgue /mɔːg; mɔːg/ n a building in which the dead bodies of unknown people are kept until they are buried or burned 陳屍所

Mor·mon /ˈmɔːmən; ˈmɔːmən/ n a member of a religious body originally formed in the US 摩門教教徒

morn /mɔːn; mɔːn/ n a morning 早晨; 拂曉

⋆⋆**morn·ing** /ˈmɔːnɪŋ; ˈmɔːnɪŋ/ n [C;U] the first part of the day, usually until the time when the midday meal is eaten 早晨; 上午: I must go to the shops some time during the morning. 上午我得抽空去商店看看。| Can't the decision wait until morning? 能不能到上午再做決定? | I'll see you in the morning. 明天上午再見面吧。| She met him in town this morning. 她今天上午在城裡遇見了他。| He didn't get home until two o'clock in the morning. 他直到凌晨兩點才到家。

mo·ron /ˈmɔːrɒn; ˈmɔːrɒn/ n a very stupid person (a word used to express disapproval) 傻子; 笨蛋〔含貶義〕**–moronic** /məˈrɒnɪk; məˈrɒnɪk/ adj

mo·rose /məˈros; məˈrəʊs/ adj bad-tempered 脾氣不好的 **–morosely** adv

mor·phine /ˈmɔːfin; ˈmɔːfiːn/ n [U] a powerful drug used for stopping pain 嗎啡

mor·sel /ˈmɔːsəl; ˈmɔːsəl/ n a very small piece of food〔食物的〕一小份〔片〕

mor·tal¹ /ˈmɔːtl; ˈmɔːtl/ adj **1** unable to live for ever 終有一死的; 不會長生不死的 – opposite 反義 **immortal 2** causing death 致死的; 致命的: a mortal wound 致命傷 **3** [only before a noun 只用於名詞前] very serious 極嚴重的: in mortal danger 處境極度危險

mortal² n a human being (a literary word; it is also often used in a humorous way) 人〔書面語; 也常表示幽默〕: We mortals can only do our best. 我們是血肉之軀, 只能盡力而為。

mor·tal·i·ty /mɔːˈtælətɪ; mɔːˈtælḷti/ n [U] the number of deaths, often from a particular cause or among a certain type of people 死亡率: Infant mortality has declined with the rise in the standard of living. 隨着生

活水準提高, 嬰兒死亡率已在下降。 **2** the fact that people die 必死性 –opposite 反義 **immortality** (for sense 2)

mor·tal·ly /ˈmɔːtlɪ; ˈmɔːtəlɪ/ *adv* in a manner that causes death 致命地: *He was mortally wounded in the fight.* 他在戰鬥中受了致命傷。

mor·tar /ˈmɔːtə; ˈmɔːtəʳ/ *n* **1** [C] a heavy gun with a short barrel, which fires explosives that fall from a great height 迫擊砲 **2** [C] a bowl made from a hard material, in which substances are crushed into very small pieces or powder 臼; 研鉢 **3** [U] a mixture of lime, sand, and water, used in building 砂漿; 灰漿

★**mort·gage¹** /ˈmɔːgɪdʒ; ˈmɔːgɪdʒ/ *n* a sum of money borrowed, especially to buy a house 〔尤指購房的〕抵押借款: *We took out a £30,000 mortgage on our new house.* 我們辦理了三萬英鎊的抵押借款買新房子。

mortgage² *v* [T] to borrow money, especially from a bank; if you do not pay back the money, you lose your house or land 抵押〔房屋、土地等〕

mor·ti·fy /ˈmɔːtəˌfaɪ; ˈmɔːtɪ̣faɪ/ *v* **mortified, mortifying, be mortified** to feel very ashamed 感到羞愧: *The teacher was mortified by his own inability to answer such a simple question.* 老師因為自己答不出這麼簡單的問題而感到丟臉。 –**mortification** /ˌmɔːtəfəˈkeɪʃən; ˌmɔːtɪ̣fˈkeɪʃən/ *n* [U]

mor·tu·a·ry /ˈmɔːtʃʊˌɛrɪ; ˈmɔːtʃuərɪ/ *n* **mortuaries** a place, especially in a hospital, where a dead body is kept until it is buried or burned 〔尤指醫院的〕停屍室, 太平間

mo·sa·ic /moˈzeɪk; məʊˈzeɪ-ɪk/ *n* [C;U] a piece of ornamental work produced by the fitting together of small pieces of coloured stone or glass to form a pattern or picture 馬賽克; 鑲嵌工藝(品)

Mos·lem /ˈmɑzləm; ˈmɒzlᵻm/ *n, adj* see 見 MUSLIM

mosque /mɑsk; mɒsk/ *n* a building in which Muslims worship 清真寺

mos·qui·to /məˈskito; məˈskiːtəʊ/ *n* **mosquitoes** a small flying insect that pricks the skin of people or animals and then drinks blood; some mosquitoes carry the disease of MALARIA 蚊子; 瘧蚊

moss /mɔs; mɒs/ *n* [U] a small green or yellow plant that grows in a thick mass on wet soil or on a wet surface 苔蘚; 地衣 – **mossy** *adj*

★**most¹** /most; məʊst/ *adv* [superlative of MUCH 是 MUCH 的最高級] **1** to the greatest degree 最: *the most comfortable hotel in the town* 鎮上最舒適的旅館 | *What annoyed me most was the way he laughed at me!* 最叫我惱火的是他嘲笑我時的樣子! **2** very 很; 十分: *It was a most enjoyable evening* 那是個令人十分愉快的夜晚。

★**most²** *det, pron* [superlative of MANY, MUCH 是 MANY, MUCH 的最高級] **1** the greatest number or amount 最大量; 最多數: *Most people go on holiday in July and August.* 大多數人七、八月份去度假。 | *I spend most of my time at home now.* 現在我大部分時間在家裡。 | *As usual, John was the one who ate the most food and drank the most wine.* 和平時一樣, 約翰是吃飯喝酒最多的一個。 | *Of course, the one that I liked best cost the most.* 當然, 我最喜歡的那個最貴。 **2 at most, at the most** a phrase used when you are giving the largest number or amount that is possible 至多; 不超過〔用於給出可能的最大數目或最高數量〕: *I would guess that at most she's thirty.* 我猜想她最多三十歲。 | *It'll take a couple of hours at the most.* 這事最多花上幾小時。 **3 for the most part** usually 通常: *Summers in this area are for the most part dry and sunny.* 夏季這個地區的氣候通常是晴朗乾燥的。 **4 make the most of something** to enjoy something as much as possible, or get the best advantage from it 盡量享受; 充分利用: *We've only got two more days here, so let's make the most of them.* 我們在這裡只能再呆兩天了, 所以要盡量利用時間。

> ■ USAGE 用法: With nouns which already have a determiner (**the, this, these, that, those, his, her,** etc.) use **most of** ☆對於已有限定詞的名詞(**the, this, these, that, those, his, her** 等) 用 **most of**: *I know* **most of** *the students who live in London.* 我認識很多住在倫敦的學生。 | *I've read* **most of** *his novels.* 我已讀過他的大部分小說。 | **most of** *the population of France* 法國人口中的大多數。 With pronouns you should also use **most of** ☆對於代名詞, 也該用 **most of**: **Most of** *us agree on this point.* 我們中的大多數人同意這個觀點。 | *I've already spoken to* **most of them.** 我已和他們中的大多數人談過。 However, with nouns that do not already have a determiner remember to use **most** (WITHOUT **of**) ☆但是, 對於沒有限定詞的名詞, 記住使用 **most** (沒有 **of**): **Most** *people* **hate** *violence.* 多數人憎惡暴力。 | **Most Americans** *seem friendly.* 大多數美國人顯得很友好。 | *I like* **most French food.** 大多數法國食品我都喜歡。

★**most·ly** /ˈmostlɪ; ˈməʊstlɪ/ *adv* mainly or usually 主要地; 通常: *The people in the room were mostly quite young.* 房間裡主要是些很年輕的人。 | *When I go to London, it's mostly on business.* 如果我去倫敦, 通常是出差。

MOT /ˌɛm o ˈti; ˌɛm əʊ ˈtiː/ *n BrE* a regular official examination of cars more than three years old, carried out to make sure that they are fit to be driven; an abbreviation for **Ministry of Transport** 〖英式〗〖縮〗〔運輸部定期對使用三年以上的機動車輛性能所做的〕車輛檢驗: *My car failed its MOT.* 我的汽車未能通過年檢。

mo·tel /moˈtɛl; məʊˈtɛl/ *n* a hotel specially built for travelling motorists 汽車旅館

moth /mɒθ; mɒθ/ *n* a winged insect which flies mainly at night; the young of some types of moth eat and make holes in clothes 蛾; 〔衣服上的〕蛀蟲

moth·ball /ˈmɒθˌbɔl; ˈmɒθbɔːl/ *n* a small ball made of a strong-smelling substance, used for keeping moths away from clothes 衛生球; 樟腦丸

moth-eat·en /ˈ·ˌ··/ *adj* destroyed, or appearing to have been destroyed, by moths (used of clothing) 蟲蛀的〔指衣物〕: *Isn't it time you threw some of those moth-eaten garments away?* 難道這時候你還不扔掉一些蛀壞的衣服嗎?

moth·er¹ /ˈmʌðə; ˈmʌðəʳ/ *n* **1** a female parent 母親: *His mother and father are both doctors.* 他的父母都是醫生。| *a mother hen and her young chicks* 母雞和牠的小雞 –see picture on page 503 見 503 頁彩圖 **2 Mother** a word used to address or talk about your female parent 媽媽〔用於稱呼或談及自己的母親〕: *Can I borrow your car please, Mother?* 媽媽, 我可以借用你的汽車嗎? **3 mother tongue** a

person's first language 母語 **4 the mother country** the country where you were born 祖國 **–motherless** *adj*

mother² *v* [T] **1** to care for someone like a mother 〔像母親般〕照管〔某人〕 **2** to treat someone with too much protectiveness and care 溺愛〔某人〕

moth·er·hood /ˈmʌðəhʊd; ˈmʌðəhʊd/ *n* [U] the state of being a mother 母親身分: *I'm still trying to adjust to motherhood.* 我正在設法適應母親的身分。 –compare 比較 FATHERHOOD

mother-in-law /ˈ·· · ·/ *n* **mothers-in-law** the mother of your husband or wife 岳母; 婆婆 –see picture on page 503 見 503 頁彩圖

moth·er·ly /ˈmʌðəlɪ; ˈmʌðəli/ *adj* having or showing the loving feelings that you expect of a mother 母親似的; 慈母般的: *She's a motherly sort of person.* 她是那種慈母一樣的人。 –**motherliness** *n* [U]

mother-of-pearl /ˌ·· ·ˈ·/ *n* [U] a hard smooth substance on the inside of certain shells, used for making ornamental articles 珍珠母

mo·tif /moˈtif; məʊˈtiːf/ *n* a subject, pattern, or idea which is repeated many times or is the most important, especially in a work of music, art, or theatre 〔尤指音樂, 藝術或戲劇作品的〕主題

mo·tion¹ /ˈmoʃən; ˈməʊʃən/ *n* **1** [U] the action or way of moving 動; 運動; 移動: *The*

HOUSE 房屋

Try to draw a picture of Colin Taylor's house. 試給柯林·泰勒的房子畫一幅畫。

Colin Taylor lives in a small detached house. There is a small garden in front of the house. On the left there is a low brick wall and on the right there is a wooden fence. A hedge separates the garden from the pavement. On the left, there is a small gate and a path which leads to the front door. On both sides of the path, there are narrow flowerbeds containing plants and small bushes. On the right, there is a small square lawn.

Just outside the gate, close to the hedge, there are a pillar box and a telephone box.

Colin Taylor's house has two storeys. There is one large window on the ground floor on the right hand side. On the left there is a small porch over the front door.

There are two smaller windows on the first floor. Colin has put his satellite dish between the two windows. A gutter runs around the house at the bottom of the roof. This collects the water which falls on the roof. A drainpipe on the left carries the water down to the ground. The chimney is on the right hand side of the roof. There is a TV aerial attached to the chimney.

柯林·泰勒住在一幢獨立式住宅裡。房子前面有個小花園, 左面是一堵矮磚牆, 右面是一道木籬笆。一道樹籬把花園和人行道分隔開來。左面有扇小門, 一條小路通往前門。小路兩側是狹窄的花壇, 種着植物和矮樹叢。右面有一個小小的正方形草坪。

就在大門外靠近樹籬處, 有一個郵筒和一個電話亭。

柯林·泰勒的房子有兩層樓。底樓的右邊有扇大的窗戶, 左面前門上方有個小門廊。

二樓有兩扇較小的窗戶。柯林把他的衛星天線安裝在兩扇窗戶之間。屋頂底下有一圈簷槽圍着房子, 把落在屋頂上的水聚集在一起。左邊的排水管把水往下排到地上。煙囪在屋頂的右邊, 電視天線則連接在煙囪上。

M

balcony
陽台

second (BrE【英式】)/third (AmE【美式】) floor
二樓

first (BrE【英式】)/second (AmE【美式】) floor
一樓

ground (BrE【英式】)/first (AmE【美式】) floor
底層，樓下

fire escape
太平梯

basement
地下室

(block of) flats (BrE【英式】)
一幢住宅樓宇/
**apartment house
(AmE【美式】)**
公寓大樓

bungalow
平房

path
小路

cottage
小屋

**terraced house (BrE【英式】)/
row house (AmE【美式】)**
聯排房屋

tree
樹

aerial/antenna (AmE【美式】)
天線

satellite dish
衛星天線

detached house
獨立式房子

chimney pot
煙囪頂管

chimney
煙囪

back door
後門

roof
屋頂

clothes line
曬衣繩

fence
圍欄

patio
(與屋子連接的)
露台，平台

drainpipe
排水管

garden
(BrE【英式】) 花園/
backyard
(AmE【美式】)
後園

gutter
簷槽

window
窗

street light
街燈

porch
門廊

windowsill
窗檻

garage
汽車庫

front door
前門

hedge
樹籬

wall
牆

flowerbed
花壇

phone box
(BrE【英式】)/
phone booth (AmE
【美式】)
電話亭

tter box
【英式】)/
ail slot
E【美式】)
信箱

drive (BrE【英式】)/
driveway (AmE【美式】)
車道

lamppost
燈柱

doorstep
門前的台階

plant
植物

litterbin
垃圾箱

awn
草坪

post/pillar box
(BrE【英式】)/
mailbox
(AmE【美式】)
郵筒

pavement (BrE【英式】)/
sidewalk (AmE【美式】)
人行道

gutter
排水溝

kerb (BrE【英式】)/
curb (AmE【美式】)
路緣

bush
叢

gate
大門

gatepost
門柱

drain
下水道

road
馬路

living room 起居室、客廳

picture
圖畫；照片

curtains
窗簾

lampshade
燈罩

frame
照片框

lamp
電燈

CDs
鐳射唱片

record player
電唱機

speaker
揚聲器

TV
電視機

video/VCR
錄影機

bookcase
書架

radio
收音機

amplifier
擴音機

tape deck
錄音座

CD (player)
鐳射唱機

hi-fi unit
高保真度音響設備/
stereo system
立體聲音響設備

ornament
裝飾品

mantelpiece
壁爐架

video tapes
錄影帶

clock
鐘

cushion
靠墊

sofa/settee/couch
（長）沙發

carpet
地毯

fireplace
壁爐

TV remote control
電視遙控器

rug
小地毯

coffee table
咖啡桌

hearth
壁爐前的地板

magazines
雜誌

armchair
扶手椅

gentle rolling motion of the ship made me feel sleepy. 船身的輕微搖動使我昏昏欲睡。| The train was already in motion when he jumped on. 他跳上火車時，車子已經開動。**2** [C] a single movement 動作; 手勢: He made a motion with his hand, as if to tell me to keep back. 他做了個手勢，好像是叫我別上前。**3** [C] a suggestion formally put before a meeting〔會議時提出的〕動議; 提議: The motion to increase the club's membership charges was defeated by 15 votes to 10. 提高俱樂部會費的動議以十票對十五票被否決了。**4** [C] fml an act of emptying your bowels〔正式〕大便 **5 go through the motions** to do something without much interest or belief that it worth doing 裝裝樣子; 走過場 **6 in slow motion** making the movements slower than in real life, especially in a film〔尤指影片中〕用慢鏡頭地 **7 set things in motion** to start things working 使〔事物〕開始運轉或工作

motion² v [I;T] to direct by means of a movement, usually with your hand〔常指〕做手勢; 示意: She motioned me into the room. 她招手要我進房間去。

mo·tion·less /ˈmoʃənlɪs; ˈməuʃənləs/ adj not moving 不動的: The cat remained

motionless, waiting for the mouse to move. 那隻貓一動也不動，等着老鼠移動。－ **motionlessly** adv

mo·ti·vate /ˈmotəˌvet; ˈməutɪ̩veɪt/ v **motivated, motivating** [T] to provide someone with a reason for doing something 構成〔某人做某事的〕動機; 促使: His attempt to get elected to parliament was motivated only by a desire for power. 他企圖當選為議員，只是出於對權力的渴望。

mo·ti·va·tion /ˌmotəˈveʃən; ˌməutɪ̩ˈveɪʃən/ n [C;U] a reason or the knowledge of a reason for doing something 動力; 誘因: How can we provide them with the motivation to learn? 我們怎樣才能給他們學習的動力?

mo·tive /ˈmotɪv; ˈməutɪv/ n a reason for action 動機; 目的: The police are questioning everyone who might have a motive to kill the man. 警方在盤問每個可能有殺害此人動機的人。| What do you think his motives were in buying the director a drink? 你認為他請董事喝酒的動機是甚麼?

mot·ley /ˈmɑtlɪ; ˈmɒtli/ adj of many different kinds (a word used to express disapproval or used in a humorous way) 不同種類的; 混雜的〔含貶義或表示幽默〕: a motley

---

LIVING ROOM 起居室, 客廳

Exercise 1 練習一

Here is a list of household items whose names have got mixed up. Unscramble the words and decide where you would expect to find them. Complete the table by putting the words in the appropriate columns. 這裡有一張家用物品的清單，項目名稱已弄亂了。把這些詞語整理一下，然後想一想你可以在哪裡找到它們。把這些詞語填入適當的欄目內，完成這張表格。

rachairm   pleenamteci   pat
lektet   palm   habt
basna wish   etlow   recaus
dwarboer   sichoun   plowil

Living room	Kitchen	Bathroom	Bedroom

Exercise 2 練習二

How does your living room differ from the one pictured opposite? Write a short paragraph describing your living room. 你的起居室和左頁畫的那一間有甚麼不同? 寫一篇短文描述一下你的起居室。

M

crowd of people 形形色色的一羣人

mo·tor¹ /'mouta; 'mouta'/ *n* a machine that changes power, especially electrical power, into movement 馬達; 發動機; 電動機: *This grass-cutting machine is driven by a small electric motor.* 這架割草機是由一台小電動機驅動的。

motor² *adj* [only before a noun 只用於名詞前] **1** driven by an engine 機動的: *a motorboat* 摩托艇; 汽艇 | *a motor scooter* 低座小型摩托車 | *a motor mower* 機動割草機 **2** related to vehicles driven by an engine, especially those used on roads 汽車的: *the motor industry* 汽車工業 | *motor racing* 汽車賽

motor³ *v* [I+adv/prep] *BrE old fash* to travel by car 〔英式, 老式〕乘汽車旅行: *We motored over to Cambridge to see some friends.* 我們開車去劍橋看望幾個朋友。

mo·tor·car /'mouta,kar; 'moutakɑː'/ *n BrE old fash* a car 〔英式, 老式〕汽車

mo·tor·cy·cle /'mouta,saikl; 'mouta,saikəl/ *n* (also 又作 **motorbike** *BrE infml* 〔英式, 非正式〕) a large heavy bicycle driven by an engine 摩托車 –**motorcyclist** *n*

mo·tor·ist /'moutarist; 'moutərɪst/ *n* a person who drives a car 駕駛汽車的人

mo·tor·ized /'mouta,raizd; 'moutəraizd/ *adj* having an engine (used of vehicles) 機動的 〔指車輛〕

mo·tor·way /'mouta,we; 'moutəwei/ *n BrE* a very wide road built for fast long-distance travel 〔英式〕高速公路

mot·tled /'motld; 'motld/ *adj* marked irregularly with different coloured spots or parts 雜色的; 斑駁的: *The underside of this snake is yellow, but its back is mottled.* 這條蛇的腹部是黃色的, 可牠的背部顏色斑駁。

mot·to /'motou; 'motou/ *n* **mottos** *or* **mottoes** a short sentence or a few words taken as the guiding principle of a person, a school, or an organization 箴言; 格言; 座右銘: *The school motto is "Never lose hope".* 這所學校的格言是"永不氣餒"。

mould¹ /mould; mould/ *n* (also 又作 **mold** *AmE* 〔美式〕) [U] **1** a soft greenish growth on bread or cheese that has been kept too long, or on objects which have been left for a long time in warm wet air 霉; 霉菌 **2** loose soft soil that is rich in decayed vegetable substances 耕作土壤; 鬆軟沃土: *He planted the seeds in a box filled with leaf mould.* 他把種子播在裝滿腐葉沃土的盒子裡。 **3** a hollow container with a particular shape, into which some soft or liquid substance is poured; when the substance hardens, it takes this shape 模子; 鑄模: *a jelly mould shaped like a rabbit* 兔型果凍模子

mould² *v* (also 又作 **mold** *AmE* 〔美式〕) [T] to give shape or form to something especially by using a mould 用模子製作; 澆

鑄: *The car body is moulded in the factory.* 汽車的車身是在工廠裡澆鑄而成的。 | *a figure of a man moulded out of clay* 用黏土塑造的人像 | *His character has been moulded more by his experiences in life than by his education.* 他的性格由生活經歷形成多於由所受教育形成。

mould·y /'mouldi; 'mouldi/ *adj* **mouldier**, **mouldiest** (also 又作 **moldy** *AmE* 〔美式〕) old, and covered with mould 發霉的: *mouldy cheese* 發霉的乾酪 | *The house has been empty for years, and smells rather mouldy.* 這座房子好些年沒人住, 發出一股子霉味。

moult /moult; moult/ *v* (also 又作 **molt** *AmE* 〔美式〕) [I] (of birds or animals) to lose feathers, fur, or hair as part of a natural process of loss and regrowth 〔鳥〕換羽; 〔動物〕脫毛

mound /maund; maund/ *n* **1** a pile of earth or stones, sometimes making a small hill 土堆, 土丘, 石岡 **2** a large pile of objects 一大堆東西: *a mound of newspapers* 一大堆報紙

mount¹ /maunt; maunt/ *n* **1** an animal on which you can ride 坐騎: *This pony is a good quiet mount for a child.* 這匹小馬性情溫和, 是孩子的好坐騎。 **2** **Mount** a word used as part of the name of a mountain 〔作為山名的一部分〕…山; …峯: *Mount Everest* 珠穆朗瑪峯, 埃佛勒斯峯

mount² *v* **1** [I;T] to get on a horse or a bicycle 騎上(馬或腳踏車): *He mounted his horse and rode away.* 他騎上馬跑開了。 | *Shall I hold it while you mount?* 你上馬時要我幫你牽住馬嗎? **2** [T] *fml* to go up 〔正式〕登上: *My grandmother can hardly mount the stairs.* 我的祖母幾乎無法上樓梯了。 **3** [I] to increase 增加: *mounting debts* 增加的債務 | *The government faced mounting opposition.* 政府面對越來越多的反對意見。 **4** [T] to fix something on a support or in a frame 安放; 鑲嵌; 裱貼: *She mounted the photograph on stiff paper.* 她把照片裱貼在硬紙板上。 **5** [T] to prepare and carry out an action 發起; 發動; 舉行: *The unions are getting ready to mount a powerful attack on the government.* 工會正準備向政府發動有力的攻勢。

mount up *phr v* [I] increase 增加: *Our debts are mounting up at an alarming rate.* 我們的債務正以驚人的速度增加。

✱**moun·tain** /'mauntn; 'mauntɪn/ *n* a very high hill 山; 山岳: *I have no wish to climb any mountains.* 我並不打算攀登任何的山。 | *mountain goats* 石山羊

moun·tain bike /'·· ,·/ *n* a special strong bicycle for riding over rough ground 山地車

moun·tain·eer /,mauntn'ir; ,mauntɪ'niə'/ *n* a person who climbs mountains as a sport or profession 登山運動員; 登山家

moun·tain·eer·ing /,mauntn'iriŋ; ,mauntɪ-

'nɪərɪŋ/ *n* [U] the sport of climbing mountains 登山運動: *Mountaineering is very popular.* 登山很流行。 —**mountaineering** *v* [only in progressive forms 只用於進行式]

moun·tain·ous /'maʊntnəs; 'maʊntʃnəs/ *adj* full of mountains 多山的: *mountainous country* 多山的國家

mourn /morn; mɔːn/ *v* [I;T] to feel or show grief, especially when someone has died 〔尤指對死者〕感到悲痛; 表示哀悼: *The old woman still mourns for her son.* 這老婦人仍在為她死去的兒子傷心。| *The whole nation mourned his death.* 舉國為他逝世而哀悼。

mourn·er /'mornə; 'mɔːnəʳ/ *n* a person who attends a funeral, especially a relative or friend of the one who is dead 哀悼者; 送葬者

mourn·ful /'mornfl; 'mɔːnfəl/ *adj* sad 悲哀的 –**mournfully** *adv*

mourn·ing /'mornɪŋ; 'mɔːnɪŋ/ *n* [U] 1 the expression of grief, especially when someone has died 〔尤指為某人的去世所表示的〕哀痛; 哀悼: *All the theatres and cinemas closed as a sign of mourning for the dead president.* 所有的劇院和電影院都停演停映, 對逝世的總統表示哀悼。 2 **in mourning** behaving or dressed in a way that expresses your grief at someone's death 穿着喪服的

*★**mouse** /maʊs; maʊs/ *n* 1 [plural is 複數為 **mice** /maɪs; maɪs/] a small furry animal with a long tail that lives in houses and in fields 老鼠; 耗子: *a field mouse* 田鼠 | *I think we've got mice in the kitchen.* 我想我們廚房裡有老鼠。 2 [plural is 複數為 **mouses**] a small box connected to a computer by a wire which you move around on a surface in order to work the computer 〔電腦〕鼠標 –see picture on page 763 見 763 頁彩圖

mousse /mus; muːs/ *n* [C;U] a dish made from cream, eggs, and other substances mixed together and then served cold 奶油凍〔一種甜點〕: *chocolate mousse* 巧克力奶油凍

mous·tache /'mʌstæʃ; mə'stɑːʃ/ *n* (also 又作 **mustache** *AmE* 【美式】) hair growing on a man's upper lip 髭; 八字鬚 –see picture on page 469 見 469 頁彩圖

mous·y /'maʊsɪ; 'maʊsɪ/ *adj* 1 a dull brown colour (used of hair) 灰褐色的〔指毛髮〕 –see picture on page 469 見 469 頁彩圖 2 unattractively plain or quiet and uninteresting (used of a person) 不討人喜歡的; 不好看的; 悄無聲息的; 乏味的〔指人〕

*★**mouth**¹ /maʊθ; maʊθ/ *n* 1 the opening in your face through which you speak and take food into your body 嘴; 口; 口腔 2 an opening, entrance, or way out 出入口: *the mouth of a cave* 洞口 | *the mouth of a river* 河口 3 **down in the mouth** unhappy 垂頭喪氣的 4 **keep your mouth shut: a** to remain silent 保持沉默 **b** to not reveal a secret 保守秘密 5 **make someone's**

mouth water to make someone eager to eat 使人垂涎欲滴: *The smells from the kitchen are making my mouth water.* 廚房裡飄來的氣味使我垂涎欲滴。 6 **put words into someone's mouth** to tell someone what to say 告訴某人說甚麼; 教某人怎麼說 7 **take the words out of someone's mouth** to say something that someone else was going to say, before they have had time to speak 搶先說出 8 **-mouthed** having the stated way of speaking (usually part of a word expressing disapproval) 有某種說話方式的 〔常用來組成貶義詞〕: *loud-mouthed* 說話嘰哩呱啦的 | *foul-mouthed* 說話下流的

mouth² /maʊð; maʊð/ *v* [T] 1 to speak or say something without understanding or sincerity 言不由衷地說; 機械地說 2 to move your lips as if you are speaking but without making any sound 不出聲地說

mouth·ful /'maʊθ,ful; 'maʊθfʊl/ *n* 1 as much food or drink as you usually put into your mouth at one time 〔食物、飲料〕一口之量: *I'm too full to eat another mouthful.* 我太飽了, 一口也不能再吃了。 2 *infml* a long word or phrase that you find difficult to say 〔非正式〕又長又拗口的詞或詞組: *Her name is quite a mouthful!* 她的名字真是又長又拗口!

mouth·or·gan /'maʊθ,ɔrgən; 'maʊθ,ɔːgən/ *n* a small musical instrument; you play it by blowing into it as you move it from side to side 口琴

mouth·piece /'maʊθ,pis; 'maʊθpiːs/ *n* 1 part of something like a musical instrument or a telephone, that you hold in or near the mouth 〔樂器的〕吹口; 〔電話機的〕送話口 2 a person or newspaper that expresses the opinions of others 代言人; 喉舌; 傳聲筒: *This newspaper is just the mouthpiece of the government.* 這份報紙只是政府的傳聲筒。

mouth·wa·ter·ing /'·,····/ *adj* so good that you feel a desire to eat the food which is smelt, seen or described 令人垂涎的: *He gave me a mouth-watering account of the dinner I missed.* 他對我沒吃到的那頓飯做了一番令人垂涎的描述。

mo·va·ble /'muvəbl; 'muːvəbəl/ *adj* (also 又作 **moveable**) able to be moved 可動的; 活動的: *toy soldiers with movable arms and legs* 手足可以活動的玩具士兵

*★**move**¹ /muv; muːv/ *v* **moved, moving** 1 [I] to change position or go to a new place 改變位置; 移動: *Sit still and don't move!* 安安靜靜地坐着別動! | *I could hear someone moving around downstairs.* 我聽到有人在樓下走來走去。 | *That bird hasn't moved for half an hour.* 那隻鳥半小時沒動了。 2 [T] to change something's position or take it to a new place 改變〔某物的〕位置; 移動; 搬動: *I can't move my legs.* 我的腿沒法動了。 | *Could you move your car, please?* 請

M

把你的汽車移動一下好嗎? **3** [I] (also 又作 **move house**) to go to a new home 搬家: *We're moving to a bigger house.* 我們要搬到一座更大的房子裡去。| *I moved house three times last year.* 我去年搬了三次家。 **4** [I + adv/prep] to advance 進展; 發展: *Events in Europe are moving very quickly now.* 歐洲事態現在進展很快。| *We seem to be moving towards a peace agreement.* 我們似乎正在向和平協定邁進。 **5** [T] to make you feel a strong emotion such as anger or sadness 感動; 激起〔情感〕: *I was very moved by her story.* 她的故事使我很感動。 **6 move someone to do something** *fml* to cause someone to do something 〔正式〕促使某人做某事: *What finally moved the prime minister to resign?* 是甚麼最終促使首相辭職? **7** [T; +that] to put forward a suggestion at a meeting 〔在會議上〕提議: *I move that we reject this application.* 我提議我們駁回這項申請。| *I wish to move an amendment to this law.* 我希望對這法律提出一項修正案。

move in *phr v* [I] to go and live in a new home 搬入, 遷入〔新居〕: *We've bought a house now, and should be able to move in next month.* 我們已經買了新房子, 相信下個月可搬進去。

move off *phr v* [I] to move away from a place 離去: *The guard blew his whistle and the train moved off.* 列車長吹響哨子, 火車就開動了。

move on *phr v* **1** [I] to change to something new 更換成〔新的事物〕: *Can we move on to the next item on our agenda?* 我們可以改談議程上的下一個項目嗎? **2** [I] to go away to a new place 離開〔去別處〕: *He stopped to look in a shop window, then moved on.* 他停下來看看商店櫥窗, 然後走開了。 **3** [T **move sbdy ↔ on**] to make someone move away from where they are 使〔某人〕走開: *He was moved on by the police.* 警察要他走開。

move over *phr v* [I] to change your position so that there is room for someone else 〔為給他人讓出地方〕移動: *Move over a bit so that I can sit down.* 挪過去一點, 那樣我可以坐下來。

move² *n* **1** a movement or an act of moving 動; 移動; 動作: *He was watching my every move.* 他在監視我的一舉一動。| *Don't make a move, or I'll shoot.* 別動, 否則我就開槍。 **2** an act of going to a new home or a new job 搬家; 換工作: *The move went very smoothly.* 搬家進行得很順利。| *I couldn't face another job move.* 我受不了又要換工作。 **3** an act of moving a piece in a game such as CHESS 一步棋: *Come on, it's your move.* 快點兒, 該你走了。 **4** an action that you take in order to gain a particular result 步驟; 行動: *The latest moves towards peace seem to have ended in failure.* 最近為通向和平採取的步驟似乎已告失敗。 **5 get a move on** *infml* to hurry up 〔非正式〕快點; 趕緊: *We'd better*

get a move on or we'll be late. 我們最好快些, 否則要遲到了。

★move·ment /ˈmuːvmənt; ˈmuːvmənt/ *n* **1** [C;U] change in position or from one place to another 移動; 走動; 活動: *Any movement can be painful when you've hurt your back.* 你背部受傷時, 動一動都可能感到疼痛。| *the movement of goods by road* 公路貨運 | *I noticed a sudden movement behind the curtain.* 我注意到簾子後面忽然動了一下。| *The police are watching this man's movements very carefully.* 警察正在密切監視這個男人的活動。 **2** [C] a group of people who make united efforts for a particular purpose 積極開展運動的團體; 運動: *The trade union movement works to obtain higher wages and better conditions.* 工會運動旨在爭取更高的工資和更好的工作條件。 **3** [C] a general development in something, often not directed by any particular person or group 動向; 傾向; 趨勢: *The movement* **towards** *complete equality for women still has a long way to go.* 男女完全平等的趨勢還有很長一段路要走。 **4** [C] one of the main parts into which many longer pieces of music are divided 樂章 **5** [C] the moving parts of a piece of machinery, especially a clock or watch 〔尤指鐘、錶的〕機件

★mov·ie /ˈmuːvɪ; ˈmuːvɪ/ *n* the usual American word for 〔美式〕= FILM

mov·ies /ˈmuːvɪz; ˈmuːvɪz/ *n* [pl] **the movies** the usual American word for 〔美式〕= the CINEMA: *Let's go to the movies!* 我們去看電影吧!

mov·ing /ˈmuːvɪŋ; ˈmuːvɪŋ/ *adj* **1** causing strong feelings, especially of pity 動人的; 感人的: *The film was so moving that we were all in tears.* 這電影感動得大家都哭了。 **2** [only before a noun 只用於名詞前] able to move 可活動的: *Oil the moving parts of this machine regularly.* 要定期給這部機器的運轉部件上油。

mow /moʊ; məʊ/ *v* **mowed, mown** /moʊn; məʊn/ *or* **mowed** [I;T] to cut grass or crops with a machine 〔用機器〕割(草); 收割(莊稼)

mow sbdy ↔ down *phr v* [T] to kill people or knock them down, especially in large numbers 〔大批〕殘殺; 摧倒: *Protesters were mown down by army guns.* 抗議者遭軍隊開槍射殺。

mow·er /ˈmoʊə; ˈməʊəʳ/ *n* a machine for cutting grass or crops 割草機; 收割機

MP /ˌɛmˈpi; ˌem ˈpiː/ *n* a person who has been elected to represent people from a particular area in parliament; an abbreviation for **Member of Parliament** 〔縮〕(下院)議員: *Michael Foot, MP* 邁克爾·弗特議員 | *our local MP* 我們本地的議員 | *the MP for Witney* 代表惠特尼的議員

mpg an abbreviation for 〔縮〕= **miles per gallon** 每加侖汽油所行英里數, 英里/加侖: *a*

car that does 35 mpg 一輛每加侖汽油行駛三十五英里的汽車

mph an abbreviation for 〔縮〕= **miles per hour** 每小時英里數，英里/小時: *driving along at 60 mph* 以每小時六十英里的速度行駛

Mr /ˈmɪstə; ˈmɪstər/ *n* [only before a noun 只用於名詞前] (also 又作 **mister**) **1** a title used to address or talk about a man who has no other title 先生〔用於稱呼或談及沒有其他頭銜的男子〕: *Mr Smith* 史密斯先生 | *Mr John Smith* 約翰·史密斯先生 **2** a title used to address men in certain official positions 先生〔用於稱呼某些有官職的男子〕: *Mr Chairman* 主席先生 | *Mr President* 總統先生

Mrs /ˈmɪsɪz; ˈmɪs1z/ *n* [only before a noun 只用於名詞前] a title used to address or talk about a married woman 太太〔對已婚女子的稱呼〕: *Mrs Jones* 瓊斯太太 | *Mrs Sarah Jones* 莎拉·瓊斯太太 –compare 比較 MISS, MS

Ms /mɪz; mɪz/ *n* [only before a noun 只用於名詞前] a title for a woman who does not wish to call herself either "Mrs" or "Miss" 女士〔用於不願被稱為"太太"或"小姐"的女子姓氏前〕

MS *n* **MSS** a written abbreviation for 〔縮〕= MANUSCRIPT

MSc /ˈɛmɛsˈsi; ˌem es ˈsiː/ (also 又作 **MS** *AmE* 〔美式〕) **1** a higher university degree; an abbreviation for **Master of Science** 〔縮〕理科碩士學位: *Jill Smith, MSc* 理科碩士吉爾·史密斯 | *an MSc from Cambridge University* 來自劍橋大學的一名理科碩士 **2** a person who has an MSc 理科碩士

Mt a written abbreviation for 〔縮〕= MOUNT¹ (2) ...山; ...峯: *Mt Everest* 珠穆朗瑪峯，埃佛勒斯峯

much¹ /mʌtʃ; mʌtʃ/ *adv* **more** /mor; mɔːr/, **most** /most; məʊst/ **1** by a great amount or degree 十分; 非常: *She's much cleverer than I am.* 她比我聰明得多。 | *We're looking forward very much to seeing you.* 我們非常盼望與你會面。 **2** not much not very often 不是經常: *We don't go out very much.* 我們不是經常外出。 | *I don't see him much these days.* 近來我不常看到他。 **3** in most ways 幾乎; 差不多: *Jane was much the same as usual.* 簡同以往幾乎一樣。

> ■ USAGE 用法: We use **much** instead of **very** before expressions like *admired, improved, commented on, talked about* (expressions containing the passive form of verbs). ☆ 在 *admired, improved, commented on, talked about* 等詞語(包含動詞的被動形式)前, 用 **much** 而不用 **very**。Compare 比較 *This picture is* **much** *admired.* and 和 *This picture is* **very** *famous.* (這幅畫非常出名。)

much² *det, pron, n* **more, most 1** used in questions asking about the amount of something that there is 多少〔於問句詢問數量〕: *How much cheese have we got left?* 我們還剩下多少乾酪? | *How much does it cost?* 這東西多少錢? **2** *fml* a large amount 〔正式〕許多; 大量: *I have much pleasure in welcoming you today.* 歡迎你今天到來, 本人十分榮幸。 | *Much of what he says is true.* 他說的很多都是實話。 **3** not much not a great amount 不多: *She doesn't earn very much money.* 她掙錢不多。 | *"Did you enjoy the party?" "Not much."* "你喜歡那次聚會嗎?" "不太喜歡。" **4** too much too great an amount 太多: *I've got far too much work to do.* 我有好多好多工作要幹。 **5** much as although 雖然: *Much as I'd love to come, I'm afraid I won't be able to.* 雖然我很想來, 恐怕也來不了。 **6** not much of a a phrase you use to say that someone or something is not very good 不十分好; 不太好: *I'm not much of a sportsman.* 我不是甚麼了不起的運動員。 **7** not up to much *infml* not very good 〔非正式〕不太好: *The film's not up to much.* 這部影片不怎麼樣。 **8** so much for a phrase you use to say that something is not possible or not helpful 不過如此〔表示某事物不可能或沒甚應用〕 **9** too much for someone too difficult for someone 對某人而言太難

> ■ USAGE 用法: **Much** is not usually used in simple statements. Instead use **a great deal of** or **a lot of** ☆ 在簡單的陳述句裡 **much** 不常用, 而用 **a great deal of** 或 **a lot of**: *She's got* **a lot of** *money.* 她有很多錢。 | *We've already collected* **a great deal of** *information.* 我們已經搜集了很多資料。 | **a lot of** *trouble* 很多麻煩 | **a great deal of** *discomfort* 很不舒服

muck¹ /mʌk; mʌk/ *n* [U] *infml* 〔非正式〕 **1** dirt 污穢: *What's that muck on the carpet?* 地毯上那髒東西是甚麼? **2** waste matter from animals, especially as used for spreading on the land 廄肥; 糞肥 –**mucky** *adj* **muckier, muckiest**

muck² *v*

muck about/around *phr v* [I] *BrE infml* to behave in a silly way 〔英式, 非正式〕胡鬧: *Stop mucking about and listen to what I'm saying.* 別胡鬧, 聽我說。

muck in *phr v* [I] *infml* to join in work or activity with others 〔非正式〕與〔別人〕一起工作[活動]: *If we all muck in we'll soon be finished.* 如果我們大家一起幹, 很快就做完。

muck sthg ↔ up *phr v* [T] *BrE infml* 〔英式, 非正式〕 **1** to spoil something 弄糟, 打亂〔某事物〕: *The change in the weather has mucked up our plans.* 天氣變化打亂了我們的計劃。 **2** to make something dirty 弄髒〔某

M

物〕: *I've mucked up my shirt, working in the garden.* 我在花園裡幹活，把衣服弄髒了。

mu·cus /ˈmjukəs; ˈmjuːkəs/ *n* [U] a liquid produced in certain parts of your body, especially your nose〔人體產生的〕黏液;〔尤指〕鼻涕

mud /mʌd; mʌd/ *n* [U] **1** very wet earth in a sticky mass, or the same substance when it has dried on something 爛泥; 泥漿: *The garden became a sea of mud.* 花園變成了泥潭。| *You've got mud on your trousers.* 你褲子上有泥漿。**2** your name is mud = people speak badly of you after you have caused trouble 你聲名掃地了

mud·dle¹ /ˈmʌdl; ˈmʌdl/ *n* a state of confusion and disorder 糊塗狀態; 混亂狀態: *I was in such a muddle that I couldn't find anything.* 我稀裡糊塗，甚麼也找不到。

muddle² *v* **muddled, muddling** [T] **1** (also 又作 **muddle sth ↔ up**) to put things into disorder 把〔東西〕弄亂: *You're muddling up my papers.* 你把我的文件弄亂了。**2** (also 又作 **muddle sbdy/sth ↔ up**) to confuse people or things, or to make someone confused 把〔人或東西〕混在一起; 使〔某人〕糊塗: *Don't muddle me up with all these different instructions.* 別給我這許多不同的指示，把我都搞糊塗了。| *I keep muddling up James with his brother.* 我經常誤以為詹姆斯是他的哥哥。

muddle along *phr v* [I] to continue in a confused manner, without a plan 混日子; 得過且過

muddle through *phr v* [I;T] to manage to do something although you do not have the necessary plans or means 胡亂應付過去; 混過去: *I expect the country will muddle through this crisis too.* 我相信這個國家同樣可以勉力應付這場危機。| *We had no idea what was expected, but we muddled through.* 我們不知道結果如何，但我們應付過去了。

mud·dled /ˈmʌdld; ˈmʌdld/ *adj* confused 糊塗的

mud·dy¹ /ˈmʌdɪ; ˈmʌdɪ/ *adj* **muddier, muddiest** covered with or containing mud 沾滿泥的; 泥潭的: *the muddy waters of the river* 渾濁的河水 | *Take off those muddy boots.* 脫掉那雙沾滿污泥的靴子吧。

muddy² *v* **muddied, muddying** [T] to make something dirty with mud 使〔某物〕沾上泥: *Your dog's muddying the kitchen floor.* 你的狗弄得廚房地板上都是泥。

mud·guard /ˈmʌdˌɡɑrd; ˈmʌdɡɑːd/ *n* a metal cover over the wheel of a vehicle to keep the mud from flying up〔汽車輪胎上的〕擋泥板

muf·fle /ˈmʌfl; ˈmʌfəl/ *v* **muffled, muffling** [T] to make a sound less easy to hear 使〔聲音〕低沉或輕微: *I heard muffled voices through the wall.* 我聽到有壓低的聲音從牆那邊傳來。

mug¹ /mʌɡ; mʌɡ/ *n* **1** a kind of large cup

with a flat bottom, straight sides, and a handle 圓筒形有柄大杯: *a mug of coffee* 一大杯咖啡 –see picture on page 244 見 244 頁彩圖 **2** *BrE infml* a foolish person who is easily deceived〔英式, 非正式〕傻瓜; 易受騙者

mug² *v* **-gg-** [T] to rob someone with violence, especially in a dark street〔尤指在黑暗的街道上〕對〔某人〕行兇搶劫 –**mugger** *n* –**mugging** *n* [C;U]

mug·gy /ˈmʌɡɪ; ˈmʌɡɪ/ *adj* unpleasantly warm but not dry (used of weather) 悶熱而潮濕的〔指天氣〕 –**mugginess** *n* [U]

Mu·ham·ma·dan /mʊˈhæmədən; mʊˈhæmɪdən/ *adj, n* see 見 MUSLIM

mul·ber·ry /ˈmʌlˌbɛrɪ; ˈmʌlbəri/ *n* **mulberries** a small dark purple fruit which can be eaten 桑椹

mulch /mʌltʃ; mʌltʃ/ *n* a covering of material, often made from decaying plants, which is put over the soil and over the roots of plants to help plants grow 土地覆蓋料; 護根〔常為腐爛的植物〕

mule /mjul; mjuːl/ *n* an animal whose parents are a donkey and a horse 騾; 騾子

mull /mʌl; mʌl/ *v* [T] to heat alcohol with sugar and other things to make a special drink 給〔酒〕加糖和其他東西並加熱: *mulled wine* 香甜的熱酒

mull sth ↔ over *phr v* [T] to consider something for a time 仔細考慮〔某事物〕: *I'm mulling over what she said.* 我在仔細考慮她所說的話。

mul·lah /ˈmʌlə; ˈmʌlə/ *n* a Muslim teacher of law and religion 毛拉〔伊斯蘭〕

mul·ti·far·i·ous /ˌmʌltəˈfɛrɪəs; ˌmʌltɪˈfeəriəs/ *adj fml* of many different types〔正式〕多種類的: *multifarious interests* 多樣的興趣 –**multifariously** *adv*

mul·ti·lat·e·ral /ˌmʌltɪˈlætərəl; ˌmʌltɪˈlætərəl/ *adj* concerning more than two groups of people, often with different opinions 多方的; 多邊的: *a multilateral agreement on world oil prices* 有關世界石油價格的多邊協議

mul·ti·ple¹ /ˈmʌltəpl; ˈmʌltɪpl/ *adj* including many different parts, things, or people 複合的; 多樣的; 多人的: *The driver of the crashed car received multiple injuries.* 出事汽車的司機多處受傷。

multiple² *n* a number which contains a smaller number an exact number of times 倍數: *3×4=12, so 12 is a multiple of 3.* 3乘4等於12, 所以12是3的倍數。

mul·ti·pli·ca·tion /ˌmʌltəpləˈkeʃən; ˌmʌltɪpliˈkeɪʃən/ *n* [U] the method of combining two numbers by adding one of them to itself as many times as the other number states 乘法(運算): *2×4=8 is an example of multiplication.* 2×4=8是乘法運算的一例。

mul·ti·pli·ci·ty /ˌmʌltəˈplɪsətɪ; ˌmʌltɪˈplɪsɪti/ *n* [sing] a large variety of things 多樣: *a multiplicity of ideas* 各種各樣的想法

mul·ti·ply /'mʌltəˌplaɪ; 'mʌltɪˌplaɪ/ v [I;T] **1** to combine numbers by MULTIPLICATION 乘; 做乘法: *to multiply 2 by 3* 2 乘以 3 | *2 multiplied by 3 (2×3) = 2 + 2 + 2.* 2 乘以 3 (2×3) = 2 + 2 + 2。 | *You added when you should have multiplied.* 你該用乘法, 而你卻用了加法。 –compare 比較 DIVIDE² (6) **2** to increase in number or make something increase in number (使)增加: *We can multiply our chances of success.* 我們可以增加成功的機會。 | *Our problems seem to be multiplying.* 我們的問題似乎在增加。

mul·ti·ra·cial /ˌmʌltɪˈreɪʃəl; ˌmʌltɪˈreɪʃəl◂/ adj consisting of or involving several races of people 多種族的

mul·ti·sto·rey /ˌmʌltɪˈstɔːrɪ; ˌmʌltɪˈstɔːri◂/ adj [only before a noun 只用於名詞前] with several levels or floors (used of a building) 多層的〔指建築物〕: *a multistorey car park* 多層停車場

mul·ti·tude /'mʌltəˌtjuːd; 'mʌltɪˌtjuːd/ n fml a large number〔正式〕大批; 許多: *A multitude of thoughts filled her mind.* 眾多的想法充塞在她的腦子裡。

mum /mʌm; mʌm/ n BrE infml (also 又作 **Mum; mom** AmE〔美式〕) mother〔英式, 非正式〕媽媽: *Can I go to the cinema please, Mum?* 媽媽我可以去看電影嗎? | *My mum's gone to work.* 我媽媽上班了。 | *Have you seen Mum?* 媽媽在哪兒?

mum·ble /'mʌmbl; 'mʌmbəl/ v **mumbled, mumbling** [I;T] to speak unclearly 含糊地說; 咕噥: *She mumbled a reply.* 她咕噥着回答。 | *I wish you wouldn't mumble when you speak to me.* 我希望你和我說話時不要咕咕噥噥。

mum·mi·fy /'mʌmɪˌfaɪ; 'mʌmɪfaɪ/ v **mummified, mummifying** [T] to preserve a dead body as a mummy (2) 將〔屍體〕製成木乃伊

mum·my /'mʌmɪ; 'mʌmi/ n **mummies** BrE〔英式〕(also 又作 **Mummy**) **1** a word for mother used especially by or to children 媽咪〔用作兒語〕: *I want my mummy!* 我要媽咪! | *Ask your mummy if she will help you.* 問問你媽咪她會不會幫你。 **2** a dead body preserved from decay by treatment with special substances, especially in ancient Egypt〔尤指古埃及的〕木乃伊

mumps /mʌmps; mʌmps/ n [U] an infectious illness common in children which causes swelling in the neck (流行性)腮腺炎

munch /mʌntʃ; mʌntʃ/ v [I;T] to eat something noisily 出聲咀嚼: *He was munching an apple.* 他在嚼一隻蘋果。 | *We sat there munching on biscuits.* 我們坐在那裡大嚼餅乾。

mun·dane /'mʌndeɪn; mʌn'deɪn/ adj ordinary, with nothing exciting or unusual in it (a word usually used to express disapproval) 平凡的; 平淡的〔常含貶義〕: *a mundane life* 平庸的生活

mu·ni·ci·pal /mjuːˈnɪsəpl; mjuːˈnɪsɪˌpəl/ adj relating or belonging to a town with its own local government 市政的: *municipal buildings* 市政府辦公大樓 | *the municipal council* 市政會

mu·ni·ci·pal·i·ty /ˌmjuːnɪsəˈpælɪtɪ; mjuːˌnɪsɪˈpælɪˌti/ n **municipalities** a town, city, or other small area, which has its own government for local affairs 自治市; 自治區

mu·nif·i·cence /mjuːˈnɪfəsns; mjuːˈnɪfɪˌsəns/ n [U] fml generous action or thought〔正式〕慷慨; 寬厚 –**munificent** adj

mu·ni·tions /mjuːˈnɪʃənz; mjuːˈnɪʃənz/ n [pl] large weapons for war, such as bombs 軍火; 軍需品〔如炸彈〕

mu·ral /'mjʊərəl; 'mjʊərəl/ n a picture which is painted on a wall 壁畫

mur·der¹ /'mɜːdə; 'mɜːdər/ n **1** [C;U] the crime of killing a human being illegally 謀殺(罪): *Police investigating the two murders believed they were committed by the same person.* 警方調查了兩件謀殺案, 認為皆由同一人所為。 | *She was found guilty of murder.* 法庭判她謀殺罪罪名成立。 | *Police are still looking for the murder weapon.* 警方仍在尋找謀殺案的兇器。 **2** [U] infml a very difficult or tiring experience〔非正式〕艱難困苦的經歷; 遭罪經歷: *It was murder putting the clock together.* 把這隻鐘裝配好真是件苦差事。 | *The traffic was murder.* 這交通真要命。

mur·der² v [I;T] to kill someone illegally and on purpose 謀殺〔某人〕: *She was murdered in the most brutal way.* 她被人用極為殘忍地謀殺了。 | *We suspect that he has murdered before.* 我們懷疑他以前殺過人。 – see 見 KILL (USAGE 用法) –**murderer** n

mur·der·ous /'mɜːdərəs; 'mɜːdərəs/ adj likely to kill someone, or expressing that possibility 殺人的; 蓄意謀殺的: *murderous intentions* 謀殺的意圖 | *a murderous expression on his face* 他臉上那一副要殺人的兇相 | *murderous road conditions* 險惡的道路狀況

murk·y /'mɜːkɪ; 'mɜːki/ adj **murkier, murkiest** dark and unpleasant 陰暗的; 昏暗的: *a murky night* 黑夜

mur·mur¹ /'mɜːmə; 'mɜːmər/ n **1** a soft low sound 低柔的聲音: *the murmur of the stream* 溪水淙淙 **2** without a murmur without complaint 無怨言地: *The children went to bed without a murmur.* 孩子們一聲也沒咕噥就上牀睡了。

murmur² v [I;T] to make a soft sound, especially when speaking in a quiet voice〔尤指低語〕發出輕聲: *a child murmuring in her sleep* 睡夢中喃喃低語的女孩子 | *As she delivered her speech, the crowd murmured their approval.* 她在演講時, 聽眾發出輕輕的讚許聲。

mus·cle¹ /'mʌsl; 'mʌsəl/ n **1** [C;U] pieces of flesh in your body joining the bones 肌肉: *I'm playing tennis to develop my arm*

M

muscles. 我在打網球鍛鍊手臂肌肉。 | *He's all muscle!* 他非常健壯! **2** [U] strength 體力; 力量: *the military muscle of the world's great powers* 世界各大國的軍事實力 **3 not move a muscle** to stay quite still 紋絲不動; 一動不動
muscle² v

muscle in *phr v* [I] *infml* to force your way into a situation where you have no right to be 《非正式》強行擠入; 強行插足: *He's trying to muscle in on the contracts that I have been responsible for winning.* 他企圖擠進來分享我負責贏得的那些合同。

mus·cu·lar /'mʌskjələˀ; 'mʌskjŭlɔˀ/ *adj* **1** connected with muscles 肌肉的: *a muscular disease* 肌肉疾病 **2** having big strong muscles 肌肉發達的; 強健的: *a muscular body* 強健的體魄

muse /mjuːz; mjuːz/ *v* **mused, musing** [I] to think deeply, forgetting about the world around you 沉思; 冥想: *She sat musing for hours.* 她一連幾小時坐着沉思默想。

*★**mu·se·um** /mjuˈzɪəm; mjuːˈzɪəm/ *n* a building where objects are kept and shown to the public because of their scientific, historical, or artistic interest 博物館: *the Museum of Modern Art* 現代藝術博物館

mush /mʌʃ; mʌʃ/ *n* [U] *infml* a soft mass of half-liquid, half-solid material, especially food (a word often used to express disapproval) 《非正式》爛糊狀東西〔尤指食物〕〔常含貶義〕: *I can't eat this mush!* 我吃不下這種爛糊東西! –**mushy** *adj* **mushier, mushiest:** *mushy potatoes* 薯泥[土豆泥] | *mushy peas* 青豆泥

mush·room¹ /'mʌʃrum; 'mʌʃruːm/ *n* a plant with a short stem and round top, often eaten and sometimes poisonous 蘑菇 –see picture on page 504 見 504 頁彩圖

mushroom² v [I] to develop or spread fast 迅速發展或擴散: *Since the opening of the first shop, new branches have mushroomed all over the country.* 自從第一家店開張以來，新的分店在全國如雨後春筍般湧現。

*★**mu·sic** /'mjuzɪk; 'mjuːzɪk/ *n* [U] **1** the arrangement of sounds in pleasant patterns and tunes 樂曲; 曲: *That's a beautiful piece of music.* 那是一首優美的樂曲。 | *What's your favourite kind of music?* 你最喜愛哪種樂曲? **2** the art of arranging sounds and tunes 音樂; 作曲法: *to study music* 學習音樂 | *a music student* 學音樂的學生 **3** a written or printed set of notes 樂譜: *a sheet of music* 一頁樂譜 | *I've lost my music.* 我把樂譜丟了。 **4 face the music** to admit to blame and accept the results 承擔行為的後果

*★**mu·sic·al¹** /'mjuzɪkl̩; 'mjuːzɪkəl/ *adj* **1** [only before a noun 只用於名詞前] sounding like music or producing music 音樂般的; 音樂的; 悅耳的: *musical instruments* 樂器 | *a rather musical way of speaking* 頗為悅耳的說話方式 **2** skilled in and fond of music 有音樂才

能的; 愛好音樂的: *a very musical child* 有音樂天份的孩子

musical² *n* a play or film with songs and often dances 音樂劇; 音樂片

music cen·tre /'·· ‚··ˀ/ *n* a piece of electrical apparatus which can play records and cassettes (CASSETTE), and also contains a radio 組合音響〔唱機、盒式磁帶錄音機和收音機合為一體〕

mu·si·cian /mjuˈzɪʃən; mjuːˈzɪʃən/ *n* a person who performs on a musical instrument 音樂家; 樂師

musk /mʌsk; mʌsk/ *n* [U] a strong-smelling substance used in making PERFUME 麝香 –**musky** *adj: a musky smell* 麝香的香味

Mus·lim /'mʌzləm; 'mʌzl̩m/ *n* (also 又作 **Moslem, Mohammedan, Muhammadan**) a person who believes in ISLAM 穆斯林; 伊斯蘭教信徒 –**Muslim** *adj: a Muslim country* 伊斯蘭教國家

mus·lin /'mʌzlɪn; 'mʌzl̩n/ *n* [U] a very fine thin cotton material, used for light dresses especially in the past 平紋細布

mus·sel /'mʌsl̩; 'mʌsəl/ *n* a small sea animal that lives inside a dark shell, and whose soft body can be eaten as food 貽貝; 淡菜 –see picture on page 504 見 504 頁彩圖

*★**must¹** /məst; məst; *strong* 強讀 mʌst; mʌst/ *v negative short form* 否定縮約式 **mustn't** [modal verb 情態動詞] **1** used to show that something is necessary or should be done 必須〔用於表示某事必要或應該做〕: *I must go or I'll be late.* 我必須走了, 否則要遲到了。 | *You mustn't tell anyone about this.* 這件事你不可以告訴任何人。 | *Dogs must be kept on a lead.* 狗須用皮帶拴住。 | *The government must do something about this problem.* 政府必須設法解決這個問題。 **2** used to show that something is very likely or certain 諒必; 一定〔用於表示很有可能〕: *You must be tired after your walk.* 你走了路以後一定是累了。 | *You must be the new English teacher.* 你一定是新來的英語老師吧。 | *There's nobody here — they must have all gone home.* 這兒沒人 ——他們想必都回家了。 –see Study Note on page 1318 見 1318 頁學習提示 **3 you must** a phrase you use when you are inviting someone to do something or suggesting that they do something nice 務必; 一定要〔用於邀請某人做某事或建議他們做某件好事〕: *You must come round for dinner one evening.* 你哪天晚上一定要過來吃飯呀。 | *You must go and see that new film.* 你一定要去看看那部新影片。 **4 I must admit, I must say** phrases you use when you are giving your opinion about something 我必須承認; 我得說〔用於對某事發表意見時〕: *I must admit I don't know very much about classical music.* 我得承認我對古典音樂懂得不多。 | *I must say I don't like the design of that new shopping centre.* 我得說我不喜歡那座新購物

中心的設計。**5 if you must know** a phrase you use when you are telling someone something but you do not think that they really need to know it 如果你一定要知道的話〔用於告訴某人其並不需要知道的事〕: *I live in London, if you must know.* 如果你一定要知道的話，我住在倫敦。

must² *n* a must *infml* something that is necessary or very important 《非正式》必不可少或十分重要的事物: *Warm clothes are a must in the mountains.* 在山裡保暖的衣服是必不可少的。

mus·tache /'mʌstæʃ; mə'stɑː/ *n* see 見 MOUSTACHE

mus·tard /'mʌstəd; 'mʌstəd/ *n* [U] a yellow-flowered plant; mustard seeds produce a hot-tasting powder which is eaten with some kinds of meat 芥菜; 芥末

mus·ter /'mʌstə; 'mʌstər/ *v* **1** [I;T] to gather in one place 集合; 聚集; 召集: *The troops mustered on the hill.* 部隊在小山上集合。| *Will you muster the troops?* 請你集合部隊好嗎? **2** [T] (also 又作 **muster sth ↔ up**) to find as much of something as possible 搜集, 激發〔某事物〕: *I'm trying to muster up the courage to speak to her.* 我在盡量鼓起勇氣和她說話。

must·n't /'mʌsnt; 'mʌsənt/ *v* short for 〔縮〕= 'must not': *You mustn't talk in class.* 你不得在課堂上講話。

must·y /'mʌstɪ; 'mʌsti/ *adj* **mustier, mustiest** smelling unpleasant, often because of age or of fresh air 發霉的; 有霉味的: *musty old books* 有霉味的舊書 | *a musty room* 有霉味的房間 –**mustiness** *n* [U]

mu·ta·tion /mjuː'teɪʃən; mjuː'teɪʃən/ *n* [C;U] the action of change in the cells of a living thing 〔生物細胞內的〕突變

mute¹ /mjuːt; mjuːt/ *adj* silent, often because you are unable to speak 緘默的; 啞的; 不會說話的 –**mutely** *adv*

mute² *n* a person who cannot speak 啞巴

mut·ed /'mjuːtɪd; 'mjuːtɪd/ *adj* made softer than is usual (used of a sound or a colour) 減弱的; 變得柔和的〔指聲音或顏色〕

mu·ti·late /'mjuːtl,eɪt; 'mjuːtḷeɪt/ *v* **mutilated, mutilating** [T] to damage something, usually by removing a part of it 使〔某事物〕殘缺不全: *The police found a badly mutilated body.* 警方發現了殘缺不全的屍體。–**mutilation** /,mjuːtl'eɪʃən; ,mjuːtḷ'eɪʃn/ *n* [C;U]

mu·ti·neer /,mjuːtṇ'ɪr; ,mjuːtḷ'nɪər/ *n* a person who takes part in a mutiny 叛變者; 反叛者

mu·ti·nous /'mjuːtṇəs; 'mjuːtḷnəs/ *adj* dissatisfied and refusing to obey orders 反叛的; 違抗命令的: *A number of crew members are becoming mutinous.* 好幾個船員開始反叛。–**mutinously** *adv*

mu·ti·ny /'mjuːtṇɪ; 'mjuːtḷni/ *n* **mutinies** [C; U] the act of taking power away from the person in charge, especially from a captain on a ship 叛變;〔尤指船上水手的〕譁變

mutiny² *v* **mutinied, mutinying** [I] to take part in a mutiny 參加叛變: *The crew has mutinied and taken over the ship.* 船員參加了叛變並接管了這艘船。

mut·ter /'mʌtə; 'mʌtər/ *v* [I;T] to speak in a low voice, often expressing anger or dissatisfaction 嘀嘀自語; 小聲抱怨: *He muttered a threat.* 他嘟噥着些威脅的話。| *She was muttering to herself.* 她在嘀嘀自語。–**mutter** *n* [sing]

mut·ton /'mʌtṇ; 'mʌtn/ *n* [U] the meat from a sheep 羊肉 –see 見 MEAT (USAGE 用法)

mu·tu·al /'mjuːtʃʊəl; 'mjuːtʃʊəl/ *adj* **1** shared by two people and directed towards each other (used of feelings) 相互的, 彼此的〔指感情〕: *Stalin and Trotsky were mutual enemies.* 斯大林和托洛茨基彼此是敵人。| *their mutual dislike* 他們彼此間的憎惡 –**mutually** *adv* **2** shared by two or more people 共同的; 共有的: *We have a number of mutual interests.* 我們有些共同的興趣。| *our mutual friend* 我們共同的朋友

muz·zle¹ /'mʌzl; 'mʌzəl/ *n* **1** the front part of an animal's face, including its nose and mouth 〔動物的〕鼻口部 **2** a covering round an animal's mouth, to prevent it from biting people 〔動物的〕口套 **3** the front end of a gun 槍口; 砲口

muzzle² *v* **muzzled, muzzling** [T] **1** to put a muzzle on an animal 給〔動物〕戴上口套 **2** to stop someone talking about something 使〔某人〕緘默: *It is a worrying attempt to muzzle the press.* 企圖遏制新聞自由的做法令人擔憂。

my /maɪ; maɪ/ *det* relating to or belonging to the person who is speaking 我的: *I went in and sat down in my chair.* 我走進去坐在我的椅子上。| *I was sitting drinking my coffee.* 我正坐着喝咖啡。

my·o·pic /maɪ'ɒpɪk; maɪ'ɒpɪk/ *adj* unable to see distant objects clearly 近視眼的

myr·i·ad /'mɪrɪəd; 'mɪriəd/ *n* *lit* a great number and variety of things 《文》極大數量; 無數 –**myriad** *adj*

my·self /mə'self; maɪ'self/ *pron* **1** used as the object of a verb or a PREPOSITION when the subject of a verb is the person who is speaking and the action is done to the same person 我自己〔用作動詞或介詞的受詞〕: *I washed myself and got dressed.* 我洗了澡, 穿上衣服。| *I looked at myself in the mirror.* 我照鏡子看看自己。| *I decided to buy myself some new clothes.* 我決定給自己買些新衣服。**2** used to add force to the word "I" 我親自; 我本人〔用以加強語氣〕: *I myself admit that it's not my best painting.* 我自己承認這不是我最好的畫作。| *I did all the decorating myself.* 我親自做了所有的粉刷工作。**3 by myself** alone, with

M

no one with me or helping me 我單獨地; 我
獨立地: *I had spent the day by myself.* 我獨自
過了一天。| *I had managed to mend the
roof by myself.* 我終於獨力補好了屋頂。

mys·te·ri·ous /mɪsˈtɪrɪəs; mɪˈstɪəriəs/ *adj*
not easily understood 神祕的; 難以理解的:
the mysterious disappearance of my brother
我兄弟神祕失蹤 | *They're being very
mysterious about their holiday plans.* 關於他
們的度假計劃, 他們顯得很神祕。 –**mysteri-
ously** *adv* –**mysteriousness** *n* [U]

★mys·te·ry /ˈmɪstrɪ; ˈmɪstəri/ *n* **mysteries 1**
[C] something which cannot be explained
or understood 神祕的事物; 難以理解的事物;
謎: *Her death is a mystery.* 她的死是個謎。**2**
[U] a strange secret quality 神祕(性); 奧妙:
stories full of mystery 充滿奧妙的故事

mys·tic /ˈmɪstɪk; ˈmɪstɪk/ *n* a person who
practises mysticism 神祕主義者

mys·tic·al /ˈmɪstɪkḷ; ˈmɪstɪkəl/ *adj* (also 又作
mystic) **1** concerning mysticism 神祕主義的
2 concerning hidden religious power and
importance 暗含宗教奧祕的 –**mystically**
/-klɪ; -kli/ *adv*

mys·ti·cis·m /ˈmɪstəˌsɪzəm; ˈmɪstɪˌsɪzəm/ *n*
[U] a search for God or religious knowledge through prayer 人神靈交; 神祕主義

mys·ti·fy /ˈmɪstəˌfaɪ; ˈmɪstɪˌfaɪ/ *v* **mystified,**
mystifying [T] to make someone confused
and unable to understand things 使〔某人〕
迷惑; 使〔某人〕莫名其妙: *I'm
completely mystified about what happened.* 我對發生的
事壓根兒迷惑不解。| *Physics mystifies me.*
物理學難住了我。 –**mystification** /ˌmɪstəfə-
ˈkeʃən; ˌmɪstɬfɬˈkeɪʃən/ *n* [C;U]

mys·tique /mɪsˈtik; mɪˈstiːk/ *n* [U] a sense
of mystery which surrounds certain things,
people, or professions 神祕感; 神祕性: *the
mystique* **of** *the film industry* 電影業的神祕感

myth /mɪθ; mɪθ/ *n* **1** [C] an old story, often
containing religious or magical ideas,
which may explain natural or historical
events 神話故事 **2** [U] such stories generally 神話〔總稱〕: *an idea common in myth* 神
話中常見的觀念 **3** [C] a false story or idea,
which may be widely believed〔可能為很多
人所相信的〕荒誕或虛構的故事或想法: *It's
a myth that men are better drivers than
women!* 男人開汽車比女人高明是鬼話!

myth·i·cal /ˈmɪθɪkḷ; ˈmɪθɪkəl/ *adj* **1** concerning myths or coming from a myth 神話的;
根據神話的 **2** not real 不真實的; 虛構的

my·thol·o·gy /mɪˈθɑlədʒɪ; mɪˈθɒlədʒi/ *n*
mythologies [C;U] stories made up in the
past to explain events 神話 –**mythological**
/ˌmɪθəˈlɑdʒɪkḷ; ˌmɪθəˈlɒdʒɪkəl/ *adj*

N, n

N, n /ɛn; en/ **N's, n's** or **Ns, ns** the 14th letter of the English alphabet 英語的第十四個
字母

N a written abbreviation for 〖縮〗= NORTH-
(ERN)

'n' /ən; ən/ short for 〖縮〗= AND: *rock 'n' roll*
搖滾樂

nab /næb; næb/ v **-bb-** [T] *infml* to catch
someone or take something quickly 〖非正
式〗逮住，捉住〔某人〕; 搶佔〔某物〕: *The thief
was nabbed as he rushed out of the bank.* 小
偷在衝出銀行時當場被抓。| *Nab that table
over there and I'll get the drinks.* 把那邊的桌
子佔下來，我來買飲料。

nag¹ /næg; næg/ v **-gg-** [I;T] to try to make
someone do something by continuously
complaining 嘮嘮叨叨; 抱怨不停〔試圖促使某
人做某事〕: *I wish you'd stop nagging — I'm
doing my best.* 但願你別再嘮叨了; 我在盡我
最大的努力。| *She's been nagging me for
ages to take her to the theatre.* 她跟我嘮叨了
很久，要我帶她去看戲。| *They finally nagged
me into taking them to the zoo.* 他們對我糾
纏不休，使我終於帶他們去了動物園。

nag² n a horse that is old or in bad condition 老馬

nag·ging /'næɡɪŋ; 'næɡɪŋ/ adj [only before
a noun 只用於名詞前] worrying or annoying
you continuously 令人煩惱不已的: *a nagging
headache* 惱人的頭痛 | *a nagging doubt* 縈
繞於心的疑團

nail¹ /nel; neɪl/ n **1** a thin pointed piece of
metal which you hammer into a wall or
two pieces of wood to fasten them
together 釘子 **2** (also 又作 **fingernail** or
toenail) the hard flat substance that covers
the top of the end of each finger and toe
指甲; 趾甲 **3 a nail in someone's coffin**
something bad which, with other bad
things, might gradually bring failure to
someone 促使某人逐步走向失敗的事物

nail² v [T] **1** [+ adv/prep] to fasten with a
nail or nails 用釘子釘牢、釘住: *She nailed a
sign to the tree.* 她把牌子釘在樹上。| *We
must nail up the windows of the old house.*
我們必須把舊房子的窗子釘死。**2** *infml* to

catch or trap 〖非正式〗抓住; 捕捉: *They've
finally nailed the thief.* 他們終於抓住了小偷。

nail down *phr v* **1** [T **nail** sthg ↔ **down**]
to fasten down, with a nail or nails 用釘子
釘牢: *Will you nail down the carpet?* 請你把
地毯釘牢好嗎? | *Shall I nail the lid down?*
我把蓋子釘牢好嗎? **2** [T **nail** sbdy ↔ **down**]
infml to force someone to agree to something or to tell you what they are thinking
〖非正式〗要〔某人〕同意〔某事〕; 要〔某人〕表態:
*Before they repair the car, nail them down to
a price.* 在他們修理汽車前，要他們確定一個價
錢。| *I can never nail her down.* 我從來也沒
法摸透她的心思。

nail·brush /'nel,brʌʃ; 'neɪlbrʌʃ/ n a small
stiff brush for your fingernails 指甲刷

nail file /'· ·/ n a small flat piece of metal
with a rough surface for shaping your
fingernails 指甲銼

nail pol·ish /'· ,··/ n see 見 NAIL VARNISH

nail var·nish /'· ,··/ *BrE*〖英式〗(**nail polish**
AmE〖美式〗) n [U] coloured or trans-
parent liquid which can be painted on
fingernails 指甲油

na·ive /nɑ'iv; naɪ'iːv/ adj (also 又作 **naïve**)
showing a lack of worldly experience in
what you believe and say 天真的; 幼稚的; 輕
信的: *They laughed at his naive remarks.* 他
們給他那幼稚的話逗得哈哈大笑。| *He told
her he was a millionaire and she was naive
enough to believe him.* 他告訴她說自己是百
萬富翁，她輕易地相信了他。–**naively, naively**
adv –**naivety, naïvety, naiveté** n [U]

na·ked /'nekɪd; 'neɪkɪ̩d/ adj **1** without any
clothes on 裸體的; 赤裸的: *a naked body* 裸
體 **2** without any covering 無遮蔽的; 無覆蓋
物的: *a naked lightbulb* 無燈罩的燈泡 | *a
naked flame* 明火 **3** not hidden or covered
up 顯露的; 無掩飾的: *the naked truth* 赤裸裸
的事實 | *naked fear* 明顯的恐懼 **4 with the
naked eye** without any instrument to help
you see 用肉眼(看): *Bacteria are too small
to see with the naked eye.* 細菌太小了，肉眼
看不見。

name¹ /nem; neɪm/ n **1** [C] the word or
words that someone or some-
thing is known by 名字; 名稱: *What's your
name?* 你叫甚麼名字? | *I've forgotten the
name of the company.* 我忘了那家公司的名
稱。| *Please print your full name and ad-
dress at the top of your exam paper.* 請用印
刷體大寫字母把你的姓名和地址寫在考卷的上
方。**2** [sing] the opinion other people have
of something 名譽; 名聲: *That firm's got a*

N

good name **for** reliability. 那家公司的信譽很好。| The slow service gave the restaurant a bad name. 慢吞吞的服務敗壞了那家餐廳的名聲。**3** [C] infml a well known person 〖非正式〗名人: He's a big name around here. 他是這一帶的大名人。**4 by name** using or saying the name of someone 使用或説出〔某人〕的名字: It's a big firm but she knows everyone by name. 這是家大公司, 但她知道每個人的名字。**5 make a name for yourself** to become well known 成名; 出名: She's made a name for herself **as** a designer. 她是以當設計師而成名的。**6 have something to your name** infml to own something 〖非正式〗擁有某物: He hasn't a penny to his name. 他已一文不名。

★**name²** v **named, naming** [T] **1** to give a name to someone 給〔某人〕取名字: They named their baby son Philip. 他們給嬰兒取名為菲利普。**2** to say what the name of someone or something is 説出〔某人或某物〕的名字[名稱]: Can you name this plant? 你能説出這種植物的名稱嗎? **3** to choose or appoint 選定; 指名, 任命: "When are you going to take me out to dinner?" "Just name the day!" "你打算甚麼時候請我出去吃飯?" "這就定個日子吧!" | She's just been named **as** the new manager. 她剛被任命為新任經理。**4 name someone after someone else** to give someone the same name as someone else 以別人的名字為某人取名: They named him after his grandfather. 他們以他祖父的名字給他取名。

name·drop /ˈneɪmˌdrɒp; ˈneɪmdrɒp/ v **-pp-** [I] to talk about famous or important people as if you know them so that other people will admire you (a word used to express disapproval) 〔在談話中〕抬出名人顯要以提高自己身價〖含貶義〗 **–namedropping** n [U]

name·less /ˈneɪmlɪs; ˈneɪmləs/ adj **1** having no name or no known name 沒有名字的; 不知其名的: the work of a nameless 13th century poet 一位不知名的十三世紀詩人的作品 | a nameless tomb 無名墓 **2** whose name you decide not to mention 不道出姓名的; 隱名的: I was told by a certain politician who will remain nameless. 這是某個隱名的政治家告訴我的。**3** too terrible to describe 不可名狀的; 可怕得難以形容的: guilty of nameless crimes 犯有醜惡不堪的罪行

name·ly /ˈneɪmlɪ; ˈneɪmli/ adv that is to say 即; 那就是: Only one person can do the job, namely you. 只有一個人能做這項工作, 那就是你。

name·sake /ˈneɪmˌseɪk; ˈneɪmseɪk/ n someone who has the same name as someone else 同姓名的人: I often get letters that are addressed to my namesake down the street. 我常收到一些寫給這條街那頭與我同姓名者的信件。

nan·ny /ˈnænɪ; ˈnæni/ n **nannies** a woman employed to take care of children in a family 〔雇來照看小孩的〕保姆

nanny goat /ˈ·· ·/ n a female GOAT 雌山羊

nap /næp; næp/ n **1** a short sleep during the day 〔在白天的〕小睡; 打盹: Grannie likes to have a short nap after lunch. 奶奶喜歡在午飯後小睡片刻。**2** the short fine threads or hairs on the surface of some cloth, which are brushed in one direction 〔某些布料表面的〕絨毛

na·palm /ˈneɪpɑːm; ˈneɪpɑːm/ n [U] a jelly made from petrol, which burns fiercely and is used in bombs 凝固汽油〔用於燃燒彈〕

nape /neɪp; neɪp/ n [sing] the back of your neck 後頸; 頸背

nap·kin /ˈnæpkɪn; ˈnæpkɪn/ n a square piece of cloth or paper used for protecting your clothes and for cleaning your hands and lips during a meal 餐巾

nap·py /ˈnæpɪ; ˈnæpi/ n BrE 〖英式〗**nappies** a piece of soft cloth or paper worn between a baby's legs and around its bottom to hold its URINE and FAECES 尿布

nar·cis·sus /nɑːˈsɪsəs; nɑːˈsɪsəs/ n **narcissuses** or **narcissi** a family of white or yellow spring flowers, including the DAFFODIL 水仙花

nar·cot·ic¹ /nɑːˈkɒtɪk; nɑːˈkɒtɪk/ n narcotics drugs which in small amounts cause sleep or take away pain, and in large amounts are harmful and habit-forming 麻醉劑; 毒品: The illegal trade in narcotics is growing. 非法的毒品買賣情況在增加。

narcotic² adj **1** taking away pain or causing sleep 麻醉的; 催眠的 **2** [only before a noun 只用於名詞前] concerning or related to drugs 麻醉毒品的

nar·rate /næˈreɪt; nəˈreɪt/ v **narrated, narrating** [T] fml to tell a story 〖正式〗敘述, 講述〔故事〕 **–narration** /næˈreɪʃən; nəˈreɪʃən/ n

nar·ra·tive /ˈnærətɪv; ˈnærətɪv/ n **1** [C;U] a story or account of events 故事; 敘事 **2** [U] the art of telling a story 講故事技巧[手法]: She's very good at narrative. 她很擅長講故事。**–narrative** adj: a narrative poem 敘事詩

nar·ra·tor /næˈreɪtə; nəˈreɪtəʳ/ n someone in some books, television shows, or plays who tells the story or explains what is happening 〔書、電視節目、戲劇等的〕敘述者; 解説員

★**nar·row¹** /ˈnærəʊ; ˈnærəʊ/ adj **1** small in distance from one side to the other, in comparison with length or with what is usual 狹窄的: a narrow street 狹窄的街道 | The gate is too narrow for a car to get through. 大門太窄, 汽車過不去。–see 見 THIN¹ (USAGE 用法) **2** not including many people, ideas, or other important facts, which is usually regarded as a bad thing 狹隘的; 有局限的: a narrow group of friends 交遊不廣 | She has a very narrow view of religion. 她對宗教持有狹隘的觀點。**3** only just successful 勉強的;〔勝勢〕微弱的: *to win by a narrow majority* 以微弱多數獲勝 | *a narrow escape* 死裡逃生 –**narrowness** n [U]

narrow[2] v [I] **1** to become narrower 變窄: *The river narrows at this point.* 這條河到這裡就變窄了。 **2** [I;T] to make a difference smaller (使)縮小〔差異〕: *The tax aims to narrow the gap between rich and poor.* 這項稅法意圖縮小貧富差距。

　　narrow sthg/sbdy ↔ **down** *phr v* [T] to reduce the number of things that you have to consider or deal with 使減少〔數字〕: *The police have now narrowed down their list of suspects.* 警方現已減少單子上列出的嫌疑犯人數。 | *I've narrowed the potential candidates down to three.* 我已經把可能入選的人縮減到三個。

nar·row·ly /ˈnærəli; ˈnærəʊli/ *adv* only just 勉強地: *We narrowly missed hitting that car!* 我們險些兒撞上那輛汽車!

narrow-mind·ed /ˌ···ˈ···◂/ *adj* unwilling to accept or try to understand ideas that are new or different from your own (a word used to express disapproval) 心胸狹窄的; 思想狹隘的〔含貶義〕: *His views are very narrow-minded.* 他的觀點非常狹隘。 –opposite 反義 **broadminded** –**narrowmindedness** n [U]

na·sal[1] /ˈnezl; ˈneɪzəl/ *adj* related to the nose 鼻的: *We breathe through our nasal passages.* 我們透過鼻腔呼吸。 –**nasally** *adv*

nasal[2] n *tech* a speech sound such as /m/, /n/, or /ŋ/ made through the nose〔術語〕鼻音〔如 /m/, /n/, /ŋ/〕 –**nasal** *adj*

nas·ty /ˈnæsti; ˈnɑːsti/ *adj* **nastier, nastiest** **1** unpleasant to see, taste, smell, touch, or experience 令人不愉快的: *nasty weather* 惡劣的天氣 | *a nasty smell* 一種難聞的氣味 **2** unkind or unpleasant in manner 不善良的; 令人不快的〔態度〕: *a nasty temper* 壞脾氣 | *He turned nasty when I said I couldn't pay him.* 我說我不能付錢給他時, 他就變得殺氣騰騰的。 **3** serious, and causing people to be hurt or killed 嚴重的; 致傷的; 致死的: *a nasty accident with one person killed* 造成一人死亡的嚴重事故 | *a nasty cut on the head* 頭上嚴重的割傷 | *It gave me a nasty shock.* 那件事使我大為震驚。 **4** in bad taste 低級趣味的: *cheap and nasty furniture* 便宜而難看的家具 –**nastily** *adv* –**nastiness** n [U]

⋆**na·tion** /ˈneɪʃən; ˈneɪʃən/ n a large group of people living in one country usually with an independent government, and sharing the same history 國民; 國家; 民族: *the African nations* 非洲國家 | *The Queen spoke to the nation.* 女王向全國人民作了講話。

⋆⋆**na·tion·al**[1] /ˈnæʃənl; ˈnæʃənəl/ *adj* **1** of or for the whole of one country 國家的: *a national holiday* 國定假日 **2** owned or controlled by the central government of a country 國有的; 國家控制的: *a national bank* 國家銀行 **3** typical of the people of a nation 民族的: *national*

dress 民族服裝 | *the national characteristics of the Welsh* 威爾斯的民族特性 **4** national **anthem** the official song of a nation, which is sung or played on certain formal occasions 國歌 **5** national **service** the system of making young people in some countries serve in the armed forces for a limited period 國民義務兵役制 **6** National **Health Service** see 見 NHS **7** National Insurance a system of insurance in Britain which is run by the government, into which workers and employers make regular payments, and which provides money for people who are unemployed, old, or ill〔英國〕國民保險制度〔指雇員和雇主定期繳納保險費, 在失業、年老或患病時能得到補助〕 **8** national **park** a large area of attractive country, beautiful plants, and wild animals which are protected by the governments so that people can visit them 國家公園 – **nationally** *adv*

national[2] n someone living abroad who belongs to another country〔僑居外國的〕國民; 僑民: *American nationals in England* 旅居英國的美國僑民 | *foreign nationals* 外國僑民

na·tion·al·is·m /ˈnæʃənlˌɪzəm; ˈnæʃənəlɪzəm/ n [U] **1** love of and pride in your country which sometimes makes people believe unfairly that their country is better than others 民族自豪感; 民族自尊心 **2** desire by a racial group to form an independent country 民族獨立的願望; 民族主義: *Scottish nationalism* 蘇格蘭民族主義

na·tion·al·ist /ˈnæʃənlɪst; ˈnæʃənəlɪst/ n someone who believes their racial group or part of the country should form an independent country 民族獨立運動的信仰者; 民族主義者: *a Basque nationalist* 巴斯克民族主義者 –**nationalist** *adj* : *the nationalist party in Wales* 威爾斯民族主義政黨

na·tion·al·is·tic /ˌnæʃənlˈɪstɪk; ˌnæʃənəˈlɪstɪk◂/ *adj* showing a great love of your country because you think it is better than others (a word used to express disapproval) 民族主義的; 國家主義的〔含貶義〕: *nationalistic election speech* 一次民族主義競選演説 –**nationalistically** /-klɪ; -kli/ *adv*

na·tion·al·i·ty /ˌnæʃəˈnælətɪ; ˌnæʃəˈnælฺ ti/ n **nationalities** [C;U] the fact of belonging to a particular country 國籍: *She lives in France but has British nationality.* 她住在法國, 但有英國國籍。 | *people of many different nationalities* 許多不同國籍的人

na·tion·al·ize /ˈnæʃənlˌaɪz; ˈnæʃənəlaɪz/ v **nationalized, nationalizing** (also 又作 **nationalise** BrE 〔英式〕) [T] (of a central government) to buy or take control of a business or industry for the state〔中央政府〕把〔企業或工業〕歸為國有; 使國有化: *The British government nationalized the railways in 1948.* 英國政府在一九四八年把鐵路收歸國

有。–**nationalization** /ˌnæʃənl̩ˈzeʃən; ˌnæʃə-nəlaɪˈzeɪʃən/ *n* [U]

na·tion·wide /ˈneʃən͵waɪd; ˌneɪʃənˈwaɪd◂/ *adj,adv* happening over a whole country 全國性的: *a nationwide search* 全國性的搜捕 | *The speech will be broadcast nationwide.* 這次講話將在全國廣播。

*★**na·tive**¹ /ˈneɪtɪv; ˈneɪtɪv/ *adj* **1** [only before a noun 只用於名詞前] connected with where you were born 出生地的: *her native language* 她的母語 | *He was never popular in his native Australia.* 他在故土澳大利亞向來不受人歡迎。 **2** first found in a particular place and not brought there by anyone 當地土生的[土產的]: *a plant native to the eastern USA* 原產於美國東部的植物 | *Pandas are native to China.* 熊貓原產於中國。 **3** belonging to someone's character from birth and therefore not learned〔品質〕天生的; 天賦的: *native ability* 天賦的才能 | *native intelligence* 天生的智力 **4** [only before a noun 只用於名詞前] *old fash* belonging to the people of poor non-European countries when considered by people who think Western customs are better 〖老式〗土人的; 土著的〔指貧窮的非歐洲人〕: *a native village* 土著村莊 **5 native speaker** someone who has learnt a particular language from birth 生來就學說某種語言的人: *a native speaker of English* 以英語為母語的人

native² *n* **1** someone who was born in a place 本地人; 本國人: *a native of New York City* 紐約市本地人 **2** *old fash* a poor non-European person living in their own country where Europeans consider themselves to be better in some way 〖老式〗土著; 土人〔指非歐洲人〕: *The government of the island treated the natives badly.* 該島的政府虐待土人。 **3** a plant or animal living naturally in a place 土生的植物或動物: *The bear was once a native of Britain.* 熊曾一度是英國的土生動物。

Na·tiv·i·ty /neˈtɪvətɪ; nəˈtɪvˌti/ *n* **the Nativity** the birth of Christ 耶穌基督誕生

NATO /ˈneto; ˈneɪtəʊ/ *n* a group of countries including the USA and Britain which give military help to each other; an abbreviation for **North Atlantic Treaty Organization** 〖縮〗北大西洋公約組織〔包括英、美等國, 相互之間有軍事援助協定〕

nat·ter /ˈnætə; ˈnætər/ *v* [I] *infml* to talk for a long time about unimportant things 〖非正式〗瞎扯; 閒聊: *She nattered on about her holiday.* 她沒完沒了地嘮叨自己的假期。 – **natter** *n* [sing] : *We had a good natter.* 我們聊得很痛快。

nat·ty /ˈnætɪ; ˈnæti/ *adj* **nattier, nattiest** *infml* neat in appearance 〖非正式〗〔外表〕整潔的: *He's a very natty dresser.* 他的穿着十分整潔。 –**nattily** *adv*

*★★**nat·u·ral**¹ /ˈnætʃərəl; ˈnætʃərəl/ *adj* **1** not caused, made, or con-

trolled by people 非人為的; 自然的: *the natural mineral wealth of a country* 國家的天然礦藏 | *death from natural causes* 自然〔正常〕死亡 **2** usual or expected 通常的; 意料之中的: *It's natural to feel nervous when you have an exam.* 考試時感到緊張是正常的。 | *It's natural for her to feel upset.* 她感到心煩意亂是很自然的。 | *She's the natural choice for the job.* 選她做這份工作是意料之中的。

> □ USEFUL PATTERNS 有用句型
> it is natural to do something; it is natural for someone to do something

3 [only before a noun 只用於名詞前] having a skill or ability from birth without being taught 〔技能等〕天生的; 生來就有的; 非習得的: *a man with a lot of natural charm* 一位天生就具有很大魅力的男子 | *a natural musician* 天生的音樂家 **4** not looking or sounding different from usual 本來的; 跟平常一樣的; 不做作的: *Try to look natural for your photograph.* 拍照的時候要自然一點。 **5 natural gas** gas which is taken from under the earth or sea and mainly burnt for cooking and heating 天然氣 **6 natural history** the study of plants, animals, and rocks 博物學 **7 natural resources** the land, forests, and mineral wealth that a country possesses 自然資源 **8 natural science** one of the sciences which deal with the natural world, BIOLOGY, chemistry, and PHYSICS 自然科學 **9 natural selection** the process by which only the plants and animals best suited to the conditions around them continue to live 自然選擇〔指動、植物適者生存不適者淘汰的過程〕–**naturalness** *n* [U]

natural² *n infml* someone who can do something very well without studying or learning 〖非正式〗天生的料子; 天才: *As an actor, he's a natural.* 他天生是當演員的料子。

nat·u·ral·ist /ˈnætʃərəlɪst; ˈnætʃərəl̩st/ *n* a person who studies plants, birds, or animals 博物學家

nat·u·ral·ize /ˈnætʃərəl͵aɪz; ˈnætʃərəlaɪz/ *v* **naturalized, naturalizing** (also 又作 **naturalise** *BrE* 〖英式〗) [T] to make someone born in one country a citizen of a different country 使〔僑民〕入籍; 使歸化: *He was naturalized after living in Britain for ten years.* 他在英國住了十年後入了英國籍。 – **naturalization** /ˌnætʃrəlɪˈzeʃən; ˌnætʃərəlaɪ-ˈzeɪʃən/ *n* [U]

*★**nat·u·ral·ly** /ˈnætʃərəlɪ; ˈnætʃərəli/ *adv* **1** not made or caused by anyone 天然地; 非人為地: *Her cheeks are naturally red.* 她的兩頰生來就是紅的。 | *Mould occurs naturally in damp places.* 潮濕的地方自然會生霉菌。 **2** having a quality with which you were born 〔品質〕天生地: *She's just naturally clever.* 她天生就聰明。 **3** without trying to look or sound different from usual 不做作地; 自然

地: *Try to speak naturally while I'm taping you.* 我給你錄音時，講話要自然。**4** of course 當然地: *"Did you win the game?" "Naturally." "你比賽贏了沒有？" "那當然。"* | *Naturally you will want to discuss the proposal with your wife.* 你當然要跟你妻子討論一下這個建議。**5** as an expected development 必然地: *That will lead naturally into the subject of money.* 那必然會遇到資金問題。**6 come naturally to someone** to be easy for someone 對某人很容易: *Swimming seems to come naturally to him.* 游泳對他似乎很容易。

★★na·ture /'neɪtʃɚ; 'neɪtʃəʳ/ *n* **1** [U] everything that exists in the world which is not made or controlled by people, such as earth, rocks, the weather, plants, and animals 大自然；自然界: *Farming on such bad land is a struggle against nature.* 在這樣貧瘠的土地上種農作物是與大自然搏鬥。**2** [C;U] the particular qualities or character of someone 性格；稟性；天性；性質: *She is generous by nature.* 她生性慷慨大方。 | *It's not in her nature to be rude.* 無禮不是她的本性。 | *What is the nature of the new chemical?* 這種新的化學元素有甚麼特性？ | *It's only human nature to want more money.* 貪錢是人的天性。**3** [sing] a kind 種類: *ceremonies of a solemn nature* 一種很莊嚴的儀式 | *He's an engineer or something of that nature.* 他是工程師或那一類的職業。**4 in the nature of things** as may be expected 可以預料: *In the nature of things there's bound to be the occasional accident.* 可以預料，偶爾的事故必定會發生。

naugh·ty /'nɔtɪ; 'nɔːti/ *adj* **naughtier, naughtiest 1** behaving badly, or not obeying a parent, teacher, or set of rules (used of children) 頑皮的；淘氣的；不聽話的〔指兒童〕: *You naughty boy! I told you not to play in the road.* 你這頑皮的孩子！我告訴過你不要在馬路上玩。**2** slightly rude or morally offensive 沒規矩的；不道德的: *a naughty joke* 低級的笑話 –**naughtily** *adv* –**naughtiness** *n* [U]

nau·se·a /'nɔzə; 'nɔːziə/ *n* [U] a feeling of sickness and desire to throw up the contents of your stomach through your mouth 噁心；嘔吐感

nau·se·ate /'nɔzɪˌet; 'nɔːzieɪt/ *v* **nauseated, nauseating** [T] **1** to make you feel sick 使噁心；使作嘔: *That smell nauseates me.* 那氣味使我噁心。**2** to make you feel strong dislike 使厭惡；憎惡: *The way he treats his wife nauseates me.* 他對待妻子的方式使我感到憎惡。–**nauseating** *adj* : *a nauseating meal* 使人噁心的飯菜 | *nauseating stupidity* 令人憎惡的愚蠢

nau·se·ous /'nɔzəs; 'nɔːziəs/ *adj* sick with a desire to throw up the contents of your stomach 令人作嘔的: *I felt nauseous in the cabin of the boat.* 我在船艙裡直想嘔吐。

nau·ti·cal /'nɔtɪkl; 'nɔːtɪkəl/ *adj* relating to sailors, ships, or sailing 船員的；船舶的；航海的

nautical mile /ˌ··· '·/ *n* a measure of distance, used at sea, equal to 1,852 metres 海里〔用於航海的長度單位。等於1852米〕

na·val /'nevl; 'neɪvəl/ *adj* relating to the navy or ships of war 海軍的；軍艦的: *a naval officer* 海軍軍官 | *naval battles* 海戰

nave /nev; neɪv/ *n* the long central part of a church where the people sit〔教堂的〕中殿

na·vel /'nevl; 'neɪvəl/ *n* a small sunken place in the middle of your stomach, left when the connection to your mother was cut at birth〔肚〕臍

nav·i·ga·ble /'nævəgəbl; 'nævɪɡəbəl/ *adj* deep and wide enough to allow ships to travel (used of water) 可通航的〔指水域〕: *The St Lawrence River is navigable from the Great Lakes to the sea.* 聖羅倫斯河自五大湖區至海均可航行。

nav·i·gate /'nævəˌget; 'nævɪɡeɪt/ *v* **navigated, navigating** [I;T] to calculate your position and the direction you should travel in, for example by using a map 導航；領航

nav·i·ga·tion /ˌnævə'geʃən; ˌnævɪ'ɡeɪʃən/ *n* [U] the planning and directing of the movements of ships or planes 航海；航空；航行: *Navigation is difficult on this river because of the rocks.* 由於有岩石，在這條河上航行是很困難的。

nav·i·ga·tor /'nævəˌgetɚ; 'nævɪɡeɪtəʳ/ *n* the officer on a ship or aircraft who plans and directs its movements〔船或飛機上的〕領航員

na·vy /'nevɪ; 'neɪvi/ *n* **1 the Navy** [+ sing/pl verb] the part of a country's military forces that fights at sea 海軍: *The Navy want to recruit more officers.* 海軍要徵募更多的軍官 **2** the ships of war belonging to a country〔國家的〕艦隊: *a small navy of ten ships* 一支十艘船的小艦隊

navy blue /ˌ·· '··/ *adj, n* [U] (also 又作 **navy**) a colour which is very dark blue 藏青色；深藍色 –see picture on page 243 見 243 頁彩圖

NB read what follows carefully (used in writing to begin a note); an abbreviation for the Latin phrase **nota bene** 〖縮〗注意〔用於書寫註釋的開頭〕

NCO /ˌɛn si 'o; ˌen siː 'əʊ/ *n* an abbreviation for 〖縮〗= NON-COMMISSIONED OFFICER

NE a written abbreviation for 〖縮〗= NORTH-EAST(ERN)

★near¹ /nɪr; nɪəʳ/ *adj* **1** not far away from something 近的；不遠的: *She walked to the nearest tree and picked an apple.* 她走到離自己最近的那棵樹前摘了一個蘋果。 | *My office is quite near.* 我的辦事處離得很近。 | *We're hoping this will happen in the near future.* 我們希望不久這就會發生。–see picture on page 764 見 764 頁彩圖 **2** close in relationship 關係近的: *He's one of my nearest relatives.* 他是我的一個近親。**3** [only before a noun 只用於名詞前] closer 較近的: *the near bank of the river* 較近的河岸

■ USAGE 用法: **Near** and **close** have almost the same meaning, but in some phrases you must use one word and not the other. We say *the near future* | *a near miss* (not **close**). But we say *a close friend* | *close behind* (not **near**). ☆**near** 和 **close** 的意義幾乎相同，但在某些短語中只能用其中之一，而不能用另一個。我們說 *the near future* (不久的將來), *a near miss* (近距脫靶) 〔不能用 **close**〕; 但是要說 *a close friend* (親密朋友), *close behind* (緊跟在後) 〔不能用 **near**〕。

---

near² adv, prep not far away in place or time 〔地點或時間〕近; 不遠: *people who live near London* 住在倫敦附近的人 | *We live quite near to the church.* 我們住在離教堂很近的地方。 | *Don't go too near the edge.* 別走得太靠邊。 | *Remind me again nearer the time.* 到時候再提醒我一下。 | *The day of the interview was getting nearer.* 離面試的日子越來越近。

near³ *v* **1** [T] to move closer to something 靠近, 接近〔某物〕: *I started to feel quite nervous as we neared the town.* 我們快到那個城鎮時, 我便開始緊張起來。 **2** [I] to come closer in time 臨近: *The time was nearing for me to leave.* 離我動身的時間越來越近。

near·by /'nɪr,baɪ; ,nɪə'baɪ◄/ *adj, adv* near to a place 附近的〔地〕: *He lives in a nearby town.* 他住在附近的一個鎮上。 | *Are there any shops nearby?* 在這附近有商店嗎?

near·ly /'nɪrlɪ; 'nɪəlɪ/ *adv* **1** almost 幾乎; 差不多: *I was nearly asleep.* 我幾乎睡着了。 | *She was ill for nearly a year.* 她生病快一年了。 | *He very nearly died.* 他幾乎死了。 **2** not nearly not at all 遠遠不; 根本不: *We haven't got nearly enough money.* 我們的錢遠遠不夠。

near·side /'nɪr,saɪd; 'nɪəsaɪd/ *adj* [only before a noun 只用於名詞前] on the side of a vehicle nearest to the edge of the road 〔車輛〕靠近路邊的一側: *the nearside back light of a car* 汽車靠邊一側的尾燈

near·sight·ed /'nɪr'saɪtɪd; ,nɪə'saɪtₗd◄/ *adj* the usual American word for 〔美式〕= SHORTSIGHTED –**nearsightedness** *n* [U]

neat /nit; niːt/ *adj* **1** arranged carefully or tidy 整潔的; 整齊的: *neat handwriting* 工整的筆跡 | *He keeps his office very neat and tidy.* 他把辦公室保持得很整潔。 | *What a neat child!* 一個多麼整潔的孩子! **2** simple and effective 乾淨利落的; 簡潔的; 巧妙的: *a neat trick* 巧妙的花招 | *There are no neat solutions to this problem.* 這個問題沒有乾淨利落的解決辦法。 **3** without ice or any

added liquid (used of alcoholic drinks) 純的; 不摻冰或水的〔指酒〕: *I like my whisky neat.* 我喜歡喝純威士忌酒。 **4** *AmE infml* very good or pleasant 〔美式, 非正式〕很好的: *That was a neat party.* 那次派對辦得很好。 –**neatly** *adv* –**neatness** *n* [U]

neb·u·lous /'nɛbjələs; 'nɛbjʊ̯ləs/ *adj* not clear (used of a plan or idea) 模糊不清的〔指計劃或思想〕: *nebulous political beliefs* 模糊的政治觀念

ne·ces·sar·i·ly /,nɛsə,sɛrəlɪ; 'nɛsₗsərₗlɪ/ *adv* **1** not necessarily not always 不總是; 未必: *Food that looks good doesn't necessarily taste good.* 好看的食物並不一定就好吃。 **2** unavoidably 必然地; 必定: *New laws are necessarily difficult to make.* 新的法律必然難以制定。

ne·ces·sa·ry /'nɛsə,sɛrɪ; 'nɛsₗsərɪ/ *adj* **1** needed 必要的; 必需的: *Food is necessary for life.* 食物是生命所必需的。 | *It's not necessary to wear a tie.* 沒有必要打領帶。 | *I'll leave you to make the necessary arrangements.* 我會讓你來作必要的安排。 | *Is it necessary for me to be at the meeting?* 我有必要出席會議嗎?

□ USEFUL PATTERNS 有用句型
it is necessary to do something; it is necessary for someone to do something

---

2 unavoidable 必定的; 必然的: *the necessary conclusion* 必然的結果 | *a necessary evil* 不可避免的壞事

ne·ces·si·tate /nə'sɛsə,tet; nₗ'sesₗteɪt/ *v* **necessitated, necessitating** [T] *fml* to make something necessary 〔正式〕使〔某物〕成為必要: *Lack of money necessitated a change of plan.* 資金的缺乏使計劃必須改變。 | *This idea would necessitate starting all over again.* 這個想法會使一切都需從頭做起。

ne·ces·si·ty /nə'sɛsətɪ; nₗ'sesₗtɪ/ *n* **necessities 1** [U] a need or condition which makes you do something 需要; 必要: *Is there any necessity for another election?* 有沒有必要再選舉一次? | *We won't buy a car until the necessity arises.* 除非真正有必要, 否則我們不會買汽車的。 | *There's no necessity to buy tickets in advance.* 沒有必要提前買票。 | *He was forced by necessity to steal a loaf of bread for his starving son.* 他是迫不得已才為挨餓的兒子偷了一條麵包。 **2** [C] something that you must have 必需品: *Food and clothing are the bare necessities of life.* 衣食是最低限度的生活必需品。 **3** of necessity in a way that is unavoidable; 無法避免地: *These examples are, of necessity, very short.* 這些例證必然是不夠充分。

neck /nɛk; nek/ *n* **1** the part of your body which joins your head to your shoulders 頸; 脖子 –see 見 PAIN (USAGE 用法) **2** the part of a garment, for example a dress or a shirt, that fits round your neck 〔衣服的〕領

N

圈 **3** a narrow part at one end of something broader 頸狀部分: *the neck of a bottle* 瓶頸 | *the neck of a violin* 小提琴的琴頸 **4 by a neck** *infml* winning or losing by a very short distance 《非正式》〔獲勝或失利〕僅一線之差 **5 neck and neck** *infml* with an equal chance of winning (used of two people or animals in a race) 《非正式》不分上下; 難分高低〔指賽事中的兩個人或兩隻動物〕: *The horses were neck and neck to the finish.* 那兩匹馬衝過終點時並駕齊驅, 不分上下。 | *The two candidates are neck and neck in the opinion polls.* 這兩個候選人在民意測驗中難分高低。 **6 up to your neck in** *infml* in or deeply concerned with a difficult situation 《非正式》深深陷入〔困境〕: *I'm up to my neck in debt.* 我已債台高築。 **7 -necked** having a certain shape or style of neck 有〔某種式樣的〕領圈的: *a V-necked dress* 有 V 形領的衣服 | *an open-necked shirt* 開領襯衫

neck·lace /ˈnɛklɪs; ˈnek-lɪs/ *n* a string of jewels or beads (BEAD), or a chain of gold or silver that a person wears around their neck 項鏈; 項圈 –see picture on page 210 見 210 頁彩圖

neck·line /ˈnɛkˌlaɪn; ˈnek-laɪn/ *n* the position of the top of a dress or garment at or below your neck 〔衣服的〕領口; 開領: *a low neckline* 低開領

neck·tie /ˈnɛkˌtaɪ; ˈnektaɪ/ *n* the usual American word for 《美式》= TIE

nec·tar /ˈnɛktə; ˈnektər/ *n* [U] **1** the sweet liquid collected by bees from flowers 〔蜜蜂採集的〕花蜜 **2** the drink of the gods in ancient Greek and Roman literature 〔古希臘、羅馬文學中〕眾神飲的酒

née /ne; neɪ/ *adv* a word used to show what a woman's family name was before she got married 娘家姓…的〔用於表示已婚婦女婚前的姓〕: *Mrs Carol Cook née Williams* 娘家姓威廉斯的卡羅爾·科克夫人

need¹ /niːd; niːd/ *n* **1** [U] the situation in which something necessary or very useful is missing or wanted 缺乏; 需要; 要求: *There's a growing need for new housing in this area.* 這個地區對新建住宅的需求在不斷增長。 | *This accident shows the need for stricter safety regulations.* 這一事故表明需要制定更嚴格的安全條例。 **2** [C] something that you want or must have 需要的東西; 必需品: *She didn't earn enough money to satisfy all her needs.* 她賺的錢不足以滿足她的全部需要。 | *The hotel staff are here to attend to your needs.* 飯店的工作人員來這兒聽取你們的需求。 **3 in need** without enough food and money 缺衣少食的; 在貧困中的: *We are collecting money for children in need.* 我們在為貧困兒童募捐。 **4 in need of something** wanting or needing something 需要某物: *The doctor told me I was in need of a holiday.* 醫生說我需要休假。 | *Please come to me if ever you're in need of help.* 你

若需要幫忙請來找我。 **5 if need be** if it is necessary 如果需要的話 **6 no need for something** a phrase you use to say that something is not necessary or not wanted 無需某事〔用於表示沒有必要做某事或不需要某物〕: *There's no need for you to be at the meeting.* 你不必出席這次會議。 | *There's no need for all that noise!* 沒有必要那樣大吵大鬧!

need² *v* [not in progressive forms 不用於進行式] *negative short form* 否定縮約形式為 **needn't 1** [T] to want something that is necessary 需要〔某物〕: *Children need milk.* 孩子們需要牛奶。 | *The soup needs more salt.* 這湯需要再加點鹽。 | *I need a holiday.* 我需要休假。 | *That jumper needs a wash.* 那件工作夾克需要洗一洗了。 –see Study Note on page 1318 見 1318 頁學習提示 **need to do something** to have to do something because it is necessary 必須做某事: *I need to talk to you.* 我必須找你談一談。 | *We need to borrow some money.* 我們需要借些錢。 | *You don't need to come if you don't want to.* 你不想來就不必來了。 **3 need not do something, needn't do something** used when you are saying that something is not necessary or not wanted 不必做某事〔用於表示沒有必要或不需要做某事〕: *You needn't be afraid.* 你 不 必 害 怕。 | *The government needn't become involved in this dispute at all.* 政府根本就不必捲入這場爭端。 | *Holidays abroad needn't be expensive.* 出國度假不一定昂貴。 | *You needn't shout at me like that!* 你不必對我那樣大喊大叫的。 | *If he had been given proper treatment he need not have died.* 要是他能得到適當的治療, 就不一定會死。

nee·dle¹ /ˈniːdl; ˈniːdl/ *n* **1** a long pointed metal pin with a hole in one end for the thread, used in sewing 針; 縫衣針 **2** a thin pointed object 針狀物: *a pine needle* 松樹的針葉 **3** a long, thin pointed piece of plastic or metal used to make woollen garments 編織用針: *knitting needles* 手工編織用的針 **4** the very small pointed jewel in a RECORD PLAYER which picks up the sound from a record 〔唱機的〕唱針 **5** a very thin hollow pointed tube, at the end of a SYRINGE, which is pushed into someone's skin to put medicine into their body 注射針 **6** a long thin pointer that shows the reading on a measuring instrument 指針; 刻針: *the needle of a compass* 羅盤指針

nee·dle² *v* **needled, needling** [T] *infml* to annoy someone with repeated unkind remarks 《非正式》〔反覆用不友好的話〕刺激, 挑逗〔某人〕: *The boys always needled Jim about being fat.* 男孩們總是用話激吉姆, 說他肥胖。 | *They needled me into losing my temper.* 他們惹得我發脾氣。

need·less /ˈniːdlɪs; ˈniːdləs/ *adj* **1** unnecessary 不必要的: *What a lot of needless trouble*

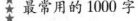

preparing for guests who don't turn up! 為沒來的客人準備了半天，真是白費工夫! **2 need-less to say** of course 不用說; 當然: *Needless to say, it rained when I left my window open.* 不用說，我沒有關上窗戶時下過雨。—**needlessly** *adv*

nee·dle·work /'nidl̩,wɜːk; 'niːdlwɜːk/ *n* [U] decorative sewing 縫紉; 刺繡: *two beautiful needlework cushion covers* 兩個漂亮的刺繡坐墊套子

need·n't /'nidn̩t; 'niːdnt/ short for 〔縮〕= "need not": *You needn't go if you don't want to.* 如果你不想去，就不必去了。

need·y /'nidɪ; 'niːdi/ *adj* **needier, neediest 1** without good food, clothing, or housing 貧困的: *a needy family* 貧困家庭 **2 the needy** poor people 窮人: *I'm collecting money to help the needy.* 我在募集資金救濟窮人。

ne·far·i·ous /nɪ'fɛrɪəs; nɪ'feəriəs/ *adj fml* immoral and wicked 〔正式〕邪惡的; 惡毒的: *nefarious activities* 邪惡的活動 —**nefariously** *adv*

neg·ate /nɪ'get; nɪ'geɪt/ *v* **negated, negating 1** [T] *fml* to take away the value or effect of something 〔正式〕使〔某事物〕無效: *The new evidence negates all previous theories.* 新的證據推翻了以前所有的理論。 **2** to say that something does not exist or 否認 —**negation** /nɪ'geʃən; nɪ'geɪʃən/ *n* [C;U]

⋆**neg·a·tive¹** /'nɛgətɪv; 'negətɪv/ *adj* **1** saying or meaning "no" 否定的: *a negative answer to my request* 對我的要求所作的否定回答 | *negative expressions like "not at all" or "not at all"* (一點也不)這種否定的用語 —opposite 反義 **affirmative 2** considering only the bad side of something 消極的; 負面的: *Don't be so negative — I think we could still win.* 別那麼消極，我認為我們仍然可以獲勝。 | *a negative attitude* 消極的態度 **3** showing no signs of what was looked for or expected 無跡象的; 陰性的: *Her pregnancy test was negative.* 她的妊娠試驗呈陰性。 **4** less than zero (used of a number) 負的〔指數字〕: *If x is positive then -x is negative.* 假如x是正的，那麼-x就是負的。 **5** *tech* having the same type of electric charge as an ELECTRON 〔術語〕負極的 —**negatively** *adv*

negative² *n* **1** a word, expression, or statement saying or meaning "no" 否定詞; 否定表達方式; 否定句: *The answer to my request was a strong negative.* 我的要求遭到了強硬的拒絕。 | *"Never" and "not at all" are negatives.* "Never" 和 "not at all" 都是否定詞語。 —opposite 反義 **affirmative 2** a photograph or film showing dark areas as light and light areas as dark and from which the pictures will be developed 〔照相或攝影的〕底片 **3 in the negative** *fml* meaning "no" 〔正式〕否定的〔地〕: *He answered in the negative.* 他作了否定的回答。

ne·glect¹ /nɪ'glɛkt; nɪ'glekt/ *v* **1** [T] to give too little attention or care to someone or

something 忽視〔某人或某事物〕; 疏忽: *You've been neglecting your work recently.* 你最近做工作一直玩忽大意。 **2** [I;T] to fail to do something because of carelessness or forgetfulness 〔因粗心或遺忘而〕漏做〔某事〕: *Don't neglect to lock the door when you leave.* 你離開時別忘了鎖門。 | *They have neglected their duties.* 他們已忘了自己的職責。

> □ USEFUL PATTERNS 有用句型
> to neglect something; to neglect to do something

neglect² *n* [U] **1** failure to take care of something properly 〔對某事物的〕疏忽: *The tenants complained about the landlord's neglect of the building.* 租戶抱怨房東忽略了樓房的維修問題。 **2** the condition something is in when it is not cared for 被疏忽的狀態: *The garden is in a state of neglect.* 花園處於無人管理的狀態。

ne·glec·ted /nɪ'glɛktɪd; nɪ'glektɪd/ *adj* showing a lack of care or attention 缺乏照管的; 被忽視的: *The children looked sad and neglected.* 孩子們看上去很傷心，而且沒人管。

ne·glect·ful /nɪ'glɛktfəl; nɪ'glektfəl/ *adj* not giving enough attention to something 疏忽的; 不留意的: *a mother who is neglectful of her children* 對自己孩子不夠關心的母親 | *neglectful of your responsibilities* 玩忽職守

neg·li·gee /,nɛglɪ'ʒe; ,negliˈʒeɪ/ *n* a woman's light, fancy garment worn over a NIGHTDRESS 女用輕便花式睡衣

neg·li·gent /'nɛglɪdʒənt; 'neglɪdʒənt/ *adj* careless or irresponsible 疏忽的; 玩忽的; 粗心大意的: *The doctor was negligent in not giving the woman a full examination.* 醫生粗心大意，沒有給那位女士作全面檢查。 —**negligently** *adv* —**negligence** *n* [U]: *The driver's negligence was the cause of the accident.* 司機的疏忽是這起事故的起因。

neg·li·gi·ble /'nɛglədʒəbl̩; 'neglɪdʒəbl̩/ *adj* so small or unimportant that it need not be considered 無關緊要的; 微不足道的: *The damage to my car is negligible.* 我車子的損壞程度很輕微。

ne·go·ti·a·ble /nɪ'goʃɪəbl̩; nɪ'gəʊʃɪəbl̩/ *adj* **1** able to be settled or changed by talking 可談判〔解決或改變〕的; 可磋商的: *The price is not negotiable.* 價錢沒有商量的餘地。 **2** able to be exchanged for money (used of a cheque or order to pay money) 可兌現現金的〔指支票或匯票〕 **3** able to be travelled through or along 可通行的: *The road is only negotiable in the dry season.* 這條道路只有在旱季才能通行。

⋆**ne·go·ti·ate** /nɪ'goʃɪˌet; nɪ'gəʊʃɪeɪt/ *v* **negotiated, negotiating 1** [I] to try to come to an agreement through talking 談判; 協商: *The government says it will not negotiate with the terrorists.* 政府聲明不會與恐怖分子談判。

2 [T] to produce an agreement or settle a piece of business through talking 透過談判達成〔協議〕或解決〔事務〕; 商定: *The trade union negotiated a new contract with the management.* 工會與資方商定了一份新合約。
3 [T] to go safely over, through, or along something 安全通過; 越過: *Will this small car negotiate that steep hill?* 這輛小汽車能安全開過那座陡峭的山嗎?

⋆ne·go·ti·a·tion /nɪˌɡəʊʃɪˈeʃən; nɪˌɡəʊʃɪˈeɪʃən/ *n* [C;U] (also 又作 **negotiations**) talks in which people with different views try to agree 談判; 協商: *Negotiations are still in progress.* 談判還在繼續進行。 | *the negotiation of new wage levels* 有關新工資標準的談判 | *The contract is under negotiation.* 合約正在商談中。

ne·go·ti·a·tor /nɪˈɡəʊʃɪˌetə; nɪˈɡəʊʃɪeɪtəʳ/ *n* someone who tries to get people with different views in business or politics to agree 談判人; 洽談人

Ne·gro /ˈniɡro; ˈniːɡrəʊ/ *n* **Negroes** someone with dark or black skin (a word that is considered offensive) 黑人〔不禮貌的用語〕

neigh /ne; neɪ/ *v* [I] to make the loud long cry of a horse 發出馬嘶聲 **–neigh** *n*

⋆neigh·bour /ˈnebə; ˈneɪbəʳ/ *n* (**neighbor** *AmE* 《美式》) **1** someone who lives next to or near someone else 鄰居: *my next-door neighbour* 我隔壁的鄰居 | *We're neighbours now.* 我們現在是鄰居了。 **2** someone sitting next to you 鄰座〔坐在旁邊的人〕

neigh·bour·hood /ˈnebə,hud; ˈneɪbəhʊd/ *n* (**neighborhood** *AmE* 《美式》) **1** [C] a small area in a town and the people living there 街坊; 鄰近地區: *a quiet neighbourhood with good shops* 擁有幾家好商店的安靜地段 | *a neighbourhood advice centre* 附近地區的諮詢中心 **2 in the neighbourhood of** near or about 在…附近; 大約: *a price in the neighbourhood of £500* 大約五百英鎊的價格

neigh·bour·ing /ˈnebərɪŋ; ˈneɪbərɪŋ/ *adj* (**neighboring** *AmE* 《美式》) [only before a noun 只用於名詞前] situated near 鄰近的; 附近的: *a bus service between the town and the neighbouring villages* 在城鎮與鄰近村莊之間的公共汽車服務

neigh·bour·ly /ˈnebəˌlɪ; ˈneɪbəlɪ/ *adj* (**neighborly** *AmE* 《美式》) friendly and helpful like a good neighbour 睦鄰的; 友善的 **– neighbourliness** *n* [U]

⋆nei·ther¹ /ˈniðə; ˈnaɪðəʳ/ *det, pron* [used with a singular verb 與動詞的單數形式連用] not one and not the other of two people or things 〔兩者之中〕無一個(的): *Neither solution is ideal.* 兩種解決辦法都不理想。 | *Neither of the roads is very good.* 這兩條公路都不是很好。 | *"Will you have tea or coffee?" "Neither."* "你要喝茶還是喝咖啡?" "都不要。" | *Neither of us wanted to go.* 我們倆都不想去。

⋆neither² *conj* **1** used in negative expressions when you are saying that two or more things are not true 既不…, 也不…〔與否定的詞組連用, 表示兩樣或兩樣以上的東西都不是真實的〕: *He neither smokes nor drinks.* 他既不抽煙, 也不喝酒。 | *I was neither shocked nor upset.* 我既不感到震驚, 也不心煩。 | *I spoke to neither my father nor my mother.* 我既不跟父親也不跟母親說話。 | *I didn't want things to end like this, and neither did anyone else.* 我不想把事情如此了結; 其他人也不想那樣做。 | *"I can't swim." "Neither can I."* "我不會游泳。" "我也不會。" **2 neither here nor there** not important 不重要的; 無關緊要的: *The fact that he owns the building is neither here nor there.* 他擁有大樓這事並不重要。

■ USAGE 用法: The word order after **neither** and **nor** is the same as the word order in a question ☆**neither** 和 **nor** 後面的語序與問句的語序相同: **Neither/Nor** *can I.* 我也不會[能]。 | **Neither/Nor** *does he.* 他也不…。 –see 見 EITHER (USAGE用法)

ne·o·lith·ic /ˌniəˈlɪθɪk; ˌniːəˈlɪθɪk◂/ *adj* of a period of history about 10,000 years ago, when people began to settle in villages, grow crops, and keep animals 新石器時代的

ne·on /ˈnian; ˈniːɒn/ *n* [U] a chemically inactive gas that is present in small amounts in the air 氖〔一種化學惰性氣體〕

neon light /ˈ ·· ·/ *n* a glass tube filled with neon which lights when an electric current goes through it, often shaped to form a sign advertising something 霓虹燈

neph·ew /ˈnefju; ˈnevjuː/ *n* the son of your brother or sister or your brother-in-law or sister-in-law 姪子; 外甥 –see picture on page 503 見 503 頁彩圖 –compare 比較 NIECE

nep·o·tis·m /ˈnɛpəˌtɪzəm; ˈnepətɪzəm/ *n* [U] the practice of favouring your relatives when you have power by getting them good jobs 重用親屬; 任人唯親

Nep·tune /ˈnɛptʃun; ˈneptjuːn/ *n* the PLANET 8th in order from the sun 海王星

⋆nerve¹ /nɝv; nɜːv/ *n* **1** [C] a very thin part inside your body which carries feelings and message between your brain and different parts of your body 神經 **2** nerves [pl] *infml* great excitement or nervousness 〔非正式〕神經緊張: *She is in a state of nerves before every examination.* 她每逢考試前非常緊張。 | *I must try and steady my nerves.* 我必須設法穩定自己的緊張情緒。 | *He's a bundle of nerves.* 他心裡亂作一團。 **3** [U] determination and courage 毅力; 勇氣: *I wanted to tell her what I thought of her but I lost my nerve.* 我想跟她說說我對她的看法, 但我沒有勇氣。 | *You need a lot of nerve to be a rock climber.* 你需要很大膽量才能成為攀岩運動

N

員。**4** [sing;U] rudeness 魯莽; 冒失; 厚顏:
*He's the dirtiest man I know, and he has the
nerve to tell me my shoes need cleaning!* 他
是我認識的最骯髒的人，而他竟有臉說我的鞋
子該擦了! | *She's got a nerve asking to bor-
row money from my father.* 她厚着臉皮向我
父親借錢。**5 get on someone's nerves** to
make someone annoyed or bad-tempered
使某人心煩; 令人惱怒: *That loud music is
getting on my nerves.* 那大聲的音樂吵得我心
煩意亂。

nerve² *v* **nerved, nerving, nerve yourself** *fml*
to give yourself courage 〖正式〗激勵自己;
鼓勵自己: *The parachutist nerved himself to
jump.* 跳傘者激勵自己往下跳。 | *She nerved
herself for the speech.* 她鼓足勇氣發言。

nerve-rack·ing /'· ,··/ *adj infml* very worrying or frightening 〖非正式〗令人十分緊張的:
*a nerve-racking journey through the high
mountains* 穿過高山峻嶺那令人十分緊張的旅
程

ner·vous /'nɜːvəs; 'nɜːvəs/ *adj* **1** frightened
or worried 提心吊膽的; 害怕的: *She's ner-
vous of being left alone in that big house at
night.* 讓她一個人留在那大房子裡過夜她很害
怕。**2** tense and easily excited 緊張的; 易激
動的: *I'm always nervous before an inter-
view.* 我面試前總是很緊張。 | *a child full of
nervous energy* 精力充沛的孩子 **3** related to
the nerves in your body 神經的; 神經性的: *a
nervous disorder* 神經紊亂 **4 nervous break-
down** serious medical condition in which a
person suffers from great anxiety, tiredness, and uncontrollable crying 神經失常 **5
nervous system** the system in people and
animals made up of the brain, SPINAL
CORD, and nerves, which receives and
passes on feelings and messages from inside and outside the body 神經系統 **6 nervous wreck** someone who is very worried
and anxious 神經極度焦慮的人 –**nervously**
adv –**nervousness** *n* [U]

■ USAGE 用法: Compare 比較 **nervous, concerned, anxious.** You can be
nervous (=rather afraid) before or
during an event ☆**nervous** 可以表示事
情發生前或發生時的 "緊張"(=相當害怕):
*I'm always nervous when I have to go
to the dentist.* 每當我須去看牙醫時總是很
緊張。You can be **concerned** (= worried) about something that is happening now, and often about another person ☆**concerned** 可以表示對正在發生的
事情，常指對別人的"關心"(=擔心): *We're
rather concerned about your father's
health.* 我們相當擔心你父親的健康。
Anxious usually means "worried about
something which might happen" ☆
anxious 通常表示"對可能發生的事情很
擔心": *I'm always anxious when the*

children go cycling on busy roads. 每當
孩子們在車輛川流不息的馬路上騎車時，
我總是很擔心。

nerv·y /'nɜːvi; 'nɜːvi/ *adj* **nervier, nerviest**
infml 〖非正式〗**1** *BrE* nervous and anxious
〖英式〗神經質的; 緊張不安的 **2** *AmE* disrespectfully rude 〖美式〗厚顏的; 粗魯的

nest¹ /nɛst; nɛst/ *n* **1** a hollow place or a
structure built of branches, feathers, and
leaves where a bird places its eggs and
brings up its young 鳥窩; 巢 **2** the home of
certain other animals or insects 〔某些動物
或昆蟲的〕穴; 窩: *an ants' nest* 蟻穴 | *a
wasps' nest* 黃蜂窩 **3** a comfortable place 安
樂窩, 舒適的地方: *They made the cottage
into a cosy nest.* 他們把小屋佈置成一個安樂
窩。**4** a place where bad people or activities are safe 藏匿處; 庇護所: *a nest of in-
trigue* 陰謀活動的庇護所 **5** a group of similar objects which fit closely inside one
another 〔由大到小可依次套疊的〕一套; 一組
(物件): *a nest of tables* 一套茶几

nest² *v* [I] to build or use a nest 築巢; 巢居:
Most birds nest in trees. 大多數的鳥在樹上築
巢。

nest egg /'· ·/ *n* an amount of money saved
for future use 儲備金

nes·tle /'nɛsl; 'nɛsəl/ *v* **nestled, nestling 1** [I
+ adv/prep; T + adv/prep] to settle warmly
or comfortably often by pressing against
something 〔舒適地〕安頓下來; 偎依: *I'd love
to nestle down in a big chair with a book.* 我
很想舒適地倚在大椅子上看書。 | *She nestled
her head on his shoulder.* 她把頭偎依在他的
肩上。**2** [I + adv/prep] to lie in a sheltered
position 位於遮掩處: *The village nestled
among the hills.* 那村莊坐落在山丘之中。

***net¹** /nɛt; nɛt/ *n* **1** [U] a material of strings,
wires, or threads twisted, tied, or woven
together with regular spaces between them
網: *net curtains* 網眼簾 **2** [C] a piece of this
woven material which is used for a particular purpose 網織品: *The fishermen put out
their nets.* 漁民拿出了他們的魚網。 | *a but-
terfly net* 捕蝶網 | *The footballer kicked the
ball into the net.* 那個足球運動員把球踢進了
球網。 | *I'm hopeless at tennis — I'm always
hitting the ball into the net.* 我打網球
沒指望了，我老是擊球落網。 | *a hair net* 髮網 |
a mosquito net 蚊帳

net² *v* **-tt-** [T] **1** to catch something in a net
用網捕捉〔某物〕: *We netted three fish.* 我們
網捕到了三條魚。**2** to cover something with
a net 用網罩住〔某物〕: *You'll have to net
those strawberries or the birds will get them.*
你必須用網罩住那些草莓，否則鳥會把它們吃
掉。**3** to get something by using skill 用技巧
得到〔某物〕: *She managed to net herself a
rich husband.* 她設法為自己弄到了一個有錢
的丈夫。**4** to gain as a profit when every-

thing else has been paid 淨得; 淨賺: *The sale netted a fat profit for the company.* 這筆買賣為公司賺了一大筆錢。 –compare 比較 GROSS[1]

★**net³** *adj* [only before or after a noun 只用於名詞前或名詞後] (also 又作 **nett** *BrE* 〖英式〗) **1** after all the things like tax, rent, and electricity have been paid 〔付清稅款、租金和電費等之後〕淨的; 純的: *net profit* 淨利潤 **2** without the container or packet 不帶容器或包裝的: *net weight* 淨重 | *This jar of coffee weighs 350 grams net.* 這瓶咖啡淨重三百五十克。 **3** net result the result when everything has been considered 最終結果: *The net result of this policy was even worse inflation.* 這項政策的最終結果是物價進一步上漲。

net·ball /ˈnetˌbɔl; ˈnetbɔːl/ *n* [U] a game usually played by women in which teams of seven players win points by throwing a ball so that it falls through one of the two high rings at the opposite ends of a court 無擋板籃球〔一種女子球類項目〕

net·ting /ˈnetɪŋ; ˈnetɪŋ/ *n* [U] string, wire, or thread made into a net 網狀物: *a fence of wire netting* 鐵絲網做的圍欄

net·tle¹ /ˈnetl; ˈnetl/ *n* a wild plant with hairs on its leaves which may sting and make red marks on the skin 蕁麻〔葉上的毛會刺人並使皮膚起紅斑〕

nettle² *v* **nettled, nettling** [T] *infml* to make someone annoyed 〖非正式〗使〔某人〕惱怒: *I was rather nettled by his rudeness.* 我被他的粗魯激怒了。

★**net·work¹** /ˈnetˌwɜrk; ˈnetwɜːk/ *n* **1** a large system of roads, wires, or lines of things that cross or meet one another 網狀系統: *Britain's railway network* 英國鐵路網 | *the network of blood vessels in the body* 體內血管網狀系統 **2** a group of people, companies, or organizations that are connected and work together 〔團體、公司或組織的〕聯絡網: *a network of restaurants in different parts of the country* 全國各地的餐飲業系統 | *a spy network* 間諜網 **3** a group of radio or television stations in different places using many of the same broadcasts 廣播網; 電視網 **4** a set of computers that are connected to each other and can be used as a means of sending and sharing information 電腦網絡

network² *v* [T] to connect computers together to share information 把〔電腦〕聯網

neu·ro·sis /njuˈrosɪs; njuˈrəusɪs/ *n* **neuroses** /-siz; -siːz/ [C;U] *tech* an illness of the mind marked by strong unreasonable fears and ideas about the outside world 〖術語〗恐懼症; 神經官能症

neu·rot·ic /njuˈrɑtɪk; njuˈrɒtɪk/ *adj* unreasonably anxious or sensitive 神經過敏的; 極為焦慮的: *She's neurotic about her children's hygiene.* 她對她孩子的衛生神經過敏。 – **neurotic** *n*

neu·ter¹ /ˈnjutɚ; ˈnjuːtəʳ/ *adj* **1** related to a class of words which are neither MASCULINE nor FEMININE 〔詞類〕中性的: *a neuter noun* 中性名詞 **2** with no sexual organs, or undeveloped sexual organs (used of plants or animals) 無性的; 無生殖器的; 生殖器發育不全的〔指動植物〕: *Worker bees are neuter.* 工蜂是無性生物。

neuter² *v* [T] to remove part of the sex organs of an animal by an operation 閹割〔動物〕

neu·tral¹ /ˈnjutrəl; ˈnjuːtrəl/ *adj* **1** without strong feelings or opinions for or against something 中立的; 不偏不倚的: *"Who do you want to win?" "Oh, I'm neutral."* "你希望誰贏?" "噢, 我保持中立。" | *neutral reporting of a political issue* 對某個政治問題不偏不倚的報道 **2** belonging to a country which is not fighting or helping either side in a war 中立國的; 非作戰國的: *neutral waters* 非作戰水域 **3** of a very pale colour such as grey or cream 淡色的; 略帶灰色的: *The carpet is a neutral colour.* 地毯是淡灰色的。 **4** containing no colour 無色的: *neutral shoe polish* 無色鞋油膏 **5** neither acid nor ALKALINE in chemistry 〔化學〕中性的 **6** having no electrical charge (used of a wire) 不帶電的〔指電線〕 – **neutrally** *adv*

neutral² *n* **1** [U] the position of the gears (GEAR) in a car in which no power is carried from the engine to the wheels 〔汽車的〕空檔: *When you start the engine, be sure the car is in neutral.* 你在發動引擎時, 一定要讓汽車處於空檔位置。 **2** [C] a neutral person or country 中立者; 中立國

neu·tral·i·ty /njuˈtrælɪti; njuːˈtrælɪti/ *n* [U] the supporting of neither side in a disagreement or war 〔意見分歧或戰爭時的〕中立; 中立地位

neu·tral·ize /ˈnjutrəlˌaɪz; ˈnjuːtrəlaɪz/ *v* **neutralized, neutralizing** (also 又作 **neutralise** *BrE* 〖英式〗) [T] **1** to stop something having an effect 使〔某物〕無效; 使中和: *The acid was neutralized with a base.* 酸被鹼中和了。 | *High taxes will neutralize increased wages.* 高稅收會抵銷增加了的工資。 **2** to make a country or area neutral by international agreement 使〔國家或地區〕中立化 –**neutralization** /ˌnjutrələˈzeʃən; ˌnjuːtrəlaɪˈzeɪʃn/ *n* [U]

neu·tron /ˈnjutrɑn; ˈnjuːtrɒn/ *n* a very small piece of matter that carries no electricity and that together with the PROTON forms the central part of an atom 中子

★**nev·er** /ˈnevɚ; ˈnevəʳ/ *adv* **1** not at any time 從不; 決不; 永不: *I've never been to Paris.* 我從未去過巴黎。 | *Never give your name and address to someone you don't know.* 千萬不要把你的姓名地址告訴不認識的人。 | *I shall never leave you.* 我決不會離開你。 | *She never finished the book she was writing.* 她寫的那本書從未完稿。 **2** never

N

ever a stronger way of saying "never" 永不; 從不; 決不〔語氣強於never〕: *You must never ever tell anyone about this.* 你無論如何也不要把這事告訴別人。

nev·er·more /ˌnɛvɚˈmɔr; ˌnevəˈmɔːʳ◂/ *adv* lit never again 《文》永不再; 決不再

★**nev·er·the·less** /ˌnɛvɚðəˈlɛs; ˌnevəðəˈles/ *adv* in spite of what someone has just said 不過; 仍然; 儘管; 然而: *The politicians admit that the tax is unpopular. Nevertheless they seem determined not to get rid of it.* 這些政客承認該稅法不受歡迎。不過他們似乎並不願意廢除它。| *Seat belts undoubtedly save lives. Many people, nevertheless, do not wear them.* 座椅安全帶無疑可以救命。不過, 很多人還是不繫安全帶。

★★**new** /nju; njuː/ *adj* **1** recently produced, made, or built 新生產的; 新製成的; 新造的: *They're going to put 150 new houses in that field.* 他們要在那塊土地上建造一百五十棟新房子。| *This idea isn't new.* 這個想法並不新鮮。| *Have you seen their new baby?* 你見到他們的新生嬰兒了嗎？| *the newest fashions* 最新的款式 | *a new system of drainage* 新建的排水系統 **2** recently bought 新買的: *We're moving to our new house in May.* 我們在五月份準備搬入新居。**3** not used or owned by anyone before 未用過的; 新的: *They sell new and used cars.* 他們出售新舊汽車。| *a brand new bicycle* 嶄新的腳踏車 **4** only recently discovered 新發現的: *new reserves of coal* 新近發現的原煤儲備 **5** new to something unfamiliar with something 不熟悉某事物: *a young clerk new to the job* 不熟悉這項工作的年輕職員 **6** new to someone not known by someone 對某人不熟悉的〔生疏的〕: *The experience was new to me.* 那次經歷對我很陌生。| *Her name is new to me.* 她的名字我很陌生。**7** recently begun or joined 剛開始的; 新加入的: *He's just started at a new school.* 他剛剛開始在一所新學校念書。| *new members of the club* 俱樂部的新成員 **8** different or another 不同的; 另外的: *I've got a new teacher.* 我有了個新的老師。| *They've gone to Australia to start a new life.* 他們已經到澳大利亞去開始過一種新的生活。| *He wants to learn a new language.* 他想學另一種語言。**9** picked or dug up when small and young (used of a crop) 未成熟就採的〔指農作物〕: *new potatoes* 時鮮的馬鈴薯〔土豆〕| *fresh new garden peas* 園地裡採的時鮮豌豆 **10** new blood, young blood young members taken into an organization to give it fresh ideas〔具有新思想的〕新成員; 新人: *We need new blood in this company.* 我們這家公司需要新成員。**11** new moon the bright thin edge of the moon seen at the beginning of its four-week cycle 新月 **12** new wave a group of people who make a conscious effort to change the styles of art, music, photography, or film making 新浪潮〔指力圖改變藝術、音樂、攝影或電影製作的傳

統風格的一批人〕**13** New Year, new year the beginning of January 新年: *Business should improve in the new year.* 生意會在新年越來越好。| *Happy New Year!* 新年快樂! **14** New Year's Day in Western countries, January 1st 元旦〔一月一日〕**15** New Year's Eve in Western countries, December 31st 除夕〔十二月三十一日〕**16** the New Testament the second half of the Bible, which tells us about the teachings of Jesus Christ and his followers〔《聖經》的〕新約全書 –compare 比較 OLD TESTAMENT **17** the New World North, Central, and South America 新世界〔指美洲大陸〕**18** new- recently 新近的: *a newborn baby* 新生嬰兒 | *a new-found friend* 新交的朋友 –**newness** *n* [U]

■ USAGE 用法: Compare 比較 **new, recent, modern, current, contemporary. New** is the general word for something that has only been in existence for a short time ☆ **new** 一般用來表示剛出現不久的事物: *a new road* 新建的馬路。**Recent** describes events that happened a short time ago ☆**recent** 用來描述不久前發生的事情: *our recent holiday* 我們最近的假日。**Modern** means "belonging to the present time or the not-too-distant past" ☆**modern** 的意思是"現代的或近代的": *an examination in* **modern** *history, from 1789 to the present* 從 1789 年至今的現代史考試。**Contemporary** means "belonging to the present" ☆**contemporary** 的意思是"當代的": *contemporary art/music* 當代藝術/音樂。**Current** describes something that exists now, but was different before and may be different again ☆**current** 表示現存的但又有別於以前的事物, 而且可能再起變化: *The* **current** *fashion is for men to have short hair.* 當今的流行式樣是男子留短髮。

---

new·com·er /ˈnju͵kʌmɚ; ˈnjuːˌkʌməʳ/ *n* someone who has recently come to a place or has started an activity 新來的人; 新手: *a newcomer to the city* 初到這個城市的人 | *I'm a newcomer to teaching.* 我在教書方面是個新手。

new·fan·gled /ˌnjuˈfæŋgld; ˌnjuːˈfæŋgəld◂/ *adj* [only before a noun 只用於名詞前] new and disapproved of by the person speaking (used of ideas or machines) 新潮而不提倡的〔指思想或機器〕: *We need better teachers, not newfangled ideas of education!* 我們需要更好的教師, 而不是新花樣的教育思想!

new-found /ˈ· ·/ *adj* recently made or discovered 新交的; 新發現的: *new-found friends* 新交的朋友 | *a new-found ability* 新發現的能力

★**new·ly** /ˈnjulɪ; ˈnjuːli/ *adv* recently 最近的: *a newly built house* 新造的房子 | *a newly* *qualified teacher* 最近剛具備資格的教師

new·ly·wed /ˈnjuːlɪˌwɛd; ˈnjuːliwed/ *n* a man or woman recently married 新婚的人: *You can tell they're newlyweds.* 你能猜出他們是新婚夫婦。 | *a newlywed couple* 新婚夫婦

★**news** /njuːz; njuːz/ *n* [U] **1** new information about a recent event 新聞; 新消息: *I've got some news of the election results.* 我得到了一些選舉結果的新聞。 | *Have you heard the news about Mary? She's going to have a baby.* 你聽到了瑪麗的消息嗎? 她快要生孩子了。 | *I'm afraid the news isn't very good.* 恐怕消息不盡如人意。 **2 the news** a regular report of recent events broadcast on radio and television〔電台及電視的〕新聞報道: *I'd like to see the news at 9 o'clock.* 我想收看九點鐘的新聞報道。 | *It'll be on the news this evening.* 今晚的新聞報道中會有這消息。 **3 that's news to me** *infml* a phrase used about something that you did not know which surprises you〔非正式〕那對我來說可是新聞〔用於因對某事一無所知而感到意外〕

news·a·gent /ˈnjuːzˌedʒənt; ˈnjuːzˌeɪdʒənt/ *n* **1** a person in charge of a shop selling newspapers and magazines 報刊經銷人: *The newsagent was shot by the thieves.* 報刊經銷人被小偷打中了。 **2 newsagent's** a shop selling newspapers, magazines and sometimes sweets and cigarettes 報刊門市部: *The newsagent's has got that new magazine.* 在報刊門市部可買到那本新出的雜誌。

news·cast·er /ˈnjuːzˌkæstə; ˈnjuːzˌkɑːstəʳ/ *n* (also 又作 **newsreader** /-ˌriːdə; -ˌriːdəʳ/) someone who reads the news on radio or television〔電台或電視台的〕新聞播音員

news con·fer·ence /ˈ· ˌ···/ *n* a meeting during which an important person gives a statement to news reporters or answers questions 記者招待會

news-flash /ˈ·· ·/ *n* a short news report on radio or television〔電台、電視播送的〕簡訊; 特別新聞: *The programme was interrupted with a news-flash about the war.* 節目因播送有關戰爭的特別新聞而中斷了。

news·let·ter /ˈnjuːzˌletə; ˈnjuːzˌletəʳ/ *n* a short report of news about a club or organization sent weekly or monthly to its members〔定期發送給俱樂部或組織成員的〕簡訊; 簡報: *the company newsletter* 公司簡訊

★**news·pa·per** /ˈnjuːzˌpepə; ˈnjuːzˌpeɪpəʳ/ *n* **1** [C] (also 又作 **paper**) a set of large folded sheets of paper containing news, articles, and advertisements, printed and sold daily or weekly 報紙; 報章: *an evening newspaper* 晚報 | *the Sunday newspapers* 星期日報 | *an interesting article in the newspaper* 報上一篇有趣的文章 **2** [U] the paper on which newspapers are printed 印上新聞的紙; 報紙: *Wrap it up in newspaper.* 用報紙把它包起來。

3 [C] a company which produces a newspaper 報社: *He works for a national newspaper.* 他在一家國有報社工作。

news·print /ˈnjuːzˌprɪnt; ˈnjuːzˌprɪnt/ *n* [U] *tech* a cheap paper used mostly for printing newspapers on〔術語〕新聞紙; 白報紙

news·reel /ˈnjuːzˌriːl; ˈnjuːzˌriːl/ *n* a short film of news made for showing in the cinema 新聞短片

news·stand /ˈnjuːzˌstænd; ˈnjuːzˌstænd/ *n* a table, often in a street or in a station, from which newspapers, and magazines are sold 書報攤

news·wor·thy /ˈnjuːzˌwɜːðɪ; ˈnjuːzˌwɜːði/ *adj* important and interesting enough to be reported as news 有新聞價值的; 值得報道的

newt /njuːt; njuːt/ *n* a small four-legged animal with a long tail which can live on land and in water 水蜥; 蠑螈

★**next¹** /nekst; nekst/ *adj* **1** nearest 最近的: *They live in the next house.* 他們住在隔壁的房子。 | *I could hear music coming from the next room.* 我可以聽見從隔壁房間傳來的音樂。 **2** coming straight after the present one 緊接在後的: *If I miss this train I'll catch the next one.* 如果我趕不上這班火車, 我就趕乘下一班。 | *Are you coming to our next meeting?* 你來參加我們的下一次會議嗎? | *I'll see you next week.* 我下星期和你碰頭。 **3 next best** the thing that is the best one except for one other 僅次於最好的; 居第二位的

★**next²** /nekst; nekst/ *adv* **1** just after something 接着; 然後: *What will you do next?* 接下去你要做甚麼? **2** on the first occasion after this one 下一次: *I'll tell you the rest when I next see you.* 下一次見面時我把其餘的事告訴你。 **3** you use "next" when you move on to the following stage in a story that you are telling 然後〔用於接着往下講故事〕: *He took the scissors from the drawer and cut a small article from the newspaper. Next, he took a large file down from a shelf behind him.* 他從抽屜裡拿出剪刀, 剪下了報紙上的一篇小文章。然後, 他從身後的架子上取下一大卷檔案。 **4** you use "next" when you move on to the next stage of a process you are describing 然後〔用於接着往下描述事情的過程〕: *The letters are taken to the sorting offices and sorted. Next, they are sent out to the main postal towns, where they are sorted again.* 信函被送到郵件分揀處加以整理分類; 然後又運往各主要郵政市鎮, 在那裡又進行分類。 **5** you use "next" when you go on to the follow-

ing instruction in a set of instructions 然後
〔用於接着往下作使用説明〕: *You select the wash temperature. Next, you put the detergent in.* 先選擇洗滌溫度; 然後把洗滌劑放入。 **6** you use "next" when you move on to make another point in an argument 下面〔用於接着往下論述另一個問題〕: *So now we've got an idea of some of the social problems in the towns. Next, I'd like to have a look at some of the social problems in the villages.* 現在我們已經了解了一些發生在城鎮的社會問題, 下面我想談談鄉村的社會問題。 **7 next to** close beside 緊靠…旁邊: *She was sitting next to Lucy.* 她坐在露西身邊。 –see picture on page 764 見 764 頁彩圖 **8 next to nothing** almost nothing 幾乎一無所有: *He earns next to nothing.* 他幾乎一分錢都沒賺到。

next-door /ˌ·ˈ·ˌ/ *adj, adv* in the next building or room 隔壁的: *next-door neighbours* 隔壁鄰居 | *The director's office is next-door.* 主任的辦公室就在隔壁。 | *We live next-door to a cinema.* 我們住在一家電影院隔壁。

next of kin /ˌ··ˈ·/ *n* [plural as 複數為 **next of kin**] *law* [+ sing/pl verb] your closest relative or relatives 《律》最近的親屬: *Her next of kin have now been informed.* 現已通知她最近的親屬。

NHS /ˌen eɪtʃ ˈes; ˌen eɪtʃ ˈes/ *n* a system of medical treatment for everyone in Britain, paid for by taxes; an abbreviation for **National Health Service** 〔縮〕〔英國〕國民保健局〔納税人均可享受免費醫療的制度〕: *Can I get my glasses on the NHS?* 我配眼鏡是否可以得到國民保健局的資助?

nib /nɪb; nɪb/ *n* the pointed piece on the end of a pen through which the ink flows 鋼筆尖

nib·ble /ˈnɪbl; ˈnɪbəl/ *v* **nibbled, nibbling** [I; T] to eat slowly with small repeated bites 啃; 一點一點地咬: *Aren't you hungry? You're only nibbling at your food.* 你不餓嗎? 你只是一點一點地啃着吃東西。 –**nibble** *n*

⭐**nice** /naɪs; naɪs/ *adj* **1** *infml* pleasant or pleasing 《非正式》令人愉快的; 使人高興的: *Have a nice time at the party.* 在派對上玩個痛快。 | *a nice piece of work* 一件好看的作品 | *a nice sunny day* 令人愉快的晴天 | *This soup tastes very nice.* 這湯的味道很好。 | *How nice to see you!* 見到你真高興! **2** kind or friendly 好心的; 友好的: *She's the nicest person I know.* 在我認識的人中間, 她最和善。 **3** *fml* showing or needing careful understanding 《正式》微妙的; 細緻的: *a nice point of law* 法律的細微之處 **4** *old fash* having high standards of moral and social behaviour 〔老式〕有教養的; 正派的: *Nice girls don't do that!* 行為端莊的女孩不會幹那種事! **5** nice and *infml* pleasantly 《非正式》宜人地: *The soup is nice and hot.* 這湯熱氣騰騰。 | *The speech was nice and short.* 那篇發言簡短扼要。 –**niceness** *n* [U]

■ **USAGE** 用法: In informal English **nice** is often used to add strength to another adjective which describes a pleasant quality. When the adjectives follow the verb "to be" (or a similar linking verb) they are joined by and ☆ 在英語的非正式文體中, **nice** 常用來修飾另一個描述良好品質的形容詞。 當形容詞緊跟在動詞 "to be" (或類似的連繫動詞) 後面時, 它們之間要用 **and** 連接: *The room was **nice** and cosy.* 房間非常舒適。 | *I know a restaurant where the food is **nice** and cheap.* 我認識一家餐廳, 那裡的食品很便宜。 | *You look **nice** and warm in that coat.* 你穿那件衣服看上去很暖和。 But when they come before the noun they should NOT be joined by and ☆ 但當它們出現在名詞前時, 就不能用 **and** 連接: *a **nice** cosy room* 一間很舒適的房間 | *a **nice** warm coat* 一件很保暖的衣服 | *a **nice** big tip for the waiter* 一筆給侍應生的可觀的小費

nice·ly /ˈnaɪslɪ; ˈnaɪsli/ *adv* **1** in a good, pleasant, kind, or skilful way 很好地; 令人愉快地; 合宜地: *Smile nicely at the camera!* 面對照相機要笑得自然一點! | *She always dresses nicely.* 她總是穿得很像樣。 **2** in an exact, or delicate way 精確地; 精細地: *a nicely calculated distance* 經過精確計算的距離 **3 do nicely** be satisfactory 令人滿意: *"Here's £10." "Thank you. That will do nicely."* "這是十英鎊。" "謝謝你, 真是太好了。" **4 doing nicely** doing well 進展良好: *The injured man is doing nicely in hospital.* 這個受傷的人在醫院裡情況進展良好。 | *James is now financial director and doing very nicely for himself.* 詹姆斯現在是財務主管, 幹得很出色。

ni·ce·ty /ˈnaɪsətɪ; ˈnaɪsəti/ *n* **niceties** a fine or delicate point 精細之處; 細節: *We haven't time to consider all the niceties of the situation.* 我們沒有時間考慮形勢的所有細節。 | *I wish she would try to observe the social niceties.* 但願她能盡量遵守社交禮節。

niche /niːtʃ; nɪtʃ/ *n* **1** a hollow place in a wall, usually made to hold a piece of art 壁龕〔常用來放置藝術品〕 **2** a suitable place, job, or position 適當的地方〔工作、職位〕: *He's found a niche for himself in the book trade.* 他在圖書行業找到了一份適合他的工作。

nick[1] /nɪk; nɪk/ *n* **1** a small accidental cut in a surface or edge 缺口; 裂口; 刻痕 **2 in good nick** *infml* in good condition 《非正式》情況好的 [RELATED PHRASE 相關詞組 **in bad nick**] **3 in the nick** *slang* in prison 《俚》監禁 **4 in the nick of time** at the last possible moment 在最後關鍵時刻: *I caught the baby in the nick of time before he fell down the stairs.* 當孩子正要從樓梯上跌下去的時候, 我一把抓住了他。

nick² v [T] **1** to make or cut a nick in something 刻痕於〔某物〕; 割傷: I nicked my chin when I was shaving this morning. 我今天早上刮鬍子時將下巴割破了。 **2** infml to steal something 〔非正式〕偷〔某物〕: Someone's nicked my bicycle. 有人偷了我的腳踏車。 **3** infml to ARREST someone 〔非正式〕逮捕〔某人〕; 抓獲: He was nicked as he ran out of the bank. 他正要衝出銀行就被抓獲。

nick·el /ˈnɪkḷ; ˈnɪkəl/ n **1** [U] a hard silver-white metal that is used in the production of other metals 鎳 **2** [C] a coin of the US and Canada worth five cents 〔美國或加拿大的〕五分硬幣

nick·nack /ˈnɪkˌnæk; ˈnɪknæk/ n see 見 KNICK-KNACK

nick·name¹ /ˈnɪkˌnem; ˈnɪkneɪm/ n a name used informally instead of someone's own name, usually given because of their character or as a short form of the actual name 綽號; 謔名: "Mac" is just my nickname — my real name is MacDonald. "麥克"只是我的綽號; 我的真名是麥克唐納。

nickname² v **nicknamed, nicknaming** [T] to give someone a nickname 給〔某人〕起綽號〔謔名〕: They nicknamed him "Fats" because of his weight. 因為他胖, 他們給他取個綽號叫"胖子"。

nic·o·tine /ˈnɪkəˌtin; ˈnɪkətiːn/ n [U] a poisonous chemical contained in tobacco 煙鹼; 尼古丁

niece /nis; niːs/ n the daughter of your brother or sister or your wife's or husband's brother or sister 姪女; 甥女 –see picture on page 503 見 503 頁彩圖 –compare 比較 NEPHEW

nif·ty /ˈnɪftɪ; ˈnɪftɪ/ adj **niftier, niftiest** infml very attractive, or clever and useful 〔非正式〕有吸引力的; 漂亮的; 精巧的: That's a very nifty outfit you're wearing! 你穿的這套衣服真時髦! | a nifty little gadget for squeezing oranges 榨橘子汁的小巧的工具

nig·gard·ly /ˈnɪgədlɪ; ˈnɪgədli/ adj **1** not generous, and unwilling to spend money or time (a word used to express disapproval) 小氣的; 吝嗇的〔含貶義〕: a niggardly offer for such a good bicycle 對於那麼好腳踏車所出的低價 | a niggardly old man 吝嗇的老頭 **–niggardliness** n [U]

nig·ger /ˈnɪgə; ˈnɪgɚ/ n a black person (a word that is considered very offensive) 黑人; 黑鬼〔此稱呼被看作是對黑人的極大侮辱〕

nig·gle¹ /ˈnɪgḷ; ˈnɪgəl/ v **niggled, niggling 1** [I] to give too much attention to finding faults in small details 過分為瑣事操心; 吹毛求疵: She niggled **over** every detail of the bill. 她對賬單的每一項都仔細查算。 **2** [T] to annoy or worry someone slightly but continually 使〔某人〕煩惱; 令人擔心: Her laziness constantly niggled him. 她的懶惰總惹他討厭。

niggle² n a small worry that you think about continually 牽腸掛肚的小事: There's a niggle at the back of my mind about something but I can't remember what. 我內心有件小事讓我牽掛, 但就是想不起來。

nig·gling /ˈnɪglɪŋ; ˈnɪgəlɪŋ/ adj [only before a noun 只用於名詞前] **1** worrying or annoying you slightly but continually 〔瑣碎而〕煩惱的; 討厭的: a niggling doubt 使人心煩的疑慮 **2** needing too much attention to detail 需要過分注重細節的; 費神的: a niggling job 繁瑣的工作

nigh /naɪ; naɪ/ adv, prep old fash 〔老式〕 **1** near 近的 **2 well nigh, nigh on** almost 幾乎: It's well nigh impossible to see any difference between the twins. 要看出這對雙胞胎的不同之處幾乎是不可能的。

★night /naɪt; naɪt/ n **1** [C;U] the dark part of each day, when the sun cannot be seen 夜晚; 黑夜: The nights are longer in winter. 冬季夜長。 | Nurses have to work at night. 護士得上夜班。 | Night began to fall and we could no longer see what we were doing. 夜幕開始降臨, 我們再也無法看清我們在做的事。 | a few nights ago 前幾夜 | Where were you on the night of 16th January? 一月十六日晚上你在哪裡? | The hotel charges £50 a night. 這家旅館的住宿費是每晚五十英鎊。 **2** [C;U] the evening 黃昏; 傍晚: We'll be out tomorrow night. 我們明天晚上要出門。 | Let's go to the cinema on Saturday night. 我們星期六晚上去看電影吧。 **3** [C;U] the period when most people are sleeping 深夜: I slept well last night. 昨天夜裡我睡得很好。 | She lay awake all night long. 她通宵沒合上眼。 **4** [C] a particular occasion or performance of something in the evening 晚會; 〔演出的〕夜場: We're going to a Scottish Burns Night tonight. 我們今晚要去參加一個紀念蘇格蘭詩人彭斯的晚會。 | the first night of a play 戲劇的首夜演出 **5** [C] the evening of a holiday 假日的夜晚: Christmas night 聖誕夜 **6 by night** during the night 在夜間: I hate travelling by night. 我不喜歡夜間旅行。 **7 night after night** infml regularly every night 〔非正式〕每晚; 夜夜: He goes out drinking night after night. 他每天晚上出去喝酒。 **8 night and day, day and night** infml all the time 〔非正式〕日日夜夜; 夜以繼日 **9 the other night** a few nights ago 幾天前的一個晚上: I saw David the other night. 我在幾天前的一個晚上見到過大衛。

night·cap /ˈnaɪtˌkæp; ˈnaɪtkæp/ n **1** a drink taken before going to bed, usually alcoholic 臨睡前喝的酒 **2** a soft cloth cap that people used to wear in bed 睡帽

night·club /ˈnaɪtˌklʌb; ˈnaɪtklʌb/ n a club open late at night where people can eat, drink, dance, and often see a show 夜總會

night·dress /ˈnaɪtˌdrɛs; ˈnaɪtdres/ n (also 又作 **nightgown** /ˈnaɪtˌgaun; ˈnaɪtgaun/) a type of loose dress, which women and girls wear in bed 〔婦女或孩子穿的〕睡袍 –see picture on page 210 見 210 頁彩圖

night·fall /ˈnaɪtfɔl; ˈnaɪtfɔːl/ n [U] the time when it begins to get dark 黄昏; 傍晚

night·ie /ˈnaɪti; ˈnaɪti/ n infml a nightdress 〖非正式〗女式睡衣

nigh·tin·gale /ˈnaɪtɪŋˌgel; ˈnaɪtɪŋgeɪl/ n a brown European bird known for its beautiful song 夜鶯

night·life /ˈnaɪtˌlaɪf; ˈnaɪtlaɪf/ n [U] evening entertainment such as bars and nightclubs (NIGHTCLUB) in towns and cities 夜生活

night·ly /ˈnaɪtli; ˈnaɪtli/ adj, adv happening every night 每夜的[地]: a play performed nightly 每晚上演的戲劇 | a nightly news broadcast 晚間新聞廣播

night·mare /ˈnaɪtˌmer; ˈnaɪtmeəʳ/ n 1 a terrible dream 惡夢 2 a terrible experience or event 恐怖的經歷或事件: Driving through that snowstorm was a nightmare. 開車穿過那場暴風雪真是可怕極了。 –nightmarish adj

night school /ˈ· ·/ n [C;U] a school or set of classes meeting in the evening, especially for people who have jobs during the day 夜校: You can learn French at night school. 你可以上夜校學法語。

night shift /ˈ· ·/ n 1 a period of time during the night, when people regularly work somewhere like a hospital or a factory 夜班: I'm on the night shift this week. 我本週上夜班。 2 the night shift [+ sing/pl verb] the group of workers who do the night shift 夜班工人: The night shift is just coming off duty. 夜班工人正下班。

night·time /ˈnaɪtˌtaɪm; ˈnaɪttaɪm/ n [U] the time each day when it is dark 夜間 –opposite 反義 **daytime**

night watch·man /ˌ· ˈ··/ n a man with the job of guarding a building at night 夜間守衛; 值夜者

nil /nɪl; nɪl/ n nothing or zero 無; 零: The new machine reduced labour costs to almost nil. 新機器把人工成本幾乎降低到零。 | Our football team won by four goals to nil. 我們的足球隊以四比零獲勝。

nim·ble /ˈnɪmbl; ˈnɪmbəl/ adj 1 quick, light, and neat in movement 〔動作〕靈活的; 輕快的; 敏捷的: a nimble climber 敏捷的爬山者 2 able to think quickly 〔思路〕敏捷的; 敏銳的: a nimble mind 敏銳的頭腦 –**nimbleness** n [U] –**nimbly** adv

nin·com·poop /ˈnɪŋkəmˌpup; ˈnɪŋkəmpuːp/ n infml a stupid person 〖非正式〗傻子; 笨蛋

nine /naɪn; naɪn/ det, n, pron 1 the number 9 〔數字〕九 2 nine times out of ten infml almost always 〖非正式〗十之八九; 幾乎總是

nine·teen /ˈnaɪnˈtin; ˌnaɪnˈtiːn◂/ det, n, pron 1 the number 19 〔數字〕十九 2 talk nineteen to the dozen infml to talk quickly and continuously 〖非正式〗喋喋不休 –**nineteenth** det, n, adv, pron

nine·ty /ˈnaɪnti; ˈnaɪnti/ det, n, pron **nineties** 1 the number 90 〔數字〕九十 2 the Nineties, the nineties the years 1990-1999 九十年代

〔1990年 – 1999年〕3 in her nineties, in their nineties, etc. aged between 90 and 99 九十歲到九十九歲的時期 –**ninetieth** /ˈnaɪntiɪθ; ˈnaɪntiɪθ/ det, n, adv, pron

nin·ny /ˈnɪni; ˈnɪni/ n **ninnies** infml a silly foolish person 〖非正式〗笨蛋; 傻瓜

ninth /naɪnθ; naɪnθ/ det, n, adv, pron 1 9th 第九(的) 2 one of nine equal parts 九分之一

nip¹ /nɪp; nɪp/ v -**pp**- 1 [T] to catch in a tight sharp hold between two points or surfaces 夾住; 箝住: I nipped my finger in the door. 我的手指被門夾了一下。 2 [I;T] to take a small bite 咬: The dog has nipped the postman on the leg. 這狗咬了郵差的腿。 3 [I +adv/prep] BrE infml to move or go quickly or for a short time 〖英式, 非正式〗急走; 快速行動: I'll nip out and buy a newspaper. 我要趕緊出去買一份報紙。 | Let's nip in there for a quick cup of tea. 我們進去趕快喝杯茶。 4 nip something in the bud to stop something before it develops very much 把某事物消滅於萌芽狀態; 防患於未然: Her plans to go out were nipped in the bud when her mother arrived for the evening. 她母親來過夜, 使得她要外出的計劃成了泡影。

nip² n [sing] 1 a coldness 寒冷; 嚴寒: There's a nip in the air today: winter's coming. 今天寒風刺骨, 冬天已至來臨了。 2 a small bite or PINCH 一夾; 一掐: I gave my fingers a nasty nip when I caught them in the door. 我的手指被卡在門縫裡, 弄得好痛。 3 infml a small amount of a strong alcoholic drink, usually spirits 〖非正式〗少量的酒: a nip of whisky 一點威士忌酒

nip·per /ˈnɪpɚ; ˈnɪpəʳ/ n infml a small child 〖非正式〗小孩

nip·ple /ˈnɪpl; ˈnɪpəl/ n 1 the dark area in the middle of each of your breasts 乳頭 2 AmE the piece of rubber on the end of a baby's bottle 〖美式〗(奶瓶的)橡皮奶頭 3 something shaped like a nipple with a small opening for oil to come out of 〔乳頭狀的〕注油口

nip·py /ˈnɪpi; ˈnɪpi/ adj **nippier, nippiest** infml 〖非正式〗1 rather cold (used of weather) 寒冷的; 刺骨的〔指天氣〕: It's nippy this morning. I wish I had a coat. 今天早上寒風刺骨, 我真想有件大衣。 2 quick in movement 〔動作〕敏捷的; 快的: My new car is really nippy. 我的新車開起來真快。

nit /nɪt; nɪt/ n 1 an egg of an insect that is sometimes found in people's hair 〔時常寄生於頭髮的〕蟲卵; 虱卵 2 infml a stupid person 〖非正式〗傻瓜; 笨蛋

nit·pick·ing /ˈnɪtˌpɪkɪŋ; ˈnɪtˌpɪkɪŋ/ n [U] the paying of too much attention to small and unimportant details 挑剔; 吹毛求疵 –**nit-picking** adj

ni·trate /ˈnaɪtreɪt; ˈnaɪtreɪt/ n [C;U] a chemical used to improve soil in order to grow crops 硝酸鹽類化肥

ni·tric ac·id /ˌnaɪtrɪk ˈæsɪd; ˌnaɪtrɪk ˈæsɪd/ n

[U] a powerful acid which eats away other substances and is used in explosives and other chemical products 硝酸

ni·tro·gen /ˈnaɪtrədʒən; ˈnaɪtrədʒən/ *n* [U] a gas that has no colour or smell, and which forms most of the earth's air 氮(氣)

ni·tro·gly·ce·rine /ˌnaɪtrəˈglɪsrɪn; ˌnaɪtrəʊ-ˈglɪsərɪn/ *n* [U] (also 又作 **nitroglycerin**) a powerful liquid explosive 硝化甘油〔一種強力液體炸藥〕

nit·wit /ˈnɪt.wɪt; ˈnɪt-wɪt/ *n infml* a silly foolish person〔非正式〕傻瓜；笨蛋

☆**no**¹ /nɒ; noʊ/ *det, adv* **1** used to show that you disagree with someone or something, or refuse to do something 不；不是〔用於表示不同意某人、某事，或拒絕做某事〕: *"Is it raining?" "No, but it's quite cold."* "在下雨嗎？""沒下，不過很冷。" | *"She's got a new job, I think." "No, she hasn't."* "我認為她找到了一份新的工作。""不，沒有。" | *"Would you like a cup of tea?" "No, thanks."* "你想喝一杯茶嗎？""不，謝謝。" | *"Can I have a word with you?" "No, not at the moment."* "我可以跟你説句話嗎？""不，現在不行。" **2** used to show that something is not allowed 不准〔用於表示某事被禁止〕: *No Smoking* 禁止吸煙 **3** not any 沒有；無: *There's no sugar in the bowl.* 缽裡沒有食糖。 | *There's no reason for you to worry.* 你毫無理由擔心。–see 見 SOME (USAGE 用法) **4** oh no a phrase used to show disappointment 啊呀不好〔用於表示失望〕

■ USAGE 用法: Compare 比較 **no** and 和 **not**. You can use **no** where the meaning is "not any" ☆**no** 可用於表示"無；非"的意思: **no** *smoking* 不准吸煙 | **no** *children* 沒有孩子 | **no** *good* 沒好處。For other meanings use **not** ☆ 用於表示其他意義: *I'm* **not** *coming.* 我不來了。 | **not** *a chance* 沒有機會 | *She's* **not** *stupid.* 她並不笨。

no² *n* a decision or an answer that says "no" 否定；拒絕: *The answer was a definite no.* 回答無疑是否定的。

no. nos. an abbreviation for〔縮〕= NUMBER

no·bil·i·ty /nəʊˈbɪləti; nəʊˈbɪləti/ *n* **1 the nobility** the group of people in certain countries of the highest social class who have titles such as DUKE and EARL 貴族(階層) **2** [U] grandness and high moral qualities 高貴；崇高；高尚

no·ble¹ /ˈnɒbl; ˈnəʊbəl/ *adj* **1** deserving praise and admiration because of unselfishness, honesty, and high morals 高尚的；崇高的: *noble and generous feelings* 高尚豪爽的情懷 **2** admirable in appearance 宏偉的；堂皇的: *a noble monument* 宏偉的紀念碑 **3** of or belonging to a high social rank which has a title 貴族的；貴族出身的: *a woman of noble birth* 貴族出身的女子

noble² *n old fash* a person of the highest social class〔老式〕貴族(成員)

no·ble·man /ˈnɒblmən; ˈnəʊbəlmən/ *n* **noblemen** /-mən; -mən/ a titled man born into the highest social class; a woman in this social class or the wife of a nobleman is called a **noblewoman** 出身高貴的人；貴族階層的人〔女性稱為 noblewoman〕

no·bly /ˈnɒbli; ˈnəʊbli/ *adv* generously and unselfishly 慷慨無私地；高尚地: *She nobly did my work as well as hers while I was ill.* 在我生病期間，她不僅做好自己的工作，而且還無私地承擔了我的工作。

☆**no·bod·y**¹ /ˈnɒˌbɒdi; ˈnəʊbədi/ *pron* (also 又作 **no one**) no person at all 沒有人: *There's nobody here at the moment.* 這兒現在沒有人。 | *No one knew anything about it.* 此事無人知曉。 | *I spoke to Jane, but to nobody else.* 我找簡談了，但沒對別人説。

nobody² *n* **nobodies** someone who is not at all important 無足輕重的人；小人物: *I don't want to be a nobody all my life.* 我不想一輩子都默默無聞。

noc·tur·nal /nɒkˈtɜːnəl; nɒkˈtɜːnl/ *adj* **1** happening at night 夜間發生的: *a nocturnal visit* 夜訪 **2** active at night 夜間活動的: *a nocturnal bird* 夜間活動的鳥 –**nocturnally** *adv*

☆**nod** /nɒd; nɒd/ *v* -**dd**- **1** [I;T] to move your head forward and down and then up again to show agreement or give a greeting 點頭〔表示同意或打招呼〕: *She nodded her head when she passed me in the street.* 她在街上和我身邊走過時向我點了點頭。 | *I asked her if she was ready to go and she nodded.* 我問她是否願意去，她點點頭。 | *They all nodded in agreement.* 他們都點頭表示同意。 **2** [I;T] to show something or give a signal by nodding 點頭示意: *"Give it to him," she said, nodding towards the boy.* "把這個給他，"她邊説邊朝那男孩點頭示意。 **3** [I] to move gently up and down 晃動；擺動: *The flowers nodded in the wind.* 花兒在風中擺動。

nod off *phr v* [I] to fall asleep, often unintentionally 打盹；打瞌睡: *The meeting was so boring I nodded off.* 會議實在枯燥無味，我不知不覺睡着了。 –**nod** *n*: *He greeted us with a nod.* 他點頭向我們打招呼。

nod·ule /ˈnɒdʒʊl; ˈnɒdʒuːl/ *n* a small hard lump or swelling 小圓塊；小瘤

No·el /nəʊˈɛl; nəʊˈɛl/ *n lit* Christmas〔文〕聖誕節

no-go ar·e·a /ˌ· ˈ· ···/ *n infml* an area controlled by a group of people who make it dangerous for anyone else to enter〔非正式〕禁區

☆**noise** /nɔɪz; nɔɪz/ *n* **1** [C;U] a sound, often unwanted, unpleasant, or confused 喧鬧聲；嘈雜聲；噪聲: *Try not to make a noise when you go upstairs — the baby's asleep.* 上樓時盡量別弄出聲，孩子在睡覺。 | *There's so much noise in this restaurant I can hardly* *hear you talking.* 這家餐廳裡太嘈雜了，我幾乎聽不見你説話。| *Seals make a very unusual noise.* 海豹會發出與眾不同的聲音。| *The washing machine's been making funny noises lately.* 最近洗衣機一直發出奇怪的雜音。**2 make a noise about something** to complain about something 埋怨某事物: *She was making a lot of noise about the lack of child care facilities.* 她為缺乏用於照料兒童的設施而大發牢騷。**3 make all the right noises** to say things which suggest that you are interested, although sometimes you are not 隨聲附和；故作踴躍: *She made all the right noises about helping us, but I know she's too lazy to do anything.* 她雖然口口聲聲説要幫助我們，但我知道她太懶，不會有行動。**4 make noises** *infml* to say something which indirectly shows your ideas or feelings 〔非正式〕口頭上表示〔看法或情態〕: *My teacher made encouraging noises when I said I wanted to go to university.* 我説我想上大學時，我的老師連聲鼓勵。

■ USAGE 用法: Compare 比較 **sound, noise, voice. Sound** is the general word for anything you hear ☆ **sound** 一般表示能聽見的任何聲音: *the sound of voices/of music/of breaking glass* 説話聲/音樂聲/打碎玻璃的聲音。**A noise** is usually a loud, unpleasant sound ☆ **noise** 常指響亮、令人不快的聲音: *Stop making so much* **noise**! 別發出那麼多噪音! **A voice** is the sound of a person speaking or singing ☆**voice** 是指人的説話聲或歌聲: *He spoke in a loud* **voice.** 他大聲地説話。

---

noise·less /ˈnɔɪzlɪs; ˈnɔɪzləs/ *adj* making no sound 無聲的；寂靜的: *The car was smooth and noiseless.* 汽車開得既平穩又無噪音。– **noiselessly** *adv*

nois·y /ˈnɔɪzɪ; ˈnɔɪzi/ *adj* **noisier, noisiest** making a lot of noise 嘈雜的；喧鬧的: *a noisy car* 噪響大的汽車 | *It's very noisy in this office.* 這間辦公室裡很嘈雜。| *This is a very noisy pub.* 這是一家十分喧鬧的酒吧。| *a noisy group of tourists* 一羣吵吵嚷嚷的觀光客 –**noisily** *adv* –**noisiness** *n* [U]

no·mad /ˈnoʊmæd; ˈnəʊmæd/ *n* a member of a tribe which does not live in one place but travels about, usually to find grass for its animals 遊牧民中的一員

no·mad·ic /noʊˈmædɪk; nəʊˈmædɪk/ *adj* not living in one fixed place, but moving from place to place 流浪的；遊牧生活的: *nomadic tribes* 遊牧部落 | *a nomadic way of life* 到處流浪的生活方式 –**nomadically** *adv*

no-man's-land /ˈ·· ·,·/ *n* [sing; U] the area of land which no one owns or controls between two borders or two opposing armies 〔兩條邊界間或敵對陣地之間的〕真空地帶；無人地帶

nom de plume /ˈnɑm də ˌplum; ˌnɒm də-ˈpluːm/ *n* **noms de plume** (*same pronunciation* 發音相同) a name a writer uses instead of their real name 筆名

no·men·cla·ture /ˈnoʊmən,kleɪtʃə; nəʊˈmenkləʊtʃər/ *n* [C;U] *fml* a system of naming things, especially in science 〔正式〕〔尤指科學上的〕命名法: *the nomenclature* **of** *chemical compounds* 化合物命名法

nom·i·nal /ˈnɑmənl̩; ˈnɒmɪnəl/ *adj* **1** in name or position but usually not in reality 名義上的；有名無實的: *The old man is only the nominal head of the business; his daughter makes all the decisions.* 那老人只是這家企業名義上的負責人，一切事情都由他的女兒決定。**2** very small (used of an amount of money) 很小的；微不足道的〔指金額〕: *The rent for the cottage is nominal.* 這小屋的租金很便宜。–**nominally** *adv*

nom·i·nate /ˈnɑmə,neɪt; ˈnɒmɪ,neɪt/ *v* **nominated, nominating** [T] **1** to suggest or name someone formally for election to a position, office, or honour 提名: *I wish to nominate Jane Morrison* **for** *president of the club.* 我想提名簡·莫里森為俱樂部主席。| *I nominate Susan to represent us.* 我提議蘇珊作為我們的代表。

□ USEFUL PATTERNS 有用句型
to nominate someone for something; to nominate someone to do something

---

2 to appoint someone to a position, office, or duty 任命；指定: *The director nominated me* **as** *his representative at the conference.* 那位董事指定我代表他出席會議。

nom·i·na·tion /ˌnɑməˈneɪʃən; ˌnɒmɪˈneɪʃən/ *n* [C;U] **1** the formal suggestion that someone is appointed to a position 提名: *His nomination* **as** *chief executive was approved by the board.* 他被提名為行政裁一事已被董事會批准。**2** someone's official appointment to a position 任命；指定: *He was delighted by his nomination* **to** *the committee.* 他對被任命為委員會成員而感到高興。

nom·i·na·tive /ˈnɑmənətɪv; ˈnɒmɪnətɪv/ *n* *tech* a particular form of a noun in certain languages, such as Latin, Greek, and German, which shows that a noun is the subject of a verb 〔術語〕主格〔指在拉丁、希臘和德語等某些語言中，名詞為動詞的主語〕 –**nominative** *adj*

nom·i·nee /ˌnɑməˈni; ˌnɒmɪˈniː/ *n* a person who has been formally suggested for a position or honour 被提名者

non-ag·gres·sion /ˌnɑnəˈgrɛʃən; ˌnɒn-əˈɡreʃən/ *n* [U] the idea that countries should not attack or fight each other 互不侵犯；不侵略: *a non-aggression pact* 互不侵犯條約

non-al·co·hol·ic /ˌ· ··ˈ·· ·/ *adj* containing no alcohol 不含酒精的: *non-alcoholic beer*

不含酒精的啤酒

non-a·ligned /ˌ· ·ˈ·ˌ/ adj not dependent on or supporting any particular powerful country or group of countries 〔國家〕不結盟的 **–non-alignment** n [U]

non·cha·lant /ˈnɑnʃələnt; ˈnɒnʃələnt/ adj showing calmness, lack of anxiety, and often lack of interest 若無其事的；漠不關心的；冷淡的: He showed a nonchalant attitude to his debts. 他對自己的債務顯得滿不在乎的樣子。**–nonchalance** n [U]: She showed a surprising nonchalance when she was awarded the trophy. 她在接受頒獎時表現出驚人的冷靜。**–nonchalantly** adv

non-com·ba·tant /ˌnɑnˈkɑmbətənt; ˌnɒn-ˈkɒmbətənt/ n someone in the armed forces who does not take part in actual fighting, for example a doctor 非戰鬥人員〔如軍醫〕

non-com·mis·sioned of·fi·cer /ˌnɑnkəˈmɪʃənd ˈɔfɪsɚ; ˌnɑnkəˌmɪʃənd ˈɒfɪsəˈ/ n (also 又作 **NCO**) a member of the armed forces who has some responsibility to command others 軍士

non·com·mit·tal /ˌnɑnkəˈmɪtl̩; ˌnɒnkəˈmɪtl̩ˌ/ adj not expressing a clear opinion or intention 〔觀點〕不明朗的；〔意圖〕不明確的: I asked him if he approved of our plan, but he was noncommittal. 我問他是否贊同我們的計劃，但他態度不明朗。**–noncommittally** adv

non·con·form·ist /ˌnɑnkənˈfɔrmɪst; ˌnɒn-kənˈfɔːm̩st ˈ/ n **1** someone who does not follow generally accepted ways of living, acting, or thinking 〔思想、行動或生活方式〕不遵照準則或規範的人: a political nonconformist 政治上不落俗套的人 | nonconformist views 不合常理的觀點 **2** **Nonconformist** a member of one of the Christian religious groups which have separated from the CHURCH OF ENGLAND 不信奉英國國教的教徒: a Nonconformist minister 不信奉國教的牧師 **–nonconformist** adj **–nonconformity, nonconformism** n [U]

non·de·script /ˈnɑndɪˌskrɪpt; ˈnɒndɪˌskrɪpt/ adj without any noticeable or interesting qualities 無明顯特徵的；平凡無奇的: Her clothes were so nondescript that I can't remember what she was wearing. 她的衣服平平常常，所以我記不得她穿的是甚麼。

★**none** /nʌn; nʌn/ pron, adv **1** not any 沒有任何東西；沒有一人: None of the money is mine. 這錢沒有一分是我的。 | None of these subjects interests me. 這些科目中沒有一個使我感興趣。 | None of my friends are going to university. 我的朋友中沒有一個打算上大學。 | Even an old car is better than none at all. 即使是輛舊汽車也總比沒有車好。 **2** **none but** fml only 〔正式〕只有 **3** **none other than** a phrase used to show that you are surprised that it is the person mentioned 不是別人而正是〔表示驚訝〕: I opened the door, and it was none other than Tom Robinson! 我打開

了門，來者不是別人而正是湯姆·羅賓遜！ **4** **none the** not at all 一點也不；毫不: He's got plenty of money now, but he seems none the happier for it. 他現在很有錢，但他似乎仍然一點也不幸福。 **5** **none too** not very 不很；不太: She came out of the meeting looking none too pleased. 她開完會出來的樣子不太高興。

■ USAGE 用法: When **none of** is followed by a plural noun it usually takes a plural verb in informal spoken English ☆在非正式的口語體英語中，當 **none of** 後面緊跟名詞的複數形式時，動詞通常用複數形式: None of us are ready yet. 我們中間尚無一人準備就緒。Some people, however, consider this to be incorrect and so in formal writing it is safer to use a singular verb ☆但有些人把這看作是錯誤的用法，因此在正式文體中，用單數形式的動詞比較穩妥: None of our factories is in operation yet. 我們的工廠尚無一家開工。

non·en·ti·ty /nɑnˈɛntəti; nɒˈnentɨti/ n **nonentities** someone without much ability, character, or importance 無能力〔個性〕的人；無足輕重的人: a weak government, full of politicians who are nonentities 一個無能政客充斥其中的軟弱政府

none·the·less /ˌnʌnðəˈlɛs; ˌnʌnðəˈlesˈ/ adv in spite of what someone has just said 儘管如此；不過: The government has introduced strict economic controls, but inflation has continued to rise nonetheless. 政府採用了嚴格的經濟掌控手段，但儘管如此，物價還在繼續上漲。 | Profits have not been as good lately. Nonetheless, Regis are hoping to expand. 利潤最近一直不理想，不過，里吉斯仍然有望得到發展。

non-e·vent /ˌ· ·ˈ·ˌ/ n infml something that is much less important, interesting, or exciting than expected 〔非正式〕遠不如所預期那樣重大、有趣或激動人心的事: The party was a real non-event; only three people came. 這個聚會真是擺擺樣子，只來了三個人。

non-ex·ist·ent /ˌnɑnɪgˈzɪstənt; ˌnɒnɪgˈzɪs-təntˈ/ adj not existing 不存在的；沒有的: This year's profits were very small; in fact, almost non-existent. 今年的利潤很薄，事實上幾乎沒有。

non-fic·tion /nɑnˈfɪkʃən; nɒnˈfɪkʃən/ n [U] writing that is about real facts or events, rather than the imagined things in poetry, plays, and stories 非小說類的寫實文學

non-flam·ma·ble /nɑnˈflæməbl̩; nɒnˈflæ-məbəl/ adj difficult or impossible to burn 不易燃的；不燃燒的

non-in·ter·ven·tion /ˌnɑnɪntɚˈvɛnʃən; ˌnɒn-ɪntəˈvenʃən/ n [U] the practice, especially by a government, of taking no part in the affairs or arguments of another person or country 不干涉〔尤指別國內政〕

non·nu·cle·ar /ˌ· ·····◂/ *adj* not using NU-CLEAR power or ENERGY 不使用核動力或核原子能的: *non-nuclear weapons* 常規武器

no-non·sense /ˌ· ·····◂/ *adj* practical and direct 實際的; 直截了當的: *a no-nonsense approach to the problem* 對問題直截了當的處理方法

non-pay·ment /nɑnˈpeɪmənt; ˌnɒnˈpeɪmənt/ *n* [U] failure to pay bills, tax, or a debt 未能支付〔賬單、稅款或債務〕: *They were taken to court for non-payment of rent.* 他們因不付租金而被起訴。

non·plussed /nɑnˈplʌst; ˌnɒnˈplʌst/ *adj* surprised and uncertain what to think or do 吃驚的; 不知所措的: *The speaker seemed completely nonplussed by my question.* 演說者似乎完全被我提出的問題所難倒。

non-pro·lif·e·ra·tion /ˌnɑnprəˈlɪfəˈreʃən; ˌnɒnprəˌlɪfəˈreɪʃən/ *n* [U] the limitation of the number and spread of NUCLEAR and chemical weapons 限止〔防止〕核武器和化學武器擴散: *a non-proliferation agreement* 防止核武器擴散協定

non·sense /ˈnɑnsɛns; ˈnɒnsəns/ *n* [U] **1** speech and writing with no meaning 無意義的話和文章: *If you leave out this paragraph, the report is nonsense.* 如果你省略這個段落, 這份報告就失去意義。| *You're talking utter nonsense.* 你是在胡說八道。**2** a word you use when you think that someone is saying something silly and untrue 愚蠢的話; 荒謬的話: "*I can't go out dressed like this.*" "*Nonsense, you look fine.*" "我不能穿這套衣服出去。""胡說, 你穿這身衣服顯得很好看。" **3** foolish behaviour 愚蠢的舉動: *Stop that nonsense, children.* 別胡鬧了, 孩子們。| *A strict teacher stands no nonsense from the pupils.* 嚴格的老師不容學生瞎胡鬧。**4 make nonsense of, make a nonsense of** to make something seem pointless and useless 使〔某事物〕顯得無意義或無用: *Remarks like that make nonsense of his claim that he is unbiased.* 那些話使他不帶偏見的自我表白失去意義。

non·sen·si·cal /nɑnˈsɛnsɪkl; nɒnˈsensˌkəl/ *adj* stupid or full of nonsense 愚蠢的; 荒謬的: *nonsensical opinions* 荒謬的意見 **–nonsensically** /-klɪ; -klɪ/ *adv*

non seq·ui·tur /nɑnˈsɛkwɪtə; ˌnɒn ˈsekwɪtər/ *n fml* a statement which does not follow from the facts or arguments which have gone before 〔正式〕前後不連貫的陳述; 不根據前提的推論

non-smok·er /ˌ· ···/ *n* someone who does not smoke 不抽煙的人 **–non-smoking** *adj*: *the non-smoking section on the plane* 禁止抽煙的飛機艙艙

non-stan·dard /nɑnˈstændəd; ˌnɒnˈstændəd/ *adj* not usually regarded as correct by educated native speakers of a language (used of words, expressions, pronunciations) 不標準的; 不規範的〔指詞彙、詞組、發音等〕

non·start·er /ˌnɑnˈstɑrtə; ˌnɒnˈstɑːtər/ *n infml* a plan or idea without any chance of success 〔非正式〕無成功希望的計劃或想法: *The idea of buying a house was a non-starter, as we didn't have enough money.* 買房子的想法不切實際, 因為我們沒有足夠的錢。

non-stick /ˌnɑnˈstɪk; ˌnɒnˈstɪk◂/ *adj* having a specially treated smooth inside surface that food will not stick to 不黏食物的: *a non-stick frying pan* 不黏底平底煎鍋

non-stop /ˌnɑnˈstɑp; ˌnɒnˈstɒp◂/ *adj, adv* without a pause or interruption 不停的〔地〕; 直達的〔地〕: *The flight from London to Singapore is non-stop.* 從倫敦到新加坡的班機是直達的。| *We worked non-stop for three days.* 我們連續工作了三天。

non-vi·o·lence /nɑnˈvaɪələns; ˌnɒnˈvaɪələns/ *n* [U] attempts to make political changes without using violence or hurting anyone 非暴力〔政治改革運動〕 **–non-violent** *adj*: *non-violent protest* 非暴力抗議 **–non-violently** *adv*

noo·dle /ˈnudl; ˈnuːdl/ *n* noodles long thin pieces of a paste made from flour, water, and eggs; the pieces are boiled until soft and eaten in soups, or with meat 麵條

nook /nʊk; nʊk/ *n* **1** *lit* a sheltered and private place 〔文〕隱蔽處: *a shady nook in the garden* 花園裡的陰涼隱蔽處 **2 every nook and cranny** every part of a place 〔某地的〕每一個角落

noon /nun; nuːn/ *n* 12 o'clock in the middle of the day 中午; 正午: *We left home at noon.* 我們中午離開了家。| *I can't come before noon.* 我中午以前來不了。

noon·day /ˈnun,de; ˈnuːndeɪ/ *n* old fash in the middle of the day 〔老式〕中午: *the noonday sun* 中午的太陽

★**no one** /ˈ· ·/ *pron* see 見 NOBODY

noose /nus; nuːs/ *n* a circle formed by the end of a cord or rope which closes more tightly as it is pulled 活繩結; 套索

nor /nɔr; nɔːʳ/ *conj* used in negative expressions when you are giving the second thing that is not true 也不; 也沒有〔用於否定後者〕: *He neither smokes nor drinks.* 他既不抽煙也不喝酒。| *I was neither shocked nor upset.* 我既不感到震驚也不心煩。| *I spoke to neither my father nor my mother.* 我既不跟父親說話也不跟母親說話。| *I wasn't pleased about what had happened, and nor was anyone else.* 我對所發生的事情很不滿意, 其他人也不滿意。| "*I can't swim.*" "*Nor can I.*" "我不會游泳。" "我也不會。"

norm /nɔrm; nɔːm/ *n* **1 norms** [pl] ways of behaving that are regarded as usual or generally acceptable 準則; 規範: *social norms* 社會準則 | *the norms of civilised society* 文明社會的準則 **2 the norm** a situation that is regarded as average or usual 平均或

一般的狀況; 標準: *Large families are no longer the norm in Western Europe.* 大家庭在西歐不再是常見模式。| *a pay increase well below the national norm* 大大低於國家標準的加薪

nor·mal /ˈnɔrml; ˈnɔːməl/ *adj* expected, usual, or average 正常的; 通常的; 平均的: *normal working hours from nine to five* 從九點到五點的正常工作時間 | *Rainfall has been above normal this July.* 今年七月份降雨量超過平均值。| *She is a normal child in every way.* 她是個各方面都正常的孩子。

nor·mal·i·ty /nɔrˈmælətɪ; nɔːˈmælɪ̩ti/ (also 又作 **normalcy** /ˈnɔrmlsɪ; ˈnɔːməlsi/ *AmE* 【美式】) *n* [U] a situation where everything is usual and as expected 正常狀態

nor·mal·ize /ˈnɔrml̩aɪz; ˈnɔːməlaɪz/ *v* **normalized, normalizing** (also 又作 **normalise** *BrE* 【英式】) [I;T] to return something to a good or friendly state (使)〔某事物〕恢復正常或友好狀態: *Relations between the two countries were slow to normalize after the war.* 戰後兩國關係的正常化恢復緩慢。| *You can normalize the situation by remaining calm.* 你保持冷靜就可以使局面恢復正常。 – **normalization** /ˌnɔrmlɪˈzeʃən; ˌnɔːməlaɪˈzeɪʃən/ *n* [U]

nor·mal·ly /ˈnɔrmlɪ; ˈnɔːməli/ *adv* **1** in the usual or expected way 正常地: *The factory is running normally again.* 工廠又在正常運作。 **2** usually 通常地: *I normally go to bed early, but I stayed up late last night.* 我通常很早睡覺, 但昨晚我睡得很晚。

north[1] /nɔrθ; nɔːθ/ *n* [U] the direction to the left of someone facing the rising sun 北; 北方: *I'm lost: which direction is north?* 我迷路了: 哪個方向是北方? | *Cheshunt is a few kilometres to the north of London.* 切森特位於倫敦北面幾公里處。 **2 the North** the northern part of a country〔國家的〕北部(地區): *The problem of unemployment is much worse in the North than in the South.* 北部的失業問題比南部更為嚴重。

north[2] *adj* **1** (also 又作 **North**) in the north or facing the north 在北方的; 面朝北的: *The north side of the house doesn't get much sun.* 房子的北面很少曬到太陽。| *He lives in North Korea.* 他住在北韓。 **2 north wind** a wind coming from the north 北風

north[3] *adv* (also 又作 **North**) **1** towards the north 向北方: *The room faces North, so it's always rather cold.* 房間朝北, 所以總是很冷。| *Edinburgh is a long way north of London.* 愛丁堡在倫敦以北很遠的地方。| *Birds fly north in summer.* 鳥在夏季飛向北方。 **2** from the north (used of a wind) 自北方〔指風〕

north·bound /ˈnɔrθˌbaʊnd; ˈnɔːθbaʊnd/ *adj* travelling towards the north 向北行的: *northbound traffic* 北行的車輛

north·east[1] /ˌnɔrθˈist; ˌnɔːθˈiːst/ (also 又作

Northeast) *n* **1** [sing;U] the direction which is half-way between north and east 東北; 東方 **2 the northeast** the northeastern part of a country〔國家的〕東北部(地區): *Houses are cheaper in the northeast.* 東北地區的房屋比較便宜。

northeast[2] *adj* [only before a noun 只用於名詞前] **1** in the northeastern part of something 在東北部的: *the northeast gate of the park* 公園的東北大門 **2 northeast wind** a wind coming from the northeast 東北風 – **northeasterly** *adj*

northeast[3] *adv* towards the northeast 向東北: *The ship sailed northeast.* 輪船向東北航行。

north-east·ern /ˌnɔrθˈistən; ˌnɔːθˈiːstən/ *adj* in or from the northeast part, especially of a country 在東北的; 來自東北的〔尤指國家〕

nor·ther·ly /ˈnɔrðəlɪ; ˈnɔːðəli/ *adj* **1** towards the north 向北的: *in a northerly direction* 朝北方向 **2** from the north (used of a wind) 來自北方〔指風〕

nor·thern /ˈnɔrðən; ˈnɔːðən/ *adj* (also 又作 **Northern**) of or in the north part of an area 北部的; 在北方的: *The northern half of the Earth is called the Northern hemisphere.* 地球的北半部稱為北半球。

nor·thern·most /ˈnɔrðən̩most; ˈnɔːðənməʊst/ *adj* furthest north 最北端的; 極北的: *the northernmost parts of Scotland* 蘇格蘭的最北部

North Pole /ˌ · ˈ ·/ *n* **the north pole** the most northern point on the surface of the earth 北極

north·ward /ˈnɔrθwəd; ˈnɔːθwəd/ *adj* going towards the north 向北的: *a northward journey* 向北的旅行 – **northwards** (also 又作 **northward** *AmE*【美式】) *adv*: *We sailed northwards.* 我們向北航行。

north·west[1] /ˌnɔrθˈwest; ˌnɔːθˈwest/ (also 又作 **Northwest**) *n* **1** [sing;U] the direction which is halfway between north and west 西北; 西北方 **2 the northwest** the northwestern part of a country〔國家的〕西北部(地區) – **northwesterly** *adj*

northwest[2] *adj* [only before a noun 只用於名詞前] **1** in the northwestern part of something 在西北的, 西北部的: *the northwest tower of the castle* 城堡的西北塔 **2 northwest wind** a wind coming from the northwest 西北風

northwest[3] *adv* towards the northwest 向西北: *Birmingham is northwest of London.* 伯明翰位於倫敦西北面。

north·west·ern /ˌnɔrθˈwestən; nɔːθˈwestən/ *adj* in or from the northwest part, especially of a country 在西北部的; 來自西北部的〔尤指國家〕

nose[1] /noz; nəʊz/ *n* **1** the part of your face above your mouth through which you smell and breathe 鼻子: *He's got a broken* nose. 他的鼻子破相了。| *She punched him on the nose.* 她一拳打在他的鼻子上。**2** the front part of something that sticks out, for example a car or plane 前端突出部分〔如車頭或機首〕**3 a nose for something** a special ability to find or recognize something 對某事物的嗅覺; 覺察力: *A newspaper reporter must have a nose for a good story.* 新聞記者對好的報道題材必須具有特殊的覺察力。**4 stick/poke your nose into** to show too great an interest in things which do not concern you 對〔自己無關的事〕過於感興趣; 探問: *Stop poking your nose into other people's affairs.* 別管別人的閒事。**5 get up someone's nose** *BrE infml* to annoy someone very much 〔英式, 非正式〕惹某人發火; 使某人惱怒 **6 keep your nose to the grindstone** to continue with hard and dull work 〔非正式〕一刻不停地做勞累單調的活 **7 turn up your nose at something** *infml* to consider something not good, interesting, or important enough for you 〔非正式〕不把某事放在眼裡; 蔑視; 嗤之以鼻 **8 under someone's nose** *infml* right in front of someone 〔非正式〕就在某人面前; 當着某人的面: *He passed me the note under the very nose of the examiner!* 他竟當着主考人的面把紙條傳給了我! **9 -nosed** having a certain shape of nose 有〔某種形態〕鼻子的: *red-nosed* 紅鼻子的 | *broken-nosed* 塌鼻樑的 | *snub-nosed* 獅子鼻的

nose² *v* **nosed, nosing** [I+adv/prep; T+adv/prep] to move or push ahead slowly or carefully 緩慢小心地前進: *I nosed the car*

out into the traffic. 我緩緩把汽車開出來駛入車流之中。| *The ship nosed along the narrow channel.* 輪船小心翼翼地沿着狹窄的海峽航行。| *The plane nosed its way down the runway.* 飛機沿着跑道緩緩行駛。

nose about/around *phr v* [I] *infml* to look at things which do not belong to you for something of interest 〔非正式〕〔在他人的物品中〕搜尋: *I found her nosing about among my private papers.* 我發現她在我的私人文件中尋找東西。

nose·bag /ˈnozˌbæg; ˈnəʊzbæg/ *n* a bag hung around a horse's head to hold its food 〔掛在馬頸上的〕飼料袋

nose·bleed /ˈnozˌblid; ˈnəʊzbliːd/ *n* bleeding from the nose 鼻出血: *James had a nosebleed earlier today after Simon hit him.* 詹姆斯給西蒙打了以後, 在今天早些時候流鼻血。

nose·dive /ˈnozˌdaɪv; ˈnəʊzdaɪv/ *v* **nose-dived, nosediving** [I] **1** (of an aircraft) to drop suddenly with the nose pointing straight down 〔飛機〕俯衝 **2** (of prices and money) to go down a lot suddenly 〔價格等〕突降; 猛跌: *Profits have nosedived in the last year.* 去年的利潤急劇下降。 **–nosedive** *n*

nosh /nɒʃ; nɒʃ/ *n* *BrE infml* [U] food 〔英式, 非正式〕食物: *Let's have some nosh before the film starts.* 電影開映前我們吃點東西吧。

nos·tal·gia /nɒˈstældʒɪə; nɒˈstældʒə/ *n* [U] a feeling of fondness and sadness for the past 戀舊; 懷舊: *The old song filled me with nostalgia.* 那首老歌使我心中充滿懷舊之情。 **–nostalgic** *adj* **–nostalgically** /-klɪ; -klɪ/ *adv*

THE OFFICE 辦公室

Exercise 1 練習一

Match the words in the box to the descriptions. Write the number of the description beside the correct word. 把方框中的詞與各描述配對起來。將各描述的號碼寫在對應單詞的旁邊。

- ☐ calculator
- ☐ disk drive
- ☐ fax machine
- ☐ photocopier
- ☐ printer
- ☐ waste paper basket
- ☐ V. D. U
- ☐ answering machine
- ☐ pencil sharpener
- ☐ stapler

1 A machine which records telephone messages.
2 A machine which sends copies of documents along telephone lines.
3 A container for paper which you don't need.
4 A machine which copies documents.
5 A machine for passing information to and from a computer.

6 A small machine which can perform calculations.
7 A small machine which uses short pieces of metal wire to join papers together.
8 A machine which prints information from a computer onto paper.
9 A machine which cuts away the wooden part of a pencil.
10 A machine with a screen which shows information from a computer.

Exercise 2 練習二

Can you explain the difference between these things? Look up the words in the dictionary if you don't know. 你能分辨出下列的物品嗎? 如果不能, 請在詞典中查一下。

1 calendar / diary
2 floppy disk / hard disk
3 paper clips / staples

calendar
月曆

noticeboard (BrE【英式】)/
bulletin board (AmE【美式】)
佈告欄

diary
(BrE【英式】)/
desk calendar
(AmE【美式】)
記事簿

pencil
sharpener
削鉛筆器

filing trays
文件盤

pencil
鉛筆

lamp
燈

rsonal
mputer
人電腦

window
視窗

printer
打印機

desk
辦公桌

printout
電腦印出的資料

typewriter
打字機

mouse
鼠標器，
滑鼠

keyboard
鍵盤

index cards
索引卡

hard disk
硬磁盤

disk drive
磁盤驅動器，
磁碟機

floppy disk
軟磁盤

calculator
計算機

(ring) binder
(環圈式)活頁封套

photocopier
複印機

word processor
文字處理機

screen
屏幕

fax machine
傳真機

v.d.u
圖像文字
顯示屏

telephone
電話

answering
machine
電話答錄機

secretary
祕書

shorthand pad
速記簿

fax
傳真

pen
鋼筆

filing cabinet
檔案櫃

pler
書機

(typist's) chair
(打字員的)椅子

paper clips
曲別針

waste-paper basket/
bin (BrE【英式】)
廢紙簍

file(s)
文件；檔案

staples
釘書釘

IBRARY
SUPERMARKET
NEWSAGENT
BAN
SAVE
SAVE
SAVE
SAVE
1
2
3
4
5
6
7
8
9
10
11
12
13
14
15
16
17
19
20
21
22
23
24
25

PREPOSITIONS 介詞

In the picture opposite the following prepositions are shown by the numbers.

在左頁的彩圖中，下列的介詞用數字表示了出來。

1 ... (going) **down** the steps
2 ... (climbing) **up** the ladder
3 ... **beside/next to** the ladder
4 ... **outside** the supermarket
5 ... **over/above** the doorway
6 ... (going) **into** the supermarket
7 ... (coming) **out of** the supermarket
8 ... (going) **through** the doorway
9 ... **between** the bank and the supermarket
10 ... (walking) **past** the newsagent's
11 ... (leaning) **against** the wall, **below/under** the sign
12 ... (standing) **by/near** the bank
13 ... **on** the motorbike
14 ... **behind** the car

15 ... **at** the crossing
16 ... (walking) **across** the road, **in front of** the car, **towards/in the direction of** the bank
17 ... (pointing) **to/at** the car
18 ... **inside/on** the bus, (looking) **through** the window
19 ... (getting) **off** the bus
20 ... (getting) **on/onto** the bus
21 ... **opposite** the bank
22 ... (walking) **away from** the bus stop
23 ... (dancing) **round** the flowerbed
24 ... (walking) **along** the pavement, **to** the bus stop
25 ... **in** the car

Choose the correct preposition or phrase in this passage.

請在下文中選出正確的介詞或詞組。

Mrs Macdonald walked **1** towards / into the railway station and went **2** near / into the ticket office, where she bought a ticket to Brighton. **3** Under / Outside her arm she carried a box, **4** inside / into which was her cat, Cleopatra. She walked **5** out of / towards the ticket office **6** to / through the newsagent where she bought a newspaper to read **7** on / on to the train. Mrs Macdonald showed her tickets to the inspector at the barrier and then she walked **8** along / beside the platform looking for a first class non-smoking compartment. She found one which was nearly empty. There was a man sitting **9** in / at the corner. Mrs Macdonald opened the door and got **10** in / into the compartment. She bent down and tried to put the box **11** under / down the seat but it was too big so she put it on the seat

12 between / beside her. Then she noticed that the man had a box on the seat **13** next to / behind him.

When the train arrived in Brighton station, Mrs Macdonald opened the box to make sure that her cat was safe. At the same moment, the man opened his box. A small dog jumped **14** out of / out the box! Mrs Macdonald's cat jumped **15** against / through the open window. The small dog tried to follow the cat but the man caught it before it got **16** out / outside the compartment. Mrs Macdonald opened the door and called to her cat. Slowly the cat came **17** towards / in the direction of her. "Come here, Cleopatra," she said "Don't be frightened." When the cat was **18** near / at her, Mrs Macdonald put her hand **19** under / down the cat's body and picked it up.

N

nos·tril /ˈnɑstrəl; ˈnɒstrɬl/ *n* one of two openings at the end of your nose, through which you breathe 鼻孔

nos·y /ˈnozɪ; ˈnəʊzɪ/ *adj* **nosier, nosiest** (also 又作 **nosey**) interested in things that do not concern you (a word used to express disapproval) 愛管閒事的; 愛打聽的〔含貶義〕: *Don't be so nosy.* 別多管閒事! – **nosiness** *n* [U]

not /nɑt; nɒt/ *adv* (also 又作 **n't** after verbs such as "be" and "have") **1** used for changing a word or expression to one with an opposite meaning 不; 沒; 不是〔用於將字或語句變成相反的意思〕: *I'm not thirsty.* 我不渴。| *It's a fox, not a dog.* 牠是狐狸, 不是狗。| *She said she wasn't frightened.* 她說她並不害怕。| *I'm afraid I'm not coming to the party.* 恐怕我不來參加派對了。| *I don't think that's very funny!* 我覺得那並不十分好笑! | *Not everyone likes this book.* 並不是每個人都喜歡這本書。| *"Is it going to rain?" "I hope not."* "會下雨嗎?" "希望不會。" **2 not** a not even one 連一個…也不〔也沒有〕: *Not a drop of rain has fallen this month.* 這個月連一滴雨也沒有下過。 **3 not that** a phrase used when you are adding something which means that what you said before is less important 並不是說…: *Where were you last night? Not that I care, of course.* 昨天晚上你在哪兒? 當然我並不在乎。–see 見 NO (USAGE 用法)

no·ta·ble¹ /ˈnotəbl̩; ˈnəʊtəbəl/ *adj* interesting, important, or excellent 顯著的; 重要的; 傑出的: *an area notable for its excellent climate* 以氣候宜人見稱的地區 | *Most of the directors are men. Miss Parker is a notable exception.* 大部分董事是男的, 帕克小姐明顯是個例外。–**notability** /ˌnotəˈbɪlətɪ; ˌnəʊtə-ˈbɪlɬti/ *n* [U]

notable² *n* a famous or important person 名人; 顯要人物

no·ta·bly /ˈnotəblɪ; ˈnəʊtəblɪ/ *adv* **1** especially or particularly 尤其; 特別: *A lot of people were absent, notably the vice-chairman.* 有很多人缺席, 特別是副主席也沒到場。 **2** noticeably 顯著地: *Prices are notably higher this year.* 今年的價格明顯上升。

no·ta·tion /noˈteʃən; nəʊˈteɪʃən/ *n* [C;U] a system of showing numbers or musical notes in writing by using signs 〔使用符號代表數目或樂譜的〕標誌法

notch¹ /nɑtʃ; nɒtʃ/ *n* **1** a V-shaped cut in a surface or edge V字形槽口: *He cut a notch in the stick with a sharp knife.* 他用一把利刀在手杖上刻了個V字形槽口。 **2** *infml* a degree or level on a scale 〔非正式〕程度; 等級: *He went up a notch or two in my estimation when he helped my father.* 他幫了我父親的忙, 使我對他的評價上升了一、二級。

notch² *v* [T] to make a notch in something 在〔某物〕上刻槽口

notch sthg ↔ **up** *phr v* [T] *infml* to reach

a total of 〔非正式〕達到…的總數: *The team notched up their third victory in a row.* 該隊在划船賽中贏得了第三場勝利。

note¹ /not; nəʊt/ *v* **noted, noting** [T; + that] *fml* to call attention to a particular fact 〔正式〕注意; 留意: *Please note that this bill must be paid within ten days.* 請注意這張賬單必須在十天之內付清。| *Note the way the writer uses the present tense for dramatic effect.* 要注意作者是如何使用現在式來取得戲劇性的效果。| *The report notes with approval the government's efforts to resolve this problem.* 這份報告以贊同的語氣説明了政府為解決這一問題所作的努力。

note sthg ↔ **down** *phr v* [T] to write something down as a record or reminder 記錄, 記下〔某事〕: *He noted down my new address.* 他記下了我的新地址。

note² *n* **1** [C] a written reminder of something 記錄; 筆記: *Make a note of how much money you spend.* 把你的開支記錄下來。| *You don't need to take notes. I'll give you a handout at the end.* 你們不用作筆記, 我最後會把講義發給大家。 **2** [C] additional information about something in a book given at the bottom of a page or at the end 註釋; 註解 **3** [C] a short informal letter 便條; 短箋: *I'll write her a note to thank her for dinner.* 我要寫封短信給她, 對她的宴請表示感謝。 **4** [C] a single musical sound of a particular length and degree of highness or lowness or the written sign for it 樂音; 音符: *I can't sing the high notes.* 我唱不了這些高音。 **5** [sing] the suggestion of a particular feeling 〔某種感情的〕口氣; 語氣; 聲調: *There was a note of anger in what he said.* 他的話中帶着怒氣。| *The report ended on an optimistic note.* 這份報告以樂觀的語氣結尾。 **6** [C] a piece of paper money 鈔票; 紙幣: *a £5 note* 一張五英鎊的鈔票 **7** of note *fml* 著名的; 顯要的: *She's a musician of great note.* 她是一位非常著名的音樂家。 **8 take note of something** to pay careful attention to something 注意某事物: *The committee took note of his objections.* 委員會注意到他反對的理由。

note·book /ˈnotbʊk; ˈnəʊtbʊk/ *n* a book in which you can make notes 筆記簿

not·ed /ˈnotɪd; ˈnəʊtɬd/ *adj* well-known because of a special quality or ability 〔因特別才能而〕著名的; 有名的: *a noted violinist* 著名的小提琴家 | *a town noted for its cheeses* 以乳酪聞名的城鎮

note·pa·per /ˈnotˌpepɚ; ˈnəʊtˌpeɪpərʳ/ *n* [U] paper for writing letters and notes on 信紙; 便箋紙

note·wor·thy /ˈnotˌwɝðɪ; ˈnəʊtˌwɜːðɪ/ *adj* interesting or worth paying attention to 值得注意的; 顯著的

noth·ing /ˈnʌθɪŋ; ˈnʌθɪŋ/ *pron* **1** no thing or things 沒有東西; 沒有事情: *There's nothing in this box.* 這個盒子

N

裡甚麼也沒有。| *She told me nothing about her plans.* 她沒有跟我提起她的計劃。| *By three o'clock I'd finished my work and had nothing to do.* 到三點鐘我完成了工作，接着便無事可做。**2** something that is not at all important 微不足道的事物: *£50 is nothing these days.* 五十英鎊在目前派不了甚麼用場。| *She means nothing to me.* 她對我來說無關緊要。**3 for nothing: a** for no money 不花錢地; 不要錢地: *When we bought the house we got all the furniture as well, for nothing.* 我們買下房子時也得到了所有的家具，都是白送的。**b** with no satisfactory result 沒有滿意結果地; 白費地: *I realized that I had spent three years studying for nothing.* 我意識到自己白花了三年時間去進行研究。**4 nothing but** only 只不過; 僅僅: *We could see nothing but trees and open fields.* 我們只能看到樹木和空曠的田野。**5 nothing like** not at all 一點也不; 完全不: *It's nothing like as cold today as it was yesterday.* 今天根本沒有昨天那樣冷。**6 nothing of the sort** a phrase used to say that something is completely untrue 哪兒的話, 沒有那回事〔表示完全否定某事物〕: *They claim that these weapons are purely defensive, but they're nothing of the sort.* 他們聲稱這些武器純粹是用作防禦，但其實並不是那麼回事。**7 nothing to do with** having no connection with someone or something 與〔某人或某物〕無關: *Keep out of this argument — it's nothing to do with you!* 別捲入這場爭論，這與你無關! **8 there's nothing for it** = there is nothing else that we can do 沒有別的辦法: *There was nothing for it but to swim across the river.* 沒有別的辦法，只好游過河去。**9 there's nothing in it** = it is completely untrue 毫不真實 **10 there's nothing to it** = it is very easy 這非常容易

noth·ing·ness /ˈnʌθɪŋnɪs; ˈnʌθɪŋɬs/ *n* [U] the state of emptiness where nothing exists 虛無; 不存在: *Is there only nothingness after death?* 人死後甚麼都不存在了嗎?

⋆**no·tice**[1]/ˈnoʊtɪs; ˈnəʊtɬs/ *n* **1** [C] a written or printed statement which gives information to the public 通告; 佈告; 啟事: *The notice on the wall says "No Smoking".* 牆上的告示寫着"不准吸煙"。**2** [U] a warning that something is going to happen 警告; 通知: *These rules may be changed without notice.* 這些規則可能不經通知就進行更改。| *The factory is closed until further notice.* 工廠將一直關閉到另行通知時為止。**3 at a moment's notice, at short notice** without having much time or advance warning to get ready 在短時間內通知: *I can leave at a moment's notice.* 我可以接到通知馬上動身。**4** [U] a formal warning to end an agreement 〔終止協議的〕正式通知: *I'm fed up with this job. I'm going to give in my notice.* 我已厭倦了這份工作，我打算提交辭職通知書。| *Our landlady has given us notice to quit.* 我們的房東已經通知我們遷出。| *If the company wants to dismiss me, they*

have to give me three months' notice. 要是公司想解雇我，他們得提前三個月通知我。**5 take no notice of** to pay no attention to someone or something 不注意〔某人或某事物〕: *Don't take any notice of what she says.* 別去理睬她所說的話。[RELATED PHRASE 相關詞組 **take notice of:** *Managers need to take notice of the report.* 經理們需要關注這篇報告。] **6 come to your notice** *fml* to become known to you 〔正式〕被人察覺; 引起注意: *It has come to my notice that you have been missing school.* 我已注意到你一直在逃學。[RELATED PHRASE 相關詞組 **bring something to someone's notice**]

⋆**notice**[2] *v* **noticed, noticing** [I;T; +(that); not in progressive forms 不用於進行式] to see or pay attention to 注意到; 看到: *She was wearing a new dress, but he didn't even notice.* 她穿着一件新衣服，但他根本就沒注意到。| *I noticed that he was looking rather nervous.* 我注意到他看上去相當緊張。| *Did you notice whether I locked the door?* 你看見我是否鎖了門? | *I noticed her leaving.* 我看見她離開的。

□ USEFUL PATTERNS 有用句型
to notice something; to notice that …;
to notice when, how, why, where, etc.;
to notice someone doing something

no·tice·a·ble /ˈnoʊtɪsəbl; ˈnəʊtɬsəbəl/ *adj* easily seen or clearly recognized 顯而易見的: *The damage to my car is hardly noticeable.* 我汽車的損壞不大明顯。| *a noticeable drop in the amount of crime* 犯罪數字的顯著下降 **–noticeably** *adv*: *Noticeably fewer people came this year.* 今年來的人顯著減少。

notice board /ˈ·· ˌ·/ *n BrE* a board on a wall, which notices may be fixed to 〔英式〕佈告欄[板]–see picture on page 763 見 763 頁彩圖

no·ti·fy /ˈnoʊtɪfaɪ; ˈnəʊtɬfaɪ/ *v* **notified, notifying** [T] to tell someone something formally 〔正式〕通知〔某人〕〔某事〕; 告知: *Have you notified the police?* 你報警了沒有? | *Please notify all staff that the inspectors will be here on Monday.* 請通知全體職工，視察人員將在星期一來這裡。**–notification** /ˌnoʊtəfəˈkeɪʃən; ˌnəʊtɬfɬˈkeɪʃən/ *n* [C;U]

⋆**no·tion** /ˈnoʊʃən; ˈnəʊʃən/ *n* an idea or belief 概念; 觀念: *I haven't the faintest notion what you're talking about.* 我對你談論的事一點也不懂。| *He is full of silly notions.* 他滿腦子的傻念頭。| *the old notion that the sun moved round the Earth* 認為太陽繞地球旋轉的舊觀念 | *notions of equality* 平等觀念

no·to·ri·e·ty /ˌnoʊtəˈraɪəti; ˌnəʊtəˈraɪətɪ/ *n* [U] fame for something bad 臭名昭著; 聲名狼藉

no·to·ri·ous /noʊˈtɔːriəs; nəʊˈtɔːriəs/ *adj* widely known for something bad 臭名昭著的; 聲名狼藉的: *a notorious thief* 聲名狼藉的

竊賊 | *This airport is notorious* **for** *its bad security.* 這個機場因安全工作不好而聲名狼藉。–see 見 FAMOUS (USAGE用法) **–notoriously** *adv*

not·with·stand·ing /ˌnɑtwɪθˈstændɪŋ; ˌnɒtwɪθˈstændɪŋ/ *prep fml* in spite of something〖正式〗儘管: *They are determined to go ahead with the plan, notwithstanding public opposition.* 儘管公眾反對，他們仍決心開始實行該計劃。| *They bought the building, cost notwithstanding.* 儘管花費很大，他們還是買下了那幢大樓。

nought /nɔt; nɔːt/ *n BrE* the number 0〖英式〗〔數字〕零: *0.6 is usually read "nought point six".* 0.6 通常讀作「零點六」。

noun /naʊn; naʊn/ *n* a word that describes a person, place, thing, quality, or action, and can be used as the subject or object of a verb; nouns are marked *n* in this dictionary 名詞 –see Study Note on page 1330 見 1330 頁學習提示

nour·ish /ˈnɜːrɪʃ; ˈnʌrɪʃ/ *v* [T] **1** to give someone the food that they need to live, grow, and stay healthy 養育; 滋養; 營養: *Milk is a nourishing drink.* 牛奶是營養豐富的飲料。| *a well-nourished baby* 營養良好的嬰兒 **2** to encourage a feeling or idea 孕育〔感情〕; 滋長〔想法〕

nour·ish·ment /ˈnɜːrɪʃmənt; ˈnʌrɪʃmənt/ *n* [U] food needed to live, grow and stay healthy 營養品; 食物: *Plants get nourishment from the soil.* 植物從土壤吸取營養。

★**nov·el¹** /ˈnɑvl; ˈnɒvəl/ *n* a book which tells a long story about people and events that are not real (長篇)小說: *"War and Peace" is a great novel by Leo Tolstoy.*《戰爭與和平》是利奧·托爾斯泰寫的偉大小說。

nov·el² *adj* new, different, and interesting 新穎的; 新奇的; 新奇的: *a novel suggestion* 新建議 | *a novel idea* 新構想

nov·el·ist /ˈnɑvlɪst; ˈnɒvəlɪst/ *n* someone who writes novels (長篇) 小說家

nov·el·ty /ˈnɑvltɪ; ˈnɒvəlti/ *n* **novelties 1** [U] the quality of being new, different, and interesting 新穎; 新奇(性): *After ten weeks of camping, the novelty had worn off.* 過了十週的野營生活，新鮮感就慢慢消失了。**2** [sing] something new and unusual 新奇事物: *I go out so rarely that is quite a novelty for me to go to the cinema last night.* 我極少出門，所以昨晚去看電影對我來說是件新奇的事。**3** [C] an unusual, cheap object often given as a small present〔常作為小禮物的〕新奇而價廉的物品: *The shops are full of Christmas novelties.* 商店裡擺滿了新奇的聖誕小裝飾品。

No·vem·ber /noˈvɛmbə; nəʊˈvembər/ *n* (also 又作 **Nov.**) *n* the 11th month of the year 十一月

nov·ice /ˈnɑvɪs; ˈnɒvɪs/ *n* **1** someone with no experience in a skill or job 新手; 生手: *When it comes to sailing, I'm a complete novice.* 關於航海，我完全是個新手。**2** someone who has recently joined a religious group to become a MONK or NUN 見習修道士〔修女〕

★**now¹** /naʊ; naʊ/ *adv* **1** at the present time 現在; 目前: *We're living in London now.* 我們目前住在倫敦。| *Most women work now.* 現在多數婦女有工作。| *It's two years now since I left Birmingham.* 我離開伯明翰至今已有兩年。**2** at the time mentioned in a story 當時; 那時: *He was feeling happier now.* 他當時感到比較幸福。**3** used when you are starting to talk about a new subject 現在〔開始談論新的題目〕: *I think that's enough on Question 5. Now, let's move on to the next question.* 我想第五個問題已經談了不少。現在我們接着談下一個問題。**4 now and then, every now and then, now and again** sometimes 時而; 偶爾 **5 now, now** a phrase you use to calm someone or to express amused disapproval of what someone says〔用於表示使某人安靜或對別人的話有異議〕: *Now, now, stop crying.* 好了，好了，別哭了。

★**now²** *conj* (also 又作 **now that**) because something has happened 既然; 由於: *Now that everyone's here we can start the meeting.* 既然大家已經到齊，我們就可以開會了。

now·a·days /ˈnaʊədez; ˈnaʊədeɪz/ *adv* at the present time 現今; 如今: *Most women work nowadays.* 如今多數婦女都有工作。

no·where /ˈnoˌhwɛr; ˈnəʊweər/ *adv* **1** in or to no place 無處; 任何地方都不: *He now had nowhere to live.* 他現在無處安身。| *I've been to Paris, but nowhere else in France.* 我到過巴黎，但沒去法國的其他地方。**2 nowhere near** not at all 一點也不; 遠遠不: *£100 will be nowhere near enough.* 一百鎊是遠遠不夠的。

nox·ious /ˈnɑkʃəs; ˈnɒkʃəs/ *adj fml* harmful or poisonous〖正式〗有害的; 有毒的: *They pour noxious chemicals into that river.* 他們把有毒的化學物質倒入那條河裡。

noz·zle /ˈnɑzl; ˈnɒzəl/ *n* a short tube fitted to the end of a HOSE or pipe to direct and control the stream of liquid or gas coming out 噴嘴; 管嘴

n't /nt; ənt/ short for〖縮〗= NOT: *hadn't | didn't | wouldn't | isn't*

nu·ance /ˈnjuːɑns; ˈnjuːɑːns/ *n* a slight delicate difference in colour, appearance, meaning, or feeling〔顏色、外表、意義、感情等的〕細微差別: *You have to be fluent at a language to understand the nuances of what people are saying.* 你必須熟練掌握一門語言，以便完全理解人們的談話內容。

nu·bile /ˈnjubl; ˈnjuːbaɪl/ *adj* young and sexually attractive (used of a girl or young woman) 年輕嫵媚的; 性感的〔指姑娘或年輕女子〕

★**nu·cle·ar** /ˈnjuklɪə; ˈnjuːklɪər/ *adj* **1** concerned with the nucleus of an atom and the way it behaves (原子)核的: *nuclear* *fission* 核裂變 | *nuclear physics* 核物理學 **2** concerned with the powerful force produced by breaking atoms up 核動力的: *a nuclear power station* 核發電站 | *nuclear energy* 核能 **3 nuclear reactor** a large machine that produces nuclear ENERGY as a means of producing electricity 核反應堆 **4** related to or using weapons that explode because of the force of atoms breaking up inside them (使用)核武器的: *nuclear war* 核戰爭 | *a nuclear missile* 核導彈 **5 nuclear-free** without any nuclear ENERGY or nuclear weapons 無核能或核武器的: *Lambeth is a nuclear-free zone.* 朗伯斯是一個無核區。

nu·cle·us /'njuklɪəs; 'njuːkliəs/ *n* **nuclei** /-klɪ,aɪ; -kliaɪ/ **1** the small group of people or things which form the central part of something larger 核心; 中心; 基礎: *These 100 books will form the nucleus of the new school library.* 這一百本書將成為學校新建圖書館藏書的基礎。 **2** the central part of an atom, made up of neutrons (NEUTRON) and protons (PROTON) 原子核 **3** the central part of almost all cells of living matter 細胞核

nude[1] /njud; njuːd/ *adj* not wearing clothes 裸體的

nude[2] *n* **1** a picture of someone not wearing any clothes 裸體畫 **2 in the nude** without any clothes on 赤身裸體: *They went swimming in the nude.* 他們去裸體游泳。

nudge /nʌdʒ; nʌdʒ/ *v* **nudged, nudging** [T] to touch or push someone gently, usually with your elbow 用肘輕碰或輕推〔某人〕: *She nudged me when he came into the room.* 他走進房間時, 她用肘輕輕推了我一下。 **–nudge** *n*: *Give me a nudge when it's time to leave.* 該走時輕輕碰我一下。

nud·is·m /'njudɪzm; 'njuːdɪzəm/ *n* [U] the practice of not wearing clothes because you think it is good for you 裸體主義〔認為實行裸體對健康有好處〕 **–nudist** *adj*: *a nudist camp* 裸體營 **–nudist** *n*

nu·di·ty /'njudətɪ; 'njuːdɪ,tɪ/ *n* [U] the state of not wearing any clothes 赤裸; 裸體: *Many people regard nudity in films as wrong.* 許多人認為影片裡有裸體鏡頭是不對的。

nug·get /'nʌgɪt; 'nʌg,ɪt/ *n* **1** a small rough lump of a precious metal, found in the earth 天然塊狀貴金屬: *a gold nugget* 天然金塊 **2** an interesting or useful piece of information 有價值的資料〔消息〕

nui·sance /'njusns; 'njuːsəns/ *n* a person, thing, or situation that causes annoyance 討厭的人〔事物、情況〕: *Sit down and stop making a nuisance of yourself.* 坐下吧, 別讓人討厭。 | *It's a real nuisance having to go back for her.* 還得為了她而趕回去, 真是討厭。

nul·li·fy /'nʌlə,faɪ; 'nʌl,ɪ,faɪ/ *v* **nullified, nullifying** [T] *fml* to cause or declare something to have no legal force 〔正式〕使〔某物〕

在法律上〕無效; 宣佈無效: *a claim nullified by the court* 被法庭宣佈無效的要求 **–nullification** /,nʌləfə'keʃən; ,nʌl,ɪfˌɪ'keɪʃən/ *n* [U]

numb[1] /nʌm; nʌm/ *adj* unable to feel or express anything 失去感覺的; 麻木的: *My hands are numb with cold.* 我的手凍僵了。 | *The anaesthetic made my arm go numb.* 麻醉劑使我的手臂失去了知覺。 | *numb* **with** *shock* 驚呆 **–numbness** *n* [U]

numb[2] *v* [T] to stop you feeling anything or behaving normally 使失去知覺; 使麻木: *The cold numbed my fingers.* 寒冷凍僵了我的手指。 | *He was numbed by his wife's death.* 他妻子的去世使他神情麻木。

✫num·ber[1] /'nʌmbə; 'nʌmbər/ *n* **1** [C] a word such as three, eight, or sixteen, or a sign such as 1, 14, or 23 which is part of the system we use to count or measure 數; 數字; 數目: *Choose any number between one and ten.* 在一和十之間任選一個數字。 | *Six is my lucky number.* 六是我的幸運數字。 **2** [C] a telephone number 電話號碼: *What's your number?* 你的電話號碼是多少? | *Do you know Jane's number?* 你知道簡的電話號碼嗎? **3** [C] a figure used to explain what you are talking about from things in an ordered list 編號; 號碼: *Who lives at number 10?* 誰住在十號? | *Please look at question number four.* 請看第四題。 **4** [C;U] [always with a plural verb 只能與複數形式的動詞連用] a quantity or amount 數量; 總數: *Large numbers of tourists visit London every year.* 每年有大批的遊客遊覽倫敦。 | *They were twelve in number.* 他們的總數是十二。 | *A small number of women are now holding key jobs.* 現在有少數婦女身居要職。 **5 a number of** several 幾個; 若干: *A number of people have complained recently.* 最近已有好幾個人發了牢騷。 **6 any number of** a lot of 許多: *Any number of people might apply for the job.* 許多人會申請這份工作。 **7** [C] a copy of a magazine printed at a particular time 〔雜誌的〕一期: *the latest number of "Vogue" magazine* 最近一期的《時尚》雜誌 **8** [C] a piece of popular music 一首流行樂曲

number[2] *v* **1** [T] to give a number to something 給〔某物〕編號: *Number the questions from 1 to 10.* 將這些問題編為一至十號。 | *All the seats are numbered.* 所有的座位都編了號。 **2** [+ complement] to reach as a total 達到…總數; 共計: *The children who were affected numbered several hundred.* 受到(疾病)感染的孩子有好幾百個。 **3 be numbered among** to be included as one of a group or set 把…包括在內; 被算作: *He is numbered among the best of modern writers.* 他被認為是最優秀的現代作家之一。

num·ber·plate /'nʌmbə,plet; 'nʌmbəpleɪt/ *BrE* 〔英式〕 *n* (**license plate** *AmE* 〔美式〕) one of two signs at the front and back of a

N

vehicle showing its official number 〔掛在車輛前後部的〕號碼牌; 牌照 –see picture on page 209 見 209 頁彩圖

Number Ten /ˌ··ˈ·/ n (**No. 10**) 10 Downing Street; the place where the British PRIME MINISTER lives 唐寧街十號〔英國首相官邸〕

nu·me·ral /ˈnjumərəl; ˈnjuˈmərəl/ n a sign that represents a number 數字; 數詞

nu·me·rate /ˈnjumə,ret; ˈnjuːmərˌt/ adj able to do calculations with numbers 有計算能力的 –**numeracy** n [U]

nu·mer·i·cal /njuˈmɛrɪkl/ adj expressed in numbers 用數字表示的: The files are kept in numerical order. 檔案是按數字順序保存的。 –**numerically** /-klɪ; -klɪ/ adv: Their army is numerically greater than ours but less well trained. 他們的軍隊在人數上比我們多, 但訓練不甚良好。

****nu·me·rous** /ˈnjumərəs; ˈnjuːmərəs/ adj many 許多的: one of my numerous relatives 我眾多親屬中的一個 | for numerous reasons 由於多種原因

nun /nʌn; nʌn/ n a member of an all-female religious group who live together in a CONVENT 修女; 尼姑

nun·ne·ry /ˈnʌnərɪ; ˈnʌnərɪ/ n nunneries old fash a building in which nuns live 〔老式〕女修道院; 尼姑庵

nup·tial /ˈnʌpʃəl; ˈnʌpʃəl/ adj [only before a noun 只用於名詞前] fml concerning marriage or the marriage ceremony 〔正式〕婚姻的; 結婚的; 婚禮的: a nuptial mass 結婚彌撒 –**nuptials** n [pl]: The nuptials were performed by the local priest. 婚禮由當地牧師主持。

****nurse**[1] /nɜːs; nɜːs/ n **1** someone, often a woman, who is trained to help a doctor or to take care of sick, hurt, or old people in a hospital 護士: a student nurse 實習護士 | Nurse Jones 瓊斯護士 | Our daughter is a nurse. 我們的女兒是護士。 | Thank you, nurse. 謝謝您, 護士。 **2** a woman employed to take care of a young child 保姆 –compare 比較 NANNY

nurse[2] v nursed, nursing **1** [T] to take care of someone who is ill 護理, 照料〔病人〕: He nursed her back to health. 她在他照料下恢復了健康。 | She spends all her time nursing her old father. 她把所有的時間都化在照料她年邁的父親上。 **2** [T] to try to cure an illness 調治〔疾病〕; 調養: She's in bed nursing a cold. 她臥床調治感冒。 **3** [I] to be a professional nurse 當職業護士: She spent some time nursing in a military hospital. 她曾一度在軍醫院當護士。 **4** [I;T] to give a baby milk from the breast 給嬰兒喂奶; 哺育乳: a nursing mother 哺乳中的母親 **5** [T] to think a lot about something 心裡老是想〔某事〕: She still nursed a grudge against her old boss. 她對過去的老闆仍然懷恨在心。 | I've always nursed a desire to be a politician. 我一直渴望當政治家。 **6** to hold someone or something lov-

ingly 摟, 抱〔某人、某物〕: The child nursed the kitten in her arms. 孩子把小貓摟在懷裡。

nurse·maid /ˈnɜːs,med; ˈnɜːsmeɪd/ n a woman employed to look after young children 保姆

nur·se·ry /ˈnɜːsərɪ; ˈnɜːsəri/ n nurseries **1** a place where small children are taken care of while their parents are at work or shopping 托兒所; 保育室 **2** an area where young plants and trees are grown to be sold or planted in other places 苗圃 **3** a small child's bedroom or playroom in a house 〔兒〕兒童臥室; 兒童遊戲室

nur·se·ry·man /ˈnɜːsərɪmən; ˈnɜːsərimən/ n nurserymen /-mən; -mən/ someone who grows plants in a nursery 苗圃工人

nursery rhyme /ˈ··· ·/ n a short, well-known song or poem for small children 兒歌; 童謠

nursery school /ˈ··· ·/ n [C;U] a school for young children between three and five years of age 〔接收三至五歲幼兒的〕幼兒園

nurs·ing /ˈnɜːsɪŋ; ˈnɜːsɪŋ/ n [U] the job of looking after people who are sick, hurt, or old 護理工作: the nursing profession 護理專業 | Have you thought of going into nursing? 你想過當護士嗎?

nursing home /ˈ·· ·/ n **1** a usually private establishment where old or sick people can live and be looked after 〔常指私人辦的〕養老院; 療養院 **2** BrE a small private hospital 〔英式〕私人小醫院

nur·ture /ˈnɜːtʃə; ˈnɜːtʃər/ v nurtured, nurturing [T] lit to care for and encourage the development of something or someone 〔文〕養育〔某人〕; 培育〔某物〕: children nurtured by loving parents 由慈愛的父母養育的孩子 | I looked at the plants I had nurtured through the winter. 我看了看我培植了一個冬天的植物。 | He nurtured a desire to be completely independent. 他滋長了徹底獨立的慾望。

nut /nʌt; nʌt/ n **1** a dry fruit which consists of a seed surrounded by a hard shell; the seed is also called a nut 堅果; 果仁: a cashew nut 腰果 **2** a small piece of metal with a hole through it for screwing onto a BOLT to fasten things together 螺母; 螺帽 **3** (also 又作 **nutter**) infml someone who seems to be mad 〔非正式〕瘋子; 怪人: He's a bit of a nut. 他有點瘋瘋癲癲。 **4** someone who likes a particular thing much more than most people can understand 對某事物入迷的人; 狂熱的人: She's a health nut. 她是個保養迷。 **5** off your nut slang mad 〔俚〕瘋的: You must be off your nut! 你一定是瘋了! **6** a hard nut to crack, a tough nut to crack infml a difficult person or situation to deal with 〔非正式〕難對付的人; 棘手的事 **7** do your nut slang to suddenly become very angry or worried 〔俚〕大發雷霆; 心煩意亂: Dad will do his nut if he finds out where *you've been.* 要是爸爸發現你去過那兒, 他會大發雷霆。

nut·case /ˈnʌtˌkeɪs; ˈnʌtkeɪs/ *n infml* a mad person 〖非正式〗瘋子

nut·crack·ers /ˈnʌtˌkrækəz; ˈnʌtˌkrækəz/ *n* [pl] a tool for cracking the shell of a nut 胡桃鉗; 軋碎堅果的鉗子: *Have we got any nutcrackers?* 我們家裡有沒有胡桃鉗?

nut·meg /ˈnʌtmɛg; ˈnʌtmɛg/ *n* [C;U] a small hard seed of a tropical tree which is made into powder and used to give a particular taste to food 肉豆蔻〖可碾粉作調味用〗

nu·tri·ent /ˈnjuːtrɪənt; ˈnjuːtrɪənt/ *n tech* a chemical or food which helps plants and animals to grow 〖術語〗營養素; 營養品

nu·tri·tion /njuːˈtrɪʃən; njuːˈtrɪʃən/ *n* [U] the process of giving and getting food to remain healthy 營養; 滋養(過程)

nu·tri·tious /njuːˈtrɪʃəs; njuːˈtrɪʃəs/ *adj* valuable to the body as food 有營養價值的; 滋養的: *a nutritious diet* 有營養的飲食

nuts /nʌts; nʌts/ *adj* [never before a noun 不能用於名詞前] *infml* 〖非正式〗**1** mad 發瘋的; 發狂的: *I'll go nuts if I have to wait much longer.* 如果我得再等下去的話, 我會發瘋的。| *He's nuts.* 他瘋了。**2 nuts about** very keen on someone or something 熱衷於〔某事物〕; 迷戀着〔某人〕: *She's nuts about Jason Donovan.* 她對傑森·唐諾文很迷戀。

nut·ty /ˈnʌtɪ; ˈnʌti/ *adj* **nuttier, nuttiest 1**

filled with nuts or tasting like them 有許多堅果的; 有堅果味的: *wine with a nutty taste* 有堅果味的酒 | *a nutty cake* 多堅果的餅 **2** *infml* mad 〖非正式〗瘋的; 瘋狂的 –**nuttiness** *n* [U]

nuz·zle /ˈnʌzl; ˈnʌzəl/ *v* **nuzzled, nuzzling** [I; T] to rub or push something gently often with the nose 〔常用鼻子〕擦, 掘或推〔某物〕: *The horse nuzzled me, looking for food.* 馬用鼻子觸碰我, 想找東西吃。| *He nuzzled up against her on the sofa.* 他在沙發上緊靠着她。

NW a written abbreviation for 〖縮〗= NORTHWESTERN

ny·lon /ˈnaɪlɒn; ˈnaɪlɑn/ *n* [U] a strong manmade material made into clothes, cords, and plastics 尼龍: *nylon thread* 尼龍線 | *a nylon shirt* 尼龍襯衫

ny·lons /ˈnaɪlɒnz; ˈnaɪlɑnz/ *n* [pl] *old fash* women's nylon stockings 〖老式〗〔婦女的〕尼龍長襪: *a pair of nylons* 一雙尼龍長襪

nymph /nɪmf; nɪmf/ *n* one of the less important goddesses of nature in Greek and Roman literature, represented as young girls 〔希臘和羅馬神話中的〕仙女

nym·pho·ma·ni·ac /ˌnɪmfəˈmeɪniæk; ˌnɪmfəˈmeɪniæk/ *n* a woman who has unusually strong sexual desires 女性色情狂 –**nymphomaniac** *adj*

O, o

O, o /o; əʊ/ **O's, o's** or **Os, os 1** the 15th letter of the English alphabet 英語的第十五個
字母 **2** (used in speech when referring to
numbers) zero〔口語中的〕零: *His phone
number is 071-283-9462.* 他的電話號碼是
071-283-9462.–see 見 ZERO (USAGE 用法)

oaf /of; əʊf/ *n* a stupid awkward person 傻
瓜, 笨蛋: *You clumsy oaf! 你這個笨蛋!*

oak /ok; əʊk/ *n* [C;U] a large tree common
in Britain or the wood of this tree〔英國常
見的〕橡樹; 橡木; 櫟樹; 櫟木: *an oak table* 櫟
木桌

OAP /ˌoʊ eˈpiː; ˌəʊ eɪ ˈpiː/ *n* someone who is
over 60 or 65 years old, and who no longer
works; an abbreviation for **old age pensioner**《縮》領取養老金者〔60 或 65 歲以上的
人〕

oar /or; ɔːr/ *n* a long pole with a wide flat
blade at one end, used to move a boat
through the water 槳; 櫓: *He pulled hard on
the oars.* 他使勁地划槳。

o·a·sis /oˈesɪs; əʊˈeɪsɪs/ *n* **oases** /-siz; -siːz/ **1**
a place in a desert where there is water
and where trees can grow〔沙漠中的〕綠洲 **2**
a pleasant place in the middle of unpleasant places〔不愉快環境中的〕舒適之處,
宜人的地方

oath /oθ; əʊθ/ *n* **oaths** /oðz; əʊðz/ **1** a solemn promise 誓約; 誓言: *The soldiers swore
an oath of allegiance.* 士兵宣誓效忠。 **2** *old
fash* an expression of strong feeling using
the name of God in a disrespectful way《老
式》詛咒; 咒罵 **3** be on oath, be under oath
law to have made a solemn promise to tell
the truth in a court of law《律》〔在法庭上〕
宣過誓要說實話

oat·meal /ˈotˌmil; ˈəʊtmiːl/ *n* [U] crushed
oats used for making dry flat cakes and
PORRIDGE 燕麥片〔用於做燕麥餅及煮粥〕

oats /ots; əʊts/ *n* [pl] a grain that is used in
PORRIDGE and fed to animals 燕麥〔用於煮
粥及餵牲口〕

ob·du·rate /ˈɒbdjərɪt; ˈɒbdʒʊrɪt/ *adj fml* refusing to change your beliefs or feelings
about something《正式》頑固的; 執拗的 –
obduracy *n* [U]

o·be·di·ent /əˈbidiənt; əˈbiːdiənt/ *adj* willing to do what you are told to do by someone, for example a parent or teacher 服從
的; 順從的; 聽話的: *an obedient child* 聽話的
孩子 | *an obedient dog* 馴服的狗 –opposite
反義 **disobedient** –**obediently** *adv* –**obedience** *n* [U]

o·bese /oˈbis; əʊˈbiːs/ *adj* very fat (過度)肥

胖的 –**obesity** *n* [U]

o·bey /əˈbe; əʊˈbeɪ/ *v* **obeyed, obeying** [I;T]
to do what you are told to do 服從; 順從; 聽
從: *Soldiers are expected to obey.* 士兵應當服
從命令。 | *Everyone has to obey the law.* 人
人都得遵守法律。–opposite 反義 **disobey**

o·bit·u·a·ry /əˈbɪtʃʊ,ɛri; əˈbɪtʃʊəri/ *n* **obitu-
aries** a formal notice in a newspaper of
someone's death, with a short account of
their life 訃告; 訃聞

★**ob·ject**[1] /ˈɒbdʒɪkt; ˈɒbdʒɪkt/ *n* **1** a thing that
can be seen or touched and is no alive〔可
見到或可觸摸的〕物件; 物體 **2** someone or
something towards which interest or another feeling is directed 對象〔指興趣或情感
所及的人或物〕: *The vase was an object of
admiration.* 那花瓶是人們欣賞之物。 | *She
had become an object of pity.* 她成了人們憐
憫的對象。**3** purpose or aim 目的; 目標: *The
object of his visit was to meet as many
people as possible.* 他訪問的目的是儘可能結
識多一些人。**4** *tech* a term used in grammar
to describe words in a certain situation; in
the sentences "John gave Mary a book"
and "John gave a book to Mary", "Mary"
is the **indirect object** of the verb, and
"book" is the **direct object**〔術語〕〔語法中
的〕受詞[賓語]〔如在 John gave Mary a
book 和 John gave a book to Mary 兩句中,
Mary 是動詞的間接受詞[賓語]; book 是直接
受詞[賓語]〕**5** no object not a difficulty 沒
有困難; 不成問題: *I want the best seats in the
theatre; money is no object.* 我要買到最佳座
位的戲票, 錢不成問題。

ob·ject[2] /əbˈdʒɛkt; əbˈdʒɛkt/ *v* **1** [I] to feel
or say that you dislike and disapprove of
something 反對〔某事物〕; 不贊成〔某事物〕:
I'll go ahead if no one objects. 要是沒有人反
對, 我就繼續進行。 | *What I object to is the
way he orders everyone around.* 我反感的是
他對各人那種差來遣去的態度。 | *They
objected to the adoption of children from
abroad.* 他們不贊成收養外國的孩子。**2** [+
(that)] to give as a reason for not doing
something 提出…作為反對的理由: *I wanted
to climb the hill, but Bill objected that he
was too tired.* 我想去登山, 但比爾表示反對,
他說他太累了。–**objector** *n*

ob·jec·tion /əbˈdʒɛkʃən; əbˈdʒɛkʃən/ *n* **1** a
statement or feeling of dislike, disapproval, or opposition 不喜歡; 不贊成; 反對:
She voiced her objection to travelling by bus.
她反對坐公共汽車旅行。**2** a reason or argu-
ment against something 異議; 反對的理由:

The only objection **to** *hiring her is that she can't drive.* 反對雇用她的唯一理由是她不會開車。

ob·jec·tio·na·ble /əbˈdʒɛkʃənəbl̩; əbˈdʒɛk-ʃənəbəl/ adj unpleasant and offensive 令人不快的; 令人反感的: *I find his behaviour quite objectionable.* 我認為他的行為十分令人討厭。 **–objectionably** adv

*★**ob·jec·tive**[1] /əbˈdʒɛktɪv; əbˈdʒɛktɪv/ adj **1** not influenced by personal feelings 客觀的, 無偏見的: *The reporter gave an objective analysis of the political situation.* 那位記者對政治形勢作了客觀的分析。 **2** based on things which can be seen and touched 客觀存在的; 真實的: *We need objective evidence before we can convict him.* 我們需要有確鑿的證據才能給他定罪。 **–objectively** adv: *Try to look at the problem objectively.* 要盡量客觀地看待這個問題。 **–objectivity** /ˌɑbdʒɛkˈtɪvətɪ; ˈɒb-dʒɛkˈtɪvḷti/ n [U]

objective[2] n an aim towards which you have to work 目標; 目的: *We've achieved our main objective — to produce a first class engine.* 我們已經達到了我們的主要目標, 就是生產一部一流的發動機。

ob·jet d'art /ˌobˈʒɛˈdɑr; ˈɒbʒeɪ ˈdɑːʳ/ n **objets d'art** (*same pronunciation* 讀音相同) a small object considered to have some artistic value 小工藝〔美術〕品

*★**ob·li·ga·tion** /ˌɑbləˈgeʃən; ˌɒbliˈɡeɪʃən/ n something which must be done because of a duty or promise 責任; 義務; 承諾: *Have a look round the shop — you're under no obligation to buy anything.* 在店裡到處看看, 你不一定非要買東西。 | *I said I would help her and I have to fulfil that obligation.* 我答應過幫助她, 現在要履行那個諾言。

ob·lig·a·to·ry /əˈblɪɡəˌtorɪ; əˈblɪɡətəri/ adj which must be done because of a law, or rule 〔按法律或規定〕必須履行的; 有義務的; 強制的: *The wearing of uniform is obligatory.* 按規定人人都必須穿制服。

o·blige /əˈblaɪdʒ; əˈblaɪdʒ/ v **obliged, obliging 1** [T] to make it necessary for someone to do something 迫使〔某人〕做某事: *He felt obliged to leave after such an unpleasant quarrel.* 在那樣一次不愉快的爭吵之後, 他覺得必須離開。 | *Falling profits obliged them to close the factory.* 利潤下降迫使他們關閉這家工廠。

□ **USEFUL PATTERNS** 有用句型
to oblige someone to do something; to be obliged to do something

2 [I;T] to be helpful to someone 幫〔某人〕的忙: *I asked Oliver to lend us his car and he was only too happy to oblige.* 我請奧利弗把他的汽車借給我們, 他非常樂意幫忙。 **3** **much obliged** *fml* very grateful 非常感謝: *I'm much obliged* **to** *you.* 我非常感謝你。 **4 I should/would be obliged if** a formal

phrase meaning that you want someone to do something 要是…我將不勝感激〔請求某人做某事時的正式用語〕: *I'd be obliged if you could make less noise.* 你們的聲音若能輕一點, 我將不勝感激。

o·blig·ing /əˈblaɪdʒɪŋ; əˈblaɪdʒɪŋ/ adj willing and eager to help 樂於助人的 **–obligingly** adv

o·blique /əˈblik; əˈbliːk/ adj **1** indirect 拐彎抹角的, 間接的: *I think what he said was an oblique reference to my driving.* 我覺得他的話是在間接提及我開車的事。 **2** sloping 斜的; 傾斜的: *an oblique line* 斜線

o·blit·er·ate /əˈblɪtəˌret; əˈblɪtəreɪt/ v **obliterated, obliterating** [T] to destroy something completely 徹底毀滅〔某物〕 **–obliteration** /əˌblɪtəˈreʃən; əˌblɪtəˈreɪʃən/ n [U]

o·bliv·i·on /əˈblɪvɪən; əˈblɪvɪən/ n [U] **1** the state of being unconscious or not noticing your surroundings 漠視; 無意識的狀態 **2** the state of being forgotten 遺忘; 被忘卻的狀態: *Her fame soon sank into oblivion* 她的名氣很快被遺忘了。

o·bliv·i·ous /əˈblɪvɪəs; əˈblɪvɪəs/ adj not noticing 不注意的; 未覺察的: *He was quite oblivious* **to** *the danger he was in.* 他完全沒有覺察到自己有危險。 | *She was oblivious* **of** *the effect she had on him.* 她並未注意到自己對他產生的影響。 **–obliviously** adv **–obliviousness** n [U]

ob·long /ˈɑblɔŋ; ˈɒblɒŋ/ n a shape with four straight sides, two long and two short, which form four right angles 長方形

ob·nox·ious /əbˈnɑkʃəs; əbˈnɒkʃəs/ adj very unpleasant or offensive 使人非常不快的; 可憎的: *He's an obnoxious little man.* 他是個討厭的小人。 **–obnoxiously** adv

o·boe /ˈobo; ˈəʊbəʊ/ n a musical instrument of the woodwind family; it is a long tube with a double REED at the top which you blow through 雙簧管

ob·scene /əbˈsin; əbˈsiːn/ adj shocking and offensive, usually in a sexual way 震驚的; 猥褻的; 淫穢的; 下流的 **–obscenely** adv **–obscenity** /əbˈsɛnətɪ; əbˈsenəti/ n **obscenities** [C;U]

ob·scure[1] /əbˈskjʊr; əbˈskjʊəʳ/ adj **1** unclear or hard to understand 不清楚的; 難解的; 晦澀的: *a speech full of obscure political jokes* 一次充滿晦澀的政治笑話的講話 **2** not well known 無名的; 名不見經傳的: *an obscure poet* 一位無名的詩人 **–obscurely** adv **–obscurity** n **obscurities** [C;U]

obscure[2] v **obscured, obscuring** [T] to make something difficult to see or understand 使〔某物〕變模糊; 使難理解; 遮掩: *The clouds obscured the moon.* 雲層遮住了月亮。 | *The report obscures the fact that prices have risen.* 這份報告掩蓋了物價已經上漲的事實。

ob·se·qui·ous /əbˈsikwɪəs; əbˈsiːkwiəs/ adj *fml* too eager to agree with someone and do what they want (a word used to express disapproval)〖正式〗巴結的; 奉承拍馬的〔含貶義〕

ob·ser·vance /əbˈzɜːvəns; əbˈzɜːvəns/ *n fml* 〖正式〗 **1** [U] the obeying or following of a law, ceremony, or custom 〔對法律、禮儀、習俗等的〕遵守, 奉行: *strict observance* **of** *the school rules* 嚴格遵守校規 | *the observance of Christmas* 奉行過聖誕節的習俗 **2** [C] a part of a religious ceremony 〔宗教的〕儀式: *religious observances* 宗教儀式

ob·ser·vant /əbˈzɜːvənt; əbˈzɜːvənt/ *adj* quick at noticing things 善於觀察的; 觀察力敏銳的 –opposite 反義 **unobservant**

***ob·ser·va·tion** /ˌɒbzəˈveɪʃən; ˌɒbzəˈveɪʃən/ *n* **1** [U] the action of noticing or watching something in order to learn about it 觀察; 注意: *During our observation of the rats, we made several new discoveries.* 我們在對老鼠的觀察中有了幾項新的發現。 | *He left by the back door to escape observation.* 他從後門離去, 避開了別人的注意。 **2** [C] something that you have learned by watching 觀察得來的資料: *The scientific observations of Professor Jones are extremely interesting.* 瓊斯教授的科學觀察記錄極其有趣。 **3** [C] a remark 言論; 評論: *She made a few general observations before a more detailed analysis.* 她先作了些一般性的評論, 然後進行詳盡的分析。 **4** [U] the ability to notice things 觀察力: *poor powers of observation* 觀察力不強 **5 under observation** carefully watched 受嚴密監視〔觀察〕: *The police are keeping him under observation.* 警方正對他進行嚴密監視。 | *She has been put under observation at the local hospital.* 她已在當地醫院接受觀察。

ob·ser·va·to·ry /əbˈzɜːvətɔːri; əbˈzɜːvətɔːri/ *n* **observatories** a place from which scientists can watch the moon, stars, and the weather 天文台; 氣象台

***ob·serve** /əbˈzɜːv; əbˈzɜːv/ *v* **observed, observing 1** [T] to watch carefully, often to learn or understand something 觀察, 觀測: *They observed the stars.* 他們觀察星體。 **2** [T; +that] *fml* to see and notice 〖正式〗看到; 注意到: *The police observed them entering the bank.* 警察看到他們走進了銀行。 | *Did you observe where they went?* 你注意到他們去了哪兒嗎? | *I observed that they were late.* 我看見他們遲到了。

□USEFUL PATTERNS 有用句型
to observe something; to observe someone doing/do something; to observe where, how, who, etc.; to observe that...

---

3 [T] to obey or follow a law or custom 遵守, 奉行〔法規或習俗〕 **4** [I; +that] to make a remark about something you have noticed 評說; 評論: *"It's going to rain,"* he observed. "要下雨了," 他說。 | *He observed that she looked rather upset.* 他説她看上去很煩惱。

ob·serv·er /əbˈzɜːvə; əbˈzɜːvər/ *n* **1** someone who sees or watches something 觀察者; 遵守者 **2** someone who attends meetings or classes to see what happens without taking part 〔出席會議、課堂等的〕觀察員; 旁聽者

ob·sess /əbˈsɛs; əbˈsɛs/ *v* [T] to fill your thoughts completely so that you think of nothing else 迷住, 使着迷

ob·sessed /əbˈsɛst; əbˈsɛst/ *adj* thinking about only one thing 牽掛的; 着迷的: *She's obsessed* **by** *the thought of another war.* 她一想到有另一場戰爭就感到困擾。 | *He's obsessed* **with** *getting fit.* 他一心想使自己身體變得健壯。

ob·ses·sion /əbˈsɛʃən; əbˈsɛʃən/ *n* something you cannot stop thinking about 縈繞於心的事物, 無法擺脱的意念 –**obsessional** *adj*

ob·ses·sive /əbˈsɛsɪv; əbˈsɛsɪv/ *adj* continually filling your thoughts so that you can think of nothing else 着迷的; 縈繞於心的: *He has an obsessive interest in death.* 他對死亡過於感興趣。

ob·so·les·cent /ˌɒbsəˈlɛsənt; ˌɒbsəˈlɛsənt/ *adj* being used less and less 逐步廢棄的; 逐漸過時的 –**obsolescence** *n* [U]

ob·so·lete /ˈɒbsəliːt; ˈɒbsəliːt/ *adj* no longer used 已廢棄的; 已過時的: *obsolete machinery* 已廢棄的機器

ob·sta·cle /ˈɒbstəkl; ˈɒbstəkəl/ *n* something which gets in the way and prevents action, movement, or success 障礙(物); 妨礙(物): *Their different religions were an obstacle* **to** *their marriage.* 他倆宗教信仰的不同是他們婚姻的一大障礙。

ob·stet·rics /əbˈstɛtrɪks; əbˈstɛtrɪks/ *n* [U] the branch of medicine concerned with the birth of children 產科學 –**obstetric** *adj* –**obstetrician** /ˌɒbstəˈtrɪʃən; ˌɒbstəˈtrɪʃən/ *n*

ob·sti·nate /ˈɒbstɪnət; ˈɒbstənət/ *adj* **1** determined not to change your opinions or behaviour 頑固的; 固執的; 倔強的: *He's a very obstinate child.* 他是個非常倔強的孩子。 **2** difficult to get rid of 難以擺脱的: *an obstinate pain* 難以治癒的疼痛 –**obstinately** *adv* –**obstinacy** *n* [U]

ob·struct /əbˈstrʌkt; əbˈstrʌkt/ *v* [T] **1** to block 阻塞; 堵住: *The accident obstructed the road.* 那起事故阻塞了道路。 **2** to prevent something from advancing 阻礙; 阻撓: *obstructing the course of justice by withholding information* 以隱瞞消息來妨礙司法公正 –**obstruction** /əbˈstrʌkʃən; əbˈstrʌkʃən/ *n* [C;U]: *an obstruction in the road* 路上的障礙物 –**obstructive** /-tɪv; -tɪv/ *adj*

***ob·tain** /əbˈten; əbˈteɪn/ *v* [T] to get something 得到, 獲得〔某物〕: *Further information can be obtained* **from** *our head office.* 進一步的資料可以向我們的總部索取。 –**obtainable** *adj*: *I'm afraid that the record you asked for is no longer obtainable.* 我恐怕你

要的唱片再也買不到了。

ob·tru·sive /əb'truːsɪv; əb'truːsɪv/ *adj* unpleasantly noticeable 過分突出而討人厭的 – **obtrusively** *adv*

ob·tuse /əb'tjus; əb'tjuːs/ *adj* **1** *fml* stupid or slow to understand〔正式〕愚笨的；遲鈍的 **2** **obtuse angle** *tech* an angle between 90° and 180°〔術語〕鈍角〔在90°至180°之間〕 –**obtusely** *adv* –**obtuseness** *n*

★ob·vi·ous /ˈɒbvɪəs; ˈɒbvɪəs/ *adj* easy to see and understand 明顯的；明白的；顯而易見的: *It's quite obvious that he's lying.* 很明顯他是在撒謊。–**obviousness** *n* [U]

★ob·vi·ous·ly /ˈɒbvɪəslɪ; ˈɒbvɪəslɪ/ *adv* it can be easily seen that 明顯地: *Obviously, you didn't read it.* 你顯然沒有讀過它。

★oc·ca·sion /əˈkeʒən; əˈkeɪʒən/ *n* **1** [C] a time when something happens〔事情發生的〕時刻，時候: *On that occasion I was not at home.* 那時我不在家。–see 見 CHANCE (USAGE用法) **2** [sing] a suitable time 時機，機會: *This is hardly the occasion for an argument.* 這根本不是爭論的時候。 **3** [sing] reason 原因；理由: *There was no occasion to be so rude to your uncle.* 你沒有理由對你叔叔那麼粗魯。 **4** [C] a special event or ceremony 特殊的事件或儀式；特殊場合: *The royal visit was quite an occasion.* 國王的訪問是一次特殊的盛會。 **5** **on occasion** from time to time 偶爾；有時

★oc·ca·sion·al /əˈkeʒənl; əˈkeɪʒənəl/ *adj* [only before a noun 只用於名詞前] happening from time to time 偶爾的；偶然的: *I get the occasional business trip abroad.* 我偶爾會出國外出差。–**occasionally** *adv*

oc·cult /əˈkʌlt; ˈɒkʌlt/ *adj* secret, magical, and mysterious 祕密的；神祕的；奧祕的 –**the occult** *n*

oc·cu·pant /ˈɒkjəpənt; ˈɒkjʊpənt/ *n fml* someone who lives, works, or is in a certain place〔正式〕居住者；佔有人: *The letter was addressed to the occupant of the house.* 這封信是寄給那屋子的住戶的。

★oc·cu·pa·tion /ˌɒkjəˈpeʃən; ˌɒkjʊˈpeɪʃən/ *n* **1** [C] a job 職業，工作 –see 見 JOB (USAGE 用法) **2** [C] something you like doing in your free time 消遣: *Gardening is a peaceful occupation.* 園藝是一項寧靜的消遣活動。 **3** [U] the act of taking control of a place or the period when that place is under your control 佔有(期)；佔領(期)；居住(期): *She was born in France during the German occupation.* 她是在德軍佔領期間在法國出生的。

oc·cu·pa·tion·al /ˌɒkjəˈpeʃənl; ˌɒkjʊˈpeɪʃənəl/ *adj* caused by or connected with your job 職業引起的；職業的: *For professional footballers, broken bones are an occupational hazard.* 對職業足球運動員來說，骨折是職業上的風險。

oc·cu·pi·er /ˈɒkjəpaɪə; ˈɒkjʊpaɪər/ *n* the person who lives or works in a place 居住者；佔用者

★oc·cu·py /ˈɒkjəˌpaɪ; ˈɒkjʊˌpaɪ/ *v* **occupied, occupying** [T] **1** to live in a building or place 居住；佔有: *Is that house occupied at present?* 那房子現在有人居住嗎？ | *His family has occupied that land for years.* 他的一家在那片土地上已住了多年。 **2** to fill a certain position, space, or time 擔任〔某職〕；佔去〔空間或時間〕: *His father occupies a senior position in the company.* 她父親在公司擔任高級職位。 | *His books occupy a lot of space.* 他的書佔了很多地方。 | *Voluntary work occupies most of his spare time.* 義務工作佔了他大部分的業餘時間。 **3** **be occupied** to spend time doing something 花時間做〔某事〕；從事: *For most of the day I was occupied in writing letters.* 那天大部分時間我都在寫信。 **4** **occupy yourself** to fill your time by keeping yourself busy doing something 使自己忙於〔某事〕: *What do you do to occupy yourself now that you're retired?* 你既已退休，還在忙些甚麼？ | *The old woman occupied herself playing cards with her neighbour.* 那位老太太成天整天玩着與鄰居玩牌。 **5** to move into and hold possession of an enemy's country or town 佔領；佔據〔敵人的國家或城鎮〕

★★oc·cur /əˈkɜː; əˈkɜːr/ *v* **occurred, occurring** [I] **1** to happen 發生: *Many accidents occur in the home.* 許多事故是在家裡發生的。–see 見 HAPPEN (USAGE用法) **2** to exist 存在: *That sound doesn't occur in his language.* 他的母語裡沒有那個音。 **3** **occur to someone** (of an idea) to come into someone's mind〔主意〕被某人想到〔想起〕: *Just as I was leaving the house, it occurred to me that I had forgotten my keys.* 我剛要出門，就想起了我忘記了帶鑰匙。

■ USAGE 用法: If you say that something "occurred" you mean that it happened ☆ 如要説 something "occurred"，意思是"某事發生了": *The accident occurred while passengers were waiting to board the plane.* 旅客在等候上飛機時，那場事故就發生了。But if you say that something "occurred to you" you mean that an idea came into your mind ☆ 但如果説 something "occurred to you"，意思是"某事被想起": *Something suddenly occurred to me while I was waiting for the plane.* (=I had an idea) 我正在等候飛機時，突然想起了一件事。Be careful, therefore, NOT to use this expression if you mean that something happened which concerned you. Instead you can say 因此要注意: 若要表示發生的事情與你有關，就不能用這個詞組，而可以這樣表達: *Something suddenly happened to me while I was waiting for the plane.* 我在等候飛機時，突然發生了意外。

oc·cur·rence /əˈkɜːəns; əˈkʌrəns/ *n* an event or happening 事件; 事故: *What a strange occurrence!* 多麼奇怪的事情! | *an everyday occurrence* 日常發生的事

★**o·cean** /ˈoʃən; ˈəʊʃən/ *n* **1** [U] the great mass of salt water that covers most of the earth 海洋: *Have you ever seen the ocean?* 你見過海洋嗎? **2** [C] (also 又作 **Ocean**) any of the great seas into which this mass is divided 洋〔指地球上的五大洋之一〕: *the Pacific Ocean* 太平洋 **–oceanic** /ˌoʃiˈænɪk; ˌəʊʃiˈænɪk◂/ *adj*

★**o·clock** /əˈklɑk; əˈklɒk/ *adv* used when you are saying what time it is …點鐘〔用於表達時間〕: *"What time is it?" "It's 9 o'clock."* "現在幾點鐘?" "九點正。"

oc·ta·gon /ˈɑktəˌgɑn; ˈɒktəgən/ *n tech* a flat figure with eight sides and eight angles〔術語〕八邊形; 八角形 **–octagonal** /ɑkˈtægənl; ɒkˈtægənəl/ *adj*

oc·tave /ˈɑktɪv; ˈɒktɪv/ *n* a space of eight degrees between musical notes 八度(音階)

Oc·to·ber /ɑkˈtobɚ; ɒkˈtəʊbəʳ/ (also 又作 **Oct.**) *n* the 10th month of the year 十月

oc·to·pus /ˈɑktəpəs; ˈɒktəpəs/ *n* a sea creature with eight arms 章魚, 八爪魚

oc·u·list /ˈɑkjəlɪst; ˈɒkjʊlɪst/ *n fml* an eye-doctor〔正式〕眼科醫生

★**odd** /ɑd; ɒd/ *adj* **1** strange and unusual 奇怪的; 古怪的: *He's such an odd man!* 他這人多麼古怪! | *It was a really odd thing to do.* 幹這事確實很奇怪。**2** [only before a noun 只用於名詞前] separated from a part or set to which it belongs 單隻的; 不成對的: *After sorting out all the washing, I was left with two odd socks.* 我整理完洗好的衣物後, 剩下兩隻不成對的短襪。**3** that cannot be divided exactly by 2 (used of numbers) 奇數的; 單數的〔不能被 2 整除的〕**4** not happening regularly 不固定的; 不規則的; 不定期的: *He likes the odd drink.* 他有時喜歡喝點酒。**5** [only after a noun 只用於名詞後] near in number〔數字〕餘的; 帶零頭的: *They lived abroad for some thirty odd years.* 他們在國外住了三十多年。**6 odd jobs** small practical jobs that you do in your home, for example mending things 零活〔如修理東西〕

odd·i·ty /ˈɑdəti; ˈɒdəti/ *n* **oddities** a strange person or thing 怪人; 奇特的東西

odd·ly /ˈɑdli; ˈɒdli/ *adv* **1** strangely 奇怪地; 古怪地: *He spoke oddly.* 他說話很奇怪。**2 oddly enough** a phrase used to introduce something that is strange 說也奇怪〔用於談到奇怪的事〕: *Oddly enough, he didn't remember his own birthday.* 說也奇怪, 他連自己的生日都不記得了。

odd·ments /ˈɑdmənts; ˈɒdmənts/ *n* [pl] pieces left over, usually from a roll of material 零碎物件; 零頭: *I'm going to make a quilt out of all these oddments.* 我要把所有這些零頭布拼成一張被子。

odds /ɑdz; ɒdz/ *n* [pl] **1** the probability that something will or will not happen〔事情發生的〕機會; 可能性: *The odds are that he will fail his exam.* 他考試可能會不及格。**2** this probability expressed in numbers when making a BET〔打賭的〕賠率: *If you bet £1 on a horse with the odds at 10 to 1 and the horse wins, you get £11 back.* 如果你用一英鎊在賠率為十比一的馬上壓注, 馬獲勝後你就可得到十一英鎊。**3 at odds with** in disagreement with 與…意見不合; 與…有矛盾 **4 it makes no odds** *BrE* it makes no difference or has no importance〔英式〕沒有差別; 無關緊要

odds and ends /ˌ · · ˈ ·/ *n* [pl] small articles without much value 零星雜物, 零碎東西

odds-on /ˌ · ˈ· ◂/ *adj* very likely to win 很可能獲勝的: *It's odds-on that he'll win.* 他很可能獲勝。| *the odds-on favourite to win* 有望獲勝的熱門馬〔競選者〕

ode /od; əʊd/ *n* a poem addressed to a person or thing 頌詩; 頌歌

o·di·ous /ˈodiəs; ˈəʊdiəs/ *adj fml* very unpleasant〔正式〕可憎的; 討厭的

o·dom·e·ter /oˈdɑmətɚ; əʊˈdɒmɪtəʳ/ *n* the usual American word for〔美式〕= MILEOMETER

o·dour /ˈodɚ; ˈəʊdəʳ/ *n* (**odor** *AmE*〔美式〕) a smell, especially an unpleasant one 氣味〔尤指〕臭氣 **–see** 見 SMELL (USAGE用法) **–odourless** *adj*

oe·soph·a·gus /iˈsɑfəgəs; ɪˈsɒfəgəs/ *n* (also 又作 **esophagus**) *tech* the food tube leading down into the stomach〔術語〕食道

★**of** /əv; əv; *strong* 強讀 ɑv; ɒv/ *prep* **1** forming part of something, relating to something, or belonging to something 屬於〔某事物〕: *One of the legs of the table was broken.* 桌子的一條腿斷了。| *the colour of her hair* 她頭髮的顏色 | *the size of the room* 房間的大小 | *the King of England* 英國的國王 | *a friend of mine* 我的一個朋友 | *the Univeristy of London* 倫敦大學 | *the economic boom of the 1980s* (二十世紀)八十年代的經濟繁榮時期 **2** made from something 由〔某物〕製成的: *a crown of gold* 金冕 **3** containing something 包含〔某物〕的: *a bag of potatoes* 一袋馬鈴薯 | *a cup of tea* 一杯茶 **4** showing something 顯示〔某物〕的: *a picture of lion* (畫有)獅子的畫 | *a map of England* 英國地圖 **5** used in expressions showing amounts〔用於表示數量〕: *two pounds of sugar* 兩磅食糖 | *a group of students* 一羣學生 | *a piece of cake* 一塊蛋糕 **6** used when giving a detailed amount〔用於表示具體的數量〕: *a pay rise of 9%* 百分之九的加薪 | *a child of eight years old* 八歲的兒童 | *a man of fifty* 五十歲的男子 **7** by 由…所著的: *the plays of Shakespeare* 莎士比亞的戲劇 **8** used when you are giving the name of a place〔用於表示地名〕: *the city of New York* 紐約市 | *the town of Stamford* 斯坦福德市 **9** used in dates〔用於表示日期〕: *the 27th of February* 2月27日 **10 of a, of an** during a period of time 在一段時間裡: *I like to go to the park of an afternoon.* 我喜歡下午去公園。

off¹ /ɔf; ɒf/ *adv, prep* **1** *adv, prep* away from a place, or no longer on or in a place 離開; 脫離; 脫落: *Keep off the grass.* 請勿進入草坪。| *She cut a piece off the loaf.* 她從麵包上切下了一片。| *The door handle's fallen off.* 門的把手脫落了。| *The car drove off.* 汽車開走了。| *My parents have gone off to America for the summer.* 我父母親已動身去美國過夏天。| *She got off the train.* 她下了火車。| *The bus stopped and I got off.* 公共汽車一停我就下了車。| *He took his shoes off.* 他脫掉了鞋子。| *A picture had fallen off the wall.* 一幅畫從牆上掉了下來。–see picture on page 764 見 764 頁彩圖 **2** *adv* not switched on (used of a light or a machine) 關掉(指電燈或機器): *Switch the light off, please.* 請把電燈關掉。| *Can you check that the cooker's off?* 你去看看爐子關了沒有, 好嗎? **3** *adv* not going to happen 不舉行的; 取消了的: *I'm afraid the party's off.* 我恐怕聚會取消了。| *The deal's off.* 交易取消了。**4** *adv, prep* away from work, either because you are ill or on holiday〔因生病或度假〕不工作; 不上班: *I've just had two weeks off.* 我剛休假兩個星期。| *It's his day off today.* 今天他放假。| *I'm off work today.* 我今天不上班。**5** *prep* leading from a road〔道路〕從…分岔: *a narrow street leading off the High Street* 從高街分岔出來的一條狹窄小街 **6** *prep* in the sea near a place 靠近…的海面: *an island off the West coast of Africa* 非洲西海岸附近的一個島嶼 **7** *adv* no longer good to eat (used of food) 不能再吃(指食物); 變質: *The milk's gone off.* 這牛奶已變質。**8** **off your food** not wanting to eat because you are ill〔因病而〕不想吃東西 **9** *prep* no longer taking a drug or a medicine regularly 不再按時服藥; 停服: *She finally managed to come off the tranquillizers.* 她終於設法克服鎮定劑。**10** **a bit off** *infml* not acceptable〔非正式〕不能接受的; 不妥當的: *I thought it was a bit off that she didn't bother to thank me.* 我認為她不肯向我說一聲謝謝是有點過分。**11** **they're off** = the people or animals in a race have started running〔比賽中的人或動物〕已經起跑 **12** **off and on** sometimes, but not continuously 斷斷續續地; 有時: *It's been raining off and on all morning.* 整個上午都在斷斷續續地下着雨。

off² *adj* **1** [never before a noun 不能用於名詞前] no longer good to eat (used of food)〔食物〕不能再吃的; 變質的: *I think this meat is off.* 我覺得這肉已變質。**2** **an off day** a day when you are not able to do things as well as you usually do, for example because you are not feeling very well 有失水準的一天〔如因身體不舒服〕**3** **the off season** the winter, when people do not go on holiday 淡季〔指人們不外出度假的冬季〕

off-col·our /ˌ· '··/ *adj infml* not well〔非正式〕身體不舒服的: *I didn't go to work that day because I felt a bit off-colour.* 那天我沒去上班, 因為我感到有點不舒服。

off-day /'·ˌ·/ *n infml* a day when you don't do things well〔非正式〕不順利的一天: *He's having a bit of an off-day.* 他今天有點不順利。

of·fence /ə'fɛns; 'ɔfɛns/ *n* (**offense** *AmE*〔美式〕) **1** [C] a crime 罪行; 違法行為: *Driving while drunk is a serious offence.* 醉酒開車是一種嚴重的違法行為。**2** [C;U] cause for hurt feelings or displeasure 冒犯; 得罪; 傷感情的因素: *He's always causing offence to his colleagues.* 他老是得罪他的同事。| *He takes offence at everything I say.* 我無論說甚麼他都會生氣。

of·fend /ə'fɛnd; ə'fɛnd/ *v* **1** [T] to hurt someone's feelings 傷害…的感情; 冒犯; 得罪: *She was very offended that I forgot her birthday.* 我忘記了她的生日, 這使她非常生氣。**2** [T] to cause someone displeasure 使〔某人〕不悅〔不快〕: *That new office block offends the eye.* 那幢新建的辦公大樓非常難看。**3** [I] to do wrong 觸犯; 違犯: *His behaviour offends* **against** *the religious laws of this country.* 他的行為觸犯了這個國家的宗教法。

of·fend·er /ə'fɛndə; ə'fɛndəʳ/ *n law* a criminal〔律〕罪犯

of·fen·sive¹ /ə'fɛnsɪv; ə'fɛnsɪv/ *adj* **1** unpleasant or causing offence 令人不快的; 冒犯的; 討厭的: *offensive behaviour* 令人不快的行為 | *an offensive remark* 令人不快的話 **2** **offensive weapon** an object used to attack someone 攻擊性武器: *He was charged with carrying an offensive weapon.* 他被指控攜帶攻擊性武器。**–offensively** *adv*

offensive² *n* **1** a continued attack 進攻; 攻勢 **2** **on the offensive** making a continued attack 採取攻勢

of·fer¹ /'ɔfə; 'ɒfəʳ/ *v* **1** [T] to hold out something to a person for acceptance or refusal 提出…〔以供接受或拒絕〕: *Offer the guests some coffee.* 給客人端些咖啡來。| *They've offered us £85,000 for the house. Shall we take it?* 他們向我們出價八萬五千英鎊買這房子。我們賣不賣? | *I've been offered a job in Canada.* 加拿大有份工作要聘請我去做。

> □ USEFUL PATTERNS 有用句型
> to offer something to someone; to offer someone something

2 [I;T] to express willingness to do something 表示願意〔做某事〕: *She offered, and I didn't say no.* 她表示願意, 我就沒反對。|

> □ USEFUL PATTERNS 有用句型
> to offer something; to offer to do something

She offered to help. 她表示願意幫忙。 | *He's always willing to offer advice.* 他總是樂於提出忠告。 **3** [T] to give something to God〔向上帝〕奉獻; 祭獻

offer² *n* **1** a statement offering to do something 提議: *Thanks for your offer of help.* 謝謝你提出幫助的建議。 **2** something which is offered 提供之物; 出價: *He made me an offer of £5.* 他向我出價五英鎊。

of·fer·ing /ˈɔfərɪŋ; ˈɒfərɪŋ/ *n* something offered, especially to God 贈品;〔尤指給神的〕供品, 祭品

off·hand /ˌɔfˈhænd; ˌɒfˈhænd◂/ *adv, adj* **1** careless and disrespectful 隨便的[地]; 不禮貌的[地]: *an offhand manner* 不禮貌的態度 **2** at once and without time to think 立即; 不假思索地: *I can't give you an answer offhand.* 我不能立即給你回答。

of·fice /ˈɔfɪs; ˈɒfɪs/ *n* **1** [C] a place where business is done 辦公室; 辦事處; 事務所: *I work in an office.* 我在一家事務所工作。 | *a ticket office* 售票處 **2** [C] (also 又作 **Office**) a government department〔政府的〕部; 局; 處: *the Foreign Office* 外交部 **3** [C;U] a position of responsibility or power, especially in government 公職; 官職: *That politician has been in office for 20 years.* 那位政治家已經在職二十年了。 | *That party has held office for over a decade.* 那個政黨執政已經十多年了。

of·fi·cer /ˈɔfəsər; ˈɒfɪsər/ *n* **1** a person in a position of command in the armed forces 軍官 **2** a person who holds a position of some importance, especially in government or a business〔政府或企業中的〕高級官員; 高級職員: *a local government officer* 地方政府官員 **3** a policeman 警察

■ USAGE 用法: **Civil servants** are people in general who work for the government, and **officials** are people who work for a government or other large organization in a position of responsibility ☆ **Civil servants** 是指政府部門的公務員; **officials** 是指為政府或其他大機構擔任負責職務的人: *A strike by* **civil servants** *could damage the government.* 公務員的罷工會使政府受損。 | **officials** *from the Department of Trade and Industry* 工商部的官員 | *British Rail* **officials** *are to hold high level meetings tomorrow.* 英國鐵道部的官員明天將舉行高級會議。 An **officer** is often a member of the armed forces in a position of command, or a member of the police force, but the word is also used in a similar way to **official** ☆ **officer** 常指軍隊中的軍官或警隊中的一員; 但也可像 **official** 那樣使用: *a cus-*

toms **officer** *at the airport* 機場的海關官員 | *the university Careers* **Officer** 大學職業諮詢職員 | *the Public Health* **Officer** 公共衛生部官員

of·fi·cial¹ /əˈfɪʃəl; əˈfɪʃəl/ *n* a person who holds a position of responsibility 官員; 高級職員; 公務員: *a union official* 工會職員 –see OFFICER (USAGE 用法)

official² *adj* approved by or connected with those in power 官方的; 公務的; 正式的: *an official investigation* 官方調查 | *The Prince is engaged — and that's official.* 王子已經訂婚, 那是官方消息。 | *He was accused of using his official car for private business.* 他因用公家的汽車辦私事而受到指責。 | *This uniform is to be worn on official occasions.* 這套制服將在正式場合穿着。

of·fi·cial·ly /əˈfɪʃəli; əˈfɪʃəli/ *adv* **1** formally or publicly 正式地; 官方地: *They have officially announced their engagement.* 他們已經正式宣佈了訂婚。 **2** according to what is said by an official but which may not be true 根據公佈所說〔但可能不是真的〕: *Officially he's on holiday but actually he's in hospital.* 據公佈說他在度假, 其實他在醫院裡。 –opposite 反義 **unofficially**

of·fi·ci·ate /əˈfɪʃiˌet; əˈfɪʃieɪt/ *v* **officiated, officiating** [I] to perform official duties 行使職務; 主持: *Who's going to officiate at your wedding?* 誰來主持你的婚禮?

of·fi·cious /əˈfɪʃəs; əˈfɪʃəs/ *adj* too eager to give orders or to offer advice (a word used to show disapproval) 愛發號施令的, 好管閒事的〔含貶義〕: *an officious manner* 愛使喚人的態度 –**officiously** *adv* –**officiousness** *n*

off·ing /ˈɔfɪŋ; ˈɒfɪŋ/ *n* **in the offing** about to happen 即將發生

off-li·cence /ˈ· ··/ *n* a shop where alcohol is sold to be taken away 持有外賣酒類執照的酒店

off-peak /ˌ· ˈ·◂/ *adj* **1** less busy 較空閒的; 非繁忙的: *Telephone charges are lower during off-peak periods.* 在非繁忙時間電話收費較低。 **2** used during less busy periods 非高峯期用的: *off-peak electricity* 非高峯時間的用電

off·set /ɔfˈsɛt; ˈɒfset/ *v* **off-set, offset, offsetting** [T] to make up for something or act as a balance to something 補償; 抵銷: *The cost of getting there was offset by the fact that it's a very cheap place to live.* 當地低廉的生活費用彌補了去那裡所需的旅費。

off·shoot /ˈɔfˌʃut; ˈɒfʃuːt/ *n* something which grows out of something else, for example a new stem or branch 新莖; 分枝

off·shore /ˌɔfˈʃor; ˌɒfˈʃɔːr◂/ *adv, adj* at a distance from the coast 在近海岸的): *Britain's offshore oil* 英國的近海石油 | *two miles offshore* 離岸兩英里

off·side /ˌɔfˈsaɪd; ˌɒfˈsaɪd◂/ *adj, adv* **1** in a position in which play is not allowed (used of certain sports) 越位(犯規)(的)〔用於某些運動項目〕 **2** the side of a vehicle farthest from the edge of the road 〔車輛〕遠離路邊一側(的)

off·spring /ˈɒfˌsprɪŋ; ˈɔfˌsprɪŋ/ *n* [U] child or children 子女, 後代: *All his offspring were musicians.* 他的子女都是音樂家。

off-white /ˌ·ˈ·◂/ *adj* having a colour that is not a pure white but with some grey or yellow in it 灰白色的; 米色的

★★ **of·ten** /ˈɒfən; ˈɔfən/ *adv* **1** many times 時常; 多次; 經常: *I often spend the afternoon reading.* 我經常在下午看書。| *I don't often see my parents.* 我不常見到父母親。**2 how often?** how many times, or how frequently? 隔多久(一次)?: *How often do you go to France?* 你隔多久去法國一次? **3** in many cases 在很多情況下; 通常: *It's often very difficult to understand what he's saying.* 通常很難聽懂他所説的話。**4 as often as not** at least half of the time 往往; 多半: *As often as not he forgets his homework.* 他往往忘了做家庭作業。**5 every so often** sometimes 有時; 偶爾 **6 more often than not** more than half of the time 經常; 多半: *More often than not she's late for school.* 她上學多半遲到。

o·gle /ˈɒgl; ˈoʊgəl/ *v* **ogled, ogling** [I;T] to look at someone with great interest, especially sexual interest 向〔某人〕做媚眼, 色迷迷地看着: *Most women hate being ogled.* 多數女子都討厭別人色迷迷地看着她們。

o·gre /ˈoʊgə; ˈoʊgɚ/ *n* **1** (in fairy stories) a frightening creature like a very large man, who is thought to eat children 〔童話中的〕吃小孩的妖魔 **2** a person who makes others afraid 可怕的人

oh /o; oʊ/ *interj* an expression of surprise, fear, or pleasure 啊, 喲, 噢, 唉〔表示驚訝、恐懼或歡樂〕

ohm /om; oʊm/ *n tech* a measure of electrical RESISTANCE 〔術語〕歐姆〔電阻單位〕

★ **oil¹** /ɔɪl; ɔɪl/ *n* [U] **1** a fatty liquid used for burning, for making machines run easily, or for cooking 油: *an oil burner* 油爐 | *engine oil* 機油 | *olive oil* 橄欖油 **2 oils** [pl] paints containing oil 油畫顏料

oil² *v* [T] to put oil onto something or rub oil onto someone 給〔某物〕加油; 給〔某人〕上油

oil·field /ˈɔɪlˌfild; ˈɔɪlfiːld/ *n* an area under which there is oil 油田

oil paint·ing /ˈ· ˌ··/ *n* **1** [U] the art of painting in oils 油畫藝術 **2** [C] a picture painted in oils 油畫

oil·rig /ˈɔɪlˌrɪg; ˈɔɪlˌrɪg/ *n* a large piece of apparatus for getting oil from underground, especially from under the sea 石油鑽台〔塔〕;〔尤指海底的〕油井設備

oil·skin /ˈɔɪlˌskɪn; ˈɔɪlˌskɪn/ *n* [C] a piece of clothing treated with oil so that water will not pass through it 防水布(衣), 油布(雨衣)

oil slick /ˈ· ·/ *n* a thin sheet of oil floating on water, especially as a result of an accident to an oil-carrying ship 〔尤指油船發生事故後漂在水面上的一層〕浮油 –see picture on page 470 見 470 頁彩圖

oil-well /ˈ· ·/ *n* a hole made in the ground in order to get oil 油井

oil·y /ˈɔɪlɪ; ˈɔɪli/ *adj* **oilier, oiliest 1** like oil 油(質)的, 似油的: *an oily liquid* 油質液體 **2** covered with or containing oil 塗有油的; 含油的: *dirty oily clothes* 沾滿油污的衣服 | *oily food* 油膩的食品 **3** too polite (a word used to show disapproval) 圓滑的, 會奉承的〔含貶義〕: *I don't like his oily manner.* 我不喜歡他那副圓滑的樣子。

oint·ment /ˈɔɪntmənt; ˈɔɪntmənt/ *n* [C;U] a substance to be rubbed on the skin for medical purposes 油膏, 軟膏; 藥膏

o·kay¹ /oˈke; oʊˈkeɪ/ *adj, adv* (also 又作 **OK**) *infml*〖非正式〗**1** all right 好, 行, 可以; 順利的[地]: *That car goes okay now.* 那汽車現在跑得不錯。| *She's OK now.* 她現在很好。**2** an expression used when asking for or expressing agreement, or giving permission 好嗎, 好的, 可以〔用於表示徵求、同意或許可〕: *Let's go there, okay?* 我們到那裡去, 好嗎? | *"Shall we go there?" "Okay."* "我們到那裡去好嗎?" "好的。" | *"Can I use your car?" "Okay."* "我可以用一下你的車嗎?" "可以。"

okay² *v* **okayed, okaying** [T] *infml* to approve something〖非正式〗批准, 許可〔某事物〕: *Has the bank okayed your request for a loan?* 銀行已經批准你的貸款要求了嗎?

okay³ *n* **okays** *infml* (also 又作 **OK**) approval or permission〖非正式〗批准; 許可: *I got the OK to leave early.* 我獲准提早離開。

★★ **old** /old; oʊld/ *adj* **1** having a particular age …歲的; …久的: *How old are you?* 你年紀多大了? | *The baby is 8 months old.* 那嬰兒八個月大了。| *a thirty-year-old man* 一名三十歲的男子 | *This castle is centuries old.* 這城堡已有幾百年的歷史。**2** having lived for a long time 年老的: *an old man* 一位老人 | *old and young people* 老年和年輕人 **3 the old** old people 老年人: *The old and the young often don't agree.* 老年人和年輕人看法往往不一致。**4** having existed or lasted for a long time 〔存在或延續〕很久的: *old and new books* 舊書和新書 | *old friends* 老朋友 | *an old building* 古老的建築 **5** having been in use for a long time and often no longer useful 陳舊的; 廢棄的: *an old pair of shoes* 一雙舊鞋 | *rather old ideas* 相當陳舊的觀念 | *I'm going to throw away these old clothes.* 我正準備扔掉這些舊衣服。**6** belonging to past times 舊時的; 古老的: *old customs* 舊風俗 | *an old civilization* 古老的文明 | *the good old days* 從前那些美好的日子 **7** former 以前的; 從前的: *He's got his old job back.* 他又重操故業了。| *my old school* 我的母校 **8 of old: a** long ago 從前的: *days of old* 從前的日子 **b** since a long time ago 很早以前: *I know him of old.* 我很早以前就認識他了。

■ USAGE 用法: **1** Compare 比較 **old, ancient, antique**. **Old** is the general word for people or things that have existed for a long time ☆ **old** 一般用來指存在很久的人或物: *an old man* 一位老人 | *an old house.* 一所舊房子。 **Ancient** means "belonging to times long ago" ☆ **ancient** 意為"(屬於)古代的": *the ancient Romans* 古羅馬人 | *ancient history* 古代歷史。 **Antique** describes something that is old and usually valuable ☆ **antique** 用以形容古老而通常有價值的東西: *an antique piece of furniture made by a famous craftsman* 一件由名工匠所做的古董家具 | *a collector of antiques* 古玩收藏家 **2** When you speak about a person, **elderly** is a polite way of saying **old** ☆在談到人時, 用 **elderly** (年長的)比用 **old** 有禮貌: Compare 比較 *an old church* (古老的教堂) and 和 *an old/elderly lady* (老婦人)。

---

old age pen·sion /ˌ· · ˈ··/ *n* [U] money paid regularly by the state to old people〔國家按期付給的〕養老金 **–old age pensioner** *n* (also 又作 **OAP**)

old boy /ˈ· ·/ *n BrE* a former pupil of a school; a woman who is a former pupil of a school is called an **old girl**〔英式〕男校友〔女校友為 **old girl**〕

old·en /ˈəʊldn; ˈəʊldən/ *adj* [only before a noun 只用於名詞前] *lit* long ago〔文〕古時的; 往昔的: *in olden days* 在昔日 | *olden times* 從前

old-fash·ioned /ˌ· ˈ···/ *adj* of a type that is no longer common or popular 老式的; 過時的: *old-fashioned ideas* 陳舊的觀念 | *old-fashioned clothes* 老式的服裝

old mas·ter /ˌ· ˈ··/ *n* a picture by an important painter of an earlier period 古典名畫家的作品

Old Tes·ta·ment /ˌ· ˈ··· ◂/ *n* the first half of the Bible, containing events before the birth of Christ〔聖經〕的)《舊約全書》

old-tim·er /ˌ· ˈ··/ *n* **1** a person who has lived somewhere or done something for a long time 老居民; 老手, 老前輩 **2** *AmE* an old man〔美式〕上了年紀的人, 老人

O lev·el /ˈ· ˌ··/ *n* the lower of the two standards of examination formerly taken at most British schools; an abbreviation for **Ordinary Level**〔縮〕普通程度(考試)〔大部分英國學校過去舉行的教育文憑考試, 分為兩級, 普通程度考試為較低的一級〕

ol·i·gar·chy /ˈɒlɪˌgɑːkɪ; ˈɒlɪˌgɑːkɪ/ *n* **oligarchies 1** [C;U] a type of government in which a few people have all the power 寡頭政治; 寡頭政治集團 **2** [C] the group who

---

govern such a state 寡頭統治集團

ol·ive /ˈɒlɪv; ˈɒlɪv/ *n* a small green or black bitter-tasting fruit which produces oil used in cooking and which can be used as food〔可食用及榨油用的〕橄欖

olive branch /ˈ·· ·/ *n* a sign of peace 橄欖枝〔和平的象徵〕

O·lym·pic Games /oˈlɪmpɪk ˌgemz; əˌlɪmpɪk ˈgeɪmz/ *n* [plural is 複數為 **Olympic Games**] (also 又作 **Olympics**) an international sports event held once every four years in different countries 奧林匹克運動會〔每隔四年一次在不同國家舉行〕 **–Olympic** *adj* [only before a noun 只用於名詞前]

o·me·ga /ˈoʊmeɡə; ˈəʊmɪɡə/ *n* the last letter of the Greek alphabet 希臘字母表的最後一個字母

ome·let /ˈɒmlɪt; ˈɒmlᵻt/ *n* (also 又作 **omelette**) eggs beaten together and cooked in hot fat in a pan 炒蛋; 煎蛋(卷): *a cheese omelet* 乳酪煎蛋卷

o·men /ˈoʊmən; ˈəʊmən/ *n* a sign that something is going to happen in the future 預兆; 徵兆: *a good omen* 吉祥之兆 | *a bad omen* 不祥之兆

om·i·nous /ˈɑmənəs; ˈɒmᵻnəs/ *adj* being a sign of something bad 不祥的, 不吉的: *ominous black clouds* 不祥的烏雲 **–ominously** *adv*

o·mis·sion /oˈmɪʃən; əʊˈmɪʃən/ *n* **1** [U] the act of leaving something out 省略; 刪節; 遺漏: *He's annoyed about his omission from the team.* 他對自己被隊裡漏掉感到很惱火。 **2** [C] something or someone that has been left out 省略的事物; 遺漏的人

o·mit /oˈmɪt; əʊˈmɪt/ *v* **omitted** [T] **1** to leave something out by mistake or on purpose 省略; 刪去; 遺漏 **2** to not do something 忘記, 疏忽〔做某事〕: *He omitted to tell me when he was leaving.* 他忘了告訴我他何時離開。

□ USEFUL PATTERNS 有用句型
to omit something, to omit to do something; to omit doing something

---

om·ni·bus /ˈɑmnəˌbʌs; ˈɒmnɪbəs/ *n* a book containing several works, especially by one writer, which have already been printed separately〔某作家的〕選集, 文集: *a Dickens omnibus* 狄更斯選集

om·nip·o·tent /amˈnɪpətənt; ɒmˈnɪpətənt/ *adj* having complete power 全能的; 有無限權力的 **–omnipotence** *n* [U]

om·nis·ci·ent /amˈnɪʃənt; ɒmˈnɪʃənt/ *adj* knowing everything 無所不知的; 博識的: *an omniscient god* 無所不知的上帝 **–omniscience** *n* [U]

✭on /ɑn; ɒn/ *adv, prep* **1** *adv, prep* touching something and supported or held by it 在…上〔表示接觸、支承等〕: *There was a lamp on the table.* 桌子上有一盞燈。 | *Put the cup*

---

on the shelf. 把杯子放到架子上。| *shelves with books on* 上面擺着書的架子 | *the pictures on the walls* 牆上的那些畫 | *There were a lot of cars on the road.* 馬路上有許多汽車。| *a blue hat with a ribbon on it* 上面繫着絲帶的藍帽子 | *Write your name on a piece of paper.* 把你的名字寫在紙上。**2** adv, prep inside a bus, train, or plane 在〔公共汽車、火車或飛機〕上: *I've never been on an aeroplane.* 我從不坐過飛機。| *The bus stopped and several people got on.* 公共汽車停下後, 好幾個人上了車。–see picture on page 764 見 764 頁彩圖 **3** prep during the day mentioned 在…的〔時候〕: *I'll see you on Tuesday.* 我在星期二和你見面。| *We're going out on Monday evening.* 我們在星期一晚上要出門。| *I always go to town on Fridays.* 我總是星期五到城裡去。| *He's leaving on July 1st.* 他於七月一日啟程。**4** adv used to show that someone continues to do something 不停地〔用於表示繼續做某事〕: *We worked on all night.* 我們整夜不停地工作。| *We talked on, and came to a village.* 我們繼續往前走, 來到了一個村莊。| *Please read on.* 請繼續讀下去。**5 have something on** to be wearing something 身穿某衣服: *He had no coat on.* 他沒有穿外衣。| *men with smart suits on* 身穿漂亮西裝的男子 **6** adv working (used of a light or a machine) 工作着的〔指電燈或機器〕: *Put the light on, please.* 請把燈打開。| *Is the cooker still on?* 爐子還開着嗎? **7** adv happening 正在發生的: *There's a new film on at the cinema in town.* 城裡那家電影院正在上映一部新影片。| *There's a dance on in the village hall tonight.* 今晚鄉村禮堂裡會舉行舞會。| *We had very little money when the war was on.* 戰爭發生那段時間, 我們手頭非常拮据。**8** prep about something 關於〔某事物〕: *a lecture on medieval history* 關於中世紀歷史的講座 | *They sell books on all subjects.* 他們出售有關各類科目的書。**9** prep taking a drug or a medicine regularly 定期吸毒; 按時服藥: *She's on five or six different drugs.* 她服用五、六種不同的藥物。**10** prep receiving an amount of money as your wage 掙〔工資〕: *She's on about £20,000 a year.* 她每年可掙大約兩萬英鎊。**11** prep used when you are saying that one thing happens as soon as another one has happened 一…就…〔表示一件事緊接在另一件事後發生〕: *On hearing of our success, she poured herself a large drink.* 她一聽說我們獲得成功, 就給自己倒了一大杯酒。| *He was greeted with cheers on his arrival.* 他一到達就受到熱烈歡迎。| *On thinking about it, I decided not to go.* 我一想到這事就決定不去。**12 on the left, on the right** at the left or right 在左邊; 在右邊: *The school is just down the road on the left.* 學校就在道路的那一頭靠右邊。| *You'll see the cinema on your right.* 你可以看到電影院在你的右邊。**13 on someone** infml paid for by

someone 〔非正式〕由某人支付: *The drinks are all on me tonight!* 今晚的飲料都由我請客! **14 from now on, from then on, etc** starting now, then, etc and continuing from that time 從現在起; 從那時起: *From now on I'll always drive within the speed limit.* 從現在起, 我一定會限速駕駛汽車。**15 on about something** talking about something for a long time and in a dull way 〔單調而冗長地〕談論: *What's he on about now?* 他又在談論些甚麼? **16 on at someone** complaining to someone or asking them to do something for a long time 以抱怨的方式說服〔某人〕, 向〔某人〕嘮叨: *She's always on at me to tidy my room.* 她老是嘮叨着要我把房間收拾一下。**17 on and off** sometimes, but not continuously 斷斷續續地; 間歇地: *It's been raining on and off all morning.* 整個上午都在斷斷續續地下雨。**18 on and on** continuing to do something for a very long time, in a way that is dull or annoying 〔以枯燥乏味並令人討厭的方式〕不停地, 繼續地: *His talk just went on and on for ages!* 他沒完沒了地說了很久! **19 not on** infml not acceptable 〔非正式〕不能接受的: *That kind of behaviour's just not on!* 那種行為簡直無法接受!

once¹ /wʌns; wʌns/ adv **1** one time and no more 一次, 一回: *I've only met him once.* 我只碰到過他一次。| *We go to the cinema once a week.* 我們每星期去看一次電影。| *I'll help you just this once.* 我只會幫你這一次。**2** some time ago 從前; 曾經: *He once lived in Rome.* 他從前住在羅馬。**3 all at once** suddenly 突然; 忽然: *All at once I heard a noise.* 我突然聽到有喧鬧聲。**4 at once: a** now, without delay 馬上; 立刻: *We set to work at once.* 我們馬上開始努力工作。**b** all together, at the same time 一起: *Everyone was talking at once.* 大家都同時談論起來。**5 for once** for this one time only 就此一次: *For once he was telling the truth.* 他只有這一次說了實話。**6 once and for all** completely and for the last time 最後一次; 一勞永逸地 **7 once in a while** sometimes 有時; 偶爾: *We go to London once in a while.* 我們偶爾到倫敦去。**8 once more, once again: a** one more time 再一次: *I'll write to her once more.* 我將再一次寫信給她。**b** now again, like before 〔像以前那樣〕再來一次: *Once again unemployment is rising.* 失業率再度上升。**9 once or twice** only a few times 一兩次; 數次 **10 once upon a time** at some time in the past; used as the beginning of a children's story 從前, 過去〔用於兒童故事的開頭〕

once² conj from the moment that something happens 一… 便; 一旦…(就…): *Once he arrives we can start.* 他一到我們就可以開始。

once-o·ver /ˈ· ˌ··/ n infml **the once-over** a quick look or examination 〔非正式〕草草過

目; 大略地檢查: *He gave the car the once-over and decided not to buy it.* 他粗略地看了一下這輛汽車, 便決定不買了。

on·com·ing /ˈɒn,kʌmɪŋ; ˈɒn,kʌmɪŋ/ *adj* [only before a noun 只用於名詞前] coming towards you 迎面而來的: *oncoming traffic* 迎面駛來的車輛

one¹ /wʌn; wʌn/ *det, n* **1** the number 1 〔數字〕一: *Only one person came.* 只有一個人來了。 | *I'll see you at one o'clock.* 我將於一點鐘和你見面。 | *one of your friends* 你的一位朋友 **2** only 唯一的: *She's the one person who can do it.* 她是唯一一可以做這件事的人。 **3** a particular or person 某一個; 某人: *I saw her one day in June.* 我在六月裡的某一天見過她。 | *You must come round for a drink one evening.* 找個晚上你一定要過來喝一杯。 | *He can't tell one tree from another.* 他分辨不出這棵樹和另一棵樹有甚麼不同。 **4** the same 同一的: *They all ran in one direction.* 他們都朝同一個方向跑去。

one² *pron* ones **1** a particular thing or person 〔特別指的人或物〕: *New houses aren't generally as well built as old ones.* 一般說來, 新房子造得不比舊房子好。 | *Is that record the one that I lent you?* 那是我借給你的唱片嗎? **2** *fml* used when you are talking about people in general 〔正式〕〔泛指〕任何人: *One should never leave one's keys lying around.* 任何人都不應該到處亂放鑰匙。

■ USAGE 用法: The use of **one** to mean "any person" is now considered to be very formal ☆用 one 表示"任何人" 現已視為非常正式的用法: **One should attempt to understand one's own culture to the best of one's ability.** 每個人都應該盡最大努力去了解自己的文化。 In conversation and in informal writing **you** is commonly used instead ☆在會話和非正式文體中, 常用 you 代替 one: *It is important to understand your own culture.* 了解自己的文化是很重要的。 | **You** can spend the day enjoying **yourself** on the beach. 你可以花一天時間在海濱玩個痛快。

one an·oth·er /ˌ· ·ˈ··/ *pron* see 見 EACH OTHER: *They hit one another.* 他們互相打起來。 | *We often stay in one another's houses.* 我們經常住在彼此的家裡。

one-armed ban·dit /ˌ· · ·ˈ··/ *n infml* a machine with one long handle, into which you put money to try to win more money 〔非正式〕獨臂強盜, 吃角子老虎〔用於賭博的長把手機器〕

one-off /ˌ· ·ˈ·/ *n infml* something done or made once only 〔非正式〕只發生〔做〕一次的事物: *Do you often go abroad on business, or is this trip just a one-off?* 你是經常到國外出差呢, 還是就這一次?

o·ner·ous /ˈɒnərəs; ˈɒnrəs/ *adj fml* difficult or troublesome 〔正式〕艱巨的; 繁重的: *an onerous duty* 繁重的職責

one·self /wʌnˈsɛlf; wʌnˈsɛlf/ *pron fml* used as the object of a verb or PREPOSITION when the subject of a verb is "one" 〔正式〕自己; 自身〔當動詞的主語是 one 時, 用作動詞或介詞的受詞〕〔賓語〕

one-sid·ed /ˌ· ·ˈ··/ *adj* **1** unfair because it takes into account only one side 片面的; 不公正的: *a one-sided view of the problem* 對問題的片面的看法 **2** with one side or team much stronger than the other 一面倒的; 一方強於另一方的: *a one-sided football match* 一面倒的足球賽

one-time /ˈwʌn,taɪm; ˈwʌn,taɪm/ *adj* former 從前的; 一度的

one-up·man·ship /ˌwʌnˈʌpmən,ʃɪp; wʌnˈʌpmənʃɪp/ *n* [U] the art of getting an advantage over others 勝人一籌的本領

one-way /ˌ· ·ˈ··/ *adj* **1** moving or allowing movement in only one direction 單向的; 單行的: *one-way traffic* 單向交通 | *a one-way street* 單行街道 **2** allowing travel to a place but not the return 單程的: *a one-way ticket* 單程票

on·go·ing /ˈɒn,gəʊɪŋ; ˈɒn,gəʊɪŋ/ *adj* continuing 持續發展的; 繼續進行的: *an ongoing situation* 不斷發展的形勢 | *ongoing discussions* 繼續進行的討論

on·ion /ˈʌnjən; ˈʌnjən/ *n* [C;U] a strong-smelling round white vegetable with a dry skin, used in cooking 洋蔥; 洋蔥頭 –see picture on page 504 見 504 頁彩圖

on·look·er /ˈɒn,lʊkə; ˈɒn,lʊkər/ *n* a person who sees something happening without taking part in it 旁觀者, 觀看者

only¹ /ˈɒnlɪ; ˈəʊnlɪ/ *adj* [only before a noun 只能用於名詞前] **1** with no others 唯一的; 僅有的: *Jane was the only one who came.* 簡是唯一一到場的人。 **2** only child a child with no brothers or sisters 獨生子女

only² *adv* **1** not more than 只; 僅僅; 才: *It took only five minutes.* 只用了五分鐘時間。 | *Only three people came.* 只有三個人來了。 **2** used to show that something happened very recently 〔用於表示某事最近剛發生〕: *This law was introduced only last year.* 這項法規去年才實施。 **3** used to show that something is sure to happen 〔用於表示某事肯定會發生〕: *Don't eat all that cake — it will only make you feel sick.* 別把蛋糕全部吃掉, 那只會使你生病。 **4** not only a phrase you use when you are giving the first of two surprising facts 不僅〔用於提到兩件意外事情中的第一件〕: *The cuts will affect not only this school but also other schools in the area.* 這些削減〔項目〕不僅會影響這家學校, 而且會影響區內的其他學校。 **5** only just hardly 幾乎不; 勉強: *I could only just lift it.* 我勉強能把它提起來。 **6** only too very 非常; 很: *What you say is only too true.* 你說的話完全

是事實。

1984 onwards 從1984年以後

only³ *conj* except that; but 可是; 不過: *He wants to go, only he can't.* 他想去, 可是沒法去。

o.n.o a written abbreviation for 〖縮〗= "**or near offer**" 或者接近的價格: *Car for sale £850 o.n.o.* 汽車的售價為八百五十英鎊, 可以還價

on·rush /ˈɑn,rʌʃ; ˈɒnrʌʃ/ *n* a strong movement forward 猛衝; 急流: *an onrush of water* 水的奔流 | *an onrush of people* 人流湧動 **–onrushing** *adj*

on·set /ˈɑn,sɛt; ˈɒnset/ *n* **the onset** the first attack or beginning of something 攻擊; 開始: *the onset of a nasty cold* 重感冒發作 | *the onset of winter* 冬天的開始

on·shore /ˈɑn,ʃɔr; ˌɒnˈʃɔːʳ◂/ *adv, adj* **1** happening on or near the shore 在岸上(的); 近岸(的): *the search for onshore oil* 近海石油的勘探 **2** moving towards the shore 向岸(的): *an onshore breeze* 吹向陸地的微風

on·side /ˈɑnˈsaɪd; ˌɒnˈsaɪd◂/ *adj, adv* in a position in certain sports in which play is allowed 〔某些體育運動中的〕沒有越位(的)

on·slaught /ˈɑn,slɔt; ˈɒnslɔːt/ *n* a fierce attack on something or someone 猛攻; 攻擊: *In his speech, the politician made a strong onslaught on the unions.* 那個政客在發言中對工會進行了猛烈抨擊。

on·to /ˈɑntu; ˈɒntə/ *before vowels* 在元音前 /ˈɑntu; ˈɒntu/ *prep* to a position or point on something or someone 到 [在]... 上: *He jumped onto the horse.* 他跳到了馬上。–see picture on page 764 見 764 頁彩圖

o·nus /ˈonəs; ˈəʊnəs/ *n* responsibility 責任: *The onus of proof lies with you.* 提供證據的責任落在你身上了。

on·ward /ˈɑnwəd; ˈɒnwəd/ *adj* [only before a noun 只用於名詞前] forward in space or time 向前的; 前進的: *the onward march of events* 事態的進一步發展 **–onwards** (also 又作 **onward** *AmE* 〖美式〗) *adv*: *We decided to travel onwards.* 我們決定繼續旅行。| *from*

oops /ʊps; ʊps/ *interj infml* an expression used when someone has made a mistake 〖非正式〗哎喲〔出錯時的用語〕: *Oops! I nearly dropped my cup of tea!* 哎喲! 我差點把這杯茶掉了!

ooze¹ /uz; uːz/ *n* [U] mud or thick liquid, especially at the bottom of a river 泥漿; 〔尤指河底的〕軟泥

ooze² *v* **oozed, oozing 1** [I+adv/prep] (of a liquid) to pass or flow slowly 〔液體〕慢慢地流, 滲出: *Blood was oozing from his wound.* 鮮血正從他的傷口慢慢滲出。**2** [T] to allow liquid to pass slowly out 使〔液體〕滲出, 冒出: *The wound was oozing blood.* 傷口正在流血。

o·pal /ˈopl; ˈəʊpəl/ *n* [C;U] a precious stone which looks like milky water with colours in it 蛋白石

o·paque /oˈpek; əʊˈpeɪk/ *adj* **1** not allowing light to pass through 不透明的; 不透光的: *opaque glass* 不透明的玻璃 **2** hard to understand 難理解的: *an opaque argument* 難理解的論據 **–opaquely** *adv* **–opaqueness, opacity** /oˈpæsəti; əʊˈpæsəti/ *n* [U]

OPEC /ˈopɛk; ˈəʊpek/ a group of countries who produce oil, and plan together how to sell it; an abbreviation for **Organization of Petroleum Exporting Countries** 〖縮〗石油輸出國組織

o·pen¹ /ˈopən; ˈəʊpən/ *adj* **1** not shut 開著的: *Come in! The door's open.* 請進! 門開了。| *with open eyes* 睜著雙眼的 **2 an open mind** not closed to new ideas 開放的思想〔指不拒絕接受新思想的〕 **3** [only before a noun 只用於名詞前] not enclosed 空曠的; 開闊的: *the open country* 廣闊的郊野 | *open fields* 空曠的田野 **4** not covered 敞開的; 無遮蓋的: *an open boat* 敞篷的船 | *Let's eat in the open air.* 我們到戶外去吃吧。| *The courtyard is open to the skies.* 這庭院沒有任何遮蓋。**5** not fastened 未繫好的: *an open shirt* 開襟襯衫 **6** spread out or unfolded 展開的; 攤開的: *an open book* 攤開的書 **7** not certainly decided 尚未決定的; 懸而未決的: *an open question* 懸而未決的問題 | *The job is still open.* 這個職位仍然懸空。**8** not hiding anything 坦率的; 公開的: *Let's be open with each other.* 讓我們彼此坦誠相見。**9** ready for business 開門營業的: *The bank isn't open yet.* 銀行還沒有開門營業。**10** that anyone can enter 對任何人開放的; 可自由參加的: *an open competition* 公開賽 **11 open to something: a** not safe from something 對某事物不設防的: *This book is open to misunderstanding.* 這本書容易引起誤解。**b** willing to receive something 願意接受的: *I'm always open to suggestions.* 我一向很樂於接受各種建議。

o·pen² *v* **1** [I;T] to make open or become open 開; 打開; 張開: *He opened the door.* 他打開了門。| *The door opened.*

門開了。| *Open your eyes.* 睜開你的眼睛。**2** [I;T] to start 開始; 展開: *The story opens in a country house.* 故事始於一所鄉間的房子。| *He opened the meeting with a welcoming speech.* 他以致歡迎辭來開始會議。| *When was the new hospital opened?* 新醫院何時開張? **3** [I;T] to begin business 開始營業: *The bank opens every morning at 9 am.* 銀行每天上午九點開始營業。| *They open their shop 7 days a week.* 他們的商店每星期營業七天。**4** [I;T] to unfold or spread out 展開; 張開: *He opened his umbrella.* 他打開了傘。| *The flowers open in the sunshine.* 花兒在陽光下盛開。**5** [T] to make it possible to use a passage by removing the things that are blocking it 開闢; 開通: *They cleared away the rocks to open the tunnel.* 他們搬掉岩石,打通了隧道。**6 open fire** to start shooting at someone or something 開火

open out *phr v* [I] to become wider 打開; 張開

open up *phr v* **1** [T **open** sthg ↔ **up**] to open something 開發; 開闢: *They opened the country up to trade.* 他們使這個國家在貿易上對外開放。**2** [I] *infml* to open a door 〖非正式〗開門: *Open up or we'll break the door down.* 開門,否則我們就把門打破。

open³ *n* [U] **1 in the open** outdoors 在戶外: *We love eating in the open.* 我們喜歡在戶外吃東西。**2 be out in the open** to become generally known (of opinions, secrets) 公開〔看法、祕密等〕: *I'm glad the news of their divorce is finally out in the open; it's so difficult to keep secrets.* 我很高興他們離婚的消息終於公開,要保守祕密很不容易。

open-air /,·· '·◄/ *adj* [only before a noun 只用於名詞前] outdoor 露天的: *an open-air theatre* 露天劇院

open-end·ed /,·· '··◄/ *adj* without stating any clear aim in advance 無預期目標的: *an open-ended discussion* 不受拘束的自由討論

o·pen·er /'opənə/ *n* a tool used for opening something 開啟工具: *a tin opener* 開罐器

open-hand·ed /,·· '··◄/ *adj* generous 慷慨的

o·pen·ing¹ /'opənɪŋ; 'ɔupənɪŋ/ *n* **1** the act of becoming open or of opening 開幕, 開張: *the opening of a new supermarket* 新超級市場的開張 **2** a hole or space 洞; 孔; 缺口: *We squeezed through an opening in the fence.* 我們從籬笆上的豁口擠過去。**3** a favourable set of conditions which will allow you to do something 有利條件; 良機: *She's looking for an opening in advertising.* 她在尋找做廣告的良機。

opening² *adj* [only before a noun 只用於名詞前] **1** coming first or at the beginning 首先的; 首次的: *The opening night of the new play went very well.* 新戲的首演夜場非常成功。**2 opening hours** the hours when a shop or business is open 〔商店或商行的〕營

業時間: *What are your opening hours?* 你們的營業時間是從幾點到幾點?

o·pen·ly /'opənlɪ; 'əupənli/ *adv* without trying to hide anything 公開地; 公然地: *They talked openly about their plans.* 他們公開談論自己的計劃。

open-mind·ed /,·· '··◄/ *adj* willing to consider new ideas and opinions 願意接受新思想的; 思想開通的

open-plan /,·· '·◄/ *adj* open, not divided into closed rooms (used of offices and buildings) 敞開式佈置的〔指辦公室和大樓的房間內隔牆極少的〕

op·e·ra /'ɒpərə; 'ɑpərə/ *n* [C;U] a musical play in which most of the words are sung 歌劇 **–operatic** /,ɒpə'rætɪk; ,ɑpə'rætɪk◄/ *adj*

op·e·rate /'ɒpə,ret; 'ɑpəreɪt/ *v* **operated, operating 1** [I;T] to work or make something work 操作; (使)運轉: *He operates the loading machine.* 他操作那台裝貨機。| *I'm not sure exactly how computers operate.* 我不能準確說出電腦是如何運作的。**2** [I] (of a business) to be in action 做生意, 經營: *We operate mainly in Europe.* 我們經營的業務主要在歐洲。**3** [I] to cut someone's body in order to remove or repair a diseased or damaged part 動手術: *I'm afraid we'll have to operate.* 恐怕我們非動手術不可了。| *They're operating on her left eye.* 他們在為她的左眼做手術。

operating thea·tre /'···· ,··/ *n* (also 又作 **theatre**) a special room in a hospital where medical operations are done 手術室

op·e·ra·tion /,ɒpə'reʃən; ,ɑpə'reɪʃən/ *n* **1** [U] **in operation** working or having an effect 操作; 運轉; 起作用; 生效: *The new system is now in operation.* 新的制度現已實行。| *When does the new law come into operation?* 這項新法律甚麼時候開始生效? **2** [C] a planned activity 〔有計劃的〕活動, 行動: *We've been asked to finance a mining operation.* 有人請求我們為採礦項目提供資金。| *a famine relief operation* 救濟饑荒活動 **3** [C] a hospital treatment to repair or remove a diseased part of someone's body 手術: *a hip replacement operation* 臀部復位手術

op·e·ra·tion·al /,ɒpə'reʃən; ,ɑpə'reɪʃənəl◄/ *adj* **1** working and ready for use 操作中的; 即可使用的: *The new machines are not yet operational.* 這些新機器未能投入使用。**2** [only before a noun 只用於名詞前] happening while a plan is in operation 〔發生於計劃〕運作中的: *We've had a few operational difficulties.* 我們遇到了幾個運作上的困難。

op·e·ra·tive¹ /'ɒpə,retɪv; 'ɑpərətɪv/ *adj* **1** working or having an effect 運轉的; 運行的: *The school should be fully operative by the new year.* 學校應該在新年時全面運行。**2 the operative word** the most suitable word 最合適的詞

operative² *n* a worker 工人; 技工

op·e·ra·tor /ˈɑpəˌretɚ; ˈɒpəreɪtəʳ/ *n* **1** a person who works a machine or a business 〔機器的〕操作人員; 〔商業的〕經營者: *a lathe operator* 機牀操作員 | *tour operators* 旅行社經營者 **2** someone who works a telephone SWITCHBOARD 〔電話的〕接線員: *I'll have to dial the operator.* 我得打給電話接線員。–see 見 TELEPHONE¹ (USAGE用法)

oph·thal·mic /ɑfˈθælmɪk; ɒfˈθælmɪk/ *adj tech* concerning the medical treatment of people's eyes 〖術語〗眼科的

☆o·pin·ion /əˈpɪnjən; əˈpɪnjən/ *n* **1** [C;U] what a person thinks about something 意見; 看法; 主張: *His opinions are always interesting.* 他的看法總是很有意思的。| *There has been a shift in public opinion.* 公眾的看法已有改變。–see 見 ACCORDING TO (USAGE 用法) **2 in my opinion** a phrase used when you are giving your opinion 照我看來〔用於表達自己的看法〕 **3 have a good/high opinion of** to think that someone or something has good qualities 對〔某人或某物〕有好感; 對〔某人或某物〕評價很高 [RELATED PHRASE 相關詞組 **have a low opinion of**]

opinion poll /·'·· ,·/ *n* a way of finding out what people think about particular events or subjects by asking them questions 民意調查: *An opinion poll of over a thousand people showed 80% in support of the government.* 民意調查表明一千多人之中有八成的人支持政府。

o·pin·ion·at·ed /əˈpɪnjənˌetɪd; əˈpɪnjəneɪtɪ̣d/ *adj* too sure that your own opinions are always right (a word used to show disapproval) 固執己見的, 武斷的〔含貶義〕

o·pi·um /ˈopɪəm; ˈəʊpɪəm/ *n* [U] a drug made from the seeds of the POPPY; it is used in medicines and as an illegal drug 鴉片

☆op·po·nent /əˈponənt; əˈpəʊnənt/ *n* **1** a person who takes the opposite side in a game or competition 對手; 敵手; 對方 **2** a person who opposes something 反對者: *He is one of the government's strongest opponents.* 他是其中一個強烈反對政府的人。

op·por·tune /ˌɑpɚˈtjun; ˈɒpətjuːn/ *adj fml* coming at the right time 〖正式〗合時的; 適時的: *an opportune remark* 合時宜的話 | *They called at an opportune moment.* 他們電話打得正是時候。–opposite 反義 **inopportune**

op·por·tun·ist /ˌɑpɚˈtjunɪst; ˌɒpəˈtjuːnɪst/ *n* a person who takes advantage of every chance for success without considering other people's needs 機會主義者 –**opportunism** *n* [U] –**opportunistic** /ˌɑpɚtjuˈnɪstɪk; ˌɒpətjuːˈnɪstɪk◂/ *adj*

☆☆op·por·tu·ni·ty /ˌɑpɚˈtjunəti; ˌɒpəˈtjuːnəti/ *n* **opportunities** [C;U] a favourable moment or occasion which allows you to do something 機會; 時機:

This job offers the opportunity to work abroad. 這份職業提供出國工作的機會。| *equality of opportunity* 機會均等 | *She had no opportunity to develop her talents.* 她沒有機會發展自己的才能。–see 見 CHANCE (USAGE用法)

> □ USEFUL PATTERNS 有用句型
> an opportunity to do something; an opportunity for someone to do something

☆op·pose /əˈpoz; əˈpəʊz/ *v* **opposed, opposing** [T] to try to prevent something because you do not agree with it 反對: *Local residents opposed the building of a new road.* 當地居民反對修築新的公路。

op·posed /əˈpozd; əˈpəʊzd/ *adj* **1** not in agreement with someone or something 反對的: *She is opposed to the death penalty.* 她反對死刑。**2** opposite or completely different from something 相對的; 相反的: *Their opinions are diametrically opposed.* 他們的意見完全相反。**3 as opposed to** rather than 而不是; 與…對比: *We're talking about business practice as opposed to theory.* 我們在談論經營的實踐, 而不是談理論。

op·po·site¹ /ˈɑpəzɪt; ˈɒpəzɪt/ *n* a person or thing that is completely different to another 對立的人〔物〕: *Black and white are opposites.* 黑和白相反。| *She is very generous, but her sister is just the opposite.* 她很慷慨, 可她的妹妹卻正好相反。

☆opposite² *adj* **1** completely different 完全不同的; 相反的: *They set off in opposite directions.* 他們朝着相反的方向出發。**2** facing 對面的; 相對的: *There were illustrations on the opposite page.* 在相對的那一頁上有些插圖。| *We live on the opposite side of the street.* 我們住在街的對面。| *There were lights on in the houses opposite.* 對面的那些房子裡亮着了燈。| *I was watching the man sitting opposite.* 我看着那坐在對面的男子。**3 opposite number** a person who does the same job as you but in a different department or organization 〔在另一部門或組織中的〕職務相同的人

opposite³ *prep* facing 在…的對面: *We live opposite the village green.* 我們住在村鎮公用綠地的對面。–see picture on page 764 見 764 頁彩圖

☆☆op·po·si·tion /ˌɑpəˈzɪʃən; ˌɒpəˈzɪʃən/ *n* **1** [U] the act of being opposed to something or fighting against it 反對; 反抗: *The changes met with a lot of opposition from the workforce.* 那些變動遭到了許多職工的強烈反對。**2 the opposition** [+sing/pl verb] the political parties who are not in power 反對黨; 在野黨: *The opposition are going to vote against the government.* 反對黨將投票反對政府。| *The opposition is united on this issue.* 反對派在這個問題上已形成共識。| *opposition groups* 反對派團體 **3** the sports team or person you are playing against 對手; 對方隊: *Two players managed to break through the opposition's defence.* 有兩個隊員設法突破了對方的防守。

op·press /əˈprɛs; əˈpres/ *v* [T] **1** to treat people in a hard and cruel way 壓迫, 壓制〔某人〕 **2** to make you feel worried or sad 使〔某人〕擔心[難過]: *The threat of war oppressed us all.* 戰爭的威脅使我們都憂心忡忡。

op·pres·sion /əˈprɛʃən; əˈpreʃən/ *n* [U] **1** the act of treating people in a hard and cruel way 壓迫; 壓制 **2** a feeling of worry or sadness 壓抑; 鬱悶

op·pres·sive /əˈprɛsɪv; əˈpresɪv/ *adj* **1** cruel and unjust 壓迫的; 暴虐的; 不公正的: *an oppressive government* 嚴苛的政府 **2** unpleasantly hot (used of the weather) 悶熱的〔指天氣〕 **3** making you feel worried or sad 壓抑的; 令人苦惱的: *an oppressive silence* 難以忍受的寂靜 –**oppressively** *adv* –**oppressiveness** *n* [U]

op·pres·sor /əˈprɛsɚ; əˈpresər/ *n* a person who rules in a cruel way 壓迫者, 暴君

opt /ɑpt; ɒpt/ *v* **1** **opt for something** to choose something 選擇某事物 **2** **opt to do something** to choose to do something 選擇做某事

opt out *phr v* [I] to choose not to take part in something 決定不參加, 決定退出

op·tic /ˈɑptɪk; ˈɒptɪk/ *adj* [only before a noun 只用於名詞前] related to the eyes 眼睛的; 視覺的

op·ti·cal /ˈɑptɪkl; ˈɒptɪkəl/ *adj* [only before a noun 只用於名詞前] **1** related to your sense of sight 視覺的; 視力的: *an optical illusion* 視錯覺, 錯視 **2** using light for recording and storing information 光的; 光學的: *an optical disk* 光盤[碟] –**optically** *adv*

op·ti·cian /ɑpˈtɪʃən; ɒpˈtɪʃən/ *n* a person who makes and sells glasses and CONTACT LENSES 眼鏡(製造)商; 配製眼鏡技師

op·tics /ˈɑptɪks; ˈɒptɪks/ *n* [U] the scientific study of light 光學

op·ti·mis·m /ˈɑptəˌmɪzəm; ˈɒptɪˌmɪzəm/ *n* [U] the belief that the future will be good, and that things will end well 樂觀; 樂觀主義 –**optimist** *n*

op·ti·mis·tic /ˌɑptəˈmɪstɪk; ˌɒptɪˈmɪstɪk◂/ *adj* feeling hopeful about the future 樂觀的 –**optimistically** /-klɪ; -kli/ *adv*

op·ti·mum /ˈɑptəməm; ˈɒptɪməm/ *adj* [only before a noun 只用於名詞前] the best possible 最佳的; 最適宜的: *optimum conditions for growing rice* 種植水稻的最佳條件

op·tion /ˈɑpʃən; ˈɒpʃən/ *n* **1** [sing] the freedom to choose whether you will do something or not 選擇的自由: *You must do it; you have no option.* 你一定要做這件事, 你沒有選擇餘地。 **2** [C] a choice 選擇: *As I see it, there are two options open to us.* 據我看來, 我們可以有兩種選擇。

op·tion·al /ˈɑpʃənl; ˈɒpʃənəl/ *adj* which may

be chosen or not chosen 可選擇的; 非強制的: *All students have to take Maths and English, but other subjects are optional.* 所有學生都必須修讀數學和英語課, 但其他科目是選修的。

op·u·lent /ˈɑpjələnt; ˈɒpjʊlənt/ *adj* very wealthy and expensive-looking 富裕的; 闊綽的 –**opulence** *n* [U]

or /ɚ; ər, *strong* 強讀 ɔr; ɔːr/ *conj* **1** used when you are giving a list of possibilities 或, 或者; 還是〔用於提到一系列的可能性〕: *Would you like coffee or tea?* 你想喝咖啡還是茶? | *I'll see you either on Monday or Tuesday.* 我星期一或者星期二來看你。 | *They cost two or three hundred pounds.* 它們的價錢為二百或三百英鎊。 | *"Bank" may mean the edge of a river. Or, it may mean a place where you can leave your money safely.* "bank" 可指"河岸", 還可以指"銀行"。 **2** otherwise 否則, 要不然: *Put your coat on or you'll be cold.* 穿上你的外衣, 否則你會覺得冷的。 | *He can't be that ill or he wouldn't have gone out.* 他不可能病得很重, 否則他就不會出去了。 **3** **or so** about 大約; 左右: *I'll be there in an hour or so.* 我大約一小時之內就到那裡。 **4** **or else** used when you mention a second possibility 否則; 要不然〔用於提到第二種可能性〕: *We could do it now or else we could leave it till the morning.* 我們可以現在做, 要不然就要明天早上才做。

o·ral /ˈɔrəl; ˈɔːrəl/ *adj* **1** spoken, not written 口頭的; 口述的: *an oral examination* 口試 **2** concerning your mouth or using your mouth 口(腔)的; 口服的: *oral hygiene* 口腔衞生 –**orally** *adv*

or·ange¹ /ˈɔrɪndʒ; ˈɒrɪndʒ/ *n* a very common reddish-yellow round fruit which is sweet and juicy and has a thick skin 柑橘; 橙 –see picture on page 504 見 504 頁彩圖

orange² *adj*, *n* [U] reddish-yellow 橘黃色的; 橙色的 –see picture on page 243 見 243 頁彩圖

o·rang·u·tang /oˈræŋuˌtæŋ; ɔːˌræŋuːˈtæŋ/ *n* (also 又作 **orang-utan**) a large monkey with reddish-brown hair and no tail 猩猩

o·ra·tion /oˈreʃən; əˈreɪʃən/ *n fml* a formal and solemn public speech 〔正式〕演說, 演講

or·a·tor /ˈɔrətɚ; ˈɒrətər/ *n* a person who is good at making formal speeches in public 演說者; 演說家 –**oratory** *n* [U]

or·bit¹ /ˈɔrbɪt; ˈɔːbɪt/ *n* the curved path of an object moving round a PLANET or the sun 〔物體繞行星或太陽運行的〕軌道 –**orbital** *adj*

orbit² *v* [I;T] to move round something in an orbit 繞...的軌道運行

or·chard /ˈɔrtʃɚd; ˈɔːtʃəd/ *n* a field where fruit trees grow 果園

or·ches·tra /ˈɔrkɪstrə; ˈɔːkɪˌstrə/ *n* a large group of people who play musical instruments together 管弦樂隊: *The orchestra meets for rehearsal every Tuesday evening.*

管弦樂隊每星期二晚上排練。–**orchestral** /ɔr-ˈkɛstrəl; ɔːˈkestrəl/ *adj* [only before a noun 只用於名詞前]

or·chid /ˈɔrkɪd; ˈɔːkɪ̥d/ *n* a plant with unusual and beautiful flowers 蘭花; 蘭科植物

or·dain /ɔrˈden; ɔːˈdeɪn/ *v* **1 be ordained** become a priest in a special ceremony 委任為牧師: *She was ordained the first woman priest of her church.* 她被委任為她的教會中的第一個女牧師。**2** [T; +that] *fml* to order something to happen〖正式〗命令; 判定

or·deal /ɔrˈdil; ɔːˈdiːl/ *n* a difficult or painful experience 苦難的經歷; 嚴峻的考驗

★**or·der**[1] /ˈɔrdɚ; ˈɔːrdər/ *n* **1** [U] the way in which things are arranged in relation to each other 次序, 順序: *The names are filed in alphabetical order.* 名字都按字母排列順序存檔。| *The items are listed in order of importance.* 這些項目都按其重要性的順序列出。| *We must work towards a new social order.* 我們一定要努力實現新的社會秩序。**2** [U] the state in which things are neatly arranged in their proper place 整齊; 井然有序: *She longed for stability and order in her life.* 她渴望生活安定又有條理。| *It only took me a few minutes to put the room in order.* 我只花了幾分鐘時間就把房間收拾乾淨。**3** [U] the state in which people are behaving well and laws or rules are being obeyed 秩序; 紀律; 治安: *He couldn't keep order in the classroom.* 他無法維持課堂的秩序。| *The police were called in to help restore order.* 警察奉召到來協助恢復治安。**4** [C] a command 命令; 指示: *You must obey my orders.* 你必須服從我的命令。| *I give the orders round here!* 這兒的一切由我指揮! **5** [C] a request to supply goods 訂購; 訂貨; 訂單: *You can either write to us or place your order by telephone.* 你可以寫信或以電話向我們訂購。**6** [C] the goods that are supplied in accordance with your request 訂購的貨物: *Your order will be sent off today and should reach you tomorrow.* 你們訂購的貨物今天寄出, 明天應該可以收到。**7** [C] a group of people who live according to a particular set of religious rules 神職人員團體 **8 in order: a** arranged in the correct way 按順序排列的: *Are those invoices in order?* 那些發票是按順序排列的嗎? **b** *fml* acceptable〖正式〗可接受的, 適當的: *It would be quite in order for you to ask for a refund of your money.* 你要求退款是非常合情合理的。**9 in order to, in order that** with a particular purpose 為了〔某一目的〕: *We went by car in order to save time.* 我們坐汽車去是為了節省時間。| *I walked quietly in order not to wake the children.* 為了不弄醒孩子們, 我走得很輕。| *The government has to continue with these policies in order that inflation can be brought down as quickly as possible.* 為了使通貨膨脹盡快回落, 政府不得不繼續推行這些政策。**10 in the order of, of the order of**

about 大約: *We spent something in the order of £50,000.* 我們花了大約五萬英鎊。**11 on order** 〔貨物〕訂購中: *The book you want is still on order and should be here next week.* 你要的書還在訂購, 下星期應該可以送來。**12 out of order: a** not arranged in the correct way 不按順序: *These papers are all out of order.* 這些文件都放得亂七八糟。**b** not working 不運轉; 出故障: *The telephone's out of order.* 電話壞了。**c** not in accordance with the rules of a formal meeting, and so not acceptable 違反〔會議〕規程: *His interruption was ruled to be out of order.* 他的打擾被定作違反了會議規則。**13 under orders** obeying someone's orders 受〔某人〕的指揮; 遵〔某人〕之命: *They claimed that they were simply acting under orders.* 他們聲稱自己只是在奉命執行任務。

★**order**[2] *v* **1** [T; +that] to give a command to someone 命令, 指示; 囑咐: *The minister has ordered an inquiry into the accident.* 部長已下令調查這起事故。| *She ordered me to leave the room.* 她命令我離開房間。| *The commander has ordered that the troops should withdraw from the area.* 指揮官已經命令部隊從這地區撤退。

□ **USEFUL PATTERNS** 有用句型
to order something; to order someone to do something; to order that…

2 [I;T] to ask for something to be brought or sent to you 訂購; 預訂: *Shall I order a taxi?* 我去叫一輛計程車好嗎? | *I've ordered a new carpet for the sitting room.* 我已經為起居室預訂了一塊新的地毯。| *The waiter came over and asked if we were ready to order.* 服務員過來問我們是否已準備點菜。**3** [T] to arrange things in a particular way 安排; 整理: *the way in which we order our lives* 我們安排生活的方式

■ **USAGE** 用法: Compare 比較 **order**, **command**, **tell**. People can **order** or **give orders** if they have the right to be obeyed ☆ 有權發號施令的可以"下命令"或"作指示"(**order** or **give orders**): *The doctor ordered me to rest for a week.* 醫生囑咐我休息一星期。**Command** has the same meaning, but is most often used in a military sense ☆ **Command** 的意思相同, 但大多用於軍事方面: *The general ordered/commanded his men to advance.* 將軍命令士兵前進。**Tell** is similar to **order** but less strong ☆ **tell** 與 **order** 的意思相似, 但語氣不如 **order** 有力: *She told me to come as early as possible.* 她叫我盡量早點來。

or·dered /ˈɔrdɚd; ˈɔːdəd/ *adj* done or arranged in a regular, tidy way 安排好的; 整

齊的; 有條理的: *In the hospital, everything was well ordered.* 醫院裡一切都井然有序。

or·der·ly¹ /'ɔrdəlɪ; 'ɔːdəli/ *adj* **1** arranged in a regular, tidy way 有條理的; 整齊的: *He did everything in an orderly manner.* 他樣樣事情都幹得有條不紊。 **2** peaceful and well-behaved 守秩序的; 品行良好的: *orderly behaviour* 規規矩矩的行為 **–orderliness** *n* [U]

orderly² *n* **1** a soldier who looks after an officer 勤務兵 **2** an untrained attendant in a hospital 〔醫院的〕勤雜工, 護理員

or·din·al /'ɔrdnəl; 'ɔːdɪnəl/ *n* (also 又作 **ordinal number** /,··· '··/) a number which shows the order of a set of things; 1st, 2nd, and 3rd are all ordinals 序數〔第一、第二和第三等都是序數〕

or·di·na·ri·ly /'ɔrdn,ɛrɪlɪ; 'ɔːdənər‚li/ *adv* usually 通常地; 慣常地: *Ordinarily, of course, we would telephone first.* 通常當然是由我們先打電話。

★**or·di·nary** /'ɔrdn,ɛrɪ; 'ɔːdənri/ *adj* **1** not unusual or special in any way 普通的; 通常的; 平常的: *I've got an ordinary sort of car, nothing special.* 我買了一輛普通的汽車, 毫無特別之處。 **2 out of the ordinary** unusual 不尋常的; 特殊的 **3 ordinary degree** a first degree that is lower than an honours degree 普通級學位

or·di·na·tion /,ɔrdn'eʃən; ,ɔːdɪ‚'neɪʃən/ *n* [C; U] the act of making someone a priest in a special ceremony 聖職授任

ore /or; ɔːr/ *n* [U] rock or earth from which metal can be obtained 礦石; 礦砂

★**or·gan** /'ɔrgən; 'ɔːgən/ *n* **1** a part of your body that has a particular purpose 器官: *Vital organs such as the liver and the heart are now being used in transplant operations.* 諸如肝和心臟等重要器官現已用於移植手術。 **2** an official organization that has a special purpose 〔官方的〕機構, 機關: *The newspaper was seen as the organ of the government.* 該報社被看作是政府的機構。 **3** a musical instrument with pipes of different lengths through which air is forced; organs are often found in churches and are played like a piano 風琴; 管風琴

or·gan·ic /ɔr'gænɪk; ɔː'gænɪk/ *adj* **1** [only before a noun 只用於名詞前] produced by or found in animals or plants 有機體的; 有機物的 **–opposite** 反義 **inorganic 2** [only before a noun 只用於名詞前] made of many parts with specialized purposes 有組織〔系統〕的: *an organic system* 有組織的系統 **3** using only natural products and no chemicals, or produced in this way 施用有機肥料的: *organic vegetables* 施有機肥料的蔬菜 | *organic farming methods* 施用有機肥料的耕作法 **–opposite** 反義 **nonorganic –organically** /-klɪ; -kli/ *adv*

or·gan·is·m /'ɔrgən,ɪzəm; 'ɔːgənɪzəm/ *n* a very small living being, especially one that can only be seen using a microscope 有機

體; 〔尤指〕微生物

or·gan·ist /'ɔrgənɪst; 'ɔːgənɪst/ *n* a musician who plays an organ 風琴手; 風琴演奏者

★**or·gan·i·za·tion** /,ɔrgənə'zeʃən; ,ɔːgənaɪ-'zeɪʃən/ *n* (also 又作 **organisation** *BrE* 【英式】) **1** [C] a group, club, or business 團體, 組織, 機構: *a charity organization* 慈善機構 **2** [U] the way in which something is arranged or planned 體制; 編制: *The merger will bring about major changes in organization.* 這次合併將引起體制上的重大變化。 **3** [U] the act of planning an event and making the arrangements for it 組織; 安排 **–organizational** *adj*

★**or·gan·ize** /'ɔrgən,aɪz; 'ɔːgənaɪz/ *v* **organized, organizing** (also 又作 **organise** *BrE* 【英式】) **1** [T] to plan and arrange an event 組織, 安排: *Who's organizing the party?* 誰在組織這次聚會? **2** [T] to arrange things in a sensible order 使〔事物〕有條理: *You need to organize your ideas better in this essay.* 你要在這篇論文中把自己的思路組織得更有條理。 **3** [I] to form into a group in order to ask for better pay and working conditions 〔為要求加薪和改善工作環境而〕組成團體 **–organizer** *n*

or·gan·ized /'ɔrgən,aɪzd; 'ɔːgənaɪzd/ *adj* (also 又作 **organised** *BrE* 【英式】) **1** well arranged and so working well 有組織的; 有效率的 **2** able to arrange things well 安排有序的; 井井有條的

or·gas·m /'ɔrgæzəm; 'ɔːgæzəm/ *n* [C; U] the moment of greatest pleasure in sexual activity 性高潮 **–orgasmic** /ɔr'gæzmɪk; ɔː'gæz-mɪk/ *adj*

or·gy /'ɔrdʒɪ; 'ɔːdʒi/ *n* **orgies 1** a wild party with a lot of alcohol and sexual activity 〔有縱酒、淫樂行為的〕狂歡會 **2** a period of a lot of activity of a particular kind 放縱的行為: *They embarked on an orgy of spending.* 他們開始大肆揮霍。

o·ri·ent¹ /'ɔrɪ,ɛnt; 'ɔːrɪənt/ *v* (also 又作 **orientate**) **orient yourself, orientate yourself: a** to discover where you are by looking at a map 〔根據地圖〕確定…的方位 **b** to become familiar with a new situation 使…熟悉〔新情況〕

o·ri·ent² /'ɔrɪ,ɛnt; 'ɔːrɪənt/ *n lit* the **Orient** the Eastern part of the world, including India, China, and Japan 〈文〉東方, 亞洲〔包括印度、中國和日本〕 **–Oriental** /,ɔrɪ'ɛntl; ,ɔːri'entl‚/ *adj*

o·ri·en·ta·tion /,ɔrɪɛn'teʃən; ,ɔːrɪən'teɪʃən/ *n* [U] aims or direction 目標; 方向

o·ri·en·ted /'ɔrɪ,ɛntɪd; 'ɔːrɪent‚d/ *adj* (also 又作 **orientated**) interested in something 對〔某事物〕感興趣的: *an export-oriented company* 以出口為主的公司

or·i·fice /'ɔrəfɪs; 'ɒrɪfɪs/ *n fml* an opening or hole 〈正式〉孔; 開口; 洞

★**or·i·gin** /'ɔrədʒɪn; 'ɒrɪdʒɪn/ *n* [C; U] **1** the

beginning or cause of something 起源; 開端; 起因: *The riot had its origins in unemployment.* 騷亂是由失業引起的。| *a word of unknown origin* 詞源不詳的詞 **2** the race or social class of your parents 血統; 出身: *a young man of West Indian origin* 一個原籍為印度西部的年輕人 | *He was proud of his working class origins.* 他為自己出身於工人階層而感到自豪。

o·rig·i·nal¹ /ə'rɪdʒənl; ə'rɪdʒɪ̯nl/ *adj* **1** [only before a noun 只用於名詞前] first or earliest 起初的; 最早的; 原始的: *The original owner of the house was the Duke of Wellington.* 這房子最早的主人是威靈頓公爵。 **2** new, different, and interesting 新穎的; 與眾不同的; 有獨創性的: *a very original idea* 非常獨到的見解 −opposite 反義 **unoriginal** **3** not copied 非抄襲; 原創作的: *We have a few original paintings.* 我們有幾幅油畫原作。 −**originally** *adv*: *My family originally came from Ireland.* 我家最初來自愛爾蘭。

original² *n* a painting or piece of writing which was the first one made, and is not a copy〔繪畫或文章的〕原作, 原文

o·rig·i·nal·i·ty /ə,rɪdʒə'næləti; ə,rɪdʒɪ̯'næliti/ *n* [U] the quality of being new, different, and interesting 獨創性; 創造力: *Her book shows great originality.* 她寫的書顯示出非凡的獨創性。

o·rig·i·nate /ə'rɪdʒə,net; ə'rɪdʒɪ̯neɪt/ *v* **originated, originating** [I] to begin to happen or exist 開始; 發源: *This TV series originated from a short story.* 這部電視連續劇取材於一部短篇小說。 −**orginator** *n*

or·na·ment¹ /'ɔrnəmənt; 'ɔːnəmənt/ *n* **1** [C] a small attractive object for show in the home 裝飾品: *Their house is full of little ornaments.* 他們的房子裡擺滿了小裝飾品。 −see picture on page 730 見 730 頁彩圖 **2** [U] something which is added to make something else more beautiful 點綴品

or·na·ment² /'ɔrnə,mɛnt; 'ɔːnəment/ *v* [T] to add attractive things to something 裝飾, 點綴

or·na·men·tal /,ɔrnə'mɛntl; ,ɔːnə'mentl◂/ *adj* intended to look attractive rather than to be useful 裝飾(用)的: *an ornamental garden pond* 裝飾性的花園池塘 −**ornamentally** *adv*

or·nate /ɔr'net; ɔː'neɪt/ *adj* having a lot of decoration 裝飾華麗的

or·ni·thol·o·gy /,ɔrnə'θɑlədʒɪ; ,ɔːnɪ̯'θɒlədʒɪ/ *n* [U] the scientific study of birds 鳥類學 −**ornithologist** *n* −**ornithological** /,ɔrnɪθə'lɑdʒɪkl; ,ɔːnɪ̯θə'lɒdʒɪkəl/ *adj*

or·phan¹ /'ɔrfən; 'ɔːfən/ *n* a child whose parents are dead 孤兒

orphan² *v* **be orphaned** to become an orphan 使成為孤兒

or·phan·age /'ɔrfənɪdʒ; 'ɔːfənɪdʒ/ *n* a place where orphans are cared for 孤兒院

or·tho·dox /'ɔrθə,dɑks; 'ɔːθədɒks/ *adj* **1** generally or officially accepted (used of ideas and beliefs) 正統的, 公認的〔指觀念和信仰〕 **2** holding accepted religious or political opinions〔宗教信仰或政治觀點〕正統的 −**orthodoxy** *n* [U]

Orthodox Church /,··· '·/ *n* **the Orthodox Church** part of the Christian church in eastern Europe〔東歐的〕東正教會

or·tho·pae·dic /,ɔrθə'pidɪk; ,ɔːθə'piːdɪk◂/ *adj* (also 又作 **orthopedic**) [only before a noun 只用於名詞前] related to the branch of medicine that deals with bones 整形外科的; 矯形手術的: *I had to see the orthopaedic specialist.* 我得去看矯形外科專家。

Os·car /'ɑskɚ; 'ɒskəʳ/ *n* an American cinema prize 奧斯卡金像獎〔美國獎勵優秀電影的年獎〕

os·cil·late /'ɑsl,et; 'ɒsɪleɪt/ *v* **oscillated, oscillating 1** [I] *tech* to keep moving backwards and forwards between two positions〔術語〕來回擺動 **2** to keep changing from one opinion or state of mind to another 動搖; 猶豫 −**oscillation** /,ɑsə'leʃən; ,ɒsɪ'leɪʃən/ *n* [C;U]

os·prey /'ɑsprɪ; 'ɒsprɪ/ *n* a large bird which catches and eats fish 鶚〔一種捕食魚的大鳥〕; 魚鷹

os·ten·si·ble /ɑs'tɛnsəbl; ɒ'stensɪ̯bəl/ *adj* [only before a noun 只用於名詞前] seeming to be true, but perhaps not really true 表面上的; 貌似真實的: *the ostensible reason* 表面上的理由 −**ostensibly** *adv*

os·ten·ta·tion /,ɑstən'teʃən; ,ɒstən'teɪʃən/ *n* [U] *fml* unnecessary show of wealth or knowledge〔正式〕〔對財富、學識的〕炫耀, 賣弄: *Having four cars and parking them outside the house is pure ostentation.* 弄來四輛汽車並把它們停在屋外, 顯然是為了炫耀。

os·ten·ta·tious /,ɑstən'teʃəs; ,ɒstən'teɪʃəs/ *adj* showing your wealth and knowledge in such a way that everybody sees it 炫耀的; 賣弄的 −**ostentatiously** *adv*

os·tra·cize /'ɑstrə,saɪz; 'ɒstrəsaɪz/ *v* **ostracized, ostracizing** (also 又作 **ostracise**) [T] to stop accepting someone as a member of a group 排斥〔某人〕: *Conscientious objectors were ostracized during the war.* 拒服兵役者在戰爭時期遭到排斥。 −**ostracism** *n* [U]

os·trich /'ɑstrɪtʃ; 'ɒstrɪtʃ/ *n* a large African bird which runs quickly but cannot fly 鴕鳥

oth·er /'ʌðɚ; 'ʌðəʳ/ *det, pron* **1** the remaining one or ones that you have not already mentioned 另一個; 另一些: *He was holding the wheel with one hand and waving with the other one.* 一隻手握著方向盤, 另一隻手揮手示意。| *One of their children is 15 years old, and the other is 12.* 他們的孩子一個十五歲, 另一個十二歲。| *Put that box over there with the other boxes.* 把那盒子和那邊其餘的盒子放在一起。| *Mary's here. Where are the others?* 瑪麗在這裡。其

他人在哪裡? **2** an additional or different person or thing 其他的[另外的]人或物: *There were two other boys with him.* 有另外兩個男孩和他在一起。| *I'd love to travel to other countries.* 我很想到別的國家旅行。| *Some people adapt to change more quickly than others.* 有些人比其他人能更快地適應變化。**3 other people** people in general, not including yourself 別人; 其他人: *She gets on well with other people.* 她和別人相處得很好。| *He's always keen to spend other people's money.* 他花別人的錢總是很起勁。**4 other than** except 除了: *There's no one here other than me.* 這裡除了我沒有別人。**5 the other day, the other night, etc** on a recent day, night, etc 不久前的一天; 不久前的一個晚上: *I saw Jane the other day.* 我前幾天見過簡。| *Your letter arrived the other morning.* 前幾天的一個上午收到了你的來信。

oth·er·wise /ˈʌðəˌwaɪz; ˈʌðəwaɪz/ *adv* **1** used when you are saying what the result would be if something did not happen or was not ture 要不然, 否則[用於表示若某事不發生或不真實可能產生的結果]: *Let's go now otherwise we'll be late.* 我們現在就走吧, 否則要遲到了。**2** in a different way 用別的方法; 另外: *She was determined to go ahead with it although I tried to persuade her otherwise.* 儘管我設法勸她, 但她還是決心繼續幹下去。**3** in every other way 在其他方面; 除此之外: *It was a bit long, but otherwise it was a good film.* 那影片是長了一點, 其他方面倒還不錯。–see Study Note on page 1325 見 1325 頁學習提示

ot·ter /ˈɑtɚ; ˈɒtəʳ/ *n* a small animal which can swim well, and catches and eats fish 水獺

ouch /aʊtʃ; aʊtʃ/ *interj* a cry expressing sudden pain 哎喲[表示突然疼痛]

ought /ɔt; ɔːt/ *v negative short form* 否定縮約式 **oughtn't** [modal verb 情態動詞] **1** used to show that you think someone has a moral duty to do something 應當, 應該[表示道義上有責任做某事]: *She ought to look after her children a bit better.* 她應該把孩子照料得好一點。| *You ought to be ashamed of yourself.* 你應該感到羞恥。| *She ought not to talk to you like that.* 她不該那樣對你說話。| *You ought to have helped her.* 你本應該幫助她。| *He ought to be punished for what he did.* 他應當為自己的所作所為而受到懲罰。**2** used when you are suggesting what someone should do, or saying that something would be a good idea 應該[表示建議某人做某事]: *You ought to see a doctor.* 你應該去看醫生。| *He ought to give up that job and find something better.* 他應該放棄那份工作, 找一份理想一點的幹。| *We really ought to buy a new car.* 我們確實該買一輛新車了。| *I ought to have bought some bread.* 我本來應該買些麵包的。| *Ought I to phone her?* 我該不該打電話給她? **3** used to show that you

expect something to happen or be true 大概會, 預料會: *They ought to win easily.* 他們應該很容易就能獲勝的。| *She ought to be home by now.* 她現在該在家了。| *The weather ought to start improving soon.* 天氣不久應該會轉好。| *They ought to have set out by now.* 他們現在也該出發了。–see Study Note on page 1318 見 1318 頁學習提示

ounce /aʊns; aʊns/ *n* (also 又作 **oz**) **1** a unit for measuring weight, equal to 28.35 grams 益司[英制重量單位, 等於 28.35 克] **2 an ounce of** a small amount 少量; 一點點: *Haven't you got an ounce of sense?* 難道你連一點兒常識都沒有嗎?

our /aʊr; aʊəʳ/ *det* connected with or belonging to the people who are speaking 我們的: *We went in and took off our coats.* 我們走進屋子, 脫掉了外衣。| *We must look after our planet for the sake of future generations.* 我們必須為我們的子孫後代着想, 好好料理我們的地球。

ours /aʊrz; aʊəz/ *pron* something connected with or belonging to the people who are speaking (屬於)我們的(東西): *This is your room, and that one over there is ours.* 這是你們的房間, 那邊的一個是我們的(房間)。| *Their house is very similar to ours.* 他們的房子與我們的(房子)很相似。

ourselves /aʊrˈselvz; aʊəˈselvz/ *pron* **1** used as the object of a verb or a PREPOSITION when the subject of a verb is the people who are speaking and the action is done to the same people 我們自己[反身代詞, 用作動詞或介詞的受詞[賓語]: *We were thrilled to see ourselves on television.* 我們在電視上看到自己時感到很激動。| *We bought a few things for ourselves.* 我們為自己買了幾樣東西。| *We've bought ourselves a new car.* 我們為自己買了輛新汽車。**2** used about the word "we" 我們親自, 我們自己[用來加強 "we" 的語氣]: *We did all the decorating ourselves.* 所有的裝飾都是我們自己幹的。**3 by ourselves** alone, with no-one with us or helping us 我們獨力地; 我們獨自地: *We spent the evening by ourselves.* 我們獨自度過了那個傍晚。| *We had managed to mend the roof by ourselves.* 我們靠自己想辦法修好了屋頂。

oust /aʊst; aʊst/ *v* [T] to force someone to leave a place or job 驅逐; 把…撤職; 罷黜: *The government has been ousted by the army.* 政府已被軍隊廢黜。

out /aʊt; aʊt/ *adv, adj* **1** *adv* not in a place, or so as to be no longer in a place 不在裡面; 向外面: *She opened her bag, and took some money out.* 她打開手提包, 拿出了一些錢來。| *The gate was open and several animals had got out.* 大門開了, 好幾隻動物跑了出去。**2** *adv* away from your home or your place of work 不在家; 不在工作單位: *I'm afraid Miss Hall is out at the* *moment.* 霍爾小姐現在怕是出去了。| *He's gone out for the afternoon.* 他下午已經出去了。| **3** *adj* not correct 不正確的: *Our calculations were out by quite a lot.* 我們的計算有不少差錯。**4** *adv* no longer batting (BAT) in a game of cricket〔板球比賽中的〕出局: *England were all out for 347.* 英格蘭隊以347分全部出局。**5** *adv, adj* no longer fashionable 不流行的, 不時髦的: *Long skirts are definitely out now.* 長裙子現在確實不時興了。**6** *adv* no longer burning (used of a fire)〔火〕熄滅: *The fire's gone out.* 火熄滅了。**7** *adv* no longer shining (used of a light)〔燈〕熄滅: *Could you turn the light out, please?* 請你把燈熄了好嗎? **8** *adv* open (used of flowers)〔花〕盛開地: *The roses are out early this year.* 玫瑰花今年開得早。**9** *adv* not acceptable 不能接受的: *I'm afraid that idea's out.* 我恐怕那個主意不能接受。**10** *adv infml* not working because of a STRIKE《非正式》在罷工中: *The men have been out for two months now.* 這些男人罷工已有兩個月了。**11 the tide is out** = the sea is at the point when it is lowest and furthest from the land 潮水退盡〔處於低位〕**12 out and about** able to get out of bed and go outside again after an illness〔病後〕能外出走動 **13 out for something** trying to get something 試圖得到某物: *They're only out for profit.* 他們只圖利潤。**14 out to do something** trying to do something 試圖做某事: *She's out to make as much money as she can from the deal.* 她一心要從這筆交易中盡量多掙些錢。

out of *prep* **1** towards the outside of something, or away from something 從〔某物〕裡面〔出來〕; 離開: *He took a small packet out of his pocket.* 他從口袋裡掏出一隻小盒子。| *She got up and walked out of the room.* 她站起身, 走出房間。| *He fell out of the window.* 他從窗子掉到了外面。| *It's time you got out of bed!* 你該是時候起牀了! – see picture on page 764 見 764 頁彩圖 **2** used when stating the relation between two numbers 從…中〔用於敍述兩個數字間的關係〕: *Four out of five people agree with the government's economic policies.* 五人之中便有四人擁護政府的經濟政策。**3** having no more of something 用完, 缺乏: *We're nearly out of petrol.* 我們的汽油快用完了。| *I'm afraid we're right out of coffee.* 恐怕我們沒有咖啡了。**4** because of a feeling that you have 出於〔某種感覺〕: *I went to see her out of curiosity.* 我去看她是出於好奇。| *He only did it out of spite.* 他是出於惡意才幹了那事的。**5** used when stating what something is made from 由…製成: *I thought I'd make the frame out of wood.* 我想我可以用木料做框架。**6 out of it** feeling sad because you are not included in something〔因在局外而〕悶悶不樂的: *All the others were enjoying themselves and I felt rather out of it.* 其他人

都玩得很痛快, 我卻因沒有參加而感到悶悶不樂。

out-and-out /ˈ···/ *adj* [only before a noun 只用於名詞前] complete 完全的; 徹頭徹尾的: *He's an out-and-out liar.* 他是個完完全全的說謊者。

out·back /ˈautbæk; ˈautbæk/ *n* **the outback** the part of Australia far away from cities, where few people live〔澳大利亞遠離城市的〕內地

out·bid /autˈbɪd; autˈbɪd/ *v* **outbid, outbid, outbidding** [T] to offer more money than someone else for something that you both want to buy 出價高於〔別人〕

out·board mo·tor /ˈaut‚bord ‚motɚ; ‚autˈbɔːd ˈməutəʳ/ *n* a motor fixed to the back end of a small boat〔裝於小船的〕舷外〔尾掛〕發動機

out·break /ˈaut‚brek; ˈautbreɪk/ *n* sudden start or appearance 突然開始〔出現〕: *After the hurricane, there was an outbreak of cholera.* 颶風過後, 又突然出現了一場霍亂。| *the outbreak of war* 戰爭的爆發

out·burst /ˈaut‚bɜst; ˈautbɜːst/ *n* a sudden powerful period of activity or expression of feeling〔感情或動作的〕爆發, 迸發: *There was an unexpected outburst of gunfire.* 突然響起了一陣意想不到的槍聲。| *an outburst of anger* 勃然大怒

out·cast /ˈaut‚kæst; ˈautkɑːst/ *n* a person who is forced to live away from other people or is not accepted by other people 被抛棄的人; 被逐出的人

out·class /autˈklæs; autˈklɑːs/ *v* [T] to be much better than someone else 遠遠勝過

***out·come** /ˈaut‚kʌm; ˈautkʌm/ *n* an effect or result 後果; 結果; 效果: *What was the outcome of the election?* 選舉的結果如何?

out·crop /ˈaut‚krɑp; ˈautkrɒp/ *n* a large area of rock which stands up out of the ground 露出地面的岩石層

out·cry /ˈaut‚kraɪ; ˈautkraɪ/ *n* **outcries** a public expression of anger〔公眾的〕吶喊, 強烈抗議: *If they try to close the railway, there'll be an outcry.* 如果他們試圖關閉那條鐵路, 一定會遭到強烈的抗議。

out·dat·ed /autˈdetɪd; ‚autˈdeɪtɪd◂/ *adj* no longer in fashion 過時的; 陳舊的

out·dis·tance /autˈdɪstəns; autˈdɪstəns/ *v* **outdistanced, outdistancing** [T] to go a lot faster than someone else in a race〔比賽中〕遠遠超過, 遙遙領先於

out·do /autˈdu; autˈduː/ *v* **outdid** /autˈdɪd; autˈdɪd/, **outdone** /autˈdʌn; autˈdʌn/, **outdoing** [T] to be better or more successful than someone else 勝過〔別人〕; 優於

out·door /ˈaut‚dor; ‚autˈdɔːʳ◂/ *adj* [only before a noun 只用於名詞前] happening or used in the open air 戶外(發生)的; 用於戶外的: *the outdoor life* 戶外生活 | *outdoor shoes* 戶外便鞋 –opposite 反義 **indoor**

out·doors /‚autˈdorz; ‚autˈdɔːz/ *adv* (also 又

作 **out of doors**) outside in the open air 在戶外; 在野外: *Go and play outdoors.* 到室外去玩吧。–opposite 反義 **indoors**

out·er /ˈaʊtə; ˈaʊtəˊ/ *adj* [only before a noun 只用於名詞前] on the outside or at a greater distance from the middle 外面的; 遠離中心的: *outer London* 倫敦市郊 | *The outer walls seem sound.* 外牆似乎完好無損。–opposite 反義 **inner**

out·er·most /ˈaʊtəˌmost; ˈaʊtəməʊst/ *adj* [only before a noun 只用於名詞前] furthest from the middle 最外面的; 離中心最遠的 – opposites 反義 **inmost, innermost**

outer space /ˌ·· ˈ·/ *n* [U] the area beyond the Earth's ATMOSPHERE 外太空

out·fit /ˈaʊtˌfɪt; ˈaʊtˌfɪt/ *n* **1** a set of clothes 全套服裝 **2** *infml* a group of people working together 《非正式》〔一起共事的〕一輩人: *I joined this outfit last year.* 我是去年開始與這幫人一起共事的。

out·flank /aʊtˈflæŋk; aʊtˈflæŋk/ *v* [T] to go round the side and attack an enemy from behind 對〔敵人〕進行側翼包圍〔攻擊〕

out·go·ing /ˈaʊtˌgoɪŋ; ˌaʊtˈɡəʊɪŋˊ/ *adj* **1** [only before a noun 只用於名詞前] leaving an important job 即將離職的: *The outgoing president was praised for his commitment to the Party.* 即將離任的總統因對黨作出了貢獻而受到讚揚。 **2** friendly and eager to make friends 友好的; 樂於交友

out·go·ings /ˈaʊtˌgoɪŋz; ˈaʊtˌɡəʊɪŋz/ *n* [pl] amounts of money that are spent 支出; 開銷: *You will have to reduce your outgoings if you want to pay off your debts.* 如果你想還清債務, 就得減少開支。

out·grow /aʊtˈgro; aʊtˈɡrəʊ/ *v* **outgrew** /-ˈgru; -ˈɡruː/, **outgrown** /-ˈgron; -ˈɡrəʊn/ [T] to grow too big or too old for something 長得太大而不適用; 年長而放棄…: *Children outgrow their shoes every few months.* 孩子們的腳長大得太快, 他們的鞋子每隔幾個月就穿不下了。

out·house /ˈaʊtˌhaʊs; ˈaʊthaʊs/ *n* a small building connected to or near a house 附屬建築物; 外屋

out·ing /ˈaʊtɪŋ; ˈaʊtɪŋ/ *n* a short pleasure trip 短途旅遊; 遠足

out·land·ish /aʊtˈlændɪʃ; aʊtˈlændɪʃ/ *adj* strange and not very pleasant 稀奇古怪的; 奇特的: *outlandish behaviour* 古怪的行為

out·last /aʊtˈlæst; aʊtˈlɑːst/ *v* [T] to last longer than something else 比…持久〔經久〕

out·law¹ /ˈaʊtˌlɔ; ˈaʊtlɔː/ *n* *old fash* a criminal who has not been caught and is hiding from the police 《老式》逃犯; 亡命之徒

outlaw² *v* [T] to declare that something is against the law 宣佈〔某事〕不合法

out·lay /ˈaʊtˌle; ˈaʊtleɪ/ *n* an amount of money that is spent for a particular purpose 開支; 費用

out·let /ˈaʊtˌlɛt; ˈaʊtlet/ *n* **1** a pipe through which a liquid or gas may go out 〔排水管或

排氣管的〕出口 **2** an activity that lets you express your ideas or feelings 〔思想或感情的〕發泄(活動) **3** an American word for 《美式》= an electrical SOCKET 電源插座

out·line¹ /ˈaʊtˌlaɪn; ˈaʊtlaɪn/ *n* **1** a line showing the shape of something 輪廓; 外形: *the outline of her face* 她臉部的輪廓 **2** the main ideas or facts of something, with no details 提綱; 大綱; 概要: *an outline of the main points of the talk* 會談要點的提綱

outline² *v* **outlined, outlining** [T] to explain a plan or idea in a general way 概述; 概括〔計劃或想法〕: *The director outlined his plans for the company's future.* 董事長概述了公司的未來規劃。

out·live /aʊtˈlɪv; aʊtˈlɪv/ *v* **outlived, outliving** [T] to live longer than someone 比〔某人〕活得長

out·look /ˈaʊtˌluk; ˈaʊtlʊk/ *n* **1** a general point of view about life 〔對人生的〕觀點, 看法: *We are now much more European in our outlook.* 我們現在的觀點更接近歐洲人的(觀點)。 **2** the way a situation is likely to develop 前景; 展望: *The weather outlook for the weekend is bad.* 本週末的天氣預料不會好。

out·ly·ing /ˈaʊtˌlaɪɪŋ; ˈaʊtˌlaɪɪŋ/ *adj* [only before a noun 只用於名詞前] far from cities 遠離城市的; 邊遠的: *Outlying villages were cut off by the heavy snow.* 邊遠的村莊因大雪而被隔絕了。

out·ma·noeu·vre /ˌaʊtməˈnuvə; ˌaʊtməˈnuːvəˊ/ *v* **outmanoeuvred outmanoeuvring** (**outmaneuver** *AmE* 《美式》) [T] to do something clever which results in you having an advantage over your opponent 智勝〔對手〕; 比〔對手〕技高一籌

out·mod·ed /aʊtˈmodɪd; aʊtˈməʊdəd/ *adj* no longer in fashion 過時的; 不再流行的

out·num·ber /aʊtˈnʌmbə; aʊtˈnʌmbəˊ/ *v* [T] to be larger in number than something 在數量上超過…; 比…多: *Women in this age-group outnumber men by three to one.* 這個年齡組別的婦女人數比男子多三分之一。

out-of-date /ˌ· · ˈ·ˊ/ *adj* no longer in fashion 過時的; 不再流行的

out-of-the-way /ˌ· · · ˈ·ˊ/ *adj* far away from cities, and so not often visited 遠離城市的; 邊遠的; 人跡罕至的

out of work /ˌ· · ˈ·ˊ/ *adj* without a job 失業的: *The number of people out of work is expected to reach 3 million by the end of the year.* 失業人數到年底預計要達到三百萬。 | *an out of work actor* 失業的演員

out·pa·tient /ˈaʊtˌpeʃənt; ˈaʊtˌpeɪʃənt/ *n* a person who receives hospital treatment without staying there at night 門診病人

out·post /ˈaʊtˌpost; ˈaʊtpəʊst/ *n* a small village at some distance from a main centre 邊遠小村莊

out·pour·ing /ˈaʊtˌpoɪŋ; ˈaʊtˌpɔːrɪŋ/ *n* a strong expression of your feelings or ideas, especially in an uncontrolled way〔感情或思想的〕不斷流露, 傾訴: *hysterical outpourings of grief* 悲痛心情的歇斯底里的吐露

★out·put /ˈaʊt.pʊt; ˈaʊtpʊt/ *n* [C;U] **1** the amount of something that is produced by a person or business 產量: *The company hopes to increase its output by 30% next year.* 公司希望明年把產量增加百分之三十。 **2** the information printed or shown on a computer〔電腦的〕輸出信息: *Run the program, then we'll have a look at the output.* 執行該程式, 然後我們來看一下輸出的信息。

out·rage¹ /ˈaʊt.redʒ; ˈaʊtreɪdʒ/ *n* **1** [U] a strong feeling of anger and shock 義憤; 憤慨: *There was a general sense of outrage at the killing.* 人們對這宗謀殺案普遍感到憤慨。 **2** [C] an event which people find very shocking 暴行; 踐踏: *Another bomb outrage has shocked the city.* 又一宗炸彈暴行震驚了全城人。

outrage² *v* **outraged, outraging** [T] *fml* to offend and shock someone greatly《正式》侵害; 觸犯

out·ra·geous /aʊtˈredʒəs; aʊtˈreɪdʒəs/ *adj* very shocking and offensive 駭人的; 粗暴的; 蠻橫無禮的: *outrageous remarks* 粗暴的言語 **–outrageously** *adv*

out·right¹ /ˌaʊtˈraɪt; aʊtˈraɪt/ *adv* **1** completely 完全地; 徹底地: *The government have banned the drug outright.* 政府已經徹底禁止毒品。 **2** openly and in a direct manner 直率地; 直截了當地: *I asked him outright what he thought.* 我直截了當地問他有甚麼想法。

out·right² /ˈaʊt.raɪt; ˈaʊtraɪt/ *adj* [only before a noun 只用於名詞前] complete 完全的; 徹底的: *an outright victory* 徹底的勝利 | *an outright refusal* 斷然的拒絕

out·set /ˈaʊt.set; ˈaʊtset/ *n* **at the outset** at the very beginning of an event 在一開始〔開頭〕: *You must tell the builders what you want at the outset.* 你必須在一開始就把你的要求告訴建築工人。 [RELATED PHRASE 相關詞組: **from the outset:** *I've been involved with the project from the outset.* 我從一開始就參加了這項工程。]

out·shine /aʊtˈʃaɪn; aʊtˈʃaɪn/ *v* **outshone** /-ˈʃɒn; -ˈʃɒn/, **outshining** [T] to do something much better than someone else 比〔別人〕更出色; 勝過

★★out·side¹ /ˈaʊt.saɪd; ˌaʊtˈsaɪd/ *n* **1** the outer part of something, or the part that is furthest from the middle 外部; 外面: *We need to paint the outside of the house.* 我們需要把房子的外牆油漆一下。 **2 at the outside** at the most 至多; 充其量: *The job will take three weeks at the outside.* 這項工作至多需要三個星期。

★out·side² /aʊtˈsaɪd; ˌaʊtˈsaɪd/ *adv, prep* **1** out of something towards the open air 在[向]外面; 在…的外面: *She opened the door and went outside.* 她打開門走了出去。 | *He was standing outside the door.* 他站在門外。 –see

picture on page 764 見 764 頁彩圖 **2** not within a group of people 外界; 不在〔某一羣體〕之內: *We had to bring in extra help from outside.* 我們只好另請外界給予幫助。

★outside³ *adj* [only before a noun 只用於名詞前] **1** on the outside of something 外面的; 外部的: *the outside walls of the house* 房子的外牆 **2** connected with people who are not within a particular group 外界的; 局外的: *We need some outside help.* 我們需要一些外界的幫助。 **3 outside chance** a very small chance 極小的可能性; 渺茫的機會: *There's an outside chance that she'll win.* 她取勝的可能性不大。 **4 outside lane** the part of a MOTORWAY or large road where cars drive more quickly〔汽車可加速行駛的〕外車道

out·sid·er /aʊtˈsaɪdə; aʊtˈsaɪdə/ *n* a person who is not a member of a particular group, or is not accepted by a group 外人; 局外人; 非成員: *I've lived here for five years but I still feel an outsider.* 我在這兒已住了五年, 但我感到自己還是個外人。

out·size /ˈaʊt.saɪz; ˈaʊtsaɪz/ *adj* larger than the usual size 特大的; 超大的: *outsize clothes* 特大號衣服 | *"What sizes do you have?" "Small, medium, large and outsize."* "你們有些甚麼尺碼?" "小號、中號、大號和特大號。"

out·skirts /ˈaʊt.skɜts; ˈaʊtskɜːts/ *n* **the outskirts** the outer area of a town 市郊; 郊區: *They live on the outskirts of Paris.* 他們住在巴黎市郊。

out·smart /aʊtˈsmart; aʊtˈsmaːt/ *v* [T] *infml* to cleverly defeat someone and gain an advantage over them《非正式》智勝〔某人〕, 比…更精明

out·spo·ken /ˈaʊt.spokən; aʊtˈspəʊkən/ *adj* expressing your opinions openly, even if they offend peopole 直言的; 坦率的

out·spread /ˈaʊt.spred; ˌaʊtˈspred◂/ *adj* spread out flat or stretched out to full width 展開的; 伸開的

★out·stand·ing /aʊtˈstændɪŋ; aʊtˈstændɪŋ/ *adj* **1** extremely good 傑出的; 優秀的 **2** not yet done or paid 未完成的; 未償付的: *I've got two essays outstanding this term.* 這個學期我還有兩篇論文未寫。 | *outstanding debts* 有待償還的債務 **–outstandingly** *adv*

out·stretched /aʊtˈstretʃt; ˌaʊtˈstretʃt◂/ *adj* stretched out as far as possible (used of your arms or hands) 伸展開的〔指胳膊或手〕

out·strip /aʊtˈstrɪp; aʊtˈstrɪp/ *v* **-pp-** [T] to be larger or more successful than someone else 超過; 勝過〔別人〕

out·ward /ˈaʊtwəd; ˈaʊtwəd/ *adj* [only before a noun 只用於名詞前] **1** away from a place 向外的; 外出的: *the outward journey* 外出旅行 **2** shown to other people (used of feelings) 外表的, 表露的〔指情感〕: *I knew he was unhappy despite his outward cheerfulness.* 他儘管表面上高興, 我知道他其實並不快樂。

out·ward·ly /ˈautwədlı; ˈautwədli/ adv in a way that is shown to other people 外表上；表面上: She seemed happy, at least outwardly. 她似乎很快樂，至少在表面上是這樣。

out·wards /ˈautwədz; ˈautwədz/ adv (also 又作 **outward** AmE 【美式】) towards the outside 朝外；向外: The door opens outwards. 這門是向外開的。

out·weigh /autˈweı; autˈweı/ v [T] to be more important than something, or have more advantages than something 比〔某事物〕更重要；勝過〔某事物〕

out·wit /autˈwıt; autˈwıt/ v -tt- [T] to cleverly defeat someone and gain an advantage over them 以機智取勝

out·worn /ˈautˈwɔrn; ˌautˈwɔːnˑ/ adj old-fashioned and no longer useful (used of ideas, beliefs and customs) 過時的，陳腐的〔指觀念、信仰和習俗〕

o·val /ˈovl; ˈəuvəl/ n a shape like that of an egg 卵形的；橢圓形的 **–oval** adj

o·va·ry /ˈovəri; ˈəuvəri/ n **ovaries** the female organ that produces eggs 卵巢

o·va·tion /oˈveʃən; əuˈveıʃn/ n fml 【正式】**1** a loud burst of APPLAUSE 熱烈鼓掌: The soloist received a thunderous ovation. 那位獨唱者受到一陣雷鳴般的掌聲歡迎。**2 standing ovation** a burst of APPLAUSE in which people stand up to show their great approval of someone〔為某人〕起立鼓掌

ov·en /ˈʌvən; ˈʌvən/ n the part of a COOKER that is like a small box, in which you put food to bake it 烤爐；烤箱

o·ver¹ /ˈovə; ˈəuvəʳ/ adv, prep **1** prep directly above something, on the top of something, or covering something 在…的上方；在…的上面；蓋在…上面: There was a picture hanging over the fireplace. 有一幅畫掛在壁爐的上方。| Put a cloth over the table. 在桌子上鋪一塊布。| She put a coat on over her jumper. 她在套頭毛衣外面穿上了一件大衣。–see picture on page 764 見 764 頁彩圖 **2** adv, prep going across from side of something to the other side, or on the other side 從一邊到〔某物〕的另一邊；在…的另一邊；越過: He jumped over the hedge. 他跳過那樹籬。| She looked at me over the wall. 她在牆的那一邊看我。| He walked quickly over the road. 他迅速走過馬路。| The shops are just over the road. 商店就在公路的那一邊。| We'll have to cross over to the other side of the river. 我們將要橫越河流到對岸。**3** adv used when you are saying where someone or something is, and are pointing to the place 在…那邊〔用於表示某人或某物在何處，並可用手指著方位〕: The telephone is over by the door. 電話在那邊靠門的地方。| Jane is over there by the window. 簡就在窗子旁邊那個地方。**4 over to** towards a place 朝〔某處〕: She walked over to the radio and switched it on. 她走到收音機旁並打開開關。| They're flying over

to America. 他們乘飛機前往美國。**5** adv, prep downwards from an upright position (落)下；(倒)下；〔從上〕往下: I fell over. 我跌倒了。| She leaned over to look at the map. 她探身去查看地圖。| He was sitting bending over his work. 他坐著俯身工作。**6** adv, prep more than a particular amount 多於；超過；在…以上: We've had over two thousand letters. 我們收到了二千多封來信。| It all happened over five years ago. 那一切發生於五年多前。| children aged seven and over 七歲和七歲以上的兒童 **7** prep about 關於: a disagreement over rates of pay 關於稅率的分歧 **8** prep during a period of time 在…期間: She gradually got better over the summer. 她在夏天期間逐漸恢復健康。| We'll talk over dinner. 我們會在晚飯時邊吃邊談。**9** adv remaining 剩餘；剩下: Was there any money over after you'd paid the bills? 你當時付賬之後還有剩餘的錢嗎？**10** adv too 太；過分地: Don't be over anxious about it. 不要為此過分憂慮。**11 all over** everywhere in a place 到處: We've been looking all over for you. 我們一直在到處找你。| They've travelled all over Europe. 他們遊遍了歐洲各地。**12 all over again** starting from the beginning again 從頭再來一次: I'm afraid you'll have to do the test all over again. 我想你得把測驗重做一遍。**13 over and done with** completely finished 全部結束: At least we've got our exams over and done with. 至少我們的考試已經全部結束了。**14 over and over again** again and again, many times 一再地；再三地

o·ver² adj [never before a noun 不能用於名詞前] finished 結束的；過去了的: I'll talk to you once the meeting's over. 會議一結束，我就要找你談話。

o·ver³ n a set of six balls that are bowled (BOWL) in a game of cricket〔板球比賽中投出六次的〕一輪投球數

o·ver·all¹ /ˌovəˈɔl; ˌəuvərˈɔːlˑ/ adj including everything or the whole of something 全部的；包括一切的；總的: The fish measured 5 feet 3 inches overall. 那條魚全長五呎三吋。| The overall cost of the repairs is more than we anticipated. 修理項目的總費用高於我們所預期的。

overall² adv generally 總的說來；大體上: Overall, the future looks bright. 總的說來，前途似乎是光明的。| This was a good attempt overall. 總的來說，這是一次不錯的嘗試。

o·ver·all³ /ˈovərɔl; ˈəuvərɔːl/ n **1** a loose coat that you wear when you are working, to protect your other clothes 工作服；防護服 **2 overalls** [pl] loose trousers and a top that you wear when you are working, to protect your other clothes〔上下連身的〕工作褲

o·ver·arm /ˈovəˌarm; ˈəuvərɑːm/ adj, adv thrown with your arm moving above your shoulder 舉手過肩的[地]: He bowled overarm. 他舉手過肩投球。

o·ver·awe /ˌovəˈɔ; ˌəuvərˈɔː/ v **overawed,**

overawing, be overawed to be filled with respect and fear 使敬畏

o·ver·bal·ance /ˌovɚˈbæləns; ˌəʊvəˈbæləns/ v **overbalanced, overbalancing** [I] to become unbalanced and fall over 失去平衡而跌倒

o·ver·bear·ing /ˌovɚˈbɛrɪŋ; ˌəʊvəˈbeərɪŋ/ adj always trying to make other people obey you or do what you want 專橫的 – **overbearingly** adv

o·ver·board /ˈovɚˌbord; ˈəʊvəbɔːd/ adv **1** over the side of a boat into the water 自船邊落入水中: He fell overboard and drowned. 他從船邊掉入水中淹死了。 **2 go overboard** infml to do something too much 【非正式】過分追求; 着迷 **3 throw something overboard** to get rid of something or not to accept an idea or plan 擺脫[抛棄]某物

o·ver·bur·dened /ˌovɚˈbɝːdnd; ˌəʊvəˈbɜː-dnd/ adj carrying or doing too much 裝載太多的; 負擔過重的: I felt overburdened with work. 我感到工作負擔太重。

o·ver·cast /ˈovɚˌkæst; ˌəʊvəˈkɑːst◂/ adj dark with clouds 天陰的; 多雲的: There was a grey, overcast sky. 灰暗的天空烏雲密佈。

o·ver·charge /ˈovɚˈtʃɑrdʒ; ˌəʊvəˈtʃɑːdʒ/ v **overcharged, overcharging** [T] to charge someone too much 對〔某人〕索價過高: The waiter overcharged us for the wine. 服務員多收了我們飲料的錢。

o·ver·coat /ˈovɚˌkot; ˈəʊvəkəʊt/ n a thick warm coat 大衣

⋆o·ver·come /ˌovɚˈkʌm; ˌəʊvəˈkʌm/ v **over-came** /-ˈkem; -ˈkeɪm/, **overcome**, **over-coming** [T] **1** to fight successfully against something such as a feeling or a problem 戰勝, 克服〔某種情感或難題〕: I managed to overcome my fear of the dark. 我設法克服了對黑暗的恐懼感。 **2 be overcome** to be made helpless, especially by a strong feeling 被壓倒; 使無能為力: overcome by smoke 被煙熏倒 | overcome with emotion 激動得不能自持

o·ver·com·pen·sate /ˈovɚˈkɑmpənset; ˌəʊvəˈkɒmpənseɪt/ v **overcompensated, overcompensating** [I] to try too hard to correct a weakness 矯枉過正; 過度補償

o·ver·crowded /ˌovɚˈkraʊdɪd; ˌəʊvəˈkraʊ-dᵻd/ adj having too many people or things inside 過分擁擠的: an overcrowded classroom 過分擁擠的教室

o·ver·do /ˌovɚˈdu; ˌəʊvəˈduː/ v **overdid** /-ˈdɪd; -ˈdɪd/, **overdone** /-ˈdʌn; -ˈdʌn/, **over-doing** [T] **1** to do something in a way which is more than is expected or more than you can manage 把〔某事〕做得過分: The love scenes in the play were a bit overdone. 劇中的愛情場面演得略嫌過火。 | When you first start jogging, you have to be careful not to overdo it. 你剛開始練慢跑時, 要當心別練得過度。 **2** to use too much of something 使用過多: Don't overdo the salt. 不要放過多的鹽。

o·ver·done /ˈovɚˈdʌn; ˌəʊvəˈdʌn/ adj cooked too much 煮得太久的

o·ver·dose /ˈovɚˈdos; ˌəʊvədəʊs/ n a dangerous amount of a drug 〔藥物的〕危險劑量: He died from an overdose of heroin. 他因服用過量的海洛因而死了。

o·ver·draft /ˈovɚˌdræft; ˈəʊvədrɑːft/ n permission from a bank to spend more money than you have in your bank account, or the amount by which you are overdrawn 〔銀行允許的〕透支, 透支額

o·ver·drawn /ˌovɚˈdrɔn; ˌəʊvəˈdrɔːn/ adj **1** having taken out more money than you had in your bank account 〔銀行賬戶〕透支的: I'm often overdrawn at the end of the month. 到了月底, 我的銀行存款往往會透支。 **2** in a state where you have taken out an amount of money lent to you by the bank 已經透支的: My account is £300 overdrawn. 我的賬戶已透支了三百英鎊。

o·ver·due /ˌovɚˈdju; ˌəʊvəˈdjuː◂/ adj late, or later than expected 逾期的; 遲到的: My library books are overdue; I should have returned them last week. 我借的圖書逾期了, 我上星期就應該還掉。 | Changes in the law are long overdue. 法律早就該作些修改了。

o·ver·es·ti·mate /ˈovɚˈɛstəˌmet; ˌəʊvərˈes-tᵻmeɪt/ v [T] **overestimated, overestimat-ing** to think that something is bigger or more important than it really is 對〔某事物〕估計過高, 評價過高: We overestimated the cost, so we still have some money left. 我們對這項費用估計過高, 因此我們還剩下一些錢。 | I think you're overestimating his abili-ties. 我認為你對他的能力評價過高。

o·ver·flow¹ /ˌovɚˈflo; ˌəʊvəˈfləʊ/ v **1** [I;T] to flow over the edges 使溢出; (使)泛濫: The river overflowed and flooded the fields. 河水泛濫, 淹沒了田地。 **2** [I+adv/prep] to move out of a place because there are too many people inside 〔因容納不下太多的人而〕擠到外面: The crowd overflowed into the street. 人羣(從裡面)湧到了街上。 **3 be overflowing** to be full of 充滿; 洋溢: His heart was overflowing with pride. 他心中充滿了自豪。 **4 full to overflowing** extremely full 滿得外溢

o·ver·flow² /ˈovɚˌflo; ˈəʊvəfləʊ/ n **1** something that overflows 溢出物: We used a bucket to catch the overflow from the gutter. 我們用水桶接住簷槽裡溢出的東西。 **2** a pipe through which water can flow out of a con-tainer when it gets too full 溢流管

o·ver·grown /ˌovɚˈgron; ˌəʊvəˈgrəʊn◂/ adj thickly covered with plants that are not growing in a controlled way 長滿〔野生植物〕的

o·ver·hang /ˌovɚˈhæŋ; ˌəʊvəˈhæŋ/ v **over-hung** /-ˈhʌŋ; -ˈhʌŋ/, **overhung** [I;T] to hang over something or stick out above it 懸於… 之上, 突出於…之上: A large tree overhangs the wall. 一棵大樹懸在牆上。 –**overhang** /ˈovɚˌhæŋ; ˈəʊvəhæŋ/ n

o·ver·haul /ˌovɚˈhɔl; ˌəʊvəˈhɔːl/ v [T] to examine something thoroughly and repair or change anything that is not working properly 徹底檢修 –**overhaul** /ˈovɚˌhɔl; ˈəʊvəhɔːl/ n

o·ver·head /ˈovɚˌhɛd; ˌəʊvəˈhed◂/ adv, adj above you 在頭頂上的(的); 架空地[的]: electricity carried by overhead wires 通過架空電線輸送的電

o·ver·heads /ˈovɚhɛdz; ˈəʊvəhedz/ n [pl] the regular costs involved in running a business 〔企業的〕經常性開支, 日常管理費用

o·ver·hear /ˌovɚˈhɪr; ˌəʊvəˈhɪə/ v **overheard** /-ˈhɚd; -ˈhɜːd/, **overheard** [T] to hear what other people are saying by accident, when they do not know that you are listening 無意中聽到; 偶然聽到: I overheard them talking about me. 我無意中聽到他們在談論我。

o·ver·heat /ˌovɚˈhit; ˌəʊvəˈhiːt/ v [I] to become too hot because of a fault 變得過熱: The kettle overheated and burnt out. 水壺過度加熱, 把水燒乾了。

o·ver·joyed /ˌovɚˈdʒɔɪd; ˌəʊvəˈdʒɔɪd/ adj [never before a noun 不能用於名詞前] extremely pleased 極其高興的; 非常欣喜的: We were overjoyed when our baby was born. 嬰兒出生時, 我們都非常高興。

o·ver·land /ˈovɚˌlænd; ˌəʊvəˈlænd◂/ adv, adj travelling across land, rather than by sea or air 經由陸路(的)

o·ver·lap¹ /ˌovɚˈlæp; ˌəʊvəˈlæp/ v **-pp-** **1** [I; T] to cover part of something else 疊蓋; 〔與某物〕互搭: a pattern of overlapping circles 圓圈互相搭接的圖案 **2** [I] to be concerned with some of the same subjects 部分重疊: History and politics overlap quite a bit. 歷史和政治有相當部分內容重疊。

o·ver·lap² /ˈovɚˌlæp; ˈəʊvəlæp/ n [C;U] the amount by which two or more things overlap each other 〔兩個或兩個以上東西的〕重疊, 互搭

o·ver·leaf /ˈovɚˌlif; ˌəʊvəˈliːf/ adv on the next page 在下一頁, 在一頁的背面

o·ver·load /ˌovɚˈlod; ˌəʊvəˈləʊd/ v [T] **1** to give someone or something too much to do or carry 使〔某人〕負擔過重; 使〔某物〕超載 **2** to damage an electrical system by connecting too many machines together 使〔電路〕超過負荷

o·ver·look /ˌovɚˈlʊk; ˌəʊvəˈlʊk/ v [T] **1** to have a view of something from above 俯瞰; 眺望: Our room overlooked the sea. 從我們的房間可以眺望大海。 **2** to not notice the importance of something 忽視; 忽略: I overlooked the dangers involved when I planned this trip. 我在計劃這次旅行時忽略了當中涉及的危險。 **3** to forgive a fault or a mistake 寬恕; 原諒: I'll overlook it this time, but don't do it again! 我這次可以不計較, 但今後可別再犯了!

o·ver·much /ˈovɚˈmʌtʃ; ˌəʊvəˈmʌtʃ◂/ adv fml too much 〖正式〗過多地; 過度地

o·ver·night /ˈovɚˈnaɪt; ˌəʊvəˈnaɪt◂/ adv, adj **1** for or during the night 夜裡(的); 在夜裡: We'll stay in Paris overnight. 我們將在巴黎過夜。 **2** happening very suddenly 突然〔發生〕; 一下子: Byron became famous overnight. 拜倫一下子名揚四海。

o·ver·pass /ˈovɚˌpæs; ˈəʊvəpɑːs/ n the usual American word for 〖美式〗= FLY-OVER

o·ver·pop·u·lat·ed /ˌovɚˈpɑpjəˌletɪd; ˌəʊvəˈpɒpjʊˌleɪtɪd/ adj having too many people living there (used of places) 人口過多[過密]的〔指地方〕

o·ver·pop·u·la·tion /ˌovɚˌpɑpjəˈleʃən; ˌəʊvəˌpɒpjʊˈleɪʃən/ n [U] the situation in which there are too many people living in a place 人口過多

o·ver·pow·er /ˌovɚˈpaʊɚ; ˌəʊvəˈpaʊə/ v [T] **1** to defeat someone by being stronger than they are 〔以較強力量〕打敗, 制服 **2** to give you a particular feeling very strongly 〔感情等〕壓倒

o·ver·rate /ˌovɚˈret; ˌəʊvəˈreɪt/ v **overrated**, **overrating** [T] to think that something is greater or better than it really is 對〔某事物〕估計過高: I think that film is overrated. 我認為那部影片被評價過高了。

o·ver·ride /ˌovɚˈraɪd; ˌəʊvəˈraɪd/ v **overrode** /-ˈrod; -ˈrəʊd/, **overridden** /-ˈrɪdn; -ˈrɪdn/, **overriding** [T] **1** to become more important than other things 比...更重要; 優先於: The fight for freedom overrode all other issues. 爭取自由的鬥爭比其他一切問題都重要。 **2** to change someone's decisions because you have the power to do so 〔用職權〕改變〔別人的決定〕

o·ver·rid·ing /ˌovɚˈraɪdɪŋ; ˌəʊvəˈraɪdɪŋ◂/ adj [only before a noun 只用於名詞前] more important than anything else 壓倒一切的; 首要的

o·ver·rule /ˌovɚˈrul; ˌəʊvəˈruːl/ v **overruled**, **overruling** [T] to officially decide that someone else's decision was wrong 否決, 駁回〔某人的決定〕: The local council has been overruled by the government. 地方議會的決定已被政府否決了。

o·ver·run /ˌovɚˈrʌn; ˌəʊvəˈrʌn/ v **overran** /-ˈræn; -ˈræn/, **overrun**, **overrunning 1** [T] to take over a place very quickly 佔領; 侵擾: Troops overran the country. 軍隊佔領了那個國家。 | The house is overrun with mice. 屋子裡鼠害猖獗。 **2** [I;T] to continue beyond a time limit 超越〔時限〕: Sorry I'm late — the meeting overran. 對不起, 我來遲了, 會議超過了規定時間才結束。

★**o·ver·seas** /ˈovɚˈsiz; ˌəʊvəˈsiːz◂/ adv, adj across the sea 在[向]海外(的); 在[向]國外(的): They've gone to live overseas. 他們已經移居國外。 | overseas students 外國留學生

o·ver·see /ˌovɚˈsi; ˌəʊvəˈsiː/ v **oversaw** /-ˈsɔ; -ˈsɔː/, **overseen** /-ˈsin; -ˈsiːn/ [T] to watch a piece of work to see that it is done properly 監督; 監視: *I'll oversee this job myself.* 我要親自監督這項工作。

o·ver·shad·ow /ˌovɚˈʃædo; ˌəʊvəˈʃædəʊ/ v [T] **1** to be taller than something and throw a shadow over it 使〔某物〕蒙上陰影; 使陰暗 **2** to make something appear less important, less successful, or less happy 使〔某事物〕顯得不重要; 使相形見絀; 使減少樂趣: *He always felt overshadowed by his brothers.* 他總覺得比他的兄弟遜色。

o·ver·shoot /ˌovɚˈʃut; ˌəʊvəˈʃuːt/ v **overshot** /-ˈʃɑt; -ˈʃɒt/, **overshot** [I;T] to go too far past a place 走得太快以致錯過〔某處〕: *We overshot the entrance and had to come back.* 我們因走得太快而錯過了入口處，結果只好往回走。

o·ver·sight /ˈovɚˌsaɪt; ˈəʊvəsaɪt/ n [C;U] something which you forget to do or fail to notice 疏忽; 失察: *I'm sorry there was no one to meet you; it was an oversight on my part.* 我很抱歉沒有人去接你, 那是我的疏忽。

o·ver·sim·pli·fy /ˌovɚˈsɪmpləˌfaɪ; ˌəʊvəˈsɪmplɪfaɪ/ v **oversimplified, oversimplified** [I; T] to make something seem simpler than it really is (使)過於簡化 –**oversimplification** /ˈovɚˌsɪmpləfəˈkeʃən; ˌəʊvəˌsɪmplɪfɪˈkeɪʃən/ n [C;U]

o·ver·sized /ˈovɚˈsaɪzd; ˌəʊvəˈsaɪzd◂/ adj (also 又作 **oversize**) too big, or bigger than usual 過大的; 特大號的

o·ver·sleep /ˈovɚˈslip; ˌəʊvəˈsliːp/ v **overslept** /-ˈslɛpt; -ˈslɛpt/, **overslept** [I] to sleep for too long, or for longer than you intended 睡得過久; 睡過了頭

o·ver·state /ˈovɚˈstet; ˌəʊvəˈsteɪt/ v **overstated, overstating** [T] to state something too strongly, making things seem greater or more important than they really are 誇大; 誇張 –**overstatement** n [C;U]

o·ver·step /ˌovɚˈstɛp; ˌəʊvəˈstɛp/ v **overstep the mark** to go beyond acceptable limits in the way that you behave 做得過分; 超越限度

o·vert /ˈovɚt; ˈəʊvɜːt/ adj fml shown in an open, public way【正式】公開的: *There have been overt moves to undermine his authority.* 已經有削弱他的權威的公開舉動。 –**overtly** adv

o·ver·take /ˌovɚˈtek; ˌəʊvəˈteɪk/ v **overtook** /-ˈtʊk; -ˈtʊk/, **overtaken** /-ˈtekən; -ˈteɪkən/, **overtaking 1** [I;T] to go past something because you are travelling faster than it is 追上; 趕上並超過: *A car overtook me just before the bend.* 就在我轉彎前, 一輛汽車超過了我。 | *All clear, you can overtake now.* 前面一路暢通, 你現在可以超車了。 **2** [T] to have an effect on you suddenly 突然產生影響: *I was overtaken by exhaustion.* 我突然累得精疲力盡。

o·ver·throw /ˌovɚˈθro; ˌəʊvəˈθrəʊ/ v **overthrew** /-ˈθru; -ˈθruː/, **overthrown** /-ˈθron; -ˈθrəʊn/ [T] to defeat a government or ruler and remove them from power 打倒; 推翻〔政府等〕 –**overthrow** /ˈ···/ n [sing]

o·ver·time /ˈovɚˌtaɪm; ˈəʊvətaɪm/ n [U] time that someone works beyond the usual working hours 超時工作(的時間), 加班時間: *I've done six hours' overtime this week.* 這個星期我加班工作了六個小時。 –**overtime** adv: *We're working overtime to finish the job.* 我們正在加班, 以便完成這項工作。

o·ver·tone /ˈovɚˌton; ˈəʊvətəʊn/ n something, such as an idea or feeling, that is suggested without being shown or stated openly 暗示; 含意; 弦外之音: *The poems have clear political overtones.* 這些詩歌帶有明顯的政治含意。

o·ver·ture /ˈovɚtʃɚ; ˈəʊvətjʊəʳ/ n **1** a musical introduction to a play or an OPERA〔戲劇或歌劇的〕序曲, 前奏曲 **2 make overtures to someone** to behave in a friendly manner to someone because you want to have a more friendly relationship with them〔為建立友好關係而向某人作出的〕建議; 姿態

o·ver·turn /ˌovɚˈtɚn; ˌəʊvəˈtɜːn/ v **1** [I] to turn something over so that it is upside down 翻轉; 傾覆: *She was in the boat when it overturned.* 船剛倒時, 她就在船上。 **2** [T] to make something turn over 使〔某物〕翻轉; 使翻倒: *The intruders had overturned all the furniture.* 闖入者把所有的家具都翻倒了。 **3** [T] to officially change a decision that someone else had made 推翻; 否決: *The verdict was overturned by the Court of Appeal.* 判決被上訴法院翻掉了。

o·ver·weight /ˈovɚˈwet; ˌəʊvəˈweɪt◂/ adj **1** too fat 太肥胖的: *Fat parents tend to have children who are overweight too.* 肥胖的父母生的孩子也往往是過胖。 **2** too heavy 超重的: *This parcel is half a kilo overweight.* 這個包裹超重半公斤。

o·ver·whelm /ˌovɚˈhwɛlm; ˌəʊvəˈwelm/ v [T] **1** to gain complete control or victory over a group of people 制服, 壓倒 **2** to give someone a particular feeling very strongly 使〔某人感情〕受到衝擊; 使不能自持: *I was overwhelmed by grief.* 我感到悲哀不已。

o·ver·whelm·ing /ˌovɚˈhwɛlmɪŋ; ˌəʊvəˈwelmɪŋ/ adj very large or very great 巨大的; 壓倒一切的; 勢不可擋的: *an overwhelming majority of voters* 壓倒性多數的投票人 | *an overwhelming feeling of guilt* 沉重的內疚感 – **overwhelmingly** adv

o·ver·work¹ /ˌovɚˈwɚk; ˌəʊvəˈwɜːk/ v **1** [I; T] to work too hard, or make someone work too hard (使)過度工作; (使)過度勞累 **2** [T] to use something too much 過度使用〔某物〕: *This soil has been overworked.* 這塊土地已經被過度使用。

overwork² n [U] too much hard work 工作過度; 過重的工作

o·ver·wrought /ˈovɚˈrɔt; ˌəʊvəˈrɔːt◂/ adj feeling very nervous and excited 過分緊張

的; 過度興奮的

ow /aʊ/ *interj* an expression used to show sudden pain 啊唷〔表示突然疼痛〕: *Ow! You stepped on my toe!* 啊唷! 你踩到我腳趾了!

*★**owe** /o; əʊ/ *v* **owed, owing** [T] **1** to have to pay money to someone because they lent it to you 欠〔債〕: *He owes me £20.* 他欠我二十英鎊。| *I'll pay what I owe you but no more.* 欠你的我會如數付清, 但不會多給。– see 見 DUE¹(USAGE用法)

□ USEFUL PATTERNS 有用句型
to owe something; to owe something to someone; to owe someone something

2 to feel grateful to someone for a quality or an ability that they have given you 感激〔某人〕: *We owe our parents a lot.* 我們深深感激我們的父母。| *I owe most of my technique to a very good music teacher.* 我大部分的技巧應歸功於一位非常出色的音樂教師。

ow·ing /ˈoʊ·ɪŋ; ˈəʊɪŋ/ *adj* [never before a noun 不能用於名詞前] still to be paid 未付的; 欠着的: *How much is owing to you?* 還欠你多少錢? | *There is still £5 owing.* 還欠五英鎊。

owing to /ˈ·· ·/ *prep* because of 由於, 因為: *We were late, owing to the snow.* 由於下雪, 我們遲到了。

owl /aʊl; aʊl/ *n* a bird that flies at night, and hunts small animals 鴞, 貓頭鷹

*★★**own**¹ /on; əʊn/ *det, pron* **1** belonging to or for a particular person 〔屬於〕自己的: *I'd love to have my own house.* 我很想有自己的房子。| *The country has its own oil so it doesn't need to import any.* 這國家有自己的石油, 因此不需要從國外進口。| *I need a room of my own.* 我需要有一間屬於自己的房間。**2** get your own back to do something to punish someone who harmed you in some way 報復〔某人〕**3** on your own alone, with no one with you or helping you 獨自地; 獨立地; 靠自己: *I spent the afternoon on my own.* 我獨自一人度過了下午。| *Did you manage to do it on your own?* 你是獨力做成那件事的嗎?

■ USAGE 用法: **Own** is used only after possessive words like ☆ own 只用於所有格形式的單詞後面, 如: *my, our,*

John's, the school's: He has his own room/a room of his own. 他有自己的房間。| *The company has its own canteen.* 公司有自己的食堂。| *Was that your own idea?* 那是你自己的想法嗎? | *Does Sue have a car of her own?* 蘇有她自己的汽車嗎? | *Is that Sue's own car?* 那是蘇自己的汽車嗎?

*★**own**² *v* **1** [T] to possess something 擁有〔某物〕: *We only rent the house, we don't own it.* 我們只是租這房子, 並不擁有它。**2** [+that] *fml* to admit something〔正式〕承認〔某事〕

own·er /ˈonɚ; ˈəʊnəʳ/ *n* a person who owns something 物主; 所有人 –**ownership** *n* [U]

ox /ɑks; ɒks/ *n* **oxen** /ˈɑksən; ˈɒksən/ a large animal like a cow, sometimes used for pulling carts or carrying things 牛, 公牛〔有時用於拉車或運貨〕

ox·ide /ˈɑksaɪd; ˈɒksaɪd/ *n* [C;U] a compound of oxygen and another chemical substance 氧化物: *iron oxide* 氧化鐵

ox·i·dize /ˈɑksə‚daɪz; ˈɒksɪ‚daɪz/ *v* **oxidized, oxidizing** (also 又作 **oxidise** *BrE*〔英式〕) [I; T] to change chemically by combining with oxygen; when metal oxidizes, it becomes RUSTY (使)氧化; (使)生鏽

ox·y·gen /ˈɑksədʒən; ˈɒksɪdʒən/ *n* [U] a gas present in the air, without colour, taste, or smell; oxygen is necessary for all forms of life on earth 氧; 氧氣

oy·ster /ˈɔɪstɚ; ˈɔɪstəʳ/ *n* a flat shellfish which is often eaten raw, and which can produce pearls (PEARL) 牡蠣, 蠔〔能生產珍珠〕

oy·ster·catch·er /ˈɔɪstɚ‚kætʃɚ; ˈɔɪstə‚kætʃəʳ/ *n* a seabird that eats shellfish 蠣鷸

oz a written abbreviation for 〔縮〕= OUNCE

o·zone /ˈozon; ˈəʊzəʊn/ *n* [U] **1** a poisonous form of oxygen 臭氧 **2** the air near the sea, which is thought to be healthy〔海邊的〕清新空氣

ozone-friend·ly /‚·· ‘···/ *adj* not harmful to the ozone round the earth 對地球臭氧層無害的

ozone lay·er /ˈ·· ‚··/ *n* **the ozone layer** a layer of ozone high above the Earth's surface which protects the Earth from harmful rays (RAY) from the sun 臭氧層 –see picture on page 470 見 470 頁彩圖

P, p

P, p /piː/ piː/ *P's, p's* or **Ps, ps** the 16th letter of the English alphabet 英語的第十六個字母

p *n* **1** [plural is 複數為 **p**] the smallest unit of money in Britain; 100p=£1 便士〔100便士=1英鎊〕: *It cost 49p.* 這東西花了四十九便士。| *a 10p piece* 一個十便士的硬幣 –see 見 PENNY (USAGE用法) **2** [plural is 複數為 **pp**] a written abbreviation for 〔縮〕= PAGE

PA /ˌpiː ˈeɪ; ˌpi ˈeɪ/ *n* BrE〔英式〕a secretary employed to look after the affairs of one person; an abbreviation for **personal assistant** 〔縮〕私人助理; 私人祕書

*pace¹ /peɪs; peɪs/ *n* **1** [sing;U] the rate at which you move forward in many activities, especially walking and running 步速, 速度: *He set off at a very fast pace.* 他以飛快的速度出發了。| *The pace of reform has been rather slow.* 改革的速度一直比較慢。**2** [C] a single step in running or walking, or the distance moved in it 一步; 步長: *The fence is ten paces from the house.* 籬笆距房子有十步遠。**3** **keep pace with** to go at the same speed as someone or something 跟上〔某人或某物〕的速度 **4** **put someone through their paces** to make someone do something as a test or proof of their abilities 測試某人的能力 **5** **set the pace** to set a speed for others to try to equal 定速度

pace² *v* **paced, pacing** [I; +adv/prep; T] to walk backwards and forwards when you are waiting or worried〔等待或憂慮時〕來回踱步: *She paced up and down, waiting for him to appear.* 她踱來踱去, 等待着他的出現。| *restlessly pacing the floor* 不安地踱來踱去

pace·mak·er /ˈpeɪsˌmeɪkə; ˈpeɪsˌmeɪkər/ *n* **1** a machine fitted under someone's skin near the heart to make it beat regularly (心臟) 起搏器 **2** a person who sets a speed that others in a race try to equal 定速度者

pac·i·fis·m /ˈpæsəˌfɪzəm; ˈpæsᵻˌfɪzəm/ *n* [U] the belief that all wars are wrong 和平主義; 反戰主義

pac·i·fist /ˈpæsəfɪst; ˈpæsᵻfᵻst/ *n* a believer in pacifism, especially one who refuses to fight in a war because of their belief 和平主義者; 反戰主義者

pac·i·fy /ˈpæsəˌfaɪ; ˈpæsᵻˌfaɪ/ *v* **pacified, pacifying** [T] to make someone stop being angry or upset and become calm, quiet, and satisfied 安撫; 使鎮靜: *to pacify a crying baby* 使正在啼哭的嬰兒安靜下來 –**pacification** /ˌpæsəfəˈkeɪʃən; ˌpæsᵻfᵻˈkeɪʃən/ *n* [U]

*pack¹ /pæk; pæk/ *v* **1** [I;T] to put things into a case or other container 把〔東西〕放入〔箱子或其他容器〕; 把〔東西〕打包: *She packed her bags and left.* 她收拾好行李包就走了。| *I'm leaving in an hour and I haven't packed yet!* 我一小時後就要出發了, 可我的行李還沒收拾呢! | *Could you pack me a few sandwiches?* 你能幫我包幾個三明治嗎? | *a packed meal* 盒裝的飯 –opposite 反義 **unpack 2** [T] to put goods into containers ready for transport or sale 把〔貨物〕裝箱〔以便運輸或出售〕: *The eggs are packed and sent off the following day.* 雞蛋裝箱後第二天運出。**3** [T] to cover, fill, or surround closely with a protective material〔用保護性材料〕覆蓋, 裹緊: *Pack some paper round the dishes so that they won't break.* 把紙裹在盤子周圍, 以防破碎。**4** [T;+adv/prep] to fit, crush, or push things into a space 塞滿; 壓緊; 擁擠: *If you pack those things down we can get some more clothes into the box.* 你如果把那些東西壓緊, 我們還可以再放幾件衣服進箱子裡。| *The hotel manager wanted to pack all of us into one small room.* 旅館老闆想把我們所有人擠進一間小房間裡。

pack sthg ↔ in *phr v* [T] BrE *infml*〔英式, 非正式〕**1** to stop doing a job or piece of work, often because you are dissatisfied or tired〔常因不滿或勞累而〕停止工作: *He used to work for Smith's, but he packed his job in.* 他以前是在史密斯的店裡上班的, 但現在他不幹了。| *It's ten o'clock. I think I'll pack it in and go to bed.* 十點鐘了, 我打算結束工作, 睡覺去了。**2** **pack it in** a phrase used to tell someone fairly rudely to stop doing something that is annoying you; used especially by parents to children 住手〔用於粗暴地叫某人停止做令你惱怒的事情, 尤用於父母對孩子講話時〕: *Pack it in, you two!* 你們兩個住手!

pack sbdy ↔ off *phr v* [T] *infml* to send someone away quickly, especially without spending time being nice to them〔非正式〕把〔某人〕打發走: *They packed their children off to boarding school at the earliest possible age.* 他們等孩子們年齡一到, 便送他們上寄宿學校去了。

pack up *phr v* [I] *infml*〔非正式〕**1** to finish work 完成工作 **2** to put all your things in boxes because you are leaving 收拾好行李 **3** BrE (used of machines) to stop working〔英式〕〔機器〕停止運轉

*pack² *n* **1** a quantity of things packed together for sale or for giving out〔準備出售或送人的〕包在一起的物品: *a pack of*

bacon 一包燻肉 | *You can't buy just one lightbulb. You have to buy a pack.* 你不能只買一隻燈泡，你必須買一盒。| *an information pack* 資料包 **2** (also 又作 **backpack**) a large bag which goes on your back and in which you can carry things 背包 **3** a number of things wrapped or tied together which a homeless person carries on their back as they travel from place to place 無家可歸者所背的家當 **4** a group of wild animals that hunt together, or a group of dogs trained together for hunting 〔野獸或獵犬的〕一羣: *a pack* **of** *hounds* 一羣獵狗 | *a wolf pack* 一羣狼 **5** a set of cards used in playing a game 〔紙牌的〕一副

★**pack·age¹** /ˈpækɪdʒ; ˈpækɪdʒ/ *n* **1** a small parcel or a large envelope with things inside it 小包；大信封 **2** a set of related things sold or offered all together 〔供買賣的〕一整套物品: *a new software package for home computers* 一套家庭電腦的新套裝軟件 | *The union has won a new package* **of** *benefits.* 工會獲得了一攬子的好處。

package² *v* **packaged, packaging** [T] **1** to put a number of things all together into a parcel 把〔幾件物品〕包成一包 **2** to put a product in a box, bag, or other wrapping for protection, easy handling, and attractive appearance 包裝〔物品〕: *attractively packaged chocolates* 包裝得很吸引人的巧克力

package deal /ˈ··· ·/ *n infml*〔非正式〕(also 又作 **package**) an agreement that includes a number of things all of which must be accepted together 一攬子交易，整批交易

package hol·i·day /ˌ·· ˈ···/ *n* a completely planned holiday arranged by a company at a fixed price 〔全程由旅行社安排且費用固定的〕包辦旅遊，包價旅遊

pack·ag·ing /ˈpækɪdʒɪŋ; ˈpækɪdʒɪŋ/ *n* [U] material used for packing goods 包裝材料: *These days the packaging often costs more than the goods.* 現在包裝材料常比商品本身還要貴。

packed /pækt; pækt/ *adj infml*〔非正式〕(also 又作 **packed out** /ˌ· ˈ·/) full of people 擠滿人的，擁擠的

pack·er /ˈpækə; ˈpækɚ/ *n* a person whose job is to pack goods for travelling or selling 打包工，包裝工

pack·et /ˈpækɪt; ˈpækɪt/ *n* **1** a small box, envelope, bag, or wrapper in which goods are packed 小包；小盒: *a packet of envelopes* 一小捆信封 | *an empty cigarette packet* 一個空煙盒 –see picture on page 244 見 244 頁彩圖 **2** *infml* a large amount of money〔非正式〕一大筆錢: *That car cost me a packet.* 那輛車花了我一大筆錢。

pack·ing /ˈpækɪŋ; ˈpækɪŋ/ *n* [U] **1** the act of putting things into cases or boxes 包裝；打包；裝箱: *I'll do my packing the night before we leave.* 我會在我們出發的前一天晚上收拾

行李。**2** material used in packing 包裝材料

packing case /ˈ·· ·/ *n* a strong wooden box in which things are packed to be stored or sent to another place 裝貨木箱

pact /pækt; pækt/ *n* an important formal agreement, often between countries 〔國家之間的〕條約；協定: *They signed a non-aggression pact.* 他們簽署了互不侵犯條約。

pad¹ /pæd; pæd/ *n* **1** a thick piece of soft material, such as plastic FOAM or cotton, used to clean or protect something, shape it, or make it more comfortable 墊，襯墊；護墊: *American footballers wear shoulder-pads for protection.* 美式足球運動員戴護肩做保護。| *Put a clean pad of cotton over the wound.* 在傷口上敷一塊乾淨的棉花團。**2** a number of sheets of paper fastened together 便簽簿: *a writing pad* 拍紙簿 **3** the ground where a HELICOPTER lands and takes off or where a ROCKET takes off 直升機場；火箭發射場 **4** the thick-skinned underpart of the foot of some animals, such as cats〔貓等動物的〕爪垫

pad² *v* **padded, padding 1** [T] to fill with soft material in order to protect, shape, or make more comfortable 填入襯墊〔護墊〕: *a coat with padded shoulders* 有墊肩的外衣 **2** [I; +adv/prep] to walk steadily and softly 穩步而行: *John rode his bicycle slowly, and his dog padded along beside him.* 約翰慢慢騎着腳踏車，他的狗輕輕地跟在後面走。

  pad *sthg* ↔ **out** *phr v* [T] to fill up space in a written article by adding unnecessary or unconnected material 拉長〔文章〕

pad·ding /ˈpædɪŋ; ˈpædɪŋ/ *n* [U] material used to pad something 襯料；襯墊

pad·dle¹ /ˈpædl; ˈpædl/ *n* **1** a short pole with a wide flat blade at one or both ends, used for moving a small boat, especially a CANOE 短槳 **2** a walk in the sea, a river, or a stream where the water is only a few centimetres deep 涉水；蹚水: *The children went for a paddle.* 孩子們涉水玩去了。

paddle² *v* **paddled, paddling 1** [I;T] to move a small light boat through water, using one or more paddles 〔用槳〕划〔小船〕 **2** [I] *BrE* to walk about in water only a few centimetres deep 〔英式〕涉水，蹚水

paddle steam·er /ˈ·· ˌ··/ *n* a steam ship which is pushed forward by large wheels 明輪船

pad·dling pool /ˈ·· ·/ *n* a container for water only a few centimetres deep for children to play in 〔供兒童玩水的〕嬉水池

pad·dock /ˈpædək; ˈpædək/ *n* a small field where horses are kept and exercised, or where horses are brought together before a race so that people can see them 〔養馬或練馬的〕小牧場，練馬場；〔賽馬前的〕馬匹檢閱場

pad·dy /ˈpædɪ; ˈpædi/ *n* **paddies** (also 又作 **paddy field** /ˈ·· ·/) a field where rice is grown in water 水稻田

pad·lock /ˈpædˌlɒk; ˈpædlɒk/ *n* a movable lock with a U-shaped metal bar, which can be used to lock things such as gates and bicycles 掛鎖 –**padlock** *v* [T]: *Did you remember to padlock the gate?* 你記得用掛鎖鎖門嗎?

pae·di·a·tri·cian /ˌpidɪəˈtrɪʃən; ˌpiːdɪəˈtrɪʃən/ *n* (**pediatrician** *AmE* 〖美式〗) a doctor concerned with children's medicine 兒科醫生

pae·di·at·rics /ˌpidɪˈætrɪks; ˌpiːdɪˈætrɪks/ *n* (**pediatrics** *AmE* 〖美式〗) [U] the branch of medicine concerned with children and their diseases 兒科學

pae·do·phile /ˈpidofaɪl; ˈpiːdəfaɪl/ *n* (**pedophile** *AmE* 〖美式〗) a person whose sexual desires are directed towards children 變童癖患者

pa·el·la /paɪˈelə; paɪˈelə/ *n* [U] a Spanish dish of rice cooked with pieces of meat, fish, and vegetables 〔用肉、魚和菜同煮的〕〔西班牙〕平鍋什錦飯

pa·gan /ˈpegən; ˈpeɪgən/ *n* a person who is not a believer in any of the chief religions of the world 異教徒

★★ **page¹** /pedʒ; peɪdʒ/ *n* **1** one or both sides of a sheet of paper in, for example, a book or newspaper 〔書、報等的〕頁: *There is a picture of a ship on page 44.* 第44頁上有張輪船的插圖。| *Someone's torn a page out of this book.* 有人從這本書中撕去了一頁。**2** (also 又作 **page boy** /ˈ· ·/) a uniformed boy servant in a hotel or club 〔旅館或俱樂部內穿制服的〕男侍童、門僮 **3** a boy attendant on a woman when she is getting married, or, in the past, on a king or queen 〔已婚婦女,或舊時國王或王后的〕男侍童

page² *v* **paged, paging** [T] to call aloud in a public place for someone who is wanted, especially through a LOUDSPEAKER 〔尤指通過擴音器〕呼喊找〔某人〕: *The hotel manager had my boss paged for me.* 旅館經理幫我在擴音器裡呼叫找我的老闆。

pag·eant /ˈpædʒənt; ˈpædʒənt/ *n* a public show or ceremony, usually out of doors, especially one in which there is a procession of people in rich dress or in which historical scenes are acted 盛大的慶典;盛裝的遊行

pag·eant·ry /ˈpædʒəntrɪ; ˈpædʒəntri/ *n* [U] a splendid show of ceremonial grandness with people in fine dress 盛大慶典場面;盛況: *the pageantry of a royal wedding* 皇家婚禮的隆重場面

pa·go·da /pəˈgodə; pəˈgəʊdə/ *n* a temple, especially a Buddhist or Hindu one built on several floors with a decorative roof at each level 〔尤指佛教或印度教的〕塔、寶塔

paid¹ /ped; peɪd/ the past tense and past participle of PAY¹ ☆ PAY¹ 的過去式及過去分詞

paid² *adj* which you receive wages for 有工資的: *a paid job* 有報酬的工作 –opposite 反義 **unpaid**

paid-up /ˌ· ˈ··◂/ *adj* having paid in full, especially in order to continue being a member of an organization 付清的、已付的〔尤指付清會費的〕

pail /pel; peɪl/ *n* a bucket 桶、水桶: *a milk pail* 牛奶桶

★ **pain¹** /pen; peɪn/ *n* **1** [U] suffering of body or mind 〔肉體或精神上的〕痛苦: *She was crying with pain.* 她疼得大喊大叫。| *He's in constant pain.* 他一直處於痛苦之中。| *His behaviour caused his parents a great deal of pain.* 他的行為令父母非常難過。**2** [C] a feeling of suffering or discomfort in a particular part of your body 〔身體局部的〕疼痛: *I've got a terrible pain in my chest.* 我胸口疼得很厲害。| *slight stomach pains* 輕微的胃痛 **3** a **pain, a pain in the neck** *infml* a really annoying person, thing, or happening 〖非正式〗令人極其討厭的人〔物、事情〕: *He can be a real pain at times.* 他有時委實是個討厭的人。**4 pains** [pl] effort 努力: *All I got for my pains was the door slammed in my face!* 我努力所換來的就是別人當着我的面摔門! **5 take great pains** to make a very big effort to do something well 不遺餘力

■ **USAGE** 用法: Remember to use the preposition **in** for expressions such as ☆記住在下列表達法中用介詞 **in**: *I've got a pain in my leg/in my neck/in my shoulder.* 我的腿〔脖子、肩膀〕疼。| *She felt a sudden pain in her back/in her chest/in her stomach.* 她突然感到背〔胸、胃〕疼。

pain² *v* [T] *fml* to cause someone to feel very unhappy 〖正式〗令〔某人〕感到痛苦

pained /pend; peɪnd/ *adj* showing that your feelings have been hurt 痛苦的; 難受的: *There was a pained silence before she replied.* 一段令人難受的沉默之後,她才回答。

pain·ful /ˈpenfəl; ˈpeɪnfəl/ *adj* causing pain or hurting 引起疼痛的; 令人痛苦的: *My wrist is really painful today.* 我的手腕今天疼得很厲害。| *a painful cut on his thumb* 大拇指上一個疼痛的傷口 | *painful memories* 令人痛苦的記憶 –**painfully** *adv*

pain·kill·er /ˈpenˌkɪlə; ˈpeɪnˌkɪlər/ *n* a medicine which lessens or removes pain 止痛藥

pain·less /ˈpenlɪs; ˈpeɪnləs/ *adj* **1** causing no pain 無痛的: *X-rays are quite painless.* X光不會引起甚麼疼痛。**2** needing no effort or hard work 不費力的: *a painless way of learning a foreign language* 一種不費力的學習外語的辦法 –**painlessly** *adv*

pains·tak·ing /ˈpenzˌtekɪŋ; ˈpeɪnzˌteɪkɪŋ/ *adj* very careful and thorough 費盡心思的; 非常小心的; 非常徹底的: *a painstaking examination of the whole area* 對整個地區的徹底

檢查 –**painstakingly** adv

***paint¹** /pent; peɪnt/ n **1** [U] liquid colouring matter which is put on a surface to protect it or make it look attractive 油漆; 塗料: *a tin of green paint* 一罐綠色油漆 | *The sign said "Wet Paint".* 牌子上寫着"油漆未乾"。**2** [C;U] colouring matter which you use for painting pictures 油彩顏料: *a box of paints* 一盒油彩顏料

***paint²** v [I;T] **1** to put paint on a surface 給…上油漆: *I wear my old clothes when I'm painting.* 我油漆東西的時候穿舊衣服。 | *She painted the door blue.* 她把門漆成藍色。 | *They painted it a bright colour.* 他們給它漆上了鮮豔的顏色。**2** to make a picture of someone or something using paint 〔用顏料〕繪畫; 畫〔人或物〕: *Who painted this picture?* 這幅畫是誰畫的? | *I wish I could paint as well as you.* 我希望能畫得和你一樣好。 | *Paint the view from your window.* 把你窗戶外面的景象畫下來。

paint·brush /ˈpent,brʌʃ; ˈpeɪntbrʌʃ/ n a brush for spreading paint on a surface 油漆刷; 畫刷, 畫筆 –see picture on page 958 見 958 頁彩圖

paint·er /ˈpentə; ˈpeɪntə/ n **1** a person whose job is painting the inside or outside of houses 油漆工 **2** a person who paints pictures 畫家: *a portrait painter* 肖像畫家

***paint·ing** /ˈpentɪŋ; ˈpeɪntɪŋ/ n **1** [U] the act of painting, or the skill of painting pictures 上油漆; 繪畫(技巧) **2** [C] a picture made by painting 圖畫; 水彩畫, 油畫

paint·work /ˈpent,wɝk; ˈpeɪntwɜːk/ n [U] a painted surface 上了漆的表面: *The paintwork on my car needs a bit of attention.* 我車子的漆面需要注意一下。

***pair¹** /pɛr; peə/ n **1** something made up of two parts that are alike and are joined and used together 一副; 一條; 一把: *a pair of trousers* 一條褲子 | *a pair of scissors* 一把剪刀 **2** two things that are alike or of the same kind, and are usually used together 一雙; 一對: *a pair of shoes* 一雙鞋 | *a pair of vases* 一對花瓶 **3** two people who are closely connected, especially a man and woman or husband and wife 〔關係密切的〕一對人; 一對夫妻: *They're a nice pair.* 他們是對模範夫妻。 *Let's ask them to dinner with the Harrisons.* 我們是對模範夫妻。我們邀請他們與哈里森一家到進晚餐吧。 | *The pair of them are going.* 他們兩個準備走了。

■ USAGE 用法: Some words like **trousers** are in the plural form, but we do not usually think of them as "more than one". If we say *Those* **trousers** *are old,* it is not clear whether we are talking about one or more than one item of clothing. To make it clear we can use **pair** or **pairs** ☆ 有些詞如 **trousers** 用作複數形式, 但我們通常不把它們視作複數。當我們說 *Those* **trousers** *are old* 時, 聽者並不清楚我們是指一條還是幾條褲子。為明白起見, 我們可以用 **pair** 或 **pairs**: *a pair of trousers* 一條褲子 | *three pairs of trousers* 三條褲子。We can use *a* **pair** of with any word in this dictionary which has "–see PAIR (USAGE)" after it. ☆ 凡本詞典中後面標有 "–see 見 PAIR (USAGE)" 的單詞, 前面均可以用 *a* **pair** of。

---

pair² v [I;T] to form into pairs 成對, 成雙

pair up phr v [I] to form into a pair for a particular purpose 〔為某一目的〕結成一對: *They paired up on holiday.* 他們兩個結對去度假。

pair sbdy ↔ **off** phr v [T] to encourage people to start a relationship 鼓勵人們交往: *My parents are always trying to pair me off with people.* 我的父母一直在鼓勵我與別人交往。

pa·ja·mas /pəˈdʒæməz; pəˈdʒɑːməz/ n [pl] see 見 PYJAMAS

pal /pæl; pæl/ n infml a close friend 〔非正式〕好朋友: *an old pal of mine* 我的一個老朋友

***pal·ace** /ˈpælɪs; ˈpælɪs/ n a large and splendid house, especially one where a king or queen officially lives 宮殿, 皇宮

pal·ae·o·lith·ic /ˌpelɪəˈlɪθɪk; ˌpæliəʊˈlɪθɪk/ adj (also 又作 **paleolithic**) of the earliest known period of human existence, the Old Stone Age, when people made weapons and tools of stone 舊石器時代的

pal·a·ta·ble /ˈpælətəbl; ˈpælətəbəl/ adj **1** pleasant to taste 美味的; 可口的 **2** agreeable to the mind 合意的

pal·ate /ˈpælɪt; ˈpælɪt/ n **1** the top part of the inside of your mouth 上腭 **2** the ability to judge food or wine 〔對佳餚美酒的〕鑑賞力

pa·la·tial /pəˈleɪʃəl; pəˈleɪʃəl/ adj large and splendid like a palace (usually used of buildings) 宮殿似的; 宏偉的〔通常指建築物〕: *a palatial hotel* 宏偉的旅館

***pale¹** /pel; peɪl/ adj **1** having little colour (used of your face or skin) 蒼白的〔指臉或皮膚〕: *a pale complexion* 蒼白的臉色 | *still pale and tired after her illness* 她病癒後仍顯得蒼白而疲乏 –see picture on page 469 見 469 頁彩圖 **2** not bright 淡的; 暗的: *pale blue* 淡藍色 | *the pale light of the moon* 暗淡的月光 –**paleness** n [U] –see picture on page 243 見 243 頁彩圖

pale² v **paled, paling** [I] to become unimportant 使顯得遜色; 相形見絀: *All our other worries paled into insignificance beside the possibility that the country would go to war.* 我們的國家可能要捲入戰爭, 這使得我們所有其他的憂慮都顯得無足輕重了。

pal·ette /ˈpælɪt; ˈpælɪ̩t/ n a board with a curved edge and a hole for the thumb, on which an artist mixes colours 調色板

pal·ings /ˈpeɪlɪŋz; ˈpeɪlɪŋz/ n [pl] a fence made of pointed pieces of wood 木柵; 柵欄

pall¹ /pɔl; pɔːl/ n **1** a low dark cloud 低沉的烏雲: *A pall of smoke hung over the city.* 一層煙霧籠罩着城市。 **2** a covering of dark cloth spread over the box in which a dead body is carried 柩衣; 棺罩

pall² v [I] to become less interesting or enjoyable 變得乏味; 使厭煩: *His new job began to pall after a while.* 一段時間以後, 他的新工作開始變得乏味起來。

pall·bear·er /ˈpɔlˌbeərə; ˈpɔːlˌbeərər/ n a person who walks beside or helps to carry the box in which the body is carried at a funeral 〔出殯時的〕扶靈人, 抬棺人

pal·let /ˈpælɪt; ˈpælɪ̩t/ n a large metal plate or flat wooden frame for lifting and moving goods, used with a special small vehicle 貨盤; 集裝架

pal·li·a·tive /ˈpælɪ̩ˌetɪv; ˈpælɪətɪv/ n something that lessens pain or a problem without removing the cause of it 緩解劑; 緩和物 **–palliative** adj: *palliative measures* 緩解措施

pal·lid /ˈpælɪd; ˈpælɪ̩d/ adj unusually or unhealthily pale (used of your face or skin) 蒼白的〔指臉或皮膚〕 **–pallor** n [sing; U]: *the unusual pallor of her skin* 她的皮膚不尋常的慘白

pal·ly /ˈpælɪ; ˈpælɪ/ adj having a friendly relationship 親密的; 友好的: *I didn't know you were pally with her.* 我不知道你同她要好。

palm /pɑm; pɑːm/ n **1** (also 又作 **palm tree** /ˈ· ·/) a tall tropical tree with no branches, but with a mass of large leaves at the top 棕櫚(樹): *a date palm* 棗椰樹 | *a coconut palm* 椰子樹 **2** the inner surface of your hand between the base of your fingers and your wrist 手掌

palm·ist /ˈpɑmɪst; ˈpɑːmɪ̩st/ n a person who claims to be able to tell someone's future by examining the lines on their palm 看掌相的人 **–palmistry** n [U]

pal·pa·ble /ˈpælpəbl; ˈpælpəbəl/ adj fml easily and clearly known by your senses or your mind 〔正式〕容易感覺到的; 明顯的: *a palpable atmosphere of mistrust* 明顯的不信任氣氛 **–palpably** adv: *What you say is palpably untrue.* 你所說的顯然與事實不符。

pal·pi·ta·tions /ˌpælpəˈteʃənz; ˌpælpɪ̩ˈteɪʃənz/ n [pl] irregular or unusually fast beating of your heart, caused by illness or too much effort 心悸, 心跳不規則

pal·try /ˈpɔltrɪ; ˈpɔːltrɪ/ adj so small that it is almost worthless 微不足道的: *The management offered us a paltry 3% increase.* 資方答應給我們的加薪幅度是微乎不足道的百分之三。

pam·pas /ˈpæmpəz; ˈpæmpəz/ n **the pampas** the large grass-covered plains in parts of South America 南美大草原

pam·per /ˈpæmpə; ˈpæmpər/ v [T] to treat too kindly 使嬌生慣養; 溺愛: *a pampered cat* 寵壞了的貓 | *Pamper your skin with our rich creamy soap.* 用我們這種柔滑細膩的香皂使你的肌膚保持細緻。

pam·phlet /ˈpæmflɪt; ˈpæmflɪ̩t/ n a small thin book with paper covers which deals usually with some matter of public interest or gives information on a product or service 小冊子

pan /pæn; pæn/ n **1** metal container used in cooking, usually with one long handle, and sometimes with a lid 鍋, 平底鍋 **2** the bowl of a LAVATORY 抽水馬桶

pan·a·ce·a /ˌpænəˈsiə; ˌpænəˈsiə/ n something that is supposed to cure any illness, or put any trouble right 萬靈藥; 萬全之策

pa·nache /pəˈnæʃ; pəˈnæʃ/ n [U] a manner of doing things that is showy and splendid 炫耀

pan·cake /ˈpænˌkek; ˈpænkeɪk/ n a thin soft flat cake made of flour, milk, and eggs, cooked in a flat pan and eaten hot with a filling, often sweet 薄煎餅

pan·da /ˈpændə; ˈpændə/ n (also 又作 **giant panda**) a large animal like a bear, with black and white fur, originally from China 大熊貓, 大貓熊

pan·de·mo·ni·um /ˌpændɪˈmoniəm; ˌpændɪ̩ˈməuniəm/ n [U] a state of wild and noisy disorder 大混亂; 喧囂

pan·der /ˈpændə; ˈpændər/ v **pander to** to provide something that satisfies unreasonable wishes 迎合: *a newspaper that panders to people's interest in sex* 一份迎合人們對性的興趣的報紙

pane /pen; peɪn/ n a single sheet of glass for use in a frame, especially a window frame 〔尤指窗格上的〕一塊玻璃

pan·el /ˈpænl; ˈpænl/ n **1** [+ sing/pl verb] a group of speakers who answer questions to inform or amuse the public, usually on a radio or television show 〔通常在廣播或電視中〕答問小組; 座談小組: *a panel game* 小組(競賽)遊戲 | *What do the panel think?* 專題討論小組的看法如何? **2** [+sing/pl verb] a committee chosen to find out about something or make a decision 〔調查某事或做出決定的〕委員會 **3** one of a number of sheets of wood, glass, or metal which fit into a frame to form a door, wall, or CEILING 〔門、牆或天花板的〕嵌板; 鑲板 **4** a board on which controls or instruments of various kinds are fastened 控制板; 儀表板

pan·elled /ˈpænld; ˈpænld/ adj (**paneled** AmE 〔美式〕) decorated or fitted with panels 飾有嵌板的; 裝有鑲板的

pan·el·ling /ˈpænlɪŋ; ˈpænəl-ɪŋ/ n (**paneling** AmE 〔美式〕) [U] a set of panels used to decorate an inside wall 〔裝飾內牆壁的〕一套嵌板

pan·el·list /'pænḷ̩ɪst; 'pænəl-ˌl̩st/ n (**panelist** AmE 【美式】) a member of a panel of people 〔廣播或電視的〕答問小組成員；座談小組成員

pang /pæŋ; pæŋ/ n a sudden sharp feeling of pain 一陣突然的劇痛: *pangs of hunger* 飢餓引起的一陣腸胃痛 | *a pang of sadness* 一陣悲痛

pan·ic¹ /'pænɪk; 'pænɪk/ n [C;U] great anxiety of fear which makes it difficult to act reasonably 恐慌；驚惶: *There was panic when the fire started.* 大火燒起來時，人們一陣恐慌。 | *She's getting into a panic now because it's only two weeks to the exams.* 由於離考試只有兩星期，她開始恐慌起來。

panic² v **panicked, panicked, panicking** [I; T] to lose control of yourself because you suddenly feel very frightened or worried 使恐慌；使驚慌失措: *The crowd panicked at the sound of the guns.* 人們一聽到槍聲，便驚慌失措起來。 | *Don't panic. It's only some fireworks going off!* 別慌，這不過是在放煙火罷了！

panic-strick·en /'·· ˌ··/ adj extremely frightened and anxious 驚慌失措的

pan·ni·er /'pænjɚ; 'pæniə/ n a basket or bag, especially one of a pair, carried on a bicycle or by a horse or donkey 馱籃；掛籃

pan·o·ra·ma /ˌpænə'rɑːmə; ˌpænə'ræmə/ n a complete view over a wide area 〔一片廣闊地區的〕全景，全貌 –**panoramic** /-'ræmɪk; -'ræmɪk/ adj: *a panoramic view of the city from the tenth floor of the building* 從這座建築物的十樓所看到的城市全景

pant /pænt; pænt/ v [I] to take quick short breaths, especially after great effort or in great heat 喘氣: *The dog panted in the heat.* 狗在炎熱的天氣裡喘着氣。 | *"Stop, stop," he panted.* "停下，停下，"他氣喘吁吁地說。

pan·ties /'pæntɪz; 'pæntiz/ n (also 又作 **pants**) [pl] a short piece of underclothing worn by women and girls 女式短內褲，短襯褲

pan·to·mime /'pæntəˌmaɪm; 'pæntəmaɪm/ n BrE 【英式】 (also 又作 **panto** /'pæntəʊ; 'pæntəʊ/ infml 【非正式】) [C;U] a funny play for children, based on a fairy story, and usually produced at Christmas 〔通常在聖誕節演出供兒童觀看的〕童話劇

pants /pænts; pænts/ n [pl] **1** BrE a piece of underclothing which men wear under trousers and women under skirts or trousers 【英式】內褲 **2** the usual American word for 【美式】= TROUSERS

pa·pa /'pɑpə; 'pɑːpə/ n AmE infml a father 【美式，非正式】爸爸

pa·pa·cy /'pepəsɪ; 'peɪpəsi/ n **the papacy** the power and office of the POPE 教皇的職權

pa·pal /'pepḷ; 'peɪpəl/ adj of or about the POPE 教皇的；有關教皇的

pa·pa·ya /pə'paɪə; pə'paɪə/ n (also 又作

pawpaw) [C;U] a large yellow-green tropical fruit 番木瓜，木瓜

pa·per¹ /'pepɚ; 'peɪpɚ/ n **1** [U] a substance used to make the pages of books, for writing on, or for wrapping parcels with 紙: *a piece of paper* 一張紙 | *a paper bag* 紙袋 | *Have you got any writing paper?* 你有書寫用紙嗎？ **2** [C] a newspaper 報紙: *Have you seen today's paper?* 你看到今天的報紙了嗎？ **3** [C] a set of printed questions used as an examination 考試卷: *We're doing both the biology papers today.* 今天我們做兩份生物學試卷。 **4** [C] a piece of writing for specialists, often read aloud 論文 **5** **papers** [pl] pieces of paper with writing on them 書寫物 **6** **papers** [pl] official pieces of paper, for example your passport, which give information about who you are and what you have the right to do 證件; 公文文件 **7** **on paper** as written down or printed, but not yet tested by experience 在紙上；理論上: *This idea seems all right on paper, but I'm not sure how it would work out in practice.* 這個主意理論上看來沒問題，但我不敢肯定實踐中是否可行。

paper² v [T] to cover a wall with decorative paper 用牆紙裱糊〔牆壁〕: *She papered the main bedroom green.* 她用綠色牆紙裱糊了主臥室。

paper over sth phr v [T] to try to hide the difficulties of something and make it look as though everything is all right 掩蓋，掩飾〔困難〕

pa·per·back /'pepɚˌbæk; 'peɪpəbæk/ n a book with a thin cardboard cover 平裝書: *This shop only sells paperbacks.* 這家商店只出售平裝書。 | *a paperback edition* 平裝版 | *Is it out in paperback yet?* 這本書的平裝版出版了嗎？

paper clip /'·· ·/ n a small piece of curved wire used for holding sheets of paper together 回形針，曲別針 –see picture on page 763 見 763 頁彩圖

paper shop /'·· ˌ·/ n a shop which sells newspapers and magazines 出售報刊雜誌的商店

pa·per·weight /'pepɚˌwet; 'peɪpəweɪt/ n a heavy object placed on top of loose papers to keep them from being scattered 鎮紙；紙壓

pa·per·work /'pepɚwɝk; 'peɪpəwɜːk/ n [U] **1** regular work of writing reports, letters, keeping records, etc. 日常文書工作 **2** **the paperwork** the papers connected with one piece of business 文件: *I'll have to go through all the paperwork again.* 我必須把所有的文件再瀏覽一遍。

pa·pi·er-mâ·ché /ˌpepɚmə'ʃe; ˌpæpieɪ'mæʃeɪ/ n [U] paper mixed with a sticky substance to form a soft mass, and used for making objects such as boxes; it is quite hard when dry 製型紙漿〔用於製紙箱等〕

pap·ri·ka /pæˈprikə; ˈpæprɪkə/ *n* [U] red pepper with a sweet taste 紅色甜辣椒

pa·py·rus /pəˈpaɪrəs; pəˈpaɪɒrəs/ *n* [U] paper made in ancient Egypt from a plant similar to grass, or the plant itself 紙莎草紙

par /pɑr; pɑːʳ/ *n* [sing] **1** in the game of GOLF, the number of strokes the average player should take to hit the ball into a hole〔高爾夫球賽的〕標準桿數 **2 below par** *infml* not in the usual or average condition of health or activity〔非正式〕〔健康或活動的〕一般水平以下 **3 on a par** equal or almost the same 相等; 幾乎相同: *Our results this year are on a par* **with** *those of our rivals.* 我們今年的成績與對手的成績差不多。

par·a·ble /ˈpærəbl; ˈpærəbəl/ *n* a short simple story which teaches a moral or religious lesson〔道德説教或宗教性的〕寓言

par·a·chute¹ /ˈpærəʃut; ˈpærəʃuːt/ *n* an apparatus which is made of cloth and is fastened to a person or an object dropped from an aircraft in order to make them fall slowly 降落傘: *a parachute jump* 跳傘

parachute² *v* **parachuted, parachuting** [I; T] to drop from an aircraft using a parachute 跳傘

pa·rade¹ /pəˈred; pəˈreɪd/ *n* **1** a public procession 遊行; 列隊行進: *The Olympic Games begin with a parade of all the competing nations.* 奧運會以所有參賽國(的運動員)列隊進場開始。 **2** an ordered procession of soldiers in front of a higher officer〔軍隊的〕檢閲, 閲兵 **3** a wide street, often beside the seashore〔常位於海濱的〕大道 **4 on parade** taking part in a parade (used of soldiers)〔指士兵〕接受檢閲

parade² *v* **paraded, parading 1** [I;T] to march in a public procession 遊行; 列隊行進: *soldiers parading in front of the Queen* 士兵在女王面前接受檢閲 | *The prisoners were paraded around the town.* 囚犯在城裡遊行。 **2** [I; + adv/prep] to walk around an area in order to attract attention 炫耀地走來走去: *Groups of lads were parading along the main street, showing off to the girls.* 成羣的少年在大街上走來走去, 向女孩子們炫耀。 **3** [T] to show something unnecessarily, just in order to gain admiration 炫耀〔某物〕: *He is always parading his knowledge.* 他總喜歡炫耀自己的學識。

par·a·dise /ˈpærəˌdaɪs; ˈpærədaɪs/ *n* **1 Paradise** Heaven 天堂, 天國 **2** a place of perfect happiness 樂園: *This hotel is a sportsman's paradise.* 這座旅館是運動員的樂園。

par·a·dox /ˈpærədɑks; ˈpærədɒks/ *n* **1** a statement which seems to be impossible, because it says two opposite things, but which has some truth in it 似非而是的雋語: *"More haste, less speed" is a paradox.* "欲速則不達"是個似非而是的雋語。 **2** an improbable combination of opposing qualities or ideas 自相矛盾的事物: *It is a paradox*

that in such a rich country there should be so many poor people. 在如此富裕的國家裡竟有這麼多的窮人, 真是自相矛盾的事。 **—para·doxical** /ˌpærəˈdɑksɪkl; ˌpærəˈdɒksɪkəl/ *adj* **—paradoxically** *adv*

par·af·fin /ˈpærəfɪn; ˈpærəfn/ *n* [U] an oil made from PETROLEUM or coal, burnt for heat and in lamps for light 煤油

par·a·gon /ˈpærəˌgɑn; ˈpærəgən/ *n* a person or thing that is a perfect model to copy 模範; 典範: *She's an absolute paragon of virtue.* 她是美德的最佳典範。

*par·a·graph /ˈpærəˌgræf; ˈpærəgrɑːf/ *n* a part of a longer piece of writing which deals with one particular idea; each new paragraph starts on a new line 段落: *Look at the third paragraph on page 23.* 看第二十三頁的第三段。

par·al·lel¹ /ˈpærəˌlɛl; ˈpærəlel/ *adj* **1** running side by side but never getting nearer to or further away from each other (used of lines and rows) 平行的, 並行的: *parallel lines* 平行線 | *The railway line runs parallel* **with** *the road.* 這條鐵軌與那條公路相平行。 | *The line is parallel* **to** *the road.* 這條線與公路相平行。 **2** of the same type and done at the same time 相類似的; 同時發生的: *Parallel experiments are carried out in London and Paris.* 實驗同時在倫敦和巴黎進行。

parallel² *n* **1** [C] a parallel line or surface 平行線; 平行面 **2** [C;U] a person or thing that is similar to another person or thing 極相似的人[物]: *There are few parallels between American football and European football.* 美式足球和英式足球鮮有相似之處。 | *an actor without parallel in the modern cinema* 近代電影界無與倫比的男演員

parallel³ *v* **-l-** (also 又作 **-ll-** *BrE*〔英式〕) [T] to equal 比得上; 與…相等: *No one has paralleled her success in business.* 在商業上沒有人像她那樣成功。

par·a·lyse /ˈpærəˌlaɪz; ˈpærəlaɪz/ *v* **paralysed, paralysing** (**paralyze** *AmE*〔美式〕) [T] **1** to make your muscles unable to move 使癱瘓: *paralysed from the neck down* 從頸部以下癱瘓 | *paralysed with fear* 嚇得無法動彈 **2** to cause something to stop working 使〔某物〕停止運行: *The electricity failure paralysed the train service.* 停電使鐵路服務陷於癱瘓。

par·al·y·sis /pəˈræləsɪs; pəˈrælɪsɪs/ *n* [U] loss of feeling in and control of your muscles 癱瘓: *suffering from partial paralysis of the arm* 手臂的局部癱瘓

par·a·lyt·ic /ˌpærəˈlɪtɪk; ˌpærəˈlɪtɪk/ *adj* **1** suffering from paralysis 癱瘓的 **2** causing paralysis 引起癱瘓的: *a paralytic stroke* 引起癱瘓的中風 **3** *infml* very drunk〔非正式〕醉醺醺的, 酩酊大醉的

par·a·med·ic /ˌpærəˈmɛdɪk; ˌpærəˈmedɪk/ *n* a person who is trained to help with the care of sick people, but who is not a doctor or a nurse 護理人員

pa·ram·e·ter /pəˈræmətə; pəˈræmˌtər/ *n* any of the established limits within which something must operate 規範; 限定要素

par·a·mil·i·tary /ˌpærəˈmɪlɪˌterɪ; ˌpærəˈmɪl-ɪˌtəri/ *adj* like or used as a regular military force 像正規軍的; 準軍事性的: *In some countries the police have paramilitary duties.* 在一些國家，警察具有輔助軍隊的職責。 | *the paramilitary organizations of Northern Ireland* 北愛爾蘭的準軍事組織

par·a·mount /ˈpærəˌmaunt; ˈpærəmaunt/ *adj* placed above all others 至上的; 首要的: *of paramount importance* 最重要的

par·a·noi·a /ˌpærəˈnɔɪə; ˌpærəˈnɔɪə/ *n* [U] a disease of the mind in which the sufferers believe that others hate them and are purposely mistreating them, or that they are a person of great importance 妄想狂; 偏執狂

par·a·noid /ˈpærənɔɪd; ˈpærənɔɪd/ *adj* **1** full of unreasonable distrust of other people 多疑的: *My father locks every door in the house when he goes out. He's absolutely paranoid about being burgled.* 我父親外出時把所有的門都鎖上。他太疑神疑鬼，怕有人來撬竊了。**2** suffering from paranoia 患妄想症的

par·a·pet /ˈpærəpɪt; ˈpærəpˌt/ *n* a low wall at the edge of a roof or bridge 〔屋頂或橋樑邊緣的〕矮護牆

par·a·pher·na·li·a /ˌpærəfəˈneɪlɪə; ˌpærəfə-ˈneɪlɪə/ *n* [U] a number of articles of various kinds, especially personal belongings or those needed for some skill or work 裝備; 隨身用品: *I keep all my photographic paraphernalia in that cupboard.* 我把自己所有的攝影器材放在那個小櫥裡。

par·a·phrase /ˈpærəˌfrez; ˈpærəfreɪz/ *v* **paraphrased, paraphrasing** [T] to re-express something in words that are easier to understand 〔用較易懂的話〕釋義, 意譯; 改述 –**paraphrase** *n*

par·a·ple·gic /ˌpærəˈplɛdʒɪk; ˌpærəˈpliː-dʒɪk/ *n* a person suffering from a condition in which they are unable to control the muscles of the lower part of their body 患下身麻痺者

par·a·site /ˈpærəˌsaɪt; ˈpærəsaɪt/ *n* **1** a plant or animal that lives on or in another and gets food from it 寄生植物; 寄生蟲 **2** a useless person who is supported by the wealth or efforts of other people 依靠他人供養的人 –**parasitic** /ˌpærəˈsɪtɪk; ˌpærəˈsɪtɪk◂/ *adj*: *a parasitic plant* 寄生植物 –**parasitically** /-klɪ; -kli/ *adv*

par·a·sol /ˈpærəˌsɔl; ˈpærəsɒl/ *n* a light UMBRELLA used for protection from the sun 太陽傘

par·a·troops /ˈpærəˌtrups; ˈpærətruːps/ *n* [pl] soldiers trained to drop from an aircraft using a PARACHUTE 傘兵部隊

par·boil /ˈpɑrˌbɔɪl; ˈpɑːbɔɪl/ *v* [T] to boil food until it is partly cooked 把〔食物〕煮到半熟

par·cel¹ /ˈpɑrsl; ˈpɑːsəl/ *n* **1** a thing or things wrapped in paper and tied or fastened for easy carrying, or posting 郵包; 包裹: *I'm taking this parcel to the post office.* 我正要把這個包裹送到郵局去寄。 | *a parcel of clothes* 一包衣服 **2** part and parcel of a most important part that cannot be separated from the whole of something 不可分割的重要部分

parcel² *v* **-ll- (-l-** *AmE* 【美式】)

parcel sthg ↔ **out** *phr v* [T] to divide something into parts or shares and give it to several people 分配, 分發〔某物〕

parcel sthg ↔ **up** *phr v* [T] to make something into a parcel 把〔某物〕打成包裹, 把…包起來

parched /pɑrtʃt; pɑːtʃt/ *adj* **1** *infml* very thirsty 〔非正式〕非常渴的 **2** dried up by the hot sun and in need of water (used of land) 〔土地〕被曬得很乾的

parch·ment /ˈpɑrtʃmənt; ˈpɑːtʃmənt/ *n* [U] **1** a writing material used especially in ancient times, made from the skin of a sheep or goat 羊皮紙 **2** a paper of good quality that looks like this material 〔一種類似羊皮紙的〕優質紙

par·don¹ /ˈpɑrdn; ˈpɑːdn/ *n* **1** official forgiveness for an illegal act, or the action of a court in forgiving someone and freeing them from punishment 赦免 **2** a word you use to ask someone to repeat something they have just said, because you did not hear it properly 對不起; 請原諒〔用於因未聽清而請對方再重複一遍〕 –see 見 SORRY¹ (USAGE 用法) **3 I beg your pardon** a very polite phrase that you use when you want someone to repeat what they have just said, or when you have done something that might offend them; you might also use it if someone said something that made you angry 對不起; 請原諒〔請別人重複所說的話時，或做了可能會令別人生氣的事時所用的非常禮貌的用語; 當別人說了令你非常生氣的話時也可用此短語〕: *I beg your pardon, I didn't quite hear you.* 對不起，我沒聽清楚你的話。 | *I beg your pardon, I didn't mean to push in front of you.* 對不起，我不是故意在前面推你的。 | *I beg your pardon, that's not true at all!* 對不起，可那完全是無稽之談!

pardon² *v* [T] **1** *fml* to forgive or excuse someone 【正式】原諒〔某人〕: *You'll have to pardon me while I just make a quick phone call.* 我很快去打個電話，請原諒。 **2** to give an official pardon to someone for an unlawful act 赦免 **3 pardon me** *AmE* excuse me 【美式】對不起: *Pardon me, could you tell me the way to the station?* 對不起，你可以告訴我去車站怎麼走嗎?

par·don·a·ble /ˈpɑrdnəbl; ˈpɑːdənəbəl/ *adj*

possible to forgive or excuse 可原諒的: *a pardonable mistake* 可原諒的錯誤

pare /pɛr; peəʳ/ *v* **pared, paring** [T] to cut away the thin outer covering, edge, or skin of something 削〔某物的覆蓋物、邊或皮〕: *to pare an apple* 削蘋果皮

pare sthg ↔ **down** *phr v* [T] to reduce something, especially a cost 削減〔尤指成本〕

★par·ent /ˈpɛrənt; ˈpeərənt/ *n* the father or mother of a person 父親; 母親: *His parents are both teachers.* 他的父母都是教師。 **–parental** /pəˈrɛntl; pəˈrentl/ *adj*

par·ent·age /ˈpɛrəntɪdʒ; ˈpeərəntɪdʒ/ *n* [U] the fact of who your parents are, including their social class 身世; 出身; 門弟: *a child of unknown parentage* 身世不明的小孩

pa·ren·the·sis /pəˈrɛnθəsɪs; pəˈrenθ₁s₁s/ *n* **1 parentheses** [pl] the usual American word for 〖美式〗= BRACKETS **2 in parenthesis** as an interruption to the main idea that you are talking or writing about 作為插入成分 **–parenthetic** /ˌpærənˈθɛtɪk; ˌpærənˈθetɪk◂/, **parenthetical** *adj*

par·ent·hood /ˈpɛrənt,hʊd; ˈpeərənthʊd/ *n* [U] the state of being a parent 做父母的身分

par ex·cel·lence /ˌpɑːʳˈɛksəˌlɑns; ˌpɑːr ˈeksəlɑːns/ *adj* [only after a noun 只用於名詞後] *lit* without equal, as the best or most typical of its kind 〖文〗無與倫比的, 最卓越的

pa·ri·ah /pəˈraɪə; pəˈraɪə/ *n* a person not accepted by society 不為社會所接受者

par·ish /ˈpærɪʃ; ˈpærɪʃ/ *n* **1** an area with a single priest in charge, and served by one main church 教區: *a parish church* 教區教堂 | *a parish priest* 教區牧師 **2** the smallest area of local government in the countryside, usually a village 鄉間的最小行政區〔通常為村莊〕

pa·rish·io·ner /pəˈrɪʃənɚ; pəˈrɪʃnəʳ/ *n* a person living in a parish 教區居民

par·i·ty /ˈpærətɪ; ˈpærₐtɪ/ *n* [U] the state or quality of being equal, especially in pay and working conditions 〔尤指報酬和工作條件〕相等: *They want parity with the car workers.* 他們想要享有與汽車工人同等的待遇。

★park¹ /pɑrk; pɑːk/ *n* **1** a large, usually grassy, enclosed piece of land in a town, used by the public for pleasure and rest 公園 **2** a large enclosed stretch of land with grass and trees round a large country house 園林, 邸園

park² *v* **1** to put a car or other vehicle somewhere for a time 停放〔車輛〕: *Don't park the car in the main road.* 不要把車停在大路上。 | *a parked car* 一輛停放的汽車 **2 be parked** to have parked your car 把車停放好: *I'm parked outside the paper shop.* 我把車停在紙品店門口。

par·ka /ˈpɑrkə; ˈpɑːkə/ *n* **1** a short coat with

a part that covers your head and is decorated with fur 帶兜帽的毛皮短大衣; 風雪大衣 **2** the usual American word for 〖美式〗= ANORAK

park·ing /ˈpɑrkɪŋ; ˈpɑːkɪŋ/ *n* [U] the leaving of a car or other vehicle in a particular place for a time 〔車輛等的〕停放

■ USAGE 用法: **1** The special open space where people can park their cars is called a **car park**. If you park your car in the street in a place which you find yourself (often between other cars) you can talk about a **parking place** or a **parking space** ☆用於專門停放車輛的場地叫做 **car park** (停車場)。如果把車停在街上自己找來的地方〔通常停在其他車輛中間〕, 這種地方可叫做 **parking place** 或 **parking space** (停車處): *I can never find a parking place outside your house!* 我在你的房子外面從來就找不到可以停車的地方! **2** The sign **"No Parking"** means that you are not allowed to park in a particular place. ☆ **"No Parking"** 的標誌表示此處禁止停車。

---

parking lights /ˈ·· ˌ·/ *n* [pl] the usual American word for 〖美式〗= SIDELIGHTS

parking lot /ˈ·· ·/ *n* the usual American word for 〖美式〗= CAR PARK

parking me·ter /ˈ·· ˌ·/ *n* an apparatus at the side of a street, into which you put money to pay for parking a car beside it for a certain time 停車計時收費器

parking tick·et /ˈ·· ˌ·/ *n* a piece of paper which is put on your car if you have parked it where it is against the law to do so; it tells you to pay some money as a punishment 違章停車罰款單

park·land /ˈpɑrk,lænd; ˈpɑːk-lænd/ *n* [U] *BrE* a large enclosed stretch of land with grass and trees round a large country house 〖英式〗邸園

par·lance /ˈpɑrləns; ˈpɑːləns/ *n* [U] *fml* a particular kind of language 〖正式〗說法; 用語: *In naval parlance, the left side of a ship is the "port" side.* 在海軍用語中, 船的左邊稱為"左舷"。

★par·lia·ment /ˈpɑrləmənt; ˈpɑːləmənt/ *n* **1** a large group of people elected by the people of a country to make laws 國會, 議會 **2 Parliament** in the United Kingdom, the main law-making body, made up of the King or Queen, the Lords, and the elected representatives of the people 英國國會: *Parliament has been debating industrial relations.* 國會裡正進行有關勞資關係的辯論。 **–parliamentary** /ˌpɑrləˈmɛntərɪ; ˌpɑːlə-ˈmentəri◂/ *adj*: *during this parliamentary session* 在此次國會會議期間

pa·ro·chi·al /pəˈrokɪəl; pəˈrəʊkiəl/ *adj* **1** too

concerned with local affairs and not taking enough interest in the wider world 地方觀念的; 狹隘的 **2** related to a PARISH 教區的

par·o·dy¹ /'pærədɪ; 'pærədi/ *n* **parodies 1** [C;U] a piece of writing or music intended to amuse by copying the style of another writer or musician 滑稽的模仿詩文; 滑稽的模仿音樂 **2** [C] a weak and unsuccessful copy 拙劣的模仿: *The trial was a parody of justice.* 這次審判是對正義的嘲弄。

parody² *v* **parodied, parodying** [T] to make a parody of something 拙劣地模仿〔某物〕

pa·role /pə'rol; pə'rəul/ *n* [U] letting someone out of prison early, on the condition that they promise to behave well 假釋: *He was released on parole to attend his daughter's wedding.* 他獲假釋出獄去參加女兒的婚禮。 **–parole** *v* [T]: *Prisoners may be paroled after serving half their sentence.* 囚犯在刑期過半後可獲假釋。

par·ox·ys·m /'pærəks,ɪzəm; 'pærəksɪzəm/ *n* a sudden uncontrollable burst of strong feeling 〔感情的〕突然爆發: *paroxysms of laughter* 一陣大笑

par·quet /'pɑr'ke; 'pɑːkeɪ/ *n* [U] small flat blocks of wood fitted together in a pattern on to the floor of a room 鑲木地板: *a parquet floor* 鑲木地板

par·rot¹ /'pærət; 'pærət/ *n* a tropical bird with a curved beak; sometimes people teach parrots to speak 鸚鵡

parrot² *v* [T] to repeat words without understanding what they mean 盲目地模仿

par·ry /'pærɪ; 'pæri/ *v* **parried, parrying** [T] **1** to cleverly avoid answering a question 機智地回避〔問題〕 **2** to turn aside an attack 擋開〔打擊〕

par·si·mo·ni·ous /,pɑrsə'monɪəs; ,pɑːsɪ'məunɪəs/ *adj fml* very unwilling to spend money 〔正式〕吝嗇的; 小氣的 **–parsimoniously** *adv* **–parsimony** /'pɑrsə,monɪ; 'pɑːsɪməni/ *n* [U]

pars·ley /'pɑrslɪ; 'pɑːsli/ *n* [U] a small plant with strong-tasting leaves, used in cooking 歐芹; 西芹

pars·nip /'pɑrsnəp; 'pɑːsnɪp/ *n* a cream-coloured vegetable which grows under the ground 防風草, 歐防風

★★part¹ /pɑrt; pɑːt/ *n* **1** [C;U] a piece of something, not all of it 部分: *Which part of the town do you live in?* 你住在城裡哪個地區? | *Part of the house was damaged in the fire.* 房屋的一部分被大火燒毀了。| *The hard part of the scheme was raising the money.* 該計劃的困難部分是籌措資金。| *Wales is part of the United Kingdom.* 威爾士是英國的一部分。 **2** [C] any of the pieces into which something is divided 劃分的部分, 份: *Cut the cake into eight parts.* 把蛋糕切成八份。| *You can see the second part of our new drama series at the same time next week.* 你可以在下週同樣時間看到我

們新的連續劇的第二集。 **3** [C] (also 又作 **spare part**) a piece of a machine which you use in place of a broken one 〔機器的〕零件; 備件: *That big garage up the top of the hill stocks parts for Renaults.* 山頂的那家大修車庫備有雷諾牌汽車的零件。 **4** [C] a character acted by an actor in a play or film 〔戲劇或電影中的〕角色: *She plays the part of an old woman who has lost her whole family.* 她演的角色是失去了所有親屬的老婦人。 **5** [C] an equal quantity 等份: *Mix two parts sand to one of cement.* 把兩份沙子和一份水泥混在一起。 **6** [C] a share or responsibility in some activity 〔活動的〕參與; 責任: *For his part in the burglary, Matthews was given two years' imprisonment.* 馬修斯由於參與盜竊, 被判監禁兩年。 **7** the usual American word for a PARTING in the hair 〔美式〕〔頭髮的〕分界 **8** **play a part in, take a part in, have a part in** to be responsible for a result to some degree, but not completely 對某種結果負有一定責任; 有…的成分: *Cheap accommodation played a part in my decision to stay in the north.* 房價低是我決定住在北部的原因之一。 **9** **take part** to do an activity with other people 參加〔活動〕: *He took part in the International Student Games.* 他參加了國際學生運動會。 **10** **take someone's part** to be on someone's side in an argument 〔辯論中〕支持某一方 **11** **for my part** *fml* speaking for myself 〔正式〕對我來說 **12** **for the most part** *fml* generally 〔正式〕就大部分而言 **13** **in part** partly 部分地 **14** **on someone's part** by someone 在某人方面; 由某人做出: *This was a serious mistake on the Government's part.* 這是政府所犯的一個嚴重錯誤。 **15** **part and parcel** an important piece which cannot be separated from the rest 不可分割的重要部分: *Getting hot is part and parcel of being a cook!* 作為廚師就不可避免地要挨熱受燙了。 **16** **the best part, the better part** most 大部分: *Registering at the university took the best part of the day.* 在大學裡註冊登記花去了大半天的時間。

part² *v* **1** [I;T] to separate 分開; 分離: *She tried to part the two fighting dogs.* 她試圖把兩隻在打架的狗分開。| *If we must part, I hope we can part friends.* 如果我們必須分手, 我希望我們分了手還是朋友。| *The clouds parted, and the sun shone down.* 雲散開了, 太陽光照到地上。| *Young children don't like to be parted from their mothers.* 年紀小的孩子不喜歡和母親分開。 **2** **part your hair** to separate your hair along a line with a comb 用梳子把頭髮分界 **3** **part company: a** to end a relationship 斷絕關係 **b** no longer to be together 跟…離別 **c** to disagree 不同意

part with sthg *phr v* [T] to get rid of something that you are fond of 捨棄〔自己喜歡的東西〕: *He hates parting with his old toys.* 他不喜歡捨棄自己的舊玩具。

part³ _adv_ part..., part... consisting partly of one thing and partly of another 部分地: _The medical exams are part written, part practical._ 醫科考試部分是筆試，部分是考實踐。

part⁴ _adj_ not complete 不完全的，部分的: _We're part owners of the land; we share with our neighbours._ 我們不是全部擁有這塊地，而是與鄰居共同擁有。

par·tial /ˈpɑːʃəl; ˈpɑːʃəl/ _adj_ **1** not complete 不完全的，部分的: _The attempt was only a partial success._ 此項努力只取得了部分成功。 **2** unfairly favouring one person or side more than another 偏袒的；不公平的 –opposite 反義 **impartial 3 partial to** _infml_ having a strong liking for 《非正式》過分喜歡；偏愛: _I'm very partial to sweet foods._ 我非常喜歡吃甜食。

par·ti·al·i·ty /ˌpɑːʃiˈæləti; ˌpɑːʃiˈælˌti/ _n_ **1** [U] the favouring of one person or side more than another 偏袒；不公平 –opposite 反義 **impartiality 2** [sing] a special liking for something 偏愛

par·tial·ly /ˈpɑːʃəli; ˈpɑːʃəli/ _adv_ **1** not completely 不完全地，部分地: _I'm partially to blame for the accident._ 我要對這次事故負部分責任。 **2** in a way that favours one person or side more than another 偏袒地；不公平地

*par·tic·i·pant /pɑːˈtɪsəpənt; pɑːˈtɪsˌpənt/ _n_ a person who takes part in an activity or event 〔活動或事件的〕參加者

*par·tic·i·pate /pɑːˈtɪsɪˌpeɪt; pɑːˈtɪsˌpeɪt/ _v_ **participated, participating** [I] _fml_ to take part in an activity 《正式》參加〔活動〕: _We were invited to participate in the discussion._ 我們獲邀請參加討論。 –**participation** /pɑːˌtɪsəˈpeɪʃən; pɑːˌtɪsˌˈpeɪʃən/ _n_ [U]

par·ti·ci·ple /ˈpɑːtəsəpl; ˈpɑːtˌsɪpəl/ _n_ a part of a verb which is used to make compound forms of the verb or as an adjective; with the verb **take** the present participle is _taking_ and the past participle is _taken_ 分詞〔例如 **take**，其現在分詞為 taking，過去分詞為 taken〕 –**participial** /ˌpɑːtəˈsɪpiəl; ˌpɑːtˌˈsɪpiəl/

par·ti·cle /ˈpɑːtɪkl; ˈpɑːtɪkəl/ _n_ a very small piece or amount 微粒；一點兒: _dust particles floating in the sunlight_ 飄浮在陽光中的塵粒 | _There wasn't a particle of truth in what he said._ 他所說的沒有一句是真的。

*par·tic·u·lar /pɑːˈtɪkjələ; pɑːˈtɪkjˌələ/ _adj_ **1** [only before a noun 只用於名詞前] special 特別的，特殊的: _There was nothing of particular importance in the letter._ 信裡沒有甚麼特別重要的內容。 **2** [only before a noun 只用於名詞前] this one and not others 特定的；特指的: _On this particular day we had got up very early._ 在這一天我們起得十分早。 **3** demanding that everything is exactly right, including the smallest details 苛求的；講究的: _She's very particular about hygiene._ 她特別講究衛生。 **4**

in particular especially 尤其；特別: _I'm interested in insects, and beetles in particular._ 我對昆蟲感興趣，尤其是甲蟲。

*par·tic·u·lar·ly /pɑːˈtɪkjələli; pɑːˈtɪkjˌələli/ _adv_ especially 尤其；特別地: _He isn't particularly clever._ 他不是特別聰明。

par·tic·u·lars /pɑːˈtɪkjələz; pɑːˈtɪkjˌələz/ _n_ [pl] the detailed facts about something 細節；詳情

part·ing /ˈpɑːtɪŋ; ˈpɑːtɪŋ/ _n_ **1** [C;U] separation 分開；離別 **2** [C] _BrE_ the line in a person's hair where they have divided it with a comb 〔頭髮的〕分縫，分界 –see picture on page 469 見 469 頁彩圖 **3 the parting of the ways** the point at which two people must separate, or a choice must be made 兩人分手的地方；抉擇的時刻

par·ti·san¹ /ˌpɑːtəˈzæn; ˈpɑːtˌˈzæn/ _adj_ looking at things from one particular point of view, and not trying to see them fairly 〔觀點〕片面的

partisan² _n_ **1** a strong supporter of someone or something 〔某人或某事的〕強硬支持者 **2** a member of an armed group that fights in secret against an enemy that has conquered its country 游擊隊員

par·ti·tion /pɑːˈtɪʃən; pɑːˈtɪʃən/ _n_ **1** [C] a thin wall that separates one part of a room from another 〔屋內的〕隔牆；隔板 **2** [U] division of a country into two or more independent countries 〔一個國家的〕瓜分；劃分；分割 –**partition** _v_ [T]: _The kitchen area was partitioned off._ 廚房被隔開了。

*part·ly /ˈpɑːtli; ˈpɑːtli/ _adv_ to some degree, but not completely 部分地: _It was partly my fault._ 這有部分是我錯。| _The problem is partly money and partly time._ 這個問題部分是因為錢，部分是因為時間。| _We didn't go, partly because the public transport was so poor._ 我們沒有去，部分原因是公共交通太糟糕了。

*part·ner¹ /ˈpɑːtnə; ˈpɑːtnə/ _n_ **1** a person or group that you share an activity with 合作者；夥伴: _Britain's partners in NATO_ 英國在北約組織中的夥伴 **2** a person that you dance with or who makes a pair with you to play a game such as tennis 舞伴；搭檔；配手: _I can't find a partner._ 我找不到搭檔。 **3** any of the owners of a business, who share the profits and losses 股東；合夥人: _She's a partner in a law firm._ 她是這家法律事務所的合夥人。 **4** a person who you are married to or who you live with, go out with, or have sex with 伴侶；配偶

partner² _v_ [T] to be someone's partner in a game or dance 〔比賽或舞蹈中〕作〔某人〕的夥伴

*part·ner·ship /ˈpɑːtnəʃɪp; ˈpɑːtnəʃɪp/ _n_ **1** [U] the state of being a partner, especially in business 〔尤指生意中的〕合夥關係: _We've been in partnership for five years._ 我們合夥已

P

經五年了。**2** [C] a business owned by two or more people who share the profits and losses 合營企業, 合股公司

part of speech /ˌ· · ˈ·/ *n* a class of words in grammar, for example nouns, verbs, and adjectives〔語法〕詞類: *What part of speech is "do" in this sentence?* "do" 在該句中是甚麼詞類?

par·took /parˈtʊk; pɑːˈtʊk/ the past tense of PARTAKE ☆ PARTAKE 的過去式

par·tridge /ˈpɑrtrɪdʒ; ˈpɑːtrɪdʒ/ *n* a middle-size bird shot for sport and food 山鶉, 鷓鴣

part-time /ˌ· ˈ·◂/ *adj* working during only a part of the regular working time 兼職的: *a part-time job* 兼職工作 | *a part-time secretary* 兼職祕書 **–part time** *adv*: *She works part time.* 她做兼職工作。

par·ty /ˈpɑrtɪ; ˈpɑːti/ *n* **parties 1** a social event at which people eat, drink, and enjoy themselves 聚會; 宴會: *We went to a party at Nicky's.* 我們去參加了尼克家的聚會。 | *We had a party to celebrate the end of the exams.* 我們為慶祝考試結束舉行了一個聚會。 | *a birthday party* 生日慶祝會 | *They gave a party for their parents' fiftieth wedding anniversary.* 他們為父母結婚五十週年舉行了一個慶祝會。 **2** [+sing/pl verb] a group of people doing something together〔一起活動的〕一夥人: *a party of schoolchildren on their way to France* 正前往法國的一羣小學生 **3** [+sing/pl verb] an organization of people with the same political aims who try to win elec-tions 政黨: *the Green Party* 綠黨 | *Three parties are contesting the election.* 有三個政黨參加大選。 **4 party politics** political activity for the advantage of your party and not your country〔從黨派利益出發的〕政黨政治: *This is not a time to play party poli-tics.* 現在不是進行黨派政治的時候。 **5 the party line: a** the official view of a political party 政黨的路線 **b** a view which the more powerful members of an organization try to force on the rest 一個組織內有勢力的成員試圖強加給其他人的觀點 **6** *law* one of the people or sides in an agreement or argu-ment〔律〕〔協議或爭執的〕一方

pass¹ /pæs; pɑːs/ *v* **1** [T] to go past a person or thing 經過, 越過〔人或物〕: *We passed the school and then saw the library in front of us.* 我們走過學校, 隨後看見圖書館就在前面。 | *She waved at me as she passed.* 她經過時朝我揮揮手。**–see** PAST¹ (USAGE用法) **2** [I+adv/prep] to move in a particular direction 穿過, 路過: *We passed through Germany on our way to Austria.* 我們去奧地利時途經德國。 | *A cloud passed across the sun.* 一片雲掠過太陽。 **3** [T; +adv/prep] to move something in a par-ticular direction 越過: *She passed the rope around the tree.* 她把繩子繞在樹上。 **4** [T] to give something to someone by putting it into their hand 把〔某物〕傳給〔某人〕; 遞給: *I*

looked at the photograph then passed it to Jane.* 我看了看照片, 然後把它遞給簡。 | *Could you pass the salt, please?* 請你把鹽遞給我好嗎? | *He passed me a glass of wine.* 他遞給我一杯酒。

□ USEFUL PATTERNS 有用句型
to pass something to someone; to pass someone something

5 [I;T] to kick, throw, or hit a ball to some-one in your own team during a game such as football〔諸如足球等比賽中〕傳球 **6** [I] (of time) to go by〔時間〕消逝: *The time seemed to pass very slowly.* 時間似乎過得很慢。 | *He gradually grew stronger as the summer passed.* 隨着夏天的過去, 他逐漸變得強壯起來。 **7** [T] to spend time in a particular way〔以某種方式〕度過, 消磨〔時間〕: *We passed an enjoyable evening together.* 我們一起度過了一個愉快的夜晚。 **8** [I] to go from one per-son's control or possession to another's 轉讓; 傳給: *When she died the house passed to her son.* 她去世時把房子傳給了她兒子。 **9** [T] to officially accept a new law or a sugges-tion 通過〔法律〕; 接受〔提議〕: *The new law will be passed next month.* 新法例將於下月通過。 **10** [I;T] to succeed in a test or an examination 通過〔考試〕: *I've finally passed my driving test!* 我終於通過了駕駛考試! | *Most of the students passed the exam.* 大部分學生通過了考試。 **11 pass judgement** to give your opinion about something, es-pecially when it is unfavourable 提出自己的看法〔尤指對某事不利的看法〕: *My job is just to collect the facts — not to pass judgement.* 我的工作只是收集事實, 而不是提供自己的看法。 **12 pass sentence** to say what some-one's punishment will be for a crime that they have done 宣佈〔對某人的〕判決 **13 pass the buck** *infml* to refuse to accept re-sponsibility for something and say that it is someone else's responsibility〔非正式〕推諉責任 **14 pass the time** to do something so that you do not feel BORED 消磨時間: *We played cards to pass the time.* 我們以玩牌來消磨時間。 **15 pass the time of day** to have a short conversation with someone that you meet 與〔某人〕寒暄 **16 pass unnoticed** to not be noticed by people 未被注意: *His odd behaviour passed unnoticed.* 他古怪的行為未引起人們的注意。 **17 pass water** *tech* to URI-NATE〔術語〕小便

pass away *phr v* [I] *euph* to die (a less di-rect word than **die**)〔委婉〕去世, 死亡〔比 **die** 含蓄的用詞〕: *She passed away peacefully in her sleep.* 她在睡夢中平靜地去世了。

pass by *phr v* [I] to go past a person or thing 經過; 走過: *She waved as she passed by.* 她經過時揮了揮手。

pass sthg ↔ **down** *phr v* [T] to give or leave something to people who are younger than you or come after you 留傳; 傳授: *The knowledge was passed down from father to son.* 父親把知識傳給了兒子。

pass off *phr v* **1** [I] to stop 停止: *The feelings of depression gradually passed off.* 抑鬱的感覺漸消失了。**2 pass off well** to take place successfully 舉行得很成功: *The meeting passed off very well.* 會議開得很順利。**3** [T **pass** sbdy/sthg **off**] to present a person or thing as something false 冒充〔某人、某物〕: *They tried to pass the painting off as a genuine Piccasso.* 他們試圖把這幅畫冒充為畢加索的真跡。| *He passed himself off as a doctor.* 他冒充醫生。

pass on *phr v* **1** [I] *euph* to die (a less direct word than **die**)〔委婉〕去世, 死亡〔比 **die** 含蓄的用詞〕: *My mother passed on last year.* 我的母親去年去世了。**2** [T **pass** sthg **on**] to give something to someone else after you have used it 將〔某物〕傳給〔別人〕: *Please read this notice and pass it on.* 請傳閱這則通告。

pass out *phr v* [I] to faint 昏過去: *I always pass out at the sight of blood.* 我總是一見血就會暈倒。

pass over sthg *phr v* [T] to not talk about something because you do not want to pay attention to it 對〔某事物〕忽略不提; 忽視: *He passed over the subject of salaries very quickly!* 他對有關工資的問題一帶而過!

pass sthg ↔ **up** *phr v* [T] to fail to take advantage of a chance to do something 放過; 錯過〔做某事的機會〕: *I'd never pass up a chance to travel.* 我決不錯失去旅遊的機會。

***pass²** *n* **1** a successful result in an examination 考試及格 **2** a piece of paper which shows that you are allowed to do something, for example enter a building 許可證; 通行證 **3** an act of passing a ball to a member of your own team in a game such as football〔足球賽等的〕傳球 **4** a narrow way which you can go through in a mountain range 山間小道 **5 make a pass at someone** to try to begin a sexual relationship with someone 向某人調謔〔挑逗〕; 勾引某人

pass·a·ble /'pæsəbl; 'pɑːsəbəl/ *adj* **1** satisfactory 令人滿意的 **2** just good enough to be accepted 尚可的; 可接受的 **3** possible to use or cross (used of roads and rivers) 能通過的; 能渡過的〔指路或河流〕

***pas·sage** /'pæsɪdʒ; 'pæsɪdʒ/ *n* **1** [C] (also 又作 **passageway**) a narrow way, especially inside a building, connecting rooms or places together 過道, 走廊〔尤指建築物內連接房間的通道〕: *It's along this passage on the left.* 它在這條走廊的左邊。**2** [C] a narrow way through 通道; 通路: *He forced a passage through the crowd.* 他從人羣中擠出一條通道。**3** [C] a natural tube which is part of your body and through which air or waste matter may pass along〔體內的〕管道: *Clear the air passages.* 清一清氣管。**4** [U] movement

from one place to another 通過; 經過; 越過: *The bridge is not strong enough to allow the passage of heavy vehicles.* 這座橋不夠堅固, 重型車輛無法通過。**5 the passage of time** the passing of time 時間的消逝 **6** [sing] a long journey by ship〔坐船的〕長途航程 **7** [C] a short part of a piece of writing or music〔文章或音樂的〕一段, 一節: *an interesting passage on page 32* 第三十二頁上的一段有趣的文章

pas·sage·way /'pæsɪdʒˌwe; 'pæsɪdʒweɪ/ *n* a passage in a building or between buildings 走廊; 通道

***pas·sen·ger** /'pæsndʒə; 'pæsɪndʒəʳ/ *n* a person, not the driver or a member of the crew, travelling in a public or private vehicle 乘客

pass·er-by /ˌpæsəˈbaɪ; ˌpɑːsəˈbaɪ/ *n* **passersby** /-sˌz-; -səz-/ a person who, by chance, is going past 途人, 過路人: *Several passersby saw the accident.* 有幾個過路人目擊了這起事故。

pas·sing¹ /'pæsɪŋ; 'pɑːsɪŋ/ *adj* [only before a noun 只用於名詞前] **1** moving or going by 通過的, 經過的: *She watched the passing cars.* 她看着來往的汽車。**2** not lasting very long 短暫的, 一時的: *She did not give the matter even a passing thought.* 她對這件事甚至連想也沒有想一下。

passing² *n* **in passing** in the course of talking about something else 順便地; 附帶地: *He was talking about Spain, and he mentioned in passing that you went there last year.* 他在談論西班牙時, 順便提到去年你曾到過那裡。

***pas·sion** /'pæʃən; 'pæʃən/ *n* [C;U] a strong, deep, often uncontrollable feeling, especially of love, hatred, or anger 強烈的情感, 激情: *The poet was expressing his burning passion for the woman he loved.* 詩人在表達他對自己熱戀的女子火一般的感情。| *He has a passion for cream cakes.* 他很愛吃奶油蛋糕。

pas·sion·ate /'pæʃənɪt; 'pæʃənɪt/ *adj* showing or filled with passion 多情的; 充滿激情的: *a passionate speech* 充滿激情的演講 | *a passionate woman* 多情的女人 | *a passionate interest in politics* 對政治的強烈興趣 – **passionately** *adv*

pas·sive¹ /'pæsɪv; 'pæsɪv/ *adj* **1** not active, but allowing things to happen to you (a word often used to express disapproval) 被動的; 消極的〔常含貶義〕: *his passive acceptance of his fate* 他消極地接受了自己的命運 **2** a verb relating to or containing as its subject the person or thing to which an action is done; in "The boy was thrown from his horse", "was thrown" is a passive verb〔動詞〕被動式的〔如在 "The boy was thrown from his horse" 中, "was thrown" 就是被動式的動詞〕 –**passively** *adv*

passive² *n* **the passive** the passive part or form of a verb〔動詞的〕被動式, 被動語態

Pass·o·ver /'pæs,ovə; 'pɑːsəuvə/ *n* [U; sing] a holiday in the Jewish religion in memory of the freeing of the Jews from Egypt〔猶太教的〕逾越節

pass·port /'pæs,port; 'pɑːspɔːt/ *n* **1** a small official book that proves which country you belong to; you use it when you enter a foreign country 護照 **2 a passport to something** a way to get something 獲取某物的手段: *Money isn't a passport to happiness.* 有錢不一定就有幸福。

pass·word /'pæs,wɜːd; 'pɑːswɜːd/ *n* **1** a secret word which you have to know in order to get into a place, such as a military area 口令; 通行密語 **2** a word you put into a computer in order to use it〔電腦的〕口令; 通行密碼

★★past¹ /pæst; pɑːst/ *adj* **1** [only before a noun 只用於名詞前] having happened or existed before the present time 過去的: *He blamed past governments for creating these problems.* 他指責過去的政府造成了這些問題。| *Things have got much worse in the past few years.* 事情在過去幾年變得更糟糕了。 **2** finished and no longer happening or existing 完成的; 結束的: *The time for talking is past — we must act now.* 談論的時間已經過去, 我們現在必須行動起來。 **3 past tense** the form of a verb that expresses an action or an event that happened before the present time〔動詞的〕過去式

★past² *adv, prep* **1** *adv, prep* used to show that someone moves up to and beyond something 越過; 經過: *We drove past the house.* 我們駕車從那所房子旁邊經過。| *He didn't stop — he just walked straight past.* 他沒有停下來, 只逕直地走了過去。–see picture on page 764 見 764 頁彩圖 **2** *prep* farther on than something 比〔某物〕更遠: *The hospital is about a mile past the school.* 醫院大約在距學校一英里遠的地方。 **3** *prep* beyond a particular time 超過〔某一時間〕: *It's just past ten o'clock.* 現在剛過十點鐘。 **4 past caring** no longer caring what happens 已經不在乎〔發生甚麼事〕

★past³ *n* **1** [sing] the time that existed before the present time 過去; 以前: *Housework is much easier now than it was in the past.* 現在做家務比以前容易多了。| *He never talks about his past.* 他對自己的過去絕口不提。 **2 the past** the past tense of a verb〔動詞的〕過去式

> ■ USAGE 用法: The past participle of **pass** is **passed** ☆ **pass** 的過去分詞是 **passed**: *The week has **passed** quickly.* 這一週很快就過去了。But the adjective from **pass** is **past** ☆但 **pass** 派生出的形容詞是 **past**: *The **past** week has been very busy.* 過去的一週很繁忙。

pas·ta /'pɑstə; 'pæstə/ *n* [U] an Italian food made, in various different shapes, from flour paste, and often covered with SAUCE or cheese; SPAGHETTI is a kind of pasta 意大利麵食〔常拌以肉醬或乾酪〕

paste¹ /pest; peɪst/ *n* [C;U] **1** a wet substance used for sticking paper together, or onto other surfaces 漿糊 **2** any soft wet mixture of powder and liquid that is easily shaped or spread 糊狀物: *Mix it all up into a paste.* 把它調成糊狀。 **3** a food made by crushing solid foods into a smooth soft mass, used for spreading on bread〔塗在麵包上的〕醬: *meat paste* 肉醬 | *fish paste* 魚醬 **4** a shining glassy substance, used to copy the appearance of real jewels〔製造人造寶石用的〕鉛質玻璃

paste² *v* **pasted, pasting** [T] to stick paper with paste 用漿糊黏貼〔紙張〕; 裱糊

pas·tel /'pæs'tel; 'pæstl/ *n* **1** [C;U] a kind of dry colour in sticks used by artists 彩色粉筆 [蠟筆] **2** [C] a picture drawn with pastels 彩色粉筆畫; 蠟筆畫

pas·teur·ize /'pæstə,raɪz; 'pɑːstʃəraɪz/ *v* **pasteurized, pasteurizing** (also 又作 **pasteurise** BrE《英式》) [T] to heat a liquid, especially milk, in a certain way in order to destroy bacteria 用巴斯德消毒法給〔液體〕消毒〔尤指牛奶〕 –**pasteurization** /,pæstərə'zeɪʃən; ,pɑːstʃəraɪ'zeɪʃən/ *n* [U]

pas·time /'pæs,taɪm; 'pɑːstaɪm/ *n* something you do to pass your time in a pleasant way 消遣; 娛樂

past mas·ter /,· ·· / *n* a person who is very skilled in a particular subject or action 能手, 老手, 高手

pas·tor·al /'pæstərəl; 'pɑːstərəl/ *adj* **1** concerning simple peaceful country life 田園生活的; 簡樸的: *a pastoral scene of cows in a meadow* 牛羣在草地上的田園景象 | *pastoral poetry* 田園詩 **2** connected with looking after people's happiness, especially their religious happiness〔尤指宗教信仰上〕提供輔導的: *The priest makes pastoral visits every Tuesday.* 牧師每週二拜訪教友。

past par·ti·ci·ple /,· ·····/ *n* a part of a verb which is used in compound forms of the verb to express an action done or happening in the past; it is sometimes used as an adjective 過去分詞: *"Done" and "walked" are the past participles of "do" and "walk".* "done" 和 "walked" 是 "do" 和 "walk" 的過去分詞。–see LIST OF IRREGULAR VERB 見"不規則動詞表"

past per·fect /,· ···/ *n* **the past perfect** a verb form used to show that one thing had happened before another in the past〔動詞的〕過去完成式: *"Had done" is the past perfect of "do".* "had done" 是 "do" 的過去完成式。

pas·try /'pestrɪ; 'peɪstrɪ/ *n* **pastries 1** [U] a mixture of flour, fat, and milk or water, eaten when baked and often used to enclose other food〔麵粉加油脂、牛奶或水的〕油酥麵團 **2** [C] a small sweet cake made with pastry 酥皮小甜餅

pas·ture /ˈpæstʃɚ; ˈpɑːstʃəʳ/ *n* [C;U] grassy land where cattle feed 牧場

pas·ty¹ /ˈpæsti; ˈpæsti/ *n* **pasties** a folded piece of pastry baked with meat and potatoes in it〔有肉和馬鈴薯的〕肉餡餅

past·y² /ˈpesti; ˈpeɪsti/ *adj* white and unhealthy-looking (used to describe someone's face)〔臉色〕蒼白的; 病態的

pat¹ /pæt; pæt/ *v* -**tt-** [T] to touch something gently and repeatedly with your hand flat, often to show kindness or pity 輕拍, 輕打〔某人〕〔常用以表示友好或同情〕: *She patted her hair into place.* 她輕拍她的頭髮, 使頭髮保持整齊。| *He patted her hand sympathetically.* 他同情地拍拍她的手。

pat² *n* **1** a light friendly touch with your hand flat 輕拍, 輕打: *He gave the dog a pat as he walked past.* 他走過時輕輕地拍了拍那隻狗。**2 a pat on the back** *infml* an expression of praise or satisfaction for something done〔非正式〕讚許, 稱讚 **3 a pat of butter** a small lump of butter 一小塊黃油

patch¹ /pætʃ; pætʃ/ *n* **1** a piece of material used to cover a hole or a damaged place 補丁, 補片 **2** a small area that looks different from the rest 斑塊; 斑點: *wet patches on the wall* 牆上一片片的潮斑 | *There will be a few patches of mist near the coast.* 近海地區將出現一團團的霧。**3** a small piece of ground 一小塊土地: *a potato patch* 一小塊馬鈴薯地 **4 a bad patch** *BrE* a time of trouble or misfortune〔英式〕不景氣時期; 倒霉時期 **5 not a patch on** *infml* not nearly as good as〔非正式〕比不上, 遠不如

patch² *v* [T] **1** to put a patch on a hole or worn place 在〔有洞或磨損處〕打補丁; 修補: *patched trousers* 有補丁的褲子 **2 patch something together** to quickly put together something which is of low quality but better than nothing 拼湊; 湊合

patch sthg ↔ up *phr v* [T] **1** to mend something with patches so that it can be used, even though it is not as good as new 修補, 修理〔某物〕: *They patched the car up well enough to get us home.* 他們草草修了車子, 使我們能夠開回家。**2 patch up a quarrel** to become friendly with someone again after a disagreement〔爭吵後〕和解; 和好

patch·work /ˈpætʃwɜːk; ˈpætʃwɜːk/ *n* [C;U] **1** material made by sewing together a lot of small pieces of cloth, of regular shape but different colours and patterns 用各色布片縫綴成的縫物; 補綴的手工: *a patchwork bedcover* 用各色布片縫製成的牀罩 **2** something that has a surface made up of lots of little pieces and looks like patchwork 由許多小塊組成的表面: *From the aircraft we could see a marvellous patchwork of fields.*

從飛機上望下去, 我們能看見一塊塊令人驚嘆的田野。

patch·y /ˈpætʃi; ˈpætʃi/ *adj* **patchier, patchiest 1** made up of patches, or appearing in patches 一塊塊的; 一片片的; 斑駁的: *patchy mist* 一團團的霧 **2** incomplete or uneven 不完整的; 不均勻的: *My knowledge of science is rather patchy.* 我的科學知識是零零碎碎的。– **patchily** *adv* –**patchiness** *n* [U]

pâ·té /ˈpæte; ˈpæteɪ/ *n* [U] a meat paste made by cutting PORK and other meat very finely and cooking it 肉醬

pa·tent¹ /ˈpetnt; ˈpeɪtnt/ *adj* **1** easy and plain to see (mostly used to describe feelings or qualities) 顯而易見的〔主要用於描述情感或性質〕: *her patent discomfort at this odd situation* 她在這種不尋常的情形下的明顯的不自在 **2** protected, by a patent, from being copied or sold by those who do not have a right to do so 有專利權的: *a patent lock* 專利鎖

patent² *n* a piece of paper from a government office called the Patent Office giving someone the right to make or sell a new invention for a certain number of years 專利證書

patent³ *v* [T] to obtain a patent for something 取得〔某物〕的專利權

patent leath·er /ˌpetnt ˈlɛðɚ; ˌpeɪtnt ˈleðəʳ◂/ *n* [U] fine very shiny leather 漆皮: *patent-leather shoes* 漆皮鞋

pa·tent·ly /ˈpetntli; ˈpeɪtntli/ *adv* clearly and plainly 明顯地, 顯然地: *a patently false statement* 明顯的謊言

pa·ter·nal /pəˈtɜːnl; pəˈtɜːnl/ *adj* **1** like a father or received from a father 父親般的; 得自父親的: *paternal love* 父愛 **2** related to a person through their father's side of the family 父系的: *my paternal grandmother* 我的祖母 –**paternally** *adv*

pa·ter·nal·is·m /pəˈtɜːnlˌɪzəm; pəˈtɜːnəlˌɪzəm/ *n* [U] a way of ruling a country or controlling a company, which treats people like children 家長式統治 –**paternalistic** /pəˌtɜːnlˈɪstɪk; pəˌtɜːnəlˈɪstɪk◂/ *adj*

pa·ter·ni·ty /pəˈtɜːnəti; pəˈtɜːnₐti/ *n* [U] *law* the fact of being the father of a child〔律〕父親的身分

✲**path** /pæθ; pɑːθ/ *n* **1** (also 又作 **pathway**) a track for people on foot 小徑; 小路: *a path through the woods* 林中小路 | *We went down the garden path.* 我們沿着花園裡的小路往前走。–see 見 WAY¹ (USAGE用法) – see picture on page 729 見 729 頁彩圖 **2** the hard raised part at the side of the street which people on foot use 人行道: *Stay on the path. Don't go out into the road.* 留在人行道上, 不要走到馬路上去。**3** a way 通道: *The police cleared a path through the crowd.* 警察把人羣分開, 闢出一條通道。**4** a line along which something moves 路線; 軌跡: *the path of an arrow* 箭的

P

飛行軌跡 | *He stepped into the path of an oncoming car.* 他走到了一部迎面而來的汽車經過的路線上。 **5** a course of action with an expected result 途徑; 方式: *Development of the railways is the path to a successful transport structure.* 發展鐵路是通向完善運輸體系的成功之路。

pa·thet·ic /pəˈθɛtɪk; pəˈθetɪk/ *adj* **1** very bad or weak when there is no good reason for it 糟糕的; 虛弱的: *The Government's treatment of the disabled is quite pathetic.* 政府對待殘疾人士的態度相當糟糕。 **2** very bad 差勁的: *He's a pathetic actor.* 他是個差勁的演員。 **3** making you feel sorry for someone 可憐的, 惹人憐憫的: *the child's pathetic cries of pain* 那個孩子令人心碎的喊痛聲 **–pathetically** /-klɪ; -kli/ *adv*: *a dog whimpering pathetically* 一隻狗可憐兮兮地在嗚咽

path·o·log·i·cal /ˌpæθəˈlɒdʒɪkl; ˌpæθəˈlɒdʒɪkəl/ *adj* **1** behaving again and again in an unreasonable way, but unable to stop yourself 〔行為〕病態的; 反常的: *a pathological liar* 病態的說謊者 **2** *infml* unreasonable and caused by the imagination only 《非正式》 不合理的; 單憑想像的: *a pathological fear of the dark* 對黑暗的莫名其妙的恐懼 **3** *tech* caused by disease, or connected with the study of disease 《術語》 由疾病引起的; 病理學的 **–pathologically** *adv*: *pathologically jealous* 嫉妒得莫名其妙的

pa·thol·o·gist /pæˈθɒlədʒɪst; pəˈθɒlədʒ ̮st/ *n* a specialist in pathology, especially a doctor who examines a dead body to find out how the person died 病理學家〔尤指驗屍醫師〕

pa·thol·o·gy /pəˈθɒlədʒɪ; pəˈθɒlədʒi/ *n* [U] the study of disease 病理學

pa·thos /ˈpeɪθɒs; ˈpeɪθɒs/ *n* [U] *lit* something in a sad situation which makes you feel very sorry for the people in it 《文》引起憐憫的事情; 傷感力

path·way /ˈpɑːθweɪ; ˈpɑːθweɪ/ *n* a path 小徑; 小路

pa·tience /ˈpeɪʃns; ˈpeɪʃəns/ *n* [U] **1** the ability to wait, or to deal with difficulties, for a long time without getting annoyed 耐心; 忍耐力: *You need a lot of patience if you want to get served in this shop.* 如果你想在這商店裡得到服務, 就需要有很大的耐心。 | *She showed great patience with them all.* 她對他們大家表現出了極大的耐心。 **–opposite** 反義 **impatience 2** a card game for one player 單人紙牌戲

⋆**pa·tient**[1] /ˈpeɪʃnt; ˈpeɪʃənt/ *adj* having or showing patience 耐心的: *Try to be patient.* 盡量耐心些。 **–opposite** 反義 **impatient –patiently** *adv*

⋆**patient**[2] *n* a person receiving medical treatment 病人: *clinics for private patients* 為自費病人開設的診所 **–see** 見 CUSTOMER (USAGE 用法)

pat·i·o /ˈpætɪˌo; ˈpætiəʊ/ *n* **patios** an area of the garden with a hard surface; it is near the house, and people use it for sitting outside 〔和房屋連接的〕露台, 平台 **–see** picture on page 729 見 729 頁彩圖

pat·ri·ot /ˈpeɪtrɪət; ˈpætrɪət/ *n* a person who loves their country 愛國者

pat·ri·ot·is·m /ˈpeɪtrɪətɪzəm; ˈpætrɪətɪzəm/ *n* [U] love for your country 愛國主義; 愛國精神 **–patriotic** /ˌpeɪtrɪˈɒtɪk; ˌpætrɪˈɒtɪk◂/ *adj*: *patriotic songs* 愛國歌曲 **–patriotically** /-klɪ; -kli/ *adv*

pa·trol[1] /pəˈtrol; pəˈtrəʊl/ *n* **1** [+sing/pl verb] a small group of soldiers who move round the outside of a military camp to make sure that the enemy do not enter it 巡邏小隊 **2** **on patrol** working in a patrol 在巡邏中

patrol[2] *v* **-ll-** [I;T] to go round an area or building at regular times to see that there is no trouble, and that no one is trying to get in or out illegally 巡邏; 巡查: *Armed guards patrol the grounds.* 這一帶有武警巡邏。

pa·trol·man /pəˈtrolmən; pəˈtrəʊlmən/ **patrolmen** /-mən; -mən/ *AmE* a policeman who regularly patrols a particular area 〔美式〕巡警

pa·tron /ˈpeɪtrən; ˈpeɪtrən/ *n* **1** a well-known person who officially supports an organization which helps people 〔對於一個團體的〕贊助人 **2** a person who supports artists, musicians, and writers by buying their works or giving them money 〔藝術家、音樂家和作家的〕資助人 **3** a person who uses a particular shop or hotel, especially regularly (老)顧客, (老)主顧

pat·ron·age /ˈpeɪtrənɪdʒ; ˈpætrənɪdʒ/ *n* [U] **1** the support given by a patron 贊助; 惠顧 **2** the right to appoint people to important positions (a word which is often used to express disapproval) 授予要職的權力, 任命權〔常含貶義〕

pat·ron·ize /ˈpeɪtrənˌaɪz; ˈpætrənaɪz/ *v* **patronized, patronizing** (also 又作 **patronise** *BrE* 《英式》) [T] **1** to behave to someone as if you think that you are better or more important than they are 以高人一等的態度對待〔某人〕: *He cannot speak to women without patronizing them.* 他一對婦女說話就盛氣凌人。 | *a patronizing smile* 盛氣凌人的笑容 **2** *fml* to be a patron of a shop or hotel 《正式》惠顧〔商店或旅館〕

patron saint /ˌ··ˈ·/ *n* a Christian holy man or woman in the past, regarded as giving special protection to a particular place or activity 守護神: *Saint Christopher is the patron saint of travellers.* 聖克里斯托夫是旅行者的守護神。

pat·ter[1] /ˈpætə; ˈpætər/ *n* **1** [sing] the sound of something hitting a hard surface lightly, quickly, and repeatedly 〔急促的〕嗒嗒聲: *the patter of rain on the window* 窗上嘀嘀嗒嗒的雨聲 **2** [U] the quick talk of a salesperson or a performer〔售貨員或演員的〕快速的講話, 急口詞, 順口溜

patter² *v* [I; +adv/prep] to make the sound of something hitting a hard surface lightly, quickly, and repeatedly 發出急促的嗒嗒聲: *The dog pattered down the stairs.* 狗篤篤地跑下樓梯。

★★**pat·tern** /ˈpætən; ˈpætən/ *n* **1** a regularly repeated arrangement especially of lines or shapes on a surface or of sounds or words 圖案;〔聲音或詞彙的〕模式: *The cloth has a pattern of red and white squares.* 這塊布有紅白方格的圖案。 **2** the way in which something usually happens or develops〔某事發生或發展的〕方式, 形式: *The illness is not following its usual pattern.* 這種病並未按其慣常的方式發展。 **3** a shape used as a guide for making something, especially a piece of paper used to show the shape of the parts of a piece of clothing〔做衣物的〕紙樣: *a dress pattern* 服裝的紙樣

pat·terned /ˈpætənd; ˈpætənd/ *adj* having a pattern 有圖案的: *a patterned carpet* 有圖案的地毯 –see picture on page 243 見 243 頁彩圖

paunch /pɔntʃ; pɔːntʃ/ *n* a fat stomach, especially a man's〔尤指男子的〕大肚皮

pau·per /ˈpɔpə; ˈpɔːpə/ *n* a person who is very poor 窮人, 貧民

★**pause¹** /pɔz; pɔːz/ *n* a short but noticeable break in activity or speech〔行動或講話的〕暫停, 停頓: *a pause in the conversation* 談話中的停頓

pause² *v* **paused, pausing** [I] to stop for a short time 暫停, 停頓: *She paused to light a cigarette, then continued reading.* 她停下來點根煙, 然後繼續看書。

pave /pev; peɪv/ *v* **paved, paving** [T] **1** to cover a path or area with a surface of flat stones〔用石塊〕鋪〔路〕: *a paved courtyard* 鋪上石塊的院子 **2** pave the way for to do something now which will make something else possible in the future 為〔某事〕鋪平道路; 為〔某事〕創造條件

pave·ment /ˈpevmənt; ˈpeɪvmənt/ *n* **1** BrE a paved surface at the side of a street for people to walk on《英式》人行道 **2** AmE the hard black part of a road that vehicles drive on《美式》硬路面 –see picture on page 729 見 729 頁彩圖

pa·vil·ion /pəˈvɪljən; pəˈvɪljən/ *n* **1** BrE a building at the side of a sports field where players can change their clothes and wash《英式》〔運動場邊的〕運動員更衣室 **2** a large decorative building used for public amusements or exhibitions (EXHIBITION), especially one intended to be used only for a short time〔供娛樂或展覽用的〕臨時展覽館

pav·ing /ˈpevɪŋ; ˈpeɪvɪŋ/ *n* [U] material used to pave a surface 鋪面材料: *a paving stone* 鋪路石

paw¹ /pɔ; pɔː/ *n* an animal's foot that has nails called claws (CLAW) and a soft part to walk on, called a PAD〔動物的〕腳爪: *a dog with an injured paw* 腳爪受傷的狗

paw² *v* [I;T] (of animals) to keep moving or rubbing something with a front foot〔動物〕用前腳爪移動〔磨擦〕: *an angry bull pawing the ground* 一頭用腳爪扒地的發怒的公牛 | *The dog was pawing at the door, trying to get out.* 那隻狗在用腳爪抓門, 試圖走出去。

pawn¹ /pɔn; pɔːn/ *v* [T] to take something to a pawnbroker, who then lends you money 典當; 抵押〔某物〕

pawn² *n* **1** a piece in the game of CHESS〔國際象棋中的〕兵, 卒 **2** an unimportant person used by someone else for their own advantage 被利用的小人物

pawn·bro·ker /ˈpɔnˌbrokə; ˈpɔːnˌbrəʊkə/ *n* a person who lends you money if you give him something of yours; if you don't pay the money back, he sells it 當鋪老闆

paw·paw /ˈpɔpɔ; ˈpɔːpɔː/ *n* see 見 PAPAYA

★**pay¹** /pe; peɪ/ *v* **paid** /ped; peɪd/, **paid 1** [I;T] to give money for something you buy 付〔款〕: *How do you want to pay? Cash or cheque?* 你打算如何付款? 用現金還是用支票? | *You must pay in dollars.* 你必須用美元付款。 | *She paid over the money.* 她付清了款。 | *She paid the girl £5.* 她付給那個女孩5英鎊。 | *She paid the money to the girl.* 她把錢付給那個女孩。 | *Who's going to pay* **for** *the drinks?* 誰來付飲料費? | *You can't take them until they've been paid* **for**. 你得付了錢才能拿走它們。 | *He paid extra to have a reserved seat.* 他多付了錢來預訂座位。

□ USEFUL PATTERNS 有用句型
to pay someone money; to pay money to someone

2 pay through the nose *infml* to pay far too much for something《非正式》付費過高; 花代價過大 **3 pay your way** to pay for what you need yourself and not have to ask for help 自己付款; 自需之物〔不求人幫助〕, 不負債 **4** [I] to be profitable 贏利; 有利可圖: *If we can't make our farm pay, we'll sell it.* 如果我們不能使農場贏利, 我們就把它賣掉。 | *It's a paying concern.* 這是家有利可圖的企業。 **5** [I;T] to give an advantage, even though it costs more or takes more effort at the beginning 合算; 有利: *It pays to get up early.* 早起〔對你〕有好處。 | *It really pays you to buy a large quantity.* 大量購買確實很合算。 | *Crime doesn't pay.* 犯罪並不划算。 **6** [I;T] to give someone wages 發給〔某人〕工資: *How much do they pay?* 他們付多少工資? | *They pay £7.50 an hour.* 他們一小時付7.5英鎊的工資。 | *We got paid weekly.* 我們按星期領取工資。 | *They pay someone to cut the grass.* 他們出錢請人割草。 **7** [T] to give money which you owe 還〔錢〕; 繳付: *Have you paid the* *electricity bill yet?* 你交電費了嗎? | *She'll have to pay her debts first.* 她首先必須還債。 **8 pay for something** to suffer because you have done something bad 為某事付出代價: *I'll make you pay for this!* 我要你為此付出代價! | *You'll pay for your late night tomorrow.* 你今天睡得這麼晚, 明天就要吃苦頭了。 **9 pay attention: a** to listen or watch carefully 仔細聽; 仔細看: *Now, pay attention or you won't know what to do.* 現在, 請認真聽, 不然你就不知道該怎麼做。 **b** to take care 注意; 當心: *Pay particular attention to the backs of your teeth.* 特別要當心你牙齒的背面。 **c** to think only about what you are supposed to be doing 集中注意力: *You've got to pay attention when you're driving. It's no good day-dreaming.* 駕車時必須全神貫注, 做白日夢可沒有好處。 **10 pay a call on someone** to make a short social visit to someone 拜訪某人 **11 pay a compliment to someone** to praise someone directly to their face 對某人說恭維話 **12 pay for itself** to save as much money as it cost 節省下與成本相等的錢: *Insulating the roof pays for itself within five years.* 給屋頂裝隔熱材料, 五年之內就能收回成本。 **13 pay lip service to** to say that you support something, but not to act as though you do 口頭上支持: *The government pays lip service to better education, but it won't provide the money.* 政府只是口頭上說要改善教育, 卻不肯提供資金。 **14 pay no attention** to take no notice 不注意 **15 pay a visit to** to make a visit to 參觀; 拜訪 **16 pay your respects** to visit someone as a way of showing your respect for them 對某人表示敬意 **17 pay your last respects** to go and see someone after they have died as a way of showing your respect for them 向〔某人的遺體〕告別

pay back *phr v* **1** [T **pay** sbdy/sthg ↔ **back**] to return money you have borrowed 還〔錢〕: *Have I paid back the £10 you lent me?* 你借給我的十英鎊我還給你了嗎? | *You must pay me back by Friday.* 你必須週五之前把錢還給我。 **2** [T **pay** sbdy ↔ **back**] to treat someone badly because they have treated you badly 向〔某人〕報復: *I'll pay you back for what you did to me!* 你這樣對待我, 我會向你報復的!

pay sthg ↔ **in** *phr v* [T] to put money into the bank 把〔錢〕存入銀行: *I've got to call at the bank and pay this cheque in.* 我必須去一趟銀行, 把這張支票存進去。 | *I paid it into my current account.* 我把錢存入了我的往來賬戶。

pay off *phr v* **1** [T **pay** sthg ↔ **off**] to finish paying money that you owe 還清〔債款〕 **2** [I] to be worth the trouble 所做的努力得到回報: *His careful preparation really paid off.* 他認真的準備工夫確實沒有白費。

pay sthg ↔ **out** *phr v* [T] to spend large amounts of money 花費〔大量的錢〕: *We*

paid out a lot of money to get the roof mended. 我們為修屋頂花了許多錢。

pay up *phr v* [I] to give someone all the money you owe them, especially unwillingly 〔尤指不情願地〕還清欠款

★pay² *n* [U] **1** money received for work 工資; 薪金: *He gets his pay every Friday.* 他每週五領工資。 | *a pay rise* 提高工資 | *Very few office cleaners get good pay.* 很少辦公室清潔工可以拿到很好的工資。 **2 in the pay of** employed by someone 被〔某人〕雇用: *He is in the pay of the enemy.* 他被敵方雇用。

■ USAGE 用法: Compare 比較 **pay, salary, wages, fee, income**. **Pay** is a general word for the money you receive for work. A **salary** is paid monthly into a bank (especially to professional people) and **wages** are paid weekly in cash (especially to people who work with their hands). A **fee** is money paid to a professional person (e.g. a lawyer) for a particular service. Your **income** is all the money you receive over a long period of time, whether from work, rents, etc. ☆ **pay** 是表示工資的一般用詞。**salary** 是每月由公司存入個人賬戶的薪水〔尤指職業人士〕。**wages** 是以現金形式支付的週薪〔尤指以手工勞動者〕。**fee** 指為特殊服務而支付給職業工作者〔如律師〕的報酬。**income** 指一個較長時期內所有的收入, 可以是工資, 也可以是房租收入等: *My total income last year was £15,000.* 我去年的總收入是一萬五千英鎊。

---

pay·a·ble /ˈpeəbl; ˈpeɪəbəl/ *adj* [never before a noun 不能用於名詞前] showing that something may or must be paid 可支付的; 應支付的: *This bill is payable within seven days.* 這張賬單必須在七天內付款。 | *Your cheque should be made payable to "The London Electricity Board".* 你的支票上應寫明支付給"倫敦電力局"。

pay·day /ˈpeˌde; ˈpeɪdeɪ/ *n* the day on which wages are paid 發薪日

PAYE /ˌpi e waɪ ˈi; ˌpi: eɪ waɪ ˈi:/ *BrE* 〔英式〕 a system by which income tax is taken away from wages before the wages are paid; an abbreviation for **pay as you earn** 〔縮〕所得稅預扣法

pay·ee /peˈi; peɪˈi:/ *n tech* a person to whom money is or should be paid 〔術語〕受款人; 收款人

pay en·ve·lope /ˈ·· ,···/ *n* the usual American word for 〔美式〕= PAY PACKET

pay·ing guest /ˌ·· ˈ·/ *n* a person who stays in someone else's house and pays money to have a room and meals 寄宿者; 房客

pay·ing-in slip /ˌ·· ˈ·/ a small form which you fill in when you pay money into your bank account 銀行存款單

★★pay·ment /ˈpeɪmənt; ˈpeɪmənt/ n **1** [U] the act of paying 支付, 付款: I enclose a cheque in payment of my account. 我附上一張支票以支付賬款。**2** [C] an amount of money that is paid 所付的金額: monthly payments for rent 每月所付的租金

pay·off /ˈpeɪˌɔf; ˈpeɪɒf/ n **the payoff: a** the end of a story when everything is explained 〔故事的〕結局 **b** the end of a number of connected acts when there is some good result 〔一連串事件的〕結果

pay pack·et /ˈ· ··/ n BrE an envelope containing wages, given to an employed person each week 〔英式〕工資袋

pay phone /ˈ· ·/ n a public telephone that you put coins into when you use it 公用投幣電話

pay·roll /ˈpeɪˌrol; ˈpeɪrəʊl/ n **1** [C] a list of workers employed by a company and the amount of wages each person is to be paid 〔公司的〕發薪名冊 **2** [sing] the total amount of wages paid in a particular company 〔公司的〕工資發放總額

PC /ˌpiː ˈsi; ˌpiː ˈsiːᵈ/ n **1** an abbreviation for 〔縮〕=PERSONAL COMPUTER **2** a male member of the British police force having the lowest rank; an abbreviation for **Police Constable** 〔縮〕〔英國的〕警員: PC Johnson 警員約翰遜 | Two PCs were attacked. 兩名警員受到襲擊。

PE /ˌpiː ˈi; ˌpiː ˈiː/ n sport and exercise done as a subject in school; an abbreviation for **physical education** 〔縮〕體育(課)

pea /pi; piː/ n a very small round green vegetable 豌豆 –see picture on page 504 見 504 頁彩圖

★peace /pis; piːs/ n **1** [U] quiet and restful conditions with nothing to worry you 平靜: She'd just like to get on with her work in peace. 她只想安安靜靜地做工作。**2** [sing;U] a condition or period in which there is no war 和平: a dangerous situation that threatens world peace 威脅全世界和平的危險局勢 | a lasting peace 持久的和平 **3** [U] a state of freedom from disorder within a country, with the citizens living according to the law 〔社會的〕太平: Peace has returned to the streets of Wigham after last Saturday night's disturbances. 自上週六晚上的騷亂之後, 威格漢姆市的街上又恢復了太平。**4** **peace and quiet** freedom from noise, interruption, and worry 平靜 **5** **peace of mind** freedom from worry (心態)平靜, 安靜 **6** **keep the peace: a** not to cause violent disorder 維持治安 **b** to stop people quarrelling 阻止人們爭吵 **7** **make your peace with someone** to bring your quarrel with someone to an end 與某人和解

peace·a·ble /ˈpisəbl; ˈpiːsəbəl/ adj disliking argument or quarrelling 不愛爭吵的; 平和的 –**peaceably** adv

peace·ful /ˈpisfəl; ˈpiːsfəl/ adj **1** quiet and untroubled 安靜的; 平靜的: to spend a peaceful day in the garden 在花園裡安靜地度過一天 **2** liking peace 愛好和平的: peaceful nations 愛好和平的國家 **3** not violent 和平的: a peaceful demonstration 和平示威 – **peacefully** adv –**peacefulness** n [U]

peace·time /ˈpis,taɪm; ˈpiːstaɪm/ n [U] a time when a nation is not at war 和平時期

peach¹ /pitʃ; piːtʃ/ n a round fruit with soft yellowish-red skin and sweet juicy flesh, and a large seed in its centre 桃子 –see picture on page 504 見 504 頁彩圖

peach² adj pale orange-pink, the colour of a peach 桃紅色的

pea·cock /ˈpi,kɑk; ˈpiːkɒk/ n a large bird with beautiful long tail feathers which have large blue-green spots like eyes; a female peacock is called a **peahen** 孔雀〔雌孔雀稱為 **peahen**〕

★peak¹ /pik; piːk/ n **1** a sharply pointed mountain top 山峯; 山頂: The mountain peaks are covered with snow all the year round. 山頂上終年覆蓋着雪。**2** the point when activity is greatest or performance is best 頂峯; 最高點: Sales have reached a new peak. 銷量已達到新的頂峯。 | The roads are full of traffic at peak hours. 在高峯時間馬路上擠滿了車輛。| The Kenyan runner was at his peak in the 1989 Games. 這位肯尼亞賽跑選手在 1989 年的運動會中達到了頂峯狀態。**3** the part of a cap which sticks out in front above your eyes to keep the sun out of them 帽舌, 帽簷

peak² v [I] to reach and pass the highest point 達到最高點, 達到高峯: Sales have now peaked, and we expect them to decrease soon. 銷量現已達到了最高點, 我們預料很快就會下降。

peal¹ /pil; piːl/ n **1** the sound of the loud ringing of bells 響亮的鐘聲[鈴聲] **2** a long, loud sound or number of sounds one after the other 響亮的聲音; 隆隆聲: a peal of thunder 隆隆的雷聲 | a peal of laughter 一陣笑聲

peal² v [I;T] to ring out or sound loudly (使)鳴響; 發出隆隆聲: All the church bells are pealed on Christmas morning. 在聖誕日的早上, 所有教堂裡的鐘都被敲響。

pea·nut /ˈpi,nʌt; ˈpiːnʌt/ n a small nut which grows in a shell under the ground, and can be eaten 花生

peanut but·ter /ˌ· ·· / n [U] a soft food which looks like brown butter, but is made of crushed peanuts; you eat it on bread 花生醬

pear /pɛr; peər/ n a sweet yellow-green juicy fruit which grows on a tree; it is about the size of an apple, but narrow at the stem end and wide at the other end 梨 –see picture on page 504 見 504 頁彩圖

pearl /pɝl; pɜːl/ n a small round hard silvery-white object found inside a shellfish called an OYSTER; pearls are used for making expensive jewellery 珍珠

pearl·y /'pɜːli; 'pɔːli/ *adj* **pearlier, pearliest** like pearls 珍珠似的: *a pale pearly grey* 珍珠般的灰白色

peas·ant /'pɛznt; 'pɛzənt/ *n* **1** a person who works on the land, especially one who owns and lives on a small piece of land 農民, 農夫 **2** a person without education or manners 缺乏教養的人

peas·ant·ry /'pɛzntrɪ; 'pɛzəntri/ *n* [+sing/pl verb] **the peasantry** all the peasants of a particular country 〔某一國家的〕農民的總稱

peat /piːt; piːt/ *n* [U] dark brown decaying plant material which takes the place of ordinary soil in certain areas; it is used for improving garden soil and for burning instead of coal 泥炭, 泥煤 **–peaty** *adj*

peb·ble /'pɛbl; 'pɛbəl/ *n* a small roundish smooth stone found especially beside the sea or in a river 卵石, 礫石

peck¹ /pɛk; pɛk/ *v* **1** [I;T] (used of birds) to take a small quick bite of something 〔鳥〕啄; 啄食: *chickens pecking in the dust* 在泥土裡啄食的小雞 | *The parrot tried to peck me.* 那隻鸚鵡想啄我。 **2 peck at your food** to eat a few small bites of your food, when you do not really want it 〔不想吃時〕隨便吃幾口食物 **3** [T] *infml* to kiss someone in a hurry or without much feeling 《非正式》輕輕地吻 〔某人〕

peck² *n* **1** an act of pecking 啄 **2** *infml* a hurried kiss 《非正式》匆匆一吻: *He gave her a quick peck on the cheek.* 他匆匆地吻了一下她的面頰。

peck·ish /'pɛkɪʃ; 'pɛkɪʃ/ *adj BrE infml* slightly hungry 《英式, 非正式》有點餓的

pe·cu·li·ar /pɪ'kjuːljə; pɪ'kjuːliɚ/ *adj* **1** strange, especially in a troubling or displeasing way 奇怪的; 乖僻的〔尤指令人不安或令人不快的〕: *This food has got a peculiar taste. Do you think it's all right?* 這食物有異味。你看它有沒有問題? **2 peculiar to** belonging only to a particular person, place, or thing 〔某人、某地、某物〕特有的; 專有的: *This style of cooking is peculiar to the southwest of the country.* 這種烹調方式是該國西南地區所特有的。

pe·cu·li·ar·i·ty /pɪˌkjuːlɪ'ærətɪ; pɪˌkjuːli'ærəti/ *n* **peculiarities 1** [U] the quality of being peculiar 奇異的性質; 獨特性 **2** [C] something which be-longs only to a particular person, place, etc 特點; 特色; 特性: *One of the peculiarities of her behaviour is that she shouts instead of talking.* 她的行為特色之一就是不好好說話, 而是大喊大叫。

pe·cu·li·ar·ly /pɪ'kjuːljəlɪ; pɪ'kjuːliɔli/ *adv* **1** especially 尤其; 特別地: *This question is peculiarly difficult.* 這個問題尤為困難。 **2** strangely 奇怪地

pe·cu·ni·a·ry /pɪ'kjuːnɪˌɛrɪ; pɪ'kjuːniɔri/ *adj fml* connected with or consisting of money

〔正式〕錢的; 金錢上的

ped·al¹ /'pɛdl; 'pɛdl/ *n* a part of a machine which you press with your foot 腳踏板: *One of the pedals has come off my bicycle.* 我的腳踏車有一個踏板掉下來了。 | *When you want to stop the car, press the brake pedal.* 你想停車的話, 就踩剎車踏板。

ped·al² *v* **-ll-** (**-l-** *AmE*《美式》) [I;T] to ride a bicycle 騎腳踏車: *She pedalled the bicycle up the hill.* 她騎腳踏車上山。 | *I was just pedalling along.* 我只是騎着車隨便走走。

pe·dan·tic /pɪ'dæntɪk; pɪ'dæntɪk/ *adj* paying too much attention to small details, and wanting everything to be done exactly according to the rules 學究式的; 迂腐的 **–pedant** /'pɛdnt; 'pɛdnt/ *n*: *Our teacher's a bit of a pedant about punctuation.* 我們的老師有點過於講究標點符號。

ped·dle /'pɛdl; 'pɛdl/ *v* **peddled, peddling** [I;T] **1** to go from place to place trying to sell small goods 挨家兜售, 沿街叫賣 **2** to sell illegal drugs 販〔毒〕 **3** to keep trying to get other people to accept your poor ideas 兜售〔差勁的主意〕

ped·dler /'pɛdlə; 'pɛdlɚ/ *n* **1** a person who sells illegal drugs 販毒者 **2** see 見 PEDLAR

ped·es·tal /'pɛdɪstl; 'pɛdɪstəl/ *n* **1** the base on which a pillar or STATUE stands 〔柱子或雕像的〕基座 **2 put someone on a pedestal** to admire someone very much although they may not really be so wonderful 推崇某人

pe·des·tri·an¹ /pə'dɛstrɪən; pə'dɛstriən/ *n* a person walking in a street, and not travelling in a vehicle 行人

pedestrian² *adj* not interesting or unusual or having much imagination 平凡的; 缺乏想像力的: *He was rather a pedestrian student.* 他是個相當平凡的學生。

pedestrian cross·ing /·ˌ··· '··/ *n* a special place for pedestrians to cross the road 人行橫道

pe·di·a·tri·cian /ˌpidɪə'trɪʃən; ˌpiːdiə'trɪʃən/ *n* see 見 PAEDIATRICIAN

pe·di·at·rics /ˌpidɪ'ætrɪks; ˌpiːdi'ætrɪks/ *n* [U] see 見 PAEDIATRICS

ped·i·gree¹ /'pɛdəˌgri; 'pɛdɪˌgriː/ *n* [C;U] the record of the specially chosen animals that a particular animal has been bred from 〔動物的〕系譜, 血統

pedigree² *adj* [only before a noun 只用於名詞前] descended from a recorded and specially chosen family, and therefore of high quality (used of animals, especially dogs) 純種的〔指動物, 尤指狗〕: *a pedigree spaniel* 純種西班牙獵犬

ped·lar /'pɛdlə; 'pɛdlɚ/ *n* (also 又作 **peddler** *AmE*《美式》) a person who goes from place to place trying to sell small articles 流動小販

pe·do·phile /'pidoˌfaɪl; 'piːdəʊfaɪl/ *n* see 見 PAEDOPHILE

peek¹ /pik; piːk/ *v* [I] *infml* to look at something quickly, especially when you should not〖非正式〗偷看，窺視: *He just had time to peek into the room before the door closed.* 他剛向房裡偷看了一眼，門便關上了。

peek² *n infml* a quick look〖非正式〗一瞥: *Just have a peek and see what the children are doing.* 稍微看一下孩子們在幹甚麼。

peel¹ /pil; piːl/ *v* **1** [T] to remove the skin from fruit or vegetables 削去〔水果、蔬菜〕的皮: *a machine that peels potatoes* 削馬鈴薯皮的機器 **2** [I] to come off in small pieces 一塊塊地脫落: *My skin always peels when I've been in the sun.* 我的皮膚在曬了太陽後總會脫皮。

peel off *phr v* **1** [T **peel** sthg ↔ **off**] to remove an outer covering from something 剝落〔某物〕的外皮: *Can you peel the label off?* 你能把標籤剝下來嗎? **2** [I] to come off in small pieces 一塊塊地脫落: *The paint was beginning to peel off.* 油漆開始一塊塊地脫落。

peel² *n* [U] the skin of those fruits and vegetables which you usually peel before you eat them〔水果、蔬菜的〕外皮: *orange peel* 橘子皮，橙皮 | *apple peel* 蘋果皮

peel·ings /ˈpilɪŋz; ˈpiːlɪŋz/ *n* [pl] pieces of skin peeled from fruit and vegetables, especially potatoes〔水果和蔬菜，尤指馬鈴薯〕削下的皮

peep¹ /pip; piːp/ *v* **1** [I] to look quickly and secretly 偷看，窺視: *His hands were covering his face, but I could see him peeping through his fingers.* 他用雙手捂着臉，但我能看見他透過指縫在偷看。 **2** [I; +adv/prep] to come partly into view 部分露出: *strands of hair peeping out from under her hat* 從她的帽子下露出來的幾縷頭髮

peep² *n* **1** a quick, incomplete, and perhaps secret look 偷看; 一瞥: *He took a peep at the back of the book to find the answers.* 他偷看了一下書的後面，想尋找出答案。 **2** a short high sound like that made by a young bird or a mouse〔小鳥或老鼠的〕唧唧叫聲 **3** a **peep** *infml* words spoken, or small sound made〖非正式〗所說的話; 嘀咕: *I don't want to hear a peep out of you until dinnertime.* 晚飯前我不希望聽見你再說一句話。

peer¹ /pɪr; pɪəʳ/ *v* [I; +adv/prep] to look very carefully or hard 注視，凝視，盯着看: *She peered through the window.* 她凝視着窗外。 | *He peered at me over the top of his glasses.* 他從眼鏡的上方盯着看我。

peer² *n* **1 peers** [pl] (also 又作 **peer group** /ˈ··/) people that you know who are the same age as you or who have the same social position 同輩; 同等社會地位的人: *The opinion of his peers is more important to him than his parents' ideas.* 對他來說，同輩人的意見要比父母的觀點更重要。 | *There's a lot of peer group pressure on teenagers.* 青少年要承受來自同齡人的很大壓力。 **2** a member of the noble ranks such as Lord in Britain 貴族

peer·age /ˈpɪrɪdʒ; ˈpɪərɪdʒ/ *n* [C;U] **1 the peerage** all the peers as a group 貴族的總稱 **2** the noble rank of a peer 貴族爵位: *After twenty years as a member of parliament she was given a peerage.* 她任國會議員二十年之後，被授予貴族爵位。

peer·ess /ˈpɪrɪs; ˈpɪərɪs/ *n* a female member of the nobility 女貴族

peer·less /ˈpɪrlɪs; ˈpɪərləs/ *adj fml* better than any other〖正式〗無雙的; 絕世的

peeved /pivd; piːvd/ *adj* annoyed 惱怒的; 生氣的

peev·ish /ˈpiːvɪʃ; ˈpiːvɪʃ/ *adj* easily annoyed by unimportant things 易怒的 – **peevishly** *adv* – **peevishness** *n* [U]

peg¹ /pɛg; pɛg/ *n* **1** a short piece of wood or other material which is fixed on a wall or door so that you can hang clothes or other things on it 掛鈎; 短釘; 栓: *Hang your coat on the peg in the hall.* 把你的衣服掛在門廳的掛鈎上。 **2** a small piece of wood which goes into a hole; pegs are used for joining things together, and also in games 短椿; 椿子 **3** a small wooden or plastic thing you use to fasten clothes to a washing line to dry〔曬衣服用的〕衣夾 **4 off the peg** not specially made for you (used of clothes) 現成的;〔指衣服〕以成衣形式 **5 square peg in a round hole** a person who is not suited to the position or group in which they are placed 不宜擔任某一職務的人 **6 take somebody down a peg** *infml* to show somebody that they are not as important as they thought they were〖非正式〗煞某人的威風，挫某人的傲氣

peg² *v* **-gg-** [T] **1** to fasten with pegs 用木釘釘牢; 用椿子固定: *Peg the clothes on the line.* 用衣夾把衣服夾在晾衣繩上。 **2** to fix prices or wages and not allow them to rise 固定〔價格或工資〕: *Wages have been pegged for 12 months.* 工資在過去的十二個月中被固定在同一水準上。

pe·jo·ra·tive /ˈpɪdʒəˌretɪv; pɪˈdʒɒrətɪv/ *adj fml* expressing disapproval or suggesting that someone or something is of little value (used of a word or phrase)〖正式〗貶義的〔指詞或詞組〕: *Many women now think the word "housewife" is pejorative, because it makes them seem unimportant.* 現在許多婦女認為"家庭主婦"一詞帶有貶義，因為該詞令她們顯得無足輕重。

pe·kin·ese /ˌpikɪnˈiz; ˌpiːkɪˈniːz/ *n* a small dog with long silky hair 北京狗，哈巴狗

pel·i·can /ˈpɛlɪkən; ˈpɛlɪkən/ *n* a large water bird which catches fish and stores them under its beak in part of its body that is like a long bag 塘鵝〔一種食魚鳥〕

pelican cross·ing /ˌ··· ˈ··/ *n* a place where people can cross the road by pressing a button at traffic lights to stop the traffic〔行人穿越馬路時可自行按亮交通燈使車輛停

下的〕自控人行橫道

pel·let /ˈpɛlɪt; ˈpɛlə̥t/ n **1** a small ball of paper, animal food, or other material 小紙團; 一小球〔動物食品〕 **2** a small metal ball that can be fired from a gun 小彈丸

pel·met /ˈpɛlmɪt; ˈpɛlmə̥t/ n a narrow piece of wood or cloth across the top of a window that hides the curtain rod〔用以遮擋窗簾掛桿的〕窗簾上框; 布帷幔

pelt¹ /pɛlt; pɛlt/ n **1** the skin of a dead animal, especially one with the fur still on it 動物的毛皮 **2 at full pelt** as fast as possible 盡快, 飛快

pelt² v **1** [T] to attack someone by throwing things at them 向〔某人〕投擲: *They pelted the police with stones.* 他們向警察投擲石塊。 **2** [I] (also 又作 **pelt down**) (of rain) to fall heavily and continuously〔雨〕下得很大: *I'm not going out there — it's really pelting down!* 我不打算去了, 雨下得真大呢! **3** [I] to run very fast 飛快地跑: *They came pelting down the hill.* 他們飛奔下山。

pel·vis /ˈpɛlvɪs; ˈpɛlvə̥s/ n the bowl-shaped frame of bones at the base of the backbone that joins your leg bones to your pelvis 骨盆 **–pelvic** adj

pen¹ /pɛn; pɛn/ n **1** a narrow metal or plastic object which contains ink, and is used to write or draw with 鋼筆,〔用墨水的〕筆 – see picture on page 763 見 763 頁彩圖 **2** a small piece of land enclosed by a fence, used for keeping animals in〔家畜的〕圍欄

pen² v **-nn-** [T] lit〔文〕 **1** to write 寫 **2** (also 又作 **pen up/in**) to shut animals in a pen 把〔動物〕關進欄中

pe·nal /ˈpiːnl; ˈpiːnl/ adj **1** about the punishment of criminals 刑罰的: *the penal system* 刑罰制度 | *the need for penal reform* 對於刑罰改革的需求 **2** for which you can be punished by law 刑事的: *a penal offence* 刑事罪

pe·nal·ize (also 又作 **penalise** BrE〔英式〕) /ˈpiːnlaɪz; ˈpiːnəl-aɪz/ v **penalized, penalizing** [T] **1** to put someone in an unfair position 使〔某人〕處於不公平的地位: *She felt penalized for having children and going to work as well.* 她感到有了孩子還要外出工作是很不公平的。 **2** in sports, to punish a player's action by giving an advantage to the other team〔運動中〕對...施罰: *Their team was penalized* **for** *intentionally wasting time.* 他們的球隊由於故意拖延時間而受罰。

pen·al·ty /ˈpɛnltɪ; ˈpɛnltɪ/ n **penalties 1** the punishment for breaking a law or rule 刑罰; 懲罰: *Fishing in this river is forbidden — penalty £5.* 禁止在這條河裡釣魚——違者罰款五英鎊。 **2** in football and other games, an advantage given to a team when the other team has broken the rules〔運動中受到的〕處罰: *We were given a penalty after one of our players was hit.* 我們的一名球員被擊中後, 我隊得到一次罰球機會。

pen·ance /ˈpɛnəns; ˈpɛnəns/ n [C;U] some-thing which you do as a punishment to show that you are sorry about something you have done wrong, according to your religion〔表示懺悔的〕自我懲罰

pence /pɛns; pɛns/ BrE〔英式〕 (also 又作 **p**) the unit of money in Britain that is smaller than a pound 便士: *There are a hundred pence to the pound.* 一英鎊等於一百便士。 | *It only cost a few pence.* 這東西只花了幾個便士。 –see 見 PENNY (USAGE用法)

pen·chant /ˈpɛntʃənt; ˈpɒnʃɒn/ n a strong liking 愛好; 嗜好: *a penchant* **for** *Indian food* 對印度食品的偏愛

pen·cil¹ /ˈpɛnsl; ˈpɛnsəl/ n a narrow wooden object which contains a thin stick of a black or coloured substance, and is used to write or draw with 鉛筆 –see picture on page 763 見 763 頁彩圖

pencil² v **-ll-** (**-l-** AmE〔美式〕) [T] to write something or mark something with a pencil 用鉛筆寫; 用鉛筆作標記

pen·dant (also 又作 **pendent**) /ˈpɛndənt; ˈpɛndənt/ n a small piece of jewellery on a chain that you wear round your neck〔戴在頸上的〕垂飾, 懸飾

pend·ing¹ /ˈpɛndɪŋ; ˈpɛndɪŋ/ prep fml while waiting for or until〔正式〕等待...; 直到...: *This decision must wait pending her return from Europe.* 這項決定要等她從歐洲回來才能作出。

pending² adj fml〔正式〕 **1** waiting to be decided or settled 待定的; 待解決的: *She put the file into a box marked "pending".* 她把文件放入一個標着"待決"的盒子中。 **2** going to happen soon 即將發生的

pen·du·lum /ˈpɛndʒələm; ˈpɛndjə̥ləm/ n a rod with a weight at the bottom which swings from side to side and works a clock 鐘擺

pen·e·trate /ˈpɛnətreɪt; ˈpɛnə̥treɪt/ v **penetrated, penetrating 1** [I;T] to get through or force a way into something that is difficult to enter 滲入; 穿透: *The sun penetrated* **through** *the thick clouds and started to shine.* 陽光透過厚厚的雲層, 開始照耀大地。 | *The car lights penetrated the darkness.* 車燈的光穿過了黑暗。 | *Japanese car manufacturers have penetrated the European market.* 日本汽車製造商已打入歐洲市場。 **2** to get inside an organization in order to get information or make it difficult for them〔為獲取信息或製造麻煩而〕滲入〔某一組織〕

pen·e·trat·ing /ˈpɛnətreɪtɪŋ; ˈpɛnə̥treɪtɪŋ/ adj **1** sharp and searching (used of a person's eyes, or the way they look at you) 銳利的〔指眼睛或目光〕 **2** able to understand clearly and deeply (used of a person's mind) 聰明的, 敏銳的〔指頭腦〕 **3** sharp and loud (used of sounds) 尖銳的, 響亮的〔指聲音〕: *a penetrating voice* 尖銳的聲音 – **penetratingly** adv

pen·e·tra·tion /ˌpɛnəˈtreɪʃən; ˌpɛnə̥ˈtreɪʃən/

n [U] **1** the act or action of penetrating 滲透; 穿透: *The army's penetration of the enemy territory has been successful.* 軍隊成功地進入了敵territory. **2** the ability to understand quickly and clearly 領悟力, 洞察力

pen friend /'· ·/ *n* a person in a foreign country who you make friends with by exchanging letters, even though you may never meet 筆友

pen·guin /'pεŋgwɪn; 'pεŋgwə̣n/ *n* large black and white bird found mainly in the Antarctic 企鵝

pen·i·cil·lin /ˌpεnɪ'sɪlɪn/, ˌpεnə̣'sɪlə̣n/ *n* [U] a substance called an ANTIBIOTIC which is used as a medicine to kill harmful bacteria in your body 青黴素, 盤尼西林

pe·nin·su·la /pə'nɪnsələ; pə̣'nɪnsjə̣lə/ *n* piece of land almost completely surrounded by water but joined to a larger mass of land 半島: *Italy is a peninsula.* 意大利是個半島.—**peninsular** *adj*

pe·nis /'pinɪs; 'pinɪ̣s/ *n* the outer sex organ of males 陰莖

pen·i·tent /'pεnətənt; 'pεnɪ̣tənt/ *adj fml* feeling or showing that you are sorry for having done wrong, and that you intend not to do so again〔正式〕後悔的; 懺悔的 –**penitently** *adv* –**penitence** *n* [U]

pen·i·ten·tia·ry /ˌpεnə'tεnʃərɪ, ˌpεnɪ̣'tεnʃə-rɪ/ *n* **penitentiaries** a prison, especially in the US〔尤指美國的〕監獄

pen·knife /'pεn,naɪf; 'pεn-naɪf/ *n* **penknives** /-ˌnaɪvz; -naɪvz/ a small knife with a blade that folds into the handle 摺疊式小刀

pen name /'· ·/ *n* a name used by a writer instead of their real name 筆名

pen·ni·less /'pεnlɪs; 'pεnɪləs/ *adj* having no money 一文不名的

pen·ny /'pεnɪ; 'pεni/ *n* **1** [plural is 複數為 **pence**] (also 又作 **p**) the smallest unit of money in Britain; there are 100 pence in one pound 便士〔一英鎊等於一百便士〕**2** [plural is 複數為 **pennies**] a small brown coin, the British coin of lowest value 便士〔硬幣〕**3** in the US and Canada, a coin worth a cent〔美國和加拿大的〕一分錢(硬幣) **4** not a penny [usually used in negatives 常用於否定] no money at all 一分錢也不用花: *It won't cost you a penny.* 這不會花你一分錢. **5** in for a penny, in for a pound if something has been begun it should be finished whatever the cost may be 一旦開始就做到底; 一不做, 二不休 **6** spend a penny a less direct expression for "go to TOILET"上廁所〔比較含蓄的講法〕**7** the penny dropped *BrE infml* the meaning of something said has finally been understood〔英式, 非正式〕終於明白; 恍然大悟

■ USAGE 用法: In British English the words **penny** and **pennies** are no longer used very much to talk about money or prices. When speaking or writing about an amount of money use **pence** or **p** ☆在英式英語中, 已經不大用 **penny** 和 **pennies** 來談論金錢和價格。口語和書面語中, 用 **pence** 或 **p** 來談論錢: *It costs twenty pence/twenty p/20 p a packet.* 這東西要二十便士一袋。| *You owe me ten pence/ten p/10 p.* 你欠我十便士。| *a ten pence piece/a 10 p piece* 十便士的一份 | *one pence/one p/1 p* 一便士

---

pen pal /'· ·/ *n AmE* the usual American word for〖美式〗= PEN FRIEND

★**pen·sion¹** /'pεnʃən; 'pεnʃən/ *n* money paid to you regularly by your employer or the government when you no longer work because you are old or ill 退休金; 養老金

pension² *v*

pension sbdy ↔ **off** *phr v* [T] to dismiss someone from a job and give them a pension 發放退休金使(提早)退休

pen·sion·a·ble /'pεnʃənəbḷ; 'pεnʃənəbəl/ *adj* giving you the right to receive a pension 有領取養老金資格的: *a pensionable job* 可領取養老金的工作

pen·sion·er /'pεnʃənə; 'pεnʃənər/ *n* a person who has stopped working and is receiving a pension 領退休金〔養老金〕的人

pen·sive /'pεnsɪv; 'pεnsɪv/ *adj* thinking about something 沉思的; 思考的: *a pensive smile* 面帶沉思的笑容

pen·ta·gon /'pεntə,gan; 'pεntəgən/ *n* **1** a flat shape with five sides and five angles 五邊形; 五角形 **2** the Pentagon the leaders of the US army and the building they work from 美國五角大樓, 美國國防部 –**pentagonal** /pεn'tægə-n̩l; pεn'tægənəl/ *adj*

pen·tath·lon /pεn'tæθlən; pεn'tæθlən/ *n* a sports event in which people have to compete in five different sports 五項全能運動

pent·house /'pεnt,haus; 'pεnthaus/ *n* a desirable set of rooms built at the top of a tall building 頂層高級公寓

pent-up /ˌpεnt'ʌp; ˌpεnt'ʌp/ *adj* shut up inside you instead of being expressed 被抑制的: *pent-up anger* 壓抑的怒火

pe·nul·ti·mate /pɪ'nʌltɪmɪt; pɪ'nʌltə̣mɪ̣t/ *adj* next to the last 倒數第二的: *the penultimate scene in the play* 戲中的倒數第二幕

pen·u·ry /'pεnjərɪ; 'pεnjə̣ri/ *n* [U] *fml* the state of being very poor〔正式〕貧窮

★**peo·ple¹** /'pipḷ; 'pipəl/ *n* **1** [pl] men, women, and children; "people" is the usual plural of PERSON 人; 人們〔"people"為 PERSON 的一般複數形式〕: *Were there many people at the party?* 有許多人參加聚會嗎? | *young people* 年輕人 | *It's hard to meet people in a foreign country.* 在

外國很難認識別人。**2 the people** [pl] all the ordinary people in a society 人民, 平民; 百姓 **3** [C] a race or nation 種族; 民族: *The Chinese are a hard-working people.* 中國人是一個勤勞的民族。| *the peoples of Africa* 非洲的各個民族

people² *v* **peopled, peopling** [T] *fml* (of people) to live in a place 〔正式〕〔人〕居住於〔某地〕: *The desert is peopled by wandering tribes.* 沙漠中居住着遊牧部落。

pep·per¹ /ˈpɛpɚ; ˈpepəʳ/ *n* **1** [U] a hot-tasting powder made from crushed seeds that you add to food 胡椒粉: *salt and pepper* 鹽和胡椒粉 **2** [C] (also 又作 **green pepper, red pepper**) a red or green hollow vegetable 辣椒 –see picture on page 504 見 504 頁彩圖 –**peppery** *adj*

pepper² *v* [T] **1** to put pepper on food 撒胡椒粉於〔食物〕上 **2** to hit with a lot of small bullets or other things 〔用子彈或其他物體〕密集射擊; 亂射

pep·pered /ˈpɛpɚd; ˈpepəd/ *adj* full of 充滿的: *Her essay was absolutely peppered with mistakes.* 她的文章確實錯誤百出。

pep·per·mint /ˈpɛpɚˌmɪnt; ˈpepəˌmɪnt/ (also 又作 **mint**) *n* **1** [U] a plant with a special strong taste, used in sweets and to make toothpaste taste nice 胡椒薄荷, 薄荷 **2** [C] a sweet with this taste 薄荷糖

pep pill /ˈ· ·/ *n slang* a PILL containing a drug which makes you think or act more quickly 〔俚〕興奮藥丸

pep talk /ˈ· ·/ *n infml* a talk which you give to people you are in charge of to encourage them to do better 〔非正式〕鼓舞士氣的講話: *Our new teacher gave us a pep talk.* 我們的新老師給我們作了一次鼓舞士氣的講話。

per /pɚ; pəʳ, *strong* 強讀 pɝ; pɜːʳ/ *prep* for each 每; 每一: *We're paid £10 per hour.* 我們的報酬是每小時十英鎊。| *Allow half a pound of meat per person.* 給每人半磅肉。

per·ceive /pɚˈsiv; pəˈsiːv/ *v* **perceived, perceiving** *fml* 〔正式〕**1** [T; +that] to see, or notice something which it is not easy to notice 感覺到; 察覺〔某事物〕: *He perceived that he was unwelcome and left.* 他察覺到自己不受歡迎, 於是便走了。| *I couldn't perceive any difference between the two sounds.* 我感覺不到這兩種聲音有甚麼差別。**2** [T] to understand something in a particular way 理解; 認為: *The new tax is perceived* **as** *an attack on the poor.* 新稅法被認為是對窮人發起攻擊。–**perceivable** *adj*

per cent /· ˈ·/ *adv* **1** parts for each 100 百分之…(的): *The restaurant has a service charge of ten per cent (10%).* 該餐館收百分之十的服務費。| *The bank has increased its interest rate by one per cent.* 銀行已將利率提高了百分之一。**2 a hundred per cent** a phrase used to show you agree with something completely 百分之百〔表示完全同意某事〕: *I*

agree with you 100 per cent. 我百分之百同意你的意見。

per·cen·tage /pɚˈsɛntɪdʒ; pəˈsentɪdʒ/ *n* an amount stated as if it is part of a whole which is 100 百分比, 百分率: *What percentage of babies die of this disease every year?* 每年死於這種疾病的嬰兒的百分比是多少? | *A high percentage* **of** *people still smoke.* 吸煙的人百分比仍然很高。

per·cep·ti·ble /pɚˈsɛptəbl; pəˈseptɪbəl/ *adj fml* noticeable 〔正式〕感覺得到的: *A barely perceptible smile crossed his face.* 他的臉上掠過一絲難以覺察的笑容。–opposite 反義 **imperceptible** –**perceptibly** *adv*

per·cep·tion /pɚˈsɛpʃən; pəˈsepʃən/ *n* **1** [U] (also 又作 **perceptiveness**) natural ability to notice and understand things 洞察力; 直覺: *a woman of great perception* 一個具有很強洞察力的女人 **2** [C] understanding of something 理解力: *Her perceptions and insight into the book were fascinating.* 她對於該書的理解和意見都令人驚嘆。**3** [U] noticing things with your senses and understanding them with your mind 感覺; 感知: *He's studying the psychology of perception.* 他在研究感知心理學。

per·cep·tive /pɚˈsɛptɪv; pəˈseptɪv/ *adj* quick to notice and understand 觀察敏銳的; 領悟力強的 –**perceptively** *adv* –**perceptiveness** *n* [U]

perch¹ /pɝtʃ; pɜːtʃ/ *v* **1** [I] (of a bird) to come to rest from flying 〔鳥〕棲息: *The birds perched on the telephone wires.* 鳥棲歇在電話線上。**2** [I;T] to sit or to put someone on the edge of something 坐在邊緣; 置於邊緣: *She perched herself on a tall chair.* 她危坐在一張高的椅子上。| *The house was perched on the edge of the cliffs.* 那所房子位於懸崖邊上。

perch² *n* **1** a branch, or rod where a bird rests 〔鳥的〕棲木 **2** a high position in which a person or building is placed 高處; 高位: *From our perch up there on top of the hill we can see the whole town.* 我們從山頂上居高臨下, 可看到城市的全景。**3 perch** [pl] a lake and river fish that is caught and eaten 鱸〔魚〕

per·co·late /ˈpɝkəˌlet; ˈpɜːkəleɪt/ *v* **percolated, percolating 1** [I] (of liquid) to pass slowly down through a material which has small holes in it 〔液體〕濾出; 濾過: *It takes several days for the rain to percolate* **through** *the rock and into the rivers.* 雨水要幾天的時間才能滲過岩石流入河裡。**2** to pass slowly from one person to another in a group 慢慢流傳: *Opposition to the Prime Minister began to percolate* **through** *all sections of the government.* 對首相所持的反對意見開始在政府的所有部門中瀰漫開來。**3** [T] (also 又作 **perk**) *infml* to make coffee in a special pot by passing hot water slowly through crushed coffee beans 〔非正式〕濾

煮〔咖啡〕–**percolation** /ˌpɜːkəˈleʃən; ˌpɜːkəˈleɪʃən/ *n* [U]

per·co·la·tor /ˈpɜːkəˌletə; ˈpɜːkəleɪtəʳ/ *n* a pot in which coffee is percolated 咖啡滲濾壺

per·cus·sion /pəˈkʌʃən; pəˈkʌʃən/ *n* **1 the percussion** [+sing/pl verb] the group of musical instruments in a band or ORCHESTRA which you play by hitting them, for example drums 打擊樂器(組): *The percussion is too loud.* 打擊樂器的聲音奏得太響了。**2 percussion instrument** a musical instrument which you play by hitting it 打擊樂器 **3** [U] the forceful striking together of two hard objects〔兩件硬物的〕撞擊

pe·remp·to·ry /pəˈrɛmptəri; pəˈremptəri/ *adj fml* showing an expectation of being obeyed at once《正式》專橫的, 霸道的 –**peremptorily** *adv*

pe·ren·ni·al¹ /pəˈrɛniəl; pəˈreniəl/ *adj* **1** happening repeatedly or lasting forever 反覆不斷的; 永久的: *Politics provides a perennial subject of argument.* 政治給人們提供了一個長期存在的辯論主題。**2** living for more than two years (used of plants) 多年生的〔指植物〕–**perennially** *adv*

perennial² *n* a perennial plant 多年生植物

★**per·fect¹** /ˈpɜːfɪkt; ˈpɜːfɪkt/ *adj* **1** the very best possible kind 完美的: *The weather was absolutely perfect.* 天氣真好極了。| *The optician said he had perfect vision.* 驗光師說他的視力一點問題也沒有。**2** having no mistakes or faults 毫無錯誤的; 完整無缺的: *a perfect set of teeth* 一副完好的牙齒 | *Her English is perfect.* 她的英語無可挑剔。**3** complete 完全的; 徹底的: *perfect strangers* 不折不扣的陌生人 **4** suitable and satisfying in every way 完全合適的; 圓滿的: *The house was perfect for a big family.* 這所房子對一個大家庭來說是最合適不過的。**5** *tech* (of the form of a verb) concerning a period of time up to and including the present (**present perfect**), past (**past perfect**), or future (**future perfect**) (as in "*She has gone*", "*She had gone*", "*She will have gone*")《語法》(動詞的)完成式的〔包括現在完成式、過去完成式、將來完成式〕〔如 "*She has gone*", "*She had gone*", "*She will have gone*"〕: *the Present Perfect tense* 現在完成式

per·fect² /pəˈfɛkt; pəˈfekt/ *v* [T] to make perfect 使完美: *She practised hard to perfect her singing voice.* 她刻苦練習, 以使嗓音達至完美。

per·fec·tion /pəˈfɛkʃən; pəˈfekʃən/ *n* [U] **1** the quality of being perfect 完美: *We don't need perfection — just a good general standard.* 我們不要求完美無缺, 只要總體上達到良好水平就可以了。**2** the process of developing completely or making perfect 達到完善的過程: *The perfection of this new medical treatment may take several years.* 這種新的醫療辦法要達到盡善盡美的地步也許還

要幾年的時間。**3 to perfection** perfectly 完美地: *The meat was done to perfection.* 這肉燒得恰到好處。

per·fec·tion·ist /pəˈfɛkʃənɪst; pəˈfekʃənᵻst/ *n* a person who is not satisfied with anything that is not perfect 完美主義者: *It takes him hours to cook a simple meal because he's such a perfectionist.* 他是個完美主義者, 所以做一頓簡單的飯也要花上幾個小時。

★**per·fect·ly** /ˈpɜːfɪktli; ˈpɜːfɪktli/ *adv* **1** so well that it would be impossible to do it better 完美地: *She understood perfectly.* 她完全懂了。**2** completely or very 徹底地; 非常: *The walls must be perfectly clean before you paint them.* 在上油漆以前, 牆壁必須一塵不染。| *You know perfectly well that you're not supposed to go in there.* 你很清楚自己不應當走進那個地方。

per·fo·rated /ˈpɜːfəˌretɪd; ˈpɜːfəreɪtᵻd/ *adj* having a lot of small holes through the surface 表面有許多小孔的: *You can separate the stamps along the perforated line.* 你可以順着齒孔線把郵票撕開。

per·fo·ra·tion /ˌpɜːfəˈreʃən; ˌpɜːfəˈreɪʃən/ *n* **1** [U] the action of perforating 打孔; 穿孔 **2** [C] a small hole made in the surface of something 表面上的小孔: *tear along the perforations* 順着齒孔撕開

★**per·form** /pəˈfɔːm; pəˈfɔːm/ *v* **1** [T] to do a piece of work 做〔工作〕; 實行, 履行: *This operation can now safely be performed by a junior doctor.* 這項手術現在可以放心讓一個初級醫生來做。**2** [I;T] to do something to amuse people 表演: *They're performing a Shakespeare play.* 他們在演一齣莎士比亞的戲劇。| *She's performing at the National Theatre.* 她正在國家大劇院演出。| *a performing elephant* 表演的大象 **3** [I] to work or operate 工作; 運行: *This car performs well in busy traffic.* 這汽車在交通擁擠時也很容易駕駛。

★★**per·form·ance** /pəˈfɔːməns; pəˈfɔːməns/ *n* **1** [C] an act of performing 表演: *The singer's performance was terrible.* 這位歌手的演出很糟糕。| *There are two performances a day.* 一天有兩場演出。**2** [U] the action of doing a piece of work 表現: *Her performance in the exam was disappointing.* 她這次考試的表現令人失望。**3** [U] the ability of a person or machine to do something well 能力; 性能: *Our team's performance needs to improve if we're going to win.* 我們的隊如果想贏, 還需要提高能力。| *a high performance car* 性能卓越的汽車

per·form·er /pəˈfɔːmə; pəˈfɔːməʳ/ *n* a person who performs, for example an actor or musician 表演者〔如演員或音樂家〕

per·fume /ˈpɜːfjuːm; ˈpɜːfjuːm/ (also 又作 **scent**) *n* [C;U] **1** a sweet or pleasant smell 香味 –see 見 SMELL (USAGE用法) **2** sweet-smelling liquid, often made from flowers, which women put on their skin 香

水 –compare 比較 AFTER-SHAVE

per·fumed /pəˈfjuːmd; ˈpɜːfjuːmd/ *adj* **1** *fml* filled with a sweet or pleasant smell《正式》芬芳的; 香的: *a garden perfumed with flowers* 飄滿花香的花園 **2** having perfume on it 噴上香水的: *a perfumed handkerchief* 噴上香水的手帕

per·func·to·ry /pəˈfʌŋktəri; pəˈfʌŋktəri/ *adj fml* done in a hurry and without thinking or caring《正式》馬虎的; 敷衍的 –**perfunctorily** *adv*

per·haps /pəˈhæps; pəˈhæps/ *adv* **1** possibly 可能地: *Perhaps their train has been delayed.* 他們的火車可能晚點了。| *This is perhaps her best novel.* 這可能是她寫的最好的一部小說。**2** used when you are asking for something politely 也許〔用於禮貌地要求某事〕: *Perhaps you could phone me later to let me know what has been decided?* 也許你可以在晚些時候打電話來, 把決定好的事告訴我。

per·il /ˈperəl; ˈperl/ *n fml*《正式》**1** [U] danger of being harmed or killed 危險 **2** [C] something that causes danger 引起危險的事物 **3 at your peril** a phrase used to warn someone that they are very unwise to do something because they are taking a serious risk 自擔風險〔用於告誡某人做某事很不明智〕

per·il·ous /ˈperələs; ˈperləs/ *adj fml* very dangerous or risky《正式》非常危險的; 冒險的 –**perilously** *adv*

pe·rim·e·ter /pəˈrɪmətə; pəˈrɪmtə/ *n* the edge all round a closed flat area 四周; 周圍: *The perimeter of the airfield is protected by guard-dogs.* 機場周圍由警犬守衛。| *a perimeter fence* 環形的籬笆圍牆 | *the perimeter of a circle* 圓周長

★**pe·ri·od** [1] /ˈpɪəriəd; ˈpɪəriəd/ *n* **1** a length of time 一段時間: *There were long periods when we had no news of him.* 我們曾有很長時間沒有得到他的消息。| *Tomorrow's weather will be dry with sunny periods.* 明天天氣乾燥, 間或有太陽。**2** a particular length of time in history, or in a person's life〔歷史或人生的〕階段; 時代; 時期: *the Victorian period* 維多利亞時代 | *She went through a difficult period after her divorce.* 她離婚後度過了一段困難時期。**3** a lesson at school 課時, 一節課: *a history period* 一節歷史課 **4** (also 又作 **menstrual period** *fml*《正式》) a monthly flow of blood from the body of a woman 月經

period [2] *adj* belonging to an earlier period in history 早期的: *period costumes* 早期的服裝

pe·ri·od·ic /ˌpɪəriˈɒdɪk; ˌpɪəriˈɒdɪk◂/ (also 又作 **periodical**) *adj* happening occasionally, usually at regular times 周期性的; 定期的: *He suffered from periodic attacks of depression.* 他患有周期性的憂鬱抑鬱。–**periodically** /-klɪ; -kli/ *adv*

pe·ri·od·i·cal /ˌpɪəriˈɒdɪkl; ˌpɪəriˈɒdɪkəl/ *n* a magazine which appears at regular times, for example every month 期刊

pe·riph·e·ral /pəˈrɪfərəl; pəˈrɪfərəl/ *adj* **1** of relatively little importance 不太重要的: *This is a subject of only peripheral interest to many men.* 這是對許多男人來說唯一無關緊要的話題。**2** on the edge of an area〔地區〕周圍的 –**peripherally** *adv*

pe·riph·e·ry /pəˈrɪfəri; pəˈrɪfəri/ *n* peripheries *fml*《正式》**the periphery** the outside area or edge 外圍; 周邊: *the periphery of the town* 城市外圍

per·i·scope /ˈperəˌskəʊp; ˈperəˌskoʊp/ *n* a long tube with mirrors fitted in it so that people in a SUBMARINE can see what is above them 潛望鏡

per·ish /ˈperɪʃ; ˈperɪʃ/ *v fml*《正式》**1** [I] to die, because of something terrible that happens 死亡; 喪生: *Almost a hundred people perished in the hotel fire last night.* 昨夜的旅館大火中差不多有一百人喪生。**2** [I;T] to decay or cause to decay (使)腐爛: *The rubber in this tyre has perished.* 這隻輪胎的橡膠腐爛了。

per·ish·a·ble /ˈperɪʃəbl; ˈperɪʃəbəl/ *adj* that goes bad quickly (used of food) 易腐爛的〔指食品〕–opposite 反義 **nonperishable**

per·ish·ing /ˈperɪʃɪŋ; ˈperɪʃɪŋ/ *adj* very cold (used of weather) 非常冷的〔指天氣〕: *the perishing winter* 非常寒冷的冬天

per·jure /ˈpɜːdʒə; ˈpɜːdʒə/ *v* perjured, perjuring, **perjure yourself** to tell lies in court even though you have promised solemnly to tell the truth 作偽證; 發假誓

per·jur·er /ˈpɜːdʒərə; ˈpɜːdʒərə/ *n* a person who tells lies in court, even though they have promised solemnly to tell the truth 作偽證者; 發假誓者

per·ju·ry /ˈpɜːdʒəri; ˈpɜːdʒəri/ *n* [U] the act of telling lies in court, even though you have promised solemnly to tell the truth 偽證; 假誓

perk [1] /pɜːk; pɜːk/ *n* (also 又作 **perquisite** /ˈpɜːkwəzɪt; ˈpɜːkwɪzɪt/ *fml*《正式》) *infml* money, goods, or other advantages that you get regularly from your work in addition to your pay《非正式》固定的福利; 津貼; 補貼: *The perks include a company car.* 津貼包括提供一輛公司的汽車。| *One of the perks of this job is free meals.* 這份工作的福利之一是免費供應膳食。

perk [2] *v*

perk up *phr v* [I;T **perk** sbdy/sthg ↔ **up**] *infml* to become more cheerful and begin to show interest, or make someone become more cheerful and begin to show interest《非正式》(使)變得快活; (使)感興趣: *I had a cup of coffee to perk me up.* 我喝了杯咖啡以振作精神。| *He perked up when the party started.* 宴會一開始他就精神為之一振。

perk·y /ˈpɜːkɪ; ˈpɜːki/ *adj* cheerful and full

of life and interest 充滿生氣的; 感興趣的 –
perkily adv –**perkiness** n [U]

perm¹ /pɜːm; pɜːm/ n infml waves or curls
put into someone's hair by chemical treatment so that they will last for several
months〖非正式〗燙髮

perm² v [T] infml to put waves or curls into
someone's hair by chemical treatment so
that they will last for several months〖非正
式〗〔用化學劑〕燙髮: I'm going to have my
hair permed tomorrow. 我明天去燙髮。

per·ma·nence /ˈpɜːmənəns; ˈpɜːmənəns/ n
[U] the state of being permanent 永久

★**per·ma·nent** /ˈpɜːmənənt; ˈpɜːmənənt/ adj
lasting for a very long time or for ever 長久
的; 永久的: a permanent job 固定的工作 |
Pollution is causing permanent damage to
the environment. 污染正在給環境造成永久性
的損害。–**permanently** adv

per·me·ate /ˈpɜːmɪˌeɪt; ˈpɜːmɪeɪt/ v **permeated**, **permeating** [I;T] to pass through or
into every part of something 滲入; 滲透:
Water permeated through the cracks in the
wall. 水從牆縫中滲進來。 | A strong desire
for political change permeated the country.
這個國家瀰漫着對政治變革的強烈渴望。

per·mis·si·ble /pəˈmɪsəbl; pəˈmɪsɪbəl/ adj
fml allowed by the rules〖正式〗允許的:
What is the maximum permissible level of
nitrates in water? 水中所含硝酸鹽的最大許可
標準是多少?

★**per·mis·sion** /pəˈmɪʃən; pəˈmɪʃən/ n [U] the
right to do something somebody
else allows you 許可, 允許; 批准: We asked
his permission to use the computer. 我們請求
他允許我們使用計算機。 | Did she give you
permission to take that? 她准許你拿那東西了
嗎? | He took the car without permission.
他未經允許便把車開走了。

per·mis·sive /pəˈmɪsɪv; pəˈmɪsɪv/ adj allowing people a great deal of or too much
freedom, especially in sexual matters (a
word often used to express disapproval)
〔尤指在性方面〕縱容的; 放任的〔常含貶義〕:
The permissive society developed during the
1960s. 性開放的社會是在六十年代形成的。
–**permissively** adv –**permissiveness** n [U]

★**per·mit¹** /pəˈmɪt; pəˈmɪt/ v **-tt- 1** [T] to allow
someone to do or have something 允許, 准
許: I cannot permit this to happen. 我不能允
許此事發生。 | The rules of the club do not
permit alcohol. 俱樂部規定不許飲酒。 | She
wasn't permitted to drive. 她沒有獲准開車。 |
permitted food colouring 允許使用的食用色
素 | the maximum permitted dose 最大允許
劑量

□ USEFUL PATTERNS 有用句型
to permit something; to permit someone to do something; to permit someone something

2 [I;T] to make it possible to happen 容許,
許可: I will come in June if my health
permits. 如果我的健康狀況許可的話, 我將於
六月份來。 | weather permitting 如果天氣允
許的話 | The facts permit no other expla-
nation. 事實不容有其他解釋。

per·mit² /ˈpɜːmɪt; ˈpɜːmɪt/ n an official written statement giving you the right to do
something 許可證: You are not allowed to
enter the building without a permit. 你沒有許
可證就不能進入大樓。

per·mu·ta·tion /ˌpɜːmjʊˈteɪʃən; ˌpɜːmjʊˈteɪ-
ʃən/ n **1** any of the ways in which a group of
things can be arranged in order 排列方式 **2**
[U] the act of changing the order of a
group of things in MATHEMATICS〔數學
的〕排列

per·ni·cious /pəˈnɪʃəs; pəˈnɪʃəs/ adj fml very
harmful〔正式〕很有害的 –**perniciously**
adv –**perniciousness** n [U]

per·nick·e·ty /pəˈnɪkɪti; pəˈnɪkɪti/ adj infml
too concerned that every small detail
should be exactly right〖非正式〗挑剔的

per·ox·ide /pəˈrɒksaɪd; pəˈrɒksaɪd/ n [U]
(also 又作 **hydrogen peroxide** fml〖正式〗)
infml a chemical liquid used to take the
colour out of dark hair and to kill bacteria
〖非正式〗過氧化氫〔用作防腐劑及漂染頭髮
劑〕

per·pen·dic·u·lar /ˌpɜːpənˈdɪkjələ; ˌpɜːpən-
ˈdɪkjələr/ adj **1** exactly upright and not
leaning to one side or the other 垂直的 **2** at
an angle of 90 degrees to a line or surface
成直角的 –**perpendicularly** adv

per·pe·trate /ˈpɜːpəˌtreɪt; ˈpɜːpətreɪt/ v **per-
petrated**, **perpetrating** [T] fml to do something wrong or criminal〔正式〕做〔壞事〕; 犯
〔罪〕–**perpetrator** n –**perpetration** /ˌpɜː-
pəˈtreɪʃən; ˌpɜːpəˈtreɪʃən/ n [U]

per·pet·u·al /pəˈpetʃʊəl; pəˈpetʃʊəl/ adj **1**
lasting for ever or for a long time 持久的;
長久的: the perpetual snow on the mountains 山上的終年積雪 **2** happening often or
all the time (a word used to express disapproval) 經常的; 不斷的〔含貶義〕: I'm tired of
your perpetual complaints. 我聽厭了你沒完
沒了的抱怨。–**perpetually** adv: He's perpetually losing things. 他老是遺失東西。

per·pet·u·ate /pəˈpetʃʊˌeɪt; pəˈpetʃʊeɪt/ v
perpetuated, **perpetuating** [T] to cause
something to continue 使〔某事〕繼續; 保存:
The tax laws perpetuate inequality between
men and women. 稅法維持了男女間的不平等
狀況。–**perpetuation** /pəˌpetʃʊˈeɪʃən; pəˌpe-
tʃʊˈeɪʃən/ n [U]

per·pe·tu·i·ty /ˌpɜːpəˈtjuːəti; ˌpɜːpəˈtjuːɪti/
n [U] fml〔正式〕in perpetuity for ever 永
遠; 永存

per·plexed /pəˈplekst; pəˈplekst/ adj confused by something difficult to understand
困惑的: She looked perplexed and asked me
to repeat what I had said. 她滿臉困惑, 叫我

再把話重複一遍。

per·plex·i·ty /pə'plɛksətɪ; pə'plɛksˌti/ *n* [U] the feeling of being confused and worried because you do not understand something 困惑

per se /ˌpɜ·'si; ˌpɜ:'seɪ/ *adv fml* considered alone and not in connection with other things〖正式〗就本身而論

per·se·cute /'pɜ·sɪˌkjut; 'pɜ:sɪkjuːt/ *v* **persecuted, persecuting** [T] to treat someone cruelly and make them suffer, especially because of their religious or political beliefs〖尤指因宗教或政治信仰不同而〗迫害 – **persecutor** *n* –**persecution** /ˌpɜ·sɪ'kju-ʃən; ˌpɜ:sɪ'kjuːʃən/ *n* [C;U]: *the persecution of the Jewish people* 對猶太人的迫害

per·se·ver·ance /ˌpɜ·sə'vɪrəns; ˌpɜ:sɪ'vɪərəns/ *n* [U] steady and continued effort 不屈不撓；堅持不懈

per·se·vere /ˌpɜ·sə'vɪr; ˌpɜ:sɪ'vɪə‹r›/ *v* **persevered, persevering** [I] to keep trying to do something although it is difficult 堅持不懈: *Learning to drive was difficult but I persevered with it.* 學習駕車很難，但我仍堅持下去。–**persevering** *adj*

per·sist /pə'zɪst; pə'sɪst/ *v* [I] **1** to continue doing something with determination in spite of opposition 堅持；執意: *If you persist in breaking the law you will go to prison.* 你如果堅持違法就會坐牢。| *Why must the government persist with this unpopular plan?* 政府為何要堅持執行這項不受歡迎的計劃？ **2** to continue to exist 繼續存在: *The cold weather will persist for the rest of the week.* 寒冷天氣將在本週餘下的時間持續下去。

per·sis·tent /pə'zɪstənt; pə'sɪstənt/ *adj* **1** continuing to do something with determination in spite of opposition 堅持的；固執的: *a persistent thief* 劣性難改的賊 | *His persistent questions really started to annoy me.* 他沒完沒了的問題真的開始使我煩厭了。 **2** continuing to exist for a long time and not going away 持續的: *a persistent cough* 持續不斷的咳嗽 –**persistence** *n* [U]: *He showed such persistence that they finally had to give him a job.* 他表現出很大的毅力，最終他們不得不給了他那份工作。–**persistently** *adv*

⋆⋆**per·son** /'pɜ·sn; 'pɜ:sən/ *n* **1** [C] [plural is 複數為 **people**] a man or woman 人: *You're just the person I wanted to see.* 你就是我想見的人。 **2** [C;U] in grammar, any of the three special forms of verbs that show who is speaking (the first person), who is spoken to (the second person) or the human being or thing being spoken about (the third person)〖語法〗人稱 **3 in person** being physically present in a place 親自: *The minister could not come in person so she sent her secretary instead.* 部長無法親自前來，所以她派了祕書代替她出席。| *After speaking so often on the telephone, I finally met her in person.* 我經常與她在電話中通話，最後終於於見到了她本人。

■ USAGE 用法: **1** The usual plural of **person** is **people**. ☆ **person** 的複數是 **people**: *The doctor sees one* **person** *at a time.* 醫生一次看一個人。| *Five* **people** *sat in the waiting room.* 有五個人坐在候診室裡。(**Persons** is very formal and is used in official writing or notices ☆ **persons** 非常正規，用於正式的文件或通知中: *He was murdered by a* **person** *or* **persons** *unknown.* 他被一個或者是幾個不知名的人殺害。) **2** Many people do not like the use of words such as **chairman** or **spokesman** to refer to women or to both sexes. If you want to avoid this use, you can often use words formed with **person** ☆ 許多人不喜歡用 **chairman** 或 **spokesman** 來指代女性或兩種性別的人。如果你要為避免這種用法，可以用 **person** 所形成的詞: *She/he is our new* **chairperson**. 她[他]是我們的新主席。| *She/he agreed to act as* **spokesperson**. 她[他]同意擔任發言人。

-person *n* a man or woman who does a particular job 做…工作的人: *She's an excellent chairperson.* 她是個很出色的主持人。| *a spokesperson for the organization* 一位該組織的發言人

per·so·na /pə'sonə; pə'səʊnə/ *n* **personas** *or* **personae** /-ni; -niː/ the sides of your character you show to other people〖顯示給別人的〗表面形象；人格面具

per·son·a·ble /'pɜ·sɴəbl; 'pɜ:sənəbəl/ *adj* attractive in appearance or character 英俊的；氣質好的

per·son·age /'pɜ·sɴɪdʒ; 'pɜ:sənɪdʒ/ *n fml* a famous or important person〖正式〗名人，要人

⋆⋆**per·son·al** /'pɜ·sɴl; 'pɜ:sənəl/ *adj* **1** relating to the feelings of a particular person rather than a group 有關個人感情的: *My personal opinion was that she should not go.* 我個人的意見是她不應該去。| *a question of personal choice* 一個屬於個人選擇的問題 **2** concerning, or belonging to a particular person 個人的；私人的: *The letter was marked "Personal".* 該信上寫着"私人信件"。| *his personal possessions* 他的私人財物 **3** concerning your body 身體的: *personal cleanliness* 個人衛生 **4** directed against a person's character or appearance in an unpleasant way 人身攻擊的: *I was upset by his personal remarks about my family.* 他對我的家人進行了人身攻擊，我感到很生氣。 **5** done by a particular person, not a representative 親自的: *The minister made a personal appearance on television.* 部長親自在電視中露面。 **6** concerning private

---

feelings or actions 有關個人感情的; 有關個人行動的: *The problem is too personal to be discussed.* 此問題有關個人隱私, 不宜討論。| *I try and keep my personal life separate from my professional life.* 我盡力將自己的私生活與工作分開。**7** in grammar, showing the person concerned 〔語法〕人稱的: *a personal pronoun* 人稱代(名)詞

personal as·sis·tant /ˌ··· ·'··/ *n* see 見 PA

personal col·umn /'··· ˌ··/ *n* a part of a newspaper that provides information or private messages for particular people 〔報紙上的〕人事欄

personal com·put·er /ˌ··· ·'··/ *n* a small computer for business or personal use 個人電腦

personal or·gan·iz·er /ˌ··· ·'··/ *n* a book with loose pages you can add to in which to keep a record of things you plan to do in the current year, appointments, names and addresses, notes, and other information you need to carry with you 備忘記事本

*★**per·son·al·i·ty** /ˌpɜ·snˌˈælətɪ; ˌpɜːsəˈnælɪti/ *n* **personalities 1** [C;U] the whole nature and character of a particular person 個性; 性格: *She has a lovely personality.* 她的性格很可愛。| *They don't get on well because of differences of personality.* 他們由於性格不同而合不來。**2** [U] interesting or exciting qualities of character 個性: *He has no personality.* 他沒有個性。**3** [C] a person who is well known to the public 名人: *a television personality* 電視名人

per·son·al·ize /'pɜ·snˌaɪz; 'pɜːsənəlaɪz/ *v* [T] **personalized, personalizing** (also 又作 **personalise** *BrE* 〔英式〕) **1** to consider something not from the facts but from the characters or relationships of the people concerned 使個人化: *Let's not personalize this argument.* 讓我們不要將這場爭端搞成針對個人。**2** to make or do something so that it is for a particular person, often by adding their name or address 在〔物品〕上標出個人姓名〔地址〕: *personalized handkerchiefs* 印有個人名字的手帕

per·son·al·ly /'pɜ·snlɪ; 'pɜːsənəli/ *adv* **1** directly and not through a representative 親自(地): *He is personally in charge of all the arrangements.* 他親自負責安排一切。**2** a word you use when you are giving your own opinion about something 就個人來說〔用於提供個人意見〕: *Personally, I thought the film was very good.* 就個人來說, 我認為這部電影很不錯。**3** as a person 作為一個人: *Personally she may be very charming, but is she a good doctor?* 她這個人也許很有魅力, 但她是個好醫生嗎? **4** directed against a particular person's character or appearance 攻擊人地: *You must not take my remarks about your work personally.* 你千萬不要把我對你的工作評論看成是對你的人身攻擊。

personal pro·noun /ˌ··· '··/ *n* a word standing for a noun and used for showing the speaker, the person spoken to, or the person spoken about; "I", "you", and "they" are personal pronouns 人稱代(名)詞〔"I", "you", 和 "they" 都是人稱代(名)詞〕

per·son·i·fy /pɜ·ˈsɑnəˌfaɪ; pɜːˈsɒnɪfaɪ/ *v* **personified, personifying** [T] to be a perfect example of something 是...的化身 –**personification** /pɜ·ˌsɑnəfəˈkeʃən; pɜːˌsɒnɪfɪˈkeɪʃən/ *n* [C;U]

*★**per·son·nel** /ˌpɜ·snˈɛl; ˌpɜːsəˈnel/ *n* [pl] all the people employed by an organization 全體職員: *army personnel* 軍隊人員 | *New personnel are needed for our operations in the Middle East.* 我們需要新的雇員來經營我們在中東的業務。

per·spec·tive /pɜ·ˈspɛktɪv; pɜːspektɪv/ *n* **1** [C] a way of thinking about something, related to your background, experience, or beliefs 〔思考問題的〕觀點; 看法: *He views everything from a political perspective.* 他從政治的角度來看待一切事物。| *an historical perspective* 歷史的觀點 **2** [U] the ability to think clearly, considering all the facts 思考能力: *She was under such stress that she lost all sense of perspective.* 她緊張得喪失了全部的判斷能力。**3 keep things in perspective** to keep a sense of what is really important and what is not important 對事物有明確的認識 [RELATED PHRASE 相關詞組 **get things into perspective**] **4** [U] the rules of drawing used by artists to give a feeling of distance and solidity to objects painted on a flat surface 〔繪畫的〕透視法: *The streets in the background are out of perspective.* 背景上的馬路沒有透視感。

per·spex /'pɜ·spɛks; pɜːspeks/ *n* (also 又作 **Perspex**) [U] *tdmk* a strong plastic material that can be used instead of glass 〔商標〕珀斯佩有機玻璃

per·spi·ca·cious /ˌpɜ·spɪˈkeʃəs; ˌpɜːspɪˈkeɪʃəs/ *adj fml* having or showing good judgment and understanding 〔正式〕善於判斷的; 有洞察力的 –**perspicacity** /-ˈkæsətɪ; -ˈkæsɪti/ *n* [U]

per·spi·ra·tion /ˌpɜ·spəˈreʃən; ˌpɜːspəˈreɪʃən/ *n* [U] *fml* liquid that comes out through your skin when you are very hot 〔正式〕汗(水); 出汗

per·spire /pɜ·ˈspaɪr; pəˈspaɪəʳ/ *v* **perspired, perspiring** [I] *fml* to lose liquid through your skin when you are very hot 〔正式〕出汗

*★**per·suade** /pɜ·ˈswed; pəˈsweɪd/ *v* **persuaded, persuading** [T] **1** to cause someone to do something they had been unwilling to do by giving good reasons 說服; 勸服: *She didn't want to come, but I persuaded her.* 她不想來, 但我說服了她。| *My mother persuaded me to buy this dress.* 我母親說服我買下了這條裙子。

---

2 to make someone feel certain that something is true 使〔某人〕相信: *He persuaded himself that things were best left as they were.* 他使自己相信事情已處理得盡可能令人滿意了。—see 見 CONVINCE (USAGE用法)

per·sua·sion /pɚˈsweʒən; pəˈsweɪʒən/ *n* **1** [U] the act of persuading someone 勸說: *I'm sure she'll agree — it just needs a little persuasion.* 我肯定她會同意——只不過需要稍微做些勸說工作。 **2** [U] the ability to influence others 說服力: *He has great powers of persuasion.* 他有很強的說服力。 **3** [C] a person or group holding a particular belief 持某一信仰的人或團體: *People of many different political persuasions attended the meeting.* 持各種不同政治信仰的人出席了這個會議。

per·sua·sive /pɚˈsweɪsɪv; pəˈsweɪsɪv/ *adj* having the power to influence other people into believing or doing something 有說服力的: *He can be very persuasive when he wants something.* 他想要得到一樣東西時，他可以很有說服力。 **–persuasively** *adv*

pert /pɜt; pɜːt/ *adj* slightly disrespectful in an amusing way 冒失的

per·tain /pɚˈten; pəˈteɪn/ *v fml* 【正式】 **pertain to** to belong to something or have a connection with it 有關，關於

per·ti·na·cious /ˌpɜtnˈeʃəs; ˌpɜːtɪˈneɪʃəs/ *adj fml* 【正式】 determined 堅持的；固執的 **– pertinacity** /-nˈæsətɪ; -ˈnæs‚ti/ *n* [U]

per·ti·nent /ˈpɜtnənt; ˈpɜːtɪˌnənt/ *adj fml* directly connected with something being considered 【正式】相關的；中肯的: *She asked several pertinent questions.* 她提了幾個切題的問題。

per·turbed /pɚˈtɜbd; pəˈtɜːbd/ *adj* [T] *fml* worried 【正式】憂慮的

pe·ruse /pəˈruz; pəˈruːz/ *v* **perused, perusing** [T] *fml* to read through something carefully 【正式】細讀；精讀〔某篇文章〕 **– perusal** *n* [C;U]

per·vade /pɚˈved; pəˈveɪd/ *v* **pervaded, pervading** [T] *fml* to be present strongly in a place 【正式】瀰漫；蔓延: *The smell of cooking pervaded the whole house.* 滿屋都是烹調的氣味。

per·va·sive /pɚˈvesɪv; pəˈveɪsɪv/ *adj* present strongly in a place (a word often used to express disapproval) 遍佈的；蔓延的〔常含貶義〕: *the pervasive influence of television* 電視無孔不入的影響 **–pervasively** *adv*

per·verse /pɚˈvɜs; pəˈvɜːs/ *adj* continuing to do something you know is wrong or unreasonable and that other people do not want you to do 一意孤行的；剛愎的: *He gets a perverse pleasure from arguing with people.* 他有一種不正常的心態，以與人爭辯。

取樂。

per·ver·sion /pɚˈvɜʒən; pəˈvɜːʃən/ *n* **1** [C; U] something that has been changed or the action of changing something so that it is no longer reasonable, right or true 歪曲: *perversion of the truth* 對事實的歪曲 **2** [C] an unnatural form of sexual behaviour 性變態

per·vert[1] /pɚˈvɜt; pəˈvɜːt/ *v* [T] **1** to cause someone to behave in ways that are considered wrong or unnatural 使〔某人〕墮落 **2** to change something and use it for a bad purpose 歪曲；誤用: *Scientific knowledge has been perverted to help cause destruction and war.* 科學知識被濫用於毀滅和戰爭。 **3** **pervert the course of justice** to prevent justice being done 濫用司法程序

per·vert[2] /ˈpɜvɜt; ˈpɜːvɜːt/ *n* a person whose sexual behaviour is not considered natural 性變態者

pe·se·ta /pəˈsetə; pəˈseɪtə/ *n* a Spanish coin, on which the Spanish money system is based 比塞塔〔西班牙貨幣單位〕

pes·si·mis·m /ˈpɛsəˌmɪzəm; ˈpesɪˌmɪzəm/ *n* [U] the habit of thinking that whatever happens will be bad 悲觀(主義) **–pessimist** *n*: *Don't be such a pessimist!* 別這麼悲觀! **–pessimistic** /ˌpɛsəˈmɪstɪk; ˌpesɪˈmɪstɪk/ *adj* **–pessimistically** /-klɪ; -kli/ *adv*

pest /pɛst; pest/ *n* **1** a small animal or insect that harms or destroys food supplies 有害的小動物；害蟲 **2** *infml* an annoying person or thing 【非正式】討厭的人〔物〕

pes·ter /ˈpɛstɚ; ˈpestə/ *v* [T] to annoy somebody by continually asking for something 糾纏〔某人要某物〕: *He keeps pestering me for money.* 他一直纏著我要錢。

pes·ti·cide /ˈpɛstɪsaɪd; ˈpestɪˌsaɪd/ *n* [C;U] a chemical substance used to kill harmful animals and insects 殺蟲劑，農藥 –see picture on page 470 見 470 頁彩圖

pes·ti·lence /ˈpɛstləns; ˈpestɪləns/ *n* [C;U] *old fash* a disease that kills large numbers of people 【老式】瘟疫

pes·tle /ˈpɛsl; ˈpesəl/ *n* an instrument with a heavy rounded end, used for crushing things in a special bowl called a MORTAR 〔搗研用的〕杵

pet /pɛt; pet/ *n* **1** an animal you keep in your home as a companion 供玩賞的動物；寵物: *a pet dog* 寵物狗 | *She keeps a monkey as a pet.* 她養了隻猴子作為寵物。 **2** a person who is specially liked by someone in power 受寵的人: *She is the teacher's pet.* 她是老師的得意門生。 **3** [only before another noun 只用於另一名詞前] something that you feel very strongly about or that you like very much 堅信之事；喜愛之物: *He's talking about his pet theories again.* 他又在談論他所篤信的理論了。 **4** **pet hate** the thing you hate most 最憎惡的事物: *Teabags are my pet hate.* 袋泡茶是我最討厭的東西。

pet² v -tt- **1** [T] to touch gently and treat lovingly 撫摸; 愛撫 **2** [I;T] *infml* to kiss and touch someone in sexual play 〔非正式〕〔男女間〕親吻; 愛撫

pet·al /ˈpetl; ˈpetl/ n one of the coloured parts of a flower 花瓣

pe·ter /ˈpiːtə; ˈpiːtə/ v

  peter out *phr* v [I] to gradually come to an end 逐漸消失

pe·tite /pəˈtiːt; pəˈtiːt/ *adj* small in an attractive way (used of women) 嬌小玲瓏的〔指女人〕–see picture on page 469 見 469 頁彩圖

pe·ti·tion¹ /pəˈtɪʃən; pəˈtɪʃən/ n a request signed by a lot of people made to a government or other official group 請願書: *Will you sign a petition against the closure of the local railway line?* 你願意在反對關閉當地鐵路的請願書上簽名嗎?

petition² v [I;T] to make a request in the form of a petition 請願; 請求: *They have petitioned the government to improve bus services.* 他們已請求政府改善公共汽車服務。

pet·ri·fy /ˈpetrəˌfaɪ; ˈpetrɪˌfaɪ/ v **petrified, petrifying 1** [T] *infml* to make someone feel very afraid 〔非正式〕使〔某人〕嚇呆: *I was so petrified by the face at the window that I couldn't move.* 我被窗外的那張臉嚇呆了, 連動也不敢動。**2** [I;T] to turn into stone 使石化: *the Petrified Forest in Arizona* 亞利桑那州的石化森林

pet·ro·chem·i·cal /ˌpetroˈkemɪkl; ˌpetrə-ˈkemɪkl/ n a chemical substance obtained from petroleum or natural gas 石(油)化(學)產品: *the petrochemical industry* 石化工業

pet·rol /ˈpetrəl; ˈpetrəl/ n *BrE* [U] a liquid obtained from petroleum, used especially for producing power in engines 〔英式〕汽油: *I need to fill the car up with petrol.* 我需要給車加滿汽油。| *a petrol station* 汽車加油站

pe·tro·le·um /pəˈtrəʊliəm; pəˈtrəʊliəm/ n [U] a mineral oil obtained from below the surface of the Earth, and used to produce petrol and various other chemical substances 石油

petrol sta·tion /ˈ·· ˌ··/ n *BrE* a place where you can buy petrol for vehicles 〔英式〕汽車加油站

pet·ti·coat /ˈpetɪˌkoʊt; ˈpetɪkəʊt/ n a thin skirt worn by women under a dress or skirt 襯裙

pet·ty /ˈpetɪ; ˈpeti/ *adj* **pettier, pettiest 1** small and not important 微不足道的; 瑣碎的: *our petty problems* 我們的小問題 **2** unkind, and too concerned with small, unimportant things (a word used to express disapproval) 心胸狹窄的; 小心眼的〔含貶義〕: *John can be very petty about money.* 約翰有時非常在乎錢。

petty cash /ˌ·· ˈ·/ n [U] an amount of money kept in an office ready for making small payments 零用現金; 小額備用金

petty of·fi·cer /ˌ·· ˈ···/ n an officer in the navy 海軍軍士長

pet·u·lant /ˈpetʃələnt; ˈpetʃʊlənt/ *adj* showing childish anger over unimportant things 愛使性子的; 任性的 –**petulantly** *adv* –**petulance** n [U]

pew /pjuː; pjuː/ n **1** a long seat for people to sit on in church 教堂的長條座椅 **2 take a pew** to sit down (a phrase which is often used in a humorous way) 坐下〔常作幽默用法〕

pew·ter /ˈpjuːtə; ˈpjuːtər/ n [U] a grey metal made by mixing lead and tin 白鑞〔錫和鉛的合金〕

pha·lanx /ˈfeɪlæŋks; ˈfælæŋks/ n **phalanxes** or **phalanges** /fəˈlændʒiːz; fəˈlændʒiːz/ any group of people or soldiers who are packed closely together for attack or defence 密集隊形; 士兵方陣

phal·lus /ˈfæləs; ˈfæləs/ n an image of the male sex organ 男性生殖器形象 –**phallic** *adj*

phan·tom /ˈfæntəm; ˈfæntəm/ n **1** an image of a dead person that appears like a shadow 幽靈 **2** something which exists only in someone's imagination 幻影, 幻象

pha·raoh /ˈfeəroʊ; ˈfeərəʊ/ n (also 又作 **Pharaoh**) title of the ruler of ancient Egypt 〔古埃及的〕法老

phar·ma·ceu·ti·cal /ˌfɑːrməˈsjuːtɪkl; ˌfɑːmə-ˈsjuːtɪkəl/ *adj* [only before a noun 只用於名詞前] connected with the production of medicines 製藥的; 藥用的: *a pharmaceutical company* 製藥公司

phar·ma·cist /ˈfɑːrməsɪst; ˈfɑːməsɪst/ n *fml* a person who prepares and sells medicines 〔正式〕藥劑師; 藥商

phar·ma·col·o·gy /ˌfɑːrməˈkɒlədʒi; ˌfɑːmə-ˈkɒlədʒi/ n [U] the scientific study of medicines and drugs 藥理學; 藥物學 –**pharmacologist** n

phar·ma·cy /ˈfɑːrməsi; ˈfɑːməsi/ n **pharmacies 1** [U] the making or giving out of medicines 製藥; 配藥 **2** [C] a shop where medicines are given out or sold 藥店; 藥房

✲phase¹ /feɪz; feɪz/ n **1** a stage of change or development 階段; 時期: *East-West relations are entering a new phase.* 東西方關係正進入一個新階段。| *the most dangerous phase of the illness* 疾病的最危險期 **2 go through a phase** to experience a particular period of change or development 經過某一階段: *The band's music is going through a boring phase at the moment.* 樂隊正在演奏一段沉悶的樂章。**3** one of the changes in the appearance of the moon as seen from the Earth at different times 〔月球的〕位相

phase² v **phased, phasing** [T] to do something gradually, in stages 分階段做〔某事〕: *a phased withdrawal of nuclear weapons* 分階段撤出核武器

  phase sthg ↔ **in** *phr* v [T] to introduce

something gradually 逐步引入〔某物〕: *The new exam system is being phased in over two years.* 新的考試制度在兩年內逐步實施。

phase sthg ↔ **out** *phr v* [T] to remove something gradually 逐步淘汰〔某物〕: *They are phasing out the old coins.* 他們在逐漸淘汰舊硬幣的使用。

PhD /ˌpiː etʃ ˈdiː; ˌpiː eɪtʃ ˈdiː/ *n* **1** an advanced university degree; an abbreviation for **Doctor of Philosophy**〔縮〕哲學博士學位 **2** a person who has gained a PhD 哲學博士

pheas·ant /ˈfeznt; ˈfezənt/ *n* [C;U] a large long-tailed bird hunted for food 雉; 野雞

phe·nom·e·nal /fəˈnɑmənl; fɪˈnɒmɪnəl/ *adj* very unusual and great 非凡的; 很大的: *She has a phenomenal memory.* 她有非凡的記憶力。 –**phenomenally** *adv*

****phe·nom·e·non** /fəˈnɑməˌnɑn; fɪˈnɒmɪˌnən/ *n* **phenomena** /-nə; -nə/ **1** something that happens in nature, science, or society, and can be seen 現象: *natural phenomena* 自然現象 | *Unemployment is not a new phenomenon.* 失業不是新現象。 **2** a very unusual person, thing, or event 非凡的人〔物或事件〕

phew /fju; fjuː/ *interj* (also 又作 **whew**) a word used to represent a whistling sound that you make when you are tired, shocked, or pleased 呸; 唷; 啐〔表示疲倦、吃驚或高興〕

phi·al /ˈfaɪəl; ˈfaɪəl/ *n* a small bottle for medicine 小藥瓶

phi·lan·thro·pist /fəˈlænθrəpɪst; fɪˈlænθrə-pɪst/ *n* a person who makes generous gifts of money to people who need it 慈善家

phi·lan·thro·py /fəˈlænθrəpɪ; fɪˈlænθrəpi/ *n* [U] giving money and help to those who need it 慈善; 仁慈 –**philanthropic** /ˌfɪlən-ˈθrɑpɪk; ˌfɪlənˈθrɒpɪk◂/ *adj*

phi·lat·e·ly /fəˈlætlɪ; fɪˈlætəli/ *n* [U] *tech* stamp collecting〔術語〕集郵 –**philatelist** *n*

phil·is·tine /fəˈlɪstɪn; ˈfɪlɪˌstaɪn/ *n* a person who has no understanding of, or interest in, art, music, or beautiful things (a word used to express disapproval) 庸俗的人; 對藝術無知的人〔含貶義〕

phi·lol·o·gy /fɪˈlɑlədʒɪ; fɪˈlɒlədʒi/ *n* [U] *tech* the study of the nature and development of words and language〔術語〕語文學 –**philologist** *n*

phi·los·o·pher /fəˈlɑsəfɚ; fɪˈlɒsəfər/ *n* **1** a person who studies or develops systems of thought about reality and the meaning of life 哲學家: *the Greek philosophers* 希臘哲學家 **2** someone who thinks deeply about life 對人生認真思考的人

phil·o·soph·i·cal /ˌfɪləˈsɑfɪkəl; ˌfɪləˈsɒfɪkəl/ *adj* **1** accepting difficulty or unhappiness calmly 達觀的 **2** of or concerning systems of thought 哲學的: *the philosophical writings of Sartre* 薩特的哲學著作 –**philosophically** /-klɪ; -kli/ *adv*

phi·los·o·phize /fəˈlɑsəˌfaɪz; fɪˈlɒsəfaɪz/ *v* **philosophized, philosophizing** (also 又作 **philosophise**) [I] to think, talk, or write about important subjects and ideas in a very serious way〔以非常嚴肅的態度〕思考〔談論或寫作〕

****phi·los·o·phy** /fəˈlɑsəfɪ; fɪˈlɒsəfi/ *n* **philosophies 1** [U] the study of the meaning of existence, reality, and knowledge 哲學 **2** [C] a set of ideas about the meaning of existence, reality, and knowledge 哲學體系: *the philosophy of Aristotle* 亞里士多德的哲學思想 **3** a set of personal beliefs about how life should be lived 人生觀

phlegm /flɛm; flem/ *n* [U] **1** the thick yellow substance produced in your nose and throat when you have a cold 痰 **2** calmness 平靜; 冷靜

phleg·mat·ic /flɛgˈmætɪk; flegˈmætɪk/ *adj fml* calm and not easily upset or worried〔正式〕冷靜的; 鎮定的 –**phlegmatically** /-klɪ; -kli/ *adv*

pho·bi·a /ˈfobɪə; ˈfəʊbiə/ *n* a strong and unreasonable fear 恐懼症: *I've got a phobia about insects.* 我極害怕昆蟲。

phoe·nix /ˈfinɪks; ˈfiːnɪks/ *n* an imaginary bird believed to burn itself and be born again from the ashes 鳳凰, 長生〔不死〕鳥

****phone¹** /fon; fəʊn/ *n* **1** a telephone 電話: *What's your phone number?* 你的電話號碼是多少? | *Could I make a phone call please?* 我可以打個電話嗎? | *a car phone* 汽車電話 **2** be on the phone: a to be talking on the telephone 在通話: *We were on the phone for an hour.* 我們在電話裏談了一個小時。 b to have a telephone in your house 家中有電話: *I'm afraid we're not on the phone.* 對不起, 我們家裏沒有電話。

phone² *v* **phoned, phoning** [I;T] (also 又作 **phone up; phone** sbdy ↔ **up**) to telephone someone 給〔某人〕打電話: *Phone me when you arrive at the station.* 你到了車站就給我打個電話。 | *He phoned to say he couldn't come.* 他來電話說, 他不能來了。 –see 見 **TELEPHONE¹** (USAGE 用法)

phone book /ˈ· ·/ *n* a book containing an alphabetical list of the names, addresses and telephone numbers of all the people who own a telephone in a certain area 電話簿

phone box /ˈ· ·/ *n* (also 又作 **phone booth** *AmE*〔美式〕) a small enclosure containing a public telephone 電話亭 –see picture on page 729 見 729 頁彩圖

phone-in /ˈ· ·/ *n* a radio or television broadcast during which telephoned questions or opinions from the public are heard 公眾打電話參與的電台[電視]直播節目

pho·net·ic /foˈnɛtɪk; fəˈnetɪk/ *adj* **1** of or concerning the sounds of human speech 語音(學)的 **2** using special letters and signs to represent the actual sounds of speech 使用

音標的, 表示發音的: *This dictionary uses a phonetic alphabet as a guide to pronunciation.* 本詞典是以音標注音的。**–phonetically** /-klɪ; -kli/ *adv*

pho·net·ics /fo'netɪks; fə'netɪks/ *n* [U] *tech* the study and science of speech sounds 〖術語〗語音學

pho·ney /'fonɪ; 'fəuni/ *adj* (also 又作 **phony**) *infml* false 〖非正式〗假的; 偽造的

phos·pho·res·cence /ˌfɑsfə'rɛsns; ˌfɒsfə'resns/ *n* [U] the giving out of light with little or no heat 發磷光, 閃磷火 **–phosphorescent** *adj*

phos·pho·rus /'fɑsfərəs; 'fɒsfərəs/ *n* [U] a poisonous yellowish substance that shines in the dark and starts to burn when brought into the air 磷

pho·to /'foto; 'fəutəu/ *n* photos *infml* a photograph 〖非正式〗照片, 相片: *holiday photos* 度假時拍的照片 | *I took a photo of the baby.* 我給嬰兒拍了張照片。

pho·to·cop·i·er /ˌfoto'kɑpɪə; 'fəutəuˌkɒpiəʳ/ *n* a machine that makes photocopies 影印機 **–see picture on page 763** 見 763 頁彩圖

pho·to·cop·y /'fotəˌkɑpɪ; 'fəutəuˌkɒpi/ *v* **photocopied, photocopying, photocopies** [C;T] to make a photographic copy of a letter or piece of writing 影印; 複印 **– photocopy** *n*: *I'll send you a photocopy of the letter.* 我把信的複印本寄給你。

photo fin·ish /ˌ··· '··/ *n* the end of a race in which the leaders finish so close together that a photograph has to be taken to show which is the winner 攝影定終局[勝負]〔競賽者的勝負以攝影來判斷〕

pho·to·gen·ic /ˌfoto'dʒenɪk; ˌfəutəu'dʒenɪk◂/ *adj* having an appearance that looks attractive when photographed (used of people)〔指人〕上鏡頭的; 適合拍照的

★pho·to·graph[1] /'fotəˌgræf; 'fəutəgrɑːf/ *n* (also 又作 **photo** *infml* 〖非正式〗) a picture of someone or something obtained by using a camera and film sensitive to light 照片: *Visitors to the castle are not allowed to take photographs.* 參觀城堡的人不許拍照。| *a black and white photograph* 一張黑白照片 | *I saw your photograph in the newspaper.* 我在報上看到了你的照片。

photograph[2] *v* [T] to take a photograph of someone or something 給〔某人或某物〕拍照: *She has photographed hundreds of famous people.* 她給數以百計的名人拍過照。

pho·tog·ra·pher /fə'tɑgrəfə; fə'tɒgrəfəʳ/ *n* a person who takes photographs as their job or for pleasure 攝影師; 拍照的人

pho·to·graph·ic /ˌfotə'græfɪk; ˌfəutə'græfɪk◂/ *adj* [only before a noun 只用於名詞前] **1** used in producing photographs 攝影(用)的: *photographic equipment* 攝影器材 **2** photographic memory an ability to remember exactly things that you have seen

照像般鮮明的記憶力 **–photographically** /-klɪ; -kli/ *adv*

pho·tog·ra·phy /fə'tɑgrəfɪ; fə'tɒgrəfi/ *n* [U] the art or process of producing photographs 攝影術; 攝影

pho·to·stat /'fotəˌstæt; 'fəutəstæt/ *v* **-tt-** [T] *tdmk* to make a photographic copy of a letter or piece of writing 〖商標〗影印; 複印 **–photostat** *n*

phras·al verb /ˌfrezl 'vɝb; ˌfreɪzəl 'vɜːb/ *n* a small group of words that act like a verb and consist of a verb with an adverb or a PREPOSITION; "run out" and "use up" are phrasal verbs 片語[短語]動詞("run out" 和 "use up" 就是片語[短語]動詞 **–see** Study Note on page 1322 見 1322 頁學習提示

★phrase[1] /frez; freɪz/ *n* **1** a small group of words that form part of a sentence or which have particular meaning 短語; 片語: *I learned a few Greek phrases on holiday.* 假期裡我學會了幾個希臘文短語。**2** a short expression, especially one that is clever 簡潔的語句; 警句

phrase[2] *v* **phrased, phrasing** [T] to express something in a particular way or using a particular kind of word 用某種方式表達; 用某種詞表達: *Her letter was phrased very carefully.* 她的信措辭很謹慎。

phrase·book /'frez,buk; 'freɪzbuk/ *n* a book giving and explaining phrases of a foreign language, for people to use when they go abroad 〔供遊客到國外旅行時用的〕外語常用語手冊

phra·se·ol·o·gy /ˌfrezɪ'ɑlədʒɪ; ˌfreɪzi'ɒlədʒi/ *n* [U] *fml* the way in which words are chosen, arranged, or used 〖正式〗措詞; 專門用詞; 術語

★phys·i·cal /'fɪzɪkl; 'fɪzɪkəl/ *adj* **1** concerning the body rather than the mind 身體的, 肉體的: *physical exercise* 體育活動, 體操 | *The doctor will give you a complete physical examination.* 醫生將給你做一次全身體格檢查。**2** concerning material things that you can see and touch 物質的: *Babies need to explore physical objects with their mouths as well as their hands.* 嬰兒需要用嘴和手去探知物體。**3** according to the laws of nature 根據自然法則的: *the physical world* 自然界 **4** [always before a noun 只能用於名詞前] concerning the natural formation of the Earth's surface 自然(界)的: *physical geography* 自然地理學

phys·i·cal·ly /'fɪzɪklɪ; 'fɪzɪkli/ *adv* **1** concerning the body 身體上, 體格上: *My elderly uncle is still physically fit, but mentally rather confused.* 我的伯伯身體仍然健康, 但頭腦已相當糊塗了。**2** according to the laws of nature 根據自然法則: *It's physically impossible to travel faster than the speed of light.* 根據自然法則, 物體的運動速度不可能超過光速。

physical train·ing /ˌ··· '··/ *n* (also 又作 **physical education** /ˌ··· ··'··/, **PT, PE**) [U] development of your body by games or exercises 身體鍛鍊

phy·si·cian /fə'zɪʃən; fɪ'zɪʃən/ *n* a doctor, especially one who treats diseases with medicines 內科醫生

phys·i·cist /'fɪzəsɪst; 'fɪzɪ̹sɪst/ *n* a person who studies physics 物理學家

phys·ics /'fɪzɪks; 'fɪzɪks/ *n* [U] the science concerned with the study of matter and natural forces such as light, heat, and movement 物理學

phys·i·ol·o·gy /ˌfɪzɪ'ɑlədʒɪ; ˌfɪzɪ'ɒlədʒi/ *n* [U] the science concerned with the study of the bodies of living things, and how they work 生理學 **–physiologist** *n* **–physiological** /ˌfɪzɪə'lɑdʒɪkl; ˌfɪzɪə'lɒdʒɪkəl/ *adj*

phys·i·o·ther·a·py /ˌfɪzɪəʊ'θɛrəpɪ; ˌfɪzɪəʊ'θerəpi/ *n* [U] the use of exercises, rubbing, or heat in the treatment of illness 物理療法 – **physiotherapist** *n*

phy·sique /fɪ'zik; fɪ'ziːk/ *n* the shape and size of someone's body 體格; 體形

pi /paɪ; paɪ/ *n* a Greek letter (Π, π) used for representing the fixed relationship between the distance round the edge of a circle and the distance across its middle; pi is almost equal to $\frac{22}{7}$ or 3.142 圓周率〔約等於 $\frac{22}{7}$ 或 3.142〕

pi·a·nist /pɪ'ænɪst; 'piːən̹ɪst/ *n* a person who plays the piano 鋼琴演奏者; 鋼琴家

pi·an·o /pɪ'æno; pɪ'ænəʊ/ *n* (also 又作 **pianoforte** /pɪˌænə'fort; pɪˌænəʊ'fɔːti/ *fml* 〔正式〕) a large musical instrument, played by pressing narrow black or white bars which make small hammers hit wire strings 鋼琴

pic·co·lo /'pɪkəˌlo; 'pɪkələʊ/ *n* a small musical instrument that looks like a FLUTE but plays higher notes 短笛

★★ pick¹ /pɪk; pɪk/ *v* [T] **1** to choose someone or something 選擇, 挑選〔某人、某物〕: *He looked at all the cakes, then picked the biggest one.* 他看了看所有的蛋糕, 然後挑了最大的一塊。| *She has been picked to play a leading role in a new film.* 她被選中擔任一部新電影的主角。 **2** to pull a flower or fruit from a plant 採, 摘: *She was picking flowers in the garden.* 她在花園裡摘花。| *They've gone strawberry-picking.* 他們去採草莓了。 **3** to remove something from a place using your hands or fingers 〔用手或手指〕挖; 剔除: *He was picking crumbs off the floor.* 他在把地板上的麵包屑撿乾淨。| *Pick all the meat off the bone.* 把骨頭上的肉都剔乾淨。 **4 pick your nose** to remove unwanted bits of MUCUS from your nose using your finger 挖鼻孔 **5 pick your teeth** to remove small bits of food from your teeth 剔牙 **6 pick a fight/quarrel** to be unpleasant to someone so that you cause a fight or quarrel 〔向某人〕尋釁打架〔吵架〕 **7 pick a lock** to unlock a lock with an instru-

ment that is not the proper key, especially so that you can steal something 撬鎖 **8 pick someone's brains** to try to find out information from someone in order to help you with a problem 向某人討教〔以解決自己的問題〕 **9 pick someone's pocket** to steal things from someone's pocket 扒竊 **10 pick your way** to walk carefully so that you do not fall or stand on things 小心地走路, 謹慎地行進: *Firemen were picking their way over the rubble.* 消防隊員小心翼翼地在瓦礫堆上走。 **11 pick a hole in something** to make a hole in something with a pointed instrument 〔用尖利的工具〕在某物上鑿個洞 **12 pick holes in something** to find lots of faults in something 挑…的毛病, 找…的過失 **13 pick and choose** to choose very carefully, considering each choice for a long time 挑挑揀揀

pick at sthg *phr v* [T] to eat only small amounts of something, as if you are not really hungry 〔彷彿不餓一般〕一點點地吃, 挑挑揀揀地吃〔食物〕

pick sbdy ↔ off *phr v* [T] to shoot people or animals by aiming at them carefully and shooting them one by one 一個接一個地瞄準〔人或動物〕後射殺

pick on sbdy *phr v* [T] to punish or blame someone unfairly because you do not like them 〔由於不喜歡而不公正地〕懲罰; 責備〔某人〕: *He's always picking on me!* 他總是跟我過不去!

pick sbdy/sthg ↔ out *phr v* [T] **1** to choose someone or something 挑選〔某人或某物〕: *She picked out a red scarf to go with her dress.* 她挑了一條紅圍巾與她的裙子相配。 **2** to see someone or something clearly 辨別出〔某人或某物〕: *She managed to pick out her sister in the crowd.* 她設法在人羣中辨認出她的妹妹。

pick up *phr v* **1** [T **pick** sbdy/sthg ↔ **up**] to take hold of something and lift it up 提起; 拾起〔某物〕: *He picked up his suitcase and walked out.* 他提起手提箱走了出去。| *Come and pick all your toys up.* 來把你的玩具都收拾起來。→ see picture on page 992 見 992 頁彩圖 **2** [T **pick** sthg ↔ **up**] to gain or obtain something 獲得; 學會: *I picked up quite a lot of French when I lived in France.* 我住在法國時學了不少法語。| *I picked up quite a few tips about painting and decorating.* 我學到了一點油漆和裝修的竅門。 **3** [T **pick** sbdy/sthg ↔ **up**] to collect someone or something from a place 取〔物〕; 接〔人〕; 接載〔人〕: *I'll pick you up at your hotel.* 我來旅館接你。| *I've got to go and pick up my coat from the cleaner's.* 我要去洗衣店取我的外衣。 **4** [T **pick** sbdy ↔ **up**] to catch a criminal 逮捕〔罪犯〕: *The thieves were picked up by the police later that day.* 那天晚些時候小偷們被警方逮捕了。 **5** [T **pick** sbdy ↔ **up**] to become friendly with someone because you want to have a sexual relationship with them 勾搭: *I could see that he was trying to pick me up.* 我看得出來他在試圖勾搭我. **6** [T **pick** sbdy ↔ **up**] to make someone feel better and stronger 使復原; 使強健: *You need a tonic to pick you up.* 你需要點補品來強身健體. **7** [T **pick** sth ↔ **up**] to be able to hear or receive something on a radio 〔在無線電中〕收聽到: *We picked up distress signals from another ship.* 我們接收到另一艘船的遇難信號. **8 pick up speed** to start to travel more quickly 增加速度: *We picked up speed when we got onto the motorway.* 我們開上高速公路後便加快了速度. **9** [I] to improve 好轉; 改善: *Trade is picking up again.* 生意又有了起色. | *The economy is starting to pick up now.* 經濟現在開始好轉.

pick² *n* **1 take your pick** to choose something 挑選某物: *I've been offered three jobs so I can take my pick.* 已經有三份工作提供給我, 所以我可以挑一下. | *Here are the prints that we've got — take your pick.* 這些是我們所有的印刷字體, 你挑吧. **2 the pick of the bunch** the best one in a group 出類拔萃者 **3** a pickaxe 鶴嘴鋤, 鎬

pick·axe /ˈpɪk.æks; ˈpɪk-æks/ *n* (**pickax** *AmE* 〔美式〕) a large tool which has a curved iron bar with two sharp points, used for breaking up rock 鶴嘴鋤, 鎬

pick·er /ˈpɪkə; ˈpɪkər/ *n* a person or machine that gathers crops 採摘者; 採集機: *potato pickers* 馬鈴薯採集機

pick·et¹ /ˈpɪkɪt; ˈpɪkḷt/ *n* someone placed outside a factory or shop during an argument with employers to prevent anyone going to work 〔罷工時被派在工廠或商店門口制止工人入內的〕罷工糾察員

picket² *v* [I;T] to stand outside a factory or shop during an argument with employers to prevent anyone going to work 〔罷工時〕用糾察包圍...〔以阻止工人上班〕: *No coal could be delivered to the factory, because the workers were picketing the gates.* 煤炭無法運至工廠, 因為工人們用糾察包圍了大門口. – **picketing** *n* [U]

pick·le¹ /ˈpɪkl; ˈpɪkəl/ *n* **1** [U] a liquid, for example salt water, used to preserve meat or vegetables 〔醃肉或蔬菜用的〕鹽水, 泡菜水 **2 pickles** vegetables preserved in liquid such as salt water 泡菜, 醃菜 **3 in a pickle** *infml* in a difficult situation 〔非正式〕在困境中

pickle² *v* **pickled**, **pickling** [T] to preserve food in liquid such as salt water 醃製〔食品〕 – **pickled** *adj*: *pickled cucumbers* 醃黃瓜

pick-me-up /ˈ··/ *n infml* a drink or a medicine that makes you feel stronger and more cheerful 〔非正式〕興奮飲料; 興奮劑

pick·pock·et /ˈpɪk.pɒkɪt; ˈpɪk.pɒkḷt/ *n* a person who steals things from people's pockets, especially in a crowd 〔尤指在人羣中偷竊的〕扒手 –see 見 THIEF (USAGE

用法)

pick-up /ˈ··/ *n* **1** the part of a record-player which receives and plays the sound from a record 〔唱機的〕唱頭 **2** a vehicle with an open body with low sides 輕型貨車

pic·nic¹ /ˈpɪknɪk; ˈpɪknɪk/ *n* **1** an occasion when you take food somewhere outdoors and eat it there 野餐: *We went for a picnic in the country.* 我們去郊外野餐. **2** food taken to eat outdoors 野餐食物: *Let's take a picnic.* 我們野餐去吧. | *a picnic lunch* 盒飯

picnic² *v* **picknicked**, **picknicking** [I] to have a picnic 去野餐

pic·to·ri·al /pɪkˈtɔːrɪəl; pɪkˈtɔːrɪəl/ *adj* connected with or using pictures 圖片的; 用圖片表示的

pic·ture¹ /ˈpɪktʃə; ˈpɪktʃər/ *n* **1** [C] a painting or drawing 畫, 圖畫: *Draw a picture of that tree.* 畫一張那棵樹的畫. –see picture on page 730 見 730 頁彩圖 **2** [C] a photograph 照片: *This is a lovely picture of the princess.* 這是一張公主的可愛的照片. **3** [sing] a person or thing that is beautiful to look at 漂亮的人〔物〕; 美麗的人〔物〕: *This garden is a picture in the summer.* 這座花園在夏季美麗如畫. **4 the picture of** the perfect example 完美的例子: *That baby is the picture of health.* 那嬰兒非常健康. **5** [sing] what is seen on a television set or at the cinema 〔電視或電影的〕畫面: *You can't get a clear picture on this set.* 這台電視機的畫面不清晰. **6** [C] an image or idea in your mind 形象: *This book gives a good picture of life in England 200 years ago.* 這本書形象地描寫了英國二百年前的生活. **7** *BrE* 〔英式〕 **the pictures** the cinema 電影院: *We went to the pictures last night.* 我們昨晚去看電影了. **8** [sing] a situation 情形; 情況; 局面: *The political picture seems to be changing.* 政治形勢似乎在起變化. **9 get the picture** to understand something 理解〔某事〕 **10 put someone in the picture** to tell someone about something that has been happening 把實情告訴某人

picture² *v* **pictured**, **picturing** [T] **1** to imagine 想像: *I can't quite picture myself as a mother.* 我很難想像自己做母親會是甚麼樣子. **2** to paint or draw someone or something to give a particular idea 畫, 繪〔某人或某物〕: *The artist has pictured him as a clown.* 那位藝術家把他畫成了小丑.

pic·tur·esque /ˌpɪktʃəˈresk; ˌpɪktʃəˈresk◂/ *adj* **1** charming or interesting enough to be made into a picture 美麗如畫的 **2** very clear, strong, and descriptive (used to describe language) 生動的, 形象化的〔用來描述語言〕

pid·dling /ˈpɪdlɪŋ; ˈpɪdlɪŋ/ *adj* small and unimportant (a word used to express disapproval) 微不足道的〔含貶義〕

pid·gin /ˈpɪdʒɪn; ˈpɪdʒ3n/ *n* [C;U] a language which is a mixture of two or more other languages 混雜語言, 洋涇濱語

pie /paɪ; paɪ/ n [C;U] **1** a pastry case filled with meat or fruit, often baked in a deep dish 餡餅: *an apple pie* 蘋果餡餅 | *meat pies* 肉餡餅 | *Have some more pie.* 再吃點餡餅吧。 **2 pie in the sky** *infml* a hopeful plan or suggestion that is unlikely to happen〔非正式〕難以實現的計劃[建議]

piece[1] /piːs; piːs/ n **1** a part of something solid which is separated from the whole or larger thing 塊; 片: *a piece of meat* 一塊肉 | *a piece of cake* 一塊蛋糕 | *pieces of wood* 幾塊木頭 **2** part of something that has broken or come off 碎片: *The glass broke into pieces.* 玻璃杯被打碎了。 **3** a single object that is an example of a certain type 件; 個; 張: *Have you got a piece of paper?* 你有一張紙嗎? | *a piece of furniture* 一件家具 | *a beautiful piece of music* 一段美妙的音樂 **4** a single example of something that is part of a set〔一套中的〕一件: *a piece of cutlery* 一件餐具 | *This tea set has a piece missing.* 這套茶具丟了一件。 **5** the separate parts which make a whole object 部分; 部件: *a 50 piece jigsaw puzzle* 有五十塊板片的拼圖 | *He cleaned all the pieces of the saxophone and put them back in the case.* 他把薩克斯管各部分都擦乾淨, 並將它們放回原來的盒子。 **6** an example or amount of something someone has made, thought, or done〔想法的〕一條;〔工作的〕一件: *She offered me a piece of advice.* 她給我提了一條意見。 | *a good piece of work* 一件完成得很出色的工作 **7** a particular coin 硬幣: *a 10p piece* 一枚十便士的硬幣 **8 go to pieces** to be so nervous that you can't do what you want to 垮下來〔指太緊張而無法做想做的事〕: *He usually plays the piano beautifully but he went to pieces in the exam.* 他平時彈鋼琴彈得很出色, 但考試時卻因過度緊張而垮了。 **9 in one piece** not hurt or damaged 未受傷的; 未受損壞的; 完整無損(的) **10 a piece of cake** something that is very easy and takes no effort 非常容易做的事 **11 take something to pieces** to take something apart 把某物拆開: *Jo took her bike to pieces to try and fix it.* 喬把她的腳踏車拆開, 試圖修復它。

piece[2] v **pieced, piecing, piece something together** to make something complete by putting different parts together 拼合, 拼湊〔某物〕: *She tried to piece the information together so she could write about what had happened.* 她盡力把信息拼湊起來, 以便把發生的事情寫出來。

pi·èce de ré·sis·tance /ˌpjɛsdəˌrezisˈtɑ̃s; piːˌes də reziːˈstɑːns/ n **pièces de résistance** (*same pronunciation* 讀音相同) the best or most important thing or event, among a number of things or events 最好的部分; 最重要的事件

piece·meal /ˈpiːsmiːl; ˈpiːsmiːl/ adj, adv bit by bit 一點一點(的), 零碎的: *We used to do the work piecemeal, but now we do everything in one operation.* 過去我們的工作是一件件地做, 現在我們把所有的事情一起做。

piece·work /ˈpiːsˌwɜːk; ˈpiːswɜːk/ n [U] work paid for by the amount that you do rather than by the hours that you work 按件計酬的工作, 計件工作

pied /paɪd; paɪd/ adj [only before a noun 只用於名詞前] coloured with two or more colours (used of certain types of birds) 雜色的〔指某些鳥類〕

pier /pɪr; pɪəʳ/ n **1** a structure built out into the sea at which boats can stop to take on or land passengers or goods〔突出於海中的〕棧橋; 突堤; 碼頭 –see picture on page 991 見 991 頁彩圖 **2** a structure like this at places where people go for holidays, where people can walk and enjoy themselves 長堤

pierce /pɪrs; pɪəs/ v **pierced, piercing** [T] **1** to make a hole in or through something with a point 刺穿; 刺破: *The needle pierced her skin.* 針刺入了她的皮膚。 **2** to be suddenly heard, seen, or felt through something else〔透過某物〕被突然看到; 聽到; 感覺到: *A loud scream pierced the silence.* 一聲響亮的尖叫劃破了寂靜。 **3 pierced ears** small holes in your ears for jewellery 穿耳環孔的耳朵

pierc·ing /ˈpɪrsɪŋ; ˈpɪəsɪŋ/ adj **1** loud and unpleasant (used of sounds) 尖銳的〔指聲音〕: *a piercing cry* 尖利的叫聲 **2** looking very hard, or going straight to the centre of something 銳利的: *He gave me a piercing look.* 他用銳利的目光看了我一眼。 **3** very strong and cold (used of wind) 刺骨的, 凜冽的〔指風〕 –**piercingly** adv

pi·e·ty /ˈpaɪəti; ˈpaɪəti/ n [U] deep respect for God and religion 虔誠

pig /pɪg; pɪg/ n **1** a fat, pink, short-legged animal kept on farms for food 豬 –see 見 MEAT (USAGE 用法) **2** an bad-mannered person who eats too much (a word used to express disapproval) 貪吃的粗人〔含貶義〕

pi·geon /ˈpɪdʒən; ˈpɪdʒɪn/ n a common, grey short-legged bird that can be eaten 鴿子

pi·geon·hole /ˈpɪdʒənˌhɒl; ˈpɪdʒɪnhəʊl/ n one of a set of small boxes in a frame on a wall in an office or on a desk for putting papers in〔牆上或書桌上的〕文件分類架, 信箱格

pigeon-toed /ˌ·· ˈ··◁/ adj having feet that point inwards 腳向內彎的, 內八字的

pig·gy·back /ˈpɪgɪˌbæk; ˈpɪgɪbæk/ n a ride given to a child who is carried in a sitting position on your back〔小孩〕騎在某人背上 –**piggyback** adj, adv

pig·gy·bank /ˈpɪgɪˌbæŋk; ˈpɪgɪbæŋk/ n a small container, often in the shape of a pig, used by children for saving coins 兒童儲蓄罐〔常為豬形〕, 撲滿

pig·head·ed /ˈpɪgˈhɛdɪd; ˌpɪgˈhedˌd◂/ *adj* being determined to continue thinking or doing something in spite of good reasons not to 頑固的; 固執的

pig·let /ˈpɪglɪt; ˈpɪglɪt/ *n* a young pig 小豬

pig·ment /ˈpɪgmənt; ˈpɪgmənt/ *n* **1** [C;U] a dry coloured powder that is mixed with oil or water to make paint 顏料(粉) **2** [U] natural colouring matter of plants and animals, for example in leaves, hair or skin 天然色素

pig·men·ta·tion /ˌpɪgmənˈteʃən; ˌpɪgmənˈteɪʃən/ *n* [U] the colouring of living things 〔生物的〕天然顏色

pig·my /ˈpɪgmɪ; ˈpɪgmi/ *n* see 見 PYGMY

pig·sty /ˈpɪgˌstaɪ; ˈpɪgstaɪ/ *n* **pigsties 1** an enclosure with a small building in it, where pigs are kept 豬圈, 豬欄 **2** *infml* a very dirty room or house 〔非正式〕骯髒的房間[房子]

pig·tail /ˈpɪgˌtel; ˈpɪgteɪl/ *n* a length of hair that has been twisted together and hangs down the back of the neck and worn by girls 辮子, 髮辮

pike /paɪk; paɪk/ *n* **1** a large fish that lives in rivers and lakes and eats other fish 狗魚 **2** a long-handled spear used in the past by soldiers fighting on foot 長矛

pil·chard /ˈpɪltʃəd; ˈpɪltʃəd/ *n* a small sea fish, often preserved in tins as food 沙丁魚

pile¹ /paɪl; paɪl/ *n* **1** [C] a number of things of the same kind placed on top of each other 堆; 疊: *There's a pile of dirty washing to do.* 有一堆骯髒衣服要洗。| *We arranged the books in piles on the floor.* 我們把書一堆堆地放在地上。**2** [C] *infml* (also 又作 **piles**) a lot 〔非正式〕許多; 大量: *I've got a pile of work to do today.* 我今天有很多工作要做。| *They've got piles of money!* 他們很有錢! **3** [sing] the soft surface of short threads on floor coverings or cloth 〔地毯或布料上的〕絨毛 **4 piles** [pl] painful swellings on a person's bottom 痔瘡

pile² *v* **piled, piling 1** [T] to put a number of things of the same kind on top of each other 堆積; 堆疊〔東西〕: *He piled the boxes one on top of the other.* 他把箱子一個個堆了起來。**2** [T] to load, fill, or cover 裝滿; 堆滿: *The bowl was piled high with fruit.* 碗裡裝滿了水果。

pile in *phr v* [I] to get into a vehicle in a disorderly way 擠入〔車輛〕: *The driver opened the door of the bus and they all piled in.* 司機一打開了公共汽車的門, 他們就蜂擁而入。

pile out *phr v* [I] to get out of a vehicle in a disorderly way 擠出〔車輛〕: *I stopped the car and the kids piled out.* 我一停車, 孩子們就蜂擁而出。

pile up *phr v* **1** [T **pile** sthg ↔ **up**] to put things one on top of another 堆積〔物品〕: *He piled up the letters on the table.* 他把信堆在桌上。**2** [I] to increase 增加: *His debts*

piled up and finally he had to sell his house. 他的債務越積越多, 最終被迫賣掉了房子。

pile-up /ˈpaɪlˌʌp; ˈpaɪlʌp/ *n infml* a traffic accident in which a number of vehicles crash into each other 〔非正式〕連環撞車

pil·fer /ˈpɪlfə; ˈpɪlfər/ *v* [I;T] to steal something small and not particularly valuable 偷竊; 小偷小摸

pil·grim /ˈpɪlgrɪm; ˈpɪlgrɪm/ *n* a person who travels to a holy place as a religious act of respect 朝聖者; 香客

pil·grim·age /ˈpɪlgrəmɪdʒ; ˈpɪlgrɪmɪdʒ/ *n* [C;U] a journey made by a pilgrim 朝聖者的旅程: *Aziz is planning to go on/make a pilgrimage to Mecca.* 阿齊茲正準備去麥加朝聖。

pill /pɪl; pɪl/ *n* **1** [C] a small ball of solid medicine, made to be swallowed whole 藥丸; 藥片: *a bottle of vitamin pills* 一瓶維生素丸 **2 the pill** a pill taken regularly by women as a means of birth control 口服避孕藥 **3 be on the pill** to take the pill as a means of birth control 服用避孕藥: *"Are you on the pill?"* "你在服用避孕藥嗎?"

pil·lage¹ /ˈpɪlɪdʒ; ˈpɪlɪdʒ/ *n* [U] *old fash* violent stealing of property 〔老式〕掠奪, 搶劫, 劫掠

pillage² *v* **pillaged, pillaging** [T] *old fash* to steal things violently 〔老式〕掠奪〔財物〕

pil·lar /ˈpɪlə; ˈpɪlər/ *n* **1** a tall round post made of stone used as a support or decoration 柱, 柱子 **2** something in this shape 柱狀物: *a pillar of smoke* 一縷煙 **3** an important member and active supporter 中堅分子, 積極支持者: *She has been a pillar of the church all her life.* 她一生都是教會的中堅。

pillar-box /ˈ··· ·/ *n BrE* a tall, round box in the street, into which letters are posted 〔英式〕郵筒, 信筒

pil·lion /ˈpɪljən; ˈpɪljən/ *n* a seat for a second person on a motorcycle, placed behind the driver 摩托車[電單車]後座

pil·low /ˈpɪlo; ˈpɪləʊ/ *n* a cloth bag filled with soft material, used to support your head while you are sleeping 枕頭

pil·low·case /ˈpɪloˌkes; ˈpɪləʊkeɪs/ *n* (also 又作 **pillow slip** /ˈ·· ·/) a washable cloth covering for a pillow 枕頭套

pi·lot¹ /ˈpaɪlət; ˈpaɪlət/ *n* **1** a person who flies an aircraft 飛行員, 飛機駕駛員 **2** a person with a special knowledge of a particular stretch of water, who is employed to go on board and guide ships that use it 〔船舶的〕領航員

pilot² *v* [T] **1** to act as pilot of an aircraft or ship 駕駛〔飛機〕; 給〔船〕領航 **2** to try out something new before it is introduced 試驗: *The scheme is being piloted in several large cities.* 該計劃正在幾個大城市中進行試驗。

pilot³ *adj* [only before a noun 只用於名詞前] done to find out if or how something works 試驗性的: *We're doing a pilot study to* *see if this product will sell well.* 我們正在做試驗性的研究, 看看該產品是否會有好銷路。

pilot light /ˈ· ·/ *n* a small gas flame kept burning all the time, used for lighting larger gas burners〔用以點燃大煤氣用具的〕常燃引火小火苗

pimp /pɪmp; pɪmp/ *n* a man who controls and makes a profit from a woman who sells sex for money〔男性〕皮條客, 妓院男老闆

pim·ple /ˈpɪmpl; ˈpɪmpəl/ *n* a small raised spot on your skin 粉刺, 丘疹 **–pimply** *adj*: *pimply skin* 長有粉刺的皮膚

pin¹ /pɪn; pɪn/ *n* **1** a short thin piece of metal, pointed at one end and used for fastening together pieces of cloth or paper 別針, 大頭針 **2** a thin piece of metal, pointed at one end and with a decoration at the other, used to position clothing, or a hat 飾針 **3** a short piece of wood or metal used as a support, for fastening things together 釘; 栓; 銷

pin² *v* **-nn-** [T; +adv/prep] **1** to fasten or join with a pin or pins〔用別針〕別住,〔用釘〕釘住: *She pinned the pieces of the dress together before sewing it.* 她用別針將裙子各部分別在一起, 然後再縫起來。| *You can pin your notice up on the noticeboard.* 你可以把通知釘在佈告板上。| *She pinned the brooch on her coat.* 她把胸針別在衣服上。–opposite 反義 **unpin 2** to keep in one position 固定; 壓住: *In the accident , he was pinned under the car.* 事故中他被壓在汽車底下。**3 pin something on someone** to fix the responsibility for something bad 把某事歸罪於某人: *Don't try to pin the blame on me.* 別想把責任推到我身上。**4 pin your hopes on someone/something** to hope that someone or something will be successful 把希望寄托在…上, 指望: *Paul has pinned his hopes on passing the exams.* 保羅已把希望寄托在通過考試這件事上了。

pin down *phr v* [T **pin** sbdy/sthg ↔ **down**] **1** to fasten down and prevent from moving 固定住: *He pinned my arms down and I couldn't move.* 他抓緊我的臂膀, 使我動彈不得。**2** to make firm arrangements or decisions 使作出保證: *I won't pin you down to a particular time; come any day next week.* 我不會迫你定出一個具體的時間; 你下週隨時都可以來。

pin·a·fore /ˈpɪnə,for; ˈpɪnəfɔːr/ *n* **1** a loose piece of clothing that does not cover your arms or back, worn over a dress to keep it clean 連胸圍裙; 圍兜 **2** (also 又作 **pinafore dress** /ˈ··· ·/) a dress that does not cover your arms, under which other clothes are usually worn 無袖連衣裙

pin·cers /ˈpɪnsəz; ˈpɪnsəz/ *n* [pl] **1** a tool made of two crossed pieces of metal which is used for holding small things tightly and pulling them 鉗子 **2** the sharp pointed nails

of certain shellfish〔甲殼動物的〕螯

pinch¹ /pɪntʃ; pɪntʃ/ *v* **1** [T] to press tightly between the thumb and a finger 捏; 掐: *He pinched her arm.* 他掐了一下她的胳膊。| *Don't pinch me!* 別掐我! **2** [I] to cause pain by being too tight 夾痛: *Don't buy the shoes if they pinch.* 如果鞋子夾腳的話, 就不要買了。**3** [T] *infml* to steal〔非正式〕偷, 盜竊: *Somebody's pinched my car!* 有人把我的車偷走了!

pinch² *n* **1** an act of pressing tightly between the thumb and the finger 捏; 掐 **2** an amount that can be picked up between the thumb and a finger 一撮, 微量: *a pinch of salt* 一撮鹽 **3 at a pinch** only just and if necessary 必要時: *I can afford to buy the books at a pinch.* 必要時我還花得起錢來買書。**4 feel the pinch** to be in difficulties because of lack of money〔由於缺錢而〕陷入困境

pinched /pɪntʃt; pɪntʃt/ *adj* thin or tired-looking (used to describe a face) 清瘦的; 疲倦的〔用來描述臉〕

pin·cush·ion /ˈpɪn,kuʃən; ˈpɪn,kuʃən/ *n* a filled bag into which PINS are stuck until they are needed 針墊

pine¹ /paɪn; paɪn/ *v* **pined, pining** [I] **1** to feel very sad and lonely, and lose interest in life so that you become ill 憔悴; 衰弱: *Uncle pined away after his wife died.* 叔叔在妻子去世後日漸憔悴。**2** to have a strong desire for something you can no longer have 渴望, 思念: *They pined for the country they had left behind.* 他們渴望着回到離開了的祖國。

pine² *n* **1** [C] (also 又作 **pinetree** /ˈpaɪn,tri; ˈpaɪntriː/) a tall tree with woody fruits and thin sharp leaves that do not drop off in winter, found especially in colder parts of the world 松樹 **2** [U] the white or yellowish soft wood of this tree 松木

pine·ap·ple /ˈpaɪn,æpl; ˈpaɪnæpəl/ *n* [C;U] a large yellow tropical fruit with a thick skin and stiff leaves on top 菠蘿

ping /pɪŋ; pɪŋ/ *v* [I] to make a short sharp ringing sound 發出砰的聲響: *The bell pinged.* 鈴"噹"地響了一聲。–**ping** *n*

ping-pong /ˈ· ·/ *n* [U] *infml*〔非正式〕see 見 TABLE TENNIS

pin·ion /ˈpɪnjən; ˈpɪnjən/ *v* [T] *fml* to prevent someone moving by holding or tying up the arms or legs〔正式〕抓住〔綁住〕手或腳〔以防止某人移動〕: *Two of them pinioned me against the wall, while a third searched my pockets.* 他們中的兩人抓住我的胳膊使我靠着牆, 第三人搜查了我的口袋。

*pink¹ /pɪŋk; pɪŋk/ *adj* **1** pale red 粉紅色的: *a pink dress* 一條粉紅色的裙子 –see picture on page 243 見 243 頁彩圖 **2 in the pink** in good health 很健康的

pink² *v* [I] (of a car engine) to make high knocking sounds because it is not working properly 〔汽車引擎有毛病時〕發出蓬蓬的響聲

pink·ish /ˈpɪŋkɪʃ; ˈpɪŋkɪʃ/ *adj* slightly pink 淺粉紅色的

pin·na·cle /ˈpɪnəkl; ˈpɪnəkəl/ *n* **1** a thin tall pointed rock or rocky mountain top 山尖; 山峰 **2** the highest point 最高點, 極點: *She reached the pinnacle of success when she moved to America.* 她移居美國時, 已達到了成功的頂峯。

pin·point /ˈpɪnˌpɔɪnt; ˈpɪnpɔɪnt/ *v* [T] **1** to find or describe the exact nature of cause of something 找出或描述〔某事物確切的性質或原因〕: *The police are trying to pinpoint the cause of the accident.* 警察正在盡力查出這起事故的原因。 **2** to show the exact position of something 指出〔某物〕的確切位置: *He pinpointed the village on the map.* 他在地圖上準確地確定了這村莊的位置。

pin·prick /ˈpɪnˌprɪk; ˈpɪnˌprɪk/ *n* a small mark made by a pin 針刺的孔

pins and nee·dles /ˌ· · ˈ··/ *n* [pl] *infml* slight continuous pricking feelings in a part of the body to which the supply of blood is returning《非正式》〔四肢的〕針刺感: *I've got pins and needles in my legs.* 我感到兩腿酸痛發麻。

pin·stripe /ˈpɪnˌstraɪp; ˈpɪnstraɪp/ *n* a pattern of thin lines repeated at regular spaces along cloth 〔布料上的〕細條花紋 – **pinstriped** *adj*

pint /paɪnt; paɪnt/ *n* **1** a unit for measuring liquids, equal to about 0.57 of a litre 品脫〔約等於 0.57 公升〕: *a pint of milk* 一品脫牛奶 **2** *infml* a drink of beer or other liquid of this amount《非正式》一品脫啤酒[飲料]: *Two pints please.* 請來兩品脫啤酒。

pin·up /ˈpɪnˌʌp; ˈpɪnʌp/ *n* a picture of an attractive person, usually a woman wearing no clothes which is often fixed to a wall 具有吸引力的人像畫〔通常為釘於牆上的裸女畫〕

pi·o·neer¹ /ˌpaɪəˈnɪr; ˌpaɪəˈnɪəʳ/ *n* **1** one of the first settlers in a new or unknown country 拓荒者 **2** a person who does something first, often in science or medicine 〔常為科學或醫學的〕先驅; 先鋒: *He was a pioneer of heart surgery.* 他是心臟手術的先驅。

pioneer² *v* [T] to begin or help in the early development of something 開闢, 創始〔某事物〕

pi·ous /ˈpaɪəs; ˈpaɪəs/ *adj* showing and feeling deep respect for God and religion 虔誠的, 信神的, 篤信宗教的 – **piously** *adv*

pip¹ /pɪp; pɪp/ *n* a small seed from a fruit 〔水果的〕種子, 果核

pip² *n* a short high-sounding note, heard on the radio to show the exact time, or as used in the operation of telephones 〔電台的〕報時信號; 〔電話的〕撥號音: *Don't put any money into the telephone until you hear the pips.* 聽到撥號音後才把錢投進電話裡去。

pip³ *v* -pp- *BrE infml*〔英式, 非正式〕**pipped**

at the post just beaten at the end of some struggle 到最後關頭被擊敗

★**pipe¹** /paɪp; paɪp/ *n* **1** a tube used for carrying liquids, air, and gas 管子, 管道: *a metal pipe* 金屬管道 | *a hot-water pipe* 熱水管道 **2** a small tube with a little bowl at one end, used for smoking tobacco 煙斗: *Grandfather lit his pipe.* 祖父點燃了煙斗。 **3** a simple musical instrument, played by blowing 管樂器 **4** pipes [pl] see 見 BAGPIPES

pipe² *v* **piped, piping** [T] to carry things like liquid or gas through pipes 用管道輸送〔液體或氣體〕

  pipe down *phr v* [I] *infml* to stop talking 《非正式》停止說話: *"Pipe down, will you!"* "你閉上嘴好不好!"

  pipe up *phr v* [I] *infml* to begin to speak or sing, especially in a high voice《非正式》〔尤指用高聲〕開始講話〔唱歌〕

piped mu·sic /ˌ· ˈ··/ *n* [U] recorded music played continuously in a public place, such as a shop or restaurant 〔在公共場所, 如商店或餐館〕不斷播放的音樂

pipe dream /ˈ· ·/ *n* an impossible hope, plan, or idea 空想; 幻想

pipe·line /ˈpaɪpˌlaɪn; ˈpaɪp-laɪn/ *n* **1** a long line of pipes, often underground, for carrying liquids or gas 〔通常為輸送液體或氣體的地下〕管道 **2 in the pipeline** on the way 在路上; 在進行中

pip·er /ˈpaɪpə; ˈpaɪpəʳ/ *n* a musician who plays on a pipe 演奏管樂器的人; 吹笛人

pip·ing¹ /ˈpaɪpɪŋ; ˈpaɪpɪŋ/ *n* **1** a number or system of tubes used for carrying liquids or gas 管道系統 **2** the act or art of playing music on a pipe 吹奏; 吹奏藝術

piping² *adv* **piping hot** very hot (used of liquids and foods) 滾燙的〔指液體和食物〕: *piping hot soup* 滾燙的湯

pi·quant /ˈpiːkənt; ˈpiːkənt/ *adj fml*《正式》**1** having a pleasant sharp taste 辛辣的, 開胃的 **2** pleasantly interesting and exciting to the mind 開心的; 令人興奮的 – **piquancy** *n* [U] – **piquantly** *adv*

pique /piːk; piːk/ *n* [U] a feeling of displeasure, especially when your pride is hurt 〔尤指自尊心受傷害時的〕生氣; 慍怒: *He left in a fit of pique.* 他一賭氣就走了。

piqued /piːkt; piːkt/ *adj* angry because your pride is hurt 〔因自尊心受傷而〕生氣的

pi·ra·cy /ˈpaɪrəsi; ˈpaɪrəsi/ *n* [U] **1** robbery carried out by pirates 海上掠奪, 海盜行為 **2** the act of stealing ideas or copying the work of others without permission 非法翻印; 盜印

pi·ra·nha /pɪˈrɑːnjə; pˈrɑːnjə/ *n* a fierce South American river fish, that will eat meat 〔南美洲一種兇殘的肉食性河魚〕水虎魚, 鋸脂鯉

pi·rate¹ /ˈpaɪrət; ˈpaɪərət/ *n* **1** a person who sails the seas attacking and robbing ships

海盗 **2** a person who copies the work of other people without official permission; for example, a person who prints and sells a book without the writer's permission 盗印者; 侵犯專利權者

pirate² v **pirated, pirating** [T] to copy and sell the work of other people without permission 非法翻印, 盗印〔他人作品〕; 侵犯專利權

pir·ou·ette¹ /ˌpɪruˈɛt; ˌpɪruˈet/ n a very fast turn made by a dancer on the front part of one foot〔舞蹈者的〕足尖旋轉

pirouette² v **pirouetted, pirouetting** [I] to dance one or more pirouettes〔舞蹈〕用足尖旋轉

Pis·ces /ˈpɪsiz; ˈpaɪsiːz/ n one of the signs of the ZODIAC 雙魚座

pis·ta·chi·o /pɪsˈtɑʃɪˌo; pɨˈstɑːʃiəʊ/ n a small green nut 開心果

pis·tol /ˈpɪstl; ˈpɪstl/ n a small gun that you hold and fire with one hand 手槍

pis·ton /ˈpɪstn̩; ˈpɪstn/ n a solid pipe-shaped piece of metal in pumps and engines that fits tightly into a tube; it moves up and down by pressure or explosion and causes other parts of the machine to move 活塞

pit¹ /pɪt; pɪt/ n **1** a large natural or man-made hole in the ground 坑: *The children were playing in the sandpit.* 孩子們在沙坑裡玩耍. **2** a deep hole dug in the ground to get coal out 煤礦, 礦坑: *He worked down the pit all his life.* 他一生都在煤礦工作. **3** a small hollow mark or place in the surface of something〔物體表面的〕小凹陷處, 凹痕 **4** **the pit of your stomach** your stomach, when you are describing a physical feeling of fear 胸口, 心窩〔用於描述恐懼的感覺〕 **5** (also 又作 **orchestra pit**) the low space in front of a theatre stage where musicians sit and play during a performance 樂池, 樂隊 **6** **the pit** the seats at the back of the ground floor of a theatre 劇場正廳後座 **7** **the pits** a place in motor racing beside a track where cars can come during a race to be examined and repaired quickly〔賽車比賽的〕修理站 **8** infml《非正式》**the pits** a person or thing that you feel a strong dislike for 討厭的人[物]: *Exams are the pits, aren't they!* 考試真令人討厭, 不是嗎! | *My little brother is the pits.* 我的弟弟很令人討厭.

pit² -tt- [T] **1** to cover something in hollow marks 使〔某物〕表面留下凹痕: *The walls had been pitted by gunfire.* 牆壁被子彈打得凹痕處處. **2** **pit your wits against** to compete against in a test of knowledge 與…鬥智

pit-a-pat /ˈ··ˌ·ˌ·/ n infml《非正式》(also 又作 **pitter-patter**) the sound or movement of a number of quick light beats on a surface 劈劈啪啪聲

***pitch¹** /pɪtʃ; pɪtʃ/ v **1** [T] to throw 投; 擲; 扔: *He pitched the ball at the batsman.* 他把球投向擊球員. **2** to fall suddenly and heavily 摔

倒; 跌倒: *She pitched heavily into the mud.* 她重重地跌進了泥漿. **3** [T] to force someone into a situation 迫使〔某人〕處於某種情形: *He was pitched into the debate by the publication of his controversial new novel.* 由於他出版了一本具爭議性的新小說, 他被迫參與了辯論. **4** [I] (of a ship) to move violently up and down〔船〕顛簸 **5** [T] to fix a sound at a particular level 定音調; 音高 [T] to arrange or deliver something at a particular level that is suitable for a particular group of people 把〔某物〕定於一程度〔以適合某一輩人的需求〕: *His speech was pitched at a level that even children could understand.* 他的演講非常淺顯, 甚至連小孩子也能聽懂. **7** [T] to set up something like a tent or camp 支起, 搭起〔帳篷等〕 **8** **pitch into someone** to attack someone, using words or physical violence〔用言詞或武力〕攻擊某人

pitch in phr v [I] infml to start to work or to help other people do a particular job 《非正式》開始工作; 幫助他人: *If we all pitch in, it shouldn't take long.* 如果我們一起動手, 就不會花費太長的時間.

pitch² n **pitches 1** [C] an area of ground with markings on it where certain sports are played〔某些體育運動的〕場地: *a football pitch* 足球場 **2** [C] the level, high or low of a particular sound 音調; 音高 **3** [sing] a high level 高水準: *Their excitement rose to fever pitch.* 他們的興奮達到了狂熱的地步. **4** [C] the amount of slope of part of a building〔建築物的〕傾斜度: *the pitch of the roof* 屋頂的傾斜度 **5** [U] a black substance used as a protective covering for ships and houses, to prevent water coming in 瀝青

pitch-black /ˌ· ˈ·◂/ adj (also 又作 **pitch-dark**) very dark indeed 漆黑的

pitched bat·tle /ˌ· ˈ·◂/ n a violent fight between armies or groups of people who are determined to win 對陣戰

pitch·er /ˈpɪtʃɚ; ˈpɪtʃəʳ/ n **1** a large container for holding and pouring liquids, usually made of clay〔通常為泥製的〕大水罐 **2** the usual American word for《美式》= JUG

pitch·fork /ˈpɪtʃˌfɔrk; ˈpɪtʃfɔːk/ n a farm tool with a long handle and two curved metal points at one end, used for lifting cut grass or HAY 乾草叉

pit·e·ous /ˈpɪtiəs; ˈpɪtiəs/ adj causing or intended to cause pity 令人憐憫的; 為取得同情的: *the piteous cries of the abandoned kittens* 被遺棄的小貓所發出的可憐叫聲 –**piteously** adv

pit·fall /ˈpɪtˌfɔl; ˈpɪtfɔːl/ n a mistake that may easily be made 易犯的錯誤: *The English spelling system provides many pitfalls for foreign students.* 英語的拼寫系統中有許多外國學生很容易犯的錯誤.

pith /pɪθ; pɪθ/ n [U] **1** a soft white substance that fills the stems of certain plants and trees 木髓 **2** a white substance just under the skin of oranges and certain other fruits 橘子等水果皮下的白色海綿層，中果皮

pit·head /ˈpɪtˌhed; ˈpɪt-hed/ *n* the entrance to a coal mine 煤礦入口，礦井口

pith·y /ˈpɪθɪ; ˈpɪθi/ *adj* **1** having a lot of pith (used of fruit) 襯皮多的〔指水果〕 **2** spoken or written in strong, direct language without wasting words〔講話或文章〕簡練的

pit·i·a·ble /ˈpɪtɪəbl; ˈpɪtɪəbəl/ *adj* worthy of pity 令人憐憫的 **–pitiably** *adv*

pit·i·ful /ˈpɪtɪfəl; ˈpɪtɪfəl/ *adj* causing or deserving pity 令人憐憫的；值得同情的: *The poor old man was a pitiful sight.* 看見那個貧窮的老人，實在令人同情不已。| *His performance on the piano was pitiful.* 他演奏鋼琴的水平低得很可憐。**–pitifully** *adv: She's pitifully thin these days.* 近來她瘦得可憐。

pit·i·less /ˈpɪtɪlɪs; ˈpɪtɪl̩s/ *adj* showing no pity 無憐憫心的；無情的: *a pitiless ruler* 無情的統治者

pit·tance /ˈpɪtns; ˈpɪtns/ *n* **a pittance** a very small amount of pay 微薄的薪水: *They pay me a pittance and then expect me to work long hours.* 他們給我少得可憐的工資，然後就指望我一天忙到晚。

pit·ted /ˈpɪtɪd; ˈpɪt̩d/ *adj* **1** covered in hollow marks 坑坑窪窪的: *pitted skin* 粗糙不平的皮膚 **2** with the stone removed 去核的: *pitted olives* 去核的橄欖

pit·ter-pat·ter /ˈpɪtɚˌpætɚ; ˈpɪtə ˌpætəʳ/ *n* see 見 PIT-A-PAT

pit·y¹ /ˈpɪtɪ; ˈpɪti/ *n* **1** [U] a feeling of sadness and sorrow for the suffering of others 同情，憐憫: *I invited you here out of pity, but you're taking advantage of my generosity.* 我是出於同情才請你到這裡來，但你卻在利用我的慷慨。**2** [sing] a sad or unfortunate situation 可惜的事，憾事: *What a pity you won't be back before I leave!* 你不會在我走之前回來，多可惜啊! | *It's a great pity you can't come to the party.* 你無法來參加晚會，太遺憾了。**3** **take pity on someone** to help someone because you feel sorry for them 由於同情而幫助某人

pity² *v* **pitied, pitying** [T] to feel sorry for the suffering of another person 同情，可憐: *I pity anyone who has to live on £40 a week.* 我同情一星期只靠四十英鎊過日子的人。| *I pity his poor wife!* 我很同情他那可憐的妻子!

piv·ot¹ /ˈpɪvət; ˈpɪvət/ *n* a fixed central point or pin on which something turns or balances 樞軸；支點

pivot² *v* **1** [I] to move around or balance on a central point 圍繞樞軸旋轉；平衡於支點上 **2** **pivot on** to depend on something 取決於，依靠〔某事〕: *The success of the venture pivots on the signing of this contract.* 此次投資是否成功取決於該合同能否簽署。

pix·ie /ˈpɪksɪ; ˈpɪksi/ *n* **pixies** a small fairy said to enjoy playing tricks on people〔喜歡捉弄人的〕小精靈

piz·za /ˈpitsə; ˈpiːtsə/ *n* [C;U] a round flat piece of DOUGH covered with a mixture of cheese, tomatoes (TOMATO), and other kinds of food and then baked 意大利薄餅〔餅上覆蓋乳酪、番茄等烘烤而成〕

pl. an abbreviation for 《縮》= PLURAL

plac·ard /ˈplækɑrd; ˈplækɑːd/ *n* a large printed or written notice or advertisement 佈告；廣告牌

pla·cate /ˈpleket; pləˈkeɪt/ *v* **placated, placating** [T] to calm someone and stop them feeling angry 安撫，使息怒 **–placatory** /ˈplɛkəˌtɔrɪ; pləˈkeɪtəri/ *adj*

P

place¹ /ples; pleɪs/ *n* **1** a particular area or position in space 地方，地點: *This is the place where the accident happened.* 這就是事故發生的地點。| *He travelled to places all over the world.* 他周遊過世界各地。| *Moscow is a very cold place in winter.* 莫斯科在冬天是個很冷的地方。| *Let's find a place where we can eat.* 我們去找個地方吃飯吧。| *cinemas and other places of entertainment* 電影院及其他娛樂場所 **2** the spot or position where something usually goes〔某物〕通常所處的位置: *She put the clock back in its place.* 她把鐘放回到原處。**3** *infml* your house or home 《非正式》住所；家: *How long have you lived in this place?* 你在這裡住了多久了? | *We all went over to John's place for coffee.* 我們都去約翰家喝咖啡了。**4** a seat 座位: *There were no places on the bus.* 公共汽車上沒有空座位。| *Is this place taken?* 這個座位有人嗎? **5** the position that you have reached when you are reading something or talking about something 讀到的地方；講到的地方: *I've lost my place.* 我找不到讀到的那頁了。| *This would be a good place for me to stop and answer some of your questions.* 在這個地方我可以停下來回答你們所提出的一些問題。**6** a position in an order 順序中的排位: *She finished the race in second place.* 她在比賽中獲得了第二名。**7** a position as a member of a team or a student at a college 位置；職位: *She's been offered a place at Cardiff University.* 她被卡迪夫大學錄取了。| *He'll take up his place on the committee next month.* 下月他將就任委員會裡的職務。**8** a position in society 社會地位: *Will this weaken Britain's place within the European Community?* 這會不會削弱英國在歐盟中的地位? | *I felt that it wasn't my place to criticize his work.* 我覺得我沒有資格批評他的工作。**9** **all over the place** in many different parts or places 在許多不同的地方: *She travels all over the place.* 她遊歷很廣。| *There were books and magazines all over the place.* 到處都是書籍和雜誌。**10** **in high places** among people who have power and high social positions 在上層社會: *There was much talk of corruption in high places.* 許多人在議論上層社會的貪污現象。**11** **in place** in the proper place 在適當的位置: *All the technical equipment was now in place.* 所有的技術設備

均已到位。**12 in place of** instead of 代替: *And now, in place of advertised programmes, there will be a special news broadcast.* 現在將有一節特別新聞廣播來代替廣告節目。**13 in the first place** in the beginning 首先; 起先: *We weren't even sure how this situation had arisen in the first place.* 首先我們甚至不敢肯定這種情況是怎樣發生的。**14 in the first place, in the second place, etc** phrases you use when you are listing reasons or ideas 首先; 其次〔用於例舉理由或觀點〕**15 out of place: a** not in the proper place 不在適當的地方: *Everything was untidy and out of place.* 所有的東西都放得亂七八糟。**b** unsuitable 不合適的: *The modern paintings looked out of place in such an old building.* 現代繪畫看上去不太適合這樣一座老房子。**16 put someone in their place** to remind someone that they are not as important as they would like to be 煞某人的氣焰 **17 take place** to happen 發生: *When did the accident take place exactly?* 事故具體是在何時發生的? **18 take the place of** to do something or be used instead of someone or something else 代替, 取代〔某人或某物〕: *Robots have now taken the place of workers in some factories.* 現在在一些工廠裡, 機械人已取代了工人。

> ■ USAGE 用法: Compare 比較 **place** and 和 **room**. Both words can mean "space that we can use". But **place** is a countable noun and we use it for a single particular piece of space ☆ 這兩個詞都可表示 "空間"。但是 **place** 是名詞, 可用來指代某種單一的空間: *This is the **place** where we keep our coal.* 這是我們貯存煤炭的地方。| *There's a **place** for you in the corner.* 角落裡有個地方給你。**Room** is uncountable and we use it for free space in general ☆ **room** 是不可數名詞, 可用來泛指未被佔用的空間: *There's no **room** for any more coal in here.* 這裡沒有再存更多煤的地方。| *Is there (any) **room** for me to sit down?* 有沒有可以讓我坐的地方?

place² /plets; plets/ v **placed, placing** [T] **1** to put something somewhere 放置〔某物〕: *He placed the book carefully on the shelf.* 他小心翼翼地把書放到書架上。**2 place an order** to order goods 訂〔貨〕: *We placed an order with them for 500 pairs of shoes.* 我們向他們訂購了五百雙鞋。**3** to state that someone has a particular position in a race or competition 〔在比賽中〕定出〔某人的〕名次: *She was placed second.* 她獲得了第二名。**4 can't place** to be unable to remember fully what someone's name is or when you last saw them 記不起〔某人的名字或最後一次見面時間〕: *I recognize his face, but I can't quite place him.* 我能認出他的面孔, 卻不太記得他的名字。**5 be well placed to do something** to have the information or other

things that are necessary in order to do something 具有做某事所需要的條件: *As we have offices all over the country, we are very well placed to carry out a national survey.* 由於我們在全國各地都有辦事處, 我們已具備了進行一次全國性調查的條件。

plac·id /'plæsɪd; 'plæsɪd/ adj calm and peaceful 平靜的; 平和的: *A placid expression hid her real feelings.* 平和的表情掩飾了她的真實感情。| *the placid surface of the lake* 平靜的湖面 **–placidly** adv

pla·gia·rism /'pleɪdʒəˌrɪzəm; 'pleɪdʒərɪzəm/ n [U] the action of taking someone's words, ideas or work and using them as if they are your own 剽竊; 抄襲: *He was accused of plagiarism in his doctoral thesis.* 他被指責在做博士論文時有剽竊行為。**–plagiarist** n

pla·gia·rize /'pleɪdʒəˌraɪz; 'pleɪdʒəraɪz/ v **plagiarized, plagiarizing** (also 又作 **plagiarise** *BrE* 〔英式〕) [I;T] to take words or ideas from someone else's work and use them as if they are your own 剽竊; 抄襲〔別人的作品〕

plague¹ /pleɪg; pleɪg/ n **1** [C;U] a very serious disease that spreads quickly, especially a particular one that produces high fever and swellings on your body 疫病, 瘟疫, 傳染病 **2** [C] a very large number of things of a type that is unpleasant, possibly harmful, and certainly very difficult to control 〔難以控制的〕災害, 禍患: *a plague of rats* 鼠災

plague² v **plagued, plaguing** [T] to annoy someone by doing some repeated action 煩擾〔某人〕: *You've been plaguing me with silly questions all day!* 你整天老是拿些愚蠢的問題來煩我!

plaice /pleɪs; pleɪs/ n [plural is 複數為 **plaice**] [C;U] a flat European fish eaten as food 鰈〔一種產於歐洲的可食用的魚〕

plaid /plæd; plæd/ n [C;U] woollen cloth, often with a special coloured pattern, which is typical of Scotland 〔蘇格蘭的〕格子花呢

plain¹ /pleɪn; pleɪn/ n **1** [C] a large stretch of flat land 〔大〕平原: *In winter they move down from the mountains to the plains below.* 在冬天, 他們從山上遷往下面的平原去。**2** [U] a simple stitch in knitting (KNIT) 〔編織的〕平針

plain² adj **1** easy to see, hear, or understand 明白的, 清楚的: *It's plain that you don't agree.* 你顯然不同意。| *Explain it in plain language.* 用簡明的話解釋一下。**2** simple, without decoration or pattern 簡單的, 簡樸的: *plain food* 清淡的食物 | *plain paper* 白紙 –see picture on page 243 見 243 頁彩圖 **3** euph not pretty or good-looking (a less direct word than ugly) 〔委婉〕相貌平平的; 不好看的〔ugly 的委婉用語〕**4** direct and honest (used of speech or writing) 直率的;

坦誠的〔指講話或寫作〕–**plainness** *n* [U]

plain choc·o·late /ˌ· ˈ··/ *n* [U] dark chocolate made without milk and with little sugar〔不加牛奶只加少量糖的〕黑［純］巧克力

plain-clothes /ˌ· ˈ·/ *adj* wearing ordinary clothes, not uniform, while on duty (used of policemen) 穿便衣的〔指警察〕

plain·ly /ˈpleɪnli, ˈpleɪnli/ *adv* clearly 明白地; 清楚地: *The child is plainly cold and hungry.* 這孩子顯然又冷又餓。

plain sail·ing /ˌ· ˈ··/ *n* [U] a course of action that is simple and without problems 十分順利, 一帆風順: *If we can persuade the bank to lend us money, the rest should be plain sailing.* 我們如果能說服銀行貸款給我們, 餘下的事該會十分順利。

plain-spo·ken /ˈpleɪnˈspoʊkən, ˌpleɪnˈspoʊkən◂/ *adj* direct and so often rude in the way you speak 直言不諱的, 不客氣的

★**plain·tiff** /ˈpleɪntɪf; ˈpleɪntɪ̣f/ *n* law a person who brings a charge against somebody in a court of law《律》原告

plain·tive /ˈpleɪntɪv; ˈpleɪntɪv/ *adj* sad 難過 的; 悲傷的: *the plaintive cries of the hungry child* 飢餓的孩子那可憐的哭聲

plait¹ /plet; plæt/ *n* (also 又作 **braid** *AmE* 《美式》) three or more lengths of something, especially hair, twisted over and under each other into one piece 辮繩; 髮辮 –see picture on page 469 見 469 頁彩圖

plait² *v* (also 又作 **braid** *AmE* 《美式》) to twist three or more lengths of something over and under each other into one piece 將〔某物〕編成辮狀

★**plan¹** /plæn; plæn/ *n* **1** an arrangement for some future activity 計劃; 安排: *Have you made any plans for tomorrow night?* 你明晚有甚麼安排嗎? | *a government plan to change the education system* 政府制定的教育體制改革計劃 **2** a list or line drawing showing how something is or will be arranged 平面圖; 示意圖: *a street-plan of London* 倫敦的街道圖 | *Have you seen the plans for the new library?* 你看過新圖書館的設計圖嗎? | *an essay plan* 文章的綱要 **3 go according to plan** to happen as planned, without any difficulties 按計劃進行

★**plan²** *v* **-nn- 1** to decide what to do and how to do it 計劃: *We planned our holiday trip in great detail.* 我們為假日旅行訂下了極為詳細的計劃。 | *What do you plan to do after you leave school?* 你離校後打算做甚麼?

□ USEFUL PATTERNS 有用句型
to plan something; to plan to do something

2 to decide how things will be arranged 安排: *They planned the layout of the kitchen with great care.* 他們為廚房的佈局做了精心安排。 **3 plan for something** to take into account something that you expect to happen when you make an arrangement 考慮到某事物: *We were planning for rain but it looks fine enough to eat outside.* 當時我們曾考慮到可能會下雨, 但現在看來天氣良好, 可以到外面吃飯。 **4 plan on something** to intend to do something 打算做某事: *How long do you plan on staying in Spain?* 你打算在西班牙逗留多久?

plan sth ↔ **out** *phr v* [T] to decide something in great detail 詳細安排〔某事物〕: *We planned everything out in advance.* 我們事先做好了一切安排。

★**plane¹** /pleɪn; pleɪn/ *n* **1** a vehicle that flies 飛機: *The plane will be landing on time.* 飛機將準時着陸。 **2** a tool with a blade that takes thin pieces off wooden surfaces to make them smooth 刨子, 平刨 –see picture on page 958 見 958 頁彩圖 **3** a flat or level surface in GEOMETRY〔幾何學中的〕平面 **4** a particular level 水平: *Let's try to keep the conversation on a friendly plane.* 讓我們盡量友好地談話吧。

plane² *v* **planed, planing** [T] to make a wooden surface smooth by taking off small pieces with a special tool 用刨子刨平〔某物〕

plan·et /ˈplænɪt; ˈplænɪ̣t/ *n* a large body in space that moves round a star, especially round the sun 行星: *the Earth and other planets* 地球與其他行星 –**planetary** /ˈplænəˌteri; ˈplænɪ̣təri/ *adj* [only before a noun 只用於名詞前]: *planetary movements* 行星運動

plan·e·tar·i·um /ˌplænəˈteriəm; ˌplænɪ̣ˈteəriəm/ *n* a building inside which lights are directed onto the CEILING to represent the stars and planets and to show how they move 天文館, 太空館

plane tree /ˈ· ·/ (also 又作 **plane**) a tree with widespreading branches and broad leaves that grows in towns 懸鈴木

plank /plæŋk; plæŋk/ *n* **1** a long flat piece of wood 長條木板 **2** a main principle of a political party's intentions〔政黨的〕政策要點, 政綱條目

plank·ton /ˈplæŋktən; ˈplæŋktən/ *n* [U] the very small forms of plant and animal life that live in water and form the food of many fish 浮游生物

plan·ner /ˈplænɚ; ˈplænəʳ/ *n* a person who plans, especially one who plans the development of towns 規劃者, 策劃人〔尤指城市規劃者〕: *city planners* 城市規劃者

★**plant¹** /plænt; plɑːnt/ *v* **1** [I;T] to put plants or seeds in the ground to grow 種植: *April is the time to plant.* 四月是種植的季節。 | *Where are you going to plant those roses?* 那些玫瑰你打算種在哪裡? **2** [T] to supply an area of land with seeds or growing plants 播種; 移植: *We're planting a small herb garden.* 我們在開闢小百草園。 | *The sides of the motorway were planted with* *trees.* 高速公路的兩旁種有樹木。 **3** [T] to place a person or thing firmly in a certain place 牢牢安置〔人或物〕: *He planted himself between Jones and the door.* 他很堅定地站在瓊斯和門之間。 **4** [T] to hide something among another person's possessions so that they will appear guilty if caught 栽贓於〔某人〕: *The drugs must have been planted on me at the airport!* 這些毒品一定是有人在機場裡栽贓到我的! **5** to send someone somewhere secretly to collect information 祕密安插〔某人〕: *Spies were planted in key ministries.* 在各個重要的部門均安插了特務。

plant sthg ↔ **out** *phr v* [T] to move plants outside to grow 把植物移植到戶外

plant² *n* **1** [C] a living thing that has leaves and roots, and usually grows in earth 植物: *Those plants need more water.* 那些植物需要多些水分。 | *the plant life of the area* 該地區的植物 | *a potato plant* 一棵馬鈴薯苗 –see picture on page 729 見 729 頁彩圖 **2** [C] a place where something, often power, is produced 工廠: *a car plant* 汽車廠 | *a power plant* 發電廠 **3** [U] heavy machinery 重型機械: *We've ordered new plant for the factory.* 我們已為工廠訂購了新的機械設備。

plan·ta·tion /plæn'teɪʃən; plæn'teɪʃən/ *n* **1** a large piece of land, especially in hot countries, on which crops such as tea, sugar, and rubber are grown 種植園〔場〕: *a rubber plantation* 橡膠園 **2** a large group of trees planted to produce wood 造林地, 林場

plant·er /'plæntə; 'plɑːntə'/ *n* a person who owns or is in charge of a large area of land on which tropical crops are grown 種植園主; 種植園管理者: *a tea planter* 茶園主

plaque /plæk; plɑːk/ *n* **1** [C] a flat metal or stone plate with writing on it, usually fixed to a wall in memory of a person or event 飾板; 匾 **2** [U] *tech* a substance that forms on your teeth, and in which bacteria live and breed 〔術語〕牙斑

plas·ma /'plæzmə/ *n* [U] the liquid part of blood 血漿

plas·ter¹ /'plæstə; 'plɑːstə'/ *n* **1** [U] a paste of lime, water, and sand, which hardens as it dries and is used to give a smooth surface, especially on walls and ceilings (CEILING) 〔塗牆等用的〕灰泥 **2 in plaster** covered with a special plaster mixture which dries and hardens to protect a broken bone 打了石膏: *His arm has been in plaster for a month now.* 他的胳膊現已打了一個月的石膏。 **3** [C;U] (also 又作 **sticking plaster**) a thin band of sticky material put on the skin to protect small wounds 〔窄條〕橡皮膏; 膏藥

plaster² *v* [T] **1** to cover a surface with plaster 用灰泥塗抹〔表面〕: *Shall we plaster the ceiling next?* 下一步我們要不要給天花板塗上灰泥? **2** to cover a surface with something, perhaps too thickly 塗上; 貼上: *The wall*

was plastered with signs. 牆上貼滿了告示。 | *She plastered cream on her face.* 她在臉上塗了奶油。

plaster cast /,·· '·/ *n* **1** a hollow copy of a stone or metal figure made out of plaster 石膏模型 **2** a case made of a special plaster, which covers a part of your body to protect or support a broken bone 石膏繃帶, 石膏夾

plas·tered /'plæstəd; 'plɑːstəd/ *adj* [never before a noun 不能用於名詞前] *infml* very drunk (a word which is often used in a humorous way) 〔非正式〕醉醺醺的〔常作幽默用法〕: *By midnight everyone was plastered!* 到了半夜, 所有的人都已喝得醉醺醺了!

plas·ter·er /'plæstərə; 'plɑːstərə'/ *n* a person whose job is to plaster the inside of houses 泥水匠, 塗灰泥工人

plaster of Par·is /,plæstə əv 'pærɪs; ,plɑːstər əv 'pærɪs/ *n* [U] a quick-drying white paste made of a mixture of powder and water, used for plaster casts or in decorative building work 熟石膏

plas·tic¹ /'plæstɪk; 'plæstɪk/ *n* [C;U] a light man-made material produced chemically from oil or coal, which can be made into different shapes when soft and keeps its shape when hard 塑料, 塑膠: *The chairs are made of plastic.* 這些椅子是塑料製成的。 | *manufacturers of plastics* 塑料生產商

plastic² *adj* **1** made of plastic 塑料製的: *a plastic spoon* 塑料匙 **2** easily formed into different shapes by pressing 可塑的 **3** [only before a noun 只用於名詞前] *fml* connected with the art of shaping forms in clay, stone, or wood 〔正式〕造型藝術的: *the plastic arts* 造型藝術

plas·ti·cine /'plæstəˌsin; 'plæstəˌsiːn/ *n* [U] *tdmk* (also 又作 **Plasticine**) a soft substance like clay, which is produced in many different colours and used by young children for making small models 〔商標〕橡皮泥, 塑膠黏土

plas·tic·i·ty /plæˈstɪsətɪ; plæˈstɪsɪti/ *n* [U] the state or quality of being easy to form into different shapes 可塑性

plastic sur·ge·ry /,·· '···/ *n* [U] the repairing of damaged parts of the body, or the improvement of parts that a person is unhappy about 整形外科; 整容手術: *She is planning plastic surgery to change the shape of her nose.* 她打算做一次整容手術以改變鼻子的形狀。

★**plate¹** /plet; pleɪt/ *n* **1** [C] a flat, usually round dish used to put food on 盤; 碟: *a dinner plate* 餐碟, 菜盤 | *a paper plate* 紙碟 **2 have a lot on your plate** have a lot of things to do 有許多事要做 **3** [C] a flat sheet of metal or glass used in building 〔建築用的〕金屬板; 玻璃板: *There was a metal plate covering the hole.* 有塊金屬板蓋在洞上。 | *plate glass window* 平板玻璃窗 **4** [C] a piece of metal outside an office with a name on it 〔辦公室的〕招牌, 名牌 **5** [U] metal covered with gold or silver 鍍金〔鍍銀〕金屬: *Those forks are silver plate; I couldn't afford silver.* 這些叉是鍍銀的, 我買不起銀叉。**6** [U] dishes made of PRECIOUS metals like silver and gold 金銀餐具 **7** [C] a picture or photograph in a book 〔書中的〕(全頁)插圖〔照片〕 **8** [C] a piece of plastic into which false teeth have been fixed 假牙牙牀

plate² *v* **plated, plating** [T] to cover a metal article thinly with another metal, especially gold, silver, or tin 鍍上〔金、銀或錫〕: *a silver-plated spoon* 鍍銀的湯匙

plat·eau /plæ'to; 'plætəʊ/ *n* **plateaus** *or* **plateaux** /-'toz; -təʊz/ **1** a large area of high level land 高原 **2** a state in which an activity has stopped developing 停滯狀態; 穩定狀態: *Business has now reached a plateau.* 現在生意已經穩定下來。

plate glass /, · '··/ *n* [U] clear glass made in large sheets for use in windows and doors 〔窗或門用的〕厚玻璃板, 平板玻璃 **–plate-glass** [only before a noun 只用於名詞前]: *plate-glass windows* 平板玻璃窗

plat·form /'plæt,fɔrm; 'plætfɔːm/ *n* **1** a raised structure on which people or things may stand 台; 平台; 講台: *We had a good view of the speakers on the platform.* 我們能清楚地看到站在講台上的演講者。| *There was a fire on an oil platform in the North Sea.* 在北海的石油鑽井平台上發生了一起火災。**2** an area beside the track at a railway station where passengers wait or get on and off trains 〔火車站的〕站台, 月台: *The train now standing at Platform 1 is the 12.15 to Birmingham.* 現停在一號站台的火車將於十二點十五分開往伯明翰。| *I'll meet you on the platform.* 我在站台上與你見面。–see picture on page 991 見 991 頁彩圖 **3** a chance for someone to tell people something 發表觀點的講台: *He used the interview as a platform for his views on ecology.* 他以那次訪問作為他發表有關生態的見解的講台。**4** what a political party says it will do if it wins an election 〔政黨選舉前發表的〕政綱

plat·ing /'pletɪŋ; 'pleɪtɪŋ/ *n* [U] a thin covering of metal 金屬外表的鍍層

plat·i·num /'plætnəm; 'plætɪnəm/ *n* [U] an expensive grey metal often used to make very valuable jewellery 鉑, 白金: *a platinum ring* 白金戒指

plat·i·tude /'plætə,tjud; 'plætɪtjuːd/ *n* a statement that is not new, interesting, or clever 陳詞濫調, 老生常談: *He speaks in platitudes.* 他說的都是老生常談。

pla·ton·ic /plə'tɑnɪk; plə'tɒnɪk/ *adj* a word used to describe relationships between friends that are not sexual 柏拉圖式的; 純精神戀愛的: *platonic love* 精神戀愛 **–platonically** /-klɪ; -klɪ/ *adv*

pla·toon /plə'tun; plə'tuːn/ *n* a small group of soldiers 〔軍隊的〕排

plat·ter /'plætɚ; 'plætəʳ/ *n* a large flat plate used for serving food 大淺盤

plau·dits /'plɔdɪts; 'plɔːdɪts/ *n* [pl] *fml* a show of pleased approval 《正式》喝采, 讚揚

plau·si·ble /'plɔzəbḷ; 'plɔːzɪbəl/ *adj* **1** seeming to be true or reasonable 似乎真實的; 似乎有理的: *His explanation sounds plausible. I think we'd better accept it.* 他的解釋似乎有理。我覺得我們最好接受這個解釋。–opposite 反義 **implausible 2** skilled in producing reasonable statements which may not be true (used of a person) 花言巧語的〔指人〕

play¹ /ple; pleɪ/ *v* **1** [I] (of children) to do things that are enjoyable and interesting, for example running and jumping and using toys 〔孩子〕玩, 玩耍: *The children were playing in the garden.* 孩子們在花園裡玩耍。| *She was playing with her toys.* 她在玩她的玩具。**2** [I;T] to take part in a game 參加〔遊戲〕: *Let's go and play football.* 我們去踢足球吧。| *Shall we play cards?* 我們玩牌好嗎? **3** [T] to compete against someone in a game 與〔某人〕比賽: *England are playing France in the final.* 英格蘭隊將在決賽中與法國隊比賽。**4** [T] to hit or kick a ball in a particular way during a game 打〔球〕; 擊〔球〕: *She played that ball very well.* 她那一球打得很漂亮。**5** [I] to be switched on and producing sounds 發出聲音: *A radio was playing in the background.* 背景裡傳來收音機的聲音。| *I could hear a record playing somewhere.* 我聽見某處正在放唱片。**6** [T] to make something produce musical sounds 使〔某物〕發出樂音; 演奏: *Can you play the piano?* 你會彈鋼琴嗎? | *The orchestra was playing beautifully.* 樂隊演奏得非常動聽。| *Let me play you a tune.* 我來彈首曲子給你聽。| *I'd like to play this tape to you.* 我想把這錄音帶放給你聽。**7** [T] to perform a part on the stage or on television 〔舞台上或電視中〕扮演〔角色〕: *The part of Hamlet was played by Laurence Olivier.* 哈姆雷特這個角色是由勞倫斯·奧立弗扮演的。**8** [T] to put a particular card down onto the table during a game of cards 出〔牌〕: *She played the Queen of Hearts.* 她打出了紅桃皇后。**9** [+ complement] to pretend to be 假裝: *The children are playing doctors and nurses.* 孩子們扮作醫生和護士在玩。| *Don't play the innocent with me!* 別在我面前裝出無辜的樣子! **10** [I+adv/prep] *lit* to move lightly and irregularly 《文》輕快而不規則地移動; 浮現: *The sunlight played on the water.* 陽光在水面上閃爍。**11 play a hose** to direct a HOSE so that the water goes in a particular direction 用水管瞄準某一方向 **12 play a joke/trick on someone** to deceive someone in some way for amusement 戲弄某人 **13 play a part, play a role** to be important and have an effect 起重要作用: *The family plays a significant part in any child's development.* 家庭在孩子的成長過程中起着

很重要的作用。**14 play for time** to cause a delay in order to gain time 為爭取時間而拖延 **15 play hard to get** to pretend not to be interested in someone sexually in order to make them more interested in you 假裝作在性方面對某人不感興趣以吸引對方 **16 play into someone's hands** to do something which gives another person an advantage over you 做對某人有利的事 **17 play it by ear** to let things develop in their own way, rather than making plans in advance 順其自然 **18 play it safe, play safe** to not take risks in order to avoid danger or difficulties 慎重行事 **19 play with fire** to take great risks 冒很大的風險，玩火 **20 play your cards right** to use the chances and advantages that you have 辦事高明: *If I play my cards right I might get a promotion out of this deal.* 如果我能應付得當，也許會由於這筆交易而獲得提升。

play along with sbdy *phr v* [T] to accept what someone says or wants, even though you do not really agree with them 假裝支持〔某人〕

play at sthg *phr v* [T] **1** to pretend to be something 假裝: *She loves playing at being the teacher.* 她喜歡扮當老師的遊戲。 **2 what are you playing at?** a phrase you use when you think that someone is doing something foolish or wrong 你在開甚麼玩笑?〔用於當你認為別人在做蠢事或錯事時〕

play sthg ↔ **back** *phr v* [T] to go through and listen to or watch something that you have just recorded 重新播放〔已錄製的錄音帶、錄像帶〕

play sthg ↔ **down** *phr v* [T] to say that something is less important than it really is 貶低，減低…的重要性: *The government's mistakes have been played down by the media.* 政府的錯誤被傳媒緩和了。

play sbdy **off against** sbdy *phr v* [T] to set one person against another in order to gain advantage for yourself 使對立，挑撥離間: *Children love to play one parent off against the other.* 孩子們喜歡在父母之間挑撥。

play on/upon sthg *phr v* [T] to use a feeling or a weakness that someone has for your own advantage 利用〔某人的感情或弱點〕: *The government has strengthened its position by playing on people's fears about a possible war.* 政府利用人們對可能發生戰爭的恐懼鞏固了自身的地位。

play up *phr v* [I;T **play** sbdy **up**] to cause difficulties for someone 給〔某人〕帶來麻煩: *The coffee machine's playing up again.* 咖啡機又出問題了。 | *My back has been playing me up recently.* 我的背近來一直隱隱作痛。 | *Have the children been playing up?* 孩子們惹麻煩了嗎?

★play² *n* **1** [U] activity that is done for amusement, especially by children 〔尤指孩子的〕玩耍，遊戲；娛樂: *Children learn a lot through play.* 孩子們能從玩耍中學到很多東西。 **2** [C] a piece of writing that is acted in a theatre or on television 戲劇；劇本；電視劇: *You must go and see the new play on in town.* 你一定要去看看在城裡上演的那部新戲。 | *I've just read a wonderful play.* 我剛看了一個非常出色的劇目。 **3** [U] the action in a sports game 運動；比賽: *We've seen some excellent play here this afternoon.* 我們今天下午在這裡看到了精彩的比賽。 **4** [U] freedom of movement caused by something not being fixed firmly in place 鬆動: *There's a bit too much play in that handle.* 那個把手太鬆了一點。 **5** [U] *lit* quick movement 〔文〕迅速的移動: *the play of sunlight on the water* 陽光在水面上的閃爍 **6 at play** playing 在玩耍: *watching the children at play* 看着孩子在玩耍 **7 bring something into play** to use something and make it have an effect 使發揮作用: *He has an awful lot of experience that he can bring into play to help solve these problems.* 他有特別豐富的經驗，可以用來解決這些問題。 [RELATED PHRASE 相關詞組 **come into play**: *Several new factors have now come into play.* 有幾個新的因素現已開始起作用。] **8 in play** (of a ball) in a position where the rules allow it to be played 〔球〕按規則在比賽狀態中 [RELATED PHRASE 相關詞組 **out of play**]

play·boy /'pleɪˌbɔɪ; 'pleɪbɔɪ/ *n* a rich man who spends his time enjoying himself 花花公子，追求享樂的富家子

★★play·er /'pleɪə; 'pleɪəʳ/ *n* **1** a person taking part in a game or sport 運動員；選手 **2** *old fash* an actor 〔老式〕演員 **3** a person who plays a musical instrument 〔樂器〕演奏者: *a piano player* 鋼琴演奏者

play·ful /'pleɪfəl; 'pleɪfəl/ *adj* **1** full of fun 活潑快樂的；愛玩的: *a playful little dog* 愛玩的小狗 **2** not intended seriously 戲謔的；鬧着玩的: *a playful kiss on the cheek* 在臉頰上鬧着玩地吻一下

play·ground /'pleɪˌgraʊnd; 'pleɪgraʊnd/ *n* a special piece of land for children to play on 〔供孩子玩耍的〕遊樂場

play·group /'pleɪˌgrup; 'pleɪgruːp/ *n* an informal school where very young children play together 幼兒園

play·house /'pleɪˌhaʊs; 'pleɪhaʊs/ *n* **playhouses** /-ˌhaʊzɪz; -ˌhaʊzᵻz/ a theatre 劇院: *the Provincetown Playhouse* 郡城劇院

playing card /'·· ·/ *n fml* 〔正式〕see 見 CARD³ (1)

play·mate /'pleɪˌmeɪt; 'pleɪmeɪt/ *n fml* 〔正式〕 (also 又作 **playfellow** /'pleɪˌfeloʊ; 'pleɪfeləʊ/) a particular child who often plays with another one 〔孩童的〕遊戲夥伴: *A lot of Mary's playmates live nearby.* 瑪麗有許多玩伴就住在附近。

play·off /'· ·/ *n* a second match played to decide a winner, when the first has not done so〔因不分勝負而進行的〕加時賽, 延長賽

play on words /ˌ·· ·'·/ *n* **plays on words** see 見 PUN

play·pen /'pleɪˌpen; 'pleɪpen/ *n* a frame enclosed by bars or a net in which a small child can play safely〔供嬰孩安全地在其中玩耍的〕遊戲圍欄

play·room /'pleˌrum; 'pleɪrʊm/ *n* a room for children to play in 兒童遊戲室

play·thing /'pleˌθɪŋ; 'pleɪˌθɪŋ/ *n* **1** a toy 玩具 **2** a person who is treated without respect by another 被玩弄的人, 玩物

play·time /'pleˌtaɪm; 'pleɪtaɪm/ *n* a short period of time, especially at a school, when children can play〔學校的〕遊戲時間

play·wright /'pleˌraɪt; 'pleɪraɪt/ *n* a writer of plays 劇作家

plc /ˌpi ɛl 'si; ˌpiː el 'siː/ *n* an abbreviation for〔縮〕= **public limited company** 公共有限公司

plea /pli; pliː/ *n* **1** *fml* a request based on strong feelings〔文〕懇求; 請求: *his plea for forgiveness* 他請求寬恕 **2** *law* a statement by a person in a court of law, saying whether or not they are guilty of a charge〔律〕答辯; 抗辯: *She has entered a plea of guilty.* 她已承認有罪。

plead /plid; pliːd/ *v* **pleaded** *or* **pled** /plɛd; pled/ *AmE*〔美式〕**1** [I] to make continual and deeply felt requests 懇求; 請求: *He pleaded* **with** *her until she agreed to do as he wished.* 他向她懇求, 直到她答應照他的願望做才罷休。 **2** [T] to give an excuse for your behaviour 為〔自己的行為〕找藉口: *The player tried to explain his poor performance by pleading injury.* 那位選手試圖以受傷為理由, 解釋自己糟糕的表現。 **3** [I] *law* to state whether or not you are guilty of a charge in a court of law〔律〕申辯; 答辯: *The man pleaded not guilty.* 那個男人不肯認罪。 **4** [I; T] to speak in support of someone or something 為〔某人或某事〕辯解: *He has promised to plead our case.* 他已答應為我們這案件辯護。 | *We need someone to plead for us.* 我們需要有人來替我們辯護。

***pleas·ant** /'plɛznt; 'plezənt/ *adj* **1** nice or enjoyable 愜意的; 舒適的: *What a pleasant surprise!* 多麼叫人又驚又喜啊! | *a flower with a pleasant smell* 氣味芬芳的花 | *pleasant weather* 宜人的天氣 **2** friendly 友好的: *She seems a pleasant woman.* 她似乎是個友善的女人。 | *Make an effort to be pleasant to our guests, will you!* 請盡量對客人們客氣點, 好不好! –opposite 反義 **unpleasant**

pleas·ant·ry /'plɛzntri; 'plezəntri/ *n* **pleasantries** a friendly remark made in conversation〔交談中的〕客氣話

***please¹** /pliz; pliːz/ *v* **pleased, pleasing 1** [I; T] to give pleasure to someone 使〔某人〕高興[滿意]: *You can't please everybody.* 你不可

能讓人人都滿意。 | *He did it to please me.* 他做此事是為了使我高興。 | *He's always eager to please.* 他總是很熱心取悅別人。 **2** [I] **as you please, whatever you please, whenever you please, etc** used when you are saying that someone can do whatever they want 只要你願意[喜歡]〔表示某人可以隨心所欲地做任何事〕: *You can come and go as you please.* 只要你願意, 來去都可以。 | *She can stay as long as she pleases.* 只要她喜歡, 她留多久都可以。 **3 if you please** *fml* a polite way of asking someone to do something〔正式〕請, 勞駕〔表示禮貌地請求某人做某事〕: *Come this way, if you please.* 請這邊走。 **4 please yourself** a phrase you use when you are angry to say that someone can do whatever they want and you do not care what they do 隨你的便〔表示生氣時說某人想怎麼做都可以, 你無所謂〕

***please²** *interj* **1** used when you are politely asking for something 請〔用於禮貌的請求〕: *Could I have a drink, please?* 請來杯飲料好嗎? | *"More coffee?" "Please."* "還要咖啡嗎?" "請再來一些。" **2** used when you are politely asking someone to do something 請〔用於禮貌地要求某人做某事〕: *Can you close the window, please?* 請你把窗關上好嗎? | *Please be quiet!* 請安靜!

***pleased** /plizd; pliːzd/ *adj* happy or satisfied 高興的; 滿意的: *I'm very pleased you decided to come.* 我很高興你決定來。 | *We're pleased* **with** *your work.* 我們對你的工作感到滿意。 | *He was looking very pleased with himself, so I knew he had passed his test.* 他看上去對自己很滿意, 所以我知道他已通過了考試。–opposite 反義 **displeased**

pleas·ing /'plizɪŋ; 'pliːzɪŋ/ *adj* giving someone pleasure or satisfaction 令人愉快的; 令人滿意的: *The results are very pleasing.* 結果很令人滿意。

plea·sur·a·ble /'plɛʒərəbl; 'pleʒərəbəl/ *adj fml* enjoyable〔正式〕愉快的; 舒適的

***plea·sure** /'plɛʒə; 'pleʒəʳ/ *n* **1** [U] the feeling of happiness or satisfaction resulting from an experience that you enjoy 高興; 愉快; 滿足: *He listened with pleasure to the beautiful music.* 他愉快地聽着美妙的音樂。 | *It gives me no pleasure to have to tell you this.* 非得由我把此事告訴你, 我並不為此感到愉快。 | *He took great pleasure in telling me that my team had lost.* 他異常興奮地告訴我說我的(球)隊輸了。–opposite 反義 **displeasure 2** [C] a cause of happiness, enjoyment, or satisfaction 令人愉快的事, 樂事: *It's been a pleasure talking to you.* 很高興能和你談話。 | *My grandmother has very few pleasures in life.* 我的祖母在生活中沒有甚麼樂趣。 **3** [U] enjoyment 消遣; 享樂: *Are you here on business or just for pleasure?* 你到這裡來是工作還是來玩? | *a pleasure trip* 遊覽 **4 it's a pleasure** a phrase used as a polite reply to someone who thanks you 別客氣

〔用於禮貌地回答他人的感謝〕[RELATED PHRASES 相關詞組 **my pleasure, pleasure**]

pleat¹/pliːt; pliːt/ v to make folds in cloth 在〔布料上〕打褶: *a pleated skirt* 有褶的裙子

pleat² n a specially pressed narrow fold in cloth〔布料上的〕褶

pleb·is·cite /'plɛbə,saɪt; 'plɛbɨsɨt/ n a direct vote of the people of a nation on a matter of national importance 公民投票: *The government plans to hold a plebiscite.* 政府計劃舉行公民投票。| *It was decided by plebiscite.* 此事是由公民投票決定的。–compare 比較 REFERENDUM

plec·trum /'plɛktrəm; 'plɛktrəm/ n a small thin piece of wood or plastic used for playing certain stringed instruments such as the GUITAR 琴撥

pled /plɛd; pled/ v AmE〖美式〗the past tense and past participle of PLEAD ☆ PLEAD 的過去式和過去分詞

pledge¹/plɛdʒ; pledʒ/ n fml〖正式〗**1** a solemn promise or agreement 誓言, 誓約, 保證: *He gave a pledge to make the company a success.* 他發誓要使公司在經營上獲得成功。**2** something valuable left with someone else as proof that you will fulfil an agreement 保證物; 抵押物 **3** something given or received as a sign of faithful love or friendship〔愛情或友誼的〕信物: *Take this ring as a pledge of our friendship.* 收下這枚戒指, 作為我們友誼的信物。

pledge²v **pledged, pledging** fml〖正式〗**1** [I; T;+that] to make a solemn promise or agreement 允諾; 發誓: *They have pledged that they will stay together.* 他們已發誓要團結一致。| *The director pledged to reduce working hours.* 董事長允諾縮短工時。| *Hundreds of people have pledged time and money to the campaign.* 數以百計的人已答應為該運動出錢出力。**2 pledge yourself to something** to promise that you will do something 保證做某事: *They pledged themselves to the fight against corruption.* 他們保證要對抗貪污。

ple·na·ry/'plinərɪ; 'pliːnəri/ adj fml〖正式〗**1** attended by everyone who has the right to do so (used of a meeting) 全體出席的〔指會議〕**2** complete (used to describe the power of government) 全權的〔指政府權力〕

plen·i·po·ten·tia·ry /,plɛnəpə'tɛnʃərɪ; ,plenɨpə'tenʃəri/ n **plenipotentiaries** a person who has complete power to act for a government or organization〔政府或組織的〕全權代表

plen·ti·ful/'plɛntɪfəl; 'plentɪfəl/ adj existing in quantities or numbers that are more than enough 多的, 豐富的: *The camp has a plentiful supply of food.* 營地有大量食物供應。

plen·ty/'plɛntɪ; 'plenti/ n [U] as much or as many as you need 大量, 充足, 豐富: *They've got plenty of money.* 他們有很多錢。| *£200*

is plenty. 有二百英鎊便足夠了。| *There are plenty more chairs in here.* 這裏還有許多椅子。

pleth·o·ra /'plɛθərə; 'pleθərə/ n fml an amount or supply much greater than is necessary〖正式〗過多, 過量

pli·a·ble /'plaɪəbl; 'plaɪəbəl/ adj (also 又作 **pliant** /'plaɪənt; 'plaɪənt/) **1** easily bent without breaking 易彎的; 柔軟的 **2** easy to persuade or to use for your own purposes (used of a person) 順從的〔指人〕–**pliability** /,plaɪə'bɪlətɪ; ,plaɪə'bɪlɨti/ n [U]

pli·ers /'plaɪəz; 'plaɪəz/ n [pl] a small tool used to remove things like nails or to bend and cut wire 鉗子, 老虎鉗 –see picture on page 958 見 958 頁彩圖

plight /plaɪt; plaɪt/ n a bad situation 困境, 苦況: *The poor girl was in a terrible plight.* 那可憐的姑娘處境異常艱難。| *the plight of homeless children* 無家可歸的兒童的困境

plim·soll /'plɪmsl; 'plɪmsəl/ n one of a pair of light shoes with a top made of heavy cloth and a flat rubber bottom, used especially for games and sports 橡皮底帆布鞋, 膠底運動鞋 –see picture on page 210 見 210 頁彩圖 –see 見 PAIR (USAGE用法)

plinth /plɪnθ; plɪnθ/ n a square block, usually made of stone, serving as the base of a pillar or STATUE〔石柱或雕像的〕底座, 基底, 柱腳

plod/plɑd; plɒd/ v **-dd-** [I;T] to walk slowly and without pleasure 沉重緩慢地走: *The old man plodded wearily home.* 那位老人拖着疲憊的步伐緩緩地走回家。| *We plodded the streets in search of a place to stay.* 我們慢慢地走在大街上, 想找一個地方停留。

plod awayphr v [I] (also 又作 **plod on**) to work steadily, especially at something uninteresting 沉悶地幹: *I'm plodding away at my work while she's out shopping.* 我正在默默地工作, 而她卻出去購物了。| *We'd better plod on with our revision.* 我們最好繼續溫習。

plod·der/'plɑdə; 'plɒdər/ n a slow, steady, but not very clever worker who often succeeds in the end 苦幹的人〔最終常獲得成功〕

plonk¹/plɑŋk; plɒŋk/ n **1** [C] the sound of something quite heavy falling or being dropped 砰的一聲〔重物掉下的聲音〕**2** [U] infml cheap wine〖非正式〗廉價酒: *How about a glass of plonk?* 來杯廉價酒怎麼樣?

plonk²v infml〖非正式〗**1** [T;+adv/prep] to put something down heavily and without care 重重地放下: *Just plonk the bags on the table.* 把袋子放在桌上就行了。**2 plonk yourself**to sit down in this way 沉重地坐下: *She plonked herself in the only armchair.* 她重重地坐在唯一的一把扶手椅子上。

plop/plɑp; plɒp/ v [I] infml to fall with a sound like something dropping smoothly into liquid〖非正式〗〔物體落入水中的〕撲通

聲: *The stone plopped into the stream.* 石頭撲通一聲掉進了河裡。 –**plop** n

plot¹ /plɑt; plɒt/ n **1** a small marked or measured piece of ground for building or growing things 小塊土地: *a building plot* 建築用地 | *I grow potatoes on the little plot of land beside the house.* 我在屋子旁邊的一小塊地裡種馬鈴薯。 **2** the set of connected events on which a story, play, or film is based 情節: *Don't tell me the plot! I might want to read it.* 別把情節告訴我! 我想自己看書。 **3** a secret plan by a group of people to do something, usually against those in power 祕密計劃; 陰謀: *a plot to kill the President* 殺害總統的陰謀

plot² v **-tt- 1** [I;T] to plan something secretly 密謀, 策劃〔做某事〕: *They're plotting against him.* 他們在密謀對付他。 | *They're plotting his downfall.* 他們在密謀要他垮台。 **2** [T] to mark the position of a moving aircraft or ship on a map 在地圖上標出〔正在運行的飛機或輪船的〕位置 **3** [T] to mark points on a piece of paper in the form of a GRAPH 繪製…圖表: *I'm plotting the monthly sales figures for each region last year.* 我正在繪出去年各地區每月銷量的圖表。 –**plotter** n

plough¹ /plau; plaʊ/ n (also 又作 **plow** AmE《美式》) **1** a farming tool with a heavy cutting blade which is used to break up and turn over the earth, especially before seeds are planted 犁 **2** any tool or machine that works like this 犁形器具: *a snowplough* 掃雪機, 雪犁

plough² v (also 又作 **plow** AmE《美式》) **1** [I;T] to break up or turn over land with a special tool 犁(地), 耕(地): *The farmers are out ploughing their fields.* 農夫們都在外面耕地。 **2** [I] to force a way or make a track through something 奮力前行: *The car ploughed through the bushes and stopped in the next field.* 汽車奮力地開過灌木叢, 停在下一塊田地裡。 **3** **plough into something** to crash into something 猛撞某物: *The car ploughed into the back of the bus.* 汽車撞上了公共汽車的尾部。 **4** **plough money into something** to put a lot of money into a business 投資於某事

  plough sthg ↔ **back** phr v [T] to put money that has been earned back into a business to build it up 將〔利潤〕再投資〔以擴展業務〕

  plough on phr v [I] **1** to continue moving with difficulty 持續奮力前行 **2** to continue doing something difficult or unpleasant 持續做〔困難或討厭的事〕: *I'm finding the book boring, but I'll plough on for a few more chapters.* 我覺得這本書沒有趣味, 但我會費點力再多看幾章。

ploy /plɔɪ; plɔɪ/ n **ploys** infml a carefully planned way of behaving to get something you want《非正式》花招; 手法: *His usual*

ploy is to pretend to be ill. 他慣用的手法就是裝病。 | *It was a ploy to avoid working.* 這是一種逃避工作的花招。

pluck¹ /plʌk; plʌk/ v **1** [T] to pull the feathers off a bird before cooking it 拔〔雞、鴨等的〕毛: *Will you pluck the chicken?* 你來拔雞毛好嗎? **2** [T] to take something, often with a quick movement 拔掉; 搶去〔某物〕: *He plucked the bill from my hand.* 他從我手裡搶去了賬單。 **3** **pluck your eyebrows** to pull out hairs from above your eyes 拔眉毛 **4** **pluck up courage, pluck up the courage to do something** to act bravely although you are afraid 鼓起勇氣〔做某事〕: *He couldn't pluck up the courage to complain.* 他鼓不起勇氣去投訴。 **5** [I;T] to play a stringed instrument by pulling at the strings with your fingers 彈奏〔弦樂器〕

pluck² n [U] infml courage《非正式》勇氣; 膽量: *Mountain climbers need a lot of pluck.* 登山者需要有很大的勇氣。

pluck·y /ˈplʌki; ˈplʌki/ adj **pluckier, pluckiest** infml brave and determined《非正式》有勇氣的; 有膽量的 –**pluckily** adv

plug¹ /plʌg; plʌg/ n **1** a small plastic object with two or three metal pins which are pushed into an electric power point to obtain power for an electrical apparatus 電源插頭 –see picture on page 958 見 958 頁彩圖 **2** a small piece of rubber or plastic used to block a hole, especially in a pipe 塞子, 栓: *She finished her bath and pulled the plug out.* 她洗完澡就把塞子拔掉。 **3** infml a favourable opinion of something like a book or record expressed in order to encourage people to buy it《非正式》〔書或唱片等物品的〕推薦; 捧場

plug² v **-gg-** [T] **1** to block or close a hole with something 堵, 塞住: *Use this to plug the hole in your boat.* 用這個把你小船上的洞塞住。 **2** infml to talk about or praise something in order to encourage people to buy or see it《非正式》推薦〔商品〕; 為〔商品〕大肆宣傳: *He's been plugging his new book on the radio.* 他一直在廣播中大肆宣傳他的新書。

  plug sthg ↔ **in** phr v [T] to connect an electrical apparatus to a supply of electricity 接上電源 –opposite 反義 **unplug**

plum /plʌm; plʌm/ n **1** [C] a sweet smooth-skinned fruit, usually red or yellow, with a single hard stone in the middle 李子, 梅 –see picture on page 504 見 504 頁彩圖 **2** [U] a dark reddish-blue colour 深紫色, 紫紅色 **3** **a plum job** a very desirable job 令人嚮往的工作

plum·age /ˈpluːmɪdʒ; ˈpluːmɪdʒ/ n [U] all the feathers on a bird〔鳥的〕全身羽毛

plumb¹ /plʌm; plʌm/ n a mass of lead tied to the end of a string, used to find out the depth of water or whether a wall is straight from top to bottom 鉛錘〔用於測水深或牆是否垂直〕: *Have you got a plumb line I could* *use?* 你有沒有鉛錘線可給我用一下?

plumb² *v* [T] *fml* 【正式】 **1** to try to find out the meaning of something 查明〔意義〕: *plumbing the deep mysteries of man's mind* 探測人內心深處的奧祕 **2 plumb the depths** to reach the lowest point of an unpleasant feeling or way of behaving 達到〔感情或行動的〕最低點: *The hero plumbs the depths of unhappiness.* 這位英雄非常不愉快。

plumb·er /ˈplʌmə; ˈplʌmɚ/ *n* a person whose job is to fit and repair water pipes 管子工

plumb·ing /ˈplʌmɪŋ; ˈplʌmɪŋ/ *n* [U] **1** all the pipes and containers for storing water in a building 〔建築物中所有的〕管道設備: *We'll need to put in new plumbing.* 我們需要鋪設新的管道系統。 **2** the work of looking after the water system in buildings 管道維修: *He specializes in plumbing and electrical repairs.* 他專門維修管道和電線線路。

plume /pluːm; pluːm/ *n* **1** a large bright feather 〔一根鮮艷的〕羽毛 **2 a plume of smoke** smoke rising high into the air 一縷煙

plum·met /ˈplʌmɪt; ˈplʌmɪt/ *v* [I] to fall steeply or suddenly 垂直落下, 驟然跌落: *The damaged aircraft plummeted to earth.* 受損的飛機直向地面墜落。 | *Prices have plummeted.* 物價已暴跌。

plump¹ /plʌmp; plʌmp/ *adj* slightly fat (a word often used to express approval) 豐滿的; 微胖的〔常含褒義〕: *a baby with plump little arms and legs* 小胳膊小腿胖乎乎的嬰孩–see picture on page 469 見 469 頁彩圖 – **plumpness** *n* [U]

plump² *v infml* 【非正式】 **1 plump for** to decide in favour of something or someone 決定贊成; 選定: *We finally plumped for the second house we looked at.* 最終我們選定所過的第二所房子。

    plump sthg ↔ **up** *phr v* [T] to make cushions (CUSHION¹) rounded and soft by shaking or knocking them into the right shape 把〔墊子〕拍鬆

plun·der¹ /ˈplʌndə; ˈplʌndɚ/ *v* [I;T] to steal goods from people or a place, often by force and during a war 掠奪, 搶劫: *Rebels plundered the farms and villages for food.* 反叛者搶劫了農場和村莊的食物。

plunder² *n* [U] goods stolen, often by force and during a war 掠奪物, 贓物

plunge¹ /plʌndʒ; plʌndʒ/ *v* **plunged, plunging 1** [I] to move suddenly in a particular direction, often downwards 向前〔向下〕突然移動: *Prices on the stock market plunged following the poor trade figures.* 股票市場價格隨着糟糕的貿易數字驟然下跌。 | *The divers plunged into the river.* 跳水的人跳進河裡去了。 **2** [T] to push something suddenly into a person or thing 猛地把〔某物〕投入[插入]: *He plunged the knife into her heart.* 他猛地把刀插入她的心臟。 **3** [I;T] to experience or

cause a sudden change in state (使)突然發生變化, 使陷入: *The room was plunged into darkness.* 房間頓時變得一片漆黑。 **4 plunge into something** to start an activity eagerly, suddenly, or giving it your complete attention 積極開始做某事; 突然開始做某事: *She plunged into her studies with terrific enthusiasm.* 她懷着極大的熱忱開始進行研究。

plunge² *n* **1** a sudden move downwards 驟降; 猛跌 **2 take the plunge** to make a difficult decision to do something 作出困難的決定〔做某事〕

plung·er /ˈplʌndʒə; ˈplʌndʒɚ/ *n* a rubber cup on the end of a handle, used for unblocking pipes 〔用於疏通管道的〕橡膠吸盤, 撬子

plung·ing /ˈplʌndʒɪŋ; ˈplʌndʒɪŋ/ *adj* showing a large area of chest 低領口的: *a dress with a plunging neckline* 一件低領口衣服

plu·per·fect /pluːˈpɜːfɪkt; pluːˈpɜːfɪkt/ *n* a tense that expresses an action completed before a particular time in the past, formed in English with "had" and a past participle 過去完成式

plu·ral /ˈpluərəl; ˈpluərəl/ *n* a word form that expresses more than one of a person or thing 複數: *"Dogs" is a plural noun.* "dogs" 是個複數名詞。 | *"Dogs" is the plural of "dog".* "dogs" 是 "dog" 的複數形式。

plus¹ /plʌs; plʌs/ *prep* and, in addition 加, 加上: *3 plus 6 is 9 (3+6=9).* 3加6等於9。 | *It costs a pound, plus ten pence for postage.* 這件東西價格為一英鎊, 另加十便士郵費。

plus² *n* (also 又作 **plus sign** /ˈ · ·/) **1** a sign (+) showing that two or more numbers are to be added together, or that a number is greater than zero 加號; 正號 **2** *infml* something that is good about a situation 〔非正式〕有利的事, 有利條件

plus³ *adj* **1** [only before a noun 只用於名詞前] greater than zero 大於零的; 正的: *a plus quantity* 正數 **2** [never before a noun 不能用於名詞前] more than the stated number 大於〔某一數字〕的: *All the children here are 12 plus.* 這裡所有的孩子都在十二歲以上。

plush /plʌʃ; plʌʃ/ *adj* comfortable and expensive 豪華的: *the town's plush new cinema* 城裡新建的豪華影院

Plu·to /ˈpluːtəʊ; ˈpluːtoʊ/ *n* the PLANET 9th in order from the sun, the most distant of the group that includes the Earth 冥王星

plu·to·crat /ˈpluːtəkræt; ˈpluːtəkræt/ *n* a person who has power because of their wealth (a word used to express disapproval) 財閥, 有錢有勢的人〔含貶義〕 –**plutocracy** *n* –**plutocratic** /ˌpluːtəˈkrætɪk; ˌpluːtəˈkrætɪk/ *adj*

plu·to·ni·um /pluːˈtəʊnɪəm; pluːˈtoʊnɪəm/ *n* [U] a substance used in the production of NUCLEAR power and weapons 鈈〔用於生產核能或核武器〕

ply¹ /plaɪ; plaɪ/ *v* **plied, plying 1 ply someone**

with something to keep supplying someone with things, especially food, drink, or questions 不斷勸〔人〕吃喝; 不斷向〔人〕提問題 **2** [I;T] old fash (of taxis, buses, and especially boats) to travel regularly 《老式》〔計程車、公共汽車, 尤指船〕定期地往返: *This ship plies between London and Australia.* 這艘船定期航行於倫敦和澳大利亞之間。 **3** lit 《文》

ply your trade to work at a particular job 從事, 經營

**ply² **n [U] a measure of the thickness of wool or rope, according to the number of threads it is made from 〔毛線或繩子的〕股: *This is four-ply wool.* 這是四股的毛線。

ply·wood /ˈplaɪˌwʊd; ˈplaɪwʊd/ n [U] strong board made of several thin sheets of wood stuck together 膠合板, 夾板

p.m. /ˌpiː ˈɛm; ˌpiː ˈem/ letters which follow numbers to show that a time is after midday 〔接在時間後面〕下午: *He caught the 5 p.m. train from Manchester.* 他趕上了由曼徹斯特開來的下午5點那一班火車。 —compare 比較 **a.m.**

P M see 見 PRIME MINISTER

pneu·mat·ic /njuːˈmætɪk; njuːˈmætɪk/ adj **1** worked by air pressure 由壓縮空氣推動的: *a pneumatic drill* 風鑽 **2** containing air 充氣: *a pneumatic tyre* 充氣輪胎

pneu·mo·ni·a /njuːˈmonjə; njuːˈməʊnɪə/ n [U] a serious disease of the lungs causing difficulty in breathing 肺炎

poach /pəʊtʃ; pəʊtʃ/ v **1** [T] to cook food in gently boiling liquid 用沸水〔或其他液體〕煮: *poached eggs* 水煮蛋 **2** [I;T] to catch animals or birds on private land without permission 侵入他人地界偷獵〔偷捕〕: *One of the villagers was caught poaching.* 有一位村民在偷獵時被當場抓獲。 | *They were charged with poaching salmon.* 他們被控偷獵鮭魚。 **3** [T] to use someone else's work or idea without permission 剽竊; 竊取〔他人的工作成果或主意〕: *All his best ideas were poached from someone else.* 他所有的好主意都是從別人那裡剽竊來的 **4** [T] to persuade someone to leave another group and join your own, either secretly or dishonestly 挖走〔人員〕, 挖角: *They are poaching all our best managers.* 他們在網羅我們最優秀的經理。 —**poacher** n

P O Box /ˌpiː əʊ ˈbɒks; ˌpiː əʊ ˈbɑːks◂/ n (also 又作 **Post Office Box** fml 《正式》) a numbered box at a post office, to which a person's letters can be sent 郵政信箱: *For further details, write to PO Box 179.* 欲知詳情, 請寫信至179號郵政信箱。

pock·et¹ /ˈpɒkɪt; ˈpɑːkət/ n **1** a small flat cloth bag sewn into or onto a garment, for keeping small articles in 衣袋, 口袋: *Do you know what's in your child's pockets?* 你知道你孩子的口袋裡裝的是甚麼東西嗎? —see picture on page 210 見 210 頁彩圖 **2** a container made by fitting a piece of cloth or

other material into the inside of a case or a car door, or onto the back of an aircraft seat, for putting things in 〔箱內、車門內、飛機座位後等的〕小袋: *You will find a list of duty-free items in the pocket in front of you.* 你會在前面的小袋裡找到一張免稅商品的清單。 **3** a small area or group that is separated from others like it 一小片; 一小羣: *pockets of mist* 一團團的霧 | *There are pockets of unemployment in the industrial areas.* 工業區內有零星的失業現象。 **4 out of pocket** having less money than you should after spending some 白花錢的, 賠錢的: *She paid for everyone and ended up badly out of pocket.* 她為每個人都付了錢, 到頭來損失慘重。 —**pocket** adj: *a pocket dictionary* 袖珍詞典

pocket² **v [T] **1 to put something into your pocket 把〔某物〕裝進口袋裡 **2** to take something for your own use dishonestly 竊取〔某物〕; 私吞〔某物〕: *We shared the bill, but John pocketed the change.* 我們平均分攤賬款, 但約翰私吞了找回的零錢。

pock·et·book /ˈpɒkɪtˌbʊk; ˈpɒkɪ̩tbʊk/ n **1** a small book or notebook 袖珍本; 小筆記本 **2** AmE a small container for carrying papers or money 《美式》小型錢包

pock·et·ful /ˈpɒkɪtˌfʊl; ˈpɒkɪ̩tfʊl/ n the amount of something that can fit into a pocket 一袋之量: *a pocketful of coins* 一袋硬幣

pocket mon·ey /ˈ·· ˌ··/ n BrE 《英式》(**allowance** AmE 《美式》) [U] money given to a child by its parents every week 〔父母給孩子的〕零用錢: *How much pocket money do you get?* 你有多少零用錢?

pock·mark /ˈpɒkˌmɑːk; ˈpɒkmɑːk/ n a hollow mark left on your skin where a raised spot has been 〔皮膚上的〕痘痕, 麻點, 麻子 —**pockmarked** adj

pod¹ /pɒd; pɒd/ n a long narrow seed container of various plants such as beans 豆莢

pod² v **-dd-** [T] to take beans and other vegetables out of their pods before cooking them 剝掉〔豆等〕的莢

podg·y /ˈpɒdʒi; ˈpɒdʒi/ adj infml short and fat 《非正式》矮胖的

po·di·um /ˈpodiəm; ˈpəʊdɪəm/ n **podiums** or **podia** /-dɪə; -dɪə/ a raised part of a floor, or a large movable block, for a performer to stand on 表演台; 講台

po·em /ˈpoːɪm; ˈpəʊɪ̩m/ n a piece of writing, carefully arranged in patterns of lines and sounds 詩; 韻文

po·et /ˈpoːɪt; ˈpəʊɪ̩t/ n a person who writes poems 詩人

po·et·ic /poˈɛtɪk; pəʊˈetɪk/ adj (also 又作 **poetical**) **1** of poets or poetry 詩人的; 詩的: *poetic language* 詩的語言 | *Some plays are written in poetic form.* 有些劇本是以詩的形式寫成的。 **2** beautiful or pleasing in a way which is similar to poetry 富有詩意的, 如詩

一般優美的 **3 poetic justice** perfect justice, by which people who do wrong are punished in a suitable way 惡有惡報, 應得的懲罰 **4 poetic licence** freedom to change facts or not obey the usual rules 改變事實的自由; 打破常規的自由; 破格

*po·et·ry /ˈpoɪtrɪ; ˈpəʊˌtrɪ/ n [U] **1** poems in general 〔總稱〕詩: *a book of poetry* 一本詩集 –compare 比較 PROSE (1) **2** a quality of beauty, grace, or deep feeling (a word used to express approval) 詩意, 詩情〔含褒義〕

poi·gnant /ˈpɔɪnənt; ˈpɔɪnjənt/ adj producing a strong feeling of sadness or pity 傷心的; 辛酸的: *poignant memories of my childhood* 我的童年的辛酸回憶 **–poignancy** n [U]

***point¹ /pɔɪnt; pɔɪnt/ n **1** [C] a sharp end of something 尖, 尖端: *Mind those scissors — they've got sharp points.* 當心那把剪刀——它有鋒利的尖端。 **2** [C] an exact position or place 〔確切的〕位置; 地點: *I showed him the point in the road where the accident had happened.* 我把事故發生的確切位置指給他看。 **3** [C] an exact moment in time 確切的時間: *It was at that point that I realized what had happened.* 到那一刻我才意識到發生了甚麼事。 **4** [C] a stage in a process when something begins to happen 階段; 程度: *Heat the water until it reaches boiling point.* 把水加熱到沸點。| *This government has brought the economy to the point of collapse.* 這政府已使經濟瀕於崩潰。| *He finally reached the point where he could no longer continue working.* 他終於到了無法繼續工作的階段。 **5** [C] a unit used for recording the SCORE in a game or competition 〔遊戲或比賽的〕分數, 得分: *We won by 12 points to 3.* 我們以十二比三獲勝。 **6** [C] a sign (.) used for separating a whole number from the decimals that follow it 小數點 **7** [C] a single fact or idea 事實; 觀點: *There are two or three points in your speech that I didn't understand.* 你的演講中有兩三點沒聽懂。| *I'd like to make a couple of points.* 我想提幾點意見。| *He quoted a whole series of figures and statistics to prove his point.* 他引用了一系列的數據來證明他的觀點。 **8 the point** the most important idea or argument 最重要的觀點〔論點〕: *Stop messing around and get to the point!* 不要兜圈子了, 有話就直說吧! | *The point is that we don't have enough money to move house.* 關鍵問題在於我們不夠錢搬家。| *I know he's nice, but that's not the point.* 我知道他是個好人, 但那不是問題的關鍵。 **9** [C] a noticeable quality or ability that someone or something has 特點; 特質: *You should wear clothes that show off your good points.* 你應當穿能襯托出你身材上過人之處的衣服。| *Work isn't her strong point.* 工作不是她的長處。 **10** [U] purpose or use 目的; 用途: *If your car's that old, there isn't much point in*

repairing it. 如果你的車那麼舊了, 修理它也沒有甚麼用處。| *He couldn't see any point in learning foreign languages.* 他看不出學外語有甚麼用處。 **11** [C] a set of holes in a wall into which you can put an electric PLUG 電源插座 **12** [C] one of the 32 marks on a compass that show direction 〔指南針的〕刻度, 方位點 **13 points** [pl] a pair of rails (RAIL) that can be moved to allow a train to change onto another track 鐵軌道岔, 轉轍器 **14 at the point of** just before something happens 就在…之前: *Even at the point of death he would not reveal his secret.* 他甚至在臨死前都不願透露那個祕密。 **15 at the point of a gun, at gun point** turning the dangerous end of a gun towards someone 用槍瞄準〔某人〕: *They were held up and robbed at gun point.* 他們被人用槍劫住, 並搶走了財物。 **16 beside the point** not important to the subject being talked about 不切題的: *The fact that he's your brother is beside the point.* 他是你的弟弟這一事實與主題無關。 **17 have a point** a phrase you use to show that you agree with something that someone has said 有道理〔用於表示同意某人所說的話〕: *You have a point, I suppose.* 我認為你言之有理。 **18 in point of fact** in fact 事實上, 實際上: *In point of fact, she's only worked for the company for two months.* 實際上, 她在這家公司只幹了兩個月。 **19 make a point of doing something** to make sure that you do something 特別注意做某事, 重視某事: *She made a point of introducing herself to all the new recruits.* 她很着重把自己介紹給所有新來的人。 **20 on the point of doing something** just about to do something 剛要做某事: *I was just on the point of phoning you.* 我剛要打電話給你。 **21 point of no return** a point at which it becomes clear that you cannot change your mind and stop doing something 有進無退〔欲罷不能〕的地步 **22 point of order** a question or statement concerned with the proper running of an official meeting 關於議事程序的問題或聲明 **23 point of view** a way of considering or judging someone or something 觀點: *Look at it from my point of view.* 請從我的角度來看那件事。| *I find it difficult to understand his point of view.* 我發覺很難理解他的觀點。 **24 take someone's point** to accept what someone has said 接受某人所說的話: *I take your point about the place needing decorating.* 我同意你所說的關於那地方需要裝修的話。 **25 to the point** covering the most important facts or ideas about a subject 切題的, 中肯的: *His speech was short and to the point.* 他的演講很短, 但很中肯。 **26 to the point of** so as to be almost 幾乎了…的程度: *Her way of speaking is direct to the point of rudeness.* 她講話的方式過於直率, 幾乎到了粗魯的地步。 **27 up to a point** partly, but not completely 部分地; you sometimes say "up to a point" when you do not really agree with what someone says, but you do not want to be rude 部分地; 在某種程度上〔用於不同意別人所説的話, 但又不想顯得不禮貌〕: *Do you think it's a good idea for mothers to go out to work?" "Up to a point, but I don't think it's a good idea for a young child to be in a nursery all day."* "你認為做母親的外出工作好不好?" "在某種程度上來講是不錯, 但我認為小孩子一天到晚在幼兒園裡不是一個好辦法。"

point² *v* 1 [I] to hold your finger out towards someone or something 指, 指向〔某人或某物〕: *She pointed at him and said, "He's the one."* 她指着他説: "就是他。" | *He pointed to the house on the corner and said, "That's where I live."* 他指着拐角處的那所房子説: "那就是我住的地方。" 2 [T] to aim or direct something towards a person or thing 用〔某物〕瞄準〔人或物〕: *He pointed the gun at her.* 他用槍瞄着她。 3 **point the finger at someone** to say that someone has done something wrong 責怪某人, 指責

point out *phr v* 1 [T **point** sbdy/sthg ↔ **out**] to indicate a person or thing by pointing 把〔人或物〕指出來: *I pointed out the house where I was born.* 我把自己出生的那所房子指出來。 | *He pointed her out to me.* 他把她指給我看。 2 [T **point** sthg ↔ **out**; +that] to state a fact so that you draw attention to it 〔為引起注意而〕指出, 指明: *He pointed out a few contradictions in my argument.* 他指出了我論證中的幾處矛盾。 | *I pointed out that I had lived in the town for a lot longer than she had.* 我指出自己住在城裡的時間比她長得多。

point to/towards sthg *phr v* [T] to suggest that something is the case 顯出, 表明〔某事物〕: *All the evidence points towards Briggs as the murderer.* 所有的證據都顯示布里格斯是殺人兇手。 | *These latest figures seem to point to the fact that the country is entering a recession.* 這些最新數據似乎都表明該國正進入經濟衰退期。

point-blank /ˌ·ˈ·◂/ *adj, adv* 1 from very close to the person or thing being shot at 近距離射擊(的): *He was shot at point-blank range.* 他被人在近距離槍殺。 | *He fired at the animal point-blank.* 他在近距離開槍射擊那隻動物。 2 forceful and direct 有力的; 直率的: *a point-blank refusal* 斷然的拒絕 | *He refused point-blank.* 他直截了當地拒絕了。

point·ed /ˈpɔɪntɪd; ˈpɔɪntⁱd/ *adj* 1 shaped to a point at one end 尖的: *long, pointed fingernails* 又長又尖的指甲 2 expressing a clear and often unfriendly message to a particular person or group 直截了當的; 有針對性的: *She looked in a pointed manner at the clock and stood up to leave.* 她以十分明確的態度看了看鐘, 我於是起身告辭了。 – **pointedly** *adv*

point·er /ˈpɔɪntə; ˈpɔɪntɚ/ *n* 1 a long stick used to point at things on a board 指物棒 2 a thin piece of metal that points to numbers on a measuring apparatus 指針 3 a useful suggestion or piece of advice 忠告; 點子: *He gave me some useful pointers about how to approach the boss.* 他給了我一些忠告, 教我如何接近老闆。 4 a type of hunting dog 指示獵犬

point·less /ˈpɔɪntlɪs; ˈpɔɪntləs/ *adj* without sense or purpose 無意義的; 無目的的: *a pointless activity* 毫無意義的活動 – **pointlessly** *adv* – **pointlessness** *n* [U]

poise /pɔɪz; pɔɪz/ *n* [U] 1 calm self-control 沉着, 泰然自若: *I admire his poise in these difficult negotiations.* 我非常欽佩他在這些艱苦的談判中的冷靜沉着。 2 a graceful way of holding your head or body upright 〔身體〕優美的姿態: *She had the poise of a ballet dancer.* 她擁有芭蕾舞演員的體態。

poised /pɔɪzd; pɔɪzd/ *adj* 1 [never before a noun 不能用於名詞前] in a delicate state of balance 在微妙的平衡狀態中的: *The sick man is poised between life and death.* 這個病人正處於生死邊緣。 2 [never before a noun 不能用於名詞前] ready to act or move 準備行動[移動]的: *The army was poised for action.* 軍隊已準備好隨時行動。 3 possessing calm self-control 沉着的, 鎮定的

poi·son¹ /ˈpɔɪzn; ˈpɔɪzən/ *n* [C;U] a substance that can harm or kill people, animals, or plants 毒藥, 毒物: *He tried to kill himself by taking poison.* 他企圖服毒自殺。 | *A number of these are poisons.* 這當中有些是毒藥。

poison² *v* [T] 1 to give poison to people or animals 給〔人或動物〕服毒藥: *We managed to poison the rats.* 我們設法毒死老鼠。 2 to put poison into or onto something 給〔某物〕加入毒藥: *Someone tried to poison the water supply.* 有人試圖在供水系統裡下毒。 | *a poisoned arrow* 毒箭 3 to spoil or ruin something 破壞, 毀壞: *Her remarks poisoned the atmosphere.* 她的話破壞了氣氛。 4 **poison someone's mind** to make someone believe bad or false things about another person 使某人對〔他人〕產生惡感: *She tried to poison her husband's mind against his sister.* 她企圖令丈夫對他的妹妹產生惡感。 – **poisoner** *n* – **poisoning** *n* [U]: *This paint has caused severe cases of lead poisoning.* 這種油漆已引發了好幾起嚴重的鉛中毒。

poi·son·ous /ˈpɔɪznəs; ˈpɔɪzənəs/ *adj* 1 containing or producing poison 有毒的: *poisonous snakes* 毒蛇 | *Don't touch these flowers; they're poisonous.* 不要碰這些花; 它們有毒。 2 intended to hurt or harm someone 惡意攻擊的: *poisonous remarks* 惡毒的話 – **poisonously** *adv*

poke /pok; pəʊk/ *v* **poked, poking** 1 [T] to push a pointed thing into someone or something 插入, 刺入〔某人或某物〕: *You* *nearly poked me in the eye with your pencil.* 你的鉛筆差點戳中我的眼睛。| *Stop poking me!* 別老是用肘推我! **2** [I;T] to appear or to show part of something through an open-ing or out of something else 伸出; 露出: *She poked her head round the door.* 她從門後探出頭來。| *His handkerchief was poking out of his sleeve.* 他的手帕從袖口中露了出來。**3** **poke fun at** to make jokes against some-one or something 嘲笑, 嘲弄〔某人或某事物〕: *They were poking fun at my hair.* 他們在拿我的頭髮開玩笑。**4** **poke your nose into something** *infml* to show interest in some-thing that does not concern you〔非正式〕管閒事, 探聽〔與自己無關的事情〕

  poke about/around *phr v infml* [I] to search〔非正式〕到處找尋: *She poked about in her bag for her ticket.* 她在手袋裡找她的票。

  poke at sbdy/sthg *phr v* [T] to make lots of small movements as you push some-thing with something pointed〔用尖的東西〕撥弄〔某物〕

poke² *n* a quick push with something pointed 撥弄

pok·er /'pəʊkə; 'pəʊkəʳ/ *n* **1** [C] a thin metal rod used to move the wood or coal in a fire in order to make it burn better 撥火棒 **2** [U] a card game usually played for money 撲克牌戲, 紙牌戲

pok·y /'pəʊkɪ; 'pəʊki/ *adj* **pokier, pokiest** *infml* uncomfortably small (used to de-scrible buildings)〔非正式〕狹小的〔指建築物〕: *a poky little house* 狹小的房屋

po·lar /'pəʊlə; 'pəʊləʳ/ *adj* [only before a noun 只用於名詞前] of or from the area around the North or South Pole 北極的; 南極的

polar bear /ˌ···ˈ·/ *n* a large white bear that lives near the North Pole 北極熊

po·lar·i·ty /pəʊˈlærətɪ; pəˈlærɟti/ *n* **polarities** [C;U] great difference 分歧; 對立: *We have observed a growing polarity between the opinions of the government and those of the trade unions.* 我們已注意到政府與那些工會之間的意見分歧越來越大。

po·lar·ize /'pəʊləˌraɪz; 'pəʊləraɪz/ *v* **polar-ized, polarizing** (also 又作 **polarise** *BrE*〔英式〕) [I;T] to move into two opposing groups (使)兩極分化: *The government's pol-icy seems to have polarized society into two classes.* 政府的政策似乎已使社會分化成兩個階級。| *Society has polarized into two classes.* 社會已分化成兩個階級。**–polariza-tion** /-rəˈzeɪʃən; -rarˈzeɪʃən/ *n* (also 又作 **po-larisation** *BrE*〔英式〕) [C;U]

Po·lar·oid /'pəʊləˌrɔɪd; 'pəʊlərɔɪd/ *n tdmk* 〔商標〕**1** [U] a substance used in glass to make light shine less brightly through it 偏振片, 偏光薄膜 **2** [C] a camera that produces a finished photograph only seconds after the picture has been taken

即影即有相機, 寶麗來一次成像照相機

***pole** /pəʊl; pəʊl/ *n* **1** a long thin round stick or post 桿; 柱; 竿: *a flagpole* 旗桿 | *tele-graph poles* 電線桿 **2** either of the two ends of the AXIS on which the Earth turns 極地 **3** one of the two points at which wires may be fixed onto an electricity-storing appa-ratus 電極 **4 poles apart** having very diff-erent views〔意見〕截然相反, 毫無共同之處

Pole *n* see 見 POLISH²

pole star /ˈ· ·/ *n* **the pole star** (also 又作 **the Pole Star, the North Star**) the bright star that is nearest to the centre of the sky in the northern part of the world 北極星

pole vault /ˈ· ·/ *n* **1** a sport in which a per-son uses a pole to jump over a high raised bar 撐竿跳高比賽 **2** a jump in this sport 撐竿跳高 **–pole-vault** *v* [I]

******po·lice¹** /pəˈliːs; pəˈliːs/ *n* [pl] **1 the police** an official body of men and women whose duty is to protect people and property, and to make sure that everyone obeys the law 警方; 警察部門: *The police are searching for him now.* 警方現正在追捕他。| *the police force* 警察部隊 | *a police car* 警車 **2** members of this official body 警察: *There were police everywhere.* 到處都有警察。

police² *v* **policed, policing** [T] to keep order in a place, usually by using police〔通常用警察〕維持〔某地〕的治安: *This area has to be carefully policed on Saturday nights.* 這地區在星期六晚上要小心地管治。

*****po·lice·man** /pəˈliːsmən; pəˈliːsmən/ *n* **po-licemen** /-mən; -mən/ (also 又作 **police offi-cer** /ˈ·· ˌ···/) a male member of a police force 男警察

police state /ˌ·· ˈ·/ *n* a country in which most activities of the citizens are con-trolled by secret political police (a phrase used to express disapproval) 警察國家〔含貶義〕

police sta·tion /ˈ·· ˌ···/ *n* the local office of a police force 警察局, 派出所

po·lice·wom·an /pəˈliːsˌwʊmən; pəˈliːsˌwu-mən/ *n* **policewomen** /-ˌwɪmən; -ˌwɪmɪn/ (also 又作 **police officer** /ˈ·· ˌ···/) a female member of a police force 女警察

******pol·i·cy** /ˈpɒləsɪ; ˈpɒlɟsi/ *n* **policies** [C; U] **1** a plan or course of action that is agreed by a political party, govern-ment, or business〔政黨、政府、公司的〕政策, 方針: *One of the party's policies is to control public spending.* 該黨的政策之一是控制公共支出。| *It's against government policy to sell weapons to that country.* 將武器售給那個國家有違政府的政策。**2** a written agreement by a company to insure health, lives or property for a stated sum of money 保險單: *an insurance policy* 保險單

po·li·o /ˈpəʊlɪəʊ; ˈpəʊliəʊ/ *n* (also 又作 **polio-myelitis** /ˌpɒlɪəʊˌmaɪəˈlaɪtɪs; ˌpəʊliəʊˌmaɪə-

'laɪtɬs/ *tech*《術語》) [U] a serious infectious disease of the nerves in your backbone, which often causes you to lose the power to move certain muscles 脊髓灰質炎, 小兒麻痺症

pol·ish¹ /'pɑlɪʃ; 'pɒlɪʃ/ *v* **1** [I;T] to make or become smooth and shiny by rubbing 磨光; 擦亮: *Polish your shoes with that brush.* 用那隻刷子把你的鞋擦亮。| *Silver polishes easily with this special cloth.* 用這種特製的布料很容易把銀器擦亮。**2** [T] to make something as perfect as possible 使〔某物〕盡量完美: *The musicians gave a very polished performance.* 音樂家們的演出十分精湛。| *This essay needs polishing.* 這篇文章需要潤飾一下。

polish sthg ↔ **off** *phr v* [T] *infml* to finish food or work quickly《非正式》迅速吃完; 迅速完成: *I must polish this report off before I leave.* 我在走之前，必須趕快寫完這份報告。

polish² *n* **1** [U] a liquid, powder, or paste used to make a surface smooth and shiny 擦光劑; 上光蠟: *a tin of shoe polish* 一罐鞋油 | *furniture polish* 家具上光蠟 **2** [sing] a rub to make a surface smooth and shiny 磨光; 擦亮: *Could you give the table a polish?* 你能把桌子擦亮嗎? **3** [sing] the smooth shine of a surface 光澤: *That hot plate will spoil the polish on this table.* 那隻滾燙的盤子會燙掉這張桌子的光澤。**4** [U] the fine quality of something, especially manners or writing〔尤指舉止或寫作的〕優雅; 完美

Po·lish¹ /'poʊlɪʃ; 'pəʊlɪʃ/ *adj* from or connected with Poland 波蘭的

Polish² *n* **1** [U] (also 又作 **the Poles**) the people of Poland 波蘭人 **2** [U] the language of Poland 波蘭語

po·lite /pə'laɪt; pə'laɪt/ *adj* having good manners, and showing respect and consideration for others 有禮貌的, 客氣的, 文雅的: *What polite children!* 多有禮貌的孩子啊! | *I wish you'd be more polite to my parents.* 我希望你對待我的父母能更禮貌一些。–opposite 反義 **impolite** –**politely** *adv* –**politeness** *n* [U]

pol·i·tic /'pɑlə,tɪk; 'pɒlɪtɪk/ *adj fml* sensible because you will gain some advantage〔正式〕明智的, 精明的: *It would be politic to agree with him.* 同意他的意見將是明智之舉。

po·lit·i·cal /pə'lɪtɪkl; pə'lɪtɪkəl/ *adj* **1** concerning politics 政治的: *a political party* 政黨 | *the loss of political freedoms* 喪失政治上的自由 | *political beliefs* 政治信仰 **2** interested in politics 對政治感興趣的: *Our students used to be more political.* 我們的學生以往對政治(比現在)更感興趣。–**politically** /-kl̩; -kli/ *adv*

po·lit·i·cal prisoner /·,··· '···/ *n* someone who is in prison because of their political beliefs 政治犯

pol·i·ti·cian /,pɑlə'tɪʃən; ,pɒlɪ'tɪʃən/ *n* a person who works in politics, especially a member of a parliament 政治家; 政客〔尤指

議員〕

pol·i·tics /'pɑlə,tɪks; 'pɒlɪtɪks/ *n* **1** [pl;U] activities concerned with power relationships or government 政治(活動): *Are you interested in politics?* 你對政治感興趣嗎? | *She takes an active part in local politics.* 她積極參與當地的政治活動。| *I try to avoid company politics.* 我盡力避免捲入公司的權力紛爭之中。**2** [U] the study of political affairs 政治學: *Politics is my main subject.* 政治是我的主要科目。| *the politics department* 政治系 **3** [pl] political opinions 政治觀點: *What are your politics?* 你的政治觀點是甚麼?

pol·ka /'polkə; 'pɒlkə/ *n* a quick simple dance for people in pairs, or the music it is danced to 波爾卡舞; 波爾卡舞曲

poll¹ /pol; pəʊl/ *n* **1 the polls** an election 選舉: *Voters go to the polls next Thursday.* 選民在下週四參加選舉投票。**2** (also 又作 **opinion poll**) a set of questions given to a number of people chosen by chance, to find out the general opinion about something or someone 民意調查, 民意測驗: *The latest poll gives the opposition a 10% lead over the Government.* 最新的民意測驗顯示反對派比政府領先百分之十。**3 poll tax** money collected by the local council from people living in the area; the money is used to help pay for local services 人頭稅: *Have you paid your poll tax?* 你納了人頭稅嗎?

poll² *v* [T] **1** to receive a certain number of votes in an election〔在選舉中〕獲得〔票數〕: *She polled 10,542 votes.* 她獲得了10542張選票。**2** to ask people for their opinions on a particular subject 進行民意測驗〔調查〕: *The majority of people polled supported the Prime Minister's decision.* 被調查的人大部分都支持首相的決定。

pol·len /'pɑlən; 'pɒlən/ *n* [U] fine yellow dust on a flower that causes other flowers to produce seeds 花粉

pollen count /'··· ·/ *n* a measure of the amount of pollen floating in the air 花粉計數〔即空氣中的花粉量〕

pol·li·nate /'pɑlə,net; 'pɒlɪneɪt/ *v* **pollinated, pollinating** [T] to make a plant able to produce seeds by bringing pollen to it 給〔植物〕傳授花粉 –**pollination** /,pɑlə'neʃən; ,pɒlɪ'neɪʃən/ *n* [U]

poll·ing /'polɪŋ; 'pəʊlɪŋ/ *n* [U] voting at an election (選舉)投票

pol·lut·ant /pə'lutnt; pə'luːtənt/ *n* [C] a substance that pollutes the air, water, or soil 污染物

pol·lute /pə'lut; pə'luːt/ *v* **polluted, polluting** [T] to make the air, water, or soil dirty or dangerous by adding harmful substances 污染〔空氣、水或土壤〕: *The river has been polluted by chemicals.* 這條河被化學物質污染了。

pol·lu·tion /pə'luʃən; pə'luːʃən/ *n* [U] **1** the

process of polluting the air, water, or soil 污染: *water pollution* 水污染 | *the pollution of the environment* 環境污染 **2** a substance that pollutes the air, water, or soil 污染物: *There's so much pollution in the air here that it's becoming dangerous to breathe!* 這裡的空氣中有大量污染物質, 以致呼吸都變得很危險!

po·lo /ˈpəʊləʊ; ˈpəʊləʊ/ *n* [U] a game played between two teams on horses, who hit the ball with long wooden hammers 馬球

polo neck /'·· ·/ *n* a high rolled collar 高領 —**polo-neck** *adj*: *a polo-neck sweater* 高領羊毛衣

pol·ter·geist /ˈpɒltəˌɡaɪst; ˈpɒltəɡaɪst/ *n* a spirit that is said to make noises and move objects around 〔會發出聲響並移動物體的〕捉弄人的鬼怪

pol·y /ˈpɒlɪ; ˈpɒlɪ/ *n* **polys** *BrE infml* 〖英式, 非正式〗see 見 POLYTECHNIC

pol·y·es·ter /ˌpɒlɪˈɛstə; ˈpɒliestər/ *n* [U] a man-made material used to make cloth 聚酯(纖維): *a polyester shirt* 一件聚酯襯衫

pol·y·eth·y·lene /ˌpɒlɪˈɛθɪ,lin; ˌpɒliˈeθəliːn/ *n* [U] the usual American word for 〖美式〗= POLYTHENE

po·lyg·a·my /pəˈlɪɡəmɪ; pəˈlɪɡəmi/ *n* [U] the practice of having more than one wife at the same time 一夫多妻制 —**polygamist** *n* —**polygamous** *adj*: *a polygamous society* 一夫多妻制的社會

pol·y·gon /ˈpɒlɪ,ɡɒn; ˈpɒlɪɡən/ *n tech* a shape that has three or more straight sides 〖術語〗多邊形

pol·y·sty·rene /ˌpɒlɪˈstaɪrin; ˌpɒlɪˈstaɪriːn/ *n* [U] a light plastic, used especially for making containers 聚苯乙烯〔尤用於製作塑料容器〕

pol·y·tech·nic /ˌpɒlɪˈtɛknɪk; ˌpɒlɪˈteknɪk/ *n* (also 又作 **poly** *infml* 〖非正式〗) a college of higher education where you can train in practical skills as well as study a wide range of subjects 理工學院, 工藝專科學院

pol·y·thene /ˈpɒlɪθin; ˈpɒlɪθiːn/ *n* (also 又作 **polyethylene** *AmE* 〖美式〗) [U] a strong, thin plastic used to cover and protect things 聚乙烯: *a polythene bag* 聚乙烯塑料袋

pom·e·gran·ate /ˈpɒm,ɡrænɪt; ˈpɒmˌɡrænɪt/ *n* a round fruit containing a lot of small seeds in a red juicy flesh 石榴

pomp /pɒmp; pɒmp/ *n* [U] grand and solemn ceremony shown on public or official occasions 隆重的慶典

pom·pous /ˈpɒmpəs; ˈpɒmpəs/ *adj* behaving or speaking in a very serious way, as if you are trying to appear more important than you are (a word used to express disapproval) 浮誇的; 自大的〔含貶義〕: *pompous language* 浮誇的語言 | *a pompous official* 自高自大的官員 —**pomposity** /pɒmˈpɒsətɪ; pɒmˈpɒsəti/ *n* (also 又作 **pompousness**) [U] —**pompously** *adv*

pond /pɒnd; pɒnd/ *n* an area of still water, smaller than a lake 池塘: *a duck pond* 養鴨池

pon·der /ˈpɒndə; ˈpɒndər/ *v* [I;T] *fml* to spend time thinking carefully about something 〖正式〗深思, 仔細考慮: *She pondered the problem for a while.* 她仔細考慮了一下這個問題。| *I need time to ponder over the best thing to do.* 我需要時間考慮一下最好的做法。

pon·der·ous /ˈpɒndərəs; ˈpɒndərəs/ *adj fml* 〖正式〗**1** slow and awkward in moving 沉重, 笨重的 **2** slow and dull (used especially of speech) 緩慢而沉悶的〔尤指演講〕 —**ponderously** *adv* —**ponderousness** *n* [U]

pong /pɒŋ; pɒŋ/ *v* [I] *BrE infml* 〖英式, 非正式〗to make an unpleasant smell 發出難聞的氣味 —**pong** *n*: *What a terrible pong!* 這味道難聞極了! —**pongy** *adj*

pon·tiff /ˈpɒntɪf; ˈpɒntɪf/ *n fml* 〖正式〗**the pontiff** see 見 POPE

pon·tif·i·cate /pɒnˈtɪfɪkɪt; pɒnˈtɪfɪˌkeɪt/ *v* **pontificated, pontificating** [I] to speak or write as if your own judgment is the only correct one (a word used to express disapproval) 自以為是地說或寫〔含貶義〕

pon·toon /pɒnˈtun; pɒnˈtuːn/ *n* **1** [C] a flat-bottomed boat fastened to others side by side to support a floating bridge across a river 〔架浮橋用的〕平底船: *a pontoon bridge* 浮橋 **2** (also 又作 **twenty-one** *AmE* 〖美式〗) [U] a card game played for money 二十一點牌戲

po·ny /ˈpɒnɪ; ˈpəʊni/ *n* **ponies** a small horse 小馬; 矮種馬

po·ny·tail /ˈpɒnɪ,tel; ˈpəʊniteɪl/ *n* a bunch of hair tied high at the back of the head 馬尾髮(型) —see picture on page 469 見 469 頁彩圖

poo·dle /ˈpudl; ˈpuːdl/ *n* a dog with thick curling hair 長鬈毛狗

pooh /pu; puː/ *interj* **1** a word you use to express your feelings when you smell something unpleasant 呸!〔表示聞到臭味〕 **2** a word used to express disbelief or disapproval 胡說!〔表示不相信或反對〕

pooh-pooh /ˌ·ˈ·/ *v* [T] *infml* to show that you consider something foolish 〖非正式〗對…〔某事〕嗤之以鼻: *They pooh-poohed the idea of health food in those days.* 那時他們對於保健食品這個主意嗤之以鼻。

☆pool¹ /pul; puːl/ *n* **1** [C] a small area of still water, usually formed naturally 水坑; 水塘; 水池: *There were little pools of rainwater in the street.* 馬路上有積了雨水的小水坑。| *a rock pool on the beach* 海灘上的石坑 **2** [C] a small amount of any liquid on a surface 一灘液體: *She was lying in a pool of blood.* 她躺在血泊之中。**3** a SWIMMING POOL 游泳池 **4** [C] a collection of money, goods, or people that may be used or shared by a number of people 集中使用的錢〔物品、人

力〕: *I can borrow a car from the company car pool.* 我可以從公司車隊借輛車。| *Give the report to someone in the typing pool.* 把報告交給打字組裡的人。**5** [U] a game played with hard coloured balls on a flat green table with pockets at the corners 落袋式枱球戲: *They were in the bar shooting pool all evening.* 他們整晚都在酒吧裡打枱球。

pool² [T] to put things together and share them 把〔物品〕集中使用，共用: *If we pool our ideas it'll be much easier.* 如果我們集思廣益，事情會容易得多。| *They pooled their resources to buy a house.* 他們集資買了一所房子。

pools /pulz; puːlz/ n BrE 〔英式〕 **the pools, the football pools** a competition in which people risk money on the results of certain football matches 猜足球賽結果的賭博

poop /pup; puːp/ n tech the back end of a ship 〔術語〕船尾

★★poor /puɪ; puɔ^r/ adj **1** having very little money and therefore a low standard of living 貧窮的，貧困的: *They were too poor to afford shoes for their children.* 他們很窮，沒錢給孩子們買鞋。| *It's a very poor country.* 這是個非常貧窮的國家。**2 the poor** the people in society who are poor 窮人: *The government must do more to help the poor and the sick.* 政府必須多做些事情來幫助窮人和病人。**3** low in quality, or below the usual standard 質量差的; 低於普通標準的: *a poor crop of beans* 豆子的收成差 | *The light was too poor to see his face.* 光線太暗，看不清他的臉。| *He has very poor eyesight.* 他的視力很差。| *It was a poor performance.* 這是一場很糟糕的演出。**4** [only before a noun 只用於名詞前] deserving sympathy 可憐的: *The poor old man had lost both his sons in the war.* 那可憐的老人在戰爭中失去了兩個兒子。**5 in poor health** ill 生病的

poor·ly¹ /ˈpuɪli; ˈpuɔli/ adv badly 糟糕地: *a poorly paid job* 一份薪水微薄的工作

poorly² adj [never before a noun 不能用於名詞前] BrE 〔英式〕 ill 〔英式〕身體不舒服的: *I'm feeling rather poorly today.* 今天我感覺不舒服。

pop¹ /pap; pɒp/ v **-pp- 1** [I;T] to burst with a short sharp sound (使) 嚓啪作響: *She popped the balloon with a pin.* 她用別針把汽球啪的一聲戳破了。| *The balloon popped.* 汽球啪的一聲爆破了。**2** [I] to make a short sharp sound 發出嚓啪的一聲: *The champagne cork popped when he pulled it out.* 他拔出香檳瓶塞時，發出了啪的一聲。**3** [I] infml to do something or go somewhere quickly or for a short time 〔非正式〕迅速地做某事 〔去某處〕: *I've just popped in to return your book.* 我趕來是還書給你的。| *I'm afraid she's just popped out to the shops.* 對不起，她剛出去逛商店了。**4** [T] infml to put something somewhere quickly 〔非正式〕迅速把

〔某物〕置於〔某處〕: *Will you pop the bread in the oven?* 你去把麵包放進烤爐裡好嗎? | *He popped his head round the door.* 他突然從門邊探出頭來。**5** [I] infml (of eyes) to show great surprise by opening wide 〔非正式〕〔眼睛由於吃驚而〕瞪大: *Her eyes almost popped out of her head when she saw me.* 她看見我時，眼睛瞪得大大的。**6 pop the question** infml to ask someone to marry you 〔非正式〕向〔某人〕求婚

★pop² n **1** [C] a sound like that of a slight explosion 輕微的爆炸聲: *There was a loud pop and the lights went out.* 他 "啪" 的一聲，燈便全熄滅了。**2** [U] modern music that has a strong beat and is popular with young people 現代流行音樂: *Do you like pop music?* 你喜歡流行音樂嗎? | *a pop star* 流行音樂歌星 **3 pop group** a group of people who sing and play pop music 流行音樂樂隊 **4** [C] AmE infml father 〔美式，非正式〕爸爸: *Can I borrow the car, pop?* 爸爸，我可以借用你的車嗎? **5** [U] infml a sweet drink containing a harmless gas 〔非正式〕有氣的飲料; 汽水

pop·corn /ˈpapˌkɔrn; ˈpɒpkɔːn/ n [U] grains of corn that are heated until they burst and are eaten with salt or sugar 爆玉米花, 爆穀

pope /pop; pəup/ n **the Pope** the head of the ROMAN CATHOLIC Church 教皇, 教宗: *the election of a new pope* 新教皇的選舉 | *Pope John Paul* 教宗若望·保祿 | *a message from the Pope* 從教皇那裡帶來的訊息

pop·lar /ˈpaplə; ˈpɒplə^r/ n [C;U] a very tall straight thin tree, or the wood from this tree 楊樹, 楊木

pop·py /ˈpapi; ˈpɒpi/ n **poppies** a plant with large, round, red flowers 罌粟

pop·u·lace /ˈpapjələs; ˈpɒpjʊləs/ n fml [U; +sing/pl verb] all the people of a country, especially the people who do not govern it 〔正式〕民眾, 百姓, 平民: *The populace no longer supports this policy.* 人民羣眾不再支持這項政策。

★★pop·u·lar /ˈpapjələ; ˈpɒpjʊlə^r/ adj **1** liked by a lot of people 流行的, 受歡迎的: *a popular TV programme* 一個受歡迎的電視節目 | *She's very popular with her students.* 她深受學生喜愛。—opposite 反義 **unpopular 2** [only before a noun 只用於名詞前] aimed at the understanding and interests of ordinary people (a word often used to express disapproval) 通俗的; 大眾化的〔常含貶義〕: *An article like this could only appear in the popular press.* 這種文章只可能出現在通俗報刊上。**3** [only before a noun 只用於名詞前] fml of the general public 〔正式〕大眾的: *popular opinion* 公眾輿論 | *the popular vote* 大眾投票

pop·u·lar·i·ty /ˌpapjəˈlærəti; ˌpɒpjʊˈlærɪti/ n [U] the quality or state of being liked by a lot of people 流行, 受歡迎, 普及: *His popu-*

larity comes from his genuine concern for others. 他受人歡迎是因為他真心地關心別人。–opposite 反義 **unpopularity**

pop·u·lar·ize /ˈpɑpjələˌraɪz; ˈpɒpjʊləraɪz/ v **popularized, popularizing** (also 又作 **popularise**) [T] **1** to make something known to and liked by a lot of people 使〔某物〕流行, 使受歡迎 **2** to make something difficult easier for ordinary people to understand 使〔某物〕通俗易懂 **–popularization** /ˌpɑpjələraɪˈzeɪʃən; ˌpɒpjʊləraɪˈzeɪʃən/ n [C;U]

pop·u·lar·ly /ˈpɑpjələli; ˈpɒpjʊləli/ adv by most people 一般地, 廣泛地: *The London Underground is popularly known as the Tube.* 倫敦地鐵一般都叫做 the Tube。

pop·u·late /ˈpɑpjəˌleɪt; ˈpɒpjʊleɪt/ v **populated, populating** [T] to fill an area with people who move or live there 使〔人〕居住於; 使移居於: *a densely-populated area* 人口稠密的地區 | *North America was mainly populated by immigrants from Europe.* 在北美居住的人大部分是歐洲來的移民。

pop·u·la·tion /ˌpɑpjəˈleɪʃən; ˌpɒpjʊˈleɪʃən/ n **1** [C;U] the number of people living in a particular area, or country 人口: *What was the population of Europe in 1900?* 1900年歐洲的人口是多少？ | *a population of 8 million* 八百萬人口 | *population levels* 人口水平 **2** [C] the people, or sometimes animals, living in an area 〔某一個地區的〕全體居民〔有時指動物羣〕: *Most of Australia's population lives near the coast.* 澳大利亞大部分人住在沿海地區。

pop·u·lous /ˈpɑpjələs; ˈpɒpjʊləs/ adj fml full of people (used of an area) 〔正式〕人口稠密的〔指地區〕

porce·lain /ˈpɔrslɪn; ˈpɔːslɪn/ n [U] a thin shiny substance made of baked clay which is used to make fine quality cups and dishes 瓷; 瓷器

porch /pɔrtʃ; pɔːtʃ/ n **1** an entrance to a house or church which has sides and a roof 〔房子或教堂的〕有頂的門廊 –see picture on page 729 見 729 頁彩圖 **2** the usual American word for 【美式】= VERANDA

por·cu·pine /ˈpɔrkjəˌpaɪn; ˈpɔːkjʊpaɪn/ n a short-legged animal that has very long stiff sharp points all over its back and sides 豪豬, 箭豬

pore¹ /pɔr; pɔːr/ n a very small hole in your skin or a leaf which allows liquid to come out 〔皮膚上的〕毛孔, 〔葉子上的〕氣孔

pore² v **pored, poring**
pore over sth phr v [T] to study something closely 鑽研〔某事物〕, 仔細地閱讀: *She's always poring over a book.* 她總是捧着書本在認真地閱讀。

pork /pɔrk; pɔːk/ n [U] meat from a pig 豬肉 –see 見 MEAT (USAGE用法) –compare 比較 BACON, HAM

porn /pɔrn; pɔːn/ n [U] infml 【非正式】see

見 PORNOGRAPHY

por·nog·ra·phy /pɔrˈnɑgrəfi; pɔːˈnɒgrəfi/ n [U] books, photographs or films showing sexual acts in a way that is meant to excite people (a word often used to express disapproval) 色情作品[書刊, 照片, 電影等]〔常含貶義〕 **–pornographer** n **–pornographic** /ˌpɔrnəˈgræfik; ˌpɔːnəˈgræfik◂/ adj: *a pornographic film* 色情電影

po·rous /ˈpɔrəs; ˈpɔːrəs/ adj allowing liquid to pass through 可滲透的: *porous soil* 滲水土壤

por·poise /ˈpɔrpəs; ˈpɔːpəs/ n a large sea animal that swims about in groups 鼠海豚

por·ridge /ˈpɔrɪdʒ; ˈpɒrɪdʒ/ n [U] a breakfast food made by boiling grain, especially oats (OAT), in milk or water 麥片粥

port /pɔrt; pɔːt/ n **1** [C] a town or an area by the water which ships arrive at and leave from 港口, 海港: *a fishing port* 漁港 | *It is one of the world's busiest ports.* 這是世界上最繁忙的港口之一。| *Port Said* 塞德港 **2** port of call a place where a ship will stop 〔輪船的〕停靠港: *Singapore is our next port of call.* 新加坡是我們下一個停靠的港市。 **3** [U] the left side of a ship or aircraft as you face the front 〔輪船或飛機的〕左舷: *The ship was leaning to port.* 船正向左舷傾斜。 **4** [U] strong sweet Portuguese wine 〔葡萄牙產的〕波爾圖紅葡萄酒

por·ta·ble /ˈpɔrtəbl; ˈpɔːtəbəl/ adj quite small, light, and easy to move or carry 便攜的; 手提式的: *a portable television* 手提式電視機

por·tal /ˈpɔrtl; ˈpɔːtl/ n fml or lit 【正式或文】 a very grand door or entrance to a building 大門; 正門入口

port·cul·lis /pɔrtˈkʌlɪs; ˌpɔːtˈkʌlɪs/ n a strong gate above an entrance to an old castle or fort, which was lowered as a protection against attack 〔古時城堡的〕吊門, 吊閘

por·ter /ˈpɔrtə; ˈpɔːtəʳ/ n **1** a person who looks after a building, such as a school or a block of flats, and who often sits near the entrance 守門人 **2** a person employed to carry travellers' bags at railway stations, airports, or hotels 〔火車站、機場、旅館等的〕行李搬運工

port·fo·li·o /pɔrtˈfoliˌo; pɔːtˈfəʊliəʊ/ n **portfolios 1** a large flat case for carrying drawings and papers in 公事包, 文件夾 **2** a set of examples of a person's work 作品選輯: *an artist's portfolio* 藝術家的作品選輯 **3** the office and duties of a government minister 部長職位

port·hole /ˈpɔrtˌhol; ˈpɔːthəʊl/ n a small circular window along the side of a ship or aircraft 〔輪船或飛機的〕舷窗

por·ti·co /ˈpɔrtɪˌko; ˈpɔːtɪkəʊ/ n **porticoes** or **porticos** a grand entrance to a building, consisting of a roof supported by pillars

〔由柱子支撐的〕門廊, 柱廊

por·tion¹ /'porʃən; 'pɔːʃən/ *n* **1** a part that can be separated from the rest, or is different from it 〔東西的〕一部分: *Keep this portion of your ticket.* 請把票的這一部分保存好。**2** an amount or share of something 〔分得的〕部分: *The driver must bear a portion of the blame for the accident.* 司機必須對這次事故負一部分責任。**3** a quantity of food for one person 〔食物的〕一份: *How many portions of meat are there?* 一共有幾份肉?

portion² *v*

portion sthg ↔ **out** *phr v* [T] to share something among a group of people 分配〔某物〕

port·ly /'portli; 'pɔːtli/ *adj* **portlier, portliest** *old fash* fat (a word which is sometimes used instead of 'fat' in order to be more polite or humorous) 〔老式〕肥胖的〔有時用來代替 'fat' 一詞以表示禮貌或幽默〕: *Men in our family tend to be rather portly.* 我們家的男人都容易發福。**–portliness** *n* [U]

port·man·teau /port'mænto; pɔːt'mæntəʊ/ *n* **portmanteaus** *or* **portmanteaux** /-toz; -təʊz/ a large travelling case that opens out into two equal parts 〔可對開的〕旅行皮箱

por·trait /'portret; 'pɔːtrɪt/ *n* **1** a painting, drawing, or photograph of a real person, especially of their face 肖像畫[照片]: *She's just painted a portrait of her mother.* 她剛給母親畫了幅肖像畫。| *a self-portrait* 自畫像 **2** a written description of a person, place or thing 〔對於人、地點或事物的〕描繪: *The book is a portrait of a country at war.* 這本書描繪了一個處於戰爭之中的國家。

por·tray /por'tre; pɔː'treɪ/ *v* **portrayed, portraying** [T] **1** to show a person or thing in a particular way, using words or pictures 描寫; 描繪: *Her book portrays women as domestic slaves.* 她的書把婦女描繪成了家庭的奴隸。**2** to act the part of a particular character in a play or film 扮演〔角色〕: *He portrays a young doctor.* 他扮演一位年輕醫生。**–portrayal** *n* [C;U]: *I particularly enjoyed his portrayal of King Arthur.* 我特別欣賞他扮演的亞瑟王。

Por·tu·guese¹ /'portʃə,giz; ,pɔːtʃʊ'giːz◂/ *adj* from or connected with Portugal 葡萄牙的

Portuguese² *n* **1 the Portuguese** the people of Portugal 葡萄牙人 **2** [U] the language of Portugal 葡萄牙語

*****pose¹** /poz; pəʊz/ *v* **posed, posing 1** [I] to sit or stand in a particular manner so that you can be drawn, painted, or photographed 擺好姿勢〔準備畫像或拍照〕: *How would you like me to pose?* 你想我擺甚麼樣的姿勢? | *I've never posed for a painting before.* 我以前從未擺過姿勢讓人畫像。**2** [I] to behave unnaturally in order to attract interest or attention (a word used to express disapproval) 裝腔作勢〔含貶義〕 **3 pose**

as someone to pretend to be someone else 裝扮成某人: *The prisoner escaped by posing as a prison officer.* 那囚犯假裝成監獄看守員逃走了。**4** [T] to be the cause of a difficulty or problem 引起〔困難或問題〕: *This new law poses several problems for the farmers.* 這項新法例給農民帶來了幾個問題。**5** [T] to ask or suggest something 提出〔某事〕; 暗示說: *That poses the question of where the party should be held.* 那便提出了晚會在哪裡舉辦的問題。

pose² *n* **1** a position, in which someone sits or stands while they are being drawn, painted, or photographed 〔畫像、拍照時的〕姿勢: *This pose is more flattering, I think.* 我覺得這姿勢更討人歡喜。**2** an unnatural way of behaving which is intended to attract interest or attention (a word used to express disapproval) 裝模作勢的舉止〔含貶義〕

posh /paʃ; pɒʃ/ *adj infml* 〔非正式〕**1** typical of people from a high social class (a word used to express disapproval) 上流社會的〔含貶義〕: *She has a rather posh accent.* 她有上流社會的口音。**2** grand and expensive-looking 宏偉的, 豪華的: *a posh hotel* 豪華旅館

*****po·si·tion¹** /pə'zɪʃən; pə'zɪʃən/ *n* **1** [C; U] the place where someone or something is 〔某人或某物的〕位置: *Can you find our position on this map?* 你能在這張地圖上找到我們的位置嗎? | *Our seats were in a very good position.* 我們的座位位置很好。| *Shall we change position?* 我們換個位置好嗎? **2** [U] the place where something is supposed to be 適當的位置: *The screws will hold the shelves in position.* 螺絲釘會固定好架子的位置。**3** [C] a situation someone is in 〔某人的〕處境, 境況: *I'm in a difficult financial position at the moment.* 現在我處於財政困境之中。| *You're putting me in an impossible position.* 你正把我推向絕境。**4 not be in a position to do something** to be unable to do something 不能做某事: *I'm afraid I'm not in a position to lend you any money.* 我恐怕我不能把錢借給你。**5** [C] the way in which someone stands, sits or lies 〔某人站、坐或躺的〕姿勢: *She slept in an uncomfortable position.* 她睡覺的姿勢很不舒服。**6** [C] the way in which something has been placed 某物所處的狀態: *The switch was in the off position.* 開關處於關的位置上。**7** [C;U] a particular place or rank in relation to others 地位; 名次: *She finished the race in second position.* 她賽跑得了第二名。**8** [C] a job that is professional, or in an office 職位, 職務: *I have a position of responsibility at the bank.* 我在銀行裡擔任責任重大的職務。**–see** 見 JOB (USAGE用法) **9** [C] an opinion about something 態度, 立場: *The government's position on this matter is clear.* 政府對此事的立場很明確。

position² *v* [T] **1** to move a person or thing

to a particular place, or so that they sit, stand, or lie in a particular way 使〔人或物〕安放〔在某一位置上〕, 使定位: *Most of the soldiers will be positioned near the border.* 大部分士兵將駐紮在邊境附近。 **2 position yourself** to move to a particular place 到某一位置: *She positioned herself beside the fire exit.* 她在緊急出口處旁找了個位置。

***pos·i·tive** /ˈpɑzətɪv; ˈpɒzˌtɪv/ *adj* **1** [never before a noun 不能用於名詞前] sure that something is true (used of a person) 肯定的; 有把握的〔指人〕: *"Are you sure this is the right number?" "Positive."* "你肯定就是這個號碼嗎?" "我肯定。" | *He was positive that he had seen the man before.* 他肯定以前見過那個男子。 **2** certain 確定的; 確實的: *The police have positive proof that it was murder.* 警方有確鑿的證據證明這是謀殺。 **3** hopeful or confident 有希望的; 有信心的: *a positive attitude to life* 對人生的樂觀態度 | *He's being very positive about the future.* 他對未來充滿了信心。 **4** helpful, decisive, or encouraging 有益的, 有建設性的; 令人鼓舞的: *She offered me some very positive advice.* 她給我提了一些十分有益的意見。 | *At least you're taking some positive steps towards solving the problem.* 最起碼你是在採取一些積極的措施來解決問題。 **5** showing signs that a substance is present (used of a medical test) 陽性的〔指醫療試驗〕 **6** greater than zero (used of a number, in MATHEMATICS) 〔數學上〕正的 **7** having the charge carried by PROTONS (used of a flow of electricity) 陽性的, 正的〔指電流〕: *The red is positive and the black is negative.* 紅的帶正電, 黑的帶負電。 **8** a word used to give force to a noun, to say that something is really true 實在的; 完全的〔用於強調名詞〕: *It's a positive pleasure to work with her.* 與她共事真是令人愉快。

pos·i·tive·ly /ˈpɑzətɪvlɪ; ˈpɒzˌtɪvlɪ/ *adv* **1** with certainty 肯定地, 有把握地: *He said quite positively that he would come.* 他相當肯定地說他要來。 **2** *infml* a word used to show that you feel strongly when you say that something is true 〔非正式〕實在地; 完全地〔強調某事符合實情〕: *This food is positively delicious!* 這東西實在好吃!

***pos·sess** /pəˈzɛs; pəˈzes/ *v* [T not in progressive forms 不用於進行式] **1** *fml* to own or have something 〔正式〕擁有〔某物〕; 具有: *They asked me if I possessed a gun.* 他們問我是否擁有一支槍。 **2** to influence or take control of someone's mind or actions 影響; 控制〔某人的思想或行動〕: *He was possessed by jealousy.* 他被嫉妒所驅使。 | *What possessed you to behave like that?* 是甚麼事使你那樣做的?

pos·sessed /pəˈzɛst; pəˈzest/ *adj fml or lit* 〔正式或文〕 controlled by an evil spirit (used of people or animals) 着了魔的〔指人或動物〕

***pos·ses·sion** /pəˈzɛʃən; pəˈzeʃən/ *n* **1** [U] the state of owning or having something 擁有; 佔有: *Possession of a large fortune does not always bring happiness.* 擁有大筆財富並不總能帶來幸福。 | *The papers are in my possession now.* 文件現在我這裡。 **2 in possession of something** having something, especially something surprising or illegal 擁有某物〔尤指驚人或非法之物〕: *He was found in possession of stolen goods.* 他被發現私藏贓物。 **3 take possession of something** to get control or become the owner of something 佔領〔佔有〕〔某物〕: *The rebels took possession of the airport.* 反叛者佔領了機場。 | *We take possession of our new house next week.* 我們下週便擁有我們的新居。 **4** [C] a piece of personal property 私有財產: *They lost most of their possessions in the fire.* 他們在火災中喪失了大部分財產。

pos·ses·sive¹ /pəˈzɛsɪv; pəˈzesɪv/ *adj* **1** wanting to have all of a person's love or attention (a word used to express disapproval) 希望佔有全部的愛〔注意力〕的〔含貶義〕: *Don't be so possessive! He's just a friend.* 別這麼愛吃醋! 他不過是個朋友罷了。 **2** unwilling to share your things (a word used to express disapproval) 佔有慾強的, 不願與人分享的〔含貶義〕: *Children can be very possessive about their toys.* 孩子們對於玩具的佔有慾可以是非常強的。 **3** showing ownership or connection (used in grammar) 表示所有權或連屬關係的; "my" and "their" are possessive adjectives 所有格的〔指語法〕〔"my" 和 "their" 是所有格形容詞〕

possessive² *n* a word or grammatical form showing ownership or connection; "hers" is a possessive 所有格; 所有格形式〔"hers" 是所有格代名詞〕

pos·ses·sor /pəˈzɛsɚ; pəˈzesəʳ/ *n fml* a person who owns something (a word that is often used in a humorous way) 〔正式〕擁有者〔常作幽默用法〕: *I was now the proud possessor of a university degree.* 我現在有令我引以為榮的大學學位。

***pos·si·bil·i·ty** /ˌpɑsəˈbɪlətɪ; ˌpɒsˌˈbɪlˌtɪ/ *n* **possibilities 1** [sing;U] the chance that something is likely to happen or to be true 可能性: *Is there any possibility that you'll be able to come tomorrow?* 你明天有可能來嗎? | *There's a slight possibility of rain.* 下雨的可能性很小。 **2** [C] something that might happen or that might be true 可能發生的事; 可能屬實的事: *War is now a strong possibility.* 戰爭現在極有可能發生。 | *"He might have left already." "Yes, it's a possibility."* "他或許已經走了。" "這有可能。"

***pos·si·ble** /ˈpɑsəbl; ˈpɒsˌbəl/ *adj* **1** that can exist, happen, or be done 可能的: *It's no longer possible to find a cheap flat in London.* 在倫敦已不可能再找到便宜的公寓了。 | *It's possible that we might be a bit late.* 我們可能會晚一會兒到。 | *Everything is possible.* 甚麼事都會發生。

it is possible to do something; it is possible that...

2 if possible if it is possible 如果可能的話 – opposite 反義 **impossible** **3** that may or may not be, happen, or be expected 可能會發生的 **4** acceptable or suitable 可以接受的; 合適的: *one of many possible answers* 許多可能的答案中的一個

★**pos·si·bly** /'pɒsəblɪ; 'pɒsɪ̯bli/ *adv* **1** in accordance with what is POSSIBLE(1) 可能地: *I'll do all I possibly can.* 我將盡我所能去做。| *You can't possibly walk 20 miles in an hour.* 你不可能一小時步行二十英里。**2** perhaps 也許，或許: *"Will you come with us tomorrow?"* *"Possibly."* "你明天和我們一起來嗎？" "可能會的。"

■ USAGE 用法: **Possibly** is commonly used in requests to make them sound less direct and, therefore, more polite ☆ **possibly** 常用於請求，以使之更加婉轉而禮貌: **Could you possibly** *give me a hand with the washing up?* 你能幫我洗碗碟嗎？| **Could I possibly** *borrow your bike this afternon?* 今天下午我能借你的腳踏車一用嗎？| **I wonder if I could possibly** *borrow £10.* 不知我可不可以問你借十英鎊。

★**post¹** /post; pəust/ *n* **1** [C] an upright wooden or metal pole fixed into the ground〔木製或金屬的〕柱，桿，樁: *a gate post* 門柱 | *a signpost* 路標 **2** the place where a race begins or ends〔比賽的〕起點或終點標誌 **3** *BrE*〔英式〕(also 又作 **mail** *AmE*〔美式〕) [C;U] the official system for sending and receiving letters 郵政: *He sent it by post.* 他通過郵局把它寄了。| *I'll put it in the post today.* 我今天去把它寄出。**4** [U] a single official collection or delivery of letters 一批郵件: *Has the afternoon post gone yet?* 下午的郵件寄走了嗎？| *Is there any post for me?* 有沒有我的郵件？**5** [C] a job 工作，職位: *I saw an advertisement for the post.* 我(在報上)看到了這個職位的招聘廣告。| *the post* **of** *head teacher* 校長這一職位 –see 見 JOB (USAGE 用法) **6** [C] a place where someone, especially a soldier, does their job 崗位〔尤指崗哨〕: *I want all soldiers at their posts by 6 a.m.* 我要求所有的士兵凌晨六點之前站崗。

post² *v* [T] **1** to show something publicly, on a wall or board 公開招貼〔布告〕: *Examination results will be posted outside the staffroom.* 考試結果將貼在教員辦公室外面。**2** *BrE*〔英式〕(also 又作 **mail** *AmE*〔美式〕) to take a letter or parcel to a post office or put one into a collection box for sending 郵寄〔信件或包裹〕: *Did you remember to post the letters?* 你記得去寄信了嗎？**3** keep

someone posted to continue to give someone all the latest news about something 不斷把最新消息告訴某人 **·4** to send someone, especially a soldier, to a particular place to work 派駐〔某人，尤指士兵〕: *John has been posted to Hong Kong.* 約翰已被派往香港工作。

post·age /'pɒstɪdʒ; 'pəʊstɪdʒ/ *n* [U] the charge for sending or delivering something by post 郵費: *The books will cost £9, including postage.* 這些書一共要九英鎊，包括郵費。

postage stamp /'·· ·/ *n fml*〔正式〕see 見 STAMP² (1)

post·al /'pɒstl; 'pəʊstl/ *adj* [only before a noun 只用於名詞前] connected with the post service 郵政的: *The postal workers are on strike again.* 郵政工人又罷工了。

postal or·der /'·· ·/ *n* a small piece of paper that can be bought from a post office and sent to someone, who can exchange it at a post office for a stated amount of money 郵政匯票

post·box /'pɒst,bɒks; 'pəʊstbɒks/ *n* **1** *BrE*〔英式〕(also 又作 **letterbox**) an official box which you put letters into if you want to send them by post 郵筒，郵箱 **2** *AmE* a small numbered box in a post office for receiving mail〔美式〕〔郵局內有編號的〕郵政信箱 –see picture on page 729 見 729 頁彩圖

post·card /'pɒst,kɑːd; 'pəʊstkɑːd/ *n* a card, often with a picture on one side, on which a message can be sent by post 明信片

post·code /'pɒst,kəʊd; 'pəʊstkəʊd/ *n BrE* a group of letters and numbers written at the end of an address so that letters will be delivered more quickly〔英式〕郵政編碼

post·date /ˌpɒst'deɪt; ˌpəʊst'deɪt/ *v* **postdated, postdating** [T] to write a date later than the actual date of writing on a letter or cheque 把〔信或支票的〕日期填遲: *I'll give you a postdated cheque.* 我會給你一張期票。

post·er /'pəʊstə; 'pəʊstər/ *n* a large printed notice or picture put up in a public place 海報: *gazing at the posters in the travel agent's window* 注視著旅行社櫥窗裡的海報

pos·te·ri·or /pɒs'tɪərɪə; pɒ'stɪərɪər/ *n* the part of your body that you sit on (a word which is often used in a humorous way) 臀部〔常作幽默用法〕

pos·ter·i·ty /pɒs'terətɪ; pɒ'sterbti/ *n* [U] *fml* people who will be born and live after your own time〔正式〕後代，子孫

post·grad·u·ate /ˌpəʊst'grædʒuɪt; ˌpəʊst'grædjuət/ *n* (also 又作 **graduate** *AmE*〔美式〕) a person doing advanced studies at a university, done after a first degree 研究生 –**postgraduate** *adj*: *postgraduate studies* 研究生的研究學習

post·hu·mous /'pɒstʃʊməs; 'pɒstʃ̍ʊməs/ *adj* coming after a person's death 死後的，身後的 –**posthumously** *adv*: *His last book was published posthumously.* 他最後一本書是在

死後才出版的。

post·ing /ˈpəʊstɪŋ; ˈpəʊstɪŋ/ *n* being sent to a job in another town or country 派駐〔其他城市或國家〕，派任

post·man /ˈpəʊstmən; ˈpəʊstmən/ *n* **postmen** /-mən; -mən/ a person employed to collect and deliver letters and parcels 郵遞員, 郵差

post·mark /ˈpəʊstˌmɑːk; ˈpəʊstmɑːk/ *n* an official mark made on letters or parcels, over the stamp, showing when and from where they are sent 郵戳 –**postmark** *v* [T]: *The parcel was postmarked London.* 包裹上印着倫敦的郵戳。

post·mas·ter /ˈpəʊstˌmɑːstə; ˈpəʊstˌmɑːstər/ *n* a person officially in charge of a post office; a female postmaster is usually called a **postmistress** 郵局局長〔女郵局局長通常稱作 **postmistress**〕

post·mor·tem /ˌpəʊstˈmɔːtəm; ˌpəʊstˈmɔːtəm/ *n* an examination of a dead body by doctors to discover the cause of death 屍體解剖, 驗屍

post·na·tal /ˌpəʊstˈneɪtl; ˌpəʊstˈneɪtl/ *adj tech* concerning the time after a birth 〔術語〕產後的: *postnatal depression* 產後抑鬱症

post of·fice /ˈ· ·ˌ··/ *n* **1** a building where you can buy stamps, send parcels, collect money paid to you by the government, and make certain payments 郵局 **2 the Post Office** the national organization which provides these services 郵政局

post·pone /pəʊstˈpəʊn; pəʊsˈpəʊn/ *v* **postponed, postponing** [T] to move to a later time 推遲, 延期: *We're postponing our holiday until August.* 我們打算把假期推遲到八月份。–**postponement** *n* [C;U]

post·script /ˈpəʊsˌskrɪpt; ˈpəʊstˌskrɪpt/ *n* (also 又作 **P.S.** *infml* 〔非正式〕) a short addition to a letter, below the place where you have signed your name 〔信末簽名後的〕附筆, 又及

pos·tu·late /ˈpɒstjʊˌleɪt; ˈpɒstʃəleɪt/ *v* **postulated, postulating** [T; +that] *fml* to suggest that something is true, often so that you can continue talking about a subject 〔正式〕假定, 假設

pos·ture¹ /ˈpɒstʃə; ˈpɒstʃər/ *n* **1** [U] the way a person holds their body when they are walking or sitting 姿勢; 姿態: *She's got very good posture.* 她的姿勢非常好。 **2** [C] a particular position of the body 某一姿勢: *She photographed me in a relaxed posture.* 她給我照了張姿勢輕鬆的照片。

posture² *v* **postured, posturing** [I] to behave unnaturally in order to attract attention or deceive people 故作姿態, 裝腔作勢〔以引人注意或欺騙別人〕

post-vi·ral syn·drome /ˌ· ··· ··/ *n* [U] an illness which makes you very tired and unable to work for many months 病毒後綜合徵〔一種令人疲憊而數月無法工作的疾病〕

post·war /ˈpəʊstˈwɔː; ˌpəʊstˈwɔːr/ *adj* [only before a noun 只用於名詞前] in the time after a war 戰後的

po·sy /ˈpəʊzɪ; ˈpəʊzi/ *n* **posies** a small bunch of flowers 小花束

***pot¹** /pɒt; pɒt/ *n* **1** [C] a round container, used especially for cooking 罐; 壺; 鍋: *I've made a big pot of soup.* 我煮了一大鍋湯。 | *pots and pans* 廚房炊具, 鍋碗瓢盆 | *a cast-iron pot* 鑄鐵鍋 –see picture on page 244 244 頁彩圖 **2** [C] (also 又作 **potful** /ˈpɒtfʊl; ˈpɒtfʊl/) the amount that a pot will hold 一罐; 一壺; 一鍋: *A pot of tea for two, please.* 請來一壺兩人喝的茶。 **3 pots of money** *infml* a large amount of money 〔非正式〕大筆錢 **4** [U] *infml* MARIJUANA 〔非正式〕大麻 **5 go to pot** *infml* to become ruined from lack of care 〔非正式〕〔因缺乏照料而〕遭到毀壞 **6 take pot luck** *infml* to take what is offered, without having any choice 〔非正式〕接受已有的東西: *Come to dinner tonight — though I'm afraid you'll have to take pot luck!* 今晚來吃飯吧——雖然我恐怕那只是一頓便飯!

pot² *v* **-tt-** [T] to put a plant in a pot filled with earth 把〔植物〕栽入花盆裡

po·ta·to /pəˈteɪtəʊ; pəˈteɪtəʊ/ *n* **potatoes** [C; U] a round white vegetable with a thin brown or yellow skin, that is cooked and served in many different ways 馬鈴薯, 土豆: *I've peeled the potatoes.* 我已給馬鈴薯削了皮。 | *baked potatoes* 烤馬鈴薯 | *Is there any mashed potato left?* 還有沒有馬鈴薯泥? –see picture on page 504 見 504 頁彩圖

potato chip /·ˈ·· ·/ *n* (also 又作 **chip**) the usual American and Australian word for 〔美式和澳式〕= a **CRISP³**

pot·bel·ly /ˈpɒtˌbɛlɪ; ˈpɒtˌbeli/ *n* **potbellies** a large round stomach (a word used to express disapproval, but usually used in a humorous way) 大肚皮〔含貶義, 但常作幽默用法〕

po·tent /ˈpəʊtnt; ˈpəʊtnt/ *adj fml* 〔正式〕 **1** very effective 非常有效的: *a potent argument* 有力的論據 **2** having a strong effect on your body or mind (used of medicines, drugs, or drinks) 有效力的; 烈性的〔指藥、毒品或酒〕 **3** able to have sex (used of a man) 具有性能力的〔指男子〕 –**potency** *n* [U]

po·ten·tate /ˈpəʊtnˌteɪt; ˈpəʊtnteɪt/ *n fml* a ruler with direct power over his or her people 〔正式〕君主, 統治者

***po·ten·tial¹** /pəˈtenʃəl; pəˈtenʃəl/ *adj* possibly going to happen or develop, although not existing at present 潛在的; 有可能的: *Every seed is a potential plant.* 每粒種子都可能長成植物。 | *She is seen as a potential Prime Minister.* 她被認為有可能成為首相。 –**potentially** *adv*

***potential²** *n* [sing; U] the possibility for developing or being developed 潛力, 潛能: *a new product with a big sales potential* 一種有很大銷售潛力的新產品 | *She has great po-*

pot·hole /ˈpɒt.həʊl/ n **1** a deep hole in a rocky area which often leads to caves underground〔多岩石地區的〕鍋穴, 壺穴 **2** a large hole in the surface of a road〔路面上的〕大洞, 坑窪

pot·hol·ing /ˈpɒt.həʊlɪŋ/ n [U] the sport of climbing down inside potholes 岩洞探險活動 –**potholer** n

po·tion /ˈpəʊʃən/ n lit a liquid mixture, given as medicine, poison, or a magic charm〔文〕〔液體狀的〕一服藥〔毒藥, 迷幻劑〕: a love potion 一服春藥

pot·shot /ˈpɒt.ʃɒt/ n infml a carelessly aimed shot〔非正式〕胡亂射擊

pot·ted /ˈpɒtɪd/ adj [only before a noun 只用於名詞前] **1** cooked and preserved in a small pot (used of meat or fish) 瓶裝的〔指肉或魚〕 **2** grown in a pot (used of a plant) 盆栽的〔指植物〕: potted palms 盆栽棕櫚 **3** produced in a short, simple form (a word used of a book, often to express disapproval) 簡略的, 簡化的〔指書, 常含貶義〕: potted biographies of world leaders 世界領導人物的小傳

pot·ter¹ /ˈpɒtə/ n a person who makes pots, dishes, etc., out of baked clay using their hands 製陶工人

potter² v

   potter about phr v [I] infml to spend time doing unimportant things in an unhurried way〔非正式〕閒蕩, 閒逛: I spent the afternoon pottering about in the garden. 我在花園裡閒蕩了一個下午。

pot·ter·y /ˈpɒtəri/ n **1** [U] the work of a potter 陶器製造 **2** [U] objects made out of baked clay 陶器: Modern pottery is usually decorated. 現代陶器一般都經過裝飾。| a pottery dish 陶碟 **3** [C] a place where pottery is made 陶器作坊; 陶瓷廠

pot·ty¹ /ˈpɒti/ adj pottier, pottiest BrE infml〔英式, 非正式〕**1** slightly mad 傻的, 瘋瘋癲癲的: That noise is driving me potty. 那噪音吵得我快發瘋了。**2 to be potty about** to like very much 對…着迷的: He's just potty about her! 他對她真是着了迷!

potty² n potties a plastic pot for children to use as a TOILET〔小孩用的〕便盆

pouch /paʊtʃ/ n **1** a small leather bag to hold tobacco or other things〔皮製的〕小煙袋; 小袋子 **2** a pocket of skin in which kangaroos (KANGAROO) and other animals carry their young〔袋鼠或其他動物的〕育兒袋

pouf /puf/ n (also 又作 **pouffe**) a drum-shaped low soft seat〔鼓形〕坐墊

poul·tice /ˈpəʊltɪs/ n a soft heated mixture, spread on a cloth and laid against your skin to reduce pain or swelling 膏藥, 泥敷劑

poul·try /ˈpəʊltri/ n **1** [pl] chickens and other farmyard birds kept for supplying eggs and meat 家禽 **2** [U] meat from chickens and other farmyard birds 家禽肉: Poultry is quite cheap nowadays. 目前家禽肉相當便宜。

pounce /paʊns/ v pounced, pouncing [I] **1** to jump on something in order to catch and eat it 猛撲; 撲向: The lioness suddenly pounced. 母獅突然猛撲上去。| The cat pounced **on** the bird. 貓猛然撲向那隻鳥。**2** to jump out and catch 突襲: Policemen were hiding in the bank, ready to pounce **on** the thieves. 警察躲在銀行裡, 準備突襲竊賊。

★pound¹ /paʊnd/ n **1** the British unit of money, divided into 100 pence 英鎊〔英國貨幣單位, 等於一百便士〕: Five pounds is usually written £5. 五英鎊通常寫作 £5。| a five-pound note 一張五英鎊的鈔票 | An eye test now costs ten pounds. 一次視力檢查現在要花十英鎊。**2 the pound** the value of British money compared with the money of other countries〔與其他貨幣相比〕英鎊的價值: What's the current exchange rate of the pound against the dollar? 英鎊兌美元現時的匯率是多少? **3** a unit for measuring weight, equal to 0.454 kilograms 磅〔重量單位, 等於 0.454 千克〕: Sugar is sold by the pound. 食糖按磅出售。| Two pounds of apples, please. 我要兩磅蘋果。| a baby weighing eight pounds three ounces (8lb 3oz) 一個體重為八磅三盎司的嬰兒 **4** a place where lost animals, or illegally parked cars, are kept by the police 走失牲畜〔貓狗〕待領處; 違章停放車輛扣押處 **5** **-pounder** something weighing a certain number of pounds …磅重的東西: I caught a five-pounder the last time I went fishing. 上次釣魚時我釣了一條五磅重的魚。

pound² v **1** [T] to crush something by hitting it repeatedly with a heavy object 搗碎, 擊碎: This machine pounds the stones into a powder. 這台機器把石頭搗成粉末。**2** [I; +adv/prep; T] to hit repeatedly, heavily, and noisily 連續猛擊: The stormy waves pounded **against** the rocks. 驚濤駭浪拍擊着岩石。| He pounded the table angrily. 他憤怒地捶打着桌子。**3 my heart pounded** a phrase used when you have a very strong feeling, such as fear or excitement 我的心砰砰地跳〔用於表示恐懼或激動〕: My heart pounded **with** excitement. 我的心激動得砰砰亂跳。–**pounding** n [sing; U]: the pounding of my heart 我的心砰砰跳

★pour /pɔː/ v **1** [T] to cause a liquid or a loose substance to flow into or out of a container 倒; 灌; 注: She poured some sugar into a bowl. 她把一些糖倒入碗裡。| Pour the dirty water away outside. 把髒水倒到外面去。**2** [T] (also 又作 **pour out**) to fill a glass or cup with a drink 倒酒〔飲料〕: Could you pour the tea? 你來倒茶好嗎? | I poured out two cups of coffee. 我倒了兩杯咖啡。**3 pour yourself/someone a drink** to fill a glass or

---

cup with a drink for yourself or someone else 給自己/某人倒杯飲料: *He poured himself a stiff whisky.* 他給自己倒了一杯濃烈的威士忌。 **4** [I; +adv/prep] to flow steadily and rapidly 不斷地流出: *Smoke was pouring from the engine.* 煙從引擎裡不斷地冒出來。 | *Water poured into the boat.* 水不斷地流進小艇裡。 | *At four o'clock children poured out of the school.* 四點鐘孩子們便從學校蜂湧而出。 **5** [I] to rain hard and steadily 〔雨〕傾瀉, 滂沱: *The rain poured* **down** *all day.* 大雨下了一整天。 | *We waited in the pouring rain.* 我們在滂沱大雨中等着。 **6 it's pouring with rain** = it's raining very hard 大雨傾盆而下

pour sth ↔ **out** *v* [T] **1** to POUR (2) 倒滿〔飲料〕 **2** to tell someone your thoughts or experiences, freely and quickly 傾吐, 傾訴: *He suddenly poured out all his troubles.* 他突然把所有的煩惱都傾訴出來。

pout /paʊt; paʊt/ *v* [I] to push forward your lips in order to show that you are annoyed or to attract sexual interest 撅嘴〔為了表示慍怒或吸引異性〕—**pout** *n*

*★**pov·er·ty** /ˈpɑvɚtɪ; ˈpɔvəti/ *n* [U] the state of being poor 貧窮, 貧困: *families living in poverty* 生活在貧困中的家庭

poverty-strick·en /ˈ··· ,·ˈ/ *adj* very poor 極度貧窮的

POW /ˌpi o ˈdʌblju; ˌpiː əʊ ˈdʌbəljuː/ see 見 PRISONER OF WAR

pow·der¹ /ˈpaʊdɚ; ˈpaʊdəʳ/ *n* **1** [C;U] a substance in the form of very small grains 粉, 粉末: *That packet of white powder the police found in his room turned out to be cocaine.* 警察在他的房間裡找到的那包白色粉末原來是可卡因。 | *These soap powders are all the same.* 這些肥皂粉都是一樣的。 **2** [U] a pleasant-smelling substance in this form which you use on your skin 〔擦在皮膚上的〕香粉: *baby powder* 嬰兒爽身粉 | *The only make-up she uses is powder and lipstick.* 她所用的唯一的化妝品是撲面粉和口紅。

powder² *v* [T] to put face powder or TALCUM POWDER on your skin 塗擦面粉; 塗茶身粉: *John powdered the baby after her bath.* 約翰在給洗過澡的嬰兒撲上爽身粉。

pow·dered /ˈpaʊdɚd; ˈpaʊdəd/ *adj* **1** produced or dried in the form of powder 粉狀的: *powdered milk* 奶粉 **2** covered with powder 塗上粉的: *powdered hair* 撲了粉的頭髮

powder room /ˈ·· ·/ *n AmE* a women's public TOILET in a theatre, hotel, restaurant, or large shop 〔美式〕〔劇院、旅館、飯店、大商店等的〕女洗手間

pow·der·y /ˈpaʊdərɪ; ˈpaʊdəri/ *adj* like powder, or easily broken into powder 粉狀的; 易變成粉的

*★**pow·er¹** /ˈpaʊɚ; ˈpaʊəʳ/ *n* **1** [sing; U] control over people, a place, or a situation 權勢, 權力; 控制權: *Now I've got him in my power!* 現在他受我支配了! | *The British Queen doesn't have any real power.* 英國女王沒有實權。 **2 be in power** to govern or control a country 執政: *This government has been in power for two years.* 這屆政府已執政兩年了。 **3 come to power** to begin to be in control of the government 執掌政權: *She came to power in 1990.* 她於1990年上台執政。 **4 return someone to power** to give someone control of the government as the result of an election 〔在選舉中獲勝後〕重新執政: *I'm hoping the Democratic Party will be returned to power.* 我希望民主黨能夠重新執政。 **5 seize power** to take control of the government 奪取政權: *The army seized power in a coup d'état.* 軍隊在一場政變中奪取了政權。 **6** [C] legal rights to act or official permission to do something 〔合法的〕權力; 職能: *He doesn't have the power to make a final decision.* 他無權做出最後的決定。 | *The police now have greater powers than they used to.* 警方現在的權力比過去大。 **7** [U] (also 又作 **powers** [pl]) a physical ability or a skill 能力; 技能: *the power* **of** *speech* 說話的能力 | *I don't have the power to see into the future, you know.* 你要知道，我沒有能力預見未來。 **8 be in/within someone's power** to be possible for someone to do 在某人的能力所及範圍之內: *I did everything in my power to help them.* 我盡自己所能幫助他們。 **9** [C] a strong and important country or group 強大的國家; 有權力[影響力]的組織: *a meeting of world powers* 一次世界強國的會議 **10 the powers that be** *infml* the people in official positions who make decisions that change our lives (a word which is often used in a humorous way) 〔非正式〕當權派; 掌權者〔常作幽默用法〕 **11** [U] **a** force that can be used to produce electricity or make a machine work 動力 **b** electricity 電力: *solar power* 太陽能 | *nuclear power* 核能 | *Switch on the power.* 打開電源開關。 | *in darkness because of a power cut* 由於斷電而處在一片漆黑之中 **12** [U] force or strength 力量: *the power of words* 言辭的力量 | *Japan's industrial power* 日本的工業實力 **13 to the power of** multiplied by itself a particular number of times (used of a number, in MATHEMATICS) 〔數學中的〕冪, 乘方: *2 to the power of 3,* or 2^3, *means* $2 \times 2 \times 2$. 二的三次方, 也就是 2^3, 表示 $2 \times 2 \times 2$。 **14 -powered** using a certain type of ENERGY 用…為能源的: *a nuclear-powered submarine* 核動力潛艇

power² *v* [T] to supply power to a vehicle or machine 為〔車輛或機器〕提供動力, 以動力驅動

*★**pow·er·ful** /ˈpaʊɚfəl; ˈpaʊəfəl/ *adj* **1** very strong, or having great power 強大的; 強而有力的: *a powerful swimmer* 游泳健將 | *a meeting of the world's most powerful nations* 世界最強國家的一次會議 | *The ship is driven by two powerful motors.* 這艘船是由兩

部高功率馬達驅動的。**2** having a strong effect 效力大的: *The minister made a powerful speech.* 部長作了一次作用很大的講話。| *a powerful drug* 強效藥 –**powerfully** *adv*

pow·er·less /'pauəlɪs; 'pauələs/ *adj* **1** not having any power or influence 無能力的; 無影響力的 **2 powerless to do something** completely unable to do something 無能力做某事: *He was powerless to stop the accident.* 他無力阻止事故的發生。–**powerlessly** *adv* –**powerlessness** *n* [U]

power sta·tion /'·· ,··/ *n* (also 又作 **power plant** /'·· ·/) a large building in which electricity is made 發電廠; 發電站 –see picture on page 470 見 470 頁彩圖

pp a written abbreviation for 〖縮〗= pages: *see pp 15-37* 見第 15-37 頁

PR /piː 'ɑr; piː 'ɑːʳ/ *n* [U] see 見 PUBLIC RELATIONS

prac·ti·ca·ble /'præktɪkəbl; 'præktɪkəbl/ *adj* that can be done successfully 可行的, 行得通的: *Is it practicable to try to grow crops in deserts?* 在沙漠中種植莊稼可行嗎? –**opposite** 反義 **impracticable** –**practicably** *adv* –**practicability** /,præktɪkə'bɪlət; ,præktɪkə'bɪlᵻti/ *n* [U]

> ■ USAGE 用法: People are beginning to use **practical** with the same meaning as **practicable**; a **practical/practicable** plan or suggestion is one that will work. **Practicable** is not used of people ☆ 人們已開始將 **practical** 與 **practicable** 用作同樣的意思。這兩個詞都可以指計劃或建議是 "可行的"。**practicable** 不用於指人。

prac·ti·cal¹ /'præktɪkl; 'præktɪkəl/ *adj* **1** concerned with real situations and actions, rather than with ideas 實際的; 實踐的: *She has finished her training but hasn't had any practical experience yet.* 她已完成了訓練, 但還沒有任何實踐的經驗。–see 見 PRACTICABLE (USAGE 用法) **2** sensible and good at dealing with real situations 切合實際的: *We've got to be practical and buy only what we can afford.* 我們必須切合實際, 只買我們買得起的東西。**3** good at doing or making things with your hands 實事求是的: *My father is very clever, but he's not very practical.* 我的父親很聰明, 但不大實事求是。**4** useful and suitable for a particular purpose 符合需要的, 實用的: *a very practical little table that folds up out of the way when it is not needed* 不需要時可摺疊好收起來的一張非常實用的小桌子 | *Their new carpet is beautiful, but I don't think white is a very practical colour.* 他們的新地毯很漂亮, 但我覺得白色不太實用。–**practicality** /,præktɪ'kælət; ,præktɪ'kælᵻti/ *n* **practicalities** [C;U]: *Please stick to practicalities.* 請不要離開實際性原則。

practical² *n* *infml* a lesson or test in which you have to do or make something, instead of writing about it 〖非正式〗實驗課; 實踐考試: *a chemistry practical* 化學實驗課

practical joke /,·· '·/ *n* a trick played on someone to make them look silly and to amuse other people 惡作劇

prac·ti·cally /'præktɪklɪ; 'præktɪklɪ/ *adv* **1** almost 幾乎, 差不多: *The holidays are practically over; there's only one day left.* 假期差不多完了, 只剩下一天了。**2** in a practical way 從實際出發

prac·tice¹ /'præktɪs; 'præktᵻs/ *v* **practiced, practicing** [I;T] the usual American spelling of 〖美式〗= PRACTISE²

practice² *n* (also 又作 **practise** *AmE* 〖美式〗) **1** [U] regularly repeated performance of an activity in order to improve your ability or skill 練習; 訓練: *It takes a lot of practice to become a good swimmer.* 要成為一個優秀的游泳運動員, 就要做大量訓練。| *He's going to football practice after school.* 放學後他去練習踢足球。| *The trainees now have six weeks teaching practice.* 學員現在要參加六星期的教學實習。–see 見 HABIT (USAGE 用法) **2 out of practice** unable to do something well because of lack of practice 疏於練習 **3 in practice** when something is actually done, rather than just talked about 付諸實行: *It sounded a good idea, but in practice it simply didn't work.* 這主意聽起來不錯, 但一付諸實踐便行不通。**4 put something into practice** to take action regarding something 把某事付諸實踐: *We've made our plans, and now we must put them into practice.* 我們已制定了計劃, 現在必須把它們付諸實踐。**5** [U] *fml* the usual way of doing something 〖正式〗習慣做法, 慣例: *Tipping is common practice in most restaurants.* 給小費是大部分餐館裡的慣例。**6** [C] an activity or habit that is regularly repeated 常規; 習俗: *religious practices* 宗教慣例 **7** [C] the business of a doctor or lawyer 〔醫生或律師的〕業務

prac·tise¹ /'præktɪs; 'præktᵻs/ *n* the usual American spelling of 〖美式〗= PRACTICE²

practise² *v* **practised, practising** (also 又作 **practice** *AmE* 〖美式〗) **1** [I;T] to regularly repeat an activity in order to improve your ability or skill 練習; 訓練: *She practises the piano for two hours every day.* 她每天練習彈兩小時鋼琴。| *I'm not very good at parking the car; I'll have to practise.* 我不太善於停車, 我得練習一下。| *He's practising doing handstands.* 他在練習倒立。**2** [T] *fml* to do 〖正式〗做, 幹; 奉行: *an old custom still practised in the smaller communities* 在小社區內仍奉行的古老習俗 **3 practise what you preach** to do yourself what you are always telling other people to do 以身作則 **4** [I;T] to do the work of a doctor or lawyer 從事

〔醫生或律師〕的職業: *She practises medicine.* 她是行醫的。| *He practises as a doctor.* 他執業為醫生。| *a practising lawyer* 執業律師 **5** [T] to act according to the ideas and customs of your religion 按宗教信仰行事: *She's a practising Muslim.* 她是個按教義行事的虔誠的穆斯林教徒。

prac·tised /ˈpræktɪst; ˈprækt̬st/ *adj* (also 又作 **practiced** *AmE*〔美式〕) skilled because of having had a lot of practice 熟練的, 精通…的 *a practised liar* 撒謊的老手 | *Our mother was practised in the art of storytelling.* 我們的母親精於講故事。

****prac·ti·tion·er** /prækˈtɪʃənə; prækˈtɪʃənər/ *n* a person who works in a profession, especially a doctor or a lawyer 執業者〔尤指醫生或律師〕: *medical practitioners* 執業醫生

prag·mat·ic /prægˈmætɪk; prægˈmætɪk/ *adj* dealing with matters in the way that seems best in the real situation, rather than following a principle or rule 務實的; 注重實效的 –**pragmatically** /-klɪ; -klɪ/ *adv*

prag·ma·tis·m /ˈprægmətɪzəm; ˈprægmətɪzəm/ *n* [U] pragmatic ways of considering things 務實的想法或做法; 實用主義 –**pragmatist** *n*

prai·rie /ˈpreəri; ˈpreəri/ *n* a wide treeless grassy plain, especially in North America 〔尤指北美的〕大草原

praise¹ /prez; preɪz/ *v* **praised, praising** [T] **1** to speak of someone or something with admiration and approval 稱讚, 讚揚: *She was praised for her achievements as a sportswoman.* 作為一名運動員, 她由於取得了成就而受到讚揚。**2** *fml or lit*〔正式或文〕to offer thanks and honour to God, especially in song〔尤指唱歌〕讚頌〔上帝〕

praise² *n* **1** [U] expression of admiration 稱讚, 讚揚: *His new film has received high praise from the critics.* 他的新電影受到影評人的高度讚揚。**2** [U] *fml or lit*〔正式或文〕worship 崇拜, 讚美: *Let us give praise to God.* 讓我們來讚美上帝吧。**3 sing the praises of** to praise very strongly 高度讚揚: *He's always singing your praises.* 他總是對你讚不絕口。

praise·wor·thy /ˈprezwɜːði; ˈpreɪzwɜːði/ *adj fml* deserving praise〔正式〕值得讚揚的 –**praiseworthiness** *n* [U]

pram /præm; præm/ *n* a four-wheeled carriage, pushed by hand, for a baby (四輪手推)嬰兒車

prance /præns; prɑːns/ *v* **pranced, prancing** [I] **1** (of a horse) to move making quick high steps〔馬〕騰躍 **2** to move or walk in a proud or excited way that attracts attention 神氣活現地走: *Jane pranced about in front of the mirror trying on the clothes.* 簡穿著新衣服在鏡子前面神氣地走來走去。

prank /præŋk; præŋk/ *n* a playful trick, not intended to harm anyone 玩笑, 惡作劇

prat·tle /ˈprætl; ˈprætl/ *v* **prattled, prattling** [I] to talk continually about unimportant or meaningless things 喋喋不休; 閒聊: *He prattled on about his job.* 他嘮嘮叨叨地談着他的工作。–**prattle** *n* [U]

prawn /prɔn; prɔːn/ *n* a small pink sea animal that you can eat, larger than a SHRIMP 對蝦, 明蝦, 大蝦

pray /pre; preɪ/ *v* [I;T;+(that)] **1** to speak to God giving thanks, or asking for help 祈禱; 禱告: *They went to the mosque to pray.* 他們到清真寺做禱告。| *I will pray to God for your safety.* 我要向上帝祈禱保佑你平安。| *They prayed that their enemies might be defeated.* 他們祈求上蒼要敵軍敗陣。**2** *infml* to hope very strongly〔非正式〕希望, 渴望: *We're praying for good weather on our wedding day.* 我們很希望在婚禮當天天氣很好。| *He prayed that she wouldn't turn around.* 他希望她不要改變主意。

****prayer** /prɛr; preər/ *n* **1** [U] the act of praying to God 祈禱, 禱告: *They believe that prayer can bring peace to the world.* 他們相信禱告能給世界帶來和平。**2** [C] a soleman request made to God 祈求: *Her prayer was answered, and her parents came home safely.* 她的祈求應驗了, 她的父母平安地回到了家。**3** [C] a fixed form of words said to God 禱詞: *The children said their prayers at bedtime.* 孩子們在睡覺的時候念了禱詞。| *a prayer book* 祈禱書 **4 prayers** [pl] a religious service for a particular group of people 祈禱儀式: *school prayers* 學校的祈禱儀式

preach /pritʃ; priːtʃ/ *v* **1** [I;T] to give a religious talk as part of a service in church 傳教; 佈道: *Christ preached to large crowds.* 基督向群眾傳教。| *The priest preached a sermon on the importance of caring for the old and sick.* 神父佈道中宣講照顧老人和病人的重要性。**2** [T] to advise or urge other people to accept something that you believe in 宣揚, 鼓吹: *She's always preaching socialism.* 她一直在宣揚社會主義。**3** [I] to give unwanted advice on matters of right and wrong 勸誡, 告誡: *The teacher preached at us about being lazy.* 老師告誡我們不要懶惰。–**preacher** *n*

pre·am·ble /ˈpriæmbl̩; ˈpriːæmbəl/ *n* an introduction to a speech or piece of writing, stating its purpose, and often using too many words 序言; 序文; 開場白

pre·ar·range /ˌpriəˈrendʒ; ˌpriːəˈreɪndʒ/ *v* **prearranged, prearranging** [T] to arrange in advance 預先安排, 預定: *The car arrived at a prearranged time.* 汽車按預定時間抵達。

pre·car·i·ous /prɪˈkɛrɪəs; prɪˈkeəriəs/ *adj* unsafe and likely to fall 危險的; 不穩的: *John was in a precarious position at the top of the ladder.* 約翰站在梯子上端一個十分不穩的位置。–**precariously** *adv* –**precariousness** *n* [U]

pre·cau·tion /prɪˈkɔʃən; prɪˈkɔːʃən/ *n* an action done to avoid something dangerous or unpleasant happening 預防措施: *You should make a copy of the disk, as a precaution.* 你應該複製這張磁盤作為預防措施。| *They've taken every precaution against theft.* 他們已採取了一切防盜措施。– **precautionary** *adj*: *a precautionary X-ray* 預防性 X 光檢查

*pre·cede /prɪˈsiːd; prɪˈsiːd/ v preceded, preceding [I;T] fml to come or go before someone or something else 〔正式〕在…之前, 先於…: The wedding was preceded by weeks of preparation. 婚禮前做了幾個星期的準備工作。| Several bodyguards preceded the President into the palace. 有幾位保鏢護在總統前面進入了大廈。–preceding adj [always before a noun 只能用於名詞前]: This is described in detail in the preceding chapter. 這在前一章已做了詳細描述。

pre·ce·dence /ˈprɪsɪdn̩s; ˈpresɪ̩dəns/ n [U] 1 the right of something to be put first because it is more important than something else 優先權: The needs of the community must take precedence over the wishes of individuals. 社區的需要比個人的意願重要。 2 in order of precedence in order of importance 按輕重緩急

pre·ce·dent /ˈpresədənt; ˈpresɪ̩dənt/ n [C;U] an action or decision that is used as an example for a similar action or decision at a later time 先例: The judge's decision has set a precedent for women seeking equal pay. 法官的判決為尋求同工同酬的婦女開創了先例。

pre·cept /ˈprɪsept; ˈpriːsept/ n a rule which guides behaviour 戒律, 格言

pre·cinct /ˈprɪsɪŋkt; ˈpriːsɪŋkt/ n 1 [C] BrE a shopping area in a town, where no cars are allowed 〔英式〕〔禁止汽車駛進的〕商業區域: a new shopping precinct 一個新的商業區 2 [C] AmE a division of a town or city for election or police purposes 〔美式〕選舉區; 警察管轄區 3 precincts [pl] the enclosed space that surrounds important buildings 〔重要建築物的〕周圍地區: It's quiet within the precincts of the old college. 那所古老學院的校園十分寧靜。

pre·cious¹ /ˈpreʃəs; ˈpreʃəs/ adj 1 of great value because of being rare or expensive 珍貴的, 寶貴的: Water is a very precious resource. 水是非常珍貴的資源。 2 very special to you 特別的: I have some precious memories of our time together. 我的記憶之中藏珍存著我們在一起的時光。 3 delicate and rather unnatural in manner 矯揉造作的: a rather precious young man 一個相當造作的年輕人 4 a word you use when you want to show your annoyance concerning something that someone else thinks is important 〔用於對別人認為是重要的事物表示不高興〕"寶貝": I wish you'd shut up about your precious car! 我希望你能閉上嘴, 不要再談你的那輛寶貝汽車!

precious² adv precious few, precious little very few or very little 非常少的: We have precious little time left. 我們只剩一點點時間了。

precious met·al /ˌ… ˈ…/ n [C;U] a valuable metal, such as gold or silver 貴重金屬〔如金或銀〕

precious stone /ˌ… ˈ…/ n a valuable jewel, such as a diamond or EMERALD 寶石〔如鑽石或綠寶石〕

pre·ci·pice /ˈpresəpɪs; ˈpresɪ̩pɪs/ n a steep side of a high mountain or cliff 懸崖, 峭壁

pre·cip·i·tate¹ /prɪˈsɪpəˌtet; prɪˈsɪpɪ̩teɪt/ v precipitated, precipitating [T] fml to make something happen quickly and suddenly 〔正式〕促成〔某事物〕突發; 加速: the fears of the public which precipitated the great economic crash of 1929 加速了 1929 年經濟大崩潰的公眾恐慌

pre·cip·i·tate² /prɪˈsɪpəˌtɪt; prɪˈsɪpɪ̩tɪt/ adj fml done in a hurry, without thinking 〔正式〕倉促的; 魯莽的 –precipitately adv

pre·cip·i·tous /prɪˈsɪpətəs; prɪˈsɪpɪ̩təs/ adj dangerously steep 險峻的, 陡峭的

pré·cis /ˈpreˈsiː; ˈpreɪsiː/ n [plural is 複數為 précis /ˈpreˈsiːz; ˈpreɪsiːz/] a short piece of writing which gives only the main points of a longer piece 摘要, 概要, 梗概

*pre·cise /prɪˈsaɪs; prɪˈsaɪs/ adj 1 exact and correct 精確的, 準確的: The measurements need to be very precise. 尺寸量度要非常精確。 2 to be precise a phrase you use when you are adding slightly more exact information to something you have just said 確切地說〔用於令信息更加精確〕: It's a little after three o'clock. Five past three, to be precise. 現在三點剛過。確切地說是三點五分。 3 careful about small details 講求精確的, 周密的: She was very precise in her calculations. 她的計算非常周密。

*pre·cise·ly /prɪˈsaɪslɪ; prɪˈsaɪsli/ adv 1 exactly 精確地, 確切地; 正好: She didn't know precisely how he made his money. 她不十分清楚他的錢是怎樣弄來的。 2 a word used to show you agree with what has been said 對, 確實如此〔表示同意對方所說的話〕: "So you think it was a mistake?" "Precisely." "這麼說你認為這是個錯誤?" "確實如此。"

pre·ci·sion¹ /prɪˈsɪʒən; prɪˈsɪʒən/ n (also 又作 preciseness /prɪˈsaɪsnəs; prɪˈsaɪsnɪ̩s/) [U] exactness 精確: The distance to the moon has been measured with great precision. (地球)到月球的距離已測量得非常精確。

precision² adj [only before another noun 只用於另一名詞前] 1 made or done with great exactness 精確的: precision bombing 精確轟炸 2 used for producing exact results 精密的: precision engineering 精密工程學

pre·clude /prɪˈklud; prɪˈkluːd/ v precluded, precluding [T] fml to make impossible 〔正

式〕使不可能; 排除: *These terrorist attacks preclude any prospect of a peaceful settlement.* 這些恐怖分子的襲擊排除了和平解決的可能性。

pre·co·cious /prɪˈkoʃəs; prɪˈkəʊʃəs/ *adj* showing unusually early development or behaviour in a way that is too grown up (used of a child) 早熟的〔指孩子〕 –**precociousness, precocity** /prɪˈkɑsətɪ; prɪˈkɒsɨ̩tɪ/ *n* [U]

pre·con·ceived /ˌprikənˈsivd; ˌpriːkən-ˈsiːvd◂/ *adj* formed in advance, without enough knowledge or experience to be true or fair (used of an idea) 先入為主的〔指想法〕 –**preconception** /-kənˈsɛpʃən; -kən-ˈsepʃən/ *n*: *I had a lot of preconceptions about America, but when I actually went there, I loved it!* 過去我對美國有許多先入之見, 但當我真的去了那裡, 我就愛上了它!

pre·con·di·tion /ˌprikənˈdɪʃən; ˌpriːkən-dɪ-ʃən/ *n* something that must be agreed to in advance if something else is to happen 先決條件, 前提: *The management have laid down certain preconditions to talks.* 資方已為談判列出了先決條件。

pre·cur·sor /prɪˈkɝsɚ; prɪˈkɜːsəʳ/ *n fml* something that exists before something else and leads to it or develops into it 〔正式〕前身; 先驅: *Here it is. The precursor of the modern car!* 請看這一部 —— 現代汽車的前身!

pred·a·tor /ˈprɛdətɚ; ˈpredətəʳ/ *n* an animal that kills and eats other animals 食肉動物; 猛獸

pred·a·to·ry /ˈprɛdəˌtorɪ; ˈpredətəri/ *adj* **1** living by killing and eating other animals 靠捕食其他動物為生的 **2** trying to take advantage of other people in order to gain something 愛敲竹槓的: *Tourists should watch out for predatory shopkeepers.* 遊客應當提防愛敲竹槓的店主。

pre·de·ces·sor /ˌprɛdɪˈsɛsɚ; ˈpriːdɨ̩sesəʳ/ *n* **1** a person who held a position before someone else 前任, 前輩: *Our new doctor is much younger than his predecessor.* 我們新來的醫生比前任醫生年輕得多。 **2** something which has now been followed by something else 原先的東西: *This latest plan to save the company seems to me no better than any of its predecessors.* 這個挽救公司的最新計劃似乎不比以前的幾個計劃好。

pre·des·ti·na·tion /prɪˌdɛstəˈneʃən; prɪˌdes-tɨ̩ˈneɪʃən/ *n* [U] the belief that God or fate has decided everything that will happen, and that no human effort can change things 宿命論, 命定論

pre·des·tined /prɪˈdɛstɪnd; prɪˈdestɨ̩nd/ *adj fml* decided in advance by God or fate 〔正式〕(命中) 注定的: *I felt we were predestined to meet.* 我覺得我們注定要遇見。

pre·de·ter·mine /ˌpridɪˈtɝmɪn; ˌpriːdɪˈtɜː-mɨ̩n/ *v* **predetermined, predetermining** [T]

to fix in advance 事先決定: *The colour of a person's eyes is predetermined by those of his parents.* 一個人眼睛的顏色是由他父母眼睛的顏色預先決定好了的。

pre·dic·a·ment /prɪˈdɪkəmənt; prɪˈdɪkə-mənt/ *n* a difficult or unpleasant situation in which you must decide what to do 困境, 尷尬的處境

pred·i·cate /ˈprɛdɪkɪt; ˈpredɨ̩kɨ̩t/ *n* the part of a sentence which tells you about the subject 〔語法中的〕謂語: *In "She is an artist", "is an artist" is the predicate.* 在 "She is an artist" 中, "is an artist" 是謂語。

pred·ic·a·tive /ˈprɛdɪˌketɪv; prɪˈdɪkətɪv/ *adj* coming after a verb (used of an adjective or phrase) 〔形容詞或短語〕用作表語的: *In "She is happy", "happy" is a predicative adjective.* 在 "She is happy" 一句中, "happy" 是表語形容詞。

***pre·dict** /prɪˈdɪkt; prɪˈdɪkt/ *v* [T;+(that)] to say in advance that something will happen 預言, 預測: *A fortune-teller predicted that she would become famous.* 一位算命先生預言她將會成名。| *Weather forecasters are predicting storms over the weekend.* 天氣預報員預告週末將有暴風雨。| *They can't predict when it might occur.* 他們預測不出這件事會在何時發生。

pre·dic·ta·ble /prɪˈdɪktəbḷ; prɪˈdɪktəbəl/ *adj* not being or doing anything unexpected (a word sometimes used to show disapproval) 墨守成規的; 可預料到的〔有時含貶義〕: *I'd say his reaction was entirely predictable!* 我會說他的反應完全是預料之中的事! | *Honestly, George, you're so predictable!* 坦白說, 佐治, 你太墨守成規了! –opposite 反義 **unpredictable** –**predictably** *adv* –**predictability** /prɪˌdɪktəˈbɪlətɪ; prɪˌdɪktəˈbɪlɨ̩tɪ/ *n* [U]

pre·dic·tion /prɪˈdɪkʃən; prɪˈdɪkʃən/ *n* **1** [C] a statement that something is likely to happen in the future 預言: *He made several wildly inaccurate predictions.* 他做了一些極不準確的預言。**2** [U] the act of saying in advance what will happen 預測

pre·di·lec·tion /ˌpridḷˈɛkʃən; ˌpriːdɪˈlekʃən/ *n fml* a special liking 〔正式〕特別愛好, 嗜好: *Charles has always had a predilection for expensive clothes.* 查爾斯一向偏愛昂貴的衣服。

pre·dis·pose /ˌpridɪsˈpoz; ˌpriːdɪˈspəʊz/ *v* **predisposed, predisposing** [T] *fml* to influence someone in advance, in a particular way 〔正式〕預先影響〔某人〕

pre·dis·po·si·tion /ˌpridɪspəˈzɪʃən; ˌpriːdɪs-pəˈzɪʃən/ *n fml* 〔正式〕**a predisposition to/towards something** a tendency to act in a particular way, or to feel or suffer a particular thing 傾向於某事物; 易受某事物感染

pre·dom·i·nance /prɪˈdɑmənəns; prɪˈdɒmɨ̩-nəns/ *n* [U] *fml* 〔正式〕**1** a greater number of something than of other similar things 佔大多數: *the recent predominance of wom-*

en in the movement 在該運動中婦女近來佔絕大多數 **2** the most influence or power 最大影響; 主要勢力: *The Japanese have long had predominance in the world's electronics markets.* 長期以來日本人在世界電子產品市場上一直佔有主導地位。

pre·dom·i·nant /prɪˈdɒmənənt; prɪˈdɒmɪˌnənt/ *adj* most powerful, noticeable, or important 最主要的; 最顯著的; 最重要的: *I'd say death is the predominant theme of her paintings.* 我認為死亡是她的繪畫作品中最重要的主題。

pre·dom·i·nant·ly /prɪˈdɒmənəntlɪ; prɪˈdɒmɪˌnəntli/ *adv* mostly or mainly 主要地, 大部分地: *The votes were predominantly in support of the government.* 選票大部分都支持政府。

pre·dom·i·nate /prɪˈdɒmɪˌneɪt/ *v* **predominated, predominating** [I] to be the most noticeable or influential, or exist in the greatest numbers 統治; 支配; 佔優勢

pre·em·i·nent /prɪˈɛmənənt; priːˈemɪnənt/ *adj fml* above all others in importance or in having a particular quality or ability 〔正式〕出類拔萃的, 傑出的: *a lawyer who is preeminent in his field* 在同行中出類拔萃的律師 **–preeminently** *adv* **–preeminence** *n* [U]

pre·empt /prɪˈɛmpt; priːˈempt/ *v* [T] to prevent something by taking action in advance which makes it ineffective or impossible 搶先行動以阻止〔某事〕; 先發制人

preen /priːn/ *v* **1 preen itself** (of a bird) to clean or smooth itself or its feathers with its beak 〔鳥〕用嘴整理〔羽毛〕**2 preen yourself** to spend a long time making yourself look neat and tidy (a word usually used to express disapproval) 精心打扮自己〔通常含貶義〕

pre·fab /ˈpriːfæb; ˈpriːfæb/ *n infml* a small house made from parts prepared in a factory 〔非正式〕預製裝配式房屋

pre·fab·ri·cat·ed /priːˈfæbrəˌkeɪtɪd; priːˈfæbrɪkeɪtɪd/ *adj* made of parts prepared in a factory ready for fitting together later (used of a building) 預製構件的〔指建築物〕

pref·ace[1] /ˈprɛfɪs; ˈprefɪs/ *n* an introduction to a book 〔書的〕序言, 前言

preface[2] *v* **prefaced, prefacing** [T] to provide a book or speech with an introduction 作為…的序言; 為〔講話〕作開場白

pre·fect /ˈpriːfɛkt; ˈpriːfekt/ *n* an older pupil who helps control other pupils, in some British schools 〔英國學校中的〕級長, 監督生

★ **pre·fer** /prɪˈfɜː; prɪˈfɜːr/ *v* **-rr-** **1** to choose one thing rather than another because you like it better 更喜歡, 寧願選擇〔其中之一〕: *Some coffee? Or would you prefer tea?* 來些咖啡嗎? 還是你喜歡茶? | *I'd prefer to live abroad if I could.* 如果可以的話, 我寧願住在國外。| *Richard prefers riding a bike to driving.* 理查德喜歡騎腳踏車多於開汽車。| *I*

think she'd prefer you not to ask that question. 我認為她寧願不向你提那個問題。| *We'd prefer that you didn't say anything about it just yet.* 我們寧願你不對此事發表甚麼評論。

□ USEFUL PATTERNS 有用句型
to prefer something to something else;
to prefer to do something; to prefer doing something; to prefer someone to do something; to prefer that...

2 prefer charges *fml* to officially charge someone with a crime 〔正式〕控告某人犯罪, 起訴

pref·er·a·ble /ˈprɛfrəbl̩; ˈprefərəbəl/ *adj* more suitable, or that you like better than something else 更合適的; 更可取的: *We accept credit cards, but cash or a cheque would be preferable.* 我們接受信用卡, 但付現金或支票更好。| *Anything is preferable to having her stay for the whole week!* 甚麼事都比她在這裡住上整整一個星期要好! **–preferably** *adv*: *Can we meet for lunch tomorrow? Preferably an early one.* 我們明天午飯時見面好嗎? 最好是早一點吃的午飯。

★ **pref·er·ence** /ˈprɛfərəns; ˈprefərəns/ *n* **1** [C; U] a liking for one thing rather than another 較喜歡的東西; 偏愛: *"Would you like to sit on the left or the right?" "It doesn't matter; I have no great preference."* "你想坐在左邊還是右邊?" "無所謂, 我沒有甚麼特別偏好。" **2** [U] special favour or consideration shown to someone 優待; 優先考慮: *In considering people for this job, we have to give preference to those with some experience.* 在為這項工作挑選工作人員的時候, 我們必須優先考慮有工作經驗的人。

pref·er·en·tial /ˌprɛfəˈrɛnʃəl; ˌprefəˈrenʃəl◂/ *adj* [always before a noun 只能用於名詞前] giving, receiving, or showing special consideration 優先的: *The minister admitted that he gave preferential treatment to people from his own party.* 部長承認他對那些和他屬同一黨派的人給予優待。

pre·fix /ˈpriːfɪks; ˈpriːfɪks/ *n* a letter or group of letters that is put at the beginning of a word to change its meaning or it use 前綴: *The prefix in "refill" is "re-", meaning "again". So "refill" means "to fill again".* "refill" 一詞的前綴為 "re-", 意思為 "再次"。所以 "refill" 的意思是 "再次填滿"。**–compare** 比較 SUFFIX

preg·nan·cy /ˈprɛɡnənsɪ; ˈpreɡnənsi/ *n* **pregnancies** [C; U] the condition of being pregnant 懷孕, 妊娠: *It is unwise to smoke during pregnancy.* 懷孕期間吸煙很不明智。| *She had a difficult pregnancy.* 她懷孕期間吃了不少苦頭。

preg·nant /ˈprɛɡnənt; ˈpreɡnənt/ *adj* **1** having a baby developing in your body (used of a woman or female animal) 〔人〕

懷孕的;〔動物〕懷胎的: *She is five months pregnant.* 她懷孕五個月了。| *She was pregnant with her second child at the time.* 當時她正懷着第二個孩子。 **2** [always before a noun 只能用於名詞前] full of important but unexpressed meaning 意味深長的; 耐人尋味的: *His words were followed by a pregnant pause.* 他說完話, 意味深長地頓了一頓。

pre·his·tor·ic /ˌpriːsˈtɔrɪk; ˌpriːhɪˈstɒrɪk◂/ *adj* of a time before history was written down 史前的: *prehistoric art* 史前藝術 – **prehistory** /priːˈhɪstəri; priːˈhɪstəri/ *n* [U]

pre·judge /priˈdʒʌdʒ; ˌpriːˈdʒʌdʒ/ *v* **pre-judged, prejudging** [T] to form an opinion about someone or something before knowing or examining all the facts 對〔某人或某事〕預先判斷, 過早判斷 – **prejudgment, prejudgement** *n* [C;U]

prej·u·dice¹ /ˈprɛdʒədɪs; ˈprɛdʒ͡ʊdɪs/ *n* [C; U] unfair feeling or opinion, formed without enough thought or knowledge, or as the result of fear or distrust 偏見; 成見: *A judge must be completely free from prejudice.* 一個法官絕不應存有任何偏見。| *He admits that he has a prejudice against women drivers.* 他承認自己對女駕駛員懷有偏見。

prejudice² *v* **prejudiced, prejudicing** [T] **1** to influence someone to have an unfair opinion about something 使〔某人〕對〔某物〕懷有偏見: *The stories I had heard about his father prejudiced me* **against** *him.* 我所聽說的關於他父親的故事使我對他產生了偏見。 **2** to harm someone's case, or expectations 損害, 不利於: *Your bad spelling may prejudice your chances of getting this job.* 拼寫錯誤連篇可能會影響你獲取這份工作的機會。

prej·u·diced /ˈprɛdʒədɪst; ˈprɛdʒ͡ʊdɪst/ *adj* having an unfair feeling or opinion 有偏見的, 有成見的: *She doesn't think Italian wine is very good, but then, as she's French, she's prejudiced!* 她認為意大利酒不太好, 但由於她是法國人, 她實際上心存偏見!

prel·ate /ˈprɛlɪt; ˈprɛl͡ət/ *n* a priest of very high rank 高級教士

pre·lim·i·na·ry¹ /prɪˈlɪmɪˌnɛri; prɪˈlɪmͺnəri/ *n* **preliminaries** something done first, to prepare for a later thing 預備工作, 初步行動: *There are a lot of preliminaries to be gone through before you can visit the prison.* 在參觀監獄之前, 有許多預備工作要做。

preliminary² *adj* [always before a noun 只能用於名詞前] coming first, to prepare for something more important later 預備的; 初步的: *The team must pass the preliminary competition before they can enter the final.* 該隊必須先通過預賽才能進入決賽。

prel·ude /ˈprɛljud; ˈprɛljuːd/ *n* [sing] **1** something that comes before and acts as an introduction to something more important 序幕; 前奏: *The political crisis may be a prelude to civil war.* 這次政治危機也許

是內戰的前奏。 **2** a short piece of music that introduces a large musical work 〔音樂作品的〕前奏曲

pre·mar·i·tal /priˈmærətl; priːˈmær͡ɪtəl/ *adj* happening before marriage 婚前的

pre·ma·ture /ˌprɪməˈtjʊr; ˈprɛmətʃəʳ/ *adj* **1** happening before the natural or expected time 過早的; 早熟的: *His premature death at the age of 32 is a great loss.* 他三十二歲即早逝是一大損失。 **2** born before expected (used of a baby) 早產的〔指嬰兒〕: *She was a tiny baby, six weeks premature.* 她是個很小的嬰兒, 早產了六個星期。 **3** done too early or too soon 過早的, 過快的; 草率的: *I think the decision was a bit premature.* 我認為該決定未免太早了一點。 – **prematurely** *adv*

pre·med·i·tat·ed /prɪˈmɛdəˌtetɪd; priːˈmed͡ɪteɪt͡ɪd/ *adj* planned in advance 事先計劃好的, 預謀的: *premeditated murder* 有預謀的兇殺

prem·i·er¹ /ˈprimɪʳ; ˈprɛmɪəʳ/ *adj* [always before a noun 只能用於名詞前] *fml* most important 〔正式〕最重要的: *Britain's premier industry* 英國最重要的工業

premier² *n* the head of the government of a country (used especially in newspapers) 總理, 首相〔尤用於報刊〕: *the Irish Premier* 愛爾蘭總理 – **premiership** *n* [U]

prem·i·ere /prɪˈmɪr; ˈprɛmɪeəʳ/ *n* (also 又作 **première**) the first public performance of a play or a film 〔戲劇或電影的〕首次公演, 首映

*****prem·ise** /ˈprɛmɪs; ˈprɛm͡ɪs/ *n* *fml* a statement or idea that you consider is true and on which you base your reasoning 〔正式〕前提: *The law is based on the premise that people are innocent until they are proved to be guilty.* 該法規的前提是人在被證明有罪之前是無辜的。

prem·is·es /ˈprɛmɪsɪz; ˈprɛm͡ɪsɪz/ *n* [pl] **1** the buildings and land that a property or business consist of 建築物及其周圍的土地: *I have warned you before to keep off my premises!* 我以前曾警告過你不要進入我的領地! | *The company is moving to new premises.* 該公司打算遷入新的地址。 **2 on the premises** in the building 在屋內: *No smoking on the premises, please.* 在屋內請勿吸煙。

pre·mi·um /ˈprimɪəm; ˈpriːmɪəm/ *n* **1** a payment made to buy insurance 保險費 **2 at a premium: a** at a higher price than usual 〔股票〕溢價, 超過面值的價格 **b** difficult to get, because of being wanted by many people 奇貨可居的: *During the summer, hotel rooms are at a premium.* 在夏季, 旅館客房供不應求。 **3 put a premium on something** to regard a quality or action as very important 重視, 注重

pre·mo·ni·tion /ˌprɪməˈnɪʃən; ˌprɛmɔˈnɪʃ͡ən/ *n* a feeling that something bad is going to happen 〔不祥的〕預感: *The day before her accident, she had a premonition* **of** *danger.*

在她發生事故的前一天, 她有種危險的預感。

pre·na·tal /priˈneɪtl; ˌpriːˈneɪtl/ *adj* the usual American word for 〖美式〗= ANTENATAL

pre·oc·cu·pa·tion /pri͵ɑkjəˈpeɪʃən; priːˌɒkjə-ˈpeɪʃən/ *n* **1** [sing;U] the state of mind in which you think about something so much that you forget about other things 全神貫注, 出神: *his total preoccupation with his health* 他對自己健康的極度關注 **2** [C] something which you think about a lot 反覆考慮的事情; 當務之急

pre·oc·cu·pied /priˈɑkjə͵paɪd; priːˈɒkjʊpaɪd/ *adj* thinking or worrying about something so that you forget about other things 全神貫注的

pre·oc·cu·py /priˈɑkjə͵paɪ; priːˈɒkjʊpaɪ/ *v* **preoccupied, preoccupying** [T] to fill your thoughts so much that you forget about other things 使…全神貫注, 使專心於; 使著迷

prep /prɛp; prep/ *n* [U] *BrE infml* 〖英式, 非正式〗 school work that is done at home 〔學校安排的〕家庭作業

★**prep·a·ra·tion** /͵prɛpəˈreɪʃən; ͵prepəˈreɪʃən/ *n* **1** [U] the act of making something ready 準備, 預備: *Teachers have a lot of preparation to do.* 教師有許多準備工作要做。| *Today we're studying food preparation and handling.* 今天我們要學習食品的準備與處理。 **2 in preparation: a** being made ready 在準備之中: *Plans for the new school are now in preparation.* 興建新學校的計劃正在籌備之中。**b** getting ready 做準備: *Paul is studying hard in preparation for his exams.* 保羅為了準備考試而努力學習。 **3 preparations** [pl] arrangements for a future event 安排; 籌備: *They've started making preparations for the wedding.* 他們已開始為婚禮進行籌備工作。 **4** [C] a mixture of substances made for use as a medicine, COSMETIC, etc. 配製品: *beauty preparations* 美容化妝品

pre·par·a·to·ry /priˈpærə͵tɔri; priˈpærətəri/ *adj* [only before a noun 只用於名詞前] done first, in order to prepare for something else 準備的, 預備的: *some preparatory talks before drawing up the contract* 簽署合同前的預備性會談

preparatory school /·ˈ···· ·/ *n* (also 又作 **prep school** *infml* 〖非正式〗) [C;U] a private school in Britain for young pupils 〔英國的〕私立小學

★★**pre·pare** /priˈpɛr; priˈpeəʳ/ *v* **prepared, preparing 1** [T] to make something ready for a future event or action 準備好〔某物〕: *She prepared the room for the guests.* 她為客人準備好了房間。| *The training will prepare you to work with computers.* 這次訓練會為你日後使用電腦做好準備。 **2** [I] to get ready to do something 準備: *They are busy preparing to go on holiday.* 他們正忙著為度假做準備。| *Will you help me prepare for the party?* 你能幫我為晚會做些準備工作嗎? **3** [T] to get food ready to

eat 準備好食物: *My job was to help prepare the vegetables.* 我的工作是幫著準備蔬菜。| *Grandma prepared us a delicious meal.* 祖母為我們準備了美味的飯菜。 **4** [T] to get someone ready to accept a new idea or situation 讓〔某人〕做好思想準備: *Prepare yourself* **for** *some bad news.* 有一些壞消息, 你做好思想準備吧。

pre·pared /priˈpɛrd; priˈpeəd/ *adj* **1** got ready in advance 事先準備好的: *The chairman read out a prepared statement.* 主席讀了一項事先準備好的聲明。 **2 be prepared to do something** to be willing to 願意做某事: *I'm not prepared to accept less than £500 for the car.* 我不打算以五百英鎊以下的價錢賣車。

pre·pon·de·rance /priˈpɒndrəns; priˈpɒn-dərəns/ *n* [sing] *fml* more of one type of person or thing than of another 〖正式〗優勢: *There is now a preponderance of women students at the college.* 該大學現在女生人數比男生多。 **–preponderantly** *adv*

prep·o·si·tion /͵prɛpəˈzɪʃən; ͵prepəˈzɪʃən/ *n* a word used with a noun or PRONOUN to show its connection with another word 介詞: *In "He walked into the house" and "She succeeded by working hard", "into" and "by" are prepositions.* 在 "He walked into the house" 和 "She succeeded by working hard" 兩句中, "into" 和 "by" 是介詞。 –see Study Note on page 1330 見 1330 頁學習提示 **–prepositional** *adj*: *"In bed" and "on top" are prepositional phrases.* "in bed" 和 "on top" 是介詞詞組。

pre·pos·ter·ous /priˈpɑstərəs; priˈpɒstərəs/ *adj* completely unreasonable and improbable 荒謬的: *That's the most preposterous idea I've ever heard!* 那是我所聽到過的最荒謬的觀點! **–preposterously** *adv*

prep school /'· ·/ *n* [C;U] *infml* 〖非正式〗 see 見 PREPARATORY SCHOOL

pre·req·ui·site /priˈrɛkwəzɪt; priːˈrekwɪzɪt/ *n fml* something that is necessary before something else can happen or be done 〖正式〗先決條件, 前提: *A good education is not a prerequisite* **for** *success in business.* 良好的教育不是在商界取得成功的先決條件。| *working in every part of the store as a prerequisite* **to** *her management training* 在商店各部門工作是她接受管理訓練的先決條件

pre·rog·a·tive /priˈrɑgətɪv; priˈrɒgətɪv/ *n fml* a special right that a particular person has 〖正式〗特權: *It is the President's prerogative to pardon a criminal.* 總統有赦免罪犯的特權。

pres·age /priˈsedʒ; ˈpresɪdʒ/ *v* **presaged, presaging** [T not in progressive forms 不用於進行式] *fml* to be a warning of something that will happen 〖正式〗預示; 預兆

Pres·by·te·ri·an /͵prɛzbəˈtɪrɪən; ͵prezbəˈtɪə-rɪən/ *n* a member of a PROTESTANT Church governed by a body of official people all of equal rank, as in Scotland 長老會教徒

pre·scribe /prɪˈskraɪb; prɪˈskraɪb/ v **prescribed, prescribing** [T] **1** to say what medicine or treatment someone needs when they are ill 開藥，開處方: *The doctor prescribed some medicine* **for** *the baby's cough.* 醫生給那個嬰兒開了些咳嗽藥。| *Take one tablet a day, or as prescribed by your doctor.* 每天服一片(藥)，或遵照醫生的處方。**2** *fml* to order something to be done 〔正式〕指定，規定: *What punishment does the law prescribe for such a crime?* 法律對這樣的罪行有何懲罰?

pre·scrip·tion /prɪˈskrɪpʃən; prɪˈskrɪpʃən/ n **1** a special written order from a doctor which allows you to get medicine 〔醫生開的〕藥，處方: *Take your prescription to the hospital pharmacist's and they'll make it up for you.* 把處方拿到醫院的藥房去，他們會給你把藥配好的。| *Children under 16 can get free prescriptions.* 十六歲以下的孩子可以免費得到醫生的處方。**2 on prescription** on the order of a doctor 憑醫生處方: *This drug is only available on prescription.* 該藥只有憑醫生處方才能購買。

★pres·ence /ˈprɛzns; ˈprɛzəns/ n **1** [U] the state of being present at a particular place 到場，出席: *She was so quiet that her presence was hardly noticed.* 她一聲不吭，幾乎無人注意到她在這裡。| *Your presence is requested at the meeting on Thursday.* 會議於星期四舉行，敬請出席。–opposite 反義 **absence 2 in the presence of someone, in someone's presence** seen or heard by someone 當着某人; 有某人在場: *The performance is to be in the presence of the Queen.* 女王將出席這場表演。**3** [C] a spirit or influence that cannot be seen but is felt to be near 〔看不見但卻能感受到的〕靈氣，鬼怪: *I could sense a strange presence in the room.* 我能感覺到房間裡有種奇怪的靈氣。**4** [sing;U] personal qualities that have a strong effect on other people (a word used to express approval) 風度，風采〔含褒義〕: *a man of great presence* 氣宇軒昂的男子 **5** [sing] soldiers or police at a particular place 駐軍; 駐場警察: *There is a strong military presence on the frontier.* 邊境地區駐守了重兵。

pres·ence of mind /ˌ··· ˈ·/ n [U] the ability to act calmly and quickly in a dangerous situation 鎮定，沉着: *A fire started in the kitchen, and John had the presence of mind to turn off the gas immediately.* 廚房裡着了火，約翰鎮定地立刻關掉了煤氣。

★pre·sent¹ /prɪˈzɛnt; prɪˈzɛnt/ v [T] **1** to give something to someone, especially at an official ceremony 贈給，獻給，呈送〔尤指在正式場合〕: *He presented a silver cup* **to** *the winner.* 他把銀杯頒給了獲勝者。| *When she left*

the company, the director presented her **with** a set of golf clubs. 她離開這家公司時，董事贈給她一套高爾夫球桿。**2** to be the cause of a problem or difficulty 引起〔問題或困難〕: *His resignation presented us with rather a tricky situation.* 他的辭職令我們的處境相當尷尬。**3** to give or show to someone in a formal way 提交; 呈送: *The committee is presenting its report next week.* 委員會定於下星期提交報告。**4** to show to the public in a theatre, cinema, etc. 上演，上映〔戲劇、電影等〕: *The local theatre company is presenting "Hamlet" next week.* 當地的劇團將於下週上演《哈姆雷特》。**5** to introduce a television or radio show 介紹〔電視劇或廣播節目〕**6** *fml* to introduce someone in an official way, especially to someone important 〔正式〕介紹〔尤指引見給重要人物〕: *May I present Mr Jobbings?* 請允許我介紹一下賈賓斯先生。**7 present itself** (of something possible) to happen 〔可能的情況〕出現，發生: *The opportunity I had been waiting for suddenly presented itself.* 我一直在等候的機會突然出現了。

★pres·ent² /ˈprɛznt; ˈprɛzənt/ n **1** something that you give to someone as a gift, often on a special occasion 禮物〔常指在特殊場合贈送的禮品〕: *They unwrapped their Christmas presents.* 他們打開了自己的聖誕禮物。**2 the present** the time that is happening now 現在: *You should live in the present — don't worry about the future.* 你應當面對的是現在——不要擔心將來。**3 the present, the present tense** the tense of a verb which expresses the time that is now or the time of speaking 現在式〔時〕**4 at present** at this time 現在 **5 for the present** now but not necessarily in the future 目前; 暫時: *Let's leave it as it is for the present.* 我們就暫且不要管它吧。

pres·ent³ /ˈprɛznt; ˈprɛzənt/ adj **1** [never before a noun 不能用於名詞前] in a particular place at a particular time 出席的，在場的: *How many people were present at the meeting?* 該會議有多少人出席? | *Small amounts of the gas are present in the atmosphere.* 大氣中含有少量這種氣體。–opposite 反義 **absent 2** [only before a noun 只用於名詞前] existing now 現存的，現在的: *It is very difficult to sell a house in the present economic climate.* 在目前的經濟氣候下，很難將房子賣掉。

pre·sen·ta·ble /prɪˈzɛntəbl; prɪˈzɛntəbəl/ adj in a good enough state to be seen, shown, or judged 像樣的; 拿得出去的: *He looked very presentable in his new suit.* 他穿着新衣服看上去儀表不俗。–**presentably** adv

★pre·sen·ta·tion /ˌprɛznˈteɪʃən; ˌprɛzənˈteɪʃən/ n **1** [C;U] the act or action of giving something to someone at a ceremony or an official occasion 頒授; 贈與: *The presentation of prizes will begin at three o'clock.* 頒獎儀式於

三點鐘開始。**2** [U] the way something looks 儀表; 外表: *Your essays are good, but you should pay more attention to presentation.* 你的文章很好，但你應該更加注意一下文章的外觀。**3** [C] the act of giving or showing something to people in a formal way 引見; 介紹: *She will give a presentation on her company at the sales conference.* 她將在銷售會議上向大家介紹一下她的公司。

pres·ent-day /ˈprɛznt ˈde; ˌprɛznt ˈdeɪ◂/ *adj* [only before a noun 只用於名詞前] of the period of time that is happening now 當今的; 現代的: *the architecture of present-day Egypt* 現今埃及的建築術

pre·sent·er /prɪˈzɛntə; prɪˈzɛntəʳ/ *n* a person who introduces a television or radio show 〔電視劇或廣播劇的〕節目主持人

pre·sen·ti·ment /prɪˈzɛntəmənt; prɪˈzɛntɨmənt/ *n fml* an unexplained uncomfortable feeling that something bad is going to happen 〔正式〕〔不祥的〕預感

pres·ent·ly /ˈprɛzntli; ˈprɛzəntli/ *adv* **1** soon 很快, 馬上: *The doctor will be here presently.* 醫生很快就到這兒。**2** after some time 過了一會兒; 不久: *They sat talking through the long, hot afternoon. Presently, an old man approached them.* 在那個炎熱而漫長的下午，他們一直坐在那裡交談。過了一會兒，一位老人向他們走了過來。**3** now 現在，目前: *The doctor is presently writing a book.* 該醫生目前正在寫一本書。

present par·ti·ci·ple /ˌ·· ˈ····/ *n tech* a form of a verb which ends in *-ing* and can be used in compound forms of the verb to show PROGRESSIVE tenses (such as *barking* in *The dog is barking*) or sometimes as an adjective (such as *barking* in *a barking dog*) 〔術語〕現在分詞〔可用於進行式，如 "The dog is barking" 中的 barking; 也可作形容詞，如 "a barking dog" 中的 barking〕

pres·er·va·tion /ˌprɛzəˈveʃən; ˌprɛzəˈveɪʃn/ *n* [U] **1** the act or action of keeping something unharmed or unchanged 維護; 保持: *The police are responsible for the preservation of law and order.* 警方負責維持治安。**2** the state of being or remaining in a particular condition after a long time 保存; 保養: *The old building is in a good state of preservation, except for the wooden floors.* 這幢舊房子除了木地板之外，其他都保養得很好。

pre·ser·va·tive /prɪˈzɜvətɪv; prɪˈzɜːvətɪv/ *n* [C;U] a chemical substance used to keep something, especially food, in good condition for a long time 〔尤指食物的〕防腐劑

pre·serve¹ /prɪˈzɜv; prɪˈzɜːv/ *v* **preserved, preserving** [T] **1** to keep someone or something alive or safe from destruction 保護; 保存: *The Town Council has spent a lot of money to preserve this remarkable old building.* 市政廳已花了許多錢來保存這幢不同尋常的舊房子。**2** to cause a condition to remain unchanged 維持: *It is the duty of the police to preserve public order.* 警方的責任是維持公共秩序。**3** to keep something, especially food, in good condition for a long time by some special treatment 保存〔尤指食物〕: *preserved fruit* 蜜餞 | *The Ancient Egyptians knew how to preserve dead bodies from decay.* 古埃及人懂得如何能保存屍體不腐爛。

preserve² *n* **1** [C;U] *old fash* (also 又作 **jam**) a sweet food made from fruit that is often spread on bread 果醬 **2** [C] an activity considered to be limited to a certain person or group of people 〔某人或少數人所參加的〕私人活動: *Politics is still very much a male preserve.* 政治仍然主要是男人活動的領域。

pre·side /prɪˈzaɪd; prɪˈzaɪd/ *v* **presided, presiding** [I] to be in charge and lead 負責, 主持: *The presiding officer reads out the result of an election.* 主持的官員宣讀了選舉結果。

preside over sthg *phr v* [T] to be in charge of a group of people gathered for a formal purpose 主持〔會議〕: *The meeting was presided over by Mr Jarrett, the chairman.* 會議是由傑瑞特主席先生主持的。

pres·i·den·cy /ˈprɛzədənsɪ; ˈprɛzɨdənsi/ *n* **presidencies 1** the position of president 總統[主席等]的職位: *Roosevelt was elected four times to the presidency of the US.* 羅斯福四度當選美國總統。**2** the length of time a person is president 總統[主席等]的任期: *two wars during his presidency* 他任期間的兩場戰爭

pres·i·dent /ˈprɛzədənt; ˈprɛzɨdənt/ *n* (also 又作 **President**) **1** the head of government in many modern states that do not have a king or queen 總統: *the President of France* 法國總統 | *President Bush* 布殊總統 **2** the head of a club or important organization 〔俱樂部或重要組織的〕會長; 首長: *the President of the Board of Trade* 商會會長 **3** *AmE* the head of a business, bank, or company 〔美式〕〔企業、銀行、公司的〕總裁; 董事長; 總經理 –**presidential** /ˌprɛzəˈdɛnʃəl; ˌprɛzɨˈdenʃəl/ *adj* [only before a noun 只用於名詞前]: *presidential advisers* 總統顧問

press¹ /prɛs; prɛs/ *v* **1** [T] to push firmly and steadily 按; 壓: *Press this button to start the engine.* 按這個按鈕來發動引擎。| *She pressed her face up against the window.* 她把臉緊貼在窗子上。**2** [T] to put weight onto something in order to flatten it 壓平〔某物〕: *She pressed the flowers between the pages of a book.* 她把花夾在書頁當中。**3** [T] to crush fruit in order to get juice out 榨〔果汁〕: *The olives are pressed in this machine.* 橄欖在這台機器中把橄欖榨成汁。**4** [T] to give clothes a smooth surface and a sharp fold by using a hot iron 熨燙〔衣服〕**5** [T] to hold firmly as a sign of friendship or love 緊握; 緊抱〔以示友情或愛情〕: *He pressed my hand warmly when we met.* 我們見面時他熱情地緊握着我的手。**6** [I;T] to strongly try to persuade or demand 敦促; 力勸: *She pressed her guest to stay a little longer.* 她極力勸說客人再多留一會兒。| *The company is pressing for a decision.* 公司急於要做決定。

press on with sth *phr v* (also 又作 **press ahead with** sth *fml* 〔正式〕) [T] to continue doing something without delay 加緊〔做某事〕: *Let's press on with our work.* 讓我們加緊工作吧。

*** press²** *n* **1 the press** [U; +sing/pl verb] newspapers and magazines, and the reporters who write for them 新聞界; 報界: *the local press* 當地報界 | *a press photographer* 新聞攝影記者 | *The press have been invited to listen to the minister's statement.* 新聞記者獲邀來聽部長發表聲明。**2** [sing] a good or bad opinion of an event or person, given by newspapers, radio, or television 新聞報道〔評論〕: *The play had a good press.* 那齣戲獲得了新聞界的好評。**3** [C] see 見 PRINTING PRESS **4** [C] (also 又作 **Press**) a business for printing books and magazines 出版社: *the Cambridge University Press* 劍橋大學出版社 **5 go to press** to start being printed 付印 **6** [C] an act of smoothing an item of clothing with a hot iron 熨, 燙 **7** [C] a machine used for pressing clothes 熨斗

press con·fer·ence /ˈ· ,···/ *n* (also 又作 **news conference**) a meeting during which an important person gives a statement or answers questions 記者招待會, 記者會

press cut·ting /ˈ· ,··/ *n* a picture or piece of writing cut out of a newspaper or magazine 剪報

pressed /prest; prest/ *adj* **pressed for** not having very much 缺乏, 不足: *I'm rather pressed for time this morning, so I'll get back to you later.* 我今天上午時間相當緊, 所以我晚些時候再來找你。

press·gang¹ /ˈpresgæŋ; ˈpresgæŋ/ *n* a band of sailors who in former times seized men for service in the navy 〔昔時〕強迫別人服海軍役的水手隊

pressgang² *v* [T] *infml* to force someone to do something unwillingly 〔非正式〕強迫〔某人〕做〔某事〕

press·ing /ˈpresɪŋ; ˈpresɪŋ/ *adj* demanding or needing urgent attention 緊迫的; 迫切的: *Pressing business matters prevented her from taking a holiday.* 緊迫的業務使她無法休假。

press·man /ˈpresmən; ˈpresmæn/ *n* **press·men** /-mən; -mən/ *BrE infml* a newspaper reporter 〔英式, 非正式〕記者

press·stud /ˈ· ·/ *n* a small round metal fastener for clothing 子母扣

press·up /ˈ· ·/ *n* a form of exercise in which you lie face down and push your body up with your arms 俯臥撐

****pres·sure¹** /ˈpreʃə; ˈpreʃər/ *n* **1** [U] the force that is produced by the weight of one thing pressing against another 壓, 壓力: *The pressure of the water*

caused the banks of the river to burst. 水壓使河堤開裂。**2** [C;U] the strength of the force produced by a gas or liquid pressing against something 〔氣體或液體所產生的〕壓力: *I'd better check the pressure in the tyres.* 我最好還是去檢查一下輪胎的壓力。| *Low atmospheric pressure means it may rain.* 低氣壓意味着可能會下雨。**3 put pressure on, bring pressure to bear on** to use strong influence or force on someone to make something happen 迫使; 給〔某人〕施加壓力: *We must put pressure on the government to change this law.* 我們必須迫使政府改變這一法律。**4** [C;U] the demands of your work, family or style of life which cause worry and problems 〔工作、家庭、或生活方式所帶來的〕重荷; 壓力: *the pressures of modern life* 現代生活的壓力 **5 under pressure** having a lot of demands made on you at the same time 在壓力之下: *He definitely works better under a certain amount of pressure.* 他在一定的壓力下確實工作得更為出色。

pressure² *v* **pressured, pressuring** [T] see 見 PRESSURIZE

pressure cook·er /ˈ·· ,··/ *n* a tightly covered metal cooking pot in which food cooks very quickly by the pressure of hot steam 壓力鍋

pressure group /ˈ·· ·/ *n* [+sing/pl verb] a group of people that actively tries to influence public opinion and government action 〔力圖對輿論及政府行動施加影響的〕壓力集團

pres·sur·ize /ˈpreʃəˌraɪz; ˈpreʃəraɪz/ *v* **pressurized, pressurizing** (also 又作 **pressurise** *BrE* 〔英式〕) [T] **1** (also 又作 **pressure**) to try to make someone do something by means of forceful demands or influence 迫使〔某人做某事〕, 對…施加壓力: *These government measures have pressurized the farmers into producing more milk.* 政府的這些措施已迫使農民生產更多牛奶。**2** to control the air pressure inside an aircraft so that the pressure does not become much lower than that on Earth 使〔飛機內部〕保持正常氣壓, 給…增壓: *a pressurized cabin* 增壓艙

pres·tige /preˈstiːʒ; preˈstiːʒ/ *n* [U] general respect or admiration felt for someone or something because of their position, history, or quality 聲望, 威望: *The old universities of Oxford and Cambridge still have a lot of prestige.* 牛津和劍橋這兩所古老的大學仍然很有聲望。

pres·ti·gious /preˈstɪdʒɪs; preˈstɪdʒəs/ *adj* having or bringing prestige 有聲望的; 帶來名望的

***pre·su·ma·bly** /prɪˈzuːməblɪ; prɪˈzjuːməblɪ/ *adv* it is reasonable to suppose that 可能; 大概: *Presumably there's a good reason for her absence, as she doesn't usually stay away from work.* 由於她一般不離開工作崗位, 所以

她缺席大概有不得已的理由。

pre·sume /prɪˈzum; prɪˈzjuːm/ v **presumed, presuming 1** [I;T;+(that)] to suppose that something is true, without having direct proof or certainty 猜想, 假定, 推測: *From the way they talked I presumed they were married.* 從他們談話的樣子看, 我猜想他們已經結婚了。| *He went missing in the war and is presumed dead.* 他在戰爭中失蹤, 所以被認為已經死亡。| *This course presumes you already know something about computers.* 這課程的前提是你對電腦已有一定的認識。**2 presume to do something** *fml* to dare to do something which you have no right to do 〔正式〕擅自做某事: *Do not presume to tell me how to do my job!* 不要自以為是來教我該怎樣做工作!

pre·sump·tion /prɪˈzʌmpʃn; prɪˈzʌmpʃən/ n **1** [C] an act of supposing that something is true 猜想, 假定, 推測: *The book is full of false presumptions.* 書裡滿是憑空的臆測。**2** [U] self-confident behaviour in doing something you have no right to do 擅自; 放肆: *I was furious at his presumption in telling people we were engaged.* 他擅自告訴別人我們已訂婚了, 這令我很氣憤。

pre·sump·tu·ous /prɪˈzʌmptʃuəs; prɪˈzʌmptʃuəs/ adj having no right to do something, but supposing you can do it because you are very self-confident (a word used to express disapproval) 放肆的; 專橫的〔含貶義〕– **presumptuously** adv

pre·sup·pose /ˌprisəˈpoz; ˌpriːsəˈpəʊz/ v **presupposed, presupposing** [T;+that] to suppose or consider one thing to be true before another thing can also be true 預先假定; 以…為前提: *All these plans presuppose that the bank will be willing to lend us the money.* 所有這些計劃是預先假定銀行願意給我們貸款。– **presupposition** /-sʌpəˈzɪʃn, -sʌpəˈzɪʃən/ n [C;U]

pre·tence /prɪˈtens; prɪˈtens/ n (also 又作 **pretense** *AmE* 〔美式〕) [sing;U] an action that is intended to deceive people or make them believe something that is not true 假裝; 虛偽: *He made a pretence of enjoying the food.* 他裝作很喜歡這食品。| *How much longer are you going to keep up this pretence that you're ill?* 你裝病還打算裝多久?

****pre·tend** /prɪˈtend; prɪˈtend/ v [I;+(that)] **1** to make something appear true, or real, when it is not 假裝: *She pretended she didn't know me when I passed her in the street.* 當我在街上從她身邊走過時, 她裝作不認識我。| *He pretended to be asleep.* 他假裝在睡覺。| *She wasn't really crying; she was only pretending.* 她沒有真哭, 只不過是在裝哭。

> □ USEFUL PATTERNS 有用句型
> to pretend to do something; to pretend
> that...

2 to imagine as a game when you are a child 〔遊戲中〕假扮; 假想: *Let's pretend we're on the moon!* 讓我們假裝是在月球上吧!

pre·tend·er /prɪˈtendə; prɪˈtendəʳ/ n a person who makes a claim to some high position, such as to be the rightful king 覬覦高位者〔如王位〕

pre·ten·sion /prɪˈtenʃn; prɪˈtenʃən/ n **1** [C] a claim to possess certain skills, qualities, or importance 自稱, 自命: *I have no pretensions as an artist, but I enjoy painting.* 我不敢自稱為藝術家, 但我喜愛繪畫。**2** [U] *fml* the quality of being pretentious 〔正式〕狂妄; 自命不凡

pre·ten·tious /prɪˈtenʃəs; prɪˈtenʃəs/ adj trying or claiming to be more important or clever than is really the case 狂妄的; 自負的: *His style of writing is really pretentious.* 他的寫作風格實在是太狂妄了。–**pretentiously** adv –**pretentiousness** n [U]

pre·text /ˈpritekst; ˈpriːtekst/ n a reason given for doing something which hides the real reason 藉口: *I went to see Richard, under the pretext of wanting to borrow a book.* 我以想借本書為藉口去見了理查德。| *She called round on some pretext or other.* 她找了點甚麼藉口來坐了一坐。–see 見 EXCUSE[2] (USAGE 用法)

****pret·ty**[1] /ˈprɪti; ˈprɪti/ adj **prettier, prettiest 1** attractive and nice to look at (used of a woman, a child, or something small) 漂亮的; 好看的〔指女人、孩子或小東西〕: *She looks much prettier with long hair than with short hair.* 她留長髮比留短髮漂亮多了。| *What a pretty little garden!* 多麼漂亮的小花園啊! | *That's a pretty colour.* 那種顏色很漂亮。| *a pretty girl* 可愛的小姑娘 –see 見 BEAUTIFUL (USAGE 用法) **2 sitting pretty** *infml* in a favourable situation (used of a person) 〔非正式〕處於有利地位〔指人〕– **prettily** adv –**prettiness** n [U]

****pret·ty**[2] adv *infml* 〔非正式〕**1** to quite a large degree 相當, 頗: *It's pretty cold today.* 今天相當冷。**2 pretty much, pretty well** almost 差不多, 幾乎: *The work is pretty much finished.* 這項工作差不多已完成了。

pre·vail /prɪˈvel; prɪˈveɪl/ v [I] *fml* 〔正式〕**1** to exist or be widespread 流行, 盛行: *A belief in magic still prevails among some tribes.* 某些部落仍然相信巫術。**2** to succeed after a struggle 戰勝: *Justice prevailed when they found him guilty and he was sent to prison.* 當他們發現他有罪時, 正義戰勝了邪惡, 他被送進了監獄。

prevail upon sbdy *phr v* (also 又作 **prevail on** sbdy) [T] *fml* to succeed in persuading someone to do something 〔正式〕說服〔某人〕做〔某事〕

pre·vail·ing /prɪˈvelɪŋ; prɪˈveɪlɪŋ/ adj [always before a noun 只能用於名詞前] **1** the most common or general in a particular place or time 普遍的; 盛行的: *prevailing attitudes* among young people 年輕人的普遍態度 **2 a prevailing wind** a wind that blows over an area most of the time 常颳的風，盛行風

prev·a·lent /ˈprɛvələnt; ˈprɛvələnt/ adj fml existing commonly, generally, or widely 〖正式〗普遍的；流行的：Eye diseases are prevalent in some tropical countries. 在一些熱帶國家眼疾很流行。**—prevalence** n [U]

pre·var·i·cate /prɪˈværəˌket; prɪˈværɪˌkeɪt/ v **prevaricated, prevaricating** [I] fml to try to hide the truth by not answering questions clearly or completely truthfully 〖正式〗支吾，搪塞；推諉 **—prevarication** /prɪˌværəˈkeʃən; prɪˌværɪˈkeɪʃən/ n [C;U]

pre·vent /prɪˈvɛnt; prɪˈvent/ v [T] **1** to stop something from happening 預防，防止〔某事的發生〕：I couldn't prevent the accident. 我無法防止這宗事故發生。| What can we do to prevent this disease spreading? 我們要做甚麼才能防止這種疾病蔓延呢？

> □ USEFUL PATTERNS 有用句型
> to prevent something; to prevent something from happening

2 to stop someone from doing something 阻止〔某人做某事〕：The police prevented them from leaving the country. 警方阻止他們離開該國。**—preventable** adj: Most of these cancers are entirely preventable. 這些癌症中的大部分是完全可以預防的。

pre·ven·tion /prɪˈvɛnʃən; prɪˈvenʃən/ n [U] the action of stopping something happening 阻止；防止，預防：crime prevention 防止犯罪 | a society for the prevention of cruelty to children 防止虐待兒童組織

pre·ven·tive /prɪˈvɛntɪv; prɪˈventɪv/ adj (also 又作 **preventative** /-tətɪv; -tətɪv/) intended to prevent something, such as crime or illness 預防性的：preventive medicine 預防性藥物

pre·view /ˈpriˌvju; ˈpriːvjuː/ n **1** a private showing of paintings or a film before they are shown to the general public 〔繪畫的〕預展；〔電影的〕預演 **2** a short written description of a book or film that is about to come out 〔書或電影的〕預告；預告性評述

pre·vi·ous /ˈprivɪəs; ˈpriːvɪəs/ adj [always before a noun 只能用於名詞前] **1** happening or existing at an earlier time 以前的；過去的：They gave me the job, even though I had no previous experience. 儘管我以前沒有經驗，他們仍把這份工作給了我。| We had a previous engagement and so we couldn't go to the party. 我們預先已有約會，故不能參加晚會了。**2** coming just before the time or place you are talking about 前的；先的：She had previously telephoned him the previous day. 她前一天打過電話給他。**3 previous to** fml before 〖正式〗在…以前

pre·vi·ous·ly /ˈprivɪəsli; ˈpriːvɪəsli/ adv be-

fore that 在那以前：Pym, of no fixed address, was found guilty of driving without due care and attention. He had previously been convicted of drunken driving. 皮姆，無固定住址，因駕車時疏忽大意而被判有罪。在此之前，他曾因酒後駕車而被判有罪。**—see** 見 AGO (USAGE 用法)

pre·war /priˈwɔr; ˌpriːˈwɔːr◂/ adj belonging to the time before a war, especially the First or Second World Wars 戰前的〔尤指第一次或第二次世界大戰前的〕：pre-war Europe 戰前的歐洲

prey¹ /pre; preɪ/ n [U] **1** an animal that is hunted and eaten by another animal 被捕食的動物；獵物 **2 a bird of prey** a bird which lives by killing and eating other animals 猛禽，捕食獵物的飛禽 **3** someone or something that is used or deceived by someone else 易上當的人或物：People like her are easy prey for a clever salesman. 像她那樣的人很容易被聰明的推銷員矇騙。**4 fall prey to** to become used or controlled by 被…利用；被…控制

prey² v

prey on sbdy/sthg phr v (also 又作 **prey upon** sbdy/sthg) [T] **1** (of an animal) to hunt and eat 〔動物〕捕食：Cats prey on birds and mice. 貓捕食鳥和老鼠。**2** (of a person) to live by using or controlling other people unfairly 〔人〕靠欺詐為生：antiques dealers who prey on old people 欺詐老年人的古董商 **3 prey on your mind** to make you worry a lot 使非常憂慮；折磨

price¹ /praɪs; praɪs/ n **1** the amount of money that you must pay in order to buy something 價格，價錢：The price is £50. 價格是五十英鎊。| House prices are rising fast. 房價正迅速上漲。| Our shops give you good value at a low price. 我們店知美價廉。| Prices have gone up again. 物價又再上漲了。**—see** 見 COST² (USAGE 用法) **2** something you have to do or suffer in order to have what you want 代價：I'm afraid the price you pay for smoking is bad health! 你吸煙的代價恐怕是你的健康受損！**3 at a price: a** for a lot of money 以很高的價錢：You can buy excellent wine here — at a price. 你可以在這裡買到好酒——但要出高價。**b** with an unwanted result 結果不盡人意 **4 at any price** by doing or suffering anything at all to get something 以任何代價：He wanted fame at any price. 他為成名不惜一切代價。

price² v **priced, pricing** [T] **1** to fix the price of something in order to sell it 定〔某物〕的售價：The chairs were very reasonably priced. 這些椅子定價很合理。**2 price yourself out of the market** to make your prices so high that people are unwilling to pay 定價過高而無人問津

price·less /ˈpraɪslɪs; ˈpraɪsləs/ adj **1** very valuable 無價的；貴重的：a priceless collec-

tion of paintings 貴重的藏畫 –see 見 WORTHLESS (USAGE 用法) **2** *old fash infml* very amusing〖老式, 非正式〗非常有趣 的

pric·ey /ˈpraɪsɪ; ˈpraɪsi/ *adj* **pricier, priciest** *infml* expensive〖非正式〗昂貴的: *Houses in this area are getting rather pricey.* 這地區的房子越來越貴。

prick¹ /prɪk; prɪk/ *n* a small sharp pain 刺痛: *She felt a sharp prick as a needle went into her finger.* 針戳進她的手指時, 她感到一陣刺痛。

prick² *v* **1** [T] to make a very small hole in something with a sharp-pointed object 刺, 戳: *She pricked the potatoes* **with** *a fork before putting them in the oven.* 她用叉把馬鈴薯叉起來放到烤爐子裡。**2** [I] to cause a light sharp pain on your skin (使) 刺痛: *Careful, Johnny! The thorns on that bush will prick you.* 約翰, 小心! 那株灌木上的荊棘會把你刺痛的。**3 prick up its ears** (of an animal) to raise its ears〔動物〕豎起耳朵 **4 prick up your ears** to listen very carefully 非常仔細地聽, 側耳傾聽: *He pricked up his ears when they started to talk about him.* 當他們開始議論到他的時候, 他豎起耳朵仔細地聽。

prick·le¹ /ˈprɪkl̩; ˈprɪkəl/ *n* a small sharp point that grows on the skin of some plants or animals〔動植物的〕刺: *The cactus was covered with tiny prickles.* 仙人掌渾身長滿了小刺。

prickle² *v* **prickled, prickling** [I] to give or feel a sensation of small sharp points sticking into your skin 感到刺痛: *I can't wear this woollen shirt — it prickles.* 我不能穿這件羊毛襯衣——它刺得我發痛。

prick·ly /ˈprɪklɪ; ˈprɪkli/ *adj* **pricklier, prickliest** **1** covered with prickles 多刺的: *prickly bushes* 多刺的灌木 **2** giving a sensation of small sharp points sticking into your skin 有刺痛感的

*★**pride¹** /praɪd; praɪd/ *n* [U] **1** a feeling of satisfaction and pleasure in something you or someone else has done, or in something you own 自豪(感); 驕傲: *He looked at the new baby with pride and happiness.* 他得意地看着那個新生嬰兒。**2 take pride/a pride in something** to feel pleased or proud about something 為…感到自豪: *They take a great pride in their daughter's success.* 他們對女兒的成功感到十分自豪。| *He takes no pride in his appearance.* 他對自己的儀表並不感到自豪。**3** self-respect 自尊(心): *I think you hurt his pride by laughing at the way he speaks English.* 我認為你嘲笑他說英語的腔調傷了他的自尊心。**4** too high an opinion of yourself or what you have done 狂妄; 自大: *His pride made him an arrogant and cold person.* 他的狂妄令他變得又自負又冷漠。**5 be someone's pride and joy** to be the most valuable and important thing or person in someone's life 成為〔某人生活中〕最可貴和最

重要的人和物: *His roses are his pride and joy.* 他的玫瑰是他最珍視的東西。**6 be the pride of** to be the most valuable thing in 是…中最珍貴的東西: *This is the pride of my collection.* 這是我的收藏品中的精品。**7 have pride of place in** to have the best or most important position in 擁有最重要的位置

pride² *v* **prided, priding, pride yourself on something** to be pleased and satisfied with yourself about something 以…自豪: *She prided herself on her ability to speak eight languages.* 她為自己能講八種語言而自豪。

*★**priest** /priːst; priːst/ *n* **1** a specially trained person in the Christian Church, who performs various religious duties〔基督教的〕牧師;〔天主教的〕神父: *the argument over having women priests* 對允不允許婦女作牧師的爭論 **2** a specially-trained person with religious duties, in many non-Christian religions〔許多基督教以外的其他宗教的〕教士; 祭司; 僧侶

■ USAGE 用法: **Priest** is a general word for someone who is in charge of the religious worship of a group of Christian people, but the word is used especially in the Roman Catholic Church. A priest in the Church of England is called a **clergyman**, and a clergyman in charge of a particular area is the **vicar** of that area. In the Nonconformist churches the usual word is **minister**. ☆ **priest** 通常是指負責一羣基督徒的宗教禮拜的牧師, 但該詞尤用來指天主教的神父。英國國教中的牧師叫 **clergyman**, 負責某一地區的牧師叫 **vicar**. 英國新教的牧師通常叫 **minister**.

---

priest·ess /ˈpriːstɪs; ˈpriːstes/ *n* a specially-trained woman with religious duties, in many non-Christian religions〔許多基督教以外的其他宗教的〕女教士

priest·hood /ˈpriːsthʊd; ˈpriːsthʊd/ *n* **the priesthood** the position of being a priest 教士的職位: *He entered the priesthood.* 他當了教士。

prig /prɪg; prɪg/ *n* a person who is very careful about rules of moral behaviour, and so thinks they behave better than other people (a word used to express disapproval) 一本正經的人, 道學先生〖含貶義〗: *Come on, Margaret, join in — don't be such a prig!* 來吧, 瑪格麗特, 一起來吧——別這麼一本正經! –**priggish** *adj* –**priggishness** *n* [U]

prim /prɪm; prɪm/ *adj* **-mm-** very formal and correct in behaviour and easily shocked by anything rude (a word that is usually used to express disapproval) 循規蹈矩的; 拘謹的〖常含貶義〗–**primly** *adv* –**primness** *n* [U]

pri·ma don·na /ˌpriːmə ˈdɒnə; ˌpriːmə ˈdɒnə/ *n* **1** the leading woman singer in an OPERA 歌劇中的主角女歌手 **2** a person who changes their mind easily and expects everyone to do as they wish (a word used to express disapproval) 喜怒無常的人; 善變的人〔含貶義〕: *Their marketing director is a bit of a prima donna.* 他們的市場部經理有點喜怒無常, 十分善變。

pri·mae·val /praɪˈmiːvl̩; praɪˈmiːvəl/ *adj* see 見 PRIMEVAL

pri·ma·ri·ly /ˈpraɪˌmɛrəlɪ; ˈpraɪmərəlɪ/ *adv* mainly or most importantly 主要地, 首要地: *The village is primarily a fishing community, but a lot of tourists come here.* 這村落主要是個漁村, 但有許多遊客到這裏來遊覽。

★**pri·ma·ry**[1] /ˈpraɪˌmɛrɪ; ˈpraɪmərɪ/ *adj* **1** main or most important 主要的, 首要的: *The primary cause of Tom's failure was simply his laziness.* 湯姆失敗的主要原因就是他太懶。 **2** primary education, primary schools education or schools for children between 5 and 11 years old, in Britain 〔英國五至十一歲兒童上的〕小學: *There's Billy's primary school teacher.* 那位是比利的小學老師。

primary[2] *n* primaries an election in the US at which people vote for someone to be their party's choice for a political office 〔美國的〕黨內初選

primary col·our /ˌ··· ˈ···/ *n* one of the three colours red, yellow, and blue; all other colours can be made by mixing these together in different ways 基色, 原色〔指紅、黄、藍〕三色之一

pri·mate[1] /ˈpraɪmɪt; ˈpraɪmeɪt/ *n* a member of the most highly developed group of animals, which includes humans and monkeys 靈長目動物〔包括人和猿〕

pri·mate[2] /ˈpraɪmɪt; ˈpraɪmɪt/ *n* (also 又作 **Primate**) a priest of the highest rank 大主教

prime[1] /praɪm; praɪm/ *adj* [always before a noun 只能用於名詞前] **1** the first or greatest 首要的, 主要的: *This is a matter of prime importance.* 這件事至關緊要。 **2** of the very best quality 質量最佳的: *a prime piece of beef* 一塊最上等的牛肉 **3** that is completely typical 典型的: *Look, over there. That's a prime example of what I was saying about office workers.* 看, 在那兒, 那就是我所說的典型辦公室職員。

prime[2] *n* [sing] **your prime** the time when you are strongest, most active, or in the best condition 全盛時期: *As a tennis player she is now in her prime, at 23.* 作為一名網球運動員, 她今年二十三歲, 正值盛年。

prime[3] *v* **primed, priming** [T] **1** to prepare someone for an event by giving them information 事先向〔某人〕提供情況: *The lawyer has been carefully primed about the case.* 律師已事先獲知了有關此案的詳細情況。 **2** to prepare wood for painting by covering it with a special liquid or paint 為〔木板〕上底色[底漆]

prime min·is·ter /ˌ· ˈ···/ (also 又作 **Prime**

Minister; also 又作 **PM** *infml* 〔非正式〕) *n* the leader of the government in certain countries 首相, 總理: *talks with the British Prime Minister* 與英國首相所進行的會談

prim·er /ˈpraɪmə; ˈpraɪmə/ *n* [C;U] a paint spread over the bare surface of wood before the main painting 〔木板上打的〕底漆, 底層塗料

prime time /ˈ· ˌ·/ *n* [U] the time when most people are thought to watch television 〔電視的〕黄金時間

pri·me·val /praɪˈmiːvl̩; praɪˈmiːvəl/ *adj* (also 又作 **primaeval**) of the earliest period of the Earth's existence 太古時代的; 原始的: *primeval forests* 原始森林

prim·i·tive /ˈprɪmətɪv; ˈprɪmɪtɪv/ *adj* **1** [always before a noun 只能用於名詞前] of an early stage of human development or human society 原始的: *In primitive societies tools were made from sharp stones and animal bones.* 在原始社會, 工具是由尖利的石頭和動物的骨頭製成的。 **2** in a simple style and without having anything more than is necessary 簡單的, 簡樸的: *Their living conditions are somewhat primitive — there's no running water, for a start.* 他們的生活條件有點簡陋——首先來說, 他們沒有自來水。 **– primitively** *adv* **–primitiveness** *n* [U]

prim·rose /ˈprɪmˌroz; ˈprɪmrəʊz/ *n* a common wild plant with pale yellow flowers 報春花

★**prince** /prɪns; prɪns/ *n* (also 又作 **Prince**) **1** a son or other near male relation of a king or queen 王子; 王孫; 親王: *He bowed to the prince.* 他向王子鞠了一躬。 | *Prince Charles* 查爾斯王子 **2** a ruler of a small country or state 小國的君主: *Prince Rainier of Monaco* 摩納哥國王雷尼爾

prince·ly /ˈprɪnslɪ; ˈprɪnslɪ/ *adj* **1** of or belonging to a prince 王子的 **2** splendid and generous 壯麗的; 慷慨的: *a princely gift* 高貴的禮物

prin·cess /ˈprɪnsɪs; ˌprɪnˈses/ *n* (also 又作 **Princess**) **1** a daughter or other near female relation of a king or queen 公主 **2** the wife of a prince 王妃: *Princess Diana* 戴安娜王妃

★**prin·ci·pal**[1] /ˈprɪnsəpl̩; ˈprɪnsəpəl/ *adj* [always before a noun 只能用於名詞前] first in importance 最重要的, 首要的: *The principal character in the book is a young woman called Scarlett O'Hara.* 本書最重要的人物是一位叫斯嘉麗·奧郝拉的年輕女子。

principal[2] *n* **1** (also 又作 **Principal**) the head of some colleges, and schools 校長; 院長 **2** a leading performer in a play or in a group of musicians 〔戲劇的〕主要演員, 主角; 〔樂團的〕首席樂手

prin·ci·pal·i·ty /ˌprɪnsəˈpælətɪ; ˌprɪnsɪˈpælɪtɪ/ *n* **principalities** a country that a prince rules 公國, 侯國, 封邑

prin·ci·pal·ly /ˈprɪnsəplɪ; ˈprɪnsɪplɪ/ *adv*

mostly 主要地: *The money is principally invested in the oil industry.* 這筆錢主要投資於石油工業上。

★**prin·ci·ple** /ˈprɪnsəpl; ˈprɪnsḷpəl/ *n* **1** [C] a general truth or rule that ideas or beliefs are based on 原則: *One of the principles of this dictionary is that it is written in simple language.* 這本辭典的編寫原則之一是使用淺顯的語言。| *Socialism is based on the principle that everyone is equal.* 社會主義是基於人人平等的原則之上的。**2 in principle** as far as the general idea is concerned 原則上: *I agree with your plan in principle, but I'm not sure if it will work in practice.* 我原則上同意你的計劃，但不敢肯定它是否切實可行。**3** [C] a law of nature or science which controls how something works 原理: *Einstein's theories form the basic principles of modern physics.* 愛因斯坦的理論構成了現代物理學的基本原理。**4** [C;U] a moral belief or rule that you follow when you do something or that guides your behaviour 道德準則, 規範: *She is a woman of great principle.* 她是個具有高尚情操的女子。| *He has no principles: he just wants to make money in any way he can.* 他沒有甚麼做人的行為準則，他只想用盡一切手段掙錢。| *I couldn't have a servant; it goes against my principles.* 我不可以要僕人，這有違我的行為準則。**5 on principle** because of a moral belief that you have 依據(自己的)道德準則: *We don't eat meat, on principle.* 我們不吃肉，是出於道義的原因。

★**print¹** /prɪnt; prɪnt/ *n* **1** [U] words printed on a page 〔印刷出來的〕字體: *I can't read small print without my glasses.* 我不戴眼鏡看不清小字體。**2** [C] a photograph or picture printed on paper 〔印於紙上的〕照片或圖畫 **3 in print: a** printed in a book or newspaper 印在書上或報上: *I was very excited to see my name in print.* 看到自己的名字登了出來，我很興奮。**b** that you can still buy (used of a book) 買得到的〔指書〕 **4 out of print** that you can no longer buy (used of a book) 買不到的，已絕版的〔指書〕 **5** [C] a mark made on a surface showing the shape of the thing pressed into it, especially a FINGER-PRINT 印痕, 痕跡〔尤指指紋〕: *the thief's prints on the door handle* 竊賊留在門把手上的指紋 | *footprints in the snow* 雪地裡的足跡

★**print²** *v* **1** [I;T] to press letters or pictures onto paper using ink in a machine 印刷: *They've printed the leaflet on the wrong paper.* 他們用錯了紙印傳單。| *The books are printed in Spain.* 這些書是用西班牙文印的。**2** [I;T] to produce books, newspapers, or magazines in large numbers 出版: *We are printing 10,000 copies of his new book.* 我們正在出版他的新書，印數為一萬冊。**3** [T] to include in a book or newspaper 刊登: *All today's newspapers have printed the minis-*

ter's speech in full. 今天所有的報紙都全文刊登了部長的講話。**4** [T] to make or copy a photograph on paper sensitive to light 沖印〔照片〕 **5** [I;T] to write without joining the letters 用印刷體書寫: *Please print the address clearly in capital letters.* 請用印刷體大寫字母把地址清楚地寫下來。

print sthg ↔ **out** *phr v* [T] (of a computer) to produce a printed record of information 〔電腦〕打印出〔資料〕

★**print·er** /ˈprɪntər; ˈprɪntə^r/ *n* **1** a person who owns or works in a printing business 印刷商; 印刷工人 **2** a machine which is connected to a computer and makes a printed record of its information 〔與電腦連接的〕打印機 –see picture on page 763 見 763 頁彩圖

print·ing /ˈprɪntɪŋ; ˈprɪntɪŋ/ *n* [U] the act or art of producing books or newspapers using a machine 印刷; 印刷術: *The invention of printing made it possible for many more people to learn to read.* 印刷術的發明使更多人有機會學會閱讀。

printing press /ˈ·· ·/ *n* (also 又作 **press**) a machine that prints books or newspapers 印刷機

print·out /ˈprɪntˌaʊt; ˈprɪntˌaʊt/ *n* [C;U] a printed record produced by a computer 〔電腦〕打印出的資料 –see picture on page 763 見 763 頁彩圖

★**pri·or¹** /ˈpraɪər; ˈpraɪə^r/ *adj* [always before a noun 只能用於名詞前] **1** that is done or exists already 事先的; 已存在的: *I was unable to attend the wedding because of a prior engagement.* 我因有約在先，所以未能出席婚禮。**2** coming first in importance 首要的; 優先的: *He felt his family had a prior claim on his time.* 他覺得有時間應首先同家人在一起。**3 prior to** *fml* before 〖正式〗在…以前: *The contract will be signed prior to the ceremony.* 該合同將在儀式之前簽署。

prior² *n* the head of a priory; a female prior is called a **prioress** 小修道院院長〔小修道院女院長稱作 **prioress**〕

★**pri·or·i·ty** /praɪˈɔrətɪ; praɪˈɒrɪti/ *n* **priorities 1 have priority, be given priority** to be treated as more important than someone or something else 有優先權: *We are treating the children first — they have absolute priority over everyone else.* 我們先招待兒童——他們理所當然地比任何人都要優先。**2** [C] something that needs attention immediately or first, before other things 優先考慮的事情: *The government should make education a priority.* 政府應優先發展教育。| *It's simply a matter of priorities.* 這不過是個孰先孰後的問題。**3 get your priorities right** to deal with the most important things first 先處理最重要的事情

pri·o·ry /ˈpraɪərɪ; ˈpraɪəri/ *n* **priories** a Christian religious house where monks (MONK) live and work together 小修道院

prise /praɪz; praɪz/ *v* **prised, prising** (also 又

P

作 **prize**) [T;+adv/prep] to move, lift, or force with a tool 用工具移動[舉起、撬開]: *We finally managed to prise the box open.* 我們最終設法撬開了箱子。

pris·m /ˈprɪzəm; ˈprɪzəm/ *n* a transparent three-sided block, made of glass, that breaks up white light into different colours 三稜鏡

★**pris·on** /ˈprɪzn̩; ˈprɪzən/ *n* **1** [C;U] a large building where criminals are kept locked up as a punishment 監獄: *The thief was sent to prison for a year.* 小偷被判入獄一年。| *locked up in a prison cell* 被關在牢房裡 **2** [sing] a place or situation which you feel you cannot escape from 監禁，無法逃脫的地方或處境: *Tom hates school; he thinks it's a prison.* 湯姆憎恨學校，他覺得它像一座監獄。

★**pris·on·er** /ˈprɪznɚ; ˈprɪzənə/ *n* **1** a person kept in a prison for a crime 囚犯，犯人: *Three prisoners were caught trying to escape.* 三名囚犯試圖逃跑時被抓獲。 **2 take someone prisoner** to seize someone in a war〔在戰爭中〕俘虜某人: *He was taken prisoner by enemy soldiers.* 他被敵軍士兵俘虜了。 **3** a person taken by force and kept somewhere against their will 被關押的人 **4 keep/hold someone prisoner** to keep someone somewhere by force 囚禁某人: *The kidnappers held him prisoner for five months.* 綁架者把他囚禁了五個月。

prisoner of war /ˌ··· · ·ˈ·/ *n* (also 又作 **POW** *infml*〔非正式〕) a soldier caught by the enemy during a war and kept as a prisoner 戰俘

pris·tine /ˈprɪstin; ˈprɪstiːn/ *adj fml* fresh, clean, and undamaged〔正式〕新鮮的；乾淨的；未損壞的: *an old book still in pristine condition* 一本仍完好無損的舊書

priv·a·cy /ˈpraɪvəsɪ; ˈprɪvəsɪ/ *n* [U] the state of being able to be alone, and not seen or heard by other people 獨處(狀況): *There's not much privacy in these flats: the walls are so thin you can hear everything your neighbour is saying.* 這些公寓裡沒有多少不受侵擾的空間：牆壁很薄，鄰居不論說甚麼話你都聽得見。

★★**pri·vate¹** /ˈpraɪvɪt; ˈpraɪvɪt/ *adj* **1** only for use by one person, and not people in general 私人的；私用的: *a room with a private bathroom* 有私人浴室的房間 | *She has a private plane.* 她有一架私人飛機。 **2** not connected with or paid for by the government, or a public service 私立的，私營的: *a private hospital* 私立醫院 | *a private bus company* 私營公共汽車公司 | *pay increases in the private sector* 私人企業工資的上漲 **3** not connected with your work or business 與工作無關的；私人的: *The Queen is on a private visit to Scotland.* 女王正在蘇格蘭進行私人訪問。| *I don't discuss my private life at the office.* 我不在辦公室裡談論我的私生活。 **4** secret and personal and

not for sharing with others 祕密的；個人的: *private papers* 祕密文件 | *I was lost in my own private thoughts.* 我沉浸於遐想之中。 **5** quiet and without lots of people 安靜的；僻靜的: *Is there a private corner where we can sit and talk by ourselves?* 有沒有個僻靜的角落可以讓我們坐下來談談？ **6 in private** without other people listening or watching 私下地 **7 a private person** someone who likes to be on their own 孤僻的人 —compare 比較 PUBLIC¹ —**privately** *adv: May I speak to you privately?* 我能和你單獨談一下嗎？

private² *n* (also 又作 **Private**) a soldier of the lowest rank 二等兵

private en·ter·prise /ˌ·· ·ˈ··/ *n* [U] see 見 CAPITALISM

private school /ˌ·· ·ˈ·/ *n* a school paid for by parents, not supported with government money 私立學校 —compare 比較 PUBLIC SCHOOL

pri·va·tion /praɪˈveʃən; praɪˈveɪʃən/ *n* [C;U] *fml* lack of the necessary things of life〔正式〕生活必需品的匱乏: *Everyone suffered privations during the war, when there wasn't enough food in the country.* 戰爭期間人人生活困難，國內沒有足夠的糧食。

pri·vat·ize /ˈpraɪvətaɪz; ˈpraɪvətaɪz/ *v* **vatized, privatizing** (also 又作 **privatise** *BrE*〔英式〕) [T] to sell a government-owned industry or organization 使私營化: *Their rail services have recently been privatized.* 他們的鐵路服務最近已私營化了。

★**priv·i·lege** /ˈprɪvlɪdʒ; ˈprɪvl̩ɪdʒ/ *n* **1** [C] a special right or advantage given only to one person or group of people 特權，特惠待遇: *You may be rich, but no one gets any special privileges in this prison.* 你可能很有錢，但在這座監獄裡，沒有人可以享受特權。 **2** [U] advantage possessed by one person or group because of their wealth, social rank, etc. (a word often used to express disapproval)〔由財富、社會地位等而享有的〕特權〔常含貶義〕: *Their oldest universities are criticized for being bastions of privilege.* 他們的那些最古老的大學被批評為特權的堡壘。 **3** [sing] a special chance to do something that gives you great pleasure 特別恩寵；榮幸: *It was a privilege to meet such a talented musician.* 能遇到這樣一位天才音樂家真是榮幸。 —**privileged** *adj: We are privileged tonight to have as our main speaker the Foreign Minister of France.* 今晚我們很榮幸地請到法國外交部長向我們發表演講。

priv·y /ˈprɪvɪ; ˈprɪvɪ/ *adj* **privy to** *fml* sharing secret knowledge of〔正式〕知道內情的: *I was not privy to the discussions.* 我對於討論的內容一無所知。

★**prize¹** /praɪz; praɪz/ *n* something of value given to someone who is successful in a game, race, or competition, or given for some action that is admired 獎；獎品: *Her roses won first prize at the flower show.* 她的

玫瑰在花展中獲得了一等獎。

prize² adj [only before a noun 只用於名詞前] **1** that has gained a prize 獲獎的: *prize cattle* 獲獎的牛 | *a prize rose* 獲獎的玫瑰 **2** given as a prize 作為獎品的: *prize money* 獎金 **3** infml worthy of a prize for quality, size, etc. (a word often used in a humorous way)〔非正式〕值得給與獎品的〔常作幽默用法〕: *The new hen has produced a prize egg!* 那隻新買來的母雞下了一隻特別大的蛋!

prize³ v **prized, prizing 1** [T] to value highly 珍視; 珍愛: *His new bicycle was his most prized possession.* 他新買的腳踏車是他最珍視的東西。 **2** [T; +adv/prep] (also 又作 **prise**) to move, lift, or force with a tool 用工具移動〔舉起、撬開〕: *With a long iron bar we prized the top off the box.* 我們用一根長鐵棍撬開了箱蓋。

pro /prəʊ; prəʊ/ n **pros 1** see 見 PROFESSIONAL² (3) **2 the pros and cons** the arguments or reasons for and against something 贊成與反對的論據〔理由〕: *We discussed all the pros and cons thoroughly.* 我們徹底地談論了正反兩方面的意見。

prob·a·bil·i·ty /ˌprɑbəˈbɪləti; ˌprɒbəˈbɪlɪti/ n **probabilities 1** [sing;U] likelihood that something will happen 可能性: *I don't think there's much probability of an agreement being reached.* 我認為達成協議的可能性不大。 | *There's a high probability that oil prices will fall next year.* 明年油價很有可能會下降。 **2 in all probability** almost certainly 幾乎可以肯定 **3** [C] an event or result that will probably happen 可能發生的事情〔結果〕: *War is a real probability in the present crisis.* 在現在的危機之下, 有可能發生戰爭。

prob·a·ble /ˈprɑbəbl; ˈprɒbəbl/ adj that has a good chance of happening or being true 有望發生的; 很有可能的: *He may just get the job, but judging from his account of the interview it doesn't seem very probable.* 他有可能獲得那份工作, 但從他所說的面試情況來看, 這種可能性似乎不太大。 | *It is probable that they will win the election.* 他們很可能贏得大選。 –**probably** adv: *We'll probably go to Greece later in the year.* 今年稍後時候我們可能去希臘。

pro·ba·tion /proˈbeʃən; prəˈbeɪʃən/ n [U] **1** a period of time during which someone's abilities are tested 試用期: *I will be on probation for the first three months of my new job.* 我的新工作頭三個月是試用期。 **2** law the system of allowing someone who has broken the law to go free if they promise to behave well and report to the court〔律〕緩刑(制度) –**probationary** adj

probation of·fi·cer /·ˈ··· ˌ···/ n a person whose job is to watch, advise, and help law-breakers who are put on probation 監視緩刑犯的官員

probe¹ /prob; prəʊb/ n **1** a long thin metal instrument used by doctors and dentists to examine a part of the body carefully (醫用)探針 **2** (also 又作 **space probe**) a machine sent into the sky to examine conditions in outer space 太空探測器 **3** a careful and thorough inquiry into a situation 深入調查

probe² v **probed, probing** [I;T] **1** to search or examine something very carefully with a long thin instrument〔用探針或探測器〕探查 **2** to make a careful and thorough inquiry into a situation 細查

prob·lem /ˈprɑbləm; ˈprɒbləm/ n **1** a difficult situation or thought about 困難, 難題: *I've got a problem with the gears on my bike.* 我的腳踏車的變速檔出了問題。 | *The problem is, I just don't have enough time.* 問題在於, 我沒有足夠的時間。 | *The unemployment problem is getting worse.* 失業問題正日益嚴重。 **2** a question connected with numbers, or facts for which an answer is needed〔數字、事實方面的〕問題, 習題: *He's only three, but he can already do simple problems in addition and subtraction.* 他只有三歲, 但已能做簡單的加減法題目了。

prob·lem·at·ic /ˌprɑbləˈmætɪk; ˌprɒbləˈmætɪk◂/ adj (also 又作 **problematical**) having difficulties and problems 有問題的: *The situation is somewhat problematic.* 形勢有些問題。

pro·ce·dure /prəˈsidʒɚ; prəˈsiːdʒəʳ/ n [C;U] a particular formal way of doing something 程序; 步驟: *Writing a cheque is quite a simple procedure.* 開一張支票是十分簡單的手續。 | *a review of government procedure* 審核政府工作的程序 –**procedural** adj

pro·ceed /prəˈsid; prəˈsiːd/ v [I] **1** fml to continue with something you have already started〔正式〕繼續做〔某事〕; 開始進行: *Now that everyone has arrived we can proceed with the meeting.* 既然大家都到了, 我們就開始開會吧。 | *The work is proceeding according to plan.* 工作正在按計劃進行。 **2** to do something, especially something rather unexpected, after someone has just said or done something〔某人剛說或剛做某事之後〕做〔尤指令人意想不到的事情〕: *We asked if anything was wrong, and he proceeded to tell us all his troubles.* 我們是否出了甚麼問題, 他於是把他所有的問題都告訴我們。 **3** fml to move in a forward direction〔正式〕朝〔某一方向〕移動, 前進: *Do not proceed across a main road without first checking your mirror.* 要先看反光鏡, 然後才能駛過大馬路。

pro·ceed·ings /prəˈsidɪŋz; prəˈsiːdɪŋz/ n [pl] **1** an action taken in law 法律行動, 訴訟: *They're taking legal proceedings against the manufacturer.* 他們正在對製造商提出訴訟。 **2** events that happen in a formal way 事件: *We had a bird's eye view of the proceedings.* 我們概覽了一下所發生的事情。

pro·ceeds /ˈprosidz; ˈprəʊsiːdz/ n [pl] money gained from selling something or from an event or activity〔銷售、事件或活動的〕收入, 收益

‡pro·cess[1] /ˈprɑsɛs; ˈprəʊsɛs/ n **1** a set of actions or changes that develop or happen naturally〔自然發生的〕過程; 變化: *the process of breathing* 呼吸過程 | *Coal was formed out of dead forests by chemical processes.* 煤是由死去的樹木通過進化學變化而形成的。**2** a continued set of actions performed in order to make or do something 步驟; 程序: *She's learning to walk again, but it's a slow process.* 她在重新學習行走, 但這是個很緩慢的過程。| *the electoral process* 選舉程序 **3 in the process** while something is or was being done 正在進行〔某事〕的時候 **4 be in the process of** to have started something and still be doing it 在做〔某事〕的過程中: *We are now in the process of moving the machines to a new factory.* 我們目前正在把機器運至新的工廠。**5** a method of treating raw materials in order to produce goods 工序, 製作流程: *an advanced process for rubber production* 生產橡膠的先進工序

process[2] v [T] **1** to treat something by a particular method 加工, 處理〔某物〕: *processed cheese* 加工好的乾酪 | *They will process a film in 24 hours.* 他們能在二十四小時內把膠卷沖洗出來。**2** to deal with information in a formal way 處理, 辦理: *Your mortgage application is still being processed.* 你的抵押貸款申請仍在審理中。**3** to put information into a computer for examination〔用電腦〕處理〔資料〕: *new techniques of data processing* 用電腦處理數據的新技術

pro·ces·sion /prəˈsɛʃən; prəˈseʃən/ n **1** [C] a line of people or vehicles moving forward in a ceremonial way〔人或車輛的〕行列: *a carnival procession* 狂歡節[嘉年華會]的遊行隊列 **2** [C;U] a continuous onward movement of people or things 列隊行進: *The workers marched in procession to the minister's office.* 工人們列隊向部長的辦公地點進發。| *to hold a procession* 舉行遊行

pro·ces·sor /ˈprɑsɛsɚ; ˈprəʊsesəʳ/ n see 見 WORD PROCESSOR

pro·claim /proˈklem; prəˈkleɪm/ v [T; +that] **1** fml to declare officially and publicly〔正式〕宣佈; 宣告: *Our country proclaimed its independence after the war.* 我們的國家在戰後宣告獨立。| *A national holiday was proclaimed.* 宣佈全國放假一日。**2** lit to show clearly〔文〕顯示; 表明: *His pronunciation proclaimed that he was an American.* 他的發音表明他是美國人。

proc·la·ma·tion /ˌprɑkləˈmeʃən; ˌprɒklə-ˈmeɪʃən/ n an official public statement 公告, 佈告; 聲明: *a royal proclamation* 王室公告

pro·cras·ti·nate /proˈkræstəˌnet; prəˈkræs-tɪˌneɪt/ v **procrastinated, procrastinating** [I] fml to repeatedly delay doing something that is necessary〔正式〕拖延, 耽擱 –

procrastination /proˌkræstəˈneʃən; prə-ˌkræstɪˈneɪʃən/ n [U]

pro·cre·ate /ˈprokriˌet; ˈprəʊkrieɪt/ v **procreated, procreating** [I;T] fml or tech to produce babies or young animals〔正式或術語〕生育, 生殖 –**procreation** /ˌprokriˈeʃən; ˌprəʊkriˈeɪʃən/ n [U]

pro·cure /proˈkjur; prəˈkjʊəʳ/ v **procured, procuring 1** [T] fml to obtain something that may be difficult to find〔正式〕獲得, 取得〔某物〕**2** [I;T] to provide a woman for someone else's sexual satisfaction 為…介紹娼妓, 拉皮條

prod /prɑd; prɒd/ v **-dd-** [I;T] **1** to push or press something or someone with a pointed object 刺, 戳: *She prodded the spider cautiously to make sure it was really dead.* 她小心地戳了戳那隻蜘蛛, 看牠是不是真的死了。**2** to urge someone to do something which they might forget 激勵; 催促〔某人〕做〔某事〕**–prod** n: *He gave the snake a prod with a stick.* 他用棍子戳了戳那條蛇。

prod·i·gal[1] /ˈprɑdɪgl; ˈprɒdɪgl/ adj fml careless and wasteful with money〔正式〕揮霍的; 奢侈的

prodigal[2] n **the prodigal returns** a person who has left to live a wasteful or immoral life is now returning (a phrase often used in a humorous way) 浪子回頭〔常作幽默用法〕

pro·di·gious /prəˈdɪdʒəs; prəˈdɪdʒəs/ adj great in size or amount and causing admiration 巨大的; 龐大的; 驚人的: *He is one of the country's most prodigious writers.* 他是該國最多產的作家之一。**–prodigiously** adv

prod·i·gy /ˈprɑdədʒi; ˈprɒdɪdʒi/ n **prodigies** a person who shows unusual and very noticeable abilities at an early age 奇才, 天才: *a child prodigy* 神童, 天才兒童

‡pro·duce[1] /prəˈdjus; prəˈdjuːs/ v **produced, producing** [T] **1** to have as a result or effect 產生〔結果或影響〕: *Gordon's jokes produced a great deal of laughter.* 高登的笑話引起了哄堂大笑。| *The two lasers combine to produce a powerful cutting tool.* 兩束激光合在一起, 形成了一把強有力的切割工具。**2** to make something, especially in large quantities〔尤指大量地〕生產: *Gas can be produced from coal.* 煤氣可從煤中提取。| *The factory produces 500 cars a week.* 這家工廠每週生產五百輛汽車。| *to produce a work of art* 創作一件藝術作品 –see 見 PRODUCTION (USAGE 用法) **3** to grow or supply 生產, 出產: *Canada produces good wheat.* 加拿大出產優質小麥。**4** to give birth to young ones or make as a natural process 生育; 生產: *Bees produce honey.* 蜜蜂產蜂蜜。**5** to show, or bring out for examination 出示, 提出, 拿出: *We had to produce our passports on the train.* 我們在火車上必須出示護照。| *He suddenly produced a gun.* 他突然拔出一支槍來。**6** to control, prepare, and present to the public 製作; 上演: *The play was badly produced*. 這齣戲製作得很糟糕.

prod·uce[2] /'prɒdjus; 'prɒdjuːs/ *n* [U] something that has been grown in large quantities 產品; 農產品: *The wine bottle was marked "Produce of Spain"*. 酒瓶上標着"西班牙產品"的字樣.

*★**pro·duc·er** /prə'djusə; prə'djuːsə[r]/ *n* 1 a person or company that produces goods, foods, or materials 生產商; 製造者: *one of the world's leading oil producers* 世界上主要的原油開採商之一 2 a person who has general control of the money for and preparation of a play, film, or broadcast 〔戲劇、電影或廣播的〕製片人, 製作人

prod·uct /'prɒdʌkt; 'prɒdʌkt/ *n* 1 something that is produced or made somewhere 產品, 出品: *a new range of kitchen products* 新系列的廚房用品 –see 見 PRODUCTION (USAGE 用法) 2 the result of experiences or certain situations 產物; 結果: *Criminals are sometimes the product of bad homes*. 罪犯有時是惡劣家庭環境的產物.

*★★**pro·duc·tion** /prə'dʌkʃən; prə'dʌkʃən/ *n* 1 [U] the act of producing something, especially for sale 〔尤指為了銷售而進行的〕生產: *This factory specializes in the production of larger cars*. 這家工廠專門生產大型汽車. | *There are problems with the production process*. 生產過程中出了問題. 2 [U] the amount of something which is produced 產量: *Oil production is falling world-wide*. 全世界的石油產量正在下降. 3 [C; U] a play, film, or broadcast, or the act of producing it 〔戲劇、電影、廣播劇的〕製作: *There are two productions of 'Hamlet' playing in London now*. 倫敦現在有兩齣《哈姆雷特》在上演. 4 [U] the act of showing something to someone 出示; 顯示: *Entry is permitted only on production of a ticket*. 出示門票才能入場.

■ USAGE 用法: Compare 比較 **production, product, produce**. **Production** is the process in which things are made ☆**production** 指生產過程: *a good rate of production* 良好的生產速度. A **production** is a play, film, etc. made for the theatre, television, etc. ☆ **production** 還指上演的戲劇、電影等: *a new production of 'Hamlet'* 新上映的《哈姆雷特》. A **product** is something made by industry ☆ **product** 指工業產品: *various industrial products* 各種各樣的工業產品. **Produce** is the general word for things from a farm, such as milk, potatoes, or wool ☆ **produce** 是諸如牛奶、馬鈴薯或羊毛等農產品的一般用詞: *a large quantity of agricultural produce* 大量的農產品.

production line /·'··· ·/ *n* a set of machines that are used to make something in a factory 生產線, 製配線

pro·duc·tive /prə'dʌktɪv; prə'dʌktɪv/ *adj* 1 useful because of having results 有成效的: *It was a productive meeting, at which some important decisions were made*. 這是個富有成效的會議, 會上做出了幾項重要決定. 2 producing a lot 多產的: *They form a productive team of workers*. 他們組成了一支多產高效的工人隊伍. –opposite 反義 **unproductive** –**productively** *adv*

pro·duc·tiv·i·ty /ˌprɒdʌk'tɪvətɪ; ˌprɒdʌk'tɪvəti/ *n* [U] the success of a company or area in making goods or growing things for sale 生產力; 生產效率: *Industrial productivity continues to increase in Japan*. 日本的工業生產能力持續增長. | *to get a productivity bonus* 獲得生產效率獎

Prof a written abbreviation for 〔縮〕= PROFESSOR

pro·fane[1] /prə'fen; prə'feɪn/ *adj fml* showing lack of respect for religion or religious things 〔正式〕褻瀆的; 不敬神的: *Smoking in a church is a profane act*. 在教堂裡吸煙是一種褻瀆神的行為.

profane[2] *v* **profaned, profaning** [T] *fml* to show a lack of respect for something religious or holy 〔正式〕褻瀆〔神明〕

pro·fan·i·ty /prə'fænətɪ; prə'fænəti/ *n* **profanities** [C;U] *fml* words or actions that show a lack of respect for religion or religious things 〔正式〕褻瀆的言詞〔舉止〕

pro·fess /prə'fes; prə'fes/ *v* [T] 1 to claim something which may not be true 自稱, 裝作; 聲稱: *We professed ignorance*. 我們裝作一無所知. | *He professes to be an expert in management skills, but I have my doubts*. 他自稱是管理技巧方面的專家, 但我對此持懷疑態度. 2 *fml* to express a feeling, opinion, or belief 〔正式〕表明〔感情、觀點或信仰〕: *She professed her surprise at the decision*. 她表明了自己對於該決定感到驚訝. –**professed** *adj* [only before a noun 只用於名詞前]: *a professed Catholic* 公開承認信仰的天主教徒

*★**pro·fes·sion** /prə'feʃən; prə'feʃən/ *n* 1 [C] a job that is socially respected because you need a high standard of education and also special training to do it 職業; 專業: *She wants to go into one of the professions; medicine, perhaps*. 她想從事一項專業, 可能是當醫生. –see 見 JOB (USAGE 用法) 2 [sing +sing/pl verb] all the people who are trained to do a particular job 同行; (某一)職業界: *There is a lot of pressure from the teaching profession for higher salaries*. 教育界為了增加工資而施加了很大壓力. | *The legal profession is extremely upset about this case*. 法律界對這件案子感到極端失望. 3 [C] *fml* a declaration of your belief, opinion, or feeling 〔正式〕〔對於信仰、觀點或感情的〕表白, 聲明: *professions of regret* 公開表示遺憾

*★★**pro·fes·sion·al**[1] /prə'feʃənl; prə'feʃənəl/ *adj* 1 [only before a noun 只用於名詞前] working in or concern-

ing a job that is socially respected because it needs a high standard of education and special training 專業的, 職業的: *You should ask a lawyer for professional advice.* 你應當去請教律師, 讓他給你一些專業意見。 **2** showing that you have great experience and high standards in what you do (a word used to express approval) 職業水準的〔含褒義〕: *It's a very professional report.* 這份報告很具職業水準。 –opposite 反義 **unprofessional 3** doing something for money rather than for interest or enjoyment 作為職業的: *a professional painter* 職業畫家 | *professional football* 職業足球 –**professionally** adv: *She was professionally trained.* 她受過職業訓練。

*professional² *n* **1** a person who is working in a job that is socially respected because it needs a high standard of education and special training 從事專門職業者, 專業人士 **2** a person who has great experience and high standards (a word used to express approval) 內行, 專家〔含褒義〕: *She's a real professional.* 她是個真正的專家。 **3** (also 又作 **pro** *infml* 〔非正式〕) a person who earns money for doing something which other people do for interest or enjoyment, for example, sport 職業選手; 職業演員: *Large prizes are encouraging tennis-players to become professionals.* 巨額獎金是要鼓勵打網球的人成為職業選手。

pro·fes·sion·al·is·m /prəˈfɛʃənlɪzm; prəˈfɛʃənəlɪzəm/ *n* [U] behaviour or skill which shows that a person has the experience and high standards that would be expected of a member of a PROFESSION (1) 專業精神; 職業技能: *I admire her professionalism.* 我很欣賞她的專業精神。

pro·fes·sor /prəˈfɛsə; prəˈfesər/ *n* (also 又作 **Professor**) **1** *BrE* a teacher of the highest rank in a university department 〔英式〕教授: *A new history professor will be appointed next term.* 下學期將委派一位新的歷史學教授。 | *Certainly, Professor Ingham.* 當然可以, 英格漢姆教授。 **2** *AmE* a teacher at a university or college 〔美式〕大學或學院教師

prof·fer /ˈprɒfə; ˈprɒfər/ *v* [T] *fml* 〔正式〕 **1** to hold something out towards someone 向〔某人〕遞上〔某物〕, 遞給: *She refused the proffered drink.* 她拒絕了別人遞給她的飲料。 **2** to offer 提供: *to proffer a suggestion* 提供建議

pro·fi·cient /prəˈfɪʃənt; prəˈfɪʃənt/ *adj* very good at something 熟練的: *She's a highly proficient swimmer.* 她是個非常熟練的游泳運動員。 –**proficiency** *n* [U]: *He's taking his cycling proficiency test.* 他正在參加腳踏車水平測試。

*pro·file /ˈprəʊfaɪl; ˈprəʊfaɪl/ *n* **1** a view of a person's face from one side 側面(像): *He had an attractive profile.* 他的側面很迷人。 **2** in profile seen from the side 從側面看: *He drew her in profile.* 他給她畫側面像。 **3** a short description of a person's life and character, that is written or broadcast 人物簡介, 傳略 **4** keep a low profile to avoid drawing attention to yourself or your actions 避免引人注目; 保持低姿態

*prof·it¹ /ˈprɒfɪt; ˈprɒfɪt/ *n* **1** [C;U] money which is earned by doing business, after all the costs are taken from it 利潤, 贏利, 收益: *He made a profit of £50,000 on the sale of his house.* 他把房子賣了, 獲利五萬英鎊。 | *Company profits have fallen this year.* 公司今年利潤下降。 | *There's not much profit in selling hats these days.* 現在出售帽子賺不了多少錢。 –opposite 反義 **loss 2** sell something at a profit to sell something for more than it cost you 高於原價出售某物, 出售某物而獲利: *She sold the car again later at a profit.* 過了些時候, 她又把車以高價賣掉了。 **3** [U] *fml* advantage which you get from something you do 〔正式〕得益, 益處

profit² *v* [T] *fml* 〔正式〕 **profit by/from something to learn or gain from something 從某事得到教益: *You must profit by my mistakes.* 你必須從我的錯誤中吸取教訓。

prof·it·a·ble /ˈprɒfɪtəbl; ˈprɒfɪtəbl/ *adj* **1** successful because of the money that is earned 贏利的, 有利可圖的: *The company has had a profitable year.* 公司去年贏利可觀。 | *Farming in this country is rarely profitable.* 在這個國家從事農業很少贏利。 **2** *fml* useful 〔正式〕有用的: *I hope you found the seminar profitable.* 我希望這次研討會對你有所裨益。 –**profitably** adv

pro·fi·teer /ˌprɒfɪˈtɪr; ˌprɒfɪˈtɪr/ *n* a person who makes large profits from people who need goods or services but cannot get them anywhere else (a word used to express disapproval) 牟取暴利者〔含貶義〕 –**profiteer** *v* [I]

profit mar·gin /ˈ·· ˌ··/ *n* the difference between the cost of producing something and the price at which it is sold 利潤幅度, 盈利率

prof·li·gate /ˈprɒflɪgət; ˈprɒflɪgət/ *adj fml* 〔正式〕 **1** wasting money or other things 揮霍的, 浪費的: *profligate spending* 揮霍的開支 **2** without morals or shame 放蕩的, 無恥的

pro·found /prəˈfaʊnd; prəˈfaʊnd/ *adj* **1** very great or strong 很大的; 強烈的: *Her death was a profound shock to all of us.* 她的死對我們所有人都是個很大的打擊。 **2** having, showing, or using great knowledge and understanding 淵博的; 深奧的: *a very profound remark* 深奧的話 –**profoundly** adv *fml* 〔正式〕: *I am profoundly grateful.* 我深為感激。

pro·fuse /prəˈfjuːs; prəˈfjuːs/ *adj* large in quantity 大量的; 充沛的; 很多的: *She offered her profuse thanks.* 她再三道謝。 –**profusely** adv – **profusion** /prəˈfjuːʒən; prəˈfjuːʒən/ *n* [sing;U]: *The room was covered in a profusion of flowers.* 房間裡放滿了花。 | *Weeds grow in profusion.* 野草叢生。

prog·e·ny /ˈprɒdʒənɪ; ˈprɒdʒəni/ *n* [U;

+sing/pl verb] *lit* someone's children (a word often used in a humorous way)〖文〗子女; 孩子〔常作幽默用法〗: *Her numerous progeny were all asleep.* 她那一大羣兒女都睡着了。

prog·no·sis /prɒɡˈnəʊsɪs; prɒɡˈnəʊsɪs/ *n* **prognoses** /-siz; -siːz/ **1** *tech* a doctor's judgment of how a particular disease will develop〖術語〗〔醫生對病情的〕預斷, 預後 —compare 比較 DIAGNOSIS **2** a judgment of how something will develop 預測

☆☆☆pro·gram¹ /ˈprəʊɡræm; ˈprəʊɡræm/ *n* **1** the instructions which a computer follows to perform an operation 電腦程序 **2** the usual American spelling for〖美式〗= PROGRAMME¹

program² *v* **-mm-** *or* **-m-** [T] **1** to give a computer the instructions it needs to perform an operation 為〔電腦〕編製程序: *The computer can be programmed to list all the people who are over 35.* 可為電腦編製程序, 把所有三十五歲以上的人的名字列出來。 **2** the usual American spelling for〖美式〗= PROGRAMME²

pro·gram·er /ˈprəʊɡræmə; ˈprəʊɡræmər/ *n* the usual American spelling for〖美式〗= PROGRAMMER

☆☆pro·gramme¹ /ˈprəʊɡræm; ˈprəʊɡræm/ *n* (**program** *AmE*〖美式〗) **1** a show or performance which is broadcast on television or radio〔電視或廣播的〕節目: *What is your favourite television programme?* 你最喜歡的電視節目是甚麼? **2** a plan of what you are going to do 計劃, 方案: *They're discussing a new research programme.* 他們正在商討一項新的研究計劃。 | *We must include shopping in the programme for tomorrow.* 我們必須把購物安排列入明天的計劃中去。 **3** printed information about performers, or things to be performed, at an event such as a concert or sports competition 節目單; 比賽程序表

programme² *v* **-mm-** (**program** *AmE*〖美式〗) [T] to make a person or thing operate in a particular way 調好〔使人或物按某種方式運作〕: *The central heating system is programmed to switch itself on in the mornings.* 中央暖氣系統已調好在清晨自行啟動。 | *Society programmes us to think like this.* 社會促使我們以這種方式思考。

pro·gram·mer /ˈprəʊɡræmə; ˈprəʊɡræmər/ *n* (**programer** *AmE*〖美式〗) a person who prepares instructions for computers 電腦程序編製員: *She's training to be a computer programmer.* 她正在接受培訓成為電腦程序編製員。

☆pro·gress¹ /ˈprəʊɡres; ˈprəʊɡres/ *n* [U] **1** movement in a particular direction 前進; 行進: *The ship made slow progress through the rough sea.* 這艘船在大風大浪中緩慢地前進。 **2** continual improvement or development 進步, 進展, 發展: *Jane is making progress in her research.* 簡正在研究中取得進展。 |

We've been following the progress of the case with interest. 我們懷着很大的興趣, 跟進着案情的發展。 **3** the idea of advancing generally in science, the organization of human society, etc.〔科學、人類社會等〕發展: *These ridiculous changes in the education system are being made in the name of progress.* 他們以發展為名, 正在對教育制度進行這些荒唐的改革。 **4 in progress** happening now 正在發生: *Repairs to the building are in progress.* 目前正在對房屋進行修繕。

pro·gress² /prəˈɡres; prəˈɡres/ *v* [I] **1** to move on 前進; 行進: *As the journey progressed he became increasingly tired.* 旅程進行得越長, 他越覺疲累。 **2** to improve or develop 進展, 發展: *We progressed from being total beginners to a high level of competence.* 我們從一竅不通的初學者逐漸變得極為稱職。 | *As the conversation progressed, her feelings became clear.* 隨着談話的展開, 她的感覺也變得明確起來。

pro·gres·sion /prəˈɡreʃən; prəˈɡreʃən/ *n* **1** [sing;U] development or improvement over time 進步; 進展 **2** a number of things which follow each other 一系列(的事情): *It was due to an unfortunate progression of events.* 這事起因於一系列不幸事件。

pro·gres·sive /prəˈɡresɪv; prəˈɡresɪv/ *adj* **1** developing or changing continuously over a period of time 有進展的; 逐漸變化的: *progressive loss of sight in old age* 老年時期視力的逐步衰退 **2** supporting or using new ideas 進步的; 革新的: *The company is very progressive in the benefits and facilities it offers its employees.* 公司在提供給雇員的福利和設施上做得非常開明。—**progressively** *adv*: *The situation got progressively worse.* 情況愈來愈壞。 | *thinking very progressively* 富有進取性地思考問題

pro·hib·it /prəˈhɪbɪt; prəˈhɪbɪt/ *v* [T] *fml*〖正式〗 **1** to forbid something by law or by a rule〔用法律或規定〕禁止: *Smoking is strictly prohibited.* 嚴禁吸煙。 **2** to make something impossible 使不可能: *His height prohibits him from becoming a policeman.* 他的身高使他不可能成為警察。

pro·hi·bi·tion /ˌprəʊɪˈbɪʃən; ˌprəʊəˈbɪʃən/ *n* **1** [U] the act of forbidding something 禁止 **2** [C] an order which forbids something〖正式〗禁令

pro·hib·i·tive /prəˈhɪbɪtɪv; prəˈhɪbɪtɪv/ *adj* costing so much that people cannot afford to do or buy something 貴得買不起的: *We wanted to buy a video recorder, but the cost was prohibitive.* 我們想買台錄影機, 但其價格貴得使人買不起。—**prohibitively** *adv*: *Meat has become prohibitively expensive.* 肉的價格已貴得使人望而卻步。

☆☆proj·ect¹ /ˈprɒdʒekt; ˈprɒdʒekt/ *n* **1** a plan to do something 計劃, 規劃, 項目: *Our current project is to build a garage.* 我們現在的計劃是建造一個車庫。 **2**

an educational activity in which students collect and present information about a subject 〔教育的〕研究項目: *We're doing a project on the history of London.* 我們正在進行一項關於倫敦歷史的研究。

pro·ject² /prə'dʒɛkt; prə'dʒɛkt/ v 1 [I] to stand out beyond an edge or surface 突出, 伸出: *The roof projects a metre beyond the walls.* 屋頂凸出牆外一米遠。 2 [T] to make something move through the air with force 發射; 投擲 3 [T] to direct light, sound, or heat into space or onto a surface 投射〔光線、聲音或熱量〕: *He's learning to project his voice so that he can be heard by a large audience.* 他正在學習把聲音擴大遠處, 以便使許多聽眾都能聽見。 | *Pictures of the earthquake were projected on a screen.* 地震的畫面被投到了屏幕上。

pro·jec·ted /prə'dʒɛktɪd; prə'dʒɛktⅼd/ adj 1 planned 計劃的: *our projected trip* 我們計劃中的旅行 2 calculated in advance 預測的: *projected unemployment figures* 預測的失業數字

pro·jec·tile /prə'dʒɛktɪl; prə'dʒɛktaɪl/ n fml an object that is shot from a gun or other weapon 〔正式〕射彈; 發射物

pro·jec·tion /prə'dʒɛkʃən; prə'dʒɛkʃən/ n 1 [C] a part of something that stands beyond an edge or surface 突出部分, 凸出物 2 [C] an amount calculated in advance 預測, 推斷: *Sales projections for next year look encouraging.* 對明年銷量的預測看起來很令人鼓舞。 3 [U] the act of projecting something 發射; 投擲

pro·jec·tion·ist /prə'dʒɛkʃənɪst; prə'dʒɛkʃⅼⅼst/ n a person who works a projector, especially in a cinema 投影機操作員〔尤指電影放映員〕

pro·jec·tor /prə'dʒɛktə; prə'dʒɛktər/ n an apparatus for showing images like films on a surface 投影機; 放映機

pro·le·tar·i·an /ˌproʊlə'tɛrɪən; ˌproʊl 'tɛrɪən/ adj of the proletariat (a word used to express disapproval) 無產階級的〔含貶義〕: *the proletarian masses* 無產階級羣眾 –**proletarian** n

pro·le·tar·i·at /ˌproʊlə'tɛrɪət; ˌproʊl 'tɛrɪət/ n the proletariat [+sing/pl verb] the class of workers who have to work for wages and do not own property 無產階級 –compare 比較 BOURGEOISIE

pro·lif·e·rate /prə'lɪfəˌret; prə'lɪfəreɪt/ v proliferated, proliferating [I] fml to increase in number rapidly 〔正式〕〔數量〕激增 –**proliferation** /proˌlɪfə'reʃən; prəˌlɪfə'reɪʃən/ n [U]

pro·lif·ic /prə'lɪfɪk; prə'lɪfɪk/ adj producing a lot of something 多產的: *Agatha Christie was a prolific writer.* 阿加莎·克里斯蒂是位多產的作家。 –**prolifically** /-klɪ; -klɪ/ adv

pro·logue /'prɒlɒɡ; 'proʊlɒɡ/ n (also 又作 **prolog** AmE 〔美式〕) 1 an introduction to a play or a long poem 〔戲劇的〕序幕; 〔長詩的〕序篇 –compare 比較 EPILOGUE 2 an event which comes before another one and often causes it to happen 事件的序幕: *The border incident proved to be just the prologue to a full-scale invasion.* 邊境的事件後來證明為為全面入侵的序幕。

pro·long /prə'lɒŋ; prə'lɒŋ/ v [T] to make something continue for a longer time 延長, 拖長, 拉長: *They're prolonging their visit because they've fallen in love with the city.* 由於他們愛上了那座城市, 所以延長了遊覽時間。

pro·longed /prə'lɒŋd; prə'lɒŋd/ adj continuing for a long time, or longer than expected 長期的; 延長的: *I am worried about his prolonged absence from school.* 我對他長期缺課感到擔憂。

prom·e·nade¹ /ˌprɒmə'ned; ˌprɒmə'naɪd◂/ n (also 又作 **prom** infml 〔非正式〕) 1 a wide path along the coast in a holiday town 海濱散步闊道 2 fml a slow walk or drive for pleasure or exercise 〔正式〕散步; 開車兜風

prom·e·nade² v promenaded, promenading [I] fml to walk slowly for pleasure or exercise 〔正式〕散步

prom·i·nent /'prɒmənənt; 'prɒmⅼnənt/ adj 1 standing out beyond a surface 突出的: *His teeth are rather prominent.* 他的牙有點向外突出。 2 famous or important 著名的; 重要的: *A number of prominent politicians will be present.* 幾位著名的政治家將會出席。 3 easily seen 明顯的, 顯著的: *She left a note for him in a prominent position.* 她在顯眼的地方給他留了張條子。 –**prominence** n [U] –**prominently** adv

pro·mis·cu·ous /prə'mɪskjʊəs; prə'mɪskjʊəs/ adj having sex with more than one sexual partner (a word used to show disapproval) 濫交的; 放蕩的〔含貶義〕: *a promiscuous girl* 放蕩的女孩 | *a promiscuous lifestyle* 放蕩的生活方式 –**promiscuously** adv –**promiscuity** /ˌprɒmɪs'kjʊtɪ; ˌprɒmⅼ'skjuⅼⅼti/ (also 又作 **promiscuousness** /prə'mɪskjʊəsⅼs/) n [U]

★prom·ise¹ /'prɒmɪs; 'prɒmⅼs/ n 1 [C] a statement that you certainly will or will not do something 承諾, 諾言: *I trust him to keep his promise.* 我相信他會信守諾言的。 | *She made a promise and then broke it.* 她答應過的, 卻食言了。 | *a promise of support* 答應給予支持的諾言 2 [U] signs or hope of success or improvement (有)希望, (有)指望: *His son is showing great promise as a footballer.* 他的兒子很有希望成為足球運動員。

★prom·ise² v promised, promising 1 [I;T] to state that you will certainly do something 承諾; 答應: *She promised to phone me later.* 她答應晚些時候打電話給我。 | *"I'm afraid I can't come this evening." "But you promised!"* "我恐怕今晚不能來。" "但你答應過的!" | *He promised that he would do his best.* 他答應盡力而為。 | *I promised her that I would* *never reveal her secret.* 我向她保證永不會泄露她的祕密。

□ **USEFUL PATTERNS** 有用句型
to promise to do something; to promise that...; to promise someone that...

---

2 [T] to state that you will certainly give something to someone 答應把〔某物〕給〔某人〕: *I've promised this book to Susan.* 我已答應把這本書給蘇珊了。| *We've promised her a puppy for her birthday.* 我們已答應在她生日時送一隻小狗給她。

□ **USEFUL PATTERNS** 有用句型
to promise something to someone; to promise someone something

---

3 [T] *fml* to show signs that something good will happen 〔正式〕有...的良好跡象: *It promises to be a fine day.* 今天天氣看來會很好。

prom·is·ing /ˈprɑmɪsɪŋ; ˈprɒmɪsɪŋ/ *adj* showing signs that something good will happen or that something will succeed 有良好跡象的; 有希望的: *That was a promising performance.* 那場演出有望成功。 **–promisingly** *adv*

prom·on·to·ry /ˈprɑməntɔrɪ; ˈprɒməntəri/ *n* **promontories** a long, narrow piece of land stretching out into the sea 海角; 岬

★**pro·mote** /prəˈmot; prəˈməut/ *v* **promoted, promoting** [T] **1** to give someone a higher position at work 提升, 晉升〔某人〕: *She's been promoted to senior editor.* 她被提升為高級編輯。 **2** to advertise a product or event 推廣, 宣傳〔產品或事件〕: *We are spending millions of pounds on promoting our new cat food.* 我們正在花幾百萬英鎊給我們新的貓糧做宣傳。 **3** to help something to develop or succeed 促進, 促成〔某事物〕: *The society's aim is to promote peace and understanding between nations.* 該協會旨在促進國與國之間的和平與理解。

pro·mot·er /prəˈmotɚ; prəˈməutəʳ/ *n* a person who arranges an event or works for the success of something 促進者; 推動者: *The concert promoters warn us that there will be a rush for tickets.* 音樂會的推廣人員提醒我們將會出現門票搶購現象。

★**pro·mo·tion** /prəˈmoʃən; prəˈməuʃən/ *n* **1** [C;U] a move to a higher position at work 提升, 晉升: *Congratulations on your promotion!* 恭喜你獲得晉升! | *good chances of promotion* 提升的機會很多 **2** [C;U] advertising, or a particular set of activities for advertising something 推廣, 宣傳(活動): *the promotion of our products on national television* 在國家電視台裡為我們的產品做的宣傳活動 | *We're mounting a new promotion.* 我正在舉行新的宣傳活動。 **3** [U] *fml* action to help something develop or succeed 〔正式〕促進; 促成: *The promotion of social values among teenagers has been neglected.* 在青少年間倡導社會價值觀念的工作被忽視了。

prompt[1] /prɑmpt; prɒmpt/ *v* [T] **1** to cause something to happen 促使〔某事發生〕: *Hunger prompted him to steal.* 飢餓促使他去偷竊。 | *News of the scandal prompted an inquiry into the conduct of local councillors.* 有關醜聞的消息促使人們對本市市政委員的操守進行調查。 **2** to remind someone, especially an actor of the next words in a speech 為〔演員〕提示台詞

prompt[2] *adj* arriving at the correct time 及時的; 準時的: *Please be prompt.* 請按時到達。 | *We request prompt payment of bills.* 我們要求立即付款。 **–promptly** *adv*: *I arrived promptly at 6 o'clock.* 我六點鐘準時到達。 **–promptness** *n* [U]

prompt[3] *adv* at a certain time exactly 準時: *The performance will start at seven o'clock prompt.* 演出將在七點鐘準時開始。

prompt·er /ˈprɑmptɚ; ˈprɒmptəʳ/ *n* (also 又作 **prompt**) a person who reminds actors of the words they forget during a performance 提詞員

prone /pron; prəun/ *adj* **1** prone to something, prone to do something likely to do something or to suffer from something 可能做某事; 可能遭遇某事: *He's prone to colds in winter.* 他在冬天很容易患上感冒。 | *People are more prone to make mistakes when they are tired.* 人累的時候較容易出差錯。 **2** *fml* lying flat, with your face and the front of your body downwards 〔正式〕俯臥的

prong /prɔŋ; prɒŋ/ *n* **1** a thin sharp-pointed part of something, especially of a fork 叉尖; 齒尖 **2** -pronged /prɔŋd; prɒŋd/ *adj* **a** having a certain number of prongs 有〔若干〕叉〔齒〕的: *a four-pronged fork* 四齒叉 **b** coming from a certain number of directions at the same time 來自〔若干〕方面的: *a two-pronged attack* 兩面夾攻

pro·noun /ˈpronaun; ˈprəunaun/ *n* a word like 'she' or 'we' that is used in place of a noun or a noun phrase 代名詞〔如"she"或"we"〕 –see Study Note on page 1330 見 1330 頁學習提示

pro·nounce /prəˈnauns; prəˈnauns/ *v* **pro·nounced, pronouncing** [T] **1** to make the sound of letters or words 發〔詞或字母〕的音: *In the word "knew", the "k" is not pronounced.* 在 "knew" 一詞中, 字母 "k" 不發音。 | *How do you pronounce his name?* 你怎麼唸他的名字? **2** *fml* to state something formally or officially 〔正式〕宣佈〔某事物〕: *The priest said: "I now pronounce you man and wife," and they were married.* 神父說: "現在我宣佈你們結為夫妻," 他們就這樣結婚了。 | *The jury pronounced their verdict.* 陪審團宣佈了判決。

---

pro·nounced /prəˈnaʊnst; prəˈnaʊnst/ *adj* very strong or noticeable 強烈的; 明顯的: *He has very pronounced ideas about politics.* 他對於政治的觀點非常明確。| *She walks with a pronounced limp.* 她走起路來明顯地一瘸一拐。

pro·nounce·ment /prəˈnaʊnsmənt; prəˈnaʊnsmənt/ *n fml* an official statement 〖正式〗聲明, 公告

pro·nun·ci·a·tion /prəˌnʌnsɪˈeɪʃən; prəˌnʌnsɪˈeɪʃən/ *n* 1 [C;U] the way in which something is spoken 發音 (法): *the normal Australian pronunciation* 正常的澳大利亞發音 | *There are several different pronunciations of this word.* 這個詞有好幾種讀法。2 [sing;U] a particular person's way of speaking a language or the words of a language 〔某人的〕發音方式: *She's always correcting my pronunciation.* 她總要糾正我的發音。

★**proof¹** /pruf; pruːf/ *n* 1 [C;U] a sign that something is certainly true 證明; 證據: *There's no proof of his guilt.* 沒有證據能表明他有罪。2 [C] a first copy of something printed, on which mistakes can be corrected before the printing process continues 校樣 3 [U; after a noun 用於名詞後] the standard of strength of some kinds of alcoholic drink 〔酒類的〕強度標準: *This whisky is 40 per cent proof.* 這種威士忌的酒精度是百分之四十。

proof² *adj* not influenced by something unpleasant 可防…的, 能抵擋…的: *His honesty is proof* **against** *temptation.* 他的誠實能經得起誘惑。

prop¹ /prɒp; prɒp/ *n* 1 a support which is placed to hold something up 支柱: *a clothes prop for the washing line* 晾衣繩的支柱 2 a person or thing that gives support to others 支撐者; 支撐物 3 an object used on the stage during the acting of a play or film 〔戲劇或電影的〕道具: *The costumes and props should be ready by Friday.* 服裝和道具應在星期五之前準備好。

prop² *v* **-pp-** [T; +adv/prep] to support something in a particular position 支撐; 把…固定於某個位置: *Prop the gate open with a brick!* 用磚�固定大門使它開着吧! | *She propped it* **against** *the shed.* 她把它靠在棚子上。

  prop sth ↔ **up** *phr v* [T] 1 to support something 支撐〔某物〕: *Prop it up* **against** *the wall.* 把它靠在牆上。2 to help something to continue 維持: *We just can't afford to prop up so many needy causes.* 我們實在無法支持這麼多需要投入物力財力的事情。

prop·a·gan·da /ˌprɒpəˈɡændə; ˌprɒpəˈɡændə/ *n* [U] ideas and information which are spread about officially, especially by a government for its own purposes 〔尤指政府的〕宣傳: *Those aren't facts; it's just propaganda.* 那些不是事實, 不過是些宣傳罷了。–

propagandist *n*: *political activists and propagandists* 政治活動的積極分子和搞政治宣傳的人

prop·a·gate /ˈprɒpəˌɡeɪt; ˈprɒpəɡeɪt/ *v* **propagated, propagating** 1 [I] *tech* to grow young plants from an original plant 〖術語〗繁殖: *Cuttings propagate easily.* 插枝很容易繁殖。2 [T] *fml* to spread ideas and information to a great number of people 〖正式〗宣傳; 傳播, 散播: *The government is able to use national newspapers and television to propagate its ideas.* 政府可以使用全國的報紙和電視來宣傳他們的主張。–**propagation** /ˌprɒpəˈɡeɪʃən; ˌprɒpəˈɡeɪʃən/ *n* [U]

pro·pel /prəˈpɛl; prəˈpel/ *v* **-ll-** [T] to move a person or thing in a certain direction, usually forwards 推進, 推動

pro·pel·ler /prəˈpɛlər; prəˈpelər/ *n* two or more blades fixed to a central bar that is turned at high speed by an engine; propellers are used for moving a ship or aircraft forwards 〔輪船或飛機上的〕螺旋槳; 推進器

pro·pen·si·ty /prəˈpɛnsətɪ; prəˈpensəti/ *n* **propensities** *fml* a tendency to behave in a particular and usually undesirable way 〖正式〗(不良)嗜好; 傾向: *She has a propensity* **to** *sudden anger.* 她很容易突然發脾氣。| *He has a propensity* **for** *getting into trouble.* 他愛惹麻煩。

★**prop·er** /ˈprɒpər; ˈprɒpər/ *adj* 1 [only before a noun 只用於名詞前] suitable and correct 合適的; 正確的: *She needs proper medical attention.* 她需要接受妥善的治療。| *These pages aren't in their proper order.* 這幾頁次序不對。| *What do you think is the proper role of the press in our society?* 你認為新聞界在我們這個社會裡應扮演甚麼樣的角色? 2 socially acceptable 合乎禮節的; 正經的: *That is not proper conduct for a girl of your age.* 對於你這個年紀的女孩子來說, 那是有失體統的行為。| *the proper thing to do* 理應做的事情 3 [after a noun 用於名詞後] itself 本身的: *We don't live in London proper.* 我們不住在倫敦城區內。

★**prop·er·ly** /ˈprɒpərlɪ; ˈprɒpəli/ *adv* in a correct or acceptable way 正確地; 適當地: *I've been learning German for years but I still can't speak it properly.* 我已學了德語好幾年, 但仍然說不好。| *I believe in doing a job properly.* 我認為凡要做事情就得做好。

proper noun /ˌ·· ˈ·/ *n* a name used for a particular person or thing and spelt with a capital letter; "James", "London", and "China" are all proper nouns 專有名詞〔"James"、"London" 和 "China" 都是專有名詞〕–compare 比較 COMMON NOUN

★**prop·er·ty** /ˈprɒpətɪ; ˈprɒpəti/ *n* **properties** 1 [U] something which you own 財產; 財物: *Always lock your car to protect your property.* 不管甚麼時候都要鎖好汽車, 以防財物丟失。2 [C;U] land, buildings, or both together 地產, 房產, 房地

產; 物業: *Property in the town centre is now very valuable.* 城中心的房地產現在非常值錢。| *There are a number of properties for sale in this street.* 這條街上有幾處房地產正在出售。**3** [C] a natural quality of something 性質; 特性: *The leaves of this plant have medicinal properties.* 這種植物的葉子具有醫藥性能。

proph·e·cy /'prɑfəsɪ; 'prɒfɨ͵sɪ/ *n* **prophecies 1** [U] the telling of future events 預言: *the art of prophecy* 預言術 **2** [C] a statement saying that something will happen in the future 預言: *his prophecies of war* 他對於戰爭的預言 | *The prophecy that he would live to be king was fulfilled.* 他將成為國王的預言果然應驗了。

proph·e·sy /'prɑfə͵saɪ; 'prɒfɨ͵saɪ/ *v* **prophesied, prophesied** [I;T;+that] to say that something will happen in the future 預言, 預示〔某物〕: *They prophesied disaster.* 他們預言要發生一場災難。| *I wouldn't like to prophesy who will win the election.* 我不想預言誰將在選舉中獲勝。| *They prophesied that there would be a bad winter.* 他們預言將有一個非常寒冷的冬天。

proph·et /'prɑfɪt; 'prɒfɨt/ *n* **1** a person who says what will happen in the future 預言者; 預言家 **2 a prophet of doom** a person who is always talking about the terrible things that they think will happen 預言災難的人 **3** a person who believes that they are directed by God to teach people religion and acceptable behaviour〔宗教的〕先知 **4 the Prophet** Mohammed, who formed the Muslim religion 穆罕默德〔伊斯蘭教創始人〕 **5** an important thinker who introduces and teaches a new idea〔新觀念的〕倡導者, 提倡者

pro·phet·ic /prə'fɛtɪk; prə'fetɪk/ *adj* (also 又作 **prophetical**) correctly telling of things that will happen in the future 預言性的; (似)先知的: *He made a number of prophetic remarks before he died.* 他去世前說了幾句預言性的話。 **–prophetically** /-klɪ; -klɪ/ *adv*

pro·pi·ti·ate /prə'pɪʃɪ͵et; prə'pɪʃɪeɪt/ *v* **propitiated, propitiating** [T] *fml* to do something to please someone who is angry or unfriendly〔正式〕安撫; 撫慰

pro·pi·tious /prə'pɪʃəs; prə'pɪʃəs/ *adj fml* favourable or likely to bring good results 〔正式〕吉利的, 吉祥的; 有利的: *It is not a propitious time to invest in oil.* 現在不是投資石油業的有利時機。

pro·po·nent /prə'ponənt; prə'pəʊnənt/ *n* a person who argues in favour of something 支持者; 鼓吹者: *an enthusiastic proponent of yoga* 一位熱心鼓吹瑜珈術的人

★pro·por·tion /prə'porʃən; prə'pɔːʃən/ *n* **1** [U] the correct relationship between the size and shape of the different parts of something 相稱, 協調; 均衡: *The painting lacks proportion.* 這幅畫比例失調。**2 in proportion** having everything of the correct

size or amount compared to other things 勻稱協調, 合乎比例: *The drawing wasn't in proportion.* 這幅畫比例不協調。[RELATED PHRASE 相關詞組 **out of proportion**] **3 keep/see things in proportion** to remember what is important and what is not important 分清主次: *Try to keep things in proportion.* 要分清事情的輕重緩急。[RELATED PHRASE 相關詞組 **get things out of proportion**] **4** [C] the amount of one thing compared to the amount of something else 比例: *What's the proportion of men to women in your office?* 你們辦公室裡男女比例是多少? **5** [C] a part or share of something 一部分: *Londoners have to spend a large proportion of their salary on rent.* 倫敦市民不得不將很大一部分工資用於房租上。**6 in proportion to: a** compared with the size of something else 與...相比: *The garage is big in proportion to the house.* 這車庫與房子相比顯得很大。**b** happening at the same rate as something else 與...速度相同: *The tax increases in proportion to the amount you earn.* 所得稅隨著你的收入按比例增長。**7 out of all proportion to something** much too great compared to something 大得與某物不成比例: *The suffering caused by the law is out of all proportion to the benefits it brings.* 這條法律給人們帶來的痛苦要遠遠超過它所帶來的好處。**8 proportions** [pl] the size and shape of something 大小, 面積; 形狀: *a building of fine proportions* 大小適中的建築物

pro·por·tion·al /prə'porʃən; prə'pɔːʃənəl/ *adj* in the correct relationship to something else 比例適當的; 成比例的: *His pay is proportional to the amount of work he does.* 他的工資與工作量相稱。 **–proportionally** *adv*

pro·por·tion·ate /prə'porʃənt; prə'pɔːʃə͵nɨt/ *adj* correct in relation to something else 相稱的; 均衡的 **–proportionately** *adv*

★★pro·pos·al /prə'pozl; prə'pəʊzəl/ *n* **1** a plan or suggestion 計劃; 建議: *There's a proposal to build a new supermarket.* 有人建議建造一座新的超級市場。| *They are discussing peace proposals.* 他們在商討和平計劃。| *She's made a proposal for new childcare facilities.* 她已提議建造新的兒童保育設施。**2** an offer of marriage 求婚

★pro·pose /prə'poz; prə'pəʊz/ *v* **proposed, proposing 1** [T;+(that)] *fml* to suggest something〔正式〕建議, 提議〔某事物〕: *He proposed delaying our decision for a few days.* 他建議我們遲幾日才做出決定。| *I propose that we all speak to the manager.* 我提議我們一起去與經理談。| *He has been proposed for membership of the club.* 有人提議讓他成為俱樂部的會員。**2 propose to do something** to intend to do something 打算做某事: *"I'm very upset about their decision." "And what do you propose to do*

about it?" 他決定感到非常不安。"
"那你打算怎麼辦?" **3** [I;T] to ask someone to marry you 向〔某人〕求婚: *He proposed to her after dinner.* 晚飯之後他向她求婚。| *He proposed marriage.* 他提議結婚。**4 propose a motion** to suggest the subject for DEBATE, and speak about why you believe in it 提出動議 **5 propose a toast** *fml* to invite people at a social gathering to raise their glasses and drink as a sign of wishing someone good luck or success 〔正式〕舉杯祝酒: *I would like to propose a toast to the bride and groom.* 我提議為新娘新郎乾杯。

prop·o·si·tion¹ /ˌprɑpəˈzɪʃən; ˌprɒpəˈzɪʃən/ *n* **1** *fml* a statement in which an opinion or judgment is expressed 〔正式〕陳述; 主張 **2** a suggestion or offer, especially in business 〔尤指商業上的〕建議, 提議: *I've got a proposition to put to you.* 我想對你提項建議。

proposition² *v* [T] *infml* to offer to have sex with someone 〔非正式〕向〔某人〕提出性要求: *I was propositioned in the hotel bar.* 有人在旅館酒吧裡向我提出非分要求。

pro·pound /prəˈpaʊnd; prəˈpaʊnd/ *v* [T] *fml* to suggest something such as a problem or a THEORY for people to consider 〔正式〕提出〔問題或理論〕供考慮

pro·pri·e·ta·ry /prəˈpraɪəˌtɛri; prəˈpraɪətəri/ *adj* sold under the name of a person or company 專有的; 專利的: *proprietary medicines* 專利藥品

pro·pri·e·tor /prəˈpraɪətɚ; prəˈpraɪətər/ *n fml* the owner of a business; a female owner of a business is sometimes called a **proprietress** 〔正式〕業主〔女業主有時稱為 **proprietress**〕

pro·pri·e·ty /prəˈpraɪəti; prəˈpraɪəti/ *n* [U] *fml* correctness of social or moral behaviour 〔正式〕禮節; 規矩: *You can trust John to behave with perfect propriety.* 約翰很懂得規矩, 你可以對他放心。

pro·pul·sion /prəˈpʌlʃən; prəˈpʌlʃən/ *n* [U] *tech* the force that moves something forward 〔術語〕推進力

pro·sa·ic /proˈzeɪ·ɪk; prəʊˈzeɪ·ɪk/ *adj* dull and uninteresting 單調的; 無聊的: *a prosaic job* 無聊的工作 **–prosaically** /-klɪ; -kli/ *adv*

pro·scribe /proˈskraɪb; prəʊˈskraɪb/ *v* **proscribed, proscribing** [T] *fml* to forbid something officially 〔正式〕禁止〔某事物〕 **–proscription** /proˈskrɪpʃən; prəʊˈskrɪpʃən/ *n* [C;U]

prose /proz; prəʊz/ *n* [U] language written in its usual form and not as poetry 散文: *He usually writes in prose.* 他通常用散文體寫作。

pros·e·cute /ˈprɑsɪˌkjut; ˈprɒsɪkjuːt/ *v* **prosecuted, prosecuting** [I;T] to bring a criminal charge against someone in a court of law 對〔某人〕起訴: *He was prosecuted for stealing.* 他因偷竊而被起訴。| *Shop-lifters warned — we always prosecute!* 店鋪盜竊者

注意——一經抓獲, 即被檢控!

✱pros·e·cu·tion /ˌprɑsɪˈkjuʃən; ˌprɒsɪˈkjuːʃən/ *n* **1** [C;U] the bringing of a criminal charge against someone 起訴, 檢控: *The sale of alcohol to children can lead to prosecution.* 出售酒類給兒童可引起訴訟。| *The police brought a successful prosecution against him.* 警方成功地對他起訴。**2 the prosecution** [U; +sing/pl verb] the lawyers who try to prove someone's guilt in a court of law 控方律師: *The prosecution is calling its final witness.* 控方律師在請最後的證人出庭。| *Mr Jones is acting for the prosecution.* 瓊斯先生任控方律師。 **–compare** 比較 **DEFENCE**

pros·e·cu·tor /ˈprɑsɪˌkjutɚ; ˈprɒsɪkjuːtər/ *n* the lawyer who tries to prove someone's guilt in a court of law 控方律師, 檢控官

✱pros·pect¹ /ˈprɑspɛkt; ˈprɒspekt/ *n* **1** [C;U] a possibility that something will happen 〔某事發生的〕可能性; 指望: *There's not much prospect of my being able to see you soon.* 我不大指望會很快再見到你。| *The prospects for a peaceful solution to the crisis are quite good.* 此次危機很有可能和平解決。**2** [sing] something which you expect to happen 預料要發生的事情: *She hates the prospect of having to live alone.* 對於不久可能要過獨身生活, 她感到很討厭。| *That's not a very cheerful prospect.* 那種可能無法令大家振作起來。**3 someone's prospects** someone's chances of being successful in their job 某人在工作上成功的可能; 前景: *His prospects are very good.* 他的前景非常好。**4** [sing] *fml* a wide or distant view 〔正式〕遠景; 視野

pros·pect² /prəˈspɛkt; prəˈspekt/ *v* [I] to look for things like gold, oil, or minerals in a particular area 勘探〔黃金、石油或礦藏〕 **– prospector** *n*

pro·spec·tive /prəˈspɛktɪv; prəˈspektɪv/ *adj* probable or expected 可能的; 預期的: *We've found a prospective buyer for the house.* 我們已找到了一位可能買這所房屋的人。

pro·spec·tus /prəˈspɛktəs; prəˈspektəs/ *n* a printed statement giving information about a university, a school, or a company 〔大學、學校或公司的〕說明書, 簡介資料

pros·per /ˈprɑspɚ; ˈprɒspər/ *v* [I] **1** to become successful and rich 成功; 興旺: *Our business has just started to prosper.* 我們的生意剛剛開始興旺起來。**2** to develop favourably 使繁榮

pros·per·i·ty /prɑsˈpɛrəti; prɒˈsperɪti/ *n* [U] success and wealth 成功; 繁榮: *We live in a period of great prosperity.* 我們生活在一個繁榮昌盛的時代。

pros·per·ous /ˈprɑspərəs; ˈprɒspərəs/ *adj* rich and successful 富強的; 繁榮的 **–prosperously** *adv*

pros·ti·tute¹ /ˈprɑstəˌtjut; ˈprɒstɪtjuːt/ *n* a person, especially a woman, who has sex with people for money 賣淫者; 妓女

prostitute² *v* **prostituted, prostituting** [T]

fml〖正式〗**1 prostitute yourself** to have sex with people for money 賣淫 **2** to use an ability for doing things which are not important and do not deserve respect, and that usually you do not have to do, especially in order to make money 廉價出賣; 濫用: *He prostituted his talent by acting in such terrible films.* 他在如此糟糕的影片中扮演角色，濫用了自己的才能。

pros·ti·tu·tion /ˌprɑstəˈtjuʃən; ˌprɒstɪˈtjuːʃən/ *n* [U] the act or work of having sex with people for money 賣淫(業)

pros·trate[1] /ˈprɑstreɪt; ˈprɒstreɪt/ *adj* **1** lying flat, with your face and the front of your body downwards 俯臥的, 匍伏的 **2** so upset or weak that you are unable to act 虛弱的; 不振的: *She was prostrate with grief.* 她因悲痛而一蹶不振。**–prostration** /prəˈstreɪʃən; prɒˈstreɪʃn/ *n* [C;U]

pros·trate[2] /ˈprɑstret; prɒˈstreɪt/ *v* **prostrated, prostrating 1 prostrate yourself** to lie face down on the ground, usually as a sign of worship〔通常為了表示敬慕〕拜倒; 匍伏 **2 be prostrated by something** to be made so weak by something that you are unable to do anything 被某事搞得異常虛弱: *She was prostrated by illness.* 她由於生病而非常虛弱。

pro·tag·o·nist /prəˈtægənɪst; prəʊˈtægənɪst/ *n* **1** a leader or supporter of an idea or purpose 倡導者, 擁護者: *Mrs Pankhurst was one of the chief protagonists of women's rights.* 潘郝斯特夫人是女權的主要倡導者之一。**2** one of the most important characters in a play, story, or actual event〔戲劇、故事或事件的〕主角; 主要人物

pro·tect /prəˈtɛkt; prəˈtekt/ *v* [T] to keep a person or thing safe from something unpleasant 保護, 維護〔人或物〕: *He raised his arm to protect his face* **from** *the blow.* 他舉起胳膊護住臉部免被擊中。| *We must protect ourselves* **against** *further attack.* 我們必須保護自己以防止進一步受到攻擊。**–protector** *n*

pro·tec·tion /prəˈtɛkʃən; prəˈtekʃn/ *n* **1** [U] the act of keeping a person or thing safe, or the state of being kept safe 保護; 防衛: *That coat's too thin to give you any protection against the cold.* 那件外衣太薄了，根本無法禦寒。| *I've hired a bodyguard for the children's protection.* 我已雇了個保鏢保護孩子們。**2** [sing] a person or thing that keeps someone or something safe 保護者; 保護物: *He bought a hat as a protection against the sun.* 他買了頂帽子以抵禦陽光。

pro·tec·tive /prəˈtɛktɪv; prəˈtektɪv/ *adj* **1** [only before a noun 只用於名詞前] giving protection against harm 保護的; 防護的: *All workers must wear protective clothing.* 所有的工人都必須穿上防護服。**2** having a desire to protect and look after someone...愛護的: *He is very protective* **towards** *his younger sister.* 他非常愛護他的小妹妹。–

protectiveness *n* [U]

pro·tec·tor·ate /prəˈtɛktərɪt; prəˈtektərɪt/ *n* a country which is controlled and protected by a more powerful nation〔由一個較強的國家支配和保護的〕保護國

prot·é·gé /ˈprɒtəˌʒe; ˈprɒtɪʒeɪ/ *n* a person who is guided and helped by someone of influence or power; a woman who is guided and helped in this way is called a **protégée** 受提攜者, 受保護者〔受提攜的女子稱為 **protégée**〕

pro·tein /ˈprotin; ˈprəʊtiːn/ *n* [C;U] a substance which is found in foods like meat and eggs, and which helps your body to grow and stay healthy 蛋白質

pro·test[1] /ˈprotɛst; ˈprəʊtest/ *n* **1** [C;U] a complaint about something 抗議, 反對: *I would like to register a protest about local services.* 我想對本地的服務機構提出抗議。| *They are demonstrating in protest against the new law.* 他們在遊行示威，反對新法。| *You should write a letter of protest to your M.P.* 你應該給你區的國會議員寫封抗議信。**2 under protest** unwillingly and complaining that something is not fair 不願意地; 不服地: *They led him away under protest.* 他們強行把他帶走了。

pro·test[2] /prəˈtɛst; prəˈtest/ *v* **1** [I] to express your disagreement or annoyance about something 反對, 抗議: *They protested* **about** *the bad food at the hotel.* 他們對旅館粗劣的食物提出抗議。| *We protested to the manager.* 我們對經理提出抗議。| *a crowd protesting* **against** *the war* 抗議戰爭的一羣人 **2** [T;+that] to state firmly that something is true when other people do not believe you 堅持說; 申明: *She protested that she was too tired to continue dancing.* 她堅持說人太累起不動舞了。| *He has always protested his innocence.* 他一直申明自己是無辜的。–

protester *n*

Prot·es·tant /ˈprɑtɪstənt; ˈprɒtɪstənt/ *adj* belonging to a part of the Christian church that separated from the ROMAN CATHOLIC Church in the 16th century 新教的〔指16世紀脫離羅馬天主教的基督教派的〕**–Protestant** *n* **–Protestantism** *n* [U]

prot·es·ta·tion /ˌprɑtəsˈteʃən; ˌprɒtɪˈsteɪʃən/ *n* *fml* a strong declaration that what you say is true〖正式〗宣言; 鄭重聲明

pro·to·col /ˈprotəˌkɑl; ˈprəʊtəkɒl/ *n* [U] the system of rules about acceptable behaviour on official occasions, which is used especially by representatives of governments 外交禮節, 禮儀

pro·ton /ˈprotɑn; ˈprəʊtɒn/ *n* a very small piece of matter present in the central part of an atom 質子

pro·to·type /ˈprotəˌtaɪp; ˈprəʊtətaɪp/ *n* the first form of something, from which all later forms develop 原型; 雛型: *They are working on the prototype* **of** *a new car.* 他們

正在設計一種新型汽車的原型。

pro·trac·ted /prəˈtræktɪd; prəˈtræktʃd/ *adj* lasting a long time 長時間的; 拖長的: *a protracted argument* 長時間的辯論 | *a protracted stay in hospital* 長期住院

pro·trac·tor /prəˈtræktə; prəˈtræktər/ *n* an instrument, usually in the form of a halfcircle, which is used for measuring and drawing angles 量角器, 分度規

pro·trude /prəˈtrud; prəˈtruːd/ *v* **protruded, protruding** [I] *fml* to stick out from a place or through a surface 〖正式〗伸出, 突出: *She saw a gun protruding from the man's pocket.* 她看見那個人的口袋裡露出了一支手槍。 | *protruding teeth* 齙牙 **–protrusion** /-ˈtruʒən; -ˈtruːʒən/ *n* [C;U]

pro·tu·ber·ance /prəˈtjubərəns; prəˈtjuːbərəns/ *n fml* something curved that stands out from a surface 〖正式〗隆起; 突出物

*****proud** /praud; praud/ *adj* **1** having or showing self-respect (a word used to express approval) 自尊的; 有自尊心的〔含褒義〕: *They are proud people despite their poverty.* 他們儘管貧窮, 但有自尊心。 **2** having too high an opinion of yourself (a word used to express disapproval) 驕傲自大的, 傲慢的〔含貶義〕: *She's too proud to mix with people like us.* 她過於高傲, 不願同我們這種人混在一起。 **3** feeling satisfaction and pleasure about something that you have done or something that someone close to you has done 自豪的, 得意的, 引以為榮的: *You should be proud of your achievements.* 你應當對自己的成就感到自豪。 | *We're all very proud of you.* 我們都為你而自豪。 | *I'm very proud to be invited to give this speech.* 我能被邀請來發表此次演講, 感到非常自豪。 | *It was a proud day for her parents.* 對她的父母來說, 這是個值得驕傲的日子。

□ USEFUL PATTERNS 有用句型
be proud of something or someone; be proud to do something; be proud that...

4 do someone proud *infml* to treat a guest very well 〖非正式〗款待客人以上賓之禮 – **proudly** *adv*

*****prove** /pruv; pruːv/ *v* **proved, proved** or **proven** /ˈpruvən; ˈpruːvən/, **proving 1** [T] to show that something is certainly real or true 證明: *He has proved his courage in battle.* 他已在戰鬥中證明了自己的英勇。 | *There is enough evidence to prove that she is guilty.* 有足夠的證據證明她有罪。 **2** [T+complement] to show over time that something has, or you have, a certain quality 證實: *It proved to be a terrible mistake.* 這被證實是個嚴重的錯誤。 | *He proved more talented than anyone had imagined.* 事實表明, 他的天賦超過了所有人的想像。

prov·en /ˈpruvən; ˈpruːvən, *Scot* ˈprovən; ˈprəʊvən/ *adj* shown to be real or true 被證

實的: *I can recommend Mr. Jones as a manager of proven ability.* 我願意推薦瓊斯先生, 證明他是位有能力的經理。

prov·erb /ˈprɑvɝb; ˈprɒvɜːb/ *n* a short wellknown saying about a general truth 格言; 諺語: *My favourite proverb is "Don't put all your eggs in one basket".* 我最喜歡的格言是 "不要把全部雞蛋放在一個籃子裡"(不要孤注一擲)。

pro·ver·bi·al /prəˈvɝbiəl; prəˈvɜːbiəl/ *adj* **1** of or from a proverb 格言的, 諺語的 **2** very widely known and talked about 廣為人知的; 廣為談論的: *his proverbial generosity* 他那人盡皆知的慷慨

*****pro·vide** /prəˈvaɪd; prəˈvaɪd/ *v* **provided, providing** [T] **1** to give or supply something to someone 提供, 供給: *The hotel provides very good meals.* 這家旅館供應豐盛的膳食。 | *The school does not provide paper for students.* 那所學校不為學生提供紙張。 | *These letters should provide us with all the information we need.* 這些信應當可以為我們提供所需要的全部信息。

□ USEFUL PATTERNS 有用句型
to provide something for someone; to provide someone with something

2 provide for someone to supply someone with all the things that they need 供養某人: *He has to provide for his elderly parents.* 他要供養他年邁的父母。 **3 provide for something** to make the necessary arrangements for a possible future event 〔可能發生的事〕做好準備: *The budget must provide for a possible increase in unemployment levels.* 這個預算必須為可能上升的失業人數做好準備。 **4 provide that** *fml* to state that something should happen or will happen 〖正式〗規定: *The law provides that ancient buildings must be preserved.* 法律規定古建築必須得到保護。

*****pro·vid·ed** /prəˈvaɪdɪd; prəˈvaɪdʃd/ *conj* (also 又作 **provided that, providing, providing that**) on condition that 如果; 條件是: *I will go, provided you go too.* 如果你去, 那我就去。 | *I'll dry the dishes, providing that you do the washing-up.* 如果你來洗碗碟, 那我就把它們擦乾。

prov·i·dence /ˈprɑvədəns; ˈprɒvɪdəns/ *n* [U] good fortune which is said to be brought by God or fate 天意; 天佑

prov·i·dent /ˈprɑvədənt; ˈprɒvɪdənt/ *adj* careful about providing for future needs 深謀遠慮的, 有遠見的

prov·i·den·tial /ˌprɑvəˈdɛnʃəl; ˌprɒvɪˈdenʃəl/ *adj fml* fortunate 〖正式〗幸運的 – **providentially** *adv*

*****prov·ince** /ˈprɑvɪns; ˈprɒvɪns/ *n* **1** [C] one of the main divisions of a country, that has its own local government 省份, 大行政區: *Eastern Province in Zambia is the most densely populated.* 贊比亞東部省是人口最稠

密的地區。**2** [U] an area of thought, knowledge, or responsibility〔思想、知識〕領域; 職責, 範圍: *Persian art is outside my province, I'm afraid.* 對不起, 波斯藝術不是我的領域。**3 the provinces** [pl] the parts of a country outside its main city 外省; 外地: *The film is new, so it is not yet being shown in the provinces.* 這是部新電影, 所以還未在外地上映。

pro·vin·cial /prə'vɪnʃəl; prə'vɪnʃəl/ *adj* **1** [only before a noun 只用於名詞前] of or from a province or the provinces 省的; 外省的; 地方上的: *a provincial newspaper* 省報 **2** having old-fashioned ideas and habits which are believed to be typical of people from the provinces 偏狹的; 粗俗的: *I found him rather narrow-minded and provincial.* 我覺得他心胸狹窄, 舉止粗俗。 –**provincialism** *n* [U]

★**pro·vi·sion**¹ /prə'vɪʒən; prə'vɪʒən/ *n* **1** [U] the act of supplying something 提供, 供給: *Local councils are responsible for the provision of books to schools.* 地方市政體負責為學校提供課本。**2 make provision for** to prepare for future needs 為〔將來的需要〕做準備; 未雨綢繆: *We must make some provision for our retirement.* 我們必須為退休做好準備。**3** [C] a condition in an agreement or law〔協議或法律的〕條文, 條款: *According to the provisions of the agreement the money must be paid back quickly.* 根據協議的條款, 那筆錢必須很快還清。**4 provisions** [pl] supplies of food and drink 糧食的供應

provision² *v* [T] *fml* to supply someone with food and other necessary things〔正式〕給〔某人〕提供食品及其他必需品

pro·vi·sion·al /prə'vɪʒənl; prə'vɪʒənəl/ *adj* existing for the present time only and likely to be changed later 暫時的, 臨時性的: *It's just a provisional arrangement.* 這不過是個臨時性的安排。–**provisionally** *adv*

pro·vi·so /prə'vaɪzəʊ; prə'vaɪzəʊ/ *n* a condition that must be fulfilled before an agreement is accepted 限制性條件, (附帶)條件: *I've agreed to do the work, with the proviso that I'm paid in advance.* 我已同意做這項工作, 但條件是工資要預付。

prov·o·ca·tion /ˌprɒvə'keɪʃən; ˌprɒvə'keɪʃən/ *n* [C;U] the act of trying to make someone angry or the state of being made angry 刺激; 激怒: *Bringing her here was a deliberate provocation.* 把她帶到這裡來是存心為了激怒她。| *She hit me, without the least provocation.* 她打了我一下, 毫無激怒我的意思。

pro·voc·a·tive /prə'vɒkətɪv; prə'vɒkətɪv/ *adj* intending to cause anger, or sexual desire 挑釁的; 挑逗的: *a provocative speech* 挑釁性的演講 | *provocative behaviour* 挑逗性行為。–**provocatively** *adv*

pro·voke /prə'vok; prə'vəʊk/ *v* **provoked, provoking** [T] **1** to make someone very

angry, especially by continually annoying them 激怒; 挑釁: *I don't want to fight, so don't provoke me.* 我不想打架, 所以別來惹我。

□ USEFUL PATTERNS 有用句型
to provoke someone; to provoke someone into doing something; to provoke someone to do something

2 to cause an unpleasant feeling or action 激起, 引起〔不愉快的感覺或行動〕: *The article provoked many letters of complaint.* 這篇文章引來了許多表示不滿的信。

pro·vok·ing /prə'vokɪŋ; prə'vəʊkɪŋ/ *adj* annoying 令人惱怒的

prow /prau; prau/ *n* the pointed front part of a ship or boat 船頭

prow·ess /'prauɪs; 'praʊᵻs/ *n* [U] *fml* great skill〔正式〕高超的技藝: *I admire his prowess as a footballer.* 我非常欣賞他的足球球藝。

prowl¹ /praul; praʊl/ *v* (also 又作 **prowl about**) [I] to move about quietly, trying not to be seen or heard 偷偷潛行, 悄悄走動: *I thought I heard someone prowling about in the garden last night.* 我覺得昨天夜裡我聽到有人在花園裡悄悄走動。–**prowler** *n*

prowl² *n* [sing] **on the prowl** moving about quietly trying not to be seen or heard 潛行

prox·im·i·ty /prɒk'sɪmətɪ; prɒk'sɪmᵻti/ *n* [U] *fml*〔正式〕**1** nearness 臨近: *We chose the house because of its proximity to the school.* 我們選中了那所房子, 因為它離學校近。**2 in the proximity of** near to a place 靠近〔某地〕

prox·y /'prɒksɪ; 'prɒksi/ *n* **proxies 1** someone who has the right to represent another person, especially as a voter at an election 代理人〔尤指代人投票者〕**2 by proxy** by sending another person to represent you 派代表: *You can vote by proxy.* 你可以讓人代你投票。

prude /pruːd; pruːd/ *n* a person who is easily shocked by things which they consider improper, especially sexual things (a word used to express disapproval)〔尤指在性方面〕過分拘謹的人; 假正經的人〔含貶義〕– **prudish** *adj* –**prudishly** *adv*

pru·dent /'pruːdnt; 'pruːdənt/ *adj* sensible and careful 謹慎的, 慎重的: *We were taught to be prudent with money.* 我們被告誡對於金錢要小心謹慎。–opposite 反義 **imprudent** – **prudence** *n* [U]

prud·er·y /'pruːdərɪ; 'pruːdəri/ *n* (also 又作 **prudishness** /'pruːdɪʃnɪs; 'pruːdɪʃᵻs/) [U] the behaviour or opinions of someone who is easily shocked by improper things, especially sexual things (a word used to express disapproval) 拘謹; 假正經〔含貶義〕

prune¹ /pruːn; pruːn/ *n* a dried PLUM 西梅乾
prune² *v* **pruned, pruning** [T] to cut off some of the branches of a tree or bush to

improve its shape and help it grow better 修剪〔枝條〕

pry /praɪ; praɪ/ v **pried, pried 1** [I] to try to find out about someone else's private affairs (a word used to express disapproval) 探查; 打聽〔含貶義〕: *Those journalists are paid to pry into the affairs of the royal family.* 那些記者被雇來探聽有關王室人員的私事。| *I'm sorry, I didn't mean to pry.* 對不起, 我沒有打聽的意思。**2** [T;+adv/prep] to force something open, or to force two things apart, using a tool or metal bar 〔用工具或金屬棍〕撬開: *I can't pry the lid off this box without breaking it.* 我不打破這個箱子就無法把蓋子撬下來。

P.S. /ˌpi ˈɛs; ˌpiː ˈes/ n infml 〔非正式〕a short addition to the end of a letter or message an abbreviation for POSTSCRIPT 〔縮〕信的附言; 又及: *Look. There's a P.S. at the bottom.* 看, 底下還有附言呢。| *...Yours sincerely, J.Smith. P.S. I shan't be able to come before Thursday.* ...J・史密斯敬上。又及, 我週四之前不能來。

psalm /sɑm; sɑːm/ n (also 又作 **Psalm**) a song or poem in praise of God 聖歌; 讚美詩

pseud /sjud; sjuːd/ n infml a person who tries to appear better than others in their knowledge, experience, and social position (a word used to express disapproval) 〔非正式〕假充在學識、經驗和社會地位上高人一等的人; 偽君子〔含貶義〕

pseu·do·nym /ˈsudn̩ˌɪm; ˈsjuːdənɪm/ n a name which a writer uses instead of his or her real name 筆名, 假名: *Eric Blair wrote under the pseudonym of George Orwell.* 埃里克・布萊爾以喬治・奧威爾的筆名寫作。

psy·che /ˈsaɪki; ˈsaɪki/ n tech or fml the human mind, soul, or spirit 〔術語或正式〕心靈; 靈魂; 精神

psy·che·del·ic /ˌsaɪkɪˈdɛlɪk; ˌsaɪkɪ̩ˈdelɪk◂/ adj **1** concerning certain drugs which cause changes in your mind and in the way your senses experience reality 〔藥物〕引起幻覺的 **2** concerning art forms which have an effect on your brain because they use strong or strange patterns and colours 〔藝術形式〕〔由於使用強烈或奇異的圖案和顏色而〕產生幻覺的

psy·chi·a·trist /saɪˈkaɪətrɪst; saɪˈkaɪətrɨst/ n a doctor who is trained to study and treat illnesses of the mind 精神科醫生

psy·chi·a·try /saɪˈkaɪətri; saɪˈkaɪətri/ n [U] the study and treatment of illness of the mind 精神病學; 精神病治療 —**psychiatric** /ˌsaɪkɪˈætrɪk; ˌsaɪkɪˈætrɪk/ adj

psy·chic /ˈsaɪkɪk; ˈsaɪkɪk/ adj (also 又作 **psychical** /-kɪkl̩; -kɪkəl/) **1** concerning strange powers or events which cannot be explained by scientists 超自然的: *They claim that his psychic powers enabled him to predict his mother's death.* 他們聲稱他的特異功

能使他預見到了母親的去世。**2** fml concerning the mind rather than the body 〔正式〕精神上的: *We are studying psychic disorders caused by great unhappiness in childhood.* 我們正在研究不愉快的童年所造成的精神失常。–**psychic** n: *Psychics were used to try and find the kidnapped girl.* 有特異功能的人被請來設法尋找被綁架的小女孩。

psy·cho·an·a·lyse /ˌsaɪkoʊˈænl̩ˌaɪz; ˌsaɪkəʊ-ˈænəlaɪz/ v **psychoanalysed, psychoanalysing** (also 又作 **psychoanalyze** AmE 〔美式〕) [T] to treat disorders of the mind by using psychoanalysis 用精神分析法治療

psy·cho·a·nal·y·sis /ˌsaɪkoʊəˈnæləsɪs; ˌsaɪkəʊ-əˈnæləsɨs/ n [U] a way of treating certain disorders of the mind by examining the sufferer's past life, feelings, and dreams in an effort to find the hidden causes of their illness 精神分析(治療法); 心理分析(治療法)

psy·cho·an·a·lyst /ˌsaɪkoʊˈænlɪst; ˌsaɪkəʊ-ˈænəl-ɨst/ n (also 又作 **analyst**) a person who is trained to treat disorders of the mind by using psychoanalysis 精神分析專家

****psy·cho·log·i·cal** /ˌsaɪkəˈlɑdʒɪkl̩; ˌsaɪkə̩lə-dʒɪkəl◂/ adj **1** concerning your mind and thoughts 心理(上)的: *Your problems are psychological and can be solved if you change your attitude.* 你的問題出在心理上, 如果你轉變態度, 問題就能得到解決。**2** [only before a noun 只用於名詞前] using psychology 心理學的: *Psychological tests are being used to analyse the personalities of job applicants.* 心理測驗現在被用來分析申請工作者的個性。–**psychologically** /-klɪ; -kli/ adv

psy·chol·o·gist /saɪˈkɑlədʒɪst; saɪˈkɒlə-dʒɨst/ n a person who is trained to study and explain how the human mind works 心理學家

****psy·chol·o·gy** /saɪˈkɑlədʒi; saɪˈkɒlədʒi/ n [U] **1** the scientific study of the mind and how it works 心理學 **2** the psychology of someone the way in which the mind of a particular person or group works 某人的心理: *We must take into account the psychology of both teachers and pupils.* 我們必須考慮到老師和學生的心理。

psy·cho·path /ˈsaɪkəˌpæθ; ˈsaɪkəpæθ/ n a person who has a serious disorder of the mind that may cause violent or criminal behaviour 精神變態者 –**psychopathic** /ˌsaɪ-kəˈpæθɪk; ˌsaɪkəˈpæθɪk◂/ adj

psy·cho·sis /saɪˈkosɪs; saɪˈkəʊsɨs/ n **psychoses** /-siz; -siːz/ [C;U] tech a serious disorder of the mind that may produce character changes 〔術語〕精神病

psy·cho·so·mat·ic /ˌsaɪkəsoʊˈmætɪk; ˌsaɪ-kəʊsəˈmætɪk◂/ n caused by fear or anxiety rather than by a disease or physical disorder 由恐懼或焦慮引起的: *Her illness appears to be psychosomatic.* 她的病似乎是由焦慮引起的。

psy·cho·ther·a·py /,saɪkoˈθerəpɪ; ,saɪkəʊ-ˈθerəpi/ *n* [U] *tech* treatment of disorders of the mind using PSYCHOLOGY rather than drugs 〔術語〕心理療法; 精神療法 – **psychotherapist** *n*

psy·chot·ic /saɪˈkɑtɪk; saɪˈkɒtɪk/ *n* *tech* a person suffering from a serious disorder of the mind which may produce character changes 〔術語〕精神病患者 –**psychotic** *adj*: *psychotic behaviour* 精神病患者行為

pt a written abbreviation for 〔縮〕= PINT(S)

PTO /,pi ti ˈo; ,pi: ti: ˈəʊ/ a request to the reader to look at the next page; it is an abbreviation for "please turn over", and is written at the bottom of a page 〔縮〕通常寫於頁下端〕請翻至下頁, 見下頁

***pub** /pʌb; pʌb/ *n* a building which is not a club or hotel, where alcohol may be bought and drunk during fixed hours and where people meet and talk 小酒館, 酒吧: *We all went down to the pub last night.* 我們昨晚都去了酒吧。

pu·ber·ty /ˈpjubɜtɪ; ˈpjuːbəti/ *n* [U] the stage in the development of your body when you are becoming an adult and you become able to have children 發育期, 青春期

pu·bic /ˈpjubɪk; ˈpjuːbɪk/ *adj* [only before a noun 只用於名詞前] concerning the area around your sexual organs 陰部的: *pubic hair* 陰毛

★**pub·lic**¹ /ˈpʌblɪk; ˈpʌblɪk/ *adj* [only before a noun 只用於名詞前] **1** concerning people in general 公眾的: *There has been a change in public opinion.* 公眾的意見已有所改變。 | *the increasing public awareness of environmental issues* 公眾對於環境問題的日益關注 **2** for everyone to use, see, or attend 公共的; 公用的: *a public library* 公共圖書館 | *public telephones* 公用電話 | *We're calling a public meeting next week.* 我們定於下週召開一次公共會議。 | *They want smoking to be banned in all public places.* 他們希望在所有公共場所禁止吸煙。 **3** connected with the government and the services it provides 政府的; 為公眾服務的: *The government is increasing public spending on health.* 政府目前正在增加醫療方面的公共開支。 **4** well-known to people in general 眾所周知的: *the prime minister and other public figures* 總理以及其他知名人士 **5** **make something public** to make something known to people, so that it is no longer secret 公開某事: *The figures have not yet been made public.* 這些數字還未公開。

★**public**² *n* [+sing/pl verb] **1 the public, the general public** people in general 公眾, 大眾, 民眾: *The park is only open to the public at weekends.* 這公園只在週末對公眾開放。 | *The public are requested to remain silent during parliamentary debates.* 在國會辯論的時候, 民眾需保持沉默。 **2** a group of people

who share an interest in a particular person or activity 某一方面的大眾: *He writes songs that he knows will please his public.* 他寫些他知道能夠取悅歌迷的曲子。 **3 in public** in the presence of other people 公開地, 當眾

pub·li·can /ˈpʌblɪkən; ˈpʌblɪkən/ *n* a person who owns or manages a PUB 小酒館[酒吧]老闆

★**pub·li·ca·tion** /,pʌblɪˈkeʃən; ,pʌblɪˈkeɪʃən/ *n* **1** [U] the act of making something known to the public 發表; 公佈: *We are waiting for the publication of the election results.* 我們在等候公佈選舉結果。 **2** [U] the process of printing something and offering it for sale to the public 出版: *The publication of his diaries caused embarrassment to other politicians.* 他的日記的出版令其他政界人士感到難堪。 **3** [C] something, such as a book or magazine, which is printed and sold to the public 出版物, 書刊: *His latest publication is by far the best.* 他最新出版的一本書是到目前為止最好的一本。

public bar /,·· ·ˈ·/ *n* a room in a PUB or a hotel which is plainly furnished, and where the cheapest prices are charged for drinks 〔酒館、旅館內收費低廉的〕公眾酒吧 —compare 比較 SALOON BAR

public con·ve·ni·ence /,·· ·ˈ···/ *n* *BrE euph* a TOILET which is provided for the public to use, often in the centre of a town (a less direct word than "toilet") 〔英式, 委婉〕〔通常在市中心的〕公眾廁所〔比 "toilet" 更加委婉〕

public house /,·· ·ˈ·/ *n* *fml* a PUB 〔正式〕小酒館, 酒吧

pub·li·cist /ˈpʌblɪsɪst; ˈpʌblɪsɪst/ *n* a person who brings something to the attention of the public, especially someone who works in advertising 廣告人員, 宣傳人員〔尤指從事廣告宣傳的人員〕

★**pub·lic·i·ty** /pʌbˈlɪsətɪ; pʌˈblɪsəti/ *n* [U] **1** public attention 公眾的注意; 張揚: *The prime minister's recent speech on the environment got a lot of publicity.* 首相近來關於環境的演講引起了公眾的很大注意。 **2** the business of bringing someone or something to the attention of the public 宣傳, 宣揚: *The recent publicity campaign has changed people's attitudes to unleaded petrol.* 近來的宣傳活動已改變了人們對於無鉛汽油的態度。

pub·li·cize /ˈpʌblɪˌsaɪz; ˈpʌblɪˌsaɪz/ *v* **publicized, publicizing** (also 又作 **publicise** *BrE* 〔英式〕) [T] to bring something to the attention of the public 使〔某事物〕引起公眾的注意, 宣傳, 宣揚: *We're using posters to publicize the contest.* 我們利用海報以宣傳這次比賽。

public pros·e·cu·tor /,·· ·ˈ····/ *n* a government lawyer who acts for the state in bringing charges against criminals in a court of law 檢察官; 公訴人

public re·la·tions /,·· ·'··/ *n* (also 又作 **PR**) **1** [pl] the relations between an organization and the general public 公共關係: *Inviting people to visit the factory would be good for public relations.* 邀請人們參觀工廠有利於促進公共關係。**2** [U] the job of encouraging good relations between an organization and the general public 公共關係工作: *He works in public relations.* 他從事公關工作。

public school /,·· ·'·/ *n* **1** *BrE* a private school for 13 to 18-year-old children who usually also live there; it is paid for by their parents〔英式〕私立寄宿中學〔學生年齡為 13 至 18 歲〕**2** *AmE* a free local state school〔美式〕〔免費的〕地方公立學校 –compare 比較 PRIVATE SCHOOL

public spir·it·ed /,·· '···/ *adj* showing a desire to serve people and do what is helpful for society 熱心公益的

★★★pub·lish /'pʌblɪʃ; 'pʌblɪʃ/ *v* [T] **1** to have a book, magazine, or piece of writing printed, and offer it for sale to the public 出版; 發行: *The book was first published in 1982.* 該書於1982年首次發行。| *He refused to publish my poem.* 他拒絕出版我的詩。**2** to make something known to the public 發表, 宣佈, 公佈: *News of his death wasn't published for several days.* 他的死訊好幾天都沒有公佈。

★pub·lish·er /'pʌblɪʃə; 'pʌblɪʃər/ *n* a person or firm whose business is to publish books, newspapers, or magazines 出版者, 出版商, 出版社

pub·lish·ing /'pʌblɪʃɪŋ; 'pʌblɪʃɪŋ/ *n* [U] the business or job of preparing books, newspapers, or magazines and offering them for sale 出版業; 出版工作: *She works in publishing.* 她從事出版業。

puce /pjus; pju:s/ *adj, n* [U] a dark pinkish purple colour 紫褐色

puck·er /'pʌkə; 'pʌkər/ *v* (also 又作 **pucker up**) [I;T] to form into folds (使)皺起: *She puckered her lips in disapproval.* 她撅起嘴表示不贊成。

pud·ding /'pʊdɪŋ; 'pʊdɪŋ/ *n* [C;U] **1** *BrE infml* the sweet dish of a meal, served after the main dish〔英式, 非正式〕布丁;〔飯後的〕甜點心: *What's for pudding, John?* 約翰, 甜點心吃甚麼? **2** a dish based on flour or rice which is usually solid and served hot〔某種〕布丁: *We're having rice pudding.* 我們在吃米布丁。| *There's a steak and kidney pudding in the oven.* 爐子上有塊牛排加腰子布丁。

pud·dle /'pʌdl; 'pʌdl/ *n* a small amount of rain water lying in a hollow place in the ground〔地上的〕水坑, 水窪: *Don't step in the puddles!* 別踩到水坑裡!

pu·er·ile /'pjuə,rɪl; 'pjʊəraɪl/ *adj fml* silly and suitable only for children〔正式〕幼稚的; 孩子氣的

puff¹ /pʌf; pʌf/ *v* **1** [I] to breathe rapidly and with effort, usually because you have been running or doing something tiring 喘粗氣: *He jumped onto the bus, puffing with exhaustion.* 他跳上了公共汽車, 累得氣喘吁吁。**2** [I;T] to blow out smoke repeatedly, in small amounts 噴出〔煙霧〕: *Don't puff cigarette smoke in my face.* 別把煙噴到我臉上。| *Smoke was puffing from the engine of the train.* 火車的引擎直冒煙。**3** [I;T] to breathe smoke into your mouth and then blow it out repeatedly 抽煙: *She was puffing away on small cigars all evening!* 她整個晚上都在抽小雪茄煙! **4** [I] to move while sending out small clouds of smoke 噴着煙移動〔行進〕: *The train finally puffed into the station.* 火車噴着煙駛進車站。

puff out *phr v* [I;T **puff** sthg ↔ **out**] to become or to make something larger, especially with air (使)〔某物〕變大〔尤指充入空氣〕: *The bird puffed out its feathers.* 那隻鳥使自己的羽毛膨鬆起來。

puff up *phr v* [I] to swell 使膨脹; 使腫脹: *My leg puffed up so that I could hardly walk.* 我的腿腫了, 幾乎無法走路。

puff² *n* **1** an act of breathing smoke into your mouth and blowing it out again 吸(煙): *He took a puff of his cigarette.* 他吸了一口香煙。**2** a sudden short rush of air or smoke〔氣流或煙的〕一陣; 一股: *The paper was blown away by a puff of wind.* 紙被一陣風吹走了。

puffed /pʌft; pʌft/ *adj* (also 又作 **puffed out**) *infml* tired and finding it difficult to breathe〔非正式〕氣喘吁吁的

puf·fin /'pʌfɪn; 'pʌfɪn/ *n* a seabird with a very large brightly coloured beak 海鸚

puff·y /'pʌfi; 'pʌfi/ *adj* **puffier, puffiest** swollen 腫大的; 鼓起的 –**puffiness** *n* [U]

pug /pʌg; pʌg/ *n* a small dog with a wide face and a flat nose 哈巴狗

pug·na·cious /pʌg'neɪʃəs; pʌg'neɪʃəs/ *adj fml* fond of quarrelling and fighting〔正式〕好鬥的 –**pugnaciously** *adv*

puke /pjuk; pju:k/ *v* **puked, puking** (also 又作 **puke** sthg ↔ **up**) [I;T] *slang* to be sick〔俚〕嘔吐: *The worst moment was when someone puked all over my dress.* 最糟糕的一刻是有人吐了我一身。–**puke** *n* [U]

★★pull¹ /pʊl; pʊl/ *v* **1** [I;T] to move something or someone towards yourself 拖過來, 拉過來: *She pulled the door open.* 她把門拉開。| *He pulled his chair up to the table.* 他把椅子拖向桌子。| *I got hold of the rope and pulled as hard as I could.* 我抓住繩子拼命拉。| *He pulled her into the kitchen.* 他把她拖入了廚房。–see picture on page 992 見 992 頁彩圖 **2** [T] to move something along 拖, 拉〔某物〕: *carts pulled by horses and ponies* 由大大小小的馬拉着的車 | *The train is pulled by a powerful engine.* 火車是由馬力強大的引擎驅動的。**3** [T] to attract people 招來, 吸引〔人〕: *She managed to pull a number of new voters.* 她設法引來一些新的投票者。| *The match pulled a crowd of 20,000.* 比賽吸引了兩萬人。**4 pull a gun** to bring out a small gun that you had kept hidden 拔出手槍: *Suddenly she pulled a gun on me.* 她突然拔出手槍對準了我。**5 pull a face** to make an expression with your face to show that you disagree with something or do not like it 拉長臉〔表示不同意或不喜歡〕**6 pull a fast one** *infml* to gain an advantage over someone by deceiving them in some way〔非正式〕欺詐〔某人〕**7 pull a muscle** to hurt a muscle in your body by stretching it too much 拉傷肌肉 **8 pull the trigger** to press the TRIGGER of a gun so that it fires 扣動扳機: *He pointed the gun at her and pulled the trigger.* 他舉槍對準她, 並扣動了扳機。**9 pull someone's leg** to tell someone things that are not true for amusement 開某人玩笑; 耍弄某人: *He said that I'd failed, but I think he was only pulling my leg.* 他說我失敗了, 但我認為他不過是在跟我開玩笑。**10 pull something to pieces** to say that something is worthless by pointing out all its faults 把某物說得一無是處 **11 pull strings** to use influence in order to get something〔為得到某事而〕施加影響力: *I think he pulled a few strings to get that job.* 我覺得他為得到那份工作使用了一些影響。**12 pull your socks up** to start making a greater effort 加緊努力 **13 pull your weight** to do your full share of work 盡本分工作

pull at sth *phr v* [T] to try to pull something towards you 拉扯: *The children pulled at her coat.* 孩子們拉扯她的衣服。

pull away *phr v* [I] (of a vehicle) to start moving away〔車輛〕駛離: *I arrived just as the bus was pulling away.* 我到達的時候, 公共汽車剛好開走了。

pull sth ↔ down *phr v* [T] to destroy a building 拆毀〔建築物〕: *A lot of the old houses have been pulled down.* 許多舊房子已被拆除。

pull in *phr v* [I] **1** (of a train) to arrive at a station〔火車〕到站, 進站: *We arrived just as the train was pulling in.* 我們到達的時候, 火車剛好進站。**2** (of a vehicle) to move to one side of the road and stop〔車輛〕開到路邊停下

pull sth ↔ off *phr v* [T] **1** to take off clothes quickly and roughly 迅速脫下〔衣服〕: *She ran in and pulled off her coat.* 她跑進來, 迅速脫下外衣。**2 pull it off** *infml* to succeed in doing something difficult〔非正式〕成功做了〔難事〕

pull sth ↔ on *phr v* [T] to put on clothes quickly and roughly 迅速穿上〔衣服〕: *She pulled on her socks and shoes.* 她快速穿上了襪子和鞋。

pull out *phr v* **1** [I] (of a train) to leave a station〔火車〕離站: *The guard blew his whistle and the train pulled out.* 列車長吹響哨子, 火車駛出了車站。**2** [I;T **pull** sbdy ↔ **out**] to leave a place or cause people to leave a place (使)離開: *The army has started to pull out of the area.* 軍隊開始從該地區撤離。| *Troops will be pulled out as soon as possible.* 軍隊將盡快撤離。**3** [I] to say that you do not want to go ahead with something that you had agreed to do 不願做〔答應做的事情〕: *I decided to pull out of the agreement.* 我決定不履行協議。

pull over *phr v* [I] (of a vehicle) to move to one side of the road and stop〔車輛〕開到路邊停下

pull through *phr v* **1** [I;T **pull through** sthg] to continue to live in spite of an illness or accident 康復; 恢復: *Will she pull through, doctor?* 她會恢復嗎, 醫生? | *It's not certain that he'll pull through the operation.* 他能否從手術中恢復過來還不敢肯定。**2** [T **pull** sbdy **through** (sthg)] to help someone to continue to live in spite of an illness or accident 使〔某人〕康復; 使〔某人〕恢復

pull together *phr v* **1** [I] to all work together for a common aim 齊心協力 **2 pull yourself together** to control your feelings and behave in a calm way 控制自己(的感情); 鎮定情緒

pull up *phr v* [I] (of a vehicle) to stop〔車輛〕停止: *A car pulled up outside the house.* 一輛汽車在屋外停了下來。

pull² n 1 an act of pulling something 拖, 拉: *I took hold of the rope and gave it a pull.* 我抓住繩子拉了一下。**2** *fml* a force which attracts you to something or makes you want to do something〔正式〕吸引力; 誘惑力: *I still felt the pull of the sea.* 我仍然能覺到大海的吸引力。

pul·let /ˈpʊlɪt; ˈpʊlɪt/ *n* a young hen 小母雞

pul·ley /ˈpʊli; ˈpʊli/ *n* an apparatus which consists of a wheel over which a rope or chain can be moved, and which is used for lifting heavy things 滑輪: *We managed to hoist up the trunk using a system of pulleys.* 我們設法用一組滑輪把箱子吊了起來。

pull·o·ver /ˈpʊlˌoʊvər; ˈpʊlˌəʊvəʳ/ *n* a woollen piece of clothing for the top half of your body, which you pull on over your head 套頭毛衣

pul·mo·na·ry /ˈpʌlmənɛri; ˈpʌlmənəri/ *adj* [only before a noun 只用於名詞前] *tech* concerning your lungs〔術語〕肺的

pulp¹ /pʌlp; pʌlp/ *n* **1** [sing;U] a soft almost liquid mass, such as the soft inside part of many fruits or vegetables 果肉; 菜心; 漿狀物: *The vegetables were boiled to a pulp.* 蔬菜被煮成了糊狀。**2** [U] wood or other vegetable materials which have been soft-ened and are used for making paper 紙漿 **3** [U] poor quality books or magazines 劣質的書

籍[雜誌]

pulp² /pʌlp/ *v* [T] to crush something so that it becomes a pulp 把[某物]壓成漿狀物

pul·pit /ˈpʊlpɪt; ˈpʊlpɪt/ *n* a small raised enclosure in a church, from which the priest talks to the worshippers [教堂中的]講壇

pul·sate /pʌlˈseɪt; ˈpʌlseɪt/ *v* **pulsated, pulsating** [I] to move or shake very regularly, like the beating of your heart 有規律地移動[振動]: *The room pulsated with the rhythm of deafening music.* 房間在隨著震耳欲聾的音樂節奏顫動起來。

pulse¹ /pʌls; pʌls/ *n* **1** [C] the regular beating of blood in the main blood tubes carrying blood from your heart, especially as it can be felt by a finger on your wrist 脈搏: *The doctor frowned as he took my pulse.* 醫生一按我的脈搏便皺起了眉頭。| *a weak pulse* 很弱的脈搏 **2** [C] a regular beat or VIBRATION, for example of music or sound [如音樂或聲音的]拍子; 節奏, 律動 **3 pulses** [pl] seeds from particular plants, such as beans, which can be eaten 豆類植物的種子; [可食用的]豆類植物

pulse² /v/ **pulsed, pulsing** [I] to move or shake very regularly, like the beating of your heart [如心臟跳動般]有規律地搏動; 跳動: *He could feel the blood pulsing through his body as he waited for the next explosion.* 在等待下一次的爆炸時, 他可以感覺到自己體內血液的搏動。

pul·ver·ize /ˈpʌlvəˌraɪz; ˈpʌlvəraɪz/ *v* **pulverized, pulverizing** (also 又作 **pulverise** *BrE* [英式]) [T] **1** to reduce something to a fine powder or dust through crushing 把[某物]壓成粉末狀 **2** *infml* to defeat someone or destroy something completely [非正式]徹底擊敗[某人]; 徹底毀壞[某物]

pu·ma /ˈpjuːmə; ˈpjuːmə/ *n* a large member of the cat family which lives in the Americas 美洲獅

pum·ice /ˈpʌmɪs; ˈpʌmɪs/ *n* (also 又作 **pumice stone** /ˈ·· ·/) [U] a light, silver-grey rock, used for rubbing surfaces smooth 浮石, 輕石[用於磨光]

pum·mel /ˈpʌməl; ˈpʌməl/ *v* **-ll- (-l- *AmE*** [美式]) [T] to hit a person or thing repeatedly, usually with your closed hand 用拳連擊[人或物]

pump¹ /pʌmp; pʌmp/ *n* a machine which is used to force liquids, air, or gas into or out of something 泵; 抽水機; 抽氣機; 打氣筒: *Pumps are used to irrigate the fields in the dry season.* 旱季時, 人們用水泵來灌溉田野。| *a petrol pump* 汽油泵

pump² *v* **1** [I;T] to empty or fill with a liquid or gas by means of a pump, or something like a pump 用泵抽出[注入]: *They had pumped all the water out of the well.* 他們用泵把井裡的水抽乾了。| *His heart was pumping fast.* 他的心跳得很快。**2 pump money into something** *infml* to spend a lot of money on something [非正式] 把大量資金投入某事: *She has pumped money into the business.* 她已在這項業務上投入了大筆資金。**3 pump someone** *infml* to ask someone a lot of questions in the hope of finding out something that you want to know [非正式] 追問, 盤問某人 **4 pump someone's hand** to shake someone's hand with force 用力握某人的手

pump sthg ↔ up *phr v* [T] to fill something with air 給[某物]充氣: *My front tyre needs to be pumped up.* 我車子的前胎需要打氣了。

pump·kin /ˈpʌmpkɪn; ˈpʌmpkɪn/ *n* [C;U] a very large, round, dark yellow fruit that grows on the ground 南瓜

pun¹ /pʌn; pʌn/ *n* an amusing use of a word or phrase that has two meanings, or of two words which have the same sound; an example of a pun is 'Seven days without water make one weak' (= 1 week) [利用有兩重含義的詞或同音異義詞的]雙關語[例如"七天沒有水使人虛弱", weak 和 week 同音, 也可理解為"七天沒有水為一週"]

pun² *v* **-nn-** [I] to make puns 使用雙關語

punch¹ /pʌntʃ; pʌntʃ/ *v* **1** [I;T] to hit a person or thing hard with your closed hand 用拳打[人或物]: *I was very tempted to punch him on the nose.* 我真巴不得在他鼻子上狠揍一拳。–see picture on page 992 見 992 頁彩圖 **2** [T] to make a hole in something using a special machine 給[某物]打孔: *He's coming to punch our tickets.* 他來給我們的車票打孔了。

punch² *n* **1** [C] a quick strong blow made with your closed hand [用拳]擊打: *She gave him a tremendous punch on the nose.* 她在他的鼻子上狠狠地砸了一拳。**2** [U] forcefulness (a word used to express approval) 有力; 效力[含褒義]: *His speech lacked punch.* 他的話缺乏力量。**3** [C] a tool or machine for cutting holes in things 打孔器 **4** [U] hot or cold drink made mainly from fruit juice and alcohol 賓治, 潘趣酒[一種主要由果汁和酒混合而成的熱飲料或冷飲料]

punch line /ˈ· ·/ *n* the last few words of a joke or story, that cause amusement or surprise [笑話或故事中引人發笑或令人吃驚的]結尾妙語

punch-up /ˈ· ·/ *n* *infml* a fight [非正式]打鬥, 鬥毆

punc·til·i·ous /pʌŋkˈtɪliəs; pʌŋkˈtɪliəs/ *adj* *fml* very exact and particular about details, especially of behaviour (a word that is usually used to express approval) [正式]注意細節的; 一絲不苟的[通常含褒義] – **punctiliously** *adv*

punc·tu·al /ˈpʌŋktʃuəl; ˈpʌŋktʃuəl/ *adj* arriving or doing things at exactly the right time 準時的; 守時的: *She's always punctual for appointments.* 她一向很準時赴約。–

punctually *adv*: *He arrived punctually at eight o'clock.* 他於八點鐘準時到達。 **–punctuality** /ˌpʌŋktʃʊˈæləti; ˌpʌŋktʃʊˈælˌti/ *n* [U]

punc·tu·ate /ˈpʌŋktʃʊˌet; ˈpʌŋktʃueɪt/ *v* **punctuated, punctuating** [T] **1** to divide a piece of writing into sentences, phrases, and other units by means of special marks, such as full stops (FULL STOP) 在〔文章〕中加標點 **2 be punctuated with/by** to be interrupted repeatedly by something 被〔某事〕不時打斷: *The match was punctuated by the cheers of supporters.* 比賽中不時響起支持者的歡呼聲。

punc·tu·a·tion /ˌpʌŋktʃʊˈeʃən; ˌpʌŋktʃʊˈeɪʃn/ *n* [U] the marks used to divide a piece of writing into sentences, phrases, and other units, for example commas (COMMA) or colons (COLON) 標點符號

punctuation mark /ˌ··ˈ··· ·/ *n* a sign such as a COMMA (,) or FULL STOP (.) that is used to divide up a piece of writing and make it easier to read 標點符號

punc·ture¹ /ˈpʌŋktʃə; ˈpʌŋktʃəʳ/ *n* a small hole in a tyre 輪胎上的小洞: *I'm afraid we've got a puncture, so we'll have to change the wheel.* 恐怕輪胎被紮破了，所以我們必須換一個。

puncture² *v* **punctured, puncturing** [I;T] to make or get a small hole in something, with the result that air or liquid can get out (被)刺穿: *The ball punctured when it fell on a broken bottle.* 球落到一個破玻璃瓶上時被戳破了。 | *He is in hospital, suffering from a punctured lung.* 他因肺部穿孔而住進了醫院。

pun·dit /ˈpʌndɪt; ˈpʌndɪt/ *n infml* a person with a lot of knowledge of a particular subject 〔非正式〕〔某一學科的〕權威, 專家

pun·gent /ˈpʌndʒənt; ˈpʌndʒənt/ *adj* **1** having a strong, sharp taste or smell 〔味道或氣味〕刺鼻的; 辛辣的 **2** clever and effective (used of speech or writing) 尖刻的, 尖銳的〔指談話或寫作〕 **–pungently** *adv* **–pungency** *n* [U]

pun·ish /ˈpʌnɪʃ; ˈpʌnɪʃ/ *v* [T] to make someone suffer for a fault or crime 處罰, 懲罰: *She was punished for talking during the lesson.* 她由於上課講話而受罰。 | *Dangerous driving should be severely punished.* 危險駕駛者應受到嚴懲。

pun·ish·a·ble /ˈpʌnɪʃəbl̩; ˈpʌnɪʃəbəl/ *adj* that can be punished by law 可受到法律制裁的, 應懲處的: *In many countries murder is punishable by death.* 在許多國家裡, 犯謀殺罪可被判處死刑。

pun·ish·ing /ˈpʌnɪʃɪŋ; ˈpʌnɪʃɪŋ/ *adj infml* making you very tired and weak 〔非正式〕使人勞累的, 吃力的: *It was a long and punishing climb to the top.* 爬到頂端是又費時又費力。

★**pun·ish·ment** /ˈpʌnɪʃmənt; ˈpʌnɪʃmənt/ *n* **1** [U] the act of making someone suffer for a fault or crime 懲罰, 處罰〔某人〕: *They won't escape punishment again.* 他們不可能再逃避懲罰了。 **2** [C] a way in which a person is made to suffer for a fault or crime 懲罰手段, 處罰方式: *In his case the punishment certainly fits the crime.* 在他的案子中, 他罪有應得。 | *She accepted her punishment without complaint.* 她毫無怨言地接受了對她的處罰。

pu·ni·tive /ˈpjuːnətɪv; ˈpjuːnɪtɪv/ *adj* intended as punishment and therefore very severe 懲罰的; 嚴懲的 **–punitively** *adv*

punk /pʌŋk; pʌŋk/ *n* **1** [U] loud, often violent music which was played in the 1970s and 1980s by and for people opposed to current social values 〔一種七十年代和八十年代期間反對現代社會價值觀的〕龐克搖滾樂 **2** [C] a person who dresses and cuts their hair in a way which is intended to shock people, and who enjoys punk music 龐克搖滾樂迷; 不良少年 **–punk** *adj*

pun·net /ˈpʌnɪt; ˈpʌnᵻt/ *n* a small square basket in which soft fruits are sold 〔出售水果用的〕小方簍, 扁籃

punt /pʌnt; pʌnt/ *n* a long narrow boat with a flat bottom, which is moved by someone pushing a long pole against the bottom of the river 〔用篙撐的〕平底船 **–punt** *v* [I;T]

punt·er /ˈpʌntə; ˈpʌntəʳ/ *n BrE infml* 〔英式, 非正式〕 **1** a person who risks money on the result of a horse race 下賽馬賭注者, 賭馬者 **2 the punters** your customers 顧客, 主顧: *It looks good, but will the punters buy it?* 它看上去不錯, 但顧客會來買嗎?

pu·ny /ˈpjuːni; ˈpjuːni/ *adj* **punier, puniest** small and weak (a word used to express disapproval) 瘦小的; 發育不良的〔含貶義〕: *He's a puny little child.* 他是個發育不良的小孩子。

pup /pʌp; pʌp/ *n* **1** see 見 PUPPY **2** a young SEAL¹ or OTTER 小海豹; 小水獺

pu·pa /ˈpjuːpə; ˈpjuːpə/ *n* **pupas** or **pupae** /-piː; -piː/ an insect in the middle stage of its development, protected by a hard covering 蛹; 成蛹狀態

★**pu·pil** /ˈpjuːpl̩; ˈpjuːpəl/ *n* **1** a person, usually a child, who is being taught (小)學生 **2** the small round black opening in the middle of the coloured part of your eye, through which light passes 〔眼睛的〕瞳孔

pup·pet /ˈpʌpɪt; ˈpʌpᵻt/ *n* **1** a figure of a person or animal that can be made to move by someone who pulls the wires or strings that are fixed to different parts of its body 木偶 **2** a cloth figure of a person or animal that can be made to move by someone who puts their hand inside it 手套式木偶 **3** a person or government that is controlled by others who are more powerful 傀儡(政府): *They invaded the country and set up a puppet government.* 他們入侵該

國，並建立了一個傀儡政府。

pup·pe·teer /ˌpʌpɪ'tɪr; ˌpʌpɪ'tɪəʳ/ n a person who performs with puppets 操縱木偶的人; 演木偶戲的人

pup·py /'pʌpɪ; 'pʌpi/ n **puppies** (also 又作 **pup**) a young dog 小狗, 幼犬

***pur·chase¹** /'pɜtʃəs; 'pɜːtʃᵻs/ v **purchased, purchasing** [T] fml to buy 〔正式〕購買, 採購: We intend to purchase a house in the country. 我們打算在鄉間買一所房子。

***purchase²** n fml 〔正式〕**1** [U] the act of buying something 購買, 採購: The purchase of the house should be completed by the end of June. 六月底以前應把房子買下來。**2** [C] something that you have bought 購買物: Can I look at your purchases, then? 那麼我能看看你買的東西嗎? **3 make a purchase** to buy something 購買東西

pur·chas·er /'pɜtʃəsə; 'pɜːtʃəsəʳ/ n fml a person who buys something from someone else 〔正式〕購買者

***pure** /pjʊr; pjʊəʳ/ adj **1** not mixed with anything else, and especially with dirt or harmful substances 純的; 純淨的: It's made of pure silver. 這是由純銀製成的。| The sea air is so pure and healthy. 海上的空氣非常純淨, 有益健康。**2** free from bad thoughts or actions 純潔的: a pure young girl 純潔的小姑娘 **3** clear 清徹的: a cloudless sky of the purest blue 碧藍無雲的天空 | The voices of the young boys were high and pure. 男孩子們的聲音高揚而清晰。**4** [only before a noun 只用於名詞前] considered only as a subject for study and not for doing or gaining anything practical 純理論的; 非實用的: He's studying pure science. 他正在學習純科學。– compare 比較 APPLIED **5** [only before a noun 只用於名詞前] infml complete 〔非正式〕完全的: By pure chance she met him again 20 years later. 完全是碰巧, 她在二十年後又重遇了他。**6 pure and simple** [never before a noun 不能用於名詞前] only 僅僅: He is motivated by a desire for power, pure and simple. 他的一舉一動僅僅是出於對權力的慾望。

pu·ree /pjʊ're; 'pjʊəreɪ/ n [C;U] food boiled to a soft half-liquid mass, with all lumps removed 〔食物煮成的〕泥; 醬: apple puree 蘋果醬 – puree v [T]

***pure·ly** /'pjʊrlɪ; 'pjʊəli/ adv **1** only 僅僅: a decision taken for purely political reasons 純粹出於政治原因而作出的決定 **2 purely and simply** a phrase you use when you want to make it very clear that there is no other reason for something 純粹地〔用於表明沒有其他原因〕: I helped him out of friendship, purely and simply. 我幫助他純粹是出於友情。

pur·ga·tive /'pɜɡətɪv; 'pɜːɡətɪv/ n a medicine that causes you to empty your bowels 瀉藥 –**purgative** adj

pur·ga·to·ry /'pɜɡətorɪ; 'pɜːɡətəri/ n [U] **1** (also 又作 **Purgatory**) a state or place in which, Roman Catholics believe, the soul of a dead person suffers for wrong-doing on earth until it is pure enough to enter Heaven 〔羅馬天主教的〕煉獄, 滌罪所 **2** a place or time when you are suffering a lot 受苦受難的〔地方〕

purge¹ /pɜdʒ; pɜːdʒ/ v **purged, purging** [T] **1** to make yourself or another person clean and free from bad thoughts or actions 淨化〔思想〕; 清除〔惡行〕: I felt the need to purge myself **of** my sins. 我覺得有必要為自己赦罪。**2** to remove unwanted people from a group or organization suddenly and often, usually by forceful means 〔通常用暴力〕清除〔異己分子〕

purge² n a set of actions intended to remove unwanted members of a group or organization suddenly and often, by force 清除異己; 清洗行動; 整肅: The president carried out a purge **of** disloyal army officers. 總統對不忠心的陸軍軍官採取了整肅行動。

pu·ri·fy /'pjʊrəfaɪ; 'pjʊərᵻfaɪ/ v **purified, purified** [T] to make a person or thing pure 使潔淨, 淨化: Has the water been purified? 水被淨化過了嗎? –**purification** /ˌpjʊrəfə'keɪʃən; ˌpjʊərᵻfᵻ'keɪʃən/ n [U]

pur·ist /'pjʊrɪst; 'pjʊərᵻst/ n a person who is very careful to do things in the correct way and to try to make sure that others do too 力求純正者: She's a terrible purist about language. 她是個極為注意語言純正的人。

pu·ri·tan /'pjʊrɪtn; 'pjʊərᵻtən/ n a person who has fixed standards of behaviour and self-control, and thinks that pleasure is unnecessary or wrong (a word usually used to express disapproval) 嚴守清規戒律的人〔通常含貶義〕 –**puritanical** /ˌpjʊrə'tænɪkl; ˌpjʊərᵻ'tænɪkəl/ adj: a puritanical attitude toward sex 在性方面的清教徒式的態度 – **puritanically** /-klɪ; -kli/ adv

pu·ri·ty /'pjʊrɪtɪ; 'pjʊərᵻti/ n [U] the quality or state of being pure 純潔; 純淨; 純正

purl /pɜl; pɜːl/ n [U] tech a simple stitch in knitting (KNIT) 〔術語〕〔編織中的〕倒針, 反針 –**purl** v [I;T]

pur·loin /pɜ'lɔɪn; pɜː'lɔɪn/ v [T] to steal something or take it without permission (a formal word which is also often used in a humorous way) 偷竊〔常作幽默用法的正式用詞〕

pur·ple /'pɜpl; 'pɜːpəl/ adj,n [U] a dark colour which is a mixture of red and blue 紫色的; 紫色 –see picture on page 243 見 243 頁彩圖

pur·port¹ /pə'port; pɜː'pɔːt/ v [T] **purport to do/be something** to claim to do something or be something 聲稱做某事〔是某物〕: His plans are not what they purport to be. 他的計劃與他們講的不一樣。

pur·port² /'pɜport; 'pɜːpɔːt/ n [U] fml the general meaning of someone's words 〔正式〕大意; 要旨: The purport of the message seemed to be that she would deal with the *situation.* 這信息的要旨似乎是, 她會處理這種情況。

★pur·pose /ˈpɜːpəs; ˈpɜːpəs/ *n* **1** [C] your reason for doing something 目的, 意圖: *What was the purpose of her visit?* 她來訪的目的是甚麼? | *Have you come to London to see your family, or for business purposes?* 你來倫敦是看望家人, 還是因公出差? **2 on purpose** intentionally 故意(地): *You broke that on purpose!* 你是故意把它打碎的! **3** [C] a use 用途: *Don't waste your money; put it to some good purpose.* 別浪費你的錢, 要花在有用的地方。 | *I haven't got a pen, but a pencil will serve the same purpose.* 我沒有鋼筆, 不過鉛筆也一樣能用。 **4 to little purpose, to no purpose** without much, or any, effect 效果甚微; 無效果: *Are you saying that I worked all night to no purpose?* 你是不是説我一整夜都白忙了? **5** [U] determination to succeed in what you want to do 決心: *Getting a job has given him a new sense of purpose.* 找到工作使他有了堅定的新目標。

purpose-built /ˌ·· ˈ·◂/ *adj* specially made for a particular use 為某用途而特製的: *a purpose-built flat* 一幢特別建造的公寓

pur·pose·ful /ˈpɜːpəsfʊl; ˈpɜːpəsfəl/ *adj* determined and having a clear purposeful stride 堅決的; 果斷的: *a purposeful stride* 堅定的腳步 —**purposefully** *adv*

pur·pose·less /ˈpɜːpəslɪs; ˈpɜːpəsləs/ *adj* without any clear aim or purpose 無目的的

pur·pose·ly /ˈpɜːpəslɪ; ˈpɜːpəsli/ *adv* intentionally 故意地: *They purposely left the letter lying around.* 他故意把信隨處放。

purr /pɜː; pɜːr/ *v* **1** [I] to make the low continuous sound which a happy cat produces in its throat, or some similar sound 〔貓高興時〕發出呼嚕聲 **2** [T] to say something in a low pleasant voice 以低沉的聲音愉快地説 —**purr** *n*

purse¹ /pɜːs; pɜːs/ *n* **1** a small leather or plastic bag that people, especially women, use to carry money in 〔尤指女用的〕錢包 — compare 比較 WALLET **2** *AmE* a bag in which a woman carries the things she needs when she goes out 〔美式〕女用手提包, 手袋

purse² *v* **pursed, pursing** [T] **purse your lips** to bring your lips together into a round shape 撅起〔嘴唇〕: *She pursed her lips to show her displeasure.* 她撅起了嘴以示不滿。

purs·er /ˈpɜːsə; ˈpɜːsər/ *n* an officer on a ship who keeps the ship's accounts and is also in charge of the travellers' comfort 〔輪船上的〕事務長

★pur·sue /pəˈsuː; pəˈsjuː/ *v* **pursued, pursuing** [T] *fml* 〔正式〕 **1** to follow someone, especially in order to catch or hurt them 追, 追捕〔某人〕: *The police realized that they were pursuing the wrong man.* 警察意識到他

們追錯了人。 **2** *fml* to be busy with an activity or interest, or continue to develop it 〔正式〕積極從事; 繼續發展: *He is pursuing his studies at the university.* 他正在大學繼續深造。 | *She was keen to pursue her interest in painting.* 她非常渴望發展她在繪畫方面的興趣。

pur·su·er /pəˈsuːə; pəˈsjuːər/ *n* a person or animal that is following another one in order to catch or hurt them 追捕者〔指人或動物〕: *She managed to escape her pursuers.* 她設法擺脱了追捕她的人。

pur·suit /pəˈsuːt; pəˈsjuːt/ *n* **1** [U] the act of following a person or thing in order to catch them 追趕; 追捕: *The police car raced through the streets in pursuit of the stolen motorbike.* 警車在街上急馳, 追趕着那輛被盜的摩托車。 **2** [U] the search for something that you want 尋找: *They emigrated to Australia in pursuit of a better life.* 他們為了追求更舒適的生活而移居澳大利亞。 **3** [C] any activity which you spend time doing, usually for pleasure 愛好: *One of his favourite pursuits was stamp collecting.* 他的愛好之一是集郵。

pur·vey /pəˈveɪ; pəˈveɪ/ *v* **purveyed, purveying** [T] *fml or tech* to supply food or other needed goods to people as a trade 〔正式或術語〕供應〔食品及其他必需品〕, 承辦…的供應 —**purveyor** *n*

pus /pʌs; pʌs/ *n* [U] a thick yellowish liquid that is produced in an infected wound 膿

★push¹ /pʊʃ; pʊʃ/ *v* **1** [I;T] to use sudden or steady pressure to move someone or something 推, 推動: *He pushed me into the water.* 他把我推進水裡去。 | *Don't push; there's room for all of us.* 別推, 我們每個人都有地方。 | *I pushed the door open and went in.* 我推開門走了進去。 | *Inflation is pushing prices up.* 通貨膨脹推高物價。 —see picture on page 992 見 992 頁彩圖 **2** [I; +adv/ prep] (also 又作 **push your way**) to move somewhere by roughly moving other people or things out of your way 擠: *She pushed past me.* 她從我旁邊擠了過去。 **3** [T] to force someone to do something, or urge them strongly to do it 迫使〔某人做某事〕; 催促: *My friends are all pushing me to enter politics.* 我的朋友都在慫恿我從政。 | *I was pushed into signing the contract.* 我被迫簽約同。 **4 push for something** to try very hard to get something, or to have something accepted 努力爭取某物; 努力使某物被接受: *Workers are pushing for higher wages.* 工人在努力爭取提高工資。 **5** [T] *infml* to try to make something more popular or attractive to people 〔非正式〕使〔某物〕更受歡迎; 使〔某物〕更具吸引力: *The company are pushing their new range of furniture.* 該公司正在推銷他們的新家具系列。 | *She is pushing the idea of free childcare for everyone.* 她正在宣傳兒童一律免費保育的主意。 **6** [T]

P

infml to sell illegal drugs〖非正式〗非法出售〔毒品〕**7 push your luck** to take an increasing risk in the hope of success〔在快要成功的情況下〕再冒更大的風險

push ahead *phr v* [I] to move forward with a plan or activity 繼續實行〔計劃〕; 繼續開展〔活動〕: *The government is pushing ahead with changes to the tax laws.* 政府正在大力推進稅法的修改工作。

push sbdy **around** *phr v* [T] *infml* to treat someone in a rough and unfair way 欺侮〔某人〕

push sbdy/sthg ↔ **aside** *phr v* [T] to pay no attention to a person or thing that you feel is not important〖非正式〗把〔人或物〕擱置一邊

push in *phr v* [I] *infml* to move in front of other people who have been waiting for something longer than you have〖非正式〗插隊

push off *phr v* [I] *infml* to go away〖非正式〗走開, 滾開: *Push off before I call the police.* 在我打電話叫警察來之前, 你快滾開。

push on *phr v* [I] *infml* to continue a journey〖非正式〗繼續旅程: *We must push on or we'll be late.* 我們必須抓緊時間, 不然要遲到了。

push sbdy/sthg ↔ **over** *phr v* [T] to make a person or thing fall over 使〔人或物〕跌倒

push sthg ↔ **through** *phr v* [T] to persuade people to accept something 説服〔某人〕接受〔某物〕: *Our M.P. has pushed through new legislation about drinking and driving.* 我們的國會議員促使有關飲酒和駕駛的新法案得到通過。

push² *n* **1** an act of pushing someone or something 推: *They gave the car a push to start it.* 為了發動車子, 他們推了它一下。**2** a planned attack and advance of great strength by an army〔軍隊的〕進攻; 推進 **3 a push for something** *infml* a determined attempt to achieve something 想獲得某物的努力 **4 give someone the push** *infml* to dismiss someone from a job〖非正式〗解雇某人: *I was given the push after 30 years.* 我在三十年後被解雇了。[RELATED PHRASE 相關詞組 **get the push**] **5 at a push** *infml* with difficulty, if it is necessary〖非正式〗不得已時, 如果真有必要: *I could do the work by Tuesday at a push.* 如有急需, 我可以在週二以前做完該項工作。

push·bike /ˈpʊʃˌbaɪk; ˈpʊʃbaɪk/ *n BrE infml* a bicycle〔英式, 非正式〗自行車, 腳踏車

push·chair /ˈpʌʃˌtʃer; ˈpʊʃtʃeəʳ/ *n* a small folding chair on wheels for pushing a small child around (摺疊式)手推嬰兒車

pushed /pʊʃt; pʊʃt/ *adj* **be pushed** *infml* to have difficulty in finding enough money or time to do something〖非正式〗〔錢或時間〕不夠用的: *I'm always rather pushed for money at the end of the month.* 每到月底, 我總是手頭很緊。

push·er /ˈpʊʃɚ; ˈpʊʃəʳ/ *n infml* a person who sells illegal drugs〖非正式〗販毒者

push·ing /ˈpʊʃɪŋ; ˈpʊʃɪŋ/ *prep infml* nearly a particular age〖非正式〗將近〔某一年齡〕: *She must be pushing forty by now.* 她現在肯定是將近四十歲了。

push·o·ver /ˈpʊʃˌovɚ; ˈpʊʃəʊvəʳ/ *n* [sing] *infml*〖非正式〗**1** something that is very easy to do or win 容易做的事; 容易獲得之物: *The examination was a pushover.* 那次考試很容易。**2** a person who can easily be persuaded 易被説服的人: *He was a pushover; he'll lend us whatever we need.* 他很容易被説服, 只要我們需要, 他甚麼東西都肯借給我們。

push-up /ˈ· ·/ *n* the usual American word for〖美式〗= a PRESS-UP

push·y /ˈpʊʃi; ˈpʊʃi/ *adj* **pushier, pushiest** *infml* too forceful in getting things done or in getting other people's attention〖非正式〗強求的; 咄咄逼人的: *Don't be so pushy — your turn will come.* 別這麼咄咄逼人——會輪到你的。

pus·sy /ˈpʊsi; ˈpʊsi/ *n* **pussies** *infml*〖非正式〗(also 又作 **puss, pussycat**) a cat, or a word for calling one to you 小貓咪

★★ **put** /pʊt; pʊt/ *v* **put, put, putting 1** [T; +adv/prep] to place or lay something in a particular place or position 把〔某物〕置於〔某處〕; 放置: *He put the letter on the table.* 他把信放在桌子上。| *She put her bags down on the floor.* 她把袋子放在地上。| *You've put too much salt in this soup.* 這碗湯裡放了太多的鹽。| *Where did I put my keys?* 我把鑰匙放到哪裡去了? –see picture on page 992 見 992 頁彩圖 **2** [T; +adv/prep] to cause someone or something to be in a particular state or condition 使〔某人或某物〕處於某種境地: *She put me in a bad mood by being late.* 她遲到了, 這令我心情不快。| *You have put me in a very awkward position.* 你令我處境非常尷尬。**3** [T; +adv/prep] to express something in words in a particular way 表達, 表述〔某事物〕: *Her ideas were cleverly put.* 她的意見表達得很巧妙。| *To put it bluntly, the whole event was a total disaster.* 不客氣地説一句, 整個事件根本是一塌糊塗。**4 put a question to someone** to ask someone a question 問某人問題: *I'd like to put this same question to the other members of the group.* 同樣這個問題, 我打算去問問組裡的其他人。**5 put a shot** to throw a heavy metal ball called a SHOT in a sporting competition 擲鉛球 **6 put an end to something** to cause something to end 結束某事: *We must put an end to these ridiculous rumours.* 我們必須制止這些可笑的謠言。**7 put it to someone** to suggest to someone that something is true 告訴某人〔某事是真的〕: *I put it to him that the police had known all along that these men were innocent.* 我告訴他警方從一開始就知道這些人是無辜的。**8 put paid to something** to ruin something or end it completely 徹底毀壞某物; 徹底結束某事: *This accident has put paid to his chances of becoming a professional athlete.* 這宗事故使他成為一名職業運動員的希望徹底破滅了。 **9 put someone to death** to kill someone 殺死某人

put sthg ↔ **about** *phr v* [T] *infml* to spread news about by telling it to people 〔非正式〕傳播, 散佈〔消息〕: *Rumours have been put about that he is working for the security forces.* 謠傳他在治安部隊裡工作。

put sthg ↔ **across** *phr v* [T] to explain something so that people can understand it 解釋, 說明〔某事物〕: *She didn't succeed in putting her ideas across very well.* 她未把觀點解釋得很清楚。

put sthg ↔ **aside** *phr v* [T] to save something so that you can use it or deal with it later 儲存備用: *I've got a bit of money put aside for a new car.* 我存了些錢準備買輛新車。

put away *phr v* **1** [T **put** sthg ↔ **away**] to put something into a safe place or into the place where it is kept 貯存; 放好: *Put your toys away, please.* 請把你的玩具收起來放好。 | *We've put a bit of money away in the building society.* 我們已在建築協會那裡存了點錢。 **2** [T **put** sbdy ↔ **away**] *infml* to send someone to prison 〔非正式〕把〔某人〕關進監獄

put back *phr v* **1** [T **put** sthg ↔ **back**] to delay something 推遲〔某事〕: *Publication has been put back by three months.* 出版時間推遲了三個月。 **2 put the clocks back** to change the time on all clocks so that they show an earlier time 把鐘往回撥

put sthg ↔ **by** *phr v* [T] to save money so that you can use it later 儲備〔錢〕: *I've got a bit of money put by for my old age.* 我已存了一些錢供養老。

put down *phr v* **1** [T **put** sthg ↔ **down**] to defeat a protest, usually by using force 鎮壓: *Troops were called in to help put down the rebellion.* 調動軍隊協助鎮壓叛亂。 **2** [T **put** sbdy ↔ **down**] *infml* to make someone feel ashamed or foolish 〔非正式〕使〔某人〕慚愧; 羞辱〔某人〕 **3** [T **put** sthg ↔ **down**] to kill an animal, usually because it is old or ill 宰殺〔通常是年老或生病的動物〕: *Two horses had to be put down after the race.* 比賽之後必須宰殺兩匹馬。

put sbdy **down for** sthg *phr v* [T] to put someone's name on a list of people who are going to do something 把〔某人〕列入名單中

put sthg **down to** sbdy/sthg *phr v* [T] to say or think that something was caused by a particular person or thing 把〔某事〕歸咎於…: *He didn't look well but I just put it down to the fact that he was tired.* 他氣色不佳, 但我相信這只是由於疲倦。

put forward *phr v* **1** [T **put** sbdy/sthg ↔ **forward**] to suggest or offer someone or something 提議; 提出: *I've put your name forward for the job of chairman of the committee.* 我已提議你當委員會的主席。 **2 put the clocks forward** to change the time on all clocks so that they show a later time 把鐘往前撥

put in *phr v* **1** [T **put** sthg ↔ **in**] to send a request or claim 提出〔要求或聲明〕: *I've put in a claim for compensation.* 我已要求獲得賠償。 **2** [T **put** sthg ↔ **in**] to spend time doing something 花費〔時間做某事〕: *I've only put in ten hours of work this week.* 本週我僅工作了十個小時。 **3** [I] (of a ship) to enter a port 〔輪船〕進港

put in for sthg *phr v* [T] to make a formal request for something 正式要求; 申請: *Unions have put in for a pay rise of 15%.* 工會已正式要求增加百分之十五的工資。

put into sthg *phr v* [T] (of a ship) to enter a port 〔輪船〕進〔港〕: *The ship had to put into Sydney for supplies.* 為了補充物資, 這艘船駛進了悉尼港。

put off *phr v* **1** [T **put** sthg ↔ **off**] to delay something until a later date 推遲〔某事〕: *The meeting's been put off until next month.* 會議推遲至下月舉行。 **2** [T **put** sbdy ↔ **off**] to tell someone that you cannot do something that you had agreed to do 推脫; 食言: *We're expecting them for dinner, but we'll have to put them off because the children aren't well.* 我們邀請了他們到來吃飯, 但現在卻要請他們不要來, 因為孩子們病了。 **3** [T **put** sbdy **off** (sbdy/sthg)] to make someone feel that they no longer like a person or thing, or that they no longer want to do something 使〔某人〕不再喜歡〔某人或某物〕: *My first week at university put me off university life completely.* 入讀大學僅一星期, 我已經十分討厭大學生活。 | *Don't tell him all the unpleasant aspects of the work — you'll put him off.* 別把這工作的各方面令人不快的情況都告訴他 —— 你那樣做會令他掃興的。

put on *phr v* **1** [T **put** sthg ↔ **on**] to put clothes onto your body 穿上〔衣服〕: *She got up and put her coat on.* 她起牀後穿上外衣。 –see 見 DRESS[1] (USAGE 用法) **2** [T **put** sthg ↔ **on**] to cause a light or a machine to work by pressing a button or turning a SWITCH 開〔電燈〕; 開動〔機器〕: *Could you put the light on, please?* 請你開燈, 可以嗎? **3** [T **put** sthg ↔ **on**] to gain weight and become fatter 增加〔體重〕: *He's put on a lot of weight recently.* 他近來胖了許多。 **4** [T **put** sthg ↔ **on**] to perform a play or show on a stage 上演〔戲劇〕 **5** [T **put** sthg ↔ **on**] to pretend to have a quality or feeling 佯裝; 假裝: *I don't believe she's really ill — I think she's just putting it on to get sympathy.* 我不相信她真的病了 —— 我認為她不過是在裝假以博得同情。 **6** [T **put** sthg **on** sthg] to add an amount to a cost or price 增加〔成本〕; 抬高

〔價格〕: *a tax increase that will put another 10p on the price of petrol* 由於加稅使得汽油價格上升十便士 **7** [T **put** sthg **on** sthg] risk money on the result of something 把錢押在〔某一結果〕上: *I've put £10 on Liverpool to win the cup.* 我已下注十英鎊, 賭利物浦隊贏得杯賽.

put sbdy **onto** sthg *phr v* [T] to tell someone information that will be useful 向〔某人〕介紹〔有用資料〕: *I phoned my solicitor and he put me onto a good lawyer.* 我打電話給我的事務律師, 他為我引見了一位優秀的律師.

put out *phr v* **1** [T **put** sthg ↔ **out**] to broadcast or print official information 播出; 出版: *The government will put out a new statement on the economy tomorrow.* 政府將於明天發表一項關於經濟方面的新的聲明. **2** [T **put** sthg ↔ **out**] to stop a fire from burning 撲滅〔火焰〕 **3** [T **put** sthg ↔ **out**] to stop a light from shining 關〔燈〕: *Don't forget to put the lights out when you leave.* 走之前不要忘記把燈關掉. **4** [T **put** sbdy **out**] to trouble or annoy someone 攪擾〔某人〕; 惹惱〔某人〕: *I felt somewhat put out by his behaviour.* 他的行為令我有點兒生氣. **5 put yourself out** to take trouble and make an effort to do something 花費功夫〔做某事〕: *He'll never put himself out to help anyone.* 他從來不肯費神幫助別人.

put sthg ↔ **over** *phr v* [T] to explain something so that people can understand it 解釋, 說明〔某事〕: *She didn't succeed in putting her ideas over very well.* 她沒把自己的想法說得很清楚.

put through *phr v* **1** [T **put** sbdy **through**] to connect someone by telephone to the person that they want to talk to 接通電話: *If you'll just hold the line for a minute I'll put you through to Mr Brown.* 請不要掛線, 我馬上把電話接到布朗先生那裡. **2** [T **put** sbdy **through** sthg] to make someone suffer something unpleasant 使〔某人〕經歷〔不愉快之事〕: *I don't want to put you through all that distress and anguish again.* 我不想讓你再次經歷那種憂傷與悲痛.

put sthg **to** sbdy *phr v* [T] to suggest something to someone 向〔某人〕建議〔某事〕: *I put my ideas to him but he didn't seem very enthusiastic.* 我把意見告訴他, 但他似乎不太熱心.

put together *phr v* **1** [T **put** sthg ↔ **together**] to make something into a single unit or group by joining or bringing together different parts 組成〔某事物〕: *We managed to put together a football team.* 我們終於組成了一支足球隊. **2 put your heads together** to all think about a problem in order to find an answer 大家一起思考問題尋找對策 **3 put together** combined 聯合在一起: *He earns more than the rest of us put together.* 他一人掙的錢比我們餘下的人掙的錢

合在一起還要多.

put up *phr v* **1** [T **put** sthg ↔ **up**] to build or raise something 建造, 舉起〔某物〕: *They're going to put up 20 new houses here.* 他們打算在此處建造二十所新的房子. | *I've never put up a tent on my own.* 我從未一個人搭過帳篷. | *She put up her umbrella.* 她撐起了傘. **2** [T **put** sthg ↔ **up**] to put a notice in a public place 張貼〔布告〕: *The exam results will be put up on the main notice board.* 考試結果將貼在主要告示牌上. | *They put up posters advertising the meeting.* 他們貼出了海報, 為此次會議做宣傳. **3** [T **put** sthg ↔ **up**] to increase a cost or price 提高〔成本〕; 抬高〔價格〕: *Most companies are expected to put their prices up by about 10% this year.* 估計今年大部分公司均會把產品價格提高約百分之十. **4** [T **put** sbdy ↔ **up**] to give someone food and lodging 給〔某人〕提供食宿: *Will you be able to put me up to-night?* 我今晚可以住在你這裡嗎? **5 put up a fight, put up resistance** to struggle to avoid something happening to you 進行反抗; 抵制: *Local groups are putting up a lot of resistance to the scheme.* 當地團體大力抵制該項計劃. | *In the end he was arrested without putting up much of a fight.* 最後, 他沒有經過多少反抗就被捕了. **6 put something up for sale** to offer something for sale 出售某物: *She's decided to put her house up for sale.* 她已決定出售她的房子.

put sbdy **up to** sthg *phr v* [T] give someone the idea of doing something bad 唆使〔某人〕做〔壞事〕: *I think it was Michael who put them up to it.* 我覺得是邁克爾唆使他們去幹此事的.

put up with sbdy/sthg *phr v* [T] to suffer someone or something unpleasant without complaining 容忍, 忍受〔某事物〕: *I won't put up with her rudeness any longer!* 她的態度粗魯無禮, 我再也不會容忍她的! | *I don't know why she puts up with him!* 我不明白她為甚麼會對他一忍再忍!

pu·ta·tive /'pjuːtətɪv/ *adj* [only before a noun 只用於名詞前] *fml* generally accepted as being something 〔正式〕公認的: *his putative parents* 他那為大家所公認的雙親

pu·tre·fy /'pjuːtrəˌfaɪ; 'pjuːtrɪˌfaɪ/ *v* putre-**fied, putrefied** [I] to decay 腐爛; 腐敗

pu·trid /'pjuːtrɪd; 'pjuːtrɪd/ *adj* very decayed and bad-smelling (usd especially of a dead animal or a plant substance) 腐爛的; 腐臭的〔尤指動物死屍或植物〕

putt /pʌt; pʌt/ *v* [I;T] to hit a GOLF ball gently along the ground towards the hole 〔高爾夫球中〕輕擊〔球〕 **–putt** *n*

put·ty /'pʌtɪ; 'pʌtɪ/ *n* [U] a soft paste, used to fix glass to window frames 〔給玻璃上框時用的〕油灰, 膩子

put-up·on /ˈ·· ·/ *adj* [never before a noun 不能用於名詞前] *infml* badly treated by someone for their own advantage 〔非正式〕

被虐待的; 被佔便宜的: *Everyone thinks I'll lend them money; I'm beginning to feel put-upon.* 人人都認為我會把錢借給他們; 我開始感覺到被人利用了。

puz·zle¹ /ˈpʌzl; ˈpʌzəl/ *v* puzzled, puzzling **1** [T] to make someone feel confused and unable to understand something 使〔某人〕困惑: *Her illness puzzled the doctor for months.* 醫生花了好幾個月時間仍無法瞭解她的病況。| *I was puzzled by his response.* 我被他的反應弄糊塗了。 **2 puzzle over something** to think about something a lot in order to understand it 對某事苦苦思索: *He was puzzling over the map, unwilling to ask for directions.* 他不願向別人問路, 便看着地圖苦苦思索。| *I've been puzzling as to why she'd said that, too.* 我也是無法弄明白她為甚麼會那樣講。–**puzzled** *adj*: *He had a puzzled expression on his face.* 他的臉上有種困惑不解的表情。

 puzzle sthg ↔ **out** *phr v* [T] to find the answer to something after a lot of thought 反覆思考之後找到答案

puzzle² *n* **1** a person or thing that you cannot understand or explain 無法理解的人或物 **2** a game or toy which is made in a way that forces you to think carefully in order to SOLVE it or put it together 智力遊戲; 智力玩具: *I do the Times crossword puzzle every day.* 我每天都做《泰晤士報》上的字謎遊戲。| *Can you help me finish this jigsaw puzzle?* 可以幫我拼好這幅拼板畫嗎?

PVC /ˌpi vi ˈsiː; ˌpiː viː ˈsiː/ *n* [U] a type of plastic 聚氯乙烯

pyg·my /ˈpɪgmɪ; ˈpɪgmi/ *n* **pygmies** (also 又作 **pigmy**) **1** a very small person, especially one belonging to certain African groups 〔尤指某些非洲部落的〕侏儒 **2** a particularly small type of animal 特別細小的動物

py·ja·mas /pəˈdʒɑːməz; pəˈdʒɑːməz/ *n* (also 又作 **pajamas** *AmE* 〔美式〕) [pl] a loose-fitting pair of trousers and short coat worn in bed, especially by men 〔尤指男用〕睡衣褲 –see picture on page 210 見 210 頁彩圖 –see 見 PAIR (USAGE 用法)

py·lon /ˈpaɪlən; ˈpaɪlən/ *n* a tall framework of steel bars used for supporting wires that carry electricity over land 高壓電線架; 電纜塔

pyr·a·mid /ˈpɪrəmɪd; ˈpɪrəmɪd/ *n* **1** a solid shape with a flat square base and three-angled sides that slope upwards to meet at a point 錐體 **2** (also 又作 **Pyramid**) a very large ancient stone building in this shape, used formerly in Egypt as the burial place of a king 〔埃及的〕金字塔 **3** the structure of an organization, in which there are fewer people at the top than lower down 金字塔式的組織結構

pyre /paɪr; paɪəʳ/ *n lit* a high pile of wood for the ceremonial burning of a dead body 〔文〕火葬用的柴堆

py·thon /ˈpaɪθən; ˈpaɪθən/ *n* a large tropical snake that kills animals for food by winding itself round them and crushing them 〔熱帶地區的〕蟒蛇

Q, q

Q, q /kju; kjuː/ **Q's, q's** *or* **Qs, qs** the 17th letter of the English alphabet 英語的第十七個字母

Q. C. /ˌkju ˈsi; ˌkjuː ˈsiː/ *n* a British lawyer of high rank; an abbreviation for QUEEN'S COUNSEL 《縮》御用大律師; 王室法律顧問: *Sir John Smithers, Q.C.* 王室法律顧問約翰·史密瑟斯爵士

quack¹ /kwæk; kwæk/ *v* [I] to make the sound that ducks make 〔鴨子〕嘎嘎地叫

quack² *n* **1** a person dishonestly claiming to have medical knowledge or skills 江湖醫生; 庸醫 **2** the sound that ducks make 鴨叫聲

quad /kwɑd; kwɒd/ *n* **1** a square open area with buildings around it, especially in a college 〔尤指學院中由建築物圍繞的〕四方庭院; 四方廣場 **2** see 見 QUADRUPLET

quad·rant /ˈkwɑdrənt; ˈkwɒdrənt/ *n* **1** a quarter of a circle 四分之一圓 **2** an instrument for measuring angles 象限儀

quad·ri·lat·er·al /ˌkwɑdrəˈlætərəl; ˌkwɒdrɪˈlætərəl◂/ *n* a shape with four straight sides 四邊形—**quadrilateral** *adj*

quad·ru·ped /ˈkwɑdrəˌpɛd; ˈkwɒdrʊˌped/ *n* an animal with four legs 四足獸

quad·ru·ple¹ /ˈkwɑdrʊpl̩; ˈkwɒdrʊpəl/ *v* **quadrupled, quadrupling 1** [T] to multiply a number or an amount by four 乘以四; 使成四倍 **2** [I] to become four times as great 成四倍: *Our profits have quadrupled this year.* 今年我們的利潤已增至四倍。

quadruple² *adj fml* four times as big as something mentioned, or four times as big as usual 《正式》四倍的

quad·ru·plet /ˈkwɑdruˌplɪt; ˈkwɒdrʊplɪt/ *n* (also 又作 **quad** *infml* 《非正式》) one of four children born to the same mother at the same time 四胞胎中的一個孩子

quag·mire /ˈkwæɡˌmaɪr; ˈkwæɡmaɪər/ *n* **1** a large area of soft wet ground 泥沼; 沼澤地 **2** a very difficult situation 困境

quail¹ /kwel; kweɪl/ *n* [C;U] a type of small bird which is often eaten 鵪鶉

quail² *v* [I] *lit* to feel afraid 《文》害怕: *He quailed at the thought of telling her about the accident.* 他一想到要把這起事故告訴她便感到害怕。

quaint /kwent; kweɪnt/ *adj* unusual or old-fashioned in an attractive way 古雅的; 古色古香的: *We visited a quaint little village in the hills.* 我們參觀了山中的一個古老的小村落。 —**quaintly** *adv*

quake¹ /kwek; kweɪk/ *v* **quaked, quaking** [I] to tremble because you are very afraid 〔由

於恐懼而〕顫抖: *She was quaking* **with** *fear.* 她嚇得渾身發抖。

quake² *n infml* 《非正式》 see 見 EARTHQUAKE

Quak·er /ˈkwekɚ; ˈkweɪkər/ *n* a member of a Christian religious group which opposes violence 基督教中的貴格會的教徒, 教友派的信徒〔該教派反對暴力〕

***qual·i·fi·ca·tion** /ˌkwɑləfəˈkeʃən; ˌkwɒlɪfɪ-ˈkeɪʃən/ *n* **1** [C] a proof that you have passed an examination 〔考試〕合格證明(書): *She has the right qualifications for the job.* 她有符合該項工作的各項證明材料。 **2** [C] a skill or quality that you need to do a particular job 資格; 資歷: *Previous experience is not an essential qualification for the job.* 以前的經驗不是獲得這份工作的必要條件。 **3** [U] the act of completing the necessary training for a particular job 取得資格 **4** [C] something which limits what has just been said 限制; 限定條件: *We support their policy statement, but with certain qualifications. Points 5 and 7 will have to be changed.* 我們支持他們的政策聲明, 但有一些條件。第五和第七點必須有所改動。

qual·i·fied /ˈkwɑləˌfaɪd; ˈkwɒlɪˌfaɪd/ *adj* **1** having the right training, knowledge, or skills to do something 合格的; 有資格的: *He's not qualified to teach young children.* 他沒有資格教小孩子。 | *You're certainly well qualified for the job.* 你當然很有資格做這份工作。 | *a qualified doctor* 合格的醫生

□ USEFUL PATTERNS 有用句型
be qualified to do something; be qualified for something

2 limited 有限度的; 有條件的: *Her response to the idea was one of qualified agreement.* 她對該觀點的反應是有保留的贊同。

***qual·i·fy** /ˈkwɑləˌfaɪ; ˈkwɒlɪˌfaɪ/ *v* **qualified, qualifying 1** [I] to pass an examination or gain the knowledge or experience necessary for a particular job 考試合格; 取得資格: *I came to this school immediately after I had qualified* **as** *a teacher.* 我一取得教師資格便馬上來了這所學校。 **2 qualify for something** to have the right to do or have something 有權做某事; 有權擁有某物: *I'm afraid you don't qualify for a pension.* 對不起, 您沒有資格領養老金。 | *We're hoping to qualify for the next round of the competition.* 我們希望能有資格進入下一輪比賽。 **3 qualify someone to do something** to allow someone to do something or give them the right to do it 讓某人做某事; 讓某人有權做某事: *This test will qualify you to fly an air-craft.* 你若能通過此次考試, 便有資格開飛機。 **4** [T] to limit what you are saying in some way 限制; 修飾: *I'd like to qualify my last re-mark.* 我想把我最後的一句話修飾一下。

qual·i·ta·tive /ˈkwɑləˌtetɪv; ˈkwɒlɪ̸tətɪv/ *adj* concerning the quality of something 定性的, 質量的 –**qualitatively** *adv*

★**qual·i·ty** /ˈkwɑlətɪ; ˈkwɒlɪ̸ti/ *n* **qualities** **1** [U] the degree to which something is good or bad 質, 質量: *The re-port criticized the poor quality of many TV programmes.* 這報道批評了許多電視節目素質低劣。 **2** [U] a very high standard 非常高的水準: *He's an actor of real quality.* 他是個非常優秀的演員。 **3** [C] something that is typical of a person or thing 特質; 特性: *Her writing has a rather sinister quality.* 她的作品總給人一種不祥的感覺。 **4** [C] a good part of some-one's character, such as kindness or honesty 〔人的〕品性; 品德: *She showed all the qualities of a great leader.* 她表現出了一位偉大的領導人所應具備的品質。

qualm /kwɑm; kwɑːm/ *n* a feeling of ner-vousness or uncertainty about an action or situation 緊張; 不安: *He seems to have no qualms about going to work abroad.* 他對於到國外去工作似乎沒有甚麼不安。

quan·da·ry /ˈkwɑndrɪ; ˈkwɒndəri/ *n* **quan-daries** a feeling of not knowing what to do 茫然; 不知所措: *I was in a quandary about whether or not to go.* 我猶豫不定, 不知道該不該去。

quan·ti·fy /ˈkwɑntəˌfaɪ; ˈkwɒntɪ̸faɪ/ *v* **quan-tified, quantifying** [T] *fml* to measure an amount or quantity of something 〔正式〕測定〔某物〕的數量: *It is difficult to quantify the value of a good education.* 很難用數量來表示良好教育的價值。 –**quantifiable** *adj*

quan·ti·ta·tive /ˈkwɑntəˌtetɪv; ˈkwɒntɪ̸tətɪv/ *adj* concerning the number or amount of something (數)量, 量的 –**quantitatively** *adv*

★**quan·ti·ty** /ˈkwɑntətɪ; ˈkwɒntɪ̸ti/ *n* **quan-tities** **1** [C] a number or amount of some-thing 量, 數量: *Police found a large quantity of illegal drugs.* 警方發現了大量違法藥品。 | *expensive cars that are manufactured in small quantities* 小量生產的昂貴的汽車 **2** [U] amount 量: *manufacturers who are more concerned with quantity than quality* 更加重視產量而非質量的生產商 **3** **in quantity** in a large numbers or amounts 大量: *We buy in quantity, and then resell most of it.* 我們大量地採購, 然後再把大部分轉賣掉。

quan·tum /ˈkwɑntəm; ˈkwɒntəm/ *n* **quanta** /-tə; -tə/ **1** *tech* a very small amount 〔術語〕很少的數量 **2** **quantum jump, quantum leap** a very important advance or improvement 重大進展; 重大改進

quar·an·tine¹ /ˈkwɔrənˌtin; ˈkwɒrəntiːn/ *n*

[U] a period of time when a person or ani-mal that may be carrying disease is kept separate from others so that the disease cannot spread 〔患病的人或動物的〕隔離檢疫期: *The dogs were put in quarantine for six months.* 這些狗被檢疫隔離了六個月。

quarantine² *v* **quarantined, quarantining** [T] to put a person or an animal in quaran-tine 對〔人或動物〕進行檢疫隔離

quar·rel¹ /ˈkwɔrəl; ˈkwɒrəl/ *n* **1** an angry ar-gument 爭吵; 吵架 **2** **have no quarrel with something** to have no reason to disagree with something 沒有理由不同意: *I have no quarrel with what the minister says.* 我沒有理由不同意部長所說的話。

quarrel² *v* **-ll- (-l- *AmE* 〖美式〗)** [I] to have an angry argument 爭吵; 吵架: *They used to quarrel all the time.* 他們以前老是沒完沒了地爭吵。 | *I don't want to quarrel with you.* 我不想和你吵架。 | *What are you two quarrel-ling about?* 你們兩個在吵甚麼? | *quarrelling over whose pen it was* 為了那是誰的鋼筆而吵

quar·rel·some /ˈkwɔrəlsəm; ˈkwɒrəlsəm/ *adj* frequently starting arguments 愛吵架的

quar·ry¹ /ˈkwɔrɪ; ˈkwɒri/ *n* **quarries 1** [C] a place on the surface of the earth from which stone or sand are dug out 採石場 **2** [sing] a person or animal that is being hunted 獵取的目標; 獵物

quarry² *v* **quarried, quarrying** [I;T] to dig out stone or sand from the surface of the earth 採〔石〕; 挖〔沙〕

quart /kwɔrt; kwɔːt/ *n* a unit for measuring liquids, equal to two pints (PINT) 夸脫〔液體的容積單位, 等於兩品脫〕

★**quar·ter¹** /ˈkwɔrtɚ; ˈkwɔːtəʳ/ *n* **1** one of four equal parts which make up a whole, ¼ 四分之一: *It's a quarter of a mile to the bus stop.* 這裡距離公共汽車站有四分之一英里。 **2** 15 minutes before or after the hour 一刻鐘; 十五分鐘: *We started at a quarter to 10 and didn't finish until quarter past.* 我們九點三刻開始, 直到十點一刻才做完。 see 見 TIME¹ (USAGE 用法) **3** a period of three months of the year, used especially for making payments 一個季度; 三個月〔尤指付款〕: *I pay my bills each quarter.* 我一個季度付一次账。 **4** a coin in the US and Canada worth 25 cents, or ¼ of a dollar 〔美國或加拿大〕二角五分的硬幣 **5** ¼ of a pound in weight 四分之一磅: *I'd like a quarter of those choco-lates, please.* 我想買四分之一磅那種巧克力。 **6** a part of a town, often one where a certain type of person lives 〔常為某一類人居住的〕城區: *the student quarter* 學生〔居住〕區 **7** a place or person from which something comes 〔某物的〕來源: *Help came from several quarters.* 援助正來自四面八方。 **8** **quarters** [pl] lodgings, especially for soldiers and their families 〔尤指士兵及其家屬的〕住處, 宿舍

quarter² *v* [T] **1** to divide something into

four parts 把〔某物〕分成四部分 **2** to provide lodgings for people, especially soldiers〔尤指為士兵〕提供住宿

quar·ter·fi·nal /ˌkwɔːtəˈfaɪnl; ˌkwɔːtəˈfaɪnl/ *n* any of the four matches in a competition; the winners of them will play in the two semifinals (SEMIFINAL) 四分之一決賽, 半準決賽

quar·ter·ly¹ /ˈkwɔːtəlɪ; ˈkwɔːtəli/ *n* a magazine which is produced four times a year 季刊

quarterly² *adv, adj* every three months 每季的[地]: *We pay the phone bill quarterly.* 我們每季度付一次電話賬單。| *the company's quarterly accounts* 該公司的季度報表

quar·ter·mas·ter /ˈkwɔːtəˌmɑːstə; ˈkwɔːtəˌmɑːstə/ *n* a military officer who is in charge of food and supplies 軍需官

quar·tet /kwɔːˈtet; kwɔːˈtet/ *n* **1** four people playing instruments or singing together 四重奏; 四重唱 **2** a piece of music written for such a group 四重奏[唱]曲

quartz /kwɔːts; kwɔːts/ *n* [U] a hard mineral substance which is used in making very exact watches and clocks 石英

quash /kwɒʃ; kwɒʃ/ *v* [T] **1** to change a legal decision or dismiss a suggestion officially 撤銷〔判決〕; 拒絕接受〔建議〕: *The high court judge quashed the decision of the lower court.* 高等法院的法官撤銷了初級法院的判決。 **2** to bring something to an end by force 鎮壓; 平息: *The army quashed the rebellion.* 軍隊平息了叛亂。

qua·ver /ˈkweɪvə; ˈkweɪvə/ *v* **1** [I] (of a voice or a sound) to shake slightly〔嗓音或聲音〕發顫 **2** [T] to say something in a shaky voice 用顫抖的聲音説 –**quaver** *n*

quay /kiː; kiː/ *n* a place, usually built of stone, where ships can land and be loaded 碼頭

quea·sy /ˈkwiːzɪ; ˈkwiːzi/ *adj* **queasier, queasiest** feeling slightly sick 令人噁心的: *I felt a little queasy when the sea got rough.* 海上風浪一大, 我就感到有點想嘔吐。–**queasiness** *n* [U]

☆**queen** /kwiːn; kwiːn/ *n* **1** (also 又作 **Queen**) a female ruler of a country who is not elected but is usually the daughter of a former king; **Queen** is also used as a title 女王〔Queen也可以用作稱號〕: *She became queen at an early age.* 她年紀很小時就做了女王。| *Queen Elizabeth II* 伊利沙白女王二世 **2** (also 又作 **Queen**) the wife of a king 皇后; 王后 **3** a woman who is considered to be, or is voted, the best of her kind 出眾的女子: *a beauty queen* 選美皇后 | *the queen of opera* 歌劇皇后 **4** the large female that leads a group of certain insects〔昆蟲中的〕后: *the queen bee* 蜂后 **5** a playing card with a picture of a queen on it〔紙牌中的〕王后: *the queen of hearts* 紅桃王后 **6** one of the pieces in a game of CHESS〔國際象棋中的〕

王后

queen·ly /ˈkwiːnlɪ; ˈkwiːnli/ *adj* like a queen or suitable for a queen 女王般的; 適合女王的

queen moth·er /ˌ·ˈ··/ *n* (also 又作 **Queen Mother**) the mother of a ruler (王)太后

Queen's Coun·sel /ˌ·ˈ··/ *n fml*〔正式〕see 見 Q.C.

queer¹ /kwɪə; kwɪə/ *adj* **1** strange 奇怪的: *It was a queer situation.* 那情景很奇特。 **2** *infml* rather ill〔非正式〕不舒服的: *I've been feeling a little queer since dinner.* 晚飯之後, 我便一直感到有點不舒服。 **3** *infml* HOMOSEXUAL (a word which is considered offensive)〔非正式〕同性戀的〔該詞被認為是不禮貌的〕

queer² *n infml* a male HOMOSEXUAL (a word which is considered offensive)〔非正式〕男同性戀者〔該詞被認為是不禮貌的〕

quell /kwel; kwel/ *v* [T] to stop opposition, violent behaviour, or unpleasant feelings 鎮壓; 壓制; 抑制: *The prime minister quelled disagreement among her ministers.* 首相消除了部長之間的分歧。

quench /kwentʃ; kwentʃ/ *v* [T] **1 quench your thirst** to drink enough so that you are no longer thirsty 喝…解渴 **2** to put out a fire using water〔用水〕撲滅〔火〕: *Firemen quenched the flames.* 消防隊員撲滅了火焰。

quer·u·lous /ˈkwerʊləs; ˈkwerələs/ *adj fml* often complaining, especially in a rather weak and unnecessary way〔正式〕嘮叨的; 愛發牢騷的

que·ry¹ /ˈkwɪərɪ; ˈkwɪəri/ *n* **queries** a question 問題; 疑問: *I've got a few queries about the salary and conditions.* 我有幾個有關工資待遇和工作條件的問題。

query² *v* **queried, querying** [T] to express doubt about something 對〔某事〕提出疑問: *The directors have queried our findings.* 董事們對我們的調查結果提出了疑問。

quest /kwest; kwest/ *n fml or lit*〔正式或文〕 **1** a search for something 探尋; 探索: *The quest for a cure is nearly over.* 很快便會找到治療的辦法。 **2 in quest of** searching for something 尋找〔某物〕

☆☆**ques·tion¹** /ˈkwestʃən; ˈkwestʃən/ *n* **1** [C] a sentence or phrase which asks for information 問題: *I asked you a question and you didn't answer.* 我問了你一個問題, 但你沒有回答。| *The question is: how was he killed?* 問題在於: 他是如何被殺的? | *Turn over your exam papers now. You must answer three questions on each subject.* 現在請把試卷翻過來。每一科目大家必須回答三個問題。 –see 見 ASK (USAGE 用法) **2** [C] a problem to be dealt with 難題; 待解決的事: *It's a question of finding enough time.* 問題是要爭取足夠的時間。 **3** [C;U] doubt 疑問; 懷疑: *There was some question as to his honesty.* 他是否誠實令人有些懷疑。| *They did it. There's no* *question* **about** *it.* 是他們做的。這是毫無疑問的。**4 beyond question** not to be doubted 毫無疑問: *Her good intentions were beyond question.* 她的好意是毫無疑問的。**5 call something into question** to express doubts about something 對某事表示懷疑 **6 in question** being considered 考慮之中的: *Let's return to the subject in question.* 讓我們回到正在考慮的問題上來。**7 out of the question** impossible or not allowed 不可能; 不允許 **8 there's no question of** a phrase you use when you want to stop someone worrying and tell them that there is no possibility of something happening 沒有…的可能〔用於安慰某人〕: *It's just a rumour. There's no question of my leaving the company.* 這不過是謠言罷了。我不可能離開公司的。

question² v [T] **1** to ask someone questions about something 詢問; 審問: *She questioned him about his past.* 她詢問了他的過去。**2** to express doubts about something 對〔某事〕表示懷疑: *I would never question her honesty.* 我絕不會懷疑她的誠實。**–questioning** *n [U]*: *They were taken to the police station for questioning.* 他們被帶到警察局接受盤問。

ques·tion·a·ble /ˈkwɛstʃənəbəl; ˈkwɛstʃənəbəl/ *adj* **1** not certain 不肯定的; 無把握的: *It's questionable whether this type of research is useful.* 這類研究是否有用還不能肯定。**2** perhaps not right or honest 可疑的: *highly questionable goings-on at the bank* 銀行中很值得懷疑的勾當 **–questionably** *adv*

ques·tion·ing /ˈkwɛstʃənɪŋ; ˈkwɛstʃənɪŋ/ *adj* showing that you want an answer to something 懷疑的: *She gave him a questioning look.* 她懷疑地看了他一眼。**–questioningly** *adv*

question mark /ˈ···/ *n* a sign (?) used to show that something you have written is a question 問號

ques·tion·naire /ˌkwɛstʃənˈɛr; ˌkwɛstʃəˈneər/ *n* a set of questions to be answered by a number of people in order to provide information 問卷〔發放給許多人回答以便提供資料〕; 調查表: *We all had to fill in a questionnaire about our working habits.* 我們所有人都必須填一張有關工作習慣的問卷。

queue¹ /kju; kjuː/ *n BrE* a line of people or vehicles waiting to do something 〔英式〕〔人或車輛的〕行列; 隊: *There was a long queue outside the cinema.* 電影院門外排着長隊。

queue² *v* **queued, queuing** *[I] BrE* 〔英式〕 (also 又作 **queue up**) to wait for something in a line of people or vehicles 排隊: *Have you been queuing for long?* 你排了很長時間的隊嗎? | *She had to queue up to pay for the books.* 她要排隊付款買書。

quib·ble /ˈkwɪbl; ˈkwɪbəl/ *v* **quibbled, quibbling** *[I]* to argue about small, unimportant points 〔在小問題上〕爭辯: *He quibbles over every penny we spend.* 我們每花一分錢,

他都要和我們爭論不休。**–quibble** *n*

⋆**quick¹** /kwɪk; kwɪk/ *adj* **1** performing an action in an unusually short time 迅速的; 快的: *a quick worker* 工作速度快的人 | *She's very quick to learn.* 她學得很快。| *You're quick at knitting.* 你織得真快啊! **2** done in a short time 迅速完成的: *a quick journey* 短程旅行 | *Have you got time for a quick drink?* 你有沒有時間去乾一杯? **3 a quick temper** a tendency to get angry very easily 急躁的性情 **4 quick as a flash** very quickly 非常迅速地 **5 quick off the mark** wasting no time before beginning to do something 〔做某事之前〕不浪費時間 **6 quick on the uptake** able to understand things very fast 能迅速理解事情 **–quickly** *adv*: *Come quickly!* 快來! **–quickness** –see 見 FASTNESS (USAGE 用法) *n [U]*

quick² *adv* quickly 迅速地: *Quick! She's coming!* 快點! 她來了! | *Come quick!* 快來! | *I need a quick-acting painkiller.* 我需要一片速效止痛片。

quick·en /ˈkwɪkən; ˈkwɪkən/ *v [I;T]* to become faster, or to make something faster (使)變快, 加快: *The music quickened, and the dancing began.* 音樂節奏越來越快, 人們開始隨之跳舞。

quick·sand /ˈkwɪksænd; ˈkwɪksænd/ *n [U]* wet sand which sucks down anyone or anything that tries to cross it 流沙

quick·step /ˈkwɪkstɛp; ˈkwɪkstɛp/ *n* a dance with small, quick steps 快步舞

quick-wit·ted /ˌ· ···◁/ *adj* quick to understand things and to act quickly 聰明的; 機敏的: *A quick-witted neighbour heard the screams and called the police.* 一位機敏的鄰居聽到尖叫聲後, 便打電話叫來了警察。

quid /kwɪd; kwɪd/ *n* [plural is 複數為 **quid**] *infml* a pound in British money 〔非正式〕一英鎊: *This dress cost me 40 quid.* 這條裙子我花了四十英鎊。

⋆**qui·et¹** /ˈkwaɪət; ˈkwaɪət/ *adj* **1** making little noise 安靜的; 輕聲的: *quiet music* 輕輕的音樂 | *a quiet voice* 輕柔的嗓音 | *I'm trying to make a phone call!* 請安靜! 我正在打電話! **2** without very much activity or excitement 平靜的, 寧靜的: *I just want a quiet life.* 我只想過寧靜的生活。| *They're having a quiet wedding.* 他們在舉行一場很平靜的婚禮。**3** calm and often silent (used of people) 鎮靜的; 安靜的〔指人〕 **4** not bright (used of colours) 素淨的; 不鮮豔的〔指顏色〕 **5** not attracting attention from other people 不引人注目的; 暗中的: *Can I have a quiet word with you?* 我能私下和你談幾句話嗎? **–quietly** *adv*: *He crept quietly down the hall.* 他悄悄地往大廳走下去。**–quietness** *n [U]*

quiet² *n [U]* **1** the state of being quiet 安靜; 寂靜: *We drove to the mountains for some peace and quiet.* 我們驅車前往山中, 享受一下祥和與安靜。**2 on the quiet** *infml* secretly

---

〖非正式〗祕密地

qui·et·en /ˈkwaɪətn; ˈkwaɪətn/ v (also 又作 **quiet** *AmE* 〖美式〗) [T] to make someone less noisy 使〔某人〕安靜: *Can't you quieten those children?* 你難道不能讓那些孩子安靜下來嗎?

quieten down *phr v* [I;T **quieten** sbdy ↔ **down**] to become less noisy, or to make someone less noisy (使)安靜下來: *She soon quietened down.* 她很快就安靜下來了。| *I was trying to quieten the children down.* 我正在設法使孩子們安靜下來。

quill /kwɪl; kwɪl/ n 1 a bird's long stiff feather, or a pen made from this 大羽毛;羽管筆 2 one of the many sharp points sticking out from the body of some animals, such as the PORCUPINE 〔動物身上的〕刺

quilt /kwɪlt; kwɪlt/ n a cover for a bed which is filled with soft, warm material 被褥;被子

quilt·ed /ˈkwɪltɪd; ˈkwɪltˌɪd/ adj made with cloth which contains soft material that is kept in place by lines of stitching 中間夾有軟物的

quin /kwɪn; kwɪn/ n (**quint** /kwɪnt; kwɪnt/ *AmE* 〖美式〗) see 見 QUINTUPLET

quince /kwɪns; kwɪns/ n a hard fruit used for making jelly 榅桲〔一種用於製果醬的水果〕

quin·ine /ˈkwaɪniːn; ˈkwaɪniːn/ n [U] a drug used for treating fevers, especially MALARIA 金雞納;奎寧〔用於治療發燒,尤其是瘧疾〕

quin·tes·sence /kwɪnˈtɛsn̩s; kwɪnˈtesəns/ n fml 〖正式〗 1 the quintessence of the perfect example of something 典型;完美的榜樣: *John is the quintessence of good manners.* 約翰是彬彬有禮的典範。 2 the central character of something 精髓 –**quintessential** /ˌkwɪntəˈsɛnʃəl; ˌkwɪntˌɪˈsenʃl/ adj – **quintessentially** adv

quin·tet /kwɪnˈtɛt; kwɪnˈtet/ n 1 five people playing instruments or singing together 五重奏;五重唱 2 a piece of music written for such a group 五重奏〔唱〕曲

quin·tu·plet /ˈkwɪntjuplɪt; ˈkwɪntjʊplˌt/ n (also 又作 **quin** infml 〖非正式〗, **quint** *AmE* infml 〖美式,非正式〗) one of five children born to the same mother at the same time 五胞胎中的一個孩子

quip /kwɪp; kwɪp/ v -pp- [I] to make a clever or amusing remark 説俏皮話 –**quip** n

quirk /kwɝk; kwɜːk/ n 1 a strange happening that is difficult to explain 奇事;巧合: *By some quirk of fate the two of us were on the same train.* 由於命運的巧妙安排,我們倆乘上了同一列火車。 2 a strange type of behaviour or part of someone's character. 奇行;怪癖: *He has some unusual quirks in his character.* 他的性格中有一些不尋常怪癖。

quis·ling /ˈkwɪzlɪŋ; ˈkwɪzlɪŋ/ n a person who helps an enemy power that has taken control of their country 〔與佔領本國的敵人合作的〕賣國賊

quit /kwɪt; kwɪt/ v quit, quit, quitting [I;T] infml 〖非正式〗 1 to stop doing something 停止做〔某事〕: *She quit smoking when she got pregnant.* 她一懷孕便戒煙了。 2 to leave your job 辭職: *I had an argument with my boss and quit.* 我跟老闆吵了一架之後便辭職了。

★ **quite** /kwaɪt; kwaɪt/ predeterminer, adv 1 to some degree 相當;頗: *He must be quite old now.* 他現在一定相當年邁了。| *It was quite expensive.* 它相當昂貴。| *Quite a lot of people came.* 相當多人來了。 2 completely 完全;十分: *Their second child is quite different.* 他們的第二個孩子完全不同。| *Are you quite sure?* 你十分肯定嗎? | *I'm not quite ready.* 我還沒有完全準備好。 3 **quite a** a phrase used to say that something is important or unusual in some way 重要的;不尋常的〔用於表示某物在某方面與眾不同〕: *Bullying is quite a problem in some schools.* 恃強凌弱的現象在一些學校裡很成問題。 4 **quite something** infml 〖非正式〗了不起的: *It's quite something to get a degree at the age of 82.* 八十二歲拿到學位實在是了不起。

■ USAGE 用法: 1 If you want to use **quite** with an adjective which comes in front of a noun, remember to put **quite** before the indefinite article (**a** or **an**) ☆如果 **quite** 用於修飾名詞前的形容詞,請記住把 **quite** 置於不定冠詞(**a** 或 **an**)之前: *The book is quite long.* 這本書的篇幅相當長。| *It's quite a long book.* 這是一本篇幅相當長的書。| *Her mouth is quite small.* 她的嘴相當小。| *She's got quite a small mouth.* 她有張相當小巧的嘴巴。 2 If you want to say something nice to somebody, it is often better to avoid the word **quite**. In sentences such as ☆如果想表示稱讚,最好避免使用 **quite**。在下列各句中: *Your shirt is quite nice.* 你的襯衫還不錯。| *This wine is quite good.* 這酒還算好。| *"Do you like my hair?" "Yes, it's quite nice."* "你喜歡我的髮型嗎?""喜歡,這種髮型還不錯"。 **quite** usually means "fairly but not very". It is safer to use **very** or **really** instead ☆ **quite** 通常表示"尚可"而不是"非常",因此最好使用 **very** 或 **really**: *Your shirt is really nice.* 你的襯衫真的不錯。| *This wine is very/extremely good.* 這酒非常好/好極了。| *Your hair looks really nice.* 你的髮型看上去挺好的。

★ **quits** /kwɪts; kwɪts/ adj infml 〖非正式〗 be **quits** to have returned to a situation in which neither of two people is at a disadvantage 互不相欠: *Now we're quits.* 我們現在誰也不欠誰。

quiv·er¹ /'kwɪvə; 'kwɪvə'/ *v* [I] to tremble slightly 微微顫抖 **–quiver** *n*: *A quiver of excitement ran down her spine.* 她感到一陣激動, 全身發抖。

quiver² *n* a container for arrows which you carry on your back 箭筒, 箭袋

quix·ot·ic /kwɪks'ɑtɪk; kwɪk'sɒtɪk/ *adj* trying to do something impossible, often to help other people 愚俠式的, 堂吉訶德式的

quiz¹ /kwɪz; kwɪz/ *n* **quizzes** a competition or game in which people try to answer questions 問答比賽[遊戲]: *a general knowledge quiz* 常識問答比賽

quiz² *v* **-zz-** [T] to ask someone questions 向〔某人〕提問: *He quizzed me about where I'd spent the evening.* 他問我昨晚去哪裡了。

quiz·zi·cal /'kwɪzɪkḷ; 'kwɪzɪkəl/ *adj* **a quizzical smile/look** a smile or look that seems to suggest that you are asking a question or showing amusement, though you are not doing it openly 〔笑容或表情〕疑問的; 嘲弄的 **–quizzically** /-klɪ; -klɪ/ *adv*

quoit /kwɔɪt; kwɔɪt/ *n* a ring that you try to throw over a small upright post in a game called **quoits** 〔擲環遊戲用的〕圈; 環

quo·rum /'kwɔrəm; 'kwɔːrəm/ *n fml* a particular number of people, without which a meeting cannot begin 〔正式〕〔會議的〕法定人數: *No decisions were made because we didn't have a quorum.* 由於不到法定人數, 我們沒有作出任何決定。

quo·ta /'kwotə; 'kwəʊtə/ *n* a limited number or share of something 定額; 限額; 配額: *Quotas have been imposed for most imports.* 大部分進口商品都有限額。| *I've done my quota of work, so I'm leaving now.* 我已幹完了自己的工作定額, 所以準備走了。

quo·ta·ble /'kwotəbḷ; 'kwəʊtəbəl/ *adj* worth quoting 值得引用的

quo·ta·tion /kwo'teʃən; kwəʊ'teɪʃən/ *n* **1** [C] (also 又作 **quote** *infml* 〖非正式〗) words taken from speech or writing and repeated exactly by someone else 引語; 引文: *Support your ideas with quotations from the play.* 請引用該劇中的話來支持你的觀點。**2** [U] the act of quoting someone or something 引用, 引述 **3** [C] (also 又作 **quote** *infml* 〖非正式〗) the calculated cost of a piece of work, given before the work is started 報價; 開價: *He gave me a quotation for installing the central heating.* 他把安裝中央暖氣系統的報價告訴了我。

quotation marks /·'··· ·/ *n* a pair of marks (" ") or (' ') showing the beginning and end of words which are being quoted 引號: *Phrases from someone else's work must always be written in quotation marks.* 從別人的作品中借用來的短語必須寫在引號之中。

***quote¹** /kwot; kwəʊt/ *v* **quoted, quoting 1** [I; T] to repeat in speech or writing someone else's exact words 引用: *He quotes from the Bible at every opportunity.* 他一有機會就引用聖經裡的話。| *That's my honest opinion, but don't quote me!* 那是我自己坦白的意見, 不過別引用我的話! | *"When a man is tired of London, he is tired of life," she quoted.* "如果一個人厭倦了倫敦, 他便厭倦了生活," 她引用別人的話說道。**2** [T] to mention an example to support your argument 引證: *She quoted several cases in which such mistakes had occurred.* 她列舉了幾宗發生過這類錯誤的實例。**3** [T] to give someone a price for your goods or services 報(價), 開(價): *We've asked two builders to quote for replacing the roof.* 我們已經讓兩家建築商就改建屋頂的費用進行報價。

quote² *n infml* 〖非正式〗**1** see 見 QUOTATION 1, 3 **2 in quotes** in QUOTATION MARKS 在引號中

R, r

R, r /ɑr; ɑːʳ/ **R's, r's** or **Rs, rs 1** the 18th letter of the English alphabet 英語的第十八個字母 **2 the three R's** reading, writing, and ARITHMETIC, thought to be the very important base of a child's education 基本三技能〔指讀、寫、算,三者為兒童教育的重要基礎〕

rab·bi /ˈræbaɪ; ˈræbaɪ/ *n* a person who is a Jewish religious leader and teacher of Jewish law 拉拜〔猶太教領袖及猶太教法學的導師〕

rab·bit[1] /ˈræbɪt; ˈræbɪt/ *n* **1** [C] a small long-eared animal that lives in a hole in the ground 兔 **2** [U] the fur or meat obtained from a rabbit 兔的毛皮; 兔肉

rabbit[2] *v* **-tt-** (also 又作 **-t-** *AmE*〔美式〕)
rabbit on *phr v* [I] to talk continuously in an uninteresting way 嘮叨不休, 抱怨: *He keeps rabbiting on* **about** *his health.* 他沒完沒了地嘮叨自己的健康如何如何。

rab·ble /ˈræbl; ˈræbl̩/ *n* a noisy disorderly crowd of people 烏合之眾; 暴民

rabble-rous·ing /ˈ·· ˌ··/ *adj* encouraging a group of people to feel or do things which are uncontrolled and violent 煽動性的; 蠱惑人心的: *a rabble-rousing speech* 煽動性的演說

rab·id /ˈræbɪd; ˈræbɪd/ *adj* **1** infected with rabies (患)狂犬病的: *a rabid dog* 瘋狗 **2** [only before a noun 只用於名詞前] unreasonably violent or strong in your opinions, particularly about politics 〔尤指政治觀點上〕狂熱的; 偏激的: *a rabid conservative* 過激的保守黨人

ra·bies /ˈreɪbiz; ˈreɪbiːz/ *n* [U] a disease of humans and certain animals, particularly dogs, which causes madness and death 狂犬病

★**race**[1] /res; reɪs/ *n* **1** [C] a competition to see which person, vehicle, or animal is the fastest 〔速度的〕賽跑; 賽船; 賽車等: *Who won the race?* 誰贏了這場比賽? | *Let's have a race!* 我們進行賽跑吧! | *a boat race* 賽船 **2 a race against time** an attempt to do or finish something in a limited amount of time 和時間賽跑; 趕時間: *We had to get her to hospital before the baby was born! It was a race against time.* 我們得在嬰兒出生以前把她送到

醫院! 這是和時間賽跑。 **3 the races** [pl] an occasion when people go to a racecourse to watch horses racing 賽馬會: *She won a lot of money at the races.* 她在賽馬會上贏了一大筆錢。 **4** [C] a struggle for power or control between people or countries 〔力量或指揮力的〕競爭; 競賽: *the arms race* 軍備競賽 **5** [C;U] any of the groups into which human beings can be divided according to physical type 人種; 種族: *the black races* 黑色人種 | *the Mongolian race* 蒙古人種 | *The law forbids discrimination on grounds of race or religion.* 法律禁止以種族區別或宗教信仰為理由實行歧視。 **6** [C] a group of people with the same history, language, and customs 〔具有相同歷史、語言和風俗習慣的〕民族: *the German race* 日耳曼民族

race[2] *v* **raced, racing 1** [I;T] to compete in a race 賽跑; 參加比賽: *She's a very good swimmer and often races.* 她是個出色的游泳選手, 經常參加比賽。 | *I'll race you to the end of the road.* 我來和你比賽一下, 看誰先跑到路的盡頭。 **2** [T] to make an animal or vehicle run a race 使〔動物或車輛〕參加比賽: *My horse has hurt his leg so I can't race him.* 我的馬傷了腿, 所以沒法讓牠參加比賽。 **3** [I+adv/prep;T+adv/prep] to go very fast or take someone somewhere very fast 使疾走; 使迅跑: *She raced off to get milk before the shop closed.* 她趕在商店關門前飛奔著去拿牛奶。 | *We raced the sick woman to hospital.* 我們急忙把那生病的女人送到醫院。 | *The holidays raced by.* 假日一眨眼就過去了。 **4** [I] (of your heart) to beat very fast 〔心臟〕疾跳

race·course /ˈresˌkɔrs; ˈreɪs-kɔːs/ *n* a track which horses race around 賽馬跑道; 賽馬場

race·horse /ˈresˌhɔrs; ˈreɪshɔːs/ *n* a horse specially bred and trained for racing 比賽用的馬

race re·la·tions /ˌ·· ·ˈ··/ *n* [pl] the behaviour of different groups of people in a society towards each other 種族關係

race·track /ˈresˌtræk; ˈreɪs-træk/ *n* a course which runners, vehicles, or horses race around 〔賽跑、賽車、賽馬用的〕跑道

ra·cial /ˈreʃəl; ˈreɪʃl̩/ *adj* **1** connected with the group of people to which someone belongs 人種的; 種族的: *racial pride* 種族優越感 | *racial origins* 種族起源 **2** existing or happening between different races of people 〔存在或發於〕種族之間的: *racial discrimination* 種族歧視 | *racial harmony* 種族和諧 **3 racial prejudice** unreasonable dislike of people of other races 種族偏見

ra·cial·is·m /ˈreʃəlˌɪzəm; ˈreɪʃəlɪzəm/ n see 見 RACISM

ra·cial·ly /ˈreʃəli; ˈreɪʃəli/ adv concerning the group of people to which someone belongs 種族上; 人種上: *Racially, there is no difference between the two nations.* 在人種上, 這兩個國家沒有區別。| *a racially mixed population* 種族混雜的人口

rac·ing /ˈresɪŋ; ˈreɪsɪŋ/ adj [only before a noun 只用於名詞前] used for racing in competitions 賽跑用的; 比賽用的: *a racing car* 賽車 | *a racing pigeon* 賽鴿; 競飛鴿

rac·ism /ˈresɪzəm; ˈreɪsɪzəm/ n (also 又作 **racialism**) [U] **1** the belief that some races of people are better than others 種族主義 **2** dislike of people or unfair treatment of people because they belong to a particular race 種族偏見, 種族歧視 −**racist** adj, n: *a racist attack* 出於種族主義的攻擊

rack¹ /ræk; ræk/ n **1** a frame or shelf with bars or hooks for holding or hanging things 擱物架; 掛物架: *He washed the dishes and put them in the plate rack to dry.* 他把碟子洗好, 放在盤碟架上晾乾。| *a luggage rack* 行李架 | *shops full of racks of clothes* 衣架上掛滿衣服的商店 **2 the rack** an instrument used in the past to cause great pain to people by stretching them on a frame 〔舊時的〕拉肢刑架 **3 rack and ruin** the ruined state of a building caused by lack of care 〔因不注意保養而造成的〕破壞, 毀壞: *The house went to rack and ruin after they moved out.* 他們搬走後, 這幢房子變得破敗不堪。

rack² v **1 be racked by/with** lit to suffer great pain or anxiety because of 〖文〗因…而深受痛苦; 受折磨: *He was racked by doubts.* 他深受疑慮的折磨。 **2 rack your brains** infml to think very hard about something 〖非正式〗苦思冥想, 絞盡腦汁

rack·et /ˈrækɪt; ˈrækɪt/ n **1** [C] (also 又作 **racquet**) a light frame with a handle across which strings are stretched; it is used for hitting the ball in various games such as tennis 〔網球等的〕球拍 **2** [sing] infml a loud noise 〖非正式〗喧嚷; 吵鬧聲: *Stop making such a racket! I can't sleep.* 別再這麼吵吵嚷嚷的! 我沒法睡覺了。 **3** [C] a dishonest way of getting money 勒索; 敲詐; 詐騙

rack·e·teer /ˌrækɪˈtɪr; ˌrækɪˈtɪə/ n someone who gets money in a dishonest or illegal way 敲詐勒索者; 詐騙者

rac·on·teur /ˌrækɒnˈtɜː; ˌrækɒnˈtɜː/ n someone who is good at telling stories in an amusing and interesting way 擅長講故事的人

rac·quet /ˈrækɪt; ˈrækɪt/ n see 見 RACKET

rac·y /ˈresi; ˈreɪsi/ adj **racier, raciest** amusing, full of life, and often dealing with sex (used of speech and writing) 近乎猥褻的〔指語言和文字〕: *Paul shocked the priest with his racy stories.* 保羅講的下流故事使神父大為震驚。

ra·dar /ˈredɑr; ˈreɪdɑːʳ/ n [U] a method of finding the position and speed of ships and aircraft by using radio waves 雷達

ra·di·ance /ˈrediəns; ˈreɪdiəns/ n [U] the quality of being radiant 發光; 發熱; 容光煥發

ra·di·ant /ˈrediənt; ˈreɪdiənt/ adj **1** [only before a noun 只用於名詞前] shining brightly 明亮照耀的; 光輝燦爛的: *the radiant sun* 光芒四射的太陽 **2** showing love, hope, or happiness in your face so that you look very attractive 容光煥發的; 喜氣洋洋的: *The bride was radiant with joy.* 新娘高興得容光煥發。− **radiantly** adv

ra·di·ate /ˈrediˌet; ˈreɪdieɪt/ v **radiated, radiating** [T] **1** to send out light or heat 發射〔光、熱〕: *a fire radiating warmth* 散發出熱量的火爐 **2** to express a good quality or feeling in your appearance or behaviour 流露; 煥發; 顯示: *Jenny absolutely radiates confidence.* 珍妮顯示出信心十足的樣子。

radiate from sth phr v [T] to come out in all directions from a central point 從〔中心〕發散: *a system of roads radiating from the town centre* 從市中心伸展出去的道路系統

ra·di·a·tion /ˌrediˈeʃən; ˌreɪdiˈeɪʃən/ n [U] **1** the giving or sending out of heat or light 〔光或熱的〕放射, 輻射 **2** amounts of RADIOACTIVITY which can seriously harm you if you are not protected against them 放射線; 輻射能: *the effects of nuclear radiation* 核輻射的影響

ra·di·a·tor /ˈrediˌetə; ˈreɪdieɪtəʳ/ n **1** an apparatus, consisting of pipes with steam or hot water passing through them, which is used for heating buildings 暖氣設備; 取暖裝置 **2** an apparatus which keeps the engine of a motor vehicle cool 〔汽車發動機的〕散熱器

★**rad·i·cal¹** /ˈrædɪkl; ˈrædɪkəl/ adj **1** thorough, complete, and at the most basic level 徹底的; 完全的; 根本的: *The government made radical improvements to the tax system.* 政府對稅收制度作了徹底的改進。 **2** in favour of rapid and great political change 激進的: *a radical priest* 激進的神父 | *radical views* 激進的觀點 −**radically** /-klɪ; -kli/ adv

radical² n a person who believes in rapid and great social and political changes 激進分子 −**radicalism** n [U]

rad·i·i /ˈrediˌaɪ; ˈreɪdiaɪ/ n the plural of RADIUS ☆ RADIUS 的複數形式

★**ra·di·o¹** /ˈrediˌo; ˈreɪdiəʊ/ n **1** [U] the sending or receiving of sounds through the air by electrical waves 無線電通訊: *Air traffic controllers were in radio contact with the ship.* 空中交通調度員通過無線電和這艘船保持聯絡。| *radio signals* 無線電信號 **2** [C] an apparatus to receive sounds broadcast in this way 無線電(設備); 收音機: *Turn on the* *radio.* 打開收音機。 –see picture on page 730 見 730 頁彩圖 **3 on the radio** broadcast by radio (無線電)廣播: *I heard it on the radio.* 我從廣播中聽到這件事。 | *Jean was on the radio again today.* 瓊今天又在播音了。 **4** [U] the radio broadcasting industry (無線電)廣播業: *Her first job was in radio.* 她的第一份工作是在廣播電台工作。 | *a radio play* 廣播劇

radio² *v* [I;T] to send a message by radio 用無線電發送(信息): *The ship radioed for help.* 這艘船發出無線電求救訊號。

ra·di·o·ac·tiv·i·ty /ˈreɪdɪˌoækˈtɪvɪtɪ; ˌreɪdɪəʊækˈtɪvɪ̥ti/ *n* [U] **1** the quality that some substances have of giving out a powerful and sometimes harmful force by breaking up atoms 放射(性) **2** the force given out in this way 放射線; 輻射能 –**radioactive** /-ˈæktɪv; -ˈæktɪv◂/ *adj*: *The train was carrying dangerous radioactive waste.* 這列火車在運載危險的放射性廢物。

ra·di·og·ra·phy /ˌreɪdɪˈɒɡrəfɪ; ˌreɪdɪˈɒɡrəfi/ *n* [U] the taking of photographs using x-rays (X-RAY), usually for medical reasons 〔常指醫用的〕X 光照相術 –**radiographer** *n*

ra·di·o·ther·a·py /ˈreɪdɪəʊˈθɛrəpɪ; ˌreɪdɪəʊ-ˈθerəpi/ *n* [U] the treatment of diseases by RADIOACTIVITY (2) 放射療法

rad·ish /ˈrædɪʃ; ˈrædɪʃ/ *n* a small strong-tasting red and white vegetable which is eaten raw 〔可生吃的紅色或白色的〕小蘿蔔 –see picture on page 504 見 504 頁彩圖

ra·di·um /ˈreɪdɪəm; ˈreɪdɪəm/ *n* [U] a rare white metal that has a high level of RADIOACTIVITY, and is used in the treatment of certain diseases 鐳

ra·di·us /ˈreɪdɪəs; ˈreɪdɪəs/ *n* **radii** /-dɪˌaɪ, -dɪaɪ/ **1** the distance of a straight line from the centre of a circle to its edge 〔圓的〕半徑 **2** a circular area which measures the same distance from a central point to its edges in all directions 半徑範圍: *The tax affects everyone within a ten-mile radius of the town.* 這項稅收涉及鎮上方圓十英里內的每個人。

R.A.F /ˌɑr e ˈɛf; ˌɑːr eɪ ˈef, *infml* 〔非正式〕 ræf; ræf/ *n* the Royal Air Force, the British airforce 〔英國〕皇家空軍: *Join the R.A.F.* 參加皇家空軍。

raf·fi·a /ˈræfɪə; ˈræfɪə/ *n* [U] the soft substance from a PALM tree, used for making hats, baskets, and mats 酒椰葉纖維〔用以編製帽子、籃子、蓆墊〕

raf·fle¹ /ˈræfl; ˈræfəl/ *n* a way of making money, especially for a good public purpose, by selling numbered tickets, some of which win prizes 〔尤指為慈善目的舉辦的〕對獎售物(活動): *He won a car in the raffle.* 他在對獎售物活動中贏得一輛汽車。 | *a raffle ticket* 對獎券

raffle² *v* **raffled, raffling** [T] to offer something as a prize in a raffle 在對獎售物活動

中以〔某物〕作獎品

raft /ræft; rɑːft/ *n* **1** a flat floating structure, usually made of pieces of wood or of barrels and used as a boat 木排; 木筏; 筏子 **2** (also 又作 **life raft**) a flat rubber boat that can be filled with air, for the use of passengers if a plane crashes or a ship sinks (橡皮充氣)救生筏

raf·ter /ˈræftɚ; ˈrɑːftə/ *n* one of the large sloping beams that hold up a roof 椽

rag /ræg; ræg/ *n* **1** [C;U] an old cloth 舊布: *He cleaned the machine with an oily rag.* 他用一塊有油污的舊布擦機器。 | *a piece of rag* 一塊舊布 **2 rags** [pl] torn old clothes 破舊衣服: *The beggar was dressed in rags.* 這乞丐衣衫襤褸。 **3** [C] *infml* a badly written newspaper 〔非正式〕(質量低劣的)報紙: *Why are you reading that rag?* 你怎麼看那種無聊的小報? **4 from rags to riches** from being very poor to being rich and successful 從赤貧走向巨富: *Her exceptional musical talent took her from rags to riches.* 她傑出的音樂才能使她從一貧如洗到家財萬貫。 **5 like a red rag to a bull** *BrE* likely to make someone very angry 〔英式〕像激怒公牛的紅布; 使(某人)怒不可遏: *Asking him to drive more carefully is like a red rag to a bull.* 叫他開車更小心都會使他暴跳如雷。 **6** [C] *BrE* a procession of college students through the streets on some particular day in the year, collecting money for a good public purpose 〔英式〕〔大學生一年一度為慈善事業而進行的〕募捐遊行

rag·a·muf·fin /ˈrægəˌmʌfɪn; ˈrægəˌmʌfɪ̥n/ *n lit* a dirty young child in torn clothes 〔文〕衣衫襤褸的髒小孩

rag·bag /ˈrægˌbæg; ˈrægbæg/ *n infml* a confused mixture of things which are different from each other 〔非正式〕雜七雜八的東西; 大雜燴: *His argument is a ragbag of disconnected facts.* 他的論據是一堆雜亂無章、互不相關的事實。

rage¹ /reɪdʒ; reɪdʒ/ *n* **1** [C;U] strong uncontrollable anger 狂怒, 盛怒: *The director's in a terrible rage.* 這董事勃然大怒。 | *The child wept with rage.* 這孩子氣得直哭。 **2 all the rage** *infml* fashionable and popular 〔非正式〕風靡, 流行: *Short hair is all the rage again.* 短髮又風靡起來。

rage² *v* **raged, raging** [I] **1** to feel extremely angry and to show this in your behaviour 發怒, 生氣: *He raged at their stupidity.* 他為他們的愚蠢大為光火。 **2** to spread or continue with great force or violence 流行; 盛行; 肆虐: *The disease raged through the city.* 這種疾病在全城迅速蔓延。 | *The argument over the new road is still raging.* 關於這條新道路的爭論仍然十分激烈。

rag·ged /ˈrægɪd; ˈrægɪ̥d/ *adj* **1** old and torn 破舊的: *a ragged shirt* 破爛的襯衣 **2** dressed in old torn clothes 衣衫襤褸的: *a ragged little boy* 衣衫襤褸的小男孩 **3** with uneven, rough edges 〔邊緣〕參差不齊的: *a ragged beard* 亂蓬蓬的鬍子 **4** imperfect and disorganized 不完善的; 雜亂無章的: *The musicians gave rather a ragged performance.* 那幾個音樂家的表演很差勁。–**raggedly** *adv* –**raggedness** *n* [U]

ra·ging /'redʒɪŋ; 'reɪdʒɪŋ/ *adj* very strong and severe 兇猛的; 嚴重的: *a raging thirst* 極度口渴

rag·time /'ræg,taɪm; 'ræɡtaɪm/ *n* [U] a type of music popular in the 1920's, of black US origin 雷格泰姆音樂〔一種起源於美國黑人的旋律, 流行於二十年代〕: *a ragtime band* 雷格泰姆樂隊

raid¹ /red; reɪd/ *n* **1** a sudden military attack in order to cause damage to the enemy 〔部隊的〕突然襲擊: *The fighter jets made a raid* **on** *the enemy camp.* 戰鬥機對敵營發動了襲擊。**2** an unexpected visit by the police, in search of criminals or illegal goods 〔警察對罪犯或贓物的〕查抄; 突擊搜捕: *Two million pounds' worth of drugs were discovered during a raid* **on** *a house in South London this morning.* 今天早晨警方在突襲查抄倫敦南區的一幢房子時, 發現了一批價值二百萬英鎊的毒品。**3** a secret or violent entering of a place to steal something 劫掠, 搶劫: *a bank raid* 搶劫銀行

raid² *v* [T] to visit or attack a place on a raid 搜捕; 襲擊: *Soldiers raided the village at dawn.* 士兵拂曉時襲擊了這村莊。–**raider** *n*

✭rail¹ /rel; reɪl/ *n* **1** [C] a fixed bar, used to hang things on or to support someone or something 橫杆; 扶手; 欄杆: *Keep your hand on the rail as you climb the steps.* 上樓梯時要扶住欄杆。| *a towel rail* 掛毛巾用的橫杆 **2** [C] one of the pair of metal bars fixed to the ground, along which a train runs 鐵路路軌: *Passengers must not cross the rails.* 乘客不准橫越鐵路路軌。**3** [U] the railway system 鐵路: *rail travel* 乘火車旅行 | *the rail strike* 鐵路(工人)罷工 **4** **by rail** by train 用火車: *The goods were sent by rail.* 這些貨物用火車運送。**5** **go off the rails** to start to behave in a strange, confused way 精神失常: *Since she lost her job, she seems to have gone off the rails.* 她自從失業以後, 精神似乎不正常了。

rail² *v* [I] *fml* to complain angrily and noisily 〔正式〕對…強烈不滿; 抱怨: *Doctors railed* **against** *the increased costs of medicines.* 醫生抱怨藥費上漲。

rail·card /'rel,kɑrd; 'reɪlkɑ:d/ *n* a card which allows you to travel on trains more cheaply 火車月票

rail·ing /'relɪŋ; 'reɪlɪŋ/ *n* one of a set of rails making up a fence 圍欄, 欄杆: *The dog got its head stuck between the railings.* 那條狗的頭夾在欄杆中間了。

rail·road /'rel,rod; 'reɪlrəʊd/ *v* [T] **1** to hurry someone into doing something unwillingly 強使〔某人〕匆忙做〔某事〕: *The workers were railroaded into signing the*

agreement. 工人們被逼着匆忙地簽訂了協議。**2** to pass a law or carry out a plan quickly in spite of opposition 〔不顧反對〕草率地強行通過〔法律〕; 匆忙執行〔計劃〕: *The chairman railroaded the plan* **through** *the committee.* 主席草率地強使委員會通過這項計劃。

✭rail·way /'rel,we; 'reɪlweɪ/ *n* (also 又作 **railroad** *AmE* 〔美式〕) **1** (also 又作 **railway line** /'‥ ‥/) a track for trains to run on 鐵道, 鐵路: *They're building a new railway to the south.* 他們在修築一條通往南方的新鐵路。**2** (also 又作 **railways** [pl]) the organization that runs trains and stations 鐵路系統: *I'm a ticket collector on the railway.* 我是火車上的查票員。

✭rain¹ /ren; reɪn/ *n* **1** [U] water falling in separate drops from the clouds 雨: *The rain fell throughout the night.* 整晚都在下雨。| *She went out in the rain without a coat.* 她沒穿外衣就冒雨出去了。| *Heavy rain destroyed the plants.* 大雨摧毀了植物。**2** [sing] a thick fall of large quantities of something 〔雨點般的〕降落物: *The car was stopped by a rain of bullets.* 雨點般的子彈使得那輛汽車停了下來。**3 the rains** [pl] the season in tropical countries when rain falls continuously 〔熱帶地區的〕雨季: *The rains came early this year.* 那年雨季來得早。

rain² *v* **1 it is raining** = rain is falling 正在下雨: *It's raining.* 下雨了。| *It began to rain hard.* 開始下大雨了。**2 rain cats and dogs** *infml* to rain very heavily 〔非正式〕下傾盆大雨 **3 be rained off** to be stopped or prevented because of rain 因下雨而受阻〔中斷〕: *Last week's football match was rained off.* 上週的足球比賽因下雨而暫停舉行。

rain down *phr v* **1** [I] to be directed at someone 對準〔某人〕: *Insults rained down* **on** *him.* 他接二連三地受到侮辱。**2** [I;T **rain** sthg **↔ down**] to fall rapidly and in large amounts 大量傾瀉: *The army rained bullets down* **on** *the village.* 軍隊向村莊掃射。

■ USAGE 用法: With the verb **to rain** you can use the adverbs **heavily** or **hard** ☆副詞 **heavily** 或 **hard** 可以和動詞 **to rain** 連用: *It rained* **heavily** *all day.* 雨整天都下得很大。| *It's raining really* **hard** *now.* 雨現在下得真大。With the noun **rain** use the adjective **heavy** ☆形容詞 **heavy** 和名詞 **rain** 連用: *The bridge was washed away by* **heavy** *rain.* 橋被大雨沖走了。If there is not very much rain, you can say ☆如果雨不大, 可以說: *It's* **not** *raining* **very hard/heavily.** 雨下得不太大。| *A* **light** *rain was falling.* 正下着微雨。

rain·bow /'ren,bo; 'reɪnbəʊ/ *n* an arch of different colours that sometimes appears in the sky immediately after rain 虹, 彩虹

rain·coat /'ren,kot; 'reɪnkəʊt/ *n* a light coat

worn to protect yourself from rain 雨衣 – see picture on page 210 見 210 頁彩圖

rain·drop /ˈreɪnˌdrɒp; ˈreɪndrɒp/ n a single drop of rain 雨點, 雨滴

rain·fall /ˈreɪnˌfɔːl; ˈreɪnfɔːl/ n [C;U] the total amount of rain or snow that falls in an area in a particular period of time〔某一地區在某一時期內的〕降雨〔雪〕量

rain for·est /ˈ· ··/ n a wet tropical forest with tall trees growing thickly together (熱帶)雨林

rain·storm /ˈreɪnˌstɔːm; ˈreɪnstɔːm/ n a sudden heavy fall of rain 暴風雨

rain·y /ˈreɪni; ˈreɪni/ adj **1** having a lot of rain 多雨的: a very rainy day 多雨的日子 | Vancouver is a rainy city. 溫哥華是個多雨的城市。**2 for a rainy day** for a future time when something may be needed 以備不時之需; 未雨綢繆: Save your money for a rainy day. 存錢以備不時之需。

R☆☆raise[1] /reɪz; reɪz/ v **raised, raising** [T] **1** to lift or move something to a higher position 舉起, 提起〔某物〕: He raised the lid of the box. 他揭起了箱蓋。| She raised her finger to her lips as a sign for silence. 她把一個手指舉到唇邊, 示意保持安靜。–see 見 RISE[1] (USAGE 用法) **2** to increase in amount, degree, or size 增加; 增大: Our rent's just been raised again. 我們的房租剛剛又給增加了。| This radiator automatically raises the temperature. 這暖氣裝置能自動提升溫度。**3 raise someone's hopes** to make someone feel hopeful that something will happen, when often it will not 喚起某人的希望〔通常並不能實現〕**4 raise your voice** to speak loudly and angrily 提高嗓門〔指大聲而生氣地說〕**5 raise yourself to your full height** to stretch your body so that you are standing very tall 站得筆直 **6** to manage to get or collect an amount of money 籌集, 募集: They're raising money for charity. 他們正進行慈善籌款。| I raised £500 by selling my car. 我把自己的汽車賣掉, 籌了五百英鎊。**7** to look after a child until it is an adult 撫養, 養育〔孩子〕: They finally got married and raised six children. 他們最終結婚了, 並養育了六個孩子。**8** to breed animals or grow crops 飼養〔動物〕; 種植〔農作物〕: They raise chickens on this farm. 他們在這個農場養雞。**9** to mention something to be talked about or given attention 提到, 提及〔某事物〕: There's an important point I want to raise. 我想提出重要的一點。**10** to cause people to do or feel something 引起: His joke raised a laugh. 他的笑話引起一片笑聲。| His long absense raised fears about his safety. 他久未露面使人們對他的安全擔心起來。| That smell raises memories of hot summer days. 那種氣味喚起了我對炎炎夏日的回憶。**11** to make something appear 使〔某事物〕出現: The car raised a cloud of dust as it rushed by. 汽車開過時揚

起了一陣塵土。

■ USAGE 用法: **Raise** and **bring up** can both be used to mean "look after and be responsible for children until they become adults". ☆**raise** 和 **bring up** 都可用來指"把孩子撫養成人": My grandmother **raised/brought up** a family of ten single-handed. 我的祖母一人把家裡的十個孩子撫養成人。Note, however, that in British English **bring up** is more commonly used if you want to talk about the process of looking after children and the way in which this happens ☆但是注意, 在英式英語中, 如果想談論照料孩子的過程及其方法, **bring up** 更常用: Bringing up children is never easy. 養育孩子從來就不容易。| She's devoted the last ten years to bringing up her daughters. 她最近十年來一心一意地養育幾個女兒。| We were brought up to respect our elders. 我們受過教養, 要尊敬長者。| a very well brought-up little boy 很有教養的小男孩

raise[2] n AmE an increase in wages〔美式〕加薪: He asked his boss for a raise. 他向老闆要求加薪。

rai·sin /ˈreɪzən; ˈreɪzən/ n a dried GRAPE used in cooking or eaten raw 葡萄乾

rake[1] /reɪk; reɪk/ n **1** a garden tool consisting of a row of metal points at the end of a long handle; it is used for making the soil level or gathering up dead leaves〔長柄帶齒的〕耙 –see picture on page 958 見 958 頁彩圖 **2** old fash a man, especially a rich one, who has had many sexual relations with women and drinks too much〔老式〕浪蕩子; 酒色之徒

rake[2] v **raked, raking 1** [I;T] to use a rake to make the ground smooth, loosen the soil, or collect leaves〔用耙子〕耙: He raked the garden paths. 他耙平了花園的小徑。| They raked up the dead leaves. 他們把枯葉耙成一堆。**2** [I+adv/prep] to search quite carefully, but rather quickly through a pile of things〔仔細而又飛快地〕搜尋: She raked through her papers to see if she could find it. 她在自己的文稿中翻尋, 看能否找到它。

rake sth ↔ **in** phr v [T] infml to earn a lot of money〔非正式〕賺大錢: He must be raking in at least £500 a week! 他一星期肯定至少賺五百英鎊! | They're absolutely raking it in! 他們絕對是在大發其財!

rake sth ↔ **up** phr v [T] infml to talk about something and remind people of something unpleasant that happened in the past〔非正式〕翻出〔不愉快的舊事〕, 重提: Please don't rake up that old quarrel again. 請不要再提過去那次爭吵了。

rake-off /ˈ· ·/ n infml a dishonest share of profits〔非正式〕〔以不正當手段獲得的〕回扣:

The taxi-driver gets a rake-off from the hotel if he takes travellers there. 這個計程車司機如果把旅遊者帶到那家旅館, 就能拿到回扣。

ral·ly¹ /'ræli; 'ræli/ *v* **rallied, rallying 1** [I;T] to come or bring together to give support for a shared purpose 〔為共同目的〕集合: *The general rallied his tired soldiers and they drove the enemy back.* 將軍讓疲憊的士兵重整旗鼓, 終於擊退了敵軍。| *Her colleagues rallied to her defence when she was fired.* 她遭解雇時, 同事都團結起來為她辯護。**2** [I] to become stronger after illness or other difficulties 〔在患病或受挫後〕恢復; 復元; 重新振作: *Prices on the stock market rallied after yesterday's falls.* 股票價格在昨天下跌後又回升了。

　rally round *phr v* [I;T **rally round** sbdy] *infml* to come together as a group to support someone 〖非正式〗團結起來支持〔某人〕: *Her friends all rallied round when she was ill.* 她生病時朋友都來幫助她。| *The teachers all rallied round the headmaster.* 教師都團結起來支持校長。

rally² *n* **rallies 1** a large public meeting to support a cause or political party (羣眾)集會 **2** a motor race over public roads 公路賽車, 汽車拉力賽 **3** a long struggle in tennis and similar games, with each player trying to win a point by hitting the ball again and again 〔網球等為爭奪一分而進行的〕長時間持續對打, 拉鋸戰

ram¹ /ræm; ræm/ *n* **1** [C] a fully grown male sheep 成年公羊 **2** [C] any machine that uses a weight to push or force things into a particular position 衝壓機 **3 RAM** [U] a computer memory holding information that is needed by the computer for a limited period, and that can be searched in any order you like; an abbreviation for Random-Access Memory 〖縮〗隨機存取記憶體

ram² *v* **-mm- 1** [I + adv/prep; T] to crash into something very forcefully 猛撞; 猛擊: *His car rammed into a large tree.* 他的汽車猛撞到一棵大樹上。**2** [T + adv/prep] to force into place with heavy pressure 猛壓, 壓實; 硬塞: *He rammed the stick into the hole.* 他把棍子埋實在洞裡。**3 ram something home** to force people to recognize or accept something 迫使承認或接受某事物: *The attack on the military base rammed home the need for tighter security.* 這次對軍事基地的襲擊使人痛感有必要採取更嚴密的安全措施。

Ram·a·dan /ˌræmə'dɑn; 'ræmədæn/ *n* the 9th month of the Muslim year, during which no food or drink may be taken between sunrise and sunset 賴買丹月, 齋戒月〔伊斯蘭教曆的第九個月, 該月內每日在日出到日落禁食〕

ram·ble¹ /'ræmbl; 'ræmbəl/ *v* **rambled, rambling 1** [I; + adv/prep] to go on a long walk in the country for pleasure 〔在鄉間進行的〕散步: *They rambled through the woods.* 他們在林間漫步。**2** [I] to talk in a disordered way without keeping to the subject 漫談; 聊天: *Since her operation she seems to ramble a lot.* 自從手術以後, 她好像常常和人閒聊。**3 ramble on** to talk or write for a long time in a disordered way 漫無邊際地閒扯[胡寫]: *He's always rambling on about his life in India.* 他總是漫無邊際地閒談着他在印度的生活。

ramble² *n* a long country walk taken for enjoyment 〔在鄉間的〕閒逛; 漫步: *We went for a ramble along the river.* 我們沿着河邊漫步。

ram·bler /'ræmblə; 'ræmblɚ/ *n* someone who goes on long walks in the country 閒遊者; 漫步者

ram·bling /'ræmblɪŋ; 'ræmblɪŋ/ *adj* **1** disordered and confused (used of speech or writing) 散漫的; 不連貫的〔指講話或文章〕: *a long and rambling letter* 一封冗長而雜亂無章的信 **2** of irregular shape and spreading over a large area 凌亂的; 蔓延的: *a rambling old house* 一幢大而無當的舊房子

ram·i·fi·ca·tion /ˌræməfə'keʃən, ˌræmɪfɪ-'keɪʃən/ *n fml* a result or effect of an action or decision which is not always clear at first 〖正式〗衍生結果; 派生影響: *I think we should consider the ramifications of this decision very carefully.* 我認為我們應該十分仔細地考慮這個決定將引起的後果。

ramp /ræmp; ræmp/ *n* an artificial slope that connects two levels 人造斜坡; 坡道: *Drive the car up the ramp.* 把汽車開上坡道。

ram·page¹ /ræm'peɪdʒ; ræm'peɪdʒ/ *v* **rampaged, rampaging** [I + adv/prep] to rush about wildly and violently 橫衝直撞: *The elephants rampaged through the forest.* 象羣橫衝直撞地穿過森林。

ram·page² /'ræmpeɪdʒ; 'ræmpeɪdʒ/ *n* **on the rampage** rushing about behaving wildly and violently 橫衝直撞; 狂暴地: *During the match, some supporters went on the rampage.* 比賽進行中, 一些支持者橫衝直撞地大鬧。

ram·pant /'ræmpənt; 'ræmpənt/ *adj* widespread and impossible to control (used of crime, disease, and false beliefs) 猖獗的, 不可控制的〔指犯罪、疾病或錯誤的信仰〕: *Malaria was rampant in that area.* 那個地區瘧疾流行。**—rampantly** *adv*

ram·part /'ræmpɑrt; 'ræmpɑːt/ *n* (also 又作 **ramparts** [pl]) a wide bank of earth or a stone wall built to protect a fort or city 〔保護城堡或城市的〕防禦土牆; 堤壘

ram·rod /'ræm,rɑd; 'ræmrɒd/ *n* **stiff/ straight as a ramrod** extremely stiff or straight in the way you walk or stand 〔走路或站立〕挺直的; 筆直的: *The soldier stood as stiff as a ramrod while waiting for his orders.* 這名士兵在等候命令時站得筆直。

ram·shack·le /'ræmʃækl; 'ræmʃækəl/ *adj* almost falling to pieces (used of a building or vehicle) 搖搖欲墜的〔指建築物或車輛〕: *a ramshackle old house* 一幢搖搖欲墜的老房子

ran /ræn; ræn/ the past tense of RUN ☆ RUN 的過去式

ranch /rɑːntʃ; rɑːntʃ/ *n* a very large farm in the US and Canada where sheep, cattle, or horses are bred 〔美國、加拿大的〕大牧場; 大農場

ranch·er /ˈrɑːntʃə; ˈrɑːntʃər/ *n* a person who owns or works on a ranch 大牧場〔農場〕主; 大牧場〔農場〕工人

ran·cid /ˈrænsɪd; ˈrænsɪd/ *adj* not fresh and with an unpleasant taste or smell (used of fatty food) 不新鮮的; 〔滋味或氣味〕酸臭的〔指油脂食物〕: *rancid butter* 變質黃油 | *a rancid taste* 腐臭味

ran·cour /ˈræŋkə; ˈræŋkər/ *n* (**rancor** *AmE* 〖美式〗) [U] *fml* a feeling of bitter, unforgiving hatred towards someone 〔正式〕深仇, 積怨 –**rancorous** *adj* –**rancorously** *adv*

rand /rænd; rænd/ *n* [plural is 複數為 **rand**] the standard money unit of South Africa, divided into 100 cents 蘭特〔南非貨幣單位, 等於100分〕

ran·dom[1] /ˈrændəm; ˈrændəm/ *adj* done or chosen without any plan, aim, or pattern 隨便的; 任意的; 胡亂的: *He fired a few random shots.* 他亂放了幾槍。 | *They need a random sample of people for the experiment.* 他們需要隨機抽樣挑出一羣人來做這項實驗。 –**randomly** *adv*

random[2] *n* **at random** without any plan, aim, or pattern 隨便地; 任意地; 胡亂地: *He chose a few people at random.* 他隨便選了幾個人。

rand·y /ˈrændɪ; ˈrændɪ/ *adj slang* full of sexual desire 〖俚〗好色的; 性慾衝動的 –**randiness** *n* [U]

rang /ræŋ; ræŋ/ the past tense of RING ☆ RING 的過去式

⭐range[1] /reɪndʒ; reɪndʒ/ *n* **1** [sing; U] the distance that a gun or other weapon can fire or within which an apparatus can operate effectively 〔槍砲的〕射程: *He shot the rabbit at close range.* 他在近距離內射中了這隻兔子。 | *medium-range nuclear weapons* 中程核武器 | *This radio transmitter only has a range of a few miles.* 這台無線電發射機的量程只有幾英里。 **2 within range** near enough to see, hear, or hit 在聽〔看〕得到的範圍內; 在射程內: *Shout as soon as she comes within range.* 等她一走到聽得見的地方, 你就叫喊。 [RELATED PHRASE 相關詞組 **out of range**] **3** [sing] the measurable limits within which something varies 變動範圍; 變化幅度: *Several cars are available within the price range.* 在這個價格範圍內能買到這幾種車。 | *I'm afraid that high note is beyond my range.* 很抱歉, 那個高音我唱不上去。 | *an age range of between 25 and 35 years old* 年齡介乎二十五歲到三十五歲之間 **4** [sing] the limits of what something

includes 範圍: *This decision lies outside the range of my responsibility.* 這項決定不在我的職責範圍之內。 **5** [sing] a group of different things which are of the same general type 一系列: *The talks will consider a range of topics important to both countries.* 這次會談將要考慮到兩國都很重要的一系列話題。 | *She uses a range of techniques to help her patients to relax.* 她採用了一系列方法來幫助病人放鬆。 **6** [C] a set of different products of the same kind sold by a shop or made by a company 系列商品; 成套產品: *We sell a wide range of gardening tools.* 我們出售門類齊全的成套園藝工具。 **7** [C] a connected line of mountains or hills 〔山脈、山丘等的〕連續, 綿亙: *The lake is to the north of a high mountain range.* 這片湖在一條高山山脈的左面。 **8** [C] an area where shooting is practised 靶場; 射擊場: *a rifle range* 步槍射擊場 **9 the range** a wide stretch of grassy land in North America where cattle feed 〔北美的〕放牧場

⭐range[2] *v* **ranged**, **ranging** **1** [I not in progressive forms 不用於進行式] to vary between particular limits 〔在一定範圍內〕變化: *The children's ages range from 5 to 15.* 孩子們的年齡在五到十五歲之間。 | *The pay ranges from £5 to £7 an hour.* 報酬每小時從五至七英鎊不等。 | *Her hobbies range from cooking to cycling.* 她的愛好從烹飪到騎腳踏車, 範圍很廣。 **2** [I] (of writing or speech) to be concerned with or include 〔文章或講話〕論及, 涉及: *Our conversation ranged over many subjects.* 我們的談話涉及很多問題。 **3** [I + adv/prep] *lit* to wander freely without a fixed purpose 〔文〕〔無固定目的地〕漫遊, 徘徊: *We ranged through deserted countryside.* 我們在荒僻的鄉間漫遊。 **4** [T+adv/prep] to arrange in rows 排列, 把…排成行: *She ranged the goods neatly in the shop window.* 她把貨物整齊地排放在商店的櫥窗裡。 | *Soldiers were ranged along the walls.* 士兵沿着牆排列成行。

rang·er /ˈreɪndʒə; ˈreɪndʒər/ *n* **1** a person who is responsible for looking after a forest or park 護林員; 公園管理員 **2** a policeman in North America who works in a country area on horseback 〔北美的〕巡邏騎警

⭐rank[1] /ræŋk; ræŋk/ *n* **1** [C;U] an official position in an organization, especially the armed forces 〔尤指軍隊裡的〕軍階, 軍銜; 官階; 職銜: *He reached the rank of general before he was 40.* 他四十歲以前獲得了將軍的軍階。 | *officers of high rank* 軍銜高的軍官 **2** [C] a line of people or things 〔人或事物的〕行, 列, 排: *Rank upon rank of ancient trees stretched to the horizon.* 一排排的古樹一直向天際延伸。 **3 join the ranks of** to become a member of a particular group of people 成為〔某一羣人中的〕一員: *She's joined the ranks of the unemployed.* 她加入了失業者的

行列[失業大軍]. **4 the ranks** [pl] the ordinary people in the armed forces and other organizations as opposed to those in high positions 士兵; 普通成員: *He rose from the ranks to become a colonel.* 他由普通士兵晉升成為上校. **5** [C;U] *old fash* social class 〖老式〗社會階層: *People of all ranks attended the ceremony.* 各階層的人都來參加典禮.

rank² *v* [I;T] to have, or to regard as having, a particular position on a scale 把...分等; 給...評定等級: *The city ranks as one of the most polluted in the country.* 這個城市被列為該國污染最嚴重的城市之一. | *a tennis-player ranked third in the world* 世界排名第三的網球選手

rank³ *adj* **1** too thick and widespread (used of a plant) 過於繁茂的; 茂盛叢生的〔指植物〕: *rank grass* 叢生的雜草 **2** very strong and unpleasant in taste or smell 〔味道或氣味〕惡臭難聞的: *rank tobacco* 難聞的煙草味 **3** [only before a noun 只用於名詞前] complete or extreme (used especially of bad qualities) 不折不扣的; 十足的〔尤指壞品質〕: *rank bad luck* 糟透的運氣 | *rank stupidity* 絕頂的愚蠢 | *The race was won by a rank outsider.* 這場比賽被一個完全不起眼的人贏了.

rank and file /ˌ·'··/ *n* **the rank and file** [+ sing/pl verb] the ordinary members of an organization as opposed to the leaders 〔某組織中與領導人相對而言的〕普通成員: *The rank and file refused to accept the committee's decision.* 會員都拒絕接受委員會的決定.

ran·kle /'ræŋkl; 'ræŋkəl/ *v* **rankled, rankling** [I] to continue to be remembered with bitterness and anger 〔回憶時〕激起怨恨, 氣忿不已: *His rudeness to me still rankles.* 他對我的粗暴無禮使我仍然怨恨難消.

ran·sack /'rænsæk; 'rænsæk/ *v* [T] **1** to search a place or building thoroughly and roughly 徹底搜索, 仔細搜查: *The police ransacked the house looking for drugs.* 警察翻箱倒櫃地搜查了這房子, 想找出毒品來. **2** to go through a place stealing and causing damage 洗劫, 劫掠: *The town was ransacked by enemy soldiers.* 這個鎮被敵軍洗劫一空.

ran·som /'rænsəm; 'rænsəm/ *n* **1** a sum of money paid to free someone who is held illegally as a prisoner 贖金: *The boy's family paid a large ransom to the kidnappers.* 這男孩的家人給綁架者付了一大筆贖金. **2 hold someone to ransom** to keep someone prisoner and demand to be given money before you will let them go 綁某人的票; 擄某人以索取贖金: *The terrorists kidnapped a priest and held him to ransom.* 恐怖分子綁架了一名牧師, 索取贖金. **–ransom** *v* [T]

rant /rænt; rænt/ *v* [I] to talk in a loud, excited, and angry way 怒氣沖沖地叫嚷; 大聲激昂地說: *The priest ranted on about the devil and all his works.* 牧師慷慨激昂地譴責

魔鬼及他的種種罪惡. | *He's ranting and raving about the way they treated him.* 他在大叫大嚷地講述他們是怎麼對待他的. **–ranting** *n*

rap¹ /ræp; ræp/ *n* **1** a quick light hit or knock 輕敲; 急拍: *I heard a rap on the door.* 我聽見輕輕的敲門聲. **2 take the rap** *infml* to be punished for something even if you did not do it 〖非正式〗〔即使沒責任也〕受罰; 代罪

rap² *v* **-pp-** [I+adv/prep; T+adv/prep] to hit quickly and lightly 輕敲; 急拍: *She rapped her pen on the table and called for silence.* 她用筆輕敲桌子, 要求大家肅靜.

rap out sthg *phr v* [T] to say sharply and suddenly 厲聲急促地說: *The officer rapped out an order.* 軍官厲聲發出了命令.

ra·pa·cious /rə'peɪʃəs; rə'peɪʃəs/ *adj fml* having an extremely strong desire to have a lot of something, especially money 〖正式〗貪婪的; 貪得無厭的: *a rapacious businessman* 貪婪的商人 **–rapaciously** *adv* **–rapacity** /rə'pæsəti; rə'pæsˌti/ *n* [U]

rape¹ /reɪp; reɪp/ *v* **raped, raping** [T] (of a man) to violently force a woman to have sex when she does not want to 強姦〔女子〕

rape² *n* **1** [C;U] the act or crime of raping someone 強姦(案): *He was sent to prison for rape.* 他因犯強姦罪而入獄. | *a rape victim* 遭強姦者 **2** [sing] *fml* spoiling or destruction 〖正式〗蹂躪; 破壞: *the rape* of *our beautiful forests* 對我們美麗森林的破壞 **3** [U] a plant grown as animal food and for oil 油菜

⋆rap·id /'ræpɪd; 'ræpˌd/ *adj* with great speed 快的, 迅速的: *The patient's recovery was rapid.* 病人復原得很快. | *The school promised rapid results in the learning of languages.* 這所學校保證(學員)能在語言學習方面迅速取得成效. | *a rapid growth in population* 人口的迅速增長 **–rapidly** *adv*: *the rapidly changing world of computer technology* 迅速變化的電腦技術領域 **–rapidity** /rə'pɪdəti; rə'pɪdˌti/ *n* [U]

rap·ids /'ræpɪds; 'ræpˌds/ *n* [pl] a part of a river where the water moves very fast over rocks 急流; 湍灘

ra·pi·er /'reɪpɪə; 'reɪpɪə'/ *n* a long thin sharp sword 輕劍

rap·ist /'reɪpɪst; 'reɪpˌst/ *n* a man guilty of forcing a woman to have sex with him 強姦犯

rap·port /ræ'pɔrt; ræ'pɔ:; / *n* [U] close and sympathetic understanding of someone's feelings or opinions 意見一致; 融洽; 和諧: *a teacher who has an excellent rapport with her class* 和她的學生關係極為融洽的老師

rap·proche·ment /raprɒʃ'mɑ̃; ræ'prɒʃmɒŋ/ *n fml* an increase in friendship between countries, groups, or people who were enemies 〖正式〗〔國家、組織或個人之間〕重修舊好, 恢復友好關係: *At last there are signs of a rapprochement between our two countries.*

R

我們兩國終於有了重新和好的跡象。

rapt /ræpt; ræpt/ *adj* so interested in something that you do not notice anything else 專心致志的, 全神貫注的: *We listened to the song with rapt attention.* 我們全神貫注地聽這首歌。

rap·ture /ˈræptʃə; ˈræptʃɚ/ *n fml* 【正式】 **1** [U] great joy and delight 狂喜: *He stared with rapture at his baby son.* 他欣喜若狂地盯着自己剛出生的兒子。 **2 go into raptures** to feel or express great delight about something 〔對某事物〕欣喜若狂: *They went into raptures about their new house.* 新房子令他們欣喜萬分。 –**rapturous** *adj: a rapturous welcome* 狂熱的歡迎 –**rapturously** *adv*

☆**rare** /rɛr; reəʳ/ *adj* **rarer, rarest 1** very unusual or uncommon 稀有的; 罕見的: *a rare disease* 罕見的疾病 | *It's very rare for him to be late.* 他很少遲到。 **2** unusually good in quality 極好的; 出類拔萃的: *his rare talent for learning languages* 他在學習語言方面出類拔萃的才能 **3** thin, with less oxygen than usual (used of air) 稀薄的〔指空氣〕: *the rare air of the mountains* 山上稀薄的空氣 **4** lightly cooked so that it is still red (used of meat) 煮得嫩的〔指肉〕 –compare 比較 WELL-DONE

■ USAGE 用法: Compare 比較 **rare** and 和 **scarce**. We use **rare** for things that are uncommon, and perhaps valuable ☆ **rare** 用於指罕見而可能有價值的東西: *a rare bird/a rare coin* 珍禽/罕見的錢幣。 We use **scarce** for ordinary useful things when we have not got enough of them ☆**scarce** 用於指一般有用而又不充足的東西: *Potatoes were scarce last winter.* 去年冬天馬鈴薯很少。 We can use **rare**, but not **scarce**, about time ☆表示時間可用 **rare**, 但不可用 **scarce**: *one of my rare* (= not happening often) *visits to Paris* 我難得幾次去巴黎觀光中的一次(=不常發生的)

rar·e·fied /ˈrɛrəfaɪd; ˈreərɪ͵faɪd/ *adj* **1** thin and with less oxygen than usual (used of air) 〔空氣〕稀薄的 **2** separate from ordinary people because of wealth, high social position, or cleverness 〔因有財富, 社會地位高或聰明而〕脫離大眾的, 小圈子的: *He moves in very rarefied circles; his friends are all lords.* 他只在非常小的圈子裡活動, 他的朋友盡是貴族。

rare·ly /ˈrɛrli; ˈreəli/ *adv* not at all often 很少, 難得, 不常: *Rarely has so much been achieved in such a short time.* 在這麼短的時間內取得如此成就實在難得。 | *She very rarely complains.* 她很少抱怨。

rar·ing /ˈrɛrɪŋ; ˈreərɪŋ/ *adj infml* 【非正式】 **1 raring to do something** very eager to do something 非常渴望做某事: *The children were raring to get out in the snow.* 孩子們渴望着到外面雪地裡去。 **2 raring to go** very keen to start 巴不得馬上開始: *Hurry up! We're raring to go.* 快點兒! 我們巴不得要走了。

rar·i·ty /ˈrɛrəti; ˈreərˌti/ *n* **rarities 1** [C] an uncommon or unusual thing 稀罕的東西; 珍品: *This type of flower is becoming something of a rarity.* 這種花逐漸變成珍品。 **2** [U] the quality of being very uncommon or unusual 稀有, 罕見: *rarity value* 珍奇

ras·cal /ˈræskl; ˈræskəl/ *n* **1** *old fash* a dishonest person 【老式】流氓; 無賴 **2** a child who misbehaves but with whom you are not really angry 小淘氣; 搗蛋鬼: *You little rascal! Where have you hidden my shoes?* 你這個小淘氣! 把我的鞋子藏到哪兒去了?

rash¹ /ræʃ; ræʃ/ *adj* acting foolishly because of not thinking enough of the possible results 魯莽的; 輕率的: *a rash decision* 草率的決定 | *I promised in a rash moment to take the children swimming.* 我未經考慮, 一時貿然答應帶孩子們去游泳。 –**rashly** *adv* – **rashness** *n* [U]

rash² *n* **1** [C] a lot of small red spots on your skin 皮疹, 疹子: *a heat rash* 熱疹 **2 come out in a rash** to become covered in a rash 出疹子: *When she eats strawberries, she comes out in a rash.* 她一吃草莓就出疹子。 **3** [sing] a number of events that happen suddenly in a short time 〔短時期內〕爆發的一連串事情: *We've had a rash of complaints at the office.* 我們辦公室裡一片抱怨聲。

rash·er /ˈræʃə; ˈræʃɚ/ *n* a thin piece of BACON 熏[鹹]肉片

rasp /rɑːsp; ræsp/ *v* [I] to make a rough unpleasant sound 發出刺耳聲: *The noise of their sawing rasped loudly in his ears.* 他們拉鋸的噪聲很大, 刺激着他的耳朵。 | *a rasping voice* 刺耳的嗓音

rasp·ber·ry /ˈræzˌbɛri; ˈrɑːzbəri/ *n* **raspberries 1** a soft sweet red berry 懸鈎子, 山莓: *a bowl of raspberries and cream* 一碗奶油山莓 –see picture on page 504 見 504 頁彩圖 **2** the bush this grows on 懸鈎子灌木 **3** *infml* a sound made by putting your tongue out and blowing; this expresses your low opinion of someone 【非正式】〔伸舌於唇外爆氣發出的〕吓聲〔表示輕蔑〕: *He blew a raspberry at the general.* 他發出吓吓聲來嘲笑那位將軍。

rat¹ /ræt; ræt/ *n* **1** a long-tailed animal related to but larger than a mouse 大老鼠 **2** *infml* a disloyal and deceiving person (a word which is often used in a humorous way) 【非正式】變節者, 判徒〔常含幽默〕: *But you promised to help us, you rat!* 可是你答應過幫助我們的, 你這言而無信的小人!

rat² *v* **-tt-** [I] *infml* to act in a disloyal way or break a promise 【非正式】變節; 背信棄義, 食言: *They said they'd help but they've ratted on us.* 他們說要幫忙, 但他們對我們食言了。

ratch·et /ˈrætʃɪt; ˈrætʃət/ *n* a toothed wheel

or bar fitted with a piece of metal that allows it to turn in one direction but not the other 棘輪; 棘齒條

rate¹ /reɪt/ *n* **1** [C] a quantity, such as a value, cost, or speed, measured by its relation to some other amount 比率, 率: *a drug with a high success rate in curing people* 治病成功率很高的藥 | *We drove at a steady rate.* 我們以平穩的速度駕車。 | *a fall in the rate of inflation* 通貨膨脹率的下降 **2** [C] a charge or payment fixed according to a standard scale〔依標準而定的〕收支款項, 費用: *They're demanding higher rates of pay.* 他們要求有更高的工資。 | *The interest rate has gone down.* 利率下降了。 **3 the rates** [pl] a local tax which was formerly paid by owners of buildings in Britain for locally provided services〔英國地方當局向房產主徵收的〕房地產稅 **4 at any rate: a** at least; used when you are giving one advantage that exists among a lot of disadvantages 無論如何; 至少〔提出諸多不利條件中存在的有利之處〕: *The house is far too small.* "Oh well, not so much to keep clean, at any rate." "這房子實在太小了。" "算了, 至少需要打掃乾淨的地方不多。" **b** used when you have said something which you are correcting because you are not really certain about it 反正〔用於對上文沒有完全的把握, 要再做進一步修正〕: *She's coming with us. At any rate, I think she is.* 她要和我們一起來。反正, 我想是這樣。 **5 at this rate, at that rate** if events continue in the same way 照這〔那〕樣發展下去; 照這〔那〕種情形: *At this rate we won't be able to afford a holiday.* 照這種情形看, 我們負擔不起度假的費用了。

rate² *v* **rated, rating** **1** [T + adv/prep] to have a particular opinion about the value or worth of someone or something 對〔某人或某事物〕評價; 估值: *She was generally rated highly as a poet.* 作為一個詩人, 她受到了普遍的高度評價。 **2** [T] to deserve 值得, 應得: *It was an item of local interest, and didn't really rate a mention in the national newspapers.* 這是本地人才有興趣的一則新聞, 不值得在全國性的報紙中提及。

ra·tea·ble val·ue /ˌreɪtəbḷ ˈvæljuː; ˌreɪtəbəl ˈvæljuː/ *adj* (also 又作 **ratable value**) a value given to a building for the purpose of calculating the rates (RATE) to be charged on it〔房地產的〕徵稅估定價值

rate of ex·change /ˌ···ˈ·/ *n* see 見 EXCHANGE RATE

rate·pay·er /ˈreɪtˌpeɪə; ˈreɪtpeɪəʳ/ *n* someone in Britain who has to pay the rates (RATE)〔英國持有不動產的〕地方納稅人

ra·ther /ˈræðə; ˈrɑːðəʳ/ *predeterminer, adv* **1** to some degree 相當, 頗: *It's rather cold today.* 今天天氣相當冷。 | *It was rather an unsuccessful day.* 那是個頗不順利的日子。 | *His behaviour rather sur-*

prised me. 他的行為使我頗為吃驚。 **2 would rather** would prefer to 寧可; 寧願: *"Shall we go and see that film?" "I'd rather stay in."* "我們去看那部電影好嗎?" "我寧可留在家裡。" | *I'd rather not talk about it.* 我寧可不談那個。 **3 rather than** instead of 寧願…也不: *I prefer to live near to my work rather than spend a lot of time travelling every day.* 我寧可住得靠近工作地點, 也不要每天在路上花很多時間來去。 **4** used when you are stating something that is opposite to what you have just said or makes what you have just said correct 恰恰相反; 〔修正上文〕更確切些: *He came home very late last night, or rather very early this morning.* 他昨晚回家很晚, 說得確切點, 就是今天凌晨才回家。

■ **USAGE** 用法: Compare 比較 **rather** and 和 **fairly. Rather** often suggests a quality that is bad or unsuitable ☆ **rather** 常表示一種壞的或不合適的性質: *I was driving rather fast.* (= too fast for the conditions on the road) 我車子開得相當快。(就道路情況而言太快了) But British speakers sometimes use **rather** about things they like very much ☆但英國人有時用 **rather** 來修飾自己很喜歡的東西: *I was rather pleased when I won the prize.* 我獲獎時頗為高興。We use **fairly** for qualities that are neither good nor bad ☆ **fairly** 用來表示既不好也不壞的性質: *I was driving fairly fast.* (= fast, but not very fast) 我車子開得挺快。(快, 但不是很快)

---

rat·i·fy /ˈrætɪfaɪ; ˈrætҙfaɪ/ *v* **ratified, ratifying** [T] *fml* to officially approve a written agreement by signing it〔正式〕簽署批准〔書面協議〕: *The heads of the two governments met to ratify the treaty.* 兩國政府的首腦會晤, 並簽署了這項條約。 **–ratification** /ˌrætəfəˈkeɪʃən; ˌrætҙfҙˈkeɪʃən/ *n* [U]

rat·ing /ˈreɪtɪŋ; ˈreɪtɪŋ/ *n* **1** [C] the position that someone or something has on a scale of values or amounts〔某人或某事物的〕受信任的程度, 評分: *The president has a favourable rating in the opinion polls.* 這位總統在民意調查中得到很高的支持率。 **2 ratings** [pl] lists showing the position of popularity of a particular song, or radio or television show〔某首歌曲、廣播或電視節目的〕受歡迎的程度; 收聽〔視〕率: *"Newsnight" has been getting excellent ratings.* "晚間新聞"一直有很高的收視率。 | *the ratings war* 收視率大戰

ra·ti·o /ˈreɪʃəʊ; ˈreɪʃɪəʊ/ *n* a figure showing the number of times one quantity contains another; it is used to show the relationship between two amounts 比, 比率, 比例: *The ratio of 10 to 5 is 2 to 1.* 十和五之比是二比一。 | *The ratio of nursing staff to doctors at this hospital is 3 to 1.* 這家醫院護理人員和醫生的比率是三比一。

---

ra·tion¹ /'ræʃən; 'ræʃən/ *n* **1** [C] a limited quantity of food, petrol, etc., allowed to each person for a period, especially during a war 〔尤指戰爭時期間對食物、汽油等的〕配給量, 定量配給 **2 rations** [pl] the amount of food given to a soldier each day 〔士兵的〕給養, 口糧

ration² *v* [T] **1** to limit someone to a fixed amount of something 定量給配〔某人〕: *On this diet, you are rationed* **to** *two eggs a week.* 按照這份飲食安排, 你每週獲配給兩個蛋。 **2** to control supplies of something 限制〔某物的供應〕, 限量: *The government had to ration petrol during the war.* 戰時政府不得不限量供應汽油。

ration sthg ↔ **out** *phr v* [T] to give out supplies in limited amounts 按定量分發〔供應物〕: *He rationed out the water to the sailors.* 他按照定額給水手發放飲用水。

ra·tion·al /'ræʃənl; 'ræʃənəl/ *adj* **1** having the ability to think and understand things clearly, and make decisions based on reason 有理智的; 有理性的; 明事理的 **2** based on reason (used of ideas and behaviour) 基於理性的; 合理的〔指觀點、行為〕: *There must be a rational explanation.* 必須有個合理的解釋。 −opposite 反義 **irrational** − **rationally** *adv*: *We must try to think rationally.* 我們必須盡量有理性地思考。 −**rationality** /,ræʃə'næləti; ,ræʃə'næl½ti/ *n* [U]

ra·tio·nale /,ræʃə'næl; ,ræʃə'nɑːl/ *n* [C;U] *fml* the reasons and principles on which a system, practice, or belief is based〔正式〕基本原理, 理論基礎: *What do you think is the rationale* **behind** *his decision?* 你認為他的決定有甚麼理論根據?

ra·tion·al·ize /'ræʃənl,aɪz; 'ræʃənəlaɪz/ *v* **rationalized, rationalizing** (also 又作 **rationalise** *BrE*〔英式〕) **1** [I;T] to think of reasons to explain unreasonable behaviour or opinions〔為不合理的行為或觀點〕找出辯護的理由; 自圓其說: *He tried to rationalize his behaviour by blaming his son.* 他試圖以責罵兒子來為自己的行為找藉口。 **2** [T] to make an organization or industry more modern and less wasteful 使〔組織或企業〕合理化: *Production was rationalized by buying new machinery.* 買了新機器後, 生產得到了合理化的改進。 −**rationalization** /,ræʃənəli-'zeʃən; ,ræʃənəlaɪ'zeɪʃən/ *n* [C;U]

rat race /'· ·/ *n* **the rat race** *infml* the endless competition for success, especially at work〔非正式〕〔尤指在工作上〕無休止的競爭: *Paul got so tired of the rat race that he went to live in the country.* 保羅對無休止的競爭深感厭倦, 於是他到鄉間定居。

rat·tle¹ /'rætl; 'rætl/ *v* **rattled, rattling 1** [I; T] to make a number of short sharp sounds like small objects knocking repeatedly against each other (使)發出連續短促的尖利聲; (使)碰撞作響; (使)發格格聲: *The beggar rattled the coins in his tin cup.* 乞丐把他的錫杯子裡的硬幣搖得格格響。 | *The windows rattled in the wind.* 窗子在風中格格作響。 **2** [I + adv/prep] to move quickly while making these noises 喀嚓喀嚓地飛快行進: *The cart rattled along the stony road.* 馬車沿着石子路喀嚓喀嚓地疾馳。 **3** [T] *infml* to make someone lose confidence and become anxious〔非正式〕使〔某人〕驚慌失措; 使〔某人〕緊張不安: *Keep calm — don't get rattled.* 保持鎮靜──不要慌亂起來。

rattle sthg ↔ **off** *phr v* [T] to say something quickly and easily from memory 迅速地背誦: *He rattled off the poem.* 他滾瓜爛熟地背了那首詩。

rattle on *phr v* [I] to talk quickly and for a long time about something unimportant 喋喋不休地說: *He rattled on about his holidays, although nobody was listening.* 雖然沒人在聽, 他仍喋喋不休地說他度假的事。

rattle through sthg *phr v* [T] to do something quickly 匆匆地做〔某事〕: *He rattled through his speech.* 他匆匆地演講了一遍。

rattle² *n* **1** [C] a baby's toy with loose pieces inside, that make a rattling noise when it is shaken〔幼兒玩的〕撥浪鼓 **2** [sing] the noise of small objects being knocked against each other〔小件物品碰撞發出的〕格格聲; 嘩嘩聲: *the rattle of milk bottles* 牛奶瓶相互撞擊時發出的嘎嘎聲

rat·tle·snake /'rætl,sneɪk; 'rætlsneɪk/ *n* (also 又作 **rattler** /'rætlə; 'rætlər/ *AmE*〔美式〕) a poisonous American snake that makes a rattling noise with its tail 響尾蛇

rat·ty /'ræti; 'ræti/ *adj infml* bad-tempered〔非正式〕壞脾氣的, 易怒的: *She always gets a bit ratty when she hasn't had enough sleep.* 她睡眠不足時總是要發點脾氣。

rau·cous /'rɔːkəs; 'rɔːkəs/ *adj* rough, loud, and unpleasant (used of sounds) 沙啞的; 粗嘎的〔指聲音〕: *raucous shouts* 沙啞的喊叫聲 −**raucously** *adv* −**raucousness** *n* [U]

raunch·y /'rɔːntʃi; 'rɔːntʃi/ *adj* **raunchier, raunchiest** *infml* having or suggesting a strong desire for sex〔非正式〕好色的; 淫穢的: *a raunchy dance* 色情舞蹈 | *a raunchy voice* 有挑逗意味的說話聲

rav·age /'rævɪdʒ; 'rævɪdʒ/ *v* **ravaged, ravaging** [T] to damage something so that it is nearly destroyed 毀壞〔某物〕; 使荒蕪: *The whole area was ravaged by forest fires.* 整個地區毀於森林大火。

rav·ag·es /'rævɪdʒɪz; 'rævɪdʒ½z/ *n* [pl] **the ravages of** the harmful effects of something 破壞的結果: *the ravages of war* 戰爭造成的破壞性後果

rave¹ /rev; reɪv/ *v* **raved, raving 1** [I] to talk wildly and with strong feeling 激烈地罵; 胡言亂語: *He was very feverish, and raved all night.* 他發高燒, 一整夜說胡話。 **2 rave about something** *infml* to speak about something with great admiration and praise〔非正式〕熱烈讚揚, 極力誇獎某事物: *Everybody raved* *about her new book.* 大家都熱烈讚揚她的新書。 **3 rave it up** *infml* to enjoy yourself in a very unworried and happy way〖非正式〗縱情歡樂; 狂歡

rave² *adj* **a rave review** a judgment about a book, film, or play that praises it very highly〖對書、電影或戲劇的〗熱烈的讚賞, 高度的評價

ra·ven /'rævən; 'reɪvən/ *n* a large shiny black bird with a deep unpleasant voice 渡鴉

rav·e·nous /'rævənəs; 'rævənəs/ *adj infml* extremely hungry〖非正式〗餓極了的 —**ravenously** *adv*

rave-up /'··/ *n infml* a very wild exciting party〖非正式〗狂歡聚會

ra·vine /rə'viːn; rə'viːn/ *n* a deep narrow valley with steep sides 溝壑; 深谷

rav·ing /'revɪŋ; 'reɪvɪŋ/ *adj, adv infml*〖非正式〗 **1** talking and behaving wildly 胡言亂語的[地]; 行為狂野的[地]: *a raving madman* 胡言亂語的瘋子 | *He's stark raving mad.* 他簡直瘋了。 **2** very great 非凡的[地], 出色的[地]: *She's hardly a raving beauty.* 她絕不是個絕色美人。 | *The party was not a raving success.* 那次聚會不很成功。

rav·ings /'revɪŋz; 'reɪvɪŋz/ *n* [pl] wild, uncontrolled talking or writing 胡言亂語, 瘋話: *the ravings of a madman* 瘋子的胡言亂語

rav·i·o·li /ˌrævɪ'olɪ; ˌrævɪ'əʊlɪ/ *n* [U] small squares of PASTA filled with meat and cooked by boiling〖意大利式〗肉餡小方餃

rav·ish /'rævɪʃ; 'rævɪʃ/ *v* [T] *lit*〖文〗 **1** to force a woman to have sex when she does not want to 強姦 **2 be ravished by** to get great pleasure and delight from the beauty of something〖因某事物而〗陶醉; 狂喜

rav·ish·ing /'rævɪʃɪŋ; 'rævɪʃɪŋ/ *adj* very beautiful and so causing great delight 極美的; 使人陶醉的: *a ravishing sight* 引人入勝的美景 —**ravishingly** *adv*

*raw /rɔ; rɔː/ *adj* **1** not cooked 生的; 未煮過的: *raw vegetables* 生的蔬菜 | *Don't cook it. I'll eat it raw.* 不要煮, 我要生吃。 **2** in a natural state 天然的: *raw silk* 生絲 | *raw cotton* 原棉 **3 raw material** a natural substance from which industrial products are made 原料〖用以生產工業品的天然物質〗: *Coal and oil are important raw materials for the manufacture of plastic.* 煤和石油是生產塑料的重要原料。 **4** not yet trained or experienced (used of a person)〖指人〗未經訓練的; 無經驗的: *intensive army courses for raw recruits* 針對剛入伍新兵的密集軍事課程 **5** painful because part of the skin has come off or is sore〖因擦掉一部分皮膚而〗疼痛的: *a raw patch where his shoe had rubbed* 被他的鞋子擦破的一塊皮 **6** unpleasantly cold and wet (used of weather) 濕冷的; 陰冷的〖指天氣〗: *a raw winter day* 濕冷的冬日 **7 get a raw deal, be given a raw deal** *infml* to be treated unfairly〖非正式〗受到不公平的對

待 —**rawness** *n* [U]

ray /re; reɪ/ *n* **1** a narrow beam of heat, light, or ENERGY 光線; 射線: *the sun's rays* 太陽光 | *a ray of light* 一束光線 | *gamma rays* 伽瑪射線 **2** a very small amount of a good feeling which might help to improve a bad situation 一線〔希望〕: *There's just one ray of hope left. Debbie may talk him into joining us.* 只剩下一線希望了。戴比可能會説服他加入到我們這裡來。

ray·on /'rean; 'reɪɒn/ *n* [U] a smooth material which looks like silk and is used for making clothes 人造絲

raze /rez; reɪz/ *v* **razed, razing** [T] *fml* to completely destroy a town or building so that no part is left standing〖正式〗把〔房屋、城鎮〕夷為平地: *An earthquake razed the city to the ground.* 一場地震把這座城市夷為平地。

ra·zor /'rezə; 'reɪzər/ *n* a sharp instrument for removing hair from your skin 剃刀: *his electric razor* 他的電動剃鬚刀

razor blade /'·· ·/ *n* a thin very sharp piece of metal that is put inside a razor〔夾在剃刀中的〕刀片

RC /ˌɑr 'si; ˌɑː 'siː/ *n* an abbreviation for〖縮〗= ROMAN CATHOLIC

Rd a written abbreviation for〖縮〗= ROAD: *17, Nelson Rd, Oxford* 牛津內爾森路十七號

re /ri; riː/ *prep* a word used when you are writing something formal, like a business letter, to show that you are going to talk about a particular subject〖用於正式文書, 如商業信件中〗關於: *re your enquiry of the 19th October* 關於你十月十九日垂詢的事

-'re /ə; ər/ *short for*〖縮〗= ARE: *We're ready, but they're not.* 我們準備好了, 但他們還沒有。 —see 見 's (USAGE 用法)

★reach¹ /ritʃ; riːtʃ/ *v* **1** [T] to arrive at or get to a place or person 抵達, 到達: *They reached London on Thursday.* 他們星期四抵達倫敦。 | *The news only reached me yesterday.* 我昨天才聽到這個消息。 **2** [I+adv/prep] to stretch out your hand or arm for some purpose 伸出〔手或手臂〕: *He reached across the table and picked up the book.* 他伸手到桌子那邊把書拿起。 | *The shopkeeper reached for a packet of tea.* 店主伸手拿了一包茶葉。 | *She reached out to hug him.* 她伸出手臂擁抱他。 **3** [I;T; not in progressive forms 不用於進行式] to be able to touch or get something by stretching out your arm or hand 伸手觸及: *Are you tall enough to reach that light switch?* 你的身高夠你用手觸到那個電燈開關嗎? | *It's no good. I can't reach.* 不好了, 我觸不到。 **4** [I+adv/prep; T; not in progressive forms 不用於進行式] to stretch as far as a particular place 延伸到〔某處〕, 伸展: *The ladder won't quite reach the roof.* 這梯子還夠不到屋頂。 | *fields reaching down to the sea* 一直延伸到海邊的田野 **5** [T] to get as far as a particular point or level 到達〔某一點或某個水平〕: *Haven't you reached the end of that book yet?* 你還沒有讀到那本書的結尾部分嗎？| *She's now reached the age of 50.* 她現在已五十歲了。| *Our sales to Japan have reached record levels.* 我們對日本的銷售已達到創紀錄的水平。**6 reach an agreement, reach a decision** to succeed in making an agreement or decision after a lot of thought or effort 達成〔協議〕: *After weeks of talks, the two sides reached an agreement.* 經過數星期的會談，雙方達成了一項協議。**7** [T] to get in touch with someone by telephone 和〔某人〕電話聯繫: *She can be reached on 72894.* 打72894能找到她。

reach sthg ↔ out *phr v* [T] to stretch out your hand or arm 伸出〔手或手臂〕: *The little girl reached out a hand to touch the doll.* 小女孩伸出手來觸摸那玩具娃娃。

reach² *n* **1 within reach: a** near enough to touch by stretching out your arm or hand 在伸手可及的範圍內: *He lay in bed with all his books within reach.* 他躺在牀上，所有的書都放在拿得到的地方。**b** a phrase used to describe a place you can travel to easily 在容易到達的範圍內: *We live within easy reach of the shops.* 我們住在離商店很近的地方。[RELATED PHRASES 相關詞組 **out of reach; beyond reach**] **2 the reaches of** large stretches of a river or of land 河段；地帶: *the upper reaches of the Nile* 尼羅河的上游

*re·act /rɪˈækt; rɪˈækt/ *v* [I] **1** to behave in a particular way as a result of a particular action or situation 作出反應: *The firm reacted* **to** *the workers' complaints by dismissing the director.* 公司對工人投訴的反應是解雇了這個董事。| *How did he react when you told him?* 你告訴他時，他反應如何？**2 react against** to behave differently to what is expected because you do not agree with something 反抗；反對: *He reacted against his father's influence by running away.* 他以離家出走來對抗父親的影響。**3** *tech* (of a substance) to change when mixed with another substance 〔術語〕〔物質〕起化學反應: *An acid can react* **with** *a base to form a salt.* 酸可與鹼起化學反應而合成鹽。

*re·ac·tion /rɪˈækʃən; rɪˈækʃən/ *n* **1** [C] something that you say or do as an answer to a particular situation 〔對某種情形的〕反應: *What was his reaction* **to** *the news?* 他對這個消息有甚麼反應？| *I made myself stand there, though my instinctive reaction was to turn and run.* 我不由自主地站在那裡，雖然我的本能反應是想轉身逃走。**2 a reaction against something** a change back to a previous belief or a change because of some opposition to something 對某事物的反抗〔對抗〕: *Their old-fashioned views are a reaction against the permissive age.* 他們的舊式觀點是反對性開放時代的一種反應。| *His wild be-*

haviour was simply a reaction against his strict schooling. 他的瘋狂行為只是對嚴厲的學校教育的反抗。**3 your reactions** how quickly your body can act 反應能力；反應靈敏度: *Now I'm going to test your reactions.* 現在我要測試一下你的反應。**4** [C;U] *tech* change caused in a chemical substance when it combines with another 〔術語〕化學反應 **5** [U] *fml* the quality of being strongly opposed to social or political change 〔正式〕〔對社會或政治變革的〕強烈反對；反動: *The revolution was defeated by the forces of reaction.* 革命被反動勢力扼殺了。

re·ac·tion·a·ry /rɪˈækʃənˌɛrɪ; rɪˈækʃənəri/ **reactionaries** a person strongly opposed to social or political change (a word used to express disapproval) 反動分子〔含貶義〕 **–reactionary** *adj*

re·ac·tiv·ate /rɪˈæktɪˌvet; rɪˈæktɪ̩veɪt/ *v* **reactivated, reactivating** [T] to make something become active or work again 使〔某物〕恢復活動；使〔某物〕再度活躍

*read¹ /rid; riːd/ *v* **read** /rɛd; red/, **read**, **reading 1** [I;T] to look at and understand printed or written signs 閱讀；看懂: *The child is learning to read.* 這孩子正在學習閱讀。| *She reads well for a six-year-old.* 對一個六歲的孩子來說，她的閱讀能力算不錯了。| *I often read a book at night.* 我常在晚上看書。| *Can you read music?* 你會看樂譜嗎？| *He can't read a map.* 他不會看地圖。**2** [I;T; +that] to learn particular information from print or writing 讀到；獲悉: *I read about the murder in the paper.* 我從報上看到了這宗謀殺案的報道。| *I read that the new director was Spanish.* 我獲悉那位新董事是西班牙人。**3** [I not in progressive forms 不用於進行式] to be written in a particular form or style 讀起來〔有某種形式或風格〕: *Her letters always read as if she copied them from books.* 她的信讀起來總是好像從書上抄來的。| *The name reads "Benson" not "Fenton".* 這個名字讀作"Benson"，而不是"Fenton"。**4** [T] to say printed or written words aloud to others 〔向其他人〕朗讀；唸: *He read the children a story.* 他給孩子們唸了一個故事。| *The teacher read a poem to the class.* 老師給全班學生朗讀了一首詩。| *The nurse read aloud to the old man.* 護士給老人朗讀。

□ USEFUL PATTERNS 有用句型
to read something to someone; to read someone something

5 [T] to show a particular amount or piece of information 指示，顯示: *The thermometer reads 33 degrees.* 溫度計顯示三十三度。| *The name on the door read Finnegan.* 門上的名字是菲納根。**6** [T] to understand someone's thoughts or feelings even if they are not directly expressed 洞察，察識〔某人的思

想或感情〕: *He can always read my mood.* 他總能察識我的情緒。**7** [T] to understand the meaning of a statement or situation in a particular way 理解: *How do you read the latest trade figures?* 你怎麼理解最近的貿易數字? | *This could be read as an attack on the government.* 這可以理解為是對政府的攻擊。**8** [T] to study a subject at university 〔在大學裡〕攻讀〔某一學科〕: *Helen's reading History at Oxford.* 海倫在牛津大學攻讀歷史。**9** **read between the lines** to understand something that is not directly expressed 看出字裡行間的意思,了解言外之意: *If you read between the lines, this letter is really a request for money.* 如果你能看出言外之意的話,這封信其實是來要錢的。**10** **-read: a** having a certain amount of knowledge gained from books (used of a person) 有學問的〔指人〕: *a well-read woman* 一位學識淵博的女士 **b** read by a certain number of people (used of a book or newspaper) 為〔某數量的人〕閱讀的〔指書、報紙〕: *a little-read novel* 很少人看的小説

read sthg into sthg *phr v* [T] to believe something means something more than what it really does 認為〔某事物〕有言外之意: *Don't read more into her reply than she intended.* 別把她回覆的意思另加揣測。

read sthg ↔ out *phr v* [T] to read aloud for others to hear 朗讀〔給別人聽〕: *Can you read out the list of names?* 你能把名單宣讀一下嗎?

read up *phr v* [I;T **read sthg ↔ up**] *infml* to become informed about a subject by reading thoroughly 〔非正式〕鑽研;用心研讀: *I'll need to read up* **on** *the tax laws to answer your question.* 我需要研究一下税務法,才能回答你的問題。

read² *n infml* 〔非正式〕[sing] **1** an act of reading 閲讀: *Can I have a read of your paper?* 我能看看你的論文嗎? **2 a good read, an excellent read** something which is enjoyable and interesting to read 好的讀物: *Her latest novel is a very good read.* 她最近的一部小説是本很不錯的讀物。

rea·da·ble /ˈriːdəbl; ˈriːdəbəl/ *adj* **1** interesting or easy to read 讀起來有趣的;易讀的 **2** written or printed in a way that is clear to read 易辨認的;〔字跡〕清晰的 **–readability** /ˌriːdəˈbɪlətɪ; ˌriːdəˈbɪlə̱ti/ *n* [U]

re·ad·dress /ˌriəˈdres; ˌriːəˈdres/ *v* [T] to write a different address on a letter that has already been delivered to your house 更改〔信件上的〕地址〔再轉寄〕: *Could you re-address my letters to the new house please?* 能否請你把我的信件轉寄到我的新房子那裡?

★**read·er** /ˈriːdə; ˈriːdər/ *n* **1** a person who reads 閲讀的人: *Are you a fast reader?* 你看書快嗎? | *My brother is a keen reader.* 我弟弟是個熱衷於讀書的人。**2** a person who reads a particular book, magazine, or newspaper 〔某種書、雜誌或報紙的〕讀者: *We*

got *a lot of letters about this from our readers.* 有關這個問題,我們收到了很多讀者的來信。

read·er·ship /ˈriːdəʃɪp; ˈriːdəʃɪp/ *n* [sing] the number or type of people who read a particular newspaper or magazine 〔某一報紙或期刊的〕讀者羣;讀者人數: *The paper has a readership of 500,000.* 這份報紙有五十萬讀者。| *a very well-educated readership* 受過良好教育的讀者(羣)

★**read·i·ly** /ˈredlɪ; ˈredɪ̱li/ *adv* **1** willingly 樂意地: *He readily agreed to their suggestion.* 他欣然同意他們的建議。**2** with no difficulty 無困難地;容易地: *This type of plug is readily available.* 這種塞子容易買到。

read·i·ness /ˈredɪnɪs; ˈredɪnɪ̱s/ *n* **1** [sing;U] willingness or eagerness 願意;樂意: *She showed a great readiness to learn.* 她表現出強烈的學習願望。**2 in readiness for** ready or prepared for something 準備就緒的: *The soldiers were lined up in readiness for the parade.* 士兵排好隊,準備接受檢閱。

★**read·ing** /ˈriːdɪŋ; ˈriːdɪŋ/ *n* **1** [U] the activity or practice of reading 讀,閲讀: *Children learn reading and writing at school.* 孩子們在學校裡學習讀書寫字。| *She loves reading.* 她愛讀書。**2** [C] an opinion about the meaning of something 看法;理解: *My reading of the law is that we needn't pay.* 我對這條法律的理解是,我們無需付錢。**3** [C] a figure shown by a measuring instrument 〔儀表上的〕讀數: *What are the temperature readings for this machine?* 這台機器的温度是多少? **4** [C] a gathering of people at which something is read aloud 朗讀〔誦〕會: *a poetry reading* 詩歌朗誦會 **5** [only before a noun 只用於名詞前] for reading 用於閲讀的: *the reading room at the library* 圖書館的閲覽室

re·ad·just /ˌriːəˈdʒʌst; ˌriːəˈdʒʌst/ *v* **1** [T] to move or put something back into a particular position 重新調整〔某物〕: *You'll have to readjust the driving mirror.* 你得重新調節汽車後視鏡的角度。**2** [I;T] to change in order to fit into a situation 使重新適應: *It's hard readjusting to work after a holiday.* 假期結束後,一時很難重新適應工作。**–readjustment** *n* [C;U]: *a period of readjustment* 調整時期

★**read·y¹** /ˈredɪ; ˈredi/ *adj* **readier, readiest 1** [never before a noun 不能用於名詞前] prepared fully for use or having the right qualities 準備就緒的: *Is breakfast ready?* 早飯準備好了嗎? | *Come on — aren't you ready yet?* 快來—你還沒準備好嗎? | *Is everything ready for the party?* 聚會的一切都準備就緒了嗎? | *These apples are nearly ready to eat.* 這些蘋果差不多可以吃了。

□ USEFUL PATTERNS 有用句型
be ready for something; be ready to do something

2 [never before a noun 不能用於名詞前] willing and eager to do or give something 願意的; 樂意的: *She's always ready to help.* 她總是樂於助人。| *He's always ready with an excuse.* 他總是愛給自己找藉口。

□ USEFUL PATTERNS 有用句型
be ready to do something; be ready with something

3 [never before a noun 不能用於名詞前] likely or about to do something 可能做; 快要〔做某事的〕: *I felt ready to cry with frustration.* 我碰了釘子, 真想大哭一場。**4** quick and easy 快的; 容易的: *a ready solution to the problem* 解決這個問題的快捷方法

ready² *interj* **Ready, steady, go!** a phrase used when telling people to begin a race 各就各位, 預備, 跑!〔用於賽跑發令時〕

ready³ *adv* [used before a past participle 用於過去分詞前] in advance 事先; 預先: *a ready-cooked dinner*〔菜餚已準備妥的〕現成的晚餐 | *You can buy the bread ready-cut.* 你可以買切好了的麵包。

ready⁴ *v fml* [T] to prepare something or someone for a particular event or purpose 〔正式〕使準備好, 預備: *The government is readying itself for the elections.* 政府正為選舉作準備。

ready-made /ˌ·· '·◂/ *adj* able to be used at once 現成的: *a ready-made suit* 成衣 | *Many shops now have ready-made curtains.* 現在很多商店都有現成的窗簾。

re·af·firm /ˌriːə'fɜːm; ˌriːə'fɝːm/ *v* [T] to state or declare something again 重申, 再確認

★**real** /'rɪəl; rɪəl/ *adj* **1** not imaginary but actually existing 真實的; 現實的: *a story of real life* 現實生活的故事 **2** true or actual 真正的; 實際的: *What was the real reason for your absence?* 你缺席的真正原因是甚麼? **3** not false 真的; 真正的: *Is this ring real gold?* 這戒指是真金的嗎? | *real leather* 真皮 **4** [only before a noun 只用於名詞前] made in the proper old way rather than a modern way 用傳統方法製作的, 純正的, 地道的: *real ale* 正宗的淡色啤酒 **5** [only before a noun 只用於名詞前] a word used when you want to add force to a statement or to show that something actually exists 完全的, 十足的〔用於加強語氣或表示某事物確實存在〕: *You're a real idiot!* 你是個十足的傻瓜! | *It's been a real pleasure to meet you.* 實在很高興認識你。**6 for real** *infml* a phrase used to show that something actually exists or happens, and is not pretended or imagined 〔非正式〕真的[地]; 確實的[地]: *I suddenly realized that the gun was for real.* 我突然意識到那把槍是真的。**7 in real terms** a phrase used to talk about the real cost or value of something; for example, if your wages increase by a certain amount but prices also increase by the same amount, in real terms you are not earning any more money 說真的; 實際上〔用於談論某事的真正價值或費用〕

real es·tate /'·· ·/ *n* [U] *law* property in the form of land and houses〔律〕不動產, 房地產

re·al·is·m /'rɪəlˌɪzəm; 'rɪəlɪzəm/ *n* [U] **1** accepting a situation as it actually is and dealing with it practically, without being influenced by your feelings 現實性; 注重實際的態度 **2** the showing of things in art and literature as they really are〔文藝創作的〕寫實主義, 現實主義 —compare 比較 ROMANTICISM, CLASSICISM —**realist** *n*

re·a·lis·tic /ˌrɪə'lɪstɪk; rɪə'lɪstɪk/ *adj* **1** sensible and reasonable 切合實際的: *Our income has got smaller, so we must be realistic and give up our car.* 我們的收入減少了, 所以我們必須面對現實, 還是把車賣了的好。—opposite 反義 **unrealistic 2** life-like (used of art or literature) 真實的; 逼真的〔指文藝作品〕: *a realistic drawing of a horse* 一幅栩栩如生的駿馬圖 —**realistically** /-kli; -kli/ *adv*

★**re·al·i·ty** /rɪ'æləti; rɪ'ælɪ̩ti/ *n* **realities 1** [U] the quality or state of existing or being real rather than imagined 真實(性); 實在: *She believes in the reality of God.* 她相信上帝是真實存在的。**2** [C;U] everything that is real or true about a situation, especially when these things are unpleasant 現實: *You'll have to face up to reality.* 你得面對現實。| *He liked to escape from reality by going to the cinema.* 他喜歡以看電影來逃避現實。| *the harsh realities of life in the desert* 沙漠中生活的殘酷現實 **3** [C] a situation which actually exists 真實的情形: *His dream of marrying Jean became a reality.* 他想娶瓊的夢想實現了。**4 in reality** a phrase used to show that something is different from what you believed or imagined 實際上〔用以表示某事物跟所認為的或想像的不同〕: *We thought they had come to repair the phone, but in reality, they were burglars.* 我們原以為他們是來修理電話的, 實際上他們是盜賊。

re·a·li·za·tion /ˌrɪələ'zeɪʃən; ˌrɪələr'zeɪʃən/ *n* (also 又作 **realisation**) **1** [sing;U] understanding or becoming conscious of something you did not know before 理解; 認識; 領悟: *I was struck by the full realization that he was guilty.* 當我充分認識到他有罪時, 我深感驚訝。**2 the realization of** the becoming real of a hope, plan, or fear〔希望、計劃或恐懼的〕實現: *Travelling there was the realization of all my dreams.* 去那裡旅遊, 我所有的夢想都實現了。

★**re·a·lize** /'rɪə‚laɪz; 'rɪəlaɪz/ *v* **realized, realizing** (also 又作 **realise**) **1** [T;+(that)] to understand or become conscious of something 認識到; 了解: *He didn't realize his mistake.* 他並未認識到自己的錯誤。| *Do you realize how late it is?* 你知道多

晚了嗎? | *She spoke such good English that I didn't realize she was German.* 她英語說得這麼好, 我沒想到她是德國人。

□ USEFUL PATTERNS 有用句型
to realize something; to realize how, where, why, etc.; to realize that

---

2 [T] to make a hope, fear, or purpose real 實現〔希望、目的〕; 使〔恐懼〕變為事實: *She realized her ambition of becoming an actress.* 她實現了當演員的抱負。| *My worst fears were realized when I saw the exam questions.* 我一看到考試題目, 就知道我最害怕的事情發生了。**3** [T] *tech* to get money by selling something 〔術語〕把〔某物〕變賣: *The company realized a considerable profit by selling the land.* 這家公司賣掉這塊土地, 賺了一大筆錢。

★real·ly /ˈrɪəlɪ; ˈrɔlɪ/ *adv* **1** truly or in fact 真正地; 實際上: *Did she really say that?* 她真的那樣說嗎? | *Tell us what really happened.* 把事情真相告訴我們。| *I've just put a sheet of plastic over the hole for now. Really, it needs mending properly.* 我現在只在洞上蓋了一塊塑料。實際上, 它要好好修補一下了。**2** to a great degree 十分; 很: *It's really cold today.* 今天非常冷。| *I was really pleased when they offered me the job.* 他們給我提供這份工作, 我真的很高興。| *I really hate him.* 我實在恨他。**3** used to show that you are interested in something or surprised by it 真的; 是嗎〔用以表示感興趣或驚訝〕: *"Have you heard, Jane's going to have a baby?" "Really?"* "你聽說簡要生孩子了嗎?" "真的?"

realm /rɛlm; relm/ *n* **1** (also 又作 **Realm**) *lit* a country which has a king or queen as its official ruler 〔文〕王國: *the defence of the Realm* 王國的防務 **2** a particular area of activity, interest, or thought 〔活動、興趣或思想的〕領域, 範圍: *This theory belongs more to the realm of science than art.* 這理論與其說屬於藝術領域, 倒不如說是屬於科學領域的。

reams /riːmz; riːmz/ *n infml* [pl] a large quantity of something written 〔非正式〕〔寫作等的〕大量: *She wrote reams of notes.* 她記了大量筆記。

reap /riːp; riːp/ *v* **1** [I;T] to cut and gather a crop of grain 收割〔莊稼〕: *The men are all out reaping.* 男的都出去收割了。| *Machines are used to reap the corn.* (人們)用機器收割穀物。**2** [T] to get something because of your hard work or thorough planning 〔因辛勤工作或周密計劃而〕得到; 獲得: *The company is now reaping the benefits of its investments.* 公司現在正從投資中獲益。

reap·er /ˈriːpə; ˈriːpɚ/ *n* a person or machine that reaps 收割者; 收割機

re·ap·pear /ˌriːəˈpɪə; ˌriːəˈpɪɚ/ *v* [I] to appear again after an absence 再出現, 重新顯露 **–reappearance** *n* [U]

re·ap·prais·al /ˌriːəˈpreɪzl; ˌriːəˈpreɪzəl/ *n fml* [C;U] careful thought about something to decide whether you should change your opinion of it 〔正式〕重新估計, 重新評價: *There needs to be a reappraisal of our trade policy.* 我們需要重新評價貿易政策。

rear¹ /rɪə; rɪɚ/ *v* **1** [T] to care for children, animals, or plants until they are fully grown 撫養〔孩子〕; 飼養〔動物〕; 培植〔植物〕: *They reared a large family.* 他們養活了一大家人。**2** [I] (also 又作 **rear up**) (of a horse) to lift the front part of the body and stand on the back legs 〔馬〕用後腿站立: *The horse reared and threw me off.* 馬用後腿直立起來, 把我摔了下來。**3 rear its ugly head** (of a problem or something unpleasant) to appear 〔問題或不愉快的事物〕出現: *Disagreement again reared its ugly head among the staff.* 員工之間又出現了意見分歧。

rear² *n* **the rear** *fml* the back 〔正式〕後部; 背: *a garden at the rear of the house* 屋後的花園 **–rear** *adj*: *a rear window* 後窗

re·arm /riˈɑːm; riˈɑːm/ *v* [I;T] to supply a country or army again with new or better weapons 重新武裝, 重整裝備: *They rearmed with modern missiles.* 他們用現代化導彈重新武裝。**–rearmament** *n* [U]

re·ar·range /ˌriːəˈreɪndʒ; ˌriːəˈreɪndʒ/ *v* **rearranged, rearranging** [T] to organize or arrange differently 重新整理[佈置], 安排]: *She rearranged the furniture in her room.* 她把房間裡的家具重新佈置過了。**–rearrangement** *n* [C;U]

★rea·son¹ /ˈriːzn; ˈriːzən/ *n* **1** [C;U] the fact or cause which explains why something happens or exists 原因, 理由: *She suddenly left without giving any reason.* 她沒有提出任何理由就突然走了。| *There is reason to believe she was murdered.* 有理由相信她是被謀殺的。| *What were his reasons for leaving his last job?* 他上次辭職是由於甚麼原因? | *The reason for the flood was all that heavy rain.* 這次洪水都是由於那場大雨引起的。| *Can you tell me the reason why you didn't come that night?* 你能告訴我你那天晚上沒有來的原因嗎? | *The animal hunts at night. For this reason, it has large ears.* 這種動物在晚間獵食, 因此牠有大耳朵。–see 見 EXCUSE² (USAGE 用法) **2** [U] the ability to think, understand, and form opinions or judgments based on facts 理智; 理性; 判斷力: *His writings appeal to emotion rather than reason.* 他的作品不是訴諸理性, 而是訴諸感情。**3** [U] good sense 道理; 情理: *He won't listen to reason.* 他不會聽從道理的。**4 by reason of** *fml* because of 〔正式〕由於...; 因為...: *He escaped punishment by reason of his youth.* 他因年輕而免於受罰。**5 for some reason** a phrase used to describe something that happens or exists although you do not know why 由於某種原因〔用於描述不知原因而發生或存在的某事物〕: *For* *some reason, she felt terribly tired.* 由於某種原因, 她感到累極了。**6 with reason** correctly 正確地: *He thinks, with reason, that I don't like him.* 他認為我不喜歡他, 這倒是真的。**7 within reason** within sensible and fair limits 合情合理地: *The bank will lend you as much as you need, within reason.* 銀行會合情合理地盡量借給你所需要的錢。

■ USAGE 用法: **1** Remember to use the preposition **for** in phrases such as ☆在下列詞組中, 記住使用介詞 **for:** *the* **reason for** *my absence* 我缺席的原因 | *the* **reason for** *his success* 他成功的原因 | *one of the* **reasons for** *doing this* 做這事的原因之一 **2** Compare 比較 **cause** and 和 **reason.** A **cause** is something which produces a result ☆ **cause** 指引起某種後果的起因: *Bad driving is the cause of many accidents.* 駕駛不當是許多事故的起因。A **reason** is something which explains an action ☆**reason** 指為某項行為動作解釋的理由: *The reason he gave for his bad driving was that he was late for work.* 他為自己駕駛不當解釋的理由是, 他上班要遲到了。

---

reason² *v* **1** [I] to think about or understand facts clearly 推理, 思考: *Animals do not have the power to reason.* 動物沒有推理能力。**2** [+that] to give an opinion or make a judgment based on careful thought 推想; 推論: *I reasoned that since she had not answered my letter she must be angry with me.* 她不回我的信, 從那時開始, 我推想她一定是生我的氣了。

reason with sbdy *phr v* [T] to try to persuade someone to be more sensible 説服, 勸告: *There's no point in trying to reason with him — he'll never change.* 想和他講道理是沒用的——他決不會改變想法。

★**rea·so·na·ble** /ˈriznəbl; ˈriːzənəbəl/ *adj* **1** sensible and fair (used of people or behaviour) 講道理的; 合情合理的〔指人或行為〕: *Be reasonable, Mary! It wasn't my fault.* 要講道理, 瑪麗! 這不是我的錯。–opposite 反義 **unreasonable 2** correct or based on good reasons 正當的; 合理的: *Scientists agree there is no reasonable explanation for these results.* 科學家承認對於這些結果沒有合理的解釋。**3** fair and not too expensive (used of prices) 公道的〔指價錢〕: *The price of bananas is quite reasonable this month.* 本月香蕉的價錢相當公道。**4** not small, but not too great either 適度的; 過得去的: *We live a reasonable distance away from my parents.* 我們住得離我的父母不算遠。–**reasonableness** *n* [U]

★**rea·son·a·bly** /ˈriznəbli; ˈriːzənəbli/ *adv* **1** fairly and sensibly 合理地; 理智地: *He said quite reasonably that he didn't agree.* 他相當得體地説他不同意。**2** quite 十分; 相當: *The*

car is in reasonably good order. 這輛汽車的性能相當好。| *They live reasonably close.* 他們住得十分近。

rea·soned /ˈriznd; ˈriːzənd/ *adj* [only before a noun 只用於名詞前] clearly thought out and sensible (used of an argument or explanation) 經過慎密思考的; 言之有據的〔指論據或解釋〕: *In a reasoned statement, the minister explained the new economic policy.* 首相在一篇有條理的聲明中解釋了新的經濟政策。

rea·son·ing /ˈriznɪŋ; ˈriːzənɪŋ/ *n* [U] the process of thinking carefully about particular facts in order to form an opinion or judgment 推理, 推論: *Your reasoning on this point was quite correct.* 你在這一點上的推理相當正確。

re·as·sure /ˌriːəˈʃʊr; ˌriːəˈʃʊər/ *v* **reassured, reassuring** [T] to comfort someone and stop them feeling anxious 使放心, 使安心: *His boss reassured him that his work was satisfactory.* 他的老闆讓他放心, 説他的工作是令人滿意的。–**reassurance** *n* [C;U]: *She won't believe it in spite of all our reassurances.* 不管我們怎樣安慰她, 她都不相信。–**reassuringly** *adv*

re·bate /ˈriːbeɪt; ˈriːbeɪt/ *n* an amount of money that is paid back to you because you have paid too much tax or rent 回扣; 部分退款: *a tax rebate* 退還部分税款

reb·el¹ /ˈrebl; ˈrebəl/ *n* a person who rebels 造反者; 反叛者; 反抗者: *She joined the rebels when her father was killed.* 她父親被殺害後, 她加入了反叛者的行列。| *Even at school Joe was a rebel who dressed differently to the others.* 即使在上學時, 喬也是個穿着與眾不同的叛逆者。

re·bel² /rɪˈbɛl; rɪˈbel/ *v* **-ll-** [I] to oppose or fight against someone in a position of control 反叛; 造反: *The people have rebelled* **against** *their foreign rulers.* 人民奮起反抗他們的外來統治者。| *Teenagers always rebel against authority.* 青少年總是反抗權威。

re·bel·lion /rɪˈbɛljən; rɪˈbeljən/ *n* [C;U] opposition to someone in a position of control 反抗; 叛亂; 造反

re·bel·lious /rɪˈbɛljəs; rɪˈbeljəs/ *adj* disobedient and hard to control 反叛的; 不易管束的: *rebellious behaviour* 叛逆行為 –**rebelliously** *adv* –**rebelliousness** *n* [U]

re·birth /riːˈbɜːθ; ˌriːˈbɜːθ/ *n* [sing] *fml* a change leading to a new development 〔正式〕再生; 新生; 復興: *the rebirth* **of** *learning in the Western world* 西方世界的學術復興

re·bound¹ /rɪˈbaʊnd; rɪˈbaʊnd/ *v* **1** [I] to fly or spring back after hitting something solid 彈回, 跳回: *The ball rebounded from the wall and I caught it.* 球從牆上彈回來, 我接住了它。**2 rebound on/upon someone** to have a bad effect on a person who has done something harmful〔做壞事的〕某人自食惡果, 自作自受: *His lies rebounded on* *himself because nobody trusted him any more.* 他的謊話使他自食其果，因為沒有人再信任他了。

re·bound² /rɪˌbaʊnd; ˈriːbaʊnd/ *n* **on the rebound** to quickly start a new relationship because you are unhappy or disappointed that another relationship has just ended 〔一種關係剛結束〕心灰意冷之餘〔迅速建立新關係〕: *He married Mary on the rebound after Sue left him.* 蘇離他而去之後，他失望之餘便娶了瑪麗。

re·buff /rɪˈbʌf; rɪˈbʌf/ *n fml* an unkind or unfriendly answer given to someone who is trying to be helpful or is asking for help 〔正式〕〔對想幫忙或請求幫助的人〕拒絕; 冷落: *Her tactful advice met only with a cruel rebuff.* 她得體的忠告只受到了冷酷的拒絕。**—rebuff** *v* [T]: *She rebuffed all my offers of friendship.* 她斷然拒絕了我的種種友好表示。

re·build /riˈbɪld; ˌriːˈbɪld/ *v* **rebuilt** /-ˈbɪlt; -bɪlt/, **rebuilt** [T] to build again or add new parts to a building or town, usually after it has been damaged 〔常在建築物或城鎮被毀壞後〕重建: *The church was rebuilt after the fire.* 這座教堂是在火災後重建起來的。

re·buke /rɪˈbjuk; rɪˈbjuːk/ *v* **rebuked, rebuking** *fml* [T] to speak severely to someone because you do not like something they have said or done 〔正式〕指責; 訓斥: *The judge rebuked the police for their behaviour.* 法官指責警察的行為。**—rebuke** *n*

re·cal·ci·trant /rɪˈkælsɪtrənt; rɪˈkælsⱼtrənt/ *adj fml* refusing to obey or be controlled, even after being punished 〔正式〕不順從的; 頑抗的: *recalcitrant children* 無法管教的孩子 **—recalcitrance** *n* [U]

★**re·call¹** /rɪˈkɔl; rɪˈkɔːl/ *v* **1** [T; +that; not in progressive forms 不用於進行式] *fml* to remember something 〔正式〕記起, 回想, 回憶起: *I can't recall the exact details of the report.* 我記不起這篇報告的確切細節了。| *I don't recall meeting her.* 我不記得見過她。| *Do you recall where he lives?* 你能想起他住在哪兒嗎? | *She recalled that there was no supermarket then.* 她記得那時沒有超級市場。

> ☐ USEFUL PATTERNS 有用句型
> to recall something; to recall doing something; to recall where, how, why, etc.; to recall that…

2 to order someone to return to a particular place 召回; 叫回: *The government recalled its ambassador when war was declared.* 宣戰以後，政府召回了大使。

re·call² /ˈriːkɔl; ˈriːkɔːl/ *n* **1** [U] the ability to remember something learned or experienced in the past 記憶力: *She has amazing recall of her early childhood.* 她對自己的幼年時代有着驚人的記憶力。**2 beyond recall** impossible to remember or change 想不起來的; 不能改變的 **3** [sing;U] the act of

ordering someone to return 召回; 叫回: *The recall of the general from abroad caused a scandal.* 從國外把將軍召回卻引出了一樁醜聞。

re·cant /rɪˈkænt; rɪˈkænt/ *v* [I;T] *fml* to say publicly that you no longer hold a former political or religious belief 〔正式〕宣佈放棄〔以前的政治或宗教信仰〕: *She recanted and became a Christian.* 她宣佈放棄原有信仰, 成為一名基督教徒。

re·ca·pit·u·late /ˌrikəˈpɪtʃəˌlet; ˌriːkəˈpɪtʃⱼleɪt/ *v* **recapitulated, recapitulating** (also 又作 **recap** /ˈrikæp; ˈriːkæp/ *infml* 〔非正式〕) [I;T] to repeat the main points of a statement or argument 扼要重述: *He recapitulated the main reasons for accepting the employers' offer.* 他把接受雇主提議的主要原因扼要地重述了一遍。**—recapitulation** /ˌrikəˌpɪtʃəˈleʃən; ˌriːkəpɪtʃⱼˈleɪʃən/ *n* [C;U]

re·cap·ture /riˈkæptʃə; riːˈkæptʃər/ *v* **recaptured, recapturing** [T] **1** to take control of or take as prisoner again 再俘虜; 再擒獲; 奪回: *The police recaptured the escaped criminal.* 警察重新捕獲了逃犯。**2** *lit* to make someone experience or feel something again 〔文〕使再次經歷; 重溫: *a book that recaptures the happiness of youth* 一本使人重溫快樂的青年時代的書

re·cede /rɪˈsid; rɪˈsiːd/ *v* **receded, receding** [I] **1** to move back or away into the distance 後退; 遠去: *She could see the lights of the ship receding on the horizon.* 她能看到輪船上的燈火在地平線上消失。**2** to become less strong or less likely 變得渺茫; 變弱: *Hopes for their safety are receding fast.* 他們安全脫險的希望很快變得渺茫了。**3 be receding** to be losing hair at the front of your head 開始從前額向後脫髮 **—see picture on page 469** 見 469 頁彩圖

re·ceipt /rɪˈsit; rɪˈsiːt/ *n* **1** [C] a piece of paper showing you have received money 收據, 收條: *Ask him to give you a receipt when you pay the bill.* 你付賬單時叫他要一張收據。**2** [U] the getting of something 收到: *Did you write to acknowledge receipt of the goods?* 你有沒有寫信確認收到了貨物? **3 receipts** [pl] the amount of money received by a business during a particular period 〔企業某段時期內的〕收入; 進款

★★**re·ceive** /rɪˈsiv; rɪˈsiːv/ *v* **received, receiving** [T] **1** *fml* to get something 〔正式〕收到, 得到, 接到〔某物〕: *Did you receive my letter?* 你收到我的信了嗎? | *The children received a lot of attention.* 孩子們備受關注。| *We've just received some good news.* 我們剛得到一些好消息。**2** to experience 經受; 遭受: *During the fight, he received a blow on the head.* 打架時, 他頭上挨了一拳。**3** to welcome a visitor, often formally 〔通常正式地〕接待〔訪客〕: *The director received her in the library.* 主管在圖書館接待她。**4 be at/on the receiving end of** *infml* to be suffering something unpleasant done by someone else 〔非正式〕遭受〔別人加在自己身上不愉快的事〕: *We were on the receiving end of several complaints.* 我們承受了好幾次投訴。

re·ceiv·er /rɪˈsiːvɚ; rɪˈsiːvə^r/ *n* **1** the part of a telephone that you hold to your ear 〔電話〕聽筒, 受話器 —see 見 TELEPHONE¹ (USAGE 用法) **2** a radio or television set 無線電接收機, 收音機, 〔電視機〕接收 **3** a person who deals in stolen property 買賣贓物者

★**re·cent** /ˈriːsn̩t; ˈriːsənt/ *adj* having happened or appeared a short time ago 近來的, 最近的: *recent history* 近代史 | *her recent trip to China* 她最近一次去中國的旅行 | *one of the most exciting developments in medicine in recent years* 近年來醫學上最激動人心的發展之一

★**re·cent·ly** /ˈriːsn̩tlɪ; ˈriːsəntlɪ/ *adv* not long ago 近來, 不久前, 最近: *I lived in London until quite recently.* 前不久我住在倫敦。 | *Mike's only recently started learning French.* 邁克只是最近才開始學法語。

re·cep·ta·cle /rɪˈsɛptəkl; rɪˈsɛptəkəl/ *n tech fml* a container 〔術語, 正式〕容器

★**re·cep·tion** /rɪˈsɛpʃən; rɪˈsɛpʃən/ *n* **1** [U] the office or department in a hotel or large organization which helps visitors and gives information 〔旅館或大機構的〕接待處: *Leave your key at reception.* 把你的鑰匙留在接待處。 **2** [C] a large formal party 招待會; 歡迎會: *a wedding reception* 婚宴 **3** [C] a particular way of behaving which shows your opinion about someone or something 接待, 迎接: *The ambassador got a cool reception from the president.* 大使受到了總統冷淡的接待。 **4** [U] the receiving of radio or television signals 〔無線電、電視的〕接收: *Radio reception isn't very good here.* 這兒的無線電接收效果不太好。

re·cep·tion·ist /rɪˈsɛpʃənɪst; rɪˈsɛpʃənɪst/ *n* a person working in an office or hotel who deals with people when they first arrive and makes appointments for people 〔旅館、辦公室的〕接待員

re·cep·tive /rɪˈsɛptɪv; rɪˈsɛptɪv/ *adj* willing to consider new ideas 〔對新思想〕樂意接受的: *He's not very receptive to my suggestions.* 他不太願意接受我的建議。 | *a receptive mind* 善於接受新事物的頭腦 —**receptively** *adv* —**receptiveness** *n* [U]

re·cess /rɪˈsɛs; rɪˈsɛs/ *n* **1** [C;U] a period of holiday during the working year 〔一年中的〕休假(期): *Parliament is in recess now.* 國會現正在休會。 | *the summer recess* 暑假 **2** [C] a space in the wall of a room for shelves or cupboards 〔室內牆壁的〕凹進處, 壁龕 **3 the recesses of** [pl] *lit* the secret inner parts of something 〔文〕隱祕處, 幽深處

★**re·ces·sion** /rɪˈsɛʃən; rɪˈsɛʃən/ *n* a period of reduced trade and business activity 經濟衰退期

★**re·ci·pe** /ˈrɛsəpɪ; ˈresəpi/ *n* **1** a set of instructions for cooking a particular type of food 烹飪法; 食譜: *a recipe for making chocolate cake* 巧克力蛋糕的做法 | *He didn't follow the recipe but it still tasted great.* 他沒有照着食譜做, 但味道還是很不錯。 | *a recipe book* 一本烹飪書 **2 a recipe for something** a way of making something likely to happen 做某事的方法, 祕訣: *These proposals look like a recipe for disaster.* 這些建議看來後患無窮。

re·cip·i·ent /rɪˈsɪpɪənt; rɪˈsɪpɪənt/ *n fml* a person who receives something 〔正式〕接受者, 收受者

re·cip·ro·cal /rɪˈsɪprəkl; rɪˈsɪprəkəl/ *adj fml* exchanged between two people or two groups of people 〔正式〕相互的; 互惠的: *a reciprocal trade agreement between two nations* 兩國間的互惠貿易協定 —**reciprocally** /-klɪ; -klɪ/ *adv*

re·cip·ro·cate /rɪˈsɪprəˌket; rɪˈsɪprəkeɪt/ *v* **reciprocated, reciprocating** *fml* [I;T] to give or do something in return 〔正式〕回報, 報答; 互給: *They invited us to their party, and we reciprocated by inviting them to ours.* 他們邀請我們參加宴會, 我們也回請了他們。

re·cit·al /rɪˈsaɪtl; rɪˈsaɪtl/ *n* **1** a performance of poetry or music, usually given by one performer 朗誦會; 獨奏會; 獨唱會: *a piano recital* 鋼琴獨奏表演 **2** *fml* an account or report 〔正式〕敘述, 述說: *He gave us a long recital of his experiences.* 他詳細地向我們敘述了他的種種經歷。

re·cite /rɪˈsaɪt; rɪˈsaɪt/ *v* [T] **recited, reciting** **1** to say a poem or other piece of writing aloud from memory 背誦: *I don't like reciting poetry in public.* 我不喜歡當眾背誦詩歌。 **2** to say a list of something aloud 列舉〔事物〕: *He recited a list of his complaints.* 他把自己的不滿一一説出。 —**recitation** /ˌrɛsəˈteʃən; ˌresɪˈteɪʃən/ *n* [C;U]

reck·less /ˈrɛklɪs; ˈrekləs/ *adj* not caring about danger or the possible bad results of your behaviour 魯莽的; 不顧後果的: *Wasn't it a bit reckless of you to leave the job before you had another one?* 你在找到別的工作之前就辭職, 不是有點輕率嗎? | *reckless driving* 魯莽駕駛 —**recklessly** *adv* —**recklessness** *n* [U]

★**reck·on** /ˈrɛkən; ˈrekən/ *v* **1** [+(that)] *infml* to think or suppose 認為; 設想: *I reckon that he'll come soon.* 我想他馬上就會來。 **2** [+ (that)] to guess or believe as a result of calculating roughly 估計; 推斷: *How much do you reckon she earns?* 你估計她掙多少錢? | *The experts reckon about 10,000 tons of grain are needed.* 專家們估計需要一萬噸穀物。 **3** [T] to calculate an amount or cost 計算: *My pay is reckoned from the 1st of the month.* 我的工資從這個月一號算起。

reckon on sthg *phr v* [T] to expect or depend on something happening 指望; 依賴〔某事物〕: *We're reckoning on a large profit.* 我們正期待着一筆大的贏利。| *You can't always reckon on seeing him.* 你不能老指望見到他。

reckon with *phr v* **1** [T **reckon with** sbdy/sthg] to have to deal with someone or something 處理〔某事〕; 對付〔某人〕: *If they try to dismiss you, they'll have the union to reckon with.* 如果他們想要解雇你, 工會就會對他們不客氣。 **2** [T **reckon with** sthg] to make your plans because you expect something 考慮到〔某事物〕: *We hadn't reckoned with the possibility that it might rain.* 我們沒料到有可能會下雨。 **3 to be reckoned with** to be treated seriously as a possible competitor or problem 值得認真對付: *The new team is already a force to be reckoned with.* 這支新球隊已成了一股不可忽視的力量, 必須認真對付。

reckon without sthg *phr v* [T] to fail to expect a possible problem when making a plan 〔訂計劃時〕未料到; 忽略: *When he decided to change his job, he reckoned without the difficulty of selling his house.* 他決定改換工作時, 沒有考慮到出售自己房子的困難。

reck·on·ing /ˈrɛkənɪŋ/ *n* [U] **1** a rough calculation 估算, 估計: *By my reckoning, it must be 60 kilometres from here to the coast.* 據我估計, 從這裡到海邊要有六十公里。 **2 day of reckoning** the time when you must be punished for a mistake or bad behaviour 報應到來之日; 受到懲罰的日子

re·claim /rɪˈklem; rɪˈklem/ *v* [T] **1** to get something back 收回〔某物〕: *I want to reclaim some of the tax I paid last year.* 我想要求退回去年繳納的部分稅款。 **2** to make land fit for use 開拓, 開墾〔土地〕: *This land was reclaimed from the sea.* 這片地是填海開拓的。 **–reclamation** /ˌrɛkləˈmeʃən; ˌrɛkləˈmeɪʃən/ *n* [U]

re·cline /rɪˈklaɪn; rɪˈklaɪn/ *v* **reclined, reclining** [I;T] to lean or lie back so that part of your body is supported (使)向後靠; (使)斜倚; (使)躺下: *in a reclining position* 斜倚着 | *She reclined her head against my shoulder.* 她把頭倚在我的肩上。

re·cluse /ˈrɛklus; rɪˈkluːs/ *n* a person who purposely lives alone and avoids other people 隱居者, 隱士, 遁世者

rec·og·ni·tion /ˌrɛkəɡˈnɪʃən; ˌrɛkəgˈnɪʃən/ *n* [U] **1** the act of being seen and known as someone or something 認識; 認出: *She hoped to avoid recognition by wearing dark glasses and a hat.* 她戴着墨鏡和帽子, 希望人們認不出她來。 **2** acceptance as legal or true 承認, 確認, 認可: *The new government has not yet received recognition from other countries.* 新政府尚未得到其他國家的承認。 **3 change beyond recognition, change out of all recognition** to change so as to be im-

possible to recognize 改變得認不出來: *Illness and age had changed her out of all recognition.* 疾病和衰老使她變得讓人認不出來了。 **4 in recognition of** in order to show official gratefulness for 作為表彰, 酬謝: *He received a large cheque in recognition of his years of service.* 他收到一張大面額支票, 作為對他多年來服務的酬謝。

rec·og·nize /ˈrɛkəɡˌnaɪz; ˈrɛkəgnaɪz/ *v* **recognized, recognizing** (also 又作 **recognise**) **1** [T] to know someone or something you have seen or heard before 辨認出: *I recognized Mary in the photograph.* 我從照片上認出了瑪麗。| *The town has changed so much you wouldn't recognize it!* 這市鎮變化很大, 你會認不出它來的! **2** [T] to officially accept something as being lawful 承認, 認可〔某事物〕: *They refused to recognize the new government.* 他們拒絕承認新政府。| *a recognized qualification in medicine* 在醫學上得到認可的資格 **3** [+(that)] to accept or agree that something is true or real 承認〔某事物為真實的〕: *I recognize that this is an unpleasant choice to make.* 我承認這是不得已作出的不愉快選擇。 **4** [T] to show official gratefulness for something 正式表揚, 表彰〔某事物〕: *The government recognized his services by making him a lord.* 政府為表彰他的服務貢獻, 授予他勳爵爵位。 **–recognizable** *adj* **–recognizably** *adv*

re·coil /rɪˈkɔɪl; rɪˈkɔɪl/ *v* [I] **1** to suddenly experience a strong feeling of fear or dislike 突然體驗〔強烈的恐懼或厭惡感〕: *She recoiled at their cruel behaviour.* 她對他們的殘酷行為厭憎不已。 **2** to move back suddenly from someone or something because you fear or dislike it 〔因恐懼或厭惡而〕畏縮, 退卻: *She recoiled from her attacker.* 她因受到襲擊而嚇得往後縮。 **–recoil** *n* [U]

rec·ol·lect /ˌrɛkəˈlɛkt; ˌrɛkəˈlekt/ *v* [T; not in progressive forms 不用於進行式] to remember 回憶; 想起; 記得: *Do you recollect her name?* 你記得她的名字嗎? | *I don't recollect meeting her.* 我不記得和她見過面。

□ USEFUL PATTERNS 有用句型
to recollect something; to recollect doing something

rec·ol·lec·tion /ˌrɛkəˈlɛkʃən; ˌrɛkəˈlekʃən/ *n* **1** [U] the power or action of remembering the past 記憶力; 回憶 **2** [C] a memory of the past 記憶中的往事: *I have a vivid recollection of that evening.* 我對於那個傍晚記憶猶新。

rec·om·mend /ˌrɛkəˈmɛnd; ˌrekəˈmend/ *v* [T] to praise someone or something as being good for a particular purpose 推薦, 介紹〔某人、某事物〕: *Can you recommend a good dictionary?* 你能給我推薦一本好詞典嗎? | *He recommended a very good book to* *me.* 他向我推薦了一本很好的書。| *They recommended him for the job.* 他們推薦他做這項工作。**2** [T; +(that)] to advise or suggest something as a correct or suitable course of action 勸告；建議：*I recommend caution in dealing with this matter.* 我建議要謹慎處理這件事。| *He recommends wearing safety equipment.* 他建議佩帶安全裝備。| *The committee has recommended that the training programme be improved.* 委員會提議培訓方案應當改進。

> □ USEFUL PATTERNS 有用句型
> to recommend something; to recommend doing something; to recommend that…

3 [T] (of a particular quality) to make something or somebody attractive 〔特質〕使〔某物或某人〕有吸引力；使受歡迎：*The hotel has nothing to recommend it except cheapness.* 這家旅館除了價錢便宜之外就無可取之處了。

*rec·om·men·da·tion /ˌrɛkəmɛnˈdeʃən; ˌre-kəmənˈdeɪʃən/ *n* **1** [C;U] the suggestion that someone or something is good for a particular purpose 推薦，介紹；稱讚：*I wrote him an excellent recommendation.* 我為他寫了一封極好的推薦信。| *They bought the car on Paul's recommendation.* 他們經保羅介紹，買了這輛車。**2** [C] the suggestion that a particular action should be done 提議，建議；勸告：*The committee's recommendations will be discussed tomorrow.* 明天將討論委員會的提議。

rec·om·pense¹ /ˈrɛkəmˌpɛns; ˈrekəmpens/ *v* **recompensed, recompensing** *fml* [T] to give a reward or payment for trouble or loss 〔正式〕酬報；賠償

recompense² *n* [sing;U] *fml* reward or payment given for causing trouble or loss, or to thank someone 〔正式〕報酬；酬金；賠償：*They received £500 as a recompense for the damage to their house.* 他們因房屋受損而得到五百英鎊的補償。

rec·on·cile /ˈrɛkənˌsaɪl; ˈrekənsaɪl/ *v* **reconciled, reconciling** [T] **1** to find agreement between ideas or situations which seem to be in opposition 調解；調和：*How do you reconcile your political principles* **with** *your religious beliefs?* 你怎樣使你的政治原則和你的宗教信仰調和起來的? **2** to have friendly relations again after a quarrel 〔爭吵後〕和解，和好：*Her parents were completely reconciled.* 她的父母和好如初了。**3 reconcile yourself to something** to accept something difficult or unpleasant without trying to change it 使接受〔困難或不愉快的事物〕：*I can't reconcile myself to living in such a boring place.* 我不甘心住在一個這麼乏味的地方。| *He never became reconciled to the death of his wife.* 他從來不願接受妻子死了的

事實。

rec·on·cil·i·a·tion /ˌrɛkənˌsɪliˈeʃən; ˌrekən-sɪliˈeɪʃən/ *n* [sing;U] the bringing back of friendly relations after a quarrel 和解，和好：*There was no hope of a reconciliation* **between** *the two families.* 這兩家人沒有和好的希望。| *There is now a spirit of reconciliation between the two nations.* 這兩國之間目前存在着修好的精神。

re·con·di·tion /ˌrikənˈdɪʃən; ˌriːkənˈdɪʃən/ *v* [T] to repair something so that it works well again 修理〔某物〕，修復：*A reconditioned engine is cheaper than a new one.* 一台修理好的發動機比新的便宜。

re·con·nais·sance /rɪˈkɑnəsəns; rɪˈkɒnɪ-səns/ *n* [C;U] the sending out of soldiers to get information about the enemy 偵察

re·con·noi·tre /ˌrikəˈnɔɪtəʳ; ˌrekəˈnɔɪtəʳ/ *v* **reconnoitred, reconnoitring** (also 又作 **re-connoiter** *AmE* 〔美式〕) [I;T] to send aircraft or a small group of soldiers near the place where an enemy is in order to get information about them 偵察〔敵情〕

re·con·sid·er /ˌrikənˈsɪdəʳ; ˌriːkənˈsɪdəʳ/ *v* [I; T] to think again about something and decide whether you need to change your opinion about it 重新考慮：*Won't you reconsider your decision to leave the club?* 你會否重新考慮退出俱樂部的決定? —**reconsideration** /ˌrikənˌsɪdəˈreʃən; ˌriːkənsɪdəˈreɪʃən/ *n* [U]

re·con·sti·tute /rɪˈkɑnstəˌtjut; riːˈkɒnstɪ-tjuːt/ *v* [T] **1** to bring an organization back into existence in a changed form 改組，重組成〔某一機構〕：*We decided to reconstitute the committee under a new chairman.* 我們決定在新主席主持下重組委員會。**2** to change dried food into its original state by adding water 加水使〔脫水食物〕復原：*reconstituted potato* 復水馬鈴薯

re·con·struct /ˌrikənˈstrʌkt; ˌriːkənˈstrʌkt/ *v* [T] **1** to rebuild a town or building after destruction or damage 〔遭受毀壞後〕重建，再建 **2** to get a complete description of something by putting together different pieces of information 〔利用各種資料〕重現〔完整的事物〕，使再現：*The police are trying to reconstruct the crime from the few clues they have.* 警察正設法根據已掌握的線索，重現整個犯案過程。—**reconstruction** /-ˈstrʌkʃən; -ˈstrʌk-ʃən/ *n* [C;U]：*a reconstruction of the events leading up to the accident* 導致事故發生的種種事件的重組

*re·cord¹ /rɪˈkɔrd; rɪˈkɔːd/ *v* **1** [T] to write down something or put it on a computer so that it can be looked at later 將〔某事物〕記錄下來：*All the statistics are recorded on this disc.* 所有的統計數字都記錄在這張磁盤上。| *How he died is not recorded.* 他是如何死的沒有記載。| *Please record the score in this book.* 請把得分記在這本書裡。**2** [I;T] to preserve sound or events so that they can be heard and seen again 錄音; 錄下: *The broadcast was recorded, not live.* 這個廣播節目是錄影的, 不是現場直播的。| *She has recorded several songs.* 她錄了幾首歌。| *The wedding ceremony was recorded on video.* 婚禮的情況記錄在錄影帶上。**3** [T] (of an instrument) to show an amount by measuring 〔儀器〕顯示, 標示: *The thermometer recorded a temperature of 28 degrees.* 溫度計上顯示出溫度為二十八度。

★rec·ord² /ˈrɛkəd; ˈrekɔːd/ *n* [C] **1** information kept as a written statement or on a computer so that it can be looked at later 記錄; 記載: *Keep a record of how much you spend.* 你花了多少錢要作一個記錄。**2** the known facts about the past behaviour or performance of a person or organization 〔人或組織的〕履歷; 歷史: *She has a long criminal record.* 她有長期的犯罪記錄。| *The company has an outstanding record in industrial relations.* 這家公司在勞資關係上表現得很出色。**3** the best figure ever reached 記錄; 最佳成績: *He broke the record for long distance swimming.* 他打破了長距離游泳的記錄。| *She holds the world record for discus throwing.* 她保持着擲鐵餅的世界記錄。**4** a circular piece of plastic on which sound is stored so that it can be played back again 唱片: *Have you heard my new record?* 你聽過我的新唱片嗎? | *He put a record on.* 他放了一張唱片。**5 off the record** *infml* unofficial and intended to be known only in private 〔非正式〕非正式的〔地〕; 不公開的〔地〕: *He told us off the record that the firm was doing badly this year.* 他私下告訴我們, 這家商行今年營業情況不好。**6 on record: a** having said something publicly 公開地說: *She is on record as having said that she opposed high taxation.* 她公開表明自己反對高稅收的立場。**b** ever recorded 記錄在案的: *It was the coldest winter on record.* 這是有記錄以來最冷的冬天。**7 put/set the record straight** to correct someone's information about or understanding of something by giving them the correct facts 澄清事實; 糾正誤解: *This article really sets the record straight.* 這篇文章確實弄清了事實。

rec·ord³ /ˈrɛkəd; ˈrekɔːd/ *adj* [only before a noun 只用於名詞前] more, faster, better, etc., than ever before 創記錄的: *a record crop of corn* 創記錄的穀物收成 | *We finished the work in record time.* 我們以創記錄的速度完成了工作。

record-break·ing /ˈ·· ˌ··/ *adj* better than the former record, especially in sport 〔尤指體育運動中〕破記錄的: *a record-breaking speed* 破記錄的速度

recorded de·liv·er·y /·ˌ·· ·ˈ··/ *n* [U] a method of sending mail through the Post Office, by which you can get proof that it has been posted and delivered 掛號郵遞

re·cord·er /rɪˈkɔrdə; rɪˈkɔːdəʳ/ *n* **1** a musical instrument that you play by blowing through a hollow tube and putting your fingers over different holes 豎笛, 直笛〔一種管樂器〕**2** a machine used for listening to or recording TAPES or CASSETTES, or watching or recording VIDEOS (磁帶)錄音機; 錄像機

★re·cord·ing /rɪˈkɔrdɪŋ; rɪˈkɔːdɪŋ/ *n* **1** a performance, speech, or piece of music that has been recorded 〔演出、講話或樂曲的〕錄音; 錄像: *the latest recording of the London Symphony Orchestra* 倫敦交響樂團最近的演出錄音 **2** the process of preserving sound or events so that they can be heard again 錄製: *recording equipment* 錄音[錄像]設備

record play·er /ˈ·· ˌ··/ *n* a machine which is used to play records 唱機 –see picture on page 730 見 730 頁彩圖

re·count¹ /rɪˈkaʊnt; rɪˈkaʊnt/ *v* [T] **1** *fml* to tell a story or describe something that happened 〔正式〕敍述〔故事〕; 描述〔某事〕: *She recounted her adventures.* 她講述了她的冒險經歷。**2** to count again 重新計算: *They had to recount the votes.* 他們不得不重新計算選票。

re·count² /ˈri,kaʊnt; ˈriːkaʊnt/ *n* a second count of votes in an election 重新計算〔選票〕, 重數

re·course /rɪˈkɔrs; rɪˈkɔːs/ *n* **1 have recourse to** to use something as a means of help 求助於, 依靠〔某事物〕: *Patients have recourse to drugs to ease their pain.* 病人依靠毒品來減輕自己的痛苦。**2 without recourse to** without making use of something 不利用〔某物〕: *We hope to solve the problem without recourse to further borrowing.* 我們希望不靠再借款來解決問題。

★re·cov·er /rɪˈkʌvə; rɪˈkʌvəʳ/ *v* **1** [I] to be well again after an illness 痊癒, 康復: *I'm still recovering from a bad cold.* 我得了重感冒, 仍有待恢復。| *He never fully recovered from the heart attack.* 他並未完全從心臟病康復過來。**2** [I] to return to a former state of body or mind 恢復: *She recovered consciousness soon after the accident.* 事故發生後不久, 她就恢復了知覺。| *The country had not yet recovered from the effects of the war.* 這個國家還未從戰爭帶來的影響中恢復過來。| *They never recovered from the shock.* 他們並未從這打擊中復原過來。**3** [T] to get back or bring back something lost or stolen 尋回, 重新獲得〔遺失或被偷走的東西〕: *The police managed to recover the stolen goods.* 警方設法找回了被盜的貨物。| *The bodies were recovered from the wreck.* (人們)從沉船上找出屍體。**4** [T] to get back the amount of money you spent 收回〔所花的錢〕: *The company recovered its investment in two years.* 這家公司兩年內收回了投資。**5** [T] to put a new cover on something 給〔某物〕換上新面: *The chairs were recovered in* *green silk.* 椅子都換上了新的綠色絲綢椅套。– **recoverable** *adj*

*★**re·cov·er·y** /rɪˈkʌvərɪ; rɪˈkʌvəri/ *n* **1** [U] the getting back of something lost or stolen 找回; 尋回: *the recovery of the stolen jewels* 找回被盜的珠寶 **2** [sing] a return to good health or a strong condition 恢復, 痊癒, 復原: *She made a quick recovery from her fever.* 她發燒很快就康復了。| *The government's policies led to an economic recovery.* 政府的政策帶來了經濟復蘇。

re·cre·ate /ˌriːkrɪˈeɪt; ˌriːkriˈeɪt/ *v* recreated, recreating [T] to make something exist or be experienced again 使(某事物)再現; 使再次經歷: *You can't recreate the past.* 你不可能使過去再現。

rec·re·a·tion /ˌrɛkrɪˈeʃən; ˌrɛkriˈeɪʃən/ *n* [C; U] a way of amusing and enjoying yourself when you are not working 消遣, 娛樂: *His only recreations are drinking beer and reading.* 他僅有的消遣是喝啤酒和看書。| *What do you do for recreation?* 你做甚麼來消遣? –**recreational** *adj*

> ■ USAGE 用法: We use **recreation** as a general word for the things people do in their spare time. Forms of recreation include **sports** such as tennis and football. They also include **hobbies,** which people do on their own, not in order to compete ☆**recreation** 是用來指人們閒暇時所做的事的一般用詞。消遣的形式包括 **sports** (運動), 如網球和足球, 也包括人們自己進行、不以競賽為目的的 **hobbies** (業餘愛好): *Her hobbies are gardening, stamp-collecting and playing the piano.* 她的業餘愛好是園藝、集郵和彈鋼琴。

re·crim·i·nate /rɪˈkrɪməˌneɪt; rɪˈkrɪmɪ̩neɪt/ *v* recriminated, recriminating *fml* [I] to blame someone for bad behaviour after they have already blamed you 〖正式〗反責; 反(控)訴 –**recriminatory** /-nə̩torɪ; -nətəri/ *adj* –**recrimination** /rɪˌkrɪməˈneʃən; rɪˌkrɪmɪ̩neɪʃən/ *n* [C;U]: *Let's make friends, instead of wasting our time on recriminations.* 我們交個朋友吧, 不要再浪費時間互相指責了。

re·cruit[1] /rɪˈkrut; rɪˈkruːt/ *n* **1** a new member of an organization 〔機構中的〕新成員: *New recruits to our music club are always welcome.* 我們的音樂俱樂部隨時歡迎新會員參加。**2** someone who has recently joined the armed services 新兵

recruit[2] *v* **1** [I;T] attract new members to join the armed forces or other organization 招募, 徵募〔新兵或新成員〕: *His job is recruiting for the Conservative Party.* 他的工作是為保守黨吸收新成員。**2** [T] to find someone to employ for a particular job 雇用, 聘用〔某人〕: *We're having a lot of diffi-*

culty recruiting well-qualified staff. 我們在招聘素質好的員工時遇到不少困難。–**recruit·ment** *n* [U]

rec·tan·gle /ˈrɛktæŋgl; ˈrɛktæŋgəl/ *n* a shape with four straight sides; the sides opposite each other are of equal length 長方形, 矩形

rec·tan·gu·lar /rɛkˈtæŋgjələ·; rekˈtæŋgjᵿlər/ *adj* in the shape of a rectangle 長方形的, 矩形的

rec·ti·fy /ˈrɛktəˌfaɪ; ˈrɛktɪ̩faɪ/ *v* rectified, rectifying *fml* [T] to correct something or change it to something better 〖正式〗改正, 糾正〔某事物〕: *Would you rectify the mistakes in my bill?* 請你糾正一下我賬單上的錯誤好嗎? | *A good manager could rectify the situation.* 一位好的管理人員能使局面改觀。–**rectification** /ˌrɛktəfəˈkeʃən; ˌrɛktɪ̩fɪ̩ˈkeɪʃən/ *n* [C;U]

rec·tor /ˈrɛktə·; ˈrektər/ *n* **1** the priest in the CHURCH OF ENGLAND who is in charge of a PARISH 〔英國教會的〕教區長 **2** the head of certain colleges and schools 〔某些學院、學校的〕院長; 校長

rec·to·ry /ˈrɛktərɪ; ˈrektəri/ *n* the house where a rector lives 教區長住所

rec·tum /ˈrɛktəm; ˈrektəm/ *n* tech the lowest end of your bowel, through which solid waste matter passes out of your body 〖術語〗直腸

re·cu·pe·rate /rɪˈkjupə̩ret; rɪˈkjuːpəreɪt/ *v* recuperated, recuperating [I] to get well or strong again after an illness 病後復原; 恢復健康: *He went to the mountains to recuperate.* 他去了山區休養。–**recuperation** /rɪˌkjupəˈreʃən; rɪˌkjuːpəˈreɪʃən/ *n* [U]

re·cur /rɪˈkɜ·; rɪˈkɜːr/ *v* -rr- [I] to happen or appear again or many times 一再發生; 反覆出現: *If the pain recurs, take this medicine.* 如果再痛的話, 就服這種藥。–**recurrence** /rɪˈkɜ·əns; rɪˈkʌrəns/ *n* [U]: *the frequent recurrence of this problem* 這個問題一再發生 –**recurrent** *adj*

re·cy·cle /riˈsaɪkl; ˌriːˈsaɪkəl/ *v* recycled, recycling [T] to treat something which has already been used so that it is fit to use again 回收利用〔用過的東西〕: *These bottles can be recycled.* 這些瓶子可以回收利用。| *a bag made of recycled paper* 再造紙做的紙袋

*★★***red**[1] /rɛd; red/ *adj* **1** of the colour of blood 紅(色)的: *Let's paint the door red.* 我們把門漆成紅色吧。| *a red dress* 紅色連衣裙 –see picture on page 243 見 243 頁彩圖 **2** of a copper colour (used of hair) 〔頭髮〕紅褐色的 **3** stronger in colour than usual because of a feeling of anger or shame (used of someone's face) 〔因生氣或羞愧而〕通紅的〔指臉〕: *She turned red with embarrassment.* 她尷尬得滿臉通紅。**4** (also **Red**) COMMUNIST (a word used to show disapproval) 赤色的; 共產黨的〔含貶義〕–**redness** *n* [U]

red² *n* **1** [C;U] a red colour 紅色: *the pinks and reds of the sunset* 深淺不一的紅色晚霞 **2** [U] red clothes 紅衣服: *dressed in red* 穿紅衣 **3 in the red** in debt 負債的; 有虧欠的; 有赤字的: *Your account is in the red.* 你的賬目有赤字。 **4** (also 又作 **Red**) a COMMUNIST 共產黨人; 共產主義者

red car·pet /ˌ· ˈ··/ *n* **the red carpet** a special ceremonial welcome to a guest 紅地毯式的歡迎儀式; 隆重歡迎: *We'll roll out the red carpet for the president.* 我們將隆重歡迎總統。

Red Cross /ˌ· ˈ·/ *n* **the Red Cross** [+sing/pl verb] an international Christian organization that looks after sick and wounded people 紅十字會: *The Red Cross is active in a lot of different countries.* 紅十字會在許多國家都很活躍。

red·cur·rant /ˌredˈkɜːrənt; ˌredˈkʌrənt◂/ *n* a small red berry or the bush on which it grows 紅醋栗(灌木)

red·den /ˈrɛdn; ˈredn/ *v* **1** [I;T] to turn red from anger or another strong feeling (因生氣或別的強烈感情而)臉紅: *Her face reddened when I mentioned Jack.* 我提到傑克時, 她便臉紅了。 **2** [T] to make something red 使(某物)變紅: *The sunset reddened the clouds.* 落日把雲霞映得通紅。

red·dish /ˈrɛdɪʃ; ˈredɪʃ/ *adj* slightly red 微紅的, 淡紅的

re·deem /rɪˈdiːm; rɪˈdiːm/ *v* [T] **1** to make a bad thing or situation slightly less bad 彌補; 補救: *Oliver's performance redeems an otherwise awful production.* 奧利弗的表演彌補了其他方面的糟糕演出。 **2 redeem yourself** to do something to improve people's opinion of you after you have behaved badly 挽回自己的聲譽: *He'll never redeem himself for hitting her.* 他打她, 因此再也挽不回自己的聲譽了。 **3** to buy back something you have given to someone in return for money 贖回(抵押品) **4 redeeming feature** a single good point in a person or thing that is bad in all other ways (壞人或壞事的)唯一可取之處: *His only redeeming feature is his honesty.* 他的唯一可取之處是誠實。

re·demp·tion /rɪˈdɛmpʃən; rɪˈdempʃən/ *n* [U] **1** the state of being saved from evil which CHRISTIANS believe was made possible by the death of JESUS CHRIST 救贖 **2 beyond/past redemption** too bad to be saved or improved 無可救藥的; 不可挽回的

re·de·ploy /ˌriːdɪˈplɔɪ; ˌriːdɪˈplɔɪ/ *v* to rearrange soldiers, workers, or apparatus in a more effective way 重新部署; 重新調配(調派) –**redeployment** *n* [U]

re·de·vel·op·ment /ˌriːdɪˈvɛləpmənt; ˌriːdɪˈveləpmənt/ *n* the knocking down and rebuilding of part of a town 重建, 重新開發

red·head /ˈrɛdˌhɛd; ˈredhed/ *n* *infml* a woman with red hair (非正式)紅髮女子: *He married a beautiful redhead.* 他和一位美麗的紅髮女郎結了婚。

red her·ring /ˌ· ˈ··/ *n* a fact or subject which is introduced to draw people's attention away from the main point 轉移注意力的事(話題)

red-hot /ˌ· ˈ·◂/ *adj* so hot that it shines red (used of metal) 熱得發紅的; 赤熱的(指金屬)

re·di·rect /ˌriːdəˈrɛkt; ˌriːdaɪˈrekt/ *v* [T] to send post in a different direction or to a new address 改寄(信件)

re·do /ˌriːˈduː; riːˈduː/ *v* **redid** /-ˈdɪd; -ˈdɪd/, **redone** /-ˈdʌn; -ˈdʌn/ [T] to do something again so that you can change it or make it better 重做, 再做(某事): *You'll have to redo your homework.* 你得重做你的家庭作業。

red·o·lent /ˈrɛdlənt; ˈredələnt/ *adj* *fml* [never before a noun 不能用於名詞前] making you think of something (正式)使人聯想起(某事物)的: *an old house redolent of mystery* 一座使人有神祕感的老房子

re·dou·ble /riːˈdʌbl; riːˈdʌbəl/ *v* **redoubled, redoubling, redouble your efforts** to greatly increase your efforts 加倍努力: *The police redoubled their efforts to find the missing child.* 警察加倍努力去尋找失蹤的孩子。

re·doub·ta·ble /rɪˈdaʊtəbl; rɪˈdaʊtəbəl/ *adj* *lit* greatly respected and feared (used of people) (文)令人敬畏的(指人): *a redoubtable opponent* 令人敬畏的對手

re·dress¹ /rɪˈdrɛs; rɪˈdres/ *v* *fml* (正式) **1** to correct an injustice or improve the situation for someone who has been treated unfairly 改正, 糾正 **2 redress the balance** to make things equal or fair again 作公正的調整, 改變不公道的局面

re·dress² /ˈriːdrɛs; rɪˈdres/ *n* *fml* [U] satisfaction or payment for something wrong that has been done (正式)賠償, 補償: *You must seek redress in the law courts for the damage to your car.* 你的汽車受到了損壞, 你應當通過法律途徑要求賠償。

red tape /ˌ· ˈ·/ *n* [U] unnecessary official rules that delay action 繁文縟節, 官樣文章

★★re·duce /rɪˈdjuːs; rɪˈdjuːs/ *v* **reduced, reducing 1** [T] to make less in size, amount, or degree 減少; 縮小; 降低: *I bought this shirt because it was reduced from £10 to £5.* 我買這件襯衣是因為價格從十英鎊跌到了五英鎊。| *He won't reduce the rent of our house.* 他不會降低我們的房租。| *a defence policy that reduces the risk of war* 減少戰爭風險的防禦政策 **2 be reduced to doing something** to be forced to behave in a particular way 被迫做某事: *She was reduced to begging for her living.* 她被迫以乞討為生。**3 reduce someone to tears** to make someone cry 使人流淚

reduce sbdy/sth to sthg *phr v* [T] **1** to change something into a simpler form 把(某事物)簡化為…: *We can reduce his argument to three simple facts.* 我們可以把他的論

據歸納為三個簡單的事實。 **2** to cause some-one or something to be in an unfortunate or bad state 使〔某人或某事物〕處於〔不幸或糟糕的地位〕: *The bomb reduced the city to ashes.* 炸彈使城市化為灰燼。| *His bad be-haviour reduces me to despair.* 他的惡劣行為讓我絕望。

☆**re·duc·tion** /rɪˈdʌkʃən; rɪˈdʌkʃən/ *n* **1** [C;U] the act of making something less in size, amount, or degree 減少; 縮小; 降低: *price reductions* 減價 **2** [C] the amount by which something is made less 減少量; 削減數: *a 2% reduction in the rate of inflation* 通貨膨脹率下降百分之二

re·dun·dan·cy /rɪˈdʌndənsɪ; rɪˈdʌndənsi/ *n* **redundancies** [C;U] **1** a case of losing your job because there is not enough work 〔因人員過剩而造成的〕裁員, 解雇: *The govern-ment action will cause a lot of redundancy among coalminers.* 政府的行動將使煤礦工人大量過剩而被裁減。| *There have been 200 redundancies at the factory.* 這家工廠已有冗員二百人。 **2 redundancy payment** an amount of money paid to someone employed by a company when they be-come redundant 裁員費, 冗員遣散費

re·dun·dant /rɪˈdʌndənt; rɪˈdʌndənt/ *adj* **1** no longer employed by a company or organization because there is not enough work 〔因人員過剩而〕被解雇的: *Seventy men at the factory were made redundant when the machines were installed.* 機器安裝好以後, 這家工廠裡有七十名工人成為冗員被辭退了。 **2** no longer needed for a particular pur-pose 多餘的, 過剩的: *The new road has made rail travel almost redundant.* 這條新建的公路使鐵路運輸幾乎變得多餘。

reed /riːd; riːd/ *n* **1** a plant with tall, hollow stems; reeds grow in wet places 蘆葦, 葦草 **2** a thin piece of wood or metal in a musi-cal instrument that produces sound when air is blown over it 〔吹奏樂器中的〕簧片

reef /riːf; riːf/ *n* a line of sharp rocks or a bank of sand above or near the surface of the sea 礁; 暗礁: *The ship was wrecked on a reef.* 船觸礁失事了。

reek /riːk; riːk/ *n* [sing] a strong unpleasant smell 濃烈的臭味, 惡臭: *a reek of tobacco and beer* 煙味和啤酒味

reek *v* [I] to smell strongly and unpleasantly of 散發出濃烈臭味, 有臭味: *His clothes reek of cigarettes.* 他的衣服散發出煙臭。

reel[1] /riːl; riːl/ *n* **1** a round object around which you wind things such as thread for sewing or film 〔縫衣線的〕卷軸; 〔電影膠片的〕卷盤 **2** a Scottish dance 〔蘇格蘭的〕里爾舞(曲), 輕快的雙人舞(曲)

reel[2] *v* **1** [I] to move unsteadily as if drunk 〔如喝醉般〕蹣跚, 躊蹌, 跌跌撞撞: *He was reeling when he left the pub.* 他蹣跚地離開酒館。 **2** [I] to be in a state of confusion or shock 糊塗; 震驚: *All these figures make my head reel.* 所有這些數字弄得我頭昏腦脹。| *The party is still reeling from its defeat in the election.* 該黨仍處於選舉失敗的震驚之中, 動搖不定。

reel sthg ↔ **off** *phr v* [T] to repeat infor-mation quickly and easily from memory 一口氣背出: *He could reel off the names of all the kings of England.* 他能一口氣背出英國所有國王的名字。

re·en·try /riːˈentrɪ; riːˈentri/ *n* [C;U] an act of entering again 再進入; 重返: *The space-craft made a successful reentry into the earth's atmosphere.* 太空船成功地重返大氣層。

re·fec·to·ry /rɪˈfektərɪ; rɪˈfektəri/ *n* **refecto-ries** a large hall, for example in a college, in which meals are served 〔學校等的〕食堂, 餐廳

☆**re·fer** /rɪˈfɜː; rɪˈfɜːr/ **-rr-** *v*

refer to *phr v* **1** [T **refer to** sbdy/sthg] to mention or speak about someone or some-thing 提到, 談及〔某人、某事〕: *Which companies did the prime minister refer to in his speech?* 首相在演講中提到了哪幾家公司? | *He didn't refer to Jack in his letter.* 他在信中沒有提到傑克。| *He referred to her simply as "my friend".* 他只稱她為"我的朋友"。 **2** [T **refer to** sthg] to look at some-thing in order to get information 查閱, 參考, 參照〔某物〕: *Refer to a dictionary if you don't know what this word means.* 如果你不明白這單詞是甚麼意思, 查一下詞典。 **3** [T **re-fer** sbdy **to** sbdy/sthg] to tell a particular person or organization about something or someone so they can do what is needed 提交〔某人或某組織〕處理: *Her doctor referred her to a specialist.* 她的醫生把她交給專科醫生治療。| *The proposal was referred to the Finance Committee.* 這項提議提交給財政委員會處理。 **4** [T **refer** sbdy **to** sthg] to suggest that someone looks at a particular piece of writing to get information they need 建議〔某人〕參考〔查閱〕: *The professor referred him to an article in the latest journal.* 教授建議他去查閱最近一期雜誌上的一篇文章。

ref·er·ee[1] /ˌrefəˈriː; ˌrefəˈri/ *n* **1** (also 又作 **ref** *infml* 〔非正式〕) an official in charge of judging certain games 〔一些比賽的〕裁判員 **2** a person who provides a statement about your character and abilities 〔性格、能力的〕證明人, 介紹人, 推薦人

■ **USAGE** 用法: **Referee** is used in connection with **basketball, boxing, football, hockey, lacrosse, rugby, snooker, squash,** and **wrestling. Um-pire** is used in connection with **bad-minton, baseball, cricket, tennis,** and **volleyball.** ☆referee (裁判)用於籃球、拳

擊、足球、曲棍球、長柄曲棍球，英式橄欖球、彩色桌球、壁球和摔跤等比賽中。**umpire** (裁判)用於羽毛球、棒球、板球、網球和排球等比賽中。

referee² v [I;T] to act as referee for a game or match 為〔比賽〕擔任裁判: *Who's going to referee Monday's game?* 星期一的比賽由誰擔任裁判?

⋆⋆ref·er·ence /ˈrɛfərəns; ˈrɛfərəns/ n **1** [C;U] an example of mentioning or talking about something or someone 談到, 提及; 涉及: *In the letter, he made no reference to his illness.* 他在信中沒有提到自己的病。| *Her remark was a nasty reference to her previous boss.* 她在説話中惡意地提到了自己的前任老闆。**2** [U] an act of looking at something for information 參考, 參閲, 查閲: *Keep this dictionary on your desk for easy reference.* 把這本詞典放在你的書桌上, 以便查閲。**3** for future reference for use in the future 供將來參考: *He kept the article for future reference.* 他保留着這篇文章以供日後參考。**4** [C] a letter written by someone about your character and ability which you use when looking for a job〔謀職時關於品行和能力的〕證明書, 介紹信, 推薦信: *She had excellent references so we hired her.* 推薦信都對她評價很高, 所以我們雇用了她。**5** [C] something that tells a reader where a piece of information came from 引文出處; 附註: *There's a list of references at the back of the book.* 書後面有參考書目。**6** in/with reference to *fml* a phrase used to show what subject you are talking or writing about〔正式〕關於〔表示自己正在談論或寫的話題或主題〕: *Dear Sir, with reference to your letter of the 15th May...* 先生, 關於您五月十五日的來信⋯

reference book /ˈ··· ·/ n a book, for example a dictionary, which you look at to get particular information about a subject 參考書, 工具書〔如詞典〕

ref·e·ren·dum /ˌrɛfəˈrɛndəm; ˌrɛfəˈrendəm/ n a direct vote by all the people of a country or area to decide on a political matter about which there is strong disagreement〔以表決有很大爭執的政治問題的〕全民投票

re·fill¹ /ˈriˈfɪl; ˌriːˈfɪl/ v [T] to fill something again 再充滿: *I'll refilled my cigarette lighter.* 我要給打火機再充氣。

re·fill² /ˈriˌfɪl; ˈriːfɪl/ n a container holding a quantity of a particular substance which is used to refill something 置換物, 添補物, 新補充物: *I bought two refills for this pen.* 我給這支筆買了兩支筆芯。

re·fine /riˈfaɪn; rɪˈfaɪn/ v **refined, refining** [T] **1** to make something pure 提煉, 精製, 精煉: *Oil must be refined before it can be used.* 石油在使用前必須經過提煉。**2** to im-

prove an idea, method, or plan by changing some of its details 對〔想法、方法或計劃〕去蕪存菁地改進; 對⋯精益求精

re·fined /riˈfaɪnd; rɪˈfaɪnd/ adj **1** made pure 精煉的; 精製的: *refined oil* 提煉過的石油〔精煉油〕**2** having good education, manners, and often an interest in art, music, and literature 優雅的, 高雅的; 有教養的: *She's so refined she eats cake with a little fork!* 她非常文雅, 吃蛋糕要用小叉子! –opposite 反義 **unrefined**

re·fine·ment /riˈfaɪnmənt; rɪˈfaɪnmənt/ n **1** [C] a small, but useful addition or improvement to a product or system 精巧的附件; 精細的改良品: *The new car has many new refinements such as a compact disc player.* 這輛新車有許多精巧的新附加裝置, 如雷射唱機。**2** [U] the process of making a substance pure 精煉, 提煉: *the refinement of sugar* 糖的精煉 **3** [U] the quality of being polite and well-educated 優雅, 高雅; 有教養: *a woman of great refinement* 非常文雅的女士

re·fin·e·ry /riˈfaɪnri; rɪˈfaɪnəri/ n **refineries** a factory for refining metals, oil, or sugar〔金屬、油或糖的〕精煉廠, 提煉廠: *a sugar refinery* 煉糖廠

⋆⋆re·flect /riˈflɛkt; rɪˈflɛkt/ v **1** be reflected to be shown as an image, for example in water or a mirror 反映, 照出〔如在水中或鏡中〕: *Clouds were reflected in the lake.* 湖裏映照出朵朵白雲。**2** [T] to throw back heat, light, or sound 反射〔熱、光或聲〕: *The material is designed to reflect the heat.* 這種材料是為反射熱而設計的。**3** [T] to express or show a feeling or belief 表達; 表現〔情感或信仰〕: *Does the letter reflect your real opinions?* 這封信是否表達了你的真正想法? **4** [T] to be the result of a particular situation or feeling 反映〔某種情況或感情〕: *The increase in crime reflects rising unemployment.* 犯罪活動的上升是由於失業人數增加所致。**5** [I] to think carefully 仔細考慮, 深思: *After reflecting for a time he decided not to go.* 仔細考慮過後, 他決定不去了。

reflect on sbdy/sthg *phr* v [T] to make something be considered in a particular way 給〔某事物〕帶來影響: *These exam results reflect badly on your school.* 這些考試成績給你們學校帶來了很壞的影響。

⋆re·flec·tion /riˈflɛkʃən; rɪˈflɛkʃən/ n **1** [C] an image reflected in a mirror or water〔鏡中的〕影像;〔水中的〕倒影: *We looked at our reflections in the lake.* 我們看着自己在湖中的倒影。**2** [U] the process by which heat, light, or sound, is reflected〔熱、光、聲的〕反射, 反照 **3** [C;U] deep and careful thought 深思; 考慮後的看法: *his reflections on Indian politics* 他對印度政治的看法 | *After a moment's reflection, she agreed to go.* 略作考慮之後, 她同意去。**4** on reflection

R

after thinking carefully 經過仔細考慮: *She admitted, on reflection, that it was foolish.* 經仔細考慮後, 她承認那是愚蠢的。 **5** [C] something that is a result or sign of a particular situation 反映: *The results of the election are an accurate reflection of the public mood.* 選舉結果確實反映了公眾情緒。

re·flec·tor /rɪˈflektə; rɪˈflektəˊ/ *n* a surface that reflects light 反射器; 反射鏡; 反射物

re·flex /ˈriːfleks; ˈriːfleks/ *n* a movement which you cannot control made by a part of the body in reply to something〔對某事物的〕反射(作用)[動作]: *The doctor hit my knee with a hammer to test my reflexes.* 醫生用鎚子敲我的膝蓋來試驗我的反射動作。

re·flex·ive /rɪˈfleksɪv; rɪˈfleksɪv/ *adj* **1 reflexive verb** a verb in which the object is always the same as the subject; for example in the sentence "He studied himself in the mirror." "He" and "himself" mean the same person 反身動詞〔如在"He studied himself in the mirror"中, "He" 和 "himself" 指同一個人〕 **2 reflexive pronoun** a word which points back to the subject of the verb; for example in the sentence "She washed herself." "herself" is a reflexive pronoun which tells us about the subject "she" 反身代詞〔如在"She washed herself."中, "herself" 是反身代詞, 指的是主語 "she"〕

re·form¹ /rɪˈfɔrm; rɪˈfɔːm/ *v* [T] to improve an organization or system by making changes to it 改革; 改良, 改進: *This law will help to reform the prisons.* 這條法律將有助於改革監獄內的情況。 **2** [I;T] to improve or change unacceptable behaviour (使)改正; (使)改過自新: *You can't reform criminals by punishing them.* 你不能用懲罰手段來改造罪犯。 | *Harry has completely reformed since he stopped taking drugs.* 哈里自從不再吸毒以後, 已完全改過自新了。

reform² *n* [C;U] a change that improves an organization or social system 改革, 革新; 改良: *The minister announced the reform of the tax system.* 部長宣佈對稅務制度進行改革。 | *Reform of unfair laws will take many years.* 對不公正的法律進行改革要花許多年時間。

Ref·or·ma·tion /ˌrefəˈmeʃən; ˌrefəˈmeɪʃən/ *n* **the Reformation** the religious movement in Europe in the 16th century leading to the establishment of the PROTESTANT churches〔十六世紀歐洲的〕宗教改革運動〔導致新教各教派的成立〕

re·for·mer /rɪˈfɔrmə; rɪˈfɔːməˊ/ *n* a person who tries to change and improve conditions in society 改革者, 改良者, 革新者

re·fract /rɪˈfrækt; rɪˈfrækt/ *v* [I;T] to make light or sound change direction when passing through a substance like glass or water at an angle (使)〔光線、聲音〕折射 **–refraction** /-ˈfrækʃən; -ˈfrækʃən/ *n*

re·frain¹ /rɪˈfren; rɪˈfreɪn/ *v* [I] **refrain from**

doing something to intentionally stop yourself from doing something 抑制[克制]不做某事: *Please refrain from smoking.* 請勿吸煙。

refrain² *n* a part of a song that you repeat a number of times when you sing the song〔歌曲中重複演唱的〕副歌

re·fresh /rɪˈfreʃ; rɪˈfreʃ/ *v* [T] **1** to make someone less hot or tired 消除…的疲勞; 使振作精神: *A hot bath will refresh you.* 洗個熱水澡會使你精神振作。 | *He refreshed himself with a glass of beer.* 他喝了杯啤酒提提神。 **2 refresh your memory** to remind you about something 喚起…的記憶: *Please refresh my memory — what was your last job?* 請幫我想想 — 你的上一份工作是甚麼?

refresher course /·ˈ···/ *n* a training course given to a group of members of the same profession so that they know about recent changes in their field 進修課程: *She attended a refresher course on modern teaching methods.* 她參加了一項現代教學法的進修課。

re·fresh·ing /rɪˈfreʃɪŋ; rɪˈfreʃɪŋ/ *adj* **1** making you feel cool and strong again after being unpleasantly hot or tired 涼爽的; 提神的: *a refreshing drink* 提神的飲料 | *a refreshing sleep* 消除疲勞的睡一覺 **2** pleasantly new and interesting 清新有趣的, 令人耳目一新的: *It's refreshing to see a film with so little violence.* 看到一部幾乎沒有暴力鏡頭的影片, 真令人耳目一新。 **–refreshingly** *adv*

re·fresh·ment /rɪˈfreʃmənt; rɪˈfreʃmənt/ *n* **1** [U] *fml* food and drink〔正式〕食品; 飲料: *We worked all day without refreshment.* 我們工作了一整天, 沒吃也沒喝。 **2 refreshments** small quantities of food and drink, usually served at a social gathering〔常在社交聚會時供應的〕茶點, 點心: *Refreshments will be served after the performance.* 演出後有茶點招待。

re·fri·ge·rate /rɪˈfrɪdʒəˌret; rɪˈfrɪdʒəreɪt/ *v* **refrigerated, refrigerating** [T] to make food or liquid cold as a way of preserving it 冷藏, 冷凍〔食物等〕: *refrigerated meat* 凍肉 **–refrigeration** /rɪˌfrɪdʒəˈreʃən; rɪˌfrɪdʒəˈreɪʃən/ *n* [U]

re·fri·ge·ra·tor /rɪˈfrɪdʒəˌretə; rɪˈfrɪdʒəreɪtəˊ/ *n* (also 又作 **fridge** *infml*〔非正式〕) a large box, usually working by electricity, in which food and drink can be kept cool in order to preserve them (電)冰箱

re·fu·el /rɪˈfjuəl; ˌriːˈfjuːəl/ *v* **-ll-** (also 又作 **-l-** *AmE*〔美式〕) [I;T] to fill up or be filled up again with FUEL (給)加油; 加注燃料: *The aircraft stopped in Cairo to refuel.* 飛機在開羅停留加油。

ref·uge /ˈrefjudʒ; ˈrefjuːdʒ/ *n* **1** [U] protection or shelter from unhappiness or physical danger 躲避; 避難; 庇護: *The prisoners sought refuge in telling stories.* 犯人們以講故事來尋找慰藉。 | *We found refuge from the* storm under a tree. 我們在一棵樹下躲避暴風雨。 **2** [C] a place which provides protection or shelter 收容所; 避難所: *She's been living in a refuge for battered wives.* 她一直住在為遭受毆打的妻子所準備的收容所裡。 **3 take refuge** to find shelter or protection 躲避; 尋求庇護

*ref·u·gee /ˌrefjuˈdʒiː; ˌrefjuˈdʒiː/ *n* a person who has been forced to leave their country for political or religious reasons, or because they have no food 避難者; 流亡者; 難民

re·fund¹ /rɪˈfʌnd; rɪˈfʌnd/ *v* [T] to give back money which has been paid to you 歸還, 退還〔錢款〕: *They refunded our money when the play was cancelled.* 比賽取消了, 他們退錢給我們。

re·fund² /ˈriːfʌnd; ˈriːfʌnd/ *n* an amount of money which is paid back to you, for example when you return unsatisfactory goods to a shop 退款, 退還: *Can I get a refund on these tickets?* 我能拿到這些票子的退款嗎?

re·fus·al /rɪˈfjuːzl; rɪˈfjuːzl/ *n* [C;U] a case of refusing to do, accept, or allow something 拒絕: *Their refusal to negotiate with us made progress difficult.* 他們拒絕和我們談判, 因此難有進展。

re·fuse¹ /rɪˈfjuːz; rɪˈfjuːz/ *v* refused, refusing **1 [I;T] to say firmly that you are not willing to accept or do something 拒絕, 不接受: *He asked her to marry him but she refused.* 他向她求婚, 可是她拒絕了。 | *She refused his offer.* 她拒絕了他的建議。 | *He refuses to do any extra work.* 他拒絕做任何額外的工作。

□ USEFUL PATTERNS 有用句型
to refuse; to refuse something; to refuse to do something

2 refuse someone something to say firmly that you will not give or allow something 拒絕給與某人以某物; 拒絕准許某人做某事: *They refused me an extension of my visa.* 他們拒絕延長我的簽證期。 | *We were refused permission to enter the country.* 我們被拒絕進入該國。

■ USAGE 用法: Compare 比較 **refuse, decline, reject, turn down. 1** You can **refuse** an invitation, a suggestion, an offer, or permission. You can **decline** an invitation, a suggestion, or an offer. You can **reject** or **turn down** a suggestion, an offer, or a plan. ☆ 我們可以 **refuse** (拒絕)一項邀請、一個建議、提議或許可; **decline** (拒絕)一項邀請、一個建議或一個提議; **reject** 或 **turn down** (拒絕)一個建議、一個提議或一項計劃。 **2 Decline** is more polite than **refuse,**

and not so strong ☆**decline** 比 **refuse** 有禮貌, 而且語氣沒有那麼強烈: *I'm afraid I must **decline** your invitation.* 對不起, 我得謝絕你的邀請。

ref·use² /ˈrefjuːs; ˈrefjuːs/ *n* [U] *fml* waste material 〔正式〕廢物, 垃圾: *When is the refuse collected?* 甚麼時候收垃圾? | *a refuse dump* 垃圾場, 垃圾站

re·fute /rɪˈfjuːt; rɪˈfjuːt/ *v* refuted, refuting *fml* [T] to prove that a person or an argument is wrong 〔正式〕反駁, 駁斥: *This argument cannot be easily refuted.* 這個論點無法輕易駁倒。 **–refutation** /ˌrefjuˈteɪʃən; ˌrefjuˈteɪʃən/ *n* [C;U]

re·gain /rɪˈgeɪn; rɪˈgeɪn/ *v* [T] to get something back 復得, 恢復: *She is slowly regaining her health.* 她正在慢慢地康復。 | *The army has regained control of the town.* 軍隊已重新控制了這個城鎮。

re·gal /ˈriːgl; ˈriːgl/ *adj* splendid enough to be fit for a king or queen 豪華的; 帝王(般)的: *regal manners* 雍容莊嚴的風度 **–regally** *adv*

re·gale /rɪˈgeɪl; rɪˈgeɪl/ *v* regaled, regaling [T] **regale someone with something** to entertain someone with jokes and stories 用〔笑話、故事〕使某人高興; 款待: *He regaled us with tales of his foreign adventures.* 他講述在外地冒險的故事, 逗得我們不亦樂乎。

re·ga·li·a /rɪˈgeɪliə; rɪˈgeɪliə/ *n* [U] ceremonial clothes and decorations, used especially on official occasions 〔尤指正式場合穿的〕盛裝; 禮服: *The mayor was dressed in full regalia.* 市長穿着華麗的禮服。

re·gard¹ /rɪˈgɑːd; rɪˈgɑːd/ *n* **1** [U] respect for someone or something 尊敬, 尊重 **2 have high regard for** to have great respect for someone or something 極其尊敬或尊重〔某人或某事〕: *I have a high regard for his abilities.* 我極為重視他的能力。 **3 hold someone/something in high regard** to have great respect for a person or thing 極其尊敬或尊重某人〔某物〕: *She has always held her son-in-law in high regard.* 她一向極其尊重自己的女婿。 [RELATED PHRASE 相關詞組 **hold someone/something in low regard**] **4** [U] attention or consideration 注意; 考慮: *You have no regard for my feelings!* 你一點也不顧及我的感情! | *The report pays little regard to the facts.* 這份報告不大顧及事實。 **5 regards** a word used to express your good wishes to someone 問候; 致意〔用於表達對某人的良好祝願〕: *Please give my best regards to your wife.* 請代我向你太太問好。 | *With kind regards, John.* 謹致問候, 約翰。 **6 with regard to, as regards** a phrase used to show which subject is being talked or written about 關於〔表示正在談到或論及的某個話題或題目〕: *With regard to your recent application, I am afraid we cannot offer you a* job. 關於您最近的申請，恐怕我們無法為您提供一份工作。

★★regard² /v/ [T] **1** to consider someone or something in a particular way〔以某種方式〕考慮，看待〔某人、某事〕: *I have always regarded him highly.* 我總是非常尊敬他。| *I regard him as my friend.* 我視他為朋友。| *She regards this painting as her best ever.* 她認為這幅畫是自己最好的作品。**2** *fml* to look at someone in a particular way〔正式〕注視，打量〔某人〕: *She regarded him thoughtfully.* 她若有所思地注視著他。

re·gard·ing /rɪˈgɑːdɪŋ; rɪˈgɑːdɪŋ/ *prep fml* a word used, especially in letters, to show what subject you are writing or talking about〔正式〕〔尤用於信件中〕關於，有關: *Regarding your recent enquiry, I enclose a college prospectus.* 關於您最近的詢問，我附上一份學院簡介。

re·gard·less /rɪˈgɑːdlɪs; rɪˈgɑːdləs/ *adv* **1** regardless of in spite of 不管；不顧: *They signed the contract regardless of their lawyer's advice.* 他們不顧律師的勸告，簽署了合同。**2** without worrying about a problem 不在意地；不顧及地: *The baby was crying, but she carried on painting regardless.* 嬰兒在哭，但她毫不在意地繼續作畫。

re·gat·ta /rɪˈgætə; rɪˈgætə/ *n* an event in which races between rowing or sailing boats take place 划船比賽；帆船比賽

re·gen·cy /ˈriːdʒənsi; ˈriːdʒənsi/ *n* [U] the period of government by a regent 攝政期

re·gent /ˈriːdʒənt; ˈriːdʒənt/ *n* (also 又作 **Regent**) a person who governs in place of a king or queen who is ill, absent, or still a child 攝政者

reg·gae /ˈrege; ˈregeɪ/ *n* [U] a type of popular music from the West Indies with a strong regular beat 雷蓋〔一種起源於西印度群島的節奏很強的流行音樂〕

★★re·gime /rɪˈʒiːm; reɪˈʒiːm/ *n* (also 又作 **régime**) **1** a particular type of government (a word often used to express disapproval) 政體，政權〔常含貶義〕: *The country is under a military regime.* 該國家處於軍事政權統治之下。**2** a particular government that rules a country (a word often used to express disapproval) 國家政府〔常含貶義〕: *The old regime killed hundreds of people.* 舊政府殺害了數以百計的人。**3** a way of life intended to improve your health 養生法: *Giving up smoking is part of my new regime.* 戒煙是我的新養生法的一部分。

re·gi·ment¹ /ˈredʒəmənt; ˈredʒəmənt/ *n* [+sing/pl verb] a large group of soldiers, commanded by a COLONEL〔軍隊的〕團 – **regimental** /-ˈmentl; -ˈmentl/ *adj* [only before a noun 只用於名詞前]: *the regimental band* 團的樂隊

re·gi·ment² /ˈredʒəˌment; ˈredʒəment/ *v* [T] to control people tightly 嚴密控制: *Children today don't like being regimented.* 現在的孩子不喜歡受嚴格的管教。– **regimented** *adj*: *a regimented society* 在嚴密控制下的社會 – **regimentation** /ˌredʒəmenˈteɪʃən; ˌredʒ-ˌmenˈteɪʃən/ *n* [U]

★★re·gion /ˈriːdʒən; ˈriːdʒən/ *n* **1** a large area of land, usually with clear borders or particular qualities 地區；區域: *Snow is expected in southern regions.* 南部地區預料會下雪。**2** an area around a particular part of your body〔身體的〕部位: *He experienced pains in the region of his heart.* 他感到心臟部位疼痛。**3** in the region of about... 大約...: *It will cost in the region of £200.* 這要花費大約二百英鎊。– **regional** *adj*: *strange regional customs* 奇異的地區風俗 – **regionally** *adv*

★register¹ /ˈredʒɪstə; ˈredʒɪstər/ *n* **1** [C] an official record 登記〔簿〕；註冊〔簿〕: *We could consult the register of births and deaths.* 我們可以查閱出生和死亡的記錄。| *a school attendance register* 學校點名冊 **2** [C;U] *tech* a way of speaking or writing which depends on the situation you are in and whether it is formal or informal〔術語〕語域

★register² /v/ **1** [I;T] to record a name or event on an official list 登記；記錄；註冊: *Have you registered the birth of the baby yet?* 你給剛生的嬰兒登記了嗎？| *The car is registered in my name.* 這輛車是以我的名字登記的。| *They registered at my hotel last night.* 他們昨晚在我的旅館登記投宿。**2** [T] (of a machine or instrument) to show an amount or a measurement〔機器或儀器〕顯示；指示: *The thermometer registered 35°C.* 溫度計顯示為攝氏三十五度。**3** [I] to show as a measurement on an instrument〔儀器上〕顯示量度: *The speed is not registering.* 速度沒顯示出來。**4** [T] to express your feelings or opinions about something 表示，流露〔感情或意見〕: *Her face registered surprise.* 她臉露驚訝之色。| *I want to register my opposition to this project.* 我要對這個方案表示反對。**5** [T] to pay more to send a letter in order to insure it against loss 以掛號郵寄〔信件〕: *You'd better register this letter.* 這封信你最好用掛號郵寄。

registered post /ˌ··· ˈ·/ *n* (also 又作 **registered mail** *AmE*〔美式〕) [U] a postal service which, for an additional charge, insures the sender of a valuable letter or parcel against loss 掛號郵寄: *I'll send it by registered post.* 我要用掛號郵寄把它寄出。

re·gis·trar /ˌredʒɪˈstrɑː; ˈredʒ-ˌstrɑːr/ (also 又作 **Registrar**) **1** a person whose job is to keep official records, for example of births and deaths 主管登記註冊的人〔如戶籍員〕；登記員 **2** a person whose job is to admit students and organize examinations at a college or university〔大學的〕註冊主任 **3** a high-level hospital doctor 專科住院醫師

re·gis·tra·tion /ˌredʒɪˈstreɪʃən; ˌredʒɪˈstreɪʃən/ *n* [U] the act of recording something on an official list 登記; 註冊: *Registration of new students takes place on Monday.* 新生註冊在星期一進行。

registration num·ber /·-ˈ·· ˌ··/ *n* the official set of numbers and letters that must be shown on the front and back of a car or other motor vehicle〔汽車或其他機動車輛的〕登記號碼; 牌照號碼

re·gis·try /ˈrɛdʒɪstrɪ; ˈredʒəstri/ *n* **registries** (also 又作 **Registry**) a place where official records are kept 登記處; 註冊處: *the Land Registry* 土地登記處

re·gress /rɪˋgrɛs; rɪˈgres/ *v fml* [I] to return to a worse or less developed state〖正式〗倒退, 退化, 退步: *The boy's behaviour regressed after his parents' divorce.* 父母離婚以後, 這男孩的行為退步了。–**regression** /-ˋgrɛʃən; -ˈgreʃən/ *n* [U]

re·gret[1] /rɪˋgrɛt; rɪˈgret/ *v* **-tt-** [T; +(that)] **1** to feel sorry about something you did and wish you had not done it 後悔, 遺憾: *Later, I regretted that I hadn't taken the job.* 後來, 我後悔自己沒有接受這份工作。| *Mary deeply regrets her decision not to have children.* 瑪麗對自己不要孩子的決定深感後悔。| *Do you regret selling the farm?* 你後悔賣掉農場嗎?

> □ USEFUL PATTERNS 有用句型
> to regret something; to regret doing something; to regret that...

2 [I; +that] *fml* a word used to show you are sorry about certain bad news〖正式〗對〔壞消息〕感到遺憾[惋惜]: *I regret that I will be unable to attend.* 很遺憾我將無法出席。| *We regret to inform you that your application has been rejected.* 我們很遺憾地告訴你, 你的申請沒有被接受。

regret[2] *n* **1** [U] a feeling of sadness or disappointment about something 惋惜; 遺憾; 懊悔: *The prime minister expressed his regret* **at** *the failure of the talks.* 首相對會談失敗表示遺憾。**2 have no regrets** not to feel sorry about something that has happened or that you have done〔對發生的事或自己做過的事〕不感後悔: *He has no regrets about leaving college.* 他對離開大學並不感到後悔。–**regretful** *adj*: *She said goodbye with a regretful smile.* 她依依不捨地一笑道別。–**regretfully** *adv*

re·gret·ta·ble /rɪˋgrɛtəbḷ; rɪˈgretəbəl/ *adj* unfortunate 不幸的; 令人遺憾的: *a regrettable mistake* 令人遺憾的錯誤 –**regrettably** *adv*: *Regrettably, teaching methods have not improved.* 令人遺憾的是, 教學方法並未得到改進。

re·group /riˋgrup; ˌriːˈgruːp/ *v* [I;T] to form into new groups, or into the same groups as before (使)重新組合, (使)重新編組

☆**reg·u·lar**[1] /ˋrɛgjələ; ˈregjᵊləʳ/ *adj* **1** repeated, with the same amount of time or space between one thing and the next 規則的, 有規律的: *His heartbeat is not very regular.* 他的心跳不太有規律。| *the regular tick of the clock* 時鐘規則的滴答聲 | *Plant the seeds at regular intervals.* 在規定的間隔距離內播種。**2** planned for the same time every day, week, or month 定時的; 定期的; 固定的: *We hold regular meetings.* 我們定期開會。| *They give regular performances throughout the summer.* 他們整個夏天都有定期演出。**3** arranged or shaped evenly 端正的; 整齊的; 勻稱的: *He had an attractive face, with regular features.* 他五官端正, 有一張迷人的臉。**4** frequent enough to be expected 習慣性的; 常規的: *James was one of my regular visitors.* 詹姆斯是我的幾個常客之一。| *his regular failure to finish the work on time* 他那經常不能按時完成工作的毛病 **5** usual 尋常的; 一般的: *Who's your regular doctor?* 你通常找哪個醫生看病? | *Our regular customers always pay cash.* 我們的老主顧總是付現鈔的。**6** following a common pattern (used in grammar) 按照規則的〔指語法〕: *The verb "to walk" is regular, while the verb "to be" is not.* 動詞"to walk"是規則動詞, 而動詞"to be"則不是。

regular[2] *n infml* a person who often goes to a particular shop or place〖非正式〗常客; 老主顧: *Mr Bennett is one of the regulars at the village pub.* 貝納特先生是鄉村酒館的常客之一。

reg·u·lar·i·ty /ˌrɛgjəˋlærətɪ; ˌregjᵊˈlærəti/ *n* [U] the situation or state of happening repeatedly 規則性; 規律性: *The building is cleaned with great regularity.* 這幢樓房要定期打掃。

*****reg·u·lar·ly** /ˋrɛgjələlɪ; ˈregjᵊləli/ *adv* **1** at regular times 有規律地; 定期地: *Take the medicine regularly three times a day.* 定時服藥, 一日三次。| *They met regularly to discuss business.* 他們定期見面討論生意的事。**2** often 經常地: *Sue regularly leaves work early.* 蘇常常很早下班。

reg·u·late /ˋrɛgjəˌlet; ˈregjᵊleɪt/ *v* **regulated, regulating** [T] **1** to control something, usually by having rules〔常以規章〕控制, 管制〔某事物〕: *Gun sales are strictly regulated by the government.* 槍的銷售受到政府的嚴格控制。**2** to control the way a machine works 調整, 調節, 校準: *Use this button to regulate the sound.* 用這個按鈕來調節音量。

☆**reg·u·la·tion** /ˌrɛgjəˋleʃən; ˌregjᵊˈleɪʃən/ *n* **1** [C] an official rule to control a particular activity 規章; 規則; 條例; 法令: *safety regulations* 安全規則 | *Don't do anything that's against the regulations.* 別做違反規章的事。**2** [U] control of a process or activity〔對過程或活動的〕管理; 管制: *the regulation* **of** *public spending* 公共開支的管制

re·gur·gi·tate /rɪˋgɝdʒəˌtet; rɪˈgɜːdʒəteɪt/ *v* **regurgitated, regurgitating** [T] *fml*〖正式〗**1** to bring back into your mouth food that

you have already swallowed 〖正式〗反芻,
(使)〔已吞嚥的食物〕回湧 **2** to repeat facts or
ideas without understanding them clearly
〔未經了解清楚而〕機械地重複〔事實或想法〕–
regurgitation /rɪ,gɜ˞'dʒə'teɪʃən; rɪ,gɜːdʒ˩'teɪ-
ʃən/ n [U]

re·ha·bil·i·tate /,rihə'bɪlə,tet; ,riːhə'bɪl˩teɪt/
v **rehabilitated, rehabilitating** [T] to help
someone live a healthy or useful life again
after they have been ill or in prison 幫助
〔某人病後或從監獄中被釋放後〕恢復正常的生
活: *The organization helps to rehabilitate
young offenders.* 這個組織幫助年輕的罪犯重
新做人. –**rehabilitation** /,rihə,bɪlə'teʃən;
,riːhəbɪl˩'teɪʃən/ n [U]

re·hash /ri'hæʃ; riː'hæʃ/ v [T] *infml* to use
the same ideas again in a new form which is
not really different or better 〖非正式〗把…
改頭換面後重新使用, 使…改變形式: *He keeps
rehashing the same old speech.* 他老是改頭
換面地重複演講的內容. –**rehash** /'ri,hæʃ;
'riːhæʃ/

re·hears·al /rɪ'hɜ˞sl; rɪ'hɜːsəl/ n [C;U] practice as preparation for a public performance 排練; 排演: *This play will need a lot of
rehearsal.* 這齣戲需要多次排練. | *Rehearsals
will take place every Saturday.* 每個星期六進
行排練.

re·hearse /rɪ'hɜ˞s; rɪ'hɜːs/ v **rehearsed, rehearsing** [I;T] **1** to practise a play, dance,
or music in order to prepare for a public
performance 排練〔戲劇、舞蹈或樂曲〕; 排演:
*The actors were rehearsing until late last
night.* 昨晚演員們一直排練到深夜. | *She's
only rehearsed the song a couple of times.* 這
首歌她只排練過幾次. **2** to think about the
words you are going to use later 複述; 默誦

re·house /ri'hauz; ,riː'hauz/ v **rehoused,
rehousing** [T] to move someone into a different or better house 給〔某人〕提供新住
房: *Many families were rehoused after the
war.* 戰後許多家庭獲安排新的住處.

reign[1] /ren; reɪn/ n **1** a period of time during which someone rules a country 君主統
治時期: *It happened in the reign of King
George IV.* 這事發生在國王喬治四世統治時
期. **2** a period of time during which a particular situation or state exists 〔某一形勢或
情況存在的〕時期: *a reign of terror* 恐怖時期

reign[2] v [I] **1** (of a king or queen) to rule a
country 〔國王或女王〕統治: *Queen Victoria
reigned for over 60 years.* 維多利亞女王在位
六十餘年. **2** *lit* to exist for a period of time
in a very noticeable or influential way 〖文〗
盛行一時: *The thunder died away and
silence reigned once more.* 雷聲逐漸消失, 萬
籟又回復寂靜. | *Anarchy reigned during the
revolution.* 革命時期一直維持無政府狀態.

re·im·burse /,riɪm'bɜ˞s; ,riːɪm'bɜːs/ v **reimbursed, reimbursing** *fml* to pay money
back to someone 〖正式〗償還, 付還: *We will
reimburse you **for** the loss of the painting.* 我

們將賠償你這幅畫的損失. | *The cost will be
reimbursed.* 費用將會償還. –**reimbursement**
n [U]

rein /ren; reɪn/ n **1** a long narrow band of
leather, by which a horse is controlled 韁繩
2 give (a) free rein to someone to give
someone the freedom to do what they like
放任, 對…不加約束: *We've given the
architects free rein in designing the building.*
我們任由建築師設計這座大樓. **3 keep a tight
rein on** to control a person or thing firmly
嚴加控制: *We intend to keep a tight rein on
public spending.* 我們打算嚴格控制公共開支.

re·in·car·nate /,riɪn'kɑrnet; ,riːɪn'kɑːneɪt/ v
**reincarnated, reincarnating, be reincar-
nated** to return to life in a new body after
dying 賦予〔靈魂〕新的肉體; 使再生; 使轉世

re·in·car·na·tion /,riɪnkɑr'neʃən; ,riːɪnkɑː-
'neɪʃən/ n **1** [U] return to life in a new body
after dying 〔靈魂的〕轉世; 再投胎: *Do you
believe in reincarnation?* 你相信投胎轉世嗎?
2 [C] the person or animal in whose body
a dead person is thought to live again 再生
化身: *He claims to be a reincarnation of
Napoleon.* 他聲稱自己是拿破崙再生.

rein·deer /'rendɪr; 'reɪndɪə˞/ n **reindeer** a
type of large deer with long branching
horns, found in northern parts of the
world 馴鹿

★**re·in·force** /,riɪn'fors; ,riːɪn'fɔːs/ v **reinforced,
reinforcing** [T] **1** to strengthen something by
adding to it 加強, 加固〔某物〕: *The knees on
Tim's trousers need reinforcing before he rubs
a hole in them.* 蒂姆的褲子膝部需要加固, 以免
磨出洞來. **2** to support or strengthen a situation, feeling, or idea 支持, 加深〔情形、感情
或想法〕: *This argument is strongly reinforced
by the latest trade figures.* 最近的貿易數字更
有力地證實了這個論點. –**reinforcement** n
[U]: *This roof needs some reinforcement.* 這
屋頂需要加固.

re·in·force·ments /,riɪn'forsmənts; ,riːɪn-
'fɔːsmənts/ n [pl] more soldiers sent to
strengthen an army 援軍, 增援部隊: *We've
sent for reinforcements.* 我們已派人去要求增
援.

re·in·state /,riɪn'stet; ,riːɪn'steɪt/ v **reinstated, reinstating** [T] to put someone
back into a position or job they held before 使〔某人〕恢復原職: *He was reinstated
after the real thief was caught.* 真正的竊賊被
抓獲後, 他恢復了原職. –**reinstatement** n [C;
U]

re·it·e·rate /ri'ɪtə,ret; riː'ɪtəreɪt/ v **reiterated, reiterating** [T; + that] to say something more than once 反覆地說, 重申〔某事
物〕: *The miners reiterated their demands for
an inquiry into the accident.* 礦工都再三要求
調查這事故. –**reiteration** /ri,ɪtə'reʃən; riː,ɪtə-
'reɪʃən/ n [C;U]

★**re·ject**[1] /rɪ'dʒɛkt; rɪ'dʒekt/ v [T] **1** to refuse
to accept or agree with something 拒絕接受

〔同意〕〔某事物〕: *She rejected my suggestion.* 她拒絕接受我的建議。| *The teachers voted to reject the government's pay offer.* 教師投票表決, 拒絕接受政府提出的工資方案。−see 見 REFUSE (USAGE 用法) **2** to throw away something because it is useless or imperfect〔因無用或有瑕疵而〕丟掉, 抛棄〔某物〕 **3** to refuse someone, especially for a job 拒絕〔某人〕〔尤指拒絕一份工作〕: *He was rejected by the army because of his poor eyesight.* 他因視力差而被拒絕入伍。**4** to behave in a cruel way to someone who expects love or kindness from you 厭棄, 嫌棄〔希望得到愛或溫暖的人〕: *He was rejected by his father.* 他遭父親嫌棄。

re·ject[2] /ˈriːdʒɛkt; ˈriːdʒekt/ *n* a product which is not accepted for use because it is damaged or imperfect 不合格品; 次品

re·jec·tion /rɪˈdʒɛkʃən; rɪˈdʒekʃən/ *n* **1** [C;U] refusal to accept or agree with something〔對某事物的〕拒絕接受〔同意〕: *Rejections of the proposal could lead to disaster.* 拒絕接受這項建議可能導致災難。**2** [C] refusal to accept a person, especially for a job〔尤指對求職者的〕拒絕: *I'm trying to get a job, but have so far received only rejections.* 我在設法找工作, 但到目前為止得到的只是拒絕。**3** [U] cruel behaviour to someone who expects love or kindness from you 厭棄, 嫌棄: *Total rejection of a child by the mother is fortunately rare.* 幸好, 孩子完全被母親厭棄的事很少發生。

re·joice /rɪˈdʒɔɪs; rɪˈdʒɔɪs/ *v* **rejoiced, rejoicing** [I] *fml lit* to feel or show great joy〔正式, 文〕高興, 歡喜: *The people rejoiced at the happy news.* 人們為這令人愉快的消息感到欣喜。| *He rejoiced over the birth of his son.* 他為兒子的出生而欣喜不已。

re·joic·ing /rɪˈdʒɔɪsɪŋ; rɪˈdʒɔɪsɪŋ/ *n* [U] *fml* great joy, shown by a large number of people〔正式〕〔許多人的〕欣喜; 歡慶

re·join·der /rɪˈdʒɔɪndə; rɪˈdʒɔɪndɚ/ *n* a quick or rude reply〔迅速或粗魯的〕回答; 反駁: *He answered me with a sharp rejoinder.* 他厲聲反駁我。

re·ju·ve·nate /rɪˈdʒuːvə‚neɪt; rɪˈdʒuːvəneɪt/ *v* **rejuvenated, rejuvenating** [T] to make someone look or feel young and strong again 使變得年輕; 使恢復青春活力: *They were completely rejuvenated by their holiday.* 度假使他們完全恢復了活力。−**rejuvenation** /rɪ‚dʒuːvəˈneɪʃən; rɪ‚dʒuːvəˈneɪʃən/ *n* [U]

re·lapse /rɪˈlæps; rɪˈlæps/ *v* **relapsed, relapsing** [I] to return to poor health or bad behaviour after an improvement 舊病復發; 故態復萌: *He soon relapsed into his bad habits.* 他很快就恢復了過去的惡習。−**relapse** /ˈriːlæps; ˈriːlæps/ *n*: *Jack had a relapse a few weeks after the operation.* 手術後幾星期, 傑克舊病復發了。

re·late /rɪˈleɪt; rɪˈleɪt/ *v* **related, relating** [T] **1** to make a connection between two things 使〔兩者〕聯繫: *The police are trying to relate the girl's disappearance to an attack which took place last week.* 警方正在試圖把這個女孩的失蹤和上週發生的一次襲擊事件聯繫起來。**2** *fml* to tell a story〔正式〕講述〔故事〕: *He related to us the events which led to his escape.* 他給我們講述了導致他逃跑的那些事。**3 relate to something: a** to concern or be connected with something 和〔某事〕有關: *secret documents relating to war crimes* 和戰爭中的罪行有關的祕密文件 **b** to feel that something has meaning for you personally 產生共鳴; 認同: *I can't relate to those kind of religious beliefs.* 我不能認同那些宗教信仰。**4 relate to someone** to understand someone and have a comfortable relationship with them 和某人和睦相處; 理解某人: *She doesn't relate very well to other women.* 她和其他婦女相處得不太好。

re·lat·ed /rɪˈleɪtɪd; rɪˈleɪtᵻd/ *adj* **1** connected by a family relationship 有親戚關係的: *She is related to me by marriage.* 她與我有姻親關係。**2** connected in some way 有關的, 相關的: *The book deals with drug addiction and related problems.* 這本書論述了毒癮和一些有關的問題。−opposite 反義 **unrelated**

re·la·tion /rɪˈleɪʃən; rɪˈleɪʃən/ *n* **1** [C] a member of your family 家屬; 親戚: *I saw a lot of my relations at the wedding.* 我在婚禮上看到許多親戚。**2** [U] the connection between one thing and another 關係; 關聯: *His argument bears no relation to the facts.* 他的論據和事實沒有關係。**3 relations** [pl] the way that two people or groups feel and behave towards each other〔兩個人或兩個團體間的〕關係; 交往: *Relations with neighbouring countries are excellent.* 和鄰國的關係非常不錯。**4 in relation to** a phrase used to talk about the size or position of something compared with something else 和…相比〔用於和其他東西相比時, 談論某物的大小或位置〕: *Her salary is high in relation to that of state school teachers.* 和公立學校的老師相比, 她的薪水是高的。| *Where is the village in relation to the lake?* 村子在湖的哪邊?

re·la·tion·ship /rɪˈleɪʃənˌʃɪp; rɪˈleɪʃənʃɪp/ *n* **1** a connection between two things 關係; 關聯: *What's the relationship between art and revolution?* 藝術和革命之間有甚麼關係? **2** the way two people or groups feel and behave towards each other〔人際或團體間的〕關係: *The police have a good relationship with local people.* 警方和當地人民之間關係良好。**3** a close friendship between two people which is often sexual〔兩人間的〕親密關係;〔常指〕性關係: *My relationship with my boyfriend has lasted six months.* 我同男朋友的關係已維持六個月。| *He isn't in a relationship at the moment.* 他這陣子沒有和別人交往。

rel·a·tive[1] /ˈrɛlətɪv; ˈrelətɪv/ *n* a member of

your family 親戚; 親屬: *My uncle is my nearest relative.* 我的叔父是我最近的親人。

*relative² adj compared to each other or to something else 比較的; 相對的: *the relative costs of building in stone and brick* 石頭與磚瓦建築的造價差距 | *After his money troubles, he's now living in relative comfort.* 他在渡過經濟困難之後，現在過著比較舒適的生活。

*rel·a·tive·ly /ˈrɛlətɪvlɪ; ˈreləlɪvli/ *adv* to quite a large degree when compared to something similar or what you might expect 比較而言; 相對地; 相當: *She walks relatively fast for a small child.* 就一個小孩而論，她算走得相當快了。| *The baby's been relatively quiet.* 這嬰兒比較安靜。

relative pro·noun /ˌ··· ˈ··/ *n tech* a word that connects a relative CLAUSE to the rest of a sentence; 'who' and 'which' can be relative pronouns 〔術語〕關係代名詞〔如 "who"和"which"〕: *In the sentence "The man who lives next door is a doctor.", "who" is a relative pronoun.* 在"The man who lives next door is a doctor."一句中，"who"是關係代名詞。

rel·a·tiv·i·ty /ˌrɛləˈtɪvətɪ; ˌreləˈtɪvⱦti/ *n* [U] the relationship between time, size, and mass, which is said to change with increased speed 相對性; 相對論: *Einstein's theory of relativity* 愛因斯坦的相對論

*re·lax /rɪˈlæks; rɪˈlæks/ *v* **1** [I;T] to calm someone, or to become calmer and less worried (使)輕鬆; 放鬆: *Sit down and relax!* 坐下來休息一下! | *The music will help to relax you.* 這音樂能助你放鬆。**2** [I;T] to make a part of your body become less stiff or tight (使)鬆弛: *His muscles relaxed.* 他的肌肉鬆弛了。| *Try to relax your shoulders.* 盡量放鬆你的肩膀。**3** [T] to make a form of control over something less severe 放寬; 使鬆懈: *The police sometimes relax the rules in special cases.* 警察有時在特殊的案件中會放寬規定。

re·lax·a·tion /ˌrilæksˈeʃən; ˌriːlækˈseɪʃən/ *n* **1** [C;U] rest and amusement, or an activity that gives you this 消遣; 娛樂: *Playing the piano is one of his favourite relaxations.* 彈鋼琴是他最喜愛的消遣之一。| *I desperately need some relaxation.* 我極需要消遣一下。**2** [U] the act of making some form of control less severe 放寬; 鬆弛; 鬆懈: *the relaxation of exchange controls* 外匯管制的放寬

re·lay¹ /ˈrile; ˈriːleɪ/ *n* [C;U] **1** (also 又作 **relay race**) a race in which each member of each team runs or swims part of the distance 〔賽跑、游泳的〕接力賽 **2** in relays using a fresh group of people or animals in the place of a tired one 輪班地; 輪流地: *The men worked in relays to repair the railway.* 工人輪班修理鐵路。**3** an apparatus that receives and passes on messages by telephone, radio, or television 〔電話、無線電或電視的〕中繼設備: *This broadcast is coming*

from America by relay. 這廣播節目是從美國轉播的。

relay² v [T] **1** to send out a radio or television signal 中繼轉發, 轉播〔無線電或電視信號〕: *The broadcast was relayed to Europe.* 這廣播節目轉播到了歐洲。**2** to pass on a message to someone else 轉達〔消息〕: *Please relay the news to the other teachers.* 請把這消息轉告給其他教師。

*re·lease¹ /rɪˈlis; rɪˈliːs/ *v* **released, releasing** [T] **1** to set free a person or animal 釋放〔人或動物〕: *The hijackers released three of the hostages.* 劫機者釋放了其中三名人質。**2** to free someone from a difficult feeling or duty 解脫; 免除: *Her awful behaviour released him* **from** *any sense of obligation.* 她的可怕行為使他解除了所有的責任感。**3** to stop holding something 放開, 鬆開〔某物〕: *He released his grip on her hand.* 他鬆開了她的手。**4** to make something move by freeing a handle 鬆開把手使〔某物〕移動: *He released the handbrake.* 他鬆開了手剎車。**5** to allow a new film or record to be shown or bought publicly 上映; 發行〔新影片或唱片〕: *The record was released recently.* 這張唱片是最近發行的。

release² n 1 [U] the act of setting someone free or of being set free 釋放: *After his release from prison he went abroad.* 他釋放出獄後便去了國外。**2** [U] the act of freeing someone from a difficult feeling or duty 解脫; 免除: *After the exam, I had such a feeling of release.* 考試結束後，我有那麼一種如釋重負的感覺。**3** [C] a new film or record that has been released 發行的新影片〔唱片〕: *I'd like to see some of the latest releases.* 我想看最近發行的一些影片。**4 on release, on general release** able to be seen at public cinemas 〔影片〕在電影院上映

rel·e·gate /ˈrɛləˌget; ˈrelⱦgeɪt/ *v* **relegated, relegating** [T] to move someone or something to a less important position 把〔某人或某事物〕降級, 貶低: *Jack was relegated* **to** *the role of assistant.* 傑克被降為助理。| *Everyone was surprised when the football team was relegated to a lower division.* 足球隊被降級，每個人都大吃一驚。

re·lent /rɪˈlent; rɪˈlent/ *v* [I] to let someone do something that you would not let them do before, or to decide not to carry out a threat 變寬容; 變溫和: *She threatened to make me pay for the damage, but then she relented.* 她起初威脅要我賠償損失，但後來她的態度緩和了。

re·lent·less /rɪˈlentlɪs; rɪˈlentləs/ *adj* continuous and strong 持續不停的; 不屈不撓的: *the relentless desert heat* 沙漠中持續的酷熱 | *relentless ambition* 百折不撓的雄心壯志 — **relentlessly** *adv*: *He beat the dog relentlessly.* 他痛打那隻狗。

*rel·e·vant /ˈrɛləvənt; ˈrelⱦvənt/ *adj* **1** directly connected with a particular subject,

R

especially one being talked or written about 有關的; 切題的: *This book isn't really relevant to my research.* 這本書和我的研究實在無關。 **2** valuable or important to someone or something 有價值的; 重要的: *This type of course is no longer relevant to nurses.* 這種課程對護士不再有甚麼價值了。 –opposite 反義 **irrelevant** –**relevance** *n* [U]: *What you say has no relevance to what we're talking about.* 你說的和我們正在談論的話題毫無關係。

re·li·a·ble /rɪˈlaɪəbl; rɪˈlaɪəbəl/ *adj* **1** that you can trust to perform well at all times 可靠的: *My memory is not very reliable.* 我的記憶力不大靠得住。 | *a reliable car* 性能可靠的汽車 **2** that you can trust to be true or to provide correct information 可信賴的: *reliable evidence* 可靠的證據 | *A reliable source told journalists the hospital would close.* 記者從可靠的消息來源, 得知這家醫院要關閉了。 – opposite 反義 **unreliable** –**reliably** *adv*: *I am reliably informed that he takes drugs.* 我從可靠的消息得知他吸毒。 –**reliability** /rɪ,laɪəˈbɪlətɪ; rɪ,laɪəˈbɪl‿ti/ *n* [U]

re·li·ant /rɪˈlaɪənt; rɪˈlaɪənt/ *adj* **reliant on** dependent on 依賴的; 信賴的: *We should not be so reliant on imported food.* 我們不應如此依賴進口食品。 –**reliance** *n* [U]

rel·ic /ˈrɛlɪk; ˈrɛlɪk/ *n* **1** a part of a holy person's body, or something that belonged to a holy person, which is kept and respected after their death 聖徒的部分遺骸〔遺物〕 **2** an old custom, idea, or thing which still exists 遺風; 遺俗; 遺物; 遺跡: *This stone axe is a relic of ancient times.* 這石斧是古代的遺物。 | *These beliefs are relics from the last century.* 這些信仰是從上個世紀傳下來的遺風。

★**re·lief** /rɪˈliːf; rɪˈliːf/ *n* **1** [sing;U] a feeling of comfort and happiness after a period of anxiety or some other unpleasant feeling 〔憂慮或不愉快的感情的〕減輕; 寬慰: *This medicine will give you some relief.* 這藥會減輕你一些痛苦。 | *To my relief, they arrived safely.* 他們平安抵達, 這使我放心了。 | *She heaved a sigh of relief when she got the contract.* 她拿到合同時, 如釋重負地鬆了一口氣。 **2** [U] money, food, or clothing provided for people in trouble 救濟; 補助: *The government sent relief to people who lost their homes in the flood.* 政府將救濟品送給在洪水中失去家園的人。

re·lieve /rɪˈliːv; rɪˈliːv/ *v* **relieved, relieving** [T] **1** to lessen pain or some other unpleasant feeling 減輕, 緩解〔痛苦或其他不愉快的感情〕: *This pill will relieve your headache.* 這藥片可緩解頭痛。 | *I went for a walk to relieve my boredom.* 我外出散步以消除厭煩的感覺。 **2 relieve someone of** to free someone of something heavy or difficult 使某人擺脫〔重物或難事〕, 解除〔某人〕的負擔: *Let me relieve you of those parcels.* 讓我來幫

你拿那些包裹吧。 | *Her letter relieved him of his anxieties.* 她的來信解除了他的憂慮。 **3** to take someone's place in a job 接替〔某人的工作〕: *Will you relieve me at 5.00?* 你五點鐘來換我的班嗎? **4 relieve someone of their duties** to dismiss someone from their position at work 解除某人的職務

re·lieved /rɪˈliːvd; rɪˈliːvd/ *adj* happy after a period of anxiety 放心的; 寬慰的: *Your mother will be very relieved to hear that you are safe.* 你的母親聽說你平安無事, 會感到很寬慰的。 | *You look relieved!* 你看來愁雲盡掃了!

★**re·li·gion** /rɪˈlɪdʒən; rɪˈlɪdʒən/ *n* **1** [U] belief in one or more gods, and the behaviour and worship connected with this 宗教信仰: *a book on religion* 一本關於宗教信仰的書 **2** [C] a particular system of belief in one or more gods and the behaviour and worship connected with this 宗教: *the Muslim religion* 伊斯蘭教

★**re·li·gious** /rɪˈlɪdʒəs; rɪˈlɪdʒəs/ *adj* **1** connected with religion 宗教的: *religious beliefs* 宗教信仰 **2** showing a strong belief in a particular religion and careful obedience to its rules (used of a person or behaviour) 篤信宗教的; 虔誠的〔指人或行為〕: *a very religious man* 一個非常虔誠的男人

re·li·gious·ly /rɪˈlɪdʒəslɪ; rɪˈlɪdʒəslɪ/ *adv* thoroughly and regularly from a sense of duty 認真徹底地; 有規律地: *He visits his mother religiously every morning.* 他每天早晨都定時去探望他的母親。

re·lin·quish /rɪˈlɪŋkwɪʃ; rɪˈlɪŋkwɪʃ/ *v* [T] *fml* to give up a position or right 〔正式〕放棄〔職位或權利〕: *He relinquished his claim to the land.* 他放棄了對那塊土地所有權的要求。

rel·ish¹ /ˈrɛlɪʃ; ˈrɛlɪʃ/ *n* **1 with relish** with great enjoyment and satisfaction 津津有味地; 享受地: *He ate the cake with relish.* 他津津有味地吃蛋糕。 **2** [C;U] a substance eaten with a meal to add taste 調味品; 佐料

rel·ish² *v* [T] to look forward to something with great enjoyment 享受地期望〔某事物〕: *John won't relish having to wash all those dishes!* 約翰可不會樂意洗那麼一大堆碟子! | *She didn't relish the prospect of explaining her decision.* 她不喜歡解釋自己的決定。

re·live /riˈlɪv; ,riːˈlɪv/ *v* **relived, reliving** [T] to remember something from the past in such detail that it is as if you experience it again 〔在想像中〕再經歷, 再體驗, 重溫: *We spent the whole morning reliving our schooldays.* 我們整個上午都在重溫我們學生時代的生活。

re·lo·cate /riˈloket; ,riːləʊˈkeɪt/ *v* **relocated, relocating** [I;T] to move to a new place (使)遷移; 重新安置: *We're relocating to the Bristol area.* 我們將遷往布里斯托爾地區。 | *The factory was relocated outside London.* 這家工廠遷出了倫敦。 –**relocation** /,rɪloˈkeʃən; ,riːləʊˈkeɪʃən/ *n* [U]

R

re·luc·tant /rɪˈlʌktənt; rɪˈlʌktənt/ *adj* unwilling, and therefore perhaps slow to act 不情願的; 勉強的: *He gave a reluctant promise.* 他勉強答應下來了。 | *He was very reluctant to help.* 他很不願意幫忙。 –**reluctance** *n* [U] –**reluctantly** *adv*

□ USEFUL PATTERN 有用句型
be reluctant to do something

re·ly /rɪˈlaɪ; rɪˈlaɪ/ *v* **relied, relying** [I] **rely on** to depend on someone or something 依賴, 指望〔某人、某事物〕: *We're relying on your support.* 我們期望得到你的支持。 | *Don't rely on his taking the job.* 別指望他會接受這份工作。 | *They rely on the river for water.* 他們用水要依靠這條河。

re·main /rɪˈmen; rɪˈmeɪn/ *v* **1** [I] to stay or be left behind after others have gone 留下; 遺留: *She remained at home with the children.* 她和孩子們留在家裡。 **2** [+ complement] to continue unchanged in a particular state or condition 保持不變; 依然: *Peter became a judge but John remained a fisherman.* 彼得成了一名法官, 但約翰仍是個漁夫。 | *The situation remained the same.* 形勢仍然未變。 | *Please remain calm!* 請保持鎮定! **3** [I] to continue to exist 繼續存在: *Little of the original building remains.* 原來的建築留存的已經很少了。 **4** **it remains to be seen** it is still unclear and will only be known in the future 留待以後才知曉: *It remains to be seen what the results of the tests will be.* 測試結果如何尚待以後分曉。

re·main·der /rɪˈmendə; rɪˈmeɪndəʳ/ *n* the **remainder** [+sing/pl verb] the rest 剩餘部分: *We'll eat the remainder of the food tomorrow.* 我們明天會把剩下的食物吃掉。

re·mains /rɪˈmenz; rɪˈmeɪnz/ *n* [pl] **1** parts which are left after the larger whole has gone or been destroyed 剩餘物; 殘骸: *the remains of dinner* 晚餐的剩飯菜 | *the remains of an old castle* 古堡的遺跡 **2** *fml* the parts of a body that are left after a person's death 〔正式〕遺骸, 遺體: *His remains lie in the churchyard.* 他的遺體安葬在教堂的墓地。

re·make /riˈmek; ˌriːˈmeɪk/ *v* **remade, remaking** [T] to make something again, usually a film which has the same story as an earlier film 重製; 〔專指〕重新攝製〔影片〕 –**remake** /ˈrimek; ˈriːmeɪk/ *n*: *It's supposed to be a remake of "Gone with the Wind".* 這應該是重新攝製的電影《飄》。

re·mand¹ /rɪˈmænd; rɪˈmɑːnd/ *v* **1** be **remanded** to be ordered to return later to a court of law to be tried for a crime 還押候審: *She was remanded for trial two weeks later.* 她被還押等候兩星期後的審判。 **2** be **remanded in custody** to be held in prison until a trial in a court of law 在押候審

remand² *n* **on remand** waiting to be tried after already appearing in court 還押候審

re·mark¹ /rɪˈmɑrk; rɪˈmɑːk/ *v* **1** [+ that] to say something 說起, 談到: *He remarked that it was getting late.* 他說天色已晚了。 | *"She was very kind to me", Ben remarked.* "她對我非常好," 本說。 **2** **remark on/upon** to notice something and talk or write about it 評論; 議論: *Everyone remarked loudly on his absence.* 大家對他的缺席都大聲地議論了一番。

remark² *n* something said or written 評述; 評論: *Hilda made some rude remarks about his appearance.* 希爾達對他的外表發表了一些粗魯的評論。

re·mar·ka·ble /rɪˈmɑrkəbl; rɪˈmɑːkəbəl/ *adj* extremely unusual or noticeable 異常的; 卓越的; 顯著的: *a most remarkable sunset* 非常壯觀的日落景象 | *Finland is remarkable for its large number of lakes.* 芬蘭以湖泊眾多而著名。 –**remarkably** *adv*: *a remarkably fine day* 異常晴朗的一天 | *He sings remarkably well.* 他的歌唱得十分出色。

re·me·di·al /rɪˈmidɪəl; rɪˈmiːdɪəl/ *adj* **1** intended to provide a cure or some improvement 治療的; 補救的: *He has to do remedial exercises for his weak back.* 他得為衰弱的背部做矯正運動。 **2** intended to help someone learn something that they find difficult or did not learn at the usual age 補習的: *a remedial reading class* 閱讀補習班 –**remedially** *adv*

rem·e·dy¹ /ˈrɛmədɪ; ˈremɪdi/ *n* **remedies 1** something that cures pain or illness 治療法; 藥物: *herbal remedies* 草藥 | *a new remedy for indigestion* 治療消化不良的新藥 **2** a means of dealing properly with a difficulty 處理〔困難的〕辦法; 補救法: *A holiday may be the best remedy for his unhappiness.* 休假一天也許是排解他的不快的最佳辦法。

remedy² *v* **remedied, remedying** [T] to correct a bad situation 糾正; 矯正; 補救: *How can we remedy this mistake?* 我們怎樣才能糾正這個錯誤呢?

re·mem·ber /rɪˈmɛmbə; rɪˈmembəʳ/ *v* **1** [I;T; +(that)] to keep in your memory people or events from the past 記得; 想起: *I definitely remember posting the letter.* 我確實記得寄了那封信。 | *I'll always remember that wonderful day.* 我會永遠記得那美妙的一天。 | *Do you remember me phoning you that afternoon?* 你記得我那天下午給你打電話嗎? | *He remembered that she worked in a pub.* 他記得她在一家酒館工作。

□ USEFUL PATTERNS 有用句型
to remember something; to remember doing something; to remember someone doing something; to remember that...

2 [I;T] to come back or bring back into your mind 記起; 回想起: *She suddenly remembered that she hadn't locked the door.* 她忽然記起她沒有鎖門。| *Can you remember where they live?* 你記得他們住哪兒嗎? **3** [I; +(that)] to take care not to forget 記住; 牢記: *Remember to post my letter!* 別忘了替我寄信! | *Remember I need the car by 10.00.* 記住我在十點鐘前要車。

□ USEFUL PATTERNS 有用句型
to remember to do something; to remember that…

4 [T] to think about someone or something with honour and respect 紀念〔某人、某事〕: *On this day, we remember those who died in the war.* 在這一天, 我們紀念那次戰爭中的死難者。**5** remember someone to someone to carry greetings from one person to another 代某人問候某人: *Please remember me to your mother.* 請代我問候你的母親。

■ USAGE 用法: Note the difference between "remember doing something" and "remember to do something". *I remember locking the door* means "I locked the door, and this event is still in my mind". *I remembered to lock the door* means "It was in my mind then that I must lock the door, and I locked it". ☆注意 "remember doing something" 和 "remember to do something" 的區別。"*I remember locking the door* (我記得鎖了門)"意思是"我鎖了門, 而且這件事還記在我的腦海裡"。"*I remembered to lock the door* (我記得鎖門)"意思是"我在腦裡記住必須鎖門, 並鎖了門"。

re·mem·brance /rɪ'mɛmbrəns; rɪ'mɛmbrəns/ *n* **1** [C;U] memory of someone or something 紀念; 懷念: *A church service was held in remembrance of those killed in the earthquake.* 教堂舉行了儀式以紀念地震中的死難者。**2** [C] something kept or given to remind you of someone or something 紀念品, 紀念物: *He gave me his photograph as a remembrance.* 他把他的照片送給我留念。

*re·mind /rɪ'maɪnd; rɪ'maɪnd/ *v* [T; +(that)] **1** to make someone remember something 使〔某人〕想起〔某事〕; 提醒: *Remind me to write to Dave.* 請提醒我給戴芙寫信。| *She reminded me that Sue was in Paris.* 她提醒我蘇在巴黎。

□ USEFUL PATTERNS 有用句型
to remind someone about something; to remind someone to do something; to remind someone that…

2 remind someone of to appear very similar to another person or thing 使某人想起 (相似的人或物): *This hotel reminds me of the one we stayed in last year.* 這家旅館使我想起我們去年住過的那一家。| *He reminds me of Mick Jagger.* 他使我想起米克·傑格。

re·mind·er /rɪ'maɪndə; rɪ'maɪndə·/ *n* **1** something that makes you remember something else 令人回憶起某事的東西, 起提醒作用的東西: *The photographs are a lasting reminder of life in the 1920s.* 這些照片總能使人回憶起二十世紀二十年代的生活。**2** a letter telling you to do something you have not done 催款信; 催還〔繳〕單: *He hasn't paid his bill. We'd better send him a reminder.* 他還沒有付賬, 我們最好寄給他一封催款信。

rem·i·nisce /ˌrɛmə'nɪs; ˌrɛmə'nɪs/ *v* **reminisced, reminiscing** [I] to talk or write with enjoyment about the past 緬懷往事, 追憶往事: *We meet to reminisce about our schooldays.* 我們聚在一起回憶學生時代的往事。–**reminiscence** *n* [C;U]

rem·i·nis·cent /ˌrɛmə'nɪsnt; ˌrɛmə'nɪsnt/ *adj* reminiscent of that reminds you of 使人聯想起…: *a taste reminiscent of strawberries* 像草莓的味道

re·miss /rɪ'mɪs; rɪ'mɪs/ *adj* [never before a noun 不能用於名詞前] *fml* careless about a duty 〖正式〗疏忽(職守)的; 懈怠的: *It was remiss of me not to answer your letter.* 沒有給你回信是我的疏忽。

re·mis·sion /rɪ'mɪʃn; rɪ'mɪʃən/ *n* [U] a decrease in the time a person has to stay in prison 〔刑期的〕縮短; 減刑: *The prisoner was given six months' remission for good behaviour.* 這個犯人因表現良好而減刑六個月。

re·mit·tance /rɪ'mɪtns; rɪ'mɪtəns/ *n* an amount of money sent by post as payment for something 匯款(額)

rem·nant /'rɛmnənt; 'rɛmnənt/ *n* **1** a small part that is left of something larger 殘餘部分; 剩餘: *We fed the dogs the remnants of our meal.* 我們用吃剩的東西餵狗。**2** a small piece of cloth left over from a larger piece and sold cheaply 〔減價出售的〕零頭布料

re·mod·el /ri'madl; ˌriː'mɒdl/ *v* **-ll-** (also 又作 **-l-** *AmE* 〖美式〗) [T] to change the shape of something, especially a room 改變〔某物、尤指房間的〕形狀: *Pat had her kitchen remodelled.* 帕特改建了她的廚房。

re·mon·strate /rɪ'mɑnstret; 'rɛmənstreɪt/ *v* **remonstrated, remonstrating** [I] *fml* to complain about something you do not approve of 〖正式〗抗議; 抱怨: *She remonstrated with the driver about the poor bus service.* 她向司機抗議公共交通服務太差勁了。

re·morse /rɪ'mɔrs; rɪ'mɔːs/ *n* a feeling of guilt and sorrow for something you have done which was wrong 悔恨; 自責: *He was filled with remorse after hitting the child.* 他打了孩子後感到悔恨不已。–**remorseful** *adj* –**remorseless** *adj*

*re·mote /rɪ'mot; rɪ'məʊt/ *adj* **1** distant in

space or time 〔空間〕遙遠的;〔時間〕久遠的: *remote stars* 遙遠的星球 | *the remote future* 遙遠的將來 | *a remote village* 偏遠的村莊 **2** not closely connected 關係疏遠的: *What is studied on the course seems rather remote* **from** *ordinary life.* 這門課程學習的內容好像和日常生活沒有甚麼關係。**3** unlikely (used of a chance or possibility) 很小的〔指機會或可能性〕: *Your chances of success are rather remote.* 你成功的可能微乎其微。**4** not friendly or interested 冷淡的; 不感興趣的: *Her behaviour was polite but remote.* 她的舉止有禮, 但十分冷漠。**—remoteness** *n* [U]

remote con·trol /ˌ·ˈ·/ *n* [C;U] a system or a small apparatus for controlling a machine from a distance by radio signals 遙控〔器〕

re·mote·ly /rɪˈmotlɪ; rɪˈməutli/ *adv* **not remotely** not even to a very small degree 一點也不: *She isn't remotely interested in what you're saying.* 她對你說的話一點也沒有興趣。

re·mov·al /rɪˈmuvl; rɪˈmuːvəl/ *n* [U] an act of taking something away or moving it 移動; 除去; 擺脫: *The teacher agreed to the removal* **of** *maps from the walls.* 老師同意把地圖從牆上拿下來。

removal van /·ˈ··· ·/ *n BrE* a large covered vehicle used for moving furniture 〔英式〕(家具)搬運車; 搬家車

★★**re·move** /rɪˈmuv; rɪˈmuːv/ *v* **removed, removing** [T] **1** to take a person or thing away 移開; 挪走; 拿去: *The parents removed their child* **from** *the school.* 這對父母把他們的孩子從學校帶走。 | *Could you remove your suitcase from the hall?* 你可不可以把你的手提箱從走廊搬開? **2** to get rid of something 除去, 去掉〔某物〕: *Please remove the mud from your shoes.* 請擦掉你鞋上的泥。 | *an operation to remove a tumour* 切除腫瘤的手術 **3** to take off clothing 脫下〔衣服〕: *She removed her jacket.* 她脫下了短上衣。**4** to dismiss someone from a job or position 把〔某人〕免職; 開除: *We voted to remove her from the committee.* 我們投票表決把她開除出委員會。**5 far removed from** very different from 與…相差甚遠: *What you now say is far removed from what you said before.* 你現在說的話和你以前說的大相徑庭。

re·mu·ne·rate /rɪˈmjunəˌret; rɪˈmjuːnəreɪt/ *v* **remunerated, remunerating** [T] *fml* to pay someone for work done 〔正式〕給〔某人〕報酬 **—remuneration** /rɪˌmjunəˈreʃən; rɪˌmjuːnəˈreɪʃən/ *n* [sing; U]: *You'll receive a small remuneration.* 你會收到一筆微薄的報酬。

re·mu·ne·ra·tive /rɪˈmjunəˌretɪv; rɪˈmjuːnərətɪv/ *adj fml* well-paid (used of work) 〔正式〕報酬豐厚的〔指工作〕

re·nais·sance /ˌrɛnəˈzɑns; rɪˈneɪsəns/ *n* **1 the Renaissance** the period in Europe between the 14th and 17th centuries, when the art, literature, and ideas of ancient Greece were discovered again and widely studied 〔歐洲十四至十七世紀的〕文藝復興(時期): *the poetry of the early Renaissance* 文藝復興早期的詩歌 **2** a period in which something becomes popular again, especially a style of art, music, or literature 〔尤指藝術、音樂或文學風格的〕復興時期

ren·der /ˈrɛndɚ; ˈrendəʳ/ *v* [T] *fml* 〔正式〕**1** to give someone something, especially help 給予; 提供〔尤指幫助〕: *You have rendered me a great service.* 你幫了我一個大忙。**2** to cause a person or thing to be in a particular state 致使; 使成為: *He was rendered helpless by the accident.* 一場事故使得他無法照顧自己。

ren·der·ing /ˈrɛndərɪŋ; ˈrendərɪŋ/ *n* (also 又作 **rendition**) a performance of a poem, play, or piece of music 演奏; 演出; 表演; 演唱: *a splendid rendering* **of** *the song* 這首歌美妙動聽的演繹

ren·dez·vous /ˈrɑndəˌvu; ˈrɒndɪˌvuː/ *n* **rendezvous** /-ˌvuz; -vuːz/ **1** an arrangement to meet at a certain time and place 約會; 會面: *John arrived late for their rendezvous.* 約翰遲到了他們的約會。**2** a place where you have arranged to meet someone 約會地點 **3** a popular place for people to meet 〔經常的〕聚會處: *This club is a rendezvous for writers.* 這個俱樂部是作家經常聚會的地方。**—rendezvous** *v* [I]

ren·di·tion /rɛnˈdɪʃən; renˈdɪʃən/ *n* see 見 RENDERING

ren·e·gade /ˈrɛnɪˌged; ˈrenɪɡeɪd/ *n* a person who gives up their old beliefs and accepts new ones (a word used to express disapproval) 叛教者; 變節者〔含貶義〕

re·new /rɪˈnju; rɪˈnjuː/ *v* **1** to begin something again 重新開始: *In the morning the enemy renewed their attack.* 早上敵軍再次發動進攻。**2** to give someone or something new life and freshness 使〔某人或某事物〕獲得新生; 使恢復: *I came back from my holiday with renewed strength.* 我度假歸來, 體力得以恢復了。**3** to put something new in the place of something of the same kind 更換; 更新〔某物〕: *to renew your library ticket* 更換借書卡 **—renewal** *n* [C;U]

re·new·a·ble /rɪˈnjuəbl; rɪˈnjuːəbəl/ *adj* **1** that can or must have a new one in its place after a certain period of time 可以更新的; 必須更換的: *All contracts are renewable.* 所有的合同都可續期。**2** that gets some more in its place as it is used or lost 可再生的: *renewable energy sources* 再生性能源

re·nounce /rɪˈnauns; rɪˈnauns/ *v* **renounced, renouncing** [T] *fml* 〔正式〕**1** to give up a claim or a right to something in a formal or official way 聲明放棄〔要求或權利〕: *He renounced his claim to the property.* 他宣佈放棄財產的所有權。**2** to say formally that you will have no more connection with someone or something 宣佈與〔某人或某事

物〕斷絕關係: *He has renounced his entire family.* 他已宣佈和整個家族脫離關係。

ren·o·vate /'rɛnə,vet; 'renəveɪt/ *v* **reno·vated, renovating** [T] to repair something and put it back into good condition 修復; 整修; 翻新: *I renovate old houses.* 我重新裝修舊房子。 **–renovation** /,rɛnə'veʃən; ,renə'veɪʃən/ *n* [C;U]

re·nown /rɪ'naʊn; rɪ'naʊn/ *n* [U] *fml* 【正式】fame 名望, 聲譽: *a painter of world renown* 一位世界知名的畫家 **–renowned** *adj*: *renowned as an inventor* 知名的發明家 **–renowned for his inventions** 因他的發明而著稱

rent¹ /rɛnt; rent/ *n* [C;U] money paid regularly for the use of something, especially a room, building, or piece of land 租用費; 〔尤指房屋或土地的〕租金: *Are you paying rent?* 你付租金嗎? | *They are charging a high rent for the flat.* 他們這套房間租金很昂貴。

*** rent²** *v* [T] **1** to pay rent for the use of something 租用, 租借〔某物〕: *I rent a room from Mrs Jones.* 我向瓊斯太太租了一個房間。 **2** to pay money for the use of something for a short time 〔短時間地〕租用: *Shall we rent a car?* 我們要不要租用一輛汽車嗎?

　rent sthg ↔ out *phr v* [T] to allow something to be used for a certain time in return for payment 出租〔某物〕: *They've rented out their house for the summer.* 他們在夏天時把房子出租。

rent·al /'rɛntl; 'rentl/ *n* **1** the amount of money that you pay to rent something 租金: *The television rental is going up again.* 電視租金又上漲了。 **2** the process of renting something out or something connected with this process 租賃: *a rental agreement* 租賃協議

rent-free /,· '··◄/ *adv, adj* without payment of rent 不收租金地〔的〕: *a rent-free flat* 免收租金的公寓 | *He lives there rent-free!* 他住在那兒, 連租金也不用付!

re·nun·ci·a·tion /rɪ,nʌnsɪ'eʃən; rɪ,nʌnsɪ'eɪʃən/ *n* [C;U] *fml* an act of giving up a claim or a connection with something 〔要求或關係的〕放棄; 斷絕

re·or·gan·ize /ri'ɔrgə,naɪz; riː'ɔːgənaɪz/ *v* **reorganized, reorganizing** (also 又作 **reorganise** *BrE* 〔英式〕) [I;T] to organize something in a different and usually better way 重新組織, 改組; 改編; 整頓: *We're reorganizing the filing system.* 我們在重新整理文件存檔系統。 **–reorganization** /,riɔrgənə'zeʃən; riː,ɔːgənaɪ'zeɪʃən/ *n* [C;U]

rep /rɛp; rep/ *n infml* 【非正式】**1** an elected representative of a group of people 代表: *Take your complaints to the union rep.* 向你的工會代表訴訟吧。 **2** (also 又作 **sales rep**) a salesman 推銷員: *Our rep will call on Monday.* 我們的推銷員星期一要來造訪。 **3** (also 又作 **repertory**) a theatre company 劇團: *the local rep* 本地劇團 | *He's in rep at Bristol.* 他加入了布里斯爾的一個劇團。

re·paid /rɪ'ped; rɪ'peɪd/ the past tense and past participle of REPAY ☆ REPAY 的過去式和過去分詞

re·pair¹ /rɪ'pɛr; rɪ'peəʳ/ *v* [T] **1** to mend something 修理; 修補〔物〕: *The TV has just been repaired.* 這台電視機剛修好。 **2** *fml* to put right something wrong 【正式】補救, 糾正, 彌補〔某事物〕: *The company is trying to repair the damage done to its reputation.* 公司正在設法彌補其聲譽上的損失。 **–repairable** *adj* **–repairer** *n*

*** repair²** *n* **1** what is done to mend something or make it work 修理; 修補: *Who is responsible for carrying out repairs to the road?* 誰負責修理那條路? **2 beyond repair** in such terrible condition that mending is no longer possible 無法修理的 **3 in good repair** in good condition 維修良好 [RELATED PHRASE 相關詞組 **in bad repair**]

rep·a·ra·tion /,rɛpə'reʃən; ,repə'reɪʃən/ *n* [U] *fml* money or help given for loss or suffering by those who caused it 【正式】補償; 賠償: *I expect you to make reparation for any damage.* 我希望你賠償一切損失。 | *We will demand reparations after the war is over.* 戰爭結束後我們要索取賠款。

rep·ar·tee /,rɛpɑ'ti; ,repɑː'tiː/ *n* [U] quick amusing remarks and replies in conversation 〔談話中〕機敏的應答: *I enjoy listening to their witty repartee.* 我很喜歡聽他們妙語連珠的對答。

re·past /rɪ'pæst; rɪ'pɑːst/ *n lit* a meal 【文】餐; 飲食

re·pat·ri·ate /ri'petri,et; riː'pætrieɪt/ *v* **repatriated, repatriating** [T] to send someone back to their own country 把〔某人〕遣送回國, 遣返: *He's being repatriated.* 他被遣送回國。 **–repatriation** /ri,petri'eʃən; ,riːpætri'eɪʃən/ *n* [U]

re·pay /rɪ'pe; rɪ'peɪ/ *v* **repaid** /-'ped; -'peɪd/, **repaid, repaying** [T] **1** to pay back what you owe 償還; 付還: *When can you repay the £5 I lent you?* 我借給你的五英鎊, 你甚麼時候還給我? | *He'll never repay me.* 他永遠不會還錢給我了。 **2** to give something in return for something given or done to you 報答; 回報: *How can I ever repay your kindness?* 我如何才能報答你的恩惠?

re·pay·a·ble /rɪ'peəbl; rɪ'peɪəbəl/ *adj* that can or must be paid back 可償還的; 必須償還的: *The money is repayable at the end of the month.* 這筆錢應在月底償還。

re·pay·ment /rɪ'pemənt; rɪ'peɪmənt/ *n* [C;U] the act of paying back money that you owe 償還; 付還: *I'm making monthly repayments on my bank loan.* 我在按月償還銀行貸款。

re·peal /rɪ'pil; rɪ'piːl/ *v* [T] to put an official end to a law 廢除, 撤銷〔法令〕 **–repeal** *n* [U]

*** re·peat¹** /rɪ'pit; rɪ'piːt/ *v* **1** [T; +(that)] to say, write, or do something again 重複; 重說〔寫/做〕: *Repeat the word after me!* 跟着我

R

唸這個詞! | *'It wasn't her,' he repeated.* "那不是她," 他重複説。 | *She repeated that she had not been there.* 她重複説她當時不在那裡。 **2** [T] to say something that you have heard or learnt 轉述〔聽到或學到的內容〕: *Don't repeat what I told you.* 不要把我告訴你的話對別人説。 **3 repeat yourself** to say or do the same thing again and again 反反覆覆地説或做; 重覆: *History seems to be repeating itself.* 歷史似乎又在重演。

repeat² *n* a broadcast on TV or radio that has been sent out before 〔電視或廣播節目的〕重演; 重播: *All these programmes are repeats!* 這些節目都是重播的!

re·peat·ed /rɪ'pitɪd; rɪ'piːtɪd/ *adj* [only before a noun 只用於名詞前] done again and again 反覆的, 再三的: *I've made repeated attempts to contact him.* 我已再三嘗試和他聯繫。 **-repeatedly** *adv*

re·pel /rɪ'pɛl; rɪ'pel/ *v* **-ll-** [T] **1** to drive someone or something back by force 擊退〔某人〕; 抵制〔某物〕: *They managed to repel the attack.* 他們設法擊退了進攻。 **2** to consider something to be very unpleasant 使人厭惡[反感]: *The smell repels me.* 這氣味使我厭惡。

re·pel·lent¹ /rɪ'pɛlənt; rɪ'pelənt/ *adj* very unpleasant 令人厭惡的; 令人反感的: *She found his behaviour repellent.* 她發現他的行為令人生厭。

repellent² *n* [C;U] a substance that drives something, especially insects, away 驅除藥; 〔尤指〕驅蟲劑: *insect repellent* 驅蟲劑 | *a mosquito repellent* 驅蚊劑

re·pent /rɪ'pɛnt; rɪ'pent/ *v* [I;T] *fml* to be sorry for something that you have done which was wrong〔正式〕悔悟; 後悔 **-repentance** *n* [U] **-repentant** *adj*

re·per·cus·sion /,ripə'kʌʃən; ,riːpə'kʌʃən/ *n* an unplanned effect of some action or event, which may only be known much later〔在意料外且可能深遠的〕反響; 影響; 後果: *The president's death had unexpected repercussions.* 總統的逝世引起了出乎意料的反響。

rep·er·toire /'rɛpə,twar; 'repətwɑːr/ *n* all the things like plays or pieces of music that a performer or theatre company can perform〔演員或劇團能演出的〕全部劇目; 保留劇目; 全部曲目: *Their repertoire includes a number of foreign plays.* 他們的保留劇目包括許多外國劇作。

rep·er·to·ry /'rɛpə,tɔrɪ; 'repətəri/ *n* **repertories** [U] the practice of performing several plays, with the same actors and in the same theatre, one after the other on different days〔同一演員陣容並在同一劇場演出的〕保留劇目輪演: *a repertory company* 輪演選定劇目的劇團 | *The play is in repertory at the National Theatre.* 這齣戲在國家劇院輪演。

rep·e·ti·tion /,rɛpɪ'tɪʃən; ,repɪ'tɪʃən/ *n* **1** [U]

the act of saying or doing something again 重説; 重做; 重複 **2** [C] something said or done again 重説[做]的事, 重複的事: *This accident is a repetition of one that happened here three weeks ago.* 這起事故是三星期前在這裡所發生的事故的重演。

rep·e·ti·tious /,rɛpɪ'tɪʃəs; ,repɪ'tɪʃəs/ *adj* containing parts that are said or done too many times (a word used to express disapproval) 重複的; 反覆的〔含貶義〕: *a repetitious speech* 內容重複的演説

re·pet·i·tive /rɪ'pɛtɪtɪv; rɪ'petɪtɪv/ *adj* said or done too many times 重複的

re·place /rɪ'ples; rɪ'pleɪs/ *v* **replaced, replacing** [T] **1** to put something back where it was 把〔某物〕放回原處: *He replaced the book on the shelf.* 他把書放回書架上。 **2** to take the place of someone or something 代替, 取代, 接替〔某人、某事物〕: *George has replaced Edward as captain of the team.* 喬治接替愛德華當了隊長。 **3** to change one thing for another that is newer or better〔以更新或更好的〕更換, 替換: *We've replaced the old adding machine with a computer.* 我們用計算機替換了舊式的加法器。 | *You'll have to replace those tyres.* 你必須更換那些輪胎了。 **-replaceable** *adj*

re·place·ment /rɪ'plesmənt; rɪ'pleɪsmənt/ *n* **1** [U] the action of replacing a person or thing 代替; 更換 **2** [C] a person or thing that takes the place of another one 代替物; 接替的人; 替換品: *We need a replacement for the secretary who's leaving.* 我們需要一個人來接替即將離職的祕書。 | *I'm Mr. Smith's replacement.* 我是來接替史密斯先生的。

re·play /ri'ple; ,riː'pleɪ/ *v* **replayed, replaying** [T] to play something, especially a match, again 重新舉行〔尤指比賽〕; 重播; 再放: *Let's replay the tape from the beginning.* 我們把磁帶從頭再放一次吧。 **-replay** /ri'ple; 'riːpleɪ/ *n*: *The score was 2-2, so there'll be a replay next Saturday.* 得分是二比二, 所以下週六要再賽一場。

re·plen·ish /rɪ'plɛnɪʃ; rɪ'plenɪʃ/ *v* [T] to fill something up again 再填[裝]滿: *I must replenish the food cupboard.* 我必須把食櫥重新裝滿。

re·plete /rɪ'plit; rɪ'pliːt/ *adj* [never before a noun 不能用於名詞前] *fml* full, especially of food and drink〔正式〕塞滿的; 飽足的

rep·li·ca /'rɛplɪkə; 'replɪkə/ *n* a close copy of a painting or other work of art〔繪畫或其他藝術作品的〕複製品; 摹本

re·ply¹ /rɪ'plaɪ; rɪ'plaɪ/ *v* **replied, replying** [I; T +that] to give an answer 回答, 答覆: *"Did you forget?" I asked. "Of course not," she replied.* "你忘了嗎?" 我問。"當然沒有," 她答道。 | *I replied that I would do it later.* 我回答説我以後會做的。 | *Have you replied to his letter?* 你回了他的信嗎? **-see 見 ANSWER (USAGE 用法)**

reply² *n* **replies** [C;U] **1** something said or

written as an answer 回答, 答覆: *I had twelve replies to my advertisement.* 我收到十二封回應廣告的來信。| *She's free to criticize me, but I demand the right of reply.* 她可以隨意地批評我，但我要求有答辯的權利。**2 in reply** as an answer to what someone has said or done 作為答覆

★**re·port**¹ /rɪˈpɔːrt; rɪˈpɔːt/ *n* **1** a spoken or written account of a situation or event 報告; 報道: *We read a report of the accident.* 我們看了這事故的報道。| *a newspaper report* 新聞報道 **2** the noise of an explosion or shot 爆炸聲; 射擊聲: *a loud report* 一聲巨響

report² *v* **1** [T; +that] to tell people about something, often because it is your job or duty 〔常因為是自己的工作或職責而〕報道, 報告〔某事〕: *He reported the accident to his insurance company.* 他向保險公司報告了這次事故。| *She reported that sixteen students had been taken ill on the trip.* 她説旅途中有十六名學生患了病。| *"He's disappeared," she reported on her return.* "他失蹤了，" 她一回來就報告説。**2 report on something** to provide information and often ideas about something 報告〔匯報〕某事: *He reported on the conference he had attended.* 他匯報了他所參加的會議的情況。| *The committee is reporting on ways of improving the Health Service.* 委員會在報告改進社會保健服務的各種方法。**3** [T] to make a complaint about someone 告發; 舉報: *The clerk was so rude that I reported him to his superior.* 辦事員十分粗魯無禮，因此我向他的上司告發他。**4** [I] to go to a person or place and say that you have arrived or that you are ready for work 報到: *I have to report for duty at 5 o'clock.* 我必須在五點鐘報到上班。| *Report to the main desk on arrival.* 到達時請至總服務台報到。

reported speech /·,·· ·ˈ·/ *n* [U] writing which shows what someone said, without using their exact words 轉告引述

re·port·er /rɪˈpɔːrtər; rɪˈpɔːtər/ *n* a person who writes about news for a newspaper, or for radio and television 記者

re·pose /rɪˈpoz; rɪˈpəʊz/ *n* [U] *fml* rest 〔正式〕休息; 歇息 –**repose** *v* **reposed, reposing** [I;T]

rep·re·hen·si·ble /ˌreprɪˈhensəbl; ˌreprɪˈhensəbl/ *adj* very bad 極惡劣的: *reprehensible behaviour* 惡劣的行為 –**reprehensibly** *adv*

★**rep·re·sent** /ˌreprɪˈzent; ˌreprɪˈzent/ *v* [T] **1** to act officially for another person or group of people 代表〔其他人或團體〕: *The workers were represented in the negotiations by the union secretary.* 工人們由工會祕書來代表談判。| *Prince Charles is representing the Queen at today's ceremony.* 查爾斯王子代表女王出席今天的典禮。**2** to be typical of something,

or of a group of people 〔典型地〕代表; 作為…典型: *She represents the typical teenager.* 她是典型青少年的代表。**3** to be a sign for another thing 象徵: *This line is supposed to represent her head.* 這條線應該是象徵她的頭。**4** to express the true nature of something 表達〔某事物的真正性質〕: *Nothing represents home more than my mother's cooking.* 沒有甚麼比我媽媽做的飯菜更能表達出家的感覺。**5** to be the result of something 是〔某事物〕的結果: *His final book represented twenty years of hard work.* 他的最後一本書是二十年辛勤工作的成果。**6** to describe or show a person or thing in a particular way 〔以某種方式〕描述, 表現〔人或物〕: *The former dictator was represented as a tyrant.* 前獨裁者被描繪成一位暴君。

★**rep·re·sen·ta·tion** /ˌreprɪzenˈteɪʃən; ˌreprɪˌzenˈteɪʃən/ *n* **1** [U] the situation of being represented by someone 代表; 代理: *They demanded political representation.* 他們要求建立政治代表制。**2** [C] something that is shown in a particular way 表示; 描繪; 象徵: *This painting is a representation of a storm at sea.* 這幅畫表現的是一場海上風暴。**3 representations** [pl] formal statements, complaints, or requests 〔正式〕陳述; 投訴; 要求: *We made representations on behalf of the political prisoners.* 我們代表政治犯提出抗議。

rep·re·sen·ta·tive¹ /ˌreprɪˈzentətɪv; ˌreprɪˈzentətɪv/ *adj* **1** typical of a particular group 有代表性的; 典型的: *Are your opinions representative of those of the other students?* 你的意見是否代表了其他學生的意見? **2** [only before a noun 只用於名詞前] related to a system of government in which people and their opinions are represented by people who speak for them 〔政府制度〕代表制的; 代議制的: *a representative council* 代議委員會

★**representative**² *n* a person acting in place of one or more others 代表; 代理人: *They sent a representative to the meeting.* 他們派了一位代表參加會議。

re·press /rɪˈpres; rɪˈpres/ *v* [T] **1** to control or hold back natural feelings 抑制, 壓制〔自然感情〕: *I could hardly repress my laughter.* 我忍不住要大笑起來。| *She tends to repress her emotions.* 她往往會壓抑自己的感情。**2** to control people by force 鎮壓; 制止 –**repressed** *adj*: *a repressed desire to steal* 受抑制的偷竊慾望 | *He's very repressed.* 他很受壓抑。–**repression** /rɪˈpreʃən; rɪˈpreʃən/ *n* [U]: *the repression of political opposition* 政治對立的鎮壓

re·pres·sive /rɪˈpresɪv; rɪˈpresɪv/ *adj* hard and cruel 鎮壓的; 殘暴的: *The country has an extremely repressive political system.* 該國的政治制度極為嚴厲而殘暴。

re·prieve¹ /rɪˈpriv; rɪˈpriːv/ *v* **reprieved, reprieving** [T] to change a sentence of death so that a person is not killed 緩期執

行〔死刑〕: *Both men have been reprieved.* 這兩個人已緩期處決。

reprieve² *n* **1** an official order delaying or ending a sentence, especially a death sentence 〔尤指死刑的〕緩刑令: *There is little hope of a reprieve.* 緩刑的希望很小。 **2** a delay before something unpleasant happens or continues 〔不快之事的〕暫時緩解

rep·ri·mand /'rɛprə,mænd; 'reprɨ,mɑːnd/ *v* [T] to give someone a serious official warning about unacceptable behaviour 申斥; 訓斥 –**reprimand** *n* [U]

re·print¹ /ri'prɪnt; ˌriː'prɪnt/ *v* [T] to print a book again when supplies have run out 〔書籍〕重印; 再版

re·print² /'ri,prɪnt; 'riː,prɪnt/ *n* a reprinted book 重印本; 再版本

re·pri·sal /rɪ'praɪzl; rɪ'praɪzəl/ *n* [C;U] violent action taken as punishment for harm done 報復(行為): *Bombs were dropped on an enemy village as a reprisal.* 向敵人的村莊投炸彈作為報復。 | *In an act of reprisal seventy men were taken prisoner.* 在一次報復行動中, 有七十人被捕入獄。

re·proach¹ /rɪ'protʃ; rɪ'prəʊtʃ/ *n* **1** [U] quiet blame 責備, 指責: *She gave me a look of reproach.* 她責備地看了我一眼。 **2** [C] a word or words of blame 責備的話, 責罵: *He can't live with his wife's constant reproaches.* 他太受不了妻子沒完沒了的責備, 使他簡直受不了。 **3** beyond reproach perfect 無可指摘的; 盡善盡美的 –**reproachful** *adj* –**reproachfully** *adv*

reproach² *v* [T] **1** to blame someone, usually in a sad and quiet way 〔常指難過而又輕聲地〕責備(某人) **2** reproach yourself to blame yourself for something that you wish you had not done 自責: *She reproached herself for not having made enough effort.* 她為自己不夠努力而自責。

rep·ro·bate /'rɛprə,bet; 'reprəbeɪt/ *n* a person of bad character 惡棍; 墮落者: *He's an old reprobate, who spends all his money on beer.* 他是個老無賴, 把錢全都買啤酒喝了。 –**reprobate** *adj*

re·pro·duce /,riprə'djus; ˌriːprə'djuːs/ *v* **reproduced, reproducing 1** [I] to produce young 繁殖, 生殖: *Some tropical fish reproduce by laying eggs.* 有些熱帶魚靠產卵繁殖。 **2** [T] to produce a copy 複製; 翻印; 重現: *a painting that reproduces every detail of the scene* 一幅把景色的每個細節再現的畫

re·pro·duc·tion /,riprə'dʌkʃən; ˌriːprə'dʌkʃən/ *n* **1** [U] the act or method of producing young 繁殖; 生殖(方式): *a book on insect reproduction* 一本關於昆蟲繁殖的書 **2** [U] the copying of things like sound and printed materials 〔有聲資料、印刷材料的〕複製; 翻印; 拷貝: *The quality of reproduction isn't very good on this recording.* 這張唱片的複製質量不是很好。 **3** [C] a copy, especially of a work of art 〔尤指藝術作品的〕複製品: *a cheap reproduction of a great painting* 一幅

偉大畫作的廉價複製品 –**reproductive** *adj* [only before a noun 只用於名詞前]: *the female reproductive organs* 女性生殖器官

re·prove /rɪ'pruv; rɪ'pruːv/ *v* **reproved, reproving** [T] *fml* to tell someone they have done something wrong 〔正式〕責備, 指摘 〔某人〕 –**reproof** /rɪ'pruf; rɪ'pruːf/ *n* [C;U]

rep·tile /'rɛptl; 'reptaɪl/ *n* a creature with a rough skin whose blood changes temperature according to the temperature around it 爬行動物; 爬蟲: *Snakes and lizards are reptiles.* 蛇和蜥蜴都是爬行動物。 –**reptilian** /rɛp'tɪlɪən; rep'tɪlɪən/ *adj*

★**re·pub·lic** /rɪ'pʌblɪk; rɪ'pʌblɪk/ *n* a nation which is usually governed by elected representatives; the head of state is a president 共和國; 共和政體

re·pub·li·can¹ /rɪ'pʌblɪkən; rɪ'pʌblɪkən/ *adj* belonging to or favouring a republic 共和國的; 共和政體的: *a republican system of government* 共和政體 | *republican ideas* 共和思想

republican² *n* **1** a person who believes in a republican system of government 擁護共和政體者, 共和主義者 **2** Republican a member or supporter of the Republican Party, one of the two largest political parties of the US 〔美國〕共和黨黨員; 共和黨的支持者

re·pu·di·ate /rɪ'pjudɪ,et; rɪ'pjuːdɪeɪt/ *v* **repudiated, repudiating** [T] *fml* to refuse to accept or recognize someone or something 〔正式〕拒絕接受; 否認〔某人、某事物〕: *He repudiated the charge of having shot his sister.* 他否認了對他槍殺自己妹妹的指控。 –**repudiation** /rɪ,pjudɪ'eʃən; rɪ,pjuːdi'eɪʃən/ *n* [U]

re·pug·nance /rɪ'pʌgnəns; rɪ'pʌgnəns/ *n* [sing; U] a feeling of strong dislike 強烈的反感; 厭惡: *She turned away from him in repugnance.* 她厭惡地從他面前轉身走開了。 –**repugnant** *adj*

re·pulse /rɪ'pʌls; rɪ'pʌls/ *v* **repulsed, repulsing** [T] **1** to cause someone to feel a strong dislike 使(某人)厭惡: *He repulses me.* 他使我反感。 **2** to drive back an enemy attack 擊退〔敵人的進攻〕

re·pul·sion /rɪ'pʌlʃən; rɪ'pʌlʃən/ *n* **1** [sing; U] a feeling of strong dislike 憎惡; 反感: *He looked with repulsion at the dead body.* 他厭惡地看着那屍體。 **2** [U] a force that pushes something away from something else 斥力; 排斥力

re·pul·sive /rɪ'pʌlsɪv; rɪ'pʌlsɪv/ *adj* extremely unpleasant 令人厭惡的; 可憎的: *a repulsive smell* 令人厭惡的氣味 | *repulsive behaviour* 令人厭惡的行為

rep·u·ta·ble /'rɛpjətəbl; 'repjʊtəbəl/ *adj* known to be good 聲譽好的; 享有聲望的: *a reputable firm of builders* 一家聲譽良好的建築公司 –opposite 反義 **disreputable** –**reputably** *adv*

★**rep·u·ta·tion** /,rɛpjə'teʃən; ˌrepjʊ'teɪʃən/ *n*

[C;U] **1** the opinion people have of a person or thing 名譽; 名聲: *This will ruin my reputation!* 這會毀掉我的名譽! | *The restaurant has a good reputation.* 這家餐館名聲很好。 | *He has a reputation for finishing work on time.* 他按時完成工作盡人皆知。 **2** **live up to your reputation** to behave in the way that people have come to expect of you 不負盛名; 名不虛傳: *He's living up to his reputation as a troublemaker.* 他是個名不虛傳的搗蛋鬼。

re·pute[1] /rɪˈpjut; rɪˈpjuːt/ n [U] fml the opinion people have of someone or something 〔正式〕名譽; 名聲: *a hotel of high repute* 一家名聲很好的旅館

re·put·ed /rɪˈpjutɪd; rɪˈpjuːtɪd/ adj generally considered to be 普遍認為的: *the reputed father of her baby* 一般認為是她那嬰兒的父親 | *She is reputed to be the richest woman in Europe.* 據說她是歐洲最有錢的女人。 –**reputedly** adv

re·quest[1] /rɪˈkwɛst; rɪˈkwest/ n **1** a polite demand 請求: *He made a request for help.* 他請求幫助。 **2** something that is asked for, especially music to be played on the radio 要求的事物〔尤指廣播中點播的音樂〕 **3** **at someone's request** because someone asked 應某人的要求: *I bought it at the request of my father.* 我應父親的要求買了它。 **4** **on request** if you ask 一經要求: *Further details are available on request.* 備有進一步的詳細資料備索。

request[2] v fml [T; +that] to ask politely 〔正式〕請求, 要求: *The judge requested silence.* 法官請求肅靜。 | *Staff have requested that we discuss this matter at the next meeting.* 全體職員已要求我們在下次會議上討論此事。 | *Guests are requested not to use the pool after 9pm.* 客人請勿於下午九時後使用游泳池。

> □ USEFUL PATTERNS 有用句型
> to request something; to request that…,
> to be requested (not) to do something

> ■ USAGE 用法: Remember that the verb **request** is transitive and is NOT, therefore, followed by a preposition. (The noun **request**, however, may be followed by the preposition **for**.) ☆記住動詞 **request** 是及物的, 所以後面不跟介詞。(但名詞 **request** 可以跟介詞 **for**。) Compare 比較: *They have **requested** more information on this issue.* 他們要求得到關於這個問題的更多資料。 | *We have received **a request for** more information on this issue.* 我們收到一份請求, 要我們就這個問題提供更多資料。

req·ui·em /ˈrikwɪəm; ˈrekwɪəm/ n a piece of music usually played or sung at a Christian ceremony (MASS) for the soul of a dead person 〔追思彌撒時的〕安魂曲

re·quire /rɪˈkwaɪr; rɪˈkwaɪər/ v **required, requiring** [T] **1** to need something 需要〔某事物〕: *This suggestion requires careful thought.* 這項建議需要仔細考慮。 **2** fml to make someone do something that is necessary 〔正式〕要求〔某人做必須做的事〕: *All passengers are required to show their tickets.* 所有的乘客都要出示車票。 | *to pass the required examinations to become a doctor* 通過各項規定的考試而成為醫生

re·quire·ment /rɪˈkwaɪrmənt; rɪˈkwaɪərmənt/ n **1** something needed or demanded 必需品; 要求的東西: *This shop can supply all your requirements.* 這家商店能供應你需要的一切東西。 **2** **meet someone's requirements** to be what someone needs or demands 符合某人的需要〔要求〕: *We can't find an office that meets our requirements.* 我們找不到一間能滿足我們要求的辦公室。

req·ui·site /ˈrɛkwəzɪt; ˈrekwɪzɪt/ n fml something that is necessary for a certain purpose 〔正式〕必需品; 必要條件: *sports requisites* 運動必需品 –**requisite** adj: *Have you got the requisite stamp on your passport?* 你的護照蓋上所需的印鑑了嗎?

req·ui·si·tion /ˌrɛkwəˈzɪʃən; ˌrekwɪˈzɪʃən/ n a formal demand for the use of something, especially by the army 正式要求; 〔尤指軍隊〕徵用: *The soldiers made a requisition for horses.* 士兵徵用了馬匹。 –**requisition** v [T]: *The army has requisitioned the local hotel.* 軍隊徵用了當地的旅館。

res·cue[1] /ˈrɛskju; ˈreskjuː/ v **rescued, rescuing** [T] to save someone or something from harm or danger 拯救, 救援〔某人、某物〕: *The boys were rescued after hours at sea.* 男孩在海上漂流了幾小時後獲救了。 – **rescuer** n

rescue[2] n [C;U] **1** an act of saving a person or thing from harm or danger 營救, 拯救: *A rescue team is trying to reach the trapped miners.* 一支救援隊正設法接近礦工被困的地方。 **2** **come/go to someone's rescue** to help someone who is in a difficult or dangerous situation 幫助〔援救〕〔處於困難或危險境地的〕某人

re·search[1] /ˈrisɚtʃ; rɪˈsɜːtʃ/ n [C;U] advanced and detailed study of a subject, in order to find out something new 研究; 探討: *research students* 研究生 | *He's doing research into the causes of cancer.* 他正從事癌症起因的研究。

research[2] v [I;T] to try and get information in order to find out something new 研究, 探究: *They are researching attitudes to health food.* 他們在研究對健康食品的看法。 | *We've been researching for three years without result.* 我們已研究了三年, 但毫無結果。 –**researcher** n

re·sem·ble /rɪˈzɛmbl; rɪˈzembəl/ v **resem-**

R

bled, resembling [T] to look or be like another person or thing 像〔他人、他物〕；與…相似: *She resembles her sister in many ways.* 她在很多方面都像她的姐姐。 —**resemblance** n [C;U]: *There's a strong resemblance* **between** *the two sisters.* 這兩姐妹非常相似。 | *Can you see a family resemblance?* 你能看出家人之間相似之處嗎？

re·sent /rɪˈzɛnt; rɪˈzent/ v [T] to feel angry or bitter about something 對〔某事物〕感到憤恨，不滿: *He resents being treated as a child.* 他討厭被人當作小孩子看待。 —**resentful** adj: *a resentful look* 忿恨不滿的神色

re·sent·ment /rɪˈzɛntmənt; rɪˈzentmənt/ n [C;U] the feeling of being angry and bitter 忿恨，不滿，怨恨: *I don't bear you any resentment.* 我對你毫無怨恨。

res·er·va·tion /ˌrɛzɚˈveʃən; ˌrezəˈveɪʃən/ n [C] **1** a doubt in your mind 保留；存疑: *I have some reservations* **about** *the truth of his story.* 我對他所說的事的真實性有些懷疑。 **2 without reservation** with no uncertainty 毫無保留地；毫不躊躇地: *I accepted his explanation without reservation.* 我毫無保留地接受了他的解釋。 **3** a piece of land set apart for North American Indians to live on〔北美印第安人的〕居留地 **4** an arrangement to make sure that something is kept for your use 預訂: *Have you made the flight reservations yet?* 你預訂了飛機座位沒有？

****re·serve¹** /rɪˈzɝv; rɪˈzɜːv/ v **reserved, reserving** [T] **1** to keep something for a special purpose 保留；保存: *These seats are reserved* **for** *old people.* 這些座位是留給老人的。 **2** to arrange for something to be kept for your use 預訂: *I need to reserve a seat on the plane.* 我要預訂一個飛機座位。

reserve² n **1** [C] a supply of something which is kept for possible future use 儲備物: *Our water reserves are low at the moment.* 目前我們的食水儲備量很少。 **2** [C] a piece of land kept for a particular purpose 保留地；保護區: *a nature reserve* 自然保護區 **3** [U] the quality of not showing your thoughts or feelings 矜持；含蓄: *the well-known reserve of the English* 英國人眾所周知的矜持 **4** [C] a player whose job is to play in a team game in place of any member who cannot play 替補隊員；預備〔後備〕隊員: *I'm a reserve for the school football team.* 我是學校足球隊的後備隊員。 **5 in reserve** ready for use if needed 留以備用

re·served /rɪˈzɝvd; rɪˈzɜːvd/ adj **1** unwilling to talk about your thoughts or feelings 沉默矜持的 **2** kept for someone's use 保留的；預訂的: *reserved seats* 預訂的座位

res·er·voir /ˈrɛzɚˌvɔr; ˈrezəvwɑːʳ/ n **1** a place where liquid is stored, especially a man-made lake that supplies water to places in the area 蓄水池；〔尤指〕水庫 **2** a supply of something that may be used if necessary 儲藏；積蓄

re·shuf·fle /riˈʃʌfl; riːˈʃʌfəl/ n a change in the positions of a number of people employed in an organization 人事變動；改組 —**reshuffle** /riˈʃʌfl; riːˈʃʌfəl/ v **reshuffled, reshuffling** [I;T]

re·side /rɪˈzaɪd; rɪˈzaɪd/ v **resided, residing** [I] fml to have your home in a particular place 〔正式〕居住；定居: *They reside overseas.* 他們在海外定居。

res·i·dence /ˈrɛzədəns; ˈrezɪdəns/ n **1** [C] fml the place where you live 〔正式〕住處，居所，住宅: *the Prime Minister's official residence* 首相的官邸 **2** [U] the situation of living in a place 居住；定居: *Payment of the tax depends on residence, not house ownership.* 納稅多少取決於居住權，而不是房屋所有權。 **3 in residence** actually living in a place 實際住在某處的: *The students are not in residence during the holidays.* 學生放假期間都不住在學校。 **4 take up residence** fml to move to a place where you are going to live〔正式〕去〔某處〕居住

****res·i·dent¹** /ˈrɛzədənt; ˈrezɪdənt/ adj **1** living in a place 居住的: *He's resident in Britain.* 他是住在倫敦的。 **2** living in the place where you work 住在工作所在地的: *Boarding schools have resident nurses.* 寄宿學校有住校的護士。 —opposite 反義 **non-resident 3** working in a place all the time 常駐的: *Is there a resident painter at the arts centre?* 藝術中心有常駐畫家嗎？

resident² n a person who lives in a place 居民；定居者；住客: *residents of Oxford* 牛津的居民 | *This hotel serves meals to residents only.* 這家旅館只向住客供膳。 —opposite 反義 **non-resident**

****res·i·den·tial** /ˌrɛzəˈdɛnʃəl; ˌrezɪˈdenʃəl◂/ adj **1** consisting of private houses, without offices or factories (used to describe an area of a town) 住宅區的；居住的〔用於描述城鎮地區〕 **2** where people live in the building 住宿的: *residential accommodation* 住處 | *a residential course* 必須住校攻讀的課程

re·sid·u·al /rɪˈzɪdʒuəl; rɪˈzɪdjuəl/ adj left over 剩餘的；殘留的

res·i·due /ˈrɛzəˌdju; ˈrezɪdjuː/ n tech what is left, especially after chemical treatment 〔術語〕〔尤指化學處理後的〕殘餘物；殘渣

****re·sign** /rɪˈzaɪn; rɪˈzaɪn/ v [I;T] **1** to leave a job or position 辭職；放棄〔工作、職位〕: *I'm considering resigning.* 我正在考慮辭職。 | *Has he resigned his post?* 他已辭職了嗎？ **2 resign yourself to something** to accept something unpleasant without complaint 聽任，順從〔不愉快的事物〕: *You must resign yourselves to waiting a bit longer.* 你們必須耐心多等一會兒。

****res·ig·na·tion** /ˌrɛzɪɡˈneʃən; ˌrezɪɡˈneɪʃən/ n **1** [C;U] a statement that you intend to leave a job or position 辭職；放棄: *You have the choice between resignation and dismissal.* 辭職還是被解雇，你自己選擇。 | *He*

handed in his resignation. 他遞交了辭職信。
2 [U] acceptance of something unpleasant 聽從, 順從: *She accepted her fate with resignation.* 她聽天由命。

re·signed /rɪˈzaɪnd; rɪˈzaɪnd/ *adj* prepared to accept something unpleasant without complaint 聽任的; 順從的: *He seems quite resigned to living alone.* 他似乎甘心情願過獨居生活。 –**resignedly** /-nɪdlɪ; -nˌˈdlɪ/ *adv*

re·sil·i·ent /rɪˈzɪlɪənt; rɪˈzɪlɪənt/ *adj* **1** able to spring back to its former shape when pressure is removed (used to describe substances) 有回彈力的; 有彈性的 (用於描述物質): *Rubber is more resilient than wood.* 橡膠的彈性比木頭大。 **2** strong enough to recover from a bad situation or event 有復原力的; 適應性強的: *He'll cope with the situation. He's very resilient.* 他會應付這局面的; 他適應力很強。 –**resilience** *n* [U]

res·in /ˈrezn; ˈrezˌ̩n/ *n* **1** [U] a thick sticky liquid obtained from certain trees 樹脂 **2** [C] any of various man-made plastic substances, used in industry 合成樹脂, 人造樹脂 –**resinous** *adj*

*❋**re·sist** /rɪˈzɪst; rɪˈzɪst/ *v* [T] **1** to fight back against attack 抵抗, 抵禦 (進攻): *They tried to resist the enemy attack.* 他們盡力抵抗敵人的進攻。 **2** to fight against something 抵制, 抗拒 (某物): *He resists any kind of change.* 他拒絕任何變革。 **3** to stop yourself accepting or doing something 按捺; 忍住: *I can't resist chocolate cake.* 我看見巧克力蛋糕就要吃。 | *She couldn't resist laughing.* 她忍不住要大笑起來。 –**resistible** *adj*

*❋**re·sist·ance** /rɪˈzɪstəns; rɪˈzɪstəns/ *n* [U] **1** refusal to accept something 反抗; 抵制: *There was a lot of resistance to the plan.* 好多人抵制這項計劃。 **2** fighting back against attack 抵抗: *resistance fighters* 抵抗運動戰士 **3** the ability of a living body not to be harmed by disease (生物體的)抵抗力: *This vaccine improves resistance to certain diseases.* 這種疫苗能增強對某些疾病的抵抗力。

re·sis·tant /rɪˈzɪstənt; rɪˈzɪstənt/ *adj* **1** unwilling to accept something 反抗的; 抵抗的: *Many teachers are resistant to new ideas.* 很多教師抵制新思想。 **2** not harmed by something 有抵抗力的: *rats that are resistant to poison* 對毒藥有抗藥力的老鼠

res·o·lute /ˈrezəˌlut; ˈrezəluːt/ *adj* firm and determined 堅定的; 有決心的; 堅毅的 –compare 比較 IRRESOLUTE –**resolutely** *adv*

*❋**res·o·lu·tion** /ˌrezəˈluʃən; ˌrezəˈluːʃn/ *n* **1** [U] strength of purpose 堅決, 堅定, 果斷: *You might be taken seriously if you showed more resolution.* 如果你表現得更堅定些, 人家也許會認真對待你。 **2** [C;U] the settling of a problem (問題的)解決; 解答: *The lawyer's advice led to the resolution of all our difficulties.* 律師的忠告幫助我們解決了全部困難。 **3** [C] a formal decision made by a group of people at a meeting (會議的)決議; 正式決

定: *A resolution to build a new road was passed easily.* 修築一條新公路的決議很容易地通過了。 **4** [C] a decision 決定; 決心: *She made a resolution to eat more healthy food.* 她決定要多吃健康食品。

*❋**re·solve**¹ /rɪˈzɑlv; rɪˈzɒlv/ *v* **resolved, resolving** **1** [T] to deal with a problem 解決, 解答 (問題): *We must find a way of resolving these difficulties.* 我們必須找到一個解決這些困難的方法。 **2** [I; +(that)] to make a decision about something 下決心, 決意(要做): *They resolved to work harder.* 他們決心更努力工作。 | *She resolved that in future she would not lose her temper.* 她決心以後不再發脾氣了。

> ◻ USEFUL PATTERNS 有用句型
> to resolve to do something; to resolve that…

resolve² *n fml* (正式) **1** [C] a decision 決心, 決意: *He made a firm resolve to be more considerate.* 他下定決心要考慮得更周全一些。 **2** [U] strength of purpose 決心; 堅決: *He showed great resolve.* 他表現出很大的決心。

res·o·nant /ˈrezˌnənt; ˈrezənənt/ *adj* strong and continuing (used of a sound) 洪亮的, 回盪的 (指聲音): *the resonant note of a bell* 洪亮的鐘聲 –**resonance** *n* [U]

*❋**re·sort** /rɪˈzɔrt; rɪˈzɔːt/ *n* **1** [C] a place to which a lot of people go on holiday 度假地; 遊覽勝地: *a tourist resort* 旅遊勝地 | *a beach resort* 海濱勝地 **2** [U] making use of something, often something bad 採取, 訴諸 (常指不好的事物): *You can all pass the examination without resort to cheating!* 你們是不靠作弊都能通過考試的! **3** **in the last resort, as a last resort** if everything else fails (其他一切都失敗後)作為最後的手段: *In the last resort we can always spend the night in the car.* 作為最後一着, 我們總還能在汽車裡過夜。

resort *v* **resort to something** to turn to something bad or unpleasant because you know no other way 求助於, 訴諸 (不良手段): *When her money ran out, she resorted to stealing.* 她花光了錢, 就去偷竊。

re·sound /rɪˈzaʊnd; rɪˈzaʊnd/ *v* [I] **1** to be heard loudly and clearly 回響, 鳴響: *Their laughter resounded through the hall.* 他們的笑聲在大廳裡響成一片。 **2** (of a place) to be filled with sound (地方)充滿聲音; 回盪: *The hall resounded with laughter.* 大廳裡回盪着笑聲。

re·sound·ing /rɪˈzaʊndɪŋ; rɪˈzaʊndɪŋ/ *adj* [only before a noun 只用於名詞前] **1** loud and clear 響亮的, 洪亮的: *a resounding crash* 響亮的撞擊聲 **2** very great 巨大的: *a resounding success* 巨大的成功

*❋**re·source** /rɪˈsors; rɪˈzɔːs/ *n* **1** something that a place possesses and that can be used 資源: *The*

country is rich in natural resources. 這個國家自然資源豐富。**2** something that you can use to help you 對人有幫助的東西: *Are there many resources available to teachers here?* 這裡有很多供教師使用的資料嗎? | *Religion is her only resource now.* 宗教是她現在唯一的慰藉。**3 leave someone to their own resources** to let someone pass the time as they wish 讓某人自己想辦法(打發時間)

re·source·ful /rɪˈsɔrsfəl; rɪˈzɔːsfəl/ *adj* good at dealing with difficulties 善於隨機應變的: *Someone as resourceful as you will be able to find a way of making money!* 像你這麼足智多謀的人應該能找到賺錢的法子! **–resourcefulness** *n* [U]

⋆⋆**re·spect**[1] /rɪˈspɛkt; rɪˈspekt/ *n* **1** [U] admiration of someone's position or personal qualities 尊敬, 尊重: *Of course I feel respect for my father.* 我當然尊敬我的父親。 | *He expects to be treated with respect.* 他期望受到尊重。 –opposite 反義 **disrespect 2** [U] attention to something 注意; 重視; 顧慮: *Drivers have no respect for speed limits.* 司機全都不注意限速規定。**3** [C] a detail or way of judging something〔判斷的〕着眼點; 細節; 方面: *The new job is better paid, but in some respects less interesting.* 這份新工作報酬較好, 但在某些方面不太有意思。 | *In this respect, the service we provide is better now.* 就這方面而言, 我們現在提供的服務更好。**4 with respect to** *fml* concerning〔正式〕關於: *With respect to your recent enquiry, I enclose a form for your insurance claim.* 關於你最近的查詢, 我隨附上一份保險索賠表格給你。**5 pay your last respects** to show honour to a person who has recently died 向某人告別悼念

respect[2] *v* [T] **1** to treat someone in a way that shows you accept their position or admire their personal qualities 尊敬, 敬重〔某人〕: *Her students don't respect her any more.* 她的學生不再敬重她。**2** to agree that something has value, even if your view is different 尊重, 重視〔某事物的價值〕: *They respect my judgment, but they are in a difficult situation.* 他們尊重我的判斷, 不過他們也有難處。**3** to act in accordance with something 顧及: *I promise to respect your wishes.* 我會應尊重你的願望。

re·spec·ta·ble /rɪˈspɛktəbl; rɪˈspektəbəl/ *adj* **1** showing or having standards that society approves of 值得尊敬的; 體面的; 正派的: *Please try to look respectable this evening!* 今天晚上請盡量表現得體面些! | *She's a respectable woman.* 她是個很正派的女子。**2** enough in amount or quality〔數量或質量〕可觀的, 足夠的; 相當好的: *I earn a respectable income.* 我掙的收入很可觀。**–respectability** /rɪˌspɛktəˈbɪlətɪ; rɪˌspektəˈbɪlɪti/ [U]

re·spect·ful /rɪˈspɛktfəl; rɪˈspektfəl/ *adj* feeling or showing respect 恭敬的; 表示尊敬的 –opposite 反義 **disrespectful**

re·spec·tive /rɪˈspɛktɪv; rɪˈspektɪv/ *adj* [only before a noun 只用於名詞前] particular and separate 各自的; 個別的: *They went home to their respective houses.* 他們各自回家了。

⋆**re·spec·tive·ly** /rɪˈspɛktɪvlɪ; rɪˈspektɪvli/ *adv* each separately in the order mentioned 各自地; 個別地: *The nurses and the miners received pay rises of 8% and 12% respectively.* 護士和礦工分別加薪百分之八和百分之十二。

re·spects /rɪˈspɛkts; rɪˈspekts/ *n* [pl] polite formal greetings 敬意; 問候: *Give my respects to your wife.* 請代我問候你太太。

res·pi·ra·tion /ˌrɛspəˈreʃən; ˌrespɪˈreɪʃən/ *n* [U] *tech* breathing〔術語〕呼吸

res·pi·ra·tor /ˈrɛspəˌretə; ˈrespɪreɪtəʳ/ *n* an apparatus that helps people to breathe 人工呼吸器

re·spi·ra·to·ry /rɪˈspaɪrəˌtɔri; rɪˈspɪrətəri/ *adj* [only before a noun 只用於名詞前] connected with breathing 呼吸的: *respiratory diseases* 呼吸道疾病

res·pite /ˈrɛspɪt; ˈrespaɪt/ *n* [C;U] pause or rest, during a time of effort, pain, or trouble〔努力、痛苦或困難的〕暫停; 暫息; 喘息: *The noise went on all night without a moment's respite.* 吵鬧聲一刻不停地持續了一整晚。 | *There was no respite from the bombing.* 轟炸一直沒有停止過。

re·splen·dent /rɪˈsplɛndənt; rɪˈsplendənt/ *adj fml or lit* bright and striking (used of appearance)〔正式或文〕燦爛的; 引人注目的〔指外表〕**–resplendence** *n* [U] **–resplendently** *adv*

⋆**re·spond** /rɪˈspɑnd; rɪˈspɒnd/ *v fml*〔正式〕**1** [I; +that] to answer someone or something 回覆; 回答: *They still haven't responded to my letter.* 他們仍未回我的信。 | *He responded that he had not been in the building at the time.* 他回答說當時他不在大樓裡。 –see 見 ANSWER (USAGE 用法) **2** [I] to act in answer to something 作出反應: *He responded to my suggestion with a laugh.* 他對我的建議報以一笑。**3** to improve as a result of something〔因某事物的結果而〕有起色; 良好反應: *The disease failed to respond to drugs.* 這個病服藥無效。 | *He doesn't respond to discipline.* 他不守紀律。

⋆⋆**re·sponse** /rɪˈspɑns; rɪˈspɒns/ *n* [C; U] **1** answer 回答: *He gave no response.* 他沒有作出回答。 | *I'm waiting for a response from the airline.* 我在等航空公司的答覆。 | *I am writing in response to your recent letter.* 我在回覆你最近的來信。**2** action or feelings caused by something 反應: *There has been little response to our appeal.* 我們的呼籲沒有甚麼反應。

⋆⋆**re·spon·si·bil·i·ty** /rɪˌspɑnsəˈbɪlətɪ; rɪˌspɒnsəˈbɪlɪti/ *n* **responsibilities 1** [U] the ability or need to deal with important matters in a correct and useful way 責任: *He's not ready for such responsibility.* 他還未準備好承擔這樣的責任。| *She's in a position of great responsibility.* 她所處的職位責任重大。**2** [U] control over someone or something in your charge, which means you must take the blame if anything goes wrong 責任: *Who has responsibility for the work of this department?* 誰負責這個部門的工作? **3** [C] something which you have the duty to do or to look after 義務; 職責; 所負責的事物: *Parents have many responsibilities.* 父母有許多責任。| *The children are our responsibility.* (養育)孩子是我們的責任。**4** responsibility for something the blame for something 對某事物負責: *I accept full responsibility for the disaster.* 我承擔這次災難的全部責任。

★**re·spon·si·ble** /rɪ'spɒnsəbl; rɪ'spɑnsᵢbəl/ *adj* **1** worthy of trust 負責可靠的: *We're looking for a responsible adult to look after the child.* 我們正在找一個負責可靠的成年人來照顧孩子。– opposite 反義 **irresponsible 2** needing a person who can be trusted with important matters 責任重大的: *a responsible job* 要職 **3** [never before a noun 不能用於名詞前] in charge of people or things, and prepared to accept blame if anything goes wrong 需負責任的; 承擔責任的: *I am responsible for making sure that the company is profitable.* 我負責確保公司有盈利。| *Who's responsible here?* 這兒由誰負責? **4** be responsible to someone to have the duty to keep someone in a higher position informed about your actions, and to accept their power over you 對〔級別較高的〕某人負責: *I'm responsible to the Board of Governors.* 我要向董事會負責。**5** be responsible for something to be the cause of something 對某事負責: *Who is responsible for breaking the mirror?* 這鏡子是誰打破的?

re·spon·si·bly /rɪ'spɒnsəblɪ; rɪ'spɑnsᵢblɪ/ *adv* in a way that shows you can be trusted 認真負責地; 可靠地: *Can I trust you to behave responsibly while I'm out?* 我外出的時候, 你能讓我相信你會認真辦事嗎? –opposite 反義 **irresponsibly**

re·spon·sive /rɪ'spɒnsɪv; rɪ'spɑnsɪv/ *adj* quick to answer or return actions, words, or feelings 〔回答〕迅速的; 〔反應〕敏捷的; 敏感的: *The child is very responsive to kindness.* 這孩子易為好意所感動。| *To what extent are politicians responsive to public opinion?* 政治家對公眾輿論敏感到何種程度? –opposite 反義 **unresponsive –responsiveness** *n* [U]

★★**rest**¹ /rɛst; rɛst/ *n* **1** [C;U] a period of freedom from any tiring activity 休息; 歇息: *We all need a rest!* 我們都需要歇一歇! | *Shall we have a rest?* 我們可以休息一下嗎? | *Will they be able to get any rest later?* 稍後他們能休息一下嗎? **2** the rest the remaining part or parts of something 剩餘部分: *He's out for the rest of the evening.* 他出外度過晚上剩餘的時間。| *Let's keep the rest of the soup for*

tomorrow. 我們把剩下的湯留到明天喝吧。| *While Tim and Anna went to get help, the rest of us stayed in the car.* 添和安娜出去求援, 我們其餘的人就留在車裡。**3** [C] a support for something 支撐物; 支架; 支座: *an armrest* 〔椅子的〕扶手, 靠枕 **4** be at rest to be still, without moving 靜止; 不動 **5** come to rest to stop 停止: *The rocks crashed down the mountainside and came to rest by the river.* 岩石沿着山坡嘩啦啦地滾下來, 在河邊停住了。**6** give something a rest *infml* to stop doing something for a period of time 〔非正式〕使某事暫停一段時間 **7** put/set someone's mind at rest to give someone information that makes them stop worrying 使某人安心

★**rest**² *v* **1** [I] to spend time free of any tiring activity 休息; 歇息: *It's good to rest after lunch.* 午飯後休息有益身心。**2** [T] to keep a part of your body still for a period of time, because it is tired or painful 使〔身體的一部分〕靜止, 使休息: *I need to rest my poor feet!* 我要讓這雙可憐的腳歇一歇了! **3** rest on *lit* to stop at the sight or thought of something 〔文〕停留; 凝視: *His eyes rested on the picture.* 他的雙眼凝視着那幅畫。**4** [I;T] to provide or be given support (使)依靠, 支撐: *Rest your bicycle against the wall.* 把你的腳踏車靠在牆上。| *She rested her head on his shoulder.* 她把頭靠在他的肩上。**5** rest assured *fml* a phrase used to stop someone worrying 〔正式〕請放心: *Rest assured, I'll be there if you need me.* 放心吧, 如果你需要我, 我會在那兒的。**6** rest your case to stop putting an argument when you are confident that you have proved your case, and leave it for other people to consider (因講夠了而)停止對〔案情〕再作說明 **7** rest with someone to be the responsibility of someone 由某人負責 *The decision rests with you.* 由你來作出決定。**8** rest on something (of an argument) to be based on something 〔論點〕以某事物為依據: *His case rested on the fragile alibi of the accused man.* 他的案情陳述以被告不在犯罪現場的不可靠證據為依據。

★**res·tau·rant** /'rɛstərənt; 'rɛstərɒnt/ *n* a place where meals are sold and eaten 餐館, 飯店

res·tau·ra·teur /ˌrɛstərə'tɜː; ˌrɛstərə'tɜːʳ/ *n* the owner of a restaurant, especially a person who also runs it 餐館老闆〔尤指本人經營者〕

rest·ful /'rɛstfʊl; 'rɛstfəl/ *adj* pleasantly peaceful 平靜的, 寧靜的; 悠閒的: *We spent a restful evening watching television.* 我們看看電視, 度過了一個悠閒的晚上。–**restfully** *adv* –**restfulness** *n* [U]

res·ti·tu·tion /ˌrɛstə'tjuːʃən; ˌrɛstᵢ'tjuːʃən/ *n* [U] *fml* the act of returning something lost or stolen to its owner, or of paying for damage 〔正式〕(把丟失或被竊之物)歸還(原

主); 賠償

res·tive /ˈrɛstɪv; ˈrɛstɪv/ *adj* **1** unable to keep still 不安靜的, 煩躁的 **2** dissatisfied and wanting change 不滿意的; 想改變的

rest·less /ˈrɛstlɪs; ˈrɛstləs/ *adj* **1** unable to keep still 不安靜的; 不耐煩的: *You were very restless last night!* 你昨晚一點也靜不下來的! **2** dissatisfied and in need of a change 得不到滿足的; 求變的: *After a year in the job, she's feeling restless.* 工作一年以後, 她覺得不滿意, 需要改變一下。 —**restlessness** *n* [U]

re·sto·ra·tive /rɪˈstorətɪv; rɪˈstɔːrətɪv/ *n fml* a drink, food, or medicine that brings back health and strength 《正式》恢復健康和體力的飲料、食物或藥物 —**restorative** *adj*: *the drink's restorative qualities* 這種飲料的滋補性能

*****re·store** /rɪˈstor; rɪˈstɔːʳ/ *v* **restored, restoring** [T] **1** to give back something lost or stolen 歸還, 交還〔丢失或被盜的東西〕: *The goods were restored to their original owners.* 那些貨物歸還原主了。 **2** to make something exist again 恢復: *The army was called in to restore law and order.* 軍隊被召來恢復治安。 **3** to make a person or thing return to its original or former condition 使復原; 修復: *A long stay in the country restored her health.* 她在鄉村裡住了一段長時間, 使她恢復了健康。 | *He makes his living restoring old buildings.* 他以整修古建築謀生。 —**restoration** /ˌrɛstəˈreʃən; ˌrɛstəˈreɪʃn/ *n* [U]: *the restoration of public order* 公共秩序的恢復 | *the restoration of a painting* 一幅畫的修復

re·strain /rɪˈstren; rɪˈstreɪn/ *v* [T] **1** to prevent someone or something from doing something 抑制, 遏制〔某人、某事物〕: *If you can't restrain your dog, you should lock him up.* 如果你管不住你的狗, 就該把牠關起來。 **2**

SPORTS 體育運動

Exercise 1 練習一

Some sports are played by individuals, others are played in teams. Can you unscramble the names of the sports to complete the table? 有些運動是個人參加的比賽項目, 另一些則需組隊參加。你能正確地寫出表中所提供的運動項目名稱嗎?

Individual		Team	
ceathletis	*athletics*	gyrbu	*rugby*
xingob		cineramA boollfat	
yingccl		bleatblask	
flog		treckic	
kingsi		cresco	
roseh caring			
miwsming			
nestin			

Exercise 2 練習二

Can you answer these questions about the sports in the picture? 你能針對彩圖中的運動項目回答這些問題嗎?

1 Which two sports are played with an egg-shaped ball?

2 In which three sports do you hit the ball with something?

3 Which sport involves water?

4 Which sport involves an animal?

5 Which three sports involve kicking a ball?

Exercise 3 練習三

Which sports are played in these places? Write the names of the sports. The number in brackets shows the number of sports. 在哪些運動項目在這些地方進行? 請寫下運動項目的名稱, 括號中的數字表示運動的數目。

pitch (4)	*cricket, American football, soccer, rugby*
track (2)	....
court (2)	....
course (2)	....
pool (1)	....
slope (1)	....
ring (1)	....

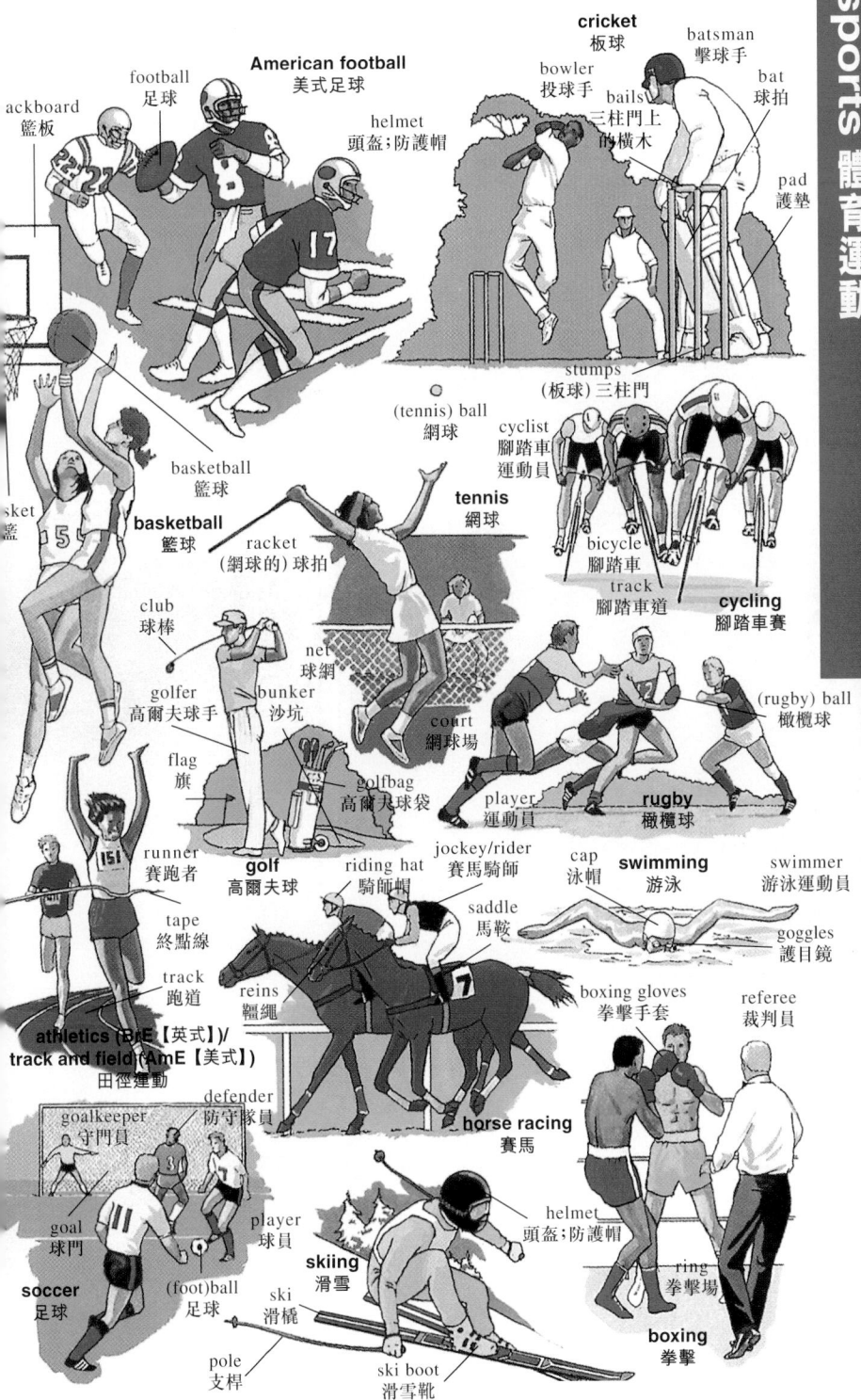

cricket
板球

bowler
投球手

bails
三柱門上
的橫木

batsman
擊球手

bat
球拍

pad
護墊

football
足球

American football
美式足球

helmet
頭盔;防護帽

ackboard
籃板

stumps
(板球) 三柱門

(tennis) ball
網球

cyclist
腳踏車
運動員

bicycle
腳踏車

track
腳踏車道

cycling
腳踏車賽

basketball
籃球

basketball
籃球

racket
(網球的) 球拍

tennis
網球

sket
籃

club
球棒

golfer
高爾夫球手

net
球網

bunker
沙坑

court
網球場

(rugby) ball
橄欖球

flag
旗

player
運動員

rugby
橄欖球

golfbag
高爾夫球袋

golf
高爾夫球

runner
賽跑者

riding hat
騎師帽

jockey/rider
賽馬騎師

saddle
馬鞍

cap
泳帽

swimming
游泳

swimmer
游泳運動員

goggles
護目鏡

tape
終點線

reins
韁繩

boxing gloves
拳擊手套

referee
裁判員

track
跑道

athletics (BrE【英式】)/
track and field (AmE【美式】)
田徑運動

defender
防守隊員

goalkeeper
守門員

player
球員

horse racing
賽馬

helmet
頭盔;防護帽

goal
球門

skiing
滑雪

ski
滑橇

ring
拳擊場

soccer
足球

(foot)ball
足球

pole
支桿

ski boot
滑雪靴

boxing
拳擊

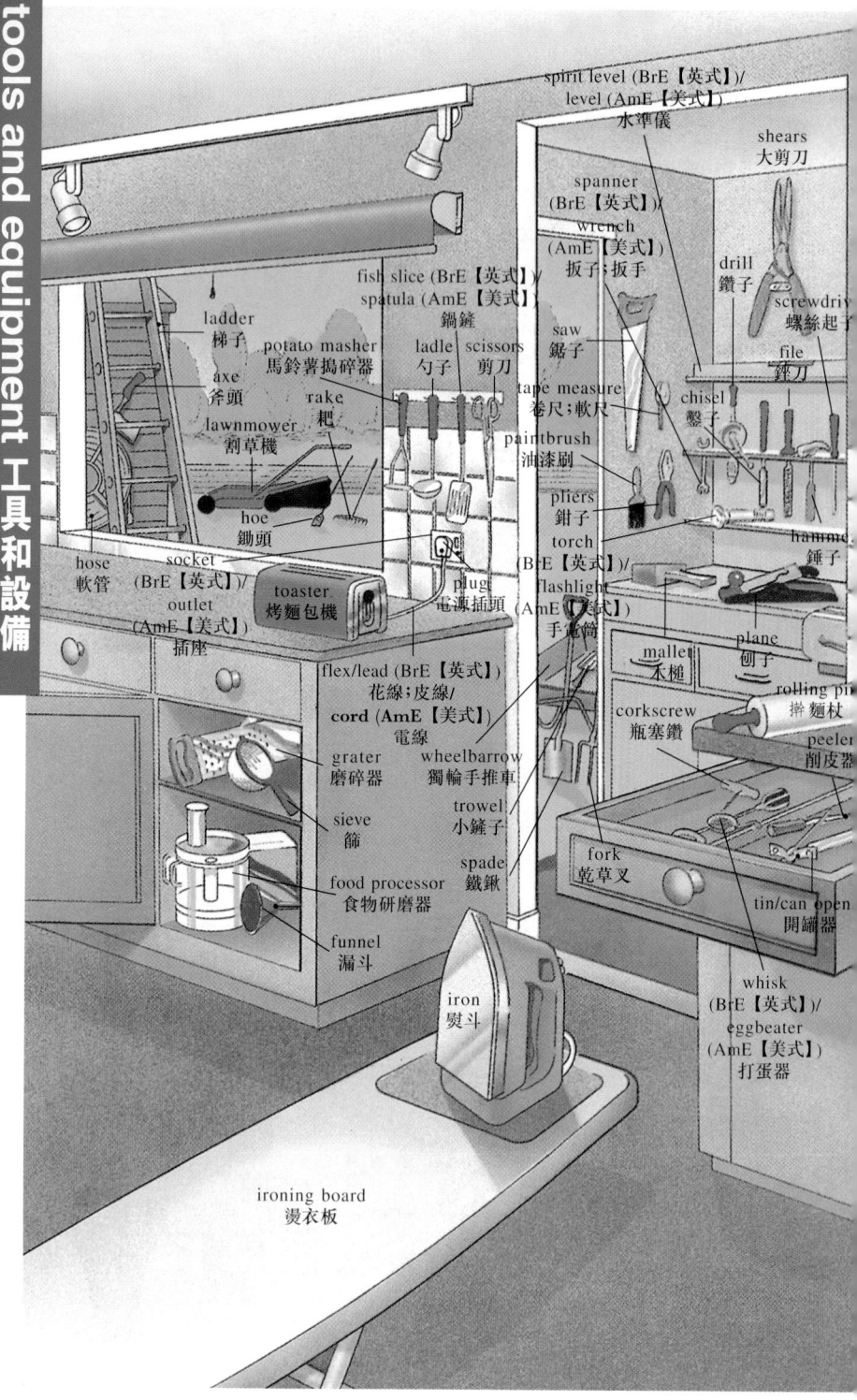

spirit level (BrE【英式】)/ level (AmE【美式】) 水準儀

shears 大剪刀

spanner (BrE【英式】)/ wrench (AmE【美式】) 扳子;扳手

drill 鑽子

screwdriver 螺絲起子

file 銼刀

fish slice (BrE【英式】)/ spatula (AmE【美式】) 鍋鏟

saw 鋸子

ladder 梯子

potato masher 馬鈴薯搗碎器

ladle 勺子

scissors 剪刀

tape measure 卷尺;軟尺

chisel 鑿子

axe 斧頭

rake 耙

paintbrush 油漆刷

lawnmower 剃草機

pliers 鉗子

torch (BrE【英式】)/ flashlight (AmE【美式】) 手電筒

hammer 錘子

hoe 鋤頭

hose 軟管

socket (BrE【英式】)/ outlet (AmE【美式】) 插座

toaster 烤麵包機

plug 電源插頭

plane 刨子

mallet 木槌

rolling pin 擀麵杖

flex/lead (BrE【英式】) 花線;皮線/ cord (AmE【美式】) 電線

corkscrew 瓶塞鑽

peeler 削皮器

grater 磨碎器

wheelbarrow 獨輪手推車

sieve 篩

trowel 小鏟子

fork 乾草叉

spade 鐵鍬

food processor 食物研磨器

tin/can opener 開罐器

funnel 漏斗

iron 熨斗

whisk (BrE【英式】)/ eggbeater (AmE【美式】) 打蛋器

ironing board 燙衣板

to control something 控制, 限制〔某事物〕: *The government tried to restrain demand for foreign goods.* 政府試圖限制對外國貨的需求。

re·strained /rɪ'strend; rɪ'streɪnd/ *adj* calm and controlled, especially when it is difficult to behave in this way〔尤指在難以辦到時〕有節制的, 克制的

re·straint /rɪ'strent; rɪ'streɪnt/ *n* **1** [U] controlled behaviour (a word usually used to express approval) 抑制, 克制, 遏制〔常含褒義〕: *I think you show great restraint in ignoring his insults.* 我認為你沒有理會他的侮辱, 表現出了極強的克制力。**2** [C;U] something that limits what you can do (a word often used to express disapproval) 約束, 管束, 限制〔常含貶義〕: *He hates the restraints of life in a small town.* 他討厭在小城鎮生活的種種限制。**3** [C;U] control over something 控制

*★**re·strict** /rɪ'strɪkt; rɪ'strɪkt/ *v* [T] to keep something within limits 限制, 限定, 約束〔某

事物〕: *The speaker restricted his comments to the situation in Europe.* 演講者只對歐洲的局勢作出評論。| *New laws have been introduced to restrict the sale of alcohol.* 已推行新法例來限制酒類的銷售。–**restriction** /-'strɪkʃən; -'strɪkʃən/ *n* [C;U]

re·strict·ed /rɪ'strɪktɪd; rɪ'strɪkt ̣d/ *adj* **1** limited 受限制的; 有限的: *The space in this house is quite restricted.* 這房子裡的空間很有限。**2** for the use of a particular group only 供特定團體專用的: *a restricted document* 內部文件 | *a restricted area* 管制地區

re·stric·tive /rɪ'strɪktɪv; rɪ'strɪktɪv/ *adj* limiting because you are not free to behave as you want 限制(性)的, 約束(性)的: *He finds the job too restrictive.* 他發覺這份工作有太多限制。

rest room /'··/ *n* the usual American word for〔美式〕= a public TOILET

*★**re·sult**¹ /rɪ'zʌlt; rɪ'zʌlt/ *v* [I] **1** to be caused by something 因〔某事物〕而產生; 是…的後果, 是…的結果: *His*

R

TOOLS AND EQUIPMENT 工具和設備

Exercise 1 練習一

Can you explain the connection between these things? 你能解釋下列物品之間的關係嗎?

1 bottle opener, corkscrew, tin opener
2 scissors, secateurs, shears
3 trowel, spade, fork, hoe

Exercise 2 練習二

Mr Sampson always makes mistakes. He always uses the wrong tools. Read these sentences and say which tool Mr Sampson should use in each case. 桑普遜先生常犯錯誤, 他總是用錯工具。請閱讀下列各句, 説出在每一種情況下他應該使用哪一種工具。

1 He uses a **ladle** to water the lawn.
2 He uses a **pair of scissors** to cut the grass.
3 He uses a **spade** to cut down trees.
4 He uses a **plane** to peel potatoes.
5 He uses a **mallet** to mash the potatoes.
6 He uses a **rolling pin** to press his trousers.
7 He uses a **screwdriver** to take the cork out of a wine bottle.
8 He uses an **iron** to make toast.
9 He uses a **chisel** to drive in a nail.
10 He uses a **saw** to open a tin of peas.

Exercise 3 練習三

Complete this passage with words from the illustration. Put in one letter for each dash. 請用彩圖中的詞語填入各空格中。每條橫線上請填入一個字母。

If you want to join two pieces of wood together, you can use a ¹h _ _ _ _ _ and a nail. Another way is to use a ²d _ _ _ _ to make a small hole in the pieces of wood and then use a ³s _ _ _ _ _ _ _ _ and a screw to join them. Alternatively, you can make a hole through both pieces of wood and slide a bolt through the hole. You should then twist a nut on the other end and tighten it with a ⁴s _ _ _ _ _ _ .

The most professional way of joining two pieces of wood is to cut a joint. First, you should use a ⁵t _ _ _ _ _ _ _ _ _ to measure the pieces carefully. Then use the ⁶s _ _ to cut the end of one piece of wood into a tongue shape. After that, use your ⁷c _ _ _ _ _ and ⁸m _ _ _ _ _ to cut a hole of the same size in the other piece of wood. Put some glue on the tongue and in the hole and stick the two pieces of wood together.

---

tiredness resulted **from** *lack of sleep.* 他的疲勞是因睡眠不足引起的。 **2 result in** to cause something 導致, 造成〔某事物〕: *The accident resulted in the death of two passengers.* 這次事故造成兩名乘客死亡。

*result² *n* **1** something that happens because of something else 結果, 成果, 效果: *His illness is the result* **of** *eating bad food.* 他的病是由於吃了變質食物所致。 **2** the situation at the end of a competition or examination 〔比賽或考試的〕比分, 成績, 結果: *I heard the football results on the radio.* 我在廣播中聽到足球比賽的結果。 | *When will you know your examination results?* 你甚麼時候可以知道考試成績? **3** the answer to a calculation 〔計算的〕結果, 答案 **4 as a result** because of something 因為, 由於〔某事物〕: *He didn't practise, and as a result he lost.* 他沒有練習, 所以輸了。 | *As a result of the warning, nobody was hurt.* 由於得到了警告, 沒有人受傷。

re·sul·tant /rɪ'zʌltənt; rɪ'zʌltənt/ *adj* [only before a noun 只用於名詞前] caused by something 從而產生的, 作為...後果的: *The drivers all sounded their horns and the resultant noise was unbearable.* 司機一齊按響喇叭, 所造成的噪音令人難以忍受。

re·sume /rɪ'zum; rɪ'zju:m/ *v* resumed, resuming *fml*〖正式〗 **1** [I;T] to begin something again after a pause〔中斷後〕重新開始: *We'll stop now and resume at two o'clock.* 我們現在停止工作, 兩點鐘再開始。 | *The negotiators resumed their discussion.* 談判者繼續討論。 **2** [T] to return to a place 重返, 回到〔某處〕: *Could we ask you, please, to resume your seats?* 可以請你們回到自己的座位嗎? **–resumption** /rɪ'zʌmpʃən; rɪ'zʌmpʃən/ *n* [U]

ré·su·mé /,rɛzu'me; 'rezjumeɪ/ *n* **1** a short account of something giving only the main points 摘要, 梗概 **2** the usual American word for〖美式〗= CV

re·sur·gence /rɪ'sɜ·dʒəns; rɪ'sɜ:dʒəns/ *n fml* [C;U] return to power, life, or activity〖正式〗復蘇; 復興: *a resurgence of nationalist feeling* 民族感情的復蘇 **–resurgent** *adj* [only before a noun 只用於名詞前]

res·ur·rect /,rɛzə'rɛkt; ,rezə'rekt/ *v* [T] to bring something back into use or fashion, or to someone's attention 使〔某物〕恢復使用〔重新流行〕; 使再受注意: *Old customs are being resurrected.* 舊風俗正在重新流行。

res·ur·rec·tion /,rɛzə'rɛkʃən; ,rezə'rekʃən/ *n* [C;U] **1** the return of something or giving something new life 恢復, 復活, 復興 **2 the Resurrection** the return to life of Christ, according to Christian belief〔基督教的〕耶穌復活

re·sus·ci·tate /rɪ'sʌsə,tet; rɪ'sʌsɪteɪt/ *v* resuscitated, resuscitating [T] to bring someone back to life 使〔某人〕蘇醒〔復活〕: *They tried to resuscitate the dying man.* 他們試圖救活這個垂危者。 **–resuscitation** /rɪ,sʌsə-

'teʃən; rɪ,sʌsɪ'teɪʃən/ *n* [U]

re·tail /'ritel; 'ri:teɪl/ *n* [U] the sale of goods to people for their own use, usually in shops 零售; 零賣: *the retail of goods* 商品零售 | *retail prices* 零售價 **–retail** *adj*: *We bought it retail.* 我們是以零售方式把它買來的。

re·tail·er /'ritelə; 'ri:teɪlər/ *n* a person who sells goods to the public 零售商

re·tain /rɪ'ten; rɪ'teɪn/ *v* [T] to keep or keep possession of something 保持, 保留, 保有: *I can't retain all that information.* 我記不住那麼多東西。 | *She sold everything, retaining only a few pieces of furniture.* 她只留下了幾件家具, 把其他的都賣了。

re·take /ri'tek; ,ri:'teɪk/ *v* retook /-'tuk; -'tʊk/, retaken /-'tekən; -'teɪkən/, retaking [T] to take something again 拿回, 取回〔某物〕: *He's retaking his physics exam.* 他在重考物理科。 | *The city has been retaken by enemy forces.* 這座城市已被敵軍奪回。 | *Can we retake the last scene, please?* 我們能否重拍最後一個鏡頭? **–retake** /'ri,tek; 'ri:teɪk/ *n*

re·tal·i·ate /rɪ'tælɪ,et; rɪ'tælieɪt/ *v* retaliated, retaliating [I] to return the harm that someone has done to you 報復, 反擊; 以牙還牙: *Two diplomats have been expelled, and their country is expected to retaliate.* 兩名外交官已被驅逐出境, 預計他們的國家將要報復。 **–retaliatory** *adj* **–retaliation** /rɪ,tælɪ'eʃən; rɪ,tæli'eɪʃən/ *n* [U]

re·tard·ed /rɪ'tardɪd; rɪ'tɑ:dɪd/ *adj* slower in development than other people 發育遲緩的, 弱智的

retch /rɛtʃ; retʃ/ *v* [I] to try to be sick 乾嘔, 噁心

re·ten·tion /rɪ'tɛnʃən; rɪ'tenʃən/ *n* [U] the state or action of keeping something 保持, 保留; 記憶: *Retention of the territory will cause problems with neighbouring countries.* 保留這片領土會跟鄰近幾個國家惹起麻煩。 **–retentive** *adj*: *He has a very retentive memory.* 他有很強的記憶力。

re·think /,ri'θɪŋk; ,ri:'θɪŋk/ *v* rethought /-'θɔt; -'θɔ:t/, rethinking [I;T] to reconsider 再思考; 重新考慮: *We'd better rethink the whole plan.* 我們最好重新考慮一下整個計劃。 **–rethink** /'ri,θɪŋk; 'ri:θɪŋk/ *n* [sing]

ret·i·cent /'rɛtəsnt; 'retɪsənt/ *adj* not saying as much as you know or feel 說話有保留的: *She was reticent about the reasons for the quarrel.* 她不肯多談這次爭吵的原因。 **–reticence** *n* [U]

ret·i·na /'rɛtnə; 'retɪnə/ *n* retinas or retinae /-ni; -ni:/ the area at the back of your eye that sends images to your brain 視網膜

ret·i·nue /'rɛtn̩,ju; 'retɪnju:/ *n* [+sing/pl verb] a group of servants and followers travelling with an important person〔重要人物的〕侍從; 隨員: *The president's retinue is arriving tomorrow.* 總統的隨員將於明天到達。

*re·tire /rɪˈtaɪr; rɪˈtaɪəʳ/ v **retired, retiring 1** [I;T] to stop working, usually because of your age (使)退休; (使)退職: *My father has retired now.* 我的父親現在已退休了。| *He was retired early because of bad health.* 他因健康狀況不佳而提前退休。**2** [I] *fml* leave a place or group of people〔正式〕退下, 引退, 離開: *The ministers retired to the committee-room to make their decision.* 部長都退席到委員會辦公室去作決定。**3** [I] *fml* to go to bed〔正式〕就寢: *Shall we retire?* 我們睡覺好嗎?

re·tired /rɪˈtaɪrd; rɪˈtaɪəd/ adj no longer working 退休了的: *My parents are both retired.* 我的父母都退休了。| *a retired doctor* 退休醫生

*re·tire·ment /rɪˈtaɪrmənt; rɪˈtaɪəmənt/ n [U] **1** the time at which a person stops working 退休[職]: *He was given a gold watch on his retirement.* 他退休時獲贈一塊金錶。**2** the period after a person has stopped working 退休期間: *He intends to spend his retirement in France.* 他打算去法國過退休生活。| *Is she in retirement?* 她退休了嗎?

re·tir·ing /rɪˈtaɪrɪŋ; rɪˈtaɪərɪŋ/ adj **1** too quiet in the company of others 不合羣的; 孤僻的; 緘默的: *a retiring man* 不合羣的人 **2** [only before a noun 只用於名詞前] when a person stops working 退休[職]的: *What's the retiring age for miners?* 礦工的退休年齡是幾歲? **3** soon to stop working 即將退休[職]的: *The retiring president wished his successor well.* 即將退職的總統祝願繼任者好運。

re·tort /rɪˈtɔrt; rɪˈtɔːt/ v [I; +that] to make a quick angry or amusing answer 回嘴, 反駁: *He retorted that it was all my fault.* 他反駁說這全是我的過錯。| *"You, of course, are perfect!" she retorted.* "你, 當然是十全十美的啦!" 她回嘴說。

re·trace /rɪˈtres; rɪˈtreɪs/ v **retraced, retracing** [T] to follow the same way again 折回, 折返: *She retraced her steps along the path to the beach.* 她沿着小道返回海灘。

re·tract /rɪˈtrækt; rɪˈtrækt/ v [I;T] **1** to admit that something you said earlier should not have been said 收回〔說過的話〕: *I would like to retract my previous remark.* 我希望收回剛說過的話。**2** to move back or in again 縮回, 縮進: *The cat retracted its claws when I screamed.* 我一尖叫, 貓便縮回了爪子。

re·treat[1] /rɪˈtrit; rɪˈtriːt/ v [I] **1** to move away, especially because you are uncomfortable or you are forced to move〔尤指因不舒服或被迫而〕退卻, 撤退: *The entire army is retreating.* 全軍正在撤退。**2** to give up something like a plan or an idea 放棄〔計劃或主意等〕: *The government seems to be retreating from its position on local taxation.* 政府似乎在地方稅收的立場上有所讓步。

retreat[2] n **1** [C;U] movement away from someone or something 退卻, 撤退: *Napoleon's retreat from Moscow* 拿破崙從莫斯科的撤退 |

The army is in retreat. 軍隊正在撤退。**2** [C; U] a place to which you can go for peace and safety 隱居所; 靜養所: *a country retreat* 鄉間靜居所 | *He's joined the monks in retreat.* 他隱退出家。**3** [C;U] removal of support for something like a plan or an idea〔對計劃或主意的〕後退; 背離: *It's a retreat from his original position on staff relations.* 這是他從原來的員工關係的立場上的倒退。

re·tri·al /riˈtraɪəl; ˌriːˈtraɪəl/ n a second trial of a legal case 再審, 複審: *Her lawyer has demanded a retrial.* 她的律師已要求複審。

ret·ri·bu·tion /ˌretrəˈbjuʃən; ˌretrɪˈbjuːʃən/ n [U] *fml* deserved punishment, sometimes believed to come from a god〔正式〕應得的懲罰, 報應: *Retribution was quick and decisive.* 報應又快又重。| *divine retribution* 上天的懲罰

re·trieve /rɪˈtriv; rɪˈtriːv/ v **retrieved, retrieving** [T] to find something and bring it back 找回, 取回〔某物〕: *I managed to retrieve the bag I had left in the train.* 我設法找回了遺忘在火車上的手提包。| *How do you retrieve information from this computer system?* 你怎麼從這電腦操作系統上檢索訊息? **2 retrieve a situation** to improve a situation that looked very bad 挽回〔糟糕的〕局面 —**retrieval** n [U]

ret·ro·grade /ˈretrəˌgred; ˈretrəgreɪd/ adj returning to something that is no longer considered good or useful 倒退的, 退步的: *Limiting the power of the unions is a retrograde step.* 限制工會權力是個倒退。

ret·ro·gress /ˈretrəˌgres; ˌretrəˈgres/ v [I] *fml* to return to a state that is no longer satisfactory〔正式〕倒退, 衰退, 退化 —**retrogression** /-ˈgreʃən; -ˈgreʃən/ n [U]

ret·ro·spect /ˈretrəˌspekt; ˈretrəspekt/ n **in retrospect** looking back on the past 回想: *In retrospect my childhood was a relatively happy one.* 回想起來, 我的兒童時代是相當快樂的。

re·tro·spec·tive /ˌretrəˈspektɪv; ˌretrəˈspektɪv/ adj **1** concerned with the past 回顧的, 回想的: *retrospective thoughts* 懷舊思緒 **2** effective from before the time they were decided on (used of laws) 有追溯效力的〔指法律〕: *retrospective legislation* 有追溯效力的法律

*re·turn[1] /rɪˈtɜrn; rɪˈtɜːn/ v **1** [I] to come or go back 返回, 回來〔去〕: *He returned home after years of travel.* 他遊歷幾年後歸家。| *She has just returned to work.* 她剛回來工作。| *Let's return to that subject later.* 我們稍後再講那個題目吧。| *The government returned to power with an increased majority.* 這屆政府以增加了的多數票重新掌權。| *I hope the good weather returns soon.* 我希望天氣馬上好起來。**2** [T] to give, put, send, or hit something back 歸還; 送回; 擊回: *Library books must be returned at the end of term.* 圖書館借的書必

須在學期結束時歸還。| *Please return the keys to the housekeeper.* 請把鑰匙歸還管家。| *She returned the vase to its place on the shelf.* 她把花瓶放回架子上。| *Complete and return the enclosed form.* 請填妥並寄回隨信所附的表格。| *I couldn't even return the ball today!* 我今天連球也不能回擊過去! **3** [T] to do or feel the same as another person 回報; 報答: *She doesn't return his feelings.* 她對他的感情不予回報。| *I hope they'll return the favour.* 我希望他們會報答恩惠。**4 return a Member of Parliament** to elect someone as a Member of Parliament 選〔某人〕為國會議員 **5 return a verdict** *law* to say in a law court if someone is guilty or not 〔律〕〔在法庭上〕宣佈〔某人有罪或無罪的〕裁決: *The jury returned a verdict of not guilty.* 陪審團作出了無罪的裁決。

★return² *n* **1** [C;U] a journey back to a place you have left, or your arrival in that place 返回, 回來: *I expect to meet him on his return.* 我盼望在他回來時和他見面。| *Since her return she has felt unsettled.* 她自從回來以後, 便感到心神不定。| *The workers agreed on a return to work.* 工人們同意復工。**2** [U] taking, giving, sending, or putting something back 放回; 送回; 退回: *The library books are due for return on Friday.* 圖書館借的書應於星期五歸還。**3 by return, by return of post** by the next post 由下一班回程郵遞送回 **4** [C] (also 又作 **return ticket**) a ticket you use on a plane, bus, or train to go somewhere and come back again 來回票, 雙程票: *Is it cheaper to buy a return than two singles?* 買一張來回票比買兩張單程票便宜嗎? **5 in return** in exchange 作為...的交換: *She helps everyone and expects nothing in return.* 她幫助大家, 不求回報。| *He sold his invention in return for a share of the profits.* 他把自己的發明成果出售, 以換得一份贏利。**6** [C;U] the profit you make when you put money into, for example, a business 收益; 盈利: *He expects a good return on his capital.* 他指望自己的資本能有很好的盈利。**7** [U] something which happens again 回復; 再現: *the return of spring* 春回大地 **8 returns** [pl] results in an election 選舉結果 **9 many happy returns** what you say to wish someone a happy birthday 〔生日祝賀語〕(恭祝)生日快樂

re·tur·na·ble /rɪˈtɜːnəbl; rɪˈtɜːnəbəl/ *adj* intended to be given or sent back after use 可回收的; 可退還的: *returnable bottles* 可退還的瓶子

re·u·nion /riːˈjuːnjən; riːˈjuːnjən/ *n* [C;U] a meeting between people who have not seen each other recently 重聚; 團聚: *an emotional reunion* 激動人心的重聚 | *There was no hope of reunion.* 沒有希望重聚了。| *a college reunion* 大學校友聚會

re·u·nite /ˌriːjuːˈnaɪt; ˌriːjuːˈnaɪt/ *v* **reunited, reuniting 1** [I;T] to meet, or help people

meet, after a period of separation (使)重聚: *Returning soldiers have been reunited with their families.* 歸來的士兵們已和家人重聚。| *It's time for all members of the party to re-unite.* 又到全體黨員聚首的時間了。**2** [T] to bring things together again (使)重新結合

rev¹ /rev; rev/ *n infml* 〔非正式〕**1 Rev** an abbreviation for 〔縮〕= REVEREND **2** *infml* 〔非正式〕see 見 REVOLUTION (4)

rev² *v* **-vv-** [I;T] *infml* (also 又作 **rev up**) to increase the speed of an engine 〔非正式〕加快〔發動機的〕轉速: *Don't rev your engine so loudly.* 不要把發動機開得那麼響。| *The engine is revving.* 發動機在加快轉速。

re·val·ue /ˌriːˈvæljuː; ˌriːˈvæljuː/ *v* **revalued, revaluing** [T] **1** to increase the exchange value of a country's money 使〔貨幣〕升值 **2** to make a new judgment about the value of something 對〔某事物〕重新評價: *We're having our paintings revalued.* 我們正在對我們的畫作重新評價。 **–revaluation** /ˌriːvæljuˈeɪʃən; ˌriːˌvæljuˈeɪʃən/ *n* [C;U]

★★re·veal /rɪˈviːl; rɪˈviːl/ *v* **1** [T] to allow someone or something to be seen 暴露; 顯露: *The front door opened to reveal a magnificent entrance hall.* 前門打開, 展現出一個富麗堂皇的大堂。**2** [T; +(that)] to make something known to people 揭露; 揭示; 透露: *She suddenly revealed that she was married.* 她突然透露她已婚。| *His expression reveals his true feelings.* 他的表情泄露了他的真實感情。**3 reveal yourself** to show yourself in a particular way, especially one that is unexpected 〔以某種方式, 尤指出乎意料地〕暴露自己身分: *She revealed herself to be a member of the royal family.* 她暴露了自己王室成員的身分。| *He revealed himself as a fraud.* 他暴露了騙子的身分。

re·veal·ing /rɪˈviːlɪŋ; rɪˈviːlɪŋ/ *adj* allowing something private or personal to be seen or known 暴露的; 顯露的: *a very revealing dress* 一件非常暴露的女服 | *Her remarks were very revealing.* 她的話發人深省。

rev·el /ˈrevl; ˈrevəl/ *v* **-ll-** (also 又作 **-l-** *AmE* 〔美式〕) [I] **1** to pass the time eating, drinking, and dancing in a noisy and sometimes wild way (an old-fashioned word which is often used in a humorous way) 虛度時光; 狂歡; 作樂〔老式詞, 常含幽默〕: *They were drinking and revelling all night.* 他們飲酒作樂, 徹夜狂歡。**2 revel in something** to enjoy something greatly 陶醉於; 沉湎於: *She revels in hearing about my problems.* 她幸災樂禍地聽別人說我的麻煩。**–reveller** (also 又作 **reveler** *AmE* 〔美式〕)

rev·e·la·tion /ˌrevlˈeɪʃən; ˌrevəˈleɪʃən/ *n* **1** [U] the making known of something secret 揭露, 揭示; 暴露 **2** [C] a surprising fact that is made known 揭露的事物; 令人意想不到的發現: *We listened to her strange revelations about her past.* 我們聽她透露她過去那些奇異

的經歷。**3** something surprising 令人驚訝的事物: *His exposure of corruption in the government was a revelation.* 他對政府內部腐敗情況的揭露令人感到驚訝。

rev·el·ry /ˈrɛvlrɪ; ˈrɛvəlrɪ/ *n* **revelries** [pl;U] wild, noisy, active entertainment 狂歡; 尋歡作樂: *Shall we join in the revelries?* 我們一起去狂歡好嗎?

re·venge¹ /rɪˈvɛndʒ; rɪˈvɛndʒ/ *v* **revenged, revenging 1 revenge yourself on someone** to take action in return for harm done to you 向某人報復 **2** [T] to take action in return for harm done to someone or something 為〔某人或某事〕報仇

revenge² *n* [U] action taken against someone who has done something to harm you 復仇, 報復: *a revenge attack* 報復性進攻 | *He took his revenge by humiliating me in public.* 他以當眾羞辱我作為報復。 | *Her house was burnt down in revenge for her statement to the police.* 她向警察作了陳述, 結果遭人報復, 房子被燒毀了。

★**rev·e·nue** /ˈrɛvəˌnju; ˈrevₐˌnjuː/ *n* [U] income that a government receives as tax or that is earned by a company 〔國家的〕稅收; 〔公司的〕收入

re·ver·be·rate /rɪˈvɜ˞bəˌret; rɪˈvɜːbərɛɪt/ *v* **reverberated, reverberating** [I] **1** to sound again and again 回響, 回蕩: *The thunder reverberated across the valley.* 雷聲在山谷中回蕩。 **2** to shake as a result of loud noises 〔因聲音響亮而〕震動: *The hall reverberated with the applause.* 大廳裡掌聲雷動。 **3** to have a strong and lasting effect 產生〔強烈而持續的〕反響: *The consequences reverberated throughout the political world.* 這些結果在政界引起了強烈的反響。 –**reverberation** /rɪˌvɜ˞bəˈreʃən; rɪˌvɜːbəˈrɛɪʃən/ *n* [C;U]

re·vere /rɪˈvɪr; rɪˈvɪəʳ/ *v* **revered, revering** [T] *fml* to feel great respect and admiration for someone 〔正式〕尊敬, 崇敬〔某人〕: *You revered your father, didn't you?* 你尊敬你的父親, 是嗎?

Rev·e·rend /ˈrɛvərənd; ˈrevərənd/ *n adv* (also 又作 **Rev** in written English) a title used to address or talk about a person holding a religious position 〔對教士的尊稱〕牧師; 大人: *The Reverend Donald Jones* 唐納德·瓊斯牧師 | *Good morning, Reverend!* 早安, 牧師!

rev·e·rent /ˈrɛvrənt; ˈrevərənt/ *adj* having or showing a feeling of great respect or admiration 恭敬的, 崇敬的 –**opposite** 反義 **irreverent** –**reverence** *n* [U]

rev·e·rie /ˈrɛvərɪ; ˈrevərɪ/ *n* [C;U] a kind of dream that you have while you are awake 幻想, 白日夢: *She fell into a reverie about the past.* 她陷入了對往事的沉思之中。

re·vers·al /rɪˈvɜ˞səl; rɪˈvɜːsəl/ *n* [C;U] a complete change 逆轉; 徹底改變: *That's a reversal of your usual position on relations with the US.* 你在同美國關係上所持的態度與平時截然不同。

re·verse¹ /rɪˈvɜ˞s; rɪˈvɜːs/ *adj* [only before a noun 只用於名詞前] **1** opposite or back 相反的; 反面的: *the reverse side of the coin* 硬幣的反面 **2 in reverse order** from the last to the first 從尾到頭: *Why are these names in reverse order?* 這些名字為甚麼顛倒排列?

reverse² *v* **reversed, reversing 1** [I;T] to move backwards (使)倒退〔轉〕; (使)反向: *He reversed the car through the gate.* 他把汽車倒着開出大門。 | *The car reversed and drove off.* 汽車倒車後退, 然後開走了。 **2** [T] to change a process, decision, or judgment completely 徹底改變, 推翻〔過程、決定或判決〕: *The judgment was reversed in a higher law court.* 這個判決被上級法院推翻了。 | *I'm trying to reverse the company's fortunes.* 我正試圖扭轉公司的命運。 **3** [T] to change round the usual order or position of things 顛倒, 改變〔正常次序或位置〕: *Today we'll reverse the usual order of the lesson, and start with a written exercise.* 今天我們改變一下通常的上課順序, 先開始上寫作課。 **4 reverse the charges** to make a telephone call which the person receiving it will pay for 〔電話〕由受話人付款 –**reversible** *adj*: *a reversible coat* 可兩面穿的大衣

reverse³ *n* **1 in reverse: a** with the controls of a vehicle in such a position that you will move backwards 〔車輛〕向相反方向地: *Put the car in reverse!* 倒車! **b** in reverse in the opposite way 倒; 逆: *His career went into reverse.* 他的事業倒退了。 **2 the reverse** the opposite 相反情況; 對立面: *He did the reverse of what we expected and bought us all a drink.* 他所做的和我們預料的相反, 他給我們大家買了飲料。

re·vert /rɪˈvɜ˞t; rɪˈvɜːt/ *v* **1 revert to something** to return to an earlier state, habit, or subject 回復〔原來的狀態、舊習慣或老話題〕: *He's stopped taking drugs now, but he may revert to taking them again.* 他現在已經停止吸毒了, 但有可能會再度吸毒。 **2 revert to someone** *law* (of property) to return to a previous owner 〔律〕〔財產〕歸還, 歸屬〔原主〕 –**reversion** /rɪˈvɜ˞ʒən; rɪˈvɜːʃən/ *n* [C;U]: *reversion to bad habits* 惡習重染

★**re·view¹** /rɪˈvju; rɪˈvjuː/ *n* **1** [C;U] a study of something 檢討, 檢查, 回顧: *After a careful review of the situation, he decided on a few changes.* 他仔細研究了形勢之後, 決定作出幾處改動。 | *The matter is open to review.* 這件事受到公開審查。 **2** [C] a magazine, newspaper, or article giving judgments on things like new books or plays 〔新書或新戲的〕評論; 評論性刊物: *a page of book reviews* 書評的一頁 **3** a show of the armed forces, in the presence of a ruler or an important general 〔軍事〕檢閱: *a naval review* 海軍檢閱 **4 under review** being considered carefully to see if changes are necessary 在仔細考慮之中: *The company's wage system is cur-*

rently under review. 公司的工資制度目前正獲重新研究。

★review² v [T] **1** to consider something carefully, especially to decide whether changes are necessary 仔細考慮〔尤指決定是否有必要作改變〕, 檢討: *The government is reviewing its education policy.* 政府在檢討教育政策。| *Your salary will be reviewed annually.* 你的工資將每年作出審核。**2** to give publicly a written or spoken opinion of something like a new book or play 公開評論〔新書、新戲等〕: *The play was well reviewed in all the newspapers.* 這齣戲受到所有報章的一致好評。

re·view·er /rɪ'vjuɚ; rɪ'vju:ɚ'/ *n* a person who gives opinions publicly on new plays, books, and other things 評論者; 評論家

re·vile /rɪ'vaɪl; rɪ'vaɪl/ *v* **reviled, reviling** [T] *fml* to express strong and angry feelings about or to someone or something〔正式〕辱罵, 謾罵〔某人、某事物〕

re·vise /rɪ'vaɪz; rɪ'vaɪz/ *v* **revised, revising 1** [T] to read through something carefully, making improvements to it 修訂, 校訂 **2** [T] to change your opinions or behaviour because of new information or more thought 改正, 修正〔看法或行為〕 **3** to change something, especially a figure, to make it more correct 訂正, 修改〔數字〕: *We are revising our estimates as news of further deaths reaches us.* 隨着死亡人數進一步增加的消息傳來, 我們正在修正我們的估計。**4** [I;T] to prepare for a test by studying 複習, 溫習〔功課〕: *I must revise for my exam.* 我必須溫習功課, 準備考試。| *Have you revised these notes yet?* 你已經複習過這些筆記了嗎?

re·vi·sion /rɪ'vɪʒən; rɪ'vɪʒən/ *n* **1** [C;U] a change made to improve something 修正; 校訂 **2** [U] study in preparation for a test 複習; 溫習: *Have you done any revision for the English exam?* 你有沒有為英語考試做過複習?

re·vi·tal·ize /ri'vaɪtḷ,aɪz; ri:'vaɪtəl-aɪz/ *v* **revitalized, revitalizing** (also 又作 **revitalise** *BrE*〔英式〕) [T] to put new strength or power into something 使具有新的活力; 使恢復元氣: *attempts to revitalize the economy* 使經濟復蘇的嘗試 –**revitalization** /,rivaɪtḷ'ze-ʃən; ri:,vaɪtəl-aɪ'zeɪʃən/ *n* [U]

re·viv·al /rɪ'vaɪvḷ; rɪ'vaɪvəl/ *n* **1** [C;U] a process in which something becomes active or popular again 復興; 重新流行; 復蘇: *There has been a revival of interest in the fashions of the 1930's.* 對三十年代的時裝又重新產生了興趣。**2** [C] a new performance of an old play after many years〔舊劇多年後的〕重演

re·vive /rɪ'vaɪv; rɪ'vaɪv/ *v* **revived, reviving** [I;T] **1** to return to consciousness or health (使)蘇醒; (使)恢復健康: *A drink might revive him.* 喝杯飲料也許會使他精神恢復過來。| *That rose will revive if you water it.* 如果你給它澆水, 那株玫瑰就會再活過來。**2** to start a custom or habit again (使)〔風俗或習慣〕復

興; (使)重新流行: *We're trying to revive old customs.* 我們在試圖使舊風俗重新興起。| *Her interest in sport is reviving.* 她對運動又開始有興趣了。

re·voke /rɪ'vok; rɪ'vəuk/ *v* **revoked, revoking** [T] to put an end to an official agreement 撤銷, 廢除〔正式協定〕: *His driving licence has been revoked.* 他的駕駛執照被吊銷了。

re·volt¹ /rɪ'volt; rɪ'vəult/ *v* **1** [I] to act violently against those in power in an attempt to change the system of government 反叛; 起義, 造反: *The people revolted against the military government.* 人民起義反抗軍政府。**2** [T] to make someone feel violent dislike and sickness (使)憎惡, (使)反感: *Such cruelty revolted him.* 這樣的暴行使他極為反感。

revolt² *n* [C;U] a violent attempt to change the way a country is governed 反叛; 造反: *The whole nation is in a state of revolt.* 整個國家處於叛亂之中。| *The revolt is over.* 叛亂已結束了。

re·volt·ing /rɪ'voltɪŋ; rɪ'vəultɪŋ/ *adj* very unpleasant indeed 令人厭惡的; 令人作嘔的: *What a revolting smell!* 好難聞的氣味啊! | *I've never had a more revolting meal.* 我從未吃過比這更難吃的飯。–**revoltingly** *adv*: *a revoltingly dirty room* 髒得令人噁心的房間

★rev·o·lu·tion /,rɛvə'luʃən; ,revə'lu:ʃən/ *n* **1** [C;U] great social change, especially the changing of a ruler or political system by force 革命; 社會大變革: *the Russian revolution* 俄國革命 **2** [C] a complete change in ways of thinking or acting〔思考或行為方式的〕徹底變革: *The invention of the aeroplane caused a revolution in travel and communications.* 飛機的發明使旅行和通訊發生了很大的變化。| *the computer revolution* 電腦革命 **3** [C;U] circular movement round a fixed point 旋轉; 繞轉: *The earth makes one revolution round the sun each year.* 地球每年繞太陽轉一圈。**4** [C] (also 又作 **rev** *infml*〔非正式〕) one complete circular movement on a central point in a machine〔機器的〕轉動一周: *a speed of 100 revolutions per minute* 每分鐘一百轉的速度

rev·o·lu·tion·a·ry¹ /,rɛvə'luʃən,ɛrɪ; ,revə'lu:ʃənəri/ *adj* **1** connected with revolution (1) 革命的; 變革的: *a revolutionary leader* 革命領袖 | *revolutionary ideas* 革命思想 **2** completely new and different 革命性的; 全新的, 完全不同的: *a revolutionary new way of growing rice* 一種全新的種稻方法

revolutionary² *n* **revolutionaries** a person who supports or takes part in a revolution (1) 革命者; 革新者

rev·o·lu·tion·ize /,rɛvə'luʃən,aɪz; ,revə'lu:-ʃənaɪz/ (also 又作 **revolutionise** *BrE*〔英式〕) *v* **revolutionized, revolutionizing** [T] to cause a complete change 使革命化; 使徹底改變: *The discovery of the new drug has revolutionized the treatment of many dis-*

eases. 這種新藥的發現徹底改變了許多疾病的治療方式。

re·volve /rɪ'vɑlv; rɪ'vɒlv/ *v* **revolved, revolving** [I] to spin round on a central point 旋轉; 繞轉: *The wheels began to revolve slowly.* 輪子開始緩緩轉動。| *revolving doors* 旋轉門
　revolve around sbdy/sthg *phr v* [T] to have something as a centre or main subject 以〔某人、某物〕為中心: *Her life revolves around her work.* 她的生活以工作為中心。

re·volv·er /rɪ'vɑlvə; rɪ'vɒlvəʳ/ *n* a type of small gun 左輪手槍

re·vue /rɪ'vjuː; rɪ'vjuː/ *n* a light theatrical show with songs, dances, and jokes〔有歌舞和說唱的〕輕鬆式演劇; 時事諷刺劇

re·vul·sion /rɪ'vʌlʃən; rɪ'vʌlʃən/ *n* [U] the feeling of finding something shocking and very unpleasant 震驚; 厭惡; 反感: *We looked away in revulsion from the scene of the accident.* 我們厭惡地轉過臉去, 不看事故現場。| *a feeling of utter revulsion* 極為厭惡的感覺

****re·ward¹** /rɪ'wɔrd; rɪ'wɔːd/ *v* [T] to give someone something because they have done something useful for you 報答, 酬報, 獎賞〔某人〕: *He rewarded the boy for bringing back the lost dog.* 他獎賞了那男孩, 因為他找回了走失的狗。| *How can I reward you for all your help?* 我該怎樣報答你的種種幫忙? | *He rewarded me with a £5 note.* 他給了我一張五英鎊的鈔票表示酬謝。

reward² *n* [C;U] something given or gained as return for work or service 報答; 報償; 酬金; 獎賞: *She got nothing as a reward for her kindness.* 她的好心沒有得到一點報償。| *The police are offering a reward for information about the robbery.* 警方將懸賞提供搶劫案情報的人。

re·ward·ing /rɪ'wɔrdɪŋ; rɪ'wɔːdɪŋ/ *adj* giving a feeling of satisfaction 令人滿意的; 值得做的: *Nursing can be a very rewarding job.* 當護士是一份很有價值的工作。

re·wind /ˌriː'waɪnd; ˌriː'waɪnd/ *v* **rewound** /-'waʊnd; -'waʊnd/, **rewound** [I;T] to make a TAPE on a TAPE-RECORDER or VIDEO-RECORDER go back to the beginning 倒回〔錄音帶或錄像帶〕: *He rewound the tape.* 他倒回磁帶。| *I had to rewind to the beginning.* 我得把帶子倒回開始的地方。

re·wire /ˌriː'waɪr; ˌriː'waɪəʳ/ *v* **rewired, re-wiring** [T] to put new electric wires into a building 給〔房屋〕裝上新電線

re·write /ˌriː'raɪt; ˌriː'raɪt/ *v* **rewrote** /-'rot; -'rəʊt/, **rewritten** /-'rɪtn; -'rɪtn/, **rewriting** [T] to write again in a different, more suitable way 改寫, 重寫 **–rewrite** /'riːˌraɪt; 'riːˌraɪt/ *n*

rhap·so·dy /'ræpsədɪ; 'ræpsədɪ/ *n* **rhapsodies** an expression of great praise and wild excitement 狂熱讚詞; 溢美之詞

rhet·o·ric /'retərɪk; 'retərɪk/ *n* [U] **1** the art of speaking or writing so as to persuade people effectively 修辭學 **2** speech or writ-

ing that sounds important, but is not really sincere or is without meaning 浮誇之詞; 華麗詞藻 **–rhetorical** /rɪ'tɔrɪk; rɪ'tɒrɪkəl/ *adj* **–rhetorically** /-klɪ; -klɪ/ *adv*

rhetorical ques·tion /·,··· '··/ *n* a question asked only for effect, and not expecting any answer〔只為取得修辭效果而不求回答的〕修辭性的疑問句

rheu·mat·ic /ru'mætɪk; ruː'mætɪk/ *adj* connected with or having rheumatism (患)風濕病的: *a rheumatic condition of the joints* 關節風濕 | *stiff rheumatic hands* 患風濕病的僵硬的雙手

rheu·ma·tism /'rumə,tɪzəm; 'ruːmətɪzəm/ *n* [U] a disease causing pain and stiffness in the joints or muscles 風濕病

rhi·no·ce·ros /raɪ'nɑsərəs; raɪ'nɒsərəs/ *n* **rhinoceros** *or* **rhinoceroses** (also 又作 **rhino** /'raɪno; 'raɪnəʊ/ *infml*〖非正式〗) a large, heavy animal of Africa or Asia, with either one or two horns on its nose and a thick skin 犀牛

rho·do·den·dron /ˌrodə'dɛndrən; ˌrəʊdə'dendrən/ *n* a bush that is grown for its large bright flowers 杜鵑(花)

rhu·barb /'rubɑrb; 'ruːbɑːb/ *n* [U] a broad-leaved garden plant whose thick red juicy stems are boiled with sugar and eaten (食用)大黃

rhyme¹ /raɪm; raɪm/ *n* **1** a word that ends with the same sound as another word 押韻詞; 同韻詞: *"Bold" and "cold" are rhymes.* "bold" 和 "cold" 是同韻詞。| *I can't find a rhyme for "donkey".* 我找不到一個和 "donkey" 同韻的詞。**2** [U] the use of words that rhyme in poetry〔寫詩的〕押韻; 同韻詞的使用: *Shakespeare sometimes wrote in rhyme.* 莎士比亞有時用押韻的方式寫作。**3** [C] a short piece of writing, using words that rhyme 押韻詩; 韻文: *a nursery rhyme* 兒歌, 童謠 | *He made up funny rhymes to make us laugh.* 他編了滑稽的順口溜逗我們發笑。

rhyme² *v* **rhymed, rhyming** [I] (of words or lines of poetry) to end with the same sound〔詞或詩行〕押韻, 成韻: *"House" rhymes with "mouse".* "house" 和 "mouse" 押韻。| *The last two lines of this poem don't rhyme properly.* 這首詩的最後兩行不怎麼押韻。

rhyth·m /'rɪðəm; 'rɪðəm/ *n* [C;U] a regular, repeated pattern of sounds or movements in speech, dancing, music, or nature〔說話、舞蹈、音樂或自然界的〕韻律; 節奏: *the exciting rhythms of African drum music* 非洲鼓樂那激動人心的節奏 | *the rhythm of the seasons* 四季循環往復的變化

rhyth·mic /'rɪðmɪk; 'rɪðmɪk/ *adj* (also 又作 **rhythmical**) having rhythm 有韻律的; 有節奏的: *the rhythmic beating of one's heart* 心臟有節奏的跳動 **–rhythmically** /-klɪ; -klɪ/ *adv*

rib¹ /rɪb; rɪb/ *n* one of the 12 pairs of bones

R

running round your chest from your SPINE to where they join at the front 肋骨

rib² v **-bb-** [T] old fash to make fun of someone in a friendly way 〖老式〗〖友善地〗戲弄〔某人〕; 取笑: All the boys ribbed him **for** keeping a pet pig. 所有的男孩因為他養了一隻小豬作寵物而取笑他。

rib·ald /ˈrɪbld; ˈrɪbəld/ adj fml humorously rude in a disrespectful way 〖正式〗下流的; 粗俗的: ribald jokes 下流的笑話 **–ribaldry** n [U]

rib·bon /ˈrɪbən; ˈrɪbən/ n [C;U] **1** a long, narrow piece of silk or other cloth used for tying your hair or for decoration 〔束髮、裝飾用的〕緞帶, 絲帶: red ribbons in her hair 她頭髮上繫的紅絲帶 **2** the piece of cloth that provides ink when you write with a machine 〔打字機的〕色帶

rib cage /ˈ··/ n the wall of ribs that encloses and protects your lungs 胸廓; 胸腔

rice /raɪs; raɪs/ n [U] a food of white or brown grains grown in wet tropical places, especially in India and China 稻; 米; 米飯: Would you like rice with your meat? 你吃肉時要不要吃點米飯?

★**rich** /rɪtʃ; rɪtʃ/ adj **1** possessing a lot of money or property 富(有)的, 有錢的: a very rich industrialist 很有錢的實業家 **2** [never before a noun 不能用於名詞前] containing a lot of a certain desirable thing 富含...的: This country is rich **in** oil. 這個國家盛產石油。 | rich in vitamins 含有豐富的維生素 **3** costly, valuable, and beautiful (used of objects) 昂貴的; 貴重的; 精美的(指東西): The walls were hung with rich silk. 牆上懸掛着昂貴的絲綢。 **4** containing a lot of cream, sugar, or eggs 含大量奶油、糖或雞蛋的; 濃郁的: a very rich Christmas cake 重糖而奶味濃的聖誕蛋糕 | The pudding was too rich for me. 這布丁對我來說太濃太甜了。 **5** good for growing plants (used of land) 肥沃的〔指土地〕: rich soil 沃土 **6** deep and strong (used of sounds and colours) 深沉的, 濃豔的〔指聲音和顏色〕: a rich dark red 濃豔的深紅色 – **richness** n [U]

rich·es /ˈrɪtʃɪz; ˈrɪtʃɪz/ n [pl] lit wealth 〖文〗財富; 財寶: Riches are worth nothing without health. 如果沒有健康, 財富沒有任何價值。 | the earth's riches 地球的資源

rich·ly /ˈrɪtʃlɪ; ˈrɪtʃli/ adv **1** in a large quantity 豐富地; 富裕地; 大量(地): richly rewarded 報酬豐厚的 | richly decorated 許多裝飾的 **2** fully 完全地, 充分地: They got the punishment they so richly deserved. 他們受到的懲罰完全是罪有應得。

rick·et·y /ˈrɪkətɪ; ˈrɪkⱨti/ adj weak and likely to break 虛弱的; 不牢靠的, 快要散架的: a rickety old cart 一輛快要散架的舊手推車

rick·shaw /ˈrɪkʃɔ; ˈrɪkʃɔː/ n a small vehicle used in East Asia for carrying passengers; they are pulled by a man either running or cycling in front 人力車, 黃包車

ric·o·chet /ˌrɪkəˈʃe; ˈrɪkəʃeɪ/ v **ricocheted** /-ˈʃed; -ʃeɪd/, **ricocheting** /-ˈʃeɪŋ; -ʃeɪɪŋ/ [I] (of a stone, or bullet) to change direction when it hits a surface at an angle 〔石頭或子彈接觸表面後〕跳飛; 反彈: The bullet ricocheted off the bridge. 子彈打在橋上反彈出去。 **–ricochet** n

rid /rɪd; rɪd/ v **rid, rid** [T] **1** fml to remove something unpleasant from a place 〖正式〗清除〔不愉快的事物〕: The new ruler rid the city **of** its corrupt officials. 新統治者使這個城市不再有腐敗官員。 **2** fml to remove something so that it no longer has any effect on you 〖正式〗擺脫〔某人〕: You must rid yourself **of** these unfortunate friends. 你必須擺脫那些倒運的朋友。 **3** be rid of to be free from something unpleasant 擺脫〔不愉快的事物〕: She was glad to be rid of her financial worries. 她很高興擺脫了財政上的煩惱。 **4** get rid of to remove something or someone you no longer want 處理掉〔某物〕; 擺脫〔某人〕: At the end of his studies he got rid of his course-books. 學業結束時他把教科書都丟掉了。 | The company quickly gets rid of poor salesmen. 這家公司很快便把差勁的推銷員開除了。 | I'll be glad to get rid of this cold. 能治好這層冒我就會很高興。

rid·dance /ˈrɪdns; ˈrɪdəns/ n Good riddance! an expression used to show you are glad that someone or something has gone 謝天謝地地總算擺脫了!〔用於表示對擺脫了某人或某事物感到高興〕

rid·den /ˈrɪdn; ˈrɪdn/ the past participle of RIDE ☆ RIDE 的過去分詞

rid·dle /ˈrɪdl; ˈrɪdl/ n **1** a difficult and amusing question to which you must guess the answer 謎, 謎語 **2** something you cannot understand 謎, 奧祕, 猜不透的事物: Where the woman disappeared to was a complete riddle. 這失蹤的女子去了哪裡完全是個謎。

rid·dled /ˈrɪdld; ˈrɪdld/ adj [only before a noun 只用於名詞前] **riddled with** full of holes 滿是洞眼的: The man's body was riddled with bullets. 這具男屍上盡是彈孔。 | The beam was riddled with woodworm. 這橫樑被木蛀蟲蛀得滿是洞。

★**ride¹** /raɪd; raɪd/ v **rode** /rod; rəʊd/, **ridden** /ˈrɪdn; ˈrɪdn/, **riding** **1** [I;T] to sit on a horse and control it 騎(馬): She rides every day. 她每天騎馬。 | He rode the new horse. 他騎了那匹新馬。 **2** [I;T] to travel in or on a vehicle 乘坐; 騎: She rode a bicycle to work. 她騎腳踏車上班。 | He rode to work on a bus. 他乘公共汽車上班。 | We rode to town in a Land Rover. 我們乘坐越野車去市鎮。 | Can you ride a motorbike? 你會騎摩托車嗎?

ride sthg ↔ **out** phr v [T] to come safely through a difficulty 渡過〔難關〕: The prime minister rode out the crisis. 首相渡過了危機。

ride up phr v [I] (of a dress or skirt) to move up away from its proper position 〔衣服或裙子〕向上掀; 向上縮起

ride² *n* **1** a journey on an animal or in a vehicle, especially for pleasure 〔尤指為娛樂而騎着動物或乘車而〕旅行: *Shall we go for a ride in the car?* 我們開車兜兜風好嗎? | *a ride in the country* 在郊外坐車兜風 | *a ride on a donkey* 騎驢兜風 **2 take someone for a ride** *infml* to deceive someone 〖非正式〗欺騙〔某人〕

rid·er /'raɪdə; 'raɪdə'/ *n* a person who rides, especially someone who rides a horse 騎師; 〔尤指〕騎馬者: *The rider was thrown off into a hedge.* 策騎者在樹籬中被甩掉。

ridge /rɪdʒ; rɪdʒ/ *n* a long narrow raised part of any surface 脊; 脊狀突起部分: *He walked along the mountain ridge.* 他沿着山脊行走。 | *He looked at the ridges in the ploughed field.* 他看着那塊犁過的田地上的壟。

rid·i·cule¹ /'rɪdɪkjuːl; 'rɪd ̣kjuːl/ *n* [U] being made fun of 嘲笑; 戲弄; 奚落: *His behaviour deserves ridicule rather than blame.* 他的行為該受到嘲笑, 而不是指責。 | *He didn't want to risk being exposed to ridicule.* 他不想冒着被人嘲笑的風險。

ridicule² *v* **ridiculed, ridiculing** [T] to laugh unkindly at someone or something 嘲笑, 奚落〔某人或某事物〕: *They all ridiculed the idea.* 他們全都嘲笑這主意。

ri·dic·u·lous /rɪ'dɪkjələs; rɪ'dɪkjələs/ *adj* silly and deserving to be laughed at 荒謬的; 可笑的: *She looks ridiculous in those tight trousers.* 她穿着那條緊身褲, 樣子很滑稽。 | *What a ridiculous suggestion!* 多麼荒唐的建議! **– ridiculously** *adv*: *The examination was ridiculously easy.* 這次考試出奇地容易。 **– ridiculousness** *n* [U]

rid·ing /'raɪdɪŋ; 'raɪdɪŋ/ *n* [U] the skill or exercise of travelling on a horse 騎術; 騎馬: *a riding lesson* 騎術訓練課

rife /raɪf; raɪf/ *adj* [never before a noun 不能用於名詞前] *lit* 〖文〗 **1** common (used of bad things) 流行的, 普遍的〔指壞事〕: *Disease and violence were rife in the city.* 疾病和暴力在這個城市裡非常普遍。 **2** full of bad things 充斥着〔壞事〕: *The city was rife with disease and violence.* 這個城市充斥着疾病和暴力。

ri·fle¹ /'raɪfl; 'raɪfəl/ *n* a gun with a long barrel, fired from the shoulder 步槍, 來復槍

rifle² *v* **rifled, rifling** [I;T] to search through and steal everything worth taking from a place 搜劫; 劫掠: *Somebody has been rifling* **through** *my files.* 有人一直在偷翻我的文件。 | *He rifled the biscuit tin.* 他把餅乾箱翻了個底朝天。

rift /rɪft; rɪft/ *n fml* 〖正式〗 **1** a narrow opening in something solid, especially in the ground 裂縫; 〔尤指〕隙裂, 裂谷: *The Great Rift Valley* 東非大峽谷 **2** a serious disagreement 不和; 裂痕: *The argument caused a rift* **between** *mother and daughter.* 這次爭論使母女間產生了裂痕。

rig¹ /rɪg; rɪg/ *v* **-gg-** [T] to arrange an event dishonestly for your own advantage 〔用欺騙手段〕操縱, 控制〔事件〕: *The election had been rigged.* 這次選舉被人操縱。

rig sthg ↔ **up** *phr v* [T] to make something out of materials that you can find quickly 〔就地取材〕草草做成〔某物〕: *The climbers rigged up a shelter to protect them from the rain.* 登山者臨時搭了個棚躲雨。

rig² *n* a large structure used when digging to find oil or gas 鑽井架; 鑽塔: *an oil rig* 油井鑽塔

rig·ging /'rɪgɪŋ; 'rɪgɪŋ/ *n* [U] all the ropes which hold up the sails on a ship 〔船的〕索具: *The ship lost most of her rigging in the storm.* 這艘船在風暴中損失了大部分索具。

⭐**right**¹ /raɪt; raɪt/ *n* **1** [U] the side of your body that does not contain your heart, or the direction that is on this side of your body 右邊, 右方: *You'll see the library on your right.* 你可以看到圖書館在你的右邊。 | *Take the first turning on the right.* 在右邊第一個路口轉彎。 **2 the Right** political parties or groups such as the Conservatives in Britain that are in favour of fewer social and political changes 右翼, 右派〔如英國保守黨〕: *Politicians on the Right are very unhappy about these reforms.* 右翼政客對這些改革十分不快。 **3** [U] things that are morally good 正當; 公正: *Children must learn the difference between right and wrong.* 孩子們必須學會分清是非。 **4** [C] something that you can claim because it is morally or legally just 正當要求; 合法權利: *Everyone over 18 has the right to vote.* 凡年滿十八歲的人都有選舉權。 | *She has a right* **to** *half your money.* 她有權分你一半的錢。 | *people campaigning for women's rights* 為婦女的權利而爭鬥的人 **5 be within your rights to do something** a phrase you use when you are saying that someone is allowed to do something because it is morally or legally just 在自身合法權利範圍之內; 不越權〔用於表示因某事正當或合法, 某人有權做此事〕: *You'd be quite within your rights to refuse to work on a Sunday.* 你完全有權拒絕在星期天工作。 **6 by rights** a phrase you use when you are saying that something should be true, although it is not 按理(說)〔用於認為某事應該如何, 但並非如此〕: *He should by rights be going to university this year, but he failed his exams and will have to retake them.* 按理說他今年該上大學, 可是他沒考上, 只好明年再考。 **7 in your own right** because of a personal claim that you have rather than because of someone else 憑自身的權利: *After the death of her husband she became the country's leader in her own right.* 丈夫死後, 她憑自身的權利成為國家的領導。 **8 in the right** having moral or legal justice on your side 正確; 有理: *I was convinced that I was in the right.* 我確信自己有理。 **9 put/set something to rights** *fml* to make something correct or just 〖正式〗整頓; 糾正〔某事物〕

right² *adj* **1** [only before a noun 只用於名詞前] on or belonging to the side of your body that does not contain your heart, or the direction that is on this side of your body 右邊的, 右方的: *Most people write with their right hand.* 大多數人用右手寫字。| *Take a right turn just after the supermarket.* 就在超級市場後面向右轉。**2** [never before a noun 不能用於名詞前] morally good or just 正當的: *I don't think it's right to let children have a lot of sweets.* 我認為讓孩子多吃糖是不對。| *She thinks it's not right for women to work when they have small children.* 她認為婦女有了小孩就不該上班。| *You were right to report it to the police.* 你報警是正當的。**3** correct or true 正確的, 對的: *Is that the right time?* 那是適當時機嗎? | *Nobody got the right answer.* 沒有人答對。| *She said that the party would be no good, and she was absolutely right.* 她說那聚會肯定會很糟糕, 這話一點也沒錯。| *I think it's the right job for you.* 我想這工作適合你。| *"Is this Piccadilly Circus?" "Yes, that's right."* "這是皮卡迪里廣場嗎?" "是的, 一點不錯。" **4 put/set something right** to change a situation that is bad to one that is good 使壞情況變好: *I'm sorry about all the trouble I've caused — I'll do my best to put things right.* 我很抱歉惹了所有這些麻煩 — 我會盡力把事情安排好。**5 That's right** a phrase you use when you agree with someone else's opinion 對呀〔用於同意他人意見〕: *"Some people really don't look after their children properly." "That's right."* "有些人確實不會照料孩子。" "對呀。" **6 right you are, right oh** phrases that you use to show that you agree to do something that someone has asked you to do 行; 好的〔表示同意做某人請求做的事〕: *"We'll see you on Saturday, then." "Right you are."* "那麼, 我們星期六再見面。" "好的。"

right³ *adv* **1** towards the right side 往右; 向右: *Go to the bottom of the road and turn right.* 走到馬路盡頭向右轉。**2** exactly in a particular place 正好〔在某處〕: *He was standing right in the middle of the lawn.* 他站在草坪的正中央。| *It's right in front of you!* 就在你面前! **3** as far as a particular place 徑直地; 一直: *Did you go right to the top of the tower?* 你一直走到塔頂了嗎? | *Go right back to the beginning.* 一直走到開頭的地方。**4** *infml* without delay at or after a particular time 〖非正式〗立即, 馬上: *We'll set off right after breakfast.* 我們在早飯後馬上出發。**5** properly or correctly 適當地; 正確地: *She had guessed right.* 她猜得對。| *Did I do it right?* 我做得對嗎? **6** used to show that you agree with someone or agree to do something 行; 好的〔用於贊同某人或同意某事〕: *"Come tomorrow." "Right,*

what time?" "明天來吧。" "行, 甚麼時候?" **7 right away** immediately 立即, 馬上: *I phoned the doctor and he said that he'd come right away.* 我打電話給醫生, 他說馬上就來。**8 right now** at this exact moment 就在此刻: *He should be getting on the train right now.* 他此刻應該上火車了。

right⁴ *v* [T] **1** to put something back into its correct position 把〔某物〕扶正; 恢復到正常位置: *The boat nearly capsized, but then righted itself.* 小船快要翻了, 但又自己翻正了。**2 right a wrong** to do something to take away the harmful or bad effects of something else 伸冤; 平反

right an·gle /ˈ· ˌ··/ *n* an angle of 90 degrees, like any of the four corners of a square 九十度角, 直角: *The fence was at right angles to the path.* 這籬笆和小路成直角。**–right-angled** *adj*

right·eous /ˈraɪtʃəs; ˈraɪtʃəs/ *adj fml* lawful and morally good 〖正式〗正直的; 義的; 正當的: *a righteous man* 正直的人 | *righteous indignation* 義憤 **–righteousness** *n* [U]

right·ful /ˈraɪtfəl; ˈraɪtfəl/ *adj* [only before a noun 只用於名詞前] *fml* according to a just and legal claim 〖正式〗依據正當要求的; 合法的: *The land was restored to its rightful owner after the war.* 這塊土地在戰後被歸還給合法的所有人。**–rightfully** *adv*

right-hand /ˌ·ˈ· ◂/ *adj* [only before a noun 只用於名詞前] **1** on or to the right side 右邊的; 向右的: *Take a right-hand turn.* 向右拐。| *on the right-hand side* 在右邊 **2 your right-hand, your right-hand man** your most useful and valuable helper 得力助手; 左右手

right-hand·ed /ˌ· ˈ··◂/ *adj* using the right hand rather than the left for most actions 慣用右手的: *Most people are right-handed.* 大多數人慣用右手。**–opposite** 反義 **left-handed**

right·ly /ˈraɪtlɪ; ˈraɪtli/ *adv* correctly 正確地: *He believed, rightly or wrongly, that she was guilty.* 他也許對也許不對, 反正他認為她有罪的。| *I don't rightly know whether she phoned on Tuesday or Wednesday.* 我不能確定她是星期二還是星期三打電話來的。

right of way /ˌ·· ˈ·/ *n* **rights of way 1** [C] a legal right to follow a path across someone else's land 〔穿過別人土地的〕通行權: *We have a right of way across his field to our house.* 我們有穿過他的田地走到家裡的通行權。**2** [U] the right of traffic to drive, or pass in front of other vehicles 〔車輛的〕超行權; 先行權: *We have right of way at this road junction.* 我們在這個交叉路口有先行權。

right wing /ˌ· ˈ·◂/ *n* [U; +sing/pl verb] the members of a political party or group, favouring fewer political changes, and CAPITALISM〔政黨或政治組織的〕右翼, 右派: *The right wing of the party is opposed to this plan.* 該黨內的右翼反對這項計劃。**–opposite**

反義 **left wing** –**right-wing** *adj: a right-wing politician* 右翼政治家 –**right-winger** *n*

ri·gid /ˈrɪdʒɪd; ˈrɪdʒɪd/ *adj* **1** hard and not able to be changed, used of rules and laws 〔指規則或法律〕嚴酷的; 無法改變的: *a rigid system of control* 嚴格的控制體系 **2** refusing to change 拒絕改變的; 僵化的: *The headmaster is very rigid in his approach.* 校長處理事情的態度很固執。 **3** stiff, and not bending easily 僵硬的; 堅硬的; 不易彎曲的: *a tent supported on a rigid framework* 由堅固的構架支撐着的帳篷 –**rigidly** *adv* –**rigidity** /rɪˈdʒɪdətɪ; rɪˈdʒɪdɪ ti/ *n* [U]

ri·gid·ly /ˈrɪdʒɪdlɪ; ˈrɪdʒɪdli/ *adv* **1** not moving 不移動地: *The soldier stood rigidly to attention.* 這名士兵動也不動地立正站着。 **2** in a very severe way 嚴酷地: *The laws were rigidly enforced.* 法律雷厲風行。

rig·ma·role /ˈrɪɡmərəʊl; ˈrɪɡmərəul/ *n* [sing; U] *infml* a long, confusing story or set of actions that seem to lack meaning or importance 〔非正式〕胡言亂語; 無聊的舉動: *She told me some rigmarole or other about having lost her keys.* 她向我說拉拉雜雜地說了一大堆關於丟失鑰匙的事。

rig·or mor·tis /ˌraɪɡər ˈmɔːrtɪs; ˌrɪɡə ˈmɔːtɪs/ *n* [U] the stiffening of the muscles after death 屍僵, 死後強直: *Rigor mortis set in a few hours ago.* 屍體幾小時前就僵硬了。

rig·or·ous /ˈrɪɡərəs; ˈrɪɡərəs/ *adj* **1** careful and thorough 縝密的; 徹底的; 嚴密的: *The new cars are given rigorous safety checks.* 新車接受了仔細徹底的安全檢查。 **2** severe and painful 嚴酷的; 艱苦的: *the rigorous hardships of the journey* 旅途上的艱難困苦 –**rigorously** *adv*

rig·our /ˈrɪɡər; ˈrɪɡə/ *n* (**rigor**, *AmE* 〔美式〕) [U] **1** hardness 艱難; 嚴格: *He deserves to be punished with the full rigour of the law.* 他應該受到法律最嚴厲的懲罰。 **2 the rigours** severe conditions 嚴酷; 艱苦: *the rigours of a Canadian winter* 加拿大冬天的嚴寒 **3** thoroughness in a subject of study 精確; 嚴密: *the rigour of scientific proof* 科學證據的嚴格精確性

rile /raɪl; raɪl/ *v* **riled, riling** [T] *infml* to make someone angry 〔非正式〕激怒, 惹惱〔某人〕; 使生氣: *I was really riled by the way he treated me.* 他對我的態度真把我惹火了。

rim /rɪm; rɪm/ *n* the outside edge or border, usually of a round or circular object 〔尤指圓形物的〕邊, 緣: *the rim of a cup* 杯口 | *the rim of a wheel* 輪框 –**rimless** *adj: She wore rimless glasses.* 她戴了一副無框眼鏡。

rind /raɪnd; raɪnd/ *n* [U] the thick, outer covering of certain foods or fruits 〔某些食物或水果的〕外皮: *a piece of lemon rind* 一片檸檬皮 | *cheese rind* 乳酪外皮 | *bacon rinds* 熏豬肉皮

★**ring¹** /rɪŋ; rɪŋ/ *n* **1** a circular metal band, usually worn on a finger 圈; 環; 〔常指〕戒指: *a wedding ring* 結婚戒指 | *a key ring* 鑰匙

圈 –see picture on page 210 見 210 頁彩圖 **2** something in the shape of a circle 環狀物; 圈狀物: *a ring of oil around the wrecked ship* 失事船隻周圍的一圈油 | *children dancing in a ring* 圍成一圈跳舞的孩子 **3** a group of people acting together in a dishonest way 〔行為欺騙的〕一夥人, 團夥, 幫派: *The police were searching for the head of the drugs ring.* 警方在搜尋毒品集團的頭目。 **4** an enclosed space with seats around it in which an activity takes place 圓形活動場地: *a boxing ring* 拳擊場 | *a circus ring* 馬戲場 **5** the sound of a bell 鈴〔鐘〕聲: *I thought I heard a ring at the door.* 我以為我聽到門鈴聲。 **6 give someone a ring** *infml* to telephone someone 〔非正式〕給某人打電話: *Give me a ring when you get home.* 你回到家時打個電話給我。 **7 run rings round someone** to do things much better than someone 幹得比某人好得多: *I tried my best, but he ran rings round me.* 我盡了力, 可是他幹得比我好得多。

★**ring²** *v* **ringed, ringed** [T] to put a ring around something 環繞; 包圍; 把〔某物〕圈出: *The teacher ringed every mistake in red.* 老師用紅筆圈出了每個錯誤。 | *Police ringed the building.* 警察包圍了那座大樓。

ring³ *v* **rang** /ræŋ; ræŋ/, **rung** /rʌŋ; rʌŋ/ **1** [T] to make a bell sound 使〔鐘〕鳴響; 按〔鈴〕: *He rang the doorbell.* 他按了門鈴。 **2** [I] to sound 鳴; 響: *The phone rang.* 電話鈴響了。 | *I could hear the church bells ringing.* 我聽得到教堂鐘聲在鳴。 **3** [I;T] to telephone 打電話: *I rang twice but got no reply.* 我打了兩次電話, 但沒有人接。 | *I'll ring you tonight.* 我今晚給你打電話。 **4** [I;T] to ring a bell because you want something 按鈴呼喚: *He rang for his secretary.* 他按鈴叫他的祕書。 | *He rang for some sandwiches.* 他按鈴要些三明治。 **5** [I] to be filled with a continuous sound 發出連續的聲響: *The theatre rang with applause.* 劇場裡響起了一陣陣的掌聲。 | *My ears were ringing.* 我的耳朵在嗡嗡作響。 **6 ring a bell** *infml* to make you remember something 〔非正式〕使記得; 使想起: *His name doesn't ring a bell.* 他的名字喚不起印象。 **7 ring false** to sound untrue 聽起來虛偽: *Her explanation rang false.* 她的解釋聽上去不真實。 [RELATED PHRASE 相關詞組 **ring true**] **8 ring the changes** to introduce variety 推出新花色

ring sbdy ↔ **back** *phr v* [I;T] to telephone later 〔稍後〕再打電話: *I'll ring you back when I've got more news.* 我有了更多消息就再打電話給你。 | *I forgot to ring back.* 我忘了回電話。

ring off *phr v* [I] to end a telephone conversation 掛斷電話: *I'd better ring off now, there's someone at the door.* 我現在還是掛斷電話吧——門口有人。

ring out *phr v* [I] to sound loudly and clearly 響亮而清晰地響起: *The climber's shouts rang out across the valley.* 登山者的喊

叫聲在山谷間響起。

ring up *phr v* [I;T **ring** sbdy ↔ **up**] to telephone 打電話: *She rang me up to say she'd be home late.* 她打電話告訴我她晚一些到家。–see 見 TELEPHONE[1] (USAGE 用法)

ring·lead·er /ˈrɪŋˌlidɚ; ˈrɪŋˌliːdəʳ/ *n* a person who leads others to do wrong or make trouble〔帶領其他人幹壞事的〕頭目，首領

ring·let /ˈrɪŋlɪt; ˈrɪŋlɪ̯t/ *n* a long hanging curl of hair 長鬈髮

ring·mas·ter /ˈrɪŋˌmæstɚ; ˈrɪŋˌmɑːstəʳ/ *n* a person whose job is directing performances in the CIRCUS ring 馬戲團領班

ring road /ˈ·ˌ·/ *n* a road that goes round the edge of a large town so that traffic need not pass through the centre 環路；環城公路

ring·side /ˈrɪŋˌsaɪd; ˈrɪŋsaɪd/ *n* **the ringside** at the edge of a ring such as in a CIRCUS 台邊；台的前排 —**ringside** *adj*: *We had ringside seats for the big fight, and saw it all.* 我們坐在拳擊場前排的位置上，所以整場比賽看得清清楚楚。

rink /rɪŋk; rɪŋk/ *n* a specially prepared indoor surface, on which people SKATE, or ROLLER-SKATE〔室內〕溜冰場；四輪溜冰鞋溜冰場: *They met at the ice rink.* 他們在溜冰場碰頭。

rinse¹ /rɪns; rɪns/ *v* **rinsed, rinsing** [T] to wash something in clean water〔用清水〕漂洗〔某物〕，沖洗: *I'll just rinse these shirts.* 我正要漂洗這些襯衫。| *Rinse your mouth out.* 漱漱你的口。

rinse² *n* **1** [C] washing in clean water 漂洗，沖洗: *Give the shirts at least three rinses.* 這些襯衫至少要漂洗三次。**2** [C;U] a liquid for colouring the hair 染髮劑: *blue rinse for grey hair* 染灰白頭髮用的藍色染髮劑

ri·ot¹ /ˈraɪət; ˈraɪət/ *n* **1** [C] a lot of violent actions by a number of people in a public place 暴亂；騷亂: *The army was called in to put down a riot.* 軍隊被召來鎮壓騷亂。**2 a riot** *infml* a very funny and successful occasion or person〔非正式〕有趣的事；成功的事〔人〕: *I hear the new show is a riot — let's go and see it!* 我聽說這齣新戲十分有趣——我們去看看吧! **3 run riot** to become violent and uncontrollable 無法無天，胡作非為，不受控制: *The football supporters ran riot through the town after their team lost.* 足球隊輸了以後，支持者在鎮上到處鬧事。

riot² *v* [I] to behave violently in a public place〔在公共場所〕鬧事，騷亂: *The crowds are rioting in the city centre.* 人羣在市中心鬧事。–**rioter** *n*

ri·ot·ous /ˈraɪətəs; ˈraɪətəs/ *adj* **1** wild and disorderly 狂亂的，暴亂的；鬧事的: *a riotous crowd* 騷亂的人羣 | *riotous laughter* 狂亂的笑聲 **2** noisy and exciting (a word used to express approval) 喧鬧的；狂歡的〔含褒義〕: *They spent a riotous night drinking and singing.* 他們喝酒高歌，度過了一個狂歡之夜。–**riotously** *adv*

rip¹ /rɪp; rɪp/ *v* **-pp-** [I;T] **1** to tear or be torn quickly and violently （被）撕破: *The sail ripped under the force of the wind.* 帆被強風颳破了。| *He ripped the cloth with his knife.* 他用小刀割破了那塊布。| *I ripped the letter open.* 我撕開信封。| *The curtains were ripped to pieces.* 窗簾被撕成了碎片。**2** to remove something quickly and often violently 猛力移去〔去除〕: *He ripped the letter from my hand.* 他從我手中奪去那封信。| *He ripped off his clothes and jumped into the pool.* 他扯掉衣服，跳入池塘。

rip sbdy ↔ **off** *phr v* [T] *infml* to charge someone far too much money〔非正式〕收費過高，敲竹槓: *They really ripped us off at that hotel.* 那家旅館着實敲了我們一筆竹槓。

rip sthg ↔ **up** *phr v* [T] to tear violently into pieces 用力撕成碎片: *Angrily, she ripped the letter up.* 一怒之下，她把信撕成碎片。

rip² *n* a long tear or cut 長裂縫；長切口: *a rip in the tyre caused by a sharp stone* 一塊尖石在輪胎上割開的裂口

rip·cord /ˈrɪpkɔrd; ˈrɪpkɔːd/ *n* the cord that one pulls to open a PARACHUTE after jumping from an aircraft〔降落傘的〕開傘索

ripe /raɪp; raɪp/ *adj* **1** fully grown and ready to be eaten (used of food and crops) 成熟的(指食物和莊稼): *a field of ripe corn* 一片成熟的莊稼 | *These apples aren't ripe yet.* 這些蘋果還未熟。**2** [never before a noun 不能用於名詞前] ready for something 準備好的；適宜…的: *land ripe for industrial development* 適合發展工業的土地 **3 the time is ripe** a suitable time has arrived for a particular action〔採取某種行動的〕時機已經成熟: *The time is ripe for a change of attitude.* 時機已經成熟，應該轉變態度了。**4 live to a ripe old age** to live until you are very old 活到高齡，年紀大: *His grandmother lived to a ripe old age.* 他的祖母活到了高齡。–**ripeness** *n* [U]

rip·en /ˈraɪpən; ˈraɪpən/ *v* [I;T] to make or become ripe （使）成熟: *The sun ripens the corn.* 日光照射使農作物成熟。| *The corn ripens in the sun.* 農作物依靠日光照射而成熟。

rip-off /ˈ·ˌ·/ *n infml* an act of charging too much〔非正式〕收費過高，敲竹槓: *"What a rip-off!"*"真是敲竹槓啊!"

rip·ple¹ /ˈrɪpl; ˈrɪpəl/ *v* **rippled, rippling 1** [I;T] to move or be made to move in gentle waves （使）起漣漪: *The wind rippled the surface of the cornfield.* 風吹過麥田，泛起一片麥浪。**2** [I] to make a sound like gently running water 發出潺潺聲: *The water rippled over the stones.* 水從石頭上流過，發出潺潺的聲音。

ripple² *n* **1** [C] a very small wave 漣漪；微波；細浪: *ripples on a pool when the wind blows* 風吹過池塘時泛起的漣漪 **2** [sing] a sound of gently running water 潺潺聲: *I heard the ripple of the stream.* 我聽到了小溪的潺潺流水聲。**3** a sound heard for a short time〔短

時間裡的〕聲音: *a ripple of laughter* 一陣陣的笑聲 | *a ripple of applause* 一陣陣的掌聲

⋆rise[1] /raɪz; raɪz/ *v* **rose** /roz; rəʊz/, **risen** /ˈrɪzn; ˈrɪzən/, **rising** [I] **1** to go up or move to a higher position 上升; 上漲: *The river is rising after the rains.* 幾場雨後河水不斷上漲。 | *Smoke rose from the factory chimney.* 煙從工廠的煙囪冒出。 | *Her voice rose higher and higher as she got more excited.* 她越來越激動, 嗓門也提得越來越高。 | *The price of bread has risen by 10% in the last year.* 麵包的價格去年上漲了百分之十。 | *The road rises steeply when you leave the village.* 這條路一出村莊就陡峭地上升。 | *He rose to an important position in the firm.* 他升任到公司的一個重要職位上。 | *My spirits rose when I heard the wonderful news.* 我聽到這個大好消息, 情緒便高漲起來。 –opposite 反義 **fall 2** to appear above the horizon 升起, 上升: *The sun rises in the east.* 太陽從東方升起。 | *The trees rose above the rooftops.* 這些樹長得高出了屋頂。 **3** *fml* to get out of bed 〔正式〕起牀: *She used always to rise at daybreak.* 她過去總是黎明即起的。 **4** to stand up 站起來, 起立: *She rose to greet her guests.* 她站起來迎接客人。 **5** to begin to be active in opposition 開始反對; 起來反抗: *The people rose **against** their cruel oppressors.* 人民奮起反抗他們殘酷的壓迫者。 **6** (of wind and storms) to become stronger 〔風和暴風雨〕增強, 變猛烈: *The storm rose without warning.* 暴風雨突然猛烈起來。 **7** to begin 起源: *The Rhine rises in Switzerland.* 萊茵河發源於瑞士。 **8** rise to the occasion to show that you can deal with a difficult situation when it happens 表現出能應付〔困難局面〕; 應付裕如

> ■ USAGE 用法: Compare 比較 **rise** and 和 **raise. Rise** is intransitive. If you **rise,** you yourself move to a higher position ☆ **rise** 是不及物動詞。如果表示從較低的位置移到較高的位置, 用 **rise**: *I rose from my seat.* 我從座位上站起來。 **Raise** is transitive. If you **raise** something you lift it to a higher position ☆ **raise** 是及物動詞。如果 **raise** 某物, 表示將某物提升至較高的位置: *We* **raised** *the ship from the seabed.* 我們從海底把船打撈上來。

rise above sthg *phr v* [T] not to allow something to have a bad effect on you 克服; 擺脫; 不受…的影響: *She was able to rise above the disadvantages of her family background.* 她能克服家庭背景這個不利條件的影響。

⋆rise[2] *n* **1** [C] an increase 上漲; 增加: *a rise in the cost of living* 生活費用的上漲 **2** [U] the act of growing greater or more powerful 興起; 興盛: *the rise and fall of the Roman Empire* 羅馬帝國的興衰 **3** [C] a small hill 小山

丘: *a house on top of a small rise* 在小山丘的頂上的一幢房子 **4** [C] *BrE* an increase in wages 〔英式〕〔工資的〕增加: *We all got a £6-a-week rise last month.* 上個月我們的週薪增加了六英鎊。 **5** give rise to to be the cause of 引起, 使發生: *The minister's comments gave rise to rumours he would soon resign.* 部長的言論引致有傳聞說他不久將辭職。

⋆risk[1] /rɪsk; rɪsk/ *n* **1** [C;U] a possibility something bad may happen 風險, 危險(性): *He was taking a risk by overtaking on a bend.* 他在轉彎處超車是在冒險。 | *There was no risk of infection.* 沒有感染的危險。 **2** [C] a danger 危險: *The house is a fire risk.* 這房子有着火的危險。 | *We took out an all risks insurance policy.* 我們辦了一份綜合險的保險單。 **3** at risk in danger 在危險中: *Babies and old people are at greatest risk in this influenza epidemic.* 嬰兒和老人在這次流行性感冒中最有被傳染的危險。 | *You really are at risk if you do not wear a seat-belt.* 你不繫安全帶真的會有危險的。 **4** at the risk of knowing something unpleasant might happen 冒…的危險〔風險〕: *He went ahead with the plan at the risk of infuriating his colleagues.* 他冒着激怒同事的危險開始實行這項計劃。 | *At the risk of seeming rude, I must refuse your request I'm afraid.* 儘管似乎很無禮, 恐怕我還是必須拒絕你的要求。 **5** at your own risk taking responsibility for what happens 〔對發生的事〕自己負責, 自擔風險(地): *People bathing here do so at their own risk.* 在此處洗澡者如有意外責任自負。 **6** run the risk of to do something knowing that a particular unpleasant thing might happen 冒險〔做某事〕: *He ran the risk of losing his job by criticizing his boss.* 他冒着丟飯碗的風險批評他的老闆。 | *They're unlikely to run the risk of holding an election before the summer.* 他們未必會冒險在夏季前舉行選舉。

risk[2] *v* [T] **1** to place something in danger 使〔某事物〕遭受危險: *Don't risk your health.* 別拿你自己的健康去冒險。 **2** to take a chance, knowing something may happen 冒…的危險: *He risked his parents' anger by marrying me.* 他不惜惹惱父母而同我結婚。

risk·y /ˈrɪskɪ; ˈrɪski/ *adj* **riskier, riskiest** rather dangerous 相當危險的, 冒險的: *You drove too fast round that corner — it was a risky thing to do.* 你開車拐過那個街角時速度太快了——這是很危險的。 –**riskily** *adv*

ri·sot·to /rɪˈzato; rɪˈzɒtəʊ/ *n* **risottos** [C;U] a dish made from rice cooked with vegetables or meat 肉〔菜〕燴飯

ris·qué /rɪsˈke; ˈrɪskeɪ/ *adj* slightly rude because it is concerned with sex (used of jokes and stories) 有傷風化的, 不雅的, 近乎淫穢的〔指笑話和故事〕

ris·sole /ˈrɪsol; ˈrɪsəʊl/ *n* a small flat or round cake made from cut up meat or fish and cooked in hot fat 炸肉丸〔肉卷〕; 炸魚丸

〔魚卷〕

rite /raɪt; raɪt/ *n* a ceremony with a serious, often religious, purpose 儀式, 典禮: *funeral rites* 葬禮

rit·u·al /ˈrɪtʃʊəl; ˈrɪtʃuəl/ *n* [C;U] one or more ceremonies or customary acts often repeated in the same form 儀式; 程序; 例行習慣: *the ritual of morning prayers in school* 學校的晨禱儀式 –**ritual** *adj*: *ritual dancing* 儀式舞蹈 –**ritually** *adv*

ri·val[1] /ˈraɪvḷ; ˈraɪvəl/ *n* a person with whom one competes 競爭對手: *Who will be his main rival in the presidential election?* 誰將是他在這次總統選舉中的主要競爭對手? 是他在這次總統選舉中的主要競爭對手?

rival[2] *adj* [only before a noun 只用於名詞前] competing 競爭的: *Michael has left and joined a rival company.* 邁克爾已離開, 加入了競爭對手的公司。

rival[3] *v* **-ll-** (**-l-** *AmE* 〔美式〕) [T] to be as good as something else 與〔某事物〕匹敵, 比得上: *Ships can't rival aircraft for speed.* 船在速度上無法同飛機相比。

ri·val·ry /ˈraɪvlrɪ; ˈraɪvəlrɪ/ *n* **rivalries** [C;U] competition 競爭; 競賽: *Should we encourage international rivalry in sport?* 我們應該鼓勵國際間的體育競賽嗎? | *fierce rivalry between the two companies* 兩家公司之間的激烈競爭

★**riv·er** /ˈrɪvə; ˈrɪvər/ *n* a wide natural stream of water flowing between banks into a lake, into another wider stream, or into the sea 河, 江: *the river Amazon* 亞馬遜河 | *The river meanders down to the sea.* 這條河蜿蜒流入大海。

riv·et[1] /ˈrɪvɪt; ˈrɪvɪt/ *n* a metal pin for fastening flat pieces of metal together 鉚釘

rivet[2] *v* [T] **1** to fasten something with rivets 鉚接〔某物〕, 〔用鉚釘〕把…固定住 **2** to attract and hold someone's attention 吸引, 引起〔某人的〕注意力: *All the people in the theatre were riveted by his performance.* 劇場裡的全體觀眾都被他的表演吸引住了。

riv·et·ing /ˈrɪvɪtɪŋ; ˈrɪvətɪŋ/ *adj* extremely interesting 非常精彩的; 引人入勝的: *a riveting book* 十分精彩的書

RN /ˌɑːˈrɛn; ˌɑːrˈɛn/ an abbreviation for 〔縮〕 = **Royal Navy**, used in titles 皇家海軍 〔用於稱呼〕: *Captain Brown, RN* 皇家海軍布朗上校

★★**road** /rod; rəʊd/ *n* **1** a prepared track of hard ground along which vehicles can travel (道)路; 公路: *Snow blocked the road.* 大雪堵塞了道路。 | *The child ran out into the road and nearly caused an accident.* 這孩子跑出馬路上去, 差點引起一場事故。 | *3, St. Mary's Road* 聖瑪麗路三號 –see 見 STREET (USAGE 用法) –see pictures on pages 729 and 991 見 729 頁和 991 頁彩圖 **2** by road travelling on a road 由公路: *The journey takes longer by road than by rail.* 坐汽車旅行比坐火車花的時間長。 **3** on the road travelling 在旅途中: *We'd been on the road for forty-eight hours and were quite exhausted.* 我們已經坐汽車旅行了四十八小時, 所以感到精疲力竭。 **4** on the road to something on the way to something 在走向某事物的途中: *on the road to disaster* 將要發生災難 –see 見 WAY (USAGE 用法)

road·block /ˈrodˌblɑk; ˈrəʊdblɒk/ *n* something which prevents traffic passing through 路障: *The police set up roadblocks to try to catch the terrorists.* 警察設置路障, 試圖捕捉恐怖分子。

road·side /ˈrodˌsaɪd; ˈrəʊdsaɪd/ *n* the roadside at or near the edge of the road 路旁, 路邊: *We ate our meal by the roadside.* 我們在路旁吃飯。 –**roadside** *adj*: *a roadside café* 路邊咖啡館

road·way /ˈrodˌwe; ˈrəʊdweɪ/ *n* the part of a road where vehicles drive 車行道: *Don't stop in the roadway.* 不要停在車行道上。

road works /ˈ· ·/ *n* [pl] a sign which means road repairs are being carried out 道路施工 〔用於告示牌上〕

road·wor·thy /ˈrodˌwɜːðɪ; ˈrəʊdˌwɜːðɪ/ *adj* in a fit condition to be driven on the road (used of a vehicle) 適於在道路上行駛的〔指車輛〕 –**roadworthiness** *n* [U]

roam /rom; rəʊm/ *v* [I; + adv/prep; T] to wander with no very clear purpose 漫步; 漫遊; 閒逛: *roaming from place to place* 到處閒逛

roar[1] /rɔr; rɔːr/ *v* **1** [I] to make a loud noise 吼叫, 怒吼, 呼嘯: *The lion roared.* 獅子在吼叫。 **2** [I; +adv/prep] to travel along very fast, making a loud noise 轟響着快速行進: *The traffic roared past.* 車輛轟隆隆地駛過。 **3** [I;T] to say or express with a deep loud continuing sound 大聲表示, 大聲説: *The crowd roared their approval.* 人羣大聲呼喊表示贊成。 | *He roared with laughter.* 他放聲大笑。

roar[2] *n* a deep loud continuing sound 吼叫; 咆哮; 轟鳴: *the roar of an angry lion* 雄獅的怒吼 | *roars of laughter* 哄然大笑聲

roar·ing /ˈrɔrɪŋ; ˈrɔːrɪŋ/ *adj* **1** making a loud noise 喧鬧的; 吼叫的; 怒號的: *roaring laughter* 喧鬧的笑聲 | *a roaring fire* 燒得旺盛的火 **2** very great 巨大的: *The play was a roaring success.* 這齣戲取得了巨大的成功。 **3** do a roaring trade to do very good business 生意興隆: *The new restaurant is doing a roaring trade.* 這家新餐館生意十分興隆。

roast[1] /rost; rəʊst/ *v* [I;T] to cook or be cooked by dry heat, either in front of an open fire or in an OVEN 烤; 烘: *roasted coffee beans* 烘過的咖啡豆 | *Roast the chicken for two hours.* 把雞烤上兩小時。 –see 見 COOK[1] (USAGE 用法)

roast[2] *n* a large piece of meat for roasting 大塊烤肉: *Let's have a nice roast for Sunday dinner.* 我們星期天晚飯好好吃頓烤肉吧。 –**roast** *adj*: *roast chicken* 烤雞 | *roast potatoes* 烤馬鈴薯

rob /rɑb; rɒb/ v -bb- [T] to take something which belongs to someone else 搶劫, 搶奪: *They planned to rob a bank.* 他們計劃搶劫一家銀行。 | *I've been robbed!* 我遭搶劫了! | *They robbed him of everything he possessed.* 他們搶走了他的所有財物。

> ■ USAGE 用法: Compare 比較 **rob** and 和 **steal.** Things are **stolen**; people or organizations are **robbed** (of things) ☆東西被偷用 **stolen**; 人或組織被劫掠用 **robbed**: *He stole my pen.* 他偷了我的鋼筆。 | *Two video recorders were stolen.* 兩台錄影機被偷走了。 | *We've been robbed!* 我們被人搶劫了! | *He was robbed of his wallet and £10 in cash.* 他被人搶了錢包和十英鎊現金。

rob·ber /ˈrɑbɚ; ˈrɒbə/ n a person who steals 盜賊; 搶劫者: *a band of robbers* 一夥強盜 –see 見 THIEF (USAGE 用法)

rob·ber·y /ˈrɑbɚɪ; ˈrɒbəri/ n **robberies** [C; U] **1** the crime of taking someone else's property 搶劫, 劫奪: *He was charged with robbery.* 他被控搶劫。 | *The robbery took place during the hours of darkness.* 那宗搶劫案發生在夜裡。 **2 daylight robbery** *infml* charging too much money 《非正式》要價太高; 敲竹槓: *£2 for a beer? It's daylight robbery!* 一杯啤酒兩英鎊? 這是敲竹槓!

robe /rob; rəʊb/ n a long flowing garment 長袍: *a bath robe* 浴袍 | *a judge's black robes* 法官的黑袍

rob·in /ˈrɑbɪn; ˈrɒbɪn/ n a small brown bird with a red breast 知更鳥, 鴝

ro·bot /ˈrobət; ˈrəʊbɒt/ n a machine that can move and do some of the work of a person 機器人: *Some of the work in the car factory is now done by robots.* 汽車製造廠裡的某些工作現在由機器人來做。

ro·bust /roˈbʌst; rəˈbʌst/ adj having or showing very good health or strength 健壯的, 強壯的

★**rock¹** /rɑk; rɒk/ v **1** [I;T] to move regularly backwards and forwards or from side to side (使)〔來回有規律地〕搖擺; 搖晃: *She rocked the child in her arms.* 她把孩子抱在懷裡輕輕搖動。 | *The boat rocked on the water.* 船在水上搖晃。 **2** [T] to cause great shock and surprise 使震驚: *The news of the president's murder rocked the nation.* 總統遇刺的消息震驚了全國。 **3 rock the boat** to spoil a good or comfortable situation 破壞良好〔舒適〕的狀況

rock² n **1** [U] a type of stone forming part of the earth's surface 岩石: *a passage cut through solid rock* 從堅硬的岩石中鑿出的通路 **2** [C] a large piece or mass of stone 大石, 岩塊: *danger from falling rocks* 石塊崩落的危險 | *ships driven onto the rocks by a storm* 被暴風刮得撞上礁石的船隻 **3** [U] *BrE* a hard sticky kind of sweet made in long

round bars 〔英式〕硬棒糖: *a stick of Brighton rock* 一根布賴頓棒糖 **4 on the rocks** with ice 加冰塊的: *whisky on the rocks* 加冰塊的威士忌 **5 their marriage is on the rocks** = their marriage is in difficulties and about to end 他們的婚姻瀕於破裂

rock bot·tom /ˌ··ˈ·◂/ n [U] the lowest point 最低點; 最低水平: *Prices have reached rock bottom.* 物價已降到最低點。

rock·er /ˈrɑkɚ; ˈrɒkə/ n **1** one of the curved pieces of wood which certain types of furniture have at the bottom so that they can be rocked backwards and forwards 〔某些家具底部的〕弧形搖板 **2** the usual American word for 〔美式〕= ROCKING CHAIR **3 off your rocker** *infml* mad 〔非正式〕發瘋, 精神失常

rock·e·ry /ˈrɑkərɪ; ˈrɒkəri/ n **rockeries** (also 又作 **rock garden**) a part of a garden laid out with rocks and low-growing plants 假山庭園, 假山園林

rock·et¹ /ˈrɑkɪt; ˈrɒkɪt/ n **1** a tube-shaped machine used for space travel, and to power bombs 火箭: *an anti-tank rocket* 反坦克火箭 | *the launch of the new American space rocket* 美國新航天火箭的發射 **2** a FIREWORK that goes high in the air and then explodes with many bright colours 火箭式煙火

rocket² v [I] to rise quickly and suddenly 猛漲, 急速上升: *The price of sugar has rocketed.* 糖價飛漲。

rocking chair /ˈ·· ·/ n (also 又作 **rocker** *AmE* 〔美式〕) a chair with special curved pieces at the bottom so that you can ROCK in it 搖椅

rocking horse /ˈ·· ·/ n a toy horse for a child to ride on; it has curved pieces at the bottom so that the child can ROCK on it 〔小孩騎的〕搖動木馬

rock 'n' roll /ˌrɑkənˈrol; ˌrɒk ən ˈrəʊl/ n (also 又作 **rock, rock and roll**) [U] popular modern dance music with a strong beat, which is played on electric instruments 搖滾樂

rock·y /ˈrɑkɪ; ˈrɒki/ adj **rockier, rockiest 1** covered with rocks 覆蓋岩石的: *a rocky path up the mountain* 上山的石頭小路 **2** unsteady 不穩定的; 搖晃的: *She felt a bit rocky after the accident.* 事故之後, 她感到有點頭暈目眩的。 –**rockiness** n [U]

rod /rɑd; rɒd/ n a long thin pole or bar of wood, metal, or plastic 〔木質、金屬或塑料的〕桿, 棒, 竿: *to go fishing with rod and line* 帶着釣竿釣線去釣魚 | *curtain rods* 掛簾子的桿 | *a rod of iron* 鐵棒

rode /rod; rəʊd/ the past tense of RIDE ☆ RIDE 的過去式

ro·dent /ˈrodn̩t; ˈrəʊdənt/ n a member of the family of small plant-eating animals with strong sharp teeth, that includes rats, mice, and rabbits 齧齒動物〔如鼠、兔等〕

R

roe /ro; rəʊ/ n [C;U] a mass of eggs or male seed in a fish, often eaten as food 〔常供食用的〕魚子

rogue /rog; rəʊg/ n old fash 〔老式〕**1** a very dishonest person 流氓, 無賴: *Don't buy a used car from that rogue.* 別買那個無賴的舊車。 **2** infml a boy who likes playing tricks 〔非正式〕調皮鬼, 小淘氣: *You little rogue — where are my shoes?* 你這個小淘氣鬼, 把我的鞋藏哪兒去了?

*role /rol; rəʊl/ n the part taken by someone in life or in any activity, especially the part of some particular actor in a play 作用; 任務; 職責;〔尤指〕角色: *Olivier played the role of Hamlet.* 奧利弗扮演哈姆雷特的角色。 | *She needed to fulfil her role as a mother.* 她要盡當母親的職責。

*roll[1] /rol; rəʊl/ n **1** a piece of a particular material that has been rolled into or around a tube 卷; 卷軸; 卷狀物: *a roll of film* 一卷膠片 | *a roll of cloth* 一卷布 **2** a small round or long loaf of bread for one person 圓麵包; 麵包卷: *little bread rolls* 小麵包卷 | *a cheese roll* 乾酪麵包卷 **3** an official list of names 〔正式〕名冊; 名錄: *The teacher called the roll.* 老師點名。 **4** [sing] a long deep sound 隆隆聲; 轟響聲: *a roll of thunder* 隆隆的雷聲 | *the roll of drums* 隆隆的鼓聲 **5** a rolling movement from side to side 滾動, 翻滾: *the slow roll of a ship on a rough sea* 船隻在洶湧的海面上的緩緩搖晃

roll[2] v **1** [I;T] to move by turning over and over, or from side to side (使)滾動; (使)轉動: *The golfer hit the ball and it rolled straight into the hole.* 高爾夫球手一擊球, 球便徑直滾進洞裡。 | *The dog rolled in the grass.* 狗在草地上打滾。 | *We rolled the barrels of wine into their correct position in the cellar.* 我們把一隻隻酒桶滾進地窖裡適當的位置上。 | *The ship rolled with the waves.* 船隨波浪左右搖晃。 **2** [I] to move steadily and smoothly 〔平穩地〕移動: *The train rolled slowly into the station.* 火車緩緩地駛進車站。 | *Tears rolled down her cheek.* 淚水順著她的臉頰滾滾流下。 **3** [T] to form into a particular shape by moving round and round 捲, 捲起; 搓: *He rolled himself a cigarette.* 他給自己捲了一支煙。 | *She rolled the clay into a ball.* 她把黏土搓成一個球。 | *She rolled the paper instead of folding it.* 她把紙捲了起來, 而不是摺起來。 **4** [T] to make something flat by pressing it down 把…輾平: *The grass needs rolling.* 這些草要輾一輾。 | *He rolled the pastry as thin as he could.* 他盡量把麵團擀得薄一些。 **5** [I] to make a long deep sound 發出隆隆聲: *The drums rolled.* 鼓聲隆隆。 **6** [I;T] (of your eyes) to move round (使)〔眼睛〕轉動: *His eyes rolled with fear.* 他嚇得眼睛溜溜地轉動。

roll about phr v [I] to move around in an uncontrolled way 無法控制地搖來轉去: *During the storm, the cargo got loose and rolled about on the deck of the ship.* 在暴風雨中, 貨物鬆動了, 在甲板上滾來滾去。

roll by phr v [I] to go steadily past 〔平穩地〕經過: *The years rolled by.* 歲月流逝。 | *The girl watched the heavy trucks roll by.* 女孩看著重型卡車平穩地駛過。

roll in phr v [I] to be received in large quantities 大量湧到: *The money came rolling in.* 鈔票滾滾而來。

roll over phr v [I;T] to move to a different position 翻轉; 側轉: *The baby rolled over.* 嬰兒翻了個身。

roll up phr v **1** [I;T roll sth ↔ up] to shape something like a tube or ball 捲起; 捲成一團: *The paper kept rolling up.* 紙一直捲着。 | *They rolled up the carpet.* 他們捲起地毯。 | *He rolled up his sleeves and started work.* 他捲起袖子, 開始工作。 **2** [I] infml to arrive 〔非正式〕到達: *John rolled up when everyone else had left.* 大家都已走了, 約翰才姍姍而來。

roll call /'··/ n [U] the time for an act of reading out a list of names to see who is there 點名(時間): *I arrived just before roll call.* 我剛好在點名前到達。

roll·er /'rolə; 'rəʊlər/ n **1** a hard tube-shaped object that rolls over and over 滾子, 滾筒, 滾軸: *The rollers under the armchair made it easy to move.* 扶手椅下面的滾軸使椅子易於移動。 **2** tubes around which women wind their hair to make it curl 捲髮筒: *She sleeps with her hair in rollers.* 她戴着捲髮筒睡覺。 **3** a big, long wave on the coast 巨浪: *The Atlantic rollers surged in.* 大西洋的巨浪奔騰而上。

roller blind /'·· ·/ n BrE a kind of curtain that rolls up and down over a window 〔英式〕捲簾

roller coast·er /'·· ‚··/ n a kind of small railway with sharp slopes and curves, popular in amusement parks 〔遊樂園中的〕過山車, 雲霄飛車

roller skate /'··· / n a frame with wheels for fitting under a shoe, or a shoe with wheels fixed on, allowing you to move quickly on any smooth surface 四輪旱冰鞋: *a boy on roller skates* 穿四輪旱冰鞋的男孩 **–roller-skate** v [I]

roll·ing /'rolɪŋ; 'rəʊlɪŋ/ adj [only before a noun 只用於名詞前] **1** rising and falling in long gentle slopes 起伏的; 延伸的: *the rolling hills of England* 英格蘭綿延起伏的山丘 **2** moving from side to side (used to describe the way someone walks) 搖擺的〔用於形容走路的樣子〕: *the rolling walk of a very fat man* 一個大胖子搖搖擺擺的步態 **3** **rolling in it** infml very rich 〔非正式〕很富有的: *Dave can pay. He's rolling in it.* 戴夫可以付錢。他很有錢。

rolling pin /'·· ·/ n a tube-shaped piece of wood or other material, used for spreading pastry out flat and thin before cooking 擀

麵杖 –see picture on page 958 見 958 頁彩圖

rolling stock /'··· ·/ *n* [U] everything on wheels that belongs to a railway, such as engines and carriages 鐵路上的各種車輛〔如機車、客車等〕

Ro·man /'rəmən; 'rəʊmən/ *n* a citizen of the ancient empire or the city of Rome 古羅馬人;羅馬城

Roman Cath·o·lic /,·· '···/ *adj* someone belonging to the **Roman Catholic Church** whose leader rules from Rome (羅馬)天主教的: *a Roman Catholic nun* (羅馬)天主教修女 –**Roman Catholicism** /,··'····· ·/ *n* [U]

ro·mance /rə'mæns; rəʊ'mæns/ *n* **1** [C] a story about a love affair 浪漫故事, 愛情故事: *She spends her time reading silly romances.* 她把時間花在閱讀傻兮兮的浪漫故事上。 **2** [U] the enjoyment of something new and exciting 傳奇色彩; 浪漫色彩: *the romance of life in the Wild West* 西部蠻荒生活的浪漫色彩 **3** [C] a love affair 風流韻事, 浪漫史: *a holiday romance* 假日韻事

Ro·ma·ni·an[1] /rə'meɪnɪən; ruː'meɪnɪən/ *adj* of or connected with Romania (關於)羅馬尼亞的

Romanian[2] *n* **1** [C] a person from Romania 羅馬尼亞人 **2** [U] the language of Romania 羅馬尼亞語

Roman nu·me·ral /,·· '···/ *n* any of a set of signs, originally used in ancient Rome for numbers, such as I, II, III, IV, V, etc. 羅馬數字〔如 I, II, III, IV, V 等〕 –compare 比較 ARABIC NUMERAL

ro·man·tic[1] /rə'mæntɪk; rəʊ'mæntɪk/ *adj* **1** showing strong feelings of love 浪漫的: *a very romantic love story* 一個很浪漫的愛情故事 **2** not practical; sometimes used to express disapproval 空想的, 不切實際的〔有時含貶義〕: *She has romantic ideas about becoming a famous actress.* 她幻想成為著名女演員。 –**romantically** /-klɪ; -kli/ *adv*

romantic[2] *n* a person with wild impractical ideas 浪漫的人; 不切實際的人: *He was a romantic who went off to the South Seas to paint pictures.* 他遠赴南海作畫, 是個浪漫的人。

ro·man·ti·cize /rə'mæntə,saɪz; rəʊ'mæntɪ,saɪz/ *v* **romanticized, romanticizing** (also 又作 **romanticise** *BrE* 〔英式〕) [I;T] to talk about things in a way which makes them seem more romantic or attractive than they really are 使浪漫化, 使具浪漫色彩: *This novel romanticizes life in the country.* 這部小說為鄉村生活加添了浪漫色彩。

romp /rɒmp; rɑmp/ *v* [I] to play noisily and roughly with a lot of running and jumping 蹦跳嬉戲; 歡鬧玩耍: *The children were romping about in the garden.* 孩子們在花園裡到處蹦跳嬉戲。 –**romp** *n*

romp·ers /'rɒmpəz; 'rɑmpəz/ *n* [pl] a one-piece garment for babies combining a top and short trousers 〔幼兒穿的〕連衫褲: *a pair*

of rompers 一套連褲童裝 –see 見 PAIR (USAGE 用法)

☆roof[1] /ruf; ruːf/ *n* **1** the outside covering on top of a building or vehicle 〔建築物或車輛的〕頂(部): *A tile has fallen off the roof.* 一塊瓦片從屋頂上掉了下來。 | *the roof of the car* 車頂 –see pictures on pages 209 and 729 見 209 頁和 729 頁彩圖 **2** the highest part of something 〔某物的〕最高部分: *the roof of his mouth* 他的上膛 | *like the roof of the world* 如同世界屋脊 **3 under someone's roof** in someone's home 在某人家裡: *It's impossible for her and her mother to live under the same roof.* 她和她的母親不可能住在一起。 **4 have a roof over your head** to have a place to live 有住處, 大家可歸 **5 hit the roof** *infml* to get extremely angry 《非正式》勃然大怒 **6 go through the roof** *infml* (of a price) to increase greatly 《非正式》〔價格〕飛漲

roof[2] *v* [T] to put a roof on a building 給〔建築物〕蓋瓦: *a house roofed with slates* 用石板瓦做屋頂的房子 –**roofed** *adj*

roof·ing /'rufɪŋ; 'ruːfɪŋ/ *n* [U] material for making or covering roofs 蓋屋頂的材料

roof rack /'·· ·/ *n BrE* a metal frame fixed on top of a car roof, for carrying things 《英式》車頂行李架

rook /rʊk; rʊk/ *n* **1** a large black European bird like a CROW 禿鼻烏鴉 **2** a piece in the game of CHESS 〔國際象棋中的〕車

☆☆room /rum; ruːm/ *n* **1** [C] a division of a building, with its own walls and floor 房間, 室: *The house has six rooms.* 這房子有六間房間。 **2** [U] enough space for a particular purpose 空間, 空地方: *There's no room to move.* 沒有活動的空間。 | *Move along and make room for me!* 坐過去一點, 給我騰個地方! | *A piano takes up a lot of room.* 一架鋼琴要佔很大的地方。

> □ USEFUL PATTERNS 有用句型
> there is room for something; there is room to do something

3 [U] a need for 需要...的地方: *There's plenty of room for improvement in his work.* 他的工作大有需要改進之處。 **4** a reason for 理由: *There's no room for doubt.* 毫無懷疑的理由。

room·mate /'rum,met; 'ruːm,meɪt/ *n* a person you share a room with 住在同室的人, 室友: *Bill and I are roommates.* 比爾和我是室友。

room ser·vice /'·· ,··/ *n* [U] a service provided by a hotel, by which food and drink are sent to a person's room 〔旅館中的〕客房用餐服務, 送食物到客房的服務: *Let's call room service and have tea sent up.* 我們給客房用餐服務部打個電話, 讓他們把茶送上來吧。

room·y /'rumɪ; 'ruːmi/ *adj* **roomier, roomiest** having plenty of space inside 寬敞的: *a roomy cupboard* 寬敞的食櫥

roost /rust; ruːst/ v [I] (of a bird) to sit and sleep for the night〔鳥〕棲息

roost·er /ˈrustə; ˈruːstəʳ/ n the usual American word for《美式》= a male chicken 雄雞

★root¹ /rut; ruːt/ n **1 roots** the part of a plant that grows down into the soil in search of food and water〔植物的〕根: *Pull the plant up by the roots.* 把這株植物連根拔起。 **2** the part of a tooth, hair, or organ that holds it to the rest of the body〔牙、毛髮或器官的〕根部 **3** the central part or cause of something 根源, 起源: *Let's get to the root of this matter.* 我們來探究一下這件事的根源吧。 **4 your roots** the place where you grew up 成長的地方, 老家 **5 put down roots** to settle in a place and feel you belong there 定居, 落地生根 **6 take root** (of plants and ideas) to become established and grow〔植物、思想〕生根, 扎根

root² v [I;T] to make or get roots (使)生根; (使)長出根來: *Try to root this plant in the garden.* 試試把這株植物栽在園子裡。 | *Do roses root easily?* 玫瑰容易生根嗎？

root about/around *phr* v [I] to search for something 搜尋；翻找: *Someone's been rooting about in my papers.* 有人老是亂翻我的文件。

root sthg ↔ **out** *phr* v [T] to get rid of something bad 根除, 肅清〔壞事物〕: *Scientists doubt whether malaria can ever be totally rooted out.* 科學家懷疑瘧疾是否能夠被完全根除。

root crop /ˈ··/ n a crop that is grown for its roots 塊根植物

root·ed /ˈrutɪd; ˈruːtᵻd/ adj [never before a noun 不能用於名詞前] unable to move or be moved 生根的, 根深蒂固的: *He stood rooted to the spot.* 他一動也不動地站在那裡。 | *a deeply rooted dislike of cats* 對貓根深蒂固的厭惡

root·less /ˈrutlɪs; ˈruːtləs/ adj without a home or any sense of belonging somewhere 無家可歸的; 無歸屬感的 **–rootlessness** n [U]

★rope¹ /rop; rəʊp/ n **1** [C;U] a strong thick cord made by twisting thinner pieces of string together 粗繩, 繩索 **2 know the ropes** to know from experience the rules and customs in a place or activity 曉得訣竅; 熟悉風土人情: *I've done this before so I know the ropes; shall I show you how to do it?* 我以前幹過這事, 所以知道竅門。我來告訴你怎麼幹好嗎？

rope² v **roped, roping** [T] to tie up with a rope〔用繩索〕捆, 綁, 紮: *The prisoners were roped together.* 犯人被綁在一起。

rope sbdy ↔ **in** *phr* v [T] *infml* to persuade someone to help《非正式》說服〔某人〕幫忙: *I've been roped in to help sell the tickets.* 我被拉去幫忙賣票。

rope sthg ↔ **off** *phr* v [T] to separate an area from the rest with ropes 用繩隔開[圈起]: *They've roped off one end of the pool.* 他們用繩子把池塘的一邊分隔開。

rope lad·der /ˈ· ，··/ n a ladder made of two long ropes connected by cross pieces of wood, rope, or metal 繩梯

ro·sa·ry /ˈrozərɪ; ˈrəʊzərɪ/ n **rosaries** a set of prayers or the string of small decorative balls used to count them in the ROMAN CATHOLIC religion〔羅馬天主教的〕玫瑰經;〔祈禱時數的〕念珠

★rose¹ /roz; rəʊz/ n **1** the sweet-smelling flower of a bush with prickly stems 薔薇科植物; 薔薇(花); 玫瑰(花) **2** a colour from pink to deep red 玫瑰(紅)色 **3 not a bed of roses** a phrase used to warn someone that something is not as pleasant or as easy as they think it will be 不是那麼稱心如意: *University life won't be a bed of roses, I can tell you!* 我可以告訴你, 大學生活可不是事事如意的!

rose² the past tense of RISE ☆ RISE 的過去式

ro·sé /ˈroze; ˈrəʊzeɪ/ n [U] light pink wine 玫瑰紅葡萄酒: *a glass of rosé* 一杯玫瑰紅葡萄酒

rose·ma·ry /ˈroz，mɛrɪ; ˈrəʊzmərɪ/ n [U] a bush with sweet-smelling leaves which are used in cooking 迷迭香〔其葉可用作調味品〕

ro·sette /roˈzɛt; rəʊˈzet/ n a BADGE made from narrow silk bands made up in the form of a rose 玫瑰花形飾物, 玫瑰花結: *The winner was given a red rosette in the riding competition.* 騎術比賽的優勝者獲得了一個紅玫瑰花結。

ros·ter /ˈrostə; ˈrostəʳ/ n a list of people who each take it in turn to do a certain job 值勤表, 勤務簿: *the duty roster* 值勤冊

ros·trum /ˈrostrəm; ˈrostrəm/ n **rostrums** or **rostra** /-trə; -trə/ a raised place for a public speaker or a music CONDUCTOR 演講台;〔樂隊的〕指揮台

ros·y /ˈrozɪ; ˈrəʊzɪ/ adj **rosier, rosiest 1** pink and healthy (used of skin colour) 紅潤的〔指膚色〕: *rosy cheeks* 紅潤的臉頰 **2** giving hope for the future〔未來〕充滿希望的; 樂觀的: *Things don't look very rosy at my firm; I'm looking for another job.* 我這家公司的前景不太妙, 我正在另找工作。 | *painting a rosy picture of the situation* 對形勢作樂觀的描繪

rot¹ /rot; rot/ v **-tt-** [I;T] to decay (使)腐爛, (使)腐朽: *The rain has rotted away the roof beams.* 雨水使屋樑腐爛了。 | *The vegetables were left to rot.* 蔬菜剩下來任其爛掉。

rot² n [U] **1** decay 腐爛, 腐朽: *an old hollow tree full of rot* 一棵中空而腐朽的老樹 | *dry rot* 乾腐, 乾朽 **2** BrE *infml* foolish remarks or ideas《英式, 非正式》蠢話; 傻主意: *Don't talk such rot!* 別講這種蠢話! **3 the rot is setting in** a situation is becoming bad 形勢在變壞

ro·ta /ˈrotə; ˈrəʊtə/ n BrE a list of people

who take turns to do a job〖英式〗勤務輪值表: *a rota for parents to drive children to school* 家長輪流開車送孩子上學 | *We can draw up a washing-up rota.* 我們可以擬一張洗碗碟的值勤表。

ro·ta·ry /'rotərɪ; 'rəutəri/ *adj* turning round a fixed point, like a wheel 旋轉的, 轉動的: *the rotary movement of the blades* 螺旋槳葉片的旋轉運動 | *a rotary lawn-mower* 旋轉割草機

ro·tate /'rotet; rəu'teɪt/ *v* **rotated, rotating** [I;T] **1** to turn round a fixed point (使)旋轉, (使)轉動: *The earth rotates once every 24 hours.* 地球每二十四小時自轉一圈。 | *You can rotate the wheel with your hand.* 你可以用手轉動輪子。 **2** to use in regular order 輪流, 交替: *We try to rotate the crops, wheat following beans and so on.* 我們試着輪種莊稼, 種豆類之後再種麥子等等。

ro·ta·tion /ro'teʃən; rəu'teɪʃən/ *n* **1** [U] the action of rotating 旋轉, 轉動; 交替: *the rotation of the earth* 地球的旋轉 | *The seasons follow each other in rotation.* 四季循環交替。 **2** [C] one complete turn round a fixed point〔旋轉的〕一圈: *The wheel made ten rotations a second.* 這輪子每秒鐘轉十圈。

ro·tis·ser·ie /ro'tɪsərɪ; rəu'tɪsəri/ *n* an apparatus for cooking meat by turning it over and over on a bar under direct heat 旋轉式烤肉架

ro·tor /'rotə; 'rəutə/ *n* a part of a machine that rotates 轉子, 旋轉部分: *helicopter rotor blades* 直升飛機的旋翼葉片

rot·ten /'rɑtn; 'rɒtn/ *adj* **1** gone bad 腐爛的, 變壞的: *rotten eggs* 壞了的雞蛋 | *a rotten apple* 爛蘋果 **2** *infml* bad or unpleasant〖非正式〗糟糕的; 不愉快的: *I feel rotten today.* 我今天覺得不舒服。 | *a rotten film* 差勁的電影 | *What a rotten thing to do to her!* 這樣對她真是太卑劣了!

ro·tund /ro'tʌnd; rəu'tʌnd/ *adj fml* fat and round〖正式〗圓圓胖胖的

rou·ble /'rubl; 'ruːbəl/ *n* a standard unit of money, or a note worth that amount, in Russia 盧布〖俄羅斯貨幣單位〗

rouge /ruʒ; ruːʒ/ *n* [U] a red substance used for colouring your cheeks 胭脂

★rough¹ /rʌf; rʌf/ *adj* **1** not even or smooth (used of a surface) 不平的, 不光滑的, 粗糙的〔指表面〕: *You need a car that will travel over rough ground.* 你需要一輛能在崎嶇不平的路面上行駛的汽車。 | *My skin feels rough and dry.* 我的皮膚摸起來又粗糙又乾。 **2** rather violent or rude 粗暴的; 粗魯的: *He is rough with his sister and hurts her.* 他對妹妹很粗暴, 還傷害她。 | *She spoke in a rough voice.* 她說話粗魯無禮。 **3** difficult and unpleasant 艱難的; 不愉快的: *Life has always been rough in this part of town.* 這部分城區的生活一直都很艱苦。 | *She's had a rough time since she lost her job.* 自從她失業以後, 就過得很艱苦。 **4** not yet finished or exact

粗略的; 不精確的: *This is the rough version of her speech.* 這是她的講辭的草稿。 | *I've only got a rough idea where it is.* 我只大概知道它在甚麼地方。 **5** having a lot of crime or violence (used of a place) 暴亂的〔指地方〕: *one of the roughest parts of town* 鎮上最混亂的地區之一 | *a rough school* 毫無秩序的學校 **6** stormy and violent (used of weather, the sea, or a sea journey) 有暴風雨的; 狂暴的〔指天氣、海洋或海上旅行〕: *a rough Channel crossing* 橫渡風浪很大的英吉利海峽 **7 be rough on someone** to be unfair on someone 對某人不公平: *It's a bit rough on him, having to do two people's work.* 他要做兩個人的工作, 這對他有點不公平。 **8 rough and ready** simple and without comfort 簡陋的, 不講究的: *rough and ready accommodation* 簡陋的住處 **–roughness** *n* [U]

rough² *n* [U] **1** uneven ground with long grass on a GOLF course〔高爾夫球場上起伏不平的〕深草區: *He lost his ball in the rough.* 他打球打到深草區, 找不到了。 **2 in rough** in an incomplete or inexact form 不完整地; 粗略地; 大致上: *Draw it in rough first.* 你先畫張草圖。 **3 rough-and-tumble** noisy fighting 混戰; 亂鬥: *the rough-and-tumble of politics* 政治上的混戰

rough³ *v* **rough it** *infml* to live in a simple way without any comforts〖非正式〗過簡單不很舒適的生活

rough *sthg* ↔ **out** *phr v* [T] to write or draw your first ideas about something 草擬〔某事物〕: *I've roughed out the conclusion for my article.* 我已草擬出文章的結論。

rough *sbdy* ↔ **up** *phr v* [T] to attack and hurt someone 攻擊, 傷害〔某人〕: *They roughed him up as a warning.* 他們打了他一頓作為警告。

rough⁴ *adv* **1** in a rather violent way 粗野地, 粗暴地: *Keep away from anyone who plays rough!* 遠離那些玩得粗野的人吧! **2 sleep rough** to sleep out of doors, without a bed 露宿: *He's been sleeping rough under the pier.* 他總是在橋墩下露宿。

rough·age /'rʌfɪdʒ; 'rʌfɪdʒ/ *n* [U] a substance contained in food substances that help your bowels to work〔食物中的〕纖維質〔幫助大便通暢〕: *Brown bread provides valuable roughage.* 黑麵包中含有有價值的纖維質。

rough·en /'rʌfən; 'rʌfən/ *v* [I;T] to make a surface uneven or rough (使)變得粗糙; (使)變得不平

rough·ly /'rʌflɪ; 'rʌfli/ *adv* **1** in a rather violent or rude manner 粗暴地, 粗野地, 粗魯地: *He pushed her roughly away.* 他粗暴地把她推開。 **2** about 大概, 大約: *There were roughly 200 people there.* 那兒大約有二百人。 | *Roughly speaking, I'd say 200.* 籠統來說有二百人。 **3** in a way which is not complete or exact 粗略地, 大致上: *Just do the calculations roughly.* 就大致上算一下吧。

rou·lette /ruˈlɛt; ruːˈlet/ *n* [U] a game of chance in which a small ball is spun round a moving wheel and falls into a hole marked with a number 輪盤賭

★**round¹** /raʊnd; raʊnd/ *adj* **1** curved in shape, like the shape of a circle, a ball, or the letter "c" 圓(形)的: *a large round plate* 大圓盤 | *small round pebbles* 小圓卵石 | *her round face* 她那張圓圓的臉 | *The earth is round, not flat.* 地球是圓的，不是扁平的。 **2** **round number, round figure** a complete number, usually one such as 10, 20, 30, etc. 整數〔如10、20、30等〕: *Let's make it 50 — that's a nice round number.* 我們把它算作五十吧——這個整數不錯。

★**round²** *adv, prep* **1** *adv, prep* moving or positioned in a circle 成圓圈(地); 圍繞(地); 旋轉(地): *The wheel was still spinning round.* 車輪仍在轉着。 | *The earth goes round the sun.* 地球圍繞着太陽轉。 | *He put his belt round his waist.* 他把皮帶繫在腰上。 | *We sat round the table.* 我們圍着桌子而坐。 | *People were standing round the fire.* 人們站在火堆周圍。 | *The children gathered round to listen to the story.* 孩子們圍成一圈聽故事。 | *a large tree measuring three metres round the trunk* 一棵樹幹周長三米的大樹 —see picture on page 764 見764頁彩圖 **2** **round and round** spinning many times in a circle 不斷旋轉地: *The wheels were spinning round and round.* 車輪一圈圈地轉着。 **3** *adv* so as to face the other way 朝反方向, 轉過來: *Turn the clock round so that I can see it.* 把鐘轉過來, 這樣我可以看到。 | *He swung round to look at me.* 他快速地轉過身來看我。 **4** *adv, prep* visiting all the parts of a place, or a lot of different places 到處; 在各處: *They spent a year just travelling round.* 他們花了一年時間, 就是到處旅行。 | *We're driving round France this summer.* 我們今年夏天將開車遊遍法國。 | *A guide showed us round the castle.* 一位導遊領我們在城堡裡四處看看。 **5** *prep* near a place 在…附近: *A lot of the people who live round here work in London.* 許多住在這裡附近的人在倫敦上班。 **6** *adv* to someone's house 到〔某人〕家: *He invited us round to his house for a meal.* 他請我們到他家裡吃飯。 | *Would you like to come round for a cup of tea?* 你想來我家喝杯茶嗎? **7** **round a corner** turning a corner or past a corner 繞過〔經過〕拐角: *He disappeared round the corner.* 他繞過拐角就不見了。 | *The post office is just round that corner.* 郵局就那那拐角處。 **8** **this way round, the other way round, the right way round, etc.** a phrase used to say which way something is facing or in which order things are placed 這個方向; 反方向; 正是這個方向〔用於表示某物的朝向或放置的次序〕: *You've got that hat on the wrong way round.* 你把那頂帽子戴反了。 | *Those two numbers should be the other way round.* 那兩個數字應該是倒

過來的。 **9** **round about: a** about 大約, 大概: *We've sold round about 200 cars this month.* 我們這個月賣掉了大約二百輛汽車。 | *It was round about five o'clock by the time we arrived.* 我們到達時大約是五點鐘。 **b** near a place 靠近: *Most of the people who live round about here have their own cars.* 大多數住在這裡附近的人都有自己的車。 | *We've met quite a few people from this village and from the villages round about.* 我們已碰到了好幾位從這村莊及鄰近村來的人。

★**round³** *n* **1** a set of events 一連串事件: *We're hoping for a new round of talks with the government.* 我們希望和政府進行新一輪會談。 | *Life seems to be a continual round of parties!* 生活似乎就是一連串的聚會! **2** a set of matches in a sports competition 〔體育比賽的〕一輪, 一回, 一局, 一場: *They were knocked out in the first round of the competition.* 他們在比賽的第一回合就被淘汰了。 **3** a regular journey that someone makes to a number of houses or offices 例行路線; 巡迴: *The milkman starts his round at five o'clock in the morning.* 送牛奶的人每天早上五點鐘開始挨家挨戶送牛奶。 | *The doctor's out on his rounds at the moment.* 醫生現在巡迴出診去了。 **4** **round of drinks** a drink for each person in a group 每人一份飲料: *Let me buy a round of drinks.* 我來給每人買一份飲料。 | *The next round's on me!* 下一回由我請客! **5** a complete game of GOLF 〔高爾夫球的〕一局 **6** one of the periods of fighting in a BOXING match 〔拳擊的〕一個回合 **7** a bullet or something else fired from a weapon 一發〔子彈或砲彈〕: *He fired a single round.* 他射出一發子彈。 | *I had only two rounds of ammunition left.* 我只剩兩發彈藥。

round⁴ *v* **round a corner** to go round a corner 繞過拐角: *She rounded the corner at 95 miles per hour.* 她以九十五英里的時速駛過轉彎處。

round sth ↔ **off** *phr v* [T] to end something in a suitable or satisfactory way 圓滿結束〔某事物〕: *Do you fancy a drink to round off the evening?* 你們想喝杯酒來圓滿結束這個晚會嗎?

round up *phr v* **1** [T **round** sth ↔ **up**] to change a figure to the next highest whole number 把〔數字〕調高為整數: *It's £2.99, so we'll round it up to £3.* 這是2.99英鎊, 那麼我們調為整數3英鎊吧。 **2** [T **round** sbdy ↔ **up**] to gather people together 把〔人〕聚攏起來: *We should be able to round up a few friends to help.* 我們應該可以找幾個朋友來幫忙的。

round·a·bout¹ /ˈraʊndəˌbaʊt; ˈraʊndəbaʊt/ *n BrE* 〔英式〕 **1** a central space at a road crossing, which cars must go round in a circle 環島〔道路交叉處的環行路〕; 環形交叉路口: *Turn left at the next roundabout.* 在下一個環形交叉路口向左轉。 —see picture on page 991 見991頁彩圖 **2** a machine on which children can ride round and round sitting on wooden animals, cars, etc. 旋轉木馬

roundabout² *adj* [only before a noun 只用於名詞前] not direct, and therefore taking longer 不直接的, 轉彎抹角的; 兜圈子的: *We arrived in Birmingham by a rather roundabout route.* 我們繞了個大圈子才到達伯明翰。| *She told me in a very roundabout way.* 她轉彎抹角地告訴我。

roun·ders /ˈraʊndəz; ˈraʊndəz/ *n* [U] a British ball game, usually played by children, in which a member of one team hits the ball and then runs round the edge of a square area 圓場棒球

round-eyed /ˌ·ˈ·◂/ *adj* with your eyes wide open, usually because you are surprised or excited 〔因驚奇或激動而〕圓睜着眼的

round-shoul·dered /ˌ·ˈ·◂/ *adj* with bent shoulders and a curved back 曲肩拱背的

round trip /ˌ·ˈ·/ *n* a journey to a place and back again 來回旅程

rouse /raʊz; raʊz/ *v* **roused, rousing 1** [I;T] to wake up, or to wake someone up 喚醒, 使醒來: *He's very hard to rouse in the morning.* 早上很難叫醒他。| *The noise roused me out of a deep sleep.* 這響聲把我從酣睡中吵醒。**2** [T] to make someone active and concerned 使〔某人〕活躍起來; 喚起: *John has roused the workers, and they are ready to strike.* 約翰已激發起工人準備罷工。| *roused from apathy* 使不要無動於衷 | *roused to action* 受激勵而行動起來

rous·ing /ˈraʊzɪŋ; ˈraʊzɪŋ/ *adj* exciting, and encouraging people to act 激動人心的; 鼓舞人〔行動〕的: *He made a rousing speech to his supporters.* 他向支持者作出了令人振奮的演講。

rout /raʊt; raʊt/ *v* [T] to defeat your enemies or opponents completely 徹底擊敗, 擊潰〔敵人或對手〕: *The invading army was soon routed.* 侵略軍很快被擊潰了。

rout sbdy ↔ **out** *phr v* [T] to find a person or thing, and often to make them move from where they are 把〔某人〕趕出去 —**rout** *n* [C;U]

route¹ /ruːt; ruːt/ *n* a way which you plan or follow from one place to another 路線, 路程: *What's the shortest route from London to Edinburgh?* 從倫敦到愛丁堡的最短路線怎麼走? | *It's not on the bus route.* 這地方不在公共汽車的路線上。

route² *v* **routed, routing** [T] to send people or things by a particular route 按特定路線發送: *All flights are being routed to Manchester.* 所有的航班都是往曼徹斯特的。

rou·tine¹ /ruːˈtiːn; ruːˈtiːn/ *n* **1** [C;U] a person's regular way of doing things 例行公事; 常規, 慣例: *I enjoy my daily routine.* 我喜歡自己的日常習慣。| *Babies have different routines.* 嬰兒的習慣各不相同。**2** [C] the performance of fixed steps, words, or actions in dance or theatre 固定舞步[動作]; 固定節目: *a dance routine* 一套舞步

rou·tine² /ˌruːˈtiːn; ˌruːˈtiːn◂/ *adj* **1** regular and usual 常規的, 例行的: *a routine medical examination* 例行的體格檢查 **2** not unusual or exciting 平凡的, 平淡的, 一般的: *a dull, routine job* 單調平淡的工作 —**routinely** *adv*

☆row¹ /rəʊ; rəʊ/ *v* **1** [I;T] to move a boat through the water using OARS 划船: *Shall we row to the island?* 我們划船去那個島好嗎? **2** [T] to carry people or things in this way 划船運載〔人或物〕: *He rowed his friends home.* 他划船送朋友回家。—**row** *n*: *They've gone for a row round the lake.* 他們去了划船遊湖。

row² /rəʊ; rəʊ/ *n* **1** a neat line of people or things side by side 〔人或物的〕一排, 一行, 一列: *I live in the row of houses beside the river.* 我住在河邊的一排房子裡。| *The only seats left were in the back row.* 剩下來的位子都是在後排的。**2 in a row** closely following each other 接連地; 連續地: *She's failed three exams in a row.* 她連續三次考試不及格。

row³ /raʊ; raʊ/ *n* [C] **1** a noisy quarrel 爭吵, 吵鬧: *My parents have had another row.* 我的父母又吵架了。**2** [sing] a noise 吵聲, 喧鬧聲: *Will you stop making such a row!* 你別再發出這樣的噪聲了, 好不好!

row⁴ /raʊ; raʊ/ *v* [I] to quarrel noisily 爭吵, 吵架: *They always row about money.* 他們老是為錢吵架。| *He never rowed with his colleagues.* 他從來不和同事爭吵。

row·dy /ˈraʊdi; ˈraʊdi/ *adj* **rowdier, rowdiest** noisy and rough 吵鬧的; 粗暴的: *Their rowdy behaviour frightened me.* 他們粗暴喧鬧的行為把我嚇壞了。—**rowdily** *adv* —**rowdiness** *n* [U]

row house /ˈrəʊ haʊs; ˈrəʊ haʊs/ *n* the usual American word for 〖美式〗= TERRACED HOUSE

row·ing boat /ˈrəʊɪŋ bəʊt; ˈrəʊɪŋ ˌbəʊt/ *n* (also 又作 **rowboat** /ˈrəʊbɒt; ˈrəʊbəʊt/ *AmE* 〖美式〗) a small boat that is moved through the water using OARS 划艇, 用槳划的小船 —see picture on page 991 見 991 頁彩圖

☆☆roy·al /ˈrɔɪəl; ˈrɔɪəl/ *adj* **1** connected with a king or queen or their family 國王的; 女王的; 王室的: *Some of the royal palaces are open to the public.* 皇宮內有些地方是向公眾開放的。| *the Royal Navy* 皇家海軍 **2 royal blue** a bright purplish-blue colour 品藍 —see picture on page 243 見 243 頁彩圖 —**royally** *adv*

Royal High·ness /ˌ·· ˈ··/ *n* a title used when you are speaking to or about a prince or princess 殿下〔用於當面稱呼或間接提到王子或公主〕: *Thank you, Your Royal Highness.* 謝謝, 殿下。| *We hope that His Royal Highness, Prince Charles, will attend.* 我們希望查爾斯王子殿下能夠光臨。

roy·al·ist /ˈrɔɪəlɪst; ˈrɔɪəlᵻst/ *n* someone who supports a king or queen, or believes that a country should be ruled by one 保皇主義者; 保皇派 —**royalist** *adj*: *He holds roy-*

alist views. 他持保皇主義者的觀點。

roy·al·ty /'rɔɪəltɪ; 'rɔɪəltɪ/ *n* **royalties 1** [U] royal power and rank 王權; 王位 **2** [+sing/pl verb] people of the royal family 王族; 皇室成員: *The flag is only raised when royalty is present.* 這面旗幟只在王室成員在場的時候才升起。 **3 royalties** [pl] a payment made to people like writers and inventors as part of the profit from sales 版稅: *All the royalties from his books were given to charity.* 他寫的書的所有版稅都捐給了慈善團體。

rpm /,ɑr pi 'em; ,ɑː piː 'em/ a measure of engine speed; an abbreviation for **revolutions per minute** 〔縮〕〔發動機的〕每分鐘轉數, 轉/分

RSVP /,ɑr ɛs vi 'pi; ,ɑːr es viː 'piː/ please reply; an abbreviation for the French phrase **répondez s'il vous plaît**, which is written on invitations 〔縮〕〔寫於請柬上的話〕請賜覆

rub¹ /rʌb; rʌb/ *v* **-bb- 1** [T] to press on a surface while you move something like your hand backwards and forwards 擦; 摩擦; 按摩: *Can you rub my back?* 你能按摩一下我的背部嗎? | *He rubbed his hands together with delight.* 他高興地揉搓着雙手。 **2** [I] to press against another surface while moving backwards and forwards 〔在另一表面上〕相互磨擦: *This tyre must be rubbing against something.* 這輪胎一定擦着甚麼東西了。 | *My new shoes have been rubbing on my heel.* 我的新鞋磨腳。 **3 rub salt into the wound** to make someone's suffering or annoyance even worse 加深〔某人的〕痛苦 **4 rub someone's nose in something** to make someone remember a mistake they have made 揭某人的舊瘡疤; 觸某人痛處 **5 rub shoulders with someone** to meet someone, especially a well-known person 和某人〔尤指知名人士〕來往 **6 rub someone up the wrong way** to annoy someone by the way you talk or act with them 〔因為說話或行為方式〕惹惱某人, 觸犯某人

rub sbdy/sthg ↔ **down** *phr v* [T] **1** to dry a person or thing 擦乾: *Rub yourself down with this towel.* 用這塊毛巾把你身上的汗擦乾。 **2** to make something smooth by rubbing it 把〔某物〕擦平滑: *Rub the door down before you paint it.* 在你塗油漆之前先要把門打磨光滑。

rub sthg ↔ **in** *phr v* [T] **1** to make a liquid go into a surface by rubbing 把〔液體〕擦入: *Rub the polish well in.* 把上光劑完全擦進去。 **2** *infml* 〔非正式〕**rub it in** to keep talking about something that another person wants to forget 不斷提起某人的不快事; 觸動某人的痛處: *"It was you who made the mistake." "I know; don't rub it in!"* "是你犯了這個錯誤。" "我知道, 別多提了。"

rub off *phr v* **1** [I;T] to come off a surface or to remove something from a surface by rubbing (被)擦掉, (被)抹掉: *The paint marks will rub off quite easily.* 油漆的污跡很容易擦去。 **2** [I] *infml* to influence someone 〔非正式〕影響〔某人〕: *I hope that some of her good humour rubs off on him.* 我希望她身上的一些幽默會對他產生影響。

rub sthg ↔ **on** *phr v* [T] to spread a liquid over a surface by rubbing 把〔液體〕擦開

rub sthg ↔ **out** *phr v* [I;T] *BrE* to disappear or to remove something, especially writing, often with a piece of rubber 〔英式〕〔尤指用橡皮〕把…擦掉: *Rub the first sentence out and start again.* 把第一句擦掉, 重新開始。 | *Will it rub out?* 要把它擦掉嗎?

rub sthg ↔ **up** *phr v* [T] to polish something by rubbing it 擦亮, 打磨光滑

rub² *n* [sing] an act of rubbing 擦; 磨擦: *Give the table a good rub with this polish.* 用這上光劑把桌子好好擦一擦。

rub·ber /'rʌbə; 'rʌbəʳ/ *n* **1** [U] a strong elastic substance, made either from the juice of a tropical tree or chemically, which can keep out water 橡膠; 合成橡膠; 橡皮: *a rubber ball* 橡皮球 | *Tyres are made of rubber.* 輪胎是用橡膠做的。 | *rubber gloves* 橡膠手套 **2** [C] a piece of this substance, which is used to remove pencil marks 橡皮擦 **3** a match in the card game of bridge 橋牌比賽

rubber band /,·· '·/ *n* a thin circular piece of rubber which is used to keep things together 橡皮筋[圈]: *Have you got a rubber band to put round these documents?* 你有沒有用橡皮筋紮一下這些文件?

rub·ber·y /'rʌbərɪ; 'rʌbəri/ *adj* elastic like rubber and rather hard 橡皮般的; 堅韌的: *This meat's a bit rubbery!* 這肉有點兒老了!

rub·bish /'rʌbɪʃ; 'rʌbɪʃ/ *n* [U] **1** waste material to be thrown away 垃圾, 廢物: *We can burn most of this rubbish.* 我們可以把這大部分垃圾燒掉。 | *a rubbish bin* 廢物箱 **2** nonsense 胡說八道; 廢話; 無意義的東西: *He's talking rubbish.* 他在說廢話。 | *Rubbish! He's never even been as far as France!* 胡說八道! 他連法國都沒有去過呢!

rub·bish·y /'rʌbɪʃɪ; 'rʌbɪʃi/ *adj infml* silly and worthless 〔非正式〕無聊的; 無價值的: *a rubbishy love story* 不值一看的愛情故事

rub·ble /'rʌbl; 'rʌbəl/ *n* [U] broken stones, bricks or other materials 碎石, 碎磚, 瓦礫: *The bomb reduced her house to a heap of rubble.* 炸彈把她的家夷為一堆瓦礫。

ru·bel·la /ru'belə; ruː'belə/ *n* [U] *tech* the medical word for GERMAN MEASLES 〔術語〕風疹; 德國麻疹

ru·by /'rubɪ; 'ruːbi/ *n* **rubies 1** [C] a dark red precious stone 紅寶石 **2** [U] the colour of this stone 紅寶石色, 深紅色 **–ruby** *adj*

ruck·sack /'rʌk,sæk; 'rʌksæk/ *n* a bag that you carry on your back, especially when you are climbing or walking 〔尤指登山或徒步旅行時用的〕背包, 背囊

rud·der /'rʌdə; 'rʌdəʳ/ *n* a wooden or metal blade at the back of a ship or aircraft that moves from side to side to control the direction 〔船的〕舵;〔飛機的〕方向舵

rud·dy /ˈrʌdɪ; ˈrʌdi/ *adj* **ruddier, ruddiest 1** pink and healthy-looking (used of a person's face) 紅潤的〔指臉色〕 **2** red 紅色的 – **ruddiness** *n* [U]

rude /rud; ruːd/ *adj* **1** not at all polite (of a person or behaviour) 粗魯〔野〕的; 無禮的 〔指人或行為〕: *It's rude to say you don't like the food.* 你説不喜歡這種食物是不禮貌的。| *Don't be so rude to your father.* 不要對你的父親這麼無禮。**2** improper and usually concerned with sex 粗俗的; 下流的: *a rude story* 粗俗的故事 **3** [only before a noun 只用於名詞前] sudden and violent 突然的; 猛烈的; 狂暴的: *a rude shock* 突如其來的震驚 | *a rude awakening* 醒悟; 突然明白 **4 rude health** excellent health 十分健壯 –**rudeness** *n* [U] – **rudely** *adv*

ru·di·men·ta·ry /ˌrudəˈmɛntərɪ; ˌruːdɪˈmentəri/ *adj* at the simplest level and often not good enough 基本的, 初步的, 粗淺的: *I have only the most rudimentary knowledge of chemistry.* 我只有最粗淺的化學知識。| *That's a rudimentary mistake.* 那是個基本錯誤。

ru·di·ments /ˈrudəmənts; ˈruːdɪmənts/ *n* [pl] **the rudiments of** the simplest parts of (used of a subject) 基礎〔部分〕;〔指科目的〕入門, 初步: *We're just trying to learn the rudiments of Italian grammar.* 我們只是在試着學習意大利語的基本語法。

rue·ful /ˈrufəl; ˈruːfəl/ *adj* feeling or showing that you are sorry about something but that you accept it 悔恨的, 後悔的: *a rueful smile* 苦笑 –**ruefully** *adv*

ruff /rʌf; rʌf/ *n* **1** a kind of stiff white collar with folds in it which was worn in Europe in the 16th century 〔十六世紀歐洲人穿的〕白色環狀硬皺領 **2** a ring of fur or feathers round the neck of an animal or bird 〔鳥獸頸部的〕環狀羽毛; 頸毛

ruf·fi·an /ˈrʌfɪən; ˈrʌfiən/ *n old fash* a bad man who is often criminal and violent 〔老式〕流氓, 暴徒, 惡棍: *He was attacked by a gang of ruffians.* 他遭到一夥暴徒的襲擊。

ruf·fle¹ /ˈrʌfl; ˈrʌfəl/ *v* **ruffled, ruffling 1** [T] to make uneven and untidy something that was neat and smooth 弄皺, 弄亂〔某物〕: *She ruffled his hair affectionately.* 她親切地撥弄他的頭髮。| *The bird ruffled up its feathers.* 鳥豎起了羽毛。**2** to annoy someone 惹惱, 打擾〔某人〕: *Don't get so ruffled.* 別生那麼大的氣。

ruffle² *n* a band of cloth sewn in folds round the neck or wrists of a garment as decoration 〔服裝的〕褶邊, 飾邊

rug /rʌg; rʌg/ *n* **1** a thick floor mat, often made of wool 小地毯 –see picture on page 730 見 730 頁彩圖 **2** a thick woollen covering which people use to keep themselves warm when travelling 〔旅行用的〕厚毛毯: *a tartan travel rug* 格子花呢旅行毛毯

*rug·by /ˈrʌgbɪ; ˈrʌgbi/ *n* (also 又作 **rugby football** /ˌ·· ˈ··/ *infml* 〔非正式〕**rugger** /ˈrʌgə; ˈrʌgəʳ/) [U] a type of ball game played by two teams; players win points by carrying or kicking an OVAL shaped ball to the opponents' end of the field 橄欖球(運動) –see picture on page 957 見 957 頁彩圖

rug·ged /ˈrʌgɪd; ˈrʌgɪd/ *adj* **1** rough and rocky 粗糙的; 多岩石的; 崎嶇的: *rugged hills* 崎嶇不平的山丘 **2** strongly built 堅固的; 結實的: *his rugged good looks* 他粗獷而英俊的面容 | *a rugged vehicle* 堅固耐用的車輛 – **ruggedly** *adv* –**ruggedness** *n* [U]

ru·in¹ /ˈruɪn; ˈruːɪn/ *n* **1** [U] the cause or state of destruction and decay 禍根; 毀滅; 滅亡; 崩潰: *The temple has fallen into ruin.* 這座廟宇已經破敗不堪。| *Drink was your father's ruin!* 酗酒毀了你的父親! **2** [C] a building that has been badly damaged or destroyed 倒塌的建築物; 廢墟: *We walked round the castle ruins.* 我們在城堡的廢墟中四處走動。**3 in ruins** badly damaged or destroyed 毀壞了的: *Invaders left the city in ruins.* 侵略者把這座城市夷為廢墟。| *By the end of her speech, her career was in ruins.* 到了她演講的尾聲, 她的事業亦已前途盡毀。

ruin² *v* [T] **1** to spoil or completely destroy a person or thing 〔完全地〕毀滅, 毀掉: *His complaints ruined the evening for everyone.* 他的牢騷搞糟了大家的這個晚上。**2** to cause someone to lose all their money 使〔某人〕傾家蕩產: *If I lose my lawsuit, the costs will ruin me.* 如果我輸了官司, 這些費用會使我傾家蕩產。–**ruined** *adj*: *a ruined city* 傾毀的城市

ru·in·ous /ˈruɪnəs; ˈruːɪnəs/ *adj* causing destruction or total loss of money 毀滅性的; 破壞性的; 導致破產的: *The cost of rebuilding will be ruinous.* 重新修建的費用會昂貴到使你破產的。–**ruinously** *adv*: *ruinously expensive* 貴得能叫人破產的, 極其昂貴的

*rule¹ /rul; ruːl/ *n* **1** [C] an instruction or principle which tells you what you must or must not do 規章; 章程; 規則: *It's against the rules to pick up the ball.* 用手撿球是違反規則的。| *Anyone caught breaking the rules will be punished.* 違反規則而被抓住的人要受懲罰。**2** [C] a statement of the usual way of doing something 習慣; 慣例; 規律: *the rules of grammar* 語法規則 **3 as a rule, as a general rule** usually 通常, 一般説來: *He works hard as a rule.* 他通常努力工作。**4 the rule** the way things usually are 慣例: *Companies providing childcare facilities are still the exception rather than the rule.* 提供託兒設施的公司仍然是例外, 不常見的。**5 rule of thumb** a rough guide to behaviour 粗略的估算: *As a rule of thumb, you should expect to pay one third of your salary on rent.* 按粗略的估算, 你預計要用三分之一的薪水交房租。**6** [U] government or control 統治; 管轄: *The*

R

country is now under foreign rule. 這個國家目前在外國人的統治下。| *the days of British rule* 英國統治的時代 **7** [C] a ruler for measuring lengths 尺: *a two foot rule* 兩英尺長的尺

rule² v **ruled, ruling 1** [I;T] to govern or have power over an area or people 統治, 管轄, 控制: *The first king ruled for 30 years.* 第一個國王統治了三十年。**2 rule the roost** to control a group of people 當家作主: *It's my mother who rules the roost at home.* 我媽媽才是在家裡當家作主的。**3** [T; + that] to make an official and often legal decision 裁決, 裁定: *The judge ruled that he should be allowed to see his children.* 法官裁定他可以去看自己的孩子。| *The committee ruled her actions unacceptable.* 委員會裁定她的行為無法讓人接受。**4** to influence or control a person, their feelings or actions 影響, 支配〔人、感情或行為〕: *Don't let yourself be ruled by your personal feelings towards him.* 別讓你對他的個人感情左右你自己。**5** [T] to draw a straight line with the help of something like a ruler〔用尺等〕劃線

rule sbdy/sthg ⟷ **out** *phr v* to dismiss something without considering it carefully〔不經過仔細考慮〕把〔某事物〕排除: *We can't rule out the possibility that he'll come.* 我們不能排除他會來的可能性。

rul·er /ˈruːlə; ˈruːləʳ/ n **1** a person who rules an area or people 統治者; 管轄者 **2** a long, flat, narrow piece of a hard material such as plastic, which has straight edges and is marked with inches or centimetres. It is used for measuring things or for drawing straight lines 尺, 直尺: *a 12-inch ruler* 十二英寸長的尺

rul·ing¹ /ˈruːlɪŋ; ˈruːlɪŋ/ n an official and usually legal decision 裁決, 裁定, 判決: *The latest EEC ruling will be unpopular with British farmers.* 歐洲共同體最近的裁決不會受到英國農民的歡迎。| *the court's ruling on the matter* 法庭對此事的判決 –compare 比較 RULE

ruling² *adj* [only before a noun 只用於名詞前] most powerful 統治的, 支配的: *It was a popular revolt against the ruling classes.* 這次反抗統治階級的起義得到了普遍支持。| *His garden is his ruling passion.* 他生活中最大的樂趣。

rum /rʌm; rʌm/ n [U] a strong alcoholic drink 朗姆酒

rum·ble /ˈrʌmbl; ˈrʌmbəl/ v **rumbled, rumbling 1** [I] to make a deep continuous rolling sound, often while moving 發出隆隆〔轆轆〕聲: *The thunder rumbled in the distance.* 遠處雷聲隆隆。| *The heavy cart rumbled through the village streets.* 笨重的馬車轆轆地在村鎮的街道上行駛。**2** *infml* to discover the truth about someone or something which was being hidden〔非正式〕察覺, 識破, 發現: *We've been rumbled; some-*

one must have told the police. 我們被發現了, 一定有人向警方告了密。–**rumble** n

ru·mi·nate /ˈruːmə.neɪt; ˈruːmɪ.neɪt/ v **ruminated, ruminating** [I] to think carefully about something 仔細考慮: *Let me ruminate over this plan of yours.* 讓我仔細思考一下你的這項計劃。–**rumination** /ˌruːməˈneɪʃən; ˌruːmɪˈneɪʃən/ n [U]

rum·mage /ˈrʌmɪdʒ; ˈrʌmɪdʒ/ v **rummaged, rummaging** (also 又作 **rummage around**) [I] to move things around while you are trying to find something 翻找, 把東西亂翻來尋找: *Who's been rummaging through my papers?* 誰亂翻我的文件來了？| *Take one, don't just rummage about!* 拿一個, 別光翻來找去！–**rummage** n

rum·my /ˈrʌmɪ; ˈrʌmɪ/ n [U] a type of simple card game 拉米紙牌戲

ru·mour /ˈruːmə; ˈruːməʳ/ n (**rumor** *AmE*【美式】) [C;U] something that is talked about but may not be true 謠言, 謠傳, 傳聞: *Rumour has it that he's found a new job at last.* 傳說他終於找到了一份新工作。| *I heard a strange rumour about Jean at the club last night.* 昨晚我在俱樂部聽到關於瓊的奇怪傳聞。| *You mustn't spread rumours.* 你不得散佈謠言。| *There are rumours of a spring election.* 謠傳要進行春季大選。

ru·moured /ˈruːməd; ˈruːməd/ v (**rumored** *AmE*【美式】) be rumoured to be talked about, although it may not be true 謠傳的, 傳聞的: *It's rumoured that Jean's getting married.* 傳聞瓊就要結婚了。| *The company is rumoured to be in serious difficulties.* 據說這家公司陷入了困境。

rump /rʌmp; rʌmp/ n the back part of an animal above the legs〔動物的〕臀部, 尾部: *rump steak* 臀肉牛排

rum·ple /ˈrʌmpl; ˈrʌmpəl/ v **rumpled, rumpling** [T] to make something like hair or clothes untidy 把〔某物〕弄皺; 使凌亂: *rumpled bedsheets* 亂皺皺的牀單

rum·pus /ˈrʌmpəs; ˈrʌmpəs/ n *infml*【非正式】**kick up a rumpus** to make a lot of noise, or a noisy disagreement〔非正式〕引起一片吵鬧; 引起口角

★★ **run¹** /rʌn; rʌn/ v **ran** /ræn; ræn/, **run, running 1** [I;T] to move along on your legs at a speed that is faster than walking 跑, 奔跑: *The people ran to meet him.* 那些人跑着去見他。| *She came running downstairs.* 她跑下樓來。| *The dog ran after a rabbit.* 那狗追着一隻兔子。| *He always runs three or four miles before breakfast.* 他在早餐前總要跑上三四英里。–see picture on page 992 見 992 頁彩圖 **2** [T; +adv/prep] to make something move quickly over or through something 使〔某物〕快速移動: *He ran his hand over the polished wood.* 他用手抹一抹那光滑的木頭。| *She ran her fingers through her hair.* 她用手指攏了攏頭髮。**3** [I; +adv/prep] to pass or go somewhere 經過, 延伸到〔某處〕: *The road runs along the river bank.* 這條路沿着河岸延伸。 | *The stream runs along the bottom of that field.* 溪流順着那塊田流到盡頭。 | *There were tears running down her face.* 淚水順着她的臉頰流下。 **4** [I] (of a bus or train) to travel somewhere at an arranged time 〔公共汽車或火車〕定時來往行駛: *That train doesn't run on a Sunday.* 那班列車星期天停駛。 **5** [T; +adv/prep] to take someone somewhere in a car 〔用車〕載送: *I'll run you home if you like.* 如果你願意的話, 我開車送你回家。 **6** [I] (of a machine) to work or be in operation 〔機器〕開動, 運轉: *Don't touch the engine while it's running.* 發動機運轉的時候不要去碰它。 | *Most cars run on petrol.* 大多數汽車靠汽油驅動。 **7** [T] to operate something or make it work 使運轉; 操作: *Can you just run the projector to check that it's working?* 你能不能開動一下放映機, 看看它是否運轉? | *We don't have enough money to run the hospital properly.* 我們沒有足夠的錢來維持這家醫院的正常運作。 | *I've got to run a couple of computer programs this afternoon.* 我今天下午得使幾個電腦程序運行。 **8** [T] to fill a bath with water 把〔浴盆〕放滿水: *I'm just running my bath.* 我正在放水洗澡。 | *Shall I run some water into the bath for you?* 要我給你在澡盆裡放些水嗎? **9 the tap is running** = water is coming out of the TAP 水龍頭開了 **10 your nose is running** = liquid is coming out of your nose 你在流鼻涕 **11 a colour runs** = a colour on a piece of clothing spreads when it gets wet 〔織物上的顏色〕滲色: *Wash that shirt in cold water otherwise the colours will run.* 用冷水洗那件襯衫, 否則顏色會掉的。 **12** [I] to be one of the people trying to be elected in an election (參加)競選: *He has decided not to run for president again.* 他已決定不再競選總統。 **13** [I] to last or continue happening for a particular period of time 持續, 繼續〔一段時間〕: *The play ran for 18 months.* 這齣戲連演了十八個月。 | *My car insurance has two months to run.* 我的汽車的保險期還有兩個月。 **14** [T] to control or be in charge of something 管理; 經營: *They run a small export business.* 他們經營一家小型出口公司。 | *We run all sorts of courses at the college.* 我們在大學裡開設了各種各樣的課程。 **15** [T] to print a story or an article 登出; 刊出: *The magazine is running a series of features on European life.* 這本雜誌正在刊登一系列有關歐洲生活的特寫。 **16 be running at** to be at a particular level 在某個水平上: *Inflation is now running at 11%.* 通貨膨脹率現在是百分之十一。 **17 be running late** to be taking longer than you had planned to do a number of things 比計劃的晚: *We were due to finish at lunch time, but we're running a bit late.* 我們應該在午飯時完工的, 但現在稍微晚了一點。 **18 run dry** (of a

well) to no longer contain any water 〔井〕乾涸 **19 run in the family** to be present in several members of a family 為家庭成員所共有: *Musical ability runs in the family.* 家中人人都有音樂天賦。 **20 run low on something** to no longer have very much of something 不再有很多的某物: *We're running a bit low on coffee.* 我們的咖啡不太多了。 **21 run short** to become less than enough 不足; 短缺: *Time is running short.* 時間很緊迫了。 **22 run short of something** to no longer have enough of something 某物不夠: *We're running short of oil.* 我們的油快用完了。

run along *phr v* [I] used when you are telling a child to go away and leave you alone 走開; 離開: *Run along and play now.* 現在走開, 去玩玩吧。

run away *phr v* [I] **1** to escape from someone or something 逃跑: *He was sent to boarding school but he ran away.* 他被送往寄宿學校, 但他逃跑了。 | *children who run away* **from** *home* 離家出走的孩子 | *He ran away with all my savings.* 他偷走了我所有的積蓄逃跑了。 **2** to go away with someone of the opposite sex 和〔異性〕私奔: *She ran away* **with** *her music teacher.* 她和她的音樂老師私奔了。

run away with sbdy *phr v* [T] to make someone lose control of themselves 使〔某人〕失去控制: *Don't let your temper run away with you.* 不要亂發脾氣。

run down *phr v* **1** [T **run** sbdy ↔ **down**] to knock down and hurt a person with a car or other vehicle 〔用汽車或其他車輛〕撞倒, 撞傷: *Don't run into the road — you'll get run down.* 別跑到馬路上去——你會被車撞倒的。 **2** [T **run** sbdy/sthg ↔ **down**] to talk about someone or something in a way that shows that you do not like or respect them 説〔某人或某事物的〕壞話, 誹謗, 詆毀: *He shouldn't run me down in public like that.* 他不該那樣當眾說我的壞話。 **3** [T **run** sthg ↔ **down**] to reduce the size or importance of something 減少; 降低; 縮減: *The coal industry is gradually being run down.* 煤礦工業正在逐漸縮減規模。

run in *phr v* **1** [T **run** sthg ↔ **in**] to use an engine gently for a while before you use it fully 使〔發動機〕試轉 **2** [T **run** sbdy ↔ **in**] *infml* to catch someone who has done something against the law 〔非正式〕拘留, 逮捕〔犯法者〕: *He was run in for possessing illegal drugs.* 他因非法藏有毒品而被捕。

run into *phr v* **1** [T **run into** sbdy/sthg] to hit someone or something with the car or other vehicle that you are driving 使〔車〕撞在〔某人或某物〕上: *I nearly ran into a lamp-post.* 我差點把車撞到路燈柱上。 **2** [T **run into** sthg] to add up to a particular amount (累計) 達到: *Her debts now ran into thousands of pounds.* 她的債務現在達到數千

英鎊。**3** [T **run into** sbdy] to meet someone by chance 偶遇，邂逅〔某人〕**4** [T **run into** sthg] to meet a problem or difficulty 遭遇〔困難或問題〕，陷於〔困境〕: *We ran into problems with the authorities.* 我們和當局之間遇到了一些問題。

run off *phr v* **1** [I] to go away with someone of the opposite sex 和〔異性〕私奔: *She's run off with the man next door.* 她和隔壁的男人私奔了。**2** [T **run** sthg ↔ **off**] to make a copy of a piece of writing on a special copying machine 複印出〔某物〕: *I'll run off a few copies for you.* 我會給你複印幾份副本的。

run out *phr v* **1** [I] to come to an end or no longer be useful or acceptable 完成；結束；期滿；耗盡: *Time is running out.* 時間剩下不多了。| *My car insurance runs out tomorrow — I must renew it.* 我的汽車保險明天到期——我得重新辦手續。**2** to no longer have enough of something 用完，沒有了: *I've run out of petrol.* 我的汽油已用完了。

run sbdy ↔ **over** *phr v* [T] to hit someone and hurt them with the car or other vehicle that you are driving 〔用車輛〕撞傷〔某人〕: *Mind you don't run that child over.* 小心別撞倒那個孩子。

run through sthg *phr v* [T] **1** to repeat something for practice 反覆練習；排練: *Let's run through the first scene again.* 我們把第一場再排練一遍。**2** to read something quickly 匆匆閱讀，瀏覽: *I'll just run through this list of figures.* 我很快地把這個數目表看一遍就可以了。**3** to be present in all the parts of something 貫穿於，普遍存在於〔某事物〕: *the prejudices that run through our society* 普遍存在於我們社會中的偏見

run sthg ↔ **up** *phr v* [T] **1** to cause bills or debts to grow 積欠〔賬單或債務〕: *I've run up debts of over £5,000.* 我已積欠了五千多英鎊的債務。**2** to raise a flag 升〔旗〕

run² *n* **1** an act of running 跑，奔跑: *I always go for a run before breakfast.* 我總是在早飯前跑步。| *a five-mile run* 五英里賽跑 **2** a journey by car or train 〔坐汽車或火車的〕旅行，旅程: *Let's go for a run in the car.* 我們開車兜兜風吧。| *We had quite a good run — it only took us 50 minutes.* 我們這次車程才花了五十分鐘，玩得真開心。**3** a period of time during which a play or film is shown every day 〔戲或影片的〕連續演出: *The play had a run of three months.* 這齣戲連演了三個月。**4** **a run of** a group of similar events coming one after another 一連串〔事件〕: *I've had a run of bad luck recently.* 我最近碰到一連串倒霉的事。**5** **a run on** a lot of buying of something 暢銷；爭購: *There's always a run on swimwear as soon as the weather warms up.* 天氣一暖和起來，游泳衣就總是很暢銷。**6** an enclosed area where animals are kept 〔禽畜的〕飼養場；放牧場: *a chicken run* 養雞場 **7** a point in a game of cricket or BASE-

BALL 〔板球或棒球的〕得分；一分 **8 a good run for your money** *infml* good results for the amount of effort that you have made or the amount of money that you have spent 〔非正式〕〔付出的努力或花的錢得到的〕良好收益；滿足 **9 in the long run** in the end, over a longer period of time 終究，最終；長遠來看: *Stone is more expensive, but in the long run it's better value.* 寶石雖然比較貴，但從長遠看它較有價值。**10 make a run for it** to try to escape by running away suddenly 試圖逃走 **11 on the run** trying to escape or hide from the police 躲藏，逃避〔警察的追捕〕: *He's been on the run for nearly two months.* 他逃避警方的追緝已差不多有兩個月了。**12 the run of** the freedom to use a place and go anywhere in a place 出入自由；使用〔某地的〕自由: *The children had the run of the house and garden.* 孩子們在這幢房子及花園裡玩耍的自由。

run·a·way /ˈrʌnəˌweɪ; ˈrʌnəweɪ/ *adj* [only before a noun 只用於名詞前] **1** out of control 失去控制的: *a runaway horse* 脫韁的馬 | *runaway inflation* 失控的通貨膨脹 **2** who has left the place where they are supposed to be 逃跑的: *a runaway child* 一個離家出走的孩子 **–run·away** *n*

run-down¹ /ˈ··/ *n* a detailed report of events 〔事件的〕詳細報告: *He gave me a run-down on everything that had happened while I was away.* 他交給我一份關於我外出期間所發生事情的詳細報告。

run-down² /ˌ· ˈ·◂/ *adj* **1** tired and rather ill 精疲力盡的，衰弱的: *When you feel run-down, it's time for a holiday!* 當你感到疲乏，就是時候放假了！**2** in bad condition 破舊的: *We stayed in an old run-down hotel.* 我們住在一家又破又舊的旅館裡。

rung¹ /rʌŋ; rʌŋ/ *n* **1** one of the cross-bars that form the steps of a ladder 梯子的橫檔，梯級 **2** a level, especially of people at work 〔尤指工作中的〕地位，等級: *I started on the bottom rung and now I run the company.* 我從底層做起，現在管理這家公司。

rung² *the past participle of* RING ☆ RING 的過去分詞

run·ner /ˈrʌnə; ˈrʌnər/ *n* **1** a person who runs, especially for sport or exercise 奔跑的人；〔尤指〕參加賽跑的人: *She's a long-distance runner.* 她是一名長跑運動員。**2** a person who carries something illegal, such as guns or drugs, from one country to another 走私者 **3** thin pieces of a material like wood which are fixed to the bottom of something and help it move easily 〔某物底部的〕滑行裝置: *sledge runners* 雪橇的滑板

runner bean /ˌ·· ˈ·/ *n* a long green bean from a climbing plant 紅花菜豆

runner-up /ˌ·· ˈ·/ *n* **runners-up** the person or team that wins second place in a race or competition 〔比賽中的〕第二名，亞軍

run·ning¹ /ˈrʌnɪŋ; ˈrʌnɪŋ/ *n* **1** [U] the act or

sport of running 跑; 賽跑 **2 in the running** with some hope of succeeding in something 有希望獲勝: *Charles is in the running for the job of director.* 查爾斯有希望得到董事之職。[RELATED PHRASE 相關詞組 **out of the running**]

running² *adj* [only before a noun 只用於名詞前] **1** flowing continuously or when you need it (used of water) 不斷流動的〔指水〕: *This hotel has hot and cold running water in every room.* 這家旅館每個房間都有冷熱自來水供應。**2** done while you are running 邊跑邊完成的: *a running jump* 助跑起跳 **3** continuous 持續的: *She and her husband have a running battle over use of the car.* 她和丈夫為用汽車的事而爭吵不休。**4 running commentary** an account of an event, usually a sports event, which is spoken while it is actually happening 〔常指比賽〕現場實況評述 **5** for or concerned with running as a sport (用於)賽跑的: *Where are my running shoes?* 我的跑鞋在哪兒? **6 in running order** working properly (used of a machine) 運轉正常的〔指機器〕**7 running costs** the money that you need to spend to keep something working 維持運轉的費用

running³ *adv* one after the other; a word used after a number and a noun 連續地〔用於數字和名詞之後〕: *She won the prize three times running.* 她連續三次獲獎。| *This is the tenth day running that it's snowed.* 雪已下了連續十天了。

run·ny /ˈrʌni; ˈrʌni/ *adj* **runnier, runniest** *infml* 〔非正式〕**1** more liquid than usual or than it should be 稀的: *This paint is too runny to use on the ceiling.* 這油漆太稀,不能用來漆天花板。**2** producing liquid, often because you have a cold (used of your nose or eyes) 〔常因傷風而〕流鼻涕〔眼淚〕的

run-of-the-mill /ˌ···ˈ·◂/ *adj* ordinary and unexciting (used to express disapproval) 一般的,普通的,平淡的〔含貶義〕: *He has a run-of-the-mill office job.* 他幹一份平平淡淡的辦公室工作。

run-up /ˈ··/ *n* **the run-up** the period of time leading up to an event, and the activities during that period 〔事件的〕前奏期; 準備活動: *There are more political broadcasts during the run-up to an election.* 在選舉的籌備期間有更多的政治性廣播。

run·way /ˈrʌnweɪ; ˈrʌnweɪ/ *n* a specially prepared hard, flat surface like a road, on which aircraft take off and land 〔飛機的〕跑道 –see picture on page 991 見 991 頁彩圖

ru·pee /ruˈpi; ruːˈpiː/ *n* a unit of money in certain countries, such as India and Pakistan, or a note or coin worth that amount 盧比〔印度、巴基斯坦等國的貨幣單位〕

rup·ture¹ /ˈrʌptʃə; ˈrʌptʃər/ *n* [C;U] **1** damage, especially to your body, which is caused by something breaking or bursting 〔尤指身體上的〕破裂,裂開: *the rupture of a blood vessel* 血管的突然破裂 **2** *fml* the ending of relations between people 〔正式〕〔關係的〕斷絕,決裂

rupture² *v* **ruptured, rupturing 1** [I;T] *fml* to break or burst 〔正式〕(使)破裂; (使)裂開 **2 rupture yourself** to give yourself a HERNIA 使〔自己〕發疝氣: *She ruptured herself trying to move the sofa.* 她想搬動沙發,結果發疝氣了。**3** [I;T] (of relations between people) to end 斷絕(關係)

★**ru·ral** /ˈrʊrəl; ˈrʊərəl/ *adj* concerning country areas and village life 農村的,田園的,鄉村生活的: *the peace and beauty of rural Britain.* 英國鄉間的平靜和美麗

ruse /ruz; ruːz/ *n* a trick to deceive someone 詭計; 詐術: *The plan was just a ruse to conceal his true intentions.* 這計劃只是個用來隱瞞他的真實意圖的詭計。

★**rush¹** /rʌʃ; rʌʃ/ *v* **1** [I;T] to move or to do something quickly 衝; 奔; 快速做: *There's plenty of time; we needn't rush.* 時間很寬裕,我們不用趕。| *The passengers rushed to get seats on the train.* 乘客衝上列車搶座位。| *Don't rush your breakfast!* 別急急忙忙地吃早飯! **2** [T] to make someone hurry 催促〔某人〕: *If you rush me, I'll do it badly.* 如果你催促我,我會做得很差的。**3** [T] to attack a person or thing suddenly 突然攻擊: *Perhaps if we all rush him at once he'll drop his gun.* 如果我們立刻一起撲上去,也許他會繳槍的。**4** [T; +adv/prep] to take a person or thing somewhere quickly 急送〔人或物去某處〕: *He was rushed to hospital.* 他被火速送往醫院。**5 rush someone off their feet** to make someone hurry too much or work too hard 使某人疲於奔命,忙碌不停: *I've been rushed off my feet all day at the office and I'm exhausted.* 我在辦公室裡整天忙得不可開交,真累壞了。**6 rush in, rush into something** to enter a situation too quickly and without thinking 倉促做某事物: *You're too young to rush into marriage.* 你太年輕,不要匆匆忙忙結婚。

rush sthg ↔ **out** *phr v* [T] to produce something very quickly 匆匆生產〔某物〕: *Publishers are rushing out biographies of the new prime minister.* 出版商正在匆匆趕印新首相的自傳。

rush sthg ↔ **through** *phr v* [T] to get something like a new law approved quickly 使〔某事物〕迅速通過

rush² *n* **1 a rush** a sudden rapid movement 衝; 奔: *We made a rush for the best seats.* 我們奔着去搶最好的座位。**2** [sing] hurry or great demand 匆忙; 大量需求: *We needn't leave yet; what's the rush?* 我們還用不着離開,着甚麼急? | *There will be a rush for tickets.* 將會有一陣搶購票子的熱潮。**3 the rush** a period of great activity 繁忙時期: *I try and buy presents before the Christmas rush.* 我設法在聖誕節購物熱潮前買禮物。|

the morning rush 早晨的紛繁忙亂 **4 rushes** tall, thin water plants whose stems are often dried and made into things like mats and baskets 燈心草

rush hour /'··/ n one of the periods in the day when people are travelling to and from work in a city and the streets are crowded 〔城市裡上下班時的〕交通擁擠時間, 高峯時刻: *Try not to travel in the rush hour.* 盡量別在交通高峯時間出門。| *rush-hour traffic* 高峯時刻的交通(擁擠情況)

rusk /rʌsk; rʌsk/ n a hard dry BISCUIT which is given to babies 〔嬰兒食用的〕麵包乾; 脆餅乾

rus·set /'rʌsɪt; 'rʌsɪt/ adj lit reddish brown 《文》赤褐色的

Rus·sian[1] /'rʌʃən; 'rʌʃən/ adj from or connected with Russia 俄羅斯的: *Russian ballet* 俄羅斯芭蕾舞

Russian[2] n **1** [C] a person from Russia 俄羅斯人 **2** [U] the language of Russia 俄語

rust[1] /rʌst; rʌst/ n [U] a reddish brown substance that forms on iron and steel when they are attacked by water or air (鐵)鏽

rust[2] v [I;T] to cover something or become covered with rust (使)生鏽: *I can't open the door because the lock has rusted.* 我沒法把門打開, 因為鎖生鏽了。–**rusted** adj

rus·tic /'rʌstɪk; 'rʌstɪk/ adj **1** concerning or typical of the country 農村的, 鄉村風味的: *The village has a certain rustic charm.* 這村莊有一種迷人的田園風貌。**2** simple (used to express approval) 粗製的; 簡樸的〔含褒義〕: *a rustic garden seat* 花園裡簡陋的椅子

rus·tle[1] /'rʌsl; 'rʌsəl/ v **rustled, rustling 1** [I; T] to make or to cause something to make soft sounds when it moves gently (使)沙沙作響: *Her long silk skirt rustled as she walked.* 她一走路, 她的綢子長裙就窸窣作響。| *Stop rustling that newspaper and listen!* 別把那張報紙弄得沙沙響, 注意聽啊! **2** [T] AmE to steal cattle or horses that are left loose in open country 《美式》偷〔野地放牧的牛馬〕

rustle sthg ↔ **up** phr v [T] to find or prepare something quickly 迅速弄到〔某物〕: *I'll rustle up something to eat while you unpack.* 你打開行李, 我趕緊去弄點兒東西吃。

rustle[2] n [sing] a soft sound caused by gentle movement 沙沙聲, 窸窣聲: *a rustle of leaves* 樹葉的沙沙聲 –**rustling** n [C;U]: *the rustling of papers in the library* 圖書館裡紙頁翻動的沙沙聲

rus·tler /'rʌslə; 'rʌslər/ n AmE a person who steals cattle or horses from open country 《美式》偷牛賊; 盜馬賊 –**rustling** n [U]: *They're suspected of cattle rustling.* 他們有偷牲口的嫌疑。

rust·y /'rʌsti; 'rʌsti/ adj **rustier, rustiest 1** covered with a reddish brown substance that forms on iron and steel when attacked by water or air 生鏽的: *a rusty nail* 生鏽的釘 **2** mostly forgotten (used of a person's knowledge or ability in a particular area) 〔指某人在某一領域中的知識或能力〕荒廢的, 荒疏的: *My French is rather rusty nowadays.* 現在我的法語有點兒荒疏了。–**rustiness** n [U]

rut /rʌt; rʌt/ n **1** a deep narrow track which a wheel leaves in soft ground 車轍 **2** a fixed and uninteresting way of life or of doing things 老規矩, 老一套, 常規: *I've got into a rut at work, but I haven't got the courage to leave.* 我在工作上已開始感到刻板乏味, 但又沒有勇氣離職。

ruth·less /'ruːθlɪs; 'ruːθləs/ adj cruel and without pity 殘酷的; 無憐憫心的; 無情的: *He has always been a ruthless manager.* 他這個經理一向冷酷無情。–**ruthlessly** adv –**ruthlessness** n [U]

rye /raɪ; raɪ/ n [U] a plant grown in cold countries for its grain and for flour 黑麥, 裸麥: *rye bread* 黑麥麵包

S, s

S, s /ɛs; es/ **S's, s's** or **Ss, ss** the 19th letter of the English alphabet 英語的第十九個字母

S a written abbreviation for 〖縮〗= SOUTH-(ERN)

-'s /z, s; z, s/ *v* **1** a short form of "is" 是的縮略形式: *What's that?* 那是甚麼? **2** a short form of "has" has 的縮略形式: *He's gone.* 他已經走了。 **3** a short form of "us" (only in the phrase **let's**) us的縮略形式〔只用於片語 let's 中〕 **4** used to show who owns something 〔用於表示所有格形式〕: *Is that Jane's coat?* 那是珍的外衣嗎?

> ■ USAGE 用法: Do not use **'s** as the short form for **is** at the end of a sentence. Compare *John's here* and *I don't know where John is.* ☆不要在句末用 **'s** 作為縮略形式代替 **is**。比較 *John's here* (約翰在這裡) 和 *I don't know where John is* (我不知道約翰在哪裡). The same is true of **'m** (short for **am**), **'re** (short for **are**), **'ll** (short for **will** or **shall**), **'d** (short for **would** or **had**), **'s** (short for **has**). ☆下列的情形相同: **'m** (am 的縮略形式), **'re** (are 的縮略形式), **'ll** (will 或 shall 的縮略形式), **'d** (would 或 had 的縮略形式), **'s** (has 的縮略形式)

Sab·bath /'sæbəθ; 'sæbəθ/ *n* **the Sabbath** a day of rest and prayer each week for followers of certain religions; Jews, for example, should not work on Saturdays 〔某些宗教所遵奉的〕安息日〔如猶太教徒星期六為安息日〕

sab·bat·i·cal /sə'bætɪkl̩; sə'bætɪkəl/ *n* a period in which a person who works in education can leave their job to travel and study while still being paid 〔教師的〕休假學年, 休假學期: *Two of the history lecturers are away on sabbatical this term.* 這學期有兩位教歷史的講師出外度休假年去了。

sa·ble /'sebl̩; 'seɪbəl/ *n* **1** [C] a small animal that lives in northern Europe and Asia 紫貂, 黑貂 **2** [U] the fur of this animal, which is used to make expensive coats 紫貂皮

sab·o·tage¹ /'sæbə‚tɑːʒ; 'sæbətɑːʒ/ *n* [U] intentional damage to an object or a plan, in order to weaken an enemy 蓄意破壞, 陰謀破壞: *The telephones were not working and the police suspected sabotage.* 電話中斷, 警方懷疑有人蓄意破壞。

sabotage² *v* **sabotaged, sabotaging** [T] to cause intentional damage to an object or a plan in order to weaken an enemy 蓄意破壞〔物體或計劃〕: *a deliberate attempt to sabotage the country's economy* 蓄意破壞國家經濟的企圖

sab·o·teur /‚sæbə'tɜː; ‚sæbə'tɜːʳ/ *n* a person who intentionally damages an object or a plan, to weaken an enemy 搞陰謀破壞者, 從事破壞活動的人

sa·bre /'sebə; 'seɪbəʳ/ *n* (**saber** *AmE* 〖美式〗) a heavy military sword, or a light sword used in FENCING 軍刀, 馬刀, 〔擊劍用的〕長劍, 佩劍

sac·cha·rin /'sækərɪn; 'sækərɪn/ *n* [U] a very sweet-tasting chemical which is used instead of sugar 糖精

sac·cha·rine /'sækə‚raɪn; 'sækəriːn/ *adj* **1** too sweet 太甜的 **2** too friendly, nice, or happy 奉承的; 過分甜蜜的; 故作多情的: *a saccharine love story* 過於纏綿的愛情故事

sach·et /'sæʃe; 'sæʃeɪ/ *n* a small paper or plastic bag containing a quantity of something, for example SHAMPOO, all of which is used at the same time 〔裝有供一次用量的洗髮劑等〕小袋; 小包 –see picture on page 244 見 244 頁彩圖

sack¹ /sæk; sæk/ *n* **1** a large bag, usually made of strong plastic cloth, which is used for carrying things like coal and grain 大袋 〔常由厚塑料布制成, 用於裝煤或穀物〕; 粗布袋: *a sack of potatoes* 一袋馬鈴薯 **2** **get the sack** *infml* to be dismissed from a job 〖非正式〗被解雇: *If you're late again, you'll get the sack.* 你要是再遲到, 你就會被解雇。[RELATED PHRASE 相關詞組 **give someone the sack**]

sack² *v* [T] **1** to dismiss someone from their job 解雇〔某人〕: *She was caught stealing and sacked immediately.* 她偷東西時當場被抓, 並馬上遭到解雇。 **2** to destroy and steal from buildings in a conquered city 毀壞; 洗劫〔被攻佔的城市〕

sack·ing /'sækɪŋ; 'sækɪŋ/ *n* [U] rough cloth for making sacks 麻袋布

sac·ra·ment /'sækrəmənt; 'sækrəmənt/ *n* an important Christian ceremony, such as marriage 聖事; 聖禮〔如婚禮〕

sa·cred /ˈsekrɪd; ˈseɪkrᵻd/ *adj* **1** holy because of a connection with God or religion 神聖的: *sacred writings* 聖典 | *sacred animals* 神聖的動物 **2** [only before a noun 只用於名詞前] connected with religion 宗教的: *sacred music* 宗教音樂 **3** serious and important in the same way that religious things are 莊嚴的; 鄭重的: *a sacred oath* 莊嚴的宣誓 –**sacredness** *n* [U]

sac·ri·fice¹ /ˈsækrəˌfaɪs; ˈsækrᵻfaɪs/ *n* [C;U] **1** the act of offering something to a god or gods in a ceremony, often by killing it 獻祭, 供奉: *The idea that anyone practises human sacrifice is ridiculous.* 實現人人獻祭的想法是很荒謬的。 **2** something that is offered in this way 供品, 祭品 **3** the act of giving up something important or useful for a particular purpose 犧牲: *She made a lot of sacrifices to help her children go to university.* 她為幫助兒女考入大學, 作出了很大的犧牲。–**sacrificial** *adj*: *a sacrificial victim* 動物祭品; 犧牲品

sacrifice² *v* [T] **sacrificed, sacrificing 1** to offer something as a sacrifice 獻祭, 供奉 **2** to give up something important or useful for a particular purpose 犧牲, 獻出〔某事物〕

sac·ri·lege /ˈsækrəlɪdʒ; ˈsækrᵻlɪdʒ/ *n* [U] treatment of a holy or widely admired thing which shows a lack of respect 褻瀆神聖: *It would be sacrilege to destroy this beautiful old building.* 毀掉這座美麗的古建築物會是褻瀆神靈的行為。–**sacrilegious** /-ˈlɪdʒəs; -ˈlɪdʒəs/ *adj*

sac·ro·sanct /ˈsækroˌsæŋkt; ˈsækrəsæŋkt/ *adj* too important to be changed in any way (a word that is often used in a humorous way) 神聖不可侵犯的〔常含幽默〕: *I never take any work home at the weekend. My weekends are sacrosanct.* 我從來不在週末把工作帶回家去做, 我的週末是神聖不可侵犯的。

★**sad** /sæd; sæd/ *adj* **1** unhappy 悲哀的; 難過的; 傷心的: *He looked sad and lonely.* 他看上去既傷心又孤獨。 | *It was a sad day for our team.* 對我們球隊來說, 那是一個傷心的日子。 **2** undesirable and often deserving blame 不合心意的; 該受責備的: *It's a sad state of affairs when our children aren't taught to read properly.* 不教孩子如何讀書是很糟糕的事。

sad·den /ˈsædn; ˈsædn/ *v* [T] to make someone feel unhappy 使傷心, 使難過: *We were saddened by the news of his death.* 我們聽到他去世的消息感到很悲傷。

sad·dle¹ /ˈsædl; ˈsædl/ *n* **1** a seat, usually made of leather, that you fit over the back of an animal such as a horse or camel 鞍; 馬鞍 **2** a seat on a bicycle or motorcycle 〔腳踏車或摩托車的〕鞍座 **3** a piece of meat from the back of a sheep 〔羊的〕脊肉

saddle² *v* **saddled, saddling** [T] **1** to put a saddle on a horse 給〔馬〕裝鞍 **2** to give someone an unpleasant duty or responsi-

bility 使〔某人〕承擔〔令人不快的責任〕; 強加: *He's saddled* **with** *a large house which he can't sell.* 他賣不出一幢大房子, 被迫承擔責任。

saddle up *phr v* [I;T **saddle** sthg ↔ **up**] to put a saddle on a horse 給〔馬〕裝鞍

sad·dle·bag /ˈsædlˌbæg; ˈsædlbæg/ *n* a bag or a pair of bags fixed to the saddle on a horse, bicycle, or motorcycle 鞍囊, 馬褡子, 〔腳踏車或摩托車的〕掛包

sa·dis·m /ˈseɪdɪzəm; ˈseɪdɪzəm/ *n* [U] pleasure, which is sometimes sexual, from cruelty to other people 施虐狂, 性虐待狂 – **sadist** *n* –**sadistic** /sæˈdɪstɪk; səˈdɪstɪk/ *adj*: *He took a sadistic delight in humiliating her.* 他以侮辱她為樂。

sad·ly /ˈsædli; ˈsædli/ *adv* **1** with feelings of unhappiness 傷心地; 悲哀地: *I watched sadly as the old man was buried.* 我難過地看着老人被埋葬。 **2** unfortunately 不幸地; 遺憾地: *Sadly, she could not attend my wedding.* 很遺憾, 她不能參加我的婚禮。

sad·ness /ˈsædnɪs; ˈsædnᵻs/ *n* [U] a feeling of unhappiness 悲哀, 憂傷

s.a.e. /ˌɛs eˈi; ˌes eɪ ˈiː/ *n* an envelope which you put a stamp on and write your own address on; you send it to someone so that they can send something back to you: an abbreviation for **stamped addressed envelope** 〔縮〕貼有郵票並寫明姓名地址的回郵信封

sa·fa·ri /səˈfɑrɪ; səˈfɑːri/ *n* a trip through wild country, especially in Africa, to hunt or watch large animals 〔尤指在非洲的〕遊獵, 探險旅行: *They're going on safari in Kenya.* 他們正在肯尼亞遊獵。

★**safe¹** /sef; seɪf/ *adj* **1** in no danger 無危險的, 安全的: *I won't feel safe until the plane has landed.* 直到飛機着陸我才會感到安全。 | *For the moment we are safe* **from** *attack.* 我們此刻沒有遭到攻擊的危險。 | *Your secret is safe with me.* 我一定給你保密。 **2 safe and sound** completely unharmed 平安無事; 完整無損: *The child was found safe and sound at her grandparents'.* 孩子在她的祖父母家找到時安然無恙。 **3** not dangerous 安全的: *Is this a safe place to swim?* 這個地方游泳安全嗎? | *Keep these papers in a safe place.* 把這些文件放在一個安全的地方。 | *a campaign for safe driving* 一場安全駕駛運動 | *a safe investment* 無風險的投資 **4** unlikely to be proved wrong 不會出錯的; 有把握的: *It's safe to say that crime will continue at a high rate this year.* 可以有把握地說, 今年的犯罪率仍會很高。 **5 in safe hands** with someone who can be trusted 與可靠的人在一起: *When the children are with my brother, I know they're in safe hands.* 孩子們和我兄弟在一起時, 我知道他們會受到妥善照料。 **6 to be on the safe side** to be sure that you are not taking a risk 確保安全; 以防萬一: *Carry a little more money with you, to be on the safe side.* 你隨身多帶點錢以防萬一。 –**safely** *adv*: *Did the parcel arrive safely?* 包裹送到時是否完好無損? | *I think I can safely say that he won't show his face in here again.* 我認為我可以有把握地說,他不會再在這兒露面了。 – **safeness** *n* [U]

safe² *n* a strong box or cupboard with thick metal sides and a lock, used for protecting valuable things from thieves 保險箱, 保險櫃

safe·de·pos·it box /'· ·,·· ·/ *n* (also 又作 **safety-deposit box** /'·· ·,·· ·/) a small box where you can store valuable objects, usually in a special room in a bank 〔銀行裡的〕貴重物品保管箱

safe·guard /'sef,gɑrd; 'seɪfgɑːd/ *v* [T] to protect something from possible harm 保護, 維護〔某事物〕: *The new laws are designed to safeguard the rights of the individual.* 這項新法律是為了保護個人權利而制定的。– **safeguard** *n*: *safeguards against the misuse of government power* 防範政府濫用權力的措施

safe·keep·ing /'sef'kipɪŋ; ,seɪf'kiːpɪŋ/ *n* [U] protection from harm or loss 保護; 保管: *Put your important papers in the bank for safekeeping.* 把你的重要文件放在銀行裡保管。

safe sex /,· '·/ *n* [U] sexual activities in which people use contraceptives (CONTRACEPTIVE) to prevent the spread of disease 〔使用避孕套以防止疾病傳染的〕安全性交; 安全房事

★**safe·ty** /'seftɪ; 'seɪftɪ/ *n* [U] freedom from danger, harm, or risk 安全; 平安; 保險: *My main concern is for the safety of my family.* 我主要關心的是我家人的安全。 | *She led the children to a place of safety.* 她把孩子們帶到了安全的地方。

safety belt /'·· ·/ *n* see 見 SEAT BELT

safety cur·tain /,·· '··/ *n* a theatre curtain which will not burn if there is a fire; it is lowered at the front of the stage 〔劇場的〕防火幕

safety pin /'·· ·/ *n* a wire pin which is bent so that its sharp point is covered when the pin is being used to fasten two things together 〔安全〕別針

safety ra·zor /'·· ,··/ *n* a RAZOR with a cover above its blade to protect your skin from being cut 〔刀片上有蓋的〕安全剃刀

safety valve /'·· ·/ *n* **1** a part of a machine which allows liquids or gas to escape when the pressure inside becomes too great 安全閥 **2** a way of expressing strong feelings, for example anger, without harming yourself or others 發泄怒氣的方式: *Sport can be a safety valve for people under stress.* 運動可以紓解人們的壓力。

sag /sæg; sæg/ *v* **-gg-** [I] to sink, bend, or hang downwards under pressure or because of lack of support 〔因受壓或缺少支撐〕下沉; 下彎; 下垂: *The branch sagged under the weight of the apples.* 樹枝在蘋果的重壓下彎曲。

sa·ga /'sɑgə; 'sɑːgə/ *n* a long story about a group of actions and events, often ones that are said to have happened a very long time ago 長篇故事, 家世小說

sa·ga·cious /sə'geʃəs; sə'geɪʃəs/ *adj lit* wise 〔文〕明智的

sage¹ /sedʒ; seɪdʒ/ *n* **1** [C] a person, especially an old man, who is wise as a result of long thinking and experience 年高望重的人; 哲人; 賢者 **2** [U] leaves from a plant, used in cooking 鼠尾草, 洋蘇草〔用於烹調〕

sage² *adj* wise as a result of experience and thinking for a long time 賢明的; 明智的: *his sage advice* 他那明智的忠告 – **sagely** *adv*

Sa·git·tar·i·us /,sædʒɪ'tɛrɪəs; ,sædʒɪ'teərɪəs/ *n* one of the signs of the ZODIAC 〔占星術中的〕人馬宮〔黃道十二宮的第九宮〕

sa·go /'sego; 'seɪgəʊ/ *n* [U] a white food substance which is used for cooking sweet dishes with milk 西米, 西穀米

said¹ /sed; sed/ the past tense and past participle of SAY ☆ SAY 過去式和過去分詞

said² *adj fml* **the said** [only before a noun 只用於名詞前] the one mentioned before 〔正式〕上述的, 該…: *Our first task was to find the murder weapon. The said weapon was discovered in Mr Law's garage.* 我們的首要任務是找到殺人兇器。上述兇器是在勞先生的車庫發現的。

sail¹ /sel; seɪl/ *n* **1** [C;U] a piece of strong cloth which moves a ship through the water when it is filled with wind 帆: *Lower the sails!* 請下帆! **2** [C] **a sail** a short trip, usually for pleasure, in a boat with a sail 乘船旅行; 〔常指〕坐船遊覽: *Let's go for a sail this afternoon.* 我們今天下午去乘船遊玩吧。 **3 set sail** to leave the shore and begin a trip at sea 啟航: *On Thursday we set sail for New York.* 我們星期四啟航去紐約。 **4** [C] any of the broad blades of a WINDMILL, which move by the force of the wind 〔風車的〕翼板

sail² *v* **1** [I +adv/prep; T] to travel on water or across an area of water in a ship or boat 〔船〕航行, 行駛: *These boats sail between the islands.* 這些船隻在兩島之間航行。 | *We sailed the Pacific in eight days.* 我們用了八天時間乘船橫渡太平洋。 **2** [T] to direct or command a ship or boat on water 駕駛〔船〕: *He sailed the ship while the captain slept.* 船長睡覺時由他駕駛船。 **3** [I] to begin a journey across water 啟航, 開船: *We sail tomorrow at 10 o'clock.* 我們明天十點鐘開船。 **4** [I + adv/prep] to move smoothly and without pausing 平穩地行進: *A flock of birds sailed across the sky.* 一羣鳥兒輕快地在天空中飛過。 | *She sailed past me without a word.* 她一聲不吭地從我身旁翩然走過。 **5 sail through** to pass some kind of test easily 順利通過〔考試〕: *All my children seem to sail through exams.* 我的孩子似乎都順利通過了考試。

sail·ing /'selɪŋ; 'seɪlɪŋ/ *n* **1** [U] the skill of

directing the course of a ship 航海術 **2** [U] the sport of travelling in or directing a small boat with sails 帆船運動 **3** [C] journey by ship 〔船的〕航班: *When is the next sailing to France?* 下一班開往法國的船甚麼時候啟航?

sail·or /'seləʳ; 'seɪləʳ/ *n* **1** a person with a job on a ship, especially one who is not a ship's officer 水手; 海員 **2 a good sailor** a person who does not become sick on boats 不會暈船的人 [RELATED PHRASE 相關詞組 **a bad sailor**]

saint *n* **1** /sent; seɪnt/ a person who is officially recognized after death as specially holy and worthy of formal honour in the Christian church 〔基督教正式追封的〕聖徒, 聖者 **2** /sent; seɪnt/ *infml* a person who is unusually unselfish or patient 〔非正式〕謙卑有慈愛的人; 極有忍耐心的人; 虔誠慈善的人: *My mother was a real saint.* 我的母親是一位真正心地善良的人。 **3 Saint** /sənt; sənt, *strong* 強讀 sent; seɪnt/ (also written as 又寫作 **St**) a title which is used before a saint's name 聖〔用於聖徒名字前的頭銜〕: *Saint Joan of Arc* 聖女貞德 | *St Francis* 聖弗蘭西斯

saint·ly /'sentlɪ; 'seɪntli/ *adj* like a saint 聖徒似的, 聖人似的; 極為聖潔的: *a saintly man* 聖人般的男人 | *She led a saintly life.* 她過着聖潔的生活。–**saintliness** *n* [U]

***sake** /sek; seɪk/ *n* **1 for someone's sake** in order to help or please someone 為了某人: *Do it for my sake.* 看在我的份上就做吧。 **2 for the sake of** for a particular purpose 了〔某一目的〕: *He's just talking for the sake of hearing his own voice.* 他說話的目的就是要聽聽自己的嗓音。 **3 for God's sake, for goodness sake, for pity's sake** phrases used to add force to what you are saying when you are annoyed 看在上帝的面上; 天哪, 哎呀; 千萬〔用於厭煩時加強請求的語氣〕: *For goodness sake, don't tell him!* 千萬別告訴他! | *For God's sake, can't you keep quiet for a minute!* 老天呀, 你們難道就不能安靜一會兒!

sa·la·cious /sə'leʃəs; sə'leɪʃəs/ *adj fml* treating sexual matters in an improper or shocking way 〔正式〕淫穢的; 褻瀆的: *a salacious film* 淫褻的電影 –**salaciously** *adv*

TRANSPORT 交通工具

Exercise 1 練習一
Which of these things can you see on a motorway? 下列哪些東西能在高速公路上看到?

bicycle	speedboat	crossroads
roundabout	lorry	motorbike
pelican crossing	bus stop	T–junction
zebra crossing	coach	level crossing

Exercise 2 練習二
What sort of power drives these vehicles? Put a tick in the correct boxes. Remember that some vehicles may have two or more different types of power. 是甚麼動力驅動這些交通工具的? 在正確的方格裡加上(√)號。記住某些交通工具可能有兩種或更多的動力。

	muscle power	wind power	petrol engine	diesel engine	jet engine	turbine engine
aeroplane						
bus						
car						
dinghy						
helicopter						
hovercraft						
liner						
lorry						
rowing boat						
speedboat						
train						
yacht						

hangar
飛機庫

control tower
機場指揮塔

aeroplane (BrE【英式】)/
airplane (AmE【美式】)
飛機

crossroads (BrE【英式】)/
intersection (AmE【美式】)
十字路口

airport
飛機場

terminal
航空客運站

runway
跑道

carriage (BrE【英式】)/
car (AmE【美式】)
車廂

roundabout
(BrE【英式】)/
traffic circle
(AmE【美式】)
環島

bus
公共汽車

helicopter
直升飛機

t-junction (BrE【英式】)
丁型路口

zebra crossing (BrE【英式】)
斑馬線

level
(BrE【英式】)/
grade (AmE【美式】)
crossing
(公路與鐵路的)
平交道口

lorry (BrE【英式】)/
truck/semi (AmE【美式】)
貨車

dual carriage
(BrE【英式】)/
divided highway
(AmE【美式】)
雙向公路

bus station
公共汽車站

jetty
突堤

footbridge
天行橋

lane
車道

railway (BrE【英式】)
train (AmE【美式】)
station
火車站

sidings
(鐵路的)
側線; 旁軌

platform
月台

dock
碼頭

ship
船

signal
鐵路信號裝置

harbour (BrE【英式】)/
harbor (AmE【美式】)
港口

taxi/cab
計程車

track
軌道

hovercraft
氣墊船

traffic lights
交通燈; 紅綠燈

lighthouse
燈塔

speedboat
快艇

pier
突堤; 碼頭

yacht
帆船

rowing boat (BrE【英式】)/
row boat (AmE【美式】)划艇

lift
舉起

kneel
跪

squat
蹲下

crouch
蹲伏

crawl
爬

lean
倚靠

throw
投擲

hold
拿著

bend
彎腰

stretch
伸展

sit
坐

pull
拉

catch
接

drag
拖

push
推

fall
跌倒

run
跑

carry
提

punch
重擊

hit
擊

skip
蹦跳

kick
踢

walk
步行

leap
跳躍

drop
掉下

pick up
撿起

march
齊步走

jump
跳越

tiptoe
踮著腳走

put down
放下

jog
慢跑

climb
攀爬

hop
單腳跳

sal·ad /'sæləd; 'sæləd/ n [C;U] a mixture of vegetables served cold and usually raw, sometimes with other foods added 沙拉, 沙律; 涼拌生菜: *We'll have a green salad with the steak, so I need to get some lettuce.* 我們要吃生菜沙拉和牛排, 所以我要弄些生菜來。| *Do you like chicken salad?* 你喜歡吃涼拌鷄肉沙拉嗎?

sa·la·mi /sə'lɑmɪ; sə'lɑːmi/ n [U] a large dark SAUSAGE with a strong taste 〔意大利的〕薩拉米香腸

sal·a·ried /'sælərɪd; 'sælərid/ adj earning a salary, as opposed to wages 有(固定)薪水的: *salaried workers* 領固定薪水的工人 | *a salaried job* 有固定薪水的工作

sal·a·ry /'sælərɪ; 'sæləri/ n **salaries** [C;U] money that you receive every month as payment for your job, especially if you are an office worker or a professional person, such as a teacher or lawyer 〔通常按月發的〕薪金, 薪水: *I get a good salary.* 我有一份很不錯的薪水。| *He's on a salary of about £20,000 a year.* 他年薪大約二萬英鎊。–see PAY[2] (USAGE 用法)

sale /sel; seɪl/ n **1 [C;U] an act or occasion of selling something 銷售, 出售: *The sale of my house hasn't been easy.* 我的房子一直很難賣掉。| *There's a second-hand clothes sale in the church hall today.* 今天教堂裡在賣二手衣服。**2 for sale** offered to anyone who wants to buy it 待售; 出售: *There are three houses for sale near us.* 我們附近有三所房子待售。| *The sign said "For sale".* 標牌上寫着"出售"。**3 on sale** in the shops for people to buy 〔商店裡的〕出售: *The latest model of this video recorder is now on sale in your high street.* 這種最新型號的錄影機目前在你們那條大街中有售。**4** [C] a special offering of goods in a shop at lower prices than usual 賤賣, 廉價出售: *I got this hat cheap in the Harrods sale.* 我是在哈羅茲大減價時以便宜價買下這頂帽子的。| *The sales are on so the streets are very crowded.* 大減價還在進行, 所以街上十分擁擠。**5 sales** [pl] the total amount of something that is sold 銷售量: *The company is hoping for improved sales this month.* 公司正期待本月的銷售量有所增加。

sales /selz; seɪlz/ adj [only before a noun 只用於名詞前] concerned with selling something 銷售的: *this year's sales figures* 今年的銷售數字 | *the sales department* 銷售部

sales·clerk /'selz,klɜk; 'seɪlzklɑːk/ n the usual American word for 〔美式〕= a SHOP ASSISTANT

sales·man /'selzmən; 'seɪlzmən/ n **salesmen**

VERBS OF MOVEMENT 動作動詞

Complete this passage with verbs from the illustration. 用彩圖中的動詞完成這段文字。

Some children are helping old Mrs Grainger in her garden. She is telling them what to do.

"Tony and Martin, **1**run down to the garden shed and get the ladder. **2**C_ _ _ _ it to the apple tree. Then I'll come and tell you what to do. Don't **3**w _ _ _ on the flowerbeds, **4**j _ _ _ over them!

Sarah and Jane, there are some carrots and a lot of weeds growing here. I want you to **5**p _ _ _ up the weeds and put them in the wheelbarrow. It's not a difficult job but I can't **6**b _ _ _ at my age. Don't get your legs dirty, **7**k _ _ _ _ on this board!

Mary and Colin, I want you to **8**c _ _ _ _ _ under those bushes and **9**p _ _ _ up those bits of paper.

Carol and John, can you see that old tree on the ground near the pond?

Can you **10**d _ _ _ it down to the end of the garden? Don't try to **11**l _ _ _ it, it's very heavy. Ah, Elaine, you're a nice tall girl. You see that beautiful peach on the tree by the wall? Can you **12**s _ _ _ _ _ _ up and get it for me?

Now, Tony and Martin, you've got the ladder, good. Now Tony, **13**l _ _ _ the ladder against the tree. Good. Martin, you must **14**h _ _ _ the ladder. Make sure it doesn't move. Tony, can you **15**c _ _ _ _ the ladder and get those apples? Be careful! Don't **16**f _ _ _ down! That's right, Tony. Can you get that big red apple? Good. Now **17**t _ _ _ _ it to me. I'll **18**c _ _ _ _ it. Be careful, don't **19**d _ _ _ it! Good. Now, I'm going to **20**s _ _ in this nice chair and enjoy the sun."

Half an hour later, old Mrs Grainger was asleep in her chair. "We mustn't wake her up," said Elaine. "Let's **21**t _ _ _ _ _ out of the garden and let her sleep."

/-mən; -mən/ a person, usually a man, whose job is to sell goods, either in a shop or directly to homes or businesses 男售貨員; 男推銷員

sales·man·ship /ˈseɪzmənˌʃɪp; ˈseɪlzmənʃɪp/ n [U] skill in selling or in persuading people to accept something 推銷術; 銷售技巧

sales·wo·man /ˈseɪzˌwʊmən; ˈseɪlzˌwʊmən/ n **saleswomen** /-ˌwɪmɪn; -ˌwɪmɪn/ a woman whose job is to sell goods, either in a shop or directly to homes or businesses 女售貨員; 女推銷員

sa·li·ent /ˈseɪliənt; ˈseɪliənt/ adj fml most noticeable or important 〔正式〕顯著的; 突出的; 重要的: Just tell me the salient points of her speech. 就把她演説的要點告訴我。

sa·line /ˈseɪlaɪn; ˈseɪlaɪn/ adj containing salt 含鹽的: a saline solution 鹽溶液

sa·li·va /səˈlaɪvə; səˈlaɪvə/ n [U] the watery liquid produced naturally in your mouth 涎, 唾液

sal·i·vate /ˈsæləˌveɪt; ˈsælɪˌveɪt/ v **salivated**, **salivating** [I] to produce more saliva than usual in your mouth, especially at the sight or thought of food 〔尤指看到或想到食物時〕分泌唾液; 流口水

sal·low /ˈsæləʊ; ˈsæləʊ/ adj yellow and unhealthy-looking (used of a person's skin) 灰黃色的, 蠟黃色的〔指人的皮膚〕

salm·on /ˈsæmən; ˈsæmən/ n [plural is **salmon**] [C;U] a large fish with silvery skin and pink flesh that is eaten as food 鮭, 三文魚, 大麻哈魚: I like salmon, but it's expensive. 我愛吃鮭魚, 但它太貴了。| smoked salmon 燻製鮭魚

sal·on /ˈsælɒn; ˈsælɒn/ n a place of business, especially for beauty treatment or the sale of expensive clothes 〔提供美容等營業性質的〕店, 廳, 院: a hairdressing salon 美髮廊

sa·loon /səˈluːn; səˈluːn/ n **1** BrE 〔英式〕(also 又作 **saloon car** /·ˈ··/) a car for four to six passengers with a firm roof and a separate enclosed space for cases, bags, and boxes, etc. 大轎車 –see picture on page 209 見 209 頁彩圖 **2** a large room on a ship for the passengers to sit in 〔輪船上的〕大客廳 **3** (also 又作 **saloon bar, lounge bar**) a comfortably furnished room in a PUB, where drinks cost a little more than in the other bars 雅座酒吧 **4** a large public drinking place typical of the western US in former times 〔昔日美國西部的〕酒館

★**salt**[1] /sɔːlt; sɔːlt/ n **1** [U] a very common white substance found in the earth and in seawater which has many uses, including giving food more taste 鹽, 食鹽: The vegetables need more salt. 這些蔬菜需多放點鹽。| Please pass the salt. 請把鹽遞過來。 **2** [C] tech a chemical substance which may form when an acid and a metal combine 〔術語〕鹽類, 氯化鈉〔酸和金屬生成的化合物〕

3 salts [pl] a mineral substance like salt which is used as a medicine or to make your bath smell sweet 鹽狀物; 瀉鹽; 浴鹽 **4 the salt of the earth** a person who is admired by other people 令人敬佩的人; 社會中堅

salt[2] v [T] to add salt to something 加鹽於〔某物〕, 給…加鹽: Have you salted the vegetables? 你給蔬菜加了鹽嗎?

salt sthg ↔ **away** phr v [T] infml to hide something, usually money, away for the future 〔非正式〕積貯, 儲蓄, 收藏〔金錢〕

salt[3] adj containing or tasting of salt 含鹽的; 鹹的: salt water 鹹水 | a salt lake 鹽湖

salt·cel·lar /ˈsɔːltˌselə; ˈsɔːltˌselər/ n a container for salt, used at meals 〔餐桌上用的〕鹽瓶

salt·wa·ter /ˈsɔːltˌwɔːtə; ˈsɔːltˌwɔːtər/ adj [only before a noun 只用於名詞前] living in or containing sea water 生於海水中的; 海水的; 鹹水的: saltwater fish 海產魚

salt·y /ˈsɔːlti; ˈsɔːlti/ adj **saltier, saltiest** containing or tasting of salt 含鹽的; 鹹的 – **saltiness** n [U]

sa·lu·bri·ous /səˈluːbriəs; səˈluːbriəs/ adj fml or lit healthy or attractive 〔正式或文〕有益健康的: This is not a very salubrious part of town. 這不是十分有益健康的城區。– **salubriousness** n [U]

sal·u·ta·ry /ˈsæljəˌteri; ˈsæljʊtəri/ adj fml useful because the effect is helpful 〔正式〕有利的, 有益的: The accident was a salutary experience; I'll never drink and drive again. 那次事故是個有益的教訓, 我再也不會酒後開車了。

sal·u·ta·tion /ˌsæljəˈteɪʃən; ˌsæljʊˈteɪʃən/ n [C;U] fml an expression of greeting through words or action 〔正式〕致敬, 致意; 行禮: He bowed in salutation. 他鞠躬致意。

sa·lute[1] /səˈluːt; səˈluːt/ v **saluted, saluting 1** [I;T] to show someone respect with a special sign, such as the raising of your right hand to your forehead 向〔某人〕致敬; 行舉手禮: to salute your commanding officer 向你的指揮官敬禮 **2** [T] fml to honour and praise 〔正式〕頌揚, 讚揚: He saluted the splendid work of the local police. 他對當地警方的出色工作表示敬意。 **3** [T] lit to greet someone with words or a sign 〔文〕向〔某人〕打招呼, 問候; 致意: He saluted his friend with a wave. 他向他的朋友揮手致意。

salute[2] n **1** [C] a military sign of respect for a person or an occasion, such as a raising of your right hand to your forehead or a ceremonial firing of guns 敬禮; 行禮 **2** [C;U] lit a greeting 〔文〕致意; 問候 **3 take the salute** (of a person of high rank) to stand while soldiers march past and salute you 〔高級官員在閲兵時〕接受敬禮; 行答禮

sal·vage[1] /ˈsælvɪdʒ; ˈsælvɪdʒ/ n [U] **1** the act of saving things from destruction, especially of saving a wrecked ship or its contents from the sea 海上救援〔尤指打撈沉船或船上貨物〕 **2** property which is saved from something that has been destroyed 搶救出的財物: *Salvage from the wreck will go to the maritime museum.* 海難中搶救出的物品將送往海事博物館。

salvage² *v* **salvaged, salvaging** [T] to save something from further damage 搶救, 挽救〔某物〕: *We were unable to salvage anything when the factory burnt down.* 工廠焚毀時, 我們無法搶救出任何東西。 | *Is there anything I can do now to salvage my reputation?* 我現在還能做些甚麼來挽回我的名譽?

sal·va·tion /sæl'veɪʃən; sæl'veɪʃən/ *n* [U] **1** the means or state of being saved from the power and effect of evil, especially in the Christian religion 〔尤指基督教的〕得救; 拯救: *praying for his salvation* 祈求(上帝的)拯救 **2** *fml* the means of saving a person or thing from loss, ruin, or destruction 〔正式〕拯救; 解救辦法: *Business was terrible, but the new tax laws were our salvation.* 生意很不景氣, 但新的稅法成了我們的救星。 **3 the Salvation Army** a Christian organization which works to help poor people and whose members wear military uniforms 〔基督教的〕救世軍

salve¹ /sæv; sælv/ *n* [C;U] an oily paste which you put on sore, cut, or burnt skin 藥膏; 軟膏

salve² *v* **salved, salving** [T] *lit* **salve your conscience** to make yourself feel less guilty 〔文〕使自己的良心得到寬慰: *He rarely visited his mother, but he sent her expensive presents to salve his conscience.* 他很少去探望母親, 但他寄給她昂貴的禮物, 來減輕自己良心上的不安。

sal·ver /'sælvə; 'sælvər/ *n* a fine metal plate, often made of silver, for serving food or drink 〔用於遞送食物或飲料的〕金屬托盤〔常爲銀器〕

sal·vo /'sælvəʊ; 'sælvoʊ/ *n* **salvos** *or* **salvoes** a firing of several guns at once, in a ceremony or battle 〔禮儀或戰鬥中的〕砲火齊發; 〔禮砲〕齊鳴

Sa·mar·i·tan /sə'mærɪtn; sə'mærɪtən/ *n* **1 a good Samaritan** a person who gives help to someone in need 行善的人; 助人爲樂的人 **2 the Samaritans** an organization which gives help to people who are extremely unhappy and need someone to talk to 撒瑪利亞會〔專爲不幸和苦悶的人排憂解難的慈善組織〕

same¹ /sem; seɪm/ *adj* **1** not changed or different 一樣的, 同一的, 原來的: *He sits in the same chair every evening.* 他每天晚上都坐在同一把椅子上。 | *I don't want to make the same mistakes again.* 我不想再犯那種錯誤。 **2** alike in every way 同樣的: *Women and men should get the same pay for doing the same jobs.* 男女應該同工同酬。 **3 one and the same** exactly the same 完全

一樣(的), 同一個(的) **4 same here** *infml* a phrase you use when you are agreeing with someone or saying that you have had a similar experience to them 〔非正式〕我也一樣〔用於表示同意某人或表示有類似經歷〕

same² *pron* the same thing 同樣的事物: *John ordered a beer, and I asked for the same.* 約翰叫了一杯啤酒, 我也要了一杯。 | *All the newspapers say the same.* 所有報紙都那樣報道。 | *Jane looks the same as ever.* 珍看上去一點也沒變樣。

same·ness /'semnɪs; 'seɪmnɪs/ *n* [U] the quality of being nearly or exactly the same 同樣; 相似; 千篇一律: *We soon got bored with the sameness of the hotel meals.* 我們很快就吃膩了旅館提供的那種千篇一律的飯菜。

sam·ple¹ /'sæmpl; 'sɑːmpəl/ *n* a small part, quantity, or number which gives you information about something or a general idea of the whole of something 樣品; 標本; 樣本: *The nurse took a blood sample for analysis.* 護士取了血液的樣本作分析。 | *These samples of a new washing powder came through the door today.* 這些新種類洗衣粉的樣品是今天有人從門縫裡塞進來的。 –**sample** *adj*

sample² *v* **sampled, sampling** [T] **1** to try or test a small part, quantity, or number of a whole thing or set of things 抽樣檢驗; 試嘗: *She sampled the wine before filling the other glasses.* 她先把酒嘗了嘗, 然後才把其他杯子倒滿。 **2** to find out about something through a short experience of it 體驗〔某事物〕: *I want to sample the pleasures of country life.* 我想體驗一下鄉村生活的樂趣。

san·a·to·ri·um /,sænə'tɔːrɪəm; ,sænə'tɔːrɪəm/ *n* **sanatoriums** *or* **sanatoria** /-rɪə; -rɪə/ (also 又作 **sanitorium, sanitarium** *AmE* 〔美式〕) a kind of hospital for sick people who need treatment or rest, often for long periods 療養院

sanc·ti·fy /'sæŋktəfaɪ; 'sæŋktɪfaɪ/ *v* **sanctified, sanctifying** [T] *fml* 〔正式〕 **1** to make something holy 使神聖: *The priest sanctified the church with a special ceremony.* 牧師進行一種特殊的儀式, 使教堂顯得神聖。 **2** to give something official approval or great importance 認可, 批准, 重視〔某事物〕: *These customs are sanctified by royal tradition.* 這些習俗得到王室傳統的認可。 –**sanctification** /,sæŋktəfə'keɪʃən; ,sæŋktɪfə'keɪʃən/ *n* [U]

sanc·ti·mo·ni·ous /,sæŋktə'məʊnɪəs; ,sæŋktɪ'moʊnɪəs/ *adj* making a show of being extremely religious or moral (a word used to show disapproval) 假裝虔誠的; 裝成正經的〔含貶義〕: *sanctimonious behaviour* 假仁假義的行爲 –**sanctimoniously** *adv*: *"I'd never do that," she said sanctimoniously.* "我絕不會幹那事," 她假裝正經地說。 –**sanctimoniousness** *n* [U]

sanc·tion¹ /'sæŋkʃən; 'sæŋkʃən/ *n* **1** [C] an action, such as the stopping of trade,

S

which is taken against a country that has behaved in an unacceptable way 〔對一個國家的〕制裁: *We will establish economic sanctions against any country that threatens to harm British citizens.* 我們將對任何威脅要損害英國公民利益的國家實行經濟制裁。**2** [C] something that is intended to force people to obey a rule or moral standard 約束力；懲處: *"What about expelling these students from the university?" "Well, of course, that is the ultimate sanction."* 「把這些學生從大學開除出去怎麼樣?」「哦，當然囉，那是極限的懲處。」**3** [U] *fml* official permission or approval 〔正式〕准許；批准；許可: *The minister is acting with the sanction of Parliament.* 部長在按照國會的批准行事。

sanction² *v* [T] *fml* to accept, approve, or permit something 〔正式〕接受；批准；准許〔某事〕: *The church would not sanction his second marriage.* 教會不會批准他第二次結婚。

sanc·ti·ty /ˈsæŋktəti; ˈsæŋktⱼti/ *n* [U] the quality of being holy or so important that it should not be questioned 神聖，莊嚴: *These men have no respect for the sanctity of human life.* 這些人不尊重人類生命的神聖。

sanc·tu·a·ry /ˈsæŋktʃuˌɛri; ˈsæŋktʃuəri/ *n* **sanctuaries 1** [C;U] a place of protection or safety from harm 避難所；庇護所: *He found sanctuary in his uncle's home.* 他躲到他叔叔家裡避難。**2** [C] an area where birds or animals are protected 鳥獸保護區 **3** [C] a building which is considered holy 聖地；聖所

sanc·tum /ˈsæŋktəm; ˈsæŋktəm/ *n* **1** a holy place 聖所；聖殿 **2 your inner sanctum** *infml* a private place or room where can be quiet and alone 〔非正式〕〔不受干擾的〕私室；密室

sand¹ /sænd; sænd/ *n* **1** [U] loose material of many fine small grains which many beaches (BEACH) and deserts are made of and which is used for making things like cement and glass 沙，沙粒，砂: *a heap of sand* 一堆沙子 | *children playing in the sand* 在沙灘上玩耍的兒童 **2 sands** [pl] a large area of sand 沙地；沙灘；沙洲: *desert sands* 荒蕪的沙洲

sand² *v* [T] **1** (also 又作 **sand** sthg ↔ **down**) to make a surface smoother by rubbing it, usually with special rough paper 〔用砂紙〕磨光，磨平: *Sand down the door-frames before painting them!* 要用砂紙把門框磨光後才能上油漆! **2** to put sand on a surface 在〔表層〕鋪上沙子

san·dal /ˈsændl; ˈsændl/ *n* a light open shoe that is worn in warm weather 涼鞋 –see picture on page 210 見 210 頁彩圖

sand·bank /ˈsændˌbæŋk; ˈsændbæŋk/ *n* a large raised mass of sand in a river or sea 〔河或海裡的〕沙丘；沙壩

sand·cas·tle /ˈsændˌkæsl; ˈsændˌkɑːsəl/ *n* a

castle made by children out of sand 〔小孩子用沙子堆成的〕沙城堡

sand·pa·per /ˈsændˌpepɚ; ˈsændˌpeɪpəʳ/ *n* [U] special rough paper which you rub on surfaces to make them smoother 砂紙 – **sandpaper** *v* [T]

sand·pit /ˈsændˌpɪt; ˈsændˌpɪt/ *n* an enclosed hole or area which contains sand for children to play in 〔供兒童玩耍的〕沙坑

sand·stone /ˈsændˌston; ˈsændstəʊn/ *n* [U] soft rock formed mainly from sand 砂岩

sand·storm /ˈsændˌstɔrm; ˈsændstɔːm/ *n* a storm in which a strong wind blows large amounts of sand about, especially in a desert 沙暴，大風沙

sand·wich¹ /ˈsændwɪtʃ; ˈsænwɪdʒ/ *n* two pieces of bread with another food between them 三文治，三明治，夾心麵包片: *She made herself a chicken sandwich.* 她親自做了雞肉三明治。

sandwich² *v* [T] to put something between two other things, often so that it cannot move 把〔某物〕夾在〔兩物之間〕: *I found myself sandwiched between a group of teenagers and a brick wall.* 我發現自己被擠在一羣青少年和一堵磚牆之間。

sandwich board /ˈ··· ·/ *n* a pair of advertising signs which hang over the front and back of a person who then walks about in public 〔掛在胸前和背後在公眾場合走動的〕夾板廣告牌

sandwich course /ˈ··· ·/ *n* a course of study in which some periods are spent working for a company 工讀交替制課程，"三文治"課程

sand·y /ˈsændi; ˈsændi/ *adj* **sandier, sandiest 1** consisting of sand 由沙構成的，沙質的: *a sandy beach* 沙灘 **2** covered in sand 覆蓋着沙的: *My towel's all sandy.* 我的毛巾上全是沙子。**3** yellowish-brown (used especially of hair) 沙色的，棕黃色的〔尤指頭髮〕 –**sandiness** *n* [U]

sane /sen; seɪn/ *adj* **1** having a healthy mind 心智健全的，神志正常的 –opposite 反義 **insane 2** sensible 理智的；明智的: *The country needs a sane education policy.* 那國家需要一種明智的教育政策。

sang /sæŋ; sæŋ/ the past tense of SING ☆ SING 的過去式

san·guine /ˈsæŋgwɪn; ˈsæŋgwⱼn/ *adj fml* quietly confident that there is no need to worry 〔正式〕十分自信的；樂觀的

san·i·ta·ry /ˈsænəˌtɛri; ˈsænⱼtəri/ *adj* **1** of or concerned with health, especially the treatment or removal of human waste substances, dirt, or infection 〔有關〕衛生的〔尤指清除廢物、髒物或傳染病〕；保健的: *Sanitary inspectors will be visiting all local restaurants.* 衛生檢查人員將巡視當地所有的餐館。**2** clean and no threat to health 清潔的；不危害健康的: *The kitchen can't be very sanitary with all those flies about.* 廚房裡到

處是蒼蠅, 不可能保持清潔衛生。

sanitary tow·el /ˈˑˑˑ, ˑˑ/ n (also 又作 **sanitary napkin** AmE 【美式】) a small mass of soft paper which a woman may wear during her PERIOD to catch the blood 衛生巾, 月經帶

san·i·ta·tion /ˌsænəˈteʃən; ˌsæn̩ˈteɪʃən/ n [U] means for protecting public health, especially by removing and treating waste 公共衛生(設施)

san·i·to·ri·um /ˌsænəˈtɔːriəm; ˌsæn̩ˈtɔːriəm/ n (also 又作 **sanitarium** /-ˈteriəm; -ˈteəriəm/) the usual American spelling of 【美式】 SANATORIUM

san·i·ty /ˈsænəti; ˈsæn̩ti/ n [U] **1** the state of having a healthy mind 心智健全, 精神正常: *She suffered temporary loss of sanity after her son's death.* 她的兒子死後, 她曾一度精神錯亂。 **2** good sense and judgment 明智; 理智; 通情達理: *We need someone to bring sanity to our meetings.* 我們需要有人來使我們的會議進行得理智一點。

sank /sæŋk; sæŋk/ the past tense of SINK ☆ SINK 的過去式

San·ta Claus /ˈsæntɪ ˌklɔz; ˈsæntə klɔːz/ n see 見 FATHER CHRISTMAS

sap[1] /sæp; sæp/ v **-pp-** [T] to weaken or destroy something, especially over a long period 〔經過長時間〕逐漸削弱, 破壞〔某事物〕: *Her long illness gradually sapped her strength.* 她那長期不癒的疾病慢慢地使她體力不支了。

sap[2] n [U] the watery liquid that carries food through a plant 〔植物的〕汁液, 樹液

sap·ling /ˈsæplɪŋ; ˈsæplɪŋ/ n a young tree 樹苗, 幼樹

sap·phire /ˈsæfaɪr; ˈsæfaɪəʳ/ n [C;U] a bright blue precious stone 藍寶石

sar·cas·m /ˈsɑːkæzəm; ˈsɑːkæzəm/ n [U] speech or writing which clearly means the opposite to what is actually said and which is often intended to hurt someone 諷刺, 挖苦, 嘲笑: *"It was a great idea to leave the dog and the cat in the same room," she pointed out with heavy sarcasm.* "把狗和貓放在同一個房間裡可真是個絕妙的主意," 她以極諷刺的口吻說道。 **–sarcastic** adj: *a sarcastic remark* 挖苦的話 | *Do you have to be so sarcastic?* 你非得那麼挖苦人不可嗎? **–sarcastically** adv

sar·dine /sɑːˈdiːn; sɑːˈdiːn◂/ v **1** a small fish sold as food in tins and often preserved in oil 〔常指油浸罐裝的〕沙丁魚 **2** like sardines infml so close together that little movement is possible 【非正式】〔像沙丁魚那樣〕緊擠在一起

sar·don·ic /sɑːˈdɒnɪk; sɑːˈdɒnɪk/ adj showing complete lack of respect for people or matters that you consider unimportant or foolish 嘲笑的; 冷嘲的; 譏諷的: *a sardonic smile* 嘲弄的微笑, 冷笑 **–sardonically** /-klɪ; -kli/ adv

sa·ri /ˈsɑːri; ˈsɑːri/ n a length of light cloth that is wrapped around your body, worn especially by Hindu women 莎麗(服)〔印度婦女裹身用的長條布〕 –see picture on page 210 見 210 頁彩圖

sa·rong /səˈrɒŋ; səˈrɒŋ/ n a piece of cloth which is wrapped around the lower part of your body and tied at the waist, worn especially by Indonesian and Malaysian women and men 紗籠, 圍裙〔印尼人及馬來人裹在腰部的長條布〕

sar·to·ri·al /sɑːˈtɔːriəl; sɑːˈtɔːriəl/ adj fml concerning men's clothes or the way they are made 【正式】男式服裝的

sash /sæʃ; sæʃ/ n a length of cloth which is worn round your waist or, usually as a mark of honour, over one shoulder 〔象徵榮譽的〕腰帶; 肩帶; 飾帶

sash win·dow /ˈˑ ˈˑˑ/ n a window consisting of two frames with glass in them, which opens by sliding one of the frames up or down 上下拉窗, 框格窗

sat /sæt; sæt/ the past tense and past participle of SIT ☆SIT 的過去式和過去分詞

Sa·tan /ˈsetn; ˈseɪtn/ n the Devil 撒旦, 魔鬼

sa·tan·ic /seˈtænɪk; səˈtænɪk/ adj **1** evil or wicked 邪惡的; 罪惡的 **2** concerning the Devil 撒旦的, 魔鬼的

sat·an·ism /ˈsetənɪzm; ˈseɪtənɪzəm/ n (also 又作 **Satanism**) [U] the worship of the Devil 對撒旦的崇拜, 魔鬼崇拜

satch·el /ˈsætʃəl; ˈsætʃəl/ n a small bag with a band for carrying over your shoulder, used by a child to carry things to and from school 小背包; 書包

sat·ed /ˈsetɪd; ˈseɪtɪd/ adj be sated with fml to have reached the point when you do not want any more of something 【正式】使厭膩, 使厭足

sat·el·lite /ˈsætlˌaɪt; ˈsæt̩laɪt/ n **1** a natural or man-made object which moves around a larger one in space 衛星; 人造衛星: *The moon is a satellite of the Earth.* 月球是地球的衛星。 | *The broadcast came from America by satellite.* 廣播節目是經人造衛星從美國傳來的。 **2** a country or some form of organization that is dependent on a more powerful one 衛星國; 附屬組織

satellite dish /ˈˑˑˑ ˈˑ/ (also 又作 DISH) n **1** the large round surface of a radio TELESCOPE 〔射電望遠鏡中巨大的〕拋物面反射器 **2** a small plate-like object which people fix to their houses so that they can receive television pictures broadcast by satellites 〔接收衛星電視圖像的小型家用的〕衛星天線, 拋物面天線 –see picture on page 729 見 729 頁彩圖

sa·ti·ate /ˈseʃɪet; ˈseɪʃieɪt/ v **satiated, satiating** [T] to satisfy someone with enough, or even too much, of something 使〔某人〕滿足; 使飽足: *We ate until everyone was completely satiated.* 我們人人都吃得酒足飯飽。

sat·in /ˈsætɪn; ˈsæt̩n/ n [U] a kind of smooth and shiny silk cloth 緞子 **–satin** adj:

satin pyjamas 緞子睡衣 –**satiny** *adj*: *satiny skin* 柔滑的皮膚

sat·ire /'sætaɪr; 'sætaɪə/ *n* [C;U] a style, especially of writing, which attempts to show the foolishness of something by making you laugh at it 諷刺; 譏諷〔尤指諷刺作品〕: *The play is a satire on the government's defence policy.* 這是個諷刺政府防衛政策的戲劇。

sa·tir·i·cal /sə'tɪrɪkl; sə'tɪrɪkəl/ *adj* (also 又作 **satiric**) using satire 使用諷刺手法的; 諷刺的 –**satirically** *adv*

sat·ir·ize /'sætəˌraɪz; 'sætɪˌraɪz/ *v* **satirized**, **satirizing** (also 又作 **satirise** *BrE* 〔英式〕) [T] to try to make people laugh at a person or thing by showing their foolishness in an amusing way, especially in a work of literature 諷刺, 譏諷〔人或物〕: *She was arrested for writing a book which satirized the president and his family.* 她因寫了一本諷刺總統及其家人的書而被捕。

***sat·is·fac·tion** /ˌsætɪs'fækʃən; ˌsætɪs'fækʃən/ *n* [U] **1** a feeling of pleasure which is the result of success 滿意; 滿足: *We get great satisfaction from improving the house ourselves.* 我們從自己動手裝修房子中得到極大的滿足。–opposite 反義 **dissatisfaction 2** *fml* the giving of something which is wanted or needed 〔正式〕賠償; 補償: *Take your complaint to the manager and demand satisfaction!* 向經理投訴並要求賠償! **3 to someone's satisfaction** so that someone is pleased or believes that something is true 令某人滿意; 使某人確信: *The work was done to her satisfaction.* 工作做得令她滿意。| *My version of events was proved to the satisfaction of the court.* 法院確信我說的都是事實。

sat·is·fac·to·ry /ˌsætɪs'fæktəri; ˌsætɪs'fæktəri/ *adj* **1** good enough 令人滿意的; 符合要求的: *Jim's examination results are not satisfactory.* 吉姆的考試成績不理想。**2** pleasing 如意的: *This year's profits are very satisfactory.* 今年的利潤十分令人滿意。–opposite **unsatisfactory** –**satisfactorily** *adv*

sat·is·fied /'sætɪsˌfaɪd; 'sætɪsˌfaɪd/ *adj* **1** pleased or contented 滿意的; 滿足的: *There goes another satisfied customer!* 又送走了一位心滿意足的顧客! **2** certain 確信的: *I am satisfied that he is telling the truth.* 我確信他是在說真話。

***sat·is·fy** /'sætɪsˌfaɪ; 'sætɪsˌfaɪ/ *v* **satisfied**, **satisfied** [T] **1** to please someone 使〔某人〕滿意; 使滿足: *Nothing I do ever satisfies my mother.* 我做甚麼都不能使母親感到滿意。| *Some people are very hard to satisfy.* 有些人很難滿足。–opposite 反義 **dissatisfy 2** to have or give what is wanted or needed 滿足〔需要〕; 符合: *First you must satisfy the college entry requirements.* 首先你必須符合學院的入學要求。| *Just satisfy my curiosity and tell me what happened next.* 就滿足一下我的好奇心, 把接下去發生的事告訴我吧。**3**

fml to persuade someone that something is true 〔正式〕使〔某人〕確信: *Can you satisfy me that you were not involved in the fight?* 你能使我相信你沒有參與打架嗎?

sat·is·fy·ing /'sætɪsˌfaɪɪŋ; 'sætɪsˌfaɪ-ɪŋ/ *adj* giving pleasure 令人滿意的; 使人滿足的: *a satisfying meal* 令人滿意的一頓飯 | *a satisfying job* 令人有滿足感的工作 –**satisfyingly** *adv*

sat·su·ma /ˌsæt'suːmə; sæt'suːmə/ *n* a fruit like a small orange, with skin that comes off easily 蜜橘

sat·u·rate /'sætʃəˌret; 'sætʃəreɪt/ *v* **saturated**, **saturating** [T] **1** to make something extremely wet 浸透, 濕透〔某物〕: *His shirt was completely saturated in blood.* 他的襯衫完全被血浸透了。| *a towel saturated with seawater* 被海水浸透的毛巾 **2** to fill something completely 使〔某物〕飽和: *The market is saturated with new products at the moment.* 目前新產品充斥市場。–**saturation** /ˌsætʃə'reʃən; ˌsætʃə'reɪʃən/ *n* [U]

Sat·ur·day /'sætədɪ; 'sætədeɪ/ *n* (also 又作 **Sat.**) the day after Friday and before Sunday 星期六

Sat·urn /'sætən; 'sætən/ *n* the PLANET which is sixth in order from the sun and is surrounded by large rings 土星

sat·ur·nine /'sætəˌnaɪn; 'sætənaɪn/ *adj* *lit* solemn and unfriendly 〔文〕嚴肅的; 不友好的; 陰沉的

sat·yr /'sætə; 'sætə/ *n* a god who is usually represented in ancient stories as half human and half goat 〔古代神話中〕半人半羊的神

sauce /sɔs; sɔːs/ *n* **1** [C;U] a thick liquid that is poured over or eaten with food 調味汁; 醬汁: *ice cream with chocolate sauce* 澆巧克力汁的冰淇淋 | *vegetables in a cheese sauce* 用奶酪醬伴的蔬菜 **2** [U] *infml* disrespectful but usually harmless remarks, such as those a disobedient child might make to an adult 〔非正式〕無禮的話: *I've had enough of your sauce; just do as you're told!* 你對我太無禮了, 就照我說的去做!

sauce·pan /'sɔsˌpæn; 'sɔːspən/ *n* a deep metal cooking pot which has a handle and usually a lid 〔有柄和蓋的〕深平底鍋 –see picture on page 244 見 244 頁彩圖

sau·cer /'sɔsə; 'sɔːsə/ *n* a small plate with curved edges which you put a cup on 茶托, 茶杯碟

sauc·y /'sɔsɪ; 'sɔːsi/ *adj* **saucier**, **sauciest** *infml* disrespectful in a way that is usually harmless and often amusing 〔非正式〕無禮的; 調皮的: *a saucy grin* 調皮的一笑 –**saucily** *adv* –**sauciness** *n* [U]

sau·na /'saʊnə; 'sɔːnə/ *n* **1** a period of sitting or lying in a room filled with hot steam, often followed by a cold bath 桑拿浴, 蒸氣浴 **2** the room where you sit 蒸氣浴室

saun·ter /'sɔntə; 'sɔːntər/ v [I +adv/prep] to walk in an unhurried way, and usually in a confident manner 閒逛; 漫步: *He sauntered off, looking as if he hadn't a care in the world.* 他悠閒地走開了，看上去若無牽無掛。– **saunter** n [sing]

saus·age /'sɔsɪdʒ; 'sɒsɪdʒ/ n [C;U] a thin tube of animal skin filled mainly with meat and bread, which is eaten hot or cold 香腸: *Sausages and chips, please.* 請來點香腸和炸馬鈴薯條。–see picture on page 504 見 504 頁彩圖

sausage roll /,·· '·/ n a small quantity of sausage meat covered in a pastry 〔包以麵皮的〕香腸卷

sau·té /so'te; 'səʊteɪ/ v **sautéed** or **sautéd**; **sautéeing** or **sautéing** [T] to cook something quickly in a little hot oil or fat 快炒; 快炸; 快煎〔食物〕: *Sauté the onions for five minutes.* 把洋葱炒五分鐘。– **sauté** adj: *sauté potatoes* 快炸的馬鈴薯

sav·age¹ /'sævɪdʒ; 'sævɪdʒ/ adj **1** extremely cruel or violent 兇猛的; 殘暴的; 兇惡的: *a savage dog* 兇猛的狗 | *a savage attack on her reputation* 對她名譽的惡毒攻擊 **2** [only before a noun 只用於名詞前] uncivilized 不文明的; 野蠻的: *savage customs* 不文明的習俗 –**savagely** adv –**savageness** n [U]

savage² n an uncivilized person 野蠻人; 未開化的人

savage³ v **savaged**, **savaging** [T] to attack a person or animal and cause them serious harm 兇猛地攻擊〔人或動物〕; 殘害: *I was savaged by a mad dog.* 我被一隻瘋狗咬傷了。

sav·ag·e·ry /'sævɪdʒrɪ; 'sævɪdʒəri/ n [U] extreme violence or cruelty 殘暴; 野蠻: *The judge was appalled by the savagery of his attack on his wife.* 他對妻子的暴行令法官震驚。

sa·van·nah /sə'vænə; sə'vænə/ n (also 亦作 **savanna**) [C;U] a flat area of grassy land without trees, in a warm country 〔熱帶的〕無樹木大草原

★★★save¹ /seɪv; seɪv/ v **1** [T] to prevent a person or thing being harmed or destroyed 救, 挽救, 拯救: *Help! Save me!* 救命! 救救我吧! | *He saved his friend* **from** *falling.* 他救了他的朋友，使他沒掉下去。 | *I managed to save some of the furniture from the fire.* 我設法從火中救出了幾件家具。 | *She saved his life.* 她救了他的命。 **2 to save your life** infml however hard you try 〔非正式〕無論多麼努力: *I couldn't pass an exam now to save my life!* 我現在無論多麼努力都無法通過考試! **3 save face** to try to keep other people's respect 保全面子: *She was late because she overslept, but she invented a car accident to save face.* 她因睡過頭而遲到，但為保全面子，她謊稱遇上交通意外。 **4** [I; T] to put something, especially money, aside for later use 儲蓄; 保存: *The children must learn to save.* 孩子一定要學會儲蓄。 | *I'm saving this pie* **for** *lunch tomorrow.* 我留

下這個餡餅作為明天的午餐。 | *She saved her strength for the last minutes of the race.* 她留著勁準備在賽跑的最後幾分鐘衝刺。 **5** [T] to avoid unnecessary waste 節省; 節約: *The council will save a lot of money by closing the leisure centre.* 關閉娛樂中心會使地方議會節省很多錢。 | *We'll save time if we go by car.* 我們要是坐汽車去，就可以節省時間。 | *If you buy the family-size box it will save you £1.* 如果你買這種家庭的大包裝，就能省下一英鎊。 **6 save your breath** to keep silent since there is no point in speaking 不必白費唇舌: *I've already made a decision, so you can save your breath.* 我已經作出決定，所以你不用白費口舌了。 **7** [T] to make it unnecessary for someone to do something 免去, 省去〔某事物〕: *If we go out to eat, it'll save me cooking tonight.* 我們出外吃飯，就省得我今晚燒飯了。 | *Save yourself a lot of trouble and pay someone to do the work.* 付錢讓別人做這工作可省去許多麻煩。 **8** [T] to stop the ball going into the net in some sports, such as football 〔足球等守門員〕救球: *He saved three goals in the first half of the match.* 他在比賽的上半場救了三球。

save on sthg phr v [T] to avoid wasting something 節省, 避免浪費〔某物〕: *We can all go in one car, to save on petrol.* 為節省汽油，我們大家可以坐一輛汽車。

save up phr v [I] to put money aside for later use 儲蓄, 存錢: *We're saving up to buy a new car.* 我們在儲錢買新汽車。

save² n a quick action by the GOALKEEPER in a game such as football, which prevents the opponents scoring a goal 〔足球等守門員的〕救球

save³ prep (also 又作 **saving**) lit except (a word rarely used in modern English)〖文〗除了〔現代英語中已很少使用〕: *Save for one old lady, the bus was empty.* 除了一個老太太之外，公共汽車上空無一人。

sav·er /'seɪvə; 'seɪvər/ n **1** a person who puts money aside for future use, especially in a bank or BUILDING SOCIETY account 儲蓄者 **2 saver** something that prevents loss or waste 節省…的裝置, 節約的器具: *The new motorway is a great time-saver for us.* 新建的高速公路為我們節省了不少時間。

★sav·ing¹ /'seɪvɪŋ; 'seɪvɪŋ/ n **1** the amount of something that is not lost or wasted 節省物的量; 節約率: *We are hoping for a 30% saving in work time lost through illness.* 我們期待著把因病假損失的工作時間省回百分之三十。 **2 savings** [pl] money which is put aside for future use, especially in a bank or BUILDING SOCIETY account 〔尤指銀行和建房互助會的〕儲蓄存款: *She won't need to touch her savings until she retires.* 她直到退休以後才需要動用她的存款。

saving² adj **1 a saving grace** a quality that makes something acceptable in spite of its weaknesses or faults 足以彌補〔某事物〕缺點

的特點; 〔彌補不足的〕可取之處: *The film's saving grace is its beautiful photography.* 這部電影的可取之處是它的攝影非常美。 **2 saving** that prevents loss or waste 節省的; 節儉的: *labour-saving devices such as microwave ovens* 諸如微波爐那樣的節省勞力的器具

sa·viour /'sevjə; 'seɪvjər/ *n* (**savior** *AmE*〖美式〗) **1 a** person who saves someone else from danger 救星; 拯救者: *She was her country's saviour during the war.* 大戰時她是國家的救星。 **2 the Saviour, our Saviour** Jesus Christ, in the Christian religion〔基督教的〕耶穌基督; 救世主

sa·vour¹ /'sevər; 'seɪvər/ *n* (**savor** *AmE*〖美式〗) [sing; U] **1 a** taste or smell 味道; 氣味 **2** the power to interest someone 情趣; 趣味

savour² *v* (**savor** *AmE*〖美式〗) [T] **1** to enjoy something, especially by tasting it slowly and purposefully 品嘗〔某物〕; 欣賞: *She drank the wine slowly, savouring every drop.* 她慢慢地喝著酒, 品嘗著每一滴的滋味。| *He savoured every minute he spent with her.* 他細細地回味與她度過的每一分鐘。 **2 savour of** (of a situation or activity) to suggest something unpleasant〔指情況或活動〕具有…的性質; 帶有〔不好〕的迹象: *His financial dealings savour of dishonesty to me.* 他的財務賬目看來對我有所隱瞞。

sa·vour·y /'sevərɪ; 'seɪvərɪ/ *adj* (**savory** *AmE*〖美式〗) **1** salty rather than sweet (used of food) 鹹的; 香辣的〔指食物〕 **2** pleasant or acceptable 令人愉快的; 受歡迎的: *Her behaviour in this affair has not been very savoury.* 她在這件事上的表現不太體面。

saw¹ /sɔ; sɔː/ the past tense of SEE ☆ SEE 的過去式

saw² *n* a hand tool or power-driven tool for cutting hard substances such as wood or metal 鋸子 –see picture on page 958 見 958 頁彩圖

saw³ *v* **sawed, sawed** or **sawn** [I;T] **1** to cut something with a saw〔用鋸〕鋸; 鋸開: *She sawed through a power cable by accident.* 她無意中鋸斷了電纜。| *He sawed the logs into firewood.* 他把原木鋸成了木柴。 **2** (also 又作 **saw at, saw away at**) to move something such as a knife backwards and forwards as if you are using a saw 拉鋸般地來回移動: *He sawed at the loaf of bread with the blunt knife.* 他用那把鈍刀像拉鋸那樣切開這條麵包。

saw sthg ↔ **off** *phr v* [T] to separate something from something larger using a saw 鋸掉〔某物〕: *Will you saw off the dead branches?* 你把那枯枝鋸掉好嗎?

saw sthg ↔ **up** *phr v* [T] to cut something into pieces with a saw 把〔某物〕鋸成小塊: *Saw this old table up so that it will fit in the dustbin.* 把這舊桌子鋸成小塊, 使它能放進垃圾桶內。

saw·dust /'sɔ,dʌst; 'sɔːdʌst/ *n* [U] a powder which is produced when wood is cut up 鋸末, 鋸(木)屑: *The floor was covered in sawdust.* 地板上滿是鋸末。

sawn /sɔn; sɔːn/ the past participle of SAW³ ☆ SAW³ 的過去分詞

sax·o·phone /'sæksə,fon; 'sæksəfəʊn/ *n* (also 又作 **sax** *infml*〖非正式〗) a metal musical instrument which you blow into, especially to play JAZZ 薩克斯管〔一種銅管樂器〕 –**saxophonist** /'sæksə,fonɪst; sæk'sɒfən‚st/ *n*

☆☆say¹ /se; seɪ/ *v* **said** /sɛd; sed/, **said**, 3rd person singular present tense 第三人稱單數現在式 **says** /sɛz; sez/ **1** [I;T; +(that)] to express something in speech 説, 講: *"I'd like another drink," he said.* 我想再喝一杯, 他説。| *She said she would come.* 她説她會來的。| *Don't believe anything he says.* 他説甚麼都不要相信。| *I said no and I mean it!* 我説了不行就是不行! | *Don't be afraid to say what you think.* 不用害怕把自己的想法説出來。| *Nobody would say you were lazy.* 沒有人會説你懶惰。| *"What's he going to do now?" "I'd rather not say."* "他現在打算做甚麼?" "我還是不説好了。" **2** [I;T; +(that)] to express something in words or by some other sign〔用言語或其他符號〕表達, 説明: *What does that notice say?* 那則佈告説些甚麼? | *My watch says 5.30.* 我的手錶上是五點三十分。| *She didn't speak, but her expression said everything.* 她沒有開口, 但她的表情足以説明一切。 **3** [T] to repeat words that you have learned 唸; 背誦: *Say your prayers before you go to bed!* 你祈完禱後才能上牀睡覺! **4 say something to yourself** to think something 心中暗想某事: *"She's lying," John said to himself.* "她在撒謊," 約翰暗自思量着。 **5 I say** a phrase used to express surprise or to get someone's attention (it is not often used in modern English) 我説呀〔用於表示驚訝, 或吸引某人注意; 在現代英語中已不常用〕 **6 say, let's say: a** suppose; you can use these expressions when you want someone to consider a situation 假定; 假如〔用以請某人考慮某事〕: *Say he refuses to help us. What are we going to do then?* 假如他拒絕幫助我們, 我們打算下一步怎麼辦? | *Say he refused to help us. What would we do then?* 假定他拒絕了幫助我們, 我們接着會幹些甚麼? **b** suppose; you can use these expressions when you are suggesting something 假設; 讓〔用於建議某事〕: *"Say we meet at 5 o'clock. How would that be?" "Well, I think that's leaving it a bit late. Let's say 4.30."* "讓我們五點鐘碰頭, 那樣的安排怎樣?" "嗯, 我覺得稍晚了一點, 定在四點半吧。" **c** for example 比如説: *Let's go somewhere hot — Italy, say.* 我們到熱一點的地方去吧, 比如説意大利。| *at an angle of, say, 60°* 比如説, 在六十度角 **7 that is to say** in other words 那就是説; 換言之 **8 they say** the general feeling of most people is 人們説, 據説〔表示大多數人的感覺〕: *They say that* *too much sugar is bad for you, but it's never done me any harm.* 據說糖吃得太多對健康沒好處，但還從未損害到我的身體。**9 to say nothing of** a phrase used to add that something else should be considered 更不用説，更談不到〔用於補充考慮事情的其他方面〕: *Three people were hurt, to say nothing of the damage to the building.* 有三個人受了傷，建築物的損壞更不用説了。**10 to say the least** a phrase used to suggest that you could express your feelings even more strongly 至少可以這樣説; 不誇張地説〔用於暗示完全可以用更強的語氣表達情感〕: *I was upset by her attitude, to say the least.* 毫不誇張地説，她的態度使我生氣。**11 You can say that again!** *infml* a phrase used when someone has just said something which you strongly agree with〔非正式〕我同意! 你説對了!〔用於完全同意某人的意見〕: *"He hasn't been very easy to work with recently." "You can say that again!"* "最近與他共事不太容易。" "你説得很對!" **12 You don't say, You don't say so!** *infml* phrases used to express surprise or, when spoken in a certain way, a lack of surprise〔非正式〕不會這樣吧! 不至於吧!〔表示驚訝，但不大驚小怪〕

> ■ USAGE 用法: Compare **say** and **tell** in these sentences ☆比較這些句子中的 **say** 和 **tell**: *He said he was tired.* 他説他累了。| *He told me he was tired.* 他告訴我説他累了。| *She said something.* 她説了幾句話。| *She told me something.* 她跟我講了一些事情。**Say** cannot have a person as its object ☆ **Say** 後面不能用人作為受詞: *Please say something.* 請説幾句吧。**Tell** often has a person as its object ☆ **tell** 後面時常用人作為受詞: *What's the problem? Please tell me.* 有甚麼問題? 請告訴我。If it has two objects, one of them must be a person ☆ **tell** 如有兩個受詞，其中一個必定是人: *Please tell me your secret.* 請把你的祕密告訴我。

say² *n* [sing;U] the right to express an opinion which is then seriously considered 發言權; 決定權: *The unions had very little say in the new pay agreement.* 工會對新制定的工資協議不大有發言權。| *I want a say in any changes to the management structure.* 我想對任何管理體制結構上的改變有發言權。

*★**say·ing** /ˈseɪɪŋ; ˈseɪ-ɪŋ/ *n* a well-known wise statement 格言; 警句; 諺語: *"There's no smoke without fire," as the saying goes.* 常言道: "無火不起火煙〔無風不起浪〕。"

scab /skæb; skæb/ *n* **1** a hard mass of dried blood which forms over a cut or wound〔傷口上結的〕痂 **2** *infml* a person who works in a place where other people are refusing to work because of a STRIKE² (2) (a word used to express disapproval)〔非正式〕拒絕

參加罷工的人〔含貶義〕, 工賊

scab·bard /ˈskæbəd; ˈskæbəd/ *n* a leather or metal tube which holds the blade of a sword 劍鞘

scab·by /ˈskæbɪ; ˈskæbi/ *adj* covered with areas of dried blood which have formed over cuts or wounds 結(滿)痂的

scaf·fold /ˈskæfl̩d; ˈskæfəld/ *n* a raised surface on which criminals were killed in the past 斷頭台; 絞刑架: *He was led to the scaffold and executed.* 他被帶上斷頭台處死。

scaf·fold·ing /ˈskæfl̩dɪŋ; ˈskæfəldɪŋ/ *n* [U] poles and boards which are used to make a frame around a building for workmen to stand on 搭腳手架〔施工架〕用的材料

scald¹ /skɔld; skɔːld/ *v* [T] **1** to burn with hot liquid〔用沸水〕燙傷: *The coffee was so hot that he scalded himself.* 咖啡太熱，他被燙傷了。| *They were scalded to death by steam from a burst pipe.* 他們被爆裂的管子噴出的蒸汽燙死了。**2** *tech* to heat a liquid like milk until it is nearly boiling〔術語〕將〔牛奶等〕加熱至接近沸點

scald² *n* a skin burn caused by hot liquid or steam〔熱水或蒸汽造成的〕燙傷

scald·ing /ˈskɔldɪŋ; ˈskɔːldɪŋ/ *adj* so hot that it can burn you 滾燙的; 灼熱的: *scalding water* 滾燙的水 **–scalding** *adv*: *a scalding hot bath* 滾燙的熱水浴

*★**scale¹** /skel; skeɪl/ *n* **1** [C] a set of numbers or standards for measuring or comparing things〔用以度量或比較的〕標準; 級別, 等級: *I am still at the bottom of the company's pay scale.* 我還在拿公司最低一級的工資。**2** [C] a set of marks, especially numbers, on an instrument which is used for measuring 標度, 刻度: *I need a ruler with a metric scale.* 我需要一把有公制刻度的尺。**3** [C] a set of numbers comparing measurements on a map or on a model with actual measurements 比例; 比率; 比例尺: *This map uses a scale of 1 inch to the mile.* 這幅地圖使用一英寸代表一英里的比例。| *a scale of 1:25,000* 1:25,000 的比例尺 **4** [C;U] the size of something, especially in relation to other things or to what is usual 規模; 大小: *He has gone into business on a large scale.* 他從事大規模的生意。**5 to scale** according to a fixed rule for reducing the size of something so that the measurements remain the same in relation to each other 按比例: *The plan of the building was carefully drawn to scale.* 這座建築物的圖紙是精確地按比例繪製的。[RELATED PHRASE 相關詞組 **out of scale**] **6 scales** [pl] a machine for weighing things 秤, 磅秤: *He weighed himself on the bathroom scales.* 他在浴室的磅秤上秤了一下體重。**7** [C] (also 又作 **scales** [pl]) a pair of pans for weighing an object by comparing it with a known weight 天平: *a laboratory scale* 實驗室用的天平 **8** [C] a set of musical notes in upward or downward order from

and to a particular note 音階: *Start by playing the scale of A.* 從A音階開始演奏。**9** [C] one of the small stiff pieces of skin which cover the body of animals like fish and snakes 〔魚、蛇等的〕鱗(片) **10** [U] a substance which forms inside pipes and pots containing boiling water 〔水管、水壺裡的〕水鏽，水垢

scale² v **scaled, scaling** [T] to climb up something steep 攀登〔陡牆等〕: *The burglar scaled the back wall and escaped.* 竊賊爬上後牆逃走了。

scale sthg ↔ **down** phr v [T] to reduce the size of something in a controlled way 〔按一定比例〕縮減: *The company has begun to scale down its operations in Africa.* 這公司已經開始相應縮減在非洲的業務。

scal·lop /ˈskɑləp; ˈskɒləp/ n (also 又作 **scollop**) **1** a sea creature which can be eaten 扇貝(的貝柱)，帶子 **2** one of a row of small curves forming an edge or pattern 扇形飾邊: *a dress with scallops around the neck* 領口有扇形飾邊的連衣裙

scal·ly·wag /ˈskælɪ,wæg; ˈskæliwæg/ n a person, especially a child, who behaves badly but without doing serious harm (a word which is often used in a humorous way) 〔尤指兒童〕搗蛋鬼；小壞蛋〔常含幽默〕

scalp¹ /skælp; skælp/ n the skin on the top of your head, where your hair grows 頭皮

scalp² v [T] (especially of North American Indians in the past) to cut the scalp off a dead enemy as a sign of victory 〔尤指舊時北美印第安人〕剝下〔打死的敵人的〕頭皮作為戰利品

scal·pel /ˈskælpɛl; ˈskælpəl/ n a small sharp knife used by doctors during operations 手術刀，解剖刀

scal·y /ˈskɛlɪ; ˈskeɪli/ adj **scalier, scaliest** covered with scales (SCALE¹ (9,10)) 多鱗的；滿是水垢的 –**scaliness** n [U]

scamp /skæmp; skæmp/ n a child who behaves badly but who you remain fond of 小淘氣；頑皮的孩子

scam·per /ˈskæmpə; ˈskæmpəʳ/ v [I + adv/prep] to run taking short quick steps, often playfully 蹦蹦跳跳地跑: *The children scampered off.* 孩子們蹦蹦跳跳地跑開了。| *The mouse scampered into its hole.* 老鼠很快地溜進了洞裡去。

scam·pi /ˈskæmpɪ; ˈskæmpi/ n [U] a dish of large prawns (PRAWN) covered in bread or flour and cooked in oil 〔裹麵包屑的〕炸大蝦

scan /skæn; skæn/ v **-nn-** [T] **1** to look quickly at something written, without reading it carefully, often looking for a particular thing 瀏覽，粗略地快看〔文章等〕: *He scanned the list of names for someone he knew.* 他瀏覽了一下名單，看看有沒有他認識的人。**2** to examine something closely, especially because you are looking for something 細看〔某物〕；〔尤指〕搜索: *The*

soldiers were scanning the sky for planes. 那些士兵在仔細觀察天空，看看有沒有飛機。– **scan** n [sing]: *a quick scan of the paper* 很快地看一看試卷 | *a brain scan* 腦掃描

scan·dal /ˈskændl; ˈskændl/ n **1** [C;U] something which public feeling considers to be immoral and shocking 引起公憤的事: *The affair caused a scandal which led to the minister's resignation.* 那件事激起了民憤，最終導致部長辭職。**2** [U] talk about someone's immoral and shocking behaviour 醜聞；流言蜚語: *All that newspaper prints is scandal!* 那份報紙上登的盡是醜聞! **3 be a scandal** to be something that you strongly disapprove of 成為反感的事；醜事: *It's a scandal that the streets aren't cleaned more often!* 街道打掃的次數那麼少，可真是丟臉!

scan·dal·ize /ˈskændl,aɪz; ˈskændəl-aɪz/ v **scandalized, scandalizing** (also 又作 **scandalise** BrE 〔英式〕) [T] to shock someone by doing something they consider morally wrong 震驚〔某人〕: *The clothes she wore to church scandalized the older people.* 她去教堂做禮拜所穿的衣服，令年長者大為震驚。

scan·dal·ous /ˈskændləs; ˈskændələs/ adj morally offensive and shocking 丟臉的；令人反感的: *scandalous behaviour* 丟臉的行為 –**scandalously** adv

Scan·di·na·vi·an¹ /,skændəˈnevɪən; ,skændɪˈneɪviən/ adj of or connected with the peoples or languages of Denmark, Norway, Sweden, Finland, and Iceland 斯堪的納維亞的〔指丹麥、挪威、瑞典和冰島的〕；斯堪的納維亞人〔語〕的

Scandinavian² n a person from one of the countries in Scandinavia 斯堪的納維亞人

scan·ner /ˈskænə; ˈskænəʳ/ n an ELECTRONIC instrument used for following or examining something closely 〔電子〕掃描器: *The plane suddenly disappeared off their scanners.* 飛機突然從他們的掃描器中消失。| *a brain scanner* 大腦掃描器

scant /skænt; skænt/ adj little, and often not enough 少量的；不足的: *He paid scant attention to what was said.* 他不大注意聽別人講話。

scant·y /ˈskæntɪ; ˈskænti/ adj **scantier, scantiest** small in size or amount, and often not enough 不多的；少量的；不足的: *a scanty breakfast* 份量不足的早餐 | *scanty information* 不充足的資料 –**scantily** adv –**scantiness** n [U]

scape·goat /ˈskep,got; ˈskeɪpgəʊt/ n a person who is blamed for something that others have done or have also done 替罪羊；代人受過的人: *I was made the scapegoat for anything that went wrong.* 凡是出了差錯，我就成了替罪羊。

scar /skɑr; skɑːʳ/ n **1** a mark on your skin from an old cut or wound 傷痕，傷疤: *The operation left a terrible scar.* 那次手術留下了一道可怕的疤痕。**2** the effect of a very unpleasant experience 〔不幸的經歷留下的〕創傷: *Both countries bear the scars of last year's war.* 去年的戰爭給兩國留下了創傷。 – **scar** *v* **-rr-** [T]: *She was scarred by the accident, both physically and emotionally.* 那次事故令她在身體上和精神上都留下了創傷。

scarce /skɛrs; skɛəs/ *adj* **1** hard to find, and often not enough 供不應求的; 缺乏的; 不足的: *Food is becoming scarce in the cities.* 城市的食品供應越來越短缺。 –see 見 RARE (USAGE 用法) –compare 比較 COMMON **2 make yourself scarce** *infml* to go away or keep away, especially in order to avoid trouble 〔非正式〕離開; 躲開〔尤指為避免麻煩〕: *He told the children to make themselves scarce.* 他囑咐孩子們要躲着點。

scarce·ly /ˈskɛrslɪ; ˈskɛəslɪ/ *adv* **1** hardly 幾乎不: *She spoke scarcely a word of English.* 她幾乎連一個英文單詞都不會講。 | *"I didn't get hurt." "That's scarcely the point, is it?"* "我沒有受傷。" "那幾乎不是問題所在, 是嗎?" –see 見 HARDLY (USAGE 用法) **2** certainly not; a word you use to express strong opposition to an idea 決不〔用於表示強烈反對某一想法〕: *We can scarcely expect the child to travel alone!* 我們決不能期望這孩子可以單獨旅行!

scar·ci·ty /ˈskɛrsətɪ; ˈskɛəsəˌtɪ/ *n* **scarcities** [C;U] a situation in which there is not enough of something 缺乏, 不足: *The floods caused a scarcity of food and drinking water.* 洪水造成了食物和飲用水的短缺。

scare[1] /skɛr; skɛəʳ/ *v* **scared, scaring 1** [T] to frighten a person or animal 恐嚇〔人或動物〕, 使驚恐: *Don't let the noise scare you: it's only the wind.* 別讓那聲音把你嚇着了, 那不過是風聲。 **2 scare someone stiff** to make someone very frightened or nervous indeed 令某人非常驚怕: *Exams scare me stiff!* 考試真是讓我怕! **3** [I] to become frightened 受驚嚇: *She's a woman who doesn't scare easily.* 她是個不容易驚慌的女人。 **4 scare someone into doing something** to frighten someone enough to make them do something 嚇得某人做某事
scare sbdy/sthg ↔ **away** *phr v* [T] (also 又作 **scare** sbdy/sthg ↔ **off**) to make a person or animal go or stay away by frightening them 將〔人或動物〕嚇跑: *We've installed a burglar alarm to scare thieves off.* 我們已經安裝了防盜鈴來嚇跑小偷。

scare[2] *n* **1** [sing] a sudden feeling of fear 驚恐, 驚嚇: *What a scare you gave me, disappearing like that!* 你那樣突然失蹤, 可把我嚇了一跳! **2** [C] a usually mistaken or unreasonable public fear 恐慌: *a recent series of bomb scares* 最近接連二連三的爆炸引起的恐慌

scare·crow /ˈskɛrˌkro; ˈskɛəkrəʊ/ *n* an object in the shape of person which is put in a field to frighten birds away from crops 稻草人

scared /skɛrd; skɛəd/ *adj* **1** frightened or worried 驚恐的, 擔驚受怕的: *He was scared of the dog.* 他害怕那條狗。 | *I'm scared of flying.* 我害怕坐飛機。 | *We're all scared that we might lose our jobs.* 我們大家都害怕失業。 | *She's scared to leave the house.* 她害怕要離開那所房子。

□ USEFUL PATTERNS 有用句型
be scared of something; be scared to do something; be scared that…

2 scared stiff, scared to death extremely frightened 嚇呆; 嚇得要死: *I was scared to death that he would return unexpectedly.* 我對他會突然回來嚇得要死。

scarf /skɑrf; skɑːf/ *n* **scarfs** or **scarves** /skɑrvz; skɑːvz/ a piece of cloth that you wear round your neck, head, or shoulders to keep warm or to look attractive 圍巾; 頭巾; 披巾 –see picture on page 210 見 210 頁彩圖

scar·let /ˈskɑrlɪt; ˈskɑːlɪt/ *adj* bright red 猩紅的, 鮮紅的: *She went scarlet with embarrassment.* 她窘得滿臉通紅。 –see picture on page 243 見 243 頁彩圖 **–scarlet** *n* [U]

scarlet fe·ver /ˌ·· ˈ··/ *n* [U] a serious disease which gives you a very sore throat and red marks on your skin 猩紅熱

scar·y /ˈskɛrɪ; ˈskɛərɪ/ *adj* **scarier, scariest** *infml* rather frightening 〔非正式〕可怕的; 嚇人的: *a scary story* 嚇人的故事

scath·ing /ˈskeðɪŋ; ˈskeɪðɪŋ/ *adj* cruel in telling people what you think about a person or thing 尖刻的; 刻薄的; 嚴厲的: *She was very scathing about my work.* 她對我的工作要求十分苛刻。 | *He makes scathing remarks about my clothes.* 他對我的衣着不留情地批評。 **–scathingly** *adv*

scat·ter /ˈskætɚ; ˈskætə/ *v* **1** [T] to spread people or things over a wide area by moving or putting them there 使分散; 驅散: *The loud noise scattered the birds.* 那聲巨響驅散了鳥羣。 | *His desk was scattered with papers.* 他的書桌上到處都是文件。 **2** [I] to move quickly in different directions 分散; 散開: *The crowd scattered when it began to rain.* 一開始下雨, 人羣就散開了。

scat·ter·brain /ˈskætɚˌbren; ˈskætəbreɪn/ *n* *infml* a careless or forgetful person 〔非正式〕粗心大意的人; 疏忽健忘的人 **–scatterbrained** *adj*

scat·ty /ˈskætɪ; ˈskætɪ/ *adj* **scattier, scattiest** *infml* 〔非正式〕 **1** careless or forgetful 粗心的; 健忘的 **2** mad 發瘋的, 精神不正常的: *Living with her would drive anyone scatty!* 誰跟她住都會變得精神不正常!

scav·enge /ˈskævɪndʒ; ˈskævɪndʒ/ *v* **scavenged, scavenging** [I;T] to search for things to eat or use among used or unwanted food or objects 在〔廢物中〕尋找〔有用之物或食物〕: *At night you see homeless*

dogs scavenging for food. 在夜裡, 你可以見到流浪狗在垃圾中尋找食物。 | *We scavenged a few useful bits and pieces from the wreck of the car.* 我們從汽車的殘骸中撿到一些有用的零件。

scav·eng·er /ˈskævɪndʒɚ; ˈskævɪ̩ndʒəʳ/ *n* **1** a creature which feeds on decaying flesh or looks for food in waste matter 食腐肉的動物 **2** a person who scavenges 拾垃圾的人

sce·na·ri·o /sɪˈnɛrɪˌo; sɪ̩ˈnɑːrɪəʊ/ *n* **scenarios 1** a brief description of the story of a film 電影腳本 **2** a possible set of events 一系列可能發生的事件: *She outlined several convincing scenarios for the outbreak of a nuclear war.* 她頗有説服力地概述了核戰爭爆發時可能出現的幾種情況。

✲✲scene /siːn; siːn/ *n* **1** [C] a part of a play, film, or book which describes the events happening in one place over a short period of time 〔戲劇的〕一場; 〔電影的〕一個鏡頭; 〔小説書的〕一節; 場面, 場景: *Is that the scene in which he kills his sister?* 那是他殺害他姐姐的一場戲嗎? | *That speech comes in Act 2, Scene 3.* 那段講話出現在第二幕第三場。 **2** [C] a view of a place, sometimes in a picture 景色; 景象〔有時可指畫面中的風景〕: *a peaceful country scene* 寧靜的鄉村景色 | *He paints street scenes.* 他畫街道景色。 –see 見 VIEW¹ (USAGE 用法) **3** [C;U] a place where something happens 事發地點: *The murder weapon was found at the scene of the crime.* 殺人兇器是在犯罪現場找到的。 | *We're moving to the country for a change of scene.* 我們搬到鄉村去住, 換換環境。 **4 on the scene: a** in or into the place where something has happened 在場; 到場: *There had been an accident of some kind, and policemen started arriving on the scene.* 有某種事故發生了, 警察開始陸續趕到現場。 **b** into public knowledge or use 為大眾了解或使用: *When did the video recorder really come on the scene?* 錄影機是在甚麼時候真正被人們接受的? **5 behind the scenes: a** out of sight of the people watching in a theatre 在後台 **b** secretly 祕密地; 在幕後: *Decisions are being made behind the scenes, and it's time we were told about them.* 決定都是暗中作出的, 也是時候讓我們知道了。 **6** [sing] *infml* an area of activity 《非正式》活動領域: *What do you think of the music scene in Britain?* 你覺得英國的音樂領域怎麼樣? | *the political scene* 政治舞台 **7 not someone's scene** *infml* not something someone finds interesting 《非正式》某人不感興趣的事物: *Discos are just not my scene.* 我對迪斯科舞不感興趣。 **8** [C] a show of anger or strong feelings, in public 發脾氣; 當眾吵鬧: *Don't make a scene here; people are watching.* 別在這兒大吵大鬧, 人們都看着呢。 | *The news caused angry scenes in Parliament.* 那消息在國會引起了怒氣沖沖的爭吵。

sce·ne·ry /ˈsinɚɪ; ˈsiːnərɪ/ *n* [U] **1** natural surroundings, especially in beautiful and open country 〔尤指鄉村美麗的〕景色, 風景 – see 見 VIEW¹ (USAGE 用法) **2** the set of painted backgrounds and furniture used on a theatre stage to give an idea of the place where the action happens 舞台佈景: *a piece of scenery* 一件道具

sce·nic /ˈsinɪk; ˈsiːnɪk/ *adj* having or showing attractive natural scenery 自然景色的; 風景優美的: *We took the scenic route along the coast.* 我們走的是沿海一帶風景優美的路線。 –**scenically** /-klɪ; -klɪ/ *adv*

scent¹ /sɛnt; sent/ *n* **1** [C] a pleasant smell 香味: *the scent of roses* 玫瑰的芳香 –see SMELL (USAGE 用法) **2** [C;U] *BrE* a sweet-smelling liquid that women put on their skin 《英式》〔女用〕香水: *a bottle of scent* 一瓶香水 **3** [C] the smell left behind by an animal 〔動物的〕遺臭, 臭跡 **4 on the scent of** making progress towards finding a person or thing 找到線索; 追蹤: *We're on the scent of the killer.* 我們在追蹤那殺手。

scent² *v* [T] **1** to feel the presence of something 察覺到〔某物〕的存在: *She scented danger.* 她察覺到有危險。 **2** (especially of animals) to smell something, usually another animal 〔尤指動物〕嗅出, 聞到〔某物, 常為另一動物〕

scent·ed /ˈsɛntɪd; ˈsentɪ̩d/ *adj* having a pleasant smell 芳香的: *scented soap* 香皂 | *rose-scented* 玫瑰香的

scep·tic /ˈskɛptɪk; ˈskeptɪk/ *n* (**skeptic** *AmE* 《美式》) a person who has doubts about the truth of other people's beliefs or claims 持懷疑態度的人; 懷疑論者

scep·ti·cal /ˈskɛptɪkl; ˈskeptɪkəl/ *adj* doubtful about one or many things that other people claim or believe 懷疑(論)的: *I'm rather sceptical about the team's chances of winning.* 我對該球隊的獲勝機會會相當懷疑。 –**sceptically** *adv*: *"It seems unlikely," he said sceptically.* "這似乎不可能," 他懷疑地説。

scep·ti·cis·m /ˈskɛptəˌsɪzəm; ˈskeptɪ̩sɪzəm/ *n* [U] doubt 懷疑(態度); 懷疑論: *a claim which is being treated with some scepticism in Washington* 華盛頓方面有所懷疑的一項聲明

scep·tre /ˈsɛptɚ; ˈseptəʳ/ *n* (**scepter** *AmE* 《美式》) a rod carried by a ruler during ceremonies as a sign of power 〔象徵君主權位的〕節杖, 權杖

✲sched·ule¹ /ˈskɛdʒul; ˈʃedjuːl/ *n* **1** a timetable 時刻表, 時間表: *Has the new train schedule been published?* 新的火車時刻表印出來了嗎? | *This is my work schedule for the rest of the month.* 這是我這個月其餘日子的工作日程表。 **2 according to schedule** in the way it was planned 按照預定計劃: *Is everything going according to schedule?* 一切都在按預定計劃進行嗎? **3 ahead of schedule, on schedule, behind schedule** before, at, or after the planned time 提前; 準時; 遲於預定時間: *We're about a week behind schedule.* 我們的計劃大約遲了一星期。

schedule² *v* **scheduled, scheduling** [T] **1** to arrange something for a certain time 安排〔某事〕; 排定; 預定: *The meeting is scheduled to take place next week.* 會議安排在下星期舉行。| *We've scheduled that trip for Friday.* 我們已經把那次旅行定在星期五舉行。**2 a scheduled flight** a flight which appears on the regular airline timetable 定期航班

scheme¹ /skim; skiːm/ *n* **1** a plan or system for something 計劃; 規劃; 方案: *He's got some new scheme to make money.* 他有一些賺錢的新計劃。| *a health insurance scheme* 健康保險方案 **2** **someone's scheme of things** the way someone wants everything around them to be 某人所希望事情的發展過程: *His sister getting married just didn't fit into his scheme of things.* 他姐姐的婚姻不如他所期待的那樣稱心。

scheme² *v* **schemed, scheming** [I] to make plans in a way that is usually secret, clever, and morally unacceptable 搞陰謀(詭計); 策劃; 圖謀: *They're scheming to get the manager sacked.* 他們正在密謀使經理被解雇。– **schemer** *n* **–scheming** *adj*

schis·m /ˈsɪzəm; ˈsɪzəm/ *n* [C;U] *fml* the separation of a group into two parts as a result of disagreement《正式》〔組織因意見分歧而〕分裂; 分派

schiz·oid /ˈskɪzɔɪd/ *adj tech* like or suffering from schizophrenia《術語》精神分裂樣的; 患精神分裂症的

schiz·o·phre·ni·a /ˌskɪzəˈfriːnɪə; ˌskɪtsəʊˈfriː-nɪə/ *n* [U] *tech* an illness of the mind which causes a person to live in their imagination and behave in strange and unexpected ways《術語》精神分裂症 **–schizophrenic** /-ˈfrenɪk; -ˈfrenɪk/ *adj, n, tech*

schol·ar /ˈskɒlə; ˈskɒlə/ *n* **1** a person with great knowledge of one or more ACADEMIC subjects 學者 **2** a person who has been given money by an organization to help pay for a course of study 獎學金獲得者 **3 a good scholar, a bad scholar** a person who is or is not good at learning things they are being taught 學習能力強的學生; 學習能力差的學生

schol·ar·ly /ˈskɒləlɪ; ˈskɒləlɪ/ *adj* concerned with serious detailed ACADEMIC study 學術性的; 學問精深的: *His new book is a scholarly work.* 他的新書是一部學術性著作。

schol·ar·ship /ˈskɒləʃɪp; ˈskɒləʃɪp/ *n* **1** [C] a sum of money given to a student by an organization to help pay for a course of study 獎學金: *He won a scholarship to Oxford.* 他獲得一份到牛津大學唸書的獎學金。**2** [U] the method or result of serious detailed ACADEMIC study 學問, 學識: *Her book is a fine piece of scholarship.* 她的書是一部學術性著作。

一部卓越的學術著作。

scho·las·tic /skoˈlæstɪk; skəˈlæstɪk/ *adj* concerning schools or teaching 學校的; 教學的

school¹ /skul; skuːl/ *n* **1** [C;U] a place of education for children 學校: *That's the new secondary school.* 那是所新辦的中學。| *I go to school by bus.* 我坐公共汽車上學。| *school uniform* 校服 **2** [U] the time spent at school〔學校的〕上課時間: *What are you doing after school?* 放學後你打算幹甚麼? **3** [C + sing/pl verb] the students and teachers at a school 全體師生: *The whole school was sorry when she left.* 她離開時, 全校師生都很難過。**4** [C;U] an establishment where a particular subject or skill is taught 專科學校: *She goes to art school in London.* 她到倫敦藝術學校上課。| *a school of dance* 舞蹈學校 **5** [C] (also **School**) a department or college of certain universities in which a particular subject is taught〔某些大學中的〕學院: *the School of Law* 法學院 **6** [C;U] the usual American word for university〔美式英語的〕大學 **7** [C] a group of people with the same style of painting, ideas, or opinions 流派, 學派: *the Dutch school of painting* 荷蘭的繪畫流派 **8 a school of thought** a group of people who have a shared opinion 思想觀點相同的一羣人: *One school of thought says that hitting a child is the best form of discipline.* 有一派人的觀點是, 打孩子是最好的管教形式。**9** [C] a large group of fish or other sea creatures swimming together〔魚或其他海生動物的〕羣

school² *v* [T] to teach or train a person or animal 教育〔人〕; 訓練〔動物〕: *The children were schooled in obedience from a very early age.* 那些孩子從小就被教育要服從別人。

school·boy /ˈskul; ˈskuːlbɔɪ/ *n* a boy who attends school〔中·小學〕男生

school·child /ˈskul, tʃaɪld; ˈskuːltʃaɪld/ *n* **schoolchildren** /-, tʃɪldrən; -tʃɪldrən/ a child who attends school 學童; 學生

school·girl /ˈskul, gɜl; ˈskuːlgɜːl/ *n* a girl who attends school〔中·小學〕女生

school·ing /ˈskulɪŋ; ˈskuːlɪŋ/ *n* [U] education at school 學校教育: *He had only five years of schooling.* 他只讀過五年書。

school·mas·ter /ˈskul, mæstə; ˈskuːl, mɑːs-tə/ *n* a male teacher at a school (a word no longer used in modern English) 男教師〔現代英語中已不再使用〕

school·mis·tress /ˈskul, mɪstrɪs; ˈskuːl, mɪs-trɪs/ *n* a female teacher at a school (a word no longer used in modern English) 女教師〔現代英語中已不再使用〕

school·teach·er /ˈskul, titʃə; ˈskuːl, tiːtʃə/ *n* a teacher at a school〔中·小學〕教師

schoo·ner /ˈskunə; ˈskuːnə/ *n* a fast sailing ship 縱帆船

sci·ence /ˈsaɪəns; ˈsaɪəns/ *n* **1** [U] knowledge which depends on testing facts and stating general natural laws, or the study which produces this knowledge 科學: *the marvels of modern science* 現代科學的奇跡 **2** [C;U] a branch of such knowledge, such as chemistry 理科的一門學科〔如化學〕: *She's taking exams in three science subjects.* 她要參加三門理科的考試。 –compare 比較 ARTS **3** [C;U] something that needs exact skill (一門)專門知識, (一門)學問: *the science of cooking* 烹飪技巧 | *military science* 軍事科學

science fic·tion /ˌ·· ˈ··/ *n* (also 又作 **sci-fi** *infml*〖非正式〗) [U] stories about imaginary worlds or imaginary scientific developments 科學幻想小說, 科幻小說

science park /ˈ·· ·/ *n* an area where there are a lot of companies that are concerned with new TECHNOLOGY and scientific study 新技術研究開發區, 高科技園地

★sci·en·tif·ic /ˌsaɪənˈtɪfɪk; ˌsaɪənˈtɪfɪk◂/ *adj* **1** [only before a noun 只用於名詞前] relating to science 科學(上)的: *The microscope is a scientific instrument.* 顯微鏡是一種科學儀器。 | *She has a scientific background.* 她有從事科學的經驗。 **2** needing or showing exact skill or use of a system 需要技術的; 顯示技能的; 有系統的: *She has a very scientific approach to any problem.* 她以非常科學的方法處理任何問題。 –opposite 反義 **unscientific** (for 2) –**scientifically** /-klɪ; -kli/ *adv*

★sci·en·tist /ˈsaɪəntɪst; ˈsaɪənˌtɪst/ *n* a person who works or studies in an area of science, especially chemistry, PHYSICS, or BIOLOGY 科學家〔尤指研究化學、物理或生物學者〕: *nuclear scientists* 核子科學家

sci-fi /ˈsaɪ ˈfaɪ; ˈsaɪ·faɪ/ *n* [U] see 見 SCIENCE FICTION

scim·i·tar /ˈsɪmətə; ˈsɪmˌtə/ *n* a curved sword, formerly used in the Middle East 〔舊時中東地區人用的〕單刀彎刀

scin·til·lat·ing /ˈsɪntlˌeɪtɪŋ; ˈsɪntˌleɪtɪŋ/ *adj* quick, clever, and interesting (used especially of speech) 才氣橫溢的〔尤指講話〕: *scintillating conversation* 才氣橫溢的談話

scis·sors /ˈsɪzəz; ˈsɪzəz/ *n* [pl] two sharp blades, fastened at the centre and with handles at one end, for cutting paper or cloth 剪刀: *Have you got any scissors?* 你有剪刀嗎？ | *There's a pair of scissors in the drawer.* 抽屜裡有一把剪刀。 | *These scissors aren't very sharp.* 這把剪刀不太鋒利。 –see PAIR (USAGE 用法) –see picture on page 958 見 958 頁彩圖

scoff /skɒf; skɒf/ *v* **1** [I] to laugh at a person or idea by making remarks that show you have a low opinion of them 嘲笑; 嘲弄; 譏笑: *They just scoffed at my suggestion.* 他們嘲笑我的建議。 **2** [T] *infml* to eat something very fast and eagerly〖非正式〗狼吞虎嚥地吃: *Don't scoff all those cakes!* 別吃光那些蛋糕！

scold /skoʊld; skoʊld/ *v* [I;T] to express anger to someone about their behaviour (a

word which is not used much in modern English) 罵; 責罵〔現代英語中已不大使用〕: *Your father will scold you if he sees this mess.* 要是你父親看到這樣雜亂, 他準會罵你。 –**scolding** *n* [C;U]: *She gave me a terrible scolding!* 她狠狠地罵了我一頓！

scol·lop /ˈskɒləp; ˈskɒləp/ *n* see 見 SCALLOP

scone /skɒn; skɒn/ *n* a small soft round cake which is eaten with butter or JAM 烤餅〔一種塗上奶油或果醬吃的小圓軟餅〕

scoop¹ /skuːp; skuːp/ *n* **1** a container, or a special tool in the shape of a deep spoon, for picking up and moving liquids or loose materials 杓子; 小鏟: *a measuring scoop* 計量用杓 **2** (also 又作 **scoopful** /-fʊl; -fʊl/) the amount held by this 一杓的量: *Two scoops of ice-cream, please.* 請來兩杓冰淇淋。 **3** an exciting report that one particular newspaper manages to print before the public hears about it anywhere else 搶先報導的新聞; 獨家新聞

scoop² *v* **1** [T + adv/prep] to pick something up with a scoop or with your hand curved in the shape of a scoop〔用杓〕舀出; 用手捧: *He scooped up a handful of sand.* 他用手捧起一堆沙。 | *Can you scoop some sugar out of that bag?* 你能從那袋裡舀出一些白糖嗎？ **2** [T + adv/prep] to move something up with one quick, smooth movement〔輕快地〕推動〔某物〕: *She scooped the books into the rubbish bin.* 她把幾本書扔進垃圾箱裡。 **3** (of a newspaper) to print an exciting news report before any other newspaper〔報紙〕搶在〔別家報紙〕之前登出新聞

scoop sth **↔ up** *phr v* [T] to pick something up with a quick smooth movement 快速地撿起, 拾起〔某物〕

scoot /skuːt; skuːt/ *v* [I] *infml* to go or go away quickly〖非正式〗快跑; 趕快離開: *Scoot, before you do any more damage!* 快跑吧, 不要再作破壞了！

scoot·er /ˈskuːtə; ˈskuːtə/ *n* **1** (also 又作 **motor scooter** *fml*〖正式〗) a small motorcycle that does not move very fast〔車速不太快的〕小型摩托車 **2** a child's vehicle with two small wheels which you move by pushing on the ground with one foot while the other foot rests on a narrow board between the wheels〔兒童遊戲用的〕踏板車

★scope /skoʊp; skoʊp/ *n* [U] **1** chance for action or thought〔供採取行動、思考的〕機會; 餘地: *There's a lot of scope for improvement in your homework, Jenny.* 珍妮, 你的家庭作業還有許多改進的餘地。 **2** the limits of a subject or activity〔課題或活動的〕範圍: *I'm afraid that is outside the scope of our research.* 我恐怕那已超出了我們的研究範圍。

scorch¹ /skɔːtʃ; skɔːtʃ/ *v* **1** [I;T] to burn slightly so that it has a mark or marks on it 燒焦, 烤焦: *I've scorched my best shirt!* 我燙焦了我那件最好的襯衫！ | *Heat it gently so* *that it doesn't scorch.* 慢慢地加熱，別讓它烤焦。**2** [T] very dry indeed as a result of heat and no rain〔因酷熱和不下雨而〕曬枯；乾枯: *The garden is absolutely scorched!* 花園被曬得極為乾枯。**3** [I + adv/prep] *infml* to travel very fast〔非正式〕高速行駛

scorch² *n* (also 又作 **scorch mark** /ˈ‧‚‧/) a mark caused by a slight burn 燒焦；焦痕

scorch‧er /ˈskɔrtʃər; ˈskɔːtʃəʳ/ *n* a scorcher *infml* a very hot day〔非正式〕大熱天, 炎熱的日子

scorch‧ing /ˈskɔrtʃɪŋ; ˈskɔːtʃɪŋ/ *adj* so hot that it can burn you 灼熱的: *It's scorching outside.* 外面驕陽似火。**–scorching** *adv*: *a scorching hot day* 火辣辣的大熱天

⋆**score¹** /skɔr; skɔːʳ/ *n* **1** [C] the number of points gained in a game, competition, or test〔比賽中的〕得分；比分；進球: *The final score was two goals to nil.* 最後的比分是 2:0。| *"What's the score so far?" "2-1."* "到目前為止的比分是多少？" "二比一。" | *He always gets high scores in IQ tests.* 他在智商測試中總是得高分的。**2** [C] **a** a written copy of a piece of music 樂譜 **b** the music for a film or play〔電影或戲劇的〕配樂 **3 a score** 20 (a word which is no longer used in modern English) 二十〔數量單位〕〔現代英語中已不再使用〕**4 scores** [pl] a large number 許多, 大量: *There were scores of people waiting.* 有許多人在等。**5** [C] a cut in a hard surface 刻痕, 劃痕 **6** [C] harm that someone did to you in the past 宿怨, 舊仇: *I've got some old scores to settle with him.* 我有一些舊賬要跟他算。**7 know the score** *infml* to know the true, often unfavourable, facts of the situation〔非正式〕知道事實真相 **8 on that score** concerning the matter that has just been mentioned 在〔剛提到的〕那一點上: *I've got enough money, so don't worry about me on that score.* 我的錢足夠用的, 所以不必為此替我擔心。

⋆**score²** *v* **scored**, **scoring 1** [I;T] to gain points in a game, competition, or test〔比賽中〕得（分）；進（球）: *"He's got the ball... And he's scored!"* "他拿到了球…他得分了！" | *How many did the England team score?* 英格蘭隊進了多少球？| *He scored three goals.* 他打進了三球。**2** [I] to record the points won in a game while it is being played〔比賽中〕記分: *Will you score for us?* 你為我們記分好嗎？**3** [I;T] to succeed in something〔某事〕獲得成功: *a well-known writer who has scored again with another popular book* 因另一本暢銷書而取得成功的知名作家 | *The bomb scored a hit on the bridge.* 炸彈擊中了大橋。**4** [I;T] to gain an advantage, especially in an argument〔尤指在辯論中〕佔上風, 駁倒（對方）: *I hate conversations where people try to score over each other.* 我討厭那種針鋒相對, 彼此力圖駁倒對方的談話。| *I hate discussing things with him; he's only interested in scoring points off his opponent.*

我討厭和他討論事情, 他只愛跟你鬥嘴。**5** [T] to cut or mark the top of a surface with a sharp instrument〔用尖器〕刻痕, 劃痕: *Score the paper before folding it.* 把紙劃上摺痕再摺疊。

score sthg ↔ **out** *phr v* [T] *fml* (also 又作 **score** sthg ↔ **through**) to draw a line firmly through written words to show they should not be read〔正式〕劃掉, 刪去〔字句等〕

score‧board /ˈskɔr‚bɔrd; ˈskɔːbɔːd/ *n* a board on which the points won in a game are recorded while the game is being played〔體育比賽的〕記分牌

scor‧er /ˈskɔrər; ˈskɔːrəʳ/ *n* **1** a person who records the points won in a game while the game is being played〔比賽中的〕記分員 **2** a player who wins points in a game〔比賽中的〕得分者

scorn¹ /skɔrn; skɔːn/ *n* **1** [U] strong and often angry feelings expressed when a person feels that something has no value 輕蔑, 鄙視: *He treats all my ideas with scorn.* 他輕蔑地對待我的一切想法。**2 heap scorn on, pour scorn on** to show that you think something has no value at all 對〔某事物〕表示蔑視 **–scornful** *adj* **–scornfully** *adv*

scorn² *v* [T] **1** to refuse to accept something because you are proud or because it is not good enough 拒絕接受；不屑（做）: *She scorned our offers of help.* 她拒絕了我們提供的幫助。| *In those days unmarried women of her age were scorned by polite society.* 在當時, 她這年紀的未婚女子受到上流社會的擯棄。**2** to feel or show strongly that a person or thing has no value 輕蔑, 鄙視〔人或物〕

Scor‧pi‧o /ˈskɔrpiˌo; ˈskɔːpiəu/ *n* one of the signs of the ZODIAC〔占星術中的〕天蠍宮〔黃道十二宮的第八宮〕

scor‧pi‧on /ˈskɔrpiən; ˈskɔːpiən/ *n* a small animal with a poisonous sting in its curving tail 蠍子

Scot /skɑt; skɒt/ *n* a person from Scotland 蘇格蘭人

scotch /skɑtʃ; skɒtʃ/ *v* [T] *fml* to put an end to something〔正式〕制止, 撲滅, 粉碎: *How can we scotch these rumours?* 我們怎樣才能粉碎這些謠言呢？

Scotch *n* (also 又作 **Scotch, Scotch whisky**) [C;U] a strong alcoholic drink (WHISKY) made in Scotland 蘇格蘭威士忌酒: *a bottle of Scotch* 一瓶蘇格蘭威士忌酒 | *Two Scotches, please.* 請來兩杯蘇格蘭威士忌酒。

scotch tape /ˌ‧ ‧ˈ‧, ˈ‧ ‧/ *n* see 見 SELLOTAPE

scot-free /ˌ‧ ‧ˈ‧/ *adj* [never before a noun 不能用於名詞前] *infml* without harm or punishment〔非正式〕未受損害的；免於受罰的: *Some of the children were punished, but the others escaped scot-free.* 一些孩子受到了懲罰, 但另一些卻安然逃脫。

Scot‧land Yard /ˌskɑtlənd ˈjɑrd; ˌskɒtlənd ˈjɑːd/ *n* [U + sing/pl verb] **1** the main office of the London police 蘇格蘭場, 倫敦警察廳 **2** the police who work there 倫敦警方

Scot·tish /'skɒtɪʃ; 'skɒtɪʃ/ *adj* (also 又作 **Scots** /skɒts; skɒts/) of or connected with Scotland 蘇格蘭(人)的

scoun·drel /'skaʊndrəl; 'skaʊndrəl/ *n* a man whose behaviour is bad, selfish, and often criminal (a word which is only used in a formal or humorous way in modern English) 惡棍, 壞蛋, 無賴〔現代英語中只用於正式場合或帶幽默含義〕

scour /skaʊr; skaʊəʳ/ *v* [T] **1** to search an area thoroughly for a person or thing 四處搜索〔人或物〕: *scouring the horizon* **for** *a ship* 走遍地平線尋找一艘輪船 **2** to clean something by rubbing its surface hard with something rough 擦淨; 擦亮〔某物〕: *Can you scour those dirty pans?* 你能把那幾隻骯髒的平底鍋擦乾淨嗎?

scour·er /'skaʊrə; 'skaʊərəʳ/ *n* a piece of rough material which is used for cleaning cooking pots 刷鍋用具

scourge /skɜːdʒ; skɜːdʒ/ *n* something that causes great suffering to someone or something else 苦難的根源; 禍端: *Jack Evans, the self-appointed scourge* **of** *the political left* 傑克·埃文斯, 那位自封的 "政治左翼" 的禍根"

scout¹ /skaʊt; skaʊt/ *n* **1** a soldier who is sent ahead to get information about the enemy 偵察員, 偵察兵 **2** (also 又作 **boy scout**) a member of an association (**the Scouts**) which trains boys to have good characters and teaches them various useful skills 男童子軍 **3** someone who tries to find suitable people for particular jobs 物色人才的人 **4 a scout around** *infml* a search of an area 〔非正式〕搜尋, 搜索: *Have a scout around for something to eat.* 到處搜一搜, 看看有甚麼吃的東西"

scout² *v*

    scout around for sth *phr v* (also 又作 **scout for** sthg) [T] to look for something in different places 四處搜索, 尋找〔某物〕: *He scouted around for a shop that sold guitars.* 他到處尋找賣吉他的商店"

scowl /skaʊl; skaʊl/ *n* an expression on a person's face which shows that they are not at all pleased 不悅之色, 怒容 **–scowl** *v* [I]: *She scowled* **at** *the pile of dirty plates.* 她看到一堆髒盤子就露出不快的神色"

scrab·ble /'skræbl; 'skræbəl/ *v* **scrabbled, scrabbling** [I] *infml* to move your fingers wildly and quickly, especially if you are looking for something 〔非正式〕扒找; 亂摸: *She scrabbled* **about** *on the floor trying to pick up all the coins.* 她在地板上亂扒, 試圖撿起所有的硬幣"

scrag·gy /'skrægɪ; 'skrægi/ *adj* **scraggier, scraggiest** thin and bony 骨瘦如柴的, 皮包骨的: *a scraggy dog* 骨瘦如柴的狗

scram /skræm; skræm/ *v* **-mm-** [I] *infml* to

go away quickly 〔非正式〕快速走開: *You're not wanted here, so scram!* 這裡不需要你, 快滾開!

scram·ble¹ /'skræmbl; 'skræmbəl/ *v* **scrambled, scrambling 1** [I + adv/prep] to move quickly, especially over a rough surface or because you are in a hurry, often using your hands to help you 爬行; 攀登: *I scrambled up the rock.* 我爬上了那塊岩石" | *She scrambled to her feet.* 她趕忙爬起身來" **2** [I+ adv/prep] to move quickly in competition with other people 爭奪; 搶先: *Customers scrambled for the few remaining loaves of bread.* 顧客爭搶剩下的幾條麵包" **3** [T] to mix things so that they are not in their usual order 把〔東西〕弄亂: *The message has been scrambled for security reasons.* 為安全起見, 訊息已經被攪亂了" **4** [T] to mix the white and yellow parts of eggs together while cooking them 炒〔蛋〕: *scrambled eggs* 炒蛋

scramble² *n* [sing] **1** hurried and often difficult movement over a rough surface 爬行; 攀登: *It's quite a scramble to get to the top of the hill.* 要往上爬一大段路才能到達山頂" **2** a disorderly struggle for something 爭奪; 搶奪: *There was an undignified scramble* **for** *the best seats.* 大家都不顧尊嚴, 爭奪最佳座位"

scrap¹ /skræp; skræp/ *n* **1** [C] a small piece 小塊; 碎片; 少量: *a scrap of paper* 一小片紙 | *There isn't a scrap of evidence that she was involved.* 沒有任何證據表示她牽涉在內" **2 scraps** [pl] bits of eatable food which are left after a meal and usually thrown away 殘羹剩飯: *Give the dog those scraps.* 把那些剩菜給狗吃" **3** [U] material which has been used, and often thrown away, but which may still have some value 廢料: *scrap metal* 廢金屬 | *scrap paper* 廢紙 **4** [C] *infml* a fight or quarrel which is not very serious 〔非正式〕爭吵; 打架: *He got into another scrap at school.* 他在上學時又跟別人吵架了"

scrap² *v* **-pp-** [T] **1** to get rid of something which is no longer useful or wanted 廢棄, 拋棄〔某物〕: *Shall we scrap these plans and start again?* 我們廢棄這些計劃, 重新開始好嗎? **2** [I] *infml* to fight or quarrel, but not very seriously 〔非正式〕爭吵; 打架

scrap·book /'skræp,bʊk; 'skræpbʊk/ *n* a book of empty pages into which you can put things like newspaper articles or pictures that you want to keep safely 剪貼簿

scrape¹ /skreɪp; skreɪp/ *v* **scraped, scraping 1** [T] to remove something from a surface with a hard object 刮除〔某物〕: *Use a knife to scrape that dry paint off the washbasin.* 用小刀刮掉臉盆上的乾油漆" **2** [T] to remove the surface of something with or on a hard object 刮(削); 擦傷〔某物〕: *Could you scrape the carrots?* 你可以把胡蘿蔔削一下嗎? | *I* *scraped my leg when I fell.* 我跌了一跤, 擦傷了腿。 **3** [I + adv/prep; T] to rub roughly against something 刮; 擦: *He scraped his chair* **against** *the wall.* 他拖着椅子擦牆而過。 | *I hate the sound of fingernails scraping* **on** *the blackboard!* 我討厭聽到手指甲刮在黑板上發出的刺耳聲! **4** **scrape a living** to manage to get just enough food or money to stay alive 收入[食物]勉強夠維持生活: *We may have to scrape by on his salary alone.* 我們也許得靠他一個人的薪水勉強度日。 **5** **scrape the bottom of the barrel** *infml* to use a person or thing that would be your last choice of all the possibilities 〔非正式〕動用最後一點財力; 起用剩下的次等人才

scrape along *phr v* (also 又作 **scrape by**) [I] to live with difficulty or with a small amount of money which is only just enough 靠…勉強度日

scrape sthg ↔ **together** *phr v* (also 又作 **scrape** sthg ↔ **up**) [T] to collect an amount of something, especially money, from different places and with difficulty 勉強湊集, 拼湊: *We should be able to scrape together enough money for a holiday this year.* 我們今年應該能湊足錢去度假。

scrape through *phr v* [I;T **scrape through** sthg] to succeed by performing in a way which is just acceptable 〔勉強地〕通過: *She scraped through the exam by one mark.* 她考試以一分之差勉強及格。

scrape² *n* **1** an act or sound of scraping 刮; 擦; 刮擦聲 **2** a sore area from which your skin has been scraped 〔皮膚的〕擦傷, 擦痕: *He suffered a few cuts and scrapes, nothing serious.* 他有幾處割傷和擦傷, 都不嚴重。 **3** *infml* a difficult situation you get into which is your own fault, but is not very serious 〔非正式〕窘境; 困境: *As a child I kept getting into scrapes.* 小時候, 我老是遇到麻煩事。

scrap heap /ˈ· ·/ *n* **1** a pile of waste material, especially metal 廢金屬堆, 廢料堆 **2** **on the scrapheap** *infml* treated as useless 〔非正式〕當作廢物處理

scrap·py /ˈskræpɪ; ˈskræpi/ *adj* **scrappier**, **scrappiest** untidy or badly organized, and often not complete 不連貫的; 雜亂的: *a scrappy report* 雜亂無章的報告

scratch¹ /skrætʃ; skrætʃ/ *v* [I;T] **1** to tear or mark a surface with something sharp or rough 抓; 抓破; 劃破: *Did the cat scratch you?* 貓抓傷你嗎? | *The table top has been scratched.* 桌面已被劃破了。 | *Your dog was scratching at the door.* 你的狗在抓門。 | *People scratch their names on the walls.* 人們在牆上刻下了自己的名字。 **2** to rub a part of your body lightly, usually with your fingernails (FINGERNAIL) 〔用手指甲〕搔〔身體〕; 搔癢: *Stop scratching those mosquito bites!* 別去搔那些蚊子叮咬的地方! | *The cat likes to be scratched behind its ears.* 貓喜歡

人搔牠的耳背。 **3** **scratch your head** to think very hard about an answer or about what you should do, often rubbing your head lightly as you do so 搔頭; 抓頭皮〔表示對問題或事情感到為難〕 **4** to remove yourself or an animal from a race or competition before it starts 〔賽馬等〕退出比賽; 棄權: *I was scratched the day before the match.* 我是在比賽前一天棄權的。 | *This horse has been scratched.* 這匹馬已被撤出比賽。 **5** **scratch the surface** to begin to deal with something, but without getting to what is really important 觸及〔某事的〕表面

scratch² *n* **1** [C] a mark or slight cut caused by something sharp or rough 劃痕; 刮痕: *The cupboard looks new, except for a few scratches.* 這櫥櫃除了有幾處劃痕之外, 看上去像新的一樣。 | *I got these scratches on my arm from picking roses.* 我的臂膀上的這幾道傷痕是在採玫瑰花時劃破的。 **2** **without a scratch** *infml* without any hurt or damage at all 〔非正式〕絲毫未受傷地, 安然無恙地: *The driver was seriously injured but his passenger escaped without a scratch.* 司機傷勢嚴重, 但他的乘客卻安然無恙。 **3** [sing] an act of rubbing a part of your body lightly 〔身體的〕搔癢: *The dog's having a good scratch.* 那隻狗正在舒適地搔癢。 **4** **from scratch** *infml* from nothing 〔非正式〕從頭做起, 從零開始: *Instead of converting the garage, let's pull it down and start again from scratch.* 我們不改建車庫了, 還是把它拆掉重建吧。 **5** **up to scratch** *infml* at or to a good enough standard 〔非正式〕達到標準; 情況良好: *The team's performance just wasn't up to scratch.* 球隊的表現並未達到水準。

scratch·y /ˈskrætʃɪ; ˈskrætʃi/ *adj* **1** rough and uncomfortable (used of clothes) 粗糙刺人的〔指衣服〕 **2** making unpleasant sounds because of scratches on its surface (used of a record) 發出沙沙聲的〔指唱片〕 **3** noisy to write with because it is damaged (used of a pen) 〔指筆因損壞而〕發刮擦聲的 **–scratchiness** *n* [U]

scrawl /skrɔl; skrɔːl/ *v* [T] to write something in a careless or untidy way 潦草地寫, 亂塗亂劃 **–scrawl** *n*: *Can you read her scrawl?* 你能看得懂她那潦草的字跡嗎?

scraw·ny /ˈskrɔnɪ; ˈskrɔːni/ *adj* so thin that the bones show through the skin (a word which is used of people or animals, and expresses disapproval) 骨瘦如柴的, 皮包骨的〔指人或動物, 含貶義〕

scream¹ /skrim; skriːm/ *v* **1** [I] to cry out loudly on a high note, in fear, pain, or excitement 〔因恐懼、疼痛或激動而〕尖聲喊叫; 驚呼: *The man was screaming with pain.* 那男人痛得尖聲喊叫。 | *I screamed for help.* 我高聲呼救。 | *He screamed out a warning.* 他尖叫着發出警告。 **2** [T; + that] to say something in this way 尖叫着說出〔某事〕: *He screamed a warning.* 他尖叫着發出警告。 |

She was screaming that her finger was trapped. 她尖叫着说, 她的手指被夾住了。| *"Get out!" he screamed.* "滾出去!" 他尖叫着。**3 scream with laughter** to laugh loudly and in an uncontrolled way 放聲大笑

scream² *n* **1** [C] a sudden loud cry or a high note expressing pain, fear, or excitement 尖叫聲: *We heard a terrible scream.* 我們聽到可怕的尖叫聲。**2** [C] a noise that sounds like this 尖銳的聲音: *screams of laughter* 尖笑聲 | *the scream of the electric saw* 電鋸發出的刺耳聲 **3** [sing] *infml* a very funny person, thing, or event 〔非正式〕極其可笑的人〔事物〕: *It was an absolute scream when she fell off her chair.* 她從椅子上跌下來時, 真是滑稽極了。

scree /skriː; skriː/ *n* [U] a mass of small loose stones on the side of a mountain 山坡上的碎石; 岩屑堆

screech /skriːtʃ; skti:tʃ/ *v* **1** [I] to make a high, sharp, and unpleasant sound 發出尖銳刺耳的聲音: *He screeched in terror.* 他發出恐懼的尖叫聲。**2** [T; +that] to say something in this way 尖聲喊叫出: *"Leave me alone!" she screeched.* "別管我!" 她尖聲叫道。| *Birds were screeching above us.* 鳥兒在我們頭上嘎嘎尖叫。| *The car screeched to a halt.* 汽車嘎的一聲突然停住了。–**screech** *n*: *a screech of brakes* 尖銳刺耳的煞車聲

screed /skriːd; skriːd/ *n* a long and usually dull speech or piece of writing 冗長的講話或文章

★★screen¹ /skriːn; skriːn/ *n* **1** a flat surface in a cinema on which a film is shown (電影)銀幕 **2 the screen, the big screen** films or the film industry 電影; 電影業: *This was written for the screen.* 這是為電影寫的劇本。**3** the front surface of an electrical instrument, on which pictures and words are shown 〔電視等的〕屏幕; 螢光屏: *the television screen* 電視機的螢光屏 | *a computer screen* 電腦的屏幕 –see picture on page 763 見 763 頁彩圖 **4** an upright frame used as a small movable wall for dividing a room, for protecting people from cold air, or for hiding things from view 屏風; 隔板; 簾; 帳: *The nurse will put some screens around your bed.* 護士會在你牀的四周豎起屏風。**5** something that protects, shelters, or hides things 掩蔽物, 遮蔽物; 屏障: *We're planting a screen of trees between the two houses.* 我們在兩幢房子之間種一排樹作為屏障。| *She runs a travel company as a screen for her drug-smuggling operation.* 她開了一家旅遊公司作為她從事毒品走私活動的一種掩護。

screen² *v* [T] **1** to shelter or protect a person or thing 遮蔽〔某物〕; 掩護〔某人〕: *He screened his eyes with his hand as he looked into the sun.* 他看太陽時用手遮住雙眼。| *I tried to screen her* **from** *their anger.* 我試圖護着她, 以免惹起他們的怒氣。**2** to show a

film or television PROGRAMME 放映〔電影〕; 播放〔電視節目〕: *His new film is being screened on BBC1 tonight.* 他的新電影將在今晚的英國廣播公司一台放映。**3** to carry out medical tests on people to make sure they do not have a particular disease 體格檢查: *All older women are now being screened for breast cancer.* 所有上了年紀的婦女現在都要作乳癌檢查。**4** to find out about people to see whether they are suitable for something 甄別, 審查: *A hundred carefully screened people were invited to have dinner with the President.* 經過仔細審查的一百人獲邀與總統共進晚餐。

screen sthg ↔ **off** *phr v* [T] to separate a part of a room from the rest 隔開〔房間〕: *We'll screen off this area here.* 我們要把這個地方隔開。

screen·ing /ˈskriːnɪŋ; ˈskriːnɪŋ/ *n* **1** [C;U] a showing of a film 〔電影的〕放映 **2** [U] the process of finding out **a** whether people are ill 體格檢查 or **b** whether people are suitable for something 人員審查

screen·play /ˈskriːnˌpleɪ; ˈskriːnpleɪ/ *n* the written conversation, description, and instructions which are used in the production of a film 電影劇本

screw¹ /skruː; skruː/ *n* **1** a metal pin which is turned to push it into a surface where it is then fixed 螺釘, 螺絲(釘): *We need four large screws to hang that cupboard on the wall.* 我們需要四顆大螺釘才能把那櫥櫃掛在牆上。**2 have a screw loose** *infml* to be slightly mad 〔非正式〕有點瘋瘋癲癲

screw² *v* **1** [T +adv/prep] to fasten with one or more screws 用螺釘固定: *It won't move; it's screwed to the floor.* 它已用螺釘固定在地板上了, 不會移動。**2** [I + adv/prep; T + adv/prep] to tighten something or fasten things together by turning 旋緊, 擰: *Screw the two pipes together end to end.* 把這兩根管子首尾相接地擰在一起。| *Screw the lid on tightly.* 把蓋子旋緊。| *The pieces screw together easily.* 這些部件很容易擰在一起。**3 screw something out of someone** *infml* to get something from someone by force or by dishonest means 〔非正式〕從某人處逼出某物; 向某人勒索某物: *See what you can screw out of him.* 看看你能逼他交出甚麼。**4 have your head screwed on** *infml* to be very sensible 〔非正式〕頭腦清醒

screw sthg ↔ **up** *phr v* [T] *infml* 〔非正式〕**1** to twist something or change its shape from the usual one 把〔某物〕揉成一團; 扭歪: *He screwed up the letter and threw it away.* 他把信揉成一團扔掉了。| *She screwed up her eyes in the bright light.* 她在刺眼的燈光下眯起了眼睛。**2** to ruin something or do it very badly 毀壞; 弄糟: *You've really managed to screw everything up this time!* 你這次真把一切都弄糟了! **3 screw up your courage** to make yourself do something that you are afraid of doing 鼓起勇氣: *He screwed up his courage and asked her to go out with him.* 他鼓起勇氣邀請她出去。

screw·driv·er /ˈskruˌdraɪvə; ˈskruːˌdraɪvəʳ/ *n* a tool with a narrow blade at one end, which is used to put screws into something or to remove them 螺絲刀，螺絲起子 –see picture on page 958 見 958 頁彩圖

scrib·ble /ˈskrɪbl; ˈskrɪbəl/ *v* **scribbled, scribbling** **1** [T] to write something carelessly or in a hurry, often so that it is hard to read 潦草地書寫: *He scribbled her a note.* 他草草地給她寫了一張便條。 **2** [I] to make meaningless marks with a pen or pencil 亂塗，亂寫: *The children will scribble on anything if you don't watch them.* 要是你不看着孩子，他們就會拿筆到處亂塗。 **–scribble** *n*

scribe /skraɪb/ *n* a person employed to copy or record things in writing, especially before the invention of printing 〔尤指印刷術發明之前的〕抄寫員

scrimp /skrɪmp; skrɪmp/ *v* **scrimp and save** to save money slowly and with difficulty by spending as little as possible 節儉地過日子，一點一滴地省錢: *She has to scrimp and save to buy clothes for the children.* 她不得不比平時節儉，省下錢來為孩子們買衣服。

script /skrɪpt; skrɪpt/ *n* **1** [C;U] the system of writing a language 〔一種語言的〕(全部)字母，字母表: *I'm learning to write the Arabic script.* 我在學寫阿拉伯文字的字母。 **2** [U] writing done by hand, especially with the letters joined 筆跡，手跡，手書 **3** [C] a written form of a speech, play, film, or broadcast 〔演講、廣播等的〕原稿；劇本: *Have the actors got their scripts yet?* 演員們拿到劇本了嗎？

scrip·ture /ˈskrɪptʃə; ˈskrɪptʃəʳ/ *n* [C;U] holy writings, especially the Bible 〔尤指〕聖經；經文；聖典 **–scriptural** *adj*

script·writ·er /ˈskrɪptˌraɪtə; ˈskrɪptˌraɪtəʳ/ *n* a person who writes the script for a film or broadcast 〔電影〕劇本作者；〔廣播或電視節目的〕撰稿人

scroll /skrol; skrəʊl/ *n* **1** a long piece of paper or animal skin for writing on 卷軸；紙卷 **2** an ancient book written on one of these 古代的書稿羊皮卷

scrooge /skrudʒ; skruːdʒ/ *n* (also 又作 **Scrooge**) *infml* a person who is not at all generous towards other people 〔非正式〕吝嗇鬼，守財奴: *Oh, go on, give something towards his leaving present — don't be such an old Scrooge!* 快，快點，送點甚麼給他作為他離開的禮物吧，別那麼吝嗇！

scrounge /skraʊndʒ; skraʊndʒ/ *v* **scrounged, scrounging** [I;T] to get something without paying for it (a word which is used to express disapproval 乞討；擅取〔含貶義〕): *He's always scrounging drinks and cigarettes off us.* 他老是跟我們討煙酒。 **–scrounger** *n*

scrub¹ /skrʌb; skrʌb/ *v* **-bb-** **1** [I;T] to clean

by rubbing hard, especially with a stiff wet brush 用力擦洗；擦淨〔尤指用硬刷擦〕: *Go on — scrub harder!* 繼續吧，加把勁去擦！ | *He's scrubbing the floor.* 他在擦洗地板。 **2** [T] *infml* to stop something that was decided earlier 〔非正式〕取消〔某事物〕: *We've had to scrub our holiday plans this year.* 我們不得不取消今年的度假計劃。

scrub² *n* **1 a scrub** an act of cleaning by scrubbing 擦洗: *Give that floor a good hard scrub.* 把那地板好好擦洗一下。 | *It needs a scrub.* 它需要擦洗一下。 **2** [U] low trees and bushes growing in poor soil 矮樹叢，灌木叢

scruff /skrʌf; skrʌf/ *n* **1 the scruff of the neck, the scruff of someone's neck** the flesh at the back of your neck, or your shirt collar 頸背[後頸]上的肉: *He grabbed me by the scruff of the neck and shook me hard.* 他揪住我的後頸使勁地甩動。 **2** *infml* a dirty and untidy person 〔非正式〕骯髒邋遢的人

scruf·fy /ˈskrʌfi; ˈskrʌfi/ *adj* **scruffier, scruffiest** dirty and untidy 骯髒的，邋遢的: *He always looks so scruffy.* 他看上去總是那麼邋遢的。 **–scruffily** *adv* **–scruffiness** *n*

scrum /skrʌm; skrʌm/ *n* (also 又作 **scrummage** /ˈskrʌmɪdʒ; ˈskrʌmɪdʒ/) *fml* 〔正式〕 **1** an organized group of players from each team pushing against each other at particular times in a game of RUGBY 〔橄欖球的〕並列爭球 **2** a disorderly struggling crowd 混亂的人羣，騷動的人羣

scrump·tious /ˈskrʌmpʃəs; ˈskrʌmpʃəs/ *adj* *infml* very good indeed (used especially of food) 〔非正式〕極好的，美味可口的〔尤指食物〕: *What a scrumptious meal!* 這頓飯真是好吃極了！

scru·ple /ˈskrupl; ˈskruːpəl/ *n* **1** [C] a moral principle which stops you from doing something that is wrong 顧忌，顧慮: *I can't work for a man who has absolutely no scruples.* 我不能為一個(良心上)沒有一點顧忌的人做事。 **2** [U] the feeling that what you do might be morally wrong 良心上的不安；內疚: *He acted completely without scruple.* 他做事完全肆無忌憚。

scru·pu·lous /ˈskrupjələs; ˈskruːpjʊləs/ *adj* **1** careful about even the smallest detail 一絲不苟的，嚴格認真的: *He is known for his scrupulous research.* 他以研究認真見稱。 **2** careful to do only what is right 小心謹慎的；是非分明的: *She is scrupulous in her business activities.* 她在業務活動中公私分明。 **–opposite** 反義 **unscrupulous** (for 2) **–scrupulously** *adv*: *The room was scrupulously clean.* 這房間一塵不染。 **–scrupulousness** *n* [U]

scru·ti·nize /ˈskrutnˌaɪz; ˈskruːtɪˌnaɪz/ *v* **scrutinized, scrutinizing** (also 又作 **scrutinise** *BrE* 〔英式〕) [T] to examine something very carefully 詳細檢查，仔細審查〔某事物〕: *She scrutinized his work before allowing him to send it to clients.* 她仔細審查了他的作品

S

後, 才允許他寄給客戶。

scru·ti·ny /'skrutn̩ɪ; 'skruːtɪ̩ni/ *n* [U] careful and thorough examination 詳細的檢查; 仔細的觀察: *Close scrutiny revealed a lot of errors.* 經過仔細的檢查, 發現了許多錯誤。

scu·ba-di·ving /'skubə ‚daɪvɪŋ; 'skuːbə ‚daɪvɪŋ/ *n* [U] a sport in which you swim under water with a container of air on your back, breathing through a tube 戴水肺的潛水, 斯庫巴潛水

scuff /skʌf; skʌf/ *v* **scuff your feet** to walk along without picking up your feet properly, damaging the surface of your shoes 拖着腳步走

sculp·tor /'skʌlptə‚; 'skʌlptər/ *n* an artist who makes sculptures 雕刻家, 雕塑家

sculp·ture¹ /'skʌlptʃə‚; 'skʌlptʃər/ *n* **1** [U] the art of shaping solid figures out of materials like stone or wood 雕刻(術), 雕塑(術): *He's gone to art school to study sculpture.* 他去了藝術學院學習雕塑。 **2** [C;U] work produced by this art 雕刻品, 雕塑品: *There are some interesting sculptures in this church.* 這座教堂裡有一些有趣的雕像。

sculpture² *v* **sculptured, sculpturing** (also 又作 **sculpt** /skʌlpt; skʌlpt/ [T]) to shape a solid work of art out of a material such as stone 雕刻, 雕塑: *figures sculptured out of marble* 用大理石雕刻成的塑像

scum /skʌm; skʌm/ *n* **1** [sing; U] an unpleasant sticky material on the surface of a liquid 浮渣, 浮垢 **2** [pl] very unpleasant people of the worst kind 卑賤的人; (社會) 渣滓, 人渣: *The police treated the protesters like scum.* 警方把抗議者當作社會敗類對待。 | *These hooligans are the scum of the earth.* 這些流氓是社會的渣滓。 –**scummy** *adj*

scur·ri·lous /'skʌrələs; 'skʌrɪ̩ləs/ *adj fml* saying extremely offensive and unfair things about someone 〖非正式〗惡言誹謗的; 辱罵的: *a scurrilous attack in the newspapers* 報紙上的毀謗性攻擊 –**scurrilously** *adv* – **scurrilousness, –scurrility** /skə'rɪləti; skə-'rɪl̩ti/ *n* [U]

scur·ry /'skɜ‚ɪ; 'skʌri/ *v* **scurried, scurried** [I + adv/prep] to move quickly with short steps 〖小步〗急跑; 急趨: *The mouse scurried away.* 老鼠急忙溜走了。

scurry² *n* [sing] a movement or sound of scurrying 急促的奔跑(聲): *I heard the scurry of feet in the hall.* 我聽到大廳裡傳來急促的腳步聲。

scut·tle /'skʌtl; 'skʌtl/ *v* **scuttled, scuttling** [I + adv/prep] to run with short quick steps in order to escape 急促逃奔: *The children scuttled away when they saw the policeman.* 孩子們看見警察便迅速逃走了。

scythe¹ /saɪð; saɪð/ *n* a long-handled tool with a curved blade, used for cutting long grass 長柄大鐮刀

scythe² *v* **scythed, scything** [I;T] to cut grass with a scythe 用大鐮刀割〔草〕

SE a written abbreviation for 〖縮〗= SOUTHEAST(ERN)

★★sea /si; siː/ *n* **1** [C;U] the salty water that covers much of the Earth's surface 海, 海洋: *boats sailing on the sea* 在海上航行的船隻 | *sea water* 海水 | *sea travel* 海上旅行 | *We sailed into quieter seas.* 我們駛入了較平靜的水域。 | *We went by sea, not by air.* 我們是坐船去的, 而不是坐飛機去的。 | *We spent a week by the sea.* 我們在海邊度過了一星期。 **2** [C] a large area of salty water smaller than an ocean, partly surrounded by land ...海〔海洋的一部分〕: *the Red Sea* 紅海 | *the Mediterranean Sea* 地中海 **3** [C] a strong movement of waves on the sea. 海浪; 波濤: *The ship ran into strong winds and heavy seas.* 船遇上了強風巨浪。 **4 at sea: a** working or travelling on the sea 在海上工作或旅行 **b** *infml* not able to understand 〖非正式〗茫然, 迷惑, 一竅不通: *I'm all at sea with these new regulations.* 我對這些新規則一竅不通。 **5 out to sea** away from the shore 離岸, 出航 **6 a sea of** a large quantity of something spread out in front of you 大量, 茫茫一片: *He looked out from the stage onto a sea of faces.* 他從舞台上往下望, 看見數不清的臉孔。

sea·bed /'si‚bɛd; 'siːbed/ the land at the bottom of the sea 海底, 海牀

sea·far·ing /'si‚fɛrɪŋ; 'siːfeərɪŋ/ *adj* [only before a noun 只用於名詞前] having strong connections with the sea and sailing (與)航海(有關)的; 以航海為業的: *a seafaring man* 海員

sea·food /'si‚fud; 'siːfuːd/ *n* [U] sea creatures that you eat 海產食品, 海味, 海鮮

sea·front /'si‚frʌnt; 'siːfrʌnt/ *n* the wide road next to the sea in a seaside town 〔城鎮的〕濱海區, 濱海大道

sea·gull /'si‚gʌl; 'siːgʌl/ *n* a rather large seabird with a loud cry 海鷗

sea·horse /'si‚hɔrs; 'siːhɔːs/ *n* a very small fish with a neck and head that look like those of a horse 海馬

seal¹ /sil; siːl/ *n* **1** an official mark put on a paper that gives information or proof to show that it is really what it seems to be 印章; 圖章: *This letter carries the royal seal.* 這封信蓋有皇家的印章。 **2 someone's seal of approval** an official mark or statement to show that someone approves of something 某人的批准: *The headmaster has given their plan his seal of approval.* 校長已經批准了他們的計劃。 **3 put/set the seal on something** to be a sign that something **a** has officially ended 某事物正式結束, 使成定局 or **b** will continue in the same way in the future 某事物繼續生效 **4** something fixed to a letter or container so that you can see whether anyone has opened it 〔信件或容器的〕封條, 封蠟, 封鉛, 火漆: *The seal on this bottle of pills is broken.* 這個藥瓶上的封條破開了。 **5 a**

tight connection in a machine, for keeping a gas or liquid in or out〔機器上防止氣體或液體進出的〕密封裝置: *The seal has worn and the machine is losing oil.* 密封裝置已經磨損, 機器在漏油。**6** a large sea animal with a tail and broad flat limbs for swimming; seals live mostly on cool sea-coasts 海豹

seal² v [T] **1** to close firmly 封, 密封: *She sealed the envelope.* 她封密了信封。| *a sealed envelope* 封了口的信封 **2** to close tightly or cover so that it is not possible for anything to get through 封閉, 封鎖: *The police sealed all the exits.* 警方封閉了所有的出口。| *We've sealed all the holes.* 我們封閉了所有的洞口。| *The meat is sealed in polythene.* 肉是用聚乙稀密封包裝的。**3** to put an official mark on something 蓋印於, 蓋章於 **4** to make something certain or formal 確定, 決定〔某事物〕: *They sealed their agreement by shaking hands.* 他們握手達成了協議。

seal sthg ↔ **in** *phr v* [T] to enclose something so that it cannot get out 把〔某物〕封住: *Brown the meat to seal in the juices.* 把肉烤成棕色, 使肉汁滲不出來。

seal sthg ↔ **off** *phr v* [T] to close something so that it is impossible to go into it or get out of it 封閉, 封鎖: *After the explosion, the area was sealed off by the police.* 爆炸發生後, 警方封鎖了該區。

sea lev·el /ˈ·ˌ··/ n [U] the level of the sea, used as a standard for measuring the height of land 海平面, 海拔: *500 metres above sea level* 海拔五百米

sea li·on /ˈ·ˌ··/ n a sea animal of the Pacific Ocean which has broad flat limbs for swimming 海獅

seam /siːm; siːm/ n **1** a line of stitches joining two pieces of cloth 線縫, 縫口 **2** a narrow band of one kind of rock between large areas of other rocks〔夾在其他岩層間的〕礦層: *a rich seam of coal* 含量豐富的煤層

sea·man /ˈsiːmən; ˈsiːmən/ n **seamen** /-mən; -mən/ a sailor 水手, 海員

sea·man·ship /ˈsiːmənˌʃɪp; ˈsiːmənʃɪp/ n [U] the skill of handling a ship and directing its course 航海術; 航海技能

seamed /siːmd; siːmd/ adj deeply lined 有深縫的; 有深皺紋的

seam·y /ˈsiːmɪ; ˈsiːmi/ adj **seamier, seamiest** rough and immoral (not used of a person) 簡陋的; 醜惡的〔不用於指人〕: *the seamy side of city life* 城市生活的陰暗面

sé·ance /ˈseɑ̃ns; ˈseɪɑːns/ n a meeting where people try to talk to dead people, or receive messages from them 降神會

sea·port /ˈsiːpɔːt; ˈsiːpɔːt/ n a large town on or near the coast to which large ships come 海港, 海濱市鎮

sear /sɪr; sɪər/ v be **seared on/into your memory** to be impossible to forget, usually because of being a very powerful experi-

ence〔常因重大經歷而〕難以忘懷; 深深烙在記憶中

★**search¹** /sɜːtʃ; sɜːtʃ/ v **1** [I;T] to look carefully and thoroughly at or in a place when you are trying to find something 搜查, 搜索, 搜尋: *We've searched the house from top to bottom.* 我們把屋子上上下下搜查了一遍。| *The police searched the woods for the little girl.* 警察搜遍樹林尋找那個小女孩。| *She searched through her pockets for a cigarette.* 她摸遍口袋想找一支煙。**2 search for something** to try to find something 尋找某物: *They are searching for the missing child.* 他們正在尋找失蹤的孩子。| *Scientists are still searching for a cure for the common cold.* 科學家仍在尋求治療感冒的方法。**3** [T] to examine a person's body and clothing to try to find something 搜身: *The police searched the thief but found nothing.* 警察搜查了小偷的身上, 但是甚麼也沒找到。**4 search your conscience** to think hard about whether you have acted correctly 反省

search sthg ↔ **out** *phr v* [T] to find by searching 找出〔某事物〕

★**search²** n **1** an act of searching 搜查, 搜尋: *a long search for the lost treasure* 長時間尋找丟失的寶藏 **2 in search of** looking for 尋找; 尋求: *in search of happiness* 尋求幸福 | *He went in search of his long-lost brother.* 他去尋找他那失蹤多年的弟弟。

search·ing /ˈsɜːtʃɪŋ; ˈsɜːtʃɪŋ/ adj determined to discover the truth 洞察的; 探究的: *She gave me a searching look.* 她用探尋的目光看了我一眼。| *a searching enquiry* 追根問底的調查 **–searchingly** adv

search·light /ˈsɜːtʃlaɪt; ˈsɜːtʃlaɪt/ n a powerful light used to find planes in the sky or people who have escaped 探照燈

search par·ty /ˈ· ˌ··/ n **search parties** [C + sing/pl verb] a group of people looking for something or someone that is lost 搜索隊: *We sent out a search party.* 我們派出了一支搜索隊。

sear·ing /ˈsɪrɪŋ; ˈsɪərɪŋ/ adj very painful and causing a burning feeling 灼痛的: *a searing pain* 一陣灼痛

sea·shell /ˈsiːʃɛl; ˈsiːʃel/ n a shell of a small sea animal (海)貝殼

sea·shore /ˈsiːʃɔːr; ˈsiːʃɔːr/ n [U] land along the edge of the sea, usually sand or rocks 海岸, 海濱

sea·sick /ˈsiːsɪk; ˈsiːˌsɪk/ adj feeling sick because of the movement of a ship on water 暈船的 **–seasickness** n [U]

sea·side /ˈsiːsaɪd; ˈsiːˌsaɪd/ n BrE **the seaside** a place by the sea where people go on holiday〔英式〕〔人們度假的〕海邊, 海濱: *a holiday at the seaside* 在海濱度假 | *a seaside town* 海濱小城 –see 見 SHORE¹ (USAGE 用法)

★**sea·son¹** /ˈsiːzn; ˈsiːzən/ n **1** one of the four parts of the year, spring, summer, autumn, and winter 季, 季

節〔如春、夏、秋、冬〕: *Autumn is my favourite season.* 秋天是我最喜愛的季節。**2** a period of time each year when something regularly happens 〔某事定期發生的〕節期; 賽季; 季節: *the rainy season* 雨季 | *the football season* 足球賽季 | *the holiday season* 度假旺季 **3 in season** easy to buy because it is the right time of year (used of fresh foods) 當令的, 應時的〔指新鮮食品〕: *It's cheaper to buy fruit and vegetables that are in season.* 購買當令水果和蔬菜比較便宜。**4 out of season: a** not easy to buy (used of fresh foods) 不當令的, 落令的〔指新鮮食品〕 **b** not at the busiest time of the year 淡季的 **5** a group of similar events, such as plays and concerts, given within a certain period 〔某些活動舉行的〕時期; 旺季; 〔戲劇或音樂會的〕會演期: *a season of Shakespeare plays* 莎士比亞戲劇會演

season² *v* [T] to give a special taste to food by adding salt, pepper, or a SPICE 〔加鹽、胡椒或香料〕給〔食物〕調味: *Season with a little paprika.* 用少量紅辣椒粉調味。

sea·so·na·ble /ˈsiznəbl; ˈsiːzənəbəl/ *adj fml* suitable or typical for the time of year 〔正式〕合乎季節的: *seasonable weather* 合時令的天氣 —**seasonably** *adv*

sea·son·al /ˈsiznəl; ˈsiːzənəl/ *adj* happening at a particular time of the year 季節(性)的: *seasonal employment in the travel industry* 旅遊業的季節性雇用

sea·soned /ˈsiznd; ˈsiːzənd/ *adj* with a great deal of experience 經驗豐富的, 老練的: *a seasoned traveller* 有經驗的旅行者

sea·son·ing /ˈsiznɪŋ; ˈsiːzənɪŋ/ *n* [U] salt and pepper or similar things that you add to food to make it taste good 調味品, 佐料

season tick·et /ˈ·· ·ˌ·/ *n* a special travel ticket that allows you to make as many journeys as you like within a certain period without having to pay each time 長期票; 季票

★★seat¹ /sit; siːt/ *n* **1** something that you sit on, for example a chair 座位〔如椅子〕: *What can we use for seats?* 我們可以用甚麼當座位? | *the back seat of a car* 汽車的後排座位 | *We sat in the best seats at the theatre.* 我們坐在劇院的最佳座位。**2 take a seat, have a seat** to sit down 坐下 **3** the part on which you sit 坐的部位: *grass stains on the seat of his trousers* 他的褲子臀部上的青草污跡 | *The seat of the chair is broken.* 椅座壞了。**4** a place as a member of an official body 席位: *At the last election, the Labour Party won 252 seats.* 在上屆選舉中, 工黨贏得了二百五十二個席位。

seat² *v* [T] **1** to have enough seats for a particular number of people 有〔某數量的人〕的座位; 可容納…人: *a large hall which seats 950* 可容納九百五十人的大廳 **2 seated** sitting 坐着 **3 Please be seated** a formal phrase used to ask someone to sit down 請

坐〔正式用語〕

seat belt /ˈ· ·/ *n* (also 又作 **safety belt**) a fixed belt fastened around a person in a car or plane to protect them from sudden movement, especially in an accident 〔飛機或汽車的〕安全帶 —see picture on page 209 見 209 頁彩圖

seat·ing /ˈsitɪŋ; ˈsiːtɪŋ/ *n* [U] seats 座位: *The hall has seating for three hundred.* 大廳可供三百人就坐。 | *the seating plan for the Football Club's annual dinner* 足球會周年晚宴座位表

sea ur·chin /ˈ· ·ˌ·/ *n* a small ball-shaped sea animal that has a hard shell with many sharp points 海膽

sea·weed /ˈsiˌwid; ˈsiːwiːd/ *n* [U] a plant that grows in the sea 海草, 海藻

sea·wor·thy /ˈsiˌwɜːðɪ; ˈsiːwɜːðɪ/ *adj* in good condition and fit for a sea voyage (used of ships) 適於航海的〔指船〕 —**seaworthiness** *n* [U]: *a certificate of seaworthiness* 適航證書

sec /sɛk; sek/ *n infml* a very short time 〔非正式〕一會兒, 片刻: *Wait a sec.* 等一會兒。

sec·a·teurs /ˌsɛkəˈtɜːz; ˈsekətɜːz/ *n* [pl] *BrE* strong scissors for cutting parts off garden plants 〔英式〕修枝剪刀

se·cede /sɪˈsid; sɪˈsiːd/ *v* **seceded, seceding** [I] *fml* to officially leave a larger country, group, or organization, especially because of disagreement 〔正式〕〔由於意見不合而〕退出, 脫離〔國家、團體或組織〕 —**secession** /sɪˈsɛʃən; sɪˈseʃən/ *n* [C;U]

se·clud·ed /sɪˈkludɪd; sɪˈkluːdɪd/ *adj* very quiet and private 幽靜的; 偏僻的: *a secluded country house* 僻靜的鄉間住宅

se·clu·sion /sɪˈkluʒən; sɪˈkluːʒən/ *n* [U] a state in which you are very quiet and private 僻靜(狀態); 隱居: *The famous actor now lives in seclusion.* 那位著名的演員現在過着隱居生活。

★★sec·ond¹ /ˈsɛkənd; ˈsekənd/ *det, adv, pron* **1** 2nd 第二; 第二的: *their second child* 他們的第二個孩子 | *The second and third volumes are missing from the set.* 這套書的第二卷和第三卷找不到了。 | *"Did you win?" "No, I came second."* "你贏了嗎?" "不, 我得了第二名。" | *Maria's just had a baby. That's her second, isn't it?* 瑪麗亞剛生了個孩子。那是她的第二胎, 是嗎? **2** when you are speaking or writing and have several points you want to make, you can order them and number them **First...**, **Second...**, **Third...**, etc. 第二〔當在講話或文章中有數個論點要表達時, 可用**First...**, **Second...**, **Third...** 等順序來編號羅列〕: *There are several reasons why the plan will not work. First, there has not been enough preparation. Second, there is not enough money.* 計劃行不通有幾個原因。首先是準備工作不夠充分; 第二是資金不足。**3 in the second place** when you have several points you want to make, you can use this expression to introduce the second one 其次〔當有幾個要點要表述時, 可用這詞組引出第二點〕: *They won't be interested in that house. In the first place, it's too far from where they work. And in the second place, it's more than they are prepared to pay.* 他們不會對那幢房子感興趣。首先, 房子離上班的地方太遠; 其次, 房價比他們預料的為高。 **4 at second hand** from other people 二手的; 得自他人的 **5 second to none** *infml* the best 〔非正式〕最好的, 首屈一指的: *As a tennis player, Ann is second to none.* 作為一名網球運動員, 安是無與倫比的。 **6 second only to something** not quite as good as something, but still very good 僅次於某事物

⋆second² *n* **1** [C] a length of time equal to 1/60 of a minute 〔時間的〕秒: *The seconds ticked by.* 時間一秒一秒地過去。 **2** [C] a very short time 一會兒, 片刻: *Hang on just a second.* 稍等片刻, 不要掛斷電話。 **3 seconds** [pl] goods sold cheaply because there is something slightly wrong with them 二等貨; 次貨, 次品

second³ *v* [T] to support a formal suggestion at a meeting so that argument or voting can follow 〔在會議上〕正式支持〔動議〕; 附議: *"Will anyone second this motion?" "I second it, Mr Chairman."* "有誰支持這項動議?" "主席先生, 我附議。"

se·cond⁴ /'sɛkənd; sɪ'kɒnd/ *v* **be seconded somewhere** *BrE fml* to be moved to a special duty for a limited time 〔英, 正式〕調派, 調任某處: *The finance officer was ill, so someone was seconded from another department to do his work.* 財務主管病了, 因此從別的部門調派了人做他的工作。

⋆sec·ond·a·ry /'sɛkən͵dɛrɪ; 'sɛkəndərɪ/ *adj* **1** not as important as something else 次要的: *The question of public transport is secondary. We must spend more on developing our road networks.* 公共交通工具的問題是次要的。我們必須投入更多的資金來發展我們的公路網。 **2 secondary education, secondary schools** education or schools for children over 11 years old, in Britain 中等教育; 中學〔指十一歲以上孩子就讀的學校〕: *Are there many good secondary schools round there?* 這兒附近有很多不錯的中學嗎? —compare 比較 PRIMARY **3** developing from something that happened earlier 隨後的; 繼發的: *a secondary infection brought on by a cold* 傷風引起的繼發性感染

secondary mod·ern /͵····'··/ *n* a school in Britain which does not prepare students for university or further study, common in the middle of the 20th century 中等學校〔英國為不能上大學或進一步深造的學生而辦的學校, 在第二十世紀中葉很常見〕

second-best /͵·· '··◂/ *adj* not quite as good as the best 僅次於最好的: *my second-best jacket* 我那件次好的茄克衫

second-class /͵·· '··◂/ *adj, adv* **1** relating to the sending of letters by a system that is slightly cheaper and slower than the fastest one 〔郵件〕二類(的)〔比一類郵件慢且便宜〕: *second-class letters* 二類信件 | *Ten second-class stamps, please.* 請給我十張二類郵票。 | *How much is second-class postage these days?* 現在寄二類信件的郵費是多少? | *I'm going to send that parcel second-class.* 我想把那包裹作為二等郵件寄出。 **2** relating to the ordinary class of travel by train or boat 〔火車或輪船〕二等(的): *a second-class ticket* 二等票 | *Two second-class returns to Birmingham, please.* 請給我兩張去伯明翰的二等來回票。 **3** not as good or important as others 次等的: *He regards women as second-class citizens.* 他把婦女看作二等公民。 —compare 比較 FIRST-CLASS

second-hand /͵·· '··◂/ *adj, adv* **1** used by an earlier owner, and not new 用過的; 舊的; 二手的: *a second-hand car* 二手汽車 | *I got this book second-hand.* 我買的這本書是二手貨。 **2** [only before a noun 只用於名詞前] dealing in goods that are not new 經營舊貨的: *a second-hand shop* 舊貨店 **3** passed on from someone else 得自他人的; 第二手的; 間接(獲得)的: *It was a second-hand report, based on what others had told him.* 那是一份根據第二手資料寫成的報告, 情況是由別人告訴他的。

⋆sec·ond·ly /'sɛkəndlɪ; 'sekəndlɪ/ *adv* (also 又作 **second**) when you are speaking or writing and you have several points to make, you can order them using **Firstly, Secondly, etc.** 第二, 其次〔當在講話或文章中有幾個要點要表述時, 可以用 **Firstly, Secondly** 等順序來陳列〕: *There are several reasons why the plan will not work. Firstly, there has not been enough preparation. Secondly, there is not enough money.* 計劃行不通有幾個原因。首先是準備不夠充分; 第二是資金不足。

second na·ture /͵·· '··/ *n* [U] a very firmly fixed habit 〔根深蒂固的〕習性, 第二天性: *It's second nature for me to lock the doors at night.* 夜間鎖門是我的第二天性。

second per·son /͵·· '··/ *n* [sing] a form of the verb that you use with "you" 第二人稱〔如 you〕

second-rate /͵·· '··◂/ *adj* not very good 二流的, 次等的: *a second-rate actor* 二流演員

second thoughts /͵·· '·/ *n* [pl] **1** doubts that a past decision or action was the correct one 重新的考慮: *We had decided to sell our house, but then we began to have second thoughts.* 我們當時已決定賣掉我們的房子, 但後來我們又有了新的考慮。 **2 on second thoughts** a phrase you use when you have suddenly changed your mind about something 經重新考慮後〔用於表示突然改變主意〕: *Let's go and see "Fury"... No, on second thoughts, there's a new French film at the*

Arts Centre. 我們去看"怒火"吧。不,再想想還有藝術中心在上映新法國電影。

se·cre·cy /'siːkrəsɪ; 'siːkrɪsi/ *n* [U] **1** the keeping of secrets 保密: *Secrecy is important to our plans.* 保密對於我們的計劃很重要。 **2** the state of being secret 祕密(狀態): *The secrecy of the plan was closely guarded.* 這項計劃必須嚴格保守。

★**se·cret¹** /'siːkrɪt; 'siːkrɪt/ *adj* **1** kept from the view or knowledge of others 祕密的; 機密的: *secret plans* 祕密計劃 | *These plans must be kept secret **from** the enemy.* 這些計劃必須保密,不能讓敵人知道。 **2** [only before a noun 只用於名詞前] doing a particular thing only when other people will not find you (used of a person) 祕密進行的〔指人〕: *She became a secret drinker.* 她老是背着人喝酒。 **–secretly** *adv*

★**secret²** *n* **1** something kept hidden or known only to a few people 祕密: *Don't tell Mary about the party. It's a secret.* 不要跟瑪麗談起聚會的事,這是祕密。 | *Can you keep a secret?* 你能保密嗎? | *It's no secret that the two men dislike each other intensely.* 這兩個人相互作對已不是甚麼祕密了。 **2** the unknown explanation of something 奧祕, 神祕的事: *the secret of how life on Earth began* 地球上生命起源的奧祕 | *What is the secret of your success?* 你的成功祕訣是甚麼? **3 in secret** unknown to other people 暗地裡, 祕密地: *The two leaders met in secret.* 兩位首腦祕密會見。

secret a·gent /ˌ·· '··/ *n* a person gathering information secretly for a foreign government 特工人員,特務,間諜

sec·re·tar·i·al /ˌsɛkrə'tɛrɪəl; ˌsekrə'teəriəl/ *adj* of or concerning the work of a secretary 祕書(工作)的: *secretarial college* 祕書學院

sec·re·tar·i·at /ˌsɛkrə'tɛrɪət; ˌsekrə'teəriət/ *n* a department that manages the affairs of a government organization 祕書處; 書記處: *the United Nations Secretariat in New York* 紐約的聯合國祕書處

★**sec·re·ta·ry** /'sɛkrətɛrɪ; 'sekrətəri/ *n* **secretaries 1** a person with the job of preparing letters, arranging meetings, and so on, for someone else 祕書: *a job as private secretary **to** the company chairman* 公司董事長私人祕書的職位 –see picture on page 763 見 763 頁彩圖 **2** (also 又作 **Secretary**) a government minister at the head of a large government department 部長; 大臣: *the Foreign Secretary* 〔英國的〕外交大臣 **3** an officer of an organization who keeps records, writes official letters, and so on 幹事; 文書: *a union secretary* 工會幹事

se·crete /sɪ'kriːt; sɪ'kriːt/ *v* **secreted, secreting** [T] **1** (of an animal or plant) to produce a liquid 〔指動、植物〕分泌〔液體〕 **2** to hide 隱藏, 藏匿

se·cre·tion /sɪ'kriːʃən; sɪ'kriːʃən/ *n* **1** [U] the production of a liquid by part of a plant or animal 分泌 **2** [C] the liquid produced 分泌液 **3** [U] the act of hiding something 隱藏

se·cre·tive /sɪ'kriːtɪv; 'siːkrɪtɪv/ *adj* fond of keeping things secret (a word usually used to express disapproval) 愛保密的; 守口如瓶的〔常含貶義〕 **–secretively** *adv* **–secretiveness** *n* [U]

secret ser·vice /ˌ·· '··/ *n* the secret government department which tries to find out the secrets of enemy countries 〔政府的〕特務機關, 特工處

sect /sɛkt; sekt/ *n* **1** a group of people with special beliefs, usually religious, which separate it from a larger group 教派 **2** an organized group of extreme people who think, unreasonably, that their ideas are the only correct ones 宗派, 派別

sec·tar·i·an /sɛk'tɛrɪən; sek'teəriən/ *adj* divided into sects or connected with the differences between sects 派別的, 宗派的: *sectarian differences* 宗派分歧 | *sectarian killings* 宗派之間的殘殺

★**sec·tion** /'sɛkʃən; 'sekʃən/ *n* **1** [C] a separate part of something 部分; 部件; 段; 組: *a bookcase which comes apart into sections* 可拆成幾個部分的書櫃 | *signals controlling each section of railway track* 控制每一段鐵路路軌的信號 | *She plays in the orchestra's woodwind section.* 她在管弦樂隊的木管樂器組演奏。 | *in the sports section of the paper* 報紙上的體育版 **2** [C;U] a representation of something as if it were cut from top to bottom and looked at from the side 斷面; 橫截面, 剖面: *The architect drew the house in section.* 建築師畫下房子的剖面圖。

★**sec·tor** /'sɛktə; 'sektə/ *n* **1** a part of a country's ECONOMY 〔國家經濟的〕部門; 界: *employment in the public and private sectors* 公營和私營部門的就業情況 | *the banking sector* 銀行界 **2** a part of a larger group 部分

sec·u·lar /'sɛkjələ; 'sekjʊlə/ *adj* not connected with a church and not religious 非宗教的; 與宗教無關的; 世俗的: *secular music* 世俗音樂

★**se·cure¹** /sɪ'kjuə; sɪ'kjuə/ *adj* **1** safe 安全的; 可靠的; 無危險的: *Make sure your money is in a secure place.* 你要確保把錢存放在安全可靠的地方。 | *a secure job* 安定的工作 | *a secure investment* 無風險的投資 **2** tightly fastened or well protected so that no one can get in or out 緊閉的; 堅固的: *a secure door* 堅固的門 | *a castle secure **from** attack* 牢不可破的城堡 **3** feeling safe and not frightened or worried 安心的, 無恐懼的, 無憂慮的: *The little boy felt secure near his parents.* 小男孩在父母身邊感到很安全。 **4** firmly fixed 牢固的; 結實的: *Are you sure that shelf is secure?* 你肯定那個架子很結實嗎? | *a secure foundation* 牢固的地基 | *a* secure belief in life after death 認為人死後仍有生命的堅定信念 –opposite 反義 **insecure** (for 1,3) –**securely** adv: securely fastened 牢牢地固定住

secure² v secured, securing [T] **1** fml to get something after a lot of effort 〖正式〗〖經過努力後〗得到〔某物〕: He's secured himself a good job. 他已經為自己找到了一份好工作。**2** to fasten tightly 關緊; 緊閉: They secured the windows when the storm began. 風暴來時, 他們關緊了窗戶。**3** to make safe 使安全; 保護: The soldiers secured the camp **against** attack. 士兵保護着營地以免受攻擊。

se·cu·ri·ty /sɪˈkjʊrəti; sɪˈkjʊərˌʃti/ n securities **1** [U] the state of being secure 安全; 安全感; 保障: Once the jewels were safely locked up in the bank, he had no more worries about their security. 珠寶一經安全地鎖在銀行裡, 他就不再擔憂了。| A job in the Civil Service offers security. 公務員的工作提供保障。| the security of a good home and a loving family 一個美好的家庭及相親相愛的家人所帶來的安全感 **2** [U] something which protects 防禦物, 保護物: The money is my security against hardship. 這筆錢可讓我應付不時之需。**3** [U] valuable property which you promise to give to a money-lender if you do not repay money you have borrowed 抵押品: What did you offer as security **for** the loan? 你拿甚麼作貸款抵押? **4** [U] arrangements to keep people safe from attack, or to keep them in or out of a building 保安措施; 安全: For security reasons passengers have to be searched. 為了保安的理由, 須對旅客進行搜身。| Tight security was in force during the President's visit. 總統訪問期間實行嚴密的保安措施。| the security forces 保安部隊 **5** [C] property in the form of shares 證券

se·dan /sɪˈdæn; sɪˈdæn/ n the usual American word for 〖美式〗= a SALOON car

sedate /sɪˈdet; sɪˈdeɪt/ adj not easily excited, and formal and unhurried in movement 鎮定的; 沉着的; 莊重的: a calm, rather sedate manner 鎮定自若、嚴肅莊重的態度 –**sedately** adv –**sedateness** n [U]

se·da·ted /sɪˈdetɪd; sɪˈdeɪtˌd/ adj made sleepy or calm with a special drug 〔因服用特種鎮靜藥而〕昏昏欲睡的 –**sedation** /-ˈdeʃən; -ˈdeɪʃən/ n: He's under sedation and resting quietly in bed. 他吃了鎮靜藥, 正在牀上安靜地休息。

sed·a·tive /ˈsɛdətɪv; ˈsɛdətɪv/ n a drug which causes sleep 鎮靜藥: The doctor gave him a sedative to help him sleep. 醫生給他服了鎮靜劑以幫助他入睡。–**sedative** adj

sed·en·ta·ry /ˈsɛdn̩ˌtɛrɪ; ˈsɛdəntərɪ/ adj fml sitting down, or done sitting down 〖正式〗坐着的; 坐着做的: a sedentary job 坐着做的工作

sed·i·ment /ˈsɛdəmənt; ˈsɛdɨmənt/ n [sing; U] solid material that settles at the bottom of a liquid 沉澱(物)

se·di·tion /sɪˈdɪʃn; sɪˈdɪʃn/ n [U] fml speaking, writing, or action intended to make people disobey a government 〖正式〗〔反政府的〕煽動性的演講、文章或行動 –**seditious** adj: a seditious speech 煽動性的演講

se·duce /sɪˈdjus; sɪˈdjuːs/ v seduced, seducing **1** [T] to persuade someone young and without sexual experience to have sex with you 引誘〔年輕或無經驗者〕發生性關係 **2** [T + adv/prep] to encourage someone to do something wrong by making it seem attractive 唆使〔某人〕做壞事; 引誘〔某人〕入歧途: The warm weather seduced me away from my studies. 暖洋洋的天氣誘使我放下了學習。–**seducer** n –**seduction** /sɪˈdʌkʃən; sɪˈdʌkʃən/ n [C;U]

se·duc·tive /sɪˈdʌktɪv; sɪˈdʌktɪv/ adj having qualities likely to seduce 誘人的; 有吸引力的: a seductive voice 誘人的嗓音 | a seductive offer of higher pay 具有吸引力的高薪 –**seductively** adv –**seductiveness** n [U]

see /si; siː/ v saw /sɔ; sɔː/, seen /sin; siːn/ **1** [I;T] to notice something with your eyes, or look at something 看; 看見; 看到: Can you see the screen? 你能看見屏幕嗎? | It was so dark that he could hardly see. 光線太暗了, 他幾乎甚麼也看不見。| I can't see anything without my glasses. 我不戴眼鏡就甚麼也看不見。| Did you see that programme on television last night? 你看了昨晚那個電視節目嗎? | Shall we go and see a film? 我們去看電影好嗎? | You must go and see the Tower of London! 你一定要去看看倫敦塔! | You ought to see how she dances! 你應該看看她跳舞的樣子! | I saw him snatch the handbag and run. 我看見他搶了手提包就跑了。| I saw you talking to them. 我看見你對他們說話。

□ USEFUL PATTERNS 有用句型
to see something/someone; to see someone do something; to see someone doing something

2 [I;T] to understand something 理解; 領會: I don't see the logic of your argument. 我不理解你論點的邏輯。| He can't see why I want the day off work. 他不明白我為甚麼要請假休息一天。| Do you see what I mean? 你明白我的意思嗎?

□ USEFUL PATTERN 有用句型
to see how/why/what…

3 you see you use this expression when you are explaining something with information which will help another person to understand 你瞧; 你知道〔用於解釋某事〕: He's very worried about driving in London. You see, he's never driven in the city before. 他很擔心在倫敦開車, 要知道他以前從來沒有在市區開過

車。**4** [T] to imagine something 想像〔某事物〕: *I can't see her lending me any money.* 我難以想像她會借錢給我。| *I don't see him changing his mind.* 我想像不出他會改變主意。| *Nobody could see him as a married man.* 沒有人能想到他是已婚男子。| *I see no great advantage in expanding the company.* 我看不出擴大公司規模有多大好處。**5** [T] to believe that someone or something has a particular quality 認為; 看作: *My mother still sees herself* **as** *a teenager.* 我的母親仍然把自己看作是十幾歲的人。| *I see his behaviour as unreasonable.* 我認為他的行為不合情理。**6** [T] to meet or visit someone 會見; 探望〔某人〕: *I'm going to see my Aunt.* 我要去探望我的姑媽。| *She's too ill to see you.* 她病得太重, 無法來看你。| *We'll see you in the cafeteria.* 我們將在自助食堂和你見面。| *You ought to see a doctor.* 你應該去看醫生。**7** [T] to find out something 查明; 弄清〔某事〕: *Let's see what time the train is.* 我們去了解一下火車到達的時間吧。| *I'll go and see if the postman's been.* 我去看看郵遞員來過沒有。**8** [T] to be present when something happens or to be the time when something happens 目睹, 經歷; 有〔某事〕發生: *In recent weeks we have seen a political crisis developing.* 我們在最近幾星期親眼目睹了政治危機的發展。| *This century has seen huge social changes.* 本世紀是社會發生巨大變化的時期。**9** **see someone somewhere** to take someone somewhere 送某人到某處: *I'll see you to the door.* 我送你到門口。**10** **see that** to make sure that something is done 確保; 務必〔做到〕: *See that you're home by eleven o'clock.* 你務必要在十一點鐘回到家。| *Will you see that all the doors are locked?* 你一定要把所有的門都鎖上, 行嗎? **11** **what does she see in him?** = what does she find attractive about him? 她覺得他有甚麼吸引力?; 她看中他甚麼? **12** **see if you can** = try to do something 盡量做〔某事〕: *See if you can get the report finished by next week.* 你盡量在下週把報告寫完。**13** **seeing that, seeing as** because 由於, 因為: *Seeing as you're still here, you might as well help us to tidy up.* 既然你還在這兒, 你倒可以幫我們收拾一下。**14** **see fit to do something** to decide to do something, usually something which you think is wrong 決定做某事〔常為錯事〕: *The government has seen fit to abolish this benefit.* 政府已決定廢除這項救濟金。**15** **see red** to suddenly become very angry 〔突然變得〕非常生氣, 狂怒 **16** **have seen better days** to be old and in bad condition 曾有過風光日子〔現在變得古老和破舊〕: *This coat's seen better days.* 這件衣服曾經時髦過一陣。**17** **see a lot of someone, not see much of someone**, etc to see someone often, not very often, etc 常見到某人/不常見到某人: *We don't see very much of Philip these days.* 我們這些日子不常見到菲利普。**18** **see the back of, see the last of** to finish doing something or finish dealing with someone 了結〔某事〕; 擺脫〔某人〕: *I'll be glad to see the back of him!* 我樂得不再與他來往! **19** **see the light: a** to understand something in the end 領悟〔某事〕; 明白過來: *He's finally seen the light and decided to scrap the project.* 他終於明白過來, 並決定放棄那項計劃。**b** to have a religious experience which makes you start believing in a particular religion 〔在宗教上〕省悟, 皈依 **20** **be seeing things** to be imagining that you can see things which are not really there 產生幻覺 **21** **I see** a phrase you use to show that you understand something 我明白了〔用於表示理解某事〕: *"You put the soap in here." "I see."* "你把肥皂放在這裡面。" "我知道了。" **22** **you see** a phrase you use to show that you are explaining something or giving a reason 你瞧〔用於表示解釋事情或提供原因〕: *"He's had an accident, you see."* "他發生了事故, 你瞧。" **23** **as I see it** = as I understand it 依我所見: *As I see it, we need to recruit a few more people.* 依我所見, 我們需要多招聘幾個人。**24** **I'll see, we'll see** a phrase you use when you do not want to decide something at once 我會考慮的; 我們會考慮的〔用於不想馬上決定某事〕: *"Will you lend me the money?" "I'll see."* "你能借錢給我嗎?" "我會考慮考慮。" **25** **let me see, let's see** a phrase you use when you are pausing to think about something 讓我想想看; 讓我們想想看〔用於停下來想某事〕: *Now, let me see, where did I put that list?* 現在讓我想想看, 我把那單子放到哪兒去了? **26** **see you, see you later** *infml* a phrase used to say goodbye to someone 〖非正式〗再見; 回頭見

■ **USAGE** 用法: Compare 比較 **see, look at, watch**. To **see** is to experience with the eyes, and it does not depend on what you want to do ☆ **see** 指用眼睛去感受, 而不取決於你想怎樣做: *I wish I could forget the terrible things I saw during the war.* 但願我能忘卻我在戰爭期間所見到的可怕的事情。*You* **look at** something if you direct your eyes to it and try to see it ☆ **look at** 指用眼睛注視並看清某物: *Sometimes you have to look at a person to understand what they mean.* 有時候你得看着說話人, 以便明白其話義。To **watch** is to look for some time at something that may move ☆ **watch** 指在一段時間內觀看會動的事物: *to* **watch** *television/a football match* 看電視; 看足球賽。Compare 比較 *I* **saw** *him cross the road* 我看見他過馬路。(= I saw the whole journey from one side to the other 我看見他過馬路的全個過程。) and *I* **saw** *him crossing the road* 我看見他正在過馬路。(= I saw him when he was halfway across 他剛

過了一半馬路時，我看見了他。) We can also **watch**, **feel**, and **hear** in these two ways. **watch**, **feel** 和 **hear** 也可用這兩種方式表達。

see about sth *phr v* [T] to make arrangements for something or deal with something 安排〔某事〕；着手辦理〔某事〕: *I've got to go to the personnel department to see about my salary.* 我得去人事部門一下我的薪水。

see sbdy ↔ **off** *phr v* [T] to go with someone to the station or airport where they are leaving from, so that you can say GOODBYE to them 給〔某人〕送行: *We saw her off at the airport.* 我們到機場為她送行。

see sbdy **out** *phr v* [T] to go to the door with someone when they are leaving a room or building 送〔某人〕到門口: *I'll see you out.* 我送你到門口。

see through *phr v* **1** [T **see through** sbdy/sth] to recognize that someone or something is false or not sincere 看穿，識破: *I saw through him immediately.* 我立即就把他看穿。 **2** [T **see** sbdy **through** (sth)] to help someone until the end of a difficult time 幫〔某人〕渡過難關: *I've only got a few pounds to see me through until I get paid.* 我只有幾英鎊，一直要用到發工資。 | *We should have enough coal to see us through the winter.* 我們應該有足夠的煤供我們度過冬天。

see to sth *phr v* [T] to deal with something or make the arragements for it 照料，處理，安排〔某事物〕: *Will you see to the holiday arrangements?* 你能否關照一下假日的安排? | *I must go and see to the dinner.* 我必須去安排晚飯了。

***seed**[1] /sid; siːd/ *n* **1** [C;U] a small thing produced by a flower from which another plant may grow 種子，籽: *grass seed* 草籽 | *Sow the seeds in moist compost.* 把種子撒在潮濕的堆肥裡。 **2** [C] the beginning of something which develops later 起因；根源: *the seeds of future trouble* 未來災難的根源 – **seedless** *adj*: *a seedless orange* 無核柑橘

seed[2] *v* **1** [I] (of a plant) to produce seed 〔植物〕結子 **2** [T] to plant seeds in a piece of ground 在〔地裡〕播種: *a newly-seeded lawn* 新近撒上種子的草坪 **3** [T] to remove seeds from fruit 給〔水果〕去核 **4** [T] (of tennis officials) to place tennis players in the order that they are likely to come in a tennis competition 〔網球隊領導層〕安排種子選手的出場順序；挑選...為種子選手: *Navratilova has been seeded second.* 納夫拉蒂洛娃已被定為二號種子選手。

seed·ling /ˈsidliŋ; ˈsiːdliŋ/ *n* a young plant grown from a seed 籽苗；幼苗

seed·y /ˈsidi; ˈsiːdi/ *adj* **seedier**, **seediest 1** having a poor, worn-out appearance 破舊的；破爛的: *a rather seedy and unpleasant*

part of the town 城中相當破爛不堪的地區 **2** *infml* slightly unwell 〔非正式〕〔身體〕不舒服的: *feeling seedy* 感到不舒服 –**seedily** *adv* – **seediness** *n* [U]

see·ing /ˈsiɪŋ; ˈsiːɪŋ/ *conj* (also 又作 **seeing that** /ˈ··/, **seeing as**) *infml* as it is true that 〔非正式〕鑑於；由於: *Seeing she's old enough to get married, I don't think you can stop her.* 由於她到了女大當嫁的年齡，我想你是阻止不了她的。

*★★**seek** /sik; siːk/ *v* **sought** /sɔt; sɔːt/, **sought** [T] *fml or lit* 〔正式或文〕 **1** to try to find or get something 試圖找到，尋找〔某物〕: *They sought shelter from the rain.* 他們在找地方避雨。 | *to seek the truth* 尋求真理 | *We shall continue to seek for a solution to this problem.* 我們將繼續尋找解決這個問題的辦法。 | *Witnesses are being sought by the police.* 警方正在尋找目擊者。 **2 seek to do something** to try to do something 試圖做某事: *The company is seeking to improve its profitability.* 公司正力圖改進它的盈利能力。 **3** to ask for 要求；請求: *You should seek advice from your lawyer.* 你應該請教你的律師。 –**seeker** *n*: *job seekers* 尋找工作的人

seek sbdy/sth ↔ **out** *phr v* [T] to look for someone or something until you find them 找出，找到〔某人或某物〕

*★★**seem** /sim; siːm/ *v* [not in progressive forms 不用於進行式] **1** [I + complement] to appear or appear to be 似乎；好像；看來: *She always seems sad.* 她總是顯得很哀愁的樣子。 | *That seems a good idea.* 那似乎是個好主意。 | *That seems like a good idea to me.* 對我來說，那似乎是個好主意。 | *There seems to be a problem of some kind.* 好像還存在某種問題。 | *There seems every hope that business will get better.* 看來生意很有希望好轉。 | *He seems to have forgotten the key.* 他好像忘了帶鑰匙。 **2 it seems that, it seems as if** it appears to be true that 看樣子...；似乎...；好像...: *It seems as if there will be an election soon.* 看來不久就要進行選舉。 | *It seems that he has forgotten the key.* 看樣子他忘了帶鑰匙。 | *It seems to me that it's a waste of time.* 依我看這是浪費時間。

seem·ing /ˈsimɪŋ; ˈsiːmɪŋ/ *adj* [only before a noun 只用於名詞前] *fml* that seems to be, but perhaps is not 〔正式〕表面上的，似乎是的: *a seeming piece of good luck which later led to all kinds of trouble* 表面上的好事，後來卻引來各種各樣的麻煩

seem·ing·ly /ˈsimɪŋli; ˈsiːmɪŋli/ *adv* as far as you can know 就某人所知；看樣子: *Seemingly, there is nothing we can do.* 看樣子我們是無能為力了。

seen /sin; siːn/ the past participle of SEE ☆ SEE 的過去分詞

seep /sip; siːp/ *v* [I] to flow slowly through very small holes 滲透，滲漏: *Water had seeped through the bathroom ceiling.* 水從浴室的天花板上滲進來。

see·saw¹ /'si,sɔ; 'si:sɔ:/ *n* a board balanced in the middle for children to sit on at opposite ends so that when one end goes up the other goes down, used for fun 蹺蹺板

seesaw² *v* [I] to move strongly and suddenly up and down 〔劇烈而突然地〕升降: *seesawing prices* 忽漲忽跌的價格

seethe /sið; si:ð/ *v* **seethed, seething** [I] **1 be seething with** to be full of people or things moving in a confused or excited way 密集，雲集: *St Peter's Square was absolutely seething with tourists.* 聖彼得廣場擠滿了旅遊觀光者。**2** to be extremely angry, although often not showing it openly 極其憤怒〔但常不外露〕: *By this time he was absolutely seething.* 至此他氣得火冒三丈。| *I silently seethed with rage at his thoughtlessness.* 我對他的粗心疏忽感到怒火中燒。

see-through /'··/ *adj* that you can see through or partly see through (used of material) 透明的; 極薄的〔指材料〕

seg·ment¹ /'sɛgmənt; 'segmənt/ *n* any of the parts into which something may be divided 部分; 片; 塊: *a large segment of the population* 大部分人口 | *a dish of orange segments* 一盤掰開的橙子

segment² /sɛg'mɛnt; seg'ment/ *v* [I;T] to divide into segments (使)分割〔成部分〕 – **segmentation** /,sɛgmən'teʃən; ,segmən'teiʃən/ *n* [sing; U]

seg·re·gate /'sɛgrɪ,get; 'segrigeit/ *v* **segregated, segregating** [T] to separate different groups 分裁〔不同的組〕; 使分離: *He went to a school where boys and girls were segregated.* 他上的學校是男女生分開的。| *Special cycle paths segregate bicycles from the rest of the traffic.* 腳踏車專用道把腳踏車和其餘的車輛分隔開。–compare 比較 INTEGRATE

seg·re·ga·tion /,sɛgrɪ'geʃən; ,segri'geiʃən/ *n* [U] **1** the separation of groups 分組; 分離 **2** the separation of a social or racial group from others, for example, by laws against using the same schools, hotels, or buses 〔社會或種族團體的〕隔離: *racial segregation* 種族隔離

seis·mic /'saɪzmɪk; 'saizmik/ *adj tech* relating to or caused by an EARTHQUAKE 〔術語〕地震的; 地震引起的

⋆**seize** /siz; si:z/ *v* **seized, seizing** [T] **1** to take hold of something quickly and forcefully 抓住〔某物〕: *He seized my hand.* 他抓住了我的手。| *She seized hold of the child and pulled it away from the road.* 她抓住孩子，把他從路上拉到一邊。**2** to take control of something by official order or by force 依法沒收; 扣押; 佔領; 奪取: *Large quantities of drugs were seized by the police.* 大量毒品被警方沒收了。| *Anti-government forces seized the television station.* 反政府的部隊佔領了電視台。**3 seize on something, seize upon something** to accept something

eagerly as soon as you get the chance 把握住，〔迫不及待地〕利用: *She seized on the chance of a trip abroad.* 她緊緊地把握住那次出國旅行的機會。**4 be seized by** to have a sudden urgent feeling 產生某種突如其來的迫切的感覺: *He was seized by a sudden desire to see his native land again.* 他突然很想重遊出生地。

    seize up *phr v* [I] *BrE* (of part of a machine or your body) to become stuck and stop working 〔英式〕〔機器部件〕卡住; 〔人體〕僵硬

sei·zure /'siʒə; 'si:ʒə/ *n* **1** [U] the act of seizing 抓住; 查封; 扣押: *The courts ordered the seizure of all her property.* 法院下令查封她的全部財產。**2** [C] a sudden attack of an illness, especially one in which your heart suddenly stops working 〔疾病〕突然發作〔尤指心臟病〕: *Her father suffered a heart seizure.* 她的父親心臟病突然發作。

sel·dom /'sɛldəm; 'seldəm/ *adv* not very often 很少, 不常: *I seldom get up before nine o'clock.* 我很少九點鐘以前起牀。

⋆**se·lect¹** /sə'lɛkt; si'lekt/ *v* [T] to choose someone or something 挑選〔某人或某物〕; 選擇: *He selected a shirt to match his suit.* 他挑選了一件襯衫來配他那套西裝。| *He was selected to play for England.* 他被選拔代表英格蘭隊去參賽。

> ☐ **USEFUL PATTERNS** 有用句型
> to select someone for something; to select someone to do something

select² *adj* **1** carefully chosen 仔細挑選的; 精選的 **2** limited to the best people 限於最好的人選使用的: *a select club* 只限於上流社會人士加入的俱樂部

⋆**se·lec·tion** /sə'lɛkʃən; si'lekʃən/ *n* **1** [U] the act of choosing 挑選; 選擇: *the selection of the England team for the World Cup* 選拔英格蘭隊參加世界杯 **2** [U] the fact of being chosen 被選中: *His selection as the new bishop was very unexpected.* 選中了他為新主教完全出乎意料。**3** [C] a thing or person that is chosen from a larger group of things or people 被挑選出的人或物; 精選品: *The orchestra played selections from Gilbert and Sullivan.* 管弦樂隊演奏了吉爾伯特和沙利文的精選作品。**4** [C] a collection of things that have been chosen, or of goods for sale 供選購的貨物: *The shop has a fine selection of cheeses.* 這家商店有很多乾酪可供選購。

se·lec·tive /sə'lɛktɪv; si'lektiv/ *adj* **1** not dealing with all, but choosing only a few for a special purpose 選擇的; 選擇性的: *selective controls on goods brought into the country for sale* 對進口的銷售品有選擇地控制 | *They accused her of being highly selective in her reporting of the war.* 他們指責她對戰爭所作的報道極具選擇性〔即沒有作全面報道〕。**2** careful in choosing 精心挑選的: *He is* always very selective when he chooses his suits. 他購買西裝時總要精心挑選。—**selectively** adv

se·lec·tor /sə'lɛktəʳ; sɪˈlektəʳ/ n a member of a committee choosing a sports team 運動隊選拔委員會的委員

***self** /sɛlf; self/ n **selves** /sɛlvz; selvz/ **1** [C;U] a person's whole nature including their character and abilities 本性, 本質; 自我, 自身: I'm feeling better, but I'm still not quite my old self. 我感到好一點了, 但還沒有完全恢復。**2** [C] a part of your nature 本性的一面: his better self 他本性中較好的一面

self-ad·dressed /ˌ· ·'·◁/ adj a **self-addressed envelope** an envelope addressed for return to the sender 寫上自己姓名地址的回郵信封: Please enclose a self-addressed envelope with your order. 請隨訂單附上寫有你自己姓名地址的回郵信封。

self-as·sur·ance /ˌ·· ·'·/ n [U] a sure belief in your own abilities 自信 —**self-assured** adj

self-ca·ter·ing /ˌ· ·'··/ adj in which you cook your own meals (used of a place where you stay) 〔指住宿處〕自己做飯的

self-cen·tred /ˌ· ·'·◁/ adj interested only in yourself, and not in other people 自我中心的; 自私的

self-con·fessed /ˌ· ·'·◁/ adj [only before a noun 只用於名詞前] admitted by yourself to be a particular kind of person 自己承認的: She is a self-confessed liar. 她自己承認是個說謊的人。

self-con·fi·dence /ˌ· ·'··/ n [U] belief in your own power to do things successfully 自信 —**self-confident** adj

self-con·scious /ˌ·'··/ adj nervous and uncomfortable about yourself, wondering what other people are thinking about you 〔因顧慮他人的看法而〕不自然的, 忸怩的, 在意的 —**self-consciously** adv —**self-consciousness** n [U]

self-con·tained /ˌ· ·'·◁/ adj **1** not depending on help from outside 不依靠外界幫助的; 獨立自足的 **2** a **self-contained flat/apartment** a set of rooms in a building to which you have your own entrance and which has its own bathroom and kitchen; they do not have to be shared with other people 有獨立設施的公寓

self-con·trol /ˌ· ·'·/ n [U] the ability to control your strong feelings 〔強烈感情的〕自(我)克)制: I felt like hitting him, but I managed to keep my self-control. 我很想動手打他, 但我設法自制。—**self-controlled** adj

self-de·feat·ing /ˌ· ·'··/ adj having the effect of preventing its own success 自我挫敗的, 弄巧成拙的: a self-defeating plan 適得其反的計劃

self-de·fence /ˌ· ·'·/ n [U] the act or skill of defending yourself from physical attack 自衛: He shot the man in self-defence. 他出於自衛而開槍打死了那個人。

self-de·ni·al /ˌ· ·'·/ n [U] the habit of not allowing yourself pleasures 克己; 自我犧牲

self-de·ter·min·a·tion /ˌ· ···'··/ n [U] the right of the people of a place to make a free decision about the form of their government, especially whether or not to be independent of another country 〔民族的〕自決(權)

self-dis·ci·pline /ˌ· ·'··/ n [U] the ability to make yourself do the things that you must do 自我約束; 自律

self-em·ployed /ˌ· ·'·◁/ adj earning money from your own business and not being paid by an employer 自己經營的, 不受僱於他人的, 自僱的

self-ev·i·dent /ˌ· ·'··◁/ adj clearly true, without need of proof 不證自明的, 顯而易見的

self-ex·plan·a·to·ry /ˌ· ·'····/ adj easy to understand and not needing any explanation (used especially of things like written instructions) 不須多加解釋的, 不言而喻的〔尤指文字說明等〕

self-gov·ern·ment /ˌ· ·'··/ n [U] government of a country or organization by its own people 自治; 獨立 —**self-governing** adj

self-im·port·ance /ˌ· ·'··/ n [U] thinking that you are more important than you really are 妄自尊大, 自負 —**self-important** adj

self-im·posed /ˌ· ·'·◁/ adj that you have forced yourself to accept (used, for example, of a duty) 自己強加的〔指責任等〕: a self-imposed limit of three cigarettes a day 只許自己每天抽三支煙的自我限制

self-in·dul·gent /ˌ· ·'··/ adj [U] allowing yourself more pleasures and comfort than you should 放縱自己的 —**self-indulgence** n [U]

self-in·terest /ˌ· ·'··/ n [U] concern for what is best for yourself, often hidden behind an appearance of caring for others 利己之心; 自私自利: It's sheer self-interest that makes her so kind to her elderly relatives. 她純粹是為了自己的利益, 才對長輩那麼孝順。

self·ish /ˈsɛlfɪʃ; ˈselfiʃ/ adj caring only about your own advantage and not caring about other people 自私(自利)的: He offered to help for purely selfish reasons. 他提供幫助完全是出於自私的理由。| Don't be so selfish! 別那麼自私自利!—**selfishly** adv —**selfishness** n [U]

self·less /ˈsɛlflɪs; ˈselfləs/ adj always thinking about other people and not yourself 無私的, 忘我的 —**selflessly** adv —**selflessness** n [U]

self-made /ˌ· ·'·◁/ adj becoming successful and wealthy by your own efforts alone 靠自己努力而成功的, 白手起家的: a self-made man 白手起家的人

self-pit·y /ˌ· ·'·/ n [U] too much pity for yourself 自憐

self·pos·sessed /ˌ· ·ˈ··◂/ *adj* confident and having control over your own feelings and actions, especially in difficult or unexpected conditions 泰然自若的; 沉着自信的〔尤指在困難或意外條件下〕 —**self-possession** *n* [U]

self-pres·er·va·tion /ˌ· ···ˈ·/ *n* [U] the natural feeling that makes you keep yourself alive or free from trouble when you are in danger 自我保存; 自我保護

self-re·li·ant /ˌ· ·ˈ··◂/ *adj* able to act without depending on help from other people 自力更生的 —**self-reliance** *n* [U]

self-re·spect /ˌ· ·ˈ·/ *n* [U] the feeling that you need not be ashamed of yourself 自尊 (心), 自重: *I refuse to ask him again. I value my self-respect.* 我不想再去問他, 我很重視自己的自尊心。

self-right·eous /ˌ· ·ˈ·◂/ *adj* too proud of your own rightness or goodness 自以為是的 —**self-righteously** *adv* —**self-righteousness** *n* [U]

self-sac·ri·fice /ˌ· ·ˈ··/ *n* [U] the giving up of your own pleasure or interests for some good or important purpose or to help others 自我犧牲 —**self-sacrificing** *adj*

self-sat·is·fied /ˌ· ·ˈ··◂/ *adj* too pleased with yourself (a word used to show disapproval) 沾沾自喜的, 自鳴得意的〔含貶義〕 —**self-satisfaction** /ˌ· ··ˈ··/ *n* [U]

self-seek·ing /ˌ· ·ˈ·◂/ *adj* doing things only to get an advantage for yourself 追求私利的, 為自己打算的: *a self-seeking politician* 追求私利的政客 —**self-seeking** *n* [U]

self-service /ˌ· ·ˈ··◂/ *adj* working on the system where you serve yourself 顧客自我服務的, 自助(式)的: *a self-service petrol station* 自助加油站 | *Many restaurants are self-service these days.* 目前許多餐廳都是自助用餐的。

self-suf·fi·cien·cy /ˌ· ·ˈ··/ *n* [U] **1** the ability to provide for your own needs without outside help 自給自足 **2** a system of farming in which the farm grows everything 〔各種農作物〕自產自銷

self-suf·fi·cient /ˌ· ·ˈ··◂/ *adj* able to provide for your own needs without outside help 自給自足的: *Britain is now self-sufficient in oil.* 英國現在石油可以自給自足。

★★**sell** /sɛl; sɛl/ *v* **sold** /sold; səʊld/, **sold 1** [I; T] to provide goods in exchange for money 賣, 出售: *Do you sell matches?* 你們賣火柴嗎? | *He sold his house and bought a boat.* 他賣掉房子, 買了一條船。 | *These days they sell bread at petrol stations.* 這些日子, 他們在加油站出售麵包。 | *She sold us her car for £4000.* 她以四千英鎊的價格把她的車子賣給了我們。 | *She sold it to us for £4000.* 她以四千英鎊把它賣給了我們。 | *It was sold before we arrived.* 我們到達以前, 它已被賣掉了。 | *We sold fifty at £5 each.* 我們以五英鎊的單價賣掉了五十個。 **2** [I] to be bought 銷售, 賣出: *Canned drinks sell well in a hot summer.* 罐裝飲料在炎熱的夏天十分暢銷。 |

□ USEFUL PATTERNS 有用句型
to sell something to someone; to sell someone something

The tickets cost too much and did not sell. 票價太高, 賣不出去。 | *They sell for about £1.* 它們的售價是一英鎊左右。 **3** [T] to make people want to buy things 促銷, 推銷: *Bad news sells news-papers.* 壞消息可使報紙增加銷路。 **4 sell someone something** *infml* to make people think that something is a good idea 〔非正式〕使某人接受某個主意: *He sold us the idea that we needed to replace our windows.* 他向我們出了個主意, 說我們必須更換窗子。 **5 be sold on something** *infml* to think that something is a really good idea 〔非正式〕覺得某想法確實不錯: *I'm really sold on this idea of taking a winter holiday.* 我覺得度寒假這個想法確實不錯。 **6 sell yourself** *infml* to make your good qualities clear to people such as employers 〔非正式〕自我推薦

sell sthg ↔ **off** *phr v* [T] **1** to sell all of one thing you own because you want the money for something else 把〔某物〕全部出售: *They have had to sell off the land to pay for the repairs to the house.* 他們不得不出售土地以支付房屋的整修費用。 **2** to sell remaining or unprofitable goods or property, usually cheaply 廉價出售, 削價賣掉: *The garden centres are selling off the garden furniture now that summer is nearly over.* 園藝中心正在削價出售園藝用具, 因為夏季就要過去了。

sell out *phr v* [I] to sell all of what was for sale, so that there is nothing left 賣光: *"Is there any bread left?" "Sorry, we've completely sold out."* "還有麵包嗎?" "對不起, 我們已經全部賣光了。" | *We've sold out of bread.* 我們賣完了麵包。 | *The tickets are sold out.* 票子都賣光了。

sell up *phr v* [I;T **sell up** sthg] to sell a business 賣掉〔產業〕: *They sold up and went to live in Spain.* 他們變賣了全部家產, 去西班牙定居。

sell·er /ˈsɛlə; ˈsɛlər/ *n* a person who sells things 賣主, 賣方

Sel·lo·tape /ˈsɛlo,tep; ˈsɛləteɪp/ *n* (also 又作 **sellotape; scotch tape** *AmE* 〔美式〕) [U] *tdmk* sticky thin clear material sold in narrow rolls, and used for sticking things such as paper or cardboard together 〔商標〕〔用於黏貼紙張等的〕透明膠帶 —**sellotape** *v* [T]

sell-out /ˈ·ˌ·/ *n* **1** an event such as a concert or sports match for which all the tickets are sold 〔音樂會、運動比賽等的〕滿座 **2** a failure to keep to your principles or promises, especially in politics 出賣, 背叛 〔尤指政治〕

selves /sɛlvz; sɛlvz/ *n* the plural of SELF ☆ SELF 的複數形式

se·man·tics /sə'mæntɪks; sɪ'mæntɪks/ *n* [U] the study of the meanings of words 語義學 **–semantic** *adj*

sem·blance /'sɛmbləns; 'sɛmbləns/ *n a/* **some semblance of** an outward appearance of something that usually does not really exist 〔常指實際不存在的〕外表, 外觀: *People were still shouting, but the chairman had managed to restore some semblance of order.* 人們仍在大聲說話, 但主席設法恢復有秩序的樣子。

se·men /'simən; 'siːmən/ *n* [U] the liquid produced by the male sex organs 精液

se·mes·ter /sə'mɛstə; sɪ'mɛstər/ *n* either of the two periods into which a year at universities in the US is divided 〔美國大學的〕學期; 半學年

sem·i /'sɛmɪ; 'sɛmiː/ *n AmE* a large lorry 【美式】大卡車; 半拖車

sem·i·cir·cle /'sɛməˌsɜkl; 'sɛmɪˌsɜːkəl/ *n* half a circle 半圓(形) **–semicircular** /ˌsɛmɪ-'sɜːkjələ; ˌsɛmɪ'sɜːkjʊlə r/ *adj*

sem·i·co·lon /'sɛməˌkolən; ˌsɛmɪ'kəʊlən/ *n* the mark (;) used to separate different members of lists and independent parts of a sentence 分號(;)

sem·i·de·tached /ˌsɛmədɪ'tætʃt; ˌsɛmɪdɪ-'tætʃt r/ *adj* that is one of a pair of houses joined to each other 兩所房子相連的, 半獨立式的 **–semidetached** *n*

sem·i·fi·nal /ˌsɛmə'faɪnl; ˌsɛmɪ'faɪnl r/ *n* one of a pair or set of matches whose winners then compete against one another to decide the winner of the whole competition 半決賽

sem·i·nar /'sɛməˌnɑr; 'sɛmɪnɑː r/ *n* **1** a study meeting for university students with a teacher 〔大學生與教師的〕研討會 **2** a meeting organized by a business in which managers, other people who work in business, or the general public can learn about a particular business subject 〔企業管理層、職工或公眾的〕專家討論會; 交流會

sem·i·na·ry /'sɛməˌnɛrɪ; 'sɛmɪnəri/ *n* **seminaries** a college for training priests 神學院

sem·i·pre·cious /ˌsɛmə'prɛʃəs; ˌsɛmɪ'prɛ-ʃəs r/ *adj* of lower value than a PRECIOUS STONE (used of a jewel or stone) 次貴重的; 半寶石的: *Set with opals and other semi-precious stones* 鑲有蛋白石和其他次貴重寶石

sem·o·li·na /ˌsɛmə'linə; ˌsɛmə'liːnə r/ *n* [U] a powder made from wheat, used in producing PASTA 粗粒麵粉〔用於製作意大利麵食〕

Sen·ate /'sɛnɪt; 'sɛnɪt/ *n* [+ sing/pl verb] the upper house of parliament in the US and some other countries 〔美國和另一些國家的〕參議院: *The Senate has voted to support the President's plans for the economy.* 參議院已經投票支持總統的經濟計劃。 **–compare** 比較 CONGRESS

sen·a·tor /'sɛnətə; 'sɛnətə r/ *n* (also 又作

Senator) a member of a Senate 參議員: *Senator John Dole* 參議員約翰·多爾

★★**send** /sɛnd; sɛnd/ *v* **sent** /sɛnt; sɛnt/, **sent 1** [T] to cause something to go to another place, often by post 送; 寄; 派; 使: *They sent a letter to her brother.* 他們給她的弟弟寄了一封信。 | *My parents send you their love.* 我父母向你致意問好。 | *A letter was sent to him.* 寄了一封信給他。 | *They sent their children to London.* 他們送孩子去倫敦。 | *She sent us to wait in her office.* 她讓我們在她的辦公室裡等。 | *He was sent to buy some milk* 他被派去買牛奶。 | *The explosion sent glass flying everywhere.* 爆炸使玻璃四處飛散。 | *Bad news sent market prices down.* 壞消息使市場價格下跌。

> □ **USEFUL PATTERNS** 有用句型
> to send something to someone; to send someone something; to send someone somewhere

2 [T + complement] to cause someone to have a particular feeling or to be in a particular state 使〔某人〕產生某種情感; 使進入某種狀態: *This noise is sending me mad!* 這噪聲可真讓我受不了! | *His boring speeches always send me to sleep.* 他那枯燥乏味的講話老是令我昏昏入睡。

send away for sthg *phr v* [T] to order goods to be sent by post 郵購〔貨物〕: *I couldn't get a lamp like this in town, so I sent away for one.* 我在城裡買不到這種電燈, 所以我郵購了一個。

send for sbdy/sthg *phr v* [T] **1** to ask someone to come by sending them a message 派人去叫〔請〕〔某人〕: *I think we'd better send for the doctor.* 我認為我們最好去請醫生來。 | *Did you send for the police?* 你派人去叫警察了嗎? **2** to ask in a message for someone or something to be brought or sent to you 要求郵寄〔某物〕來; 要求〔某人〕來: *I'm going to send for the entry form for that competition.* 我準備要求把那次比賽的參賽表格郵寄來。 | *The chief of police sent for reinforcements.* 警長要求增援。

send sthg ↔ **off** *phr v* [T] **1** to post something 郵寄〔某物〕: *Have you sent the cheque off?* 你把支票寄出了沒有? **2** to send a footballer off the field because of bad behaviour or a serious breaking of the rules 〔足球運動員因犯規而〕判罰下場

send sthg ↔ **on** *phr v* [T] to send something from someone's old address to their new address 轉寄〔信件〕到新地址: *The landlady sent on all my mail.* 女房東把我所有的信件都轉寄(到新地址)給我。

send sthg ↔ **out** *phr v* [T] **1** to broadcast 〔用無線電〕發出: *The ship sent out an SOS.* 那艘輪船發出了緊急求救信號。 **2** to send from one particular point 發出; 放出: *We haven't sent the invitations out yet.* 我們尚未

發出邀請。| *The sun sends out light.* 太陽光芒四射。

send-off /'··/ n infml an occasion when a lot of people gather together to say GOODBYE to someone who is leaving 〔非正式〕送行(會), 告別(會): *The team were given a great send-off at the airport.* 在機場上, 這隊伍受到熱烈的歡送。

se·nile /'sinaɪl; 'si:naɪl/ adj weak in mind or body because of old age 老年的, 衰老的 – **senility** /sə'nɪlətɪ; sɪ'nɪl˧ti/ n [U]

se·ni·or[1] /'sinjə; 'si:niəʳ/ n a person who is older or higher in rank than another person 年長者; 前輩; 上級: *He's my senior.* 他是我的上司。

senior adj 1 older or of higher rank 較年長的; 地位較高的: *He is senior to me.* 他年紀比我大。2 of high rank 高級的: *a meeting of the most senior army officers* 最高級將領的會議

Senior n [after n 用於名詞後] especially AmE the older 〔尤美〕較年長者: *John Smith Senior* 老約翰·史密斯

senior cit·i·zen /,··· '···/ n euph an old person, especially one over the age of 60 or 65 (a less direct expression than "old person" or "pensioner", though sometimes not liked by older people) 〔委婉〕老年人; 已屆退休年齡的公民〔尤指六十歲以上的女人或六十五歲以上的男人〕

se·ni·or·i·ty /sin'jɔrətɪ; ˌsi:ni'ɒr˧tɪ/ n [U] the quality of being senior in rank or age 年長; 級別高; 資歷深

sen·sa·tion /sen'seʃən; sen'seɪʃən/ n 1 [C;U] a physical feeling 〔肉體的〕感覺, 知覺: *Since the accident he's had no sensation in the left side of his face.* 事故之後, 他的左臉失去了知覺。| *It gave me a strange tingling sensation.* 它使我產生了一種奇怪的刺痛感。2 [C] a general feeling in your mind or body that you cannot describe exactly 〔難以準確描述的〕感受, 感覺: *I had the sensation that I was being watched.* 我覺得有人在監視我。3 [C] a state of excited interest or the unexpected event that leads to it 激動; 轟動: *The discovery caused a great sensation.* 這個發現是個〔引起了〕很大的轟動。| *The victory of the newcomer Perry over the champion Potter was a sensation.* 新人佩里戰勝冠軍波特, 成了轟動一時的新聞。

sen·sa·tion·al /sen'seʃənl; sen'seɪʃənəl/ adj 1 causing or intended to cause excited interest 引起轟動的; 聳人聽聞的: *a sensational murder* 引起轟動的謀殺案 | *a sensational news report* 聳人聽聞的新聞報道 2 infml wonderful 〔非正式〕極好的, 了不起的: *You won? That's sensational!* 你贏了? 那真好極了! – **sensationally** adv

sen·sa·tion·al·is·m /sen'seʃənl,ɪzəm; sen'seɪʃənəlɪzəm/ n [U] the intentional producing of excitement or shock, for example, by books or magazines of low quality 〔低級書刊等的〕煽情的手段; 嘩眾取寵

sense[1] /sens; sens/ n 1 [C] a way in which a person can know about the physical world, for example, through sight or hearing 感官; 官能〔如視覺或聽覺〕: *When you have a cold, you sometimes lose your sense of smell.* 人患感冒時, 有時會失去嗅覺。2 [C;U] good practical understanding and judgment 領悟; 見識; 判斷力: *Haven't you got enough sense to come in out of the rain?* 難道你就不懂得跑進來避雨嗎? | *a successful man with good business sense* 具有生意眼光的成功人士 3 there's no sense in infml there's no good reason for 〔非正式〕沒有道理〔做某事〕: *There's no sense in going by boat when the plane is just as cheap and much quicker.* 乘船去是沒有道理的, 因為乘飛機一樣便宜, 而且快得多。4 a sense of direction the ability to know where you are or where you are going 方向感: *Tom has absolutely no sense of direction — he's always getting lost.* 湯姆毫無方向感 —— 他老是迷路的。5 a sense of humour an ability to see what is funny in a situation 幽默感: *I like John. He's got a good sense of humour.* 我喜歡約翰, 他很有幽默感。| *Don't look so cross! Where's your sense of humour?* 別發那麼大的火! 你的幽默感到哪兒去了? 6 [sing] a feeling 感覺: *a sense of fear* 恐懼感 | *a sense that someone was standing behind him* 感覺到有人站在他的身後 7 [sing] a belief in the importance of something 〔對某事物重要性的〕信念; 觀念: *a strong sense of justice* 強烈的正義感 8 [C] a meaning 意義, 意思: *I'm using the word "man" in its broadest sense, meaning both men and women.* 我用的"man"這個詞是取其最廣的涵義, 既指男人也指女人。9 make sense: a to have a clear meaning 有明確的意義: *No matter how you read it, this sentence doesn't make sense.* 這句子不管你怎麼讀, 意思都不通。b to be a wise course of action 明智的; 有道理的: *It makes sense to take care of your health.* 注意身體健康是明智的。10 make sense of/out of something to understand something 理解某事物 11 in a sense, in one sense if something is looked at from only one point of view 在某種意義上: *Yes, in a sense I agree with you, but the issue goes much deeper than that.* 對, 在某種意義上我同意你的觀點, 但問題要比那深入得多。

sense[2] v sensed, sensing [T;+(that)] to have a feeling about something without being told directly 感覺到〔某事物〕, 覺察到, 意識到: *The horse sensed danger and stopped.* 這匹馬意識到有危險就停了下來。| *She sensed that her husband was worried.* 她覺察到她丈夫心中不安。

sense·less /'senslɪs; 'sensləs/ adj 1 foolish or without a purpose 愚蠢的; 漫無目的的: *senseless violence* 愚蠢的暴行 2 unconscious

失去知覺的, 不省人事的 **–senselessly** adv **– senselessness** n [U]

sen·si·bil·i·ty /ˌsɛnsəˈbɪlətɪ; ˌsɛnsˌ₅ˈbɪlˌ₅ti/ n **sensibilities** [C;U] fml tender or delicate feeling 〖正式〗感情; 敏感: She plays the piano with great sensibility. 她彈鋼琴彈得很有感情。

★**sen·si·ble** /ˈsɛnsəbl; ˈsɛnsˌ₅bəl/ adj reasonable and practical 合理的; 切實可行的; 明智的: a sensible child 懂事的孩子 | a sensible plan 切合實際的計劃 **–sensibly** adv: You acted very sensibly. 你表現得十分通情達理。

■ USAGE 用法: Do not confuse **sensible** and **sensitive**. A **sensible** person is one who is reasonable and practical, and who has good judgment ☆不要混淆 **sensible** 和 **sensitive**。**sensible** person 是指一個人既"通情達理和切合實際", 又具有"判斷力": She was very **sensible** in the way she dealt with a dangerous situation. 她對付危險情況的辦法非常切實可行。A **sensitive** person is one who is very conscious of other people's feelings and opinions ☆ **sensitive** person 是指對別人的感情和看法敏感的人: She was **sensitive** enough not to ask too many questions about his unhappy childhood. 她是個非常敏感的人, 因此對他那不幸的童年沒有問及太多。| You shouldn't be so **sensitive** — I didn't mean anything bad in what I said. 你不應該那麼敏感, 我的話沒有惡意。

★**sen·si·tive** /ˈsɛnsətɪv; ˈsɛnsˌ₅tɪv/ adj **1** quick to show or feel the effect of something 敏感的; 靈敏度高的: sensitive to cold 對冷敏感的 | light-sensitive photographic paper 感光相紙 | a sensitive pair of scales 靈敏度高的天平 **2** showing delicate feelings or judgment 感情細膩的; 判斷力強的: a sensitive performance 演技細膩的演出 | a sensitive actor 演技細膩的男演員 –opposite 反義 **insensitive** –see 見 SENSIBLE (USAGE 用法) **3** easily offended (a word often used to express disapproval) 容易生氣的; 神經過敏的 〔常含貶義〕: For goodness sake, don't be so sensitive! 看在上帝的面上, 別那麼神經過敏! **4** needing to be dealt with very carefully 需要小心處理的, 要慎重處理的敏感: This is rather a sensitive issue. 這是個相當棘手的問題。| sensitive official papers 機密的官方文件 **–sensitively** adv **–sensitivity** /ˌsɛnsəˈtɪvətɪ; ˌsɛnsˌ₅ˈtɪvˌ₅ti/ n (also 又作 **sensitiveness** /ˈsɛnsətɪvnɪs; ˈsɛnsˌ₅tɪvnˌ₅s/) [U]

sen·so·ry /ˈsɛnsərɪ; ˈsɛnsəri/ adj of the physical senses 感官的; 感覺上的: sensory perception 感官的感覺

sen·su·al /ˈsɛnʃuəl; ˈsɛnʃuəl/ adj **1** interested in the pleasure of the body, especially in sex 肉體上的; 肉慾的; 性感的: her

sensual curves 她那性感的(女性)曲線 **2** of the senses 感官上的: sensual experiences 感官上的經歷 **–sensuality** /ˌsɛnʃuˈælətɪ; ˌsɛnʃuˈælˌ₅ti/ n [U]

sen·su·ous /ˈsɛnʃuəs; ˈsɛnʃuəs/ adj causing pleasant feelings of the senses 引起感官快感的; 舒服的: The cat stretched itself with sensuous pleasure. 貓舒服地伸展身體。**–sensuously** adv **–sensuousness** n [U]

sent /sɛnt; sɛnt/ the past tense and past participle of SEND ☆ SEND 的過去式和過去分詞

★**sen·tence¹** /ˈsɛntəns; ˈsɛntəns/ n **1** a group of words that, in writing, begins with a capital letter and ends with a FULL STOP 句子: It was a fantastic story. It was absolutely gripping from the very first sentence. 那故事寫得非常出色, 從第一個句子開始就引人入勝。| Where's the verb in this sentence? 這個句子的動詞在哪裡? **2** a punishment for a criminal who has been found guilty in court 判決; 宣判: The sentence was ten years in prison. 判刑是入獄十年。| the death sentence 死刑

sentence² v **sentenced, sentencing** [T] (of a judge or court) to give a punishment to someone 〔法官或法庭〕宣判; 判決: He was sentenced **to** three years in prison. 他被判處三年徒刑。

sen·ti·ment /ˈsɛntəmənt; ˈsɛntˌ₅mənt/ n [C; U] **1** tender feelings 柔情; 脆弱的感情, 多愁善感: There's no place for sentiment in this business! 處理這件事情可不能感情用事! **2** an opinion which comes from feeling 意見, 觀點; 情緒: strong public sentiment on the question of unemployment 公眾對失業問題的強烈情緒

sen·ti·ment·al /ˌsɛntəˈmɛntl; ˌsɛntˌ₅ˈmɛntl◂/ adj **1** having or coming from tender feelings rather than reasonable or practical ones 感情(上)的: The clock doesn't work very well, but we keep it for sentimental reasons. 這隻鐘走得不準了, 但因為是感情上的緣故, 我們還保留着它。**2** showing too much of such feelings, especially of a weak or silly kind 多愁善感的; 感傷的: sentimental love stories 傷感的愛情故事 **–sentimentally** adv **–sentimentality** /-mɛnˈtælətɪ; -mɛnˈtælˌ₅ti/ n [U]

sen·ti·nel /ˈsɛntənl; ˈsɛntɪnəl/ n old fash a guard 〖老式〗哨兵, 崗哨

sen·try /ˈsɛntrɪ; ˈsɛntri/ n **sentries** a soldier standing as a guard outside a building or entrance 哨兵, 崗哨

sep·a·ra·ble /ˈsɛpərəbl; ˈsɛpərəbəl/ adj able to be separated from something else 可分開的, 可分離的

★**sep·a·rate¹** /ˈsɛpəˌret; ˈsɛpəreɪt/ v **separated, separating 1** [I;T] to set or move apart (使)分開, (使)分離: They tried to separate the two men who were fighting. 他們盡力把在打架的那兩個男子拉開。| He separated the boys

---

from *the girls.* 他們把男孩和女孩分開。| *The crowd pressed round us, and I got separated from my friends.* 人羣把我們團團圍住, 我和我的朋友走散了。| *In discussing teachers' pay, the issues of their hours of work and types of work must be clearly separated.* 在討論教師薪酬時, 工作時間和工作種類這兩個問題必須明確分開。**2** [I;T] to break or divide up into parts 使分散; 分成: *War separated the family.* 戰爭拆散了這個家庭。| *The children separated into four groups.* 孩子們分成了四組。**3** [T] to keep apart 分隔, 隔開: *two communities separated by religious differences* 因宗教分歧使兩個社區隔離 **4** [I] (of a husband and wife) to decide to live apart, especially by a formal agreement 〔夫妻〕分居〔尤指通過正式協議〕

★**sep·a·rate²** /'sepərɪt; 'sepɚɪt/ *adj* **1** [never before a noun 不能用於名詞前] apart 分開的, 分離的: *Keep the onions separate from the bread, or they'll make it smell.* 洋葱和麵包要分開放置, 否則麵包會沾上味。**2** different 不同的, 不一樣的: *This word has three separate meanings.* 這個單詞有三個不同的意思。**3** not shared with another person 單獨的; 各自的: *We have separate rooms.* 我們各有自己的房間。–**separateness** *n* [U] –**separately** *adv: They left separately.* 他們各自離開了。

sep·a·ra·ted /'sepəreɪtɪd; 'sepəreɪt̬ɪd/ *adj* living apart, especially by a formal agreement (used of a husband and wife) 分居的〔尤指協議分居的夫妻〕

sep·a·ra·tion /ˌsepə'reʃən; ˌsepə'reɪʃən/ *n* **1** [U] movement apart 分離, 分開: *the separation of the rocket* 火箭的分體 **2** [C;U] the state of being separate or living apart 分離狀態; 分居 *the separation of government and administration* 政府和行政的分離 | *He was unhappy because of his separation from his mother.* 他因與母親分離而感到悶悶不樂。**3** [C] *law* a formal agreement by a husband and wife to live apart 《律》〔夫婦的〕分居〔協議〕–compare 比較 DIVORCE

sep·a·rat·ist /'sepə,retɪst; 'sepərətɪst/ *n* a member of a group that wants to become separate from a larger political or religious organization〔政治或宗教組織的〕分離主義者

se·pi·a /'sipɪə; 'siːpɪə/ *n* [U] the brown colour of early photographs〔舊照片的〕紅褐色

Sep·tem·ber /sep'tembə; sep'tembɚ/ *n* (also 又作 **Sept.**) the 9th month of the year 九月

sep·tic /'septɪk; 'septɪk/ *adj* infected by disease bacteria 病菌感染的; 膿毒性的

sep·ul·chre /'seplkə; 'sepəlkɚ/ *n biblical* a large TOMB where a person was buried《聖經》墳墓; 塚 –**sepulchral** /sə'pʌlkrəl; sə'pʌlkrəl/ *adj*

se·quel /'sikwəl; 'siːkwəl/ *n* **1** a book or film which continues the action of an earlier one〔書或電影的〕續集, 續篇 **2** something that follows something else, especially as a

result 後續; 後果

★**se·quence** /'sikwəns; 'siːkwəns/ *n* **1** [C] a group of things arranged in an order, especially following one another in time 按順序排列的一組事物, 一連串: *a strange sequence of events* 一連串古怪的事件 **2** [U] the order in which things or events follow one another 先後次序, 順序: *Please keep the cards in the correct sequence.* 請把這些卡片按正確次序放好。| *The slides were all in order, except for two that were slightly out of sequence.* 幻燈片都按順序排列, 只有兩張次序不對。

se·quin /'sikwɪn; 'siːkwɪn/ *n* a small shiny piece of metal or plastic sewn onto a piece of clothing for decoration〔裝飾衣服用的〕金屬或塑料小圓片, 閃光裝飾片

ser·e·nade¹ /ˌserə'ned; ˌserə'neɪd/ *n* a song or other music sung or played in the open air at night, especially to a woman by a lover〔尤指男子給所愛的女子演唱或演奏的〕小夜曲

serenade² *v* **serenaded, serenading** [T] to sing or play a serenade to someone 對〔某人〕唱〔奏〕小夜曲

se·rene /sə'rin; sə'riːn/ *adj* completely calm and peaceful 寧靜的; 平靜的: *a serene summer night* 寧靜的夏夜 –**serenely** *adv* –**serenity** /sə'renəti; sə'renət̬i/ *n* [U]

serf /sɜf; sɜf/ *n* a person forced to stay and work on their master's land, in the Middle Ages in Europe and until the 19th century in Russia〔歐洲中世紀和俄國十九世紀以前的〕農奴

ser·geant /'sardʒənt; 'saːdʒənt/ *n* **1** a NONCOMMISSIONED OFFICER of middle rank in the army or air force〔陸軍或空軍的〕中士, 軍士 **2** a police officer with next to the lowest rank 警察小隊長; 巡佐

sergeant ma·jor /ˌ·· '··◂/ *n* a NONCOMMISSIONED OFFICER of the highest rank in an army 軍士長

se·ri·al /'sɪrɪəl; 'sɪrɪəl/ *n* a written or broadcast story appearing in parts at fixed times 連載小說; 連續劇: *He's the star of a popular TV serial.* 他是一部受歡迎的電視連續劇的明星。

se·ri·al·ize /'sɪrɪəl,aɪz; 'sɪrɪəlaɪz/ *v* **serialized, serializing** (also 又作 **serialise** *BrE*《英式》) [T] to print or broadcast something in a number of parts, not all at once 連載; 連播 –**serialization** /ˌsɪrɪələ'zeʃən; ˌsɪrɪələ'zeɪʃən/ *n* [C;U]

serial num·ber /'··· ,··/ *n* a number printed on a large number of similar things, so that you can tell them apart 順序號碼, 連續編號: *The police know the serial numbers of the stolen bank-notes.* 警方知道被偷的鈔票的連續編號。

★**se·ries** /'sɪrɪz; 'sɪriːz/ *n* [plural is 複數為 **series**] a group of things of the same kind, coming one after another

一系列; 連續(的事物): *a television series about modern art* 關於現代藝術的電視系列片 | *After a series of unsuccessful attempts, he has at last passed his driving test.* 他在連續幾次失敗的嘗試後, 終於通過了駕駛考試。 | *The British team will be playing a series of matches in Australia this winter.* 英國隊今年冬天將在澳大利亞參加一系列的比賽。

se·ri·ous /'sɪrɪəs; 'sɪərɪəs/ *adj* **1** very bad and worrying 嚴重的: *serious damage* 嚴重的損毀 | *serious crime* 嚴重的罪行 | *A serious situation is developing in Fleetwood, where floods have devastated the town.* 弗利特伍德正陷入嚴峻的局面, 洪水已經吞沒了市鎮。 | *a serious illness* 重病 **2** solemn and not joking or cheerful 嚴肅的; 莊重的; 認真的: *a serious expression on his face* 他臉上嚴肅的表情 | *Are you serious about looking for a new job?* 你是真的要找一份新的工作嗎? **3** concerned with important things 重要的; 重大的: *a serious artist* 重要的藝術家 | *a serious newspaper article* 一篇嚴肅的報刊文章 – **seriousness** *n* [U]

se·ri·ous·ly /'sɪrɪslɪ; 'sɪərɪəslɪ/ *adv* **1** in a serious way 嚴肅地; 嚴重地; 認真地: *She likes art but has never studied it seriously.* 她喜歡藝術, 但從未認真學習過。 | *seriously ill in hospital* 病重住院 **2** a word you use when you are surprised at something someone has just said, and are asking them if they really mean it 當真地〔用於對某人的話表示吃驚〕: *"I'm going to emigrate." "Seriously?"* "我打算移居國外。" "真的嗎?" **3 take something seriously** to treat something as important and needing thought and attention 認真對待某事

ser·mon /'sɜːmən; 'sɜːmən/ *n* a talk given as part of a church service 佈道, 講道

ser·pent /'sɜːpənt; 'sɜːpənt/ *n lit* a snake 〔文〕蛇

ser·rat·ed /sɛˈreɪtɪd; sɪˈreɪtɪd/ *adj* having a row of connected V-shapes like teeth 鋸齒狀的; 有鋸齒的: *a serrated edge* 鋸齒狀的邊 | *a serrated knife* 鋸齒刀

ser·vant /'sɜːvənt; 'sɜːvənt/ *n* a person who is paid to work for another person in their house 僕人, 傭人: *They have two servants, a cook and a gardener.* 他們有兩個僕人: 一個廚師和一個園丁。

serve ¹ /sɜːv; sɜːv/ *v* **served, serving 1** [I; T] to work in the army or another organization or for an important person (為…)服務; 服役; 任職: *He served under Mrs Thatcher in the Department of Education and Science.* 他在戴卓爾夫人手下的科學教育部任職。 | *They served on the committee.* 他們在委員會擔任委員。 | *He served in the Korean War.* 他參加了朝鮮戰爭。 **2** [T] to provide something useful for people 供應〔有用之物〕: *Travellers from Essex to Kent are served by the M25*

motorway. M25 高速公路為來往於埃塞克斯郡和肯特郡的旅行者帶來便利。 | *a single pipeline serving all the houses with water* 給所有房子供水的一條水管 **3** [I;T] to put food ready for people to eat 侍候〔進餐〕; 端上〔食物〕: *Shall I serve the meat?* 我可以把肉端上嗎? | *fish served with potatoes and beans* 與馬鈴薯和豆子一同上桌的魚 | *Breakfast is served from 8.15 until 10 a.m.* 早餐從上午八時十五分至十時供應。 | *All the recipes serve six people.* 所有這些食譜可供六人吃。 | *She served us a lemon pudding.* 她給我們端上了檸檬布丁。 **4** [I;T] to provide a customer in a shop with attention and help 接待〔顧客〕: *Are you being served?* 有人接待你嗎? **5** [T] to spend time in prison 服刑, 坐牢: *He served ten years for murder.* 他因謀殺服刑十年。 **6** [I;T] to do a job, often a job which is usually done by something else 用作; 起…的作用: *The entrance hall also serves as a dining-room.* 這門廳又作飯廳。 | *This polythene sheet should serve to keep out the rain.* 這種聚乙稀塑料布可用來遮雨。 **7** [I;T] to hit the ball first to start a game such as tennis 〔網球等〕發(球), 開(球) **8 it serves you right** = you deserve the trouble you've got 活該; 給某人應得的懲罰

serve sthg ↔ out *phr v* [T] to put food on people's plates 把〔食物〕分給大家

serve up *phr v* [I;T **serve sthg ↔ up**] to put food on people's plates, especially when you have cooked it yourself 端上〔食物〕並分給大家〔尤指親自做的飯菜〕

serve² *n* (also 又作 **service**) the ability to hit, the act of hitting, the ball to start a game such as tennis 〔網球等〕發球: *She has a strong serve.* 她的發球很有力。

serv·er /'sɜːvə; 'sɜːvə/ *n* a specially shaped tool for putting a particular kind of food onto a plate 分菜用具〔指大調羹、叉子等〕: *a pair of salad servers* 一副上沙拉用的叉匙

ser·vice¹ /'sɜːvɪs; 'sɜːvɪs/ *n* **1** [U] attention to customers in a shop, or to business customers, or to guests in a hotel or restaurant 〔對商店、企業、旅館或餐館的顧客的〕服務; 接待: *The food was excellent, but the service was rather slow.* 食物挺不錯, 可就是服務太慢。 **2** [U] work done for someone else 效勞: *He was given an award for his service to the blind.* 他因為服務盲人而獲獎。 | *He died in the service of his country.* 他為國捐軀。 **3** [U] employment in an organization, or by a person 任職: *He resigned after twenty years' service.* 他任職二十年後辭職。 **4** [C] a particular job or kind of work offered to the public 〔為公眾提供的〕特別服務: *The centralized hotel booking system is a useful service for overseas visitors.* 集中的旅館預訂制度為海外遊客提供了有效用的服務。 | *a free information service* 免費信息服務 **5 services: a** work done for someone else 幫

助; 服務: *You may need the services of a lawyer.* 你可能需要一位律師的幫助。 **b** useful work done by businesses for their customers but which does not produce goods 非生產性勞動; 服務性行業: *service occupations such as hairdressing* 諸如理髮等服務性行業 **6 services** [C plural is 複數為 **services**] a place on a very big road where people can stop to use the restaurant and the toilets (TOILET) and buy petrol 〔提供飲食、汽油等的〕路邊服務站: *On the way up to Scotland we stopped at the Scratchwood Services.* 去蘇格蘭的途中,我們在斯格拉奇伍德路邊服務站稍作停留。 **7** [C] an organization or system which does something useful for the public 公用事業; 公用機構: *the National Health Service* 國民保健制度 | *the Fire Service* 消防服務 | *a delivery service* 送遞業務 **8 the services: a** the army, navy, and air force 三軍〔陸軍、海軍、空軍〕 **b** the supply of water, electricity, and gas 水、電和煤氣的供應 **9** [U] work done in the army, navy, or air force 兵役: *He's on service in the Far East.* 他在遠東服兵役。 **10** [C] *BrE* a particular area of government responsibility 〔英式〕政府部門: *the foreign service* 外交部門 **11** [C] the regular examination and repair of a machine, for example a car or washing-machine 〔機器的〕定期檢修,維修: *I've got to take the car in for a service on Monday.* 星期一我得把汽車送進去維修一下。 **12** [C] regular public buses, trains, planes, or boats between one place and another 定期來往於兩地的公共汽車、火車、飛機或輪船: *an hourly service between Manchester and London* 曼徹斯特與倫敦之間每小時一班的班車〔航班〕 **13** [C] a fixed form of public worship 禮拜; 〔宗教〕儀式: *She attended the evening service at St Stephen's.* 她參加了聖斯蒂芬教堂的晚禱儀式。 **14** [C] a set of plates and dishes, or a set of tea plates, cups, and saucers (SAUCER) 一套餐具; 一套茶具: *a dinner service* 正餐餐具 **15** [C] (also 又作 **serve**) the ability to hit the ball, or the act of hitting it, at the beginning of a game such as tennis 〔網球等的〕發球 **16 in service** in use or able to be used 在使用的; 能使用的 **17 out of service** not in use or able to be used 不在使用的; 不能使用的: *We regret that the photocopier is out of service.* 我們感到很遺憾,複印機不能用了。

service² *v* **serviced, servicing** [T] to examine a machine and repair it or put in good condition 檢修,維修,保養: *We have the car serviced once a year.* 我們一年一次把汽車送去維修。

ser·vi·cea·ble /'sɜːvɪsəbḷ; 'sɜːvḷsəbəl/ *adj* fit to use and suitable for a purpose 適用的; 耐用的: *a serviceable pair of shoes* 一雙耐穿的鞋

service charge /'·· ·/ *n* money added to a restaurant bill in order to pay for the

waiter or waitress who serves you 〔加在飯館賬單上的〕服務費: *a 10% service charge* 百分之十的服務費

ser·vice·man /'sɜːvɪs,mæn; 'sɜːvḷsmən/ *n* **servicemen** /-mən; -mən/ a man in the army, navy, or AIRFORCE 軍人

service sta·tion /'·· ,··/ *n* (also 又作 **garage** *BrE* 〔英式〕) a place that sells petrol 〔汽車〕加油站

ser·vi·ette /ˌsɜːvi'ɛt; ˌsɜːviˈet/ *n BrE* a small square of cloth or paper which you use at meals to keep your clothes, fingers, and lips clean 〔英式〕餐巾

ser·vile /'sɜːvḷ; 'sɜːvaɪl/ *adj* too eager to do what someone else wants, and giving them too much respect 卑賤的; 奴性的; 屈從的 – **servility** /sɜːˈvɪlətɪ; sɜːˈvɪlḷti/ *n* [U]

ser·vi·tude /'sɜːvə,tjud; 'sɜːvḷtjuːd/ *n* [U] *lit* the condition of a slave or of someone who is forced to obey another person all the time 〔文〕奴隸狀態; 奴役: *a life of servitude* 奴役生活

ses·sion /'sɛʃən; 'seʃən/ *n* **1** a meeting of an organization or court 會議; 開庭: *a session of the United Nations Security Council* 聯合國安全理事會會議 **2** a period in the year when a parliament or court meets 會期; 開庭期 **3** a period of time used for a particular activity 〔進行某項活動的〕一段時間: *a dancing session* 一次跳舞的聚會

set¹ /sɛt; set/ *v* **set, set, setting 1** [T + adv/prep] to put something somewhere carefully 放置〔某物〕,安放: *The waiter set a plate of food down in front of me.* 服務員把一盤食物放在我的前面。 | *She picked up the ornament and set it on the table.* 她撿起裝飾品放到桌上。 **2** [T] to fix or establish a rule, time, or level 制定〔規則〕; 確定〔時間〕〔標準〕: *The price has been set at £1000.* 定價為一千英鎊。 | *I always try to set a good example to the children.* 我總是盡量為孩子們樹立良好的榜樣。 **3 set someone/something doing something** to cause someone or something to start doing something 使〔某人或某物〕開始做某事: *Your remarks have set me thinking.* 你的話引起我的思考。 | *He pushed the switch to set the wheel turning.* 他按下開關,使輪子開始轉動。 **4** [T] to give a piece of work to someone 〔給某人〕指派〔工作〕: *Who's setting the exam this year?* 今年誰出考題? | *She forgot to set us any homework.* 她忘了給我們佈置家庭作業。

> ☐ USEFUL PATTERNS 有用句型
> to set something for someone; to set someone something

5 [T] to show the action of a story or play as happening in a particular place 為〔故事或戲劇〕設置背景: *The story is set in 17th century Spain.* 這個故事以十七世紀的西班牙為背

景。**6** [T] to fix something into a surface 鑲，嵌: *a gold ring with three diamonds set into it* 鑲有三顆鑽石的金戒指 **7** [T] to put a broken bone into a fixed position so that it will mend 使〔折骨〕復位，癒合 **8** [I] (of a broken bone) to become mended in a fixed position 接合〔折骨〕 **9** [I] to become solid 凝固: *It will take two or three days for the concrete to set.* 水泥要兩、三天時間才能凝固。**10** [T] to arrange your hair while it is wet so that it has a particular style when it dries〔頭髮〕梳理成一定髮型 **11 set a table** to put plates, glasses, and other things onto a table ready for people to have a meal 擺好餐具準備開飯 **12 set a trap** to prepare a trap 設置圈套 **13 the sun sets** = the sun disappears from the sky at the end of the day 太陽落山 **14 set eyes on** to see someone or something 看見〔某人或某物〕: *I'd never set eyes on him before.* 我以前從未見過他。**15 set fire to something, set something on fire** to cause something to burn 放火燒某物: *Vandals had broken in and set fire to the building.* 破壞分子闖入，並放火燒了大樓。**16 set foot** to go into or onto a place 進入; 踏上: *You will never set foot in this house again!* 你再也別想踏進這個家! **17 set free** to allow someone or something to go free 釋放〔某人〕; 放出〔某物〕: *Hundreds of political prisoners have been set free.* 數以百計的政治犯已被釋放。**18 set sail** to start sailing 起航: *The boat is due to set sail tomorrow evening.* 小船定在明天晚上起航。**19 set store by something** a phrase you use when you are saying how important you think something is 重視某事物〔用於表示某事至關重要〕: *We don't set much store by paper qualifications.* 我們並不十分強調資歷。**20 set the pace** to fix the speed for other people to follow 定出步速 **21 set the scene for something** to make it possible for something to happen 使某事可能發生: *This agreement set the scene for future arguments and disagreements.* 這項協議可能導致將來的爭吵與不和。**22 set to music** to write music for a piece of writing 為〔歌詞〕譜曲: *The poems have been set to music.* 這些詩已被譜成了曲。**23 set to rights** to make something right or correct 糾正, 校正〔某事物〕 **24 set to work** to start working 開始工作: *I think we should set to work as soon as possible.* 我認為我們應該盡早開始工作。**25 set your heart on something** to decide that you want something very strongly 決心得到某物: *I've really set my heart on a holiday this summer.* 我已下決心今年夏天真的要去度假。**26 set your teeth on edge** (of a very unpleasant taste or sound) to give you an unpleasant feeling〔令人不舒服的味道或聲音〕使人感到難受

set about sthg *phr v* [T] to start doing something 開始，着手〔做某事〕: *We set about tidying the room.* 我們開始收拾房間。

set against *phr v* **1** [T set sthg **against** sthg] to consider one thing along with something else that is different or opposite 抵銷: *This defeat has to be set against a whole series of recent successes.* 這次失敗抵銷了最近一連串的成功。**2** [T set sbdy **against** sbdy] to make someone dislike or oppose another person 使〔某人〕與〔另一人〕對立: *a war which set family against family* 一場使家族之間產生對立的戰爭

set sbdy/sthg ↔ **apart** *phr v* [T] to make someone or something clearly different from others 使〔某人或某物〕與眾不同: *His deprived background set him apart from other children.* 他那貧苦的出身使他不同於其他孩子。

set sthg ↔ **aside** *phr v* [T] **1** to save something for a special purpose〔為特殊用途〕留出, 節省〔某物〕: *I'm trying to set aside a bit of money to pay for a holiday.* 我想盡量積攢點錢, 以便支付度假費用。**2** to pay no attention to a particular idea or belief 對〔某一想法或信念〕置之不理: *We must try to set aside our individual ambitions and work for the common good.* 我一定要拋開個人的抱負, 為共同的利益而奮鬥。

set back *phr v* **1** [T set sbdy/sthg ↔ **back**] to cause someone or something to not make as much progress as they should 使…耽誤; 使…延緩: *The bad weather has set back the building work.* 惡劣的天氣已經使建築工程推遲了。| *That illness really set him back.* 那場疾病確實耽誤了他的事。**2** [T set sbdy **back**] *infml* to cost someone a particular amount of money《非正式》使〔某人〕花費〔一筆錢〕: *The new car set me back £6000.* 這輛新汽車花了我六千英鎊。**3 be set back** to be at a distance from a road, not right next to a road 把…置於距〔公路〕一定距離處: *The house is well set back from the road.* 這所房子與公路有相當一段距離。

set down *phr v* **1** [T set sbdy ↔ **down**] to stop a car and let someone get out 讓〔某人〕下車: *Could you set me down just by the library?* 你能讓我就在圖書館那兒下車嗎? **2** [T set sthg ↔ **down**] *fml* to write something down《正式》寫下〔某事〕, 記錄: *I felt the need to set my feelings down in writing.* 我覺得有必要把我的感受記錄下來。

set in *phr v* [I] (of something unpleasant) to begin and seem likely to continue for a long time〔不愉快的事〕來臨〔並且可能持續一段時間〕: *In the afternoon the rain really set in.* 下午果然下起雨來。

set off *phr v* **1** [I] to begin a journey 出發, 動身, 啟程: *We set off early the next morning.* 我們第二天一大清早就出發了。**2** [T set sthg ↔ **off**] to cause something to explode or make a loud noise 使〔某物〕爆炸; 發出很大噪音: *The bomb could be set off at any time.* 炸彈隨時都可能會爆炸。| *Children had set off the fire alarm.* 孩子們弄響了火警鐘。**3** [T set sthg ↔ **off**] to cause something to start happening 引起，觸發〔某事的發生〕: *The relaxation of the licensing laws set off a sudden boom in the drinks industry.* 售酒法的放寬使釀酒業發展迅速。

set on *phr v* **1** [T **set on** sbdy] to attack someone 攻擊〔某人〕 **2** [T **set** sthg **on** sbdy] to cause an animal to attack someone 使〔動物〕攻擊〔某人〕: *They set the dogs on him.* 他們放出狗來咬他。

set out *phr v* **1** [I] to begin a journey 出發，起程，動身: *We set out* **for** *London.* 我們出發去倫敦。 **2 set out to do something** to start with the purpose of doing something〔帶着某目的〕開始做某事: *It seems that he set out to destroy the company.* 他似乎開始了破壞公司的活動。 **3** [T **set** sthg ↔ **out**] to explain facts or ideas clearly 闡明，解釋〔某事物〕: *The reasons for my decision are set out in my report.* 我作此決定的理由已在我的報告中闡明。 **4** [T **set** sthg ↔ **out**] to arrange or spread things out in order 安排，擺放〔物品〕: *The meal was set out on a long table.* 飯菜擺放在一張長桌子上。

set up *phr v* **1** [T **set** sthg ↔ **up**] to put or build something somewhere 安放，豎起〔某物〕: *Roadblocks have been set up by the police.* 警察已經設置了路障。 **2** [T **set** sthg ↔ **up**] to make the preparations for something and start it working 創立，建立，設立: *The council set up a committee to look into ways of creating more jobs in the area.* 議會設立了一個委員會來調查該地區可提供更多就業機會的途徑。 **3** [I;T **set** sbdy **up**] to establish yourself or someone else in a new business 使…開業: *She left the company where she had been working and set up on her own.* 她離開了她一直效力的公司，自己做起生意來了。 | *He set himself up as a painter and decorator.* 他幹起了油漆和裝飾工來。 **4** [T **set** sbdy **up**] *infml* to make someone seem guilty of something that they did not do〔非正式〕枉害，誣陷〔某人〕: *He claims that the police set him up.* 他聲稱警方陷害他。

★★ **set²** *adj* **1** fixed and not able to be changed 固定不變的: *The meals are all a set price.* 飯菜的價格都是固定的。 | *I have to study at set hours every day.* 我每天必須在固定的時間學習。 | *He has very set ideas about what a marriage should be like.* 婚姻該是甚麼樣子，他有自己的固定看法。 **2 set book** a book that students must study for an examination 必讀課本 **3 be set to do something** to be ready to do something 準備好做某事: *We were all set to leave when the phone rang.* 我們都準備好啟程時，電話突然響了。 **4 be set on doing something** to be determined to have or do something 決心做某事: *Everyone has told him how dangerous it is, but he still seems set on going.* 人人都告訴他那有多危險，但他好像還是決

意要去。

set³ *n* **1** a group of things that belong together 一組，一套: *I need a new set of gardening tools.* 我需要一套新的園藝工具。 | *We are now facing a whole new set of problems.* 我們現在正面臨整整一批全新的問題。 **2** a machine on which you can watch television broadcasts〔收看電視節目的〕接收裝置: *a television set* 電視機 | *We can't watch television at the moment — our set's broken.* 我們現在無法看電視，我們的電視機壞了。 **3** the scenery for a play or film〔戲劇或電影的〕佈景 **4** a group of games in a tennis match〔網球比賽的〕一盤

set-back /'sɛt,bæk; 'sɛtbæk/ *n* a return to a less good position 退步，倒退，挫折: *She seemed better after her illness but then she had a sudden setback.* 她病後似乎有了好轉，但後來病情又突然急轉直下。 | *Hopes of an early end to the dispute have suffered a severe setback.* 早日結束爭端的希望已嚴重受挫。

set-square /'sɛt,skwɛr; 'sɛtskweə^r/ *n BrE* a flat three-sided plate used for drawing straight lines and angles exactly〔英式〕〔製圖用的〕三角板，三角尺

set-tee /se'ti; se'ti:/ *n BrE* (also 又作 **sofa**) a comfortable seat for more than one person, with a back and arms 長靠椅，長沙發 – see picture on page 730 見 730 頁彩圖

★ **set-ting** /'sɛtɪŋ; 'setɪŋ/ *n* **1** the surroundings of a place 環境；背景: *high mountains forming a beautiful setting for a holiday* 高山環抱，形成優美的度假環境 | *Our story has its setting in ancient Rome.* 我們的故事以古羅馬為背景。 | *a diamond in a gold setting* 鑲在黃金底座的鑽石 **2** one of the positions at which you can set the controls of something〔調節某物的〕定位: *Turn the fridge to the coldest setting.* 把冰箱調節到最冷的位置。

★ **set-tle** /'sɛtl; 'setl/ *v* **settled, settling** **1** [I;T] to put an end to an argument or a problem 平息〔爭端〕；解決〔難題〕: *They agreed to settle their differences and work together.* 他們同意消除分歧，攜手共事。 **2** [T] to decide 決定: *I'm going to settle this question once and for all.* 我要把這個問題一勞永逸地定下來。 | *That's the holiday settled, then.* 那麼，就那樣定下假期了。 **3 settle a bill** to pay a bill 支付賬單 **4** [I] to go and live somewhere 移居；定居: *They got married and settled in Manchester.* 他們結了婚，在曼徹斯特定居。 | *They left Pakistan and settled in Canada.* 他們離開巴基斯坦，移居加拿大。 **5** [I] to land 降落；停留於: *The large bee settled briefly on the flower.* 大蜜蜂飛到花上稍作停留。 **6** [I] to sink slowly to the bottom 慢慢下沉: *The sand settled on the bottom of the pond.* 沙子沉到了池塘底。 **7** [I;T] to make or become quiet and calm (使)安靜下來；平靜下來: *I think I need to take something to settle my stomach.* 我覺得我需要吃點東西來緩解胃部

不適。**8 settle someone somewhere** to sit someone down and make them comfortable 把某人安頓於某處: *She settled the little boy on the sofa.* 她把小男孩安頓在沙發上。 | *She settled herself in her chair.* 她舒適地在椅子上坐下。

settle down *phr v* [I] **1** to become calmer and less active and noisy 平靜下來, 安靜下來: *Settle down now, children, and go to sleep.* 現在安靜下來吧, 孩子們, 去睡覺吧。 **2** to start to lead a quieter life in one place 開始過安定的生活: *At the age of thirty he decided it was time to marry and settle down.* 他在三十歲時決定應該結婚並安頓下來。 **3** to become used to a new way of life or something such as a new job or a new school 習慣於〔新的生活方式、工作或學校〕: *How are you settling down in your new school?* 你在新學校裡適應得怎樣? **4** to get comfortable somewhere where you intend to stay for a time 舒舒服服地坐下〔躺下〕: *After tea she settled down in the armchair with her book.* 她吃過茶點, 就拿起她的書舒適地在扶手椅上坐下來。 | *He settled down for a sleep.* 他舒適地躺下睡覺。 **5** to stop thinking about other things and attend to one particular thing 安下心來〔做某事〕: *Settle down to your homework.* 安下心來做你的功課吧。 | *He settled down to do his accounts.* 他專心地計算他的賬目。

settle for sth *phr v* [T] to accept something less than you hoped for 勉強接受: *The miners are asking for a 10% pay rise, but they'd probably settle for 8%.* 礦工要求增加百分之十的工資, 但他們大概會勉強接受百分之八。

settle in *phr v* [I] to get used to something such as a new place to live or a new job 習慣於〔新的家或工作〕: *How are you settling in?* 你習慣得怎樣?

settle on sbdy/sthg *phr v* [T] to decide on one of the things you have been considering 決定; 選定: *We liked all the colours, but in the end we settled on green.* 我們喜歡所有的顏色, 但最終選定綠色。

settle up *phr v* [I] **1** to pay your debts 付清欠賬: *You pay for now and I'll settle up later.* 你現在付賬, 稍後我來結清。 **2** (of two or more people) to pay and receive what is owed 〔兩人或多人之間〕結清該付該收的賬目: *We settled up at the end of the evening.* 我們在傍晚結束時清一下賬目。

★**set·tled** /ˈsɛtld; ˈsɛtld/ *adj* unlikely to change 不大可能改變的: *settled weather* 穩定的天氣 | *settled habits* 固定的習慣

★**set·tle·ment** /ˈsɛtlmənt; ˈsɛtlmənt/ *n* **1** [C] a formal agreement or decision ending an argument or question 〔爭吵或問題的〕解決; 和解; 協議: *the settlement of the miners' dispute* 礦工糾紛的解決 | *We've reached a settlement with the defence lawyers.* 我們已經和辯護律師達成協議。 **2** [C] a place where

people live 村落: *a settlement on the edge of the desert* 沙漠邊緣的村落 **3** [U] the movement of a new population into a place to live there 移民, 殖民: *the settlement of the American West* 往美國西部的移民 **4** [C] a payment of money claimed 結賬

set·tler /ˈsɛtlə; ˈsɛtlə[r]/ *n* one of a large number of people who go to live in a new area 移民, 殖民者: *early settlers in Australia* 澳大利亞的早期移民

set-up /ˈ··/ *n* [sing] the way something is organized 組織(方式); 結構; 設置; 安排: *He's new to the office and doesn't know the set-up yet.* 他新到這個辦事處, 還不了解這裡的組織結構。

sev·en /ˈsɛvən; ˈsɛvən/ *det, n, pron* the number 7 〔數字〕七

sev·en·teen /ˌsɛvənˈtin; ˌsɛvənˈtiːn/ *det, n, pron* the number 17 〔數字〕十七 **–seventeenth** *det, n, pron, adv*

sev·enth /ˈsɛvənθ; ˈsɛvənθ/ *det, n, pron, adv* **1** 7th 第七 **2** one of seven equal parts 七分之一

sev·en·ty /ˈsɛvəntɪ; ˈsɛvəntɪ/ *det, n, pron* **seventies 1** the number 70 〔數字〕七十 **2 the seventies** (also 又作 **the 70's**) the years from 1970 to 1979 七十年代〔從1970年至1979年〕: *He first became famous in the seventies.* 他在七十年代開始出名。 **3 in your seventies** aged between 70 and 79 在七十多歲〔七十到七十九歲之間〕: *She's in her seventies now.* 她現在七十多歲了。 **–seventieth** *det, n, pron, adv*

sev·er /ˈsɛvə; ˈsɛvə[r]/ *v* [T] *fml* 〖正式〗 **1** to cut through something completely 切斷, 割斷〔某物〕: *His arm was severed from his body in the accident.* 在事故中他的一條胳膊被撞得與身子分離了。 | *a severed artery* 截斷的動脈 **2** to bring something completely to an end 斷絕, 中斷〔某事物〕: *Britain has severed diplomatic relations with Ruritania.* 英國已同魯里坦尼亞王國斷絕了外交關係。

★★**sev·er·al** /ˈsɛvərəl; ˈsɛvərəl/ *det, n, pron* some, or a few 幾個, 數個: *Several people came to congratulate me after the performance.* 演出結束之後, 好幾個人來向我表示祝賀。 | *I've made several visits to London this month.* 這個月我已去了倫敦幾次。 | *There were several hundred people there.* 那兒有好幾百人。 | *Several of us had travelled down from Scotland.* 我們當中好幾個人是從蘇格蘭旅行來的。

★**se·vere** /səˈvɪr; sɪˈvɪə[r]/ *adj* **1** not kind or gentle 嚴厲的; 嚴峻的; 嚴肅的: *a severe look on her face* 她臉上嚴肅的神情 | *severe military rules* 嚴格的軍紀 **2** very bad 嚴重的; 劇烈的: *severe pain* 劇痛 | *the severest winter for ten years* 十年來最寒冷的冬天 | *severe traffic congestion* 嚴重的交通擁塞 **–severely** *adv*: *severely disabled* 〔肢體〕嚴重殘疾的 **– severity** /səˈvɛrətɪ; sɪˈverɪtɪ/ *n* [U]: *the severity of winter in Norway* 挪威冬天的嚴寒

sew /so; sɔʊ/ v **sewed, sewn** /son; sɔʊn/ [I;T; +adv/prep] to join pieces of cloth together using a needle and thread〔用針線〕縫; 縫製〔衣服〕: *I used to hate sewing before I got a sewing machine.* 我買縫紉機以前最討厭做針線活。| *She sewed a row of sequins along the pocket.* 她沿着口袋縫了一排圓形小光片。

sew sthg ↔ on *phr v* [T] to fix something on to a piece of cloth using a needle and thread 縫上〔某物〕: *Would you sew on this button for me?* 請你幫我縫上這顆鈕扣好嗎?

sew sthg ↔ up *phr v* [T] **1** to close or repair something by sewing 縫合, 縫補〔某物〕 **2** sewn up *infml* decided and arranged in detail (used of a business deal, etc.)〔非正式〕作了具體安排〔指一筆交易等〕: *The People's Party have got the election sewn up: they're sure to win.* 人民黨已對選舉作了具體部署: 他們必定獲勝。

sew·age /ˈsjuɪdʒ; ˈsjuːɪdʒ/ n [U] the waste material and water from people's houses and from industry carried away in large pipes under the ground〔從下水道排出的住家和工業的〕污水, 污物

sew·er /ˈsoə; ˈsjuːəʳ/ n a man-made passage or large pipe under the ground for carrying away water and waste material 污水管, 下水道, 陰溝

sew·ing /ˈsoɪŋ; ˈsɔʊɪŋ/ n [U] **1** work that you are doing with a needle and thread 縫紉活, 針線活 **2** the activity of making or mending something with a needle and thread 縫製; 縫補

sewing ma·chine /ˈ··· ,·/ n a machine which you use to sew pieces of cloth together 縫紉機

sewn /son; sɔʊn/ the past participle of SEW ☆ SEW 的過去分詞

★**sex** /sɛks; sɛks/ n **1** [U] the condition of being either male or female 性別: *In the space marked "sex", put an "M" for male or an "F" for female.* 在標明"sex(性別)"這一欄裡填上"M"代表男性, 填上"F"代表女性。 **2** [C] the set of all male or all female creatures〔總稱〕男性或女性: *a member of the opposite sex* 異性 **3** [U] the physical act between two people in which the sex organs are brought together 性交, 性行為: *Do you think sex outside marriage is wrong?* 你認為婚外性行為是錯誤的嗎? **4** have sex (of two people) to perform the physical act in which the sex organs are brought together〔兩人〕發生性關係 **5** [U] all the activity connected with the sex act 性活動, 性行為: *There's a lot of sex and violence in this film.* 這部電影中有許多性行為和暴力的情節。

sex·is·m /ˈsɛksɪzəm; ˈsɛksɪzəm/ n [U] the idea or belief that members of one sex (usually men) are more able and clever than those of the other sex; it is often used to suggest that certain jobs should only be done by members of one particular sex (a

word used to show disapproval)〔常指對女性的〕性別歧視, 性別偏見〔含貶義〕

sex·ist /ˈsɛksɪst; ˈsɛksᵻst/ adj showing sexism 表現出性別歧視的: *I'm tired of his sexist jokes about women drivers!* 我聽膩了他那些歧視女司機的笑話! —**sexist** n

sex·less /ˈsɛkslɪs; ˈsɛksləs/ adj **1** not showing any interest in sex 性冷淡的 **2** not exciting to someone of the opposite sex 缺乏性感的

★**sex·u·al** /ˈsɛkʃʊəl; ˈsɛkʃʊəl/ adj connected with sex 與性有關的: *sexual reproduction* 有性繁殖 | *sexual excitement* 性興奮 | *the fight against sexual discrimination* 反對性別歧視的鬥爭 —**sexually** adv: *sexually attractive* 具有性吸引力的

sexual in·ter·course /,··· '···/ n (also 又作 **intercourse**) [U] the physical act in which a male and a female bring their sex organs together 性交

sex·u·al·i·ty /,sɛkʃʊˈælᵻti; ,sɛkʃʊˈælᵻti/ n [U] fondness for or interest in sexual activity 性慾; 性興趣

sex·y /ˈsɛksɪ; ˈsɛksi/ adj **sexier, sexiest** exciting in a sexual way 性感的, 引起性慾的: *sexy girls* 性感女郎 | *sexy pictures* 性感畫片 | *sexy clothes* 性感的衣服 —**sexily** adv

SF /,ɛs ˈɛf; ,es ˈef/ n an abbreviation for〔縮〕= SCIENCE FICTION

Sgt n a written abbreviation for〔縮〕= SERGEANT

sh /ʃ; ʃ/ interj (also 又作 **shh**) you say this when you want people to be quiet 噓〔用於叫別人安靜〕: *Sh! You'll wake the baby!* 噓! 你會把嬰兒吵醒的!

shab·by /ˈʃæbɪ; ˈʃæbi/ adj **shabbier, shabbiest 1** in poor condition because of being old and worn 破舊的; 破爛的: *a shabby old coat* 一件破舊的外衣 **2** wearing old worn clothes 衣衫襤褸的 **3** ungenerous 吝嗇的; 卑鄙的: *What a shabby trick, making me walk home!* 多麼卑劣的惡作劇, 害得我要步行回家! —**shabbily** adv: *shabbily dressed* 衣着破爛的 | *The company she worked for treated her very shabbily.* 她效力的那家公司對她很不公平。 —**shabbiness** n [U]

shack /ʃæk; ʃæk/ n a small roughly built building 簡陋的小木屋

shack·le /ˈʃækl; ˈʃækəl/ v **shackled, shackling** [T] **1** to put into shackles 戴上鐐銬 **2 to be shackled** to have your freedom limited 受束縛: *shackled by old customs* 受舊習俗束縛

shack·les /ˈʃæklz; ˈʃækəlz/ n [pl] **1** two joined metal rings for fastening around the wrist or ankle of a person such as a prisoner to prevent movement 手銬; 腳鐐 **2** lit something that prevents freedom of action or expression〔文〕枷鎖, 桎梏, 束縛物

shade[1] /ʃed; ʃeɪd/ n **1** [U] shelter from direct light, especially from sunlight outdoors, made by something blocking it 蔭, 背陰處:

sitting in the shade **of** *a tree* 坐在樹蔭下 –see 見 USAGE 用法 **2** [C] something that keeps out light or its full brightness 遮光物; 罩子: *a lampshade* 燈罩 | *a green eyeshade* 綠色的遮光眼罩 **3** [C] a degree of colour 顏色的深淺度; 色調: *a lighter shade of blue* 較淺的藍色 **4** [C] a slight difference 細微的差別: *a word with several shades of meaning* 語義有幾種細微差別的單詞 **5** [sing] a little bit 一點; 少許: *That music is just a shade too loud.* 那音樂太響了一點。 **6** [C] *lit* a GHOST 〔文〕鬼魂, 幽靈

■ USAGE 用法: Compare 比較 **shade** and 和 **shadow**. We can use **shade** for any place sheltered from the sun. In this meaning **shade** is uncountable ☆ **shade** 用於指任何遮住陽光的地方。用作這種意思時, **shade** 為不可數名詞: *Let's find some shade.* 我們找個陰涼處吧。 We can use **shadow** for the dark shape made by blocking a strong light. In this meaning **shadow** is countable ☆ **shadow** 可用於指因擋住強光而形成的黑影子。用作這種意思時, **shadow** 為可數名詞: *Under the floodlights, each player in the football match had four **shadows**.* 在泛光燈下, 足球比賽中的每個球員都有四個黑影。

shade² *v* **shaded, shading 1** [T] to shelter from direct light or heat 遮蔽〔光和熱〕: *She shaded her eyes from the sun.* 她遮住眼睛以阻擋陽光。 **2 shade into something** not to have a clear difference from something else 逐漸融入〔某物〕

★**shad·ow¹** /ˈʃædəʊ; ˈʃædəʊ/ *n* **1** [C] the clear dark shape of an object made on a surface behind it when the sun or a strong light falls on it 陰影; 影子: *As the sun set, the shadows became longer.* 太陽落山時, 影子就會變長。 | *The tree cast its shadow on the wall.* 樹把影子投在牆上。 –see 見 SHADE¹ (USAGE 用法) **2 a shadow of your former self** very much weaker or less powerful than you used to be 虛弱得同從前判若兩人: *After his illness he was only a shadow of his former self.* 他病後瘦弱得同從前判若兩人。 **3 There's not a shadow of doubt that...** There isn't the slightest doubt that... 毫無疑問...

shadow² *v* [T] to follow and watch someone closely and secretly 釘〔某人〕的梢; 跟蹤; 尾隨: *She was shadowed everywhere by the secret police.* 她到處受到祕密警察的監視。

shadow cab·i·net /ˌ·· ˈ····/ *n* **the shadow cabinet** a group of the leading politicians of the main opposition party in Parliament, who each study the work of a particular government minister 〔指由反對黨主要人物組成的〕影子內閣

shad·ow·y /ˈʃædəʊɪ; ˈʃædəʊɪ/ *adj* **1** not very

clear in people's minds because little is known about it 朦朧的; 〔因了解甚少而〕難以捉摸的: *a shadowy and little-known historical figure* 一位難以捉摸而又鮮為人知的歷史人物 **2** dark and full of shadows 多陰的; 幽暗的: *the shadowy depths of the forest* 森林深處陰暗的地方 **3** hard to see 難以看清的; 模糊的

shad·y /ˈʃeɪdɪ; ˈʃeɪdɪ/ *adj* **shadier, shadiest 1** sheltered from sunlight 遮擋陽光的; 背陰的: *a shady spot under the trees* 樹下的陰涼處 **2** producing shade, giving the shade 成蔭的: *shady trees* 成蔭的樹 **3** *infml* illegal or not very honest 〔非正式〕非法的; 不誠實的; 不可靠的: *a shady politician* 不誠實的政客 | *a shady deal* 不正當的交易

shaft /ʃɑːft; ʃɑːft/ *n* **1** the deep and narrow hole in the ground by which you enter a mine 豎井; 通風井: *a mine shaft* 礦井 **2** the tall narrow space in which a lift goes up and down 〔電梯上下的〕井: *a lift shaft* 電梯井 **3** a bar which turns, or around which a belt or wheel turns, to pass power through a machine 〔機器的〕傳動軸, 旋轉軸: *a propeller shaft* 螺旋槳軸 **4** a narrow line of light 〔光〕束: *a shaft of sunlight* 一道陽光 **5** the long handle of a spear, hammer, axe, etc. 〔矛、錘、斧等的〕長柄

shag·gy /ˈʃægɪ; ˈʃægɪ/ *adj* **shaggier, shaggiest 1** long and very untidy (used of hair or material) 長而不整齊的〔指毛髮或材料〕: *a shaggy beard* 蓬亂的鬍子 **2** covered with long untidy hair 長滿蓬亂長毛的: *a shaggy dog* 長毛狗

★**shake¹** /ʃeɪk; ʃeɪk/ *v* **shook** /ʃʊk; ʃʊk/, **shaken** /ˈʃeɪkən; ˈʃeɪkən/, **shaking 1** [I;T] to move quickly up and down and backwards and forwards (使)搖動; 震動; 抖動: *The explosion shook the house.* 爆炸使房子搖晃起來。 | *The house shook.* 房子搖動了。 | *She was shaking with anger.* 她氣得渾身發抖。 | *Shake the bottle before use.* 使用前先把瓶子搖一下。 | *She shook the sand from her shoes.* 她抖掉了鞋子裡的沙。 **2 shake hands** to take someone's right hand in your own and shake it when you are introduced to them, greet them, say GOODBYE to them, or reach a formal agreement with them 握手〔用於介紹、問候、道別時〕: *They shook hands with each other.* 他們互相握手。 **3** [T] to upset 使心緒不寧: *She was badly shaken by the news.* 她被那個消息弄得心煩意亂。 **4 shake your head** to move your head from side to side to say "no" 搖頭〔表示"不"〕

shake sbdy/sthg ↔ **off** *phr v* [T] to get rid of or escape from something or someone 擺脫〔某人〕; 從〔某事物〕中解脫: *I've had a bad cold for weeks — I just can't shake it off.* 我患重感冒已有幾個星期了, 我就是沒法治好它。 | *The crooks managed to shake off the police car.* 那些壞蛋設法甩掉了警車。

shake sthg ↔ **out** *phr v* [T] to open or

spread something with a shaking movement 抖開[某物], 把…抖乾淨: *He shook out the dirty mat.* 他把髒蓆子抖乾淨了。

shake sthg ↔ **up** *phr v* [T] **1** to make big changes in an organization 改組，重新組織: *The new chairman is really going to shake up the company.* 新任董事長真的準備對公司進行改組。**2** to mix by shaking 搖勻

shake² *n* an action of shaking 搖動；抖動: *She answered "no" with a shake of the head.* 她搖着頭回答說"不"。| *Give the duvet a good shake.* 把羽絨被好好抖一抖。

shak·en /ˈʃeɪkən/ the past participle of SHAKE ☆ SHAKE 的過去分詞

shake-up /ˈ··/ *n* a set of big changes in an organization 〔組織的〕改組: *a government shake-up with three ministers losing their jobs* 政府大改組令三名部長丟了官職

shak·y /ˈʃeɪkɪ; ˈʃeɪki/ *adj* **shakier, shakiest 1** shaking or unsteady, for example because of nervousness or weakness 〔因緊張或虛弱而〕顫抖的；搖晃的 **2** not solid or firm 不穩固的；不結實的；不堅定的: *a shaky ladder* 不牢的梯子 | *shaky in her beliefs* 她的信念不堅定 **–shakily** *adv*

shale /ʃeɪl; ʃeɪl/ *n* [U] soft rock which naturally divides into thin sheets 頁岩

shall /ʃəl; ʃəl, *strong* ʃæl; ʃæl/ *v negative short form* 否定縮約式為 **shan't** [modal verb 情態動詞] **1** used with "I" and "we" to show that you are going to do something or intend to do something 將要，會〔與I和we連用表示將要或打算做某事〕: *We shall see you on Saturday.* 我們將在星期六和你見面。| *I shall have to go soon.* 我得馬上就走。| *I shall be furious if they're late!* 要是他們遲到，我會非常生氣! | *I shan't be at work tomorrow.* 我明天不去上班。| *When I see him, I shall tell him about it.* 我見到他時會把這事告訴他。**2** *fml* used with "you", "he", "she", "it", and "they" to show that something will certainly happen or you promise to make it happen《正式》必定；必須〔與you, he, she, it 和they 連用表示某事必定要發生或承諾使某事發生〕: *The murderer shall be caught and punished.* 兇手一定要抓獲懲處。| *The work shall be completed by the 15th July.* 這項工作必須在七月十五日前完成。| *You shall not get away with this!* 你決不可以把這東西帶走! –see Study Note on page 1318 見 1318 頁學習提示 –see 見 'S (USAGE 用法) **3 shall I** a polite way of asking someone if they would like you to do something …好嗎?〔問某人是否同意你做某事的客套用語〕: *Shall I answer the phone for you?* 我替你接電話好嗎? | *Shall I open the window?* 我打開窗戶好嗎? **4 shall we** a way of suggesting to someone that you should both do something or all do something …好嗎?〔用於向某人建議一起做某事〕: *Shall we go out tonight?* 我們今夜出去好嗎?

shal·lot /ʃəˈlɒt; ʃəˈlɒt/ *n* a vegetable like a small onion 青葱

shal·low /ˈʃæləʊ; ˈʃæləʊ/ *adj* **1** not deep 淺的: *the shallow end of the swimming pool* 游泳池的淺水區 | *Her breathing was very shallow.* 她的呼吸很淺[弱]。**2** lacking deep or serious thinking 〔思想〕膚淺的；淺薄的: *a shallow thinker whose opinions aren't worth much* 其見解沒有多大價值的淺薄的思想家 **– shallowness** *n* [U]

sham¹ /ʃæm; ʃæm/ *n* something false pretending to be the real thing 假貨；假象: *He seemed to be very concerned about her but it was all a sham.* 他好像很關心她，但其實都是假裝的。**–sham** *adj*

sham² *v* **-mm-** [T] to pretend that you have got an illness or other condition which you have not really got 假裝〔生病等〕: *He isn't really ill. He's shamming.* 他不是真的生病，而是在裝病。

sham·ble /ˈʃæmbl; ˈʃæmbəl/ *v* **shambled, shambling** [I; +adv/prep] to walk awkwardly, dragging your feet 蹣跚而行，拖着腳走: *an old man shambling along the street* 沿着街道蹣跚而行的老人

sham·bles /ˈʃæmblz; ˈʃæmblz/ *n* [sing] *infml* something very disorderly or which should have been much better organized《非正式》混亂的場面；凌亂: *After the party the house was a shambles.* 聚會過後，屋子裡亂七八糟。| *The whole event was a total shambles.* 整件事弄得一塌糊塗。

shame¹ /ʃeɪm; ʃeɪm/ *n* **1** [U] the painful feeling you have when you have done something wrong or silly, or when a relative or close friend has 羞恥，羞愧，慚愧: *I feel no shame for my action: I did what was right.* 我對自己的行為問心無愧，我做的對。| *I was filled with shame when I realized how badly I'd behaved at the party.* 當我意識到我在聚會上表現得多麼無禮時，心中十分羞愧。**2 bring shame on someone** to make people think that someone deserves blame 使蒙受恥辱: *Your bad behaviour brings shame on the whole school.* 你的惡劣行為使全校蒙受恥辱。**3 What a shame!, What a shame that...** an expression you use when you are disappointed or sorry 太遺憾了!〔用於表示失望或遺憾〕: *What a shame that it rained on the day of your wedding!* 多可惜啊，你舉行婚禮那天下雨了! **4 put someone or something to shame** to show someone or something to be less good by comparison 使相形見拙: *Your beautiful garden puts my few little* *flowers to shame.* 你那美麗的花園使我那幾株小花相形見拙。

shame² *v* **shamed, shaming** [T] **1** to make someone feel ashamed 使〔某人〕感到羞愧; 使丟臉: *He shamed his family by being sent to prison.* 他被關進了監獄，使全家人感到丟臉。 **2 shame someone into doing something** to make someone feel so bad about not having done something that they then do it 使某人感到羞愧而做某事

shame·faced /ˈʃeɪm.feɪst; ʃeɪmˈfeɪst◂/ *adj* showing suitable shame 慚愧的; 羞怯的: *Looking suitably shamefaced, he apologized for being so rude.* 他對自己的粗魯表示道歉，看上去很慚愧。 –**shamefacedly** /-ˈfeɪstlɪ; -ˈfeɪ-sɪ̩dli/ *adv*

shame·ful /ˈʃeɪmful; ˈʃeɪmfəl/ *adj* very bad and which you ought to be ashamed of 可恥的; 丟臉的: *the most shameful disregard for other people's safety* 對別人安全置之不理的最可恥的行為 –**shamefully** *adv*

shame·less /ˈʃeɪmlɪs; ˈʃeɪmləs/ *adj* **1** feeling no shame 無羞恥感的; 不要臉的: *an immodest and shameless person* 一個不正派的無恥之徒 **2** done without shame 無恥的; 傷風敗俗的: *shameless disloyalty* 無恥的不忠 – **shamelessly** *adv*: *quite shamelessly asking for more money* 厚顏無恥地要更多的錢

sham·poo¹ /ʃæmˈpuː; ʃæmˈpuː/ *n* **shampoos** **1** [C;U] a soapy liquid which you use for washing something, especially your hair 洗髮劑; 洗滌劑: *creamy shampoo for dry hair* 乾洗頭髮適用的乳狀洗髮劑 **2** [C] an act of shampooing 洗頭, 洗髮: *an appointment at the hairdressers' for a cut and shampoo* 到理髮店剪髮洗頭的預約

shampoo² *v* **shampooed, shampooing** [T] to wash with shampoo 用洗髮劑〔洗滌劑〕洗

sham·rock /ˈʃæmrɒk; ˈʃæmrɑk/ *n* [C;U] a type of small plant with three round leaves on each stem, used as the national sign of Ireland 三葉草〔愛爾蘭的國花〕

shan·dy /ˈʃændɪ; ˈʃændi/ *n* **shandies** [C;U] *BrE* a drink made from a mixture of beer and LEMONADE or GINGER ALE〔英式〕香迪酒〔攙薑汁或檸檬汁的啤酒〕

shan't /ʃænt; ʃɑnt/ a short form of "shall not" ☆ "shall not" 的縮約式: *Shall I go, or shan't I?* 我應該去，還是不應該去?

shan·ty town /ˈʃæntɪ.taʊn; ˈʃænti.taʊn/ *n* a town or part of a town made up of small houses roughly built out of things such as old packing cases; poor people live there〔城市的〕貧民窟; 棚戶區〔居民〕

shape¹ /ʃeɪp; ʃeɪp/ *n* **1** [C;U] the appearance or form of something; circles, squares, and triangles (TRIANGLE) are shapes 形狀; 外形; 形態: *The sign was triangular in shape.* 符號是三角形的。 | *a cake in the shape of a heart* 心形的蛋糕 | *We saw a shape through the mist but we couldn't see who it was.* 我們在霧中看到一個人影，但看不清是誰。 **2** [U]

infml a good state or condition〔非正式〕〔良好的〕狀態, 情況: *He's taking lots of exercise to get into shape.* 他做許多運動以鍛鍊身體。 | *What do you do to keep in shape?* 你是怎樣保持身體健康的? | *Our garden is in good shape after the rain.* 我們的花園在雨後情況良好。 **3 take shape** to begin to be like the finished form 成形; 形成: *ideas taking shape in his mind* 在他的腦子裡形成的想法 – **shapeless** *adj*

shape² *v* **shaped, shaping** [T] **1** to make something into a particular form 使〔某物〕成形: *The bird shaped its nest from mud and sticks.* 鳥兒用泥土和樹枝做成鳥巢。 | *We watched in amazement as she shaped the clay* **into** *a pot.* 我們驚訝地看着她用黏土捏成罐子。 **2** to influence strongly 強烈地影響: *His experience of the war shaped his whole outlook.* 他那戰爭的經歷對他的人生觀產生了重大影響。

   shape up *phr v* [I] to develop well 進展良好: *Our holiday plans are shaping up well.* 我們的度假計劃進展良好。

shaped /ʃeɪpt; ʃeɪpt/ *adj* having a certain shape 有〔某種〕形狀的: *a cloud shaped like a camel* 形狀像駱駝的雲 | *a heart-shaped cake* 心形蛋糕

shape·ly /ˈʃeɪplɪ; ˈʃeɪpli/ *adj* **shapelier, shapeliest** having a good-looking shape (used especially of a woman) 體態美觀的, 身材好的〔尤指女人〕–**shapeliness** *n* [U]

★★share¹ /ʃeər; ʃeər/ *v* **shared, sharing 1** [I; T] to join with other people in owning, using, or doing something 分享; 共有; 分擔: *We haven't got enough books for everyone. Some of you will have to share.* 我們的書不夠每人一本，你們有些人得合着一起看。 | *Everyone in the house shares the same bathroom.* 家裡的人都共用一個浴室。 | *He's sure we'll win the match, but I don't share his faith in the team.* 他肯定我們會贏這場比賽，但我沒有他對球隊的那種信念。 | *I share the house* **with** *my brother.* 我和我的兄弟合住一所房子。 **2** [T] (also 又作 **share out**) to divide and give out in shares 分配; 均分: *His property was shared* **between** *his children.* 他的財產由他的孩子們平分了。 **3 share something with someone** to tell someone about an idea or some news 將某事〔如想法或消息〕告訴某人

★★share² *n* **1** [sing] a part in something which you have, do, or use with other people 一份: *If you want a share* **of** *the pay, you'll have to do your share of the work.* 如果你想得到一份報酬，就得做好你該分擔的那一份工作。 | *Children should have a share* **in** *deciding which subjects they study.* 孩子們應可參與決定學習哪些課程。 **2** [C] any of the equal parts into which the ownership of a company may be divided 股份: *She owns 5000 shares in the company.* 她擁有公司的五千股股份。 | *a dividend of*

---

ten pence per share 每股十便士的股息 | Share prices rose yesterday. 昨天股價上漲了。

share·hold·er /'ʃɛr,holdɚ; 'ʃeə,həʊldəʳ/ n a person who owns shares in a company 股東

shark /ʃark; ʃɑːk/ n a very large fish with sharp teeth that is dangerous to people 鯊魚

★sharp¹ /ʃarp; ʃɑːp/ adj 1 having a thin cutting edge or a fine point 鋒利的, 銳利的, 尖的: a sharp knife 鋒利的小刀 | a sharp needle 尖針 –opposite 反義 **blunt** 2 quick and sensitive 敏銳的; 靈敏的: a sharp mind 敏銳的頭腦 | sharp eyes 靈敏的眼睛 3 causing a sensation like that of cutting or biting 似刀割的; 刺骨的: a sharp wind 刺骨的寒風 4 very sour 很酸的: a sharp taste 濃烈刺鼻的味道 5 pointed, not gently rounded 尖突的; 不圓的: a sharp nose 尖鼻子 | a sharp bend 急轉的彎道 6 sudden and big 急劇的: a sharp rise in prices 價格猛漲 7 clear 清晰的, 清楚的: a sharp photographic image 清晰的影像 | a sharp distinction between first and second class degrees 一等學位和二等學位的顯著區別 8 severe and sudden (used of a pain) 劇烈的〔指疼痛〕–opposite 反義 **dull** 9 quick and strong 猛烈的: a sharp blow on the head 頭部受到的猛擊 10 intended to hurt (used of words) 尖刻的〔指言詞〕: a sharp scolding 尖刻的責罵 11 [only after a noun 只用於名詞後] tech higher than the main note (used of musical notes) 〔術語〕升半音的〔指音符〕: Rachmaninov's Piano Concerto No 1 in F sharp minor 升F小調的拉赫瑪尼諾夫鋼琴協奏曲 12 slightly too high (used of a note in music) 偏高的〔指音符〕 – **sharply** adv: Prices have risen sharply. 價格急劇上漲。 | "I don't care," he replied sharply. "我可不在乎," 他尖刻地回答。– **sharpness** n [U]

sharp² n a sharp note in music 升半音; 升半音號

sharp³ adv [after a noun 用於名詞後] 1 exactly at the stated time 準時, 正: The meeting starts at three o'clock sharp. 會議三點正開始。 2 slightly higher than the note you are trying to sing or play 〔音〕偏高

sharp·en /'ʃarpən; 'ʃɑːpən/ v [I;T] to make or become sharp or sharper 削尖, 使尖銳: to sharpen a knife 把刀磨尖 | His voice sharpened 他的嗓音變得很尖。

sharp·en·er /'ʃarpənɚ; 'ʃɑːpənəʳ/ n something that you use to sharpen things 磨削的工具: a pencil sharpener 鉛筆刨

shat·ter /'ʃætɚ; 'ʃætəʳ/ v 1 [I;T] to break suddenly into small pieces (使)粉碎; (使)破碎: A stone shattered the window. 一塊石頭打碎了窗戶。 | The glass shattered. 玻璃摔碎了。 2 [T] to destroy something totally 使破滅: Hopes of reaching an agreement were shattered. 達成協議的希望徹底破滅。 3 be **shattered by** something to begin to feel extremely upset and unhappy because of

something that has happened 因發生某事而心煩意亂

shat·tered /'ʃætɚd; 'ʃætəd/ adj 1 very unhappy because you have had a sudden shock 〔因受意外打擊而〕感到傷心的; 感到震驚的 2 infml very tired 〔非正式〕筋疲力盡的: I felt completely shattered. 我感到筋疲力盡。

shat·ter·ing /'ʃætɚrɪŋ; 'ʃætərɪŋ/ adj 1 very upsetting 令人極度不安的: Failing the entrance exam was a shattering blow to his hopes of a career in the Civil Service. 沒通過入學考試對他從事政府文職工作的願望是個沉重的打擊。 2 infml very tiring 〔非正式〕令人極度疲勞的: a shattering day at work 工作極度勞累的一天

shave¹ /ʃev; ʃeɪv/ v shaved, shaving 1 [I;T] to cut hair from your face or another part of your body 刮〔鬍子〕; 剃〔毛髮〕: I've shaved off my beard. 我已經刮掉了鬍子。 | I cut myself while I was shaving. 我在刮鬍子時把自己的臉刮破了。 | Do you shave your legs? 你剃腿上的毛嗎? 2 [T] to cut off very thin pieces from a surface 刨, 削: She shaved the bottom off the door to make it close properly. 她把門的底部刨去使它能關緊。 3 -shaven /'ʃevən; 'ʃeɪvən/ having been shaved 刮過的; 剃過的: a shaven head 剃了的頭 | No, he hasn't got a beard. He's clean-shaven. 不, 他一根鬍子也沒有, 他的面修得很乾淨。

shave² n an act or result of shaving 剃鬚, 刮鬍子, 修面, 刮臉: He had a quick shave. 他很快地刮了刮鬍子。

shav·er /'ʃevɚ; 'ʃeɪvəʳ/ n an electric tool for shaving 電動剃鬚刀

shav·ings /'ʃevɪŋz; 'ʃeɪvɪŋz/ n [pl] very thin curly pieces of wood cut from a larger piece (木頭)刨花

shawl /ʃɔl; ʃɔːl/ n a piece of cloth which a woman wears over her head or shoulders or which is wrapped round a baby 〔女用〕披肩, 圍巾; 〔嬰兒用的〕襁褓

★she¹ /ʃɪ, ʃi, strong 強讀 ʃi; ʃiː/ pron [used as the subject of a verb 用作動詞的主語] the female person or animal who has already been mentioned 她; 〔指雌性動物〕牠: "Where's Mary?" "She's gone to the cinema." "瑪麗在哪裡?" "她去了看電影。"

she² n a female animal 女性, 雌性: Is your dog a he or a she? 你的狗是公的還是母的? | a she-goat 母山羊

sheaf /ʃif; ʃiːf/ n sheaves /ʃivz; ʃiːvz/ 1 a handful of papers 一紮〔文件〕; 疊: She had a sheaf of notes in front of her. 她面前放着一疊筆記。 2 a bunch of grain plants cut and tied together and left to dry in the field 一束; 一捆〔莊稼〕

shear /ʃɪr; ʃɪəʳ/ v sheared, sheared or shorn /ʃɔrn; ʃɔːn/ [T] to cut wool off a sheep 剪羊毛

shear off phr v [I] tech (especially of thin rods, pins, etc.) to break in two under a sideways force 〔術語〕〔尤指細桿、別針等〕折

斷, 扭斷

shears /ʃɪrz; ʃɪəz/ *n* [pl] large heavy scissors, used for example for cutting grass〔修剪草地等用的〕大剪刀 –see picture on page 958 見 958 頁彩圖

sheath /ʃiθ; ʃiːθ/ *n* **sheaths** /ʃiðz; ʃiːðz/ **1** a close-fitting case for a knife or sword blade〔刀、劍的〕鞘 **2** covering worn over a man's sex organ while he is having sex, used as a means of birth control or as a protection against disease 陰莖套; 避孕套

sheathe /ʃið; ʃiːð/ *v* **sheathed, sheathing** [T] to put into a sheath 把…插入鞘

sheaves /ʃivz; ʃiːvz/ *n* the plural of SHEAF ☆ SHEAF 的複數形式

shed¹ /ʃed; ʃed/ *n* a simple building usually used for storing things 棚屋, 小屋〔常用於存放物品〕: *We keep our old newspapers in the shed.* 我們把舊報紙放在棚屋裡。| *a toolshed* 工具房 | *a cattle shed* 牲口棚 | *a woodshed* 木柴房 | *a garden shed* 園具棚

shed² *v* **shed, shed, shedding** [T] **1** (of a plant or animal) to throw off something naturally〔植物或動物〕使〔某物〕自然脫落: *trees shedding their leaves in autumn* 秋天落葉的樹 | *Some snakes shed their skin each year.* 有些蛇每年都要蛻皮。 **2** to get rid of something 去掉〔某物〕, 除掉: *With costs rising, many firms are shedding labour.* 由於成本上升, 許多公司在削減勞動力。| *I need to shed a few pounds before I can get into my new trousers.* 我需要減少幾磅體重, 才能穿上我這條新褲子。 **3 shed a load** (of a LORRY) to drop the goods being carried by accident〔指卡車〕〔意外〕掉落貨物: *There are long tailbacks on the A21 near Tonbridge where a lorry has shed its load.* 在塘橋附近的A21路段有一輛卡車的貨物掉下來, 使受阻的車輛排起了長陣。 **4 shed blood** to kill or hurt people 流血〔犧牲〕: *It is hoped that the crisis can be solved without any blood being shed.* 希望這場危機能不造成流血事件而得到解決。 **5 shed light on something** to help to explain something 使某事清晰 **6 shed tears** to cry 流淚: *His mother shed a few tears when he left for Australia.* 他動身去澳大利亞時, 他媽媽流下了眼淚。

she'd /ʃid; ʃid, *strong* 強讀 ʃid; ʃiːd/ **1** a short form of "she would" ☆ "she would" 的縮約式: *She said she'd try.* 她說她要試試。 **2** a short form of "she had" ☆ "she had" 的縮約式: *She'd been there before.* 她以前到過那裡。

sheen /ʃin; ʃiːn/ *n* [sing; U] brightness on a surface 光輝, 光澤: *hair with a beautiful sheen* 有美麗光澤的頭髮

sheep /ʃip; ʃiːp/ *n* [plural is 複數為 **sheep**] **1** an animal that eats grass and is kept for its wool and its meat 羊, 綿羊: *a flock of sheep* 一羣羊 –see 見 MEAT (USAGE 用法) **2 the sheep and the goats** those who are good, clever, and successful, and those who are

not 好人與壞人; 聰明人與笨蛋; 成功者與失敗者: *a difficult examination, intended to separate the sheep from the goats* 旨在區分優劣的嚴格考試

sheep·dog /ʃip,dɔg; ˈʃiːpdɒg/ *n* a type of dog that can be trained to control sheep 牧羊犬

sheep·ish /ˈʃipɪʃ; ˈʃiːpɪʃ/ *adj* slightly uncomfortable because you have done something foolish 羞怯的, 腼腆的; 侷促不安的: *a sheepish smile* 腼腆的微笑 –**sheepishly** *adv* –**sheepishness** *n* [U]

sheep·skin /ˈʃip,skɪn; ˈʃiːpˌskɪn/ *n* the skin and wool of a sheep 綿羊皮: *a sheepskin coat* 羊皮大衣 | *a sheepskin rug* 羊皮毯子

sheer¹ /ʃɪr; ʃɪər/ *adj* **1** [only before a noun 只用於名詞前] pure and not mixed with anything else 純粹的, 不攙雜的; 全然的: *He won by sheer determination.* 他全靠決心取勝。| *It was sheer luck.* 那純屬運氣。 **2** very steep 陡峭的: *a sheer cliff* 陡峭的懸崖 **3** very thin and almost transparent 極薄的; 幾乎透明的: *ladies' sheer stockings* 婦女的透明長統絲襪

sheer² *adv* straight up or down 垂直地; 陡峭地: *The mountain rises sheer from the plain.* 這座山從平原上拔地而起。

⋆**sheet** /ʃit; ʃiːt/ *n* **1** a large piece of cloth used under you or on top of you in a bed; the sheets are next to you in a bed 牀單; 被單: *We change the sheets every week.* 我們每星期換牀單。 **2 a sheet of paper** a single flat piece of paper 一張紙: *a sheet of headed notepaper* 一張帶信頭的信紙 | *wrapped in a sheet of newspaper* 用一張報紙包起來的 **3** a broad area or piece of something thin 一大片; 薄片: *a sheet of ice over the lake* 湖上的一層冰 | *sheet metal* 金屬片

sheikh /ʃik; ʃeɪk/ *n* (also 又作 **sheik**) an Arab chief or prince〔阿拉伯國家的〕酋長; 王子: *Sheikh Yamani of Saudi Arabia* 沙特阿拉伯的亞馬尼酋長

⋆**shelf** /ʃelf; ʃelf/ *n* **shelves** /ʃelvz; ʃelvz/ a long board fixed against a wall or in a cupboard so that things can be kept on it〔牆壁或櫃櫥的〕架子, 擱板: *a book-shelf* 書架 | *some new shelves for the kitchen* 一些新安裝的廚架

shell¹ /ʃel; ʃel/ *n* **1** [C;U] the hard covering of an egg, nut, or of some sea animals 蛋殼; 堅果殼; 貝殼: *The sea shore was covered with shells.* 海邊到處是貝殼。| *a nutshell* 堅果殼 | *some pieces of eggshell* 幾片蛋殼 **2** [C] the frame of a building〔房屋的〕框架, 骨架 **3** [C] an explosive for firing from a large gun 砲彈: *shells bursting all around* 四處爆炸的砲彈

shell² *v* **1** [T] to remove from a natural shell or POD 剝去〔殼、莢〕: *to shell peas* 剝豌豆莢 **2** [I;T] to fire shells at a place or at the enemy 砲擊〔某地或敵人〕: *The enemy lines were weakened by shelling before the attack.* 敵人的陣線在進攻前被砲擊所削弱。

shell out *phr v* [I;T **shell out** sthg] *infml* to pay money unwillingly〖非正式〗(不情願地)付款: *I'm going to have to shell out for some new tyres soon.* 我馬上就要花錢買幾個新輪胎。

she'll /ʃɪl; ʃɪl; *strong* 強讀 ʃil; ʃiːl/ a short form of "she will" 〝she will〞的縮約式: *She'll come if she can.* 她要是能來就一定會來。

shell·fish /ˈʃɛlˌfɪʃ; ˈʃɛlˌfɪʃ/ *n* [plural is 複數為 **shellfish**] **1** any small animal that lives in the sea and has a shell 甲殼類動物, 貝類動物 **2** such animals as food 甲殼類(食物), 貝類(食物): *I don't like any shellfish except lobsters.* 除了龍蝦之外, 我不喜歡別的貝類食物。

shel·ter¹ /ˈʃɛltə; ˈʃɛltɚ/ *n* **1** [U] protection, especially from bad weather or danger 遮蔽, 庇護〔尤指避雨或脫險〕: *In the storm I took shelter under a tree.* 下暴雨時我在樹下躲避。| *The refugees are in urgent need of food and shelter.* 難民急需食品和棲身之地。**2** [C] a building that protects you from weather or danger 隱蔽處, 庇護所: *a bus shelter* 公共汽車候車亭

shelter² *v* **1** [T] to protect someone or something from bad weather or danger 庇護, 遮蔽: *This blind shelters the plants from the sun.* 這個遮簾遮蔽那些植物, 以免日光照射。**2** [I] to stay in a place in order to be protected from bad weather or danger 躲避, 避難: *In the rain people were sheltering in the doorways of shops.* 下雨時人們都在商店門口避雨。**3** [T] to give a homeless person a place to stay in 收留〔無家可歸的人〕**4** [T] to look after someone while they hide in your house 庇護〔逃犯〕

shel·tered /ˈʃɛltəd; ˈʃɛltəd/ *adj* **1** protected from bad weather, especially wind 可避風雨的: *a sheltered spot in the garden* 花園裡的避風處 **2** kept away from the hard facts of life 受庇護的; 與現實生活隔離的: *She had led a sheltered life and was quite unprepared for city living.* 她一直過着受庇護的生活, 對城市生活毫無準備。

shelve /ʃɛlv; ʃɛlv/ *v* **shelved, shelving 1** [T] to put a plan on one side and do nothing about it at the present time 擱置〔計劃〕: *We've had to shelve our holiday plans because Tom's mother is ill.* 我們不得不把度假計劃擱置一邊, 因為湯姆的母親病了。**2** [I] (of the seashore) to slope〔海岸〕漸漸傾斜

shelves /ʃɛlvz; ʃɛlvz/ *n* the plural of SHELF ☆ SHELF 的複數形式

shelv·ing /ˈʃɛlvɪŋ; ˈʃɛlvɪŋ/ *n* [U] shelves 擱板

shep·herd¹ /ˈʃɛpəd; ˈʃɛpəd/ *n* someone whose job it is to look after sheep 牧羊人

shepherd² *v* [T] to look after a group of people by going with them and making sure they get to the right place 帶領, 引導, 照管: *We shepherded the children into the bus.* 我們照管着孩子們上公共汽車。

sher·iff /ˈʃɛrɪf; ˈʃɛrɪf/ *n* (also 又作 **Sheriff**) an elected officer in the US responsible for making sure that people do not break the law〔美國的〕縣治安官: *Sheriff Wyatt appointed four deputies.* 懷亞特警官任命了四位副手。

sher·ry /ˈʃɛrɪ; ˈʃɛri/ *n* **sherries 1** [U] strong wine from Spain, often drunk in Britain before a meal 雪利酒〔產於西班牙的一種烈性葡萄酒, 在英國通常飯前飲用〕**2** [C] a small glass of this 一小杯雪利酒

she's /ʃɪz; ʃiz, *strong* 強讀 ʃiz; ʃiːz/ **1** short for 〔縮〕= "she is": *She's working in an office.* 她在辦公室工作。**2** short for 〔縮〕= "she has": *She's got a new job.* 她找到了新的工作。

shh /ʃ; ʃ/ *interj* see 見 SH

shield¹ /ʃild; ʃiːld/ *n* **1** a large flat piece of metal or wood which, in the past, soldiers held in front of them to protect them from weapons 盾 **2** a protective cover, especially on a machine to protect the person operating it from moving parts〔機器的〕護蓋, 護罩: *an eye shield over his bad eye* 蓋在他壞眼上的護目罩 **3** a formal and colourful sign for a family, town, team, or other group; the sign has the shape of a shield〔表示家族、城市、球隊或其他社團的〕盾形標誌符; 盾形徽章 **4** a prize in the shape of a shield which you might win in a competition for something such as sport or public speaking 盾形錦標

shield² *v* [T] to protect someone or something 保護, 庇護〔某人或某物〕: *She lied to the police to shield her friend.* 她對警察説謊以掩護她的朋友。| *That wall will shield us from the wind.* 那堵牆會保護我們免受風的侵襲。

*****shift¹** /ʃɪft; ʃɪft/ *v* **1** [I;T] to move 移動, 轉移: *The wind shifted from the south to the west.* 風由南轉吹向西。| *I want to try and shift this sand before lunch.* 我想盡量在午飯前把這堆沙子搬走。| *It's stuck fast and we can't shift it.* 它卡得很牢, 我們搬不動。| *Don't try to shift the blame onto me!* 別想把罪責推到我身上! **2** [I] to change slightly 改變, 轉變: *Public opinion has shifted on this issue.* 公眾對這個問題的看法已經改變。**3 shift for yourself** to do your best to look after yourself even if you do not do it very well〔即使不行也要〕自謀生計

shift² *n* **1** a change in position or direction〔位置或方向的〕改變, 轉變: *a shift in the wind* 風向的改變 | *a shift in public opinion* 公眾輿論的轉變 **2** one of the work periods, usually eight hours, in a place such as a factory which is open many hours a day〔工廠裡通常八小時的〕輪班工作時間: *He's on the night shift this week.* 他這星期上夜班。**3** [+sing/pl verb] a group of workers working together for one of these periods 輪班職工: *The early shift came on at six a.m.* 早班工人上午六點鐘上班。

shift·less /ˈʃɪftlɪs; ˈʃɪftləs/ *adj* without any

sense of responsibility or the ability to organize anything 沒出息的; 無能的

shift·y /'ʃɪfti; 'ʃɪfti/ *adj* **shiftier, shiftiest** looking dishonest 不老實的, 詭詐的

shil·ling /'ʃɪlɪŋ; 'ʃɪlɪŋ/ *n* **1** a unit of money in use in Britain until 1971; it was equal to 5 new pence; there were 12 old pennies in a shilling and 20 shillings in a pound 先令〔1971 年之前英國的貨幣單位, 等於新的五便士; 但舊時十二便士為一先令, 二十先令為一英鎊〕**2** an amount of money in some African countries equal to 100 cents 先令〔某些非洲國家的貨幣單位, 等於一百分〕

shim·mer¹ /'ʃɪmə; 'ʃɪmɚ/ *v* [I] to shine with a soft trembling light 閃閃發光: *water shimmering in the moonlight* 月光下閃閃發光的水

shimmer² *n* [sing] a soft trembling shining effect 微光, 閃光: *the shimmer of candlelight in the old church* 古老的教堂裡那微微閃爍的燭光

shin¹ /ʃɪn; ʃɪn/ *n* the bony front part of your leg between your knee and your ankle 脛(部)

shin² *v* **-nn-** **shin up something** to climb something such as a tree or pole quickly and easily, using your hands and legs〔用手和腿〕輕快地爬〔樹或柱子〕: *She shinned up a tree to get a better view.* 她爬到樹上, 以便看得更清楚。

shine¹ /ʃaɪn; ʃaɪn/ *v* **shone** /ʃɒn; ʃɒn/, **shone, shining** **1** [I] to give out light 發光; 照耀: *It's a lovely day. The sun is shining.* 今天天氣晴朗, 陽光燦爛。**2** [I] to look bright〔看上去〕發亮: *The polished surface shone in the sun.* 磨光的表面在太陽下發着亮光。| *eyes shining with happiness* 流露出快樂神色的眼睛 **3** [T] to point a lamp at something 把〔燈〕照向〔某物〕: *Shine your torch over here.* 用你的手電筒往這兒照。**4** [T] to make something bright by rubbing 擦亮〔某物〕: *Shine your shoes before you go out.* 出門前把你的鞋子擦亮。**5** [I] to show special ability 顯露才華: *She's a good student generally, but chemistry is where she really shines.* 她總的來說是個好學生, 而在化學方面表現尤為突出。

shine² *n* [sing] **1** brightness 光輝, 光澤, 光亮: *The wooden surface had a beautiful shine.* 這木質表面有漂亮的光澤。**2** an act of polishing shoes 擦, 磨: *These shoes need a shine.* 這雙鞋子需要擦一擦。

shin·gle /'ʃɪŋɡl; 'ʃɪŋɡəl/ *n* [U] small rough rounded pieces of stone found on a shore〔海邊的〕小圓石

shin·y /'ʃaɪni; 'ʃaɪni/ *adj* **shinier, shiniest** bright with light which is thrown back from the surface〔從表面反射而〕發亮的, 閃亮的: *a shiny new coin* 一枚閃閃發亮的新硬幣

ship¹ /ʃɪp; ʃɪp/ *n* a large boat for carrying people or goods on the sea: 船; 艦: *The ship sailed at 9.30 a.m. She was called the Princess Elizabeth.* 輪船上午九點三十分起航,

船名為伊麗莎白公主號。| *We went by plane, but sent all our furniture by ship.* 我們是坐飛機去的, 但所有的家具都用船託運。| *Life on board ship was enormous fun.* 船上的生活好玩極了。–see 見 BOAT (USAGE 用法) – see picture on page 991 見 991 頁彩圖

ship² *v* **-pp-** [T] to send large articles by ship or by another vehicle 用船〔或別的交通工具〕運送〔大件物品〕: *I'm flying to America but my car is being shipped over.* 我坐飛機去美國, 但我的汽車正由船運送。

ship·ment /'ʃɪpmənt; 'ʃɪpmənt/ *n* **1** [C] a load of goods sent together, usually by ship and usually from one country to another 一批貨物〔常由船從一國運往另一國〕: *A large shipment of grain has just arrived.* 一大批穀物剛剛運到。**2** [U] the action of sending goods 裝載, 裝運: *articles lost in shipment* 裝運時遺失的物件

ship·per /'ʃɪpə; 'ʃɪpɚ/ *n* a person or company who sends goods, usually by ship and usually from one country to another 托運人[公司]; 航運商: *wine shippers* 酒類托運人

ship·ping /'ʃɪpɪŋ; 'ʃɪpɪŋ/ *n* [U] **1** ship traffic 船運 **2** ships as a group 船舶〔總稱〕**3** the sending and delivery of something, usually by ship and usually from one country to another 運送, 運輸: *a shipping charge of £15* 十五英鎊運輸費

ship·wreck¹ /'ʃɪp,rɛk; 'ʃɪp-rek/ *n* [C;U] the destruction of a ship when it hits something at sea or sinks 海難, 船隻失事

shipwreck² *v* **be shipwrecked** to be on a ship when it is destroyed because it hits something at sea or sinks 遭遇海難: *They were shipwrecked off the Irish coast.* 他們在愛爾蘭沿海遭遇到海難。| *a shipwrecked sailor* 遭海難的水手

ship·yard /'ʃɪp,jɑrd; 'ʃɪp-jɑːd/ *n* a place where ships are built or repaired 船塢, 造船廠; 修船廠

shirk /ʃɜːk; ʃɝːk/ *v* [I;T] to avoid something or do something badly because you are lazy〔因偷懶而〕逃避〔某事或做某事〕: *We mustn't shirk on the cleaning.* 我們不應該逃避清潔工作。| *You mustn't shirk your responsibilities.* 你不可以逃避自己的責任。– **shirker** *n*

★shirt /ʃɜːt; ʃɝːt/ *n* a piece of clothing which you wear on the upper part of your body, usually made of light cloth, with a collar, coverings for your arms, and buttons down the front opening 襯衫, 恤衫 –see picture on page 210 見 210 頁彩圖

shirt·sleeves /'ʃɜːt,slivz; 'ʃɝːtsliːvz/ *n* [pl] **in your shirtsleeves** wearing nothing over your shirt 只穿襯衫: *On hot days the men in the office work in their shirtsleeves.* 在大熱天裡, 辦公室裡的男士都是只穿襯衫上班。

shirt·y /'ʃɜːti; 'ʃɝːti/ *adj infml* bad-tempered and rude〔非正式〕脾氣壞的; 粗暴的

---

shiv·er¹ /'ʃɪvə; 'ʃɪvəʳ/ v [I] to shake because you are cold or frightened 〔因冷或害怕而〕顫抖, 哆嗦: *It was so cold that we were all shivering.* 天太冷了, 我們都凍得發抖。 **–shivery** *adj*

shiver² n **1** a shaking movement caused by cold or fear 〔因寒冷或害怕而引起的〕顫抖, 發抖: *The strange noise sent a shiver down my spine.* 那奇怪的聲音令我毛骨悚然。 **2** give someone the shivers *infml* to make someone feel afraid 〖非正式〗使某人顫慄, 使某人發顫

shoal /ʃol; ʃəʊl/ n **1** a large group of fish swimming together 魚羣, 一大羣魚 **2** in **shoals** in large numbers 大量, 許多: *People arrived in shoals.* 一大羣人來了。

✹✹shock¹ /ʃak; ʃɒk/ n **1** [C;U] the feeling you get after something unexpected and usually very unpleasant has suddenly happened, or you have received an unexpected piece of bad news 震驚, 驚駭: *His death came as a great shock to us all.* 他的死令我們大家都十分震驚。 | *The survivors of the earthquake are still in a state of deep shock.* 地震的倖存者仍處於極度驚駭之中。 | *I had a shock when I saw how thin she had grown.* 我看到她長得那麼瘦不禁大吃一驚。 | *Oh, it's only you! You gave me a shock.* 噢, 原來是你啊! 你讓我吃了一驚。 | *Her granddaughter's new clothes were a bit of a shock.* 她的孫女的新衣服有點令人吃驚。 **2** [C;U] a violent force from something such as an explosion, a crash, or a hard blow 〔爆炸、碰撞、重擊等引起的〕震動, 衝擊: *The shock of the explosion was felt far away.* 爆炸引起的震動在很遠的地方都能感覺到。 **3** [C;U] the sudden violent effect of electricity passing through someone's body 電擊, 觸電: *Don't touch that wire! You'll get a shock.* 別碰那電線! 你會觸電的。 **4** [U] *tech* the poor medical condition of someone who has had an accident and whose heart and lungs are not working properly 〖術語〗休克: *suffering from minor injuries and shock* 受了輕傷並有點休克

shock² v [I;T] to make someone feel very upset, angry, or unpleasantly surprised (使)震驚; 使憤慨; 使受打擊: *I was shocked by his sudden death.* 他的突然去世使我感到震驚。 | *We were all shocked by her rudeness.* 她的粗魯行為使我們都感到震驚。 | *Take no notice. She's only doing it to shock.* 不用理會她, 她幹這事只是嚇唬人。

shock·ing /'ʃakɪŋ; 'ʃɒkɪŋ/ adj **1** very upsetting, wrong, or immoral 令人震驚的; 非常錯誤的; 大逆不道的: *a shocking accident* 令人震驚的事故 | *shocking and scandalous behaviour* 令人震驚的醜惡行為 **2** *infml* very bad 〖非正式〗極壞的; 糟糕的: *What a shocking waste of time!* 這樣浪費時間, 真不像話! **– shockingly** *adv*: *shockingly underpaid* 工資低得驚人

■ **USAGE** 用法: Remember that **shocked** and **shocking** usually give the idea that you disapprove of something very strongly or that you find it offensive. If you do not want to give this meaning, you should use another expression. For example ☆記住: **shocked** 和 **shocking** 通常表示強烈反對某事, 或覺得某事令人感到討厭。如果不表示上述意思, 就應該用另外的詞表達, 例如: *My first day at school in England was rather strange/disturbing.* 我在英格蘭上學的第一天感到很不自在〔非常不安〕。 | *When I arrived in New York I felt completely disorientated.* 我到達紐約時完全感到茫然失惜。 | *I found the British education system very strange/confusing.* 我發覺英國的教育制度很不可思議〔莫名其妙〕。

shod /ʃad; ʃɒd/ adj *lit* provided with shoes 〖文〗穿着鞋的: *poor badly-shod children* 穿着破鞋的窮孩子

shod·dy /'ʃadi; 'ʃɒdi/ adj **shoddier, shoddiest 1** made or done badly or carelessly 劣質的; 粗製濫造的: *shoddy goods* 劣質貨品 | *shoddy workmanship* 劣等工藝 **2** ungenerous or dishonourable 卑劣的, 卑鄙的: *a shoddy trick* 卑鄙的伎倆 **–shoddily** *adv* **– shoddiness** *n* [U]

✹shoe /ʃu; ʃuː/ n **1** the thing you wear on each of your feet to protect them from the hard ground; shoes are sometimes made of leather 鞋: *He took off his shoes.* 他脫掉鞋子。 | *a new pair of shoes to match her dress* 一雙和她的連衣裙相配的新鞋 –see 見 PAIR (USAGE用法) –see picture on page 210 見 210 頁彩圖 **2** in someone's shoes in someone else's position, experiencing what they have to experience 處於某人的處境; 經歷某人的事情: *I'm glad I'm not in his shoes!* 我很幸運, 沒有遇到他那樣的情況。

shoe·lace /'ʃuˌles; 'ʃuːleɪs/ n a thin cord that you use to tie the front parts of your shoe together 鞋帶 –see 見 PAIR (USAGE 用法)

shoe·string /'ʃuˌstrɪŋ; 'ʃuːˌstrɪŋ/ n **on a shoestring** on a very small amount of money 極少的錢: *He started his business on a shoestring and built it up.* 他用很少的資金創業, 然後逐步發展起來。

shone /ʃon; ʃɒn/ the past tense and past participle of SHINE ☆ SHINE 的過去式和過去分詞

shoo¹ /ʃu; ʃuː/ *interj* a word said, usually not angrily, to animals or small children when you want them to go away 噓〔將動物或小孩趕走時發出的聲音, 通常並不生氣〕

shoo² v [T] **shooed, shooing** to make children or animals go somewhere by repeatedly waving your arms at them and telling them to go 〔揮手〕趕走〔孩子或動物〕; 噓走:

S

He shooed the children out of the kitchen. 他把孩子趕出了廚房。

shook /ʃuk; ʃuk/ the past tense of SHAKE ☆ SHAKE 的過去式

☆**shoot¹** /ʃut; ʃuːt/ *v* **shot** /ʃat; ʃɒt/, **shooting 1** [T] to hit, wound, or kill with a gun 射擊; 射傷; 射死: *He shot a bird.* 他射中了一隻鳥。 | *He was shot three times in the arm.* 他的胳膊中了三槍。 | *She shot him dead.* 她開槍打死了他。 **2** [I;T] to fire a gun 開槍: *I'm coming out with my hands up. Don't shoot.* 我就舉手出來，別開槍。 **3 shoot at** to aim a gun at someone or something and fire it 〔某人或某物〕射擊: *He shot at the bird, but missed.* 他開槍打那隻鳥，但沒打中。 **4** [I;T] to aim the ball at the place which gets you a point in games such as football and BASKETBALL〔足球、籃球等〕射(門); 投(籃); 射門〔或投籃〕得分: *Murano shot the winning goal just 30 seconds from the end.* 穆拉諾隊就在終場前三十秒射入了致勝的一球。 | *Go on! Shoot!* 衝上去! 射門! **5** [I + adv/prep; T + adv/prep] to move or send something suddenly or quickly 投射; 噴出; 快速發出; 疾馳: *Blood shot out of the wound.* 血從傷口處噴出。 | *He shot past me without speaking.* 他不發一言地從我身邊飛馳而過。 | *She shot him an angry look.* 她向他投以氣憤的一眼。 | *They shot questions at us for over an hour.* 他們連珠砲似地向我們提問達一個多小時。 | *The force of the gas in a bottle of champagne can shoot the cork across the room.* 香檳酒瓶內的氣壓可使噴出的軟木塞穿越房間。 **6** [I;T] to use a camera to make a film 拍攝: *"Room Downstairs" was shot in Italy.* "樓下的房間"是在意大利拍攝的。 **7** [I; T] to shoot birds or animals for sport 打獵: *He shoots most weekends.* 他週末大多數去打獵。 | *duck shooting* 獵殺野鴨 | *We go shooting in Scotland every autumn.* 我們每年秋天都去蘇格蘭打獵。

shoot sbdy/sthg ↔ **down** *phr v* [T] **1** to bring down and destroy a plane by shooting it when it is in the air 擊落〔飛機〕 **2** to say, sometimes without cause and without showing any respect for the person who had it, that an idea is no good at all 斷然否定〔某人的觀點〕: *another good idea shot down by the chairman* 被主席斷然否決的另一個好提案

shoot out *phr v* [I;T **shoot** sthg ↔ **out**] to move fast out of somewhere 突然伸出(來): *The snake shot out its tongue.* 那條蛇突然伸出舌頭來。 | *Its tongue shot out.* 牠的舌頭突然伸出來。

shoot up *phr v* [I] to go upwards, increase, or grow quickly 急升; 飛漲: *Flames shot up into the air.* 火焰直衝上天空。 | *Prices have shot up lately.* 最近物價飛漲。

shoot² *n* **1** the first part of a plant to appear above ground, or a new growth from a plant 嫩芽; 新枝 **2** an occasion for shooting

birds or animals 射獵場〔會〕: *a weekend shoot* 週末射獵場

shoot·ing /ʃutɪŋ; ʃuːtɪŋ/ *n* **1** [C] an act of wounding someone with a gun 射傷; 槍殺: *politically-motivated shootings* 有政治動機的槍殺(事件) **2** [U] the sport of shooting birds or animals 射獵

shooting star /ˌ··· ˈ·/ *n* (also 又作 **falling star**) a piece of matter from space which burns brightly as it passes through the Earth's air 流星

☆**shop¹** /ʃap; ʃɒp/ *n* **1** (**store** *AmE*【美式】) a room or building where goods are regularly kept and sold 商店, 店鋪: *the local village shop* 當地村莊的店鋪 | *The shops in town close at 5.30.* 城裡的商店五點半關門。 | *a bookshop* 書店 | *a sweetshop* 糖果店 **2** a place where things are made or repaired 工場, 車間: *the body shop in a car factory* 汽車廠的車身製造車間 | *a repair shop* 修理車間

shop² *v* -pp- [I] to go to the shops and buy things or try to find things you want to buy 去買東西, 購物: *I was shopping for some new clothes, but I couldn't find anything.* 我想買一些新衣服，但一件(稱心的)也沒找到。 | *I hate shopping.* 我討厭買東西。 | *People's shopping habits are changing now that we have the big out-of-town superstores.* 由於有了大型的城外超級商場，人們的購物習慣正在改變。 | *He's gone shopping for a present for his mother.* 他去了買禮物給媽媽。 —**shopper** *n* —see 見 CUSTOMER (USAGE 用法)

shop around *phr v* [I] to compare prices in different shops 比較各家商店的價格; 逐店比貨選購: *It pays to shop around for the lowest price.* 為買到最便宜的東西而逐家比較是值得的。

shop as·sis·tant /ˈ·· ·ˌ··/ *n* (**salesclerk** *AmE*【美式】) a person who serves buyers in a shop 店員; 售貨員

shop floor /ˌ· ˈ·◂/ *n* **1 the shop floor** the ordinary workers, as opposed to the managers〔相對於資方的〕勞方: *They need to take more notice of shop floor opinion.* 他們要對勞方的意見多加注意。 **2 on the shop floor** with or by the ordinary workers 在工廠生產區: *The decision was very popular on the shop floor.* 該決定很受生產工人的歡迎。

shop·keep·er /ˈʃap,kipə; ˈʃɒp,kiːpəʳ/ *n* (**storekeeper** *AmE*【美式】) a person who owns and runs a small shop 店主, 店東

shop·lift·ing /ˈʃap,lɪftɪŋ; ˈʃɒp,lɪftɪŋ/ *v* [only in progressive forms 只用於進行式] taking things from a shop without paying for them 商店盜竊: *She was caught shoplifting.* 她在商店盜竊當場被捕。 | *Shoplifting is on the increase.* 店鋪盜竊案件正在增加。 —**shoplifter** *n* —see 見 THIEF (USAGE 用法)

☆**shop·ping** /ˈʃapɪŋ; ˈʃɒpɪŋ/ *n* [U] **1** all the things that you need to buy or that you have bought on one trip to the shops 需購

買或已購買的物品: *Put the shopping on the table.* 把買來的東西放在桌上。| *Can I carry some of your shopping for you?* 我來幫你拿一些你買的東西, 好嗎? | *Put it on the shopping list.* 把它寫在購物單上。| *It's in my shopping bag.* 它在我的購物袋裡。**2 do the shopping** to go to the shops and buy things, especially the everyday things you need such as food 買東西, 購物〔尤指購買所需日用品〕: *My husband always does the shopping.* 買東西的事都由我丈夫做。

shopping cen·tre /'·· ,··/ *n* a group of shops of different kinds planned and built together in one area 購物中心

shop·soiled /'ʃɒp,sɔɪld; 'ʃɒpsɔɪld/ *adj BrE* slightly damaged or dirty from being in a shop for a long time〔英式〕在商店裡陳列得舊了的

shop stew·ard /, ·'··/ *n* an officer elected by trade union members in a particular place of work〔基層工會選出來的〕工會代表

shore¹ /ʃɔr; ʃɔːr/ *n* [C;U] **1** the land along the edge of the sea or other large area of water〔海或湖等大水域的〕濱, 岸: *walking along the shore* 沿着海岸散步 | *a boat about a mile from the shore* 離岸約一英里處的一條船 **2 on shore** on land, as opposed to at sea 在岸上: *The sailors got into trouble while they were on shore.* 那些水手在岸上惹了麻煩。

> ■ USAGE 用法: Compare 比較 **coast, shore, beach** and 和 **seaside**. The **coast** is the edge of an area of land where it meets the sea. Use it particularly when thinking about the position of a place on the map ☆ **Coast** 指陸地與海交界的邊緣處, 特別用於指地圖的地理位置: *the French* **coast** 法國海岸 | *the north* **coast** *of Spain* 西班牙北海岸 | *a house on the Suffolk* **coast** 薩福克海岸上的一所房子。**Shore** is the usual word for the land on the edge of a sea or lake ☆ **Shore** 常指海或湖邊的土地: *We walked along the rocky* **shore.** 我們沿着佈滿岩石的海濱步行。| *The waves broke on the opposite* **shore.** 波浪衝到對岸激起浪花。A **beach** is part of the shore that is smooth, without cliffs or rocks ☆ **Beach** 指平坦而無懸崖或岩石的沙灘: *The children are building sandcastles on the* **beach.** 孩子們在沙灘上堆沙堡。| *Rows of bodies lay sunbathing on the* **beach.** 一排排的人躺在沙灘上沐日光浴。The **seaside** is used to talk about the area near the sea when we think of it as a place for a holiday or enjoyment ☆ **Seaside** 用來表示靠近海的度假或遊樂場所: *We always take the children to the* **seaside** *in August.* 我們總是在八月份帶孩子到海邊去玩。

shore² *v* **shored, shoring**

shore sth ↔ **up** *phr v* [T] to strengthen or give support to something weak or in danger of failing 支撐, 加強〔某物〕: *government action to shore up farm prices* 政府支持農產品價格的行動 | *They shored up the damaged buildings.* 他們把損壞的樓房支撐起來。

shorn /ʃɔrn; ʃɔːn/ **1** the past participle of SHEAR ☆ SHEAR 的過去分詞 **2 be shorn** to have too much hair cut off 毛髮剪得過短的

short¹ /ʃɔrt; ʃɔːt/ *adj* **1** not long 短的: *a short break in the middle of the lesson* 課間的短暫休息 | *a short pencil* 短鉛筆 | *a short article on the front page* 頭版上的短篇文章 | *She has her hair short these days.* 這些日子她留着短髮。–see picture on page 469 見 469 頁彩圖 **2** not as tall as usual 矮的: *the shortest boy in the class* 班上最矮的男孩 | *a rather short tower* 相當低的塔 –see picture on page 469 見 469 頁彩圖 –opposite 反義 **tall 3** not enough 短缺的; 不夠的: *short measure* 份量不足 | *short rations* 不足的配給量 | *The team is one man short.* 該隊還缺少一人。**4 short of: a** lacking something or not having enough of something 缺乏; 不足: *short of money* 缺錢 | *short of breath* 呼吸短促 | *We've got most of the equipment we need, but we're still short of a thermometer.* 我們弄到了所需的大部分設備, 但還缺少一個溫度計。**b** if something does not happen or is not done 除非, 除了: *Short of a miracle, the harvest is going to fail.* 除非奇跡出現, 否則會失收了。**5 be short for something** to be a short way of saying a longer word or expression〔某物的〕簡稱〔縮略形式〕: *"Rep" is short for "representative".* Rep 是 *representative* 的縮略形式。| *"What's 'Cindy' short for?" "Lucinda."* "Cindy (仙迪)是甚麼的簡稱?" "Lucinda. (露辛達)。" **6 for short** as a shorter way of saying the same name 作為簡稱: *My name is Alexander, Al for short.* 我的名字叫 Alexander (阿歷山大), 簡稱 Al。| *the Association of South-East Asian Nations, or Asean for short* 東南亞國家聯盟, 簡稱為 Asean (東盟) **7 be short with someone** to be a little rude to someone, not speaking to them much because you are in a hurry or they annoy you〔因忽忙或不高興而〕怠慢某人; 對某人無禮 **8 have a short temper, be short-tempered** to be the sort of person who gets angry very quickly 容易發脾氣〔發怒〕 **9 in short** you use this expression when you have talked or written in detail about something and you want to make sure that people understand exactly what you mean by giving them the main idea or ideas again in few words and clearly; you use **in short** to tell them that you are going to SUMMARIZE your ideas 總之, 簡而言之〔在詳細論述了某事之後, 為使聽話人或讀者準確

理解意思, 可用 **in short** 引出簡練的語句來概括要點): *It tests both spoken and written English. It demands the ability to communicate as well as a knowledge of grammar and vocabulary. Candidates are required to do extensive reading. In short, this is a very well-designed examination.* 該考題包括測試口頭英語和筆試。考生需要有溝通的能力和詞匯及語法知識。考生須進行泛讀。簡言之, 這是一份設計得十分嚴謹的試題。**10 go short** to have less than you really need 短缺, 缺少: *The mother will sometimes go short in order to make sure that the children have enough.* 為了確保孩子們夠吃, 母親時常會吃不飽。| *We went short of food for a few days.* 我們好幾天都沒有東西吃了。**11 at short notice** without being given much time to prepare 在短時間內〔沒有充分準備時間〕: *When John Raven had an accident another actor took over his part at short notice.* 約翰·拉文發生事故後, 另一位演員接到通知馬上接替他的角色。**12 be in short supply** to be able to be obtained only in small quantities or with difficulty because there is not enough 供應不足: *Water was in short supply.* 水的供應不足 | *Skilled engineers are in short supply now that business is booming again.* 由於業務又再蓬勃起來, 有經驗的工程師供不應求。**13 in the short term** looked at over only a short period of time 從短期看: *In the short term inflation will continue to rise, but we should begin to see a fall by mid-summer.* 通貨膨脹在短期內還會持續上升, 但到了仲夏我們應該開始看到回落。**14 make short work of** *infml* to deal with quickly and easily 〔非正式〕迅速處理掉, 輕易處理掉 **15 be short on something** *infml* not to have enough of a desirable quality 〔非正式〕欠缺某物: *The trouble with her is that she's long on talk, but short on action.* 她的缺點在於說的多, 做的少。**16 short and sweet** not lasting very long and saying only what is necessary 簡短扼要, 直截了當 **–shortness** n [U]

short² *adv* **1** just before reaching a certain point 達不到目標地 **2** suddenly 突然地

short³ *n* **1 shorts** [pl] **a** trousers ending at or above your knees 〔只到膝部的〕短褲 **b** the usual American word for 〖美式〗= UNDERPANTS **2** [C] a drink of strong alcohol, such as WHISKY or RUM, that has nothing added to it to make it weaker 〔不攙任何成分的〕烈酒〔如威士忌、朗姆酒等〕 **3** [C] *infml* 〖非正式〗–see 見 SHORT CIRCUIT

short·age /ˈʃɔːtɪdʒ; ˈʃɔːtɪdʒ/ *n* a situation in which you do not have enough of something 不足, 缺少: *food shortages during the war* 戰爭期間食物短缺 | *an acute shortage of skilled workers* 熟練工人的嚴重缺乏

short·bread /ˈʃɔːtbrɛd; ˈʃɔːtbred/ *n* (also 又作 **shortcake**) [U] a thick hard sweet BISCUIT made with a lot of butter 牛油甜酥餅

short-change /ˌ· ˈ·/ *v* **short-changed, short-changing** [T] **1** to give back too little money to someone who has paid you for something 少找錢給〔某人〕 **2** to treat someone badly by not giving them as much as you should 〔以盡量少給東西〕虐待〔某人〕: *There's a general feeling that the children of single-parent families have been short-changed by the new system.* 人們普遍感到, 單親家庭的孩子已受到新制度的虧待。

short cir·cuit¹ /ˌ· ˈ··/ *n* the touching of two electrical wires that should not touch; a short circuit usually makes the electricity go off 〔電的〕短路

short-circuit² *v* [I;T] to have a short circuit or to cause one in something (使)短路

short·com·ing /ˈʃɔːtˌkʌmɪŋ; ˈʃɔːtˌkʌmɪŋ/ *n* a fault 缺點, 短處: *In spite of all his shortcomings I still like him.* 雖然他有那麼多缺點, 但我還是喜歡他。

short cut /ˌ· ˈ·/ *n* **1** a quicker and more direct way of getting somewhere than the usual way 近路, 捷徑: *They took a short cut through the fields.* 他們穿過田野抄了個近路。**2** a quicker way of doing something; sometimes it is not as good as the usual way and people choose it because they are lazy or dishonest 捷徑, 快捷的辦法〔有時並不理想, 但人們由於懶惰或不誠實而選用〕

short·en /ˈʃɔːtn; ˈʃɔːtn/ *v* [I;T] to make or become shorter 變短, 縮短: *Shorten this report to 2000 words.* 把這篇報告縮短到二千字。

short·fall /ˈʃɔːtfɔl; ˈʃɔːtfɔːl/ *n* less than is needed or expected 缺少; 不足: *Owing to the drought, there will be a shortfall in wheat supplies this year.* 由於乾旱, 今年的小麥將供應不足。

short·hand /ˈʃɔːthænd; ˈʃɔːthænd/ *n* [U] a system of rapid writing using signs for letters and words 速記(法): *Her secretary made some notes in shorthand.* 她的祕書用速記作了些記錄。

short-hand·ed /ˌ· ˈ··/ *adj* see 見 SHORT-STAFFED

short list /ˈ· ·/ *n* *BrE* a list of a small group of people from which the person who will get a job or prize is chosen 〖英式〗決選名單〔挑選最終獲得工作或獎品的少數候選人的名單〕: *I think I'm on their short list.* 我想我已被列入他們的決選名單。**–short-list** *v* [T]: *He's been short-listed for the director's job.* 他已被列入董事職務的決選名單。

short-lived /ˌ· ˈ·/ *adj* lasting only a short time 短暫的, 持續不久的

★short·ly /ˈʃɔːtli; ˈʃɔːtli/ *adv* **1** soon 不久, 很快: *He will be back shortly.* 他很快就會回來。| *We received your message shortly after landing.* 我們在飛機著陸後不久就收到了你的口信。**2** in an impatient way 不耐煩地; 唐突地: *She answered me rather shortly.* 她很不耐煩地回答我。

short·sight·ed /ˈʃɔːtˈsaɪtɪd; ˌʃɔːtˈsaɪtɪd◂/ *adj* **1** unable to see things clearly if they are not close to your eyes 近視的 **2** not considering the likely future effects of something 目光短淺的，無遠見的: *You need to think of the future; don't make a short-sighted decision.* 你要考慮一下將來，不要作目光短淺的決定。– **shortsightedly** *adv* – **shortsightedness** *n* [U]

short-staffed /ˌ· ˈ·/ *adj* (also 又作 **short-handed**) with too few workers 人手不足的

short-term /ˌ·ˈ·◂/ *adj* having an effect within or for a short time 短期的，暫時的: *This is only a short-term solution to our problems.* 這對於我們的問題是個暫時的解決辦法。– **short term** *n* [sing]: *Profits will fall in the short term.* 利潤會在短期內下降。

short wave /ˌ· ˈ·◂/ *n* [U] radio broadcasting or receiving using waves of less than 120 metres in length 短波〔波長在一百二十米以下的無線電波〕: *Our only means of sending a message was by short-wave radio.* 我們發送信息的唯一方法是用短波無線電。

shot¹ /ʃɒt; ʃɒt/ the past tense and past participle of SHOOT ☆ SHOOT 的過去式和過去分詞

shot² *n* **1** [C] an act of firing a gun 射擊；開槍: *He fired three shots.* 他開了三槍。| *I heard a shot outside.* 我聽到外面有槍聲。**2** [C] an act of kicking or hitting a ball to make a point in a game 射門；投籃(得分): *His shot went wide of the goal.* 他把球射偏了。| *Well done! That was a good shot!* 做得好! 那球射得很精彩! **3 a good shot, a crack shot** a person who shoots very skilfully [RELATED PHRASE 相關詞組 **a poor shot**] 優秀的射手，神射手 **4** [U] non-explosive metal balls for shooting from some kinds of guns 〔不會爆炸的〕彈丸: *We couldn't eat the rabbit, as it was full of lead shot.* 我們不能吃那野兔，它裡面全是鉛沙彈。**5** [C] a photograph, or a picture seen in a film 照片；〔電影的〕一個鏡頭: *He got some wonderful action shots.* 他有一些精彩的動作連續鏡頭。**6** [C] an INJECTION of a drug 注射，(一)針: *The doctor gave me a shot of penicillin.* 醫生給我打了一針青霉素。**7** [C] *infml* an attempt to do something 〔非正式〕試圖；嘗試: *I'm not much good at sewing, but I'll have a shot at mending it.* 我不太擅長縫紉，但我會試着把它補一下。**8 a shot in the dark** *infml* a guess, without having any knowledge of something 〔非正式〕瞎猜，亂猜: *I was surprised that I got the answer right: it was a complete shot in the dark.* 我對自己能答對感到意外: 我完全是瞎猜的。**9 like a shot** *infml* quickly and eagerly 〔非正式〕立刻，馬上: *He offered me the job, and I accepted like a shot.* 他給我那份工作，我馬上就接受了。

shot·gun /ˈʃɒtɡʌn; ˈʃɒtɡʌn/ *n* a gun which fires shot, used for shooting birds and animals 獵槍

should /ʃəd; ʃəd; *strong* 強讀 ʃud; ʃud/ *v negative short form* 否定縮約式 **shouldn't** [modal verb 情態動詞] **1** used to show that you think someone has a moral duty to do something 應該〔用於表示道義上的責任〕: *The government should do something to help these people.* 政府應該做點事情去幫助這些人。| *You should be ashamed of yourself.* 你應該為自己感到羞恥。| *You shouldn't tell lies.* 你不應該撒謊。| *He should have gone to prison for what he did.* 他本應該為他的所作所為去坐牢。**2** used when you are saying that something would be a good idea 應該〔用於表示某個想法不錯〕: *You should see a doctor.* 你應該去看醫生。| *He should go to college and get himself some qualifications.* 他應該上大學，為自己取得一些資格。| *We should sell this house and buy a bigger one.* 我們應該把這房子賣了，買一所大一點的。| *I really should be going soon.* 我真的該馬上走。| *We should have booked in advance.* 我們本應該事先預訂。| *Should I phone her to check that she's there?* 我是否應該給她打個電話，看看她在不在那裡? **3** used when you are saying that you expect something to happen or to be true 應該〔用於表示期待某事發生或推論〕: *They should be here soon.* 他們應該馬上就到這裡。| *It should be easy.* 這事應該很容易。| *He should have got my letter by now.* 他現在該收到我的信了。| *We shouldn't have to wait long.* 我們應該不用等很長時間。**4** *fml* used with "I" and "we" in sentences with "if", when you are saying what you would do 〔正式〕將會〔在帶 if 從句的句子中與 I 和 we 連用表示說話者的意願〕: *I should be very surprised if he came now.* 如果他現在來，我會感到非常驚訝。**5** used in some sentences after "that" 〔某些句子中用於 that 之後〕: *It's odd that he should say that.* 奇怪的是他竟會那樣說。| *We arranged that she should meet us in London.* 我們安排了她在倫敦和我們會面。**6** *fml* used when you are talking about things that might happen in the future 〔正式〕〔用於表示將來〕: *If we should miss the train, we'll come by car.* 如果我們錯過了那班火車，就會坐汽車來。| *Should you remember his name, please let me know.* 要是你想起他的名字，請告訴我。–see Study Note on page 1318 見 1318 頁學習提示 **7 I should** a phrase you use when you are giving advice to someone 〔表示給某人忠告的用語〕: *I should get that roof mended if I were you.* 我要是你的話，我就會把那屋頂修補一下。| *"What shall I do about the car?" "I should take it to a garage."* "我該對這汽車怎麼辦呢?" "我會把它送去修理廠。" **8 I should like** a polite way of saying that you want something 我想〔表示想做某事的客氣說法〕: *I should like to ask a question.* 我想問一個問題。**9 I should think** I believe 我相信: *I* *should think he's about fifty.* 我相信他大約有五十歲。| *"Will you be able to come tonight?" "I should think so."* "今晚你能來嗎？" "我想我能來。" **10 I should have thought** a phrase you use when you are giving your opinion and saying that you expected something to be true 我以為〔用於表示期待某事是真的〕: *I should have thought that was obvious.* 我原以為那是顯而易見的!

✶shoul·der¹ /ˈʃoldər; ˈʃəuldər/ *n* **1** [C] the part of your body between your neck and the tops of your arms 肩，肩膀: *Put my jacket round your shoulders.* 把我的茄克衫披在你的肩上。| *She glanced over her shoulder nervously.* 她緊張地回頭掃了一眼。**2 shoulders** [pl] the parts of a piece of clothing that cover this part of your body 〔衣服的〕肩部: *a jacket with padded shoulders* 有墊肩的茄克衫 **3 a shoulder to cry on** someone from whom you get sympathy 能給予安慰的人

shoulder² *v* [T] **1** to put something heavy across your shoulders 挑起〔重擔〕 **2** to accept something such as responsibility or blame 擔負，承擔〔責任等〕: *Local residents are being asked to shoulder the cost of the damage.* 當地居民正被要求承擔這筆損毀的費用。

shoulder blade /ˈ··· / *n* either of the two flat bones on each side of your back 肩胛〔骨〕

should·n't /ˈʃudnt; ˈʃudnt/ a short form of "should not" 的縮略形式: *You shouldn't laugh at him.* 你不應該笑他。

should've /ˈʃudəv; ˈʃudəv/ a short form of "should have" 的縮略形式: *You should've come earlier — it's too late now.* 你本該早點來的，現在太晚了。

✶shout¹ /ʃaut; ʃaut/ *v* [I;T] to say something very loudly or speak very loudly 呼喊，叫: *"Help!" he shouted.* "救命啊!" 他大聲喊叫。| *There's no need to shout; I can hear you.* 不必大聲喊叫，我能聽見你的聲音。| *He's always shouting at his children.* 他老是對着孩子大喊大叫。| *We shouted to him to look where he was going.* 我們大聲喊他，看他往哪兒。

shout sbdy ↔ **down** *phr v* [T] to prevent someone from being heard by shouting at them 大喝〔某人〕倒采: *The speaker tried to reply but he was shouted down by the opposition.* 發言者想反駁，但被反對的人大喝倒采。

shout sthg ↔ **out** *phr v* [T] to suddenly shout loudly 突然呼喊: *She shouted out a warning and I managed to jump clear.* 她突然大聲警告，我就跳開了。

shout² *n* a loud cry or call 呼喊，喊叫: *a warning shout* 警告的呼喊聲 | *shouts of delight from the crowd* 人羣的歡呼聲

shove /ʃʌv; ʃʌv/ *v* **shoved, shoving** [I;T] **1** to push in a quick, rough way 推；猛推；亂塞: *I shoved the papers into my bag.* 我把文件胡亂塞進手提包裡。| *People always push and*

shove to squeeze into the trains. 人們總是你推我擠地爭着上火車。**2 Shove off!** *infml* a phrase used when you are telling someone rudely to go away 〔非正式〕走開!〔用於粗魯地叫某人離開〕—**shove** *n*: *It's stuck. Give it a shove.* 它卡住了，使勁推它一下。

shov·el¹ /ˈʃʌvl; ˈʃʌvəl/ *n* a long-handled tool with a flat broad surface at the bottom, used for lifting and moving earth, snow, sand, or coal 鏟子，鐵鏟

shovel² *v* **-ll- (-l- *AmE* 〔美式〕) 1** [I;T] to use a shovel to move and lift something 鏟去〔某物〕: *shovelling snow* 鏟雪 | *He shovelled the snow away.* 他把雪鏟掉了。**2** [T] to push quickly into a place 很快塞入: *She shovelled the papers into a drawer.* 她把文件胡亂塞進抽屜裡。| *Don't shovel the chips into your mouth! Eat properly.* 別把那麼多炸馬鈴薯條塞進嘴裡! 慢慢吃。

✶show¹ /ʃo; ʃəu/ *v* **showed, shown** /ʃon; ʃəun/ *or* **showed 1** [T] to allow or cause something to be seen 把〔某物〕給人看，出示，顯示: *He was showing them his holiday photographs.* 他在給他們看他度假的照片。| *She never shows her feelings.* 她從不表露她的感情。| *I had to show my ticket to the inspector.* 我得向查票員出示票子。| *Show me that cut.* 讓我瞧瞧那個傷口。| *This picture shows us all practising.* 這張照片把我們在練習的情景展現出來。

> ◻ **USEFUL PATTERNS** 有用句型
> to show something; to show something to someone; to show someone something

2 show someone how to do something to do something so that someone can watch and learn 向某人示範怎樣做某事: *He showed us how to catch rabbits.* 他向我們示範怎樣捉兔子。**3 show your face** to make an appearance 露面，出現: *I don't think he'd dare show his face here after his behaviour last week.* 我認為他在上星期那樣表現之後不敢在這裡露面。**4** [T] to make something clear 表明，説明〔某事物〕: *The figures show a 9% increase in inflation.* 這些數字説明通貨膨脹上升了百分之九。| *His comments showed that he didn't understand.* 他的評論證明他並不明白。| *Her behaviour shows you how bitter she feels.* 她的行為向你表明她感到多麼痛苦。| *This report shows the accident to have been the driver's fault.* 這項報告表明事故是司機的失誤造成的。**5 it goes to show** it proves the point 事實證明: *Running away from the police, he fell under a bus... which just goes to show that crime doesn't pay!* 他逃離警方時給公共汽車撞倒...這就證明了犯罪沒有好結果! **6** [I] to appear or be noticeable 顯現，顯現: *Don't worry about that bit of dirt; it won't show.* 別為那點污跡苦惱，那並不明顯。| *The lights showed faintly* *through the mist.* 燈光在霧中隱約可見。**7 have nothing/not much to show for something** to have no or not much gain or profit from something 在某事物上沒有〔沒多大〕成果〔成績〕: *We worked hard all night, but didn't have much to show for it when dawn came.* 我們整整幹了一夜，但天亮時卻沒做出甚麼成績來。**8** [T] to behave with a particular feeling towards someone 向〔某人〕表示〔某種感情〕: *They showed their enemies no mercy.* 他們對敵人沒有一點憐憫的表示。| *You should show more respect to your parents!* 你應該對你的父母表現出多一點尊敬! **9 show someone somewhere** to go with someone and guide them 給某人帶路: *I'll show you to your seat.* 我帶你到你的座位上去。| *Could you show the gentleman in, please, Wendy?* 溫迪，請你領這位先生進去，好嗎? **10 show someone the door** to make it clear to someone that they are not welcome and must leave 〔因不受歡迎而〕攆某人出去，給某人下逐客令 **11** [I;T] to offer a film for people to watch 放映〔電影〕: *They're showing six hours of cartoons on children's TV today.* 今天他們將在兒童電視節目中放映六小時的動畫片。

show off *phr v* **1** [I] to try to get other people's attention and admiration 炫耀，誇耀: *He came first in that exam, and he's been showing off ever since.* 那次考試他得了第一名，自此以後他一直在炫耀自己。**2** [T **show** sbdy/sthg ↔ **off**] to show someone or something that you are proud of to as many people as possible 炫耀〔某人或某物〕: *showing off her new car* 炫耀她的新車

show sbdy ↔ **round/around** *phr v* [T] to act as a guide to someone on their first visit to a place 帶領〔某人〕參觀〔某地〕: *Before you start work, I'll show you round the office.* 你開始工作之前，我會帶你到辦公室各處看看。

show up *phr v* **1** [T **show** sthg ↔ **up**] to cause something to be easily seen 使〔某物〕顯眼: *The bright light really shows up the cracks in the wall.* 明亮的燈光確使牆上的裂縫十分顯眼。**2** [T **show** sbdy ↔ **up**] to behave in a way that makes someone feel ashamed of you 使〔某人〕蒙受羞辱，使〔某人〕難堪: *Now, don't show me up when we have dinner with my boss!* 好啦，我們在和老闆吃飯時，可別讓我難堪! **3** [I] *infml* to arrive at a place where you are expected 〔非正式〕來到; 出席: *He didn't show up at the party until after midnight.* 他直到午夜後才在聚會上露面。

show² *n* **1** a performance in a theatre or on radio or television, especially one that is not very serious in its contents 演出，〔廣播或電視上的〕表演: *tickets for a variety show* 觀看綜藝表演的票子 **2** a collection of things for the public to look at 展覽，展覽會: *the village flower show* 村裡

的花展 **3 on show** being shown to the public 正在公開展出: *All the items will be on show until Wednesday.* 所有物品將展出到星期三為止。**4 a show of something: a** a showing of a particular quality 某物的顯示: *The army put on a show of strength.* 部隊展示了強大的軍力。**b** an outward appearance, as opposed to what is really happening 外觀; 外表〔相對於真實情況〕: *I made a show of interest, but I really didn't care about their problems.* 我表面上對他們的問題感興趣，其實根本不關心。**5 a show of hands** a vote taken by counting the raised hands of the voters 舉手表決 **6 for show** for appearance only 只為裝門面，只為了給人看: *It's all done for show — it doesn't mean a thing.* 幹這事全是為了裝門面，其實毫無意義。

show busi·ness /'· ˌ··/ *n* (also 又作 **showbiz** /'ʃəbɪz; 'ʃəʊbɪz/ *infml* 【非正式】) [U] the business of entertaining in television, films, or the theatre 娛樂性行業，娛樂界〔指電視、電影或戲劇〕: *She's in show business.* 她從事娛樂性行業。

show·down /'ʃo,daun; 'ʃəʊdaʊn/ *n infml* the settlement of a disagreement through an argument 【非正式】攤牌，一決勝負〔指通過爭論解決分歧〕

show·er¹ /'ʃauəʳ; 'ʃaʊəʳ/ *n* **1 a** an act of washing yourself by standing under running water 淋浴: *I'll just have a quick shower.* 我只是很快地洗個淋浴。**b** a place where you wash yourself like this 淋浴間: *He's in the shower.* 他在淋浴間裡。**c** the apparatus under which you wash yourself 淋浴器，淋浴用的噴頭: *The plumber is putting in a new shower.* 管子工在安裝新的淋浴器。**2** a short period of light rain 陣雨: *Scattered showers are expected this afternoon.* 預計今天下午有零星陣雨。**3** a fall of many small things or drops of water 〔許多小東西或液體的〕灑落: *a shower of confetti* 一陣灑落的五彩碎紙屑

shower² *v* **1** [I] to pour down in a shower 陣雨般落下; 下陣雨: *Nuts showered down from the tree.* 堅果從樹上如陣雨般落下。**2** [T] to scatter something heavily on someone or something 使〔某物〕大量灑落: *The pipe burst, showering us with oil.* 管道爆裂了，濺了我們一身油。

show·er·y /'ʃauərɪ; 'ʃaʊərɪ/ *adj* raining sometimes, but not for long 下陣雨的

show·ing /'ʃoɪŋ; 'ʃəʊɪŋ/ *n* **1** [C] an act of letting the public see something 展覽，展示: *There's a showing of his latest paintings at the art gallery.* 他近期的繪畫作品正在美術館裡展出。**2** [sing] performance 表現: *On their current showing, the party should do well in the election.* 根據他們目前的表現，該政黨有望在選舉中獲勝。

show·jump·ing /'· ˌ··/ *n* [U] a sport in which riders, one at a time, jump their horses over a course of fences 騎馬跳越障

礙運動 –**showjumper** n

show·man /'ʃəmən; 'ʃəʊmən/ n **showmen** /-mən; -mən/ **1** a person whose business is producing entertainment for the public 娛樂節目主持人: *a fairground showman* 露天遊樂會的演出主持人 **2** a person who likes to gain public attention 愛出風頭的人: *Our local doctor is a bit of a showman.* 我們的地方醫生有點愛出風頭。

shown /ʃon; ʃəʊn/ the past participle of SHOW ☆ SHOW 的過去分詞

show-off /'··/ n infml a person who behaves in a way intended to make others admire them 【非正式】愛炫耀的人: *I know he's a good player, but I don't like him because he's such a show-off.* 我知道他是個優秀的運動員，但我不喜歡他，因為他太愛炫耀自己。

show·room /'ʃo,rum; 'ʃəʊrʊm/ n a shop where goods for sale can be looked at 〔商品樣品的〕陳列室: *a car showroom* 汽車陳列室

show·y /'ʃoɪ; 'ʃəʊi/ adj **showier, showiest** too colourful or bright, but without much real value or beauty 過分豔麗的; 顯眼的; 賣弄的

shrank /ʃræŋk; ʃræŋk/ the past tense of SHRINK ☆ SHRINK 的過去式

shrap·nel /'ʃræpnəl; 'ʃræpnəl/ n [U] small pieces of metal scattered from an exploding bomb 砲彈碎片

shred¹ /ʃred; ʃred/ n **1** a small narrow piece of paper or material torn or roughly cut off 碎片; 碎條: *His coat was torn to shreds.* 他的外衣被撕成碎片。 **2 not a shred** not even a small bit 沒有絲毫…的: *He doesn't have a shred of evidence.* 他沒有絲毫證據。

shred² v **-dd-** [T] to cut or tear into small pieces 切碎; 撕碎: *shredded cabbage* 切碎的白菜

shrew /ʃru; ʃruː/ n **1** a small animal like a mouse with a long pointed nose 尖鼠, 鼩鼱〔一種長着長尖鼻子，外形似鼠的小動物〕 **2** old fash a bad-tempered woman 【老式】潑婦, 悍婦

shrewd /ʃrud; ʃruːd/ adj **1** quick to understand and judge a situation 機靈的; 精明的: *He's shrewd enough to turn things to his own advantage.* 他很精於使事情轉化為對自己有利的。 **2** well-reasoned and likely to be right 有理的; 可能對的: *a shrewd guess* 相當精確的猜測 **–shrewdly** adv

shriek /ʃrik; ʃriːk/ v [I;T] to cry out in a high voice 尖聲喊叫, 發出尖叫聲: *"Help!" she shrieked.* "救命!" 她尖聲呼叫。 | *They were all shrieking with laughter.* 他們都尖聲大笑起來。 **–shriek** n: *She gave a shriek of terror.* 她發出了一聲驚駭的尖叫聲。

shrill /ʃrɪl; ʃrɪl/ adj high and sharp (used of sound) 尖銳的, 刺耳的〔指聲音〕: *a shrill whistle* 刺耳的汽笛聲 **–shrilly** /'ʃrɪlɪ; 'ʃrɪli/ adv

shrimp /ʃrɪmp; ʃrɪmp/ n a small sea creature with many legs and a long tail, used as food 〔小〕蝦

shrine /ʃraɪn; ʃraɪn/ n a holy or respected place 聖地; 神殿; 神祠: *the shrine of St Augustine* 聖奧古斯丁神殿

shrink¹ /ʃrɪŋk; ʃrɪŋk/ n **shrank** /ʃræŋk; ʃræŋk/, **shrunk** /ʃrʌŋk; ʃrʌŋk/ **1** [I;T] to become smaller or make something become smaller 〔使〕收縮, 〔使〕皺縮, 〔使〕縮小: *You shouldn't wash that jumper in the washing machine — it will shrink.* 你可不要用洗衣機洗那件套衫，它會縮水的。 | *Oh no! I've shrunk my best cardigan in the wash.* 啊呀不好啦! 我最好的這件開襟羊毛衫洗後縮水了。 | *shrinking profits* 正在縮減的利潤 **2 shrink from something** to avoid or move away from something because you are afraid of it 從某事物退縮〔畏縮〕: *He shrank from the thought of having to kill anyone.* 他一想到要去殺人就退縮了。

shrink² n infml a PSYCHIATRIST (a word which is often used in a humorous way) 【非正式】精神病醫生; 精神分析學家〔常含幽默〕

shrink·age /'ʃrɪŋkɪdʒ; 'ʃrɪŋkɪdʒ/ n [U; sing] a decrease in the size or amount of something 收縮, 皺縮, 縮小: *There has been further shrinkage in the size of the workforce.* 職工人數已進一步減少。

shriv·el /'ʃrɪvl; 'ʃrɪvəl/ v **-ll-** (**-l-** AmE 【美式】) [I;T] to dry out, or make something dry out, and twist into small folds 〔使〕枯萎, 〔使〕乾枯: *The plants shrivelled up in the heat.* 植物在炎熱的天氣裡枯萎了。

shroud¹ /ʃraud; ʃraʊd/ n **1** the cloth used for wrapping a dead body 裹屍布 **2** something that covers and hides 覆蓋物; 遮蔽物: *A shroud of secrecy surrounds the plan.* 這項計劃神祕莫測〔籠罩在神祕之中〕。

shroud² v **be shrouded in** to be hidden by something 被〔某物〕遮蔽, 掩蓋: *Everything was shrouded in fog.* 大霧籠罩着一切。 | *The case was shrouded in mystery.* 箱子被神祕地藏了起來。

shrub /ʃrʌb; ʃrʌb/ n a low bush 灌木(叢)

shrub·be·ry /'ʃrʌbəri; 'ʃrʌbəri/ n **shrubberies** [C;U] part of a garden with a lot of shrubs 灌木叢(區)

*★**shrug** /ʃrʌg; ʃrʌg/ v **-gg-** [I;T] (also 又作 **shrug your shoulders**) to raise your shoulders as an expression of doubt or lack of interest 聳〔肩〕〔表示懷疑或不感興趣等〕: *She just shrugged and said, "I don't care."* 她只是聳聳肩膀説: "我不在乎。" | *He shrugged his shoulders and wouldn't reply.* 他聳了聳肩卻不作回答。 **–shrug** n: *She just gave a shrug.* 她只是聳了聳肩膀。

shrug sthg ↔ **off** phr v [T] to treat something as if it is not really serious or important 把〔某事物〕看得無足輕重; 對〔某事物〕滿不在乎: *You can't just shrug off something* *like this as if it didn't exist!* 你可不能就像它不存在似的不理不睬!

shrunk /ʃrʌŋk; ʃrʌŋk/ *the past tense and past participle of* SHRINK ☆ SHRINK 的過去式和過去分詞

shrunk·en /ˈʃrʌŋkən; ˈʃrʌŋkən/ *adj* that has been shrunk 乾枯的; 收縮的: *shrunken heads* 乾癟的腦袋

shud·der /ˈʃrʌdə; ˈʃʌdər/ *v* [I] **1** to shake uncontrollably for a moment with fear or strong dislike 〔因恐懼或憎惡而〕打顫, 戰慄, 發抖: *He saw the body on the floor, and shuddered.* 他看到地板上的屍體便嚇得發抖。 **2 I shudder to think of something** I don't like to think about something at all 怕想一點也不敢想某事: *I shudder to think of how often I told her I hated the boss.* 一想到我常對她說我恨老闆, 我就不敢再想了。 | *"What will you have to pay?" "I shudder to think!"* "你得付出甚麼樣的代價?" "我根本不敢設想!" **3 shudder to a halt** (of a vehicle) to stop, shaking at the same time 〔車輛〕顫動着停住: *The bus shuddered to a halt.* 公共汽車顫動着停了下來。 –**shudder** *n*: *She gave a shudder of repulsion.* 她反感得打了個寒顫。

shuf·fle /ˈʃʌfl; ˈʃʌfəl/ *v* **shuffled, shuffling 1** [I] to walk slowly, without lifting your feet off the ground properly 拖着腳步走: *The old woman shuffled home.* 那位老婦拖着緩慢的腳步回家。 **2** [I;T] to move your feet around impatiently or nervously, or move around in your chair like this 坐立不安: *Stop shuffling your feet!* 你別坐立不安的樣子! **3** [I;T] to mix up the order of playing cards 洗(牌): *Your turn to shuffle.* 輪到你洗牌了。 –**shuffle** *n*: *Give the cards a shuffle.* 洗一洗牌。

shun /ʃʌn; ʃʌn/ *v* **-nn-** [T] to avoid on purpose 〔故意地〕避開, 迴避: *He was shunned by the other prisoners.* 其他囚犯都避開他。 | *Few politicians shun publicity.* 能避免出風頭的政治家寥寥無幾。

shunt /ʃʌnt; ʃʌnt/ *v* [T] to move objects or people, especially to a less important place 將(人或物)轉至次要的地方: *The trains were shunted to a railway siding.* 火車被轉到了岔道。 | *I've been shunted off to the branch office.* 我已被轉調到分行辦事處工作。

shush /ʃʌʃ; ʃʊʃ/ *interj* a word used when telling someone to be quiet 噓〔用於叫某人安靜下來〕別作聲: *Shush! Don't cry!* 噓, 別哭了!

★**shut** /ʃʌt; ʃʌt/ *v* **shut, shut, shutting 1** [I;T] to close something 關上, 關閉, 合上: *Please shut the gate.* 請關上大門。 | *He shut his eyes and tried to sleep.* 他閉上眼睛打算睡覺。 | *She shut the book.* 她合上了書。 | *The doors shut, and the train moved off.* 門關上後, 火車開走了。 **2** [T + adv/prep] to lock or catch something inside or outside something 把...關在裡面(外面): *He shut himself in his room to think.* 他把自己關在房間裡思考。 | *She shut her skirt in the door*

and tore it. 她的裙子夾在門縫裡給扯破了。 **3** [I;T] to close 打烊, 停止營業: *The shops shut at 5.30.* 商店五點半停止營業。 | *He lost his job when they shut the factory.* 他們關閉工廠後, 他就失業了。

shut sbdy ↔ **away** *phr v* [T] to keep someone locked up away from other people 把〔某人〕關起來; 隔離: *He shut himself away in an attic and nobody knew he was there.* 他把自己關在閣樓裡, 沒有人知道他在那兒。

shut down *phr v* [I;T **shut sthg** ↔ **down**] (of a business) to close and stop working (使)〔企業〕關閉, 停業: *He was made redundant when the pit shut down.* 礦井關閉時, 他成為冗員被裁減了。

shut sthg ↔ **off** *phr v* [I] to disconnect 切斷, 關掉: *Don't forget to shut off the gas when you go on holiday.* 你去度假時別忘了關掉煤氣。

shut up *phr v* **1** [I] *infml* to stop talking 〔非正式〕閉嘴, 住口: *Now shut up for a minute and listen!* 現在歇會兒嘴聽着! | *"So I said..." "Shut up!"* "所以我就說..." "住口!" **2** [T **shut sbdy** ↔ **up**] *infml* to prevent someone from talking 〔非正式〕堵住〔某人的〕嘴: *He was going to tell the newspapers, so we gave him £1000 to shut him up.* 他要告訴報界, 所以我們給了他一千英鎊堵住他的嘴。 **3** [T **shut sbdy/sthg** ↔ **up**] to keep enclosed 把〔某人〕關起來: *They shut him up in a cupboard until he confessed.* 他們把他關在櫥櫃裡, 直到他招供為止。

shut·down /ˈʃʌtdaʊn; ˈʃʌtdaʊn/ *n* a stopping of work or operation 停工, 停業

shut·ter /ˈʃʌtə; ˈʃʌtər/ *n* **1** [C] a part of a camera which opens when a photograph is taken, to let light onto the film 〔照相機的〕快門 **2 shutters** [pl] wooden or metal covers that can be unfolded in front of a window 百葉窗

shut·tle¹ /ˈʃʌtl; ˈʃʌtl/ *n* an air, bus, or train service which makes frequent journeys between two places 〔於兩地之間行走的〕穿梭運輸; 穿梭運輸的交通工具〔如飛機、汽車或火車〕: *There is a shuttle between the station and the university.* 火車站與大學之間有短程往返的穿梭運行班車。

shuttle² *v* **shuttled, shuttling** [I;T] to move between two places often or regularly 穿梭般來回運行: *The new trains shuttle passengers across the town.* 一列列新火車往返穿梭市內運送旅客。

shut·tle·cock /ˈʃʌtlkɑk; ˈʃʌtlkɒk/ *n* a small light feathered object hit across a net in the game of BADMINTON 羽毛球

shy¹ /ʃaɪ; ʃaɪ/ *adj* **shyer, shyest** (also 又作 **shier, shiest**) **1** nervous and uncomfortable in the company of other people 怕陌生的; 害羞的, 腼腆的: *When the children met the Queen, they were too shy to speak.* 孩子們見到女王時腼腆得話也不敢講。 | *a shy* smile 羞怯的微笑 **2** unwilling to come near people (used of animals) 不願近人的, 膽怯的〔指動物〕 **3 shy** afraid of or hating 害怕...的; 不喜歡...的: *She's camera-shy and hates being photographed.* 她怕上鏡頭, 因此不愛拍照片。 | *He's not ill — he's just work-shy.* 他沒有病, 只是討厭上班。 **–shyly** *adv* **–shyness** *n* [U]

shy² *v* **shied, shying** (of a horse) to make a sudden movement through fear 〔馬〕驚退; 驚跳: *My horse shied at the dog, and I fell off.* 我的馬因怕狗而驚跳起來, 把我摔了下來。

shy away from sth *phr v* to avoid doing something unpleasant 避開〔做不愉快的事〕: *She tends to shy away from accepting responsibility.* 她往往逃避責任。

sib·ling /'sɪblɪŋ; 'sɪblɪŋ/ *n fml* a brother or sister 〔正式〕兄弟; 姐妹

*sick¹ /sɪk; sɪk/ *adj* **1** suffering from an illness 患病的, 有病的: *My uncle is sick in hospital.* 我的叔叔因病住院了。 **2** [only before a noun 只用於名詞前] for illness 因病的: *sick pay* 病假工資 | *He's got two weeks' sick leave.* 他請了兩週病假。 **3 be off sick** not to be at work because of illness 因病缺勤, 休病假: *Sarah's off sick this week.* 莎拉本週病了沒有上班。 **4 be sick** to throw up what is in your stomach 嘔心; 嘔吐 **5 feel sick** to feel as if you are going to throw up what is in your stomach 感到噁心: *He began to feel rather sick when the ship started to move.* 船一開動, 他就覺得要吐。 **6 make someone sick** *infml* to give someone feelings of annoyance or strong dislike 〔非正式〕使某人感到厭惡: *Your complaining makes me sick!* 你的牢騷令我厭惡! **7 sick of, sick to death of, sick and tired of** *infml* annoyed with and tired of 〔非正式〕討厭...; 厭倦...: *I'm sick of sitting around waiting for him.* 我討厭乾坐着等他。 **8** not treating death or cruelty in a properly serious way 令人毛骨悚然的: *That's a really sick joke. I don't find it funny at all.* 那笑話真是令人毛骨悚然, 我覺得一點兒也不可笑。

sick² *n* [pl] **the sick** people who are ill 病人

sick·en /'sɪkən; 'sɪkən/ *v* **1** [T] to cause strong feelings of dislike, anger, or shock 使作嘔; 使厭惡; 使震驚: *Their hypocrisy sickens me.* 他們的虛情假意令我噁心。 | *His head hit the floor with a sickening thud.* 他的頭砰的一聲撞在地板上, 讓人嚇一大跳。 **2** [I] to become ill 生病: *The animal began to sicken and soon died.* 那頭動物患了病, 不久就死了。 **3 sicken for something** to be about to become ill 有生某種病的症狀: *She's got a high temperature; maybe she's sickening for something.* 她在發高燒, 可能是得了甚麼病。

sick·ly /'sɪklɪ; 'sɪklɪ/ *adj* **sicklier, sickliest 1** weak and unhealthy 病弱的, 不健康的: *a sickly child* 多病的孩子 | *a sickly-looking plant* 長勢不好的植物 **2** looking or smelling unpleasant or unhealthy 病態的; 令人作嘔

的: *His face was a sickly yellow.* 他的臉色是病態的黃色。 | *a foul sickly smell* 令人作嘔的臭味

sick·ness /'sɪknɪs; 'sɪknɪs/ *n* **1** [U] the condition of being ill or unhealthy 患病; 疾病: *Put up a notice: Closed due to staff sickness.* 把通知貼上: 職員生病, 特此停業。 **2** [U] the condition of feeling or being sick 噁心; 嘔吐: *Morning sickness is one of the first indications of pregnancy.* 晨吐是懷孕的一個早期症狀。 **3** [C;U] a particular form of illness 某一種病: *sleeping sickness* 昏睡病

★side¹ /saɪd; saɪd/ *n* **1** a surface of something that is not its top, bottom, front, or back 旁邊, 側面: *The front door is locked: we'll have to go around to the side of the house.* 前門鎖了, 我們只好繞到屋子的側面去。 | *Standing on either side of her were her sons.* 站在她兩旁的是她的兒子。 | *I sat down by his side.* 我在他的旁邊坐下。 **2** any of the flat surfaces of something 〔平面的〕面; 表面: *A cube has six sides.* 立方體有六個面。 | *Which side of the box do you put the label on?* 你把標籤貼在箱子的哪一面? **3** either of the two surfaces of a thin flat object 〔薄平物體的〕兩面中的一面: *Write on only one side of the paper.* 只在紙的一面書寫。 | *The queen's head is on one side of a pound coin.* 女王的頭像鑄在一英鎊硬幣的一面。 **4** the right or left part of your body between the shoulder and the top of the leg 〔人體的〕側邊; 肋: *I've got a pain all down my left side.* 我的整個左肋疼痛。 **5 side by side** next to one another 肩並肩地, 並排地: *We sat side by side on a long wooden bench.* 我們並排坐在木板凳上。 **6** an edge or border 邊, 緣: *A square has four equal sides.* 正方形有四條等邊。 | *We had a picnic by the side of the road.* 我們在公路邊野餐旅行。 **7** a slope 斜坡: *a beautiful spot halfway up the side of the hill* 半山腰的一個美麗的景點 **8** a place or division according to a real or imaginary central line 〔以物體實際或想像中的中線分成的〕部分, 半, 邊: *She lives on the other side of town.* 她住在城市的另一邊。 | *Cars drive on the left side of the road in England.* 在英國, 汽車是靠左行駛的。 **9** one of the different points of view in an argument 〔爭論中的〕一方的看法: *Don't just listen to my side of things — ask him too!* 別只聽我的一面之言, 也該去問問他。 | *Try to look at all sides of the question before deciding.* 在作出決定前, 要盡量從問題的各方面來考慮。 **10** one of the two people or groups in a quarrel or war 〔爭吵或戰爭的〕一派, 一方: *In most wars neither side wins.* 在大多數戰爭中, 哪一方都說不上是贏家。 | *Whose side are you on?* 你支持[站在]哪一方? **11 on someone's side: a** agreeing with someone and ready to support them in an argument 〔爭論中〕支持某一方: *I'm on your side — I think you've been treated very* *badly.* 我支持你——我覺得你一直受到虐待。**b** relating to someone's relatives or family history 家系, 血統: *He's Scottish on his mother's side.* 他的母系是蘇格蘭血統。 **12** [+sing/pl verb] a sports team 運動隊: *Our side are winning.* 我們隊節節勝利。 | *My brother's side is always losing.* 我兄弟的隊老是輸球。 **13 take sides** to support one person against another in an argument 支持一方; 袒護: *Don't ask me to decide — I'm not taking sides!* 別讓我作決定——我不會偏袒任何一方! **14 on the side** as an additional activity, often a dishonest one 作為兼職; 作為副業: *He runs a little business on the side.* 他經營小店作為副業。 **15 on the high side, on the low side, etc.** *infml* a phrase you use to show that you think something is a little high, low, etc. 〖非正式〗偏高; 偏低: *I like the house but I think the price is on the high side.* 我喜歡這房子, 但我覺得價格偏高。 | *She's on the small side for her age.* 她人長得比實際年齡要矮小。 | *I ought to lose some weight — I'm a bit on the plump side at the moment.* 我該減肥了——我現在有點過胖。 **16 put on/to one side** to keep for possible use later 暫擱一邊以備後用 **17 -sided** having a particular number or type of sides 有...邊的; 有...面的: *an eight-sided coin* 一個八邊形的硬幣 | *a steep-sided valley* 陡峭的山谷

side² *adj* [only before a noun 只用於名詞前] **1** at, from, or towards the side 在邊上的; 從側面來的; 向一側的: *a side door* 側門 **2** besides the main or regular thing 枝節的; 副的: *Certain drugs have harmful side effects.* 某些藥物產生有害的副作用。 | *We serve curry with a selection of side dishes.* 我們應咖喱食品, 還配上一些精選的小菜。 **3 a side street, a side road** a narrow, less important street 〔旁邊的〕小街, 小道, 橫街

side³ *v* **sided, siding**
    side with sbdy *phr v* [T] to support one person or group in a quarrel or fight 〔爭吵或打架時〕支持一方: *She always sides with her son* **against** *the teachers.* 她總是支持她的兒子和老師作對。

side·board /ˈsaɪdˌbɔːd; ˈsaɪdbɔːd/ *n* **1** [C] a long low cupboard, used to hold dishes and glasses 餐具櫃 **2 sideboards** [pl] (also 又作 **sideburns** /-ˌbɜːnz; -bɜːnz/ *AmE* 〖美式〗) hair grown on the sides of a man's face 〔男子的〕鬢角

side·car /ˈsaɪdˌkɑr; ˈsaɪdkɑːʳ/ *n* a small vehicle fastened to the side of a motorcycle for carrying passengers 〔附於摩托車旁的〕邊車; 邊斗

side ef·fect /ˈ··ˌ·/ *n* **1** an effect that a drug has on you in addition to curing illness or pain 〔藥物的〕副作用: *Sleeping pills often have harmful side effects.* 安眠藥常產生有害的副作用。 **2** an event that is not planned and happens in addition to the main result 意外事件; 意外後果: *One side effect of in-*

flation is unemployment. 通貨膨脹的後果之一是失業問題。

side·lights /ˈsaɪdˌlaɪts; ˈsaɪdlaɪts/ *n* [pl] the small lights at the front of a vehicle 〔車輛前面的〕側燈 –see picture on page 209 見 209 頁彩圖

side·line /ˈsaɪdˌlaɪn; ˈsaɪdlaɪn/ *n* **1** an activity done in addition to your regular job 副業, 兼職 **2 sidelines** [pl] the lines marking the length of a football field or tennis court 〔足球場或網球場的〕邊線

side·long /ˈsaɪdˌlɒŋ; ˈsaɪdlɒŋ/ *adj* directed sideways 向旁邊的, 斜的: *a sidelong glance* 斜視的一瞥

side·show /ˈsaɪdˌʃəʊ; ˈsaɪdʃəʊ/ *n* **1** a small show at a fair or CIRCUS with amusements or games 〔馬戲團的〕穿插表演, 雜耍 **2** an unimportant activity compared to a more serious main one 附帶活動; 次要事情

side·step /ˈsaɪdˌstɛp; ˈsaɪdstɛp/ *v* **-pp-** [T] to avoid something dangerous or unpleasant 避開〔危險事物〕; 迴避〔不快之事〕: *The minister neatly sidestepped the reporter's questions.* 部長巧妙地迴避了記者的提問。

side·tracked /ˈsaɪdˌtrækt; ˈsaɪdtrækt/ *v* **get sidetracked** to leave an important activity and start an unimportant one 放下重要的事而去做次要事情, 轉移目標: *I started to cook dinner but got sidetracked reading the recipe book.* 我開始是做飯, 但接着卻轉移目標, 看起烹飪書來。

side·walk /ˈsaɪdˌwɔk; ˈsaɪdwɔːk/ *n* the usual American word for 〖美式〗= a PAVEMENT

side·ways /ˈsaɪdˌweɪz; ˈsaɪdweɪz/ *adv, adj* to or towards one side 向一邊的, 向一側的: *to step sideways* 向旁邊跨出一步 | *a sideways jump* 橫跳

sid·ing /ˈsaɪdɪŋ; ˈsaɪdɪŋ/ *n* a short railway track connected to the main track, used to park carriages when they are not being used 〔鐵路的〕側線, 旁軌 –see picture on page 991 見 991 頁彩圖

si·dle /ˈsaɪdl; ˈsaɪdl/ *v* **sidled, sidling** [I] to walk in a nervous or uncertain way as if you do not want to be noticed 〔鬼祟地〕側身而行: *He sidled up to the stranger and tried to sell him the stolen ring.* 他鬼鬼祟祟地走近那陌生人, 企圖想把偷來的戒指賣給他。

siege /siːdʒ; siːdʒ/ *n* **1** [C;U] a military operation in which an army surrounds a place and blocks supplies and help, in order to force the people inside to come out and admit they are defeated 〔軍隊的〕包圍, 圍困 **2** [C] a situation in which an armed criminal keeps people as prisoners in a building 〔持槍歹徒對大樓裡的人進行的〕包圍

si·es·ta /sɪˈɛstə; siˈestə/ *n* a short sleep after the midday meal which people have in hot countries 〔氣候炎熱國家的〕午睡

sieve¹ /sɪv; sɪv/ *n* **1** a tool made of wire or plastic net on a frame, used for separating large and small solid bits, or solid things from liquid 篩(子); 濾網: *Use a sieve to get out the lumps.* 用篩子去除塊粒。–see picture on page 958 見 958 頁彩圖 **2 a head/memory like a sieve** *infml* a very poor memory〔非正式〕記憶力極差

sieve² *v* **sieved, sieving** [I] to put a liquid or a dry substance through a sieve 篩; 濾: *Sieve the flour first.* 先把麵粉篩一下。| *Sieve out the stones from the soil.* 把石塊從土壤中篩出。

sift /sɪft; sɪft/ *v* **1** [T] to put a dry substance through a sieve 篩 **2** [I;T] to examine things in a mass or group 篩選; 細查: *sifting through her papers to find his letter* 從她的文件中仔細地尋找他的信

sigh¹ /saɪ; saɪ/ *v* [I] to let out a deep breath slowly as a way of expressing tiredness, sadness, or pleasure 嘆氣, 嘆息; 悲嘆: *She sighed heavily.* 她重重地嘆了一口氣。

sigh² *n* an act or sound of sighing 嘆氣, 嘆息(聲): *We all breathed a sigh of relief when she left.* 她走後我們都鬆了一口氣。| *She gave a little sigh of contentment.* 她滿意地舒了一口氣。

★sight¹ /saɪt; saɪt/ *n* **1** [U] the ability to see 視力, 視覺: *He lost his sight in a road accident.* 他在一次交通事故中喪失了視力。**2** [sing; U] an act of seeing something, or an occasion when you see it 看見: *I always faint at the sight of blood.* 我一見到血就會暈倒。| *The house is hidden from sight by a row of trees.* 那幢房子被一排樹遮住了, 人們看不見。| *I had my first sight of land for three weeks.* 我三個星期以來首次見到陸地。| *Do you believe in love at first sight?* 你相信一見鍾情嗎? **3** [C] something that is seen 情景, 景象: *the familiar sight of the postman going along the street* 郵差沿街走着的熟悉情景 **4** [U] the range of what can be seen 眼界, 視域: *The boat was within sight of land.* 那艘船已接近陸地。| *Keep out of sight until the police have gone.* 別露面, 直到警察離去。| *There's no end in sight.* 一眼望不到頭〔一望無際〕。**5 a sight** something which looks very bad or so foolish that it cannot be taken seriously 難看〔滑稽〕的模樣: *What a sight you are, with paint all over your clothes!* 你全身衣服都是油漆, 這樣子多難看! **6 a sight** *infml* a lot〔非正式〕很多, 大量: *This hotel's a sight better than the place I usually stay at.* 這家旅館比我常住的那地方好得多。**7 the sights** the places that are interesting to see 值得看的地方; 名勝: *We'll take you to see the sights of London.* 我們將帶你去遊覽倫敦的名勝。**8 sights** [pl] a part of an instrument or weapon which helps you to aim correctly〔儀器或武器上的〕瞄準器; 準星 **9 set your sights on something** to try very hard to obtain or become something 力求, 志在…: *She'd set her sights on going to college.* 她要全力以赴考取大學。**10 catch sight of** to see something suddenly〔突然〕看見〔某物〕: *I*

caught sight of her hurrying away. 我看見她匆匆離去。[RELATED PHRASE 相關詞組 **lose sight of:** *I lost sight of her in the crowd.* 我在人羣中再也看不見她。]

sight² *v* [T] to get a sudden or quick view of someone or something after looking for them for a long time〔尋找很長時間後〕突然看到; 發現: *The missing child has been sighted in London.* 失蹤的孩子已經在倫敦被發現。| *We sighted a falcon and some other rare birds.* 我們發現一隻獵鷹和其他一些罕見的鳥。–**sighting** *n*

sight·ed /ˈsaɪtɪd; ˈsaɪtɪd/ *adj* (of a person) not blind〔人〕非盲的, 有視力的: *Both blind and sighted learners will benefit from the new library system.* 雙目失明和視力健全的學習者都會從新的圖書館體制得益。

sight·see·ing /ˈsaɪtˌsiɪŋ; ˈsaɪtˌsiːɪŋ/ *n* [U] going about as a tourist on holiday, visiting places of interest 觀光, 遊覽: *Allow three days for sightseeing in Paris.* 給予三天時間遊覽巴黎。

★sign¹ /saɪn; saɪn/ *n* **1** a mark that always has a particular meaning 符號, 記號: *signs of military rank* 軍階符號 | *the minus sign* 負號 **2** a movement of your body giving a particular meaning〔身體的〕示意動作, 姿勢; 手勢: *She put her finger to her lips as a sign to be quiet.* 她把手指放在嘴唇邊, 示意大家安靜下來。**3** a board or notice giving information or a warning 標誌, 指示牌, 告示牌: *Pay attention to the road signs.* 要注意路標。| *There was a "No Smoking" sign on her door.* 她的門上有一塊"禁止吸煙"的告示牌。**4** something that shows the presence or likely future existence of something else 徵兆, 跡象: *Swollen ankles can be a sign of heart disease.* 腫脹的腳踝可能是心臟病的徵兆。| *There are signs that the economy is improving.* 有跡象表明經濟在好轉。**5 a sign of the zodiac** any of the 12 divisions of the year represented by groups of stars〔黃道十二宮之一〕宮, 星座

★sign² *v* **1** [I;T] to write your name on a paper or letter for official purposes 簽名, 署名: *The papers are ready to be signed.* 這些文件已準備好, 可以簽字了。| *She signed the cheque.* 她在支票上簽了名。| *Can you sign here please?* 請在這裡簽個字, 好嗎? **2 sign on the dotted line** to agree to something, especially by signing a contract 簽字同意〔某事〕〔尤指簽署合同〕

sign sth ↔ **away** *phr v* [T] to give something up formally by signing a paper 簽字放棄〔某物〕: *He signed away his share in the property.* 他簽字放棄他在那筆財產中應得的一份。

sign for sth *phr v* [T] to sign your name to show that you have received something 簽收

sign in *phr v* [I] to write your name when arriving at a hotel or club 簽到 [RE-

LATED PHRASE 相關詞組 **sign out**]

sign on *phr v* **1** [I] to officially agree to work or study by signing a contract 簽約受雇; 報名進修: *He signed on with the Army.* 他正式簽約加入軍隊。| *You could sign on for a computer course.* 你可以報名參加電腦班。**2** [T **sign** sbdy ↔ **on**] to officially give someone a job 簽約雇用〔某人〕: *The foreman has signed on several new men this week.* 這星期工頭已經雇用了好幾個新工人。**3** [I] to say officially that you are unemployed so that you can receive money from the state 辦理失業登記〔以獲得救濟金〕

sign up *phr v* **1** [I] to sign an agreement to do something 簽約做〔某事〕; 報名參加: *I've signed up to take a course at the local college.* 我已報名修讀本地學院開設的一門課程。**2** [T **sign** sbdy ↔ **up**] to get someone to sign an agreement to do something 使〔某人〕簽約: *Our manager's just signed up two new players.* 我們的經理剛與兩位球員簽約。

★sig·nal¹ /ˈsɪɡnl; ˈsɪɡnəl/ *n* **1** a sound or action intended to give a message 信號; 暗號: *A red lamp is often used as a danger signal.* 紅燈常被用作危險的信號。| *smoke signals* 煙霧信號 **2** a piece of railway apparatus like traffic lights to tell train drivers whether to stop 〔鐵路的〕信號裝置 –see picture on page 991 見 991 頁彩圖 **3** a sound, image, or message sent by waves 〔電波傳送的〕訊息; 圖像; 訊號: *We live too far from the city to get a strong television signal.* 我們住的地方離城市太遠，無法收到清晰的電視圖像。| *radar signals* 雷達訊號

signal² *v* **-ll-** (**-l-** *AmE* 〖美式〗) **1** [I] to give a signal 發信號, 打信號: *The general signalled for the attack to begin.* 將軍發信號表示開始進攻。**2** [T] to express, warn, or tell by a signal 用信號表示〔警告〕: *The policeman signalled the traffic to move forward.* 警察用信號指示車輛前進。| *Both sides have signalled their willingness to start negotiations.* 雙方已經表示願意開始談判。**3** [T] to be a sign or proof of 是…的標誌; 標誌着: *This defeat signalled the end of the war.* 這次失敗標誌着戰爭的結束。

signal³ *adj* [only before a noun 只用於名詞前] *fml* very noticeable and important 〖正式〗顯著的; 重要的: *a signal achievement* 顯著的成就 –**signally** *adv*

sig·na·to·ry /ˈsɪɡnətri; ˈsɪɡnətəri/ *n* **signatories** *fml* any of the people or countries that sign an agreement 〖正式〗〔協議的〕簽署者; 簽約國

sig·na·ture /ˈsɪɡnətʃə; ˈsɪɡnətʃəʳ/ *n* a person's name written in their own handwriting, at the end of a letter, cheque, or official paper 署名, 簽名, 簽字: *a petition with four thousand signatures* 一份有四千人簽名的請願書 | *I couldn't decipher his signature.* 我認不出他的簽名。

★sig·nif·i·cance /sɪɡˈnɪfɪkəns; sɪɡˈnɪfɪkəns/ *n* [U] importance and meaning 重要性; 意義: *The discovery of oil is of great significance to the country's economy.* 石油的發現對該國的經濟具有重大的意義。| *It doesn't matter; it's of no significance.* 沒關係, 這並不重要。

★sig·nif·i·cant /sɪɡˈnɪfɪkənt; sɪɡˈnɪfɪkənt/ *adj* **1** large or noticeable 重大的; 顯著的; 值得注意的: *a significant increase in crime* 犯罪活動的顯著增加 **2** having a special meaning 意義深長的, 有特殊意義的: *a significant discovery* 有重大意義的發現 –**significantly** *adv*

sig·ni·fy /ˈsɪɡnəfaɪ; ˈsɪɡnɪfaɪ/ *v* **signified**, **signified** [T] *fml* to have a particular meaning 〖正式〗意味着; 表示: *This latest shift signifies a real change in foreign policy.* 最近這次〔領導層的〕更迭意味着外交政策將有實質性的改變。

sign lan·guage /ˈ· ˌ··/ *n* [U] a language expressed by a system of hand movements, as used by people who cannot speak or hear properly 〔聾啞人用的〕手勢語, 手語

sign·post /ˈsaɪnpost; ˈsaɪnpəʊst/ *n* a road sign showing directions and distances 路標

Sikh /sik; siːk/ *n* a member of a religious group that began in Northern India; the religion developed from HINDUISM but believes that there is only one god 〔印度北部的〕錫克教; 錫克教教徒 –**Sikhism** *n*

si·lage /ˈsaɪlɪdʒ; ˈsaɪlɪdʒ/ *n* [U] grass or other green plants cut and stored for cattle food 青貯飼料

★si·lence¹ /ˈsaɪləns; ˈsaɪləns/ *n* [C;U] **1** total quietness 寂靜, 無聲: *The silence was broken by a loud cry.* 一聲大喊打破了寂靜。**2** in silence without speaking or making a noise 沉默地; 靜靜地: *She received the bad news in silence.* 她默不作聲地承受了那個壞消息。| *We walked downstairs in silence.* 我們默默地走下樓去。**3** failure or refusal to mention something 緘默, 沉默: *I can't understand the government's silence on European issues.* 我無法理解政府對歐洲問題所保持的沉默。

silence² *v* **silenced silencing** [T] to make someone stop making a noise or expressing their opinions 使〔某人〕安靜; 使停止發表意見: *The enemy's guns were silenced by repeated bombings.* 敵人的砲火因遭到輪番轟炸而沉寂了。| *He silenced us with a menacing look.* 他用威脅的目光示意我們別作聲。

si·lenc·er /ˈsaɪlənsə; ˈsaɪlənsəʳ/ *n* an apparatus on a gun or on a car EXHAUST PIPE to reduce noise 〔槍或汽車排氣管的〕消音器, 減聲器

★si·lent /ˈsaɪlənt; ˈsaɪlənt/ *adj* **1** not saying anything 不作聲的, 沉默的: *He looked thoughtful and was silent for a moment.* 他看來是在思考, 因此沉默了片刻。| *a silent film* 無聲電影 | *She was silent on her plans for the company.* 她閉口不談她為公司所作的計劃。**2** without any noise 安靜的, 寂靜無聲

的: *the silent hours of the night* 夜晚的寂静時分 **3** not pronounced (of a letter in a word) 不發音的〔指單詞中的某個字母〕: *The "k" in "know" is silent.* 在"know"這個單詞中，"k"是不發音的。–**silently** *adv*

sil·hou·ette[1] /ˌsɪluˈɛt; ˌsɪlu'et/ *n* a shadow-like solid shape against a light background 〔淺色背景上的〕黑色輪廓像，側面影像，剪影: *His silhouette appeared on the curtain.* 他的側影映在窗簾上。

silhouette[2] *v* be silhouetted to appear as a silhouette 使現出輪廓[黑色影像]: *The hills were silhouetted* **against** *a wonderful pink sunset.* 絢麗的淡紅色落日餘暉襯映出小山的輪廓。

sil·i·con /ˈsɪlɪkən; 'sɪlɪkən/ *n* [U] a non-metallic substance that is found in clay, sand, and stone 硅

silicon chip /ˌ··· '·/ *n* a small ELECTRONIC part used in a computer 〔用於電腦或其他電子機械中的〕硅片

silk /sɪlk; sɪlk/ *n* [U] fine smooth thread which is made into cloth 絲; 絲綢: *a black silk dress* 黑色的絲綢連衫裙

silk·en /ˈsɪlkən; 'sɪlkən/ *adj lit* soft, smooth, and shiny 〔文〕柔軟光潔的: *silken hair* 柔軟光潔的頭髮

silk·worm /ˈsɪlkˌwɜm; 'sɪlkwɜːm/ *n* an insect which produces a substance used to make silk 蠶

silk·y /ˈsɪlkɪ; 'sɪlki/ *adj* **silkier, silkiest** soft, smooth, or shiny 絲一樣的，柔軟光潔的，有光澤的人: *the cat's silky fur* 貓的柔軟光滑的皮毛 –**silkiness** *n* [U]

sill /sɪl; sɪl/ *n* the shelf at the base of a window, either inside or outside a building 窗台，檻

sil·ly /ˈsɪlɪ; 'sɪli/ *adj* **sillier, silliest** foolish or not sensible 傻的，愚蠢的; 缺乏理智的: *Don't be silly!* 別那麼傻! | *It was pretty silly of you to forget your keys.* 你忘了帶鑰匙，真是糊塗。

si·lo /ˈsaɪlo; 'saɪləʊ/ *n* **1** a tall tower on a farm for storing SILAGE 〔貯藏青飼料的〕青貯塔 **2** an underground base from which a NUCLEAR weapon may be fired 導彈地下發射井

silt[1] /sɪlt; sɪlt/ *n* [U] loose sand or mud carried along in a river 〔水流夾帶的〕泥沙; 淤泥

silt[2] *v* **silt up** *phr v* [I;T **silt** sthg ↔ **up**] to fill up or become filled with silt (使)淤塞

sil·ver[1] /ˈsɪlvə; 'sɪlvə(r)/ *n* [U] **1** a soft precious metal, greyish-white in colour, that can be brightly polished, and is used in jewellery and for making coins 銀 **2** coins made from this metal, or having that colour 銀幣: *Could you give me £1 in silver, please?* 請你給我一枚一英鎊的銀幣，好嗎? **3** knives, forks, spoons, or dishes for the table, made from this metal 銀餐具: *The silver sparkled on the banquet table.* 銀餐具在宴會桌上閃閃發亮。 **4** a silver medal 銀獎章 [獎牌]

sil·ver[2] *adj* **1** made of silver 銀製的: *silver earrings* 銀耳環 **2** silver medal a piece of silver that you win when you come second in a race or competition 〔比賽中贏得第二名的〕銀牌 **3** greyish-white or silver in colour 銀白色的: *a silver-haired old man* 銀髮老人

silver birch /ˌ·· '·/ *n* a tree with a greyish-white trunk 白樺(樹)，紙皮樺

silver ju·bi·lee /ˌ·· '···/ *n* the 25th ANNIVERSARY of an important event 二十五周年紀念，銀禧紀念

sil·ver·smith /ˈsɪlvəˌsmɪθ; 'sɪlvəsmɪθ/ *n* a person who makes things out of silver 銀(器)匠

silver wed·ding /ˌ·· '··/ (also 又作 **silver wedding anniversary** /ˌ·· '···,···/) *n* the 25th ANNIVERSARY of a wedding 銀婚〔結婚二十五周年紀念〕

sil·ver·y /ˈsɪlvərɪ; 'sɪlvəri/ *adj* **1** like silver in shine and colour 銀一樣的，有銀色光澤的 **2** *lit* having a pleasant musical sound 〔文〕〔聲音〕銀鈴般悦耳的; 清脆的: *silvery bells* 清脆悦耳的鐘聲

★★**sim·i·lar** /ˈsɪmələ; 'sɪmələ(r)/ *adj* like or of the same kind 相似的，類似的: *bread, cake, and other similar foods* 麵包、糕餅以及諸如此類的食品 | *We appear to have similar problems.* 我們好像有類似的問題。

sim·i·lar·i·ty /ˌsɪməˈlærɪti; ˌsɪmɪ'lærɪti/ *n* **similarities** [C;U] the quality of being alike 相似性，類似性: *Despite the age difference, there are many similarities between the two brothers.* 這兄弟倆儘管年齡不同，但有許多相似之處。 | *There's a certain similarity with the earlier version.* 這與以前的版本有某種相似之處。

sim·i·lar·ly /ˈsɪmələli; 'sɪmələli/ *adv* in a similar way; you can use this word when the point you are making is like the one before 相似地〔用於正在表述的要點與前者相似〕: *Art students will be charged extra for materials. Similarly, catering students will have to pay for their ingredients.* 藝術系學生所用的材料要另外收費。同樣地飲食服務系的學生也需要付錢買(烹調)原料。

sim·i·le /ˈsɪməlɪ; 'sɪmɪli/ *n* an expression in which someone or something is described as being similar to someone or something else 明喻: *"As white as snow" is a simile.* "像雪一樣潔白"是明喻。

sim·mer /ˈsɪmə; 'sɪmə(r)/ *v* [I;T] to cook food gently in liquid at just below boiling point 用文火煮，煨，燉: *Let the soup simmer.* 讓湯放在文火上慢慢煮。 | *Simmer the beans for two hours.* 把豆子煨上兩個小時。 –see 見 COOK[1] (USAGE 用法) –**simmer** *n* [sing]: *Bring the potatoes to a simmer.* 用文火煮馬鈴薯。

simmer down *phr v* [I] *infml* to become calmer after being angry 〔非正式〕冷靜下來; 息怒: *I was so furious that I went for a*

S

walk to simmer down. 我火冒三丈, 所以出去走走冷靜一下。

sim·per /'sɪmpə; 'sɪmpɚ/ *v* [I] to smile in a silly way 傻笑 —**simper** *n*

⭐ **sim·ple** /'sɪmpl; 'sɪmpəl/ *adj* **simpler, simplest 1** plain, and not decorated or fancy 簡單的, 簡易的: *The meal was simple but well-prepared.* 飯菜雖然簡單, 但做得不錯。**2** easy to understand or do 簡明易懂的: *There's quite a simple explanation.* 解釋十分簡單易明。| *It's a simple job, nothing complicated to worry about.* 這份工作簡單易做, 沒有甚麼複雜的事情要操心。**3** consisting of only one thing or part 結構單一的: *A knife is one of the simplest of tools.* 刀是最簡單不過的一種工具。| *Bacteria are simple forms of life.* 細菌是生物的原始形態。**4** without anything added or mixed (of something non-physical) 單純的, 純粹的 〔指非物質的東西〕: *She did it for the simple reason that she had no choice.* 她幹那事純粹是因為別無選擇。**5** (also 又作 **simpleminded**) foolish or weak-minded 頭腦簡單的; 愚蠢的: *I'm afraid old Jack is a bit simple.* 我恐怕老傑克頭腦有點簡單了。

sim·ple·ton /'sɪmpltən; 'sɪmpəltən/ *n old fash* a weak-minded trusting person 〔老式〕傻瓜; 容易受騙的人

sim·plic·i·ty /sɪm'plɪsɪtɪ; sɪm'plɪsɪti/ *n* [U] the quality of being simple 簡單, 簡易, 單純, 簡明: *He believes everything you tell him, with childlike simplicity.* 他相信你對他說的一切, 頭腦像孩子一樣單純。| *The main advantage of the new scheme is its simplicity.* 新方案的主要優點是簡明扼要。

sim·pli·fy /'sɪmpləˌfaɪ; 'sɪmplɪˌfaɪ/ *v* **simplified, simplifying** [T] to make something easier to understand or do 使簡明, 使簡易: *Try to simplify your explanation for the children.* 你要設法解釋得簡單些, 好讓孩子們明白。—**simplified** *adj* —**simplification** /ˌsɪmpləfə'keʃən; ˌsɪmplɪfɪ'keʃən/ *n* [U]

⭐ **sim·ply** /'sɪmplɪ; 'sɪmpli/ *adv* **1** in a simple way 簡單地, 簡易地, 簡樸地: *On her small income they live very simply.* 他們靠着她微薄的收入過着十分簡樸的生活。**2** just or only 僅僅, 只不過: *I'd like to help. It's simply a question of money.* 我樂意幫忙, 那只不過是錢的問題。**3** really 真正地; 簡直: *It was simply wonderful.* 那真是好極了。| *I simply couldn't believe him.* 我簡直無法相信他。

sim·u·late /'sɪmjʊˌlet; 'sɪmjʊˌleɪt/ *v* **simulated, simulating** [T] *fml* to give the effect or appearance of 〔正式〕冒充; 模擬: *The wood is carved to simulate rock.* 木頭被雕刻以模仿岩石。| *Reality can now be simulated on screen.* 如今現實生活可以在屏幕上模擬出來。—**simulation** /ˌsɪmjə'leʃən; ˌsɪmjʊ'leɪʃən/ *n* [C;U]: *computer simulations* 計算機的模擬(研究)

sim·u·lat·ed /'sɪmjəˌletɪd; 'sɪmjʊˌleɪtɪd/ *adj* made to look or feel like the real thing 仿造的: *a simulated fur coat* 仿裘皮大衣

sim·ul·ta·ne·ous /ˌsaɪml'tenɪəs; ˌsɪməl'teɪniəs/ *adj* happening at the same time 同時發生的: *There was a flash of lightning and a simultaneous crash of thunder.* 一道閃電發出, 同時響起了雷聲。—**simultaneously** *adv*

sin¹ /sɪn; sɪn/ *n* [C;U] an offence against God or a religious law 罪孽, 罪惡, 過失: *guilty of the sin of pride* 驕傲罪 | *You must ask God for forgiveness for your sins.* 你必須請求上帝寬恕你的罪過。

sin² *v* **-nn-** [I] to do something wicked 違反戒律; 犯罪: *You have sinned* **against** *God.* 你已經得罪了上帝。

⭐ **since** /sɪns; sɪns/ *adv, prep, conj* **1** *adv, prep, conj* starting at a time in the past and continuing until the present 從那以後, 自從…以來: *It's a long time since our last holiday.* 自從我們上次度假以來, 已經過了很長時間了。| *I've lived here since 1982.* 我從1982年起就住在這兒了。| *I've worked abroad since leaving university.* 我自大學畢業後一直在國外工作。| *We've been friends ever since we left school.* 我們自從畢業後一直是朋友。**2** *conj* as a particular fact is true 既然; 因為: *Since you can't answer my question, I'll have to ask someone else.* 既然你不能回答我的問題, 我只好問別人了。

sin·cere /sɪn'sɪr; sɪn'sɪɚ/ *adj* real, true, or honest 真誠的, 由衷的: *a sincere apology* 真誠的道歉 | *I don't think she was completely sincere in what she said.* 我認為她所說的話並不完全是出自衷心。

sin·cere·ly /sɪn'sɪrlɪ; sɪn'sɪəli/ *adv* **1** in a sincere way 真誠地, 由衷地: *a sincerely held belief* 真誠奉行的信仰 **2 Yours sincerely** the usual way of ending a letter that begins "Dear Mr…", "Dear Ms…", etc. 謹啟, 謹上 〔常用於"親愛的××先生", "親愛的××女士"開頭的信的末尾〕—compare 比較 FAITHFULLY(3)

sin·cer·i·ty /sɪn'sɛrətɪ; sɪn'sɛr,ti/ *n* [U] the quality of being sincere 真誠, 誠實, 誠意

si·ne·cure /'saɪnɪˌkjʊr; 'saɪnɪˌkjʊɚ/ *n* a well-paid job with few duties (a word used to express disapproval) 工作清閒而報酬優厚的職位, 閒職〔含貶義〕

sin·ew /'sɪnju; 'sɪnjuː/ *n* [C;U] a strong cord in your body which connects a muscle to a bone 肌腱

sin·ew·y /'sɪnjəwɪ; 'sɪnjuːi/ *adj* thin, with strong muscles 肌肉發達的, 強壯的

sin·ful /'sɪnfəl; 'sɪnfəl/ *adj* wicked or seriously wrong 罪惡的, 罪孽深重的; 極為錯誤的 —**sinfully** *adv* —**sinfulness** *n* [U]

⭐ **sing** /sɪŋ; sɪŋ/ *v* **sang** /sæŋ; sæŋ/, **sung** /sʌŋ; sʌŋ/ **1** [I;T] to make musical sounds with your voice 唱, 歌唱: *I can hear the birds singing.* 我能聽見鳥兒在歌唱。| *The children were singing Christmas carols.* 孩子們在唱聖誕頌歌。| *Would you like me to sing* *you a song?* 你想要我給你唱首歌嗎? **2 sing someone's praises** to praise someone highly 歌頌某人 **–singer** *n: an opera singer* 歌劇演員 | *She's a good singer.* 她是位出色的歌唱家。

sing. an abbreviation for 〖縮〗= SINGULAR

singe /sɪndʒ; sɪndʒ/ *v* **singed, singeing** [T] to burn slightly on the surface or edge 燒焦...的表面〔邊沿〕: *I'm afraid the iron was too hot — I've singed your shirt.* 我怕是熨斗太燙了——我把你的襯衣燙焦了。**–singe** *n*

sing·ing /ˈsɪŋɪŋ; ˈsɪŋɪŋ/ *n* [U] the art or sound of singing 唱歌, 演唱; 歌聲: *I'm taking singing lessons.* 我在上唱歌課。| *He could hear the singing down in the valley.* 他可以聽到山谷下面傳來的歌聲。

★★ **sin·gle**¹ /ˈsɪŋgl; ˈsɪŋgəl/ *adj* **1** [only before a noun 只用於名詞前] only one 唯一的: *A single tree gave shade from the sun.* 唯一的一棵樹能遮住陽光, 提供了陰涼處。| *Not a single one of my friends offered to help me.* 我的朋友中沒有一個肯主動幫助我。**2** [only before a noun 只用於名詞前] separate 各自的, 單獨的: *There's no need to write down every single word I say.* 沒有必要記下我說的每一個字。| *You do that every single time.* 你每一次都那樣做。**3** having only one part 單一的, 單個的: *For strong sewing use double, not single, thread.* 為了縫得牢固些, 用雙線, 而不要用單線。| *Inflation is now down to single figures.* 通貨膨脹現已降至單位數了。**4** unmarried 獨身的, 未婚的: *I intend to stay single for a while yet.* 我還是想繼續過一陣單身的日子。**5 a single bed, a single room** a bed or room for only one person 單人牀; 單人房間 **6 a single ticket** *BrE* a ticket for a trip from one place to another but not for the return journey〖英式〗單程票

single² *n* **1** *BrE* a ticket for a one-way journey〖英式〗單程票: *Two singles to Borchester, please.* 請給我兩張去波切斯特的單程票。**2** a small record with only one song on each side〔每面只錄一首歌曲的〕曲唱片 **3 singles** a game of tennis, BADMINTON, or SQUASH between two players〔網球、羽毛球等的〕單打比賽: *I prefer to play doubles; singles is too exhausting.* 我喜歡打雙打, 單打比賽太令人筋疲力竭了。

single³ *v* **single, singling**
  single sbdy/sthg ↔ **out** *phr v* [T] to choose one person or thing from a group for special treatment 把〔個別的人或物〕挑選出來: *He was singled out for special praise.* 挑選他來作特別表揚。

single file /ˌ·· ˈ·/ *adv* **in single file** in a line one behind another 排成單行; 成一路縱隊: *We walked in single file down the corridor.* 我們排成單行在通道上走。

single-hand·ed /ˌ·· ˈ··◄/ *adv* on your own, without help from other people 獨力地, 無人幫助的: *He rebuilt his house single-*

handed. 他獨力重建了自己的房子。**–single-handed** *adj: a single-handed voyage across the Atlantic* 橫渡大西洋的單人航行

single-mind·ed /ˌ·· ˈ··◄/ *adj* having one clear purpose 一心一意的, 專一的: *He's quite single-minded about his work.* 他對自己的工作專心致志。**–single-mindedly** *adv* **– single-mindedness** *n* [U]: *I admire his single-mindedness.* 我欽佩他的全神貫注。

sin·gly /ˈsɪŋglɪ; ˈsɪŋgli/ *adv* separately 單個地, 各自地: *Some guests came singly, others in groups.* 有些客人個別前來, 有的則成羣結隊而來。

sing-song¹ /ˈsɪŋˌsɒŋ; ˈsɪŋsɒŋ/ *adj* repeatedly rising and falling (used of the voice) 有起伏節奏的〔指嗓音〕: *She has a lovely sing-song intonation.* 她的語調帶有動聽的節奏。

sing-song² *n* an occasion when a group of people sing songs together for pleasure〔自娛的〕唱歌聚會: *We had a bit of a sing-song after the game.* 比賽之後, 我們在一起唱了一會兒歌。

sin·gu·lar /ˈsɪŋgjələ; ˈsɪŋgjəlɚ/ *n* a word in the form which represents only one〔詞的〕單數形式: *The singular of "mice" is "mouse".* "mice"的單數形式是"mouse"。

sin·gu·lar·ly /ˈsɪŋgjələlɪ; ˈsɪŋgjələli/ *adv fml* particularly〖正式〗特別地, 格外地: *a singularly unsuccessful attempt to gain publicity* 為博得名聲的極不成功的嘗試

sin·is·ter /ˈsɪnɪstə; ˈsɪnɪstɚ/ *adj* seeming to be frightening and evil 不吉祥的, 凶兆的; 險惡的: *a sinister look on his face* 他臉上險惡的神情 | *a rather sinister figure dressed in black* 一個身穿黑衣服的相當兇險的人物

★ **sink**¹ /sɪŋk; sɪŋk/ *v* **sank** /sæŋk; sæŋk/, **sunk** /sʌŋk; sʌŋk/ **1** [I;T] to go down or make something go down below a surface, especially below the surface of water or to the bottom of the water (使)下沉, 沉沒: *The ship slowly sank* **beneath** *the waves.* 船慢慢沉到海浪下面。| *The sun sank below the horizon.* 太陽落到了地平線下。| *They sank the ship with bombs.* 他們用炸彈擊沉了那艘船。**2** [I] to go down in number, strength, or value〔數量、力量、價值等〕下降, 減弱, 減少: *The population of the village has sunk from 100 to 27.* 村裡的人口已從一百人減少至二十七人。| *His voice sank to a whisper.* 他的聲音低得幾乎聽不見。| *The value of money sank as inflation increased.* 貨幣因通貨膨脹的上升而貶值。**3** [I] to fall or sit down, especially because of tiredness or lack of strength〔尤因疲倦或無力而〕倒下, 坐下: *He fainted and suddenly sank to the ground.* 他突然昏倒在地上。| *She sank gracefully into the armchair.* 她動作優美地在扶手椅上坐下。**4 my heart sank, my spirits sank** = I lost confidence or hope 我的心情變得沉重; 我的情緒變得低落: *My heart sank when I realized how much work I still had to do.* 當我意識到我還有許多工作要做時, 我

的心情就變得沉重了。**5** [T] to put money into 投入〔資金〕: *I've sunk all my money into buying this house.* 我已經把所有的錢都投下來買這所房子。**6 sink a well** to dig a well 挖井 –**sinkable** *adj*

sink in *phr v* [I] **1** to become fully understood 被充分理解: *The news was a terrible shock to her. I don't think it's really sunk in yet.* 這消息對她是個沉重的打擊。我認為她還未真正理解。**2** to enter a solid through the surface 滲入, 透入: *Quick! If the ink sinks in it'll be harder to remove it.* 快! 如果墨水滲入, 那就很難洗掉。

sink into *phr v* [T] **1** [**sink** sthg **into** sthg] to put, force, or go into 放入; 插入; 進入: *The dog sank its teeth into the meat.* 那條狗使勁地咬住那塊肉。**2** [**sink into** sthg] to pass gradually into a less active or worse state 陷入〔消極或糟糕的狀態〕: *I sank back into a dreamless sleep.* 我沉沉地睡着了, 一夜無夢。*He sank further into debt.* 他的債務越來越重。

sink² *n* **1** a large basin in a kitchen, used especially for washing pans, dishes, etc. 〔廚房中的〕洗滌槽 **2** the usual American word for 〖美式〗= WASHBASIN

sin·ner /'sɪnə; 'sɪnə'/ *n biblical* a person who has disobeyed God 〖聖經〗罪人, 犯罪者

sin·u·ous /'sɪnjuəs; 'sɪnjuəs/ *adj lit* 〖文〗**1** twisting like a snake 〔動作〕柔美的: *a sinuous belly dance* 婀娜多姿的肚皮舞 **2** having many bends or curves 彎曲的, 蜿蜒的: *a sinuous mountain track* 蜿蜒的山路

si·nuses /'saɪnəsɪz; 'saɪnəsịz/ *n* [pl] the air passages just behind your nose 鼻竇 –**sinus** *adj*: *a sinus infection* 鼻竇炎

sip¹ /sɪp; sɪp/ *v* -**pp-** [T] to drink, taking only a little at a time 小口地喝, 啜飲, 呷: *She sipped politely at her drink.* 她有禮貌地呷一口飲料。

sip² *n* a very small amount of a drink 一小口的量, 一啜之量: *She took another sip of her tea.* 她又喝了一小口茶。

si·phon /'saɪfən; 'saɪfən/ *v* (also 又作 **syphon**) [T] **1** to draw out a liquid from one place through a tube by sucking it up the tube and letting it out in another place 用虹吸管吸出〔液體〕: *Siphon the liquid into a clean container.* 用虹吸管把液體抽到一個乾淨的容器裡。*Someone's siphoned off all our petrol!* 有人用虹吸管吸光了我們的汽油! **2** to cause something to change from one use or direction to another 使〔某物〕改變用途[方向]: *We need a new road to siphon off some of the traffic from the town centre.* 我們需要修建一條新的公路來疏導市中心的交通。–**siphon** *n*

*sir /sɜ; sɔ'; *strong 強讀* sɜ; sɜ:'/ *n* **1** a respectful way of addressing a man 先生; 閣下〔對男子的尊稱〕: *Thank you, sir.* 謝謝你, 先生。*"Excuse me, sir." "Yes?" said his*

teacher absently. "對不起, 先生。""甚麼事?" 他的老師心不在焉地說。**2 Sir** a title used before the name of a KNIGHT or BARONET 爵士〔用作爵士或男爵名字前的稱號〕: *We've got Sir Harold Wilson on the programme today.* 我們邀請了哈羅德·威爾遜爵士來參加今天的節目。*Good morning, Sir Harold.* 早安, 哈羅德爵士。**3 Dear Sir** a formal way of beginning a letter to a man 敬啟者〔用於寫給男子的正式信件的開頭〕: *Dear Sir, I would like to apply for the position advertised in "The Times" this week.* 敬啟者: 我想申請在本週《泰晤時報》上刊登的這個職位。

sire¹ /saɪr; saɪə'/ *n* **1** the father of an animal, especially of a dog or a horse 雄性種獸〔尤指種馬或種狗〕**2 Sire** a way of addressing a king (no longer used in modern English) 〔國王〕陛下〔現代英語中已不再使用〕

sire² *v* [T] **sired, siring** to be the father of a dog or a horse 〔狗或馬的〕配種, 繁殖: *This horse has sired several race winners.* 這匹馬已經繁殖了好幾匹比賽優勝馬。

si·ren /'saɪrən; 'saɪərən/ *n* **1** an apparatus on ships, police cars, and other vehicles used to make a loud warning sound 汽笛; 警報器: *the wail of the sirens in the distance* 遠處警報器的呼嘯聲 **2** *lit* a beautiful woman who is dangerous to men 〖文〗妖豔而危險的女人

sir·loin /'sɜlɔɪn; 'sɜːlɔɪn/ *n* (also 又作 **sirloin steak** /ˌ·· '·/) [C;U] a piece of good quality BEEF cut from the lower back 上等的牛腰肉, 西冷牛扒

sis·sy /'sɪsɪ; 'sɪsɪ/ *n* **sissies** (also 又作 **cissy**) *infml* a weak cowardly boy 〖非正式〗膽小的男孩; 娘娘腔的小子

★★sis·ter¹ /'sɪstə; 'sɪstə'/ *n* **1** a female relative with the same parents 姐; 妹; 姊妹: *Joan and Mary are sisters.* 瓊和瑪麗是姐妹。*Joan is Mary's sister.* 瓊是瑪麗的姐姐[妹妹]。–see picture on page 503 見 503 頁彩圖 **2 a** a nurse in charge of a hospital WARD 護士長: *the night sister* 夜班護士長 **b** the title for this job 護士長〔用作稱呼〕: *Sister Brown* 布朗護士長 *Can you help me, Sister?* 你能幫我一下嗎, 護士長? **3 a** a NUN or a woman member of a religious group 修女; 女教友: *a Christian sister* 基督教修女 **b** the title for this 修女; 女教友〔用作稱呼〕: *Sister Mary Grace* 瑪麗·格雷斯修女 *the Sisters of Mercy* 慈善修女會

sister² *adj* closely related or in the same group 關係密切的; 同一團體的: *a sister ship* 姊妹船 *We have a sister school in Tokyo.* 我們在東京有個姊妹學校。

sis·ter·hood /'sɪstəhʊd; 'sɪstəhʊd/ *n* **1** [U] a strong sisterly friendship between women 姐妹關係; 姐妹情誼 **2** [C + sing/pl verb] a society of women leading a religious life 婦女宗教團體

sister-in-law /'···,·/ *n* **sisters-in-law 1** the sister of your husband or wife 夫或妻的姐妹; 姑子; 姨子 –see picture on page 503 見503頁彩圖 **2** the wife of your brother 兄或弟的妻子; 嫂子; 弟媳

sis·ter·ly /'sɪstɚlɪ; 'sɪstəlɪ/ *adj* typical of a loving sister 姊妹般的, 親如姊妹的

☆☆sit /sɪt; sɪt/ *v* **sat** /sæt; sæt/, **sat, sitting 1** [I] to rest in a position in which your weight is on your bottom, usually on a chair 坐: *She was sitting on a large sofa.* 她坐在大沙發上。| *He was sitting at his desk working.* 他坐在書桌前工作。| *a group of people sitting in the corner of the room* 坐在房間角落的一羣人 –see picture on page 992 見992頁彩圖 **2** [I] to lower yourself so that you are sitting on something 坐下, 就座: *She walked in and sat on the floor.* 她走進房間就地坐下。**3** [T] to make someone sit somewhere 使〔某人〕坐在〔某處〕: *She sat the child on her knee.* 她讓孩子坐在她的膝蓋上。| *He sat me in a corner and told me all about his problems.* 他讓我坐在角落裡, 然後把他的問題都告訴了我。**4** [I] (of an object) to be in a particular place or position 〔物體〕坐落在; 位於: *The building sits in 10 acres of grounds.* 大樓坐落於十英畝的場地中。| *The village sits on the top of a small hill.* 村莊坐落在小山頂上。| *The books just sit on the shelves without ever being read.* 書本只是擱在架子上, 從未有人看過。**5** [I] (of an official group) to have a meeting 〔官方團體〕開會: *The court sits every morning.* 法庭每天上午開會。**6** [T] to take an examination 參加〔考試〕: *He decided to sit the exam despite the fact that he hadn't done much work.* 儘管他不太用功, 但還是決定參加考試。| *I'm sitting my finals next month.* 我下個月參加期終考試。**7 sit tight** to stay in the same place and do nothing 留在原處, (穩坐)不動: *If your car breaks down, sit tight and wait for the police.* 如果你的車壞了, 就停在原地等警察來。

■ **USAGE** 用法: **1** Sit can be followed by various prepositions depending on the noun which comes next ☆ **sit** 後面可接不同的介詞, 取決於介詞後面的名詞: *You sit on a sofa/a settee/a stool/a bench/the floor/a wall.* 你坐在沙發〔長沙發、椅子、長櫈、地板、牆〕上。| *You sit in an armchair/a seat in a theatre/a seat in a car/the back or front row.* 你坐在扶手椅〔劇院的座位、汽車的座位、後排或前排〕裡。| *You sit at a table/a desk.* 你坐在桌子〔書桌〕前。It can also depend on the meaning you want to give. Compare 介詞的選用還可取決於所要表達的意思, 請比較: *He sat at his desk working.* 他坐在書桌前工作。(= at a chair in front of his desk 坐在他書桌前的椅子

上) | *He sat on his desk swinging his legs.* 他坐在書桌上擺動着雙腿。(= on top of his desk 坐在他的書桌上面) **2** With the word **chair** you can use either on or in. If the chair is hard and has no arms use on; if it is soft or has arms use in. ☆ 在**chair** 這個詞前既可以用 on 又可以用 in。在沒有扶手的硬座椅子前用 on; 在有扶手的軟座椅子前用 in。

sit about/around *phr v* [I] to spend time just resting and doing nothing 閒坐着, 無所事事: *We spent the days sitting around talking.* 我們天天坐着閒聊。

sit back *phr v* [I] to not take an active part in something 在一旁閒着〔不積極參加〕: *Just sit back and enjoy yourselves.* 坐下來好好享受一下吧。

sit down *phr v* **1** [I] to move to a sitting position after you have been standing 坐下: *Come in and sit down.* 請進來坐下。**2 sit yourself down** to move to a sitting position after you have been standing 就座: *He walked in and sat himself down by the fire.* 他走進屋子, 並在爐火旁就坐。**3** [T **sit** sbdy **down**] to make someone sit somewhere 讓〔某人〕坐下: *She sat me down and gave me a cup of tea.* 她讓我坐下, 並給我倒了一杯茶。

sit in on sthg *phr v* [T] to be present during a meeting but not take part in it 列席〔會議〕; 旁聽: *I asked if I could sit in on the board meeting* 我問我是否可以列席董事會會議。

sit on sthg *phr v* [T] **1** to be a member of an official group that has regular meetings 擔任...的成員: *He sits on several committees.* 他擔任好幾個委員會的委員。**2** *infml* to keep something but not take action on it 〖非正式〗拖延〔某事〕不處理: *He's been sitting on my letter for weeks!* 他已拖了好幾個星期不給我回信!

sit sthg ↔ **out** *phr v* [I] to remain sitting or do nothing until something has finished 坐着而不參加〔直到結束〕

sit through sthg *phr v* [I] to remain sitting until something has finished 坐到結束: *We had to sit through three hours of speeches.* 我們只好坐着聽完三小時的演講。

sit up *phr v* **1** [I] to rise to a sitting position after you have been lying down 坐起來: *He heard a noise and sat up in bed.* 他聽見響聲便在牀上坐了起來。**2** [T **sit** sbdy **up**] to help someone into a sitting position after they have been lying down 幫助〔某人〕坐起來: *We managed to sit him up and give him a drink.* 我們設法讓他坐起來, 並給他喝了一杯飲料。**3** [I] to stay up and not go to bed 不睡, 熬夜: *We sat up waiting for her to come home.* 我們熬夜等她回家。

sit·com /'sɪt,kɑm; 'sɪtkɒm/ *n infml* (also 又

作 **situation comedy**) a form of humorous show on radio or television, in which the same characters appear in different situations each week〔非正式〕情景喜劇〔一種同一批角色每週在電視或廣播中表演不同情景的喜劇〕

★**site¹** /saɪt; saɪt/ *n* a place where something happens or is positioned 地點, 現場, 遺址, 地方: *th site of the Battle of Waterloo* 滑鐵盧戰場遺址 | *a caravan site* 旅行拖車停車場 | *the site for a new business centre* 新商務中心的選址

site² *v* **sited, siting** [T] to build or position in a particular place 使坐落於〔某處〕: *We refused to have a factory sited so near to the school.* 我們不接受工廠坐落在離學校那麼近的地方。

sit-in /'··/ *n* a public act of dissatisfaction and anger by a group of people who go into a place and stay sitting there for a long time 靜坐示威抗議: *There's a sit-in at the local hospital because of government cut-backs.* 由於政府削減經費, 當地醫院裡有人在靜坐抗議。

sit-ting¹ /'sɪtɪŋ; 'sɪtɪŋ/ *n* **1** a period of time spent seated 一次坐着…的時間: *I read the book in a single sitting.* 我坐着一口氣看完了這本書。 **2** one of the times for serving a meal 一次就餐時間: *The first sitting for school dinners is at 12.30.* 學校正餐的第一次就餐時間為十二點半。 **3** a meeting of an official body such as a law court or government〔法庭〕的開庭;〔政府機構的〕開會: *It was the first sitting of the House since the Prime Minister's return.* 那是首相回來後的第一次議院會議。

sitting² *adj* [only before a noun 只用於名詞前] **1** currently having a seat on an official body 現任的, 在任期內的: *The sitting member will be hard to defeat in the election.* 要在選舉中擊敗現任議員是很難的。 **2** **a sitting tenant** *BrE* a person currently renting a particular flat or house as their home〔英式〕〔公寓或房屋的〕現租戶, 現住的房客: *We can't sell the flat unless the sitting tenant leaves.* 我們要等到現租戶搬走才能出售公寓。

sitting room /'·· ·/ *n BrE* a room in a home where people sit and rest〔英式〕起居室; 會客室

sit-u-at-ed /'sɪtʃuˌetɪd; 'sɪtʃueɪtˌd/ *adj* [never before a noun 不能用於名詞前] in a particular place 位於〔某處〕的, 坐落在〔某處〕的: *His office was very conveniently situated.* 他的辦事處所處的位置十分方便。

■ **USAGE** 用法: **Situated** is a rather formal word. If you are speaking, or writing, in ordinary informal English it often sounds more natural NOT to use it. ☆ **Situated** 是個相當正式的詞。當你以普通的非正式英語說話或書寫時,

不使用該詞常顯得更為自然。Compare 比較: *The Royal Hotel is conveniently situated in the centre of the town* (in an advertisement) 皇家飯店位於便捷的市中心(用於廣告) | *The emergency exits are situated at the rear of the plane* (in an official notice) 緊急出口位於飛機的後部(用於官方的告示) and 以及: *My house is in the centre of the town* (in a personal letter) 我家在市中心(用於私人信件) | *The toilets are at the back of the plane* (in a conversation) 廁所在飛機的後部(用於會話)。

★**sit-u-a-tion** /ˌsɪtʃuˈeʃən; ˌsɪtʃuˈeɪʃən/ *n* **1** a position or condition at the moment 形勢, 處境, 狀況, 局面: *the economic situation* 經濟形勢 | *Well, that's the situation as I see it.* 好了, 那就是我所看到的局勢。 **2** the place and surroundings of a building or town〔建築物或城市的〕地點, 位置: *The cottage is in a beautiful situation.* 村舍坐落在一個風景美麗的地方。 **3** *old fash* a job〔舊式〕工作; 職業: *the "Situations Vacant" advertisements in the newspaper* 報紙上的"招聘"廣告

situation com-e-dy /ˌ···· '···/ see 見 SITCOM

six /sɪks; sɪks/ *det, n , pron* **1** the number 6〔數字〕六 **2** **at sixes and sevens** *infml* confused and not organized〔非正式〕亂七八糟

six-pence /'sɪkspəns; 'sɪkspəns/ *n* an old silver coin in Britain〔英國舊時的〕六便士(硬幣)

six-teen /sɪksˈtin; ˌsɪksˈtiːn◂/ *det, n, pron* the number 16〔數字〕十六 −**sixteenth** *det, n, pron, adv*

sixth /sɪksθ; sɪksθ/ *det, pron, adv, n* **1** 6th 第六(個) **2** one of six equal parts 六分之一

sixth form /'·· ·/ *n* [sing/pl verb] the top class with the oldest pupils, in a British school〔英國中學的〕六年級, 中六: *She got her GCSEs last year and is now in the sixth form.* 她去年獲得了普通中等教育證書, 現在已上六年級了。

sixth sense /ˌ· '·/ *n* [sing] an ability to see or know things by INSTINCT 第六感, 直覺

six-ty /'sɪkstɪ; 'sɪksti/ *det, n, pron* **sixties 1** the number 60〔數字〕六十 **2** **the Sixties, the sixties** the years 1960-1969 二十世紀六十年代〔1960年至1969年〕 **3** **in his sixties, in their sixties** aged between 60 and 69 在〔某人的〕六十歲到六十九歲之間 −**sixtieth** *det, n, pron, adv*

siz-a-ble /'saɪzəbl; 'saɪzəbəl/ *adj* (also 又作 **sizeable**) rather large 相當大的: *He has a sizeable income.* 他的收入相當可觀。

★**size¹** /saɪz; saɪz/ *n* **1** [C;U] how big or small something is 大小, 尺寸, 規模: *What's the size of your back garden?* 你家的後花園有多大? | *Their army is about* *half the size of ours.* 他們部隊的規模大約只有我們的一半左右。 | *hailstones the size of golf balls* 像高爾夫球那麼大的雹塊 **2** [U] the fact of being big 大, 巨大: *We're the only company of any size outside London.* 我們是倫敦市郊唯一的大公司。 | *The sheer size of the building amazed me.* 建築物之龐大使我大為驚訝。 **3** [C] a standard measure for clothes, shoes, and other things you buy 〔服裝、鞋子等的〕號, 碼: *There's a special offer on the giant-size pack.* 特大號的包裝以特別優惠價出售。 | *What shoe size do you take?* 你穿幾號鞋? | *I need a larger size.* 我要大一點的尺碼。 **4** -sized (also 又作 -size) of a certain size or number …型號的: *medium-sized* 中型的 | *a good-sized crowd* 一大羣人

size[2] *v* **sized, sizing**

size sbdy/sthg ↔ **up** *phr v* [T] to form an opinion about 估計, 判斷: *He sized up the new boy critically.* 他以挑剔的目光來判斷那新來的男孩。

size·a·ble /ˈsaɪzəbl̩; ˈsaɪzəbəl/ *adj* see 見 SIZABLE

siz·zle /ˈsɪzl̩; ˈsɪzəl/ *v* **sizzled, sizzling** [I] to make a sound like food cooking in hot fat 〔油煎時〕發出嘶嘶聲: *There were sausages sizzling in the pan.* 香腸在鍋裡嘶嘶作響。

skate[1] /sket; skeɪt/ *n* **1** (also 又作 **ice skate**) a special boot for moving on ice, with a metal blade beneath it 溜冰鞋 **2** (also 又作 **roller skate**) a special boot with four wheels beneath it, for moving quickly on a smooth surface 旱冰鞋 **3** get/put your skates on *infml* to hurry 〔非正式〕趕緊(做) **4** a large flat sea fish 鰩〔一種體大扁平的海魚〕

skate[2] *v* **skated, skating** [I] to move about on ice skates 滑冰, 溜冰: *We skated around the edge of the lake.* 我們在湖的邊緣處滑冰。 –**skater** *n*

skate over sthg (also 又作 **skate round** sthg) *phr v* [T] to avoid talking about something in detail 輕描淡寫地帶過〔某事〕: *He always skates round the subject.* 他對這個題目總是避而不談。

skate·board /ˈsket,bɔːd; ˈskeɪtbɔːd/ *n* a short board with two wheels at each end for standing on and riding, for fun 滑板

skein /sken; skeɪn/ *n* a loosely wound length of thread or wool 〔紗或線的〕一束, 一絞: *a couple of skeins of pink tapestry wool* 幾絞粉紅色的壁毯毛線

skel·e·ton[1] /ˈskelətn; ˈskelətən/ *n* **1** the framework of bones in a human or animal body 〔人或動物的〕骨骼 **2** something forming a framework 骨架; 框架: *the steel skeleton of a tall building* 高大建築物的鋼筋骨架 **3** have a skeleton in the cupboard to keep a secret from the past which makes you feel anxious and uncomfortable 有不可外揚的家醜; 隱情

skeleton[2] *adj* [only before a noun 只用於名詞前] just enough to keep going 最基本的; 骨幹的: *British Rail managed to keep a skeleton service running during the strike.* 英國鐵路設法在罷工期間維持最基本的服務。

skep·tic /ˈskeptɪk; ˈskeptɪk/ *n* see 見 SCEPTIC

sketch[1] /sketʃ; sketʃ/ *n* **1** a quick rough drawing 素描, 草圖, 速寫: *He made a quick sketch of the house.* 他作了一幅房子的素描。 | *a charcoal sketch* 炭筆素描 **2** a short description in words 略述, 概述: *a brief biographical sketch of the author* 作者的生平概述 **3** a short humorous scene on stage or television that is part of a larger show 詼諧短劇: *I enjoyed the show. My favourite sketch was the one about the dead parrot.* 我很愛看那次演出, 最喜歡的是有關那頭死鸚鵡的那幕滑稽戲。

sketch[2] *v* [I;T] to draw quickly or roughly 繪素描; 草擬

sketch sthg ↔ **in** *phr v* [T] to give the details of something 詳細說明〔某事物〕: *Can you sketch in the events that led to their decision?* 你能否詳細地說明一下事情, 以便他們作出決定?

sketch sthg ↔ **out** *phr v* [T] to give a short description of something 簡要描述, 草擬〔某事〕: *The Minister sketched out his plans for the next two years.* 部長簡要描述了後兩年計劃的構想。

sketch·y /ˈsketʃɪ; ˈsketʃi/ *adj* **sketchier, sketchiest** not thorough or complete 不徹底的, 不完全的, 粗略的: *a sketchy knowledge of history* 零碎的歷史知識 –**sketchily** *adv* –**sketchiness** *n* [U]

skew·er[1] /skjuə; ˈskjuːər/ *n* a long wooden or metal pin for holding pieces of food together while cooking 〔烤肉用的〕串肉籤, 烤肉叉

skewer[2] *v* [T] to push a skewer through food 〔用串肉籤〕串起〔食物〕

ski[1] /ski; skiː/ *n* one of a pair of long narrow pieces of wood, plastic, or metal which you fasten to your boots when travelling on snow 滑雪板; 滑橇 –see 見 PAIR (USAGE 用法)

ski[2] *v* **skied, skiing** [I] to go on skis 滑雪: *We're going skiing at Christmas.* 我們要在聖誕節去滑雪。 | *I learnt to ski in the Alps.* 我是在阿爾卑斯山脈學滑雪的。 –**skier** *n* –see picture on page 957 見 957 頁彩圖

skid /skɪd; skɪd/ *v* **-dd-** [I] to slip sideways out of control (used of a vehicle) 打滑, 滑向一側〔指車輛〕: *Be careful not to skid on that icy surface.* 當心別在那冰面上打滑。 | *The car skidded off the road.* 汽車滑到了路邊。 –**skid** *n*: *The car went into a skid.* 汽車向前滑行。

skil·ful /ˈskɪlfəl; ˈskɪlfəl/ *adj* (**skillful** AmE 〔美式〕) **1** having skill 有技巧的, 熟練的: *a very skilful driver* 非常熟練的司機 **2** showing

skill 顯示技巧的: *her skilful handling of the situation* 她處理局勢的熟練技巧 **–skilfully** *adv*

skill /skɪl; skɪl/ *n* **1** [U] an ability to do something very well 技巧; 熟練: *a pilot of great skill* 技藝嫻熟的飛行員 | *He handled the negotiations with both skill and tact.* 他應付談判問題既老練又有策略。 **2** [C] the ability to do a particular thing 〔專門〕技術, 技能, 技藝: *Reading and writing are related skills.* 閱讀和寫作是有關聯的技能。 | *basic computer skills* 電腦基本技術 | *management skills* 管理技巧

skilled /skɪld; skɪld/ *adj* **1** having skill 有技能的, 熟練的: *skilled workers* 技術熟練的工人 **2** needing skill 需要技能的: *a highly skilled job* 一項需要高度技能的工作

skill·et /ˈskɪlɪt; ˈskɪlət/ an American word for 〖美式〗= FRYING PAN

skill·ful /ˈskɪlfəl; ˈskɪlfəl/ *adj* see 見 SKILFUL

skim /skɪm; skɪm/ *v* **-mm- 1** [T] to remove something from the surface of a liquid 從液體表面上撇去〔某物〕: *skim the cream off the milk* 撇去牛奶上的奶脂 **2** [I;T] to read quickly to get the main ideas 瀏覽, 略讀: *Just skim the first chapter.* 只要把第一章瀏覽一下就行了。 | *I skimmed* **through** *a few of the replies.* 我粗略地看了幾封回信。 **3** [I;T + adv/prep] to move or to make something move swiftly over a surface (使)掠過, (使)擦過: *The children were skimming stones across the pond.* 孩子們用石頭在池溏面上打水漂。 | *A seagull skimmed the waves.* 一隻海鷗掠過了浪尖。

skimp /skɪmp; skɪmp/ *v* [I;T] to use less money, time, or material than is really needed 少花, 省用〔錢、時間或材料〕: *The old lady had been skimping* **on** *food to save money.* 那位老婦為了省錢而吃省吃儉用。 | *Don't skimp the essays or you'll fail the exam.* 寫短文別偷工減料, 否則你考試會不及格。

skimp·y /ˈskɪmpɪ; ˈskɪmpi/ *adj* **skimpier, skimpiest** too small in size or quantity 〔大小〕不夠的;〔數量〕不足的: *a skimpy meal* 份量很少的一頓飯 | *shivering with cold in a skimpy little dress* 穿着過小的衣服直凍得發抖

★**skin¹** /skɪn; skɪn/ *n* **1** [U] the natural outer covering of your body 皮, 皮膚: *a skin disease* 皮膚病 | *Babies have soft skin.* 嬰兒有柔嫩的皮膚。 **2** [C;U] the part of an animal body used for leather, fur, etc. 獸皮, 毛皮: *a sheepskin coat* 羊皮大衣 | *The skins are sent to the tannery.* 獸皮送到製革廠去(加工)。 **3** [C] **a** a natural outer covering of some fruits and vegetables 〔水果、蔬菜的〕外皮: *banana skins* 香蕉皮 | *onion skins* 洋葱皮 **b** the outer covering of a SAUSAGE 〔香腸的〕腸衣 **4** [C;U] the solid surface that forms over some liquids when they get cool 〔某些液體冷卻時形成的〕表皮, 薄層: *Paint forms a skin if you don't seal the tin properly.* 如果你

不及時封口, 桶裡的油漆就會形成一層皮。 | *the skin on the custard* 蛋奶沙司表層結的皮 **5** **by the skin of your teeth** *infml* with very little time or space remaining 〖非正式〗差點就沒…: *We caught the train by the skin of our teeth.* 我們差一點就趕不上火車。 **6** **no skin off my nose** *infml* not something that will annoy or harm me 〖非正式〗與我毫不相關: *If she won't accept my help that's her problem — it's no skin off my nose.* 如果她不願接受我的幫助, 那便是她的問題, 這與我毫不相干。 **7** **skin and bone/bones** *infml* very thin 〖非正式〗極瘦, 瘦得皮包骨: *The cattle were all skin and bone after the drought.* 乾旱之後, 牛都瘦得皮包骨頭。 **8** **-skinned** having a certain type or colour of skin 具有〔某種〕皮膚[膚色]的: *pale-skinned* 皮膚蒼白的 | *smooth-skinned* 皮膚光滑的

skin² *v* **-nn-** [T] to remove the skin from 剝去…的皮; 擦破…的皮: *She skinned the rabbit for me.* 她為我剝去兔子的皮。 | *I skinned my elbow.* 我擦破了肘部的皮。

skin-deep /ˌ·ˈ·◂/ *adj* only on the surface 表面的, 膚淺的: *Their differences of opinion are only skin-deep.* 他們的意見分歧只是表面的。

skin·flint /ˈskɪn.flɪnt; ˈskɪn.flɪnt/ *n* a person who is very mean 吝嗇鬼; 小氣的人

skin·ny /ˈskɪnɪ; ˈskɪni/ *adj* **skinnier, skinniest** too thin (a word used to express disapproval) 皮包骨的〔含貶義〕 –see THIN¹ (USAGE 用法)

skint /skɪnt; skɪnt/ *adj* [never before a noun 不能用於名詞前] *BrE slang* completely without money 〖英式, 俚〗不文一名的, 身無分文的

skin-tight /ˌ·ˈ·◂/ *adj* fitting extremely tightly (used of clothes) 緊身的〔指衣服〕

skip¹ /skɪp; skɪp/ *v* **-pp- 1** [I] to move in a light dancing way, jumping from one foot to the other 蹦跳; 蹦跳着走: *The little boy skipped along at his mother's side.* 小男孩在媽媽旁邊蹦蹦跳跳地往前走。 **2** [I] to jump up and down over a rope as a game or as exercise 跳(繩): *Boxers skip to keep fit.* 拳擊運動員用跳繩來保持身體健壯。 –see picture on page 992 見 992 頁彩圖 **3** [I] to move in no fixed order 無次序地轉換, 隨意移動: *The speaker kept skipping from one subject to another.* 演講者不斷地從一個話題跳到另一個話題。 **4** [T] to leave out on purpose 〔故意〕跳過, 略去: *You can skip Chaper 3; it's not relevant.* 你可以跳過第三章, 這一章無關緊要。 | *Never skip a meal.* 千萬不要少吃一頓飯。

skip² *n* **1** a light quick jumping movement 蹦跳 **2** a large metal container used for holding old bricks or other heavy things to be taken away 〔用於裝舊磚瓦或其他重物的〕大鐵桶, 廢料桶

skip·per /ˈskɪpə; ˈskɪpəʳ/ *n infml* a captain of a ship or sports team 〖非正式〗船長;〔運動隊的〕隊長

skir·mish¹ /ˈskɜːmɪʃ; ˈskɜːmɪʃ/ *n* **1** a short

rough fight 小規模戰鬥; 小衝突 **2** a short sharp argument 小爭論, 小爭執

skirmish² v [I] to fight in a skirmish 進行小規模戰鬥, 發生小衝突

skirt¹ /skɜ:t; skɝt/ n a piece of clothing worn by women and girls which fits around the waist and hangs down 〔女用的〕裙子: *a knee-length skirt* 長及膝部的裙子 | *a straight skirt* 直筒裙 –see picture on page 210 見 210 頁彩圖

skirt² v [T] **1** (also 又作 **skirt round/around**) to go around the edge of 繞…的邊緣走; 繞過: *The bus skirted the roadworks.* 公共汽車繞過了道路施工工地。 **2** to be around the edge of an area 位於〔某地區〕的邊緣[外圍]: *The motorway skirts the city centre.* 高速公路位於市中心的外圍。 **3** (also 又作 **skirt round/around**) to avoid dealing with a difficult question or problem 繞開〔問題〕, 避開: *Don't keep skirting round the main issue — get to the point!* 別對主要問題避而不談, 要抓住要點!

skirting board /'··· / n [C;U] *BrE* a board fixed along the base of a wall in a room 〔英式〕踢腳板, 壁腳板

skit·tle /'skɪtl; 'skɪtl/ n **1** [C] a bottle-shaped object used in the game of skittles 〔撞柱戲的〕瓶狀木柱 **2 skittles** [U] the game in which a player tries to knock down these objects with a ball 撞柱遊戲

skive /skaɪv; skaɪv/ v **skived, skiving** [I] *BrE infml* to avoid work, often by staying away from a place 〔英式, 非正式〕逃避工作, 偷懶: *She's always skiving off.* 她老是逃避工作。 | *Were you skiving on Monday, or were you really at the dentist?* 你在星期一是故意偷懶, 還是真的去看牙醫了? –**skiver** n

skulk /skʌlk; skʌlk/ v [I] to stay quietly in a place because you do not want to be noticed 躲藏, 隱伏: *robbers skulking behind the bushes, ready to jump out* 潛伏在灌木叢後隨時準備衝出的強盜

skull /skʌl; skʌl/ n **1** the bone of your head which encloses your brain 頭顱骨, 頭骨 **2 the skull and crossbones** a sign for death or danger, used on PIRATE flags in former times 骷髏旗〔舊時海盜用作旗幟上的標誌, 象徵死亡或危險〕

skull·cap /'skʌl,kæp; 'skʌlkæp/ n a simple close-fitting cap for the top of the head 無檐便帽

skunk /skʌŋk; skʌŋk/ n a small black and white North American animal which gives off a very bad smell when attacked 臭鼬〔產於北美, 受到攻擊時會放出惡臭〕

★**sky** /skaɪ; skaɪ/ n **skies 1** [C;U] the space above the Earth where you can see the clouds, sun, moon, and stars 天(空): *There's a bit of blue sky between the clouds.* 烏雲之間露出了一小片藍天。 | *The rocket shot up into the sky.* 火箭射上了天空。 **2 the sky's the limit** *infml* there is no upper limit 〔非

正式〕毫無限制

sky-high /,·'··/ adv infml to a very high level 〔非正式〕極高地; 天一般高地: *Prices have gone sky-high.* 物價飛漲。 –**sky-high** adj: *sky-high mortgage rates* 極高的抵押借款率

sky·light /'skaɪ,laɪt; 'skaɪlaɪt/ n a window in a roof 天窗

sky·line /'skaɪ,laɪn; 'skaɪlaɪn/ n a shape or view made by scenery, especially tall buildings, against the background of the sky 〔以天空為背景映出的〕輪廓(線)〔尤指高大的建築物〕

sky·scrap·er /'skaɪ,skreɪpə; 'skaɪ,skreɪpɚ/ n a very tall modern city building 摩天大樓

slab /slæb; slæb/ n a thick flat piece of something 厚板, 厚片: *The patio was made of stone slabs.* 平台是由石板鋪成的。 | *a thick slab of fruit cake* 一塊厚厚的水果蛋糕

slack¹ /slæk; slæk/ adj **1** not stretched tight 不緊的, 鬆弛的: *a slack rope* 鬆垂的繩子 **2** not firm 鬆懈的; 不嚴的: *slack discipline* 鬆懈的紀律 **3** careless or without firmness 馬虎的; 疏忽的: *You're getting very slack in your work!* 你的工作越來越馬虎了! | *Discipline in the classroom is too slack.* 課堂紀律太鬆弛。 **4** not busy 不忙的, 清閒的: *Business is slack just now.* 目前生意很清淡。 –**slackly** adv –**slackness** n [U]

slack² v [I] not to work well or quickly enough 疏忽; 怠慢; 鬆懈: *Stop slacking!* 不要偷懶了! –**slacker** n

slack³ n **1 the slack** the part of a rope or wire that hangs loose 〔繩子、鐵絲的〕鬆垂部分 **2 slacks** [pl] *old fash* trousers for wearing informally 〔老式〕便褲, 寬鬆的長褲

slack·en /'slækən; 'slækən/ v [I;T] **1** to make or become slower or less active (使)放慢, (使)減緩: *We slackened our pace as we reached town.* 我們快到市區時便放慢了腳步。 **2** to make or become looser (使)放鬆, (使)鬆弛: *She was too frightened to slacken her grip on my arm.* 她太害怕了, 緊抓著我的胳膊不放。

slacken off phr v [I] to become slower or less active 變緩慢, 變蕭條: *Business has slackened off recently.* 最近生意清淡起來。

slag heap /'slæg ,hip; 'slæg ,hiːp/ n a hill made of waste material from mines and factories 礦渣堆

slain /slen; sleɪn/ the past participle of SLAY ☆ SLAY 的過去分詞

slake /slek; sleɪk/ v **slaked, slaking** *lit* **slake your thirst** to satisfy your thirst by having a drink 〔文〕解渴

slam¹ /slæm; slæm/ v **-mm- 1** [I;T] to shut loudly and with great force 使勁關閉, 砰地關上: *Please don't slam the door.* 請別使勁地關門。 | *The door slammed shut behind him.* 門在他身後砰地一聲關上了。 **2** [T + adv/prep] to throw down quickly and violently 使勁扔; 猛推; 砰地放下: *He* slammed the papers down on the desk. 他把文件往書桌上使勁一扔。 | I slammed the receiver down. 我砰地一聲放下電話聽筒。 **3** [T] (used in newspapers) to attack with words 〔用於報紙〕猛烈抨擊: "What's today's headline?" "Teachers slam education cuts." "今天報紙的標題是甚麼？" "教師猛烈抨擊教育開支的削減。"

slam² n the act or the noise of a door closing violently 關門〔砰時〕的一聲: He shut the door with a slam. 他砰的一聲關上了門。

slan·der¹ /ˈslɑːndə; ˈslɑːndɚ/ n [C;U] a spoken report about someone that is intentionally false and harms them 誹謗, 詆毀, 中傷

slander² v [T] to say false things about someone in order to harm them 對〔某人〕誹謗, 詆毀 **—slanderous** adj

slang /slæŋ; slæŋ/ n [U] very informal words and expressions often used only by a particular social group 俚語: Slang often goes in and out of fashion quickly. 俚語常常是流行得快, 過時得也快。 | American slang 美國俚語 | "I'm skint" is a slang expression meaning "I haven't got any money". "I'm skint"是俚語表達法, 意思為"我身無分文"。 **—slangy** adj

slant¹ /slɑːnt; slɑːnt/ v [I;T] to put or to be at an angle (使)傾斜: The sitting room floor slants towards the window. 起居室的地板朝窗子方向傾斜。 **2 be slanted** to be reported in a way which favours one particular opinion 有傾向性地報道: His account was obviously slanted towards the government's view. 他的報道顯然是傾向於政府的觀點。

slant² n **1** [sing] a slanting direction or position 傾斜；斜面: a steep upward slant 向上的陡峭斜面 | That shelf is on a slant. 那個架子是斜的。 | a line drawn at a slant 畫的一條斜線 **2** [C] a particular way of looking at or expressing news or facts 〔對新聞或事實的〕看法, 觀點: an interesting new slant on the presidential elections 對總統選舉的新鮮有趣的看法

slap¹ /slæp; slæp/ n **1** a quick blow with the flat part of your hand 一拳；一拍；一巴掌: She gave him a slap on the cheek. 她打了他一記耳光。 **2 a slap in the face for someone** an action that seems to be intended to harm or upset someone 侮辱某人

slap² v **-pp-** [T] **1** to hit quickly with the flat part of your hand 〔用手掌〕擊；拍；摑: She slapped his wrist playfully. 她頑皮地拍拍他的手腕。 | He slapped his friend on the back. 他拍拍他朋友的背。 **2** to place roughly or carelessly 〔隨意地〕塗抹；〔隨便地〕扔置: He was slapping paint onto the wall. 他往牆上隨意塗漆。 | She slapped the meal down on the table. 她往桌上亂扔飯菜。

slap³ adv infml (also 又作 **slap-bang**) directly, suddenly and forcefully 〔非正式〕直接地；突然；猛烈: The car ran slap into a tree.

汽車猛地撞在一棵樹上。 | I ran slap-bang into my boss. 我一頭撞上了我的老闆。 | I dropped a whole tin of paint slap-bang in the middle of the carpet. 我把一整桶油漆倒到地毯的正中央。

slap·dash /ˈslæp,dæʃ; ˈslæpdæʃ/ adj hasty and careless 匆促的, 草率的: a slapdash piece of work 一件草率的工作

slap·stick /ˈslæp,stɪk; ˈslæp,stɪk/ n [U] humorous acting with fast violent action and simple jokes 〔動作激烈的〕打鬧劇: slapstick comedy 打鬧喜劇

slap-up /ˈ· ·/ adj a slap-up meal BrE infml a large and excellent meal 〔英, 非正式〕一頓佳餚美餐

slash¹ /slæʃ; slæʃ/ v **1** [T] to make a long deep cut 砍；砍出〔深長口子〕: We slashed a path through the bushes. 我們在灌木叢中砍出一條路來。 | The cinema seats have been slashed. 電影院的座位被割破了。 **2 slash at something** to make wild long sweeping strokes in the direction of something 亂擊某物 **3** to reduce an amount of time or money greatly 大幅度削減〔價格或時間〕: It's the last day of the sale and prices have really been slashed. 這是大減價的最後一天, 價格確實已經大幅度削減。

slash² n **1** a long sweeping cut 長切口；砍痕 **2** a DIAGONAL line that separates letters, words, or numbers 〔分隔字母、單詞或數字的〕斜線符號: "2/4" can be read as "two slash four". "2/4"可讀成"2 斜線 4"。

slat /slæt; slæt/ n a thin flat piece of wood or plastic 〔木頭或塑料的〕細長板條: It's difficult to clean the slats of Venetian blinds. 百葉窗的板條很難擦乾淨。 **—slatted** adj

slate¹ /sleɪt; sleɪt/ n **1** [U] a dark grey rock that is easily split into flat thin pieces 板岩, 板石 **2** [C] a thin flat piece of this rock used for covering a roof 石板瓦

slate² v **slated, slating** [T] **1** to cover a roof with slates 用石板瓦蓋〔屋頂〕 **2** to judge a book, play, or film severely 嚴厲批評〔書、戲劇或電影〕: The critics really slated his latest production. 評論家非常嚴厲地批評了他的最新作品。

slaugh·ter¹ /ˈslɔːtə; ˈslɔːtɚ/ n [U] **1** the killing of many people or animals in a cruel way 屠殺, 殺戮 **—see** 見 KILL¹ (USAGE 用法) **2** the killing of animals for meat 屠宰

slaughter² v [T] **1** to kill many people cruelly or wrongly 屠殺, 殘殺: They slaughtered thousands of innocent people. 他們屠殺了成千上萬無辜的人。 **2** to kill an animal, especially for food 屠宰〔動物〕

slaugh·ter·house /ˈslɔːtə,haʊs; ˈslɔːtəhaʊs/ n (also 又作 **abattoir**) a building where farm animals are killed for meat 屠宰場

slave¹ /sleɪv; sleɪv/ n **1** a person who is owned by another person and must work for them 奴隸 **2 a slave to something, a slave of something** a person completely under the control of a particular thing 完全受某事物支配的人: *He's a slave to drink.* 他是個酒鬼。 | *We're all slaves of habit.* 我們都是受習慣支配的人。

slave² *v* **slaved, slaving** [I] to work hard 刻苦工作, 苦幹: *She slaved for him all her life.* 她拼命為他工作了一輩子。 | *I've been slaving away all weekend in the garden.* 我整個週末都一直在花園裡辛辛苦苦地工作。

slave driv·er /'·‚ '··ʳ/ *n infml* a person who makes other people work very hard〔非正式〕逼使人拼命幹活的人

slav·er /'sleɪvəʳ; 'slævəʳ/ *v* [I] to let SALIVA come out of your mouth 垂涎, 淌口水

sla·ve·ry /'sleɪvərɪ; 'sleɪvəri/ *n* [U] **1** the system of having slaves 奴隸制度: *When was slavery abolished?* 奴隸制是何時廢除的? **2** the condition of being a slave 奴隸的身分: *sold into slavery* 被販賣為奴隸

slav·ish /'sleɪvɪʃ; 'sleɪvɪʃ/ *adj* **1** copied very closely or exactly from something else 一味模仿的, 盲從的: *a slavish translation* 逐字硬譯的翻譯 **2** showing complete obedience to the idea of serving someone or dependence on them 奴性的; 卑屈的: *slavish devotion to duty* 奴隸般地忠於職守 **–slavishly** *adv*

slay /sle; sleɪ/ *v* **slew** /slu; slu:/, **slain** /slen; sleɪn/ [T] *lit* to kill violently〔文〕殘殺

slea·zy /'slizɪ; 'sli:zi/ *adj* **sleazier, sleaziest** cheap, dirty, and not respectable 低劣的; 骯髒的; 不體面的: *a sleazy hotel in a poor part of town* 貧困城區的低格廉價的旅館 **– sleaziness** *n* [U]

sledge¹ /sledʒ; sledʒ/ *n* (also 又作 **sled** /slɛd; sled/) a vehicle for sliding along on snow or ice, used in play and sport or for carrying heavy loads 雪車, 雪橇〔用於娛樂、運動或運載重物〕

sledge² *v* **sledged, sledging** [I] *BrE* to go down slopes on a sledge for fun〔英式〕乘雪橇〔滑下斜坡〕

sledge·ham·mer /'sledʒ‚hæmər; 'sledʒ‚hæmʳ/ *n* a large heavy hammer 大錘

sleek /slik; sli:k/ *adj* **1** smooth and shining (used of hair) 光滑的, 油亮的〔指毛髮〕 **2** looking rich or expensive and stylish 豪華的; 時髦的: *a sleek sports car* 時髦的跑車

sleep¹ /slip; sli:p/ *n* **1** [U] the natural state of rest in which your eyes are shut and your mind and body are unconscious for a period of time 睡眠, 睡覺: *I haven't had enough sleep lately.* 我最近睡眠不足。 **2** [sing] a period of sleeping 睡眠時間: *I need a short sleep after lunch.* 我吃完午飯需要小睡片刻。 **3 go to sleep, get to sleep** to begin to sleep 入睡, 睡着: *I couldn't get to sleep last night.* 我昨晚睡不着覺。 **4 go to sleep** (of a part of your body) to lose all sense of feeling〔肢體〕麻木: *I've been sitting here so long that my foot's gone to sleep.* 我一直坐在這裡, 太久連腳都麻木了。 **5 put to sleep:**

euph to kill a sick or hurt animal painlessly〔委婉〕無痛處死, 人道毀滅〔有病痛的動物〕: *The dog had been so badly injured that the vet had to put him to sleep.* 那條狗傷勢嚴重, 所以獸醫只好把牠人道毀滅。

sleep² *v* **slept** /slɛpt; slept/ **1** [I] to rest in sleep 睡, 睡覺: *I didn't sleep very well last night.* 我昨晚睡得不太好。 | *I usually sleep for at least seven hours a night.* 我通常每晚至少睡七小時。 | *We like to sleep late on Sundays.* 我們喜歡在星期日睡懶覺。 **2** [T] to provide sleeping-places for a number of people 為〔某數量的人〕提供住宿: *The sofa folds down to sleep two.* 這沙發可以翻下睡兩個人。 **3 sleep like a log** *infml* to sleep deeply without moving〔非正式〕睡得很熟 **4 sleep on something** to spend a night considering a problem 徹夜考慮〔問題〕: *I'm not sure. Can I sleep on it and let you know my decision in the morning?* 我不肯定。可否讓我今晚考慮一下, 明天早上把決定告訴你? **5 sleep rough** to sleep outdoors because you have nowhere to go 在戶外睡覺, 露宿

sleep in *phr v* [I] to sleep late in the morning〔早上〕睡過頭; 睡懶覺: *We slept in after the party.* 聚會之後, 我們都睡過了頭。

sleep sthg ↔ **off** *phr v* [T] to get rid of the effects of drink, food, or drugs by sleeping 用睡眠消除...: *He drank too much wine and went home early to sleep it off.* 他喝酒過量, 便早早地回家把醉意睡掉。

sleep together *phr v* [I] (used of two people who are not married to each other) to have sex〔未婚男女〕性交

sleep with sbdy *phr v* [T] to have sex with someone 與〔某人〕發生性關係

sleep·er /'slipər; 'sli:pəʳ/ *n* **1** a person sleeping 睡眠者, 睡覺的人: *He's a heavy sleeper, very difficult to wake.* 他是個睡得很熟的人, 不易叫醒。 **2** a train with beds for sleeping through a journey at night〔火車的〕臥鋪 **3** a heavy piece of wood used to support a railway track〔鐵路的〕枕木, 軌枕

sleeping bag /'·· ·/ *n* a large warm bag for sleeping in, especially when camping 睡袋〔尤指露營用的〕

sleeping pill /'·· ·/ *n* (also 又作 **sleeping tablet** /'·· ‚··/) a PILL containing a medicine which helps a person to sleep 安眠藥〔片〕

sleep·less /'sliplɪs; 'sli:pləs/ *adj* **1 a sleepless night** a night during which you do not sleep 不眠之夜: *We spent a sleepless night waiting for news.* 我們為等消息度過了一個不眠之夜。 **2** not able to sleep 睡不着的, 失眠的: *He lay sleepless on his bed.* 他躺在牀上睡不着覺。 **–sleeplessness** *n* [U]

sleep·walk /'slip‚wɔk; 'sli:p‚wɔ:k/ *v* [I] to walk around while you are asleep 夢遊: *Do you know that you've been sleepwalking?* 你知道自己一直在夢遊嗎? **–sleepwalker** *n*

sleep·y /'slipɪ; 'sli:pi/ *adj* **sleepier, sleepiest**

S

1 tired and ready for sleep 困倦的, 昏昏欲睡的 **2** without much activity or noise 不熱鬧的; 冷清的: *a sleepy country town* 冷清的鄉村小鎮 –**sleepily** *adv* –**sleepiness** *n* [U]

sleet /sliːt; sliːt/ *n* [U] a mixture of rain and snow 雨夾雪, 凍雨

sleeve /sliːv; sliːv/ *n* **1** a part of a piece of clothing that covers your arm 衣服袖子: *a dress with long sleeves* 長袖連衣裙 –see picture on page 210 見 210 頁彩圖 **2** a stiff envelope in which a record is kept 唱片套 **3** **have something up your sleeve** to keep an idea or plan secret for use at the right time in the future 有錦囊妙計, 留有後手 **4** -**sleeved** having sleeves of a certain length or shape 有…袖子的: *a short-sleeved shirt* 短袖襯衫 –**sleeveless** *adj*

sleigh /sle; sleɪ/ *n* a vehicle which slides along over snow, pulled by a horse 〔馬拉的〕雪車, 雪橇

sleight of hand /ˌslaɪt əv ˈhænd; ˌslaɪt əv ˈhænd/ *n* [U] a quick skilful movement of your hands, which other people cannot see 巧妙敏捷的手法: *He made a coin disappear by sleight of hand.* 他以巧妙的變戲法使一枚硬幣不見了。

slen·der /ˈslɛndə; ˈslɛndər/ *adj* **1** attractively thin and graceful 苗條的, 纖細的: *a slender woman* 苗條的女子 –see 見 THIN[1] (USAGE用法) **2** small and hardly enough 微少的, 不足的: *You have only the slenderest chance of success.* 你只有很微的成功機會。 –**slenderness** *n* [U]

slept /slɛpt; slɛpt/ the past tense and past participle of SLEEP ☆ SLEEP 的過去式和過去分詞

sleuth /sluːθ; sluːθ/ *n old fash* a person whose job is to find out information about criminals 〔老式〕偵探

slew[1] /sluː; sluː/ *v* (**slue** *AmE* 〔美式〕) [I;T] to turn or swing violently or make something turn or swing violently (使)〔某物〕急轉; (使)旋轉: *He lost control of the car and it slewed round.* 他控制不住汽車, 它打起轉來。

slew[2] the past tense of SLAY ☆ SLAY 的過去式

slice[1] /slaɪs; slaɪs/ *n* **1** a thin flat piece cut from something 〔切下的〕薄片, 片: *a slice of bread* 一片麵包 | *Cut the cake into slices.* 把蛋糕切成幾片。 **2** a kitchen tool for lifting and serving pieces of food 〔分菜用的〕鏟子 **3** a shot in sports like GOLF and tennis, which makes the ball go to one side rather than straight ahead 〔高爾夫球和網球中的〕削球, 側旋球

slice[2] *v* **sliced, slicing** **1** [T] to cut into slices 把…切成薄片: *a sliced loaf* 切片麵包 | *She sliced up the meat.* 她把肉切成薄片。 **2** [I;T] to cut with something sharp 用刀切: *I sliced into my finger with a vegetable knife.* 我用切菜刀切傷了手指。 **3** [I;T] to hit a ball to one side in various sports 〔體育運動中〕削(球);

斜擊(球)

slick[1] /slɪk; slɪk/ *adj* **1** clever or attractive, but often not honest 圓滑的: *a slick salesman* 圓滑的推銷員 **2** spoken too easily to be right or true 花言巧語的: *slick excuses* 巧妙的藉口 –**slickly** *adv* –**slickness** *n* [U]

slick[2] *n* (also 又作 **oil slick**) a quantity of oil floating on the sea or a lake 〔海面或湖面的〕浮油

slick[3] *v*

slick sthg ↔ **down** *phr v* [T] to make your hair flat and shiny with water or oil 〔用水或油〕使〔頭髮〕光滑

slid /slɪd; slɪd/ the past tense and past participle of SLIDE ☆ SLIDE 的過去式和過去分詞

*****slide[1]** /slaɪd; slaɪd/ *v* **slid** /slɪd; slɪd/ **slid, sliding 1** [I;T] to go or make something go smoothly over a surface (使)滑行, (使)滑動: *He slid his glass across the table.* 他把玻璃杯滑到桌子那邊。 | *The children like sliding down the stairs.* 孩子們喜歡順着樓梯滑下。 **2** [I + adv/prep] to go silently and unnoticed 悄悄地走, 溜走: *She slid out of the room when no one was looking.* 她趁沒人看見的時候溜出了房間。 **3** **let something slide** *infml* to pay no attention to something, often because of laziness 〔非正式〕對〔某事物〕聽其自然

slide[2] *n* **1** a slipping movement over a surface 滑動, 打滑 **2** an apparatus for sliding down 滑梯: *a children's playground slide* 兒童遊樂場的滑梯 **3** a fall 滑落, 跌落: *How can we stop the slide in living standards?* 我們怎樣才能制止生活水準的下降? | *a landslide* 滑坡 | *a rock slide* 岩崩 **4** a piece of photographic film through which you shine light to show a picture 幻燈片: *They showed us the slides of their holiday.* 他們給我們放映了他們度假時拍的幻燈片。 | *a slide show* 放映幻燈片 **5** a small glass plate on which you put something that you want to examine under a microscope 〔顯微鏡的〕載物玻璃片 **6** a decorative fastener worn in your hair 〔裝飾用的〕髮夾

sliding scale /ˌ·· ˈ·/ *n* a system of pay or taxes calculated by rates which may vary according to changing conditions 〔工資或稅額按情況變化而調整的〕浮動折算制

*****slight[1]** /slaɪt; slaɪt/ *adj* **1** small in amount 少量的, 微小的: *There's a slight improvement in his condition.* 他的情況略有改善。 **2** thin and delicate 纖細的; 瘦小的: *a rather slight old lady* 一位相當纖弱的老婦 **3** **not in the slightest** not at all 一點也不, 根本不: *"Do you mind if I open the window?" "Not in the slightest: please do."* "你介意我打開窗戶嗎?" "一點也沒關係, 請便。"

slight[2] *v* [T] to treat someone without respect 怠慢〔某人〕 –**slightingly** *adv*

slight[3] *n* rude behaviour, not showing respect 冒犯; 輕視: *I'm afraid he took your re-*

mark as a slight **on** *his work.* 我怕他把你的話當作是對他工作的一種冒犯。

★**slight·ly** /'slaɪtlɪ; 'slaɪtli/ *adv* **1** a little bit 稍微，輕微地: *"Do you know her?" "Only slightly".* "你認識她嗎？" "只稍有了解。" | *He was slightly drunk.* 他喝得有點兒醉了。**2** in a slight way 瘦小地; 不結實地: *a small, slightly-built man* 一個身材瘦小的男子

slim¹ /slɪm; slɪm/ *adj* **slimmer, slimmest 1** attractively thin and well-shaped (used of people) 苗條的，修長的，纖細的〔指人〕: *She's pretty, with a lovely slim figure.* 她長得可愛俊俏，體形苗條動人。–see 見 THIN¹ (USAGE 用法)–see picture on page 469 見 469 頁彩圖 **2** slight or unlikely (used of a hope or probability) 微小的，渺茫的〔指希望或可能性〕: *Our chances of winning are slim.* 我們獲勝的希望很渺。**3** thinner than usual 較薄的: *a slim paperback book* 薄薄的平裝本

slim² *v* **-mm-** [I] to try to lose weight 盡力減輕體重，變苗條: *I don't want any cake: I'm slimming.* 我甚麼蛋糕都不吃，我在減肥。– **slimmer** *n* –**slimming** *n* [U]: *a slimming club* (減肥)健美俱樂部

slime /slaɪm; slaɪm/ *n* [U] a thick slippery liquid 黏液: *a snail's trail of slime* 蝸牛的黏液痕跡

slim·y /'slaɪmɪ; 'slaɪmi/ *adj* **slimier, slimiest 1** unpleasantly slippery 黏性的; 泥濘的 **2** *infml* friendly and pleasant in an insincere way 【非正式】虛偽的; 奸詐的: *He's such a slimy do-gooder.* 他是一個十分虛偽的慈善家。

sling¹ /slɪŋ; slɪŋ/ *v* **slung** /slʌŋ; slʌŋ/, **slung, slinging 1** [T] to throw something roughly 【非正式】扔，擲，拋〔某物〕: *Sling the empty boxes in the corner.* 把空盒子扔在角落裡。**2** [T + adv/prep] to put something in a position quickly and carelessly so that it hangs down〔隨手地〕放，搭〔某物〕: *He slung his coat over his shoulder.* 他把上衣搭在肩上。**3** [T; + adv/prep] to hang with a rope〔用繩子〕吊起，掛起: *The line of flags was slung up between two trees.* 一排旗幟掛在兩棵樹之間。

sling² *n* **1** a piece of cloth for supporting a damaged arm or hand〔支撐傷臂或斷手的〕懸帶，吊帶 **2** an apparatus of ropes or cloth for carrying things 吊索，吊具: *a babysling* 娃娃繫帶 **3** a length of string with a piece of leather in the middle, used in former times for throwing stones 彈弓;〔舊時的〕投石器

slink /slɪŋk; slɪŋk/ *v* **slunk** /slʌŋk; slʌŋk/, **slunk** [I] in a slow, quiet, and secretive way 悄悄地走，偷偷溜走: *The leopard slunk back into the darkness.* 豹偷偷溜回黑暗中。

★**slip¹** /slɪp; slɪp/ *v* **-pp- 1** [I] to slide a short distance out of place by accident, or to fall by sliding 滑倒; 滑落: *My foot slipped and I nearly fell.* 我的腳一滑，差點跌倒。| *The hammer slipped and hit my fingers.* 錘子滑落，砸在我的手指上。**2** [I] to get worse or

lower 變壞; 下降: *Standards are slipping in this hotel.* 這家旅館的水準在下降。| *Output has slipped by 15% this year.* 今年的產量下降了百分之十五。**3** [I+adv/prep] to move smoothly, secretly, or unnoticed 悄悄地走; 溜走: *She slipped into the room when no one was looking.* 她趁沒有人注意的時候溜進了房間。| *As the years slipped by, I thought less about her.* 隨著歲月的流逝，我把她漸漸淡忘了。**4** [T] to put or give smoothly, secretly, or unnoticed 偷偷地給，悄悄地塞給: *He slipped the waiter a five pound note to get a good table.* 他偷偷塞給侍者五英鎊，以便得到好的桌位。| *He slipped the papers quietly into his briefcase.* 他悄悄地把文件塞進公事包內。**5 let something slip** to say something without intending to 無意中說出某事，說漏嘴: *He carelessly let slip the date of the election to a reporter.* 他不小心向記者說出了選舉的日期。**6 slip your mind** to be forgotten or unnoticed 被忘記; 未被注意: *I'm sorry I forgot your birthday: it completely slipped my mind.* 對不起，我忘了你的生日: 我忘得一乾二淨。

slip into sthg *phr v* [T] to put a piece of clothing on 穿上〔衣服〕

slip sthg ↔ **off** *phr v* [T] to take off a piece of clothing 脫掉〔衣服〕

slip sthg ↔ **on** *phr v* [T] to put on a piece of clothing 穿上〔衣服〕: *I slipped my coat on and went out.* 我穿上衣服就出去了。

slip out of sthg *phr v* [T] to take off a piece of clothing 脫掉〔衣服〕

slip up *phr v* [I] to make a slight mistake 犯小錯，疏忽: *The secretary slipped up and forgot to post the letter.* 祕書粗心大意，忘了寄信。

slip² *n* **1** a small mistake 差錯，失誤: *"Oh no! That's not right; I've made a slip somewhere."* "噢不! 那是不對的，我在某處出了差錯。" | *a slip of the tongue* 口誤 **2** a small piece of paper 小紙條: *He scribbled his phone number on a slip of paper.* 他在紙條上草草寫下了他的電話號碼 **3** a woman's undergarment worn under a dress or skirt 女式長襯裙 **4 slip of a boy/girl** a small thin young person 瘦小的男孩〔女孩〕: *She's just a slip of a girl.* 她只是個瘦小的女孩。**5 give someone the slip** *infml* to escape from someone who is chasing you 【非正式】逃避追逐的人，甩掉某人

slipped disc /ˌ·'·/ *n* a painful displacement of one of the connecting parts between the bones of your back 椎間盤脫出

slip·per /'slɪpə; 'slɪpɚ/ *n* a loose soft shoe worn indoors〔室內穿的〕拖鞋，便鞋: *a comfortable old pair of slippers* 一雙舒適的舊拖鞋 –see 見 PAIR (USAGE 用法) –see picture on page 210 見 210 頁彩圖

slip·per·y /'slɪpərɪ; 'slɪpɚi/ *adj* **1** wet or smooth and difficult to hold or to stand on 滑的，滑溜的: *Drive carefully: the roads are*

wet and slippery. 開車小心點, 路上又濕又滑。
2 *infml* not to be trusted 〖非正式〗狡猾的;
不可靠的: *He looks a slippery character.* 他看
來是個品性狡猾的人。**3 be on a slippery**
slope to become worse and find it difficult
to stop 〔變壞而〕難以自拔: *Once you've given*
in to temptation you're on the slippery slope.
你一旦經不住誘惑, 以後就無法抵制得住。

slip road /' · ·/ *n BrE* a road for driving onto
or off a MOTORWAY 〖英式〗〔連接高速公路
的〕岔道, 支路

slip·shod /'ʃɪpˌʃɒd; 'slɪpʃɒd/ *adj* done in a
careless or untidy way 馬虎的, 草率的: *a*
slipshod piece of work 一件馬虎的工作

slip-up /' · ·/ *n* a slight mistake 差錯, 疏忽, 失
誤

slip·way /'ʃɪp,weɪ; 'slɪpweɪ/ *n* a track
sloping down into the water for moving
ships into or out of the water 船台; 下水滑
道

slit[1] /slɪt; slɪt/ *v* **slit, slit, slitting** [T] to make
a long narrow cut in something carefully
or intentionally 切開; 撕開: *She slit the en-*
velope open with a knife. 她用小刀裁開信
封。| *His throat had been slit.* 他的喉嚨已被
切開。

slit[2] *n* a long narrow cut or opening 狹長的
切口, 裂縫: *I could see a light through the slit*
under the door. 我可以看到從門下的縫隙透進
來的光。

slith·er /'slɪðə; 'slɪðəʳ/ *v* [I + adv/prep] **1** to
move in a slipping or twisting way like a
snake 蜿蜒地滑行 **2** to slide unsteadily
while trying to walk 搖晃不穩地滑動: *She*
slithered across the ice. 她搖搖晃晃地滑過冰
面。

sliv·er /'slɪvə; 'slɪvəʳ/ *n* a small thin sharp
piece cut or torn off something 裂片, 碎片:
a sliver of glass from the broken window 破
窗上的一塊玻璃碎片

slob /slɒb; slɒb/ *n infml* a lazy or carelessly-
dressed person 〖非正式〗懶散的人; 衣冠不整
的人

slob·ber /'slɒbə; 'slɒbəʳ/ *v* [I] to have SA-
LIVA running from your mouth, like a
baby 淌口水, 流涎

slog[1] /slɒg; slɒg/ *v* **-gg-** [I] *infml* to work
hard at something difficult or dull 〖非正式〗
拼命地幹苦活, 賣力苦幹: *I don't want to slog*
away for years in a factory. 我不想在工廠裡
苦幹幾年。

slog[2] *n* [sing] *BrE infml* tiring work which
requires a lot of effort 〖英式, 非正式〗艱苦
的工作: *It's a hard slog up to the top of the*
hill. 登上山頂的這段路很難走。

slo·gan /'sləʊgən; 'sloʊgən/ *n* a short easily-
remembered phrase with a political or advertising message 口號, 標語

sloop /sluːp; sluːp/ *n* a small sailing ship wih
one MAST 單桅小帆船

slop /slɒp; slɒp/ *v* **-pp- 1** [I] (used of a
liquid) to go over the side of a container

〔液體〕溢出, 濺出: *Some of the soup slopped*
over the edge of the bowl. 有些湯從碗邊溢了
出來。**2** [T] to cause a liquid to do this 使溢
出, 使濺出: *I've slopped some coffee on the*
floor. 我把一些咖啡濺到地板上了。

***slope**[1] /sləʊp; sloʊp/ *v* **sloped, sloping** [I] to
be at an angle 傾斜, 成斜坡: *a sloping roof*
傾斜的屋頂 | *The road slopes up slightly at*
this point. 路在這個地方微微向上傾斜。

slope off *phr v* [I] *BrE infml* to go away
quietly, often in order to avoid work 〖英式,
非正式〗〔常為逃避工作而〕溜走, 開小差

slope[2] *n* **1** a surface that slopes 斜面, 斜坡: *a*
ski slope 滑雪斜坡 | *a steep slope* 陡坡 **2 a**
slope of 30 degrees = the angle at which
something slopes is 30 degrees 三十度的坡
度

slop·py /'slɒpɪ; 'slɒpi/ *adj* **sloppier, slop-**
piest 1 loose and very informal (used of
clothes) 寬鬆的; 不整潔的〔指衣服〕: *He wore*
jeans and a sloppy old jumper. 他穿着牛仔褲
和寬鬆的舊套頭毛衣。**2** not careful or
thorough enough 草率的, 馬虎的: *a sloppy*
piece of writing 一篇寫得草率的文章 **3** foolish in showing feelings 庸俗地傷感的: *sloppy*
romantic love songs 庸俗傷感的浪漫愛情歌
曲 **–sloppily** *adv* **–sloppiness** *n* [U]

slops /slɒps; slɒps/ *n* [pl] **1** food waste for
feeding to animals 〔餵動物的〕食物殘渣 **2**
liquid waste from food or drinks 〔食物或飲
料的〕剩汁, 泔水

slosh /slɒʃ; slɒʃ/ *v* [I] **1** to go through water
or mud 涉水, 在泥濘中行進: *We sloshed*
along through the puddles. 我們艱苦地在水
坑涉水前進。**2** (of liquid) to move about
against the sides of a container 〔液體〕〔在
容器中〕晃動

sloshed /slɒʃt; slɒʃt/ *adj infml* drunk 〖非正
式〗喝醉的: *He was completely sloshed at the*
party. 他在聚會上喝得酩酊大醉。

slot[1] /slɒt; slɒt/ *n* **1** a narrow opening in a
machine or container 狹孔, 狹縫, 槽: *to put*
a coin in the slot 把硬幣放入投幣口 **2** *infml*
a position in a list or system 〖非正式〗〔名單或
系列中的〕位置; 檔位: *the 7 o'clock slot on*
the radio 電台七點鐘這一檔節目

slot[2] *v* **-tt-** [I;T] to go or to put something
into a space where it fits (被)放入空位〔孔或
縫〕: *The lid slots into the grooves, like this.*
蓋子可以這樣插入槽裡。

sloth /sləʊθ; sloʊθ/ *n* **1** [U] *fml* laziness 〖正
式〗懶惰, 懶散 **2** [C] a slow-moving animal
of Central and South America 〔中南美洲
的〕樹懶

sloth·ful /'sləʊfəl; 'sloʊθfəl/ *adj fml* lazy 〖正
式〗懶惰的, 懶散的 **–slothfully** *adv*

slot ma·chine /' · ·,·/ *n* a machine which
you operate by putting in coins (投幣)自動
售貨機

slouch /slaʊtʃ; slaʊtʃ/ *v* [I] to sit, stand, or
walk in a tired round-shouldered way 沒精
打采地坐[站或走]: *Sit up properly — don't*

slouch! 坐好一點, 別無精打采的! **–slouch** *n* [sing]

slough /slʌf; slʌf/ *v*

slough sthg ↔ **off** *phr v* [T] to get rid of something 擺脫〔某事物〕; 脱落〔某物〕: *The snake sloughs off its skin every few months.* 蛇每隔幾個月蜕皮一次。

slov·en·ly /'slʌvnlɪ; 'slʌvənlɪ/ *adj* untidy and careless 不整潔的; 馬虎的: *a slovenly piece of work* 一件馬虎的工作 **–slovenliness** *n* [U]

★**slow¹** /slo; sləu/ *adj* **1** moving or happening without much speed (速)慢的: *a slow train* 慢車 | *slow music* 節拍緩慢的音樂 | *the slow erosion of rock by wind and rain* 風雨對岩石的緩慢侵蝕 **2** not very clever 遲鈍的: *some of the slower pupils* 一些較遲鈍的學生 **3** showing a time that is earlier than the correct time (used of clocks and watches) 〔時間上〕慢了的〔指鐘錶〕: *The station clock is two minutes slow.* 火車站的鐘慢了兩分鐘。 **–slowly** *adv* **–slowness** *n* [U]

★**slow²** *adv* slowly 慢慢地, 緩慢地: *You're going too slow.* 你走得太慢了。 | *slow-moving traffic* 移動緩慢的車輛

slow³ *v*

slow sbdy/sthg ↔ **down** *phr v* (also 又作 **slow** sbdy/sthg ↔ **up**) [I;T] to start to move or happen more slowly, or to make someone or something do this (使)〔某人或某事物〕慢下來, (使)減速: *Slow down, there's a bend ahead.* (車)開得慢一點, 前面有個彎道。 | *His bad leg slows him down a lot.* 他的傷腿使他走得很慢。 | *Business slows up in summer.* 夏天的生意變得清淡。

slow·coach /'slo,kotʃ; 'sləʊkəʊtʃ/ *n* BrE *infml* a person who does something too slowly〔英, 非正式〕做事緩慢的人

slow mo·tion /,·'··/ *n* [U] movement which takes place at a much slower speed than in real life, especially in a film 慢動作; 〔尤指〕慢鏡頭: *They showed the goal again in slow motion.* 他們用慢鏡頭把進球重放了一遍。

sludge /slʌdʒ; slʌdʒ/ *n* [U] **1** thick mud 淤泥, 軟泥 **2** dirty waste oil in an engine〔發動機內的〕油污, 油垢

slue /sluː/ *v* **slued** sluding [I; T] the usual American spelling of SLEW¹〔美式〕= SLEW¹

slug¹ /slʌg; slʌg/ *n* **1** a small soft limbless creature, like a SNAIL but with no shell 蛞蝓, 鼻涕蟲 **2** a lump or piece of metal 金屬小塊 **3** *AmE* a bullet〔美式〕子彈 **4** *AmE* a small quantity of an alcoholic drink drunk in one swallow〔美式〕〔酒的〕一口的量: *a slug of whisky* 一口威士忌酒

slug² *v* **-gg-** [T] to strike with a heavy blow 重擊, 猛打

slug·gish /'slʌgɪʃ; 'slʌgɪʃ/ *adj* slow-moving and without strength 動作慢的; 無力氣的: *a sluggish stream* 水流緩慢的小溪 | *I was feeling rather sluggish.* 我感到渾身無力。 **–**

sluggishly *adv*

sluice¹ /slus; sluːs/ *n* a passage for water with a gate through which the flow can be controlled 水閘, 水門, 閘門

sluice² *v* **sluiced, sluicing** [T] to wash with floods of water〔用大水〕沖洗: *We sluiced out the cowshed.* 我們用水沖洗了牛棚。

slum /slʌm; slʌm/ *n* **1** (also 又作 **the slums**) a city area of poor living conditions and old unrepaired buildings 貧民窟, 貧民區: *They've moved out of the slums to a much better area.* 他們已經從貧民窟搬到了條件不錯的地區。 | *I grew up in a slum.* 我是在貧民區長大的。 **2** *infml* a very untidy place〔非正式〕很髒的地方: *Your room is an absolute slum!* 你的房間真是髒透了!

slum·ber /'slʌmbə; 'slʌmbəʳ/ *n lit* sleep〔文〕睡眠: *waking from her slumbers* 她從睡眠中醒來 | *in a deep slumber* 在沉睡中 **–slumber** *v* [I]

slump¹ /slʌmp; slʌmp/ *v* [I] **1** (of a person) to fall heavily or in a heap〔人〕沉重地倒下: *He slumped into his chair.* 他猛地倒在椅子上。 **2** to fall suddenly by a large amount 暴跌, 劇降: *Sales have slumped in the last month.* 上個月的銷售額已大幅下降。

slump² *n* **1** a time of seriously bad business conditions and unemployment〔生意和就業的〕不景氣, 蕭條 **2** a sudden fall in an amount or value 暴跌, 劇降: *There's been a slump in demand for electrical goods.* 電器產品的需求已大幅度下降。

slung /slʌŋ; slʌŋ/ the past tense and past participle of SLING ☆ SLING 的過去式和過去分詞

slunk /slʌŋk; slʌŋk/ the past tense and past participle of SLINK ☆ SLINK 的過去式和過去分詞

slur¹ /slɝ; slɜːʳ/ *v* **-rr-** [T] to pronounce words unclearly, often because you are ill or drunk〔常因患病或喝醉酒而〕含糊地説話: *I find him hard to understand because he slurs his speech.* 他説話含糊不清, 使我難以理解。

slur² *n* an unfair damaging remark 誹謗, 中傷, 詆毁: *He has cast a slur on the company's good name.* 他中傷了公司的好名聲。

slurp /slɝp; slɜːp/ *v* [I;T] *infml* to drink noisily〔非正式〕咕嘟咕嘟地喝: *The children slurped their milkshakes greedily.* 孩子們咕嘟咕嘟地大喝奶昔。

slush /slʌʃ; slʌʃ/ *n* [U] **1** wet, melted snow 半融化的雪, 雪泥 **2** *infml* literature, films, concerned with silly love stories〔非正式〕無聊的愛情故事〔文學作品; 影片〕**–slushy** *adj* **slushier, slushiest**

slut /slʌt; slʌt/ *n* **1** a woman who is considered to be immoral 蕩婦; 妓女 **2** an untidy lazy woman 邋遢女人; 懶女人 **–sluttish** *adj*

sly /slaɪ; slaɪ/ *adj* **slier** *or* **slyer, sliest** *or* **slyest 1** clever in deceiving 狡猾的, 狡詐的:

My granddad was a sly old fox. 我的爺爺是個狡猾的老狐狸。 **2** showing that you know something that others do not know 詭祕的: She gave a sly smile. 她詭祕地笑一笑。 **3 on the sly** infml secretly 〖非正式〗祕密地，偷偷地 **–slyly, slily** adv **–slyness** n [U]

smack¹ /smæk; smæk/ v [T] **1** to hit with your open hand 〔用手掌〕摑，打，拍: She smacked his leg. 她打在他的腿上。 | Don't smack me! 別打我了! **2 smack your lips** to open and close your lips noisily 咂嘴 **3 smack of something** to remind you of something 使人想到某事物: His plan smacks of disloyalty to me. 他的計劃對我有不忠的味道。

smack² n **1** [C] a quick forceful blow with an open hand 〔用掌的〕猛擊: If you don't stop making that noise, you'll get a smack! 如果你不停止發出那種噪音，你就要挨揍了! **2** [sing] a loud sharp noise 劈啪聲: The book landed on the floor with a loud smack. 那本書啪的一聲落在地板上。 **3** [C] a small sailing boat 單桅小漁船

smack³ adv infml 〖非正式〗 **1** with force 猛烈地: The car ran smack into a wall. 汽車猛然撞在牆上。 **2** exactly in a place 恰好; 不偏不倚: She lives right smack in the middle of the town. 她就住在城鎮的正中心。

small /smɔl; smɔːl/ adj **1** not large in size, weight, or amount 〔尺寸、重量或數量等〕小的: a book written for small children 一本為兒童寫的書 | The Indian elephant is smaller than the African elephant. 印度象比非洲象小。 | She's rather small for her age. 就她這年齡來說，她算是矮小的。 –see picture on page 469 見 469 頁彩圖 –see 見 LITTLE (USAGE用法) **2** not important 〔重要性〕小的: We'll have to make a few small changes, that's all. 我們將不得不作些小變動，僅此而已。 | He's a small businessman. 他是做小本生意的。 **3 the small ads** short advertisements in a newspaper which people can use to buy or sell things, or to find or offer a job or a place to live 〔報紙上的分類〕小廣告 **4 the small hours** the early morning hours just after midnight 午夜後至天亮前的幾個小時，凌晨時分 **5 small wonder** it's not surprising 不奇怪; 難怪: Small wonder you're fed up — Small wonder you're fed up with the job, the hours are terrible. 難怪你要厭煩了，你應該多出去走走。 –**small** adv: He writes so small I can hardly read it. 他的字寫得太小，我難以看清楚。 –**smallness** n [U]

small change /ˌ·'·/ n [U] money in coins of small value 小額硬幣，零錢

small·hold·ing /'smɔlˌhəʊldɪŋ; 'smɔːlˌhəʊldɪŋ/ n a small piece of land used for farming 小片農田 –**smallholder** n

small-mind·ed /ˌ·'···◂/ adj having mean and selfish interests 心胸狹窄的，氣量小的 –**small-mindedness** n [U]

small-scale /ˌ·'·◂/ adj **1** happening within a small area or with small numbers or quantities 小規模的: a small-scale operation involving only a few local people 只有幾個當地人參與的小規模行動 **2** showing a large area, without much detail (used of maps) 小比例尺的〔指地圖〕

small talk /'··/ n [U] conversation about unimportant subjects 閒談, 聊天

small-time /ˌ·'·◂/ adj unimportant 無關緊要的: a small-time criminal 一名罪輕的刑事犯

smarm·y /'smɑrmɪ; 'smɑːmi/ adj **smarmier, smarmiest** BrE infml unpleasantly and falsely polite 〖英式, 非正式〗奉承的, 諂媚的; 拍馬屁的

smart¹ /smɑrt; smɑːt/ adj **1** neat and stylish in appearance 整潔的; 時髦的: You look very smart in that new shirt. 你穿那件新襯衫看上去很帥。 **2** clever 聰明的: He's a very smart young man. 他是個很聰明的年青人。 **3** quick and sharp 猛烈的; 厲害的: a smart blow on the head 在頭上狠狠的一擊 **4** connected with wealthy or fashionable people 時髦人士的, 講究時髦的: a smart restaurant 格調時髦的餐館 | He took me to a very smart party. 他帶我去參加了一個十分時髦的聚會。 –**smartly** adv –**smartness** n [U]

smart² v [I] **1** to sting for a short time 刺痛, 短暫劇痛: His knee was smarting. 他的膝蓋感到一陣劇痛。 **2** to feel hurt or upset about an unkindness 感到傷心〔痛苦〕: She was still smarting over his criticism. 她對他的批評仍感到很難受。

smart·en /'smɑrtn; 'smɑːtn/ v
smarten up phr v [I;T **smarten** sbdy/sthg ↔ **up**] to become or make something look neat or stylish (使)〔某物〕整潔, (使)變得時髦: We smartened the office up with a new coat of paint. 我們新刷一層油漆使辦公室煥燃一新。 | Try to smarten yourself up for the interview. 你要盡量打扮得漂亮點去面試。

smash¹ /smæʃ; smæʃ/ v **1** [I;T] to break something into pieces violently 打碎, 打破〔某物〕: I nearly smashed the window. 我差點兒把窗子打破。 | The plate smashed on the floor. 盤子在地上摔了個粉碎。 –see 見 BREAK (USAGE用法) **2** [I;T] to crash into something solid 猛衝, 猛撞: They smashed their way out of the building. 他們奪路衝出大樓。 | The waves smashed on to the beach. 浪濤拍擊着海灘。 **3** [T] to hit a ball with a hard downward attacking shot 〔運動中〕殺〔球〕, 扣〔球〕

smash² n **1** the sound of a violent breaking 破碎聲: the smash of glass breaking 玻璃的碎裂聲 **2** a powerful blow 猛擊, 猛撞 **3** (also 又作 **smash-up**) a violent car accident 撞車事故, 車禍: There was a terrible smash-up on the motorway last night. 昨夜在高速公路上發生了一起嚴重的車禍。 **4** a hard downward attacking shot in games such as tennis 〔網球的〕殺球, 扣球 **5** (also 又作 **smash hit**) a very successful new play, film, book, or song 轟動一時極為成功的新劇、電影、書或歌曲: *a new smash musical* 轟動一時的新音樂劇

smashed /smæʃt; 'smæʃt/ *adj* [never before a noun 不能用於名詞前] *slang* drunk or under the influence of drugs 〔俚〕喝醉的; 麻醉的

smash·ing /'smæʃɪŋ; 'smæʃɪŋ/ *adj BrE infml* excellent 〔英式，非正式〕極好的，了不起的: *We had a smashing holiday.* 我們度過了一個極快活的假期。

smat·ter·ing /'smætərɪŋ; 'smætərɪŋ/ *n* a smattering of a little knowledge about 略知，淺知: *I have a smattering of Italian.* 我懂一點點意大利語。

smear¹ /smɪr; smɪəʳ/ *n* **1** a dirty oily mark 油漬; 污點: *There's a smear of grease on your forehead.* 你的前額上有油脂痕跡。 **2** an untrue charge made against someone to try to turn public feelings against them 誹謗，污衊，詆毀: *The newspapers ran a smear campaign* **against** *him.* 報界掀起了一陣誹謗他的浪潮。 | *a right-wing smear* 右翼人士的誹謗 **3 a smear test** a medical test for CANCER of the CERVIX 塗片標本試驗〔一種探查子宮頸癌的方法〕

smear² *v* **1** [T] to spread a thin covering of a sticky or greasy substance over the surface of something 〔用黏或膩的東西〕塗抹於〔某物的表面〕: *She smeared sun tan lotion all over herself.* 她在全身塗上了防曬護膚液。 | *Smear the dish with butter.* 在碟子上塗黃油。 **2** [I] to spread across a surface, leaving a dirty mark 沾染; 弄污: *Be careful, the paint may smear.* 小心，油漆會沾你一身。

*★**smell**¹ /smɛl; smɛl/ *v* **smelled** *or* **smelt** /smɛlt; smɛlt/, **smelled** *or* **smelt** **1** [I] to have or use the sense of the nose 嗅，聞，有嗅覺: *I've got a cold and I can't smell very well.* 我得了感冒，嗅覺不靈。 **2** [T; + (that)] to notice or recognize the smell of something 嗅出，聞到〔某物〕: *Come and smell these roses. They're wonderful.* 來聞聞這些玫瑰花，它們的味真香。 | *I could smell that the milk wasn't fresh.* 我聞得出牛奶不新鮮。 | *I can smell burning.* 我聞到了焦味。 **3** [I; + adv/prep; + complement] to have a particular smell 〔聞起來〕有特定的氣味: *This wine smells like honey.* 這酒有一股蜂蜜味。 | *The room smelt of stale beer.* 房間裡散發出一股不新鮮的啤酒味。 | *This book smells old.* 這本書有一股霉味。 **4** [I] to have an unpleasant smell 發出臭氣: *The meat had started to smell.* 這肉已開始發臭。 **5** [T] to feel that something, especially danger or trouble, is about to happen 覺察到〔危險或困難將要發生〕 **6 smell a rat** *infml* to become conscious that something is wrong 〔非正式〕感到事情不妙 **smell** sthg ↔ **out** *phr v* [T] **1** to discover something by smelling 嗅出，聞出〔某物〕: *The hounds smelt out a fox.* 獵犬嗅出有狐狸。 **2** to work hard so that you find out

---

something that someone is trying to keep hidden 查出〔某物〕

smell² *n* **1** [U] the ability to use your nose 嗅覺: *I've got an excellent sense of smell.* 我的嗅覺非常敏銳。 **2** [C] the effect that something has on your nose 氣味: *There's a nice smell of coffee in the restaurant.* 餐館裡散發出一股咖啡香味。 | *I love the smell of baking.* 我喜歡烘烤（麵包）的氣味。 | *What's that awful smell?* 那是甚麼難聞的氣味? **3 have a smell** to smell something 聞，嗅〔某物〕: *Have a smell of this wine: is it all right?* 聞聞這酒，沒問題吧?

■ USAGE 用法: A **smell** can be either good or bad ☆ **smell** 可以表示香味，也可以表示臭味 做飯菜的香味: *a wonderful smell of cooking* 做飯菜的香味 | *a strong smell of rotten eggs* 刺鼻的臭蛋味。 If you do not say whether it is good or bad, you usually mean that it is bad ☆ 若不表明是香味還是臭味，則通常是指臭味: *What's that smell in the bathroom?* 那浴室裡是甚麼氣味? (= it smells bad 聞上去很臭) **Odour** is a rather formal word usually meaning a bad smell ☆ **Odour** 一詞相當正式，常指臭味: *A new disinfectant which destroys household odours instantly!* （這是）一種立即消除屋內臭味的新型消毒劑! **Stink** is an informal word meaning a very strong, bad smell ☆ **Stink** 是表示“惡臭味”的非正式用詞 ☆ *Phew! What a stink!* 唷! 多麼臭的氣味! **Scent** and **perfume** can both be used for pleasant, sweet smells ☆ **Scent** 和 **perfume** 都用以表示“香味”: *the sweet scents of a garden in springtime* 春季花園裡散發的芳香 | *The perfume of roses filled the room.* 房間裡充滿了玫瑰的芬芳。

smell·y /'smɛlɪ; 'smɛlɪ/ *adj* **smellier, smelliest** unpleasant smelling 發臭的，有臭味的: *smelly old socks* 發臭的舊短襪

smelt /smɛlt; smɛlt/ *v* **1** the past tense and past participle of SMELL ☆ SMELL 的過去式和過去分詞 **2** [T] to melt metal-containing earth in order to separate and remove the metal 熔煉〔礦石〕; 煉取〔金屬〕

*★**smile**¹ /smaɪl; smaɪl/ *n* an expression on your face in which your mouth moves upwards at the corners to show happiness 微笑，笑容: *She gave a shy smile.* 她腼腆地笑一笑。 | *He welcomed me with a smile.* 他微笑著對我表示歡迎。

*★**smile**² *v* **smiled, smiling** **1** [I] to have or give a smile 微笑: *He smiled at me.* 他向我微笑。 | *She smiled with satisfaction.* 她露出滿意的微笑。 **2** [T] to express with a smile 以微笑表示: *She smiled her approval.* 她微微一笑表示讚許。 –**smilingly** *adv*

smirk /smɜrk; smɜːk/ *v* [I] to smile in a silly

satisfied way 傻笑, 得意地笑

smith /smɪθ; smɪθ/ *n* a person who makes things out of metals such as gold, silver, or iron〔金、銀、鐵等的〕金屬工匠: *a blacksmith* 鐵匠 | *a goldsmith* 金匠 | *a gunsmith* 造槍工人

smith·e·reens /ˌsmɪðəˈrinz; ˌsmɪðəˈriːnz/ *n* **into/to smithereens** *infml* into very small bits〔非正式〕成碎片: *The glass was smashed to smithereens.* 玻璃被打得粉碎。

smit·ten /ˈsmɪtn; ˈsmɪtn/ *adj* **be smitten** to have a sudden strong feeling, especially of approval, for something or someone 被突然打動; 迷住: *He only spoke to her for a moment, but he was absolutely smitten.* 他跟她只説了一會兒話, 但他被徹底迷住了。

smock /smɑk; smɒk/ *n* a loose piece of clothing like a long shirt 寬鬆罩衣

smog /smɑg; smɒg/ *n* [U] an unhealthy mixture of FOG and smoke which is found in the air in some industrial cities 煙霧〔某些工業城市上空煙和霧的有害混合物〕–see picture on page 470 見 470 頁彩圖

*★**smoke**[1] /smok; sməʊk/ *n* **1** [U] the white, grey, or black gas produced when something burns 煙: *There's a lot of smoke coming from that bonfire.* 那堆篝火冒出了很多的煙。 | *a puff of smoke* 一團煙 | *the smell of tobacco smoke* 吸煙的氣味 **2** [C] an act of smoking tobacco 抽煙: *There's just time for a cup of coffee and a smoke.* 有時間喝杯咖啡抽支煙了。 **3 go up in smoke** to end without results, especially suddenly (突然)成為泡影, 化為烏有

*★**smoke**[2] *v* **smoked, smoking 1** [I;T] to light something containing tobacco and breathe in the smoke from it 抽煙: *Do you mind if I smoke?* 你介意我抽煙嗎? | *He smokes a pipe.* 他抽煙斗。 **2** [I] to send out smoke 冒煙: *The chimneys were smoking on the industrial estate.* 工業區的煙囱在冒煙。

smoke sbdy/sthg ↔ **out** *phr v* [T] to fill a place with smoke to force a person or animal to come out from hiding 用煙把〔躲藏的人或動物〕熏出

smoked /smokt; sməʊkt/ *adj* **1** preserved by hanging in smoke 煙熏保存的; 熏製的: *smoked mackerel* 熏製鯖魚 | *smoked meats* 熏肉 **2** darkened by the colour of smoke 被熏黑的: *smoked glass* 熏黑的玻璃 | *smoked quartz* 熏黑的石英

smok·er /ˈsmokɚ; ˈsməʊkər/ *n* **1** a person who smokes 吸煙者 **2** a railway carriage where smoking is allowed 〔火車上的〕吸煙車廂 –opposite 反義 **non-smoker**

smoke·screen /ˈsmokˌskrin; ˈsməʊkskriːn/ *n* **1** a cloud of smoke produced in order to hide a place or an activity from your enemy〔用以遮蔽陣地或活動以防敵人發現的〕煙幕 **2** something which hides your real intentions〔用以掩蓋自己真實意圖的〕煙幕, 障眼法: *It wasn't easy to find out as they had*

thrown up a bit of a smokescreen. 他們放了點煙幕使其本意難以了解。

smok·ing /ˈsmokɪŋ; ˈsməʊkɪŋ/ *n* [U] the practice or habit of breathing in tobacco smoke from cigarettes or a pipe 吸煙, 抽煙: *I'm trying to give up smoking.* 我正在努力戒煙。 | *The sign says "No smoking".* 告示上寫着"不准吸煙"。

smok·y /ˈsmoki; ˈsməʊki/ *adj* **smokier, smokiest 1** full of smoke 充滿煙的: *a smoky bar* 煙霧瀰漫的酒吧 | *I hate this smoky atmosphere.* 我不喜歡這種煙霧騰騰的空氣。 **2** with the taste or appearance of smoke 有煙熏味的; 煙灰色的: *smoky-tasting fish* 有煙熏味的魚 | *a smoky-blue uniform* 藍灰色的制服 –**smokiness** *n* [U]

smol·der /ˈsmoldɚ; ˈsməʊldər/ *v* the usual American spelling of SMOULDER ☆〔美式〕= SMOULDER

*★**smooth**[1] /smuð; smuːð/ *adj* **1** without any holes or lumps in its surface 平滑的, 光滑的; 平坦的: *a baby's smooth skin* 嬰兒光滑的皮膚 | *a smooth road* 平坦的路 | *The tyres were worn smooth.* 輪胎被磨平了。 **2** without lumps (of a liquid mixture) 無結塊的; 調勻的〔指液體混合物〕: *Beat the mixture until smooth.* 把混合物攪拌至調勻為止。 **3** even in movement, without sudden changes 平穩的: *He brought the car to a smooth stop.* 他把汽車平穩地煞住。 **4** free from problems or difficulties 順利的, 無困難的: *a smooth journey* 一帆風順的旅程 | *progress in this matter has not been smooth* 這件事的進展不大順利 **5** too pleasant or polite in manner (used of a man) 圓滑的; 過分殷勤的〔指人〕: *I don't trust that man; he's far too smooth.* 我不相信那人, 他太圓滑了。 –**smoothly** *adv* –**smoothness** *n* [U]

smooth[2] *v* [T] to make something smooth 使平滑, 使光滑: *He smoothed down his hair.* 他把頭髮捋平。 | *This face cream is good at smoothing* **away** *wrinkles.* 這種面霜消除皺紋效果良好。

smooth sthg ↔ **out** *phr v* [T] to move your hands over something to make it smooth〔用手〕弄平〔某物〕

smooth sthg ↔ **over** *phr v* [T] to make something less important or less of a problem 緩和, 減輕〔某物〕: *We managed to smooth over the bad feeling in the office.* 我們設法緩解了辦公室裡的不良情緒。

smoth·er /ˈsmʌðɚ; ˈsmʌðər/ *v* [T] **1** to cover completely 厚厚地覆蓋: *I threw a blanket down to smother the flames.* 我扔下一條毯子把火撲滅。 | *The cake was smothered* **with** *chocolate icing.* 蛋糕上蓋了一層巧克力霜。 **2** to control your feelings so that other people do not notice them 抑制, 壓抑〔情感〕: *I tried to smother my anger.* 我強忍怒火。 **3** to cover someone's face with something so that they cannot breathe 使窒息, 悶死: *She'd been smothered with a pillow.* 她

是給枕頭悶死的。**4 to give too much love and protection** 過分寵愛，溺愛：*Don't smother the child; let him make his own mistakes.* 不要溺愛孩子，讓他出點差錯吧。

smoul·der /ˈsmoʊldər; ˈsməʊldəʳ/ *v* (**smolder** *AmE*〖美式〗) [I] **1** to burn slowly without a flame 用文火悶燒 **2** *lit* to have violent feelings inside you that you do not show〖文〗〔強烈情緒〕悶在心裡，鬱積：*Inside, I was smouldering with anger.* 我的內心鬱積着滿腔怒火。

smudge¹ /smʌdʒ; smʌdʒ/ *v* **smudged, smudging 1** [T] to make something look dirty and unclear because you have touched it 弄髒〔某物〕：*I'm afraid I've smudged your signature.* 我怕弄髒了你的簽名。**2** [I] to become dirty and unclear because of being touched 變髒：*The ink has smudged.* 墨水被抹開留下了污跡。

smudge² *n* a dirty mark 污點，污跡

smug /smʌg; smʌg/ *adj* **smugger, smuggest** too pleased with yourself because you think you are good or clever 沾沾自喜的，自鳴得意的：*a smug expression on her face* 她臉上沾沾自喜的表情 | *He's unbearably smug about getting into university.* 他對考進大學自鳴得意，令人受不了。**–smugly** *adv* **–smugness** *n* [U]

smug·gle /ˈsmʌgl; ˈsmʌgəl/ *v* **smuggled, smuggling** [T] to take goods or people from one country to another illegally 非法私運〔貨物或人〕，走私：*The drugs had been smuggled in by a gang.* 毒品已被一夥歹徒私運入境。| *smuggling refugees into Europe* 偷渡進入歐洲的難民 **–smuggler** *n* **–smuggling** *n* [U]

smut /smʌt; smʌt/ *n* **1** [C;U] a small piece of dirt that makes dark marks 污點，污跡 **2** [U] morally offensive books, stories, pictures, or remarks 淫穢作品；淫詞穢語

smut·ty /ˈsmʌtɪ; ˈsmʌti/ *adj* **smuttier, smuttiest** rather rude and morally improper 下流的，淫穢的：*a smutty joke* 淫穢的笑話 **–smuttily** *adv* **–smuttiness** *n* [U]

snack /snæk; snæk/ *n* a quick light meal 快餐；點心，小食，小吃：*I haven't got time for lunch, I'll just have a snack.* 我沒有時間吃午飯，我只吃點小食。

snack bar /ˈ· ·/ *n* a place where you can buy snacks and drinks 小吃部，小食店

snag¹ /snæg; snæg/ *n* a small unexpected difficulty〔意外的〕小困難，麻煩：*It's a good idea. The only snag is, we haven't any money.* 這是個好主意，唯一的困難是我們身無分文。

snag² *v* [T] to pull a thread in clothing by catching it on something sharp 使鈎破；使戳破：*Oh no! I've snagged my jumper on your rose bush.* 啊呀不好了！我的套頭毛衣被你那玫瑰叢鈎破了。

snail /sneɪl; sneɪl/ *n* **1** a small slow-moving creature with a soft body and a hard shell on its back 蝸牛 **2 at a snail's pace** at a very slow speed 非常緩慢的速度

snake¹ /sneɪk; sneɪk/ *n* a long thin REPTILE with no legs, often having a poisonous bite 蛇

snake² *v* **snaked, snaking** [I] (also 又作 **snake its way**) to move in a twisting way 蜿蜒前進：*The train snaked its way through the mountains.* 火車蜿蜒地穿過羣山。

snake charm·er /ˈ· ,· ·/ *n* a person who entertains people by controlling snakes, for example by playing music〔用音樂聲馴蛇的〕玩蛇人，弄蛇人

***snap¹** /snæp; snæp/ *v* **-pp- 1** [I;T] to break suddenly with a sharp cracking noise 突然折斷：*The branch snapped under all the snow.* 樹枝在雪的重壓下折斷了。| *I snapped the stick in half.* 我把棍子折成兩截。**2** [I;T] to move into a particular position with a sharp noise 啪地移動：*The lid snapped shut.* 蓋子啪地一聲蓋上了。**3 snap your fingers** to make a noise by moving your second finger quickly across your thumb, usually to attract attention 捻手指使劈啪作響〔常用來引起別人注意〕**4** [I] (used of animals) to try to bite〔動物〕咬：*The dog snapped at my ankles.* 那條狗使勁地咬我的腳踝。**5** [I] to speak quickly in a sharp, unfriendly way 厲聲説；急促地説：*"You're late!" she snapped.* "你遲到了!" 她厲聲説。| *I'm sorry I snapped at you.* 對不起，我不該讓你厲聲地説話。**6** [T] *infml* to photograph〖非正式〗拍照 **7 snap out of it** *infml* a phrase used when you are telling someone to stop feeling unhappy and be cheerful again〖非正式〗打起精神來，重新振作起來〔用於開導某人擺脱苦悶不快的心境〕

snap sth ↔ **up** *phr v* [T] to buy quickly and eagerly 搶購：*We snapped up lots of bargains in the sales.* 我們在大減價時搶購了許多便宜貨。

snap² *n* **1** [C] a sudden sharp sound 喀嚓聲；劈啪聲 **2** [C] *infml* an informal photograph〖非正式〗快照，快相：*holiday snaps* 假期中拍攝的快照 **3** [U] a children's card game in which players shout "Snap!" when they see two cards which are the same 呼"同"牌戲〔一種兒童玩的牌戲，玩牌者搶先認出兩張相同的牌即呼"同"(snap)〕

snap³ *adj* [only before a noun 只用於名詞前] done in haste and without careful thought 倉促的，匆忙的：*a snap decision* 倉促的決定

snap·py /ˈsnæpɪ; ˈsnæpi/ *adj* **1** speaking in a sharp, unfriendly way 厲聲説話的；沒好氣的 **2 a snappy dresser** a person who wears stylish, fashionable clothes 穿着時髦的人 **3 Make it snappy! Look snappy** *infml* Hurry up!〖非正式〗趕快! 快一點!

snap·shot /ˈsnæpʃɒt; ˈsnæpʃɒt/ *n* an informal photograph 快照：*holiday snapshots* 假期中拍的快照

snare¹ /sneə; sneəʳ/ *n* **1** a trap for catching

birds or small animals 〔捕捉鳥獸等的〕陷阱、羅網 **2** something which attracts you, but is really a trap for you 圈套, 陷阱

snare² v **snared, snaring** [T] to catch in a snare 〔用陷阱、羅網等〕捕捉, 誘捕: *We snared a couple of rabbits.* 我們捕捉到幾隻野兔。

snarl¹ /snɑrl; snɑ:l/ v [I] **1** (of an animal) to make a fierce angry sound and show its teeth 〔動物〕狂吠, 嗥叫: *a snarling dog* 狂吠的狗 **2** to say something in a fierce angry way 咆哮

snarl² n the expression an animal has or the sound it makes when it snarls 狂吠, 嗥叫 (聲)

snarled /snɑrld; snɑ:ld/ adj **snarled up** blocked or confused 堵塞; 混亂: *Traffic was badly snarled up near the accident.* 車禍現場附近的交通極為混亂。

snarl-up /ˈ··/ n infml a confused situation 〔非正式〕混亂的狀態, 一團糟

snatch¹ /snætʃ; snætʃ/ v [T] **1** to get hold of something quickly and forcefully 奪走〔某物〕: *The thief snatched her handbag and ran off.* 小偷搶了她的手提包就跑。 **2** to make use of time or a chance quickly 抓住時機(做): *I snatched a moment at lunchtime to read your letter.* 我在吃午飯時抓緊時間看了你的來信。 **3 snatch at something** to try to get something or to take it eagerly 設法抓住某物; 渴望得到某物: *You must snatch at any opportunity to go abroad.* 你一定要抓住任何出國的機會。 –**snatcher** n

snatch² n **1** make a snatch at to try to get something by snatching 設法奪取〔某物〕: *He made a snatch at the ball but just missed.* 他奮力地搶球, 但沒有接住。 **2** a short and incomplete period of something 片刻; 片段: *We slept fitfully, in snatches.* 我們睡得不安穩, 時睡時醒。 | *I heard a snatch of their conversation.* 我聽到了他們的一段談話。

sneak¹ /snik; sni:k/ v **1** [I + adv/prep] to go quietly and secretly 潛行, 偷偷地走: *He sneaked past the guard.* 他偷偷地從衛兵身邊溜過。 **2** [T] to take secretly or cleverly 偷偷地拿〔看、做〕: *We sneaked the food up to our rooms.* 我們偷偷地把食物拿到我們的房間去。 | *I sneaked a look at his diary.* 我偷偷地看了一下他的日記。

sneak up phr v [I] to come quietly and secretly 偷偷地走近: *Don't sneak up behind me like that!* 別那樣偷偷地跟在我的身後! | *Our teacher has a nasty habit of sneaking up on you when you're not working.* 我們的老師有個令人討厭的習慣: 在你不做功課的時候悄悄地走到你的身邊。

sneak² n infml a person who informs officials that you have done something wrong (a word used to express disapproval) 〔非正式〕向上司打小報告的人; 向...告密的人〔含貶義〕

sneak-er /ˈsnikə; ˈsni:kə/ n the usual American word for 〔美式〕= PLIMSOLL or

TRAINER

sneak-ing /ˈsnikɪŋ; ˈsni:kɪŋ/ adj [only before a noun 只用於名詞前] secret and not openly expressed 暗中的, 私下的: *I have a sneaking suspicion that he knows about us.* 我心中暗暗懷疑他對我們很了解。

sneak-y /ˈsniki; ˈsni:ki/ adj **sneakier, sneakiest** infml acting or done secretly and deceitfully 〔非正式〕偷偷摸摸的, 鬼鬼祟祟的 –**sneakiness** n [U]

sneer¹ /snɪr; snɪə/ v [I] **1** to have an unpleasant expression on your face, with a one-sided smile 嗤笑, 嘲笑, 譏笑 **2** to speak or to behave as if something is not worthy of serious attention 蔑視, 不屑一顧: *Don't sneer at their religion.* 不要蔑視他們的宗教信仰。 –**sneeringly** adv

sneer² n the expression on someone's face when they sneer, or a sneering remark 嗤笑, 譏笑, 冷言冷語

sneeze /sniz; sni:z/ v **sneezed, sneezing** [I] to suddenly blow down your nose noisily in an uncontrolled way, for example when you have a cold 打噴嚏: *The dust made him sneeze.* 灰塵使他打噴嚏。 –**sneeze** n: *He gave a sudden sneeze.* 他突然打了個噴嚏。

snick-er /ˈsnɪkə; ˈsnɪkə/ v [I] to laugh quietly to yourself, in a disrespectful way 暗笑, 竊笑

snide /snaɪd; snaɪd/ adj amusing but unfair and hurtful 譏諷的, 挖苦的: *a snide remark* 挖苦的話

sniff¹ /snɪf; snɪf/ v **1** [I] to breathe air up into the nose with a sound 以鼻吸氣: *She sniffed, trying hard not to cry.* 她抽泣著, 盡力不哭出來。 **2** [I;T] to smell something by breathing air up into the nose 嗅, 聞: *The dogs sniffed at my shopping bag.* 那幾條狗聞了聞我的購物袋。 | *"That's a nice perfume," she said, sniffing the air.* "那是種不錯的香水," 她嗅著空氣說。 | *I'm afraid your son's been sniffing glue.* 我遺憾地告訴您, 您的兒子一直在吸膠煙。 **3 not to be sniffed at** not to be refused without careful thought, or because of pride 對...不可嗤之以鼻, 對...不可瞧不起: *A good offer like that is not to be sniffed at.* 對那麼好的提議不可輕視。

sniff sthg ↔ **out** phr v [T] infml to discover after searching 〔非正式〕查出; 嗅出: *The police dogs finally sniffed out the drugs.* 警犬最終嗅出了毒品。

sniff² n **1** the sound you make when you sniff 以鼻吸氣聲 **2 have a sniff** infml to smell 〔非正式〕聞, 嗅: *Have a sniff of this perfume.* 請聞一下這種香水。

snif-fle /ˈsnɪfl; ˈsnɪfəl/ v **sniffled, sniffling** (also 又作 **snuffle**) [I] to sniff repeatedly, as if you are crying or have a cold 〔哭泣或感冒時不斷〕抽鼻子 –**sniffle** n

snig-ger /ˈsnɪgə; ˈsnɪgə/ v [I] to laugh quietly to yourself in a disrespectful way 暗笑, 竊笑 –**snigger** n

snip¹ /snɪp; snɪp/ *n* **1** a short quick cut made with scissors 〔剪刀的〕剪口 **2** *BrE infml* a surprisingly cheap article for sale 〔英式, 非正式〕廉價品

snip² *v* **-pp-** [I;T] to cut something with scissors, especially in short quick strokes 〔用剪刀快速〕剪〔某物〕: *Just snip a hole in the paper here.* 就在紙上這個地方剪個洞。| *Keep still while I snip around your ears!* 我給你耳朵周圍剪頭髮時請別動!

snipe /snaɪp; snaɪp/ *v* **sniped, sniping** [I] **1** to shoot at people from a hidden position 伏擊, 狙擊: *People were sniping at us from above.* 有人從上面向我們射擊。 **2** to attack someone with unpleasant remarks 〔用言詞〕中傷〔某人〕: *He should learn to work with his colleagues instead of sniping at them.* 他應當學會如何與同事一起工作, 而不是用言詞中傷他們。**–sniper** *n*

snip·pet /ˈsnɪpɪt; ˈsnɪpɪt/ *n* a small bit of something 一點點; 小片, 片斷: *a snippet of information* 一點零星的信息 | *snippets of conversation* 談話的片段

sniv·el /ˈsnɪvl; ˈsnɪvəl/ *v* **-ll-** (also 又作 **-l-** *AmE* 〔美式〕) [I] to cry, act, or speak in a weak complaining way 啜泣; 哭訴: *If you fail, don't come snivelling back to me.* 你如果失敗的話, 不要回到我這裡來哭訴。**–sniveller** *n*

snob /snɑb; snɒb/ *n* **1** a person who dislikes those considered to be of a lower social class, and admires people of a higher social class (a word used to express disapproval) 勢利小人〔含貶義〕 **2** a person who is proud of having greater knowledge or better taste than others (a word used to express disapproval) 恃才傲物的人, 自命不凡的人〔含貶義〕: *She's a musical snob who despises all pop music.* 她自以為是懂音樂, 看不起所有的流行音樂。**–snobbish** *adj* **– snobbishly** *adv*

snob·be·ry /ˈsnɑbəri; ˈsnɒbəri/ *n* [U] the feelings, behaviour, or language of a snob 勢利的行為或言詞; 恃才傲物

snoo·ker¹ /ˈsnukər; ˈsnuːkər/ *n* [U] a game played on a table covered with green cloth; players must knock coloured balls into pockets at the edge of the table, using long sticks 彩色桌球, 落袋台球

snooker² *v* [T] *infml* to trap or trick someone so that they cannot act as they wish 〔非正式〕使〔某人〕陷入困境

snoop /snup; snuːp/ *v* [I] to look into other people's property or activities without permission 管閒事; 探聽: *I caught him snooping around in my office.* 我發覺他在我的辦公室到處窺探。**–snooper** *n*

snoot·y /ˈsnuti; ˈsnuːti/ *adj* **snootier, snootiest** *infml* showing that you feel more important than others (a word used to express disapproval) 〔非正式〕妄自尊大的, 傲氣的〔含貶義〕: *Now that he's rich, he's too snooty to*

be interested in his old friends. 他現在富有了, 妄自尊大得對老朋友也沒有甚麼興趣了。**– snootily** *adv*

snooze /snuz; snuːz/ *v* **snoozed, snoozing** [I] *infml* to have a short, light sleep 〔非正式〕小睡, 打盹 **–snooze** *n*: *I'm going to have a snooze after lunch.* 我準備在午飯後小睡一會。

snore¹ /snɔr; snɔːʳ/ *v* **snored, snoring** [I] to breathe noisily through your nose and mouth while you are asleep 打鼾: *How can I stop him snoring?* 我如何才能讓他停止打鼾呢? **–snorer** *n*

snore² *n* a noisy way of breathing while you are asleep 打鼾(聲)

snor·kel /ˈsnɔrkl; ˈsnɔːkəl/ *n* an air tube that allows a swimmer to breathe under water 〔用於潛水的〕通氣管 **–snorkel** *v* [I]: *Do you want to go snorkelling?* 你想使用通氣管潛泳嗎?

snort /snɔrt; snɔːt/ *v* [I] to make a noise by blowing air through your nose, to express feelings like anger or impatience 哼着鼻子〔表示憤怒或不耐煩〕**–snort** *n*

snout /snaʊt; snaʊt/ *n* the long nose of animals like pigs 〔豬等動物的〕長鼻子, 口鼻部

★snow¹ /sno; snəʊ/ *n* **1** [U] water frozen into soft white pieces that fall like rain in cold weather and cover the ground 雪 **2 the snows** [pl] *lit* falls of snow 〔文〕降雪

snow² *v* [I] (of snow) to fall 降雪, 下雪: *Look! It's snowing.* 看! 下雪了。

snow·ball¹ /ˈsno,bɔl; ˈsnəʊbɔːl/ *n* a ball made of snow pressed together, which children throw at each other 雪球

snowball² *v* [I] to grow at a faster and faster rate 像雪球似地迅速增大: *The effect of rising prices has snowballed.* 物價上漲的影響像雪球似地迅速增大。

snow·bound /ˈsno,baʊnd; ˈsnəʊbaʊnd/ *adj* blocked or kept indoors by heavy snow 被雪困阻的, 被雪封閉的

snow·drift /ˈsno,drɪft; ˈsnəʊˌdrɪft/ *n* a deep bank of snow formed by the wind 雪堆

snow·drop /ˈsno,drɑp; ˈsnəʊdrɒp/ *n* a small white European flower which appears in the early spring 雪花蓮〔歐洲一種開於早春的小白花〕

snowed in /ˌ·ˈ·/ *adj* unable to go anywhere because of deep snow 被大雪困住: *We were snowed in for three days last winter.* 去年冬天我們被大雪困了三天。

snowed un·der /ˌ·ˈ··/ *adj* having more work to do than you can easily deal with 有幹不完的工作: *I'm completely snowed under at the moment.* 我目前正忙得不可開交。

snow·fall /ˈsno,fɔl; ˈsnəʊfɔːl/ *n* **1** [C] a fall of snow 降雪 **2** [sing;U] the amount of snow that falls 降雪量: *an average snowfall of five inches per year* 每年平均五英寸的降雪量

S

snow·flake /ˈsnoˌflek; ˈsnəʊfleɪk/ *n* one of the soft white pieces of frozen water which fall as snow 雪片, 雪花

snow·man /ˈsnoˌmæn; ˈsnəʊmæn/ *n* **snowmen** /-mɛn; -men/ a figure of a person made out of snow 雪人

snow·plough /ˈsnoplaʊ; ˈsnəʊplaʊ/ *n BrE* 〖英式〗(**snowplow** *AmE* 〖美式〗) a vehicle for pushing snow off roads or railways 雪犁, 掃雪機

snow·storm /ˈsnoˌstɔrm; ˈsnəʊstɔːm/ *n* a very heavy fall of snow, especially when blown by strong winds 暴風雪, 雪暴

snow-white /ˌ· ˈ· ◂/ *adj* as white as snow 雪白的

snow·y /ˈsnoɪ; ˈsnəʊi/ *adj* **snowier, snowiest** **1** covered in or full of snow 被雪覆蓋的; 積雪的, 多雪的: *snowy mountains* 雪山 | *snowy weather* 下雪的天氣 **2** pure white 雪白的: *snowy white hair* 雪白的頭髮

Snr *n* an abbreviation for 〖縮〗= SENIOR

snub¹ /snʌb; snʌb/ *v* **-bb-** [T] to treat someone rudely, usually by paying them no attention or by making an unkind remark 冷落〔某人〕: *I said hello, but she just snubbed me and walked on.* 我(向她)打招呼, 但她理也不理我, 徑直往前走。–**snub** *n*

snub² *adj* **snub nose** a short, flat nose 短而扁的鼻子

snuff /snʌf; snʌf/ *n* [U] tobacco made into a powder which you breathe up through your nose 鼻煙: *a snuff box* 鼻煙盒 | *a pinch of snuff* 一撮鼻煙

snuf·fle /ˈsnʌfl; ˈsnʌfəl/ *v*, *n* [I] to make a noise inside your nose, often because you have a cold 〔常因感冒而〕抽鼻子

snug /snʌg; snʌg/ *adj* **1** warm and comfortable 溫暖舒適的: *a snug little room with a warm fire* 生着火的溫暖舒適的小房間 **2** fitting closely (used to describe clothes) 合身的, 貼身的〔用以形容衣服〕

snug·gle /ˈsnʌgl; ˈsnʌgəl/ *v* **snuggled, snuggling** [I] to settle into a warm comfortable position 舒適地蜷伏, 偎依: *Snuggle up to me and I'll keep you warm.* 偎依着我, 我會使你暖和的。

so¹ /so; səʊ/ *adv* **1** used when you are talking again about something that has already been mentioned 如此, 如是〔用於提及已經提到過的事情〕: *"Will you be coming to the party tonight?" "I think so."* "你今晚來參加晚會嗎?" "我打算來。" | *He hopes he'll get the job and I hope so too.* 他希望他能得到那份工作, 我也希望如此。| *Are you married? If so, please give your wife's name.* 你結婚了嗎? 如果結婚了, 請說出你太太的名字。 **2** used when you are making sure that you have understood something that you have been told 這麼說〔用於確認自己已理解別人所說的話〕: *So he didn't go to America after all.* 這麼說她最終還是沒有去美國。| *So she didn't get the job?* 這麼說他沒

有得到那份工作? **3** used when you are going to tell someone something again, but more briefly, to make sure that they have understood 也就是說〔用於以簡明的方式再次把自己的話重複一遍, 以確保聽者理解〕: *The Birmingham factory produces sweets. The other section of the business, the one in Derby, is concerned with soft drinks. So we've got sweets in Birmingham and soft drinks in Derby.* 伯明翰的工廠生產糖果。該公司的另外一家廠, 也就是在德比的那一家, 負責生產汽水。這也就是說我們在伯明翰生產糖果, 在德比生產汽水。 **4** used when you are describing something by showing it with your hands 如此, 這樣〔用於做手勢描繪某物〕: *Then you have to fold the paper so.* 然後你必須把紙這樣摺。| *It was about so big.* 大約有這麼大。 **5** to such a degree, to a very great degree 如此, 這麼, 那麼: *He was so fat that he couldn't get through the door.* 他太胖了, 無法通過這門。| *He's a lovely child, and so clever.* 他是個可愛的孩子, 還那麼聰明。 –see 見 SUCH (USAGE用法) **6** also 也, 又: *"I need a drink." "So do I."* "我要杯飲料。" "我也要一杯。" | *"Ann can play the piano." "So can Sally."* "安會彈鋼琴。" "莎莉也會。" **7 and so on, and so forth** used to say that there are lots of other things that you could add to a list 等等〔用於表示仍有許多其他東西可列舉〕: *The place was full of junk – old furniture, paintings, and so on.* 那個地方滿是垃圾 — 舊家具、圖畫等等。 **8 so as to** in order to do something 為了: *She put her arms up so as to protect herself.* 她舉起胳膊以保護自己。 **9 so long** *infml* GOODBYE 〖非正式〗再見 **10 so much for…** you use this phrase when you are disappointed that something has not happened 這就是…, …就只有這些〔用於因某事沒有發生而感到失望〕: *I see they've appointed another man as Head of Department. So much for equality!* 聽說他們已指派另一個人當系主任了。這就是所謂的平等!

so² *conj* **1** therefore 因此, 所以: *It was dark so I couldn't see very well.* 天很黑, 所以我看得不太清楚。| *It was quite late so I went to bed.* 時間已不早了, 所以我就睡覺了。 **2** (also 又作 **so that**) with the purpose that 目的是, 為了: *I put the heating on so that the house would warm up.* 我打開暖氣以使房間暖和起來。| *Put your umbrella up so you don't get wet.* 你把傘撐起來, 免得被淋濕。 **3 so what?** *infml* a phrase you use to show that you think that something is not at all important 〖非正式〗那有甚麼了不起?〔用於認為某事無足輕重〕

so³ *adj* [never before a noun 不能用於名詞前] true 真實的: *Is that really so?* 真是那樣的嗎? | *You know very well that just isn't so.* 你很清楚情況並非如此。

soak¹ /sok; səʊk/ *v* [I;T] **1** to put something in liquid and leave it there 浸, 泡: *Leave the* *dirty clothes to soak.* 把髒衣服浸泡一下。| *Soak the bread in milk.* 把麵包放在牛奶裡泡。| *I'm going to soak in the bath for a while.* 我準備到浴缸裡去泡一會兒。**2** (of a liquid) to get into something and make it very wet 〔液體〕浸濕, 浸透, 滲透: *The ink had soaked throught the thin paper.* 墨水已滲透了那張薄紙。

soak *sthg* ↔ **up** *phr v* [T] **1** to take in liquid 吸乾〔液體〕: *Use a cloth to soak up the water.* 用布把水吸乾。**2** *infml* to take in the sun through your skin《非正式》曬太陽: *He's at the beach soaking up some sunshine.* 他在海灘上沐日光浴。

soak² *n* **1** an act of leaving something in liquid 浸, 泡: *Give the clothes a good soak before you wash them.* 先把衣服好好地浸泡一下才洗。**2** *infml* a person who is frequently drunk《非正式》酒徒; 酒鬼

soaked /sokt; səukt/ *adj* [never before a noun 不能用於名詞前] thoroughly wet 濕透的: *You're soaked! Take off those wet clothes!* 你全身濕透了! 快把濕衣服脫下來!

soak·ing /'sokɪŋ; 'səukɪŋ/ *adj* very wet indeed 濕透的: *My coat's soaking wet.* 我的外衣濕透了。| *I'm soaking!* 我全身濕透了!

so-and-so /'··,·/ *n* **1** [U] a person or thing that has not been named and is usually one of a group of similar people 某某人; 某某事: *When Mrs So-and-so comes into the shop, make her feel welcome.* 當某某夫人走進商店時, 要讓她感到受歡迎。**2** [C] a person who has done something bad (a word used to express disapproval) 傢伙, 小子〔含貶義〕: *The so-and-so charged me £20 for ten minutes' work!* 那小子只幹了十分鐘, 卻開價要二十英鎊!

soap¹ /sop; səup/ *n* [U] a product made from fat and used for washing 肥皂: *a bar of soap* 一塊肥皂 | *soap powder* 肥皂粉 — **soapy** *adj* **soapier, soapiest**: *soapy water* 肥皂水

soap² *v* [T] (also 又作 **soap yourself**) to rub soap on or over yourself 給〔自己〕抹上肥皂: *I was just soaping myself in the bath when the telephone rang.* 我正在浴缸裡往身上塗肥皂, 就在這時電話鈴響了起來。

soap op·e·ra /'· ,···/ *n* a continuing television or radio story about the lives and problems of imaginary characters 〔電視或電台的〕連續劇, 肥皂劇

soar /sor; sɔː/ *v* [I] *lit*《文》**1** to fly 飛翔: *birds soaring over the hills* 在山上飛翔的鳥兒 **2** to rise far or fast 驟升: *The temperature soared to 35℃.* 氣溫驟升至攝氏三十五度。| *soaring prices* 飛漲的物價 | *The cliffs soar 500ft into the air.* 懸崖聳入天際, 有五百英尺高。

sob /sab; sɒb/ *v* **-bb-** [I] to cry while breathing in sudden short bursts 抽泣, 嗚咽: *The little boy was sobbing in the corner.* 小男孩在角落裡抽泣。| *She sobbed herself to sleep.*

她抽泣到睡着了。—**sob** *n*: *"Don't be so nasty to me!" she said with a sob.* "別對我這麼兇!" 她抽泣着說。

so·ber¹ /'sobə; 'səubə/ *adj* **1** not drunk 未喝醉的 **2** thoughtful, serious, or solemn 沉思的; 認真的; 嚴肅的 **3** plain and dull 樸素的; 素淡的: *a sober dress* 一條樸素的裙子 — **soberly** *adv* —**sobriety** /sə'braɪətɪ; sə'braɪəti/ *n* [U]

sober² *v*

sober up *phr v* [I;T] **sober** *sbdy* **up**) to lose or take away the effects of alcohol (使)酒醒: *I hope this coffee sobers him up.* 我希望這杯咖啡能使他酒醒。| *You'd better sober up before your wife sees you!* 在你太太看到你之前, 你最好醒醒酒!

so·ber·ing /'sobərɪŋ; 'səubərɪŋ/ *adj* making you become serious or thoughtful 令人嚴肅的; 使人沉思的: *Her illness had a sobering effect on her.* 她的病令她變得嚴肅了。

★so-called /,·'·◂/ *adj* [only before a noun 只用於名詞前] **1** wrongly named 所謂的; 名不符實的: *so-called Christians who show no love to anyone* 對任何人都沒有愛心的所謂基督教徒 **2** known by a particular name 叫做...的, 號稱的: *Do you mean the so-called "Gang of Five"?* 你指的是所謂的"五人集團"嗎?

soc·cer /'sakə; 'sɒkə/ *n* [U] *BrE* football《英式》足球: *a soccer match* 一場足球比賽 | *Do you play soccer at school?* 你在學校踢足球嗎? —see picture on page 957 見 957 頁彩圖

so·cia·ble /'soʃəbl; 'səuʃəbəl/ *adj* fond of being with other people 愛好交際的, 喜歡與人交往的 —**sociability** /-ʃə'bɪlətɪ; -ʃə'bɪljᵻti/ *n* [U]

★★so·cial /'soʃəl; 'səuʃəl/ *adj* **1** concerning human society or its organization 社會的, 有關社會的: *social change* 社會變革 | *social, political, and economic systems* 社會、政治和經濟制度 **2** based on rank in society 社會地位上的; 社會階層上的: *people of different social classes* 不同社會階層的人 **3** relating to activities that you do with other people in your free time 社交的, 交際的: *We have an active social life.* 我們的社交生活很活躍。**4** forming groups or living together by nature 羣居的: *social insects such as ants* 螞蟻等羣居昆蟲 —**socially** *adv*

so·cial·is·m /'soʃəl,ɪzəm; 'səuʃəlɪzəm/ *n* [U] a set of beliefs which aims for the establishment of a society in which every person is equal 社會主義

so·cial·ist¹ /'soʃəlɪst; 'səuʃəlᵻst/ *n* **1** a believer in socialism 社會主義者 **2** a member of a socialist political party 社會黨黨員

socialist² *adj* of, concerning, or following socialism 社會主義的: *socialist principles* 社會主義原則 | *a socialist government* 社會主義政府

so·cial·ize /'soʃə,laɪz; 'səuʃəl-aɪz/ *v* **social-**

S

ized, socializing (also 又作 **socialise** *BrE* 〖英式〗) [I] to spend time with other people in a friendly way 與⋯交往: *There will be no socializing during business hours!* 辦公時間不許進行社交活動!

social sci·ence /ˌ·· ˈ··/ *n* [C;U] the study of people in society 社會科學: *I intend to study social science.* 我打算學習社會科學。| *the importance of social sciences such as economics or politics* 諸如經濟學或政治學等社會科學的重要性

social sci·en·tist /ˌ·· ˈ···/ *n* a person who studies or teaches social science 研究或教授社會科學的人

social se·cu·ri·ty /ˌ·· ·ˈ··/ *n* *BrE* 〖英式〗 (**welfare** *AmE* 〖美式〗) [U] a system that allows money to be paid to people who have no job or little money 社會保障制度

social serv·ic·es /ˌ·· ·ˈ··/ *n* [pl] *BrE* 〖英式〗 the services provided by the government for people in need 〖英式〗社會福利事業

social work /ˈ·· ·/ *n* [U] work done to improve bad social conditions and help people in need 社會福利工作 **–social worker** *n*

S **☆☆so·ci·e·ty** /səˈsaɪətɪ; səˈsaɪəti/ *n* **societies 1** [C;U] a large group of people with shared customs and laws 社會: *That is unacceptable in our society.* 在我們的社會中, 那是不可接受的。| *Far Eastern societies* 遠東各國的社會 | *in Western society* 在西方社會中 **2** [U] people living together, considered as a whole 羣體; 團體: *Society has a right to expect obedience to the law.* 社會羣體有權要求人人遵守法律。**3** [C] an organization of people with similar aims and interests 社團, 協會: *a film society* 電影協會 **4** [U] *fml* the company of others 〖正式〗交際, 交往: *I prefer to spend time in the society of my friends.* 我喜歡和朋友交往, 消磨時間。**5** (also 又作 **Society**) [U] the fashionable people in an area 上流社會, 社交界: *Her marriage to a road-sweeper shocked London Society.* 她嫁給了馬路清潔工, 這令倫敦的上流社會大為吃驚。

so·ci·ol·o·gy /ˌsəʊʃɪˈɒlədʒɪ; ˌsəʊsiˈɒlədʒi/ *n* [U] the study of societies and human behaviour in groups 社會學 **–sociologist** *n* – **sociological** /ˌsəʊʃɪˈlɒdʒɪkl; ˌsəʊsiəˈlɒdʒɪkəl/ *adj*

sock /sak; sɒk/ *n* **1** a garment which covers your foot and is usually worn inside a shoe 短襪 –see 見 PAIR (USAGE用法) –see picture on page 210 見 210 頁彩圖 **2 pull your socks up** *BrE infml* to stop being lazy and start working hard 〖英式, 非正式〗加緊努力工作

sock·et /ˈsakɪt; ˈsɒkɪt/ *n* an opening into which something fits 承口, 窩, 插座: *eye sockets* 眼窩 | *Could you fit an electric light bulb into that socket?* 你能把電燈泡插到那個插座裏去嗎? –see picture on page 958 見 958 頁彩圖

sod /sad; sɒd/ *n* [C;U] earth with grass and roots growing in it 草地, 草皮, 草坪

so·da /ˈsodə; ˈsəʊdə/ *n* [U] **1** see 見 SODA WATER **2** the usual American word for 〖美式〗= POP² (2): *a bottle of orange soda* 一瓶橘子汽水

soda wa·ter /ˈ·· ˌ··/ *n* [U] water filled with gas 蘇打水: *Whisky and soda, please.* 請來一杯加蘇打水的威士忌酒。

sod·den /ˈsadn; ˈsɒdn/ *adj* extremely wet 極濕的: *sodden clothes* 濕透的衣服

so·di·um /ˈsodɪəm; ˈsəʊdɪəm/ *n* [U] a silver-white metal that is found only in combination with other substances 鈉

so·fa /ˈsofə; ˈsəʊfə/ *n* a comfortable seat long enough for two or three people to sit on (長)沙發 –see picture on page 730 見 730 頁彩圖

☆soft /sɒft; sɒft/ *adj* **1** easily pressed into a different shape 軟的, 柔軟的: *a soft cushion* 軟墊子 | *His foot sank into the soft snow.* 他的腳陷入鬆軟的雪中。**2** smooth and delicate to the touch 柔滑的, 細嫩的: *soft skin* 柔滑的皮膚 **3** restful and pleasant to the senses, especially to your eyes 〔感覺上, 尤指視覺上〕柔和的, 不刺目的: *soft lights* 柔和的光線 | *soft colours* 柔和的色彩 **4** quiet 輕柔的: *soft music* 輕柔的音樂 | *a soft voice* 輕柔的嗓音 **5** *infml* not severe enough 〖非正式〗不夠嚴厲的: *Don't let him do that; you're too soft with him.* 別讓他那樣做, 你對他管得太鬆了。**6 soft drink** a drink containing no alcohol 〔不含酒精的〕軟性飲料, 汽水 **7** allowing soap to spread easily (used of water) 軟性的〔肥皂容易起泡〕〔指水〕: *We're lucky that the local water here is quite soft.* 我們很幸運, 當地的水質比較軟。**8** not of the strongest, most harmful kind 不是最強烈的; 不是最有害的: *soft pornography* 軟性色情文學 | *soft drugs like cannabis* 大麻之類的軟性毒品 **9** *infml* foolish or mad 〖非正式〗愚蠢的; 瘋狂的: *Have you gone soft in the head?* 你瘋了嗎? **10** easy 容易的, 輕鬆的: *a soft job* 一件輕鬆的工作 | *Selling the company would be the soft option, but I want to try and make a success of it.* 把公司賣掉是最省事的選擇, 但我想試試讓公司的經營獲得成功。**–softly** *adv* **–softness** *n* [U]

soft-boiled /ˌ·ˈ· ·◂/ *adj* boiled for a short time so that the inside is still soft (used of an egg) 煮得半熟的〔指蛋〕

soft·en /ˈsɒfən; ˈsɒfən/ *v* **1** [I;T] to make something or to become softer, more gentle, less hard, or less severe (使)變軟; (使)變輕柔; (使)變溫和: *This cream softens dry skin.* 這種潤膚霜可使乾燥的皮膚變得柔滑。| *His attitude towards children softened when he had a son of his own.* 當他有了自己的兒子以後, 他對待孩子的態度就變得溫和了。**2 soften the blow** to make unpleasant news easier to accept 使壞消息變得易於接受, 使緩

和打擊

soften sbdy ↔ **up** *phr v* [T] to make someone feel good so that they will do something for you 打動, 使〔某人〕軟化

soft·heart·ed /'sɔft'hɑrtɪd; ,sɒft'hɑːtɪd◂/ *adj* kind and sympathetic 心腸軟的, 好心腸的 –**soft-heartedness** *n* [U]

soft·spok·en /,· '···◂/ *adj* having a gentle voice 聲音柔和的, 説話斯文的

✸**soft·ware** /'sɔft,wɛr; 'sɒftweər/ *n* [U] lists of instructions that must be given to a computer in order to make it perform operations; these lists are called programs (PROGRAM) 電腦軟件: *Is there any new software for this machine?* 有沒有供這台機器使用的新軟件?

soft·wood /'sɔft,wʊd; 'sɒftwʊd/ *n* [U] wood that comes from particular trees and is easy to cut 軟木材

sog·gy /'sɑgi; 'sɒgi/ *adj* **soggier, soggiest** unpleasantly wet 黏濕的, 濕透的: *The ground is still soggy from yesterday's rain.* 由於昨天下過雨, 地上仍然濕漉漉的。| *If you boil the vegetables for too long, they'll go soggy.* 蔬菜如果煮的時間過長, 就會變得濕乎乎的。

✸**soil¹** /sɔɪl; sɔɪl/ *n* [U] **1** the top covering of the earth, in which plants grow 泥土, 土壤: *fertile soil* 肥沃的土壤 | *poor soil* 貧瘠的土壤 **2** the land that forms part of a country 國土: *It was his first experience of being on foreign soil.* 那是他首次踏上異國的土地。– see 見 LAND¹(USAGE用法)

soil² *v* [T] to make something dirty 使〔某物〕變髒: *Your shirt collar is badly soiled.* 你的襯衫領子很髒。

sol·ace /'sɑlɪs; 'sɒlɪs/ *n* [C;U] something that provides comfort when you are unhappy or worried 安慰, 慰藉

so·lar /'solə; 'səʊlər/ *adj* of, from, or using the sun or its light 太陽的; 太陽光的: *solar power* 太陽能 | *a solar heating system* 太陽能暖氣系統 –compare 比較 LUNAR

solar sys·tem /'··, ···/ *n* **1 the solar system** the sun together with the bodies that move around it 太陽系 **2** [C] a system like this around another star 恒星系

sold /sold; səʊld/ *v* the past tense and past participle of SELL ☆ SELL 的過去式和過去分詞

solder¹ /'sɑdə; 'sɒldər/ *n* [U] soft metal which is used to join together other metal surfaces 焊料, 焊錫

solder² *v* [T] to join or repair metal with solder 焊接: *I'll solder those pipes together.* 我會把那些管子焊起來。

✸**sol·dier¹** /'soldʒə; 'səʊldʒər/ *n* a member of an army 士兵

soldier²

soldier on *phr v* [I] *BrE* to continue doing something in spite of difficulties 〖英式〗克服困難做〔某事〗, 繼續幹下去

✸**sole¹** /sol; səʊl/ *n* **1** [C] the bottom surface of your foot 腳底, 腳掌 **2** [C] the part of a sock, shoe, or boot that covers the bottom of your foot 〔襪、鞋、靴的〕底部 **3** [C;U] a flat white fish eaten as food 鰨〔魚〕

sole² *v* **soled, soling** [T] to put a new surface on the bottom of a shoe 換鞋底: *I'd better get my shoes soled.* 我最好給鞋子換鞋底。

sole³ *adj* [only before a noun 只用於名詞前] **1** only 唯一的, 僅有的: *The sole survivor of the crash was a baby.* 這場車禍中唯一的幸存者是一名嬰兒。**2** not shared with another person 獨佔的: *You have sole responsibility for this department.* 你專責代表這個部門。

sole·ly /'solli; 'səʊl-li/ *adv* only 僅僅, 獨一無二地: *I did it solely for your own good.* 我僅僅是為了你才這樣做的。

sol·emn /'sɑləm; 'sɒləm/ *adj* **1** serious 嚴肅的: *His expression was unusually solemn.* 他的神情異常嚴肅。**2** formal 正式的; 隆重的: *a solemn promise* 鄭重的承諾 –**solemnly** *adv* –**solemnity** /sə'lɛmnəti; sə'lemnəti/ *n* [U]

so·li·cit /sə'lɪsɪt; sə'lɪsɪt/ *v* **1** [I;T] *fml* to ask for something such as help or support 〖正式〗請求, 懇求〔幫助或支持等〕: *Beggars are not allowed to solicit in public places.* 乞丐不得在公共場所乞討。| *We intend to solicit the views of all our members.* 我們打算徵求一下我們所有成員的意見。**2** [I] to offer to have sex for money 〔妓女〕拉客: *The police charged her with soliciting.* 警方控告她拉客賣淫。

✸**so·lic·i·tor** /sə'lɪsətə; sə'lɪsɪtər/ *n* a lawyer who gives advice, prepares legal cases, and appears in lower law courts 〔解答疑難、準備案件並出席下級法庭的〕事務律師

so·lic·i·tous /sə'lɪsɪtəs; sə'lɪsɪtəs/ *adj* *fml* concerned or anxious to help 〖正式〗關切的, 關心的 –**solicitously** *adv* –**solicitousness** *n* [U]

✸**sol·id¹** /'sɑlɪd; 'sɒlɪd/ *adj* **1** hard, so that it keeps its shape 固體的: *The milk had frozen solid.* 牛奶已凍結了。| *a solid lump of fat* 一塊固體油脂 **2** tightly packed together, with no empty space inside 實心的: *solid rubber tyres* 實心橡膠輪胎 | *solid rock* 堅實的岩石 **3** without spaces or breaks 不中斷的, 連續的: *She overtook another car on a solid white line.* 她在連續白線上超過了另一輛車。| *I waited for three solid hours.* 我等了整整三個小時。**4** [only before a noun 只用於名詞前] completely of one material 〔金屬〕純質的: *a solid gold watch* 純金手錶 **5** strong and dependable 堅固的; 可靠的: *solid furniture* 堅固的家具 | *solid evidence* 有力的證據 **6** continuous and useful 連續的; 有用的: *I need to get a few years' solid work experience.* 我需要有幾年實在的工作經驗。**7** *tech* having length, width, and height 〖術語〗立體的: *A sphere is a solid figure.* 球體是立體形的。–**solidly** *adv* –**solidity** /sə'lɪdəti;

saˈlɪdⱼ̩ti/ n [U]

solid² n **1** something that is firm and keeps its shape 固體: *Water becomes a solid when it freezes.* 水在結冰時變成固體。 **2 solids** non-liquid food 固體食物, 非流質食物: *He is still too ill to take solids.* 他仍病得很重, 無法吃固體食物。 **3** tech a figure with length, width, and height〖術語〗立體

sol·i·dar·i·ty /ˌsɑləˈdærəti; ˌsɒlɪˈdærⱼ̩ti/ n [U] agreement among a group of people about their common interests, aims, or standards 團結, 一致

so·lid·i·fy /səˈlɪdəˌfaɪ; səˈlɪdⱼ̩faɪ/ v **solidified, solidifying** [I;T] to make something or to become hard or firm (使)變得堅硬 **–so·lidification** /səˌlɪdəfəˈkeɪʃən; səˌlɪdⱼ̩fⱼ̩ˈkeɪʃən/ n [U]

so·lil·o·quy /səˈlɪləkwɪ; səˈlɪləkwi/ n **soliloquies** a speech especially in a play where you speak your thoughts aloud to yourself〖劇中的〗獨白; 自言自語

sol·i·ta·ry /ˈsɑləˌtɛrɪ; ˈsɒlⱼ̩təri/ adj **1** spending a lot of time alone 孤獨的: *He's a rather solitary young man.* 他是個頗為孤獨的年輕人。 **2** done alone 獨自完成的: *Reading is usually a solitary activity.* 閱讀一般是一個人的活動。 **3** standing alone, away from others 孤僻的; 偏僻的: *a solitary building* 一座偏僻的房子 **4** single 單個的: *Can you give me one solitary piece of proof for what you say?* 對於你所說的話, 你能給我提供一項證據嗎? **5 in solitary confinement** alone in a prison cell without seeing the other prisoners 單獨監禁 [RELATED PHRASE 相關詞組 **in solitary**]

sol·i·tude /ˈsɑləˌtjud; ˈsɒlⱼ̩tjuːd/ n [U] the state of being alone and away from other people 孤獨, 孤寂

so·lo¹ /ˈsoloʊ; ˈsəʊləʊ/ n **solos** a piece of music played or sung by one person 獨奏曲; 獨唱曲 **–compare** 比較 DUET

so·lo² adj done by one person alone 獨自完成的, 單獨的: *my first solo flight* 我的首次單獨飛行 **–solo** adv: *Have you ever flown solo?* 你有沒有單獨飛行過?

so·lo·ist /ˈsoloʊ-ɪst; ˈsəʊləʊⱼ̩st/ n a person who performs a piece of music written for one person to play or sing alone 獨奏者; 獨唱者

sol·stice /ˈsɑlstɪs; ˈsɒlstⱼ̩s/ n either the shortest or the longest day in the year; in the northern half of the world the **winter solstice** is December 21 or 22 and the **summer solstice** is June 21 or 22 至, 至日〖北半球的冬至為12月21日或22日, 夏至為6月21日或22日〗

sol·u·ble /ˈsɑljəbəl; ˈsɒljⱼ̩bəl/ adj **1** that will become part of a liquid when mixed with it 可溶的: *Salt is soluble in water.* 鹽可以溶於水。 **2** to which an answer can be found 可以解決的: *a soluble problem* 可以解決的問題 **–opposite** 反義 **insoluble**

so·lu·tion /səˈluʃən; səˈluːʃən/ n **1** [C] an answer to a difficulty or problem 答案; 解決辦法: *It's difficult to find a solution that we can all agree on.* 很難找到我們大家都同意的解決辦法。 | *the solution to yesterday's crossword* 昨日縱橫字謎遊戲的答案 **2** [U] ways of dealing with a difficulty or problem 解決; 解答: *We're investigating approaches to the solution* **of** *domestic problems.* 我們正在研究對付國內問題的解決辦法。 **3** [C;U] a liquid containing a solid or gas mixed into it 溶液, 溶劑: *chemical solution* 化學溶液

solve /sɑlv; sɒlv/ v **solved, solving** [T] to find an answer to something or way of dealing with it 解決, 解答〖問題〗: *I'm trying to solve the problem.* 我正在試圖解決這個問題。 **–solvable** adj

sol·vent¹ /ˈsɑlvənt; ˈsɒlvənt/ adj having enough money to pay all that you owe 有還債能力的 **–opposite** 反義 **insolvent** **–solvency** n [U]

solvent² n [C;U] a liquid that can DISSOLVE(2) a substance 溶劑: *Alcohol and petrol are useful solvents.* 酒精和汽油是很有效的溶劑。

som·bre /ˈsɑmbɚ; ˈsɒmbər/ adj BrE 〖英式〗 (also 又作 **somber** AmE 〖美式〗) **1** sad and serious 憂鬱的; 嚴肅的: *a sombre speech* 嚴肅的講話 **2** dark and dull 昏暗的, 暗淡的: *a sombre business suit* 一套顏色暗淡的(成套)西服 **–somberly** adv

some /səm; səm, strong 強讀 sʌm; sʌm/ det, pron **1** a certain amount or number 一些, 有些, 某些: *Some parts of the country are very cold in winter.* 該國有些地方冬天非常冷。 | *He asked for money and I gave him some.* 他問我要錢, 我給了他一些。 | *Some of the stories are very good.* 這些故事中有一些非常不錯。 **2** used when you mention an unknown person or thing 某一(個)〖用於提及不知道的人或物〗: *There must be some reason for it.* 其中肯定有某種原因。 | *She met some man while she was living in Italy.* 她住在意大利時遇到了某個男子。 **3** **some... or other** a phrase used when you mention an unknown person or thing 某一, 某個; 某些〖用於提及不知道的人或物〗: *I read it in some book or other.* 我在某本書裡看到過。

■ USAGE 用法: In negative sentences we use **any** and **no** instead of **some** ☆ 在否定句中, 我們用 **any** 和 **no** 代替 **some**: *I haven't* **any** *socks.* 我沒有襪子。 | *I have* **no** *socks.* 我沒有襪子。 In questions we usually use **any** ☆ 在疑問句中, 我們常用 **any**: *Is there* **any** *chance that he'll pass the exam?* 他有沒有機會通過考試? But we use **some** in offers, suggestions, and requests ☆ 但在提議、建

議和請求中，我們用 **some**: *Would you like* **some** *tea?* 你想要些茶嗎？ | *Shall we have* **some** *tea?* 我們喝杯茶怎麼樣？ | *Can I have* **some** *tea, please?* 請問我能喝點茶嗎？ The same is true of compounds of **some, any**, and **no** such as **something, anyone, nobody**. ☆ 上述用法也適用於 **some, any** 和 **no** 構成的複合詞，如 **something, anyone, nobody**。

***some·bod·y** /'sʌm,bɑdɪ; 'sʌmbɒdi/ *pron* (also 又作 **someone**) a person, but not a particular one and not one who is known 某人，有人: *There's somebody on the telephone for you.* 有人打電話找你。 | *You'd better ask someone to help you.* 你最好叫人來幫你一把。 | *I thought the parcel was for me, but it was for somebody else.* 我本以為這包裹是給我的，但其實是給別人的。 −see 見 EVERYBODY (USAGE 用法)

some·day /'sʌm,de; 'sʌmdeɪ/ *adv* (also 又作 **some day**) at some future time 將來總有一天，有朝一日: *Perhaps someday I'll be rich.* 也許有一天我會富有起來。

***some·how** /'sʌm,haʊ; 'sʌmhaʊ/ *adv* **1** in some way that is not known 不知怎樣地；以某種方式: *We'll get the money somehow.* 我們會想辦法找點錢回來的。 | *Somehow the thieves had managed to get in through a tiny bathroom window.* 那些竊賊不知用甚麼辦法從浴室的一扇小窗鑽了進去。 **2** for some reason that is not clear 因某種不明的原因: *Somehow I don't trust him completely.* 不知為甚麼，我並不完全信任他。

***some·one** /'sʌm,wʌn; 'sʌmwʌn/ *pron* see 見 SOMEBODY

som·er·sault /'sʌmə,sɔlt; 'sʌməsɔːlt/ *v* to do a rolling backward or forward movement in which your feet go over your head while your body stays close to the ground 翻觔斗 −**somersault** *n*

***some·thing** /'sʌmθɪŋ; 'sʌmθɪŋ/ *pron* **1** a thing that is not known or not described in detail 某物，某事: *I could see something moving in the bushes.* 我能看見有東西在灌木叢中移動。 | *I think I've dropped something.* 我想我丟了些甚麼東西。 | *I'm worried that something might have happened to him.* 我很擔心他也許發生了些甚麼事。 **2 or something** a phrase used when you are not completely sure what a thing is, or are suggesting other possibilities 是甚麼的，或是…之類〔用於表示不能完全肯定或是提出其他可能性〕: *It must have been eaten by a fox or something.* 那東西肯定是被狐狸或其他甚麼動物吃掉了。 | *Let's go to a film or something.* 讓我們去看場電影或幹點別的甚麼事情。 **3 something like: a** rather like 有點像: *It looked something like a potato.* 它看上去有點像馬鈴薯。 **b** about 大約: *There were something like 1000 people on the march.* 約有一千人參加了遊行。 **4 something to do with** having a connection with 同…有關: *I don't know exactly what his job is, but it's something to do with oil.* 我不大知道他確實是做甚麼工作的，但我知道是有關石油方面的。 **5 that's something** a phrase used to say that at least there is one good thing 還算是不錯〔用於表示至少還有一件好事〕: *At least we didn't lose any money. That's something!* 最起碼我們沒有損失金錢。那已經算是不錯了!

some·time¹ /'sʌm,taɪm; 'sʌmtaɪm/ *adv* at some uncertain time in the past or the future 在〔過去或將來的〕某個時候: *Our house was built sometime around 1905.* 我們的房子建於1905年左右。 | *You must come and visit us sometime.* 你甚麼時候有空一定要來探望我們。

sometime² *adj* [only before a noun 只用於名詞前] *fml* former 〔正式〕以前的，昔日的: *the sometime chairman of British Rail* 前英國鐵路部部長

***some·times** /'sʌm,taɪmz; 'sʌmtaɪmz/ *adv* on some occasions but not on others 有時，偶爾: *Sometimes I drive to work and sometimes I walk.* 我有時開車去上班，有時走路去上班。

***some·what** /'sʌm,hwɑt; 'sʌmwɒt/ *adv fml* slightly 〔正式〕略微，稍稍，有點: *He looked cold, and somewhat lonely.* 他看上去冷冰冰的樣子，還有幾分孤獨。 | *The news somewhat surprised me.* 這消息令我有點吃驚。 | *The experience of being in prison has changed him somewhat.* 坐牢的經歷使他有了點改變。

***some·where** /'sʌm,hwɛr; 'sʌmweəʳ/ *adv* **1** in or to some place 某處；在某地；到某地: *She's on holiday somewhere in Spain.* 她在西班牙某地度假。 | *I'm looking for my bag — it must be somewhere.* 我在找我的手提包──它一定是放到了甚麼地方了。 **2** used when you are giving a number that is not exact 大約，左右〔用於表示不確切的數字〕: *somewhere between 40 and 60 students* 大約四十到六十個學生之間

***son** /sʌn; sʌn/ *n* a male child 兒子 −compare 比較 DAUGHTER −see picture on page 503 見 503 頁彩圖

so·na·ta /sə'nɑtə; sə'nɑːtə/ *n* a piece of music for one or two instruments, one of which is a piano 奏鳴曲

***song** /sɔŋ; sɒŋ/ *n* **1** [C] a piece of music with words for singing 歌曲: *a love song* 情歌 | *folk song* 民歌 | *They're playing our song.* 他們在演奏我們的歌曲。 **2** [U] the act of singing 歌唱: *After a few drinks, we burst into song.* 幾杯酒過後，我們唱起歌來。 **3** [C; U] the musical sound that a bird makes 鳥鳴聲，鳥語: *the song of the blackbird* 黑鸝的鳴聲 **4 for a song** cheaply 便宜地: *I bought that old wardrobe for a song.* 我以很便宜的價錢買了那個舊衣櫃。 **5 make a song and**

dance about something to be unnecessarily annoyed or worried about something 沒必要為某事感到生氣或憂慮: *Stop making such a song and dance about the washing-up and do it!* 別為了洗幾隻碗而嘮嘮叨叨了，快去洗吧!

song·bird /'sɔŋ.bɜːd; 'sɒŋbɜːd/ *n* a bird that can sing well 鳴鳥, 鳴禽

son·ic /'sɑnɪk; 'sɒnɪk/ *adj* of or relating to sound waves 聲波的, 音波的

son-in-law /'···/ *n* **sons-in-law** the husband of your daughter 女婿 –compare 比較 DAUGHTER-IN-LAW –see picture on page 503 見 503 頁彩圖

son·net /'sɑnɪt; 'sɒnᵻt/ *n* a 14-line poem with a formal pattern of line endings 十四行詩

so·nor·ous /sə'nɔrəs; 'sɒnərəs/ *adj fml* having a pleasantly full sound 〔正式〕聲音洪亮的: *a sonorous bell* 洪亮的鐘聲 | *a sonorous voice* 洪亮的聲音

★★**soon** /sun; suːn/ *adv* **1** a short time from now, or a short time after the time mentioned 很快, 不久, 即刻: *I hope to hear from him soon.* 我希望不久能收到他的信。| *He died soon after he retired.* 他退休後不久便去世了。| *We should arrive soon after lunch.* 我們應在午飯後不久到達那裡。**2 as soon as** after something has happened without any delay 一...就..., 盡快: *I'll phone you as soon as I hear any news.* 我一得到任何消息便會打電話給你。**3 no sooner...than** a phrase you use to say that after one thing has happened something else happens without any delay 一...就...〔用於表示一件事緊接着另一件事發生〕: *No sooner had she sat down than the phone rang.* 她剛坐下電話鈴便響了。**4 sooner or later** a phrase used to say that something is certain to happen, either soon or after a time 遲早, 總有一天: *Don't worry, you'll find a job sooner or later.* 別擔心, 你遲早會找到工作的。**5 the sooner the better** a phrase used to say that you would like something to happen as soon as possible 越快越好: *The sooner she leaves home the better.* 她越快離家越好。**6 would just as soon, would sooner** phrases you use to say that you would prefer to do something 寧可, 寧願〔用於表示喜歡做某事〕: *I'd sooner die than spend my life in a wheelchair.* 我寧願死也不願意終生坐在輪椅上。

soot /sut; sʊt/ *n* [U] black powder produced by fires, and often found in a chimney 煤灰, 煙灰 –**sooty** *adj* **sootier, sootiest**

soothe /suð; suːð/ *v* **soothed, soothing** [T] **1** to make someone who is angry or anxious feel calmer 使〔某人〕平靜; 安慰: *A nice cup of tea will soothe your nerves.* 一杯好茶會使你的神經放鬆下來。| *soothing words* 安慰的話 **2** to make something less painful 減輕〔疼痛〕: *I need something to soothe my sore*

throat. 我需要點甚麼藥來減輕我喉嚨的疼痛。| *soothing cream* 鎮痛藥膏

★**so·phis·ti·cat·ed** /sə'fɪstɪˌketɪd; sə'fɪstᵻkeɪtᵻd/ *adj* **1** experienced in social life and behaviour 老於世故的, 老練的: *a sophisticated young woman* 一位老於世故的年輕女子 –opposite 反義 **unsophisticated 2** showing intelligent understanding 精通的; 熟練的: *a sophisticated response* 巧妙的問答 **3** not simple 複雜的, 精密的: *sophisticated machinery* 精密的機器 –**sophistication** /sə,fɪstɪ'keʃən; sə,fɪstᵻ'keɪʃən/ *n* [U]

sop·o·rif·ic /,sɑpə'rɪfɪk; ,sɒpə'rɪfɪk◂/ *adj* that makes you fall asleep 催眠的: *a soporific drug* 催眠的藥物 | *soporific speeches* 令人昏昏欲睡的演講

sop·ping /'sɑpɪŋ; 'sɒpɪŋ/ *adv, adj* extremely wet 極濕地[的]: *Our clothes are sopping wet.* 我們的衣服都濕透了。

sop·py /'sɑpi; 'sɒpi/ *adj* **soppier, soppiest** *BrE infml* too full of tender feelings like sorrow and love and therefore rather silly 〔英式, 非正式〕多愁善感的: *a soppy film* 過於傷感的電影 | *You're getting soppy about him!* 你對他的感情太豐富了!

so·pra·no /sə'præno; sə'prɑːnəʊ/ *n* **sopranos** a high singing voice of a woman or young boy 女高音; 男童聲最高音

sor·cer·er /'sɔrsərə˞; 'sɔːsərəʳ/ *n* a person believed to perform magic by using the power of evil spirits; a female sorcerer is called a **sorceress** 巫師術士, 施魔法者〔女巫師被稱作 **sorceress**〕–**sorcery** *n* [U]

sor·did /'sɔrdɪd; 'sɔːdᵻd/ *adj* **1** unpleasant and shameful 卑鄙的, 可恥的: *a sordid attempt to cheat his brother* 想欺騙他兄弟的可恥企圖 **2** very dirty and unpleasant 骯髒的, 髒亂的: *a rather sordid little house* 一所髒兮兮的小房子 –**sordidly** *adv* –**sordidness** *n* [U]

sore¹ /sor; sɔːʳ/ *adj* **1** painful because of infection, hard use, or a wound 〔因感染、過度用力或受傷而〕疼痛的, 酸痛的: *I've got a sore throat.* 我喉嚨痛。| *His feet are so much running.* 跑了這麼多路後, 他的腿很酸痛。**2** *infml* angry and upset 〔非正式〕憤怒的; 心煩意亂的: *She was sore at losing to a younger opponent.* 她輸給了比她年輕的對手, 感到很氣惱。**3** very serious 非常嚴重的: *The bridge is in sore need of repair.* 那座橋極需修繕。**4 a sore point** a subject that makes someone uncomfortable or upset 惹人惱怒的話題: *Don't mention drinking and driving – it's a sore point with him since he lost his licence.* 別提酒後駕車的事—自從他被吊銷駕駛執照後, 這話題就令他心煩意亂。–**soreness** *n* [U]

sore² *n* a place on the body that is painful, often because of infection 〔常因感染而造成的〕身體上的痛處

sore·ly /'sorli; 'sɔːli/ *adv fml or lit* greatly 〔正式或文〕非常, 極: *John has been sorely* *missed since he emigrated to Australia.* 自從約翰移民澳大利亞後, 大家都非常想念他.

sor·row¹ /'sɒrəʊ; 'sɒrəʊ/ *n fml* 〖正式〗 **1** [U] unhappiness 悲傷, 悲哀, 難過; 懊悔, 悔恨: *I felt great sorrow at her death.* 她的去世令我極為難過. | *He expressed deep sorrow for what he had done.* 他對自己的所作所為表示非常難過. **2** [C] a situation that makes you sad 令人悲哀〔難過〕的情景: *the sorrows of old age* 年邁所帶來的悲哀 –**sorrowful** *adj* –**sorrowfully** *adv*

sorrow² *v* [I] *lit* to experience or express sad feelings 〖文〗感到難過, 表示悲傷: *The sorrowing relatives gathered around his grave.* 悲傷的親戚聚集在他的墳墓周圍.

sor·ry /'sɒrɪ; 'sɒrɪ/ *adj* **sorrier, sorriest 1** [never before a noun 不能用於名詞前] sad 難過的, 悲傷的, 愧疚的: *I'm so sorry about your husband's death.* 對於你丈夫的去世我感到很難過. | *He was sorry to hear the news of the accident.* 聽到出事的消息, 他覺得很難過. | *I'm sorry to have to tell you this.* 很遺憾, 我不得不把這告訴你. **2** [never before a noun 不能用於名詞前] unhappy about your past actions 後悔的, 悔恨的; 抱歉的: *If you're really sorry, I'll forgive you.* 你如果真的感到後悔, 我就原諒你. | *He's sorry that he made you cry.* 他很抱歉把你弄哭了. **3 Sorry, I'm sorry** a phrase used to tell someone that you are unhappy about the effect on them of your speech or behaviour 對不起〔用於對自己的言行表示抱歉〕: *Sorry, I'm late.* 對不起, 我遲到了. | *Sorry! Did I hurt you?* 對不起! 我傷了你嗎? **4 Sorry, I'm sorry** a phrase used as a polite expression to show you do not agree with something that has been said 對不起〔用於禮貌地表示不同意某事〕: *Sorry, but I think you're wrong.* 對不起, 但我認為你錯了. **5 Sorry, I'm sorry** a phrase used to refuse permission politely 對不起〔用於禮貌地表示不允許〕: *Sorry, but you can't go in there.* 對不起, 你不能進去. **6** a word used to ask someone to repeat what they said 對不起〔用於請對方重複剛說過的話〕: *Sorry? What did you say?* 對不起, 你說甚麼? **7** a word used to correct yourself when you say the wrong thing 對不起〔用於更正自己所說的話〕: *He's six, sorry, seven years old.* 他今年六歲, 哦對不起, 他七歲了. **8 be/feel sorry for someone** to feel pity for someone 為某人感到惋惜: *I felt so sorry for him when he failed his exams.* 他考試失敗了, 我很為他感到惋惜. **9 feel sorry for yourself** to feel pity for yourself 為自己感到難過: *Stop feeling sorry for yourself and decide what you're going to do next!* 別再為自己感到難過了, 決定下一步準備做甚麼吧! **10** terrible (used of the appearance or condition of a person or thing) 糟糕的; 可憐的〔用於人或物的外表或情況〕: *He was a sorry sight in his dirty old clothes.* 他穿着髒兮兮的舊衣服, 一副可憐相.

■ USAGE 用法: In British English you may say **(I'm) sorry** to people when you accidentally touch them, or push against them, or get in their way (for example, if you step on someone's foot). In American English you say **Excuse me.** In both British and American English you can say **Sorry?** when you do not hear what someone says. You can also say **Pardon (me)?** but this is more common in American English. ☆ 在英式英語中, 如果你不小心碰到了別人〔如踩了別人的腳〕, 或推了別人, 或擋了別人的路, 你可以說 **(I'm) sorry**. 在美式英語中則說 **Excuse me.** 如果沒有聽清楚別人所說的話, 在英式和美式英語中都可以說 **Sorry?**. 你可以說 **Pardon (me)?**, 這在美式英語中更常見.

sort¹ /sɔrt; sɔːt/ *n* **1** a type or kind of person or thing 〔人或物的〕種, 類: *What sort of food do you like?* 你喜歡哪一類食物? | *There were all sorts of people there.* 那裡有各種各樣的人. | *It looks like an insect of some sort.* 牠看上去有點像某種昆蟲. –see 見 KIND¹ (USAGE 看法) **2** *infml* a person of a particular type 〖非正式〗某種人: *She's a good sort.* 她是個好人. **3 of sorts** of poor quality 質量差的: *He's a writer of sorts.* 他勉強算是個作家. **4 out of sorts** feeling unwell or annoyed 身體不舒服; 心緒不佳 **5 sort of** *infml* used when you are saying that something is true in some way 〖非正式〗有點, 有幾分: *It's sort of round and green, a bit like a lettuce.* 它有點圓有點綠, 樣子像生菜. | *I sort of thought you might say that.* 我有點覺得你也許會那麼說. | *It was a sort of dog-like creature.* 那東西看上去有點像狗.

sort² *v* [T] to put things in order or in place according to their type 把〔物品〕分類; 揀選: *The letters are all sorted here before being sent off for delivery.* 投遞之前, 所有的信件都在此分類. | *Can you sort these clothes into two piles, please?* 你能把這些衣服分成兩堆嗎?

sort sthg ↔ **out** *phr v* [T] **1** to put things into groups according to their type 把〔物品〕分類; 揀出: *I'm just sorting out the papers that can be thrown away.* 我正在把要扔掉的文件挑出來. **2** to solve a problem or difficulty 解決〔問題或困難〕: *We've got a few little problems to sort out.* 我們有幾個小問題要解決.

sort through sthg *phr v* [T] to look through a number of things in order to find the ones that you want 查看並挑選出〔某物〕: *He was sorting through a pile of papers on his desk.* 他在整理桌上的一堆文件.

sor·tie /'sɔːti; 'sɔːti/ *n* **1** a short attack made by an army from a position of defence 出擊, 突擊 **2** a short trip into an unfamiliar place 異域的短暫旅行, 探索 **3** a short experience of an unfamiliar situation 陌生環境中的短暫體驗: *His first sortie into the world of film-making wasn't very successful.* 他初次涉足電影界並不十分成功.

SOS /ˌɛs,oˈɛs; ˌes əu 'es/ *n* letters used as an international signal when help is needed, especially by ships in trouble 〔尤指遇難船隻發出的〕國際通用呼救信號

so-so /'··/ *adj, adv infml* not very bad and not very good 【非正式】馬馬虎虎的〔地〕; 一般的〔地〕: *The food was good, but the room so-so.* 吃的東西不錯, 但房間一般. | *"Does he play the piano well?" "So-so."* "他鋼琴彈得好嗎?" "還過得去."

sot·to vo·ce /ˌsɑtoˈvotʃi, ˌsɑtəʊˈvəʊtʃi/ *adv* in a soft voice so that other people cannot hear 低聲地〔不讓別人聽見〕

souf·flé /'sufle; 'suːfleɪ/ *n* [C;U] a light dish made from beaten eggs, flour, and milk, and then baked 蛋奶酥: *cheese soufflé* 乾酪蛋奶酥 | *a chocolate soufflé* 巧克力蛋奶酥

sought /sɔt; sɔːt/ *n* the past tense and past participle of SEEK ☆ SEEK 的過去式和過去分詞

soul /sol; səʊl/ *n* **1** [C] the part of a person that is believed to exist even after the body has died 靈魂: *She's dead, but her soul's in heaven.* 她雖然死了, 但她的靈魂進了天堂. **2** [U] the special quality of deep, sincere feeling 真摯, 誠摯; 內涵: *It was a stylish performance but it lacked soul.* 這是一次有氣派但缺乏內涵的演出. **3** [C] the true nature of something 精神; 精髓: *the soul of our nation* 我們的民族精神 **4 the soul of something** a fine example of a quality 典範, 化身: *Your son is the soul of charm.* 你的兒子是魅力的化身. **5** [U] see 見 SOUL MUSIC: *a soul group* 靈樂演唱組 **6 keep body and soul together** to have enough money and food to live 勉強維持生活 **7** [C] a person 人: *You mustn't tell this to a soul.* 這事你千萬不要告訴別人. | *She's a dear old soul.* 她是個可愛的老太太.

soul-des·troy·ing /'· ·ˌ··/ *adj* extremely uninteresting 極為枯燥的: *He's got a soul-destroying job in a factory.* 他在工廠裡做極為枯燥的工作.

soul·ful /'solfl; 'səʊlfəl/ *adj* full of feeling, especially great sadness 充滿感情的〔尤指悲哀〕: *a soulful look* 充滿深情的眼神 **–soulfully** *adv* **–soulfulness** *n* [U]

soul·less /'sollıs; 'səʊl-ləs/ *adj* with no warm or friendly human qualities 無人情味的: *a soulless office building* 一幢冷冰冰的辦公大樓

soul mu·sic /'· ·ˌ··/ *n* [U] a type of popular music often sung by black musicians and that expresses strong feelings 〔黑人表達強烈情感的〕靈樂

☆sound¹ /saʊnd; saʊnd/ *n* **1** [C;U] something that can be heard 聲音: *the sound of voices* 嗓音 | *strange sounds from the next room* 隔壁房間傳來的奇怪的聲音 | *Does sound travel through these walls?* 聲音能穿過這些牆壁嗎? **2 the sound of something** an idea that you get from something you read or hear 語意, 含意: *From the sound of it, I'd say the matter was serious.* 聽起來, 我認為事態很嚴重. **3** [C] a stretch of water connecting two larger areas of water 海峽 **–soundlessly** *adv*

☆sound² *v* **1** [I] (of something said or heard) to produce a particular quality or effect 〔話語〕聽起來: *Your idea sounds a good one.* 你的主意聽起來不錯. | *Does this sentence sound right?* 這句話聽起來對不對? | *It sounds as if you'll need a new car if the damage is as bad as they say.* 如果汽車損壞的情況有他們說的那麼嚴重, 你似乎就應該去買部新的. **2** [I;T] to make a noise, often as a signal 發出聲音〔常用作信號〕: *Sound your horn to warn the other driver!* 按響喇叭提醒另一個司機! | *The dinner bell sounded.* 晚飯的鐘聲響了. **3** [T] to pronounce something 讀出: *Can you sound those letters?* 你能當眾讀出那些信件嗎?

sound off *phr v* [I] to express a strong opinion, usually to people who are not interested (a phrase used to express disapproval) 大發議論; 高談闊論〔含貶義〕: *He's always sounding off about the behaviour of young people.* 他總在大談特談年輕人的言行舉止.

sound sbdy ↔ **out** *phr v* [T] to try to find out someone's opinion or intention 試探〔某人的〕意見或意向

☆sound³ *adj* **1** in good condition 完好的, 無損的: *in sound health* (身體) 很健康 | *a sound construction* 完好的建築 **2** good and dependable 良好的; 可靠的: *We're pleased with the company's sound performance this year.* 我們對公司今年的良好表現感到滿意. | *a sound candidate for the job* 做這份工作的合適人選 **3** based on truth or good judgment 據實的; 審慎的: *sound advice* 審慎的忠告 **4 sound asleep** sleeping deeply 酣睡 **–soundly** *adv* **–soundness** *n* [U]

sound ef·fects /'··ˌ·/ *n* [pl] sounds produced to give the effect of natural noises in a broadcast, play, or film 〔廣播、戲劇、電影的〕音響效果

sound·proof¹ /'saʊnd,pruf; 'saʊndpruːf/ *adj* to and from or through which sound cannot pass 隔音的: *a soundproof room* 隔音室 | *soundproof material* 隔音材料

soundproof² *v* [T] to make a place soundproof 使〔某處〕隔音: *He's soundproofed the bedroom so that he can practise playing his drums.* 他給臥室裝上了隔音設施, 以便他能練習打鼓.

---

sound·track /'saʊnd,træk; 'saʊndtræk/ *n* the recorded sound, especially the music from a film〔尤指〕電影配樂

soup /sup; suːp/ *n* [U] liquid food, usually containing small pieces of meat, fish, or vegetables that have been boiled 湯

sour¹ /saʊr; saʊəʳ/ *adj* **1** having a bitter taste 酸的, 有酸味的: *sour green apples* 帶酸味的青蘋果 **2** having an unpleasant taste produced by the chemical action of bacteria 酸腐的: *sour milk* 變酸的牛奶 **3** bad-tempered 壞脾氣的: *He gave me a sour look.* 他狠狠地看了我一眼。 **4 sour grapes** the act of pretending to dislike something that you really want quite badly, because you know that you cannot have it 酸葡萄〔由於得不到某物而裝作不喜歡〕 **5 turn sour** become unpleasant 變得不愉快: *Relationships in the office have turned sour.* 辦公室中的關係已經惡化。[RELATED PHRASE 相關詞組 **go sour**] –**sourly** *adv* –**sourness** *n* [U]

sour² *v* [I;T] **1** to make or become sour (使)變酸: *I added lemon juice to make soured cream.* 我加入檸檬汁製成酸奶油。 **2** to make or become unpleasant (使) 變得不愉快: *His bad temper soured the atmosphere.* 他的壞脾氣破壞了氣氛。

source /sors; sɔːs/ *n* **1** a place, person, or thing from which something comes 來源, 出處: *Can you find the source of the engine trouble?* 你能找出引擎出毛病的原因嗎? | *Have you any other source of income apart from your job?* 除了工作, 你還有沒有其他收入來源? | *the source of the rumour* 謠言的出處 **2** the place where a stream of water starts〔河流的〕源頭, 水源: *Where is the source of the River Thames?* 泰晤士河的源頭在哪裡? **3** a person or book that provides information 消息來源〔指人或書等〕: *A government source confirmed that tax cuts were unlikely.* 據來自官方的消息證實, 減稅的可能性不大。

south¹ /saʊθ; saʊθ/ *n* **1** [U] the direction to the right of a person facing the rising sun 南, 南面, 南方: *Is that way south?* 那條路是往南面的嗎? | *It's to the south of here.* 那個地方在這裡的南面。 **2 the south** the southern part of a country which is further south than the rest〔一國的〕南部, 南方地區: *The South of England is warmer than the North.* 英格蘭南部比北部暖和。 | *He lives in the South.* 他住在南方。

south² *adj* **1** (also 又作 **South**) in the south or facing the south 南方的, 向南的: *He lives on the south side of the park.* 他住在公園的南面。 **2 south wind** a wind coming from the south 南風

south³ *adv* (also 又作 **South**) towards the south 向南, 在南方: *Let's travel south.* 我們往南走吧。 | *It's south of here.* 它在這裡的南面。

south·bound /'saʊθ,baʊnd; 'saʊθbaʊnd/ *adj* travelling towards the south 往南行的: *To get to Oxford Circus, take the southbound train.* 要去牛津廣場, 請乘搭往南開的火車。

south·east¹ /,saʊθ'ist; ,saʊθ'iːst◂/ *n* (also 又作 **Southeast**) **1** [sing; U] the direction that is halfway between south and east 東南, 東南方 **2 the southeast** the southeastern part of a country〔一國的〕東南部, 東南地區

southeast² *adj* [only before a noun 只用於名詞前] **1** in the southeastern part of something 東南部的: *the southeast corner of the park* 公園的東南角 **2 southeast wind** a wind coming from the southeast 東南風 –**southeasterly** *adj*

southeast³ *adv* towards the southeast 向東南方: *These windows face southeast.* 這些窗戶面向東南方。

south·east·ern /,saʊθ'istən; ,saʊθ'iːstən/ *adj* in or from the southeast part, especially of a country〔尤指一國的〕東南部的; 來自東南部的

south·east·ward /,saʊθ'istwəd; ,saʊθ'iːstwəd/ *adj fml* going towards the southeast〔正式〕朝東南方行進的 –**southeastwards** (also 又作 **southeastward** *AmE*〔美式〕) *adv*

south·er·ly /'sʌðəˈli; 'sʌðəli/ *adj* **1** towards the south 向南的: *the southerly shore of the lake* 湖的南岸 **2** coming from the south (used of a wind) 來自南方的〔指風〕: *warm southerly winds* 溫暖的南風

south·ern /'sʌðən; 'sʌðən/ *adj* (also 又作 **Southern**) in or from the south part of an area〔某地〕南部的; 來自〔某地〕南部的: *the southern US* 美國南部 | *the warm southern sun* 南方地區溫暖的陽光

South·ern·er /'sʌðənə; 'sʌðənəʳ/ *n* a person who lives in or comes from the southern part of a country〔一國的〕南方人

south·ern·most /'sʌðən,most; 'sʌðənməʊst/ *adj fml* furthest south〔正式〕最南端的: *the southernmost station on the railway line* 最南邊的鐵路站

south pole /ˌ · '·/ *n* **the South Pole** the point furthest south on the surface of the earth, and the land around it 南極

south·ward /'saʊθwəd; 'saʊθwəd/ *adj* going towards the south 向南行的: *a southward journey* 去南方的旅行 –**southwards** (also 又作 **southward** *AmE*〔美式〕) *adv*: *We travelled southwards for several days.* 我們往南方旅行了好幾天。

south·west¹ /,saʊθ'wɛst; ,saʊθ'wɛst◂/ *n* **1** [sing; U] the direction which is halfway between south and west 西南, 西南方 **2 the southwest** the southwestern part of a country〔一國的〕西南部, 西南地區

southwest² *adj* [only before a noun 只用於名詞前] **1** in the southwestern part of something 西南部的: *the southwest mountains* 西南部的山脈 **2 southwest wind** a wind coming from the southwest 西南風 –

southwesterly *adj*

southwest³ *adv* towards the southwest 向西南方: *We'll sail southwest.* 我們的船將往西南方行駛。

south·west·ern /ˌsaʊθˈwɛstə:n; ˌsaʊθˈwestən/ *adj* in or from the southwest part, especially of a country 〔尤指一國的〕西南部的; 來自西南部的

south·west·ward /ˌsaʊθˈwɛstwəd; ˌsaʊθˈwestwəd/ *adj fml* going towards the southwest 《正式》朝西南方行進的 **–southwestwards** (also 又作 **southwestward** *AmE* 《美式》) *adv*

sou·ve·nir /ˌsuvəˈnɪr; ˌsuːvəˈnɪər/ *n* an object bought on holiday or on a trip to remind you about it 紀念品, 紀念物: *I bought this bag as a souvenir of my visit to London.* 我買了這手提包作為我去倫敦旅遊的紀念物。

sou·west·er /ˌsaʊˈwɛstə; saʊˈwestər/ *n* a hat made of shiny material, worn especially by sailors to keep their heads dry during storms 〔尤指水手在暴風雨中所戴的〕油布防水帽

sove·reign¹ /ˈsɑvrɪn; ˈsɒvrɪn/ *n* **1** (also 又作 **Sovereign**) a king or queen 國王; 女王 **2** a British gold coin used in the past with a value of £1 英國從前的一英鎊金幣

sovereign² *adj* **1** highest and greatest (used of power) 最高的; 最大的〔指權力〕; 至高無上的: *Sovereign power must lie with the people.* 主權必須屬於人民。 **2** independent and self-governing (used of a country) 獨立自主的〔指國家〕: *a sovereign state* 主權國家 **–sovereignty** *n* [U]

So·vi·et /ˈsovɪɪt; ˈsəʊvɪˌɛt/ *adj* from or connected with the former USSR 前蘇聯的, 蘇維埃的: *the Soviet Union* 蘇聯 | *a Soviet official* 蘇聯的官員

sow¹ /saʊ; saʊ/ *n* a fully grown female pig 〔已成年的〕母豬

sow² /so; səʊ/ *v* **sowed, sown** /son; səʊn/ *or* **sowed, sowing 1** [I;T] to plant or scatter seeds 播(種): *We'll sow grass in that field.* 我們準備在那塊田裡撒上草籽。 | *It's time for sowing.* 是播種的時節了。 | *This land is being sown with wheat.* 這片地裡正在播撒小麥的種子。 **2** [T] *fml or lit* to make an unpleasant feeling or situation develop 《正式或文》傳播, 使產生〔令人不快的感覺或情形〕: *The newspapers are sowing doubt and despair.* 報紙正在向讀者散播疑慮和絕望。

soy·a bean /ˈsɔɪə.bin; ˈsɔɪə.biːn/ *n* (also 又作 **soybean** /ˈsɔɪbin; ˈsɔɪbiːn/) a plant native to Asia which produces oil and is eaten as food 大豆, 黃豆

spa /spɑ; spɑː/ *n* a place with a spring of mineral water where people come to be cured of disease or to improve their general health 礦泉療養地: *spa water* 礦泉水 | *a spa town* 一個有礦泉的城鎮

space¹ /spes; speɪs/ *n* **1** [C;U] an empty area 空地; 空間: *Is there enough space at the table for 10 people?* 桌子夠不夠地方坐十個人? | *Keep some space between you and the car ahead.* 和前面這輛汽車保持一定距離。 | *a parking space* 停車處 **2** [U] that area the surrounds all objects and continues outwards in all directions without limits 空中; 天空: *the concepts of time and space* 時空概念 | *He was just staring into space.* 他兩眼只是望着天空。 **3** [U] the area outside the earth's air, where other heavenly bodies move 太空: *The satellite is travelling through space.* 衛星在太空中運行。 | *a space station* 太空站 | *in outer space* 在外空間 **4** [U] the feeling that a place is large and open, without too many things in it 空曠(的感覺): *A wonderful sense of space was created by clever furnishing.* 巧妙的家具擺設在房間裡創造出了一種很奇妙的空曠感覺。 **5** [C;U] the amount of room that you have on a page or time in a talk to deal with something 空白處; 空餘時間: *I haven't got enough space to discuss other people's research.* 我沒空討論其他人的研究情況。 **6** [sing] a period of time 一段時間: *Within the space of three years, he had become champion jockey.* 在三年時間裡, 他已成為賽馬的冠軍騎師。

space² *v* **spaced, spacing** [T] to arrange things with spaces or periods of time between them 〔空間或時間上〕隔開: *Space the desks two metres apart.* 把這兩張桌子隔開兩米。 | *Space the activities through the day.* 把一天內各項活動的時間隔開。

space sthg/sbdy ↔ **out** *phr v* [T] to position people or things with spaces or periods of time around them 〔空間或時間上〕把〔人或物〕隔開: *The flowers were neatly spaced out at 6 inch intervals.* 花兒排列得非常整齊, 相互之間有六英寸的距離。 | *Space out the ice-creams so that the children don't get sick!* 把吃冰淇淋的時間隔開點, 免得孩子們生病!

space·craft /ˈspes.kræft; ˈspeɪs.krɑːft/ *n* **spacecraft** a vehicle able to travel in space 太空船, 宇宙飛船

space·ship /ˈspes.ʃɪp; ˈspeɪs.ʃɪp/ *n* a vehicle for carrying people through space 太空船, 宇宙飛船

spa·cious /ˈspeʃəs; ˈspeɪʃəs/ *adj* large, so that there is room to move around 寬敞的 **–spaciousness** *n* [U]

spade /sped; speɪd/ *n* **1** a tool with a blade and a long handle, used for digging the earth 鏟; 鍬 –see picture on page 958 見958頁彩圖 **2 spades** a set of playing cards which has one or more figures shaped like a black pointed leaf printed in black 〔紙牌〕黑桃: *the six of spades* 黑桃六點

spa·ghet·ti /spəˈɡɛti; spəˈɡeti/ *n* [U] Italian food consisting of long strings made from a paste of flour and water 意大利麵條, 意大利粉: *I'll have spaghetti, please.* 請給我來一

客意大利麵條。

span¹ /spæn; spæn/ n **1** the distance between the two limits of something 〔某物的〕兩個界限間的距離: *The bird had a wing span of over a metre.* 那隻鳥的翼展超過一米。**2** a length of time during which something lasts 〔某事物持續的〕一段時間: *I've got a very short memory span.* 我的記憶力很短暫。

span² v **-nn-** [T] **1** to stretch over a certain area 跨越，橫跨: *A bridge spanned the stream.* 一座橋橫跨小河。**2** to last a certain length of time 持續: *His army career spanned four decades.* 他的戎馬生涯持續了四十年。

span·gle /'spæŋgl; 'spæŋgəl/ n a small piece of shiny metal or plastic used to decorate clothes or hair 〔用以裝飾衣服或頭髮的〕閃光金屬片，閃光飾片 — **spangled** adj

span·iel /'spænjəl; 'spænjəl/ n a type of dog with long ears and rather long hair 西班牙獵犬〔一種長毛垂耳狗〕

Span·ish¹ /'spænɪʃ; 'spænɪʃ/ adj from or connected with Spain 西班牙的: *the Spanish Civil War* 西班牙內戰

Spanish² n **1 the Spanish** the people of Spain 西班牙人 **2** [U] the language of Spain 西班牙語: *I'm learning Spanish at evening classes.* 我在夜校學習西班牙語。

spank /spæŋk; spæŋk/ v [T] to hit someone with your open hand, especially on their bottom 用手掌打〔某人，尤指打在屁股上〕: *Do it now, or I'll spank you!* 現在就做，不然我就要打你的屁股了！ — **spank** n — **spanking** n: *If you don't stop that noise, you'll get a good spanking!* 如果你還發出那種聲音，你要狠狠地挨一頓揍了！

span·ner /'spænə; 'spænər/ n BrE a metal hand tool with jaws or a hollow end which you use to twist something into or out of its place 〔英式〕扳手，扳子 — see picture on page 958 見 958 頁彩圖

spar¹ /spɑː; spɑːr/ n a thick pole, especially one used on a ship to support sails or ropes 圓材〔尤指用作桅杆、帆桁等〕

spar² v **-rr-** [I] **1** to BOX without hitting the other person hard, usually because you are practising 〔通常在拳擊練習中〕輕擊〔某人〕**2** to argue, usually in quite a friendly way 〔通常友好地〕爭辯: *Here the minister can be seen sparring with newspaper reporters.* 在這裡可以看見部長與報社記者爭辯。

spare¹ /speə; speər/ v **spared, sparing** [T] **1** to make someone or something free to do something or to be used 使〔某人〕可自由做〔某事〕；使撥出，騰出，讓給: *Can you spare me five minutes?* 你能抽出五分鐘和我談談嗎？ | *We're so busy that no one can be spared for any other work.* 我們非常忙，誰都抽不出來做其他工作。| *Could you spare your car for a while?* 你的車能讓出來用一會兒嗎？**2** to leave someone or something unharmed 使〔某人或某物〕不受傷害: *Take my*

money but spare my life! 把我的錢拿走，饒我一命吧！| *In the event of war not even children will be spared.* 戰爭連小孩子都不會放過。**3** to avoid making someone do or listen to something unpleasant 使〔某人〕不必做〔聽〕: *Spare me all the details of the meeting — just tell me about what they decided.* 不要說會議的細節，只要把他們的決定告訴我就行了。| *He was spared having to identify the body.* 他不必去認屍了。**4** [usually used in negatives and questions 常用於否定句和疑問句] to avoid doing, using, or spending something 避免做〔某事〕；避免使用〔花費〕〔某物〕: *No trouble was spared to make sure they enjoyed themselves.* 為使他們盡情歡樂而不遺餘力。**5 something to spare** something that is not really needed but could be used 多餘之物: *Let's go! There's no time to spare.* 我們快走吧！沒有時間了。| *I've got money to spare.* 我有多餘的錢。

spare² adj **1** kept for use when needed 備用的: *a spare tyre* 備用輪胎 | *a spare room* 備用房間 **2** free from other activities or use 空餘的；剩餘的: *It's something to do in her spare time.* 這是她可以在空餘時間裡做的事情。| *Have you got a spare piece of paper?* 你有沒有多餘的紙？**3** rather thin 很瘦的: *her spare figure* 她瘦削的身材

spare³ n a second object of the same kind that is kept for possible use 備用品: *This tyre is damaged. Have you got a spare?* 這輪胎壞了。你有備用的嗎？

spar·ing /'speərɪŋ; 'speərɪŋ/ adj using or giving little 省着用的，節儉的: *Be sparing in the amount of salt you add.* 少加點鹽。 — **sparingly** adv: *Apply this cream sparingly.* 塗這種霜劑時要省着點用。

spark¹ /spɑːk; spɑːk/ n **1** a small piece of burning material thrown out by a fire or by the striking together of two hard objects 火花，火星 **2** a flash of light produced by electricity 電火花 **3** a very small but important amount of a quality 〔某種品質的〕一點點: *a spark of intelligence* 一點機智 **4 bright spark** infml a clever person (a word usually used to mean the opposite of this) 〔非正式〕聰明的人〔常指相反的意思〕: *Some bright spark was caught cheating in the exam today.* 今天考試時有個要小聰明的人作弊，被當場抓住了。

spark² v [I] to produce a spark 產生火花；產生火星

spark sthg ↔ **off** phr v [T] BrE to be the direct cause of something 〔英式〕導致〔某事〕: *What sparked off the quarrel?* 是甚麼事引起了這場爭吵？

spar·kle /'spɑːkl; 'spɑːkəl/ v **sparkled, sparkling** [I] **1** to shine in small flashes 閃閃發光，閃爍: *a diamond that sparkled in the sunlight* 鑽石在陽光下閃閃發亮 **2** to be clever and full of life 機智活躍: *She sparkles in company.* 她在公司裡非常活躍。 — **sparkle**

n [C;U]

spark plug /ˈ··/ *n* a part in an engine which makes an electric spark to fire the petrol 〔引擎的〕火花塞

spar·row /ˈspærəʊ; ˈspærəʊ/ *n* a small brown bird very common in many parts of the world 麻雀

sparse /spɑːs; spɑːs/ *adj* limited in number or amount 數量有限的; 稀少的 **–sparsely** *adv*: *a sparsely populated area* 人口稀少的地區 **–sparseness** *n* [U]

spar·tan /ˈspɑːtn; ˈspɑːtn/ *adj* simple and without comfort 簡樸的; 艱苦的: *spartan accommodation* 簡樸艱苦的住宿環境

spas·m /ˈspæzəm; ˈspæzəm/ *n* **1** a sudden uncontrolled tightening of the muscles 〔肌肉的〕痙攣, 抽筋 **2** a sudden violent effort, feeling, or act 〔努力、感情或動作的〕突發, 發作: *spasms of pain* 陣陣疼痛

spas·mod·ic /spæzˈmɒdɪk; spæzˈmɒdɪk/ *adj* **1** of or like a spasm 痙攣(性)的: *spasmodic pain* 痙攣性疼痛 **2** happening for short periods of time but not continuously 間歇性的, 一陣陣的: *spasmodic increases in the population* 間歇性的人口增長 **–spasmodically** /-klɪ; -klɪ/ *adv*

spas·tic /ˈspæstɪk; ˈspæstɪk/ *n* a person suffering from a disease in which some parts of the body cannot be controlled 患肌肉痙攣性麻痺的人 **–spastic** *adj*

spat /spæt; spæt/ *v* the past tense and past participle of SPIT ☆ SPIT 的過去式和過去分詞

spate /spet; speɪt/ *n BrE* a large number or amount of something 〔英式〕大量, 許多: *There has been a spate of accidents on this bend.* 這個彎道發生了多次交通事故。

spa·tial /ˈspeʃəl; ˈspeɪʃəl/ *adj fml* connected with size, shape, or position 〔正式〕〔有關大小、形狀、位置等〕空間的 **–spatially** *adv*

spat·ter /ˈspætə; ˈspætər/ *v* [I;T] to cover something with drops of liquid 濺, 灑: *The car spattered my clothes with mud.* 那輛車把泥漿濺到了我的衣服上。| *A little oil spattered on the wall.* 有一點油濺到了牆上。

spat·u·la /ˈspætjʊlə; ˈspætjʒlə/ *n* a tool with a wide flat blade, for spreading, mixing, or lifting soft substances 抹刀, 刮鏟

spawn¹ /spɔːn; spɔːn/ *v* **1** [I;T] (of fish and certain other creatures) to lay eggs in large quantities 〔魚或其他動物〕大量產(卵) **2** [T] to produce something in large numbers 大量產生〔某物〕, 釀成: *The computer industry has spawned hundreds of new companies.* 由於電腦工業的發展, 數以百計的新公司紛紛設立。

spawn² *n* [U] the eggs of fish and certain other creatures that live in water 〔魚和其他水生動物的〕卵

speak¹ /spik; spiːk/ *v* **spoke** /spok; spəʊk/, **spoken** /ˈspokən; ˈspəʊkən/, **speaking 1** [I] to say things by using your voice 說, 講:

Most children begin to speak between the ages of one and two. 大部分孩子在一到兩歲之間開始講話。| *She's been unable to speak since the accident.* 事故之後, 她喪失了說話能力。| *I haven't spoken to Robert for a few months.* 我有好幾個月沒有跟羅伯特說話了。| *We spoke about the new contract.* 我們談及新的合同。**2** [T] to express or say something in words 表達, 說〔某事物〕: *They were convinced the prisoner was not speaking the truth.* 他們堅信囚犯沒有說出真相。**3** **be on speaking terms with someone, be speaking to someone** to be friendly with someone, especially someone with whom relations are often difficult 與某人〔尤指難以相處的人〕和睦相處 **4** **speak badly/well of someone** to say bad or good things about someone 說某人的壞話[好話] **5** **speak for yourself** a phrase used to show that you disagree with someone's opinion and are annoyed that they thought you agreed 你只代表你自己說話〔用於表示你不同意某人的觀點, 故而對他認為你已同意了他的觀點表示不快〕: *"I'm sure we'll do well." "Speak for yourself!"* "我敢肯定我們會做得好。" "你只說你自己吧!" **6** **speak your mind** to say exactly what you think 直言不諱 **7** **to speak of** worth mentioning 值得一提: *"Did you do anything interesting at the weekend?" "Nothing to speak of."* "週末你有沒有做點有趣的事?" "沒有甚麼值得一提的。" **8** [I] to make a speech 發表演說: *She makes a lot of money speaking to groups of businessmen.* 她對許多商人發表演說, 掙了很多錢。**9** [T] to be able to talk in a particular language 講〔某種語言〕: *She can read Italian but she can't speak it.* 她看得懂意大利文, 但不會講。| *Do you speak English?* 你講英語嗎? | *We need a French-speaking secretary.* 我們需要一位會講法語的秘書。**10** [I] to express thoughts, ideas or feelings in a way that does not use words 〔以說話之外的方式〕表達〔思想、觀點或感情〕: *Actions speak louder than words.* 行動勝於言語。**11** **so to speak** as one might say, although it is not strictly true 可以說, 可謂

speak for sbdy *phr v* [T] to act for a person or group by expressing their thoughts or opinions to other people 為〔人或團體〕發表思想或觀點: *I'm speaking for those who cannot be present at this meeting today.* 我現在代表那些今天無法到會的人發表講話。

speak out *phr v* [I] to state your opinions freely and boldly 自由而大膽地說出〔自己的觀點〕: *The newspaper spoke out against the government's decision.* 這份報紙明確地反對政府的決定。

speak up *phr v* [I] **1** to speak more loudly 大聲地說, 提高聲音說: *Please speak up so that people at the back can hear you.* 請說得大聲一點, 以便後面的人也能聽見。**2** to state your opinions freely and boldly 自由而大膽

地说出〔自己的觀點〕: *If you disagree, you should speak up.* 如果你不同意, 就直截了當地說出來。

☆☆speak·er /ˈspikɚ; ˈspiːkəʳ/ *n* **1** a person making a speech 演講者; 發言人: *an interesting speaker* 一位談笑風生的演講者 **2** a person who speaks a language 講某種語言的人: *a speaker of English* 講英語的人 **3** see 見 LOUDSPEAKER

speak·ing¹ /ˈspikɪŋ; ˈspiːkɪŋ/ *n* **public speaking** the art of speaking formally to groups of people 公開演說

speaking² *adv* **1 speaking of something** a phrase used to introduce a different but related subject 説起某事〔用以引入一個新的但卻是相關的話題〕: *Speaking of John, is he feeling better these days?* 説到約翰, 對了, 他近來覺得好些了嗎? **2 speaking as someone** a phrase used to show that what you are saying is based on your own experience 作為某人來説〔用於表示所説的話基於自己的親身經歷〕: *Speaking as a lover of poetry I have to say that I have little respect for modern poets.* 作為一名詩歌愛好者, 我不得不説我不大看得起現代詩人。 **3** a word used with another adverb to make clear the limits of the subject area you are talking about ...説來; 就...來説〔同另外一個副詞連用表示講話所涉及到的範圍〕: *Generally speaking, British people are quite polite.* 一般來説, 英國人是相當有禮貌的。 | *Technically speaking, she's a legal adviser rather than a lawyer.* 從專業水平上來講, 她是個法律顧問, 而不是律師。

spear¹ /spɪr; spɪəʳ/ *n* a pole with a sharp point at one end, used in the past as a weapon 長矛

spear² *v* [T] to stick a pointed object into something 用尖的物體刺入〔某物〕: *He speared a piece of meat with his fork.* 他用叉子叉起一塊肉。

spear·head /ˈspɪrˌhɛd; ˈspɪəhed/ *n* the person or group that leads an attack on something〔進攻某物的〕先鋒; 先頭部隊: *the spearhead of the movement* 該行動的先頭部隊 — **spearhead** *v* [T]: *The attack on slavery was spearheaded by William Wilberforce.* 攻擊奴隸制度是由威廉·威爾伯福斯發起的。

spear·mint /ˈspɪrˌmɪnt; ˈspɪəˌmɪnt/ *n* [U] a common plant used to give a strong fresh taste to sweets and other substances 留蘭香(植物)

☆☆☆spe·cial¹ /ˈspɛʃəl; ˈspeʃəl/ *adj* not ordinary or usual 特殊的, 特別的: *A special train was provided for the football supporters.* 有一輛專門的列車接載那足球啦啦隊。 | *a special friend of mine* 我的一位特別的朋友 | *Of course my birthday is a special occasion!* 我的生日當然是個特殊的日子啦!

special² *n* something that is not of the usual or ordinary kind 特別的東西: *a two-hour television special* 長達兩小時的電視特別節目

☆spe·cial·ist /ˈspɛʃəlɪst; ˈspeʃəlˌɪst/ *n* a person who has particular knowledge in an area of work, study, knowledge, or training 專家; 專科醫生: *a heart specialist* 心臟專科醫生 | *He's a specialist in Roman coins.* 他是研究古羅馬硬幣的專家。

spe·ci·al·i·ty /ˌspɛʃɪˈælətɪ; ˌspeʃɪˈælˌtɪ/ **specialities** (**specialty** /ˈspɛʃəltɪ; ˈspeʃəltɪ/ *AmE* 〖美式〗) **1** an area of work or study that someone knows a lot about 專業; 專門研究: *Her speciality is ancient Greek poetry.* 她專門研究的領域是古希臘詩歌。 **2** a particularly fine product for which a person or place is known〔某人或某地的〕特產: *Fish baked in pastry is the speciality of this restaurant.* 魚餡餅是這家餐館的特色菜。

spe·cial·ize /ˈspɛʃəlˌaɪz; ˈspeʃəlaɪz/ *v* **specialized, specializing** (also 又作 **specialise** *BrE* 〖英式〗) [I] to limit what you do in your work or studies to particular areas or subjects 專門從事; 專門研究: *She's a doctor who specializes in tropical diseases.* 她是專門醫治熱帶病的醫生。 — **specialization** /ˌspɛʃəlɪˈzeʃən; ˌspeʃəlaɪˈzeɪʃən/ *n* [C;U]

spe·cial·ized /ˈspɛʃəˌlaɪzd; ˈspeʃəlaɪzd/ *adj* (also 又作 **specialised** *BrE* 〖英式〗) developed for one particular use or in one particular field of knowledge 專用的; 專門的: *specialized tools* 專用工具 | *specialized knowledge* 專門知識

spe·cial·ly /ˈspɛʃəlɪ; ˈspeʃəli/ *adv* **1** for one particular purpose or person 專門地; 特定地: *I made a cake specially for you.* 我特意為你做了一個蛋糕。 **2** more than usual 特殊地; 特別地: *It's not specially hot today.* 今天不是特別熱。

☆spe·cies /ˈspiʃiz; ˈspiːʃiːz/ *n* **species** a group of plants or animals of the same kind, which are alike in all important ways and can breed together〔動植物的〕物種, 種

☆☆spe·cif·ic /spɪˈsɪfɪk; spəˈsɪfɪk/ *adj* **1** detailed and exact 詳細的, 明確的, 確切的: *You say that your factory is in the South of England. Can you be a bit more specific?* 你説你的工廠在英格蘭南部。你能説得再具體一點嗎? **2** particular 特定的, 特殊的: *The book was aimed at a specific group.* 該書是為某一羣人而寫的。 | *My research deals with customs specific to West Africa.* 我專門研究西非特有的風俗習慣。 — **specifically** /-klɪ; -kli/ *adv*: *They specifically told us not to go there.* 他們明確地告訴我們不要到那裡去。 | *a book written specifically for schoolchildren in Nigeria* 專為尼日利亞的學童寫的書

spe·ci·fi·ca·tion /ˌspɛsəfəˈkeʃən; ˌspesˌfɪˈkeɪʃən/ *n* **1** [C;U] any or all of the part of a detailed plan, description, or set of instructions 規格; 規格説明: *According to the specifications, this wire should go into that hole.* 按照規格説明, 這根電線應該穿過那個孔。 | *Are you sure this was made to* *specification?* 你肯定這是按照規格説明書製造的嗎? **2** [C] something that is stated or demanded 聲明之事; 要求之事: *None of the candidates meet our specifications.* 沒有一位候選人符合我們的要求。

spe·ci·fics /spɪˈsɪfɪks; spɪˈsɪfɪks/ *n* [pl] the details of a subject that need to be considered〔需要考慮的〕細節, 詳情: *Could you give me a few specifics?* 你能給我提供一些細節嗎? | *Let's talk about the specifics.* 我們來談一下細節問題吧。

*****spe·ci·fy** /ˈspɛsəˌfaɪ; ˈspɛsɪˌfaɪ/ *v* **specified, specifying** [T; + that] **1** to mention something exactly 確切地提及, 載明, 詳述〔某事〕: *Be careful to specify every relevant point.* 注意要把每個相關問題具體説明。**2** to state what is necessary 指明〔需要之物〕: *The rules specify what must be done in cases of disagreement.* 規則清楚載明如有不同意見時必須如何處理。

spe·ci·men /ˈspɛsəmən; ˈspɛsɪmɪn/ *n* **1** a single thing that is a typical example of its kind 樣本; 標本: *a fine specimen of a mountain lion* 一隻山獅的精製標本 **2** a small amount of something that shows what the whole thing is like 樣品; 抽樣: *The doctor will need a specimen of your blood for testing.* 醫生需要你的血樣做檢查。

spe·cious /ˈspiʃəs; ˈspiːʃəs/ *adj fml* seeming true or correct but in fact not so〔正式〕似是而非的: *a specious argument* 似是而非的論據 **–speciously** *adv* **–speciousness** *n* [U]

speck /spɛk; spɛk/ *n* a small spot or mark 斑點, 污點: *I've got a speck of dirt in my eye.* 我的眼睛裡有點灰塵。

speck·le /ˈspɛkl; ˈspɛkəl/ *n* a small coloured mark, especially one of a large number of similar marks〔彩色的〕小斑點 **–speckled** *adj*: *speckled birds' eggs* 有斑點的鳥蛋

spec·ta·cle /ˈspɛktəkl; ˈspɛktəkəl/ *n* **1 spectacles** (also 又作 **specs** *infml*〔非正式〕) glasses that help people to see better 眼鏡: *I can't see a thing without my spectacles.* 我不戴眼鏡甚麼也看不見。**2** a grand public show or scene 壯觀的場面〔景象〕**3** a scene that is unusual and interesting 不平常的場面, 異常的現象 **4 make a spectacle of yourself** to do something silly that makes people look at you 出醜, 出洋相

spec·tac·u·lar¹ /spɛkˈtækjələ; spɛkˈtækjələr/ *adj* very special and splendid 壯觀的, 宏偉的 **–spectacularly** *adv*

spectacular² *n* a special entertainment 特別節目, 精彩的節目: *a television spectacular with lots of famous stars* 明星眾多、場面浩大的電視節目

spec·ta·tor /ˈspɛkteɪtɚ; spɛkˈteɪtər/ *n* a person who watches an event or sport without taking part〔事件或運動項目的〕旁觀者, 觀眾

spec·tre /ˈspɛktɚ; ˈspɛktər/ *n* (**specter** *AmE*〔美式〕) a spirit without a body 鬼魂, 幽靈

spec·trum /ˈspɛktrəm; ˈspɛktrəm/ *n* **spectra**

/-trə; -trə/ **1** the set of bands of coloured light into which a beam of light may be separated 光譜 **2** a range of any of various kinds of waves 頻譜: *a sound spectrum* 聲譜 **3** a range of different opinions, feelings, or subject areas 系列, 範圍, 幅度: *We found a wide spectrum of opinions on this issue.* 我們發覺對這個問題的看法眾説紛紜, 莫衷一是。

spec·u·late /ˈspɛkjəˌlet; ˈspɛkjʊˌleɪt/ *v* **speculated, speculating 1** [I; +that] to consider what might be true but without enough proof to be sure 推測, 猜測: *Many people have been speculating about whether the situation will lead to war.* 許多人一直在猜測, 這樣的形勢發展下去會否引起戰爭。| *He speculated that she might have gone to France.* 他推測她也許去了法國。**2** [I] to try to make money by taking a business risk 投機買賣: *He speculated in commercial property.* 他做的是商業地產的投機生意。| *They made a lot of money by speculating on the price of gold.* 他們通過投機買賣黃金掙了許多錢。**–speculator** *n* **–speculative** *adj*: *a speculative investment* 投機性的投資

spec·u·la·tion /ˌspɛkjəˈleʃən; ˌspɛkjʊˈleɪʃən/ *n* **1** [U] thoughts about what might happen 推測, 猜測: *The politician's remarks gave rise to speculation about his future.* 這位政治家的講話引起了人們對他的前途有所猜測。**2** [C; U] taking a risk in order to make money〔為掙錢而進行的〕冒險; 投機: *His speculations on the Stock Market led to a considerable loss.* 他在股票市場上的投機活動令他損失慘重。

sped /spɛd; spɛd/ the past tense and past participle of SPEED ☆ SPEED 的過去式和過去分詞

*****speech** /spitʃ; spiːtʃ/ *n* **1** [C] a formal talk to a group of listeners 演講, 演説: *In an angry speech, the MP criticized the government's action.* 國會議員在演講中怒氣沖沖地批評了政府的行動。| *I'm making a speech at the club dinner tomorrow.* 我將在明天俱樂部舉辦的晚宴上發表演説。**2** [U] the ability to speak or the act of speaking 説話能力; 説話: *She is researching speech development in children.* 她在研究兒童語言能力的發展。**3** [U] way of speaking 説話方式: *His speech was slow and hesitant.* 他説話慢吞吞的, 而且猶豫不決。**4** [U] spoken language 口語: *That phrase sounds all right in speech but not in writing.* 那個詞組在口語裡聽起來沒問題, 但用在書面表達就不合適。

speech·less /ˈspitʃlɪs; ˈspiːtʃləs/ *adj* unable to speak at a particular moment because of strong feeling or shock〔由於強烈的感情或震驚而一時〕説不出話的: *He was speechless with anger.* 他氣得一句話也説不出來。**–speechlessly** *adv* **–speechlessness** *n* [U]

*****speed¹** /spid; spiːd/ *n* **1** [C;U] the rate at which something moves or happens 速度, 速率: *The car was travelling at a speed of 30* *mph.* 這輛車以每小時三十英里的速度行駛。| *Modern trains can achieve speeds in excess of 200 miles per hour.* 現代化的火車可以達到每小時二百英里以上的速度。| *We work at different speeds.* 我們工作的速度快慢不一。| *It's for measuring speed.* 這是用來測定速度的。–see 見 FASTNESS (USAGE 用法) **2** [U] very fast movement 快速, 迅速: *The team won because of their speed with the ball.* 該隊由於擊球速度快而贏得了比賽。**3 at speed** very fast 很快地, 高速地: *The car was travelling at speed.* 那輛車開得很快。

speed² *v* **speeded** *or* **sped** /spɛd; sped/, **speeding 1** [I + adv/prep] to move or happen quickly 迅速移動; 迅速發生: *We were enjoying ourselves so much that the time sped quickly by.* 我們玩得非常開心, 所以覺得時間過得很快。| *He jumped into his car and sped off into the night.* 他跳進汽車, 在夜色之中飛馳。**2** [T] to make something move or happen fast 使〔某物〕迅速移動; 使〔某事〕迅速發生: *Security guards sped the President to the waiting helicopter.* 警衛人員把總統快速送到那正在等候的直升飛機。**3** [I only in progressive forms 只用於進行式] to break the speed limit 超過速度限制: *The driver was fined for speeding.* 司機因超速駕駛而被罰款。| *She was speeding when the police stopped her.* 警察截停她的時候, 她正在超速駕駛。

speed up *phr v* [I;T **speed** sbdy/sthg ↔ **up**] to go faster or to make something or someone go faster (使)加速: *Production of the new car was speeded up.* 新車的生產加快了速度。| *We had to speed up to meet the new targets.* 為了達到新的目標, 我們必須加快速度。

speed·boat /'spid,bot; 'spi:dbəut/ *n* a small power boat built to travel at high speed (高速)快艇 –see picture on page 991 見 991 頁彩圖

speed·om·e·ter /spɪ'dɑmətə; spɪ'dɒmɪtə'/ *n* an instrument in a vehicle that shows how fast it is going 〔車輛的〕速度計 –see picture on page 209 見 209 頁彩圖

speed·way /'spid,we; 'spi:dweɪ/ *n* **speedways 1** [U] a type of motorcycle racing 摩托車賽 **2** [C] the track where this racing is done 摩托車賽車道, 賽車跑道

speed·y /'spidɪ; 'spi:dɪ/ *adj* **speedier, speediest 1** fast 迅速的, 快速的: *We wished him a speedy recovery.* 我們希望他能很快康復。**2** able to move fast 能快速移動的: *It's a speedy little car.* 這是一部速度很快的小汽車。–**speedily** *adv* –**speediness** *n* [U]

spell¹ /spɛl; spel/ *v* **spelt** /spɛlt; spelt/ *or* **spelled, spelling 1** [T] to say or write in order the letters of a word (用字母)拼寫: *My surname is spelt S-M-Y-T-H.* 我的名字拼作 S-M-Y-T-H。**2** [I] to know the correct letters in words 正確地拼寫: *He writes well, but he can't spell.* 他寫的字很好, 但不會拼

字。**3** [T] to form a word 〔字母〕拼成〔單詞〕: *B-O-O-K spells "book". B-O-O-K* 拼成 *"book".* **4** [T] to mean something 意味着〔某事物〕: *This vote spells defeat for the government.* 這表決結果意味着政府的失敗。–**speller** *n*

spell sthg ↔ **out** *phr v* [T] **1** to explain something in a very detailed way 詳細解釋〔某事物〕: *The government is spelling out its plans in a party political broadcast.* 政府正在黨派的政治宣傳廣播中詳盡地解釋其計劃。**2** to write or say a word letter by letter 逐個字母寫〔讀〕出〔單詞〕

spell² *n* **1** a condition caused by the use of magical power 着魔, 中邪: *He put a spell on her.* 他對她施了魔咒。**2** the words used to cause magic power 咒語 **3 be under someone's spell** to be in the power of someone 被某人迷住 **4** a period of time 一段時間: *He spent a spell in prison.* 他被監禁了一段時間。| *a hot spell* 一段炎熱的日子

spell·bound /'spɛl,baʊnd; 'spelbaʊnd/ *adj* [never before a noun 不能用於名詞前] with your attention held as if by magic 出神的, 着迷的: *The children sat spellbound as the old man told his story.* 老人講故事的時候, 孩子們都聽得入了迷。

spell·ing /'spɛlɪŋ; 'spelɪŋ/ *n* [C;U] the way of forming words from letters 拼寫(法): *Her spelling has improved.* 她的拼寫有了進步。| *English and American spellings of some words are different.* 有些單詞的英式和美式拼法是不同的。

spelt /spɛlt; spelt/ the past tense and past participle of SPELL ☆ SPELL 的過去式和過去分詞

spend /spɛnd; spend/ *v* **spent** /spɛnt; spent/, **spending 1** [I;T] to pay money 花費〔金錢〕: *They spent their last dollars on a good meal.* 他們把最後的一些錢用來好好吃了一頓。| *How much do you want to spend?* 你準備花多少錢? **2** [T] to pass or use time 度過〔時間〕, 消磨〔時間〕: *Come and spend the weekend with us.* 來和我們一起週末吧。| *He spent three years working overseas.* 他在海外工作了三年。| *I spent a lot of time planning this trip.* 我花了許多時間計劃這次旅行。**3 spend a penny** a less direct expression for 'go to the TOILET' 去廁所〔委婉語〕

spend·thrift /'spɛnd,θrɪft; 'spend,θrɪft/ *n* a person who spends money wastefully 揮霍的人, 浪費金錢的人

spent¹ /spɛnt; spent/ *adj fml* used up 〔正式〕用盡的: *a spent force* 已失去影響力的勢力

spent² the past tense and past participle of SPEND ☆ SPEND 的過去式和過去分詞

sperm /spɝm; spɜːm/ *n* **sperm** *or* **sperms 1** [C] a cell produced by the sex organs of a male animal, which is able to unite with the female egg to produce new life 精子, 精蟲 **2** [U] the liquid from the male sex organs in which these cells swim 精液

spew /spjuː; spjuː/ v 1 [I;T] to send out in a flood (使)噴出, (使)湧出: *The burst pipe was spewing out water.* 水正從破裂的管子湧出來。 2 [I] *infml* to VOMIT〖非正式〗嘔吐

sphere /sfɪr; sfɪəʳ/ n 1 a round object 球, 球形, 球體 2 an area of existence, action, or activity〔存在、行動或活動的〕範圍: *His main sphere of influence is the world of banking.* 他主要的勢力範圍是在金融界。 3 a group of people with the same interests and activities 興趣愛好等相同的一羣人

spher·i·cal /'sferɪkəl; 'sferikəl/ adj in the form of a sphere (1) 球的, 球形的

sphinx /sfɪŋks; sfiŋks/ n an ancient Egyptian image of a lion with a human head〔古埃及的〕獅身人面像

spice¹ /spaɪs; spais/ n 1 [C;U] a vegetable product often used in powder form for giving a taste to other foods 香料; 調味品: *herbs and spices* 香草與香料 | *a pinch of mixed spice* 一撮混合香料 2 [U] interest or excitement 興趣; 趣味: *I need some jokes to add spice to the speech.* 我需要一些笑話來給我的講話增添些趣味。

spice² v spiced, spicing [T] to add spice to something 加香料於〔某物〕; 使增添趣味

spice sthg ↔ **up** phr v [T] to make something interesting 使〔某事物〕變得有趣: *He spiced up his speech with some jokes.* 他用了幾個笑話使演講變得有趣一些。

spick-and-span /ˌspɪkən'spæn; ˌspɪk ən 'spæn/ adj clean, bright, and tidy 乾淨的; 明亮的; 整潔的

spic·y /'spaɪsɪ; 'spaisi/ adj spicier, spiciest 1 containing or tasting of SPICE¹ (1) 加有香料的; 有香(料)味的; 味辛辣的: *I don't like spicy food.* 我不喜歡加有香料的食物。 2 exciting and perhaps slightly improper or rude 刺激的; 略帶淫穢的: *spicy stories* 略帶淫意的故事

spi·der /'spaɪdər; 'spaidəʳ/ n a small creature with eight legs which makes threads into nets for catching insects 蜘蛛

spi·der·y /'spaɪdərɪ; 'spaidəri/ adj long and thin like the legs of a spider〔如蜘蛛腿般〕細長的: *the old lady's spidery writing* 那位老婦人寫的細長字體

spike¹ /spaɪk; spaik/ n 1 a piece of metal with a point at one end 金屬釘狀物: *There are spikes along the top of the fence.* 籬笆頂上有許多尖頭。 | *I bought running shoes with spikes on the soles.* 我買了一雙帶釘的跑鞋。 2 something long and pointed 長而尖的東西 –**spiky** adj spikier, spikiest *infml*〖非正式〗: *spiky hair* 豎直而尖刺的頭髮

spike² v spiked, spiking [T] 1 to put a spike through something 用金屬釘釘入 2 to add a little alcohol to a drink 加烈酒於〔飲料〕

spill /spɪl; spil/ v spilled *or* spilt /spɪlt; spilt/, spilling 1 [I;T] to pour out accidentally, especially over the edge of a container 灑出, 溢出; 濺出: *My hand slipped and I spilt my*

drink. 我的手一滑, 飲料濺了出來。 | *There was some spilt milk on the floor.* 一些牛奶灑到了地上。 2 **spill the beans** *infml* to tell a secret before you should〖非正式〗泄露祕密

spill out phr v [I] (used of people) to come out of a place in large numbers〔人〕大量湧出: *The congregation spilled out into the street.* 集會羣眾湧到了街上。

spin¹ /spɪn; spin/ v spun /spʌn; spʌn/, spinning [I;T] 1 to make thread by twisting cotton or wool 將〔棉花或羊毛〕紡成〔紗、線〕: *She spent her days spinning.* 她整天在紡紗。 | *She spun the wool into thread.* 她把羊毛紡成了紗線。 2 to turn round and round fast 快速旋轉: *The child was fascinated by the spinning top.* 那孩子被那快速旋轉的陀螺迷住了。 | *He spun the coin on the table.* 他把硬幣放在桌上旋轉。 | *Let the washing spin before you put it out to dry.* 先讓衣服在脫水機裡轉一轉, 再拿出去晾乾。 3 **be spinning** to feel confused and perhaps DIZZY: 感到困惑而頭暈: *My head is spinning with all this new information.* 這些新的資料令我頭暈。 4 **spin a yarn** to tell a story which is not completely true 編造故事, 講故事

spin sthg ↔ **out** phr v [T] to make something last longer than it should 延長〔某事〕

spin² n 1 a short pleasure trip 兜風; 短途旅行: *We went for a spin in the new car.* 我們坐新車去兜風。 2 **in a spin** in a state of confusion because something unexpected has happened〔因發生意外而〕驚慌

spin·ach /'spɪnɪdʒ; 'spinidʒ/ n [U] a vegetable with broad green leaves 菠菜

spin·al /'spaɪnl; 'spainl/ adj relating to the row of bones in your back 脊椎的: *a spinal injury* 脊椎受傷

spin·dle /'spɪndl; 'spindl/ n 1 a round pointed rod around which you twist the thread when you are spinning 紡錘; 紗錠 2 a machine part around which another part turns〔機器的〕軸

spin·dly /'spɪndlɪ; 'spindli/ adj long, thin, and weak-looking 細長的; 瘦弱的: *a young horse with spindly legs* 兩腿纖弱的小馬

spin dri·er /ˌ·'··/ n (also 又作 **spin dryer**) an electric machine used to get water out of wet clothes 旋轉式脫水機

spin-dry /ˌ·'··/ v spin-dried, spin-drying [T] to remove water from wet clothes in a machine that spins them round and round〔用旋轉式脫水機〕脫乾〔衣服〕, 旋乾〔洗好的衣服〕

spine /spaɪn; spain/ n 1 (also 又作 **spinal column** /ˌ·'··, ·,··/, **backbone**) the row of bones down the centre of the back of humans and some animals 脊椎骨, 脊柱 2 the end of a book where the pages are fastened together 書脊 3 a sharp point found on plants or animals〔動植物的〕尖刺

spine·less /'spaɪnlɪs; 'spainlis/ adj without moral courage 沒有骨氣的: *He's too spine-*

less to protest. 他太懦弱了, 連抗議都不敢。 –
spine·less·ly *adv* –**spinelessness** *n* [U]

spin·ney /'spɪnɪ; 'spɪnɪ/ *n* **spinneys** *BrE* a
small area of trees and low plants 〔英式〕
灌木林, 小樹叢

spinning wheel /'·· ·/ *n* a small machine
used in the past to make thread 〔昔時的〕紡
車

spin-off /'·· ·/ *n* a useful product or result
besides the main one 副產品; 附帶產生的結
果: *The non-stick frying pan is an industrial
spin-off from space research.* 不黏鍋是太空
研究的工業副產品。

spin·ster /'spɪnstə; 'spɪnstə / *n old fash* an
unmarried woman, especially an older one
(a word sometimes used to express disapproval) 〔老式〕未婚女子〔尤指老處女〕〔有時
含貶義〕

spi·ral¹ /'spaɪrəl; 'spaɪrəl/ *n* a curve winding round and round a central point or
line 螺旋狀: *a spiral staircase* 螺旋形樓梯

spiral² *v* **-ll-** *BrE* 〔英式〕 (also 又作 **-l-** *AmE*
〔美式〕) [I] **1** to move up or down in a
spiral 盤旋上升〔下降〕: *The damaged plane
spiralled towards the earth.* 受損壞的飛機向
地面盤旋而下。 **2** (of an amount or level) to
move up more and more quickly 〔數量或水
平〕飛快上升: *spiralling prices* 飛漲的物價 **3**
spiral down (of an amount or level) to fall
more and more quickly 〔數量或水平〕飛快下
降

spire /spaɪr; spaɪə / *n* a tower rising steeply
to a point, often found on a church 塔尖;
尖頂〔常指教堂頂端〕

★spir·it¹ /'spɪrɪt; 'spɪrɪt/ *n* **1** [C] a person's
soul or mind 心靈, 精神: *His spirit was
troubled.* 他的精神受到困擾。 **2** [C] a presence without physical form, often of a person who is dead 幽靈, 靈魂: *evil spirits* 惡
鬼 | *the spirit of the dead man* 死人的靈魂 **3**
the spirit of something the central quality
or inner nature of something 〔某物的〕本質;
精神: *the spirit of the age* 時代精神 **4** [U]
great strength of purpose 志氣, 毅力; 氣魄:
a man of great spirit 很有志氣的男子 **5** a way
of feeling or thinking 心情; 態度: *He took
the criticism in the right spirit.* 他以正確的態
度接受了批評。 | *Her spirits rose.* 她心情興
奮。 **6 spirits** [pl] strong alcoholic drink 烈
酒: *He likes wine but never drinks spirits.* 他
喜歡喝酒, 但從不喝烈酒。 **7 high spirits**
feelings of happiness and enjoyment 高興,
快樂: *The children were in high spirits at the
thought of their holiday.* 孩子們一想到假期便
十分高興。 [RELATED PHRASE 相關詞組
low spirits] **8 team spirit** a feeling of
working for the good of a group, not just
for yourself 團體精神

spirit² *v* [T] to take a person or thing to or
from a place in a secret mysterious way 祕
密地帶走〔人或物〕: *She was spirited away
through the back door before her fans could*

see her. 她的擁躉還未看見她, 她便神祕地從後
門被人帶走了。

spir·it·ed /'spɪrɪtɪd; 'spɪrɪ̩tɪd/ *adj* **1** active
and excited 活躍的; 激烈的: *a spirited quar-
rel* 激烈的爭吵 | *He made a spirited defence
of the proposal.* 他情緒激昂地為該項提議作
辯解。 **2 -spirited** having a certain kind of
feeling 有...感情的: *high-spirited* 情緒高漲
的 | *public-spirited* 熱心公益的

spirit lev·el /'·· ,··/ *n* (also 又作 **level** *AmE*
〔美式〕) an instrument that shows whether
a surface is level 水準儀 –see picture on
page 958 見 958 頁彩圖

spir·i·tu·al¹ /'spɪrɪtʃuəl; 'spɪrɪ̩tʃuəl/ *adj* **1**
concerning non-physical things like
thoughts, feelings and beliefs 精神的; 心靈
的: *our spiritual nature* 我們的精神本質 **2** re-
ligious 宗教的: *spiritual songs* 聖歌 | *an ad-
viser in spiritual matters* 宗教事務的顧問 –
spiritually *adv*

spiritual² *n* a religious song sung originally
by the black peoples of the US 〔美國的〕黑
人靈歌

spir·i·tu·al·is·m /'spɪrɪtʃuəl,ɪzəm; 'spɪrɪ̩tʃulɪ-
zəm/ *n* [U] the belief that dead people may
send messages to living people, often
through a person with special powers 招魂
術, 降靈說 –**spiritualist** *n*

spit¹ /spɪt; spɪt/ *v* **spat** /spæt; spæt/ (also 又
作 **spit** *AmE* 〔美式〕), **spitting** [I;T] **1** to
force a small amount of liquid from your
mouth 吐口水; 吐痰: *He spat on the ground.*
他把痰吐在地上。 | *He's very ill and spitting
blood.* 他病得很重, 並且吐血。 **2 be spitting**
to be raining very lightly 下小雨: *It's still
spitting outside.* 外面仍在下小雨。 **3 be the
spitting image of** to look exactly like
another person or thing 酷似〔他人或他物〕:
She's the spitting image of her mother. 她跟
母親長得一模一樣。 **4** *infml* 〔非正式〕 **within
spitting distance** very close 非常近的: *They
live within spitting distance of his office.* 他
們住在他的辦公室旁邊。

spit sth **↔ out** *phr v* [T] **1** to force liquid
or food from your mouth 吐出〔口水或食
物〕: *He tasted the meat and spat it out.* 他嘗
了嘗那塊肉, 然後吐了出來。 **2** to say something with force, because you are angry 憤
怒地說出: *He spat out his criticisms of his
wife.* 他憤怒地說出了對妻子批評的話。

spit² *n* **1** [U] the liquid that is produced in
your mouth 唾液; 口水 **2** [C] a thin pointed
rod which is stuck through a piece of meat
before the meat is cooked over a fire 烤肉
叉

★spite¹ /spaɪt; spaɪt/ *n* [U] **1** the desire to hurt
someone or annoy them 〔傷害或激怒某人
的〕惡意: *I'm sure he only told them out of
spite.* 我肯定他是出於惡意才告訴他們的。 **2 in
spite of** although something is true 儘管; 雖
然: *We managed to enjoy ourselves in spite
of the rain.* 儘管下雨, 我們仍玩得很高興。 |

She had very little money. In spite of that, she managed to send her son to university. 她的錢很少，儘管如此，她仍設法送兒子去上了大學。

spite² *v* **spited, spiting** [T] to try to hurt or annoy someone 故意傷害或激怒〔某人〕: *He only did it to spite me.* 他那樣做不過是為了要我生氣。

splash¹ /splæʃ; splæʃ/ *v* [I;T] **1** (of liquids) to fall or strike against something in small drops 〔液體〕激濺; 飛濺: *The rain splashed on the window pane.* 雨打在窗的玻璃上。| *The car drove through the puddle and splashed my legs.* 車駛過水坑，把我的腿濺濕了。| *Paint splashed onto the carpet.* 油漆濺到地毯上。**2** to move liquid in a noisy way 濺濺: *The children had great fun splashing about in the pool.* 孩子們在水塘裡潑水，玩得非常開心。| *He splashed after-shave onto his skin.* 他把剃鬚後用的潤膚香水噴濺到皮膚上。

splash out *phr v infml* [I] to spend a lot of money on something 《非正式》在〔某物〕上花費許多錢: *They splashed out on a video camera.* 他們花了許多錢買了一台攝像機。

splash² *n* **1** the movement or noise made by splashing 激濺聲; 飛濺聲: *I fell into the water with a splash.* 我噗通一聲跌進水中。**2** a small amount of something that has fallen or been added 〔落下或加入的〕一點點東西: *a splash of paint on the floor* 地上的油漆斑點 | *A splash of red gave life to the picture.* 一點紅色為整幅畫增添了生動的色彩。| *a splash of vodka* 一點伏特加

splat /splæt; splæt/ *n* [sing] a noise of something wet hitting a surface 〔濕物擊中表面的〕啪嗒聲 **—splat** *adv*

splen·did /'splendɪd; 'splendɪd/ *adj* **1** grand in appearance 壯觀的; 堂皇的; 華麗的: *a splendid golden crown* 華麗的金色皇冠 **2** excellent 極好的; 優秀的: *a splendid piece of work* 一件極好的作品 | *You've got the job? Splendid!* 你得到了那份工作? 太棒了! **—splendidly** *adv*

splen·dour /'splendə; 'splendər/ *n* (**splendor** *AmE* 《美式》) [C;U] grand beauty 壯觀; 堂皇; 華麗: *He lived in great splendour.* 他過着富麗堂皇的生活。| *the splendours of the autumn landscape* 秋天的壯麗景色

splice /splaɪs; splaɪs/ *v* **spliced, splicing** [T] **1** to join two things together 拼接; 黏接〔兩物〕: *Can you splice the ends of the tape together?* 你能把這盤音帶的兩頭黏接起來嗎? **2** *infml* 《非正式》**get spliced** to get married 結婚

splint /splɪnt; splɪnt/ *n* a flat piece of wood or metal used for keeping a broken bone in position 〔固定斷骨的〕夾板

splin·ter /'splɪntə; 'splɪntər/ *n* **1** [C] a small sharp piece that has broken off something, especially something made of wood 〔尤指木頭的〕尖片; 碎片: *I've got a splinter in my*

finger. 我的手指上扎了一根刺。| *a splinter of glass* 玻璃碎片 **2** [only before a noun 只用於名詞前] a group that has separated from a larger one 〔大團體分裂出來的〕派別: *They quarrelled with the party leader, and formed a splinter group.* 他們與黨派領袖發生爭執後, 分裂出來形成了一個小派別。

splinter² *v* [I;T] to break into small pieces (使)裂成碎片

*split¹ /splɪt; splɪt/ *v* **split, splitting 1** [I;T] to break apart along the whole length 劈開; (使)裂開: *His coat had split down the back.* 他的外衣背面綻開了。| *He split the wood with one blow from his axe.* 他用斧頭一下子把木頭劈開了。**2** [I;T] to divide into separate parts or groups 分開; 分離: *We split into two groups, and searched the forest.* 我們分成兩組搜查樹林。| *The book is split into 12 chapters.* 這本書分為十二章。| *a quarrel which split the Liberal Party* 一次導致自由黨分裂的爭吵 | *Who was the first person to split the atom?* 誰是第一個使原子裂變的人? **3** [T] to divide something among people 分配; 均分〔某物〕: *I'll come with you, and we'll split the cost of the petrol.* 我和你一起來, 我們平攤汽油費用吧。**4 split the difference** to fix a figure halfway between two figures already mentioned 妥協, 折中; 讓步: *He wanted £60 for the chair and I offered £40, so in the end we split the difference.* 那把椅子他想賣六十英鎊, 我願出四十英鎊, 最後我們互相讓步。**5 split hairs** to talk about something at a level of unnecessary detail 在雞毛蒜皮上爭辯 **6 split your sides** to laugh a lot at something that is extremely funny 笑得前仰後合, 捧腹大笑

split off *phr v* [I;T **split** sthg ↔ **off**] to break off from the main part 〔從主體上〕分裂出來

split up *phr v* **1** [I] to end a relationship or marriage 斷絕關係; 離婚: *After two unhappy years John and Mary decided to split up.* 經過了兩年不愉快的日子後, 約翰和瑪麗決定分手了。**2** [I] to go in different directions 朝不同方向前進: *The group split up to try to find food.* 隊伍分頭去尋找食物。**3** [T **split** sthg ↔ **up**] to divide into smaller parts 分成小部分

split² *n* **1** a cut or break made when something splits 裂口; 裂縫: *I'm just mending a split in my trousers.* 我剛在補褲子上的裂縫。**2** a division or separation within a group 〔團體內部的〕分裂; 分歧: *a split in the Labour Party* 工黨的分裂

split-lev·el /ˌ· '··◂/ *adj* built so that different parts of the same room or floor of a building are at different heights 〔建築物〕錯層式的: *a split-level bathroom* 錯層式浴室。

split sec·ond /ˌ· '··◂/ *n* a very short moment 一瞬間; 一剎那: *For a split second, I thought I had made a mistake.* 那一瞬間, 我以為我犯了個錯誤。**—split-second** *adj*: *Split-*

second timing is crucial to the success of this operation. 分秒不差是這項行動成功的關鍵。

split·ting /'splɪtɪŋ; 'splɪtɪŋ/ *adj* very painful (used of a headache) 劇痛的〔指頭痛〕

splut·ter¹ /'splʌtər; 'splʌtə/ *n* a noise like liquid or air being forced out of something with difficulty 噼拍聲、畢剝聲

splutter² *v* [I] **1** to speak with difficulty, as if confused 困難而慌亂地說: *"But-but..." he spluttered.* "但是...但是..."他結結巴巴地說。**2** to make a noise like liquid or air being forced out of something with difficulty 發出噼啪聲: *I spent the day coughing and spluttering in bed.* 我一整天都在牀上嗆得咳個不停。

spoil¹ /spɔɪl; spɔɪl/ *v* **spoiled** *or* **spoilt** /spɔɪlt; spɔɪlt/, **spoiling 1** [T] to stop something being good 破壞; 損壞: *The visit was spoilt by an argument.* 那次探訪被一次爭吵破壞了。| *He spoiled the soup by putting too much salt in it.* 他放了太多鹽, 把湯糟蹋了。**2** [I] to decay or lose good qualities 腐爛; 變質: *The fruit has spoilt in the hot sun.* 水果在烈日下腐爛了。**3** [T] to treat someone too well 溺愛, 寵壞〔某人〕: *You spoil that child!* 你把那孩子寵壞了! **4 spoil yourself** to treat yourself very well 優待自己: *Have another chocolate. Go on, spoil yourself!* 再吃塊巧克力吧。來, 享受一下! **5 be spoiling for something** to be eager for trouble or for a fight 一心想找麻煩或打架

spoil² *n* **the spoils** things taken without payment, usually by an army or by thieves 掠奪物; 贓物: *I expect they are dividing up the spoils.* 我想他們正在分贓。

spoil·sport /'spɔɪl،spɔrt; 'spɔɪlspɔːt/ *n* a person who puts an end to someone else's fun 令人掃興的人

spoilt /spɔɪlt; spɔɪlt/ the past tense and past participle of SPOIL ☆ SPOIL 的過去式和過去分詞

spoke¹ /spok; spəʊk/ *n* any of the bars which connect the outer ring of a wheel to the centre, such as on a bicycle 輪輻, 輻條

spoke² *v* the past tense of SPEAK ☆ SPEAK 的過去式

spok·en /'spokən; 'spəʊkən/ *v* **1** the past participle of SPEAK ☆ SPEAK 的過去分詞 **2 -spoken** speaking in a certain way 以某種方式說話的: *He was well-spoken and obviously good at his job.* 他善於辭令, 顯然工作也做得很出色。

☆spokes·man /'spoksmən; 'spəʊksmən/ *n* **spokesmen** /-mən; -mən/ a person chosen to speak officially for a group; a female **spokesperson** is called a **spokeswoman** 發言人〔女發言人稱為 **spokeswoman**〕

sponge¹ /spʌndʒ; spʌndʒ/ *n* **1** [C;U] a simple sea creature which grows a light frame full of small holes, or the substance which this creature consists of 海綿〔一種海洋生物〕; 海綿組織 **2** [C;U] a piece of rub-

ber, plastic, or sponge which is full of holes and that you use for washing your body 海綿〔用多孔的橡膠、塑膠或海綿製成, 用於洗澡〕 **3** [C;U] *BrE*〔英式〕see 見 SPONGE CAKE

sponge² *v* **sponged, sponging** [T] **1** to clean something with a soft wet cloth or sponge〔用濕布或海綿〕清潔, 擦拭: *Sponge the surfaces lightly with a damp cloth.* 用濕布輕輕地擦拭表面。**2** to remove liquid in this way〔用海綿〕吸掉〔液體〕: *I'll just sponge the blood from the wound.* 我就去把傷口上的血吸掉。**3 sponge on/off someone** to take advantage of someone's generous nature in order to get money and other things from them as a gift (a phrase used to express disapproval) 詐取某人的錢財〔含貶義〕: *At 25, he's still sponging off his parents.* 他二十五歲了, 還要依賴父母生活。**–sponger** *n*

sponge·bag /'spʌndʒ،bæg; 'spʌdʒbæg/ *n* a small bag that you take with you when you travel, and in which you carry the things you need to keep yourself clean and fresh 盥洗用具袋

sponge cake /'··/ *n* [C;U] a light cake made from eggs, sugar, and flour 鬆軟蛋糕: *I've made a sponge cake.* 我做了一個鬆軟蛋糕。| *Would you like some sponge cake?* 你想來點鬆軟蛋糕嗎?

spong·y /'spʌndʒɪ; 'spʌndʒɪ/ *adj* **spongier, spongiest** soft and wet, like a sponge 海綿似的; 濕軟的: *The grass is spongy after the rain.* 雨後草地又軟又濕。**–sponginess** *n* [U]

spon·sor¹ /'spɑnsər; 'spɒnsə/ *n* **1** a person or business that provides the money for something like a sports event, often in return for advertising their products at the event〔體育比賽等的〕贊助人; 贊助商: *We interrupt this programme to hear a few words from our sponsor.* 我們打斷一下現在的節目, 請我們的贊助人講幾句話。**2** a person or business that agrees to give money to a good cause if another person succeeds in doing something special〔如果某人能做成某事便肯出資的〕贊助人; 贊助商: *I am looking for sponsors for my marathon run on behalf of the Save the Children Fund.* 我準備為"拯救孩子基金會"進行馬拉松長跑, 現正在尋找贊助商。**3** a person that takes responsibility for formally putting forward a suggestion 提案人, 倡議者

spon·sor² *v* [T] **1** to pay for something, usually in return for advertising particular products 贊助〔某事物〕: *The research programme was sponsored by tobacco companies.* 該研究計劃是由幾家煙草公司贊助的。**2** to agree to give someone money for a good cause if they succeed in doing something special〔如果某人能做成某事便〕出錢贊助: *a sponsored charity run* 受贊助的慈善活動 **3** to put forward a formal suggestion 正式提出〔建議〕; 倡議

S

spon·ta·ne·ous /spɑn'tenɪəs; spɒn'teɪnɪəs/ *adj* happening naturally, without planning 自然發生的; 自動的: *A spontaneous cheer rose from the crowd.* 人羣自發地喝起采來。 – **spontaneously** *adv* – **spontaneity** /ˌspɑntə-'niətɪ; ˌspɒntə'neɪətɪ/ *n* [U]

spoof /spuf; spuːf/ *n* a funny false copy or description of something 滑稽的模仿〔描述〕: *a magazine spoof of university life* 雜誌上描述大學生活的幽默小品

spook /spuk; spuːk/ *n infml* 〔非正式〕 **1** a spirit, especially one that appears to frighten people 幽靈; 鬼 **2** *AmE* 〔美式〕 see 見 SPY

spook·y /'spukɪ; 'spuːkɪ/ *adj* **spookier, spookiest** *infml* 〔非正式〕 frightening 可怕的, 駭人的: *a spooky old house* 陰森恐怖的老房子 | *It gets spooky here after dark.* 這個地方在天黑之後很陰森。

spool /spul; spuːl/ *n* a wheel around which things like wire, camera film, or TAPE are wound 〔電線、電影膠片或音帶等的〕卷軸

spoon[1] /spun; spuːn/ *n* **1** an object used for mixing, serving, and eating food 匙, 調羹: *a wooden spoon* 一隻木匙 **2** see 見 SPOON-FUL: *Two spoons of sugar, please.* 請加兩匙糖。

spoon[2] *v* [T] to use a spoon to pick something up and put it somewhere 用匙舀〔某物〕: *Spoon the mixture into individual dishes.* 用調羹把混合物舀到個別的盤子裡。

spoon-feed /'···/ *v* **spoonfed** /-ˌfɛd; -fed/, **spoonfeeding** [T] **1** to feed someone, often a baby, with a spoon 用匙餵〔常指嬰兒〕 **2** to teach someone everything they need to know, or do everything for them, so that they do not need to think for themselves 對〔某人〕進行填鴨式教育; 向〔某人〕灌輸

spoon·ful /'spun,ful; 'spuːnfʊl/ *n* **spoonfuls** *or* **spoonsful** (also 又作 **spoon**) the amount that a spoon will hold 一匙之量: *Add two teaspoonfuls of sugar.* 請加兩匙糖。

spo·rad·ic /spə'rædɪk; spə'rædɪk/ *adj* happening for short irregular periods, but not continuously 零星的; 偶爾發生的: *sporadic fighting* 零星的戰鬥 – **sporadically** /-klɪ; -klɪ/ *adv*

spore /spor; spɔːʳ/ *n* a very small cell produced by some plants, which is able to develop into a new plant 〔某些植物的〕芽孢; 孢子

spor·ran /'spɑrən; 'spɒrən/ *n* a special kind of bag worn by men in Scotland as part of their national dress 〔蘇格蘭男子所佩帶的〕毛皮袋

*sport[1] /sport; spɔːt/ *n* **1** [C;U] a game or activity done for physical exercise or pleasure 運動; 體育運動: *Do you think football is an exciting sport?* 你認為足球是不是一項激烈的運動? | *I've never been very keen on sport.* 我對體育運動向來不太感興趣。 | *a sports shop* 體育用品商店 – see 見 REC-REATION (USAGE 用法) **2** [C] a person who accepts defeat or a joke without becoming angry or upset 輸得起的人; 開得起玩笑的人: *You're a good sport!* 你真是個胸懷磊落的人! **3** [U] fun 玩笑: *I only said it in sport!* 我不過是開個玩笑吧!

■ USAGE 用法: **Game** and **match** are both used when talking about sports. Use **game** for an occasion when people meet to take part in a particular sporting activity ☆ **game** 和 **match** 都用作談論體育運動。當人們在一起參加某項運動時用 **game**: *Let's have a game of tennis.* 我們來打一場網球吧。 | *They meet for a game of squash every Monday.* 他們每個星期一都一起去打壁球。 | *The children were having an informal game of cricket on the back lawn.* 孩子們在後院的草坪上玩板球。 Use **match** for more public occasions when two people or teams are competing ☆ 當兩個人或兩支隊伍公開進行競賽時用 **match**: *The teams are in training for the big match.* 那些隊伍都在為大賽進行訓練。 | *a cricket match on the village green* 在村裡的草地上進行的板球比賽 | *a football match* 一場足球賽

---

sport[2] *v* [T] to wear something that you appear proud of 炫耀; 賣弄: *She came in today sporting a fur coat.* 她今天穿着毛皮大衣來炫耀一番。

sport·ing /'spɔrtɪŋ; 'spɔːtɪŋ/ *adj* **1** [only before a noun 只用於名詞前] of or concerning sports 運動的: *a painter of sporting scenes* 專畫運動場景的畫家 **2** fair and generous, especially in sports 〔尤指在運動中〕公正大度的; 有運動家風度的: *It was very sporting of them to let our team go first.* 他們十分大方, 讓我們隊先走。 **3 a sporting chance** a good possibility 很大的可能性: *He stands a sporting chance of winning, I think.* 我認為他很可能獲勝。 – **sportingly** *adv*

sports car /'··/ *n* a fast car, that is usually low with a roof that opens 跑車〔車身較低, 通常為敞篷的〕

sports·man /'spɔrtsmən; 'spɔːtsmən/ *n* **sportsmen** /-mən; -mən/ a person who plays a lot of sport; a woman who plays a lot of sport is called a **sportswoman** 運動員〔女運動員稱為 **sportswoman**〕

sports·man·ship /'spɔrtsmən,ʃɪp; 'spɔːtsmənʃɪp/ *n* [U] a spirit of fair play and generous behaviour when winning or losing 公正大度的精神, 體育精神

spot[1] /spɑt; spɒt/ *n* **1** [C] a small round area on a surface which is different in colour from the main area 點; 斑點: *a white dress with blue spots* 有藍色斑點的白色衣服 **2** [C] a raised mark on your skin, sometimes caused by disease〔有時由疾病引起的皮膚上的〕紅斑; 丘疹: *I'm covered in spots.* 我出了一身丘疹。**3** [C] a dirty mark 污跡: *He tried to remove the spot on his sweater with soap and water.* 他盡力用肥皂和水來洗去毛衣上的污跡。**4** [C] a place known for a particular quality or event〔由於某種特點或某事件而聞名的〕地點: *For many years Spain was a favourite holiday spot.* 許多年來, 西班牙一直是度假的勝地。| *This was the spot where we first met.* 這是我們第一次見面的地點。**5 on the spot: a** at the place where something is happening 在現場: *He had a heart attack in the theatre but luckily there was a doctor on the spot.* 他在劇院裡突然心臟病發作, 但幸好有位醫生在場。**b** without stopping to consider 立即, 即刻: *Of course, I resigned on the spot.* 我當然馬上就辭職了。**6** [sing] a small amount 少量: *How about a spot of tea?* 來點茶怎麼樣? | *I felt a spot of rain.* 我感覺到有一點點雨。**7 be in a spot** to be in a difficult position 處於困境中: *With no electricity, we were really in a spot.* 由於停電, 我們真的陷入了困境。**8 put someone on the spot** to put someone in a difficult position 使某人處於困境中: *The question really put the Prime Minister on the spot.* 這個問題委實令首相十分尷尬。

spot² v **-tt-** [T] to recognize a person or thing 認出〔人或物〕: *I spotted a friend in the crowd.* 我在人羣中認出一位朋友。

spot·less /ˈspɒtlɪs; ˈspɒtləs/ adj completely clean 十分乾淨的: *a spotless house* 十分乾淨的房子 **–spotlessly** adv **–spotlessness** n [U]

spot·light¹ /ˈspɒt,laɪt; ˈspɒtlaɪt/ n **1** [C] a powerful lamp with a narrow beam that can be directed at a particular place, used especially in theatres 聚光燈〔尤用於劇院內〕 **2 in the spotlight** receiving a lot of public attention 引人矚目的

spotlight² v **spotlit** or **spotlighted, spotlighting** [T] to direct attention towards something 使受注意〔某事物〕; 突出: *He's written an article spotlighting the difficulties of school-leavers.* 他寫了一篇文章, 提醒人們注意離校生的困難。

spot·ted /ˈspɒtɪd; ˈspɒtɪd/ adj with a pattern of spots on it 有斑點的: *a spotted dress* 有斑點的裙子 –see picture on page 243 見243頁彩圖

spot·ter /ˈspɒtə; ˈspɒtər/ n a person who keeps watch for a particular thing 監視者; 觀察者: *a train spotter* 火車觀察員

spot·ty /ˈspɒti; ˈspɒti/ adj **spottier, spottiest** BrE infml with spots〔英式, 非正式〕有斑點的; 有污點的: *a spotty teenager* 長雀斑的少年人 | *spotty material* 有污點的材料

spouse /spauz; spauz/ n law a husband or wife〔律〕配偶〔指夫或妻〕

spout¹ /spaut; spaut/ v **1** [I;T] to come out or be made to come out in a forceful stream 噴出; 湧出: *Water spouted from*

the rock. 水從岩石中噴出來。| *The volcano erupted, spouting lava high into the air.* 火山爆發了, 把岩漿高高地噴向空中。**2** [T] to pour out in a stream of words 滔滔不絕地講: *She's always spouting Shakespeare.* 她總是滔滔不絕地談論莎士比亞的作品。

spout² n an opening from which liquid comes out of 噴口, 噴嘴: *the spout of a teapot* 茶壺嘴

sprain /spreɪn; spreɪn/ v [T] to damage a joint in the body by twisting it suddenly 扭傷〔關節〕: *He sprained his ankle playing football.* 他踢足球時扭傷了足踝。**–sprain** n: *a nasty sprain* 嚴重扭傷

sprang /spræŋ; spræŋ/ v the past tense of SPRING¹ ☆ SPRING¹的過去式

sprat /spræt; spræt/ n a small fish found in the sea, used as food 小西鯡

sprawl /sprɔːl; sprɔːl/ v **1** [I] to lie or sit with your arms and legs stretched out 伸開四肢躺〔坐〕: *She sprawled out in a comfortable chair.* 她伸開四肢坐在一張舒適的椅子上。**2** [I] to stretch over a large area of land, often in an unattractive way 蔓延, 擴展: *The city sprawls for miles in each direction.* 這座城市向四面八方擴展了幾英里。**–sprawl** n: *dreadful urban sprawl* 可怕的城市胡亂擴張〔現象〕

spray¹ /spreɪ; spreɪ/ n **1** [U] water blown in very small drops 水花; 浪花; 飛沫: *We parked the car by the sea and it got covered in spray.* 我們把汽車停在海邊, 結果被浪花濺濕了。**2** [C;U] liquid in a can or container forced out under pressure 噴霧液體: *insect spray* 殺蟲噴劑 | *hair spray* 噴髮定型劑 **3** [C] a container that is used to hold this liquid 噴霧器: *a spray of touch-up paint for the car* 給汽車補漆用的噴霧器 **4** [C] leaves and flowers growing on a branch or arranged decoratively 帶花葉的小枝; 枝狀飾物: *a spray of lilies* 一簇百合花

spray² v [I;T] to scatter or be scattered under pressure 噴, 噴灑: *to spray paint on a wall* 把油漆噴到牆上 | *I spray a wall with paint* 在牆上噴油漆 | *They sprayed the President's car with bullets.* 他們用槍掃射總統的座駕。

☆spread¹ /spred; spred/ v **spread, spreading 1** [I;T] to open or stretch out 展開; 伸展: *a ship with sails spread* 張着帆的船 | *He spread his hands.* 他攤開雙手。**2** [I] to cover a large area or period of time〔空間或時間上〕佔; 覆蓋; 分佈: *His interests now spread over several subjects.* 現在他的興趣包括好幾門學科。| *Payments will be spread over two years.* 款項將分兩年付清。**3** [T] to put a covering on something〔在某物上〕塗, 敷: *to spread butter on bread* 把黃油塗在麵包上 **4** [I;T] to reach or have an effect on more people or things 傳播, 蔓延: *The fire spread quickly.* 火勢迅速蔓延。| *The disease is spread by touch.* 這種病通過接觸傳染。**5** [I;

T] to make or become widely known (使)變得廣為人知: *If I tell you this secret, don't spread it around.* 如果我把這個祕密告訴你，不要把它告訴別人。| *The news spread quickly.* 消息傳得很快。

spread² *n* **1** [sing] the act or action of spreading 傳播，蔓延: *the spread of a disease* 疾病的傳播 | *the spread of information* 信息的傳播 **2** [C] a variety 種類；幅度；範圍: *a spread of interests* 各種興趣 | *The students' ages show a wide spread.* 學生的年齡有很大差距。**3** [C] a newspaper or magazine article or an advertisement running across one or more pages 佔一版或多版的報刊文章[廣告]: *a two-page spread* 橫跨兩版的篇幅 **4** [C] a large or grand meal 盛宴；宴席: *Our host had a fine spread waiting for us.* 主人家為我們準備了豐盛的宴席。**5** [C;U] a soft food for spreading on bread 塗麵包的軟質食物，塗食品的醬: *a tube of cheese spread* 一管乾酪醬

spread-ea·gle /ˌ·ˈ··/ *v* to be spread-eagled to be in a position with arms and legs spread out 伸開四肢放: *lying spread-eagled on the bed* 伸開四肢躺在牀上

spree /spriː/ *n* a time of free and wild fun, spent enjoying yourself 縱情狂歡

sprig /sprɪɡ; sprɪɡ/ *n* a small end of a stem or branch with leaves 帶葉的小枝: *a sprig of parsley* 一根西芹

spright·ly /ˈspraɪtlɪ; ˈspraɪtli/ *adj* **sprightlier, sprightliest** cheerful and active 愉快的；活潑的: *a sprightly old man* 精力充沛的老人 –**sprightliness** *n* [U]

spring¹ /sprɪŋ; sprɪŋ/ *v* **sprang** /spræŋ; spræŋ/, **sprung** /sprʌŋ; sprʌŋ/, **springing 1** [I] to jump 跳；跳躍: *She sprang to her feet.* 她一躍而起。**2** [T] to produce without warning 突然出示；突然拿出: *We sprang the news on him.* 我們突然把那消息告訴他。**3** [I] to be the result of 由…產生；源自: *Her hatred of men springs from her childhood.* 她對男人的憎恨源於少女時期。**4** [I] to start being active 開始活動: *I turned the key and the engine sprang to life.* 我轉動鑰匙，引擎便起動了。**5 spring a leak** to begin to let in water through a crack 從縫隙中開始漏水

spring up *phr v* [I] to happen or appear quickly 迅速發生；迅速出現: *A wind suddenly sprang up.* 突然刮起了一陣風。| *Towns sprang up in the desert when gold was found there.* 在沙漠裡發現了黃金以後，一些城鎮便在那裡拔地而起。

spring² *n* **1** [U;C] (also 又作 **Spring**) the season between winter and summer in which leaves and flowers appear 春天，春季 **2** [C] a place where water comes up naturally from the ground 泉 **3** [C] a length of metal wound around, which returns to its original shape after being pushed 彈簧；彈條: *a watch-spring* 手錶的發條 | *What an uncomfortable chair! It needs new springs.*

這椅子太不舒服了! 需要換新的彈簧了。**4** [U] the quality of this object 彈性: *There's not much spring in this old bed.* 這張舊牀沒有多少彈性。**5** [C] a sudden large jump 突然的跳躍: *The cat made a sudden spring at the mouse.* 貓突然撲向老鼠。

spring·board /ˈsprɪŋˌbord; ˈsprɪŋbɔːd/ *n* **1** a strong board which bends and helps you jump higher 跳板；踏跳板 **2** something which makes an action or activity possible 〔使行動或活動成為可能的〕跳板；起點: *a springboard to success* 成功的跳板

spring-clean /ˌ·ˈ··/ *v* [I;T] to give a place a thorough cleaning, especially in the spring 春季大掃除 –**springclean** *n*

spring·y /ˈsprɪŋɪ; ˈsprɪŋi/ *adj* **springier, springiest** returning quickly to its original shape after being pressed 有彈性的

sprin·kle /ˈsprɪŋkl; ˈsprɪŋkəl/ *v* **sprinkled, sprinkling** [T] to scatter in drops or small grains 灑，撒: *Sprinkle sugar on the strawberries.* 把糖撒在草莓上。

sprin·kler /ˈsprɪŋklə; ˈsprɪŋklər/ *n* an apparatus for scattering drops of water 灑水器: *a garden sprinkler* 花園灑水器

sprin·kling /ˈsprɪŋklɪŋ; ˈsprɪnklɪŋ/ *n* a small quantity 少量: *a sprinkling of snow* 少量的雪

sprint¹ /sprɪnt; sprɪnt/ *v* [I] to run for a short distance at your fastest speed 〔短距離〕全速衝刺 –**sprinter** *n*

sprint² *n* **1** a short run 短跑 **2** a short race 短跑比賽: *the 100 metres sprint* 一百米短跑

sprite /spraɪt; spraɪt/ *n* a fairy, especially a playful one 小精靈，小仙子

sprout¹ /spraʊt; spraʊt/ *v* [I; T] to grow or send up new growth (使)生長；發芽: *We could see the leaves sprouting on the trees.* 我們可以看見樹木長出了葉子。

sprout² *n* **1** a new growth on a plant 芽; 苗 **2** see 見 BRUSSELS SPROUT

spruce¹ /spruːs; spruːs/ *n* [C;U] a tree with short needle-shaped leaves found in northern parts of the world 雲杉(木)

spruce² *adj* tidy and clean 整潔的 –**sprucely** *adv*: *sprucely dressed* 穿戴得整潔漂亮

spruce³ *v* **spruced, sprucing, spruce yourself up** to make yourself look neat and tidy 把自己打扮得整潔漂亮: *He spruced himself up for the interview.* 為了面試，他把自己打扮得漂標亮亮。

sprung /sprʌŋ; sprʌŋ/ *v* the past participle of SPRING¹ ☆ SPRING¹的過去分詞

spry /spraɪ; spraɪ/ *adj* active (used especially of old people) 活潑的；敏捷的〔尤指老年人〕: *a spry old lady* 一位矯捷的老婦人

spud /spʌd; spʌd/ *n infml* a potato 《非正式》馬鈴薯，土豆

spun /spʌn; spʌn/ *v* the past tense and past participle of SPIN¹ ☆ SPIN¹的過去式和過去分詞

spur¹ /spɜ; spɜːr/ *n* **1** a sharp pointed object worn on the heel of a rider's boot to help control a horse 馬刺 **2** something acting to encourage an activity 鼓勵, 激勵: *The news was a spur to continued effort.* 這消息起了激勵人們繼續努力的作用。**3 on the spur of the moment** without preparation or planning 一時衝動之下; 即席

spur² *v* **-rr-** [T] **1** to kick a horse with spurs 以馬刺策[馬] **2** to urge to faster action or greater effort 鼓勵, 勵激: *She spurred on her team.* 她鼓勵她的隊伍。

spu·ri·ous /'spjʊriəs; 'spjuəriəs/ *adj* **1** false or pretended 虛假的; 偽裝的: *a spurious signature* 偽造的簽名 | *spurious sympathy* 假裝的同情 **2** based on incorrect reasoning 不合邏輯的: *a spurious argument* 不合邏輯的爭論 **–spuriously** *adv* **–spuriousness** *n* [U]

spurn /spɜ·n; spɜ:n/ *v* [T] to refuse 拒絕: *She spurned all offers of help.* 她拒絕了一切幫助。

spurt¹ /spɜ·t; spɜ:t/ *n* **1** a short sudden increase of effort 〔努力的〕迸發; 衝刺: *a spurt of activity* 活躍程度突然增大 **2** a sudden rush 噴湧: *a spurt of blood* 一股血 | *a spurt of interest* 一陣興趣 **3 put a spurt on** to hurry 抓緊, 趕快: *She put a spurt on and passed the other runners.* 她加了一把勁, 超越了其他賽跑選手。

spurt² *v* [I] **1** to flow out suddenly 突然流出: *Water spurted from the broken pipe.* 水從破裂的管子湧了出來。**2** to increase your speed suddenly and for a short time 突然加速: *We spurted past the bus.* 我們突然加速, 超越了那輛公共汽車。

sput·ter /'spʌtɚ; 'spʌtəʳ/ *v* **1** [I;T] to say or speak in confusion 慌亂地說 **2** [I] to make repeated soft explosive sounds 發出連續的輕微爆裂聲: *The car's engine sputtered for a moment and then died.* 汽車引擎噼噼啪啪地響了一會兒便熄火了。**–sputter** *n*

spy¹ /spaɪ; spaɪ/ *n* **spies** a person employed to find out secret information 間諜, 特務; 密探

spy² *v* **spied, spying 1** [I] to watch secretly 祕密監視: *He's always spying on his neighbours.* 他總是在偷偷監視他的鄰居。 **2** [I] to act as a spy 做間諜 **3** [T] *lit* to catch sight of 〔文〕看見: *She spied her friend in the crowd.* 她在人羣中看見了朋友。

sq a written abbreviation for 〔縮〕= square: *6 sq metres* 六平方米

squab·ble /'skwɒbl; 'skwɒbəl/ *v* **squabbled, squabbling** [I] to have a quarrel over something unimportant 〔為瑣事而〕爭吵, 口角: *What are you children squabbling about now?* 你們這些小孩子在吵甚麼? **–squabble** *n*

★**squad** /skwɑd; skwɒd/ *n* [C + sing/pl verb] a group of people working as a team 〔在一起工作的〕小組, 小隊: *The bomb squad has arrived.* 炸彈處理小組已經到了。

squad·ron /'skwɑdrən; 'skwɒdrən/ *n* [C; + sing/pl verb] a group belonging to the armed forces 〔軍隊的〕中隊: *The squadron*

is ready for duty. 中隊已準備好去執行任務。

squal·id /'skwɑlɪd; 'skwɒlɪd/ *adj* very dirty or unpleasant 骯髒的, 污穢的: *squalid living conditions* 骯髒的居住環境 **–squalidly** *adv*

squall /skwɔl; skwɔ:l/ *n* a sudden strong wind 颮〔一陣狂風〕**–squally** *adj*

squal·or /'skwɑlɚ; 'skwɒlɔʳ/ *n* [U] dirty, unhealthy, and unpleasant conditions 骯髒, 污穢: *living in squalor in a filthy room* 住在一個骯髒的房間裡

squan·der /'skwɑndɚ; 'skwɒndəʳ/ *v* [T] to use up foolishly 浪費, 亂花: *The government is squandering our money on nuclear weapons.* 政府正在把我們的錢浪費在生產核武器上。

★**square¹** /skwɛr; skweəʳ/ *n* **1** a shape with four straight sides of equal length forming four right angles 正方形: *Draw a square with sides of 10 centimetres.* 畫一個邊長為十公分的正方形。| *a square of cloth* 一塊正方形的布 **2** an open space in a city, often in the shape of a square 〔常為方形的〕廣場: *The market is held in the square.* 集市在廣場上舉辦。| *He lives in Norfolk Square.* 他住在諾弗克廣場。**3** a number equal to another number multiplied by itself 平方; 自乘: *16 is the square of 4.* 16是4的平方。**4** a tool with a straight edge and often in the shape of an L which is used for drawing and measuring right angles 直角尺, 曲尺; 直角規 **5 square one** *BrE* the very beginning 〔英式〕開始; 起點: *All my papers were lost in the fire, so now I'm back to square one.* 我所有的文件都被大火燒掉了, 所以現在我只好重新開始。**6 square root** the number which when multiplied by itself equals a particular number 平方根: *3 is square root of 9.* 3是9的平方根。

square² *adj* **1** having four equal sides and four right angles 正方形的: *A handkerchief is usually square.* 手帕通常是正方形的。| *a square tower* 方形塔 **2** like a square in shape 〔形狀上〕如正方形的; 四方的: *a square jaw* 方下巴 | *square shoulders* 寬寬的肩膀 **3** being a measurement of area equal to that of a square with sides of a particular length 〔面積〕平方的: *144 square inches equal 1 square foot.* 144平方英寸等於1平方尺。**4** being the stated length on all four sides 見方的; 等邊的: *The room is 6 metres square.* 這個房間為六平方米見方。**5** [never before a noun 不能用於名詞前] paid and settled 付清的, 結清的: *Our account is all square.* 我們的賬全部結清了。**6** [never before a noun 不能用於名詞前] equal in points 得分相同的: *The teams are square at one match each.* 兩隊各勝一場, 打成平手。**7 square deal** fair and honest treatment 公正的待遇; 公平的交易: *I don't think I'm getting a square deal at that garage.* 我認為那家修車庫對我不夠公道。**8 a square meal** a good satisfying meal 一頓飽餐 **–squareness** *n* [U]

square³ *v* **squared, squaring 1** [T] to make something into a shape with a straight edge and right angles 使成方形: *He squared off the end of the piece of wood.* 他把那塊木頭的一端鋸成方形。**2** [T] to mark squares on 在…上劃正方形: *squared paper* 方格紙 **3** [T] to multiply a number by itself once 自乘一次: *2 squared equals 4.* 2 的平方是4。**4** [I;T] to fit a particular explanation or standard (使)符合解釋[標準]: *His statement doesn't square with the facts.* 他的陳述與事實不符。**5** [T] to settle 結清; 解決: *I squared my account at the store.* 我跟那家商店結清了賬。

square up *phr v* [I] to settle a bill 付賬單, 結清: *Let's square up — how much do I owe you?* 我們把賬算清吧——我欠你多少錢?

square⁴ (also 又作 **squarely**) *adv* directly 直接地: *He looked her square in the eye.* 他正視着她的眼睛。

squash¹ /skwɑʃ; skwɒʃ/ *v* **1** [I;T] to force or be forced into a flat shape or a small space 壓扁; 擠入: *I sat on my hat and squashed it.* 我把帽子坐扁了。| *May I squash in next to you?* 可否讓我擠在你的旁邊? **2** [T] to force into silence or inactivity 壓制; 鎮壓: *She felt squashed after so much criticism.* 在遭到了諸多批評之後, 她感到無話可說。

squash² *n* **1** the act of being forced into a small space 擠壓: *There was quite a squash in the train.* 火車上相當擁擠。**2** [U] a game played in a walled court with rackets (RACKET¹) and a rubber ball 壁球 **3** [U] *BrE* a sweet fruit drink《英式》果汁飲料: *a glass of orange squash* 一杯橙汁飲料

squat¹ /skwɑt; skwɒt/ *v* **-tt-** [I] **1** to sit with your legs bent and your weight on your feet 蹲, 蹲坐 –see picture on page 992 見 992 頁彩圖 **2** to live in a place without permission 擅自佔住〔某處〕

squat² *adj* unpleasantly short or low 粗矮的; 矮胖的: *It's a rather squat building, isn't it?* 這幢樓矮得很難看, 對不對?

squat·ter /'skwɑtə; 'skwɒtə'/ *n* a person who lives in a building without permission 擅自佔用房屋的人

squawk /skwɔk; skwɔ:k/ *v* [I] to make a loud rough-sounding cry, especially as made by birds〔尤指鳥類〕發出粗厲的叫聲: *hens squawking at the sight of a cat* 一見到貓就亂叫的母雞 –**squawk** *n*

squeak /skwik; skwi:k/ *v* [I] to make a very high sounding noise 吱吱作響: *a squeaking door* 吱吱作響的門 –**squeak** *n: the squeak of a mouse* 老鼠的吱吱叫聲 –**squeaky** *adj* **squeakier, squeakiest**: *a squeaky voice* 尖細的嗓音

squeal /skwil; skwi:l/ *v* [I] to make a long very high sound or cry 發出長而尖的聲音〔叫聲〕: *squealing tyres* 吱吱作響的輪胎 | *squealing pigs* 高聲尖叫的豬 –**squeal** *n: squeals of delight from the children* 孩子們高興得尖叫

squeam·ish /'skwimɪʃ; 'skwi:mɪʃ/ *adj* easily shocked by unpleasant things 易受驚的: *It's a violent film, so don't go if you're squeamish.* 這是部暴力影片, 所以如果你容易受驚嚇的話, 那就不要去看。–**squeamishly** *adv* –**squeamishness** *n* [U]

squeeze¹ /skwiz; skwi:z/ *v* **squeezed, squeezing 1** [T] to press 擠; 壓; 榨: *to squeeze an orange* 榨橘子 | *squeeze the water out of a wet cloth* 把濕布的水擠出來 **2** [I;T] to fit by forcing or pressing 擠; 塞: *The train was full but I squeezed in anyway.* 火車上坐滿了人, 但我還是擠了進去。**3** [T] to force out by pressure 擠出: *to squeeze toothpaste out of a tube* 把牙膏從牙膏筒裡擠出來

squeeze² *n* **1** [C] an act of pressing 壓迫; 擠壓: *She gave his hand a gentle squeeze.* 她輕輕地捏了他的手一下。**2** [C] a small amount squeezed out 擠出的微量: *a squeeze of lemon juice* 擠出一點檸檬汁 **3** [sing] the state of being pressed together 擁擠: *There's room for one more, but it'll be a squeeze.* 這裡還能再容納一個人, 但會相當擠。**4** [C] a difficult state of affairs caused by short supplies or tight controls〔因供應短缺或嚴格控制所引起的〕困境; 緊迫: *a credit squeeze* 信貸緊縮

squelch /skweltʃ; skweltʃ/ *v* [I] to make a wet sucking sound, for example when stepping through mud 發出吱嘎聲〔如走在泥漿中〕–**squelch** *n*

squid /skwɪd; skwɪd/ *n* a sea creature with 10 arms at one end of a long body 槍烏賊, 魷魚

squig·gle /'skwɪgl; 'skwɪgəl/ *n infml* a short wavy or twisting line《非正式》波狀或彎曲的短線: *What do these squiggles on the map mean?* 地圖上的這些曲線代表甚麼? –**squiggly** *adj*

squint¹ /skwɪnt; skwɪnt/ *v* [I] **1** to look at something with almost closed eyes 眯着眼睛看 **2** to be unable to position both eyes to look in the same direction at once 斜視

squint² *n* a disorder of the eye muscles causing the eyes to look in two different directions 斜視(眼), 斜視症

squire /skwaɪr; skwaɪə'/ *n* in the past, the main landowner in a country area of England〔昔時英國的〕大地主, 鄉紳

squirm /skwɜm; skwɜ:m/ *v* [I] to twist your body about, as if from discomfort or nervousness〔彷彿因不適或緊張而〕扭動身體; 侷促不安: *questions that made him squirm* 令他侷促不安的問題

squir·rel /'skwɜrəl; 'skwɪrəl/ *n* a small animal with a long furry tail that lives in trees and eats nuts 松鼠

squirt¹ /skwɜt; skwɜ:t/ *v* [I;T] to force or be forced out in a thin stream 使噴出; 噴射: *to squirt oil into a lock* 往鎖裡噴點油 | *The oil squirted all over his trousers.* 油噴得他的

褲子上到處都是。**2** [T] to hit with a stream of liquid 向...噴射〔液體〕: *I was squirted with water.* 有人向我噴水。

squirt² *n* a quick thin stream of liquid 噴出的細流

SRN /ˌɛs ɑr ˈɛn; ˌɛs ɑːr ˈen/ a written abbreviation for 〖縮〗= STATE REGISTERED NURSE

Ssh /ʃ; ʃ/ *interj* see 見 SH

St *n* **1** a written abbreviation for 〖縮〗= STREET: *Regent St* 瑞琴街 **2** an abbreviation for SAINT, used before the person's name 〖縮〗聖...〔用於人名前〕: *St Andrew* 聖安德魯

stab¹ /stæb; stæb/ *n* **1** a wound made by a pointed weapon 刺傷, 戳傷: *a stab in the chest* 胸部的刺傷 **2** a sudden painful feeling 一陣刺痛, 一陣劇痛: *a stab of guilt* 一陣內疚 **3** have a stab at to try to do something 嘗試做〔某事〕: *Have a stab at answering question 3.* 試解答第三個問題。

stab² *v* -bb- [I;T] **1** to strike forcefully with a pointed weapon 刺, 戳: *Julius Caesar was stabbed to death.* 裘利斯·凱撒被刺死了。| *The murdered girl had been stabbed with a knife.* 遇害的女孩是被人用刀刺死的。**2** stab someone in the back to attack someone who trusted you 背後中傷被信任你的人; 背叛某人

stab·bing¹ /ˈstæbɪŋ; ˈstæbɪŋ/ *adj* sharp and sudden (used of pain) 突然而劇烈的〔指疼痛〕

stabbing² *n* an attack when someone is stabbed 刺傷事件

sta·bil·i·ty /stəˈbɪlətɪ; stəˈbɪlɪ̩ti/ *n* [U] the state of being fixed and unlikely to change 穩定, 穩固: *the stability of their marriage* 他們穩固的婚姻 –opposite 反義 **instability**

sta·bil·ize, stabilizing (also 又作 **stabilise** BrE 〖英式〗) [I;T] to make or become firm or steady (使)穩固, (使)穩定: *The price of coffee has been rising and falling, but has now stabilized.* 咖啡的價格時上時下, 但現已穩定下來了。–**stabilization** /ˌsteɪbləˈzeʃən; ˌsteɪbɪ̩laɪˈzeɪʃən/ [U]

sta·bil·iz·er /ˈsteɪbəˌlaɪzə; ˈsteɪbɪ̩laɪzər/ *n* (also 又作 **stabiliser** BrE 〖英式〗) an apparatus or chemical that stabilizes something 穩定器; 穩定劑: *a ship's stabilizers* 船的穩定器

sta·ble¹ /ˈsteɪbl; ˈsteɪbəl/ *n* **1** a building for keeping horses in 馬廄, 馬房 **2** a group of racing horses with one owner 〔一個馬主所擁有的〕一羣賽馬

stable² *v* **stabled, stabling** [T] to put or keep in a stable 置於馬房

stable³ *adj* not easily moved, upset, or changed 穩定的, 穩固的: *a stable chair* 穩固的椅子 | *a stable relationship* 穩定的關係 –opposite 反義 **unstable** –**stably** *adv*

stack¹ /stæk; stæk/ *n* **1** an orderly pile 〔疊放

整齊的〕一堆, 一疊: *a stack of books* 一堆疊放整齊的書 **2 stacks** *infml* a large amount or number 〖非正式〗大量, 許多: *stacks of work to do* 有大量的工作要做

stack² *v* **1** [T] (also 又作 **stack sthg ↔ up**) to make into a neat pile 疊成堆; 堆放: *They stacked the chairs at the back of the hall.* 他們把椅子疊放在大廳後面。**2 be stacked with** to be full of 堆滿: *The shop was stacked with goodies.* 商店裡堆滿了可口的食物。

sta·di·um /ˈsteɪdɪəm; ˈsteɪdiəm/ *n* **stadiums** or **stadia** /-dɪə; -diə/ a large sports ground with rows of seats built around a sports field 運動場, 體育場

staff¹ /stæf; stɑːf/ *n* **1** [C + sing/pl verb] the group of people who do the work of an organization 員工, 全體工作人員: *The school's teaching staff is excellent.* 該校的全體教員都很優秀。| *a staff of 15* 十五位工作人員 | *She's on the staff of the new university.* 她是那所新大學的職員。**2** [C] a thick stick used as a support or as a sign of office 拐杖; 權杖

staff² *v* [T] to provide the workers for something 為〔某部門〕配備工作人員: *a hospital staffed with 20 doctors* 一家有二十位醫生的醫院

stag /stæg; stæg/ *n* a fully grown male deer 成年雄鹿

stage¹ /steɪdʒ; steɪdʒ/ *n* **1** [C] a period in a course of events 階段; 時期: *The plan is still in its early stages.* 該計劃仍處於初期階段。**2** [C] a part of a journey 一程; 站; 一段路: *We travelled by easy stages, stopping often along the way.* 我們沿途走走停停, 從容不迫地旅行。**3** [C] the raised floor on which plays are performed in a theatre 舞台: *The actor was on stage for hours.* 這位演員在台上已演了數小時。**4 the stage** work in the theatre 戲劇工作: *When she was five years old, she decided that she wanted to go on the stage.* 她五歲時就下決心要做戲劇演員。**5 set the stage** to carry out the preparations so that something can happen 為〔某事的發生〕做準備: *The stage was set for a great victory.* 為了大獲全勝, 已做好了準備工作。

stage² *v* **staged, staging** [T] **1** to perform or arrange for public show 上演; 演出; 舉辦: *stage an art show* 舉辦一場藝術展 | *stage a football match* 舉辦足球賽 **2** to make something happen, especially for public effect 使〔某事〕發生; 發起〔尤指為引起公眾的反應〕: *stage a one-day strike* 發起罷工一天

stage·coach /ˈsteɪdʒˌkoʊtʃ; ˈsteɪdʒˌkəʊtʃ/ *n* in the past, a closed horse-drawn vehicle for carrying passengers 〔昔時的〕驛馬車: *to travel by stagecoach* 坐驛馬車旅行

stage fright /ˈ· ·/ *n* [U] nervousness felt when performing in public 怯場

stage man·age /ˈ· ,· · ·/ *v* [T] to organize an event, often without people knowing 對...

S

進行幕後安排: *The riots were stage managed by opponents of the government.* 暴動是由政府的反對派在幕後策劃的。

stage man·ag·er /'· ,···/ *n* a person in charge of what happens on a stage during a performance 舞台監督

stag·ger¹ /'stægə; 'stægəʳ/ *v* **1** [I] to move unsteadily on your feet 蹣跚; 搖搖晃晃地行走: *a drunk staggering across the street* 搖搖晃晃地過馬路的醉漢 **2** [T] to arrange at different times 〔時間上〕錯開: *Our holidays are staggered; John's off for a week, then I'm off for a week.* 我們的假期是錯開的: 約翰休息一週, 然後是我休息一週。

stagger² *n* an unsteady movement of a person who finds it difficult to walk 蹣跚; 搖晃不穩的腳步: *She gave a stagger as she began to feel faint.* 她開始感到頭暈時, 身體搖晃了一下。

stag·gered /'stægəd; 'stægəd/ *adj* very surprised 令人吃驚的: *I was staggered when I found out the truth.* 我發現真相時大吃一驚。

stag·ger·ing /'stægərɪŋ; 'stægərɪŋ/ *adj* almost unbelievable 令人難以置信的: *a staggering rise in the cost of petrol* 汽油費驚人地暴漲 –**staggeringly** *adv*

stag·ing /'stedʒɪŋ; 'steɪdʒɪŋ/ *n* **1** [C;U] the action or art of performing a play 〔戲劇的〕演出; 演技: *a new staging of "Hamlet"* 重新上演的《哈姆雷特》 **2** [U] movable boards and frames for standing on 活動台架

stag·nant /'stægnənt; 'stægnənt/ *adj* **1** not flowing or moving (used of water) 不流動的〔指水〕 **2** inactive 不活躍的; 不景氣: *Business is stagnant at the moment.* 目前商業發展不景氣。–**stagnantly** *adv*

stag·nate /'stægnet; stæg'neɪt/ *v* **stagnated, stagnating** [I] to stop developing 停滯; 不發展 –**stagnation** /stæg'neʃən; stæg'neɪʃən/ *n* [U]

staid /sted; steɪd/ *adj* serious and dull 嚴肅呆板的 –**staidly** *adv* –**staidness** *n* [U]

stain¹ /sten; steɪn/ *v* [I;T] **1** to change the colour of something, in a way that is lasting 沾污; 染污: *teeth stained by years of smoking* 因吸煙多年而熏黃了的牙齒 **2** to darken chemically 〔用化學品〕染色: *to stain the chairs to match the dark table* 給椅子染色, 使它和深色的桌子相配

stain² *n* [C;U] **1** a stained place or spot 污跡; 污點: *blood stains on my shirt* 我襯衫上的血跡 **2** a chemical for changing the colour of wood 〔木材的〕染色劑; 着色劑

stained glass /,·· '·◂/ *n* [U] coloured glass used to make pictures or patterns in windows 彩色玻璃

stain·less steel /,·· '·◂/ *n* [U] a type of metal not easily attacked by RUST 不銹鋼: *a set of stainless steel knives* 一套不銹鋼刀具

*stair /ster; steəʳ/ *n* **1 stairs** [pl] a set of steps that go from one floor of a building to another 樓梯: *Granny had difficulty climb-*

ing the stairs. 外婆爬樓梯有點困難。 **2** [C] a step in a set of stairs 樓梯的一級

stair·case /'ster,kes; 'steəkeɪs/ (also 又作 **stairway** /-,we; -weɪ/) *n* a set of stairs with its supports and side parts 〔有扶手和欄杆的〕樓梯

*stake¹ /stek; steɪk/ *n* **1** [C] a share in something, such as a business, that gives you an interest in whether it succeeds 股份; 利害關係: *Young people need the feeling that they have a stake in the country's future.* 年輕人應當感覺到國家的前途與他們休戚相關。 | *The company sold its 15% stake in the commercial bank.* 這家公司出售了其百分之十五的商業銀行股份。 **2 at stake** at risk 在危險狀況下: *Hundreds of jobs are at stake if the mine closes.* 如果礦場關閉, 數以百計的人將瀕於失業的境地。 **3 stakes** [pl] the things you can win or lose when doing something risky 賭金; 賭注: *They always play cards for high stakes.* 他們玩牌戲的賭注總是很大的。 **4** [C] a pointed wooden post which is driven into the ground and used as a support for something 椿; 柱

stake² *v* **staked, staking** [T] **1** to risk money or your public position on the result of something 把〔錢或地位〕押下來賭: *I've staked all my hopes on you.* 我把所有的希望都寄托在你身上了。 | *The President is staking his reputation on a successful outcome to the talks.* 總統對會談的成功很有信心, 他把自己的名譽都押在這上面了。 **2 stake a claim** to state that you have a right to something 聲明擁有: *He staked a claim to the land where he'd found gold.* 他聲明擁有他發現金的那塊土地。

stal·ac·tite /stə'læktaɪt; 'stæləktaɪt/ *n* a sharp piece of rock which points down from the roof of a cave; a stalactite is formed over a long time by water dripping from the roof 鐘乳石

stal·ag·mite /stə'lægmaɪt; 'stæləgmaɪt/ *n* a sharp piece of rock which points up from the floor of a cave, and is formed by water coming down in drops 〔鐘乳石洞中的〕石筍

stale /stel; steɪl/ *adj* **1** no longer fresh (used of food or air) 不新鮮的〔指食物或空氣〕: *stale bread* 不新鮮的麵包 **2** not new or exciting 陳舊的; 乏味的: *She told the same stale jokes again!* 她又講那則老掉牙的笑話了! **3** without new ideas or life, because you have done the same thing for too long (used of a person) 倦怠的; 沒勁的〔指人〕: *I'm getting stale in this job — I need a change.* 這個工作我已感到厭倦了, 需要換一換工作。–**staleness** *n* [U]

stale·mate /'stel,met; 'steɪlmeɪt/ *n* [U; sing] **1** a situation in which neither side in an argument or competition can get an advantage 〔爭論或比賽中的〕僵局 **2** a position in the game of CHESS from which neither player can win 〔國際象棋的〕和棋; 僵棋

---

stalk¹ /stɔk; stɔːk/ *v* **1** [T] to quietly follow a person or animal while staying hidden and waiting to catch or kill them 潛伏跟蹤; 潛近〔人或動物〕: *The hunter stalked the lion for two days.* 獵人跟蹤那頭獅子已兩天了。**2** [I] to walk stiffly, proudly and angrily 〔憤怒地〕大踏步走: *She stalked out of the house in a rage.* 她怒氣沖沖地大步大步走出了屋子。

stalk² *n* **1** the main stem of a plant supporting its leaves, fruits or flowers 〔植物的〕莖, 梗 **2** the part of a fruit or leaf which connects it to a plant or tree 〔果實或葉子的〕柄

stall¹ /stɔl; stɔːl/ *n* **1** an indoor enclosure for an animal 〔牲畜的〕棚; 廄: *cattle in their stalls* 關在畜欄裡的牛 **2** a large table in a public place from which you sell something or give information about something 攤檔, 攤位: *a market stall* 市場的攤位 **3 the stalls** the seats on the main level of a theatre in front of the stage 正廳前排座位

stall² *v* **1** [I] (used of an engine) to stop suddenly because of a lack of power 〔指引擎〕由於動力不足而〕熄火, 停止轉動: *The car stalled on the hill.* 汽車在山上熄火了。**2** [T] to make an engine stop suddenly because of a lack of power 〔由於動力不足而〕使〔引擎〕熄火: *Inexperienced pilots often stall their planes.* 缺乏經驗的飛行員常常使飛機的引擎熄火。**3** [I] *infml* to delay doing something until a later time 〔非正式〕推遲, 拖延: *Stop stalling and answer my question!* 別拖延, 回答我的問題!

stal·lion /ˈstæljən; ˈstæljən/ *n* a fully-grown male horse kept for breeding 種馬

stal·wart¹ /ˈstɔlwət; ˈstɔːlwət/ *adj* strong and determined 堅定的, 堅決的: *He's a stalwart supporter of the organization.* 他是那個組織的堅定支持者。**–stalwartly** *adv*

stalwart² *n* a firm, dependable follower of an organization or political party 〔組織或政黨的〕忠實擁護者

sta·men /ˈsteɪmən; ˈsteɪmən/ *n* the male part of a flower which produces POLLEN 〔花的〕雄蕊

stam·i·na /ˈstæmənə; ˈstæmɪnə/ *n* [U] the strength of body or mind to keep doing something tiring 耐力, 毅力: *You need great stamina to run the 10,000 metres.* 你需要有極大的耐力才能跑一萬米。

stam·mer¹ /ˈstæmə; ˈstæmər/ *v* [I;T] to speak with difficulty, repeating sounds and pausing, either habitually or because of excitement or fear 口吃地說, 結結巴巴地說: *She stammers when she feels nervous.* 她緊張的時候就會口吃。| *He stammered his thanks.* 他結結巴巴地道了謝。**–stammerer** *n*

stammer² *n* [sing] the habit of stammering when you speak 口吃, 說話結巴: *Ben's got a slight stammer.* 賓有一點兒口吃。

stamp¹ /stæmp; stæmp/ *v* **1** [I] to walk with noisy, heavy steps 重步走; 踩着腳走: *She was stamping about in the cold trying to keep her feet warm.* 為了使腳保持暖和, 她在寒風中跺着腳走來走去。| *He stamped out of the room angrily.* 他生氣地跺着腳走出了房間。**2 stamp your foot/feet** to lift your foot and bring it down forcefully 跺腳: *"I won't do it", said the child, stamping her feet.* "我不要這樣做", 那小女孩跺着腳說。**3 stamp on** to intentionally put your foot down hard on something 用力踩: *She stamped on the bee and killed it.* 她用力把蜜蜂踩死了。**4** [T] to mark a word or sign on a paper or a letter by pressing with a special tool 在〔紙或信上〕蓋印: *The immigration officer stamped my passport.* 移民局官員在我的護照上蓋印。**5** [T] to clearly show that somebody or something has a particular quality or is of a particular type 表明〔某人或某物〕具有某種特點; 把…歸入〔某一類〕: *The roof stamps the church as Victorian in design.* 屋頂的樣式表明該教堂的設計風格是維多利亞式的。| *His years in the army had stamped him with an air of brisk authority.* 服役多年已使他養成了一種利索潑辣的作風。

stamp sth ↔ out *phr v* [T] to completely put an end to something bad 徹底消滅〔壞事〕: *The new law will help to stamp out the illegal drugs trade.* 新法例將有助於杜絕非法的毒品交易。

stamp² *n* **1** (also 又作 **postage stamp** *fml* 〔正式〕) a small piece of paper sold by the post office for sticking on a letter or parcel before you post it 郵票: *a twenty pence stamp* 一枚二十便士的郵票 **2** a small piece of wood or metal which is covered with ink and then prints a mark on a surface, or the mark that it makes 圖章; 印記: *The stamp in the library book shows it must be returned tomorrow.* 從圖書館借的書上的印記表明, 這本書必須明天歸還。**3** a mark which shows a particular quality 特徵; 標記: *His music bears the stamp of his passionate personality.* 他的音樂反映出他熱情的個性。

stam·pede¹ /stæmˈpid; stæmˈpiːd/ *n* **1** a sudden rush of frightened animals 〔動物的〕驚逃; 奔竄 **2** a sudden rush to do something by a crowd of people 爭先恐後的行動; 蜂擁: *There's been a stampede to buy gold before the price goes up.* 在金價上漲之前, 人們爭先恐後地搶購黃金。

stampede² *v* **stampeded, stampeding** [I] **1** to rush suddenly and wildly 突然狂奔; 奔逃: *The angry crowd stampeded through the town.* 憤怒的羣眾在城裡奔逃。| *stampeding elephants* 受驚而狂奔的象羣 **2** [T] to make animals rush wildly or suddenly 使〔動物〕驚逃: *The fire stampeded the cattle.* 大火使牛羣驚逃。

stance /stæns; stɑːns/ *n* **1** a way of standing 站立的姿勢, 站姿 **2** a way of thinking shown in a position which you state publicly 立場; 態度: *What's the government's stance on ter-*

rorism? 政府對恐怖主義持甚麼態度？

stanch /stæntʃ; stɑːntʃ/ *v* –see 見 STAUNCH

★★stand[1] /stænd; stænd/ *v* **stood** /stʊd; stʊd/, **stood 1** [I] to support yourself upright on your feet 站, 站立: *I had to stand all the way home on the bus.* 我不得不站着乘公共汽車回家。| *She was standing by her desk.* 她站在課桌旁。**2** [I] to rise so that you are standing 站起來: *The teacher asked them to stand.* 老師叫他們站起來。**3** [T] to make someone stand somewhere 使〔某人〕站在〔某處〕: *He stood the child on the wall.* 他讓孩子站在牆頭上。**4** [I; + adv/prep] to move in a particular direction when you are standing 站着朝某個方向移動: *The police told the crowd to stand back.* 警察要求人羣向後站。| *She stood aside to let me past.* 她站到一旁讓我走過去。**5** [I] to have a particular height 高度是…: *The building stands over 200 feet high.* 這幢大樓高度超過二百英尺。**6** [I] to be in an upright position somewhere 位於; 豎立, 屹立: *The house stands on the corner of the High Street.* 那座房子位於高街的轉角處。| *Few houses were left standing after the explosion.* 爆炸過後, 剩下沒倒的房子寥寥可數。**7** [T] to put something somewhere in an upright position 使〔某物〕豎立起: *Stand the ladder against the wall.* 把梯子靠在牆上。| *She stood the clock on the mantelpiece.* 她把鐘放在壁爐台上。**8** [I] to be at a particular level 處於某一水平: *Inflation now stands at 11%.* 現在的通貨膨脹率是百分之十一。**9** [I] to remain unchanged 保持不變: *My offer of help still stands.* 我答應幫助你的承諾不會變。**10** [T] to be good enough or strong enough to bear something 承受; 經得起: *This work will hardly stand close examination.* 這項工作經不起仔細的檢查。**11 can't stand** to dislike something strongly or be unable to bear it 極討厭; 無法忍受: *I can't stand getting up early.* 我討厭早起。| *I couldn't stand listening to him any more.* 我不能忍受再聽他講下去了。| *She can't stand noise.* 她受不了噪音。–see 見 BEAR[2] (USAGE 用法) **12 stand someone something** to pay for a meal or a drink for someone 為某人付…款; 請…客: *Let me stand you lunch.* 我來請你吃午飯吧。**13** [I] to be one of the people trying to be elected in an election 參加選舉, 競選: *He has decided not to stand for Parliament again.* 他已決定不再競選國會議員了。**14 stand to do something** to be likely to do something 可能做某事: *She stands to inherit £20,000 when her father dies.* 她父親去世時, 她有可能會繼承兩萬英鎊。**15 stand a chance** to have a chance of succeeding 有成功的可能, 有機會: *You don't stand a chance of getting that job!* 你沒有機會得到那份工作！ **16 stand idle** to not be in use 未被使用: *The machines have been standing idle since the strike began.* 自從罷工開始後, 機器都被閒置

起來了。**17 stand in the way of something** to prevent something from happening 阻礙某事的發生: *He accused the minister of standing in the way of progress.* 他指責部長阻礙事情的發展。**18 standing on your head** very easily 很容易地: *I could do that standing on my head.* 我可以毫不費力地把那件事做好。**19 stand on your own two feet** to be able to live without help from other people 自立 **20 it stands to reason** = it is clear 理所當然: *It stands to reason that we've got to invest in other fuel sources before oil runs out.* 在石油被用盡以前, 我們必須投資開發其他能源, 這是理所當然的。**21 stand trial** to be tried in a court 在法庭上受審

stand by *phr v* **1** [T **stand by** sbdy/sthg] to continue to support someone or something 繼續支持〔某人或某事〕: *I still stand by my decision to sack him.* 我仍然決定把他解雇。**2** [I] to do nothing while something unpleasant is happening 袖手旁觀: *We can't stand by and watch while people die of cold on our streets.* 我們不能袖手旁觀, 看着人們凍死在街上。**3** [I] to be ready to help or do something if you are needed 做好〔幫助或做某事的〕準備: *Fire and ambulance services are standing by in case the celebrations get out of hand.* 消防隊與醫療隊正在候命, 以防慶祝活動失控。

stand down *phr v* [I] to give up your position so that someone else can take it up 讓位, 退出: *He stood down in favour of a younger candidate.* 他把職位讓給了一個年紀較輕的候選人。

stand for sthg *phr v* [T] **1** to represent a word or phrase 代表〔一個詞或片語〕: *What does PTO stand for?* PTO代表甚麼？**2** to support an idea or set of ideas 支持〔觀點〕: *I am opposed to this prime minister and everything that he stands for.* 我反對這位首相, 也反對他所支持的一切觀點。**3 won't stand for something** to refuse to accept something 拒絕接受某事物; 容忍: *I won't stand for his rudeness any longer!* 我再也不會容忍他的粗魯了!

stand in *phr v* [I] to take someone's place or do their job while they are away 暫時代替〔某人〕: *I'm standing in for the chairman while he's on holiday.* 主席休假期間由我來代替他。

stand out *phr v* [I] **1** to have a colour or shape that can easily be seen 〔由於顏色鮮豔或形狀特別而〕突出; 顯眼: *The words on the sign stood out clearly.* 標誌上的字很顯眼。**2** to be clearly much better than the rest 傑出; 突出: *She stands out as the best poet of her generation.* 她在同代人中是最傑出的詩人。

stand up *phr v* **1** [I] to stand 站, 站立: *I've been standing up all day.* 我已站了一整天。| *He stood up when I came into the room.* 我

走進房間時, 他站了起來。**2** [T **stand** sthg ↔ **up**] to put something somewhere in an upright position 使(某物)直立於(某處): *The dustbin had fallen over so I stood it up again.* 垃圾箱倒了, 所以我又把它擺好。**3** [I] to stay in good condition after hard use 經久耐用: *It's a good little car that will stand up to a lot of rough treatment.* 這是部非常好的小汽車, 很經得起亂碰亂撞。**4** [I] to be accepted as true 可信, 站得住腳: *This evidence will never stand up in court.* 這項證據無法在法庭上站得住腳。

stand up for sbdy/sthg *phr v* [T] to defend someone or something against attack 保護; 維護: *You must stand up for your rights.* 你必須維護自己的權利。| *At last he's learning to stand up for himself.* 他最終學會了如何保護自己。

stand up to sbdy *phr v* [T] to refuse to accept unjust treatment from someone 拒絕接受(某人的)不公正待遇

stand² *n* **1** a small outdoor shop 售貨攤位: *an ice-cream stand* 賣冰淇淋的攤子 **2** a piece of furniture for putting something on (置物的)座, 架: *an umbrella stand* 傘架 | *a music stand* 樂譜架 **3** the place in a court where people stand when they are being questioned (法庭中的)證人席 **4 stands** [pl] buildings at a sports ground; they have open fronts and rows of seats or places where people can stand (運動場的)看台; 觀眾席 **5 make a stand** to make a strong attempt to defend yourself 反抗, 抵抗: *The retreating army made a last stand just on the border.* 撤退中的軍隊就在邊界處進行了最後一次抵抗。**6 make a stand, take a stand** to state your ideas strongly (強烈地)表明自己的立場: *The prime minister took a firm stand on the question of import controls.* 首相在控制進口的問題上立場很堅定。

★**stan·dard¹** /ˈstændəd; ˈstændəd/ *n* **1** a level or degree of quality which is considered acceptable 水準; 標準; 規格: *This teacher sets high standards for his pupils.* 這位老師給學生定下高標準。| *Watch-makers work to a high standard of precision.* 手錶工人力求達到高度精密的標準。| *I'm afraid this work is below the standard required.* 我恐怕這項工作沒有達到規定的標準。**2** an accepted level used to make comparisons 基準, 標準: *By European standards, this is a low salary.* 按照歐洲的標準來看, 這是很低的工資。**3 standards** [pl] principles which influence people's morals and behaviour 道德標準: *I'm shocked by the moral standards of teenagers today!* 我對現今少年人的道德標準感到震驚!

★**standard²** *adj* **1** usual or ordinary 通常的; 普通的: *It's standard practice now to search passengers at airports.* 在機場搜查乘客現已是例行的做法。**2** [only before a noun 只用於名詞前] generally recognized as correct or ac-

ceptable 標準的; 規範的: *The students want to learn standard pronunciation.* 學生想學習標準的發音。**3** widely used in order to understand a particular subject (used of books) (在某一學科的教授方面)廣泛使用的; 有權威的(指書): *It's the standard text for medical students.* 這是醫科學生的標準課本。

stan·dard·ize /ˈstændədˌaɪz; ˈstændədaɪz/ *v* **standardized, standardizing** (also 又作 **standardise** *BrE* 〔英式〕) [T] to change things so that they are alike in every case 使…標準化; 使符合規格: *Efforts to standardize spelling in English have not been a success.* 英語拼寫標準化的努力並沒有成功。| *The toys are produced using standardized parts.* 這些玩具是用標準部件製造的。— **standardization** /ˌstændədaɪˈzeɪʃən; ˌstændədaɪˈzeɪʃən/ *n* [U]

standard lamp /ˈ·· ·/ *n* *BrE* a lamp on a tall base which stands on the floor 〔英式〕落地燈

standard of liv·ing /ˌ··· ···/ (also 又作 **living standard**) *n* the degree of wealth and comfort in everyday life that a person, group, or country has 生活水準[水平]: *This region enjoys a high standard of living.* 這個地區的生活水準很高。| *She had to adapt to a lower standard of living.* 她不得不適應較低的生活水準。

stand·by /ˈstændˌbaɪ; ˈstændbaɪ/ *n* **standbys 1** a person or thing that is kept ready to be used if needed 備用的人或物: *If the electricity fails, the hospital has a standby generator.* 如果停電, 醫院裡還有一台備用發電機。| *Powdered milk is a good standby in an emergency.* 奶粉是緊急情況下很好的備用品。**2 on standby a** ready to act at any time 待命; 隨時準備行動: *A special team of police were on standby during the game.* 比賽期間, 警察的特遣部隊隨時待命。**b** able to travel on a plane just before it takes off if there is a seat nobody wants 等待剩餘機票, 候補

stand-in /ˈ·· ·/ *n* a person who takes the place or job of somebody else for a time 代替別人工作的人

stand·ing¹ /ˈstændɪŋ; ˈstændɪŋ/ *adj* [only before a noun 只用於名詞前] continuing in use or force 持續的; 常備的: *We have a standing invitation: we can visit them whenever we like.* 我們獲得長期有效的邀請, 可隨時去拜訪他們。| *His meanness has become a standing joke among his friends.* 他的吝嗇已在朋友間成為一個講不厭的笑話。

stand·ing² *n* [U] **1** rank or position, particularly according to the opinion of other people 名望; 身分, 地位: *a lawyer of high standing* 很有名望的律師 | *The company's standing has been badly damaged by the scandal.* 公司的聲望因這醜聞而大受損害。**2** period during which something has existed 存在期, 持續時間: *an agreement of several* *years' standing* 有效期長達數年的協議

standing or·der /ˌ·· '··/ *n* [C;U] *BrE* an order to your bank to pay a fixed amount of money from your account to a particular person or organization at regular times 〔英式〕〔要求銀行定期付款的〕長期自動轉賬委託

stand·off·ish /ˈstændˈɒfɪʃ; stændˈɒfiʃ/ *adj* rather formal and unfriendly 冷淡的; 不友好的 **–standoffishly** *adv*

stand·point /ˈstændˌpɔɪnt; ˈstændpɔɪnt/ *n* a position from which things are seen and opinions formed 立場; 看法: *from the standpoint of the ordinary voter* 從一般投票人的立場來看

stand·still /ˈstændˌstɪl; ˈstændˌstɪl/ *n* [sing] a condition of no movement or activity 靜止; 停頓: *She brought the car to a standstill.* 她把汽車停了下來。

stank /stæŋk; stæŋk/ *v* the past tense of STINK ☆ STINK 的過去式

stan·za /ˈstænzə; ˈstænzə/ *n* a group of lines forming a division of a poem 〔詩的〕節, 段

sta·ple[1] /ˈsteɪpl; ˈsteɪpəl/ *n* **1** a small piece of thin wire which is pushed through sheets of paper to hold them firmly together 釘書釘 –see picture on page 763 見 763 頁彩圖 **2** a food that forms the regular and most important part of somebody's usual meals 主要食品: *Rice is a staple in the region.* 米飯是該地區的主要食品。 **3** a main product that is produced or sold 主要產品: *Bananas and sugar are the staples of Jamaica.* 香蕉與糖是牙買加的主要產品。

staple[2] *v* **stapled, stapling** [T] to fasten with wire staples 用釘書釘釘住

sta·pler /ˈsteɪplə; ˈsteɪplər/ *n* a small instrument used to push wire staples into paper 釘書機 –see picture on page 763 見 763 頁彩圖

star[1] /stɑr; stɑːr/ *n* **1** a very large mass of burning gas in space which is seen as a bright point of light in a clear sky 星; 恆星: *stars twinkling in the sky* 在空中閃爍的星星 **2** an object or shape with five or more points coming out of it 星狀, 星形: *The walls were decorated with gold stars.* 牆壁上畫着金色的星星作為點綴。 **3** an object or sign in the shape of a star which is worn as a mark of office or rank, or as a measure of quality 〔表示職位或質量的〕星章: *a four-star general* 四星上將 | *The guidebook awarded the hotel five stars.* 這本旅遊指南將這家旅館定為五星級。 **4 the stars** the signs of the ZODIAC, regarded as determining your fate 星象, 星宿: *She always reads the stars in the newspaper.* 她總會閱讀報紙上有關星象算命的專欄。 **5** a famous or very skilful performer 明星: *a film star* 電影明星 | *a football star* 足球明星 **6** see 見 ASTERISK[1] **–starless** *adj*

star[2] *v* **-rr-** **1** [T] to have as the most important performer 以…為主角; 由…主演: *an*

old film starring Charlie Chaplin 由查理·卓別林主演的舊電影 **2** [I] to appear in a film or play as the most important performer 主演〔電影或戲劇〕: *Clint Eastwood will star in a new thriller.* 奇連·伊士活將主演一部新的恐怖片。 **3** [T] to mark with one or more stars 加上星號

star·board /ˈstɑrˌbɔːrd; ˈstɑːbəd/ *n* [sing] the right side of a ship or aircraft as you face forward 〔船舶、飛機的〕右舷, 右側 **–op-posite 反義** PORT[3]

starch[1] /stɑrtʃ; stɑːtʃ/ *n* **1** [C;U] a white tasteless substance found in food such as rice, bread, and potatoes 澱粉: *Avoid eating so much starch if you want to lose weight.* 如果你想減肥, 那就不要吃這麼多含澱粉的食物。 **2** [U] a product used for stiffening cloth 〔用以漿布的〕漿粉

starch[2] *v* [T] to stiffen with starch 給…上漿: *starched collars* 漿過的衣領 | *starched tablecloths* 漿過的桌布

starch·y /ˈstɑrtʃi; ˈstɑːtʃi/ *adj* **starchier, starchiest** **1** full of starch 含大量澱粉的: *starchy foods* 含大量澱粉的食物 **2** *infml* stiffly correct and formal in manner 〔非正式〕拘泥的; 刻板的

star·dom /ˈstɑrdəm; ˈstɑːdəm/ *n* [U] the state of being a very famous performer 明星的地位

stare /stɛr; steəʳ/ *v* **stared, staring** [I] **1** to look steadily at someone or something for a long time 凝視; 盯着看: *He sat staring into space, thinking deeply.* 他坐在那裡凝望着天空, 陷入了沉思。 | *She stared at him in horror.* 她驚恐地瞪着他。 **2 stare someone in the face** (used of an answer to a problem) to be very clear 〔指問題的答案〕清清楚楚的: *The solution is staring us in the face — let's borrow the money.* 解決的辦法很清楚 — 我們去借錢。 **–stare** *n*: *She gave him a long cool stare.* 她冷冷地盯着他看了好一會。

stare sbdy **out** *phr v* [T] to make a person look away by looking at them steadily for a long time 盯得〔某人〕把目光移開

star·fish /ˈstɑrˌfɪʃ; ˈstɑːˌfɪʃ/ *n* **starfish** or **starfishes** a flat sea creature with five arms forming a star shape 海星〔一種海洋動物〕

stark[1] /stɑrk; stɑːk/ *adj* **1** very bare or severe in appearance 〔外表〕光禿禿的; 無裝飾的; 粗陋的: *the stark silhouette of rocks against the sky* 光禿禿的岩石輪廓襯托着天空的背景 **2** very hard and unpleasant 嚴酷的; 苛刻的: *The film conveys the stark realities of life for the poor.* 電影反映了窮人嚴酷的生活現實。 **–starkly** *adv*

stark[2] *adv* **1 stark naked** *infml* wearing nothing at all 〔非正式〕赤裸裸的, 一絲不掛的 **2 stark raving mad** *infml* completely mad 〔非正式〕完全瘋的

star·let /ˈstɑrlɪt; ˈstɑːlɪt/ *n* a young actress who has had small parts in some films and hopes to become famous 演配角並希望成名

的年輕女電影演員

star·light /'stɑːlaɪt; 'stɑːlaɪt/ *n* [U] the light given by the stars 星光

star·ling /'stɑːlɪŋ; 'stɑːlɪŋ/ *n* a common greenish-black European bird 歐椋鳥

star·ry /'stɑːrɪ; 'stɑːri/ *adj* **starrier, starriest** filled with stars 佈滿星星的: *a starry winter sky* 滿天星斗的冬夜

starry-eyed /ˌ·· '··◂/ *adj* full of unreasonable or silly hopes 充滿幻想的

Stars and Stripes /ˌ·· '·◂/ *n AmE* the flag of the United States of America (a phrase which sounds too solemn for ordinary use) 〖美式〗星條旗, 美國國旗〔一般使用似乎過於隆重〕

star-stud·ded /'· ˌ··◂/ *adj infml* using many famous performers 〖非正式〗明星雲集的: *a star-studded cast* 明星薈萃的演員陣容

★**start¹** /stɑːt; stɑːt/ *v* **1** [I;T] to begin an activity and continue doing it 開始: *As everyone's here, can we start?* 人都到齊了, 我們可以開始嗎? | *He started working here a week ago.* 他一週前開始在這裏工作。| *The bus didn't come, so we started to walk home.* 公共汽車沒有來, 於是我們開始步行回家。| *He wants to start guitar lessons.* 他想開始上吉他課。

□ USEFUL PATTERNS 有用句型
to start something; to start to do something; to start doing something

2 [I; T] to bring or come into existence (使)存在, (使)出現; 開創, 建立: *How did the trouble start?* 麻煩是怎樣引起的? | *Who started that rumour?* 那個謠言是誰造的? | *She's trying to start a sports club.* 她正在努力成立一個體育俱樂部。**3** [I;T] to take place or make something take place (使)發生: *The concert started late.* 音樂會遲了開始。| *We only started dinner at ten o'clock.* 我們十點鐘才開始吃飯。**4** [I;T] to begin operating or make something begin operating 啟動, (使)發動: *Oh no! The car won't start.* 哎不! 汽車發動不起來。| *He's had a lot of trouble starting the truck.* 他費了好大的工夫才把貨車發動起來。**5** [I] to begin a journey 出發旅行, 啟程, 動身: *It's a long way, so we'll have to start early.* 路程很遠, 所以我們必須早點出發。**6** [I] to begin work 開始工作; 着手: *You're hired — when can you start?* 你已被錄用, 甚麼時候可以開始上班? | *In this office, we start at eight every morning.* 我們這辦事處每天早上八點鐘開始辦公。**7** [I] to go from a particular point or time 從〔某一點或某一時間〕開始, 自…起: *Prices start at £5.00.* 價錢從五英鎊起。| *Starting from Monday, the lunch break will be longer.* 從週一開始, 午餐時間將會延長。**8** [I] to move suddenly in an uncontrolled way because of fear or surprise 驚起, 嚇一跳: *The touch on his shoulder made him start.* 他的肩膀被拍了一

下, 使他嚇了一跳。**9 to start with: a** first; when there are several points you want to make, you can use this expression before or after the first one 首先, 第一點〔當有好幾點需要表述時, 可在第一點之前或之後使用這片語〕: *There were several reasons why he fell from power. To start with, there was his policy on Europe. Then there was his aggressive manner.* 他下台的原因有好幾個。首先是他對待歐洲的政策。其次是他放肆的態度。**b** you use this expression when you give a reason for something which has just been mentioned; you think that this reason by itself is very strong, but you are suggesting that it is not the only one 首先來説〔表示一個很重要但卻不是唯一的理由〕: *I don't think he's got a chance. I mean, he hasn't got the right qualifications to start with, has he?* 我認為他沒有機會。我的意思是, 首先來説, 他不具備各項適合的條件, 不是嗎? **c** first; you use this expression when you are talking about the first of several events 首先〔在講到數件事情中的第一件時用〕: *We had soup to start with. Then we had a lovely piece of beef. And then for pudding we had lemon mousse.* 我們首先喝了湯。然後吃了塊很美味的牛排。再下去的甜點我們吃的是檸檬奶油凍。**d** first; you can use this expression when you are going to give the first of a number of instructions 首先〔在給出一系列指令的第一條時用〕: *To start with, switch on. Then key in the code word.* 首先打開電源, 然後鍵入指令。**e** at first; you use this expression when you say what happens at the beginning of a period of time when it is different or may be different from what happens later 開始時, 起初〔在提及一段時間內發生或有可能發生不同的事情時, 説到首先發生的事情時用〕: *To start with, we'll use the old cooker. There's an old electric one there. Then later on, we'll probably get a gas one.* 起初, 我們會用舊爐子。那裏有一個舊的電爐。以後, 我們可能會去買個煤氣爐。

start off *phr v* **1** [I] to have your first job 做第一份工作: *Bill started off in marketing.* 比爾的第一份工作是從事市場銷售業務。| *They started off as dancers.* 他們開始時是當舞蹈演員的。**2** [I;T **start** sthg ↔ **off**] to do the first stage of an activity 開始〔活動〕: *I always start off the first lesson by discussing the students' aims.* 我上第一課總是先討論學生要達到的目標。

start out *phr v* [I] to begin in a particular state or position which later changes 以〔某種狀態或地位〕開始: *The building started out as a library, but was then used as a school.* 這大樓一開始被用作圖書館, 後來改為學校。

start sthg ↔ **up** *phr v* to set up a new business or organization 開創〔企業〕; 建立〔組織〕: *They're starting up a restaurant.* 他們正在開辦一家餐館。

★**start²** *n* [C; sing] **1** the beginning of an ac-

tivity or situation〔活動或形勢的〕開始, 開端:
The start of the race had to be delayed. 比賽
開始的時間只好推遲。| *It's late — we'd bet-
ter make a start on the cooking.* 時間不早了,
我們最好開始做飯吧。| *From the start I
disliked him.* 我從一開始就討厭他。**2** the
first part of something 開頭部分: *The start
of the film was rather dull.* 影片的開頭部分
頗乏味。| *The start of the term is very tiring
for teachers.* 學期的開始階段總令老師感到很
疲勞。**3** a sudden uncontrolled movement
because of surprise or fear 吃驚, 驚起: *I
woke up with a start.* 我驚醒了。**4 for a start**
you use this expression when you are making the first of several points you could
make 首先, 第一〔當有好幾點需要表述時用〕:
*I don't think she'll get the job. She's too
young, for a start.* 我認為她得不到那份工作。
首先, 她年紀太輕了。

start·er /'stɑrtɚ; 'stɑːtər/ *n* **1** the first course
of a meal 第一道菜: *Would you like soup or
melon as a starter?* 第一道菜你們想喝湯還是
吃甜瓜? **2** a person who gives the signal for
a race to begin〔賽跑的〕發令員 **3** an instrument for starting a car or engine〔汽車或引
擎的〕起動裝置

start·le /'stɑrtl; 'stɑːtl/ *v* **startled, startling**
[T] to make someone have a sudden sur-
prise or shock 使〔某人〕吃一驚: *You startled
me! I didn't hear you come in.* 你嚇了我一
跳! 我沒有聽見你進來。–**startled** *adj: She
looked at me startled.* 她吃驚地看着我。

starv·a·tion /stɑr'veɪʃən; stɑːˈveɪʃən/ *n* [U]
suffering or death caused by lack of food
飢餓; 餓死

starve /stɑrv; stɑːv/ *v* **starved, starving 1** [I]
to die or suffer greatly from lack of food
餓死; 挨餓: *They got lost in the desert and
starved to death.* 他們在沙漠中迷路而餓死了。|
*Thousands could starve if the crops fail
again.* 如果糧食再次歉收, 可能會有數以千計
的人挨餓。**2** [T] to make a person or animal suffer or die by not giving them food
使挨餓; 使餓死: *She's ready to starve herself
to lose weight.* 為了減肥, 她打算挨餓。**3**
infml〔非正式〕**be starving** be very hungry
十分飢餓: *I'm starving — let's have lunch.* 我
餓壞了——我們去吃午飯吧。**4 be starved of**
to not have enough of something you need
缺乏; 渴望得到: *a child starved of affection*
渴望受人疼愛的孩子

state[1] /stet; steɪt/ *n* **1** [C; sing] a condition in
which a person or thing is 狀態, 狀況:
*Doctors are worried about his state of
health.* 醫生很擔心他的健康狀況。| *The
survivors are still in a state of shock.* 倖存者
仍處於驚慌狀態。| *The room was in an
awful state.* 這房間亂糟糟的。**2 in a state**
infml to be very nervous or anxious〔非正
式〕緊張; 焦慮: *Paul always got into a real
state during exams.* 保羅在考試時總是非常緊
張。**3 in no fit state** not healthy or calm

enough to do something 健康狀況不佳; 不
夠冷靜: *Immediately after the accident, she
was in no fit state to talk to the police.* 事故
剛才過去, 她還未平靜下來, 所以無法跟警察談
話。**4** [C] a country considered as a political organization〔作為政治組織的〕國家:
*Most former colonies have become self-
governing states.* 以前的殖民地大多數成了自
治的國家。**5** [C] a smaller, partly self-
governing area into which a large country
is divided 州; 邦: *the State of California* 加利
福尼亞州 | *Queensland is one of the states
of Australia.* 昆士蘭是澳大利亞的一個州。**6**
[U] (also 又作 **State**) the government or
political organization of a country 國家; 政
府: *Should industry be controlled by the
state?* 工業是否應當由政府控制? | *State
secrets* 國家機密 **7** [U] the formality and
ceremony connected with a ruler or head
of government 正式的儀式, 盛禮: *The
Queen made a state visit to Canada.* 女王對
加拿大進行了國事訪問。**8 the States** *infml*
the United States of America〔非正式〕美
國

state[2] *v* **stated, stating** [T+(that)] *fml* to say
or express in speech or writing〔正式〕説,
説明, 陳述, 聲明: *This book states the case
for women's rights very clearly.* 這本書對女權
問題敍述得十分清楚。| *Please state your
name and address.* 請説出你的姓名與地址。|
*The witness stated that he had never seen
her before.* 證人稱他從未見過她。

state·ly /'stetli; 'steɪtli/ *adj* **statelier,
stateliest 1** grand, graceful and rather formal 堂皇的; 優雅的; 正式的: *a row of tall,
stately towers* 一排雄偉高大的塔 | *a stately
manner* 優雅的舉止 **2 stately home** a large,
old house of historical interest which can
be visited by the public〔具有歷史價值並可
供人參觀的〕堂皇宅第–**stateliness** *n* [U]

state·ment /'stetmənt; 'steɪtmənt/ *n*
1 [C] a written or spoken
declaration made formally〔正式的〕聲明; 陳
述: *The police took down the witness's state-
ment.* 警方記下了目擊者的陳述。| *In a
statement made last night, the Minister
announced important tax cuts.* 部長在昨晚發
表的一項聲明中, 宣佈了重要的減税措施。**2**
[C] a piece of paper from your bank which
lists the amount of money paid or received
and the total in your account〔銀行的〕結算
表; 財務報表 **3** [sing; U] expression in
words 表達; 措詞: *You need to provide a
clearer statement of your goals.* 你需要更加
清楚地表述你的目的。

states·man /'stetsmən; 'steɪtsmən/ *n*
statesmen /-mən; -mən/ an experienced
political leader who is widely respected for
being wise and honourable; a female
statesman is called a **stateswoman** 政治家
〔女政治家稱為 **stateswoman**〕–**statesman-
ship** *n* [U]

stat·ic /ˈstætɪk; ˈstætɪk/ *adj* **1** not moving, changing, or developing 靜止的; 不變的; 穩定的: *Prices remained static on the stock exchange.* 股票交易所的價格保持穩定。 **2 static electricity** electricity which does not flow in a current but collects on the surface of objects 靜電

sta·tion[1] /ˈsteɪʃən; ˈsteɪʃən/ *n* **1** a building by a railway where trains stop regularly for passengers or goods 火車站: *a station platform* 火車站台 | *We took a taxi to Euston Station.* 我們坐計程車去尤斯頓火車站。–see picture on page 991 見 991 頁彩圖 **2** a building from which buses start their journey 公共汽車站: *a coach station* 長途汽車站 –see picture on page 991 見 991 頁彩圖 **3** a building that is a centre for a particular service or activity 〔提供某種服務或進行某種活動的〕局, 所, 站: *a police station* 警察局 | *a petrol station* 加油站 **4** an organization that broadcasts on television or radio 廣播電台; 電視台: *I can't get many foreign stations on this little radio.* 我用這個小收音機收聽不到許多外國電台。 **5** a small military establishment 〔軍隊的〕駐地, 基地: *a naval station* 海軍駐地 **6** *old fash* someone's position or rank 〔老式〕地位; 職位: *She married a man beneath her station.* 她嫁給了一個地位比她低的人。

station[2] *v* [T] **1** to make someone stay in a particular place so that they can stop trouble if necessary 部署〔某人〕於; 設置: *Guards were stationed around the prison.* 監獄周圍佈置了警衛人員。 **2 be stationed** to be sent to a particular place for military duty 〔軍隊、士兵〕駐紮: *For most of the war, he was stationed in Europe.* 他在戰爭中的大部分時間都被派駐歐洲。

sta·tion·a·ry /ˈsteɪʃənəri; ˈsteɪʃənəri/ *adj* not moving 不動的, 靜止的: *The car was stationary when the accident happened.* 事故發生時, 那輛車沒有開動。

sta·tion·er /ˈsteɪʃənə; ˈsteɪʃənə/ *n* a person or shop that sells stationery 文具商; 文具店

sta·tion·er·y /ˈsteɪʃənəri; ˈsteɪʃənəri/ *n* [U] materials for writing such as paper, ink, and pencils 文具

station wag·on /ˈ·· ˌ··/ *n* the usual American word for 〔美式〕= ESTATE CAR

stat·is·ti·cian /ˌstætəˈstɪʃən; ˌstætɪˈstɪʃən/ *n* a person who works with statistics 統計學家; 統計員

sta·tis·tics /stəˈtɪstɪks; stəˈtɪstɪks/ *n* **1** [pl] facts or information based on studying a collection of numbers 統計資料, 統計數字: *These statistics show there are 57 deaths per 1,000 of population.* 這些統計資料表明每一千人中有五十七人死亡。 | *official statistics* 官方統計數字 **2** [U] the science of studying numbers in order to get facts or information 統計學: *Statistics is a branch of mathematics.* 統計學是數學的一個分支。 –

statistical *adj* **–statistically** /-kli; -kli/ *adv*

stat·ue /ˈstætʃu; ˈstætʃuː/ *n* something which looks like a person or animal, made in stone or metal 雕像, 塑像

stat·u·esque /ˌstætʃuˈesk; ˌstætʃuˈesk/ *adj* tall, large and graceful (used of women) 身材高大而體態優美的〔指婦女〕

stat·u·ette /ˌstætʃuˈet; ˌstætʃuˈet/ *n* a very small statue which you put on a table or shelf 〔放於桌上或書架上的〕小雕像, 小塑像

stat·ure /ˈstætʃə; ˈstætʃə/ *n* [U] *fml* 〔正式〕 **1** a person's natural height 身高, 身材: *She hadn't yet grown to her full stature.* 她的個子還沒有長到應有的高度。 **2** someone's importance, position and influence 地位; 影響力: *He's a politician of considerable stature, respected by people from all parties.* 他是位具有相當地位的政治家, 為各黨派的人士所尊敬。

sta·tus /ˈstetəs; ˈsteɪtəs/ *n* [U] **1** your social rank or position considered in relation to other people 社會地位; 職位: *What's his status in the company?* 他在公司內的職位是甚麼? **2** [U] social recognition and importance 重要地位, 重要身分: *They think that having a big car gives them status.* 他們認為有輛大型的轎車會使他們顯得很有身分。 **3** [U] the legal or official position of a person or organization 〔人或組織的〕法律地位: *What's your status in this country? Are you a citizen?* 你在這國家的身分是甚麼? 是公民嗎? **4** [sing] the stage a situation has reached, or its importance at a particular time 狀況, 情形: *What's the status of the talks between the two countries?* 兩國的會談已進行到何種程度了? **5 status symbol** something that you have which shows your social status, or what you would like it to be 地位 [身分] 的象徵: *For some people a pedigree dog is more of a status symbol than a pet.* 對某些人來說, 一隻純種狗與其說是寵物, 倒不如說是一種地位的象徵。

status quo /ˌstetəsˈkwo; ˌsteɪtəsˈkwəʊ/ *n* **the status quo** the existing situation at a particular time 現狀

stat·ute /ˈstætʃut; ˈstætʃuːt/ *n fml* a law written down formally 〔正式〕法規, 法令

stat·u·to·ry /ˈstætʃutori; ˈstætʃutəri/ *adj fml* fixed or controlled by law 〔正式〕法定的, 依照法令的: *statutory control of wages* 法定的工資管制

staunch[1] /stɔntʃ; stɔːntʃ/ *adj* dependably loyal 堅定的; 忠誠的: *a staunch friend* 忠誠的朋友 **–staunchly** *adv*

staunch[2] *v* (also **stanch** *AmE* 〔美式〕) [T] to stop a flow, especially the flow of blood from a wound 制止流動〔尤指血液從傷口流出〕

stave /stev; steɪv/ *v* staved, staving

stave sthg **↔ off** *phr v* [T] to prevent or keep away for a time 避開, 擋開: *They had just enough food to stave off hunger.* 他們的

食物剛好足夠, 不用挨餓。

****stay¹** /ste; steɪ/ v **1** to remain somewhere 停留, 逗留, 留下: *I stayed late at the party last night.* 我昨晚在宴會上逗留得很晚。| *I'm sorry I can't stay, but my husband's waiting.* 對不起我不能留下來, 我的丈夫在等我。| *Can you stay for dinner?* 你能留下來吃頓飯嗎? **2** to live in a place for a while as a guest or visitor 〔作為客人或來訪者〕暫住於〔某處〕, 留宿: *My cousin's coming to stay next week.* 我的表弟下星期會來住。| *They're staying at a hotel.* 他們住在旅館裡。**3** to continue to be in a particular place, situation or state 留在原地; 保持原狀, 維持: *Please stay where you are.* 請呆着不要動。| *The price has gone down, but I don't think it'll stay down.* 價格下跌了, 但我認為它不會一直保持不漲。| *The weather stayed warm all week.* 整個星期天氣都很暖和。| *I can't stay awake another minute!* 我睏得不能再支持多一分鐘! **4 stay away** to keep away from someone or something to avoid trouble 遠離〔某人或某物〕: *Stay away from my daughter!* 遠離我的女兒! **5** infml 〖非正式〗**stay put** to remain somewhere 停在原地, 不動: *Just stay put while I answer the phone.* 在原地等我, 我去接電話。

stay in phr v [I] to remain at home 呆在家中: *In the evenings, we usually stay in and read.* 晚上我們通常留在家裡看書。

stay on phr v [I] to remain after the usual or expected time for leaving 〔在通常或預定的時間以後〕繼續留下: *Are you going to stay on at school after sixteen?* 你打算在十六歲以後仍繼續上學嗎?

stay out phr v [I] **1** to remain away from home 不在家中: *Her mother was very worried when she stayed out so late.* 她這麼晚還不回家, 她的母親非常擔憂。**2** to continue to be on strike 繼續罷工: *The miners stayed out for months.* 礦工罷工已有數月了。

stay up phr v [I] to remain out of bed past the usual time 〔超過睡覺時間而〕不去睡覺: *We sometimes let the children stay up late.* 我們有時讓孩子們晚一點睡。

> ■ **USAGE** 用法: Compare 比較 **stay** and 和 **live**. Use **stay** when you are talking about a short period of time and **live** for longer periods ☆ 談到短期居住用 **stay**, 長期居住用 **live**: *I'm going to live in London, but I'll stay at a hotel until I can find a suitable house.* 我打算長期住在倫敦, 但在找到合適的房子以前, 我先住在旅館裡。

stay² n [C] a limited period of living in a place 停留, 逗留; 暫住: *a short stay in hospital* 短期住院 | *During my stay in Paris, I went to many museums.* 我在巴黎停留時, 參觀了許多博物館。

stead·fast /'stɛd,fæst; 'stedfɑ:st/ adj **1** faithful and loyal 忠誠的: *a steadfast friend* 忠誠的朋友 **2** firm and unchanging 堅定不移的: *steadfast in your beliefs* 信仰堅定 **–steadfastly** adv

***stead·y¹** /'stɛdɪ; 'stedi/ adj **steadier, steadiest 1** not moving or shaking 穩固的, 不動搖的: *Keep the ladder steady.* 把梯子扶穩。| *His hand was steady as he lit the candle.* 點蠟燭時, 他的手很穩定。**2** moving or developing in an even, regular way 〔移動或發展〕穩固的, 穩定的: *a steady growth in industry* 工業的穩步發展 **–opposite** 反義 **unsteady** (for senses 1, 2) **3** staying at about the same level with few changes 平穩的: *We drove at a steady speed.* 我們以平穩的速度駕車前行。**4** dependable and sensible (used of people) 可靠的, 穩健的〔指人〕**5 a steady job** a job which is likely to continue 穩定的工作 **–steadily** adv **–steadiness** n

steady² v **steadied, steadying 1** [I;T] to make or become more calm or still (使)平靜, 使穩定, 使穩固: *She steadied the boat as they reached the port.* 他們到達港口的時候, 她把船穩住了。| *The pound has steadied after early losses on the market.* 英鎊在外匯市場下跌之後, 現在已經穩定下來。**2 steady yourself** to make yourself less nervous and confused 使自己鎮靜: *He steadied himself before answering my question.* 他在回答我的問題前, 先使自己鎮靜下來。

steak /stek; steɪk/ n [C;U] a thick flat piece of meat or fish 肉排; 魚排; 扒: *How would you like your steak done, sir?* 先生, 你喜歡你的牛排燒到幾成熟? | *stewing steak* 燉牛肉 | *a salmon steak* 三文魚扒

***steal** /stil; sti:l/ v **stole** /stol; stəʊl/, **stolen** /'stolən; 'stəʊlən/, **stealing 1** [I;T] to take something belonging to someone without their permission and with no intention of giving it back 偷竊, 偷: *She used to steal money from her father's drawer.* 她以前經常從父親的抽屜裡偷錢。| *He was sent to prison for stealing.* 他由於盜竊而入獄。| *My bicycle was stolen last week.* 我的腳踏車上星期被偷走了。**–see** 見 ROB (USAGE 用法) **–see** 見 THIEF (USAGE 用法) **2** [I] to move secretly and quietly 偷偷地移動: *He stole out of the house without anyone seeing him.* 他悄悄地溜出了房子, 沒有人看見他。**3 steal the scene/show** to get all the praise and attention expected by someone else at a public event 搶出風頭

stealth /stɛlθ; stelθ/ n [U] the action of acting secretly and quietly so that nobody notices you 祕密的行動: *Stealth is something any hunter has to learn.* 悄悄地行動是任何一個獵人都必須學會的事情。**–stealthy** adj **stealthier, stealthiest**: *She gave a stealthy glance at her watch.* 她悄悄地看了一下手錶。**–stealthily** adv

***steam¹** /stim; sti:m/ n [U] **1** hot gas produced by boiling water 蒸汽, 水蒸氣: *Clouds* of steam rose from the machine. 陣陣水蒸氣從機器裡冒出來。 **2** power produced by putting steam under pressure 蒸汽動力, 蒸汽壓力: *The engines are driven by steam.* 發動機是由蒸汽驅動的。| *a steam locomotive* 蒸汽火車頭 **3 let off steam** to get rid of strong feelings or active strength kept under control 發洩強烈的情感[過剩的精力]: *Young children need to let off steam by running around outside.* 小孩子要到外面跑一跑, 以消耗他們過剩的精力。| *I let off steam by shouting at the dog.* 我對着狗大叫了一番, 以發洩怒氣。

steam² *v* **1** [I] to produce steam 產生蒸汽, 冒熱氣: *steaming hot coffee* 冒着熱氣的咖啡 **2** [I] to travel by steam power 靠蒸汽動力行駛: *The ship steamed into the harbour.* 輪船駛入了港口。 **3** [T] to cook by heating with steam 蒸, 用蒸汽烹調: *Lightly steam the vegetables.* 把蔬菜稍微蒸一下。 –see 見 COOK¹ (USAGE 用法) **4** [T] to use steam to open something 用蒸汽打開[某物]: *He steamed open the letter.* 他用蒸汽把信打開。

steam up *phr v* **1** [I] to be covered with steam 蒙上蒸汽: *Her glasses steamed up when she came into the warm room.* 她一走進那暖洋洋的房間, 眼鏡上就結了一層水蒸氣。 **2** *infml* 〖非正式〗 **be/get steamed up** to be or become cross or upset 生氣; 難過: *She got pretty steamed up when I told her the news.* 我把消息告訴她時, 她變得很生氣。

steam·er /'stimɚ; 'stiːməʳ/ *n* see 見 STEAMSHIP

steam·roll·er¹ /'stim,rolɚ; 'stiːm,rəʊləʳ/ *n* a heavy vehicle with very wide wheels for making road surfaces flat 蒸汽壓路機

steamroller² *v* [T] *infml* to force someone to do what you want by using all your power or influence 〖非正式〗壓迫[某人做某事]: *He was steamrollered into signing the agreement.* 他被迫簽了協議。

steam·ship /'stim,ʃip; 'stiːm,ʃip/ *n* (also 又作 **steamer**) a large ship driven by steam power 汽船, 大輪船

steed /stid; stiːd/ *n lit* a horse for riding 〖文〗馬; 駿馬

*steel¹ /stil; stiːl/ *n* [U] a hard strong metal containing mainly iron and used for making things like tools, machines, and parts of buildings 鋼, 鋼鐵

steel² *v* [T] **steel yourself** to harden yourself enough to do something unpleasant 使自己堅強起來: *He steeled himself to go in and say he was sorry.* 他硬着頭皮走進去說了聲抱歉。

steel·works /'stil,wɝks; 'stiːlwɜːks/ *n* [plural is 複數為 **steelworks**] [C +sing/pl verb] a factory where steel is made 煉鋼廠

steel·y /'stili; 'stiːli/ *adj* **steelier, steeliest 1** blue-grey in colour like steel 似鋼鐵的; 冷冰冰的: *steely blue eyes* 冷冰冰的藍眼睛 **2** hard and strong 鋼鐵般的; 堅硬的; 強硬的: *steely*

determination 鋼鐵般的決心

steep /stip; stiːp/ *adj* **1** rising or falling at a large angle 陡峭的, 險峻的: *This hill's too steep to ride up.* 這座山太陡了, 騎馬上不去。 **2** showing a large increase or decrease 大起大落的: *a steep rise in prices* 價格的急劇上漲 **3** *infml* unreasonably expensive 〖非正式〗過高的, 太昂貴的: *He's asking £500 for his old car, which I think is a bit steep.* 他那輛舊車索價五百英鎊, 我覺得太貴了。 –**steeply** *adv* –**steepness** *n* [U]

steeped /stipt; stiːpt/ *adj* thoroughly filled or familiar with 充滿…的; 精通…的: *an ancient building steeped in history* 充滿着歷史氣息的古老建築 | *a tribe steeped in the traditions of the past* 處處遵循昔日傳統的部落

stee·ple /'stipl; 'stiːpəl/ *n* a church tower with the top rising to a point 〔教堂的〕尖塔

stee·ple·chase /'stipl,tʃes; 'stiːpəltʃeɪs/ *n* a race for people or horses in which they have to jump over fences or other objects 障礙賽跑; 障礙賽馬

steer¹ /stir; stɪəʳ/ *v* **1** [I;T] to control a ship or vehicle so that it goes in a particular direction 駕駛〔船或車輛〕; 操縱〔船或車的方向盤〕: *He steered the car carefully into the garage.* 他把車小心翼翼地開進車庫裡。 | *Bill steered with one hand while adjusting the radio with the other.* 比爾一隻手操縱方向盤, 用另一隻手調校收音機。 **2** [T] to guide someone to where you want them to go 引導〔某人〕到…: *She steered the visitors towards the garden.* 她領着客人參觀花園。 **3 steer the conversation** to try to change the subject of a conversation in a way that nobody notices 話題引開: *She tried to steer the conversation towards less painful topics.* 她盡量把談話引向不那麼令人傷心的話題上去。 **4 steer clear of** to avoid 避開, 從…脫身

steer² *n* a male animal of the cattle family with its sexual organs removed 閹牛

steering wheel /'·· ·/ *n* the wheel which you turn to control the direction in which a car or other vehicle moves 駕駛盤, 方向盤; 舵輪 –see picture on page 209 見 209 頁彩圖

stel·lar /'stɛlɚ; 'steləʳ/ *adj tech* of or concerning the stars 〖術語〗星的, 與星有關的

stem¹ /stɛm; stem/ *n* **1** the central part of a plant above the ground from which the leaves or flowers grow 〔植物的〕莖; 〔樹木的〕幹 **2** the narrow upright part of a wine glass or similar container which supports the bowl 〔酒杯或類似容器的〕莖狀部分; 柄, 腳: *the stem of a wine glass* 酒杯的腳

stem² *v* **-mm-** [T] to stop the flow or spread of 阻止, 止住〔流或傳播〕: *How can we stem the flow of blood?* 我們如何才能止血?

stem from sthg *phr v* [T] to have as an origin or cause 源自, 來源於: *This problem stems from poor management in the* *company.* 這問題是由公司管理不善所造成的。

stench /stentʃ/ stentʃ/ *n fml* a strong bad smell 〔正式〕強烈的臭味, 惡臭

sten·cil[1] /'stɛnsəl; 'stensəl/ *n* a piece of card, metal, or plastic, in which patterns or letters have been cut – by putting ink or paint through these holes you make patterns or letters on the surface below 〔鏤有圖案或文字的〕模板, 型板

stencil[2] *v* **-ll- (-l-** *AmE* 〔美式〕) [T] to print by using a stencil 用模板印刷

★**step**[1] /stɛp; step/ *n* **1** the action of lifting one foot and putting it down in front of the other in order to move along 步, 腳步: *Take two steps forward and two steps back.* 向前跨兩步, 再向後退兩步。| *With every step I took the load got heavier.* 我每走一步都覺得負荷愈來愈重。**2** the sound made when you take a step 腳步聲: *I heard steps outside.* 我聽到外面有腳步聲。**3** the distance covered in one step 步幅, 一步(之距離): *There's a newsagent just a few steps down the road from the butcher.* 距離肉店只有幾步遠的地方有個報攤。**4** a flat narrow surface, often one in a set of surfaces each higher than the one before, on which you put your foot for climbing up and down to different levels 梯級, 台階: *Mind the step outside the door.* 小心門外的台階。| *She was standing on the church steps.* 她站在教堂的台階上。| *A flight of steps led to the house.* 屋前有一段台階。**5** an action in a set of actions which aims to produce a particular result 步驟, 措施: *Our first step towards improving efficiency was to buy modern equipment.* 為提高效率, 我們的第一步是要購買現代化的設備。**6** a stage in a process 階段; 進程: *Scientists here are a few steps ahead of the rest of the world.* 這裡的科學家與世界上其他地方的科學家相比要領先幾步。**7** a movement of the feet in dancing 舞步: *She learned the new steps quickly.* 她很快就學會了新的舞步。**8 steps** a ladder which folds 摺疊梯, 梯櫈 **9 in step** to move your left and right leg at the same time as other people 步伐一致: *soldiers marching in step* 士兵步伐一致向前行進 [RELATED PHRASE 相關詞組 **out of step**] **10 step by step** gradually moving from one stage to the next 一步一步地, 逐漸地: *Step by step he learned the rules of the game.* 他逐漸學會了比賽的規則。

★**step**[2] *v* **-pp-** [I] **1** to lift one foot up and put it down in front of the other in order to move along 踩; 邁步; 跨步: *She stepped on a spider.* 她踩到了一隻蜘蛛。| *He stepped forward to receive his prize.* 他走向前去領獎。**2 step into the breach** to do a job which someone else had said they would do but could not 代別人做某事, 挺身相助: *When she was taken ill her son stepped into the breach and organized the event instead.* 她生病了, 所以她的兒子代替她組織這活動。**3 step out**

of line to act differently from other people or from what is expected 行動與眾不同; 表現與預期不同

step back *phr v* [I] to try to consider something in a new and different way 以另一種方式考慮〔某事〕: *Let's step back a minute and think again.* 我們退一步再考慮一下吧。

step down (also 又作 **step aside**) *phr v* [I] to leave a job or official position 離職, 讓位, 下台: *He's seventy years old and believes it's time to step down as chairman.* 他七十歲了, 覺得是時候辭掉主席一職。

step in *phr v* [I] to begin to take part in a difficult situation in order to improve it 干涉, 插手, 介入: *If the dispute gets any worse the government will have to step in.* 如果紛爭進一步加劇, 政府便不得不進行干涉。

step sthg ↔ **up** *phr v* [T] *infml* to increase in size or speed 〔非正式〕使增加; 使加快: *We'll have to step up the work to finish by June.* 我們必須加快工作, 在六月份以前完成。

step·broth·er /'stɛp,brʌðə; 'step,brʌðəʳ/ *n* a male person whose father or mother has married your father or mother 異父或異母的哥哥或弟弟

step·fa·ther /'stɛp,fɑðə; 'step,fɑːðəʳ/ *n* a man who is not your natural father, but who your mother has married 繼父

step·lad·der /'stɛp,lædə; 'step,lædəʳ/ *n* a ladder which folds 可摺疊的梯子, 梯櫈

step·moth·er /'stɛp,mʌðə; 'step,mʌðəʳ/ *n* a woman who is not your natural mother, but who your father has married 繼母

steppe /stɛp; step/ *n* **the steppes** a large area of land without trees, especially in the Soviet Union 〔尤指俄羅斯的〕無樹的大草原, 乾草原

stepping stone /'··· /*n* **1** a way of improving or becoming more successful 改進的辦法; 達到成功的手段: *Are good exam results a stepping stone to a more successful job?* 優異的考試成績是獲得理想工作的階梯嗎? **2** one of a row of large stones, which you walk on to cross a river 〔過河用的〕踏腳石

step·sis·ter /'stɛp,sɪstə; 'step,sɪstəʳ/ *n* a female person whose father or mother has married your father or mother 異父或異母的姊姊或妹妹

ster·e·o[1] /'stɛrɪo; 'sterɪəʊ/ *n* **stereos** a record player or sound system which gives out sound from two different places by means of two speakers (SPEAKER) 立體聲音響設備

stereo[2] (also 又作 **stereophonic** /,stɛrɪə'fɑnɪk; ,sterɪəʊ'fɒnɪk/ *fml* 〔正式〕) *adj* using a system of sound recording or broadcasting in which sound comes from two different places 立體聲的: *a stereo recording* 立體聲錄音 | *a stereo record player* 立體聲唱機

ster·e·o·type[1] /'stɛrɪə,taɪp; 'sterɪətaɪp/ *n* a fixed set of ideas or image which many people wrongly believe represents a particular person or thing 固定模式; 老套: *The characters in the film are just stereotypes, with no individuality.* 這部電影中的角色不過是一些俗套人物, 沒有個性可言。| *racial stereotypes* 種族陳規

stereotype² *v* **stereotyped, stereotyping** [T] to have a fixed idea or image of a general type which you wrongly believe represents a particular person or thing 使定型; 使...模式化: *You can't stereotype policemen — they're all different.* 你不能把警察都看成是千篇一律的 — 他們是不一樣的。

ster·ile /ˈstɛrəl; ˈsteraɪl/ *adj* **1** unable to produce babies (used of people or animals) 不能生育的(指人或動物) **2** very clean and free from harmful bacteria 無菌的, 消過毒的: *The operation was performed in sterile conditions.* 手術在無菌的環境下進行。**3** lacking new thought or imagination 缺乏新意的; 無想像力的: *His theory is based on a few sterile ideas.* 他的理論是以幾個毫無新意的觀點作為基礎的。– **sterility** /stəˈrɪlɪti; stəˈrɪlɪti/ *n* [U]

ster·il·ize /ˈstɛrəˌlaɪz; ˈsterɪ̩laɪz/ *v* **sterilized, sterilizing** (also 又作 **sterilise** *BrE* 〖英式〗) [T] **1** to make clean and free from harmful bacteria 殺菌消毒, 使無菌 **2** be sterilized to have an operation so that you are unable to have children 做絕育手術, 使失去生育能力 – **sterilization** /ˌstɛrələˈzeʃən; ˈsterɪ̩laɪˈzeɪʃən/ *n* [U]

ster·ling¹ /ˈstɜ·lɪŋ; ˈstɜːlɪŋ/ *n* [U] *tech* the type of money used in Britain, based on the pound (£) 〖術語〗〖以英鎊為基礎的〗英國貨幣: *The value of sterling has risen.* 英國貨幣升值了。| *£200 sterling* 二百英鎊

sterling² *adj* [only before a noun 只用於名詞前] *fml* of the highest standard 〖正式〗最高標準的: *Her sterling work was much appreciated.* 她出色的工作贏得了許多稱讚。

stern¹ /stɜ·n; stɜːn/ *adj* very firm and severe 嚴格的; 嚴肅的; 嚴厲的: *a stern teacher* 嚴格的老師 | *a stern look* 嚴厲的神情 | *stern discipline* 嚴厲的紀律 – **sternly** *adv* – **sternness** *n* [U]

stern² *n* the back end of a ship 船尾

steth·o·scope /ˈstɛθəˌskop; ˈsteθəskəʊp/ *n* a medical instrument which is used for listening to your heart and breathing; it consists of two tubes which go in the doctor's ears and a round part that goes on your chest 聽診器

ste·ve·dore /ˈstivəˌdor; ˈstiːvɪ̩dɔːʳ/ *n BrE* a person whose job is loading and unloading ships 〖英式〗碼頭裝卸工人

stew¹ /stju; stjuː/ *n* [C;U] a dish of meat and vegetables cooked together slowly in liquid 燉肉; 燉菜

stew² *v* [I;T] **1** to cook slowly and gently in liquid 燉, 燜, 煨 –see 見 COOK¹(USAGE 用法) **2 stew in your own juice** *infml* to be

left to suffer as a result of your own actions 〖非正式〗自作自受

stew·ard /ˈstjuwɚd; ˈstjuːəd/ *n* **1** a man who serves passengers on a ship, train, or plane; a woman who does this is called a **stewardess** 〔輪船、火車或飛機上的〕乘務員, 服務員〖女服務員稱為 **stewardess**〗 **2** one of the people who arrange a public event, such as a horse race 〔一項公眾活動, 如賽馬的〕籌備者

*stick¹ /stɪk; stɪk/ *n* **1** a long thin piece of wood which has been cut or has fallen off a tree 樹枝, 枝條: *He drew in the sand with a stick.* 他用樹枝在沙堆上畫畫。**2** (also 又作 **walking stick**) a thin rod of wood or metal used to support your body when walking 手杖, 拐杖: *Since the accident she's had to walk with a stick.* 自從那次事故以後, 她便不得不用拐杖走路。**3** a long thin piece of something 一根; 一支: *a stick of celery* 一根芹菜

*stick² *v* **stuck** /stʌk; stʌk/, **sticking 1** [T] to push a pointed object into or through something 把〔尖物〕插入, 把〔尖物〕刺入: *Don't stick pins into the chair!* 不要把大頭針插到椅子上去! | *She stuck her fork into the meat.* 她把叉扎到肉裡。**2** [T] to fix something to something else by using GLUE or a similar substance 黏, 貼: *His job is to stick labels on the boxes.* 他的工作是往箱子上貼標籤。**3** [I] to become or remain fixed to something or in a particular position 黏住: *Oh no! This stamp won't stick!* 哎, 不! 這張郵票黏不住! | *The paint was still wet, so the handle stuck to my hand.* 油漆還未乾, 所以把手黏住了我的手。| *She couldn't get the door to open — it kept sticking.* 她打不開這門, 它卡住了。**4** [T] *infml* to put 〖非正式〗放置: *He stuck his coat down on the chair.* 他把外衣放到椅子上面。**5 can't stick** *infml* to hate something or someone and feel that you cannot bear them 〖非正式〗討厭〔某人、某事〕; 無法忍受: *I just can't stick his voice.* 我就是無法忍受他的聲音。**6 stick in your mind** *infml* to be remembered for a long time 〖非正式〗歷久不忘 **7 stick your neck out** *infml* to do or say something which could cause yourself harm or difficulty 〖非正式〗冒險〔做或說某事〕: *I admire her for sticking her neck out and refusing to do what was expected.* 我很敬佩她敢於冒風險, 拒絕做他人要她做的事情。

stick around *phr v* [I] *infml* to wait somewhere, often because you hope something good will happen 〖非正式〗逗留; 等待〔常因為希望有好事發生〕

stick at sthg *phr v* [T] to continue to work hard at something difficult 堅持做〔困難之事〕: *By really sticking at it, she's improved her tennis a lot.* 她堅持去上訓練課, 因此網球技藝提高了許多。

stick by sbdy *phr v* [T] *infml* to continue

to support 〖非正式〗繼續支持: *She always sticks by her friends.* 她總會支持她的朋友。

stick out *phr v* **1** [T; **stick** sthg ↔ **out**] to make something come out from inside 伸出〔物〕: *Don't stick your tongue out at me!* 別對我伸舌頭! **2** [I] to be positioned beyond something 突出: *The roof sticks out at least a metre in front of the door.* 屋頂突出門外至少有一米。 **3** [I] *infml* to be clearly seen or noticed 〖非正式〗顯眼; 使注目: *Her unusual hairstyle makes her really stick out in a crowd.* 她不同尋常的髮型令她在人羣中顯得十分突出。 **4 stick it out** to continue in a difficult situation without giving up 堅持下去: *I don't like this course, but I'm determined to stick it out.* 我不喜歡這門課, 但決心堅持下去。 **5 stick out like a sore thumb** *infml* to seem very much out of place 〖非正式〗顯得很不合適, 顯得礙眼

stick out for sthg *phr v* [T] to refuse to accept anything less than or different from what you first asked for 堅持要求〔拒絕接受不如或不同於先前所要的東西〕: *In spite of management's refusal, the union are sticking out for a 10% increase in wages.* 儘管資方不同意, 工會仍堅持要求工人的工資增加百分之十。

stick to sthg *phr v* [T] **1** to continue to behave according to a decision, plan or agreement 繼續執行〔決定、計劃或協議〕: *I've decided to stick to my original idea.* 我決定堅持我原來的觀點。 **2** to remain near to someone or something 呆在〔某人或某物〕附近: *If you stick to main roads, you won't get lost.* 如果你一直走在大路上, 就不會迷失方向。

stick together *phr v* [I] to stay loyal to each other (used of two or more people) 赤誠相待; 團結一致〔指兩個或兩個以上的人〕

stick up ↔ **up** *phr v* [T] to put on a wall 貼在牆上: *The room will look better if you stick up some pictures.* 在牆上貼幾幅畫, 房間看上去就顯得漂亮多了。

stick up for sbdy/sthg *phr v* [T] to support and defend a person or belief 維護〔人或信念〕: *Thanks for sticking up for me in the argument.* 謝謝你在辯論中支持我。

stick with sbdy/sthg *phr v* [T] *infml* to stay close or loyal to someone 〖非正式〗與〔某人〕在一起; 忠於〔某人〕: *Stick with me and you'll get rich!* 跟着我, 你就會富起來!

stick·er /ˈstɪkə; ˈstɪkɚ/ *n* a small piece of paper with a picture or writing on it which you stick to things 貼紙, 標貼: *political stickers on car windows* 貼在汽車玻璃上的政治宣傳標籤

stick-in-the-mud /ˈ··· ˌ·/ *n* **stick-in-the-muds** *infml* a person who will not change or accept new things 〖非正式〗頑固守舊者, 墨守成規的人

stick·ler /ˈstɪklə; ˈstɪklɚ/ *n* a person who demands a particular quality from themselves and other people 堅持要做到〔某種品質〕的人: *She's a stickler for the truth.* 她是個堅持實事求是的人。

stick·y /ˈstɪkɪ; ˈstɪkɪ/ *adj* **stickier, stickiest 1** covered with or containing a substance which sticks to anything it touches 黏的, 黏性的: *sticky sweets* 黏牙的糖果 | *sticky labels* 黏貼標籤 **2** *infml* awkward or difficult (used of a situation) 〖非正式〗棘手的, 困難的〔指情況〕: *He put me in a very sticky position by telling me his secrets.* 他把祕密告訴我, 使我很為難。 **3** unpleasantly hot and wet (used of weather) 炎熱的, 潮濕的〔指天氣〕 **4 come to/meet a sticky end** *infml* to suffer ruin, dishonour or death 〖非正式〗不好的下場, 悲慘的結局 — **stickiness** *n* [U]

stiff¹ /stɪf; stɪf/ *adj* **1** not easily bent or changed in shape 不易彎曲的, 不易變形的: *stiff paper* 硬紙 | *stiff new shoes* 硬邦邦的新鞋 | *Beat the egg whites until stiff.* 把蛋白打到發稠。 **2** painful when moved (used of muscles or joints in the body) 一動就疼的, 僵直的〔指肌肉或關節〕: *She felt very stiff the day after her first exercise class.* 第一節體育課後, 她感到肌肉發僵, 一動就疼。 **3** not easily moved 不易移動的: *I couldn't turn the key — the lock's very stiff.* 我轉不動鑰匙, 那鎖很緊。 **4** *formal* and not friendly (used of behaviour) 拘謹的; 冷淡的〔指舉止〕: *a stiff smile* 牽強的微笑 **5** *infml* 〖非正式〗**a stiff drink** a drink which contains a large amount of strong alcohol 烈酒 **6** difficult or severe 艱難的; 嚴厲的: *a stiff examination* 一場艱難的考試 | *The judge gave him a stiff sentence.* 法官給他判了重刑。 — **stiffly** *adv* — **stiffness** *n* [U]

stiff² *adv infml* extremely 〖非正式〗極度地: *scared stiff* 極為害怕 | *bored stiff* 厭倦極了 | *frozen stiff* 凍僵 | *worried stiff* 極為擔心

stiff·en /ˈstɪfən; ˈstɪfən/ *v* **1** [I] to suddenly become still and tense because you are angry or afraid 〔由於憤怒或恐懼而〕一下子變得生硬〔緊張〕: *He stiffened at her rude remarks.* 他聽到她無禮的説話, 態度頓時變強硬了。 **2** [I;T] to make or become more difficult to bend or move (使)變得難以彎曲〔移動〕: *a shirt with a stiffened collar* 硬領襯衫 **3** [I;T] to make firmer or more severe (used of behaviour) (使)更堅定〔指行為〕: *Your comments will only stiffen his resolve.* 你的評論只會更加堅定他的決心。

sti·fle /ˈstaɪfl; ˈstaɪfəl/ *v* **stifled, stifling** [I;T] **1** to make or become unable to breathe properly because of heat or a lack of fresh air (使)窒息, (使)透不過氣來: *The gas stifled them.* 煤氣令他們窒息。 | *a stifling hot day* 悶熱的一天 **2** to prevent from happening or developing 阻止; 抑制: *The government stifled all opposition.* 政府壓制了所有反對的意見。

stig·ma /ˈstɪɡmə; ˈstɪɡmə/ *n* **stigmas** a feeling of shame or dishonour 恥辱: *There is a stigma about having to ask for money.* 向人

要錢是種恥辱。

stile /staɪl; staɪl/ *n* two wooden steps which must be climbed to cross a fence or wall around a field〔攀越籬笆或圍牆時用的〕梯磴；階梯

sti·let·to /stɪˈlɛto; stɪˈletəʊ/ *n* **stilettos 1** a knife with a very sharp narrow blade, used as a weapon 短劍，匕首 **2 stiletto heel** a high thin heel of a woman's shoe〔女鞋上的〕細高跟

⋆⋆**still¹** /stɪl; stɪl/ *adv* **1** used to say that something is continuing to happen or continuing to be true 仍然，還: *Is the secretary still here?* 祕書還在這裡嗎? | *Do you still live in Birmingham?* 你仍住在伯明翰嗎? | *Is John still working?* 約翰還在工作嗎? **2** even so 可是，然而，儘管如此: *I knew that I wouldn't win, but I still think it was unfair that I came last.* 雖然我知道我不會贏，但得了最後一名，我仍認為有些不公平。 | *I know he's done a terrible thing, but he's still my father.* 我知道他做了件糟糕的事情，但他終究是我的父親啊。 | *I'm not very happy about it. Still, it's no use worrying, is it?* 對此我不大高興。雖是這樣，擔心仍是無濟於事的，是嗎? **3** used for making comparisons stronger 更，還要〔強調比較級〕: *It's cold now and it will be colder still tonight.* 現在很冷，今晚會更冷。

still² *adj* **1** not moving 不動的，靜止的: *Keep still while I brush your hair.* 不要動，我給你刷頭髮。 **2** quiet and calm 安靜的，平靜的: *The house was still.* 屋子裡一片寂靜。 **3** not containing gas (used of drinks) 不含氣體的〔指飲料〕: *still orange juice* 無汽橙汁 **–stillness** *n* [U]

still³ *v* [T] *lit* to make someone quiet and calm〖文〗使安靜；使靜止

still⁴ *n* **1** [C] a photograph taken from a film〔電影的〕劇照 **2** [U] *lit* quietness and calm〖文〗安靜；平靜

still·born /ˈstɪlbɔrn; ˈstɪlbɔːn/ *adj* born dead 死產的，夭折的

stilt /stɪlt; stɪlt/ *n* **1** a wooden or metal pole which supports a building above ground or water level〔木製或金屬的〕支柱 **2** one of a pair of poles, with a supporting piece for your foot, with which you can walk raised above the ground 高蹺 **–see** 見 PAIR (USAGE 用法)

stilt·ed /ˈstɪltɪd; ˈstɪltɪd/ *adj* very formal and unnatural (used of behaviour or conversation) 生硬的，不自然的〔指行為或談話〕

stim·u·lant /ˈstɪmjələnt; ˈstɪmjʊlənt/ *n* a drug or other substance which makes your body more active for a time 興奮劑: *Coffee is a stimulant.* 咖啡是一種興奮劑。

stim·u·late /ˈstɪmjəˌlet; ˈstɪmjʊleɪt/ *v* **stimulated, stimulating** [T] **1** to make something become more active or develop more quickly 刺激: *Light stimulates plant growth.* 光能促進植物生長。 | *Lowering of interest rates should stimulate the*

economy. 降低利率應當能刺激經濟增長。 **2** to fill someone with new ideas and interest 鼓勵，激勵〔某人〕: *Going back to college has really stimulated her.* 重返大學的想法給了她莫大的鼓勵。 **3** to make a part of someone's body move or behave in a particular way 刺激〔身體某部分以某種方式活動〕: *It's a chemical which stimulates the production of hormones.* 這是一種能刺激體內產生荷爾蒙的化學品。**–stimulation** /ˌstɪmjəˈleʃən; ˌstɪmjʊ-ˈleɪʃən/ *n* [U]

stim·u·lus /ˈstɪmjələs; ˈstɪmjʊləs/ *n* **stimuli** /-ˌlaɪ, -laɪ/ **1** something which encourages activity or development 刺激物；促進物: *Building new shops will be a stimulus for business in the area.* 建造新商店將帶來刺激本地商業的發展。 **2** something which fills you with new ideas and interest 起鼓舞或激勵作用的事物: *He loves the stimulus of living in a big city.* 他喜歡住在大城市裡的那份刺激。 **3** something which makes a part of your body move or act 刺激身體的東西〔使其能夠興奮或活動〕

sting¹ /stɪŋ; stɪŋ/ *v* **stung** /stʌŋ; stʌŋ/, **stinging 1** [I;T] (used of plants and insects) to hurt by pricking with a poison〔指植物或昆蟲〕叮，螫，刺: *He was stung by a wasp.* 他被一隻大黃蜂螫了一下。 | *The leaves of these plants sting.* 這些植物的葉子會刺人。**–see** 見 BITE² (USAGE 用法) **2** [I;T] to feel or make someone feel a sharp pain (使)感到刺痛: *My eyes are stinging from the smoke.* 我的眼睛被煙燻得發疼。 | *Careful — these chemicals will sting your eyes!* 小心 — 這些化學藥品會使你的眼睛感到刺痛! **3** [T] to make someone feel hurt and cross 激怒〔某人〕: *What you said so casually really stung him.* 你隨口所說的話實激怒了他。

sting² *n* **1** the sharp organ of some animals which stings〔動物的〕刺，螫針: *Does a bee die when it loses its sting?* 蜜蜂失去螫針會死嗎? **2** a sharp pain in a part of your body〔身體的〕刺痛: *the sting of salt rubbed into a wound* 鹽擦入傷口的刺痛感 **3 take the sting out of** to remove the difficult or bad part of a situation 去除困難部分；去除不好的部分: *News of winning the competition took the sting out of her dismissal.* 比賽獲獎的消息使她覺得被解雇一事不再那麼難過。

stin·gy /ˈstɪndʒɪ; ˈstɪndʒɪ/ *adj* **stingier, stingiest** very mean 吝嗇的，小氣的: *He's really stingy with his money.* 他在金錢方面十分吝嗇。**–stinginess** *n* [U]

stink /stɪŋk; stɪŋk/ *v* **stank** /stæŋk; stæŋk/, **stunk** /stʌŋk; stʌŋk/, **stinking** [I] **1** to have a strong unpleasant smell 有難聞的氣味: *The room stank of garlic.* 房間裡有大蒜的臭味。**–see** 見 SMELL (USAGE 用法) **2** *infml* to have an unpleasant or offensive quality〖非正式〗令人討厭: *Frankly, your attitude stinks!* 老實說，你的態度令人討厭! **–stink** *n*

stint¹ /stɪnt; stɪnt/ *v* [I; T] to give too small

an amount of something 節省; 吝嗇: *Don't stint on the cream when you make the cake.* 做蛋糕時, 別吝嗇放奶油。

stint² *n* a limited period of work 短期的工作: *After a stint in the army, he opened a shop.* 他服了一段時間的兵役後, 開了一片店。

stip·pled /'stɪpld; 'stɪpəld/ *adj* painted or covered with small dots 點畫的, 點刻的

stip·u·late /'stɪpjə,let; 'stɪpjʊleɪt/ *v* **stipulated, stipulating** [T; +(that)] to state clearly as a necessary condition of an agreement 〔在協議中〕規定, 講明〔條件〕: *The company stipulated payment in advance.* 公司規定必須事先支付費用。

stip·u·la·tion /,stɪpjə'leʃən; ,stɪpjʊ'leɪʃən/ *n* [C;U] a statement of conditions 規定; 條件; 條款: *My only stipulation is that I am given a share in the profits.* 我提的唯一條件是分一份利潤。

★stir¹ /stɜ; stɜːr/ *v* **-rr-** **1** [T] to mix a liquid using a spoon or something similar 攪拌, 攪動: *He stirred his coffee.* 他攪了攪咖啡。 **2** [I] to move slightly from one position to another 輕輕地移動: *She stirred in her sleep.* 她在睡夢中輕輕地動了一下。 **3** [T] (used of the wind) to make something move slightly 〔指風〕使〔某物〕微動: *A breeze gently stirred the surface of the lake.* 一陣微風使湖面泛起了漣漪。 **4** [T] to produce a strong feeling in someone 激起〔某人的強烈感情〕, 惹起: *His speech stirred the crowd to anger.* 他的話激起了群眾的憤怒。 **5 stir yourself** to make yourself move 使自己走動, 活動: *We finally stirred ourselves from the fire and went to bed.* 我們終於從爐火旁起身睡覺去了。

stir sthg ↔ up *phr v* [T] to cause trouble 引起〔麻煩〕: *Don't stir things up again by refusing to go there.* 別因為拒絕去那裡而再惹麻煩了。

stir² *n* **1** [C] an act of stirring 攪拌, 攪動: *Give the mixture a few stirs.* 把混和物攪拌幾下。 **2** [sing] strong public feeling 公眾的強烈感情; 轟動: *His resignation has created quite a stir.* 他的辭職引起了相當大的轟動。

stir·rup /'stɪrəp; 'stɪrəp/ *n* a metal piece that you put your foot in when you are riding a horse 馬鐙

stitch¹ /stɪtʃ; stɪtʃ/ *n* **1** [C] a short piece of thread sewn into a piece of material to join two edges together or for decoration 縫線, 針腳: *The stitches are so small and neat that you can't see them.* 針腳又小又整齊, 你幾乎看不出來。 **2** [C] a turn of the wool round the needle in knitting (KNIT) 〔編織時的〕一針, 一鈎: *Make sure there are 20 stitches on the needles.* 織針上必須要有二十針。 **3** [C] a piece of thread which sews the sides of a wound together 〔縫合傷口的〕縫線: *The cut needed 15 stitches.* 這個傷口需要縫十五針。 **4** [sing] a sharp pain in your side, caused by too much exercise or laughter 〔由於運動或大笑而引起的〕脅部的劇

痛: *She had a bad stitch from running.* 她由於跑步而引致脅部一陣劇痛。 **5 in stitches** *infml* laughing uncontrollably 〔非正式〕忍不住大笑: *His jokes had us all in stitches.* 他的笑話讓我們都笑得前仰後合。

stitch² *v* **1** [I;T] to sew 縫, 縫補: *Will you stitch a button on this shirt?* 你把鈕扣縫到這件襯衫上好嗎? **2** [T] to sew the edges of a wound together using a special needle 縫合〔傷口〕: *The doctor stitched the cut.* 醫生縫合了傷口。

stoat /stot; stəʊt/ *n* a small brown furry animal that eats other animals 白鼬

★stock¹ /stak; stɒk/ *n* [C;U] money lent to a government or company, on which interest is paid 證券; 公債: *stocks and shares* 公債與股票 | *government stock* 政府公債 **2** [C] a supply of something for use 儲備; 庫存: *How long will the country's stocks of coal last?* 該國煤的儲備量還可以用多久? | *We've bought a good stock of food for the weekend.* 我們已為週末購買了充足的食物。 **3** [U] the total supply of goods for sale in a shop 〔商店的〕存貨, 現貨: *There wasn't much stock left after the sale.* 大減價之後, 商店裡的存貨剩得不多了。 **4 in stock** held ready for sale by a shop 〔商店裡〕有現貨待售: *I'm afraid we have no red ones in stock at the moment.* 對不起, 我們的現貨中目前沒有紅色的。 [RELATED PHRASE 相關詞組 **out of stock**] **5** [U] farm animals, especially cattle, sheep, or pigs 牲畜〔尤指牛、羊、或豬〕 **6** [U] a liquid made from the juices of meat, vegetables, or fish used in cooking 〔用肉、蔬菜或魚製成的供烹飪用的〕原湯 **7** [U] the people from whom someone is descended 祖先, 世系: *He comes from good farming stock.* 他出身於富農家庭。 **8 take stock** to stop for a while to consider a situation so you can make a decision 斟酌; 權衡: *He took stock of his situation and decided he needed a long holiday.* 他考慮了一下自己的處境, 然後決定去休長假。

stock² *v* [T] **1** to keep supplies of goods to sell 備貨〔以供出售〕: *That shop stocks all types of shoes.* 那家商店備有各式各樣的鞋子。 **2** to fill 裝滿: *a shop well stocked with goods* 一家存滿商品的商店

stock up *v* [I] to buy a full store of goods in case you cannot get them later 充分儲備: *Bad weather was expected, so we stocked up on food.* 天氣估計會變壞, 所以我們儲備了一些食物。

stock·ade /stak'ed; stɒ'keɪd/ *n* a wooden fence built for defence 〔作防禦用的〕木柵欄, 圍椿

stock·brok·er /'stak,brokə; 'stɒk,brəʊkər/ *n* a person whose job is buying and selling stocks (STOCK¹) and shares (SHARE¹) 證券和股票經紀人

stock ex·change /'··,·/ *n* **1** the place where stocks (STOCK¹) and shares (SHARE¹) are

S

bought and sold 證券交易所, 股票交易所 **2 the Stock Exchange** (also 又作 **the stock market**) the business of buying and selling stocks (STOCK¹) and shares (SHARE¹) 證券交易(業)

stock·ing /ˈstɑkɪŋ; ˈstɒkɪŋ/ n **1** a close-fitting piece of clothing which covers your feet and legs; stockings are usually worn by women and made of nylon (女用)長統襪 –see 見 PAIR (USAGE 用法) **2 in your stockinged feet** wearing stockings or socks, but no shoes 穿着襪子〔但未穿鞋〕

stocking cap /ˈ·· ·/ n the usual American word for a 〖美式〗= WOOLLY HAT

stock·ist /ˈstɑkɪst; ˈstɒkⅰst/ n a person or firm that keeps a particular sort of goods for sale 存有某種貨物供出售的商人[商店]: This firm is a stockist of "Woofo" dog food. 這家商號出售"沃福"牌狗糧。

stock mar·ket /ˈ·· ··/ n see 見 STOCK EXCHANGE

stock·pile /ˈstɑkpaɪl; ˈstɒkpaɪl/ v **stockpiled, stockpiling** [T] to keep a large store of food or weapons, especially because they might become difficult to get for future use 大量貯備〔食物或武器〕 –**stockpile** n

stock-still /ˌ·ˈ·◂/ adv without the slightest movement 一動不動地, 靜止地: She stood stock-still and listened. 她一動不動地站在那裡聽。

stock·tak·ing /ˈstɑkteɪkɪŋ; ˈstɒkˌteɪkɪŋ/ n [U] the making of a list of all the goods held in a business or shop 清點存貨, 盤點

stock·y /ˈstɑki; ˈstɒki/ adj **stockier, stockiest** short, strong and solid (used of people) 矮胖的; 粗壯的〔指人〕 –see picture on page 469 見 469 頁彩圖

stodg·y /ˈstɑdʒi; ˈstɒdʒi/ adj **stodgier, stodgiest 1** unpleasantly filling and heavy (used of food) 油膩的; 不易消化的〔指食物〕 **2** dull and uninteresting 乏味的, 索然無味的: a stodgy old schoolmaster 一位令人乏味的老校長

sto·ic·al /ˈstoɪkḷ; ˈstəʊɪkəl/ (also 又作 **stoic**) adj patient and uncomplaining through suffering or difficulties 堅忍的; 無怨言的 – **stoically** /-klɪ; -kli/ adv –**stoicism** /-ɪˌsⅰzəm; -ɪsⅰzəm/ n [U]: He bore all his misfortunes with stoicism. 他以堅忍的態度承受了所有的不幸。

stoke /stok; stəʊk/ v **stoked, stoking** [T] (also 又作 **stoke** sth **up**) **1** to add wood or coal to a fire so that it burns more strongly 給〔火〕添加木材或煤 **2** to make an unpleasant feeling or disagreement even stronger 使更加不悅[討厭]: Your letter of complaint will only stoke up his resentment. 你的投訴信只會使他更加憎恨。

stole¹ /stol; stəʊl/ n a long straight piece of material worn on the shoulders by women at formal social occasions 女用披肩

stole² v the past tense of STEAL ☆ STEAL

的過去式

sto·len /ˈstolən; ˈstəʊlən/ v the past participle of STEAL ☆ STEAL 的過去分詞

stol·id /ˈstɑlɪd; ˈstɒlⅰd/ adj showing no excitement when strong feelings might be expected 喜怒不形於色的, 無動於衷的 –**stolidly** adv

*****stom·ach¹** /ˈstʌmək; ˈstʌmək/ n **1** [C] the organ in the body where food is digested (DIGEST) 胃 **2** [C] the front part of your body below your chest 腹部: He sat with his hands folded across his stomach. 他雙手交疊在腹部坐在那裡。| She lay on her stomach. 她俯臥着。 **3** liking or desire for something unpleasant 〔對於令人不快之事的〕慾望, 興趣: I've got no stomach for a fight. 我沒興趣打架。

stomach² v [T] **can't stomach** to hate something or someone and feel that you cannot bear them 無法忍受: I can't stomach his jokes. 我無法忍受他的笑話。

stom·ach·ache /ˈstʌmək,ek; ˈstʌmək,eɪk/ n [C;U] continuing pain in the stomach 胃痛; 肚子痛: The pills really helped to get rid of my stomachache. 藥片確實使我的胃不再痛了。–see 見 ACHE² (USAGE 用法)

stomp /stɑmp; stɒmp/ v [I] infml to walk with heavy steps 〖非正式〗以重步走路: He stomped up the stairs in a rage. 他怒氣沖沖地重步走上樓梯。

*****stone¹** /ston; stəʊn/ n **1** [C] a small piece of rock 石頭, 石塊: He threw a stone at the dog. 他向狗扔了一塊石頭。 **2** [U] a solid mineral substance often used for building 〔常作建築用的〕石料: stone steps 石階 | walls made of stone 石頭砌成的牆 **3** [C] a single hard seed inside certain fruits 〔水果的〕核; 籽: She swallowed a cherry stone. 她吞下了櫻桃核。 **4** [C] a jewel 寶石: These stones are worth a lot of money. 這些寶石很值錢。 **5** [C] (plural is 複數為 **stone** or **stones**) a unit used in Britain for measuring weight, equal to 14 pounds or 6.35 kilograms 咕, 英石〔英國重量單位, 等於14磅或6.35公斤〕: He weighs 13 stone. 他的體重是十三英石。 **6 stone cold** extremely cold (used of things) 極冷的〔指物體〕 **7 stone deaf** completely unable to hear 完全聾的 **8 a stone's throw** a short distance 短距離: It's only a stone's throw from his house to the station. 他的住所距車站很近。

stone² v **stoned, stoning** [T] to throw stones at someone, especially as a punishment 向〔某人〕擲石頭〔尤指作為懲罰〕: The criminal was stoned to death. 那罪犯被石頭砸死了。

Stone Age /ˈ· ·/ n **the Stone Age** the earliest period of man's history, when all tools were made of stone 石器時代

stoned /stond; stəʊnd/ adj [never before a noun 不能用於名詞前] infml very drunk or under the influence of drugs 〖非正式〗醉醺醺的; 〔吸毒後〕神智恍惚的

stone·ma·son /ˈston͵mesn̩; ˈstəʊn͵meɪsən/ (also 又作 **mason**) *n* a person whose job is cutting stone into shape for building 石匠

stone·ware /ˈston͵wɛr; ˈstəʊnweəʳ/ *n* [U] pots and other containers made from a special clay that contains a hard stone 粗陶器; 石製容器

stone·work /ˈston͵wɜk; ˈstəʊnwɜːk/ *n* [U] the parts of a building made of stone 建築物的石造部分

ston·y /ˈstonɪ; ˈstəʊnɪ/ *adj* **stonier, stoniest 1** containing or covered with stones 多石的, 石質的; 鋪着石塊的: *stony ground* 碎石地 **2** showing no pity or feeling 冷酷的, 無情的: *Their pleas were heard in stony silence.* 他們的請求未得到任何反應。 **–stonily** *adv*

stood /stʊd; stʊd/ *v* the past tense and past participle of STAND ☆ STAND 的過去式和過去分詞

stool /stul; stuːl/ *n* **1** a seat without a supporting part for your back or arms 櫈子: *a piano stool* 鋼琴櫈 **2** *tech* a piece of solid waste matter passed from the body〖術語〗糞便

stoop /stup; stuːp/ *v* [I] **1** to bend your upper body forwards and down 俯身, 彎腰: *He had to stoop to get through the entrance.* 他得彎腰過那道門。 **2** to habitually stand or wait with your head and shoulders bent〔習慣性地〕彎腰曲背站立 **–stoop** *n* [sing]: *an old woman with a stoop* 駝背的老婦人

stoop to sthg *phr v* [T] to reach a low standard of behaviour by doing something immoral 降低身分做〔某事〕: *I wouldn't stoop to stealing money.* 我決不會降低自己的身分去偷錢。

stop¹ /stap; stɒp/ *v* **-pp- 1** [I;T] to no longer continue an action or activity 停止〔行動或活動〕: *Stop making such a noise!* 別再發出這種噪音了! | *Apply pressure on the wound to stop the bleeding.* 用力壓住傷口止血。 | *She stopped her piano lessons because they were too expensive.* 由於學費太貴, 她停止去上鋼琴課了。 | *Stop! What do you think you're doing?* 住手! 你以為你在幹甚麼?

2 [T] to prevent something from happening or someone from doing something 阻礙; 阻止: *I'm going, and you can't stop me.* 我要走了, 你擋不了我。 | *You must try to stop her telling such lies.* 你必須設法阻止她這樣撒謊。 | *How can I stop the dog barking all night?* 我怎樣才能使那條狗不整夜吠叫呢? | *You'd better stop Joe from telling them about it.* 你最好阻止喬把這件事告訴他們。 **3** [I;T] to end or make something end (使)結束, 終止: *The rain finally stopped.* 雨終於停

了。 | *The referee stopped the fight by sending one player off the field.* 裁判將一名隊員罰出場外, 從而停止了毆鬥。 **4** [I] to interrupt a journey or activity before continuing〔旅行或活動〕暫停, 中止: *We stopped for tea in a village café.* 我們在村莊咖啡館停下來喝茶。 | *I don't usually stop at every word I don't recognize.* 遇上不認識的詞語, 我一般不是每次都停下來的。 **5** [I;T] to no longer move or make someone or something no longer move (使)停下來, 停止: *She started to run, but then stopped.* 她開始跑步, 但又停了下來。 | *Stop the bus — I want to get off.* 把公共汽車停下來, 我要下車。 **6** [I;T] to no longer work or to turn something off 停止運轉; 關掉〔某物〕: *His watch keeps stopping.* 他的手錶老是停下來。 | *Stop the video please.* 請關掉錄影機。 **7** [T] to prevent money from being paid 停付: *The bank stopped his cheque because he had no money in his account.* 銀行停付他的支票, 因為他的賬戶裡已經沒有錢了。 **8 stop at nothing** to be ready to do anything, even something wrong or dangerous, in order to get what you want〔為了得到想要的東西〕不擇手段 **9 stop short of** to stop yourself from doing something, or before reaching a dangerous point 決定停止做〔某事〕決定 *He stopped short of actually accusing her of the theft.* 他沒有真的控告她偷竊。 | *She slammed on the brakes and stopped just short of the cliff edge.* 她猛踩煞車制, 車剛好在懸崖邊上停了下來。

stop off *phr v* [I] *infml* to interrupt a journey to make a short visit to friends or a particular place〔非正式〕作短暫停留〔以拜訪朋友或參觀某地〕: *Let's stop off for tea at Aunt Betty's.* 讓我們在貝蒂阿姨那裡停下來喝杯茶吧。 | *On our way north, we stopped off in York.* 我們往北上的途中, 在約克市稍作停留。

stop² *n* **1** an act of stopping or the state of being stopped 停止, 中止, 停留: *We went straight there without making any stops.* 我們未作任何停留, 直接抵達那裡。 | *The guide said that the next stop was the National Gallery.* 導遊說下一個參觀處是國家美術館。 | *Since the war, work on the project has come to a complete stop.* 自從戰爭爆發以來, 這項工程已完全中止了。 **2** a place on a road or railway line where buses or trains stop for passengers〔公共汽車或火車的〕車站: *a bus stop* 公共汽車站 | *The next stop is Oxford.* 下一站是牛津站。 **3** a dot used to show where a sentence ends 句號 **4 put a stop to** to prevent something undesirable from continuing 制止; 結束: *The new law has put* *a stop to all the tax evasion of the last few years.* 新法例制止了過去幾年中所發生的各種逃稅活動。**5 pull out all the stops** to do everything possible to succeed in something 竭盡全力: *He pulled out all the stops to complete the work in time.* 他為如期完成工作而竭盡全力。

stop·cock /'stɒp,kɒk; 'stɒpkɒk/ *n* a tap (TAP) which controls the flow of water or gas in a pipe 管道閥門; 旋塞

stop·gap /'stɒp,gæp; 'stɒpgæp/ *n* something that fills a need for a short time until something better can be found 臨時替代物; 臨時應急措施: *They've lent us an old bed as a stopgap until our new one is delivered.* 在我們的新牀送來之前, 他們借給我們一張舊牀臨時一用。

stop·o·ver /'stɒp,ovə; 'stɒp,əʊvə/ *n* a short stay between parts of a journey, for example a long plane journey [旅行中的]中途停留

stop·page /'stɒpɪdʒ; 'stɒpɪdʒ/ *n* **1** a blocked state which stops something from moving, for example in a pipe [諸如管道等的]阻塞, 堵塞 **2** the act of stopping work in order to show disagreement with an employer 停工 [表示與僱主有分歧]: *Stoppages in the steel industry have increased.* 鋼鐵製造業內的罷工事件有所增加。 **3 stoppages** [pl] money officially taken from your pay, usually before you get it [工資中的]扣除額: *stoppages for tax and insurance* 工資中扣除用作繳稅和支付保險費的部分

stop·per /'stɒpə; 'stɒpər/ *n* an object which fits in and closes the opening to a bottle or other container 塞子; 阻塞物

stop press /ˌ·'·◂/ *n* **the Stop Press** the latest news, added to a newspaper after the main part has been printed 報紙開印後臨時插入的最新消息

stop·watch /'stɒpwɒtʃ; 'stɒpwɒtʃ/ *n* a watch which can be stopped and started at any time, so that you can measure exactly how long something takes 秒錶, 跑錶

⋆**stor·age** /'storɪdʒ; 'stɔːrɪdʒ/ *n* [U] **1** the act of keeping something somewhere until it is needed, or a place to keep things 儲藏; 貯存地, 倉庫: *storage space* 儲存空間 | *Her furniture is in storage until she finds a new house.* 她在找到新房子以前把家具存放在倉庫裡。 **2** the process of keeping information on a computer [電腦的]信息儲存: *Storage on these discs is very simple.* 將信息儲存在這些磁盤裡是十分簡單的。

⋆⋆**store**[1] /stor; stɔːr/ *v* **stored, storing** [T] **1** to keep something somewhere for future use 貯藏, 儲存: *Washing powder is stored in the cupboard on the left.* 洗衣粉放在左邊的櫥櫃裡。 **2** to keep information on a computer or in your memory 存入 [電腦或記憶內]: *I could see her storing away the details in her mind.* 我看得出她把細節都記了起來

在心裡。

⋆**store**[2] *n* **1** a supply of something kept for use in the future 儲備; 儲藏物: *This animal makes a store of nuts for the winter.* 這種動物為冬天儲藏大量堅果。 **2** a large building in which goods are stored 倉庫, 儲藏處 **3** a large shop 大商店: *a furniture store* 家具店 | *a department store* 百貨公司 **4** the usual American word for 〔美式〕= shop 店鋪: *the local village store* 當地村裡的商店 **5 in store** about to happen 即將發生: *There's a nasty shock in store for him.* 他會遇到一件使他震驚的事。 **6 set great store by** to feel that something is very important 十分重視[某事物]: *He sets great store by his sister's ability.* 他很重視他妹妹的才能。

store·house /'stor,haus; 'stɔːrhaus/ *n* a thing or person full of interesting and useful ideas or information 知識寶庫; 知淵博的人: *The book is a wonderful storehouse of techniques for teachers.* 那本書載有大量精湛的教學技能。

store·room /'stor,rum; 'stɔːrum/ *n* a room where goods are kept till needed 貯藏室

sto·rey /'stori; 'stɔːri/ (**story** AmE 〔美式〕) *n* **1** a floor or level in a building [建築物的]層: *There are three storeys including the ground floor.* 包括底樓一共有三層。 **2 -storeyed** (**-storied** AmE 〔美式〕) having a certain number of storeys 有…層的: *a six-storeyed block of flats* 一幢六層的公寓

stork /stork; stɔːk/ *n* a large bird, with a long beak and legs, which lives close to water 鸛

⋆**storm**[1] /storm; stɔːm/ *n* **1** bad weather conditions with strong wind and often rain, lightning and thunder 暴風雨: *crops damaged by heavy storms* 被暴風雨毀壞的莊稼 | *a sandstorm* 沙暴 **2** a show of strong or angry feeling [情感的]激發, 爆發: *The General's speech was greeted with a storm of abuse.* 將軍的演講引起了一陣怒罵。 **3 storm in a teacup** *infml* a lot of trouble or worry about something unimportant 〔非正式〕小題大作, 茶杯裡掀起的大風波 **4 take by storm** (used of a performer or performance) to get the great approval of [指表演者或演出]博得[觀眾]讚賞: *Her singing took New York by storm.* 她的演唱在紐約大受歡迎。

storm[2] *v* **1** [T] to attack violently 猛烈攻擊: *Angry crowds stormed the building.* 憤怒的羣眾圍攻了那座大樓。 **2** [I] to move violently and noisily because you are angry 氣沖沖地走: *He stormed out of the room.* 他怒氣沖沖地走出房間。

storm·y /'stormɪ; 'stɔːmi/ *adj* **stormier, stormiest 1** very rainy and windy 有暴風雨的: *stormy weather* 暴風雨天氣 | *a stormy day* 暴風雨天 **2** full of strong disagreements and angry feelings 憤怒的; 激烈的: *a stormy meeting* 爭論激烈的會議 | *a stormy relationship* 惡劣的關係

sto·ry /ˈstɔːrɪ; ˈstɔːri/ n **stories 1** an account of people and events, real or imagined〔真實或虛構的〕故事; 敘述: She wrote a story **about** space exploration. 她寫了一個有關太空探險的故事。| an extraordinary life story 一個非同尋常的寫實故事 | He promised to tell the children a story. 他答應給孩子們講故事。| The story of our friendship began when we were students. 我們的友誼可從我們的學生時代開始說起。**2** an article in a newspaper or magazine, or a piece of news on the radio or television〔報刊上的〕文章;〔廣播或電視上的〕新聞報道: The main story this week is about Poland. 本週主要的新聞是有關波蘭的。**3** a false description of events 謊言, 假話: She told me some story about missing the train. 她對我撒謊說她誤了火車。| His teacher shouted at him for telling stories. 老師大聲訓斥他說謊。**4** **it's the same story/the same old story** it's the same undesirable situation which has happened again …情況也一樣: It's the same old story — the addicts need money for drugs, so they steal to get it! 又是那老一套, 吸毒者需要錢去買毒品, 所以他們就去偷! **5** **only part of the story/not the whole story** a phrase used when you think you cannot completely understand a situation, because you don't have enough information about it 只是部分情況; 不是全部情況〔用於因沒有足夠的信息而認為無法完全理解某一情況〕

stout¹ /staut; staut/ adj **1** rather fat and heavy 肥胖的: He became stout as he grew older. 他隨着年齡的增加而發胖了。–see picture on page 469 見 469 頁彩圖 **2** strong and thick 粗壯的, 結實的: a stout pair of boots 一雙結實的靴子 **3** [only before a noun 只用於名詞前] strong and determined 堅強的; 堅定的; 勇敢的: a stout supporter of the team 該隊的堅定支持者 –**stoutly** adv: He stoutly defended her against criticism. 他勇敢地為她辯護, 反駁那些批評的意見。–**stoutness** n [U]

stout² n [U] a strong dark beer (烈性)黑啤酒

stout·heart·ed /ˈstautˈhɑːtɪd; ˌstautˈhɑːtɪd◂/ adj lit brave and determined〔文〕勇敢的; 堅定的

stove /stəuv; stov/ n an apparatus used for cooking or for heating a room〔煮食或取暖用的〕爐子

stow /stəu; sto/ v [T] to put something away neatly so that it is not in the way 把..整齊地收起來, 堆裝: The ship's cargo is stowed in the hold. 船的貨物都裝好放在大艙裡。| You can stow your bags **away** under the desks. 你們可以把書包收起來放到課桌下面。

stow·a·way /ˈstəuəˌweɪ; ˈstouəˌweɪ/ n a person who hides on a ship or plane to get a free journey or to escape from somewhere〔輪船或飛機的〕偷乘者

strad·dle /ˈstrædl; ˈstrædl/ v **straddled, straddling** [T] **1** to have one leg on either side of something 跨立; 跨坐; 兩腿叉開而坐: He sat straddling the fence. 他跨坐在柵欄上。**2** to be on either side of a place 橫跨於〔某地〕的兩邊: The village straddles the canal. 那村莊橫跨運河的兩岸。

strag·gle /ˈstrægl; ˈstrægl/ v **straggled, straggling 1** to move or spread untidily or unevenly 零亂地伸展; 蔓延: A few huts straggled across the countryside. 有幾間茅舍零星地散佈於鄉間。**2** to arrive singly or in small groups separate from a main group 單獨或零散地到達; 掉隊: Runners were still straggling in hours after the winners had arrived. 在取勝者跑完數小時後, 仍然有選手陸續到達終點。–**straggler** n

strag·gly /ˈstræglɪ; ˈstrægəli/ adj **stragglier, straggliest** growing or spreading out untidily 散亂的; 蔓延的: straggly hair 蓬亂的頭髮

straight¹ /streɪt; streɪt/ adj **1** not bent or curved 直的: Draw a straight line. 劃一條直線。| a straight road 筆直的馬路 | I hate having such straight hair. 我討厭自己的頭髮長得這麼直。–see picture on page 469 見 469 頁彩圖 **2** level or upright 水平的; 直立的: Put the mirror straight. 把鏡子放正。| That fence post isn't straight. 那根籬笆樁子沒有放直。**3** with no water added (used of an alcoholic drink) 未摻水的 (指酒類飲料) **4** serious 嚴肅的; 正統的: This is his first straight play. 這是他的第一齣正統戲劇。**5** **straight answer** an honest answer 坦率的回答 **6** **straight choice** a simple choice between two things〔兩樣東西中的〕簡單選擇 **7** **straight face** a serious face 嚴肅的面容

straight² adv **1** in a straight line 筆直地: Go straight down this road and you'll see the school. 順着這條路一直向前走, 你就會看到那所學校。| It's straight in front of you. 它就在你面前。**2** directly and without delay 直接地, 不拖延地: She came in and went straight to bed. 她進來後便逕直上牀睡覺去了。

straight³ n **the straight** the straight part of a road or race track〔馬路或跑道的〕直道部分

straight·a·way /ˈstreɪtəˌweɪ; ˌstreɪtəˈweɪ/ adv at once and without delay 立即, 立刻: The doctor came straightaway. 醫生立刻來了。

straight·en /ˈstreɪtn; ˈstreɪtn/ v [I;T] to become straight or to make something straight or tidy 使〔某物〕變直; 把〔某物〕弄正: There's a series of bends, and then the road straightens. 經過一個一個的彎道後, 路變得筆直了。| He straightened his tie. 他把領帶弄正了。

  straighten out phr v **1** [I;T **straighten sthg ↔ out**] to become straight or to make something straight 使變直 **2** [T **straighten sthg ↔ out**] to remove the confusions or difficulties in a situation 解除〔困惑〕; 解決

〔困難〕: *It will take ages to straighten out his business affairs.* 要把他的公司事務理清需要很長時間。

straighten up *phr v* **1** [I] to stand upright from a position in which your body is bent 站直, 挺起身來 **2** [T **straighten** sthg ↔ **up**] to make something tidy 把〔某物〕弄整潔: *Straighten your room up and put your things away.* 整理一下你的房間, 把東西收拾好。

straight·for·ward /ˌstret'fɔrwəd; ˌstreɪt'fɔ:-wəd/ *adj* **1** simple and easy to do or understand 簡單的, 易懂的; 易做的: *She thought the exam questions were very straightforward.* 她認為考試題目十分簡單。 **2** honest and open (used of a person or their behaviour) 誠實的; 坦率的〔指人或行為〕: *He's always been very straightforward about what he wants.* 他對於自己想要的東西一向直言不諱。 –**straightforwardly** *adv*

straight·laced /ˈstret‚lest; ˈstreɪt'leɪst◂/ *adj* having severe, rather old ideas about correct morals 〔道德方面〕極拘謹的, 古板的

strain¹ /stren; streɪn/ *n* **1** [C] a breed of plant or animal 〔植物或動物的〕種類; 血統: *This strain of wheat can grow during a cold spring.* 這種小麥遇上春寒也能夠生長。 **2** [sing] a particular quality in someone's character which can be passed from parents to children 〔由父母遺傳下來的〕氣質, 性情: *There's a strain of madness in the family.* 這一家人都有瘋瘋癲癲的傾向。 **3 the strains** *lit* notes of music 〔文〕旋律: *She heard the strains of a well-known song as she approached the house.* 她走近那所房子時, 聽到了一首名曲的旋律。

strain² *v* **1** [T] to damage or weaken a part of your body by using it awkwardly or too much 損傷, 扭傷〔身體的某一部分〕: *You'll strain your eyes reading in such bad light.* 你在這麼暗的地方看書會傷害眼睛的。 | *Bob strained a muscle while gardening.* 鮑勃在花園裡幹活時拉傷了肌肉。 **2** [T] to separate a liquid from a solid by using a container with small holes in it 過濾: *He strained the vegetables.* 他把菜濾了一下。 **3** [T] to force something beyond usual or acceptable limits 使〔某事物〕超過極限: *My patience has been strained to the limit.* 我的忍耐力已到了極限。 | *Having two more children to feed strained their budget even further.* 多養兩個孩子令他們大大超出了預算。 **4** [I;T] to make a great effort to do something 使勁, 努力做〔某事〕: *She had to strain her ears to hear the announcement.* 她不得不豎起耳朵去聽那項宣佈。 | *You look as if you're straining to understand me.* 看來你好像在設法聽懂我的話。

strain³ *n* **1** [C;U] the force causing something to be tightly pulled or stretched 拉力, 張力: *The rope broke under the strain of supporting such a heavy load.* 支撐這些重物的拉力很強, 繩子拉斷了。 **2** [C] a state in which someone or something is forced to do more than is acceptable 過重的負擔: *The additional work put a great strain on him.* 額外的工作給他帶來了很大的負擔。 | *Reducing the bus service has placed a great strain on the trains.* 減少公共汽車服務給鐵路帶來了很大負擔。 **3** [U] a state of anxiety and worry 擔憂, 憂慮, 壓力 *She's under a lot of strain at the moment; her child's very ill.* 她目前十分擔憂, 她的孩子病得很厲害。 | *Strain is often caused by overwork.* 壓力常由過度工作而引起。 **4** [U] damage to a part of the body caused by using it awkwardly or too much 〔由於使用不當或使用過度而導致的身體某一部分的〕損傷, 扭傷, 拉傷: *eye strain* 眼睛受損

strained /strend; streɪnd/ *adj* **1** unfriendly and lacking in trust 緊張的; 勉強的; 不信任的: *Relations between the couple became strained.* 這對夫婦之間的關係變得緊張起來。 **2** nervous and tired 緊張的; 疲勞的: *You're looking strained — are you working too hard?* 你看上去很疲倦, 是工作太辛苦了嗎?

strain·er /ˈstrenə; ˈstreɪnəʳ/ *n* an instrument used for separating solids from liquids 濾器, 濾網: *a tea strainer* 濾茶器

strait /stret; streɪt/ *n* **1** a narrow passage of water between two areas of land 海峽: *the Straits of Dover* 多佛爾海峽 | *the Strait of Gibraltar* 直布羅陀海峽 **2 straits** an extremely difficult situation, such as illness or lack of money 困境〔如生病或缺錢〕: *When my father lost his job, we were in desperate straits.* 父親失業後, 我們陷入了極大的困境。

strait·jack·et /ˈstret‚dʒækɪt; ˈstreɪt‚dʒækɪt/ *n* a garment which holds the arms down, preventing a mad person from harming themselves or other people 〔給瘋子穿以束縛其手臂的〕約束衣

strand /strænd; strænd/ *n* **1** a single thin piece or thread 〔繩、線等的〕股; 縷: *Many strands are twisted together to form a rope.* 許多股線擰在一起成為一根繩。 **2 a** part of a story, belief or situation 〔故事、信仰或情況的〕一部分: *At the end of the book the different strands of the plot come together.* 在這本書的結尾, 故事情節的不同線索都聯到一起了。

strand·ed /ˈstrændɪd; ˈstrænd‚ɪd/ *adj* **1** left on the shore and unable to get back to the sea 擱淺的: *The boat was left stranded when the tide went out.* 潮水退去了, 小船擱淺了。 **2** in a very difficult situation, unable to get away 處於困境的, 一籌莫展的: *There I was, stranded in a foreign country with no money.* 我當時在那兒, 一文不名, 一籌莫展地流落在異邦。

★strange /strendʒ; streɪndʒ/ *adj* **1** unusual, surprising, and difficult to understand 不尋常的, 奇怪的, 奇特的; 令人費解的: *It's strange you've never met him.* 很奇怪你居然沒有遇到

過他。| *She's got a strange habit of stroking her nose when she's thinking.* 她有個怪習慣, 就是在思考時要摸鼻子。| *The doctor thought her strange behaviour was caused by stress.* 醫生認為她那奇怪的舉止是由於緊張所致。**2** unfamiliar or not known before 陌生的, 不熟悉的: *Tell the children not to talk to strange people.* 告訴孩子不要同陌生人講話。| *The city I grew up in, now seems very strange to me.* 我在這個城市長大, 現在對我來說卻似乎很陌生。**–strangely** adv: *Strangely, I've never seen that television show before.* 說也奇怪, 我竟從未看過那個電視節目。**–strangeness** *n* [U]

strang·er /'strendʒɚ; 'streɪndʒəʳ/ *n* **1** a person who is unfamiliar to you 陌生人: *A complete stranger waved to me in the street.* 一個我根本不認識的人在大街上向我招手。**2** a person in an unfamiliar place 異鄉人: *I'm a stranger in this town. Can you tell me the way to the station?* 我對這個城市很陌生。你能告訴我到車站該怎麼走嗎? **3 to be a stranger to something** to feel completely unfamiliar with a particular situation 對某種情況根本不熟悉: *Pam's no stranger to living abroad.* 帕姆對海外的生活已習以為常。

stran·gle /'stræŋgl; 'stræŋgəl/ *v* **strangled, strangling** [T] **1** to kill a person or animal by pressing on their throat 掐死, 扼死〔人或動物〕 **2** to prevent something from growing or developing 阻止〔某事物〕生長或發展, 扼殺: *The government's policies are slowly strangling the economy.* 政府的政策正在逐漸扼殺經濟的發展。**–strangulation** /ˌstræŋgjə'leʃən; ˌstræŋgjʊ'leɪʃən/ *n*: *Death was caused by strangulation.* 死因是由絞扼引致窒息。

stran·gle·hold /'stræŋgl̩hold; 'stræŋglhəʊld/ *n* a strong control or influence which prevents development 束縛, 壓制: *A few large companies have a stranglehold on the production of cars.* 幾家大公司控制了汽車的生產。

strap¹ /stræp; stræp/ *n* a strong narrow band of leather or other material, used to fasten things together or to carry something 帶子, 皮帶: *a watch strap* 手錶帶 | *The strap on my bag is broken.* 我的書包帶斷了。

strap² *v* **-pp-** [T] to fasten in place with straps 用帶子固定, 捆綁: *She strapped the bag onto her back.* 她用帶子把包捆在背上。

strap·ping /'stræpɪŋ; 'stræpɪŋ/ *adj* [only before a noun 只用於名詞前] big, strong and healthy 高大健壯的, 魁梧的: *a fine, strapping man* 英俊而魁梧的男人

stra·ta /'stretə; 'strɑːtə/ *n* plural of STRATUM ☆ STRATUM 的複數形式

strat·a·gem /'strætədʒəm; 'strætədʒəm/ *n* a clever trick or plan to deceive an enemy or get what you want 〔誘騙敵人或為了得到想要之物的〕計謀, 計策

stra·te·gic /strə'tidʒɪk; strə'tiːdʒɪk/ *adj* **1** done as part of a plan intended to help you succeed in something 戰略性的: *The union took a strategic decision to sign the agreement.* 工會作出了一項戰略性的決定, 同意簽署協議。**2** connected with defence or war 防禦的; 戰爭的: *secret purchases of strategic materials* 祕密購買戰略物資 **–strategically** /-klɪ; -kli/ *adv*

strat·e·gy /'strætədʒɪ; 'strætədʒi/ *n* **strategies 1** [U] the art of planning something skilfully, particularly a war 兵法; 戰略: *The general was a master of strategy.* 將軍精通兵法。**2** [C] a particular plan for gaining success in an activity 計策, 謀略: *marketing strategies* 推銷策略 **–strategist** *n*

strat·i·fied /'strætəˌfaɪd; 'strætɪfaɪd/ *adj* divided into separate levels 分層的: *The society will become increasingly stratified as more people lose their jobs.* 隨着更多人失業, 社會將進一步分化。| *stratified rock* 成層岩 **–stratification** /ˌstrætəfə'keʃən; ˌstrætɪfɪ'keɪʃən/ *n* [U]

strat·os·phere /'strætəˌsfɪr; 'strætəsfɪəʳ/ *n* **the stratosphere** the outer band of air which surrounds the earth, starting at about ten kilometres above the earth 平流層, 同溫層 **–compare** 比較 ATMOSPHERE

stra·tum /'stretəm; 'strɑːtəm/ *n* **strata** /-tə; -tə/ **1** a band of one of the different kinds of rock which make up the levels of the earth's surface 岩層 **2** a group of people in society similar in class or education 社會階層: *What people eat differs widely in each social stratum.* 不同階層的人的飲食有很大差別。

straw /strɔ; strɔː/ *n* **1** [U] dried yellow stems of grain plants such as wheat 稻草, 麥稈, 禾稈: *a straw hat* 草帽 **2** [C] a thin dried stem of wheat, rice, etc. 稻草稈, 麥稈 **3** [C] a thin paper or plastic tube for sucking up liquid 〔紙或塑料製的〕吸管: *She drank the juice through a straw.* 她用吸管喝果汁。

straw·ber·ry /'strɔˌbɛrɪ; 'strɔːbəri/ *n* **strawberries** a small red juicy fruit which is soft and grows on plants near the ground 草莓: *strawberries and cream* 草莓拌奶油 | *strawberry ice cream* 草莓冰淇淋 **–see picture on page 504** 見 504 頁彩圖

stray¹ /stre; streɪ/ *v* **strayed, straying** [I] **1** to wander away from the proper path or place 迷路, 走失: *Some of the sheep strayed into the neighbour's field.* 一些羊迷了路, 走到附近的田裡去了。**2** to be unable to keep to a particular subject, and to think or talk about other things instead 離題: *During the talk, his thoughts strayed.* 談話時, 他的想法偏離了主題。

stray² *n* **strays** an animal lost from its home or having no home 走失的家畜, 迷路的動物

stray³ *adj* [only before a noun 只用於名詞前] **1** wandering or lost from home 迷路的,

走失的, 流浪的: *stray cats* 流浪貓 **2** separated from things of the same kind 零落的: *He was hit by a stray bullet.* 他被流彈擊中。

streak¹ /strik; striːk/ *n* **1** a thin line or band, different from what surrounds it 〔與周圍不同的〕線條, 條紋: *Streaks of grey began to appear in her black hair.* 在她的黑髮中開始出現一縷一縷的灰白頭髮。 **2** a particular quality, often bad, which sometimes appears in someone's behaviour 〔通常為不好的〕品質, 個性特徵: *There's a streak of cruelty in his character.* 他的性格中有幾分殘酷。 **3** repeated success or failure for a period 連勝; 連敗: *I was on a winning streak, and made a lot of money.* 有一段時期我不斷贏, 賺了不少錢。

streak² *v* **1** [I+adv/prep] to move very fast 飛奔, 飛跑: *The cat streaked across the road with the dog behind it.* 那隻貓飛奔過馬路, 狗在後面緊追。 **2** [T] to cover with streaks 使佈滿條紋: *His face was streaked with dirt.* 他臉上有一條條污跡。

streak·y /ˈstrikɪ; ˈstriːki/ *adj* **streakier, streakiest** **1** marked with streaks 有條紋的: *streaky paintwork* 有條紋的漆面 **2** **streaky bacon** BACON which has lines of fat in it 五花熏豬肉

stream¹ /strim; striːm/ *n* **1** a natural flow of water smaller than a river 小河, 小溪: *a mountain stream* 山澗 **2** a continuous flow of people or vehicles 川流不息的人〔車輛〕: *A steady stream of visitors came to see him in hospital.* 人們川流不息地來醫院探望他。 | *a stream of traffic* 川流不息的車輛 **3** a large number of remarks or questions 一連串的話或問題: *Her speech was followed by a stream of questions.* 她演講完之後, 人們提了一連串的問題。 **4** a group of school pupils of the same age and ability who are taught together 因年齡相同或能力相近而編在同一班的學生: *She's in the top stream.* 她在最好的班級裏。 **5** **go with the stream** to follow what most people do or think in a particular situation 隨大流, 順應潮流 [RELATED PHRASE 相關詞組 **go against the stream**]

stream² *v* **1** [I+adv/prep] to flow fast and strongly 奔流; 湧流: *The pipe broke and water streamed onto the floor.* 管子破裂了, 水湧到了地板上。 | *Tears streamed down her cheeks.* 她淚流滿臉。 **2** [I+ adv/prep] to move quickly in a mass 湧動; 魚貫而行: *The crowd streamed out of the football stadium.* 人羣從足球場湧出來。 **3** [T] *BrE* to group people together according to age and ability 〔英式〕〔按年齡和能力〕分組: *The pupils are streamed into four ability groups.* 學生按能力的高低分成四組。 **4** [I+adv/prep] (of light) to shine brightly through something 〔光〕透過: *Vera opened the curtains and the light streamed in.* 維拉拉開窗簾, 光線透了進來。

stream·er /ˈstrimɚ; ˈstriːməʳ/ *n* a long narrow piece of coloured paper used for decorating a room when there is a party 〔宴會時屋內裝飾用的〕長條彩色紙帶

stream·line, streamlining /ˈstrimˌlaɪn; ˈstriːmlaɪn/ *v* **streamlined, streamlining** [T] **1** to make something into a long smooth shape which moves easily through water or air 使〔某物〕成流線型: *a streamlined racing car* 流線型賽車 **2** to make a business, organization, or process simpler and able to work more effectively 簡化〔企業、組織或過程〕使效率更高: *How can we streamline production?* 我們如何才能簡化生產程序以提高效率呢?

street /strit; striːt/ *n* **1** a road in a town or village with houses or other buildings on one or both sides 街, 街道: *101 Oxford Street* 牛津街101號 | *a narrow street* 狹窄的街道 **2** connected with activities that take place outside the house in a town 有關街道的: *homeless people living on the streets* 流落街頭的無家可歸的人 | *street musicians* 街頭演奏的音樂家 | *street life* 街頭生活 **3** **streets ahead** *infml* much better than something else 〔非正式〕比⋯好得多 **4** **up your street** in your area of interest or activity 在你的興趣〔活動〕範圍內: *Tell Tim about the book — it's right up his street.* 跟添説一下那本書, 那是他感興趣的東西。

■ USAGE 用法: **1** A **street** is in the middle of a town, and usually has shops and buildings. A **road** can be in the town or country, and usually leads to another town, or another part of a town. ☆ **street** 在城鎮中間, 兩邊通常有商店和建築物。**road** 可以在城裏, 也可以在鄉間, 一般通向另外一個城鎮或一個鎮的另一個地區。 **2** British speakers often say **in** a street/road ☆英國人常説 **in** a street/road: *the shops in the High Street* 大街上的商店 | *a house in Bristol Road* 在布里斯托街上的一所房子。American speakers often say **on** a street/road ☆美國人常説 **on** a street/road: *the stores on Main Street* 大街上的商店 | *a house on Boston Road* 在波士頓街上的一所房子

street·car /ˈstritˌkar; ˈstriːtkaːʳ/ *n* the usual American word for 〔美式〕 = TRAM

strength /strɛŋθ; strɛŋθ/ *n* **1** [C;U] the quality of being physically strong 力量, 力氣; 壯力; 強健: *He does weight-training to build up his strength.* 他練舉重以增強體力。 | *They pushed with all their strength, but the car didn't move.* 他們用盡力氣推車, 但車子還是動也不動。 **2** [U] the quality of being brave and determined in a difficult situation 堅強; 毅力: *With great strength of character, she continued working throughout her illness.* 她憑藉着非凡的毅力, 在生病期間

繼續工作。**3** [U] influence or power 影響; 力量: *the strength of the multinational companies* 跨國公司的強勢 **4** [C] a particular quality which makes someone or something effective or forceful 長處, 優勢: *the strengths and weaknesses of the argument* 該論點的長處與短處 | *His strength as a writer is the clarity of his style.* 作為一名作家, 他的優點是寫作風格十分明晰。**5** [U] closeness in a relationship 〔關係的〕緊密: *The strength of their marriage was badly affected by all his trips abroad.* 他一次又一次的海外旅行嚴重影響到他們緊密的婚姻關係。**6** [U] the total amount of people 人數, 人力: *Membership of the club is growing in strength.* 俱樂部成員的總數正大量增加。**7 below strength** having fewer members than are needed 人數不足, 缺員: *The police force is 400 below strength.* 警隊現時人數不足, 還缺四百人。[RELATED PHRASE 相關詞組 **at full strength**] **8 from strength to strength** with continuing success 不斷壯大: *Our new company is going from strength to strength.* 我們的新公司日益壯大。**9 in strength** in large numbers 大量: *By 10 a.m. the football supporters were arriving in strength.* 大批足球隊的擁躉在十點鐘前抵達。**10 on the strength of** persuaded or influenced by 為…說服; 受…影響: *We bought this car on the strength of his advice.* 我們聽從他的意見買下了這輛汽車。

*★**strength·en** /'strεŋθən; 'strεŋθən/ v **1** [I;T] to make or become more powerful (使)變強; 加強: *If we can find more witnesses, it'll strengthen your case.* 我們如果能找到更多目擊證人, 便會使你在此案中更加有利。| *Last year popular feeling against the war strengthened.* 去年公眾對這場戰爭的反對情緒變得愈來愈強烈。**2** [I;T] (of relations between people or groups) to make or become closer 〔人或集團的關係〕(使)更緊密: *Relations between the two countries strengthened after the treaty was signed.* 條約簽定以後, 兩國之間的關係變得更鞏固。| *The college wants to strengthen its links with industry.* 該學院希望加強與工業界的聯繫。**3** [T] to become more determined 使變得堅定: *She felt strengthened by his support.* 她感到他的支持更堅定了她的決心。**4** [T] to make something physically stronger 使〔某物〕更加牢固: *The bridge was strengthened with metal supports.* 金屬支架使大橋更加牢固。

stren·u·ous /'strεnjuəs; 'strεnjuəs/ *adj* needing great effort or activity 需要很大氣力的; 要花功夫的: *a strenuous climb* 艱苦的攀登 | *strenuous exercise* 費力的運動 | *a strenuous effort* 極大的努力 **–strenuously** *adv* **–strenuousness** *n* [U]

*★**stress**[1] /strεs; strεs/ *n* **1** [C;U] pressure caused by the difficulties of life which makes you feel worried or tense 壓力, 緊張: *He's under stress because he has too much work to do.* 由於工作實在太多, 他感到壓力很大。| *He hated the stress of living in a big city.* 他討厭生活在大城市裡所受到的壓力。| *Her headaches seem to be caused by stress.* 她的頭痛似乎是由於受到壓力引起的。**2** [C; U] force of weight caused by something heavy 壓力, 重量: *The old bridge collapsed under the stress of heavy vehicles.* 那座舊橋在重型車輛的壓力下坍塌了。**3** [C] the degree of force you put on something like a beat in music or a word or part of a word when you say it 重音, 重讀: *In "under", the main stress is on "un".* 在 "under" 一詞中, 重音在 "un" 上。**4** [U] a special importance 重要性, 重點; 強調: *The stress on discipline is noticeable in the school.* 學校明顯強調紀律。

stress[2] *v* [T] **1** to give particular importance to a matter when talking or writing about it 強調, 着重: *She stressed the need for careful spending.* 她強調必須謹慎用錢。**2** to give force to a beat in music or to a word or part of a word when you say it so that it sounds a little louder than what is around it 重讀: *The word "machine" is stressed on the second syllable.* "machine" 一詞的第二個音節要重讀。

stress·ful /'strεsfəl; 'strεsfəl/ *adj* causing a feeling of stress 有壓力的, 緊張的: *a stressful job* 壓力很大的工作

stress mark /'··/ *n* a mark to show that stress falls on a certain part of a word 重音符號

*★**stretch**[1] /strεtʃ; strεtʃ/ *v* **1** [I;T] to make or become wider or longer (使)變寬; (使)變長: *I tried stretching the shoes, but they still didn't fit.* 我試著把鞋撐大一點, 但還是不合腳。| *Be careful the jumper doesn't stretch when you wash it.* 洗毛衣的時候小心別把它拉長了。**2** [I+adv/prep] to spread out in space or time 〔空間或時間上〕延伸, 延續: *The forest stretched for miles.* 森林綿延數英里。| *The project will now have to stretch on into the new year.* 這項工程現在不得不拖延到新的一年了。| *The desert stretched away into the distance.* 沙漠向遠方伸展。**3** [I;T] to straighten your limbs or body to full length 伸展肢體: *She got out of bed and stretched.* 她起牀後伸了個懶腰。| *Stretch your arms above your head.* 把胳膊舉過頭頂。–see picture on page 992 見 992 頁彩圖 **4** [I not in progressive forms 不用於進行式] to be elastic 有彈性: *Rubber bands stretch.* 橡皮筋是有彈性的。**5** [T] to pull something tightly so that it reaches its full length or width 把〔某物〕拉緊, 拉直: *She stretched the rope between the two poles.* 她把繩子拉直, 綁在兩根柱子上。**6** [T] (of a job) to make use of all your ability and skills 〔工作〕用盡某人的技能: *She left the company because she didn't feel she was being stretched enough.* 她離開了公司, 因為她覺得自己的能力並沒有得到充分發揮。**7** [T] to push something beyond its proper or natural limits 使〔某事

物〕超出正常限度: *His awful behaviour really stretches my patience.* 他那可惡的舉止令我忍無可忍。| *The hospital was stretched to the limit with so few staff.* 在醫護人員這麼少的情況下, 這家醫院已發揮了最大作用。**8 stretch your legs** go for a short walk 散散步

  stretch out/stretch yourself out *phr v* [I; T stretch sth ↔ out] to lie with your legs and arms at full length 伸直四肢地平躺: *The cat stretched out in front of the fire.* 那隻貓在爐火前伸展四肢。| *She stretched herself out on the couch.* 她伸開四肢躺在長沙發上。

stretch² *n* **1** [C] an act of stretching your body 〔身體的〕伸展, 舒展: *I stood up and had a good stretch.* 我站起身舒服地伸了個懶腰。**2** [U] the ability to increase in length or width 彈性, 伸縮性: *For these costumes we need fabric with plenty of stretch.* 我們需要用彈性強的織物來做這些服裝。**3** [C] a level area of land or water 一片陸地; 一片水域: *a pleasant stretch of coast* 一段怡人的海岸 **4** [C] a continuous period of time 持續的一段時間: *As part of her training she spent a stretch caring for the disabled.* 作為訓練的一部分, 她有一段時間專門照顧殘疾人士。**5 at a stretch** without stopping or having a break 不停地, 連續地: *The prisoners were made to stand for hours at a stretch.* 囚犯被迫連續站立數小時。**6 by no/any stretch of the imagination** a phrase you use when you want to show that you find it impossible to believe that something is true 無論怎樣想像〔用於表示無法相信某事〕: *By no stretch of the imagination could she be called a competent driver.* 不管你怎麼想, 她都不能算是一個合格的司機。

stretch·er /ˈstretʃə; ˈstrɛtʃɚ/ *n* a long piece of thick material with poles on either side on which a sick person can be carried 〔抬病人用的〕擔架

strew /struː; struː/ *v* **strewed, strewn** /struːn; struːn/ *or* **strewed** [T] **1** to scatter irregularly 撒, 散播: *There were papers strewn all over the floor.* 地上撒滿了文件。**2** to lie scattered 散佈於: *The path was strewn with flowers.* 小徑上撒滿了花。

strick·en /ˈstrɪkən; ˈstrɪkən/ *adj* experiencing strongly the effects of trouble, illness or some other problem 受困擾的; 患病的: *stricken with polio* 患小兒麻痺症的 | *stricken by doubts* 為疑慮所困擾的 | *Supplies were rushed to the drought-stricken area.* 救濟物資被迅速運往受旱災影響的地區。

strict /strɪkt; strɪkt/ *adj* **1** severe in demanding obedience to rules of behaviour 嚴格的, 嚴厲的: *They are very strict with their children.* 他們對孩子十分嚴格。| *a strict teacher* 嚴格的老師 **2** which must be followed 必須遵從的: *He had strict instructions not to tell anyone.* 他得到嚴格指示不許告訴任何人。**3** exact 精確的: *This is a rather strict interpretation of the facts.* 這是對事實比較精

確的解釋。**–strictly** *adv* **–strictness** *n* [U]

stric·ture /ˈstrɪktʃə; ˈstrɪktʃɚ/ *n fml*〔正式〕**1** severe blame or disapproval 譴責, 指責: *The judge was severe in his strictures.* 法官的譴責很嚴厲。**2** something that limits both physically and morally 〔人身或道德上的〕限制, 約束: *Because of our religion, there are certain strictures on what we eat.* 由於宗教原因, 我們所吃的食物要受某些限制。

stride¹ /straɪd; straɪd/ *v* **strode** /strod; strəʊd/, **stridden** /ˈstrɪdn; ˈstrɪdn/, **striding** [I; + adv/prep] to walk with long steps or cross with one long step 大步行走; 大步跨過: *She strode up to the front door and knocked.* 她大步走到前門處敲門。| *He strode across the stream.* 他大步跨過小溪。–see 見 WALK¹ (USAGE 用法)

stride² *n* **1** a long step in walking 大步, 闊步 **2 make great strides** to improve or do well 突飛猛進 **3 take something in one's stride** to accept and deal with something easily 從容應付某事物: *Some people would have been shocked, but she takes it all in her stride.* 有些人可能會大吃一驚, 但她卻能從容應付。

stri·dent /ˈstraɪdnt; ˈstraɪdənt/ *adj* **1** with a hard unpleasant sound 刺耳的: *She always talks in such a strident voice.* 她說話總是這麼刺耳。**2** unpleasantly strong or loud in your opinions or demands 〔表達意見或要求時〕喧囂的: *a strident political campaign* 一場喧囂的政治運動 **–stridently** *adv*

strife /straɪf; straɪf/ *n* [U] trouble or disagreement between people 紛爭, 爭吵: *family strife* 家庭糾紛 | *The city was torn apart by political strife.* 這個城市被政治紛爭弄得四分五裂。

***strike¹** /straɪk; straɪk/ *v* **struck** /strʌk; strʌk/, **struck, striking 1** [T] to hit someone or something 打, 擊〔某人或某物〕: *He struck her several times on the face.* 他打了她的臉好幾下。**2** [I] to attack someone or something 襲擊, 進攻: *The army struck at dawn.* 軍隊在黎明時分發動了進攻。**3** [I] (of something unpleasant) to happen suddenly 〔不快的事〕突然發生: *Suddenly disaster struck.* 突然間, 災難降臨了。**4** [T] to give you a particular feeling or idea 給…留下某種感覺或印象: *How does the room strike you?* 你覺得這房間如何? | *He strikes me as being a very clever man.* 他給我留下的印象是他很聰明。**5** [T] to come into your mind 使突然想到: *Suddenly a terrible thought struck me.* 我突然產生了一個可怕的念頭。| *It struck me that I had made a terrible mistake.* 我突然意識到我犯了一個嚴重的錯誤。**6** [I] to stop working because of a disagreement, usually over pay 罷工: *The unions are threatening to strike if their pay demands are not met.* 工會威脅說, 如果他們提出的增加工資的要求得不到滿足, 就會舉行罷工。**7** [T] to discover something 發現〔某事物〕: *The*

company say that they have struck oil under the Irish sea. 公司宣稱他們已在愛爾蘭海底發現了石油。**8** [I+adv/prep] to start going in a particular direction 朝〔某個方向〕進發: *We struck east towards the hills.* 我們朝着東邊的山崗進發了。**9** [I;T] (of a clock) to make a sound to show what time it is 〔鐘〕敲響報時: *The clock struck three.* 鐘敲了三點。**10 strike a balance** to do something that is between two extremes 達到平衡: *It's hard to strike a balance between caution and boldness.* 膽大而又謹慎很難兩全。**11 strike a bargain** to come to an agreement with someone 達成協議 **12 strike a blow for something** to do something which helps towards gaining a particular thing 為…而奮鬥: *She struck a blow for women's rights.* 她為爭取女權而奮鬥。**13 strike a chord** to give you feelings of understanding or sympathy 引起共鳴; 打動… **14 strike a light, strike a match** to light a match 點火柴 **15 be struck dumb** to be so shocked that you cannot speak 吃驚得説不出話來 **16 strike fear/terror into someone's heart** to make someone feel very afraid 令某人感到恐懼 **17 strike it rich** to suddenly become very wealthy 發橫財, 暴富 **18 strike while the iron is hot** to do something while the occasion is still favourable 趁熱打鐵, 趁機行事 **19 within striking distance of** very near to a place 十分靠近

strike back *phr v* [I] to do something to attack someone who has attacked or harmed you 反擊, 反攻

strike down *phr v* **be struck down** to be harmed by something 受到〔某物〕傷害: *We were all struck down by a strange illness.* 我們都得了一種奇怪的病。

strike sbdy ↔ off *phr v* [T] to take someone's name off an official list so that they are no longer a member of a professional body 把〔某人〕從〔職業登記冊上〕除名

strike up *phr v* **1** [T **strike up** sthg] to start a friendship with someone 與〔某人〕建立〔友誼〕: *They struck up a friendship on the plane.* 他們在飛機上結識了。**2** [I;T **strike up** sthg] to start to play music 開始演奏〔音樂〕: *The band struck up a lively march.* 樂隊開始演奏一首輕快的進行曲。

***strike² n* **1** a time when people do not work because they want more pay or better conditions of work 罷工; 罷課; 罷市: *The strike lasted for two months.* 罷工持續了兩個月。**2 on strike** not working because of a strike 在罷工: *The workers have been on strike for three weeks now.* 工人已罷工三星期了。| *They're threatening to go on strike.* 他們威脅説要罷工。**3** an attack 進攻; 襲擊: *The air force have carried out dozens of air strikes against enemy targets.* 空軍對敵方目標空襲了幾十次。

strik·er /'straɪkə; 'straɪkɚ/ *n* **1** a person on strike 罷工的人; 罷課者; 罷市者 **2** a player in football who attacks 〔足球的〕前鋒, 攻擊球員

strik·ing /'straɪkɪŋ; 'straɪkɪŋ/ *adj* **1** very noticeable or unusual 引人注目的; 驚人的: *There were striking similarities between the two books.* 這兩本書之間有一些驚人的相似之處。**2** beautiful in an unusual way 極為漂亮的: *What a striking woman!* 多漂亮的女人啊! **–strikingly** *adv*

❋string¹ /strɪŋ; strɪŋ/ *n* **1** [C;U] narrow cord made of threads twisted together 繩; 〔由幾股合成的〕線: *She tied the parcel up with string.* 她用繩子把包裹捆起來。| *a ball of string* 一團繩子 | *The keys are hanging on a string.* 鑰匙掛在繩子上。**2** [C] a thin piece of wire stretched tightly across a musical instrument to produce sound 〔樂器的〕弦 **3 the strings** [+ sing/pl verb] the set of players in an ORCHESTRA who play instruments with strings 〔樂隊的〕弦樂組 **4** [C] a set of things connected together on a thread 一串: *She wore a string of pearls.* 她戴着一串珍珠〔項鏈〕。| *a string of onions* 一串洋葱 **5** [C] a set of things or events which follow each other closely 一連串, 一系列〔東西或事件〕: *We've had a string of complaints about that programme.* 我們已收到了對那個節目的一連串投訴。| *He appeared in a string of horror films.* 他在一系列恐怖片中飾演角色。**6 no strings attached** a phrase used of something which is given to you with no conditions 不附加條件: *The company paid for me to do the course with no strings attached.* 公司出錢讓我去參加學習班, 不附加任何條件。

string² *v* strung, strung

string sbdy along *phr v* *infml* [T] to falsely encourage someone's hopes 《非正式》使〔某人〕空抱希望; 哄騙: *He will never be paid the money they promised him; they're just stringing him along.* 他永遠得不到他們答應付給他的錢, 他們不過是在哄騙他罷了。

string sthg ↔ out *phr v* [I;T] to spread out in a line 使擺成一行, 使排成一條線: *He strung out 12 pairs of socks on the washing line.* 他把十二雙襪子在晾衣繩上晾成一排。| *Small shops were strung out along the motorway.* 高速公路旁排滿了小商店。

string sthg ↔ together *phr v* [T] to put things together to make one thing 拼湊: *She felt so tired that she could hardly string a sentence together.* 她感到太累了, 幾乎連一句完整的話都説不出來了。

string sthg ↔ up *phr v* [T] to hang something high 把…掛起來: *They strung up coloured lights round the room.* 他們在房間各處掛起了彩燈。

string bean /ˌ· '·/ *n* the American word for 〔美式〕= RUNNER BEAN

strin·gent /'strɪndʒənt; 'strɪndʒənt/ *adj* severe (used of rules or conditions) 嚴格的〔指規定〕; 緊迫的〔指情況〕: *stringent* *restrictions* 嚴格的限制 **–stringently** *adv –* **stringency** *n*

string·y /'strɪŋɪ; 'strɪŋi/ *adj* **stringier, stringiest** containing hard narrow pieces (used of food) 多纖維的; 多筋的〔指食物〕: *The meat was so stringy we could hardly chew it.* 這塊肉的筋太多，我們幾乎嚼不動。 **–stringiness** *n* [U]

strip¹ /strɪp; strɪp/ *v* **-pp- 1** [T] to remove parts of something or the covering on its surface 除去〔一部分〕; 剝去〔表皮〕: *Elephants stripped the leaves from the trees.* 大象從樹上摘下葉子。| *You'll have to strip the walls before painting.* 上油漆前，你必須先把牆壁表面鏟乾淨。 **2** [I;T] to undress 脫衣服: *He stripped and jumped into the water.* 他脫掉衣服跳進水裡。| *The customs officials stripped and searched him.* 海關人員把他的衣服脫掉後對他進行搜身。

strip sbdy **of** sthg *phr v* [T] to remove someone's rights or possessions 剝奪〔權利〕; 沒收〔財物〕: *The military court stripped him of his rank and house.* 軍事法庭撤銷了他的職務，沒收了他的房子。

strip off *phr v* [I;T **strip off** sthg] to take off your clothes 脫衣服

★**strip²** *n* **1** a narrow piece of paper or other material 條, 帶, 窄條狀物 **2** a narrow area 狹長的地帶: *a strip of water* 狹長的水域

strip car·toon /ˌ· ·'·/ *n* the usual British word for〔英式〕= COMIC STRIP

stripe /straɪp; straɪp/ *n* **1** a long narrow band which is different in colour from what surrounds it 紋彩; 斑紋: *She wore a sweater with red and black stripes.* 她穿了一件紅黑條紋的毛衣。 **2** a narrow band of colour on someone's uniform which shows their rank〔制服上的〕級別紋彩

strip·pa·gram /'strɪpəgræm; 'strɪpəgræm/ *n* a person who is paid to visit someone on a special occasion and undress in front of them〔被雇來的特殊場合的〕脫衣表演者

strip·per /'strɪpə; 'strɪpəʳ/ *n infml* a performer in a striptease〔非正式〕脫衣舞表演者

strip·tease /'strɪpˌtiz; 'strɪptiːz/ *n* (also 又作 **strip show** /'· ·/) [C;U] a performance in which someone takes off their clothes to music in a sexually exciting way 脫衣舞(表演)

strip·y /'straɪpɪ; 'straɪpi/ *adj* **stripier, stripiest** (also 又作 **stripey**) covered in stripes of colour 有條紋的: *a stripy pattern* 有條紋的圖案 –see picture on page 243 見243頁彩圖

strive /straɪv; straɪv/ *v* **strove** /strov; strəʊv/, **striven** /'strɪvən; 'strɪvən/, **striving** [I] *fml* to struggle hard to get or do something〔正式〕奮鬥，努力: *She strove for recognition as an artist.* 她為要被人們認可為藝術家而奮鬥。| *The company is striving to improve its public image.* 該公司正在努力改善它的公眾形象。

strode /strod; strəʊd/ *v* the past tense of STRIDE ☆ STRIDE 的過去式

stroke¹ /strok; strəʊk/ *v* **stroked, stroking** [T] to pass your hand gently and slowly over something 輕撫, 撫摸〔某物〕: *The cat likes being stroked.* 那隻貓喜歡讓人撫摸。

stroke² *n* **1** a sudden illness in part of someone's brain which can cause death or loss of movement in certain parts of their body 中風: *She had to walk with a stick after she had a stroke.* 她中風以後得靠拐杖走路。 **2** a line or mark made by a single movement of your brush or pen when painting or writing 一筆, 一劃: *With a few quick strokes, she sketched his face.* 她很快畫了幾筆，就把他的臉勾畫出來。 **3** a movement of the arms repeated when swimming or rowing〔游泳或划船時的〕一划, 划水: *He swam across the lake with strong confident strokes.* 他充滿自信地用力划水，就這樣游過了那個湖。 **4** a method of swimming 泳姿, 游法: *Breaststroke is a tiring stroke.* 蛙泳是一種令人疲累的泳式。 **5** the sound made by a clock at a given time〔鐘的〕敲擊聲, 鳴聲: *At the twelfth stroke, we all started cheering.* 鐘敲到第十二下的時候，我們大家開始歡呼起來。 **6** a soft, gentle movement of your hand across something 輕撫, 撫摸: *He gave the dog a stroke.* 他輕輕撫了那隻狗一下。 **7 a stroke of luck** an unexpected piece of good luck 意想不到的好運: *What a stroke of luck you were still there.* 你居然還在那裡，真太走運了。 **8 a stroke of genius** a very clever idea 非常聰明的主意: *It was a stroke of genius to take this route.* 走這條路實在聰明。 **9 at a stroke/in one stroke** at once and with a single firm action 一下子; 一舉: *Don't believe politicians who promise to improve things in one stroke.* 別相信那些保證一下子便能改善局面的政客。 **10 not do a stroke of work** a phrase you use to describe someone who does not do any work 甚麼事也不做〔用以描述某人不做任何事情〕: *As far as I can tell, she's never done a stroke of work in her life.* 據我所知，她一輩子甚麼事也不做。

stroll /strol; strəʊl/ *v* [I] to walk, especially slowly, for pleasure 散步, 漫步 –see 見 WALK¹ (USAGE 用法)

★**strong** /strɒŋ; strɒŋ/ *adj* **1** physically powerful and able to use great force or effort 強壯的, 健壯的: *He must be very strong to be able to carry that box.* 他能舉起那隻箱子，身體一定很強壯。| *strong arms* 粗壯的臂膀 **2** having great power or influence 強有力的, 強大的: *a strong personality* 堅強的性格 | *strong leadership* 強有力的領導 | *Before the war it was one of the world's strongest nations.* 該國在戰前是世界上最強大的國家之一。 **3** not easily broken, changed or destroyed 結實的; 堅固的; 堅定的: *strong furniture* 結實的家具 | *a strong will* 堅強的意志 | *strong beliefs* 堅定的信念 |

a strong economy 強大的經濟 | *a strong relationship* 穩固的關係 **4** having a powerful effect on the mind or senses 強烈的, 濃烈的: *a strong smell* 強烈的氣味 | *She makes a strong impression on everyone she meets.* 她給每一個認識她的人都留下了深刻的印象。 **5** great in value or degree 〔價值或程度〕高的, 大的: *I told him in the strongest possible terms that he needed to change his behaviour.* 我用最強烈的措詞告訴他, 他應該改變自己的行為方式。 | *strong suspicions* 疑心重 **6** containing a lot of the substance which gives taste or produces particular effects 〔味道〕濃烈的; 高效的: *The tea is too strong for me.* 這茶對我來說太濃了。 | *strong drugs* 強效的藥物 **7** showing a high likelihood of success 很可能成功的: *There's a strong possibility that Spain will win the match.* 西班牙很可能贏得這場比賽。 | *She's a strong candidate for the job.* 她很可能獲得這份工作。 **8** [only after a noun 只用於名詞後] having the stated number of members 人數達...的: *The organization is now 500 strong.* 該組織的成員現達五百人之多。 **9** good 擅長於...的: *One of the plan's strong points is its clarity.* 該計劃的優點之一就是清楚易懂。 | *The school's very strong on teaching reading.* 該校在教授學生閱讀方面很有名。 **10** still going strong still continuing actively, even after a long time 〔長時間後〕仍然活躍; 精力充沛: *The club's still going strong after all these years.* 這麼多年來, 該俱樂部仍然運作良好。

strong·box /ˈstrɒŋˌbɒks; ˈstrɔŋbɒks/ *n* a metal box which you can lock to keep valuable things safe in 保險箱, 保險櫃

strong·hold /ˈstrɒŋˌhəʊld; ˈstrɔŋhəʊld/ *n* **1** a strongly defended place or position 據點, 要塞: *a guerilla stronghold* 游擊隊的據點 **2** a place where a particular way of life or belief is common 〔某種生活方式或信仰的〕盛行地, 大本營: *The clubs are a stronghold of male privilege.* 這些俱樂部是保持男人特權的大本營。

strong lan·guage /ˌ· ˈ···/ *n* [U] swearing and curses 罵人的話, 激烈的語言

strong-mind·ed /ˌ· ˈ···◂/ *adj* firm and determined in your beliefs and opinions 〔信仰或觀點〕堅定的, 果斷的 **–strongmindedness** *n* [U]

strong room /ˈ· ·/ *n* a room, for example in a bank, with a special thick door and walls, where valuable objects can be kept 〔銀行等貯藏貴重物品的〕保險庫

strove /strəʊv; strəʊv/ *v* the past tense of STRIVE ☆ STRIVE 的過去式

struck /strʌk; strʌk/ *v* the past tense and past participle of STRIKE ☆ STRIKE 的過去式和過去分詞

struc·tur·al /ˈstrʌktʃərəl; ˈstrʌktʃərəl/ *adj* of or concerning structure 結構上的: *a structural fault* 結構上的缺陷 **–structurally** *adv*

struc·ture¹ /ˈstrʌktʃə; ˈstrʌktʃəʳ/ *v* **1** [U] the way in which parts are arranged or organized into a whole 結構, 構造: *the structure of the brain* 大腦的構造 | *the financial structure of the company* 公司的財務結構 | *the structure of a sentence* 句子的結構 **2** [C] something which has been built, especially a building 〔尤指〕建築物, 結構物: *The hospital is a tall, brick structure.* 這家醫院是一座高大的磚建築物。

structure² *v* **structured, structuring** [T] to arrange something carefully in an organized way 構造; 組織〔某事物〕: *You'll need to structure the argument in the report more carefully.* 你需要在報告中更仔細地把論據組織一下。

strug·gle¹ /ˈstrʌɡl; ˈstrʌɡəl/ *v* **struggled, struggling** [I] **1** to make very great efforts to do something difficult 作出努力; 奮鬥: *She struggled up the stairs with her heavy bags.* 她提着沉重的行李艱辛地走上樓梯。 | *Many young writers have to struggle* **for** *recognition.* 許多年輕作家為了獲得人們的認可而努力奮鬥。 **2** to move violently in order to get free 〔為獲自由而〕掙扎, 搏鬥: *He struggled* **against** *his attacker.* 他與襲擊他的人進行搏鬥。 | *They struggled to get out of the burning car.* 他們掙扎着要爬出那輛燒着的汽車。

  struggle on *phr v* [I] to continue to do something although it is very difficult 繼續做〔困難的事情〕: *Hungry and exhausted, the climbers struggled on.* 儘管又餓又累, 登山運動員仍然繼續向山上攀登。

struggle² *n* a great effort to do something difficult 努力; 奮鬥; 掙扎: *the nation's struggle* **for** *independence* 該國為爭取獨立而鬥爭 | *With a struggle, he controlled his temper.* 他努力控制住了自己的脾氣。 | *Three people were hurt in the struggle.* 在這場爭鬥之中有三人受傷。

strum /strʌm; strʌm/ *v* **-mm-** [I;T] to play a stringed musical instrument quickly and informally 隨意彈奏, 撥弄〔弦樂器〕: *She was strumming loudly* **on** *her guitar.* 她大聲撥弄着吉他。

strung /strʌŋ; strʌŋ/ *v* the past tense and past participle of STRING ☆ STRING 的過去式和過去分詞

strut¹ /strʌt; strʌt/ *v* **-tt-** [I] to walk proudly with your chest pushed forwards 趾高氣揚地走: *The male bird strutted in front of the female.* 雄鳥在雌鳥面前趾高氣揚地走。

strut² *n* a piece of wood or metal holding the weight of a part of a building 〔建築物中木質或金屬的〕樑, 支柱

stub¹ /stʌb; stʌb/ *n* **1** the short end of a cigarette or pencil which is left when the rest has been used 〔香煙或鉛筆的〕殘根, 殘頭; 煙蒂; 鉛筆頭 **2** the small piece of a cheque or ticket which you keep as a record after use 〔支票或票據的〕票根, 存根

stub² *v* **-bb-** [T] to hurt your toe by hitting it against something 踢傷〔腳趾〕

stub sthg ↔ **out** *phr v* [T] to stop a cigarette from burning by pressing the end against something 捻滅, 捻熄〔香煙〕

stub·ble /'stʌbl; 'stʌbəl/ *n* [U] the short stiff remains of wheat or a man's beard after it has been cut〔小麥收割後的〕殘茬; 鬍子茬, 短鬚 **–stubbly** *adv*

stub·born /'stʌbən; 'stʌbən/ *adj* **1** determined and having a strong will 倔強的; 固執的: *She's so stubborn that she'll never listen to your advice.* 她太倔強了, 絕對不會聽從你的忠告。 **2** difficult to move or remove 不易移動的; 很難除去的: *stubborn stains* 不易洗掉的污跡 **–stubbornly** *adv* **–stubbornness** *n* [U]

stub·by /'stʌbɪ; 'stʌbi/ *adj* **stubbier, stubbiest** short and thick 粗短的, 矮胖的: *his stubby fingers* 他粗短的手指

stuck¹ /stʌk; stʌk/ *adj* [never before a noun 不能用於名詞前] **1** fixed in position and impossible to move 固定不動的: *The door's stuck; we'll have to get out through the window.* 門卡住了, 我們得從窗子爬出去。| *His finger got stuck in the hole.* 他的手指卡在洞孔裡了。 **2** *infml* unable to continue doing something〔非正式〕不能繼續做的, 難住的: *We'll really be stuck if the bank won't lend us the money.* 如果銀行不肯借錢給我們, 那我們就真的進退兩難了。| *I'm stuck — can you help me solve this problem?* 我真的給難倒了, 你能幫我解決這個問題嗎? **3** unable to get away from a place 困住的: *She's stuck at home all day with the children.* 她給困在家裡整天照料孩子。

stuck² *v* the past tense and past participle of STICK ☆ STICK 的過去式和過去分詞

stuck-up /ˌ· '·◂/ *adj infml* very proud and unfriendly because you think you are very important〔非正式〕目中無人的, 傲慢的: *She's too stuck-up to speak to her old friends.* 她太傲慢了, 不屑跟老朋友說話。

stud /stʌd; stʌd/ *n* **1** a number of horses or other animals kept for breeding 種馬羣; 留種的雄畜 **2** a small piece of metal which sticks out from a surface and is used to prevent slipping or for decoration 防滑釘; 飾釘: *The ground's wet — you'll need boots with studs.* 地面潮濕, 你得穿有防滑釘的靴子。 **3** a small piece of metal or another substance worn in the ear for decoration 耳墜: *a pair of gold studs* 一對金耳墜

stud·ded /'stʌdɪd; 'stʌdɪd/ *adj* covered with studs or other small objects 覆有飾釘〔或其他小物體〕的: *a ring studded with diamonds* 一枚嵌有鑽石的戒指 | *a star-studded sky* 繁星滿佈的天空

☆ stu·dent /'stjudnt; 'stjuːdənt/ *n* **1** a person who is studying at a place of education or training 學生: *a university student* 大學生 | *students at second-*

ary school 中學生 **2** a person with an interest in a particular subject 學者, 研究者〔即對某一學科感興趣的人〕: *a student of human nature* 一位研究人性的學者

stud·ied /'stʌdɪd; 'stʌdɪd/ *adj* carefully considered or planned before being expressed 深思熟慮的; 預先計劃的: *She asked about his wife with studied informality.* 她假裝隨便問及他的太太。

☆ stu·di·o /'stjudɪ,o; 'stjuːdɪəʊ/ *n* **studios 1** a workroom for a painter or photographer〔畫家或攝影師的〕工作室 **2** a room from which broadcasts are made 播音室, 錄音室: *a television studio* 電視錄製室 **3** a place where cinema films are made 電影製片廠: *Pinewood studios* 松林電影製片廠

stu·di·ous /'stjudɪəs; 'stjuːdɪəs/ *adj* fond of reading and studying 好學的, 用功的: *a studious young man* 用功的青年人 **–studiously** *adv* **–studiousness** *n* [U]

☆ stud·y¹ /'stʌdɪ; 'stʌdi/ *n* **studies 1** [U] the act of learning about a subject 學習; 讀書: *She spent the afternoon deep in study.* 她整個下午都在埋首學習。 **2 studies** subjects studied 學科: *the Department of African Studies* 非洲研究系 **3** [C] a thorough enquiry into a particular subject including a piece of writing 研究: *She's made a study of Shakespeare's comedies.* 她對莎士比亞的喜劇作了研究。| *the latest studies on the effects of drugs* 有關藥效的最新研究 **4** [C] a room in a house used for studying or private work 書房: *She writes all her letters in the study.* 她所有的信都是在書房裡寫的。 **5** a drawing or painting of a detail done to prepare for a larger work〔繪畫的〕試畫

☆ stud·y² *v* **studied, studying 1** [I;T] to spend time learning a subject 學習, 攻讀: *She studies French.* 她學習法語。| *She's studying to be a doctor.* 她在攻讀醫科。 **2** [T] to examine carefully 仔細檢查: *Before leaving they studied the map.* 臨走前他們認真看過地圖。| *Jack studied her face closely.* 傑克仔細地看了看她的臉。

☆ stuff¹ /stʌf; stʌf/ *n* [U] *infml*〔非正式〕 **1** a substance of any sort 材料, 東西: *What's this sticky stuff on the floor?* 地上這黏乎乎的東西是甚麼? | *There are one or two interesting stories, but the rest is pretty boring stuff.* 有一兩個有趣的故事, 但其餘的都是些頗無聊的東西。 **2** a group of things 一堆物品: *I can't carry all my stuff in this bag.* 我不可能把自己全部的物品都放進這袋子裡。 **3 know your stuff** to be skilful in or know a lot about a particular subject〔某方面〕內行, 拿手: *We asked him to fix the car because we thought he really knew his stuff.* 我們請他修理汽車, 因為我們認為他在這方面十分內行。

stuff² *v* **1** [T] to fill something with a substance 填塞; 塞滿: *The bag was stuffed full of old toys.* 袋子裡塞滿了舊玩具。| *They stuff the pillows with feathers.* 他們往枕頭裡

塞羽毛。**2** [T] to push something into something else quickly and untidily 胡亂地塞入: *She stuffed the letter into her pocket.* 她把信塞進口袋裡。**3 stuff yourself** *infml* to eat a lot of food〖非正式〗使吃飽: *The children were stuffing themselves with sweets.* 孩子們在大吃糖果。**4** [T] to fill a chicken, piece of meat or vegetable with a mixture of finely cut-up food before you cook it 塞填佐料，填餡於: *In Greece, peppers are stuffed with meat and rice.* 在希臘，人們在辣椒中塞入肉和米飯作填料。**5** [T] to fill the skin of a dead animal so that it looks real 剝製〔死獸的皮〕成標本: *the stuffed head of a deer* 製成標本的鹿頭 **6 get stuffed** *BrE* a very rude phrase used when you are angry or annoyed with someone〖英式〗走開，滾開〔生氣時所用的很不禮貌的短語〕: *He wanted to borrow my car again, but I told him to get stuffed.* 他又想來借我的車，但我叫他滾開。

stuff·ing /'stʌfɪŋ; 'stʌfɪŋ/ *n* [U] **1** material used as a filling for something 填塞物: *Old clothes were used as a stuffing for the cushions.* 用舊衣服作為墊子的填塞物。**2** a mixture of food placed inside a piece of meat, chicken, or vegetable before cooking〔烹飪前塞入肉、雞、蔬菜中的〕餡，填料

stuff·y /'stʌfɪ; 'stʌfɪ/ *adj* **stuffier, stuffiest** unpleasantly hot with little fresh air 悶熱的; 空氣不新鮮的: *a stuffy room* 悶熱的房間 **2** dull and full of old ideas 乏味的; 守舊的: *a stuffy organization* 守舊的組織 | *a stuffy person* 古板的人 −**stuffily** *adv* −**stuffiness** *n* [U]

stum·ble /'stʌmbl̩; 'stʌmbəl/ *v* [I] **stumbled, stumbling 1** to put your foot down awkwardly while walking or running so you start to fall 絆跌, 絆腳: *She stumbled in the dark and hurt her knee.* 她在黑暗之中絆了一跤，膝蓋受了傷。**2** to stop or make mistakes in speaking or reading aloud 結結巴巴地講話: *She stumbled over the long word.* 她結結巴巴地讀出那個長字。−**stumble** *n*

stumble across sthg *phr v* (also 又作 **stumble on** sthg) [T] to find or discover something by chance 偶然發現〔某物〕: *Scientists have stumbled on a possible cure for the disease.* 科學家偶然發現了一種治療這疾病的方法。

stumbling block /'··· ·/ *n* something which prevents action or development 障礙物, 絆腳石: *The biggest stumbling block to an agreement is the attitude of the employers.* 達成協議的最大障礙是雇主的態度。

stump¹ /stʌmp; stʌmp/ *n* **1** the small part of something left after the rest has been cut off or broken down 殘根; 殘段: *a tree stump* 樹椿 | *the stump of a tooth* 牙的殘根 | *the stump of a pencil* 鉛筆頭 **2 stumps** the three upright pieces of wood at which the ball is thrown in the game of cricket〔板球的〕三門柱

stump² *v* **1** [I +adv/prep] to walk heavily 沉重地走, 跺着腳走: *He stumped angrily up the stairs.* 他怒氣沖沖地跺着腳走上樓梯。**2** [T] *infml* to put an unanswerable question to someone〖非正式〗使〔某人〕為難; 難倒: *He was stumped by the journalist's question.* 他被記者的提問題難倒了。

stump up sthg *phr v* to pay money unwillingly〔不情願地〕付錢: *Yet again you're asking your father to stump up the money for new clothes!* 可你又在讓父親出錢給你買新衣服了!

stump·y /'stʌmpɪ; 'stʌmpɪ/ *adj* **stumpier, stumpiest** short and thick 粗短的; 粗矮的: *stumpy little fingers* 粗短的小手指

stun /stʌn; stʌn/ *v* **-nn-** [T] **1** to make someone unconscious or confused by hitting them on the head 把〔某人〕打暈 **2** to shock or surprise someone very much 使〔某人〕震驚[吃驚]: *He seemed stunned by the news.* 他似乎對這個消息感到大為震驚。| *a stunned silence* 驚呆的沉默

stung /stʌŋ; stʌŋ/ *v* past tense and past participle of STING ☆ STING 的過去式和過去分詞

stunk /stʌŋk; stʌŋk/ *v* past tense of STINK ☆ STINK 的過去式和過去分詞

stun·ning /'stʌnɪŋ; 'stʌnɪŋ/ *adj* **1** extremely attractive or beautiful 極有魅力的; 極為美麗的: *She looks stunning in that dress.* 她穿着那件裙子豔麗無比。**2** very surprising or unexpected 令人吃驚的; 意想不到的: *a stunning result* 意想不到的結果 −**stunningly** *adv*

stunt¹ /stʌnt; stʌnt/ *v* [T] to prevent the full growth or development of something 阻礙〔某物〕的生長[發育]: *A bad diet may stunt growth in children.* 飲食不良會阻礙孩子的發育。

stunt² *n* **1** an act of dangerous physical skill 特技, 絕技: *One of his stunts in the film was to drive a car off a mountain.* 他在電影裡的其中一項特技動作是駕車衝下懸崖。**2** an action which gains public attention 引人注目的舉動, 噱頭: *Dressing in funny costumes was a publicity stunt to raise money for the children's hospital.* 穿着滑稽的服裝是為兒童醫院籌款的噱頭。

stunt man /'·· ·/ *n* a person who does dangerous acts in a film so that the actor does not have to do them; a female stuntman is called a **stuntwoman** 男特技演員〔女特技演員稱為 **stuntwoman**〕

stu·pe·fied /'stjuːpɪ̩faɪd; 'stjuːpɪ̩faɪd/ *adj* **1** very surprised 非常吃驚的: *He was stupefied to see her there.* 他看見她在那裡，感到十分吃驚。**2** unable to think or feel 失去思考能力的; 失去感覺的: *He was in a stupefied state from all the drugs.* 他吸了所有那些毒品後，陷入一種沒有感覺的狀態。−**stupefaction** /ˌstjuːpəˈfækʃən; ˌstjuːpɪ̩ˈfækʃən/ *n* [U]

stu·pen·dous /stjuːˈpendəs; stjuːˈpendəs/ *adj* extremely large or good 極大的; 極好的,

了不起的: *a stupendous mistake* 極為嚴重的錯誤 | *We had a stupendous time at the party.* 我們在晚上度過了極美好的時光。

★stu·pid /ˈstjuːpɪd; ˈstjuːpɪd/ *adj* **1** silly or foolish 笨的, 愚蠢的: *a stupid person* 愚蠢的人 | *I think you were stupid to agree with him.* 我認為你很愚蠢, 居然會同意他的話。 **2** [only before a noun 只用於名詞前] *infml* a word you use for a thing when you find it annoying or you do not like it〔非正式〕〔指事物〕無聊的, 討厭的: *This stupid drawer won't open.* 這隻討厭的抽屜打不開。 **–stupidly** *adv* **–stupidity** /stjuːˈpɪdəti; stjuːˈpɪdə-ti/ *n*

stu·por /ˈstjuːpə; ˈstjuːpər/ *n* a state in which you cannot think or use your senses properly 恍惚; 昏迷: *He lay on the bed in a drunken stupor.* 他躺在牀上, 醉得不省人事。

stur·dy /ˈstɜːdi; ˈstɜːdi/ *adj* **sturdier, sturdiest** strong and unlikely to break or be hurt 強壯的; 結實的: *a sturdy horse* 一匹壯實的馬 | *a sturdy wooden desk* 一張結實的木桌子 **–sturdily** *adv* **–sturdiness** *n* [U]

stut·ter /ˈstʌtə; ˈstʌtər/ *v* [I] to speak with difficulty because you cannot easily say the first sound of a word 口吃; 結結巴巴地說: *"I c– c– can't help it,"* she stuttered. "我忍…忍…忍不住呀。" 她結結巴巴地說。 **–stutterer** *n* **–stutter** *n*

sty /staɪ; staɪ/ *n* (also 又作 **stye**) an infected swollen place on the eyelid 瞼腺炎, 麥粒腫

★★style¹ /staɪl; staɪl/ *n* **1** [C;U] a general way of doing something which expresses the belief of the particular person or group doing it 風格, 作風: *an informal style of management* 不拘禮節的管理方式 | *African styles of leadership* 非洲式的領導風格 **2** [C;U] someone's typical way of behaving or thinking 行為方式; 思考方式: *I wouldn't tell you lies — that's not my style.* 我不會對你說謊, 那不是我做的事。 | *In characteristic style, he insisted on paying for everybody.* 他作風獨特, 堅持要為所有的人付賬。 **3** [U] high quality or grace in manner, social behaviour, or appearance 風度, 儀態: *Although she has very little money, she always dresses with great style.* 她儘管沒甚麼錢, 但穿着一向很體面。 | *His salary allows him to live in style.* 他的工資收入令他可以很體面地生活。 | *I hate this singer's music, but I admit she has style.* 我討厭這位女歌手的音樂, 但我承認她很有風采。 **4** [C] fashion in clothes 時尚; 時裝: *The latest styles look really good on young people.* 最新式的時裝穿在年輕人身上着實漂亮。 **5** [C] the way that something looks 式樣; 外表: *They sell leather jackets in different colours and styles.* 他們出售不同顏色、不同式樣的皮茄克。 | *This hotel is similar in style to the others in the chain.* 這座旅館的式樣與它的連鎖旅館很相像。 | *Your new hair style really suits you.* 你的新髮型很適合你。 | *a painting in the*

style of Picasso 一幅畢加索風格的畫 **6** [C;U] a particular choice of words or manner of expression which is typical of a writer or speaker 文體, 文風: *The letter is written in a very formal style.* 這封信是用正式文體寫成的。 | *He's an interesting writer, but I don't like his style.* 他是個很有意思的作家, 但我不喜歡他的文風。 **7 -style** in the manner of a certain person or place …式樣的; …風格的: *I liked my hamburgers cooked American-style.* 我喜歡美式漢堡包。

style² *v* **styled, styling** [T] to arrange or form something in a certain pattern or shape 設計; 使符合某種式樣: *She had her hair styled by a famous hairdresser.* 她的頭髮由一位著名的髮型師來做。

styl·ish /ˈstaɪlɪʃ; ˈstaɪlɪʃ/ *adj* fashionable and attractive 時髦的, 入時的: *He's a stylish dresser.* 他是個穿着入時的人。 **–stylishly** *adv* **–stylishness** *n* [U]

styl·ist /ˈstaɪlɪst; ˈstaɪlɪst/ *n* –see 見 HAIRDRESSER

styl·is·tic /staɪˈlɪstɪk; staɪˈlɪstɪk/ *adj fml* of or concerning style in writing or art〔正式〕文體上的; 藝術風格上的: *Can you see stylistic differences between the original painting and the copy?* 你能看出畫的原作品和複製品之間在風格上的區別嗎? **–stylistically** /-klɪ; -kli/ *adv*

styl·ize /ˈstaɪlaɪz; ˈstaɪlaɪz/ *v* **stylized, stylizing** (also 又作 **stylise** *BrE*〔英式〕) [T] *fml* to present something in a work of art in a fixed unnatural style rather than as in real life〔正式〕使〔藝術作品〕格式化

sty·lus /ˈstaɪləs; ˈstaɪləs/ *n* **styluses,** *or* **styli** /-laɪ, -laɪ/ the instrument on a RECORD PLAYER that looks like a needle and picks up the sound signals from a record〔唱機的〕唱針

suave /swɑːv; swɑːv/ *adj* having charming manners which you sometimes use insincerely to get what you want (used of men) 彬彬有禮的; 殷勤的〔指男子〕 **–suavely** *adv*

sub /sʌb; sʌb/ *n infml* **1** an abbreviation for〔縮〕= SUBSCRIPTION **2** an abbreviation for〔縮〕= SUBMARINE

sub·com·mit·tee /ˈsʌbkəˌmɪti; ˈsʌbkəˌmɪti/ *n* [C + *sing/pl verb*] a smaller group formed from a larger committee to deal with a certain matter in more detail〔委員會下的〕小組委員會

sub·con·scious¹ /ˌsʌbˈkɑnʃəs; ˌsʌbˈkɒnʃəs/ *adj* not fully known or understood by the conscious mind (used of thoughts and feelings) 下意識的, 潛意識的〔指思想或感情〕 –see 見 CONSCIOUS (USAGE 用法) **–subconsciously** *adv*

subconscious² *n* (also 又作 **unconscious**) **the subconscious** the hidden thoughts and feelings you have in your mind that you are not conscious of, but which influence your behaviour 下意識, 潛意識

sub·con·ti·nent /sʌbˈkɑntənənt; ˌsʌbˈkɒntɨ-nənt/ *n* a large mass of land made up of a number of different countries 次大陸

sub·di·vide /ˌsʌbdəˈvaɪd; ˌsʌbdɨˈvaɪd/ *v* **subdivided, subdividing** [T] to divide something into smaller parts 把〔某物〕再分，細分: *The house is being subdivided into four flats.* 這棟房子被分成四間公寓房。 –**subdivision** /-dəˈvɪʒən; -dɨˈvɪʒən/ *n* [U]

sub·due /səbˈdju; səbˈdjuː/ *v* **subdued, subduing** [T] **1** to bring something under your control, often by force 〔常用武力〕使屈服；征服: *Napoleon subdued most of Europe.* 拿破崙征服了大半個歐洲。 | *She tried to subdue her anger.* 她試圖抑制自己的憤怒。 **2** to make a colour or light less bright 使〔顏色或光線〕柔和

sub·dued /səbˈdjud; səbˈdjuːd/ *adj* **1** not as bright or loud as usual 〔光線、聲音〕柔和的，緩和的: *subdued lighting* 光線柔和的照明 | *a subdued voice* 壓低的説話聲 **2** unnaturally quiet in behaviour 沉默的；克制的: *You're very subdued — is anything the matter?* 你怎麼一聲不吭，出了甚麼事嗎?

sub·hu·man /sʌbˈhjumən; sʌbˈhjuːmən/ *adj* behaving in a completely unacceptable way 〔行為〕沒有人性的；低於人類的: *Anyone who can do such a terrible thing must be subhuman.* 做這種可怕事的人一定是沒有人性的。

★★**sub·ject¹** /ˈsʌbdʒɪkt; ˈsʌbdʒɪkt/ *n* **1** something which is being talked or written about 〔談話或寫作的〕主題，題目: *He always tries to change the subject when I mention how dirty the flat is.* 每次我提到他的公寓太髒，他就想把話題岔開。 | *The subject of her book is the steel industry.* 她這本書的主題是鋼鐵工業。 **2** a word used in grammar to describe the part of the sentence which represents the person or thing that performs the action of the verb or about which something is stated 主語，主詞: *In the sentence "Mary hit John", "Mary" is the subject of the sentence.* 在"瑪麗打了約翰"一句中，"瑪麗"是句子的主語。 **3** a branch of knowledge studied in a school, college, or university 學科，科目: *She's taking six subjects in her examinations.* 她準備參加六個學科的考試。 **4** a person who lives in a particular country and owes loyalty to the state or royal leader 國民，臣民: *British subjects* 英國國民 | *the King's subjects* 國王的臣民 | *a subject of the King* 國王的一位臣民 **5** something represented in art 〔藝術的〕題材，主題: *The subject of the painting is the Battle of Waterloo.* 這幅畫的主題是滑鐵盧戰役。

subject² *adj* **1** likely to be influenced by something 易受…影響的；可能(有)…的: *The arrangements are subject to change next year.* 這些安排明年可能會有變化。 **2** governed by or dependent on something

受〔某事物〕支配的；依靠〔某事物〕的: *These outdoor concerts are subject to the local health regulations.* 這些戶外音樂會都受當地有關健康規定的管束。

sub·ject³ /səbˈdʒɛkt; səbˈdʒekt/ *v* [T] to limit someone's freedom by bringing them under your control 使服從；支配〔某人〕 –**subjection** /-ˈdʒɛkʃən; -ˈdʒekʃən/ *n* [U]

subject sbdy to sthg *phr v* [T] to make someone experience something, usually something unpleasant 使〔某人〕遭受〔不快之事〕: *He subjected us to unpleasant walks in the cold.* 他讓我們在寒風中散步。

sub·jec·tive /səbˈdʒɛktɪv; səbˈdʒektɪv/ *adj* strongly influenced by personal feelings rather than facts 主觀的: *This is a very subjective judgment of her abilities.* 這是對她能力的一種非常主觀的判斷。 –**subjectively** *adv* –**subjectivity** /ˌsʌbdʒɛkˈtɪvəti; ˌsʌbdʒek-ˈtɪvɨti/ *n* [U]

subject to /ˈsʌbdʒɪkt tʊ; ˈsʌbdʒɪkt tʊ (*as for to*)/ *prep* depending on 取決於: *Our plans may change subject to the weather.* 我們的計劃可能會因為天氣而改變。

sub·ju·gate /ˈsʌbdʒə͵get; ˈsʌbdʒʊˌgeɪt/ *v* **subjugated, subjugating** [T] **1** to conquer and take control of a group of people 使屈服；征服: *The northern tribes were subjugated in the war.* 北方的部落在戰爭中被征服了。 **2** be subjugated made less important than something else 退居次要地位: *Her needs were always subjugated to those of her parents.* 她與父母有不同需要時，父母的需要總是先得到滿足。 –**subjugation** /ˌsʌbdʒə-ˈgeʃən; ˌsʌbdʒʊˈgeɪʃən/ *n* [U]

sub·junc·tive /səbˈdʒʌŋktɪv; səbˈdʒʌŋktɪv/ *n* a special form (MOOD) of the verb used in certain languages to express doubt, wishes, a dependent verb, etc. 假設語氣，虛擬語氣 –**subjunctive** *adj*

sub·let /sʌbˈlɛt; sʌbˈlet/ *v* **sublet, sublet, subletting** [I;T] (of a person who rents property from its owner) to rent part of a property to someone else 〔租房人〕轉租，分租: *He rents the house and sublets a room to a friend.* 他租了一所房子，然後把其中一間房間分租給一個朋友。

sub·lime /səˈblaɪm; səˈblaɪm/ *adj lit* very noble or wonderful and causing deep feelings 《文》高尚的，崇高的；令人讚嘆的；莊嚴的: *sublime music* 莊嚴的音樂 –**sublimely** *adv*

sub·ma·rine¹ /ˈsʌbməˌrin; ˈsʌbməriːn/ *n* (also 又作 **sub** *infml*《非正式》) a type of ship which can travel under water 潛水艇

submarine² *adj tech* growing or used under or in the sea 《術語》海中的，海底的: *submarine plant life* 海生植物 | *a submarine cable* 海底電纜

sub·merge /səbˈmɜrdʒ; səbˈmɜːdʒ/ *v* **submerged, submerging 1** [I;T] to go or make something go under the surface of water

(使)沒入水中, (使)潛入水中: *The submarine submerged, then rose to the surface.* 潛水艇潛入了水中, 然後又浮出水面。| *dangerous submerged rocks* 危險的暗礁 | *Submerge the photographic plates in fluid.* 把感光板浸在溶液裡。**2 submerge yourself in something** to give all your time and attention to something 用全部時間和精力做某事, 埋首於: *He completely submerged himself in local politics.* 他完全地投入到當地的政治活動中去了。

sub·mis·sion /səbˈmɪʃən; səbˈmɪʃən/ *n* **1** [U] an acceptance of someone else's power over you 屈服, 屈從: *He battered his opponent into submission.* 他打得對手屈服了。**2** [C] the sending of an official paper or plan to someone so they can decide whether to accept it or not 呈送, 提交: *All submissions must be received by October 30.* 所有的提議必須在十月三十日前提交。

sub·mis·sive /səbˈmɪsɪv; səbˈmɪsɪv/ *adj* gentle and too willing to obey orders 恭順的; 服從的 –**submissively** *adv* –**submissiveness** *n* [U]

*★**sub·mit** /səbˈmɪt; səbˈmɪt/ *v* **-tt- 1** [I;T] to accept someone else's power over you (使)屈服, (使)屈從: *He was losing the fight, but he refused to submit.* 他眼看就要被打敗了, 但他決不屈服。**2** [T] to offer an official paper or plan for consideration 提交〔文件或計劃〕: *You'll have to submit the proposal to the committee.* 你必須把這個建議提交委員會。

sub·nor·mal /ˌsʌbˈnɔrml; ˌsʌbˈnɔːməl/ *adj* having less ability of mind than is usual 〔智力〕低於正常的, 弱智的: *a school for the educationally subnormal* 弱智人士學校

sub·or·di·nate[1] /səˈbɔrdnɪt; səˈbɔːdɪnət/ *n fml* a person of a lower rank or position 〔正式〕屬下, 部下

subordinate[2] *adj* less important than something else 從屬的, 次要的: *Everything else is subordinate to the need for conserving heat.* 其他任何事情與保暖相比都是次要的。| *a subordinate clause* 從句

sub·or·din·ate[3] /səˈbɔrdə,net; səˈbɔːdɪ,neɪt/ *v* **subordinated, subordinating** *fml* to put in a position of less importance 〔正式〕使...居於次要地位: *He subordinated his ideas to the general good of the group.* 他把個人觀點置於全組的利益之下。–**subordination** /sə,bɔrdəˈneʃən; sə,bɔːdɪˈneɪʃən/ *n* [U]

sub·poe·na /səˈpinə; səˈpiːnə/ *v* **subpoenaed, subpoenaeing** *law* to give someone a written order to attend a court of law 〔律〕〔以傳票〕傳喚〔某人〕出庭 –**subpoena** *n*: *He received a subpoena last week.* 他上星期收到了一張傳票。

sub·scribe /səbˈskraɪb; səbˈskraɪb/ *v* **subscribed, subscribing 1 subscribe to** to agree with a particular belief or opinion 贊同〔信仰或觀點〕: *I've never been able to subscribe to such a peculiar theory!* 我根本不能贊同這樣一個奇怪的理論! **2** [I] to pay money in order to regularly receive a magazine or newspaper 訂閱〔雜誌或報紙〕: *I subscribe to a weekly women's magazine.* 我訂了一份婦女週刊。**3** [I] to regularly give money in support of some good cause 捐助, 定期捐款: *She subscribes to a society which helps to protect animals.* 她定期捐款給一個動物保護協會。

sub·scrib·er /səbˈskraɪbɚ; səbˈskraɪbəʳ/ *n* **1** a person who pays to regularly receive a magazine or newspaper 〔雜誌或報紙的〕訂閱者, 訂戶 **2** a person who pays for the use of a service over a period of time 用戶: *a telephone subscriber* 電話用戶 **3** someone who regularly gives money to support a good cause 捐助者, 贊助者

sub·scrip·tion /səbˈskrɪpʃən; səbˈskrɪpʃən/ *n* an amount of money given regularly by people who belong to an organization, support a good cause, or regularly receive a particular magazine or newspaper 捐款; 訂閱費; 會員費

*★**sub·se·quent** /ˈsʌbsɪ,kwɛnt; ˈsʌbsɪ,kwənt/ *adj fml* existing or coming after something else, sometimes as a result of it 〔正式〕後來的, 隨後的: *We made plans for a visit, but subsequent difficulties with the car prevented it.* 我們原計劃去參觀, 但後來由於車子出了問題而未能成行。–**subsequently** *adv*: *An investigation revealed that some letters were taking as long as three days to arrive. Subsequently, a more efficient system was introduced.* 一項調查顯示有些信件要三天才能抵達收信地。後來, 便採用了一套效率更高的郵政體制。| *She claimed to be a wealthy aristocrat, but it subsequently emerged that she was the daughter of a car salesman.* 她自稱是位富有的貴族, 但後來有人發現她是汽車推銷員的女兒。

sub·ser·vi·ent /səbˈsɝvɪənt; səbˈsɜːvɪənt/ *adj* **1** willing to do what others want (a word used to show disapproval) 屈從的, 卑屈的〔含貶義〕**2** considered as less important than another thing 次要的: *All other considerations were subservient to the need for a quick profit.* 所有其他的考慮因素比起迅速獲利的需要都來得次要。–**subserviently** *adv* –**subservience** *n* [U]

sub·side /səbˈsaɪd; səbˈsaɪd/ *v* **subsided, subsiding** [I] **1** (of a building or land) to sink gradually to a lower level 〔建築物或土地〕下沉, 下陷 **2** to become less violent or strong 平息, 減弱: *We could only go out once the storm subsided.* 我們只有等暴風雨過後才能出去。| *Pam's anger subsided when I explained the situation.* 我把情況解釋了一番後, 帕姆的怒氣便平息了。

sub·si·dence /səbˈsaɪdns; səbˈsaɪdəns/ *n* [U] the sinking of land or buildings to a lower

S

level〔土地或建築物的〕沉降，下陷

sub·sid·i·a·ry¹ /'sʌbsɪdɪ,ɛrɪ; səb'sɪdiəri/ *adj* connected with but of less importance than something else 次要的；附屬的：*The secretarial college offers a foreign language as a subsidiary subject.* 祕書學院設置了一門外語作為副科。

subsidiary² *n* **subsidiaries** a company which is part of a larger company 子公司；附屬機構：*British Tyres is a subsidiary of the British Rubber Company.* 英國輪胎公司是英國橡膠公司的子公司。

sub·si·dize /'sʌbsə,daɪz; 'sʌbs ɪ daɪz/ *v* **subsidized, subsidizing** (also 又作 **subsidise** *BrE* 〖英式〗) [T] (of governments or large organizations) to pay part of the costs of something in order to keep prices lower or help an organization〔政府或大機構〕補貼，資助：*In our school you can buy subsidized meals.* 在我們的學校，你可以買到獲補貼的伙食。| *Farmers have been heavily subsidized by the government.* 農民得到政府的大量補貼。—**subsidization** /,sʌbsədə'zeʃən; ,sʌbs ɪ daɪ'zeɪʃən/ *n* [U]

sub·si·dy /'sʌbsədɪ; 'sʌbs ɪ di/ *n* **subsidies** money paid, by a government or other organization, in order to keep prices lower or support a public service 補貼，津貼

sub·sist /səb'sɪst; səb'sɪst/ *v* [I] to stay alive on very small amounts of money or food〔靠很少的錢或食物〕生存，維持生活：*They subsisted on bread and water.* 他們靠麵包和水生存下去。—**subsistence** *n* [U]：*subsistence farming* 自給農業

sub·son·ic /sʌb'sɑnɪk; ,sʌb'sɒnɪk/ *adj* flying very fast but below the speed of sound 亞音速的：*subsonic aircraft* 亞音速飛機

★**sub·stance** /'sʌbstəns; 'sʌbstəns/ *n* **1** [C] a material or type of matter 物質：*radioactive substances* 放射性物質 | *Heroin is an illegal substance.* 海洛因是一種違禁品。**2** [U] *fml* the truth 〖正式〗事實：*There is no substance in these rumours.* 這些謠傳中沒有一句是真話。**3** the substance of the most important part of what someone says〔某人所說的〕最重要的部分；實質部分：*The substance of their theory is given in the last chapter.* 他們理論的實質性內容出現在最後一章裡。

sub·stan·dard /sʌb'stændəd; ,sʌb'stændəd/ *adj* below an acceptable standard 低於標準的：*I'm afraid this work is substandard.* 對不起，這項工作並不合格。

★**sub·stan·tial** /səb'stænʃəl; səb'stænʃəl/ *adj* **1** large in size or value 重大的；有重大價值的：*The new director made substantial changes.* 新董事作出了重大變動。| *He earns a substantial amount of money.* 他掙的錢很可觀。**2** large and strongly made 大而堅固的：*a substantial wooden desk* 又大又堅固的木桌子

sub·stan·tial·ly /səb'stænʃəlɪ; səb'stænʃəli/ *adv* **1** mainly or generally 主要地；大體上：

There are one or two differences, but the plans are substantially the same. 這些計劃有一兩處的差異，但總體上是一樣的。**2** by a large amount 大量地，可觀地：*Conditions in the prison have improved substantially.* 監獄的情況已得到很大改善。

sub·stan·ti·ate /səb'stænʃɪ,et; səb'stænʃieɪt/ *v* **substantiated, substantiating** [T] *fml* to prove the truth of something 〖正式〗證明〔某事〕有根據，證實：*Can you substantiate your claim?* 你能證明你的指控有根據嗎？—**substantiation** /səb,stænʃɪ'eʃən; səb,stænʃi'eɪʃən/ *n* [U]

sub·sti·tute¹ /'sʌbstə,tjut; 'sʌbst ɪ tjuːt/ *n* **1** a person or thing acting or used in place of another 代替者；代替物；代用品：*If you don't have butter, you could use margarine as a substitute.* 要是你沒有黃油，可以用人造黃油作為代用品。| *Our teacher was ill, so we were taught by a substitute.* 老師病了，所以由代課老師來給我們上課。**2 no substitute** a phrase used when you believe something cannot be used instead of something else in a way that is satisfactory 無法替代：*Expensive toys are no substitute for a parent's love.* 昂貴的玩具無法替代父母的愛。

substitute² *v* **substituted, substituting 1** [T] to use something or someone in place of another 以〔某物或某人〕代替〔另一物或另一人〕：*They don't like potatoes, so we substituted rice.* 他們不喜歡吃馬鈴薯，所以就用米飯來代替。**2** [I] to be used instead of something or someone else 代替；取代：*If Mary doesn't arrive I'll have to substitute for her.* 如果瑪麗不來，只好由我來替她了。—**substitution** /,sʌbstə'tjuʃən; ,sʌbst ɪ 'tjuːʃən/ *n* [C; U]

sub·ter·fuge /'sʌbtə,fjudʒ; 'sʌbtəfjuːdʒ/ *n* [C;U] a trick or dishonest way of doing something 詭計；花招

sub·ter·ra·ne·an /,sʌbtə'renɪən; ,sʌbtə'reɪniən◂/ *adj* underground 地下的：*subterranean rivers* 地下河

sub·ti·tles /'sʌb,taɪtlz; 'sʌb,taɪtlz/ *n* [pl] words printed over a film in a foreign language to translate what is being said〔外國電影的〕字幕：*a French film with English subtitles* 有英文字幕的法國電影

sub·tle /'sʌtl; 'sʌtl/ *adj* **subtler, subtlest 1** cleverly indirect in getting what you want 精明的；狡猾的：*He wasn't exactly subtle in the way he offered us a bribe.* 他向我們行賄的手段並不十分高明。| *a subtle plan* 巧妙的計劃 **2** very clever and good at noticing fine details 敏銳的，靈敏的：*a subtle mind* 敏銳的頭腦 **3** pleasant and delicate 微妙的：*a subtle taste* 難以名狀的味道 | *a subtle purple* 難以描述的紫色 **4** not easily noticed or explained 細微的；難以捉摸的：*There's been a subtle change in their relationship since she started working.* 自從她開始工作以後，他們的關係發生了細微的變化。—**subtly**

adv: *subtly different* 有細微差別的

sub·tle·ty /ˈsʌtltɪ; ˈsʌltɪ/ *n* **1** [U] the ability to notice fine details and to use them in a clever way 精明; 狡猾; 敏銳: *He argued his case with great subtlety.* 他很機敏地為他的案子辯護。**2** [sing] the quality of not being easily noticed or explained 細微之處; 微妙: *The film is remarkable for the subtlety of its images.* 這部電影在攝影方面拍得特別精細。**3** [C] an idea, thought, or detail which is not easily noticed 易被忽略的觀點[想法; 細節]: *I think the translator missed some of the subtleties of the original.* 我認為譯者漏譯了原作中的一些細節。

sub·tract /səbˈtrækt; səbˈtrækt/ *v* [T] to do a sum by taking one number or amount away from another; for example if you subtract 10 from 30 you get 20 減, 減去 – **subtraction** /-ˈtrækʃən; -ˈtrækʃən/ *n* [C;U]

sub·urb /ˈsʌbɜːb; ˈsʌbɜːb/ *n* an outer area of a town or city, where people live 市郊, 郊區, 近郊: *a suburb of London* 倫敦市郊 | *I live in the suburbs.* 我住在郊區。 – **suburban** /səˈbɜːbən; səˈbɜːbən/ *adj*: *suburban living* 住在市郊的生活

sub·ur·bi·a /səˈbɜːbɪə; səˈbɜːbiə/ *n* [U] the suburbs (a word often used to show disapproval) 都市郊區〔含貶義〕

sub·ver·sive /səbˈvɜːsɪv; səbˈvɜːsɪv/ *adj* aiming to destroy established ideas and those in power 顛覆性的; 破壞性的: *The government wants to ban this magazine because they consider it to be subversive.* 政府想要禁止這本雜誌的刊行, 因為他們認為它是顛覆性的。| *a subversive influence* 破壞性的影響 – **subversive** *n*: *The peace campaigners were regarded as subversives by the police.* 和平運動成員被警方認為是顛覆分子。 – **subversively** *adv* – **subversiveness** *n* [U]

sub·vert /səbˈvɜːt; səbˈvɜːt/ *v* [T] *fml* to try to destroy the power and influence of a government or established ideas〔正式〕顛覆〔政府〕; 破壞〔觀念〕 – **subversion** /-ˈvɜːʃən; -ˈvɜːʃən/ *n* [U]

sub·way /ˈsʌbweɪ; ˈsʌbweɪ/ *n* **1** a path under a road or railway by which it can be crossed safely 地下通道, 地道 **2** the usual American word for an underground railway〔美式〕地下鐵道, 地鐵: *It's quicker to go by subway.* 坐地鐵去會更快。

suc·ceed /səkˈsiːd; səkˈsiːd/ *v* **1** [I] to manage to do something 成功, 達成: *If you try hard, you'll succeed.* 你如果努力, 就會成功。| *Jan finally succeeded in passing her driving test.* 簡最終通過了駕駛考試。**2 succeed in doing something** to manage to do something 做成某事: *He succeeded in putting out the fire.* 他把火撲滅了。**3** [I] to be done or completed with a favourable result (順利) 完成: *If the plan succeeds, he'll be very wealthy.* 如果該計劃能夠成功, 他就會十分富有。 – compare 比較 FAIL **4** [T] to follow

after something in time 緊接着〔某事物〕: *A silence succeeded his words.* 他講話後緊接着是一片沉默。 – compare 比較 PRECEDE **5** [T] to be the next person to get a particular position or job 繼任, 繼位: *Mr White will succeed the chairman when he resigns.* 主席辭職以後, 懷特先生將繼任他的職位。

suc·cess /səkˈses; səkˈses/ *n* **1** [U] the act of getting the result you aimed for 成功, 成就: *We had no success in finding a new flat.* 我們沒有找到新的寓所。| *a low success rate* 低成功率 **2** [C] a person or thing that is very favourably accepted or reaches a high position 成功的人; 成功的事[物]: *His new play was a great success.* 他的新戲非常成功。| *I've no doubt Joyce will make a success of her new business.* 我絲毫不懷疑喬伊斯將使她的新企業獲得成功。

suc·cess·ful /səkˈsesfəl; səkˈsesfəl/ *adj* **1** having got the result you aimed for 成功的; 有成果的: *My attempt to make a cake wasn't successful.* 我的蛋糕做得不成功。| *successful peace talks* 成功的和談 **2** having reached a high position, for example in your job 達到很高地位的, 出人頭地的〔如在工作上〕: *a successful journalist* 成功的新聞工作者 **3** very favourably accepted 受歡迎的: *a very successful opera* 很受歡迎的歌劇 – opposite 反義 **unsuccessful** – **successfully** *adv*

suc·ces·sion /səkˈseʃən; səkˈseʃən/ *n* **1** [C] a number of people or things following each other closely 連續不斷的人[事物]: *A succession of visitors interrupted his work.* 來訪者接踵而來, 打斷了他的工作。**2** [U] the act of being the next person with the right to a particular position 繼承, 繼任: *If the king dies the succession passes to his son.* 如果國王去世, 繼承權則傳給他的兒子。**3 in succession** following each other 一連串地: *His words came out in quick succession.* 他連珠砲似地說話。| *We went to Oxford for the third weekend in succession.* 我們連續第三個週末去牛津了。

suc·ces·sive /səkˈsesɪv; səkˈsesɪv/ *adj* following each other 連續的: *He was late for work on three successive days.* 他連續三天上班遲到。 – **successively** *adv*

suc·ces·sor /səkˈsesə; səkˈsesər/ *n* a person who takes someone's job or position when they leave 繼承人; 繼任者: *The director's successor starts next week.* 主管的繼任者於下週開始工作。

suc·cinct /səkˈsɪŋkt; səkˈsɪŋkt/ *adj* clearly expressed in a few words 簡潔的, 簡明的 – **succinctly** *adv* – **succinctness** *n* [U]

suc·cour¹ /ˈsʌkə; ˈsʌkər/ *n* (**succor** *AmE*〔美式〕) [U] *fml & lit* help given in difficulty〔正式和文〕援助, 救濟

succour² *v* [T] *fml & lit* to give help to someone in difficulty〔正式和文〕援助, 救濟〔某人〕

suc·cu·lent /ˈsʌkjələnt; ˈsʌkjl̩ənt/ *adj* pleasantly juicy (a word used to express approval) 多汁的〔含褒義〕: *a succulent fruit* 多汁的水果 **–succulence** *n* [U]

suc·cumb /səˈkʌm; səˈkʌm/ *v* [I] *fml* 〔正式〕 **1** to stop opposing a desire or strong influence 屈服於〔慾望或影響力〕: *He eventually succumbed to our offer to buy his company.* 他最終被說服接受我們購買他公司的提議。 **2** to suffer the bad effects of an illness 患〔病〕: *She succumbed to cholera and died.* 她得了霍亂後去世了。

★★such /sʌtʃ; sʌtʃ/ *predeterminer, det, pron* **1** so great, or to so great a degree 如此的, 這樣的: *Don't be such a fool!* 別這麼傻! | *They're such nice people.* 他們是如此好人。 **2** like the one or ones mentioned 這類的, 這樣的: *We spent the money on knives, forks, plates, and other such things.* 我們花錢買了刀、叉、盤子等這一類東西。 | *He shouted "Get out!" or some such remark.* 他大叫"滾出去"或諸如此類的話。 **3** such as for example 例如: *You should take up a sport such as tennis or badminton.* 你應該參加體育運動, 如網球或羽毛球。

■ USAGE 用法: Compare 比較 **such** and **so**. **Such** often comes in the pattern **such** followed by an adjective, followed by a noun ☆ **such** 常用的句型是 **such** 後面跟形容詞和名詞: **such** *interesting people* 這麼有趣的人。 **So** comes before an adjective alone ☆ **so** 出現在單獨使用的形容詞前面: *The people are* **so** *interesting* 這些人這麼有趣, or before *much, many, few* ☆或者出現在 *much, many, few* 前面: **so** *much money* 這麼多錢 | **so** *many people* 這麼多人 | **so** *few inquiries* 這麼少的詢問

such·like /ˈsʌtʃ͵laɪk; ˈsʌtʃlaɪk/ *pron, determiner infml* things of the kind already mentioned 〔非正式〕同類的事物: *Do you enjoy plays, films, and suchlike?* 你喜歡看戲劇、電影這一類東西嗎? | *tennis, cricket, and suchlike summer sports* 網球、板球以及這一類的夏季體育運動項目

suck /sʌk; sʌk/ *v* **1** [I;T] to draw liquid into your mouth by using your lips and the muscles at the side of your mouth 嘬, 吮吸: *She was sucking milk through a straw.* 她用吸管喝牛奶。 **2** [I;T] to hold something in your mouth and move your tongue around it, for example in order to eat it 含在嘴裡吮食: *Tim's always sucking a sweet.* 蒂姆總是含着一顆糖。 | *The baby was sucking its thumb.* 嬰兒在吮拇指。 **3** [T + adv/prep] to draw something forcefully in a particular direction 用吸力吞沒〔某物〕, 把…捲入: *Powerful currents sucked the boat under water.* 激流把船捲到水底。 **4** be sucked into something to become unwillingly part of something unpleasant 捲入某事之中: *He was sucked into a life of crime.* 他被捲入犯罪生活中。

suck·er /ˈsʌkə; ˈsʌkɚ/ *n* **1** the organ on some animals or insects by which they can hold on to surfaces 〔動物或昆蟲身上的〕吸盤: *Flies have suckers on their feet.* 蒼蠅的腳上有吸盤。 **2** a small piece of rubber which sticks to a surface 橡膠吸盤: *The hook is attached to the wall by means of a sucker.* 掛鈎是用吸盤吸在牆上的。 **3** *infml* a foolish person who is easily cheated or deceived 〔非正式〕易受騙的人; 傻瓜: *You're a sucker to believe all his stories!* 你真是個傻子, 竟會相信他的一派胡言!

suck·le /ˈsʌkl; ˈsʌkəl/ *v* **suckled, suckling 1** [T] to feed a baby or young animal with milk from the breast 給〔嬰兒或小動物〕餵奶 **2** [I] (of a baby or young animal) to feed by sucking from the breast 〔嬰兒或小動物〕吮吸〔母乳〕, 吸…的奶

suc·tion /ˈsʌkʃən; ˈsʌkʃən/ *n* [U] **1** the process of removing air or liquid from a container or space so that another substance is drawn in by the resulting pressure 抽吸; 空吸〔抽掉空氣或液體使另一種物質因壓力而被吸入〕: *Dust is drawn into a vacuum cleaner by suction.* 灰塵被吸力吸入真空吸塵器。 **2** the process of making one surface stick to another by removing the air between them 相吸〔把兩個物體表面之間的空氣抽掉從而使之吸附在一起〕: *The toy sticks to tables through suction.* 玩具被吸附在桌面上。

★sud·den /ˈsʌdn; ˈsʌdn/ *adj* **1** happening or coming quickly and unexpectedly 突然的, 迅速而意外的: *a sudden illness* 突發疾病 | *a sudden increase in the price of petrol* 石油價格的突然上漲 **2** all of a sudden unexpectedly and quickly, so that you are surprised 突然, 突如其來地: *All of a sudden, the lights went out.* 燈突然熄滅了。 **–suddenly** *adv* **–suddenness** *n* [U]

suds /sʌdz; sʌdz/ *n* (also 又作 **soapsuds**) [pl] the bubbles formed by soap when mixed with water 肥皂泡沫

sue /su; sjuː/ *v* **sued, suing** [I;T] to bring a legal claim against someone because of some loss or damage you have suffered 〔因受到損失而〕起訴, 控告: *If you don't return our property, we'll sue.* 如果你不把財物還給我們, 那我們就去控告你。 | *Mr James sued him for libel.* 詹姆斯先生控告他誹謗。

suede /sweɪd; sweɪd/ *n* (also 又作 **suède**) [U] soft leather with a slightly rough surface 絨面革, 仿麂皮: *suede shoes* 絨面革皮鞋

su·et /ˈsuɪt; ˈsuːɪt/ *n* [U] hard fat from an animal, used in cooking 板油, 硬脂肪油

★★suf·fer /ˈsʌfə; ˈsʌfɚ/ *v* **1** [I] to experience pain, difficulty, or loss 遭受痛苦, 受損失: *He died quickly, he didn't suffer very much.* 他死得很快, 沒有受多少痛苦。 | *The economy is bound to suffer if in-*

flation increases. 如果通貨膨脹加劇, 經濟勢必受到打擊。| *She suffered terribly when her marriage broke up.* 她的婚姻破裂後, 她痛苦不堪。**2** [T] to experience a situation in which something painful or unpleasant happens to you 經受, 承受〔痛苦或不愉快之事〕: *If you break the law you must be prepared to suffer the consequences.* 你如果犯法, 就要準備好承擔後果。| *He suffered the humiliation of being forced to resign.* 他蒙受被迫辭職的羞辱。| *Doctors suffer a lot of stress at work.* 醫生在工作時會感受到很大的壓力。**3** [I] to become gradually worse in quality through lack of care and attention〔由於缺乏照顧和注意而〕變壞, 變糟: *He started to drink a lot and his work suffered.* 他開始酗酒, 工作也因此受到影響。

suffer from sth *phr v* [T] to experience something painful or unpleasant either habitually or over a long period of time〔經常或長期〕患有〔病痛〕; 為…所苦: *Pete's always suffered from headaches.* 皮特老是頭痛。| *The company has suffered from inefficient management.* 公司的管理效率一直很低。

suf·fer·ance /'sʌfrəns/ *n* on **sufferance** with permission, though not welcomed 勉強容許, 容忍: *He's only here on sufferance.* 他只是勉強獲准留在這裡。

suf·fer·er /'sʌfərə; 'sʌfərəʳ/ *n* a person who suffers from a particular illness 患〔某種病〕者: *headache sufferers* 頭痛病患者

suf·fer·ing /'sʌfrɪŋ; 'sʌfərɪŋ/ *n* [C;U] great pain or difficulty which someone experiences 痛苦; 困難: *There was a great deal of suffering during the war.* 戰爭期間, 人們飽受痛苦。| *She never complained about her sufferings.* 她從不抱怨自己遭受的痛苦。

suf·fice /sə'faɪs; sə'faɪs/ *v* **sufficed, sufficing** [I; not in progressive forms 不用於進行式] *fml* to be enough〔正式〕足夠: *His income suffices for her needs.* 她的收入足夠她個人的開銷。

suf·fi·cien·cy /sə'fɪʃənsi; sə'fɪʃənsi/ *n* [sing] *fml* enough of something for a particular need or purpose〔正式〕足夠, 充足

suf·fi·cient /sə'fɪʃənt; sə'fɪʃənt/ *adj* enough for a particular need or purpose; a rather formal word for **enough** 足夠的, 充足的〔**enough** 的比較正式的用詞〕: *The hospital have sufficient supplies of the drug.* 醫院有足夠的藥品供應。| *This money should be sufficient to buy new furniture.* 這些錢足夠用來買新家具了。—**sufficiently** *adv*: *He wasn't sufficiently experienced to do the job.* 他經驗還不足以勝任這份工作。

suf·fix /'sʌfɪks; 'sʌfɪks/ *n* a letter or group of letters that is put at the end of a word in order to change its meaning or use; for example if you add the suffix *-ness* to *kind* you get the word *kindness* 後綴〔如在 *kind* 的後面加上 -ness 就能構成 *kindness*〕—compare 比較 PREFIX

suf·fo·cate /'sʌfə,ket; 'sʌfəkeɪt/ *v* **suffocated, suffocating** [I;T] to die or make someone die because of lack of air (使)窒息而死 —**suffocation** /,sʌfə'keʃən; ,sʌfə'keɪʃən/ *n* [U]

suf·frage /'sʌfrɪdʒ; 'sʌfrɪdʒ/ *n* [U] the right to vote for the government of your choice 選舉權, 投票權

suf·fra·gette /,sʌfrə'dʒɛt; ,sʌfrə'dʒet/ *n* a woman in Britain in the early 20th century who was a member of a group which tried to obtain for women the right to vote〔英國二十世紀初的〕為婦女爭取選舉權的女性

*★**sug·ar¹** /'ʃugə; 'ʃʊgəʳ/ *n* [U] a sweet white or brown substance obtained from plants and used in food 糖: *I take sugar in tea, but not in coffee.* 我在茶裡放糖, 但不在咖啡裡放糖。

sugar² *v* [T] to put sugar in 加糖於: *Did you sugar my tea?* 你給我的茶加糖了嗎?

sug·ar·y /'ʃugəri; 'ʃʊgəri/ *adj* **1** containing sugar 含糖的, 甜的 **2** too nice or kind to be sincere 甜蜜的, 甜言蜜語的; 媚人的: *a poem full of sugary sentiment* 一首充滿甜情蜜意的詩

*★**sug·gest** /səg'dʒɛst; sə'dʒest/ *v* [T] **1** to give someone an idea to consider 建議, 提議: *I'd like to suggest an alternative plan.* 我想提出另外一個計劃。| *I suggest that we leave now.* 我建議我們現在就走。

> ☐ USEFUL PATTERNS 有用句型
> to suggest something; to suggest doing something; to suggest that someone (should) do something

2 to say that someone or something is good for a particular purpose because you know from your own personal experience 推薦: *Can you suggest a good hotel?* 你能推薦一家好的旅館嗎? | *She suggested Bill for the job.* 她推薦比爾來做這份工作。**3** to make a new thought or idea appear in someone's mind 使人想到: *I'm not suggesting that you are responsible for the problem.* 我並不是在説你要對這個問題負責。**4** to give signs of something 表明, 顯示, 暗示: *Her expression suggested anger.* 她臉上的表情顯示她生氣了。| *The figures suggest an improvement in health care.* 這些數字顯示醫療保健已有了改善。

sug·ges·ti·ble /səg'dʒɛstəbl; sə'dʒestl̩bəl/ *adj* easily influenced (used of people) 易受影響的〔指人〕: *She's at a very suggestible age.* 她正處於容易受影響的年齡。

*★**sug·ges·tion** /səg'dʒɛstʃən; sə'dʒestʃən/ *n* **1** [C] an idea given for consideration 建議, 提議: *The teacher made some useful suggestions to help us in the examination.* 老師提了幾項有益的建議幫助我們應付考試。| *Can I make a suggestion?* 我可以提個建議嗎? **2** [U] the act of saying what someone might

do in a particular situation 提議(的行動): *I went there on your suggestion.* 我是根據你的提議去那裡的。**3** [sing] a slight sign 細微的跡象, 蛛絲馬跡: *She speaks with a suggestion of a foreign accent.* 她說話時稍有點外國口音。| *There are suggestions that she might change her mind.* 有跡象顯示她也許會改變主意。

sug·ges·tive /səgˈdʒestɪv; səˈdʒestɪv/ *adj* **1** which makes you think of something 引起聯想的; 暗示的: *The painting is suggestive of spring.* 這幅畫使人聯想到春天。**2** showing thoughts of sex 性挑逗的, 有色情意味的: *a suggestive remark* 一句性挑逗的話 **–suggestively** *adv*

su·i·cid·al /ˌsuəˈsaɪdl; ˌsuːɪ̩ˈsaɪdl◂/ *adj* **1** wanting to kill yourself 有自殺傾向的: *He was feeling positively suicidal.* 他一心想自殺。| *It was a hospital ward for suicidal patients.* 這是治療有自殺傾向的人的病房。**2** likely to lead to death or destruction 可能會導致死亡或毀滅的: *They made a suicidal attempt to climb the mountain in a snowstorm.* 他們試圖在暴風雪中冒死登山。**–suicidally** *adv*

su·i·cide /ˈsuəˌsaɪd; ˈsuːɪ̩ˌsaɪd/ *n* **1** [C;U] the act of killing yourself 自殺: *She tried to commit suicide.* 她企圖自殺。**2** [U] a course of action someone chooses to follow which destroys their position in society 自取滅亡的行為: *It would be political suicide to hold an election now.* 現在舉行選舉無異於在政治上自取滅亡。

suit¹ /sut; suːt/ *n* **1** a set of clothes made of the same material, including a short coat with trousers or skirt 一套衣服; 套裝: *a tweed suit* 一套花呢衣服 | *a dark suit* 一套深色衣服 –see picture on page 210〔見 210 頁彩圖〕**2** a set of clothes used for a particular purpose〔用於某種目的的〕服裝: *a bathing suit* 一套泳裝 **3** one of the four kinds of cards used to play a game of cards 同花色的一組紙牌 **4** –see 見 LAWSUIT

★**suit²** *v* [T] **1** to be convenient or acceptable 方便, 適合: *It's a small house but it suits our needs.* 這是所不大的房子, 但卻適合我們的需要。| *Would it suit you if I arrived in the evening?* 如果我晚上到來對你方便嗎? **2** to match or look good on someone 同〔某人〕相配, 相稱: *That colour doesn't suit him.* 那個顏色不適合他。**3** to have the right qualities or be of the right kind for something 與…相適應, 適合: *As a couple, Steve and Mary are ideally suited.* 作為夫妻, 史蒂夫和瑪麗是天造地設的一對。**4 suit yourself** *infml* to do what you like without thinking too much about other people〔非正式〕隨自己的意願行事: *"I don't feel like going out tonight." "Suit yourself."* "今晚我不想出去。" "隨你的便好了。"

★**sui·ta·ble** /ˈsutəbl; ˈsuːtəbəl/ *adj* right or acceptable for a particular situation or pur-

pose 合適的, 適合的: *Is she suitable for the job?* 她合適做這項工作嗎? | *It's a flat suitable for a large family.* 這是套適合一個大家庭居住的公寓。–opposite 反義 **unsuitable** – **suitably** *adv*

suit·case /ˈsutˌkes; ˈsuːtkeɪs/ *n* a large flat box with handles which you use to carry clothes and possessions when travelling 手提箱, 衣箱, 皮箱

suite /swit; swiːt/ *n* **1** a set of rooms in a hotel〔旅館的〕套房 **2** a set of matching furniture for a room 一套家具: *a suite of dining-room furniture* 一套飯廳家具 **3** a piece of music with several loosely connected parts 音樂組曲

sui·tor /ˈsutə; ˈsuːtə/ *n fml* a man wishing to marry a particular woman〔正式〕求婚者

sulk /sʌlk; sʌlk/ *v* [I] to be silently bad-tempered for a time because you are angry about something 生悶氣, 慍怒: *My son sulked all afternoon because I didn't buy him that toy train.* 由於我沒有給兒子買那部玩具火車, 他整個下午都在生悶氣。**–sulk** *n*: *She's in one of her sulks again!* 她又在生氣了! **–sulky** *adj* **sulkier, sulkiest** **–sulkily** *adv*

sul·len /ˈsʌlɪn; ˈsʌlən/ *adj* **1** silently showing dislike and bad temper 悶悶不樂的, 慍怒的: *She's a rather sullen-looking woman.* 她是個樣子總有點悶悶不樂的女人。| *He looked at me with sullen resentment.* 他滿臉不高興的看着我。**2** dark and unpleasant 陰沉的: *a sullen sky* 陰沉的天空 **–sullenly** *adv* **–sullenness** *n* [U]

sul·phur /ˈsʌlfə; ˈsʌlfər/ *n* (**sulfur** *AmE*〔美式〕) [U] a yellow substance which smells unpleasant 硫, 硫磺

sul·tan /ˈsʌltn; ˈsʌltən/ *n* a ruler in some Muslim countries, especially in the past 蘇丹〔尤指昔時某些伊斯蘭教國家的統治者〕

sul·ta·na /sʌlˈtænə; sʌlˈtɑːnə/ *n* a small seedless dried GRAPE 無核小葡萄乾

sul·try /ˈsʌltrɪ; ˈsʌltri/ *adj* **sultrier, sultriest 1** hot and uncomfortable (used of weather) 悶熱的〔指天氣〕**2** showing strong sexual attraction or desire (used of a woman or her appearance) 性感的, 撩人的〔指女子或其外表〕: *a sultry smile* 撩人的一笑 **–sultriness** *n* [U]

★**sum¹** /sʌm; sʌm/ *n* **1** a simple calculation, such as adding or dividing 簡單的計算, 算術〔如加或除〕: *The children learn to do sums at school.* 孩子們在學校裡學習簡單的計算。**2** an amount of money 一筆金錢: *I've spent a large sum of money on repairing the car.* 我花了一大筆錢修理汽車。| *Huge sums of money were wasted by the previous government.* 大筆大筆的巨額資金被前任政府浪費掉了。

sum² *v*

sum up *phr v* **-mm- 1** [I;T sum sth ↔ up] to list the main points of a formal conversation or argument that has gone before 總結, 概括: *John, would you sum up, please?* 約翰, 你來總結一下好嗎?｜*Let's sum up the main arguments on each side.* 讓我們把雙方的主要論點概括一下吧。**2** [T **sum** sbdy/sthg ↔ **up**] to describe a person or thing in a few words, or to make a quick judgment of them 概要地描述; 迅速地判斷: *He summed up the situation immediately, and decided not to become involved.* 他立刻對形勢作了判斷, 決定不介入去。**3 to sum up** you can use this expression when you are going to give the main ideas from a talk, a piece of writing, or a meeting at the end of it 概括地說〔用於總結講話、文章或會議的要點〕: *...then in 1991 she opened her fiftieth shop. To sum up, she's an example of a thoroughly successful business woman.* ...然後在1991年她又開辦了第五十家商店。總括來說, 她是女實業家的傑出典範。

sum·mar·ize /ˈsʌməˌraɪz; ˈsʌməraɪz/ *v* **summarized, summarizing** (also 又作 **summarise** *BrE*〔英式〕) [T] to make a short account which includes only the main points out of something longer 總結, 概括

sum·ma·ry¹ /ˈsʌmrɪ; ˈsʌməri/ *n* **summaries 1** a short account of something giving only the main points 摘要, 總結: *Here is a summary of the article.* 這是那篇文章的摘要。**2 in summary** a phrase used to show that you are going to list the main points of the discussion or argument that has gone before 概括地說〔用於總結討論或爭論的要點〕

summary² *adj fml* done at once, without considering the matter further〔正式〕立即的; 即決的; 當場 *Any employee caught stealing faces summary dismissal.* 任何被發現偷盜的雇員都會被當場解雇。**–summarily** *adv*

★★sum·mer /ˈsʌmɚ; ˈsʌmə/ *n* (also 又作 **Summer**) [C;U] the season between spring and autumn when the sun is hot 夏天, 夏季: *It was a beautiful summer.* 那是個美麗的夏天。｜*summer clothes* 夏裝 **– summery** *adj*: *a summery dress* 夏天穿的裙子

sum·mer·house /ˈsʌmɚˌhaʊs; ˈsʌməhaʊs/ *n* a small building in a garden where you can sit in warm weather〔花園內的〕涼亭

sum·mer·time /ˈsʌmɚˌtaɪm; ˈsʌmətaɪm/ *n* [U] the period of summer 夏天, 夏季

summing-up /ˌ·· ˈ·/ *n* **summings-up** a speech giving the main points of a discussion or argument that has gone before, especially by a judge at the end of a court case〔尤指法官對案件的〕總結

★sum·mit /ˈsʌmɪt; ˈsʌmɪt/ *n* **1** the top of a mountain 山頂, 山峯: *After a 3 hour climb, we reached the summit.* 攀登了三個小時之後, 我們到達了山頂。**2** [sing] the highest level 頂點, 頂峯: *She has reached the summit of her career.* 她已到達了事業的頂峯。**3** a

meeting between heads of state 政府首腦會議, 高峯會: *The leaders of six nations are attending today's summit in Moscow.* 六個國家的領導人參加今天在莫斯科舉行的政府首腦會議。

sum·mon /ˈsʌmən; ˈsʌmən/ *v* [T] *fml* to order someone to come to a certain place〔正式〕召喚, 召見, 傳喚〔某人〕: *I was summoned to the manager's office.* 我被召進經理辦公室。

summon up sthg *phr v* [T] to find a certain quality, especially courage, inside yourself when you need it 鼓起〔勇氣〕; 振作〔精神〕: *She summoned up all her strength and kicked the door open.* 她用足了全身力氣把門踢開。

sum·mons¹ /ˈsʌmənz; ˈsʌmənz/ *n* an official order to appear somewhere, especially in a court of law〔法庭的〕傳票

summons² *v* [T] to give an official order to someone to appear in court 傳喚〔某人〕出庭

sump·tu·ous /ˈsʌmptʃʊəs; ˈsʌmptʃʊəs/ *adj* grand and expensive 豪華的, 奢侈的: *a sumptuous feast* 盛宴 **–sumptuously** *adv* **– sumptuousness** *n* [U]

★★sun¹ /sʌn; sʌn/ *n* **1 the sun** the burning star in the sky, from which the earth receives light and heat 太陽 **2** [C;U] light and heat from the sun 陽光: *Don't sit in the sun for too long.* 別在陽光下坐得太久。｜*Let's lie outside and get some sun.* 我們躺在外面曬曬太陽吧。**3** [C] a star round which other bodies turn〔有衛星的〕恆星

sun² *v* **-nn-** [T] **sun yourself** to sit or lie in the sun 曬太陽: *She was sunning herself in the garden.* 她在花園裡曬太陽。

sun·bathe /ˈsʌnˌbeð; ˈsʌnbeɪð/ *v* **sunbathed, sunbathing** [I] to sit or lie in strong sunlight in order to make your body brown 曬日光浴 **–see** 見 BATH² (USAGE 用法) **–sunbather** *n*

sun·beam /ˈsʌnˌbim; ˈsʌnbiːm/ *n* a thin line of sunlight 陽光(光束), (一道)日光

sun·burn /ˈsʌnˌbɝn; ˈsʌnbɜːn/ *n* [U] sore, red skin from spending too much time in strong sunlight〔皮膚的〕曬傷 **–sunburnt** *adj*

sun·dae /ˈsʌndɪ; ˈsʌndeɪ/ *n* a dish made from ice cream and fruit 聖代冰淇淋, 新地

Sun·day /ˈsʌndɪ; ˈsʌndi/ *n* (also 又作 **Sun.**) the day between Saturday and Monday 週日, 星期日

Sunday school /ˈ·· ·/ *n* [C;U] religious education for Christian children on a Sunday〔基督教兒童的〕主日學校

sun·dial /ˈsʌnˌdaɪəl; ˈsʌndaɪəl/ *n* an apparatus, used especially in former times, which shows the time when the sun shines according to where the shadow of a pointer falls〔舊時的〕日晷, 日規

sun·down /ˈsʌnˌdaʊn; ˈsʌndaʊn/ *n* see 見

SUNSET

sun·dry /ˈsʌndrɪ; ˈsʌndri/ *adj* [only before a noun 只用於名詞前] various 各種各樣的: *books, pens, and sundry other items* 書、筆、和各種各樣的其他物品

sun·flow·er /ˈsʌnˌflaʊə; ˈsʌnˌflaʊəʳ/ *n* a plant with a large yellow flower, and seeds which are used to make cooking oil 向日葵

sung /sʌŋ/ *v* the past participle of SING ☆ SING 的過去分詞

sun·glass·es /ˈsʌnˌglæsɪz; ˈsʌnˌglɑːsɪ̱z/ *n* [pl] glasses with dark glass in them which you wear to protect your eyes from the sun 墨鏡，太陽眼鏡

sunk /sʌŋk; sʌŋk/ *v* the past participle of SINK ☆ SINK 的過去分詞

sunk·en /ˈsʌŋkən; ˈsʌŋkən/ *adj* 1 below the surface, especially of the water 沉沒的: *a sunken ship* 一艘沉船 2 below the surrounding surface 凹陷的，下陷的: *sunken eyes* 凹陷的眼睛

sun·lamp /ˈsʌnˌlæmp; ˈsʌnˌlæmp/ *n* (also 又作 **sunray lamp** /ˈsʌnreɪ ˌlæmp; ˈsʌnreɪ ˌlæmp/) a lamp which you can use to make your skin brown 太陽燈，紫外線燈〔用以使膚色變黑〕

sun·light /ˈsʌnˌlaɪt; ˈsʌnlaɪt/ *n* [U] natural light from the sun 陽光，日光

sun·lit /ˈsʌnˌlɪt; ˈsʌnˌlɪt/ *adj* brightly lit by the sun 陽光照耀的，陽光普照的

sun·ny /ˈsʌnɪ; ˈsʌni/ *adj* **sunnier, sunniest** 1 full of bright sunlight 陽光充足的: *a sunny room* 陽光充足的房間 | *a sunny day* 陽光明媚的日子 2 cheerful 快活的: *a sunny smile* 歡樂的笑容 −**sunnily** *adv*

sun·rise /ˈsʌnˌraɪz; ˈsʌnraɪz/ *n* [C;U] the time in the morning when the sun appears 黎明；日出(時分): *We got up at sunrise.* 我們黎明時分起牀。

sun·set /ˈsʌnˌsɛt; ˈsʌnset/ *n* 1 (also 又作 **sundown**) [U] the time when the sun disappears as night begins 黃昏；日落(時分): *They stopped work at sunset.* 他們日落時收工。 2 [C] the colours that the sun leaves in the sky as it disappears in the evening 落日的餘暉；晚霞: *What a beautiful sunset.* 多麼美麗的晚霞啊。

sun·shade /ˈsʌnˌʃed; ˈsʌnʃeɪd/ *n* see 見 PARASOL

sun·shine /ˈsʌnˌʃaɪn; ˈsʌnʃaɪn/ *n* [U] light and heat from the sun 陽光: *I was sitting in the garden, enjoying the sunshine.* 我坐在花園裡享受著明媚的陽光。

sun·stroke /ˈsʌnˌstrok; ˈsʌnstrəʊk/ *n* (also 又作 **heatstroke**) [U] an illness caused by spending too much time in the hot sun 中暑: *If you don't come inside soon, you'll get sunstroke!* 如果你不快些進來，你就會中暑的!

sun·tan /ˈsʌnˌtæn; ˈsʌntæn/ *n* (also 又作 **tan**) skin which has turned brown in the hot sun 皮膚曬黑: *I'm trying to get a suntan.* 我正試圖把皮膚曬黑。−**suntanned** *adj*

su·per /ˈsupə; ˈsuːpəʳ/ *adj* 1 *infml* wonderful 〔非正式〕非常好的: *a super cook* 一位了不起的廚師 | *The party was super!* 派對棒極了! 2 very large or high quality 極大的；超級的: *Oil is carried in supertankers.* 石油是由超級油輪運送的。

su·per·an·nu·at·ed /ˌsupəˈænjuˌetɪd; ˌsuːpərˈænjueɪtɪ̱d/ *adj fml* old and not as useful as in the past 〔正式〕老的；老式的: *superannuated ideas* 陳舊的觀念

su·per·an·nu·a·tion /ˌsupəˌænjuˈeʃən; ˌsuːpərˌænjuˈeɪʃən/ *n* [U] *fml* money paid to provide an income for when you are too old to work 〔正式〕退休金，養老金

su·perb /suˈpɜb; sjuːˈpɜːb/ *adj* excellent 出色的，卓越的: *The food was superb.* 食物好極了。−**superbly** *adv*

su·per·cil·i·ous /ˌsupəˈsɪliəs; ˌsuːpəˈsɪliəs/ *adj* showing that you think other people are less important than you are (a word used to show disapproval) 自負的，高傲的〔含貶義〕 −**superciliously** *adv* −**superciliousness** *n* [U]

su·per·fi·cial /ˌsupəˈfɪʃəl; ˌsuːpəˈfɪʃəl/ *adj* 1 on or near the surface 表面的；表皮的: *Despite all the blood, they were only superficial cuts.* 儘管出了這麼多血，它們也只是割破表皮罷了。 2 showing no deep understanding or serious thought (a word used to show disapproval) 膚淺的，淺薄的〔含貶義〕: *His understanding of scientific laws is very superficial.* 他對科學定律的理解十分膚淺。 | *She's a rather superficial person.* 她是個相當淺薄的人。−**superficially** *adv* −**superficiality** /ˌsupəˌfɪʃɪˈælətɪ; ˌsuːpəˌfɪʃɪˈæl̩ti/ *n* [U]

su·per·flu·ous /suˈpɜfluəs; suːˈpɜːfluəs/ *adj* not necessary, or more than is needed 多餘的；不必要的 −**superfluously** *adv* −**superfluousness** *n* [U]

su·per·hu·man /ˌsupəˈhjumən; ˌsuːpəˈhjuːmən/ *adj* beyond usual human powers 超人的，超出常人能力的: *superhuman strength* 非凡的力量

su·per·im·pose /ˌsupərɪmˈpoz; ˌsuːpərɪmˈpəʊz/ *v* **superimposed, superimposing** [T] to put something on top of something else, but so that you can still see what is below 使重疊，使〔某物〕疊加於〔另一物〕: *They superimposed one film image on another.* 他們把一個電影圖像疊加在另一個圖像上。

su·per·in·tend /ˌsupərɪnˈtɛnd; ˌsuːpərɪnˈtend/ *v* [T] to be in charge of and direct an activity 主管，監督，指導〔活動〕

su·per·in·tend·ent /ˌsupərɪnˈtɛndənt; ˌsuːpərɪnˈtendənt/ *n* 1 a person who is in charge of a place or activity 主管人；負責人；監督人 2 a British police officer of high rank 〔英國的〕警察長，警司

su·pe·ri·or¹ /səˈpɪrɪə; suːˈpɪərɪəʳ/ *adj* 1 of higher rank, class, or quality 高級的；上等的: *He is superior to me at work.* 工作上他是我的上司。 | *This is superior wool.* 這是高級

羊毛。–opposite 反義 **inferior 2** showing that you consider yourself better than other people 有優越感的; 高傲的: *a superior smile* 傲慢的一笑 –**superiority** /sə,pɪəri'ɒrəti; su:,pɪəri'ɒrḷti/ *n* [U]

superior² *n* a person of higher rank 上級, 上司: *I'll have to ask my superiors about that.* 關於那個問題, 我得去問一下我的上級。–compare 比較 INFERIOR

su·per·la·tive¹ /sə'pɜːlətɪv; su:'pɜːlətɪv/ *n* the form of a word which expresses more of a quality than anything else 最高級(形式): *The superlative of "good" is "best".* "good" 的最高級形式是 "best"。–compare 比較 COMPARATIVE –see Study Note on page 1311 見 1311 頁學習提示

superlative² *adj fml* 【正式】**1** excellent 最出色的, 最卓越的: *This wine is of superlative quality.* 這種酒品質超羣。**2** expressing more of a quality than anything else 最高級的: *the superlative form of the adjective* 該形容詞的最高級形式

su·per·man /'supə,mæn; 'su:pəmæn/ *n* **supermen** /-mən; -mən/ a man, usually in a story, who has much greater powers of mind and body than other people 超人, 具有超常能力的人

su·per·mar·ket /'supə,markɪt; 'su:pə,mɑ:kḷt/ *n* a large shop where you collect the food and other goods you need, and pay for them all on your way out 超級市場

su·per·nat·u·ral /,supə'nætʃrəl; su:pə'nætʃərəl/ *adj* not explained by natural laws but by powers which cannot be completely understood 超自然的: *She has supernatural powers which she uses to harm her enemies.* 她擁有超自然的力量, 可以用來傷害她的敵人。–compare 比較 UNNATURAL –**supernaturally** *adv*

su·per·sede /,supə'sid; ,su:pə'si:d/ *v* **superseded, superseding** [T] to put something else in the place of something which is no longer satisfactory 代替, 取代〔某事物〕: *That computer has now been superseded by a smaller one.* 那台電腦已被一台更小型的所取代。

su·per·son·ic /,supə'sɑnɪk; ,su:pə'sɒnɪk/ *adj* faster than the speed of sound 超音速的: *a supersonic aircraft* 超音速飛機 –compare 比較 SUBSONIC

su·per·star /'supə,star; 'su:pəstɑ:r/ *n* an extremely famous performer, especially a singer or a film actor 超級巨星〔尤指歌星或電影演員〕

su·per·sti·tion /,supə'stɪʃən; ,su:pə'stɪʃən/ *n* [C;U] a belief which is not based on reason 迷信: *The 14th floor is immediately above the 12th because of superstition about the number 13.* 因為人們對於數字十三的迷信, 十四樓就在十二樓上面。–**superstitious** *adj*: *a superstitious fear of black cats* 由於迷信而對黑貓有所恐懼 –**superstitiously** *adv*

su·per·struc·ture /'supə,strʌktʃə; 'su:pə-,strʌktʃər/ *n* something built above the main part of a building or ship 上層建築; 〔船舶的〕上部結構

su·per·vise /,supə'vaɪz; 'su:pəvaɪz/ *v* **supervised, supervising** [I;T] to make sure that work or some other activity is done properly 監督; 管理: *Who is going to supervise the examination?* 誰來監考? –**supervisor** *n* –**supervisory** *adj* –**supervision** /,supə'vɪʒən; ,su:pə'vɪʒən/ *n* [U]: *The work was done under my supervision.* 這項工作是在我的監督之下完成的。

sup·per /'sʌpə; 'sʌpər/ *n* [C;U] the last meal of the day 晚飯, 晚餐 –see 見 DINNER (USAGE 用法)

sup·plant /sə'plænt; sə'plɑ:nt/ *v* [T] *fml* to take the place of another person or thing 〔正式〕代替, 取代〔人或物〕

sup·ple /'sʌpl; 'sʌpəl/ *adj* bending or moving easily 伸屈自如的; 靈活的; 柔軟的: *You need to be supple to be a good gymnast.* 你的身體必須十分靈活, 才可以成為一名出色的體操運動員。| *a supple material* 一種柔韌的材料 –**suppleness** *n* [U]

sup·ple·ment¹ /'sʌpləmənt; 'sʌplḷmənt/ *n* a thing which is added to something else 補充物: *The colour supplement is inside the main part of the newspaper.* 彩色增刊夾附在報紙中。

sup·ple·ment² /'sʌplə,mɛnt; 'sʌplḷment/ *v* [T] to add something to another thing 增補, 補充〔某物〕: *He supplements his wages by working as a gardener at weekends.* 他在週末去做園丁, 以補充工資收入。

sup·ple·men·ta·ry /,sʌplə'mɛntəri; ,sʌplḷ'mentəri◂/ *adj* additional 附加的, 補充的: *This water supply is supplementary to the main system.* 這供水系統是用來補充主要水源的。

sup·pli·er /sə'plaɪə; sə'plaɪər/ *n* a person or firm that provides something, especially goods 供應人; 供應商: *We're expecting a delivery from the suppliers.* 我們在等供應商送貨給我們。

⋆**sup·ply¹** /sə'plaɪ; sə'plaɪ/ *v* **supplied, supplying** [T] to provide something 向...提供〔某物〕: *The council supplies free books to schools.* 市政廳免費給學校提供書本。| *All employees are supplied with a uniform.* 所有的雇員都獲提供一套制服。

□ **USEFUL PATTERNS** 有用句型
to supply something to someone; to supply someone with something

⋆**supply²** *n* **supplies 1** [C] an amount of something that can be used 供應量, 供給量: *a large supply of food* 大量供給的食物 **2 in short supply** difficult to find 供應不足, 短缺: *Meat is in short supply at the moment.* 目前肉類短缺。**3 supplies** things that are necessary for daily life, especially for a fixed period of time 日常用品: *The climb will take a week, so you'll need to carry a lot of supplies with you.* 這次攀登需要一個星期, 所以你必須攜帶許多日常用品。 **4** [U] an amount of something that can be produced and provided 供應: *The stability of the economy depends on a balance of supply and demand.* 經濟的穩定取決於供求是否平衡。 **5** [C] a system of providing something 供應系統: *We've had problems with the water supply.* 我們的供水系統有問題。

supply and de·mand /·,····'·/ *n* [U] the relation between the amount of goods for sale and the amount that customers want to buy, which has a strong influence on prices in a free market system 供求關係

★**sup·port**[1] /sə'pɔːrt; sə'pɔːt/ *v* [T] **1** to help, encourage, or approve of someone's ideas or actions because you want them to succeed 支持〔某人的觀點或行動〕: *Do you support the union's demand for higher wages?* 你支持工會所提的增加工資的要求嗎? | *Which football team do you support?* 你支持哪一支足球隊? **2** to provide money or food for a person or animal to live on 供養; 飼養: *She has a large family to support.* 她要供養一個大家庭。 | *Fields like these support thousands of different insects.* 這種田地裡養着數以千計的昆蟲。 **3** to bear the weight of a person or thing 支撐, 承受〔重量〕: *Can those shelves support so many books?* 那些書架承受得了這麼多書嗎? **4** to help someone keep their balance 扶持: *Give your grandfather your arm and support him up those steps.* 你用胳膊攙住你的祖父, 扶他上台階。 **5** to help show that something is true 證明, 證實: *I've found historical evidence to support my ideas.* 我已找到歷史上的證據來證實我的觀點。

★**support**[2] *n* **1** [U] encouragement and help 支持: *Thank you for all the support you have given us.* 謝謝你給我們的支持。 **2 in support of** to show approval of a person, idea or action 支持: *We are demonstrating in support of animal rights.* 我們為了支持動物的權力而遊行。 **3** [U] money which is provided for a person to live on or to help a business 生活費; 資金: *When his parents died he was left with no means of support.* 父母去世後, 他喪失了生活來源。 | *Financial support to the airline will protect jobs for a while.* 給這家航空公司財政支援將使就業機會繼續保持一段時間。 **4** [C] something which bears the weight of something else 支撐物; 承重物: *The supports under the bridge are beginning to crack.* 橋樑的支座開始裂開了。

★**sup·port·er** /sə'pɔːrtə; sə'pɔːtəʳ/ *n* a person who gives help, encouragement, or approval to a person, group, idea, or activity 支持者, 擁護者: *Liverpool supporters danced*

in the street after the match. 比賽之後, 利物浦隊的支持者在街上起舞。 | *He's a loyal supporter of the Prime Minister and her policies.* 他是首相及其政策的忠實擁護者。

★**sup·pose**[1] /sə'pɒz; sə'pəʊz/ *v* **supposed, supposing 1** [+ (that)] to consider something to be probably true 猜想, 料想, 推測: *I suppose he's gone home.* 我料想他已回家去了。 | *Do you suppose she'll agree?* 你猜她會同意嗎? **2 I suppose** a phrase used to show **a** that you believe something although you do not want to believe it or you are still not certain〔儘管你不願相信或不能肯定, 但仍然相信某事〕認為, 相信: *I suppose you're right.* 我認為你是對的。 **b** that you will probably agree to something although you do not like the idea〔儘管不喜歡某一觀點, 但仍然很可能表示同意〕: *Well, he could come with us, I suppose.* 哦, 我想他可以和我們一起來。 **c** that you are making a guess based on the information you have〔根據已知信息進行猜測〕: *He must have lived here for about 3 years, I suppose.* 我猜他在這裡一定已經了三年左右。 **3 be supposed to: a** to be expected to do something because of duty, law or custom〔由於責任、法律或習俗而〕應該做〔某事〕: *You're supposed to wear a seat belt in the car.* 在車裡你應當繫上安全帶。 | *We're not supposed to smoke in here.* 我們不應該在這裡抽煙。 **b** *infml* to be generally considered to be〔非正式〕被普遍認為: *It is supposed to be a really good film.* 它被普遍認為是一部真正出色的影片。 **4 suppose, supposing a** you use these words when you want someone to consider a particular situation and the results that would follow from it 如果, 假如; 萬一〔用於希望某人考慮某種情形及其後果〕: *Suppose he refuses to help us. What are we going to do then?* 假如他拒絕幫助我們, 那我們怎麼辦呢? | *Supposing he refused to help us. What would we do then?* 假如他拒絕幫助我們, 那我們怎麼辦呢? **b** you can use these words when you are suggesting something 何不; 讓...〔用於表示建議〕: *"Suppose we meet at five o'clock. How would that be?" "Well, I think that's leaving it a bit late. Supposing we say half past four."* "我建議我們五點鐘見面。你看怎麼樣?" "唔, 我覺得那樣的話就有點晚了。何不四點半見面呢?"

suppose[2] *conj* (also 又作 **supposing**) if 如果, 假定: *Suppose she finds out, what would we do then?* 如果她發現了, 那我們怎麼辦呢?

sup·pos·ed·ly /sə'pɒzɪdlɪ; sə'pəʊzỉdlɪ/ *adv* according to what people believe 據認為, 據推測; 一般看來: *Supposedly, she's a rich woman.* 據推測, 她是個有錢的女人。

sup·po·si·tion /,sʌpə'zɪʃən; ,sʌpə'zɪʃən/ *n fml* [C;U] a guess, or something that is believed to be true because it is probable〔正式〕猜想, 推測: *The Minister's claims for the economy are pure supposition.* 部長那有關經

濟狀況的聲明純屬猜測。

sup·press /səˈprɛs; səˈprɛs/ *v* [T] **1** to stop something becoming known 隱瞞; 藏匿: *News of his arrest was suppressed by the police.* 有關他被捕的消息被警察隱瞞了。**2** to control your feelings so that they are not expressed 壓制, 克制: *She smiled, suppressing her anger.* 她強壓怒火, 笑了一笑。**3** to put an end to an activity, often by force 鎮壓: *Armed opposition to the government was quickly suppressed.* 反對政府的武裝叛亂很快被鎮壓下去了。**–suppression** /-ˈprɛʃən; -ˈprɛʃən/ *n* [U]

su·prem·a·cy /səˈprɛməsɪ; səˈprɛməsi/ *n* [U] power which is greater than any other 最高權力 [權威]: *The country's supremacy at sea was unchallenged for fifty years.* 國家的海上霸權五十年來未受到挑戰。

su·preme /səˈprim; suˈpriːm/ *adj* **1** highest in position and usually the most powerful 最高的; 最有權力的; 至高無上的: *A final decision on the case will be made by the Supreme Court.* 本案將由最高法院作出最終決定。**2** greatest or highest in degree 程度最高的, 極度的: *This matter is of supreme importance.* 這件事最為重要。**–supremely** *adv*

sur·charge /ˈsɜːtʃɑrdʒ; ˈsɜːtʃɑːdʒ/ *n* an amount that you must pay in addition to the usual amount 附加費, 額外費用: *The surcharge on airline tickets is to cover increased oil prices.* 飛機票的附加費是用來支付上漲的油價的。

⋆⋆sure /ʃʊr; ʃʊə/ *adj* **1** [never before a noun 不能用於名詞前] certain about something 有把握的, 確信的: *I think so, but I'm not absolutely sure.* 我想是這樣的, 但我沒有絕對的把握。 | *Are you quite sure that this is the right bus?* 你肯定就是這部公共汽車嗎? | *I'm not sure whether he's telling the truth.* 我不肯定他是否在說謊話。 | *I'm not quite sure about that.* 那件事我還不能十分肯定。

□ USEFUL PATTERNS 有用句型
be sure of/about something; be sure who, why, whether, etc.; be sure that…

2 [never before a noun 不能用於名詞前] certain to happen 必定會發生的: *It's sure to rain while we're out.* 我們出去的時候肯定會下雨。**3 sure of something** certain to get something 肯定能得到某物, 有把握得到…: *He can be sure of a warm welcome.* 他有信心會受到熱烈的歡迎。**4 sure of someone** certain that someone can be trusted 肯定某人值得信賴: *You can be quite sure of John. When he says he'll do something, he does it.* 你對約翰可以放心, 他說過的事就一定會做的。**5 make sure: a** to find out for certain 查明; 確定: *I'll just make sure that the car's locked.* 我這就去看一下, 以確保汽車已上鎖。**b** to arrange that something will cer-

tainly happen 確保 [某事發生]: *Make sure you get here before midnight.* 你要確保在午夜之前到達這裡。**6** giving information that is certain [信息] 確鑿無疑的: *It's a sure sign that he's angry with me.* 這一點我確無疑地表明他很惱火。**7 sure of yourself** confident about your own abilities, actions and opinions 有自信心 **8 Be sure…** Don't forget to do something 不要忘記…: *Be sure to take an umbrella.* 不要忘記帶雨傘。**9 sure enough** as expected 不出所料 **–sureness** *n* [U]

■ USAGE 用法: Compare 比較 **sure** and 和 **certain**. We can use **sure** in the same way as **certain** in sentences like these ☆ 在以下的句子中, **sure** 的用法與 **certain** 的用法一樣: *I'm **sure**/**certain** that he'll come tomorrow.* 我肯定他明天會來。 | *He's **sure**/**certain** to come tomorrow.* 他明天肯定會來。 But we cannot use **sure** after **it** in sentences like this ☆ 但在這樣的句子中, **sure** 不能用在 **it** 後面: *It is **certain** that he'll come tomorrow.* 他肯定會來。

sure² *adv* **1** *AmE infml* certainly [美式, 非正式] 的確, 一定, 當然: *Sure I will.* 我當然會的。 | *She sure is tall.* 她的確很高。**2 for sure** certainly true 毫無疑問: *She won't lend you any money; that's for sure.* 她不會借錢給你, 這是毫無疑問的。

⋆⋆sure·ly /ˈʃʊrlɪ; ˈʃʊəli/ *adv* **1** a word used to show you believe someone to be true or correct 當然; 肯定 [用於表示相信某人是正確的]: *She's surely one of the greatest women of her time.* 她肯定是當時最偉大的女性之一。**2** a word used to express surprise that something might not be true 想必, 諒必 [用於對某事可能不符合事實表示吃驚]: *Surely you remember him?* 想必你還記得他吧? | *You know him, surely?* 想必你認識他吧? **3** *AmE* of course [美式] 當然

■ USAGE 用法: In British English **surely** is often used to show in an indirect way that you disapprove of something or that you disagree with something which has been said ☆ 在英式英語中, **surely** 常被用來間接地表示不贊成或不同意某事: **Surely** *he's finished by now!* 他現在總該做完了吧! (= he's too slow 他太慢了) | **Surely** *you didn't mean that.* 您一定不是那個意思吧。(= I don't agree with what you said 我不同意您說的話) | **Surely** *she'll write and let us know.* 她當然會寫信告訴我們的。(= I don't agree with your suggestion that she won't write 您說她不會寫信來, 這話我不同意) If you do not want to give this meaning, use **I'm sure** in-

般)洶湧向前: *The crowd surged past him.* 人
羣從他身邊湧過。

sur·geon /ˈsɜˈdʒən; ˈsɜːdʒən/ *n* a doctor
who performs medical operations 外科醫生

★sur·ge·ry /ˈsɜˈdʒəri; ˈsɜːdʒəri/ *n* **surgeries 1**
[U] the performing of medical operations
外科(手術): *He needed immediate surgery to
prevent another heart attack.* 他需要立刻動
手術,以防心臟病復發。 **2** [C] *BrE* a place
where doctors or DENTISTs treat people
〔英式〕診所 **3** [C;U] a time when doctors,
DENTISTs and Members of Parliament see
people who need their help〔醫生、牙醫的〕
診療時間;〔國會議員的〕接待時間: *He holds a
surgery every Saturday morning.* 他每星期六
上午接見市民。

sur·gi·cal /ˈsɜˈdʒɪkl; ˈsɜːdʒɪkəl/ *adj* **1** used in
operations 外科手術(用)的: *a surgical knife*
手術刀 **2** needing an operation 需要動手術
的: *surgical treatment for cancer* 癌症的手術
治療 –**surgically** /-klɪ; -kli/ *adv*

sur·ly /ˈsɜˈlɪ; ˈsɜːli/ *adj* **surlier, surliest** rude
and unpleasant 粗魯的,無禮的: *He gave me
a surly look.* 他狠狠地看了我一眼。

sur·mise /səˈmaɪz; səˈmaɪz/ *v* **surmised, sur-
mising** [I;T; +(that)] *fml* to guess that
something might be true〔正式〕猜測,猜
想 –**surmise** *n*

sur·mount /səˈmaʊnt; səˈmaʊnt/ *v* [T] *fml*
to deal with a problem successfully〔正式〕
克服〔困難〕 –**surmountable** *adj*

sur·name /ˈsɜˈneɪm; ˈsɜːneɪm/ *n* your family
name 姓: *Alan's surname is Smith.* 阿倫姓史
密斯。–see 見 FIRST NAME (USAGE 用
法) –compare 比較 FIRST NAME

sur·pass /səˈpæs; səˈpɑːs/ *v* [T] *fml* to do
more of something or to do something
better than other people or what is
expected〔正式〕超過,超出: *Her exam
results surpassed all our expectations.* 她的考
試成績超出了我們的一切預料。

sur·plus /ˈsɜˈplʌs; ˈsɜːpləs/ *n* an amount that
is more than what is needed or used 盈餘;
剩餘: *Some countries continue to produce
an oil surplus.* 一些國家繼續在生產過剩的石
油。–**surplus** *adj*: *These chairs are surplus
to our requirements.* 這些椅子比我們需要的
要多。| *surplus milk* 多餘的牛奶

★sur·prise¹ /səˈpraɪz; səˈpraɪz/ *n* **1** [U] the
feeling caused by something unexpected
驚訝,驚奇: *To my surprise I won the competition.* 使我驚奇的是,我居然贏了這場比賽。**2**
[C] something unexpected which happens
or is arranged by others 出乎意料的事: *Her
visit was a very pleasant surprise.* 她的來訪真
令人又驚又喜。| *I've got a surprise for you.*
我有件意想不到的事要告訴你。| *a surprise
birthday party* 令人意想不到的生日會 **3 take
someone by surprise** to happen when a
person is not expecting it 使某人吃驚:
*When he offered me the job it took me com-
pletely by surprise.* 當他説想把那份工作給我

stead ☆ 如果不想表達這層含義,就用
I'm sure: I am sure *he's finished by
now.* 我肯定他已做完了。(= I believe he
has finished 我認為他已做完了。) | **I'm
sure** *she'll write.* 我肯定她會寫信的 (= I
believe she will write 我認為她會寫信
的)

surf¹ /sɜˈf; sɜːf/ *n* [U] white water formed by
waves when they break on the shore or on
rocks 拍岸的浪花

surf² *v* [I] to ride on a special narrow board
over breaking waves 滑浪,作衝浪運動: *We
could take our surfboards to the beach and
go surfing.* 我們可以拿衝浪板到海灘上去衝
浪。–**surfer** *n*

★sur·face¹ /ˈsɜˈfɪs; ˈsɜːfɪs/ *n* **1** the outside or top of something 面,
表面: *the earth's surface* 地球表面 | *Don't
scratch the surface of the table!* 別刮桌面! |
*The insects hovered on the surface of the
pond.* 昆蟲在池塘面飛來飛去。**2** what is
clear in a situation and not hidden 外表;表
面現象: *The level of staff unhappiness only
came to the surface when people started
leaving the company.* 當職員開始離開公司時,
他們的不快才表露出來。**3 on the surface**
judging quickly, without careful thought or
a deeper understanding 從表面看來: *On the
surface it seems a good idea.* 從表面上看,這
似乎是一個好主意。[RELATED PHRASES
相關詞組 **below the surface, beneath the
surface:** *Below the surface he's a very unhappy man.* 他實際上是個非常不開心的人。]

surface² *v* **surfaced, surfacing 1** [I] to come
to the top of a body of water 浮到水面: *She
surfaced to take in air.* 她浮出水面吸氣。**2**
[I] to appear again after time has passed
〔一段時間後〕重新露面: *We heard no news of
him for years, and then he surfaced in Hong
Kong.* 我們好幾年沒有他的消息,後來他在香
港重新露面。**3** [T] to cover something with
hard material 用…覆蓋: *The roads are being
surfaced.* 路正在鋪設之中。

surface³ *adj* **surface mail** letters and
parcels that travel by land and sea 普通郵
件,平郵

sur·feit /ˈsɜˈfɪt; ˈsɜːfɪt/ *n fml* too large an
amount, especially of food〔正式〕〔尤指食
物〕過量: *This year farmers have produced a
surfeit* **of** *corn.* 今年農民出產了過量的玉
米。| *He's suffering from a surfeit* **of** *choco-
late.* 他由於巧克力吃得過多而不舒服。

surge¹ /sɜˈdʒ; sɜːdʒ/ *n* **1** a sudden strong
feeling 一陣強烈感情;洶湧,澎湃: *He felt a
surge of anger.* 他感到怒火中燒。**2** a sudden
increase in some kind of activity〔活動的〕
激增: *a surge in the electric current* 電流的突
然增強

surge² *v* **surged, surging** [I; + adv/prep] to
move forward like powerful waves〔如巨浪

時, 我完全為之愕然。

sur·prise² v **surprised, surprising** [T] to cause someone to feel surprise 使〔某人〕吃驚, 使驚奇: *The taste surprised him.* 那種味道令他吃了一驚。| *I was surprised to hear that his wife had left him.* 聽到他的妻子已離他而去, 我感到很意外。| *They surprised us with a visit.* 他們突然造訪, 令我們大吃一驚。

*sur·pris·ing /səˈpraɪzɪŋ; səˈpraɪzɪŋ/ adj causing a feeling of surprise 令人吃驚的, 出人意料的, 驚人的: *It's not surprising that they lost.* 他們輸了, 這並不令人感到驚訝。| *He was a man of surprising youth.* 他的年紀那麼輕, 令人頗為吃驚。–**surprisingly** adv

sur·real·is·m /səˈrɪəlˌɪzm; səˈrɪəlɪzəm/ n [U] a modern style of art and literature in which the artist connects unrelated images and objects 超現實主義 –**surrealist** adj, n

sur·real·is·tic /səˌrɪəlˈɪstɪk; səˌrɪəˈlɪstɪk/ adj **1** (also 又作 **surreal** /səˈrɪəl; səˈrɪəl/) strange, with the qualities of dreams rather than real life 奇異的; 夢幻般的 **2** concerning or in the style of surrealism 超現實主義的

sur·ren·der /səˈrendə; səˈrendəʳ/ v **1** [I] to admit that you have been beaten 投降: *With no alternative left, the army surrendered.* 由於別無選擇, 軍隊便投降了。| *They've surrendered* **to** *the enemy forces.* 他們已向敵軍投降了。 **2** surrender **to something** to allow something to control what you do or feel 屈服於某事物: *He surrendered to the temptation of an expensive meal.* 他經不起誘惑, 花很多錢吃了一頓。 **3** [T] fml to give up something that you value 〔正式〕放棄〔某事物〕: *I surrender any claim I have to the money.* 我放棄對這筆錢的所有權利。–**surrender** n [U]

sur·rep·ti·tious /ˌsʌrəpˈtɪʃəs; ˌsʌrəpˈtɪʃəs/ adj done or experienced secretly 偷偷摸摸的, 鬼鬼祟祟的: *a surreptitious kiss* 偷偷的一吻 –**surreptitiously** adv –**surreptitiousness** n [U]

*sur·round¹ /səˈraʊnd; səˈraʊnd/ v [T] **1** to be or go around something on every side of it 環繞, 圍繞〔某物〕: *The prison is surrounded* **by** *a high wall.* 監獄四周圍着高牆。| *The police surrounded the house.* 警察包圍了那所房子。 **2** to be near a person or thing all the time 圍住〔人或物〕: *She was surrounded by good friends.* 她周圍總有許多好朋友。| *Dangers will surround us until we leave here.* 我們離開這兒之前, 危險一直包圍着我們。 **3** to surround **yourself with something** to make sure that people or things are near you 使自己身邊環繞某物: *He surrounded himself with every material comfort.* 他讓自己給各種物質享受包圍着。

surround² n an edge, especially a decorative one 邊, 緣, 圍飾〔尤指作裝飾用〕: *a surround for a fireplace* 壁爐的飾邊

sur·round·ing /səˈraʊndɪŋ; səˈraʊndɪŋ/ adj [only before a noun 只用於名詞前] around and near a particular place 附近的, 周圍的: *There are few villages in the surrounding area.* 在周圍地區村莊很少。–see 見 ENVIRONMENT (USAGE 用法)

sur·round·ings /səˈraʊndɪŋz; səˈraʊndɪŋz/ n [pl] the area around a particular place 周圍地區; 環境: *The castle looked out of place in its surroundings.* 該城堡與周圍的環境很不協調。 **2** living conditions 生活環境: *She grew up in comfortable surroundings.* 她是在舒適的環境下長大的。

sur·veil·lance /səˈveləns; sɜːˈveɪləns/ n [U] a close watch kept on someone, especially someone believed to have criminal intentions 〔尤指對有犯罪嫌疑的人所進行的〕監視: *The police have been keeping him under surveillance.* 警方一直在監視他。

*sur·vey¹ /səˈveɪ; səˈveɪ/ v **surveyed, surveying** [T] **1** to look carefully at a person or place, one part at a time 審視, 仔細察看〔人或地區〕: *He surveyed the surrounding countryside.* 他仔細察看了周圍的郊外地區。 **2** to examine every area of a subject or situation 全面研究: *His article surveys research findings over the last 20 years.* 他的文章回顧了二十年來的研究成果。 **3** to examine the condition of a building 鑑定, 檢查〔房屋〕: *Has the house been properly surveyed?* 這所房子被認真檢查過了嗎? **4** to make a map of an area of land 測量, 勘測; 測繪〔地圖〕 **5** to find out what a group of people think or do, usually by asking them questions 調查〔民意〕

sur·vey² /ˈsɜːveɪ; ˈsɜːveɪ/ n **1** a general view of a place, subject or situation 縱覽; 概況: *You must include a survey of the relevant literature in your essay.* 你在文章中必須把有關的文獻概況寫進去。 **2** a careful examination of a building, especially for someone who may buy it 〔尤指為購房者所作的〕房屋鑑定: *We were not going to buy the house without a satisfactory survey.* 若是沒有令人滿意的房屋鑑定報告, 我們就不打算買那所房子。 **3** a careful examination of an area of land in order to make a map 測繪 **4** an examination of people's behaviour or opinions, usually based on questions you ask them 調查: *We're conducting a survey* **of** *drinking habits.* 我們正在做一項飲酒習慣的民意調查。

sur·vey·or /səˈveɪə; səˈveɪəʳ/ n a person whose job is to examine the condition of buildings or map areas of land 〔房屋的〕鑑定人; 〔土地的〕勘測員, 測量師

*sur·viv·al /səˈvaɪvl; səˈvaɪvəl/ n **1** [U] the state of continuing to live or exist after a difficult or dangerous situation 〔困難或危險的情況發生之後的〕幸存, 殘存; 生存: *We had little hope of survival.* 我們幸存的希望很渺茫。 **2** [C] something which has continued to exist from an earlier time 殘存物; 遺跡;

遺風

*sur·vive /səˈvaɪv; səˈvaɪv/ v survived, sur-
viving 1 [I;T] to continue to live or exist
after a difficult or dangerous situation〔困
難或危險的情況發生之後〕幸存, 殘存; 生存下
來: She survived the accident. 她在事故中死
裡逃生。| Four people were killed; only one
survived. 四個人罹難; 只有一人生還。2 [T] to
live longer than another person 比〔另一個
人〕活得長: He survived both his children. 他
活得比他兩個孩子都要長。3 [I;T] to live
through a difficult situation without
serious hurt or harm 經歷〔困難時期〕之後還
存在: It's been a year of emotional ups and
downs, but at least we survived! 過去的一年
在感情上充滿波折, 但最起碼我們挺過去了! –
survivor n: There were no survivors of the
plane crash. 空難之中沒有生還者。

sus·cep·ti·ble /səˈsɛptəbl; səˈsept ḷ bəl/ adj 1
easily influenced 易受影響的: He is very susceptible to other people's suggestions. 他很容
易受別人的建議影響。2 likely to suffer from
or as a result of something 易被感染的: I'm
highly susceptible to the cold. 我特別容易得
感冒。–susceptibility /sə,sɛptəˈbɪlətɪ; sə,sep-
tḷˈbɪl ḷ ti/ n [U]

*sus·pect¹ /səˈspɛkt; səˈspekt/ v [T] 1 [+
(that)] to feel that something may exist or
be true 懷疑〔某事物〕: At first, we suspected
that he was lost. 起先, 我們懷疑他失蹤了。|
They suspect corruption. 他們懷疑有貪污的
情況出現。2 to believe that someone may
be guilty 認為〔某人〕有嫌疑, 懷疑〔某人〕有罪:
They suspect him of murder. 他們懷疑他謀
殺。3 to have doubts about whether you
can trust a person or way of behaving 對…
有疑心, 不信任: He helped me but I suspect
his motives. 他幫了我一把, 但我對他的動機表
示懷疑。

sus·pect² /ˈsʌspɛkt; ˈsʌspekt/ n a person
who is thought to be guilty, especially of a
crime 嫌疑犯, 可疑分子

suspect³ adj that is perhaps not to be
trusted 可疑的, 令人懷疑的: I find her loyalty
increasingly suspect. 我覺得她的忠誠愈來愈
可疑。

sus·pend /səˈspɛnd; səˈspend/ v [T] 1 to
hang from above 吊, 懸, 掛: We could sus-
pend a rope from that tree. 我們可以把一根
繩子吊在那棵樹上。2 to hold something still
in liquid or air 使〔某物〕懸浮: Dust
remained suspended in the empty room. 塵
埃懸浮在那空房間裡。3 to delay or stop
something for a period of time 暫緩; 暫停:
The investigation has been suspended until
the autumn. 調查已經暫停, 要到秋天再進行。
4 to prevent someone from belonging to a
group or continuing in a job for a time,
usually because of bad behaviour〔通常由
於行為惡劣而〕被暫停會員資格; 使暫停工作:
She was suspended from school for taking
drugs. 她由於吸毒而被停學。

sus·pend·er /səˈspɛndə; səˈspendəʳ/ n 1 a
fastener hanging down from a belt to hold
a woman's stockings up〔女用的〕吊襪帶 –
see picture on page 210 見 210 頁彩圖 2
suspenders the American English word
for〚美式〛= BRACES

sus·pense /səˈspɛns; səˈspens/ n [U] a state
of uncertain expectation 懸而未決的狀況;
懸念; 掛慮, 不安: We waited in suspense for
our test results. 我們焦急不安地等待着測驗結
果。| a story of mystery and suspense 充滿
神祕感與懸念的故事

sus·pen·sion /səˈspɛnʃən; səˈspenʃən/ n 1
[U] the act of suspending a person or
thing or the state of being suspended 暫緩;
暫停 2 [C;U] the apparatus fixed to the
wheels of a vehicle to lesson the effects of
rough road surfaces〔車輛避震用的〕懸架

sus·pi·cion /səˈspɪʃən; səˈspɪʃən/ n 1 [C] a
feeling that something may exist or be true
懷疑: I have a suspicion that he's right. 我懷
疑他可能是對的。2 [C;U] a feeling that
someone may be guilty or that something
may be wrong 嫌疑; 疑心: She treats us with
great suspicion. 她對我們存有很大的疑心。|
He has his suspicions about the company
finances. 他對公司的財務狀況存有疑心。|
He's under suspicion of murder. 他涉嫌謀
殺。| The police have their suspicions
about who killed him. 警方對於是誰殺了他
有所懷疑。3 above suspicion most certainly
not guilty 不受懷疑的: The dead man's family is above suspicion. 死者的家屬不受懷疑。
4 [sing] a slight amount or taste of something 少量, 一點兒: There's a suspicion of
onion in the soup. 湯裡有一丁點兒洋葱。

sus·pi·cious /səˈspɪʃəs; səˈspɪʃəs/ adj 1 not
trusting a person or situation 懷疑的, 疑心
的: She was suspicious of our intentions. 她
對我們的企圖有所懷疑。| His statement
made the police suspicious. 他的話令警方生
疑。2 causing a lack of trust in others 令人
懷疑的, 可疑的: His behaviour has been very
suspicious. 他的行為很可疑。–suspiciously
adv: behaving suspiciously 行為可疑的 |
suspiciously well-behaved 表現好得令人懷疑

*sus·tain /səˈsten; səˈsteɪn/ v [T] 1 to keep
someone strong, alive, or happy 使〔某人〕
維持〔強壯、活力或快活〕: A good breakfast
will sustain us through the day. 一頓豐富的
早餐能維持我們一天的精力。2 to continue
something over a long period 使〔某事〕持
續: She owes her success to sustained hard
work. 她把成功歸功於堅持不懈的艱苦努力。|
He couldn't sustain his interest in the job. 他
無法維持他對這份工作的興趣。3 to suffer
something 遭受, 蒙受: They sustained severe
injuries in the accident. 事故中他們受了重
傷。4 to support something heavy 支持, 承
受〔重物〕

sus·te·nance /ˈsʌstənəns; ˈsʌstənəns/ n [U]
fml food and drink, or its value to people's

health and strength 〖正式〗食物, 糧食; 營養

svelte /svɛlt; svɛlt/ *adj* attractively thin and stylish (used especially of a woman) 苗條動人的〔尤指婦女〕

SW *n, adj* a written abbreviation for 〖縮〗= SOUTHWEST(ERN)

swab[1] /swɑb; swɒb/ *n* a piece of cotton wool used to clean wounds or to hold liquid for medical tests 〔清洗傷口或吸取液體作檢驗用的〕藥棉, 棉花棒

swab[2] *v* **-bb-** [T] (also 又作 **swab down**) to clean something with water, especially floors on a ship 〔用水〕擦洗〔尤指船上的地板〕

swag·ger /'swæɡə; 'swæɡɚ/ *v* [I+adv/prep] to walk with a proud, swinging movement 大搖大擺地走: *He swaggered down the street after his victory.* 他獲勝後大搖大擺地走在街上。–**swagger** *n*: *He walks with a swagger.* 他大搖大擺地走。

swal·low[1] /'swɒlo; 'swɒləo/ *v* **1** [T] to move something down your throat from your mouth 吞下, 嚥下: *Try to swallow a little soup.* 來試試嚥下一口湯。**2** [I] to make the same movement of the throat, especially as a sign that you are nervous 嚥口水〔表示緊張〕: *He swallowed, and then began his talk.* 他嚥了一下口水, 然後開始講話。**3** [T] *infml* foolishly to accept something as true 〖非正式〗輕信, 盲目地相信〔某事物〕: *I swallowed the whole story.* 我竟完全相信了那個說法。**4** [T] to hide your feelings or control them with difficulty 隱藏〔感情〕; 抑制〔感情〕: *She swallowed her pride and apologised.* 她抑壓住自己的驕傲, 說了聲抱歉。

swallow up *phr v* [T **swallow** sbdy/sthg ↔ **up**] to cause a person or thing to disappear into something larger 使〔人或物〕消失, 吞沒: *Higher living costs have swallowed up our pay rise.* 上漲的生活費用已經抵銷了我們增加的工資。

swallow[2] *n* a small bird with pointed wings and a double-pointed tail 燕子

swam /swæm; swæm/ *v* the past tense of SWIM ☆ SWIM 的過去式

swamp[1] /swɒmp; swɒmp/ *n* [C;U] an area of soft, wet land 沼澤(地) –compare 比較 MARSH –**swampy** *adj*

swamp[2] *v* [T] **1** to fill something with water, usually causing it to sink 淹沒〔某物〕: *The boat was swamped by high waves.* 小艇被大浪淹沒了。**2** to have a much larger quantity of something than you can deal with 使應付不來: *We've been swamped by inquiries.* 接連不斷的詢問令我們應接不暇。

swan /swɒn; swɒn/ *n* a large white bird with a long neck, which lives on rivers and lakes 天鵝

swank·y /'swæŋkɪ; 'swæŋkɪ/ *adj* **swankier, swankiest** *infml* too fashionable or expensive 〖非正式〗時髦的; 豪華的: *a really*

swanky party 十分豪華的宴會

swap[1] /swɒp; swɒp/ *v* **-pp-** (also 又作 **swop**) [I;T] *infml* to exchange things 〖非正式〗交換: *The manager has agreed that we can swap jobs.* 經理已同意我們交換工作。| *I'll swap any of my stamps for that one of yours.* 我願意用任何一枚郵票來換你的那一枚。| *Well, I prefer your coat – do you want to swap?* 哦, 我比較喜歡你的外衣, 你想交換一下嗎?

swap[2] *n* (also 又作 **swop**) *infml* an exchange 〖非正式〗交換: *Shall we do a swap?* 我們來個交換好嗎?

swarm[1] /swɔrm; swɔ:m/ *n* [C; +sing/pl v] **1** a large group of insects that move together 移動中的一大羣〔昆蟲〕: *a swarm of bees* 一大羣蜜蜂 **2** a large number of people moving at the same time 移動中的一大羣〔人〕: *swarms of students* 一羣羣學生

swarm[2] *v* [I+adv/prep] **1** to move in a large group 成羣移動, 蜂擁: *People came swarming out of the building.* 人們從那建築物裏蜂擁而出。| *Ants swarmed all over me.* 螞蟻爬滿了我的身上。**2 swarm with something** to be full of moving crowds 擠滿〔人羣〕: *The place was swarming with tourists.* 這地方遊客雲集。

swar·thy /'swɔrðɪ; 'swɔ:ðɪ/ *adj* **swarthier, swarthiest** with a dark skin (used of a person) 皮膚黝黑的〔指人〕

swas·ti·ka /'swɒstɪkə; 'swɒstɪkə/ *n* a cross with each arm bent back at a right angle, which was used as a sign by NAZIs in Germany 卐字形〔德國納粹黨的標誌〕

swat /swɒt; swɒt/ *v* **-tt-** [T] to hit an insect with a flat object, especially to kill it 拍擊〔昆蟲〕

sway /swe; sweɪ/ *v* **swayed, swaying 1** [I] to move slowly from side to side 搖動, 擺動: *The trees swayed in the wind.* 樹在風中輕輕地搖曳。**2** [T] to influence someone 影響〔某人〕, 使改變: *Don't be swayed by promises that may be false.* 別受那些可能是虛假的承諾所影響。–**sway** *n* [U]

swear /swɛr; sweə/ *v* **swore** /swor; swɔ:/, **sworn** /sworn; swɔ:n/, **swearing 1** [I] to use bad language 咒罵: *Don't swear at me!* 不要罵我! **2** [I;T +(that)] to make a formal promise 發誓, 宣誓: *He swore that he would never see her again.* 他發誓今後再也不見她了。| *She swore to tell the truth.* 她發誓所講的是實情。**3** [T] to make a person promise something formally 使〔某人〕發誓, 使〔某人〕宣誓: *I've been sworn to secrecy.* 我被迫發誓保守祕密。**4 swear by something** to claim that something is particularly useful 聲稱某物很有用處: *He swears by cold baths for keeping healthy.* 他說洗冷水浴對保持健康有好處。**5 swear to something** to say that something is certainly true 保證某事是真的: *I couldn't swear to it, but I think he lied.* 我不能保證這是真的, 但我認為他撒了謊。

swear in *phr v* [T **swear** sbdy ↔ **in**] to make someone promise formally that they will tell the truth or that they will be loyal and honest in their new position 使〔某人〕發誓; 使〔某人〕宣誓就職: *The new president was sworn in.* 新總統宣誓就職。

swear·word /ˈswɛr,wɜ˞d; ˈsweəwɜːd/ *n* a rude word used to express anger or lack of respect 罵人的話, 詛咒

sweat[1] /swɛt; swet/ *n* **1** [U] liquid which comes out through your skin when you are hot or frightened 汗, 汗水: *Sweat was running down her face.* 汗水順著她的臉淌下來。 **2 in a sweat, in a cold sweat** covered in sweat, usually from fear 〔通常由於恐懼〕一身冷汗 **3** [sing; U] *infml* hard work 〔非正式〕艱苦的工作: *Digging that hole was a real sweat.* 挖那個洞實在是件苦差事。

sweat[2] *v* **1** [I] to produce liquid that comes out through your skin because you are hot or frightened 出汗, 冒汗: *He was sweating in the intense heat.* 他在酷暑中渾身冒汗。 **2** [I] to work very hard 辛勤地工作: *We sweated day and night to get the work finished in time.* 我們日以繼夜地拼命幹, 力求把工作按時完成。 **3 sweat it out** to manage in an unpleasant situation until it ends 〔在不利的情況下〕堅持到底, 忍受到底: *They had to sweat it out until help arrived.* 他們不得不堅持到有人來幫忙為止。

sweat·er /ˈswɛtə˞; ˈswetə˞/ *n* a warm garment which covers the upper part of your body, including your arms 毛衣, 套頭毛衣

sweat·shirt /ˈswɛt,ʃɜ˞t; ˈswet-ʃɜːt/ *n* a loose garment made of thick cotton which covers the upper part of your body, including your arms 圓領長袖運動衫—see picture on page 210 見 210 頁彩圖

sweat·y /ˈswɛtɪ; ˈswetɪ/ *adj* **sweatier, sweatiest 1** wet from heat or fear (used of people) 〔由於炎熱或恐懼〕有汗的, 汗水濕透的〔指人〕: *sweaty feet* 滿是汗水的雙腳 **2** unpleasantly hot, making you sweat 酷熱的; 使人出汗的: *sweaty weather* 悶熱的天氣 | *sweaty work* 使人出汗的工作

swede /swid; swiːd/ *n* [C;U] a round yellow vegetable which grows under the ground 蕪菁甘藍〔一種蔬菜〕

*****sweep**[1] /swip; swiːp/ *v* **swept** /swɛpt; swept/, **swept, sweeping 1** [T] to clean something or remove it by brushing 掃, 打掃: *He swept the floor.* 他打掃地板。 | *She swept the dirt into the street.* 她把灰塵掃到街上。 **2** [I; T+adv/prep] to move something completely 徹底去除〔某事物〕: *All thought of revenge was swept from my mind.* 所有要報復的念頭在我心中徹底消失了。 **3** [I; + adv/prep; T; + adv/prep] to move quickly and powerfully 橫掃, 掠過: *The crowd swept through the gates.* 人羣衝過數道大門。 | *A storm swept over the country.* 一場暴風雨橫掃全國。 | *The boat was swept out to sea.* 小

船被沖到海裡去了。 **4** [I;T + adv/prep] to spread quickly 迅速傳播: *The news swept across the country.* 這消息迅速傳遍全國。 **5** [I +adv/prep] (of a person) to move with pride in a certain direction 〔人〕趾高氣揚地朝〔某一方向〕走: *She swept angrily from the room.* 她憤怒地從房裡走了出來。 **6** [I + adv/prep] to form a long curve 蜿蜒; 伸展: *Hills sweep round the bay.* 羣山環抱著海灣。 **7** [T] to look around a place 環視: *The security camera swept the store.* 保安攝像機環視著整個商店。 **8 sweep the board** to win almost everything in a competition 〔在比賽中〕大獲全勝 **9 sweep someone off their feet** to attract someone so strongly that they fall in love with you immediately 使某人神魂顛倒 **10 sweep something under the carpet** to hide something that you want to keep secret 隱藏某事, 把某事掩蓋起來

sweep up *phr v* [I;T **sweep** sthg ↔ **up**] to remove something from the floor by sweeping it 清掃, 掃掉

sweep[2] *n* **1** an act of sweeping 掃, 打掃: *This room needs a good sweep.* 這房間需要好好打掃一下。 **2** a swinging movement of your arm 〔臂膀的〕揮動: *with a sweep of his sword* 他的劍一揮 **3** a long curved shape 連綿彎曲的形狀: *the long sweep of the distant hills* 延綿的遠山 **4** the wide range of a subject 一個主題所包含的範圍: *the broad sweep of her argument* 她的論說涉及面很廣

sweep·er /ˈswipə˞; ˈswiːpə˞/ *n* a person or thing that sweeps 打掃的人; 清掃器: *a road-sweeper* 馬路清潔工 | *a carpet sweeper* 地毯清潔器

sweep·ing /ˈswipɪŋ; ˈswiːpɪŋ/ *adj* **1** important and covering a wide range of things 全面的; 徹底的: *They are making sweeping changes to the health service.* 他們正在對社會保健制度進行全面改革。 **2** too general 籠統的; 總括的: *That's a rather sweeping statement.* 那是一句很籠統的話。

sweep·stake /ˈswip,stek; ˈswiːpsteɪk/ *n* a way of risking money on the result of a horserace 〔賽馬的〕賭金全贏制

*****sweet**[1] /swit; swiːt/ *adj* **1** containing or tasting of sugar 甜的: *This tea is too sweet for me.* 這茶對我來説太甜了。 | *I eat a lot of sweet things between meals.* 我在各餐飯之間吃許多甜食。 –opposite 反義 **bitter 2** pleasant to your senses 悦耳的; 芬芳的; 令人感覺愉快的: *What sweet music!* 多麼悦耳的音樂啊! | *I love the sweet smell of freshly-picked flowers.* 我喜歡新近摘揀的鮮花的芳香。 **3** attractive (used especially of small or young people and things) 可愛的〔尤指小孩或小東西〕: *Your little boy looks sweet in his new coat.* 你的小男孩穿上新衣服, 樣子很可愛。 **4** kind or gentle 和藹的, 溫柔的: *It was sweet of you to think of me.* 你想起了我, 真體貼人啊。 | *She has such a sweet smile.* 她的笑容如此溫柔。 **5 have a sweet tooth** to enjoy eating sweet things 喜歡吃甜食 **6 in someone's own sweet time, in someone's own sweet way** at the time or in the way that suits a person and not others 在自己的時間; 用自己的方式: *I expect he'll do it in his own sweet time.* 我希望他會在自己的時間裡把事情做好。**7 keep someone sweet** to do something to please someone so that they don't get angry〔做某事〕令某人高興, 討好某人 – **sweetly** *adv* **–sweetness** *n* [U]

sweet² *n BrE*〖英式〗**1** [C] a sweet thing such as chocolate which is eaten for pleasure 糖果 –see 見 also 又作 CANDY **2** [C;U] (also 又作 **dessert, pudding**) sweet food served at the end of a meal〔飯後的〕甜點, 甜品

sweet corn /'··/ *n* [U] see 見 CORN

sweet·en /'switn̩; 'swiːtn̩/ *v* **1** [I;T] to make or become sweeter (使)變甜, 加糖於: *Shall I sweeten your coffee?* 我給你的咖啡加些糖好嗎? | *Apples sweeten as they become ripe.* 蘋果熟了就會變甜。**2** [T] (also 又作 **sweeten** sbdy **up**) *infml* to give something to someone or do something for them in order to persuade them to help you〖非正式〗籠絡, 討好〔某人〕: *You'll have to sweeten her up before you ask her for a loan.* 你得先籠絡她一下才能開口向她借錢。

sweet·ener /'switn̩ə; 'swiːtnər/ *n* **1** a substance used instead of sugar to make food and drink taste sweet〔代替糖的〕甜料 **2** something that you give someone to make a request or a deal more attractive 籠絡物, 賄賂物

sweet·heart /'swit,hɑrt; 'swiːthɑːt/ *n* a person that you love or a way of addressing them 愛人, 戀人; 親愛的〔用於稱呼〕: *Have you had a good day, sweetheart?* 親愛的, 今天過得愉快嗎?

sweet·meat /'swit,mit; 'swiːtmiːt/ *n* a sweet or any food in the past made of or preserved in sugar 糖果, 蜜餞

sweet pea /,··/ *n* a climbing plant with sweet-smelling flowers 香豌豆

swell¹ /swɛl; swel/ *v* **swelled, swollen** /'swolən; 'swoulən/ *or* **swelled, swelling 1** [I] (also 又作 **swell up**) to become larger and rounder 膨脹; 腫脹: *My ankle has swollen up.* 我的足踝腫了起來。**2** [I;T] to make or become something larger in size (使)變大: *The army has swollen to twice its normal size.* 軍隊的規模已增大到平時的兩倍。| *Refugees are swelling the camps.* 難民擠滿了難民營。**3** [I;T] to fill into a curved shape (使)隆起; (使)鼓起: *Wind swelled the sails.* 風吹得船帆鼓了起來。**4** [I;T] (of strong feelings) to grow suddenly or to have a sudden effect on someone〔強烈感情〕突然增加; 突然影響〔某人〕: *My heart swells with pride when I hear him sing.* 聽他唱歌時, 我的心中充滿了自豪。

swell² *n* **1** [C] the movement of large

stretches of the sea up and down 大浪; 巨浪 **2** [sing] an increase of sound 音量增強

swell³ *adj AmE infml* very good or nice〖美式, 非正式〗卓越的, 出色的: *a swell teacher* 出色的老師

swell·ing /'swɛlɪŋ; 'swelɪŋ/ *n* [C;U] a place on your body that has become larger and rounder than usual〔身體上的〕腫脹處, 腫塊: *I've got a nasty swelling on my foot.* 我腳上有一處地方腫得很厲害。

swel·ter·ing /'swɛltərɪŋ; 'sweltərɪŋ/ *adj infml* very hot indeed〖非正式〗酷熱的: *It's sweltering in here!* 這裡熱死人了!

swept /swɛpt; swept/ the past tense and past participle of SWEEP ☆ SWEEP 的過去式和過去分詞

swerve /swɜv; swɜːv/ *v* **swerved, swerving 1** [I] to move suddenly in another direction 突然轉向: *The car swerved to avoid the dog.* 為了避開那隻狗, 汽車突然轉向。| *The ball swerved in the air.* 球在空中突然改變了方向。**2** [I] to change your intentions 改變意向 – **swerve** *n*

swift¹ /swɪft; swɪft/ *adj fml* quick〖正式〗迅速的: *He's a swift runner.* 他是個跑得很快的賽跑運動員。| *I'm hoping for a swift response.* 我希望很快得到答覆。**–swiftly** *adv* **–swiftness** *n* [U]

swift² *n* a small bird with long wings which eats insects 雨燕

swig /swɪg; swɪg/ *v* **-gg-** [T] *infml* to drink in large amounts〖非正式〗大口大喝: *He was swigging brandy straight from the bottle.* 他大口大口地喝瓶裡的白蘭地。**–swig** *n*: *a swig of beer* 一大口啤酒

swill¹ /swɪl; swɪl/ *v* [T] **1** to wash something by pouring large amounts of water over it 沖洗 **2** to drink something in large amounts 大喝, 痛飲

swill² *n* [U] waste food that is fed to pigs 泔腳飼料, 豬食

swim¹ /swɪm; swɪm/ *v* **swam** /swæm; swæm/, **swum** /swʌm; swʌm/, **swimming 1** [I] to move through water using arms and legs or a tail 游泳: *Shall we swim to the island?* 我們游到島上去好嗎? | *Fish are swimming back into the lake.* 魚正游回湖裡。| *He goes swimming every morning.* 他每天早晨去游泳。**2** [T] to cross a certain distance by doing this 游〔一段距離〕: *I can swim the river twice without stopping.* 我可以一口氣在這條河裡游個來回。| *She swam 2 kilometres.* 她游了兩公里遠。**3** [I] to be full of or covered with liquid 充滿〔液體〕, 浸: *All the food was swimming in fat.* 所有的食物都浸在油裡。**4** [I] to seem to move or be confused 眩暈: *One drink and the room was swimming.* 只喝了一杯, 就覺得房間在搖來搖去。| *My head was swimming.* 我的頭發暈。**–swimmer** *n*

swim² *n* an act or period of swimming 游泳: *Let's go for a swim!* 我們去游泳吧!

swim·ming /'swɪmɪŋ; 'swɪmɪŋ/ *n* [U] the activity or sport of swimming 游泳(運動) –see picture on page 957 見 957 頁彩圖

swimming bath /'·· ·/ *n* (also 又作 **swimming baths**) a public place specially built for swimming, usually indoors 〔通常為室內的〕公共游泳池

swimming cos·tume /'·· ,··/ *n* (also 又作 **swimsuit**) a piece of clothing worn for swimming 游泳衣

swimming pool /'·· ·/ *n* a pool specially built for swimming in 游泳池: *They've got a swimming pool in their garden.* 他們的花園裡有個游泳池。

swimming trunks /'·· ·/ *n* [pl] an article of clothing worn by men for swimming 〔男用的〕游泳褲

swim·suit /'swɪm,sut; 'swɪmsuːt/ *n* see 見 SWIMMING COSTUME

swin·dle /'swɪndl; 'swɪndl/ *v* **swindled, swindling** [T] to cheat someone, especially to get their money 欺騙, 騙取〔某人的錢財〕: *He's swindled me out of £100!* 他騙走了我一百英鎊! –**swindle** *n*: *a big bank swindle* 一宗銀行大詐騙案 –**swindler** *n*

swine /swaɪn; swaɪn/ *n* **swine 1** *old fash or tech* a pig〔舊式或術語〕豬: *swine fever* 豬瘟 **2** *infml* a nasty, unpleasant person〔非正式〕下流坯, 討厭鬼: *Give that back, you swine!* 把那東西還給我, 你這討厭的傢伙!

***swing¹** /swɪŋ; swɪŋ/ *v* **swung** /swʌŋ; swʌŋ/, **swung, swinging 1** [I;T] to move backwards and forwards from a fixed point 擺動, 搖擺: *They were swinging their arms as they walked.* 他們邊走邊晃動胳膊。| *The sign was swinging in the wind.* 招牌在風中擺動着。| *The children were swinging on a rope.* 孩子們抓着繩子盪來盪去。**2** [I;T] to move in a curve 旋轉: *The door swung open.* 門旋轉着開了。**3 swing at something or someone** to move your arm up in an attempt to hit a person or thing 舉起胳膊打某物或某人: *I jumped out of the way as he swung at me.* 他舉起手打我, 我跳開了。**4** [I;T+adv/prep] to turn quickly 迅速轉身: *He swung round and faced his attacker.* 他突然轉過身, 面對着襲擊他的人。| *She swung the car into the drive.* 她迅速把汽車調頭, 開到了車道上。**5** [I] (of opinions or feelings) to change from one extreme to another〔觀點或感應〕轉變: *Public opinion has swung against the government.* 公眾興論已轉而反對政府。**6** [I] *infml* (of music or parties) to be full of life〔非正式〕〔音樂或晚會〕充滿活力 **7 swing into action** to act quickly 迅速行動

swing² *n* **1** a swinging action or movement 擺動, 晃動: *Would you like a swing on my rope?* 你想抓着我的繩子盪一下嗎? **2** a seat hanging on ropes or chains, on which children play 鞦韆: *We've bought a swing for the garden.* 我們買了個鞦韆放在花園裡。**3** a great change in opinion or feelings〔觀點或感情的〕巨大轉變: *There's been a big swing in public opinion since the election.* 自從選舉以來, 公眾興論有了很大的轉變。**4** a kind of music played by bands in the 1930s〔三十年代的〕搖擺樂 **5 get into the swing of something** to become used to a particular activity and do it well 適應某一活動: *It took me a year to get into the swing of teaching.* 我花了一年時間才適應教書的工作。**6 go with a swing** to be successful and full of life 成功; 充滿活力: *All our parties go with a swing.* 我們所有的晚會都很成功。

swing·ing /'swɪŋɪŋ; 'swɪŋɪŋ/ *adj old fash*〔老式〕**1** full of life 活躍的, 充滿活力的: *a swinging party* 熱鬧的晚會 | *a swinging part of town* 氣氛活躍的城鎮 **2** fashionably free and active 趕時髦的; 活躍的: *swinging teenagers* 趕時髦的青少年 –**swingingly** *adv* –**swinger** *n*

swipe¹ /swaɪp; swaɪp/ *n* a sweeping blow which may or may not hit a person or thing 擊, 擊打: *He took a swipe at me with his newspaper.* 他用報紙來打我。

swipe² *v* **swiped, swiping 1** [I] to try to hit a person or thing with a quick swing of your arm 〔揮臂〕猛擊: *He swiped wildly at the ball, and missed completely.* 他拼命地揮臂打球, 卻撲了個空。**2** [T] *infml* to steal〔非正式〕偷竊: *Someone's swiped my book!* 有人偷了我的書!

swirl /swɜːl; swɜːl/ *v* [I] to move in circles 旋轉: *The water swirled about his feet.* 水在他的腳邊打旋。–**swirl** *n*: *with a swirl of her skirt* 裙子打旋 | *swirls of smoke* 繚繞上升的煙

swish¹ /swɪʃ; swɪʃ/ *v* **1** [I;T] to move quickly through the air with a whistling sound〔在空中〕嗖嗖地飛過 **2** [I] (of cloth) to move with a soft sound〔衣服〕沙沙作響 –**swish** *n*

swish² *adj infml* fashionable and expensive〔非正式〕時髦的; 昂貴的: *We went to a very swish restaurant.* 我們去了一家非常豪華的餐館。

***switch¹** /swɪtʃ; swɪtʃ/ *n* **1** an apparatus for controlling the flow of an electric current 開關: *a light switch* 電燈開關 **2** a sudden change or exchange 突然的改變: *We were confused by the last-minute switch in textbooks.* 課本在最後一刻改了, 這把我們搞糊塗了。**3** a small thin stick 細棒

switch² *v* [I;T] to change or exchange 改變; 變化: *They switched places.* 他們換了住處。| *He got tired of teaching and switched to painting.* 他對教書感到厭倦了, 於是改行繪畫。

switch off *phr v* **1** [I;T **switch** sthg ↔ **off**] to turn off an electric light or apparatus by pushing a switch 把〔電燈或電器〕關掉: *Could you switch the television off?* 你可以把電視關掉嗎? **2** [I] to stop paying attention 不注意; 不理睬: *She switches off if you mention the subject.* 你一提及這個話題, 她便不理不睬。

switch on *phr v* **1** [I;T **switch** sthg ↔ **on**] to turn on an electric light or apparatus by pushing a switch 把〔電燈或電器的〕開關打開: *Switch on the computer!* 打開電腦的開關! **2** [T **switch** sthg ↔ **on**] to start showing a certain kind of behaviour 開始表現出〔某種行為方式〕: *Switch on the charm and he'll do whatever you want.* 施展你的魅力, 這樣你叫他做甚麼他就會做甚麼。

switch over *phr v* [I] **1** to change a habit completely 徹底地改變〔習慣〕: *People are switching over* **to** *low calorie drinks.* 人們正在紛紛轉飲低熱量的飲料。 **2** to change from one radio or television station to another 轉換〔電台或電視頻道〕, 轉台: *This programme is boring — can we switch over?* 這個節目太乏味了, 我們轉台好不好?

switch·board /ˈswɪtʃˌbɔrd; ˈswɪtʃbɔːd/ *n* a central board which connects different telephone lines in the same company〔一個公司的〕電話交換台, 電話總機: *a switchboard operator* 電話總機接線員

swiv·el /ˈswɪvl; ˈswɪvəl/ *v* **-ll-** *BrE*《英式》|| **-l-** *AmE*《美式》(also 又作 **swivel round**) [I;T] to turn round while remaining in the same place (使)〔在原地〕旋轉 **-swivel** *n*: *a swivel chair* 旋轉椅

swol·len¹ /ˈswolən; ˈswəʊlən/ *adj* **1** bigger than usual 腫大的, 隆起的: *Her foot was very swollen after her accident.* 事故發生之後, 她的腳腫得很厲害。 **2** [only before a noun 只用於名詞前] greater than is reasonable 過大的; 誇大的: *She has a swollen opinion of herself.* 她自以為了不起。

swollen² *v* the past participle of SWELL ☆ SWELL 的過去分詞

swoon /swun; swuːn/ *v* [I] *old fash* to fall as you lose consciousness《老式》暈倒 **-swoon** *n*

swoop¹ /swup; swuːp/ *v* [I] **1** to descend suddenly from the sky 飛撲: *The bird swooped to catch a fish.* 鳥飛撲下來捕魚。 **2** to move towards a place quickly and without warning 突然襲擊: *The police swooped* **on** *the thieves' hiding place.* 警方突襲了竊賊的藏身之處。

swoop² *n* **1** a sudden movement down from the sky 飛撲 **2** a sudden and unexpected movement towards a place 突襲: *Five people were arrested in a dawn swoop* **on** *their houses.* 在黎明時分的突襲中, 有五人在家中被捕。 **3** **at one fell swoop, in one fell swoop** all at the same time 馬上, 立即

swop /swɑp; swɒp/ *v, n* see SWAP

sword /sord; sɔːd/ *n* a weapon with a long sharp blade 刀; 劍

sword·fish /ˈsordˌfɪʃ; ˈsɔːdfɪʃ/ *n* **swordfish** *or* **swordfishes** a large fish with a long, thin upper jaw 箭魚, 劍魚

swords·man /ˈsordzmən; ˈsɔːdzmən/ *n* **swordsmen** /-mən; -mən/ a person who is trained to fight with a sword 劍客, 劍手

swore /swor; swɔːʳ/ *v* the past tense form of SWEAR ☆ SWEAR 的過去式

sworn /sworn; swɔːn/ *v* **1** the past participle of SWEAR ☆ SWEAR 的過去分詞 **2** **sworn enemies** people who have an extreme and long lasting dislike of each other 不共戴天的敵人

swot¹ /swɑt; swɒt/ *n* *BrE infml* a person who studies extremely hard and is usually disliked for this《英式, 非正式》書呆子; 死讀書的人

swot² *v* **-tt-** (**grind** *AmE*《美式》) [I] *infml* to study hard, especially in preparation for an examination《非正式》苦讀〔尤指為考試作準備〕: *I'm swotting* **for** *tomorrow's test.* 我在為明天的測驗苦讀。

swot up *phr v* [I] to learn as much as possible about a subject quickly 臨急抱佛腳地學習〔某一門功課〕: *He's swotting up* **on** *international law.* 他正在拼命地學國際法。

swum /swʌm; swʌm/ *v* the past participle of SWIM ☆ SWIM 的過去分詞

swung /swʌŋ; swʌŋ/ *v* the past tense form and the past participle of SWING ☆ SWING 的過去式和過去分詞

syc·a·more /ˈsɪkəˌmor; ˈsɪkəmɔːʳ/ *n* [C;U] a type of tree, or the hard wood that comes from it 懸鈴木

syc·o·phant /ˈsɪkəfənt; ˈsɪkəfənt/ *n* a person who tries too hard to please important people, especially by praising or agreeing with them, for personal advantage (a word used to show disapproval) 諂媚奉承的人, 拍馬屁者〔含貶義〕 **-sycophantic** /ˌsɪkəˈfæntɪk; ˌsɪkəˈfæntɪk/ *adj*

syl·la·ble /ˈsɪləbl; ˈsɪləbəl/ *n* a word or part of a word which contains one vowel sound 音節: *There are two syllables in "window".* "window" 一詞有兩個音節。| *"Exciting" is a three syllable word.* "exciting" 是個三音節的詞。

syl·la·bus /ˈsɪləbəs; ˈsɪləbəs/ *n* **syllabuses** *or* **syllabi** /-baɪ; -baɪ/ an arrangement of subjects for a particular course of study 教學大綱, 課程大綱: *Is Shakespeare on next year's literature syllabus?* 莎士比亞戲劇被列入了明年文學課的教學大綱嗎?

*****sym·bol** /ˈsɪmbl; ˈsɪmbəl/ *n* **1** a sign or object which represents something else 象徵; 標誌: *This wedding ring is a symbol of our love.* 這隻結婚戒指象徵着我們之間的愛情。| *What's the symbol for a church on this map?* 這幅地圖上甚麼標誌代表教堂? **2** a letter or figure which represents a sound, number, or chemical substance 符號: *"H_2O" is the symbol for water.* "H_2O" 是水的符號。

sym·bol·ic /sɪmˈbɑlɪk; sɪmˈbɒlɪk/ *adj* (also 又作 **symbolical** /-lɪk; -lɪkəl/) used or seen as representing something else 象徵(性)的: *The Queen's visit is symbolic* **of** *the friendship between the two countries.* 女王的訪問象徵着兩國間的友誼。 **-symbolically** /-klɪ;

-kli/ *adv*

sym·bol·is·m /'sɪmbḷ,ɪzəm; 'sɪmbəlɪzəm/ *n* [U] the use of symbols to represent things, especially in literature, planting, and film 〔尤指文學、繪畫、電影中的〕象徵主義(手法)

sym·bol·ize /'sɪmbḷ,aɪz; 'sɪmbəlaɪz/ *v* **symbolized, symbolizing** (also 又作 **symbolise** in British English 〖英式〗) [T] to be used or seen as a symbol of something else 象徵，代表(某事物): *Cars like these symbolize capitalism at its worst.* 這一類的汽車象徵了資本主義制度最糟糕的情況。

sym·met·ri·cal /sɪ'mɛtrɪkl; sɪ'metrɪkəl/ *adj* (also 又作 **symmetric**) balanced in size, shape, or arrangement 對稱的: *a symmetrical design* 對稱的圖案 –opposite 反義 **asymmetric** –**symmetrically** /-klɪ; -kli/ *adv*

sym·me·try /'sɪmɪtrɪ; 'sɪm⅟₂tri/ *n* [U] **1** exact balance in the arrangement of one or more things 對稱(性) **2** the pleasant effect of such a balance 對稱美，勻稱

sym·pa·thet·ic /,sɪmpə'θɛtɪk; ,sɪmpə'θetɪk/ *adj* **1** feeling or showing pity for another person's problems or suffering (表示)同情的: *She was sympathetic when I explained why I hadn't done the work.* 我解釋了為何沒有做那項工作時，她表示同情。 **2** understanding and usually approving of someone's behaviour or opinions 表示贊同的: *He was sympathetic to my idea.* 他贊同我的觀點。 –opposite 反義 **unsympathetic** – **sympathetically** /-klɪ; -kli/ *adv*

sym·pa·thize /'sɪmpə,θaɪz; 'sɪmpəθaɪz/ *v* **sympathized, sympathizing** (also 又作 **sympathise** in British English 〖英式〗) [I] **1** to feel or show pity for another person's problems or suffering 同情: *It's hard to sympathize with such a difficult man.* 他這麼一個難相處的人很難得到別人同情。 **2** to understand and usually approve of someone's behaviour or opinions 贊同: *I sympathize with most of her political views.* 我贊同她大部分的政治觀點。 –**sympathizer** *n*

sym·pa·thy /'sɪmpəθɪ; 'sɪmpəθi/ *n* **1** [C;U] a feeling or expression of pity for the problems or sufferings of another person 同情，同情心: *She pressed his hand in sympathy.* 她緊握着他的手表示同情。 | *I didn't get much sympathy from the doctor.* 我不大得到醫生的同情。 **2** [U] understanding and usually approval of someone's behaviour or opinions 贊同: *I have a lot of sympathy for his point of view.* 我十分贊同他的觀點。

sym·pho·ny /'sɪmfənɪ; 'sɪmfəni/ *n* **symphonies** a piece of music written for an OR-CHESTRA 交響樂，交響曲

*****symp·tom** /'sɪmptəm; 'sɪmptəm/ *n* a sign of illness or of something bad 症狀；徵候: *The first symptom is a high temperature.* 起初的症狀是發高燒。 | *The number of homeless people is a symptom of social decay.* 無家可歸的人的數量是社會衰落的徵兆。 –**sympto-**

·matic /,sɪmptə'mætɪk; ,sɪmptə'mætɪk/ *adj*

syn·a·gogue /'sɪnə,gɔg; 'sɪnəgɒg/ *n* a place where Jews meet for religious worship 猶太教堂

syn·chro·nize /'sɪŋkrə,naɪz; 'sɪŋkrənaɪz/ *v* **synchronized, synchronizing** (also 又作 **synchronise** in British English 〖英式〗) **1** [T] to set clocks and watches so that they show the same time 把〔鐘錶〕撥至同一時間 **2** [I;T] to happen or make things happen at the same time or speed (使)同時發生，(使)同步發生: *They synchronized their steps.* 他們使步伐配合一致。 –**synchronization** /,sɪŋkrənə'zeʃən; ,sɪŋkrənaɪ'zeɪʃən/ *n* [U]

syn·di·cate¹ /'sɪndɪkɪt; 'sɪndɪk⅟₂t/ *n* [C + sing/pl verb] a group of people or companies that come together for a particular purpose, especially a business plan 商業財團；企業聯合組織；辛迪加: *The hotel is being built by a syndicate of local businessmen.* 本地企業家聯合會正在修建該旅館。

syn·di·cate² /'sɪndɪ,ket; 'sɪndɪ⅟₂keɪt/ *v* **syndicated, syndicating** [T] to print something in a number of different newspapers or magazines 在不同的報刊上同時發表: *My article has been syndicated in local papers all over the country.* 我的文章已在全國各地的地方性報紙上發表。 –**syndication** /,sɪndɪ'keʃən; ,sɪnd⅟₂'keɪʃən/ *n* [U]

syn·drome /'sɪn,drom; 'sɪndrəʊm/ *n* a set of signs, qualities or events which are typical of a general condition 綜合徵，綜合症狀；〔具有共同性的〕一系列事件

syn·o·nym /'sɪnə,nɪm; 'sɪnənɪm/ *n* a word with the same meaning as another word 同義詞: *"Sad" and "unhappy" are synonyms.* "sad" 和 "unhappy" 是同義詞。

sy·non·y·mous /sɪ'nɑnəməs; s⅟₂'nɒn⅟₂məs/ *adj* meaning the same or having a strong association with a particular thing (與…)同義的: *Football matches are becoming synonymous with crowd violence.* 足球比賽成為羣眾暴亂的同義詞。 –**synonymously** *adv*

sy·nop·sis /sɪ'nɑpsɪs; s⅟₂'nɒps⅟₂s/ *n* **synopses** /-siz; -si:z/ a short account of something longer, like the contents of a book or the story of a film 〔如書或影片故事的〕概要，摘要

syn·tax /'sɪntæks; 'sɪntæks/ *n* [U] the rules of grammar which are used for ordering words in a sentence 句法 –**syntactic** /sɪn'tæktɪk; sɪn'tæktɪk/ *adj* –**syntactically** /-klɪ; -kli/ *adv*

syn·the·sis /'sɪnθəsɪs; 'sɪnθ⅟₂s⅟₂s/ *n* **synthe-ses** /-siz; -si:z/ [C;U] the combination of different things or ideas 〔事物或觀念的〕綜合；合成: *Our beliefs are a synthesis of Eastern and Western religions.* 我們的信仰是東西方宗教的綜合體。 –compare 比較 ANALYSIS

syn·the·size /'sɪnθə,saɪz; 'sɪnθəsaɪz/ *v* **synthesized, synthesizing** (also 又作 **synthe-sise** in British English 〖英式〗) [T] to produce something by combining different ideas or chemicals 綜合; 合成〔某物〕

syn·thet·ic /sɪnˈθɛtɪk; sɪnˈθɛtɪk/ *adj* made by humans and not natural 人造的, 合成的: *I prefer cotton to synthetic material.* 我寧願要棉花, 也不要合成材料。**–synthetic** *n* **–synthetically** /-klɪ; -klɪ/ *adv*

syph·i·lis /ˈsɪflɪs; ˈsɪflɨs/ *n* [U] a serious illness caught by having sex with an infected person 梅毒

sy·phon /ˈsaɪfən; ˈsaɪfən/ *n, v* see 見 SIPHON

sy·ringe[1] /ˈsɪrɪndʒ; sɨˈrɪndʒ/ *n* a tube used in medicine for putting liquids such as drugs into your body or for removing small amounts of blood 注射器, 注射筒; 洗滌器

syringe[2] *v* **syringed, syringing** [T] to treat a part of your body by removing something from it with a syringe 用洗滌器清洗, 噴洗

syr·up /ˈsɪrəp; ˈsɪrəp/ *n* [U] thick, sweet liquid 糖漿 **–syrupy** *adj*

★★sys·tem /ˈsɪstəm; ˈsɪstəm/ *n* **1** [C] a group of related parts working together 系統, 體系: *the postal system* 郵政體系 | *London's transport system* 倫敦的交通體系 **2** [C] your body as a whole, or certain parts of it working together 〔身體的〕系統: *Too many nuts are bad for your digestive system.* 果仁吃得太多有損你的消化系統。**3** [C] an ordered set of ideas or

methods 制度: *The problem is with the British parliamentary system.* 問題在於英國的國會制度。| *We need systems that will make our work easier.* 我們需要一些制度來使工作做起來容易一些。**4** [U] organization 組織; 秩序; 條理: *You need some system in your study methods.* 你必須在學習方法上安排得有條理一些。**5 the system** the rules and methods of a society or organization 社會制度; 組織制度: *She's trying to beat the system and avoid paying tax.* 她企圖與社會制度抗爭而逃稅。**6 get something out of your system** to express strong feelings in some way so that you do not have to continue controlling them 發洩強烈的感情

sys·te·mat·ic /ˌsɪstəˈmætɪk; ˌsɪstɨˈmætɪk◂/ *adj* thorough and done according to a careful plan 系統化的, 有條理的: *The police made a systematic search of the room.* 警察徹底搜查那個房間。**–systematically** /-klɪ; -klɪ/ *adv*

sys·te·ma·tize /ˈsɪstəmə,taɪz; ˈsɪstɨmətaɪz/ *v* **systematized, systematizing** (also 又作 **systematise** in British English 《英式》) [T] to arrange and order things according to a careful plan 使…系統化: *Our marketing strategies must be systematized.* 我們的推銷策略必須系統化。**–systematization** /ˌsɪstəmətəˈzeʃən; sɪstɨmətaɪˈzeɪʃən/ *n* [U]

T, t

T, t /ti; tiː/ **T's, t's 1** the 20th letter of the English alphabet 英語的第二十個字母 **2 to a T** infml exactly〔非正式〕恰到好處: *That hat suits her to a T.* 那頂帽子對她再合適不過了。

ta /ta; tɑː/ interj infml thank you〔非正式〕謝謝

tab /tæb; tæb/ n **1** a small piece of cloth or paper fixed to something and giving information about it〔繫到某物上的布或紙製的〕標籤: *We've been asked to sew name tabs into the children's school clothes.* 學校要求我們在孩子的校服上縫上名字標籤。 **2** infml AmE a bill〔非正式，美式〕賬單 **3 keep tabs on** infml to pay careful attention to what is happening or what someone is doing〔非正式〕密切注意: *Keep tabs on your spending.* 小心計算你自己的開支。

tab·by /'tæbɪ; 'tæbi/ n **tabbies** a cat with dark bands on its brown or grey fur (虎)斑貓

★★**ta·ble**[1] /'tebl; 'teɪbəl/ **1** a piece of furniture with a flat top supported by one or more legs 桌子; 枱子: *a kitchen table* 廚房間的桌子 | *A table for two, please, near the back of the restaurant.* 請給我一張靠餐廳裡面的兩個座位的桌子。 **2** [+ sing/pl verb] the people sitting at a table 同席的人; 在座的人: *The whole table got up as she entered the room.* 她走進房間裡，全桌的人都站了起來。 **3** a set of facts or figures arranged in rows across and down the page 表; 表格: *Table 1 shows our profits over the last 3 years.* 圖表一顯示我們過去三年的盈利情況。

table[2] v **tabled, tabling** [T] to formally suggest something to be talked about in a meeting 建議把〔某事〕列入議程

ta·ble d'hôte /ˌtebl 'dot; ˌtɑːbəl 'dəʊt/ n a fixed price meal in a hotel or restaurant〔旅館或餐廳的〕定餐, 客飯

ta·ble·spoon /'tebl,spun; 'teɪbəlspuːn/ n **1** a large spoon used for serving food 湯匙 **2** (also 又作 **tablespoonful** /-,ful; -fʊl/) the amount that a tablespoon holds 一湯匙之量: *a tablespoon of flour* 一湯匙麵粉

tab·let /'tæblɪt; 'tæblɪt/ n **1** medicine in a small, hard form 藥片: *Take two tablets before every meal.* 每頓飯前服兩片藥。 **2** a flat piece of a hard material like stone, with words cut into it 碑; 匾額 **3** fml a small block of soap〔正式〕一塊肥皂

table ten·nis /'··,··/ n [U] an indoor game played on a table by two or four players who hit a small ball to each other across a net 乒乓球

tab·loid /'tæblɔɪd; 'tæblɔɪd/ n a newspaper with small pages, a lot of pictures, and little serious news〔版面小、圖片多、嚴肅新聞少的〕小報

ta·boo /tə'bu; tə'buː/ n a strong religious or social custom which forbids certain behaviour or speech 禁忌; 忌諱: *There is a taboo on eating meat.* 吃肉犯忌 **–taboo** adj: *Is that a taboo subject?* 那是一個忌諱的話題嗎?

tab·u·late /'tæbjə,let; 'tæbjᵿleɪt/ v **tabulated, tabulating** [T] to arrange facts or figures in rows or lists 把〔事實或數字〕列成表 **–tabular** /'tæbjələr; 'tæbjᵿlər/ adj: *This information would be clearer in tabular form.* 這資料如果列成表就會更清楚。 **–tabulation** /ˌtæbju'leʃən; ˌtæbjᵿ'leɪʃən/ n [U]

ta·cit /'tæsɪt; 'tæsɪt/ adj shown or understood without being put into words 心照不宣的: *We had a tacit agreement to cooperate with each other.* 我們達成了互相合作的默契。 **–tacitly** adv

ta·ci·turn /'tæsə,tɜn; 'tæsɪˌtɜːn/ adj fml tending to speak very little and sometimes appearing unfriendly〔正式〕沉默寡言的 **–taciturnity** /ˌtæsə'tɜnɪtɪ; ˌtæsɪˈtɜːnɪti/ n [U]

tack[1] /tæk; tæk/ n **1** [C] a small nail with a sharp point and flat head 平頭釘; 大頭釘: *carpet tacks* 地毯釘 **2** [C] infml a method of doing something different to one used before〔非正式〕〔與先前不同的〕方法: *If that doesn't work, I'll try a different tack.* 如果那樣不行，我就再換一種方法。 **3** [C;U] a course or change in direction of a sailing ship which allows the wind to fill its sails〔帆船〕搶風航向; 搶風調向 **4** [C] a long loose stitch used to fasten pieces of cloth together before sewing them properly 粗縫針腳

tack[2] v **1** [T + adv/prep] to fasten something to a solid surface with a small, sharp nail〔用釘〕釘住, 固定〔某物〕: *She tacked a notice to the board.* 她把通知釘在佈告欄上。 **2** [I + adv/prep] to sail in a particular direction so that the ship's sails catch the wind〔帆船〕搶風航行 **3** [T] to fasten pieces of cloth together with long loose stitches before sewing them properly〔用大針腳〕粗縫: *You tack the curtains and I'll sew them.* 你把那些窗簾粗縫一下，然後我來把它們縫起來。

tack sthg ↔ **on** phr v [T] infml to add something not originally planned to the end of something already prepared〔非正

式』臨時添加: *She tacked a few words on to her sister's letter.* 她在姐姐寫的信上添了幾句。

*tack·le¹ /ˈtækl; ˈtækəl/ *n* **1** [C] an attempt to take the ball away from an opponent in certain sports 搶球: *What a fine tackle by the England captain!* 英格蘭隊隊長這個球搶得多棒! **2** [U] the apparatus used in a sport 運動器具: *Don't forget to bring your fishing tackle.* 別忘了帶釣具。 **3** [U] a system of ropes and wheels for lifting or pulling things 滑輪組

tackle² *v* **tackled, tackling 1** [T] to take action to deal with something 處理, 解決〔某事物〕: *How can we tackle this problem?* 我們如何來處理這個問題? **2** [I;T] to try to take the ball away from an opponent in certain sports 搶球 **3** [T] *infml* to try to stop someone, often by attacking them 〔非正式〕〔常通過攻擊〕阻止〔某人〕: *My husband tackled the burglar and made him drop everything.* 我丈夫扭住了竊賊, 迫使他丟下手上的東西。 **4** [T] to speak to someone directly and honestly so as to deal with a problem 直接了當地講; 交涉: *You'll have to tackle her parents about her bad behaviour.* 你必須找她的父母直接談談她行徑惡劣的問題。

tack·y /ˈtæki; ˈtæki/ *adj* **tackier, tackiest 1** sticky 黏的: *The paint is still tacky so don't touch it.* 油漆還未乾, 所以請不要碰它。 **2** *infml* unpleasant and of poor quality 〔非正式〕不合意的; 質量差的: *Many souvenirs are really tacky.* 許多紀念品質量低劣。

tact /tækt; tækt/ *n* [U] the ability to do or say the right thing at the right time so that no offence is given 圓滑; 機智: *He used great tact to resolve the conflict.* 他極為機智地解決了矛盾。 **–tactful** *adj*: *I appreciate your tactful handling of a difficult situation.* 我很欣賞你能夠機智地擺脫困境。 **–tactfully** *adv* **–tactless** *adj*: *His tactless remark upset her greatly.* 他說的話很不乖巧, 令她十分生氣。

tac·tic /ˈtæktɪk; ˈtæktɪk/ *n* **1** a means of getting a desired result 手段: *I respect her aims but not her tactics!* 我贊成她的目的, 但不贊成她的手法! **2 tactics** [pl] the organization of military forces to win a battle 戰術; 兵法: *A general should be skilled in tactics.* 將軍應該精通兵法。 **–tactical** *adj*: *a tactical decision* 策略性的決定 | *tactical skill in battle* 戰術技巧

tac·tile /ˈtæktl; ˈtæktaɪl/ *adj fml* related to or experienced by touch 〔正式〕觸覺的

tad·pole /ˈtædpol; ˈtædpəʊl/ *n* a small black water creature with a long tail that grows into a FROG or TOAD 蝌蚪

tag¹ /tæg; tæg/ *n* **1** [C] a small piece of some material fixed to something to give information about it 標籤: *Is there a price tag on that dress?* 那條裙子上有價格標籤嗎? **2** [U] a chasing game played by children 捉迷藏 **3** [C] a phrase added to a sentence to give it more importance or make it a question 附

加句; 附加問句

tag² *v* **-gg-** [T] to fasten a small piece of some material to something to give information about it 給〔某物〕加上標籤: *We've tagged all our sheep.* 我們給所有綿羊加了標籤。

tag along *phr v* [I] to go with other people who often do not particularly want you to be with them 緊跟; 尾隨: *Wherever I went, my little sister used to tag along.* 不論我到那兒, 我的小妹妹都要跟着我一起去。

tag sthg ↔ on *phr v* [T] to add something to the end of something already written or said 附加〔某物〕: *Her objections were casually tagged on at the end of the report.* 她的反對意見只簡單地附加在報告的末尾。

*tail¹ /tel; teɪl/ *n* **1** the movable part at the end of an animal's body 尾巴: *The dog wagged its tail with pleasure.* 那條狗高興地搖動尾巴。 **2** anything like a tail in appearance or position 尾狀物: *the tail of a plane* 飛機尾部 **3 tails** [pl] see 見 TAILCOAT **4 tail end** the last part of something 末尾部分: *the tail end of the film* 電影的結尾 **5** *infml* a person employed to watch and follow someone 〔非正式〕〔雇來的〕盯梢者: *He's got a tail on his wife.* 他雇人尾隨他的太太。 **6 on someone's tail** close behind someone or near to finding them 跟蹤某人: *The police are on his tail.* 警方正在跟蹤他。 **7 tails** [pl] the side of a coin which does not have the head of a ruler on it 〔硬幣的〕反面

tail² *v* [T] **1** to follow someone and watch what they do 跟蹤〔某人〕: *The police have been tailing me.* 警察一直在跟蹤我。 **2** to take the ends off small fruit and vegetables before cooking or eating them 去除〔水果或蔬菜的〕末梢

tail off *phr v* [I] to become less in quantity, strength, or quality 減少; 減輕; 變差: *His voice tailed off as he saw his father's expression.* 他看見父親的表情, 聲音便放輕了。

tail·coat /ˈtel,kot; ˌteɪlˈkəʊt/ *n* (also 又作 **tails**) a man's formal evening coat with the lower back part divided into two 燕尾服

tai·lor¹ /ˈtelə; ˈteɪləʳ/ *n* a person who makes clothes to particular measurements, especially for men 〔尤指男裝〕裁縫

tailor² *v* [T] **1** to make or change something so that it is suitable for a particular situation 使〔某物〕符合〔某一情況〕; 改變〔某物〕使其符合〔某一情況〕: *We can tailor the insurance policy to meet your needs.* 我們可以適當修改保險單條款以符合你的要求。 **2** to make clothes by cutting and sewing cloth to particular measurements 裁剪〔布料〕

tailor-made /ˌ···ˈ·◂/ *adj* **1** specially made or extremely suitable for a particular purpose or person 特製的; 特別合適的: *The job is tailor-made for John.* 這項工作非常適合約翰。 **2** specially made to fit the wearer (used of clothes) 定製的〔指衣服〕: *a tailor-*

made suit 一套定製的衣服

taint /teɪnt; teɪnt/ v [T] to make a person or thing less pure and desirable 污染; 玷污: *He is tainted by his friendship with corrupt businessmen.* 他由於與腐敗的商人交往而名聲受損。 –**taint** n [sing]: *The taint of dishonesty ruined his reputation.* 不誠實這一污點毀了他的名譽。

★**take**[1] /tek; teɪk/ v **took** /tʊk; tʊk/, **taken** /'tekən; 'teɪkən/, **taking** [T] **1** to put your hand round something and hold it, especially when someone has offered it to you 拿住, 握住〔尤指某人把東西給你時〕: *She took his arm and led him across the road.* 她扶着他的胳膊，領他過了馬路。| *He held out the letter and I took it.* 他遞過信，我接了過來。| *Shall I take your coat?* 我來幫你拿外衣好嗎? **2** to remove something from a place or from someone's possession 拿開; 拿出: *I took the scissors out of the drawer.* 我從抽屜裡拿出剪刀。| *She opened her purse and took out some money.* 她打開錢包，拿出一些錢。| *Who's taken my pen?* 誰拿了我的鋼筆? **3** to carry someone or something from one place to another 把〔某人或某物〕從一個地方帶到另一個地方: *I think I'll need to take some work home this evening.* 我覺得今晚有必要把一部分工作帶回家裡去做。| *We can take you to the station if you like.* 如果你喜歡，我們可以送你到車站。| *It's time to take the children to school.* 該送孩子們上學了。 **4** to do something 做〔某事〕: *Let's take a walk.* 我們去散散步吧。| *Can I take a look at the baby?* 讓我看嬰兒可以嗎? **5 take a bus/taxi/train** to go somewhere by bus, taxi, or train 乘公共汽車/出租車/火車: *Shall we take a taxi to the station?* 我們坐出租車去車站好嗎? **6** to travel along a particular road 順着某條路行進: *We took the motor-way as far as Birmingham.* 我們順着高速公路一直開到伯明翰。 **7 take a seat** to sit down 坐下; 落座 **8** to swallow medicine, especially regularly 〔尤指定時地〕服〔藥〕: *Take two tablets three times a day.* 這種藥片每日三次，一次兩片。 **9** to accept or receive something 接受, 收到〔某物〕: *I offered her £1,000 for the car, but she wouldn't take it.* 我出一千英鎊買那輛車，但她不肯接受我的意思。| *You never take my advice.* 你從來不肯接受我的意見。| *Why should I take the blame?* 為甚麼要我來負責任? **10** to need something 需要〔某物〕: *It takes a lot of time to create a beautiful garden.* 建一座美麗的花園要花費很多時間。| *It took us three hours to get home.* 我們花了三個小時才到家。| *It takes a lot of courage to do what he's done.* 要像他那樣去做，需要很大的勇氣。 **11** to record or measure something 記錄, 測量〔某物〕: *He took my name and address.* 他記下了我的名字和地址。| *The nurse took my temperature.* 護士量了量我的體溫。 **12** to understand something in a particular way 〔以某種方式〕

理解〔某事物〕: *I took his remarks as a compliment.* 我把他的話看作是讚揚。 **13** to have a particular feeling when something happens 感受; 有某種情緒: *She took it very badly when her father died.* 父親去世時，她極為難過。| *He never takes me seriously.* 他從不認真考慮我的意見。 **14** to consider something or think about it 考慮, 思考〔某事物〕: *Many countries in Africa regularly experience food shortages. Let's take Ethiopia, for example.* 非洲許多國家經常食品短缺。就拿埃塞俄比亞作為例子吧。 **15** to have a particular opinion about something 持有〔某種觀點〕: *She takes the attitude that people should sort out their own problems.* 她認為人們應當自己想辦法解決自身的問題。 **16** to start renting a house or flat 開始租〔房子或公寓〕: *We took a small flat in London.* 我們在倫敦租了間小公寓。 **17** to seize a place by force 武裝佔領〔某地〕: *Troops have taken the capital city.* 軍隊已佔領了首都。 **18** to give someone a lesson 給〔某人〕上課: *I take the students for French and German.* 我教學生法語和德語。 **19** to wear a particular size of clothes or shoes 穿〔某一尺寸的〕衣服或鞋: *What size do you take?* 你的尺碼是多少? **20 be taken ill** to become ill suddenly 突然生病 **21 can't take** to be unable to accept or bear something 無法接受; 無法忍受: *I can't take his constant criticism.* 我受不了他喋喋不休的批評。 **22 I take it** = I suppose 我認為: *I take it you know what you're doing.* 我相信你知道自己在幹甚麼。 **23 take it from me** = believe me 相信我 **24 take leave of someone** *fml* to say GOODBYE to someone 〔正式〕與某人道別 **25 take something as read** to accept that something is true without questioning it 毫不懷疑地接受某事 **26 take place** to happen 發生: *When did the accident take place?* 事故是何時發生的? **27 take your own life** to kill yourself 自殺

take aback *phr v* **be taken aback** to be very surprised and shocked 大吃一驚; 震驚

take after sbdy *phr v* [T] to look or behave like someone in your family 長得像; 舉止像: *She takes after her mother.* 她很像她的母親。

take sthg ↔ **apart** *phr v* [T] to separate something into the small pieces that it is made of 把〔某物〕拆開

take sthg ↔ **back** *phr v* [T] **1** to take something to the place where you got it from 把〔某物〕放回原處: *These shoes don't fit — I'll have to take them back.* 這雙鞋不合腳——我得把它放回原處去。 **2** to agree to receive something back 同意收回: *The machine was obviously faulty, but the shop refused to take it back.* 這台機器明顯有問題，但商店拒絕退貨。 **3** to admit that you were wrong in something that you said 承認說錯了話: *I'm sorry — I take that back.* 很抱歉——我收回那些話。

take sthg ↔ **down** *phr v* [T] **1** to separate a structure into pieces so that it is no longer standing 把〔某一建築〕拆開: *Engineers are taking down the bridge.* 工程師正在拆那座橋。 **2** to write down a piece of information 寫下〔資料〕: *She took down my phone number.* 她寫下了我的電話號碼。

take in *phr v* **1** [T take sbdy ↔ **in**] to provide a home for someone 接納, 收留〔某人〕: *My sister agreed to take me in for a while.* 姐姐同意我在她那裡暫住一些日子。 **2** [T take sthg ↔ **in**] to make clothes smaller or narrower 把〔衣服〕改小 **3** [T take sthg ↔ **in**] to understand something 理解〔某事〕: *There were too many facts to take in all at once.* 事實太多, 無法馬上全部理解。 **4** [T take sbdy ↔ **in**] to deceive someone 欺騙〔某人〕

take off *phr v* **1** [T take sthg ↔ **off**] to remove a piece of clothing 脫下〔衣服〕: *She came in and took her coat off.* 她進來以後脫掉了外衣。 **2** [I] (of a plane) to rise into the air 〔飛機〕起飛, 升空 **3** [T take sbdy ↔ **off**] *infml* to copy someone's speech or ways of behaving 〔非正式〕模仿〔某人的講話或舉止〕 **4** [T take sthg ↔ **off**] to not go to work for a particular period of time 休息; 不工作: *I'm taking a couple of weeks off.* 我準備休息幾個星期。

take on *phr v* **1** [T take sbdy ↔ **on**] to start to employ someone 開始雇用〔某人〕: *We're taking on a new secretary this week.* 本週我們聘請了一位新祕書。 **2** [T take on sthg] to start to have a particular quality 開始有〔某種品質〕: *His face took on an expression of dismay.* 他的臉上流露出沮喪的神情。 **3** [T take sbdy ↔ **on**] to start a fight or competition with someone 開始與〔某人〕打鬥〔競爭〕 **4** [T take sthg ↔ **on**] to accept responsibility for something 對〔某事〕負責: *I've taken on too much work.* 我已承擔了太多的工作。

take out *phr v* **1** [T take sthg ↔ **out**] to remove something from a place 把〔某物〕拿掉 **2** [T take sbdy ↔ **out**] to take someone to a place such as a restaurant or theatre 把〔某人〕帶到〔餐館或劇院等處〕: *She's taking me out for a meal tonight.* 她今晚帶我出去吃飯。 **3** take out insurance to obtain insurance 投保: *Have you taken out life insurance yet?* 你有沒有投保人壽險? **4** take it out of you to make you feel very tired 使你感到非常疲勞

take sthg out on sbdy *phr v* [T] to express your own feelings by making someone else suffer 向〔別人〕發泄〔情緒〕; 拿〔別人〕出〔氣〕: *When he's had a bad day he takes it out on the children.* 他白天不順心, 就拿孩子出氣。

take sthg ↔ **over** *phr v* [T] to gain control over something or responsibility for it 接收, 接管〔某物〕: *The company has been taken over by a Dutch firm.* 該公司已由一家荷蘭企業接管。 | *Sarah will take over my job when I leave.* 我走了以後薩拉將接管我的工作。

take to *phr v* **1** [T take to sbdy/sthg] to like someone or something straight away 立刻喜歡〔某人或某物〕: *I took to him as soon as I met him.* 一見面我就喜歡上他了。 **2** take to doing something to begin doing something regularly 開始經常做某事: *He's taken to staying out late.* 他開始晚回家了。 **3** take to your bed to go to bed because you are ill 由於生病而臥床

take sthg ↔ **up** *phr v* [T] **1** to start doing an activity, usually for pleasure 開始某項活動〔通常為了娛樂〕: *He took up writing poetry while he was still at school.* 他還在上學的時候便開始寫詩。 **2** to use a particular amount of time or space 佔用〔時間或空間〕: *Books take up a lot of space.* 書本佔用很多地方。 | *The visit took up the whole of Sunday.* 參觀用去了週日一整天的時間。 **3** to continue something 繼續〔某事〕: *I'll take up the story where I left off yesterday.* 我接着昨天停下的地方把故事繼續講下去。

take sbdy **up on** sthg *phr v* [T] **1** to accept an offer that someone has made to you 接受〔提議〕: *I'd like to take you up on your offer of a meal.* 你請吃飯, 我樂意奉陪。 **2** to question something that someone has said 對〔某人所說的事情〕進行提問: *I'd like to take you up on that last point.* 我想問一問最後那一點的有關情況。

take up with *phr v* **1** [T take sthg **up with** sbdy] to ask someone about something 就〔某事〕詢問〔某人〕: *I think I need to take this matter up with my lawyer.* 我覺得這事有必要詢問一下我的律師。 **2** [T take up with sbdy] *infml* to become friendly with someone 〔非正式〕與〔某人〕密切交往

take upon *phr v* take it upon yourself to do something to do something even though no one has asked you to do it 主動提出做某事

take² *n* a scene that is filmed as part of a film or television broadcast 電影〔電視〕鏡頭

take·a·way /ˈteɪkəweɪ; ˈteɪkəweɪ/ *n* **1** a shop from which cooked meals are taken away to be eaten 外賣餐館: *Let's get some food from the Chinese takeaway.* 我們去那家外賣中餐館去買些吃的吧。 **2** a hot cooked meal which you buy in a shop but eat somewhere else 外賣餐點: *an Indian takeaway* 印度外賣餐點—**takeaway** *adj*: *a takeaway meal* 一頓外賣飯菜

ta·ken /ˈteɪkən; ˈteɪkən/ the past participle of TAKE ☆TAKE 的過去分詞

take·off /ˈteɪkɒf; ˈteɪkɒf/ *n* **1** [C;U] the beginning of a flight, when a plane leaves the ground 〔飛機〕起飛: *It was a smooth takeoff.* 飛機平穩地起飛了。 **2** *infml* an amusing copy of someone's behaviour 〔非正式〕滑稽的模仿: *He does takeoffs of leading politicians.*

他能模仿政治風雲人物的舉止。

take·over /'tek,ovə; 'teɪk,əʊvəʳ/ n [C;U] **1** an act of gaining control of a company, by buying most of its shares 〔通過收購大部分股票而對某公司的〕接管 **2** an act of gaining control of a country or organization, often by force 〔對國家或組織的〕佔領: a military takeover. 軍事佔領

tak·ings /'tekɪŋz; 'teɪkɪŋz/ n [pl] receipts of money from sales 營業收入: We were counting the day's takings. 我們在清點當天的營業收入。

tal·cum pow·der /'tælkəm ,paudə; 'tælkəm ,paudəʳ/ (also 又作 **talc** /tælk; tælk/ infml 《非正式》) n [U] very fine powder which you put on your body to dry it or make it smell nice 爽身粉; 撲粉

***tale** /tel; teɪl/ n **1** a story of imaginary events, expecially exciting ones 〔尤指刺激的〕故事: She told us tales of adventure. 她說給我們聽一些驚險故事。 **2** a written or spoken account of a real situation or event 〔書面或口頭的〕陳述; 記述: tales of life in the desert 對於沙漠生活的記述 **3** a false or unkind story about another person, particularly a child, told so they will be punished 謊言; 謠言: How can I stop Susie telling tales? 我如何才能制止蘇茜說謊?

***tal·ent** /'tælənt; 'tælənt/ n [C;U] a special natural ability 天才; 天賦: She shows great artistic talent. 她表現出卓越的藝術才華。 | He's looking for a way to use his talents. 他盼望有機會一展所長。 | a talent for drawing 繪畫的天賦 –see 見 GENIUS (USAGE 用法) –**talented** adj: a very talented actor 才華橫溢的演員

tal·is·man /'tælɪzmən; 'tælɪzmən/ n an object which is believed to have magic powers to protect people and bring them luck 避邪物; 護身符

***talk**¹ /tɔk; tɔːk/ v **1** [I] to use words to express yourself in speech 說話; 講話: I want to talk to you about something. 我想和你談一些事情。 | The baby's just learning to talk. 嬰兒剛開始學講話。 **2** [T] to discuss or express something in words 談論, 表達〔某人〕: We're sick of people talking politics. 對於人們談論政治我們已經厭倦了。 | Talk sense! 講點道理吧! | Don't talk rubbish! 別說廢話! **3** [I] infml to give secret information, usually unwillingly 《非正式》〔通常為不情願地〕提供祕密的信息: The suspect refused to talk. 嫌疑犯拒絕透露實情。 **4** [T] to speak a particular language 講〔某種語言〕: Shall we talk French? 我們講法語好嗎? **5** [I] to give an informal speech about something 作非正式的報告: She'll talk on ancient history. 她準備作一個關於古代史的報告。 **6** [I] to talk about other people's actions and private lives 議論〔他人的行動和私生活〕: The neighbours are already talking about us. 鄰居已經在說我們的閒話了。 **7**

talking of something you use this expression in conversation when you are introducing a new subject which is slightly related to the last one 說到某事〔用於引入一個與剛才所說的話有一點聯繫的新話題〕: Then we had an enormous dinner and went to bed. Talking of food, did you know they've got Italian Christmas cakes in the delicatessen? 然後我們飽餐一頓後上牀睡覺。說到吃的東西, 你知不知道那家熟食店裡有意大利聖誕蛋糕賣? **8 talk your way out of something** to avoid something, especially trouble, by explaining or persuading someone 靠解釋或說服某人而避免麻煩 **9 talk shop** to talk about work 談論工作: Please stop talking shop! 請不要再談公事了! **10 now you're talking!** = now what you are saying is something that is really interesting to me 現在說的話還有點意思 **11 talk of the devil!** an expression used when a person being discussed suddenly enters the room 說誰誰到了〔用於表示正在談及的人突然進入房間〕 **12 you can talk** = you are as guilty of that as the person you mentioned 你居然有臉說別人: He steals? You can talk — what's the company name on that pen you're using? 他偷東西? 你居然有臉說這話——你手裡那支鋼筆上刻的是哪家公司的名字?

talk back phr v [I] to answer someone in a rude manner 還嘴; 反唇相譏

talk down phr v **1** [T **talk** sbdy/sthg ↔ **down**] to help the pilot of a plane to land by giving spoken instructions 〔透過無線電〕指示〔飛行員〕着陸: The radar has failed, so we'll have to talk the planes down. 雷達失靈了, 所以我們必須透過無線電指示飛機着陸。 **2** [I] to talk to someone as if you are more important than they are 以高人一等的口氣對〔某人〕講話: I dislike doctors who talk down to their patients. 我討厭那些用高人一等的口氣對病人講話的醫生。

talk sbdy **into** sthg phr v to persuade someone to do something 說服〔某人〕做〔某事〕: He talked me into selling my car. 他說服我把車賣了。

talk sbdy **out of** sthg phr v to persuade someone not to do something 勸阻〔某人〕做〔某事〕

talk sthg ↔ **over** phr v [T] to discuss something thoroughly 詳細討論: Can't we talk it over without arguing? 我們能不能心平氣和地討論一下?

talk sbdy ↔ **round** phr v [T] to persuade someone to change their mind 說服〔某人〕改變主意: He didn't want to come but we talked him round. 他不想來, 但我們說服他改變了主意。

***talk**² n **1** [C] a conversation 講話: I had a long talk with Mrs Jones today. 今天我與瓊斯太太作了一番長談。 **2** [C] an informal speech 非正式演講〔講話〕: She's gone to a talk on American politics. 她去聽有關美國

政治的講話。**3 talks** [pl] formal discussions 會談: *Most European leaders will be attending the talks in Rome.* 大部分歐洲國家領導人將參加在羅馬舉行的會談。**4** [U] a particular way of speaking 説話方式: *baby talk* 嬰兒説話的方式 **5** [U] speech which may be meaningless or give false information 空話; 謊言: *His threats were just talk.* 他的威脅不過説説而已。| *There's been a lot of talk about Linda and Paul.* 有許多有關琳達和保羅的傳言。

talk·a·tive /ˈtɔkətɪv; ˈtɔːkətɪv/ *adj* fond of talking 愛説話的; 話多的

talk·er /ˈtɔkə; ˈtɔːkəʳ/ *n* a person who talks in a particular way 〔以某種方式〕講話的人: *He's a fast talker.* 他講話速度很快。

⋆**tall** /tɔl; tɔːl/ *adj* **1** of greater than average height 高的: *a tall man* 高個子男人 | *a tall building* 高樓 | *tall trees* 高大的樹木 –see picture on page 469 見 469 頁彩圖 **2** used when giving measurements 有...高〔用於表示高度〕: *2 metres tall* 兩米高 | *How tall are you?* 你個子有多高? **3 tall order** a request that is difficult to carry out 很難達到的要求 **4 tall story** a story that is difficult to believe 難以置信的故事

tal·low /ˈtælo; ˈtæləʊ/ *n* [U] hard animal fat used for making candles 〔用於製蠟燭的〕動物硬脂

tal·ly¹ /ˈtælɪ; ˈtæli/ *n* **tallies** a record of points or amounts kept as you go along 記分; 記賬: *Please keep a tally of what you spend.* 請記下你的開支賬目。

tally² *v* **tallied, tallying** [I] to be the same as something else in all details 符合; 完全一致: *Your figures don't tally* **with** *mine.* 你的數字和我的不符。| *The two accounts don't tally.* 這兩種描述不完全一致。

tal·on /ˈtælən; ˈtælən/ *n* one of the sharp curved nails on the feet of some hunting birds 猛禽的利爪

tam·bou·rine /ˌtæmbəˈrin; ˌtæmbəˈriːn/ *n* a circular frame with skin stretched over it and small metal plates round the edge, which is shaken or beaten to make a musical sound 鈴鼓

tame¹ /tem; teɪm/ *adj* **1** trained to live with people (used of animals) 馴服的; 馴養的〔指動物〕: *a tame lion* 馴服的獅子 **2** *infml* unexciting 〔非正式〕枯燥無味的: *a tame football match* 平淡的足球賽 **3** obedient or always willing to help (a word used to express disapproval) 過於溫順的〔含貶義〕: *Haven't you got a tame politician you could ask about this?* 你們難道就找不到一位容易驅策的政界人士可一問這件事嗎? –**tamely** *adv* –**tameness** *n* [U]

tame² *v* **tamed, taming** [T] **1** to train an animal to be gentle and live with people 馴服〔動物〕**2** to bring something dangerous or violent under control 控制住〔危險或狂暴的事物〕: *Scientists have not yet tamed nature.*

科學家至今還未完全征服自然。–**tamer** *n*

tam·per /ˈtæmpə; ˈtæmpəʳ/ *v* **tamper with** to touch or make changes in something without permission 擅自撥弄; 擅自改變: *My car wouldn't start after he tampered with it.* 他撥弄過之後, 我的車就無法開動了。

tam·pon /ˈtæmpɒn; ˈtæmpɒn/ *n* a hard mass of cotton that a woman pushes inside her to collect the blood during her PERIOD 〔女子月經時用的〕棉塞

tan¹ /tæn; tæn/ *v* **-nn-** **1** [I;T] to make or become brown as a result of being in strong sunlight (使)曬成棕色: *This cream will help you to tan.* 這種乳液可以迅速令皮膚曬成棕色。| *She lay tanning her legs.* 她躺在那裡曬她的腿。**2** [T] to change animal skin into leather 把〔動物毛皮〕製成皮革

tan² *n* see 見 SUNTAN

tan³ *adj* yellowish brown in colour 棕黃色的, 棕褐的 –see picture on page 243 見 243 頁彩圖

tan·dem /ˈtændəm; ˈtændəm/ *n* **1** a bicycle built for two riders sitting one behind the other 〔兩人一前一後同騎的〕雙人自行車 **2 in tandem** working closely together 密切合作: *We'll be working on the project in tandem.* 我們將在那個項目中密切合作。–**tandem** *adv*: *They rode tandem.* 他們在騎雙人自行車。

tang /tæŋ; tæŋ/ *n* a strong taste or smell 強烈的味道〔氣味〕: *the tang of the sea air* 海上空氣的強烈氣味。–**tangy** *adj*

tan·gent /ˈtændʒənt; ˈtændʒənt/ *n* **1** a straight line that touches the outside of a curve but does not cut across it 切線 **2 go off at a tangent** *infml* to change suddenly from one course of speech, thought, or action to another 〔非正式〕突然改變話題、思路或行動 –**tangential** /tænˈdʒɛnʃəl; tænˈdʒɛnʃəl/ *adj*

tan·ge·rine /ˌtændʒəˈrin; ˌtændʒəˈriːn/ *n* [C;U] a small sweet orange with a loose skin 橘子

tan·gi·ble /ˈtændʒəbl; ˈtændʒəbl/ *adj* clear and certain enough to be felt or noticed 清楚的; 清晰的; 明顯的: *We need tangible proof of her guilt.* 我們需要有她罪行的確鑿證據。–**tangibly** *adv* –**tangibility** /ˌtændʒəˈbɪlɪtɪ; ˌtændʒəˈbɪləti/ *n* [U]

tan·gle¹ /ˈtæŋgl; ˈtæŋgəl/ *v* **tangled, tangling** [I;T] **1** to make or become a mass of twisted threads (使)纏繞在一起: *This thread tangles easily.* 這種線很容易纏在一起。–opposite 反義 **untangle** **2 tangle with someone** *infml* to quarrel with someone 〔非正式〕與某人爭吵 **3 be tangled up in** to be caught in rope or wires 被〔繩或線〕纏住: *My scarf got tangled up in the barbed wire fence.* 我的圍巾被有刺鐵絲圍欄纏住了。

tangle² *n* **1** a confused mass of threads 纏在一起的線團: *a tangle* **of** *wool* 絞成一團的毛線 | *Your hair's in a tangle.* 你的頭髮亂了。**2** a state of confusion 混亂狀態: *My business* *affairs are in a real tangle.* 我的業務一團糟。

tan·go /'tæŋgəʊ; 'tæŋɡoʊ/ n tangos a dance with a strong beat of South American origin 探戈舞 –**tango** v [I]

tank /tæŋk; tæŋk/ n **1** a large container for storing liquid or gas 〔盛液體或氣體的〕大容器: *a fish tank* 魚缸 | *There's enough petrol in the tank for the drive to Oxford.* 油箱裡有足夠的汽油可以開到牛津。**2** a large, military vehicle with a gun and heavy armour, which moves on metal belts 坦克車

tan·kard /'tæŋkəd; 'tæŋkəd/ n a large cup with a handle, usually used for drinking beer 大啤酒杯

tank·er /'tæŋkə; 'tæŋkər/ n a ship or road vehicle specially built for carrying large quantities of gas or liquid 〔運送氣體或液體的〕輪船, 車輛: *an oil tanker* 一艘油輪

tan·ner /'tænə; 'tænər/ n a person whose job is making animal skins into leather 製革工人

tan·noy /'tænɔɪ; 'tænɔɪ/ n BrE tdmk a system of loudspeakers (LOUDSPEAKER) for giving information to the public 〔美式, 商標〕擴音器

tan·ta·lize /'tæntl,aɪz; 'tæntəlaɪz/ v **tantalized, tantalizing** [T] to encourage a strong desire for something that you do not actually allow a person or animal to enjoy 誘發無法滿足的慾望: *He's been tantalizing with the promise of foreign travel.* 他一直在說要讓我們出國旅行, 以此來吊我們的胃口。| *a tantalizing smell* 令人垂涎的氣味

tan·ta·mount /'tæntə,maʊnt; 'tæntəmaʊnt/ adj **tantamount to** the same, in effect, as something else 等於: *Her answer is tantamount to a refusal.* 她的回答等於是拒絕。

tan·trum /'tæntrəm; 'tæntrəm/ n a sudden uncontrolled attack of anger, especially by a child 〔尤指小孩〕突然發怒: *Does he often have these tantrums?* 他經常這樣發脾氣嗎?

tap¹ /tæp; tæp/ n **1** an apparatus for letting liquid or gas out of a pipe or container 水龍頭; 開關: *Could you turn the hot tap off, please?* 請你把熱水龍頭關掉好嗎? **2 on tap: a** from a barrel 取自桶的: *Is the beer on tap or in bottles?* 啤酒是桶裝的還是瓶裝的? **b** ready for use when needed 可供使用的: *We have all the information we need on tap.* 所有需要的資料我們都準備好了。**3** a gentle knock on something 輕擊; 輕敲: *I felt a tap on my shoulder.* 我覺得有人在我肩膀上輕輕拍了一下。

tap² v **-pp- 1** [I;T] to knock gently on something 輕擊; 輕敲: *I tapped on the window to announce my arrival.* 我輕輕地敲敲窗, 讓他們知道我到了。| *She tapped her fingers impatiently on the desk.* 她用手指不耐煩地敲敲課桌。**2** [T] to use something or take something from a supply 利用, 使用〔供應之物〕: *The country's mineral wealth has never really been tapped.* 該國的礦產資源從未認真

開採過。**3** [T] to make a secret telephone connection so that you can listen to other people's conversations 竊聽〔電話〕: *The phones of foreign diplomats have been tapped.* 外國外交官的電話遭到了竊聽。**4** [T] to take liquid from a tree through a hole in its trunk 〔在樹幹上〕開孔導出液體: *They are tapping rubber trees.* 他們在採橡膠。

tap danc·ing /'· ,··/ n [U] a kind of dancing in which dancers use special shoes to beat time to the music with their feet 踢躂舞 – **tap dancer** n

tape¹ /tep; teɪp/ n **1** [U] a special narrow plastic band on which sound or images can be recorded 〔錄音或錄像用的〕磁帶: *I've got the match on tape.* 我把比賽錄下來了。| *Record the opera on this blank tape.* 在這盤空白磁帶上把歌劇錄下來。**2** [C] a length of narrow plastic on which sound or images have been recorded 〔錄過音或錄過像的〕磁帶: *I want to buy a tape of Michael Jackson's songs.* 我想買一盤米高積遜的歌曲磁帶。**3** [C;U] a long, very narrow piece of material used for tying things like parcels 〔用以捆紮包裹等物的〕帶子 **4** [C] a long, narrow piece of material which is stretched across a course to show the end point of a race 〔賽跑比賽的〕終點線

tape² v **taped, taping** **1** [I;T] to record something on a TAPE RECORDER, CASSETTE RECORDER or VIDEO RECORDER 錄音; 錄像: *He tapes a lot of business conversations.* 他錄下了許多商業會談。**2** [T] to fasten or fix something using tape which sticks 用黏貼膠帶捆紮: *She taped the box closed.* 她用黏貼膠帶把箱子捆封。**3 have something or someone taped** infml to understand exactly how to deal with a person or situation 〔非正式〕知道如何對付某事或某人: *After a month in the new job, I had it taped.* 新工作做了一個月以後, 我便清楚該怎麼幹了。

tape deck /'· ·/ n a machine that records and plays back sound 錄音座 –see picture on page 730 見 730 頁彩圖

tape mea·sure /'· ,··/ n a long narrow band of cloth or steel with centimetres marked on it, which is used for measuring things 卷尺 –see picture on page 958 見 958 頁彩圖

ta·per¹ /'tepə; 'teɪpər/ v [I;T] to become or to make something gradually narrower towards one end 〔靠近尾端〕越來越細

taper off phr v [I] to gradually become less in size or quantity 逐漸變小; 逐漸變少: *Enthusiasm for the project has been tapering off.* 人們對於該計劃的熱情越來越低。

taper² n a very long thin candle 細蠟燭

tape re·cord·er /'· ·,··/ n a machine that records and plays back sound 錄音機

tap·es·try /'tæpɪstrɪ; 'tæpɪstri/ n **tapestries** [C;U] heavy cloth onto which a picture is sewn or woven 掛毯; 織錦: *There were beautiful tapestries on the walls.* 牆壁上有美麗的掛毯。| *tapestry chair covers* 織錦椅套

tape·worm /ˈtep,wɜːm; ˈteɪpwɜːm/ *n* a long flat worm that can live inside the bodies of people and animals 絛蟲

tap·i·o·ca /ˌtæpɪˈoka; ˌtæpɪˈəʊkə/ *n* [U] small white grains of food made from the tropical CASSAVA plant 木薯澱粉

tar /tar; tɑːʳ/ *n* [U] a black substance, thick and sticky when it is hot and hard when it is cold, which is used for making roads 柏油; 焦油瀝青

ta·ran·tu·la /təˈræntʃələ; təˈræntjʊlə/ *n* a large hairy poisonous SPIDER 多毛毒蜘蛛

tar·dy /ˈtardɪ; ˈtɑːdɪ/ *adj lit* slow to act or happen〔文〕緩慢的

✽tar·get /ˈtargɪt; ˈtɑːɡɪt/ *n* **1** an object, building, or place which is aimed at, especially with a gun or bomb 靶子; 目標: *We are trained to hit moving targets.* 我們受過訓練打擊移動目標。**2** a person or thing that people blame, laugh at, or attack 批評、嘲笑或攻擊的對象: *He is the target of many jokes.* 他是許多人開玩笑的對象。**3** an amount or result which you hope to reach 目標; 目的: *The company has failed to meet its production targets.* 公司未能達到生產目標。

tar·iff /ˈtærɪf; ˈtærɪf/ *n* **1** a list of fixed prices charged for services, especially in a hotel 收費表; 價目表: *Compare the room tariffs in the two hotels.* 把兩家旅館的房間價目表比較一下。**2** a tax collected by a government, usually on goods coming into a country〔進口貨物的〕關稅

tar·mac /ˈtar,mæk; ˈtɑːmæk/ *n* **1** [U] a mixture of TAR and small stones used for making road surfaces〔鋪路用的〕柏油碎石 **2** **the tarmac** an area covered with this substance, especially one where planes wait before taking off 柏油碎石鋪成的地面〔尤指停機坪〕

tar·nish /ˈtarnɪʃ; ˈtɑːnɪʃ/ *v* **1** [I;T] to become or to make a metal object less bright (使)變暗; 使〔金屬物體〕失去光澤: *These silver spoons tarnish easily unless they are polished.* 這些銀匙不擦亮便很容易失去光澤。| *Wet weather can tarnish brass.* 潮濕的天氣會使黃銅失去光澤。**2** [T] to make something less perfect 損害〔某物〕: *The scandal has tarnished the reputation of several politicians.* 這一樁醜聞已使好幾位政治家的名譽受損。–**tarnish** *n* [U]

tar·ot /ˈtæro; ˈtærəʊ/ *n* the telling of a person's future using a set of 22 special cards〔用一套二十二張的紙牌進行的〕算命: *tarot cards* 算命用的紙牌

tar·pau·lin /tarˈpɔlɪn; tɑːˈpɔːlɪn/ *n* [C;U] heavy material which is covered with a special substance to prevent water passing through it (焦油)防水帆布

tar·ra·gon /ˈtærə,gɑn; ˈtærəɡən/ *n* [U] a plant which is used to give food a special taste〔調味用的〕龍蒿

tart¹ /tart; tɑːt/ *n* **1** [C;U] a circle of pastry cooked with fruit or some other filling in it 果餡餅: *a piece of apple tart* 一塊蘋果餡餅 **2** [C] *infml* a woman or girl who is considered to be sexually immoral〔非正式〕淫婦

tart² *adj* **1** unpleasantly sharp in taste 辛辣的, 酸的: *These apples are too tart to eat raw.* 這些蘋果生吃太酸。**2** unpleasantly sharp or unkind in speech〔話語〕尖酸的; 尖刻的: *We were hurt by her tart comments on our efforts.* 她尖刻地批評我們所做的事, 令我們很傷心。

tar·tan /ˈtartn; ˈtɑːtn/ *n* [C;U] woollen cloth woven with bands of different colours and widths crossing each other, which is typically from Scotland; many patterns have an association with a particular Scottish family 蘇格蘭格子呢絨〔許多圖案花紋與某一家族有緊密的聯繫〕

tar·tar /ˈtartɚ; ˈtɑːtəʳ/ *n* **1** [C] a fierce person, often a woman, with a violent temper 脾氣暴躁的人〔常為婦女〕**2** [U] a hard substance that forms on your teeth 牙石; 齒垢

tartar sauce /ˈ···, ·/ *n* [U] (also 又作 **tartare sauce**) a cold, thick liquid that is eaten with fish〔吃魚用的〕塔塔調味醬

✽✽task /tæsk; tɑːsk/ *n* **1** a piece of work, often difficult, that has to be done〔常為困難的〕工作; 任務: *I was given the task of sweeping the floors.* 掃地的任務落到了我頭上。| *She finds looking after her father a difficult task.* 她感到照料父親是項艱苦的工作。**2** **take someone to task** to scold someone severely 嚴厲批評某人: *She was taken to task for her negative attitude.* 她由於態度消極而受到嚴厲批評。

task force /ˈ· ·/ *n* [+sing/pl verb] a group of people, especially military people, who are sent to a place for a special purpose 特別工作組〔尤指特遣部隊〕

task·mas·ter /ˈtæsk,mæstɚ; ˈtɑːsk,mɑːstəʳ/ *n* a person who gives other people a lot of work to do 給他人安排大量工作的人: *Our teacher's a hard taskmaster.* 我們的老師總喜歡安排許多作業給我們。

tas·sel /ˈtæsl̩; ˈtæsəl/ *n* a bunch of threads tied together at one end and hung on things like curtains for decoration 穗; 纓; 流蘇

✽taste¹ /test; teɪst/ *v* **tasted, tasting 1** [T] to judge the taste of food or drink by putting a little into your mouth 嘗; 品嘗: *Do you want to taste the wine?* 這酒你想嘗一下嗎? **2** [T] to experience the sensation of food or drink in your mouth 嘗出…的味道: *After a spicy main course, I can't taste the pudding.* 吃了一道辛辣的主菜之後, 我嘗不出甜膩的味道了。**3** [I] to have a particular taste 有某種

味道: *These oranges taste nice.* 這些橘子吃起來很甜。| *This soup tastes of chicken.* 這碗湯有雞肉的味道。**4** [T] to experience something for a short time 體驗〔某事物〕: *Now that he has tasted the freedom of living alone, he doesn't want her back.* 他已嘗到了一個人獨自生活的自由，所以不希望她回來。

taste² *n* **1** [C;U] the sensation of saltiness, sweetness and so on that you have when something is put in your mouth 味道: *I like the taste of Indian food.* 我喜歡印度菜的味道。| *This cake has very little taste.* 這塊蛋糕沒有甚麼味道。| *I've got a cold, so I've lost my sense of taste.* 我患了感冒，所以甚麼味道都嘗不出來。**2** [C] a small quantity of food or drink that you try 〔嘗味道用的〕少量食物或飲料: *Have a taste of the soup and tell me what you think.* 嘗一下這碗湯，然後告訴我你認為怎麼樣。**3** [C] a short experience of something 體驗: *It was his first taste of freedom.* 他初嘗自由的滋味。**4** [C;U] the ability to choose and judge things which are attractive or of good quality 品味；判斷能力；鑑賞力: *She has good taste in clothes.* 她懂得挑選有品味的衣服。**5 a taste for something** a liking for something 喜歡: *I am trying to develop a taste for shellfish.* 我嘗試培養吃貝類食物的興趣。**6 in bad taste** not at all suitable for a particular time or occasion 很不合時宜: *His behaviour at the funeral was in very bad taste.* 他參加葬禮時行為失當。[RELATED PHRASE 相關詞組 **in good taste**]

taste·ful /'teɪstfəl; 'teɪstfəl/ *adj* showing someone's ability to choose what is attractive or of good quality 有品味的；有鑑賞力的: *The room was decorated in tasteful shades of pink.* 這個房間是用不同層次的粉紅色裝飾而成，顯得很有品味。–**tastefully** *adv*

taste·less /'teɪstlɪs; 'teɪstləs/ *adj* **1** providing no sensation when it is put in your mouth 沒有味道的: *tasteless medicine* 無味的藥片 **2** showing someone's lack of ability to decide what is attractive or of good quality 沒有品味的；沒有鑑賞力的: *tasteless furniture* 沒有品味的家具 **3** offensive to other people's feelings of what is suitable 不得體的: *He made a number of tasteless remarks about her sick father.* 他談及她患病的父親時，説了些不得體的話。–**tastelessness** *n* [U]

tast·er /'teɪstə; 'teɪstər/ *n* a person whose job is to test the quality of food and drink by tasting them 專職品嘗食品和酒的人: *a wine taster* 品酒師

tast·y /'teɪsti; 'teɪsti/ *adj* **tastier, tastiest 1** with a strong and pleasant taste 美味的: *a tasty meal* 美味的一餐 **2** *infml* sexually attractive 〔非正式〕性感的

tat·tered /'tætəd; 'tætəd/ *adj* old and torn 破舊的；破爛的: *tattered clothes* 破舊的衣服

tat·ters /'tætəz; 'tætəz/ *n* **in tatters: a** torn in many places (used of clothes) 破爛的〔指衣服〕: *His shirt was in tatters after the fight.*

打鬥之後，他的襯衫撕破了。**b** destroyed 毀壞的: *The conflict left her career in tatters.* 此次衝突把她的事業給毀了。

tat·too¹ /tæ'tu; tə'tu:/ *v* [T] to draw pictures or write on someone's skin using a sharp tool and coloured inks 紋身: *A heart was tattooed on his chest.* 他的胸口刺上了一個心形花紋。

tattoo² *n* **1** words or a picture drawn on someone's skin using a sharp tool and coloured inks 紋身；刺花 **2** a rapid beating of military drums played as a signal 〔作為信號的〕速擊軍鼓 **3** an outdoor military show with music 〔配有音樂的〕戶外軍事表演

tat·ty /'tæti; 'tæti/ *adj* **tattier, tattiest** *infml* untidy, dirty, and in bad condition 〔非正式〕不整潔的；邋遢的: *tatty clothes* 邋遢的衣服 –**tattily** *adv* –**tattiness** *n* [U]

taught /tɔt; tɔ:t/ the past tense and past participle of TEACH ☆ TEACH 的過去式和過去分詞

taunt /tɔnt; tɔ:nt/ *v* [T] to try to make someone angry or unhappy by making unkind remarks about their weak points 嘲弄；譏笑: *He was taunted by other children about his weight.* 他因為身體超重而受到其他孩子的嘲弄。–**tauntingly** *adv* –**taunt** *n*

Tau·rus /'tɔrəs; 'tɔ:rəs/ *n* one of the signs of the ZODIAC 金牛宮

taut /tɔt; tɔ:t/ *adj* **1** stretched tight 繃緊的: *Pull the rope until it's taut!* 把繩子拉緊! **2** showing signs of anxiety 顯得焦慮: *Her face was taut and pale with worry.* 她因憂慮而神情緊張，臉色蒼白。–**tautly** *adv* –**tautness** *n* [U]

tau·tol·o·gy /tɔ'tɒlədʒi; tɔ:'tɒlədʒi/ *n* **tautologies** [C;U] a statement in which you say the same thing twice using different words 重複；贅述: *It is a tautology to say that he sat alone by himself.* 如果説他一人獨自坐在那裡，這便是重複。–**tautological** /,tɔtə'lɒdʒɪkl; ,tɔ:tə'lɒdʒɪkəl/ *adj*

tav·ern /'tævən; 'tævən/ *n* *old fash* a pub 〔老式〕酒館

taw·dry /'tɔdri; 'tɔ:dri/ *adj* **tawdrier, tawdriest** bright and highly decorated but cheap and of poor quality 俗麗而不值錢的: *tawdry jewellery* 俗麗而不值錢的首飾 –**tawdriness** *n* [U]

taw·ny /'tɔni; 'tɔ:ni/ *adj* brownish yellow in colour 茶色的

✦tax¹ /tæks; tæks/ *v* [T] **1** to take a certain amount of money from income or the price of goods and services in tax 徵税: *Most luxury goods are taxed at 15%.* 大部分的奢侈品都要徵百分之十五的税。| *The government plans to tax small businesses more heavily.* 政府打算增加對小型企業的税收。**2** to make heavy demands on a person 使〔人〕負重擔: *The child really taxes my patience.* 這孩子真令我忍無可忍。| *It was a long, taxing journey.* 那是又長又累的旅行。

tax² *n* [C;U] money collected by the government from your income or property, or goods and services that you pay for, which is used to support public services 稅; 稅款: *Taxes on alcohol and cigarettes have gone up again.* 對煙酒徵的稅又增加了。| *Half of my salary goes in tax.* 我工資的一半都納了稅。| *a plan to impose a tax on betting* 對賭博進行徵稅的計劃

tax·a·ble /ˈtæksəbl; ˈtæksəbəl/ *adj* that can or must be taxed 可徵稅的; 必須徵稅的: *taxable income* 應納稅的收入

***tax·a·tion** /tækˈseɪʃən; tækˈseɪʃən/ *n* [U] **1** the collection of money in tax by the government 徵稅; 課稅: *We must increase taxation if we are to spend more on the health service.* 要增加醫療保健的經費就必須加稅。**2** the amount of money that people have to pay in tax 稅; 稅款

tax-free /ˌ·ˈ·◂/ *adj* with no tax to pay 免稅的: *tax-free income* 免稅的收入 **–tax-free** *adv*: *Artists can live there tax-free.* 藝術家住在那裡可以不用交稅。

tax·i¹ /ˈtæksɪ; ˈtæksi/ *n* [C;U] (also 又作 **taxi-cab** /ˈtæksɪˌkæb; ˈtæksikæb/ *fml* 〖正式〗) **1** a car and driver which can be hired by members of the public 計程車; 出租汽車: *Shall I call a taxi?* 我叫輛計程車好嗎? **–see** picture on page 991 見 991 頁彩圖 **2 by taxi** travelling in a taxi 坐計程車; 乘出租車: *Shall we go by taxi?* 我們坐計程車去好嗎?

tax·i² *v* **taxied, taxiing** [I] (of a plane) to move slowly along the ground before taking off or after landing 〔飛機起飛前或着陸後〕在地面滑行

tax·i·der·my /ˈtæksəˌdɜːmɪ; ˈtæksɪˌdɜːmi/ *n* [U] the art of preserving and filling the skins of dead animals, so that they look like living creatures 動物標本剝製術 **–taxi-dermist** *n*

taxi rank /ˈ··· / (also 又作 **taxi stand**) *n* a place where taxis wait for passengers 計程車[出租車]候客站

tax·pay·er /ˈtæksˌpeə; ˈtæksˌpeɪər/ *n* a person who pays part of their income as tax 納稅人

TB /ˌtiː ˈbiː, ˌtiː ˈbiː/ an abbreviation for 〖縮〗= TUBERCULOSIS

tbs [plural is 複數為 **tbs**] a written abbreviation for 〖縮〗= TABLESPOON

***tea** /tiː; tiː/ *n* **1** [U] the dried leaves of a bush grown mainly in Asia 茶葉: *a packet of tea* 一袋茶 **2** [C;U] a hot brown drink made by pouring boiling water onto these leaves 茶; 茶水: *Would you like a cup of tea?* 你要喝杯茶嗎? | *Two teas with milk and sugar, please.* 請給我們兩杯加奶和糖的茶。**3** [C;U] a small meal served in the afternoon, or a main meal served in the early evening 下午茶; 黃昏茶點: *What are we having for tea today?* 我們今天下午茶吃甚麼? **–see** 見 DIN-NER (USAGE 用法) **4** [U] a drink made

like tea but using the leaves or flowers of other plants 〔用其他植物的葉子或花沏成的〕茶: *a glass of mint tea* 一杯薄荷茶

tea-bag /ˈtiːbæg; ˈtiːbæg/ *n* a small bag with tea leaves inside, which you put into boiling water to make tea 袋泡茶

tea cad·dy /ˈ·ˌ··/ *n* **tea caddies** a small tin in which tea is kept 茶葉罐

***teach** /tiːtʃ; tiːtʃ/ *v* **taught** /tɔːt; tɔːt/, **taught, teaching** [I;T; +(that)] **1** to give knowledge, training, or lessons in a particular subject or skill 教; 傳授: *She teaches history.* 她教歷史。| *Mary teaches politics to university students.* 瑪麗在大學裡教政治。| *I teach young children swimming.* 我教小孩子游泳。| *My religion teaches that war is wrong.* 我所信仰的宗教宣稱戰爭是錯的。| *He taught the boys to play cricket.* 他教男孩子打板球。| *I taught them what to do.* 我告訴他們該做甚麼。

> □ USEFUL PATTERNS 有用句型 to teach someone; to teach something; to teach someone to do something; to teach someone that...

2 teach someone a lesson to punish someone so that they do not repeat what they have done 給某人一個教訓: *I'm going to stop your pocket money to teach you a lesson.* 作為教訓，我打算不給你零錢花了。

***teach·er** /ˈtiːtʃə; ˈtiːtʃər/ *n* a person who teaches, especially at a school or college 〔尤指學校或大學的〕教師、老師: *He's a music teacher.* 他是個音樂老師。| *a secondary school teacher* 中學老師

> ■ USAGE 用法: **Teacher** is not usually used as a form of address. It is usual for students to call their teachers by their names, either formally (**teacher** 一般不用作稱呼。學生通常以名字稱呼老師，可以用正式的稱呼): *Good morning* **Ms Smith/Mr Jones.** 早上好，史密斯老師/瓊斯老師, or informally (也可以用非正式的稱呼): *Good morning* **Mary/Bill.** 早上好，瑪麗/比爾。

teach·ing /ˈtiːtʃɪŋ; ˈtiːtʃɪŋ/ *n* **1** [U] the work of a teacher 教學工作: *Most of my teaching is in the mornings.* 我教的課大部分在上午。**2** [C] the moral, political or religious beliefs taught, often by a person of historical importance 〔通常由偉人傳授的〕道德、政治、或宗教信仰: *the teachings of Confucius* 孔子的教誨

tea co·sy /ˈ·ˌ··/ *n* **tea cosies** a thick cover put over a teapot to keep the tea hot 茶壺保暖罩

tea·cup /ˈtiːˌkʌp; ˈtiːˌkʌp/ *n* a cup from which you drink tea 茶杯

teak /tiːk; tiːk/ *n* [U] a very hard wood

which is used for making furniture and ships 柚木

tea·leaf /'tiːlif; 'tiːliːf/ *n* **tealeaves** /-livz; -liːvz/ one of the small pieces of leaf used for making tea 茶葉

team[1] /tiːm; tiːm/ *n* [+sing/pl verb] **1** a group of people who work together or play a game or sport together 〔一起工作、遊戲或運動的〕隊; 組: *He's in the school cricket team.* 他是學校的板球隊隊員。| *A team of management consultants has been called in to advise us.* 請來了一隊管理顧問給我們提意見。| *Do you enjoy team games?* 你喜歡參加集體遊戲嗎? **2** two or more animals pulling the same vehicle 〔同拉一輛車的〕一組動物: *a team of horses* 一組拉車的馬

team[2] *v*

team up *phr v* [I] to work with another person for a particular purpose 與〔另外一個人〕合作: *I've teamed up with Jane to write the book* 我與珍妮合作寫這本書。

team spir·it /ˌ·'··/ *n* [U] the feeling of loyalty among members of a team working together for the success of the group as a whole 協作〔集體〕精神; 團隊精神

team·work /'tiːmwɜːk; 'tiːmwɜːk/ *n* [U] the ability of a group to work well together 協作; 配合

tea·pot /'tiːpɒt; 'tiːpɒt/ *n* a container with a handle and a SPOUT, from which tea is poured into cups 茶壺 –see picture on page 244 見 244 彩圖

*tear[1] /tɪr; tɪəˈ/ *n* **1** a drop of salty liquid that runs from your eye when you are unhappy or in pain 眼淚: *Tears streamed down her face.* 眼淚順着她的臉淌了下來。 **2** in tears crying 哭泣: *He was so upset, he was almost in tears.* 他很難過, 幾乎要哭了。

*tear[2] /ter; teəˈ/ *v* **tore** /tor; tɔːˈ/ **torn** /torn; tɔːn/ **1** [T] to make irregular holes in cloth or paper, or to pull material apart leaving irregular edges 撕破; 撕裂: *Just tear the paper down the middle!* 只要把紙順着中間撕開就行了! | *You've torn your trousers again, you careless boy.* 你這粗心的孩子, 又把褲子撕破了。–see 見 BREAK (USAGE 用法) **2** [T+adv/prep] to remove a person or thing by force 用力排除; 撕掉: *You tear the paper off the walls and I'll paint them.* 你把牆上的紙撕掉後我來上油漆。| *She tore herself from his grasp and ran.* 她掙脫他的手後跑開了。 **3** [I] to split, leaving irregular holes or edges 裂開; 被撕破: *This material tears easily.* 這種料子很容易撕破。 **4** [I + adv/prep] to move at great speed 飛奔: *She tore down the road to catch the post.* 為了趕上發信的時間, 她順着馬路飛奔而去。 **5** in a tearing hurry in a great rush to get somewhere 火速地 **6** tear a strip off someone *infml* to scold someone severely 《非正式》嚴厲責備某人 **7** tear into someone to express your

anger with someone, usually in words 〔通常用言詞〕對某人發火 **8** be torn to be unable to choose between two or more things or courses of action 無法選擇; 舉棋不定: *I'm torn between going with her and staying with the children.* 我不知是與她一起去還是留在孩子身邊好。

tear sthg apart *phr v* [T] to divide an organization or country by causing great trouble 分裂〔組織或國家〕: *The country was torn apart by the civil war.* 該國被內戰搞得四分五裂。

tear sbdy ↔ away *phr v* [T] to make someone leave a place or stop doing something although they do not want to 強令〔某人〕離開〔某地〕; 強令〔某人〕停止做〔某事〕: *He couldn't tear himself away from the T.V.* 他終日沉迷於看電視, 無法自拔。

tear sthg ↔ down *phr v* [T] to destroy or use force to remove a building 拆毀〔建築物〕: *All the flats are being torn down.* 所有的公寓大樓正在拆毀。

tear sthg ↔ up *phr v* [T] to destroy something made of paper by pulling it into pieces 撕碎〔紙張〕: *He tore up every photograph he had of her.* 他把他所有她的照片都撕碎了。

tear[3] /ter; teəˈ/ *n* a hole or split in cloth or paper where it has been torn 〔布或紙的〕破洞; 裂縫

tear·a·way /'terə,we; 'teərəweɪ/ *n infml* a wild youth who is difficult to control 《非正式》小流氓; 暴徒

tear·drop /'tɪr,drɑp; 'tɪədrɒp/ *n* a single tear that falls from your eye when you are crying 淚滴; 淚珠

tear·ful /'tɪrfʊl; 'tɪəfəl/ *adj* crying or on the point of crying 哭泣的; 淚汪汪的 **–tearfully** *adv* **–tearfulness** *n* [U]

tea·room /'tiːrum; 'tiːruːm/ *n* a small restaurant where tea and light meals are served 茶館

tease /tiz; tiːz/ *v* **teased, teasing** [I;T] **1** to laugh at playfully or unkindly or make jokes about 嘲笑; 取笑: *They teased me at school because I wore glasses.* 由於我戴眼鏡, 所以他們在學校裡取笑我。 **2** to annoy a person or animal by offering or threatening something without actually meaning it 開玩笑: *He doesn't mean it; he's only teasing.* 他不是當真的, 不過是在開玩笑罷了。 **3** tease something out of someone to persuade someone to tell you something even though they are unwilling 說服某人告訴你某事〔儘管他們並不情願〕 **–tease** *n*: *Don't be such a tease!* 別老是這樣開玩笑!

teas·er /'tizər; 'tiːzəˈ/ *n infml* a difficult question, for example in a competition 《非正式》難題〔如在比賽中所遇見者〕

tea·spoon /'ti,spun; 'tiːspuːn/ *n* **1** a small spoon used for mixing sugar into tea or coffee 茶匙 **2** (also 又作 **teaspoonful**) the amount of something that this spoon holds —茶匙之量: *I take two teaspoons of sugar in my coffee.* 我在自己的咖啡裡放了兩茶匙糖。

teat /tit; ti:t/ *n* **1** a rubber object with a hole in it, fixed to a bottle for a baby to suck liquids through 橡皮奶嘴 **2** the part of the flesh on the body of a female animal through which a baby sucks its mother's milk 奶頭

tea·time /ˈtiˌtaɪm; ˈti:taɪm/ *n* [U] the time in the afternoon when people have tea 下午喝茶時間

tea towel /ˈ·ˌ··/ *n* a cloth for drying things like cups and plates after they have been washed 擦拭杯盤用的布

tech /tɛk; tek/ *n* see 見 TECHNICAL COL-LEGE

★**tech·ni·cal** /ˈtɛknɪkl; ˈteknɪkəl/ *adj* **1** having special and usually practical knowledge, especially of an industrial or scientific subject 〔尤指工業或科技方面〕有技術的: *technical experts* 技術專家 | *This book is too technical for a child to understand.* 這本書對於孩子來講，技術性太強，所以無法理解。 **2** of or related to a particular subject, especially a practical or scientific one 〔尤指實用或科技方面〕技術上的: *technical training* 技術訓練 | *The book is full of technical terms.* 該書內容滿是術語。 –**technically** /-klɪ; -kli/ *adv*

technical col·lege /ˈ···ˌ··/ *n* (also 又作 **tech** *infml* 【非正式】) a college that provides courses in practical subjects related to particular jobs, as well as in arts and social sciences for students who have left school 工學院〔提供某些職業、藝術和社會科學方面的實用課程〕

tech·ni·cal·i·ty /ˌtɛknɪˈkælətɪ; ˌteknə̩ˈkæ-lə̩ti/ *n* **technicalities 1** a detail of a rule which is carefully followed 〔嚴格遵循的〕規定細節: *He could not be tried for the crime because of a technicality in the law.* 由於一個法律上的規定而無法對他的罪行進行審判。 **2** the technicalities the small details of a process or method 技術細節: *He's interested in the technicalities of paper-making.* 他對於製紙過程的細節非常感興趣。

tech·ni·cian /tɛkˈnɪʃən; tekˈnɪʃən/ *n* a skilled worker, especially in science or industry 技術人員

★**tech·nique** /tɛkˈnik; tekˈni:k/ *n* **1** [C] a way of doing some practical or specialist activity 技術: *I am practising new photographic techniques.* 我正在練習新的攝影技術。 **2** [U] skill in doing something practical, artistic, or connected with sport 技巧: *She is working with her new piano teacher to improve her technique.* 她請新的鋼琴老師協助提高自己的演奏技巧。

★**tech·nol·o·gy** /tɛkˈnɑlədʒɪ; tekˈnɑlədʒi/ *n* **technologies** [C;U] the branch of knowledge or activity deal-

ing with scientific and industrial methods and their practical use in industry 〔科學和工業的〕技術: *We haven't got the technology to compete with the Japanese in electronics.* 在電子工業方面，我們沒有足與日本進行競爭的技術。 –**technologist** *n* –**technological** /ˌtɛknəˈlɑdʒɪkl; ˌteknəˈlɑdʒɪkəl/ *adj*: *The computer is the result of recent technological advances.* 這台電腦是新近科技發展的成果。 –**technologically** /-klɪ; -kli/ *adv*

ted·dy bear /ˈtɛdɪ bɛr; ˈtedi beəʳ/ (also 又作 **teddy**) *n* a toy bear filled with soft material 玩具熊

te·di·ous /ˈtidɪəs; ˈti:diəs/ *adj* long and very uninteresting 冗長乏味的: *tedious political speeches* 冗長乏味的政治演説 –**tediously** *adv* –**tediousness** *n* [U]

tee /ti; ti:/ *n* the small object from which the player first hits the ball in a game of GOLF 高爾夫球座

teem /tim; ti:m/ *v* [I] **1** to be crowded with living, moving creatures 充滿〔活動的生物〕: *The river was teeming with fish.* 河裡到處是魚。 **2** *infml* to rain very heavily 【非正式】下大雨

teen·age /ˈtinedʒ; ˈti:neɪdʒ/ *adj* [only before a noun 只用於名詞前] **1** concerning teenagers or for teenagers 青少年的: *teenage fashions* 青少年中流行的時尚 **2** (also 又作 **teenaged**) between 13 and 19 years old 十三至十九歲的: *a teenage boy* 十幾歲的男孩

teen·ag·er /ˈtinedʒɚ; ˈti:neɪdʒəʳ/ *n* a young person between 13 and 19 years old 青少年: *The audience consisted mainly of teenagers.* 觀眾大部分是青少年。 –see 見 CHILD (USAGE 用法)

teens /tinz; ti:nz/ *n* [pl] the period of a person's life between the ages of 13 and 19 青少年時期〔十三至十九歲〕: *She's in her teens now.* 她正值青少年時期。

tee shirt /ˈtiʃɚt; ˈti:ʃɜ:t/ *n* see 見 T-SHIRT

tee·ter /ˈtitɚ; ˈti:təʳ/ *v* **1** [I+adv/prep] to stand or move in an unsteady way 站立不穩; 步履蹣跚: *She teetered along the street in her high-heeled shoes.* 她穿着高跟鞋，步履蹣跚地走在街上。 **2** teeter on the brink, teeter on the edge to be close to a terrible state or event 處於…的邊緣: *The company is teetering on the brink of financial ruin.* 公司在財政上已瀕於垮台。

teeth /tiθ; ti:θ/ the plural of TOOTH ☆ TOOTH 的複數

teethe /tið; ti:ð/ *v* **teethed, teething** [I] (of babies) to grow teeth for the first time, often painfully 〔嬰兒〕長乳牙: *The poor child is teething.* 那可憐的孩子正在長乳牙。

tee·to·tal /ˈtiˈtotl; ˌti:ˈtəʊtl/ *adj* never drinking alcohol 滴酒不沾的; 絕對戒酒的: *I've been teetotal since I realised I had a drinking problem.* 我知道自己有酗酒的問題後，從此滴酒不沾。 –**teetotaller** *BrE* 【英式】 (**teetotaler** *AmE* 【美式】) *n*

tel·e·com·mu·ni·ca·tions /ˌtɛləkə,mjunə-
ˈkeɪʃənz; ˈtelikəmjuːnⅰˈkeɪʃənz/ *n* [pl] the
sending or receiving of messages by telephone, television, telegraph, or radio 電信

tel·e·gram /ˈtɛlə,græm; ˈtelⅰgræm/ *n* a
message sent by telegraph which is delivered to someone 電報

tel·e·graph /ˈtɛlə,græf; ˈtelⅰgrɑːf/ *n* [U] a
method of sending messages along wire by
electric or radio signals 打電報: *Send it by
telegraph.* 打電報發送消息。 –**telegraph** *v*
[T]: *We telegraphed her the news.* 我們打電
報把消息告訴她。 –**telegraphic** /ˌtɛlə'græ-
fɪk; ˌtelⅰˈgræfɪk◂/ *adj* –**telegraphically** /-klⅰ;
-kli/ *adv*

telegraph pole /'··· ·/ (also 又作 **telegraph
post**) *n* a pole for supporting telephone
and telegraph wires 電線桿

te·lep·a·thy /təˈlɛpəθɪ; tⅰˈlepəθi/ *n* [U] the
sending of thoughts from one person's
mind to another's without speaking or
writing or any ordinary use of the senses
心靈感應 –**telepathic** /ˌtɛlɪˈpæθɪk; ˌtelⅰˈpæ-
θɪk◂/ *adj* –**telepathically** /-klⅰ; -kli/ *adv*

★**tel·e·phone¹** /ˈtɛlə,fon; ˈtelⅰfəun/ *n* (also 又
作 **phone** *infml* 〖非正式〗) a machine used
for speaking to someone who is a long way
away from you 電話: *I need to make a tele-
phone call.* 我要打個電話。| *He's on the
telephone to his mother.* 他正在給母親打電
話。| *Can I use your telephone?* 我可以借用
你的電話嗎? –see picture on page 763 見
763 頁彩圖

telephone² (also 又作 **phone** *infml* 〖非正
式〗) *v* **telephoned, telephoning 1** [I;T] to
speak to someone by telephone 給〔某人〕打
電話: *Did you telephone Bob?* 你有沒有打電
話給鮑勃? | *I telephoned to invite them.* 我
打電話邀請他們。| *She telephoned the news
to her brother.* 她打電話把消息告訴了哥哥。**2**
[T] to ring the number of a person you
want to speak to by telephone 撥〔某人的〕
電話號碼: *I've been telephoning him all
morning but he's not there.* 我給他撥了一上
午的電話,但他不在。| *You can't telephone
London direct from here.* 你無法在這裡直接
打電話到倫敦。

■ **USAGE** 用法: If you want to **telephone** your mother (or **phone** her, or
ring her (**up**) or **call** her) you **dial** her
number. If you want your mother to
pay for the call you ask the **operator**
for a **reverse charge call** (or a **collect
call** in America) and the operator will
connect you. The phone will **ring** and
your mother may **answer** by picking
up the **receiver.** If she is busy she may
ask you to **call back** later. When she
finishes speaking to you she will **hang
up** (= replace the receiver). If she is

---

already **on the phone** when you call
her, her number is **engaged** (British
English) or **busy** (American English).
☆如果你想給母親打電話,你可以撥她的
號碼。如果你想讓她付款,你可以讓接線
員為你接打對方付款電話,接線員便會為你
接通電話。電話鈴響後,母親可能會拿起
聽筒聽電話。如果她正在忙,也許會請你
晚些時候再打。話講完之後,她會掛斷電
話。如果你給她打電話時她正在用電話,
她的電話就是"佔線"。

telephone booth /'··· ·/ *n* a small
enclosed space in a public place, where
you can make telephone calls 公用電話亭

telephone ex·change /'··· ·,·/ *n* (also 又作
exchange) a central place where telephone
connections are made 電話總機〔交換台〕

te·leph·o·nist /təˈlɛfənɪst; tⅰˈlefənⅰst/ *n* a
person who works in a telephone exchange
or answers the telephone in a company or
organization 〔公司或組織的〕電話接線員

tel·e·pho·to lens /ˌtɛləfoto ˈlɛnz; ˌtelⅰfəu-
təu ˈlenz/ *n* an additional part for a camera
that allows you to take clear pictures of
distant objects 〔照像機的〕長焦距鏡頭

tel·e·scope¹ /ˈtɛlə,skop; ˈtelⅰskəup/ *n* a
long scientific instrument which makes distant objects appear nearer and larger 望遠
鏡

telescope² *v* **telescoped, telescoping** [I;T]
to become or to make something shorter,
usually by sliding one part over another
(使)套疊; (使)套入

tel·e·scop·ic /ˌtɛləˈskɑpɪk; ˌtelⅰˈskɒpɪk◂/ *adj*
1 making distant objects appear nearer
and larger 能望遠的: *a telescopic lens* 望遠鏡
頭 **2** made of parts that slide over one
another to make the whole thing shorter
套疊式的

tel·e·van·gel·ist /ˌtɛləˈvændʒəlɪst; ˌtelⅰ-
ˈvændʒⅰlⅰst/ *n* a person who tries to persuade people to become CHRISTIANS by
talking to them over the television;
televangelists often ask people to send
them money 在電視中規勸人們信仰基督教的
人

tel·e·vise /ˈtɛlə,vaɪz; ˈtelⅰvaɪz/ *v* **televised,
televising** [T] to broadcast something on
television 在電視中播送〔某事〕: *The whole of
the World Cup will be televised.* 世界杯賽的全
部比賽將在電視上轉播。

★**tel·e·vi·sion** /ˈtɛlə,vɪʒən; ˈtelⅰˌvɪʒən/
n (also 又作 **telly, TV**
infml 〖非正式〗) **1** [C;U] an electrical apparatus which broadcasts pictures and
sound 電視機: *Shall I turn the television on?*
我扭開電視機好嗎? | *What's on television
this evening?* 今天晚上電視播映甚麼節目? **2**
[U] the things that are broadcast on television 電視節目: *Do you watch much tele-*

vision? 你電視節目看得多嗎? | *a television programme* 電視節目 **3** [U] the business of recording and broadcasting pictures and sound 電視節目製作業: *the television industry* 電視業

> ■ USAGE 用法: Remember to use the preposition **on** for expressions such as ☆請記住在下面這一類的短語中用介詞 **on**: *I saw it **on** television.* 我是在電視上看到的。 | *The Prime Minister appeared **on** television last night.* 首相昨夜出現在電視上了。 | *What's **on** telly/on T.V. tonight?* 電視今晚播映甚麼節目?

tel·ex /ˈtɛlɛks; ˈtɛlɛks/ *n* **1** [U] a method of sending printed messages by electrical signals 電傳: *Send it by telex.* 用電傳把它發出去。 **2** [C] a message sent in this way 電傳電文: *A telex has arrived from Hong Kong.* 從香港來了一份電傳。 **3** [C] a special machine for sending these messages 電傳機: *The telex operator will send it for you.* 電傳機操作員會給你發出去的。 **–telex** *v* [I;T]: *We'll telex our charges to you immediately.* 我們即刻電傳收費表給你。

★★**tell** /tɛl; tɛl/ *v* told /told; təʊld/, **telling 1** [T] to express something in words 告訴〔某人〕: *Did you tell Joan about Paul?* 你把保羅的事情告訴瓊了嗎? | *John told us he'd seen you in town.* 約翰告訴我們說他在城裡看見你了。 | *Can you tell me what time the party starts?* 可以告訴我晚會何時開始嗎? | *Are you telling me the truth?* 你告訴我的是實情嗎? –see 見 SAY¹ (USAGE 用法)

> □ USEFUL PATTERNS 有用句型
> tell someone (about) something; to tell someone that; tell someone what, why, how, etc.

2 [T] to advise someone to do something 勸告; 提醒: *I told him to see a doctor if he was worried.* 我勸他如果擔心的話就去看醫生。

> □ USEFUL PATTERNS 有用句型
> to tell someone to do something; to tell someone that...

3 [T] to order someone to do something 命令, 吩咐〔某人〕做〔某事〕: *Children should do as they're told!* 小孩子應該照着吩咐的去做! | *I told her not to be late.* 我叫她不要遲到。 –see 見 ORDER² (USAGE 用法) **4** [T] to let someone know something 讓〔某人〕知道〔某事〕: *This light tells you if the machine is on or off.* 這盞燈顯示機器是否開着。 **5 I told you so** a phrase used when you warned someone that something would happen and it did 我警告過你的〔用於曾告訴某人某事將會發生, 而後來果然發生〕: *"It didn't work." "I*

told you so." "這機器無法開動。" "這我警告過你的。" **6 time will tell** = we will know some time in the future 將來才會知道: *Only time will tell whether they have made the right decision.* 他們的決定是否正確有待日後證實。 **7 tell the time** to read the time from a clock or watch 看錶; 看時間 **8 be able to tell** to recognize or judge the truth of something. 辨認出; 判斷: *It was so dark I couldn't tell it was you.* 當時太暗了, 我並沒有認出是你。 | *I can't tell the difference between the twins.* 這對雙胞胎我無法分辨。 | *"Which team will win?" "Who can tell?"* "哪支隊伍會贏?" "誰曉得?" **9 there's no telling** it is not possible to know 無法得知: *There's no telling when the situation will improve.* 無法知道情況何時會好轉。 **10** [I] to have a bad effect on someone 對〔某人〕有不利影響: *The long hours of difficult work are starting to tell on us.* 長時間艱苦工作開始令我們的效率降低。 **11** [I] to pass someone's secret to another person 告密; 泄密: *If I show you what I did, will you promise not to tell?* 如果我給你看我做了甚麼東西, 你是否答應不會告訴別人? | *You won't tell on me, will you?* 你不會去揭發我吧? **12 you're telling me** *infml* a phrase used when you agree with someone completely 一點不錯〔用於表示完全同意某人所說的話〕 **13 tell you what, I tell you what** an expression used in informal conversation when you are going to suggest a good idea you have just had 聽我的〔用於閒談之中提出剛剛想到的好主意〕: *I tell you what — why don't you put the table against the other wall?* 聽我的 —— 為何不把桌子靠在另外一堵牆上呢?

tell sbdy ↔ **off** *phr v* [T] to scold someone 責備〔某人〕: *She tells me off for the smallest mistakes.* 就是極微小的錯誤, 她也會責備我。

tell·er /ˈtɛlə; ˈtɛlər/ *n* **1** a person employed to receive and pay out money in a bank 〔銀行的〕出納員 **2** a person who counts votes during an election 〔選舉時的〕計票人

tell·ing /ˈtɛlɪŋ; ˈtɛlɪŋ/ *adj* **1** very effective 有效的: *a telling argument* 有力的論證 **2** showing your feelings, even if you intend to hide them 顯示感情的: *a telling remark* 心裡話

tell·tale¹ /ˈtɛlˌtɛl; ˈtɛltɛl/ *n infml* a person who passes on other people's secrets, knowing that they will be punished 〔非正式〕告密者

telltale² *adj* [only before a noun 只用於名詞前] making something clear that is intended to be hidden 泄露祕密的: *A telltale look of jealousy in his eyes contradicted his calm manner.* 他雖然態度平靜, 但目光中卻流露出嫉妒之情。

tel·ly /ˈtɛlɪ; ˈtɛlɪ/ *n* [C;U] –see 見 TELEVISION (USAGE 用法)

te·mer·i·ty /təˈmɛrətɪ; təˈmɛrəti/ *n* [U] *fml*

bold confidence which is not suitable and often not polite 〖正式〗魯莽; 莽撞: *He had the temerity to ask for higher wages at the end of his first week's work.* 他如此魯莽, 竟然在開始工作的第一個週末便要求增加工資。

tem·per¹ /'tɛmpə; 'tɛmpəʳ/ *n* **1** [C;U] an angry state of mind 發火; 憤怒: *Jone's in a temper.* 約翰正在發脾氣。 | *a fit of temper* 一陣怒火 **2 fly into a temper, get into a temper, lose your temper** to become angry suddenly 火冒三丈; 勃然大怒 **3 keep your temper** to stay calm 保持平靜 **4** [C;U] a particular nature or state of mind, especially with regard to how easily you get angry 脾氣; 性情: *She has such a sweet temper.* 她的脾氣真好。 | *He could never control his temper.* 他一向控制不住自己的脾氣。 **5 -tempered** having a certain kind of nature or state of mind 有...脾氣的: *She's a bad-tempered old lady.* 她是個脾氣惡劣的老太太。 **6** [U] *tech* the degree to which a metal has been made hard or strong 〖術語〗金屬硬度

tem·per² *v* [T] **1** *tech* to make metal harder and stronger by heating it and then making it cool 〖術語〗把〔金屬〕煉硬 **2** *fml* to make something less severe or difficult 〖正式〗使〔某事物〕緩和: *His words were harsh, but he tempered them with a smile.* 他的話很刺耳, 但他用微笑來緩和了語氣。

tem·per·a·ment /'tɛmprəmənt; 'tɛmpərəmənt/ *n* [C;U] a person's nature, which influences their way of thinking or acting 性情; 氣質: *Their marriage succeeds because their temperaments are so similar.* 由於性情相近, 他們的婚姻很成功。

tem·per·a·men·tal /ˌtɛmprəˈmɛntl; ˌtɛmpərəˈmɛntl◂/ *adj* **1** having frequent and sudden changes of feelings 性情多變的: *The actor was so temperamental that people refused to work with him.* 那位演員性情多變, 人們都拒絕與他共事。 **2** caused by or related to a person's nature 由氣質引起的; 本性的: *She had a temperamental dislike of competitive sports.* 她生性不喜歡競技性的運動項目。 –**temperamentally** *adv*

tem·per·ance /'tɛmprəns; 'tɛmpərəns/ *n* [U] **1** *fml* self-control 〖正式〗自我克制; 節制 **2** total avoidance of alcoholic drinks 完全戒酒

tem·per·ate /'tɛmprɪt; 'tɛmpərɪt/ *adj* **1** showing self-control 節制的: *temperate behaviour* 克制的行為 **2** never very hot or cold 溫和的: *Britain has a temperate climate.* 英國的氣候很溫和。

★tem·per·a·ture /'tɛmprətʃə; 'tɛmpərətʃəʳ/ *n* [C;U] **1** the degree of heat or coldness of a person, thing, or place 溫度: *The average temperature in London is 15°C.* 倫敦的平均氣溫是攝氏十五度。 | *The constant changes in temperature made me ill.* 溫度不斷變化使我生病。 **2 have a temperature, run a temperature** to have a higher body tempera-

ture than usual 發燒: *You're not going out while you've got a temperature!* 你還發着燒, 不許外出! **3 take someone's temperature** to measure the temperature of someone's body 量某人的體溫: *Get the thermometer and I'll take your temperature.* 把溫度計拿來, 我來給你量一下體溫。

tem·pest /'tɛmpɪst; 'tɛmpˌɪst/ *n lit* a violent storm 〖文〗暴風雨

tem·pes·tu·ous /tɛmˈpɛstʃʊəs; tɛmˈpɛstʃʊəs/ *adj* **1** stormy 暴風雨的; 狂暴的: *the tempestuous sea* 波濤洶湧的大海 **2** full of strong feelings and arguments 激烈的; 劇烈的: *a tempestuous meeting* 充滿火藥味的會議 –**tempestuously** *adv* –**tempestuousness** *n* [U]

tem·ple /'tɛmpl; 'tɛmpəl/ *n* **1** a building used for worship in certain religions 寺院; 寺廟: *a Buddhist temple* 佛教寺廟 **2** one of the two flat places on each side of your forehead 太陽穴

tem·po /'tɛmpo; 'tɛmpəʊ/ *n* **tempos** *or* **tempi** /-pi; -piː/ **1** *tech* the speed at which music is played 〖術語〗〔音樂的〕速度; 拍子: *Let's try that again at a faster tempo.* 我們用快一點的速度再演奏一遍。 **2** the speed at which something happens 〔某事發生的〕速度; 節奏: *I found it difficult to adjust to the tempo of city life.* 我發覺很難適應城市生活的節奏。

tem·po·ral /'tɛmpərəl; 'tɛmpərəl/ *adj fml* 〖正式〗 **1** related to practical material affairs, as opposed to religious affairs 世俗的: *the temporal power of the state* 國家的世俗權力 **2** related to or limited by time 時間的; 受時間限制的: *"When" is a temporal conjunction.* "when" 是一個表示時間的連接詞。

★tem·po·ra·ry /'tɛmpəˌrɛrɪ; 'tɛmpərəri/ *adj* lasting only for a limited time 臨時的; 短暫的: *a temporary holiday job* 假期裡的臨時工作 –compare 比較 PERMANENT –**temporarily** /'tɛmpəˌrɛrəlɪ; 'tɛmpərərˌli/ *adv*: *I was temporarily delayed.* 我受到阻延耽擱了一會兒。

tempt /tɛmpt; tɛmpt/ *v* [T] **1** to try to persuade someone to do something which may be unwise or immoral 引誘, 慫恿〔某人〕做...: *He tried to tempt me to cheat in the examination.* 他慫恿我在考試中作弊。 | *Another firm is trying to tempt her away from her present job with an offer of more money.* 另外一家公司正試圖以更高的薪水吸引她離開現在的工作。 | *Leaving your car open might tempt someone into stealing it.* 車門開着不鎖會引來小偷把車偷走。

□ USEFUL PATTERNS 有用句型
to tempt someone to do something; to tempt someone with something; to tempt someone into doing something

2 to try to attract someone to do something that you want them to do 吸引〔某人〕做〔某事〕: *His mother tried to tempt him by preparing delicious meals.* 他母親試圖用豐盛的飯菜引起他的興趣。**3 be tempted to do something** to want to do something but to be unsure if it is the right thing to do 被某事打動: *It's a very attractive offer and I'm tempted to accept.* 這個提議很有吸引力，我動心了，準備接受。

temp·ta·tion /tɛmpˈteʃən; tempˈteɪʃən/ *n* **1** [U] a state in which you feel persuaded to do something which may be wrong 誘惑: *I resisted the temptation to smoke a cigarette.* 我抵擋住了吸煙的誘惑。**2** [C] a situation or thing which may persuade you to do something wrong 有誘惑力的事物: *the temptations of a big city* 大城市的各種誘惑

tempt·ing /ˈtɛmptɪŋ; ˈtʌmptɪŋ/ *adj* attractive, but perhaps not the right thing to do 有誘惑力的: *It's tempting to believe that I'll be promoted soon.* 想像着不久便會得到提升，實在叫人心動。| *a tempting offer* 一項誘人的提議**—temptingly** *adv*

ten /tɛn; tɛn/ *det, n, pron* the number 10 〔數字〕十

ten·a·ble /ˈtɛnəbl; ˈtɛnəbəl/ *adj fml*〔正式〕**1** reasonable and able to be successfully defended (used of an argument or belief) 有道理的，站得住腳的〔指論點或信仰〕: *Her views are no longer tenable.* 她的觀點再也站不住腳了。**—opposite** 反義 **untenable 2** that can be held by someone for a certain length of time (used of an office or position) 可保持一段時間的〔指職位〕: *How long is the post tenable* **for?** 這一職位的任期是多久？

te·na·cious /tɪˈneʃəs; tʃˈneɪʃəs/ *adj* determined, and not easily accepting defeat 堅忍不屈的; 不屈不撓的: *She has proved a very tenacious opponent of the new road scheme.* 她堅決反對新的修路計劃，立場十分堅定。 **—tenaciously** *adv* **—tenacity** /-ˈnæsətɪ; -ˈnæsˌ‖ti/ *n* [U]

ten·an·cy /ˈtɛnənsɪ; ˈtɛnənsɪ/ *n* **tenancies** [C;U] the use of a room, land, or building for which rent has been paid, or the length of time you have this use for 租賃; 租賃時間: *a tenancy agreement* 租賃協議 | *rights of tenancy* 租賃權限

★**ten·ant** /ˈtɛnənt; ˈtɛnənt/ *n* a person who pays rent for the use of a room, building, or land 房客; 租戶; 佃戶: *a council tenant* 市建房屋的租戶

★**tend** /tɛnd; tɛnd/ *v* **1** [I] to do or happen often or usually 經常做; 經常發生: *Janet tends to get angry if you ask her stupid questions..* 如果你問詹尼特愚蠢的問題，她常常會發火。| *It tends to rain here a lot in spring.* 春天這裡經常下雨。**2** [T] *fml* to look after someone or something in a caring way〔正式〕照顧，照料〔某人或某物〕: *She tended her husband lovingly during his ill-*

ness. 她在丈夫患病期間無微不至地照料他。| *a farmer tending his sheep* 看管綿羊的農民

☐ **USEFUL PATTERN** 有用句型
to tend to do something

tend to sthg/sbdy *phr v* [T] to pay attention to someone or something 注意，照顧〔某人或某物〕: *The nurses tended to the soldiers' wounds.* 護士護理士兵的傷口。

★**ten·den·cy** /ˈtɛndənsɪ; ˈtɛndənsɪ/ *n* **tendencies 1** a part of your character which makes you likely to think or behave in a particular way〔性格的〕傾向: *He's always had a tendency* **towards** *frivolity.* 他總喜歡說些輕浮的話。| *She has a tendency to shout when she gets angry.* 生氣時她喜歡大喊大叫。

☐ **USEFUL PATTERN** 有用句型
have a tendency to do something

2 a general development towards a certain situation or condition 趨勢: *There is a growing tendency for people to work at home instead of in offices.* 有一個越來越普遍的趨勢，就是人們不是在辦公室裡而是在家裡上班。

ten·der¹ /ˈtɛndɚ; ˈtɛndɚ/ *adj* **1** easy to bite through 嫩的: *tender meat* 嫩肉 **2** painful or sensitive 疼痛的; 敏感的: *His wound is still tender.* 他的傷口仍然很疼。**3** gentle and loving 溫柔的; 溫存的: *tender loving care* 體貼入微的照顧 **4** [only before a noun 只用於名詞前] *lit* young and inexperienced 《文》年幼而無經驗的: *He was sent to boarding school at the tender age of eight.* 他入讀寄宿學校時只得八歲。**—tenderly** *adv* **—tenderness** *n* [U]

tender² *n* **1** a statement of the price you would charge for doing a job or providing goods 報價; 開價 **2** a vehicle carrying coal or water, pulled behind a railway engine 〔火車頭後面的〕煤車或水車

tender³ *v* [T] *fml* to formally offer or give something《正式》提供〔某物〕: *"Passengers must tender the exact fare."* "乘客必須付足車費。" | *The minister tendered his resignation.* 部長提交了辭呈。**2** [I] to make a formal offer to do a job or provide goods at a certain price 報價; 投標: *Several firms have tendered* **for** *the new road building contract.* 已有數家公司投標，爭取修建新馬路的合約。

ten·der·heart·ed /ˈtɛndɚˈhɑrtɪd; ˌtɛndə-ˈhɑːtʃd◂/ *adj* easily made to feel love, pity, or sorrow 軟心腸的 **—tenderheartedly** *adv*

ten·don /ˈtɛndən; ˈtɛndən/ *n* a thick strong cord that connects a muscle to a bone 腱; 筋

ten·dril /ˈtɛndrɪl; ˈtɛndr̩l/ *n* a thin curling stem by which a climbing plant fastens itself to something〔攀籐植物的〕卷鬚

ten·e·ment /ˈtɛnəmənt; ˈtɛnˌmənt/ *n* large building divided into flats in the poorer areas of a city 低價公寓; 貧民住宅

ten·et /ˈtɛnɪt; ˈtɛnɪt/ *n fml* a principle or belief〖正式〗信條; 信念: *the tenets of the Christian religion* 基督教的信條

ten·ner /ˈtɛnə; ˈtɛnəʳ/ *n BrE infml* £10 or a ten pound note〖英式, 非正式〗十英鎊; 十英鎊的紙幣

***ten·nis** /ˈtɛnɪs; ˈtɛnɪs/ *n* [U] a game played between two or four people who use rackets (RACKET) to hit a small ball backwards and forwards across a low net dividing a specially marked level court 網球(運動): *Would you like a game of tennis?* 你想打場網球嗎? | *a tennis ball* 網球 –see picture on page 957 見 957 頁彩圖

tennis shoe /ˈ·· ·/ *n* the usual American word for a〖美式〗= PLIMSOLL

ten·or /ˈtɛnə; ˈtɛnəʳ/ *n* **1** a male singer with a high voice 男高音歌手 **2** a musical instrument with quite a low range of notes 次中音樂器 **3** **the tenor of** *fml* the general meaning of〖正式〗大意: *I understood the tenor of his speech but not the details.* 我理解他演講的大意, 但沒聽懂其中的細節。 –**tenor** *adj*

tense¹ /tɛns; tɛns/ *n* [C;U] any of the forms of a verb that show whether you are talking about the past, the present, or the future〔動詞的〕時態: *"I have eaten" is the present perfect tense.* "我已吃過了"是現在完成時態。

tense² *adj* **1** stretched tight or stiff 緊張的; 僵硬的: *tense muscles* 僵硬的肌肉 **2** nervous and anxious: 緊張焦慮的: *I'm always tense before an exam.* 考試前我總是很緊張。 **3** causing feelings of worry and nervousness 令人緊張的: *a tense moment before we heard the news* 聽到消息前那緊張的一刻 –**tensely** *adv*

tense³ *v* **tensed, tensing** [I;T] to become tight and stiff 變緊張; 變僵硬: *I saw her tense up when the phone rang.* 電話鈴響的時候, 我見她十分緊張。 | *Tense your muscles, please!* 請(把你的肌肉繃緊)好好準備!

***ten·sion** /ˈtɛnʃən; ˈtɛnʃən/ *n* **1** [U] the degree of tightness of a wire or rope 繃緊度; 拉緊度: *Don't tighten the violin strings too much as they can snap under the tension.* 不要把小提琴的弦繃得太緊, 這樣的話它們可能會繃斷。 **2** [C;U] a feeling of anxiety or fear 焦慮; 恐懼: *He's suffering from nervous tension.* 他神經十分緊張。 | *racial tensions in South Africa.* 南非種族間的緊張關係。 | *The border dispute has been a continuing source of tension.* 邊界爭端是不斷導致緊張關係的一個原因。 **3** [U] *tech* electric power〖術語〗電力; 電壓: *Danger! High tension wires.* 危險! 那是高壓電線。

tent /tɛnt; tɛnt/ *n* a movable shelter made of cloth or plastic material, supported by poles and ropes and used by campers to sleep in 帳篷: *Where shall we pitch the tent?*

我們把帳篷支在哪裡?

ten·ta·cle /ˈtɛntəkl; ˈtɛntəkəl/ *n* a long thin boneless arm on certain creatures, used for moving, seizing, or touching 觸角; 觸手: *the tentacles of an octopus* 鱆魚的觸手

ten·ta·tive /ˈtɛntətɪv; ˈtɛntətɪv/ *adj* **1** not certain or complete 不確定的; 不完全的: *We've made tentative plans for a holiday but haven't really decided yet.* 我們初步構思了好幾個度假計劃, 但還未決定選哪一個。 **2** done carefully and slowly without much confidence 猶豫的; 遲疑的: *a tentative smile* 怯生生的一笑 –**tentatively** *adv*

ten·ter·hooks /ˈtɛntə,hʊks; ˈtɛntəhʊks/ *n* **on tenterhooks** worried or excited about something that will happen soon 焦慮不安

tenth /tɛnθ; tɛnθ/ **1** *det, pron, adv* 10th 第十(個) **2** one of ten equal parts 十分之一

ten·u·ous /ˈtɛnjʊəs; ˈtɛnjuəs/ *adj* very thin or weak (used of an idea or connection) 薄弱的, 不牢固的〔指意見或連結〕: *There is only a tenuous link between the film and the book on which it is based.* 電影與原著間沒有太大的聯繫。

ten·ure /ˈtɛnjə; ˈtɛnjəʳ/ *n* [U] *fml*〖正式〗**1** the legal right to use land or buildings〔土地或房子的〕使用權: *conditions of tenure* 使用條件 **2** The length of time you keep a job or position 任期

tep·id /ˈtɛpɪd; ˈtɛpɪd/ *adj* **1** only slightly warm (used of liquids) 微溫的〔指液體〕 **2** not showing much interest 不太感興趣的: *a rather tepid welcome* 不太熱烈的歡迎

***term¹** /tɜːm; tɜːm/ *n* **1** one of the periods of time into which the school or university year is divided 學期: *the summer term* 夏季學期 | *Do we have end-of-term exams?* 我們有期終考試嗎? **2** a fixed or limited period of time 期限; 期限: *The President is elected for a four-year term.* 總統當選後任期四年。 | *a term of imprisonment* 刑期 **3** a word or expression used in a particular activity, profession, or subject 術語: *a medical term* 醫學術語 | *terms of abuse* 罵人的話 **4** **in the long term** over a long period of time 從長遠看: *In the long term we will make a profit.* 長遠來看我們是會有盈利的。 [RELATED PHRASE 相關詞組 **in the short term**] **5** **terms** the conditions under which you make an agreement〔協議的〕條件: *We're trying to negotiate the loan on favourable terms.* 我們正在進行協商, 力爭以優惠的條件獲取貸款。 | *terms of employment* 雇用條件 **6** **in terms of** from the point of view of 從...觀點看: *In terms of sales, the book hasn't been successful.* 從銷售的角度來看, 該書並不成功。 *In business terms the project isn't viable.* 從商業角度看, 該計劃是不可行的。 **7** **be on good terms with** to be friendly with someone 與〔某人〕和睦相處 **8** **come to terms with** to accept something unpleasant 接受〔令人不快的事物〕: *I think I've come to*

---

terms with losing my job now. 我覺得自己已經接受了失業這一現實。**9 in no uncertain terms** clearly and angrily 明確地；憤怒地: *He told me in no uncertain terms to go away.* 他憤怒地叫我走開。**10 think in terms of, talk in terms of** to consider something as a possibility 考慮做〔某事〕: *We're thinking in terms of investing the money in property.* 我們正在考慮投資地產業。**11 terms of reference** the limits of an enquiry or report 調查範圍；報告範圍: *This problem is outside the committee's terms of reference.* 這一問題超出了委員會的調查權限。

term² *v* [T] to name or describe someone or describe as a particular thing 把〔某人或某物〕稱為: *The chairman of this parliament is termed the "Speaker".* 本議會的主席稱為"議長"。

ter·mi·nal¹ /ˈtɜːmənl; ˈtɝːmɪ̯nəl/ *adj* concerning or having an illness that will cause death 〔疾病〕致命的, 晚期的: *terminal cancer* 晚期癌症 | *terminal patients* 患絕症的病人 – **terminally** *adv*: *a hospice for the terminally ill* 患絕症病人的收容所

terminal² *n* **1** an apparatus usually consisting of a keyboard and a SCREEN by which you can give instructions to a computer and get information from it 〔電腦的〕終端機 **2** a place where people, planes, and other vehicles begin or end a journey 〔人、飛機或車輛的〕終點(站)；航空客運站 –see picture on page 991 見 991 頁彩圖 **3** a point at which connections can be made to an electric system 〔電路的〕接頭

ter·mi·nate /ˈtɜːməˌneɪt; ˈtɝːmɪ̯neɪt/ *v* **terminated, terminating** [I;T] *fml* to bring or come to an end 〔正式〕(使)終止; (使)結束: *Your contract has been terminated.* 已經終止了你的合約。 | *The meeting terminated successfully.* 會議圓滿結束。 –**termination** /ˌtɜːməˈneɪʃən; ˌtɝːmɪ̯ˈneɪʃən/ *n* [U]

ter·mi·nol·o·gy /ˌtɜːməˈnɑlədʒi; ˌtɝːmɪ̯ˈnɑːlədʒi/ *n* [U] a system of specialized words and expressions used in a particular science, profession, or activity 術語: *I don't understand scientific terminology.* 我不懂科學術語。

ter·mi·nus /ˈtɜːmənəs; ˈtɝːmɪ̯nəs/ *n* the end of a railway or bus line 〔鐵路或公交線路的〕終點站

ter·mite /ˈtɜːmaɪt; ˈtɝːmaɪt/ *n* a tropical insect like an ant that destroys wood, and builds hills of earth 白蟻

ter·race /ˈterɪs; ˈterɪ̯s/ *n* **1** *BrE* a row of houses joined to each other 〔英式〕〔互相連接的〕一排房屋 **2** a flat outdoor area next to a building or on the roof , where you can sit or have your meals 〔房屋的〕平台, 陽台 **3** one of the wide steps from which you can watch a football match 〔足球比賽的〕看台 **4** a flat piece of ground cut in the slope of a hill where crops are grown 梯田

ter·raced /ˈterɪst; ˈterɪ̯st/ *adj* **1** having flat pieces of ground cut in the side of a hill like large steps on which crops can be grown 梯田的 **2 terraced house** a house which is part of a row of houses joined together 聯排房屋〔一排相連房屋中的一所〕 –see picture on page 729 見 729 頁彩圖

ter·ra·cot·ta /ˌterəˈkɑtə; ˌterəˈkɑːtə/ *n* [U] hard reddish brown baked clay 赤陶土

ter·rain /təˈreɪn; teˈreɪn/ *n* [U] an area of land, and whether it is rough, smooth, easy or difficult to cross 地形；地域；地帶: *rocky terrain* 岩石地帶

ter·ra·pin /ˈterəpɪn; ˈterəpɪ̯n/ *n* a type of small water TURTLE 甲魚

ter·res·tri·al /təˈrestriəl; tɪ̯ˈrestriəl/ *adj* **1** related to the Earth, rather than the moon, or space 地球的 **2** *tech* living on land, rather than in water or in the air 〔術語〕陸地的；陸棲的；陸生的: *a terrestrial animal* 陸棲動物

★ter·ri·ble /ˈterəbl; ˈterəbl̩/ *adj* **1** very serious 嚴重的: *a terrible accident* 嚴重的事故 **2** *infml* very bad or of poor quality 〔非正式〕很糟的；質量差的: *You look terrible — are you ill?* 你看上去氣色不好——是病了嗎? | *a terrible play* 糟糕的戲 **3** causing great dislike or fear 令人厭惡的; 令人害怕的: *There was a terrible noise and then a loud crash.* 可怕的聲音之後是非常響的碰撞聲。

ter·ri·bly /ˈterəbli; ˈterəbli/ *adv* **1** very badly 非常糟糕地: *He played that game terribly.* 他那場比賽表現很糟糕。 **2** *infml* very 〔非正式〕非常: *I've been terribly worried about you.* 我非常擔心你。 | *It wasn't a terribly good film.* 這不是一部特別好的影片。

ter·ri·er /ˈteriə; ˈteriɚ/ *n* a type of small dog originally used for hunting 㹴〔一種小獵犬〕

ter·rif·ic /təˈrɪfɪk; təˈrɪfɪk/ *adj infml* 〔非正式〕 **1** very good or enjoyable 極好的; 快樂的: *a terrific party* 氣氛非常好的聚會 **2** very great 非常大的: *She drove at a terrific speed.* 她把車開得飛快。

ter·rif·i·cal·ly /təˈrɪfɪkli; təˈrɪfɪkli/ *adv infml* very 〔非正式〕 非常: *It's terrifically cold today.* 今天非常冷。

ter·ri·fy /ˈterəˌfaɪ; ˈterɪ̯faɪ/ *v* **terrified, terrifying** [T] to fill someone with terror or fear 令〔某人〕感到恐懼: *Heights terrify me!* 一到高處我就害怕!

ter·ri·to·ri·al /ˌterəˈtoriəl; ˌterɪ̯ˈtoːriəl/ *adj* **1** relating to the land a country controls 領土的 **2 territorial waters** the sea near a country's coast over which that country has legal control 領海

★ter·ri·to·ry /ˈterətori; ˈterɪ̯tɔri/ *n* **territories** **1** [C;U] the land that the government of a country controls 領土: *British territories* 英國領土 | *We travelled through unknown territory.* 我們通過了一片不明地帶。 **2** [C;U] a piece of land which an animal defends as belonging to it alone 〔動物的〕領地 **3** [C] an area of interest or an area for which someone is responsible 感興趣的領域；責任範圍: *I never deal with the engineers' salaries: that's Peter's territory.* 我從來不管工程師的薪資問題，那是彼得負責的範圍。

ter·ror /ˈtɛrə; ˈtɛrəʳ/ *n* **1** [U] extreme fear 恐怖；恐懼: *He had a look of terror on his face.* 他臉上露出驚恐的神情。| *The children ran away in terror.* 孩子們驚慌地跑開了。**2** [C] someone or something that makes you very frightened 令人恐懼的人或物: *the terrors of war* 戰爭的恐怖

ter·ror·is·m /ˈtɛrə,rɪzəm; ˈterərɪzəm/ *n* [U] the use of violence or the threat of violence to obtain political demands 恐怖主義；恐怖手段 **–terrorist** *adj, n*: *Terrorists have claimed responsibility for the bomb blast that killed 20 people.* 恐怖主義分子聲稱對導致二十人喪生的炸彈爆炸事件負責。

ter·ror·ize /ˈtɛrə,raɪz; ˈterəraɪz/ *v* **terrorized, terrorizing** (also 又作 **terrorise** *BrE* 〔英式〕) [T] to frighten someone or force them into doing something by using threats or violence 脅迫〔某人〕做〔某事〕: *The cashier was terrorized into handing over the money.* 出納員在威脅之下交出了錢。

terror-strick·en /ˈ·· ,···/ *adj* (also 又作 **terror-struck** /ˈ·· ,·/) extremely frightened 極度恐懼的

terse /tɜs; tɜːs/ *adj* using very few words, sometimes in a way which seems rude 簡短生硬的 **–tersely** *adv*

ter·tia·ry /ˈtɜʃɪ,ɛrɪ; ˈtɜːʃəri/ *adj* **1** *fml* at a third stage of development 〔正式〕第三階段的 **2 tertiary education** education at the level of college or university 高等教育

TESL /ˈtɛsl; ˈtesəl/ *n* [U] the teaching of English to people who live in an English speaking country and who don't speak English as their first language; an abbreviation for **the Teaching of English as a Second Language** 〔縮〕作為第二語言的英語教學

test[1] /tɛst; tɛst/ *n* **1** a number of questions or exercises to find out how good someone is at something or how much they know 考試；測驗: *a history test* 歷史測驗 | *I've passed my driving test.* 我已通過了駕駛測驗。**2** the using of something to see how it works 試驗；測試: *Before buying the car I went for a test drive.* 買下這輛汽車之前，我先開車試了試。| *atom bomb tests* 核彈試驗 **3** a short medical check on part of your body 身體檢查: *an eye test* 視力檢查 | *a blood test* 驗血 **4 put something to the test** to find out the qualities of something by using it in certain conditions 檢驗某物

test[2] *v* [T] **1** to find out how much someone knows by asking them questions 考試；測驗 **2** to find out what something is like or how well it works 試驗；測試: *These wet roads*

really *test a car's tyres.* 這些潮濕的路面對於汽車輪胎是不折不扣的考驗。| *I must have my eyes tested.* 我必須檢查一下我的視力。| *He prodded the fruit, testing it **for** ripeness.* 他用手撳了撳水果，看看它是否熟了。

tes·ta·ment /ˈtɛstəmənt; ˈtestəmənt/ *n fml* something that shows or proves something else very clearly 〔正式〕證明: *The aircraft is a testament to its designer's skill.* 這架飛機就是其設計者高超技術的明證。

test case /ˈ· ·/ *n* a case in a court of law which establishes a particular principle, which is then used as a standard for other cases 判例；案例

tes·ti·cle /ˈtɛstɪkl; ˈtestɪkəl/ *n* one of the two round organs below a man's PENIS which produce SPERM 睾丸

tes·ti·fy /ˈtɛstə,faɪ; ˈtestɪfaɪ/ *v* **testified, testifying** [I+(that)] to make a solemn statement about what is true 作證；證實: *The teacher testified **to** the pupil's ability.* 老師證明了那個學生的能力。| *One witness testified that he'd seen the robbery.* 有一位證人說他親眼目睹了搶劫案。| *She can't testify **against** her husband.* 她不可以提供不利於丈夫的證詞。

tes·ti·mo·ni·al /,tɛstəˈmonɪəl; ,testɪˈməʊnɪəl/ *n* a formal written statement about someone's character and abilities 〔品德、能力的〕證明書，推薦書

tes·ti·mo·ny /ˈtɛstə,monɪ; ˈtestɪməni/ *n* [C; U] a formal statement, as made by a witness in a court of law 〔法庭上的〕證詞

test match /ˈ· ·/ *n* (also 又作 **test**) one of a group of cricket or RUGBY matches played between teams of different countries 〔板球或橄欖球的〕國際比賽

test pi·lot /ˈ· ,··/ *n* a pilot who flies new aircraft in order to test them 〔新型飛機的〕試飛員

test tube /ˈ· ·/ *n* a small tube of thin glass, closed at one end, used in scientific tests 〔科學實驗用的〕試管

test-tube ba·by /ˈ·· ,··/ *n* a baby started outside a mother's body and then planted inside her to develop naturally 試管嬰兒

tes·ty /ˈtɛstɪ; ˈtesti/ *adj infml* impatient and bad tempered 〔非正式〕不耐煩的；脾氣急的 **–testily** *adv*

tet·a·nus /ˈtɛtənəs; ˈtetənəs/ *n* [U] a serious disease caused by infection in a cut or wound, which stiffens the muscles, especially of your jaw 破傷風

tête-à-tête /ˈtetəˈtet; ,teɪt ɑː ˈteɪt/ *adv* talking together in private 私下談話: *We dined tête-à-tête.* 我倆單獨一起進餐。**–tête-à-tête** *n*: *a cosy tête-à-tête* 一次愉快的密談

teth·er /ˈtɛðə; ˈteðə/ *n* **1** a rope or chain to which an animal is tied 〔繫動物的〕拴繩，拴鏈 **2 at the end of your tether** having used up all your patience and strength and unable to manage any longer 忍無可忍；山窮

水盡 **–tether** v [T]: *a dog tethered to a post* 拴在柱子上的一條狗

text /tɛkst; tɛkst/ n **1** [U] writing, for example in a book 〔書本的〕文字: *Children's books often have more pictures than text.* 兒童書通常圖畫比文字多。| *This computer prints out text very fast.* 這台電腦的文字打印速度很快。 **2 the text** the exact original words or printed form of a speech, article, or book 〔演講、文章或書籍的〕原文: *The text of the President's speech is in today's newspaper.* 總統演講的原文刊登在今天的報紙上。 **3** [C] a sentence from the Bible that a priest reads and talks about in church 〔神父在教堂中閱讀及談論的〕聖經經句 **4** [C] a book which students studying a certain subject have to read 課本; 教材: *"Hamlet" is a set text this year.* 《哈姆雷特》一書是今年的規定教材。

text·book /ˈtɛkst,bʊk; ˈtɛkstbʊk/ n a standard book for the study of a particular subject 課本; 教科書

tex·tile /ˈtɛkstl; ˈtɛkstaɪl/ n any material made by weaving 紡織品: *a textile factory* 紡織廠 | *silk and cotton textiles* 絲織品和棉織品

tex·ture /ˈtɛkstʃɚ; ˈtɛkstʃəˈ/ n [C;U] how rough or smooth, coarse or fine something feels when you touch it 質地; 質感: *the delicate texture of her skin* 她細膩的皮膚 | *a soil with a loose sandy texture* 疏鬆的沙質土壤

than /ðən; ðən; *strong* 強讀 ðæn; ðæn/ conj, prep used when you are comparing two things 比〔用於比較兩個事物〕: *She's older than me.* 她年紀比我大。| *He's older than I am.* 他年紀比我大。| *He earns more than I do.* 他掙的錢比我多。| *They were away for more than a week.* 他們外遊一個多星期。

thank /θæŋk; θæŋk/ v [T] **1** to show or tell someone that you are pleased that they helped you or gave you something 感謝〔某人〕: *I thanked him for his advice.* 我感謝他給我忠告。| *How can I ever thank you? You've been so helpful.* 我應該如何謝你呢? 你幫了我很大的忙。

□ USEFUL PATTERNS 有用句型
to thank someone for something; to thank someone for doing someting

2 thank you (also 又作 **thanks** infml 〔非正式〕) an expression used to show that you are grateful to someone 謝謝〔用於對某人表示感謝〕: *Thank you for the present.* 謝謝你的禮物。| *Do you want some tea? No, thank you.* 你要喝茶嗎? 不用了, 謝謝。 **3 have yourself to thank** to be responsible for something bad 怪自己: *You've only got yourself to thank for the accident.* 這起事故只能怪你自己。 **4 thank God, thank goodness, thank**

heaven an expression of pleasure that something unpleasant or worrying has ended 謝天謝地〔用於表示令人不快或令人憂慮的事情結束〕: *Thank God my son's alive!* 謝天謝地, 我的兒子還活著!

thank·ful /ˈθæŋkfəl; ˈθæŋkfəl/ adj glad that something good has happened or grateful for something 高興的; 感謝的: *I was thankful to be free of the problem.* 我很高興擺脫了這問題的困擾。| *I'm very thankful that I don't have to look after elderly relatives.* 我很慶幸自己不必照顧年邁的親戚。 **–thankfully** adv **–thankfulness** n [U]

thank·less /ˈθæŋklɪs; ˈθæŋkləs/ adj not likely to be rewarded with thanks or praise 不大會得到感激或表揚的: *He has the thankless task of organizing the rubbish collection.* 他負責組織收集垃圾這項吃力不討好的工作。

thanks /θæŋks; θæŋks/ n [pl] **1** words which show how pleased you are that someone has helped you or done something for you 感謝的話: *Give thanks to God.* 感謝上帝 | *I'll get no thanks for all this hard work.* 我做了這麼多辛苦的工作, 卻無法得到人們的感謝。 **2 thanks to** because of 因為; 由於: *Thanks to your stupidity, we lost the game.* 都是因為你糊塗, 我們才輸掉比賽。

thanks·giv·ing /ˌθæŋksˈgɪvɪŋ; ˌθæŋksˈgɪvɪŋ◂/ n [U] **1** an expression of gratefulness to God 對上帝的感恩 **2 Thanksgiving** a holiday in the U.S. in November on which God is thanked for the year's crops 感恩節

thank-you /ˈθæŋk,ju; ˈθæŋkjuː/ n an expression of thanks 表示感謝: *a special thank-you for all your help* 對你的幫助特表謝意 | *a thank-you letter* 一封感謝信

that[1] /ðæt; ðæt/ det, pron those /ðoz; ðəʊz/ **1** the person or thing that is further away in place or time 那個〔人或物〕: *You look in this room and I'll look in that one over there.* 你檢查這個房間, 我去檢查那邊的一間。| *That's my boss over there.* 那位是我的老闆。| *What's that?* 那是甚麼? **2** the person or thing already stated or known about 已提及或已知的人或物: *I've got a meeting at two o'clock, but I'll be free after that.* 兩點鐘我要開一個會, 但會開完以後我就有空了。| *I never want to see that man again!* 我再也不想見那個人了! | *"We're getting a pay rise next month." "That's good."* "下個月我們加薪了。" "那不錯。" **3 that's it** a phrase you use to say that something is finished 就這樣〔用於表示某事已結束〕 **4 that's that** a phrase you use to say that there is nothing more to say or do 就這麼定了〔用於表示再沒有可說或可做的事情〕 **5 that is, that is to say: a** phrases used when you are going to explain a word that you think people may not have understood 換句話說〔用於解釋別人可能還未理解的事情〕: *The wood is then decorticated. That is, the bark is all taken off the outside.* 然後給木頭

去皮。換句話說, 也就是把樹皮全部剝掉。**b** phrases used when you are going to say something more exactly a second time, perhaps because you think that you were not very clear or gave the wrong idea the first time 也就是說〔用於進一步詳細說明某事〕: *He's going to do the garage again. That is, he's going to change the roof.* 他準備再修整一下車庫。也就是說, 他準備把屋頂換掉。

that² *adv infml* 【非正式】**not that** not very 不那麼; 不太: *I didn't like the film that much.* 我不太喜歡這部電影。

that³ *conj* /ðət; ðət; *strong* 強讀 ðæt; ðæt/ **1** used after certain nouns, verbs, and adjectives 〔用於某些名詞、動詞、和形容詞後面〕〔引導子句〕: *Is it true that you're leaving?* 你是不是真的要走了? | *I think that I'd better leave now.* 我認為我最好現在就走。| *There's no proof that she was here.* 沒有證據表明她來過這裡。**2** who or which 〔代表人或物〕〔引導子句〕: *It was George that told me.* 是喬治告訴我的。| *Did you see the letter that came today?* 你看見今天收到的那封信嗎? | *Did you get the books that I sent you?* 你收到我寄給你的書嗎? | *He's the one person that I trust completely.* 他是我完全信賴的人。

> ■ USAGE 用法: **1** We can only leave out the relative pronoun **that** when it is the object of the verb ☆ **that** 只有作動詞的受詞才能省略: *She's the woman* (**that**) *I love.* 她就是我所愛的女人。**2** We can only use **that** instead of **who** or **which** when we limit the meaning of a noun to show which one(s) we mean ☆ 當我們為了表明所指的東西而限制一個名詞的含義時, 才可以用 **that** 代替 **who** 或 **which**: *I'll stay with my brother — the one* **who/that** *lives in Leeds.* 我打算和我哥哥住在一起 —— 就是住在利茲的那個哥哥。We cannot use **that** when we simply add extra information 如果我們只是加上額外的信息時, 不能使用 **that**: *This is my father,* **who** *lives in London.* 這是我父親, 他住在倫敦。**3** In ordinary speech we often leave out **that** before a noun clause, especially after common verbs of saying and thinking ☆ 平時講話時, 我們在名詞子句前常常省略 **that,** 尤其是在表示說和想等普通動詞後: *She said* (**that**) *it wasn't true.* 她說那與事實不符。| *I think* (**that**) *you're right.* 我認為你是對的。

thatch /θætʃ; θætʃ/ *n* [U] roof covering made of STRAW or reeds (REED) 茅草屋頂 —**thatched** *adj*: *Our house has a thatched roof.* 我們的房子有個茅草蓋的屋頂。| *a thatched cottage* 屋頂用茅草覆蓋的小屋

thaw /θɔ; θɔː/ *v* **1** [I;T] to change from a solid frozen state to become liquid or soft because of an increase in temperature 融化; 解凍: *The snow is thawing.* 雪在融化。| *Make sure that the chicken is properly thawed* **out** *before you cook it.* 雪藏雞在煮之前務必要解凍。**2 it's thawing** = it's becoming warm enough for snow and ice to melt 冰雪正在融化: *It's starting to thaw.* 冰雪開始融化。**3** [I] (of a person) to become friendlier or less formal 〔人〕變得友善[隨便] —**thaw** *n*

the¹ /ðə, ði; ðə, ði; *strong* 強讀 ði; diː/ *definite article, det* **1** used before singular and plural nouns when it is understood who or what you mean 〔用於名詞的單數或複數形式前指已知的事物〕: *The sun is shining.* 太陽發出光芒。| *I spoke to her on the telephone.* 我在電話裡和她談過了。**2** used as part of some names 〔用作名字的一部分〕: *the Rhine* 萊茵河 | *the Alps* 阿爾卑斯山 **3** used before an adjective to make it into a noun 〔用於形容詞前使其名詞化〕: *We must help the poor.* 我們必須幫助窮人。| *emergency aid to feed the hungry* 對飢餓的人所進行的緊急援助 **4** used before a singular noun when you are talking about something in general 〔用於名詞單數形式前表示類別〕: *The lion is a wild animal.* 獅子是一種野獸。**5** used before the names of musical instruments 〔用於樂器名稱前〕: *She plays the violin.* 她拉小提琴。**6** each 每一; 每: *He's paid by the hour.* 他的報酬按時計算。**7** used in dates 〔用於日期〕: *Monday the seventh of January.* 一月七日星期一。**8** used in front of numbers to talk about a period of ten years 〔用於表示年代〕: *the 1940s* 二十世紀四十年代 | *He was born in the fifties.* 他出生於五十年代。**9** most important or most fashionable 最重要的; 最流行的: *It's the place to go!* 那才是個好去處!

the² *adv* used in comparisons 〔用於比較〕: *The more you eat the fatter you will get.* 你吃得越多長得越胖。| *He's the cleverest child in the class.* 他是班上最聰明的孩子。

thea·tre /'θɪətə˞; 'θɪətə˞/ *n* (**theater** *AmE* 【美式】) **1** [C] a building with a stage on which plays are performed 劇院; 劇場: *London's theatres* 倫敦的劇院 | *Shall we go to the theatre?* 我們去看戲好嗎? **2** [sing;U] the study of plays and the work of people who write, produce, or act in plays 戲劇研究; 戲劇: *I'm interested in the theatre.* 我對戲劇很感興趣。| *modern Russian theatre* 現代俄羅斯戲劇 **3** [C] a large room with each row of seats placed higher than the one in front 階梯式大廳: *a lecture theatre* 大講堂 **4** [C] see 見 OPERATING THEATRE

the·at·ri·cal /θɪ'ætrɪkl; θɪ'ætrɪkl/ *adj* **1** related to or for the theatre 戲劇的; 劇院的: *a theatrical company* 劇團 **2** showy and not natural (used of behaviour) 炫耀的, 做作的 〔指行為〕 —**theatrically** /-klɪ; -klɪ/ *adv*

thee /ði; ðiː/ *pron* you (a word which is no longer used in modern English) 你〔現代英語中不再使用〕

theft /θɛft; θɛft/ *n* [C;U] the act or crime of taking something which does not belong to you 偷竊: *The police reported an increase in theft.* 據警方報道，偷竊案件的數量有所增加。 | *the theft of a car* 偷汽車

★**their** /ðər; ðə^r; *strong* 強讀 ðɛr; ðeə^r/ *det* **1** relating to or belonging to people, animals, or things that have already been mentioned 他們的；她們的；牠們的；它們的〔指已提及的人、動物或物品〕: *They went in and took off their coats.* 他們走了進去，脫下外衣。 | *Students have to work hard to pass their exams.* 學生必須努力學習才能考試及格。 **2** *infml* relating to or belonging to a person who has already been mentioned, when it has not been stated whether the person is a man or a woman〔非正式〕他們的〔指已提及的未表明是男是女的人〕: *Someone had come in and left their suitcase in the hall.* 有人進來後留下了手提包在大廳裡。

theirs /ðɛrz; ðeəz/ *pron* something relating to or belonging to the people, animals, or things that have already been mentioned 他們的；她們的；牠們的；它們的〔所有格代名詞〕: *Our house is very similar to theirs.* 我們的房子和他們的很相像。

★**them** /ðəm; ðəm; *strong* 強讀 ðɛm; ðem/ *pron* [used as the object of a verb 用作動詞受詞] **1** the people, animals, or things that have already been mentioned 他們；她們；牠們；它們〔指已提及及的人、動物、或物品〕: *Where are my shoes? I can't find them.* 我的鞋在哪兒？我找不到。 −see 見 ME (USAGE 用法) **2** *infml* the person who has already been mentioned, when it has not been stated whether the person is a man or a woman〔非正式〕他們〔指已提及及但未表明是男是女的人〕: *Someone came into the office looking for you, so I gave them your phone number.* 有人到辦公室裡來找你，於是我把你的電話號碼告訴他們了。

★**theme** /θiːm; θiːm/ *n* **1** the subject of a talk or piece of writing〔談話、寫作的〕主題 **2** a simple tune on which a piece of music is based〔音樂的〕主題，主旋律 **3** an idea which is repeated a number of times in a work of art or literature〔藝術或文學作品的〕主題

theme song /ˈ· ·/ *n* (also 又作 **theme tune**) a song or tune played often during a musical play or film〔音樂劇或電影的〕主題歌，主題曲

★**themselves** /ðəmˈsɛlvz; ðəmˈselvz/ *pron* **1** used as the object of a verb or a PREPOSITION when the subject of a verb is plural and the action is done to the same people〔反身代名詞〕他們自己，她們自己，牠們自己〔用作動詞或介詞的受語〕: *They consider themselves to be quite well off.* 他們認為自己相當富有。 | *They had* bought themselves a new car. 他們為自己買了部新車。 | *They're very pleased with themselves.* 他們對自己非常滿意。 **2** used to add force to the word "they", or to the names of people or animals〔用於對 they 進行強調〕: *They had done all the decorating themselves.* 所有的裝修工作都是他們自己幹的。 **3** **by themselves** alone, with no one with them or helping them 獨自；依靠自己: *They had spent the day by themselves.* 他們獨自度過了一天。 | *They had managed to mend the roof by themselves.* 他們自己修好了屋頂。

★**then**[1] /ðɛn; ðen/ *adv* **1** at a particular time in the past or the future 當時；那時: *We lived in the country then.* 當時我們住在鄉下。 | *I'll probably be dead by then.* 到那時我很可能已經死了。 **2** after that 然後: *He poured himself a drink and then sat down.* 他為自己倒了杯飲料，然後坐了下來。 | *The letters are collected from postboxes. They are then taken to the sorting office.* 郵筒內的信件首先由郵遞員收集，然後就送往分類處。 **3** used in sentences with "if" 那麼〔用於有 if 的子句〕: *If you want to go home, then go.* 你如果想回家，那就走吧。 | *If I get any news then I'll phone you.* 我一有消息就打電話通知你。 **4** used when you are adding something to what you have just said 此外；另外: *We have to think about how to avoid such accidents in the future. Then there's the question of compensation for the victims of this accident.* 我們必須考慮一下以後如何避免這類事故。另外，還有給此次事故的受害者賠償的問題。 **5** used when you are reminding people of the main points in what has been said, or when you are showing the real meaning of earlier points 如此看來；這樣一來: *The main problem facing the government, then, is the economy.* 如此看來，政府所面臨的主要問題就是經濟問題。 **6** **but then** used when you are giving a piece of information which goes against what has just been said 但是；然而: *We could just repair the roof, but then that won't solve the problem completely.* 我們可以單單把屋頂修好，但那樣子並沒有徹底解決問題。

then[2] *adj* [only before a noun 只用於名詞前] at that time in the past 當時的: *the then president of the country* 該國當時的總統

thence /ðɛns; ðens/ *adv fml* from there〔正式〕從那裡: *They travelled to Paris and thence to the South of France.* 他們去了巴黎，又從那裡前往法國南部。

theo·lo·gian /θiəˈlodʒən; θiəˈləʊdʒən/ *n* a person who has studied theology 神學家；宗教研究家

the·ol·o·gy /θiˈɑlədʒi; θiˈɒlədʒi/ *n* [U] the study of God and religious beliefs 神學；宗教研究 −**theological** /ˌθiəˈlɑdʒɪkl; ˌθiəˈlɒdʒɪkl/ *adj*

theo·rem /ˈθiərəm; ˈθɪərəm/ *n tech* a statement in the science of numbers that can be shown to be true by reasoning〖術語〗〔數學中的〕定理

theo·rize /ˈθɪəˌraɪz; ˈθɪəraɪz/ v **theorized, theorizing** (also 又作 **theorise** BrE〖英式〗) [I] fml to form a set of ideas about how something works〖正式〗建立理論

theo·ry /ˈθɪərɪ; ˈθɪərɪ/ n **theories 1** [C] an explanation for something which is reasonable or scientifically acceptable, but which has not yet been proved to be true 理論; 學說: Darwin's theory of evolution 達爾文的進化論 | The detective's theory is that the murderer was well known to the victim. 偵探認為被害人與兇手熟識。**2** [U] the general principles for the study of an art or science as opposed to practical skill in it 科學原理; 理論: musical theory 音樂理論 | There will be two chemistry exams; one on theory and one will be practical. 將有兩場化學考試; 一場考理論, 一場考實踐。**3 in theory** a phrase used to describe the way something should happen but may not in practice 理論上〔用於描述某事應該如何發生而實際上卻未必如此〕: In theory the train should arrive at 9.15, but it's usually late. 按理說列車應該於九時十五分到達, 但通常會遲到。 –**theorist** n –**theoretical** /ˌθɪəˈretɪkl; θɪəˈretɪkəl/ adj: theoretical science 理論科學 | a theoretical possibility 理論上可能發生的事情 –**theoretically** /-əklɪ; -klɪ/ adv: Theoretically it's my job, but in fact I don't do it. 按理說這是我的工作, 但實際上我是不做的。

ther·a·peu·tic /ˌθerəˈpjuːtɪk; ˌθerəˈpjuːtɪk◂/ adj **1** related to the treating or curing of a disease 治療疾病的: a therapeutic diet 治療性的飲食 **2** having a good effect on your health or state of mind 有益健康的: I find sewing very therapeutic. 我覺得做針線活對身體很有益處。

ther·a·py /ˈθerəpɪ; ˈθerəpɪ/ n **therapies** [C; U] the treatment of illnesses of the mind or body without drugs or operations〔不用藥物或手術的〕療法: She's going to give me some heat therapy. 她準備給我進行熱療。 –**therapist**: a speech therapist 語言矯正專家

there /ðeə; ðeər/ adv **1** in or to that place 在那裡; 往那裡: They've lived there for ten years. 他們在那裡住了十年。| Look over there. 往那邊看。| Could you put it down there, please? 請你把它放到那裡好嗎? | That man over there might know. 那邊的那個人也許知道。**2** at that point 在那一點: I read to the bottom of the page and decided to stop there. 我看到那一頁的下方, 決定停在那裡不看了。**3** used for drawing attention to someone or something〔用於引起注意〕: There goes John. 約翰走了。**4 there and then, then and there** at that time and place 當時當地; 當場立即: He asked me to marry him there and then. 他要我當時就同他結婚。**5 there, there** a phrase you use to comfort someone 好啦, 好啦〔用於安慰某人〕: There, there, don't cry. 好啦, 好啦, 不要哭了。**6 there you are: a** a phrase

you use when you are giving someone something that they want 給你〔用於把某人想要的東西遞給他〕**b** a phrase you use when you have been proved to be right 你瞧〔用於證明自己正確〕: There you are. I said it wouldn't work. 你瞧, 我說過這樣不行。

there pron **there is, there are** a phrase used to show that someone or something exists or happens 有〔用於表示客觀存在〕: There's a cat on the roof. 屋頂上有隻貓。| There are some letters for you. 有你的幾封信。| There was a knock on the door. 有人敲門。| Is there a telephone near here? 這附近有沒有電話?

there·a·bouts /ˌðeərəˈbaʊts; ˌðeərəˈbaʊts/ adv near a particular place, time, or number〔地點、時間或數量等〕附近; 大約; 左右: I'll see you at six o'clock or thereabouts. 我在六點鐘左右見你。

there·af·ter /ðerˈæftə; ðeərˈɑːftər/ adv fml after a particular time or event〖正式〗在那以後; 此後: He left the country in 1979 and thereafter I heard nothing from him. 他在1979年離開該國, 此後我再也沒有他的消息了。

there·by /ðerˈbaɪ; ðeəˈbaɪ/ adv fml by doing or saying a particular thing〖正式〗由此; 從而; 因而: He became a British citizen, thereby gaining the right to vote. 他成了英國公民, 因此獲得了投票權。

there·fore /ˈðerˌfoːr; ˈðeəfɔːr/ adv for the reason that has just been stated 所以; 因此: This engine uses less fuel and is therefore better for the environment. 這種引擎節省燃料, 所以對於環境的危害較小。| You have repeatedly failed to deliver the goods on time. We therefore feel that we have no alternative but to find another supplier. 你不止一次地沒有按時交貨。所以我們別無選擇, 只好另找一家供應商。–see Study Note on page 1325 見 1325 頁學習提示

there·in /ðerˈɪn; ðeərˈɪn/ adv fml because of the fact or situation that has just been stated〖正式〗鑑於上述事實〔情況〕

there·up·on /ˌðerəˈpɒn; ˌðeərəˈpɒn/ adv fml at the moment when something happens and as a result of it〖正式〗於是; 因此: She told him that she was at last free, and thereupon he fell to his knees and asked her to marry him. 她說自己終於獲得了自由, 於是他跪下來向她求婚。

therm /θɜːm; θɜːm/ n tech a measurement of heat used in Britain for measuring the amount of gas people use〖術語〗撒姆〔英國用於計算用戶的煤氣使用量的單位〕

ther·mal /ˈθɜːml; ˈθɜːməl/ adj relating to, producing, or caused by heat 熱量的; 產生熱量的; 由熱量引起的: thermal energy 熱能

ther·mo·me·ter /θəˈmɒmətə; θəˈmɒmɪtər/ n an instrument for measuring and showing temperature 溫度計; 寒暑表; 體溫計

ther·mos flask /ˈθɜːməsˌflæsk; ˈθɜːməs-**

/flɑːsk/ (also 又作 **thermos** *AmE* 〖美式〗) *n* tdmk a container used to keep drinks either hot or cold 〖商標〗熱水瓶，保溫瓶

ther·mo·stat /ˈθɜːmə,stæt; ˈθɜːməstæt/ *n* an apparatus that keeps a room or machine at a particular temperature by disconnecting and reconnecting a supply of heat when necessary 恒溫器

the·sau·rus /θɪˈsɔːrəs; θɪˈsɔːrəs/ *n* a book of words put in lists according to their meaning rather than in an alphabetical list 同義詞詞典

these /ðiːz; ðiːz/ *det, pron* the plural of THIS ☆THIS的複數形式

the·sis /ˈθiːsɪs; ˈθiːsɪs/ *n* **theses** /-siːz; -siːz/ **1** a long piece of writing done for a university degree 〔為取得大學學位所寫的〕論文 **2** an opinion put forward as a statement and supported by reasoned argument 學術論文

they ★★★ /ðe; ðeɪ/ *pron* [used as the subject of a verb 用作動詞的主語] **1** the people, animals, or things that have already been mentioned 他們；牠們；它們〔指已提及的人、動物、或物品〕: *My parents live in Newcastle. They moved there two years ago.* 我的父母住在紐卡斯爾。他們是兩年前搬去的。| *Take these books — they might be useful.* 把這些書拿去吧——它們也許會有用。| *These ideas aren't new. They've been around for years.* 這些觀點並不新穎。它們已流傳好幾年了。**2** people in general 人們〔總稱〕: *They say it might snow tonight.* 據說今晚可能下雪。**3** *infml* a person who has already been mentioned, when it is not known whether the person is a man or a woman 〖非正式〗他們〔指已提及但未表明是男是女的人〕: *I met someone the other day who said that they knew you.* 前幾天我碰上了個説認識你的人。

they'd /ðed; ðeɪd/ **1** short for 〖縮〗= "they had": *If only they'd been here.* 他們要是來過這裡就好了。**2** short for 〖縮〗= "they would": *They'd never believe you.* 他們絕不會相信你的。

they'll /ðel; ðeɪl/ **1** short for 〖縮〗= "they will" **2** short for 〖縮〗= "they shall"

they're /ðer; ðəʳ; *strong* 強讀 ðeə; ðeəʳ/ short for 〖縮〗= "they are"

they've /ðev; ðeɪv/ short for 〖縮〗= "they have"

thick¹ ★ /θɪk; θɪk/ *adj* **1** having a large distance between opposite surfaces 厚的: *thick walls* 厚厚的牆 | *a thick layer of snow* 厚厚的一層雪 **2** used when giving measurements 厚的〔用於測量〕: *The castle walls are two metres thick.* 城堡的牆壁有兩米厚。| *How thick are the walls?* 那些牆壁有多厚? **3** not flowing easily (used of a liquid) 稠的，濃的〔指液體〕: *thick soup* 濃湯 **4** made of many things grouped closely together 稠密的；茂密的: *a thick forest* 茂密的森林 | *thick black hair* 濃濃的黑髮 **5** **thick with** full of or covered

with 充滿的; 覆滿的: *The air was thick with smoke.* 空氣中濃煙瀰漫。**6** not clear in sound (used of a voice) 聲音不清晰的〔指嗓音〕: *a thick accent* 很重的口音 **7** difficult to see through 難以看透的: *thick mist* 濃霧 **8** *infml* stupid (used of a person) 〖非正式〗愚蠢的〔指人〕 **9 as thick as thieves** *infml* very friendly 〖非正式〗很友善的 –**thick** *adv: The flowers grew thickest near the wall.* 花在靠近牆的地方長得最為茂盛。–**thickly** *adv*

thick² *n* **1 in the thick of** in the middle of 在…中間: *in the thick of the fight* 在毆鬥之中 **2 through thick and thin** through both good and bad times 在任何情況下

thick·en /ˈθɪkən; ˈθɪkən/ *v* **1** [I] to become more closely packed together 變得愈加緊密: *The forest thickens to the north.* 愈往北，森林愈茂密。**2** [I] (of smoke or mist) to become more solid and difficult to see through 〔煙或霧〕變濃 **3** [I,T] to make or become more solid (使)變厚: *Thicken the soup by adding flour.* 加入些麵粉使湯變稠。

thick·et /ˈθɪkɪt; ˈθɪkɪt/ *n* a thick growth of bushes and small trees 灌木叢

thick·ness /ˈθɪknɪs; ˈθɪknɪs/ *n* [C;U] the quality or degree of being thick 厚(度); 濃(度): *The length of nails you need depends on the thickness of the planks.* 你所需的釘子的長度視乎木板的厚度。

thick·set /,θɪkˈset; ,θɪkˈset◂/ *adj* having a broad strong body 體格粗壯的

thick-skinned /,···◂/ *adj* not easily offended by anything unpleasant said about, or to you 厚臉皮的; 不易發怒的

thief /θiːf; θiːf/ *n* **thieves** /θiːvz; θiːvz/ a person who steals things, usually without violence 賊; 小偷

> ■ USAGE 用法: Compare 比較 **thief, burglar, robber, shoplifter, pickpocket. Thief** is a general word for a person who **steals**. A **burglar** steals from houses after **breaking in**. A **robber** is often more violent and steals from people, banks and organizations. A **shoplifter** takes things from shops without paying. A **pickpocket** steals from the pockets and bags of people in crowds. ☆ **thief** 是小偷的普通用詞。**burglar** 是闖入房屋偷東西的竊賊。**robber** 更加野蠻，從人、銀行、或機構裡偷東西。**shoplifter** 是從商店裡偷東西的人。**pickpocket** 在人羣中偷取人們錢夾和背包中的東西。

thieve /θiːv; θiːv/ *v* **thieved, thieving** *old fash* [I] to steal things 〖老式〗偷竊

thigh /θaɪ; θaɪ/ *n* the top part of your leg between your knee and your HIP² 大腿

thim·ble /ˈθɪmbl; ˈθɪmbəl/ *n* a small hard cap put over your finger to protect it when you are sewing 頂針; 針箍

☆thin¹ /θɪn; θɪn/ *adj* **-nn-** **1** having a small distance between opposite surfaces 薄的: *The ice is too thin to skate on.* 冰太薄, 不能在上面滑冰。| *thin cloth* 薄布 **2** having little fat on your body 瘦的: *She looked thin after her illness.* 她病癒以後看上去很瘦。–see 見 USAGE 用法–see picture on page 469 見 469 頁彩圖 **3** watery (used of a liquid) 稀的, 薄的〔指液體〕: *thin soup* 清湯 **4** not very large in quantity 數量不大的: *Your hair's getting very thin on top.* 你頭頂的頭髮變得十分稀疏。**5** weak 虛弱的: *Your argument is a bit thin.* 你的論點不太充實。| *a thin excuse* 理由不充分 **6 thin on the ground** *infml* not easily found because not present in large numbers 〔非正式〕稀少; 難以找到 **–thin** *adv*: *Don't cut the bread so thin.* 不要把麵包切得這麼薄。**–thinly** *adv*: *Spread the butter thinly.* 薄薄地塗上一層黃油。| *a thinly populated area* 人口稀少的地區 | *a thinly disguised attempt to cheat us* 幾乎不加掩飾地想公然欺騙我們 **–thinness** *n* [U]

■ USAGE 用法: **1 Thin** is a general word to describe people who have little or no fat on their bodies. To describe people as **thin** in a good way we use **slim** or **slender** ☆ thin 是用來形容人瘦的普通用詞。若是形容人苗條, 可以用 **slim** 或 **slender**: *I wish I were as slim/slender as you* 我如果可以跟你一樣苗條就好了, *or* **lean** ☆或者可以用 **lean** (=thin in a strong and healthy way 清瘦而健康): *a lean, muscular body.* 清瘦強健的身體。If people are too thin they are **skinny** (informal), **underweight,** or (worst of all) **emaciated** ☆如果過瘦, 那麼就是 **skinny**〔非正式〕, **underweight,** 或者 **emaciated**〔最嚴重〕: *He looks very **skinny/underweight** after his illness.* 他病癒之後看上去瘦得皮包骨頭。| *The prisoners were* **emaciated.** 囚犯瘦弱不堪。**2** We can use **thin** for things ☆我們可以用 **thin** 來形容物體: *a thin pole* 一根細竹竿, but we usually do not use it for flat surfaces or openings. Instead we say **narrow** ☆但我們不用 **thin** 來描述平面或開口。**thin** **narrow:** *a narrow road* 狹窄的道路 | *a narrow bed* 狹窄的牀 | *a narrow gap.* 狹窄的縫隙。

---

thin² *v* **-nn-** **1** [T] (also 又作 **thin** sthg ↔ **down**) to make a liquid more watery 使〔液體〕變稀: *You should thin the paint with turpentine.* 你應當用松節油稀釋一下油漆。**2** his **hair is thinning** = he is starting to lose his hair 他的頭髮開始脫落

☆thing /θɪŋ; θɪŋ/ *n* **1** any object, especially an object that cannot or need not be named 東西: *What's that thing you've got on your head?* 你頭上那是甚麼東西? | *I*

opened the door and the first thing I saw was a cloud of smoke. 我打開門, 首先看見的東西是一團煙。**2 not a thing** nothing 無物: *I haven't got a thing to wear.* 我沒有穿的衣服。| *It's so dark I can't see a thing.* 太黑了, 我甚麼也看不見。**3** a fact, statement, or idea 事實; 話語; 觀點: *What a nasty thing to say to your sister!* 你怎麼對姐姐說這樣難聽的話! | *One thing is certain: I'm not lending him any money again.* 有一件事是肯定的: 我再也不會把錢借給他了。| *He says the first thing that comes into his head.* 他想到甚麼就會說甚麼。**4** an action, activity, or event 行動; 活動; 事件: *What's the next thing we have to do?* 我們要做的下一件事是甚麼? | *I hope I'm doing the right thing in accepting this job.* 我希望自己接受這份工作的做法是正確的。| *She might resign, which is the last thing we want.* 她也許會辭職, 這是我們最不願意看到的事情。**5 things** [pl] **a** your personal possessions 私人物品: *Pack your things, we're going to leave.* 把你的物品收拾好, 我們準備走了。**b** the general situation at a particular time 形勢; 情況: *Cheer up! Things could be worse.* 不用太擔心! 情況也不算太壞。**6** a person or animal, usually when expressing your feelings about them 人或動物〔用於表達個人對於他們的感情時〕: *Our dog's been quite ill, poor thing.* 我們的狗病得很厲害, 真可憐。**7 the thing** *infml* something necessary or desirable〔非正式〕必需的東西; 想要的東西: *A glass of cold beer is just the thing on a hot day.* 一杯冰凍啤酒正是大熱天理想的飲料。| *The main thing is to keep calm.* 最重要是保持鎮定。**8 do your own thing** *infml* to do what is satisfying to you personally〔非正式〕做自己喜歡的事情 **9 for one thing** you use this expression when you give a reason for something which has just been mentioned; you think that the reason by itself is very strong, but you are suggesting that it is not the only one 一方面〔用於表示原因; 此此短語表明這是個十分重要的原因, 但也暗示這不是唯一的原因〕: *I don't think now's a good time for expanding. For one thing, interest rates are high. And for another, wages are still rising fast.* 我認為現在不宜擴大生產規模。一方面, 利率很高; 另一方面, 工資仍然上漲得很快。[RELATED PHRASE 相關詞組 **for another thing:** *For one thing, it's expensive. And for another thing, I don't think it's very good.* 一來它很貴。二來我認為它並不是那麼好。] **10 have a thing about** *infml* to have a strong like or dislike for〔非正式〕非常喜歡; 非常討厭 **11 make a thing of** *infml* to give too much importance to something〔非正式〕過分強調: *I disagree with you, but let's not make a thing of it.* 我不同意你的觀點, 但不要把這點看得太重。**12 it's a good thing** = it's lucky 很幸運: *It's a good thing George can't hear us!* 幸好喬治聽不到我們講話!

thing·a·ma·jig /ˈθɪŋəməˌdʒɪg; ˈθɪŋməˌ¦dʒɪg/ *n* (also 又作 **thingumajig, thingamabob** /ˈθɪŋəmə.bɑb; ˈθɪŋəm¦bɒb/, **thingummy** /ˈθɪŋəmi/) *infml* a person or thing whose name you have forgotten or do not know〔非正式〕那個人;那樣東西〔對忘記了名字或不知道名字的人或物的代稱〕: *a new thingamajig for opening bottles* 一個開瓶子的新玩藝兒

★★think¹ /θɪŋk; θɪŋk/ *v* **thought** /θɔt; θɔːt/, **thought 1** [I;T] to use your mind to have thoughts and form opinions 考慮; 思考: *She thought for a moment before answering me.* 她在回答我的問題前考慮了一下。| *Think hard before you answer.* 回答以前認真想一想。| *I need some time to think before I can reach a decision.* 我在作出決定以前需要些時間考慮一下。| *What are you thinking about?* 你在想甚麼? | *You look as though you're thinking great thoughts.* 你看上去好像在考慮重大問題。 **2** [T;+(that)] to have something as your opinion 認為;覺得: *I think he's wrong about this.* 我認為他在這件事上錯了。| *I think it was Jane, but I'm not sure.* 我認為是簡,但我不敢肯定。| *What do you think **about** the plans?* 你認為那些計劃怎麼樣? | *I'm not sure what I think **of** Tom.* 我不清楚自己對湯姆的看法如何。| *We didn't think we'd be this late.* 我們不知道會這麼晚。| *"Do you think it will rain?" "Yes, I think so."* "你覺得會下雨嗎?""我看會的。" | *"Will she get the job?" "I don't think so."* "她應徵那份工作會成功嗎?""我認為不會。" | *I think myself very lucky.* 我認為自己十分幸運。 **3** to have something as an idea 想出主意: *I've thought of a brilliant solution to our problem.* 我想出了一個解決問題的絕好辦法。| *I can think of two possible reasons for the delay.* 我想到了兩個理由,有可能便是今次延期的原因。 **b** to remember something 想起某事: *I can't think of his name at the moment.* 我現在想不起他的名字。 **c** to consider that something is the thing mentioned 想到某事: *I will always think of Birmingham as my home.* 我將永遠把伯明翰當作自己的故鄉。| *I don't think of him as a friend.* 我沒有把他當作朋友看待。 **4** **be thinking about/of doing something** to be considering doing something 考慮做某事: *I'm thinking of giving up my studies and getting a job.* 我正在考慮放棄學業,找份工作。| *Have you ever thought about emigrating?* 你考慮過要移民嗎? **5** **think about someone, think of someone** to consider someone's needs or wishes 考慮某人的需要或願望: *She never thinks about anyone but herself.* 她從不考慮到別人,只顧她自己。 **6** **come to think of it** a phrase you use when you have just remembered something or had an idea 想起來了〔用於剛剛想起某事或想出某主意〕: *Come to think of it, I've met him before.* 想起來了,我以前遇見過

他。**7** **think a lot of, not think much of**, etc to have a high or low opinion of someone or something 看重; 看輕: *He thinks a lot of you.* 他很器重你。| *I don't think much of this food.* 我認為這食物不怎麼樣。 **8** **think aloud** to speak your thoughts as they come 自言自語 **9** **think better of it** to decide not to do something when you have considered it more carefully〔認真考慮後〕打消念頭: *I was going to tell her, but I thought better of it.* 我本打算告訴她,但細想之後改變了主意。 **10** **think nothing of doing something** to consider that something is easy or usual 認為某事簡單或普通: *She thinks nothing of walking three miles to work every day.* 她認為每天走三英里去上班沒有甚麼了不起。 **11** **think the world of someone** to be very fond of someone 非常歡喜某人: *He thinks the world of his children.* 他非常喜歡他的孩子。 **12** **think the worst** to believe that something bad or unpleasant has happened 認為發生了糟糕的或討厭的事情: *When someone's late I always think the worst.* 如果有人遲到,我就會以為出事了。 **13** **think twice** to consider carefully before you do something 認真考慮: *Think twice before you agree to work for her.* 你答應為她工作前要好好考慮一下。 **14** **think well/highly of** to have a good opinion of someone or something 對〔某人或某事物〕評價很好〔很高〕: *I think very highly of her.* 我對她的印象非常好。

think back *phr v* [I] to remember something that happened in the past 想起〔過去的事情〕

think sthg ↔ **over** *phr v* [T] to think about something carefully 認真考慮: *It's a good offer but I'll have to think it over.* 這提議不錯,但我必須認真考慮一下。

think sthg ↔ **through** *phr v* [T] to consider all the details and aspects of something 考慮〔某事〕各方面的細節: *It's an interesting idea and I want to spend some time thinking it through.* 這個主意很有意思,我想花點時間仔細考慮一下。

think sthg ↔ **up** *phr v* [T] to create an idea in your mind 想出〔主意〕: *I haven't thought up an excuse yet.* 我還沒有想出藉口。

think² *n* have a **think** to use your mind to have thoughts and form opinions 思考; 考慮: *I need to have a think **about** this.* 這件事我需要考慮一下。

think·er /ˈθɪŋkə; ˈθɪŋkəʳ/ *n* someone who uses their mind well, often producing new and interesting ideas 思想家: *one of the great thinkers of the 18th century* 十八世紀偉大的思想家之一

think·ing /ˈθɪŋkɪŋ; ˈθɪŋkɪŋ/ *n* [U] **1** the act of using your mind to produce thoughts 思考; 考慮: *I've been doing some thinking about our next project.* 我一直在考慮我們下一個計劃。 **2** a way of thinking or view of something 思考方式; 觀點: *What's the government's thinking on this matter?* 政府對此事的觀點如何? | *To my way of thinking, it's all wrong.* 在我看來, 這事情全錯了。

thin·ner /ˈθɪnə; ˈθɪnəʳ/ *n* [U] a liquid added to paint to make it spread more easily 〔油漆的〕稀釋劑

third /θɜːd; θɜːd/ *det, pron, adv* **1** 3rd; when you have several points you want to make, you can order them and number them "First,...", "Second,...", "Third,..." etc. 第三〔要表述幾個論點時, 可以用"第一,...", "第二,...", "第三,..." 等等將其順序排列〕: *There are several reasons why the plan will not work. First, there has not been enough preparation. Second, there is not enough money. Third, it is too complicated.* 該計劃不會起作用的原因有好幾個。第一, 準備不足。第二, 資金不夠。第三, 過於複雜。**2** *n* one of three equal parts 三分之一(1/3) **3** *n* the lowest class of British university degree 〔英國大學學士學位〕三級榮譽學位: *She got a third in Chemistry.* 她得了化學系三級榮譽學位。

third·ly /ˈθɜːdli; ˈθɜːdli/ *adv* as the third in a set of facts or reasons; when you have several points you want to make, you can order them and number them "Firstly,...", "Secondly,...", "Thirdly,...", etc. 第三〔若有數個論據或原因需要陳述時, 可以用"第一,...", "第二,...", "第三,..." 等等將其順序排列下〕: *There are several reasons why the plan will not work. Firstly, there has not been enough preparation. Secondly, there is not enough money. Thirdly, it is too complicated.* 該計劃不會起作用的原因有幾個。第一, 準備不足。第二, 資金不夠。第三, 過於複雜。

third par·ty /ˌ···◂/ *n tech* 〔術語〕**1** a person in a law case or agreement who is not one of the two main people concerned 〔法律案件或合約中的〕第三方 **2** **third party insurance** a type of insurance under which your insurance company will pay money to anyone or anything damaged by you 第三者責任保險〔保險公司負責賠償你對任何人或物所造成的損害〕

third per·son /ˌ···◂/ *n* **the third person** a form of the verb that you use with "he", "she", "it", or "they" 第三人稱: *"They are" is the third person plural of "to be".* they are 是 to be 的第三人稱複數形式。

third-rate /ˌ···◂/ *adj* of very poor quality 三流的; 劣質的

Third World /ˌ···◂/ *n* **the Third World** the industrially less developed countries of the world in Asia, South America, and Africa 第三世界

thirst¹ /θɜːst; θɜːst/ *n* **1** [sing] a sensation of dryness in your mouth caused by the need to drink 口渴: *Running five miles gave me quite a thirst.* 跑了五英里之後, 我口乾舌燥。| *a thirst-quenching drink* 解渴的飲料 **2** [U] lack of drink for a long time 長時間乾渴:

They died of thirst. 他們因乾渴而死亡。**3 a thirst for** a strong desire for something 渴望: *the thirst for excitement* 渴望刺激

thirst² *v* **thirst for/after something** to have a strong desire for something 渴望某物: *Our people thirst for independence.* 我們的人民渴望獨立。

thirst·y /ˈθɜːsti; ˈθɜːsti/ *adj* **thirstier, thirstiest 1** feeling the need to drink something, or making you feel this need 口渴的: *Salty food makes me thirsty.* 鹹的食物令我非常口渴。| *Chopping firewood is thirsty work.* 劈柴是使人口渴的活兒。**2** **thirsty for** having a strong desire for something 渴望〔某事物〕: *She was thirsty for power.* 她渴望獲得權力。— **thirstily** *adv*

thir·teen /θɜːˈtiːn; ˌθɜːˈtiːn◂/ *det, n, pron* the number 13 〔數字〕十三 — **thirteenth** *det, n, pron, adv*

thir·ty /ˈθɜːti; ˈθɜːti/ *det, n, pron* **1** the number 30 〔數字〕三十 **2** **the thirties, the Thirties** the years 1930-1939 三十年代〔1930年至1939年〕**3** **in her thirties, in their thirties, etc.** aged between 30 and 39 三十幾歲〔三十至三十九歲之間〕— **thirtieth** *det, n, pron, adv*

this¹ /ðɪs; ðɪs/ *det, pron* these /ðiːz; ðiːz/ **1** the person or thing that is nearer in place or time 〔人或物〕這個: *You look in this room and I'll look in that room over there.* 你檢查這房間, 我去檢查那邊的一間。| *I saw Mrs Jones this morning.* 今天早上我遇見瓊斯太太。| *What's this?* 這是甚麼? **2** *infml* a certain 〔非正式〕某個: *This man came up to me and asked me for money.* 這個人走來問我要錢。

this² *adv infml* as much as this 〔非正式〕這麼; 這樣: *I've never been out this late before* 我從未在外面逗留到這麼晚。

this·tle /ˈθɪsl; ˈθɪsəl/ *n* a wild plant with prickly leaves and purple flowers 薊〔野生, 葉片帶刺, 開紫花〕

thith·er /ˈθɪðə; ˈðɪðəʳ/ *adv old fash* to that place 〔老式〕到那裡

thong /θɒŋ; θɔŋ/ *n* a narrow length of leather used as a fastening or a whip 〔用以繫物、作鞭子的〕皮帶, 皮條

thorn /θɔːn; θɔːn/ *n* **1** a small sharp-pointed growth on a plant 刺; 棘: *the thorns on a rose bush* 玫瑰叢枝上的刺 **2** **thorn in your flesh/side** a continual cause of annoyance or problems 肉中刺; 眼中釘

thorn·y /ˈθɔːni; ˈθɔːni/ *adj* **1** having sharp-pointed growths 有刺的; 多刺的 **2** difficult to deal with 棘手的; 難處理的: *a thorny problem* 棘手的問題

thor·ough /ˈθʌrə; ˈθʌroʊ/ *adj* **1** complete and careful 徹底的: *a thorough search* 徹底的搜查 **2** very careful to cover every detail 細緻的: *She's slow but very thorough.* 她動作很慢, 但很細緻。— **thoroughly** *adv*: *We thoroughly enjoyed ourselves.* 我們玩得很痛快。—

thoroughness n [U]

thor·ough·bred /ˈθɜːo,brɛd; ˈθʌrəbred/ n a horse whose parents were both of very good breed 純種馬

thor·ough·fare /ˈθɜːo,fɛr; ˈθʌrəfeəʳ/ n fml a main road in a town or city《正式》大道; 大街

those /ðoz; ðəʊz/ det, pron the plural of THAT ☆THAT 的複數形式

thou /ðaʊ; ðaʊ/ pron biblical you《聖經》汝; 你: "Thou shalt not kill." "汝不許殺生。"

though[1] /ðo; ðəʊ/ conj 1 in spite of something 儘管; 雖然: I recognized her at once, though I hadn't seen her for ten years. 儘管十年沒見, 我立刻就認出了她。| I enjoy it even though it's hard work. 儘管很辛苦, 但我很喜歡這工作。2 but 但是: I think she's away at the moment, though I'm not sure. 我認為她現時不在家, 但我不敢肯定。3 as though as if 好像: She looks as though she's been crying. 她看上去像哭過的樣子。

though[2] adv in spite of something 儘管: Gardening is quite hard work. I enjoy it, though. 種花種草不是件容易事, 儘管如此, 我還是很喜歡。

thought[1] /θɔt; θɔːt/ n 1 [U] the action of thinking 思考; 思索: She sat deep in thought. 她坐在那裡沉思。2 [U] serious consideration 認真考慮: Give the matter plenty of thought before you accept. 請先好好考慮一下才決定是否接受。3 [C] an idea or opinion 觀點; 意見: What are your thoughts on the subject? 你對這個問題的觀點如何? | "Yes, the thought had crossed my mind." "是的, 這個意見我已想到了了。" 4 [U] a particular way of thinking 思想(方法): modern thought 現代思想 5 [sing] something that someone has done or offered to do for you 心意; 關心: Thank you for the flowers: it was a very kind thought. 謝謝你送的花: 你真是有心人。| With no thought for her own safety, she jumped in the river to help him. 她不顧個人安危, 跳入河裡救他。

thought[2] the past tense and past participle of THINK ☆THINK 的過去式和過去分詞

thought·ful /ˈθɔtfəl; ˈθɔːtfəl/ adj 1 showing that you are thinking deeply 沉思的: The girl looked thoughtful and sad. 這個女孩看上去心事重重, 滿腹憂愁。2 paying attention to the feelings of other people 體貼的; 周到的: It was very thoughtful of you to visit me. 謝謝你費心來看望我。| a thoughtful present 想得很周到的禮物 **–thoughtfully** adv – **thoughtfulness** n [U]

thought·less /ˈθɔtlɪs; ˈθɔːtləs/ adj careless or selfish 馬虎的; 自私的: It was thoughtless of you to forget Mum's birthday. 你忘記了母親的生日, 太粗心了。**–thoughtlessly** adv – **thoughtlessness** n [U]

thou·sand /ˈθaʊznd; ˈθaʊzənd/ det, n, pron the number 1,000〔數字〕一千 **–thousandth**

det, n, pron, adv

thrash /θræʃ; θræʃ/ v 1 [T] to hit someone hard with a whip or stick as a punishment 鞭打, 棒打〔某人〕2 [T] to defeat someone thoroughly in a game〔比賽中〕徹底擊敗〔某人〕3 [I+adv/prep] to move wildly about from pain or fear〔由於疼痛或恐懼而〕翻騰: The fish thrashed about in the net. 魚在網中翻騰。

thrash sth ↔ out phr v [T] to reach agreement about a problem or produce a decision by talking about it in detail 徹底討論〔以達成協議或做出決定〕: After a long argument we thrashed out a plan. 經過長時間的爭辯後, 我們終於訂出了一個計劃。| We need to thrash this out. 我們需要好好探討一下這事情。

thrash·ing /ˈθræʃɪŋ; ˈθræʃɪŋ/ n a severe beating or defeat 痛打; 大敗

thread[1] /θrɛd; θred/ n 1 [C;U] very thin cord, made by spinning cotton, wool, or silk, used in sewing or weaving 線〔棉、毛、絲等紡成的〕2 [C] a line of reasoning connecting the parts of an argument or story 思路; 脈絡: I've lost the thread **of** your argument. 我沒有抓住你論說的思路。3 [C] a raised line around the outside of a screw 螺紋

thread[2] v [T] 1 to pass a thread through something 把線穿過〔某物〕: I can't thread this needle. 我無法把線從這根針的線孔中穿過去。| Let's thread the beads onto a string. 我們把珠子穿在一根線上吧。2 **thread your way through** to move carefully and with difficulty through something where there is very little space 小心穿過; 費力擠過

thread·bare /ˈθrɛd,bɛr; ˈθredbeəʳ/ adj worn very thin (used of material and clothes) 磨薄了的〔指布料和衣服〕

threat /θrɛt; θret/ n 1 [C;U] a warning that someone will hurt or punish you if you do not do what they say 威脅: I obeyed, but only under threat of punishment. 我只是由於害怕會受到懲罰才遵從的。| They used the threat of strike action to enforce their demands. 他們以罷工相威脅, 迫使對方接受他們提出的要求。2 [C] a possible danger 潛在的危險: Some people see computers as a threat to their jobs. 有人認為電腦會對他們工作構成威脅。3 **threat of** a warning or possibility of future problems 預兆; 可能性: The clouds brought a threat of rain. 烏雲密佈, 可能要下雨。| The threat of bankruptcy hung over the company. 公司始終存在着倒閉的可能性。

threat·en /ˈθrɛtn; ˈθretn/ v 1 [I;T] to say that you will do something bad or hurtful 威脅; 揚言: I was threatened **with** a beating if I didn't obey. 我如果不聽話, 就有捱打的危險。| She threatened to murder me. 她威脅說要殺我。2 [T] seem likely to harm, spoil, or ruin something 危及, 威脅到〔某事物〕:

□ USEFUL PATTERNS 有用句型
to threaten to do something; to threaten someone with something

The new motorway threatens the peace of the village. 新的高速公路威脅到村莊的平靜。| *He thinks his job is threatened.* 他認為自己的工作受到了威脅。**3** [I] seem likely to happen 有可能發生: *The incident threatens to ruin his chances in the election.* 這起事故會影響他選舉獲勝的可能性。**4** [T] to warn that something bad may happen 預示〔不好的事〕發生: *The black clouds threatened rain.* 烏雲密佈表示快要下雨了。**–threatening** *adj* **– threateningly** *adv*

three /θri; θriː/ *det, n, pron* the number 3 〔數字〕三

three-di·men·sion·al /ˌ···ˈ···◂/ *adj* (also 又作 **three-D, 3-D** /ˈθriːdi; ˌθriːˈdiː◂/) having length, depth, and height 立體的; 三維的: *The painting gives a wonderful 3-D effect.* 這幅畫有很強的立體感。| *a three-dimensional model* 立體模型

three-quar·ter /ˌ·ˈ··◂/ *adj* [only before a noun 只用於名詞前] consisting of three of the four equal parts of something 四分之三的: *The game lasted for 2¾ hours.* 比賽持續了兩小時四十五分鐘。

thresh /θreʃ; θreʃ/ *v* [I;T] to separate the grain from corn or wheat by beating it 〔穀物〕脫粒

thresh·old /ˈθreʃold; ˈθreʃhəʊld/ *n* **1** the doorway or a piece of wood or stone fixed beneath the doorway which is the entrance to a building 門檻 **2** the lowest level at which something begins to happen or operate 〔某事物發生或運作的〕最低水平, 起點: *She has a low pain threshold.* 她的痛覺閾值低。| *tax thresholds* 納稅起點 **3 on the threshold of** on the point of finding or starting something new 即將發現〔開始〕: *Scientists are now on the threshold of a better understanding of how the brain works.* 科學家在了解大腦活動方面快將進入新的階段。

threw /θruː; θruː/ the past tense of THROW ☆THROW 的過去式

thrift /θrɪft; θrɪft/ *n* [U] wise and careful use of money and goods 節儉; 節省 **–thrifty** *adj*

thrill¹ /θrɪl; θrɪl/ *v* [I;T] to get or give a very strong feeling of excitement, pleasure, or fear (使)興奮; (使)高興; (使)恐懼: *We were thrilled at your news.* 你的消息令我們很興奮。| *I was thrilled to hear your news.* 聽到你的消息, 我很興奮。| *Fast driving really thrills me.* 開快車實在令我感到刺激。

thrill² *n* a sudden, very strong feeling of excitement, pleasure, or fear 興奮; 高興; 恐懼

thrill·er /ˈθrɪlə; ˈθrɪləʳ/ *n* a book, play, or film that tells a very exciting story, usually of crime and violence 驚險小説〔戲劇; 電影〕

thrive /θraɪv; θraɪv/ *v* **throve** /θrəʊv; θrəʊv/

or **thrived, thriven** /ˈθrɪvən; ˈθrɪvən/, **thriving** [I] to develop well and be healthy or successful 繁榮; 興旺; 成功: *Business is thriving.* 生意興隆。| *He thrives on hard work.* 他由於工作努力而獲得成功。

***throat** /θrəʊt; θrəʊt/ *n* **1** the passage from the back of your mouth to your lungs and stomach 咽喉; 喉嚨: *a sore throat* 喉嚨痛 **2** the front of your neck 喉部; 喉頭: *They had cut his throat.* 他們切斷了他的喉嚨。**3 at each other's throats** fighting or arguing violently 激烈打鬥〔辯論〕

throat·y /ˈθrəʊti; ˈθrəʊti/ *adj* low and rough (of someone's voice) 低沉的〔指嗓音〕: *a throaty cough* 沙啞的咳嗽聲

throb /θrɒb; θrɒb/ *v* **-bb-** [I] to beat strongly and regularly 跳動; 悸動: *My heart was throbbing with excitement.* 我很激動, 心怦怦直跳。**–throb** *n*

throes /θrəʊz; θrəʊz/ *n* [pl] **1** *lit* violent, sudden pains 《文》突然的劇痛: *death throes* 臨終的痛苦 **2 in the throes of** struggling with 與...搏鬥: *a country in the throes of war* 在戰爭的苦難中掙扎的國家

throm·bo·sis /θrɒmˈbəʊsɪs; ˌθrɒmˈbəʊsɪs/ [U] *tech* the condition of having a thickened or solid mass of blood in a blood tube or your heart 《術語》血栓形成

throne /θrəʊn; θrəʊn/ *n* **1** the ceremonial chair of a king or queen 王座; 皇座 **2 the throne** the position of being king or queen 王位; 皇位: *She was only fifteen when she came to the throne.* 她繼位時年僅十五歲。| *the power behind the throne* 暗中操縱君王的勢力

throng¹ /θrɒŋ; θrɒŋ/ *n* [+sing/pl verb]a large crowd of people 大羣的人: *Throngs of people are gathering outside the palace.* 宮殿外聚集了很多人。| *a throng of admirers* 一批崇拜者

throng² *v* [I] to go in large groups of people 成羣地走: *People thronged to see the play.* 成羣結隊的人前去看那齣戲。

throt·tle¹ /ˈθrɒtl; ˈθrɒtl/ *v* **throttled, throttling** [T] to seize someone tightly by the throat and so stop them breathing 掐〔某人〕脖子; 使窒息

throttle² *n* a part of a pipe that opens and closes to control the flow of petrol or oil into an engine 節流閥; 油門

***through¹** /θruː; θruː/ *adv, prep* **1** *adv, prep* from one side of something to the other 從一邊到另一邊; 穿過: *Water flows through this pipe.* 水流過這根管子。| *We couldn't see through the mist.* 在霧中我們看不見東西。| *I opened the gate and let them through.* 我把門打開, 放他們過去。**–**see picture on page 764 見 764 頁彩圖 **2** *prep* by means of something 通過; 依靠: *This crisis could be solved through negotiation.* 這場危機可以通過談判來解決。**3** *adv, prep* from the beginning to the end of something 從頭至尾: *I don't think that he will live through the night.* 我認為他活不過今晚。| *I've read through the report.* 我看過這篇報告了。| *She read the letter through.* 她把信從頭到尾看了一遍。| *She stopped the tape half way through.* 磁帶放了一半, 她就按停了錄音機。**4** *adv, prep* successfully to the end of something 順利通過: *Did you get through your exams?* 你通過考試了嗎? **5** *prep* among all the parts of something 在…之間: *I was looking through the papers on my desk.* 我當時在翻寫字枱上的文件堆。**6** *adv infml* finished 〔非正式〕完成的: *Are you through yet?* 你做完了嗎? **7 through and through** completely 完全地; 徹底地

‡**through**² *adj* [only before a noun 只用於名詞前] going all the way to a place 直達的: *a through train* 直達列車

‡**through·out** /θruːˈaʊt; θruːˈaʊt/ *adv, prep* **1** in every part of something 在…各處: *There were celebrations throughout the country.* 全國各地都舉行了慶祝活動。| *The house has been recently painted throughout.* 房子最近徹底粉刷了一遍。**2** from the beginning to the end of something 從頭到尾: *The party continued throughout the night.* 晚會開了一夜。| *He remained loyal throughout.* 他始終保持忠誠。

‡**throw**¹ /θro; θrəʊ/ *v* **threw** /θruː; θruː/, **thrown** /θron; θrəʊn/, **throwing** **1** [I;T] to send through the air by moving your arm back and then quickly forwards, letting go of whatever you are holding 扔; 投; 拋; 擲: *It's my turn to throw.* 該輪到我扔了。| *She threw the javelin 100 metres.* 她把標槍投了一百米遠。| *Someone threw a stone at me.* 有人朝我扔了塊石頭。| *Throw the ball to Grandad.* 把球拋給爺爺。| *Could you throw me the newspaper, please?* 請把報紙扔給我好嗎? –see picture on page 992 見 992 頁彩圖

□ **USEFUL PATTERNS** 有用句型

to throw something; to throw something at someone; to throw something to someone; to throw someone something

---

2 throw yourself to move suddenly and forcefully 突然而有力地移動: *She threw herself down on the bed.* 她重重地躺倒在牀上。**3** [T+adv/prep] to put on or take off clothes quickly and carelessly 迅速而馬虎地穿上或脫掉〔衣服〕: *He threw off his clothes and jumped into the water.* 他迅速脫掉衣服跳入水中。| *She threw a shawl around her shoulders.* 她隨手在肩上披了條圍巾。**4** [T] to make someone fall to the ground 使〔某人〕摔倒在地: *The horse threw him.* 那匹馬把他摔在地上。**5** [T] to send light or sound in a particular direction 〔朝某個方向〕傳送光線或聲音: *The sun threw shadows on the grass.* 太

陽把影子投射在草地上。**6** [T+adv/prep] to cause someone suddenly to be in a particular state 使〔某人〕突然陷於某種狀態: *The new system has thrown us all into confusion.* 新的系統把我們都搞糊塗了。**7** [T] *infml* to arrange or give a party or dinner 〔非正式〕舉行〔宴會或晚宴〕**8** [T] *infml* to confuse or shock 〔非正式〕迷惑; 使…震驚: *His remarks threw me for a moment.* 他的話使我愣了一陣子。**9 throw a fit** to have a sudden attack of uncontrolled temper 突然發脾氣 **10 throw the book at someone** *infml* to make all possible legal or police charges against someone 〔非正式〕指控某人 **11 throw yourself at someone: a** to rush violently towards someone 拼命衝向某人 **b** to attempt forcefully to win the love of someone 向某人獻媚 **12 throw yourself into something** to do or take part in something eagerly and actively 積極做某事

throw sthg ↔ **away** *phr v* [T] **1** to lose something by foolishness 浪費〔某事物〕: *He threw away the chance of a good job.* 他浪費了獲得一份好工作的機會。**2** to get rid of something that you do not want 扔掉〔不需要的東西〕: *Are you throwing all those books away?* 你準備把這些書都扔掉嗎?

throw sthg ↔ **in** *phr v* [T] *infml* to supply something in addition, without increasing the price 〔非正式〕免費添加; 額外奉送: *The room costs fifteen pounds a night, with meals thrown in.* 這房間住一個晚上要十五英鎊, 包括膳食。

throw sthg ↔ **off** *phr v* [T] to free yourself from something 擺脫〔某事物〕: *It took me a week to throw off that cold.* 我那感冒過了一個星期才好。

throw sthg ↔ **open** *phr v* [T] to allow people to enter a place 允許〔人們〕進入; 對…開放: *They have decided to throw the gardens open to the public.* 他們已決定將花園對公眾開放。

throw out *phr v* **1** [T **throw** sthg ↔ **out**] to refuse to accept something 拒絕接受〔某事物〕: *The committee threw out my suggestions.* 委員會拒絕接受我的建議。**2** [T **throw** sbdy/sthg ↔ **out**] to get rid of or force someone to leave 去除〔某物〕; 強迫〔某人〕離開: *Why don't you throw out that old sofa and get a new one?* 你為何不把那個舊沙發扔掉再去買個新的? | *He was thrown out of the hotel because he was wearing jeans.* 他由於穿著牛仔褲而被趕出旅館。

throw together *phr v* **1** [T **throw** sthg **together**] to make something quickly 迅速製作〔某物〕: *I just threw the meal together.* 我胡亂做了一頓飯。**2 throw people together** to bring people together so that they get to know each other 使人們相遇或相識: *I think it was luck which threw us together at that party.* 我想我們在晚會上相識真是運氣。

throw up *phr v* **1** [I] *infml* to be sick 〔非正

式〕生病 **2** [T **throw** sthg ↔ **up**] to make something move from the ground into the air 扔到空中; 揚起: *Mud was thrown up by the cars in front.* 前面的車把泥漿濺了起來。**3** [T **throw** sthg ↔ **up**] to produce something 產生〔某物〕: *The discussion has thrown up a lot of good ideas.* 這場討論提出了許多好主意。

throw² *n* **1** an action of moving your arm back and then forwards quickly letting go of whatever you are holding 扔; 投; 抛; **2** the distance to which something is thrown 〔某物〕投擲的距離: *a throw of 100 metres* 擲了一百米遠 | *a record throw* 破紀錄的一擲

thrush /θrʌʃ; θrʌʃ/ *n* a small bird with a brownish back and a spotted breast 畫眉〔鳥〕

thrust¹ /θrʌst; θrʌst/ *v* **thrust, thrusting 1** [T+adv/prep] to push something forcefully and suddenly 猛推; 猛塞: *We thrust our way through the crowd.* 我們從人羣中擠了過去。**2 thrust something on/upon someone** to force someone to accept something 強迫某人接受某物: *All this publicity was thrust upon her.* 公眾的注意力全部向她投去。

thrust² *n* **1** a forceful push 刺; 戳: *a sword thrust* 用劍一刺 **2 the thrust of** the main meaning or central point of 要旨; 中心點: *The thrust of her argument was that all interference in industry was wrong.* 她的中心論點就是對工業進行任何干預都是錯的。

thud /θʌd; θʌd/ *n* a dull sound as caused by a heavy object falling to the ground or hitting something soft 重擊聲: *He fell to the floor with a thud.* 他砰的一聲倒在地上。– **thud** *v* [I+adv/prep]

thug /θʌg; θʌg/ *n* a violent person 暴徒; 惡棍

thumb¹ /θʌm; θʌm/ *n* **1** the short thick finger which is set apart from the other four (大)拇指 **2 thumbs up** an expression of satisfaction, victory, or approval 翹起大拇指〔表示滿意、勝利或贊成〕**3 under somebody's thumb** *infml* under the control or influence of someone〔非正式〕在某人的控制〔影響〕下

thumb² *v* [I;T] *infml* to ask for a free ride from passing motorists by holding out your thumb〔非正式〕〔翹起拇指〕要求搭便車: *He thumbed a lift to London.* 他搭便車到了倫敦。

thumb through sthg *phr v* [T] to look through a book quickly 瀏覽〔書籍〕

thumb·nail¹ /ˈθʌmneɪl; ˈθʌmneɪl/ *n* the nail on the upper outer edge of your thumb 拇指指甲

thumbnail² *adj* [only before a noun 只用於名詞前] **thumbnail sketch** a very short description or account 極簡短的描述或敍述

thumb·tack /ˈθʌmtæk; ˈθʌmtæk/ *n* the usual American word for 〔美式〕= DRAWING PIN

thump¹ /θʌmp; θʌmp/ *v* **1** [T] to hit some-

one forcefully with the hand tightly closed 〔用拳〕重擊〔某人〕: *I'll thump you on the nose!* 小心我一拳打扁你的鼻子! **2** [I] to produce a loud, dull sound by beating, falling or walking heavily 發出沉重的聲音: *The excitement made her heart thump.* 她激動得心怦怦直跳。

thump² *n* the dull sound of a heavy blow 重擊聲

thun·der¹ /ˈθʌndə; ˈθʌndər/ *n* [U] the loud explosive noise that follows a flash of lightning 雷聲: *Can you hear the thunder?* 你聽見雷聲嗎? | *thunder and lightning* 雷電交加

thunder² *v* **1 it thunders, it is thundering** =there are loud explosive noises following flashes of lightning 打雷: *Our dog is always afraid when it thunders.* 每逢打雷我們的狗都會很害怕。**2** [I] to make a very loud deep sound 發出沉重的響聲: *The guns thundered in the distance.* 遠處傳來隆隆的槍砲聲。 | *"Get out!" he thundered.* "滾出去!" 他大聲咆吼說。

thun·der·bolt /ˈθʌndə,bolt; ˈθʌndəbəʊlt/ *n* **1** a flash of lightning and crash of thunder together 雷電 **2** a sudden event which causes great shock 令人震驚的事件

thun·der·clap /ˈθʌndə,klæp; ˈθʌndəklæp/ *n* a single loud crash of thunder 一聲雷響

thun·der·ous /ˈθʌndərəs; ˈθʌndərəs/ *adj* extremely loud 震耳欲聾的: *thunderous applause* 震耳欲聾的掌聲

thun·der·storm /ˈθʌndə,storm; ˈθʌndəstɔːm/ *n* a storm of heavy rain with thunder and lightning 雷雨; 雷暴

thun·der·struck /ˈθʌndə,strʌk; ˈθʌndəstrʌk/ *adj* [never before a noun 不能用於名詞前] very surprised indeed 震驚的

thun·der·y /ˈθʌndəri; ˈθʌndəri/ *adj* giving signs that thunder is likely (used of the weather) 有打雷徵兆的〔指天氣〕

Thurs·day /ˈθɜːzdi; ˈθɜːzdi/ (also 又作 **Thur** or **Thurs**) the day between Wednesday and Friday 星期四

★★thus /ðʌs; ðʌs/ *adv fml* 【正式】**1** in this way or for this reason 如此; 因此: *The new machines will work faster, thus reducing our costs.* 新機器運轉的速度會更快, 可以減低成本。 | *We had been told to expect help from local people. Thus, we were quite unprepared for the hostility we found.* 我們獲悉當地的人會幫助我們, 因此受到敵視時頗感意外。 | *Put a plastic bag over the plants to keep them moist. This prevents the soil drying out and there is thus less need to water them.* 把塑料袋套在植物上保濕。這樣可以防止土壤乾燥, 毋須經常澆水。**2 thus far** up until now 至此; 迄今

thwart /θwɔːt; θwɔːt/ *v* [T] to prevent someone or something from succeeding 阻止〔某人或某事〕獲得成功: *My plans were thwarted by the weather.* 我的計劃因天氣而受阻。

thyme /taɪm; taɪm/ n [U] the dried leaves of a plant, used for giving a special taste to food 百里香葉〔用作調味料〕

thy·roid /'θaɪrɔɪd; 'θaɪrɔɪd/ n (also 又作 **thy·roid gland** /'··,·/) an organ in your neck that controls the development of your mind and body 甲狀腺

ti·a·ra /taɪ'erə; tiˈɑːrə/ n a piece of jewellery like a small crown which can be worn on the head by women on formal occasions 冕狀頭飾

tic /tɪk; tɪk/ n a sudden uncontrolled movement of the muscles, usually in your face 〔常指臉部的〕肌肉抽搐

tick¹ /tɪk; tɪk/ n **1** the short regularly repeated sound of a clock or watch 〔鐘錶的〕滴答聲 **2** a mark ✓ put against an answer or a name on a list to show that it is correct or that a person is present 〔表示答案正確或人已到場的〕記號, 勾號 **3 a tick** BrE infml a moment 〔英式, 非正式〕片刻: I'll be down in a tick. 我一會兒就下來。 **4** a very small insect-like creature that fixes itself to animals and sucks their blood 蜱; 扁蝨

tick² v **1** [I] to make a regularly repeated short sound, for example like a clock or watch 發出滴答聲〔如鐘錶〕 **2** [T] to mark something with a tick, to show that it is correct or has been dealt with 打勾做記號 〔表明正確或已做好〕: All his answers had been ticked. 他的答案全部打了勾。 **3 what makes someone tick** what makes someone excited or want to live in a particular way 令某人興奮[以某種方式生活或做事]的原因

tick off phr v infml 〔非正式〕 **1** [T **tick** sbdy/sthg ↔ **off**] to remove something or someone from a list by ticking that word or name 劃掉; 劃掉: I've ticked off everything that I've bought. 我已把買好的東西都從清單上勾掉。 **2** [T **tick** sbdy ↔ **off**] to speak angrily to someone 斥責〔某人〕: He ticked me off because I was late. 由於我遲到了, 他大聲地呵斥我。

tick over phr v [I] to continue working at a slow, steady rate 緩慢而勻速地繼續工作: The car's engine was ticking over. 汽車的引擎在空轉。| Work in the office has been ticking over while you've been on holiday. 在你度假的這些日子裡, 辦公室裡大家工作起來慢吞吞的。

✱tick·et /'tɪkɪt; 'tɪkɪt/ n **1** a printed piece of paper or card which shows that a person has paid for a journey on a bus or train, or entrance into something like a cinema 車票; 門票; 入場券: a bus ticket 公共汽車票 | Entrance to the theatre is by ticket only. 只有憑票才能進入劇場。 **2** a piece of card or paper that shows the price or size of an object for sale 價目牌; 標籤 **3** a printed notice showing that you have parked your car in a place where you are not allowed to park it 違章停車通知單: a parking ticket

違章停車罰款單 **4** a list of people put forward by one political party in an American election 〔美國政黨的〕候選人名單

tick·le /'tɪkl; 'tɪkəl/ v **tickled, tickling 1** [T] to touch someone's body lightly with your fingers to make them laugh 搔癢〔使某人發笑〕 **2** [I;T] to touch or be touched lightly by something in a rather annoying way 〔輕觸〕(使)發癢: These rough sheets tickle. 這些粗麻墊扎得我發癢。 **3** [T] to delight or amuse you 使高興; 使發笑: I was tickled by her description of the wedding. 她對婚禮的描述令我覺得很有趣。

tickle² n [C;U] a feeling of being touched lightly by something 輕觸的感覺; 癢感

tick·lish /'tɪklɪʃ; 'tɪklɪʃ/ adj **1** easily made to laugh because your body is sensitive to tickling 怕癢的 **2** difficult (used of a problem) 困難的〔指問題〕: a ticklish situation 棘手的情況

tid·al /'taɪdl; 'taɪdl/ adj **1** related to the tide 潮汐的: tidal currents 潮流 **2 tidal wave** a very large dangerous ocean wave 海嘯

tid·bit /'tɪd,bɪt; 'tɪd,bɪt/ n the usual American word for 〔美式〕= TITBIT

tide¹ /taɪd; taɪd/ n **1** the regular movement of the sea level up and down the shore 潮; 潮汐: The sea comes right up to the cliffs when the tide is in. 漲潮時海水順着懸崖上湧。| Strong tides make swimming dangerous. 在洶湧的潮水中游泳很危險。 **2** the direction in which the opinion of a lot of people is moving 〔輿論的〕傾向: The tide of public opinion seems to be turning against the government. 公眾輿論似乎開始轉向反對政府。

tide² v

tide sbdy **over** phr v [t] to help someone through a difficult period 幫助〔某人〕度過〔困難時期〕: Can you lend me ten pounds, to tide me over the next few days? 請借給我十英鎊, 讓我熬過這幾天行可以嗎?

tide·mark /'taɪd,mɑːk; 'taɪdmɑːk/ n **1** the highest point reached by a tide on the shore 潮汐最高點 **2** a mark round the inside of a bath that shows the level of the water before it was emptied 〔浴缸水位留下的〕垢痕

tid·ings /'taɪdɪŋz; 'taɪdɪŋz/ n [pl] old fash news 〔老式〕消息

ti·dy¹ /'taɪdɪ; 'taɪdi/ adj **tidier, tidiest 1** neat and orderly in appearance or habits 〔外表或習慣〕整潔的; 愛整潔的: It's a very tidy house. 這是所非常整潔的房子。| She's so tidy! 她多麼整潔! **2** infml quite large (used of amounts of money) 〔非正式〕很大的〔指錢的數量〕: a tidy income 收入很多 **–tidily** adv **–tidiness** n [U]

tidy² v **tidied, tidying**

tidy sthg ↔ **up** phr v [I;T] to make a place neat 把〔某處〕收拾得整整齊齊: When are you going to tidy your room up? 你打算何時把房間收拾乾淨?

tidy sthg ↔ **away** *phr v* [T] to put something out of sight or out of the way 把〔某物〕收拾好: *Could you tidy away your homework so that we can have dinner?* 請你把家庭作業本收起來, 給我們地方吃晚飯可以嗎?

***tie¹** /taɪ; taɪ/ *n* **1** (also 又作 **necktie** *AmE* 〔美式〕) a band of cloth worn round the neck and tied in a knot at the front 領帶 **2** a cord or string used for fastening something 繩子; 帶子 **3 ties** [pl] something that unites 〔人與人之間的〕紐帶; 關係: *family ties* 家庭關係 | *ties of friendship* 友誼的紐帶 **4 a tie** something that limits your freedom 束縛; 約束: *Young children can be a tie.* 小孩子可成為累贅。 **5** a result of a competition in which the competitors have the same number of points or votes 〔比賽的〕平局; 不分勝負: *There was a tie for first place.* 有兩位選手並列第一名。

***tie²** *v* **tied, tying 1** [T+adv/prep] to fasten something whth a cord, string, or rope 捆; 綁; 繫: *You have to tie this label onto your suitcase.* 你必須把這個標籤繫在手提箱上。 | *She tied her horse to the gate.* 她把馬拴在大門上。 **2** [I;T] to fasten by drawing together and knotting 繫上; 打結: *Can you tie your own shoe laces yet?* 你會自己繫鞋帶嗎? | *My dress ties at the back.* 我的衣服帶子繫在後面。 **3** [I] to be equal in a competition 〔比賽〕平手; 不分勝負: *Two teams have tied for second place.* 有兩支隊伍並列第二名。 **4 be tied to** to be connected to 與…有聯繫: *Salary increases are tied to inflation rates.* 工資的增長和通貨膨脹率掛鈎。

tie sbdy **down** *phr v* [T] **1** to limit someone's freedom 限制〔某人的〕自由: *She feels her job is tying her down.* 她覺得被自己的工作束縛住。 **2** to force someone to make a decision 強迫〔某人〕做決定: *He tied him down to a date for the meeting.* 她強迫他定下了開會的日期。

tie in with sthg *phr v* [I] to be in agreement with something 與〔某物〕相符: *This story doesn't tie in with the facts.* 這個故事與事實不符。

tie sthg ↔ **up** *phr v* [T] **1** to fasten something with cord, string, or rope 捆綁〔某物〕: *Make sure you've tied up that parcel securely before you post it.* 你在郵寄那個包裹之前注意把它綁好。 | *She tied it up with string.* 她用繩子把它捆了起來。 **2** to put money into an account or business so that it cannot be used for anything else 凍結〔資金〕 **3** to connect one fact with another one 把〔事實〕聯繫起來: *The police are trying to tie up his escape from prison with the murder.* 警方嘗試把他越獄的案件同謀殺案聯繫起來。

tied up /ˌ·'·/ *adj* very busy 非常繁忙的: *I'm afraid I can't come, I'm rather tied up at work this week.* 我恐怕來不了, 因為本週我相當忙碌。

tier /tɪr; tɪəʳ/ *n* one of a number of levels rising one above another 〔一〕層: *Their wedding cake had three tiers.* 他們的結婚蛋糕是三層的。

tiff /tɪf; tɪf/ *n* a slight quarrel 吵嘴; 口角: *a lovers' tiff* 情侶間的吵嘴

ti·ger /'taɪgə; 'taɪgəʳ/ *n* a large fierce Asian wild cat that has yellow fur with black bands; a female tiger is called a **tigress** 虎; 老虎〔母虎稱作 **tigress**〕

***tight¹** /taɪt; taɪt/ *adj* **1** fitting part of your body closely 緊身的: *tight shoes* 擠腳的鞋子 **2** leaving no free room or time 〔空間或時間上〕擠滿的, 排滿的: *The children sat in a tight little group.* 孩子們坐在那裡, 擠成一堆。 | *tight schedule* 排得滿滿的日程表 **3** firmly fixed in place 緊的; 牢的: *This drawer is so tight I can't open it.* 這個抽屜非常緊, 我拉不開。 **4** well ordered or firmly controlled 組織嚴密的; 嚴格控制的: *There was tight security at the airport when the President's plane arrived.* 總統的專機抵達時, 機場的保安措施非常嚴密。 **5** stretched out as far as possible 拉緊的; 繃緊的: *The cover of the drum has to be stretched until it's really tight.* 鼓的表面得拉到繃緊為止。 **6** not generous with money 吝嗇的 **7** [never before a noun 不能用於名詞前] *infml* drunk 〔非正式〕喝醉的 **8 in a tight corner/spot** in a difficult position 在困境之中 **–tightly** *adv*

tight² *adv* closely or firmly 緊密地; 牢固地: *She held the baby tight.* 她緊緊地抱著嬰兒。 | *Close your eyes tight.* 把眼睛緊緊閉上。 | *Hold tight!* 抓緊!

tight·en /'taɪtn; 'taɪtn/ *v* **1** [I;T] to make something more firmly fixed in place or hold more firmly 固定〔某物〕; 緊握〔某物〕: *These screws need tightening.* 這些螺絲需要緊一下。 | *She tightened her grip on the steering wheel.* 她用力握緊方向盤。 **2** [I;T] to stretch as far as possible 拉緊; 繃緊 **3** [T] to control something more firmly 對〔某事物〕加強控制: *Security at the palace has been tightened.* 皇宮內加強了保安工作。 **4 tighten your belt** *infml* to try to live on less money 〔非正式〕節衣縮食: *We just can't afford to go on like this, we'll have to tighten our belts.* 我們不能再這樣過日子, 必須設法節衣縮食。

tighten up *phr v* [I;T **tighten** sthg ↔ **up**] to make something firmer or more severe 使〔某物〕更牢固; 使〔某事〕更嚴格: *The government is tightening up on the drinking and driving laws.* 政府正逐步把有關酒後駕車的條例訂得更嚴。

tight·fist·ed /ˌtaɪt'fɪstɪd; ˌtaɪt'fɪstˌd◂/ *adj infml* very unwilling to give or share money 〔非正式〕吝嗇的; 小氣的

tight·rope /'taɪtrop; 'taɪt-rəup/ *n* a tightly stretched rope or wire, high above the ground, on which performers walk and do tricks 〔供走鋼絲者表演用的〕鋼絲

tights /taɪts; taɪts/ *n* [pl] a very close-fitting garment made of thin material covering the legs and lower part of the body; tights are usually worn by women〔婦女用的〕褲襪 –see 見 PAIR (USAGE 用法) –see picture on page 210 見 210 頁彩圖

tile /taɪl; taɪl/ *n* a thin square piece of baked clay or other material used for covering roofs, walls, or floors 瓦; 瓷磚; 地磚: *polystyrene ceiling tiles* 聚苯乙烯天花板瓷磚 | *slate roof tiles* 屋頂石板瓦 | *white bathroom tiles* 浴室白瓷磚 –**tile** *v* **tiled, tiling** [T]

till¹ /tɪl; tɪl/ *prep, conj* until 直到; 至: *Let's wait till tomorrow.* 我們等到明天吧。 | *Drive straight on till you get to the school.* 駕車筆直往前走, 一直到學校為止。

till² *n* a drawer where money is kept in a shop〔商店內〕放錢的抽屜

till³ *v* [T] *old fash* to cultivate the ground〔舊式〕耕〔地〕

til·ler /ˈtɪlə; ˈtɪlər/ *n* a long handle fastened to the RUDDER of a boat so that it can be turned easily 舵柄

tilt¹ /tɪlt; tɪlt/ *v* [I;T] to slope or make something slope by lifting one end of it (使)傾斜

tilt² *n* **1** [C;U] a position in which one end of something is higher than the other 傾斜: *She wore her hat at a tilt.* 她歪戴着帽子。 | *with a tilt of the head* 頭一歪 **2 at full tilt** *infml* at full speed〔非正式〕全速

★**tim·ber** /ˈtɪmbə; ˈtɪmbər/ *n* **1** [U] wood or trees to be used for building〔建築用的〕木材; 木料 **2** [C] a wooden beam 木樑

★★**time¹** /taɪm; taɪm/ *n* **1** [U] a measurable quantity that we measure in minutes, hours, days, and years 時間: *Young children have no concept of time.* 小孩子沒有時間概念。 **2** [sing; U] a period of time 一段時間: *It takes a long time to get there by car.* 坐車到那裡去要花很長時間。 | *I spend quite a lot of time reading.* 我花很多時間看書。 | *I never have enough time to do things properly.* 我永遠都沒有足夠的時間把事情做好。 | *I waited for a short time, then went home.* 我等了一會兒就回家了。 | *After a time the phone rang.* 過了一會兒電話鈴響了。 **3** [U] a system of measuring time 計算時間的制度: *British Summer Time* 英國夏令時間 **4** [C] a particular point in time which is stated in hours and minutes〔具體的〕時間; 鐘點: *"What's the time?" "It's one o'clock."* "現在幾點了?" "一點鐘。" | *"What time shall we leave?" "Ten o'clock."* "我們幾點鐘出發?" "十點鐘。" | *I must find out the times of trains to London.* 我必須查一下去倫敦的各列車的開車時間。 **5** [C; U] a particular moment or occasion 時候; 時刻; 次數: *It's time to leave.* 該出發了。 | *Do you remember the time the car broke down?* 你記得汽車是何時拋錨的嗎? | *I'll tell him the news next time I see him.* 我下次見到他就把消息告訴他。 | *I've tried to phone several times.* 我已試着打過好幾次電話了。 | *This is the second time this week that she's been*

late. 這是她本週內第二次遲到了。 | *Now is the time to tackle these problems.* 現在該來解決這些問題了。 **6** [C] a period in history〔歷史上的〕時代: *in ancient times* 在古代 | *in the time of Queen Victoria* 在維多利亞女王時代 **7** [U] the rate or speed at which a piece of music is played〔音樂演奏的〕速度; 拍子 **8 times** [pl] used when you are comparing things and saying how much bigger, smaller, etc one thing is than the other thing 倍〔用於比較〕: *This machine is better, but it's three times more expensive.* 這台機器較好, 但要貴三倍。 | *This show is five times as popular as any other show on television.* 這個節目的收視率比其他電視節目要高五倍。 **9 about time** a phrase you use to say that something should be done now 是做...的時候〔用於表示該做某事〕: *Isn't it about time you got married?* 你難道還不該結婚嗎? **10 ahead of time** before the time when something should be done 提前: *We finished ahead of time.* 我們提前完成了。 **11 ahead of your time** too modern or too original for the period of history in which you live 過於現代化; 過於創新 **12 all the time** continuously 一直: *She just works all the time.* 她一直不停地工作。 **13 at one time** in the past 在過去; 從前: *At one time I wanted to be a dentist.* 我曾經想成為一名牙科醫生。 **14 at the same time** in spite of this 儘管如此; 只是: *I feel disappointed, but at the same time I'm determined to try again.* 我感到很失望。儘管如此, 我仍決心再試一次。 **15 at times** sometimes 有時: *At times I felt very lonely.* 有時我感到很孤獨。 **16 before your time** before you were born 在你出生以前 **17 for the time being** for the moment, until something else is arranged 暫時: *You can stay with us for the time being.* 你可以暫時和我們住在一起。 **18 from time to time** sometimes, but not very often 有時; 偶爾: *I see Mary from time to time.* 我偶爾會遇到瑪麗。 **19 have no time for something** *infml* to dislike something〔非正式〕討厭某物: *I haven't got much time for people like him.* 我不太喜歡像他那樣的人。 **20 have the time of your life** to spend a very enjoyable time 過得很開心 **21 in good time** at the right time or early 準時; 提早: *If we set off at 9 o'clock we should get there in good time.* 如果我們九時出發, 我們可以提早抵達那裡。 **22 in time** after a period of time 過些時間: *She'll get over the shock in time.* 過些時間她就會從打擊中恢復過來。 **23 in a day's time, in a week's time, etc** after a day, a week, etc 一天之後; 一週之後: *I'll see you again in two weeks' time.* 過兩個星期我再來看你。 **24 in time to do something** early enough to do something 趕得上做某事: *We arrived in time to see the beginning of the parade.* 我們到了那裡正好趕上遊行開始。 **25 in your own good time** when you are ready to do something 當自己準備好〔做某事〕: *She'll get in touch with me in her own good time.* 她準備好便會跟我聯繫的。 **26 take time** to need time in order to happen 需要時間: *It takes time for people's attitudes to change.* 人的心態需要時間才可以改變。 **27 take your time** to do something slowly 慢慢做某事 **28 time after time, time and again** repeatedly or on many occasions 反覆; 許多次: *She came out with the same excuses time after time.* 她多次使用同一藉口。 **29 two at a time, three at a time,** etc in groups of two, three, etc 一次兩個; 一次三個; 等等: *She ran up the stairs two at a time.* 她一步二格地跑上樓梯。 **30 work against time** to be trying to do something before a particular time 趕時間工作

■ USAGE 用法: **1** Compare 比較 **spend time, pass time, waste time.** If we **spend** time on something we use time sensibly, or in ways that are neither good nor bad ☆ **spend** 指理智地使用時間, 或指一般地花費時間: *to spend time doing English homework* 花費時間做英語家庭作業。 If we have too much time which we try to fill we may **pass** the time ☆ **pass** 表示時間太多, 需要消磨: *Listening to the radio helped me to pass the time.* 我聽收音機消磨時間。 If we use time badly and without success we **waste** time ☆ **waste** 表示時間花得不當, 未獲成功: *I wasted a lot of time trying to find a parking space.* 我浪費了許多時間尋找泊車位。 **2** At 11.45 it is *a quarter to twelve* in British English but *a quarter to/of twelve* in American English. At 12.15 it is *a quarter past twleve* in British English but *a quarter past/after twelve* in American English. ☆ 11:45 在英式英語中用 *a quarter to twelve* 表示, 在美式英語中用 *a quarter to/of twelve* 表示。12:15 在英式英語中用 *a quarter past twelve* 表示, 在美式英語中用 *a quarter past/after twelve* 表示。

---

time² *v* **timed, timing** [T] **1** to arrange for something to happen at a particular time 安排〔某事〕的時間: *We timed our visit to co-incide with the arts festival.* 我們把訪問的時間安排在藝術節期間。 **2** to measure the speed with which something happened 測定〔某物〕的速度: *We timed our journey — it took two hours.* 我們計算了一下花在路上的時間——是兩個小時。

time bomb /'··/ *n* **1** a bomb that can be set to explode at a particular time 定時炸彈 **2** a situation that is likely to become dangerous or difficult to handle 隨時發生危險[困難]的情況: *Until we deal with unemployment properly, we are sitting on a time bomb.* 如果無法妥善處理失業問題, 我們面對的便是一個

隨時會爆的定時炸彈。

time-hon·oured /'·,··/ *adj fml* respected because of age or long use 〔正式〕由於年久而受尊重的: *a time-honoured custom* 歷史悠久的風俗

time-keep·er /'taɪm,kipɚ; 'taɪm,ki:pəʳ/ *n* a person who records the time of competitors in a race or work done by others 〔比賽中的〕記時員

time lag /'··/ *n* the period of time between two connected events 〔相關事件的〕時間間隔

time·less /'taɪmlɪs; 'taɪmləs/ *adj* lasting forever or not changed by time 永恆的: *the timeless beauty of the stars* 羣星永恆之美

time lim·it /'·,··/ *n* a period of time within which something must be done 時限; 期限

time·ly /'taɪmlɪ; 'taɪmli/ *adj* happening at just the right time 及時的: *a timely warning* 及時的警告

tim·er /'taɪmɚ; 'taɪməʳ/ *n* a machine that measures or records time 計時器: *Don't forget to set the timer on the video.* 別忘了把錄像機上的計時器定好時間。 | *an egg timer* 煮蛋計時器

times /taɪmz; taɪmz/ *prep* multiplied by a particular number 乘; 乘以: *What's thirteen times six?* 十三乘以六等於多少?

time·scale /'taɪm,skel; 'taɪmskeɪl/ *n* the length of time during which something happens or develops 〔某事發生或發展的〕一段時間

time·ta·ble /'taɪm,tebl; 'taɪm,teɪbəl/ *n* a table of the times at which buses and trains arrive and leave or at which classes in a school or college take place 〔公共汽車、火車的〕時刻表; 〔學校裡的〕課程表 **–timetable** *v* **timetabled, timetabling** [T]: *The meeting was timetabled to begin at two o'clock.* 會議定在兩點鐘開始。 | *It is timetabled for two o'clock.* 這事情安排在兩點鐘。

time warp /'··/ *n* a situation which seems to belong to another period of history 時間異常[錯位]: *Visiting these distant villages is like being in a time warp. Nothing has changed for centuries.* 參觀這些偏遠的村莊就像是處於時間異常的情況中一樣。這裡數個世紀以來都沒有多少變化。

time·worn /'taɪm,wɔrn; 'taɪmwɔ:n/ *adj lit* showing signs of having been used for a long time 〔文〕用得很久的

tim·id /'tɪmɪd; 'tɪmɪd/ *adj* not confident or courageous 膽怯的 **–timidly** *adv* **–timidity** /tɪ'mɪdətɪ; tɪ'mɪdʒti/ *n* [U]

tim·ing /'taɪmɪŋ; 'taɪmɪŋ/ *n* [U] the choosing of exactly the right moment to do something so as to get the best effect 時間的選擇; 時機的掌握: *a dancer with perfect timing* 動作恰到好處的舞蹈演員 | *We must get the timing right.* 我們必須掌握好時間。

tim·o·rous /'tɪmərəs; 'tɪmərəs/ *adj fml* ner-

---

vous and easily frightened 〔正式〕緊張而膽
小的 **–timorously** adv

tin¹ /tɪn; tɪn/ n 1 [U] a soft whitish metal,
used to cover metal objects with a protective shiny surface 錫 2 [C] a small metal
container in which food or drink is sold or
stored 罐子: *a tin of beans* 一罐豆 | *a biscuit
tin* 餅乾罐 | *a tin of peaches* 一罐桃子 –see
picture on page 244 見 244 頁彩圖

tin² v **-nn-** [T] to preserve food by packing
it in a tin 用罐裝〔食物〕**–tinned** adj: *tinned
sardines* 罐裝沙丁魚

tinc·ture /ˈtɪŋktʃə; ˈtɪŋktʃər/ n [C;U] a medical substance mixed with alcohol 酊劑

tin·der /ˈtɪndə; ˈtɪndər/ n [U] fml any material that catches fire easily 〔正式〕易燃物:
The plants are as dry as tinder. 草木極為乾
燥，一點就著。

tin·foil /ˈtɪnˌfɔɪl; ˈtɪnfɔɪl/ n [U] a very thin
sheet of shiny metal, used as a protective
wrapping for food 〔包裝食品用的〕錫紙

tinge /tɪndʒ; tɪndʒ/ n a tinge of a small
amount of colour or feeling 一絲〔色彩或感
覺〕: *There was a tinge of sadness in her
voice.* 她的聲音裡流露出一絲絲悲哀。**–tinged**
adj: *Her black hair was tinged with grey.* 她
的黑髮中出現了一些花白的頭髮。

tin·gle /ˈtɪŋgl; ˈtɪŋgəl/ v **tingled, tingling** [I]
to feel a slight prickly sensation 有刺痛感:
My fingers tingled with the cold. 我的手指凍
得發疼。**–tingle** n: *I felt a tingle of excitement.* 我感到一陣激動。

tin·ker¹ /ˈtɪŋkə; ˈtɪŋkər/ n a person who
travels from place to place mending metal
pots or pans 〔走街串巷的〕補鍋匠

tinker² v [I] to try to repair or improve
something by making small changes but
without a fixed plan 胡亂修理: *Don't tinker
with my television.* 不要胡亂修理我的電視機。

tin·kle /ˈtɪŋkl; ˈtɪŋkəl/ v **tinkled, tinkling** [I;
T] to make light ringing sounds 發出叮噹
聲: *The bell tinkled as he opened the shop
door.* 他打開店門的時候，鈴叮噹作響。**–
tinkle** n

tin·ny /ˈtɪnɪ; ˈtɪni/ adj 1 cheaply and badly
made (used of something metal such as a
car) 廉價而質差的〔指金屬製品，如汽車〕 2
having a thin metallic sound 發微弱金屬聲
的: *a tinny bell* 聲音細微的鈴鐺

tin o·pen·er /ˈ·ˌ·ˌ·/ n a tool for opening
tins of food 開罐器 –see picture on page
958 見 958 頁彩圖

tin·sel /ˈtɪnsl; ˈtɪnsəl/ n [U] threads of shiny
metallic material on a string used for decoration at Christmas 〔聖誕節裝飾用的〕金屬
絲，光片

tint¹ /tɪnt; tɪnt/ n a pale or delicate shade of
a colour 淺色; 淡色

tint² v [T] to give a slight colour to something 給〔某物〕淡淡地著色: *I'm going to have
my hair tinted.* 我打算把頭髮染一下。

✷ti·ny /ˈtaɪnɪ; ˈtaɪni/ adj extremely small 極小

的; 細小的

✷tip¹ /tɪp; tɪp/ n 1 the pointed or thin end of
something 尖端; 末梢: *the tip of your nose* 你
的鼻尖 | *a town at the southern tip of India*
印度南端的一座城鎮 2 a place where un-
wanted waste is left 垃圾場 3 a small
amount of money given in addition to the
official price to someone who has done
something for you 小費: *Shall I leave the
waiter a tip?* 我應該給服務員小費嗎? 4 on
the tip of your tongue forgotten for the
moment but should soon be remembered
一時想不起來: *Oh, what's her name? It's on
the tip of my tongue.* 哦，她叫甚麼名字來着?
我一下子想不起來了。5 the tip of the ice-
berg a small part of a much larger situation or problem 〔某種情況或問題的〕一小
部分 6 a helpful piece of advice 有用的意見;
忠告: *Take a tip from the experts.* 接受專家的
忠告吧。| *useful tips on gardening* 有關園藝
工作的竅門

tip² v **-pp-** 1 [I;T] to move so that something
is no longer level or straight up (使)〔某物〕
傾斜: *He tipped his chair back and looked
thoughtful.* 他向後翹起椅子坐着，一臉沉思。2
[T] to pour something carelessly from one
container into another 把〔某物〕隨意倒入
〔另一容器〕: *She tipped the flour into the
bowl.* 她把麵粉倒入碗裡。3 [I;T] to give a
small amount of money to someone for
something they have done for you 給〔某
人〕小費 4 to consider someone most likely
to do something 認為〔某人〕極可能做〔某事〕:
*MacTavish is widely tipped as being the next
chairman.* 大家普遍認為麥克塔維什將當選下
一任主席。

tip sbdy ↔ **off** phr v [T] to give someone
a warning or a piece of secret information
給〔某人〕警告〔通風報信〕: *The police were
tipped off that a bank robbery was being
planned.* 警方獲悉有人正在謀劃搶劫銀行。

tip sthg ↔ **over** phr v [T] to move something so that it turns or leans too far 使〔某
物〕傾覆: *Sit down or you'll tip the boat over.*
你坐下來，不然會把船弄翻的。

tip-off /ˈ·ˌ·/ n a piece of secret information
or warning 祕密消息; 警告: *a tip-off about
the robbery* 有關搶劫的祕報

tip·ple /ˈtɪpl; ˈtɪpəl/ n infml an alcoholic
drink 〔非正式〕酒: *What's your favourite
tipple?* 你最喜歡喝哪種酒?

tip·ster /ˈtɪpstə; ˈtɪpstər/ n a person who
gives advice about the likely winner of
horse and dog races 〔賽馬或賽狗中〕提供消
息和情報的人

tip·sy /ˈtɪpsɪ; ˈtɪpsi/ adj slightly drunk 微醉的

tip·toe¹ /ˈtɪpˌtəʊ; ˈtɪptəʊ/ n on tiptoe on your
toes, with the rest of the feet raised above
the ground 踮着腳

tiptoe² v [I] to walk quietly and carefully on
your toes 踮着腳走 –see picture on page
992 見 992 頁彩圖

ti·rade /'taɪred; taɪ'reɪd/ n a long, angry speech 長篇而憤怒的演講

tire¹ /taɪr; taɪə˞/ v **tired, tiring 1** [I;T] to feel weak and in need of a rest 感到疲勞: *a tiring day* 令人疲勞的一天 | *After walking for two hours I began to tire.* 走了兩個小時之後, 我開始感到累了。 **2 tire of something** to become uninterested in something 厭倦某物: *She never tires of talking about her work.* 對於談論自己的工作, 她從不感到厭倦。

tire sbdy ↔ **out** phr v [T] to make someone very tired 使〔某人〕感到疲勞: *The children have completely tired me out.* 孩子們把我搞得精疲力竭。

tire² n see 見 TYRE

☆**tired** /taɪrd; taɪəd/ adj **1** needing to rest or sleep 疲勞的; 勞累的 **2 be tired of something** become uninterested in or annoyed by something 厭倦某物: *I'm tired of your stupid remarks.* 我聽厭了你那些蠢話。 **3 tired out** unable to do much more 非常疲倦: *I'm tired out so I'll go to bed.* 我十分疲倦, 要去睡覺了。 **—tiredness** n [U]

tire·less /'taɪrlɪs; 'taɪələs/ adj never needing a rest 不知疲倦的: *a tireless worker* 不知疲倦的工作者 **—tirelessly** adv

tire·some /'taɪrsəm; 'taɪəsəm/ adj annoying 討厭的: *a tiresome child* 討厭的孩子

☆**tis·sue** /'tɪʃu; 'tɪʃuː/ n **1** [U] animal or plant cells which are similar in form and purpose and make up a particular organ 〔動植物細胞的〕組織: *lung tissue* 肺組織 | *leaf tissue* 葉片組織 **2** [U] (also 又作 **tissue paper**) light thin paper used for wrapping or packing things which might get broken 〔包裝用的〕薄紙, 綿紙: **3** [C] a piece of soft paper used for blowing your nose on 紙巾: *a box of tissues* 一盒紙巾 **4 a tissue of lies** something that is completely untrue 一派謊言

tit /tɪt; tɪt/ n **1** a woman's breast (a word which some people consider not to be polite) 〔婦女的〕乳房〔有些人認為用該詞不禮貌〕 **2** a small European bird 山雀〔一種歐洲小鳥〕

tit·bit /'tɪt,bɪt; 'tɪt,bɪt/ n (also 又作 **tidbit** AmE 《美式》) a small piece of particularly nice food 少量的美食

tit for tat /,···'·/ n infml something unpleasant you do to someone in return for something unpleasant they did to you 〔非正式〕以牙還牙之舉

tit·il·late /'tɪtl,eɪt; 'tɪtl̩,leɪt/ v **titillate, titillating** [T] to excite someone pleasantly, especially sexually 使〔某人〕興奮〔尤指在性方面〕: *a titillating piece of news* 一則刺激的新聞 **—titillation** /,tɪtl'eʃən; ,tɪtl̩'leɪʃən/ n [U]

tit·i·vate /'tɪtə,vet; 'tɪtl̩,veɪt/ v **titivated, titivating** [I;T] infml to make yourself look pretty or tidy 〔非正式〕打扮

ti·tle /'taɪtl; 'taɪtl/ n **1** a name given to a book, painting, or play 〔書籍、繪畫、戲劇的〕

名稱, 題目, 標題: *The title of the play is "Hamlet".* 那齣戲的名稱叫《哈姆雷特》。 **2** a word or name, such as "Mr", "Lady", "Doctor", or "General", used before a person's name as a sign of their position in society or profession 稱呼; 頭銜〔如"先生"、"女士"、"醫生"、"將軍"〕 **3** the position of unbeaten winner in certain sports competitions 冠軍: *Tonight they will be fighting for the title.* 今晚他們將爭奪冠軍。

ti·tled /'taɪtld; 'taɪtld/ adj having a high position in society and a noble title, such as "Lord" 有爵位的; 有貴族頭銜的

title deed /'·· ·/ n a paper showing a person's legal right of ownership of property 房地產契據

title-hold·er /'··,···/ n a person or team who is at present the unbeaten winner of a sports competition 冠軍(保持者)

title role /'·· ·/ n the main character in a play, after whom the play is named 劇名角色: *He played the title role in "Macbeth".* 他在《麥克白》中飾演麥克白。

tit·ter /'tɪtə; 'tɪtə˞/ v [I] to laugh in a nervous or silly way 神經質的笑; 傻笑 **—titter** n

tit·tle-tat·tle /'tɪtl,tætl; 'tɪtl̩ ,tætl/ n [U] infml talk about other people's lives or activities (a word used to express disapproval) 〔非正式〕閒聊〔含貶義〕

tit·u·lar /'tɪtʃələ; 'tɪtʃ˞l̩ə˞/ adj holding a title but not having the duties or power of office 掛名的; 名義上的

T-junc·tion /'ti ,dʒʌŋkʃən; 'tiː ,dʒʌŋkʃən/ n BrE a place where two roads join in the shape of a T 《英式》〔道路的〕T形交叉 —see picture on page 991 見 991 頁彩圖

☆**to¹** /tə; tə; before vowels 元音前 tu; tʊ; strong 強讀 tu; tuː/ prep **1** towards someone or something, or in the direction of someone or something 往; 向; 朝: *She threw the ball to me.* 她把球扔給我。 | *Is this the road to London?* 這條路通往倫敦嗎? | *She gave the book to me.* 她把書遞給我。 | *He rushed to the door.* 他跑向門口。 | *I'm writing a letter to my mother.* 我正在給母親寫信。 | *My daughter will go to school next year.* 我的女兒明年上學。 —see picture on page 764 見 764 頁彩圖 **2 to yourself** for yourself 為自己: *I want a room to myself.* 我想要一間自己住的房間。 **3** before a certain hour 在〔某一鐘點〕以前: *It's five to four.* 現在是三點五十五分。 | *We have to leave by a quarter to eleven.* 我們最遲要在十點四十五分出發。 **4** per 每: *There are 100 pence to the pound.* 一鎊等於一百便士。 **5 to the left, to the right** on the left or right 在左面; 在右面: *To your left you will see the Houses of Parliament.* 你可以看見議會大樓在你左面。 | *Turn your head to the right.* 把頭向右轉。 **6** used in showing how someone feels when something happens 令〔用於表示某人的感覺〕: *To my surprise he handed me the enve-*

lope. 他把信封交給我，令我感到十分意外。| *To our dismay, he still wasn't home by midnight.* 他直到午夜仍未回家，我們都很沮喪。

to² /tu; tuː/ *adv* **1** into a position of being shut but not locked 到關上的位置: *The wind had blown the door to.* 風把門吹得關上了。| *Could you just close the door to?* 請你把門關上，可以嗎? **2 to and fro** moving backwards and forwards or from side to side 來回地; 往復地: *The pendulum swung to and fro.* 那鐘擺來回擺動。| *She was walking to and fro in front of the building.* 她在大樓前面走來走去。

to³ /tə; tə; *before vowels* 元音前 tu; tuː; *strong* 強讀 tu; tuː/ used with verbs to form the INFINITIVE〔與動詞一起使用構成不定式〕: *I don't want to go.* 我不想去。| *You ought to understand.* 應該明白。| *They made an attempt to land.* 他們試圖登陸。| *I need some scissors to cut this string.* 我要一把剪刀把這根繩子剪斷。| *I was very sorry to leave them.* 離開他們我感到很難過。

■ USAGE 用法: It is sometimes considered bad English to put any other word between **to** and the verb that follows it, making a "split infinitive" ☆將別的詞置於 **to** 和動詞中間，形成"分裂不定式"，有時被認為是彆腳的英語: *He was wrong to suddenly leave like that.* 他那樣突然離去的做法是錯的。Some people consider that this should be ☆ 有人認為應當這樣說: **to leave** *suddenly*, or even *suddenly* **to leave**. But sometimes there is no better place to put **to** ☆但有時沒有放置 **to** 的更佳位置: *Your job is* **to** *really understand these problems.* 你的任務是徹底了解這些問題。| *She likes* **to** *half close her eyes and view the paintings from a distance.* 她喜歡半閉着眼睛從遠處欣賞這些畫。

toad /tod; təʊd/ *n* an animal like a large FROG 蟾蜍; 癩蛤蟆

toad·stool /'tod,stul; 'təʊdstuːl/ *n* a poisonous, uneatable type of FUNGUS that looks like the MUSHROOM 毒蘑菇; 毒蕈

to-and-fro /ˌ··'·/ *adj* forwards and backwards or from side to side 來回的; 往復的: *a to-and-fro movement* 往復運動 **–to and fro** *adv*: *The pendulum swung to and fro.* 那鐘擺來回擺動。

toast¹ /tost; təʊst/ *v* [T] to make food such as bread or cheese brown, by holding it close to heat 烘烤〔食品〕: *toasted crumpets* 小圓烤餅 –see 見 COOK¹ (USAGE 用法)

toast² *n* **1** [U] bread made brown by being heated 烤麵包; 吐司: *toast and marmalade* 柑橘醬吐司 **2** [C] a call on other people to drink wine together to express good wishes for someone 祝酒, 乾杯: *He proposed a toast* **to** *the bride and groom.* 他提議

為新郎新娘乾杯。**3 the toast** someone who is greatly loved and admired 極受人愛戴的人: *the toast of Broadway* 百老匯的大紅人

toast³ *v* [T] to drink and wish for the success and happiness of someone 向〔某人〕祝酒: *He was toasted by all his friends.* 他的朋友全都向他祝酒。

toast·er /'tostə; 'təʊstəʳ/ *n* an electric apparatus for toasting bread 烤麵包機 –see picture on page 958 見 958 頁彩圖

to·bac·co /tə'bæko; tə'bækəʊ/ *n* [U] a plant or its large leaves, prepared for smoking in cigarettes and pipes 煙草, 煙葉

to·bac·co·nist /tə'bækənɪst; tə'bækən‚st/ *n* **1** a person who sells tobacco and cigarettes 煙草店老闆 **2 tobacconist's** a shop that sells tobacco and cigarettes 煙草店: *I've run out of cigarettes and the tobacconist's will be closed by now.* 我的煙都抽完了，煙草店現在估計也關門了。

to·bog·gan /tə'bɒgən; tə'bɒgən/ *n* a board curved up at the front, for carrying people over snow 平底雪橇 **–tobogган** *v* **-nn-** [I]: *The children love to go tobogganning down the hill.* 孩子們喜歡坐在雪橇上滑下山。

to·day /tə'de; tə'deɪ/ *adv, n* **1** this present day 今天; 今日: *Today is Tuesday.* 今天是星期二。| *Today is my birthday.* 今天是我的生日。| *I've got to go shopping today.* 我今天必須去買東西。**2** this present time 現在; 目前: *the young people of today* 現在的年輕人 | *People travel more today than they used to.* 人們現在外出旅遊要比以前多。

tod·dle /'tɒdl; 'tɒdl/ *v* **toddled, toddling** [I] to walk with short unsteady steps, like a small child does〔像孩子一樣〕蹣跚地走行

tod·dler /'tɒdlə; 'tɒdləʳ/ *n* a small child who has just learnt to walk 剛學步的小孩 – see 見 CHILD (USAGE 用法)

toe¹ /to; təʊ/ *n* **1** one of the five parts at the end of each foot 腳趾 **2 on your toes** ready for action 隨時準備行動

toe² *v* **toed, toeing. toe the line** to obey orders 服從命令

toe·nail /'to,nel; 'təʊneɪl/ *n* the NAIL on a toe 腳趾甲

tof·fee, toffy /'tɒfɪ; 'tɒfɪ/ *n* [C;U] a hard brown sweet made by boiling sugar and butter 太妃糖: *a sticky toffee* 黏性太妃糖 | *toffee apples* 太妃糖蘋果

to·geth·er /tə'geðə; tə'geðəʳ/ *adv* **1** so as to be joined or in a group 一起, 一道: *Tie the ends together.* 把末端繫在一起。| *Add these numbers together.* 把這些數字加在一起。| *The people gathered together to protest.* 人們聚集在一起舉行抗議活動。**2** with one another 與〔另外一個〕一起: *We went to school together.* 我們一起去上學。| *Together these two companies account for 90% of all sugar production.* 這兩間公司所生產的糖佔了全部糖產量的百分之九

十。**3** at the same time 同時: *Why do all the bills seem to come together?* 為甚麼所有的賬單似乎都是同時收到的? **4** *infml* in control of life and with no problems with your feelings【非正式】有自制力的; 能控制自己感情的: *She seems to be really together.* 她似乎很有自制力。 **5** together with as well as 連同; 和...一道: *They sent me an application form, together with some leaflets telling me about the company.* 他們將申請表連同一些公司的介紹資料一併寄給我。

to·geth·er·ness /təˈgɛðənɪs; təˈgeðən̩s/ *n* [U] a feeling of being united and friendly with other people 團結; 友情

tog·gle /ˈtɑgl; ˈtɒgəl/ *n* a small, shaped bar of wood used as a button 套索釘; 棒形鈕扣

togs /tɑgz; tɒgz/ *n* [pl] *infml* clothes【非正式】衣服

toil /tɔɪl; tɔɪl/ *v lit*【文】**1** [I] to work hard and without tiring 辛苦而不知疲倦地工作 – see 見 WORK¹ (USAGE 用法) **2** [I+adv/prep] to move with tiredness, difficulty, or pain 吃力地移動: *The slaves toiled up the hill pulling the heavy blocks.* 奴隸拖着沉重的石頭吃力地往山上爬。**–toil** *n* [U]

toi·let /ˈtɔɪlɪt; ˈtɔɪləɪt/ *n* **1** [C] a large bowl connected to a pipe, used for getting rid of your body's waste matter 廁所, 抽水馬桶: *Where's the toilet please?* 請問廁所在哪兒? | *Please flush the toilet.* 請把抽水馬桶沖洗一下。**2** [C] a room with a toilet in 廁所; 洗手間 **3** [U] *old fash* the act of washing, dressing yourself, and taking care of your appearance【老式】打扮; 梳妝; 裝束

toilet pa·per /ˈ···,··/ *n* [U] thin paper for cleaning your body when waste matter has been passed from it 衛生紙; 手紙

toi·let·ries /ˈtɔɪlɪtrɪz; ˈtɔɪlətriz/ *n* [pl] things you use when washing or taking care of your body, such as soap, face cream, etc. 化妝用品

toilet roll /ˈ··· ·/ *n* a roll of toilet paper 衛生紙卷

toilet wa·ter /ˈ··,··/ *n* [U] a pleasant-smelling but not very strong PERFUME 化妝水; 花露水

to·ken /ˈtokən; ˈtəukən/ *n* **1** something which is not very large or very important in itself, but which represents something important 表誌; 象徵: *All the family wore black as a token of their grief.* 全家人都佩戴黑紗以示哀悼。| *a token payment* 象徵性的報酬 | *a token strike* 象徵性罷工 **2** a card or a piece of metal used instead of money, for a particular purpose〔用於某一用途的〕代幣: *a book token* 購書券 | *You need to buy a token for the car-wash.* 你應當為洗車服務買一張代價券。

told /told; təuld/ the past tense and past participle of TELL ☆ TELL 的過去式和過去分詞

tol·er·a·ble /ˈtɑlərəbl; ˈtɒlərəbəl/ *adj* fairly

good, or good enough to be tolerated 尚可的; 可忍受的: *a tolerable heat* 可以忍受的熱量 **–tolerably** *adv*

tol·er·ance /ˈtɑlərəns; ˈtɒlərəns/ *n* **1** [C;U] the ability to suffer pain or hardship without being damaged〔對於疼痛或艱苦的〕忍耐力: *He has no tolerance to cold.* 他一點也不畏寒。**2** [U] the quality of allowing people to behave in a way that may not please you, without becoming annoyed 容忍; 忍受 **3** [U] the quality of allowing different opinions to your own to be tolerated〔觀點上的〕寬容

tol·e·rate /ˈtɑləreɪt; ˈtɒləreɪt/ *v* **tolerated, tolerating** [T] to allow something you do not like to be practised or done 容忍〔某物〕: *I can't tolerate bad manners.* 我無法容忍惡劣的態度。–see 見 BEAR² (USAGE用法) **–tolerant** *adj*

tol·e·ra·tion /ˌtɑləˈreʃən; ˌtɒləˈreɪʃən/ *n* [U] the quality of allowing people to hold different opinions or beliefs or to behave in a way that may not please you, without becoming annoyed 容忍; 寬容: *religious toleration* 對於其他宗教的容忍

toll¹ /tol; təul/ *n* **1** a tax paid to use a road or bridge〔道路、橋樑的〕通行費, 使用費 **2** the death toll the number of people who have died in an accident 死亡人數: *The death toll has now risen to 20.* 死亡人數現已增加至二十。

toll² *v* [I;T] to ring slowly and repeatedly 緩慢而反覆地敲響: *The bells tolled to commemorate the tragedy.* 他們敲鐘哀悼這場悲劇。**–toll** *n* [sing]: *the toll of the bell* 鐘響

to·ma·to /təˈmeto; təˈmɑːtəu/ *n* **tomatoes 1** [C;U] a soft red fruit eaten as a vegetable 番茄, 西紅柿: *six ripe tomatoes* 六隻成熟的番茄 | *tomato soup* 番茄湯 –see picture on page 504 見 504 頁彩圖 **2** [C] the plant on which this fruit grows 番茄秧: *This is the month to plant out your tomatoes.* 這是個適合種植番茄的月份。

tomb /tum; tuːm/ *n* a grave, especially a large decorated one above ground 墳, 墓

tom·boy /ˈtɑm,bɔɪ; ˈtɒmbɔɪ/ *n* a young girl who likes to be rough and noisy 頑皮的小姑娘, 愛打打鬧鬧的女孩

tomb·stone /ˈtum,ston; ˈtuːmstəun/ *n* a stone put up over a grave bearing the name, date of birth and death of the dead person 墓碑

tom·cat /ˈtɑm,kæt; ˈtɒmkæt/ (also 又作 **tom** /tɑm; tɒm/ *infml*【非正式】) *n* a male cat 雄貓

tome /tom; təum/ *n lit* a large book【文】厚厚的書, 大部頭書

★**to·mor·row** /təˈmɔro; təˈmɒrəu/ *adv, n* **1** the day after today 明天: *Tomorrow is Wednesday.* 明天是星期三。| *I'm going to London tomorrow.* 我打算明天去倫敦。| *I'll see you tomorrow evening.* 我明天晚上見你。

2 the future 將來, 未來: *This could be the food crop of tomorrow.* 這也許會成為未來的糧食作物。

tom-tom /ˈtɒmˌtɒm; ˈtɒm tɒm/ *n* a long narrow drum, beaten with the hands〔狹長的〕手鼓

ton /tʌn; tʌn/ *n* **tons** *or* **ton 1** a unit for measuring weight equal in Britain to 2,240 pounds and in the US to 2,000 pounds 噸〔重量單位, 在英國一噸等於2,240磅, 在美國一噸等於2,000磅〕**2** (also 又作 **tonne, metric ton**) a unit for measuring weight equal to one thousand kilograms 噸, 公噸〔重量單位, 等於1000公斤〕**3** *infml* a very large quantity or weight〔非正式〕大量; 很重的: *I bought tons of food.* 我買了大量食物。| *This book weighs a ton!* 這本書重不得了! **4 come down on someone like a ton of bricks** to punish or speak to someone very severely 嚴厲懲罰〔斥責〕某人

☆tone¹ /tɒn; tʌn/ *n* **1** [C] the quality of sound of a musical instrument or singing voice〔樂器或嗓音的〕音質, 音色: *That piano has a beautiful tone.* 那架鋼琴的音色優美。**2** [C] a particular manner of expression 腔調, 語氣: *to speak in low tones* 用低沉的語氣説話 | *I don't like your tone of voice.* 我不喜歡你的腔調。**3** [C] a variety of a colour 色調, 色彩的層次: *a picture painted in tones of blue* 以各種藍色調繪成的畫 **4** [U] the general quality or mood of something 風氣; 氣氛: *the tone of our neighbourhood* 我們這一帶地區的風氣 **5** [C] a fixed separation between musical notes in a scale 音級, 音程: *There is a tone between B and C sharp.* B 調與升 C 調之間相隔一個音程。| *a semi-tone* 半音

tone² *v* **toned, toning**

tone sth ↔ **down** *phr v* [T] to reduce the violence or force of something 減弱〔某物〕, 緩和: *You must tone down your language; stop swearing.* 你説話必須客氣點, 不要咒罵別人。

tone in *phr v* [I] to match 與...相配: *Your hat and shoes tone in well with your dress.* 你的鞋帽與裙子很相配。

tone sbdy/sth ↔ **up** *phr v* [T] to make stronger and more healthy 使...更強健: *Swimming is the best way to tone up your body.* 游泳是最佳的健身方法。

tone-deaf /ˌ· ˈ·◂/ *adj* unable to tell the difference between musical notes 不能辨別音調的

tone·less /ˈtɒnlɪs; ˈtəʊnləs/ *adj* lacking colour and looking lifeless 單調的, 平板的; 無生氣的: *a toneless voice* 單調的聲音

tongs /tɒŋz; tɔŋz/ *n* [pl] an instrument with two movable arms, used for holding or lifting things 夾子, 鉗子: *She used the tongs to put the coal onto the fire.* 她用鉗子把煤夾到爐火上去。

☆tongue /tʌŋ; tʌŋ/ *n* **1** [C] the soft part inside your mouth, used for tasting and speaking 舌(頭) **2** [U] a cow's tongue, used as food 牛舌頭〔用作食物〕**3** [C] an object shaped like a tongue 舌狀物: *tongues of flame* 火舌 **4** [C] *lit* a spoken language〔文〕口語; 語言: *My native tongue is English.* 我的母語是英語。**5 hold your tongue** to be silent 緘口不言 **6 with your tongue in your cheek** *infml* saying something without meaning it seriously〔非正式〕言不由衷地

tongue-tied /ˈ··/ *adj* unable to speak freely because you are nervous〔由於緊張而〕説不出話的, 張口結舌的

tongue twist·er /ˈ·· ˌ··/ *n* a word or phrase difficult to say quickly 繞口令

ton·ic /ˈtɒnɪk; ˈtɒnɪk/ *n* anything which increases health or strength 增進健康的事物; 增強信心的東西: *Country air is a good tonic.* 鄉間的空氣對健康很有益。| *The doctor gave me a special tonic.* 醫生給了我一種特別的滋補藥。| *a tonic for depression* 治療抑鬱的藥 **–tonic** *adj*

tonic wa·ter /ˈ·· ˌ··/ (also 又作 **tonic**) [U] gassy water with a slightly bitter taste, often added to alcoholic drinks〔常加於酒中的〕奎寧水: *a gin and tonic* 杜松子酒加奎寧水

☆to·night /təˈnaɪt; təˈnaɪt/ *adv, n* this present night, or the night that follows today 今晚: *It's very cold tonight.* 今晚非常冷。| *I'll see you tonight.* 我今天晚上見你。

ton·nage /ˈtʌnɪdʒ; ˈtʌnɪdʒ/ *n* [U] the total weight or size of something expressed in TONS 總噸位

tonne /tʌn; tʌn/ *n* **tonnes** *or* **tonne** see 見 TON

ton·sil /ˈtɒnsl̩; ˈtɒnsəl/ *n* one of two small organs at the sides of your throat near the back of your tongue 扁桃體, 扁桃腺

ton·sil·li·tis, tonsilitis /ˌtɒnslˈaɪtɪs; ˌtɒnsl̩ˈlaɪtl̩s/ *n* [U] infection of the tonsils 扁桃體炎, 扁桃腺炎

☆☆too /tu; tuː/ *adv* **1** also 又, 也, 還: *She bought me a book and a box of chocolates too.* 她給我買了一本書, 還買了一盒巧克力。| *I was very excited and a bit nervous too.* 我非常激動, 也有點緊張。| *"I'm absolutely fed up." "I am too."* "我徹底厭了。""我也一樣。" **2** more than is needed or wanted 過於, 太: *You're going too fast.* 你走得太快了。| *This dress is too small for me.* 這件衣服我穿起來太小了。| *It's too cold to go swimming.* 天氣太冷, 不能去游泳。**3 not too** not very 不太: *He wasn't too pleased when I told him I was leaving.* 我告訴他我準備離開時, 他不太高興。

■ USAGE 用法: **1** Compare 比較 **too** and 和 **very**. **Too** usually suggests something bad or unsuitable ☆ **too** 通常暗示出不好或不合適的事物: *It's too* cold today 今天太冷了 (so I don't want to go out 所以我不打算外出). **Very** suggests that something is neither good nor bad ☆ **very** 則有不好不壞的含義: *It's **very** cold today* 今天很冷 (but I have a warm coat, so the temperature is no problem 但我有件保暖的外衣, 所以溫度低並不要緊). **2** We can use **too** before adjectives on their own ☆ 我們可以在形容詞前單獨使用 **too**: *This coffee is **too** sweet.* 這咖啡太甜了。But we cannot use **too** before an adjective followed by a noun; thus we cannot put **too** before *sweet* in *this sweet coffee.* Notice also the word order in these two sentences ☆ 但我們不能把 **too** 放在後面跟有名詞的形容詞前面, 所以在*this sweet coffee* 中, *sweet* 前面不能加上 **too**. 請注意下列兩句的詞序: *The day is **too** hot./It's **too** hot a day.* 天氣太熱了。

took /tʊk; tʊk/ the past tense of TAKE ☆ TAKE 的過去式

***tool** /tul; tuːl/ *n* **1** any instrument such as an axe, hammer, or spade for doing special jobs 工具; 用具 –see 見 MACHINE (USAGE 用法) **2** a person dishonestly used by someone for their own purposes 被利用的人: *The king was just a **tool** of the military government.* 那國王不過是軍政府的一個工具罷了。 **3** **down tools** *infml* to stop working as a protest 〔非正式〕罷工

toot /tuːt; tuːt/ *v* [I;T] to make a short warning sound with a horn or whistle 〔用喇叭或口哨〕發出短促的警報聲: *The car drivers **tooted** their horns.* 那些汽車司機都按喇叭以示警告。 **–toot** *n*

***tooth** /tuːθ; tuːθ/ *n* **teeth** /tiːθ; tiːθ/ **1** one of the small hard white bony objects in your mouth, used for biting and tearing food 牙齒 **2** **teeth** the pointed parts on a comb, SAW or ZIP 〔梳子、鋸子或拉鏈的〕齒 **3** **long in the tooth** *infml* old 〔非正式〕年老的 **4** **tooth and nail** fighting very violently 猛烈地, 激烈地

tooth·ache /ˈtuːθˌek; ˈtuːθ-eɪk/ *n* [C;U] a pain in a tooth 牙痛 –see 見 ACHE² (USAGE 用法)

tooth·brush /ˈtuːθˌbrʌʃ; ˈtuːθbrʌʃ/ *n* a small brush used for cleaning your teeth 牙刷

tooth·paste /ˈtuːθˌpest; ˈtuːθpeɪst/ *n* [U] a substance used for cleaning your teeth 牙膏

tooth·pick /ˈtuːθˌpɪk; ˈtuːθˌpɪk/ *n* a small pointed piece of wood used for removing food stuck between your teeth 牙籤

***top¹** /tɑp; tɒp/ *n* **1** the highest or upper part of something 頂(部), 上端: *at the top of the page* 在這頁的上端 | *They live on the top floor.* 他們住在頂樓。 | *the top of my desk* 我的書桌上面 | *the table top* 桌面 **2** **the top** the best or most important position 最佳位置; 最重要位置: *He started life at the bottom and worked his way to the top.* 他從最低層幹起, 然後一步步升到了最高層。 –compare 比較 BOTTOM **3** a cover 蓋子: *I can't unscrew the top of this bottle.* 我擰不開這個瓶蓋。 | *I wish you'd put the top back on the toothpaste.* 我希望你能把牙膏蓋蓋好。 **4** a piece of clothing that you wear on the upper part of your body 上衣: *a skirt with a matching top* 一條配有上衣的裙子 **5** a child's toy that spins and balances on its point 〔作玩具的〕陀螺 **6** **at the top of your voice** as loudly as possible 放聲地, 扯着喉嚨 **7** **at top speed** very fast 以最高速度 **8** **get on top of you** *infml* to be too much for you 〔非正式〕〔太多〕使受不了: *This work is getting on top of me.* 這項工作使我越來越受不了。 **9** **on top** over or above 在上面: *a cake with cream on top* 表面有奶油的蛋糕 **10** **on top of** in addition to 此外; 另外: *She's got all this extra work to do. And, on top of that, her mother's ill.* 她有這麼多額外的工作要做。此外, 她的母親還病了。 | *On top of your basic pension you'll get a disability allowance.* 你除了基本養老金以外, 還可以得到傷殘津貼。

***top²** *v* **-pp-** [T] **1** to form or be a top for something 形成頂端; 成為上部: *a cake topped with cream* 表面澆了奶油的蛋糕 **2** to be higher, better, or more than something 高於; 好於; 多於〔某物〕: *Their profits have topped ours this year.* 今年他們的利潤比我們的高。 **3** **top the bill** to be the chief actor or actress in a play 領銜主演

top sthg ↔ **up** *phr v* [T] **1** to fill up a partly empty container 注滿〔容器〕: *We need to top the car up with petrol.* 我們給汽車注滿汽油。 | *Shall I top your glass up for you?* 我給你把玻璃杯倒滿好嗎? **2** to bring an amount of money up to an acceptable level 使〔金錢數量〕達到可以接受的水準: *The director's salary is topped up by a share in the company's profits.* 董事的薪金由公司利潤分成補足。

top³ *adj* **1** at the top 頂端的; 最高的: *the top step* 最高的梯級 **2** best 最好的: *Fred is our top man.* 弗雷德是我們當中最好的一個。 | *top of the class* 班中的頂尖份子

to·paz /ˈtopæz; ˈtəʊpæz/ *n* [C;U] a precious stone cut from a transparent yellowish mineral 黃玉(礦)

top·coat /ˈtɑpˌkot; ˈtɒpkəʊt/ *n* **1** a long, warm coat worn over other clothes in cold weather 外套 **2** **the topcoat** the last covering of paint to be put on a surface 表層油漆, 外塗(保護)層

top dog /ˌ · ˈ ·/ *n infml* the person in the most important position 〔非正式〕領導人, 首領

top hat /ˌ · ˈ ·/ *n* a man's tall silk hat worn only on formal occasions 〔男士在正式場合戴的〕高頂禮帽

top-heav-y /ˌ·ˈ···◂/ *adj* not properly balanced because there is too much weight at the top 頭重腳輕的

⋆**top-ic** /ˈtɑpɪk; ˈtɔpɪk/ *n* a subject for conversation, talk, or writing〔談話、演講或文章的〕題目，論題，話題

top-ic-al /ˈtɑpɪkl; ˈtɔpɪkəl/ *adj* related to a subject of present interest 熱門話題的: *Recent events have made this film very topical.* 近來發生的事情使這部影片成為很熱門的話題。 –**topically** /-klɪ; -klɪ/ *adv*

top-less /ˈtɑplɪs; ˈtɔpləs/ *adj* with the upper part of the body, including the breasts, bare (used of a woman or a piece of clothing) 上身裸露的，無上裝的: *a topless swimsuit* 袒胸泳裝 | *a topless dancer* 無上裝舞蹈員

top-most /ˈtɑpˌmost; ˈtɔpməʊst/ *adj* [only before a noun 只用於名詞前] highest 最高的; 頂端的: *the topmost branches of the old oak tree* 老橡樹上最高的那些樹枝

to-pog-ra-phy /toˈpɑgrəfɪ; təˈpɔgrəfɪ/ *n* [U] the science of describing or mapping the character of a place, especially the shape and height of the land 地形學 –**topographical** /ˌtɑpəˈgræfɪkl; ˌtɔpəˈgræfɪkəl/ *adj*

top-ping /ˈtɑpɪŋ; ˈtɔpɪŋ/ *n* [C;U] something put on top of food to make it look or taste nicer〔食物表面的〕配料，澆料: *cream topping* 表層奶油

top-ple /ˈtɑpl; ˈtɔpəl/ *v* **toppled, toppling** **1** [I] to become unsteady and fall over 倒下, 倒塌: *She toppled from the ladder.* 她從梯子上摔了下來。 **2** [I;T] to lose power, or to make someone lose their power (使)失去權力: *a scandal that could topple the government* 使政府垮台的醜聞

topple over *phr v* [I] to become unsteady and fall over 倒下, 倒塌: *Watch out! The bricks nearly toppled over.* 小心! 磚頭快塌下來了。

top-se-cret /ˌ·ˈ···◂/ *adj* to be kept very secret 絕密的: *top-secret military information* 絕密的軍事情報

top-sy-tur-vy /ˌtɑpsɪˈtɜvɪ; ˌtɔpsɪˈtɜːvɪ/ *adj, adv* in a state of confusion 混亂的[地]

torch /tɔrtʃ; tɔːtʃ/ *n* **1** *BrE* a small electric light that you carry in your hand〔英式〕手電筒 –see picture on page 958 見 958 頁彩圖 **2** a mass of burning material tied to a stick and carried to give light 火炬 **3** the usual American word for〔美式〕= BLOW-LAMP

torch-light /ˈtɔrtʃˌlaɪt; ˈtɔːtʃlaɪt/ *n* [U] light produced by torches 手電筒光; 火炬光: *a torchlight procession* 火炬遊行

tore /tɔr; tɔːʳ/ the past tense of TEAR ☆ TEAR 的過去式

tor-ment¹ /ˈtɔrmɛnt; ˈtɔːment/ *n* **1** [C;U] very great pain or suffering 巨大的痛苦, 折磨: *He suffered torments.* 他遭受了巨大的痛苦。 **2** [C] someone or something that causes this 引起巨大痛苦的人或物: *That child is a torment to his parents.* 那個孩子令他的父母苦惱不堪。

tor-ment² /tɔrˈmɛnt; tɔːˈment/ *v* [T] to make someone suffer pain or annoyance 折磨〔某人〕, 使痛苦: *The boy tormented his little sister.* 那個男孩折磨他的小妹妹。 –**tormentor** *n*

torn /tɔrn; tɔːn/ the past participle of TEAR ☆TEAR 的過去分詞

tor-na-do /tɔrˈnedo; tɔːˈneɪdəʊ/ *n* **tornadoes** *or* **tornados** a very violent wind that spins at great speed 龍捲風

tor-pe-do /tɔrˈpido; tɔːˈpiːdəʊ/ *n* **torpedoes** a bomb shaped like a tube that travels under the sea and is used to destroy ships 魚雷 –**torpedo** *v* [T]: *We torpedoed the enemy ships.* 我們用魚雷擊中了敵艦。

tor-pid /ˈtɔrpɪd; ˈtɔːpɪd/ *adj fml* moving slowly〔正式〕遲緩的, 遲鈍的: *a torpid mind* 遲鈍的腦子 –**torpor** /ˈtɔrpə; ˈtɔːpəʳ/ *n* [U]

tor-rent /ˈtɔrənt; ˈtɔrənt/ **1** a violently rushing stream 急流, 湍流: *The rain fell in torrents.* 大雨傾盆而下。 | *A torrent of water swept down the valley.* 急流自山谷奔騰而下。 **2** a large amount of unpleasant language 大量的難聽話: *a torrent of abuse* 罵不絕口 –**torrential** /təˈrɛnʃəl; tɒˈrenʃəl/ *adj: torrential rain* 傾盆大雨

tor-rid /ˈtɔrɪd; ˈtɒrɪd/ *adj lit*〔文〕**1** very hot 灼熱的, 炎熱的: *the torrid desert sun* 沙漠中灼熱的太陽 **2** concerning strong uncontrolled feelings 感情熾烈的: *a torrid story of sex and violence* 赤裸裸地描寫性與暴力的故事

tor-so /ˈtɔrso; ˈtɔːsəʊ/ *n* the human body without the head and limbs 人體軀幹〔不包括頭與四肢〕

tor-toise /ˈtɔrtəs; ˈtɔːtəs/ *n* a slow-moving land animal with a hard shell (陸)龜

tor-toise-shell /ˈtɔrtəsˌʃɛl; ˈtɔːtəʃel/ *n* [U] the hard brown and yellow shell of the tortoise or TURTLE, used for making combs and ornaments 龜甲, 玳瑁殼〔用於製成梳子或裝飾品〕

tor-tu-ous /ˈtɔrtʃuəs; ˈtɔːtʃuəs/ *adj* **1** twisted and winding 彎曲的, 曲折的: *a tortuous mountain road* 蜿蜒的山路 **2** not simple or direct 間接的, 轉彎抹角的: *They found out the truth by tortuous means.* 他們通過間接的手段獲悉了實情。

tor-ture¹ /ˈtɔrtʃə; ˈtɔːtʃəʳ/ *n* **1** [U] the act of causing severe pain, done out of cruelty or to find out information 嚴刑拷問; 酷刑; 刑訊: *instruments of torture* 刑具 **2** [C;U] severe pain or suffering 折磨: *the tortures of jealousy* 嫉妒引起的痛苦

torture² *v* **tortured, torturing** [T] to cause great pain to a person or animal out of cruelty, or as a punishment 施以酷刑; 折磨: *The prisoner was tortured to make him admit to the crime.* 他們對囚犯施以酷刑, 逼他認

T

罪。 **–torturer** *n*

To·ry /ˈtɔrɪ; ˈtɔːri/ *n, adj* **Tories** a member of the British CONSERVATIVE Party 英國保守黨黨員: *The Tories never supported the bill.* 保守黨黨員從不贊成此議案。 **–Tory** *adj:* *Tory principles* 英國保守黨的各項(政治)原則

toss¹ /tɔs; tɒs/ *v* **1** [T+adv/prep] to throw something 扔, 擲, 拋: *He tossed the ball to me.* 他把球扔給我。 **2** [I;T] to move about rapidly or make something move rapidly (使)搖擺; (使)顛簸: *The boat was tossed about in the stormy sea.* 小船在波濤洶湧的大海中顛簸着。 | *He tossed about in his sleep.* 他翻來覆去睡不着。 | *The horse tossed its head back.* 那匹馬猛地把頭往後一仰。 **3** [T] to mix food lightly so as to cover it in sauce 輕輕地攪拌〔食品〕: *Toss the salad in the dressing* 把沙拉在佐料中攪拌一下。 **4** [I; T] to throw a coin to decide something according to which side lands face upwards 抛硬幣〔以決定某事〕: *There's only one cake and two of us, so let's toss for it.* 我們兩個人只有一塊蛋糕, 那麼就抛硬幣決定讓誰吃。

toss sthg ↔ **off** *phr v* [T] to produce something quickly with little effort 輕而易舉地完成〔某物〕: *She tossed off a few ideas for advertising the new product.* 她很輕易地就想出了幾個給新產品做廣告的主意。

toss² *n* **1** a sudden backward movement 突然的後仰: *She gave a quick toss of her head.* 她的頭突然迅速往後一仰。 **2 the toss** an act of tossing a coin to decide something 抛硬幣〔決定某事〕: *Our team won the toss, so we play first.* 我們隊抛硬幣贏了, 因此由我們隊開球。

toss-up /ˈ··/ *n* [sing] *infml* an even chance 〔非正式〕均等的機會: *It's a toss-up between the two of them as to who will get the job.* 他們兩個人得到那份工作的機會均等。

tot¹ /tɔt; tɒt/ *n* **1** a very small child 小娃娃: *a tiny tot* 小不點兒 **2** a small amount of a strong alcoholic drink 少量(烈酒): *a tot of rum* 一點點朗姆酒

tot² *v*

tot sthg ↔ **up** *phr v* [T] to add up 把…加起來: *Now tot up the subtotals.* 現在把各部分總和加起來。

★to·tal¹ /ˈtɔtl; ˈtəʊtl/ *adj* complete 總共的; 完全的: *the total population of Britain* 英國的人口總數 | *total silence* 萬籟俱寂 **–totally** *adv: I totally agree with you.* 我完全同意你的意見。

★total² *n* **1** a number or quantity obtained by adding other amounts together 總數, 總額: *Add these numbers together and tell me the total.* 把這些數字加起來, 然後把總和告訴我。 | *A total of two hundred people visited the castle.* 共有二百人參觀了城堡。 **2 in total** as a total 總計, 合計: *In total, there were two hundred visitors.* 參觀者總計有二百人。

total³ *v* **-ll-** (**-l-** *AmE* 〔美式〕) [T] to add up to a particular amount 總計為, 合計是: *Your*

debts total one thousand pounds. 你的債務總計為一千英鎊。

to·tal·i·tar·i·an /ˌtəʊˌtæləˈtɛrɪən; təʊˌtælɪˈtɛəriən/ *adj* based on a political system in which one political group controls everything and does not allow opposition parties to exist 極權主義的 **–totalitarianism** *n* [U]

to·tal·i·ty /təʊˈtæləti; təʊˈtælɪti/ *n* [U] *fml* completeness 〔正式〕完全; 整體, 全部

tot·ter /ˈtɔtə; ˈtɒtə/ *v* [I+adv/prep] to move or walk in an unsteady way 搖搖晃晃; 蹣跚: *The old lady tottered down the stairs.* 老婦人搖搖晃晃地走下樓梯。

tot·ter·y /ˈtɔtəri; ˈtɒtəri/ *adj* unsteady and shaky 蹣跚的; 不穩的

tou·can /ˈtuːkæn; ˈtuːkən/ *n* a brightly-coloured tropical bird with a large beak 鵎鵼〔熱帶的一種羽毛豔麗的巨喙鳥〕

★touch¹ /tʌtʃ; tʌtʃ/ *v* **1** [I;T] to feel something with your hands or another part of your body 觸摸, 碰: *Visitors are asked not to touch the paintings.* 參觀者請勿觸摸那些繪畫作品。 | *You can look, but don't touch.* 你可以看, 但不許觸摸。 **2** [I;T] to be right next to something with no space between 觸及, 貼到; 接觸: *The branches were hanging down and touching the water.* 樹枝低垂, 貼到了水面。 | *We were standing close together with our shoulders touching.* 我們肩靠肩緊緊地站在一起。 **3** [T] to eat, drink, or take action with something 吃〔飲〕〔某物〕; 接觸〔某事物〕: *I never touch alcohol.* 我從不喝酒。 | *I haven't touched my work all weekend.* 整個週末我連碰也沒碰我的工作。 **4** [T] to make you feel sad 令〔人〕感動, 觸動: *a very touching story* 非常動人的故事 **5** [T] to make you feel grateful 令〔人〕感激: *I was very touched by her kindness.* 她親切的態度令我非常感激。 **6 touch and go** uncertain as to whether something will succeed or not 無把握的: *The doctors have said it's touch and go whether she'll live.* 醫生都說不能肯定她是否能活下去。 **7 touch wood** a phrase you use when you touch something made of wood in order to avoid bad luck 摸摸木頭以希望無災無難〔用於為避免惡運〕: *I haven't been ill at all this winter — touch wood.* 我今年整個冬天都未生病 — 希望好運常在。

touch down *phr v* [I] **1** (of a plane) to land 〔飛機〕着陸, 降落 **2** to press the ball down and get a point in a game of RUGBY 〔橄欖球賽中〕觸地得分

touch on sthg *phr v* [T] to mention something in just a few words 提及〔某事〕: *He only touched on the subject of water pollution.* 他只是略微提了一下水污染的事情。

touch sthg ↔ **up** *phr v* [T] to improve something by making small changes or additions 修改, 修飾〔某事物〕

★touch² *n* **1** [U] the sense by which you know whether something is hard, smooth, rough, hot, etc 觸覺: *Its fur was soft to the touch.* 牠的皮毛摸起來很柔軟。 **2** [C] an act of touching something 觸摸: *He felt the touch of her hand on his shoulder.* 他感覺到她的手摸了一下他的肩膀。 **3 a touch** a small amount of something 少量, 些微 **4** [C] a small detail that improves something 修飾, 潤色: *I'm just putting the finishing touches to the picture.* 我現在不過是在給這幅畫作最後修飾。 **5** [sing] someone's way of doing something, especially when it shows skill 做事的方式, 手法, 技巧〔尤指顯示技巧時〕: *I seem to be losing my touch.* 我的技巧似乎在日益生疏起來。 **6 get in touch with someone** to write to someone or telephone them 與某人聯繫: *I'm trying to get in touch with my brother.* 我正在設法與我的兄弟取得聯繫。 **7 in touch** speaking or writing to someone regularly 保持聯繫: *Are you still in touch with John?* 你還有跟約翰保持聯繫嗎? | *We must keep in touch.* 我們必須保持聯繫。 **8 in touch with something** knowing the latest information about a subject 掌握某學科的最新資料: *I try to keep in touch with what's going on in Linguistics.* 我力圖掌握語言學方面的最新進展。 [RELATED PHRASE 相關詞組 **out of touch with something**] **9 lose touch** to stop seeing someone, writing to them or telephoning them 失去聯繫: *I lost touch with her years ago.* 我多年以前就跟她失去了聯繫。

touch-and-go /ˌ···ˈ·◂/ *adj* risky and with an uncertain result 冒險的; 無把握的: *It was touch-and-go whether he would get there in time.* 他是否會及時趕到那裡是沒有把握的。

touched /tʌtʃt; tʌtʃt/ *adj* [only after a noun 只用於名詞後] **1** feeling grateful 感激的; 受感動的: *I was very touched by their present.* 我很感激他們送我禮物。 **2** *infml* slightly mad 〔非正式〕神經有點不正常的

touch·stone /ˈtʌtʃˌston; ˈtʌtʃstəʊn/ *n* something used as a test or standard 試金石; (檢驗)標準

touch·y /ˈtʌtʃi; ˈtʌtʃi/ *adj* easily offended and over-sensitive 易怒的; 過敏的

***tough¹** /tʌf; tʌf/ *adj* **1** strong and not easily weakened 強壯的, 強健的: *Only tough breeds of sheep can live in the mountains.* 只有強壯品種的羊才能在山區生存。 | *He won't give up, he's really tough.* 他不會放棄; 他真正能刻苦耐勞 **2** difficult to cut or eat 割不開的; 咬不動的: *tough meat* 老得咬不動的肉 **3** difficult to do and demanding effort 困難的, 費力的: *a tough lesson* 難應付的一課 **4** rough and hard 粗暴的; 強硬的: *The government will get tough with people who avoid paying taxes.* 政府將對逃稅的人採取強硬措施。 | *a tough criminal* 狂暴的罪犯 **5** *infml* unfortunate 〔非正式〕不幸的: *Tough luck!* 真倒霉! | *Life is tough on single parents.* 對於單身父母來講, 生活確是艱難。 **–toughness** *n* [U]

tough² *n infml* a rough, violent person such as a criminal 〔非正式〕流氓, 惡棍

tough·en /ˈtʌfn; ˈtʌfən/ *v* [T] to make someone or something stronger 使〔某人〕更堅強; 使〔某物〕更堅韌: *toughened steel* 韌鋼 | *The experiences of the last few months had toughened her.* 過去數月來的經歷使她變得堅強起來。

tou·pee /tuˈpe; ˈtuːpeɪ/ *n* a piece of false hair that fits over a place on a man's head where his hair no longer grows (男用)假髮

***tour¹** /tur; tʊəʳ/ *n* **1** a journey during which several places are visited 旅遊, 旅行: *a tour round Europe* 歐洲漫遊 **2 on tour** travelling to a lot of different places 巡迴〔到許多地方〕: *The National Theatre is on tour in the North.* 國家劇團正在北方巡迴演出。 **3** a short trip to or through a place 參觀, 遊覽: *We went on a guided tour round the castle.* 我們在嚮導的帶領下參觀了城堡。 **4** a period of duty at a single place, especially abroad 公差; 海外服務期: *a two-year tour in Germany* 駐德國的兩年任期

tour² *v* [I;T] to travel around a particular area 旅遊, 觀光: *We're touring Italy for our holidays.* 我們準備去意大利觀光度假。 | *a touring holiday* 旅遊度假

tour de force /ˌtʊrdəˈfɔːrs; ˌtʊə də ˈfɔːs/ *n fml* a show of strength or skill 〔正式〕絕技, 拿手好戲

tour·is·m /ˈtʊrɪzm; ˈtʊərɪzəm/ *n* [U] **1** the business of providing holidays for tourists 旅遊業 **2** travelling for pleasure 旅遊, 觀光

***tour·ist** /ˈtʊrɪst; ˈtʊərˌɪst/ *n* a person travelling for pleasure 旅行者, 遊客, 觀光客: *Oxford is full of tourists in summer.* 到了夏季, 牛津到處都是觀光客。 | *I'm not a tourist, I live here!* 我不是遊客, 我是住在這裡的!

tour·na·ment /ˈtɜːnəmənt; ˈtʊənəmənt/ *n* a number of competitions between players, played until the most skilful wins 錦標賽, 聯賽: *a tennis tournament* 網球錦標賽 | *a chess tournament* 國際象棋錦標賽

tour·ni·quet /ˈtʊrnɪˌket; ˈtʊəniket/ *n* a band of cloth or something soft, twisted tightly round a limb to stop it bleeding 止血帶

tou·sle /ˈtaʊzl; ˈtaʊzəl/ *v* **tousled, tousling** [T] to make someone's hair untidy 弄亂〔某人的頭髮〕

tout /taʊt; taʊt/ *v* [I] to try to persuade people to buy or use your goods or services 兜售, 推銷: *touting for business* 拉生意 **–tout** *n*: *a ticket tout* 賣黃牛票者, 票販子

tow¹ /to; təʊ/ *v* [T] to pull a vehicle along by a rope or chain 拖, 拉〔車輛〕

tow² *n* **1 on tow** being towed 被拖的: *a vehicle on tow* 被拖着走的一輛車 **2 in tow** *infml* following closely behind 〔非正式〕緊跟着: *She arrived with her children in tow.* 她的孩子們緊跟在她後面一起到達。

***to·wards** /tordz; təˈwɔːdz/ *prep* (also 又作 **toward** *AmE* 〔美式〕) **1** in the direction of something 朝〔某個〕方向:

She walked towards the door. 她朝着門口走去。| *He was standing with his back towards me.* 他背對着我站着。| *We are heading towards an economic crisis.* 我們正逐步走向經濟危機。–see picture on page 764 見 764 頁彩圖 **2** not long before a particular time 接近，將近，快要到〔某一時間的〕: *Towards the end of the afternoon it began to rain.* 近傍晚時開始下雨了。**3** in relation to 關於；對於: *the government's attitude towards education* 政府對於教育的態度 | *What are his feelings towards you?* 他對你的感覺如何？ **4** to pay for some of the cost of something 用於；為了: *We save £20 a week towards our holiday.* 我們每週節省二十英鎊準備度假用。

tow·el¹ /taul; ˈtauəl/ *n* a piece of cloth or paper used for drying wet things 毛巾；紙巾: *a bath towel* 浴巾 | *paper towels* 紙巾 | *a linen tea towel* 亞麻布茶巾

towel² *v* **-ll- (-l-** *AmE* 【美式】) [T] to rub or dry something with a towel 用〔毛巾或紙巾〕擦拭〔擦乾〕

tow·el·ling /ˈtauəlɪŋ; ˈtauəlɪŋ/ *n* [U] (**toweling** *AmE* 【美式】) thick, soft cloth, used for making towels 毛巾布: *a towelling bath robe* 毛巾布浴袍

★**tow·er¹** /ˈtauə; ˈtauəʳ/ *n* **1** a tall, narrow building standing alone or forming part of another building 塔；塔樓: *the Tower of London* 倫敦塔 | *the Eiffel Tower* 艾菲爾鐵塔 **2** a tower of strength a person who gives help and encouragement 可提供幫助和鼓勵的人；靠山

tow·er² *v* [I;+adv/prep] to be very tall, especially in relation to the surroundings 高聳，屹立: *The mountains towered over the town in the valley* 高山聳立在山谷中的小鎮邊上。

tower block /ˈ·· ·/ *n* a tall building containing flats or offices 高層建築物

★**town** /taun taun/ *n* **1** [C] a place with many buildings where people live and work; a town is larger than a village, but smaller than a city 市鎮，城鎮 –see picture on page 470 見 470 頁彩圖 **2** [U] the business or shopping centre of such a place 商業區；市區: *We went to town to do some shopping today.* 我們今天到市區裡去購物。**3** [C+sing/pl verb] the people who live in a town 鎮民，市鎮居民: *The whole town is in agreement about the plan.* 全鎮居民都同意這項計劃。**4** [U] life in towns and cities in general 都市生活: *I like the town better than the country.* 我喜歡都市生活多於鄉村生活。| *to leave the country for the town* 離開鄉下到城裡去 **5** go to town *infml* to act freely especially by spending a lot of money 【非正式】揮金如土 **6** go out on the town *infml* to enjoy yourself in town, especially at night 【非正式】〔尤指晚上〕到城內尋歡作樂

town coun·cil /ˌ· ˈ··/ *n* [+sing/pl verb] *BrE* the people elected to govern a town 【美式】

市議會: *The town council does not have support for this policy.* 市議會不支持這項政策。

town hall /ˌ· ˈ·/ *n* the building used for local government offices and public meetings 市政廳

town·ship /ˈtaunʃɪp; ˈtaunʃɪp/ *n* in South Africa, a place where non-white citizens live 〔南非的〕有色人種居住區

towns·peo·ple /ˈtaunz͵pipl; ˈtaunz͵piːpəl/ *n* **the townspeople** the people who live in a town 市鎮居民

tow·path /ˈto͵paθ; ˈtoʊpə͵θ /-͵pæθ; -paːθ/ *n* **towpaths** /-͵pæðz; -paːðz/ a path along the side of a river or CANAL where people can walk 〔拉船用的〕縴道

tow rope /ˈ· ·/ *n* a rope used for pulling vehicles 〔用於拖車輛的〕拖繩，拖纜

tox·ic /ˈtɒksɪk; ˈtɒksɪk/ *adj fml* poisonous 【正式】有毒的: *a toxic drug* 毒藥 | *toxic waste from a factory* 工廠排出的有毒廢物 – **toxicity** /-ˈsɪsətɪ; -ˈsɪs͵ti/ *n* [U]

tox·i·col·o·gy /͵tɒksɪˈkɒlədʒɪ; ͵tɒksɪˈkɒlədʒi/ *n* [U] the scientific and medical study of poisons 毒理學 –**toxicologist** *n*

tox·in /ˈtɒksɪn; ˈtɒks͵n/ *n* a poison produced by bacteria in a plant or animal body 〔植物或動物體內細菌產生的〕毒素

toy¹ /tɔɪ; tɔɪ/ *n* an object for children to play with 玩具: *Children love getting new toys to play with.* 孩子們喜歡玩新的玩具。| *a toy shop* 玩具店

toy² *adj* [only before a noun 只用於名詞前] **1** used to play with 用作玩耍的，作玩具的: *a toy soldier* 玩具兵 | *a toy clock* 玩具鐘 **2** smaller than the usual kind (used of dogs) 體型小的〔指狗〕，供人玩賞的: *a toy poodle* 小小的寵物貴賓狗

toy³ *v*

toy with sthg *phr v* [T] **1** to play with something without any purpose 耍弄〔某物〕: *a child toying with its food* 在擺弄食物的小孩 **2** to be considering something, but not very seriously 不認真地考慮: *She toyed with the idea of changing her job.* 她不很認真地想要換個工作。

trace¹ /tres; treɪs/ *v* **traced, tracing** [T] **1** to look for and find something 尋找，追尋〔某物〕，追蹤，跟蹤 **to**: *The criminal was traced to London.* 該罪犯被追蹤，終於發現其在倫敦。| *I can't trace the letter you sent me.* 我找不到你寄給我的那封信。**2** to copy the lines on a drawing, using transparent paper 〔用透明紙張〕描摹 **3** to discover and describe the history or development of something 探索；追溯〔某物的歷史或發展〕: *It was a most interesting talk tracing the development of the Labour movement.* 這個演講追溯工人運動的發展，非常有趣。

trace² *n* **1** [C;U] a mark or sign showing the former presence or passing of something or someone 蹤跡；行蹤；遺跡: *The police found no trace* **of** *the man.* 警方找不到那個

人的行蹤。 | *lost without trace* 消失得無影無蹤 **2** [C] a very small amount of something 微量; 痕跡: *Traces of poison were found in the dead man's blood.* 在死者的血液裡發現了微量的毒素。

trac·ing /'treɪsɪŋ; 'treɪsɪŋ/ *n* a copy of a map or drawing made by tracing 摹圖, 描圖

★**track**¹ /træk; træk/ *n* **1** a rough path or road 小道, 小徑: *a farm track* 農場的小道 –see 見 WAY¹ (USAGE 用法) **2 off the beaten track** quiet and not near people or other buildings 偏僻的, 人跡罕至的: *It's difficult to find them — they live quite off the beaten track.* 很難找到他們的——因為他們住得很偏僻。 **3** a line or number of marks left by a person, animal or vehicle 足跡; 蹤跡; 軌跡: *The trapper followed the fox's tracks.* 獵人循着狐狸的足跡向前走。 | *tyre tracks* 車輪的痕跡 **4 to be on someone's track** to be following and trying to catch someone 追捕某人: *The police are on his track and hope to catch him soon.* 警方正在對他進行追捕, 希望很快便能抓到他。 **5** an area especially prepared for running or racing [比賽用的]跑道: *track and field events* 田徑項目 **6** the metal lines on which a train runs [火車的]鐵軌: *Something had been thrown onto the track.* 有甚麼東西被扔在鐵軌上了。 | *railway tracks* 火車軌軌 –see picture on page 991 見 991 頁彩圖 **7** one of the songs or pieces of music on a record or TAPE [唱片或磁帶中的]一首歌曲: *I love the last track on this album.* 我喜歡這張唱片中最後的一首歌。 **8 be on the right track** to be thinking in the right way 思考的方向正確 [RELATED PHRASE 相關詞組 **be on the wrong track**] **9 cover/hide your tracks** not to leave signs of where you have been and what you have been doing 隱匿行跡; 掩蓋所做之事 **10 have a one track mind** *infml* to give all your attention to one thing only [非正式] 只思考一樣東西 **11 keep track of sbdy/sthg** to be sure that you know what is happening or where someone is 掌握某人的行蹤; 跟上某事的進展 [RELATED PHRASE 相關詞組 **lose track of sbdy/sthg**] **12 stop (dead) in your tracks** to stop suddenly 突然停止

track² *v* [T] to follow the track of something or someone in order to catch them 追蹤, 跟蹤; 追捕 –**tracker** *n*: *police tracker dogs* 警方的搜索警犬

    track sbdy/sthg ↔ **down** *phr v* [T] to find someone or something by hunting or searching 追捕到; 搜尋到: *I finally tracked him down in Paris.* 我終於在巴黎找到了他。

track and field /ˌ··· '··/ *n* [sing] the usual American word for [美式]= ATHLETICS

track·suit /'træk,suːt; 'træksuːt/ *n* a warm loose-fitting suit worn for informal occasions or when training for sport [非正式場合穿的]寬大的衣服; [運動員訓練時所穿的]運動服 –see picture on page 210 見 210 頁彩圖

tract /trækt; trækt/ *n* **1** *fml* a short article, especially about a religious, political, or moral subject [正式][尤指有關宗教、政治或道德方面的]短文 **2** a wide stretch of land 一大片土地: *immense tracts of open wasteland* 一望無際的荒地 **3** *tech* a system of related organs in your body with one purpose [術語][身體的](器官)系統: *the digestive tract* 消化系統

traction en·gine /'trækʃən ˌendʒən; 'trækʃən ˌendʒɪn/ *n* a large vehicle, used in the past for pulling heavy loads [昔時的]牽引機車

trac·tor /'træktə; 'træktə/ *n* a motor vehicle with large wheels and thick tyres, used for pulling farm machinery or other heavy objects 拖拉機

★**trade**¹ /tred; treɪd/ *n* **1** [U] the buying and selling of goods 買賣, 貿易: *a trade agreement between England and France* 英法之間的貿易協定 | *He made his money in trade.* 他通過做買賣掙錢。 **2** the trade a particular business or industry 行業: *the cotton trade* 棉花業 | *He's in the tourist trade.* 他從事旅遊業。 –see 見 JOB (USAGE 用法) **3** [C] a job, especially one needing special skills [尤指需要專門技巧的]職業, 手藝: *He insisted that his son should learn a trade.* 他堅持要讓他的兒子學一門手藝。 **4 do a good trade, do a roaring trade** carry out a successful business 生意興隆: *The shop does a good trade on Saturdays.* 那商店在星期六的生意不錯。

★**trade**² *v* **traded, trading 1** [I] to carry on trade 做生意, 做買賣: *He trades in meat.* 他做肉類的生意。 | *Britain is now trading with Eastern Europe.* 英國現正在與東歐進行貿易往來。 **2** [T] to buy, sell, or exchange 買; 賣; 用…交換(貨物): *They traded their clothes for food.* 他們用衣服換取食品。

    trade sthg ↔ **in** *phr v* [T] to give something in part payment for something new 折價換購: *He traded his old car in for a new one.* 他把舊車折價換購了一輛新車。 –**trade-in** /'··/ *n*

trade·mark /'tred,mɑrk; 'treɪdmɑːk/ *n* **1** a special mark on a product to show that it is made by a particular producer (註冊)商標 **2** a thing that is typical of a person or company [表現出人或公司的]特徵, 特點

trad·er /'tredə; 'treɪdə/ *n* a person who buys and sells goods 商人, 經商者

trades·man /'tredzmən; 'treɪdzmən/ *n* **tradesmen** /-mən; -mən/ a person who buys and sells goods, especially a shopkeeper 商人; 店主

trade un·i·on /ˌ· '···/ *n* (also 又作 **trades union**) an organization of workers set up to represent their interests and to deal as a group with the employers 工會 –**trade unionism** *n* [U] –**trade unionist** *n*

trade wind /ˈ···/ *n* a tropical wind 信風, 貿易風〔一種熱帶風〕

tra·di·tion /trəˈdɪʃən; trəˈdɪʃən/ *n* **1** [U] the passing down of opinions, beliefs, practices, and customs from the past to the present〔觀點、信念、習慣、風俗等的〕世代相傳, 因襲: *respect for tradition* 尊重習俗 **2** [C] an opinion, belief, or custom passed down in this way 傳統; 習慣: *It is a tradition that women get married in long white dresses.* 女人結婚時穿白色長裙是一種傳統風俗。 **–traditional** *adj*: *the traditional English breakfast* 傳統的英式早餐 **–traditionally** *adv*

traf·fic¹ /ˈtræfɪk; ˈtræfɪk/ *n* [U] **1** all the vehicles moving in a place 交通: *rush-hour traffic* 繁忙時間的交通 | *air traffic control* 空中交通管制 **2** buying and selling goods illegally 非法買賣〔交易〕: *the traffic in endangered species* 非法買賣瀕臨滅絕的動物 | *the traffic in cocaine* 販賣可卡因

traffic² *v* **trafficked, trafficking**

　　traffic in sth *phr v* [T] to carry on trade of an unlawful kind 非法買賣: *He was found to be trafficking in stolen goods.* 他被人發現在販賣贓物。 **–trafficker** *n*

traffic jam /ˈ·· ·/ *n* a long line of vehicles that cannot move because the road is blocked 交通阻塞, 塞車 –see picture on page 470 見 470 頁彩圖

traffic lights /ˈ··· /*n* [pl] a set of coloured lights used for controlling and directing traffic on roads 交通信號燈, 交通燈, 紅綠燈: *Watch out! The traffic lights are about to change.* 小心! 交通燈就要變了。 –see picture on page 991 見 991 頁彩圖

traffic war·den /ˈ·· ,·/ *n* a person whose job is to check that vehicles are not parked in the wrong place 交通督導員

tra·ge·dy /ˈtrædʒədɪ; ˈtrædʒɪdɪ/ *n* **tragedies** **1** [C] a serious play that ends sadly 悲劇: *Shakespeare's "Hamlet" is a very famous tragedy.* 莎士比亞的《哈姆雷特》是一部非常有名的悲劇。 **2** [U] these plays considered as a group〔集體名詞〕悲劇作品 **3** [C;U] a terrible, unhappy, or unfortunate event 悲劇性事件, 慘劇, 慘事: *It was a tragedy that she died so young.* 她這麼年輕就去世了, 真是太慘了。 **–tragic** *adj*: *a tragic hero* 悲劇中的英雄人物 | *a tragic accident* 可悲的意外 **–tragically** /-klɪ; -klɪ/ *adv*

trail¹ /trel; treɪl/ *v* **1** [I+adv/prep; T+adv/prep] to drag or be dragged behind 拖; 拖在後面: *Her long skirt trailed in the mud.* 她的長裙在泥漿裡拖曳着。 | *The child was trailing a toy train on a string.* 那孩子用繩子拖着一輛玩具火車。 **2** [T] to follow the tracks of a person or animal 跟蹤: *The hunters trailed the tiger for five hours.* 獵人追蹤那隻老虎追蹤了五小時。 **3** [I+adv/prep] to walk in a tired way, often behind someone else〔常跟在別人後面〕無精打采地走, 拖沓地走: *The defeated army trailed back to camp.*

那支打了敗仗的軍隊無精打采地走回營地。 **4** [I] to grow over or along the ground 長滿, 蔓生 **5** **be trailing** to be behind in a competition〔競爭中〕落後: *The Conservative Party was trailing in the opinion polls.* 保守黨在民意測驗中落後。

　　trail away *phr v* [I] (also 又作 **trail off**) to become slowly quieter or weaker〔聲音〕緩慢變輕, 緩慢變弱: *He was unable to complete what he wanted to say and his voice just trailed away.* 他沒辦法把想要說的話講完, 聲音越來越輕了。

trail² *n* **1** the track or smell of a person or animal〔人或動物的〕蹤跡; 臭跡 **2** a path across rough country 鄉間小道, 小徑 **3** a stream of dust or smoke behind something which is moving〔追隨某一移動物體的〕一陣灰塵或煙霧 **4** **be on the trail of** someone or something to be following or trying to find someone or something 追蹤某人或某物

trail·er /ˈtrelɚ; ˈtreɪləʳ/ *n* **1** a framework like a table with wheels onto which things can be loaded to be pulled by another vehicle 拖車: *a car pulling a boat on a trailer* 用拖車拖着一艘小艇的汽車 **2** an advertisement for a new film, showing small parts of it〔電影〕預告片 **3** the usual American word for〖美式〗= CARAVAN

train¹ /tren; treɪn/ *n* **1** a line of connected railway carriages drawn by an engine 列車, 火車: *I've got to catch that train!* 我必須去趕那班火車! **2** **by train** travelling in a train 乘火車: *It's cheaper to go by train.* 坐火車去更便宜。 **3** a chain of related events or thoughts 一系列, 一連串〔事件、想法〕: *The telephone rang and interrupted my train of thought.* 電話鈴響了, 打斷了我的思路。 **4** a part of the back of a long dress that spreads over the ground 裙裾, 長裙的下襬 **5** a long line of moving people, vehicles, or animals〔人、車輛或動物的〕長隊, 一長列

train² *v* **1** [I;T] to give or be given teaching and practice in a profession or skill 訓練; 培養; 接受訓練: *The army trains soldiers to fight.* 軍隊訓練士兵如何作戰。 | *She is training to be a doctor.* 她正在被培養成為一名醫生。 | *He spends two hours a day training for the race.* 他為了參加比賽, 每天花兩小時操練。

□ **USEFUL PATTERNS** 有用句型
to train for something; to train someone for something; to train to do something; to train someone to do something

2 [T+adv/prep] to point a gun at something or someone 把槍瞄準〔某物或某人〕 **3** [T] to direct the growth of a plant 修整〔植物〕

train·ee /trenˈi; treɪˈniː/ *n* a person who is being trained 接受訓練的人: *a trainee reporter* 實習記者 | *He's still a trainee.* 他仍然在接受訓練。

train·er /ˈtrenɚ; ˈtreɪnəʳ/ *n* **1** a person who trains someone 訓練人, 教練員: *He always follows the advice of his trainer.* 他一向遵從教練員的意見。**2 trainers** *BrE* [pl] special shoes worn for running or for informal occasions 〖英式〗〔跑步或非正式場合穿的〕運動鞋 –see picture on page 210 見 210 頁彩圖

train·ing /ˈtrenɪŋ; ˈtreɪnɪŋ/ *n* [C;U] **1** instruction for a particular job or activity 培訓, 訓練: *The company gave me an excellent training.* 公司為我提供了優秀的培訓。**2 be in training** to be preparing for an event by exercising and eating suitable food 〔運動員〕在進行訓練: *He's in training* for *the match next week.* 他正在為下週的比賽進行訓練。

trait /tret; treɪt/ *n* a particular quality of someone or something 特性, 品質: *Generosity is her best trait.* 慷慨是她的最大的特點。

trai·tor /ˈtretɚ; ˈtreɪtəʳ/ *n* someone who is disloyal, especially to their country 叛徒; 賣國賊

tra·jec·to·ry /trəˈdʒɛktɚri; trəˈdʒektəri/ *n* **trajectories** *tech* the curved path of an object moving through the air 〖術語〗〔抛射物的〕軌道, 彈道: *the trajectory of a bullet* 子彈的彈道

tram /træm; træm/ *n* (also 又作 **tramcar** /ˈtræm͵kɑr; ˈtræmkɑːr/) a vehicle for the public, driven by electricity, that runs along metal lines in the road 有軌電車

tramp¹ /træmp; træmp/ *v* [I+adv/prep; T] to walk a long way, steadily but in a tired way 徒步; 長途步行: *They tramped through the woods all day.* 他們一整天都在森林裡到處走。| *She tramped the streets looking for work.* 她在街上到處奔走找工作。

tramp² *n* **1** a person with no home or job, who wanders from place to place 流浪漢 **2** [sing] the sound of heavy walking 沉重的腳步聲: *the tramp of the soldiers' feet on the road* 士兵走在馬路上的重重的腳步聲 **3** a long walk 長距離行走

tram·ple /ˈtræmpl; ˈtræmpəl/ *v* **trampled, trampling 1** [T] to step heavily on something and damage it 踐踏, 踩: *trampled grass* 被踐踏的草 **2 trample on someone** *infml* to behave in an unfair or cruel way towards someone 〖非正式〗粗暴對待某人: *He trampled on people's feelings.* 他踐踏了別人的感情。

tram·po·line /ˌtræmpəˈlin; ˈtræmpəliːn/ *n* an apparatus consisting of a sheet of material held to a metal frame by springs, on which people can jump up and down 蹦床, 彈床

trance /træns; trɑːns/ *n* a condition of your mind where you are not in control of your thoughts and feelings, and may be controlled by someone else 恍惚; 出神: *She was in a deep trance.* 她精神極度恍惚。

tran·quil /ˈtrænkwɪl; ˈtræŋkwɪl/ *adj* calm and peaceful 平靜的, 寧靜的; 平和的: *a tranquil lake* 平靜的湖 | *a tranquil smile* 平和的微笑 –**tranquillity** (**tranquility** *AmE* 〖美式〗) /trænˈkwɪlətɪ; træŋˈkwɪlˌti/ *n* [U]

tran·quil·ize /ˈtrænkwɪˌlaɪz; ˈtræŋkwɪˌlaɪz/ *v* **tranquillized, tranquillizing** (also 又作 **tranquillise** *BrE* 〖英式〗) [T] **be tranquillized** to be given a drug which makes you calmer and less anxious 〔服藥後〕使鎮定下來

tran·quil·liz·er /ˈtrænkwɪˌlaɪzɚ; ˈtræŋkwɪˌlaɪzəʳ/ (also 又作 **tranquilliser** *BrE* 〖英式〗) *n* a drug used for making a person calm 鎮靜劑, 安定藥

trans·act /trænsˈækt; trænˈzækt/ *v* [T] to carry a piece of business through to an agreement 辦理, 處理〔事務〕

*trans·ac·tion /trænsˈækʃən; trænˈzækʃən/ *n* a piece of business 交易; 要處理之事

trans·at·lan·tic /ˌtrænsətˈlæntɪk; ˌtrænzət-ˈlæntɪk◂/ *adj* **1** on the other side of or across the Atlantic Ocean 大西洋彼岸的; 橫跨大西洋的: *a transatlantic military base* 一個在大西洋彼岸的軍事基地 | *transatlantic flights* 橫越大西洋的航班 **2** concerning countries on both sides of the Atlantic Ocean 大西洋兩岸國家的: *a transatlantic agreement* 大西洋兩岸國家的協定

tran·scend /trænˈsɛnd; trænˈsend/ *v* [T] *lit* to go beyond the limits of something 〖文〗超越〔界限〗: *The wish for peace transcended political differences.* 人們對和平的願望超過了政治上的分歧。

tran·scen·den·tal /ˌtrænsɛnˈdɛntl; ˌtræn-senˈdentl/ *adj* *fml* going beyond human knowledge, thought, belief, and experience 〖正式〗超越人類知識[思想、信念、經驗]的; 先驗的: *transcendental truths* 先驗的真理

trans·con·ti·nen·tal /ˌtrænskɑntəˈnɛntl; ˌtrænzkɒntˈnentl/ *adj* crossing a CONTINENT 橫貫大陸的: *a transcontinental railway* 橫貫大陸的鐵路

tran·scribe /trænˈskraɪb; trænˈskraɪb/ *v* **transcribed, transcribing** [T] **1** to make a full written copy of something 抄寫, 謄寫 **2** to arrange a piece of music for an instrument or voice other than the original 改編〔樂曲〕 –**transcription** /-ˈskrɪpʃən; -ˈskrɪpʃən/ *n*

tran·script /ˈtrænˌskrɪpt; ˈtrænskrɪpt/ *n* a written or printed copy of something that was spoken 〔講話的〕文字記錄; 抄本

*trans·fer¹ /trænsˈfɝ; trænsˈfɜːʳ/ *v* **-rr- 1** [I;T] to move from one place or job to another within the same organization 轉移; 遷移; 調動: *The office was transferred* from *Belfast* to *Dublin.* 辦事處從貝爾法斯特遷至都柏林。| *He is hoping to be transferred* to *another team.* 他希望能夠轉往其他球隊。 **2** [T] to take something from one person and give it to another 把〔某物〕從一人轉至另一人, 使轉移: *Responsibility for staff was* *transferred* **to** *the company secretary.* 對職員所負的責任轉移給了公司祕書。**3** [T] to move from one place to another 使從一處移至另一處: *The money will be transferred to your account.* 這筆錢將會轉入你的賬上。—**transferable** *adj*

★**trans·fer²** /'trænsfɜ˞; 'trænsfɜ:ʳ/ *n* **1** [C;U] a move to another place or job 轉移; 遷移; 調動: *He wants a transfer to another team.* 他希望調到其他球隊去。| *the transfer of funds to a new account* 將資金轉到新的賬戶上 **2** [C] a drawing or pattern for sticking or printing onto a surface 貼畫; 供轉印的圖樣: *He had a transfer of Mickey Mouse on his T-shirt.* 他的T恤上印有一幅米老鼠的圖畫。

trans·fer·ence /træns'fɜ˞əns; 'trænsfərəns/ *n fml* [U] the moving of something to a different person or place 〔正式〕轉移; 移交

trans·fixed /træns'fɪkst; træns'fɪkst/ *adj lit* unable to move or think because of terror or shock 〔文〕嚇呆的, 驚呆的

★**trans·form** /træns'fɔrm; træns'fɔ:m/ *v* [T] to change something completely in form, appearance, or nature 徹底改變〔形狀、外表或性質〕: *The area of wasteland was transformed into a park.* 那片荒地被改造成了一個公園。—**transformation** /,trænsfɚ'meɪʃən; ,trænsfə'meɪʃən/ *n* [C;U]

trans·form·er /træns'fɔrmɚ; træns'fɔ:məʳ/ *n* an apparatus for changing electrical force from one VOLTAGE to another 變壓器

trans·fu·sion /træns'fjuʒən; træns'fju:ʒən/ *n* [C;U] a medical process when the blood of one person is given to someone else 輸血: *The driver had to have a blood transfusion after the accident.* 這位駕駛員在事故發生以後要接受輸血。

tran·si·ent /'trænʃənt; 'trænzɪənt/ *adj* lasting for only a short time 短暫的: *transient happiness* 短暫的快樂 —**transience** *n* [U]

tran·sis·tor /træn'zɪstɚ; træn'zɪstəʳ/ *n* **1** a small electrical apparatus, used in radios or televisions 晶體管, 電晶體 **2** (also 又作 **transistor radio**) a small radio which is easy to carry 晶體管收音機, 半導體收音機

tran·sit /'trænsɪt; 'trænsɪt/ *n* **in transit** being moved from one place to another 運輸, 運送: *His luggage got lost in transit.* 他的行李在運輸中遺失了。

★**tran·si·tion** /træn'zɪʃən; træn'zɪʃən/ *n* [C;U] a change from one state or condition to another 轉變; 過渡: *We hope there will be a peaceful transition to the new system.* 我們希望能和平過渡到新的制度。| *a city in transition* 變化中的城市 —**transitional** *adj*: *a transitional period* 過渡時期

tran·si·tive /'trænsətɪv; 'trænsɪtɪv/ *adj tech* needing a direct object (used of verbs) 〔術語〕及物的〔指動詞〕: *In the sentence "I broke the cup", "broke" is a transitive verb.* 在 "I broke the cup" 一句中, "broke" 是及物動詞。—see Study Note on page 1328 見 1328 頁學習提示

trans·late /træns'let; træns'leɪt/ *v* **translated, translating 1** [I;T] to change speech or writing from one language into another 翻譯〔語言〕: *The book was translated from French into English.* 這本書由法語譯成英語。**2** [T] to change from one form into another 轉化〔形式〕: *A politician should translate ideas into action.* 政治家應當把政治觀點付諸實踐。—**translator** *n* —**translation** /-'leʃən; -'leɪʃən/ *n* [C;U]: *I've only read Tolstoy's books in translation.* 我只看過托爾斯泰小說的譯本。| *an excellent translation* 一部出色的譯作

trans·mis·sion /træns'mɪʃən; trænz'mɪʃən/ *n* **1** [U] sending or passing something to a person or place 傳送, 傳遞 **2** [C;U] something broadcast by television or radio 〔電視或廣播上的〕播送節目 **3** [C] the parts of a vehicle that carry power from the engine to its wheels 〔車輛的〕傳動裝置

trans·mit /træns'mɪt; trænz'mɪt/ *v* **-tt- 1** [I;T] to send out electric signals, messages, and news 發送〔電信號、信息和新聞〕, 播送 **2** [T] to carry something from one person, place, or thing to another 傳送; 傳播; 傳染: *How is the disease transmitted?* 這種疾病是如何傳播的?

trans·mit·ter /træns'mɪtɚ; trænz'mɪtəʳ/ *n* an apparatus that sends out radio or television signals 〔廣播或電視信號的〕發射器

trans·par·en·cy /træns'pɛrənsɪ; træn'spær-ənsɪ/ *n* **transparencies 1** [C] a piece of photographic film, on which a picture can be seen when light is passed through 幻燈片 **2** [U] the state of being transparent 透明(性)

trans·par·ent /træns'pɛrənt; træn'spærənt/ *adj* **1** able to be seen through 透明的: *Glass is transparent.* 玻璃是透明的。| *Her silk dress was almost transparent.* 她的絲裙幾乎是透明的。**2** clearly recognized 清晰易辨的: *His honesty was transparent.* 他的誠實是顯而易見的。—**transparently** *adv*

tran·spire /træn'spaɪr; træn'spaɪəʳ/ *v* **transpired, transpiring** *fml* 〔正式〕**1** [+ that] to become known at a later date 〔晚些時候〕為人所知, 透露出來: *It later transpired that the minister had lied about the money in parliament.* 人們後來知道部長在國會上就那筆款項撒了謊。**2** [I] to happen 發生: *Let's wait and see what transpires.* 我們等着瞧會發生甚麼事情。

trans·plant¹ /træns'plænt; træns'plɑ:nt/ *v* [T] **1** to move something from one place to another 遷移〔某物〕 **2** to move an organ or part of the body from one person to another 移植〔器官〕—**transplantation** /,trænsplæn'teʃən; ,trænsplɑ:n'teɪʃən/ *n* [U]

trans·plant² /'trænsplænt; 'trænsplɑ:nt/ *n* the medical operation in which an organ or part of the body is moved from one person to another 器官的移植(手術): *a heart transplant* 心臟移植手術

trans·port¹ /'trænsport; 'trænspɔːt/ *n* (also 又作 **transportation** /,trænspə'teʃən; ,trænspɔː'teɪʃən *AmE*〖美式〗) **1** [U] the moving of goods or people from one place to another 運輸, 運送: *The transport of goods by air is very costly.* 空運貨物非常昂貴。**2** [U] a means or system of carrying passengers or goods from one place to another 運輸工具; 運輸系統: *a public transport system* 公共交通系統 | *I'd like to go to the concert, but I've no transport.* 我想去聽音樂會, 但沒有交通工具。

■ USAGE 用法: **1** For most methods of transport use **by** when you are talking about how someone gets to a place ☆表示人乘坐交通工具前往某處大多用 **by**: *She came by car/taxi/bus/tube/plane, etc.* 她乘汽車[計程車; 公共汽車; 地鐵; 飛機等]到這裡來。But for walking use **on foot** ☆但步行則要用 **on foot**: *She came on foot.* 她是步行到這裡來的。**2** When talking about events which happen while you are using a particular form of public transport use **on** ☆談論在某種交通工具上發生的事情時用 **on**: *I met Jim on the train/on the bus/on the boat/on the plane/on the tube.* 我在火車上[公共汽車上; 船上; 飛機上; 地鐵裡]遇見了吉姆。

trans·port² /træns'port; træn'spɔːt/ *v* [T] to carry goods or people from one place to another 運輸, 運送〔貨物或人〕 –**transportable** *adj*

trans·pose /træns'poz; træn'spəʊz/ *v* **transposed, transposing** [T] **1** to change the order or position of two or more things 改變〔順序或位置〕, 調換: *By mistake the printers transposed the letters of that word.* 印刷工不小心把那個詞的字母順序調換了。**2** to change the key of a piece of music 使〔樂曲〕變調

trans·ves·tite /træns'vɛstaɪt; trænz'vestaɪt/ *n* a person, usually a man, who likes to wear the clothes of the opposite sex 好穿異性服裝的人, 易裝癖者 –**transvestism** /-tɪzm; -tɪzəm/ *n* [U]

trap¹ /træp; træp/ *n* **1** an apparatus for catching and holding animals〔動物的〕捕捉器; 陷阱: *a mouse trap* 老鼠夾 **2** a plan for deceiving and tricking a person 圈套; 謀計; 陷阱 **3** an unpleasant or dangerous situation from which it is difficult to free yourself〔難於擺脫的〕困境 **4** a light two-wheeled vehicle pulled by a horse 雙輪輕便馬車 **5** *infml* your mouth〖非正式〗嘴: *Shut your trap.* 閉上你的嘴。

trap² *v* -**pp**- [T] to catch in a trap or by a trick 誘捕; 設圈套: *He trapped foxes and sold their fur.* 他誘捕狐狸, 然後出售牠們的毛皮。 | *He trapped me into admitting I had done it.* 他誘使我承認了是我做的。**2 be trapped: a** to be unable to move or escape from somewhere 被困住: *We were trapped in the lift for four hours.* 我們在電梯內被困了四小時。**b** to be unable to free yourself from a difficult or unpleasant situation 無法擺脫困境: *She was trapped at home with five children.* 她有五個孩子, 因而被束縛在家裡。

trap·door /'træpdor; 'træpdɔː/ *n* a small door covering an opening in a floor or roof〖地板或屋頂上的〗活板門; 活動天窗

tra·peze /træ'piz; trə'piːz/ *n* a short bar hung from two ropes, used by acrobats (ACROBAT) and gymnasts (GYMNAST)〖雜技或體操中的〗高鞦韆

trap·pings /'træpɪŋz; 'træpɪŋz/ *n* [pl] articles of dress or decoration, especially those which show someone's social position〔尤指顯示社會地位的〕服飾: *He possessed all the trappings of high office.* 他擁有一位高官所具備的全部服飾。

trash /træʃ; træʃ/ *n* [U] **1** something worthless or of low quality 無價值之物, 劣質物品, 廢物 **2** the usual American word for〖美式〗= RUBBISH (1)

trash·can /'træʃ,kæn; 'træʃkæn/ *n* the usual American word for〖美式〗= DUSTBIN

trash·y /'træʃɪ; 'træʃɪ/ *adj* **trashier, trashiest** worthless 毫無價值的: *a trashy novel* 一文不值的小說

trau·ma /'trɔmə; 'trɔːmə/ *n* **1** [U] damage to your mind caused by a sudden shock or terrible experience 精神創傷: *an accident resulting in great trauma and suffering* 導致精神和肉體上重大創傷的事故 **2** [C] an extremely upsetting experience 痛苦的經歷: *the trauma of her son's death* 她喪子之痛

trau·mat·ic /trɔ'mætɪk; trɔː'mætɪk/ *adj* extremely upsetting 極為痛苦的; 造成創傷的 –**traumatically** /-klɪ; -klɪ/ *adv*

trav·el¹ /'trævl; 'trævl/ *v* -**ll**- (also 又作 **-l-** *AmE*〖美式〗) **1** [I] to make a journey from one place to another 旅行: *He travelled across the States on a Greyhound bus.* 他乘坐灰狗巴士在美國各地旅行。–see 見 TRAVEL² (USAGE 用法) **2** [I+adv/prep/T] to move from one place to another 從一地到另一地: *At what speed does light travel?* 光速是多少? | *The news travelled fast.* 消息很快傳播開來。 | *We travelled thousands of miles.* 我們走了數千英里。**3 travel light** to travel without much LUGGAGE 輕裝旅行

trav·el² *n* **1** [U] the activity of travelling 旅行; 移動 **2 travels** [pl] journeys made in foreign countries 在國外的旅行

■ USAGE 用法: Compare 比較 **travel, travels, journey, voyage, trip. Travel** is the general activity of moving from place to place ☆ **Travel** 指由一個地方到另一個地方的一般移動: *He came home after years of foreign* **travel**. 他在外國遊歷多年之後，終於回到了家中。We use **travels** when a person goes to different places over a period of time ☆ 一個人在一段時間內到不同的地方去，則用 **travels**: *Did you go to Rome during your* **travels** *round Europe?* 你在歐洲旅遊的時候去羅馬了嗎? We use **journey** when we think of the time spent or the distance covered in going from one particular place to another ☆ 當我們考慮到旅行的時間和距離時，則用 **journey**: *a 60-hour* **journey** *by train from Paris to Moscow* 乘火車從巴黎到莫斯科的六十小時的行程。We use **voyage** for a journey by sea ☆ 海上的旅行用 **voyage**: *The* **voyage** *from England to Australia used to take several months.* 在過去，從英國到澳大利亞坐船需要數月之久。A **trip** is a short journey, or one on which you spend only a short time in another place, then come back ☆ **trip** 指短途旅行，或在另外一地僅度過一小段時間後即返回的旅行: *We'll have time for a* **trip** *to France next weekend.* 下週末我們會有時間去一趟法國。

travel a·gen·cy /ˈ·· ˌ···/ *n* **travel agencies** a business that arranges people's holidays and journeys 旅行社

travel a·gent /ˈ·· ˌ··/ *n* a person who owns or works in a travel agency 旅行社老闆; 旅行代理人

trav·el·ler /ˈtrævlə; ˈtrævələr/ *n* (also 又作 **traveler** *AmE* 《美式》) a person who is on a journey 旅行者, 旅客

traveller's cheque /ˌ··· ·/ *n* a cheque sold by a bank to a person intending to travel abroad, exchangeable at most banks for the money of the particular country 旅行支票

tra·verse /ˈtrævəs; ˈtrævɜːs/ *v* **traversed, traversing** [T] *fml* to pass across, over, or through something 《正式》通過, 穿過; 橫貫

trav·es·ty /ˈtrævɪstɪ; ˈtrævə̩stɪ/ *n* **travesties** a copy, account, or example of something that gives a completely false idea of it 歪曲模仿; 嘲弄: *His trial was a complete travesty of justice.* 對他進行審判簡直是對正義的嘲弄。

trawl¹ /trɔl; trɔːl/ *v* [I;T] to fish with a very large net 用拖網捕魚; *boats out trawling the lake for fish* 在湖中用拖網進行捕魚的船

trawl² *n* a large wide fishing net that is drawn along the sea bottom 拖網

trawl·er /ˈtrɔlə; ˈtrɔːlər/ *n* a fishing vessel that uses a trawl 拖網漁船

tray /tre; treɪ/ *n* a flat piece of wood or metal with raised edges, used for carrying small articles 托盤, 淺盤: *The waitress put the plates on a tray and carried them into the dining room.* 女服務員把盤子放在托盤上, 然後端入餐廳。

treach·e·rous /ˈtrɛtʃərəs; ˈtrɛtʃərəs/ *adj* **1** disloyal 不忠誠的, 背叛的 **2** full of hidden dangers 充滿潛在危險的: *treacherous currents* 充滿危險的水流 **–treacherously** *adv*

treach·e·ry /ˈtrɛtʃərɪ; ˈtrɛtʃərɪ/ *n* [U] disloyalty and deceit 不忠, 背叛

trea·cle /ˈtrikl; ˈtriːkəl/ *n* [U] a thick sticky dark liquid made from sugar 糖漿

tread¹ /trɛd; trɛd/ *v* **trod** /trɒd; trɑd/, **trodden** /ˈtrɒdn̩; ˈtrɑdn̩/, **treading 1** [I] to walk or step on something 踩, 踏, 在〔某物〕上面走: *Don't tread on the flowers!* 不要踐踏花草! **2** [I] to walk in a special way 〔以某種方式〕行走: *She trod carefully between the flowers.* 她小心翼翼地在花叢中走。**3** [T] to press on something firmly with your feet 用力踩〔某物〕: *They crush the juice out of the fruit by treading it.* 他們用腳把水果的汁液踩出來。**4 tread on someone's toes** to offend someone 冒犯某人 **5 tread water** to stay upright in deep water with your head above the surface, by moving your legs 〔游泳時〕踩水

tread² *n* **1** [sing] the sound made when walking 腳步聲: *We recognized John's heavy tread.* 我們聽出是約翰的沉重的腳步聲。**2** [C; U] the raised pattern on a tyre 〔輪胎上凸起的〕紋路 **3** [C] the part of a stair on which you place your foot 〔樓梯的〕踏面板, 梯面

trea·son /ˈtrizn; ˈtriːzən/ *n* [U] the crime of disloyalty to your country, for example by telling its secrets to an enemy 叛國罪, 通敵罪 **–treasonable** *adj*

trea·sure¹ /ˈtrɛʒə; ˈtrɛʒər/ *n* **1** [U] wealth in the form of things like gold, silver, or jewels 金銀財寶, 寶藏 **2** [C] a very valuable object 珍品, 珍寶: *The gallery has many wonderful art treasures.* 該展覽館收藏了許多藝術珍品。

treasure² *v* **treasured, treasuring** [T] to regard something as very valuable 珍惜, 珍視〔某物〕

trea·sur·er /ˈtrɛʒərə; ˈtrɛʒərər/ *n* a person in charge of the money belonging to an organization 財務主管, 司庫

trea·su·ry /ˈtrɛʒərɪ; ˈtrɛʒərɪ/ *n* **the Treasury** the government department that controls and spends public money 財政部: *The treasury is spending less this year.* 財政部今年準備減少支出。

treat¹ /trit; triːt/ *v* [T] **1** to act or behave towards someone in a particular way 對待〔某人〕: *She treats us like children.* 她把我們當孩子看待。**2** to handle something in a particular way 處理〔某事〕: *This glass must be treated with care.* 這玻璃杯使用時要小心。| *He treated the idea as a joke.* 他把這個主意當作是笑話。**3** to try to cure an illness by medical means 治療〔疾病〕: *a new drug to treat this disease* 治療這種疾病的新藥 **4** to buy or give someone something special 款待〔某人〕: *I'm going to treat myself to a holiday in Spain.* 我準備自己花錢去西班牙度假。 **5** to put a special substance on something to protect it or give it a special quality 〔用特別物質〕處理: *The wood has been treated to make it waterproof.* 木頭表面已作了防水處理。 –**treatable** *adj*

treat² *n* **1** something special that gives pleasure 令人愉快的事: *It's a great treat for her to go to London.* 去倫敦對她來說是件難得的樂事。 **2** It's my treat = I will pay for everything 我來付賬〔請客〕

trea·tise /'triːtɪs; 'triːɪs/ *n* a book or article, written in a formal way, that examines a particular subject 專題著作, 專題論文

treat·ment /'triːtmənt; 'triːtmənt/ *n* **1** [C;U] the methods used to make a sick person better 治療, 療程: *He's gone to hospital for special treatment.* 他已住院接受特殊治療。 **2** [U] behaviour towards someone 對待〔某人〕態度: *His treatment of his mother is awful.* 他對待母親的態度很惡劣。

treat·y /'triːtɪ; 'triːti/ *n* **treaties** a formal agreement between countries 條約

tre·ble¹ /'trebl; 'trebəl/ *n* **1** [C] a person with a high singing voice 能唱最高音的人 **2** [U] the upper half of the whole range of musical notes 最高音部

treble² *adj, adv* **1** made up of three things or three parts 由三部分組成的[地] **2** producing a high sound or able to sing in a high voice 能產生出高音的[地], 能唱出高音的[地]

treble³ *predeterminer* three times as much 三倍的: *He earns treble my wages.* 他的收入是我的三倍。 | *The house is worth treble what we paid for it.* 這房子的價錢已值我們購買時的三倍。

treble⁴ *v* **trebled, trebling** [I;T] to make or become three times as large as before (使)成為三倍: *My salary has trebled over the last ten years.* 過去十年間, 我的工資增加了三倍。

tree /triː; triː/ *n* a tall plant with a wooden trunk, branches, and leaves 樹(木): *an apple tree* 蘋果樹 | *the trees in the wood* 林中的樹木 –see picture on page 729 見729頁彩圖

trek /trek; trek/ *v* **-kk-** [I+adv/prep] to make a long hard journey 長途跋涉; 徒步旅行 – **trek** *n*: *a long trek through the mountains* 在山區中的徒步旅行

trel·lis /'trelɪs; 'trelɪs/ *n* a light upright wooden frame used as a support for climbing plants 〔支撐緣緣植物的〕棚架

trem·ble /'trembl; 'trembəl/ *v* **trembled, trembling** [I] to shake because you are cold or afraid 〔由於寒冷或恐懼〕發抖, 顫抖, 震顫, 戰慄: *You're trembling but there's*

nothing to be frightened of. 沒有甚麼可怕的東西, 你發甚麼抖呀。 | *His voice trembled with fear.* 他嚇得聲音在發抖。 –**tremble** *n*

tre·men·dous /trɪ'mendəs; trɪ'mendəs/ *adj* **1** very great in size, amount, or degree 極大的; 極多的: *This plane travels at a tremendous speed.* 這架飛機以極快的速度飛行。 | *a tremendous explosion* 巨大的爆炸(聲) **2** wonderful 極好的: *We went to a tremendous party last night.* 昨晚我們去參加了一個妙極了的聚會。

trem·or /'tremə; 'tremər/ *n* a shaking movement 震動, 顫抖: *an earth tremor* 小地震 | *a tremor of fear* 因恐懼而發抖

trench /trentʃ; trentʃ/ *n* a long narrow hole cut in the ground 溝, 渠, 壕

trend /trend; trend/ *n* **1** a general tendency or change in direction in the way a situation is developing 趨勢, 傾向: *the trend of rising unemployment* 失業率上升的趨勢 | *the latest trends in women's clothes* 婦女服裝的最新發展趨勢 **2** set a trend to start a new fashion 開創新潮流

trend·set·ter /'trend,setə; 'trend,setər/ *n infml* a person who starts a new fashion 〔非正式〕創新潮流者

trend·y /'trendɪ; 'trendi/ *adj* **trendier, trendiest** *BrE infml* very fashionable 〔英式, 非正式〕時髦的; 流行的: *a trendy club* 時髦的俱樂部 –**trendiness** *n* [U]

trep·i·da·tion /,trepə'deɪʃən; ,trepə'deɪʃən/ *n* [U] *fml* a state of anxiety 〔正式〕恐慌, 惴惴不安: *in fear and trepidation* 處於恐懼和焦慮之中

tres·pass /'trespəs; 'trespəs/ *v* [I] to go onto privately owned land without permission 擅入, 未經許可進入〔私人領地〕 –**trespasser** *n*

tres·tle /'tresl; 'tresəl/ *n* a wooden beam fixed to a pair of legs, used as a support for a table 〔桌子的〕支架

tri·al /'traɪəl; 'traɪəl/ *n* **1** [C;U] the legal process of hearing and judging a person or case in a court 審判, 審訊: *The murder trial lasted six weeks.* 謀殺案的審訊持續了六星期。 **2** on trial being tried in court 在審訊中: *She's on trial for robbery.* 她因搶劫正在法庭受審。 **3** stand trial to be tried in a court 〔在法庭〕受審訊: *He stood trial for the murder of his wife.* 他由於殺害了妻子而受審。 **4** [C] a test to find out how good something is 試驗: *The car is now undergoing trials.* 這車正在進行試驗。 | *a trial period* 試用期 **5** on trial being tested 在試驗中: *For the first few months in my new job I was very much on trial.* 新工作剛開始的幾個月中, 我經受了許多考驗。 **6** [C] a cause of worry or trouble 引起憂慮或麻煩的事物: *That boy is quite a trial to his teachers.* 那個男孩很會給他的老師惹麻煩。 **7 trials** [pl] unpleasant things 討厭的事情: *the trials and tribulations of bringing up children* 撫養孩子的艱辛與困苦 **8 trial and error** a way of getting satisfactory results by trying several methods and learning from your mistakes 反覆試驗: *learning to cook by trial and error* 經過反覆試驗來學習烹調

tri·an·gle /ˈtraɪˌæŋgl; ˈtraɪæŋgəl/ *n* **1** a flat shape with three straight sides and three angles 三角形 **2** a small three-sided musical instrument made of steel, played by being struck with a steel rod 三角鐵〔一種打擊樂器〕 **–triangular** /traɪˈæŋgjələ; traɪˈæŋgjʊlɚ/ *adj*: *a triangular piece of land* 一塊三角形的地

tribe /traɪb; traɪb/ *n* a group of people of the same race, beliefs, and language under the leadership of a chief or chiefs 部落: *American Indian tribes* 美國的印第安部落 – **tribal** *adj*: *tribal music* 部落音樂

tribes·man /ˈtraɪbzmən; ˈtraɪbzmən/ *n* **tribesmen** /-mən; -mən/ a male member of a tribe 部落中的男性成員

trib·u·la·tion /ˌtrɪbjəˈleɪʃən; ˌtrɪbjʊˈleɪʃən/ *n* [C;U] *fml* trouble, grief, and suffering 〔正式〕艱難, 苦難: *the trials and tribulations of modern life* 現代生活的艱難困苦

tri·bu·nal /trɪˈbjunl; traɪˈbjuːnəl/ *n* a court of people officially appointed to deal with special matters 審裁團; 特別法庭: *The rent tribunal has ordered that my rent be reduced.* 租務審裁處下令減低我的租金。

trib·u·ta·ry /ˈtrɪbjəˌtɛrɪ; ˈtrɪbjʊˈtəri/ *n* **tributaries** a stream or river that flows into a larger one 〔河流的〕支流: *the tributaries of the Rhine* 萊茵河的支流

trib·ute /ˈtrɪbjut; ˈtrɪbjuːt/ *n* [C;U] **1** something done, said, or given to show respect or admiration for someone 〔表示敬意或敬仰的〕禮物; 頌辭: *We pay tribute to his courage.* 我們對他的勇氣表示敬佩。 **2 a tribute to** something which shows the excellent result or effect of something else 〔顯示出事物具有出色效果的〕標示, 產物: *Their exam results are a tribute to the school.* 他們的考試結果顯示出學校的實力。 **3** payment made by one ruler or country to another as the price of peace 〔一國向另一國交納的〕貢金, 貢物

trick¹ /trɪk; trɪk/ *n* **1** an act needing special skill, especially done to confuse or amuse people 戲法, 把戲: *magic tricks* 魔術戲法 | *No one understood how I did the card tricks.* 沒有人知道我是如何用紙牌來變戲法的。 **2** a clever and useful skill 竅門; 技巧: *John taught me the trick of getting a fire to burn well.* 約翰教我生火的竅門。 **3** something done to deceive someone or make them look foolish 詭計; 惡作劇: *He got the money by a trick.* 他要花招拿到了那筆錢。 **4** the cards played or won in one part of a game of cards 〔牌戲中打出或贏得的〕一圈牌, 一墩牌 **5 play a trick on someone** to do something to deceive someone 欺騙某人 **6 do the trick** *infml* to fulfil your purpose 〔非正式〕達到目的: *This medicine ought to*

do the trick and get rid of your cough. 這種藥應該可以達到治好你咳嗽的目的。

trick² *adj* [only before a noun 只用於名詞前] *infml* 〔非正式〕 **1** made for playing tricks 變戲法用的, 用於特技的: *trick photography* 特技攝影 **2 trick question** a question which seems clear but is full of hidden difficulties 捉弄人的問題

trick³ *v* [T] to deceive or cheat someone 欺騙〔某人〕: *She tricked me into admitting responsibility.* 她哄騙我承認責任。

trick·e·ry /ˈtrɪkərɪ; ˈtrɪkəri/ *n* [U] the use of tricks to deceive or cheat 欺騙, 欺詐

trick·le /ˈtrɪkl; ˈtrɪkəl/ *v* **trickled, trickling** [I+adv/prep] **1** to flow in drops or in a thin stream 一滴滴地流, 涓涓地流: *Blood trickled down his face.* 血一滴一滴地從他的臉頰上流下。 **2** to move gradually in small groups 〔小羣人〕慢慢移動: *Refugees are trickling home now that the war is over.* 戰爭已結束, 難民正慢慢地返回家園。 **–trickle** *n*

trick·y /ˈtrɪkɪ; ˈtrɪki/ *adj* **trickier, trickiest** **1** difficult to handle or deal with 棘手的; 難處理的 **2** clever and deceitful 狡猾的, 詭計多端的: *a tricky politician* 狡猾的政客 **–trickiness** *n* [U]

tri·cy·cle /ˈtraɪsɪkl; ˈtraɪsɪkəl/ *n* a cycle with three wheels, two at the back and one at the front, which is often ridden by small children 〔幼兒騎的〕三輪腳踏車

tried¹ /traɪd; traɪd/ *adj* found to be good by testing 試驗證明可行的, 考驗過的: *a tried and tested method* 經過實驗證明為可行的辦法

tried² the past tense and past participle of TRY¹ ☆ TRY¹ 的過去式和過去分詞

tri·fle¹ /ˈtraɪfl; ˈtraɪfəl/ *n* **1** [C] a thing of little value or slight importance 不值錢的東西; 瑣事: *wasting your money on trifles* 把錢浪費在微不足道的東西上 **2** [C;U] a dish made with fruit, jelly, and cream 〔用水果、果凍和奶油做成的〕甜點心 **3 a trifle** *fml* slightly 〔正式〕略微, 有點兒: *He's a trifle angry.* 他有點生氣了。

trifle² *v* **trifle with someone** to treat someone without seriousness or respect 小看某人, 輕視某人: *The general is not a man to be trifled with.* 這位將軍不可小看。

tri·fling /ˈtraɪflɪŋ; ˈtraɪflɪŋ/ *adj* of little importance or value 微不足道的, 不重要的

trig·ger¹ /ˈtrɪgɚ; ˈtrɪgɚ/ *n* the small piece of metal that you press to fire a gun 〔槍的〕扳機

trigger² *v* [T] (also 又作 **trigger** sthg ↔ **off**) to start a chain of events 引發〔一系列事件〕: *Price increases trigger off demands for wage increases.* 物價上漲引發了人們要求加薪。

trig·o·nom·e·try /ˌtrɪgəˈnɑmətrɪ; ˌtrɪgəˈnɒmɪtri/ *n* [U] the branch of MATHEMATICS that deals with the relationship between the sides and angles of triangles (TRIANGLE) 〔數學的〕三角學

tri·lat·e·ral /traɪˈlætərəl; ˌtraɪˈlætərəl/ *adj* including three groups or countries 三個團體的; 三國的; 三邊的: *a trilateral agreement* 三邊協定 **–trilaterally** *adv*

trill /trɪl; trɪl/ *n* **1** *tech* the rapid repeating of two musical notes〖術語〗顫音 **2** the short, sharp, repeated sounds of a bird〔鳥的〕囀鳴 **–trill** *v* [I]

tril·o·gy /ˈtrɪlədʒɪ; ˈtrɪlədʒɪ/ *n* **trilogies** a group of three related things like books or plays connected by common subject matter〔小說或戲劇的〕三部曲

trim /trɪm; trɪm/ *v* **-mm-** [T] **1** to make something neat, even, or tidy by cutting 修剪; 整修〔某物〕: *My hair needs trimming.* 我的頭髮需要修剪一下。| *a neatly trimmed beard* 修剪得很整齊的鬍鬚 **2** to decorate the edge of something 裝飾〔某物的邊緣〕: *a coat trimmed with fur* 鑲有毛邊的外衣 **3** to reduce something by taking away unnecessary parts 減少, 削減: *The theatre has to trim its costs.* 劇院必須降低成本。

trim sthg ↔ **off** *phr v* [T] to cut something off because it is not necessary 剪除; 除去: *She trimmed off the fat before cooking the meat.* 她煮那塊肉前把肥肉全部剔除了。

trim² *adj* **1** tidy and attractive in appearance 整潔的, 整齊的: *trim gardens* 修整得很好的花園 **2** thin and fit 苗條的: *a trim figure* 苗條的身材

trim³ *n* **1** an act of cutting 修剪: *She gave my hair a good trim.* 她把我的頭髮好好的修剪了一下。**2** in good physical condition 良好的身體狀況: *The team was in good trim for the match.* 這支球隊為這場比賽已做好準備。

tri·mes·ter /traɪˈmɛstər; trɪˈmestər/ *n* the usual American word for a TERM at a school or college〖美式〗一學期

trim·mings /ˈtrɪmɪŋz; ˈtrɪmɪŋz/ *n* [pl] something added to the main thing, often for decoration 裝飾品; 附加品: *duck served with all the trimmings* 有一切配菜的鴨肉

trin·ket /ˈtrɪŋkɪt; ˈtrɪŋkɪt/ *n* a small object or piece of jewellery of low value 小件飾物; 不值錢的珠寶

tri·o /ˈtriːo; ˈtriːəʊ/ *n* **trios 1** [+sing/pl v] a group of three people, especially musicians〔尤指音樂家〕三人小組 **2** a piece of music written for three singers or musicians 三重唱〔奏〕樂曲

⋆trip¹ /trɪp; trɪp/ *v* **-pp- 1** [I] to catch your foot and lose your balance 絆, 絆倒: *He tripped over a stone and fell to the ground.* 他在石頭上絆了一跤, 跌倒在地上。**2** [T] to make someone lose their balance by making them fall over something, for example your foot 使〔某人〕絆倒: *He stopped the thief by tripping him.* 他把小偷絆倒將其截住。**3** [I+adv/prep] to move or dance with quick light steps 輕快地走〔跳舞〕: *The little girl tripped lightly down the path.* 小女孩邁着輕快的步伐走在小路上。

trip up *phr v* [I; T **trip** sbdy ↔ **up**] **1** to fall or to make someone fall (使)〔某人〕跌倒 **2** to make a mistake or make someone make a mistake (使)〔某人〕犯錯誤: *He tripped up over the details of the contract.* 他在合同的細節問題上出了錯誤。| *He tripped me up by asking confusing questions.* 他用把人弄糊塗的問題令我出錯。

trip² *n* a journey from one place to another 旅行: *He went on a trip to Europe.* 他到歐洲旅行。| *a business trip* 出差 | *a day trip to the country* 郊外一日遊 **–see** 見 TRAVEL² (USAGE用法)

tri·par·tite /traɪˈpɑːtaɪt; traɪˈpɑːtaɪt/ *adj* having three parts or including three groups of people 由三部分組成的; 三個團體的

tripe /traɪp; traɪp/ *n* [U] **1** the wall of the stomach of the cow, pig or ox, eaten as food〔作食物用的〕牛肚; 豬肚 **2** *infml* worthless or stupid talk or writing《非正式》廢話; 瞎說或瞎寫的東西: *Why do you read such tripe?* 你為甚麼讀這種無聊的東西?

tri·ple¹ /ˈtrɪpl; ˈtrɪpəl/ *v* **tripled, tripling** [I; T] to grow to or be made to grow three times greater in size or amount (使)增至三倍

triple² *adj* **1** having three parts 有三部分的 **2** repeated three times 三重的; 三倍的: *a triple dose of medicine* 三倍的劑量

trip·let /ˈtrɪplɪt; ˈtrɪplɪt/ *n* any of three children born to the same mother at the same time 三胞胎中的一個

trip·li·cate /ˈtrɪplɪket; ˈtrɪplɪkɪt/ *adj* consisting of three parts that are exactly alike 一式三份的: *triplicate copies of the contract* 一式三份的合同 **–triplicate** *n*: *The contract has been written in triplicate.* 該合同一式三份。

tri·pod /ˈtraɪpɑd; ˈtraɪpɒd/ *n* a frame with three legs, used for standing a camera on〔照相機的〕三腳架

trip·per /ˈtrɪpə; ˈtrɪpər/ *n* *old fash* a person on a pleasure trip《老式》遊客

trite /traɪt; traɪt/ *adj* used too often to be effective or interesting (used of an idea or remark) 陳腐的〔指觀點或話語〕

tri·umph¹ /ˈtraɪəmf; ˈtraɪəmf/ *n* **1** [C] a complete victory or success 勝利; 成功: *a triumph **over** the enemy* 大勝敵軍 | *his examination triumph* 他在考試中取得的優異成績 **2** [U] a feeling of joy and satisfaction caused by success 勝利的歡欣; 成功的喜悅: *shouts of triumph* 勝利的歡呼 **–triumphant** /traɪˈʌmfənt; traɪˈʌmfənt/ *adj*: *a triumphant army* 得勝的軍隊 **–triumphantly** *adv*

triumph² *v* [I] to gain victory or success, especially in dealing with a difficult situation or opponent 戰勝, 得勝: *She triumphed **over** a disabling illness.* 她戰勝了殘疾。

tri·um·phal /traɪˈʌmfl̩; traɪˈʌmfəl/ *adj* related to or marking a triumph 勝利的, 凱旋的: *a triumphal arch* 凱旋門

triv·i·a /ˈtrɪvɪə; trɪvɪə/ *n* [pl] unimportant or useless things 瑣事; 微不足道的東西

triv·i·al /ˈtrɪvɪəl; ˈtrɪvɪəl/ *adj* **1** of little importance 不重要的, 瑣碎的: *Why do you get angry over such trivial matters?* 你為何為這些瑣碎的事情生氣? **2** ordinary 普通的: *trivial everyday duties* 普通的日常事務 –**triviality** /ˌtrɪvɪˈælətɪ; ˌtrɪviˈæl ̥ti/ *n* **trivialities** [C; U]

trod /trɑd; trɒd/ the past tense of TREAD ☆ TREAD 的過去式

trod·den /ˈtrɑdn̩; ˈtrɒdn/ the past participle of TREAD ☆ TREAD 的過去分詞

trol·ley /ˈtrɑlɪ; ˈtrɒli/ *n* **1** a small low cart which you push by hand and use to carry heavy things 手推車 **2** *BrE* a small table on wheels from which food and drinks are served〔英式〕送食品飲料的手推車

trol·ley·bus /ˈtrɑlɪˌbʌs; ˈtrɒlibʌs/ *n* a bus that draws power from electric wires running above it 無軌電車

trom·bone /trɑmbon; trɒmˈbəʊn/ *n* a large brass musical instrument with a long sliding tube played by blowing 長號, 伸縮喇叭〔一種樂器〕–**trombonist** *n*

*★**troop**[1] /trup; truːp/ *n* **1** a band of people or animals〔人或動物的〕一羣: *a troop of monkeys* 一羣猴子 **2** a group of soldiers on horses or in armoured vehicles 騎兵隊; 裝甲部隊 **3** troops [pl] soldiers 士兵: *The general inspected the troops.* 將軍檢閱了部隊。

troop[2] *v* [I+adv/prep] to move together in a group 成羣結隊而行: *Everyone trooped into the meeting.* 人們成羣結隊地進入會場。

troop·er /ˈtrupɚ; ˈtruːpər/ *n* a soldier of the lowest rank, especially in the CAVALRY〔軍階最低的〕裝甲士兵〔尤指騎兵〕

tro·phy /ˈtrofɪ; ˈtrəʊfi/ *n* **trophies 1** a prize given for winning a race or competition 獎品, 獎杯, 獎牌 **2** something taken after much effort, especially in war or hunting〔尤指戰爭或狩獵中的〕戰利品; 獵獲物: *Hunting trophies hung on the wall.* 狩獵得來的戰利品都掛在牆上。

trop·ic /ˈtrɑpɪk; ˈtrɒpɪk/ *n* **1** one of the two imaginary lines drawn around the world; the line drawn at about $23\frac{1}{2}°$ north of the EQUATOR is called **the tropic of Cancer** and the line $23\frac{1}{2}°$ south **the tropic of Capricorn** 回歸線〔北回歸線稱為 **the tropic of Cancer**; 南回歸線稱為 **the tropic of Capricorn**〕**2 the tropics** the very hot area found between the tropic of Cancer and the tropic of Capricorn 熱帶(地區)

trop·i·cal /ˈtrɑpɪkl; ˈtrɒpɪkəl/ *adj* **1** relating to the tropics 熱帶的: *tropical flowers* 熱帶花卉 | *the tropical sun* 熱帶的陽光 **2** very hot and wet 炎熱潮濕的: *tropical weather* 酷熱的天氣 –**tropically** /-klɪ; -kli/ *adv*

trot[1] /trɑt; trɒt/ *n* [sing] **1** a fairly quick movement made by a horse between a walk and a GALLOP〔馬的〕小跑 **2** a fairly fast human speed between a walk and a run〔人的〕慢跑, 快步 **3 on the trot** *infml* one after another〔非正式〕一個接一個地: *She won three matches on the trot.* 她連續贏了三場比賽。**4 be on the trot** to be very busy 非常忙碌地, 馬不停蹄地: *I've been on the trot since yesterday.* 我從昨天開始就一直忙個不停。

trot[2] *v* **-tt- 1** [I+adv/prep] to move fairly fast 小跑, 慢跑: *The little girl trotted along behind her father.* 小女孩跟在父親身後慢跑。**2** [I] (of an animal, especially a horse) to move with a movement between a walk and a GALLOP〔動物, 尤指馬〕小跑

trot·ter /ˈtrɑtɚ; ˈtrɒtər/ *n* a pig's foot eaten as food〔用作食品的〕豬蹄

*★**troub·le**[1] /ˈtrʌbl; ˈtrʌbəl/ *v* **troubled, troubling 1** [T] to make you feel worried or anxious 令〔人〕憂慮或焦急: *What's troubling you?* 甚麼事情使你心神不定? **2** [T] to cause inconvenience to someone 給〔某人〕添麻煩, 令〔某人〕不便: *I'm sorry to trouble you, but could you possibly help me?* 對不起, 麻煩你了, 不過你能幫我個忙嗎? | *May I trouble you for the salt?* 麻煩你幫我遞一下鹽好嗎? **3 not trouble to do something** to not make the effort to do something because it is inconvenient〔由於不便而〕不必做某事: *Don't trouble to write when you're away.* 你外出期間不用寫信了。–**troubling** *adj*: *a troubling report* 令人不安的報告

trouble[2] *n* **1** [U] a medical condition or illness 疾病: *Her mother suffers from heart trouble.* 她的母親患有心臟病。**2 troubles** [pl] problems 問題; 麻煩事: *He told me all his troubles.* 他把他所有的麻煩事都告訴了我。| *Put all your troubles behind you and make a new start.* 把你的問題都擱在腦後, 再重新開始吧。**3 the trouble** something which causes a problem 引起麻煩的事: *The trouble with you is that you believe everything people tell you.* 你的問題在於你相信別人告訴你的一切。| *What's the trouble?* 出了甚麼事啦? **4** [U] difficulty 困難: *I don't anticipate any trouble getting them to agree.* 我認為要讓他們同意不會有任何困難的。| *I had quite a lot of trouble finding your house.* 我費了好大的勁兒才找到你家。**5** [U] fighting or disagreement 戰鬥; 紛爭: *They sent in troops to deal with the trouble at the border.* 他們派出軍隊去解決邊境地區的紛爭。**6** [U] effort or inconvenience 費力; 不便: *The boss took the trouble to explain the situation to me.* 老闆特地把情況解釋給我聽。| *Of course I'll help — it's no trouble at all.* 我當然會幫忙的, 這一點也不麻煩。**7 in trouble** in difficulty, often because you have done something wrong〔常由於做錯事而〕在困境中: *Her son kept getting into trouble with the police.* 他的兒子老是和警察惹上麻煩。**8 ask for trouble,**

look for trouble to behave in a way that causes a difficulty or danger 自找麻煩: *Driving like that he's just asking for trouble.* 他那樣開車是在自找麻煩。

■ USAGE 用法: In the phrases **to have trouble with something** and **to have trouble doing something** the word trouble is *always uncountable* (NEVER plural) ☆在詞組 **to have trouble with something** 和 **to have trouble doing something** 中，trouble 一詞總是用作不可數名詞〔不用複數形式〕: *I'm having trouble with my essay.* 我在論文上遇到了麻煩。| *I had real trouble explaining things to my friends.* 我在向朋友們解釋事情時，遇到了很大的麻煩。

---

troubled /ˈtrʌbld; ˈtrʌbəld/ *adj* suffering from problems 煩惱的; 有問題的: *His face had a troubled look.* 他的臉上有種困擾的神情。| *She's been troubled by a bad back for years.* 多年以來她一直受到背痛的困擾。| *a troubled region* 動亂的地區

troub·le·mak·er /ˈtrʌblˌmekɚ; ˈtrʌbəlˌmeɪkəʳ/ *n* a person who keeps on causing trouble 惹事生非的人

troub·le·shoot·er /ˈtrʌblˌʃutɚ; ˈtrʌbəlˌʃuːtəʳ/ *n* a person employed to remove causes of trouble, usually in an organization〔通常在一個機構內雇用的〕解決問題的人;〔機器等的〕檢修人員

troub·le·some /ˈtrʌblsəm; ˈtrʌbəlsəm/ *adj* causing trouble or anxiety 引起麻煩的; 令人焦慮的: *a troublesome tooth* 令人痛楚的牙齒

trough /trɒf; trɒf/ *n* **1** a long narrow container used to hold water or food for animals〔餵動物的〕食槽 **2** a long narrow hollow area, for example between two waves 浪谷 **3** *tech* an area of lower pressure between two areas of high pressure〔術語〕低壓槽

troupe /trup; truːp/ *n* a group of singers, actors or dancers 歌唱團; 劇團; 舞蹈團

troup·er /ˈtrupɚ; ˈtruːpəʳ/ *n* a member of a troupe〔演藝團的〕團員

trou·sers /ˈtrauzɚz; ˈtrauzəz/ *n* [pl] an outer garment covering your body from the waist down, with one part for each leg 褲子, 長褲: *a pair of blue trousers* 一條藍色長褲 –see 見 PAIR (USAGE 用法) –see picture on page 210 見 210 頁彩圖 **–trouser** *adj* [only before a noun 只用於名詞前]: *a trouser leg* 褲腿

trous·seau /truˈso; ˈtruːsəʊ/ *n* **trousseaux** or **trousseaus** /-soz; -səʊz/ *old fash* the personal possessions, especially clothes, that a woman brings with her when she marries〔老式〕嫁妝

trout /traut; traut/ *n* [plural is 複數為 **trout**] [C; U] a river fish with darkish spots on its brown skin, used for food 鱒魚

trow·el /ˈtrauəl; ˈtrauəl/ *n* **1** a tool with a flat blade for spreading cement or PLASTER 鏝刀泥刀, 抹子 **2** a small garden tool with a curved blade for digging small holes〔園藝用的〕小泥鏟 –see picture on page 958 見 958 頁彩圖

tru·ant /ˈtruənt; ˈtruːənt/ *n* **1** a pupil who stays away from school without permission 逃學的小學生 **2 play truant** to stay away from school without permission 曠課, 逃學: *If you saw John in town this morning he must have been playing truant.* 如果你今天上午在城裡看到約翰的話, 那他肯定是逃學了。 **– truancy** *n* [U]: *We have a high level of truancy at this school.* 這學校的逃學情況很嚴重。

truce /trus; truːs/ *n* an agreement between two enemies to stop fighting for a short time 停戰協定

★**truck** /trʌk; trʌk/ *n* **1** a large motor vehicle used for carrying goods in large quantities 貨車, 卡車: *Heavy trucks aren't allowed to cross this bridge.* 重型貨車不得駛過這條橋。**2** *BrE* an open railway vehicle for carrying goods〔英式〕鐵路敞篷貨車: *coal trucks* 煤車

truc·u·lent /ˈtrʌkjələnt; ˈtrʌkjʊlənt/ *adj* bad-tempered and always willing to quarrel 暴躁的; 好鬥的 **–truculence** *n* [U]

trudge /trʌdʒ; trʌdʒ/ *v* **trudged, trudging** [I+adv/prep] to walk with heavy steps, slowly and with effort 腳步沉重地走: *The soldiers trudged wearily through the mud.* 士兵邁着沉重的腳步, 疲憊不堪地走過泥地。 **– trudge** *n*

★★**true** /tru; truː/ *adj* **truer, truest 1** in accordance with fact or reality 符合事實的, 真實的: *a true story* 真實的故事 | *Is the news true?* 這消息是真的嗎? | *Is it true you're going away?* 你是真的要走嗎? **2** real and sincere 真正的; 真誠的: *true love* 真摯的愛 | *I have a true interest in your future.* 我對你的未來真的很感興趣。 **3** faithful and loyal 忠實的; 忠誠的: *a true friend* 忠實的朋友 | *He remained true to his principles.* 他仍然信守自己的原則。 **4** exact 準確的, 確切的: *a true copy* 正本 **5** a good example of a particular thing 標準的; 地道的: *a true Frenchman* 地道的法國人 | *true competition* 名副其實的競爭 **6** correctly fitted or placed〔安裝、放置〕正確的: *If the door's not exactly true it won't close properly.* 門如果沒有裝好就關不上。 **7 come true** to happen just as you wished or expected 實現, 成真 **8 true to form/type** behaving or acting just as you would expect〔行為〕一如既往 **9 true to your word** doing what you promised to do 信守諾言

true-life /ˌ· ·◂/ *adj* [only before a noun 只用於名詞前] based on fact 基於事實的, 真實的: *a true-life adventure story* 一個真實的冒險故事

---

truf·fle /ˈtrʌfl; ˈtrʌfəl/ *n* **1** a FUNGUS that grows underground and is considered good to eat〔可食用的〕塊菌 **2** a type of soft sweet 巧克力軟糖

tru·is·m /ˈtruːɪzəm; ˈtruːɪzəm/ *n* a statement that is so clearly true that there is no need to say it 自明之理, 不言而喻的話

*tru·ly /ˈtruːli; ˈtruːli/ *adv* **1** exactly 準確地, 確切地: *He cannot truly be described as stupid, but he is lazy.* 確切地說, 他不能算是愚蠢, 而是懶惰。 **2** really 真正地: *I am truly grateful to you.* 我衷心感激你。 | *a truly beautiful view* 非常美麗的景色 **3 yours truly** a phrase used at the end of a formal letter before the signature 敬上, 謹上〔用於正式信函結尾處署名之前〕 **4** a word used to show strongly that you are telling the truth 的確, 真的〔用於加強語氣〕: *No, truly, I didn't break the window.* 沒有, 真的, 我沒有打碎玻璃窗。

trump¹ /trʌmp; trʌmp/ *n* **1** any card of a suit chosen to be of the highest value in a particular card game〔牌戲中的〕王牌, 將牌 **2 come/turn up trumps** to behave in a generous or helpful way, especially unexpectedly〔尤指出人意料地〕慷慨相助 **3 your trump card** the best or most effective thing you can do to gain advantage over someone 王牌, 絕招

trump² *v* **[T]** to beat a card by playing a trump〔牌戲〕出王牌贏〔一牌〕

trump sthg ↔ up *phr v* **[T]** to invent a reason or story falsely 捏造〔罪名〕: *The President wanted to get rid of him, so he was sent to prison on a trumped-up charge.* 總統想除掉他, 因此以誣告的罪名把他關進了監獄。

trum·pet¹ /ˈtrʌmpɪt; ˈtrʌmpət/ *n* **1** a brass wind instrument, played by pressing three buttons in various combinations 小號, 喇叭 **2** a loud cry made by an elephant 象的吼叫聲

trumpet² *v* **[I] 1** to play a trumpet 吹小號 **2** (of elephants) to make a loud sound〔象〕吼叫 **–trumpeter** *n*

trun·cate /ˈtrʌŋkeɪt; trʌŋˈkeɪt/ *v* **truncated, truncating [T]** *fml* to shorten something by cutting a part or end off it《正式》把〔某物〕截短: *a truncated report* 被刪減過的報告

trun·cheon /ˈtrʌntʃən; ˈtrʌntʃən/ *n* a short thick stick carried as a weapon by British policemen 警棍

trun·dle /ˈtrʌndl; ˈtrʌndl/ *v* **trundled, trundling [I+adv/prep; T+adv/prep]** to move or be made to move slowly and heavily on wheels (使) 沉重地滾動: *An old lady was trundling a cart along the street.* 一位老太太推着一輛車子在街上慢吞吞地走着。

trunk /trʌŋk; trʌŋk/ *n* **1** the thick main stem of a tree 樹幹 **2** the human body apart from the head and limbs〔人的〕軀幹 **3** a large box in which clothes or belongings are stored or packed for travel〔旅行用的〕大箱子, 衣箱 **4** the very long nose of an el-ephant 象鼻 **5** the usual American word for the BOOT of a car《美式》〔汽車的〕行李箱 **6 trunks** a garment worn by men for swimming〔男用的〕游泳褲

trunk call /ˈ· ·/ *n* a telephone call made over a long distance 長途電話

trunk road /ˈ· ·/ *n* a main road 公路幹線

*trust¹ /trʌst; trʌst/ *n* **1 [U]** firm belief in the honesty or worth of someone or something 信任, 信賴: *I don't place any trust in his promise.* 我根本不相信他的許諾。 | *It took the teacher a long time to gain the children's trust.* 老師花了很長時間才取得了孩子們的信任。 **2 [U]** responsibility for something important or valuable 職責: *a position of trust* 要職 **3 [U]** care 照顧: *After their parents' death the children were put in my trust.* 孩子們的父母去世後, 他們便交給我來照顧。 **4 [C; U]** an arrangement for the holding and controlling of money and property for someone else〔錢財的〕託管: *money held in trust for a child* 為一個孩子代管的錢 | *She set up a trust for the benefit of her grandchildren.* 她為孫兒建立了一筆信託基金, 以便其將來能夠受益。 **5 take something on trust** to accept something as true without proof 憑信用接受某物

*trust² *v* **1 [T]** to have faith in someone or something and believe in their honesty 信任, 相信〔某人或某事物〕: *Don't trust him, he's dishonest.* 別相信他, 他不誠實。 | *Trust my judgment!* 相信我的判斷吧! **2 [T]** to believe someone or something will act properly and successfully 信賴〔某人或某事物〕: *That actor can always be trusted to give an excellent performance.* 那位演員演出總是十分出色, 令人非常放心。 | *Can I trust you to look after my best interests?* 我能信任你把我的最大利益交給你來照管嗎?

□ **USEFUL PATTERNS** 有用句型
to trust someone to do something

---

3 [T] to give or tell someone something important 把重要東西交給〔某人〕; 把重要事情告訴〔某人〕: *I trusted Tom with my secret.* 我放心把祕密告訴了湯姆。 **4 [+(that)]** to believe that something is right or true 相信〔某事〕正確〔真實〕: *She trusted her information was correct.* 她相信她的資料是正確的。 **5 trust in** to have faith in someone or something 信任, 信賴〔某人或某事物〕 **6 Trust you!** a phrase used when someone behaves in a way that is typical of them 又來這一套了!〔用於某人以慣常的方式做出舉動時〕: *Trust him to ask a question just at the wrong moment.* 他肯定又要在不對的時候問問題。

trust·ee /trʌˈstiː; trʌsˈtiː/ *n* a person or firm that legally holds and controls property for someone else〔財產的〕託管人; 託管公司

trust·ful /ˈtrʌstfəl; ˈtrʌstfəl/ *adj* (also 又作

trusting) ready to believe in the sincerity of others 容易信任別人的: *the trustful nature of a small child* 小孩子容易信任他人的天性 – **trustfully** *adv*

trust·wor·thy /ˈtrʌstˌwɜ˞ðɪ; ˈtrʌstˌwɜːðɪ/ *adj* dependable and responsible 可靠的, 值得信賴的 –**trustworthiness** *n* [U]

trust·y /ˈtrʌstɪ; ˈtrʌstɪ/ *adj* **trustier, trustiest** *old fash* faithful 〖老式〗可靠的, 忠誠的: *My trusty old car will get us home safely.* 我那輛可靠的舊車能夠把我們安全地送回家。

★**truth** /truθ; truːθ/ *n* **truths** /truðz; truːðz/ **1** [U] that which is in accordance with fact and reality 真相, 事實, 實情: *You must always tell the truth.* 你必須永遠講真話。**2** [U] the quality of being true 真實性: *I don't doubt the truth of his information.* 我不懷疑他這個消息的真實性。**3** [C] a fact or principle accepted as true 真理: *the truths of science* 科學真理 **4 in truth** *fml* really 〖正式〗事實上 **5 to tell you the truth** a phrase to make it clear you are being honest 說句老實話〖用於表示自己態度坦誠〗: *To tell you the truth , I don't like him at all.* 說實話, 我一點也不喜歡他。

truth·ful /ˈtruθfəl; ˈtruːθfəl/ *adj* **1** true to the facts 符合事實的, 真實的: *a truthful account of what happened* 對於所發生事情的如實報道 **2** honest 誠實的: *a truthful boy* 誠實的男孩 –**truthfully** *adv* –**truthfulness** *n* [U]

★★**try¹** /traɪ; traɪ/ *v* **tried, trying 1** [I;T] to attempt to do something 嘗試做〖某事〗: *I don't think I can do it but I'll try.* 我覺得我做不了這件事, 但願意試一試。| *Please try to come.* 請盡量想辦法來。| *Don't try and do too much at once.* 不要試着一次做得太多。

□ USEFUL PATTERNS 有用句型
to try something; to try to do something

2 [T] to do something or use something so that you can find out if it is effective or enjoyable 試做, 試用〖某物〗: *Have you tried this new soap?* 你試用過這種新肥皂嗎? | *It seems a good idea; I'll try it.* 聽起來是個好主意, 我要試試。| *I tried waterskiing on holiday but didn't like it.* 假期裡我試試去滑水, 但發覺並不喜歡這項運動。

□ USEFUL PATTERNS 有用句型
to try something; to try doing something

3 [T] to examine a person in a court of law to decide if they are guilty 審問, 審判〖某人〗: *They're going to try him for murder.* 他們將以謀殺罪審判他。**4** [T] to go to a person or place to find out if they can give you what you want 找〖人〗, 到〖某處〗〖以試圖得到想要的東西〗: *I tried four shops before I got the shoes I wanted.* 我跑了四家商店才買

到自己想要買的鞋。**5** [T] to attempt to open a door or windows 試圖打開〖門或窗〗: *I think the door's locked but I'll try it just in case.* 我認為門已上鎖了, 不過我想去推推試試, 以防萬一。

■ USAGE 用法: **1** You can make **try** stronger by using **hard** ☆可以用 **hard** 來加強 **try** 的語氣: *He isn't very good at English, but he* **tries hard.** 他的英語並不太好, 但他很努力學習。**2** Compare 比較 **try to do** *something* and **try doing** *something*. If you **try to do** *something* you make an effort to do it, but without success ☆ **try to do** 表示努力做某事, 但不成功: *I tried to finish the work, but I didn't have enough time.* 我就着完成那項工作, 但沒有足夠的時間。If you **try doing** *something* you do it in order to see what will happen ☆ **try doing** 表示試着做做, 以便看一下會有甚麼結果: *If the machine doesn't work,* **try giving** *it a kick.* 如果這台機器不運轉, 那麼踢它一腳試試。

---

try sthg ↔ **on** *phr v* [T] to put on an article of clothing to see if it fits 試穿〖衣物〗

try² *n* **tries 1** an attempt 嘗試, 試: *Let me have a try.* 讓我來試一下。| *It was a good try but it didn't succeed.* 這是一次很好的嘗試, 但不成功。**2** points that you win in a game of RUGBY by putting the ball down behind the opposing team's GOAL〖橄欖球賽中的〗觸地所得的分

tsar /tsɑr; zɑːr/ *n* (also 又作 **czar, tzar**) the ruler of Russia before 1917〔在1917年以前統治俄國的〕沙皇

tset·se fly /ˈtsɛtsɪ flaɪ; ˈtetsɪ flaɪ/ *n* (also 又作 **tsetse**) a blood-sucking African fly that causes disease 舌蠅, 采采蠅〔非洲一種吸吮人血並會引起疾病的昆蟲〕

T-shirt /ˈtiˌʃɜrt; ˈtiː ʃɜːt/ *n* (also 又作 **tee shirt**) a close-fitting piece of clothing with a round neck and short sleeves (SLEEVE) which you wear on the upper part of your body T恤, 短袖汗衫 –see picture on page 210 見 210 頁彩圖

tsp [plural is 複數為 **tsps**] a written abbreviation for 〖縮〗= TEASPOON 茶匙: *one tsp of salt* 一茶匙鹽

tub /tʌb; tʌb/ *n* **1** a round or OBLONG container, for packing, storing, or washing things〔存放、洗濯用的〕缸, 盆 –see picture on page 244 見 244 頁彩圖 **2** *AmE* a bath〖美式〗浴缸

tu·ba /ˈtjubə; ˈtjuːbə/ *n* a large brass wind instrument that produces low notes〔樂器〕大號

tub·by /ˈtʌbɪ; ˈtʌbɪ/ *adj* **tubbier, tubbiest** *infml* short and fat〖非正式〗矮胖的

★**tube** /tjub; tjuːb/ *n* **1** a hollow round pipe of

metal, glass, or rubber often used for holding liquids 〔裝液體用的金屬、玻璃、或橡膠製成的〕管子 **2** a long thin metal container, fitted with a cap, for holding things like TOOTHPASTE or paint 〔裝牙膏或顏料等有蓋的〕金屬管 –see picture on page 244 見244 頁彩圖 **3** a hollow pipe or organ in your body 〔身體內的〕管(道): *the bronchial tubes* 支氣管 **4 the tube** *BrE* the underground railway in London 〔英式〕〔倫敦的〕地(下)鐵(道): *He hates going on the tube.* 他討厭乘坐地鐵。 **5 by tube** travelling on the tube 乘地鐵: *I usually go by tube.* 我一般乘地鐵去。

tu·ber /'tjubə; 'tjuːbəʳ/ *n* a fleshy swollen underground stem, such as the potato 塊莖 〔如馬鈴薯〕

tu·ber·cu·lo·sis /tjuˌbɜːkjəˈləʊsɪs; tjuːˌbɜːkjᵿˈləʊsᵻs/ *n* [U] (also 又作 **TB**) a serious infectious disease that attacks the lungs 肺結核 –**tubercular** /tjuˈbɜːkjələˈ; tjuːˈbɜːkjᵿləʳ/ *adj*

tub·ing /'tjubɪŋ; 'tjuːbɪŋ/ *n* [U] metal or plastic in the form of a tube 〔金屬或塑料〕管(道)

tu·bu·lar /'tjubjələ; 'tjuːbjᵿləʳ/ *adj* like a tube or made from a tube 管狀的; 管製的: *tubular metal furniture* 用金屬管製成的家具

T.U.C. /ˌti ju ˈsi; ˌtiː juː ˈsiː/ an organization of TRADES UNIONS in Britain; an abbreviation for **Trades Union Congress** 〔縮〕英國工會聯合會; 工會代表大會

tuck¹ /tʌk; tʌk/ *v* [T+adv/prep] **1** to put something into a desired or convenient position 把…藏到 *a book tucked under his arm* 夾在他腋下的一本書 **2** to put the end of a piece of clothing under another so that it looks tidy 把〔衣服的一端〕塞進: *Tuck your shirt into your trousers.* 把你的襯衫下襬塞進褲子裡去。

tuck sthg ↔ away *phr v* [T] to put something in a safe or hidden place 把〔某物〕藏好: *She's got a lot of money tucked away.* 她把許多錢藏了起來。

tuck in *phr v* **1** [I] *infml* to eat eagerly 〔非正式〕狼吞虎嚥 **2** [T **tuck sbdy ↔ in**] to make someone comfortable in bed by pulling the covers tight 把〔某人的〕被子蓋好

tuck² *n* **1** [C] a flat fold of material sewn into a garment for decoration or to give it a particular shape 〔衣服的〕縫褶 **2** [U] *BrE old fash* food, especially cakes and sweets as eaten by school children 〔英式, 老式〕〔尤指小學生愛吃的〕糖果糕點: *a tuck shop* 糖果糕點舖

Tues. an abbreviation for 〔縮〕= Tuesday

Tues·day /'tjuzdɪ; 'tjuːzdɪ/ *n* the day between Monday and Wednesday 星期二

tuft /tʌft; tʌft/ *n* a bunch of hair, feathers, or grass 一簇, 一束〔頭髮、羽毛或草〕 –**tufted** *adj*

tug¹ /tʌg; tʌg/ *v* [I;T] to pull something with force or much effort 用力拖, 拉: *We tugged,*

and the rope broke. 我們用力一拉, 繩子便斷了。| *The little child tugged his mother's arm.* 那個小孩子用力拉母親的臂膀。

tug² *n* **1** a sudden strong pull 猛拉, 猛拽 **2** see 見 TUGBOAT

tug·boat /'tʌgˌbot; 'tʌgbəʊt/ *n* (also 又作 **tug**) a small powerful boat used for guiding large vessels into or out of harbours 拖船

tug-of-war /ˌ···ˈ·/ *n* a test of strength in which two teams pull against each other on a rope 拔河(比賽)

tu·i·tion /tjuˈɪʃ*ə*n; tjuːˈɪʃ*ə*n/ *n* [U] teaching, especially of people in small groups 〔尤指小規模的〕教學, 講授: *tuition fees* 學費 | *He needs extra tuition in physics.* 他需要補習物理。

tu·lip /'tjuləp; 'tjuːlᵻp/ *n* a garden plant that grows from a BULB and has large colourful cup-shaped flowers 鬱金香

tum·ble¹ /'tʌmbl; 'tʌmbəl/ *v* **tumbled, tumbling 1** [I] to fall or roll over suddenly, helplessly, or in a disordered way 跌倒, 摔倒, 滾下: *The child tripped and tumbled down the stairs.* 孩子絆了一下, 從樓梯上滾了下去。| *The water tumbled over the rock.* 水從岩石上奔騰而過。 **2 tumble to something** *infml* to understand something suddenly 〔非正式〕忽然明白某事: *It was a long time before she tumbled to what I meant.* 過了許久她才忽然明白我的意思。

tumble² *n* a fall 跌倒

tumble dry·er /ˈ·· ˌ·ˈ·/ *n* (also 又作 **tumble drier**) an electric machine which is used to dry washing 滾筒式乾衣機

tum·bler /'tʌmblə; 'tʌmbləʳ/ *n* a drinking glass with no handle or stem 平底無腳酒杯

tum·my /'tʌmɪ; 'tʌmɪ/ *n* **tummies** *infml* your stomach 〔非正式〕肚子: *a tummy ache* 肚子痛

tu·mour /'tjumə; 'tjuːməʳ/ *n* (**tumor** *AmE* 〔美式〕) a mass of diseased cells in your body 腫瘤, 腫塊

tu·mult /'tjumʌlt; 'tjuːmʌlt/ *n* [C;U] *fml* confused noise and excitement 〔正式〕吵鬧; 混亂; 激動 –**tumultuous** /tjuˈmʌltʃʊəs; tjuːˈmʌltʃuəs/ *adj*: *a tumultuous welcome* 鬧哄哄的歡迎場面 –**tumultuously** *adv*

tu·na /'tjunə; 'tjuːnə/ *n* [C;U] a large sea fish, used for food 金槍魚, 吞拿魚: *a tin of tuna fish* 一罐金槍魚

tun·dra /'tʌndrə; 'tʌndrə/ *n* **the tundra** a cold treeless plain in the far north of Europe, Asia, and North America 〔北極的〕凍原, 凍土帶

tune¹ /tjun; tjuːn/ *n* **1** an arrangement of musical notes that form a pleasing sound 曲調, 旋律: *Do you know the tune to this song?* 你知道這首歌的曲調嗎? | *a catchy tune* 容易記住的旋律 **2 change your tune** to change your opinion or behaviour 改變觀點〔態度〕 **3 in tune: a** producing the correct musical notes 合調: *The piano is now in tune.* 現在這架鋼琴的音調很準。| *She can't sing in tune.* 她唱歌走調。**b** in agreement or sympathy 一致, 協調: *His ideas were in tune with mine.* 他的觀點與我的一致。[RELATED PHRASE 相關詞組 **out of tune**] **4 to the tune of** by an amount of 總計: *We were overcharged to the tune of fifty pounds.* 我們被多收了五十英鎊。

tune² *v* **tuned, tuning** [T] **1** to set a musical instrument so that it produces the proper notes 為〔樂器〕調音 **2** to put an engine in good working order 把〔引擎〕調好

tune in *phr v* [I] to set a radio to receive broadcasts from a particular radio station 收聽〔廣播節目〕: *We always tune in to the BBC at nine o'clock.* 我們總是在九點鐘收聽英國廣播公司的節目。

tune·ful /ˈtjuːnfʊl; ˈtjuːnfəl/ *adj* having a pleasing tune 曲調優美的 **–tunefully** *adv*

tune·less /ˈtjuːnlɪs; ˈtjuːnləs/ *adj* unmusical and unpleasant to listen to 不成調的, 不悅耳的 **–tunelessly** *adv*

tun·er /ˈtjuːnə; ˈtjuːnɚ/ *n* **1** the part of a radio or television that changes the signals into sound and pictures 〔收音機或電視機的〕調諧器, 頻道選擇器 **2** a person who tunes musical instruments 樂器調音師: *a piano tuner* 鋼琴調音師

tu·nic /ˈtjuːnɪk; ˈtjuːnɪk/ *n* **1** a loose outer piece of clothing without arms which reaches to your knees 〔無袖的〕外袍 **2** a short coat worn by policemen or soldiers as part of a uniform 〔警察或士兵作為制服穿的〕短上衣

tuning fork /ˈ··· ·/ *n* a small steel instrument that produces a fixed musical note when struck, used in tuning musical instruments 〔為樂器調音用的〕音叉

★tun·nel¹ /ˈtʌnl; ˈtʌnl/ *n* an underground or underwater passage 地道; 隧道

tunnel² *v* **-ll-** (also 又作 **-l-** *AmE* 〔美式〕) [I] to make a tunnel under or through a hill or river 挖隧道

tur·ban /ˈtɜːbən; ˈtɜːbən/ *n* **1** a head-covering consisting of a long length of cloth wound round your head 頭巾 **–see picture on page 210** 見 210 頁彩圖 **2** a woman's small tight-fitting hat 女用頭巾帽

tur·bine /ˈtɜːbɪn; ˈtɜːbaɪn/ *n* an engine or motor driven by the pressure of liquid or gas 渦輪機

tur·bo·charg·er /ˈtɜːbəʊˌtʃɑːdʒə; ˈtɜːbəʊˌtʃɑːdʒɚ/ *n* a FAN in a car which makes it work better and is driven by waste gas from the engine 渦輪增壓器 **–turbocharge** *v* **turbocharged, turbocharging** [T]: *My car has a small engine, but it's been turbocharged so it's very powerful.* 我的車引擎不大, 但由於裝置了渦輪增壓器, 所以馬力很大。

tur·bot /ˈtɜːbət; ˈtɜːbət/ *n* [plural is 複數為 **turbot**] [C;U] a large fish with a flat body,

used for food 大菱鮃〔一種扁平的大海魚〕

tur·bu·lence /ˈtɜːbjələns; ˈtɜːbjʊləns/ *n* [U] **1** the state of being violent and uncontrolled 騷亂, 騷動 **2** irregular and violent movement of air or water 〔空氣或水的〕湍流, 不穩定的強氣流: *The flight was very uncomfortable because of turbulence.* 由於有不穩定的強氣流, 這段航程很不舒服。

tur·bu·lent /ˈtɜːbjələnt; ˈtɜːbjʊlənt/ *adj* violent and stormy 騷亂的; 狂暴的: *turbulent weather* 惡劣的天氣 | *a turbulent period of history* 歷史上動蕩不安的時期

tu·reen /tʊˈriːn; tjʊˈriːn/ *n* a large deep dish with a lid, from which soup is served 〔帶蓋的〕大湯碗

turf¹ /tɜːf; tɜːf/ *n* **turfs** *or* **turves** /tɜːvz; tɜːvz/ **1** [U] a surface made of soil with thick grass growing on it 草皮, 草坪: *the smooth turf of a bowling green* 草地滾木球場上平滑的草皮 **2** [C] a small piece of thick grass with soil 一塊草皮: *She bought some turfs for her lawn.* 她買了些草皮來修補她的草坪。 **3 the turf** the sport or world of horse-racing 賽馬(界)

turf² *v* [T] to cover a piece of land with turf 用草皮覆蓋〔土地〕

turf sbdy ↔ out *phr v* [T] *infml* to throw someone out 〔非正式〕趕走〔某人〕: *He's been turfed out of his house because he hasn't paid the rent.* 他由於不付房租而被趕了出來。

turf ac·coun·tant /ˈ· ·, ··/ *n* a BOOKMAKER 〔賽馬的〕賭注登記者

tur·gid /ˈtɜːdʒɪd; ˈtɜːdʒɪd/ *adj* too solemn, uninteresting, and difficult to understand (used of a piece of writing) 浮誇的, 艱澀的〔指文章〕

tur·key /ˈtɜːkɪ; ˈtɜːki/ *n* [C;U] a large bird bred for its meat which is used as food, particularly on special occasions 火雞

Turk·ish¹ /ˈtɜːkɪʃ; ˈtɜːkɪʃ/ *adj* from or connected with Turkey 土耳其的

Turkish² **1 the Turkish** the people of Turkey 土耳其人 **2** [U] the language of Turkey 土耳其語

tur·moil /ˈtɜːmɔɪl; ˈtɜːmɔɪl/ *n* [sing; U] a state of confusion, excitement, and anxiety 混亂; 騷亂: *The whole town was in turmoil.* 整座城鎮處於一片混亂之中。| *I was thrown into a complete turmoil by the news.* 聽了這消息, 我心裡亂哄哄的。

*★★***turn¹** /tɜːn; tɜːn/ *v* **1** [I] to move round 轉動: *The wheel turned slowly.* 車輪緩緩轉動。 **2** [T] to make something move round 使〔某物〕轉動: *She turned the key in the lock.* 她轉動鎖裡的鑰匙。| *He turned the picture round to face the wall.* 他將圖畫轉過來面對着牆壁。| *She turned the bottle upside down.* 她把瓶子倒了過來。 **3** [I] to move your body or your head so that you can see in another direction 轉動〔身體或頭部〕: *He turned and waved.* 他轉過身來揮揮

手。 | *She turned round to look at him.* 她轉過頭來看他。 **4** [I+adv/prep] to change the direction in which you are moving 改變方向: *She turned down a side street.* 她轉彎沿着一條橫街走去。 | *The car turned into the car park.* 汽車轉彎駛進了停車場。 **5** [T] to make a car or other vehicle change the direction in which it is moving 使〔車輛〕改變行駛方向: *She turned the car into a narrow lane.* 她把汽車轉進一條狹窄的小巷裡。 **6 turn a corner** to move round a corner 拐過彎角: *The car turned the corner and disappeared.* 汽車拐過街角便消失了。 **7** [I] to become something different 變為，變成: *The water had turned into ice.* 水已變成了冰。 | *Their amusement turned to horror when they realized what had really happened.* 當他們明白到究竟發生了甚麼事情以後，他們的歡欣變成了恐懼。 | *The grass had all turned brown in the dry weather.* 在乾旱的天氣裡，草都變得枯黃。 –see 見 BECOME (USAGE用法) **8** [T] to make something into something different 使〔某物〕變成: *They plan to turn the building into a hotel.* 他們打算把這建築物改造成一座旅館。 | *The heat had turned the milk sour.* 炎熱的天氣使牛奶變酸了。 **9** [T] to reach a certain age or time 達到〔某一年齡或時間〕: *He's just turned 40.* 他剛過四十歲。 | *It's just turned three o'clock.* 剛到三點鐘。 **10 turn a blind eye** to pretend not to notice something bad 對…假裝看不見; 對…熟視無睹 **11 turn tail** to run away 逃跑 **12 turn the tables** to change from being in a weak position to being in a strong position 〔地位〕轉弱為強 **13 turn your attention/thoughts to something** to start thinking about something 把注意力轉移到某事; 開始考慮某事: *Now let's turn our attention to the problems of the Third World.* 現在讓我們把注意力轉移到第三世界的問題上。 [RELATED PHRASE 相關詞組 **your attention/thoughts turn to something**] **14 turn your hand to something** to begin to do something that needs skill 着手做〔需要技巧的事情〕 **15 turn your stomach** to make you feel sick 使感到噁心

turn against *phr v* [I;T **turn** sbdy **against** sbdy/sthg] to start disliking someone or something, or cause someone else to start disliking someone or something (使)開始討厭; (使)反目: *She seems to have turned against me.* 她似乎開始與我作對。

turn away *phr v* **1** [I] to look in another direction so that you do not have to look at something 移開目光: *I tried to talk to her but she turned away.* 我想和她講話，但她卻把目光移開了。 **2** [T **turn** sbdy ↔ **away**] to refuse to allow someone to enter a place 拒絕〔某人〕進入〔某地方〕

turn back *phr v* **1** [I] to return in the same direction that you have come from 返回，折回: *We had to turn back because of the*

snow. 由於下大雪，我們不得不折返了。 **2** [T **turn** sbdy ↔ **back**] to make someone return in the same direction that they have come from 使〔某人〕返回，使〔某人〕折回

turn down *phr v* **1** [T **turn** sthg ↔ **down**] to reduce the heat produced by a heater or the sound produced by a raido or record player 把〔取暖器、收音機或唱機〕開小; 調低 **2** [T **turn** sbdy ↔ **down**] to refuse a request that someone has made to you 拒絕〔要求〕: *I applied for the job but they turned me down.* 我申請那份工作，但他們拒絕了我。 – see 見 REFUSE (USAGE用法)

turn in *phr v* **1** [I] *infml* to go to bed 〔非正式〕去睡覺 **2** [T **turn** sbdy ↔ **in**] to give someone to the police 把〔某人〕交給警方

turn off *phr v* **1** [T **turn** sthg ↔ **off**] to cause something to stop operating by turning a button or SWITCH 關掉〔開關〕: *Shall I turn the television off?* 我把電視關掉好嗎? **2** [I;T **turn off** sthg] to leave a road 離開〔馬路〕: *We turned off the main road onto a country lane.* 我們離開大路，走上了一條鄉間小道。

turn on *phr v* **1** [T **turn** sthg ↔ **on**] to cause something to start operating by turning a button or SWITCH 打開〔開關〕: *He turned on the light.* 他開了燈。 **2** [T **turn on** sbdy] to attack someone suddenly 突然襲擊〔某人〕 **3** [T **turn** sbdy **on**] to make someone feel sexually interested 挑逗〔某人〕, 使產生快感 **4** [T **turn** sthg **on** sbdy] to direct a weapon towards someone 把武器瞄準〔某人〕: *He shot his wife then turned the gun on himself.* 他槍殺了妻子，然後把槍對準了自己。

turn out *phr v* **1** [T **turn** sthg ↔ **out**] to cause something to stop shining 關上，關掉〔燈〕: *She turned out the light.* 她關上了燈。 **2** [I] to gather for a public event 聚集: *Crowds of people turned out to welcome the troops home.* 人們成群結隊地迎接返家的軍隊。 **3** [T **turn** sthg ↔ **out**] to produce something 生產，製造〔某物〕: *The factory turns out 3000 cars a day.* 那工廠一天生產三千輛汽車。 **4 turn out to be** to be shown to be in the end 結果(是)，證明(是): *His story turned out to be true.* 他的說法後來證明是真的。 **5** [T **turn** sbdy **out**] to force someone to leave a place 迫使〔某人〕離開，趕走

turn over *phr v* **1** [T **turn** sthg ↔ **over**] to think about something 考慮〔某事〕: *I've been turning the idea over in my mind.* 我心裡一直在考慮這個主意。 **2** [T **turn** sthg ↔ **over**] to give something to someone who has a right to have it 把〔某物〕移交〔某人〕 **3** [T **turn** sbdy **over**] to give someone to the police 把〔某人〕交給警方

turn to *phr v* **1** [T **turn to** sbdy] to go to someone for help 求助於〔某人〕: *I don't know who I can turn to.* 我不知該向誰求助。 **2** [T **turn to** sthg] to start doing something 開始做〔某事〕: *Some young people turn to* *crime.* 一些年輕人開始走上犯罪之路。 **3** [T **turn to** sthg] to go to a particular page in a book 把書翻至〔某一頁〕: *Turn to page 27.* 翻 到第二十七頁。

turn up *phr v* **1** [I] to be found or discovered 被發現: *The missing bag turned up under an old railway bridge.* 那失去的手 提包在一座舊的鐵路橋下被發現。 **2** [T **turn** sthg ↔ **up**] to find something 找到〔某物〕: *Police have turned up some interesting new evidence.* 警方已找到一些令人感興趣的新線 索。 **3** [I] to arrive somewhere 到達〔某地〕: *They turned up late as usual.* 他們如常地遲 到了。 **4** [T **turn** sthg ↔ **up**] to increase the heat produced by a heater or the sound produced by a radio or record player 把〔取 暖器、收音機或唱機〕開大, 調大 **5** [T **turn** sthg ↔ **up**] to shorten a piece of clothing 把〔衣服〕捲起, 褶起

★★turn² *n* **1** an act of turning 轉動, 旋轉: *He gave the handle a couple of turns.* 他轉了幾下把手。 **2** a change of direction 〔方向的〕改變, 轉向: *Take the next turn on the right.* 在下一個路口向右轉。 **3** a change or development 變化; 發展: *We were all surprised by this latest turn of events.* 事件的最 新發展令我們很吃驚。 | *There seems to have been a turn for the worse.* 事情似乎變得 更糟了。 **4** the chance or right to do something that other people have done or are going to do 〔依次做某事的〕機會: *It's my turn to drive next.* 下次輪到我開車了。 | *Can I have a turn on your bicycle?* 我能輪流騎一 下你的腳踏車嗎? **5** *infml* an attack of an illness 〔非正式〕〔疾病的〕發作, 發病: *He's had one of his turns.* 他的病又發作了一次。 **6** a short performance in a show 一小段節目 **7** **the turn of the century** the period at the end of one century and the beginning of the next 世紀末的交替時間 **8** **a good turn** a useful or helpful action 有用〔有益〕的行為 **9** **done to a turn** perfectly cooked 〔菜〕燒得恰 到好處 **10** **in turn** one after the other 依次: *Each of the candidates was interviewed in turn.* 各候選人依次接受訪問。 **11** **take turns, take it in turns** to do something one after the other 輪流做〔某事〕: *We took it in turns to carry the suitcase.* 我們輪流抬手提箱。 | *We took turns at driving the car.* 我們輪流駕 車。

turn·coat /ˈtɜːn,kəʊt; ˈtɜːnkəʊt/ *n* someone who changes their political party, principles, or loyalty (a word used to express disapproval) 叛黨者, 變節者, 叛徒〔含貶義〕

turn·ing /ˈtɜːnɪŋ; ˈtɜːnɪŋ/ *n* a place where one road branches off from another 拐彎 處: *You'll find a telephone down the first turning on the left.* 你在第一個拐彎處向右轉 便能找到電話。

turning point /ˈ··· / *n* a point in time when an important change takes place 轉折點: *a turning point in the country's industrial de-*

velopment 該國工業發展的一個轉折點

tur·nip /ˈtɜːnɪp; ˈtɜːnɪp/ *n* [C;U] a round vegetable which grows underground and is used as food 蕪菁, 大頭菜, 蘿蔔 –see picture on page 504 見 504 頁彩圖

turn-out /ˈtɜːn,aʊt; ˈtɜːnaʊt/ *n* the number of people who attend a meeting or other event 出席人數: *They usually get a turnout of a hundred or more at their meetings.* 他們 舉行的會議通常有一百多人出席。

turn·o·ver /ˈtɜːn,əʊvə; ˈtɜːn,əʊvə/ *n* [U] the amount of business done, workers hired, or articles sold in a particular period 營業 額; 人事變動率; 銷售量: *a turnover of £5,000 a week* 一週營業額為五千英鎊

turn·stile /ˈtɜːn,staɪl; ˈtɜːnstaɪl/ *n* a small gate with four metal arms, spinning round on a central post, which allows people to pass one at a time 〔入口處的〕旋轉式柵門

turn·ta·ble /ˈtɜːn,teɪbl; ˈtɜːn,teɪbəl/ *n* the flat, round, spinning surface on a record player where a record is played 〔唱機上的〕 轉盤

turn-up /ˈ··/ *n* a narrow band of cloth turned upwards at the bottom of a trouser leg 〔褲腿的〕捲邊

tur·pen·tine /ˈtɜːpən,taɪn; ˈtɜːpəntaɪn/ *n* [U] (also 又作 **turps** /tɜːps; tɜːps/ *infml* 〔非正 式〕) a thin liquid, used for making paint thin or removing it 松節油

tur·quoise¹ /ˈtɜːkwɔɪz; ˈtɜːkwɔɪz/ *n* [U] a bluish-green, precious stone 綠松石

turquoise² *adj* a colour that is bluish-green 青綠色的 –see picture on page 243 見 243 頁彩圖

tur·ret /ˈtɜːrɪt; ˈtʌrɪt/ *n* a small tower, usually at a corner of a larger building 塔樓, 角塔

tur·tle /ˈtɜːtl; ˈtɜːtl/ *n* an animal that lives in water, with a soft body covered by a hard horny shell 龜, 海龜

tusk /tʌsk; tʌsk/ *n* a very long pointed tooth on certain animals such as the elephant 〔象等動物的〕長牙

tus·sle /ˈtʌsl; ˈtʌsəl/ *v* **tussled, tussling** [T] to fight roughly without weapons 扭打, 格 鬥 –**tussle** *n*

tut *interj* a sound made by sucking in air and moving your tongue behind your teeth, used to express slight disapproval or annoyance 嘖〔用於表示輕微不滿或惱怒〕

tu·tor /ˈtuːtə; ˈtjuːtər/ *n* **1** a teacher who gives private instruction to a single pupil or a very small class 家庭教師, 私人教師 **2** in British universities, a teacher who directs the studies of a number of students and teaches small groups of students 〔英國大學 中的〕導師 –**tutor** *v* [I;T]: *Mr Smith is tutoring Tom in Latin.* 史密斯先生在教導湯 姆學拉丁文。

tu·to·ri·al /tuːˈtɔːrɪəl; tjuːˈtɔːrɪəl/ *adj* related to a tutor or his or her duties 導師的; 導師 職責的

tutorial² *n* a lesson given by a tutor 輔導課, 導師個別指導課

tux·e·do /tʌkˈsido; tʌkˈsiːdəʊ/ *n* the usual American word for『美式』= DINNER JACKET

TV /ˌtiˈvi; ˌtiː ˈviː◂/ *n* see 見 TELEVISION

twad·dle /ˈtwɑdl; ˈtwɒdl/ *n* [U] *infml* nonsense『非正式』胡說八道

twang /twæŋ; twæŋ/ *v* [T] to pull the strings on a musical instrument such as a GUITAR so that they make a quick ringing sound〔撥吉他等的弦〕使發撥弦聲

tweak /twik; twiːk/ *v* [T] to pull and twist something, especially someone's ear or nose, with a sudden movement 捏, 擰, 扭〔尤指某人的耳朵或鼻子〕–**tweak** *n*

tweed /twid; twiːd/ *n* [U] coarse woollen cloth 粗花呢: *a tweed suit* 粗花呢套裝

tweet /twit; twiːt/ *v* [I] to make the short high noise of a small bird〔小鳥〕啾啾地叫 –**tweet** *n*

twee·zers /ˈtwizəz; ˈtwiːzəz/ *n* [pl] a small metal tool with two parts joined together at the end, used for picking up small objects or pulling out hairs 鑷子, 小鉗子

twelve /twɛlv; twelv/ *det, n, pron* the number 12〔數字〕十二 –**twelfth** /twɛlfθ; twelfθ/ *det, n, pron, adv*

twen·ty /ˈtwɛntɪ; ˈtwenti/ *det, n, pron* **1** the number 20〔數字〕二十 **2 the Twenties, the twenties** the years from 1920 to 1929〔從1920 年至 1929 年的〕二十年代 **3 in her twenties, in their twenties, etc.** aged between 20 and 29〔從二十歲到二十九歲〕二十多歲 –**twentieth** *det, n, pron, adv*

twenty-one /ˌ·· ˈ·◂/ *det, n, pron* the number 21〔數字〕二十一

twice /twaɪs; twaɪs/ *predeterminer, adv* two times 兩次; 兩倍: *I've read the book twice.* 那本書我讀了兩遍。| *He eats twice the amount that I eat.* 他的食量比我大一倍。| *He works twice as hard as anyone else.* 他在工作上付出的努力比別人多一倍。

twid·dle /ˈtwɪdl̩; ˈtwɪdl/ *v* **twiddled, twiddling 1** [I;T] to move your fingers to twist or turn something, often in a purposeless way〔用手指漫無目的地〕捻弄; 玩弄: *He irritated me by constantly twiddling* **with** *his pencil.* 他不斷地捻弄鉛筆, 這令我感到煩厭。**2 twiddle your thumbs** to waste your time doing nothing useful 無所事事

twig /twɪg; twɪg/ *n* a small thin woody stem growing from a branch 嫩枝, 細枝

twi·light /ˈtwaɪˌlaɪt; ˈtwaɪlaɪt/ *n* [U] the time when day is about to become night 黃昏, 薄暮時分

twin /twɪn; twɪn/ *n* **1** either of two children born to the same mother at the same time 雙胞胎之一: *Jean and John are twins.* 瓊和約翰是雙胞胎。| *my twin sister* 我的孿生妹妹 **2** either of two things which are closely connected or very like each other 兩個緊密相聯的事物之一: *twin towns* 姐妹城 | *twin beds* 兩張單人牀

twine¹ /twaɪn; twaɪn/ *n* [U] strong cord or string made by twisting threads together 兩股(或以上)的線[繩]

twine² *v* **twined, twining** [I+adv/prep; T+adv/prep] to twist 捻; 盤繞: *The stems twined round the tree trunk.* 莖盤繞着樹幹。| *She twined the ribbon in her hair.* 她把絲帶盤在頭髮上。

twinge /twɪndʒ; twɪndʒ/ *n* **1** a sudden sharp pain 一陣劇痛: *a twinge of toothache* 一陣牙痛 **2** a sudden unpleasant feeling 一陣不快: *a twinge of regret* 一陣遺憾

twin·kle /ˈtwɪŋkl; ˈtwɪŋkəl/ *v* **twinkled, twinkling** [I] **1** to shine with an unsteady light 閃爍, 閃亮: *stars twinkling in the sky* 在天空中閃爍的星星 **2** (of your eyes) to show pleasure, excitement, and amusement 眼睛〔因愉悅而〕發亮: *Her eyes twinkled.* 她的雙眼閃閃發亮。–**twinkle** *n* [sing]: *a twinkle of delight in his eyes* 他眼中閃現出愉悅的光芒

twin·kling /ˈtwɪŋklɪŋ; ˈtwɪŋklɪŋ/ *n* **in a twinkling, in the twinkling of an eye** *infml* in a moment『非正式』片刻, 不久, 轉瞬間

twirl /twɝl; twɜːl/ *v* [I;T] to turn round and round quickly (使)迅速旋轉 –**twirl** *n*

twist¹ /twɪst; twɪst/ *v* **1** [T] to wind something in a particular direction 擰, 捻, 搓, 盤〔某物〕: *They made a rope by twisting threads.* 他們用線捻了一根繩子。| *She twisted her hair round her fingers to make it curl.* 她用手指盤繞自己的頭髮使其鬈曲。**2** [T] to turn 旋轉, 轉動: *Twist the handle and the box will open.* 轉一下把手, 箱子就會打開。| *For this exercise, you need to twist your head more.* 這項運動需要你多轉動頭部。**3** [T] to change the shape of something by bending it 扭動, 扭彎, 扭曲〔某物〕: *The child twisted the wire into the shape of a star.* 那孩子把金屬絲扭成一顆星星的形狀。**4** [T] to damage a part of your body by moving it suddenly or awkwardly 扭傷〔肢體〕: *She's twisted her ankle.* 她扭傷了腳踝。**5** [I] to bend 彎曲: *The river twisted through the valley.* 河流蜿蜒流過山谷。

twist² *n* **1** [C] an act of turning something in a particular direction 擰, 扭, 捻, 搓: *Give the lid a twist.* 扭一下蓋子。**2** [C;U] something, such as thread or rope made by twisting two or more lengths together 捻[搓]成的東西 **3** [C] a bend 彎曲: *a road with a lot of twists in it* 有許多彎道的馬路 **4** [C] an unexpected change or development 意外的轉折[發展]: *a strange twist of fate* 命運的突變 –**twisty** *adj*: *a twisty road* 彎彎曲曲的馬路

twist·er /ˈtwɪstɚ; ˈtwɪstəʳ/ *n* a dishonest person who cheats other people 騙子

twit /twɪt; twɪt/ *n infml* a stupid fool『非正式』笨蛋

twitch¹ /twɪtʃ; twɪtʃ/ *v* [I;T] to move or make

something move suddenly and quickly (使)抽搐, (使)抽動: *Her lips twitched nervously.* 她的雙唇緊張得顫動起來。| *The horse twitched its ears.* 馬抽動着耳朵。

twitch² *n* **1** a repeated sudden movement of a muscle which you cannot control 抽搐, 顫動 **2** a sudden quick pull 猛的一拉

twit·ter /'twɪtɚ; 'twɪtə^r/ *v* [I] **1** (of a bird) to make a number of short high sounds 〔鳥〕啾啾叫 **2** (of a person) to talk quickly and nervously 〔人〕喊喊喳喳地講: *always twittering on about something unimportant* 喋喋不休地談些瑣事 –**twitter** *n* [U]: *the twitter of birds in the trees* 鳥在樹林中的鳴叫

two /tu; tuː/ *det, n, pron* **1** the number 2 〔數字〕二 **2 in two** into two parts 分成兩部分: *cut it in two* 一切為二

two-faced /'tuːfest; ,tuː'feɪst◂/ *adj* deceitful and dishonest in the way you behave to other people 兩面派的, 奸詐的

two-piece /, · · ◂/ *adj* [only before a noun 只用於名詞] consisting of two matching parts (used of clothes) 兩件一套的〔指衣服〕: *a two-piece suit* 兩件一套的西服 –**two-piece** *n*

two-way /, · · ◂/ *adj* moving or allowing movement in both directions 雙向的: *a two-way mirror* 雙向鏡 | *two-way traffic* 雙向交通〔車流〕

ty·coon /taɪ'kun; taɪ'kuːn/ *n* a businessman or industrialist with great wealth and power 〔工商界的〕巨頭, 大亨, 大班

ty·ing /'taɪŋ; 'taɪ-ŋ/ the present participle of TIE² ☆ TIE² 的現在分詞

type¹ /taɪp; taɪp/ *n* **1** [C] a particular class or group of people or things which share important common qualities and are different from those outside the group or class 種類, 類型: *What type of plant is this?* 這是哪一種植物? | *She's the type of person that I admire.* 她是我所崇拜的那種人。| *There have been several incidents of this type recently.* 近來發生了數宗這類事件。**2** [C] a person of the stated kind 某一種類的人: *She's an odd type.* 她是個古怪的人。| *a sporty type* 喜歡運動的那種人 **3 not my type** a phrase you use to describe a person you do not particularly like 跟我合不來〔用於描述不太喜歡的人〕**4** [U] the size or style of printed letters used in a piece of writing 〔印刷用的〕字體

type² *v* **typed, typing** [I;T] to write something using a machine such as a TYPEWRITER or WORD PROCESSOR 〔用打字機或文字處理機〕打字

　　type sthg ↔ **up** *phr v* [T] to type something that was written by hand 把〔手寫的東西〕打印成文

type·cast /'taɪpˌkæst; 'taɪpkɑːst/ *v* **typecast, typecasting** [T] to repeatedly give an actor the same kind of part 給〔演員〕分配同一類型的角色: *He's always typecast as a murderer because his face looks rather evil.* 他總

是被分派演殺人犯, 因為他看上去兇相畢露。

type·face /'taɪpˌfes; 'taɪpfeɪs/ *n* the size and style of the letters used in printing 〔活字的〕字體

type·writ·er /'taɪpˌraɪtɚ; 'taɪpˌraɪtə^r/ *n* a machine that prints letters or numbers by means of keys which you press with your fingers 打字機 –see picture on page 763 見 763 頁彩圖

type·writ·ten /'taɪpˌrɪtn; 'taɪpˌrɪtn/ *adj* written using a typewriter 打字的, 用打字機打出的

ty·phoid /'taɪfɔɪd; 'taɪfɔɪd/ *n* an infectious disease causing fever and often death, caused by bacteria in food or drink 傷寒 (病)

ty·phoon /ˌtaɪ'fun; ˌtaɪ'fuːn◂/ *n* a very violent tropical storm 颱風

ty·phus /'taɪfəs; 'taɪfəs/ [U] an infectious disease that causes severe fever and is carried by fleas (FLEA) 斑疹傷寒

typ·i·cal /'tɪpɪkḷ; 'tɪpɪkəl/ *adj* **1** showing the main signs and qualities of a particular kind, group, or class 典型的: *a typical eighteenth-century church* 一座典型的十八世紀教堂 | *a typical British summer* 典型的英國夏天 **2** showing the usual behaviour or manner of someone 〔舉止、行為〕一向如此的, 典型的: *It was typical of him to arrive so late.* 他一向都是到得這麼遲的。

typ·i·cally /'tɪpɪkli; 'tɪpɪkli/ *adv* **1** usually 通常, 一般: *She typically works from six in the morning till midnight.* 她通常六點鐘開始工作, 一直幹到午夜。**2** showing the usual signs or qualities of a particular group 典型地: *a typically American solution* 典型的美國式解決辦法

typ·i·fy /'tɪpəˌfaɪ; 'tɪp-ˌfaɪ/ *v* **typified, typifying** [T] to serve as a typical example 作為典型: *the high quality that typifies all his work* 他的作品一向具有的高質量 | *He typifies the Englishman abroad.* 他是海外英國人的典型代表。

typ·ist /'taɪpɪst; 'taɪp-st/ *n* a secretary employed mainly for typing (TYPE²) letters 打字員

tyr·an·nize /'tɪrəˌnaɪz; 'tɪrənaɪz/ *v* **tyrannized, tyrannizing** (also 又作 **tyrannise** *BrE* 〖英式〗) [I;T] to use power over a person, country or people with unjust cruelty 對…施暴政

tyr·an·ny /'tɪrənɪ; 'tɪrəni/ *n* [U] **1** the use of cruel or unjust power to control a person or country 暴政, 專制 **2** government by a cruel ruler with complete power 專制政治 – **tyrannical** /tɪ'rænɪkḷ; t-'rænɪkəl/ *adj*

ty·rant /'taɪrənt; 'taɪərənt/ *n* **1** a ruler with complete power, who rules cruelly and unjustly 暴君 **2** a person in control of other people who behaves in a severe and unfair way to them 專橫殘暴的人

tyre /taɪr; taɪə^r/ *n* (**tire** *AmE* 〖美式〗) a thick piece of rubber, usually filled with air, that fits round a wheel 輪胎: *a car tyre* 汽車輪

胎 −see picture on page 209 見 209 頁彩圖
tzar /tsɑːr; zɑːʳ/ *n* 見 see TSAR

U, u

U, u /juː; juː/ **U's, u's** or **Us, us** the 21st letter of the English alphabet 英語的第二十一個字母

u·biq·ui·tous /juːˈbɪkwətəs; juːˈbɪkwɪ̩təs/ adj fml appearing, happening, or done everywhere 【正式】無處不在的; 普遍存在的; 到處進行的

ud·der /ˈʌdə; ˈʌdəʳ/ n the part of a female animal like a cow where milk is produced 〔母牛等的〕乳房

UFO /ˌjuːɛfˈo; ˈjuːfəʊ/ n UFO's a mysterious object seen in the sky; some people think that UFO's are space vehicles bringing creatures from another world; an abbreviation for UNIDENTIFIED FLYING OBJECT 【縮】不明飛行物; 飛碟

ugh /ux; ʊx/ interj an expression of dislike 唷; 呀; 呸〔表示厭惡〕: Ugh! This medicine tastes nasty. 啊! 這種藥真難吃。

ug·ly /ˈʌɡlɪ; ˈʌɡli/ adj **uglier, ugliest 1** unpleasant to look at 醜陋的; 難看的: an ugly face 難看的臉 | Some parts of the city are rather ugly. 這個城市中的某些地方相當令人不快。 **2** very unpleasant and sometimes violent 討厭的;〔有時〕暴力的: An ugly scene developed in the crowd when a group of boys started fighting. 一羣男孩打鬥起來時, 人羣中出現了可怕的大吵大鬧的場面。 | in an ugly mood 乖戾的脾氣 **–ugliness** n [U]

UHF /ˌjuː eɪtʃ ˈef; juː eɪtʃ ˈef/ n [U] the method used for sending television pictures; an abbreviation for **ultrahigh frequency**【縮】超高頻〔發射電視圖像的方法〕

UK /ˌjuː ˈkeɪ; juː ˈkeɪ◂/ n **the UK** Great Britain and Northern Ireland; an abbreviation for **United Kingdom**【縮】(大不列顛及北愛爾蘭)聯合王國

u·ku·le·le /juːkəˈleɪli; ˌjuːkəˈleɪli/ n a musical instrument like a small GUITAR 尤克萊利琴〔一種狀如小吉他的樂器〕

ul·cer /ˈʌlsə; ˈʌlsəʳ/ n a rough place on your skin or inside your body which may bleed or produce poisonous matter 潰瘍: a stomach ulcer 胃潰瘍 | mouth ulcers 口腔潰瘍

ul·te·ri·or /ʌlˈtɪərɪə; ʌlˈtɪəriəʳ/ **an ulterior motive** a reason for doing something that is not the one you say 別有用心的動機: He has an ulterior motive for seeing her: he's going to ask for some money. 他來看她是別有用心的: 他是來要錢的。

*★**ul·ti·mate** /ˈʌltəmɪt; ˈʌltɪ̩mɪ̩t/ adj [only before a noun 只用於名詞前] **1** last 最後的; 最終的: The ultimate responsibility lies with the President. 最後的責任由總統承擔。 **2 the ultimate** infml greatest or best 【非正式】最大的; 最佳的: This is the ultimate bicycle. You'll never find a better one. 這是最好的一輛腳踏車。你再也找不到比這輛更好的了。 | Her house was the ultimate in luxury. 她的房子最為豪華。

ul·ti·mate·ly /ˈʌltəmɪtlɪ; ˈʌltɪ̩mɪ̩tli/ adv in the end 最後; 最終: Many gave their opinions, but ultimately the decision lay with the President. 眾人各抒己見, 但最後還得由總統作出決定。

ul·ti·ma·tum /ˌʌltəˈmeɪtəm; ˌʌltɪ̩ˈmeɪtəm/ n **ultimatums** or **ultimata** /-tə; -tə/ a statement of something that must be done under a threat of force 最後通牒; 哀的美敦書: They gave us this ultimatum: if we didn't move out of the house before the end of the week, they would throw us out. 他們向我們發出最後通牒: 要是我們週末之前不搬出這座房子, 他們要把我們趕出去。

ul·tra·ma·rine /ˌʌltrəməˈrin; ˌʌltrəməˈriːn/ n [U] a very bright blue colour 佛青色; 深藍色 **–ultramarine** adj

ul·tra·son·ic /ˌʌltrəˈsɑnɪk; ˌʌltrəˈsɒnɪk◂/ adj above the range of human hearing 超聲(波)的

ul·tra·vi·o·let /ˌʌltrəˈvaɪəlɪt; ˌʌltrəˈvaɪəlɪ̩t◂/ adj beyond the purple end of the colour SPECTRUM and unable to be seen by human beings 紫外(線)的: Use suncream to protect your skin from ultraviolet light. 用防曬霜保護皮膚使其免受紫外線的傷害。

um·bil·i·cal cord /ʌmˌbɪlɪkl ˈkɔːd; ʌmˌbɪlɪkəl ˈkɔːd/ n the tube of flesh which joins a baby to its mother before birth 臍帶

um·brage /ˈʌmbrɪdʒ; ˈʌmbrɪdʒ/ n **take umbrage** to show that your feelings have been hurt (為…)生氣; (對…)表示不快; (因…)傷感情

um·brel·la /ʌmˈbrelə; ʌmˈbrelə/ n **1** an arrangement of cloth over a folding frame with a handle, used for protection against rain 雨傘 **2** a single organization that includes many others〔包含其他許多組織的〕一個組織

um·pire¹ /ˈʌmpaɪr; ˈʌmpaɪəʳ/ n a judge in charge of a game〔比賽的〕裁判

umpire² v **umpired, umpiring** [I;T] to act as umpire for a game 當裁判

ump·teen /ˈʌmpˈtin; ˌʌmpˈtiːn◂/ det, n, pron infml a large number 【非正式】無數; 大量; 許多: I've seen that film umpteen times. 那部電影我已看過無數次了。 **–umpteenth** n, det:

That's the umpteenth time I've told you not to do that! 我對你不知説過多少次了，別那麼做！

UN /ˌjuː ˈɛn; ˌjuː ˈen/ *n* an international organization that tries to help relations between different countries; an abbreviation for **United Nations** 〖縮〗聯合國

un·a·bat·ed /ˌʌnəˈbeɪtɪd; ˌʌnəˈbeɪtɪ̩d/ *adj* without losing force 不減弱的；不衰退的: *The storm continued unabated.* 風暴持續着，絲毫沒有減弱。

★**un·a·ble** /ʌnˈebl̩; ʌnˈeɪbəl/ *adj* unable to do something not having enough power, skill, knowledge, time, or money to do something 不能的，不會的，無能力的: *He was unable to open the door.* 他無法開門。| *I'm afraid I'll be unable to attend the meeting tomorrow.* 我恐怕無法參加明天的會議。

un·a·bridged /ˌʌnəˈbrɪdʒd; ˌʌnəˈbrɪdʒd/ *adj* not shortened (used of a book or play) 未刪節的，未節略的〔指書或戲劇〕

un·ac·com·pa·nied /ˌʌnəˈkʌmpənid; ˌʌnəˈkʌmpənid/ *adj* **1** alone 獨自的；無人陪伴的: *Children unaccompanied by an adult will not be admitted.* 沒有成人帶領的兒童不准入內。**2** without music 無伴奏的: *an unaccompanied song* 無伴奏歌曲

un·ac·coun·ta·ble /ˌʌnəˈkaʊntəbl̩; ˌʌnəˈkaʊntəbəl/ *adj* **1** not easily explained 莫名其妙的，無法解釋的；難以説明的: *unaccountable behaviour* 無法解釋的行為 **2** not held responsible (used of people in public office) 不負責任的〔指政府機關工作人員〕 – **unaccountably** *adv*

un·a·dul·te·rat·ed /ˌʌnəˈdʌltəˌretɪd; ˌʌnəˈdʌltəreɪtɪ̩d/ *adj* **1** not mixed with impure substances 無雜質的；不攙雜的 **2** complete 完全的: *unadulterated nonsense* 一派胡言

un·af·fect·ed /ˌʌnəˈfɛktɪd; ˌʌnəˈfektɪ̩d/ *adj* **1** not changed in any way 無變化的；未改變的: *People in the south of the country were unaffected by the food shortages in the north.* 住在該國南部的人民沒有受到北方食品短缺的影響。**2** natural in behaviour or character 〔行為或性格〕自然的，不矯揉造作的: *the unaffected delight of a child* 孩子發自內心的喜悦

un·aid·ed /ʌnˈedɪd; ʌnˈeɪdɪ̩d/ *adj* without help from anyone else 無助的；獨力的: *It has to be your own unaided work.* 這工作得由你獨力來幹。| *He is now able to walk unaided.* 他現在能夠不靠支撐走路。

u·nan·i·mous /juːˈnænəməs; juːˈnænɪməs/ *adj* **1** all agreeing 一致同意的: *The voters were unanimous.* 投票人一致同意。**2** agreed by everyone 得到一致贊同的: *a unanimous decision* 一致同意的決定 –**unanimously** *adv* –**unanimity** /ˌjuːnəˈnɪmətɪ; juːnəˈnɪmɪ̩ti/ *n* [U]

un·ap·proa·cha·ble /ˌʌnəˈprotʃəbl̩; ˌʌnəˈprəʊtʃəbəl/ *adj* not very friendly, and so difficult to talk to 難以親近的；無法接近的

un·armed /ʌnˈɑrmd; ʌnˈɑːmd/ *adj* not carrying weapons 不帶武器的；徒手的

un·as·sum·ing /ˌʌnəˈsumɪŋ; ˌʌnəˈsjuːmɪŋ/ *adj* quiet in manner 〔態度〕沉靜的，不傲慢的

un·at·tached /ˌʌnəˈtætʃt; ˌʌnəˈtætʃt/ *adj* **1** not connected 不連接的；無關係的 **2** not married or in a serious relationship 未結婚的；沒有訂婚的

un·at·tend·ed /ˌʌnəˈtɛndɪd; ˌʌnəˈtendɪ̩d/ *adj* without being watched 沒人照料的: *Your car is quite likely to get damaged if you leave it unattended.* 你的汽車如果沒人照看，很可能會給弄壞。

un·a·wares /ˌʌnəˈwɛrz; ˌʌnəˈweəz/ *adv* **1** without noticing 出其不意地；不知不覺地 **2** take someone unawares to surprise someone 使某人大吃一驚

un·bal·anced /ʌnˈbælənst; ʌnˈbælənst/ *adj* **1** slightly mad (used of people) 失常的，神經錯亂的〔指人〕: *He became a bit unbalanced after his wife died.* 妻子死後，他的精神有點失常。**2** not fair and exact (used of writing and reports) 不公平的，不確切的〔指文章、報告〕: *an unbalanced account* 片面的報道

un·bear·able /ʌnˈbɛrəbl̩; ʌnˈbeərəbəl/ *adj* too bad to be put up with 不能忍受的: *unbearable heat* 難以忍受的炎熱 | *The pain was unbearable.* 疼痛實在難忍受。–**unbearably** *adv*

un·be·lie·va·ble /ˌʌnbɪˈlivəbl̩; ˌʌnbɪ̩ˈliːvəbəl/ *adj* **1** very surprising 極其驚人的: *It's unbelievable how many children she has!* 她竟有那麼多孩子，真叫人難以相信！**2** excellent 優秀的；傑出的: *My weekend in Paris was unbelievable.* 我在巴黎過的週末好得令人難以置信。–**unbelievably** *adv*

un·bend·ing /ʌnˈbɛndɪŋ; ʌnˈbendɪŋ/ *adj* refusing to change opinions, or decisions 堅定的；不妥協的

un·born /ʌnˈbɔrn; ʌnˈbɔːn/ *adj* not yet born 未出生的

un·bound·ed /ʌnˈbaʊndɪd; ʌnˈbaʊndɪ̩d/ *adj* limitless 無限的；無邊際的: *unbounded admiration* 無限的欽佩

un·bri·dled /ʌnˈbraɪdl̩d; ʌnˈbraɪdld/ *adj lit* not controlled 〖文〗不加控制的；不受約束的: *unbridled anger* 不加克制的怒火

un·bur·den /ʌnˈbɜrdn̩; ʌnˈbɜːdn/ *v* unburden yourself to someone to tell someone about your secret problems so that you feel better about them 向某人吐露心事消除〔心靈〕上的負擔

un·but·ton /ʌnˈbʌtn̩; ʌnˈbʌtn/ *v* [T] to unfasten the buttons on something 解開〔某物上的〕鈕扣

un·called-for /ʌnˈkɔld ˌfɔr; ʌnˈkɔːld fɔːr/ *adj* not deserved or right 不值得的；不適宜的；多此一舉的: *Such rudeness is quite uncalled-for.* 這樣粗魯簡直是無緣無故的。

un·can·ny /ʌnˈkænɪ; ʌnˈkæni/ *adj* mysterious 不可思議的，神祕的: *It seemed uncanny* *to hear her voice from the other side of the world.* 從世界的另一端聽到她的聲音似乎很不可思議。**–uncannily** *adv*

un·cared-for /ʌnˈkɛrdˌfɔr; ʌnˈkeəd fɔːʳ/ *adj* not well looked after 未經好好照顧[料理]的: *His face is dirty and his clothes are uncared-for.* 他的臉很髒，衣服也沒洗燙過。

un·ce·re·mo·ni·ous /ˌʌnsɛrəˈmoniəs; ˌʌnserɪˈməuniəs/ *adj* **1** informal 隨便的；不拘禮節的: *an unceremonious but sincere welcome* 不拘形式但誠摯的歡迎 **2** not done politely 無禮的；唐突的: *She finished the meal with unceremonious haste.* 她狼吞虎咽地吃完了飯。**–unceremoniously** *adv*

un·cer·tain /ʌnˈsɝtn; ʌnˈsɜːtn/ *adj* **1** not sure 不確定的: *I'm uncertain how to get there.* 我不清楚怎樣才能到達那裡。| *a man of uncertain origin* 出身不明的人 **2** undecided or unable to decide 未作決定的；無法斷定的: *Our holiday plans are still uncertain.* 我們的度假計劃還沒有定下來。**3** changeable 無常的；易變的: *uncertain weather* 變幻莫測的天氣 **–uncertainly** *adv* **–uncertainty** *n* [C;U]

un·char·i·ta·ble /ʌnˈtʃærətəbl; ʌnˈtʃærɪtəbəl/ *adj* not kind or fair in judgments〔評判〕嚴厲的，無情的，苛刻的: *an uncharitable remark* 苛刻的評論

un·chart·ed /ʌnˈtʃɑrtɪd; ʌnˈtʃɑːtɪd/ *adj* lit not known well enough for maps or other records to be made of it〔文〕地圖上未標明的；無紀錄的: *the uncharted forests of Brazil* 巴西未經勘探的森林

un·checked /ʌnˈtʃɛkt; ʌnˈtʃekt◂/ *adj* not prevented from developing 不受抑制的；未受制止的: *The disease spread unchecked.* 該疾病未能得到控制而蔓延開來。

un·cle /ˈʌŋkl; ˈʌŋkəl/ *n* the brother of your father or mother, or the husband of your aunt 伯父；叔父；舅父；姑丈；姨丈: *He's my uncle.* 他是我叔父。| *Take me swimming, Uncle Jack!* 傑克叔叔，帶我去游泳吧! **–see** picture on page 503 見 503 頁彩圖

un·clean /ʌnˈklin; ʌnˈkliːn◂/ *adj* not considered pure in a religious way〔宗教上認為〕不潔淨的: *In ancient times lepers were thought to be unclean.* 在古代，麻瘋病人被認為是不潔淨的。

un·com·for·ta·ble /ʌnˈkʌmfɚtəbl; ʌnˈkʌmftəbəl/ *adj* not comfortable 不舒服的；不自在的: *an uncomfortable chair* 不舒適的椅子 | *I felt uncomfortable when John and Jane started arguing with each other.* 約翰和簡開始爭論起來時，我感到很不自在。**–uncomfortably** *adv*: *uncomfortably close to the fire* 離火堆太近不舒服

un·com·mit·ted /ˌʌnkəˈmɪtɪd; ˌʌnkəˈmɪtɪd◂/ *adj* [to] not having given loyalty to any one thing, group or belief 不受約束的；獨立於〔任何事物、團體或信仰〕的: *She hasn't yet decided her position and wants to remain uncommitted.* 她還沒有決定自己的立場，想保

持中立。

un·com·mon /ʌnˈkɑmən; ʌnˈkɒmən/ *adj* rare or unusual 罕見的；不尋常的: *It's quite uncommon for someone not to have a television these days.* 現在沒有電視機的人相當少見。

un·com·pro·mis·ing /ʌnˈkɑmprəˌmaɪzɪŋ; ʌnˈkɒmprəmaɪzɪŋ/ *adj* refusing to change ideas or decisions 不妥協的；不讓步的；堅定的: *He is uncompromising in his demands.* 他對於自己的要求不肯讓步。**–uncompromisingly** *adv*

un·con·cerned /ˌʌnkənˈsɝnd; ˌʌnkənˈsɜːnd/ *adj* not worried or anxious 不憂慮的；不擔心的: *She seemed quite unconcerned about not having a job.* 她對自己沒有工作好像毫不擔心。**–unconcernedly** /-ndlɪ; -nɪ̯dli/ *adv*

un·con·di·tion·al /ˌʌnkənˈdɪʃənl; ˌʌnkənˈdɪʃənl/ *adj* completely without conditions or limitations 無條件的；無限制的: *The rebels want unconditional freedom for all their political prisoners.* 叛亂者要求給他們所有的政治犯無條件的自由。**–unconditionally** *adv*: *They surrendered unconditionally.* 他們無條件投降了。

un·con·scious[1] /ʌnˈkɑnʃəs; ʌnˈkɒnʃəs/ *adj* **1** in a state that is like sleep when you do not know what is happening, caused by an accident or illness 失去知覺的；不省人事的: *After the car crash I was unconscious for several hours.* 撞車以後，我昏迷不醒了幾個小時。**–see** 見 CONSCIOUS (USAGE 用法) **2** not meant intentionally 不知不覺的；無意的: *His sexist comment was quite unconscious.* 他的性別主義的評論是無意的。**3** without knowing about something 未察覺的；未察覺的: *Susan was unconscious of the fact that Bill was attracted to her.* 蘇珊沒有意識到比爾對她產生了好感。**–unconsciously** *adv* **–unconsciousness** *n* [U]

unconscious[2] *n* the unconscious **–see** 見 SUBCONSCIOUS

un·co·op·e·ra·tive /ˌʌnkoˈɑpəˌretɪv; ˌʌnkəuˈɒpərətɪv/ *adj* unwilling to work with other people, or help them, or do what they want when they ask 不願合作的；不抱合作態度的

un·cork /ʌnˈkɔrk; ʌnˈkɔːk/ *v* [T] to open a bottle by removing the CORK 拔去〔瓶子的〕塞子

un·couth /ʌnˈkuθ; ʌnˈkuːθ/ *adj* behaving and speaking in a rough and rude way〔行為〕粗野的；〔語言〕粗魯的

un·cov·er /ʌnˈkʌvɚ; ʌnˈkʌvəʳ/ *v* [T] **1** to remove a covering from something 揭去〔某物〕的蓋子；移去〔某物〕的覆蓋物 **2** to discover 揭露，發現: *The police uncovered a plan to shoot the President.* 警方揭露了一項槍殺總統的計劃。

un·crit·i·cal /ʌnˈkrɪtɪkl; ʌnˈkrɪtɪkəl/ *adj* not willing or able to make judgments about whether something is good or bad 不加批

評的; 不作評論的 **–critically** /-klɪ; -kli/

un·cut /ʌnˈkʌt; ˌʌnˈkʌt◂/ *adj* **1** not made shorter (used of books, films, or plays) 〔書〕未刪節的; 〔影片或戲劇〕未剪輯的 **2** not having the surface cut and shaped (used of a precious stone like a diamond) 未經琢磨的; 未雕琢的〔指鑽石或其他寶石〕

un·daunt·ed /ʌnˈdɔntɪd; ʌnˈdɔːntɪd/ *adj* not at all discouraged by danger or difficulty 無畏的; 勇敢的; 大膽的

un·de·cid·ed /ˌʌndɪˈsaɪdɪd; ˌʌndɪˈsaɪdl̩d/ *adj* in doubt and not having made a decision 遲疑不決的; 未作決定的: *The jury were still undecided after discussing the trial for six hours.* 陪審團對審訊討論了六個小時, 仍然未作出判決。| *A lot of people are still undecided about who they're going to vote for.* 許多人仍在猶豫該選誰。

un·de·ni·a·ble /ˌʌndɪˈnaɪəbl; ˌʌndɪˈnaɪəbəl/ *adj* certainly true 無可爭辯的; 不可否認的: *Picasso was an undeniable genius.* 畢加索是個不可否認的天才。 **–undeniably** *adv*

★un·der /ˈʌndɚ; ˈʌndəʳ/ *adv, prep* **1** *prep* directly below something or covered by something 在〔某物〕下方; 在〔某物〕底下; 在〔某物〕裡面: *There's a box of papers under the table.* 桌子下面有一箱文件。| *He squeezed under the fence.* 他擠到籬笆下面。 | *She was wearing a cream blouse under her jumper.* 她在套頭毛衣裡面穿了一件米色的襯衫。 | *These animals spend most of their time under water.* 這些動物大部分時間都在水底。–see picture on page 764 見 764 頁彩圖 **2** *adv, prep* less than a particular amount 少於〔某個數量〕: *It costs under £5.* 價格不到五英鎊。| *children under seven years old* 七歲以下的兒童 | *children aged eight and under* 八歲及八歲以下的兒童 **3** *prep* working for someone and controlled or guided by them 在〔某人〕手下工作; 在〔某人〕支配[指導]下: *I've got three junior secretaries under me.* 我手下有三個初級祕書。 | *He's studying under one of the world's leading physicists.* 他在世界上其中一位傑出的物理學家的指導下進行研究。 **4** *prep* during the rule of someone 在〔某人〕統治下: *What was it like living in Spain under Franco?* 在佛朗哥統治下的西班牙生活情況是怎樣的呢? | *new laws brought in under the conservative government* 保守黨政府統治時制訂的新法律 **5** *prep* used to say where a piece of information is kept in a system 屬於; 歸入: *It's filed under "I" for "Invoices".* 這個歸入"I"檔, "I"代表發票。 **6** *prep* using a particular name, usually one which is not your real name 用〔某個名字, 尤指化名〕: *I booked into the hotel under the name of Shaw.* 我用肖這個名字登記旅館。 | *He wrote a great many books under various names.* 他用不同的名字寫了大量的書。 **7** *adv* not enough 低於; 少於: *The project has been under-financed and under-staffed.* 這個工程資金短缺, 人手不足。

8 **under age** too young by law to do certain things such as drive a car or drink alcohol 未成年的; 未達到法定年齡的〔如駕車或喝酒〕

un·der·arm /ˈʌndɚˌɑrm; ˈʌndərɑːm/ *adj, adv* thrown without moving your hand above your shoulder 用手不過肩的[地]

un·der·car·riage /ˈʌndɚˌkærɪdʒ; ˈʌndəˌkærɪdʒ/ *n* the wheels of an aircraft and the frame they are connected to 〔飛機的〕起落架

und·er·charge /ˌʌndɚˈtʃɑrdʒ; ˌʌndəˈtʃɑːdʒ/ *v* **undercharged, undercharging** [I;T] to charge too little money for something 少收〔某物〕的價錢: *They undercharged him by £6.* 他們少收了他六英鎊。

un·der·clothes /ˈʌndɚˌkloðz; ˈʌndəkləʊðz/ *n* [pl] (also 又作 **underclothing** [U]) clothes that you wear next to your body under other clothes 內衣

un·der·coat /ˈʌndɚˌkot; ˈʌndəkəʊt/ *n* a covering of paint put onto a surface as a base for a top covering of paint 底漆; 內塗層

un·der·cov·er /ˌʌndɚˈkʌvɚ; ˌʌndəˈkʌvəʳ/ *adj, adv* acting secretly in order to get information 暗中進行的[地]; 祕密從事的[地]: *an undercover agent* 密探; 特工 | *a police officer working undercover* 從事祕密工作的警官

un·der·cur·rent /ˈʌndɚˌkɝənt; ˈʌndəˌkʌrənt/ *n* **1** a hidden current of water beneath the sea's surface 潛流; 底流 **2** a feeling or opinion that is hidden beneath the surface of a situation 潛伏的情緒[意見]: *Wherever I went in the city I felt an undercurrent of danger.* 無論我去這城市中的哪個地方, 我都能感到潛在的危險。

un·der·cut /ˌʌndɚˈkʌt; ˌʌndəˈkʌt/ *v* **undercut, undercut, undercutting** [T] to sell goods or services more cheaply than another shop 削價出售或提供服務

un·der·dog /ˈʌndɚˌdɔg; ˈʌndədɒg/ *n* a person or country that is weaker and not expected to succeed 處於劣勢的人[國家]

un·der·done /ˌʌndɚˈdʌn; ˌʌndəˈdʌn◂/ *adj* not completely cooked 半生不熟的; 煮得過嫩的

un·der·es·ti·mate /ˌʌndɚˈɛstəˌmet; ˌʌndərˈestl̩meɪt/ *v* **underestimated, underestimating** [I;T] to think that something or someone is not as valuable, great or able as it really is 低估; 看輕: *The builder underestimated how much the job would cost by £200.* 建造者對這項工程的花費低估了二百英鎊。 | *Don't underestimate a baby's ability to understand what you're saying.* 不要低估嬰兒對你的話的理解力。 **–underestimate** /-təmɪt; -tl̩mɪt/ *n*: *£1.2m is almost certainly an underestimate.* 一百二十萬英鎊幾乎可以肯定是估價過低了。

un·der·foot /ˌʌndɚˈfut; ˌʌndəˈfut/ *adv* under your feet when you are walking 在腳下:

The grass was wet underfoot. 腳下的草是濕的。

un·der·go /ˌʌndə'go; ˌʌndə'gəʊ/ *v* **underwent** /-'went; -'went/, **undergone** /-'gɔn; -'gɒn/ [T] to experience something that is unpleasant or necessary 經歷, 遭受〔不好的事〕: *His mother is undergoing treatment for cancer.* 他母親正在接受癌症治療。

un·der·grad·u·ate /ˌʌndə'grædʒuɪt; ˌʌndə-'grædʒʊ̩t/ *n* a university student who has not yet taken their first degree〔尚未取得學位的〕大學生, 大學本科生

un·der·ground¹ /ˌʌndə'graʊnd; ˌʌndə-'graʊnd/ *adv* under the surface of the ground 在地(面)下: *an underground cave* 地下洞穴 | *The waste is buried underground.* 垃圾埋在地下。

underground² /ˌʌndə'graʊnd; ˌʌndə'graʊnd/ *adj* secret, unofficial, or illegal 祕密的; 非官方的; 不合法的: *The underground political movement opposing the government is very well organized.* 反對政府的地下政治運動組織非常嚴密。

underground³ *n* a railway system in which the trains run in passages below the ground, especially the system in London〔尤指英國倫敦的〕地下鐵道: *We travelled across London on the underground.* 我們乘地鐵穿過倫敦。 | *We went by underground.* 我們是坐地鐵去的。 | *a map of the London Underground* 倫敦地鐵圖

un·der·growth /ˈʌndəˌgroθ; ˈʌndəgrəʊθ/ *n* [U] bushes and plants growing under the trees in a wood〔長在樹下的〕下層灌木叢: *thick undergrowth* 密的矮樹叢 | *They cleared a path through the undergrowth.* 他們從灌木叢中闢出一條路來。

un·der·hand /ˈʌndəˈhænd; ˌʌndəˈhænd/ *adj* done dishonestly and secretly 欺詐的; 祕密的: *He acquired all that money in a very underhand manner.* 他用極為狡詐的手段弄到了那筆錢。

un·der·lie /ˌʌndə'laɪ; ˌʌndə'laɪ/ *v* **underlay** /-'le; -'leɪ/, **underlain** /-'len; -'leɪn/, **underlying** [T] to be a hidden cause of something 形成〔某事〕潛在的原因, 成為…的基礎: *Social problems and poverty underlie much of the crime in today's cities.* 社會問題和貧窮構成了當今城市中許多罪案的原因。

un·der·line /ˌʌndə'laɪn; ˌʌndə'laɪn/ *v* **underlined, underlining** [T] **1** to draw a line under a word to make it noticeable 在…下劃線 **2** to show the importance of something 表明〔某事物的〕重要性; 強調, 使突出: *Accidents at work underline the need for better safety standards.* 工作中發生的事故突出了制訂更高安全標準的必要。

un·der·manned /ˌʌndə'mænd; ˌʌndə'mænd◂/ *adj* not having enough workers 人員不足的

un·der·men·tioned /ˌʌndə'menʃənd; ˌʌndə-'menʃənd◂/ *adj fml* mentioned later in a letter, contract, or in legal writing〔正式〕

un·der·mine /ˌʌndə'maɪn; ˌʌndə'maɪn/ *v* **undermined, undermining** [T] to weaken or slowly destroy 削弱; 逐漸破壞: *My confidence was undermined by his constant criticism.* 他老是批評我, 令我漸漸喪失了信心。 | *The storm badly undermined the seawall.* 暴風雨嚴重侵蝕了防波堤。

un·der·neath¹ /ˌʌndə'niθ; ˌʌndə'niːθ/ *adv, prep* **1** *adv, prep* under or below 在…下面; 在…底下: *There was a dog underneath the table.* 桌子底下有條狗。 | *She wore a white blouse underneath her jumper.* 她在套頭毛衣裡穿了一件白色襯衫。 **2** *adv* used when you are describing what someone feels but does not show to other people 在心底〔用於描述某人未向他人表現的感覺〕: *She smiled, but underneath she was furious.* 她微微一笑, 可是心裡怒火中燒。

underneath² *n* [sing] the bottom or lower surface of something 下面; 下部; 底部

un·der·nour·ished /ˌʌndə'nʌrɪʃt; ˌʌndə'nʌ-rɪʃt/ *adj* not healthy or well developed because of lack of food or the right kind of food 營養不足的; 營養不良的 **–undernourishment** *n* [U]

un·der·pants /ˈʌndəˌpænts; ˈʌndəpænts/ *n* [pl] a short piece of clothing worn under trousers by men and boys〔男裝〕內褲; 襯褲 **–see** 見 PAIR (USAGE 用法) **–see picture on page 210** 見 210 頁彩圖

un·der·pass /ˈʌndəˌpæs; ˈʌndəpɑːs/ *n* a road or path that goes under another road 地下通道; 下穿交叉道

un·der·priv·i·leged /ˌʌndə'prɪvəlɪdʒd; ˌʌn-də'prɪvl̩ɪdʒd◂/ *adj* not having the advantages of other people〔人〕得不到基本權利的; 社會地位低下的

un·der·rate /ˌʌndə'ret; ˌʌndə'reɪt/ *v* **underrated, underrating** [T] to have too low an opinion of something 對〔某事物〕評價過低: *We underrated his powers as a speaker.* 我們低估了他作為演說家的能力。 | *His music has been very underrated in the past.* 他的音樂過去十分遭到輕視。

un·der·shirt /ˈʌndəˌʃɜt; ˈʌndəʃɜːt/ *n* the usual American word for VEST【美式】內衣背心

un·der·side /ˈʌndəˌsaɪd; ˈʌndəsaɪd/ *n* the lower side or surface 下面; 下側: *The underside of our car is ever so rusty.* 我們汽車的底部老是生鏽。

un·der·signed /ˌʌndə'saɪnd; ˌʌndəsaɪnd/ *n* [pl] **the undersigned** the people who have signed a letter or contract〔信或合同的〕簽名者, 署名人

un·der·sized /ˌʌndə'saɪzd; ˌʌndə'saɪzd◂/ *adj* too small or smaller than usual 比一般尺寸小的

un·der·staffed /ˌʌndə'stæft; ˌʌndə'stɑːft/ *adj* not having enough workers 人員不足的; 人手不夠的: *The office is understaffed since*

the secretary left. 祕書離職以後, 辦公室顯得人手不足。

☆un·der·stand /ˌʌndəˈstænd; ˌʌndəˈstænd/ v **understood** /-ˈstʊd; -ˈstʊd/, **understood** [not in progressive forms 不用於進行式] **1** [I;T] to know or get the meaning of words or ideas 懂得; 理解; 明白: *She tried to explain the theory to me but I didn't really understand.* 她設法向我解釋這個理論, 可是我沒有真正弄懂。| *I can't understand modern art.* 我不懂現代藝術。| *He can understand quite a lot of English but he can't speak very much.* 他能看懂許多英語, 但他能説的不多。| *I found the lecture hard to understand.* 我發現這講座難以聽懂。**2** [T] to know someone's character and know why they act in the way they do 領會, 了解〔某人的性格和行為〕: *I've known Emily for 15 years but I still can't understand her.* 我認識艾米莉有十五年了, 但仍不能了解她。| *I can understand how you feel.* 我能理解你的感受。**3** [+ (that)] *fml* to know something because you have been told 《正式》得知; 獲悉: *I understand you're coming to work for us.* 我得知你要來為我們工作。**4** [+(that)] to think something is the case even if this has not been stated directly 認為〔某事物〕理所當然; 視〔某事物〕不言而喻: *I thought it was understood that we would get paid extra for working at the weekend.* 我認為我們在週末工作當然應該得到額外的報酬。**5** make yourself understood to make your meaning clear to others 使別人理解自己的意思: *I don't really speak German but I can make myself understood.* 我實際上不説德語, 但我能表達自己的意思。– **understandable** *adj*: *I think his reaction was understandable.* 我認為他的反應是可以理解。– **understandably** *adv*: *He was understandably angry.* 他生氣是理所當然的。

un·der·stand·ing¹ /ˌʌndəˈstændɪŋ; ˌʌndəˈstændɪŋ/ n **1** [U] knowledge of something or of what something means 理解; 了解; 明白: *Helen has very little understanding of music.* 海倫只懂那麼一點點音樂。**2** [U] sympathy towards and knowledge of a person's character 相互理解; 同情; 和睦: *There is a deep understanding between them.* 他們彼此相知甚深。**3** [C] a private informal agreement 〔非正式的、私下的〕協定, 協議: *We have come to an understanding.* 我們私下達成了一項協議。

understanding² *adj* sympathetic and kind 同情的; 通情達理的: *She was very understanding when I told her my problem.* 我向她訴説我的問題, 她非常同情。

un·der·state /ˌʌndəˈsteɪt; ˌʌndəˈsteɪt/ v **understated, understating** [T] to make something seem less important than it is 淡化〔某事物〕的重要性; 輕描淡寫地陳述〔某事物〕: *The government understated the seriousness of the problem.* 政府對該問題的嚴重性只作了

un·der·state·ment /ˈʌndəˌsteɪtmənt; ˈʌndəˌsteɪtmənt/ n a statement which is not strong enough 不充分的陳述, 輕描淡寫的陳述: *To say the film wasn't very good is an understatement: it was absolutely awful!* 説這部影片不好是一種低調的説法: 它簡直糟透了!

un·der·stood /ˌʌndəˈstʊd; ˌʌndəˈstʊd/ the past tense and past participle of UNDERSTAND ☆ UNDERSTAND 的過去式和過去分詞

un·der·stud·y /ˈʌndəˌstʌdɪ; ˈʌndəˌstʌdɪ/ n **understudies** an actor who learns the part of another actor in a play and can act that part if necessary 預備演員, 替角

☆un·der·take /ˌʌndəˈteɪk; ˌʌndəˈteɪk/ v **undertook** /-ˈtʊk; -ˈtʊk/, **undertaken** /-ˈteɪkən; -ˈteɪkən/, **undertaking 1** [T] to start work on 着手做; 從事: *She undertook the training of the new staff.* 她着手培訓新員工。**2** undertake to do something to promise or agree to do something 許諾, 答應做某事: *She undertook to pay the money back within six months.* 她答應在六個月之內還清欠款。

un·der·tak·er /ˈʌndəˌteɪkə; ˈʌndəˌteɪkəʳ/ n a person whose job it is to arrange funerals 承辦喪葬者; 殯儀員

un·der·tak·ing /ˌʌndəˈteɪkɪŋ; ˌʌndəˈteɪkɪŋ/ n **1** a job that is started and someone is responsible for 任務; 事業; 企業: *To start a new business can be a risky undertaking.* 創辦新企業是一件冒險的事情。**2** a promise 保證; 許諾: *The council has given an undertaking to improve local services.* 地方議會已保證要改善本地的服務質量。

un·der·tone /ˈʌndəˌton; ˈʌndətəʊn/ n a quiet voice 低聲, 小聲: *He spoke in an undertone.* 他低聲説話。

un·der·took /ˌʌndəˈtʊk; ˌʌndəˈtʊk/ the past tense of UNDERTAKE ☆ UNDERTAKE 的過去式

un·der·wa·ter /ˈʌndəˌwɔtə; ˌʌndəˈwɔːtəʳ◂/ adj, adv used or done below the surface of the water 在水下(的); 供水下用的: *an underwater camera* 水下攝影機 | *Richard loves swimming underwater.* 理查喜愛在水底游泳。

un·der·wear /ˈʌndəˌwɛr; ˈʌndəweəʳ/ n [U] clothes worn next to your body under other clothes 內衣; 襯衣

un·der·weight /ˈʌndəˌwet; ˌʌndəˈweɪt◂/ adj weighing too little 重量不足的; 未達標準重量的: *He is several pounds underweight.* 他比標準體重輕幾磅。–see 見 THIN¹ (USAGE 用法)

un·der·went /ˌʌndəˈwɛnt; ˌʌndəˈwent/ the past tense of UNDERGO ☆ UNDERGO 的過去式

un·der·world /ˈʌndəˌwɜld; ˈʌndəwɜːld/ n **1** in ancient stories the place where the spirits of the dead live 〔古代故事中的〕陰間,

地府 **2** the criminal world 罪犯社會; 黑社會

un·de·si·ra·ble[1] /ˌʌndɪˈzaɪrəbḷ; ˌʌndɪˈzaɪrə-bḷ/ *adj fml* 〔正式〕 **1** unpleasant with a possible bad effect 令人不快的; 可能有不良效果的: *Many drugs have undesirable side-effects.* 很多藥物有不良的副作用。 **2** not socially acceptable 不合社會道德標準的

undesirable[2] *n* a person thought of as socially unacceptable 不良分子; 不受歡迎的人

un·de·vel·oped /ˌʌndɪˈvɛləpt; ˌʌndɪˈveləpt/ *adj* **1** without industry or modern farming (used of a place or country) 不發達的; 未發展的〔指地方或國家〕 **2** not built on (used of land) 未開發的〔指土地〕

un·dis·tin·guished /ˌʌndɪˈstɪŋgwɪʃt; ˌʌndɪˈstɪŋgwɪʃt◂/ *adj* ordinary, without any special qualities 普通的; 無特徵的

un·di·vid·ed /ˌʌndəˈvaɪdɪd; ˌʌndɪˈvaɪdḷd◂/ *adj* **1** complete 完整的; 全部的: *The children gave me their undivided attention while I read them a story.* 我給孩子們讀一個故事時, 他們專心致志地聽。 **2** having no divisions 未分開的

un·do /ʌnˈdu; ʌnˈduː/ *v* **undid** /-ˈdɪd; -ˈdɪd/, **undone** /-ˈdʌn; -ˈdʌn/ [T] **1** to unfasten something that is tied, sewn, or connected 解開, 鬆開, 打開: *I can't undo the knot in this string.* 我解不開這繩子上的結。 | *He undid the buttons on his shirt.* 他解開了襯衫的鈕扣。 | *I undid my sewing because it was wrong.* 我把針線活拆開, 因為縫錯了。 —opposite 反義 **do up** 2 to remove the effects of something 消除〔某事物〕效果: *It will be difficult to undo your mistakes.* 要彌補你的錯誤是很困難的。

un·do·ing /ʌnˈduɪŋ; ʌnˈduːɪŋ/ *n* [sing] the cause of ruin or failure 毀滅或失敗的原因; 禍根: *Alcohol was his undoing.* 酗酒是他墮落的原因。

un·done[1] /ʌnˈdʌn; ʌnˈdʌn◂/ *adj* **1** unfastened or loose 解開的, 鬆開的: *Your shoelace has come undone.* 你的鞋帶鬆開了。 **2** not done 未做的; 未完成的: *I've got a pile of work that is still undone.* 我還有一堆工作未做。

undone[2] the past participle of UNDO ☆ UNDO 的過去分詞

*****un·doubt·ed** /ʌnˈdautɪd; ʌnˈdautḷd/ *adj* known for certain to be true 無疑的; 肯定的 **–un·doubtedly** *adv*: *The story is undoubtedly true.* 這故事是千真萬確的。

un·dreamed-of /ʌnˈdrimdɒv; ʌnˈdriːmd əv/ *adj* (also 又作 **undreamt-of** /ʌnˈdremtɒv; ʌnˈdremtəv/) better than could have been imagined 〔好得〕夢想不到的, 意外的: *undreamed-of wealth* 意想不到的財富

un·dress /ʌnˈdrɛs; ʌnˈdres/ *v* **1** [I] to take your clothes off 脫衣服: *The doctor asked me to undress.* 醫生叫我脫去衣服。 **2** **get undressed** to take your clothes off 脫衣服: *I got undressed and went to bed.* 我脫掉衣服,

上牀去睡。 **3** [T] to take off someone's clothes 脫去〔某人〕的衣服: *He undressed the baby and put her in the bath.* 他給嬰兒脫去衣服, 把她放進浴缸裡。

un·due /ʌnˈdju; ʌnˈdjuː◂/ *adj* [always before a noun 只能用於名詞前] more than is necessary or suitable 過度的; 過分的: *She left with undue haste.* 她過分匆忙地離去了。

un·du·late /ˈʌndjəˌlet; ˈʌndjʊˈleɪt/ *v* **undulated, undulating** [I] to move or have slopes like waves rising and falling 波動; 起伏: *undulating hills* 起伏的山丘

un·du·ly /ʌnˈdjulɪ; ʌnˈdjuːli/ *adv* too much 過度地; 過分地: *His parents did not seem unduly worried.* 他父母似乎並不過分地憂慮。

un·earth /ʌnˈɝˈθ; ʌnˈɜːθ/ *v* [T] to dig up or find something 發掘, 掘出〔某物〕: *The dog unearthed a bone in the garden.* 狗在花園裡掘出一塊骨頭。

un·earth·ly /ʌnˈɝˈθlɪ; ʌnˈɜːθli/ *adj* **1** strange and unnatural 奇怪的; 不自然的: *There was an unearthly presence in the room.* 這房間裡有點怪異。 **2** *infml* very early or very late and inconvenient 〔非正式〕早或遲得不合理的: *I had to get up at an unearthly hour to get to the airport.* 我得一大早起牀, 趕去機場。

un·eas·y /ʌnˈizɪ; ʌnˈiːzi/ *adj* **uneasier, uneasiest** uncertain, worried, or anxious 不穩定的; 擔心的; 憂慮的: *He feels uneasy about the future.* 他為將來感到憂慮。 **–uneasily** *adv* **–uneasiness** (also 又作 **unease** /ʌnˈiz; ʌnˈiːz/ *lit* 〔文〕) *n* [U]

un·e·co·nom·ic /ˌʌnikəˈnamɪk; ˌʌniːkəˈnɒmɪk/ *adj* not producing enough profit 不經濟的, 沒有效益的: *These old coal mines are quite uneconomic.* 這些舊煤礦沒有甚麼效益。 **–uneconomically** /-klɪ; -kli/ *adv*

un·e·co·nom·i·cal /ˌʌnikəˈnamɪkəl; ˌʌniːkə-ˈnɒmɪkəl/ *adj* wasteful or expensive 浪費的; 昂貴的: *It's uneconomical to buy such small packets.* 買這些這麼小的袋子真是浪費。 | *She uses no end of water. She's very uneconomical.* 她沒完沒了地用水, 真是浪費。 **–uneconomically** *adv*

un·ed·u·cat·ed /ʌnˈɛdʒə̩ketɪd; ʌnˈedjʊˈkeɪ-tḷd/ *adj* not having had much education 缺乏教養的, 沒受過教育的

*****un·em·ployed** /ˌʌnɪmˈplɔɪd; ˌʌnɪmˈplɔɪd◂/ *adj* **1** not having a job 失業的: *He's an unemployed actor.* 他是個失業的演員。 **2** **the unemployed** the people who do not have a job 失業者

*****un·em·ploy·ment** /ˌʌnɪmˈplɔɪmənt; ˌʌnɪm-ˈplɔɪmənt/ *n* [U] **1** the number of people in a society without a job 失業人數: *The level of unemployment has increased by 5000 this month.* 這個月失業人數增加了五千人。 **2** the situation of not having a job 失業(狀態): *Unemployment can be very depressing for people.* 失業可令人十分沮喪。

un·en·light·ened /ˌʌnɪnˈlaɪtnd; ˌʌnɪnˈlaɪ-tənd/ *adj* not having knowledge or understanding of something 愚昧無知的; 未經啟蒙的: *a very unenlightened policy* 愚昧的政策

un·en·vi·a·ble /ʌnˈenvɪəbl; ʌnˈenviəbəl/ *adj* difficult and unpleasant 為難的; 令人不快的: *The policeman had the unenviable job of telling the woman that her husband had been killed.* 這名警察有件為難的差事: 告訴那女人她的丈夫被殺害了。

un·e·qual /ʌnˈikwəl; ʌnˈiːkwəl/ *adj* **1** not of equal size, value or strength 〔尺寸、價值或力氣〕不相等的: *The two bags were unequal in weight.* 這兩個袋子重量不等。 **2** not the same or treated fairly 不相同的; 不平等的: *The women workers complained about unequal pay and conditions.* 女工抱怨工資和待遇不平等。 **3** unequal to something not having enough strength or ability to do something 不勝任某事的: *He was unequal to the job.* 他不能勝任這項工作。 —**unequally** *adv*

un·e·qualled /ʌnˈikwəld; ʌnˈiːkwəld/ *adj* (**unequaled** *AmE* 【美式】) better than any other 無與倫比的: *Her record as a tennis champion is unequalled.* 她作為一名網球冠軍的紀錄是無與倫比的。

un·e·quiv·o·cal /ˌʌnɪˈkwɪvəkl; ˌʌnɪˈkwɪvəkəl/ *adj* totally clear in meaning 意思明確的 – **unequivocally** /-klɪ; -kli/ *adv*

un·er·ring /ʌnˈɜrɪŋ; ʌnˈɜːrɪŋ/ *adj* without making a mistake 不犯錯誤的; 不出差錯的: *With unerring aim she hit the ball into the hole.* 她瞄得準確, 把球擊入洞中。

un·e·ven /ʌnˈivən; ʌnˈiːvən/ *adj* **1** not smooth, flat, straight, or regular 不光滑的; 不平坦的; 不規則的; 崎嶇的: *The road surface is very uneven here.* 這兒的路面十分凹凸不平。 **2** not equal or balanced 不平等的; 不均衡的: *The match is going to be very uneven because Jones has much more experience than Freeman.* 這場比賽不會是勢均力敵的, 因為瓊斯比弗里曼有經驗得多。 —**unevenly** *adv* —**unevenness** *n* [U]

un·fail·ing /ʌnˈfelɪŋ; ʌnˈfeɪlɪŋ/ *adj* continuous and always present 連續不斷的; 永恆的; 無窮盡的: *My parents' unfailing support has helped me to succeed.* 父母始終如一的支持幫助我成功。 —**unfailingly** *adv*

un·faith·ful /ʌnˈfeθfəl; ʌnˈfeɪθfəl/ *adj* having a sexual relationship with someone else when you are already married or have a partner 〔對配偶或戀人〕不忠貞的

un·fath·o·ma·ble /ʌnˈfæðəməbl; ʌnˈfæðəməbəl/ *adj* which cannot be understood 無法理解的; 深不可測的

un·fa·vou·ra·ble /ʌnˈfevrəbl; ʌnˈfeɪvərəbəl/ *adj* (**unfavorable** *AmE* 【美式】) **1** not good and not what you would like 不好的; 不利的: *The dollar's exchange is very unfavourable at the moment.* 美元的兌換目前十分不利。 **2** showing disapproval 不贊同的; 反對的: *Most of the reviews of the film were unfavourable.* 這部影片的大多數評論都是不贊

同的。—**unfavourably** *adv*

un·feel·ing /ʌnˈfilɪŋ; ʌnˈfiːlɪŋ/ *adj* cruel and not sympathetic towards others 無情的; 冷酷的: *My old boss was horrible — totally cold and unfeeling.* 我的舊老闆很可怕——完全是冷酷無情的。

un·flag·ging /ʌnˈflægɪŋ; ʌnˈflægɪŋ/ *adj* without getting tired or stopping 不倦的; 不鬆懈的: *She has an unflagging interest in her work as a teacher.* 她對當教師這份工作有着毫不減退的興趣。

un·flinch·ing /ʌnˈflɪntʃɪŋ; ʌnˈflɪntʃɪŋ/ *adj* without fear when in danger or difficulty 〔遇到危險或困難〕無所畏懼的

un·fold /ʌnˈfold; ʌnˈfəʊld/ *v* **1** [T] to open something from a folded position 展開; 打開: *She took the letter out of the envelope and unfolded it carefully.* 她從信封裡取出信, 小心翼翼地打開。 **2** [I] to develop and become clear 逐漸呈現; 展示: *The film gets more and more interesting as the story unfolds.* 隨着故事的展開, 這部影片越來越有趣。

un·fore·seen /ˌʌnforˈsin; ˌʌnfɔːˈsiːn◂/ *adj* not expected in advance 未預見到的; 意想不到的: *Due to unforeseen circumstances publication has been delayed.* 由於意外的情況, 出版被耽擱了。

un·for·get·ta·ble /ˌʌnfɚˈgetəbl; ˌʌnfəˈgetəbəl/ *adj* not easy to forget 難以忘懷的: *We had the most unforgettable holiday travelling around China.* 我們在中國各地旅遊, 度過了一個難忘的假期。

un·for·tu·nate¹ /ʌnˈfɔrtʃənɪt; ʌnˈfɔːtʃənɪt/ *adj* **1** having bad luck which is usually not deserved 不幸的; 倒霉的: *He is a poor, unfortunate man with no home or family.* 他是個不幸的窮人, 無家可室。 **2** producing a bad result 產生不良後果的; 不合適的: *She telephoned at a rather unfortunate moment.* 她在很不合適的時刻打電話來。

unfortunate² *n* someone who has an unlucky life that you feel sorry for 不幸的人

*****un·for·tu·nate·ly** /ʌnˈfɔrtʃənɪtlɪ; ʌnˈfɔːtʃənɪtli/ *adv* a word used to say you are sorry or disappointed about something 令人遺憾地; 可惜〔用於表示對某事物感到難過或失望〕: *Unfortunately they've sold the house to someone else.* 真遺憾, 他們把房子賣給別人了。 | *"Will you be there tomorrow?" "No, unfortunately not."* "你明天在那兒嗎?" "不, 恐怕不在。"

un·found·ed /ʌnˈfaundɪd; ʌnˈfaʊndɪd/ *adj* without any supporting facts 無事實根據的: *The newspaper story was quite unfounded.* 那報上的報道實在沒有事實根據。

un·furl /ʌnˈfɜl; ʌnˈfɜːl/ *v* [T] to unroll and open a flag or sail 展開, 揚起〔旗或帆〕

un·gain·ly /ʌnˈgenlɪ; ʌnˈgeɪnli/ *adj* awkward and ungraceful in movement 〔行動〕笨拙的; 不優雅的 –**ungainliness** *n* [U]

un·gov·er·na·ble /ʌnˈgʌvɚnəbl; ʌnˈgʌvənəbəl/ *adj fml* not controllable 〔正式〕無法控制的, 難駕馭的

un·gra·cious /ʌnˈgreʃəs; ʌnˈgreɪʃəs/ *adj* not polite or friendly 不友善的; 不禮貌的 **–ungraciously** *adv*

un·grate·ful /ʌnˈgretfəl; ʌnˈgreɪtfəl/ *adj* not showing any thanks when someone is kind or generous 忘恩負義的; 不領情的: *Don't think I'm ungrateful, but I can't accept your offer.* 別以為我不領情, 可是我不能接受你的提議。 **–ungratefully** *adv*

un·guard·ed /ʌnˈgɑrdɪd; ʌnˈgɑːdɪd/ *adj* careless about what you say 〔說話〕不留神的: *an unguarded moment* 一不留神

un·hap·pi·ly /ʌnˈhæpɪlɪ; ʌnˈhæpḷli/ *adv* **1** in a sad way 不幸福地; 不愉快地 **2** *fml* unfortunately 〔正式〕不幸地; 令人遺憾地: *Unhappily, we could not finish the work.* 很遺憾, 我們無法完成工作。

★**un·hap·py** /ʌnˈhæpɪ; ʌnˈhæpi/ *adj* **unhappier, unhappiest 1** sad 不幸福的; 難過的: *She had an unhappy marriage.* 她的婚姻不幸福。 **2** worried and not pleased 不滿的; 不快的: *She was unhappy* **about** *the children going out alone.* 她為孩子們單獨外出感到不高興。 **–unhappiness** *n* [U]

un·health·y /ʌnˈhelθɪ; ʌnˈhelθi/ *adj* **unhealthier, unhealthiest 1** not generally in good health 不健康的; 有病的: *He looks thin and unhealthy.* 他看上去瘦瘦的, 一副有病的樣子。 **2** likely to cause bad health 對健康不利的; 對身心有害的: *an unhealthy climate* 不利於健康的氣候 | *Too much salt is unhealthy.* 食鹽過多對健康有害。 **3** unnatural 反常的, 病態的: *an unhealthy interest in murder* 對謀殺案有興趣的病態心理 **–unhealthily** *adv*

un·heard /ʌnˈhɜrd; ʌnˈhɜːd/ *adj* go unheard not to be listened to 沒聽到的: *Her complaints went unheard.* 她的抱怨無人理會。

unheard-of /·ˈ··/ *adj* very unusual 前所未聞的: *It's unheard-of to pass the examination so young.* 這麼年輕就通過這項考試真是前所未聞。

un·hinge /ʌnˈhɪndʒ; ʌnˈhɪndʒ/ *v* **unhinged, unhinging** [T] to cause someone to become unbalanced in their mind 使〔精神〕錯亂; 使失常: *His terrible experience unhinged him.* 他那恐怖的經歷使他發瘋。 | *He's really quite unhinged.* 他真的大為失常。

un·hook /ʌnˈhʊk; ʌnˈhʊk/ [T] **1** to remove something from a hook 從鈎上取下〔某物〕 **2** to unfasten the hooks of something 解開〔某物〕的搭扣: *She unhooked her necklace and put it in a box.* 她解開項鍊的搭扣, 把它放在盒子裡。

u·ni·corn /ˈjunɪˌkɔrn; ˈjuːnɪˌkɔːn/ *n* an imaginary animal like a horse with one horn growing from its forehead 〔傳說中身體似馬的〕獨角獸

un·i·den·ti·fied /ˌʌnaɪˈdɛntɪˌfaɪd; ˌʌnaɪˈden-tɪ̥faɪd/ *adj* whose name or origin is not known 身分不明的: *An unidentified man was seen near the scene of the murder.* 謀殺現場的附近曾出現過一個身分不明的人。

unidentified fly·ing ob·ject /·····,··· ,· ·ˈ··/ *n* see 見 UFO

u·ni·form¹ /ˈjunəˌfɔrm; ˈjuːnɪ̥fɔːm/ *n* [C;U] a certain type of clothing which all members of a group wear, for example in the army, a school, or the police 〔軍人、學生或警察的〕制服: *British policemen wear dark blue uniforms.* 英國警察穿深藍色制服。 | *Have we got to wear school uniform?* 我們得穿校服嗎? **–uniformed** *adj*: *Two uniformed policemen came to the door.* 兩個穿制服的警察來到門口。

uniform² *adj* always the same and never changing 一樣的; 一貫的; 不變的: *All the windows were painted a uniform colour.* 所有的窗戶都漆成清一色的顏色。 **–uniformity** /-ˈfɔrmətɪ; -ˈfɔːmḷti/ *n* [U] **–uniformly** *adv*

u·ni·fy /ˈjunəˌfaɪ; ˈjuːnɪ̥faɪ/ *v* **unified, unifying** [T] **1** to join together to make one whole 統一; 使成一體: *Spain was unified in the 16th century.* 西班牙在十六世紀統一。 **2** to make all the same 使相同; 使一致: *The company wishes to unify its computer systems.* 這家公司希望使它的電腦系統一元化。 **–unification** /ˌjunəfəˈkeʃən; ˌjuːnɪ̥fḷ-ˈkeɪʃən/ *n* [U]

u·ni·lat·er·al /ˌjunɪˈlætərəl; ˌjuːnɪˈlætərəl◂/ *adj* **1** done by or having an effect on only one side in an agreement 單方面的; 單邊的 **2 unilateral disarmament** one country removing its NUCLEAR weapons without waiting for other countries to do the same 單方面(核)裁軍

un·im·pea·cha·ble /ˌʌnɪmˈpitʃəbl; ˌʌnɪm-ˈpiːtʃəbəl/ *adj fml* that should not be doubted 〔正式〕無可置疑的

un·in·formed /ˌʌnɪnˈfɔrmd; ˌʌnɪnˈfɔːmd◂/ *adj* showing a lack of knowledge and information 無知的; 對情況不了解的: *an uninformed opinion* 無根據的觀點

un·in·hab·i·ta·ble /ˌʌnɪnˈhæbɪtəbl; ˌʌnɪn-ˈhæbɪ̥təbəl/ *adj* unfit to live in 不適宜居住的

un·in·hib·it·ed /ˌʌnɪnˈhæbɪtɪd; ˌʌnɪnˈhɪb-tɪ̥d/ *adj* free in what you say and do without worrying about what other people think 無拘無束的; 隨意的

un·in·terest·ed /ʌnˈɪntərɪstɪd; ʌnˈɪntrɪ̥stɪ̥d/ *adj* not interested 不感興趣的 **–see** 見 DISINTERESTED (USAGE 用法)

un·in·ter·rupt·ed /ˌʌnɪntəˈrʌptɪd; ˌʌnɪntə-ˈrʌptɪ̥d/ *adj* continuous 不間斷的; 連續的

★**u·nion** /ˈjunjən; ˈjuːnjən/ *n* **1** [U] the act of joining or state of being joined into one 聯合; 合併; 結合: *the union of East and West Germany* 東德和西德的合併 **2** [C] a group of countries or states joined together 聯邦; 聯盟: *the Soviet Union*

蘇聯 **3** [C +sing/pl v] a club or society which represents a group of workers, or a profession 協會; 聯合會; 工會: *Do you belong to a union?* 你是工會成員嗎? | *The Students' Union are holding elections today.* 學生會今天進行選舉。**4** [C] *fml* a marriage 〖正式〗婚姻: *a union blessed by the Church* 由教會主持的婚姻

u·nion·ize /ˈjunjənˌaɪz; ˈjuːnjənaɪz/ *v* **unionized, unionizing** (also 又作 **unionise** *BrE* 〖英式〗) [I;T] to form a TRADE UNION or arrange a union for a particular industry (使) 成立工會; (使) 成立聯合組織 – **unionization** /ˌjunjənɪˈzeʃən; ˌjuːnjənaɪˈzeɪʃn/ *n* [U]

Union Jack /ˌ·· ˈ·/ *n* the national flag of Great Britain 英國國旗

*★**u·nique** /juˈnik; juːˈniːk/ *adj* **1** the only one of its type 唯一的; 僅有的: *Each person's voice is unique.* 每個人的嗓音都是不同的。**2** related to one person, place, or thing only 獨特的; 獨一無二的: *Kangaroos are unique to Australia.* 袋鼠是澳大利亞獨有的。**3** *infml* unusual 〖非正式〗不平常的, 罕見的: *She has a rather unique singing style.* 她有一種特別的演唱風格。–**uniquely** *adv* –**uniqueness** *n* [U]

> ■ USAGE 用法: Because **unique** means "the only one" many people do not consider it correct to use **unique** with the meaning "unusual", or to use expressions like *fairly/rather* **unique**. 因為 **unique** 意為"唯一的", 所以很多人認為用 **unique** 表示"不平常"的意思, 或使用諸如 *faily/rather* **unique** 之類的表達法是不正確的。

u·ni·sex /ˈjunɪsɛks; ˈjuːnɪˌseks/ *adj infml* which can be used by both men and women 〖非正式〗男女通用的, 不分男女的: *a unisex hairdresser* 為男女理髮的理髮師

u·ni·son /ˈjunəsn; ˈjuːnəsn/ *n* **in unison: a** in perfect agreement 一致 **b** together 一起: *"Yes!" they answered in unison.* "是!" 他們一起回答。

*★**u·nit** /ˈjunɪt; ˈjuːnɪt/ *n* **1** something such as a group of things or people that forms a single and complete whole within something larger 〔構成一個整體的事物或人的〕單位, 單元: *an army unit* 一支軍隊 | *The family is a small social unit.* 家庭是社會最小的基本單位。**2** a piece of furniture which can be fitted with others of the same type 〔配套家具的〕組合件: *a kitchen unit* 一件廚房設備組合件 **3** an amount or quantity used as a standard of measurement 〔計量用的〕單位, 單元: *The pound is the standard unit of money in Britain.* 英鎊是英國的標準貨幣單位。

U·ni·tar·i·an /ˌjunəˈtɛriən; ˌjuːnɪˈteəriən/ *adj* of a branch of the Christian church 〔基督教的〕一位論教派的 –**Unitarian** *n*

u·nite /juˈnaɪt; juːˈnaɪt/ *v* **united, uniting** [I; T] to join together into one and act together 聯合; 團結; 合併: *The threat of a foreign attack united the government and its opponents.* 外敵入侵的威脅使政府和反對派聯合起來。

*★**u·nit·ed** /juˈnaɪtɪd; juːˈnaɪtɪd/ *adj* **1** joined in a state of agreement 團結的; 和睦的: *They are a very united family.* 他們是一個非常和睦的家庭。**2** all together 一致的; 統一的: *We must make a united effort to help.* 我們必須一起努力, 提供幫助。**3** [only before a noun 只用於名詞前] (also 又作 **United**) joined in an organization 聯合的; 聯盟的: *the United States of America* 美利堅合眾國 | *the United Nations* 聯合國

*★**u·ni·ty** /ˈjunətɪ; ˈjuːnɪtɪ/ *n* [U] state of being joined together in agreement 結合; 團結; 統一: *Political leaders always try to show there is unity in their party.* 政治領導人總力圖顯示自己的黨派很團結。

*★**u·ni·ver·sal** /ˌjunəˈvɝsl; ˌjuːnɪˈvɜːsl◂/ *adj* **1** for or concerning all the people in the world, or everyone in a particular group 全體的; 普遍的: *There was universal agreement to stop the plan.* 全體同意終止這項計劃。| *Love is a subject of universal interest.* 愛情是一個普遍感興趣的問題。**2** concerning the whole world 全世界的: *The dangers of pollution are universal.* 污染的危害全世界都存在。–**universally** *adv* –**universality** /ˌjunəvɝˈsæləti; ˌjuːnɪvɜːˈsælɪti/ *n* [U]

*★**u·ni·verse** /ˈjunəvɝs; ˈjuːnɪvɜːs/ *n* all space and everything that exists in it 宇宙; 天地萬物: *Stars fill every part of the universe.* 星球存在於宇宙的每一個部分。

*★**u·ni·ver·si·ty** /ˌjunəˈvɝsəti; ˌjuːnɪˈvɜːsɪti/ *n* **universities** [C;U] a place of education at the highest level, where degrees are given 大學: *Which university did you go to?* 你上的是哪家大學? | *Jean is a university professor.* 瓊是位大學教授。 | *"Has he got a job?" "No, he's still at university."* "他有工作嗎?" "沒有, 他還在上大學。" | *They've passed their exams and they're going to university in September.* 他們通過了考試, 九月份進大學。| *She went to Leeds University.* 她上的是利茲大學。| *She went to the University of Leeds.* 她進了利茲大學。

un·kempt /ˌʌnˈkɛmpt; ˌʌnˈkempt◂/ *adj* having very untidy clothes and hair 〔頭髮〕未梳理的; 〔衣服〕凌亂的

un·kind /ˌʌnˈkaɪnd; ˌʌnˈkaɪnd◂/ *adj* cruel, unfriendly, or unpleasant to people 〔對人〕嚴酷的; 不仁慈的; 不友好的; 不客氣的 –**unkindly** *adv* –**unkindness** *n* [C;U]

*★**un·known** /ˌʌnˈnon; ˌʌnˈnəʊn◂/ *adj* **1** not known 不知道的; 未知的: *The cause of the disease is unknown.* 疾病的原因不明。**2** not famous or familiar 不出名的; 不熟悉的: *Un-*

til recently these fruits were unknown outside Asia. 這些水果直到最近才為亞洲以外的人所熟悉。

un·law·ful /ʌnˈlɔfəl; ʌnˈlɔːfəl/ *adj* against the law 不合法的; 非法的: *an unlawful action* 非法行為 **–unlawfully** *adv*

un·leash /ʌnˈliʃ; ʌnˈliːʃ/ *v* [T] to allow strong or violent forces or feelings to come out 發出, 發泄; 釋放〔強烈的力量或感情〕: *Enormous forces are unleashed in a thunderstorm.* 雷暴中釋放出巨大的能量。

un·leav·ened /ʌnˈlevənd; ʌnˈlevənd/ *adj* made without YEAST, and therefore flat (used of bread) 未經發酵的; 不含酵母的〔指麵包〕

★★un·less /ənˈles; ʌnˈles/ *conj* except if something happens 除非; 若不: *Do not leave the building unless you are instructed to do so.* 除非你接到指示, 別離開這幢房子。 | *Unless the government agrees to give extra money, the theatre will have to close.* 除非政府同意另外給錢, 否則這家劇院得關門了。

> ■ USAGE 用法: Do not use **unless** when you are talking about imaginary events. Use **if...not** instead ☆談論想像的事情時不要用 **unless**, 用 **if...not** 代替: *If we weren't so poor* (imaginary because we are poor) *we could go on holiday.* 如果我們不這麼窮〔這是想像的, 因為我們很窮〕, 我們就能去度假了。 | *She would have died* (imaginary) *if the doctor had not arrived on time.* 如果醫生沒及時趕到, 她就死了〔想像的〕。 **Unless** cannot be used in these sentences. ☆**unless** 不能用於上述這些句子中。

★un·like[1] /ʌnˈlaɪk; ʌnˈlaɪk/ *adj* [never before a noun 不能用於名詞前] different 不同的: *She's very unlike her mother. They're completely unlike.* 她一點不像她母親。 她們毫無相似之處。

unlike[2] *prep* it's unlike him to... = it's not typical of him to... 這不是... 的特點: *It's unlike him to be late. He's usually on time.* 遲到可不像是他做的事, 他通常很準時。

★un·like·ly /ʌnˈlaɪklɪ; ʌnˈlaɪkli/ *adj* not likely 未必的; 不大可能的: *He may come, but it's very unlikely.* 他也許會來, 但這可能性不大。 | *They're unlikely to be at home before six o'clock.* 他們六點以前不大可能在家。 | *It seems unlikely that they'll come now.* 他們似乎未必會來。

> □ USEFUL PATTERNS 有用句型
> be unlikely to do something; it is unlikely that...

–unlikeliness (also 又作 **unlikelihood**) *n* [U]

un·load /ʌnˈlod; ʌnˈləʊd/ *v* **1** [T] to remove goods from a vehicle or container 〔從車輛上或集裝箱裡〕卸下〔貨物〕: *Can you help me unload the car?* 你能幫我卸下汽車上的貨嗎? **2** [I] to have goods removed 卸貨: *The trucks unload as soon as they arrive at the warehouse.* 貨車一到達倉庫就開始卸貨。 **3** [I; T] to remove the bullets from a gun or film from a camera 退出〔槍中的〕子彈; 退出〔相機中的〕膠卷

un·lock /ʌnˈlak; ʌnˈlɒk/ *v* [T] to unfasten the lock on something 開〔某物〕的鎖: *That door is quite difficult to unlock.* 那扇門上的鎖很難打開。

un·looked-for /ʌnˈlʊktˌfɔr; ʌnˈlʊkt fɔːr/ *adj lit* unexpected 〔文〕出乎意料的; 意外的

un·loos·en /ʌnˈlusn̩; ʌnˈluːsən/ *v* [T] to make something less tight 放鬆, 鬆開〔某物〕: *He unloosened his tie when he got outside.* 他一走到外面, 就鬆開了領帶。

un·luck·y /ʌnˈlʌkɪ; ʌnˈlʌki/ *adj* **unluckier, unluckiest** not lucky 不幸的; 倒霉的, 不吉利的: *People say it's unlucky to walk under a ladder.* 人們說從梯子下面走過是不吉利的。 | *She's been unlucky with her car — it's always breaking down.* 她坐那輛車真倒霉, 它總是發生故障。

un·made /ʌnˈmed; ʌnˈmeɪd◂/ *adj* **1** not made ready for sleeping in (used of a bed) 〔指牀〕未鋪好的 **2** not having a hard surface, but just made of earth (used of roads) 〔指路面〕未鋪好的

un·mask /ʌnˈmæsk; ʌnˈmɑːsk/ *v* [T] to show the hidden truth about someone or something 暴露, 揭露〔真相〕

un·men·tio·na·ble /ʌnˈmenʃənəbl̩; ʌnˈmenʃənəbəl/ *adj* too unpleasant to be spoken of 說不出口的; 不宜提及的

un·mis·ta·ka·ble /ˌʌnmɪˈstekəbl̩; ˌʌnmɪˈsteɪkəbəl/ *adj* too clear and recognizable to be thought of as anything else 明白無誤的; 不會弄錯的: *the unmistakable sound of a baby crying* 不會叫人弄錯的嬰兒啼哭的聲音 **–unmistakably** *adv*

un·mit·i·gat·ed /ʌnˈmɪtəˌgetɪd; ʌnˈmɪtᵻˌgeɪtᵻd/ *adj* [always before a noun 只用於名詞前] bad in every way and not to be excused 壞透的; 無法原諒的: *I knew we should never have done it. It's been an unmitigated disaster.* 我知道我們本來完全不該幹這事, 這完全是一場災難。

un·moved /ʌnˈmuvd; ʌnˈmuːvd/ *adj* showing no sympathy or feelings 不感動的; 無動於衷的

un·nat·u·ral /ʌnˈnætʃərəl; ʌnˈnætʃərəl/ *adj* **1** not what is usual, expected, or normal 反常的; 不自然的: *It's unnatural for him to have a rest after a meal.* 他飯後休息是很反常的事。 | *It's unnatural for a child to spend so much time with adults.* 一個孩子和大人一起度過這麼多時間是很反常的。 | *Those tomatoes are so red they look unnatural.* 這些番茄紅得很不自然。

□ **USEFUL PATTERNS** 有用句型
it is unnatural to do something; it is unnatural for someone to do something

2 false and not sincere 虛假的; 不真誠的: *an unnatural laugh* 造作的笑容 –**unnaturally** *adv*: *It was unnaturally quiet when I arrived.* 我到達時，那裡出奇地安靜。

un·ne·ces·sa·ry /ʌnˈnɛsəˌsɛrɪ; ʌnˈnɛsəsəri/ *adj* not needed or more than is needed 不必要的; 不需要的: *It's unnecessary to spend too much time on this job.* 沒有必要在這項工作上花太多時間。 | *It was unnecessary for you to ask.* 你沒必要問。 | *I want to avoid any unnecessary expenses on the trip.* 我想避免旅途中一切不必要的花費。

□ **USEFUL PATTERNS** 有用句型
it is unnecessary to do something; it is unnecessary for someone to do something

–**unnecessarily** /ʌnˈnɛsəˌsɛrəlɪ; ʌnˈnɛsəsərˌli/ *adv*: *unnecessarily rude* 不必要地粗魯

un·nerve /ʌnˈnɜːv; ʌnˈnɜːv/ *v* **unnerved, unnerving** [T] to take away someone's courage or confidence 使喪失勇氣; 使失去信心: *The accident unnerved him and he hasn't driven since.* 那次事故使他失去了信心，從此他再也沒開過車。 | *an unnerving experience* 令人喪失信心的經歷 | *He seemed quite unnerved by the experience.* 他似乎因那次經歷而失去了信心。

un·ob·tru·sive /ˌʌnəbˈtruːsɪv; ˌʌnəbˈtruːsɪv/ *adj* not too noticeable and not getting in people's way; a word used to express approval 不引人注目的; 不顯眼的〔含褒義〕: *The builders tried to be as unobtrusive as possible.* 建造商盡量做到不引人注目。–**unobtrusively** *adv*

un·of·fi·cial /ˌʌnəˈfɪʃəl; ˌʌnəˈfɪʃəl/ *adj* not arranged or said formally or officially 非官方的; 非正式的: *The workers have organized an unofficial strike.* 工人組織了一次未經工會認可的罷工。–**unofficially** *adv*: *They told her unofficially that she had got the job.* 他們非正式地告訴她，她得到了那份工作。

un·or·tho·dox /ʌnˈɔːθəˌdɑks; ʌnˈɔːθədɒks/ *adj* not according to usual beliefs or methods 非正統的; 標新立異的: *It's an unorthodox medical treatment but it's definitely helping.* 這是一種非正統的治療法，但肯定有用。

un·pack /ʌnˈpæk; ʌnˈpæk/ *v* [I;T] to take things out of a case or box 從〔箱子或盒子裡〕取出: *I'm just going to unpack my suitcase.* 我正要打開行李〔取出裡面的東西〕。

un·par·al·leled /ʌnˈpærəˌlɛld; ʌnˈpærəleld/ *adj* so great that nothing is equal or better 無與倫比的; 空前的: *an unparalleled success* 空前的成功

un·pick /ʌnˈpɪk; ʌnˈpɪk/ *v* [T] to remove the stitches from a piece of sewing 拆去〔衣料上的縫線〕

un·pleas·ant /ʌnˈplɛzənt; ʌnˈplezənt/ *adj* **1** not pleasant or enjoyable 令人不愉快的; 討厭的: *an unpleasant smell* 難聞的氣味 **2** unkind or rude and unfriendly 不和善的; 粗魯的; 不友好的: *My brother was very unpleasant to me when I was little.* 在我小時候，哥哥對我很是無禮。–**unpleasantly** *adv* –**unpleasantness** *n* [U]

un·pre·ce·dent·ed /ʌnˈprɛsəˌdɛntɪd; ʌnˈprɛsˌdentˌd/ *adj* never having happened or been done before 沒有先例的; 空前的; 前所未有的: *Such winds were quite unprecedented and caused widespread damage.* 這種風前所未有，造成了廣泛的損失。

un·pre·ten·tious /ˌʌnprɪˈtɛnʃəs; ˌʌnprɪˈtenʃəs/ *adj* not trying to appear important or wealthy 不鋪張的; 不招搖的; 不炫耀的: *They are rich but have an unpretentious lifestyle.* 他們很有錢，但是生活方式樸實無華。–**unpretentiously** *adv* –**unpretentiousness** *n* [U]

un·prin·ci·pled /ʌnˈprɪnsəpld; ʌnˈprɪnsˌpld/ *adj* done without caring about behaving honestly and morally 不講道德原則的; 不正直的: *He is totally unprincipled about money.* 他在金錢方面完全不講道德原則。

un·prin·ta·ble /ʌnˈprɪntəbl̩; ʌnˈprɪntəbl/ *adj* too rude or offensive to be repeated in writing (used of what someone says)〔指某人說的話因過於粗魯或無禮而〕不宜刊印的

un·pro·fes·sion·al /ˌʌnprəˈfɛʃənl̩; ˌʌnprəˈfeʃənl/ *adj* not behaving according to the standards of a particular profession 違反行規的; 非專業的 –**unprofessionally** *adv*

un·pro·voked /ˌʌnprəˈvokt; ˌʌnprəˈvəʊkt◂/ *adj* not caused by anything that was done before 無緣無故的: *an unprovoked attack* 無緣無故的攻擊

un·qual·i·fied /ʌnˈkwɑləˌfaɪd; ʌnˈkwɒlˌfaɪd/ *adj* **1** not having suitable knowledge or qualifications (QUALIFICATION) 不合格的; 無資格的: *inexperienced and unqualified young people* 既缺乏經驗又無資格的年輕人 | *She is unqualified to teach in Britain.* 她沒有資格在英國教書。

□ **USEFUL PATTERNS** 有用句型
be unqualified to do something; be unqualified for something

2 not limited 無限制的; 無條件的; 絕對的: *unqualified praise* 絕對的稱讚

un·ques·tio·na·ble /ʌnˈkwɛstʃənəbl̩; ʌnˈkwestʃənəbəl/ *adj* certain and not to be doubted 確實的; 毫無疑問的 –**unquestionably** *adv*: *She is unquestionably our best player.* 她無疑是我們最出色的選手。

un·rav·el /ʌnˈrævl̩; ʌnˈrævəl/ *v* **-ll-** (also 又作 **-l-** *AmE*【美式】) **1** [I;T] to become or cause to become undone or untied 解開; 拆

散 **2** [T] to find out the truth about something when it is not simple 解釋，闡明，弄清楚

un·real /ʌnˈrɪəl; ʌnˈrɪəl◂/ adj seeming imaginary or unlike reality (used of an experience) 想像的，不真實的〔指經歷〕

un·rea·so·na·ble /ʌnˈriznəbl; ʌnˈriːzənəbəl/ adj **1** beyond what is fair, acceptable, or sensible 超越情理的；過分的；不合理的: She claimed that her ex-husband's behaviour had been totally unreasonable. 她聲稱前夫的行為實在無理。 **2** too great (used of an amount or cost) 過大的，過高的〔指數量或費用〕 –**unreasonably** adv –**unreasonableness** n [U]

un·rea·son·ing /ʌnˈriznɪŋ; ʌnˈriːzənɪŋ/ adj not using the power of reason 不憑理智的；不講理的

un·re·lent·ing /ˌʌnrɪˈlɛntɪŋ; ˌʌnrɪˈlɛntɪŋ◂/ adj continuous and often done very purposefully, without worrying about what other people feel 不鬆懈的；不屈不撓的: a week of unrelenting activity 一個星期的緊張不懈的活動 –**unrelentingly** adv

un·re·lieved /ʌnrɪˈlivd; ʌnrɪˈliːvd◂/ adj continuous and never varied (used of something unpleasant) 未減輕的；無變化的〔指不愉快的事物〕: unrelieved anxiety 未減輕的焦慮

un·re·mit·ting /ˌʌnrɪˈmɪtɪŋ; ˌʌnrɪˈmɪtɪŋ◂/ adj never stopping 不停的；持續的

un·re·quit·ed /ˌʌnrɪˈkwaɪtɪd; ˌʌnrɪˈkwaɪtʒd◂/ adj fml **unrequited love** love that is not given in return〔正式〕單戀

un·re·served /ʌnrɪˈzɝvd; ʌnrɪˈzɜːvd◂/ adj complete and without doubts or limits 完全的；無保留的；無限制的: You have my unreserved admiration. 我對你無限欽佩。 –**unreservedly** /-vdlɪ; -vʒdlɪ/ adv

un·rest /ʌnˈrest; ʌnˈrest/ n [U] dissatisfaction and anger causing trouble in society〔社會的〕不安，不穩，動亂: Unemployment causes a lot of social unrest. 失業引起很多社會動亂。

un·re·strained /ʌnrɪˈstrend; ʌnrɪˈstreɪnd◂/ adj not held back or controlled 未受抑制的；無節制的: unrestrained anger 不加克制的怒氣

un·roll /ʌnˈrol; ʌnˈrəʊl/ v [I;T] to open from a rolled position 鋪開，展開〔捲着的東西〕: They unrolled the carpet. 他們把地毯鋪開。

un·ru·ly /ʌnˈrulɪ; ʌnˈruːlɪ/ adj **unrulier, unruliest** uncontrollable and wild in behaviour 難控制的；不守規矩的: unruly children 難管教的兒童 –**unruliness** n [U]

un·said /ʌnˈsɛd; ʌnˈsed/ adj thought of but not spoken〔想到而〕未說出來的: She left her criticisms unsaid. 她沒把批評的話說出口。

un·sa·vour·y /ʌnˈsevərɪ; ʌnˈseɪvərɪ/ adj (**unsavory** AmE〔美式〕) unpleasant or morally unacceptable 令人不快的；〔道德上〕令人厭惡的: He's a rather unsavoury character. 他是個聲名狼藉的人。

un·scathed /ʌnˈskeðd; ʌnˈskeɪðd/ adj not harmed 未受傷害的: He escaped from the accident completely unscathed. 他在這次事故中脫險，完全沒有受到傷害。

un·screw /ʌnˈskru; ʌnˈskruː/ v [T] **1** to remove something by undoing the screws that hold it in place 從…旋出螺絲 **2** to undo a screw top by turning it 旋開〔螺絲蓋〕，擰開: I can't unscrew the top of this bottle. 我旋不開這瓶子的蓋。

un·scru·pu·lous /ʌnˈskrupjələs; ʌnˈskruːpjʒləs/ adj not caring about honesty and fairness 無道德原則的；不擇手段的: They use very unscrupulous business methods. 他們採用不擇手段的經營方法。 –**unscrupulously** adv –**unscrupulousness** n [U]

un·seat /ʌnˈsit; ʌnˈsiːt/ v [T] to remove someone from a position of power 奪去〔某人〕的席位；革除〔某人的職位〕

un·seem·ly /ʌnˈsimlɪ; ʌnˈsiːmlɪ/ adj fml not suitable in behaviour in a situation where politeness or seriousness is needed〔正式〕〔行為〕不適宜的，不得體的 –**unseemliness** n

un·set·tle /ʌnˈsɛtl; ʌnˈsetl/ v **unsettled, unsettling** [T] to make someone feel anxious, dissatisfied, or worried 使〔某人〕不安；使焦急；使擔憂: The sudden changes unsettled her. 突如其來的變化使她心神不寧。

un·set·tled /ʌnˈsɛtld; ʌnˈsetld◂/ adj **1** changeable and uncertain (used of a situation) 易變的，不穩定的〔指形勢〕: The weather will be rather unsettled over the next few days. 接下來的幾天裏，天氣變化將很大。 **2** feeling anxious, worried, and unable to keep your mind on one thing 不安的；心神不寧的 **3** not decided or agreed 未決定的；未解決的: Their argument is still unsettled. 他們的爭論尚未得到解決。

un·set·tling /ʌnˈsɛtlɪŋ; ʌnˈsetlɪŋ/ adj making you feel anxious, dissatisfied, or worried 令人不安的: All these changes are very unsettling. 這些變化全都令人十分不安。

un·sha·kea·ble /ʌnˈʃɛkəbl; ʌnˈʃeɪkəbəl/ adj (also 又作 **unshakable**) firm in what you believe〔信念〕堅定不移的，不可動搖的: an unshakeable belief in God 對上帝堅定不移的信仰

un·sight·ly /ʌnˈsaɪtlɪ; ʌnˈsaɪtlɪ/ adj not pleasant to look at 難看的，不悅目的 –**unsightliness** n [U]

un·skilled /ˌʌnˈskɪld; ʌnˈskɪld◂/ adj **1** not trained for a particular type of job 未受專門訓練的；不熟練的: unskilled workers 非熟練工人 **2** not needing special skill 不需要特殊技能的: an unskilled job 不需要特殊技能的工作

un·so·phis·ti·cat·ed /ˌʌnsəˈfɪstɪˌketɪd; ˌʌnsəˈfɪstʒˌkeɪtʒd◂/ adj having simple likes and dislikes and not having much experience of the world and society 頭腦簡單的；不諳世故的；天真的；單純的

un·sound /ʌnˈsaʊnd; ˌʌnˈsaʊnd◂/ adj **1** not healthy, strong, or in good condition 不健康的; 不結實的; 情況不佳的: *Most of the building is in good condition but the roof is unsound.* 這幢房子大部分地方都不錯, 可是屋頂結構不堅固。 **2** not having a firm base in reason and fact 〔理由或事實〕不充分的, 無根據的: *an unsound argument* 缺乏根據的論點

un·spea·ka·ble /ʌnˈspiːkəbl; ʌnˈspiːkəbəl/ adj very bad and totally undeserving of respect 壞透了的; 惡劣得説不出口的: *His behaviour has been unspeakable.* 他的行為都叫人説不出口。 **–unspeakably** adv: *unspeakable cruel* 殘酷得無法形容

un·stuck /ʌnˈstʌk; ʌnˈstʌk/ adj come unstuck to fail 失敗: *His plans came unstuck.* 他的計劃受挫了。

un·stud·ied /ʌnˈstʌdid; ʌnˈstʌdid/ adj fml natural, and not the result of a lot of effort 〔正式〕自然的; 不故意造作的

un·swerv·ing /ʌnˈswɜːvɪŋ; ʌnˈswɜːvɪŋ/ adj firm in your aims or purpose 〔對目標或目的〕堅定不移的 **–unswervingly** adv

un·tan·gle /ʌnˈtæŋgl; ˌʌnˈtæŋgəl/ v **untangled, untangling** [T] to take out knots and straighten things that have been twisted together 解開〔糾結〕; 理順〔纏繞之物〕, 整理: *Can you untangle these wires?* 你能解開這些纏在一起的電線嗎?

un·tapped /ʌnˈtæpt; ˌʌnˈtæpt◂/ adj not yet being used 未利用的; 未開發的: *The sea is an untapped source of power.* 海洋是有待開發的能力資源。

un·ten·a·ble /ʌnˈtɛnəbl; ʌnˈtenəbəl/ adj impossible to defend (used of a belief or an argument) 站不住腳的, 不堪一擊的〔指信仰或論點〕

un·thin·ka·ble /ʌnˈθɪŋkəbl; ʌnˈθɪŋkəbəl/ adj too terrible to imagine happening 難以想像的; 不可思議的: *The prospect of a nuclear war is unthinkable.* 真難以想像發生核戰爭會是怎麼一片景象。

un·think·ing /ʌnˈθɪŋkɪŋ; ʌnˈθɪŋkɪŋ/ adj done or said without thinking about the effect 不考慮後果的; 輕率的 **–unthinkingly** adv

un·ti·dy /ʌnˈtaɪdi; ʌnˈtaɪdi/ adj **untidier, untidiest** not neat or well arranged 不整潔的; 不整齊的: *His bedroom is always untidy.* 他的臥室總是亂七八糟的。 **–untidiness** n [U]

un·tie /ʌnˈtaɪ; ʌnˈtaɪ/ v **untied, untying** [T] to undo something that is tied, such as a knot 解開; 鬆開〔結等縛紮的東西〕: *This knot is really tight. I can't undo it.* 這個結真緊, 我解不開。

★until /ənˈtɪl; ʌnˈtɪl/ prep, conj (also 又作 **till**) **1** up to a particular time 直到〔某個時間〕為止: *Wait until tomorrow.* 等到明天。 | *We'll stay here until the others arrive.* 我們將在這兒一直等到其他人來。 **2** not until only when it is a particular time 直到〔某個時間〕才: *I'm afraid your watch won't be ready until tomorrow.* 恐怕你的錶要到明

天才能修好。

un·time·ly /ʌnˈtaɪmli; ʌnˈtaɪmli/ adj fml 〔正式〕 **1** happening too soon 〔發生〕過早的: *Her death at the age of 29 was most untimely.* 她二十九歲去世實在是太早了。 **2** not suitable for the occasion 不合時宜的: *an untimely remark* 不合時宜的話 **–untimeliness** n [U]

un·tir·ing /ʌnˈtaɪrɪŋ; ʌnˈtaɪrɪŋ/ adj not stopping or showing tiredness in what you are doing 不懈的; 不倦的 **–untiringly** adv

un·told /ʌnˈtold; ʌnˈtəʊld◂/ adj **1** too great to be counted or measured 數不清的; 不可計量的: *The war caused untold damage and suffering.* 戰爭帶來了不可估量的損害和痛苦。 **2** not told or expressed 未説過的; 未加以敍述的: *The story remained untold for years.* 這故事多年來未對外講述過。

un·to·ward /ʌnˈtord; ˌʌntəˈwɔːd/ adj fml unexpected and unfortunate 〔正式〕意外的; 不幸的; 不順利的: *Nothing untoward happened on the journey.* 旅途中沒有發生甚麼不如意的事。

un·truth /ʌnˈtruθ; ʌnˈtruːθ/ n fml something that is not true 〔正式〕不真實的東西; 假話, 謊言

un·truth·ful /ʌnˈtruθfəl; ʌnˈtruːθfəl/ adj dishonest and telling lies 不誠實的; 説謊的: *She made untruthful statements to the police.* 她向警察撤了謊。 **–untruthfully** adv

un·used¹ /ʌnˈjuzd; ˌʌnˈjuːzd◂/ adj not used 未用過的: *There was a lot of unused space in the house.* 這房子裡有許多未動用的地方。

un·used² /ʌnˈjust; ʌnˈjuːst/ adj **unused to** to having no experience of something 對...不習慣的: *He is unused to such hot weather.* 他不習慣這麼熱的天氣。 | *unused to doing his own washing* 不習慣他自己洗衣服

★un·u·su·al /ʌnˈjuʒʊəl; ʌnˈjuːʒuəl/ adj **1** uncommon and not what is expected 不平常的; 異常的: *There's been an unusual amount of extra work this month.* 這個月額外的工作量異常的大。 | *It's unusual for us to go out much in the evenings.* 我們晚上多次外出是很少有的。 **2** different and interesting 與眾不同的; 獨特的: *What an unusual name!* 多獨特的名字啊!

un·u·su·al·ly /ʌnˈjuʒʊəli; ʌnˈjuːʒuəli/ adv **1** in an unusual way 不尋常地 **2** more than is common 非常; 異常: *We had an unusually hot summer this year.* 今年我們過了一個非常炎熱的夏天。

un·veil /ʌnˈvel; ˌʌnˈveɪl/ v [T] to remove a covering from a painting or sign on a building 除去〔畫上〕罩布; 揭去〔建築物上〕的覆蓋物: *The Queen will unveil a plaque to open the new hospital.* 女王為新醫院主持開幕儀式, 揭開了牌匾的罩布。

un·war·rant·ed /ʌnˈwɒrəntɪd; ʌnˈwɒrəntd̩/ adj unwelcome and done without good reason 沒有根據的; 無正當理由的: *This is a totally unwarranted use of public money.* 這

完全是對公款的不當使用。

un·well /ʌnˈwɛl; ʌnˈwɛl/ *adj* [never before a noun 不能用於名詞前] ill 有病的, 不舒服的

un·wield·y /ʌnˈwildɪ; ʌnˈwiːldɪ/ *adj* large, heavy, and awkward to move 〔龐大得〕難以移動的; 笨重的; 不靈便的: *a large, unwieldy box* 又大又笨重的箱子

un·wind /ʌnˈwaɪnd; ʌnˈwaɪnd/ *v* **unwound** /-ˈwaʊnd; -ˈwaʊnd/, **unwound** 1 [I;T] to pull out or undo something wrapped round something else 解開〔纏繞之物〕; 展開〔捲起的東西〕: *I unwound some cotton from the reel.* 我從線團裡繞出了一些棉線。 **2** [I] *infml* to do something restful after working hard 〔非正式〕放鬆; 鬆弛: *She had a long bath to unwind after a hectic day at the office.* 在辦公室裡忙碌了一整天以後, 她好好泡了個浴才能鬆馳下來。

un·wit·ting /ʌnˈwɪtɪŋ; ʌnˈwɪtɪŋ/ *adj* without knowing about or without intending to do something 不知情的; 非故意的 –**unwittingly** *adv*: *She made the mistake quite unwittingly.* 她無意中犯了這個錯誤。

un·wound /ʌnˈwaʊnd; ʌnˈwaʊnd/ the past tense and past participle of UNWIND ☆ UNWIND 的過去式和過去分詞

un·zip /ʌnˈzɪp; ˌʌnˈzɪp/ *v* **-pp-** [T] to open something by undoing a long metal fastener called a ZIP 拉開〔某物〕的拉鏈

★★ up¹ /ʌp; ʌp/ *adv, prep* **1** *adv, prep* in or towards a higher place or position, away from the floor or the ground 在…的上端; 向上; 向更高處; 在[向]樓上: *She lifted the box up onto the shelf.* 她把那個箱子搬到架子上去。 | *The dog jumped up when it saw us.* 狗看見我們就跳起來。 | *He stood up.* 他站了起來。 | *I picked the letter up off the floor.* 我從地板上撿起這封信。 | *I wound the car window up.* 我把車窗搖上來。 | *He turned his collar up against the rain.* 他翻起衣領來擋雨。 | *A bird was flying high up in the air.* 一隻鳥在高空飛翔。 | *He was jumping up and down.* 他跳上跳下。 | *He ran up the hill.* 他跑上山坡。 | *The water got up my nose.* 水嗆入我的鼻子裡。 | *Her office is up those stairs.* 她的辦公室在那條梯子上。 –see picture on page 764 見 764 頁彩圖 **2** *adv* out of bed 起牀: *I got up quite early this morning.* 今天早晨我起牀挺早。 | *Are you up yet?* 你起牀了嗎? **3** *adv* in or towards the North 在[向]北面: *We're travelling up to Scotland this evening.* 我們今晚北上蘇格蘭。 **4** *adv* showing increase 由低到高; 由小到大: *Production has gone up this year.* 今年產量上升了。 | *Please turn the radio up.* 請把收音機開大點聲音。 **5** *adv* near or towards a person or thing 靠近; 向: *He came up to me and asked my name.* 他向我走過來, 問我叫甚麼名字。 | *We didn't get right up to the paintings to have a close look.* 我們沒有逕直走近那些畫去仔細看。 **6** *adv* completely finished, or so as to be completely finished 完; 光; 盡: *Eat up your meat.* 吃光你的肉。 | *Time's up!* 時間到了! | *My three weeks were up and I had to go back to work.* 三星期過完了, 我得回去上班。 **7** *adv* divided into pieces 成碎片; 分離: *He tore up the newspaper.* 他把報紙撕碎了。 | *They divided up the money.* 他們把錢分了。 **8** *adv* so as to be together 在一起: *Please add up these numbers.* 請把這些數字加起來。 | *Collect up the fallen apples.* 把落下的蘋果收攏在一起。 **9** *adv* in operation (used of a computer) 在運作中(指電腦): *Is the computer back up yet?* 電腦恢復運行了嗎? **10 up the road, up the street** further along or at the far end of the road or street 沿着馬路而去; 在路的較遠處: *He ran up the road.* 他沿着道路跑去。 | *They live just up the road.* 他們就住在路的那一邊。 **11 up a river** along a river against the direction of the current 向河的上游; 逆流 **12 the road is up** = the road is being repaired 路面正在修理〔施工〕 **13 not up to much** *infml* not very good 〔非正式〕不太好: *The food's not up to much here.* 這兒的食物不太好。 **14 up and about** no longer in bed and ill 病癒; 不再臥牀: *You'll soon be up and about again.* 你很快又可以下牀走動了。 **15 up and down** backwards and forwards along something 來來回回; 往返地: *running up and down the road* 沿着馬路來回跑 | *He was pacing up and down the room.* 他在房間裡來回踱步。 **16 ups and downs** a mixture of good and bad experiences 興衰; 浮沉: *We've had a lot of ups and downs in life.* 我們經歷了生活中的浮沉起伏。 **17 up against something** having to face something 面臨〔某事物〕: *I thought of all the problems we were up against.* 我考慮到我們面臨的所有難題。 **18 up against it** having a lot of problems or difficulties 面臨許多問題〔困難〕: *We were really up against it!* 我們真的面臨困難了! **19 up to** as much as or as many as 多達: *He can earn up to £20,000 a year.* 他一年能掙二萬英鎊。 | *The room can hold up to 200 people.* 這房間最多可容納二百人。 **20 up to, up until** until 一直到: *I've never thought about it up to now.* 我直到現在才想到這事。 | *She lived at home right until she got married.* 她結婚前一直都住在娘家。 **21 up to something: a** *infml* busy doing something bad 〔非正式〕忙於做壞事: *I think he's up to something.* 我想他是在搞甚麼。 | *What are they up to?* 他們在搞甚麼鬼? **b** *infml* good enough for something 〔非正式〕勝任某事: *I'm not sure if she's really up to that job.* 我不肯定她是否真的勝任那項工作。 | *My German isn't up to translating his letter.* 我的德語還不足以翻譯他的那封信。 **22 up to someone** someone's choice or responsibility 由某人選擇; 由某人負責: *It's up to you to do it yourself.* 這應該由你自己去做。 | *It's up to her to decide whether or not to go on the course.* 是否上這門課由她自己決定。 **23 what's up?** *infml* =

what's the matter? 〖非正式〗甚麼事?

up² *adj* showing increase 上升的; 增加的: *Inflation is up by 2%.* 通貨膨脹率上升了百分之二。

up³ *v* **-pp-** *infml* 〖非正式〗 **1** [T] to increase something 提高, 增加〔某物〕: *Oil companies have simply upped the price of petrol.* 石油公司儘量提高了汽油的價格。 **2 up and do something** to do something suddenly and unexpectedly 突然做某事: *She just upped and left!* 她突然站起來走了!

up-and-com·ing /ˌ· '···/ *adj* likely to succeed in the future 有前途的: *an up-and-coming actress* 大有前途的女演員

up·braid /ʌp'bred; ˌʌp'breɪd/ *v* [T] *fml* to speak angrily to someone because they have done something wrong 〖正式〗責罵, 斥責〔某人〕

up·bring·ing /'ʌpˌbrɪŋɪŋ; 'ʌpbrɪŋɪŋ/ *n* [sing] the way someone is cared for and taught to behave by their parents 撫育, 養育; 教養: *They had a very strict upbringing.* 他們受到了嚴格的教養。

up·date /ʌp'det; ˌʌp'deɪt/ *v* **updated, updating** [T] **1** to make something more modern or fashionable 更新〔某事物〕; 使現代化; 使不落後 **2** to give the latest information 提供最新的信息 /'ʌpdet; 'ʌpdeɪt/ *n*: *And now over to Peter Potter for an update on the travel situation in London this morning.* 以下由彼得·波特為我們介紹倫敦今晨最新的交通情況。

up·end /ʌp'end; ˌʌp'end/ *v* [T] to make something stand on one end 使〔某物〕倒立, 倒放: *We'll have to upend the cupboard to get it through the door.* 我們得把碗櫥倒過來才能抬過這門。

up·grade /ʌp'gred; ˌʌp'greɪd/ *v* **upgraded, upgrading** [T] **1** to give someone or something a higher or more important position or rank 提升〔某人〕; 使〔某事物〕升級 **2** to improve the standard of something 提高〔某事物〕的標準: *British Rail's decision to upgrade the track between London and Brighton* 英國鐵道部提高倫敦和布賴頓之間鐵軌標準的決定

up·heav·al /ʌp'hivl; ʌp'hiːvəl/ *n* [C;U] a great change causing worry and confusion 激變; 劇變; 動亂: *Moving house will be a big upheaval.* 搬家會引起很大的變化。

up·held /ʌp'held; ʌp'held/ the past tense and past participle of UPHOLD ☆ UPHOLD 的過去式和過去分詞

up·hill /'ʌp'hɪl; 'ʌp'hɪl/ *adj, adv* **1** going towards the top of a hill 上坡的; 上山的: *walking uphill* 向山上走 —opposite 反義 **downhill 2** difficult and needing a lot of effort 艱難的; 費力的: *Teaching this class is an uphill struggle.* 教這一班學生是一項艱難的奮鬥。

up·hold /ʌp'hold; ˌʌp'həʊld/ *v* **upheld** /-'held; -'held/, **upheld** [T] **1** to support

and defend something 堅持, 維護〔某事物〕: *We must uphold the right to free speech.* 我們必須維護自由言論的權利。 **2** to declare something to be right and correct 認可, 確認〔某事物〕: *The appeal judge upheld the court's decision.* 上訴法官維持法院的判決。

up·hol·ster /ʌp'holstə; ʌp'həʊlstəʳ/ *v* [T] to cover furniture with soft material to make it comfortable 為〔家具〕裝襯墊[套子]: *an upholstered chair* 裝上套子的椅子 —**upholsterer** *n*

up·hol·ster·y /ʌp'holstəri; ʌp'həʊlstəri/ *n* [U] material that makes a comfortable covering and filling for seats and other furniture 家具套子〔襯料〕

up·keep /'ʌpˌkip; 'ʌpkiːp/ *n* [U] the act or cost of keeping something repaired and in order 保養(費); 維修(費): *We can no longer afford the upkeep of a large house.* 我們再也負擔不起一幢大房子的維修費用了。

up·land /'ʌplənd; 'ʌplənd/ *adj* being the higher land in an area 高地的; 高原的; 山地的: *the upland areas of the country* 鄉間的高山地區

up·lifting /ʌp'lɪftɪŋ; ʌp'lɪftɪŋ/ *adj* encouraging you morally 〔在道德方面〕促進的; 提高的

upon /ə'pɒn; ə'pɒn/ *prep fml* on 〖正式〗在…上: *He lay upon the floor.* 他躺在地上。 | *We acted upon your advice.* 我們遵照你的意見辦事。

up·per¹ /'ʌpə; 'ʌpəʳ/ *adj* [always before a noun 只能用於名詞前] **1** higher 較高的, 上面的: *the upper part of the body* 上身 **2** higher than or above something else that is similar 較上的; 上層的: *Passengers may smoke on the upper floor of the bus.* 乘客可以在公共汽車的上層吸煙。 **3 the Upper House** the House of Lords in the British parliament 〔英國議會的〕上議院 **4 have/get the upper hand** to have or get control in a situation 佔…的上風

upper² *n* the top part of a shoe or boot 鞋面, 鞋幫; 靴統

upper class /ˌ·· '·◂/ *n* [+sing/pl verb] **the upper class** or **the upper classes** a small social class of families with a lot of land and money and who often have noble titles 上流社會; 上等階層: *The upper classes usually send their children to private school.* 上層社會的人通常把他們的孩子送往私立學校。 —**upper-class** *adj*

up·per·most /'ʌpəˌmost; 'ʌpəməʊst/ *adv, adj* **1** facing up or in the highest position 最高的; 在最高處: *Insert the paper with the shiny side uppermost.* 把亮閃閃的一面朝上, 將這張紙插進去。 **2** being the most important thing 最重要地[的]: *Your happiness is uppermost in my mind.* 你的快樂是我心目中最重要的事。

up·right¹ /'ʌpˌraɪt; 'ʌp-raɪt/ *adj* **1** standing or sitting with a very straight back 挺直的; 筆直的: *She woke up and sat upright in bed.* 她

醒了，筆直地坐在牀上。 **2** taller than some other kinds of the same thing 竪(式)的: *an upright piano* 竪式鋼琴 | *Is it an upright freezer or a chest freezer?* 這是直立式冰箱還是櫃式冰箱? **3** honest, fair, and responsible 正直的; 公平的; 負責的: *an upright citizen* 誠實正直的市民

upright² *adv* standing in an upright position 筆直地; 挺拔地; 直立地

up·ris·ing /ˈʌp.raɪzɪŋ; ˈʌp.raɪzɪŋ/ *n* an act of the ordinary people suddenly and violently opposing those in power 起義; 暴動

up·roar /ˈʌp.rɔr; ˈʌp.rɔːʳ/ *n* [sing;U] angry shouting and noise, often done as a protest 吵鬧; 喧嚣; 騷動

up·root /ʌpˈrut; ˌʌpˈruːt/ *v* **1** [T] to pull a plant out of the earth by the roots 把〔植物〕連根拔起 **2 uproot yourself** to move away from your home and familiar surroundings 離開家園或熟悉的環境: *The family uprooted themselves and went to live abroad.* 這一家人離鄉別井, 去國外居住。

up·set¹ /ʌpˈsɛt; ʌpˈset/ *v* **upset, upset, upsetting** [T] **1** to make someone feel unhappy and anxious about something 使〔某人〕生氣; 使心煩意亂: *He didn't mean to upset you.* 他不是故意使你心煩意亂的。 **2** to knock something over accidentally 〔不小心〕打翻, 弄翻〔某物〕: *I upset a bottle of ink on the carpet.* 我把一瓶墨水打翻在地毯上。 **3** to cause something to change suddenly and become unsettled and confused 打亂, 攪亂〔某事物〕: *Our plans were upset by the change in the weather.* 天氣的變化打亂了我們的計劃。 | *The election results will upset the government's confidence.* 選舉結果將動搖政府的信心。 **4** to cause a slight illness in the stomach 使〔腸胃〕不適: *That wine has upset my stomach.* 那種酒使我的胃感到不舒服。

up·set² /ʌpˈsɛt; ʌpˈset/ *adj* **1** feeling unhappy and anxious about something 不安的; 不快的; 心煩意亂的: *She was very upset about her parents' divorce.* 她對父母的離異感到十分煩惱。 **2** slightly ill 不適的: *I think it must have been that seafood that's given me this upset stomach.* 我想一定是吃了那種海鮮才弄得我的胃不舒服。

up·set³ /ˈʌp.sɛt; ˈʌpset/ *n* **1** [C;U] the act of causing sudden change and confusion 打亂; 攪亂 **2** [C] an illness of your stomach that lasts only a short time 〔腸胃的〕不適: *a tummy upset* 肚子不舒服

up·set·ting /ʌpˈsɛtɪŋ; ʌpˈsetɪŋ/ *adj* making you feel unhappy and anxious 令人心煩意亂的: *If people are rude to you, it's very upsetting.* 如果人們對你態度粗魯, 這真叫人心煩意亂。

up·shot /ˈʌp.ʃɑt; ˈʌpʃɒt/ *n* **the upshot** the result in the end 結局, 結果: *The upshot of the negotiations was a new trade agreement.* 談判的結果是達成了一項新的貿易協定。

up·side down /ˌʌp.saɪdˈdaʊn; ˌʌpsaɪdˈdaʊn/ *adv* **1** in a position with the top facing down and the bottom facing up 顛倒地; 倒置地 **2** untidy and in disorder 亂七八糟(地), 混亂地: *Everything's upside down in this house.* 這房子裡的所有東西都亂七八糟。

up·stage¹ /ˌʌpˈstedʒ; ˌʌpˈsteɪdʒ/ *adv* towards the back of the stage in the theatre 向舞台後面(的); 在舞台後部(的)

up·stage² /ˈʌp.stedʒ; ʌpˈsteɪdʒ/ *v* **upstaged, upstaging** [T] to take attention away from someone else in order to get attention for yourself 搶〔別人〕的鏡頭; 喧賓奪主

up·stairs /ʌpˈstɛrz; ˌʌpˈsteəz/ *adj, adv* situated on or going to an upper floor in a building 在樓上(的); 往樓上(的): *She went upstairs to her bedroom.* 她上樓去自己的臥室。 | *We could hear a party in the flat upstairs.* 我們可以聽到樓上房間有聚會。 | *"Where is she?" "Upstairs."* "她在哪兒?" "樓上。" | *The children watched from an upstairs window.* 孩子們從樓上的窗口看下來。

up·start /ˈʌp.stɑrt; ˈʌpstɑːt/ *n* a person who has risen suddenly to a high position and takes advantage of their new power (a word used to express disapproval) 新貴, 暴發戶〔含貶義〕

up·stream /ˌʌpˈstrim; ˌʌpˈstriːm/ *adv, adj* moving against the current of a river or stream 向上游(的); 逆流(的): *We travelled upstream for a few miles.* 我們逆流而上了幾英里。

up·surge /ˈʌp.sɝdʒ; ˈʌpsɜːdʒ/ *n* a sudden large rise in something 急劇上升; 突然的高漲: *There has been an upsurge in the number of violent films on television recently.* 最近電視裡的暴力影片數目突然增多。

up·tight /ˈʌp.taɪt; ˌʌpˈtaɪt/ *adj infml* angry and nervous about something without saying so 〔非正式〕生氣的; 緊張的: *He's been very uptight recently.* 他最近很緊張不安。

up-to-date /ˌ· ·ˈ·◂/ *adj* **1** modern and new 現代的; 新式的: *Our school uses all the most up-to-date teaching methods.* 我們學校採用所有最新的教學法。 **2** having all the latest information 包含最新信息的: *an up-to-date newspaper* 包含所有最新消息的報紙 **3 bring/keep someone up-to-date** to give someone all the latest information 提供某人的最新信息: *Peggy's letters keep me up-to-date with all the family's news.* 佩吉的信把家裡最新的消息告訴我。

up·ward /ˈʌp.wəd; ˈʌpwəd/ *adj* going up 向上的: *the upward movement of prices* 物價的上漲

up·wards /ˈʌp.wədz; ˈʌpwədz/ *adv* (also 又作 **upward** *AmE* 〔美式〕) **1** going, looking, or facing up 向上地; 向上部: *The plane moved gently upwards.* 飛機緩緩上升。 | *I looked upwards towards his window.* 我朝着他的窗戶看上去。 **2 upwards of** more than 多於…, …以上: *There were upwards of 3000*

people at the rally. 集會上有三千多人。

u·ra·ni·um /juˈreɪnɪəm; jʊˈreɪnɪəm/ *n* [U] a heavy white metal that is a simple substance; uranium is RADIOACTIVE and is used to make NUCLEAR weapons 鈾〔放射性元素, 用於製造核武器〕

U·ra·nus /ˈjʊərənəs; ˈjʊərənəs/ *n* the PLANET seventh in order from the sun 天王星〔太陽系第七個行星〕

★**ur·ban** /ˈɜːbən; ˈɜːbən/ *adj* of a town or city 城市的, 都市的: *Most people live in urban areas.* 大多數人住在城市裡。

ur·bane /ɜːˈbeɪn; ɜːˈbeɪn/ *adj* polite and confident in any social situation 彬彬有禮的; 溫文爾雅的

ur·ban·i·za·tion /ˌɜːbənɪˈzeɪʃən; ˌɜːbənaɪˈzeɪʃən/ *n* [U] the process of turning the country into town 城市化, 都市化

★**urge¹** /ɜːdʒ; ɜːdʒ/ *v* **urged, urging 1** urge someone to do something, to try very hard to persuade someone to do something 力勸; 慫恿: *He urged me to think again.* 他力勸我再考慮一下。 **2** [T] to suggest very strongly that something is important or necessary 竭力主張; 強烈要求: *The committee urged the need for action to control pollution.* 委員會強烈要求採取措施控制污染。 **3** [T +adv/prep] to encourage someone or to try to persuade them to move faster 鼓勵; 驅策; 推進: *He urged me towards the check-in desk.* 他催我快點去報到櫃台。

urge sbdy ↔ **on** *phr v* [T] to encourage someone or to try to persuade them to do something 鼓勵〔某人〕; 試圖説服〔某人做某事〕: *Their supporters urged them on.* 他們的支持者鼓勵了他們。

urge² *n* **1** a strong desire 強烈的慾望 **2** have/get the urge to do something feel the desire to do something 很想做某事: *She suddenly got an urge to go back to New York.* 她突然很想回紐約去。

ur·gent /ˈɜːdʒənt; ˈɜːdʒənt/ *adj* very important and needing to be dealt with without delay 緊急的; 緊迫的; 需迅速處理的: *It's not urgent. It can wait till tomorrow.* 這件事不急切, 可留待明天才做。 **–urgently** *adv* **–urgency** *n* [U]

u·ri·nal /ˈjʊərɪnl̩; ˈjʊərɪnl̩/ *n* a men's LAVATORY for urinating 〔男用的〕小便盆; 小便處

u·ri·nate /ˈjʊərəˌneɪt; ˈjʊərəˌneɪt/ *v* **urinated, urinating** [I] to pass urine from your body 小便, 排尿

u·rine /ˈjʊərɪn; ˈjʊərɨn/ *n* [U] liquid waste material passed from your body 尿

urn /ɜːn; ɜːn/ *n* **1** a large decorative container in which the ashes of a dead person are kept 骨灰甕 **2** a large container in which large quantities of tea or coffee may be heated and kept 〔可以煮熱咖啡或茶的〕大茶水壺; 咖啡壺

★**us** /əs; əs; *strong* 強讀 ʌs; ʌs/ *pron* [used as the object of a verb 用作動詞的賓語]

the people who are speaking 我們: *Did he see us?* 他看見我們嗎? | *That house is too small for us.* 那房子對我們來説太小了。 | *He bought us all a drink.* 他給我們大家都買了飲料。 –see 見 ME (USAGE 用法)

US /ˌjuː ˈes; juː ˈes/ *n* (also 又作 **USA** /ˌjuː es ˈeɪ; ˌjuː es ˈeɪ/) an abbreviation for 〔縮〕= United States of America 美國: *the US navy* 美國海軍

us·age /ˈjuːsɪdʒ; ˈjuːzɪdʒ/ *n* **1** [U] the way something is used or the degree to which something is used 使用方法; 使用程度 **2** [C; U] a generally accepted way of using a language or the way a particular word is used 〔語言的〕慣用法; 〔某個詞的〕用法: *modern English usage* 現代英語用法

★**use¹** /juːs; juːs/ *n* **1** [U] the act or fact of using something 用; 使用: *Do you approve of the use of guns by the police?* 你贊成警察用槍嗎? **2** [U] the ability or right to use something 運用能力; 使用權: *He lost the use of his legs after his accident.* 他在事故後雙腿殘廢了。 | *My mother gave me the use of the car while she was away.* 我母親外出時讓我用她的汽車。 **3** [C; U] the purpose or reason for using something 用途; 用處: *A food processor has several different uses.* 食物研磨器有幾種不同的用途。 **4** [U] the usefulness or advantage in something 效用; 益處: *Is this book any use?* 這本書有用嗎? | *What's the use of worrying?* 擔心有甚麼用呢? **5** in use being used 在使用中 **6** of use useful 有用的 **7** make use of something to use something in order to succeed in doing something 利用某物: *I make use of my spare time by studying.* 我利用空閒時間學習。

★**use²** /juːz; juːz/ *v* **used, using** [T] **1** to put something into action or employ it for a purpose 用, 使用〔某物〕: *The company now uses a computer to do all its accounts.* 這家公司現在用電腦來計算所有的賬目。 | *Do you know how to use a video camera?* 你知道怎樣用攝像機嗎? | *We used the money to buy a car.* 我們用這筆錢買了一輛汽車。 | *He never uses buses.* 他從來不坐公共汽車。 | *We are using the world's resources at an alarming rate.* 我們在以驚人的速度消耗世界上的資源。 | *The car's using too much oil.* 這輛車耗油量太大了。 **2** *derog* to treat someone unfairly for your own advantage without considering that person 〔貶義〕〔為私人利益〕利用〔某人〕; 自私地對待〔某人〕: *I realised he was just using me but I was still in love with him.* 我明白他只是在利用我, 但我仍然愛他。 **–usable** *adj*

use sthg ↔ **up** *phr v* [T] to finish the supply of something completely 用完; 耗盡: *Who's used up all the paper?* 誰把紙都用完了?

used¹ /juːzd; juːzd/ *adj* which has already been owned by someone else 用過的; 舊的; 二手的: *used cars* 舊汽車

used² /just; juːst/ *adj* **used to** accustomed to something 習慣於〔某事〕的: *to get used to English food* 開始習慣英國的食物 | *I'm not used to getting up so early.* 我不習慣起得那麼早。

□ USEFUL PATTERNS 有用句型
be used to something; be used to doing something

used to /'just tə; 'juːst tə/ *v negative short form* 否定縮略形式 **usedn't to** [modal verb 情態動詞] used to show that something happened often, regularly, or always in the past 慣常〔用於表示某事過去經常、總是或有規律地發生〕: *I used to go swimming on Saturdays.* 我以前經常在星期六去游泳。| *People used to think that the earth was flat.* 人們過去認為地球是扁平的。| *I used not to like gardening, but I love it now.* 我過去不喜歡園藝, 可現在卻愛上了它。| *Didn't she used to live in Germany?* 她過去不是住在德國嗎? | *Used you to work in a bank?* 你以前是在銀行工作嗎? | *I don't play tennis much these days, but I used to.* 我最近不太打網球, 可是過去常打。| *I never used to eat cakes, but I eat a lot now.* 我以前從不吃蛋糕, 但現在吃得很多。–see Study Note on page 1318 見1318頁學習提示

■ USAGE 用法: **1** Used to has various negative forms. Some people think that *He used not to...* is the only correct form, but *He didn't use to...* and *He didn't used to...* are both very common. *He never used to...* is also frequently used. ☆**used to** 有各種否定形式。有些人認為 *He used not to...* 是唯一正確的形式, 但 *He didn't use to...* 和 *He didn't used to...* 也很常用。*He never used to...* 也經常使用。**2** In ordinary conversation the most natural question forms are **Did(n't) he use to...?/Did(n't) he used to...?** but note that the more formal form **Used(n't) he to...** also exists. ☆在普通的會話中最自然的疑問形式是 **Did(n't) he use to...?/Did(n't) he used to...?** 但注意, 更正式的形式 **Used(n't) he to...** 也可使用。

★★**use·ful** /'jusfəl; 'juːsfəl/ *adj* **1** helpful and having a practical purpose 有用的; 實用的; 有益的: *This guide to London is a really useful book.* 這本倫敦導遊手冊真是有用。| *Jane gave me some useful advice.* 簡給了我一些有用的忠告。**2** helpful 有幫助的: *She's a useful person to have around.* 她是個在旁很幫得了忙的人。–**usefulness** *n* [U]

use·less /'juslıs; 'juːsləs/ *adj* not of any use 無用的; 無效的: *This knife is so blunt it's use-*

less! 這把刀子鈍得全無用處! –**uselessly** *adv* –**uselessness** *n* [U]

★**us·er** /'juzɚ; 'juːzə/ *n* a person or thing that uses something, especially a product or service 用戶, 〔尤指產品或服務的〕使用者: *Will users please note that from next week the photocopier will be switched off at 5.30 pm.* 請用戶注意, 從下週起複印機下午五時三十分關掉。| *telephone users* 電話用戶 | *users of large quantities of water* 用水大戶

us·er-friend·ly /ˌ···'··◂/ *adj* easy to understand and use (used especially of computers) 易懂的; 容易使用的, 易操作的〔尤指電腦〕

ush·er¹ /'ʌʃɚ; 'ʌʃə/ *n* a person who shows people to their seats at a wedding, or in a cinema or theatre 〔婚禮、影院或劇場的〕引座員, 招待員

ush·er² *v* [T +adv/prep] *fml* to bring people to a place by showing them the way 《正式》引, 領; 招待: *She ushered the guests into the room.* 她把客人引進房內。

usher sthg ↔ in *phr v* to be the cause of or start of something new and important 創始, 開始〔新的或重要的事物〕: *The bombing of Hiroshima ushered in the nuclear age.* 對廣島的轟炸標誌着原子時代的到來。

ush·er·ette /ˌʌʃɚˈɛt; ˌʌʃə'ret/ *n* a woman who shows people to their seats in a cinema 〔電影院裡的〕女引座員

USSR /ˌju ɛs ɛs 'ɑr; ˌjuː es es 'ɑːʳ/ an abbreviation for 《縮》= Union of Soviet Socialist Republics, the Soviet Union 蘇聯; 蘇維埃社會主義共和國聯盟

★**u·su·al** /'juʒuəl; 'juːʒuəl/ *adj* **1** as happens, or is done most often, or as is expected 通常的; 平常的; 慣常的: *We had lunch at our usual table by the window.* 我們在窗旁平常吃飯用的桌子前吃午飯。**2** **as usual** as is common or has happened many times before 像往常一樣; 照例: *As usual, Marc was the last to arrive.* 跟往常一樣, 馬爾克是最後一個到的。

★★**u·su·al·ly** /'juʒuəlɪ; 'juːʒuəli/ *adv* generally, or as is expected 通常地, 平常地, 慣常地: *I'm not usually so late.* 我平時並不來得這麼遲。| *The baby usually wakes up at seven.* 嬰兒通常七點睡醒。

u·surp /juˈzɝp; juːˈzɜːp/ *v* [T] *fml* to take power or a position from someone without having the right to do so 《正式》篡奪; 奪取〔某人的權力、地位〕

u·su·ry /'juʒərɪ; 'juːʒəri/ *n* [U] *old fash* the practice of lending money at a very high rate of interest 《老式》放高利貸

u·ten·sil /ju'tɛnsl; juː'tensəl/ *n* a tool or object used in the kitchen 器皿; 用具: *kitchen utensils* 廚房用具

u·te·rus /'jutərəs; 'juːtərəs/ *n* **uteruses** or **uteri** /-raɪ; -raɪ/ *tech* a woman's WOMB 《術語》子宮

u·til·i·ty /juˈtɪlətɪ; juːˈtɪlᵻti/ *n* **utilities 1** [U] usefulness 功用; 效用; 實用 **2** [C] any useful service for the public, such as the bus service, water supply, or electricity supply 公用事業〔如公共汽車、自來水、電等〕

u·til·ize /ˈjutḷ͵aɪz; ˈjuːtᵻ͵laɪz/ *v* **utilized, utilizing** (also 又作 **utilise** *BrE*〔英式〕) [T] *fml* to use something in a practical way〔正式〕利用, 使用〔某物〕: *Solar panels utilize energy from the sun.* 太陽電池板利用太陽能。 – **utilization** /͵jutḷaɪˈzeʃən; ͵juːtᵻlaɪˈzeɪʃən/ *n* [U]

ut·most /ˈʌt͵most; ˈʌtməʊst/ *adj* [always before a noun 只能用於名詞前] **1** of the greatest degree 極度的; 最大的: *with her utmost strength* 盡她最大的力量 **2 do your utmost** to make the greatest possible effort 竭盡全力: *They did their utmost to save their marriage.* 他們竭盡全力挽救自己的婚姻。

u·to·pi·a /juˈtopɪə; juːˈtəʊpiə/ *n* (also 又作 **Utopia**) an imaginary perfect society 烏托邦; 理想中的完美社會 –**utopian** *adj*

ut·ter¹ /ˈʌtɚ; ˈʌtɚʳ/ *adj* [always before a noun 只能用於名詞前] complete and total 完全的; 徹底的; 十足的: *It was an utter waste of time.* 這完全是浪費時間。| *He's an utter fool.* 他是個十足的傻瓜。–**utterly** *adv*

ut·ter² *v* [T] to make sounds or speak words 發出聲音; 説〔話〕: *She didn't utter a word all evening.* 她整個晚上一言不發。

ut·ter·ance /ˈʌtərəns; ˈʌtərəns/ *n fml*〔正式〕**1** [C;U] the act of speaking 説話; 發聲 **2** [C] something that a person says 言辭; 言語; 言論

U-turn /ˈju͵tɝn; ˈjuː tɜːn/ *n* **1** a turning movement in a car, taking you back in the direction you came from〔車輛的〕U形轉彎, 180度轉彎, 掉頭 **2** a complete change in plans or actions〔計劃或行動的〕180度的轉變, 完全的改變: *a U-turn in government policy* 政府政策上的 180 度的大改變

U

V, v

V, v /viː; viː/ **V's, v's** *or* **Vs, vs** the 22nd letter of the English alphabet 英語的第二十二個字母

v a written abbreviation for 〔縮〕= VERB

V¹ /viː/ *n* a thing shaped like the letter V V字形物: *She cut the material out in a V.* 她把料子剪成V字形狀。

V² a written abbreviation for 〔縮〕= VOLT

v. /viː; viː/ see 見 VERSUS

va·can·cy /ˈveɪkənsɪ; ˈveɪkənsɪ/ *n* **vacancies** [C] **1** a room in a hotel or guest house that is not being used 〔旅店或賓館中的〕空房 **2** an unfilled job or position 空職; 空缺: *We have a vacancy* **for** *a driver at the moment.* 目前我們有一個駕駛員的空缺。

va·cant /ˈveɪkənt; ˈveɪkənt/ *adj* **1** not being used or lived in (used of a seat, room, house, or space) 未被佔用的, 未住人的〔指座位、房間、房屋或空間〕: *We looked all over town for a vacant room.* 我們找遍全鎮, 想尋一個空房間。| *The toilet is vacant now.* 廁所現在沒人。 **2** not filled at the moment (used of a job) 空缺的〔指工作〕: *The job was advertised in the "Situations Vacant" section of the newspaper.* 這個職位空缺的廣告在報紙的"招聘"欄中刊出。 **3** showing that you are not interested in something or are not thinking about anything 不感興趣的; 無聊的; 茫然的: *There was a vacant expression on his face.* 他臉上一副茫然的神情。 **–vacantly** *adv*: *He stared vacantly into space.* 他茫然若失地凝視空中。

va·cate /ˈveɪket; vəˈkeɪt/ *v* **vacated, vacating** [T] to stop using or living in a place 不再使用或居住; 騰出; 搬出: *Guests must vacate their rooms by 11 am.* 客人必須在上午十一點以前退房。

★**va·ca·tion** /ˈveɪkeʃən; vəˈkeɪʃən/ *n* **1** the usual American word for 〔美式〕= HOLIDAY: *We'll take our vacation in July.* 我們七月休假。 **2** on vacation *AmE* on holiday 〔美式〕在度假 **3** a period of holiday when universities are closed 〔大學的〕假期: *the summer vacation* 暑假 **–vacation** *v AmE* 〔美式〕[I]: *My parents are vacationing in Europe.* 我父母在歐洲度假。

vac·cin·ate /ˈvæksn̩ˌet; ˈvæksn̩ˌneɪt/ *v* **vaccinated, vaccinating** [T] to put vaccine into someone's body as a protection against a disease 給〔某人〕接種疫苗 **–vaccination** /ˌvæksn̩ˈeʃən; ˌvæksn̩ˈneɪʃən/ *n* [C;U]: *He's had his vaccination* **against** *typhoid.* 他已接種過傷寒疫苗了。

vac·cine /ˈvæksin; ˈvæksiːn/ *n* [C;U] a sub-stance containing a form of a disease which is used to protect people against that disease 疫苗; 菌苗

vac·il·late /ˈvæsl̩ˌet; ˈvæsl̩ˌleɪt/ *v* **vacillated, vacillating** [I] to be continually changing from one opinion or feeling to another 〔看法或感情〕搖擺, 猶豫, 躊躇: *Charles vacillated* **between** *hope and fear.* 查爾斯遊移於希望和恐懼之間。 **–vacillation** /ˌvæsəˈleʃən; ˌvæsl̩ˈleɪʃən/ *n* [C;U]

vac·u·ous /ˈvækjʊəs; ˈvækjʊəs/ *adj fml* showing no sign of ideas or thought 〔正式〕無思想的; 無知的; 空洞的: *a totally vacuous remark* 十分空洞的話

vac·u·um¹ /ˈvækjʊəm; ˈvækjʊəm/ *n* **1** a space that has no air or gas in it 真空 **2** a feeling of emptiness and loss 空虛: *Her death left a vacuum in his life.* 她去世以後, 他的生活變得空虛。

vacuum² *v infml* [I;T] to clean with a vacuum cleaner 〔非正式〕用真空吸塵器打掃: *I've been vacuuming all morning.* 我整個上午都在吸塵。| *I've vacuumed the stairs.* 我用吸塵器打掃了樓梯。

vacuum clean·er /ˈ··· ˌ··/ *n* a machine which cleans the floor by sucking up dirt in a flow of air 真空吸塵器

vacuum flask /ˈ··· ·/ *n* see 見 THERMOS FLASK

vag·a·bond /ˈvægəˌbɑnd; ˈvægəbɒnd/ *n old fash* a person who lives a wandering life and is thought to be lazy or worthless 〔老式〕流浪者; 懶漢; 浪子

va·ga·ries /vəˈgɛrɪz; ˈveɪgəriz/ *n* [pl] unusual or unexpected changes in a situation 變幻莫測: *the vagaries of love* 愛情變幻無常

va·gi·na /vəˈdʒaɪnə; vəˈdʒaɪnə/ *n* the passage which leads from the outer sex organs of women or female animals, to the organ in which young are formed 陰道 **–vaginal** *adj*

va·grant /ˈveɪgrənt; ˈveɪgrənt/ *n* a person who has no home or work and goes from place to place 流浪者 **–vagrancy** *n* [U]

vague /veɪg; veɪg/ *adj* **1** not clear in shape or easy to see 模糊的: *I could see the vague shape of another car through the fog.* 我在霧中看見另一輛汽車模糊的輪廓。 **2** not clearly expressed or explained 〔表達或解釋〕不清楚的, 含糊的: *Her directions to the house were rather vague and we got lost.* 她告訴我們去那座房子的走法說得並不明確, 結果我們迷了路。 **3** not clear or certain in your mind 〔腦子裡〕影影綽綽的, 不確定的: *Our plans are still*

a bit vague. 我們的計劃還沒怎麼確定。| *I've got a vague idea who she is.* 我依稀知道她是誰。**4** not behaving or expressing yourself clearly 〔行動或表達方面〕優柔的; 不明確的: *John is a very dreamy, vague sort of person.* 約翰是那種十分喜愛幻想, 優柔寡斷的人。– **vaguely** *adv* –**vagueness** *n* [U]

vain /veɪn; veɪn/ *adj* **1** full of pride and admiration for yourself, your appearance, and your abilities 自負的; 自視過高的; 愛虛榮的 **2** without a successful result 徒勞的; 無結果的: *The teacher made a vain attempt to get the children to obey.* 老師想叫孩子守紀律, 但是徒勞無功。**3 in vain** without success 徒然; 白費氣力: *We tried in vain to make him change his mind.* 我們企圖使他改變主意, 結果是白費氣力。– **vainly** *adv*

val·ance /ˈvæləns; ˈvæləns/ *n* a pretty cover that hangs from the frame of a bed to the floor 牀沿掛布

vale /veɪl; veɪl/ *n lit* a broad low valley 〔文〕谷; 山谷: *the Vale of Evesham* 埃弗沙姆谷

val·en·tine /ˈvæləntaɪn; ˈvæləntaɪn/ *n* a greeting card sent to someone you love on **Saint Valentine's Day** (February 14th) 情人卡〔在聖瓦倫丁節(二月十四日)送給情人的賀卡〕

val·et /ˈvælɪt; ˈvælɪt/ *n* **1** a male servant, who looks after a man's clothes, cooks his meals, etc. 〔為男主人照料衣食等的〕貼身男僕 **2** someone who cleans and presses clothes in a hotel 〔旅館中洗燙衣服的〕服務員

val·i·ant /ˈvæliənt; ˈvæliənt/ *adj lit* very brave in a dangerous situation like a war 〔文〕〔在危險的情況下, 如戰爭中〕勇敢的, 英勇的 –**valiantly** *adv*

val·id /ˈvælɪd; ˈvælɪd/ *adj* **1** based on strong reasons 有充分理由的; 確鑿的: *I hope you have a valid excuse for arriving late at work.* 我希望你有充分的理由解釋上班遲到的原因。**2** that can be legally used at a certain time 有效驗的; 可合法使用的: *Your train ticket is valid for three months.* 你的火車票有效期為三個月。–opposite 反義 **invalid 3** *law* written or done in a proper way so that a court of law would agree with it 〔律〕具有法律效力的; 依法有效的 –**validity** /vəˈlɪdətɪ; vəˈlɪdɪti/ *n*: *The judge did not question the validity of the statement.* 法官對此陳述的真實性沒有表示懷疑。

val·i·date /ˈvæləˌdeɪt; ˈvælɪdeɪt/ *v* **validated, validating** *fml* [T] to make legal or prove to be correct 〔正式〕使合法化; 證實: *In order to validate the agreement between yourself and your employer, you must both sign it.* 為了使你和僱主間的協議生效, 你們雙方都必須簽字。–**validation** /ˌvælɪˈdeɪʃən; ˌvælɪˈdeɪʃən/ *n* [C;U]

Val·i·um /ˈvæliəm; ˈvæliəm/ *n tdmk* [U] a drug for making people feel calmer or less anxious 〔商標〕安定〔一種鎮靜藥〕

val·ley /ˈvælɪ; ˈvæli/ *n* the land lying between two lines of hills or mountains, often with a river running through it 谷, 山谷〔其間常有河流流過〕

val·our /ˈvælə; ˈvælər/ *n lit* (**valor** *AmE* 〔美式〕) [U] great bravery, especially in war 〔文〕〔尤指在戰爭中〕英勇, 勇猛

*★**val·u·able** /ˈvæljʊəbl; ˈvæljuəbəl/ *adj* **1** worth a lot of money 很值錢的; 貴重的: *a valuable diamond* 貴重的鑽石 **2** very useful 很有用的; 寶貴的: *Your help has been very valuable.* 你的幫助非常寶貴。

> ■ USAGE 用法: Remember that **invaluable** is NOT the opposite of **valuable**! The word **invaluable** is NOT used to talk about prices or money. It means "extremely useful" ☆記住 **invaluable** 不是 **valuable** 的反義詞! 單詞 **invaluable** 不用於談論價格或金錢, 意思是"極為有用的": *Their advice proved **invaluable** to us on our journey.* 他們的忠告證明對我們的旅途非常有用。| *Your assistance has been **invaluable**.* 你的幫助非常寶貴。If you want to describe things which have no value, you can use the word **worthless** ☆如果要描述無價值的事物, 可以用單詞 **worthless**: *The metal looked like gold, but in fact it was completely **worthless**.* 這種金屬看起來像金子, 可實際上毫無價值。

val·u·a·bles /ˈvæljʊəblz; ˈvæljuəbəlz/ *n* [pl] things that you own, such as jewellery, that are worth a lot of money 貴重物品〔如首飾〕: *You should put your valuables in the bank.* 你應該把貴重物品存放在銀行裡。

val·u·a·tion /ˌvæljʊˈeɪʃən; ˌvæljuˈeɪʃən/ *n* [C; U] a calculation of how much money something is worth 估價: *We asked for a valuation **of** the house.* 我們要求做這座房子的估價。

*★★**val·ue**[1] /ˈvæljuː; ˈvæljuː/ *n* **1** [U] the usefulness or importance of something 用處; 重要性: *My grandmother's advice was of great value to me.* 我祖母的忠告對我大有用處。| *Their research is interesting but has little practical value.* 他們的研究很有意思, 但是沒甚麼實用價值。**2** [C;U] the amount of money that something is worth if it is sold or exchanged 價值; 交換價值: *The value **of** the pound has fallen recently.* 英鎊的幣值最近下跌了。| *The insurance company put a value of $1,000 on the picture.* 保險公司給這幅畫投保一千美元。| *The thieves took some clothes and books, but nothing of great value.* 竊賊偷去了一些衣服和幾本書, 但沒甚麼值錢的東西。**3** [U] worth compared with the amount paid 等值; 上算: *We offer the best value in town – only £6.50 for a three course meal.* 我們的價錢在鎮上最公道——三道菜的晚餐只消六鎊半。| *The large packet of soap powder is better value*

than two small ones. 大盒肥皂粉要比兩小盒更合算。 **4 value for money** worth the amount paid 有所值的; 合算的: *A weekly ticket is value for money because you can use it as often as you like.* 一星期通用的客票很合算, 因為你可以隨意多次使用。 – **valueless** *adj*

value² *v* **valued, valuing** [T] **1** to calculate how much money something is worth 給〔某物〕估價: *The piano is valued at £4,000.* 這架鋼琴估價為四千英鎊。 **2** to consider something to be very important 重視; 尊重: *I've always valued your friendship very highly.* 我一向高度珍視你的友誼。

value-ad·ded tax /‚···'·'·/ *n* see 見 VAT

val·u·er /'væljuə; 'væljuər/ *n* a person whose work is to decide how much money things are worth 估價人

val·ues /'væljuz; 'væljuːz/ *n* [pl] principles and beliefs about what is important in life and how people should behave 標準; 準則: *Moral values have changed a lot in the last 50 years.* 最近五十年來道德標準變化很大。

valve /vælv; vælv/ *n* **1** part of a pipe or tube which opens and shuts in order to control the flow of liquid, air, or gas passing through it 閥; 活門: *You put air into a bicycle tyre through the valve.* 你通過氣嘴把空氣打入腳踏車輪胎。 **2** a closed glass tube with no air in it, used for controlling a flow of electricity, as formerly in radio or television 電子管; 真空管

vam·pire /'væmpaɪə; 'væmpaɪər/ *n* an evil spirit which is believed to live in a dead body and suck people's blood while they are asleep 吸血鬼〔傳說是寄身於屍體, 吸食睡覺者血液的惡鬼〕

van /væn; væn/ *n* **1** a road vehicle smaller than a LORRY which is used for carrying goods or people 小型客貨車: *a delivery van* 送貨車 | *a police van* 警車 | *a van driver* 客貨車司機 –see picture on page 209 見 209 頁彩圖 **2** a covered railway carriage for goods and sometimes people 廂式鐵路貨車; 棚車: *Put your bicycle in the guard's van.* 把你的腳踏車放在守車裡。

van·dal /'vændl; 'vændl/ *n* a person who intentionally damages or destroys public property 故意破壞公共財產者: *All the seat-covers on the train were ripped by vandals.* 列車上所有的椅套都被蓄意破壞者撕破了。

van·dal·is·m /'vændl‚ɪzəm; 'vændəl‚ɪzəm/ *n* [U] intentional and pointless damage and destruction of public property 故意破壞公共財產

van·dal·ize /'vændl‚aɪz; 'vændəl‚aɪz/ *v* **vandalized, vandalizing** (also 又作 **vandalise** *BrE* 〔英式〕) [T] to damage or destroy a piece of public property intentionally 故意破壞〔公共財產〕: *We can't use any of the public telephones round here; they've all been vandalized.* 這裡的公用電話沒有一個可

以用, 全部受到蓄意破壞。

vane /veɪn; veɪn/ *n* a flat blade on an instrument that makes it possible to use the force of wind or water to drive certain machines 〔某些機器的〕翼, 葉片: *the vanes of a propeller* 螺旋槳的葉片

van·guard /'væn‚gɑrd; 'væŋgɑːd/ *n* **1** [+sing/pl verb] the soldiers marching at the front of an army 前衛; 先頭部隊 **2 in the vanguard of** in the leading position in any course of development 〔在發展過程中〕處於領導位置: *Scientists are in the vanguard of technological development.* 科學家是技術發展的前驅。

va·nil·la /və'nɪlə; və'nɪlə/ *n* [U] a substance obtained from a tropical plant, used to give its special taste to certain sweet foods 香草香精: *vanilla ice cream* 香草冰淇淋

van·ish /'vænɪʃ; 'vænɪʃ/ *v* [I] **1** to disappear suddenly 突然不見; 消失: *With a wave of his hand, the magician made the rabbit vanish.* 魔術師一揮手兔子便不見了。 **2** to cease to exist 不復存在; 滅絕: *Many types of animal have now vanished from the earth.* 地球上原有的許多種動物現已絕種。 **3 vanish into thin air** to disappear suddenly and with no explanation 〔不可思議地〕突然消失

van·i·ty /'vænəti; 'vænɪti/ *n* [U] being extremely proud of yourself, your appearance, and your abilities 自負; 自大; 虛榮

van·quish /'væŋkwɪʃ; 'væŋkwɪʃ/ *v lit* [T] to defeat someone completely 《文》徹底擊敗〔某人〕

van·tage point /'væntɪdʒ ‚pɔɪnt; 'vɑːntɪdʒ ‚pɔɪnt/ *n* a good position from which to see something 〔觀看某事物的〕有利位置

va·por·ize, vaporizing /'veɪpə‚raɪz; 'veɪpəraɪz/ *v* **vaporized, vaporizing** (also 又作 **vaporise** *BrE* 《英式》) [I;T] to change into vapour (使)蒸發; (使)汽化: *Water vaporizes when boiled.* 水沸時就變為蒸氣。

va·pour /'veɪpə; 'veɪpər/ *n* (**vapor** *AmE* 《美式》) **1** [C;U] a liquid in the form of a gas such as mist or steam 霧氣; 水氣: *A cloud is a mass of vapour in the sky.* 雲是天空中的水氣團。 **2** [U] *tech* the gas to which a liquid or solid can be changed by the action of heat 《術語》蒸氣: *water vapour* 水蒸氣

var·i·a·ble¹ /'vɛrɪəbl; 'veərɪəbəl/ *adj* **1** likely to change at any time 易變的; 多變的: *The winds today will be light and variable.* 今天的風小但風向多變。 **2** that can be changed intentionally 可變的: *The speed of the toy boat is variable.* 玩具船的速度是可變的。 – **variability** /‚vɛrɪə'bɪləti; ‚veərɪə'bɪl‚ti/ *n* [U]

variable² *n fml* something which can vary in quantity or size 《正式》變量; 可變值; 可變物: *The time of the journey depends on a number of variables, such as the amount of traffic on the road.* 旅途所需時間取決於諸多不定因素, 如路上交通的擁擠情況。

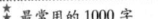

var·i·ance /ˈvɛrɪəns; ˈveəriəns/ *n* **at variance with** in opposition to and not in agreement with 有分歧; 不一致: *What he did was at variance with company policy.* 他的所作所為和公司的政策不相符合。

var·i·ant¹ /ˈvɛrɪənt; ˈveəriənt/ *adj* [always before a noun 只能用於名詞前] different and varying 不同的; 變化的: *There are many variant spellings in English.* 英語裡有許多字是有不同拼法的。

variant² *n* a different form, for example of a word or phrase 〔單詞或詞組等的〕變體, 異體

★**var·i·a·tion** /ˌvɛrɪˈeɪʃən; ˌveəriˈeɪʃən/ *n* [C;U] a change in degree, amount, or quantity 〔程度、數量的〕變化, 變動: *There are great variations in house prices in different parts of the country.* 在這個國家的不同地方, 房價有很大的差異。| *This story is just a variation on his last book.* 這個故事只是對他的上一本書做了些變動而已。

var·i·cose veins /ˌværɪˌkos ˈvenz; ˌværɪˌkəʊs ˈveɪnz/ *n* a medical condition in which the blood vessels of the leg have become very swollen 〔腿部的〕靜脈曲張

var·ied /ˈvɛrɪd; ˈveərid/ *adj* **1** of different kinds 各種各樣的: *The students come from varied backgrounds.* 學生們來自各種各樣的背景。| *The restaurant has a very varied menu.* 這家餐館的菜看豐富多彩。**2** not staying the same and having changing qualities 多變化的; 改變的: *She has led an interesting and varied life.* 她過着有趣多彩的生活。

var·ie·gat·ed /ˈvɛrɪˌgetɪd; ˈveərigeɪtɪd/ *adj* marked irregularly in spots, lines, or areas of different colours (used of a flower or leaf) 斑駁的, 雜色的〔指花和葉〕

★**va·ri·e·ty** /vəˈraɪətɪ; vəˈraɪəti/ *n* **varieties 1** [U] difference in quality, type, or character 〔質量、種類或特徵的〕變化, 多樣化: *You need a lot of variety in your diet.* 你的膳食要多樣化。**2 a variety of** a group containing different sorts of the same thing 種種; 各種: *These T-shirts are available in a wide variety of colours.* 這些T恤有各種各樣的顏色供挑選。**3** [C] a type which is different from others in the same group 種類; 品種: *different varieties of bananas* 不同品種的香蕉 **4** [U] a theatre or television show including singing, dancing, jokes, and acts of skill 〔歌舞、滑稽、雜耍的〕綜藝節目: *a variety show* 綜藝表演

★**var·i·ous** /ˈvɛrɪəs; ˈveəriəs/ *adj* **1** different from each other 不同的; 各種各樣的: *There are various ways of getting there but we always go by train.* 去那兒有各種不同的方法, 但我們總是坐火車。**2** [always before a noun 只能用於名詞前] several or a number of 幾個的; 許多的: *Various people said they had seen the accident.* 許多人說他們目擊了這宗事故。**–variously** *adv*

var·nish¹ /ˈvɑrnɪʃ; ˈvɑːnɪʃ/ *n* [C;U] a liquid which gives wood a hard shiny surface 清漆; 罩光漆; 凡立水

varnish² *v* [T] to cover with a liquid which gives a hard shiny surface 給…上清漆: *You should varnish the shelves to protect the wood.* 你該給架子上清漆以保護木頭。

★**var·y** /ˈvɛrɪ; ˈveəri/ *v* **varied, varying** [I;T] to be, make, or become different (使)變化; (使)不同; 改變: *Children need a varied, balanced diet.* 兒童需要豐富均衡的飲食。| *The quality of her work never varies.* 她的工作質量一貫保持穩定。

vase /ves; vɑːz/ *n* a glass or clay container, used to put flowers in 花瓶 –see picture on page 244 見 244 頁彩圖

va·sec·to·my /væsˈɛktəmɪ; vəˈsektəmi/ *n* **vasectomies** [C;U] an operation for removing a man's ability to become a father by cutting the small tube that carries his SPERM 輸精管切除術

★**vast** /væst; vɑːst/ *adj* very large and wide or great in size or amount 巨大的; 廣闊的; 浩瀚的; 大量的; 巨額的: *The vast plains stretch for 600 miles.* 遼闊的平原綿延六百英里。

vast·ly /ˈvæstlɪ; ˈvɑːstli/ *adv* very much 非常: *That restaurant is vastly overpriced!* 那家飯店定價實在過高!

★**vat** /væt; væt/ *n* a very large barrel or container for holding liquids 〔盛液體的〕大桶, 大缸, 甕

VAT /ˌviˈeti, væt; ˌviː eɪ ˈtiː, væt/ *n* [U] a tax in Britain and some other European countries added to the price of an article; an abbreviation for VALUE-ADDED TAX 〔縮〕〔英國和其他一些歐洲國家的〕價值附加稅, 增值稅

vault¹ /vɔlt; vɔːlt/ *n* **1** a roof formed by a number of arches 拱頂; 穹頂 **2** (also 又作 **vaults**) an underground room in which the bodies of the dead are placed, or in which valuable things are stored 地下室; 墓穴; 地窖 **3** a jump made by vaulting 撐竿跳

vault² *v* [I +adv/prep; T] to jump over something using your hands or a pole to gain more height 〔用手支撐或撐竿〕跳躍: *He vaulted over the gate and ran away.* 他越過大門逃走了。

VCR /ˌvi si ˈɑ; ˌviː siː ˈɑːʳ/ an American word for 〔美式〕= a VIDEO recorder

VDU /ˌvi di ˈju; ˌviː diː ˈjuː/ *n* an apparatus with a SCREEN which shows information from a computer or WORD PROCESSOR; an abbreviation for **visual display unit** 〔縮〕顯示電腦或文字處理機內部信息的帶熒屏的〕直觀顯示裝置; 圖像文字顯示屏 –see picture on page 763 見 763 頁彩圖

've /v; v, əv/ short for 〔縮〕= HAVE: *We've finished.* 我們幹完了。

veal /vil; viːl/ *n* [U] meat from a very young cow 小牛肉 –see 見 MEAT (USAGE 用法)

veer /vɪr; vɪəʳ/ *v* [I +adv/prep] to turn or change direction 改變方向; 轉向: *The car* *was out of control and suddenly veered across the road.* 汽車失去控制, 突然轉向橫衝過馬路。

*vege·ta·ble /'vɛdʒətəbl; 'vɛdʒtəbəl/ *n* a plant that is grown for food to be eaten in the main part of a meal, rather than with sweet things 蔬菜: *meat and vegetables* 肉和蔬菜 | *green vegetables such as cabbage and spinach* 諸如卷心菜和菠菜等綠色蔬菜

veg·e·tar·i·an /,vɛdʒə'tɛrɪən; ,vɛdʒ ɪ'tɛərɪən/ *n* a person who does not eat meat or fish 素食者 **–vegetarian** *adj*: *a vegetarian restaurant* 素菜館 **–vegetarianism** *n* [U]

veg·e·tate /'vɛdʒə,tet; 'vɛdʒ ɪ'teɪt/ *v* **vegetated, vegetating** [I] to live life without any interests or social activity 過枯燥單調、缺乏社交的生活

veg·e·ta·tion /,vɛdʒə'teʃən; ,vɛdʒ ɪ'teɪʃən/ *n* [U] plants in general〔總稱〕植物, 草木: *the colourful vegetation of the tropical rainforest* 豔麗的熱帶雨林植物

ve·he·ment /'viəmənt; 'vɪəmənt/ *adj* using strong and violent words 強烈的; 激烈的; 猛烈的: *She made a vehement attack on the government's policies.* 她對政府的政策作了猛烈的抨擊。**–vehemently** *adv* **–vehemence** *n* [U]

*ve·hi·cle /'viɪkl; 'viːɪkəl/ *n* **1** something such as a bicycle, car, or bus, which moves or carries people and goods 交通工具; 車輛 **2** *fml* something which can be used to send or carry something else〔正式〕傳播工具; 媒介物: *Television has become an important vehicle for spreading political ideas.* 電視已成為宣傳政治思想的重要媒介。

ve·hic·u·lar /vi'hɪkjɔlə; viː'hɪkj ɪlə/ *adj fml* concerning vehicles on roads〔正式〕車輛的: *vehicular traffic* 車輛往來

veil /vel; veɪl/ *n* **1** a covering of fine cloth or net for the face, worn by women, sometimes for religious reasons〔婦女的〕面紗, 面罩 **2 a veil of** something which covers or hides something else 遮蓋物; 掩飾物: *a veil of mist* 一層薄霧 | *There was a veil of secrecy over the army's activities.* 軍隊的活動蒙着一層神秘的面紗。

veiled /veld; veɪld/ *adj* **1** wearing a fine cloth or net over the face 蒙上面紗的 **2** hidden and not expressed directly 隱藏的; 掩飾的; 不明言的: *veiled threats* 隱含的威脅

vein /ven; veɪn/ *n* **1** a tube that carries blood from any part of your body to your heart 靜脈 **2** a thin line which runs in a pattern through leaves and the wings of certain insects〔植物的〕葉脈;〔昆蟲的〕翅脈 **3** a crack in rock which is filled with useful metal 岩脈; 礦脈: *a vein of silver* 銀礦脈 **4 in the same vein** with the same general meaning or style 有相同的意味或風格: *The newspaper has had many letters in the same vein complaining about the article.* 這份報紙收到了很多來信, 都用同一種語調抱怨那

篇文章。

ve·loc·i·ty /və'lɑsəti; vɪ'lɒs ɪti/ *n* **velocities** *tech* [C;U] speed in a certain direction, or rate of movement〔術語〕速度; 速率

ve·lour /və'lur; və'luə/ *n* [U] a heavy cloth with a soft surface 絲絨; 天鵝絨

vel·vet /'vɛlvɪt; 'velv ɪt/ *n* [U] a finely-woven cloth with a soft furry surface 天鵝絨; 絲絨; 立絨

vel·vet·y /'vɛlvɪtɪ; 'velv ɪti/ *adj* very soft and like velvet 天鵝絨般的; 柔軟光滑的

ve·nal /'vinl; 'viːnl/ *adj fml*〔正式〕**1** acting unfairly or wrongly, in return for money or other rewards 貪贓的; 貪污的 **2** done, not for honest reasons, but for money 為錢而幹的; 受賄而為的

ven·det·ta /vɛn'dɛtə; ven'detə/ *n* a long-lasting and violent argument between families 家族間的血仇; 世仇

ven·ding ma·chine /'vɛndɪŋ mə,ʃin; 'vendɪŋ mə,ʃiːn/ *n* a machine which you can buy drinks or chocolate from by putting money into it〔出售飲料或巧克力的〕自動售貨機

vend·or /'vɛndə; 'vendə/ *n* **1** someone who sells things from a cart or small vehicle 小販: *a street vendor* 街頭小販 **2** *law* the seller of a house or land〔律〕〔房地產的〕賣主, 賣方

ve·neer /və'nɪr; v ɪ'nɪə/ *n* **1** [C;U] a thin covering of good quality wood put on the surface of a cheaper material 飾面薄板; 裝飾板 **2** [sing] an outer appearance which hides something unpleasant〔掩蓋令人不快的事物的〕外表; 虛飾: *a veneer of good manners* 彬彬有禮的外表

ven·e·ra·ble /'vɛnərəbl; 'venərəbəl/ *adj* considered to deserve great respect or honour (used of someone or something old) 值得敬重的, 令人崇敬的〔指老人或古物〕

ven·e·rate /'vɛnə,ret; 'venəreɪt/ *v* **venerated, venerating** *fml* [T] to treat with great respect and honour〔正式〕敬重; 崇敬 **–veneration** /,vɛnə'reʃən; ,venə'reɪʃən/ *n* [U]

ven·geance /'vɛndʒəns; 'vendʒəns/ *n* [U] **1** punishment given to someone for harm they have done to you or your family 報復; 復仇: *The bombing was an act of vengeance by terrorists.* 這次轟炸是恐怖分子的一次報復行動。**2 with a vengeance** *infml* to a greater degree than expected or usual〔非正式〕極度地; 過度地: *The wind's blowing with a vengeance today.* 今天狂風大作。

venge·ful /'vɛndʒfəl; 'vendʒfəl/ *adj lit* showing a strong desire to punish someone for the harm they have done to you〔文〕復仇心切的; 報復心強的

ven·i·son /'vɛnɪzn; 'ven ɪzən/ *n* [U] meat from a deer 鹿肉 **–see** 見 MEAT (USAGE 用法)

ven·om /'vɛnəm; 'venəm/ *n* [U] **1** liquid

poison which certain snakes, insects, and other creatures use when they bite or sting you〔某些蛇、昆蟲或其他生物的〕毒液 **2** full of hatred and bad feeling 惡毒；惡意；痛恨: *He spoke about his ex-boss with venom and anger.* 他談起前任老板時就咬牙切齒，怒氣衝天。–**venomous** *adj*: *a venomous insult* 惡毒的侮辱

vent¹ /vɛnt; vɛnt/ *v* [T] to express strong feelings by directing them at someone or something 發泄〔強烈的感情〕: *Don't vent your anger* **on** *the children, it's not their fault!* 別在孩子們身上出氣，這不是他們的錯!

vent² *n* **1** a hole, opening, or pipe by which gases, smoke, air, or liquid can enter or escape from an enclosed space 通風孔；排氣口；開口；管道 **2** a long narrow straight opening at the bottom of a coat, at the sides or back〔衣服下部、兩側或背部的〕開衩 **3** **give vent to** to express something freely 任意表達〔某事物〕；發泄: *He gave vent to his frustration by kicking the door.* 他踢門發泄一腔失望之情。

ven·ti·late /ˈvɛntl̩ˌet; ˈventl̩leit/ *v* **ventilated, ventilating** [T] to allow fresh air into a room or building 使〔房間或建築物〕通風，通氣: *The bar was smoky and badly ventilated.* 酒吧裡煙霧瀰漫，通風不好。

ven·ti·la·tion /ˌvɛntl̩ˈeʃən; ˌventɪˈleiʃən/ *n* [U] a way of making the air fresh in a room or building 空氣流通；通風設備: *There was no ventilation in the office except for a small high window.* 除了一扇在高處的小窗戶以外，辦公室裡沒有通風設備。

ven·ti·la·tor /ˈvɛntl̩ˌetɚ; ˈventɪleitər/ *n* **1** a machine for ventilating a room or building 通風設備 **2** a machine which helps someone to breathe 呼吸器

ven·tril·o·quis·m /vɛnˈtrɪləˌkwɪzəm; ven-ˈtrɪləkwɪzəm/ *n* [U] the art of speaking without moving your lips so that the sound seems to come from somewhere else 腹語術〔嘴唇不動，聲音似乎來自別處的一種口技〕–**ventriloquist** *n*

ven·ture¹ /ˈvɛntʃɚ; ˈventʃər/ *v* **ventured, venturing 1** [I + adv/prep] to go somewhere, especially if it could be dangerous〔尤指冒險〕去某處: *He hasn't ventured out of the house since his accident.* 出了事故以後，他不敢冒險走出這座房子了。**2** [T] to dare to say something you are not sure about 敢說〔某事〕: *If I may venture an opinion, I think we should say no and wait for a better offer.* 恕我大膽直言，我想我們應該拒絕，再等一個更好的提議。**3** **venture into something** to risk doing something that may be dangerous 冒險做〔可能有危險的〕某事: *I would never venture into business without plenty of money.* 沒有一大筆錢，我是絕不會冒險經營的。

venture² *n* something you decide to do where there is a risk of failure as well as a chance of success 冒險；投機活動

ven·ue /ˈvɛnju; ˈvenjuː/ *n* a place where something is arranged to happen〔某事的〕舉辦地點，舉行場所: *The venue* **for** *the talks has not been announced for security reasons.* 由於安全上的原因，會談地點還沒宣佈。

Ve·nus /ˈvinəs; ˈviːnəs/ *n* the PLANET second in order from the sun, and next to the earth 金星；太白星

ve·ran·da /vəˈrændə; vəˈrændə/ *n* (also 又作 **verandah**) an open area with a floor and a roof on the outside of a house 遊廊；走廊；陽台: *When the evenings were warm we sat outside on the verandah.* 黃昏和暖之時，我們就坐在外面的陽台上。

verb /vɝb; vɜːb/ *n* a word or phrase that is used to describe an action, experience, or state (in the sentences *"She wrote a letter", "He feels hungry"* and *"I get up at seven o'clock", "wrote", "feels"* and *"get up"* are verbs) 動詞〔在句子 *"She wrote a letter", "He feels hungry"* 和 *"I get up at seven o'clock"* 中，*"wrote", "feels"* 和 *"get up"* 都是動詞〕–see Study Note on page 1330 見 1330 頁學習提示

verb·al /ˈvɝbl̩; ˈvɜːbəl/ *adj* **1** spoken, not written 口頭的；非書面的: *a verbal agreement* 口頭協議 **2** connected with words and their use 言辭的；用言辭的

verb·al·ize /ˈvɝbl̩ˌaɪz; ˈvɜːbəlaɪz/ *v* **verbalized, verbalizing** *fml* (also 又作 **verbalise** *BrE*【英式】) [I;T] to express something in words 用言語表達

verb·al·ly /ˈvɝbl̩i; ˈvɜːbəli/ *adv* in spoken words and not in writing 口頭上

verbal noun /ˌ·· ·ˈ·/ *n* a noun which comes from a verb, describes an action or experience, and ends in "-ing" (in the sentence *"The building of the bridge was slow work", "building"* is a verbal noun) 動名詞〔在句子 *"The building of the bridge was slow work"* 中，*"building"* 是動名詞〕

ver·ba·tim /vɝˈbetɪm; vɜːˈbeɪtɪm/ *adj, adv* repeating the actual words exactly 一字不差的[地]；逐字的[地]: *She could remember his words verbatim even though it was so long ago.* 雖然事隔很久，她還能一字不差地記得他的話。

ver·bi·age /ˈvɝbɪɪdʒ; ˈvɜːbi-ɪdʒ/ *n* [U] too many unnecessary words in speech or writing〔談話或寫作中的〕冗詞，贅語

ver·bose /vɝˈbos; vɜːˈbəʊs/ *adj fml* using or containing too many words【正式】囉嗦的；累贅的；冗長的: *The speech was verbose and boring.* 這篇講話冗長乏味。

ver·dant /ˈvɝdnt; ˈvɜːdənt/ *adj lit* covered with fresh green plants or grass【文】青翠的；碧綠的

ver·dict /ˈvɝdɪkt; ˈvɜːdɪkt/ *n* **1** the official decision made in a court of law, at the end of a trial〔法庭的〕裁決: *Members of the jury, what is your verdict? Guilty, or not guilty?* 陪審團諸位，你們如何裁決? 有罪還是無罪? **2**

infml a statement giving someone's opinion or judgment of something 〖非正式〗定論; 判斷; 意見: *What's your verdict on the film?* 你對這部影片看法如何?

verge[1] /vɜːdʒ; vɝdʒ/ *n* **1** the edge or border of a road or path, usually covered with grass 路邊; 路肩〔常為植草邊沿〕 **2 on the verge of** very near to 接近於; 瀕於: *The two countries are on the verge of war.* 兩國處於戰爭的邊緣。| *She was very upset and on the verge of crying.* 她非常不安, 快要哭出來了。

verge[2] *v* **verged, verging, verge on something** to be similar to a particular quality 近似於某事物: *His strange behaviour sometimes verges on madness.* 他的古怪舉止有時近於瘋狂。

ver·i·fy /ˈvɛrəˌfaɪ; ˈverᵻfaɪ/ *v* [T; +that] to make sure that a fact or statement is true 證實, 核實〔某事物〕: *The police can now verify people's personal details on their computer files.* 警方現在能夠通過電腦檔案核實人們的個人詳細資料。| *We have to verify that you are the true owner of the house before lending you any money.* 在貸款給你之前, 我們得證實你是這座房子的真正主人。–**verifiable** *adj* –**verification** /ˌvɛrɪfɪˈkeɪʃən, ˌverᵻfᵻˈkeɪʃən/ *n* [U]

ver·i·si·mil·i·tude /ˌvɛrəsəˈmɪləˌtjuːd; ˌverᵻsᵻˈmɪlᵻtjuːd/ *n fml* [U] the quality of seeming to be true and real 〖正式〗貌似真實; 逼真

ver·i·ta·ble /ˈvɛrətəbl̩; ˈverᵻtəbəl/ *adj* [always before a noun 只能用於名詞前] a word used to make a description more forceful 名副其實的, 十足的〔用以使描述更有力〕: *The meal was a veritable feast.* 這頓飯真是名副其實的盛宴。

ver·mil·ion /vəˈmɪljən; vəˈmɪljən/ *adj,n* [U] a bright reddish-orange colour 朱紅色(的); 鮮紅色(的)

ver·min /ˈvɜːmɪn; ˈvɝmᵻn/ *n* [pl] **1** small animals or birds that cause damage and are difficult to control 害獸; 害鳥: *To a farmer foxes are vermin because they steal and kill chickens.* 對農民來說, 狐狸是一種害獸, 因為牠們偷雞吃雞。 **2** unpleasant biting insects that live on the body of humans or animals 寄生蟲, 害蟲〔如蚤、蝨等〕

ver·mouth /ˈvɜːmuːθ; vɝˈmuːθ/ *n* [U] a drink made from wine with the taste of certain plants added to it 苦艾酒; 味美思酒

ver·nac·u·lar /vəˈnækjələ; vəˈnækjᵊlɚ/ *n* the native, spoken language of a country or area 本國語; 本地話; 方言; 土話: *His poetry is written in the vernacular because of the south.* 他的詩用南方方言寫的。

ver·ru·ca /veˈruːkə; vəˈruːkə/ *n* a small hard growth on the bottom of a person's foot 〔長在腳底的〕疣; 肉贅

ver·sa·tile /ˈvɜːsətaɪl; ˈvɝsətl̩/ *adj* **1** having many different skills and being able to change quickly from one kind of activity to another 有多種技能的; 多才多藝的: *He's a very versatile actor.* 他是個十分多才多藝的演員。 **2** having many different uses 多用途的; 多功能的; 萬用的: *Nylon is a versatile material.* 尼龍是一種用途廣泛的材料。 –**versatility** /ˌvɜːsəˈtɪlətɪ, ˌvɝsəˈtɪləti/ *n* [U]

verse /vɜːs; vɝs/ *n* **1** [U] written language arranged in lines, with a pattern of repeated beats as in music, and often with words of matching sound at the end of some lines 詩; 詩體; 韻文: *a book of comic verse* 幽默詩集 **2** [C] a set of lines which forms one part of a poem or song 詩節: *The song has four verses.* 這首歌有四詩節歌詞。 **3** [C] a group of sentences that together form one numbered division of one of the books of the BIBLE〔《聖經》中標有號碼的〕節

versed /vɜːst; vɝst/ *adj* **well versed in** having a thorough knowledge of or skill in a subject 精通於…

ver·sion /ˈvɜːʒən; ˈvɝʒən/ *n* **1** one person's account of an event〔個人對事件的〕描述; 説法: *The two newspapers gave different versions of what happened.* 這兩家報紙對發生的事件説法不一。 **2** a slightly different form, copy, or style of something〔略有不同的〕變化形式, 變體, 版本: *Monet painted many different versions of the flowers in his garden.* 莫奈為他園子裡的花作了許多不同的畫。 **3** a form of written or musical work which is different in some way from the original 改寫本; 經改編的樂曲: *a film version of the book* 根據這本書改編的影片

ver·sus /ˈvɜːsəs; ˈvɝsəs/ *prep* (also 又作 **v., vs.**) in opposition to or against, especially in a game of sport〔尤指在體育比賽中的〕以…為對手; 對: *The England versus Australia cricket match is starting today.* 英格蘭對澳大利亞的板球比賽今天開始。

ver·te·bra /ˈvɜːtəbrə; ˈvɝtᵻbrə/ *n* **vertebrae** /-briː, -briː/ one of the small hollow bones down the centre of your back, which form your SPINE 脊椎; 椎骨

ver·te·brate /ˈvɜːtəˌbret; ˈvɝtᵻbrᵻt/ *adj,n tech* an animal, bird, or fish which has a backbone 〖術語〗〔獸、鳥、魚等〕有脊椎的; 脊椎動物

ver·ti·cal /ˈvɜːtɪkl̩; ˈvɝtɪkəl/ *adj* pointing up and down in a straight line and forming an angle of 90 degrees with a flat surface like the ground 垂直的; 直立的; 豎的: *vertical lines* 垂直線; 豎線 –**vertically** /-klɪ, -kli/ *adv*

ver·ti·go /ˈvɜːtɪɡəʊ; ˈvɝtɪɡoʊ/ *n* [U] a feeling of sickness caused by looking down from a great height〔從高處下望產生的〕眩暈, 頭暈

verve /vɜːv; vɝv/ *n* [U] a strong feeling of enjoyment 歡快

very[1] /ˈvɛrɪ; ˈveri/ *adv* **1** to a great degree 很; 頗; 非常: *It's very warm today.* 今天很暖和。| *He's not very old.* 他不

太老。| *It's a very exciting book.* 這是一本激動人心的書。| *The traffic was moving very slowly.* 交通擠塞，車流緩慢。| *Thank you very much.* 非常感謝。**2** used with SUPERLATIVE adjectives or with words like "same", "own", "first", and "last" to make them stronger 極其；完全；真正地〔與形容詞最高級或 "same", "own", "first", "last" 連用加強語氣〕: *It's the very best film I've seen this year.* 這是我今年看過的最佳影片。| *He was the very last to finish.* 他是最後一個完成的。| *I'd love to have my very own boat.* 我好想自己擁有一條小船。**3 very much so** a phrase you use to agree with someone strongly 正是如此〔用以堅定地同意某人的話〕: *"The government seems to be in some difficulty now." "Oh, very much so."* "政府目前似乎處境困難。" "說得對，正是如此。" **4 very well** a phrase you use when you are agreeing to do something that you do not really want to do 那好吧〔用以表示同意做一些並非真的喜歡做的事〕

> ■ USAGE 用法: We can say **very** *big* or *the* **very** *biggest,* but the comparative form is **much** *bigger.* ☆可以説 **very** *big* 或 *the* **very** *biggest,* 但比較級是 **much** *bigger*。

very² *adj* [only before a noun 只用於名詞前] exact 確實的；正是的: *He's the very man I've been looking for.* 他正是我一直在找的人。| *I missed the very beginning of the film.* 我錯過了電影最前面的部分。| *He was determined to climb to the very top of the mountain.* 他決心爬到山的最頂上。

ves·pers /ˈvɛspəz; ˈvɛspəz/ *n* [U] the evening service in some divisions of the Christian church 〔某些基督教派中的〕晚禱，晚課

ves·sel /ˈvɛsl; ˈvɛsəl/ *n fml* 〔正式〕**1** a round container, such as a glass, pot, or bucket, for holding liquids 〔盛液體的〕容器，器皿〔如玻璃杯、罐、桶等〕**2** a ship or large boat 船；艦: *a fishing vessel* 漁船

vest /vɛst; vɛst/ *n* **1** *BrE* a piece of clothing worn next to the skin under a shirt 〔英式〕內衣；汗背心 –see picture on page 210 見 210 頁彩圖 **2** the usual American word for 〔美式〕= WAISTCOAT

vest·ed /ˈvɛstɪd; ˈvɛstɪd/ *adj fml* 〔正式〕**1 vested in** given as a legal right to a person or group 〔人或團體〕獲授予[賦予]〔法律權力〕: *The power to make new laws is vested in the government by the people.* 人民授予政府制訂新法律的權力。**2 vested interest** a strong reason for doing something, because you will gain something from it 既得利益: *The tobacco companies have a vested interest in claiming that cigarette smoking isn't harmful.* 煙草公司聲稱吸煙無害是因為他們對此有既得利益。

ves·ti·bule /ˈvɛstəˌbjul; ˈvɛstɪˌbjuːl/ *n fml* an entrance area or room just inside the outside door of a building 〔正式〕〔建築物的〕門廳，前廳

ves·tige /ˈvɛstɪdʒ; ˈvɛstɪdʒ/ *n* a small part that remains of something big or important that once existed 殘餘；遺跡: *This stone is the last vestige of the old castle.* 這塊石頭是古城堡的最後遺跡。

vest·ments /ˈvɛstmənts; ˈvɛstmənts/ *n fml* [pl] ceremonial clothes worn by priests for church services 〔正式〕〔牧師主持宗教儀式時穿的〕法衣，祭服

ves·try /ˈvɛstrɪ; ˈvɛstrɪ/ *n* **vestries** a room in a church where the priest puts on his ceremonial clothes 〔教堂的〕法衣室

vet¹ /vɛt; vɛt/ *n* (also 又作 **veterinary surgeon** *fml* 〔正式〕) a trained animal doctor 獸醫

vet² *v* **-tt-** *infml* [T] to examine carefully to make sure something or someone is acceptable for a particular purpose 〔非正式〕審查〔某事物或某人〕: *Everyone who works with military secrets must be thoroughly vetted.* 工作上涉及軍事機密的人必須嚴格審查。

vet·e·ran /ˈvɛtərən; ˈvɛtərən/ *n* **1** someone who has a lot of experience in something, especially in war 老手；經驗豐富的人；〔尤指〕老兵，老戰士: *Grandfather is a veteran of the First World War.* 祖父是參加過第一次世界大戰的老兵。**2 veteran car** a car made before 1919 1919年前製造的老式汽車 **–veteran** *adj* [always before a noun 只能用於名詞前]: *a veteran politician* 資深政客

vet·e·ri·nar·i·an /ˌvɛtərəˈnɛriən; ˌvɛtərəˈneəriən/ *n* the usual American word for 〔美式〕= VET

vet·e·ri·na·ry /ˈvɛtərəˌnɛri; ˈvɛtərɪnəri/ *adj* [always before a noun 只能用於名詞前] connected with the medical care and treatment of sick animals 獸醫的: *veterinary science* 獸醫學

veterinary sur·geon /ˈ···· ˌ··/ *n* see 見 VET

ve·to¹ /ˈvito; ˈviːtəʊ/ *n* **vetoes** [C;U] the official power to refuse permission for something 否決（權）: *The Presidential right of veto.* 總統的否決權。

veto² *v* **vetoed, vetoing** [T] to refuse to allow something 否決〔某事物〕: *The President vetoed the plan.* 總統否決了這項計劃。

vex /vɛks; veks/ *v old fash* [T] to make someone feel angry 〔老式〕使〔某人〕惱火 **– vexation** /vɛkˈseɪʃən; vekˈseɪʃən/ *n* [C;U]

VHF /ˌvi eɪtʃ ˈɛf; ˌviː eɪtʃ ˈef/ *n* [U] the radio wave band of 30 to 300 million HERTZ; an abbreviation for **very high frequency** 〔縮〕〔30-300兆赫的〕甚高頻

vi·a /ˈvaɪə; ˈvaɪə/ *prep* **1** travelling or sent through a place on the way to somewhere else 經由；經過；取道: *We flew to Athens via*

Paris and Rome. 我們取道巴黎和羅馬飛往雅典。 **2** using a particular person or thing 使用; 借助: *These television pictures came via satellite.* 這些電視圖像是通過衛星傳送來的。 | *I sent Mary a message via her sister.* 我通過瑪麗的姐姐帶口信給她。

vi·a·ble /ˈvaɪəbl; ˈvaɪəbəl/ *adj* able to succeed without any problems 可望成功的: *Your idea is interesting, but not really economically viable.* 你的想法很有趣, 但在經濟上不可行。 –**viability** /ˌvaɪəˈbɪləti; ˌvaɪəˈbɪlɪti/ *n* [U]

vi·a·duct /ˈvaɪəˌdʌkt; ˈvaɪədʌkt/ *n* a long high bridge which carries a road or railway line across a valley 〔架於山谷上的公路或鐵路〕高架橋

vi·brant /ˈvaɪbrənt; ˈvaɪbrənt/ *adj* **1** exciting and full of life 有活力的; 活躍的: *Hong Kong is a vibrant, fascinating city.* 香港是個充滿生機而又迷人的城市。 **2** bright and strong (used of colour or light) 〔色彩〕鮮明的; 〔光線〕明亮的。

vi·brate /ˈvaɪbret; vaɪˈbreɪt/ *v* **vibrated, vibrating** [I;T] to shake quickly with a slight movement that may often be felt rather than seen (使)震動; (使)顫動: *The music was so loud, the whole house was vibrating.* 音樂太響, 整座房子都在震動。 | *You make the sound by vibrating the tongue against the teeth.* 你用舌頭抵住牙齒顫動, 發這個聲音。

vi·bra·tion /vaɪˈbreʃən; vaɪˈbreɪʃən/ *n* [C;U] a slight continuous shaky movement 震動; 顫動; 振動: *Can you feel the vibrations of the ship's engines?* 你有沒有感覺到輪船發動機在振動? | *If you touch the machine you will feel the vibration.* 如果你用手觸摸機器, 你會感覺到震動。

vic·ar /ˈvɪkə; ˈvɪkər/ *n* a priest in the Church of England who is in charge of an area 〔英國國教的〕教區牧師 –see 見 PRIEST (USAGE 用法)

vic·ar·age /ˈvɪkərɪdʒ; ˈvɪkərɪdʒ/ *n* the house of a vicar 教區牧師的住宅

vi·car·i·ous /vaɪˈkeriəs; vɪˈkeəriəs/ *adj* experienced indirectly through watching or reading about other people and not doing something yourself 通過他人的經驗感受的; 間接感受到的: *People can get a vicarious pleasure from reading about the lives of rich families.* 通過閱讀有關富豪家族生活的文章, 人們得到間接感受的樂趣。

vice /vaɪs; vaɪs/ *n* **1** [U] criminal behaviour connected with sex, drugs, and immoral practices 罪惡行為〔指淫亂、吸毒、不道德行為〕 **2** [C] a bad or immoral part of a human character 〔人品上的〕邪惡; 道德敗壞 **3** [C] *infml* a bad habit 〔非正式〕惡習; 壞習慣: *Smoking is my only vice.* 吸煙是我唯一的惡習。 **4** (**vise** *AmE* 〔美式〕) a tool with metal jaws that can be tightened, used for holding an object firmly so that you can work on it with both hands 老虎鉗; 枱鉗

vice-chan·cel·lor /ˌ· ˈ···/ *n* the person who controls the affairs of a university 〔大學中主持事務的〕副校長

vice·roy /ˈvaɪsrɔɪ; ˈvaɪsrɔɪ/ *n* a king's or queen's representative ruling for them in another country 〔代表國王或女王在另一國進行管轄的〕總督

vice ver·sa /ˌvaɪsi ˈvɜːsə; ˌvaɪs ˈvɜːsə/ *adv* and the same is true in the opposite situation from the one just stated 反過來也一樣; 反之亦然: *When she wants to go out, he wants to stay in, and vice versa.* 她想外出時, 他寧願留在家裡, 反之亦然。

vi·cin·i·ty /vəˈsɪnəti; vɪˈsɪnɪti/ *n* [U] **1** the surrounding area 周圍地區; 近處: *There were no good schools in the vicinity.* 附近沒有好學校。 **2** in the vicinity of near to 在…附近; 與…接近: *a restaurant in the vicinity of the hotel* 旅館附近的餐館

vi·cious /ˈvɪʃəs; ˈvɪʃəs/ *adj* **1** cruel and showing the desire to hurt people 惡毒的; 兇殘的; 惡意的: *He gave the dog a vicious blow with his stick.* 他用手杖惡狠狠地打了那條狗一下。 **2** dangerous and likely to hurt people 惡性的; 險惡的: *a vicious-looking knife* 一把兇光閃閃的刀 –**viciously** *adv* – **viciousness** *n* [U]

vicious cir·cle /ˌ·· ˈ··/ *n* a situation in which the effect of one problem creates another, and causes the first problem to return 惡性循環: *Crime leads to prison, which leads to unemployment, which leads to crime. It's a vicious circle.* 由於犯罪而入獄, 由於入獄而失業, 由於失業而又再犯罪。這是個惡性循環。

vic·tim /ˈvɪktɪm; ˈvɪktɪm/ *n* **1** a person or animal that is harmed or killed by someone, or by something unpleasant happening to them 受害者; 犧牲者; 罹難者: *Four people were killed in the explosion, but police have not yet named the victims.* 爆炸中有四人喪生, 但警方尚未公佈遇難者的姓名。 **2** someone or something that suffers as a result of something unpleasant happening 〔不愉快的事的〕承受者; 罹病者; 受騙者: *She was a victim of cancer.* 她是個癌症患者。

vic·tim·ize /ˈvɪktɪmˌaɪz; ˈvɪktɪmaɪz/ *v* **victimized, victimizing** (also 又作 **victimise** *BrE* 〔英式〕) [T] to cause someone to suffer unfairly 使〔某人〕受害, 受迫害: *When she lost her job, she felt she'd been victimized because of her political views.* 她丟了工作, 感到自己是因政治觀點而受迫害的。 – **victimization** /ˌvɪktɪməˈzeʃən; ˌvɪktɪmaɪˈzeɪʃən/ *n* [U]

vic·tor /ˈvɪktə; ˈvɪktər/ *n lit* a winner in a battle or competition 〔文〕勝利者; 獲勝者

Vic·to·ri·an /vɪkˈtoːriən; vɪkˈtɔːriən/ *adj*, *n* **1** belonging to or living in the time when Victoria was the Queen of Britain (1837-1901) 維多利亞女王時代(1837-1901)的; 維多利亞女王時代的人: *Victorian furniture* 維多利亞

女王時代的家具 | *Florence Nightingale was a famous Victorian.* 弗羅倫斯‧南丁格爾是著名的維多利亞女王時代人物。 **2** having the strong moral opinions of the society at the time of Queen Victoria, especially believing in hard work and strict sexual morals 有很強的維多利亞時代道德觀的〔尤指提倡苦幹, 嚴守兩性道德規範〕

★**vic·to·ry** /'vɪktəri; 'vɪktəri/ *n* **victories** [C;U] the act of winning or state of having won in war or in any kind of struggle 勝利; 戰勝; 獲勝: *We will lead our party to victory in the next election!* 我們要率領本黨在下屆選舉中獲勝! | *Tonight's game will see another victory for Italy over the Dutch team.* 今晚的比賽意大利隊肯定會戰勝荷蘭隊。 –**victorious** /vɪk-'tɔːriəs; vɪk'tɔːriəs/ *adj*: *the victorious team* 獲勝隊

★**vid·e·o¹** /'vɪdɪˌo; 'vɪdiəʊ/ *n* **1** [U] recording and showing moving pictures, film, or television using special TAPE called VIDEO-TAPE 錄像; 錄影: *I've got the children on video.* 我把孩子們錄了像。 | *Teachers now use a lot of video in the classroom.* 教師現在在課堂上大量使用錄像。 **2** [C;U] (also 又作 **video cassette**) a container holding video-tape 盒式錄像帶 –see picture on page 730 見 730 頁彩圖 **3** [C] (also 又作 **video recorder** *fml* 〔正式〕) a machine which records pictures and sound using video-tape 錄影機, 錄像機: *You can record two programmes at the same time on this video.* 你可以用這台錄像機同時錄兩個節目。 | *Rewind the video.* 把錄像機裡的錄像帶倒一下。 –see picture on page 730 見 730 頁彩圖 **4** [C] a film or television broadcast recorded on videotape 錄像電影或電視節目: *Let's rent a video to watch tonight.* 我們今晚租部錄像片來看看吧。

video² *v* (also 又作 **videotape**) [T] to record something on videotape 把〔某事物〕錄在錄像帶上: *I must remember to video the last episode tonight.* 我必須記住今晚把最後一集錄下來。

video cas·sette /ˌ··· ·'·/ *n* see 見 VIDEO

video re·cord·er /'··· ·ˌ··/ *n* see 見 VIDEO

vid·e·o·tape¹ /'vɪdɪoˌtep; 'vɪdiəʊteɪp/ *n* [U] a long narrow band of MAGNETIC material on which television pictures and sound are recorded 錄像(磁)帶, 錄影帶

videotape² *v* [T] see 見 VIDEO

vie /vaɪ; vaɪ/ *v* **vied, vying** [I] to compete against someone for something 與〔某人〕競爭〔某事物〕: *They are vying with each other for the job as captain.* 他們彼此競爭船長這一職務。

★**view¹** /vju; vjuː/ *n* **1** [U] the ability to see something from a particular place 視力; 視線: *My view of the harbour was blocked by the new buildings.* 新樓房擋住了我的視線, 我看不到港口了。 | *If you stand here you'll get a better view of the pro-cession.* 如果你站在這裡, 就可以更清楚地看到遊行隊伍。 **2** [C] the things that you can see from a particular place 看到的東西;〔從某處看到的〕景色: *The view from the top of the hill was superb.* 從山頂看出去景色美極了。 | *a hotel with lovely views* 可以看到秀麗景色的旅館 **3** [U] a position in which something can be seen 視野: *The sea was now in view.* 現在大海在望。 | *A range of hills came into view.* 山脈出現在眼前。 | *The valley was hidden from view by mist.* 溪谷隱藏在霧靄之中, 看不見了。 **4** [C] a personal opinion or belief about something 見解; 信念; 看法; 觀點: *He has very strong views on education.* 他對教育的觀點很強硬。 | *In my view, he should never have been offered the job in the first place.* 在我看來, 原先壓根兒就不該給他這份工作。 **5 in view of something** taking something into consideration 鑑於某事物; 考慮到某事物: *In view of his age and ill health, the police have decided not to prosecute him.* 考慮到他的年齡和健康狀況, 警方決定不予起訴。 **6 on view** being shown to the public 在展出: *These paintings will be on view at the British Museum until next month.* 這些畫作將在大英博物館一直展出到下個月為止。 **7 with a view to doing something** with the aim of doing something 以做某事為目標: *We decorated the house with a view to selling it.* 我們把房子粉刷一新, 以便出售。

■ USAGE 用法: Compare 比較 **view, scenery, scene, landscape. View** is countable. We use **view** to talk about all the things we can see at a distance from a particular place ☆ **View** 是可數的。用 **view** 來談論從相當距離外的某處可以看到的全部事物: *You'll get a fine view of the town from the top of the hill.* 從山頂望出去, 你可以飽覽小鎮風光。 **View** can be countable but **scenery** is uncountable. We use **scenery** to talk about the beautiful or ugly appearance of part of the country ☆**View** 是可數的, 但 **scenery** 是不可數的。 **scenery** 用來談論鄉村的一些地方是否美麗: *We passed through some magnificent scenery on our journey through Scotland.* 我們在橫穿蘇格蘭的旅途中看到了一些壯觀的景色。 **Scene** is countable. A **scene** is what you see both close up and at a distance, and may include people and movement ☆ **scene** 是可數的。 **scene** 是指近距離和遠距離看見的事物, 可以包括人及其活動: *a happy scene of children playing in the park* 孩子們在花園中玩耍的歡樂景象。 **Landscape** is countable. We use **landscape** for any combination of hills, valleys, fields, etc. in a particular area ☆ **landscape** 是可數的。

用 **landscape** 指某地的山丘、溪谷、田地的總和: *The **landscape** was typical of Scotland, with high mountains, lakes, and deep valleys.* 高山、湖泊、深谷, 這景色是典型的蘇格蘭風光。

view² v [T] **1** to look at or examine something carefully 仔細觀察, 察看〔某事物〕: *Several possible buyers have already been to view the house.* 幾位有興趣購買的人已來看過房子了。**2** to consider something in a particular way 考慮, 看待〔某事物〕: *They viewed the future with some alarm.* 對於未來的日子, 他們感到惶恐不安。| *I viewed his action as a breach of trust.* 我認為他的行為背信棄義。

view·er /'vjuə; 'vjuːr/ n a person watching television 電視觀眾

view·point /'vjuˌpɔɪnt; 'vjuːpɔɪnt/ n your general opinions and way of thinking about something 觀點; 看法

vig·il /'vɪdʒəl; 'vɪdʒ⅟l/ n [C;U] **1** watching and guarding something or someone, usually at night〔常指在夜間的〕監視, 戒備, 值夜: *There was an all-night vigil outside the prison.* 監獄外有人徹夜守衛。**2 keep vigil** to watch and guard something or someone 監視, 警戒〔某人或某事〕

vig·i·lant /'vɪdʒələnt; 'vɪdʒ⅟lənt/ adj fml continually watchful or on guard〔正式〕警惕的; 警戒的; 警覺的: *A vigilant police force helps to control crime.* 經常保持警覺的警隊有助遏制罪案。**–vigilance** n [U]

vig·i·lan·te /ˌvɪdʒə'læntɪ; ˌvɪdʒ⅟'lænti/ n a member of an unofficial organization which keeps order and punishes crime when it thinks the police is not keeping order properly 治安維持會成員

vig·our /'vɪgə; 'vɪgər/ n (**vigor** AmE〔美式〕) [U] forceful strength or activity of body or mind 體力; 精力; 活力 **–vigorous** adj: *She made a vigorous speech in defence of the government.* 她作了一篇慷慨激昂的演説為政府辯護。**–vigorously** adv

vile /vaɪl; vaɪl/ adj **1** hateful and wicked 卑鄙的; 可恥的; 惡劣的: *He was a vile man who treated everyone badly.* 他是個卑鄙的人, 對所有的人都很壞。**2** infml nasty or unpleasant〔非正式〕討厭的; 糟透的; 討厭的: *The walls were a vile shade of green.* 這牆的顏色綠得難看死了。

vil·i·fy /'vɪlɪˌfaɪ; 'vɪl⅟faɪ/ v **vilified, vilifying** fml [T] to say bad things about someone or something〔正式〕污蔑, 詆毀, 中傷〔某人或某事〕

vil·la /'vɪlə; 'vɪlə/ n a pleasant house with a garden in the country or used for holidays〔在鄉間或供度假用的〕別墅: *We're renting a villa in the south of France for the summer holidays.* 我們在法國南部租了一幢夏天度假用的別墅。

vil·lage /'vɪlɪdʒ; 'vɪlɪdʒ/ n a small group of houses and other buildings in a country area 鄉村; 村莊: *She lives in a village in the mountains.* 她住在山間的一個村莊裡。

vil·lager /'vɪlɪdʒə; 'vɪlɪdʒər/ n a person who lives in a village 鄉村居民; 村民

vil·lain /'vɪlən; 'vɪlən/ n **1** a wicked man, or the main bad character in an old play, film, or story〔舊時戲劇、影片或小説中的〕壞蛋, 主要反派角色: *The villain always gets caught at the end of the story.* 壞蛋一般都會在故事末尾被抓。**–opposite** 反義 **hero 2** infml a criminal〔非正式〕罪犯

vil·lainy /'vɪlənɪ; 'vɪləni/ n [U] lit wicked behaviour〔文〕邪惡行為

vin·ai·grette /ˌvɪnə'grɛt; ˌvɪn⅟'grɛt/ n [U] a sharp-tasting mixture of oil and VINEGAR which is put on salads (SALAD) 醋油沙拉汁〔油、醋合成的濃烈沙拉調味品〕

vin·di·cate /'vɪndəˌket; 'vɪnd⅟keɪt/ v **vindicated, vindicating** [T] to show that someone or something is free from blame 證明〔某人或某事〕無辜或無罪; 證明正確: *The report clearly vindicates the company's actions.* 這一報告證明公司的行動是正確的。**–vindication** /ˌvɪndə'keʃən; ˌvɪnd⅟'keɪʃən/ n [sing]

vin·dic·tive /vɪn'dɪktɪv; vɪn'dɪktɪv/ adj wanting to harm someone who has harmed you 有報復心的; 想復仇的

vine /vaɪn; vaɪn/ n **1** a climbing plant that produces bunches of juicy green or purple fruit 葡萄藤 **2** any creeping or climbing plant 藤本植物

vin·e·gar /'vɪnɪgə; 'vɪnɪgər/ n [U] an acid-tasting liquid used in preserving or adding taste to food 醋

vine·yard /'vɪnjəd; 'vɪnjəd/ n a piece of land planted with vines for wine production 葡萄園

vin·tage¹ /'vɪntɪdʒ; 'vɪntɪdʒ/ adj [always before a noun 只能用於名詞前] **1** made in a particular year and of high quality (used of wines) 某一年佳釀的〔指酒〕: *a bottle of vintage claret* 一瓶某年佳釀的法國波爾多紅葡萄酒 **2** of high quality and lasting value 優質的; 享有盛名的: *a vintage silent film* 一部久負盛名的默片 **3 vintage car** a car made between 1919 and 1930 生產於1919年至1930年間的汽車

vin·tage² n a fine wine produced in a particular year 某年釀的美酒: *a 1982 vintage* 1982年釀的美酒

vi·nyl /'vaɪnɪl; 'vaɪn⅟l/ n [U] firm plastic which you can bend; it is used for making records and floor and chair coverings 乙烯基(塑膠)

vi·o·la /vɪ'olə; vi'əʊlə/ n a stringed musical instrument, a little larger than a VIOLIN 中提琴

vi·o·late /'vaɪəˌlet; 'vaɪəleɪt/ v **violated, violating** [T] **1** to take no notice of a promise or agreement 違反, 違背〔諾言或協議〕:

This action violates the international agreements on protecting wild animals. 這種行為違反了保護野生動物的國際協議。 **2** to break into or spoil a place that should be respected 褻瀆, 冒犯〔應受尊敬之地〕 **–violation** /ˌvaɪə'leɪʃən; ˌvaɪə'leɪʃən/ n [C;U]: *They have been fishing in our waters, in violation of the recent agreement.* 他們違反了最近的協定, 在我們的水域捕魚。

★**vi·o·lence** /'vaɪələns; 'vaɪələns/ n [U] **1** very great feeling or action 〔感情或行動的〕猛烈, 激烈, 強烈: *The violence of the storm was very frightening.* 暴風雨之猛烈令人膽戰心驚。 **2** the use of physical force to hurt or harm someone 暴力〔行為〕: *There is a lot of violence on television these days.* 近來電視中出現大量暴力行為。 | *robbery with violence* 暴力搶劫

★**vi·o·lent** /'vaɪələnt; 'vaɪələnt/ adj **1** using physical force to hurt or harm someone 暴力的; 強暴的: *He was a violent man who had attacked his wife before.* 他是個兇狂的人, 以前曾毆打過自己的妻子。 | *a violent storm* 猛烈的暴風雨 | *There were violent clashes between police and demonstrators.* 警察和示威者之間產生了暴力衝突。 **2** produced by damaging physical force 暴力引起的: *He died a violent death.* 他橫遭慘死。 **3** using great force in your actions or language, especially because you are angry 〔行為或言語〕猛烈的, 激烈的〔尤因生氣〕: *She has a violent temper.* 她脾氣暴躁。 **–violently** adv

vi·o·let /'vaɪəlɪt; 'vaɪəlɪt/ n **1** [C] a small plant with sweet-smelling purple flowers 紫羅蘭 **2** [U] a bluish purple colour 紫羅蘭色; 藍紫色 **–violet** adj

vi·o·lin /ˌvaɪə'lɪn; ˌvaɪə'lɪn/ n a four-stringed musical instrument which you hold under your chin and play by drawing a BOW across the strings 小提琴 **–violinist** n

VIP /ˌvi aɪ 'pi; ˌviː aɪ 'piː/ n a person who is given special treatment because they are famous or important; an abbreviation for **very important person** 〔縮〕〔因有名或重要而受到特別對待的〕要人, 大人物: *the VIP lounge at the airport* 機場貴賓室

vi·per /'vaɪpə; 'vaɪpər/ n a small poisonous snake 小毒蛇

vir·gin¹ /'vɜːdʒɪn; 'vɜːdʒɪn/ n a person, usually a woman or girl, who has never had sexual relations with a member of the opposite sex 處女 **–virginal** adj

virgin² adj lit untouched or unspoiled 〔文〕未受損傷的; 未玷污的: *no footmarks on the virgin snow* 潔白的雪地上沒有腳印

vir·gin·i·ty /və'dʒɪnəti; vɜːˈdʒɪnˌ̩ti/ n [U] the state of being a virgin 童貞; 處女身分: *She was 19 when she lost her virginity.* 她十九歲時失去童貞的。

Virgin Mar·y /ˌvɜːdʒɪn 'mɛri; ˌvɜːdʒɪn 'mɛəri/ n in the Christian religion, Mary, the mother of Christ 〔基督教中的〕聖母

瑪麗亞

Vir·go /'vɜːgo; 'vɜːgəʊ/ n one of the signs of the ZODIAC 室女宮

vir·ile /'vɪrəl; 'vɪraɪl/ adj full of male qualities such as physical strength and sexual power (used to express approval) 有男子氣概的, 有男性生殖力的〔含褒義〕: *a virile young sportsman* 充滿陽剛活力的年輕運動員

vi·ril·i·ty /və'rɪləti; vəˈrɪlˌ̩ti/ n [U] male sexual power or male qualities in general (used to express approval) 〔總稱〕男性生殖力, 男子氣概〔含褒義〕

vir·tu·al /'vɜːtʃəl; 'vɜːtʃʊəl/ adj [only before a noun 只用於名詞前] in fact though not in name 實際上的〔並非名義上的〕: *The king was so much under the influence of his wife that she was the virtual ruler of the country.* 國王深受王后的影響, 以至她成了國家的實際統治者。

★**vir·tu·al·ly** /'vɜːtʃʊəlɪ; 'vɜːtʃʊəli/ adv almost 差不多, 幾乎: *The dinner's virtually ready. I've only got to make the salad.* 飯菜差不多準備好了, 我只要再做個沙拉就成了。

★**vir·tue** /'vɜːtʃu; 'vɜːtʃuː/ n **1** [U] goodness, nobleness, and worthiness 善; 德; 高尚: *a man of the highest virtue* 道德極為高尚的人 **2** [C] any good quality of character or behaviour 美德; 德行: *Among her many virtues are loyalty, courage, and truthfulness.* 她有許多美德, 如忠誠、勇敢和率真。 **3** [C;U] an advantage 優點; 長處: *One of the virtues of this curtain material is that it's easily washable.* 這種窗簾料子的優點之一是洗滌方便。 **4** by virtue of as a result of 因為; 由於; 憑藉: *Though she isn't British by birth, she's a British citizen by virtue of her marriage to an Englishman.* 雖然她沒有英國血統, 但她通過和英國人結婚而成為英國公民。

vir·tu·o·so /ˌvɜːtʃʊ'oso; ˌvɜːtʃʊ'əʊzəʊ/ n a very skilful performer in one of the arts, especially music 藝術大師〔尤指大演奏家〕

vir·tu·ous /'vɜːtʃəs; 'vɜːtʃʊəs/ adj doing the right thing morally 品行良好的; 道德高尚的 **–virtuously** adv

vir·u·lent /'vɪrjələnt; 'vɪrᵍlənt/ adj **1** full of hatred (used of a feeling) 惡毒的, 充滿憎惡的〔指感情〕 **2** very powerful, quick-acting, and dangerous to life or health (used of a poison or disease) 劇毒的, 致命的, 惡性的〔指毒藥或疾病〕 **–virulence** n [U]

vi·rus /'vaɪrəs; 'vaɪərəs/ n a living thing even smaller than bacteria which causes infectious disease 病毒: *the common cold virus* 普通感冒病毒 | *virus infections* 病毒感染 **–viral** /'vaɪrəl; 'vaɪərəl/ adj

vi·sa /'vizə; 'viːzə/ n an official mark put onto a PASSPORT giving a foreigner permission to enter, pass through, or leave a particular country 〔護照上的〕簽證: *Do Americans need a visa to visit Britain?* 美國人到英國去是否要簽證?

vis·age /'vɪzɪdʒ; 'vɪzɪdʒ/ n lit your face 〔文〕

臉; 面容

vis·à·vis /ˌviːzəˈviː; ˌviːz ɑː ˈviː/ *prep fml*〖正式〗 **1** with regard to 關於; 對於 **2** when compared to 同...相比: *This year's profits show an improvement vis-à-vis last year's.* 今年的利潤同去年相比有所增長。

vis·count /ˈvaɪkaʊnt; ˈvaɪkaunt/ *n* (also 又作 **Viscount**) a British nobleman〖英國的〗子爵

vis·count·ess /ˈvaɪkaʊntɪs; ˈvaɪkauntɪs/ *n* (also 又作 **Viscountess**) the wife of a viscount, or a woman with the rank of viscount 子爵夫人; 女子爵

vis·cous /ˈvɪskəs; ˈvɪskəs/ *adj* thick and sticky and not flowing easily (used of liquids) 黏稠的〖指液體〗

vis·i·bil·i·ty /ˌvɪzəˈbɪlətɪ; ˌvɪzəˈbɪlɪtɪ/ *n* [U] the degree of clearness with which objects can be seen according to the weather 可見度; 能見度: *We had a splendid view of the mountains because of the very good visibility.* 由於能見度極好, 我們看到了壯麗的山景。| *The mist was so thick that visibility was down to only ten meters.* 霧非常濃, 能見度降到了只有十米。

*vis·i·ble /ˈvɪzəbl; ˈvɪzəbəl/ *adj* able to be seen 看得見的; 可見的 –opposite 反義 **invisible** –**visibly** *adv*: *He was visibly anxious about the examination.* 他顯然在為考試而焦慮。

⚹vi·sion /ˈvɪʒən; ˈvɪʒən/ *n* **1** [U] the ability to see 視力; 視覺: *When I had my eyes tested the optician said that my vision was perfect.* 我檢查眼睛時, 驗光師說我的視力非常好。**2** [U] the ability to imagine how things could be done differently in the future 想像力; 洞察力; 眼光; 遠見: *a man of vision* 有遠見的人 | *We need someone with real vision to take over the company.* 我們需要具有真知灼見的人來接管公司。**3** [C] something seen in a dream, in your imagination, or as a religious experience 夢幻; 幻想; 幻覺: *She had a vision in which God seemed to appear before her.* 她在幻覺中看見上帝似乎出現在她面前。| *He has a clear vision of the future he wants for his children.* 他對孩子們的未來有着清楚的憧憬。**4 have visions of doing something** to think that something will happen 認為某事將會發生: *There was so much traffic on the way to the airport that I had visions of missing the plane.* 去機場的路上交通那麼擁擠, 我想我要趕不上飛機了。

vi·sion·a·ry /ˈvɪʒənˌɛrɪ; ˈvɪʒənəri/ *adj, n* **visionaries** a person who has a vision of how things could be done differently in the future 有眼力的人; 有預見的人

⚹⚹vis·it¹ /ˈvɪzɪt; ˈvɪzɪt/ *v* [I;T] to go and spend time with a person or in a place 訪問; 拜訪; 探望; 在...逗留: *Aunt Jane usually visits us for two or three weeks in the spring.* 簡姑媽通常每年春天到我們家住上兩三個星期。| *While we're in Europe we ought to visit Holland.* 我們在歐洲逗留時, 應該去荷

蘭遊覽。| *When we were in London we visited the Tower twice.* 我們在倫敦的時候去倫敦塔參觀了兩次。| *Visiting hours in the hospital are from 4.30 to 6.00.* 醫院的探視時間從四時三十分到六時。

*visit² *n* an action or time of visiting 訪問; 參觀; 遊覽: *He makes several visits back home every year.* 他每年都要回家探親幾次。| *We've just had a visit from the police.* 警察剛剛來我們這裡巡視過。| *I think you should pay a visit to the doctor about your arm.* 我想你該到醫生那裡去治一下你的胳膊。

vis·i·ta·tion /ˌvɪzəˈteɪʃən; ˌvɪzəˈteɪʃən/ *n fml* a formal visit by someone in charge, usually in order to discover whether things are in good order〖正式〗視察; 巡視

⚹vis·it·or /ˈvɪzɪtə; ˈvɪzɪtər/ *n* a person who visits 訪問者; 來客; 參觀者; 遊客: *Visitors to the castle are asked not to take photographs.* 城堡參觀者請勿拍照。

vi·sor /ˈvaɪzə; ˈvaɪzər/ *n* the part of a HELMET which is moved down to protect your face when you are doing something such as riding a motorcycle〖頭盔上的〗面甲, 面罩

vis·ta /ˈvɪstə; ˈvɪstə/ *n* a distant view, to which your eyes are directed between narrow limits, for example by rows of trees〖從成排的樹中看出的〗長條形景色, 遠景

*vi·su·al /ˈvɪʒʊəl; ˈvɪʒuəl/ *adj* experienced by or connected with seeing 視覺的; 視力的: *a strong visual impact* 強烈的視覺效果 | *The visual arts are painting, dancing, and the cinema, as opposed to music and literature.* 視覺藝術和音樂、文學相對, 指的是繪畫、舞蹈和電影。–**visually** *adv*: *Visually the chair is very pleasing, but it's uncomfortable to sit on.* 這把椅子很好看, 但坐上去不舒服。

visual aid /ˌ··· ˈ·/ an object such as a picture, map, or film which teachers show people to help them learn 直觀教具〖如圖片、地圖或影片〗

vi·su·al·ize /ˈvɪʒʊəlˌaɪz; ˈvɪʒuəlaɪz/ *v* **visualized, visualizing** (also 又作 **visualise** *BrE*〖英式〗) [T] to form a picture of something or someone in your mind 設想, 想像〖某事物〗: *He described the place carefully and I tried to visualize it.* 他細緻地把那地方描繪了一遍, 我盡量想像那幅圖景。| *Can you visualize living on the moon?* 你可以想像在月球上居住的情景嗎? | *I can't visualize him as a bank clerk. He's too dreamy.* 我無法想像他當銀行職員。他太愛夢想。–**visualization** /ˌvɪʒʊələˈzeɪʃən; ˌvɪʒuəlaɪˈzeɪʃən/ *n* [U]

> □ USEFUL PATTERNS 有用句型
> to visualize something; to visualize doing something; to visualize someone as something

⚹vi·tal /ˈvaɪtl; ˈvaɪtl/ *adj* **1** very necessary or very important 必不可少的; 極其重要的: *This point is vital to my argument.* 這一點對

我的論據極為重要。 | *Your support is vital for the success of my plan.* 我的計劃是否成功, 你的支持是非常重要的因素。**2** *fml* full of life and force〔正式〕充滿活力的; 生氣勃勃的: *Their leader's vital and cheerful manner filled his men with courage.* 指揮官朝氣蓬勃和歡欣愉快的神態使士兵勇氣倍增。

vital sta·tis·tics /ˌ·· ·ˈ··/ *n* [pl] **1** *infml* the measurements of a woman's body round the chest, waist, and hips (HIP); people use this expression when they are talking about how attractive a woman's body is〔非正式〕女性三圍〔胸圍、腰圍、臀圍〕尺寸 **2** certain official facts about people's lives, especially their births, marriages, and deaths 人口統計資料〔尤指對出生、結婚、死亡的統計〕

vi·tal·i·ty /vaɪˈtælətɪ; vaɪˈtælḷtɪ/ *n* [U] strength and life 生命力; 生機; 活力: *He has a pleasant voice, but his singing lacks vitality.* 他有一副好嗓子, 但他的演唱缺乏生氣。

vi·tal·ly /ˈvaɪtlɪ; ˈvaɪtl-ɪ/ *adv* **vitally important** extremely important 至關重要的: *It is vitally important to switch off the electricity before attempting to repair the television.* 在準備修理電視機之前先切斷電源是至關重要的。

vit·a·min /ˈvaɪtəmɪn; ˈvɪtəmḷn/ *n* [C;U] a chemical substance which is present in certain foods, and is important for growth and good health 維他命; 維生素: *This type of bread has added vitamins.* 這種麵包內加有多種維生素。 | *Oranges contain vitamin C.* 柑橘含有維生素C。

vit·re·ous /ˈvɪtrɪəs; ˈvɪtrɪəs/ *adj tech* of or like glass〔術語〕玻璃(般)的: *The cooker is finished with white vitreous enamel.* 這炊具最外面的一層是玻璃般的白色琺瑯。 | *vitreous rocks* 玻璃狀的岩石

vit·ri·ol·ic /ˌvɪtrɪˈɒlɪk; ˌvɪtrɪˈɒlɪk◂/ *adj* bitter and violent (used of a feeling or its expression) 尖刻的、辛辣的〔指感情或感情的表達〕: *a vitriolic attack on the Government's plans for cuts in public services* 猛烈抨擊政府計劃縮減公共服務

vi·va·cious /vaɪˈveɪʃəs; vɪˈveɪʃəs/ *adj* attractively full of life (used especially of women) 活潑的; 快活的〔尤指婦女〕 –**vivacity** /-ˈvæsətɪ; -ˈvæsḷtɪ/ *n* [U]

viv·id /ˈvɪvɪd; ˈvɪvɪd/ *adj* **1** bright or strong in colour〔色彩〕鮮豔的, 明亮的: *a vivid flash of lightning* 耀眼的閃電 | *vivid red hair* 鮮紅的頭髮 **2** producing sharp clear pictures in your mind 生動的; 逼真的: *a child with a vivid imagination* 想像力活躍的孩子 | *a vivid description* 生動的描寫 –**vividly** *adv*

viv·i·sec·tion /ˌvɪvəˈsekʃən; ˌvɪvḷˈsekʃən/ *n* [U] the practice of performing operations on living animals in order to increase medical knowledge〔動物的〕活體解剖

vix·en /ˈvɪksn; ˈvɪksən/ *n* a female fox 雌狐

viz /vɪz; vɪz/ *adv fml* that is to say; you use

viz when you have already mentioned a general group and you are now going to mention all the particular things in it〔正式〕即, 就是〔用於已提到一個大類, 將要敍述其中所有的事物時〕: *On most English farms you'll find only four kinds of animal, viz horses, sheep, cattle, and pigs.* 在大多數英國農莊裡, 你只會看到四種家畜, 即馬、羊、牛和豬。

vo·cab·u·la·ry /vəˈkæbjəˌlerɪ; vəˈkæbjŭlərɪ/ *n* **vocabularies 1** [U] words 詞彙: *After we'd done the grammar exercise, we learnt some new vocabulary.* 完成語法練習以後, 我們學習了一些新的詞彙。**2** [C;U] all the words you know in a language 詞彙量: *Our baby's just starting to talk. He's got a vocabulary of about ten words.* 我們的孩子剛開始說話。他會講十來個單詞了。 | *the average vocabulary of an intermediate student* 中級水平學生的平均詞彙量 **3** [C;U] the words used in a particular subject or situation〔用於某個課題或某種情況的〕語彙: *I find it difficult to understand the vocabulary of the lawcourts.* 我發覺很難理解法庭語彙。

vo·cal /ˈvokl; ˈvəʊkəl/ *adj* **1** [only before a noun 只用於名詞前] related to your voice 嗓音的;〔用嗓子〕發聲的: *The tongue is one of the vocal organs.* 舌是發音器官之一。 | *I like instrumental music better than vocal music.* 和聲樂相比, 我更喜歡器樂。**2** *infml* expressing yourself freely and noisily in words〔非正式〕暢所欲言的; 發言熱烈的: *She was very vocal at the meeting.* 她在會議上發言非常熱烈。 –**vocally** *adv*

vocal cords /ˈ·· ·/ *n* (also 又作 **vocal chords**) [pl] the pair of thin bands of muscle in your throat that produce sound when you talk or sing 聲帶

vo·cal·ist /ˈvoklɪst; ˈvəʊkəlḷst/ *n* a singer of popular songs, especially one who sings with a band〔尤指有樂隊伴奏的通俗歌曲的〕歌手

vo·ca·tion /vəˈkeɪʃən; vəˈkeɪʃən/ *n* **1** [C;U] a strong desire to do a particular kind of work, usually work that helps other people, combined with a natural ability for it 稟賦: *She's a good doctor because she has a real vocation for looking after people who are ill.* 她是個好醫生, 因為她善於照料病人。**2** [C] a job that you really want to do and that you have a natural ability for, usually one that helps other people 天職; 使命: *Teaching children is more than just a way of making money: it's a vocation.* 教育兒童不僅僅是一種掙錢的手段: 它是一項使命。**3** [sing] a special call from God to be a priest, NUN, or MONK〔來自上帝的要求擔任牧師、修女或道士的〕神召, 天命

vo·ca·tion·al /vəˈkeɪʃənl; vəʊˈkeɪʃənəl/ *adj* preparing for a particular type of job 為某種職業作準備的: *vocational training for pilots* 導航員的職業培訓

vo·cif·er·ous /vəˈsɪfərəs; vəˈsɪfərəs/ *adj fml* noisy in the expression of your ideas〖正式〗叫喊的; 喧鬧的: *vociferous demands for higher wages* 大聲疾呼要求提高工資

vod·ka /ˈvɑdkə; ˈvɒdkə/ *n* [U] a strong, colourless, and almost tasteless alcoholic drink, first made in Russia and Poland 伏特加〔一種最早出產於俄國和波蘭的烈酒〕

vogue /voɡ; vəʊɡ/ *n* **1** the fashion or custom at a certain time 時尚; 流行; 風行; 時髦: *High boots were the vogue for women last year.* 去年婦女流行穿高統靴。| *There was a vogue for painting stripes on your car.* 曾流行過在汽車上漆條紋。**2 in vogue** fashionable 時髦; 正在流行: *Long hair for men is no longer in vogue.* 男子留長髮不再流行了。

[RELATED PHRASE 相關詞組 **out of vogue**]

★★voice /vɔɪs; vɔɪs/ *n* **1** [C] the sound you hear when someone speaks 說話聲; 嗓音: *We could hear the children's voices in the garden.* 我們可以聽到花園裡孩子們的聲音。| *He spoke in a very loud voice.* 他高聲講話。**2** [C;U] an opinion 意見; 看法: *The Government should listen to the voice of the people.* 政府應該聽取人民的意見。**3** [C] a person or newspaper that expresses the opinions of a group 代言人; 喉舌: *He became the recognized voice of the West Indian community in Britain.* 他成了英國西印度羣島人士社區公認的代言人。**4** [C;U] in grammar, the system for choosing an active or PASSIVE verb form depending on whether the subject of the sentence does something (**active voice**) or has something happen to it (**passive voice**)〔動詞的〕語態〔包括主動語態和被動語態〕**5** give voice to something to express an idea 發表意見 **6** have a voice in something to be able to say what you think about something and influence what happens 能夠說出對某事的看法並影響發生的事: *Parents feel that they should have a voice in the school rules.* 家長們認為他們對校規應該有發言權。**7 in good voice** singing well 唱得好 **8 keep your voice down** to speak more quietly 壓低聲音說 **9 -voiced** having a voice of the stated kind 有某種聲音的: *loud-voiced* 大聲的

> ■ USAGE 用法: Notice how the preposition **in** is used in sentences such as ☆注意介詞 **in** 在如下句子中的用法: *She spoke in a soft/angry voice.* 她柔聲〔怒聲〕說話。| *He replied in a loud/gentle voice.* 他大聲〔輕聲〕回答。| *Does he always talk in that high-pitched voice?* 他老是那樣尖聲說話嗎?

voice² *v* **voiced**, **voicing** [T] to express something in words, especially forcefully〔用言詞, 尤指有力地〕表達: *The councillor voiced the feeling of the meeting when he de-*

manded action to improve the water supply. 這位議員要求採取行動改善供水問題, 這表達了會議的精神。

void¹ /vɔɪd; vɔɪd/ *adj* **1** [never before a noun 不能用於名詞前] *fml* empty〖正式〗空的; 空無所有的: *That part of the town is completely void of interest for visitors.* 遊客對城鎮的那個地段完全不感興趣。**2** *law* having no legal force (used of official agreements)〖律〗無效的〔指正式協議〕: *A contract signed by a child is void.* 由兒童簽署的協議是無效的。

void² *n* [sing] **1** an empty space, especially the space around our world and beyond the stars 空間;〔尤指〕太空: *A ball of fire seemed to fall out of the void, disappearing before it reached the earth.* 一個火球似乎從天外飛降而來, 在到達地面前悄然消失了。**2** a feeling of something lacking in your life 空虛感: *The child's death left a painful void in his parents' lives.* 孩子的死給父母的生活留下了痛苦的空虛感。

vol /vɑl; vɒl/ *n* a written abbreviation for〖縮〗= VOLUME²

vol·a·tile /ˈvɑlətl; ˈvɒlətaɪl/ *adj* **1** likely to change quickly and unexpectedly 易變的; 變化無常的: *a volatile situation* 變化無常的局勢 **2** *tech* easily changing into a gas (used of a liquid or substance)〖術語〗易揮發的, 易散發的〔指液體或物質〕 **–volatility** /ˌvɑləˈtɪlə-tɪ; ˌvɒləˈtɪlɪtɪ/ *n* [U]

vol·au·vent /ˌvoˌloˈvɑ̃; ˌvɒl əʊ ˈvɒn/ *n* a small very light pastry case filled with something such as meat or chicken〔以肉或雞等為餡的〕酥皮餡餅

vol·ca·no /vɑlˈkeno; vɒlˈkeɪnəʊ/ *n* **volcanoes** or **volcanos** a mountain with a large opening called a CRATER at the top through which melting rock called LAVA, steam, and gases escape from time to time with explosive force from inside the earth 火山: *An active volcano may explode at any time.* 活火山隨時都可能爆發。| *an extinct volcano* 死火山 **–volcanic** /-ˈkænɪk; -ˈkæn-ɪk/ *adj*: *volcanic rocks* 火山岩 | *volcanic activity* 火山活動

vole /vol; vəʊl/ *n* a small short-tailed animal of the rat and mouse family〔短尾的〕田鼠

vo·li·tion /voˈlɪʃən; vəˈlɪʃən/ *n fml* [U] **of your own volition** of your own free choice in choosing a course of action〖正式〗出於自己的選擇; 自願: *I didn't ask him to go. He went of his own volition.* 我沒叫他去, 他是自願去的。

vol·ley /ˈvɑlɪ; ˈvɒlɪ/ *n* **1** a lot of shots fired at the same time〔槍砲等的〕羣射, 齊發: *A volley of shots was heard.* 聽到一陣齊發的槍聲。**2** continuous shouting by someone in a quarrel or attack〔吵架或攻擊時的〕連續叫喊: *a volley of abuse* 一陣咒罵 **3** in tennis, a shot in which a player hits a ball which has not touched the ground first〔網球中球落地

前的)截擊

vol·ley·ball /ˈvɑlɪˌbɔl; ˈvɒlibɔːl/ n [U] a game in which a large ball is struck by hand across a net without being allowed to touch the ground 排球(運動)

volt /volt; vəʊlt/ n a standard measure of the force of electrical current along wires 〔電壓單位〕伏(特)

volt·age /ˈvoltɪdʒ; ˈvəʊltɪdʒ/ n [C;U] electrical force measured in volts 電壓; 伏特數

volte-face /ˌvalt.fas; ˌvɒltˈfɑːs/ n [sing] fml a change to a completely opposite opinion or course of action 〔正式〕〔意見、行動的〕完全改變, 大轉變

vol·u·ble /ˈvaljəbl; ˈvɒljʊbəl/ adj talking with a great flow of words (a word often used to express disapproval) 〔説話〕滔滔不絕的, 流利的〔常含貶義〕

✲vol·ume /ˈvaljəm; ˈvɒljuːm/ n 1 [U] loudness of sound 音量; 響度: The television seems a bit loud. Could you turn the volume down? 電視聲音太響了, 減少一點音量好嗎? 2 [U] size or quantity thought of as measurement of the space filled by something 體積; 容積; 容量: The volume of this container is 100,000 cubic metres. 這個容器的容積是十萬立方米。 3 [C] a book, especially one of a set of the same kind 書籍; 〔尤指一套書中的〕卷, 冊: We have a set of Dicken's works in 24 volumes. 我們有一套二十四卷的狄更斯著作集。 4 [C;U] the amount of something 〔某物的〕量: The volume of passengers on the railways is increasing again. 鐵路的客運量又在日益增加。

vol·u·mi·nous /vəˈlumənəs; vəˈluːmɪnəs/ adj 1 very loose and full and made using a lot of cloth (used of clothes) 寬鬆的, 肥大的〔指衣服〕: a voluminous skirt 寬鬆的裙子 2 containing a lot or able to hold a lot 容量大的; 體積大的: a voluminous shopping bag 容量很大的購物袋 | a voluminous report 冗長的報告

✲vol·un·ta·ry /ˈvalənˌtɛri; ˈvɒləntəri/ adj 1 done of your free choice and not because you are forced 自願的; 自己選擇的: He made a voluntary statement to the police. 他自願向警方作供。 2 done unpaid 無償的: She does voluntary work with old people. 她和老人一起做志願工作。 –**voluntarily** /ˈvalənˌtɛrəli; ˈvɒləntərɪli/ adv: He made the promise quite voluntarily. I didn't force him to. 他完全自願地作出了承諾, 我並沒強迫他。

vol·un·teer¹ /ˌvalənˈtɪr; ˌvɒlənˈtɪə/ n 1 a person who offers to do something 自願〔做某事〕者 2 a person who is willing to do something unpaid 願意無償做某事者; 志願者: This work costs us nothing. It's all done by volunteers. 這項工作我們沒花分文, 全是由志願者做的。

volunteer² v 1 [I;T] to offer to do something 自願做〔某事〕: He volunteered to help me move. 他主動提出幫我搬家。 | He volun-

teered me **for guard duty!** 他自作主張地分配我去擔任守衛的任務!

□ USEFUL PATTERNS 有用句型
to volunteer for something; to volunteer someone for something; to volunteer to do something

2 [I] to offer to join the armed forces of your own free will 自願參軍 3 [T] to tell someone something without being asked 把〔某事〕主動告訴〔某人〕: She volunteered the information. 她主動透露消息給我知道。

vo·lup·tu·ous /vəˈlʌptʃuəs; vəˈlʌptʃuəs/ adj suggesting or expressing sexual pleasure (used especially of women) 性感的, 勾起情慾的〔尤指女子〕: The dancer's movements were slow and voluptuous. 舞者的動作緩慢而又具挑逗性。 | She had a large voluptuous mouth. 她有一張性感的大嘴。

vom·it¹ /ˈvamɪt; ˈvɒmɪt/ v [I;T] to throw up food and drink from your stomach through your mouth (使)嘔吐; 吐: The smell made me want to vomit. 這氣味使我想吐。

vomit² n [U] food and drink that has come back up from your stomach and out of your mouth 嘔吐物

voo·doo /ˈvudu; ˈvuːduː/ n (also 又作 **Voodoo**) [U] a set of magical beliefs and practices, used as a form of religion in the West Indies 〔流行於西印度羣島的〕伏都教, 巫術

vo·ra·cious /voˈreʃəs; vəˈreɪʃəs/ adj fml 〔正式〕1 eating or desiring large quantities of food 貪吃的; 食量大的 2 very eager for something and always wanting more 貪婪的; 飢渴的; 渴求的: She's a voracious reader. 她是個如飢似渴的讀者。

vor·tex /ˈvorteks; ˈvɔːteks/ n **vortexes** or **vortices** /-təˌsiz; -tɪˌsiːz/ a mass of water or air turning around a hollow central part which sucks things in; you see a vortex when water leaves a bath 旋渦; 旋風

✲vote¹ /vot; vəʊt/ v **voted, voting** 1 [I;T; + (that)] to express your choice officially from among the possibilities offered, usually by marking a piece of paper, or by raising your hand at a meeting 投票; 〔投票或舉手等〕表決; 發表意見: You're only 16. You're too young to vote. 你才16歲, 還沒到投票的年齡。 | Did you vote **for** Neil Kinnock at the last election? 在上次選舉中你是否投了內爾·基諾克的票? | The railway workers have voted to go back to work on Monday. 鐵路工人已投票贊成星期一恢復工作。 | The sign said "Vote Labour". 標語牌上寫着"投工黨的票"。 | The Liberal Democrats voted **against** closing more railway lines. 自由民主黨人投票反對關閉更多的鐵路線。 | Parliament is to vote **on** dog licences again. 議會將就養狗證的問題再次投票表決。 | They voted that the meeting be adjourned. 他們建議會議

暫停。

2 [T] to agree to provide something as the result of a vote 投票通過提供〔某物〕: *Parliament has voted the town a large sum of money for a new road.* 議會投票通過撥一大筆款項給該鎮修建新道路。**3** [T] *infml* to agree as the general opinion〔非正式〕一致認為: *The party was voted a great success.* 大家一致認為這次聚會非常成功。

***vote**² *n* **1** [C] a process of making a choice or decision by allowing people to give their opinion and then seeing which choice is most popular 投票; 表決: *The question will be settled by a vote.* 這個問題將由投票來解決。**2 take a vote on something, put something to the vote, put something to a vote** to vote on something 就某事投票表決 **3** [C] an official expression of one person's opinion in an election〔選舉中的〕票, 選票: *There were 15 votes in favour of my suggestion, and 23 against.* 我的提議得到了十五票贊成，二十三票反對。| *He will certainly not get my vote at the next election.* 下次選舉他肯定得不到我的選票。| *The total number of votes cast was 38.* 總投票數是三十八票。| *James Smith got 14,000 votes.* 詹姆士·史密斯得到了一萬四千票。**4** [sing] the total number of votes by a particular set of people〔特定人群的〕投票總數: *In elections in New York, the Irish vote is very important.* 在紐約的選舉中，愛爾蘭人的選票十分重要。**5 the vote: a** the total number of votes in an election〔選舉中的〕投票總數: *The Greens won over 10% of the vote.* 格林一家贏得了超過十分一的選票。**b** the right to vote in political elections〔政治選舉中的〕選舉權, 投票權: *In Britain, people get the vote at the age of 18.* 英國人十八歲就有選舉權。**6 vote of thanks** a public expression of thanks 公開致謝: *Mrs Jones proposed a vote of thanks to Dr Brown for his interesting talk.* 瓊斯太太提議大家鼓掌感謝布朗博士作了有趣的演講。

vot·er /'vəʊtə; 'votɚ/ *n* a person who votes 選舉人; 投票人

vouch /vaʊtʃ; vautʃ/ *v* **vouch for: a** to say that you know from your personal experience that someone or something is dependable 為〔某人或某事〕作證: *I've read this report carefully and I can vouch for its accuracy.* 我仔細讀過這份報告，我可以保證它的精確性。**b** to take responsibility for someone's future good behaviour 為〔某人的未來行為〕擔保: *I'll vouch for my son's future behaviour, officer.* 我會擔保我兒子以後規規矩矩的，長官。

vouch·er /'vaʊtʃə; 'vautʃɚ/ *n* a ticket that is used instead of money for a particular purpose〔可代替金錢用於某一用途的〕票券: *a travel voucher* 旅行憑單 | *Some firms give their workers luncheon vouchers, which they can use to buy a meal.* 有些公司發給職工午餐券，用來購買飯菜。

vow¹ /vaʊ; vau/ *n fml* a solemn promise〖正式〗誓約; 誓言: *All the men took a vow of loyalty to their leader.* 士兵都宣誓效忠他們的指揮官。

vow² *v* [T; +(that)] to declare or swear solemnly that you will do something 發誓要做〔某事〕: *When young Ernie was caught stealing he vowed he'd never do it again.* 少年歐尼爾偷竊時被人抓住，發誓再也不會偷東西了。

vow·el /'vaʊəl; 'vauəl/ *n* a speech sound in which you let your breath out without any stop or any closing of the air passage in your mouth 元音: *The vowels in the English alphabet are a, e, i, o, and u.* 英語的元音字母是 a, e, i, o 和 u。

voy·age /'vɔɪɪdʒ; 'vɔɪ-ɪdʒ/ *n* a long journey made by boat or ship or in space〔長途〕航海, 航空: *The voyage from England to India used to take six months.* 從英國到印度的航行過去要六個月。| *a voyage to the moon* 月球之行 –see 見 TRAVEL² (USAGE 用法)

vs. /vɜːsəs; 'vɜːsəs/ see 見 VERSUS

vul·gar /'vʌlɡə; 'vʌlɡɚ/ *adj* **1** very rude, low, or bad-mannered and going against the accepted standards of polite society 粗魯的; 粗野的; 粗俗的: *Putting food into your mouth with a knife is considered vulgar in Britain.* 用刀把食物送進嘴裡在英國被認為是粗魯的。| *vulgar language* 粗話 **2** showing a lack of fine feeling or good judgment in the choice of what is beautiful〔審美眼光〕庸俗的, 低級的: *The house was full of costly, but very vulgar furniture.* 這房子裡放滿了昂貴卻又俗氣的家具。–**vulgarly** *adv*

vul·gar·i·ty /vʌl'ɡærəti; vʌl'ɡærl̩ti/ *n* **vulgarities 1** [U] the quality of being vulgar 粗俗; 粗野; 庸俗 **2** [C] an example of vulgar speech or action 粗俗語; 庸俗行為

***vul·ne·ra·ble** /'vʌlnərəbl; 'vʌlnərəbl/ *adj* easily hurt in body or mind〔身心〕易受傷害的; 脆弱的: *We're in a vulnerable position here, with the enemy on the hill above us.* 敵人居高臨下盤踞山上，我們在這裡處於易受攻擊的位置。| *She looked so young and vulnerable.* 她看上去十分年輕而又脆弱。| *Your arguments are vulnerable to criticism.* 你的論點易受批評。–**vulnerability** /ˌvʌlnərə'bɪlɪti; ˌvʌlnərə'bɪl̩ti/ *n* [U]

vul·ture /'vʌltʃə; 'vʌltʃɚ/ *n* a large ugly tropical bird which feeds on dead animals 禿鷲

vy·ing /'vaɪɪŋ; 'vaɪ-ɪŋ/ the present participle of VIE ☆ VIE 的現在分詞

W, w

W, w /ˈdʌblju; ˈdʌbəljuː/ *W's, w's* or *Ws, ws* the 23rd letter of the English alphabet 英語的第二十三個字母

W 1 a written abbreviation for 〖縮〗= WEST **2** a written abbreviation for 〖縮〗= WATT (S)

wad /wɑd; wɒd/ *n* **1** a thick soft mass of material 柔軟的填塞物: *Put wads of cotton wool in your ears to keep out the noise.* 用棉花球塞着耳朵以阻擋噪音。 **2** a thick collection of things such as pieces of paper 〔紙等的〕一疊: *a wad* **of** *bank notes* 一疊鈔票

wad·dle /ˈwɑdl; ˈwɒdl/ *v* **waddled, waddling** [I+adv/prep] to walk with short steps, moving your body from one side to the other, like a duck 〔如鴨子般〕搖搖擺擺地走: *The fat man waddled up to her.* 那個胖男人一搖一擺地向她走去。 —**waddle** *n*

wade /wed; weɪd/ *v* **waded, wading** [I] **1** to walk through water which is quite deep 涉水, 蹚水: *We had to wade across the river.* 我們必須蹚過那條河。 **2** **wade through something** *infml* to read a lot of writing which is not very interesting 〔非正式〕費力也看〔冗長乏味的文章〕: *I waded through that report last night.* 我昨夜總算是啃完了那份報告。

wa·fer /ˈwefɚ; ˈweɪfəʳ/ *n* **1** a very thin BISCUIT, eaten especially with ice cream 〔尤指與冰淇淋同吃的〕威化餅乾, 薄脆餅 **2** a thin round piece of bread used in the Christian religious ceremony of COMMUNION 〔基督教聖餐時所吃的〕聖餅

waf·fle¹ /ˈwɑfl; ˈwɒfəl/ *n* a large light cake marked with squares, common in the US 〔美國常見的〕瓦夫餅, 蛋奶烘餅

waffle² *v* **waffled, waffling** [I] *BrE infml* to talk or write in words that may sound good but do not really say anything 〔英式, 非正式〕講得聽但無意義的話; 胡扯: *Stop waffling and answer the question!* 別東拉西扯, 請回答問題! —**waffle** *n* [U]: *The teacher said my essay was just a load of waffle.* 老師說我的作文不過是廢話連篇。

waft /wɑft; wɑːft/ *v* [I+adv/prep; T+adv/prep] to move lightly (使)飄蕩, (使)漂浮: *Cooking smells wafted along the hall.* 燒菜的氣味順着走廊飄過來。

wag /wæg; wæg/ *v* **-gg-** [I;T] to shake something quickly and repeatedly from side to side 搖擺; 擺動: *Look at the dog's tail wagging — he must be pleased to see us!* 你看那狗在搖尾巴——牠一定很高興見到我們! | *He wagged his finger at me.* 他對我擺了擺手指。 —**wag** *n*

*wage¹ /wedʒ; weɪdʒ/ *n* [sing] (also 又作 **wages** [pl]) the money you are paid each week for your work, especially if you do unskilled work 〔尤指幹粗活所得的〕薪金, 工資: *a weekly wage of £128* 週薪一百二十八英鎊 | *The company's wage bill is over two million pounds a year.* 公司一年要付給雇員二百多萬英鎊的工資。 | *I can't afford to do anything until I get my wages.* 在拿到工資以前, 我沒有錢幹任何事。 —see 見 PAY² (USAGE用法)

wage² *v* **waged, waging** [T] *fml* to begin and continue a struggle of some kind 〔正式〕進行, 開展, 發動〔戰鬥〕: *The police are waging a campaign against drug-pushers in the city.* 警方正在市內開展一場打擊毒販的運動。 | *They are waging a war which they cannot win.* 他們正在發動一場無法贏得的戰爭。

wa·ger /ˈwedʒɚ; ˈweɪdʒəʳ/ *v fml* 〔正式〕 **1** [T] to risk money on the result of a future event 打賭: *I'll wager you £5 that John fails his driving test.* 我敢和你打賭五英鎊, 約翰肯定通不過他的駕駛考試。 | *He wagered £10 on an unknown horse.* 他把十英鎊的賭注押在一匹不知名的馬上。 **2** [+(that)] to be sure about something 肯定: *I'll wager he's there by now.* 我敢肯定他現在已經到那兒了。 —**wager** *n*: *How about a wager on the final of the World Cup?* 我們來賭一下世界杯的結果如何?

wag·gle /ˈwægl; ˈwægəl/ *v* **waggled, waggling** [I;T] to move frequently from side to side 搖擺: *Can you waggle your ears?* 你的耳朵會來回動嗎? —**waggle** *n*

wag·on /ˈwægən; ˈwægən/ *n* **1** (**wagon** *AmE* 〔美式〕) a strong four-wheeled vehicle, mainly for heavy loads, drawn by horses or oxen 〔由馬或牛拖拉的〕四輪運貨車: *The American pioneers crossed the continent in covered waggons.* 美國早期的拓荒者使用有篷的四輪運貨馬車橫跨了北美大陸。 **2** (also 又作 **goods waggon**) a railway goods vehicle with an open top 〔敞篷的〕鐵路貨車

waif /wef; weɪf/ *n lit* an uncared-for or homeless child 〔文〕流浪兒: *a pitiful little waif* 可憐的小流浪兒

wail /wel; weɪl/ *v* [I] to cry out with a long sad sound suggesting grief or pain 痛哭, 慟哭: *The wind wailed in the chimney all night.* 風整夜在煙囱裡呼嘯着。 | *"She's taken my apple," he wailed.* "她搶走了我的蘋果。" 他哭叫着。 | *She wailed with grief.* 她傷心地嚎啕大哭。 —**wail** *n*: *with a wail of despair* 絕望的痛哭

waist /west; weɪst/ n **1** the narrow part of your body just above your hips (HIP): 腰(部): *a slim waist* 纖細的腰身 **2** the part of a piece of clothing that goes round your waist〔衣服的〕腰身部分: *It's a nice skirt, but too big round the waist.* 這件裙子不錯，但腰身太大。

waist·coat /'west.kot; 'weɪskəʊt/ n BrE a piece of clothing with buttons and no arms that you wear on the upper part of your body, usually over a shirt and under a JACKET; it is usually worn as part of a suit〔英式〕背心 –see picture on page 210 見 210 頁彩圖

waist·line /'west.laɪn; 'weɪstlaɪn/ n **1** an imaginary line round the waist which you use to judge how fat someone is 腰圍: *No sugar for me, thanks — I'm watching my waistline.* 我不要放糖，謝謝，我正在注意控制腰圍呢。 **2** the position of the waist of a piece of clothing〔衣服的〕腰身: *Low waistlines are the fashion this year.* 今年低腰身的衣服很流行。

wait¹ /wet; weɪt/ v **1** [I] to stay without doing anything until someone comes or something happens 等待；等候: *Hurry up! We're waiting.* 快點! 我們在等你呢。| *Try not to keep her waiting.* 盡量不要讓她等。| *Our business can wait until after dinner.* 我們的事可以等吃完飯再說。| *I'm waiting for Jack.* 我在等傑克。| *We waited 20 minutes for a bus.* 我們等公共汽車等了二十分鐘。| *We're waiting to see the doctor.* 我們在等著看醫生。| *They're waiting for the children to come home.* 他們在等孩子回家。

> □ USEFUL PATTERNS 有用句型
> to wait for someone/something; to wait to do something; to wait for someone to do something

2 I can't wait = I am very eager to do or experience something 我等不及了〔要做某事了〕: *He's passed his driving test. He can't wait to tell his father.* 他通過了駕駛考試，所以急著要把此事告訴他的父親。| *"The party's tomorrow, isn't it?" "Yes. I can't wait!"* "派對在明天舉行，是嗎?" "是啊。我真等不及了!" **3** wait and see to find out soon, when it is the right time 等著瞧；你很快就會知道: *"What's for dinner?" "Wait and see."* "晚飯吃甚麼?" "你馬上就會知道的。" | *"Do you think John will be better before Christmas?" "We'll just have to wait and see."* "你覺得聖誕節前約翰的情況會好轉嗎?" "這我們得等等看了。" **4** you wait!, just you wait! a phrase used when you are warning someone about something that will happen to them or something that they will learn soon 等著瞧吧〔用於警告某人將會發生某事或他們將獲悉某事〕: *I'll get even with you — you wait!* 我不會放過你的——走

着瞧吧! | *Just you wait! You'll find he's not nearly as easy to work for as you think.* 你等着瞧吧! 你會發現他不像你想像中那麼容易侍候的。

wait about/around phr v [I] to wait a long time for someone or something you are expecting, usually without having much to do〔長時間〕等待: *We got everything ready sooner than we thought, so now we're just waiting around for the big day.* 我們所有的準備工作都比預期的提前完成，所以現在就只等着這重要的日子來臨了。

wait on sbdy phr v [T] **1** to serve someone food in a restaurant〔餐館中〕侍候〔顧客〕 **2** to attend someone as a servant 照料〔某人〕；服侍〔某人〕 **3** wait on someone hand and foot to do everything for someone, often including things they could perfectly well do for themselves 無微不至地照顧某人: *Her children expect her to wait on them hand and foot.* 她的孩子們指望她能無微不至地照顧他們。

wait up phr v [I] infml to delay going to bed〔非正式〕等候着不睡: *Don't wait up for me. I shall be home very late.* 不要等着我不睡，我要很晚才回家。

> ■ USAGE 用法: Compare 比較 **wait for** and 和 **expect**. **Waiting** is a kind of activity. If you **wait for** someone or something, you arrange your time-table or actions and perhaps stay in one place, so that you are ready ☆ Waiting 是一種活動。如果你 **wait for**〔等候〕某人或某事，你就會安排好你的日程表或行動，也可能在一個地方等，做好準備: *"Why are you standing there?" "I'm waiting for John."* "你站在那裡幹甚麼?" "我在等約翰。" **Expecting** is a state of mind. If you **expect** someone or something, you think the person will come or the event will happen, but you will probably not stay in one place or make special arrangements ☆ **expecting** 是種心理狀態。如果你 **expect**〔盼望〕某人或某事，實際上就是你認為某個人要來或某事要發生，但你不大可能在一個地方等或做出特別的安排: *I'm expecting the postman.* 我預料郵遞員會來。| *We're expecting a cold winter.* 我們預計將會有一個寒冬。

wait² n **1** [sing] a period of waiting 等待；等候: *We had a long wait for a bus.* 我們等公共汽車等了很久。 **2** lie in wait for someone to hide, waiting to attack someone 伏擊某人: *The robbers were lying in wait for him.* 那些搶劫犯埋伏着準備對他下手。

wait·er /'wetər; 'weɪtəʳ/ n a person who serves food at the tables in a restaurant〔餐廳〕服務員，侍應生

waiting list /'··· / n a list of people who

want something, such as treatment in hospital or a job 等候者名單: *She's on the waiting list* **for** *a kidney transplant.* 她已被列入等候者名單，準備接受腎臟移植。

waiting room /ˈ··/ *n* a room for people who are waiting, for example to see a doctor 等候室; 候診室; 候車室

wai·tress /ˈweɪtrɪs; ˈweɪtrɪs/ *n* a woman who serves food at the tables in a restaurant (餐廳)女服務員, 女侍應生

waive /weɪv; weɪv/ *v* **waived, waiving** [T] *fml* to use your power to decide to behave in a particular case as if a rule or a right did not exist〔正式〕宣佈放棄〔權利〕; 宣佈取消〔規則〕: *We cannot waive this rule except in case of serious illness.* 除非患上嚴重的疾病, 這條規定非執行不可。

***wake¹** /weɪk; weɪk/ *v* **woke** /wok; wəʊk/ *or* **waked, woken** /ˈwokən; ˈwəʊkən/ *or* **waked, waking 1** [I; T] to stop being asleep 睡醒, 醒來: *I usually wake at eight o'clock.* 我通常在八點鐘醒來。| *We were woken by an almighty bang.* 我們被一聲巨響驚醒了。**2** **your waking hours** the hours you spend not in bed and asleep 不睡覺的時間: *She spends all her waking hours working.* 她把睡覺以外的時間都用在工作上。

  wake up *phr v* **1** [I;T **wake** sbdy **up**] to stop being asleep 睡醒, 醒來: *I woke up at six o'clock.* 我六點鐘醒來。| *What time shall I wake you up in the morning?* 早上我應該幾點鐘叫醒你? | *They were woken up by someone knocking at the door.* 他們被敲門聲弄醒了。| *Wake up, Jimmy. It's seven o'clock!* 醒醒, 吉米! 七點鐘啦! **2** [I] to start to pay attention 開始注意: *Wake up at the back there!* 後面的人注意! | *When he had his first child, he woke up* **to** *his responsibilities a bit.* 當他有了第一個孩子後, 他開始有點意識到自己的責任了。

wake² *n* **1** a track left by a ship in water〔船開過後留下的〕航跡, 尾波, 尾流 **2 in the wake of** following as a result of 隨着…而來; 作為…的結果: *There was a great deal of hunger and disease in the wake of the war.* 戰爭之後, 饑荒和疾病緊隨而來。**3** a gathering to watch and grieve over a dead person on the night before the burial, especially in Ireland〔尤指愛爾蘭的〕喪葬前夜的守靈, 守夜

wake·ful /ˈwekfəl; ˈweɪkfəl/ *adj* not able to sleep 不能入睡的, 失眠的: *a wakeful night* 不眠之夜

wak·en /ˈwekən; ˈweɪkən/ *v* [I;T] *lit* to wake〔文〕使…醒來, 弄醒: *We were wakened by a loud bang.* 我們被一聲巨響驚醒了。

****walk¹** /wɔk; wɔːk/ *v* **1** [I;T] to move forward in a natural way by putting one foot in front of the other 走, 行走, 步行: *Do you walk to work, or do you come by bus?* 你是步行上班, 還是乘公共汽車上班? | *We walked ten miles.* 我們走了十英里。| *She likes walking.* 她喜歡步行。| *He was*

walking along the rope. 他沿着繩子往前走。- see picture on page 992 見 992 頁彩圖 **2 go walking** to walk for pleasure in the country 散步: *We went walking in the French Alps.* 我們在法國的阿爾卑斯山區散步。**3** [T] to walk along 沿着…走: *tired out after walking the streets of London all day* 在倫敦的街上走了一整天之後, 累得精疲力竭 **4 walk the dog** to take your dog for a walk 遛狗, 帶狗散步 **5 walk someone somewhere** to walk with someone to a particular place, often to protect them on their way〔通常為了保護而〕送某人到某處: *I'll walk you to the bus stop.* 我送你到公共汽車站去。**6 walk all over someone** to make someone do exactly what you want, without considering their needs and feelings〔不顧及別人的需要和感情而〕令某人做你希望他們做的事情; 欺負某人

 ■ USAGE 用法: Compare 比較 **walk, stroll, stride, march.** Walk is the usual word for moving on foot at a normal speed. If you **stroll** you walk a short distance, slowly or lazily, probably for pleasure. If you **stride** you walk with long steps and if you **march** you walk with firm regular steps, like a soldier. ☆ **walk** 常用於指以正常速度步行。**stroll** 指為了散心而進行的短距離的、緩慢而放鬆的散步。**stride** 指大步行走; **march** 指像士兵一樣堅定地齊步走。

---

walk away with sthg *phr v* [T] to obtain a prize or job very easily 輕易地獲得〔獎品或工作〕

walk in on sbdy *phr v* [T] to surprise someone by going into a room unexpectedly 突然闖入而使〔某人〕吃驚

 walk into sthg *phr v* [T] **1** to find yourself in a bad situation because you were not careful to avoid it 不小心陷入〔困境〕: *He walked right into the trap.* 他正好陷入了那個陷阱。**2** to obtain a job very easily 輕易地獲得〔工作〕

walk off with sthg *phr v* [T] *infml*〔非正式〕**1** to steal something 偷竊〔某物〕: *Someone's walked off with my bicycle.* 有人偷了我的腳踏車。**2** to win something easily 輕易地贏得〔某物〕: *She walked off with first prize.* 她輕而易舉地獲得了頭獎。

walk out *phr v* [I] **1** to leave suddenly especially because you disapprove of something〔尤指由於對某事持不同意見而〕退席, 突然離開 **2** (of a group of workers) to stop work and leave your workplace as a strong complaint about something〔工人團體〕罷工

 walk out on sbdy *phr v* [T] *infml* to leave someone suddenly, especially in a time of trouble〔非正式〕〔尤指在困難的時候〕突然離開〔某人〕: *He just walked out on his wife and family without saying a word!* 他一句話也沒説就扔下太太和家人一走了之!

walk² /wɔːk/ *n* **1** a journey on foot 步行; 散步: *Let's go for a short walk.* 我們去散散步吧。| *Shall we have a walk this afternoon?* 今天下午我們去散步好嗎? | *I think I'll just take a walk down to the village.* 我打算到村裡走走。| *The station's just a ten-minute walk from here.* 從這裡走到車站只需十分鐘。**2** a path for walking along 供步行的路徑: *There is a beautiful walk along the river.* 河邊有一條美麗的人行道。**3** the particular way of walking of one person 走路的方式: *I recognized him quite a long way off because of his walk.* 從他的走路姿勢看, 我很遠就認出他來了。

walk·ie-talk·ie /ˌwɔːkɪˈtɔːki/ *n infml* a two-way radio that can be carried, allowing you to talk as well as listen 〖非正式〗步話機, 無線電對講機

walking stick /'··· / *n* a stick that you use to support yourself when you are walking 手杖

walk·man /'wɔːkmən/ *n tdmk* (also 又作 **Walkman**) a very small machine for playing music, which has small EARPHONES and is carried around by the user 〖商標〗隨身聽, 〔可隨身攜帶使用耳筒的〕袖珍放音機

walk of life /ˌ··ˈ·/ *n* **walks of life** a position in society 社會階層; 行業, 職業

walk·out /'wɔːkˌaʊt/ *n* the action of leaving a meeting or organization as an expression of disapproval or complaint 退席; 退會

walk·o·ver /'wɔːkˌəʊvə/ *n infml* a very easy victory 〖非正式〗輕易獲得的勝利

★★**wall**¹ /wɔːl/ *n* **1** a narrow upright structure, made of stone or brick, which encloses something 牆; 圍牆: *a garden surrounded by stone walls* 一個由石牆圍起來的花園 | *the ancient city walls of Cairo* 開羅的古城牆 **2** the side of a building or a room 〔房間內的〕牆壁: *Hang that picture on the wall.* 把那幅畫掛在牆上。| *They painted the walls pink.* 他們把牆刷成了粉紅色。–see picture on page 729 見 729 頁彩圖 **3** the inner surface of something hollow 內壁, 隔層: *the walls of blood vessels* 血管壁 –**walled** *adj*: *an old walled town* 一座有城牆的古城

wall²

wall sthg ↔ **off** *phr v* [T] to separate a place with one or more walls 用牆隔開: *This part of the house is walled off because it has a dangerous floor.* 由於地板很危險, 所以房間的這一部分用牆隔開了。

wal·let /'wɔlɪt/ *n* a small flat leather case for holding cards and paper money, usually carried by a man in his pocket 〔常指男用的〕皮夾子

wal·lop /'wɔləp/ *v* [T] *infml* to hit very hard 〖非正式〗重擊: *I'll wallop you if you hit your sister again!* 你如果再打你的妹

妹, 我就揍你一頓!

wal·low /'wɔləʊ/ *v* [I] **1** to allow yourself to continue to experience an unpleasant feeling for longer than you need to 沉浸在〔某種不愉快的感情中〕: *I wish you'd stop wallowing in self-pity!* 我希望你不要再自嘆自憐了! **2** to move or roll about happily in mud or water 〔在泥或水中〕快活地打滾: *Pigs enjoy wallowing in mud.* 豬喜歡在泥中打滾。–**wallow** *n*

wall·pa·per /'wɔːlˌpeɪpə/ *n* [U] thick decorative paper to cover the walls of a room 壁紙, 牆紙 –**wallpaper** *v* [T]: *We've decided to wallpaper the bedroom.* 我們打算給臥室貼上壁紙。

wal·nut /'wɔːlnʌt/ *n* **1** [C] a nut which you can eat; it has a round rough shell 胡桃 **2** [C;U] the tree that produces these nuts, or its wood 胡桃樹

wal·rus /'wɔːlrəs/ *n* **walruses** an animal which looks like a SEAL, lives in the sea, and has two long teeth which point downwards from its face 海象

waltz¹ /wɔːls/ *n* **1** a piece of music with three beats in each bar 華爾茲舞曲: *a waltz by Strauss* 施特勞斯所作的一首華爾茲舞曲 **2** a rather slow dance for two people done in time to this music 華爾茲舞

waltz² *v* **1** [I] to dance a waltz 跳華爾茲舞 **2** [I+adv/prep] *infml* to move in a particular direction easily and confidently 〖非正式〗輕快而自信地走: *Pam waltzed up to her and gave her a kiss.* 帕姆大膽地向她走去, 吻了她一下。

wan /wɒn/ *adj lit* ill, weak, and tired in appearance 〖文〗面容憔悴的; 有倦容的: *The prisoners looked pale and wan.* 那些囚犯看上去臉色蒼白, 面容憔悴。

wand /wɒnd/ *n* a thin stick used by a person who does magic tricks 〔魔術師用的〕魔杖: *He waved his magic wand and pulled a rabbit out of the hat.* 他一揮魔杖, 便從帽子裡變出了一隻兔子。

wan·der /'wɒndə/ *v* **1** [I;T] to walk through an area without a fixed aim 漫遊; 閒逛: *The poor child was found wandering the streets.* 那個可憐的孩子被發現在馬路上徘徊。| *Tourists wandered idly through the old city.* 遊客在古城中閒逛。**2** [I] (of your thoughts) to begin to move on to other things 〔思想〕走神, 精神恍惚: *I found my attention wandering.* 我發覺自己的注意力集中不起來。–**wanderer** *n*

wan·der·lust /'wɒndəˌlʌst/ *n* [U] a strong desire to travel to places which are far away 旅遊慾

wane¹ /weɪn/ *v* **waned, waning** [I] **1** (of a feeling or condition) to become gradually smaller or less 〔感覺或情況〕逐漸變弱; 逐漸變少: *Her affection for him began to wane.* 她對他的感情開始變得冷淡起來。| *the waning power of the king* 國王日漸削弱的權

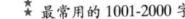
W

力 **2** (of the moon) to become smaller 〔月亮〕虧

wane² *n* **on the wane** becoming smaller, weaker, or less 變小; 變弱; 變少: *The government's popularity is on the wane.* 政府越來越不受歡迎。

wan·gle /'wæŋgl; 'wæŋgəl/ *v* **wangled, wangling** [T] *infml* to get something from someone by persuading them in a clever or dishonest way 〔非正式〕用巧計獲得〔某物〕; 哄騙: *I managed to wangle an invitation out of George.* 我略施小計便從喬治手中弄到了一張請帖。

wan·na /'wɒnə; 'wɒnə/ **1** want to 想(做)... **2** want a 想要〔某物〕

■ USAGE 用法: **Want to** and **want a** are sometimes pronounced in this way in informal speech. They may be written **wanna** in stories to show an informal way of speaking, especially in American English ☆在非正式的談話中，**want to** 和 **want a** 有時會發成這個音。它們在故事裡可以寫成 **wanna** 以表示非正式的講話方式。尤其是在美式英語中: *I don't* **wanna** *go.* 我不想去。(= I don't want to go.) | **Wanna** *drink?* 想來杯飲料嗎? (=Do you want a drink?)

want¹ /wɒnt; wɒnt/ *v* **1** [I;T] to feel a desire or wish for something 想要〔某物〕: *Do you want a drink?* 你想要杯飲料嗎? | *What do you want for your birthday?* 你想要甚麼生日禮物? | *He wants to leave soon.* 他想快些離開。| *Do you want me to help you?* 你要我幫忙嗎? | *I want that work finished by Tuesday.* 我希望那項工作能在星期二以前完成。| *She doesn't want people coming in and out all day.* 她不想讓人一天到晚進進出出。–see 見 WANNA (USAGE用法)

□ USEFUL PATTERNS 有用句型
to want something; to want to do something; to want someone to do something; to want something done

2 [I] *infml* should or ought 〔非正式〕應該，理應: *You want to leave early so as to miss the traffic.* 你應該早些出發以避開交通的高峯時間。| *You want to see a doctor about that cough.* 你應該找醫生治理一下咳嗽。

□ USEFUL PATTERN 有用句型
want to do something

3 be wanted to be searched for by the police 被警方追捕, 被通緝: *He is wanted for murder.* 他由於謀殺而被警方通緝。| *They're wanted for questioning.* 警方正尋找他們接受審問。**4** [T] *infml* to need 〔非正式〕需要: *This job wants doing this week.* 這項工作需要在這個星期做。| *The house wants paint-*

ing. 房子需要油漆一下。

□ USEFUL PATTERN 有用句型
to want doing

want for *phr v infml* 〔非正式〕**want for nothing** to have everything that you need 甚麼都不缺乏: *His children wanted for nothing except his love.* 除了他的愛, 他的孩子們甚麼都不缺。

want² *n* **1 for/from want of** because of a lack or absence of something wanted or needed 由於缺乏〔某物〕: *The plants died for want of water.* 植物因缺水而枯死。| *We watched television, for want of anything better to do.* 因為沒有更好的事情可做, 我們看電視。**2** [U] *fml* severe lack of things necessary to life 〔正式〕窮困, 匱乏: *They had lived all their lives in want.* 他們一輩子都生活在窮困之中。**3 wants** [pl] the things you want 需要的東西: *My wants are few and soon satisfied.* 我需要的東西不多, 很快便能滿足。

want·ing /'wɒntɪŋ; 'wɒntɪŋ/ *adj fml* 〔正式〕**be found wanting** to be considered not good enough 被認為不夠好: *Her new invention was tested and found wanting.* 她的新發明經測試證明不合格。

wan·ton /'wɒntən; 'wɒntən/ *adj* intentionally causing damage or harm for no reason 肆意的; 惡意的: *wanton cruelty* 任意肆虐

★★war¹ /wɔː; wɔːr/ *n* **1** [C;U] a period of armed fighting between nations or countries 戰爭(時期): *He fought in both World Wars.* 他參加過兩次世界大戰。| *Is war ever necessary?* 戰爭是必要的嗎? | *a prisoner of war* 戰俘 **2 at war** fighting 戰鬥; 作戰: *England and France were still at war with each other.* 當時英法仍在交戰。**3 go to war** to begin fighting a war 開戰: *The navy is preparing to go to war.* 海軍正在備戰。**4** [C] a struggle against something bad, or a strong competition between groups 鬥爭; 競爭: *the war against disease* 與疾病鬥爭 | *a trade war* 貿易戰 **5 have been in the wars** *infml* to have been hurt or damaged 〔非正式〕受過創傷或損壞: *Your car looks as if it's been in the wars!* 你的車似乎損壞了!

war² *v* **-rr-** [I] *lit* to fight a war 〔文〕作戰, 打仗: *a meeting between the generals of the warring forces* 交戰雙方的將軍的會晤

war·ble /'wɔːbl; 'wɔːbəl/ *v* **warbled, warbling** [I] (of birds) to sing with a clear, continuous, yet varied voice 〔鳥〕啼囀, 鳴叫, 清晰婉轉地唱 **–warble** *n*

★ward¹ /wɔːd; wɔːd/ *n* **1** a large room with beds in a hospital, usually for people all needing treatment of the same kind 病房: *the maternity ward* 產科病房 **2** a division of a city, especially for political purposes 選區, 行政區: *Which ward does she represent* *on the council?* 她在地方議會內代表哪個選區? **3** a child who is officially under the protection of a law court or a person who is not their parent 受監護人

ward² *v*

ward sthg ↔ **off** *phr v* [T] to protect yourself against something bad or unpleasant 防止，抵擋〔不好的事〕: *I've managed to ward off a cold this winter by taking these tablets.* 我吃這些藥片，以防今年冬天患上感冒。

war·den /ˈwɔːdn; ˈwɔːdn/ *n* **1** a person who looks after a place and the people in it 看守人；管理員: *the warden of an old people's home* 養老院管理員 **2** an official who helps to see that certain laws are obeyed〔監督執行某些法規的〕監察員: *a traffic warden* 交通值勤員 **3** *AmE* the head of a prison〔美式〕監獄長

ward·er /ˈwɔːdə; ˈwɔːdəʳ/ *n* a prison guard 監獄看守人，獄警

war·drobe /ˈwɔːdrob; ˈwɔːdrəub/ *n* **1** a cupboard in which you hang up clothes 衣櫃 **2** a collection of clothes belonging to one person〔個人的〕全部服裝: *She bought a new summer wardrobe.* 她買了新的夏裝。

ware·house /ˈwɛəhaus; ˈweəhaus/ *n* **warehouses** /-ˌhauzɪz; -hauzɪz/ a large building for storing things, especially things that are going to be sold〔尤指儲存待售貨品的〕倉庫

wares /wɛəz; weəz/ *n* [pl] *lit* articles for sale in the street or a market〔文〕〔馬路或市場上出售的〕小貨品: *The baker travelled round the town selling his wares.* 麵包師在城裡兜售他的麵包。

war·fare /ˈwɔːfɛə; ˈwɔːfeəʳ/ *n* [U] military activity against an enemy 戰爭；戰鬥: *chemical warfare* 化學戰

war·head /ˈwɔːhed; ˈwɔːhed/ *n* the explosive front end of a bomb or MISSILE〔炸彈或導彈的〕彈頭

war·i·ly /ˈwɛərəli; ˈweəlɪli/ *adv* in a very careful way 小心翼翼地 **—wariness** *n* [U]

war·like /ˈwɔːlaɪk; ˈwɔːlaɪk/ *adj* liking war or skilled in war 好戰的；善戰的: *a warlike nation* 好戰的國家

☆**warm¹** /wɔːm; wɔːm/ *adj* **1** having or producing heat which is pleasant, but not strong enough to be hot 暖熱的；溫熱的: *warm milk* 溫牛奶 | *a warm fire* 暖融融的爐火 | *a warm sunny day* 陽光明媚的溫暖的日子 **2** able to keep in the heat and protect you from the cold 保暖的: *warm clothes* 保暖衣服 **3** showing very friendly feelings 熱情的；熱烈的: *warm support for the local team* 對於本地球隊的熱情支持 | *warm friendship* 熱烈的友誼 | *a warm welcome* 熱烈的歡迎 **4** giving a pleasant feeling of cheerfulness or comfort 令人愉快的；令人舒適的: *warm colours* 暖色 | *a warm voice* 親切的聲音 **—warmly** *adv*: *They greeted each other warmly.* 他們熱情地互相打招呼。

warm² *v* [T] to make something hotter 加熱；使暖和: *They warmed their hands over the fire.* 他們把手放在爐火上取暖。

warm to sbdy/sthg *phr v* [T] *infml* to begin to like someone or become more interested in something〔非正式〕開始喜歡〔某人〕；對〔某物〕更加感興趣: *The students immediately warmed to their new teacher.* 學生立刻對他們的新老師產生了好感。 | *The more he spoke, the more he warmed to his subject.* 這話題他越說越起勁。

warm up *phr v* **1** [I;T **warm** sthg ↔ **up**] to make or become hotter 使變得更熱: *The room soon warmed up.* 房間很快便暖和起來了。 | *You'll have to warm the engine up a bit first.* 你首先要把引擎預熱一下。 **2** [T **warm** sthg ↔ **up**] to reheat cooked food 給〔熟食〕加熱: *We can warm up the leftovers for supper.* 我們可以把剩菜熱一下作晚餐。 **3** [I] to get ready for a performance or event by practising just before it starts 做準備活動；熱身: *The singers are already warming up for the concert.* 歌手們已在為音樂會熱身。

warm³ *n* **the warm** a warm place, state, or condition 溫暖的地方；溫暖的狀態: *Come into the warm, out of the cold.* 別站在冷風裡，到這暖和的地方來。

warm-blood·ed /ˌ· ˈ·· ◂/ *adj tech* having a body temperature that remains fairly high whether the temperature of the surroundings is high or low〔術語〕溫血的

warm-heart·ed /ˌ· ˈ··· ◂/ *adj* kind and friendly towards other people 熱心的，熱情的

war·mon·ger /ˈwɔːmʌŋgə; ˈwɔːˌmʌŋgəʳ/ *n* a person who encourages people to prepare for or start a war (a word used to express disapproval) 戰爭販子〔含貶義〕

warmth /wɔːmθ; wɔːmθ/ *n* [U] **1** the state or quality of making someone feel warm 溫暖: *the warmth of the fire* 爐火的溫暖 | *His light jacket provided little warmth.* 他那件單薄的茄克衫不保暖。 **2** kind, friendly, and generous behaviour 熱情；熱烈: *She was loved for her warmth and humour.* 她由於熱情幽默而備受喜愛。

warm-up /ˈ· ·/ *n* a period of gentle exercising in preparation for a sports event〔體育運動的〕熱身，準備: *After a 15-minute warm-up, the game began.* 在十五分鐘的熱身準備後，比賽開始了。

☆**warn** /wɔːn; wɔːn/ *v* **1** [I;T+(that)] to tell someone of a possible future problem or danger so they can try to prevent it or avoid it 告誡；提醒: *The morning paper warned of serious delays at the airport.* 晨報提醒大家注意機場的嚴重誤點。 | *He warned his students that they would have to work very hard to pass.* 他告誡學生必須非常努力才能通過考試。 | *I warn you it's going to be very cold.* 我提醒你天氣會變得很冷的。 | *Her boss had warned her about difficult customers.* 她的老闆已提醒過她有些顧客很

難應付。

□USEFUL PATTERNS 有用句型
to warn of something; to warn someone
of something; to warn that...; to warn
someone that...

2 [T] to advise someone not to do something because of a possible problem or
danger in the future 警告〔某人不要做某事〕:
*I warned her not to go near the dog, but she
ignored me.* 我警告過她不要走近那條狗，但她
不聽我的話。

＊warn·ing /ˈwɔːnɪŋ; ˈwɔːnɪŋ/ *n* [C;U] something which tells someone of a possible
problem or danger 警告; 提醒: *The enemy
attacked without warning.* 敵人不宣而戰。|
*The health department have issued warnings
about the disease.* 衛生部已就該種疾病發出
了警告。| *Let this experience be a warning
to you.* 就讓此次經歷成為你的一次教訓吧。

warp¹ /wɔːp; wɔːp/ *v* **1** [I;T] to make or become bent and damaged, often because of
heat or water〔常因熱或水分而〕彎曲; 使...歪
曲: *This wood warps easily in damp
conditions.* 這木料受潮就很容易變形。| *The
record was warped from the sun.* 唱片由於受
到日光照射而變形了。**2** [T] to strongly influence someone or something in a bad way
給〔某人或某物〕施加不良影響; 使有偏見: *Her
attitude to men was warped by several bad
experiences.* 她因為有過幾次不幸的經歷而對
男人產生了偏見。**—warped** *adj: the warped
mind of a killer* 殺手的變態心理

warp² *n* a twist or fault 扭曲; 缺陷

war·path /ˈwɔːpæθ; ˈwɔːpɑːθ/ *n* **on the
warpath** *infml* angry and looking for someone to fight or punish〔非正式〕怒沖沖準備
爭吵或打架

war·rant¹ /ˈwɒrənt; ˈwɒrənt/ *n* an official order signed by a judge which allows the
police to do something such as search
someone's house 搜查令; 逮捕令: *The
magistrate issued a warrant for his arrest.* 地
方治安官發出了對他的逮捕令。

warrant² *v* [T] *fml* to make something
seem right or reasonable〔正式〕使〔某事物〕
有正當理由: *The tiny crowd didn't warrant
such a huge police presence.* 沒有必要出動這
麼多警察來對付這一小羣人。

war·ran·ty /ˈwɒrənti; ˈwɒrənti/ *n* under
warranty covered by a GUARANTEE 受到
保障; 在保修期內: *We'll repair your car without charging because it's still under warranty.* 我們將免費修理你的汽車，因為它仍在
保修期內。

war·ren /ˈwɒrɪn; ˈwɒrən/ *n* **1** a system of
underground passages in which a number
of rabbits live 兔子的地下洞穴，野兔羣居地 **2**
a place in which too many people live, or
in which you can get lost easily 擁擠的地區;
容易迷路的地方: *a warren of narrow old*

streets 狹窄擁塞的老街區

war·ri·or /ˈwɔːriə; ˈwɒriəʳ/ *n lit* a soldier or
experienced fighter〔文〕戰士, 勇士, 武士: *a
noble warrior* 優秀的戰士

war·ship /ˈwɔːʃɪp; ˈwɔːˌʃɪp/ *n* a naval ship
with guns used for war 軍艦, 戰艦

wart /wɔːt; wɔːt/ *n* **1** a small hard swelling
on the skin of your face or hands〔臉或手
上的〕疣, 瘊子, 肉贅 **2 warts and all** not failing to mention the bad parts 不隱瞞缺點

war·time /ˈwɔːtaɪm; ˈwɔːtaɪm/ *n* [U] a
period of time during which there is a war
戰時

war·y /ˈwɛrɪ; ˈwɛəri/ *adj* **warier, wariest**
careful about something because it is new
or could cause problems 謹慎的; 小心翼翼
的: *The staff are wary of the new proposals.*
職員對於新的建議都持審慎態度。

was /wəz; wəz; *strong* wɒz; wɒz/ the
past tense of BE, 1st and 3rd person singular ☆ BE 的第一和第三人稱單數過去式: *He
was angry.* 他很生氣。| *I was at home.* 我在
家。

＊wash¹ /wɒʃ; wɒʃ/ *v* **1** [T] to clean something
with water and soap〔用水和肥皂〕洗, 洗滌:
This shirt needs washing. 這件襯衫需要洗一
洗。| *He washed his hands.* 他洗了下手。|
*Can you wash those marks off the chair,
please?* 請你把椅子上的那些污跡洗掉好嗎? **2**
[I] (also 又作 **wash up** *AmE*〔美式〕) to
clean yourself or a part of your body with
water and soap 洗臉; 洗手; 洗澡: *Jack
washed and went to bed.* 傑克梳洗了一下便
睡覺了。**3** [I] to be able to be cleaned with
soap and water without being damaged 耐
洗: *These clothes only wash in cold water.* 這
些衣服只可用冷水洗。**4** [I+adv/prep] *lit* to
flow over or against something〔文〕流過;
拍打; 沖刷: *The waves washed against the
shore.* 浪濤拍打着海岸。**5** [T+adv/prep] to
be carried by water (被水)沖走, 沖掉: *The
waves washed him off the rocks into the sea.*
海浪把他從岩石上捲入海中。**6 it won't wash**
= I don't believe it 我不相信: *It's a good
story, John, but it just won't wash with me.*
這故事不錯, 約翰, 但我就是不信。**7 wash
your hands of** *infml* to refuse to be responsible for〔非正式〕不願干管: *I wash my hands
of you and all your wild ideas!* 我再也不管你
和你的那些荒唐的念頭了!

wash sthg ↔ away *phr v* [T] to carry
something away with the force of moving
water 沖走〔某物〕: *farm animals washed
away by the floods* 被洪水沖走的農場牲口

wash sthg ↔ down *phr v* [T] **1** to clean
something large with a lot of water 用水沖
洗〔大的物體〕: *The walls need to be washed
down.* 牆壁需要用水沖洗一下。**2** to drink
something while eating or as soon as you
have finished eating 邊吃東西邊喝飲料;〔用
飲料〕吞服〔食物〕: *We washed our hamburgers down with some beer.* 我們一邊喝着

W

啤酒, 一邊吃着漢堡包。

wash out phr v **1** [I;T **wash** sthg ↔ **out**] to remove or be removed by washing (被)洗掉: *Did she manage to wash that dirty mark out of her coat?* 她有辦法把外衣上的污跡洗掉嗎? | *Do you think these ink spots will wash out?* 你覺得這些墨跡能洗掉嗎? **2 be washed out** to be prevented because of rain〔由於下雨而〕取消: *The football match was washed out.* 足球賽由於大雨而取消了。

wash up phr v infml〖非正式〗**1** [I] BrE to wash the dishes, knives, forks, etc., after a meal〖英式〗〔飯後〕洗餐具: *Who's going to wash up tonight, then?* 那麼今晚誰來洗碗呢? **2** [T **wash** sbdy/sthg **up**] (of waves) to bring someone or something onto land〔浪濤〕把〔某人或某物〕沖上陸地: *The sea washed up the body of the drowned sailor.* 海浪把淹死的水手的屍體沖到了岸邊。

wash² n **1 have a wash** to wash yourself, especially your hands and face 洗手; 洗臉: *She had a quick wash.* 她很快洗了一下手。**2 give someone/something a wash** to wash someone or something 替某人洗澡; 清洗某物: *Give the car a good wash.* 把車好好洗一下。**3 in the wash** being washed 正在洗: *I'm afraid all your shirts are in the wash.* 恐怕你的襯衫正在洗。

wash·a·ble /ˈwɒʃəbl; ˈwɒʃəbəl/ adj able to be washed without damage 可洗的; 耐洗的: *Is this cushion cover washable?* 這墊子套能洗嗎?

wash·ba·sin /ˈwɒʃˌbesn̩; ˈwɒʃˌbeɪsən/ n (**washbowl** /-ˌbol; -ˌboʊl/ AmE 〖美式〗) a large bowl fixed to the wall for washing your hands and face; it is usually found in a bathroom〔常指浴室間裡的〕洗臉盆

washed-out /ˌ·ˈ·◂/ adj **1** extremely tired 極為疲乏的: *She felt completely washed-out after working all night.* 她工作了一夜, 感到疲憊不堪。**2** very pale in colour 褪了色的: *washed-out old curtains* 褪了色的舊窗簾

wash·er /ˈwɒʃə; ˈwɒʃər/ n a ring of metal, rubber, or plastic between two pipes, which makes a better, tighter joint 墊圈〔金屬、塑料或橡膠做的扁環〕

wash·ing /ˈwɒʃɪŋ; ˈwɒʃɪŋ/ n [U] clothes or things like sheets which need to be washed, or are being washed or dried 待洗〔正在洗; 洗好〕的衣物: *I'll just hang the washing out to dry.* 我這就去把洗好的衣服掛出去晾乾。| *a pile of dirty washing* 一堆要洗的髒衣服

washing ma·chine /ˈ···,·/ n a machine for washing clothes 洗衣機

washing-up /ˌ···ˈ·/ n [U] the activity of washing the dirty plates, forks, knives, etc., that have been used to prepare and eat a meal 洗碗碟: *It's your turn to do the washing-up.* 輪到你來洗碗碟了。| *I hate washing-up.* 我討厭洗碗碟。| *a bottle of washing-up liquid* 一瓶餐具洗滌劑

wash·out /ˈwɒʃˌaʊt; ˈwɒʃ-aʊt/ n infml a failure〖非正式〗失敗: *His plan was a complete washout.* 他的計劃徹底失敗。

wash·room /ˈwɒʃˌrum; ˈwɒʃrʊm/ n AmE euph a room containing a TOILET (a less direct word than TOILET)〖美式, 委婉語〗盥洗室, 廁所〔TOILET 的委婉用詞〕

was·n't /ˈwɒznt; ˈwɒzənt/ short for 〖縮〗= "was not": *I wasn't at school yesterday.* 昨天我沒有上學。

wasp /wɒsp; wɒsp/ n a yellow and black insect similar to the bee, which stings 黃蜂

wast·age /ˈweɪstɪdʒ; ˈweɪstɪdʒ/ n fml [sing] loss, or lack of proper use〖正式〗損耗, 浪費: *this terrible wastage of our resources* 這嚴重浪費我們的資源

***waste¹** /weɪst; weɪst/ n **1** [sing; U] a wrong or unnecessary use of something 浪費; 濫用: *These new weapons are a waste of public money.* 購買這些新式武器是浪費公帑。| *The meeting was a complete waste of time.* 那次會議完全是浪費時間。| *The staff are thinking of ways to prevent waste.* 職員正在想辦法防止浪費。**2** [U] used substances, from which the valuable parts have been removed 廢物, 廢料: *A lot of poisonous waste from the chemical works goes into the river.* 化工廠的許多有毒廢料被排放到河裡。| *Waste from the body passes out from the bowels.* 體內的廢物是從腸道排泄出去的。| *the body's waste products* 體內的廢物 **3 wastes** [pl] lit a large empty area of land 〖文〗大片荒地: *No crops will grow on these stony wastes.* 這些滿是石頭的荒地種不出莊稼。| *the Arctic wastes* 北極地區的荒地 **4 go to waste** to remain unused 被浪費掉: *It's a shame to let this food go to waste.* 讓這些食物白白浪費掉, 真可恥。

***waste²** v **wasted, wasting 1** [T] to use something wrongly or use too much of something 浪費; 濫用〔某物〕: *I've wasted a lot of money on that useless car.* 我在那輛沒用的汽車上浪費了許多錢。| *Don't waste time on unimportant details.* 別把時間浪費在無關重要的細節上。**2 waste a chance, waste an opportunity** not to use a chance to do something 浪費機會 **3 be wasted on someone** to be too good for someone to recognize such high quality〔品質太好而令某人〕不懂欣賞: *His jokes were completely wasted on his students.* 他的笑話學生聽不懂, 白白浪費了。

waste away phr v [I] to become very weak and thin because of illness or lack of food〔由於疾病或缺乏食物而〕日益消瘦

***waste³** adj [only before a noun 只用於名詞前] **1** got rid of because of being used, worthless, or damaged 廢棄的; 無用的: *waste material from nuclear power plants* 核電廠的廢料 | *waste paper* 廢紙 **2 waste land, waste ground** an area of land that is not being used or cared for 荒地: *The waste ground beside the railway was covered with*

weeds. 鐵路旁的荒地長滿了野草。

wa·sted /ˈweɪstɪd/ *adj* [only before a noun 只用於名詞前] useless and unnecessary 無用的; 沒有必要的: *a wasted journey* 沒有價值的旅行

waste·ful /ˈweɪstfəl; ˈweɪstfl/ *adj* tending to waste things 浪費的: *wasteful habits* 浪費的習慣

waste·pa·per bas·ket /ˈweɪstˌpeɪpə ˈbæskɪt; ˌweɪstˈpeɪpə ˌbɑːskɪt/ *n* (also 又作 **wastebasket** /ˈweɪstˌbæskɪt; ˈweɪstˌbɑːskɪt/ *AmE* 〖美式〗) a small container on the floor of a house or office in which you put unwanted paper 廢紙簍 –see pictures on pages 244 and 763 見 244 頁與 763 頁彩圖

⋆⋆**watch**¹ /wɒtʃ; wɒtʃ/ *v* **1** [I;T] to look at a person or object which is doing something, or at an activity or event, for a period of time, and pay attention to it 觀看; 注視: *Do you watch much television?* 你看電視看得多嗎? | *They watched the sun set.* 他們看着夕陽西下。 | *Watch how to do this.* 注意看這事情怎麼做。 | *The children watched to see what would happen.* 孩子們注視着會發生甚麼事情。 –see 見 SEE (USAGE用法) **2** [T] to look at or follow carefully and secretly 監視; 跟蹤: *The police have been watching the house for weeks.* 警方數星期來一直監視着那所房子。 | *I felt I was being watched.* 我感覺被人監視着。 **3** [T; +(that)] to take care of or pay attention to 照顧; 注意: *I'll watch the baby if you want to pop out.* 要是你想出去一下, 那我來看孩子。 | *Watch that milk doesn't boil over.* 注意不要讓牛奶煮溢。 | *You'll have to watch what you say when you talk to the general.* 你跟將軍談話時要留心自己所講的話。 **4 Watch it!** *infml* Be careful! 〖非正式〗小心!: *Hey! Watch it! There are glasses in that box.* 喂! 小心! 那隻盒子裡有玻璃杯。 **5 watch your step** a phrase used to warn someone to be careful in their behaviour: 注意自己的言行〔用於警告某人〕*You'd better watch your step, or you'll be fired!* 你最好注意一下自己的言行, 不然會被解雇的! –**watcher** *n*

watch out *phr v* [I] *infml* to be careful to avoid something unpleasant 〖非正式〗注意〔以避開某事物〕: *Watch out! There's a car coming.* 注意! 有輛車開過來了。

watch over sbdy/sthg *phr v* [T] to protect and take care of 看守, 守護〔某人、某物〕

⋆**watch**²*n* **1** a small clock worn on your wrist 錶; 手錶: *My watch has stopped.* 我的錶停了。 –see picture on page 210 見 210 頁彩圖 **2 the watch** one or more guards ordered to watch a place or a person 值班警衛: *The night watch comes on duty at six o'clock.* 值夜班的人六點鐘來上班。 **3 keep watch** to look around carefully for signs of danger, so that you can warn other people 放哨, 望風, 監視 **4 keep a close/careful watch on** to carefully give your attention to something

密切注意〔某事物〕: *The government is keeping a close watch on rising prices.* 政府正密切注意物價的上漲。

watch·dog /ˈwɒtʃˌdɒg; ˈwɒtʃˌdɒg/ *n* **1** a fierce dog kept to guard property 看門狗 **2** a person or group that tries to prevent dishonest or illegal behaviour by companies or other organizations 〔被公司或其他組織雇來防止不誠實或非法舉動的〕監察者, 監察團: *The government appointed a committee to act as a watchdog on the steel industry.* 政府委任了一個委員會作為鋼鐵業產業的監督機構。

watch·ful /ˈwɒtʃfəl; ˈwɒtʃfl/ *adj* careful to notice things 警惕的, 提防的; 注意的: *From then on, she was watchful* **for** *any sign of activity in the empty house.* 從那以後, 她便很警惕地注意着那幢空房子是否有任何活動的跡象。

watch·mak·er /ˈwɒtʃˌmeɪkə; ˈwɒtʃˌmeɪkər/ *n* a person who makes or repairs watches or clocks 鐘錶製造〔修理〕工; 鐘錶匠

watch·man /ˈwɒtʃmən; ˈwɒtʃmən/ *n* **watchmen** /-mən; -mən/ a guard of a building 〔看守建築物的〕警衛: *Call the night watchman if there is any trouble tonight.* 今晚如果有甚麼麻煩, 就打電話給值班警衛。

watch·word /ˈwɒtʃˌwɜːd; ˈwɒtʃwɜːd/ *n* a word or phrase that expresses a principle of a particular group of people 格言; 口號; 標語: *"Caring and sharing" is their watchword.* "互相關心與分享"是他們的座右銘。

⋆⋆**wa·ter**¹ /ˈwɒtə; ˈwɔːtər/ *n* **1** [U] the most common liquid on the Earth, which falls from clouds as rain and forms rivers, lakes, and seas; people and animals need water to live 水: *The prisoner was given only bread and water.* 只給那個犯人麵包和水。 | *Turn on the hot water now.* 現在把熱水龍頭擰開。 | *sea water* 海水 | *bathwater* 洗澡水 **2** [U] a large amount or area of water 水域: *He's fallen in the water.* 他掉進水裡了。 | *They ran down to the edge of the lake and dived into the water.* 他們跑到湖邊, 然後跳進水裡。 | *The flood had left most of the town under water.* 洪水把城鎮的大部分地區都淹沒了。 **3 waters** [pl] the sea around a country which is considered to belong to it 領海, 海域: *The boat was caught fishing in Norwegian waters.* 那艘小船在挪威海域捕魚時被扣。 **4 in hot water** *infml* in trouble 〖非正式〗在困境中: *We'll get into hot water if the teachers hear about this.* 如果老師聽說此事, 那我們就麻煩了。 **5 it's water under the bridge** = you should stop worrying about it because it has already finished and there's nothing you can do about it now 事情已過去, 你就不必擔心了

water²*v* **1** [T] to pour water on the soil so that plants can grow 灌溉; 澆水: *It's very dry: we must water the garden.* 天氣很乾燥, 我們必須給園子澆點水。 | *Mike watered the* *roses yesterday.* 邁克昨天給玫瑰花澆過水了。 **2** [I] (of your eyes) to become filled with tears〔眼睛〕充滿淚水: *The pain made her eyes water.* 她痛得流出了眼淚。 **3** [I] (of your mouth) to become filled with SALIVA, the liquid that helps you to eat food, usually because you have seen something that you would like to eat〔嘴〕流口水: *The sight of the cake made his mouth water.* 他看見蛋糕饞得直流口水。

water sthg ↔ **down** *phr v* [T] to weaken a liquid by adding water to it 攙水沖淡; 加水稀釋: *This beer has been watered down!* 這啤酒已經攙過水了! **2** to make a speech or report less forceful by removing any strong opinions from it 減弱〔演講或報告的〕力量: *The Minister's statement had been watered down so as not to offend anyone.* 部長的聲明被加以淡化了, 以免激怒任何人。

wa·ter·borne /ˈwɔtəˌbɔrn; ˈwɔːtəbɔːn/ *adj* carried by water 由水運送〔傳播〕的: *water-borne diseases* 由水傳播的疾病

wa·ter·col·our /ˈwɔtəˌkʌlə; ˈwɔːtəˌkʌlə/ *n* (**watercolor** *AmE*〔美式〕) **1 watercolours** [pl] coloured paints that are mixed with water and used for painting pictures 水彩顏料: *She mostly paints in watercolours.* 她大部分畫都是用水彩顏料畫的。 **2** [C] a picture painted using watercolours 水彩畫: *Have you sold any more watercolours lately?* 你最近有再售出水彩畫嗎?

wa·ter·cress /ˈwɔtəˌkrɛs; ˈwɔːtəkres/ *n* [U] a plant with leaves which taste hot, grown in water and used as food 水田芥〔水生植物, 葉辛辣, 用作食物〕

wa·ter·fall /ˈwɔtəˌfɔl; ˈwɔːtəfɔːl/ *n* water that falls straight down over rocks, often from a great height 瀑布

wa·ter·front /ˈwɔtəˌfrʌnt; ˈwɔːtəfrʌnt/ *n* [sing] a part of a town, or a piece of land, near an area of water 濱水地區: *We strolled along the waterfront.* 我們沿着海濱散步。

wa·ter·hole /ˈwɔtəˌhol; ˈwɔːtəhəul/ *n* a pool in a dry country where wild animals go to drink〔乾旱之處野生動物的飲水的〕水池, 水坑

watering can /ˈ··· ·/ *n* a container with a long SPOUT, for watering garden plants 灑水壺

wa·ter·logged /ˈwɔtəˌlɑgd; ˈwɔːtəlɒgd/ *adj* **1** full of water and so unable to float (used of boats) 灌滿水的〔指船〕 **2** completely full of water (used of land) 浸透水的〔指土地〕: *The footballers couldn't play because the ground was waterlogged.* 由於地上全是水, 球員無法踢足球。

water main /ˈ·· ·/ *n* a large underground pipe carrying a supply of water〔地下的〕自來水總管道, 主輸水管

wa·ter·mark /ˈwɔtəˌmark; ˈwɔːtəmaːk/ *n* a mark made on paper by the maker seen only when it is held up to the light〔紙張上

的〕水印(圖案)

wa·ter·mel·on /ˈwɔtəˌmɛlən; ˈwɔːtəˌmelən/ *n* [C;U] a large round fruit with green skin, juicy red flesh, and black seeds 西瓜

wa·ter·proof¹ /ˈwɔtəˈpruf; ˈwɔːtəpruːf/ *adj* which does not allow water to go through 防水的, 不透水的: *Is the tent waterproof?* 這帳篷防水嗎? **–waterproof** *v*: *The walls were water-proofed with a special material.* 牆壁上塗有特殊材料, 所以能防水。

waterproof² *n* a coat which does not let water go through 防水層

wa·ter·shed /ˈwɔtəˌʃɛd; ˈwɔːtəʃed/ *n* a time or event over which marks a very important change in a person's life or a country's history〔人生或國家歷史的〕轉折點, 重要關頭: *Leaving her first job was a watershed in her life.* 她辭去第一份工作是她一生中的轉折點。

wa·ter·side /ˈwɔtəˌsaɪd; ˈwɔːtəsaɪd/ *n* **the waterside** the edge of a river, lake, or sea 水邊; 河邊; 湖邊; 海邊

water ski /ˈ·· ·/ *v* [I] to do the sport in which you move over water on skis (SKI), pulled by a boat 滑水: *She loves to go water skiing.* 她喜歡滑水。 **–water skiing** *n* [U]: *Water skiing is becoming a popular sport.* 滑水逐漸成為一項很受歡迎的運動項目。

wa·ter·tight /ˈwɔtəˌtaɪt; ˈwɔːtətaɪt/ *adj* **1** through which no water can go 不透水的: *a watertight box* 不透水的箱子 **2** produced with great care, so there is no possibility of mistakes or unintended results 嚴密的; 無懈可擊的: *a watertight argument* 無懈可擊的論點 | *a watertight plan* 嚴密的計劃

wa·ter·way /ˈwɔtəˌwe; ˈwɔːtəweɪ/ *n* a long passage of water along which ships can travel, such as part of a river 水路; 航道: *Canals and rivers form the inland waterways of a country.* 運河與河流構成一個國家的內陸航道。

wa·ter·works /ˈwɔtəˌwɜks; ˈwɔːtəwɜːks/ *n* [pl] a building in which supplies of water for the public are cleaned 公共供水廠

wa·ter·y /ˈwɔtərɪ; ˈwɔːtəri/ *adj* **1** containing too much water 含水過多的: *watery soup* 稀湯 **2** very pale in colour 色淡的; 暗淡的: *a watery sun* 暗淡的陽光

watt /wɑt; wɒt/ *n* a measure of electrical power 瓦特〔電力的計量單位〕: *Put a 100 watt bulb in that lamp.* 在那盞燈上安裝一隻一百瓦的燈泡。

★wave¹ /wev; weɪv/ *v* **waved, waving 1** [I] to hold your arm up in the air and move your hand, for example to greet someone 揮手; 招手: *She waved excitedly.* 他激動地揮着手。 | *We waved goodbye to them.* 我們向他們揮手告別。 | *He waved frantically at us to get out of the way.* 他拼命朝我們揮手讓我們閃開。 **2** [T] to hold something in your hand and move it quickly from side to side 揮動〔某物〕: *The children waved their flags as the*

President's car passed. 總統的汽車經過時, 孩子們揮動他們的旗子。**3** [T+adv/prep] to show someone the direction they should go by signalling with your hand 對〔某人〕揮手以示方向: *The policeman waved the traffic on.* 警察指揮車輛繼續前進。| *He waved his students away impatiently.* 他不耐煩地揮手讓學生們走開。**4** [I] to move in the air, from side to side or up and down 飄動; 飄揚: *The branches waved in the wind.* 樹枝在風中擺來擺去。

wave sthg ↔ **aside** *phr v* [T] to treat an idea or suggestion as unimportant 對〔觀點或建議〕置之不理: *She waved his objections aside.* 她對他的反對置之不理。

*wave² *n* **1** the movement of your hand when waving 揮手, 招手: *The actress gave the crowd a wave.* 女演員向人羣揮了揮手。**2** a raised line of water on the surface of the sea or other area of water, caused when the water rises or falls 波浪, 波濤: *In bad weather, we get very large waves pounding on the shore.* 在惡劣的天氣下, 我們可看到巨浪衝擊着海岸。**3** an evenly curved part of your hair 〔頭髮的〕鬈曲: *natural waves in her hair* 她頭髮的天然鬈曲 **4** a sudden increase in a particular feeling or way of behaviour which can spread uncontrollably 〔情緒的〕突然波動; 〔活動的〕突發高潮: *The police are worried about the recent wave of violence.* 警方對於最近的暴力泛濫憂心忡忡。| *A wave of panic spread through the crowd.* 一陣惶恐的情緒在人羣之中蔓延。**5** a form in which some forms of ENERGY, such as light and sound, travel 〔某些能量, 如光和聲的〕波: *radio waves* 無線電波 | *sound waves* 聲波

wave band /'··/ *n* a set of sound waves of similar lengths, used especially for broadcasting by radio 〔無線電的〕波段

wave·length /'wevˌleŋθ; 'weɪvlenθ/ *n* **1** a radio signal sent out on radio waves that are a particular distance apart 波長 **2 on the same wavelength** to have similar opinions to someone, so that you understand each other well 〔與某人〕意見相近 [RELATED PHRASE 相關詞組 **on a different wavelength**]

wa·ver /'wevə; 'weɪvəʳ/ *v* [I] **1** to be unsteady or uncertain in a belief or decision 猶豫不決, 舉棋不定: *He wavered between accepting and refusing.* 他猶豫不決, 不知是接受還是拒絕。| *Her confidence in his abilities never wavered.* 他從不懷疑自己的能力。**2** to move slightly 輕快的移動; 搖晃: *The flame wavered and then went out.* 火焰閃了閃後便熄滅了。

wav·y /'wevɪ; 'weɪvɪ/ *adj* having regular curves 波形的, 波狀的: *wavy hair* 鬈髮 | *a wavy line* 波浪形線條

wax¹ /wæks; wæks/ *n* [U] **1** a solid substance made of fats or oils, which changes to a thick liquid when melted; it is often used to make candles 蠟 **2** the soft yellow substance found in your ears 耳垢

wax² *v* **1** [T] to put wax on a surface as a polish 給…打蠟: *The floor was waxed every Thursday.* 每星期四給地板打蠟。**2 wax and wane** (of the moon) to gradually increase and decrease in size or amount 〔月亮〕圓缺, 盈虧: *The moon waxes and wanes every month.* 月亮每月一次盈虧。

wax·work /'wæks,wɝk; 'wækswɜːk/ *n* **waxworks 1** a model of a famous person made in wax 蠟像 **2 waxworks** a place where you can see waxworks 蠟像館

*way¹ /we; weɪ/ *n* **1** [C] a road or path that you need to follow in order to reach a place 路, 道路: *Is this the way to the station?* 這是通往車站的路嗎? | *Could you show me the way out, please?* 請你把出路指給我看好嗎? **2** [sing] the distance that you have to travel in order to reach a place 路程; 距離: *Is it a long way to Manchester?* 去曼徹斯特的路遠嗎? | *She complained all the way home.* 她在回家的路上不停地抱怨。**3 lose your way** to become lost and not know how to find the place that you are looking for 迷路 **4 on the way** while travelling to a place 在途中: *We'll stop and have lunch on the way.* 我們會在途中停下來吃頓午飯。| *I was on my way to work.* 當時我正在上班的路上。**5** [C] a direction 方向: *Come this way.* 請這邊走。| *He was looking the other way so he didn't see me.* 他在朝另一個方向看, 所以沒有看見我。**6 the right way round, the right way up** facing in the right direction 朝着正確的方向: *Have I got this picture the right way round?* 這幅畫找掛得方向對不對? [RELATED PHRASE 相關詞組 **the wrong way round/up**] **7** [C] a manner or method of doing something 〔做事的〕方式, 方法: *There are several ways in which you can pay.* 你有幾種付款方式。| *What's the best way to clean leather furniture?* 清潔皮製家具最好的方法是甚麼? | *There must be a better way of keeping food fresh.* 肯定有更好的辦法保持食物新鮮。

□ USEFUL PATTERNS 有用句型
a way to do something; a way of doing something

8 ways [pl] small bits of behaviour that are typical of a particular person 〔某人的〕習性, 舉止: *We were very fond of him in spite of his annoying little ways.* 儘管他有些令人困擾的小動作, 我們仍很喜歡他。**9 in a way, in some ways, etc** used when you are saying that something is true partly but not completely 從某種程度上說〔用於表示某事部分正確〕: *In a way I think she's right.* 在某種程度上, 我認為她是對的。| *I agree with you in* *some ways.* 我部分同意你的觀點。 **10 in the way** in a place or position that prevents you from going somewhere 擋住去路; 礙事: *I can't get past — that suitcase is in the way.* 我過不去, 那隻箱子擋住了去路。 | *I got up to leave, but she stood in my way.* 我起身離去, 但她擋住了我的去路。 **11 out of the way: a** not in a place or position that prevents you from going somewhere 不擋路; 不礙事: *Could you move that box out of the way?* 你能把那隻箱子搬開嗎? | *Get out of my way!* 走開, 別擋我的路! **b** finished 完成; 結束: *I'll be happier once the exams are out of the way.* 考試一結束, 我就會開心點。 **12 out of someone's way** not near to a place where someone is going 不靠近某人要去的地方: *Can you give me a lift home, if it's not too far out of your way?* 如果我家離你的目的地不太遠的話, 我能搭你的車回去嗎? **13 by the way** a phrase you use when you want to talk about something that is not directly concerned with what you have just been talking about 順便説; 另外〔用於想談論與剛才所説的話無直接聯繫的事物〕: *We'll discuss this at the meeting later. By the way, did you tell Steven about the meeting?* 我們稍後在會上再討論此事。順便問一句, 你把開會的事告訴史蒂文了嗎? **14 by way of** a way of doing something 作為: *He handed me his card by way of introduction.* 他把名片遞給我, 算作是自我介紹。 **15 can't have it both ways** a phrase you use to tell someone that they have to choose between two possibilities, but they cannot have both 不能兩全其美 **16 get your own way** to do or get what you want 做到想做的事; 得到想要的東西 **17 go out of your way to do something** to make a great effort to do something 千方百計做某事: *She seemed to be going out of her way to be nice to me.* 她似乎在想盡辦法待我好。 **18 have a way with** to be able to form good relationships with a particular type of people 能與〔某類人〕和睦相處: *He has a way with children.* 他善於和孩子們相處。 **19 out of someone's way** to avoid seeing or talking to someone 避免遇見某人; 避免與某人談話 **20 under way** taking place 正在發生: *Discussions between management and unions are now under way.* 勞資雙方的討論正在進行之中。 **21 No way** No 不: *"Are you going to help Mary again?" "No way!"* "你還準備再次幫助瑪麗嗎?" "不!"

■ **USAGE** 用法: **1** We do not use **way** when we are thinking of a particular **road, path,** or **track** ☆ **way** 不用來表示特定的 **road, path** 或 **track**: *We followed a muddy* **path** *through the forest.* 我們沿着一條泥濘的小路穿過了樹林。| *We walked to the village along a narrow* **track** *instead of taking the main* **road.** 我們沿着一條窄窄的小路走到村裡, 而不是順着一條大路。

2 By the way. Although this expression seems to suggest that we are going to add unimportant information, we often use it to introduce a topic which is very important to us ☆儘管 **By the way** 似乎是在暗示我們打算談及不重要的事情, 但實際上我們常用此短語來引入一個非常重要的話題: **By the way,** *is it all right if I don't pay you the money I owe you just yet?* 順便問一句, 如果我不把欠你的錢還給你行不行?

way² *adv* far 遠: *The film was made way back in 1929.* 那部影片早在1929年就拍攝了。| *We're way behind with our work.* 我們的工作遠遠沒有跟上進度。

way·lay /ˌweˈleɪ; weɪˈleɪ/ *v* **waylaid** /-ˈled; -ˈleɪd/, **waylain** /-ˈlen; -ˈleɪn/ [T] to wait for someone and stop them going somewhere, for example because you want to talk to them 〔為了説話而〕攔截〔某人〕: *She waylaid me as I was leaving the meeting.* 當我正準備離開會場時, 她攔住了我。

way-out /ˌ··◂/ *adj infml* very modern, but strange or unusual 〔非正式〕新潮的; 新奇的: *way-out clothes* 新潮的服裝

way·side /ˈweˌsaɪd; ˈweɪsaɪd/ *n* **the wayside** the side of the road (a word no longer used in modern English) 路邊〔現代英語中不再使用〕

way·ward /ˈwewəd; ˈweɪwəd/ *adj* difficult, changeable, and not easily guided 反覆無常的; 不聽勸的; 任性的: *wayward behaviour* 反覆無常的行為 | *a wayward son* 任性的兒子

WC /ˌdʌbljuˈsi; ˌdʌbljuˈsiː/ *n* a TOILET 廁所

we /wɪ; wi; *strong* 強讀 wi; wiː/ *pron* [used as the subject of a verb 用作動詞的主語] the people who are speaking 我們: *Shall we go for a drink?* 我們去喝點飲料好嗎? | *We all enjoyed the film.* 我們都很喜歡這部影片。

weak /wik; wiːk/ *adj* **1** lacking physical strength or power 弱的, 虛弱的: *I still feel a bit weak after my illness.* 病癒以後, 我仍然覺得有些虛弱。| *a weak heart* 衰弱的心臟 | *weak eyes* 視力差的眼睛 **2** not firm or determined in character 懦弱的; 軟弱的: *The teacher's so weak that the children do what they like.* 那位老師太軟弱了, 孩子們因此為所欲為。| *a weak and indecisive leader* 軟弱而優柔寡斷的領導 **3** easily broken, defeated, or destroyed 易碎的; 易擊敗的; 易毀壞的: *The shelf's too weak to hold all those books.* 架子不夠堅固, 支撐不住那麼多書。| *a weak team* 弱隊 **4** containing too much water and lacking taste 稀薄的; 淡的: *weak soup* 稀湯 | *weak tea* 淡茶 **5** lacking skill or ability in a particular area 〔在某方面〕缺乏

技巧[能力]的: *The article is weak* **on** *facts.* 那篇文章實據不足。| *She's weak* **at** *maths.* 她的數學很差。**6** lacking the ability to persuade or force people 缺乏說服力的; 沒有力量的: *a weak argument* 不充分的論據 **7** faint (used of light or sounds) 淡的, 輕的〔指光或聲音〕 —**weakly** *adv*

weak·en /'wikən; 'wi:kən/ *v* [I;T] **1** to make or become less powerful or less physically strong (使)變弱: *She weakened as the illness got worse.* 她病情惡化, 身體越來越虛弱。| *a country weakened by war and disease* 被戰爭和疾病拖垮的國家 | *Years of carrying heavy boxes had weakened his back.* 多年來扛重箱子令他的背部變得非常衰弱。| *These disputes have weakened the government's position.* 這些紛爭削弱了政府的地位。**2** to make or become less determined (使)變得猶豫: *Nothing could weaken her resolve to become a doctor.* 任何事情都不能動搖她成為一名醫生的決心。| *Their sense of responsibility never weakened.* 他們的責任感從未減弱過。

weak·ling /'wiklɪŋ; 'wi:k-lɪŋ/ *n* a person lacking physical strength or strength of purpose 虛弱的人; 意志薄弱的人

*****weak·ness** /'wiknɪs; 'wi:knɪs/ *n* **1** [U] the state of lacking strength in your body or character 虛弱; 軟弱; 薄弱: *The symptoms are general weakness and nausea.* 症狀是全身虛弱, 有噁心的感覺。| *The parents accused the headteacher of weakness.* 家長都譴責校長過於軟弱。**2** [C] an imperfect part of something 缺陷; 弱點: *The cost of your plan is its main weakness.* 你的計劃成本高是其主要缺點。| *a structural weakness in the building* 建築物結構上的缺陷 **3** [C] a fault in someone's character〔性格上的〕弱點, 缺點: *His weakness is refusing to accept criticism.* 他的缺點就是不肯接受批評。**4** [C] a strong liking for something which is bad for you〔對於不良事物的〕嗜好, 癖好: *I've got a real weakness for chocolate.* 我特別愛吃巧克力。

weal /wil; wi:l/ *n* a red mark on the skin where you have been hit or beaten 紅腫; 傷痕; 鞭痕

*****wealth** /wɛlθ; welθ/ *n* **1** [U] the state of owning a large amount of money and possessions 富有; 富裕: *It was a decade of wealth and affluence.* 那是豐足富裕的十年。**2** [U] money and possessions 錢財; 財富: *His wealth increased year by year.* 他的財富逐年增多。**3** **a wealth of** *fml* a large number or amount of〔正式〕大量, 豐富: *a wealth of examples* 大量的例子

wealth·y /'wɛlθɪ; 'welθɪ/ *adj* **wealthier**, **wealthiest** having a lot of money or other valuable possessions 有錢的, 富裕的: *a wealthy family* 富有的家庭 | *Nigeria was comparatively wealthy in those days.* 在那個時候, 尼日利亞相對較為富裕。

wean /win; wi:n/ *v* [T] **1** to accustom a young child to eat food instead of its mother's milk 使〔小孩〕斷奶: *Most babies are weaned by the time they are one.* 大部分的嬰兒在一歲時斷奶。**2** to gradually help someone to stop doing something that is bad for them 幫助〔某人〕逐漸戒除〔壞習慣〕: *How can we wean him* **from** *his habit of getting drunk every night?* 我們如何才能讓他逐漸戒除每晚喝酒的習慣呢?

*****weap·on** /'wɛpən; 'wepən/ *n* an object used to attack people, such as a gun or bomb 武器: *nuclear weapons* 核武器

*****wear**[1] /wɛr; weər/ *v* **wore** /wɔr; wɔːr/, **worn** /wɔrn; wɔːn/ **1** [T] to have something on your body, especially as clothing 穿, 戴〔尤指衣物〕: *He's wearing a new coat.* 他穿了一件新衣服。| *Does your brother wear glasses?* 你的弟弟戴眼鏡嗎? | *She's wearing a pearl necklace.* 她戴了一條珍珠項鏈。| *It is compulsory to wear seat belts when you are driving in England.* 在英國開車必須繫上安全帶。–see 見 DRESS[1] (USAGE用法) **2** [T] to have your hair in a particular style 蓄〔髮〕: *She wore her hair tied in a ribbon.* 她用絲帶把頭髮束起來。**3** [I; T] to weaken or damage by continued use 磨損; 磨壞: *I like this shirt, but the collar has worn.* 我很喜歡這件襯衫, 但領子已經磨損了。| *a worn carpet* 磨損的地毯 [T+adv/prep] to produce by continuous use〔由於不斷使用而〕造成; 磨成: *You've worn a hole in your sock.* 你的襪子上磨出了一個洞。| *The villagers have worn a path through the fields.* 村民在田裡踩出了一條小路。**5** **wear well/badly** to last in good or bad condition 耐用; 不耐用: *This coat will wear well if you look after it properly.* 要是你愛護一點, 這件外套將很耐穿。**6** **wear thin** to become less acceptable because of being used too much〔由於使用過多而〕變得越來越難以令人接受: *I felt sorry for Jackie at first, but now all her moaning about her husband is beginning to wear a bit thin.* 起初我為傑姬感到難過, 可是現在她對丈夫的悲嘆令我逐漸有點厭煩了。

wear away *phr v* [I;T **wear** sthg ↔ **away**] to gradually disappear or make something disappear from continuous use (使)磨損, 磨掉: *Over the centuries, the wind has worn the rocks away.* 經過幾個世紀, 風已漸漸把岩石磨掉了。

wear down *phr v* **1** [I;T **wear** sthg ↔ **down**] to become, or make something become, gradually smaller or thinner (使)逐漸變小: *My shoes are badly worn down at the heels.* 我的鞋後跟磨損得很厲害。**2** [T **wear** sbdy/sthg ↔ **down**] to gradually lessen somebody's strength or strength of purpose 逐漸減弱〔某人的〕力量[決心]: *We wore down their opposition after several hours' argument.* 爭論了數小時以後, 我們終於把他們的反對意見壓了下去。

wear off *phr v* [I] (of a feeling or effect)

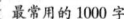

to be slowly reduced until it disappears 〔感覺或效果〕逐漸消失: *The pain is wearing off.* 疼痛漸漸消退了。

wear on *phr v* [I] to pass slowly in time 〔時間〕緩慢過去: *The day wore on.* 長日漫漫。

wear out *phr v* **1** [I;T **wear** sthg ↔ **out**] to be or become useless from use 磨壞; 穿破: *Her shoes wear out quickly when she goes walking.* 她一走路, 鞋便很快磨壞了。| *worn-out old shoes* 穿破的舊鞋 **2** [T **wear** sbdy ↔ **out**] to tire someone greatly 使〔某人〕精疲力竭: *If you don't stop working you'll wear yourself out.* 如果你不停止工作, 就會把自己弄得精疲力盡。

wear² *n* [U] **1** clothes of a particular type or for a particular purpose 〔某種〕服裝: *evening wear* 晚裝 | *footwear* 鞋 **2** (also 又作 **wear and tear**) continuous use which weakens or damages something 磨損, 損耗: *This carpet is already showing signs of wear.* 這條地毯已經有磨損的跡象了。 **3** the quality of lasting in use 耐用性: *There's still plenty of wear in these tyres.* 這些輪胎還能用很長時間。

wear·ing /ˈwɛrɪŋ; ˈwɛərɪŋ/ *adj* tiring 使人疲累的; 使人厭倦的: *It's a very wearing job.* 那是很令人厭倦的工作。

wear·i·some /ˈwɪrɪsəm; ˈwɪərisəm/ *adj* making you feel tired and annoyed 使人疲倦的; 使人厭煩的: *a wearisome task* 令人厭煩的任務

wear·y¹ /ˈwɪrɪ; ˈwɪəri/ *adj* **wearier, weariest** very tired 非常疲勞的: *You look rather weary after your long journey.* 你經過長途跋涉的旅程之後, 看上去相當疲勞。| *a weary smile* 疲憊的笑容 **–wearily** *adv* **–weariness** *n* [U]

weary² *v* **wearied, wearying** [I] to become tired of and lose interest in something 對〔某事〕感到厭倦; 對〔某事〕失去興趣: *He soon wearied of his job at the bank.* 他很快就厭倦了他在銀行的工作。

wea·sel /ˈwizl; ˈwiːzəl/ *n* a small thin furry animal which can kill other small animals 黃鼠狼

✲weath·er¹ /ˈwɛðɚ; ˈweðəʳ/ *n* [U] **1** the condition of wind, rain, sunshine, snow, etc., at a certain time or over a period of time 天氣, 氣象: *good weather* 好天氣 | *severe weather conditions* 惡劣的天氣情況 | *What will the weather be like tomorrow?* 明天的天氣如何? **2 under the weather** *infml* not very well 〔非正式〕身體不太舒服

weather² *v* **1** [T] to pass safely through difficulty 渡過〔難關〕: *The government will need to weather this crisis to win the next election.* 政府若要贏得下屆大選, 就需要渡過這場危機。 **2** [I;T] to change or be changed in shape or colour because of wind or other weather conditions (使)風化: *Rocks weather until they are worn away.* 岩石不斷風化, 直到磨損掉為止。

weather-beat·en /ˈ·· ˌ··/ *adj* brown and lined from being outdoors in bad weather (used of your face or skin) 飽經風霜的〔用於指臉或皮膚〕

weath·er·cock /ˈwɛðɚˌkɑk; ˈweðəkɒk/ *n* (also 又作 **weather vane**) a small metal object which shows the direction the wind is blowing by turning round in the wind; it is often shaped like a male chicken and fixed to the top of a building 風標, 風信雞

weather fore·cast /ˈ·· ˌ··/ *n* a description of what future weather conditions are likely to be, for example on the radio 天氣預報

weath·er·man /ˈwɛðɚˌmæn; ˈweðəmæn/ *n* **weathermen** /-mən; -mən/ a person whose job is to describe likely weather conditions on television and the radio 〔電視台或電台的〕天氣預報員

weave¹ /wiv; wiːv/ *v* **wove** /wov; wəʊv/, **woven** /ˈwovən; ˈwəʊvən/, **weaving 1** [I] to make material by crossing threads under and over each other on a LOOM 編織: *Do you know how to weave?* 你會編織嗎? **2** [T] to make something by twisting parts together 編, 織〔某物〕: *to weave a basket* 編一隻籃子

weave² *v* **weaved, weaving** [I;+adv/prep] to move along, changing direction frequently to avoid hitting anything 穿插行進: *Taxis wove through the traffic.* 計程車在車流中穿來穿去。

weave³ *n* the way in which a material is woven and the pattern formed by this 編法; 編織法: *a loose weave* 鬆織法

weav·er /ˈwivɚ; ˈwiːvəʳ/ *n* a person whose job is to weave cloth 織布工

web /wɛb; web/ *n* **1** a net of thin threads made by a SPIDER to catch other insects 蜘蛛網 **2** a detailed arrangement or network 周密的安排; 網絡: *a complex web of relationships* 複雜的關係網

webbed /wɛbd; webd/ *adj* **webbed feet** feet which have skin between the toes, as on a duck's foot 蹼足

wed /wɛd; wed/ *v* **wedded** *or* **wed** [I;T] *lit* to marry 〔文〕結婚

we'd /wɪd; wɪd; *strong* 強讀 wid; wiːd/ **1** short for 〔縮〕 = "we had": *We'd arranged to meet in town.* 我們已約好在城裡見面。 **2** short for 〔縮〕 = "we would": *We'd love to meet him.* 我們都喜歡見到他。

wed·ded /ˈwɛdɪd; ˈwedɪd/ *adj* **wedded to something** agreeing with something and supporting it strongly 執著於某事, 堅持某事: *The government is firmly wedded to the idea of cutting taxes.* 政府堅決支持減稅。

✲wed·ding /ˈwɛdɪŋ; ˈwedɪŋ/ *n* a marriage ceremony, especially with a party or meal afterwards 婚禮: *Have you been invited to their wedding?* 你被邀請參加他們的婚禮了嗎?

wedding ring /'·· ·/ *n* a gold ring, used in the marriage ceremony and worn to show that you are married 結婚戒指

wedge¹ /wɛdʒ; wedʒ/ *n* **1** a V-shaped piece of wood, with one thin end and one quite wide end, used for example for holding a door open 楔子，三角木 **2** something shaped like a wedge 楔形物: *a big wedge of chocolate cake* 一大塊切成楔形的巧克力蛋糕 **3 the thin end of the wedge** something which seems unimportant but will open the way for more serious things of a similar kind 看上去不重要但會有嚴重後果的事

wedge² *v* **wedged, wedging** [T+adv/prep] to fix something firmly into a place or a position, for example with a wedge 用楔子把〔某物〕抵住；把…擠入: *Wedge the door open.* 用楔子把門抵住，讓它開着。| *I was wedged into a corner.* 我被擠到了角落裡。

wed·lock /'wɛdlɑk; 'wedlɒk/ *n* [U] *old fash* 〔老式〕**1** the state of being married 已婚狀況 **2 born out of wedlock** born of unmarried parents 非婚生的；私生的

Wednes·day /'wɛnzdɪ; 'wenzdi/ *n* (also 又作 **Wed.** or **Weds.**) the day between Tuesday and Thursday 星期三

wee /wi; wiː/ *adj dialect* very small 〔方言〕非常小的: *a wee child* 很小的孩子，幼兒

weed¹ /wid; wiːd/ *n* **1** a wild plant that grows where you do not want it to grow 雜草，野草: *The garden's full of weeds.* 園中長滿了雜草。**2** a person who has a thin, weak body 瘦弱的人

weed² *v* [I;T] to remove weeds from a place 除去〔某處〕的雜草: *I spent the afternoon weeding the garden.* 我一個下午都在園子裡除草。

  weed sbdy/sthg ↔ **out** *phr v* [T] to get rid of things or people that you do not want 去除〔不需要的物或人〕: *We need to weed out incompetent teachers.* 我們需要淘汰不稱職的老師。

weed·y /'widɪ; 'wiːdi/ *adj* **weedier, weediest** *infml* having a thin, weak body 〔非正式〕瘦弱的

W★**week** /wik; wiːk/ *n* **1** a period of seven days, usually starting on Sunday or Monday 週，星期: *The flight to Accra goes twice a week.* 飛往阿克拉的航班一星期有兩班。| *I'll see you next week.* 我下週見你。**2** the period of time during which you work, for example in a factory or office 工作週: *She works a 60-hour week.* 她一週工作六十小時。| *The five-day week is usual in most firms.* 大部分公司都實行每週五天工作制。**3 Monday week, Tuesday week, etc.** a week after Monday, Tuesday, etc 一週後的星期一、星期二等等: *She's coming on Sunday week.* 她下個星期日來。**4 a week on Monday, a week tomorrow, etc.** a week after the stated day 〔所提及日子的〕一週以後: *He'll be back a week on Saturday.* 他下

週六回來。| *I'll see you a week tomorrow, then.* 那麼我明天起一週之後見你。| *a week next Tuesday* 下星期二起一週之後 **5 week in, week out** happening every week, without change or rest 一週接一週的

week·day /'wik,de; 'wiːkdeɪ/ *n* one of the days of the week, except Saturday or Sunday 工作日，週日〔不包括星期六和星期日〕: *We're only open on weekdays.* 我們只在工作日營業。

★**week·end** /'wik'end; ,wiːk'end◂/ *n* Saturday and Sunday 週末〔指星期六和星期日〕: *See you at the weekend.* 週末見。

week·ly¹ /'wiklɪ; 'wiːkli/ *adj, adv* happening or appearing once a week or every week 每週一次的〔地〕: *my weekly visit to the hospital* 我每週一次的醫院探訪 | *a weekly magazine* 週刊 | *We meet twice weekly.* 我們一週見面兩次。

weekly² *n* **weeklies** a magazine or newspaper which appears once a week 週刊；週報

weep /wip; wiːp/ *v* **wept** /wɛpt; wept/, **wept** [I] *lit* to let tears fall from your eyes 〔文〕流淚；哭泣: *I could weep when I think of all the money we've lost.* 我一想到我們丟了那麼多錢，我就要哭了。–**weep** *n*

weep·y /'wipɪ; 'wiːpi/ *adj infml* feeling sad and wanting to cry 〔非正式〕想哭的

weigh /we; weɪ/ *v* **1** [T] to find the weight of something by using a special machine 稱〔某物〕的重量: *Have you weighed yourself lately?* 你最近稱過體重沒有? | *The packets are all weighed before they leave the factory.* 這些小包在出廠前都稱過重量。**2** [+complement] to have a particular weight 重量有…: *It weighs six kilos.* 它有六公斤重。| *I weigh less than I used to.* 我的體重比以前輕了。**3 weigh a ton** *infml* to be extremely heavy to carry 〔非正式〕極其沉重 **4** [T] to consider something carefully 衡量；權衡〔某事〕: *He weighed the ideas in his mind.* 他在心裡權衡這些意見。**5 weigh anchor** to raise the ANCHOR of a boat or ship so that it can move 〔船〕起錨

  weigh down *phr v* **1** [T **weigh** sbdy/sthg **down**] to make someone or something heavier, so that they cannot move easily 使〔某人或某物〕變得沉重〔而無法輕易移動〕: *I was weighed down with the shopping.* 我提着買來的東西頗感費力。**2** [T **weigh** sbdy **down**] to make someone feel worried 令〔某人〕感到憂慮: *I was weighed down by my responsibilities.* 我承擔的責任令我十分憂慮。

  weigh on sbdy *phr v* [T] to make someone feel worried 使〔某人〕憂慮: *His lack of money weighed on his mind.* 他由於缺錢而滿腹憂愁。

  weigh sthg ↔ **out** *phr v* [T] to measure an amount of something by weighing it 稱出〔某物〕的重量: *I weighed out half a kilo of flour and added it to the mixture.* 我稱了半

公斤麵粉, 把它加入了混合物中。

weigh sbdy/sthg ↔ **up** phr v [T] to try to understand or form an opinion about someone or something 估量, 權衡〔某人或某物〕: *She eyed him carefully for a while, weighing him up.* 她仔細地打量了他一番, 估摸着他的來歷。

☆**weight¹** /wet; weɪt/ n **1** [U] the heaviness of something, which can be measured in units such as kilos 重量: *What's the baby's weight?* 那嬰兒有多重? **2** put on weight (of a person) to become heavier〔人〕體重增加: *He's put on a lot of weight recently.* 最近他的體重增加了許多。[RELATED PHRASE 相關詞組 lose weight: *I'm trying to lose weight.* 我正在努力減肥。] **3** [C] a piece of metal of a standard heaviness, which can be balanced against a substance to measure an equal heaviness of that substance 砝碼; 秤砣: *Put a one-kilo weight in the scales.* 在天平上加一個一公斤重的砝碼。**4** [C] a heavy object 重物: *You shouldn't lift heavy weights after an operation.* 你在手術之後不應當舉重物。**5** [U] value or importance 價值; 重要性: *These latest findings add more weight to his theories.* 這些最新的研究成果增加了他的理論的重要性。| *Her ideas don't carry much weight around here.* 她的觀點在這裡不太受到重視。**6** pull your weight to join in work equally with others 盡自己的力量工作; 盡本分 **7** throw your weight about/around to give orders to other people, because you think that you are important 作威作福 **8** a weight off your mind something that you do not have to worry about any more 不必再擔心的事情

weight² v [T] to put a weight on something to make it heavier 加重物於〔某物〕: *Fishing nets are weighted so that they sink in the water.* 魚網加上了重物, 所以能沉在水裡。

weight sthg ↔ **down** phr v [T] to make something heavier so that it cannot move easily 使〔某物〕變得更加沉重〔而無法輕易移動〕

weight·ed /wetɪd; weɪtɪd/ adj [never before a noun 不能用於名詞前] giving advantage to one particular person or group 對〔一方〕有利的: *The system of elections is weighted in favour of the main political parties.* 選舉制度對主要政黨有利。

weight·ing /wetɪŋ; weɪtɪŋ/ n [U] BrE additional pay given because of the high cost of living in a certain area, usually London〔英式〕〔某地區因生活費高而得到的〕額外補貼: *The salary is £15,000 a year, including London weighting.* 年薪為一萬五千英鎊, 其中包括倫敦地區的額外補貼。

weight·less /wetlɪs; weɪtləs/ adj having no weight, for example because a person or thing is flying in space 沒有重量的; 失重的 – **weightlessness** n [U]

weight lift·ing /ˈ· ,· ·/ n [U] the sport of lifting specially shaped weights above your head 舉重(運動) – **weight lifter** n

weight·y /weti; weɪti/ adj **weightier, weightiest** important and serious 重要的; 重大的: *weighty decisions* 重大決定

weir /wɪr; wɪər/ n a wall across a river, which stops or controls the flow of the water above it 堰堤, 攔河壩

weird /wɪrd; wɪəd/ adj strange and unusual 古怪的; 奇異的: *weird shapes in the mist* 霧氣中奇異的形狀 | *He has some weird ideas.* 他有一些怪念頭。

weird·o /wɪrdoʊ; wɪədəʊ/ n infml someone who behaves in a strange and unusual way〔非正式〕古怪的人

☆**wel·come¹** /welkəm; welkəm/ v **welcomed, welcoming** [T] **1** to meet or greet someone you are pleased to see 迎接, 歡迎〔某人〕: *The Queen welcomed the President when he arrived.* 總統抵達時, 女王上前迎接。| *They welcomed him with flowers.* 他們以鮮花歡迎他。**2** to be pleased about something that has happened or has been said 樂於接受〔某事物〕: *We welcome these changes in the law.* 我們歡迎這些法律上的改動。| *They welcomed my suggestion.* 他們欣然接受我的建議。

☆**welcome²** adj **1** acceptable and received with pleasure 受歡迎的: *You are always welcome at my house.* 歡迎你隨時來我家作客。| *All suggestions will be welcome.* 歡迎提出任何建議。**2** make someone welcome to behave in a friendly way towards someone, to show that you are pleased to see them 使某人感到受歡迎; 款待某人 **3** be welcome to do something to be allowed to do something 被允許做某事: *No one has ever done it before, but you're welcome to have a try.* 以前沒有人做過這事, 不過你可以試試。**4** You're welcome a polite phrase used when someone has thanked you for something 不用謝; 別客氣〔用於回答別人的感謝〕: *"Thank you!" "You're welcome."* "謝謝!" "別客氣。"

welcome³ interj a word used when you want to show that you are pleased to see someone who has just arrived somewhere 歡迎〔用於對剛剛到達某地的人表示歡迎〕: *Welcome home!* 歡迎歸來! | *Welcome to England.* 歡迎到英國來。

welcome⁴ n a friendly greeting given to someone who has just arrived somewhere 歡迎, 迎接: *We were given a warm welcome when we arrived.* 我們抵達時受到了熱烈歡迎。

weld /weld; weld/ v [T] to join metals by pressing or melting them together when they are hot 焊接〔金屬〕 – **weld** n: *a weld in the pipe* 管道上的焊縫

weld·er /weldər; weldə/ n a person whose job is to weld metal 焊工

☆**wel·fare** /welfer; welfeə/ n [U] **1** a per-

W

son's general comfort, good health, and happiness 幸福; 健康: *We're only thinking of his welfare: we want him to be happy in his new school.* 我們不過是在為他的幸福着想, 希望他在新的學校裡過得愉快。 **2** help that is given to people who are poor or have social problems (社會)福利: *She's interested in doing welfare work.* 她熱心於福利工作。 **3** money that is given to poor people in the US 〔美國的〕福利救濟金

welfare state /ˌ··ˈ·/ *n* a system of health care, unemployment pay, etc., that is provided by the government 福利國家; 福利制度

★★**well**¹ /wɛl; wel/ *adv* **better** /ˈbɛtər; ˈbetər/, **best** /bɛst; best/ **1** in a way that is good or satisfactory 好; 令人滿意地: *She paints very well.* 她畫得很好。 | *He was clean and well dressed.* 他乾乾淨淨, 衣着考究。 | *I can't hear very well.* 我的聽力不佳。 **2** thoroughly 徹底地, 完全地: *I don't know John very well.* 我不太了解約翰。 | *You haven't washed that very well.* 那個東西你洗得不太乾淨。 **3** very much 非常: *I can't reach it — it's well above my head.* 我夠不着——它遠遠高過了我的頭頂。 | *He finished well within the time allowed.* 他早早做完了。 **4** as well also 又, 也: *I'd like a sandwich, please, and a cup of tea as well.* 我想要一份三明治, 也要一杯茶。 **5** as well as in addition to something else 另外; 而且: *I'm learning French as well as German.* 我正在學法語, 而且還在學德語。 **6** just as well a phrase you use to say that it is good that something has happened 不妨, 倒也不錯〔用於表示所發生的事無妨〕: *I forgot to bring my other bag, which was just as well because it would have been heavy to carry round.* 我忘了帶我的另一個手提袋, 不過這倒不錯, 因為它太重了。 **7** well and good satisfactory 令人滿意的 **8** well and truly completely 徹底地; 完全地: *He was well and truly drunk.* 他喝得爛醉了。 **9** well done a phrase you say to someone when they have done something successfully 做得好〔表示某人成功地做了某事〕 **10** well out of it lucky to be free from a situation 幸而不受牽累 **11** well up on something knowing a lot about something 非常了解某事, 熟識

★★**well**² *adj* **better, best** [never before a noun 不能用於名詞前] **1** healthy 健康的: *My mother's not very well at the moment.* 我的母親現在身體不太好。 | *I don't feel very well.* 我感覺不太舒服。 **2** all is well everything is in a satisfactory state 一切正常 **3** it's all very well a phrase you use when you are annoyed about something that someone has done ...是好的, 可是...〔用於對某人所做的某事表示不滿〕: *It's all very well for you to say you're sorry, but I've been waiting here for two hours!* 你是該說聲對不起的, 可是我在這裡已等了兩小時啦!

well³ *interj* **1** used when you are surprised by something 呀, 啊〔表示驚訝〕: *Well, what a surprise.* 呀, 這真叫人吃驚。 | *So they're getting divorced, are they? Well, well.* 這麼說他們在鬧離婚, 是嗎? 唷, 原來如此。 **2** used when you are pausing before you speak, or when you are uncertain about something 嗯, 這個嘛〔用於說話前暫停或不敢肯定時〕: *"Are you sure about that?" "Well, I think so. It's what I was told."* "你肯定嗎?" "嗯, 我想是的吧。別人是這麼告訴我的。" **3** used when you are continuing a story 於是〔用於繼續講述〕: *Well, then she said that they're thinking of emigrating.* 於是, 她接着說他們正在考慮移民。 **4** used when you are correcting the idea before 哦〔用於更正前述的觀點〕: *There's no problem at all. Well, maybe there's a small problem.* 這完全沒問題。哦, 也可能會有點小麻煩。 —see Study Note on page 1325 見 1325 頁學習提示 **5** oh well a phrase you use when you are trying to be cheerful about something bad that has happened 算了〔用於試圖使自己樂觀時〕: *Oh well, things could be worse, I suppose.* 噢, 算了, 我想事情本來也許會更糟。

well⁴ *n* **1** a hole in the ground from which water is taken 井, 水井 **2** a hole in the ground from which oil is taken 油井

well⁵ *v*

    well up *phr v* [I] (of tears) to come into your eyes 〔眼淚〕湧出: *Tears welled up in her eyes.* 她的眼淚奪眶而出。

we'll /wɪl; wil; *strong* 強讀 wil; wiːl/ short for 〔縮〕 = "we will" or 或 "we shall"

well-ad·vised /ˌ·· ···/ *adj* you would be well-advised a phrase used when you are suggesting that someone should do something 你應該...〔用於建議某人做某事〕: *You would be well-advised to see the doctor about that pain.* 你應該去找醫生看看身上那疼痛的地方。

well-bal·anced /ˌ· ···◂/ *adj* sensible and not having any unreasonable feelings of fear, jealousy, etc. 理智的, 情緒穩定的: *a happy, well-balanced child* 快樂、情緒穩定的孩子

well-be·ing /ˈwɛlˌbiːɪŋ; ˌwelˈbiːiŋ/ *n* [U] a person's good health and happiness 健康; 幸福: *The warm summer weather always gives me a sense of wellbeing.* 夏季溫暖的天氣總令我有一種健康、幸福的感覺。

well-bred /ˌ· ···◂/ *adj* old fash polite, and having good manners 〔老式〕有教養的; 有禮貌的

well-brought-up /ˌ·· ···◂/ *adj* taught to behave in a polite and acceptable way (used of children) 有禮貌的, 懂道理的〔指孩子〕

well-built /ˌ·ˈ·◂/ *adj* having a strong body with large muscles 體格健壯的 —see picture on page 469 見 469 頁彩圖

well-con·nect·ed /ˌ· ···◂/ *adj* knowing or related to people of power and social importance 有門路的; 與有勢力或有社會地位的人有關係的

well-done /ˌ·ˈ·◂/ *adj* cooked thoroughly, for quite a long time 熟透的; 煮透的

well-earned /ˌ·ˈ·◂/ *adj* much deserved 應得的: *a well-earned rest after so much hard work* 辛辛苦苦工作之後應該有的休息

well-es·tab·lished /ˌ·ˈ·ˈ·◂/ *adj* having existed successfully for quite a long time 地位穩固的; 存在已久的

well-found·ed /ˌ·ˈ·◂/ *adj* based on facts 基於事實的, 有事實根據的: *Our fears proved to be well-founded.* 我們的恐懼證明是有道理的。

well-groomed /ˌ·ˈ·◂/ *adj* having a very neat clean appearance 穿戴整潔的

well-heeled /ˌ·ˈ·◂/ *adj infml* rich 〖非正式〗富有的

well-in·formed /ˌ·ˈ·ˈ·◂/ *adj* knowing a lot about several subjects or about one particular subject 〔在數門或某門學科上〕學識淵博的; 〔對某一問題〕非常熟悉的

wel·ling·ton /ˈwɛlɪŋtən; ˈwelɪŋtən/ *n* (also 又作 **wellington boot** /ˌ··· ˈ·/, **welly** *infml* 〖非正式〗) a rubber boot which keeps your feet and legs dry 防水橡膠靴, 長統橡膠雨靴

well-in·ten·tioned /ˌ·ˈ·ˈ·◂/ *adj* doing something in the hope of helping someone, though often failing 〔儘管結果失敗〕善意的; 出於好心的: *It was a well-intentioned effort to help, but disaster followed.* 本是好心好意去幫忙, 可是災難卻接踵而至。

well-known /ˌ·ˈ·◂/ *adj* known by many people 有名的, 人所共知的: *It's a well-known fact that too much sugar is bad for you.* 眾所周知, 吃糖太多是有害的。–see 見 FAMOUS (USAGE用法)

well-mean·ing /ˌ·ˈ·◂/ *adj* doing something in the hope of helping someone, though often failing 本是善意的; 出於好心的〔但卻不成功〕: *a well-meaning effort* 出於好心所作的努力

well-meant /ˌ·ˈ·◂/ *adj* done in the hope of helping someone, but unsuccessful 本是善意的; 出於好心的〔但卻不成功〕: *His actions were always well-meant.* 他的舉動本意總是好的。

well-nigh /ˈ·ˈ·/ *adv fml* almost 〖正式〗幾乎

well-off /ˌ·ˈ·◂/ **better-off, best-off** *infml* 〖非正式〗**1** rich 富有的: *They're very well-off.* 他們非常有錢。 **2 well-off for something** having plenty of something 有充足的〔某物〕: *We're quite well-off for space here.* 我們這裡有很多空間。 **3 you don't know when you're well-off** = you're more fortunate than you know 你身在福中不知福

well-read /ˌ·ˈ·◂/ *adj* having read many books and learnt a lot from them 博覽羣書的

well-spok·en /ˌ·ˈ·◂/ *adj* speaking in a polite, correct way, like an educated person 説話得體的

well-thought-of /ˌ·ˈ·◂/ *adj* liked and admired by a lot of people 受人喜愛的, 受到普遍好評的

well-timed /ˌ·ˈ·◂/ *adj* said or done at the most suitable time 合時宜的: *well-timed advice* 適時的忠告

well-tried /ˌ·ˈ·◂/ *adj* often used before and known to work well 經常使用後證明效果良好的: *well-tried methods* 反覆試驗過證明效果良好的方法

well-wish·er /ˈ·ˌ··/ *n* a person who gives good wishes to another on a special occasion 祝福者

well-worn /ˌ·ˈ·◂/ *adj* said too often, and so having little meaning 老生常談的

wel·ly /ˈwɛlɪ; ˈwelɪ/ *n* **wellies** see 見 WELLINGTON

Welsh¹ /wɛlʃ; welʃ/ *adj* of or connected with Wales 威爾士的: *the Welsh mountains* 威爾士的羣山

Welsh² *n* **1 the Welsh** the people of Wales 威爾士人 **2** the language of Wales 威爾士語

welt /wɛlt; welt/ a raised mark on your skin, for example from a hit by a whip 鞭痕; 〔被毆打後的〕腫塊

wel·ter /ˈwɛltə; ˈweltər/ *n* **a welter of things** a disordered mixture of things 混亂的事物: *a welter of confused policies* 一堆雜亂無章的政策

wench /wɛntʃ; wentʃ/ *n* a young woman (a word which is no longer used in modern English) 少婦〔現代英語中不再使用〕

wend /wɛnd; wend/ *v lit* 〖文〗**wend your way** to move or travel slowly 緩慢地移動

went /wɛnt; went/ the past tense of GO ☆ GO 的過去式

wept /wɛpt; wept/ the past tense and past participle of WEEP ☆WEEP 的過去式和過去分詞

were /wə; wər; *strong* 強讀 wɜ; wɜːr/ *negative short-form* 否定縮約式 **weren't** /wɜːnt; wɜːnt/ the past tense of BE ☆ BE 的過去式

we're /wɪr; wɪər; *strong* 強讀 wɪr; wiːər/ *short for* 〖縮〗 = "we are"

were·wolf /ˈwɪrˌwʊlf; ˈweəwʊlf/ *n* **werewolves** /-ˌwʊlvz; -wʊlvz/ a man in some stories who sometimes turns into a WOLF 〔某些故事中〕會變成狼的人, 狼人

west¹ /wɛst; west/ *n* **1** [U] the direction in which the sun sets 西, 西面, 西邊: *The road goes through the town centre from east to west.* 這條路從東到西橫穿市中心。 **2 the West** the western part of the world, especially western Europe and the United States 西方世界〔尤指歐洲和美國〕: *Leaders from the West have been invited to peace talks in Moscow.* 西方各國領導人獲邀出席在莫斯科舉行的和談。 **3 the west** the western part of a country 國家的西部

west² *adj* **1** in or towards the west 在西方的; 朝西的: *West Africa* 西非, 非洲西部 **2 west wind** a wind blowing from the west 西風

west³ *adv* (also 又作 **West**) **1** towards the west 朝西: *We travelled west for three days.* 我們向西走了三日。| *She sat facing West, watching the sun go down.* 她朝西坐着，望着太陽落山。**2** from the west (used of a wind) 從西面來的〔風〕

west·bound /'wɛst,baʊnd; 'wɛstbaʊnd/ *adj* travelling towards the west 向西行的: *To get to London Airport, take the westbound train.* 要去倫敦機場，請坐西行列車。

West End /ˌ· '·◂/ *n* **the West End** the western part of central London, where the shops and theatres are 倫敦西區

west·er·ly /'wɛstəlɪ; 'wɛstəli/ *adj* **1** towards the west 朝西的: *We set off in a westerly direction.* 我們向西出發了。**2** coming from the west (used of a wind) 從西面來的〔風〕

★**west·ern¹** /'wɛstən; 'wɛstən/ *adj* (also 又作 **Western**) **1** belonging to the west part or area of a country 西部的: *Western Scotland* 蘇格蘭西部 **2** relating to the people of Europe or the United States 西方的: *the Western way of life* 西方的生活方式 | *Western technology* 西方的技術

western² *n* (also 又作 **Western**) a story or film about life in the West of the US in the past 〔美國的〕西部小說，西部影片

west·ern·er /'wɛstənə; 'wɛstənə/ *n* a person who lives in Europe or the United States 西方人

west·ern·ize /'wɛstə,naɪz; 'wɛstənaɪz/ *v* (also 又作 **westernise** *BrE* 〔英式〕) **be westernized** to start to use the customs and behaviour typical of Europe and the United States 使西方化; 使西化

West In·di·an /ˌ· '·· ·/ *adj* from or relating to the West Indies 西印度羣島的: *West Indian cooking* 西印度羣島的烹飪

west·ward /'wɛstwəd; 'wɛstwəd/ *adj* going towards the west 向西行的: *a westward journey* 向西的旅行 –**westwards** (also 又作 **westward** *AmE* 〔美式〕) *adv*: *We travelled westwards for several days.* 我們向西行了數日。

★**wet¹** /wɛt; wɛt/ *adj* **1** covered with liquid and so not dry 濕的: *My shoes had got wet in the rain.* 我的鞋被雨水弄濕了。| *My hair's all wet now!* 我的頭髮現在全濕了! **2** rainy 多雨的; 下雨的: *wet weather* 多雨的天氣 | *We can't go out, it's too wet.* 我們不能出去, 雨太大了。**3** still sticky, and not yet dry or solid 未乾的; 未固化的: *The sign said "Wet paint".* 標牌上寫着"油漆未乾"。| *The cement's still wet.* 水泥還未乾。**4** *infml* lacking strength of mind 〔非正式〕怯懦的: *Don't be so wet! You can do it, if you try!* 別這麼膽小! 你做得到的, 試試看吧! **5 wet blanket** a person who discourages other people and prevents them enjoying themselves 掃興的人, 潑冷水的人 –**wetness** *n* [U]

wet² *n* **1 the wet** rainy weather 雨天: *Don't go out in the wet.* 下雨天別出去。**2** *infml* a

person in the British CONSERVATIVE Party who is not politically extreme 〔非正式〕〔英國保守黨內的〕溫和派

wet³ *v* **wet** *or* **wetted, wet** *or* **wetted, wetting** [T] **1** to make something wet 使〔某物〕變濕, 弄濕: *Wet the cloth and clean the table with it.* 把布濕一下, 然後擦淨桌子。**2 wet the bed, wet yourself** to pass water from your body, in bed or in your clothes, because you cannot control your body 尿牀; 遺尿

wet suit /' ·· / *n* a piece of clothing made of rubber, worn by people who do water sports 潛水服

we've /wɪv; wiv; *strong* 強讀 wiv; wi:v/ *short for* 〔縮〕= "we have"

whack¹ /hwæk; wæk/ *v* [T] to hit someone or something with a hard blow 用力擊打〔某人或某物〕

whack² *n* **1** a hard blow 重擊 **2 your whack** *infml* your fair share of something 〔非正式〕〔公平的〕一份

whacked /hwækt; wækt/ *adj* [never before a noun 不能用於名詞前] *infml* very tired 〔非正式〕非常疲勞的

whack·ing /'hwækɪŋ; 'wækɪŋ/ *adj infml* very big 〔非正式〕非常大的: *They live in a whacking great house in Hollywood.* 他們住在好萊塢一幢非常大的房子裡。

whale /hwel; weɪl/ *n* **1** a very large animal which lives in the sea, and looks like a fish but is a MAMMAL 鯨 **2 have a whale of a time** *infml* to enjoy yourself very much 〔非正式〕玩得很開心, 有非常愉快的時光

whal·ing /'hwelɪŋ; 'weɪlɪŋ/ *n* [U] the hunting of whales 捕鯨〔業〕

wharf /hwɔrf; wɔ:f/ *n* **wharfs** *or* **wharves** /hwɔrvz; wɔ:vz/ a place where ships can be tied up to unload goods 碼頭

★**what** /hwɑt; wɒt/ *predeterminer, det, pron* **1** used in questions about a thing that is not known 甚麼〔用於疑問句中, 指某未知的事物〕: *What are you doing?* 你在做甚麼? | *What colour is it?* 它是甚麼顏色的? | *What time is it?* 幾點鐘了? | *What did he say?* 他說了些甚麼? **2** the thing or things that ...的事物: *She told me what to do.* 她告訴我該做甚麼。| *I know what you mean.* 我明白你的意思。| *Show me what you bought.* 給我看看你買的東西。| *I gave her what books I had.* 我把自己有的書都給她了。–see WHICH (USAGE用法) **3** used to show surprise 多麼, 甚麼, 真(是)〔用於表示驚訝〕: *What a strange thing to say!* 說這樣的話可真奇怪! | *What beautiful weather.* 多好的天氣啊。| *You did what?* 你做甚麼了? **4** *infml* used when someone has called your name and you want to show that you have heard them and are listening 〔非正式〕甚麼事, 怎麼了〔用於回應別人的呼喚〕: "*Mary?*" "*What?*" "*Have you fed the dog?*" "瑪麗?" "甚麼事?" "你餵過狗了嗎?" **5 what for** *infml* why 〔非正式〕為甚麼: "*I'm going to Paris.*" "*What*

for?" "我準備去巴黎。" "去幹甚麼呢?" |
What did you do that for? 你為甚麼那樣做?
6 what if what would happen if 如果...那會
怎麼樣: *What if we get delayed and miss the
train?* 如果我遲到誤了火車那會怎樣? **7 what
with** *infml* because of something〔非正式〕
因為: *What with all this extra work, I haven't
had time to do any gardening.* 由於這些額外
的工作, 我沒有時間去做園藝活。 **8 what's
more** used to introduce an additional point
which is stronger than the one before 更重
要的是, 而且〔用於說出更為重要的一點〕:
*She's just the person to help you. She's lived
in Turkey. What's more, she speaks Turkish.*
她正是可以幫助你的人。她住在土耳其。而且,
她還會講土耳其語。

what·ev·er¹ /hwɑt'ɛvə; wɒt'evəʳ/ *det,
pron* **1** *det, pron* no mat-
ter what thing 無論甚麼, 不管甚麼: *These
animals will eat whatever they can find.* 這些
動物能找到甚麼就吃甚麼。 | *Use whatever
information you can find.* 你不管找到甚麼資
料都要用。 | *Whatever you do, don't be late.*
不管做甚麼都不要遲到。 –see 見 EVER
(USAGE用法) **2** *pron infml* anything else
like the thing mentioned〔非正式〕...甚麼
的; 任何類似的東西: *Anyone carrying bags,
boxes, or whatever was stopped by the
police.* 誰要是帶背包、盒子之類的物品, 都被警
察叫住了。 **3** *pron* used when you are surprised and are asking "what" 甚麼〔用於表
示驚訝〕: *Whatever is it?* 它到底是甚麼? |
Whatever did you do that for? 你那樣做到底
是為了甚麼? **4** *pron infml* it doesn't matter
which 〔非正式〕無所謂, 隨便怎樣: "*Shall we
go to a film, the theatre, or for a meal?*"
"*Whatever.*" "我們去看電影、去看戲, 還是去
吃飯?" "無所謂。"

whatever² *adj* (also 又作 **whatsoever**) **none
whatever, nothing whatever, etc** none at
all, nothing at all, etc 一點也不: *I know
nothing whatever about it.* 這事我一無所
知。 | *She had no money whatever.* 她一點錢
也沒有。

wheat /hwit; wiːt/ *n* [U] a plant from whose
grain flour is made, or its grain 小麥: *a field
of wheat* 小麥田

whee·dle /'hwidl; 'wiːdl/ *v* **wheedled,
wheedling 1 wheedle someone into doing
something** to persuade someone to do
something by being pleasant to them 哄騙
〔某人做某事〕 **2 wheedle something out of
someone** to obtain something from someone by pleasant persuading 從〔某人那裡〕哄
騙得到〔某物〕: *He managed to wheedle five
pounds out of his father.* 他用花言巧語從他
父親那裡騙得五英鎊。

★wheel¹ /hwil; wiːl/ *n* **1** a circular object with
an outer frame which turns around an in-
ner part; wheels are used for making
vehicles move and for making machinery
work 輪子; 車輪 –see picture on page 209

見 209 頁彩圖 **2** the wheel used to guide
and turn a car or other vehicle 駕駛盤, 方向
盤: *She was sitting behind the wheel of her
car.* 她坐在自己的車子的方向盤後面。

wheel² *v* **1** [T+adv/prep] to move something
which has wheels, by pushing it 推動〔有輪
子的東西〕: *The nurse wheeled the table up to
the bed.* 護士把桌子推到牀邊。 **2** [I] (of
birds) to fly round and round in circles
〔鳥〕盤旋: *Birds were wheeling above us.* 鳥
兒在我們的頭上盤旋。

wheel round/around *phr v* [I] to turn
round suddenly 突然轉身: *He wheeled
round and looked at me.* 他突然轉過身來看
着我。

wheel·bar·row /'hwil,bæro; 'wiːl,bærəʊ/ *n*
a small cart with one wheel at the front,
two legs, and two handles at the back for
pushing 獨輪手推車: *Put those stones in the
wheelbarrow.* 把那些石頭放到獨輪手推車
裡。 –see picture on page 958 見 958 頁彩圖

wheel·chair /'hwil'tʃer; 'wiːltʃeəʳ/ *n* a chair
with large wheels used by a person who
cannot walk 輪椅

wheeling and deal·ing /,····'··/ *n* [U] making deals in a skilful, and perhaps dishonest, way 使用手段, 投機取巧: *The issue
was only decided after a great deal of political wheeling and dealing.* 只有用盡許多政治手
段, 該問題才得到解決。

wheeze /hwiz; wiːz/ *v* **wheezed, wheezing** [I]
to make a noisy whistling sound when you
breathe 喘息: *By the time he reached the top
of the stairs he was panting and wheezing.* 他
在登上樓梯最上面的一級時, 已是氣喘吁吁
了。 –**wheeze** *n*

wheez·y /'hwizi; 'wiːzi/ *adj* making a noisy
whistling sound when you breathe 發出喘
息聲的: *a wheezy cough* 氣喘吁吁的咳嗽

whelk /hwɛlk; welk/ *n* a sea animal which
lives in a shell, and is sometimes used as
food 蛾螺, 油螺

★when /hwɛn; wen/ *adv, conj* **1** at what
time 甚麼時候: *When are they ar-
riving?* 他們甚麼時候到? | *She'll tell us
when we can come in.* 她會告訴我們何時可
以進來的。 **2** at a particular time 當...時:
*When I left school I didn't know what I
wanted to do.* 我當初離校時不知道自己想幹
甚麼。 **3** considering a particular fact 考慮到
〔某一情況〕: *I can't explain anything when
you won't listen.* 你不願聽的時候, 我甚麼也無
法解釋。 **4** although 雖然; 儘管: *She's always
complaining about being hard up, when in
fact she's got loads of money.* 她總是抱怨手
頭緊, 儘管她實際上很有錢。

whence /hwɛns; wens/ *adv* from where (a
word that is no longer used in modern
English) 從那裡〔現代英語中不再使用〕: *They
returned to the land whence they had come.*
他們回到了他們來的那個地方。

★when·ev·er /hwɛn'ɛvə; wen'evəʳ/ *adv* **1** at

whatever time 無論何時, 每當: *I go and visit him whenever I'm in town.* 我每次進城都去拜訪他。 | *Come round whenever you like.* 你無論甚麼時候想來就來。 **2** used when you are surprised and are asking "when" 究竟何時〔用於表示驚訝〕: *Whenever did you have time to do this?* 你哪兒來的時間做這件事?

where /hwɛr; weər/ *adv, conj, pron* in or to which place 在哪裡; 往哪裡: *Where do you live?* 你住在哪裡? | *Where are the keys?* 鑰匙在哪裡? | *Where are you going?* 你去哪兒? | *the office where I work* 我工作的辦公室 | *Sit where you like.* 你想坐在哪裡就坐在哪裡。

where·a·bouts¹ /ˌhwɛrəˈbaʊts; ˌweərəˈbaʊts/ *adv, conj* used in questions when you are asking the question "where" 在哪裡〔用於表示強調〕: *Whereabouts do you live?* 你住在哪裡?

whereabouts² /ˈhwɛrəˌbaʊts; ˈweərəbaʊts/ *n* [U+sing/pl verb] the place where someone or something is 行蹤; 下落; 去向: *Nobody knows his whereabouts.* 無人知道他的去向。

where·as /hwɛrˈæz; weərˈæz/ *conj* used when you are stating something that is opposite to what you have just said 然而, 但是〔用於陳述相反的話〕: *They spend all their money on their house, whereas we prefer to spend ours on travelling.* 他們把所有的錢花在房子上, 可是我們寧願拿錢去旅遊。

where·by /hwɛrˈbaɪ; weəˈbaɪ/ *adv fml* by which or by means of which 〔正式〕由此; 藉以: *We need a better system whereby we can calculate our future costs.* 我們需要一個更加完善的制度, 以便能核算將來的成本。

where·in /hwɛrˈɪn; weərˈɪn/ *adv, conj fml* in what or in which〔正式〕在哪方面; 在那兒

where·u·pon /ˌhwɛrəˈpɒn; ˌweərəˈpɒn/ *conj fml* after which〔正式〕在此以後; 於是: *One of them called him a liar, whereupon a fight broke out.* 他們當中有人說他撒謊, 於是他們便打起來了。

wher·ev·er /hwɛrˈɛvər; weərˈevər/ *adv, conj* **1** in or to whatever place 無論在何處; 無論到哪裡: *Sit wherever you like.* 你想坐在哪裡就坐在哪裡好了。 | *Wherever you go, I will go with you.* 不管你去哪裡, 我都跟著你。 **2** used when you are surprised and are asking "where" 在哪裡; 往哪裡〔用於表示驚訝〕: *Wherever have you been?* 你到底去哪裡了?

where·with·al /ˈhwɛrwɪðˌɔl; ˈweəwɪðɔːl/ *n fml*〔正式〕 **the wherewithal to do something** the money that you need to do something 做某事需要的金錢: *I haven't got the wherewithal to pay you.* 我沒有錢付給你。

whet /hwɛt; wet/ *v* **-tt-** [T] **1** *lit* to sharpen something〔文〕磨尖〔某物〕; *She whetted her knife on the stone.* 她在石頭上磨刀。 **2 whet your appetite** to make you wish for more 激起更大的興趣或慾望: *The experience had whetted my appetite* **for** *adventure.* 這次經歷更加激發了我去冒險的興趣。

wheth·er /ˈhwɛðər; ˈweðər/ *conj* **1** used to show a choice between different possibilities 是否〔用於表示兩種可能性中的選擇〕: *He asked me whether I enjoyed my work or not.* 他問我是否喜歡自己的工作。 | *I'll find out whether she's ready.* 我去看看她是不是準備好了。 | *Tell me whether or not you like it.* 告訴我你喜不喜歡它。 **2** used to show that it does not matter which is chosen or which is true 不論, 不管〔用於表示無論選擇某一事物或無論是否符合事實都沒關係〕: *I'll go whether you come with me or not.* 不管你是否和我一起去, 我都會去。 | *All couples will benefit whether they have children or not.* 不論是否有孩子, 所有的夫婦都會得益。

whew /hwju; hjuː/ *interj* see 見 PHEW

which /hwɪtʃ; wɪtʃ/ *det, pron* **1** used in questions when there is a choice to be made 哪一個〔用於選擇疑問句中〕: *Which shoes shall I wear, the red ones or the brown ones?* 我應該穿哪雙鞋, 是紅色的還是棕色的? | *Which of these books is yours?* 這些書當中哪一本是你的? **2** used to show what thing or things someone means …的那個, …的那些〔用於表示某人所指的事物〕: *Did you see the letter which came this morning?* 你看到今早送來的那封信了嗎? | *This is the book which I told you about.* 這就是我給你提到過的那本書。 **3** used to add more information to a sentence〔用於在句子中補充信息〕: *We went back to their house, which is lovely.* 我們回到了他們的房子, 那所房子很漂亮。 | *She said she's been waiting for half an hour, which wasn't true.* 她說她已等了半小時, 這不是真的。

> ■ **USAGE** 用法: Compare 比較 **which** and 和 **what. 1** Use **which** when the choice is from a particular group of things or people ☆當要在某一組物或人中做出選擇時, 用 **which: Which** *colour do you want, red or blue?* 你想要哪一種顏色, 紅的還是藍的? We use **what** when the choice is from an unknown number of things or people ☆當要在一組未知的物或人中做出選擇時, 用 **what: What** *colour would you like your new car to be?* 你喜歡的新車是甚麼顏色的? **2 Which** can be followed by *of*, but **what** cannot be followed by *of* ☆ **which** 後可以跟 *of*, 但 **what** 不可以: **Which** *of the puppies do you like best?* 你最喜歡哪一隻小狗?

which·ev·er /hwɪtʃˈɛvər; wɪtʃˈevər/ *det, pron* **1** any one whatever 無論哪個: *Take whichever seat you like.* 你想坐哪個位置就坐哪個吧。 | *It has the same result whichever way you do it.* 無論你用甚麼方法做, 結果都是一樣的。 **2** used when you are surprised and are asking "which" 哪個〔表示驚訝〕: *Whichever road did you come along?* 你到底是順着哪條路來的?

whiff /hwɪf; wɪf/ *n* a smell which you smell for just a short time 一陣氣味: *I caught a whiff of her perfume as she walked past me.* 她從我身旁走過時, 我聞到一股香水味。

⋆⋆**while**¹ /hwaɪl; waɪl/ *n* **a while** a length of time, usually a short one 一段時間, 〔常指〕一會兒: *After a while she fell asleep.* 過了一會兒, 她睡着了。 | *We had to wait a little while.* 我們得等一會兒。

⋆**while**² *conj* (also 又作 **whilst** *BrE* 〖英式〗) **1** during the time when something is happening 當…時, 在…時: *I read a lot while I was at college.* 我讀大學時看了許多書。 | *I always listen to the radio while I'm cooking.* 我做飯的時候, 總愛聽着收音機。 **2** although 儘管: *While I agree with a lot of what you say, I still can't accept your conclusions.* 儘管你所説的很多我都同意, 但我還是不能接受你的結論。

while³ *v* **whiled, whiling**

while sthg ↔ **away** *phr v* [T] to spend time in a lazy way 消磨〔時間〕: *She whiled away the hours sunbathing in the garden.* 她在花園裡曬太陽以消磨時間。

whim /hwɪm; wɪm/ *n* a sudden idea or wish, often one that is not reasonable 一時的興致; 突然產生的念頭: *I was tired of pandering to her whims.* 對於要迎合她的那些古怪念頭, 我已感到厭倦了。 | *A soldier won't fight very hard for a leader who is going to shoot him on a whim.* 一個一時興起便會槍殺士兵的領導人, 士兵是不願意為他賣命的。

whim·per /ˈhwɪmpə; ˈwɪmpəʳ/ *v* [I] **1** to make small weak cries of fear or pain 嗚咽, 啜泣 **2** to say something in a small trembling voice 顫聲地説, 啜泣着説: *"Don't hurt me!" he whimpered.* "不要傷害我!" 他啜泣着説。 **–whimper** *n*: *The dog gave a whimper of pain.* 那條狗痛得嗚嗚叫。

whim·si·cal /ˈhwɪmzɪkl; ˈwɪmzɪkəl/ *adj* strange and amusing 古怪而可笑的 **–whimsically** *adv*

whine /hwaɪn; waɪn/ *v* **whined, whining** [I] **1** to make a high sad cry or sound 悲鳴, 哀號: *The dog was whining at the door.* 狗在對着門大聲哀叫。 | *The machinery clattered and whined.* 機器發出轟隆隆的響聲。 **2** to complain in an unnecessarily sad voice 悲切地抱怨, 哀訴: *Stop whining, child!* 別哭哭啼啼了, 孩子! **–whine** *n*: *the whine of an aircraft engine* 飛機引擎的轟鳴聲

whinge /hwɪndʒ; wɪndʒ/ *v* **whinged, whinging** *or* **whingeing** [I] *infml* to complain often and unnecessarily 〖非正式〗抱怨; 嘮叨: *Stop whingeing about it and just get on with it!* 別再抱怨了, 還是繼續幹下去吧!

whin·ny /ˈhwɪni; ˈwɪni/ *v* **whinnied, whinnying** [I] (of a horse) to make a gentle sound 〔馬〕輕聲地嘶叫 **–whinny** *n*

whip¹ /hwɪp; wɪp/ *n* **1** a long piece of rope or leather fastened to a handle, used for hitting animals or people 鞭子 **2** a member of Parliament who is responsible for making other members of his or her party attend at voting time 政黨的紀律委員〔負責敦促該黨議員在投票時出席的議員〕

whip² *v* **-pp- 1** [T] to beat someone with a whip 鞭打〔某人〕 **2** [T+adv/prep] to move something quickly 迅速移動〔某物〕: *He whipped out his gun.* 他突然拔出槍。 | *She whipped off her coat.* 她迅速脱掉了外套。 **3** [I+adv/prep] (of the wind) to move very quickly across something 〔風〕掃過〔某物〕: *The wind whipped across the fields.* 風掃過田野。 **4** [T] to beat cream or eggs until they are stiff 攪拌〔奶油或雞蛋〕直至變稠, 打成糊狀: *apple pie with whipped cream* 加入攪打奶油的蘋果餅

whip sthg ↔ **up** *phr v* [T] **1** to cause feelings to become stronger 使〔感情〕變得強烈: *They're trying to whip up support for the new political party.* 他們正設法激起人們來支持新政黨的情緒。 **2 whip up a meal** to make a meal quickly 匆匆做一頓飯

whip·ping /ˈhwɪpɪŋ; ˈwɪpɪŋ/ *n* a beating with a whip 鞭笞, 鞭打

whip-round /'··/ *n BrE infml* a collection of money among a group of people to give to one member or to buy something for one member 〖英式, 非正式〗湊錢; 募捐: *We're having a whip-round for old Fred — he's leaving, you know.* 我們正在湊錢給老弗德買禮物——你知道, 他要走了。

whir /hwɜ; wɜ/ *v* **-rr-** [I] see 見 WHIRR

whirl¹ /hwɜl; wɜl/ *v* **1** [I;T+adv/prep] to move round and round very fast 迅速旋轉: *the whirling dancers* 旋轉起舞的舞蹈員 | *The leaves were picked up by the wind and whirled into the air.* 樹葉被風吹起來, 轉着圈地飄向天空。 **2 my head is whirling** = I am extremely excited and confused 〔因過於激動〕我頭都暈了

whirl² *n* **1** very fast and rather confused movement or activity 旋轉; 紛亂: *the whirl of the dancers* 舞蹈員的旋轉舞步 | *The sales department was a whirl of activity.* 銷售部裡人們忙忙碌碌, 一片混亂。 **2 in a whirl** very confused and puzzled 迷惑的; 糊塗的: *My head's in a whirl; let me sit down and think quietly.* 我的腦子很亂, 讓我坐下來靜靜地想一想。 **3 give something a whirl** *infml* to try something new and see if it works 〖非正式〗試試某事物: *It's an unusual idea, but I think we should give it a whirl.* 這個主意不同尋常, 不過我覺得我們應該試試。

whirl·pool /ˈhwɜl‚pul; ˈwɜlpuːl/ *n* a place with circular currents of water in a sea or river, which can pull objects down into it 〔海中或河中的〕漩渦

whirl·wind /ˈhwɜl‚wɪnd; ˈwɜlwɪnd/ *n* **1** a tall round body of air moving rapidly forward, which can destroy things in its path 旋風 **2** [only before another noun 只用於另一名詞前] happening very quickly 迅速發生的: *a whirlwind romance* 旋風式的風流韻事

whirr /hwɜːʳ; wɜːʳ/ *v* (also 又作 **whir**) [I] to make a regular sound like something turning and beating against the air 發出呼呼聲: *the whirring sound of the engine* 引擎發出的呼呼聲 **–whirr, whir** *n*: *the whirr of the sewing machine* 縫紉機發出的嗡嗡聲

whisk¹ /hwɪsk; wɪsk/ **1** a small tool for beating eggs or cream 攪拌器: *an egg whisk* 打蛋器 –see picture on page 958 見 958 頁彩圖 **2** a quick light movement 掃; 拂: *The cow brushed off the flies with a whisk of its tail.* 母牛用尾巴拂走身上的蒼蠅。

whisk² *v* **1** to move something with a quick sweeping movement 掃, 拂: *The horse whisked its tail.* 馬在甩動尾巴。 **2** [T+adv/prep] to move or remove quickly 迅速移動; 迅速拿掉: *She whisked the cups off the table.* 她突然把杯子從桌上拿走了。 | *The President was whisked off to the airport.* 總統被匆匆送往機場。 **3** [T] to beat eggs or cream to get air into them 攪打〔雞蛋或奶油〕

whis·ker /ˈhwɪskəʳ; ˈwɪskəʳ/ *n* **1** one of the long stiff hairs that grow near the mouth of an animal such as a cat or rat〔貓或老鼠等動物的〕鬚 **2 whiskers** [pl] hair growing on the sides of a man's face 連鬢鬍子, 頰鬚, 髯

whis·key /ˈhwɪskɪ; ˈwɪskɪ/ [U] WHISKY made in Ireland or the US〔愛爾蘭或美國生產的〕威士忌酒

whis·ky /ˈhwɪskɪ; ˈwɪskɪ/ *n* **whiskies 1** [U] a strong alcoholic drink made from grain, produced especially in Scotland〔尤指產於蘇格蘭的〕威士忌酒: *a bottle of whisky* 一瓶威士忌酒 **2** [C] a glass of whisky 一杯威士忌酒

★whis·per /ˈhwɪspəʳ; ˈwɪspəʳ/ *v* **1** [I;T] to speak very quietly, so that only a person very near you can hear 低語, 耳語: *The children were whispering in the corner.* 孩子們在角落裡交頭接耳。 | *"Listen!" she whispered.* "聽著!"她輕聲說。 | *He whispered a warning and then vanished.* 他低聲警告了一聲便消失了。 **2** [I] (of the wind or leaves) to make a soft sound〔風或樹葉〕發沙沙聲 **– whisper** *n*: *She spoke in a whisper.* 她低聲說。

whis·tle¹ /ˈhwɪsl; ˈwɪsəl/ *n* **1** a simple musical instrument that makes a high clear sound when air or steam is forced through it 哨子; 汽笛: *The referee blew his whistle for a free kick.* 裁判吹響了哨子, 示意發任意球。 **2** the high clear sound made by forcing air or steam through a whistle or through your lips 哨子聲; 口哨聲; 汽笛聲: *He gave a loud whistle of surprise.* 他吹了一聲響亮的口哨表示吃驚。

whistle² *v* **whistled, whistling 1** [I] to make a high clear sound by forcing air through

your lips or through a whistle 吹口哨; 吹哨子; 鳴汽笛: *He whistled to his dog.* 他對着他的狗吹了聲口哨。 | *She was whistling merrily.* 她高興地吹起口哨。 | *The train whistled as it left the station.* 火車駛出車站時拉響了汽笛。 **2** [T] to produce music by doing this 用口哨吹奏〔曲子〕: *He was whistling that tune again.* 他又在吹那個調子了。 **3** [I+adv/prep] to move with a whistling sound 呼嘯着移動: *The wind whistled in the chimney.* 風在煙囱裡呼呼作響。

★white¹ /hwaɪt; waɪt/ *adj* **whiter, whitest 1** of the colour of milk, snow, and salt 白色的: *white paint* 白油漆 | *white hair* 白髮 — see picture on page 243 見 243 頁彩圖 **2** pale in colour 淡色的; 蒼白的, 慘白的: *white wine* 白葡萄酒 | *Her face was white with fear.* 她嚇得臉色發白。 **3** belonging to a race with a pale skin 白種人的 **4** with milk or cream (used of tea or coffee) 加牛奶的, 加奶油的〔指茶或咖啡〕 **–whiteness** *n* [U]

white² *n* **1** [U] the colour which is white 白色: *a woman dressed in white* 穿着白色衣服的女人 **2** [C] a person of a race with a pale skin 白種人: *There were both whites and blacks at the meeting.* 出席會議的既有白人也有黑人。 **3** [C] the white part of your eye 眼白 **4** [C;U] the part of an egg which is colourless but becomes white after cooking 蛋清, 蛋白: *Beat three egg whites until stiff.* 攪打三個雞蛋的蛋清直到變稠。

white-col·lar /ˌ··ˈ··◂/ *adj* [only before a noun 只用於名詞前] concerning people who work in offices or at professional jobs, rather than doing hard or dirty work with their hands〔從事非體力勞動的〕白領階層的: *a white-collar union* 白領階層的工會

white el·e·phant /ˌ·ˈ···/ *n* something that is useless and unwanted, especially something that costs a lot of money 無用而昂貴的東西

White·hall /ˈhwaɪtˌhɔːl; ˈwaɪtˌhɔːl/ *n* [+sing/pl verb] the British government, especially the government departments rather than Parliament 英國政府〔尤指各政府部門而不是國會〕

white-hot /ˌ·ˈ·◂/ *adj* extremely hot (used of metal) 白熱的〔指金屬〕

White House /ˈ··/ *n* **the White House** [+sing/pl verb] the official Washington home of the President of the United States, or the US government 白宮〔美國總統或政府的官邸〕

white knight /ˌ·ˈ·/ *n* a person or organization that puts money into a business company to save it from being taken over by another company〔為某公司提供資金使其免於被收購的〕救星, 救急的人或組織

white lie /ˌ·ˈ·/ *n* a harmless lie 無傷大雅的謊言

whit·en /ˈhwaɪtn; ˈwaɪtn/ *v* [I;T] to make or

become white, or more white (使)變白; 漂白: *I must whiten my tennis shoes.* 我得把我的網球鞋刷白。

white pa·per /ˌ· ˈ··/ *n* an official report from the British government on a certain subject 白皮書〔英國政府就某一問題所做的正式報告〕: *a new white paper on education* 一份新的有關教育問題的白皮書

white spir·it /ˌ· ˈ··/ *n* [U] a strong liquid made from petrol, used for example for making paint thinner〔稀釋油漆用的〕石油溶劑

white·wash¹ /ˈhwaɪˌwɑʃ; ˈwaɪtwɒʃ/ *n* **1** [U] a white mixture made from LIME and water, used especially for painting walls〔尤指刷牆用的〕石灰水 **2** [C;U] an attempt to hide a mistake or bad action 掩飾; 粉飾: *The report was simply a whitewash.* 這個報告不過是掩飾真相罷了。

whitewash² *v* [T] **1** to cover something with whitewash 用石灰水粉刷: *whitewashing the farm buildings* 用石灰水粉刷過的農場屋舍 **2** to try to hide a mistake or bad action 掩飾; 粉飾〔壞事〕

whith·er /ˈhwɪðə; ˈwɪðər/ *adv, conj lit* to where〔文〕去哪裡: *Whither is he going?* 他往哪裡去?

whit·ing /ˈhwaɪtɪŋ; ˈwaɪtɪŋ/ *n* **whiting** *or* **whitings** a sea fish used for food 牙鱈〔一種可食用的海魚〕

whit·tle /ˈhwɪtl; ˈwɪtl/ *v* **whittled, whittling** [T] to cut wood to a smaller size by taking off small thin pieces 削〔木頭〕

whittle sthg ↔ **down** *phr v* [T] (also 又作 **whittle** sthg ↔ **away**) to reduce by a continuous and gradual process 逐漸減少; 削減: *Can't you whittle down the wedding list any more?* 你難道不能把結婚禮品表上的內容再減少一些嗎? | *We're whittling away at their sales figures.* 我們正在削減他們的銷售數字。

whizz¹ /hwɪz; wɪz/ *v* **-zz-** (also 又作 **whiz**) [I+adv/prep] *infml* to move very fast, often making a noisy sound as if rushing through the air〔非正式〕颼颼地飛馳: *Cars were whizzing past.* 一輛輛汽車颼颼地飛馳而過。

whizz² *n* (also 又作 **whiz**) **1** [sing] a noisy sound like something rushing through the air 颼颼聲 **2** [C] *infml* someone who is very fast or skilled at the stated activity〔非正式〕〔某項活動的〕快手, 高手, 能手: *She's an absolute whiz at cards.* 她絕對是個玩牌高手。

whizz kid /ˈ· ·/ *n infml*〔非正式〕(also 又作 **whiz kid**) a person who is very successful at an early age because of their natural skill or cleverness 神童; 年青有為的人

who /hu; huː/ *pron* **1** used in questions about a person that is not known 誰〔用於問句〕: *Who are you?* 你是誰? | *Who's at the door?* 誰在門口? | *Who won the race?* 誰贏了這場比賽? **2** used to show which person or people someone means

...的人〔用於指代提及的人〕: *The woman who wrote this letter works in a hospital.* 寫這封信的那個女人在醫院工作。 | *Do you know the people who live here?* 你認識住在這裡的人嗎? | *The man who I talked to had lived in the town all his life.* 跟我說話的那個男人在城裡住了一輩子。 **3** used to add more information about a person or people〔用於對一句話補充信息〕: *I had lunch with my sister, who lives nearby.* 我與妹妹共進午餐, 她就住在附近。

■ USAGE 用法: Except in very formal language we can use **who** instead of **whom** as an object in questions. ☆除非在非常正式的英語中, 我們一般可以用 **who** 來代替 **whom** 作為疑問句中的受詞〔賓語〕。Thus we can say 因此我們可以說 **Who** *did you see?* 你看見誰了? instead of the more formal 來代替比較正式的下列說法 **Whom** *did you see?* 你見到誰了? or 或 **Who** *were you dancing with?* 你在和誰跳舞? instead of the more formal 來代替比較正式的下列說法 *With* **whom** *were you dancing?* 你在和誰跳舞?

who'd /hud; huːd/ **1** short for〔縮〕= "who had" **2** short for〔縮〕= "who would"

who·dun·it /huˈdʌnɪt; ˌhuːˈdʌnɪt/ *n infml* (also 又作 **whodunnit**) a story or film about a murder that is concerned with finding out who did it〔非正式〕〔追查誰是兇手的〕偵探小說; 偵探電影

who·ev·er /huˈevə; huːˈevər/ *pron* **1** whatever person 無論是誰, 不管是甚麼人: *I'll take whoever wants to come.* 誰想來我就帶誰來。 | *Whoever it is, I don't want to see them.* 無論是誰, 我都不想見。 **2** used when you are surprised and are asking "who" 究竟誰〔表示驚訝〕: *Whoever can that be at this time of night?* 這麼晚會是誰呢?

whole¹ /hol; həʊl/ *adj* **1** not divided or cut in half 完整的: *a tin of whole peaches* 一罐整個的桃子 | *Swallow the tablet whole.* 把整片藥片吞下去。 **2** [only before a noun 只用於名詞前] all the 全部的: *I spent the whole day in bed.* 我一整天都躺在床上。 | *He drank a whole bottle of wine.* 他喝了一整瓶葡萄酒。

whole² *n* **1** **the whole of** all of something 全部, 整個: *The whole of the morning was wasted.* 整個上午都被浪費掉了。 **2** something which is complete and is made up of several parts 整體: *We must regard the education system as a whole.* 我們必須把教育體系看作是一個整體。 **3** **on the whole** in general 總的來說: *On the whole I agree with you.* 總的來說, 我同意你的觀點。

whole·food /ˈholˌfud; ˈhəʊlfuːd/ *n* [C;U] food that is in a simple natural form, without anything removed or added〔未經加工

的〕天然食品

whole-heart-ed /ˌˈ ˈ···◂/ *adj* giving all that you can of the stated quality 全心全意的: *You have my whole-hearted support.* 我全心全意地支持你。 **–wholeheartedly** *adv*

whole-meal /ˈhol,mil; ˈhəʊlmiːl/ *adj* (also 又作 **wholewheat**) made without removing the covering of the grain (used of flour or bread) 全麥的〔指麵粉或麵包〕

whole-sale /ˈhol,sel; ˈhəʊlseɪl/ *adj, adv* **1** related to the selling of goods in large quantities and usually at low prices 批發的: *a wholesale supplier of office machinery* 批發辦公用機器的供應商 | *She buys the materials wholesale.* 她成批地購進那些材料。 **2** to a very great degree and without people troubling to make moral judgments (usually used of something bad) 大規模的; 不分青紅皂白的〔常指壞事〕: *wholesale slaughter* 大屠殺

whole-sal-er /ˈhol,selə; ˈhəʊ,seɪlər/ *n* a businessman who sells goods wholesale 批發商

whole-some /ˈholsəm; ˈhəʊlsəm/ *adj* **1** good for your body 有益健康的: *wholesome food* 有益健康的食品 **2** having a good or desirable moral effect 在道德上有益的; 有益於身心健康的

whole-wheat /ˈhol'hwit; ˈhəʊlwiːt/ *n* see 見 WHOLEMEAL

who'll /hul; huːl/ short for 〔縮〕 = "who will"

whol-ly /ˈholi; ˈhəʊ-li/ *adv* completely 完全地, 全部地: *I don't think he was wholly to blame for the accident.* 我認為他不應對此事故負全部責任。 | *To be fair, it's not wholly her fault.* 平心而論, 這不完全都是她的過錯。

whom /hum; huːm/ *pron* the form of WHO that is used in formal English when it is the object of a verb or PREPOSITION 誰〔在正式英語中用作動詞或介詞的受詞[賓語]〕: *Whom did you see?* 你看見的是誰? | *a man whom she had met on holiday* 她在度假時遇到的一個男人 –see 見 WHO (USAGE用法)

whoop /hup; wuːp/ *v* [I] to make a loud cry, usually a happy one 大叫, 呼喊: *whooping with delight* 高興地大喊大叫 **–whoop** *n*

whoo-pee /ˈhwupi; wuːˈpiː/ *interj old fash* a word that people say when they are very happy and excited 〔老式〕好呀! 哈哈!〔用於表示高興和激動〕

whoop-ing cough /ˈhupɪŋ,kɔf; ˈhuː-pɪŋ kɒf/ *n* [U] a disease which causes you to cough a lot and then make a lot of noise as you breathe in 百日咳

whoops /hups; wʊps/ *interj* (also 又作 **oops**) a word that people say when someone has fallen over, dropped something, or made a mistake 哎喲〔用於跌倒時或不小心把某物掉到地上時, 或犯了錯誤時〕: *Careful now... Whoops!* 小心...哎喲!

whoosh /hwuʃ; wuʃ/ *v* [I+adv/perp] to move

quickly with a rushing sound 嗖嗖地迅速移動: *The train whooshed past.* 火車飛馳而過。 **–whoosh** *n*

whop-per /ˈhwapə; ˈwɒpər/ *n infml* 〔非正式〕 **1** something which is surprisingly big 特大的東西, 龐然大物: *Did you catch that fish? What a whopper!* 你抓到那條魚了嗎? 好大的傢伙! **2** a big lie 彌天大謊

whop-ping /ˈhwapɪŋ; ˈwɒpɪŋ/ *adv, adj* [only before a noun 只用於名詞前] *infml* extremely big 〔非正式〕極大的

whore /hor; hɔːr/ *n* a woman who earns money by having sex with anyone who will pay for it 妓女

who're /ˈhuə; huːər/ short for 〔縮〕 = "who are"

whorl /hwɜ·l; wɜːl/ *n* the shape which a line makes when going round in a SPIRAL, for example in some seashells 螺旋紋

who's /huz; huːz/ **1** short for 〔縮〕 = "who is": *Who's he talking about?* 他在談論誰? **2** short for 〔縮〕 = "who has": *Who's he brought to the dinner?* 他帶誰一起去赴宴了?

whose /huz; huːz/ *det, pron* used when you are asking who something belongs to or stating who something belongs to 誰的〔用於提問或陳述〕: *Whose house is this?* 這是誰的房子? | *Whose is that car?* 那是誰的汽車? | *That's the man whose house was burnt down.* 那就是房子被燒毀的人。

who've /huv; huːv/ short for 〔縮〕 = "who have": *I know some people who've been there.* 我認識一些去過那裡的人。 | *Who've you been staying with?* 你一直和誰在一起?

why /hwaɪ; waɪ/ *adv, conj* **1** for what reason 為甚麼: *Why did you do it?* 你為甚麼做這件事? | *I don't know why he got so angry.* 我不知為何會如此生氣。 | *I can see now why it won't work.* 現在我明白它為甚麼不起作用了。 | *There must be a reason why he refused.* 他之所以拒絕, 其中肯定有原因。 **2 why not** a way of suggesting to someone what they should do 為甚麼不〔用於建議某人做某事〕: *If your car's broken down, why not go by bus?* 如果你的車壞了, 那為甚麼不乘公共汽車去呢? | *Why don't you phone him?* 你為何不打電話給他?

wick /wɪk; wɪk/ *n* **1** a piece of twisted thread in a candle, which burns as the WAX melts 蠟燭芯 **2** a piece of material in an oil lamp which burns and gives light 〔油燈的〕燈芯 **3 get on someone's wick** *infml* to annoy someone 〔非正式〕煩擾某人

wick-ed /ˈwɪkɪd; ˈwɪkɪd/ *adj* **1** extremely bad morally 邪惡的; 缺德的: *a wicked man* 邪惡的人 | *the wicked witch* 邪惡的巫婆 | *a wicked waste of money* 對金錢無理的浪費 **2** playful in a rather troublesome or bad way 搗蛋的; 淘氣的: *a wicked smile* 頑皮的一笑 **–wickedly** *adv* **–wickedness** *n* [U]

wick-er-work /ˈwɪkə,wɜ·k; ˈwɪkəwɜːk/ *n*

(also 又作 **wicker**) [U] objects made from weaving together thin branches or reeds (REED) 柳條製品: *wickerwork furniture* 柳編家具

wick·et /'wɪkɪt; 'wɪk ḁt/ *n* **1** the set of three sticks at which the ball is thrown in cricket 〔板球的〕三柱門 **2** the area of grass between the two wickets in a cricket match 〔板球的〕兩個三柱門之間的草地

★**wide**¹ /waɪd; waɪd/ *adj* **wider, widest 1** measuring a large amount from side to side or from edge to edge 寬的, 寬闊的: *a wide road* 寬闊的大道 | *The gate isn't wide enough for me to drive the car through.* 門不夠寬, 所以我的汽車開不進去。**2** used when giving measurements …寬〔用於測量〕: *How wide is the doorway?* 門有多寬? | *The river is about ten metres wide.* 河大約有十米寬。**3** covering or including a large range of things 廣泛的; 廣闊的: *She has very wide interests.* 她的興趣很廣泛。| *books on a wide variety of subjects* 課題廣泛的書籍 **4** (also 又作 **wide open**) fully open 充分張開的, 開得很大的: *wide eyes* 圓睜着的眼睛 **5 wide of the mark** very far from being correct 完全錯誤的

wide² *adv* **1** to a great distance from side to side, or to the greatest distance possible 盡量遠地; 充分地: *He stood with his legs wide apart.* 他兩腿叉開地站着。| *Spread your arms wide.* 把手臂盡量伸開。| *"Open wide,"* *said the dentist.* "(嘴)張大點兒," 牙醫說道。| *The window was wide open.* 窗戶大開着。**2** far away from the right point (used in sport) 遠離目標的〔用於運動〕: *The ball went wide.* 球飛得遠遠的。| *His shot was wide of the goal.* 他的一槍距靶心很遠。

wide-a·wake /ˌ·'··◂/ *adj* fully awake 完全清醒的

wide-eyed /ˌ·'·◂/ *adj* **1** with your eyes fully open because you are very surprised 〔由於驚訝而〕睜大眼睛的 **2** showing a willingness to accept or admire things without questioning them 單純的; 天真的: *He found her wide-eyed innocence very appealing.* 他覺得她的天真無邪很吸引人。

★**wide·ly** /'waɪdlɪ; 'waɪdli/ *adv* **1** over a wide range of things or places 廣泛地: *She has read widely.* 她博覽群書。| *They have travelled widely.* 他們遊歷很廣。**2** by many people 由許多人: *It's widely believed that the government will lose the election.* 人們普遍認為政府將在大選中失利。**3** to a large degree 在很大程度上: *widely different opinions* 迥然不同的意見

wid·en /'waɪdn; 'waɪdn/ *v* [I;T] to make or become wider (使)變寬: *They're widening the road.* 他們正在拓寬這條路。| *The river widens out here.* 河流在此變得越來越寬。| *We'll have to widen the scope of our operation.* 我們必須拓寬業務範圍。

★**wide·spread** /'waɪd'spred; 'waɪdspred/ *adj* existing or happening in many places or among many people 廣泛流傳的; 普遍的: *The disease is becoming more widespread.* 這種疾病正更廣泛地蔓延。| *a widespread belief in his innocence* 普遍認為他是無辜的

wid·ow /'wɪdo; 'wɪdəʊ/ *n* **1** a woman whose husband has died 寡婦, 遺孀 **2** a woman whose husband is often away doing the stated activity 活寡婦〔指丈夫因經常外出參加某項活動而獨處的婦女〕: *a golf widow* 〔丈夫沉溺於高爾夫球而被棄留家中的〕高爾夫球活寡婦

wid·owed /'wɪdod; 'wɪdəʊd/ *adj* left alone after the death of your husband or wife 守寡的; 成了鰥夫的

wid·ow·er /'wɪdowɚ; 'wɪdəʊəʳ/ *n* a man whose wife has died 鰥夫

wid·ow·hood /'wɪdo,hʊd; 'wɪdəʊhʊd/ *n* [U] the state or period of being a widow 孀居; 守寡

width /wɪdθ; wɪdθ/ *n* [C;U] size from one side to the other side 寬度, 闊度, 廣度: *What is its width?* 它的寬度是多少? | *The garden is six metres in width.* 這個花園有六米寬。

wield /wild; wiːld/ *v* [T] **1** to carry a weapon and be prepared to use it 揮動〔武器〕: *They rushed at him, wielding their knives.* 他們揮着小刀向他衝過去。**2** to have and use power or influence 運用, 使用〔權力或影響力〕: *She wields a lot of power in the government.* 她在政府中有很大的影響力。

★**wife** /waɪf; waɪf/ *n* **wives** /waɪvz; waɪvz/ the woman to whom a man is married 妻子: *This is my wife, Jenny.* 這是我的妻子珍妮。| *the President and his wife* 總統夫婦 –see picture on page 503 見 503 頁彩圖

wife·ly /'waɪflɪ; 'waɪfli/ *adj* having or showing the good qualities of a wife (a word which is usually used humorously in modern English) 賢淑的, 賢惠的〔現代英語中常含幽默〕

wig /wɪg; wɪg/ *n* a covering of hair for someone's head, used because they no longer have any hair or to hide their real hair 假髮: *I'm sure she's wearing a wig.* 我敢肯定她戴了假髮。

wig·gle /'wɪgl; 'wɪgəl/ *v* **wiggled, wiggling** [I;T] to move in small side-to-side, up-and-down, or turning movements (使)擺動; (使)扭動: *She wiggled her fingers to check they were OK.* 她動動她的手指, 看看是否沒事兒。| *a rabbit wiggling its nose* 一隻抽動着鼻子的兔子 **–wiggle** *n*: *with a wiggle of her hips* 扭擺着她的屁股 | *writing full of strange wiggles* 滿是奇形怪狀扭來扭去的字體

wig·wam /'wɪgwɑm; 'wɪgwæm/ *n* a tent of the type used by some North American Indians 〔某些北美印第安人住的〕棚屋

★**wild**¹ /waɪld; waɪld/ *adj* **1** living or growing in natural conditions and having natural qualities, and not bred, grown, or produced by humans 野生的; 天然出產的; 不

馴服的: *wild animals in the jungle* 森林裡的野生動物 | *a bunch of wild flowers* 一束野花 | *wild honey* 天然蜂蜜 **2** violent and uncontrollable in behaviour 〔行為〕不受控制的, 狂熱的: *A wild man leapt out of the bushes at them.* 一個狂人躍出樹叢撲向他們。 | *She rushed out with a wild look in her eyes.* 她衝了出去, 眼中流露出狂野的神情。 | *a pop star who drives women wild **with** desire* 一位令女人神魂顛倒、想入非非的流行歌星 **3** violent (used of weather or the sea) 狂暴的, 猛烈的〔指天氣或海洋〕: *a wild wind* 一陣狂風 **4** showing strong feelings 感情強烈的; 激動的: *His speech was greeted with wild applause.* 他的演講贏得了熱烈的掌聲。 **5** having or showing lack of thought or control 雜亂的; 輕率的: *a wild guess* 亂猜 | *a wild throw* 亂投 **6 be wild about** *infml* to like very much 〔非正式〕極其喜愛, 着了魔的: *My son's absolutely wild about racing cars.* 我的兒子對賽車着了魔。 **–wildness** *n* [U]

wild² *adv* **run wild** to behave as you like, without any control over you 失去控制; 失去約束: *Some parents just seem to let their children run wild.* 有些家長似乎只聽任孩子們肆無忌憚。

wild³ *n* **the wild** the natural state in which an animal usually lives 野生〔狀態〕: *The lion escaped and returned to the wild.* 獅子逃回荒野中去了。

wil·der·ness /ˈwɪldənɪs; ˈwɪldənɪ̩s/ *n* **1** any place where there is no sign of human presence or control 荒無人煙的地區: *a city which is fast becoming a lawless wilderness* 一個正在迅速變成沒有法紀的蠻荒城市 **2 the wilderness** an area of land with little natural life, especially a desert 荒野; 〔尤指〕荒漠 **3 in the wilderness** far from the centre of an activity 遠離活動的中心: *Churchill spent years in the political wilderness before he led Britain through the war.* 邱吉爾在領導英國度過戰爭年代之前在野多年。

wild·fire /ˈwaɪldˌfaɪr; ˈwaɪldfaɪ̩r/ *n* **like wildfire** extremely fast 野火似地, 極快地: *The news spread like wildfire.* 這消息迅速地傳播開來。

wild-goose chase /ˌ·ˈ···/ *n infml* a completely useless search 〔非正式〕白費力氣的搜尋; 徒勞之舉

wild·life /ˈwaɪldˌlaɪf; ˈwaɪldlaɪf/ *n* [U] animals and plants which live in natural conditions 野生生物: *The island is full of interesting wildlife.* 島上到處都是有趣的野生生物。

wild·ly /ˈwaɪldlɪ; ˈwaɪldlɪ/ *adv* **1** in a way that shows a lack of thought or control 不受控制地; 輕率地: *He ran wildly down the street.* 他沿着大街狂奔。 | *His answer was wildly wrong.* 他的回答大錯特錯。 **2** *infml* extremely 〔非正式〕極其: *I'm afraid I'm not wildly enthusiastic about the idea.* 恐怕我對這主意不是極感興趣。

wil·ful /ˈwɪlfəl; ˈwɪlfəl/ *adj* **1** showing the intention of doing exactly what you want 任性的; 固執的: *a wilful child* 任性的孩子 **2** done on purpose 故意的, 存心的: *wilful damage to the farmer's crops* 故意損壞農民種的莊稼 **–wilfully** *adv* **–wilfulness** *n* [U]

wi·li·ness /ˈwaɪlɪnɪs; ˈwaɪlɪn̩s/ *n* [U] cleverness at using tricks and deceit to get what you want 狡猾; 詭計多端

★will¹ /wɪl; wɪl/ *v* negative short form 否定縮約式 **won't** [modal verb 情態動詞] **1** used to show that something is going to happen in the future 將, 將要, 會〔用於表示某事將要發生〕: *It will probably rain tomorrow.* 明天大概要下雨。 | *What will you do if you lose your job?* 如果失業了, 你將會幹甚麼? | *I won't be at home this evening.* 我今晚不在家。 –see 見 'S (USAGE用法) **2** used to show that someone is willing to do something 要, 願〔用於表示某人願意做某事〕: *I won't go!* 我不願去! | *No one will take the job.* 沒有人願意接受這項工作。 | *The door won't shut.* 這扇門關不上。 **3** used to show that something always happens or can happen 總是, 能〔用於表示某事一直發生或能夠發生〕: *Oil will float on water.* 油總是浮在水上。 | *Accidents will happen.* 事故總是會發生的。 | *Will your car hold six people?* 你的汽車能坐六個人嗎? **4** used to show that you think something is very likely or certain 大概; 可能〔用於表示認為某事很有可能或確定〕: *That will be Jack at the door.* 門口的人大概是傑克。 | *They will be in France by now.* 現在他們大概已到了法國。 **5** used to show that someone often or always does something unpleasant or annoying 老是〔用於表示某人經常或總是做令人不快或令人惱火的事〕: *She will keep talking when I'm trying to work!* 我想要工作的時候, 她老是說個沒完! –see Study Note on page 1318 見 1318 頁學習提示 **6 will you** a rather direct way of asking someone to do something 請你...好嗎〔用於非常直接地請求某人做某事〕: *Will you post a letter for me, please?* 請你給我寄封信好嗎? | *Shut the door, will you?* 關上門, 好嗎? | *You won't tell him, will you?* 你不會告訴他的, 是吧? | *Will you be quiet!* 你安靜一點好不好! **7 will you have** a polite way of offering something to someone 你要不要...〔用於有禮貌地向某人提供某物〕: *Will you have a cup of tea before you go?* 你走之前要不要喝杯茶? **8 you will** a way of ordering someone to do something 必須〔用於命令某人做某事〕: *You will do as you are told!* 照吩咐你的去做!

★will² *v* [T] **1 will someone to do something** to try to make someone do something by using the power of your mind 用意志力驅使某人做某事: *I was willing him to stop but he walked straight past.* 我想讓他停下來, 可是他徑直走過去了。 **2** to leave money or possessions to someone when you die, by

writing it in your will 立遺囑將〔錢財等〕遺贈〔某人〕

will³ *n* **1** [C;U] the strength of purpose to do something and the power or ability to do it 意志; 毅力; 決心; 意圖: *He no longer has the will to live.* 他再也沒有求生的意志。| *a battle of wills* 意志的較量 | *She didn't believe in free will.* 她不相信自由意志。**2** [U] what is wished or intended by someone who has power 〔有權力者的〕意願, 意旨: *He saw her death as God's will.* 他把她的死看作是上帝的意旨。**3** [C] a written statement in which a person says what should happen to their money and property after they die 遺囑: *He decided that it was time he made a will.* 他決定該立遺囑了。| *She left me £5,000 in her will.* 她在遺囑中留給我五千英鎊。**4** at will when and how you want 任意; 隨意: *She can turn on the tears at will.* 她可以隨意地一下子流出眼淚。

*★**will·ing** /ˈwɪlɪŋ; ˈwɪlɪŋ/ *adj* **1** ready to do something 願意〔做某事〕的; 樂意的: *We can start right now, if you're ready and willing.* 如果你準備好又願意的話, 我們可以馬上開始。| *Is she willing to help?* 她願意幫忙嗎?

> □ USEFUL PATTERN 有用句型
> be willing to do something

2 acting eagerly and without being forced 自願的: *a willing helper* 樂於助人的人 − **willingly** *adv* −**willingness** *n* [U]

wil·low /ˈwɪləʊ; ˈwɪləʊ/ *n* a tree which grows near water, with long thin branches 柳樹

wil·low·y /ˈwɪləwɪ; ˈwɪləʊɪ/ *adj* pleasantly tall, thin, and graceful 苗條的; 婀娜多姿的: *a girl with a willowy figure* 身材苗條的姑娘

will·pow·er /ˈwɪlˌpaʊə; ˈwɪlˌpaʊəˈ/ *n* [U] strength of purpose 意志力: *He keeps saying he'll stop smoking, but he hasn't got any willpower.* 他老是說要戒煙, 可是他一點意志力也沒有。

wil·ly-nil·ly /ˌwɪlɪˈnɪlɪ; ˌwɪlɪˈnɪli/ *adv* even though most people may not want it 不管願不願意〔即使大多數人不接受〕: *They introduced the new law willy-nilly.* 他們不管你願不願意, 就實施了新法令。

wilt /wɪlt; wɪlt/ *v* [I] **1** (of a plant) to become less fresh, bend, and start to die 〔植物〕枯萎, 凋謝: *The flowers are wilting.* 花兒正漸漸凋謝。**2** (of a person) to become tired and weaker 〔人〕變得疲倦, 變得虛弱: *I'm wilting in this heat.* 這麼熱的天氣使我變得沒精打采。

wil·y /ˈwaɪlɪ; ˈwaɪli/ *adj* **wilier, wiliest** very clever in using tricks, especially for getting what you want 狡猾的; 詭計多端的: *a wily negotiator* 狡猾的談判者

wimp /wɪmp; wɪmp/ *n infml* a weak or useless person, especially a man 〔非正式〕懦弱無用的人〔尤指男人〕−**wimpy, wimpish** *adj*

*★★**win¹** /wɪn; wɪn/ *v* **won** /wʌn; wʌn/, **won**, **winning** **1** [I;T] to be the best or first in a struggle, competition, or race 〔在鬥爭、競賽或比賽中〕獲勝, 贏: *Who won?* 誰贏了? | *She won the race.* 她在賽跑中獲勝了。| *I never win at cards.* 我玩牌從來贏不了。| *The winning team got a silver cup.* 獲勝的隊得到了一個銀杯。**2** [T] to be given something because you are successful in any kind of competition 贏得, 獲得〔某事物〕: *She won a prize for the painting.* 她的畫獲了獎。| *He won a gold medal in the 100 metres.* 他獲得了一百米賽跑的金牌。| *Congratulations! You've won a chance to meet your favourite pop star.* 恭喜你! 你得到了和你最喜愛的流行樂歌星見面的機會。**3** [T] to gain something by effort or ability 〔經努力或憑能力〕奪得, 博得〔某事物〕: *The scheme eventually won the support of the city council.* 該計劃最終贏得了市政會的支持。| *By her hard work she won herself a place.* 她憑着艱苦的努力為自己贏得了一個席位。**4** I can't win = I will not get what I want whatever I do 我無論如何也得不到我想要的東西 **5** you win *infml* a phrase used when you are admitting, rather unwillingly, that someone is right, or agreeing in the end to do what they want 〔非正式〕算你贏了〔用於表示相當不情願地承認某人正確或最終同意做某人要求的事〕**6** win the day to be successful after a lot of argument 〔經過大量爭論以後〕成功, 勝利

> ■ USAGE 用法: Compare 比較 **win, gain, earn.** You can **win** or **gain** something as a result of great effort or ability ☆ **win** 或 **gain** 可以表示經過巨大的努力或通過才能得到某物: *He won/gained everyone's approval by his hard work.* 他努力工作, 贏得大家的讚許。You can **gain** something useful or necessary whether or not you deserve it ☆ **gain** 可以用來表示得到有用或必要的事物, 而不論是否應得: *He gained everyone's attention by banging the table with his fist.* 他砰地一拳砸在桌子上, 引起了大家的注意。You can **earn** something which you deserve ☆ **earn** 指得到應得的事物: *Take a rest now. You've earned it!* 現在休息一下吧。你是應該歇歇了! You can also **earn** money for work you do ☆做工掙錢也可以用 **earn**: *She's earning £300 a week at present.* ☆她目前一週掙三百英鎊。

win sbdy ↔ **over** *phr v* (also 又作 **win** sbdy ↔ **round**) [T] to gain someone's support by persuading them 〔通過說服〕爭取〔某人〕的支持: *I'm sure we'll be able to win him round to our way of thinking in the end.* 我肯定我們最終能說服他支持我們的想法。

*★**win²** *n* a victory or success 勝利, 贏: *Our team's had three wins and two defeats this season.* 這個賽季我們隊的戰績三勝二負。

wince /wɪns; wɪns/ v **winced, wincing** [I] to move the top of your body back a little bit suddenly, often making a twisted expression with your face, as if drawing away from something painful or unpleasant 〔因痛苦或不愉快的事而〕退縮，畏縮；臉部肌肉抽搐: *She touched the snake, wincing slightly.* 她觸到那條蛇時本能地退縮了。 | *He winced when I told him how much the repairs would cost.* 我告訴他修理費要花多少錢時，他不由得心裡一征。 **–wince** n

winch /wɪntʃ; wɪntʃ/ n a machine for pulling up heavy objects by means of a rope or chain that is wound around a turning part 絞車；起貨機 **–winch** v [T+adv/prep]: *They winched the car out of the ditch.* 他們用絞車把汽車從溝裡吊上來。

⭐⭐**wind¹** /wɪnd; wɪnd/ n **1** [C;U] a strongly moving current of air 風: *The bridge is closed due to high winds.* 因風太大，那條橋給關閉了。 | *a 70-mile-an-hour wind* 時速七十英里的風 | *The clothes on the washing line flapped in the wind.* 晾衣繩上的衣服在風中飄動。 | *A sudden gust of wind blew the door shut.* 突然一陣大風把門關上了。 **2 get your wind** to breathe properly or regularly again 恢復正常呼吸 **3** [U] air or gas in the stomach 胃氣；腸氣: *Small babies often get wind.* 幼嬰肚子常會脹氣。 **4** [U] *infml* words without meaning 〔非正式〕空談；廢話 **5 get wind of** *infml* to hear about something, especially accidentally or unofficially 〔非正式〕〔尤指偶然或非正式地〕聽到〔某事〕的風聲: *If anyone gets wind of our plans, we'll be in trouble.* 要是有人得知我們的計劃，我們就會陷入困境。 **6 there is something in the wind** something that people are trying to keep secret is about to happen or is being done 〔人們力圖保密的某事〕即將發生，正在進行中 **7 put the wind up someone** *infml* to make someone become afraid or anxious 〔非正式〕使某人害怕或焦急

■ USAGE 用法: **Wind** is a general word for a moving current of air. A **breeze** is usually a pleasant, gentle wind ☆ **wind** 是風的一般用語。**breeze** 常指令人愉快的微風: *A light, summer breeze was blowing.* 一陣夏日輕柔的微風吹拂。 A **gust** is a strong, sudden rush of air ☆ **gust** 指強烈而突然的風: *A sudden gust blew the door shut.* 突然一陣風把門關上了。 A **gale** is a very strong wind ☆ **gale** 是指猛烈的風: *Our chimney was blown down in a gale.* 我們的煙囪在大風中被颳倒了。

---

wind² /wɪnd; wɪnd/ v [T] to cause someone to be breathless or to have difficulty in breathing 使〔某人〕透不過氣〔氣喘吁吁〕: *He was badly winded by the fall.* 他跌得久久喘不過氣來。

wind³ /waɪnd; waɪnd/ v **wound** /waʊnd; waʊnd/, **wound 1** [T+adv/prep] to turn or twist something repeatedly around something else 包；裹；纏繞: *The nurse wound the bandage round his arm.* 護士在他的手臂上包紮繃帶。 | *He wound the wool into a ball.* 他把毛線繞成一個球。 **2** [T+adv/prep] to move something by turning a handle or pressing a button 〔轉動把手等〕使移動: *She wound down the car window.* 她搖下車窗。 | *Can you wind the video forward again, please?* 請你把錄像再快進一下好嗎? | *The film had finished, so he wound it back.* 影片放完了，所以他把它倒回去。 **3** [T] to turn part of a machine round and round, in order to make it work 給〔機器〕上發條: *Can you wind that clock for me?* 你能給我上一下那個鬧鐘的發條嗎? **4** [I+adv/prep] to follow a twisting course, with a lot of changes of direction 彎曲前進；曲折而行；迂迴: *The path winds through the woods.* 小路蜿蜒穿過樹林。

wind down *phr v* **1** [T **wind** sthg ↔ **down**] to bring something to an end gradually 使〔某事物〕逐步結束: *The company is winding down its business in Hong Kong.* 公司正在逐漸縮減在香港的業務。 **2** [I] (of a clock or machine) to work more slowly before at last stopping 〔鐘或機器〕越走越慢而終於停下；使停止運作 **3** [I] (of a person) to rest and become calmer or less active after work or excitement 〔人〕放鬆，平靜下來

wind up *phr v* **1** [I;T **wind** sthg ↔ **up**] to bring something to an end 使〔某事〕結束: *I think we should wind up the meeting now.* 我想我們現在該結束會議了。 | *The company's being wound up.* 這家公司正要結束營業。 **2** [T **wind** sthg ↔ **up**] to turn part of a machine round and round, in order to make it work 給〔機器〕上發條: *He wound up his watch.* 他給錶上發條。 **3** [I+adv/prep] *infml* to put yourself in a certain state or place accidentally 〔非正式〕〔意外地〕落得〔某種境地〕: *You'll wind up in hospital if you drive so fast.* 如果你開得這樣快，會落得個進醫院的下場。 **4** [T **wind** sbdy ↔ **up**] *infml* to annoy someone on purpose, usually playfully 〔非正式〕故意惹惱〔某人，尤指開玩笑地〕: *Don't take any notice — she's just trying to wind you up.* 別當真——她只是想惹你生氣。

wind·bag /ˈwɪndˌbæg; ˈwɪndbæg/ n *infml* a person who talks too much, especially about uninteresting things 〔非正式〕誇誇其談者；空話連篇者

wind·break /ˈwɪndˌbrek; ˈwɪndbreɪk/ n a fence, wall, or line of trees intended to give some protection from the wind 防風籬；防風牆；防風林

wind·fall /ˈwɪndˌfɔl; ˈwɪndfɔːl/ n **1** an unexpected lucky gift, especially of money 意外的收穫；〔尤指〕橫財 **2** a piece of fruit that

---

has fallen off a tree 被風吹落的果子

wind·ing /ˈwaɪndɪŋ; ˈwaɪndɪŋ/ *adj* having a twisting turning shape 彎曲的; 蜿蜒的: *a winding road through the old town* 穿過舊城鎮的蜿蜒道路 | *winding stairs* 盤旋式樓梯

wind in·stru·ment /ˈwɪnd ˌɪnstrəmənt; ˈwɪnd ˌɪnstrʊmənt/ *n* any musical instrument played by blowing air through it 管樂器

wind·mill /ˈwɪndˌmɪl; ˈwɪndˌmɪl/ *n* a building containing a machine that crushes grain, provides electricity, or pumps water, it is driven by large sails which are turned round by the wind 風車; 風力磨坊

★★win·dow /ˈwɪndo; ˈwɪndəʊ/ *n* **1** a glass-filled opening in the wall of a building or in a vehicle, to let in light and air 窗, 窗戶; 櫥窗: *Open the bedroom window.* 打開臥室的窗戶。| *looking in all the shop windows* 朝每個櫥窗裡看 –see picture on page 729 見 729 頁彩圖 **2** *tech* one of the number of areas into which a computer's SCREEN can be divided, each of which is used to show a particular type of information 〔術語〕〔電腦上顯示分類信息的〕視窗

window box /ˈ··· / *n* a box full of earth outside a window, in which plants can be grown 窗口花壇, 窗台花箱

window dress·ing /ˈ·· ˌ·· / *n* [U] **1** arranging goods in a shop window to attract customers 櫥窗佈置 **2** something that tries to attract people to an idea or activity in a rather dishonest way, by giving special attention only to the good things about it 粉飾門面; 弄虛作假; 炫耀

win·dow·pane /ˈwɪndoˌpen; ˈwɪndəʊpeɪn/ *n* a single whole piece of glass in a window 〔一整塊〕窗玻璃

window-shop·ping /ˈ·· ˌ·· / *n* [U] looking at the goods in shop windows without intending to buy anything 逛街看商店櫥窗: *We wandered along Oxford Street, just window-shopping.* 我們沿着牛津街閒逛, 光是瀏覽商店的櫥窗。

win·dow·sill /ˈwɪndoˌsɪl; ˈwɪndəʊˌsɪl/ *n* the flat shelf formed by the piece of wood or stone below a window 窗楣, 窗台 –see picture on page 729 見 729 頁彩圖

wind·pipe /ˈwɪndˌpaɪp; ˈwɪndpaɪp/ *n* the tube which forms an air passage from your throat to the top of your lungs 氣管

wind·screen /ˈwɪndˌskrin; ˈwɪndskriːn/ *n* (**windshield** *AmE* 【美式】) the piece of glass or transparent material across the front of a vehicle, which the driver looks through 〔汽車的〕擋風玻璃 –see picture on page 209 見 209 頁彩圖

windscreen wip·er /ˈ·· ˌ·· / *n* (also 又作 **wiper, windshield wiper** *AmE* 【美式】) a thin piece of metal with a piece of rubber along it, which clears rain from a

windscreen 〔汽車擋風玻璃上的〕刮水器 –see picture on page 209 見 209 頁彩圖

wind·shield /ˈwɪndˌʃild; ˈwɪndʃiːld/ *n* the usual American word for 【美式】= a WINDSCREEN

wind·sock /ˈwɪndˌsɑk; ˈwɪndsɒk/ *n* a tube-shaped piece of material, fastened to a pole at airports to show the direction of the wind 〔套筒形的〕風向袋, 風標

wind·surf /ˈwɪndˌsɝf; ˈwɪndˌsɜːf/ *v* [I] to move along on the water on a flat board with a sail 風帆滑浪 –**windsurfing** *n* [U] **windsurfer** *n*

wind·swept /ˈwɪndˌswɛpt; ˈwɪndswept/ *adj* **1** open to the wind (used of a place) 當風的 〔指地方〕: *a bare windswept plain* 光禿禿的當風的平原 **2** untidy, as if blown by the wind (used of a person) 被風吹亂的〔用於人〕: *her windswept appearance* 她被吹得蓬頭散髮的樣子

wind tur·bine /ˈwɪnd ˌtɝbɪn; ˈwɪnd ˌtɜːbaɪn/ *n* a machine with large flat sails which are turned by the wind to produce electricity 風力渦輪機

wind·y /ˈwɪndɪ; ˈwɪndi/ *adj* **windier, windiest** with a lot of wind 多風的, 風大的: *windy weather* 刮風天 | *a windy hillside* 風很大的山坡

★wine /waɪn; waɪn/ *n* [C;U] an alcoholic drink made from grapes (GRAPE) or other fruit 葡萄酒; 果子酒: *I'd like a glass of red wine, please.* 請給我一杯紅葡萄酒。| *a dry white wine* 乾白葡萄酒 | *the wines of Alsace* 阿爾薩斯產的酒 | *home-made apple wine* 家釀蘋果酒

wine bar /ˈ·· / *n* *BrE* a place where you can buy wine and light meals 【英式】〔供應葡萄酒和便餐的〕酒吧

★wing /wɪŋ; wɪŋ/ *n* **1** a movable part of the body of a bird or insect, which it uses for flying 〔鳥或昆蟲的〕翼, 翅膀: *The parrot flapped its wings noisily.* 鸚鵡吵吵嚷嚷地拍打着翅膀。**2** one of the large flat parts which stand out from each side of a plane and support it in flight 機翼 **3** a part of a structure which stands out from the main or central part 〔主要或中心部分的〕側面伸出物, 側翼: *the west wing of the hospital* 醫院的西翼樓 **4** *BrE* the side part of a car that covers the wheels 【英式】〔汽車的〕擋泥板, 翼子板: *a badly dented wing* 癟得很厲害的擋泥板 –see picture on page 209 見 209 頁彩圖 **5** the position or player on the far right or left of the field in a game such as football 〔足球等運動中的〕邊鋒, 側翼隊員: *He came racing down the right wing.* 他沿右翼奔過來。**6** a group within a political party or organization, whose members have aims or opinions that are different from the main part of the organization 〔政黨或政治組織內部的〕翼, 派別: *The government will have to change their plans to satisfy the right*

W

wing of the party. 政府將不得不改變計劃以取悅黨內的右翼。**7 the wings** [pl] the sides of a stage, where an actor is hidden from the people watching the play 舞台的兩側; 舞台側面 **8 under someone's wing** being protected or helped by someone 在某人的庇護下: *The older boys took the new pupils under their wing*. 舊生照料和指導新生。

wing·er /ˈwɪŋə; ˈwɪŋəʳ/ *n* a player who attacks down one side of the field, in games such as football 〔足球等運動中的〕邊鋒隊員

wing·span /ˈwɪŋˌspæn; ˈwɪŋspæn/ *n* the distance from the end of one wing to the end of the other, when both of them are stretched out 翼展, 翼幅

wink[1] /wɪŋk; wɪŋk/ *v* [I;T] **1** to close and open one eye rapidly, usually as a signal between people, especially of amusement or a shared secret 〔單眼〕眨眼; 使眼色; 眨眼示意: *He winked at her, and she realized he was only pretending to be angry*. 他朝她眨眨眼, 於是她明白他只是假裝生氣。**2** (of a light) to flash on and off 〔光〕閃爍: *The driver winked his lights at us*. 駕駛員向我們一閃一閃地打着燈光信號。| *fireflies winking in the dark* 在黑暗中一閃一閃的螢火蟲 **3 wink at something** to pretend that you have not noticed something bad or illegal 〔對壞事或不合法的事〕睜一隻眼閉一隻眼, 裝作沒看見

wink[2] *n* **1** a winking movement 眨眼; 眨眼示意: *with a wink of approval* 眨眼以示贊同 | *She gave me a knowing wink*. 她會心地朝我眨眨眼。**2 not get a wink of sleep, not sleep a wink** not to be able to sleep at all 沒法睡着: *I didn't get a wink of sleep last night*. 昨晚我沒有睡過。

win·ner /ˈwɪnə; ˈwɪnəʳ/ *n* a person or animal that has won or that people think is likely to win 獲勝者; 可能獲勝的人〔動物〕

win·ning /ˈwɪnɪŋ; ˈwɪnɪŋ/ *adj* very attractive 很吸引人的; 迷人的: *a winning smile* 動人的微笑

win·nings /ˈwɪnɪŋz; ˈwɪnɪŋz/ *n* [pl] money which has been won 贏得的錢

*★***win·ter**[1] /ˈwɪntə; ˈwɪntəʳ/ *n* (also 又作 **Winter**) [C;U] the coldest season of the year, between autumn and spring 冬天, 冬季: *a very cold winter* 非常寒冷的冬季 | *We went skiing last winter*. 我們去年冬天去了滑雪。| *Does it snow here in winter?* 這裡冬天下雪嗎?

winter[2] *v* [I+adv/prep] to spend the winter in a particular place 在〔某地〕過冬: *to winter in a warm country* 在一個溫暖的國家過冬

win·ter·time /ˈwɪntəˌtaɪm; ˈwɪntətaɪm/ *n* [U] the winter 冬季, 冬天: *Heating bills are highest in the wintertime*. 暖氣費在冬天花得最多。

win·try /ˈwɪntri; ˈwɪntri/ *adj* (also 又作 **wintery**) very cold, like it is in winter 寒冷的; 冬天似的: *wintry clouds* 冬雲 | *a wintry*

scene 寒冬的景色

wipe[1] /waɪp; waɪp/ *v* **wiped, wiping 1** [T] to rub a surface in order to remove dirt or liquid 擦, 拭; 擦淨; 揩乾: *Wipe your shoes on the mat*. 在墊子上擦淨鞋子。| *He wiped the table with a damp cloth*. 他用一塊濕布擦桌子。| *Come on, stop crying and wipe your eyes*. 好了, 別哭了, 把眼淚擦乾吧。| *Let's do the dishes — you wash and I'll wipe*. 我們來收拾餐具吧 — 你洗我擦。**2** [T+adv/prep] to remove something by doing this 擦去, 擦掉〔某物〕: *She wiped the tears away*. 她擦去眼淚。| *wipe the crumbs off the table onto the floor*. 把桌子上的麵包屑擦到地上。**3 wipe a tape, wipe something off a tape** to remove the sounds or pictures that were recorded on a TAPE[1] (2) 抹掉磁帶上的錄音或錄像: *I'm afraid I wiped your film off that video*. 恐怕我把你的影片從那錄影帶上抹去了。

wipe sthg ↔ down *phr v* [T] to rub a large surface with a cloth in order to remove dirt or liquid 〔用布把一大塊表面〕擦乾淨: *Wipe down the walls before you start painting*. 漆油漆前先把牆擦乾淨。

wipe sbdy/sthg ↔ out *phr v* [T] to destroy or remove completely 徹底消滅; 勾銷: *The cost of the new machinery has wiped out all our profits this year*. 購買新機器的費用花光了我們今年的全部利潤。

wipe sthg ↔ up *phr v* [T] to remove liquid or dirt from something with a cloth 〔用布〕揩乾, 拭淨: *Wipe up that mess!* 把那攤髒東西揩乾淨! | *Please wipe that milk up*. 請把那些牛奶揩乾淨。

wipe[2] *n* a movement in which something is rubbed against something else 擦, 揩, 拭, 抹: *Give the baby's nose a good wipe*. 好好擦一擦這嬰孩的鼻子。

wip·er /ˈwaɪpə; ˈwaɪpəʳ/ *n* see 見 WIND-SCREEN WIPER

*★***wire**[1] /waɪə; waɪəʳ/ *n* **1** [C;U] a piece of thin metal in the form of a thread 金屬絲, 金屬線: *a wire fence* 金屬絲籠笆 | *The string wasn't strong enough, so we used wire*. 繩子不夠結實, 所以我們用了金屬線。**2** [C;U] a piece of metal like this used for carrying electricity from one place to another 電線: *Connect the blue wires together*. 把藍色的電線連結在一起。**3** [C] the usual American word for 〖美式〗a TELEGRAM

wire[2] *v* **wired, wiring** [T] **1** (also 又作 **wire sthg ↔ up**) to connect up wires in something, especially in an electrical system 裝上電線: *I've wired that plug up*. 我已給這個插座裝上了電線。**2** *AmE* to send a TELEGRAM to someone 〔尤指〕給〔某人〕發電報: *He wired me the results of the examination*. 他打電報告訴我考試的成績。

wire·less /ˈwaɪəlɪs; ˈwaɪələs/ *n* [C;U] old fash a radio 〖老式〗無線電; 無線電收音機

wire-tap·ping /ˈ·ˌ··; ˈ·ˌ··/ *n* [U] listening secretly to other people's telephone conversations 〔對電話的〕竊聽

wir·ing /'waɪrɪŋ; 'waɪərɪŋ/ *n* [U] the arrangement of the wires that form the electrical system in a building 〔房屋內的〕電氣線路: *This old wiring needs replacing.* 這條舊線路需要更換了。

wir·y /'waɪrɪ; 'waɪəri/ *adj* **wirier, wiriest** rather thin, but with strong muscles 瘦而結實的: *a wiry body* 瘦而結實的身體 **–wiriness** *n* [U]

wis·dom /'wɪzdəm; 'wɪzdəm/ *n* [U] **1** knowledge, experience, and good judgment 知識; 經驗; 智慧: *an old man respected for his great wisdom* 一位因才智超羣而受到尊敬的長者 **2** good sense and judgment 明智: *They questioned the wisdom of going to a country that was at war.* 去一個正在打仗的國家, 他們懷疑這是否明智。

wisdom tooth /'··· / *n* **wisdom teeth** one of the four large back teeth in humans, which do not usually appear until the rest of the body has stopped growing 智牙, 智齒

wise /waɪz; waɪz/ *adj* **1** having or showing good sense and judgment, and the ability to understand what happens and to decide on the right action to take 英明的; 明智的; 明察善斷的: *a wise old woman* 一位明智的老婦 | *a wise decision* 英明的決定 | *It was wise of you to leave when you did.* 當時你走是很明智的。 **2 get wise to** *infml* to begin to understand that someone is being dishonest 〔非正式〕開始了解〔某人不誠實〕 **3 get wise** *AmE infml* to find out about something〔美式, 非正式〕發覺 **4 none the wiser** unable to understand something even though someone has tried to explain it 〔即使某人盡力解釋後〕仍不明白: *He went into how it worked in great detail, but I was still none the wiser!* 他詳詳細細地講述了它是怎麼運行的, 但我仍然不明白! **–wisely** *adv*

wise·crack /'waɪz,kræk; 'waɪzkræk/ *n* a clever joking remark 俏皮話; 妙語

wise guy /'·· / *n infml* a person who thinks he knows more than other people 〔非正式〕自作聰明的人

wish¹ /wɪʃ; wɪʃ/ *v* **1** [+(that)] to want a particular situation to exist, when this is either impossible or very unlikely 但願〔表示不可能或可能性很小的願望〕: *I wish I could fly.* 要是我會飛就好了。 | *I wish I were a bird.* 但願我是隻鳥。 | *He wished he'd never mentioned it.* 他但願自己並不曾提過那件事。 | *I wished that the ground would open and swallow me up.* 我恨不得地面裂開把我吞沒。 **2 wish for something** to think of something that you would like very much and hope to get it, or that it will happen 渴望某事物: *"I made a wish." "What did you wish for?"* "我許了個願。" "你祈求些甚麼呢?" **3** [I;T] *fml* to want 〔正式〕想要: *The newspapers can print whatever they wish.* 報紙想登甚麼就登甚麼。 | *Do you wish to see the wine list, sir?* 先生, 您想看一下酒類清單嗎? **4 wish someone something** to hope that someone has something 祝願某人有某事物: *We wish you a merry Christmas.* 我們祝你聖誕快樂。 | *I wish you luck!* 祝你走運! **5 I would not wish something on someone** = I would not want someone else to have to suffer the same experience that I have suffered 我不想某人重蹈我的覆轍: *It was a terrible ordeal, one that I wouldn't wish on my worst enemy.* 這是一場可怕的磨難, 就是我的死敵我也不願他碰上。

wish² *n* **1** a feeling of wanting something 希望: *I am sure everyone shares my wish for these peace talks to succeed.* 我肯定大家都和我一樣, 希望這些和談成功。 | *He asked me to respect her last wishes and not tell her parents.* 他請我尊重她最後的心願, 別告訴她的父母。 **2** an attempt to make a particular thing happen by thinking about it very hard, especially when it could only happen by magic 願望: *Blow out the candles and make a wish.* 吹滅蠟燭, 許個願吧。 **3** a thing that you wish for 希望的事; 想要的東西: *I'm sure you'll get your wish one day.* 我能肯定你總有一天會得到你想要的東西。 **4 best wishes** hopes that someone is well and happy 〔對某人健康快樂的〕良好祝願: *Please give your parents my best wishes.* 請代我向你父母致以良好的祝願。 | *She sends her best wishes to you both.* 她向你倆問好。

wishful think·ing /,·· '··/ *n* [U] a strong belief that something you want very much to happen will happen, when in fact it is very unlikely to 如意算盤; 痴心妄想: *He's convinced she thinks he's wonderful — talk about wishful thinking!* 他滿以為她覺得他很棒 — 真是痴心妄想!

wish·y-wash·y /'wɪʃɪ,wɑʃɪ; 'wɪʃɪ ,wɒʃɪ/ *adj* without clear aims and principles 沒有明確目標和原則的: *rather wishy-washy ideas* 頗空洞的主意

wisp /wɪsp; wɪsp/ *n* **1** a thin or delicate untidy piece of something 一小把; 一小束; 一縷: *a wisp of hair* 一縷頭髮 **2** a small thin twisting bit of smoke or steam 〔煙和蒸汽的〕一縷 **–wispy** *adj*

wist·ful /'wɪstfəl; 'wɪstfəl/ *adj* thoughtful and rather sad, especially because of a wish which may not be satisfied, or thoughts of past happiness which may not return 惆悵的; 留戀的; 思念的: *She left, with a wistful glance over her shoulder.* 她戀戀不捨地回頭瞥了一眼才離去了。 **–wistfully** *adv*: *He thought wistfully of days gone by.* 他留戀地追想過去的日子。

wit /wɪt; wɪt/ *n* **1** [U] the ability to say things which are both clever and amusing 〔說話〕風趣 **2 have the wit to do something** to be clever or sensible enough to do something 有做某事的才智: *He hadn't the wit to say no.* 他笨得連說一聲拒絕的話都不會。 **3 at your**

W

wits' end made too worried by difficulties to know what to do next 智窮計盡; 全然不知所措 **4 frighten/scare someone out of their wits** to frighten someone very much 嚇壞某人 **5 have/keep your wits about you** to be ready to act sensibly 隨機應變; 保持頭腦清醒: *You need to keep your wits about you when you're driving in London.* 在倫敦駕車你得保持頭腦清醒。 **6 -witted** having a particular type of ability or understanding 有...智能的; 有...才能的: *quick-witted* 有機智的 | *dim-witted* 愚蠢的; 傻的

witch /wɪtʃ; wɪtʃ/ *n* a woman who is believed to have magic or evil powers 女巫, 巫婆

witch·craft /'wɪtʃ,kræft; 'wɪtʃkrɑːft/ *n* [U] the performing of magic to make things happen 巫術; 魔法

witch·doc·tor /'wɪtʃ,dɑktə; 'wɪtʃ,dɒktəʳ/ *n* a person in some societies who is believed to have magical powers and is able to cure people 巫醫: *the tribe's witchdoctor* 部落的巫醫

witch-hunt /'··/ *n* a search for people whose political views are disliked or who are thought, sometimes falsely, to be responsible for something that has gone wrong, so that they can be made to suffer or be removed from power 對持不同政見者的追查; 政治迫害

with /wɪð; wɪð/ *prep* **1** by or next to something, or among or included in something 在〔某物〕旁邊; 在〔某物〕之中; 包括在〔某物〕內: *Put this book with the others.* 把這本書和其他的放在一起。 | *Connect this wire with the other one.* 把這根電線接在另一根上。 | *Mix the flour with some milk.* 用一些牛奶把麵粉調和。 | *He was sitting with his friends.* 他和他的朋友坐在一起。 **2** used to show that people do something together 跟, 同, 和〔用於表示人們一起做某事〕: *He never plays with his brother.* 他從來不和弟弟一起玩。 | *Girls rarely fight with each other.* 女孩們很少互相打架。 **3** using something 用; 以; 藉: *Cut it with scissors.* 用剪刀剪開。 | *This photo was taken with my new camera.* 這幅照片是用我的新照相機拍的。 **4** having something 具有, 帶有: *a man with a beard* 長着鬍子的人 | *a book with a green cover* 有綠色封面的書 **5** showing a particular way of behaving 〔表示行為方式〕: *Please handle the box with care.* 請小心搬動這個箱子。 | *He fought with great courage.* 他非常勇敢地戰鬥。 **6** supporting a person or an idea 支持〔人或觀點〕: *We're all with you in this.* 在這方面我們都支持你。 **7** able to understand what someone is saying 能理解〔某人的話〕: *I'm not quite with you.* 我不太明白你的話。 **8** relating to something 對於; 關於: *What's the problem with the car?* 這汽車有甚麼問題? | *Be patient with them.* 對他們耐心些。 **9** because of something 因為; 由於: *With John away at university we've got more*

room in the house. 由於約翰上了大學, 我們房子裡的地方寬敞一些了。 **10** in the same direction as the wind or the movement of water 順着〔風或水流〕: *sailing with the wind* 順風航行

★**with·draw** /wɪð'drɔ; wɪð,drɔː/ *v* **withdrew** /-'dru; -'druː/, **withdrawn** /-'drɔn; -'drɔːn/ **1** [T] to take away or take back 收回; 取回; 提取: *The drug has been withdrawn from the market.* 這種藥已從市場上收回了。 | *I'd like to withdraw some money, please.* 我想提一些錢。 **2** [T] to take back something that was said or offered because it was wrong or must be changed 〔因錯誤或必須更改而〕收回〔說過的話或提議〕: *I think you should withdraw that last remark.* 我認為你應該收回最後那句話。 **3** [I;T] to move away or move back (使)撤出; 撤回: *The two men withdrew from the room while the others voted for who should be chairman.* 當其他人投票選舉主席時, 這兩個人退出了房間。 | *He has withdrawn his armies.* 他撤回了他的部隊。 **4** [I;T] to decide that you or someone else will not take part in something 不參加, 退出: *She withdrew from the election.* 她退出了選舉。 | *He withdrew his horse from the race.* 他讓他的馬退出了比賽。

★**with·draw·al** /wɪð'drɔəl; wɪð'drɔːəl/ *n* **1** [C; U] the taking or moving away of something 收回; 取回; 撤回; 退出: *a gradual withdrawal of troops* 部隊的逐步撤退 | *withdrawal of financial support* 撤銷資助 **2** [C] an amount of money that you take out of your bank account 提款 **3** **withdrawal symptoms** the unpleasant effects suffered by someone when they stop taking a drug 脫癮症狀〔戒毒過程中產生的症狀〕

with·drawn /wɪð'drɔn; wɪð'drɔːn/ *adj* quiet and thoughtful and not very willing to meet or talk to other people 孤僻的; 內向的; 不合羣的

with·er /'wɪðə; wɪðəʳ/ *v* [I] **1** (of a plant) to become dry and then to die 〔植物〕乾枯, 枯萎 **2** (of a part of your body) not to have grown and developed properly 〔身體的一部分〕發育不全, 萎縮 **3** to get weaker and, in the end, die away 變枯槁; 消失: *Our hopes of being rescued gradually withered.* 我們獲救的希望逐漸破滅了。

with·er·ing /'wɪðərɪŋ; 'wɪðərɪŋ/ *adj* withering look a way of looking at someone which is intended to make them feel ashamed 令人感到羞愧的一瞥: *The teacher gave me a withering look.* 老師咄咄逼人地瞥了我一眼。

with·hold /wɪð'hold; wɪð'həʊld/ *v* **withheld** /-'hɛld; -'held/, **withheld** [T] to refuse to give something to someone 拒絕給予: *He was accused of withholding information from the police.* 他被指控不向警方提供情報。

★**with·in** /wɪð'ɪn; wɪð'ɪn/ *adv, prep* **1** *fml* inside something 〔正式〕在〔某

W

物〕裡面; 在〔某物〕內部: *They have an important role within the community.* 他們在這個社區裡起着重要的作用。| *A voice came from within the house.* 房子裡傳來了一把聲音。**2** not going beyond something 在〔某物〕之內; 不出: *We must keep within these spending limits.* 我們必須控制這些開銷。**3** before a particular amount of time is finished 在〔一定時間〕以內: *We should be there within an hour.* 我們應該在一小時內到那兒。| *You should hear something within a day or two.* 你應該在一兩天內聽到點風聲。

★★★**with·out** /wɪðˈaʊt; wɪðˈaʊt/ *adv, prep* **1** not having or not using something 沒有, 不, 無: *Don't go out without your coat.* 不穿外套不要出去。| *I managed to do it without any help.* 我設法在沒有得到任何幫助的情況下做成了這事。| *There's no milk, so we'll have to manage without.* 沒有牛奶, 我們只好不加牛奶了。**2 without doing something** not doing something 不做某事; 未做某事: *He left without saying goodbye.* 他沒有道別就走了。| *Can you clean it without breaking it?* 你能把它洗乾淨而又不弄破嗎?

with·stand /wɪθˈstænd; wɪðˈstænd/ *v* **withstood** /-ˈstʊd; -ˈstʊd/ **withstood** [T] to remain unharmed or unchanged by something 經受住〔某事物〕; 承受: *Children's furniture must withstand rough treatment.* 孩子用的家具必須經得起粗用。

★**wit·ness¹** /ˈwɪtnɪs; ˈwɪtn̩ɪ̵s/ *n* **1** a person who sees something happen and can describe it to other people 目擊者: *There were no witness to the accident.* 那起事故沒有目擊者。**2 be witness to something** *fml* to see something happen 〖正式〗目擊某事物 **3** a person who tells in a court of law what they saw happen or what they know about someone 〔法庭上的〕證人: *a witness for the prosecution* 原告一方的證人 **4** someone who is present at the signing of an official paper and who also signs it, to show that they saw it being signed 〔在文件上簽字證明該文件的簽署的〕見證人, 連署人

witness² *v* [T] **1** to see something happen 目擊〔某事物〕: *Did anyone witness the accident?* 有人親眼目睹這次事故嗎? **2** to be present when an official paper is being signed and then to add your signature to show this 在〔文件〕上簽名作證, 連署: *Will you witness my signature?* 你願意在我的簽名旁連署嗎?

witness box /ˈ···/ *n* (also 又作 **witness stand** *AmE* 〖美式〗) the raised area where witnesses stand in court when they are being questioned 〔法庭的〕證人席, 證人台

wit·ter /ˈwɪtə; ˈwɪtəʳ/ *v* [I] to talk for a long time about something unimportant or uninteresting 嘮叨瑣碎事: *What are you wittering on about?* 你嘮嘮叨叨地在煩些甚麼?

wit·ti·cis·m /ˈwɪtəˌsɪzəm; ˈwɪtɪ̵sɪzəm/ *n* a clever and amusing remark 妙語; 俏皮語; 詼諧話

wit·ty /ˈwɪtɪ; ˈwɪti/ *adj* **wittier, wittiest** having or showing a clever mind and an amusing way of expressing your thoughts 機智的; 詼諧的; 妙趣橫生的: *a witty speaker* 講話風趣的人 | *a witty remark* 妙語; 詼諧話 –**wittily** *adv*

wives /waɪvz; waɪvz/ the plural of WIFE ☆ WIFE 的複數形式

wiz·ard /ˈwɪzəd; ˈwɪzəd/ *n* **1** a man in children's stories who has magic powers 〔兒童故事裡的〕男巫, 術士 **2** someone who is very good at something 能手; 奇才: *He's a financial wizard.* 他是個理財能手。

wiz·ened /ˈwɪznd; ˈwɪzənd/ *adj* old and dried up, with lines in the skin 乾枯的; 乾縮的; 乾癟的: *wizened apples* 皺癟了的蘋果 | *a wizened old lady* 皮膚乾而皺的老太太

wk a written abbreviation for 〖縮〗= WEEK

wob·ble /ˈwɑbl̩; ˈwɒbəl/ *v* **wobbled, wobbling** [I;T] to move unsteadily from side to side (使)搖晃; (使)搖擺; (使)顫動: *Who's wobbling the table?* 誰在搖晃桌子? | *The jelly wobbled about.* 果子凍在顫動着。–**wobble** *n*: *with a wobble in his voice* 嗓音顫抖地

wob·bly /ˈwɑblɪ; ˈwɒbli/ *adj* moving unsteadily from side to side 搖晃的; 顫動的: *wobbly handwriting* 歪歪扭扭的字跡

woe /wo; wəʊ/ *n lit* 〖文〗 **1** [U] great sorrow 悲哀; 悲傷: *a tale of woe* 悲哀的故事 **2 woes** [pl] problems 難題, 困難: *He poured out all his woes.* 他說出了自己所有的困難。

woe·ful /ˈwofəl; ˈwəʊfəl/ *adj* **1** very sad 悲傷的, 憂愁的: *woeful eyes* 憂鬱的眼神 **2** *fml* very bad 〖正式〗極壞的, 糟透的: *a woeful lack of understanding* 非常缺乏諒解 –**woefully** *adv*

woke /wok; wəʊk/ the past tense of WAKE ☆ WAKE 的過去式

wok·en /ˈwokən; ˈwəʊkən/ the past participle of WAKE ☆ WAKE 的過去分詞

wolf¹ /wʊlf; wʊlf/ *n* **wolves** /wʊlvz; wʊlvz/ a wild animal of the dog family which hunts other animals in a group 狼

wolf² *v* [T] (also 又作 **wolf** sthg ↔ **down**) to eat food very quickly 狼吞虎嚥地吃〔食物〕: *He wolfed his meal down.* 他狼吞虎嚥地吃了飯。

★★★**wom·an** /ˈwʊmən; ˈwʊmən/ *n* **women** /ˈwɪmɪn; ˈwɪmɪn/ **1** [C] a fully grown human female 成年女子; 婦人: *Is your doctor a man or a woman?* 你的醫生是男的還是女的? **2** [U] women in general 〔總稱〕女人 **3** [C] a man's wife or girlfriend, in some societies; this use is considered offensive in most Western countries 〔某些社會中的〕妻子, 女朋友〔這種用法在大多數西方國家中被認為是無禮的〕 **4 woman** a rude way of speaking to a woman when you are angry 婆娘〔生氣時對婦女的粗魯稱呼〕: *Sit*

W

★★★ 最常用的 1000 字　★★ 最常用的 1001-2000 字　★ 最常用的 2001-3000 字

down, woman. 坐下，婆娘。

wom·an·hood /ˈwʊmən,hʊd; ˈwʊmənhʊd/ *n* [U] the time when someone is considered a woman and not a girl 女子成年期

wom·an·izer /ˈwʊmən,aɪzə; ˈwʊmənaɪzəʳ/ *n* (also 又作 **womaniser** *BrE* 〖英式〗) a man who likes to have sexual relationships with a lot of women 沉溺於女色者; 玩弄女性者 – **womanizing** *n* [U]

wom·an·ly /ˈwʊmənlɪ; ˈwʊmənli/ *adj* having or showing the qualities suitable for a woman 有女子氣質的; 女人特有的: *She showed a womanly concern for their health.* 她對他們的健康表現出女性特有的無微不至的關懷。

womb /wum; wuːm/ *n* the part of a woman's body where a baby develops before it is born 子宮

wom·en·folk /ˈwɪmɪn,fok; ˈwɪmɪnfəʊk/ *n* [pl] *infml* women or female relatives 〖非正式〗婦女; 女眷

won /wʌn; wʌn/ the past tense and past participle of WIN ☆ WIN 的過去式和過去分詞

★**won·der¹** /ˈwʌndə; ˈwʌndəʳ/ *v* **1** [I;T] to express a wish to know something, silently or in words 對〔某事物〕感到疑惑[好奇]; 想知道: *I wonder if she knows we're here.* 我不知道她是否曉得我們在這裡。| *"Do you think they'll get married?" "I wonder."* "你認為他們會結婚嗎?" "我也不知道。" | *I wonder what really happened.* 我想知道究竟發生了甚麼事。| *I was just wondering about my car. Will it be fixed by Thursday?* 我在想我的汽車怎麼樣了, 到星期四能修好嗎?

□USEFUL PATTERNS 有用句型
to wonder if/whether...; to wonder who, what, why, etc.; to wonder about something

2 [I;+that] to be surprised about something 〔對某事物〕感到驚訝: *I wondered at his rudeness.* 我對他的粗魯感到驚訝。| *I wonder that he can come back here after what happened.* 事情發生後, 他還能回到這兒來, 我覺得奇怪。**3 I wonder if** a phrase you use when you want to ask politely for something 我不知道是否〔用於要禮貌地詢問某事〕: *I wonder if I could have some more tea?* 我不知道我是否可以再喝些茶? | *I was wondering if you could give me a lift.* 我不知道你是否能讓我搭你的車。

■ USAGE 用法: Compare 比較 **wonder** and 和 **admire**. You can **wonder** at (=be very much surprised at) both good and bad things ☆對好事和壞事都可以用 **wonder at**: *We wondered at the magnificent buildings/the dreadful poverty in the city.* 我們對城市中宏偉的建築

[可怕的貧窮]感到驚異。You **admire** good things, without being surprised by them ☆ **admire** 表示欣賞好的事物, 並不對此感到驚訝: *I have always admired Shakespeare's plays.* 我一直很欣賞莎士比亞的劇作。

wonder² *n* **1** [U] a feeling of strangeness, surprise, and admiration 驚奇; 驚訝; 驚嘆: *She gazed in wonder, seeing snow for the first time.* 她第一次看見雪, 驚奇地凝視着。| *He was filled with wonder at the sight of his newly-born son.* 他看到新生的兒子感到十分驚嘆。**2** [C] someone or something that makes you feel surprise and admiration 奇事; 奇物; 奇才; 奇跡; 奇觀: *the wonders of modern science* 現代科學的奇跡 **3 it's a wonder** *infml* it's surprising 〖非正式〗真想不到; 令人驚奇的是: *It's a wonder that you recognized me after all these years.* 真想不到這麼多年之後你還認得出我。**4 no wonder, it's no wonder, it's small wonder** it's not surprising 難怪; 不足為奇: *"I got to bed at 5 a.m." "Well, no wonder you're so tired."* "我清晨五點才睡。" "喔, 難怪你這麼疲倦。" **5 work wonders, do wonders** to bring extremely good results 創造奇跡; 取得驚人的成效: *He looked so tired before, but his holiday has worked wonders.* 他原先看上去十分疲倦, 但休假(對他)產生了奇效。

wonder³ *adj* [only before a noun 只用於名詞前] extremely good 極好的; 奇妙的: *a new wonder drug which they hope will cure cancer* 一種他們希望可以治癒癌症的新的神丹妙藥

★**won·der·ful** /ˈwʌndəfəl; ˈwʌndəfəl/ *adj* **1** causing great pleasure 令人驚喜的: *wonderful news* 令人驚喜的消息 **2** deserving admiration 令人驚嘆的; 奇妙的: *a wonderful advance in computer science* 電腦科學的奇妙進展 –**wonderfully** *adv*

won·der·ment /ˈwʌndəmənt; ˈwʌndəmənt/ *n* [U] *lit* a feeling of strangeness, surprise, and admiration 〖文〗驚奇; 驚訝; 驚嘆

won·drous /ˈwʌndrəs; ˈwʌndrəs/ *adj* causing great admiration 令人驚嘆的

won·ky /ˈwɒŋki; ˈwɒŋki/ *adj BrE infml* unsteady and likely to break, fall, or fail 〖英式, 非正式〗不穩的; 搖晃的; 要倒的: *That table's a bit wonky!* 那張桌子有點搖晃晃!

wont¹ /wʌnt; wəʊnt/ *n fml* 〖正式〗**as is someone's wont** as someone often does 像某人慣常那樣: *He spoke for too long, as is his wont.* 他發言太長了, 他總是這樣的。

wont² *adj* **be wont to do something** to be in the habit of doing something 慣於做某事: *He is wont to express himself rather forcefully on that subject.* 他慣於在那個問題上發表宏論。

won't /wont; wəʊnt/ short for 〖縮〗 = "will not": *I won't go!* 我不去!

woo /wu; wuː/ v **wooed, wooed, wooing** [T] **1** to try to get someone's support 爭取〔某人〕的支持: *Politicians try to woo voters before an election.* 政客在選舉前盡力爭取選民的支持。**2** (of a man) to try to persuade a woman into love and marriage (a word no longer used in modern English, except humorously) 〔男子〕向〔女子〕求愛, 求婚〔除了作幽默用法外, 在現代英語中不再使用〕

★**wood** /wud; wʊd/ n **1** [U] the substance of which trees are formed, which is cut and used for various purposes, for example, burning, making paper, or making furniture 木, 木材, 木料; 木頭, 木柴: *Put some more wood on the fire.* 往火裡再添些木柴。| *a polished wood floor* 擦得光亮的木地板 **2** [C] (also 又作 **woods** [pl]) a place where a lot of trees grow together, smaller than a forest 樹林; 林地: *We went for a walk in the woods.* 我們去樹林中散步。

wood·cut·ter /'wud,kʌtə; 'wʊd,kʌtəʳ/ n a man whose job is to cut down trees 伐木工人

wood·ed /'wudɪd; 'wʊdɪd/ adj covered with trees 長滿樹木的: *a densely wooded hillside* 樹木繁茂的山坡

★**wood·en** /'wudn; 'wʊdn/ adj **1** made of wood 木製的: *a wooden spoon* 木匙 **2** stiff and expressionless 僵硬的; 沒有表情的: *I thought her performance was rather wooden.* 我認為她的表演相當呆板。

wood·land /'wud,lænd; 'wʊdlənd/ n [U] an area of land covered with trees 林地; 林區: *large areas of woodland* 大片林地 | *woodland birds* 林地鳥類

wood·peck·er /'wud,pɛkə; 'wʊd,pekəʳ/ n a bird with a long beak, with which it can make holes in trees and pull out insects 啄木鳥

wood·wind /'wud,wɪnd; 'wʊd,wɪnd/ n [U+sing/pl verb] the set of tube-shaped musical instruments which are played by blowing 木管樂器

wood·work /'wud,wɝk; 'wʊdwɜːk/ n [U] **1** the parts of a house that are made of wood 〔房屋的〕木建部分 **2** the skill of making wooden objects 木工手藝

wood·worm /'wud,wɝm; 'wʊdwɜːm/ n **1** [C] the small wormlike young of certain beetles (BEETLE), which eat holes in wood 蛀木蟲; 木蠹 **2** [U] the damage done by these creatures 蛀木蟲害

wood·y /'wudɪ; 'wʊdi/ adj **1** having a lot of trees 長滿樹木的: *a woody valley* 樹木茂盛的山谷 **2** like wood 木頭似的: *plants with woody stems* 木莖植物

woof /wuf; wʊf/ n, interj infml a word used for describing the sound made by a dog 〔非正式〕狗吠聲; 汪汪(聲)

wool /wul; wʊl/ n [U] **1** the soft thick hair which sheep and some other animals have on their bodies 羊毛 **2** thick thread or cloth made from this 毛線; 絨線; 毛織物: *another ball of wool for my knitting* 我編織用的另一團毛線 | *a wool suit* 毛料套裝 **3** **pull the wool over someone's eyes** to trick someone or hide the facts from them 蒙騙〔某人〕

wool·len /'wʊlɪn; 'wʊlən/ adj (also 又作 **woolen** AmE 〔美式〕) made of wool 羊毛製的: *a woollen coat* 羊毛外衣

wool·lens /'wʊlɪnz; 'wʊlənz/ n (also 又作 **woolens** AmE 〔美式〕) [pl] clothes made of wool 毛織衣; 毛料衣服

wool·ly¹ /'wʊlɪ; 'wʊli/ adj **1** made of wool or like wool 羊毛製的; 像羊毛的: *woolly socks* 羊毛短襪 **2** showing a lack of clear thinking (used of people or their thoughts) 不清楚的, 糊塗的〔指人或思想〕

woolly² n **woollies** infml a piece of clothing made of wool 〔非正式〕毛衣; 羊毛內衣: *winter woollies* 冬季毛衣

woolly hat /,·· '·/ n BrE a close-fitting hat worn to keep the head and ears warm 〔英式〕羊毛帽 –see picture on page 210 見 210 頁彩圖

woolly-head·ed /,·· '···/ adj tending not to think clearly or have sensible ideas 糊塗的; 懵懂的

woo·zy /'wuzɪ; 'wuːzi/ adj infml unsteady or confused 〔非正式〕頭昏眼花的; 糊塗的

★**word**¹ /wɝd; wɜːd/ n **1** [C] the smallest piece of a language which has a meaning; the letters or sounds of a word do not usually change and in English a written word has a space on either side 詞; 單詞; 字: *What's the French word for "mouse"?* "mouse" 的法語單詞是甚麼? | *For homework I'd like you to write an essay of about 500 words.* 我要你們寫一篇五百字左右的短文作為家庭作業。**2** **put something into words** to express something clearly 把某事物用言語表達出來 **3** **in your own words** not repeating what someone else has said 用自己的話 **4** **in other words** a phrase used when you are repeating an idea in other words because you think that people may not have understood the real meaning behind the words and you need to explain it 換言之, 也就是說〔用於自覺得別人也許並未理解言外的真正意思, 而需要再加解釋〕: *It goes on horizontally. In other words, it goes from side to side, not from top to bottom.* 它是水平移動的。也就是說, 從一邊到另一邊, 而不是由上至下的。| *The company has to reduce labour costs. In other words, some of us are going to lose our jobs.* 公司得降低勞動力成本。也就是說, 我們有些人要失業了。–see Study Note on page 1325 見 1325 頁學習提示 **5** **in a word** making a short general statement of the main points of something 簡言之, 總之, 一句話: *It's a long story. In a word, I quit.* 說來話長, 總之, 我辭職了。**6** **not in so many words** not expressed clearly and directly, but only suggested 不明確地;

不直截了當地 [RELATED PHRASE 相關詞組 in so many words] **7 word for word: a** in exactly the same words 逐字地, 一字不變地: *Tell me what she said, word for word.* 一字不改地告訴我, 她説了甚麼。 **b** by translating each word of one language into a word in another language, rather than giving the meaning of whole phrases and sentences 逐字地; 直譯地 **8 get a word in edgeways** to manage to say something 插嘴: *She went on and on about her holiday, and I couldn't get a word in edgeways.* 她沒完沒了地談論她的假期, 我沒法插嘴。 **9 have a word with, have a few words with** to have a short conversation with someone, usually in private and about something you do not want other people to hear 和某人説幾句話〔常指私下或不願讓別人聽見〕: *Peter, could I have a word with you after class, about your homework?* 彼得, 下課後我可以和你談談關於家庭作業的事嗎? **10 have a good word for** to say pleasant things about 説好話: *She never has a good word for her brother.* 她從未為她的弟弟説過一句好話。 **11 put in a good word for** to say something good about someone to someone who is important 替〔某人〕向重要的人美言: *Could you put in a good word for me with the headmaster?* 你能替我向校長美言幾句嗎? **12 have words** to argue angrily 吵嘴, 口角 **13 have the last word** to make the last decision or remark in a conversation or argument〔在談話或爭論中〕作最後的決定[評論] **14 not a word** nothing at all of what has been said or written〔説的或寫的〕一點也不: *I don't believe a word of what she says.* 我對她的話一句也不相信。 | *The music was so loud that I couldn't hear a word of what he was saying.* 音樂太響了, 他説的話我一句也聽不到。 **15 a word of advice** some advice 一些忠告: *Let me give you a word of advice.* 我來給你一些忠告吧。 [RELATED PHRASE 相關詞組 **a word of warning** 16 [U] a message or piece of news 信息, 消息: *The hostage sent word that he was alive and well.* 那人質傳來音信説他還活着, 狀況很好。 **17 give the word, say the word** to tell someone to start doing something 告訴〔某人〕開始做〔某事〕; 發出命令: *When I give the word, you may open your exam papers.* 我發出命令, 你們就可以打開試卷。 **18** [sing] a promise 諾言; 保證: *I give you my word that I won't tell anyone* 我向你保證我不會告訴任何人。 | *She always keeps her word.* 她一向守諾言。 **19 take someone's word for it** to accept what someone says as correct without any other proof〔沒有任何證據而〕相信某人的話 **20 by word of mouth** in speech rather than in writing 用口頭〔而非筆頭〕 **21 from the word go** from the beginning 從一開始 **22 my word, upon my word** expressions of surprise (phrases no longer used in modern

English) 噯呀!〔表示吃驚, 在現代英語中不再使用〕 **23 too...for words** *infml* a phrase you use when you want to say that a quality is very strong; it is usually a quality you disapprove of 〔非正式〕實在太..., ...得難以言傳〔用於表示某種性質很強烈, 常用於不贊成〕: *Honestly, the government's thinking on this is too muddle-headed for words.* 説實話, 政府在這方面的見解實在太愚蠢了。

**word² ** *v* [T] to choose particular words to express something 用言語表達〔某事〕; 措辭: *He worded the explanation well.* 他的解釋措辭得體。 | *a carefully-worded apology* 措辭謹慎的道歉

word·ing /ˈwɜːdɪŋ; ˈwɝːdɪŋ/ *n* [U] the words and phrases chosen to express something 措辭, 用詞: *Let's discuss the wording of the advertisement.* 讓我們來討論一下這廣告的措辭吧。

word-per·fect /ˌ····◂/ *BrE* (**letter-perfect** *AmE* 【美式】) *adj* repeating or remembering every word of something completely correctly 【英式】 熟記得一字不錯的: *Her speech was word-perfect.* 她的講辭背得滾瓜爛熟。

word pro·cess·or /ˈ· ····/ *n* a small computer used for typing (TYPE) letters and reports, and storing information 文字處理機 –see picture on page 763 見 763 頁彩圖 –**word processing** *n* [U]

word·y /ˈwɜːdɪ; ˈwɝːdi/ *adj* using or containing too many words 話太多的, 冗長的, 囉嗦的: *a wordy explanation* 囉嗦的解釋

wore /wɔː; wɔːr/ the past tense of WEAR ☆ WEAR 的過去式

★★ **work¹** /wɜːk; wɝːk/ *n* **1** [U] activity which uses effort and is done for a particular purpose, not for pleasure 工作; 勞動; 作業: *It was hard work digging the garden.* 在花園裡掘土是件辛苦的工作。 | *I've been busy doing work in the house.* 我在屋裡忙着幹活。 **2 at work** doing some work 在工作, 在幹活, 在勞動: *He was sitting watching some men at work on the roads.* 他在坐着看一些工人修路。 **3 get to work, set to work** to start doing some work 開始工作, 開始幹活: *We'd better set to work on this decorating.* 我們最好開始這項裝修吧。 **4** [U] a job 職業; 業務: *What work do you do?* 你是幹甚麼工作的? | *He's not home from work yet.* 他還沒有下班。 | *She's still at work.* 她還在上班。 | *Do you enjoy your work?* 你喜歡你的工作嗎? –see 見 JOB (USAGE用法) **5 in work** with a job 有工作, 有職業: *The number of people in work has increased over the last three years.* 近三年來就業人數有所增加。 **6 out of work** with no job but wanting a job 失業: *Many people have been out of work for more than a year.* 許多人失業已有一年多了。 **7** [U] the tasks that you have to do in your job 活計; 任務: *I've had to bring some work home with me this evening.* 今晚我得帶些活

兒回家去做。| *I've got a lot of work to do at the moment.* 我現在有許多工作要做。**8** [U] something that a person has produced by working or by doing their job 工作成果; 產品: *The garden looks lovely and it's all my own work.* 這花園看上去很美麗, 這可都是我的勞動成果。**9** [U] a study that has been done on a particular subject 〔對某一課題的〕研究: *Recent work in this area suggests that men are more likely to get this disease than women.* 最近在這方面所作的研究表示男人比女人更有可能患上這種疾病。| *A lot of work has been done* **on** *this subject.* 對這個課題已進行了大量研究。**10** [C] a piece of art produced by writing, painting, etc. 著作; 〔藝術〕作品: *the works of Shakespeare* 莎士比亞的著作 **11 have your work cut out** to have something very difficult to do 面臨艱苦的工作: *You'll have your work cut out to get that job finished by next week.* 你得在下週之前設法完成那項工作。

> ■ USAGE 用法: Compare 比較 **work, labour, toil.** We can use **work** as a general word for all activities of the mind or body, pleasant or unpleasant. For unpleasant and tiring work we can use **labour** or (more literary) **toil** ☆ **work** 一詞可用於泛指各種愉快或不快的腦力及體力活動。對令人厭煩及疲倦的工作可以用 **labour** 或更正式的: **toil**: *Clearing the field of stones took ten days of backbreaking* **labour/toil**. 清理這滿是石頭的場地花了十天累人的工夫。

⁑work² *v* **1** [I] to be active or use effort in order to do something 做工作; 幹活; 勞動: *I've been working in the garden all afternoon.* 我整個下午都在花園裡幹活。| *He's working* **on** *a new book at the moment.* 他目前在寫一本新書。**2** [T] to make someone be active or use effort 使工作; 使幹活; 使勞動: *The teachers work us far too hard.* 老師逼得我們太苦了。**3** [I] to be employed 受雇用; 做工: *She works in an office.* 她在一個辦事處工作。| *He works as a salesman.* 他當推銷員。| *She works for a large computing firm.* 她為一家大規模的電腦公司工作。**4** [I] to operate properly 正常運轉: *This light doesn't work.* 這盞燈不亮了。**5** [T] to make a machine operate 使〔機器〕運轉; 開動; 操作: *He showed us how to work the coffee machine.* 他給我們示範怎樣操作咖啡機。**6** [I] to be successful 起作用; 取得成效: *I'm sure her plan won't work.* 我肯定她的計劃行不通。**7** [+complement] to become 變得: *The handle had worked loose.* 把手已經鬆了。**8 work against the clock** to work quickly because you have to finish a job by a particular time 〔為在某個時間以前完成任務而〕加快工作; 搶時間做 **9 work your way** to manage to get somewhere gradually by

using a lot of effort 費勁地到達某處: *He managed to work his way to the front of the crowd.* 他費勁地擠到了人墓前面。**10 work yourself into a rage/temper** to become very angry 大發雷霆 **11 work to rule** to obey exactly the rules of your work but do nothing more, as a way of showing that you are unhappy about something 死扣規章而少幹活; 怠工 **12 work wonders** to have very good results 創奇跡; 產生極好的效果

> □ USEFUL PATTERNS 有用句型
> to work something out; to work out how, why, who, etc.; to work out that...

2 [I] to have an answer which can be calculated 〔被〕算出: *The cost works out* **at** *£6 a night.* 費用算下來是六英鎊一晚。**3** [I] to be successful or develop 成功; 發展: *I hope the new job works out for you.* 我希望新工作會使你獲益。| *I wonder how their ideas worked out in practice.* 我不知道他們的想法如何實踐。**4** [T **work** sthg ↔ **out**] to plan or decide something 制訂出; 決定〔某事物〕: *I've drawn up the main outlines but we'll work out the details later.* 我已草擬了主要的提綱, 稍後我們將制訂出細節。**5** [I] *infml* to exercise 〔非正式〕鍛鍊: *She's working out in the gym.* 她在健身房裡鍛鍊身體。

work sthg ↔ **off** *phr v* [T] to get rid of by work or activity 〔用勞動或其他活動〕消除, 排除: *He worked off his anger by going for a run.* 他去跑了一圈發泄怒氣。

work on sthg *phr v* [T] to give your attention to doing something 致力於〔某事物〕: *I haven't found out her name yet, but I'm working on it.* 我尚未找到她的名字, 但我正抓緊辦。

work out *phr v* **1** [T **work** sthg ↔ **out**] to find by reasoning or calculating 推斷出; 計算出: *Have you worked the answer out?* 你算出答案了嗎? | *The police can't work out how the thieves entered the building.* 警察弄不懂竊賊是如何進入這座大樓的。| *She'd worked out that it would cost over £100.* 她算出這要花一百多英鎊。

work up *phr v* **1** [T **work** sbdy **up**] to make someone angry or upset 使〔某人〕生氣; 使心煩意亂: *She's worked herself up into a terrible state about her exam.* 她被考試弄得心煩意亂極了。**2** [I;T **work** sthg ↔ **up**] to develop or move towards 發展; 向前: *I've worked up quite a thirst playing tennis.* 我對打網球漸漸上了癮。| *I'm not ready to give blood yet, but I'm working up* **to** *it.* 我還沒準備好捐血, 可是我正在打算呢。

work·a·hol·ic /ˌwɜːkəˈhɒlɪk; ˌwɜːkəˈhɒlɪk/ *n* a person who likes to work too hard or who is unable to stop working 醉心於工作的人; 工作狂

work·bench /ˈwɜːkˌbentʃ; ˈwɜːkbentʃ/ *n* a table with a hard surface for working on with tools 工作枱: *a carpenter at his work-bench* 在工作枱上幹活的木匠

work·day /'wɜˑk,de; 'wɜːkdeɪ/ *n* (also 又作 **working day** /ˌ·· '·/) **1** a day which is not a holiday 工作日 **2** the amount of time during which you work each day 工作日〔一天的工作時數〕

worked up /ˌ· '·◂/ *adj* [never before a noun 不能用於名詞前] unhappy, angry and worried 不快的; 生氣的; 擔心的: *Don't get so worked up about it!* 別為此事這麼生氣!

★**work·er** /'wɜˑkə˞; 'wɜːkə˞/ *n* **1** someone who does a particular type of job 做某種工作的人: *office workers* 辦公室職員 | *farm workers* 農業工人 **2** someone who works in a particular way 以某種方式工作的人; 工作者: *She's a hard worker.* 她是個勤奮的工作者。 **3** someone employed by other people, usually to do physical work and not management 工人,〔常指〕體力勞動者: *a factory worker* 工廠工人

work·force /'··/ *n* [sing+sing/pl verb] all the people who work in an industry or a factory 全體在職人員; 勞動力: *The entire workforce is out on strike.* 全體工人都在外罷工。

★**work·ing** /'wɜˑkɪŋ; 'wɜːkɪŋ/ *adj* [only before a noun 只用於名詞前] **1** relating to or used for work (涉及)工作用的, 工作上的: *The diplomats had a working breakfast with the President.* 外交官和總統共進工作早餐。 | *working clothes* 工作服 | *working capital* 營運資本, 周轉資金 **2** having a job that is paid 有工作的; 有職業的: *childcare facilities for working mothers* 為職業婦女提供的兒童保育設施 **3 the working day, the working week** the number of hours that you spend each day or week at work 工作日; 工作週: *How long is your working day?* 你的工作日有多長時間? **4** used as a base for planning how to do something (used of an idea) 可作為基礎的; 起作用的〔指主意〕: *a working theory* 切實可行的理論 **5 a working knowledge of** enough practical knowledge to do something〔做某事的〕足夠的實用知識: *I have a working knowledge of car engines and can do most repairs.* 我對汽車引擎構造有實用的知識, 能應付大部分的修理工作。 **6 be in working order** to be operating properly 正常地運轉

working class /ˌ·· '·◂/ *n* **the working class, the working classes** the social class to which people belong who work with their hands, for example in factories or mines 工人階級, 勞動階級 —**working-class** *adj*

working par·ty /'·· ˌ··/ *n* a committee which examines a particular subject and reports what it finds 專題調查委員會, 特別工作組

work·ings /'wɜˑkɪŋz; 'wɜːkɪŋz/ *n* [pl] the way in which something works or operates 工作方式; 運行方式: *I shall never understand the workings of her mind.* 我永遠搞不懂她的思維方式。

work·load /'wɜˑk,lod; 'wɜːkləʊd/ *n* the amount of work you are expected to do in a particular period of time〔一定時間內的〕工作量: *She has a very heavy workload.* 她有很重的工作負擔。

work·man /'wɜˑkmən; 'wɜːkmən/ *n* **workmen** /-mən; -mən/ a man who works with his hands, in a particular skill or trade 工人; 工匠: *The workmen fixed the water system.* 工人修好了供水系統。

work·man·like /'wɜˑkmən,laɪk; 'wɜːkmən-laɪk/ *adj* having or showing the qualities of a good workman 技術熟練的; 有技巧的: *her workmanlike methods* 她熟練的技法

work·man·ship /'wɜˑkmən,ʃɪp; 'wɜːkmən-ʃɪp/ *n* [U] skill in making things 手藝; 工藝: *good workmanship* 精細的工藝 | *Look at the workmanship on this carved desk.* 看這張雕花書桌的工藝多麼精湛。

work of art /ˌ· ·'·/ *n* **works of art 1** something, for example a painting, which is produced by an artist 藝術作品〔如繪畫〕: *Rodin's "The Thinker" is one of many works of art in the museum.* 羅丹的"思想者"是博物館裡眾多藝術品中的一件。 **2** something which has been produced with great skill 精緻的東西: *Did you see her wedding dress? It was a real work of art.* 你看到她的結婚禮服了嗎? 真是精緻得很。

work·out /'wɜˑk,aʊt; 'wɜːkaʊt/ *n infml* a period of physical exercise and training〖非正式〗鍛鍊, 訓練(時間)

works /wɜˑks; wɜːks/ *n* [plural is 複數為 **works**] a factory or other industrial place of work 工場; 工廠: *a gas works* 煤氣廠

★**work·shop** /'wɜˑk,ʃap; 'wɜːkʃɒp/ *n* **1** a room or place where machines are built or repaired 車間, 工場 **2** an occasion when a group of people meet and work together in order to share and develop ideas about a subject 研討會, 研習班: *a two-day workshop on management techniques* 為期兩天的管理技巧研討會

work-shy /'··/ *adj* not liking work and trying to avoid it (a word used to express disapproval) 不願工作的, 偷懶的〔含貶義〕

work·top /'wɜˑk,tap; 'wɜːktɒp/ *n* a flat surface on top of a piece of kitchen furniture where you can prepare food〔廚房家具供備餐之用的〕工作枱, 工作面

work-to-rule /ˌ·· '·/ *n* a form of working which causes activity to become slower, because attention is paid to every point in the rules, even when unnecessary, and no additional work is done, in order to support a claim for more money〔死扣規章制度以降低工作效率的〕怠工, 按章工作〔以要求加薪〕

★**world** /wɜˑld; wɜːld/ *n* **1 the world** the Earth, on which we live 世界; 地

球: *the richest man in the world* 世界上最富有的人 | *I'd love to sail round the world.* 我愛環球旅行。–see 見 EARTH¹ (USAGE用法) **2 the world** people generally 世人; 眾人; 人類: *We don't want the whole world to know about it.* 我們不想讓人人都知道這件事。**3 the ... world** a group of living things 〔生物〕界: *the animal world* 動物世界 **4 the ... world** a part or area of the world that has a particular character 世界〔世界的〕某一特定部分或地區〕: *the developing world* 發展中國家 | *the industrialized world* 工業化地區 **5 the world of** ... a particular area of human activity 〔人類活動的〕領域, 界: *the world of football/the football world* 足球界 **6** the way someone thinks and lives 思考方式; 生活方式: *He's in a world of his own.* 他沉浸在自己的世界裡。| *a glimpse into my son's world* 對我兒子的內心世界的窺探 **7** a PLANET or star system which may contain life 〔可能有生命存在的〕天體, 星球: *a strange creature from another world* 來自另一個星球的奇怪生物 **8 a world of** *infml* a large amount of 《非正式》大量, 無數: *That holiday did me a world of good.* 那次休假對我大有好處。| *There's a world of difference between thinking about it and doing it.* 這件事想是一回事, 做起來是另一回事, 兩者相差甚遠。**9 for all the world as if** exactly as if 正像, 恰似 **10 in the world** a phrase used to make your question or statement more forceful 究竟, 到底〔用於加強語氣〕: *What in the world are you doing?* 你到底在做甚麼? **11 not for the world** a phrase used to say that you certainly do not want to do something 無論如何不, 決不〔用於表示肯定不做某事〕: *I wouldn't hurt her for the world.* 我無論如何不會傷害她。**12 out of this world** *infml* wonderful 《非正式》非凡的; 極好的 **13 the best of both worlds** the advantages which each choice offers, without having to choose between them 兩全其美; 各取其長 **14 worlds apart** completely different 截然不同的: *Their ways of life are worlds apart.* 他們的生活方式是截然不同的。

world-class /ˌ·ˈ·◂/ *adj* among the best in the world 世界第一流水平的: *a world-class footballer* 世界第一流水平的足球員

world·ly /ˈwɜːldli; ˈwɜːldli/ *adj* **1** related to the pleasures of this physical life, rather than the things of the spirit 塵世的, 物質世界的, 世上的 **2** knowing a lot about life 世故的 **3 worldly goods** the things that you own 所擁有的財產 –**worldliness** *n* [U]

worldly-wise /ˌ··ˈ·◂/ *adj* experienced and knowing a lot about the way people can behave 善於處世的; 老於世故的

world pow·er /ˌ· ˈ··/ *n* a powerful country whose trade and politics have an effect on other parts of the world 世界強國

world·wide /ˈwɜːldˈwaɪd; ˌwɜːldˈwaɪd◂/ *adj, adv* in or over all the world 遍及全球的;

〔地〕; 在全世界: *French cheeses are famous worldwide.* 法國的乾酪聞名世界。

worm¹ /wɜːm; wɜːm/ *n* **1** a small thin tube-like creature with no backbone or legs which lives in the earth 蟲; 蠕蟲 **2 have worms** to have a small worm or worms living in your body and possibly causing illness 〔體內〕有寄生蟲

worm² *v* **1** [I+adv/prep] (*also* 又作 **worm your way**) to move slowly and with difficulty, often by twisting 蠕動; 慢慢前行: *We wormed our way through the crack in the wall.* 我們慢慢地從牆上的裂縫處爬出來。**2 worm your way into** something to make yourself accepted by someone, gradually and sometimes dishonestly 漸漸〔有時不誠實地〕獲取某物, 千方百計地獲取某物: *He wormed his way into her confidence.* 他漸漸博得了她的信任。| *worming their way into fashionable society* 躋身上流社會 **3** [T] to give an animal medicine to get rid of worms in its body 〔用藥物〕給〔動物〕驅蟲

worn /wɔːn; wɔːn/ the past participle of WEAR ☆ WEAR 的過去分詞

worn-out /ˌ· ˈ·◂/ *adj* **1** no longer usable because of so much use in the past 用壞的; 穿舊的; 不能再用的: *worn-out shoes* 穿破了的鞋子 **2** [never before a noun 不能用於名詞前] very tired 精疲力盡的: *She was worn-out after three sleepless nights.* 三天三夜她都沒合眼, 弄得疲憊不堪。

★**wor·ried** /ˈwɜːrɪd; ˈwʌrɪd/ *adj* anxious 焦慮的, 擔心的: *a worried frown on her face* 她一臉焦慮, 愁眉不展 | *He seems worried about* something. 他似乎在擔心甚麼事。| *They are worried that the hijackers will make further demands.* 他們擔心劫機者會進一步提出要求。–**worriedly** *adv*

★**wor·ry¹** /ˈwɜːri; ˈwʌri/ *v* **worried, worrying 1** [T] to make someone anxious or uncomfortable 使擔心, 使焦慮: *It worries me that he's working so hard.* 他工作得那麼賣力, 令我擔心。| *a very worrying state of affairs* 令人非常擔心的局面 **2** [I] to be anxious about something 擔心, 為…發愁: *Worrying about your health can make you ill.* 你老是擔心自己的健康, 那會鬧出病來的。| *Don't worry!* 別擔心! **3 not to worry** = it doesn't matter 沒關係 **4** [T] (of a dog) to chase and bite an animal 〔狗〕追咬〔動物〕

worry² *n* **worries 1** [U] a feeling of fear and uncertainty about something 擔心, 煩惱, 憂慮: *She is a great source of worry to her parents.* 她是令父母憂心的最大根源。**2** [C] something that makes you anxious 令人擔心〔發愁〕的事物: *The profit and loss figures have prompted worries over the company's future.* 那些盈虧數字引起了(大家)對公司前途的憂慮。

worse¹ /wɜːs; wɜːs/ *adj* **1** [comparative of BAD, BAD 的比較級] less good 更壞的; 更差的; 更糟的: *The weather was much worse*

than we had expected. 天氣比我們預計的糟得多。**2** [never before a noun 不能用於名詞前] more ill〔病情〕更重的, 更加惡化的: *He's worse than he was last week.* 他的病情比上星期重了。**3 none the worse for something** not harmed by something 沒有遭〔某事物〕傷害

worse² *adv* [comparative of BADLY, BADLY 的比較級] in a way that is less good or less satisfactory 更糟地; 更差地; 更壞地: *You're behaving worse than an animal!* 你的行為比畜牲還不如。

worse³ *n* [U] **1** something that is worse 更壞〔差〕的事物: *I thought that what had happened was bad enough, but worse was to follow.* 我以為發生的事夠糟了, 不料更糟的事還在後頭。**2 change for the worse** a bad change 變得更壞的情況

wors·en /ˈwɜːsn; ˈwɜːsən/ *v* [I;T] to make or become more difficult, worrying, or unpleasant (使)變得更壞, (使)惡化: *The situation has worsened.* 局勢惡化了。| *the worsening economic crisis* 日趨嚴重的經濟危機

wor·ship¹ /ˈwɜːʃəp; ˈwɜːʃɪp/ *n* **1** strong feelings of love, respect, and admiration for someone, usually God 崇拜, 崇敬, 敬仰: *They bowed their heads in worship.* 他們低下了頭以示崇拜。**2** a religious service 禮拜(儀式): *They attended worship.* 他們去做了禮拜。**3 Your Worship** the polite way of addressing a MAYOR or MAGISTRATE 閣下〔對市長或地方法官的禮貌稱呼〕

worship² *v* **-pp-** (**-p-** *AmE*〖美式〗) **1** [I;T] to show great respect, admiration, and love for someone 崇拜, 崇敬, 敬仰: *He worships the ground she walks on.* 他對她崇拜得五體投地。| *His admirers worshipped at his feet.* 他的崇拜者拜倒在他的腳下。| *Let us worship God by singing hymn number 23.* 我們來唱第二十三首讚美詩敬拜上帝吧。**2** [I] to attend a church service 做禮拜: *They worship regularly at this church.* 他們定期在這教堂做禮拜。**—worshipper** *n*

worst¹ /wɜːst; wɜːst/ *adj* [superlative of BAD, BAD 的最高級] [only before a noun 只用於名詞前] most bad 最壞的, 最差的: *This is the worst accident for years.* 這是幾年來最嚴重的事故。| *He's the worst driver I know.* 他是我所知的最差的司機。

worst² *adv* [superlative of BADLY, BADLY 的最高級] the most badly 最壞地, 最差地: *Who suffered worst?* 誰受苦最深? | *He must be the worst dressed man I've ever met.* 他肯定是我碰到過的衣著最差的人。

worst³ *n* **1** the worst the thing or part that is most bad 最壞的事; 最差的部分: *The worst is yet to come.* 最壞的事還在後頭呢。| *Go on, tell me the worst.* 繼續說吧, 把最壞的消息告訴我。**2 at worst** if the worst thing happens 在最壞的情況下 **3 if the worst comes to the worst** if the worst situation happens 如果最壞的情況出現的話

wor·sted /ˈwʊstɪd; ˈwʊstɪ̩d/ *n* [U] wool cloth 毛料: *a worsted suit* 毛料衣服

★**worth¹** /wɜːθ; wɜːθ/ *prep* **1** having the value mentioned 相當於...的價值; 值...: *This house is worth a lot of money.* 這幢房子值一大筆錢。| *a necklace worth £2,000* 價值二千英鎊的項鏈 **2** having possessions and money with the value mentioned 擁有價值...的財產: *She's worth at least a million pounds.* 她擁有價值至少一百萬英鎊的財產。**3** good enough or useful enough for you to do the thing mentioned 值得; 具有〔去做〕的價值: *It's a film that's really worth seeing.* 這是部很值得看的影片。| *It's well worth making the effort to learn to drive.* 很值得花一番功夫去學會駕駛。| *I suppose it's worth a try.* 我想這值得一試。**4 worth it** good, useful, or enjoyable 有用處的; 值得去做的: *Don't lock the door — it's not worth it.* 不要鎖門, 用不著啊。| *The food is expensive there, but it's worth it.* 那裡的食物很貴, 但物有所值。**5 worth your while** useful or helpful to you and so deserving the effort that is needed〔有用或有幫助而〕值得付出努力的: *It would be worth your while to write to companies asking if they have any job vacancies.* 寫封信給公司問問他們是否有職位空缺, 這是值得你去做的。

★**worth²** *n* [U] **1** value 價值: *Most of the jewellery was of little or no worth.* 那些珠寶大多數沒有甚麼價值, 或者毫無價值。**2** the quantity that a particular amount of money will buy or pay for 值一定金額的數量: *Several thousands of pounds' worth of clothing was ruined in the fire.* 價值數千英鎊的衣服毀於這場火災。| *The storm did thousands of pounds' worth of damage.* 暴風雨造成了價值幾千英鎊的損失。**3** the amount of something that will last for a particular time〔某物的〕能持續一段時間的量: *I've only got two weeks' worth of work left on this project.* 在這個項目上, 我只剩下兩星期的工作。

worth·less /ˈwɜːθlɪs; ˈwɜːθləs/ *adj* **1** of no value or use 無價值的; 沒用處的: *I'm afraid it's completely worthless.* 我恐怕這是一錢不值。| *a worthless action* 毫無價值的行動 **2** with no good qualities 品質不良的; 不中用的: *a worthless member of society* 不中用的社會成員

■ USAGE 用法: Compare 比較 **worthless** and 和 **priceless.** We use **worthless** about things that are of no value ☆ **worthless** 用於指沒有價值的事物: *The stone looked like a diamond, but it was completely worthless.* 這石頭看上去像鑽石, 但毫無價值。But we use **priceless** about things that are very valuable indeed 但 **priceless** 則指十分貴重、值錢的東西: *a priceless painting by Van Gogh* 梵高的一幅貴重的名畫

worth·while /ˈwɜːθˈhwaɪl; ˌwɜːθˈwaɪl◂/ adj deserving the effort needed, or the time and money spent 值得花努力〔時間、金錢〕的: *I think "Save the Children" is a worthwhile charity to support.* 我認為"救救孩子"是一項值得支持的慈善事業。| *We queued for ages, but it was worthwhile. The concert was fantastic!* 我們排了老半天的隊，可是還算值得。音樂會棒極了！

wor·thy /ˈwɜːðɪ; ˈwɜːði/ adj **1** [only before a noun 只用於名詞前] deserving respect or serious consideration 值得尊敬的; 值得重視的: *a worthy opponent* 值得重視的對手 | *worthy aims* 值得為之努力的目標 **2** deserving 值得…的, 應…的: *worthy of admiration* 值得欽佩的 | *I don't feel worthy to receive all this praise.* 我覺得不該得到所有這些讚揚。**3** -**worthy** deserving of something 值得〔某事物〕的: *a praiseworthy action* 值得讚揚的行動 | *a newsworthy event* 值得報道的事件

★★**would** /wʊd; wʊd/ v negative short form 否定縮約式 **wouldn't** [modal verb 情態動詞] **1** used when someone said or thought that something was going to happen, or when they intended to do something 將, 將會〔用於過去將來式〕: *They said it would be fine.* 他們說過天會晴的。| *She said that she would come.* 她說過她會來。| *I knew she would be annoyed.* 我知道她會不高興的。–see 見 's (USAGE 用法) **2** used when you are talking about what is likely or possible 會〔用於談論可能的事情〕: *I would be very surprised if he came now.* 如果他現在來, 我會非常吃驚。| *A fall in the price of oil would have serious consequences for our economy.* 石油價格下降會給我們的經濟帶來嚴重的後果。**3** used to say that you are willing to do something 要, 肯〔表示願意做某事〕: *She would do anything for her parents.* 她肯為父母做任何事。**4** used to show that something happened regularly in the past 總是, 老是〔用於表示某事在過去有規律地發生〕: *We used to work in the same office and we would often have coffee together.* 我們以前在同一個辦公室工作, 並且經常一起喝咖啡。–see Study Note on page 1318 見 1318 頁學習提示 **5 would like, would love** a polite way of saying that you want something 想要〔禮貌地表示要某物〕: *I would love a cup of tea!* 我想要一杯茶！| *Would you like a biscuit?* 你想要塊餅乾嗎？**6 would you** a polite way of asking someone to do something 〔有禮貌地請求某人做某事〕: *Would you post this for me, please?* 請你替我寄這個, 好嗎？| *Shut the door, would you?* 請關門, 行嗎？**7 wouldn't, would not** used to say that someone refused to do something 不肯〔用於表示某人拒絕做某事〕: *I tried to talk to her, but she wouldn't listen.* 我盡量和她說話, 但她不肯聽。**8 I would a** phrase you use when you are giving advice to someone 我會〔用於勸告某人〕: *"What shall I do about the cat?" "I would have it put down."* "我該拿這隻貓怎麼辦？" "要是我就會把牠放下來。" | *I would get rid of that car if I were you.* 如果我是你, 我會把那輛車扔了的。**9 I would think, I would have thought** a phrase you use when you are giving your opinion 我(本)想〔用於發表意見〕: *I would think that the company must be in financial difficulty.* 我想公司一定是財政上有麻煩了。| *I would have thought that she would be pleased to get the job.* 我原想她會很高興得到這份工作的。

wound¹ /waʊnd; waʊnd/ the past tense and past participle of WIND³ ☆ WIND³ 的過去式和過去分詞

wound² /wuːnd; wuːnd/ n a damaged place in your body, usually a hole or tear through your skin made by a weapon such as a gun or knife 〔常指武器所致的〕傷, 創傷; 傷口: *a bullet wound* 槍傷 | *The wound is healing fast.* 傷口癒合得很快。

wound³ /wuːnd; wuːnd/ v [T] **1** to damage someone's body with a weapon such as a gun or knife 〔用槍或刀等〕使受傷; 傷害〔某人〕: *Was he badly wounded?* 他傷得很重嗎？**2** to hurt someone's feelings and make them feel unhappy 傷害〔某人的感情〕: *He has really wounded her pride.* 他大大傷害了她的自尊心。

> ■ USAGE 用法: Compare the use of **wound, injure,** and **hurt** when we talk of damage to the body. You can be **wounded** from an attack in which a gun, a sword, or a knife is used. You can be **injured** when any other weapon is used (such as a heavy stick or a bomb), or in an accident ☆當談到對身體的傷害時, 比較一下 **wound, injure** 和 **hurt** 的用法。受到槍、劍、刀的攻擊而負傷可以用 **wounded**, 用其他任何武器〔如棍棒或炸彈〕致傷或在事故中受傷用 **injured**: *He was injured in a car crash.* 他在一次撞車事故中受了傷。Both **wound** and **injure** are more serious than **hurt** ☆用 **wound** 和 **injure** 比用 **hurt** 嚴重: *She slipped and hurt her knee.* 她滑了一跤, 跌傷了膝蓋。

wove /wov; wəʊv/ the past tense of WEAVE ☆ WEAVE 的過去式

wov·en /ˈwovən; ˈwəʊvən/ the past participle of WEAVE ☆ WEAVE 的過去分詞

wow /waʊ; waʊ/ interj infml an expression of surprise and admiration 【非正式】呀, 哇〔表示驚奇和羨慕〕: *Wow! Look at her new car!* 哇! 看看她的新汽車!

W.P.C. /ˌdʌbljuː piː ˈsiː; ˌdʌbljuː piː ˈsiː/ a female member of the British police force having the lowest rank; an abbreviation for **Woman Police Constable** 〔縮〕〔英國職銜最低的〕女警察

wran·gle /ˈræŋgl; ˈræŋgəl/ v **wrangled,
wrangling** [I] to have an angry or noisy argument 爭論; 吵架; 爭吵: *The boys were
wrangling over whose turn it was.* 那些男孩
為了該輪到誰而爭吵。 –**wrangle** n

wrap¹ /ræp; ræp/ v [T+adv/prep] **-pp-** to put
something around something else to cover
or protect it 包, 裹〔某物〕: *I wrapped the
book in brown paper before I posted it.* 我先
用了棕色包裝紙把書包好, 然後寄出。 | *I
wrapped the rug around his legs to keep him
warm.* 我在他的腿上圍了一條毯子, 給他保暖。

  wrap up *phr v* **1** [T **wrap** sthg ↔ **up**] to
put paper around a parcel or present 〔用
紙〕包, 裹〔禮物等〕 **2** [I] to wear warm
clothes 穿得暖和: *It's cold outside. Wrap up
well.* 外面很冷, 穿得暖和些。 **3** [T **wrap** sthg
↔ **up**] *infml* to complete a meeting or an
agreement 〔非正式〕結束〔會議〕; 締結〔協議〕

wrap² n a piece of material which is worn
around a woman's shoulders 〔女性的〕披肩;
圍巾

wrapped /ræpt; ræpt/ *adj* **wrapped up in**
giving all your attention and care to something 專心致志於〔某事物〕: *She's wrapped up
in some project at work at the moment.* 她現
在正專心致志地在做進行中的項目。

wrap·per /ˈræpə; ˈræpɚ/ n a piece of
paper or plastic which covers a book or
sweet when you buy it 包裝紙

wrap·ping /ˈræpɪŋ; ˈræpɪŋ/ n [C;U] **1** paper
or other material used for covering and
protecting something 包裝紙; 包裝材料:
*Don't take the wrapping off. It might get
damaged.* 別把包裝紙拿掉, 會弄壞它的。 **2**
wrapping paper coloured paper that you
put around a present 〔禮品的〕包裝紙

wrath /ræθ; rɒθ/ n [U] *lit* great anger 〔文〕
憤怒; 憤慨: *the wrath of God* 上帝的震怒, 天
怒 –**wrathful** *adj*

wreak /rik; riːk/ v *lit* 〔文〕 **1** **wreak havoc** to
cause a lot of damage 造成巨大破壞 **2**
wreak vengeance on someone to make
someone suffer because they have harmed
you in some way 向某人報復

wreath /riθ; riːθ/ n **1** a circular arrangement of flowers or leaves, especially one
put on a grave 〔尤指葬禮等中使用的〕花圈;
花環 **2** a curling piece of smoke, mist, or
gas 〔煙、霧等的〕圈

wreathe /rið; riːð/ v **wreathed, wreathing**
[T] *lit* 〔文〕 **1** **wreathed in, wreathed with**
completely covered or surrounded by
something 環繞; 包圍; 覆蓋 **2** **wreathed in
smiles** smiling very happily 滿臉笑容

wreck¹ /rɛk; rɛk/ n **1** [C] a ship which has
sunk or been partly destroyed on rocks 沉
船; 失事船; 遇難船: *Divers went down to the
wreck.* 潛水員潛到失事的船上。 | *You can
see the wreck when the tide's out.* 潮水退了
以後, 你可以看到那艘觸礁的船。 **2** [C;U] the
destruction of a ship by sinking or by

crashing into rocks 〔失事船舶的〕殘骸:
*There have been hundreds of wrecks on that
coast.* 那個岸上有數百艘船的殘骸。 | *The
wreck of the Titanic shocked everyone.* "泰坦
尼克"號的殘骸令大家震驚。 **3** [U] the state
of being ruined or destroyed 破壞; 毀壞: *the
wreck of all our plans* 我們所有計劃的破壞 **4**
[C] something or someone in a very bad
state 處於很差狀態的人或物: *She's a complete wreck after her illness.* 她病了一場後元
氣大傷。 | *He's still driving round in that old
wreck.* 他還開着那輛殘破不堪的舊車到處走。

wreck² v [T] to destroy something 破壞, 毀
壞〔某物〕: *The ship was wrecked on the
rocks.* 那船觸礁失事。 | *The weather has
completely wrecked our plans.* 天氣徹底破壞
了我們的計劃。

wreck·age /ˈrɛkɪdʒ; ˈrɛkɪdʒ/ n [U] the
broken parts of something that has been
destroyed 〔被毀物的〕殘骸: *The wreckage of
the car lay all across the road.* 馬路上到處都
是汽車的殘骸。

wren /rɛn; rɛn/ n a very small brown
European bird 鷦鷯

wrench¹ /rɛntʃ; rɛntʃ/ v [T] **1** to pull something hard with a twisting or turning movement 猛扭, 猛擰, 猛扳: *He slammed the door
so hard that he wrenched the handle off.* 他
非常用力地關門, 連門把手也擰掉了。 **2** to
twist and damage a joint of your body 扭傷
〔關節〕: *She fell awkwardly and wrenched
her ankle.* 她狠狠地摔倒了, 扭傷了腳踝。

wrench² n **1** an act of twisting and pulling
猛扭, 猛擰, 猛拉 **2** **be a wrench** to be painful
or difficult because you have to leave
somone or something 離別的痛苦 **3** a metal
tool for turning and undoing nuts 活動扳
手, 活動扳鉗

wrest /rɛst; rɛst/ v [T+adv/prep] *fml* to pull
something away from someone roughly
〔正式〕強奪; 猛拉: *She wrested the gun out
of his hands.* 她從他手裏把槍奪走。

wres·tle /ˈrɛsl; ˈrɛsəl/ v **wrestled, wrestling**
1 [I;T] to fight by holding on to someone
and trying to throw them to the ground 摔
跤; 搏鬥: *She wrestled with her attacker.* 她奮
力和襲擊她的人搏鬥。 **2** **wrestle with something** to try to deal with something difficult 努力解決難以處理的事物

wres·tling /ˈrɛslɪŋ; ˈrɛslɪŋ/ n [U] a sport in
which two people wrestle and each tries to
throw the other to the ground 摔跤〔運動〕 –
wrestler n

wretch /rɛtʃ; rɛtʃ/ n **1** a poor or unhappy
person 不幸的人; 可憐的人: *unlucky
wretches with no homes* 無家可歸的苦命人 **2**
someone, especially a child, who has done
something bad 〔尤指小孩〕淘氣鬼; 傢伙

wretch·ed /ˈrɛtʃɪd; ˈrɛtʃɪd/ *adj* **1** very poor
or unhappy 可憐的; 不幸的 **2** unpleasant
and annoying 討厭的; 令人苦惱的: *Wretched
child! Why can't she behave?* 討厭的孩子! 她

為甚麼不能規規矩矩的?

wrig·gle /ˈrɪɡl; ˈrɪɡəl/ v **wriggled, wriggling 1** [I] to twist your body from side to side 蠕動, 扭動: *He wriggled uncomfortably on the hard chair.* 他在硬椅子上不舒服地扭動着身體。| *They wriggled through the gap.* 他們扭動着鑽過了裂縫。**2** [T] to move a part of your body from side to side or up and down 使〔身體的一部分〕扭動: *Wriggle your toes.* 扭一下你的腳趾頭。**3 wriggle out of something** *infml* to avoid doing something unpleasant or taking the blame for something 〔非正式〕避免做不愉快的事; 逃避責任 – **wriggle** n

wring /rɪŋ; rɪŋ/ v **wrung** /rʌŋ; rʌŋ/, **wrung 1** [T] (also 又作 **wring** sthg ↔ **out**) to twist and press something to remove water from it 把〔某物〕擰乾; 絞出〔水〕: *Wring those wet things out.* 把那些濕東西擰乾。**2 wring your hands** to twist your hands together as though washing them, as a sign of worry or grief 絞緊雙手〔顯示焦急或悲傷〕**3 wring something's neck** to kill something by twisting its neck 用擰脖子的方法殺死動物等 **4 wringing wet** extremely wet 濕得能絞出水來, 濕淋淋的 –**wring** n

wrin·kle[1] /ˈrɪŋkl; ˈrɪŋkəl/ n **1** a line in something which is folded or crushed 皺褶 **2** a line on an old person's skin 〔老年人的〕皺紋 –**wrinkly** adj

wrinkle[2] v **wrinkled, wrinkling** [I;T] to form into lines or folds (使)起皺紋, (使); 皺起: *the wrinkled face of the old man* 老人佈滿皺紋的臉

wrist /rɪst; rɪst/ n the joint between your hand and the lower part of your arm 腕, 腕關節

wrist·watch /ˈrɪst,wɒtʃ; ˈrɪstwɒtʃ/ n a watch made to be fastened on a person's wrist 手錶

writ /rɪt; rɪt/ n an official legal paper telling someone to do or not to do a particular thing 令狀, 書面命令; 傳票

write /raɪt; raɪt/ v [I;T] **wrote** /rot; rəʊt/, **written** /ˈrɪtn; ˈrɪtn/, **writing 1** to make letters or words, especially by using a pen or pencil on paper 寫, 書寫, 寫字: *The children are learning to write.* 孩子們在學寫字。| *Write the address on the envelope.* 在信封上寫下地址。**2** to make something, such as a book or play, by writing 寫〔書或劇本〕, 寫作: *She's written several books already.* 她已寫了幾本書。| *Have you written that report yet?* 你已寫了那份報告嗎? | *She writes for the stage.* 她是個劇作家。**3** to produce and send a letter to someone 寫(信); 寄(信): *She wrote* **to** *me last month.* 她上個月寫信給我。| *I've written a letter to the local newspaper.* 我寫過一封信給當地報紙。| *He wrote me a letter.* 他給我寫一封信。| *I wish he would write more often.* 我希望他常常來信。| *He wrote to tell me the news.* 他寫信告訴我這個消息。|

She wrote asking for money. 她寫信來要錢。

write back *phr v* [I;T **write** sthg ↔ **back**] to write a letter replying to one you have received 回信

write sthg ↔ **down** *phr v* [T] to record information or speech by writing it 寫下, 記下〔信息或説話〕: *Write your idea down while it's clear in your mind.* 趁你還記得清楚時, 把你的想法寫下來。| *I wrote down everything you told me.* 我把你告訴我的一切都寫了下來。

■ USAGE 用法: In informal American English you can say ☆在非正式的美式英語中可以説: *I'll write you next week.* 我下星期寫信給你。| *Please write me soon.* 請盡快寫信給我。This is NOT generally acceptable in British English. Instead you should say ☆這在英式英語中一般不能接受。相反你該説: *I'll write* **to** *you.* 我會寫信給你。| *I'll write you a letter.* 我會寫封信給你。| *Please write* **to** *me.* 請寫信給我。| *Please write me a letter soon.* 請盡快寫信給我。

write in *phr v* [I] to send a letter to a firm, asking for something or giving an opinion 給〔公司等〕寫信索取〔某物〕; 提供書面意見: *We wrote in* **for** *a free book, but the firm never replied.* 我們寫信去索取贈書, 但公司從沒有答覆。

write off *phr v* **1** [T **write** sbdy/sthg ↔ **off**] to regard someone or something as being lost or having failed 取消, 把…勾銷; 認定…失敗: *The newspapers wrote him off* **as** *a failure, but he proved them wrong.* 報章把他説成是失敗者, 但他(用事實)證明他們錯了。| *We'll have to write our holiday off. We can't afford it now.* 我們得取消度假, 我們現在負擔不起。**2** [I] to write to a firm, especially to buy something 〔尤指〕函購: *She wrote off* **for** *the book, because the shop didn't have it.* 書店沒有那本書, 她就寫信去函購。

write sthg ↔ **out** *phr v* [T] **1** to write something in full 全部寫出: *to write out a report* 寫出一篇報告 **2** to write something official 寫〔正式文件〕: *to write out a cheque* 開支票

write sthg ↔ **up** *phr v* [T] to write something again in a complete and useful form 重新整理; 詳細地記述: *to write up your notes* 重新整理筆記

write-off /ˈ·· / n a vehicle that has been so badly damaged that it cannot be repaired 報廢的車輛

writ·er /ˈraɪtɚ; ˈraɪtəʳ/ n a person who writes, especially as a job 作者; 〔尤指〕作家

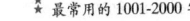

write-up /'··/ *n infml* a written report which gives a judgment about a play or a new product 〔非正式〕〔對戲劇或新產品的〕評論文章: *The concert got a good write-up in the local paper.* 那場音樂會大受當地報紙的讚揚。

writhe /raɪð; raɪð/ *v* **writhed, writhing** [I] to twist your body because you are in great pain 〔因劇痛而〕扭動身體, 蠕動: *writhing in agony* 極度痛苦地扭動

*★**writ·ing** /'raɪtɪŋ; 'raɪtɪŋ/ *n* **1** [U] the activity of writing, especially books 書寫; 寫作: *Writing is a difficult way of earning a living.* 靠寫作維生是很困難的。 **2** [U] the style which a person writes by hand 筆跡, 字跡: *I can't read the doctor's writing.* 我看不明那位醫生的筆跡。 **3** [U] something that has been written 文字: *There was writing all over the walls.* 牆上到處都是字。 **4** in writing written on paper 以書面形式寫下來: *You must get the agreement down in writing.* 你必須把協議以書面形式寫下來。 **5 writings** [pl] all the books and other things that someone has written 著作: *Darwin's scientific writings* 達爾文的科學著作

writing pa·per /'·· ‚··/ *n* [U] smooth, good quality paper for writing letters on 書寫紙; 信紙

writ·ten /'rɪtn̩; 'rɪtn̩/ the past participle of WRITE ☆ WRITE 的過去分詞

wrong[1] /rɒŋ; rɒŋ/ *adj* **1** not correct 不正確的, 錯誤的: *the wrong answer* 錯誤的答案 | *That clock's wrong.* 那鐘不準。 | *You're completely wrong.* 你全錯了。 **2** not suitable 不合適的, 不適當的: *That style is wrong for your hair.* 那種髮式不適合你。 | *This is the wrong time to ask for a pay rise.* 這個時候要求增加工資是不合適的。 **3** [never before a noun 不能用於名詞前] not morally acceptable 不道德的: *It's wrong to tell lies.* 說謊是不對的。 | *Stealing is wrong.* 偷東西是錯的。 **4 get the wrong end of the stick** to understand something wrongly 完全誤解 **–wrongly** *adv*

wrong[2] *adv* **1** wrongly 錯誤地, 不對, 不正確地: *You've spelt the word wrong.* 你把那個單詞拼錯了。 **2 get it wrong** to misunderstand something 誤解, 曲解〔某事物〕 **3 go wrong:**

a to make a mistake 搞錯, 弄錯: *This sum isn't right, but I can't see where I went wrong.* 總數算出來不對, 但我看不出是哪兒弄錯了。 **b** to develop in an unsatisfactory way 出現問題: *After five years, their marriage suddenly went wrong.* 過了五年以後, 他們的婚姻突然出現問題了。 **c** to stop working properly 有毛病, 出故障: *The car's gone wrong.* 汽車出毛病了。 | *Something's gone wrong* **with** *the car.* 這汽車出故障了。

wrong[3] *n* **1** [U] behaviour that is not morally acceptable 邪惡; 壞事: *You're old enough to know right from wrong.* 你這麼大了, 該能辨別是非了。 **2** [C] *fml* bad or unjust action 〔正式〕不公正的行為; 冤屈: *He did you a terrible wrong.* 他大大冤枉了你。 **3 in the wrong** mistaken or deserving blame 弄錯; 應受指責: *Which of the two drivers was in the wrong?* 這兩位司機中, 哪一位該負責任?

wrong[4] *v* [T] *lit* to treat someone very unfairly 〔文〕不公正地對待〔某人〕; 冤枉〔某人〕

wrong·do·ing /'rɒŋˈduːɪŋ; 'rɒŋˌduːɪŋ/ *n* [U] *fml* bad, evil, or illegal behaviour 〔正式〕壞事; 惡行; 不法行為 **–wrongdoer** *n*

wrong·ful /'rɒŋfəl; 'rɒŋfəl/ *adj fml* unjust or illegal 〔正式〕不公正的; 非法的: *wrongful imprisonment* 非法監禁 **–wrongfully** *adv*

wrote /rəʊt; rəʊt/ the past tense of WRITE ☆ WRITE 的過去式

wrought /rɔːt; rɔːt/ *adj lit* made or done 〔文〕製造的; 做成的

wrought i·ron /‚· '··◂/ *n* [U] iron shaped into a useful form or pleasing pattern 鍛鐵; 熟鐵: *a wrought-iron gate* 鍛鐵做的閘門

wrung /rʌŋ; rʌŋ/ the past tense and past participle of WRING ☆ WRING 的過去式和過去分詞

wry /raɪ; raɪ/ *adj* showing that you do not like a situation very much, or that you do not really believe something, or find it slightly amusing 做鬼臉的, 露出怪相的; 苦笑的〔表示厭惡、不相信或覺得好玩〕: *a wry expression* 怪相 | *"I'm not invited," he said with a wry smile.* "我沒受到邀請," 他苦笑着說。 **–wryly** *adv*

X, x

X, x /ɛks; eks/ **X's, x's** *or* **Xs, xs** the 24th letter of the English alphabet 英語的第二十四個字母

x *n* a sign used in MATHEMATICS for a quantity that is not known but which can be calculated 〔數學中的〕未知數: *If 3x=6, x=2.* 假設3x=6，則x=2。

X *n* **1** [U] a letter that you use instead of a name when you do not want people to know the name 某人〔不想讓人知道名字時用的代替字母〕: *the victim, whom we shall call Mrs X* 這位遇難者，我們叫她某某太太 **2** [C] a film which is considered unsuitable for young people under 18 〔十八歲以下青少年不宜觀看的電影的標記〕: *"Terrors of the Grave" is an X.* "墓地驚魂"是部 X 級影片。

xen·o·pho·bi·a /ˌzɛnə'fobɪə; ˌzenə'fəʊbiə/ *n* [U] unreasonable fear and dislike of foreigners or strangers 對外國人或陌生人的無端恐懼和厭惡 **–xenophobic** *adj*

xe·rox /'zɪrɑks; 'zɪərɒks/ *v* [T] *tdmk* (also 又作 **Xerox**) to make a photographic copy of something printed or written on a special electric copying machine 〔商標〕〔用靜電複印機〕複印〔印刷品〕，影印 **–xerox** *n*: *Copy the letter on the xerox.* 用複印機複印這封信。| *Make a xerox of the letter.* 把這封信複印一下。

X·mas /'krɪsməs; 'krɪsməs, 'eksməs/ *n* [U] *infml* Christmas 〔非正式〕聖誕節

x-ray /'ɛksˈre; 'eks reɪ/ *v* [T] (also 又作 **X-ray**) to photograph, examine, or treat someone by means of x-rays 給…照 X 光; 用 X 光攝影、檢查或治療: *They x-rayed her leg to find out if the bone was broken.* 他們用 X 光檢查她的腿部，看看骨頭是否斷了。

X-ray *n* **1** a powerful unseen beam of light which can pass through substances that are not transparent, and which is used especially for photographing medical conditions inside your body X 光; X 射線 **2** a photograph taken using this X 光片

xy·lo·phone /'zaɪlə,fon; 'zaɪləfəʊn/ *n* a musical instrument made up of a set of flat wooden bars which produce musical notes when struck with small wooden hammers 木琴

Y, y

Y, y /waɪ; waɪ/ **Y's, y's** *or* **Ys, ys** the 25th letter of the English alphabet 英語的第二十五個字母

yacht /jɑt; jɒt/ *n* a boat with sails or a motor, used for pleasure 帆船; 遊艇 –see picture on page 991 見 991 頁彩圖

yacht·ing /ˈjɑtɪŋ; ˈjɒtɪŋ/ *n* [U] the sport or activity of sailing or racing in a yacht 駕駛帆船[遊艇]; 帆船運動[比賽]: *Yachting can be very expensive.* 快艇運動可以是很昂貴的。–**yachting** *v* [only in progressive forms 只用於進行式]: *We're going yachting next weekend.* 我們下週末會乘帆船出去玩。

yam /jæm; jæm/ *n* a tropical climbing plant whose root is eaten as a vegetable 薯蕷; 山藥

yank /jæŋk; jæŋk/ *v* [I] *infml* to pull something suddenly and sharply 〖非正式〗用力猛拉; 使勁拉: *He yanked the rope.* 他猛地拉了一下繩子。–**yank** *n*: *Give it a yank.* 使勁拉一下。

Yank *n* *infml* (also 又作 **Yankee** /ˈjæŋkɪ; ˈjæŋki/) a citizen of the United States of America (a word which is considered slightly offensive) 〖非正式〗美國人; 美國佬〔被認為略有些不禮貌〕

yap /jæp; jæp/ *v* **-pp-** [I] **1** (of dogs) to make short sharp excited noises 〔狗〕尖聲狂吠 **2** *infml* to talk noisily and about unimportant things 〖非正式〗哇啦哇啦地說話 –**yap** *n*

★**yard** /jɑrd; jɑːd/ *n* **1** a unit for measuring length, equal to 3 feet or about .914 metres 碼〔長度單位, 等於3英尺或0.914米〕: *The target was about 100 yards away.* 靶子在大約一百碼開外。**2** *AmE* a garden behind a house 〖美式〗後院 **3** an enclosed or partly enclosed area next to a building 〔房子附近的〕庭院: *a churchyard* 教堂庭院 **4** an enclosed area used for a particular business 〔作某一用途的〕場所: *a shipyard* 船塢 | *a coalyard* 煤場

yard·stick /ˈjɑrdˌstɪk; ˈjɑːdˌstɪk/ *n* a standard of measurement or comparison 〔衡量或比較的〕標準; 尺度: *Is money the only yardstick of success?* 金錢是衡量成功與否的唯一標準嗎?

yarn /jɑrn; jɑːn/ *n* **1** [U] thread made of wool or cotton 紗; 線 **2** [C] *infml* a long story, often one that is not true 〖非正式〗〔常為不真實的〕故事; 奇談

yawn /jɔn; jɔːn/ *v* [I] **1** to open your mouth wide and breathe in deeply, because you are tired 打呵欠 **2** (of a hole) to be or become wide open 〔洞〕張開; 豁開: *The hole yawned before him.* 他面前有個口子很大的洞。| *a yawning crack* 豁開的裂縫 –**yawn** *n*: *I gave a loud yawn, but he just kept on talking.* 我大聲打了個呵欠, 可他還是講個不停。

yd a written abbreviation for 〖縮〗=YARD

yeah /jɛ; jeə/ *adv* *infml* yes 〖非正式〗是, 對的

★**year** /jɪr; jɪəʳ/ *n* **1** a period of 365 or 366 days, divided into 12 months, beginning on January 1st and ending on December 31st 年; 曆年 **2** a period of 365 days measured from any point 一年(時間): *He's three years old.* 他三歲。| *I arrived here two years ago today.* 我兩年前的今天來到這裡。| *I've known him for years.* 我認識他已有多年了。**3** a period of about a year in the life of an organization or system 〔機構或組織進行活動的〕年度: *We take our examinations in June, at the end of the school year.* 我們在六月學年末時參加考試。| *the financial year* 財政年度 **4** **all the year round, all year round** during the whole year 整年; 一年到頭 **5** **the year dot** *infml* a very long time ago 〖非正式〗很久很久以前: *That hat went out of fashion in the year dot!* 那帽子很久很久以前就不流行了!

year·ling /ˈjɪrlɪŋ; ˈjɪəlɪŋ/ *n* a young horse between one and two years old 一周歲至兩周歲之間的小馬

year·ly /ˈjɪrlɪ; ˈjɪəli/ *adj* [only before a noun 只用於名詞前] **1** every year or once a year 每年的; 一年一次的: *a yearly meeting* 年會 **2** concerning or lasting for a period of one year 持續一年的; 一年的: *a yearly season ticket* 年度季票 –**yearly** *adv*: *We meet twice yearly.* 我們一年見面兩次。

yearn /jɜn; jɜːn/ *v* [I] *lit* **yearn for something, yearn to do something** to have a strong, loving, or sad desire for something 〖文〗渴望, 盼望; 懷念: *They yearned to return home.* 他們渴望回家。–**yearning** *n* [C;U]

yeast /jist; jiːst/ *n* [U] a form of very small plant life that is used in making bread, and for producing alcohol in beer and wine 酵母(菌)

yell /jɛl; jel/ *v* [I;T] to say, shout, or cry something loudly 叫喊; 叫嚷: *He yelled out orders.* 他高聲地發號施令。| *Don't yell at me like that!* 別對我那樣大喊大叫! –**yell** *n*: *yells of excitement* 興奮的叫喊

★**yel·low** /ˈjɛlo; ˈjeləʊ/ *adj* of a colour like that of butter, gold, or the middle part of an egg 黃(色)的: *a yellow flower* 黃花 –see picture on page 243 見 243 頁彩圖 **–yellow** *n* [U]: *dressed in yellow* 穿着黄衣 **–yellow** *v* [I]: *The paper had yellowed with age.* 那紙因年代久遠而泛黃了。

yelp /jɛlp; jɛlp/ *v* [I] to make a high sharp sound, especially because of pain or excitement 〔尤因痛苦或激動而〕尖叫, 叫喊: *The dog yelped when I hit it.* 那條狗被我打了一下, 發出一聲尖叫。**–yelp** *n*: *He gave a yelp of delight.* 他高興地尖叫起來。

yen /jɛn; jɛn/ *n* **1** [plural is 複數為 **yen**] the standard unit of money in Japan 日圓〔日本的貨幣單位〕**2** [sing] a strong desire 渴望; 癖好: *He has a yen to travel.* 他渴望去旅遊。| *a sudden yen* **for** *some chocolate* 突然極想吃些巧克力

★★**yes** /jɛs; jɛs/ *adv* **1** used when you are agreeing with someone or agreeing to do something 是〔用於表示同意〕: *"Do you like him?" "Yes."* "你喜歡他嗎?" "是的。" | *"I think these people should be locked up." "Yes, I agree."* "我想應該把這些人關起來。" "是呀, 我同意。" | *"Lock the door when you leave." "Yes, alright."* "你走時鎖上門。" "好的。" **2** used to show that you are listening to someone and want them to continue speaking 嗯, 是〔用於表示在聽某人說話並要其說下去〕: *"John?" "Yes?" "Have you got my scissors?"* "約翰?" "嗯?" "你拿了我的剪刀嗎?"

yes-man /ˈjɛsˌmæn; ˈjɛs mæn/ *n* **yes-men** /-ˌmɛn; -mɛn/ a person who always agrees with their employer or leader (a word used to express disapproval) 唯唯諾諾的人〔含貶義〕

★★**yes·ter·day** /ˈjɛstədɪ; ˈjɛstədɪ/ *adv, n* **1** the day before today 昨天: *Yesterday was Sunday.* 昨天是星期天。| *I saw her yesterday afternoon.* 我昨天下午見到過她。| *Did you go to the meeting yesterday?* 你昨天去了開會嗎? **2** the past 過去; 往日: *the fashions of yesterday* 往日的流行式樣

★★**yet**¹ /jɛt; jɛt/ *adv* **1** used in questions to ask if something has happened already 已經〔用於疑問句中〕: *Is she home yet?* 她已經回家了嗎? –see 見 JUST² (USAGE 用法) –see 見 ALREADY (USAGE 用法) **2** not yet: **a** not up till now 迄今還沒有; 尚未: *He's not home yet.* 他還沒有回家。| *I haven't finished yet.* 我尚未完成。**b** not now, but later 不是現在〔而是以後〕: *Don't tell anyone yet.* 現在別告訴任何人。**3** in the future 將來還⋯⋯; 終歸; 遲早: *We may win yet.* 我們遲早會贏的。| *The plan may yet succeed.* 這項計劃將來還有成功的一天。**4** used to make a word stonger 〔用於加強語氣〕再; 還: *He made yet another mistake.* 他又犯了另一個錯誤。| *I had to listen to his story yet again.* 我不得不再聽一遍他的故事。

yet² *conj* even so 然而; 可是: *She's a funny girl, yet you can't help liking her.* 她是個滑稽可笑的姑娘, 可是你仍會禁不住喜歡她。

yew /ju; juː/ *n* a tree with small leaves that are always green and small red berries 紫杉樹

yield¹ /jild; jiːld/ *v* **1** [T] to give or produce something 產生, 出產〔某物〕: *His business yields big profits.* 他的生意獲利豐厚。**2** [I;T] to admit defeat or give up control of something 讓步; 放棄: *The government will yield under pressure from the opposition.* 政府會在反對派的壓力下作出讓步。| *We were forced to yield our position* **to** *the enemy.* 我們被迫把陣地放棄給了敵人。**3** [I] to bend or break because of a strong force 〔因壓力太大而〕彎曲; 折斷: *The shelf was beginning to yield under the weight of the boxes.* 架子在盒子的重壓下開始彎了。

yield² *n* the amount of something that is produced 產量; 收益: *The yield per acre is very small.* 每英畝的產量很小。| *a yield of 5p per share* 每股五便士的收益

yip·pee /ˈjɪpi; jɪˈpiː/ *interj infml* a word that you say when you are delighted, happy or successful 〔非正式〕嗨〔用於表示歡欣鼓舞等〕: *"You've won." "Yippee!"* "你們贏了。" "嗨!"

yo·del /ˈjodəl; ˈjəʊdl/ *v* **-ll-** (also 又作 **-l-** *AmE* 〔美式〕) [I] to sing with many rapid changes between your natural voice and a very high voice 用真假嗓音變換地唱; 用岳得爾調唱(歌)

yo·ga /ˈjogə; ˈjəʊgə/ *n* [U] a system of exercises which help you to control your body and your mind 瑜珈(修行法)

yog·hurt /ˈjogət; ˈjɒgət/ *n* (also 又作 **yogurt, yoghourt**) [C;U] milk that has turned thick and slightly sour through the action of certain bacteria; yoghurt is eaten, not drunk 酸乳酪

yoke¹ /jok; jəʊk/ *n* **1** a wooden frame used to fasten animals together when they are pulling a vehicle (牛)軛 **2** a frame worn across a person's shoulders and used for carrying things 軛狀扁擔 **3** **the yoke of** the cruel or hard rule or control of 奴役; 束縛; 管轄: *freed from the yoke of military government* 從軍政府的統治下掙脫出來

yoke² *v* **yoked, yoking** [T] to join two animals together with a yoke 給〔牲口〕套上軛

yo·kel /ˈjokl; ˈjəʊkəl/ *n* a simple or foolish country person (a word usually used in a humorous way) 鄉下佬〔常含幽默〕

yolk /jok; jəʊk/ *n* [C;U] the yellow central part of an egg 蛋黃

yon·der /ˈjɑndə; ˈjɒndə/ *adj, adv* over there (a word which is no longer used in modern English) 那邊的; 在那邊〔現代英語中不再使用〕: *Walk to yonder hill.* 走到那邊的小山去。| *the house yonder* 那邊的房子

yonks /jɑŋks; jɒŋks/ *n* [U] *infml* a long time 〔非正式〕很長一段時間; 很久: *I haven't seen him for yonks.* 我很久沒有見到他了。| *That*

was yonks ago! 那是很久以前了!

⁂you /juː; jə; *strong* 強讀 juː; juː/ *pron* [used as the subject or object of a verb 用作動詞的主語或賓語] **1** the person or people who are being spoken to 你; 你們: *You must all listen carefully.* 你們都必須仔細聆聽着。| *Shall I get you a drink, John?* 約翰, 我給你拿杯飲料好嗎? **2** people in general 任何人: *It's not good for you to eat too much meat.* 吃肉太多(對你)沒有好處。| *You can't believe what politicians say.* 誰也不能相信政客說的話。

you'd /juːd; jəd; *strong* 強讀 juːd; juːd/ short for〖縮〗= "you had" or 或 "you would"

you'll /juːl; jəl; *strong* 強讀 juːl; juːl/ short for〖縮〗= "you will" or 或 "you shall"

⁂young¹ /jʌŋ; jʌŋ/ *adj* **younger** /ˈjʌŋɡə; ˈjʌŋɡər/, **youngest** /ˈjʌŋɡəst; ˈjʌŋɡəst/ **1** in an early stage of life, growth, or development 年輕的; 幼小的; 新生的; 新發展的: *a young girl* 小女孩 | *They have three young children.* 他們有三個幼兒。| *Most of the teachers here are quite young.* 這裡大多數的老師都很年輕。| *These young plants are doing well.* 這些幼苗長得不錯。 **2** related or suitable for young people 年輕人的; 適合年輕人的: *That style's too young for her.* 那種式樣把她顯得太年輕了, 不大適合她。

young² *n* [pl] **1** the young young people considered as a group 年輕 **2** young animals 幼小的動物; 崽; 雛: *The lion fought to protect her young.* 那頭獅子為保護幼獅而搏鬥。

young·ster /ˈjʌŋstə; ˈjʌŋstər/ *n* a young person 年輕人; 小伙子

⁂your /juː; jər; *strong* 強讀 juː; jɔːr/ *det* **1** relating to or belonging to the person or people who are being spoken to 你的; 你們的: *Your hands are dirty.* 你的手很髒。| *Could you all leave your books on that table?* 你們都把書留在那張桌子上好嗎? **2** relating to or belonging to people in general 任何人的: *These boots really keep your feet warm.* 這靴子真能使你的腳保暖。

you're /juː; jə; *strong* 強讀 juː; jɔːr/ short for〖縮〗= "you are"

⁂yours /juːz; jɔːz/ *pron* **1** something related to or belonging to the person or people who are being spoken to 你(們)的〔所有物〕: *Our house is very similar to yours.* 我們的房子和你們的很相似。 **2** Yours, Yours faithfully, Yours sincerely a polite phrase that you write at the end of a letter before your name 你的; 你的忠實的; 你的真摯的〔寫於信末署名前的客套語〕: *Yours sincerely, John Brown.* 你的真摯的, 約翰·布朗。

■ USAGE 用法: **Yours faithfully/Yours truly** are used to end a formal letter that begins *Dear Sir/Madam* etc.

Yours sincerely is very commonly used to end a less formal letter that begins *Dear Mr Smith/Ms Jones* etc. In informal letters many endings are possible, for example **Yours** and **Best wishes.** ☆ **Yours faithfully/Yours truly** 用於以 Dear Sir/Madam (親愛的先生〔夫人〕)等開頭的正式書信的結尾。 **Yours sincerely** 常常用於以 Dear Mr Smith/Ms Jones (親愛的史密斯先生〔瓊斯太太〕)等開頭的不太正式書信的結尾。 在非正式的信中, 很多結尾都可以使用, 如 **Yours** 和 **Best wishes**。

⁂your·self /jɔːˈsɛlf; jəˈself/ *pron* **yourselves** /-ˈsɛlvz; -ˈselvz/ **1** used as the object of a verb or a PREPOSITION when the subject of a verb is the person who is being spoken to and the action is done to the same person〔反身代詞〕你自己; 你們自己: *You'll hurt yourself.* 你會弄傷你自己的。| *You should look at yourself in the mirror!* 你該照照鏡子! | *Why don't you buy yourself some new clothes?* 你為甚麼不給自己買些新衣服? **2** used to add force to the word "you" 你親自, 你本人〔用以加強語氣〕: *You admitted yourself that you hadn't been very successful.* 是你自己承認你不是很成功的。| *I'm afraid you'll have to carry your bags yourselves.* 恐怕你們得自己拿自己的袋子了。 **3** by yourself alone, with no one with you or helping you 你單獨地; 獨力地: *You'll have to spend quite a lot of time by yourself.* 你得自己一個人度過好一大段時間了。| *Can you manage to lift that box by yourself?* 你能設法獨自把那個箱子提起來嗎?

⁂youth /juːθ; juːθ/ *n* **youths** /juːðz; juːðz/ **1** [U] the period of time when you are young 青少年時代; 青春(時期): *In my youth I used to play football.* 我在青年時代常踢足球。 –see 見 CHILD (USAGE 用法) **2** [C] a young man (a word often used to express disapproval)〔男性的〕年輕人; 小伙子〔常含貶義〕: *a gang of youths* 一幫小伙子 **3** the youth [pl] young men and women considered as a group 男女青年, 青年人: *The youth of today are better educated.* 今天的青年人受過更好的教育。

youth·ful /ˈjuːθfəl; ˈjuːθfəl/ *adj* **1** having the qualities of young people 年輕人特有的; 洋溢着青春活力的: *his youthful enthusiasm* 他那份年輕人的熱情 **2** young 年輕的: *our youthful prime minister* 我們年富力強的首相 –**youthfully** *adv*

youth hos·tel /ˈ· ˌ··/ *n* a place where young people can stay cheaply when they are travelling around on holiday〔為在假期旅遊的年輕人所設的廉價〕青年招待所, 青年旅舍

you've /juːv; jəv; *strong* 強讀 juːv; juːv/ *v* short for〖縮〗= "you have"

yo·yo /ˈjojo; ˈjəʊjəʊ/ *n* a toy made of a thick

circular piece of wood, metal, or plastic, which can be made to move up and down a piece of string which is tied to it 悠悠, 搖搖〔一種可用繩索拉上拉下的玩具〕

yule /juːl; juːl/ *n lit* (also 又作 **Yule**) Christmas 〖文〗聖誕節

yule·tide /ˈjuːltaɪd; ˈjuːltaɪd/ *n lit* (also 又作 **Yuletide**) the Christmas season 〖文〗聖誕節

yup·pie /ˈjʌpɪ; ˈjʌpɪ/ *n* (also 又作 **yuppy**) a young person in a professional job with a high income, especially one who enjoys having an expensive and fashionable way of life (a word often used to express disapproval) 雅皮士, 優皮士〔尤指喜歡過時髦生活並有高收入的青年, 常含貶義〕

Z, z

Z, z /zi; zed/ **Z's, z's** or **Zs, zs** the 26th and last letter of the English alphabet 英語的第二十六個〔最後一個字母〕

za·ny /'zeni; 'zeini/ *adj* strange, foolish, and amusing 裝傻逗趣的; 滑稽可笑的

zap /zæp; zæp/ *v infml*〔非正式〕**1** [T] to attack or destroy someone or something 攻擊, 破壞〔某人或某物〕**2** [I+adv/prep] to move somewhere quickly or forcefully 快速移動

zeal /zil; ziːl/ *n* [U] great eagerness 熱心; 熱忱; 渴望: *carried away by revolutionary zeal* 被革命的熱情吸引住

zeal·ous /'zeləs; 'zeləs/ *adj* very keen 熱心的; 熱情的; 積極的: *zealous in doing his duty* 他熱心盡職 | *zealous supporters of the government* 政府的狂熱支持者 —**zealously** *adv*

ze·bra /'zibrə; 'ziːbrə/ *n* an African animal that looks like a horse and has black and white lines all over its body 斑馬

zebra cross·ing /ˌ·· '··/ *n* a set of black and white lines painted on a road in Britain, to show that people have the right to cross the road in that place〔街道上塗有黑白相間顏色, 表示行人可由此穿越馬路的〕斑馬線, 人行橫道線 –see picture on page 991 見 991 頁彩圖

ze·nith /'zinɪθ; 'zenˌθ/ *n* [sing] the point at which something is at its most successful 最高點; 頂點; 頂峯: *Rome's power reached its zenith under the emperor Trajan.* 羅馬帝國的勢力在圖雷真皇帝的統治下達到了頂峯。

ze·ro[1] /'ziro; 'zɪərəʊ/ *n* **zeros** or **zeroes 1** the name of the sign 0 and of the number it stands for〔數字〕零 **2** the point between + and – on a scale〔刻度上的〕零點; 零位 **3** the temperature on the CENTIGRADE scale at which water freezes〔氣溫的〕零度: *It was five below zero last night.* 昨晚的氣溫是零下五度。–**zero** *adj* [only before a noun 只用於名詞前]: *conditions of zero gravity* 失重的條件 | *Our target is zero inflation.* 我們的目標是通脹率為零。

■ **USAGE** 用法: In British English **zero** is NOT used when saying telephone numbers. Use **0** (pronounced "oh" /o; əʊ/) instead. ☆在英式英語中説電話號碼時不用 **zero,** 而用 **0**〔發音 "oh" /o; əʊ/〕代替。

zero[2] *v*

zero in on sthg *phr v* [T] **1** to aim a weapon directly at something 把〔武器〕直接瞄準〔某物〕**2** to give all your attention to something 集中注意力於〔某事物〕

zest /zɛst; zest/ *n* [U] a feeling of eager excitement 熱情; 熱忱: *She entered into the work with zest.* 她滿懷熱情地投入工作。| *a zest for life* 對生活充滿熱情

zig·zag[1] /'zɪgzæg; 'zɪgzæg/ *n* a line shaped like a row of touching w's 曲折線條; 之字形線條: *a zigzag path* 之字形的小徑

zigzag[2] *v* **-gg-** [I] to go in a zigzag 曲折前進, 呈之字形移動: *The path zigzags up the hill.* 這條小路向山頂蜿蜒而上。

zinc /zɪŋk; zɪŋk/ *n* [U] a bluish-white metal that is used in the production of other metals 鋅

zip[1] /zɪp; zɪp/ *n* (also 又作 **zip fastener** /ˌ· '··/ *BrE*〔英式〕, **zipper** /'zɪpə; 'zɪpəʳ/ *AmE*〔美式〕) a fastener made of two sets of metal or plastic teeth and a sliding piece that draws them together; zips are often used to fasten clothes 拉鏈: *Do my zip up, would you?* 請幫我拉上拉鏈, 好嗎? –see picture on page 210 見 210 頁彩圖

zip[2] *v* **-pp- 1** [T] to put something into a particular condition using a zip 用拉鏈拉開或扣上〔某物〕: *Zip the sleeping bag together.* 把睡袋的拉鏈扣上。**2** [I+adv/prep] to move quickly and forcefully 快速而有力地移動: *The bullet zipped past my head.* 子彈颼的一聲飛過我的頭頂。

zip up *phr v* **1** [T **zip** sthg ↔ **up**] to fasten something with a zip 用拉鏈扣上: *He zipped the bag up.* 他拉上了袋子的拉鏈。| *She zipped up her dress.* 她拉上了裙子的拉鏈。– opposite 反義 **unzip 2** [T **zip** sbdy **up**] to fasten someone into something with a zip 給某人拉上拉鏈: *Would you zip me up? I can't reach.* 你能幫我拉上拉鏈嗎? 我觸不着。

zip code /'· ·/ *n AmE* a series of numbers and letters that is part of an address〔美式〕郵政編碼

zo·di·ac /'zodɪæk; 'zəʊdiæk/ *n* **the zodiac** a picture which shows an imaginary belt through space along which the sun, the moon, and the planets (PLANET) travel; the zodiac is divided into 12 equal parts, which each have names, and is used by people who believe that the stars influence a person's character and fate 黃道十二宮圖〔指太陽、月亮及鄰近行星所構成的假想帶, 分成十二宮, 每個宮都按星座命名〕: "*Which sign of the zodiac are you?*" "*I'm a Gemini.*" "你是屬於哪個星座的?" "我是雙子宮的。"

zom·bie /ˈzɑmbɪ; ˈzɒmbi/ *n* a person who does not seem to know where they are or what they are doing 行動呆板的人: *I was so tired I was wandering about like a zombie.* 我累極了，四處遊蕩，像個遊魂。

*★**zone** /zon; zəʊn/ *n* a division or area marked off from others by particular qualities 地區; 地帶; 區域: *a war zone* 戰區 | *the US postal zones* 美國郵區

zoo /zu; zuː/ *n* **zoos** a park where many kinds of living animals are kept for people to look at or study 動物園

zo·ol·o·gy /zoˈɑlədʒɪ; zʊˈɒlədʒi/ *n* [U] the scientific study of animals, and of where and how they live 動物學 –**zoologist** *n* –**zoological** /ˌzoəˈlɑdʒɪkl; ˌzuːəˈlɒdʒkəl/ *adj*

zoom /zum; zuːm/ *v* [I+adv/prep] **1** to increase rapidly 急升; 猛漲: *Prices have zoomed up in the last year.* 去年物價急劇上漲。 **2** *infml* (of a driver or vehicle) to go quickly and noisily 〔非正式〕〔司機或車輛〕隆隆地疾行: *Jack went zooming past in his new car.* 傑克開着新車呼嘯地駛過。

zoom in *phr v* [I] (of a camera) to move quickly from a distant view to a close view of something 〔攝影機〕拉近, 推近: *The camera zoomed in on the child's face.* 攝影機向孩子的臉部推近。

zoom lens /ˈ··/ *n* a camera LENS which can move quickly between a distant and a close-up view 可變焦距透鏡

zuc·chi·ni /zuˈkinɪ; zʊˈkiːni/ *n* [plural is 複數為 **zucchini**] the usual American word for 〔美式〕= a COURGETTE

Answer Key 練習答案

Picture exercises 彩圖練習

CAR

Exercise 1

1. (back) door 2. ignition 3. clutch pedal 4. rear-view mirror 5. headlights 6. fuel gauge 7. indicators 8. brake 9. petrol cap

CLOTHES

Exercise 1

1. red t-shirt 2. green slippers 3. blue raincoat 4. red dressing gown 5. red tie

Exercise 2

	belt	collar	sleeves	pockets	lapels	buttons
jeans	?	X	X	✔	X	✔
raincoat	?	✔	✔	✔	✔	✔
nightdress	X	?	?	X	X	?
tracksuit	X	?	✔	?	X	X
waistcoat	X	X	X	✔	X	✔
gloves	X	X	X	X	X	X
sandals	X	X	X	X	X	X
scarf	X	X	X	X	X	X

COLOURS AND PATTERNS

black [7], blue [5], green [6], grey [3], pink [4], red [1], white [8], yellow [2]

CONTAINERS

Exercise 1

1. bucket 2. churn 3. bottles 4. crates 5. kettle 6. teapot 7. cups 8. saucers 9. jug

Exercise 2

	wood	plastic	glass	china	paper	metal
bag	X	✔	X	X	✔	X
bottle	X	✔	✔	X	X	X
crate	✔	✔	✔	X	X	X
cup	X	✔	?	✔	✔	X
saucepan	X	X	X	X	X	✔
box	✔	✔	X	X	X*	X
jug	X	✔	✔	✔	X	?
vase	X	X	✔	✔	X	X
tube	X	✔	X	X	X	✔

*Note that boxes are often made of CARDBOARD, a sort of thick, stiff paper. 注意：箱子一般以硬紙板製成。

ENVIRONMENTAL PROBLEMS

1. mixture 2. smog 3. power 4. chimneys 5. clouds 6. rain 7. forests 8. spray 9. pesticides 10. chemicals 11. blood

FAMILY TREE

Exercise 1

1. father 2. father-in-law 3. wife 4. husband 5. granddaughter 6. daughter-in-law 7. aunt 8. parents

Exercise 2

1H, 2I, 3J, 4B, 5D, 6F, 7E, 8C, 9G, 10A

Puzzle

His son

FOOD

Exercise 3

1. eggs 2. milk 3. butter 4. mushrooms 5. cheese 6. ham 7. onions 8. bananas

LIVING ROOM

Exercise 1

armchair, kettle, washbasin, wardrobe, mantelpiece, lamp, towel, cushion, tap, bath, saucer, pillow

living room	kitchen	bathroom	bedroom
armchair	kettle	washbasin	wardrobe
lamp	towel	towel	lamp
cushion	tap	tap	cushion
mantelpiece	saucer	bath	pillow

OFFICE

Exercise 1

1. answering machine 2. fax machine 3. waste paper basket 4. photocopier 5. disk drive 6. calculator 7. stapler 8. printer 9. pencil sharpener 10. VDU

Exercise 2

1. both show the days and dates of the year; a calendar usually shows a month at a time, and is hung on a wall, and a diary usually shows a week at a time, and is in the form of a book.
2. both are devices used in a COMPUTER to store data; a floppy disk can be removed from the computer, but a hard disk cannot.
3. both are metal devices for holding sheets of paper together; paper clips are more easily removable and reusable than staples, which make holes in the paper.

PREPOSITIONS

1. into 2. into 3. Under 4. inside 5. out of
6. to 7. on 8. along 9. in 10. into 11. under
12. beside 13. next to 14. out of 15. through
16. outside 17. towards 18. near 19. under

SPORTS

Exercise 1

Individual	Team
athletics	rugby
boxing	American football
cycling	basketball
golf	cricket
skiing	soccer
horse racing	
swimming	
tennis	

Exercise 2

1. rugby, American football
2. cricket, golf, tennis
3. swimming
4. horse racing
5. rugby, soccer, American football

Exercise 3

pitch — cricket, American football, soccer, rugby
track — cycling, athletics
court — tennis, basketball
course — horse racing, golf
pool — swimming
slope — skiing
ring — boxing

TOOLS AND EQUIPMENT

Exercise 1

1. These are all items used for opening things
2. These are all items used for cutting things
3. These are all items used for digging in the ground.

Exercise 2

1. hose 2. lawnmower 3. (an) axe
4. potato peeler 5. potato masher
6. (an) iron 7. corkscrew 8. (a) toaster
9. hammer 10. tin opener

Exercise 3

1. hammer 2. drill 3. screwdriver 4. spanner
5. tape measure 6. saw 7. chisel 8. mallet

TRANSPORT

Exercise 1

Things you can see on a motorway — lorry, coach, motorbike (only if it is very powerful)

Exercise 2

	muscle power	wind power	petrol engine	diesel engine	jet engine	turbine engine
aeroplane	X	X	X	X	✓	X
bus	X	X	✓	✓	X	X
car	X	X	✓	✓	X	X
dinghy	✓	X	X	X	X	X
helicopter	X	X	X	X	✓	✓
hovercraft	X	X	X	X	✓	✓
lorry	X	X	X	✓	X	X
rowing boat	✓	X	X	X	X	X
ship	X	X	X	✓	X	✓
speedboat	X	X	✓	X	X	X
train	X	X	X	✓	X	X
yacht	X	✓	X	X	X	X

VERBS OF MOVEMENT

1. run 2. carry 3. walk 4. jump 5. pull 6. bend
7. kneel 8. crawl 9. pick 10. drag 11. lift
12. stretch 13. lean 14. hold 15. climb 16. fall
17. throw 18. catch 19. drop 20. sit 21. tiptoe

Study Note exercise 學習提示練習

WORD CLASSES OR 'PARTS OF SPEECH'

noun	verb	adjective	adverb
weekend	went	last	quite
seaside	took	cold	rather
group	had	disappointed	fortunately
friends	arrived	warmer	
sandwiches	was	wonderful	
picnic	felt		
beach	got		
weather	had		
time			

pronoun	preposition	conjunction
I	to	and
We	with	When
us	of	so
we	with	and
we	on	
it		
we		

Study
Notes

學 習 提 示

STUDY NOTE 學習提示

Comparative and superlative adjectives 形容詞的比較級和最高級

Comparative and superlative forms of adjectives are used to show an increase in quality, quantity, or degree.

形容詞的比較級和最高級形式用來表示質量、數量或程度上的增加。

Comparatives and superlatives are formed in various ways.

比較級和最高級形式的構成方式有多種。

*The girls are all quite **tall**. Meg is **taller than** Gill. Sue is **the tallest** of the three.*

這些女孩都長得相當高。梅格長得比吉爾高。蘇是她們當中長得最高的。

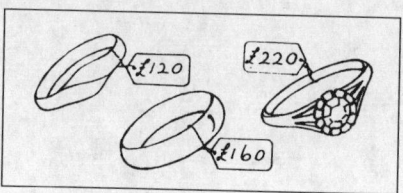

*These rings are **expensive**. The gold ring is **more expensive than** the silver one. The diamond ring is **the most expensive** of all.*

這些戒指都很昂貴。金戒指比銀戒指貴。其中鑽石戒指是最貴的。

1. Adjectives of one syllable 單音節的形容詞

By adding **-er** or **-est** to the end of the word:

在詞尾加上 **-er** 或 **-est**：

tall	taller	tallest
rich	richer	richest

If the adjective already ends in **-e** you only need to add **-r** or **-st**:

如果形容詞以 e 結尾，只需加 **-r** 或 **-st**：

nice	nicer	nicest
rare	rarer	rarest

Sometimes, when the adjective ends in a single consonant, you need to double the final con-sonant before forming the comparative and superlative. The dictionary tells you when you need to do this:

有時形容詞詞尾只有一個子音字母，在構成比較級和最高級形式時，要雙寫這個子音字母。本詞典對這類詞有註明：

big /bɪg; bɪg/ *adj* **bigger, biggest**

big	bigger	biggest
fat	fatter	fattest

2. Adjectives of two syllables 雙音節的形容詞

If the word ends in **-y**, change the **-y** to **-i** and then add **-er** or **-est**. The dictionary tells you when you need to do this:

如果形容詞以 **-y** 結尾，要把 y 變為 i，然後加上 **-er** 或 **-est**。本詞典對這種情況有註明：

heav·y /ˈhɛvɪ; ˈhevi/ *adj* **heavier, heaviest**

heavy	heavier	heaviest
happy	happier	happiest

If the adjective does NOT end in **-y**, then form the comparative and superlative using **more** and **most**:

如果形容詞不是以 **-y** 結尾的，構成比較級或最高級形式時要分別加上 **more** 和 **most**：

useful	more useful	most useful
famous	more famous	most famous

3. Adjectives of three syllables or more 三音節或更多音節的形容詞

Form the comparative and superlative using **more** and **most**.

加上 **more** 或 **most** 來構成比較級或最高級形式。

expensive	more expensive	most expensive
comfortable	more comfortable	most comfortable

4. 'Irregular' Comparatives and Superlatives
不規則的比較級和最高級形式

Some adjectives use a completely different word for the comparative and superlative forms. You can find these 'irregular' forms in the dictionary:

有些形容詞的比較級和最高級形式與原詞完全不同, 本詞典列出了這些不規則的變化:

---

good[1] /gʊd; gʊd/ *adj* **better, best**

good	better	best
bad	worse	worst

NOTE
There are some exceptions to these general rules. The most important to remember are:

註:
此外還有些特殊的規則, 特別要記住的是:

For adjectives which are formed from a verb and end in **-ed** or **-ing**, always use **more** and **most** for the comparative and superlative:

由過去分詞與現在分詞構成的形容詞, 即以 **-ed** 或 **-ing** 結尾的形容詞, 總是加上 **more** 或 **most** 來構成比較級和最高級形式的:

bored	more bored	most bored
boring	more boring	most boring

Adjectives which start with the negative prefix **un-** can use **-er** and **-est** even if they have three syllables:

以否定前綴 **un** -開首的形容詞, 即使有三個音節, 也可以加上 **-er** 或 **-est** 來構成比較級和最高級形式:

unhappy	unhappier	unhappiest

STUDY NOTE 學習提示

Countable and uncountable nouns 可數與不可數名詞

Countable nouns 可數名詞

apple and **chair** are both COUNTABLE nouns, because they are things we can count; there can be more than one of them:

apple 和 **chair** 都是可數名詞，因為它們是可以數的東西，數目可以不止一個：

three apples
三個蘋果

two chairs
兩把椅子

an apple
一個蘋果

a chair
一把椅子

These nouns can be used in the plural and can be used with a or an when they are singular.

這些名詞可以以複數形式出現，而用作單數時，前面可以冠以 **a** 或 **an**。

In the dictionary, [C] means countable, and [U] means uncountable, If a noun does not have a [C] or a [U] printed by it, this means that is always countable.

在本詞典中，[C] 表示可數，[U] 表示不可數。如果一個名詞的後面沒有註明 [C] 或 [U]，這就是說，這個名詞在任何情形下都是可數名詞。

Uncountable nouns 不可數名詞

sand and **water** are UNCOUNTABLE nouns, because they are substances which cannot be counted:

sand 沙　　　　*water* 水

sand 和 **water** 是不可數名詞，因為它們是無法數的東西：

These nouns are not usually used in the plural.

這些名詞通常不用複數形式。

There are some nouns, like **love** and **beauty** (ABSTRACT nouns) which cannot be counted because they are not physical things like apples and chairs. These are uncountable nouns too.

有些名詞，如 **love** 和 **beauty**（抽象名詞）也不能數，因為它們不像蘋果和椅子那樣是具體的東西，所以也是不可數名詞。

nouns that are both countable and uncountable 同時是可數與不可數的名詞

Some nouns, like **light** and **coffee**, can be [C] (countable) in one meaning and [U] (uncountable) in another. When they are [C] they can become plural. When they are [U] they cannot. For example:

有些名詞，如 **light** 和 **coffee**，在某種意義上是可數名詞，而在另一種意義上是不可數名詞。當用作可數名詞時，就可以變成複數；用作不可數名詞時，就沒有複數形式。例如：

[U] *the light of the sun* 〔不可數〕陽光

[C] *Turn on the lights* 〔可數〕開電燈

[U] *a jar of coffee*
〔不可數〕一瓶咖啡

[U] *a pot of coffee*
〔不可數〕一壺咖啡

[C] *Three coffees please.* 〔可數〕請來三杯咖啡。

plural and singular nouns 複數與單數名詞

Some nouns, like **trousers** are used only in the plural, i.e. they take a plural verb. These nouns are marked [pl] in the dictionary.

有些名詞，如 **trousers**，只用複數形式，也就是說，它們與複數形式的動詞連用。這類名詞在本詞典中用 [pl] 標出：

trou·sers /ˈtraʊzəz; ˈtraʊzəz/ *n* [pl] an outer garment covering your body from the waist down, with one part for each leg 褲子，長褲: *a pair of blue trousers* 一條藍色褲子

Some nouns, like **feel**, are usually used only in the singular. These nouns are used with a and an, and are marked [sing] in the dictionary:

有些名詞，如 **feel**，通常只用單數形式。這類名詞前面冠以 **a** 或 **an**，在本詞典中用 [sing] 標出：

feel[2] *n* [sing] **1** the sensation that you experience when you touch and feel something 觸覺；手感: *The skin has a rough feel.* 皮膚摸上去很粗糙。

more and less 較多和較少

The list below shows you which words to use with [C] and [U] nouns to show quantity. They answer questions like *How many?* and *How much?*
下表説明可數與不可數名詞在表示數量時可與哪些詞連用。這些詞常用來回答以 How many（多少個）和 How much（多少）發問的問題。

How many (多少?)
(use with [C] nouns) (與可數名詞連用)

all

How much (多少?)
(use with [U] nouns) (與不可數名詞連用)

every, all
Every *student /* **all** *the students came to the meeting.* 每個學生/ 全體學生都來參加會議。

most
Most *of my friends came to the party.* 我大多數的朋友都來參加晚會。

many, a lot of
Many *people walk to school every day.* 很多人每天步行上學。| *I spoke to* **a lot of** *people.* 我跟很多人講過話。

some, several
Some *of these apples taste sour.* 這些蘋果中有幾個是酸的。| **Several** *people were waiting for the bus.* 有幾個人在等公共汽車。

not many, only a few
There are **not many/ only a few** *tickets left.* 票子剩下不多了/票子只剩下幾張了。

not ... any, no, none
He couldn't answer **any** *of the exam questions.* 他一道試題都答不出來。| *There are* **no** *eggs left;* **none** *at all.* 沒有雞蛋剩下，一隻也沒有了。

none

all
He ate **all** *the bread* 他吃光了所有的麵包。

most
He spends **most** *of his time reading.* 他用大部分時間來讀書。

much, a lot of, a great deal of
Much *of what he says is true.* 他説的話大多是對的。| *He ate* **a lot of** *bread.* 他吃了很多麵包。| *She did* **a great deal of** *work.* 她做了很多工作。

some
There's **some** *bread in the cupboard.* 食櫥裡有一些麵包。

little, not much
There's only **a little / not much** *room left.* 只剩下一點兒 / 不多的空間。

not ... any, no, none
He didn't give me **any** *help.* 他沒有給予我任何幫助。| *There's* **no** *petrol in the car,* **none** *at all.* 汽車沒有汽油了，一點也沒有了。

---

some and any some 和 any

any is usually used instead of **some** in questions and sentences with *not*.
在疑問句和否定句中，通常用 **any**，不用 **some**：

Have you got **any** *eggs/milk?* 你有雞蛋/牛奶嗎?
No, I haven't got **any** *eggs/milk.* 不，我沒有雞蛋/牛奶。

It is also possible to use **some** in a question, especially when you expect the answer to be *yes*:
在疑問句中也能用 **some**，尤其是當你希望對方給予肯定的回答時：

Could you spare **some** *eggs/milk, please?* 請問你有雞蛋/牛奶嗎?
Would you like **some** *more coffee?* 你要再喝點咖啡嗎?

Some common mistakes with uncountable nouns 有關不可數名詞的一些常見錯誤

If a noun is marked [U], do NOT use it in the plural. If a particular meaning of a noun is marked [U], do not use it in the plural with this meaning:
如果一個名詞被標明是不可數名詞, 則不能以複數形式出現。如果一個名詞在某個義項上被標明是不可數名詞, 也不能用複數形式:
— We need some more informations.
　我們需要更多的消息。
— They've just bought a lot of new furnitures.
　他們剛買了很多新家具。
— I must wash my hairs tonight.
　今晚我一定要洗洗我的頭髮。

If a noun, or a meaning of a noun, is marked [U], do NOT use it with **a** or **an** in sentences like these:
如果一個名詞或其中的一個義項被標明是不可數的, 名詞前面便不能冠以 a 或 an:

— The hotel is surrounded by a beautiful scenery.
　這旅館四周的景色很美。
— We are having a really fine weather at the moment.
　此時此刻天氣好極了。
— She gave me a very good advice.
　她給了我很好的勸告。

Remember that uncountable nouns are used WITHOUT an article in general statements like these:
記住, 有些不可數名詞在用作泛指時, 不用加定冠詞:
— The crime is a problem in most big cities.
　罪案是大多數大城市的一個問題。
— She wrote an article about the role of women in the society.
　她寫了一篇有關婦女社會地位的文章。
— He is studying the medicine.
　他正在學醫。

STUDY NOTE 學習提示

Grammatical patterns 語法結構

When you are writing in English it is helpful to know if a word is usually followed by a particular kind of grammatical pattern. This dictionary helps you in various ways.
如果你知道一個詞通常和哪些特殊的語法結構結合在一起使用，這會對你的英語寫作有很大的幫助。本詞典將通過不同的方式給你提供這方面的知識。

1 Grammar codes 文法代號

The following codes tell you which grammatical patterns can follow a word:
以下這些代號表明一個詞後面可以接哪類型的語法結構：

+ *that*

In this entry the code [+ that] tells you that **contend** can be followed by a clause introduced by **that**. The example gives you more help with how to use the word.
在這詞條中，代號 [+that] 表示 **contend** 後面可以接由 **that** 引導的子句。例句則進一步說明該詞的具體用法。

> **con·tend** /kən'tɛnd; kən'tɛnd/ *v* **1** [T; +that] to claim that something is true 聲稱〔某物為真〕: *The lawyer contended that she had not returned home until 11.00.* 律師稱她十一點鐘才回家。

+ *adv/prep*

In this entry the code [I + adv/prep] tells you that, when it means "to come or go to a place in large numbers," the verb **flood** is intransitive. It also tells you that it must be followed by an adverb or a preposition. So you can say, *The letters came flooding in*, or *The spectators flooded onto the pitch*. But you should NOT say, *The spectators flooded.* ✗
下列詞條中代號 [I+adv/prep] 表示，當動詞 **flood** 作"大量湧到"解時，是不及物的，而且後面必須接一個副詞或介詞。所以可以說 *The letters came flooding in.*（信件大量地湧到。）或 *The spectators flooded onto the pitch.*（觀眾湧向球場。），而不能說 *The spectators flooded.* ✗

> **flood²** *v* .... **2** [I+adv/prep] to come or go to a place in large numbers 大量湧到: *Requests for information flooded in after the advertisement.* 廣告登出之後，索取資料的信件潮湧般寄來。| *Settlers flooded from Europe to America in the 19th century.* 在十九世紀，歐洲移民紛紛湧到了美國。

+ *complement*

This entry tells you that the verb **become** is not usually used alone but should be followed by a complement. The examples show you what kind of complements you can use.
下列詞條表示動詞 **become** 通常不單獨使用，而要加上一個補語。例句指出可以加上怎樣的補語。

> **be·come** /bɪ'kʌm; bɪ'kʌm/ *v* became /bɪ'kem; bɪ'keɪm/, become, becoming **1** [+complement] to begin to be something 變為；成為: *He became king in 1938.* 他於 1938 年成為國王。| *The weather became warmer.* 天氣變暖和了。

2 Patterns shown in red print 用紅色顯示的結構

Some words are nearly always used with the same grammatical pattern. And some words are always used with a particular pattern when they have a particular meaning. The dictionary shows you these patterns in special red print before giving you the definition.
有些詞幾乎總是和同一類型的語法結構一起使用的，而有些詞只有在具有某種含義時才與某種語法結構結合使用。本詞典在釋義前用紅色標明這些結構。

This entry shows you that, when it means "to try to do something", the verb **seek** is always followed by the infinitive with 'to'. The examples give you more help with how to use it.
下面這個詞條表明當 **seek** 的意思是"試圖做某事"時，總是後接 **to** 引出的不定式結構。例句則進一步說明該詞的具體用法。

> **seek** /sik; siːk/ *v* sought /sɔt; sɔːt/, sought [T] *fml or lit* 〔正式或文〕 **2 seek to do something** to try to do something 試圖做某事: *The company is seeking to improve its profitability.* 公司正力圖改進它的盈利能力。

3 Useful patterns 有用句型

When you are writing in English it can sometimes be difficult to know which pattern to use after a particular word. There are some words which you will need to use quite frequently in your writing but which might give you problems because of their grammatical patterns. This dictionary gives you **extra** help with these words by suggesting some patterns for you to use.

The USEFUL PATTERNS note at the first meaning of **consider** gives you some patterns to use with this verb when it means "to think about something carefully".

在英語寫作中，一個詞的後面接甚麼語法結構有時是一個難點。有些詞在寫作中經常會出現，但它們的語法結構卻是一個問題。本詞典將就此作出補充說明，指出常見的語法結構。

有用句型中註明動詞 **consider** 的第一個義項"考慮"常和哪些語法結構一起使用。

> **con·sid·er** /kənˈsɪdə; kənˈsɪdɚ/ *v* **1** [I;T] to think about something carefully 認真考慮〔某事〕: *I'm considering changing my job.* 我正考慮轉換工作。| *We need some time to consider.* 我們需要一些時間來考慮。
>
> □USEFUL PATTERNS 有用句型
> to consider; to consider something; to consider doing something

This tells you that you can say:
這表明你可以說：
— *Consider carefully before making up your mind.*✓
（做出決定之前要好好考慮。）
— *I'm considering your offer.*✓
（我正在考慮你的提議。）
— *She's considering going abroad.*✓
（她正在考慮出國。）

You should, therefore, avoid mistakes such as:
因此，你應該避免這樣的錯誤：
— *I'm considering to change my job.*✗
（我正考慮換個工作。）

The USEFUL PATTERNS note at the first meaning of **confess** gives you some patterns to use with this verb when it means "to admit to a fault or crime".

有用句型註明動詞 **confess** 的第一個義項"承認〔錯誤或罪行〕"常和哪些語法結構一起使用。

> **con·fess** /kənˈfɛs; kənˈfes/ *v* **1** [I;T; +(that)] to admit to a fault or crime 承認〔錯誤或罪行〕；坦白: *It's time to confess.* 該是坦白的時候了。| *He has confessed* **to** *the murder.* 他承認犯了謀殺罪。| *She confessed all her crimes.* 她供認了全部罪行。| *Jean confessed that she'd eaten all the cakes.* 瓊承認她把所有的蛋糕吃掉了。
>
> □USEFUL PATTERNS 有用句型
> to confess; to confess something; to confess to something; to confess to doing something; to confess that...

This tells you that you can say:
這表明你可以說：
— *They made him confess.*✓
（他們使他招供了。）
— *He's already confessed his part in the crime.*✓
（他已經承認了自己在犯罪活動中的所作所為。）
— *She confessed to the theft.*✓
（她承認偷東西。）
— *She confessed to opening/to having opened the letter.*✓
（她承認她拆開了信。）
— *They confessed that they had lost the money.*✓
（他們承認把錢丟失了。）

You should, therefore, avoid mistakes such as:
因此，你應該避免這樣的錯誤：
— *She confessed to have opened the letter.*✗
（她承認她拆開了信。）

Example 例句

Remember that, in addition to looking at codes and patterns, you should always read the example sentences. These will give you a lot of help with finding out how to use the word you are looking up.

要記住除了注意語法代號和語法結構之外，還要讀例句。這對你掌握所查的詞的具體用法很有幫助。

STUDY NOTE 學習提示

─Modal verbs 情態動詞─

Modal verbs are a small group of verbs that are used with other verbs to change their meaning in the sentence in various ways. The English modal verbs are: **can, could, may, might, shall, should, will, would, must, ought to,** and **used to. Need** and **dare** also behave like modals in some cases. Table 1 explains the grammar of modal verbs — how they are used in forming sentences. Table 2 describes the various meanings that modal verbs are used to express.

情態動詞為數不多, 它們與其他動詞連用, 以不同方式改變這些動詞在句中的意思。英語中的情態動詞有: **can, could, may, might, shall, should, will, would, must, ought to** 和 **used to**。**Need** 和 **dare** 有時也作為情態動詞使用。表一介紹情態動詞的語法, 即它們如何用作構成句子。表二則描述如何用情態動詞表達各種不同的意見。

Table 1 表一 : **grammar** 語法

In their grammar, modal verbs are different from most other verbs in the following ways:
在語法方面, 情態動詞與大多數其他動詞有以下不同之處:

1. they are followed by an infinitive verb without **to**:
   情態動詞後接不加 **to** 的動詞不定式:
   *I **can** swim.* 我會游泳。
   *You **must** go.* 你必須去。

   but **ought** and used are followed by **to+** infinitive:
   但 **ought** 和 **used** 則後接 **to+** 動詞不定式:
   *You **ought** to go.* 你應該去。
   *They **used** to live in London.* 他們過去住在倫敦。

2. they have no **-s** in the 3rd person singular:
   它們的第三人稱單數不加 **-s**:
   *She **can** swim.* 她會游泳。
   *He **must** go.* 他必須去。

3. they form questions without using **do**, with the subject coming after the modal verb:
   它們在構成問句時不用 **do**, 而是將主詞放在情態動詞後面:
   Can I go now? 我現在可以去嗎?
   Dare you ask her? 你敢問她嗎?
   Ought we to tell the police? 我們應該告訴警方嗎?
   Will the train be late? 火車會遲來嗎?

   the question form of **used to** is either **used to** 的問句形式可以是:
   *Did they **use** to live there?* or 或 *Did they **used** to live there?* 他們過去住在那裡嗎?

4. they form negatives by adding **not** or **n't**, but without using **do** or **did**.
   它們變作否定式時只需加 **not** 或 **n't**, 不用加 **do** 或 **did**:
   *I **couldn't** / **could not** lift it.* 我提不起它。
   *It **won't** / **will not** rain.* 天不會下雨。
   *You **oughtn't** / **ought not** to do that.* 你不應該去做那件事。

   the negative form of **used to** is either **used to** 的否定式是
   *They **didn't** use to / used to live here* or (less common) 或 (較少用) *They **usedn't** to / used not to live here.* 他們過去不住在這裡。

5. in indirect speech (when you are describing what someone else said) these modals change their form:

在間接引述中，情態動詞可以改變形式：

can: *"I can speak French."* "我會說法語。" *She said that she **could** speak French.* 她說她會說法語。

may: *"We may not be able to come."* "我們可能來不了。" *They said they **might** not be able to come.* 他們說他們可能來不了。

shall: *"Shall I post the letter?"* "我把信拿去寄好嗎？" *She asked if she **should** post the letter.* 她問她是否應該把信拿去寄。

will: *"We will probably be late."* "我們很可能會遲到。" *They said they **would** probably be late.* 他們說他們很可能會遲到。

the other modals do not usually change their form. For example:

其他情態動詞通常不改變形式，例如：

"I would like some coffee." "我想要點咖啡。" *She said she **would** like some coffee.* 她說她想喝點咖啡。

"You ought to work harder." "你應該更努力工作。" *He told me I ought to work harder.* 他叫我應該更努力工作。

Table 2 表二 ： meaning 語義

Modal verbs are used for many different purposes. The most common ones are:
情態動詞有許多不同的用途，最常見的有：

1. talking about ability 表示能力	*She can speak French.* 她會說法語。 *I could swim when I was five.* 我五歲時就會游泳。 *I couldn't lift it — it was too heavy.* 我提不起它 — 太重了。	**could** describes ability in the past, but expressions like **was able to** or **managed to** are often used instead: **could** 是表示能力的過去式，但很多時候用 **was able to** 或 **managed to** 代替： *With John's help I was able to lift it / managed to lift it.* 有了約翰幫忙，我能把它提起來。
2. asking for and giving permission 請求或允許	*You can go now if you like.* 你喜歡的話現在可以去。 *Students may borrow up to six books.* 學生最多可以借六本書。 *Could we go now, please?* 請問現在我們可以去嗎？ *Might I open the window?* 我可以開窗嗎？	**can** is the usual word for asking for and giving permission. **May** is more formal. **Could** and **might** are polite ways of asking for (but not giving) permission. **can** 通常都用作請求或允許，**may** 則是較正式的用法。**could** 和 **might** 是請求允許的禮貌形式。
3. making requests 提出請求	*Will you / would you / could you close the door, please?* 請關上門好嗎？ *Can you help me to lift this?* 你可否幫我把它提起來嗎？	**will, would** and **could** are more polite than **can** for making requests. 提出請求時用 **will, would** 和 **could** 比用 **can** 更有禮貌。

4. making offers and suggestions 提出建議	*Shall I open it for you?* 我替你把它打開好嗎？ *Shall we go to the cinema?* 我們去看電影好嗎？ *Can I help you with your bags?* 我來替你拿提包好嗎？ *I'll carry your bags if you like.* 要是你喜歡的話，我來替你拿提包吧。	**shall** is used only with **I** and **we** in offers and suggestions. 如用於提出建議，**shall** 只與 **I** 和 **we** 同用。
5. showing something is necessary 表示必須	*You **must** finish this work today.* 你必須今天完成這項工作。 *I **have** to go / I've to go now.* 我現在必須離去。 *I **must** phone my mother.* (=I feel a strong duty to do this.) 我必須打電話給母親。	**had to** is used to describe what was necessary in the past: **had to** 用以表示必須的過去式： *I **had to** leave early yesterday.* 昨天我必須提早離開。
6. showing that something is not necessary 表示不必	*You **needn't** finish it today.* (=but you can if you want to.) 你不必今天完成 (＝但你想的話也可以)。 *You **don't have** to finish it today.* 你不用今天完成。 *I **needn't have / didn't need** to put on my thick coat.* 我本不用穿上厚外衣。	
7. giving advice 給予意見	*You **should / ought** to see the doctor.* 你應該去看醫生。 *He **shouldn't have / oughtn't to have** said that.* 他是不應該那樣說。 *You **could** have told me you were going to be late!* (= I wish you had told me) 你是可以告訴我你會遲到的 (＝我希望你告訴了我)！ *You **might** knock before you come in!* (=I am annoyed because you did not knock) 你進來前可以先敲門吧 (＝你沒有敲門，所以我生氣了)。	
8. talking about future events or what you intend to do in the future 表示將來的事或要做的事	*It **will** probably rain tomorrow.* 明天很可能會下雨。 *We **shall** be away next week.* 下星期我們會不在。	**shall** is usually used only with **I** and **we**, and is less common than **will** for talking about the future. 表示將來的事情時，**shall** 通常只與 **I** 和 **we** 同用，也較 **will** 少用。

9. talking about the past 表示過去	*We **used to** work in the same office.* 我們以往在同一個辦事處工作。 *We **would** often go to the cinema together.* 我們以前常一起去看電影。	**would** is used to describe an action in the past only if it is a repeated action. **would** 只用於描述以往重複做的行為。
10. talking about what is possible but not certain 表示可能	*It **may / might** snow tonight.* 今晚可能會下雪。 *Don't touch that wire — it **could** be dangerous.* 別碰那根電線,那可能有危險。 *Learning English **can** be fun.* (=is sometimes fun) 學英語可以很有樂趣 (＝有時很有樂趣)。	**might** and **could** make something sound less likely than **may.** **might** 和 **could** 表達的可能性比 **may** 的低。
11. talking about what is probable 表示很有可能的事	*They **should have / ought to have** arrived by now.* (= I expect they leave, but I am not certain) 他們現在應該已經到了 (＝我預料他們已到達,但不肯定)。	
12. talking about what you believe to be certain 表示肯定	*You've been working all day — you **must** be tired.* (=I'm sure you are) 你工作了一整天,你一定很累了 (我肯定你很累)。 *Her office is empty — she **must** have gone home* (= I'm sure she has) 她的辦公室裡沒有人,她一定是已經回家了 (我肯定她已經回家)。	**can't** is the opposite of **must** in this meaning, showing that something is certainly not true: 如用作這個意思, **can't** 便是 **must** 的相反,表示某事肯定不對: *You haven't done any work — you **can't** be tired.* (=I'm sure you're not) 你一點工作也沒做,你不可能會累的 (＝我肯定你不累)。 *Her car is still here — she **can't** have gone home yet.* 她的汽車還在這兒,她不可能已經回家了。

STUDY NOTE 學習提示

─Phrasal verbs 片語／短語動詞─

In this dictionary a verb is called a phrasal verb if it consists of two or more words. One of these words is always a verb; the other may be an adverb or a preposition (or sometimes both together). The meaning of a phrasal verb is often quite different from the meaning of the verb on its own. For example, **look into** (= investigate) and **look after** (= take care of) have quite separate meanings from **look**.

在本詞典中，由兩個或兩個以上的詞構成的動詞稱為片語／短語動詞。這類片語其中必有一個動詞，另外有一個副詞或一個介詞（或兩者都有）。片語／短語動詞的含義往往不同於片語中動詞本身的含義。例如：**look into**（調查；檢查）和 **look after**（照顧；照料）和動詞 **look** 本身的含義就不同了。

How are phrasal verbs listed? 片語／短語動詞是如何排列的？

Phrasal verbs are listed in alphabetical order underneath the entry for the main verb. They are marked *phr v*.
In this entry **cry off** and **cry out for** are phrasal verbs listed under the entry for **cry**.

片語／短語動詞按字母順序，列於該主要動詞詞條之下，註明 *phr v*。
下列詞條中，片語／短語動詞 **cry off** 和 **cry out for** 就列於主要動詞 **cry** 這個詞條下面：

★cry¹ /kraɪ; kraɪ/ *v* **cried, cried, crying 1** [I] to produce tears from your eyes usually, as a sign of sadness 哭；哭泣：*She cried when she heard of her friend's death.* 她聽到朋友的死訊時哭了。| *The children cried for their father.* 孩子們哭着要找爸爸。**2** [I] to speak loudly or shout, usually with fear or excitement〔常因害怕或興奮而〕大聲喊叫：*"Run, run!" he cried.* "快跑，快跑!"他喊道。| *"That's wonderful!" she cried.* "那太棒了!"她叫道。

cry off *phr v* [I] *infml* to fail to fulfil a promise or agreement〔非正式〕食言；毀約：*He said he'd help, but then he cried off.* 他説好幫忙的，可是卻打了退堂鼓。

cry out *phr v* [I] to shout loudly, usually with fear or pain〔常因害怕或疼痛而〕大聲喊叫：*He cried out in pain.* 他痛得大喊大叫。

Sometimes the main verb of a phrasal verb is not used alone.
This entry shows you that **gad** is not used as a verb by itself, but only as part of the phrasal verb **gad about**.

有時片語／短語動詞的主要動詞不能單獨使用。這個條目表明，**gad** 不能單獨作動詞使用，只能作為片語／短語動詞 **gad about** 的一個組成部分來用。

gad /gæd; gæd/ *v* **-dd-**
　　gad about *phr v* [I; T **gad about** sthg] *infml* to travel round a place to enjoy yourself〔非正式〕遊蕩，閒逛：*He's always gadding about.* 他總是到處遊蕩。| *She's away, gadding about Europe.* 她人不在，現正在歐洲到處遊蕩。

Transitive or intransitive? 及物還是不及物？

Phrasal verbs, like all verbs, may be transitive or intransitive and are marked [T] or [I] accordingly. These sample entries show that **grow out of** is a transitive verb and **grow up** is an intransitive verb.

片語／短語動詞和動詞一樣，可以是及物動詞，也可以是不及物動詞，分別註明 [T] 或 [I]。
這些例子表明 **grow out of** 是及物的，而 **grow up** 則是不及物的。

grow out of sthg *phr v* [T] **1** to become too big or too old for something 長得太高或太大而不適於〔某事物〕：*She's grown out of all her clothes.* 她長大了，所有的衣服都穿不下。| *Most children grow out of wetting the bed.* 大部分孩子長大了就不會再尿牀。

grow up *phr v* [I] **1** (of people) to develop from a child into a man or woman〔人〕長大；成人

Some phrasal verbs can be used both transitively and intransitively.

有些片語／短語動詞既可以是及物的，也可以是不及物的。

— sometimes with similar meanings like **join in**:

— 有時在兩種情況下意義相近，如 **join in**:

> **join in** *phr v* [I;T **join in** sthg] to take part in an activity 參加〔活動〕: *Sarah never joins in, but prefers to play on her own.* 莎拉從不與別人一起玩，她喜歡獨自玩耍。| *We all joined in the singing.* 我們大家一起唱歌。

— sometimes with different meanings like **wrap up**:

— 有時在兩種情況下意義不同，如 **wrap up**:

> **wrap up** *phr v* **1** [T **wrap** sthg ⌐ **up**] to put paper around a parcel or present 用〔紙〕包, 裹〔禮物等〕 **2** [I] to wear warm clothes 穿得暖和: *It's cold outside. Wrap up well.* 外面很冷, 穿得暖和些。

Position of the direct object 直接受詞／賓語 的位置

When a phrasal verb is transitive [T], the dictionary shows you where to put the direct object. You should look at the beginning of the entry to see how the verb is written.

This entry tells you the the direct object of **pick on** always comes at the end of the phrasal verb.

對於及物的片語／短語動詞，本詞典會註明受詞／賓語在句中的位置。請注意動詞詞條開頭部分的寫法。

這個詞條表明片語／短語動詞 **pick on** 的直接受詞／賓語總是接在其後:

> **pick on** sbdy *phr v* [T] to punish or blame someone unfairly because you do not like them〔由於不喜歡而不公正地〕懲罰；責備〔某人〕: *He's always picking on me!* 他總是跟我過不去!

In a few cases, such as **get up**, the direct object must always come between the two parts of the phrasal verb.

有些情況下, 直接受詞〔賓語〕置於構成片語〔短語〕動詞的兩個部分之間, 如 **get up**:

> **get up** *phr v*
> **2** [T **get** sbdy **up**] to make someone rise from their bed 使〔某人〕起牀:
> *Can you go and get the children up?* 你能去把孩子們叫起來嗎?

For very, many phrasal verbs, however, the direct object can appear in either position. This is shown in the dictionary by the symbol ⌐.

在大多數情況下, 直接受詞／賓語可置於上述兩個位置的其中一個, 這種情況在本詞典中用符號 ⌐ 標出:

> **hand** sthg ⌐ **in** *phr v* [T] to give something to someone in a position of authority 上交；提交；呈交: *Please hand in your books at the end of the lesson.* 下課時請把書交上來。

This entry shows you that you can say either **Hand in** *your papers* or **Hand** *your papers* **in**. Note, however, that with the verbs of this type, when the direct object is a pronoun it MUST be put between the two parts of the phrasal verb.

上述詞條表明 **Hand in** *your papers* 和 **Hand** *your papers* **in** 兩種説法都可以。然而, 要注意的是這種類型的動詞, 如果它的直接受詞／賓語是代名詞, 則必須置於片語／短語動詞的兩部分之間。

Hand in your papers. 把考卷交上來。
Hand them in. 把它們交上來。
They knocked down the building. 他們拆除了那建築物。
They knocked it down. 他們把它拆除了。

More than one object 多於一個受詞／賓語

Some transitive phrasal verbs can have more than one object. The dictionary will show you where to put these.

This entry tells you that **put down to** has two objects; the first comes after **put** and the second after **to**.

有些及物的片語／短語動詞可以有一個以上的受詞／賓語。本詞典會註明這些受詞／賓語的位置。

下面這個詞條表明 **put down to** 有兩個受詞／賓語, 第一個放在 **put** 之後, 第二個則放在 **to** 之後。

---

put sthg **down to** sbdy/sthg *phr v* [T] to say or think that something was caused by a particular person or thing 把〔某事〕歸咎於…: *He didn't look well but I just put it down to the fact that he was tired.* 他氣色不佳, 但我相信這只是由於疲倦。

STUDY NOTE 學習提示

──Sentence connectors 句子的連接詞──

When you are writing it is important that your reader understands the connection between the things that you are saying.
寫作時, 讓讀者理解文章內容之間的聯繫是十分重要的。

What is the connection between these two sentences?
下面兩個句子之間有甚麼聯繫?

There has been a serious rise in food prices this year. 今年食品價格大幅度上漲。
The price of meat has doubled since March. 自三月份以來肉的價格漲了一倍。

The second sentence gives an example of the idea in the first sentence.
第二個句子對第一個句子提出的觀點舉出了一個例子。

You can help people to understand that you are saying by showing how one idea is connected to another. To show connections, you can use words and phrases such as **for example**, **however** and **on the other hand**.
指出一個意思和另一個意思之間的關係有助於讀者理解句子所表達的內容。你可以用一些單詞或片語來連接各個意思, 如: **for example, however** 和 **on the other hand**。

By using **for example**, the connection between the two sentences can be shown:
用 **for example** 來連接上面兩個句子, 可以這樣說:

*There has been a serious rise in food prices this year. **For example**, the price of meat has doubled since March.* 今年食品價格大幅度上漲, 例如自三月份以來肉的價格就漲了一倍。

Position 位置

These connecting words can go in various places. For example, they can go:
這些連接詞可以放在不同的位置上, 如:

—— at the beginning of a sentence 在句首
*We see that you have an income of less than £2000 a year. **Accordingly**, we have decided to offer you free tuition.* 我們明白你一年的收入不足二千英鎊, 因此我們決定給你免去學費。

—— after the subject 在主詞後
*Seat belts undoubtedly save lives. Many people, **however**, do not wear them.* 安全帶無疑能救人性命, 然而很多人卻不繫上它。

—— at the end 在句末
*Tim's not coming to the concert. He says he's too busy. He hasn't got any money, **in any case**.* 蒂姆不來參加音樂會了, 他說他很忙, 再說他也沒有錢。

What sort of connections are there? 句子之間有甚麼關係?

You use sentence connectors to show connections like these:
連接詞用於表示句子間的各種關係:

—— you are making an argument stronger by adding another idea 補充一層意思, 增強論點的說服力:
*I don't think I'm going to Scotland for Christmas. It's such a long way. **Besides**, I haven't much money left.* 我想我聖誕節不會去蘇格蘭了, 路太遠, 而且我也沒剩下甚麼錢。

—— you are listing a group of things 列舉一組事實:
*There are several reasons why the plan will not work. **First**, there has not been enough preparation. **Second**, there is not enough money.* 計劃無法實施的原因有幾個。第一, 沒有足夠的準備; 第二, 沒有足夠的錢。

— the next idea is unexpected after the idea before 表示轉折：

*The room was very small. It was very comfortable, **however**.* 這房間很小，但很舒服。

— you are talking about the result of the situation described in the first sentence 表示結果：

*You have repeatedly failed to deliver the goods on time. We **therefore** feel that we have no alternative but to find another supplier.* 你們已經好幾次沒有按時送貨了，因此我們覺得別無選擇，只有另找供應商。

— you are saying in what order events happened 表示事情發生的順序：

*The letters are collected from postboxes. They are **then** taken to the sorting office.* 信從郵筒中取出，然後被送到分揀處。

— you are giving an example of the idea in the sentence before 舉例說明前句的意思：

*Roman civilization was very advanced technologically. They had underfloor central heating, **for instance**.* 羅馬文明在技術方面十分先進，例如，他們當時已有了地下中央供暖系統。

— you are concluding the idea in the sentence before 表示概括總結：

*This examination tests both spoken and written English. It demands the ability to communicate, as well as a knowledge of grammar and vocabulary. Candidates are required to do extensive reading. **In short**, this is a very good examination.* 這項考試不僅測試英語口語，還要測試書面英語。它測試語言交際能力和語法及詞匯知識，考生還需要作廣泛的閱讀。簡而言之，這是一次很好的考試。

— you are explaining the idea before 對前文的意思作出解釋：

*The company has to reduce labour costs. **In other words**, some of us are going to lose our jobs.* 公司不得不降低人工成本。換言之，我們中的一些人將會失業。

How does the dictionary help you with sentence connectors? 本詞典怎樣幫助你學會使用句子連接詞？

This dictionary gives you a lot of help with sentence connectors. 本詞典針對句子連接詞為你提供了很多有用的幫助。

It explains when you use them 解釋使用場合：

in other words 換言之；也就是說
you use this phrase when you are repeating an idea in other words because you think that people may not have understood the real meaning behind the words and you need to explain it.
如果你認為讀者可能不理解某句話的言下之意，你便需要換一個說法對此作出解釋說明。這時你可以使用這個片語。

It gives you examples which are long enough for you to see how they connect sentences 用長例句來說明這些詞連接句子的用法：

in the second place 其次
*They won't be interested in that house. In the first place, it's too far from where they work. And **in the second place**, it's more than they are prepared to pay.* 他們不會對那所房子有興趣的，首先是那兒離他們工作的地方太遠，其次是價錢也比他們預算的要貴。

It shows you in the examples where you can put sentence connectors 指出句子連接詞在句中的位置：

for example 例如；比方說
*There has been a serious rise in food prices this year. The price of meat, **for example**, has doubled since March.* 今年食品價格大幅度上漲，例如自三月份以來肉的價格就漲了一倍。

*Seeds are naturally protected in various ways. **For example**, they are usually hard on the outside.* 種子本身有各種自我保護的方式，比方說，它們外殼堅硬。

*He seems to have been rather an unpleasant man. He used to throw his rubbish into the garden next door, **for example**.* 看來他以前是個令人討厭的傢伙，比方說他過去常把垃圾扔在鄰家的花園裡。

The dictionary helps you not only with the sentence connectors you use when you are writing, but also with those you use when you are speaking:

關於句子連接詞, 本詞典不僅在書面英語方面為你提供了幫助, 而且也涉及到它們在口語中的用法。

well 不過

You say "well" when you are changing or correcting the idea before. 如果你想改變或糾正前面所表達的意思, 你可以說 "**Well**":

There's no problem at all. **Well**, *maybe there's a small problem.* 根本就沒問題。不過, 也許有個小問題。

The following passage shows how some important sentence connectors work. 下面這段話用以說明句子連接詞是何等重要。

*Most scientists nowadays accept the idea of the greenhouse effect, that is, the dangerous increase in temperature of the earth's atmosphere as a result of human activities. There are those, **however**, who think that the danger has been greatly exaggerated. **Indeed**, there are a few who think that the present increase is simply part of the normal cycle of climate variation.*

*The rise in temperature began with the Industrial Revolution. **At first**, it was very slow, but now it is gathering speed. **As a result**, the Government are beginning to introduce laws to control the causes of the greenhouse effect. They are **also** trying to find ways in which to lessen the effect of human activities on the atmosphere. **For example**, they are investigating the use of wind power as a source of electricity. **Eventually**, the people of the world will be forced to consume less. **Otherwise**, the earth will be destroyed.*

　　如今大多數科學家都接受了 "溫室效應" 這個觀念, 即地球大氣溫度升高這種危險的現象正是人類活動的結果。然而, 也有人認為這種危險被遠遠誇大了。事實上, 有些人認為目前的氣溫升高只是正常的氣候變化循環的一部分。

　　氣溫升高是從工業革命開始的。開始時, 這種變化十分緩慢, 而現在速度卻逐漸加快。因此, 政府已着手制定法例對溫室效應的根源加以控制。此外, 他們也正在努力尋找減少人類活動對大氣污染的方法。例如, 他們對利用風力發電作了研究。最終, 全世界的人將不得不減少耗費, 否則, 地球會遭到毀滅。

STUDY NOTE 學習提示

Transitive and intransitive verbs 及物與不及物動詞

Transitive verbs 及物動詞

Ann	loves	apples.
安	愛吃	蘋果。

love, **hit**, **thank** and **enjoy** are all transitive verbs. This means that they must be followed by a noun or noun phrase as a direct object. If you take away the direct object, the sentence no longer makes sense.

love, hit, thank 和 enjoy 都是及物動詞, 即它們的後面必須跟名詞或名詞片語作為直接受詞。假如去掉了直接受詞／賓語, 句子就沒有意義了。

subject 主詞	verb 動詞	object 受詞
Ann (安愛吃蘋果。)	loves	apples.
Sue (蘇喜歡打網球。)	enjoys	playing tennis.
She (她擊球。)	hit	the ball.
We (我們感謝老師。)	thanked	our teacher.

Note that you can add other nouns after the verb, but these are NOT direct objects:

注意動詞後面可以再跟其他名詞, 但這些不是直接受詞／賓語。

We enjoy playing tennis <u>after work</u>. 我們喜歡下班後打網球。
She hit the ball <u>hard</u>. 她重重地擊球。
We thanked our teacher <u>for her help</u>. 我們感謝老師對我們的幫助。

In the dictionary transitive verbs are shown like this: [T]
在本詞典中, 及物動詞是這樣表示的:[T]

thank /θæŋk; θæŋk/ *v* [T] **1** to show or tell someone that you are pleased that they helped you or gave you something 感謝〔某人〕: *I thanked him for his advice.* 我感謝他給我忠告。| *How can I ever thank you? You've been so helpful.* 我應該如何謝你呢? 你幫了我很大的忙。

Intransitive verbs 不及物動詞

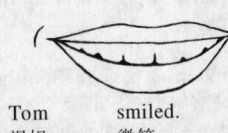

Tom	smiled.
湯姆	微笑。

smile, **sneeze**, **arrive** and **rise** are all intransitive verbs. This means that their meaning is complete without a direct object.

smile, sneeze, arrive 和 rise 都是不及物動詞, 即使不跟直接受詞／賓語, 其意思都是完整的。

subject 主語	verb 動詞
Tom (湯姆微笑。)	smiled.
Ann (安打噴嚏。)	sneezed.
The train (火車已經到了。)	has arrived.
The sun (太陽正在升起。)	is rising.

Note that you can add other nouns after the verb, but these are NOT direct objects:

注意動詞後面可以跟其他名詞, 但它們不是直接受詞／賓語。

Tom smiled <u>happily</u>. 湯姆快樂地微笑。
The train has arrived <u>at platform 12</u>. 火車已到達十二號站台。
The sun is rising <u>over the mountains</u>. 太陽升過山頭。

In the dictionary intransitive verbs are shown like this: [I]
在本詞典中, 不及物動詞是這樣表示的:[I]

rise[1] /raɪz; raɪz/ *v* **rose** /rəʊz; rəʊz/, **risen** /ˈrɪzn; ˈrɪzən/ **rising** [I] **1** to go up or move to a higher position 上升; 上漲: *The river is rising after the rains.* 幾場雨後河水不斷上漲。| *Smoke rose from the factory chimney.* 煙從工廠的煙囪冒出。

Verbs which can be both transitive and intransitive 及物兼不及物動詞

Many English verbs can be used either transitively or intransitively. 許多英語動詞, 既可作及物動詞, 也可作不及物動詞。

— sometimes with different meanings as in **study**:

如 **study** 有時有幾個不同的意思:

study² *v* **studied, studying 1** [I;T] to spend time learning a subject 學習, 攻讀: *She studies French.* 她學習法語。| *She's studying to be a doctor.* 她在攻讀醫科。

— sometimes with different meanings as in **fence**:

如 **fence** 有時有幾個不同的意思:

fence² *v* **fenced, fencing 1** [I] to fight with a long thin pointed sword as a sport 擊劍 **2** [T] to put a fence round something 把〔某物〕用籬笆[柵欄]圍起

The dictionary shows you when a verb can be both [I] and [T]. Read the examples carefully to find out how it is used in the two different ways. 本詞典會告訴你一個動詞在甚麼時候既可作及物動詞, 也可作不及物動詞。細讀例句, 看看動詞在這兩種不同的情況下是如何使用的。

Verbs which are followed by complements 後接補語的動詞

Some verbs, like **become**, **seem** and **appear**, do not have [I] or [T] in their dictionary entry. Instead they are followed by the code [+complement]. This means that they must be followed by another word for their meaning to be complete. These words can be nouns, adjectives, or adverbs, and they always tell us something about the subject of the sentence. Read the examples carefully to find out what kind of word is normally used.

有些動詞, 如 **become, seem** 和 **appear**, 後面沒有 [I] 或 [T] 的符號, 卻註明 [+complement] 的符號, 即表示這些動詞後面必須接一個詞, 意思才會完整。所接的詞可以是名詞、形容詞或副詞。這些詞都會顯示出一些關於句子主詞的內容。細讀下面這個例子, 看看這類詞的一般用法。

be·come /bɪˋkʌm; bɪˈkʌm/ *v* **became** /bɪˋkem; bɪˈkeɪm/, **become, becoming 1** [+complement] to begin to be something 變為; 成為: *He became king in 1938.* 他於 1938 年成為國王。| *The weather became warmer.* 天氣變暖和了。

STUDY NOTE 學習提示

━Word classes or 'parts of speech' 詞類━

In order to use a word correctly you need to know what word class (or "part of speech") it belongs to. Is it a noun, a verb, an adjective, etc.?

All the words in this dictionary have a label which tells you which word class they belong to. You will find a list of these labels in the dictionary.

To see some examples of the most common word classes and how they are used, look at the passages below. The passages are all the same except that a different word class has been underlined in each one.

要正確使用一個詞，你需要先了解詞的詞類（在句中充當的句子成份）。究竟那是名詞、動詞、形容詞、還是其他詞類呢？

詞典中所列的詞都有一個標籤，註明詞的詞類。你可以在縮略語表中找到。

以下是一些最常見的詞類的例子及其用法。請讀這幾段文字。這幾段文字都是一樣的，但每一段中劃有橫線的詞詞類是不同的。

Nouns 名詞 *(n)*

Yesterday when I finished <u>work</u> I went to the <u>cinema</u> with my <u>sister</u>. We really enjoyed the <u>film</u>, which was a <u>comedy</u> and very funny. Afterwards we were incredibly hungry, so I took her to <u>dinner</u> at a Chinese <u>restaurant</u>.

Verbs 動詞 *(v)*

Yesterday when I <u>finished</u> work I <u>went</u> to the cinema with my sister. We really <u>enjoyed</u> the film, which <u>was</u> a comedy and very funny. Afterwards we <u>were</u> incredibly hungry, so I <u>took</u> her to dinner at a Chinese restaurant.

Adjectives 形容詞 *(adj)*

Yesterday when I finished work I went to the cinema with my sister. We really enjoyed the film, which was a comedy and very <u>funny</u>. Afterwards we were incredibly <u>hungry</u>, so I took her to dinner at a <u>Chinese</u> restaurant.

Adverbs 副詞 *(adv)*

<u>Yesterday</u> when I finished work I went to the cinema with my sister. We <u>really</u> enjoyed the film, which was a comedy and <u>very</u> funny. <u>Afterwards</u> we were <u>incredibly</u> hungry, so I took her to dinner at a Chinese restaurant.

Pronouns 代名詞 *(pron)*

Yesterday when <u>I</u> finished work <u>I</u> went to the cinema with my sister. <u>We</u> really enjoyed the film, <u>which</u> was a comedy and very funny. Afterwards <u>we</u> were incredibly hungry, so <u>I</u> took <u>her</u> to dinner at a Chinese restaurant.

Prepositions 介詞 *(prep)*

Yesterday when I finished work I went <u>to</u> the cinema <u>with</u> my sister. We really enjoyed the film, which was a comedy and very funny. Afterwards we were incredibly hungry, so I took her <u>to</u> dinner <u>at</u> a Chinese restaurant.

Conjunctions 連詞 *(conj)*

Yesterday <u>when</u> I finished work I went to the cinema with my sister. We really enjoyed the film, which was a comedy <u>and</u> very funny. Afterwards we were incredibly hungry, <u>so</u> I took her to dinner at a Chinese restaurant.

昨天，我完成了工作後，便和妹妹一起去電影院。那是一部非常有趣的喜劇電影，我們真的很喜歡。看完電影之後，我們餓極了，於是我帶她去一家中國餐館吃飯。

Read this passage. For each word, decide which word class it belongs to and write it in the correct place in the table below. The first four have been done for you.

閱讀這一段文字, 判斷每一個詞的詞類, 並將它們分別寫在下表的正確位置上。前四個詞已經做好了。

Last weekend I went to the seaside with a group of friends. We took sandwiches with us and had a picnic on the beach. When we arrived, the weather was quite cold, so we felt rather disappointed. Fortunately it soon got warmer and we had a wonderful time. 上個週末, 我和一羣朋友去海邊。我們帶了三明治在海灘上野餐。我們到達的時候, 天氣很冷, 所以我們覺得有點失望。幸好, 天氣漸漸暖和起來, 後來我們玩得很開心。

Noun	Verb	Adjective	Adverb	Pronoun	Preposition	Conjunction
weekend	went	last		I		

STUDY NOTE 學習提示

─Words followed by prepositions 後接介詞的詞語─

Many English nouns, verbs and adjectives are commonly followed by prepositions, If you do not know which preposition to use with a particular word, look it up in this dictionary. 英語中許多名詞、動詞和形容詞通常都後接介詞。如果你不知道一個詞該和哪個介詞連用，請在本詞典中查閱該詞的詞條。

The dictionary helps you in two main ways:
本詞典主要通過兩種主要的方式為你提供這方面的幫助：

1 Many words can be used either alone or together with a preposition. When this is the case the dictionary tells you which prepositions you can use by showing them in the examples in special dark print.

許多詞既可以單獨使用，也可以後接介詞，如有這樣的情況，本詞典會在例句中用粗黑體標示可以接在詞後的介詞。

This entry tells you that the adjective **bored** can be used alone. But it can also be used with the preposition **with**.

下面這個詞條表示 **bored** 這個形容詞可以單獨使用，也可以後接介詞 **with**。

> **bored** /bɔːd; bɔːd/ *adj* **1** tired and uninterested 厭倦的: *The students all looked bored.* 學生們看上去都不耐煩了。| *She was bored* **with** *her job.* 她厭倦了自己的工作。

This entry tells you that the verb **borrow** can be used alone. But it can also be used with the preposition **from**. The examples show that you usually **borrow** a thing **from** a person.

下面這個詞條表示 **borrow** 這個動詞可以單獨使用，但也可以後接介詞 **from**。例句表示通常是從某人處借得某物。

> **bor·row** /ˈbɒrəʊ; ˈbɒrəʊ/ *v* [T] **1** to take something for a certain time, intending to return it 借〔某物〕: *Can I borrow your dictionary for a moment?* 我能借你的詞典用一下嗎?| *I borrowed £5* **from** *my mother.* 我向媽媽借了五英鎊。

This entry tells you that the verb **console** can be used alone. But it can also be used with the prepositions **for** and **with**. The examples show that you usually **console** somebody **for** something bad that has happened to them. And that you **console** them **with** something nice that you give them or do for them.

下面這個詞條表示 **console** 這個動詞可以單獨使用，也可以後接介詞 **for** 和 **with**。例句表示用法通常是 **console**〔某人〕**for**〔一些發生在他們身上的不好的事〕，及 **console**〔某人〕**with**〔一些好的事物〕。

> **con·sole¹** /kənˈsəʊl; kənˈsəʊl/ *v* **consoled,** **consoling** [T] **1** to give comfort or sympathy to someone in times of disappointment or sadness 安慰〔某人〕: *Nothing will console her* **for** *the loss of her dog.* 她的狗死了，沒有甚麼事情能安慰得了她。| *She tried to console me* **with** *a cup of tea.* 她給我一杯茶，試圖來安慰我一下。

This entry tells you that the noun **risk** can be used alone. But it can also be used with the preposition **of**. The examples show you that you should use **of** in order to give more details about the risk.

下面這個詞條表示 **risk** 這個名詞可以單獨使用，也可以後接介詞 **of**。例句表示可以用 **of** 來指出風險的具體內容。

> **risk¹** /rɪsk; rɪsk/ *n* **1** [C;U] a possibility something bad may happen 風險, 危險 (性): *He was taking a risk by overtaking on a bend.* 他在轉彎處超車是冒險的。| *There was no risk* **of** *infection.* 沒有感染的危險。

2 Some words are never used alone but are always used with particular prepositions. Some other words are nearly always used with particular prepositions in order to express particular meanings. When this is the case the dictionary shows both the main word and the preposition in special dark print. 有些詞從不單獨使用，只能後接介詞。其他一些詞常常後接介詞來表達特殊的含義。在這種情況下，本詞典用粗體來顯示主要的詞和其後的介詞。

This entry tells you that the adjective **riddled** is always used with the preposition **with**.

下面這個詞條表示 **riddled** 這個形容詞總是和介詞 **with** 一起使用的。

rid·dled /ˈrɪd|d; ˈrɪdld/ *adj* [only before a noun 只用於名詞前] **riddled with** full of holes 滿 是洞眼的: *The man's body was riddled with bullets.* 這具男屍上盡是彈孔。| *The beam was riddled with woodworm.* 這橫樑被木蛀 蟲蛀得滿是洞。

This entry tells you that when the verb **consist** means "to be made up of a number of things" it is used with the preposition **of**. But when it means "to be really" it is used with the preposition **in**. 下面這個詞條表示 **consist** 這個動詞解釋為 "組 成" 時, 要和介詞 **of** 連用。但是當 **consist** 解作 "在於, 存在於" 時則要後接介詞 **in**。

con·sist /kənˈsɪst; kənˈsɪst/ *v* **1 consist of something** to be made up of a number of things 由某物組成: *The city of New York consists of five boroughs.* 紐約由五個行政 區組成。| *a delivery of supplies, consisting mainly of food and medicines* 一批主要包括 食物和藥品的貨物 **2 consist in something** to be really〔實際〕在於某物: *For me, the pleasure of the meal consisted entirely in the conversation — the food was terrible.* 對我 來說, 那頓飯的樂趣完全在於席間的談話 —— 飯菜本身糟糕透了。

This entry tells you that the noun **search** is followed by the preposition **of** when it is in the fixed phrase **in search of**. 下面這個詞條表示 **search** 這個名詞在固定片語 **in search of** 中, 一定要後接介詞 **of**。

search² *n* **1** an act of searching 搜查, 搜尋: *a long search* **for** *the lost treasure* 長時間尋 找丟失的寶藏 **2 in search of** looking for 尋 找; 尋求: *in search of happiness* 尋求幸福 | *He went in search of his long-lost brother.* 他去尋找他那失蹤多年的弟弟。

NOTE Remember that there are also many verbs where a word which looks like a preposition makes up part of the meaning, for example **come across** (= discover), **look into** (= investigate) etc. These are considered to be *phrasal verbs* and are listed in this dictionary as separate headwords in alphabetical order under the main verb. 注意: 要記住, 還有許多動詞在後面加上了一個看 似是介詞的詞, 構成了某個特殊的含義, 如 **come across** (遇見; 碰上), **look into** (調查; 研究) 等。 這些被視作片語／短語動詞, 單獨作為詞頭, 按字 母順序列在主要動詞下面。

(See STUDY NOTE: **Phrasal verbs** on page 1322)
(見 1322 頁學習提示: 片語／短語動詞)

New Words

新词

A, a

abled /ˈeɪbḷd; ˈeɪbld/ adj 體格健全的; 無殘疾的

ableism /ˈeɪblɪzəm; ˈeɪblɪzəm/ n [U]〔雇用勞工時的〕體能歧視; 體格健全至上主義

abortuary /əˈbɔrtʃuərɪ; əˈbɔːtʃuərɪ/ n AmE【美式】墮胎手術門診部〔用作貶義〕

access /ˈækˌsɛs; əkˈses/ v [T] 存取; 訪問; 觸及內心的情緒

account card n〔某商店發放的〕商店賒購卡

acid cloud n [C;U] 酸雲〔含高濃硫酸和硝酸的霧或雲〕

acid house n [U] 迷幻狂舞熱〔指青年人以聽豪斯搖滾樂和服用迷幻藥入迷而狂舞的時尚〕

acidic /æˈsɪdɪk; əˈsɪdʒk/ adj 迷幻狂舞的

actioner /ˈækʃənə; ˈækʃənəʳ/ n〔一種有暴力行為的〕動作影片

action figure n〔能活動的〕玩具人

activewear /ˈæktɪvˌwɛr; ˈæktɪvweəʳ/ n [U] 運動服

activity holiday n〔尤指為參加運動或表演而放的〕活動假日

add-in n, adj〔電腦〕附件; 附加 (的)

adultescent /ˌædʌlˈtɛsnt; ˌædʌlˈtesənt/ n 中青年

adultism /ˈædʌltɪzəm; ˈædʌltɪzəm/ n 成人歧視

adultify /əˈdʌltɪfaɪ; əˈdʌltɪfaɪ/ v 使〔兒童〕成人化

aerobicize /eəˈrobɪsaɪz; eəˈrəʊbɪsaɪz/ v [I] 做有氧操

affinity credit card n (also 又作 **affinity card**) 愛心信用卡, 慈善信用卡〔用於通過購物來為慈善性機構提供資金〕

affluenza /ˌæfluˈɛnzə; ˌæfluˈenzə/ n 富裕病〔一種因財富過多而引起的失衡心態〕

agg /æg; æg/ n BrE slang【英俚】暴力行為

agony aunt n BrE, infml【英式, 非正式】"為你解憂專欄"女作家, 解答讀者疑難的專欄女作家

agony column n BrE, infml【英式, 非正式】〔報刊上的〕"為你解憂專欄", "答讀者問專欄"

agony uncle n BrE【英式】〔尤指在報紙、電台等上〕解答讀者 [聽眾] 疑難的男撰稿人 [主持人], 私事諮詢專欄作家

airhead /ˈɛrˌhɛd; ˈeəhed/ n slang【俚】沒頭腦的人, 傻瓜

airmiss /ˈɛrmɪs; ˈeəmɪs/ n 飛機險撞事故

airport fiction n [U] 航空小說〔一種在機場售賣、供乘客在飛行途中閱讀的通俗小說〕

air time n〔電話的〕通話時間

alcohol abuse n 酗酒

alcopop /ˈælkopɑp; ˈælkəʊpɒp/ n 含酒精汽水

A-list /ˈeɪlɪst; ˈeɪlɪst/ adj 高級別的; 頂尖的

aliterate /əˈlɪtərɪt; əˈlɪtərʒt/ adj, n 不愛讀書的 (人); 不習慣讀書的 (人)

all-fired adj AmE infml【美式, 非正式】難以置信的; 極大的

all-seater adj〔體育場〕全座位的, 觀眾均有座位的

alpha female n 女性至上論者

alpha male n 大男子主義者

alternative /ɔlˈtɜnətɪv, lˈtɜːnətɪv/ n 1〔具有環境保護意識的〕另類生活方式 2 主張另類生活方式的人

alternative rock n 另類搖滾樂

alternativism /ɔlˈtɜnətɪvɪzəm; lˈtɜːnətɪvɪzəm/ n 另類主義〔指提倡非傳統價值觀或方法〕

ambulance chaser n 乘人之危謀利者; 趁火打劫者

Amerasian /ˌæməˈreʒən; ˌæməˈreɪʒən/ n 美亞混血兒〔尤指在越戰期間父為美國軍人母為越南人的混血兒〕

anadig /ˈænəˌdɪg; ˈænədɪg/ n 數字顯示及指針式兩用手錶

anchorette /ˌæŋkəˈrɛt; æŋkəˈret/ n AmE【美式】〔廣播或電視〕新聞節目女主持人

anchorperson /ˈæŋkəˌpɜsn; ˈæŋkəˌpɜːsən/ n〔廣播或電視〕新聞節目主持人

android /ˈændrɔɪd; ˈændrɔɪd/ n〔故事中似人的〕機器人

andropause /ˈændroˌpɔz; ˈændrəʊpɔːz/ n 男性更年期

angel /ˈendʒəl; ˈeɪndʒəl/ n BrE【英式】護士, 白衣天使

angel dust n [U]〔一種服用後產生迷幻作用的〕天使粉

animatronics /ˌænəməˈtrɑnɪks; ænɪməˈtrɒnɪks/ n 動物機器人製造技術

anklebiter /ˈæŋkḷˌbaɪtə; ˈæŋkḷˌbaɪtəʳ/ n infml【非正式】小不點兒; 小傢伙

answerer /ˈænsərə; ˈɑːnsərəʳ/ n AmE【美式】電話答錄機

answerphone /ˈænsəˌfon; ˈɑːnsəfəʊn/ n BrE【英式】電話答錄機

antenuptial /ˌæntɪˈnʌpʃəl; ˌæntɪˈnʌpʃəl/ adj law【律】婚前的

anti-ageing adj〔皮膚〕抗老化的

anti-ager n 抗老化藥物

anti-viral adj 抗病毒的〔指電腦軟件〕

antivirus /ˈæntɪˌvaɪrəs; ˌæntɪˈvaɪərəs/ n〔抗電腦病毒的〕疫苗

antsy /ˈæntsɪ; ˈæntsɪ/ adj infml【非正式】易怒的; 焦躁的

aquacise /ˈækwəsaɪz; ˈækwəsaɪz/ n [U] 淺水練習

arenaball /əˈrinəˌbɔl; əˈriːnəbɔːl/ n 室內美式足球

arm-twist v 對〔某人〕施加壓力

arrestee /əˌrɛsˈti; əˌresˈtiː/ n AmE【美式】被捕者

artificial intelligence n 人工智能

asylee /əˈsaɪli; əˈsaɪliː/ n〔常指在美國尋求避難的〕流亡者

ATB n 1 abbrev【縮】= advanced technology bomber〔美國採用隱形技術製造的〕高級技術轟炸機 2 abbrev【縮】= all terrain bike 全地形腳踏車

ATM n abbrev【縮】= automated teller machine 自動提款機

attention deficit disorder n tech【術語】注意

力缺乏症〔多見於兒童〕

attraction /ə'trækʃən; ə'trækʃən/ n 偏愛; 癖好

Aum Shinrikyo n 奧姆真理教〔日本的一個邪教組織〕

automaker /ˈɔːtəˌmeɪkə; 'ɔːtəˌmeɪkər/ n AmE【美式】汽車製造商

automated teller machine n 自動提款機

avian flu n 禽流感

awfulize /ˈɔːfəlaɪz; 'ɔːfəlaɪz/ v AmE【美式】把事情想像得太糟

B, b

baby boomer n 生育高峯期出生的人〔指第二次世界大戰結束時出生的一代人〕

baby break n〔婦女的〕停職育嬰期; 產假

baby bust n 出生率驟降

babynap /ˈbeɪbɪnæp; 'beɪbɪnæp/ v [T] 綁架〔幼兒〕

babywipe /ˈbeɪbɪwaɪp; 'beɪbɪwaɪp/ n 嬰兒濕紙巾

back belt n 護腰帶

back-door adj 走後門的

back-end adj 後期的〔指工程費用〕

back office n 股票 [證券] 交易結算室

back up phr v 備份複製〔電腦數據〕

bagger /ˈbæɡə; 'bæɡər/ n〔超級市場為顧客把所購物品放入紙袋的〕裝袋工

bagstuffer /ˈbæɡˌstʌfə; 'bæɡstʌfər/ n 小型宣傳品〔尤指大量散發的廣告傳單〕

bagumble /ˈbæɡʌmbl; 'bæɡʌmbəl/ n 大批量貨品的廉價售賣

bail bandit n 在保釋期內犯罪的人

ballpark /ˈbɔːlˌpɑːk; 'bɔːlpɑːk/ n slang【俚】情況; 情境

bancassurance /ˌbæŋkəˈʃʊərəns; 'bæŋkəʃɔːrəns/ n [U] 銀行保險〔尤指人壽保險〕

bandog /ˈbændɒɡ; 'bændɒɡ/ n 雜交狗〔一種由叭喇狗和大獒犬交配而成的狗〕

bang on phr v [I] BrE infml【英式, 非正式】嘮嘮叨叨

bankroll /ˈbæŋkrəʊl; 'bæŋkrəʊl/ v 支付大筆的錢

barbify /ˈbɑːbɪˌfaɪ; 'bɑːbɪfaɪ/ v 使芭比化〔指某種女性打扮得像芭比娃娃玩具一樣艷麗, 但缺乏品味〕〔含貶義〕

barfly /ˈbɑːˌflaɪ; 'bɑːflaɪ/ n AmE infml【美式, 非正式】〔常泡在酒吧的〕酒吧友

basehead /ˈbeɪshed; 'beɪshed/ n slang【俚】服用強效純可卡因的人

bash /bæʃ; bæʃ/ n **1** slang【俚】〔流浪漢住的〕棲身所 **2** infml【非正式】盛大聚會或慶祝活動

bazillion /bəˈzɪljən; bə'zɪljən/ n infml【非正式】大量, 許多

beach volleyball n 沙灘排球

beat box n infml【非正式】手提大功率盒式錄音機

Beck /bek; bek/ n slang【俚】猶太青少年

beefcake /ˈbiːfkeɪk; 'biːfkeɪk/ n [U] slang【俚】健美男子

bells and whistles n infml【非正式】**1** 華而不實的裝飾 **2**〔計算機軟件應用程序中那些不實用的〕附屬項目

belt bag n 腰帶包

beltway /ˈbeltweɪ; 'beltweɪ/ n 環城公路

belly bomber n AmE slang【美俚】濃香小漢堡包

Bermies /ˈbɜːmɪz; 'bɜːmɪz/ n AmE infml【美式, 非正式】〔長及膝蓋的〕百慕大短褲

bezzle /ˈbezl; 'bezəl/ n 貪污收益

B-girl n 嬉蹦樂 (或快板歌) 女性表演者

bibliophagic /ˌbɪblɪəˈfædʒɪk; ˌbɪblɪə'fædʒɪk/ adj 博覽羣書的

bicoastal /baɪˈkəʊstl; baɪ'kəʊstl/ adj (美國) 東西海岸的

bigamy /ˈbɪɡəmɪ; 'bɪɡəmɪ/ n 重婚

big bang n 大變革; 劇變

Big Dry n 大旱災, 長期乾旱

big hair n 大背頭〔一種男式髮型〕

Big Wet n〔澳大利亞的〕大雨季

Bikercise /ˈbaɪkəsaɪz; 'baɪkəsaɪz/ n 健身腳踏車運動

billionaire /ˌbɪljəˈnɛə; ˌbɪljə'neər/ n 億萬富翁

bimbette /bɪmˈbet; bɪm'bet/ n AmE infml【美式, 非正式】〔年青〕女流行歌手

bimbo /ˈbɪmbəʊ; 'bɪmbəʊ/ n infml【非正式】**1** 愚蠢而性感的女郎 **2** 笨蛋; 白痴

bimboy /ˈbɪmbɔɪ; 'bɪmbɔɪ/ n 虛有其表的男性青年

bin /bɪn; bɪn/ v [T] 把〔某物〕扔入廢紙簍

binge drinking n [U] 酗酒

bin-liner n〔放在垃圾桶內的〕大塑料袋

bioastronomy /ˌbaɪəəˈstrɒnəmɪ; ˌbaɪəʊə'strɒnəmɪ/ n [U] 生物天文學

biodiversity /ˌbaɪəʊdaɪˈvɜːsətɪ; ˌbaɪəʊdaɪ'vɜːsɪti/ n [U] 生物多類狀態; 生物多樣性

biodrama /ˈbaɪəʊˌdrɑːmə; ˌbaɪəʊ'drɑːmə/ n 傳記體戲劇

biogas /ˈbaɪəʊˌɡæs; 'baɪəʊˌɡæs/ n [U]〔可用作燃料的〕生物氣

bio-house n〔由自然材料構成的〕生物屋

biological clock n 生物鐘, 生理時鐘〔生物體內的一種可控制進食、調節睡眠的週期性節律〕

biological parent n 親生父母

biopic /ˈbaɪəʊˌpɪk; 'baɪəʊˌpɪk/ n infml【非正式】傳記片

bird flu n 禽流感

bird-strike n 飛機與鳥相撞

birth-mother n〔尤指將私生子送人領養的〕未婚母親

birth parent n 生父; 生母

bizzy /ˈbɪzɪ; 'bɪzɪ/ n BrE slang【英俚】警察

black /blæk; blæk/ adj 需要保密的

Black Monday n〔股市狂跌的〕黑色星期一

bladdered /ˈblædəd; 'blædəd/ adj slang【俚】醉的

blades /bleɪdz; 'bleɪdz/ n [pl] 刀刃式溜冰鞋

blag /blæɡ; blæɡ/ v [I] BrE slang【英俚】說假話; 哄騙

bland out phr v 墨守成規; 怕擔風險〔用作貶義〕

blinding /ˈblaɪndɪŋ; 'blaɪndɪŋ/ adj〔光線〕強烈

的;〔疼痛〕劇烈的

blow off *phr v AmE infml*【美式, 非正式】離開

blow out *phr v slang*【俚】取消

blunt /blʌnt; blʌnt/ *n AmE slang*【美俚】大麻煙卷

bluppy /ˈblʌpɪ; ˈblʌpi/ *n* 黑人雅皮士

blush wine *n* 玫瑰紅酒

B-movie *n*〔低成本、質素不高的〕二流電影

boardsail /ˈbordˌseil; ˈbɔːdseɪl/ *v* [I] 作風帆衝浪運動

boardsailing /ˈbordˌseiliŋ; ˈbɔːdseɪlɪŋ/ *n* [U] 風帆衝浪

bobbing and peering *n* 彎腰拉客〔指妓女為拉生意而俯身朝沿街開過的車內看〕

body count *n* [C; U] 死亡人數

body double *n*〔電影的〕替身演員

bodyism /ˈbɑdiɪzəm; ˈbɒdiɪzəm/ *n* [U] 體形歧視; 外貌歧視

boffo /ˈbafo; ˈbɒfəʊ/ *adj AmE infml*【美式, 非正式】極好的、了不起的

bog-standard *adj BrE infml*【英式, 非正式】一般的; 乏味的

bolt-on *adj* 附加的, 另外的

bonesetter /ˈbonˌsɛtə; ˈbəʊnˌsetər/ *n* 正骨師, 正骨專家

bonk[1] /baŋk; bɒŋk/ *v* [T] *BrE infml*【英式, 非正式】與〔某人〕性交

bonk[2] *n BrE infml*【英式, 非正式】性交

bonk-happy *adj* 對性交持隨意態度的

bonk journalism *n* 桃色新聞業〔指熱衷於報道名人的風流韻事的新聞活動〕

bonsai /ˈbansai; ˈbɒnsaɪ/ *n* [C; U] 盆景, 盆栽 (藝術)

boofer /ˈbafo; ˈbuːfər/ *n AmE slang*【美俚】毒販

bookfairy /ˈbukˌfɛri; ˈbʊkˌferi/ *n infml*【非正式】經營古舊 (珍本) 書籍的人

boombox /ˈbumbaks; ˈbuːmbɒks/ *n slang*【俚】揚聲器; 立體聲音響器材

boom cut *n slang*【俚】一砲打響的音響製品

boomer[1] /ˈbumə; ˈbuːmər/ *n* 生育高峰期〔指第二次世界大戰後 1945－1952年間〕出生的人

boomer[2] *n slang*【俚】〔為同夥作案創造條件的〕鬧事者

boomerang kid *n* 回歸家庭的子女〔指成年子女回家與父母同住〕

boomflation /ˈbumˌfleʃən; ˈbuːmfleɪʃən/ *n* [U] 繁榮通貨膨脹〔指經濟發展中高消費引起的通貨膨脹〕

boosterism /ˈbustərɪzəm; ˈbuːstərɪzəm/ *n* [U] 商業化的廣告宣傳花招

boot sale *n BrE*【英式】雜物廉價銷售

boot up *phr v* [T]〔電腦〕引導

bordello /borˈdɛlo; bɔːˈdeləʊ/ *n* **bordellos** *AmE*【美式】妓院

boroscope /ˈborəˌskop; ˈbɔːrəˌskəʊp/ *n* 光纖檢查鏡〔用於檢查無法進入的部件的儀器〕

bottled water *n* 瓶裝純淨水

bounce /ˈbauns; ˈbaʊns/ *n*〔股價的〕反彈

bovine spongiform encephalopathy (*abbrev* 縮寫為 **BSE**) *n* 牛海綿狀組織腦病病, 瘋牛症〔指牛的神經系統疾病〕

box /baks; bɒks/ *v* [T] *infml*【非正式】用電視播放

boxers /ˈbaksəz; ˈbɒksəz/ *n* [pl] *infml*【非正式】拳擊褲, 平腳短褲

boy toyer *n infml*【非正式】有年輕男性情侶的老婦人

bozo /ˈbozo; ˈbəʊzəʊ/ *n AmE slang*【美俚】笨蛋, 傻瓜

brain death *n* [U] *tech*【術語】腦死亡

brain spa *n* 健腦療養中心〔常播放柔和的音樂等以緩解人們的緊張情緒〕

brandable /ˈbrændəbl; ˈbrændəbəl/ *adj* 具有名牌效應的

breakout /ˈbrekˌaut; ˈbreɪkaʊt/ *n* 發皮疹

brewpub /ˈbrupʌb; ˈbruːpʌb/ *n AmE*【美式】自釀啤酒的酒館

brill /bril; bril/ *adj BrE*【英式】極好的, 絕妙的

bring-down *n* [U] 失望, 失勢

brio /ˈbrio; ˈbriːəʊ/ *n* [U] 個人風格; 活力

Britpop /ˈbritpap; ˈbrɪtpɒp/ *n* [U] *infml*【非正式】英國的流行音樂

brittle-bone disease *n infml*【非正式】骨質疏鬆症

broadband /ˈbrɑdbænd; ˈbrɔːdbænd/ *n*【術語】寬頻 (帶)

brown /braun; braʊn/ *n* 棕色皮膚的亞洲人〔尤指印度人或巴基斯坦人〕

browse /brauz; braʊz/ *v* [T] 瀏覽〔尤指在電腦的萬維網上〕

browser /ˈbrauzə; ˈbraʊzər/ *n*〔電腦的〕瀏覽器

bruncher /ˈbrʌntʃə; ˈbrʌntʃər/ *n* 早午餐合在一起吃的人

B-school *n* 商學院

bubble /ˈbʌbl; ˈbʌbəl/ *n* 泡泡劇〔一種新的電視連續劇〕

bubblegum /ˈbʌblˌgʌm; ˈbʌbəlgʌm/ *n*〔以青少年為對象的〕"泡泡糖" 搖滾樂 [影片]

bubble skirt *n* (also 又作 **bubble**) 泡泡裙〔一種鼓起的短裙〕

buddy[1] /ˈbʌdi; ˈbʌdi/ *n* 愛滋病患者之友〔自願陪伴並幫助愛滋病患者的人〕

buddy[2] *v* [T] 充當〔愛滋病患者〕之友

bufferism /ˈbʌfərɪzəm; ˈbʌfərɪzəm/ *n* [U] 老派主義〔指對現代方式蔑視和不容忍的保守態度〕

bullet train *n* 子彈火車, 高速列車

bullish /ˈbuliʃ; ˈbʊlɪʃ/ *adj* 樂觀的; 有信心的

bum bag *n BrE infml*【英式, 非正式】腰包, 腰袋

bummed /bʌmd; bʌmd/ *adj AmE infml*【美式, 非正式】失望的; 厭煩的

bummed out *adj AmE infml*【美式, 非正式】失望的; 沮喪的

bummer /ˈbʌmə; ˈbʌmər/ *n* [C] *infml*【非正式】令人不快的事; 不願做的工作

bump /bʌmp; bʌmp/ *v* [T]〔航空公司因超額預訂而〕擠掉〔乘客的〕座位

bungee jumping *n* 綁緊跳〔一種在腳踝上繫上橡皮索從高處往下跳的運動〕, 笨豬跳

bunny slopes *n* [pl] 適合初學者滑雪的坡地

buppie /ˈbʌpi; ˈbʌpi/ *n slang*【俚】黑人雅皮士

burb /bɜb; bɜːb/ *n* [pl] 郊區

burgery /ˈbɜgəri; ˈbɜːgəri/ *n* 漢堡包店

burst out *phr v* 複印分發〔原件的〕副本

busperson /ˈbʌsˌpɜsn; ˈbʌspɜːsən/ *n AmE*【美式】〔餐廳的〕侍者助手

butterfly effect *n* 蝴蝶效應〔指一件看上去微不足道的小事會逐漸產生巨大而深遠的影響〕

butthead /ˈbʌthed; ˈbʌthed/ *n AmE slang*【美俚】白痴; 笨蛋

butty /ˈbʌtɪ; ˈbʌti/ *n BrE infml*【英式, 非正式】三明治, 三文治

buy into *phr v* 捲入

C, c

cable bug *n* 電纜蟲〔一種會起皮膚發炎小塵粒〕

cable-ready *adj* 可接收有線電視的

cable up *phr v* [I] (使) 與有線電視系統相連網

caff /kæf; kæf/ *n BrE infml*【英式, 非正式】收費低廉的小餐館

can-do *adj* 有進取心的; 積極的; 樂觀的

canteen culture *n* "食堂"文化, 下層組織文化〔指某一機構中獨立的、半自治的下層組織的集體觀點和行為〕

cantina /kænˈtiːnə; kænˈtiːnə/ *n* 酒店; 小酒吧

caplet /ˈkæplɪt; ˈkæplɪt/ *n* 膠囊藥片

carbuncle /ˈkɑːbʌŋkl; ˈkɑːbʌŋkəl/ *n BrE*【英式】煞風景的建築物

carbuncular /kɑːˈbʌŋkjələ; kɑːˈbʌŋkjələr/ *adj*〔建築物〕難看的, 醜陋的

cardboard city *n* 卡紙板城區〔指無家可歸者用紙板箱搭建臨時住所的城區〕

cardholder /ˈkɑːdˌhəʊldə; ˈkɑːdhəʊldər/ *n* 信用卡〔賒購卡〕持有者

cardmember /ˈkɑːdˌmembə; ˈkɑːdmembər/ *n* 信用卡〔賒購卡〕持有人

card swipe *n*〔信用卡的〕磁卡譯碼機

care card *n*〔儲存病歷檔案的〕護理智能卡

carjacking /ˈkɑːdʒækɪŋ; ˈkɑːdʒækɪŋ/ *n* 汽車劫持

carplane /ˈkɑːpleɪn; ˈkɑːpleɪn/ *n*〔一種可地面行駛和空中飛行的〕汽車飛機

car toppable *adj* 可放在汽車頂上運送的

cashflow /ˈkæʃfləʊ; ˈkæʃfləʊ/ *v* [T] 承擔...的營運費用; 向...提供流動資金

cashless /ˈkæʃlɪs; ˈkæʃləs/ *adj* 不用現金的; 用信用卡等結算的

cassingle /kæˈsɪŋgl; kæˈsɪŋgəl/ *n* 單碟盒式磁帶〔其內容與一張唱片相同〕

casual Friday *n* 星期五便裝日

casualism /ˈkæʒuəˌlɪzəm; ˈkæʒuəlɪzəm/ *n* [U] 雇用臨時工, 雇用零工

catastrophize /kəˈtæstrəˌfaɪz; kəˈtæstrəfaɪz/ *v AmE*【美式】小題大做

cathart /kəˈθɑːt; kəˈθɑːt/ *v* [T] 宣泄〔憂慮或緊張感〕

CDMA *n abbrev*【縮】= code division multiple access 碼分多路接達, 數碼分割多重存取〔一種通訊制式〕

CD-R *n abbrev*【縮】= compact disk-recordable〔只可寫入資料一次的〕單寫式光碟片

CD-ROM *n abbrev*【縮】= compact disc read-only memory 大容量光盤唯讀存儲器, 唯讀光碟

CD-ROM drive *n* 只讀光盤驅動器, 唯讀光碟機

CD-RW *n abbrev*【縮】= compact disk-rewritable〔可寫入、擦去及重寫資料的〕可重寫式光碟片

celebutante /sɪˈlebjuˌtɑːnt; sɪˈlebjʊtɑːnt/ *n* 初入時髦階層者

cellular phone *n* 蜂窩式流動電話

CFC *n abbrev*【縮】= chlorofluorocarbon 含氯氟烴

CFC-free *adj* 無含氯氟烴的

chain-chew *v* [T] 一塊接一塊地嚼〔口香糖〕

chalkface /ˈtʃɔːkfeɪs; ˈtʃɔːkfeɪs/ *n* 教室

challenged /ˈtʃælɪndʒd; ˈtʃælɪndʒd/ *adj* 殘疾的; 缺乏的; 不足的

champagne socialist *n* "香檳"社會主義者, 闊佬社會主義者〔生活方式奢侈得與其所宣稱的社會主義相違背的人〕

chancy /ˈtʃænsɪ; ˈtʃɑːnsi/ *adj* 偶然 (發生) 的

chapess /ˈtʃæpɪs; ˈtʃæpəs/ *n BrE infml*【英式, 非正式】女人

charbroil /ˈtʃɑːbrɔɪl; ˈtʃɑːbrɔɪl/ *v* 炭烤

charge card *n*〔商店發給的〕賒購卡, 記賬卡

charge-hand *n BrE*【英式】領班; 工頭

charge nurse *n BrE*【英式】護士長

chargepayer /ˈtʃɑːdʒˌpeə; ˈtʃɑːdʒpeɪər/ *n* 地方稅〔人頭稅〕納稅人

chartist /ˈtʃɑːtɪst; ˈtʃɑːtɪst/ *n* **1** 股市行情分析員 **2** 暢銷唱片灌製者

chat room *n*〔電腦網站的〕聊天室, 交談室

chemical ecology *n*〔化學生態學〔指環境和生物體中的化學物質對生命影響的研究〕

cherry pick *phr v* 擇優選取, 作出最佳選擇

chicken /ˈtʃɪkɪn; ˈtʃɪkɪn/ *n slang*【俚】少年男妓

chickfurter /ˈtʃɪkˌfɜːtə; ˈtʃɪkfɜːtər/ *n* 雞肉香腸

chiddler /ˈtʃɪdlə; ˈtʃɪdlə/ *n* 幼兒

chill /tʃɪl; tʃɪl/ *n slang*【俚】悠閒的晚會

chill out *phr v* [I] *AmE infml*【美式, 非正式】〔緊張或興奮之後〕平靜下來

Chinese restaurant syndrome *n* [U] 中國餐館綜合症〔指因過量食用含穀氨一鈉的味精而引起頭暈和心悸等症狀〕

Chinglish /ˈtʃɪŋglɪʃ; ˈtʃɪŋglɪʃ/ *n, adj* 中式英語; 中式英語

chocoholic /ˌtʃɒkəˈhɒlɪk; ˌtʃɒkəˈhɒlɪk/ *n infml*【非正式】嗜食巧克力的人

chopsocky /tʃɒpˈsɒkɪ; tʃɒpˈsɒki/ *n*〔尤指東方的〕武打片

ciguatera toxin *n* (also 又作 **ciguatoxin**) 雪卡毒素〔某些魚類所含的毒素〕

cineplex /ˈsɪnɪˌplɛks; ˈsɪnɪpleks/ *n*〔由多個放映廳組成的〕綜合電影院

cinnamint /ˈsɪnəˌmɪnt; ˈsɪnəmɪnt/ *n* [U] *AmE*【美式】肉桂薄荷〔一種調味料〕

clergyperson /ˈklɜːdʒɪˌpɜːsn; ˈklɜːdʒɪpɜːsən/ *n* 牧師〔可指男或女牧師〕

clerking /ˈklɑːkɪŋ; ˈklɑːkɪŋ/ *n*〔醫生所作的與病人交談的〕書面記錄

client-server *n*〔電腦〕用戶與服務器連網系統

clocker /ˈklɒkə; ˈklɒkər/ *n* 倒撥汽車計程器的人

clocking /ˈklɒkɪŋ; ˈklɒkɪŋ/ *n* 倒撥汽車計程器

clogs /klɒgz; klɒgz/ *n* [pl] *BrE infml*【英式, 非正式】死亡

clonk¹ /klɒŋk; klɒŋk/ *n infml*【非正式】噹啷聲

clonk² *v* [I] *infml*【非正式】發出噹啷聲

close-in *adj AmE*【美式】近市中心的

closeout /ˈkloz,aut; ˈkləʊzaʊt/ *n AmE*【美式】〔因企業關閉而〕清倉出售的物品

closure /ˈkloʒə; ˈkləʊʒəʳ/ *n* [U]〔沉重或不快經歷的〕解脫

clumpy /ˈklʌmpɪ; ˈklʌmpi/ *adj* 笨重的〔常指鞋〕

clunker /ˈklʌŋkə; ˈklʌŋkəʳ/ *n AmE*【美式】老爺車, 破車

clunky /ˈklʌŋkɪ; ˈklʌŋki/ *adj* 笨拙的, 拙劣的

cluster suicide *n*〔短時期內在同一地區發生的〕成羣自殺事件, 連鎖自殺

cocooning /kəˈkunɪŋ; kəˈkuːnɪŋ/ *n* 過着繭式生活; 閉門獨處

cod fax *n* 騙局

co-exclusive *adj* 為雙方專用的

cohab /koˈhæb; kəʊˈhæb/ *n infml*【非正式】未婚同居的人

cold-calling *n* [U] 不請自來的推銷〔指主動打電話和上門推銷產品或投資等金融服務〕

cold-faxing *n* [U] 不請自來的傳真〔徑自用傳真發送未經索取的資料〕

cold fusion *n* 冷核聚變〔指用一般的溫度產生能量〕

cold surgery *n* [U] 冷手術〔一種治療慢性病的非急診手術〕

collectomania /kə,lɛktəˈmenɪə; kə,lektəˈmeɪniə/ *n* 收藏癖; 積聚狂

colour-blind *adj* 無膚色偏見的; 無種族歧視的

colour commentator *n* 講解繪聲繪色的體育評論員

comede /kəˈmid; kəˈmiːd/ *v* [I] *infml*【非正式】〔向觀眾〕講笑話; 當喜劇演員

come from *phr v* [I] *AmE*【美式】持有某種意圖或觀點

comfort woman *n*〔第二次世界大戰期間被日本軍人當作性奴隸的〕慰安婦

comms /kɑmz; kɒmz/ *n infml*【非正式】通訊

compactor /kəmˈpæktə; kəmˈpæktəʳ/ *n* 垃圾壓實機

compact video disc *n* 激光影碟, 雷射影碟

company doctor *n* 公司顧問〔對管理和財務狀況不佳的公司進行分析和治理的顧問〕

comper /ˈkɑmpə; ˈkɒmpəʳ/ *n* 參加有獎競賽迷

comping /ˈkɑmpɪŋ; ˈkɒmpɪŋ/ *n* 參加有獎競賽的嗜好

compote /ˈkampot; ˈkɒmpəʊt/ *n* [C; U] 糖水水果, 蜜餞

computer fiction *n* [U] (also 又作 **interactive fiction**) 電腦小說; 互動式小說

computer nerd *n*〔因不善交際而〕整天泡在電腦前的人〔通常指男子〕

computer porn *n* 電腦色情 (作品)

computer virus *n* 電腦病毒

conciliator /kənˈsɪlɪetə; kənˈsɪlɪeɪtəʳ/ *n* 調解人

confrontive /kənˈfrʌntɪv; kənˈfrʌntɪv/ *adj* 直言不諱的; 不加掩飾的

consultancy /kənˈsʌltənsɪ; kənˈsʌltənsi/ *n* 諮詢機構

contactless /ˈkɑntæktlɪs; ˈkɒntæktləs/ *adj* 無接觸的〔指可以遙控操作某些電子設備〕

continuous assessment *n* [U]〔對學生學習情況的〕持續性評估

contract killer *n* 雇用殺手

contrarian /kənˈtrɛrɪən; kənˈtreərɪən/ *n* 持相反意見者; 別出心裁者

convenience store *n AmE*【美式】〔晝夜營業的〕便利店

conventional wisdom *n* [U] 大眾觀點, 普遍的看法

conwoman /ˈkɑn,wumən; ˈkɒnwʊmən/ *n* 女騙子

cook-chill *n*〔食品間餐時重新加熱的〕預煮速凍供膳法

cooldown /ˈkul,daun; ˈkuːldaʊn/ *n*〔劇烈運動後的〕恢復正常體能狀態

copycat /ˈkɑpɪ,kæt; ˈkɒpɪkæt/ *n infml*【非正式】模仿他人行為 [衣着等] 的人; 無創造性的模仿者

cordless phone *n* 無線電話

corpocrat /ˈkɔrpəkræt; ˈkɔːpəkræt/ *n* 商業公司的高級行政人員或董事

correspondence course *n* 函授課程

cost-cutting *n* [U]〔工程及生意等的〕降低成本

couch dancing *n*〔私人聚會上表演的〕脫衣舞

couch potato *n* (also 又作 **couch spud**) *AmE infml*【美式, 非正式】老泡在電視機前的人; 終日懶散的人

coulis /ˈkulɪ; ˈkuːli/ *n* [pl]〔較稀薄的〕水果醬

counterperson /ˈkauntə,pɜsn; ˈkaʊntəpɜːsən/ *n AmE*【美式】店員

coupledom *n* (異性) 長期同居

courseware /ˈkɔrs,wɛr; ˈkɔːsweəʳ/ *n* 課程軟件

course-work *n* [U] 課程作業

courtesy car *n* (also 又作 **courtesy coach**)〔旅館提供的到機場等免費接客的〕迎賓車

cover story *n*〔雜誌的〕封面故事

cowhorn bars *n* [pl] *infml*【非正式】〔腳踏車的〕牛角式把手

crack /kræk; kræk/ *n* [U] 強效純可卡因

cracker /ˈkrækə; ˈkrækəʳ/ *n* 非法存取他人電腦資料的人

crackerjack /ˈkrækə,dʒæk; ˈkrækədʒæk/ *n AmE slang*【美俚】極出色的人或物

crackhead /ˈkræk,hɛd; ˈkrækhed/ *n slang*【俚】吸服強效可卡因的癮君子

cram school *n* (also 又作 **cramoschool**) 強化學校; 補習學校

creative¹ /krɪˈetɪv; kriˈeɪtɪv/ *adj euph*【委婉】超出常規的; 超出法定限度的

creative² *n* 廣告設計人員; 廣告宣傳策劃者

cred /krɛd; kred/ *n slang*【俚】可靠性; 可信性

credence /ˈkridns; ˈkriːdəns/ *n* 可信性; 可靠性

crime club *n* 犯罪俱樂部; 作案團夥

criminality /,krɪmɪˈnæləti; ,krɪmɪˈnæləti/ *n* [U] 犯罪行為

crinkly /ˈkrɪŋklɪ; ˈkrɪŋkli/ *n slang*【俚】老人

crispbread /ˈkrɪspbrɛd; ˈkrɪspbred/ *n* [C;U] 薄脆餅乾

cross-dresser *n* 有異性裝扮癖的人

cross-dressing *n* [U] 異性裝扮癖

crossover /ˈkrɔsovə; ˈkrɒsəʊvəʳ/ *n* 橋; 跨路線橋

cross-over store *n* 跨系列保健物品自選商店

cross-ownership *n*〔同時擁有報紙和電台控制權的〕交叉所有權

cross training n〔體育項目和健身活動交替進行的〕交叉鍛鍊

cruciverbalist /ˌkrusəˈvɜːblɪst; ˌkruːsɪ̩ˈvɜːbəlɪst/ n 做縱橫填字謎的人

crumbly /ˈkrʌmblɪ; ˈkrʌmbli/ n (also 又作 **crumblie**) slang【俚】老人

crusty /ˈkrʌstɪ; ˈkrʌsti/ n BrE【英式】硬殼族〔指身穿舊衣到處遊蕩的青年〕

cut /kʌt; kʌt/ n slang【俚】〔密紋唱片中的〕一首歌曲或曲子;〔唱片的〕一段錄音

cutesy /ˈkjutsɪ; ˈkjuːtsi/ adj infml【非正式】矯揉造作的

cutting edge n [S; U] **1**〔尤指言語等的〕尖刻, 尖銳 **2** 先鋒地位

cyberamics /ˌsaɪbəˈræmɪks; ˌsaɪbəˈræmɪks/ n [U] 電腦人學 [技術]

cybercafe /ˈsaɪbəkəˌfe; ˌsaɪbəˈkæfeɪ/ n (also 又作 **cybercafé**) 互聯網咖啡室, 電腦咖啡室〔設有連接互聯網的電腦供人使用〕

cyber campus n〔利用網上教學的〕虛擬校園, 網上校園

cyber crime n [C;U] 電腦犯罪; 網絡犯罪

cyber criminal n 電腦罪犯; 黑客

cyberculture /ˈsaɪbəˌkʌltʃə; ˈsaɪbəˌkʌltʃəʳ/ n [C; U] 電腦文化

cyberia /ˈsaɪbərɪə; ˈsaɪbəriə/ n 網絡世界

cyber-investing n 電腦化金融投資

cyberize /ˈsaɪbəraɪz; ˈsaɪbəraɪz/ v [T] 使網絡化; 使聯網

cybernaut /ˈsaɪbəˌnɔt; ˈsaɪbənɔːt/ n 電腦網絡漫遊者

cybernetics /ˌsaɪbəˈnɛtɪks; ˌsaɪbəˈnetɪks/ n [U] 控制論〔對信息在機器、大腦和神經系統中的傳遞和控制的研究〕, 模控學 **– -ic** adj **– -ically** /-klɪ; -kli/ adv

cyberphobia /ˌsaɪbəˈfobɪə; ˌsaɪbəˈfəʊbiə/ n 電腦恐懼症

cyberphobic /ˌsaɪbəˈfobɪk; ˌsaɪbəˈfəʊbɪk/ n 畏懼電腦的人; 恐電腦症患者

cyber pirate n 電腦軟件侵權者

cyber police n [U]〔專門對付網上犯罪的〕網路警察

cyberpunk /ˈsaɪbəˌpʌŋk; ˈsaɪbəpʌŋk/ n **1** 描述由電腦網絡控制的未來暴力社會的科學幻想小說 **2** 上述科幻小說作家

cyberspace /ˈsaɪbəˌspes; ˈsaɪbəspeɪs/ n [U]〔由電腦網絡組成的〕網際空間

cyberspeak /ˈsaɪbəˌspik; ˈsaɪbəspiːk/ n 網絡用語

cybersurf /ˈsaɪbəˌsɜf; ˈsaɪbəsɜːf/ v [I] 網絡漫遊

cyber surfer n 網際漫遊者

cyberworld /ˈsaɪbəˌwɜld; ˈsaɪbəwɜːld/ n 網絡世界

D, d

dag /dæg; dæg/ n AmE slang【美俚】討厭的人; 愚蠢的人

daggy /ˈdægɪ; ˈdægi/ adj AmE slang【美俚】討厭的; 乏味的

dataflow /ˈdetəˌflo; ˈdeɪtəfləʊ/ n〔電腦技術的〕數據流, 資料流程

data highway n 信息 (高速) 公路

data warehouse n〔電腦中的〕數據倉

date rape n 約會強姦〔男子約會女子, 然後把她強姦〕

dawn raid n BrE【英式】晨襲〔尤指在一天交易開市時突然買下某上市公司大量股票的行動〕

daytimer /ˈdeˌtaɪmə; ˈdeɪtaɪməʳ/ n 白晝迪斯科舞會〔指為亞洲青年舉辦的下午場〕

dazzle gun n 眩目槍〔一種利用激光束使攻擊者目眩並能破壞光學傳感器運作的武器〕

dead-ass adj AmE slang【美俚】死氣沉沉的; 無足輕重的

dead-cat bounce n infml【非正式】死貓式反彈〔指股價在持續走低後的虛假回升〕

dead parrot n BrE infml【英式, 非正式】"死鸚鵡", 無可挽回的事物

dead-tree adj 過時的; 陳舊的

deal /dil; diːl/ n 街上兜售的毒品〔如大麻、海洛因等〕

death star n 星狀投鏢〔一種由金屬片製成的鋒利武器〕

decaf /ˈdiˈkæf; diːˈkæf/ n infml【非正式】脫咖啡因的咖啡

deccie /ˈdɛsɪ; ˈdesi/ n 室內裝飾迷

declinist /dɪˈklaɪnɪst; dɪˈklaɪnɪ̩st/ n, adj 持衰落論的 (人)

decompress /ˌdikəmˈprɛs; ˌdiːkəmˈpres/ v [I] 放鬆, 鬆弛

decor fossil n 裝飾用的化石

decryption /ˌdiˈkrɪpʃən; ˌdiːˈkrɪpʃən/ n [U]〔電腦的〕解密, 解碼

Deep House n 迷幻靈歌〔由迷幻狂舞曲發展而成的一種迪斯科音樂〕

deep-set adj 深陷的〔常指眼睛〕

def /dɛf; def/ adj slang【俚】了不起的, 棒極的

defalcation /ˌdifælˈkeʃən; ˌdiːfælˈkeɪʃən/ n [U] 盜用公款, 虧空公款

defence breed n 防衛種犬, 警衛犬

defensive medicine n [U] 防範性治療〔醫生為減少病人投訴而採取的一種謹慎保守的治療方法〕

dekalogy /dɪˈkælədʒɪ; dɪˈkælədʒi/ n 十卷 (套) 叢書

demerge /dɪˈmɜdʒ; diːˈmɜːdʒ/ v [T] 把〔合併的大公司〕分成獨立公司

demerger /dɪˈmɜdʒə; diːˈmɜːdʒəʳ/ n 合併大公司的分拆

demo /ˈdɛmo; ˈdeməʊ/ v [T] 示範; 展示

demolitional /ˌdɛməˈlɪʃənl; ˌdeməˈlɪʃənəl/ adj 拆毀的; 破壞 (性) 的

dep /dɛp; dep/ v [T] infml【非正式】擔任代表; 充當代理人

dependency culture n [U] 依賴性的社會風氣〔指習慣於依賴政府的福利制度的生活方式〕

deselect /ˌdisəˈlɛkt; ˌdiːsɪ̩ˈlekt/ v [T] euph【委婉】不讓……入選; 把……排斥在外

desktop /ˈdɛskˌtɑp; ˈdesktɒp/ adj, n **1** 台式電腦 (的), 桌上電腦 (的) **2**〔電腦中的〕桌面, 工作台

des res *n BrE infml*【英式, 非正式】〔在設計或地段方面頗具特色的〕理想住宅

destabilize /ˌdiˈsteblaɪz; ˌdiːˈsteɪbəlaɪz/ *v* [T] (also 又作 **destabilise**) 使...不穩定

destination shopper *n* 有明確目標的購物者

destination wedding *n* 旅遊結婚

detailing /dɪˈtelɪŋ; ˈdiːteɪlɪŋ/ *n* 小件裝飾品

detox /ˈditɑks; dɪˈtɒks/ *n infml*【非正式】戒毒; 戒酒

dialogue box *n* 〔電腦屏幕上的〕對話框, 對話方塊

dickhead /ˈdɪkhɛd; ˈdɪkhed/ *n slang*【俚】蠢人, 無能的人

dictionarate /ˌdɪkʃənəret; ˈdɪkʃənərɪt/ *adj* 精通詞典的, 善於使用詞典的

digital camera *n* 數碼相機

digital highway *n* 信息 (高速) 公路

digiteer /ˌdɪdʒɪˈtɪə; ˌdɪdʒɪˈtɪəʳ/ *n* 電腦能手

digithead /ˈdɪdʒɪtˌhɛd; ˈdɪdʒɪthed/ *n* 電腦迷

dink /dɪŋk; dɪŋk/ *n AmE slang*【美俚】傻瓜

Dinky /ˈdɪŋkɪ; ˈdɪŋkɪ/ *n* "頂客族"〔指收入可觀而無子女的雙職工〕

directory /dəˈrɛktərɪ; ˈdaɪˈrektəri/ *n* 〔電腦中的〕目錄

dirty dancing *n* [U] (also 又作 **touch dancing**) 接觸舞, 貼身舞

dirty trick *n* 卑鄙行為 [手段]

disadaptive /ˌdɪsəˈdæptɪv; ˌdɪsəˈdæptɪv/ *adj* 使不適應的

Discman /ˈdɪskmən; ˈdɪskmən/ *n* 〔可攜式播放音樂光碟的〕光碟隨身聽

disconsider /ˌdɪskənˈsɪdə; ˌdɪskənˈsɪdəʳ/ *v* [T] 對...評價不高

disempower /ˌdɪsɪmˈpaʊə; ˌdɪsɪmˈpaʊəʳ/ *v* [T] 剝奪...的權利

disfluency /dɪsˈfluənsɪ; dɪsˈfluːənsi/ *n* [U] 言語障礙, 口吃

disimprove /ˌdɪsɪmˈpruv; ˌdɪsɪmˈpruːv/ *v euph*【委婉】(使) 變得更糟, (使) 惡化

disney /ˈdɪznɪ; ˈdɪzni/ *v* [T] 按迪士尼式主題樂園建造

Disneyfication /ˌdɪznɪfəˈkeʃən; ˌdɪznɪfɪˈkeɪʃən/ *n* [U] 迪士尼樂園化〔一種對真實事件等所作的庸俗的商業化模仿〕

diss /dɪs; dɪs/ *v slang*【俚】不尊敬; 貶低; 羞辱

dissensus /dɪˈsɛnsəs; dɪˈsensəs/ *n* 意見分歧

distance learning *n* [U] 遙距教育〔如通過函授, 電視或互聯網等課程進行的教育〕

distant-water nation *n* 遠海捕魚國家

ditsy /ˈdɪtsɪ; ˈdɪtsi/ *adj* (also 又作 **ditzy**) *slang*【俚】呆傻的

dittohead /ˈdɪtoˌhɛd; ˈdɪtəʊhed/ *n* 應聲蟲; 追隨者

do /du; duː/ *v* [T] *slang*【俚】服用〔毒品〕

dockny /ˈdɑknɪ; ˈdɒkni/ *n* 〔倫敦東部重新開發的〕碼頭住宅區居民

docu-fantasy *n* 文獻幻想片

docutainment /ˌdɑkjəˈtɛnmənt; ˌdɒkjəˈteɪnmənt/ *n* (also 又作 **infotainment**) 記實娛樂性節目

dog /dɑg; dɒg/ *n BrE slang*【英俚】電話

dog-and-pony *v* [T] *AmE infml*【美式, 非正式】〔利用過分的宣傳或強行推銷的手段〕企圖影響〔某人〕

doggy bag *n* 〔餐館供顧客打包用的〕剩菜袋; 狗食袋

dollar diplomacy *n* [U]〔為在外國謀取更大經濟利益的〕金元外交

dollar shop *n* 〔前蘇聯等國家使用美元的〕外匯商店

domain name *n* 〔互聯網的〕域名, 定義域名稱

doning /ˈdon-ɪŋ; ˈdəʊnɪŋ/ *n* 捐贈, 贈送

doom and gloom *n* 前景暗淡; 無望

doomsayer /ˈdumˌseə; ˈduːmˌseɪəʳ/ *n* 預言災難的人

doper /ˈdopə; ˈdəʊpəʳ/ *n* 毒品販子

dork /dɔrk; dɔːk/ *n AmE slang*【美俚】蠢貨; 笨蛋

dorkish /ˈdɔrkɪʃ; ˈdɔːkɪʃ/ *adj* (also 又作 **dorky**) *AmE slang*【美俚】愚蠢的

DOS *n abbrev*【縮】= disk operating system 磁碟作業系統, 磁盤操作系統

dot ball *n* 〔板球中〕未得分的投球

double life *n* 雙重生活〔常指人格和身分〕

double whammy *n* 雙重打擊; 雙重厄運

doughnutting /ˈdonʌtɪŋ; ˈdəʊnʌtɪŋ/ *n* 呈環形圍聚在由電視轉播的發言議員周圍〔國會議員在電視轉播會議實況時聚在一起坐在發言議員周圍, 以給人印象, 他或她講話時會場上坐滿了聽眾〕

down-dressing *n* 便裝

download /ˈdaʊnˌlod; ˈdaʊnləʊd/ *v* 〔電腦〕下載

downmarketing /ˌdaʊnˈmɑrkɪtɪŋ; ˌdaʊnˈmɑːkɪtɪŋ/ *n* [U] 迎合低層次市場需要的廣告策略

downplay /ˌdaʊnˈple; ˌdaʊnˈpleɪ/ *v* [T] 對〔某事物〕輕描淡寫; 貶低

downsize /ˈdaʊnsaɪz; ˈdaʊnsaɪz/ *v* [T] *euph*【委婉】裁減〔員工〕

downspin /ˈdaʊnˌspɪn; ˈdaʊnˌspɪn/ *n* 〔房價的〕急劇下跌;〔經濟形勢等的〕急轉直下

dpi *n* (also 又作 **DPI**) *abbrev*【縮】= dots per inch 每英寸點數〔解像度單位〕

dramedy /ˈdræmədɪ; ˈdræmədi/ *n AmE*【美式】電視喜劇性正劇

dream team *n* 夢幻組合; 夢想隊伍〔常由最佳人選組成〕

dream ticket *n AmE*【美式】黃金搭檔, 完美組合〔尤指競選總統和副總統職位的兩位候選人〕

dress-down Friday *n AmE*【美式】穿著隨便的星期五

drink-driver *n BrE*【英式】酒後駕車者

drop-dead *adv AmE*【美式】異常地; 非凡地; 卓越地

droughted /ˈdraʊtɪd; ˈdraʊtɪd/ *adj* 遭受旱災的

drug around *v slang*【俚】吸毒成癮

druggie /ˈdrʌgɪ; ˈdrʌgi/ *n AmE infml*【美式, 非正式】吸毒成癮的人

dry beer *n* 〔酒精含量較高而無甜味的〕乾啤酒

dry humour *n* 冷面幽默

dry law *n AmE*【美式】禁止售酒法

dry slope *n* 〔常設在室內的〕人造滑雪坡

DTP *n abbrev*【縮】= desktop publishing 桌上出版

dumb card *n* 啞卡〔一種帶有磁條的信用卡或借方卡〕

dumbo /ˈdʌmbo; ˈdʌmbəʊ/ n BrE infml【英式, 非正式】醉漢〔指血中酒精含量超過法定限額的駕車商人〕

dump on phr v AmE slang【美俚】嚴厲地批評

dumpster /ˈdʌmpstə; ˈdʌmpstəʳ/ n AmE【美式】大型垃圾箱

DVD n abbrev【縮】= digital versatile disc (also 又作 **digital video disc**) 數碼影碟; 數字式多功能光盤

dweeb /dwib; dwi:b/ n AmE slang【美俚】討厭的蠢人

E, e

E n abbrev【縮】= ecstasy "狂喜" 迷幻藥〔一種搖頭丸〕

earner /ˈɜnə; ˈɜ:nəʳ/ n 1 掙工資的人 2 贏利的企業

ear-sight n 耳視覺〔能給微弱聲音定位的靈敏聽覺〕

earthbound /ˈɜθbaʊnd; ˈɜ:θbaʊd/ adj 1 附着於地面的 2 朝着地球移動的 3 世俗的; 缺乏想像力的

earth-shattering adj 驚天動地的; 影響深遠的

easy-listening adj 易聽懂的; 輕鬆的〔常指音樂〕

eatery /ˈitəri; ˈi:təri/ n AmE infml【美式, 非正式】飯店; 餐館

eating disorder n 進食障礙〔由心理障礙引起的暴食或厭食〕

e-banking n (also 又作 **electronic banking**) [U] 電子銀行業務

Ebonics /ˈɛbɒniks; ˈebɒniks/ n [pl] 黑人英語

e-book n 電子書

E-business n [U] (also 又作 **e-business**) 電子業務

e-card n〔經網絡傳送的〕電子賀卡

eco-car n〔對環境無污染的〕生態汽車

ecocide /ˈikoˌsaid; ˈi:kəʊˌsaid/ n [U] 生態滅絕

eco-friendly adj 對生態環境無害的

eco-labelling n [U] 加貼生態保護標籤

e-commerce n [U] (also 又作 **electronic commerce**) 電子商務; 電子貿易

econobox /ɪˈkɒnəˌbɒks; ɪˈkɒnəˌbɒks/ n 經濟汽車; 小型車

economical /ˌikəˈnɒmɪkḷ; ˌi:kəˈnɒmɪkl/ adj euph【委婉】故意隱瞞的

Economy Class Syndrome n 經濟艙綜合症〔長時間在經濟艙內坐着, 因缺少活動而導致血栓形成的病症〕

eco-refugee n 生態難民, 生態災害避難者

ecosystem /ˈikoˌsɪstəm; ˈi:kəʊˌsɪstḷm/ n [U] 生態系 (統)

ecotourism /ˈikoˌturɪzm; ˈi:kəʊˌtʊərɪzəm/ n [U] 生態 (保護) 旅遊〔指到未受污染的自然風景區度假而不對環境造成污染〕

eco-warrior n〔為環保而抗議興建公路、核電站的〕環保戰士

ECU n abbrev【縮】= European Currency Unit 歐洲貨幣單位〔1999 年之前使用〕

edge city n〔興建於大城市市郊的〕邊緣城

edgy /ˈɛdʒɪ; ˈedʒi/ adj slang【俚】趕時髦的; 前衛的

editrix /ˈɛdɪtrɪks; ˈedɪtrɪks/ n 女編輯

edutainment /ˌɛdjuˈteɪnmənt; ˌedjuˈteɪnmənt/ [U]〔多媒體〕教育娛樂資料; 寓教於樂

effing and blinding n [U] infml【非正式】咒罵; 講髒話

E-fit n abbrev【縮】= electronic facial identification technique 電子面部鑑定技術〔根據儲存於電腦中的一系列可在熒光屏上拼合的面貌特徵製作容貌拼圖人頭像的電子系統〕

E-free adj〔食品〕無添加劑的

eldercare /ˈɛldəˌkɛr; ˈeldəˌkeəʳ/ n [U] 對老人的照料

electrics /ɪˈlɛktrɪks; ɪˈlektrɪks/ n [pl] infml【非正式】電線及有關組件

electronica /ɪˌlɛkˈtrɒnɪkə; ɪˌlekˈtrɒnɪkə/ n [U] 電子流行音樂

electronic mailbox n 電子郵箱

electronic publishing n 電子出版業

electronic road pricing n 電子道路收費

electronic shopping n [U]〔通過有線電視和互聯網進行的〕電子購物

electronic tag n 電子監控牌〔一種用於監視假釋的罪犯的監視器〕

electronic tagging n [U] 電子監控〔一種對假釋的罪犯進行監視的方法〕

electronic text n〔可在電腦上閱讀的〕電子文本

electronic transfer n 電子轉賬〔用電腦將資金從一賬戶轉入另一賬戶〕

electronic virus n 電腦病毒, 電子病毒

El Niño n 1 厄爾·尼諾海流〔指太平洋東部海域的一支暖流〕2 厄爾尼諾現象〔影響全球氣候的氣象變化〕

e-mail[1] n [C, U] (also 又作 **email**) 電子郵件

e-mail[2] v [T] 發送電子郵件

e-mail address n 電子郵件地址, 電郵地址

e-mail bomb n〔含有大量資料或病毒而導致接收者系統故障的〕電子郵件炸彈

emotional abuse n [U] 精神虐待

Emotional Quotient n (also 又作 **EQ**) [sing] 情緒商數〔一種可用量表測試的某人的交際及情緒控制能力〕

empathize /ˈɛmpəθaɪz; ˈempəθaɪz/ v [I]〔對他人的情感、經歷〕有同感, 產生共鳴

encash /ɪnˈkæʃ; ɪnˈkæʃ/ v [T] fml【正式】兌現〔支票等〕

encryption /ɪnˈkrɪpʃən; ɪnˈkrɪpʃən/ n [U] tech【術語】加 (編) 密 (碼)

end-stop v 突然結束; 最終結束

entry-level adj〔尤指電腦〕初入門的, 初級水平的

environmental psychology n 環境心理學〔一門科學, 旨在研究人們所處的環境在心理上產生的影響以及人們對自然環境構築的心理框架〕

epigraph /ˈɛpɪɡræf; ˈepɪɡrɑ:f/ n 銘文; 短語

escrima /ɛsˋkrimə; esˈkriːmə/ n 棍棒術〔用棍棒打鬥的武術〕

estimate in phr v [I] 估計到達（時間）

ethno-medicine n [U] 民族醫學，民間醫術

Euro /ˋjuro; ˈjʊərəʊ/ n (also 又作 **euro**) 歐羅，歐元〔歐盟各成員國共同使用的統一貨幣，1999 年起使用〕

evenings /ˋivnɪŋz; ˈiːvnɪŋz/ adv 在（任何）晚上，每晚（地）

e-wallet n 電子錢包〔用於網上付款〕

exclude /ɪkˋsklud; ɪkˈskluːd/ v [T] 開除〔行為不良的學生〕

executive /ɪgˋzɛkjutɪv; ɪgˈzekjətɪv/ adj 特級的；豪華的

executive flu n 行政長官病毒綜合徵，肌痛腦脊髓炎

exemplar /ɪgˋzɛmplɚ; ɪgˈzemplɑ/ n fml【正式】楷模；典型；範本

exmatriculate /ˌɪksməˋtrɪkjəˌlet; ˌɪksməˈtrɪkjʊleɪt/ v [T] 將〔學生〕除名，開除〔學生〕

exotica /ɪgˋzɑtɪkə; ɪgˈzɒtɪkə/ n [pl] 奇異事物，新奇事物

expatriatism /eksˋpetrɪˌetɪzəm; eksˈpætri-eɪtɪzəm/ n [U] 長期留居國外，長期在國外旅行

expensed /ɪkˋspɛnst; ɪkˈspenst/ adj 所有費用由雇主支付的

explete /ɪkˋsplit; ɪkˈspliːt/ v [I] 使用咒罵語；咒罵

externality /ˌɛkstɚˋnælˌətɪ; ˌeksɜːˈnælɪti/ n [U] 〔某項活動的〕外在影響，附帶影響

extract /ɪkˋstrækt; ɪkˈstrækt/ v [T] 摘要發表〔文章〕

extreme /ɪkˋstrim; ɪkˈstriːm/ adj 〔某些運動項目〕極危險的，需超人毅力的

extreme sports n [pl] 極限運動

extremist /ɪkˋstrimɪst; ɪkˈstriːmɪst/ n 極限運動員

eyeball /ˋaɪbɔl; ˈaɪbɔːl/ v [T] 觀察，〔用眼睛〕打量

eyephone /ˋaɪfon; ˈaɪfəʊn/ n 視像耳機〔一種頭戴式微型電視屏幕耳機〕

eyeprint /ˋaɪprɪnt; ˈaɪprɪnt/ n 眼印〔根據視網膜內靜脈圖來識別人的身分〕

eyewear /ˋaɪˌwɛr; ˈaɪweə/ n [U] 護目鏡

e-zine n 電子雜誌

F, f

fabby /ˋfæbɪ; ˈfæbi/ adj BrE infml【英式，非正式】極好的，絕妙的

face-off n 對抗；正面交鋒

face time n 1 〔在電視上或公眾場合的〕露臉；曝光 2 〔在社交場合的〕會面

facilitator /fəˋsɪlɪtetɚ; fəˈsɪlɪteɪtɑ/ n 推動事物順利進行的人或物

facility trip n euph〔由公司支付作為廣告安排的〕公費旅遊，公出

fact-find n 實情調查

factory shop n (also 又作 **factory outlet**) 工廠直銷店

factpack /ˋfæktˌpæk; ˈfæktˌpæk/ n〔關於某項目的〕整套專題資料

fact-sheet n 專題介紹單張

fade cream n 增白霜，淡化霜

fairy cake n BrE【英式】〔供一人食用的〕小精靈蛋糕

family credit n 家庭信貸〔英國為有子女的低收入家庭提供的社會保險津貼〕

famously /ˋfeməslɪ; ˈfeɪməsli/ adv 公開地；驚人地

fandemonium /ˌfændɪˋmonɪəm; ˌfændɪ-ˈməʊniəm/ n [U]〔對影視、體育名星的〕支持者的狂熱仰慕，追星狂熱

fandom /ˋfændəm; ˈfændəm/ n [U]〔尤對科幻小說和電影的〕狂熱愛好者；科幻迷

fanny pack n AmE【美式】腰帶包

fantasy /ˋfæntəsɪ; ˈfæntəsi/ n 迷幻劑

fanzine /ˋfænzin; ˈfænziːn/ n〔尤指通俗音樂的〕愛好者雜誌

FAQ n abbrev【縮】= frequently asked questions〔電腦的〕常見問題

fashion-conscious adj 講究時髦的；熱衷於趕時髦的

fashion victim n 不惜代價趕時髦者；趕潮流受害者〔用作貶義〕

fastlink /ˋfæstˌlɪŋk; ˈfɑːstlɪŋk/ n 高速公路連接路段

fast track n (also 又作 **fast-track**) 快速成功之路；捷徑

fattist /ˋfætɪst; ˈfætɪst/ adj (also 又作 **fatist**) 歧視〔詆毀〕肥胖者的

fattyism /ˋfætɪɪzəm; ˈfæti-izəm/ n [U] infml【非正式】對肥胖者的歧視〔苛待〕

faux /fo; fəʊ/ adj 仿造的；假冒的

fave /fev; feɪv/ adj, n 特別受喜愛的（人或物）

faxable /ˋfæksəbl; ˈfæksəbəl/ adj 可用傳真機通訊的

fax hacker n 用傳真機濫發信息的人

fax-on-demand n [U] 即時傳真〔用戶通過通訊網絡，用電話撥號讓傳真機收取資料的系統〕

faxphone /ˋfæksˌfon; ˈfæksfəʊn/ n 傳真電話

feeb /fib; fiːb/ n 瘦弱的人〔用作貶義〕

feel-bad adj 令人沮喪的〔尤指經濟狀況〕

feel-good adj 令人感到樂觀幸福的〔尤指經濟和物質方面〕

feminal[1] /ˋfɛmɪnl; ˈfemɪnəl/ adj 娘娘腔的；〔男子〕女人氣的

feminal[2] n 娘娘腔的男子

fender-bender n infml【非正式】〔無人受傷的〕小車禍

fenland /ˋfɛnlænd; ˈfenlænd/ n [U]〔英國的〕沼澤地

fertigation /fɝtɪˋgeʃən; fɜːtɪˈgeɪʃən/ n [U] 灌肥，灌溉施肥〔一種通過滴灌系統源源不斷給植物澆灌肥水的農業施肥法〕

film-on-demand n 電影點播，自選影院（有線電視的一種服務）

Filofax /ˋfaɪlofæks; ˈfaɪləʊfæks/ n 活頁日記簿〔用作專利名〕

filofax /ˈfɪləˌfæks; ˌfɪləˈfæks/ n [I] 盜竊〔某人〕的備忘記事本 (以期勒索錢財)

filofiction /ˌfɪləˈfɪkʃən; ˌfɪləˈfɪkʃən/ n tdmk【商標】備忘記事本版式小說〔一種以適合裝入記事本的版式發行的小說〕

firewall /ˈfaɪrˌwɔl; ˈfaɪəwɔːl/ n〔電腦中防止系統被入侵的〕防火牆

first-ever adj 有史以來 (第一次) 的, 史無前例的

fiscal /ˈfɪskl̩; ˈfɪskəl/ n 財政年度, 會計年度

fitness centre n 健身中心

fitness walking n 健身步行

flake /flek; fleɪk/ n AmE infml【美式, 非正式】易動搖的人, 不可靠的人 (用作貶義)

flame /flem; fleɪm/ v [T]〔以電子郵件〕抨擊, 辱罵; 開火

flash /flæʃ; flæʃ/ n infml【非正式】俗艷; 炫耀

flashback /ˈflæʃˌbæk; ˈflæʃbæk/ n 往事歷歷, 回憶閃現

flash-bang n infml【非正式】閃爆彈; 眩暈彈

flat-bed scanner n 平台式掃描器, 平板掃描器

flatline /ˈflætlaɪn; ˈflætlaɪn/ v [I] 1 死亡 2 完全失效 [失敗]

flatliner /ˈflætlaɪnə; ˈflætlaɪnəʳ/ n 1 心跳停止的人 2 沒有活力的人

flatmate /ˈflætmet; ˈflætmeɪt/ n 合住公寓者

flatten /ˈflætn̩; ˈflætn/ v [T] 壓縮; 精簡

flesh-pressing n infml【非正式】與大批人一一握手〔尤用於競選活動〕

flip chart n〔可逐頁翻開展示的〕活動掛圖

flip-flop v [I] AmE【美式】完全改變觀點; 看法大轉變

flip phone n 翻蓋式手提電話

flume ride n AmE【美式】激流飛船, 急水滑坡〔常見於露天遊樂場的一種娛樂活動〕

fly-drive n, adj〔假期〕空陸聯遊 (的)〔包括來回機票和租車費用 (的)〕

foaf /fof; fəʊf/ n〔越傳越離譜的〕傳奇故事, 民間傳說

fogey phone n 老式電話機, 懷舊電話機

folding /ˈfoldɪŋ; ˈfəʊldɪŋ/ n infml【非正式】紙幣, 錢

folk hero n 民族英雄

food coma n〔因進食物過多而引起的〕食物昏迷

foodie /ˈfudi; ˈfuːdi/ n infml【非正式】美食家

foodie-ism /ˈfudi-ɪzəm; ˈfuːdi-ɪzəm/ n 美食主義

food stamp n AmE【美式】〔政府發給貧民的〕食品券

forensic evidence n 科學鑑證

forthold /ˈfortˌhold; ˈfɔːθəʊld/ v〔他人不在時〕代為處理事務

forty winks n [pl] infml【非正式】(一個) 盹, 小睡〔尤在白天〕; 午睡

forward-thinking adj 有遠見卓識的

fractality /frækˈtælɪti; fræk'tælɪti/ n 呈不規則碎片形的

fragrance /ˈfregrəns; ˈfreɪgrəns/ v 使散發香氣

frauditor /ˈfrodɪtə; ˈfrɔːdʒtəʳ/ n 檢查詐騙賬務的審計員

free-fall n 自由下跌〔指股價等的大幅度下跌〕

freeride /ˈfriraɪd; ˈfriːraɪd/ v [I] 自由滑雪

freeware /ˈfriwɛr; ˈfriːweəʳ/ n [U]〔電腦的〕免費軟件, 自由軟件

fresh /frɛʃ; freʃ/ adj slang【俚】極好的; 絕妙的

friendly fire n [U]〔因失誤〕向自己人開火; 誤殺

frit /frɪt; frɪt/ adj BrE【英式】受驚的, 驚恐的

front edge n 先鋒

front-line adj〔處在衝突〕第一線的, 首當其衝的

front-load v [T] 將...提前

front office n〔股票交易所裡進行股票買賣的〕交易室

frosted jeans n [pl] 水磨牛仔裝

frug /frʌg; frʌg/ v [I] 迪斯科音樂伴奏跳舞

fruitarian /fruˈtɛriən; fruː'teəriən/ n 只食水果的人

fudge and mudge n 不表態; 推諉

full-frills adj 花色品種多樣化的

full frontal n 正面全裸像

funboard /ˈfʌnbord; ˈfʌnbɔːd/ n 快速帆板

functional food n [U] 功能食品; 保健食品, 健康食品

fundie /ˈfʌndi; ˈfʌndi/ n 原教旨主義者; 有強烈信仰 [信念] 的人〔如宗教、政治、環保等〕

fundraiser /ˈfʌndrezə; ˈfʌndreɪzəʳ/ n〔專為慈善或非營利機構〕募款者; 籌資者

funk up v [T] AmE【美式】使鮮亮; 使活潑熱烈

fun run n 公益長跑

futuristically /ˌfjutʃəˈrɪstɪkl̩ı; ˌfjuːtʃə'rɪstɪkli/ adv 在未來, 在將來

fuzzword /ˈfʌzwɜd; ˈfʌzwɜːd/ n〔力求委婉的〕模糊用詞

fuzzy logic n〔電腦的〕模糊邏輯

G, g

gabfest /ˈgæbfɛst; ˈgæbfest/ n infml【非正式】長時間的聚談〔會議〕

game plan n (also 又作 **gameplan**) 周密計劃的行動方案

game show n〔電視上請名人參加的〕有獎遊戲節目

gangbang /ˈgæŋˌbæŋ; ˈgæŋˌbæŋ/ n slang【俚】輪姦 — **gang-bang** v [I; T]

gang-banger n AmE slang【美俚】少年犯罪集團成員

gang-banging n AmE slang【美俚】少年犯罪活動

gangbuster /ˈgæŋˌbʌstə; ˈgæŋbʌstəʳ/ adj AmE infml【美式, 非正式】棒極的

garbology /garˈbɒlədʒi; gɑː'bɒlədʒi/ n [U]【美式】垃圾處理學

gas-cooled adj 氣冷的; 用氣體冷卻的

gastrodrama /ˌgæstroˈdræmə; ˌgæstrəʊ-'drɑːmə/ n 美食戲, 果腹戲〔尤指由觀眾參與飲食的以飲食為主要內容的戲劇演出〕

gastronome /ˈgæstrəˌnɒm; ˈgæstrənəʊm/ n 美食家; 講究吃喝的人

gated community *n* 封閉式社區

Gawd /gɔd; gɔːd/ *n interj infml*【非正式】上帝; 天哪

gazillion /gəˈzɪljən; gəˈzɪljən/ *n infml*【非正式】無數; 大量

geddit /ˈgedɪt; ˈgedɪt/ *interj BrE infml*【美式, 非正式】懂嗎?〔用以開玩笑地或諷刺性地引起對雙關語, 影射語或其他被認為是巧妙的修辭或俏皮話的注意〕

geek /gik; giːk/ *n slang*【俚】令人討厭的人; 傻瓜; 呆子〔指不合潮流的人〕

geeky /ˈgikɪ; ˈgiːki/ *adj slang*【俚】令人討厭的

geep /gip; giːp/ *n* 山綿羊〔由山羊與綿羊交配而生〕

gender /ˈdʒɛndə; ˈdʒendəʳ/ *v* [T] 使性別化

gender-bender *n slang*【俚】(歌手或藝人)男扮女裝或女扮男裝者

gender gap *n* 性差距〔男性與女性在政治等問題上的分歧導致選舉上的差別〕

genderist /ˈdʒɛndərɪst; ˈdʒendərɪst/ *adj* 帶性別歧視的

generalist /ˈdʒɛnərəlɪst; ˈdʒenərəlɪst/ *n* 多面手, 通才

gene therapy *n* [U]〔用遺傳工程消除遺傳缺陷的〕基因治療

genethic /dʒəˈnɛθɪk; dʒəˈneθɪk/ *adj* 遺傳工程涉及的倫理問題的

genetic fingerprinting *n* [U] 遺傳基因紋印鑑證

genetic mother *n* 基因母親〔指贈卵子的母親〕

genetic testing *n* 基因測定

geneware /ˈdʒɪnweə; ˈdʒiːnweəʳ/ *n* 基因件 [品]〔用於人工輸入植物細胞以改變其遺傳結構的基因〕

gesturism /ˈdʒɛstʃərɪzm; ˈdʒestʃərɪzəm/ *n*〔從事政治等活動僅僅為了〕裝腔樣子; 擺花架子

getaway /ˈgɛtəweɪ; ˈgetəweɪ/ *n AmE*【美式】〔能藉以擺脫緊張繁忙的日常工作的〕度假屋, 隱居別墅

get-together *n*〔公司的〕合併

get up *v slang*【俚】〔在牆上等〕亂塗亂寫, 塗畫

giant-killer *n*〔體育比賽中的〕擊敗強隊者; 以弱勝強者

gigabyte /ˈgɪgəˌbaɪt; ˈgɪgəbaɪt/ *n* (also 又作 **GB**)〔電腦的〕吉字節, 千兆字節, 十億位元組

gimme /ˈgɪmɪ; ˈgɪmi/ *n infml*【非正式】容易得到的東西; 輕而易舉的事

gimme cap *n slang*【俚】廣告帽

girocracy /dʒaɪˈrɒkrəsɪ; dʒaɪˈrɒkrəsi/ *n BrE*【英式】依靠領取社會保險金的階層

GIS *n abbrev*【縮】= Geographic Information System 地理資訊系統〔一種電子地圖技術〕

gizmo /ˈgɪzmo; ˈgɪzməʊ/ *n*〔尤指實用而精巧的〕裝置; 小玩藝

glam /glæm; glæm/ *n infml*【非正式】富裕的中年人

glasnost /ˈglæsnɒst; ˈglɑːsnɒst/ *n* [U]〔尤指前蘇聯政治的〕開放政策

glitterati /ˌglɪtəˈrɑːtɪ; ˌglɪtəˈrɑːti/ *n* [pl] *infml*【非正式】〔尤指娛樂圈、體育界的〕名流; 知名人士; 風雲人物

global village *n* 地球村〔藉着電訊聯繫, 地球被視作單一的社區〕

globby /ˈglɒbɪ; ˈglɒbi/ *adj infml*【非正式】浮誇的, 誇張的

gloomster /ˈglumstə; ˈgluːmstəʳ/ *n infml*【非正式】悲觀主義者;〔尤指〕預言災難者

goal hanger *n* 機會主義者〔用作貶義〕

gobsmack /ˈgɒbˌsmæk; ˈgɒbˌsmæk/ *v* [T] *BrE infml*【英式, 非正式】使全然不知所措; 使窘困不堪

gob-struck *adj BrE infml*【英式, 非正式】全然不知所措的; 困窘不堪的

gofer /ˈgofə; ˈgəʊfəʳ/ *n infml*【非正式】替人辦雜事的人, 跑腿的辦事員

go-get *v* [I] *infml*【非正式】有抱負; 奮發向上

go-getter *n* 積極進取的人; 意志堅決能成事的人

go-kart /ˈgo ˌkart; ˈgəʊ kɑːt/ *n BrE*【英式】微型 (單座) 賽車

golden goal *n* 黃金入球, 金球〔足球加時賽中射入的定勝負的球〕

golden goodbye *n*〔退休時發給的〕大筆退休金

golden hello *n infml*【非正式】調職補償金

golden mean *n* [(the) S] 中庸之道

goldfishing /ˈgold ˌfɪʃɪŋ; ˈgəʊld ˌfɪʃɪŋ/ *n*〔配以議會議員在會議廳發言的無聲連續鏡頭對議項進行的〕透視式電視新聞評述

gold-plate *v* [T] 為...巧立名目; 為...做表面文章

gold standard *n* 優質標準

gomer /ˈgomə; ˈgəʊməʳ/ *n slang*【俚】無望治癒的住院病人

goodfella /ˈgʊdfelə; ˈgʊdfelə/ *n* 黑手黨成員; 歹徒

gorilla /gəˈrɪlə; gəˈrɪlə/ *n BrE slang*【英俚】一千英鎊

goth /gɒθ; gɒθ/ *n* 哥特式 (莊嚴低沉的) 搖滾樂; 哥特式搖滾樂樂師

gouger /ˈgaʊdʒə; ˈgaʊdʒəʳ/ *n*〔愛爾蘭的〕小流氓, 小暴徒

GPS *n abbrev*【縮】= Global Positioning System 全球定位系統, 人造衛星定位系統

grabby /ˈgræbɪ; ˈgræbi/ *adj infml*【非正式】立即引人注目的

grabshot /ˈgræb ˌʃɒt; ˈgræbʃɒt/ *n* 抓住機會 (匆匆) 拍下的照片

gradualism /ˈgrædʒʊəlɪzm; ˈgrædʒʊəlɪzəm/ *n* 漸進主義

graf /graf; grɑːf/ *n slang*【俚】塗寫 [塗鴉] 藝術〔作為藝術表現形式的塗鴉〕

granny creche *n*〔某些大公司提供的〕老人休息所

granny dumping *n* [U] 遺棄老人

granny farm *n BrE*【英式】養老院

grant-in-aid *n* grants-in-aid **1** 補助金 **2** 地方補助金

grant-maintained school *n*〔英國擬議中的〕政府撥款補助的中學

graze¹ /grez; greɪz/ *v* [I] 成天不停地進食

graze² *v* [I]〔不停變換頻道〕觀看不同電視節目的片斷

greasy spoon *n AmE infml*【美式, 非正式】骯髒的廉價餐館〔用作貶義〕

green audit *n* 環境保護檢查〔審核〕

greenbacking /ˈgrin ˌbækɪŋ; ˈgriːnbækɪŋ/ *n infml*【非正式】資金供給; 資助

greenery /ˈgrinəri; ˈgriːnəri/ n [U] 對環境問題的關注

greening /ˈgrinɪŋ; ˈgriːnɪŋ/ n [U] **1** 城市綠化 **2** 環保意識

greenism /ˈgrinɪzəm; ˈgriːnɪzəm/ n [U] 環保主義；對自然環境保護的關注

green laner n (also 又作 **greenroader**) 愛在未鋪築路面的鄉間道路上駕車的人

green manure n [U] 綠肥〔指用作肥料的植物〕

greenster /ˈgrinstə; ˈgriːnstə/ n 環境保護政策的擁護者，綠色政策提倡者

greenwashing /ˈgrinˌwʊʃɪŋ; ˈgriːnˌwɒʃɪŋ/ v, n "刷傷"，粉飾，掩蓋〔指把嚴重危害環境的產品冒充成有益於環保的產品〕

grey[1] /gre; greɪ/ adj 老年人的

grey[2] v [I]〔人口〕老化

gridlock /ˈgrɪdˌlɑk; ˈgrɪdlɒk/ n [U] **1** 交通大堵塞 **2** 故障；停滯

grockling /ˈgrɑklɪŋ; ˈgrɒklɪŋ/ n 遊覽名勝

groundscraper /ˈgraʊndˌskrepə; ˈgraʊndˌskreɪpə/ n 低層大樓〔公寓〕

group practice n [C; U]〔幾名醫生聯合開業的〕聯合醫療

groupware /ˈgrupˌwɛr; ˈgruːpweə/ n 協同件，羣件，組件〔電腦軟硬件包，使終端聯網，在某一終端輸入資料以更新中央資源，為各個終端所利用〕

GSM n abbrev【縮】＝ Global System for Mobile Communications 全球流動通訊系統

grump /grʌmp; grʌmp/ v [T] 怒氣沖沖地說

guanxi /gwanˈsi; gwɑːnˈsiː/ n 關係〔在中國尤指為獲取個人私利結成的人際關係網〕

guest beer n "客座"啤酒〔指某一家公司釀製的而在另一個啤酒廠開的酒店或出售各種牌子酒的小酒店限期經銷的啤酒〕

guest worker n 客籍工人，外來打工者

guff /gʌf; gʌf/ n [U] infml【非正式】廢話；無價值的意見

gunship /ˈgʌnʃɪp; ˈgʌnʃɪp/ n 裝甲直升機，武裝飛機

gutted /ˈgʌtɪd; ˈgʌtɪd/ adj BrE infml【英式，非正式】**1** 精疲力盡的 **2** 極其吃驚與失望的

gym rat n slang【俚】健身迷

H, h

haar /hɑr; hɑː/ n 哈霧〔伴有毛毛細雨的濕冷海霧〕

hacked off adj infml【非正式】不滿的；厭倦的

hackette /hæˈkɛt; hæˈket/ n infml【非正式】女記者〔用作貶義〕

hackling /ˈhæklɪŋ; ˈhæklɪŋ/ n infml【非正式】年輕的記者

haemorrhage /ˈhɛmərɪdʒ; ˈhemərɪdʒ/ n〔因不斷減少而造成的〕大量流失

hair-restorer n [C; U] 毛髮再生劑

half-care n [U] 半自立護理〔養老院為有一定自我護理能力的老人提供的一種協助性護理〕

hammer /ˈhæmə; ˈhæmə/ n 業餘無線電愛好者

handbag /ˈhændˌbæg; ˈhændbæg/ v, n 用手提包攻擊

hand-held computer n (also 又作 **hand-held PC**) 掌上型電腦

handset /ˈhændˌsɛt; ˈhændˌset/ n 電話聽筒

hands-off adj 不干涉的；不插手的

hands-on adj 親自動手的；親身實踐的

hang-up n〔電腦〕意外停機；突停

happening /ˈhæpənɪŋ; ˈhæpənɪŋ/ adj slang【俚】時髦的；最新式的

happy hour n〔在酒吧中以優惠價消費的〕快樂時光；優惠時間

harassed /həˈræst; ˈhærəst/ adj 精疲力盡的；勞累不堪的

hardball /ˈhɑrdbɔl; ˈhɑːdbɔːl/ n [U] 棒球

hard copy n tech [U]【術語】硬副本，硬拷貝〔尤指電腦打印出的信息資料〕

hard-earned adj 得來不易地

hard-faced adj 鐵石心腸的；冷酷無情的

hard-fought adj 歷盡艱辛得來的

hard hat n (also 又作 **safety helmet**) 安全帽，頭盔

hard landing n "硬着陸"，〔經濟大發展一段時間之後出現的〕突然衰退

hard-luck story n〔為博同情而述說的〕不幸事，苦惱事〔常用作貶義〕

hard rock n [U] 硬搖滾樂〔一種節奏急迫、聲音喧鬧的搖滾樂〕

hard sell n 強行推銷 (法)

hard-wired adj〔生理及心理特徵〕固有的，根深蒂固的

hard-won adj 艱苦得來的

harvest /ˈhɑrvɪst; ˈhɑːvɪst/ v [T]〔從剛死去的人身上〕摘取器官

hate mail n [U]〔通常匿名的〕攻擊性信件

haut ton n 上流社會

have nots n 一貧如洗的人，窮人

haves /hævz; hævz/ n 富人

HDTV n abbrev【縮】＝ high definition television 高清晰度電視

head /hɛd; hed/ n AmE slang【美俚】有毒癮的人，癮君子

headcase /ˈhɛdkes; ˈhedkeɪs/ n BrE slang【英俚】狂暴的人；瘋子

headcount /ˈhɛdkaʊnt; ˈhedkaʊnt/ n 人數統計；〔雇員的〕人數

headhunt[1] /ˈhɛdˌhʌnt; ˈhedhʌnt/ v [T] 獵頭，物色〔人才〕；挖〔人才〕

headhunt[2] n 物色人才的活動，獵頭行動

headhunter /ˈhɛdˌhʌntə; ˈhedˌhʌntə/ n 物色人才的人

heads-up adj 信心十足且神氣活現的

head-to-head adj〔爭論、競爭等〕面對面的

health tax n 保健稅

health tourism n [U] 健身旅遊 (業)〔提供許多健身活動〕

heft /hɛft; heft/ n infml【非正式】影響 (力)；分量

heightism /ˈhaɪtɪzəm; ˈhaɪtɪzəm/ n [U] 身高歧視〔對身材高大的婦女和矮小男子的歧視〕

heightist /ˈhaɪtɪst; ˈhaɪtɪst/ *adj* 歧視身高的

heliculture /ˈhɛlɪˌkʌltʃə; ˈhɛlɪ̩kʌltʃə/ *n* 蝸牛養殖

heli-skiing *n* 乘直升飛機上高山滑雪

heli-tele *n* 直升機上的電視機或攝像機（的使用）

helo /ˈhelo; ˈheləo/ *n AmE slang*【美俚】直升機

help desk *n*〔為用戶解決電腦問題的〕維修組

heptathlon /hɛpˈtæθlən; hepˈtæθlɒn/ *n*〔田徑〕七項全能項目

herbivory /hɜˈbɪvəri; hɜːˈbɪvəri/ *n* 食草（的習性）; 以植物為食物的習慣

her indoors *n BrE infml*【英式, 非正式】內人; 悍婦

heritage /ˈhɛrɪtɪdʒ; ˈherɪtɪdʒ/ *adj* 歷史遺留的; 懷舊傳統的

heritage tourism *n* 歷史文化名勝旅遊業

heritize /ˈhɛrɪtaɪz; ˈherɪ̩taɪz/ *v* [T] 將…改變為懷舊形象

high-end *adj*〔技術產品〕先進而昂貴的; 高檔的

high-five *n* 舉手擊掌〔以示祝賀, 歡快等情緒〕

high-flying *adj* 很有抱負的; 雄心勃勃的

high-top *n* 高幫運動鞋〔如打棒球和籃球所用〕

hijab /ˈhaɪˌdʒæb; ˈhaɪˌdʒæb/ *n* 穆斯林婦女所戴的面紗或頭巾

himbo /ˈhɪmbo; ˈhɪmbəo/ *n slang*【俚】年輕英俊的男子

hip-hop *n* 嬉蹦舞樂曲

hip house *n* 嬉蹦豪斯樂曲

hip pocket *v* [T] *AmE*【美式】私藏〔某物〕

hit /hɪt; hɪt/ *n tech*【術語】〔互聯網站用以記錄用戶的〕網頁到訪次數, 瀏覽次數

hole-in-the-wall *n BrE infml*【英式, 非正式】〔銀行外面牆上的〕自動提款機

holiday centre *n BrE*【英式】度假中心; 度假村

holiday home *n*〔常在宜人風景區的〕度假別墅

home banking *n* 家庭銀行業務

home cinema *n* 家庭影院

home office *n* 家庭辦公室

home page *n tech*【術語】〔互聯網的〕主頁, 首頁

home parole *n* [U]〔美國的〕家庭保外假釋

home shopping *n* 電視購物

homophobia /ˌhoməˈfobɪə; ˌhəoməˈfəobɪə/ *n* [U] 恐同性戀症; 對同性戀者的敵視

hook /hʊk; hʊk/ *n infml*【非正式】〔流行樂曲中〕一段容易上口的曲調; 一段疊歌樂曲

hoolivan /ˈhulɪvæn; ˈhuːlɪ̩væn/ *n* 防暴攝像車

horsiculture /ˈhɔrsɪˌkʌltʃə; ˈhɔːsɪ̩kʌltʃə/ *n* [U] *BrE*【英式】養馬業開發

hospitel /ˈhɑspɪˌtɛl; ˈhɒspɪˈtel/ *n* 旅館式醫院

hot-button *adj AmE*【美式】〔問題等〕熱門的;〔政治等〕具轟動效應的

hot-desking *n* [U]〔為省下辦公室空間與費用而設的〕共用辦公桌制度

hot housing *n* [U] 超前培養〔指為培養智力超羣的人才而對幼兒進行高度集中的教育和訓練〕

hot money *n* 游資, 熱錢

hot potato *n infml*【非正式】難於處理的事情, 棘手之事

House /haʊs; haʊs/ *n* (also 又作 **house** 或 **house music**) 豪斯音樂; 迷幻狂舞樂

house-husband *n* 操持家務的丈夫

house-sit *v* [I] 代看房屋, 照管空屋

house-sitter *n* 替人看管房屋的人

HTML *n abbrev*【縮】= Hypertext Markup Language 超文本標記語言

http *n abbrev*【縮】= Hypertext Transfer Protocol 超文本傳輸協定

huaquero *n*〔在祕魯、玻利維亞和智利〕從墓中盜竊古物的人, 盜墓人

huffer /ˈhʌfə; ˈhʌfə/ *n BrE*【英式】法式夾心棍子麵包

humanesque /ˌhjumeˈnɛsk; ˌhjuːmeɪˈnesk/ *adj* 似人類的; 具有人類特性的

humanoid /ˈhjumənɔɪd; ˈhjuːmənɔɪd/ *adj* 具人的形狀 [特性] 的

human resources *n* [pl] **1** 人力資源 **2**〔公司的〕人力資源部

humanware /ˈhjumənˌwɛr; ˈhjuːmənweə/ *n* 人件〔指作為電腦模擬系統組成部分的人〕

humongous /hjuˈmʌŋgəs; hjuːˈmʌŋgəs/ *adj* (also 又作 **humungous**) 巨大的; 極大的

hush money *n infml* [U]【非正式】〔不讓醜事張揚出去的〕封嘴錢

hyperdrive /ˈhaɪpəˌdraɪv; ˈhaɪpədraɪv/ *n*（活動）高度緊張;（工作）極度繁忙

hyperinflation /ˌhaɪpəɪnˈfleʃən; ˌhaɪpərɪnˈfleɪʃən/ *n* [U] 惡性通貨膨脹

hyperlink /ˈhaɪpəˌlɪŋk; ˈhaɪpəlɪŋk/ *n* 超連結, 超級鏈結

hypermedia /ˈhaɪpəˌmidɪə; ˈhaɪpəmiːdɪə/ *n* [U] *tech*【術語】超媒體〔包括文字、影像等媒體〕

hyperspace /ˈhaɪpəˌspes; ˈhaɪpəspeɪs/ *n* [U] 超空間, 多維空間

hypertext /ˈhaɪpəˌtɛkst; ˈhaɪpəˈtekst/ *n* 超級文本, 超文本

I, i

ice /aɪs; aɪs/ *n slang*【俚】冰毒〔一種興奮性毒品〕

iced jeans *n* [pl] 砂洗牛仔褲

icon /ˈaɪkɑn; ˈaɪkɒn/ *n* **1** 偶像; 代表性的人或物 **2**〔電腦屏幕上顯示的代表所指謂的事物的〕圖示, 圖標

ICQ *n abbrev*【縮】= "I seek you" 網際呼叫器〔一種電腦軟件, 用戶可經互聯網搜尋對方並即時在屏幕上交談或互發訊息〕

ideas man *n* 出謀劃策者, 謀士

idle money *n* 閒置資金, 游置

IFA *n abbrev*【縮】= independent financial adviser〔不受屬於金融機構的〕獨立金融顧問

iffy /ˈɪfɪ; ˈɪfɪ/ *adj infml*【非正式】可疑的; 未確定的

ikat *n* 紮染綢〔亞洲生產的一種傳統絲綢品, 在織綢前緯紗經過紮染以產生特殊的朦朧圖案〕

ill-concealed *adj*〔尤指情緒〕掩飾得不好的

ill-conceived *adj* 考慮欠周到的; 不明智的

illiterature /ɪˈlɪtərətʃə; ɪˈlɪtərətʃə/ *n* [U] 算不上文學的作品

imaging /ˈɪmɪdʒɪŋ; ˈɪmɪdʒɪŋ/ n [U] 意象療法〔一種以想像快樂時光來消除緊張的治療法〕

immoralization /ɪˌmɒrəlaɪˈzeɪʃən; ɪˌmɔːrəlaɪˈzeɪʃən/ n [U] (also 又作 **immoralisation**) 認為某人道德敗壞

immuno-compromised adj 免疫系統受損的

impaired /ɪmˈpɜːd; ɪmˈpeəd/ adj 能力衰減的

import /ˈɪmˌpɔːt; ɪmˈpɔːt/ v [T] tech〔術語〕將數據從其他電腦或應用程式中〕輸入

impro /ˈɪmprəʊ; ˈɪmprəʊ/ n [U] (also 又作 **improv**) 即興演出〔常有觀眾參與的直播節目〕

inbox /ˈɪnbɒks; ɪnˈbɒks/ n〔電腦的〕收信信箱, 收件匣

incentivize /ɪnˈsɛntɪvaɪz; ɪnˈsentɪvaɪz/ v [T] (also 又作 **incentivise**) 以物質刺激 [鼓勵]

inclusive tour n 一切費用包括在內的旅遊, 包價旅遊

income support n [U]〔英國政府為低收入者提供的〕收入保障津貼

in-depth adj 深入徹底的; 透徹詳盡的

indie /ˈɪndɪ; ˈɪndi/ n infml【非正式】獨立唱片公司; 獨立樂隊

industrial-strength adj 優質的

industrial tourism n [U] 工業旅遊〔指度假者到他人的工作場所去參觀的旅遊〕

industrial tribunal n 勞資法庭〔負責裁決勞資糾紛〕

industry-wide adj 全行業的

infanticide /ɪnˈfæntɪˌsaɪd; ɪnˈfæntɪsaɪd/ n 1 [C; U] infml【正式】殺嬰罪 2 [C] tech【術語】殺嬰者

info /ˈɪnfəʊ; ˈɪnfəʊ/ n [U] infml【非正式】信息; 資料

infobahn /ˈɪnfəʊbɑːn; ˈɪnfəʊbɑːn/ n 信息高速公路

infomercial /ˌɪnfəʊˈmɜːʃəl; ˌɪnfəʊˈmɜːʃl/ n〔電視中看似客觀介紹的〕商品資訊節目; 專題廣告片

infonaut /ˈɪnfənɔːt; ˈɪnfənɔːt/ n 信息用戶〔即互聯網用戶〕

infopreneurial industry n 信息設備工業, 電子設備工業

information anxiety n [U] 資訊焦慮 (感)〔擔心無力應付現代通信手段及大量信息而產生的焦慮〕

information consultant n (also 又作 **information broker**) 資訊顧問, 資訊經紀〔收集資訊並向客戶提供資訊的人〕

information crime n [C; U] 信息犯罪〔如不經同意打開別人的電腦文件、竊取資料等〕

information highway n 資訊高速公路〔通過光纖電纜連通電腦的通訊系統〕

information overload 信息超載〔因信息量過大以致令人無所適從〕

information retrieval n tech [U]【術語】資訊檢索, 信息檢索〔尤指從電腦存儲的資料中查找出所需的資訊或信息〕

infotainment /ˈɪnfəʊˈtenmənt; ˌɪnfəʊˈteɪmmənt/ n 資訊娛樂片

in-house adj 公司內部的; 機構內部的

in-joke n 圈內笑話〔某個小圈子裡的人才能意會的笑話〕

ink-jet printer n 噴墨打印機

in-line skate n〔輪子排成直線的〕直排輪式溜冰鞋

in-service adj 在職期間 (進行) 的

install v 安裝〔電腦程式、軟件〕

intellectronics /ɪntˌlɛkˈtrɒnɪks; ɪnˌtʃlekˈtrɒnɪks/ n [U] 人工智能電子學

intellectual property n [C; U] 知識財產

intelligent knowledge-based system n 智能知識庫系統〔一種能在某專業中自行解題和作決定的功能〕

interactive fiction n 互動式小說, 交互式小說〔電腦磁盤上情節分類的小說; 讀者可自由選擇並用軟件自行創作〕

interactive media n〔電腦的〕交互媒體, 互動媒體

interactive services n〔通過電視、電話提供的電視購物等服務的〕互動式服務

interactive video n〔電腦的〕交互 [對話] 電視, 互動電視

intercom /ˈɪntəˌkɒm; ˈɪntəkɒm/ n 內部通話系統

interface¹ /ˈɪntəˌfes; ˈɪntəfeɪs/ n〔電腦的〕接口程序, 界面程式

interface² v [I] 交流; 交談

interline /ˌɪntəˈlaɪn; ˌɪntəˈlaɪn/ v [I] 中途轉車

Internaut /ˈɪntəˌnɔt; ˈɪntənɔːt/ n 互聯網用戶

Internet /ˈɪntəˌnet; ˈɪntənet/ n (also 又作 **the Net**) 國際互聯網, 因特網

interwar /ˌɪntəˈwɔr; ˌɪntəˈwɔːr/ adj 兩次戰爭之間的

into /ˈɪntə; ˈɪntə/ prep 關於…, 有關…

Internot /ˈɪntəˌnɒt; ˈɪntənɒt/ n 互聯網盲〔指未曾使用過互聯網的人〕

in-towner n AmE【美式】住在鬧市區的人

Intranet /ˈɪntrəˌnet; ˈɪntrənet/ n tech【術語】內聯網

in-your-face adj infml【非正式】厚顏無恥的; 放肆無禮的

IP n abbrev【縮】= Internet Protocol 互聯網協定, 網際協議

IP address n abbrev【縮】= Internet Protocol address 互聯網協定位址〔表示主機所在的數字型態位址〕, 網際協議地址

IPR n abbrev【縮】= intellectual property rights 知識產權

ISBN n abbrev【縮】= international standard book number 國際標準書號

ISDN n abbrev【縮】= integrated service digital network 綜合服務數碼式網絡

ISO /ˈaɪsəʊ; ˈaɪsəʊ/ n abbrev【縮】= International Organization for Standardization 國際標準化組織

ISO standard n 國際標準化組織標準

ISP n abbrev【縮】= Internet service provider 網絡服務供應商〔提供互聯網服務〕

ISSN n abbrev【縮】= international standard serial number 國際標準期刊編號

item /ˈaɪtəm; ˈaɪtəm/ n [sing] infml【非正式】情侶; 性伴侶

IT n abbrev【縮】= information technology 資訊技術

ITV n abbrev【縮】= interactive television service 互動電視服務

J, j

Jack /dʒæk; dʒæk/ *n BrE slang*【英俚】票面為五十英鎊的紙幣

jacket crisp 帶皮炸的馬鈴薯 [土豆] 片

jacks /dʒæks; dʒæks/ *n* [pl] 拋接子遊戲

jailbait /ˈdʒelbet; ˈdʒeɪlbeɪt/ *n slang*【俚】未成年女子

jangle /ˈdʒæŋgl̩; ˈdʒæŋgəl/ *v* [I] 説長道短; 傳播流言蜚語

janny /ˈdʒæni; ˈdʒæni/ *n infml*【非正式】學校管理員〔用於蘇格蘭式英語〕

Japanimation /dʒəˌpænɪˈmeʃən; dʒəˌpænɪˈmeɪʃən/ *n* [U] 日本卡通片

Japglais /dʒæpˈglei; dʒæpˈgleɪ/ *n* [U] 日式英語

Java /ˈdʒɑːvə; ˈdʒɑːvə/ *n* [U] *tech*【術語】"爪哇"語言, Java 語言〔尤指萬維網頁上的編程語言〕

jazzerati /ˈdʒæzəˌræti; ˈdʒæzəˌræti/ *n* [pl] 著名的爵士樂樂師

jazzercise /ˈdʒæzəˌsaiz; ˈdʒæzəsaɪz/ *n* 爵士健身操

jelly shoes *n* [pl]〔由塑料模壓成的色彩繽紛的〕果凍涼鞋

jetfoil /ˈdʒetfɔil; ˈdʒetfɔɪl/ *n* 噴流水翼船

jet-ski *n* 噴氣式滑水橇

jet skiing *n* 噴氣式滑水車運動

Jiffy bag *n BrE*【英式】〔郵寄易碎物品用的〕有襯墊的信封

jiggy /ˈdʒigi; dʒɪgi/ *adj slang*【俚】激動的

job-hunt *v* [I] 求職, 找工作

job search *n* 求職, 找工作

jock /dʒak; dʒɒk/ *n* ...迷, ...愛好者

joined-up *adj* 成熟老練的

joiner /ˈdʒɔɪnə; ˈdʒɔɪnə^r/ *n* 拼貼照片

Joint Chiefs of Staff *n* [pl] 參謀長聯席會議〔美國總統和軍事顧問班子〕

jokesmith /ˈdʒoksmiθ; ˈdʒəʊksmɪθ/ *n* 笑話作家; 喜劇藝人

jokestress /ˈdʒokˌstres; ˈdʒəʊkstres/ *n* 女喜劇演員

jolly /ˈdʒali; ˈdʒɒli/ *n slang*【俚】老年富翁, 闊佬

joy-firing *n* 歡慶性開槍

JPEG *n abbrev*【縮】= Joint Photographic Experts Group〔電腦的〕聯合攝影專家組〔一種影像壓縮格式〕

judgemental /dʒʌdʒˈment̩l; ˌdʒʌdʒˈmentəl/ *adj* 苛刻挑剔的

juice /dʒus; dʒuːs/ *v* [T] *slang*【俚】使觸電死亡; 用電刑處死

juice box *n* 盒裝果汁

jump /dʒʌmp; dʒʌmp/ *v* [T] *AmE*【美式】交換; 交流

jumping /ˈdʒʌmpiŋ; ˈdʒʌmpɪŋ/ *adj*〔尤指地方、事件等〕充滿生氣的; 令人激動的

jump-rope *n AmE*【美式】跳繩 (遊戲)

junior college *n*〔美國的兩年制〕初級學院

junior school *n*〔英國七至十一歲兒童上的〕小學

junk e-mail *n* [U]〔為推銷商品等而主動發送的〕宣傳電子郵件, 垃圾郵件

junk fax *n*〔由傳真機大批量傳出的〕宣傳傳真, 垃圾傳真

junk mail *n* [U] 宣傳郵件, 垃圾郵件〔指廣告信、募捐信等〕

Juppy /ˈdʒupi; ˈdʒuːpi/ *n infml*【非正式】日本優皮士

K, k

karaoke /ˌkɑrəˈoke; kɑːrɑːˈəʊkeɪ/ *n* [U] 卡拉OK, 影音伴唱機

karoshi /kæˈrofi; kæˈrəʊʃi/ *n* [U]〔工作勞累過度引起的〕猝死

kebab /kɪˈbæb; kʃˈbæb/ *v* 使陷於困境; 使苦不堪言

keratotomy /ˌkɛrəˈtatəmi; ˌkerəˈtɒtəmi/ *n*〔矯正視力的〕角膜切開術

keyhole surgery *n* [U]〔運用光纖導管和微型器械進行的〕微型切口手術

keylock /ˈkilək; ˈkiːlɒk/ *n* 遙控鎖栓裝置

kicking /ˈkikiŋ; ˈkɪkɪŋ/ *adj slang*【俚】激動人心的; 熱烈的

kick-start *v* [T] 推動, 啟動〔某事物〕

kideo /ˈkidɪo; ˈkɪdɪəʊ/ *n* 適合兒童口味的節目或錄像

kidware /ˈkɪdˌwɛr; ˈkɪdweə^r/ *n* 兒童軟件

killer cell *n* 殺傷細胞〔一種能殺死癌細胞的白細胞〕

killjoy /ˈkɪlˌdʒɔɪ; ˈkɪldʒɔɪ/ *adj* 破壞他人樂趣的

kilobyte /ˈkɪləbaɪt; ˈkɪləbaɪt/ *n* (also 又作 **K**)〔電腦訊息的〕千字節

kiss-and-tell *adj* 詳細披露個人隱私的

kiss-off *n AmE slang*【美俚】〔突然的〕解雇

knee-jerk *v* 作出本能的反應

kwik cricket *n* 少年板球

L, l

laddish /ˈlædɪʃ; ˈlædɪʃ/ *adj BrE*【英式】〔男子〕粗野的, 不羈的

lager lout *n BrE*【英式】酗酒鬧事者〔尤指成羣醉後鬧事的青年〕

lamp /læmp; læmp/ *v slang*【俚】放鬆, 鬆弛

LAN /læn; læn/ *n abbrev*【縮】= local area network 區域網, 局部 (地區) 網 (絡)

La Niña *n* 拉尼娜現象〔影響全球氣候的氣象變化〕

landfill¹ /ˈlændfɪl; ˈlændfɪl/ n〔以土埋方式處理垃圾的〕垃圾場

landfill² v [T] 將〔某物〕埋在垃圾填築地

landsailing /ˈlændˌseɪlɪŋ; ˈlændˌseɪlɪŋ/ n [U]〔陸地上進行的〕快艇車運動

lapel mike n〔掛在翻領上的〕佩帶式話筒

lap pool n〔約三英尺寬四英尺深的〕小游泳池〔常用於健身〕

laptop computer n 便攜式電腦, 膝上型電腦

laser disc n (also 又作 **LD**) 雷射影碟, 激光視盤

laser-print v [T] 激光 [雷射] 打印

laser printer n 激光 [雷射] 打印機

laser scanner n 激光 [雷射] 掃描器

lasertripsy /ˈleɪzəˈtrɪpsɪ; leɪzəˈtrɪpsɪ/ n [U] 激光碎石術〔一種利用激光消除膀胱結石、腎結石的技術〕

latte /ˈlæte; ˈlɑːteɪ/ n 牛奶咖啡

launcher /ˈlɔːntʃə; ˈlɔːntʃəʳ/ n〔導彈等的〕發射裝置, 發射器

LCD n abbrev〔縮〕= liquid crystal display 液晶顯示

leading-edge adj〔尤指技術上〕最先進的; 尖端的

lean /lin; liːn/ adj〔通過削減不必要的成本而〕更高效的, 更具競爭力的

learner-centred adj 以學生為中心的; 按學習者興趣與需要的

least-worst adj 別無選擇的選擇 (的)

lethal /ˈliθəl; ˈliːθəl/ adj 以武器形式進行的

let-out n BrE【英式】藉口, 託辭

libero /ˈlɪbərəʊ; ˈlɪbərəʊ/ n〔足球賽中在最後的防守線上左右巡遊的〕自由防守隊員; 自由後衛

life-expired adj 廢棄不用的; 壽終正寢的

lifestyle /ˈlaɪfstaɪl; ˈlaɪfstaɪl/ n 1〔適合消費者的〕生活方式 2〔旨在滿足某種生活方式的〕營銷策略

lig¹ /lɪg; lɪg/ n BrE infml【英式, 非正式】〔燈紅酒綠的〕時髦場所

lig² v [I] 不勞而獲

line manager n 生產線經理; 部門管理人

lipblock /ˈlɪpblɒk; ˈlɪpblɒk/ n [C;U] 護唇霜

liposuction /ˈlaɪpəsʌkʃən; ˈlɪpəʊsʌkʃən/ n [U] 脂肪抽吸術〔使用化學品和吸管去除多餘脂肪的美容術〕

lip-sync n (also 又作 **lip-synch**)〔電影等中的〕對口型;〔演唱會中的〕放錄音對口型; 假唱

listeria /lɪˈstɪərɪə; lɪˈstɪərɪə/ n [U] 李司忒氏菌〔一種細菌, 可導致食物中毒〕

listing /ˈlɪstɪŋ; ˈlɪstɪŋ/ n [U] 1〔電腦〕打印清單 2 tech【術語】掛牌, 上市

lite /laɪt; laɪt/ adj〔食物〕低脂的; 清淡的

litterpick /ˈlɪtəpɪk; ˈlɪtəpɪk/ n [U] 垃圾大清除活動

living will n 生前遺囑〔某人健在時合法簽署的書面聲明〕

load /lod; ləʊd/ v [T] 裝入, 載入〔電腦程式〕

loadsamoney /ˈlɒdzəmʌnɪ; ˈləʊdzəmʌnɪ/ n [U] BrE infml【英式, 非正式】巨額財富, 腰纏萬貫

loan shark n 高利貸者, "大耳窿"

lock down n slang【俚】禁閉

logic bomb n〔電腦的〕邏輯炸彈〔暗中設定程序, 在特定邏輯條件下發作, 具破壞性〕

lombard /ˈlɒmbɑːd; ˈlɒmbəd/ n slang【俚】有錢而蠢笨的人, 愚笨的富人〔用作貶義〕

longbeard /ˈlɒŋbɪəd; ˈlɒŋbɪəd/ n infml【非正式】老 (年) 人, 長者

long-haul adj〔尤指飛機〕長途運輸的

long vacation n (also 又作 **long vac**) infml【非正式】〔尤指大學的〕暑假

lookism /ˈlʊkɪzəm; ˈlʊkɪzəm/ n 容貌歧視

looksmanship /ˈlʊksmənʃɪp; ˈlʊksmənʃɪp/ n [U] 形象優化術, 形象塑造術

loose cannon n AmE【美式】〔不屬於任何派別〕我行我素的人; 不易控制的人

loose end n 未了結的部分; 未交待清楚的事

lounge music n [U] 休閒音樂

love handles n [pl] 腰間贅肉

low-cal adj 低卡路里的, 低熱量的

low-end adj 廉價的; 低檔的; 面向普通消費者的

low-tech n, adj 低技術 (的)

lunch-bucket adj AmE infml【美式, 非正式】勞工階級的; 藍領階層的

lupus erythematosus n [U] 紅斑狼瘡

luv /lʌv; lʌv/ n BrE infml【英式, 非正式】親愛的, 寶貝兒〔用於稱呼語或書面告別語中〕

M, m

macro economics n [U] 宏觀經濟學, 總體經濟學

mad /mæd; mæd/ adj slang【俚】不同凡響的; 刺激 (感官) 的〔尤為二十世紀九十年代參加電子樂狂舞會者所使用〕

mad cow disease n (also 又作 BOVINE SPONGIFORM ENCEPHALOPATHY) 瘋牛病

mad-dog v [T] slang【俚】冷眼盯着

magalog /ˈmægəˌlɒg; ˈmægəlɒg/ n 雜誌般的大開本郵購商品廣告目錄

magic bullet n infml【非正式】靈丹妙藥; 神奇療法

magic realism n [U] lit【文】魔幻現實主義〔將真實與超現實或夢幻相結合的文學形式〕

magnetic resonance imaging n [U] (also 又作 **MRI**) 磁共振成像〔一種檢查人體內部器官的診斷技術〕

mahosker /məˈhɒskə; məˈhɒskəʳ/ n slang【俚】錢〔常指支票〕

mail bomb n 郵件炸彈

mailbox /ˈmelbɒks; ˈmeɪlbɒks/ n〔電腦的〕電子郵箱

mailout /ˈmelaʊt; ˈmeɪlaʊt/ n (also 又作 **mailshot**) 郵寄的廣告傳單; 推銷信

mainframe /ˈmenfrem; ˈmeɪnfreɪm/ n〔大型電腦的〕主機, 中央處理機

majorly /ˈmedʒəlɪ; ˈmeɪdʒəlɪ/ adv 重大地, 極端, 非常

makeover /ˈmekˌovə; ˈmeɪkəʊvəʳ/ n 改頭換面

maladministration /ˌmælədˌmɪnəˈstreɪʃən; ˌmæləd.mɪnɪˈstreɪʃən/ n [U] 管理不善; 弊政

mam /mæm; mæm/ *n BrE infml*【英式，非正式】媽媽

mamou /ˈmæmu; ˈmæmuː/ *n* 重要事情

manga /ˈmæŋɡə; ˈmæŋɡə/ *n*〔常指日本的〕漫畫書, 連環畫冊〔主人公常具有超人能力, 書中充滿暴力與性幻想〕

man-trained *adj*〔指狗〕受訓後按指令攻擊人的

marginalize /ˈmɑːdʒɪnlaɪz; ˈmɑːdʒɪnəlaɪz/ *v* [T] (also 又作 **marginalise**) 歧視; 排斥; 使…游離於事物中心之外

mariculture /ˈmærəˌkʌltʃə; ˈmærɪˌkʌltʃəʳ/ *n* [U] 海洋養殖業

marital rape *n*〔丈夫對妻子的〕婚內強姦

markdown /ˈmɑːkˌdaʊn; ˈmɑːkdaʊn/ *n* 標低的價格; 減價數

marketeer /ˌmɑːkɪˈtɪr; ˌmɑːkɪˈtɪəʳ/ *n* 在某類市場做買賣的商人, 營銷專家

marketization /ˌmɑːkɪtəˈzeʃən; ˌmɑːkɪtaɪˈzeɪʃən/ *n* [U] *BrE*【英式】(also 又作 **-sation**) 市場化〔指使變成自由市場經濟〕

market-making *n* 製造旺市, 製造旺市者的活動

masculinism /ˈmæskjəˈlɪnɪzəm; ˈmæskjɡˈlɪnɪzəm/ *n* [U] 大男子主義, 男權主義〔維護男子在社會中的支配地位並宣揚作為男性特徵的品質〕

massage /məˈsɑːʒ; ˈmæsɑːʒ/ *v* [T] 奉承, 恭維;〔苦口婆心地〕爭取

massage parlour *n euph*【委婉】〔可提供色情服務的〕按摩院

masterclass /ˈmæstəˌklæs; ˈmɑːstəklɑːs/ *n* 專家講習班, 專家評講課; 大師班

maternity leave *n* 分娩假期, 產假

mawashi *n* 相撲運動員的腰布

maxi-series *n* 大型電視系列片, 長篇電視連續劇

MB *n abbrev*【縮】= megabyte 兆字節, 百萬位元

McJob /ˈmækdʒɑb; ˈmækdʒɒb/ *n* 薪酬低且沒有前途的工作

meat-and-potatoes *adj infml*【非正式】首要的, 基本的

mechatronics /ˌmɛkəˈtrɑniks; ˌmekəˈtrɒniks/ *n* [U] 機械電子學〔尤指運用電腦設計和操作機器〕

mediagenic /ˌmidiəˈdʒɛnɪk; ˌmiːdɪəˈdʒenɪk/ *adj*〔尤指電視上〕適宜於傳媒宣揚的, 形象對公眾有吸引力的

meet-and-greet *n* 見面會

mega /ˈmɛɡə; ˈmeɡə/ *adj infml*【非正式】宏大的; 盛大的; 精彩的

megahertz /ˈmɛɡəhɜːts; ˈmeɡəhɜːts/ *n* (also 又作 **MHz**) 兆赫; 百萬赫

megahit /ˈmɛɡəhɪt; ˈmeɡəhɪt/ *n* 極其成功的產品或作品

megaplex /ˈmɛɡəplɛks; ˈmeɡəpleks/ *n* (also 又作 **multiplex**)〔擁有很多放映廳的〕大型電影城

megaseller /ˈmɛɡəˌsɛlə; ˈmeɡəseləʳ/ *n* 1 熱門暢銷書 2 熱門暢銷書作者

megastar /ˈmɛɡəˌstɑr; ˈmeɡəstɑːʳ/ *n* 非常著名的巨星

megathon /ˈmɛɡəˌθɑn; ˈmeɡəθɒn/ *n* 馬拉松式活動〔尤指馬拉松式的電視節目〕

meld /mɛld; meld/ *v* 融合; 合併

meller /ˈmɛlə; ˈmeləʳ/ *n slang*【俚】攝製成影片的通俗劇

meltdown /ˈmɛltdaʊn; ˈmeltdaʊn/ *n* [C;U]〔某種體系的〕崩潰, 失靈; 大災難

memorabilia /ˌmɛmərəˈbɪliə; ˌmemərəˈbɪliə/ *n* 與某名人或往事有關的紀念品

memorial /məˈmɔriəl; mɪˈmɔːriəl/ *n AmE*【美式】紀念某死者的慈善捐款

memorious /məˈmɔriəs; mɪˈmɔːriəs/ *adj* 記憶力強的

men's movement *n* [U] 男性解放運動〔旨在改變對男性社會角色的傳統看法〕

men's room *n AmE*【美式】男廁所, 男洗手間

mentally challenged *adj* 精神或智力有障礙的

mentee /mɛnˈti; menˈtiː/ *n* 受輔導者

mercy killing *n* [C; U] = EUTHANASIA 安樂死

metamessage /ˌmɛtəˈmɛsɪdʒ; ˌmetəˈmesɪdʒ/ *n* 隱含的信息; 言外之意, 弦外之音

meteor shower *n* 流星雨

MFN Treatment *n abbrev*【縮】= most-favoured-nation treatment 最惠國待遇

mica /ˈmaɪkə; ˈmaɪkə/ *n slang*【俚】有精神病的吸毒者

microbiology /ˌmaɪkrobaɪˈɑlədʒɪ; ˌmaɪkrəʊbaɪˈɒlədʒɪ/ *n* [U] 微生物學

micro-economics *n* [U] 微觀經濟學

microelectronics /ˌmaɪkroɪˌlɛkˈtrɑniks; ˌmaɪkrəʊɪˌlekˈtrɒniks/ *n* [U] 微電子學, 微電子技術

micromachine /ˌmaɪkroməˈʃin; ˌmaɪkrəʊməˈʃiːn/ *n* 微型機械裝置; 微型玩具車

microrobot /ˌmaɪkroˈrobət; ˌmaɪkrəʊˈrəʊbɒt/ *n* 超微型機械人裝置

microserf /ˈmaɪkroˌsɜf; ˈmaɪkrəʊˈsɜːf/ *n* 網絡奴〔指沉溺於網絡的人〕

microwaveable /ˈmaɪkrəˌweɪvəbl; ˈmaɪkrəweɪvəbl/ *adj* 適合用微波爐烹調或加熱的

Middle America *n* [U] 美國中產階級〔尤指在宗教及政治上態度保守的階層〕

Middle England *n* [U]〔倫敦以外區域的〕英國中產階級

middle management *n* 中層管理人員

middlemarket /ˈmɪdlˈmɑrkɪt; ˌmɪdl'mɑːkɪt/ *adj* 中檔品市場的; 適合中等消費者的

middlescene /ˌmɪdlˈɛsns; mɪdə'lesəns/ *n*〔充滿憂慮及心理問題的〕煩惱中年期

MIDI *n abbrev*【縮】= Musical Instrument Digital Interface（電子）樂器數字化接口,（電子）樂器數位化介面

mid-life *adj* 中年期的, 中年的

mid-range *adj* 一般的, 中檔的

mid-term *adj, n* 1〔政府、總統等任期〕中期（的） 2〔學期〕期中的

milk round *n* 巡迴招聘〔大公司通過走訪、介紹、晤談來招聘大學畢業生〕

millennium bug *n* (also 又作 **Y2K bug**)〔電腦的〕千年蟲〔電腦無法辨識公元 2000 年年序所出現的問題〕

minder /ˈmaɪndə; ˈmaɪndəʳ/ *n* 1〔受人雇用的〕保鏢 2 政治顧問

mind-set *n* 心理定勢; 既定看法; 固有心態

minibar /ˈmɪnibar; ˈmɪnibɑːʳ/ *n* 小酒櫃（常見於旅館客房內）

minibreak /ˈmɪniˌbrek; ˈmɪnibreɪk/ *n* 暫停片刻; 短休假〔如週末〕

MiniDisc /ˈmɪnɪˌdɪsk; ˈmɪnɪdɪsk/ *n* (also 又作 **MD**) 小型雷射 [激光] 唱片

miniseries /ˈmɪnɪˌsɪrɪz; ˈmɪnɪˌsɪərɪz/ *n* [pl] 小型電視連續劇

mini-vegetable *n* 微型蔬菜, "迷你" 型蔬菜 [一種經特殊栽培的蔬菜種]

mistreater /mɪsˈtriːtə; mɪsˈtriːtər/ *n* 施虐者, 苛虐者

mixer /ˈmɪksə; ˈmɪksər/ *n* 唱片剪接放音員, 音樂混合播放能手

mobile /ˈməʊbl; ˈməʊbaɪl/ *n* (also 又作 **mobile phone**) 手機, 流動電話

mockumentary /ˌmɒkjəˈmentərɪ; mɒkjəˈmentəri/ *n* 模擬記錄片, 仿製記錄片

modem /ˈməʊˌdɛm; ˈməʊdəm/ *n tech* [術語] [電子] 調制解調器, 數據機

moisturize /ˈmɔɪstʃəˌraɪz; ˈmɔɪstʃəraɪz/ *v* [T] (also 又作 **moisturise**) 用潤膚霜滋潤皮膚

monetize /ˈmʌnɪˌtaɪz; ˈmʌnɪˌtaɪz/ *v* [T] 把…兌換成金錢 [現金]

moneyman /ˈmʌnɪmən; ˈmʌnimən/ *n infml* [非正式] 專業理財人士; 金融家; 財政家

monitor /ˈmɒnɪtə; ˈmɒnɪtər/ *n* [電腦的] 顯示器

monkey /ˈmʌŋkɪ; ˈmʌŋki/ *n slang* [俚] 攝影師

monkey-wrench *v* [T] 破壞; 阻撓

monkey wrencher *n AmE slang* [美俚] 阻撓者; 破壞者

mood drug *n* 情緒藥物

mook /mʊk; mʊk/ *n* 期刊式圖書, 雜誌式圖書

moonball /ˈmuːnbɔːl; ˈmuːnbɔːl/ *n* [網球] 高吊弧線球, 月亮球

moonwalking /ˈmuːnwɔːkɪŋ; ˈmuːnwɔːkɪŋ/ *n* 跳 (走) 登月式舞步 [一種雙腳交替將腳尖向腳跟位置滑動, 身體向後滑行的舞步]

moral majority *n* 道德多數派; 衛道派

morphing /ˈmɔːfɪŋ; ˈmɔːfɪŋ/ *n* [U] 圖像變形技術

mosh[1] /mɒʃ; mɒʃ/ *v* [T] [搖滾舞會上] 快節奏狂舞

mosh[2] *n* 狂舞

mosh pit *n* [舞台前的] 狂舞區

motherese /ˌmʌðəˈriːz; ˌmʌðəˈriːz/ *n* [U] 母親用語

motormouth /ˈməʊtəˌmaʊθ; ˈməʊtəˌmaʊθ/ *n infml* [非正式] 喋喋不休的人, "馬達嘴"

mouse /maʊs; maʊs/ *v* [I] 用滑鼠操作

mouse potato *n slang* [俚] 網蟲, 滑鼠迷 [指喜歡長時間泡在電腦前的人]

mouthfeel /ˈmaʊθfiːl; ˈmaʊθfiːl/ *n* [進食者對食品的] 口感, 口味

movers and shakers *n* [pl] 有權勢的人

MP3 *n abbrev* [縮] = MPEG Audio Layer 3 動態影像專家壓縮標準音頻層面 3 [一種音樂壓縮及儲存技術]

MP3 player *n* 便攜式 MP3 數字音樂播放器

MPEG *n abbrev* [縮] = Moving Pictures Experts Group 動態影像專家小組壓縮標準

mudger /ˈmʌdʒə; ˈmʌdʒər/ *n infml* [非正式] 推諉者, 搪塞者

mug shot *n slang* [俚] [用於公事的] 臉部照片

mule /mjuːl; mjuːl/ *n* [常指過境的] 偷運毒品者

multi-gym /ˈmʌltɪˌdʒɪm; ˈmʌltɪdʒɪm/ *n* (also 又作 **multi gym**) 1 多功能健身器; 組合型健身器

2 [配備各種健身器材的] 健身房

multimedia /ˌmʌltɪˌmiːdɪə; ˌmʌltiˌmiːdiə/ *n* [U] (also 又作 **multi-media**) 1 [電腦系統的] 多媒體 2 運用多種媒介的通信技術

multiple personality disorder *n* [U] 多種人格障礙 [一種精神病症, 患者具有分離而矛盾的人格]

multiplex /ˈmʌltəˌplɛks; ˈmʌltəpleks/ *n* 有許多放映廳的電影院

mush-mouthed *adj AmE infml* [美式, 非正式] 張口結舌的, 結結巴巴的

musicality /ˌmjuːzɪˈkælətɪ; ˌmjuːziˈkæləti/ *n* [U] 音樂才華

mystery tour *n* [旅客事先不知道目的地的] 神祕旅遊

N, n

naff /næf; næf/ *adj BrE* [英式] 過時的; 不時髦的

nail-biting *adj* 令人萬分緊張的; 使人坐立不安的

namecheck /ˈneɪmtʃɛk; ˈneɪmtʃek/ *v* [T] *AmE infml* [美式, 非正式] 點 [某人的] 名, 提及 [某人的] 名字

narcodollars /ˈnɑːkəˌdɒləz; ˈnɑːkəʊˌdɒləz/ *n* [pl] 毒品美元 [指通過非法銷售毒品賺取的美元]

narrowband /ˈnærəˌbænd; ˈnærəʊbænd/ *n* [電腦的] 窄頻

narrowcast /ˈnærəkæst; ˈnærəʊkɑːst/ *v* [T] [為特定範圍的觀眾服務的電視節目等的] 小範圍播送

natural auralism *n* 自然聽覺療法 [對於天生耳聾但仍殘留一些聽覺者採用的一種治療方法]

nature reserve *n* 自然保護區

nature tourism *n* 自然風光旅遊; 自然生態旅遊

naturopath /ˈneɪtʃərəˌpæθ; ˈneɪtʃərəʊpæθ/ *n* 自然療法者 [不用危險藥物, 用改變食物等辦法治病的療法]

near-death experience *n* 瀕死經歷; 死而復生經歷 [通常包括穿越黑暗隧道, 看到盡頭亮光等]

neato /ˈniːtəʊ; ˈniːtəʊ/ *adj slang* [俚] 非常好的

need-blind *adj* [招生時] 不考慮學生支付能力的

negativity /ˌnɛɡəˈtɪvɪtɪ; ˌnegəˈtɪvəti/ *n* [U] 消極態度; 消極性

neighbourhood watch *n* 鄰里聯防, 街坊聯防 [指鄰里間自願相互照看居舍安全]

Neo-Geo *n* (also 又作 **neo-geo**) 1 新幾何 (圖形) 抽象派 2 新幾何 (圖形) 抽象派畫家

neonatal /ˌniːəʊˈneɪtl; ˌniːəˈneɪtl/ *adj* 新生兒的; 新生期的

neo-poverty *n* [U] 新貧困 [原先經濟情況尚佳, 因失業, 離婚等原因而遭受的貧困狀況]

nerd /nɜd; nɜːd/ n AmE slang【美俚】笨人, 無用的人

nerdish /ˈnɜdɪʃ; ˈnɜːdɪʃ/ adj (also 又作 **nerdic**) AmE slang【美俚】笨得令人生厭的

nerve gas n [U]〔戰爭中用作化學武器的〕神經性毒氣

net /nɛt; net/ n 電腦網絡

netcast /ˈnɛtkæst; ˈnetkɑːst/ n, v 網絡廣播; 網絡播出

net generation n 網代〔使用互聯網的一代〕

nethead /ˈnɛtˌhɛd; ˈnethed/ n〔使用互聯網的〕網迷, 網癡

netiquette /ˈnɛtɪˌkɛt; ˈnetɪket/ n [U] 網上禮儀〔指使用電子郵件、聊天室等作網上交流時應有的禮儀〕

netizen /ˈnɛtɪzən; ˈnetɪzən/ n〔使用互聯網的〕網民

netnews /ˈnɛtˌnjuz; ˈnetnjuːz/ n 網絡消息

net surf phr v 網絡漫遊

netter /ˈnɛtə; ˈnetər/ n (also 又作 **nettie**) 使用互聯網的人, 網民

neural network 又作 **neural net** n 神經式網絡〔指電腦分別對多種信息作綜合性而非步進式處理的功能〕

neurocomputer /ˌnjʊərəkəmˈpjutə; ˌnjʊrəkəmˈpjuːtər/ n〔採用神經網絡操作法的〕神經式電腦

newsgroup /ˈnjuzˌgrup; ˈnjuːzgruːp/ n〔互聯網上的〕新聞討論組, 新聞組

NICAM /ˈnaɪkæm; ˈnaɪkæm/ n abbrev【縮】= Near Instantaneously Compounded Audio Multiplex System 麗音 (系統)〔觀眾收看電視時可選擇立體聲或不同語言播出的系統〕

niche /nɪtʃ; nɪtʃ/ n 有利可圖的市場

nigga /ˈnɪgə; ˈnɪgə/ n slang【俚】黑人

nilk /nɪlk; nɪlk/ n abbrev【縮】= no income lots of kids〔指社會下層的〕無收入而多子女者

nip and tuck n infml【非正式】整容手術〔將皮繃緊或抽去累贅脂肪〕

no brainer n AmE infml【美式, 非正式】不費腦筋的事; 輕而易舉的事

noddy suit n〔士兵穿的〕防化服, 防毒制服

no-fly zone n〔軍事飛機〕禁飛區

no-frills adj 簡樸的; 無裝飾的; 只提供基本服務的

no-hoper n infml【非正式】無用的人; 注定失敗的人

noir /nwar; nwɑː/ adj〔指藝術作品, 尤其指電影〕黑色的, 病態的, 憤世嫉俗的

non-issue n 不重要的事

non-lethal adj AmE【美式】〔食品, 醫療品、金錢等外國援助〕非軍事性的, (純粹) 出於人道的

noodle /ˈnudl̩; ˈnuːdl̩/ v [I]〔在電腦鍵盤上〕胡亂擊鍵

nook-nook n slang【俚】熱衷於迷幻狂舞的年輕樂迷

nootropic /ˌnuəˈtropɪk; ˌnuːəʊˈtrəʊpɪk/ n, adj 健腦藥; 健腦的

notebook /ˈnotˌbuk; ˈnəʊtbʊk/ n 筆記簿型電腦

no-show n 訂了〔火車、飛機等〕座位而沒有搭乘的人, 不能如約出現的人

nostalgiast /nɑˈstældʒɪst; nɒˈstældʒɪst/ n 懷舊的人, 留戀過去的人

nuisance call n 騷擾電話

nuke /nuk; njuːk/ v [T] 徹底摧毀, 完全粉碎

numbing /ˈnʌmɪŋ; ˈnʌmɪŋ/ adj 驚呆的; 呆滯麻木的

numerati /njuməˈrɑti; njuːməˈrɑːtiː/ n infml【非正式】金融奇才

nurturance /ˈnɜtʃərəns; ˈnɜːtʃərəns/ n [U] 精心養育, 撫育

nutmeg /ˈnʌtmɛg; ˈnʌtmeg/ v [T] BrE infml【英式, 非正式】傳腿間球使〔對方球員〕出醜

nutraceutical /ˌnjutrəˈsutɪk; ˌnjuːtrəˈsjuːtɪkəl/ n 營養食品; 營養藥膳

O, o

oatsy /ˈotsɪ; ˈəʊtsi/ adj 十分活躍的; 自命不凡的

ob-gyn n 婦產科醫生

obscurantism /əbˈskjʊrəntɪzəm; ˌɒbskjʊˈræntɪzəm/ n [U] fml【正式】蒙昧主義, 愚民政策

oceanarium /ˌoʃəˈnɛrɪəm; ˌəʊʃəˈneərɪəm/ n -s or -ria 大型海洋水族館

OCR n abbrev【縮】= optical character recognition 光符識別法, 感光字元辨識

office /ˈofɪs; ˈɒfɪs/ v [I] AmE【美式】在辦公室辦公

off-limits adj 禁止入內的

off-line adj 離線的, 線外的

OL n abbrev【縮】= office lady 在辦公室工作的年輕女子

old-established adj 早已存在的; 悠久的

omnimax film n 全天域電影

on-demand printing n [U]〔可按訂戶需要而小量印刷的〕按需求即時印刷

on-demand system n 請求式系統, 即付系統

one-man business n 個人經營, 一人企業, 獨資經營

one-price n 不二價〔即不許討價還價〕

one-stop adj 單獨一處就可提供各種服務的; 一應俱全的; 一步到位的; 一站式的

one-under n slang【俚】跳軌自殺案件 [案例]〔指跳入迎面而來的地鐵火車的路軌而自殺的案例〕

online /ˈɑnˌlaɪn; ˈɒnlaɪn/ adj (also 又作 **on-line**)〔電腦〕聯機的,〔與計算機〕繫線的, 在線的

on-screen adj, adv 在計算機 [電腦] 屏幕上看到的 [地]

open-dated adj 無日期限制的

open-door adj〔政策、制度等〕(門戶) 開放的

open-mike adj 自願者即興表演的

optical fiber cable n 光纖電纜

optimize /ˈɑptəˌmaɪz; ˈɒptɪmaɪz/ v [T] fml【正式】使〔某事〕完美, 使最優 [佳] 化

opt-out n 決定不參加

orature /ˈorəˌtʃə; ˈɒrətʃər/ n 口述文學〔指通過吟誦和回憶一代代傳下來的文學〕

ornery /ˈɔrnərɪ; ˈɔːnəri/ *adj AmE infml*【美式, 非正式】脾氣壞的; 不合作的

osteoporosis /ˌɑstɪəpəˈrosɪs; ˌɒstiəupə'rəusiŋ/ *n* [U] 骨質疏鬆症

otherly abled *adj euph*【委婉】〔生理或心理〕有(某種)障礙的

otherness /ˈʌðərnəs; ˈʌðənəs/ *n* [U] *fml*【正式】奇異的特質; 異常性

outbox /ˈaʊtˌbɑks; aʊt'bɒks/ *n*〔電腦的〕發信信箱, 寄件匣

outpace /ˌaʊtˈpes; ˌaʊt'peɪs/ *v* [T] 比...跑得快; 超越; 勝過

outperform /ˌaʊtpərˈfɔrm; ˌaʊtpə'fɔːm/ *v* [T] 比...做得好; 勝過

outplacement /ˈaʊtplesmənt; 'aʊtpleɪsmənt/ *n* [U]〔為被裁職員〕謀新職

outsource /aʊtˈsɔrs; aʊt'sɔːs/ *v* [I, T] 1 外購〔商品, 尤零部件〕 2〔以簽約方式〕將工作 [生意] 轉包出去

ovate /ˈovet; 'əʊveɪt/ *v* [T]〔為某人〕熱烈鼓掌歡呼

ovenable /ˈʌvənəbl̩; 'ʌvənəbəl/ *adj* 可用於烤爐中的; 耐烘 [烤] 的

ovenproof /ˈʌvənˌpruf; 'ʌvənpruːf/ *adj* 適用於烤箱的; 耐烤的

overcapacity /ˌovərkəˈpæsətɪ; ˌəʊvəkə'pæsɪti/ *n* [U] 生產能力過剩

overclass /ˈovərˌklæs; 'əʊvəklɑːs/ *n* 上層階級

overfishing /ˌovərˈfɪʃɪŋ; ˌəʊvə'fɪʃɪŋ/ *n* [U]〔對魚〕過度捕撈

overhoused /ˌovərˈhaʊzd; ˌəʊvə'haʊzd/ *adj* 住房面積過大的

overstayer /ˌovərˈsteər; ˌəʊvə'steɪər/ *n*〔超過簽證規定日期的〕逾期居留者

over-the-top *adj* 過分的, 過度的

over-the-toppery *n* 浮誇行為

overuse /ˌovərˈjuz; ˌəʊvə'juːz/ *v* 濫用; 過度使用

overwrite /ˌovərˈraɪt; ˌəʊvə'raɪt/ *v* [T] *tech*【術語】蓋寫, 重寫

own goal *n*〔因笨拙無能而〕損害自己的行為; 自打嘴巴

oxygen bar *n* 氧氣吧, 吸氧吧〔提供純氧氣的休息場所〕

P, p

package tour *n* (also 又作 **package holiday**)〔全程由旅行社安排且費用固定的〕包辦旅遊, 包價旅遊

pack rape *n* 輪姦

pacy /ˈpesɪ; 'peɪsi/ *adj* 快速移動的; 節奏快的

page /pedʒ; peɪdʒ/ *n*〔電腦的〕網頁

pager /ˈpedʒər; 'peɪdʒər/ *n* 傳呼機

pageview /ˈpedʒˌvju; 'peɪdʒvjuː/ *n*〔電腦的〕頁視〔指一次網頁訪問〕

paintball /ˈpentˌbɔl; 'peɪntbɔːl/ *n* [sing] 彩彈遊戲

palm-print recognition *n*〔電腦的〕掌紋辨析

palmtop /ˈpɑmtɑp; 'pɑːmtɒp/ *n* 掌上型電腦

paparazzo /ˌpæpəˈrætso; ˌpæpə'rætsəʊ/ *n* **-zi** /-sɪ, -si/ [一般用複數] 對名人作獵奇報道的記者 [攝影師]

paperless office *n* 無紙辦公室

paper round *n* 送報工作 [服務]

para /ˈpærə; 'pærə/ *n infml*【非正式】傘兵

parenting /ˈpɛrəntɪŋ; 'peərəntɪŋ/ *n* [U] 父母對子女的關懷照顧

park home *n* (also 又作 **trailer, trailer home**)〔大型〕活動住房, 拖車房屋

Parkinson's disease *n* [U] 帕金森氏病, (老年性) 震顫麻痺

party animal *n infml*【非正式】熱衷於社交聚會的人

party-goer *n* (喜歡經常) 參加社交聚會的人

party-poop *n* (also 又作 **party-pooper**) *infml*【非正式】聚會上令人掃興的人, 煞風景的人

patch /pætʃ; pætʃ/ *n* 膏藥

paternity leave *n* [U] 陪產假〔丈夫為陪伴待分娩妻子而享有的有薪假〕

patterning /ˈpætənɪŋ; 'pætənɪŋ/ *n* [U] 1〔將形狀、事件、組成部分按一形式進行的〕設計, 安排 2〔通過模仿、重複而達成的〕模式

pay-per-view *n*〔電影的〕付費點播服務

PCS *n abbrev*【縮】= personal communications system 個人通訊系統〔一種無線電話通訊規格〕

PDA *n abbrev*【縮】= personal digital assistant 個人數碼助理〔一種袖珍電腦〕

pedalo /ˈpɛdəlo; 'pedələʊ/ *n* 腳踏式小遊船

pedestrianize /pəˈdɛstrɪənaɪz; pɪ'destriənaɪz/ *v* [T]〔將街道〕改為行人區

penalty shoot-out *n*〔足球賽中的〕罰點球決勝

people carrier *n*〔約八個座位的〕小型客車

Pepsification /ˌpɛpsɪfɪˈkeʃən; ˌpepsɪfɪ'keɪʃən/ *n* [U] 百事可樂化〔通過企業、產品來擴大 (美國) 文化影響〕

perp /pɜrp; pɛːp/ *n infml*【非正式】罪犯

personal communicator *n* 個人通訊設備〔具流動電話、傳呼機等多功能的袖珍通訊裝置〕

personal organizer *n* 小型個人記事電腦

personal planner *n* 個人記事本

phat /fæt; fæt/ *adj slang*【俚】絕妙的; 時髦的; 精彩的

phonaholic /ˌfonəˈhɑlɪk; ˌfəʊnə'hɒlɪk/ *n infml*【非正式】(also 又作 **phonoholic**) 打電話迷

phone-tapping *n* [U]〔利用電子設備進行的〕電話竊聽

photodegradable /ˌfotodɪˈgredəbl̩; ˌfəʊtəʊdɪ'greɪdəbəl/ *adj* 可被光分解的

photofit /ˈfotofɪt; 'fəʊtəʊfɪt/ *n* 拼圖相〔警方根據證人提示拼出的犯人圖像〕

phreaker /ˈfrikər; 'friːkər/ *n* 盜用長途電話的人

pic /pɪk; pɪk/ *n infml*【非正式】插圖〔尤指照片〕

picture-perfect *adj* 完美的; 理想的

picturesome /ˈpɪktʃərsəm; 'pɪktʃəsəm/ *adj* 惹人的; 引人注目的; 上照的

picture window *n*〔透過一大塊玻璃觀風景的〕觀景窗

pigeon /ˈpɪdʒən; 'pɪdʒən/ *v* [T] 通過鴿子傳遞〔某物〕

PIN *n abbrev*【縮】= Personal Identification Number 個人識別 [身分] 號

pinger /ˈpɪŋɡə; ˈpɪŋɡəˀ/ *n infml*【非正式】微波爐

pipehead /ˈpaɪpˌhɛd; ˈpaɪphed/ *n* 吸毒的人

pipework /ˈpaɪpwɜːk; ˈpaɪpwɜːk/ *n* [U] 管道系統; 管道

pitchperson /ˈpɪtʃˌpɜːsn; ˈpɪtʃˌpɜːsən/ *n AmE*【美式】強行推銷生意的人; 游說者

placing /ˈplesɪŋ; ˈpleɪsɪŋ/ *n* 排名, 排行

planetism /ˈplænɪtɪzəm; ˈplænɪtɪzəm/ *n* [U] 地球環境保護 (主義)

plore /plor; plɔːr/ *n*〔博物館的〕探索性展覽品〔一種示範科學原理操作的展覽品〕

ploms /plɑmz; plɒmz/ *n* 自憐, 自哀

plonker /ˈplɑnkə; ˈplɒnkəˀ/ *n BrE slang*【英俚】笨蛋, 無能之輩

plug-and-play *adj* 隨插即用的, 即插即用的

plug-in *n*〔電腦的〕外掛程式, 插入式軟件

plugumentary /ˌplʌɡjəˈmɛntərɪ, ˌplʌɡjəˈmentəri/ *n infml*【非正式】略帶宣傳性或廣告性的記錄片〔含在客觀求實但含有宣傳性或廣告性內容的電影或電視記錄片〕

PNETS *n abbrev*【縮】= Public Non-Exclusive Telecommunication Services 公共非專利通訊服務

pogo /ˈpogo; ˈpəʊɡəʊ/ *v* [I] 作原地跳躍舞蹈

point-and-shoot *n* 傻瓜相機

polluter /pəˈlutə; pəˈluːtəˀ/ 污染者; 污染源〔指製造污染的人、組織或工業〕

POP *n abbrev*【縮】= post office protocol 郵件通訊協定, 郵局規約〔網上傳送電子郵件的協定〕

popette /ˈpɑpˌɛt; ˌpɒˈpet/ *n* 年輕的流行樂女歌星

popmobility /ˌpɑpməˈbɪlətɪ; ˌpɒpməʊˈbɪlɪti/ *n* [U]〔強節奏的〕流行音樂體操

popstrel /ˈpɑpstrəl; ˈpɒpstrel/ *n* 年輕的流行樂女歌手

populuxe /ˈpɑpjuˌlʌks; ˈpɒpjʊlʌks/ *adj* 庸俗奢侈的, 品味不高的

pop-up menu *n* 彈出式選單, 彈出式選項屏

Portakabin /ˈpɔrtəˌkæbɪn; ˈpɔːtəkæbɪn/ *n* 活動房屋, 移動房屋

portal /ˈpɔrtl; ˈpɔːtl/ *n* (also 又作 **portal site**)〔電腦〕入口網站, 門戶網站

Portaloo /ˈpɔrtəlu; ˈpɔːtəluː/ *n* 流動廁所

posey /ˈpozi; ˈpəʊzi/ *adj* (also 又作 **posy**) 擺門面的; 裝腔作勢的

Post-It *n* (also 又作 **Post-it**) 報事貼便條紙〔商標名〕

post-modernism 後現代主義〔二十世紀八十年代的一種藝術流派, 特徵為新舊形式的奇妙混合〕

power dressing *n* [U] 專業着裝〔以顯自信、高效等〕

powerhouse /ˈpaʊəˌhaʊs; ˈpaʊəhaʊs/ *v* 1 [I] *slang*【俚】精力充沛地走動 [移動] 2 [T] 有力地領導

power line *n*〔尤指從電腦供電至家庭及工廠的〕電纜, 輸電線

power-striding *n AmE*【美式】大踏步走, 跨步走〔以鍛鍊身體〕

prat /præt; præt/ *n BrE slang*【英俚】笨蛋, 蠢貨

pre-loaded *adj* 預載的, 預裝的

prenup /ˈpriˈnʌp; priːˈnʌp/ *n* 婚前協議

preppy /ˈprɛpɪ; ˈprepi/ *n* (also 又作 **preppie**) *AmE infml*【美式, 非正式】私立學校的學生

prepster /ˈprɛpstə; ˈprepstəˀ/ *n* 富家子弟

presale /ˈpriˈsel; priːseɪl/ *n* 售前展覽〔在拍賣前為競買人提供機會以檢查貨品的展覽會〕

preschooler /ˈpriskulə; ˈpriːskuːləˀ/ *n* 學齡前兒童

presence /ˈprɛzns; ˈprezəns/ *n* [U]〔公司在某一市場的〕地位, 活動

presentational /ˌprɛznˈteʃənl; ˌprezənˈteɪʃənəl/ *adj*〔尤指用現代技術將新產品〕展示的, 介紹的

pret /prɛt; pret/ *adj*〔服裝〕現成的, 成衣的

pre-teen *n* (also 又作 **preteenager**) 十歲左右的兒童

primo /ˈpraɪmo; ˈpraɪməʊ/ *adj slang*【俚】一流的; 上等的

proactive /proˈæktɪv; prəʊˈæktɪv/ *adj* 率先採取行動的; 採取主動的

pro-am *n, adj* 包括職業和業餘選手在內的 (比賽)

programmable /ˈprogræməbl; ˈprəʊɡræməbəl/ *adj*〔電腦〕可編程的

programming /ˈprogræmɪŋ; ˈprəʊɡræmɪŋ/ *n*〔電腦〕程序設計, 編程技術 [方法], 程式規劃

promo /ˈpromo; ˈprəʊməʊ/ *adj, n infml*【非正式】宣傳 (的); 廣告 (的)

props /prɑps; prɒps/ *n* [pl] *slang*【俚】尊敬, 敬重

psychedelia /ˌsaɪkəˈdeliə; ˌsaɪkəˈdeliə/ *n* [U]〔由迷幻藥激發靈感的〕迷幻音樂 [藝術, 文化]

psycho /ˈsaɪko; ˈsaɪkəʊ/ *n infml*【非正式】精神失常者; 瘋子

psychobilly /ˈsaɪkoˌbɪlɪ; ˈsaɪkəʊˌbɪli/ *n* 瘋狂搖滾樂〔以五十年代搖滾樂為基礎但帶有八十年代暴力與瘋狂色彩的搖滾樂〕

pubescent /pjuˈbɛsnt; pjuːˈbesənt/ *adj* 青春期的, 發育期的

public works *n* [pl] 公共工程, 市政工程〔如建造道路、醫院、學校〕

puff /pʌf; pʌf/ *n slang*【俚】大麻

pull /pul; pʊl/ *v* [T] 1 撤回; 撤銷; 終止 2 逮捕; 捕捉

pull-down menu *n* 下拉選項屏 [單]

pump-priming *n* 刺激經濟的政府投資

punchbag /ˈpʌntʃbæg; ˈpʌntʃbæg/ *n*〔練拳擊用的〕吊袋, 沙袋 [包]

punker /ˈpʌŋkə; ˈpʌŋkəˀ/ *n* "龐克"搖滾樂迷

pushback /ˈpʊʃbæk; ˈpʊʃbæk/ *n* 推遲飛機的起飛時間

Q, q

Qigong /ˈtʃiɡoŋ; ˈtʃiːɡəʊŋ/ *n*〔漢語〕氣功

quad bike *n*〔體育或娛樂用的〕四輪摩托車

quaffable /ˈkwɑfəbl; ˈkwɒfəbəl/ *adj* 〔酒〕可暢飲的

qualifier /ˈkwɑləˌfaɪə; ˈkwɒlɪfaɪəʳ/ *n* 預選賽; 資格賽

quality time *n* 好時光; 過得有意義的時間〔尤指上班族父母與孩子共度的時光〕

quant /kwant; kwɒnt/ *n* 股市分析員

quietize /ˈkwaɪətaɪz; ˈkwaɪətaɪz/ *v* [T] 給...隔音

R, r

rad /ræd; ræd/ *adj slang*【俚】〔因時髦〕引人讚嘆的; 頂呱呱的

ragazine /ˈrægəˌzin; ˌrægəˈziːn/ *n* 小報

raiding party *n* 突擊小組; 搜查小組

ranching /ˈræntʃɪŋ; ˈrɑːntʃɪŋ/ *n* 牧場經營〔管理〕

R and B /ˈɑr ən ˈbi; ˌɑːr ən ˈbiː/ *n abbrev*【縮】＝ rhythm and blues [U] 節奏勃魯斯〔一種勃魯斯和黑人音樂混雜的通俗音樂〕

random breath test *n* (also 又作 **RBT**) 隨機呼吸檢測〔對司機進行的隨機抽查, 以確定體內酒精含量是否超過規定〕

rangy /ˈrendʒɪ; ˈreɪndʒɪ/ *adj* 身材修長的, 苗條的

ranking /ˈræŋkɪŋ; ˈræŋkɪŋ/ *n* 排名

rap /ræp; ræp/ *n* [U] 繞舌歌, 快板歌〔源自黑人街頭音樂, 配以強烈節奏唸出歌詞〕

rare groove *n*〔黑人〕靈歌爵士樂

ratchet up [down] *v* [T]〔強度、費用、頻率〕變高〔低〕

rat-run *n infml*【非正式】〔車輛為避開高峯期而走的〕小路, 旁道

rat run *v* [I]〔車〕繞道走小路〔以避開交通阻塞〕

ratted /ˈrætɪd; ˈrætɪd/ *adj BrE slang*【英俚】喝醉了的

rattle /ˈrætl; ˈrætl/ *v* [T]〔習語 **rattle somebody's cage**〕激怒〔某人〕

rave party *n BrE*【英式】〔在空置建築物舉行的〕大型狂歡舞會

readmit /ˌriəd`mɪt; ˌriːəd`mɪt/ *v* [T] **1** 再次接納〔某人, 使其成為組織或團體成員〕**2** 再次入院〔治療舊病〕

reality show *n* (also 又作 **reality program**)〔根據真人真事製作的〕社會傳真電視節目

reality TV *n* 社會傳真電視

real-time *adj tech*【術語】〔電腦〕即時處理的; 實時的

rear-end *v* [T] 撞入〔另一車輛〕的尾部, 尾追撞擊

reboot /ˌri`but; riː`buːt/ *v* [T]〔電腦〕重新啟動

rebounder /rɪ`baundə; rɪ`baundəʳ/ *n* 蹦跳牀

red-eye *n AmE infml*【美式, 非正式】通宵航班, 夜航航班

red tag *n*〔圖書銷售的〕特價

reedsman /ˈridzmən; ˈriːdzmən/ *n infml*【非正式】簧管樂器〔尤指薩克斯管〕吹奏者

reflected glory *n* [U] 因他人而得的榮耀; 借光得來的榮耀〔用作貶義〕

reformist /rɪ`fɔrmɪst; rɪ`fɔːmɪst/ *adj* 溫和改革派的, 改良主義的

refusenik /rɪ`fjuznɪk; rɪ`fjuːznɪk/ *n infml*【非正式】拒守規則〔規定〕的人; 拒絕合作者

reintroduce /ˌriɪntrə`djus; ˌriːɪntrə`djuːs/ *v* [T]〔使動、植物〕重回棲息〔生長〕地

reinvent /ˌriɪn`vɛnt; ˌriːɪn`vent/ *v* [T] 徹底革新, 完全改變

relational /rɪ`leʃnl; rɪ`leɪʃənl/ *adj fml*【正式】表示關係的

relief /rɪ`lif; rɪ`liːf/ *n* [U] *euph*【委婉】性滿足

rematch /`rimætʃ; `riːmætʃ/ *n* 重賽〔常因首場打成平局而進行〕

reporterette /rɪˌpɔrtə`rɛt; rɪˌpɔːtə`ret/ *n*（年輕）女記者

representational /ˌrɛprɪzən`teʃənl; ˌreprɪzən`teɪʃənl/ *adj*〔尤指藝術上〕具象派的; 寫實派的

research and development *n* (also 又作 **R and D**) 研究與開發

reset /`riˌset; riː`set/ *v*〔電腦〕復位, 重新設置

reshape /ˌri`ʃep; riː`ʃeɪp/ *v* [T] 重塑, 重整

residency /`rɛzədənsɪ; `rezɪdənsɪ/ *n* [C;U] *fml*【正式】**1** 永久居住權 **2**〔藝術家等〕常駐某地工作的一段日子

reskill /ˌri`skɪl; riː`skɪl/ *n*〔為掌握現代企業技能而進行的〕再培訓

respectify /rɪ`spɛktɪˌfaɪ; rɪ`spektɪfaɪ/ *v* [T] 使受尊重

restart /ˌri`start; riː`stɑːt/ *n*〔電腦〕重新啟動

restructure /ˌri`strʌktʃə; riː`strʌktʃəʳ/ *v* [T] 重新組織, 調整, 改組

retrain /ˌri`tren; ˌriː`treɪn/ *v* [T] 培訓〔某人〕做新工作或使用新設備

re-tread *n infml*【非正式】〔經培訓〕重新就業者;〔經整修〕重新啟用的東西

retro /`rɛtro; `retrəʊ/ *adj*〔早年流行款式〕重新流行的; 流行懷舊款式的

retro-chic *n* 不久前流行過的時髦〔時尚〕

retrophilia /ˌrɛtrə`filɪə; ˌretrə`fɪlɪə/ *n* 懷舊, 對過去時尚的偏愛〔用作貶義〕

returner /rɪ`tɜnə; rɪ`tɜːnəʳ/ *n*〔尤指女性停職一段時間後〕重新工作的人

rework /ˌri`wɜk; ˌriː`wɜːk/ *v* [T] 改進; 修訂

rewritable /ˌri`raɪtəbl; ˌriː`raɪtəbəl/ *adj*〔電腦〕可重寫的

riot gear *n* [U]〔警察的〕防暴裝備

riot girl *n AmE slang*【美俚】叛逆女孩〔年輕激進的女權主義者〕

rip /rɪp; rɪp/ *v* [T] *AmE slang*【美俚】口頭攻擊; 責罵

road kill *n AmE infml*【美式, 非正式】〔馬路當中〕被車輾死的動物

roadshow /`rodʃo; `rəʊdʃəʊ/ *n* **1** 巡迴演出〔隊〕**2** 路邊展覽

roadstop /`rod,stap; `rəʊdstɒp/ *n AmE*【美式】路邊飲食店; 路邊咖啡室

roam-a-phone *n* 手提式電話機, 手機

robotics /ro`batɪks; rəʊ`bɒtɪks/ *n* [U] 機器人（製造或使用）學

robug /ro`bʌg; rəʊ`bʌg/ *n* 爬蟲式遙控爬高機械〔指利用兩端裝有吸盤的雙腿能在垂直表面上向上爬動的遙控裝置〕

rock-hard *adj* 極其堅硬的; 非常結實的

rock jock *n* 攀岩愛好者

rockumentary /ˌrɑkjəˈmɛntəri; ˌrɒkjʊˈmentəri/ *n* (以)搖滾樂(為特色的)紀錄影片; 搖滾紀實作品

role-play *n* [C; U] 角色扮演〔模仿某人的行為舉止作為訓練或心理治療的方法〕– **role-play** *v* [I; T]

role-playing game *n* 角色扮演遊戲

rollade /ˈroled; ˈrəʊleɪd/ *n* 滾動百葉窗

rollerblade /ˈrolɚˌbled; ˈrəʊləbleɪd/ *n*〔輪子成一排直線的〕刀〔刃〕式旱冰鞋

rolling /ˈrolɪŋ; ˈrəʊlɪŋ/ *adj* 定期進行的

rolling drunk *adj* 爛醉如泥的

rolling news *n sing* (二十四小時)循環播放新聞

roll over *v* [T] *infml*【非正式】徹底擊敗; 使慘敗

rootsy /ˈrutsɪ; ˈruːtsi/ *adj*〔音樂〕地道的; 樸實的

rough stuff *n* [U] *infml*【非正式】野蠻行為; 粗暴舉止

rubber bullet *n*〔防暴警察用於驅散人羣的〕橡皮子彈

rubblehead /ˈrʌblˌhɛd; ˈrʌbəlhed/ *n slang*【俚】白痴; 傻瓜

rug /rʌg; rʌg/ *n infml*【非正式】假髮

rug rat *n AmE slang*【美俚】小傢伙; 小孩

runway /ˈrʌnˌweɪ; ˈrʌnweɪ/ *n*〔在狹長的台上所作的〕模特兒時裝表演

S, s

sad /sæd; sæd/ *adj* 令人鄙視的; 招人白眼的〔用作貶義〕

safarist /səˈfɑrɪst; səˈfɑːrɪst/ *n*〔尤指在非洲的〕狩獵旅遊者

safe haven *n* 安全區, 保護區〔為保護弱勢宗教團體或少數民族免遭迫害而設〕

saggy /ˈsægɪ; ˈsægi/ *adj* 下陷的; 下垂的; 鬆弛的

sampling /ˈsæmplɪŋ; ˈsɑːmplɪŋ/ *n* [U] 拼盤歌曲; 剽竊拼湊歌曲

sand surfing *n* [U] 沙地衝浪, 衝沙

sandwich class *n* 夾縫階層, 夾心階層〔既拿不到補助又不很富裕的中等收入階層〕

sanpro /ˈsænpro; ˈsænprəʊ/ *n euph*【委婉】衛生保護用品〔指防止月經出血帶來的難堪〕

saturation bombing *n tech*【術語】密集轟炸

save /sev; seɪv/ *v*〔電腦〕存儲, 保存

savvy /ˈsævɪ; ˈsævi/ *adj infml*【非正式】精明的; 狡猾的

scaf /skæf; skæf/ *n AmE infml*【美式, 非正式】既美觀又有益的產品

scally /ˈskælɪ; ˈskæli/ *n slang*【俚】浪子

scamster /ˈskæmstɚ; ˈskæmstəʳ/ *n* 騙子

scan /skæn; skæn/ *v tech*【用掃瞄器】掃瞄

schlock /ʃlɑk; ʃlɒk/ *n* [U] *AmE slang*【美俚】價次的東西; 粗製濫造的東西

schlocker /ˈʃlɑkɚ; ˈʃlɒkəʳ/ *n AmE slang*【美俚】廢物〔可指人或物〕

schlumpy /ˈʃlʌmpɪ; ˈʃlʌmpi/ *adj* 不修邊幅的

schmozzle /ˈʃmɑz; ˈʃmɒzəl/ *n* 亂糟糟的事情〔局面〕

scorch /skɔtʃ; skɔːtʃ/ *v* [T] *AmE infml*【美式; 非正式】嚴辭苛責; 口頭攻擊

score draw *n*〔足球賽的〕平局, 打平

scratch card *n* 刮刮卡〔刮去表層蠟後顯示是否中獎〕

screen saver *n*〔電腦〕屏幕保護程序, 螢幕保護程式

screenwriter /ˈskrinˌraɪtɚ; ˈskriːnraɪtəʳ/ *n* 電影劇本作家

scroll *v* [T] *tech*【術語】〔在電腦屏幕上〕從上到下移動〔資料等〕, 捲頁, 捲動

sea change *n* 巨變

seajack /ˈsiˌdʒæk; ˈsiːdʒæk/ *n* 海上劫持(船隻)

search engine *n*〔互聯網上的〕搜尋引擎

seasonal affective disorder *n* [U] *tech*【術語】季節性抑鬱症

secessionist /sɪˈsɛʃənɪst; sɪˈseʃənɪst/ *n tech*【術語】分離[裂]主義者〔指通常因文化、種族、宗教原因主張將部分領土分離出去的人〕

secret ballot *n* 無記名投票

seeker /ˈsikɚ; ˈsiːkəʳ/ *n* 追求...者; 喜愛...者

self-congratulation *n* [U] 沾沾自喜, 洋洋自得

self-contradictory *adj* 自相矛盾的

self-inflicted /ˌsɛlfɪnˈflɪktɪd; ˌselfɪnˈflɪktɪd/ *adj*〔損傷、創傷〕自己施加的

sell-by date *n* 銷售限期〔商品的最後使用日期〕; 保質期

sell-through *adj*〔錄像帶等〕只賣不出租的

semidetached /ˌsɛmədɪˈtætʃt; ˌsemɪdɪˈtætʃt/ *adj*〔對某團體〕半心半意的; 三心二意的

semi-skimmed *adj*〔奶類〕半脫脂的

serial killer *n* 連續殺手

serious /ˈsɪrɪəs; ˈsɪəriəs/ *adj infml*【非正式】大量的; 過多的

seriously /ˈsɪrɪəslɪ; ˈsɪəriəsli/ *adv* 極其, 非常

server /ˈsɝvɚ; ˈsɜːvəʳ/ *n*〔電腦〕伺服器, 服務器

settledown /ˈsɛtlˌdaʊn; ˈsetldaʊn/ *adj*〔開始時期熱鬧一陣後〕趨於穩定的

sex line *n* 色情電話; 性熱綫

sex out *v* 盡情享受性刺激; 性生活放縱

sex tour *n* 性旅遊

sexual abuse *n*〔長輩對兒童的〕性侵犯, 性濫用

sexual harassment *n*〔尤指在工作時所遇到的〕性騷擾

sex worker *n euph*【委婉】職業妓女

shakers /ˈʃekɚz; ˈʃeɪkəz/ *n* [pl] *infml*【非正式】有權勢的人

shapesuit /ˈʃep,sut; ˈʃeɪpsuːt/ *n* (also 又作 **shapewear**)〔女用〕展現曲線美的緊身衣

shareholding /ˈʃɛrholdɪŋ; ˈʃeəˌhəʊldɪŋ/ *n* 持股; 股權

shareowner /ˈʃɛrˌonɚ; ˈʃeərəʊnəʳ/ *n* 股東, 股票持有人

shareware /ˈʃɛrwɛr; ˈʃeəweəʳ/ *n* [U]〔使用者在試用期後需付費的〕共享軟件, 試用軟件

shelftalker /ˈʃɛlftɔkɚ; ˈʃelftɔːkəʳ/ *n* 書架廣告條〔貼於書架上作宣傳用途〕

shellfire /ˈʃɛlfaɪə; ˈʃɛlfaɪɚ/ n [U] 砲擊

shell-like n infml【非正式】耳朵

sheltered workshop n〔供殘疾人士工作的〕庇護工場

ship /ʃɪp; ʃɪp/ v [T] 推出〔產品等〕

shipjacker /ˈʃɪpˌdʒækə; ˈʃɪpˌdʒækɚ/ n (海上)劫船者, 海盜

shoot-'em-up n infml【非正式】1〔西部〕槍戰片 2〔電腦〕槍殺遊戲

shop front n 店面, 店堂

short-haul adj 短途的〔尤指空運〕

short-run adj 短暫的, 短期的

short-tennis n〔兒童玩的〕短場網球〔一種運動項目〕

short-termism n [U] tech【術語】短期效益主義〔只顧眼前利益而不惜犧牲長期保障的做法〕

shoutline /ˈʃautlaɪn; ˈʃautlaɪn/ n infml【非正式】醒目標題〔置於推銷廣告材料開頭簡短的引人注目的詞語, 以粗體字印刷, 突出銷售特色〕

shutout /ˈʃʌtˌaut; ˈʃʌtaut/ n AmE【美式】被排在成功之門外的人, 與成功無緣的人

signage /ˈsaɪnɪdʒ; ˈsaɪnɪdʒ/ n [U]〔總稱〕標誌; 指示牌

signature dish n〔某位廚師的〕拿手菜, 名菜

significant other n 至關重要的那一位〔指配偶或情人〕

singlehood /ˈsɪŋglhud; ˈsɪŋgəlhud/ n 單身男子〔女子〕身分; 獨身狀態

Singlish /ˈsɪŋglɪʃ; ˈsɪŋglɪʃ/ n 新加坡(式)英語

sister city n 姊妹城市〔指兩國間互相建立正式關係並經常有文化交流的城市〕

site /saɪt; saɪt/ n tech【術語】(also 又作 **Website**)〔電腦〕網站, 站點

sit-up n 仰臥起坐

sizist /ˈsaɪzɪst; ˈsaɪzɪst/ adj (also 又作 **sizeist**) 對身材高大者歧視的

skate dancing n [U] 冰上舞蹈

skell /skɛl; skɛl/ n AmE【美式】〔尤指睡地鐵站的〕無家可歸者, 流浪漢

skifield /ˈskiˌfild; ˈskiːfiːld/ n〔有多處滑雪場的〕山區滑雪場

skin-dive v [I]〔不帶笨重呼吸裝備, 不穿潛水衣地〕潛泳, 潛水, 裸潛 – **skin diver** n – **skin diving** n [U]

skinhead /ˈskɪnˌhɛd; ˈskɪnhɛd/ n〔尤指英國的〕短髮族(男)青年; 光頭暴徒, 光頭幫成員

skip park n〔配備大鐵櫃供存放可再利用廢物的〕廢物棄置場

skippering /ˈskɪpərɪŋ; ˈskɪpərɪŋ/ n [U] slang【俚】搶佔空屋〔未經許可或不付房租而佔據空屋居住〕

skit /skɪt; skɪt/ n [(on)] 幽默諷刺短劇

ski-through adj AmE【美式】可滑雪穿過的

skorts /skɔrts; skɔːts/ n [pl]〔女式〕裙褲, 裙式短褲

sky-box n AmE【美式】(運動場的)摩天豪華包廂〔指陳設豪華的包廂, 在運動場高處, 觀看比賽一清二楚〕

slacker /ˈslækə; ˈslækɚ/ n infml【非正式】懶散的人; 無生活目標的人

slam-dunk v [T] 1〔籃球比賽中〕扣籃, 塞籃 2 AmE infml【美式, 非正式】徹底擊敗; 斷然拒絕

slanger /ˈslæŋgə; ˈslæŋgɚ/ n AmE slang【美俚】販毒者

slap /slæp; slæp/ v [T] infml【非正式】處〔某人〕以罰款

slaphead /ˈslæphɛd; ˈslæphed/ n slang【俚】〔常指男性〕禿頂, 禿子, 光頭〔常作貶義〕

slapper /ˈslæpə; ˈslæpɚ/ n BrE slang【英俚】蕩婦, 淫婦; 淫娃

slaughter /ˈslɔtə; ˈslɔːtɚ/ v [T] 強烈譴責

sleeperette /ˌslipəˈrɛt; ˌsliːpəˈret/ n 小臥鋪, 臥鋪座〔旅客可自行調節的靠背睡椅〕

slimebag /ˈslaɪmˌbæg; ˈslaɪmbæg/ n slang【俚】歹徒, 惡棍

slimline /ˈslɪmlaɪn; ˈslɪmlaɪn/ adj〔外型〕細瘦的

slinger /ˈslɪŋə; ˈslɪŋɚ/ n slang【俚】販毒者

slo-mo n infml【非正式】(also 又作 **slowmo**)〔電影、錄像中的〕慢動作

slugfest /ˈslʌgfɛst; ˈslʌgfest/ n infml【非正式】激烈的爭奪; 激烈的爭論

smallish /ˈsmɔlɪʃ; ˈsmɔːlɪʃ/ adj 較小的; 頗小的

small print n (also 又作 **fine print**) [(the) U]〔協議或合約中故意弄得容易忽略或難懂的〕難懂的條文; 附屬細則

smallsat /ˈsmɔlˌsæt; ˈsmɔːlˌsæt/ n 小型通訊衛星

smart card n 智能卡, 智慧卡〔一種帶有內置存儲芯片的信用卡或賒購卡, 可記錄申卡購物每次交易的情況〕

smart house n (also 又作 **smart building**) 智能屋, 智慧型房屋〔內部設施由電子裝置控制〕

smart phone n 智能電話〔能自動撥號、識別來電號碼等〕

smiley /ˈsmaɪlɪ; ˈsmaɪli/ n〔以漫畫表現的〕笑臉;〔電子郵件中常用的〕表情符號

smoke and mirrors n 假象, 煙幕

smoking gun n 實證, 確鑿的罪證

snag-tooth n (also 又作 **snaggle-tooth**) 歪牙; 凸牙

snail mail n [U]〔蝸牛〕郵遞〔電腦使用者用來指一般郵遞, 因其比電子郵件緩慢得多〕

snake hips n [pl]〔尤指男子〕瘦削的臀部; 苗條的臀圍

sneak preview n 內部預報; 非正式展覽;〔影片〕預映

sniffer-dog n infml【非正式】嗅探犬〔常用來尋找毒品或炸藥〕

sniffy /ˈsnɪfi; ˈsnɪfi/ adj infml【非正式】鄙視的, 輕視的; 反對的

snowboarding /ˈsnobɔrdɪŋ; ˈsnəubɔːdɪŋ/ n [U] 滑板滑雪

snowsurfing /ˈsnoˌsɜfɪŋ; ˈsnəuˌsɜːfɪŋ/ n [U] 衝浪式滑雪

snuff /snʌf; snʌf/ v [T] slang【俚】殺害, 殺死

snuff movie n infml【非正式】有兇殺鏡頭的色情電影

social climber n 趨炎附勢者, 一心往上爬的人

social drinker n 只在應酬時喝酒的人

soft copy n [U] tech【術語】〔電腦的〕軟拷貝, 軟體複本〔指儲存在電腦中或在螢幕上顯示而不以紙張印出的資訊〕

SOHO /ˈsoho; ˈsəuhəu/ n abbrev【縮】= small office home office 小型家庭辦公室; 甦活

sound bite n〔在電台或電視上播出的〕聲明的節錄

sound card n〔電腦的〕聲效卡, 音效卡

sound-carrier *n* 載聲媒介, 錄音媒介〔如唱片等〕

space heater *n AmE*【美式】〔用電或燃料的〕小型供暖器

space-nap /ˈspeɪsnæp; ˈspeɪsnæp/ *n* 太空綁架〔指人被外星生物綁架進牠們的太空船〕

spam *v* [I; T]〔在互聯網上〕把同一信息廣泛傳送到不同地方

spam mail *n*〔在網上傳送的內容無聊或是推銷產品的〕無聊電子郵件, 垃圾郵件

Spanglish /ˈspæŋɡlɪʃ; ˈspæŋɡlɪʃ/ *n* 西班牙英語

sparky /ˈspɑːki; ˈspɑːki/ *adj BrE infml*【英式, 非正式】充滿活力的; 激情的; 強烈的

specialism /ˈspeʃəlɪzəm; ˈspeʃəlɪzəm/ *n* 專業; 專門領域

speed bump *n*〔橫置馬路上以防止車輛速度過快的〕路面減速裝置

speed-metal *n* 快節奏重金屬搖滾樂

spend /spend; spend/ *n* 可供花費的金額

spendolas /ˈspendˌoʊləz; ˈspendələz/ *n* [pl] *infml*【非正式】錢

spinsterish /ˈspɪnstərɪʃ; ˈspɪnstərɪʃ/ *adj* 老處女般的; 怪癖的〔常作貶義〕

splatter /ˈsplætə; ˈsplætər/ *n* 暴力兇殺影片

splurchaser /ˈsplɜːtʃəsə; ˈsplɜːtʃəsər/ *n* 隨意購物者

spoken for *adj* 已有所屬的; 已被預訂的

sports bar *n AmE*【美式】〔不停地播放電視體育節目的〕體育酒吧

sports day *n BrE*【英式】〔學校的〕運動日, 校運會

sportswear /ˈspɔːtsweə; ˈspɔːtsweər/ *n* [U] 運動服

spousal abuse *n* [U] 虐待配偶〔夫妻之間一方對另一方所作的生理或心理的虐待〕

spray-on *adj* 噴霧式的

spree /spriː; spriː/ *n* 陣發性的暴行; 放肆的暴力行為

spree killer *n* 殺人狂

spring-loaded *adj*〔機械裝置〕裝有彈簧的

squeeze /skwiːz; skwiːz/ *n AmE slang*【美俚】異性密友; 情人

squid /skwɪd; skwɪd/ *n BrE infml*【英式; 非正式】英鎊

staff doctor *n* 醫師〔在英國介於高級住院醫師和會診醫師之間〕

stagecraft /ˈsteɪdʒˌkrɑːft; ˈsteɪdʒkrɑːft/ *n* [U] 舞台表演技巧

stair-step *v* [I] 爬樓梯

stakeholder /ˈsteɪkˌhoʊldə; ˈsteɪkhoʊldər/ *n*〔公司或企業的〕股東, 分享利潤者

stalker /ˈstɔːkə; ˈstɔːkər/ *n* 尾隨者; 糾纏不休的人

stall out *phr v slang*【俚】用車後行李箱為攤位售貨

stand-alone *adj* 獨立的; 獨立操作的

stand-off *n* 未達成協議的局面; 僵局

stand-to *n tech*【術語】戰鬥準備

starter home *n*〔新婚夫婦〕首次購買的樓房

start-up *n*〔公司等的〕創業

stasis /ˈsteɪsɪs; ˈsteɪsɪs/ *n* [U; C] *fml*【正式】停滯狀態

stealth /stelθ; stelθ/ *n* 隱形術〔指飛機避開雷達

steam /stiːm; stiːm/ *v* [T] 結幫搶劫

steamer /ˈstiːmə; ˈstiːmər/ *n* 結幫搶劫者

step aerobics *n* 踏板健身操

sticking-point *n*〔討論、談判中的〕分歧點, 障礙

sticksman /ˈstɪksmən; ˈstɪksmən/ *n infml*【非正式】鼓手

stonewashed /ˈstoʊnwɒʃt; ˈstoʊnwɒʃt/ *adj* (also 又作 **granite-washed**)〔牛仔褲等〕石磨的

stonking /ˈstɒŋkɪŋ; ˈstɒŋkɪŋ/ *adj BrE slang*【英俚】印象深刻的; 令人激動的

storymercial /ˌstɔːriˈmɜːʃəl; ˌstɔːriˈmɜːʃəl/ *n* 故事廣告片

street /striːt; striːt/ *adj* 街頭文化的; 有街頭風格的

street-fighter *n infml*【非正式】爭強好鬥分子

street style *n* [U] 街頭風格, 街頭時尚〔指具有現代都市文化特徵的服飾及音樂風格〕

stressed-out *adj slang*【俚】因心理緊張而被壓垮的

strike-rate *n* 命中率; 成功率

strip center *n*〔建在公路沿線的〕購物中心

strip mall *n* 零售中心

strongling /ˈstrɒŋlɪŋ; ˈstrɒŋlɪŋ/ *n* [U]（矮小但）強健的人; 力氣大的人

strongman /ˈstrɒŋmæn; ˈstrɒŋmæn/ *n* 強權人物; 鐵腕人物

stun gun *n* 高壓電槍

subculture /ˈsʌbˌkʌltʃə; ˈsʌbkʌltʃər/ *n* 亞文化羣（的行為、信仰、習俗）〔社會中具獨特性, 其行為常不獲多數人認同的一羣人〕

subdirectory /ˌsʌbdəˈrektəri; ˌsʌbdaɪˈrektəri/ *n*〔電腦的〕子目錄

subjectivism /səbˈdʒektɪvɪzəm; səbˈdʒektɪvɪzəm/ *n* [U] *tech*【術語】主觀主義, 主觀論

substance abuse *n* 毒癮

sugar daddy *n*〔在年輕女人身上大花錢財以換取性好處或友誼的〕老色迷, 闊乾爹

sugar mummy *n* 甜娘子〔指以年青男子為情侶的年紀較大的女性〕

suicide bomber *n* 自殺投彈者, 敢死 [捨身] 投彈者〔不顧自己生命進行炸彈襲擊的人〕

suicide mission *n* 自殺性任務; 有去無回的使命

suit /suːt; suːt/ *n* 西裝階層〔只關心經銷或財務, 不關心產品製造的公司行政人員〕

summitry /ˈsʌmɪtri; ˈsʌmɪtri/ *n* 首腦會議, 最高級會議

sunrise job *n*〔有發展前途的〕朝陽職業, 新興職業

sunset job *n*〔無保障的〕夕陽職業

super G *n* 超大回轉 [彎道] 滑雪賽

superhighway /ˌsuːpəˈhaɪweɪ; ˌsuːpəˈhaɪweɪ/ *n*〔電腦〕信息高速公路

supermodel /ˈsuːpəˌmɒdl; ˈsuːpəmɒdl/ *n* 超級名模

supersite /ˈsuːpəˌsaɪt; ˈsuːpəsaɪt/ *n* 超大型廣告牌

supremo /səˈpriːmoʊ; suːˈpriːməʊ/ *n BrE*【英式】高層領導人; 最高權威

surf¹ /sɜːf; sɜːf/ *n* 瀏覽

surf² *v* [I; T] 瀏覽

sushi /ˈsuʃɪ; ˈsuːʃi/ n [U] 壽司〔一種日本食品〕

suspenser /səˈspɛnsə; səˈspɛnsəʳ/ n infml【非正式】懸念電影

sussed /sʌst; sʌst/ adj BrE slang【英俚】知情的; 見多識廣的; 被發現的

sweatpants /ˈswɛtpænts; ˈswɛtpænts/ n [pl] 寬鬆運動褲

sweats /swɛts; swets/ n AmE infml【美式, 非正式】田徑服

swell /swɛl; swel/ n infml【非正式】高薪的未婚女子

swingbeat /ˈswɪŋbit; ˈswɪŋbiːt/ n [U] 強節奏搖擺舞曲

swinging /ˈswɪŋɪŋ; ˈswɪŋɪŋ/ adj infml【非正式】〔式樣、舉止等〕新潮的, 時尚的

swipe¹ /swaɪp; swaɪp/ v 在解碼器上刮擦〔信用卡〕

swipe² n 電子解碼器, 刷卡機

switchgear /ˈswɪtʃˌgɪr; ˈswɪtʃgɪəʳ/ n [U]〔電路的〕開關裝置

swoonsome /ˈswunsəm; ˈswuːnsəm/ adj slang【俚】十分迷人的; 極有吸引力的

synergy /ˈsɪnədʒɪ; ˈsɪnədʒi/ n 協同效率, 聯合增效〔指商業中兩個單獨的單位聯合在一起比獨立時更能有效地發揮潛力〕

T, t

tabloid TV n〔報道名人新聞或小道消息等以迎合廣大觀眾的〕通俗小報式電視節目

tack /tæk; tæk/ n 髒亂不堪

tag /tæg; tæg/ v [T] slang【俚】在…上噴塗留名

tagger /ˈtægə; ˈtægəʳ/ n slang【俚】〔在公共場所的牆上等〕噴塗留名者

tag sale n AmE【美式】宅前標價出售

take /tek; teɪk/ n [sing] infml【非正式】觀點; 態度; 看法

talk show n 清談廣播(節目)

tamper-evident adj〔包裝等〕防拆封的

targa /ˈtɑːgə; ˈtɑːgə/ n 可卸式敞篷跑車

tastemaker /ˈtestˌmekə; ˈteɪstmeɪkəʳ/ n 引導時尚潮流者

tax avoidance n [U]（合法）避稅

tax break n 減稅優惠, 稅額優惠

tax evasion n 逃稅, 偷稅, 漏稅

tax-exempt adj 免稅的

taxiway /ˈtæksɪwe; ˈtæksɪweɪ/ n 飛機滑行道

team player n 良好的合作夥伴

techie /ˈtɛkɪ; ˈteki/ n infml【非正式】技術專家〔尤指電腦技師〕

technical knockout n 技術性擊倒〔拳擊比賽以一方因受傷過重等原因無法再繼續比賽而告終〕

techno-babble n〔太專業的〕行話,〔難懂的〕技術用語〔用作貶義〕

technophobe /ˈtɛknofob; ˈteknəʊfəʊb/ n 恐懼新技術的人

technothriller /ˈtɛknoˌθrɪlə; ˈteknəʊˌθrɪləʳ/ n 科技驚險小說

telco /ˈtɛlko; ˈtelkəʊ/ n 電信公司

telebanking /ˈtɛləˌbæŋkɪŋ; ˈteliˌbæŋkɪŋ/ n [U] 遠程銀行事務處理

telebook /ˈtɛləˌbuk; ˈtelibʊk/ n 電視劇劇情說明書

teleconference /ˈtɛləˈkɑnfərəns; ˈteliˈkɒnfərəns/ n（可視）電話會議, 電訊會議, 遠程電信會議

teledish /ˈtɛləˌdɪʃ; ˈteliˌdɪʃ/ n〔接收衛星電視節目的〕碟形天線

tele-education n [U] 電信遠程教育

telefax /ˈtɛləˌfæks; ˈteliˌfæks/ n 電話網傳真

telemarketing /ˈtɛlɪˈmɑrkɪtɪŋ; ˈteliˈmɑːkɪtɪŋ/ n [U] 電話推銷

telemarketer /ˈtɛlɪˈmɑrkɪtə; ˈteliˈmɑːkɪtəʳ/ n 電話推銷員

telephone tapping n [U] (also 又作 **phone tapping**)〔裝有竊聽器的〕電話竊聽

teleputer /ˈtɛlɪˈpjutə; ˈteliˈpjuːtəʳ/ n〔可連接互聯網的〕聯網電視機

test ban n 國與國之間停止核試驗的協定

test-drive v [T] 試驗; 嘗試

testing /ˈtɛstɪŋ; ˈtestɪŋ/ adj 費力的; 棘手的

theatricality /θiˌætrɪˈkælətɪ; θiˌætrɪˈkæləti/ n [U]〔尤指事件或行為的〕誇張的風格; 戲劇化的效果

thigh-high n 長統襪, 高幫襪

think tank n [C + sing./pl. v] 智囊團

thin-skinned adj〔對批評或羞辱〕敏感的; 臉皮薄的; 容易生氣的

thoughtcast /ˈθɔtˌkæst; ˈθɔːtkɑːst/ n 思維模式

three-peat n, v（贏得）三連冠

thriftnik /ˈθrɪftnɪk; ˈθrɪftnɪk/ n 專挑便宜貨的人; 節儉得過分的人

tie-in n **1** 搭賣, 搭配推銷 **2**〔和新的影片、電視劇、體育比賽等有關的〕關聯性產品〔如唱片、圖書, 玩具等〕

tight-knit adj〔家庭、社區〕緊密團結的; 關係密切的

time capsule n 時代文物錦囊, 當代史料儲存器

time-consuming adj 花費大量時間的, 耗時的

time frame n〔完成某項工作規定的〕時限;〔電腦的〕時框

time out n AmE【美式】〔活動, 競賽中的〕暫停, 休息（片刻）

time-span n 一段時間, 一個時段

TMD n abbrev【縮】= Theater Missile Defense 戰區導彈防禦系統

toast /tost; təʊst/ adj infml【非正式】完蛋的; 陷於困境的

toasty /ˈtostɪ; ˈtəʊsti/ adj AmE【美式】溫暖舒適的

tofu /ˈtofu; ˈtəʊfuː/ n [U] (also 又作 **bean curd**) 豆腐

tollbooth /ˈtolˌbuθ; ˈtəʊlbuːθ/ n 收費亭 [站]

toner /ˈtonə; ˈtəʊnəʳ/ n **1** [U] 碳粉 **2** [U, C] 潤膚水 [霜]; 柔膚水 [霜]

toolbar /ˈtulbar; ˈtuːlbɑːʳ/ n〔電腦軟件視窗中的〕工具列

top gun n 一流飛行員, 頂尖人物

topline /ˈtɑpˌlaɪn; ˈtɒplaɪn/ v [I; T] 扮演主角, 擔任主要角色

top-shelf *adj* 最新設計的; 最現代化的

tosh /tɒʃ; tɒʃ/ *n* [U] *BrE infml*【英式; 非正式】廢話

tosser /ˈtɒsər; ˈtɒsər/ *n infml*【非正式】沒用的人; 廢物

touchdown /ˈtʌtʃˌdaʊn; ˈtʌtʃdaʊn/ *n* [U]〔美式橄欖球式〕持球觸地得分

touchy-feely *adj infml*【非正式】觸摸 (心理) 治療的; 喜歡以身體接觸來表達感情的 (用作貶義)

tough-minded *adj* 意志堅定的; 不多愁善感的

townscape /ˈtaʊnskeɪp; ˈtaʊnskeɪp/ *n* 城市風景, 市鎮風光

toyboy /ˈtɔɪbɔɪ; ˈtɔɪbɔɪ/ *n BrE infml*【英式, 非正式】男妓, 男伴, 小白臉〔通常被年長富有的女性所供養〕

toytoon /ˈtɔɪtun; ˈtɔɪtuːn/ *n* 玩具動畫片〔片中角色常被製成模型玩具供購買〕

trackpants /ˈtrækˌpænts; ˈtrækpænts/ *n* [pl] 田徑褲, 長運動褲

trade-in *n* 折價物, 貼換物

traffic calming *n* [U] 車輛減速措施

traffic cop *n AmE infml*【美式, 非正式】交通警察

tragicomedy /ˌtrædʒɪˈkɑmədɪ; ˌtrædʒɪˈkɒmədi/ *n* [C; U] 悲喜劇 (體裁) **--comic** *adj*

tranche /trænʃ; trɑːnʃ/ *n* 部分; 份

transdermal /trænsˈdɜməl; trænsˈdɜːməl/ *adj* 滲入皮膚後起 (保健 [治療]) 作用的

transnational /ˌtrænzˈnæʃnl; ˌtrænzˈnæʃnəl/ *adj* 跨國 (經營) 的

trash /træʃ; træʃ/ *n AmE slang*【美俚】便攜式電腦, 膝上型電腦

trendoid /ˈtrɛndɔɪd; ˈtrɛndɔɪd/ *n* 時尚狂

triathlon /traɪˈæθlən; traɪˈæθlən/ *n* 鐵人三項賽; 三項全能運動〔包括游泳、腳踏車和長跑在內的連續進行的三項長距離競賽〕

triff /trɪf; trɪf/ *adj slang*【俚】絕妙的; 了不起的

trim trail *n* 越野慢跑跑道

trolly-dolly *n slang*【俚】空 (中小) 姐

trou /traʊ; traʊ/ *n infml*【非正式】褲子

trouble shooting *n* [U]〔電腦〕故障查找 [檢修] 法, 找錯, 故障追查

tug-of-love *n BrE infml*【英, 非正式】"愛之拔河", 孩子監護權的爭奪〔報紙用語〕

tummytuck /ˈtʌmɪtʌk; ˈtʌmɪtʌk/ *n euph infml*【委婉, 非正式】腹部整形術, 收腹手術

turf war *n*〔地盤和勢力範圍的〕爭奪戰

twisted /ˈtwɪstɪd; ˈtwɪstɪd/ *adj*〔心智或行為〕反常的, 怪異的

two-wag mirror *n* 單向透明玻璃鏡〔一面可透視, 另一面則為普通鏡子〕

tycoonography /ˌtaɪkuˈnɑgrəfɪ; ˌtaɪkuːˈnɒgrəfi/ *n*〔企業界的〕巨頭傳記

U, u

UCAS *n abbrev*【縮】= universities and colleges admissions service〔英國〕大學入學申請辦事處

ufology /juˈfɑlədʒɪ; juːˈfɒlədʒi/ *n* [U] 不明飛行物學; 飛碟學

unambitious /ˌʌnæmˈbɪʃəs; ˌʌnæmˈbɪʃəs/ *adj* **1** 無大抱負的 **2** 不新奇的, 平淡無奇的

unauthorized /ʌnˈɔθəˌraɪzd; ʌnˈɔːθəraɪzd/ *adj* 未經授權的

unban /ʌnˈbæn; ʌnˈbæn/ *v* [T] 消 [解] 除禁令

unblock /ʌnˈblɑk; ʌnˈblɒk/ *v* [T] 清除障礙; 疏通管道

uncap /ʌnˈkæp; ʌnˈkæp/ *v* [T] 取消對……上限

uncapped /ʌnˈkæpt; ʌnˈkæpt/ *adj BrE*【英式】〔體育運動〕未曾加入過國家隊的

uncaring /ʌnˈkɛrɪŋ; ʌnˈkeərɪŋ/ *adj* 不關心他人疾苦的〔用作貶義〕

uncool /ʌnˈkul; ʌnˈkuːl/ *adj slang*【俚】落伍的; 不時髦的, 過時的

un-customed *adj* 未付關稅的; 違禁的

undated /ʌnˈdetɪd; ʌnˈdeɪtɪd/ *adj* 未標明日期的; 日期不明的

underage /ˈʌndərˈedʒ; ˌʌndərˈeɪdʒ/ *adj* 未成年的; 未及法定年齡的; 年齡太小的

underclass /ˈʌndəˌklæs; ˈʌndəklɑːs/ *n* 下層社會

unemployable /ˌʌnɪmˈplɔɪəbl; ˌʌnɪmˈplɔɪəbəl/ *adj*〔因缺乏技能、資歷而〕不能找到工作的; 不能雇用的

unfazed /ʌnˈfezd; ʌnˈfeɪzd/ *adj* 不擔心的; 不慌不忙的

ungreen /ʌnˈgrin; ʌnˈgriːn/ *adj* 對環境有害的

unheralded /ʌnˈhɛrəldɪd; ʌnˈherəldɪd/ *adj* 未預先警告的

unheeded /ʌnˈhidɪd; ʌnˈhiːdɪd/ *adj* 遭忽視的, 未注意的

unimpress /ˌʌnɪmˈprɛs; ˌʌnɪmˈpres/ *v* [T] 未能給〔某人〕留下深刻印象

unitary /ˈjunɪtɛrɪ; ˈjuːnɪtri/ *adj* 單一的; 統一的; 整體的

unmet /ʌnˈmɛt; ʌnˈmet/ *adj*〔要求〕未得到滿足的; 未達到的

unmissable /ʌnˈmɪsəbl; ʌnˈmɪsəbəl/ *adj* 不容錯過的

unplugged /ʌnˈplʌgd; ʌnˈplʌgd/ *adj*〔流行樂隊〕不用電子樂器的

unscoopy /ʌnˈskupɪ; ʌnˈskuːpi/ *adj infml*【非正式】缺少獨家新聞報道的; 不提供內幕消息的

unseeing /ʌnˈsiɪŋ; ʌnˈsiːɪŋ/ *adj* 視而不見的

unsuspected /ˌʌnsəˈspɛktɪd; ˌʌnsəˈspektɪd/ *adj* 未受注意的; 意外的

unzip /ʌnˈzɪp; ʌnˈzɪp/ *v*〔電腦〕解壓

up and running *adj* 順利進行的; 現時可行的

upchuck /ˈʌpˌtʃʌk; ˈʌptʃʌk/ *v* [I] *infml*【非正式】嘔吐

upcoming /ˈʌpˌkʌmɪŋ; ˈʌpkʌmɪŋ/ *adj* 即將發生的

upfield /ʌpˈfild; ʌpˈfiːld/ *adj, adv*〔指球場〕在前場 (的)

up-front *adj infml*【非正式】爽直的; 性格外向的

up-frontness *n infml*【非正式】爽直; 性格外向

upload /ˈʌpˌlod; ˈʌpˌləʊd/ *v* [T]〔電腦〕上裝 [加載], 上載

upscale /ˈʌpˌskel; ˈʌpskeɪl/ *adj* 身居高位的, 上層的, 高層次的, 高檔的

upsize /ˈʌpˈsaɪz; ˌʌpˈsaɪz/ *v* [I;T] 擴大〔某事

物〕的規模

upskill /ˌʌpˈskɪl; ˌʌpˈskɪl/ v [T] 提高…的技術

upstaff /ˌʌpˈstæf; ˌʌpˈstɑːf/ v [T] (為…) 增加員工

urgicenter /ˈɜːdʒɪˌsentə; ˈɜːdʒɪˌsentər/ n 急診中心

ursaphobic /ˌɜːsəˈfobɪk; ˌɜːsəˈfəʊbɪk/ adj 害怕熊的

utilitarianism /ˌjutɪləˈteriənˌɪzm; ˌjutɪlɪ-ˈteəriənˌɪzm/ n [U] 功利主義; 實利主義

V, v

vaccine /ˈvæksin; ˈvæksiːn/ n tech 【術語】抗電腦病毒軟件

vaccinology /ˌvæksɪˈnɑlədʒɪ; ˌvæksɪˈnɒlədʒi/ n [U] 疫苗 [菌苗] (接種) 學

value-added n 增值, 增值價值 [指物品在生產過程中的每一階段價值都有所增加]

vanity publisher n 作者自費出版社 [由作者自己支付出書的費用]

VCD n abbrev【縮】= video compact disc 視像光碟

veejay /ˈvidʒe; viːˈdʒeɪ/ n (also 又作 **VJ**) 電視音樂節目主持人

veep /vip; viːp/ n AmE infml【美式, 非正式】副總統

vegeburger /ˈvedʒɪˌbɜːgə; ˈvedʒɪˌbɜːgər/ n (also 又作 **veggieburger**) 素餡漢堡包

veggie /ˈvedʒɪ; ˈvedʒi/ n infml【非正式】素食主義者, 食素者

veg out phr v [T] slang【俚】過呆板單調的生活

veinprint /ˈvenprɪnt; ˈveɪnprɪnt/ n 〔手背上的〕靜脈紋

velocious /vəˈləʃəs; vɜːˈləʃəs/ adj fml【正式】快速的, 高速的

vid /vɪd; vɪd/ n infml【非正式】電視短片

video camera n (also 又作 **video cam**) 攝像機

video conferencing n 視像會議, 電視會議

videodical /ˌvɪdɪˈɑdɪkl; ˌvɪdɪˈɒdɪkəl/ n 期刊式錄像, 錄像雜誌

videofit /ˌvɪdɪoʊˈfit; ˌvɪdɪəʊˈfit/ n 〔模擬通輯犯的〕電腦拼圖成像

video jockey n 電視短片節目主持人

video-mail n 錄像郵件

video-on-demand n (also 又作 **VOD**) 視頻點播, 視像自選服務 [系統]

video phone n 視像電話

videozine /ˈvɪdɪoʊˌzin; ˌvɪdɪəʊˈziːn/ n 期刊式錄像帶

vidkid /ˈvɪdkɪd; ˈvɪdkɪd/ n AmE【美式】沉迷於觀看電視或錄像的兒童, 兒童電視迷

viral infection n 〔電腦的〕病毒感染

viropause /ˈvaɪrəpɔz; ˈvaɪrəpɔːz/ n 男性更年期

virtual /ˈvɜːtʃuəl; ˈvɜːtʃuəl/ adj 〔電腦〕虛擬的〔實際不存在, 但能讓使用者看得到〕

virtual reality n 〔電腦〕虛擬真實

---

virus /ˈvaɪrəs; ˈvaɪrəs/ n 電腦病毒

visagiste /ˌvizɑˈʒist; ˌviːzɑːˈʒiːst/ n 美容師; 化妝師

Voguing /ˈvogɪŋ; ˈvəʊgɪŋ/ 又作 **Vogueing** /ˈvogɪŋ; ˈvəʊgɪŋ/ n 時裝表演舞 [一種糅合了模特兒時裝表演的動作和姿勢的舞蹈, 由豪斯音樂伴奏]

voice mail n 話音郵件 (系統)

volumizer /ˈvɑljəmˌaɪzə; ˈvɒljəmˌaɪzər/ n 濃髮劑, 頭髮增密劑

volunteerism /ˌvɑlənˈtɪrɪzm; ˌvɒlənˈtɪərɪzm/ n [U] 自願社會服務

W, w

wack /wæk; wæk/ adj 無用的; 二流的

waitperson /ˈwetˌpɜsn; ˈweɪtˌpɜːsən/ n 〔餐館等的〕男 [女] 服務員, 侍者

waitron /ˈwetrən; ˈweɪtrən/ n 侍者, 服務員 [指男性或女性]

wake-up call n 警鐘 [用作比喻]

walk-in /ˈwɔkɪn; ˈwɔːkɪn/ adj 〔租屋〕即可入住的

walkthrough /ˈwɔkθru; ˈwɔːkθruː/ n 電腦歷險遊戲指南

walk-up n AmE【美式】宣傳攻勢

wall-mounted adj 固定在牆上的, 釘於牆面的

wallpaper /ˈwɔlˌpepə; ˈwɔːlˌpeɪpər/ n [C; U] 電腦桌面牆紙

WAN n abbrev【縮】= wide area network 廣域網絡, 廣區網絡, 寬廣區域網絡

wannabee /ˈwɑnəˌbi; ˈwɒnəˌbi/ n AmE slang【美式】盲目崇拜名人的人, 名人仰慕者

WAP n abbrev【縮】= Wireless Application Protocol 無線應用通訊協定 [一種通訊制式]

wardrobing /ˈwɔrdˌrobɪŋ; ˈwɔːdˌrəʊbɪŋ/ n [U] 1 選購和配備一系列的服裝, 選置行頭 2 [像購置服裝那樣] 積聚一系列個人用品

war game n 1 〔摹擬實際戰爭的〕軍事演習, 戰爭演習 2 [成人玩的] 戰棋; 戰爭遊戲

waribashi /ˌwerəˈbæʃɪ; ˌweərʒˈbæʃi/ n 一次性筷子, 衛生筷

warm call n 〔事先安排的〕熱身上門推銷; 熱身推銷電話

war-torn adj 飽受戰爭摧殘的〔指某一地方〕

wasm /ˈwɑzəm; ˈwɒzəm/ n infml【非正式】過時的主義或理論

water-colourist n 水彩畫家

wave-sailing n 帆艇滑浪

waxed /wækst; wækst/ adj 防水的; 防雨的

wayport /ˈweˌpɔrt; ˈweɪpɔːt/ n 中轉機場 [供中途停留轉接航班而不是目的地的機場]

weaponize /ˈwepənˌaɪz; ˈwepənaɪz/ v [T] (also 又作 **weaponise**) 把…改裝成武器; 將…武器化

web /wɛb; web/ n, v (漫遊) 萬維網

webcam /ˈwɛbˌkæm; ˈwebkæm/ n 網絡攝像機

webonomics /ˌwɛbəˈnɑmɪks; ˌwebəˈnɒmɪks/ n 網絡經濟學, 網路經濟學

web page *n* 網頁

website /ˈwɛbsaɪt; ˈwebsaɪt/ *n* 網站

webster /ˈwɛbstə; ˈwebstɚ/ *n* 網絡用戶

websurf /ˈwɛb,sɜːf; ˈwebsɜːf/ *v* [I; T]（在…）作網絡漫遊

webzine /ˈwɛb`ziːn; ˌwebˈziːn/ *n* 網絡雜誌

weeklong /ˈwiːklɒŋ; ˈwiːklɔːŋ/ *adj* 為期一週的, 長達一週的

weightism /ˈweɪtɪzəm; ˈweɪtɪzəm/ *n* [U] 體重歧視

wellness /ˈwɛlnɪs; ˈwelnɪs/ *n* 身心健康

well-thought-out *adj* 精心策劃的, 細密安排的

well-trodden *adj*〔道路〕往來頻繁的; 常有人走動的

well-wedged *adj BrE slang*【英俚】富裕的; 有錢的

wet bike *n*〔用滑橇在水面上推動的〕水上摩托車

wet food *n* 含水包裝食品〔相對脫水食品而言〕

whammy /ˈhwæmɪ; ˈwæmɪ/ *n AmE infml*【美式, 非正式】厄運; 打擊

wheeler /ˈhwiːlə; ˈwiːlɚ/ *n slang*【俚】精明的經營者 [經商者]

wheelie-bin *n* 有輪的垃圾箱

whistleblower /ˈhwɪslˌbloə; ˈwɪsəlˌbloʊɚ/ *n* 阻止某人 [某事] 的人; 告發者

white-breaded *adj* 中產階級的

white-glove *adj* 服務質量一流的; 上等級的

white-knuckle *adj* 令人極緊張的, 使人捏把汗的

white-out *n*〔大得使人看不見東西的〕暴風雪

white top *n AmE infml*【美式, 非正式】白髮蒼蒼的體弱老人; 年邁體弱的老年人

white water *n* [U] 急流, 湍急的水流

wicket gate *n*〔裝在大門邊的〕側門, 邊門

wideband /ˈwaɪd`bænd; ˈwaɪdbænd/ *n* 寬帶, 寬頻

widget /ˈwɪdʒɪt; ˈwɪdʒɪt/ *n infml*【非正式】小裝置; 小器具

wild /waɪld; waɪld/ *n AmE*【美式】打劫鬧事; 結幫搶劫案

wine-head *n infml*【非正式】嗜酒者

winery /ˈwaɪnərɪ; ˈwaɪnərɪ/ *n* 釀酒廠; 葡萄酒廠

winie /ˈwɪnɪ; ˈwɪnɪ/ *n* 嗜酒者, 酒迷, 佳釀品嘗迷

win-win situation *n* 雙贏局面, 雙方獲利局面〔一種雙方均有利可圖的局面〕

wipe /waɪp; waɪp/ *v* [T]〔在電腦終端上〕刷（信用卡等）

wired /waɪrd; waɪəd/ *adj slang*【俚】緊張不安的; 焦慮的

wirehead /ˈwaɪrˌhɛd; ˈwaɪəhed/ *n* 電腦迷

wobbly /ˈwɑblɪ; ˈwɒblɪ/ *n BrE infml*【英式, 非正式】怒不可遏, 盛怒

wolf /wʊlf; wʊlf/ *n slang*【俚】**1** 少年流氓 **2** 肆無忌憚的新聞記者

wolf pack *n slang*【俚】**1**〔在公共場合鬧事的〕少年匪幫 **2** 媒體狼群〔指一羣肆無忌憚的新聞記者〕

womanist /ˈwʊmənɪst; ˈwʊmənɪst/ *n* 爭取女權主義者

wonder /ˈwʌndə; ˈwʌndɚ/ *v* [I] 詢問

woofer /ˈwʊfə; ˈwuːfɚ/ *n infml*【非正式】富裕的中老年人

woopie /ˈwupɪ; ˈwuːpiː/ *n BrE infml*【英式, 非正式】老年雅皮士; 富有的老年人

word bite *n* 簡短醒目的宣傳廣告; 引人注目的標語

workaholicism /ˈwɜːkə`hɒlɪsɪzəm; ˈwɜːkəˈhɒlɪsɪzəm/ *n* [U] 工作狂熱, 工作迷戀

workaphile /ˈwɜːkəˌfaɪl; ˈwɜːkəˌfaɪl/ *n* 工作迷; 工作狂

workmate /ˈwɜːkmet; ˈwɜːkmeɪt/ *n BrE*【英式】同事, 工作夥伴

workstation /ˈwɜːkˌsteʃən; ˈwɜːkˌsteɪʃən/ *n*〔辦公室內設有電腦的〕工作站, 操作崗位

World Wide Web *n* (also 又作 **WWW**) 萬維網, 全球資訊網

wrinkly /ˈrɪŋklɪ; ˈrɪŋkli/ *n slang*【俚】老 (年) 人

write-down *n*〔資產等價值的〕降低, 劃減

WTO *n abbrev*【縮】= World Trade Organization 世界貿易組織

X, x

X *n slang*【俚】搖頭丸〔一種毒品〕

x¹ *n*〔寫在信或賀卡上的符號, 表示〕親吻, 吻

x² *n abbrev*【縮】= excluding 不包括

x-rated *adj* 極為可怕的; 充滿暴力的

Y, y

Y2K *n abbrev*【縮】= Year 2000 公元二千年

Y2K bug *n*〔電腦〕千年蟲

Y2K problem *n* 二千年問題, 千年蟲問題〔因電腦用兩位數字表示年份而無法辨識公元二千年所出現的問題〕

yacht people *n* [pl]〔自香港移居國外的〕富裕移民; 遊艇階層

yah /jɑ; jɑː/ *adv BrE slang*【英俚】〔英國人表示嘲笑等的〕是呀, 對呀

yard sale *n* 現場銷售, 院子買賣

yearlong /ˈjɪr`lɒŋ; ˈjɪəlɒŋ/ *adj* 整年一年的; 持續一年的

year-on-year *adj*〔數字、價格〕與上年同期相比的

year-round *adj* 全年的, 一年到頭的

yeepie /ˈjipɪ; ˈjiːpiː/ *n infml*【非正式】活躍老人, 有活動能力的老人

yobbish /ˈjɑbɪʃ; ˈjɒbɪʃ/ *adj BrE*【英式】粗魯的; 粗暴的

yoof /juf; juːf/ *n* [U] *slang*【俚】年輕人

young fogey *n BrE*【英式】保守的青年; 青年穩健派

youth cottage *n* 青年招待所, 青年之家

youthocracy /juˋθɒkrəsɪ; juːˈθɒkrəsi/ n [sing]〔有帶動時尚走向, 具購買力的〕青年人小圈子, 年青一族

yuan /juˋɑn; jʊˈɑːn/ 元〔中國貨幣單位〕

yup /jʌp; jʌp/ n infml【非正式】雅皮士

yupperware /ˋjʌpəˏwɛr; ˈjʌpəweə/ n 雅皮士家用餐具

yuppiedom /ˋjʌpɪdəm; ˈjʌpɪdəm/ n 1 雅皮士特性 2 雅皮士族

yuppiefy /ˋjʌpɪˏfaɪ; ˈjʌpɪfaɪ/ v [T] 使雅皮士化

Z, z

zap /zæp; zæp/ v [T] 1 使更充滿力量, 使更刺激, 使更有活力 2〔通過電腦網絡〕傳送

zapper /ˋzæpə; ˈzæpəʳ/ n AmE【美式】〔計程車的〕計程表快撥器〔一種用以勒索車費的裝置〕

zebra /ˋzibrə; ˈziːbrə/ AmE slang【美俚】美式足球裁判

Zen /zɛn; zen/ n [U] 禪, 禪宗〔起源於中國, 後傳至日本, 以靜坐沉思企求進入精神集中的境界〕

zero-emission vehicle n 零排放汽車; 無廢氣汽車

zero tolerance n [U]〔打擊罪犯的〕強硬政策

Zift /zɪft; zɪft/ n 受精卵植入輸卵管的授精 (法)

zillionaire /ˏzɪljənˋɛr; ˏzɪljəˈneəʳ/ n 超級富豪

zinger /ˋzɪŋə; ˈzɪŋəʳ/ n infml【非正式】風趣的話; 尖銳的反駁

zip /zɪp; zɪp/ n 壓縮〔電腦檔案〕

zip disk n〔電腦〕極碟

zip drive n〔電腦〕極碟驅動器, 極碟磁碟機

zootique /zooˋtik; zuːəˈtiːk/ n 景觀動物園〔將動物放在模擬大自然的生態環境中並為觀看者提供舒適參觀設施的景觀化動物園〕

Appendices

附 録

Word Building 構詞法

Word beginnings 詞頭

a-¹ /ə; ə/ (makes adjectives and adverbs 構成形容詞和副詞) **asleep** sleeping 睡着的 | **alive** living 活着的

a-² /e, æ, ə; eɪ, æ, ə/ not 不, 非: **atypical** not typical 不典型的

aero- /ˈeroː; ˈeərəʊ/ relating to air 空氣(的): **aerodynamics** the study of forces on a body moving through air 空氣動力學

Afro- /ˈæfro; ˈæfrəʊ/ relating to Africa 非洲(的): **Afro-Asian** relating to both Africa and Asia 亞非的

ambi- /ˈæmbɪ; ˈæmbɪ/ both; double 兩(者); 雙: **ambiguous** having more than one possible meaning; unclear 多義的; 模棱兩可的 | **ambidextrous** able to use both hands equally well 兩手都能熟練使用的

Anglo- /ˈænglo; ˈæŋgləʊ/ relating to England 英國[英格蘭](的): **Anglo-American** relating to both England and America 英美的

ante- /ˈæntɪ; ˈæntɪ/ before (在…)之前: **antenatal** relating to the time before birth 出生前的 –compare 比較 **post-**

anti- /ˈæntɪ; ˈæntɪ/ **1** having a feeling or opinion against 〔在感情或觀點上〕反(對): **antinuclear** opposing the use of nuclear weapons and power 反對使用核武器[核能]的 –compare 比較 **pro- 2** opposite to or of 相反的: **anticlimax** a much less satisfying end (CLIMAX) than expected 遠不能令人滿意的結局 | **anticlockwise** in the opposite direction to the movement of the hands of a clock 逆時針方向的 **3** preventing or acting against 防(止)的: **antifreeze** a liquid put into water in a car to stop it from freezing 〔汽車〕防凍劑

arch- /ɑːtʃ, ɑrk; ɑːtʃ, ɑːk/ chief; first 主要的; 首要的: **archbishop** a chief bishop 大主教

astro- /ˈæstrə, əˈstrɑ; ˈæstrəʊ, ˈæstrə/ relating to the stars, planets and space 行星的; 太空的; 宇宙的: **astronomy** the study of the planets and stars 天文學

audio- /ˈɔːdɪˌo; ˈɔːdiəʊ/ also 又作 **audi-** /ˈɔːdɪ; ˈɔːdi/ relating to sound and hearing 聲音的; 聽覺的: **audio-visual** using or relating to both sound and sight 視聽的

auto- /ˈɔːtə; ˈɔːtəʊ/ **1** self 自己的: **autobiography** a book about one's own life written by oneself 自傳 **2** without help 自行, 自動: **automatic** working by itself without human operation 自動的

be- /bɪ; bɪ/ (makes verbs 構成動詞) to make; become; treat as 使; 成為; 對待: **belittle** to say that a person or thing is small or unimportant 輕視; 貶低

bi- /baɪ; baɪ/ two; twice 兩, 二, 雙: **biplane** a plane with two wings 雙翼飛機 | **bilingual** able to speak two languages equally well 能説兩種語言的 | **biweekly** happening once every two weeks, or twice a week 兩週一次的; 一週兩次的

bio- /ˈbaɪo; ˈbaɪəʊ/ relating to life and living things 生命的, 生物的: **biochemistry** the scientific study of the chemistry of living things 生物化學 | **biodegradable** able to be broken down into harmless products by the action of living things 能被生物分解成無害物質的

by- /baɪ; baɪ/ **1** less important 次要的: **by-product** something formed in addition to the main product 副產品 **2** near 附近: **bypass** a road near a city or town so that drivers can go around it rather than through it 〔繞過城鎮的〕旁道

centi- /ˈsentɪ; sentɪ/ also 又作 **cent-** /ˈsent; sent/ 100; 100th (一)百; 百分之一: **Centigrade** a scale of temperature in which water boils at 100° 攝氏 | **centimetre** a measurement of length=0.01 metres 厘米(= 1/100 米)

co- /ko; kəʊ/ together; with 共同, (和…)一起: **co-worker** a person with whom one works 同事; 合作者

contra- /ˈkɒntrə; ˈkɒntrə/ opposite; against 相反; 反, 防(止): **contradict** to say the opposite of (a statement, opinion, etc.) 反對〔説法、觀點等〕

counter- /ˈkaʊntər; ˈkaʊntəʳ/ opposite; against 相反; 反對: **counter-revolution** a movement opposing a revolution 反革命 | **counterattack** an attack opposing another attack 反攻, 反擊

cross- /krɒs; krɒs/ going across or between 跨越, 橫過: **cross-Channel** going across the Channel 橫渡(英吉利)海峽的 | **cross-cultural** going between two or more cultures 涉及多種文化的

de- /di, dɪ; diː, dɪ/ the reverse or opposite of 逆向; 相反: **de-emphasize** to make less important 降低重要性, 貶低 | **devalue** to make (the value of something such as a currency) less 使〔貨幣等〕貶值

deca- /ˈdekə; ˈdekə/ also 又作 **dec-** /dek; dek/ ten 十: **decade** a period of ten years 十年(期)

deci- /ˈdesɪ; ˈdesi/ a tenth part 十分之一: **decilitre** 0.1 litres 分升(= 1/10 升)

dis- /dɪs; dɪs/ **1** the opposite of 相反: **discontented** not happy; not contented 不滿的 | **disagree** to have a different opinion; not agree 不同意 **2** to change back; remove 消

除; 中斷: **disconnect** to remove a connection of (something, especially something electrical) 切斷〔電源〕

en- /ɪn, ɛn; en, ɪn/ *also* 又作 **em-** /əm; ɪm; *strong* 強讀 em; em/ (*makes verbs* 構成動詞) **1** to put in, on, or around 放入; 放在…上; 放在…周圍: **encase** to cover completely (as) with a case 把…裝入箱內; 包起 | **enclose** to put a wall or fence around 用圍牆〔籬笆〕圍住 **2** to make; cause to be 使成為: **enlarge** to make larger 放大 | **empower** to give (someone) the right or power to do something 授權〔某人〕, 使〔某人〕有…的權力

equi- /ˈɛkwə, ˈikwɪ; ˌekwɪ, ˌiːkwɪ/ equal 相等的: **equidistant** equally distant 等距(離)的 | **equivalent** (of amount, number, etc.) same; equal〔量、數等〕相同的; 相等的

Euro- /ˈjuro; ˈjʊərəʊ/ European 歐洲的: **Eurovision** an organization for exchanging television and radio programmes in Europe 歐洲電視廣播節目交換組織

ex- /ɛks; eks/ no longer being; former 從前的, 前任的: **ex-husband** a man who was a woman's husband, but who is now DIVORCED from her 前夫

extra- /ˈɛkstrə; ˈekstrə/ beyond; outside 超出…的, 在…之外: **extrasensory** beyond the five senses of sight, smell, sound, taste and touch 超感官的

fore- /for; fɔːʳ/ **1** earlier; before 預先; **foresee** to guess what is going to happen in the future 預見 **2** placed in front of; before; front part of 置於…前面的; …的前部: **forearm** the front part of the arm, below the elbow 前臂 | **forefront** the most forward place 最前方

geo- /ˈdʒio; ˈdʒiːəʊ/ relating to the earth 地球的: **geology** the study of the materials (soil, rocks, etc.) which make up the earth 地質學 | **geography** the study of the seas, rivers, towns, etc., on the surface of the earth. 地理學

hecto- /ˈhɛkto; ˈhektəʊ/ 100 百: **hectolitre** 100 litres 百升

hetero- /ˈhɛtərə; ˈhetərə/ other; different 異; 雜: **heterogeneous** of (many) different kinds 不同種類的 | **heterosexual** attracted to people of the opposite sex 異性戀的 – compare 比較 **homo-**

homo- /ˈhomo; ˈhəʊməʊ, ˈhɒmə-/ same; like 同: **homogeneous** formed of parts of the same kind 同類的 | **homosexual** attracted to people of the same sex 同性戀的 –compare 比較 **hetero-**

hyper- /ˈhaɪpə; ˈhaɪpəʳ/ above or too (much) 超過; 過於: **hypercritical** too critical 吹毛求疵的

in- /ɪn; ɪn/ **1** also **il-** /ɪl; ɪl/, **im-** /ɪm; ɪm/, **ir-** /ɪr; ɪr/ not 不, 非: **inexact** not exact 不確切的 **2** in; into; on 在…裡面; 進入; 在…上面: **inset** something put in as an addition into something else 插入物

■ USAGE 用法: **in-** meaning "not" usually changes to **il-** before *l* 作"不、非"解的 **in-** 在 *l* 前通常變成 **il-**: **illegal** not legal 非法的; **im-** before *b*, *m*, or *p* 在 *b*, *m* 或 *p* 前通常變成 **im-**: **imbalance** lack of balance 不平衡 | **immobile** not mobile 不動的 | **impatient** not patient 不耐煩的; **ir-** before *r* 在 *r* 前通常變成 **ir-**: **irregular** not regular or even; not usual 不規則的; 不合常規的

inter- /ˈɪntə; ˈɪntəʳ/ between; among 在…之間: **international** having to do with more than one nation 國際的 | **intermarriage** marriage between members of different groups, families, etc.〔不同團體、家庭等的〕之間通婚

intra- /ˌɪntrə; ˌɪntrə/ *also* 又作 **intro-** /-trə; -trəʊ/ inside 在內部: **introspection** looking into one's own thoughts and feelings 內省, 反省 | **intravenous** inside a VEIN 靜脈內的

kilo- /ˈkɪlə; ˈkɪlə/ 1,000 千: **kilogram** 1,000 grams 公斤, 千克; **kilometre** 1,000 metres 公里, 千米

macro- /ˈmækro; ˈmækrəʊ/ large; great 大的, 宏觀的: **macroeconomics** the study of the economics of a country or countries 宏觀經濟學

mal- /mæl; mæl/ bad; wrong 壞, 不當, 不良: **malformation** the condition of being shaped wrongly 畸形 | **malfunction** a fault in the operation of a machine 機器故障

mega- /ˈmɛgə; ˈmegə/ **1** million 百萬: **megawatt** 1,000,000 watts (WATT) of electricity 百萬瓦特 **2** *infml* unusually large or great【非正式】極大的, 巨大的: **megastar** a star who is extremely famous and popular 天皇巨星

micro- /ˈmaɪkro; ˈmaɪkrəʊ/ **1** very small 微(小的): **microcomputer** a very small computer 微型電腦 **2** a millionth 百萬分之一: **microsecond** a millionth (0.000 000 1) of a second 微秒

mid- /mɪd; mɪd/ middle 中(間): **midpoint** a point at or near the centre or middle 中點 | **midway** halfway or in a middle position 中途

milli- /ˈmɪlɪ; ˈmɪlɪ/ a thousandth 千分之一, 毫: **milligram** 1,000th (=0.001) of a gram (a measurement of weight) 毫克〔重量單位〕 | **millimeter** 1,000th (=0.001) of a meter (a measurement of length) 毫米〔長度單位〕

mini- /ˈmɪnɪ; ˈmɪni/ *infml* very small【非正式】非常小的: **minibreak** a short holiday 短期休假

mis- /mɪs; mɪs/ **1** bad; wrong 壞, 不當, 錯: **misspelling** a wrong spelling 拼寫錯誤 | **misjudge** to have a wrong opinion of 錯誤判斷 **2** the opposite of 相反: **mistrust** not to trust 不信任

mono- /ˈmɒno; ˈmɒnəʊ, ˈmɒnə/ one; single

單; 一: **monorail** a railway with only one rail 單軌 | **monopoly** a situation where only one person or group sells a particular thing, produces something, etc. 壟斷 | **monosyllabic** (of a word) having one syllable〔詞語〕單音節的

multi- /ˈmʌltɪ; ˈmʌltɪ/ many; more than one 多: **multicoloured** having many colours 多色的 | **multistorey** (of a building) having many levels or floors〔指建築物〕多層的

neo- /ˈnio; ˈniə; ˈniːəʊ; ˈniːə/ new; a later kind of 新的; 新型的: **neoclassical** a new or later kind of classical style 新古典主義的: *the neoclassical architecture of America* 美國的新古典主義建築

non- /nɑn; nɒn/ not 不，非: **nonstop** without stopping before the end 不停的 | **nonpayment** not having paid 未交付: *He is in trouble for nonpayment of taxes.* 他由於未繳稅而惹上麻煩。

out- /aʊt; aʊt/ **1** outside 在外面: **outdoors** in the open air 戶外 **2** more than; beyond 多於; 超過: **outgrow** to grow too big for 長得太大: *The girl has outgrown her clothes.* 那女孩個子長得衣服都穿不下了。

over- /ˈovə; ˈəʊvəʳ/ **1** too much 過多，過於: **overexcited** too excited 過於興奮的 | **overpopulation** the condition of having too many people (in a country)〔一個國家的〕人口過多 **2** across; above 跨過; 在...上面: **overland** across or by land 陸上的, 經由陸路的

photo- /ˈfoto; ˈfəʊtəʊ/ **1** light 光: **photo-electric cell** an instrument which starts an electrical apparatus working by means of light 光電池 **2** photography 攝影(的): **photocopy** (to make) an exact copy of (a letter, drawing, etc.) using a special machine (PHOTOCOPIER) 複印; 複印件

post- /post; pəʊst/ after; later than 在...後, 遲於: **postwar** belonging to the time after a war 戰後的 | **postpone** to put off to a later time 延遲

pre- /pri; priː/ before 在...之前: **prewar** before a war 戰前的 | **preschool** relating to children who are too young to go to school 學齡前的

pro- /pro; prəʊ/ in favour of 支持; 贊成: **pro-education** in favour of education 重教育 –compare 比較 **anti-**

pseudo- /ˈsjudo; ˈsjuːdəʊ/ not real; false 假, 偽: **pseudonym** a false name, used especially by a writer of books 筆名 | **pseudomodern** seeming to be (but not) modern 假時髦的

psycho- /ˈsaiko; ˈsaikəʊ/ *also* 又作 **psych-** /saik; saik/ relating to the mind 心理: **psychotherapy** the treatment of disorders of the mind 心理療法 | **psychology** the study of the mind and of behaviour 心理學

quadri- /ˈkwadrɪ; ˈkwɒdrɪ/ *also* 又作 **quadr-** /kwadr; kwɒdr/ four 四: **quadrilateral** (a figure) with four sides 四邊的

quasi- /ˈkwezaɪ; ˈkwɑzɪ; ˈkwɑːzɪ; ˈkweizaɪ/ seeming or like 類似; 偽: **quasi-scientific** seeming to be scientific 偽科學的

quin- /kwin; kwin/ five 五: **quintet** (music for) five players or singers together 五重奏(曲); 五重唱(曲)

re- /ri, rɪ; riː, rɪ/ again 再，重: **remake** to make (especially a film) again 重新製作〔尤指電影〕| **rethink** to think about again 重新考慮

■ USAGE 用法: When **re-** means "again", it is pronounced /riː/. In other words beginning with **re-**, it is usually pronounced /rɪ/ (or /riː/ before a vowel). Compare **recover** (to get better) /rɪˈkʌvə; rɪˈkʌvəʳ/ and **recover** (to cover again) /ˌriːˈkʌvə; ˌriːˈkʌvəʳ/ ☆當 **re-** 作「再、又」解時，讀音為 /riː/。在其他以 **re-** 為詞頭的單詞中，**re-** 的讀音通常為 /ri/（或在元音前讀作 /riː/）。比較 **recover** (恢復) /rɪˈkʌvə; rɪˈkʌvəʳ/ 和 **recover** (重新蓋上) /ˌriˈkʌvə; ˌriːˈkʌvəʳ/

---

self- /sɛlf; self/ of or by oneself, independent 自己的; 獨自的: **self-explanatory** that explains itself 不言自明的 | **self-control** control of oneself 自制 | **self-employed** working for oneself 自雇的

semi- /ˈsɛmɪ; ˈsemɪ/ **1** half 半: **semicircle** half a circle 半圓 **2** partly 部份(地): **semisolid** partly solid and partly liquid 半固態, 凝固狀態 | *a semi-detached house* a house partly joined to another house by one shared wall 半獨立式房屋

sub- /sʌb; sʌb/ **1** under 在...之下: **submarine** a ship which can travel under water 潛水艇 **2** a smaller part of 更小部分的: **subregion** a small part of a region 分區 **3** less than 低於, 次於: **subhuman** having less than human qualities 低於人類的

super- /ˈsupə; ˈsuːpəʳ/ greater or more than 超, 過於: **supersonic** faster than the speed of sound 超音速的 | **superstar** a very famous and popular performer 超級巨星

tele- /ˈtɛlɪ; ˈtelɪ/ **1** at or over a long distance 遠(距離): **telescope** an instrument for looking at objects that are far away 望遠鏡 | **telephone** an electrical apparatus for talking to other people a long distance away 電話 **2** using a telephone 使用電話的: **telesales** the sale of goods by telephone 電話銷售 **3** using or for television 使用電視的, 為電視的: **televangelism** trying to convert people to religion by means of television 電視福音佈道活動

thermo- /ˈθɜmo; ˈθɜːməʊ/ heat 熱: **thermometer** an instrument for measuring temperature 溫度計 | **thermodynamics** the study of the relationship between heat and mechanical energy 熱力學

trans- /træns, trænz; træns, trænz/ **1** across;

on the other side of 橫越; 在…另一邊:
transatlantic crossing, on the other side
of, or concerning countries on both sides
of the Atlantic 橫越大西洋的 **2** change 變化:
transform to change completely in form,
appearance, or nature 改變〔形狀、外表或性
質〕

tri- /traɪ; traɪ/ three 三: **triangle** a flat figure
with three straight sides 三角形

ultra- /ˈʌltrə; ˈʌltrə/ **1** beyond 超: **ultrasonic**
(of sound waves) beyond the range of hu-
man hearing 超聲波的 **2** very; excessively
極(度): **ultramodern** very modern 極為現代
化的 | **ultramarine** a very bright blue
colour 深藍色

un- /ʌn; ʌn/ **1** (*makes adjectives and adverbs*
構成形容詞和副詞) not 不, 非, 否: **un-
comfortable** not comfortable 不舒服的 |
unhappy not happy 不高興的 | **unwashed**
not washed 未洗的 **2** (*makes verbs* 構成動
詞) to make the opposite of; reverse 使…相
反: **undress** to take one's clothes off 脫衣
服 | **unlock** to unfasten the lock of 開鎖 |
untie to undo (a knot or something tied)
解開〔繩結或捆縛之物〕

vice- /vaɪs; vaɪs/ next in rank or importance
副; 次: **vice-president** the person next in official rank below a president 副總統; *the
Vice-President of the United States* 美國副總
統

Word endings 詞尾

-ability, -ibility /əˈbɪlətɪ; əˈbɪlˌḷti/ (*makes
nouns from adjectives ending in* -able, -ible
加在以 -able, -ible 結尾的形容詞後構成名詞)
flexibility the quality of being flexible
(=easy to bend or change) 柔韌性 | **reli-
ability** the quality of being reliable; able to
be trusted 可靠性

-able, -ible /əbl; əbəl/ (*makes adjectives* 構
成形容詞) **1** able to be …ed 能夠被…的:
washable able to be washed 可洗滌的 |
drinkable that can be drunk 可以飲用的 **2**
showing or having 顯示…的; 有…: **knowledgeable** having a good deal of knowledge
博學的 | **reasonable** showing or having
reason or good sense 合情合理的

-age /ɪdʒ; ɪdʒ/ (*makes nouns* 構成名詞) **baggage** all the bags and containers with
which a person travels 行李 | **storage** a
place for storing goods 貯藏所, 倉庫 |
passage the action of going across, by,
over, etc. 通過; 穿過

-al /əl; əl/ *also* 又作 **-ial 1** (*makes
adjectives* 構成形容詞) **political** of or concerning politics 政治的 **2** (*makes nouns* 構
成名詞) **arrival** the act of arriving 抵達 |
refusal the act of refusing 拒絕

-an /ən; ən/ *also* 又作 **-ian, -ean 1** (*makes
adjectives and nouns from names of places
or people* 接於地名和人名後構成形容詞和名
詞) **American** a person belonging to or
connected with America 美國人; 美國的 |
Christian a person who believes in the
teachings of Jesus Christ 基督徒 **2** (*makes
adjectives* 構成形容詞) **Dickensian** of or
like Dickens or his books (似)狄更斯的; 狄
更斯著作的 **3** (*makes nouns from words
ending in* -ic, -ics, *and* -y 加在以 -ic, -ics,
和 -y 結尾的單詞後構成名詞) **historian** a
person who studies and/or writes about
history 歷史學家

-ance, -ence /əns; əns/ (*makes nouns* 構成名
詞) **1 importance** the quality or state of be-
ing important 重要性 | **patience** the qual-
ity of being patient 耐性 **2** an example
of …的動作: **performance** an act of PER-
FORMING in a play, film, etc. 演出, 表演

-ant, -ent /ənt; ənt/ **1** (*makes adjectives* 構成
形容詞) **pleasant** pleasing to the senses,
feelings, or mind 愉快的 | **different** un-
like; not of the same kind 不同的 **2** (*makes
nouns* 構成名詞) **servant** a person who
works for another in the other's house 僕
人 | **student** a person who is studying at a
school, college, etc. 學生 | **disinfectant** a
chemical used to DISINFECT 消毒劑 | **de-
odorant** a substance that removes unpleasant smells (ODOURS) 除臭劑

-ar /ə; ɑr; ə; ɑːr/ **1** (*makes nouns* 構成名詞)
see 見 -ER² **2** (*makes adjectives* 構成形容詞)
muscular having big muscles; strong-look-
ing 肌肉發達的; 健壯的

-arian /ɛrɪən; eərɪən/ (*makes nouns and
adjectives* 構成名詞和形容詞) **vegetarian**
someone who does not eat meat or fish 素
食者 | **librarian** a person who is in charge
of or helps to run a library 圖書管理員

-ary /ərɪ; ərɪ/ **1** (*makes nouns* 構成名詞) a
person or thing connected with or a place
for 與…有關的人[物、場所]: **library** a building or room which contains books that can
be read and usually borrowed 圖書館 **2**
(*makes adjectives* 構成形容詞) **customary**
established by custom; usual 習慣的

-ate /ɪt, et; ḷt, eɪt/ **1** (*makes adjectives* 構成形
容詞) showing; full of 顯出…的; 充滿…的:
considerate showing consideration for 考慮
周到的 **2** (*makes verbs* 構成動詞) to act as;
cause to become 使成為: **activate** to cause
to be active 使活躍 | **regulate** to bring or-
der or method to; make REGULAR 使有規
則 **3** (*makes nouns* 構成名詞) a group of
people (與…有關的)一羣人: **electorate** all
the people in a place or country who can
vote (全體)選民

-ation /ˈeʃən; ˈeɪʃən/ (*makes nouns* 構成名詞) **declaration** an act of declaring 宣告 | **hesitation** an act of hesitating (=pausing in or before an action) 猶豫 | **exploration** the act or an action of exploring (EXPLORE) (=to travel to a place for the purpose of discovery) 勘探

-ative /ətɪv; ətɪv/ (*makes adjectives* 構成形容詞) **imaginative** using or having imagination 有想像力的 | **talkative** liking to talk a lot 健談的

-ator /etə; eɪtəʳ/ (*makes nouns* 構成名詞) a person or thing that does something 做某事的人或物: **narrator** a person who NARRATES 敍述者 | **generator** a machine which makes energy, usually electricity 發電機

-cide /saɪd; saɪd/ (*makes nouns* 構成名詞) kill 殺害: **suicide** the act of killing oneself 自殺 | **insecticide** a chemical substance made to kill insects 殺蟲劑

-cracy /krəsɪ; krəsɪ/ (*makes nouns* 構成名詞) a government or class characterized by ... 以...為特徵的政體: **democracy** a government that is DEMOCRATIC; government by elected representatives of the people 民主政治

-cy /sɪ; sɪ/ (*makes nouns* 構成名詞) **accuracy** the quality of being ACCURATE (=exact and correct) 精確(性)

-d /d, t; d, t/ see 見 -ED

-dom /dəm; dəm/ (*makes nouns* 構成名詞) **1** the state of being (something) (某種)狀態: **boredom** the state of being BORED (= uninterested because something is dull) 厭倦 **2 kingdom** the country ruled by a king or queen 王國: *the United Kingdom* 聯合王國

-ean /ɪən; ɪən/ see 見 -AN

-ed, -d /d, ɪd, t; d, ᵻd, t/ **1** (*makes regular past tenses and past participles* 構成規則動詞的過去式和過去分詞) *we* **laughed** 我們笑了 | *I have* **waited**... 我已等了... | *a man* **wanted** *by the police* 被警方通緝的人 **2** (*makes adjectives* 構成形容詞) *a* **bearded** *man* (=a man with a beard) 留鬍鬚的人 | *a long-* **tailed** *cat* 長着大尾巴的貓

-ee /i; iː/ (*makes nouns* 構成名詞) **1** somebody to whom something is done 〔某種動作的〕受動者: **employee** a person who is employed 雇員 | **trainee** a person who is being trained 受訓者 | **refugee** a person who has been driven from his/her country 難民 **2** somebody who is or does something 做〔某事〕的人: **absentee** a person who is absent from work, etc. 缺席者

-eer /ɪə; ɪəʳ/ (*makes nouns* 構成名詞) a person who does an activity 參加某種活動的人: **mountaineer** a person who climbs mountains 登山者 | **profiteer** someone who makes large profits in times of war or difficulty 牟取暴利的人

-en /ən; ən/ (*makes adjectives* 構成形容詞) made of 由...製成的: **golden** of or like gold

黃金的 | **wooden** made of wood 木製的 **2** (*makes verbs* 構成動詞) to cause to be or to have 使成為; 變得: **darken** to make or become dark 〔使〕變暗: *The sky darkened after sunset.* 太陽落山後, 天空變黑了。 | **soften** to make or become soft 〔使〕變軟

-ent /ənt; ənt/ see 見 -ANT

-er¹, -r /ə; əʳ/ (*makes the comparative of short adjectives and adverbs* 構成一些音節不多的形容詞和副詞的比較級) **hotter** more hot 更熱 | **safer** more safe 更安全 –see Study Note on page 1311 見 1311 頁學習提示

-er², -ar, -or, -r /ə; əʳ/ (*makes nouns* 構成名詞) **1** a person who does an activity 參加某種活動的人: **footballer** a person who plays football 足球運動員 | **teacher** a person who teaches 老師 | **liar** a person who tells lies 説謊者 | **actor** a person who acts 演員 | **writer** a person who writes 作家 **2** a person who lives in (a place) 住在〔某地〕的人: **Londoner** a person who lives in London 倫敦人 | **villager** a person who lives in a village 村民 **3** a thing that does something 做〔某事〕的東西: **cooker** an apparatus on which food is cooked under direct heat 炊具 | **heater** a machine for heating air, water, etc. 取暖器; 加熱器

-ery, -ry /ərɪ; ərɪ/ (*makes nouns* 構成名詞) the art of or quality of ...的技藝; ...的質量: **cookery** the art of cooking 烹飪術 | **bravery** the quality of being brave 勇敢 **2** a place where something is done 做〔某事〕的地方: **bakery** a place where bread is baked and/or sold 麵包烘房; 麵包店

-es /ɪz; ᵻz/ see 見 -S

-ese /iz; iːz/ (*makes adjectives and nouns* 構成形容詞和名詞) relating to a country, its language or people, or a style ...國的; ...語的; ...人; ...風格: **Japanese** of or relating to the people, language, or country of Japan 日本人; 日語; 日本的 | **journalese** in the style of the language used in newspapers 新聞文體

-esque /ɛsk; esk/ having a manner or style like 有...樣式的; 有...風格的: **picturesque** looking like a picture 如畫的: *a picturesque old village* 風景如畫的古老村莊

-ess /ɪs; ᵻs, es/ female 女性; 雌性: **actress** a woman who acts in plays and films 女演員 | **lioness** a female lion 母獅

-est, -st /ɪst; ᵻst/ (*makes the superlative of many short adjectives and adverbs* 構成許多音節不多的形容詞和副詞的最高級) **highest** the most high 最高: *Mount Everest is the highest mountain in the world.* 埃佛勒斯峰是世界上最高的山峯。 | **hottest** the most hot 最熱的: *the hottest day of the year* 一年中最熱的一天 –see Study Note on page 1311 見 1311 頁學習提示

-ette /ɛt; et/ (*makes nouns* 構成名詞) small 小...; **kitchenette** a small kitchen 小廚房

-fold /fold; fəʊld/ (*makes adjectives* 構成形容

詞) times; multiplied by 倍; 重: **fourfold** four times (an amount) 四倍

-ful¹ /fl; fəl; fəl/ (*makes adjectives* 構成形容詞) **delightful** causing delight; highly pleasing 令人愉快的 | **painful** causing pain 疼痛的

-ful² /ful; ful/ (*makes nouns* 構成名詞) the amount that a container holds 充滿…所容納之量: **cupful** the amount held by a cup 一杯之量 | **spoonful** the amount held by a spoon 一匙之量

-fy /faɪ; faɪ/ see 見 -IFY

-gram /græm; græm/ (*makes nouns* 構成名詞) a message delivered by a person as an amusing surprise, often on someone's birthday …信, 卡〔常在某人的生日時傳送的玩笑性質的信息〕: **kissagram** someone paid to deliver a message and also to kiss the person they are delivering it to 被雇來祝賀並送上親吻的人

-hood /hud; hud/ (*makes nouns* 構成名詞) the state or period of being …狀態; …時期: **childhood** the time or condition of being a child 孩童時代 | **womanhood** the state or period of being a woman 女子成年期

-ial /ɪəl; ɪəl/ see 見 -AL

-ian /ɪən; ɪən/ see 見 -AN

-ibility /ə'bɪlɪti; ə'bɪlɪ,ti/ see 見 -ABILITY

-ible /əbl; ḷbəl/ see 見 -ABLE

-ic /ɪk; ɪk/ (*makes adjectives* 構成形容詞) **poetic** of, like, or connected with poets or poetry (像)詩人的; 詩(一般)的 –see 見 -ICAL (USAGE 用法)

-ical /ɪkl; ɪkəl/ (*makes adjectives* 構成形容詞) connected with 與…有關的: **historical** connected with history 有關歷史的

> ■ USAGE 用法: Some pairs of words ending in **-ic** and **-ical** have different meanings. For example, **historic** means 'having a long history' or 'being remembered in history', but **historical** means 'something that happened in the past' or 'relating to the study of history'. ☆有些以 **-ic** 和 **-ical** 結尾的單詞意思並不一樣。例如, **historic** 解作 "歷史悠久的"或"有歷史紀念意義的", 而 **historical** 則解作"歷史上發生的"或"歷史學的"。

-ics /ɪks; ɪks/ (*makes nouns* 構成名詞) a science or particular activity …學; 某項活動: **economics** the scientific study of the way industry and trade produce and use wealth 經濟學 | **athletics** the sport of exercising the body by running, jumping, etc. 體育運動

-ie /ɪ; i/ see 見 -Y (2)

-ify /ɪfaɪ; ḷfaɪ/ also 又作 **-fy** (*makes verbs* 構成動詞) to make or become 使; 變成: **purify** to make pure 使變純淨 | **simplify** to make simple 簡化 | **clarify** to make clearer or

easier to understand 使清楚易懂

-ing /ɪŋ; ɪŋ/ **1** (*makes the present participle of verbs* 構成動詞的現在分詞) *she's* **sleeping** 她在睡覺 | *I'm* **waiting** *for you.* 我在等你。 **2** (*makes nouns from verbs* 由動詞構成名詞) **Running** *keeps you healthy.* 跑步能使你保持健康。 | *a* **sleeping** *pill* (=a pill to help a person sleep) 安眠藥 | *a beautiful* **painting** 一幅美麗的圖畫 | **Painting** *is fun.* 繪畫是很有趣的。

-ise /aɪz; aɪz/ see 見 -IZE

-ish /ɪʃ; ɪʃ/ (*makes adjectives* 構成形容詞) **1** relating to a country, its language, or people …國的; …語的; …人的: **British** of Britain 英國的 | **Swedish** of Sweden 瑞典的 **2** like; typical of 像…; 有…特徵的: **childish** (a word often used to express disapproval) of or typical of a child 〔常含貶義〕孩子氣的 | **foolish** like a fool; without good sense; stupid 傻瓜似的; 蠢的 **3** rather 稍微…的, 有點…的: **reddish** slightly red 微紅的 | **smallish** rather small 稍為小的 **4** approximately 大約, …左右: **fortyish** about forty 四十歲左右 | **sixish** at about 6 o'clock 六點鐘前後

-ism /ɪzəm; ɪzəm/ (*makes nouns* 構成名詞) **1** the ideas, principles, or teaching of 思想; 主義: **socialism** a belief in equality and public ownership 社會主義 | **Buddhism** a religion of east and central Asia, based on the teachings of the Buddha 佛教(教義) **2** a practice or activity 實踐; 行動: **terrorism** the practice of using violence to obtain political demands 恐怖主義 **3** a quality or characteristic 性質; 特點: **heroism** the quality of being a HERO (=someone who acts with great courage) 英雄品質

-ist /ɪst; ḷst/ **1** (*makes nouns and adjectives* 構成名詞和形容詞) a follower of a movement …主義的: **socialist** a person who believes in SOCIALISM 社會主義者 **2** (*makes nouns* 構成名詞) someone who studies, produces, plays, or operates …家; …操作者: **guitarist** someone who plays the guitar 吉他手 | **pianist** someone who plays the piano 鋼琴家 | **machinist** a person who operates a machine 機器操作者 | **linguist** someone who studies language 語言學家 | **novelist** someone who writes NOVELS 小説家

-ite /aɪt; aɪt/ (*makes nouns and adjectives* 構成名詞和形容詞) a follower of a movement 支持…的人: **Trotskyite** a supporter of Trotsky's ideas 托洛斯基分子

-ity /əti; ḷti/ also 又作 **-ty** (*makes nouns* 構成名詞) the quality or an example of …的性質; 狀態: *It was an act of* **stupidity** *to drive so fast.* 車開得這麼快是很愚蠢的行為。 | **cruelty** *to animals* 虐待動物

-ive /ɪv; ɪv/ (*makes adjectives* 構成形容詞) having a tendency, character, or quality 有…傾向的; 有…特點的; 有…性質的: **creative**

creating new ideas and things 有創造性的 | **descriptive** that describes 描述性的 | **explosive** that can explode 爆炸性的
-ize, -ise /aɪz; aɪz/ (*makes verbs* 構成動詞) **popularize** to make popular 使普及化 | **legalize** to make legal 使...合法化 | **criticize** to find fault with; judge severely 批評

■ USAGE 用法: Both **-ize** and **-ise** are used in British English, but only **-ize** is generally used in American English. ☆在英式英語中, **-ize** 和 **-ise** 都可使用, 但在美式英語中, 一般只使用 **-ize**。

-less /ləs; ləs/ (*makes adjectives* 構成形容詞) **1** without 無, 沒有: **hopeless** without hope 沒有希望的 | **painless** causing no pain 無痛的 | **careless** without taking care 不小心的 | **powerless** without power or strength 沒有權力的; 沒有氣力的 **2** that never ...s; that cannot be ...ed 不...的; 不能...的: **tireless** never getting tired 不知疲倦的 | **countless** that cannot be counted 數不清的
-let /lɪt; lɪt/ (*makes nouns* 構成名詞) small 小...: **booklet** a small book, usually with paper covers 小冊子 | **piglet** a young pig 小豬
-like /laɪk; laɪk/ (*makes adjectives* 構成形容詞) like or similar to 像...的, 與...相似的: **childlike** of or typical of a child 孩子般的
-logy /lədʒɪ; lədʒi/ see 見 -OLOGY
-ly /lɪ; li/ **1** (*makes adverbs from adjectives* 加在形容詞後構成副詞) *Please drive* **carefully.** 請小心駕駛。 | *The man was walking very* **slowly.** 那個男人正慢慢地走。 **2** (*makes adjectives and adverbs* 構成形容詞和副詞) happening regularly 每隔...時間: **hourly** happening every hour 每小時一次的 | **daily** happening each day 每日的 **3** (*makes adjectives* 構成形容詞) having the manner of 有...態度的: **motherly** having or showing the love, kindness, etc., of a mother 慈母般的 **4** (*makes adverbs* 構成副詞) from a particular point of view 從某種觀點來看: *Some people didn't like the film, but* **personally** *I thought it was very good.* 有些人不喜歡那部電影, 但就我個人來說, 我認為它拍得很好。
-ment /mənt; mənt/ (*makes nouns from verbs* 由動詞構成名詞) **1** the act or result of ...的行動; ...的結果: **government** the act or method of ruling a country 〔國家的〕統治 | **encirclement** the action or result of making a circle around something 包圍 | **development** the action or result of developing 發展; 進展 **2** the condition of ...的狀態: **confinement** the state of being CONFINED (enclosed within limits); the time during which a woman about to give birth has to stay in bed 受限制狀態; 分娩期
-most /most; məʊst/ (*makes the superlative of some adjectives and adverbs* 構成某些形容詞和副詞的最高級) most 最: **topmost**

nearest the top 最高的; 最上面的 | **northernmost** nearest the north 最北部的
-ness /nɪs; n↓s/ (*makes nouns* 構成名詞) **goodness** the quality of being good 優良; 優秀 | **loudness** the quality of being loud 響度
-ology /ˈɑlədʒɪ; ɒlədʒi/ (*makes nouns* 構成名詞) the science or study of ...學: **geology** the study of the materials which make up the earth 地質學 | **sociology** the scientific study of societies and human groups 社會學
-or /ə/; ər/ see 見 -ER
-ory /ərɪ; əri/ **1** (*makes adjectives* 構成形容詞) **satisfactory** causing SATISFACTION; good enough 令人滿意的 **2** (*makes nouns* 構成名詞) place or thing used for 作...用的場所或物品: **observatory** a place where scientists look at stars, etc. 天文台
-ous /əs; əs/ (*makes adjectives* 構成形容詞) **dangerous** able to or likely to cause danger 危險的 | **spacious** having a lot of space 寬敞的
-phile /faɪl; faɪl/ (*makes nouns* 構成名詞) a person who is attracted to 愛好...的人: **Anglophile** a person who likes England 親英分子
-philia /ˈfɪlɪə; ˈfɪliə/ (*makes nouns* 構成名詞) love of 愛好: **Anglophilia** a love of England 親英態度 –compare 比較 **-phobia**
-phobia /ˈfobɪə; ˈfəʊbiə/ (*makes nouns* 構成名詞) very strong fear or dislike 恐懼, 憎惡: **Anglophobia** a dislike of England 仇英心理 | **claustrophobia** a fear of being in a closed space 幽閉恐懼 –compare 比較 **-philia**
-ry /rɪ; ri/ see 見 -ERY
-s, -es /z, s, ɪz; z, s, ɪz/ **1** (*makes the plural of nouns* 構成名詞的複數形式) *one* **cat,** *three* **cats** 一隻貓, 三隻貓 | *one* **glass,** *two* **glasses** 一隻玻璃杯, 兩隻玻璃杯 **2** (*makes the third person singular of the present tense of verbs* 構成動詞現在式第三人稱單數的形式) *she* **sings** 她唱歌 | *He* **likes** *reading.* 他喜歡閱讀。 | *He* **watches** *television.* 他看電視。
-ship /ʃɪp; ʃɪp/ (*makes nouns* 構成名詞) **1** the state or condition of having or being ...的狀態; 有...的狀態: **friendship** the condition of having a friendly relationship 友誼 | **partnership** the state of being a partner, especially in business 合夥 **2** skill; craft 技巧, 技術: **scholarship** the knowledge, work or method of SCHOLARS 學問; 學術成就; 學術研究 | **workmanship** skill in making things 工藝 | **musicianship** skill in performing or judging music 音樂技巧; 音樂鑑賞力
-some /səm; səm/ **1** (*makes nouns* 構成名詞) **twosome** a group of two people or things 兩人一組; 兩件一組 **2** (*makes adjectives* 構成形容詞) causing; producing 引起...的, 產生...的: **fearsome** causing fear 令人恐懼的 | **troublesome** causing trouble 引起麻煩的

-ster /stə; stə^r/ (*makes nouns* 構成名詞) a person who does an activity or who is of a certain group 參加...活動的人; 某一類別的人: **youngster** a young person 年輕人

-th /θ; θ/ (*makes adjectives from numbers, except for those ending in 1, 2, or 3* 加在 1, 2 或 3 以外的數字後面構成形容詞) **sixth** 第六 | **hundredth** 第一百 | **fortieth** 第四十

-ty /tɪ; tɪ/ see 見 -ITY

-ule /juːl; juːl/ a small kind of 小...: **globule** a drop of liquid 一小滴

-ure /jə; jə^r/ (*makes nouns from verbs* 由動詞構成名詞) **closure** the act of closing 關閉 | **failure** lack of success; failing 失敗

-ward /wəd; wəd/ *also* 又作 **-wards** /wədz; wədz/ (*makes adjectives and adverbs* 構成形容詞和副詞) in the direction of 朝...方向: **backward** directed toward the back, the beginning, or the past 向後的 | **homeward** going toward home 回家的

-ware /wɛr; weər/ (*makes nouns* 構成名詞): **hardware** metal goods for the home and garden, such as pans, tools etc. 金屬器具 | **ironware** goods made from iron 鐵器

-ways /wez; weɪz/ see 見 -WISE

-wise /waɪz; waɪz/ *also* 又作 **-ways 1** (*makes adjectives and adverbs* 構成形容詞和副詞) in the manner or direction of 以...方式; 朝...方向: **lengthise** in the direction of the length 縱向的 | **clockwise** in the direction in which the hands of a clock move 按順時針方向 **2** (*often infml* 常作非正式) (*makes adverbs* 構成副詞) with regard to 在...方面 **moneywise** with regard to money 在金錢方面: *I'm having a lot of problems moneywise.* 我在金錢方面碰到了許多麻煩。

-y /ɪ; i/ **1** (*makes nouns* 構成名詞) **jealousy** a JEALOUS feeling 嫉妒 | **sympathy** pity for the suffering of another 同情 **2** *also* 又作 **-ie** (*infml* 〔非正式〕) (*makes nouns* 構成名詞) names for people 〔用於人名、稱謂〕: **granny** grandmother (外)祖母 | **Jamie** James 傑米 **3** (*makes nouns* 構成名詞) names for animals, used especially by small children 〔尤指幼兒使用的動物名稱〕: **doggy** dog 狗狗 **4** (*makes adjectives* 構成形容詞) **noisy** making a lot of noise 吵鬧的 | **sunny** having bright sunlight 陽光明媚的

List of irregular verbs 不規則動詞表

The list below shows those verbs that have irregular past tense, PAST PARTICIPLE, or PRESENT PARTICIPLE forms.

The INFINITIVE form is shown first, e.g. **begin**

2 = past tense, e.g. *As I was walking home it* **began** *to rain.*

3 = past participle, e.g. *It had already* **begun** *to rain before I left home.*

4 = present participle, e.g. *It is just* **beginning** *to rain now.*

The number **2/3** means that the past tense and past participle are the same form. The pronunciation of each form is shown at its own place in the dictionary.

下表所列的動詞均有不規則的過去式、過去分詞或現在分詞形式。

列在前面的是不定式／不定詞，例如：**begin**

2 ＝ 過去式，例如：*As I was walking home it* **began** *to rain.* 我回家時，天開始下雨。

3 ＝ 過去分詞，例如：*It had already* **begun** *to rain before I left home.* 我離家前天已經開始下雨。

4 ＝ 現在分詞，例如：*It is just* **beginning** *to rain now.* 現在剛開始下雨。

2/3 ＝ 表示該詞的過去式與過去分詞的詞形相同。每種形式的讀音分別見於本詞典各有關詞條。

abide¹ 2/3 abided 4 abiding

abide² 2 abode 3 abided 4 abiding

arise 2 arose 3 arisen 4 arising

awake 2 awoke 或 awaked 3 awaked 或 awoken 4 awaking

be — 見 BE

bear 2 bore 3 borne 4 bearing

beat 2 beat 3 beaten 或 beat 4 beating

become 2 became 3 become 4 becoming

befall 2 befell 3 befallen 4 befalling

begin 2 began 3 begun 4 beginning

behold 2/3 beheld 4 beholding

bend 2/3 bent 4 bending

bereave 2/3 bereaved 或 bereft 4 bereaving

beseech 2/3 besought 或 beseeched 4 beseeching

beset 2/3 beset 4 besetting

bet 2/3 bet 或 betted 4 betting

bid¹ 2/3 bid 4 bidding

bid³ 2 bade 或 bid 3 bidden 或 bid 4 bidding

bide 2 bode 或 bided 3 bided 4 biding

bind 2/3 bound 4 binding

bite 2 bit 3 bitten 4 biting

bleed 2/3 bled 4 bleeding

bless 2/3 blessed 或 blest 4 blessing

blow 2 blew 3 blown 4 blowing

break 2 broke 3 broken 4 breaking

breed 2/3 bred 4 breeding

bring 2/3 brought 4 bringing

broadcast 2/3 broadcast ‖ 又作 broadcasted 【美式】4 broadcasting

build 2/3 built 4 building

burn 2/3 burnt 或 burned 4 burning

burst 2/3 burst 4 bursting

buy 2/3 bought 4 buying

cast 2/3 cast 4 casting

catch 2/3 caught 4 catching

chide 2 chided 或 chid 3 chid 或 chidden ‖ 又作 chidded【美式】4 chiding

choose 2 chose 3 chosen 4 choosing

cleave 2 cleaved 或 cleft 或 clove 3 cleaved 或 cleft 或 cloven 4 cleaving

cling 2/3 clung 4 clinging

clothe 2 clothed ‖ 又作 clad 【美式】3 clad ‖ 又作 clothed【美式】4 clothing

come 2 came 3 come 4 coming

cost 2/3 cost 4 costing

creep 2/3 crept 4 creeping

cut 2/3 cut 4 cutting

dare 2/3 dared 4 daring

deal 2/3 dealt 4 dealing

dig 2/3 dug 4 digging

dive 2 dived ‖ 又作 dove【美式】3 dived 4 diving

do — 見 DO

draw 2 drew 3 drawn 4 drawing

dream 2/3 dreamed 或 dreamt 4 dreaming

drink 2 drank 3 drunk 4 drinking

drive 2 drove **3** driven **4** driving

dwell 2/3 dwelt 或 dwelled **4** dwelling

eat 2 ate **3** eaten **4** eating

fall 2 fell **3** fallen **4** falling

feed 2/3 fed **4** feeding

feel 2/3 felt **4** feeling

fight 2/3 fought **4** fighting

find 2/3 found **4** finding

flee 2/3 fled **4** fleeing

fling 2/3 flung **4** flinging

fly 2 flew **3** flown **4** flying

forbear 2 forbore **3** forborne **4** forbearing

forbid 2 forbade 或 forbad **3** forbidden 或 forbid **4** forbidding

forecast 2/3 forecast 或 forecasted **4** forecasting

foresee 2 foresaw **3** foreseen **4** foreseeing

foretell 2/3 foretold **4** foretelling

forget 2 forgot **3** forgotten **4** forgetting

forgive 2 forgave **3** forgiven **4** forgiving

forsake 2 forsook **3** forsaken **4** forsaking

forswear 2 forswore **3** forsworn **4** forswearing

freeze 2 froze **3** frozen **4** freezing

get 2 got **3** got 尤用於【英式】‖ gotten【美式】 **4** getting

gild 2/3 gilded 或 gilt **4** gilding

give 2 gave **3** given **4** giving

go 2 went **3** gone **4** going

grind 2/3 ground **4** grinding

grow 2 grew **3** grown **4** growing

hang¹ 2/3 hung **4** hanging

hang² 2/3 hanged **4** hanging

have — 見 HAVE

hear 2/3 heard **4** hearing

heave¹ 2/3 heaved **4** heaving

heave² 2/3 hove **4** heaving

hew 2 hewed **3** hewed 或 hewn **4** hewing

hide 2 hid **3** hidden **4** hiding

hit 2/3 hit **4** hitting

hold 2/3 held **4** holding

hurt 2/3 hurt **4** hurting

keep 2/3 kept **4** keeping

kneel 2/3 knelt【英式】‖ 又作 kneeled【美式】 **4** kneeling

knit 2/3 knit 或 knitted **4** knitting

know 2 knew **3** known **4** knowing

lay 2/3 laid **4** laying

lead 2/3 led **4** leading

lean 2/3 leant 尤用於【英式】‖ leaned 尤用於【美式】 **4** leaning

leap 2/3 leapt 尤用於【英式】‖ 又作 leaped 尤用於【美式】 **4** leaping

learn 2/3 learned 或 learnt **4** learning

leave 2/3 left **4** leaving

lend 2/3 lent **4** lending

let 2/3 let **4** letting

lie¹ 2 lay **3** lain **4** lying

lie² 2/3 lied **4** lying

light 2/3 lit 或 lighted **4** lighting

lose 2/3 lost **4** losing

make 2/3 made **4** making

mean 2/3 meant **4** meaning

meet 2/3 met **4** meeting

mislay 2/3 mislaid **4** mislaying

mislead 2/3 misled **4** misleading

misspell 2/3 misspelt 或 misspelled **4** misspelling

misspend 2/3 misspent **4** misspending

mistake 2 mistook **3** mistaken **4** mistaking

misunderstand 2/3 misunderstood **4** misunderstanding

mow 2 mowed **3** mown 或 mowed **4** mowing

outbid 2 outbid **3** outbid ‖ 又作 outbidden【美式】 **4** outbidding

outdo 2 outdid **3** outdone **4** outdoing

outshine 2/3 outshone **4** outshining

overcome 2 overcame **3** overcome **4** overcoming

overdo 2 overdid **3** overdone **4** overdoing

overhang 2/3 overhung **4** overhanging

overhear 2/3 overheard **4** overhearing

override 2 overrode **3** overridden **4** overriding

overrun 2 overran **3** overrun **4** overrunning

oversee 2 oversaw **3** overseen **4** overseeing

overshoot 2/3 overshot **4** overshooting

oversleep 2/3 overslept **4** oversleeping

overtake 2 overtook **3** overtaken **4** overtaking

overthrow 2 overthrew **3** overthrown **4** overthrowing

partake 2 partook 3 partaken 4 partaking

pay 2/3 paid 4 paying

prove 2 proved 3 proved 或 proven 4 proving

put 2/3 put 4 putting

quit 2 quit 3 quit 或 quitted 4 quitting

read 2/3 read 4 reading

rebuild 2/3 rebuilt 4 rebuilding

redo 2 redid 3 redone 4 redoing

relay 2/3 relayed 4 relaying

remake 2/3 remade 4 remaking

rend 2/3 rent ‖ 又作 rended【美式】 4 rending

repay 2/3 repaid 4 repaying

rewrite 2 rewrote 3 rewritten 4 rewriting

rid 2 rid 或 ridded 3 rid 4 ridding

ride 2 rode 3 ridden 4 riding

ring[2] 2/3 ringed 4 ringing

ring[3] 2 rang 3 rung 4 ringing

rise 2 rose 3 risen 4 rising

run 2 ran 3 run 4 running

saw 2 sawed 3 sawn ‖ 又作 sawed【美式】 4 sawing

say 2/3 said 4 saying

see 2 saw 3 seen 4 seeing

seek 2/3 sought 4 seeking

sell 2/3 sold 4 selling

send 2/3 sent 4 sending

set 2/3 set 4 setting

sew 2 sewed 3 sewn ‖ 又作 sewed【美式】 4 sewing

shake 2 shook 3 shaken 4 shaking

shave 2/3 shaved 4 shaving

shear 2 sheared 3 sheared 或 shorn 4 shearing

shed 2/3 shed 4 shedding

shine[1] 2/3 shone 4 shining

shine[2] 2/3 shined 4 shining

shoot 2/3 shot 4 shooting

show 2 showed 3 shown ‖ 又作 showed【美式】 4 showing

shrink 2 shrank 或 shrunk 3 shrunk 或 shrunken 4 shrinking

shut 2/3 shut 4 shutting

sing 2 sang 3 sung 4 singing

sink 2 sank ‖ 又作 sunk【美式】3 sunk ‖ 又作

sunken【美式】4 sinking

sit 2/3 sat 4 sitting

slay 2 slew 3 slain 4 slaying

sleep 2/3 slept 4 sleeping

slide 2/3 slid 4 sliding

sling 2/3 slung 4 slinging

slink 2/3 slunk 4 slinking

slit 2/3 slit 4 slitting

smell 2/3 smelt 尤用於【英式】‖ smelled 尤用於【美式】 4 smelling

smite 2 smote 3 smitten ‖ 又作 smote【美式】 4 smiting

sow 2 sowed 3 sown 或 sowed 4 sowing

speak 2 spoke 3 spoken 4 speaking

speed 2/3 sped ‖ 又作 speeded【美式】 4 speeding

spell 2/3 spelt 尤用於【英式】‖ spelled 尤用於【美式】 4 spelling

spend 2/3 spent 4 spending

spill 2/3 spilled 或 spilt 4 spilling

spin 2/3 spun 4 spinning

spit 2/3 spat ‖ 又作 spit【美式】 4 spitting

split 2/3 split 4 splitting

spoil 2/3 spoiled 或 spoilt 4 spoiling

spread 2/3 spread 4 spreading

spring 2 sprang ‖ 又作 sprung【美式】 3 sprung 4 springing

stand 2/3 stood 4 standing

steal 2 stole 3 stolen 4 stealing

stick 2/3 stuck 4 sticking

sting 2/3 stung 4 stringing

stink 2 stank 或 stunk 3 stunk 4 stinking

strew 2 strewed 3 strewn 或 strewed 4 strewing

stride 2 strode 3 stridden 4 striding

strike 2 struck 3 struck ‖ 又作 stricken【美式】 4 striking

string 2/3 strung 4 stringing

strive 2 strove 3 striven ‖ 又作 strived【美式】 4 striving

swear 2 swore 3 sworn 4 swearing

sweep 2/3 swept 4 sweeping

swell 2 swelled 3 swollen 或 swelled 4 swelling

swim 2 swam 3 swum 4 swimming

swing 2/3 swung 4 swinging

take 2 took 3 taken 4 taking
teach 2/3 taught 4 teaching
tear 2 tore 3 torn 4 tearing
tell 2/3 told 4 telling
think 2/3 thought 4 thinking
thrive 2 throve 或 thrived 3 thrived 或 thriven 4 thriving
throw 2 threw 3 thrown 4 throwing
thrust 2/3 thrust 4 thrusting
tread 2 trod 3 trodden 或 trod 4 treading
unbend 2/3 unbent 4 unbending
undergo 2 underwent 3 undergone 4 undergoing
understand 2/3 understood 4 understanding
undertake 2 undertook 3 undertaken 4 undertaking
undo 2 undid 3 undone 4 undoing
unwind 2/3 unwound 4 unwinding
uphold 2/3 upheld 4 upholding

upset 2/3 upset 4 upsetting
wake 2 woke 或 waked 3 woken 或 waked 4 waking
waylay 2/3 waylaid 4 waylaying
wear 2 wore 3 worn 4 wearing
weave[1] 2 wove 3 woven 4 weaving
weave[2] 2/3 weaved 4 weaving
wed 2/3 wedded 或 wed 4 wedding
weep 2/3 wept 4 weeping
wet 2/3 wet 或 wetted 4 wetting
win 2/3 won 4 winning
wind[2] 2/3 winded 4 winding
wind[3] 2/3 wound 4 winding
withdraw 2 withdrew 3 withdrawn 4 withdrawing
withhold 2/3 withheld 4 withholding
withstand 2/3 withstood 4 withstanding
wring 2/3 wrung 4 wringing
write 2 wrote 3 written 4 writing

Geographical Names 地名

Afghanistan /æfˈɡænəˌstæn; æfˈɡænɨstɑːn/ 阿富汗 **Afghan** /ˈæfɡən; ˈæfɡæn/
◆ *person* 人: **Afghanistani** /æfˌɡænəˌstænɪ; æfˌɡænɨˈstɑːni/, **Afghan**

Africa /ˈæfrɪkə; ˈæfrɪkə/ 非洲 **African** /ˈæfrɪkən; ˈæfrɪkən/

Alaska /əˈlæskə; əˈlæskə/ 阿拉斯加 **Alaskan** /əˈlæskən; əˈlæskən/

Albania /ælˈbeɪnɪə; ælˈbeɪnɪə/ 阿爾巴尼亞 **Albanian** /ælˈbeɪnɪən; ælˈbeɪnɪən/

Algeria /ælˈdʒɪrɪə; ælˈdʒɪrɪə/ 阿爾及利亞 **Algerian** /ælˈdʒɪrɪən; ælˈdʒɪrɪən/

America /əˈmɛrɪkə; əˈmerɨkə/ 美洲; 美國 **American** /əˈmɛrɪkən; əˈmerɨkən/

Angola /æŋˈɡolə; æŋˈɡəʊlə/ 安哥拉 **Angolan** /æŋˈɡolən; æŋˈɡəʊlən/

Antarctic /æntˈɑrktɪk; ænˈtɑːktɪk/ 南極 (地區) **Antarctic**

Antigua /ænˈtiɡə; ænˈtiːɡə/ 安提瓜島 **Antiguan** /ænˈtiɡən; ænˈtiːɡən/

Arctic /ˈɑrktɪk; ˈɑːktɪk/ 北極 (地區) **Arctic**

Argentina /ˌɑrdʒənˈtinə; ˌɑːdʒənˈtiːnə/ 阿根廷 **Argentinian** /ˌɑrdʒənˈtinɪən; ˌɑːdʒənˈtɪnɪən/

Armenia /ɑrˈminɪə; ɑːˈmiːnɪə/ 亞美尼亞 **Armenian** /ɑrˈminɪən; ɑːˈmiːnɪən/

Asia /ˈeʃə; ˈeʒə; ˈeʃə, -ʒə/ 亞洲 **Asian** /ˈeʃən; ˈeʒən; ˈeʃən, -ʒən/

Atlantic /ətˈlæntɪk; ətˈlæntɪk/ 大西洋 **Atlantic**

Australia /ɔˈstreljə; ɒˈstreɪlɪə/ 澳大利亞, 澳洲 **Australian** /ɔˈstreljən; ɒˈstreɪlɪən/

Austria /ˈɔstrɪə; ˈɒstrɪə/ 奧地利, 奧國 **Austrian** /ˈɔstrɪən; ˈɒstrɪən/

Azerbaijan /ˌɑzəˌbaɪˈdʒɑn; ˌæzəbaɪˈdʒɑːn/ 阿塞拜疆 **Azerbaijani** /ˌɑzəˌbaɪˈdʒɑnɪ; ˌæzəbaɪˈdʒɑːni/

Bahamas /bəˈhɑməz; bəˈhɑːməz/ 巴哈馬 **Bahamian** /bəˈhemɪən; bəˈheɪmɪən/

Bahrain /bɑˈren; bɑːˈreɪn/ 巴林 **Bahraini** /bɑˈreni; bɑːˈreɪni/

Baltic /ˈbɔltɪk; ˈbɒːltɪk/ 波羅的海 **Baltic**

Bangladesh /ˈbæŋɡləˌdɛʃ; ˌbæŋɡləˈdeʃ/ 孟加拉國 **Bangladesh**
◆ *person* 人: **Bangladeshi** /ˈbæŋɡləˌdɛʃɪ; ˌbæŋɡləˈdeʃi/

Barbados /bɑrˈbedoz; bɑːˈbeɪdɒs/ 巴巴多斯, 巴貝多 **Barbadian** /bɑrˈbedɪən; bɑːˈbeɪdɪən/

Belgium /ˈbɛldʒɪəm; ˈbeldʒəm/ 比利時 **Belgian** /ˈbɛldʒən; ˈbeldʒən/

Belize /bɛˈliz; bəˈliːz/ 伯利茲 **Belizean** /bɛˈlizɪən; bəˈliːzɪən/

Benin /bəˈnɪn; bəˈniːn/ 貝寧 **Beninese** /ˌbɛnɪˈniz; ˌbeniˈniːz/

Bermuda /bəˈmjudə; bəˈmjuːdə/ 百慕大, 百慕達 **Bermudan** /bəˈmjudən; bəˈmjuːdən/

Bhutan /buˈtɑn; buːˈtɑːn/ 不丹 **Bhutani** /buˈtɑnɪ; buːˈtɑːni/

Bolivia /bəˈlɪvɪə; bəˈlɪvɪə/ 玻利維亞 **Bolivian** /bəˈlɪvɪən; bəˈlɪvɪən/

Bosnia and Herzegovina /ˈbɑznɪə ənd ˌhɜːtsəɡoˈvinə; ˌbɒznɪə ənd ˌhɜːtsəɡəʊˈviːnə/ 波斯尼亞-黑塞哥維那 **Bosnian** /ˈbɑznɪən; ˈbɒznɪən/

Botswana /bɑtsˈwɑnə; bɒtˈswɑːnə/ 博茨瓦納, 波札那 **Botswanan** /bɑtsˈwɑnən; bɒtˈswɑːnən/
◆ *person* 人: **Motswana** /mɑtˈswɑnə; mɒtˈswɑːnə/ 又作 **Batswana** /bætˈswɑnə; bætˈswɑːnə/

Brazil /brəˈzɪl; brəˈzɪl/ 巴西 **Brazilian** /brəˈzɪljən; brəˈzɪlɪən/

Brunei /bruˈnaɪ; ˈbruːnaɪ/ 文萊 **Bruneian** /bruˈnaɪən; bruːˈnaɪən/

Bulgaria /bʌlˈɡɛrɪə; bʌlˈɡeərɪə/ 保加利亞 **Bulgarian** /bʌlˈɡɛrɪən; bʌlˈɡeərɪən/

Burkina Faso /burkinə ˈfæsoʊ; buəˌkiːnə ˈfæsəʊ/ 布基納法索 **Burkinese** /ˌbɜːkɪˈniz; ˌbɜːkɪˈniːz/
◆ *person* 人: **Burkinian** /bɜˈkɪnɪən; bɜːˈkɪnɪən/

Burma /ˈbɜːmə; ˈbɜːmə/ 緬甸 **Burmese** /bɜˈmiz; bɜːˈmiːz/

Burundi /bəˈrʌndɪ; bʊˈrʊndi/ 布隆迪, 蒲隆地 **Burundian** /bəˈrʌndɪən; bʊˈrʊndɪən/

Cambodia /kæmˈbodɪə; kæmˈbəʊdɪə/ 柬埔寨 (舊名為 **Kampuchea**) **Cambodian** /kæmˈbodɪən; kæmˈbəʊdɪən/

Cameroon /ˌkæməˈrun; ˌkæməˈruːn/ 喀麥隆 **Cameroonian** /ˌkæməˈrunɪən; ˌkæməˈruːnɪən/

Canada /ˈkænədə; ˈkænədə/ 加拿大 **Canadian** /kəˈnedɪən; kəˈneɪdɪən/

Caribbean /ˌkærəˈbiən; ˌkærɪˈbiːən/ 加勒比 **Caribbean**

Cayman Islands /ˈkemən ˈaɪləndz; ˈkeɪmən ˌaɪləndz/ 開曼羣島 **Cayman Island** /ˈkemən ˈaɪlənd; ˌkeɪmən ˈaɪlənd/
◆ *person* 人: **Cayman Islander** /ˈkemən ˈaɪləndə; ˌkeɪmən ˈaɪləndə/

Central African Republic /ˌsɛntrəl ˈæfrɪkən rɪˈpʌblɪk; ˈsentrəl ˌæfrɪkən rɪˈpʌblɪk/ 中非共和國

Ceylon /sɪˈlan; sɪˈlɒn/ 錫蘭 (斯里蘭卡的舊稱)

Chad /tʃæd; tʃæd/ 乍得 **Chadian** /ˈtʃædɪən; ˈtʃædɪən/

Chile /ˈtʃɪlɪ; ˈtʃɪli/ 智利 **Chilean** /ˈtʃɪlɪən; ˈtʃɪlɪən/

China /ˈtʃaɪnə; ˈtʃaɪnə/ 中國 **Chinese** /ˈtʃaɪnɪz; ˌtʃaɪˈniːz/

Colombia /kəˈlʌmbɪə; kəˈlʌmbɪə/ 哥倫比亞 **Colombian** /kəˈlʌmbɪən; kəˈlʌmbɪən/

Commonwealth of the Independent States /ˈkɑmənˌwɛlθ əv ðɪ ˌɪndɪˈpɛndənt stet; kɑmənwelθ əv ðɪ ˌɪndɪˈpendənt steɪt/ 獨立國家聯合體 (獨聯體)

Congo /ˈkɑŋɡo; ˈkɒŋɡəʊ/ 剛果 **Congolese** /ˈkɑŋɡoˌliz; ˌkɒŋɡəˈliːz/

Costa Rica /ˌkɑstə ˈrikə; ˌkɒstə ˈriːkə/ 哥斯達黎加, 哥斯大黎加 **Costa Rican** /ˈkɑstə ˈrikn̩; ˌkɒstə ˈriːkən/

Croatia /kro`eʃə; krəʊ'eɪʃə/ 克羅地亞 **Croatian** /kro'eʃən; krəʊ'eɪʃən/

Cuba /`kjubə; 'kju:bə/ 古巴 **Cuban** /`kjubən; 'kju:bən/

Cyprus /`saɪprəs; 'saɪprəs/ 塞浦路斯 **Cypriot** /`sɪprɪət; 'sɪprɪət/

Czech Republic /tʃɛk rɪ`pʌblɪk; tʃek rɪ'pʌblɪk/ 捷克 (共和國) **Czech** /tʃɛk; tʃek/
◆ *person* 人: **Czech**

Denmark /`dɛnmark; 'denma:k/ 丹麥 **Danish** /`denɪʃ; 'deɪnɪʃ/
◆ *person* 人: **Dane** /den; dem/

Dominica /`dɒmɪnɪkə; ,dɒmə'ni:kə/ 多米尼加, 多明尼加 **Dominican** /də`mɪnɪkən; ,dɒmə'ni:kən/

Dominican Republic /de`mɪnɪkən rɪ`pʌblɪk; də,mɪnɪkən rɪ'pʌblɪk/ 多米尼加共和國, 多明尼加共和國 **Dominican** /də`mɪnɪkən; də'mɪnɪkən/

Ecuador /`ɛkwə,dɔr; 'ekwədɔ:/ 厄瓜多爾 **Ecuadorian** /,ɛkwə'dorɪən; ,ekwə'dɔ:rɪən/

Egypt /`idʒəpt; 'i:dʒɪpt/ 埃及 **Egyptian** /ɪ`dʒɪpʃən; ɪ'dʒɪpʃən/

El Salvador /ɛl `sælvə,dɔr; el 'sælvə,dɔ:/ 薩爾瓦多 **Salvadorian** /sælvə`dɔrɪən; ,sælvə'dɔ:rɪən/

England /`ɪŋglənd; 'ɪŋglənd/ 英格蘭; 英國 **English** /`ɪŋglɪʃ; 'ɪŋglɪʃ/
◆ *person* 人: 單數: **Englishman** /`ɪŋglɪʃmən; 'ɪŋglɪʃmən/ (女性: **-woman** /-wʊmən; -wʊmən/) 複數: **Englishmen** /`ɪŋglɪʃmən; 'ɪŋglɪʃmən/ *people* 人民: **English**

Equatorial Guinea /,ikwə`tɔrɪəl `gɪnɪ; ekwə,tɔ:rɪəl 'gɪnɪ/ 赤道幾內亞 **Equatorial Guinean** /,ikwə`tɔrɪəl `gɪnɪən; ekwə,tɔ:rɪəl 'gɪnɪən/

Eritrea /,ɛrɪ`trɪə; ,erɪ'treɪə/ 厄立特里亞 **Eritrean** /,ɛrɪ`treɪən; ,erɪ'treɪən/

Estonia /ɛ`stonɪə; e'stəʊnɪə/ 又作 **Esthonia** 愛沙尼亞 **Estonian** /ɛ`stonɪən; e'stəʊnɪən/

Ethiopia /,iθɪ`opɪə; ,i:θɪ'əʊpɪə/ 埃塞俄比亞, 衣索比亞 **Ethiopian** /,iθɪ`opɪən; ,i:θɪ'əʊpɪən/

Europe /`jurəp; 'jʊərəp/ 歐洲 **European** /,jurə`pɪən; jʊərə'pi:ən/

Fiji /`fidʒi; 'fi:dʒi:/ 斐濟, 飛枝 **Fijian** /fɪ`dʒɪən; fi:'dʒi:ən/

Finland /`fɪnlənd; 'fɪnlənd/ 芬蘭 **Finnish** /`fɪnɪʃ; 'fɪnɪʃ/
◆ *person* 人: **Finn** /fɪn; fɪn/

France /fræns; fra:ns/ 法國 **French** /frɛntʃ; frentʃ/
◆ *person* 人: 單數: **Frenchman** /`frɛntʃmən; 'frentʃmən/ (女性: **-woman** /-,wʊmən; -wʊmən/) 複數: **Frenchmen** /`frɛntʃmən; 'frentʃmən/ *people* 人民: **French**

Gabon /ga`bõ; gæ'bɒn/ 加蓬, 加彭 **Gabonese** /,gæbə`niz; ,gæbə'ni:z◄/

Gambia /`gæmbɪə; 'gæmbɪə/ 岡比亞, 甘比亞 **Gambian** /`gæmbɪən; 'gæmbɪən/

Georgia /`dʒɔrdʒə; 'dʒɔ:dʒə/ 喬治亞, 格魯吉亞 **Georgian** /`dʒɔrdʒən; 'dʒɔ:dʒən/

Germany /`dʒɝmənɪ; 'dʒɜ:mənɪ/ 德國 **German** /`dʒɝmən; 'dʒɜ:mən/

Ghana /`gɑnə; 'gɑ:nə/ 加納, 迦納 **Ghanaian** /gɑ`neɪən; gɑ:'neɪən/

Gibraltar /dʒɪ`brɔltə; dʒɪ'brɔ:ltə/ 直布羅陀 **Gibraltarian** /,dʒɪbrɔl`tɑrɪən; ,dʒɪbrɔ:l'teərɪən/

Greece /gris; gri:s/ 希臘 **Greek** /grik; gri:k/

Grenada /grɪ`nedə; grə'neɪdə/ 格林納達 **Grenadian** /grɪ`nedɪən; grə'neɪdɪən/

Guatemala /,gwatə`malə; gwa:tə'mɑ:lə/ 危地馬拉, 瓜地瑪拉 **Guatemalan** /,gwatə`malən; ,gwa:tə'mɑ:lən/

Guiana /gɪ`anə; gi'ɑ:nə/ 圭亞那 (高原) **Guianan** /gɪ`anən; gi'ɑ:nən/

Guinea /`gɪnɪ; 'gɪnɪ/ 幾內亞 **Guinean** /`gɪnɪən; 'gɪnɪən/

Guyana /gaɪ`ænə; gaɪ'ænə/ 圭亞那 **Guyanese** /,gaɪə`niz; ,gaɪə'ni:z◄/

Haiti /`hetɪ; 'heɪtɪ/ 海地 **Haitian** /`hetɪən; 'heɪʃən/

Holland /`halənd; 'hɒlənd/ 又作 **Netherlands** 荷蘭 **Dutch** /dʌtʃ; dʌtʃ/

Honduras /hɑn`durəs; hɒn'djʊərəs/ 洪都拉斯, 宏都拉斯 **Honduran** /hɑn`durən; hɒn'djʊərən/

Hong Kong /`hɑŋ `kɑŋ; 'hɒŋ 'kɒŋ/ 香港

Hungary /`hʌŋgrɪ; 'hʌŋgərɪ/ 匈牙利 **Hungarian** /hʌŋ`gɛrɪən; hʌŋ'geərɪən/

Iceland /`aɪslənd; 'aɪslənd/ 冰島 **Icelandic** /aɪs`lændɪk; aɪs'lændɪk/
◆ *person* 人: **Icelander** /`aɪs,lændə; `aɪs,ləndə/

India /`ɪndɪə; 'ɪndɪə/ 印度 **Indian** /`ɪndɪən; 'ɪndɪən/

Indonesia /,ɪndo`niʃə, -ʒə; ,ɪndə'ni:ʒə, -zɪə/ 印度尼西亞 **Indonesian** /,ɪndo`niʃən, -zɪən; ,ɪndə'ni:ʒən, -zɪən/

Iran /ɪ`ræn, i`ran; ɪ'rɑ:n, -æn/ 伊朗 **Iranian** /ɪ`renɪən; ɪ'reɪnɪən/

Iraq /ɪ`rɑk; ɪ`ræk; ɪ'rɑ:k; -æk/ 伊拉克 **Iraqi** /ɪ`rɑkɪ; ɪ'rɑ:ki, -æki/

Irish Republic /,aɪrɪʃ rɪ`pʌblɪk; ,aɪərɪʃ rɪ'pʌblɪk/ 愛爾蘭共和國 **Irish** /`aɪrɪʃ; 'aɪərɪʃ/
◆ *person* 人: 單數: **Irishman** /`aɪrɪʃmən; 'aɪərɪʃmən/ (女性: **-woman** /-,wʊmən; -,wʊmən/) 複數: **Irishmen** /-mən; -mən/ *people* 人民: **Irish**

Israel /`ɪzrɪəl; 'ɪzreɪl/ 以色列 **Israeli** /ɪz`relɪ; ɪz'reɪlɪ/

Italy /`ɪtlɪ; 'ɪtəlɪ/ 意大利, 義大利 **Italian** /ɪ`tæljən; ɪ'tælɪən/

Ivory Coast /`aɪvərɪ kost; ,aɪvərɪ 'kəʊst/ 象牙海岸 **Ivorian** /,aɪ`vɔrɪən; ,aɪ'vɔ:rɪən/

Jamaica /dʒə`mekə; dʒə'meɪkə/ 牙買加 **Jamaican** /dʒə`mekən; dʒə'meɪkən/

Japan /dʒə`pæn; dʒə'pæn/ 日本 **Japanese** /,dʒæpə`niz; ,dʒæpə'ni:z◄/

Jordan /`dʒɔrdn; 'dʒɔ:dn/ 約旦 **Jordanian** /dʒɔr`denɪən; dʒɔ:'deɪnɪən/

Kampuchea /,kæmpu`tʃɪə; ,kæmpʊ'tʃɪə/ 柬埔寨, 高棉 **Kampuchean** /,kæmpu`tʃɪən; ,kæmpʊ'tʃi:ən/ 又作 **Cambodian** /kæm`bodɪən; kæm'bəʊdɪən/

Kazakhstan /,kazak`stan; ,kæzæk'stɑ:n/ 又作 **Kazakstan** 哈薩克 **Kazakh** /kə`zæn; kə'zæk/ 又作 **Kazak**

Kenya /`kɛnjə; `kɪnjə; 'kenjə, 'ki:-/ 肯尼亞

Kenyan /ˈkɛnjən; ˈkinjən; ˈkenjən, ˈkiː-/

Korea /koˈrɪə; kəˈrɪə/ 朝鮮, 韓國 **Korean** /koˈrɪən; kəˈrɪən/

Kuwait /kuˈwaɪt; kʊˈweɪt/ 科威特 **Kuwaiti** /kuˈweɪtɪ; kʊˈweɪtɪ/

Laos /lauz; ˈlɑːɒs, laʊs/ 老撾, 寮國 **Laotian** /leˈoʃən; ˈlaʊʃən/

Latvia /ˈlætvɪə; ˈlætvɪə/ 拉脫維亞 **Latvian** /ˈlætvɪən; ˈlætvɪən/

Lebanon /ˈlɛbənən; ˈlebənən/ 黎巴嫩 **Lebanese** /ˌlɛbəˈniz; ˌlebəˈniːz◂/

Lesotho /ləˈsutu; ləˈsuːtuː/ 萊索托 **Sesotho** /səˈsutu; səˈsuːtuː/

◆ *person* 人: 單數: **Mosotho** /məˈsutu; məˈsuːtuː/; 複數: **Basotho** /bəˈsutu; bəˈsuːtuː/

Liberia /laɪˈbɪrɪə; laɪˈbɪərɪə/ 利比亞, 賴比瑞亞 **Liberian** /laɪˈbɪrɪən; laɪˈbɪərɪən/

Libya /ˈlɪbɪə; ˈlɪbɪə/ 利比亞 **Libyan** /ˈlɪbɪən; ˈlɪbɪən/

Liechtenstein /ˈlɪktənˌstaɪn; ˈlɪktənstaɪn/ 列支敦士登, 列支敦斯登 **Liechtenstein**

◆ *person* 人: **Liechtensteiner** /ˈlɪktənˌstaɪnɚ; ˈlɪktənstaɪnə/

Lithuania /ˌlɪθjuˈenɪə; ˌlɪθjuˈeɪnɪə/ 立陶宛 **Lithuanian** /ˌlɪθjuˈenɪən; ˌlɪθjuˈeɪnɪən◂/

Luxemburg /ˈlʌksəmˌbɝg; ˈlʌksəmbɜːg/ 盧森堡 **Luxemburg**

◆ *person* 人: **Luxemburger** /ˈlʌksəmˌbɝgɚ; ˈlʌksəmbɜːgə/

Macau /məˈkau; məˈkaʊ/ 又作 **Macao** 澳門

Macedonia /ˌmæsəˈdonɪə; ˌmæsɪˈdəʊnɪə/ 馬其頓 **Macedonian** /ˌmæsəˈdonɪən; ˌmæsəˈdəʊnɪən/

Madagascar /ˌmædəˈgæskɚ; ˌmædəˈgæskəʳ/ 馬達加斯加 **Malagasy** /ˌmæləˈgæsɪ; ˌmæləˈgæsɪ◂/

Malawi /məˈlawi; məˈlɑːwi/ 馬拉維, 馬拉威 **Malawian** /məˈlawiən; məˈlɑːwiən/

Malaysia /məˈleʒə; məˈleɪzɪə/ 馬來西亞 **Malaysian** /məˈleʃən, -ʒən; məˈleɪziən/

Maldives /ˈmældaɪvz; ˈmældaɪvz/ 馬爾代夫 **Maldivian** /mælˈdɪvɪən; mælˈdɪvɪən/

Mali /ˈmalɪ; ˈmaːli/ 馬里, 馬利 **Malian** /ˈmalɪən; ˈmaːlɪən/

Malta /ˈmɔltə; ˈmɔːltə/ 馬耳他, 馬爾他 **Maltese** /mɔlˈtiz; mɔːlˈtiːz◂/

Mauritania /ˌmɔrɪˈtenɪə; ˌmɒrɪˈteɪnɪə/ 毛里塔尼亞, 茅利塔尼亞 **Mauritanian** /ˌmɔrɪˈtenɪən; ˌmɒrɪˈteɪnɪən/

Mauritius /mɔˈrɪʃəs; məˈrɪʃəs, mɔː-/ 毛里求斯, 模里西斯 **Mauritian** /mɔˈrɪʃən; məˈrɪʃən, mɔː-/

Mediterranean /ˌmɛdətəˈrenɪən; ˌmedɪtəˈreɪnɪən/ 地中海 **Mediterranean**

Melanesia /ˌmɛləˈniʒə; ˌmɛləˈniːzɪə/ 美拉尼西亞 **Melanesian** /ˌmɛləˈniʒən; ˌmɛləˈniːzɪən/

Mexico /ˈmɛksɪˌko; ˈmeksɪkəʊ/ 墨西哥 **Mexican** /ˈmɛksɪkən; ˈmeksɪkən/

Micronesia /ˌmaɪkroˈniʒə; ˌmaɪkrəʊˈniːzɪə/ 密克羅尼西亞 **Micronesian** /ˌmaɪkrəˈniʒən; ˌmaɪkrəʊˈniːzɪən/

Monaco /ˈmanəˌko; ˈmɒnəkəʊ/ 摩納哥 **Monegasque** /ˈmanɪˌgæsk; ˌmɒnɪˈgæsk/

Mongolia /maŋˈgolɪə; mɒŋˈgəʊlɪə/ 蒙古 **Mon-**

-golian /maŋˈgolian; mɒŋˈgəʊlɪən/

◆ *person* 人: **Mongolian** 或 **Mongol** /ˈmaŋgəl; ˈmɒŋgɒl/

Montserrat /ˌmantsəˈræt; ˌmɒntseˈræt/ 蒙特塞拉特島 **Montserratian** /ˌmantsəˈreʃən; ˌmɒntseˈreɪʃən/

Morocco /məˈrako; məˈrɒkəʊ/ 摩洛哥 **Moroccan** /məˈrakən; məˈrɒkən/

Mozambique /ˌmozəmˈbɪk; ˌməʊzəmˈbiːk/ 莫桑比克 **Mozambiquean** /ˌmozəmˈbɪkən; ˌməʊzəmˈbiːkən/

Namibia /nəˈmɪbɪə; nəˈmɪbɪə/ 納米比亞 **Namibian** /nəˈmɪbɪən; nəˈmɪbɪən/

Nauru /naˈuru, naˈru; naˈuːruː, naːˈ ruː/ 瑙魯, 諾魯 **Nauruan** /ˌneɪaˈruən; naːˈuːruən, naːˈruːən/

Nepal /nɪˈpɔl; nɪˈpɔːl/ 尼泊爾 **Nepalese** /ˌnɛpəˈliz; nepəˈliːz/

The Netherlands /ðə ˈnɛðɚləndz; ðə ˈneðələndz/ 荷蘭 **Dutch** /dʌtʃ; dʌtʃ/

◆ *person* 人: 單數: **Dutchman** /ˈdʌtʃmən; ˈdʌtʃmən/ (女性: **-woman** /-ˌwumən; -ˌwʊmən/) 複數: **Dutchmen** /-mən; -mən/ *people* 人民: **Dutch**

New Zealand /njuˈzilənd; njuːˈziːlənd/ 新西蘭, 紐西蘭 **New Zealand, Maori** /ˈmaurɪ; ˈmaʊəri/

◆ *person* 人: **New Zealander** /njuˈziləndɚ; njuːˈziːləndə/

Nicaragua /ˌnɪkəˈragwə; ˌnɪkəˈrægjuə/ 尼加拉瓜 **Nicaraguan** /ˌnɪkəˈragwən; ˌnɪkəˈrægjuən/

Niger /ˈnaɪdʒɚ; niˈʒɛə; ˈnaɪdʒɚ, niːˈʒeə/ 尼日爾, 尼日 **Nigerien** /niˈʒɛərɪən; niːˈʒeərɪən/

Nigeria /naɪˈdʒɪrɪə; naɪˈdʒɪərɪə/ 尼日利亞, 奈及利亞 **Nigerian** /naɪˈdʒɪrɪən; naɪˈdʒɪərɪən/

Norway /ˈnɔrwe; ˈnɔːweɪ/ 挪威 **Norwegian** /nɔrˈwidʒən; nɔːˈwiːdʒən/

Oman /oˈmæn; əʊˈmaːn/ 阿曼 **Omani** /oˈmænɪ; əʊˈmaːni/

Pacific /pəˈsɪfɪk; peˈsɪfɪk/ 太平洋 **Pacific**

Pakistan /ˌpakɪˈstan; ˌpakɪˈstæn; ˌpaːkɪˈstaːn, ˌpækɪˈstæn/ 巴基斯坦 **Pakistani** /ˌpakɪˈstanɪ; ˌpaːkɪˈstaːni, ˌpækɪˈstæni/

Palestine /ˈpæləsˌtaɪn; ˈpæləstaɪn/ 巴勒斯坦 **Palestinian** /ˌpæləsˈtɪnɪən; ˌpæləˈstɪnɪən/

Panama /ˈpænəˌma; ˈpænəˌmaː; ˌpænəˈmaː◂/ 巴拿馬 **Panamanian** /ˌpænəˈmenɪən; ˌpænəˈmeɪnɪən/

Papua New Guinea /ˌpæpjuə njuˈgɪni; ˌpæpuə njuː ˈgɪni/ 巴布亞新幾內亞 **Papuan** /ˈpæpjuən; ˈpæpjuən/

Paraguay /ˈpærəˌgwe; ˈpærəgwaɪ/ 巴拉圭 **Panaguayan** /ˌpærəˈgween; ˌpærəˈgwaɪən/

Persia /ˈpɝʒə; ˈpɜːʃə, -ʒə/ 波斯 (伊斯的舊稱)

Peru /pəˈru; pəˈruː/ 祕魯 **Peruvian** /pəˈruvɪən; pəˈruːvɪən/

Philippines /ˈfɪləˌpinz; ˈfɪlɪˈpiːnz/ 菲律賓 **Philippine** /ˈfɪləˌpin; ˈfɪlɪˈpiːn/

◆ *person* 人: **Filipino** /ˌfɪləˈpino; fɪlɪˈpiːnəʊ/

Poland /ˈpolənd; ˈpəʊlənd/ 波蘭 **Polish** /ˈpolɪʃ; ˈpəʊlɪʃ/

◆ *person* 人: **Pole** /pol; pəʊl/

Polynesia /ˌpaləˈniʒə; ˌpɒlɪˈniːzɪə/ 波利尼西亞 **Polynesian** /ˌpaləˈniʒən; ˌpɒlɪˈniːzɪən/

Portugal /ˋpɔrtʃəgl; ˈpɔːtʃʊgəl/ 葡萄牙 **Portuguese** /ˋpɔrtʃəˏgiz; ˏpɔːtʃʊˈgiːzˏ/

Puerto Rico /ˏpwɛrtəˋriko; ˏpwɜːtəʊˈriːkəʊ/ 波多黎各 **Puerto Rican** /ˏpwɛrtəˋrikən; ˏpwɜːtəʊˈriːkən/

Qatar /ˋkatar; kʌˈtɑːr/ 卡塔爾, 卡達 **Qatari** /ˋkatarɪ; kʌˈtɑːriː/

Quebec /kwɪˋbɛk; kwɪˈbek/ 魁北克 **Quebecois** /kwɪˋbɛkə; kebeˈkwɑ/

Romania /roˋmenjə; ruːˈmeɪnɪə/ 羅馬尼亞 **Romanian** /roˋmenɪən; ruːˈmeɪnɪən/

Russia /ˋrʌʃə; ˈrʌʃə/ 俄羅斯 **Russian** /ˋrʌʃən; ˈrʌʃən/

Rwanda /ruˋɑndən; ruˈændə/ 盧旺達, 盧安達 **Rwandan** /ruˋɑndən; ruˈændən/

Saudi Arabia /ˋsɔˏudɪ əˋrebɪə; ˏsaʊdɪ əˈreɪbɪə/ 沙特阿拉伯, 沙烏地阿拉伯 **Saudi Arabian** /ˋsɔˏudɪ əˋrebɪən; ˏsaʊdɪ əˈreɪbɪən/
　◆ *person* 人: **Saudi** 或 **Saudi Arabian**

Scotland /ˋskɑtlənd; ˈskɒtlənd/ 蘇格蘭 **Scottish** /ˋskɑtɪʃ; ˈskɒtɪʃ/ 或 **Scots** /skɑts; skɒts/
　◆ *person* 人: 單數: **Scot** 或 **Scotsman** /ˋskɑtsmən; ˈskɒtsmən/ (女性: **-woman** /-wumən; -wʊmən/) 複數: **Scotsmen** /-mən; -mən/ *people* 人民: **Scots**

Senegal /ˏsɛnɪˋgɔl; ˏsenɪˈɡɔːl/ 塞內加爾 **Senegalese** /ˏsɛnɪgəˋliz; ˏsenɪgəˈliːzˏ/

Seychelles /seˋʃɛlz; seɪˈʃelz/ 塞舌爾 **Seychellois** /ˏseˏʃɛlˋwa; ˏseɪʃelˈwɑː/

Siam /saɪˋæm; saɪˈæm/ 暹羅〔泰國的舊稱〕

Sierra Leone /sɪˋɛrəlɪˋonɪ; sɪˏerə lɪˈəʊn/ 塞拉利昂, 獅子山 **Sierra Leonean** /sɪˋɛrə lɪˋonɪən; sɪˏerə lɪˈəʊnɪən/

Singapore /ˋsɪŋgəˏpor; ˏsɪŋəˈpɔːr/ 新加坡 **Singaporean** /ˏsɪŋgəˋporɪən; ˏsɪŋəˈpɔːrɪən/

Slovak Republic /ˋslovak rɪˋpʌblɪk; sləʊ væk rɪˈpʌblɪk/ 斯洛伐克共和國 **Slovak** /ˋslovæk; ˈsləʊvæk/
　◆ *person* 人: **Slovak**

Slovenia /sloˋvinɪə; sləʊˈviːnɪə/ 斯拉維尼亞 **Slovene** /sloˋvɪn; ˈsləʊviːn/
　◆ *person* 人: **Slovenian** /sloˋvinɪən; sləʊˈviːnɪən/

Somalia /səˋmalɪə; səʊˈmɑːlɪə/ 索馬里, 索馬利 **Somali** /səˋmalɪ; səʊˈmɑːliː/

South Africa /saʊθ ˋæfrɪkə; saʊθ ˈæfrɪkə/ 南非 **S. African** /saʊθ ˋæfrɪkən; saʊθ ˈæfrɪkən/

Soviet Union /ˋsovɪɪt ˋjunjən; ˏsəʊvɪət ˈjuːnjən, sɒ-/ 蘇聯 **Soviet** /ˋsovɪɪt; ˈsəʊvɪət, sɒ-/ 或 **Russian** /ˋrʌʃən; ˈrʌʃən/

Spain /spen; speɪn/ 西班牙 **Spanish** /ˋspænɪʃ; ˈspænɪʃ/
　◆ *person* 人: **Spaniard** /ˋspænjəd; ˈspænjəd/

Sri Lanka /ˏsrɪˋlæŋkə; srɪː ˈlæŋkə/ 斯里蘭卡 **Sri Lankan** /ˏsrɪˋlæŋkən; srɪː ˈlæŋkən/

Sudan /suˋdæn; səˈdæn, -ˈdɑːn/ 蘇丹 **Sudanese** /ˏsudəˋniz; ˏsuːdəˈniːzˏ/

Sumatra /suˋmatrə; suːˈmɑːtrə/ 蘇門答臘 **Sumatran** /suˋmatrən; suːˈmɑːtrən/

Surinam /ˏsurɪˋnam; ˏsʊərɪˈnæm/ 蘇里南, 蘇利南 **Surinamese** /ˏsurɪnɑˋmis; ˏsʊərənɑːˈmiːzˏ/

Swaziland /ˋswazɪˏlænd; ˈswɑːzɪlænd/ 斯威士蘭, 史瓦濟蘭 **Swazi** /ˋswazɪ; ˈswɑːziː/

Sweden /ˋswidn; ˈswiːdn/ 瑞典 **Swedish** /ˋswidɪʃ; ˈswiːdɪʃ/
　◆ *person* 人: **Swede** /swid; swiːd/

Switzerland /ˋswɪtsələnd; ˈswɪtsələnd/ 瑞士 **Swiss** /swɪs; swɪs/

Syria /ˋsɪrɪə; ˈsɪrɪə/ 敍利亞 **Syrian** /ˋsɪrɪən; ˈstrɪən/

Tahiti /tɑˋhitɪ; təˈhiːtiː/ 塔希提島, 大溪地 **Tahitian** /tɑˋhitɪən; təˈhiːʃən/

Taiwan /ˏtaɪˋwan; ˏtaɪˈwɑːn/ 台灣 **Taiwanese** /ˏtaɪwɑˋniz; ˏtaɪwəˈniːzˏ/

Tanzania /ˏtænzəˋnɪə; ˏtænzəˈnɪə/ 坦桑利亞, 坦尚尼亞 **Tanzanian** /ˏtænzəˋnɪən; ˏtænzəˈnɪən/

Thailand /ˋtaɪlənd; ˈtaɪlænd, -lənd/ 泰國 **Thai** /taɪ; taɪ/

Tibet /tɪˋbɛt; tɪˈbet/ 西藏 **Tibetan** /tɪˋbɛtn; tɪˈbetn/

Timor, East /ist ˋtimor; ˏiːst ˈtiːmɔːr/ (東) 帝汶 **Timorese** /timoˋriz; ˏtiːmɔːˈriːz/

Togo /ˋtogo; ˈtəʊgəʊ/ 多哥 **Togolese** /ˏtogoˋliz; ˏtəʊgəˈliːzˏ/

Tonga /ˋtɑŋgə; ˈtɒŋgə/ 湯加, 東加 **Tongan** /ˋtɑŋgən; ˈtɒŋgən/

Trinidad & Tobago /ˋtrɪnəˏdæd ən təˋbego; ˈtrɪnɪdæd ən təˈbeɪgəʊ/ 特立尼達和多巴哥, 千里達 —— 托貝哥 **Trinidadian** /ˏtrɪnəˋdædɪən; ˏtrɪnɪˈdædɪən/ **Tobagan** /təˋbegən; təˈbeɪgən/

Tunisia /tjuˋnɪʃə; tjuːˈnɪzɪə/ 突尼斯 **Tunisian** /tjuˋnɪʃɪən; tjuːˈnɪzɪən/

Turkey /ˋtɝkɪ; ˈtɜːkiː/ 土耳其 **Turkish** /ˋtɝkɪʃ; ˈtɜːkɪʃ/
　◆ *person* 人: **Turk** /tɝk; tɜːk/

Uganda /juˋgændə; juːˈgændə/ 烏干達 **Ugandan** /juˋgændən; juːˈgændən/

Ukraine /ˋjukren; juːˈkreɪn/ 烏克蘭 **Ukranian** /juˋkrenɪən; juːˈkreɪnɪən/

United Arab Emirates /ˋjuˋnaɪtɪd ˋærəb ˋmɪrɪt; juːˈnaɪtɪd ˈærəb ˈemɪrɪts/ 阿拉伯聯合酋長國 **Emirian** /əˋmɪrɪən; eˈmɪərɪən/

United Kingdom of Great Britain and Northern Ireland /ˋjuˋnaɪtɪd ˋkɪŋdəm əf gret brɪtən ənd ˏnɔrðɚ ˋaɪrlənd; juːˏnaɪtɪd ˈkɪŋdəm əv greɪt ˏbrɪtən ənd ˏnɔːðn ˈaɪələnd/ 聯合王國, 大不列顛及北愛爾蘭聯合王國, 英國 **British** /ˋbrɪtɪʃ; ˈbrɪtɪʃ/
　◆ *person* 人: **Briton** /ˋbrɪtn; ˈbrɪtn/ **Britisher** /ˋbrɪtɪʃɚ; ˈbrɪtɪʃər/【美式】; *people* 人民: **British**

United States of America /juˋnaɪtɪd ˏstets əv əˋmɛrɪkə; juːˏnaɪtɪd ˏsteɪts əv əˈmerɪkə/ 美利堅合眾國, 美國 **American** /əˋmɛrɪkən; əˈmerɪkən/

Upper Volta /ˋʌpɚ ˋvaltə; ˏʌpər ˈvɒltə/ 上沃爾特, 上伏塔 (布基納法索的舊名)

Uruguay /ˋjurəˏgwe; ˈjʊərəgwaɪ/ 烏拉圭 **Uruguayan** /ˏjurəˋgwean; ˏjʊərəˈgwaɪən/

Uzbekistan /ˏʌzbekɪˋstan; ˏʊzbekɪˈstɑːn/ 烏茲別克 **Uzbek** /ˋʌzbɛk; ˈʊzbek/

Vatican City /ˋvætɪkən ˋsɪtɪ; ˏvætɪkən ˈsɪti/ 梵蒂岡

Venezuela /ˏvɛnəˋzwilə; ˏvenɪˈzweɪlə/ 委內瑞拉 **Venezuelan** /ˏvɛnəˋzwilən; ˏvenɪˈzweɪlən/

Vietnam /ˏviɛtˋnam; ˏvjetˈnæm/ 越南 **Vietnamese** /vi‚ɛtnəˋmiz; ˏvjetnəˈmiːzˏ/

Wales /welz; weɪlz/ 威爾士 **Welsh** /wɛlʃ; welʃ/
♦ *person* 人: 單數: **Welshman** /ˈwelʃmən;
'welʃmən/ (女性: **-woman** /-wumən; -wʊ-
mən/) 複數: **Welshmen** /-mən; -mən/ *people* 人
民: **Welsh**

West Samoa /wɛst səˈmoə; ˌwest səˈməʊə/ 西
薩摩亞 **Samoan** /səˈmoən; səˈməʊən/

Yemen /ˈjɛmən; 'jemən/ 也門 **Yemeni** /ˈjɛmənɪ;
'jeməni/

Yugoslavia /ˌjugoˈslɑvɪə; juːgəʊˈslɑːvɪə/ 南斯拉
夫 **Yugoslavian** /ˌjugoˈslɑvɪən; juːgəʊˈslɑːvɪən/
♦ *person* 人: **Yugoslav** /ˈjugoˈslɑv; 'juːgəʊslɑːv/

Zaire /zəˈirə; zaɪˈɪə/ 扎伊爾, 薩伊 **Zairean** /zəˈirən;
ˌzaɪˈɪərɪən/

Zambia /ˈzæmbɪə; 'zæmbɪə/ 贊比亞, 尚比亞
Zambian /ˈzæmbɪən; 'zæmbiən/

Zimbabwe /zɪmˈbabwe; zɪmˈbɑːbweɪ/ 津巴布韋
Zimbabwean /zɪmˈbabweən; zɪmˈbɑːbweɪən/

Numbers, Signs and Symbols 數字及符號

Numbers 數字

Cardinal 基數		Ordinal 序數		Roman 羅馬數字	
1	one	1st	first	1	I (i)
2	two	2nd	second	2	II (ii)
3	three	3rd	third	3	III (iii)
4	four	4th	fourth	4	IV (iv)
5	five	5th	fifth	5	V (v)
6	six	6th	sixth	6	VI (vi)
7	seven	7th	seventh	7	VII (vii)
8	eight	8th	eighth	8	VIII (viii)
9	nine	9th	ninth	9	IX (ix)
10	ten	10th	tenth	10	X (x)
11	eleven	11th	eleventh	11	XI (xi)
12	twelve	12th	twelfth	12	XII (xii)
13	thirteen	13th	thirteenth	13	XIII (xiii)
14	fourteen	14th	fourteenth	14	XIV (xiv)
15	fifteen	15th	fifteenth	15	XV (xv)
16	sixteen	16th	sixteenth	16	XVI (xvi)
17	seventeen	17th	seventeenth	17	XVII (xvii)
18	eighteen	18th	eighteenth	18	XVIII (xviii)
19	nineteen	19th	nineteenth	19	XIX (xix)
20	twenty	20th	twentieth	20	XX (xx)
21	twenty-one	21st	twenty-first	40	XL (xl)
22	twenty-two	22nd	twenty-second	50	L (l)
23	twenty-three	23rd	twenty-third	60	LX (lx)
24	twenty-four	24th	twenty-fourth	70	LXX (lxx)
30	thirty	30th	thirtieth	80	LXXX (lxxx)
40	forty	40th	fortieth	90	XC (xc)
50	fifty	50th	fiftieth	100	C (c)
60	sixty	60th	sixtieth	400	CD (cd)
70	seventy	70th	seventieth	500	D (d)
80	eighty	80th	eightieth	900	CM (cm)
90	ninety	90th	ninetieth	1000	M (m)
100	one hundred	100th	one [the] hundredth		
1,000	one thousand			1702	MDCCII
10,000	ten thousand			1999	MCMXCIX
100,000	one hundred thousand			2000	MM
1,000,000	one million			2001	MMI

$\overline{X} = 10 \times 1{,}000 = 10{,}000$

$\overline{C} = 100 \times 1{,}000 = 100{,}000$

$\overline{M} = 1{,}000 \times 1{,}000 = 1{,}000{,}000$

Dates 日期

Jan. 8 = January eight

Jan. 8th = January (the) eighth

8 January, 1999 = the eighth of January nineteen ninety-nine

January 8, 1999 = January (the) eighth nineteen ninety-nine

*注意：在英式英語中，日期的寫法為日／月／年，如 28／03／99，而美式英語為月／日／年，如 03／28／99。

英式寫法	美式寫法
6 January, 1998	January 6, 1998
6th January, 1998	January 6th, 1998
6 Jan. 1998	Jan. 6, 1998
6th Jan. 1998	Jan. 6th, 1998
6 Jan. '98	Jan. 6th 1998
6th Jan. '98	1.6. '98
6 Jan. 98	1.6.98
6th Jan. 98	1/6/1998
6.1. '98	1/6/98
6.1.98	
6/1/1998	
6/1/98	

35 B.C. = Thirty-five B.C.〔Before Christ 公元前〕

AD 65 = AD sixty-five〔Anno Domini 公元〕

*注意：一般來説 AD 可以不寫。

1073 = ten seventy-three

1900 = nineteen hundred

1960 = nineteen sixty

2000 = the year two thousand

2001 = twenty oh one/two thousand and one

1960s = nineteen sixties 二十世紀六十年代

Time 時間

09:00	nine o'clock; nine a.m.; nine hundred (hours) 上午九時正
09:08	nine eight; eight past nine 上午九時零八分
09:15	nine fifteen; a quarter past nine 上午九時十五分；上午九時一刻
09:30	nine thirty; half past nine 上午九時三十分；上午九時半
09:45	nine forty-five; a quarter to ten 上午九時四十五分；上午九時三刻
09:56	nine fifty-six; four to ten 上午九時五十六分
12:00	twelve o'clock; at noon; twelve hundred (hours) 中午十二時正
14:12	fourteen twelve; two twelve p.m. 下午二時十二分
24:00	twenty-four hundred (hours); at midnight 午夜十二時正

Common fractions 分數

$\frac{1}{4}$ = a (或 one) quarter   四分之一 ; $2\frac{1}{4}$ = two and a quarter   二又四分之一

$\frac{1}{2}$ = a (或 one) half   二分之一 ; $2\frac{1}{2}$ = two and a half   二又二分之一

$\frac{3}{4}$ = three quarters   四分之三 ; $3\frac{3}{4}$ = three and three quarters   三又四分之三

$\frac{5}{16}$ = five sixteenths   十六分之五 ; $4\frac{5}{16}$ = four and five sixteenths   四又十六分之五

Decimal fractions 小數

0.125 = (nought) point one two five

0.15 = (nought) point one five

0.5 = (nought) point five

6.57 = six point five seven

28.32 = twenty eight point three two

Mathematical Expressions 數學符號

+	plus; and	加
−	minus	減
×	times; (is) multiplied by; by	乘
÷	(is) divided by	除以
±	plus or minus; approximately	加或減；正負；近似
Σ	summation of; sum; sigma	總和
=	equals; is equal to	等於
≠	is not equal to; does not equal	不等於；不相等
≈	is approximately equal to	約等於；近似於
≡	is equivalent to; is identical with	全等於；恒等於
<	is less than	小於
≤	is less than or equal to	小於或等於
>	is greater/more than	大於
≥	is greater than or equal to	大於或等於
⊂	is included in; is a subset of	被包括於；是...集合的子集
∈	is an element of (a set)	屬於...(集合) 的元素；屬於
⊃	includes	包括
→, ⇒, ⊃	implies	蘊涵
%	per cent	百分之...；百分率
3:9	three to nine	三比九
2:6::3:9	proportion: two is to six as three is to nine	比例：二比六等於三比九
α	varies as; is proportional to	(校正比或反比) 變化；與...成 (正比或反比的) 比例
∞	infinity	無限大
√	square root	平方根
∛	cube root	立方根
x^2	x squared	x 平方
x^3	x cubed	x 立方
x^4	x to the power of four; x to the fourth power	x 四次方
π	pi	圓周率
∠	angle	角
∟	right angle	直角
‖	is parallel to	平行於
⊥	is perpendicular to	垂直於
°	degree	度
′	foot; minute	英尺；分
″	inch; second	英寸；秒
∵	because	因為；由於
∴	therefore; hence	所以

Chemical Elements 化學元素表

符號	名稱	符號	名稱
Ac	Actinium 錒	Mg	Magnesium 鎂
Ag	Silver 銀	Mn	Manganese 錳
Al	Aluminium 鋁	Mo	Molybdenum 鉬
Am	Americium 鋂	N	Nitrogen 氮
Ar	Argon 氬	Na	Sodium 鈉
As	Arsenic 砷	Nb	Niobium 鈮
At	Astatine 砹	Nd	Neodymium 釹
Au	Gold 金	Ne	Neon 氖
B	Boron 硼	Ni	Nickel 鎳
Ba	Barium 鋇	No	Nobelium 鍩
Be	Beryllium 鈹	Np	Neptunium 錼
Bi	Bismuth 鉍	O	Oxygen 氧
Bk	Berkelium 錇	Os	Osmium 鋨
Br	Bromine 溴	P	Phosphorus 磷
C	Carbon 碳	Pa	Protactinium 鏷
Ca	Calcium 鈣	Pb	Lead 鉛
Cd	Cadmium 鎘	Pd	Palladium 鈀
Ce	Cerium 鈰	Pm	Promethium 鉕
Cf	Californium 鐦	Po	Polonium 釙
Cl	Chlorine 氯	Pr	Praseodymium 鐠
Cm	Curium 鋦	Pt	Platinum 鉑
Co	Cobalt 鈷	Pu	Plutonium 鈈
Cr	Chromium 鉻	Ra	Radium 鐳
Cs	Caesium 銫	Rb	Rubidium 銣
Cs	Copper 銅	Re	Rhenium 錸
Dy	Dysprosium 鏑	Rf	Rutherfordium 鑪
Er	Erbium 鉺	Rh	Rhodium 銠
Es	Einsteinium 鑀，鎄	Rn	Radon 氡
Eu	Europium 銪	Ru	Ruthenium 釕
F	Fluorine 氟	S	Sulphur 硫
Fe	Iron 鐵	Sb	Antimony 銻
Fm	Fermium 鐨	Sc	Scandium 鈧
Fr	Francium 鈁	Se	Selenium 硒
Ga	Gallium 鎵	Si	Silicon 矽，硅
Gd	Gadolinium 釓	Sm	Samarium 釤
Ge	Germanium 鍺	Sn	Tin 錫
H	Hydrogen 氫	Sr	Strontium 鍶
Ha	Habnium 𨧀	Ta	Tantalum 鉭
He	Helium 氦	Tb	Terbium 鋱
Hf	Hafnium 鉿	Te	Tellurium 碲
Hg	Mercury 汞	Th	Thorium 釷
Ho	Holmium 鈥	Ti	Titanium 鈦
I	Iodine 碘	Tl	Thallium 鉈
In	Indium 銦	Tm	Thulium 銩
Ir	Iridium 銥	U	Uranium 鈾
K	Potassium 鉀	V	Vanadium 釩
Kr	Krypton 氪	W	Tungsten 鎢
La	Lanthanum 鑭	Xe	Xenon 氙
Li	Lithium 鋰	Y	Yttrium 釔
Lu	Lutetium 鑥	Yb	Ytterbium 鐿
Lr	Lawrencium 鐒	Zn	Zinc 鋅
Md	Mendelevium 鍆	Zr	Zirconium 鋯

Weights and Measures 度量衡單位

Units of length　長度單位

		1 **millimetre** (毫米／公厘)	= 0.03937 inch (英寸／吋)
10 mm	=	1 **centimetre** (厘米／公分)	= 0.3937 inch (英寸／吋)
10 cm	=	1 **decimetre** (分米／公寸)	= 3.937 inches (英寸／吋)
10 dm	=	1 **metre** (米／公尺)	= 39.37 inches (英寸／吋)
10 m	=	1 **decametre** (十米／公丈)	= 10.94 yards (碼)
10 dam	=	1 **hectometre** (百米／公引)	= 109.4 yards (碼)
10 hm	=	1 **kilometre** (公里／千米)	= 0.6214 mile (英里／哩)

		1 **inch** (英寸／吋)	= 2.54 cm
12 inches (英寸／吋)	=	1 **foot** (英尺／呎)	= 0.3048 m
3 feet (英尺／呎)	=	1 **yard** (碼)	= 0.9144 m

Units of weight　重量單位

		1 **milligram** (毫克／公絲)	= 0.015 grain (格令／喱)
10 mg	=	1 **centigram** (厘克／公毫)	= 0.154 grain (格令／喱)
10 cg	=	1 **decigram** (分克／公釐)	= 1.543 grains (格令／喱)
10 dg	=	1 **gram** (克／公克)	= 15.43 grains (格令／喱) = 0.035 ounces (盎司)
10 g	=	1 **decagram** (十克／公錢)	= 0.353 ounce (盎司)
10 dag	=	1 **hectogram** (百克／公兩)	= 3.527 ounce (盎司)
10 hg	=	1 **kilogram** (千克／公斤)	= 2.205 **pounds** (磅)
1000 kg	=	1 **tonne** (噸) (metric ton (公噸))	= 0.984 (long) ton (長噸)
			= 2204.62 pounds (磅)

Units of capacity　容量單位

		1 **millilitre** (毫升／公撮)	= 0.00176 **pint** (品脫)
10 ml	=	1 **centilitre** (厘升／公勺)	= 0.0176 pint (品脫)
10 cl	=	1 **decilitre** (分升／公合)	= 0.176 pint (品脫)
10 dl	=	1 **litre** (升／公升)	= 1.76 pint (品脫) = 0.22 UK gallon (英加侖)
10 l	=	1 **decalitre** (十升／公斗)	= 2.20 gallons (加侖)
10 dal	=	1 **hectolitre** (百升／公石)	= 22.0 gallons (加侖)
10 hl	=	1 **kilolitre** (千升／公秉)	= 220.0 gallons (加侖)

2 pints (品脫)	=	1 **quart** (夸脫)	= 1.137 dm³
4 quarts (夸脫)	=	1 (UK) **gallon** (英加侖)	= 4.546 dm³

Square measure　面積單位

		1 **square millimetre** (平方毫米／公厘)	= 0.00155 square inch (平方英寸)
100 mm²	=	1 **square centimetre** (平方厘米／公分)	= 0.1550 square inch (平方英寸)
100 cm²	=	0.01 **square metre** (平方米／公尺)	= 0.01196 square yard (平方碼)
100 m²	=	1 **are** (公畝)	= 119.6 square yards (平方碼)
100 ares	=	1 **hectare** (公頃)	= 2.471 acres (英畝)
100 ha	=	1 **square kilometre** (平方公里)	= 247.1 acres (英畝)

		1 **square inch** (平方英寸)	= 645.16 mm²
144 square inches (平方英寸)	=	1 **square foot** (平方英尺)	= 0.0929 m²
9 square feet (平方英尺)	=	1 **square yard** (平方碼)	= 0.8361 m²
4840 square yards (平方碼)	=	1 **acre** (英畝)	= 4047 m²
640 acres (英畝)	=	1 **square mile** (平方英里)	= 259 ha

Cubic measure　體積單位

		1 cubic centimetre (立方厘米／公分)	= 0.06102 cubic inch (立方英寸)
1000 cm³	=	1 cubic decimetre (立方分米／公寸)	= 0.03532 cubic foot (立方英尺)
1000 dm³	=	1 cubic metre (立方米／公尺)	= 1.308 cubic yards (立方碼)

		1 cubic inch (立方英寸)	= 16.39 cm³
1728 cubic inches (立方英寸)	=	1 cubic foot (立方英尺)	= 0.02832 m³
			= 28.32 dm³
27 cubic feet (立方英尺)	=	1 cubic yard (立方碼)	= 0.7646 m³
			= 764.6 dm³

Circular measure　圓弧單位

		1 second (秒)	= 4.860 μ rad
60 seconds (秒)	=	1 minute (分)	= 0.2909 μ rad
60 minutes (分)	=	1 degree (度)	= 17.45 μ rad
			= π/180 rad
45 degrees (度)	=	1 oxtant (八分之一圓)	= π/4 rad
60 degrees (度)	=	1 sextant (六分之一圓)	= π/3 rad
90 degrees (度)	=	1 quadrant or (象限) 或	
		1 right angle (直角)	= π/2 rad
360 degrees (度)	=	1 circle or 或	
		1 circumference (圓周)	= 2π rad

Temperature　溫度

$$°Fahrenheit (華氏) = \left(\frac{9}{5}°C\right) + 32 \qquad °Celsius (攝氏) = \frac{5}{9}(°F-32)$$

Metric prefixes　公制詞首

		Abbreviation 縮寫	Factor 階乘／因子			Abbreviation 縮寫	Factor 階乘／因子
tera-	太拉，百億	T	10^{12}	deca-	十	da	10^{1}
giga-	吉，十億	G	10^{9}	deci-	分	d	10^{-1}
mega-	百萬	M	10^{6}	centi-	厘	c	10^{-2}
kilo-	千	k	10^{3}	milli-	毫	m	10^{-3}
hecto-	百	h	10^{2}	micro-	微	μ	10^{-6}

Punctuation 標點符號

.

full stop; period 句號

1. 用於句子的結尾

   I am John. This is my dog. 我是約翰。這是我的狗。

2. 用於縮略語

   p.m.; Apr.; Waterloo Rd.

,

comma 逗號

1. 用於連接並列的項目或子句，但在 *and* 之前可以略去

   He read all kinds of books, ancient and modern, Chinese and foreign. 他看了各種各樣的書，古今中外的都有。

   He lifted his rifle, aimed at the target and shot, but missed it. 他舉起步槍，瞄準目標開槍，但沒打中。

2. 用於非限定性的關係子句

   Tom, my elder brother, advised me to take more exercise. 我哥哥湯姆勸我要多運動。

3. 用於表示句子中的短暫停頓

   Although it was raining, we went to the park. 雖然下雨，但我們仍然到公園去。

4. 用於直接引述

   "It's cold," she said. "天氣很冷，"她說。

;

semicolon 分號

用於分隔長句中已含有逗號的部分 (通常為並列子句)

It's late; I must be getting home. 太晚了，我必須回家去了。

We have more knowledge, but less sense; more medicine, but less wellness. 我們的知識豐富了，領悟力卻弱了；醫學發達了，健康卻差了。

:

colon 冒號

1. 用於列出清單或下文各項

   We visited several major cities in Europe: Paris, Lyon, London, Rome, Milan and Berlin. 我們遊覽了歐洲多個主要城市：巴黎、里昂、倫敦、羅馬、米蘭和柏林。

2. 用於解釋或說明主句

   The weather will be like this tomorrow: cloudy with scattered showers at night. 明天的天氣會是這樣：天陰，晚間有零星驟雨。

? **question mark 問號**

用於直接疑問句的結尾　　　　　*Who's that girl?* 那女孩是誰?
Are you joking? 你在開玩笑吧?

! **exclamation mark 感嘆號**

用於表示強烈感情 (如震驚、　　　*Watch out!* 小心!
大怒、欣喜等) 的句子或詞語　　　*What beautiful weather!* 多好的天氣!
的結尾　　　　　　　　　　　　*Bang!* 砰!

– **hyphen 連字符**

用於構成複合詞　　　　　　　　*sixty-five* 六十五; *non-profit-making* 非營利的;
self-confidence 自信

— **dash 破折號**

1. 用於補充說明或評語　　　　*Don't hang about — we have to set off!* 別慢吞吞
的, 我們得起程了!

They are giving away flowers — free, of course. 他
們在分送花朵, 當然是免費的。

2. 用於表示說話中斷　　　　*I didn't mean that —* 我不是這個意思 —

"" " **quotation marks, inverted commas 引號**

' '

1. 用於直接引述　　　　　　*"I'm ready," said Jenny.* "我準備好了," 珍妮說。
"See you." "再見。"

2. 用於引語、名稱等　　　　*"Titanic" won the Oscar for Best Film.* "鐵達尼
號"贏得奧斯卡最佳影片的金像獎。

"Use by May 3" was printed clearly on the label.
標籤上清楚寫明"五月三日前食用"。

3. 用於表示特殊用法或引起注意　*The "unsinkable" ship hit a rock and sank to the
bottom of the sea.* 那艘"不沉"的船觸礁沉到了海
底。